2009
STANDARD POSTAGE
STAMP CATALOGUE
ONE HUNDRED AND SIXTY-FIFTH EDITION IN SIX VOLUMES

VOLUME 2
COUNTRIES OF THE WORLD
C-F

EDITOR	James E. Kloetzel
ASSOCIATE EDITOR	William A. Jones
ASSISTANT EDITOR /NEW ISSUES & VALUING	Martin J. Frankevicz
ASSISTANT EDITOR	Charles Snee
VALUING ANALYST	Steven R. Myers
ADMINISTRATIVE ASSISTANT/IMAGE COORDINATOR	Beth L. Brown
DESIGN MANAGER	Teresa M. Wenrick
ADVERTISING	Phyllis Stegemoller
CIRCULATION / PRODUCT PROMOTION MANAGER	Tim Wagner
VICE PRESIDENT/EDITORIAL AND PRODUCTION	Steve Collins
PRESIDENT	William Fay

Released May 2008
Includes New Stamp Listings through the May 2008 *Scott Stamp Monthly* Catalogue Update

Copyright© 2008 by

Scott Publishing Co.

911 Vandemark Road, Sidney, OH 45365-0828
A division of AMOS PRESS, INC., publishers of *Scott Stamp Monthly, Linn's Stamp News, Coin World* and *Coin World's Coin Values*.

Table of Contents

See Volume 1 for United States, United Nations and Countries of the World A-B
See Volume 3 through 6 for Countries of the World, G-Z.

Volume 3: G-I
Volume 4: J-O
Volume 5: P-Sl
Volume 6: So-Z

Copyright Notice

Trademark Notice

Vol. 2 Number Additions, Deletions & Changes

Number in 2008 Catalogue	Number in 2009 Catalogue

Canada
1156a	deleted
1157a	deleted
new	1191b
new	1191c
1682	1681
1687	1682
1692	1684
1693	1685
1694	1686
1695	1687
1696	1688
1687	1689
1698	1690
1699	1691
1700	1692
1701	1693
1702	1694
1703	1695
1705	1698
1706	1699
1707	1700
1714	1696
1714B	1697
new	1945b
new	1969a

Cape of Good Hope
new	178a

Cayman Islands
new	19b

Central African Republic
new	1368
new	1369

Chile
842A	843
843	844
844	845
845	846
846	847
846A	848
847	849

People's Republic of China
2204	2202
2206	2203
2207	2204

Christmas Island
327	326
328	327
329	328
330	329
330A	330
342	341
383	382
386	383
390	384
391	385
392	386
394	387

Colombia
905A	906
906	907
907	908
907A	909
908	910
913	912

Colombia
1000	999
1001	1000
1002	1001
C8a	deleted

People's Republic of Congo
890	889
893	890
894	891
898	892

Croatia
new	1a
new	2a
new	3a
new	5a
new	8a
new	9a
new	9b
new	10a
new	11a
new	12a
new	16a
new	17a
new	17b
new	20a
new	21a
new	24a
new	24b
new	25a
new	25b
200	199
201	200
206	201
207	202
207a	206a
new	J1a
J1a	J1b
new	J1c
new	J2a
new	J3a
new	J4a

Czechoslovakia
new	1878a

Czech Republic
2890A	2891
2891	2892
2891A	2893
2891B	2894
2892	2895
2893	2896
2894	2897
2895	2898

Dahomey
new	47a
new	64a

Dalmatia
new	1a
new	3a
new	5a
new	5b

Denmark
1115a	deleted

Dubai
new	108a

Eritrea
new	J23a
new	J27a

Estonia
243A	244
244	245
245A	246
246	248
247	249
248	250
249	251
250	252
251	253

Falkland Islands
new	254b

Fiji
new	J6a

Finland
new	M9

Fiume
1	deleted
new	1a
7	deleted
new	7a
12	deleted
new	12a
20	deleted
new	20a
23	deleted
new	23a
30	deleted
new	30a
32	deleted
new	32a
43	deleted
new	43a

France
2N1-2N10	475-476H
505-523A	504-523
2N11-2N20	523A-523J

French Offices in China
18	deleted
new	18a
20	deleted
new	20a
21	deleted
new	21a
24	deleted
new	24a
25	deleted
new	25a
27	deleted
new	27a
28	deleted
new	28a
31	deleted
new	31a
32	deleted
new	32a
33	deleted
new	33a

French Guiana
new	12a
new	13a
new	17b

Scott Publishing Co.

SCOTT 911 VANDEMARK ROAD, SIDNEY, OHIO 45365 937-498-0802

Dear Scott Catalogue User:

Another new record in value changes.

Just last month we were able to announce that there were more value changes in Volume 1 of the *2009 Scott Standard Postage Stamp Catalogue* than there had been in any single volume since the Standard catalogues went to six volumes in 1996. More than 58,000 value changes were recorded in Volume 1. Well, records are kept in order to be broken, and we can now announce that this Volume 2 Standard catalogue of 2009 has set still another record, with 59,217 value changes well spread throughout the countries herein.

One of the main reasons for this enormous quantity of upward value changes is the same phenomenon that we witnessed when we prepared the 2006 catalogues: worldwide currency fluctuations that have seen the U.S. dollar drop against other strong currencies. We suspect that almost all Scott catalogue users have read reports concerning the significant devaluation during the past year of the U.S. dollar in relation to virtually every other major currency in the world. The euro, British pound, Australian dollar, New Zealand dollar, Canadian dollar, Swiss franc and Japanese yen all have gained significant strength in relation to the U.S. dollar.

The market for stamps denominated in euros, British pounds, Canadian dollars and other various foreign currencies are largely made in the home countries, and anyone who wants to compete for those stamps must compete with those home-country buyers who are using their own strong currencies. This means that it will take more U.S. dollars to buy those stamps, and it will take more U.S. dollars for U.S. dealers to replenish their stocks.

Being a retail value catalogue, Scott must react to this situation. Catalogue values for a great many better stamps (not to mention the values for many recent issues that are generally valued at about double face value) must rise to the correct retail level in U.S. dollars in order to reflect the actual market and to ensure that the U.S. and international stamp markets mesh properly for the benefit of all concerned.

Of course, there are many value changes made throughout the catalogue based on the basic laws of supply and demand rather than the currency fluctuations already mentioned. Each year, thousands of value changes are made that are not tied in any way to currency questions. These additional changes in stamp values will help to swell the total number of value changes in this year's catalogues.

Where are the value changes in Volume 2?

Value changes are not concentrated in only a few countries or a few areas. There are eighteen disparate countries in Volume 2 each with more than 1,000 value changes. First in value changes is France with 7,236 changes and with 2,393 additional changes in the French Offices Abroad. Other countries in Volume 2 with large numbers of value changes are Canada (5,505 changes with an additional 1,046 changes in the Provinces), Czechoslovakia (3,235), Denmark (3,128), Finland (2,630), Egypt (2,491), Dominica (2,371), Ethiopia (2,220), Ecuador (1,965), China (1,914), Central African Republic (1,826), Chad (1,667), Cook Islands (1,574), Croatia (1,498), Cayman Islands (1,208), Comoro Islands (1,120), Eritrea (1,104) and Cyprus (1,064).

The strong euro helps explain the enormous number of value increases in France. Classics tend to rise 10 to 20 percent, exemplified by the 1850 40c orange on yellowish paper, Scott 7, which rises to $3,750 unused and $450 used, from $3,250 unused and $400 used in the 2008 Volume 2. Values for the 1927 Strasbourg Exhibition souvenir sheet, Scott 241, rise significantly to $1,000 unused, $2,150 mint never hinged and $1,000 used, from $675 unused, $1,600 mint never hinged and $700 used last year. Generally higher values continue to run through all France listings up through the modern issues.

If the 5,505 value changes in Canada suggest to the reader that almost every value in the country must have changed, that would be a correct supposition. When the 2008 Volume 2 was revalued, the Canadian dollar was worth approximately 85¢ in U.S. funds. Today the two currencies essentially are on par. That is almost a 20 percent rise in the value of the Canadian dollar versus the U.S. dollar.

When this currency situation combines with a fairly active market for a country, especially in the rarer classics, some startling value increases result. The 3p red Beaver stamp of 1851 on laid paper, Scott 1, increases to $27,500 unused and $1,150 used, from $20,000 unused and $950 used in the 2008 Volume 2. The 12p black Queen Victoria, Scott 3, rises to $110,000 unused and $85,000 used, from $80,000 unused and $60,000 used last year.

Significant value increases continue through the difficult early issues of Canada. Beginning with the 1897 Jubilee issue, value increases are somewhat smaller but are still universal. The ever-popular 50¢ Bluenose of 1929, Scott 158, shows increases of 10 percent to $220 unused, $440 mint never hinged and $65 used, from $200 unused, $400 mint never hinged and $60 used in the 2008 Volume 2. The only real slowdowns in the size of value increases come with the definitive sets from 1935 through 1946, which show little or no movement. Otherwise, the momentum of value increases continues throughout the country.

In the modern period, the 1999-2000 Millennium sheetlets of four, Scott 1818-1834, rise significantly to $6 each from $4.50 each last year. The sheet of six of the 2003 48¢ National Hockey League Stars, Scott 1971, jumps to $20 mint never hinged from $15 in 2008, and the self-adhesive pane of six, Scott 1972, moves to $55 mint never hinged from $45. Back-of-the-Book issues show scant to modest increases only. All in all, Canada collectors will want to pay close attention to this year's value changes.

Some final thoughts.

A short time ago, in response to our appeal for color scans or loaned stamps from collectors or dealers to bring our color image project closer to a successful conclusion, dealer George Holschauer of Colonial Stamp Co. loaned Scott a very significant group of British Commonwealth stamps. He has now come through again, this time coming up with more than 120 valuable stamps which were needed for color representation in the catalogues. Some of these items replace old black and white images, some are unused stamps replacing current used examples, while still others are new images of items not previously pictured in the catalogues. These stamps have now been scanned, and they will make it into the catalogues this year and next. We wish to express our deep appreciation to George Holschauer for his generous support of our color image project.

As usual, there are new footnotes and notes modified for clarity and accuracy throughout the catalog to aid collectors. See the Volume 2 Number Additions, Deletions & Changes listing in the introduction on page 4A for listing changes, including many new lettered minor numbers in several countries, plus new major numbers in Central African Republic, Finland and France.

The new France majors represent a new classification of old Scott 2N1-2N10 and 2N11-2N20. These stamps had been incorrectly considered to be Allied Military Government stamps since their first listing in 1947. They are now properly classified as regular France issues Scott 475-476H and 523A-523J. An article in the May 2008 *Scott Stamp Monthly* by Associate Editor Bill Jones explains this transformation in detail.

A hobby is a great gift. Enjoy.

James E Kloetzel

James E. Kloetzel/Catalogue Editor

Acknowledgments

Our appreciation and gratitude go to the following individuals who have assisted us in preparing information included in this year's Scott Catalogues. Some helpers prefer anonymity. These individuals have generously shared their stamp knowledge with others through the medium of the Scott Catalogue.

Those who follow provided information that is in addition to the hundreds of dealer price lists and advertisements and scores of auction catalogues and realizations that were used in producing the catalogue values. It is from those noted here that we have been able to obtain information on items not normally seen in published lists and advertisements. Support from these people goes beyond data leading to catalogue values, for they also are key to editorial changes.

A special acknowledgment to Liane and Sergio Sismondo of The Classic Collector for their extraordinary assistance and knowledge sharing that has aided in the preparation of this year's Standard and Classic Specialized Catalogues.

A. R. Allison Ryukyu Philatelic Specialist Society
AMEXFIL (Asociacion Mexicana de Filatelia)
Roland Austin
Robert Ausubel (Great Britain Collectors Club)
Jack Hagop Barsoumian (International Stamp Co.)
William Batty-Smith
Jules K. Beck (Latin American Philatelic Society)
Vladimir Berrio-Lemm
George G. Birdsall (Northland Auctions)
John Birkinbine II
Keith & Margie Brown
Bernard Bujnak
Alan C. Campbell
Tina & John Carlson (JET Stamps)
Richard A. Champagne (Richard A. Champagne, Inc.)
Henry Chlanda (Liberian Philatelic Society)
Bob Coale
Leroy P. Collins III (United Postal Stationery Society)
Frank D. Correl
Andrew Cronin (Canadian Society of Russian Philately)
Tony L. Crumbley (Carolina Coin & Stamp, Inc.)
Stephen R. Datz
Tony Davis
Kenneth E. Diehl
Bob Dumaine
Mark Eastzer (Markest Stamp Co.)
Esi Ebrani (Iran Philatelic Study Circle)
Paul G. Eckman
Marty Farber
Leon Finik (Loral Stamps)
Henry Fisher
Jeffrey M. Forster
Robert S. Freeman
Ernest E. Fricks (France & Colonies Philatelic Society)
Bob Genisol (Sultan Stamp Center)
Michael A. Goldman (Regency Superior, Ltd.)
Daniel E. Grau
Joe Hahn (Associated Collectors of El Salvador)
Jerone Hart
John B. Head
Bruce Hecht (Bruce L. Hecht Co.)
Clifford O. Herrick (Fidelity Trading Co.)
George W. Holschauer
Philip J. Hughes (Croatian Philatelic Society)

Doug Iams
Eric Jackson
N. M. Janoowalla
Peter C. Jeannopoulos
Richard Juzwin (Richard Juzwin PTY LTD)
John Kardos (The Stamp Gallery)
Allan Katz (Ventura Stamp Co.)
Stanford M. Katz
Patricia A. Kaufmann
William V. Kriebel
William A. Litle
Gary B. Little (Luxembourg Collectors Club)
Pedro Llach (Filatelia Llach S.L.)
George Luzitano
Dennis Lynch
Leo Malz
Robert L. Markovits (Quality Investors, Ltd.)
Marilyn R. Mattke
William K. McDaniel
Gary N. McLean
Mark S. Miller (India Study Circle)
Allen Mintz (United Postal Stationery Society)
William E. Mooz
Brian Moorhouse
David Mordant
Gary M. Morris (Pacific Midwest Co.)
Peter Mosiondz, Jr.
Bruce M. Moyer (Moyer Stamps & Collectibles)
Richard H. Muller (Richard's Stamps)
James Natale
Robert Odenweller (AIEP)
Albert Olejnik
Mark Parren
John E. Pearson (Pittwater Philatelic Service)
John Pedneault
Donald J. Peterson (International Philippine Philatelic Society)
Stanley M. Piller (Stanley M. Piller & Associates)
Todor Drumev Popov
Peter W. W. Powell
Stephen Radin (Albany Stamp Co.)
Ghassan D. Riachi
Omar Rodriquez
Michael Rogers (Michael Rogers, Inc.)
Mehrdad Sadri (Persiphila)
Richard H. Salz
Alex Schauss (Schauss Philatelics)
Jacques C. Schiff, Jr. (Jacques C. Schiff, Jr., Inc.)
Charles F. Shreve (Spink Shreves Galleries)
Bernard Seckler (Fine Arts Philatelists)
Guy Shaw

Jeff Siddiqui
Sergio & Liane Sismondo (The Classic Collector)
Christopher Smith
Jay Smith
Jerry Summers
Scott R. Trepel (Siegel Auction Galleries)
Steve Unkrich
Philip T. Wall
Daniel C. Warren
Richard A. Washburn
Ed Wener (Indigo)
Don White (Dunedin Stamp Centre)
Robert F. Yacano (K-Line Philippines)
Ralph Yorio
Val Zabijaka
Michal Zika
John P. Zuckerman (Siegel Auction Galleries)
Alfonsa G. Zulueta, Jr.

Addresses, Telephone Numbers, Web Sites, E-Mail Addresses of General & Specialized Philatelic Societies

Collectors can contact the following groups for information about the philately of the areas within the scope of these societies, or inquire about membership in these groups. Aside from the general societies, we limit this list to groups that specialize in particular fields of philately, particular areas covered by the Scott Standard Postage Stamp Catalogue, and topical groups. Many more specialized philatelic society exist than those listed below. These addresses are updated yearly, and they are, to the best of our knowledge, correct and current. Groups should inform the editors of address changes whenever they occur. The editors also want to hear from other such specialized groups not listed.

Unless otherwise noted all website addresses begin with http://

American Philatelic Society
100 Match Factory Place
Bellefonte PA 16823-1367
Ph: (814) 933-3803
www.stamps.org
E-mail: apsinfo@stamps.org

American Stamp Dealers Association
Joseph Savarese
3 School St. Suite #205
Glen Cove NY 11542
Ph: (516) 759-7000
www.asdaonline.com
E-mail: asda@erols.com

International Society of Worldwide
  Stamp Collectors
Terry Myers, MD
9463 Benbrook Blvd. #114
Benbrook TX 76126
www.iswsc.org
E-mail: executivedirector@iswsc.org

Royal Philatelic Society
41 Devonshire Place
London, United Kingdom W1G 6JY
www.rpsl.org.uk
E-mail: secretary@rpsl.org.uk

Royal Philatelic Society of Canada
PO Box 929, Station Q
Toronto, ON, Canada M4T 2P1
Ph: (888) 285-4143
www.rpsc.org
E-mail: info@rpsc.org

Young Stamp Collectors of America
Janet Houser
100 Match Factory Place
Bellefonte PA 16823-1367
Ph: (814) 933-3820
www.stamps.org/ysca/intro.htm
E-mail: ysca@stamps.org

Groups focusing on fields or aspects found in worldwide philately (some may cover U.S. area only)

American Air Mail Society
Stephen Reinhard
PO Box 110
Mineola NY 11501
www.americanairmailsociety.org
E-mail: sreinhard1@optonline.net

American First Day Cover Society
Douglas Kelsey
PO Box 16277
Tucson AZ 85732-6277
Ph: (520) 321-0880
www.afdcs.org
E-mail: afdcs@aol.com

American Revenue Association
Eric Jackson
PO Box 728
Leesport PA 19533-0728
Ph: (610) 926-6200
www.revenuer.org
E-mail: eric@revenuer.com

American Topical Association
Ray E. Cartier
PO Box 57
Arlington TX 76004-0057
Ph: (817) 274-1181
americantopicalassn.org
E-mail: americantopical@msn.com

Errors, Freaks and Oddities
  Collectors Club
Jim McDevitt
3561 Country Court, North
Mobile AL 36619-5335
Ph: (251) 607-9253
www.efo.org
E-mail: cwouscg@aol.com

First Issues Collectors Club
Clark Buchi
P.O. Box 453
Brentwood TN 37024-0453
www.firstissues.org
E-mail: orders@firstissues.org

The Joint Stamp Issues Society
Pascal LeBlond
60-600 Rue Cormier
Gatineau, QC, Canada J9H 6B4
jointissues.ovh.org
E-mail: jointissues@yahoo.com

National Duck Stamp Collectors
  Society
Anthony J. Monico
PO Box 43
Harleysville PA 19438-0043
www.ndscs.org
E-mail: ndscs@hwcn.org

No Value Identified Club
Albert Sauvanet
Le Clos Royal B, Boulevard des Pas
Enchantes
St. Sebastien-sur Loire, France 44230
E-mail: alain.vailly@irin.univ nantes.fr

The Perfins Club
Kurt Ottenheimer
462 West Walnut St.
Long Beach NY 11561
Ph: (516) 431-3412
E-mail: oak462@optonline.net

Postage Due Mail Study Group
John Rawlins
13, Longacre
Chelmsford
United Kingdom, CM1 3BJ
E-mail: john.rawlins2@ukonline.co.uk.

Post Mark Collectors Club
David Proulx
7629 Homestead Drive
Baldwinsville NY 13027
E-mail: stampdance@baldcom.net

Postal History Society
Kalman V. Illyefalvi
8207 Daren Court
Pikesville MD 21208-2211
Ph: (410) 653-0665
E-mail: kalphyl@juno.com

Precancel Stamp Society
Arthur Damm
176 Bent Pine Hill
North Wales PA 19454
Ph: (215) 368-6082
E-mail: shirldamm@comcast.net

United Postal Stationery Society
Stuart Leven
1445 Foxworthy Ave. #187
San Jose, CA 95118-1119
www.upss.org
E-mail: poststat@gmail.com

United States Possessions Philatelic
  Society
Geoffrey Brewster
6453 E. Stallion Rd.
Paradise Valley AZ 85253
Ph: (480) 607-7184

Groups focusing on U.S. area philately as covered in the Standard Catalogue

Canal Zone Study Group
Richard H. Salz
60 27th Ave.
San Francisco CA 94121-1026

Carriers and Locals Society
John D. Bowman
PO Box 74
Grosse Ile MI 48138
Ph: (205) 222-7314
www.pennypost.org
E-mail: jbowman@stx.rr.net

Confederate Stamp Alliance
Gen. Francis J. Crown
PO Box 278
Capshaw AL 35742-0278
Ph. (302) 422-2656
www.csalliance.org
E-mail: csaas@knology.net

Hawaiian Philatelic Society
Kay H. Hoke
PO Box 10115
Honolulu HI 96816-0115
Ph: (808) 521-5721

Plate Number Coil Collectors Club
Ronald E. Maifeld
PO Box 54622
Cincinnati OH 45254-0622
Ph: (513) 231-4208
www.pnc3.org
E-mail: president@pnc3.org

Ryukyu Philatelic Specialist Society
Mrs. Laura Edmonds, Secy.
PO Box 240177
Charlotte NC 28224-0177
Ph: (704) 519-5157
www.ryukyustamps.org
E-mail: secretary@ryukyustamps.org

United Nations Philatelists
Blanton Clement, Jr.
P.O. Box 146
Morrisville PA 19067-0146
www.unpi.com
E-mail: bclemjr@yahoo.com

United States Stamp Society
Executive Secretary
PO Box 6634
Katy TX 77491-6631
www.usstamps.org
E-mail: webmaster@usstamps.org

U.S. Cancellation Club
Roger Rhoads
6160 Brownstone Ct.
Mentor OH 44060
www.geocities.com/athens/2088/
uscchome.htm
E-mail: rrrhoads@aol.com

U.S. Philatelic Classics Society
Rob Lund
2913 Fulton
Everett WA 98201-3733
www.uspcs.org
E-mail: membershipchairman@uspcs.org

Groups focusing on philately of foreign countries or regions

Aden & Somaliland Study Group
Gary Brown
PO Box 106
Briar Hill, Victoria, Australia 3088
E-mail: garyjohn951@optushome.com.au

American Society of Polar
  Philatelists (Antarctic areas)
Alan Warren
PO Box 39
Exton PA 19341-0039
Ph: (847) 421-7655
www.polarphilatelists.org
E-mail: cjenner00@yahoo.com

Andorran Philatelic Study Circle
D. Hope
17 Hawthorn Dr.
Stalybridge, Cheshire, United Kingdom
SK15 1UE
http://apsc.free.fr
E-mail: apsc@free.fr

Australian States Study Circle of
    The Royal Sydney Philatelic Club
Ben Palmer
GPO 1751
Sydney, N.S.W., Australia 2001

Austria Philatelic Society
Ralph Schneider
PO Box 23049
Belleville IL 62223
Ph: (618) 277-6152
www.austriaphilatelicsociety.com
E-mail: rsstamps@aol.com

American Belgian Philatelic Society
Edward de Bary
11 Wakefield Dr. Apt. 2105
Asheville NC 28803
groups.hamptonroads.com/ABPS
E-mail: belgam@charter.net

Bechuanalands and Botswana Society
Neville Midwood
69 Porlock Lane
Furzton, Milton Keynes, United
Kingdom MK4 1JY
www.nevsoft.com
E-mail: bbsoc@nevsoft.com

Bermuda Collectors Society
Thomas J. McMahon
PO Box 1949
Stuart FL 34995
www.bermudacollectorssociety.org

Brazil Philatelic Association
William V. Kriebel
1923 ManningSt.
Philadelphia PA 19103-5728
Ph: (215) 735-3697
E-mail: kriebewv@drexel.edu

British Caribbean Philatelic Study
    Group
Dr. Reuben A. Ramkissoon
3011 White Oak Lane
Oak Brook IL 60523-2513
Ph: (630) 963-1439
www.bcpsg.com
E-mail: rramkissoon@juno.com

British North America Philatelic
    Society (Canada & Provinces)
H. P. Jacobi
6-2168 150A St.
Surrey, B.C., Canada V4A 9W4
www.bnaps.org
E-mail: pjacobi@shaw.ca

British West Indies Study Circle
W. Clary Holt
PO Drawer 59
Burlington NC 27216
Ph: (336) 227-7461

Burma Philatelic Study Circle
Michael Whittaker
1, Ecton Leys, Hillside
Rugby, Warwickshire, United Kingdom,
CV22 5SL
E-mail: whittaker2004@ntlworld.com

Ceylon Study Group
R. W. P. Frost
42 Lonsdale Road, Cannington
Bridgewater, Somerset, United
Kingdom TA5 2JS
E-mail: rodney.frost@tiscali.co.uk

Channel Islands Specialists Society
Moira Edwards
86, Hall Lane, Sandon,
Chelmsford, United Kingdom, CM2
7RQ
E-mail: am012e5360@blueyonder.co.uk

China Stamp Society
Paul H. Gault
PO Box 20711
Columbus OH 43220
www.chinastampsociety.org
E-mail: secretary@chinastampsociety.org

Colombia/Panama Philatelic Study
    Group (COPAPHIL)
Thomas P. Myers
7411 Old Post Road #1
Lincoln NE 68506
www.copaphil.org
E-mail: tpmphil@hotmail.com

Association Filatelic de Costa Rica
Giana Wayman
c/o Interlink 102, PO Box 52-6770
Miami, FL 33152
E-mail: scotland@racsa.co.cr

Society for Costa Rica Collectors
Dr. Hector R. Mena
PO Box 14831
Baton Rouge LA 70808
www.socorico.org
E-mail: hrmena@aol.com

Croatian Philatelic Society (Croatia
    & other Balkan areas)
Ekrem Spahich
502 Romero, PO Box 696
Fritch TX 79036-0696
Ph: (806) 273-5609
www.croatianstamps.com
E-mail: eckSpahich@cableone.net

Cuban Philatelic Society of America
Ernesto Cuesta
PO Box 34434
Bethesda MD 20827
www.philat.com/cpsa
E-mail: ecuesta@philat.com

Cyprus Study Circle
Jim Wigmore
20 Gilpin Close, Dawlish
Devon, United Kingdom EX7 9SZ
www.cyprusstudycircle.org/index.htm
E-mail: jameswigmore@aol.com

Society for Czechoslovak Philately
Phil Rhoade
28168 Cedar Trail
Cleveland MN 56017
www.csphilately.org
E-mail: philip.rhoade@mnsu.edu

Danish West Indies Study Unit of
    the Scandinavian Collectors Club
Arnold Sorensen
7666 Edgedale Drive
Newburgh IN 47630
Ph: (812) 853-2653
dwistudygroup.com
E-mail: valbydwi@hotmail.com

East Africa Study Circle
Jonathan Smalley
1 Lincoln Close
Tweeksbury, United Kingdom B91 1AE
easc.org.uk
E-mail: jpasmalley@tiscali.co.uk

Egypt Study Circle
Mike Murphy
109 Chadwick Road
London, United Kingdom SE15 4PY
Dick Wilson: North American Agent
egyptstudycircle.org.uk
E-mail: egyptstudycircle@hotmail.com

Estonian Philatelic Society
Juri Kirsimagi
29 Clifford Ave.
Pelham NY 10803
Ph: (914) 738-3713

Ethiopian Philatelic Society
Ulf Lindahl
21 Westview Place
Riverside CT 06878
Ph: (203) 866-3540
home.comcast.net/~fbheiser/ethiopia5.
htm
E-mail: ulindahl@optonline.net

Falkland Islands Philatelic Study
    Group
Carl J. Faulkner
Williams Inn, On-the-Green
Williamstown MA 01267-2620
www.fipsg.org.uk
Ph: (413) 458-9371

Faroe Islands Study Circle
Norman Hudson
28 Enfield Road
Ellesmere Port, Cheshire, United
Kingdom CH65 8BY
www.faroeislandssc.org.
E-mail: jntropics@hotmail.com

Former French Colonies Specialist
    Society
BP 628
75367 Paris Cedex 08, France
www.colfra.com
E-mail: clubcolfra@aol.com

France & Colonies Philatelic Society
Edward Grabowski
741 Marcellus Drive
Westfield NJ 07090-2012
www.drunkenboat.net/frandcol/
E-mail: edjjg@alum.mit.edu

Germany Philatelic Society
PO Box 6547
Chesterfield MO 63006
www.gps.nu

German Democratic Republic
    Study Group of the German
    Philatelic Society
Ken Lawrence
PO Box 98
Bellefonte PA 16823-0098
Ph: (814) 422-0625
E-mail: apsken@aol.com

Gibraltar Study Circle
David R. Stirrups
34 Glamis Drive
Dundee, United Kingdom DD2 1QP
E-mail: drstirrups@dundee.ac.uk

Great Britain Collectors Club
Timothy Bryan Burgess
3547 Windmill Way
Concord CA 94518
www.gbstamps.com/gbcc
E-mail: Pennyred@earthlink.net

Hellenic Philatelic Society of
    America (Greece and related
    areas)
Dr. Nicholas Asimakopulos
541 Cedar Hill Ave.
Wyckoff NJ 07481
Ph: (201) 447-6262
E-mail: nick1821@aol.com

Haiti Philatelic Society
Ubaldo Del Toro
5709 Marble Archway
Alexandria VA 22315
www.haitiphilately.org
E-mail: u007ubi@aol.com

Hong Kong Stamp Society
Dr. An-Min Chung
3300 Darby Rd. Cottage 503
Haverford PA 19041-1064

Society for Hungarian Philately
Robert Morgan
2201 Roscomare Rd.
Los Angeles CA 90077-2222
www.hungarianphilately.org
E-mail: h.alan.hoover@hungarianphilately.
org

India Study Circle
John Warren
PO Box 7326
Washington DC 20044
Ph: (202) 564-6876
www.indiastudycircle.org
E-mail: warren.john@epa.gov

Indian Ocean Study Circle
Mrs. S. Hopson
Field Acre, Hoe Benham
Newbury, Berkshire, United Kingdom
RG20 8PD

Society of Indo-China Philatelists
Ron Bentley
2600 North 24th Street
Arlington VA 22207
www.sicp-online.org
E-mail: ron.bentley@verizon.net

Iran Philatelic Study Circle
Mehdi Esmaili
PO Box 750096
Forest Hills NY 11375
www.iranphilatelic.org
E-mail: m.esmaili@earthlink.net

Eire Philatelic Association (Ireland)
David J. Brennan
PO Box 704
Bernardsville NJ 07924
eirephilatelicassoc.org
E-mail: brennan704@aol.com

Society of Israel Philatelists
Paul S. Aufrichtig
300 East 42nd St.
New York NY 10017

Italy and Colonies Study Circle
Andrew D'Anneo
1085 Dunweal Lane
Calistoga CA 94515
www.icsc.pwp.blueyonder.co.uk
E-mail: audanneo@napanet.net

International Society for Japanese
    Philately
Kenneth Kamholz
PO Box 1283
Haddonfield NJ 08033
www.isjp.org
E-mail: isjp@isjp.org

Korea Stamp Society
John E. Talmage
PO Box 6889
Oak Ridge TN 37831
www.pennfamily.org/KSS-USA
E-mail: jtalmage@usit.net

Latin American Philatelic Society
Jules K. Beck
30 1/2 Street #209
St. Louis Park MN 55426-3551

Latvian Philatelic Society
Aris Birze
569 Rougemount Dr.
Pickering, ON, Canada L1W 2C1

Liberian Philatelic Society
William Thomas Lockard
PO Box 106
Wellston OH 45692
Ph: (740) 384-2020
E-mail: tlockard@zoomnet.net

Liechtenstudy USA (Liechtenstein)
Paul Tremaine
PO Box 601
Dundee OR 97115
Ph: (503) 538-4500
www.liechtenstudy.org
E-mail: editor@liechtenstudy.org

Lithuania Philatelic Society
John Variakojis
3715 W. 68th St.
Chicago IL 60629
Ph: (773) 585-8649
www.filatelija.lt/lps/and
www.withgusto.org/lps/index.htm
E-mail: variakojis@earthlink.net

Luxembourg Collectors Club
Gary B. Little
7319 Beau Road
Sechelt, BC, Canada V0N 3A8
http://lcc.luxcentral.com
E-mail: gary@luxcentral.com

Malaya Study Group
David Tett
PO Box 34
Wheathampstead, Herts, United
Kingdom AL4 8JY
www.m-s-g/org/uk
E-mail: davidtett@aol.com

Malta Study Circle
Alec Webster
50 Worcester Road
Sutton, Surrey, United Kingdom SM2
6QB
E-mail: alecwebster50@hotmail.com

Mexico-Elmhurst Philatelic Society
International
David Pietsch
PO Box 50997
Irvine CA 92619-0997
E-mail: mepsi@msn.com

Society for Moroccan and Tunisian
Philately
206, bld. Pereire
75017 Paris, France
members.aol.com/Jhaik5814
E-mail: splm206@aol.com

Natal and Zululand Study Circle
Dr. Guy Dillaway
PO Box 181
Weston MA 02493
www.nzsc.demon.co.uk

Nepal & Tibet Philatelic Study
Group
Roger D. Skinner
1020 Covington Road
Los Altos CA 94024-5003
Ph: (650) 968-4163
fuchs-online.com/ntpsc/
E-mail: colinhepper@hotmail.co.uk

American Society of Netherlands
Philately
Hans Kremer
50 Rockport Ct.
Danville CA 94526
Ph: (925) 820-5841
www.angelfire.com/ca2/asnp
E-mail: hkremer@usa.net

New Zealand Society of Great Britain
Keith C. Collins
13 Briton Crescent
Sanderstead, Surrey, United Kingdom
CR2 0JN
www.cs.stir.ac.uk/~rgc/nzsgb
E-mail: rgc@cs.stir.ac.uk

Nicaragua Study Group
Erick Rodriguez
11817 S.W. 11th St.
Miami FL 33184-2501
clubs.yahoo.com/clubs/nicara-
guastudygroup
E-mail: nsgsec@yahoo.com

Society of Australasian Specialists/
Oceania
Henry Bateman
PO Box 4862
Monroe LA 71211-4862
Ph: (800) 571-0293 members.aol.
com/stampsho/saso.html
E-mail: hbateman@jam.rr.com

Orange Free State Study Circle
J. R. Stroud
28 Oxford St.
Burnham-on-sea, Somerset, United
Kingdom TA8 1LQ
E-mail: richardstroudph@gofast.co.uk

Pacific Islands Study Circle
John Ray
24 Woodvale Avenue
London, United Kingdom SE25 4AE
www.pisc.org.uk
E-mail: info@pisc.org.uk

Pakistan Philatelic Study Circle
Jeff Siddiqui
PO Box 7002
Lynnwood WA 98046
E-mail: jeffsiddiqui@msn.com

Centro de Filatelistas
Independientes de Panama
Vladimir Berrio-Lemm
Apartado 0823-02748
Plaza Concordia Panama, Panama
E-mail: panahistoria@gmail.com

Papuan Philatelic Society
Steven Zirinsky
PO Box 49, Ansonia Station
New York NY 10023
Ph: (718) 706-0616
www.communigate.co.uk/york/pps
E-mail: szirinsky@cs.com

International Philippine Philatelic
Society
Robert F. Yacano
PO Box 100
Toast NC 27049
Ph: (336) 783-0768
www.theipps.info
E-mail: ryacano@triad.rr.com

Pitcairn Islands Study Group
Nelson A. L. Weller
619 Flick Circle
Thomasville NC 27360
Ph: (336) 475-4558
www.pisg.net
E-mail: nalweller@aol.com

Plebiscite-Memel-Saar Study Group
of the German Philatelic Society
Clay Wallace
100 Lark Court
Alamo CA 94507
E-mail: clayw1@sbcglobal.net

Polonus Philatelic Society (Poland)
Chris Kulpinski
9350 E. Palm Tree Dr.
Scottsdale AZ 85255
Ph: (480) 585-7114
www.polonus.org
E-mail: ctk@kulpinski.net

International Society for
Portuguese Philately
Clyde Homen
1491 Bonnie View Rd.
Hollister CA 95023-5117
www.portugalstamps.com
E-mail: cjh1491@sbcglobal.net

Rhodesian Study Circle
William R. Wallace
PO Box 16381
San Francisco CA 94116
www.rhodesianstudycircle.org.uk
E-mail: bwall8rscr@earthlink.net

Rossica Society of Russian Philately
Edward J. Laveroni
P.O. Box 320997
Los Gatos CA 95032-0116
www.rossica.org
E-mail: ed.laveroni@rossica.org

St. Helena, Ascension & Tristan Da
Cunha Philatelic Society
Dr. Everett L. Parker
719 Moosehead Lake Rd.
Greenville ME 04441-9727
Ph: (207) 695-3163
ourworld.compuserve.com/homep-
ages/ ST_HELENA_ASCEN_TDC
E-mail: eparker@midmaine.net

St. Pierre & Miquelon Philatelic
Society
David Allen
2159 W. 47 Avenue
Vancouver, BC, V6M 2M6, Canada
Ph: (604) 263-0029
E-mail: dallen@axion.net

Associated Collectors of El Salvador
Joseph D. Hahn
1015 Old Boalsburg Rd. Apt G-5
State College PA 16801-6149
www.elsalvadorphilately.org
E-mail: joehahn2@yahoo.com

Fellowship of Samoa Specialists
Jack R. Hughes
PO Box 1260
Boston MA 02117-1260
members.aol.com/tongaJan/foss.html

Sarawak Specialists' Society
Stu Leven
PO Box 24764
San Jose CA 95154-4764
Ph: (408) 978-0193
www.britborneostamps.org.uk
E-mail: stulev@ix.netcom.com

Scandinavian Collectors Club
Donald B. Brent
PO Box 13196
El Cajon CA 92020
www.scc-online.org
E-mail: dbrent47@sprynet.com

Slovakia Stamp Society
Jack Benchik
PO Box 555
Notre Dame IN 46556

Philatelic Society for Greater
Southern Africa
Alan Hanks
34 Seaton Drive
Aurora, ON, L4G 2KI, Canada
Ph: (905) 727-6993
www.psgsa.thestampweb.com
Email: alan.hanks@sympatico.ca

Spanish Philatelic Society
Robert H. Penn
1108 Walnut Drive
Danielsville PA 18038
Ph: (610) 767-6793

Sudan Study Group
c/o North American Agent
Richard S. Wilson
53 Middle Patent Road
Bedford NY 10506
www.sudanphilately.co.uk
E-mail: dadu1@verizon.net

American Helvetia Philatelic
Society (Switzerland,
Liechtenstein)
Richard T. Hall
PO Box 15053
Asheville NC 28813-0053
www.swiss-stamps.org
E-mail: secretary2@swiss-stamps.org

Tannu Tuva Collectors Society
Ken Simon
513 Sixth Ave. So.
Lake Worth FL 33460-4507
Ph: (561) 588-5954
www.tuva.tk
E-mail: fpo09501@yahoo.com

Society for Thai Philately
H. R. Blakeney
PO Box 25644
Oklahoma City OK 73125
E-mail: HRBlakeney@aol.com

Transvaal Study Circle
J. Woolgar
PO Box 379
Gravesend, DA11 9EW, United
Kingdom
www.transvaal.org.uk

Ottoman and Near East Philatelic
Society (Turkey and related areas)
Bob Stuchell
193 Valley Stream Lane
Wayne PA 19087
www.oneps.org
E-mail: rstuchell@msn.com

Ukrainian Philatelic & Numismatic
Society
George Slusarczuk
PO Box 303
Southfields NY 10975-0303
www.upns.org
E-mail: Yurko@warwick.net

Vatican Philatelic Society
Sal Quinonez
1 Aldersgate, Apt. 1002
Riverhead NY 11901-1830
Ph: (516) 727-6426
www.vaticanphilately.org

British Virgin Islands Philatelic
Society
Giorgio Migliavacca
PO Box 7007
St. Thomas VI 00801-0007
www.islandsun.com/FEATURES/
bviphil9198.html
E-mail: issun@candwbvi.net

West Africa Study Circle
Dr. Peter Newroth
Suite 603
5332 Sayward Hill Crescent
Victoria, BC, Canada V8Y 3H8
www.wasc.org.uk/

Western Australia Study Group
Brian Pope
PO Box 423
Claremont, Western Australia,
Australia 6910

Yugoslavia Study Group of the
   Croatian Philatelic Society
Michael Lenard
1514 North 3rd Ave.
Wausau WI 54401
Ph: (715) 675-2833
E-mail: mjlenard@aol.com

Topical Groups

Americana Unit
Dennis Dengel
17 Peckham Rd.
Poughkeepsie NY 12603-2018
www.americanaunit.org
E-mail: info@americanaunit.org

Astronomy Study Unit
John Budd
29203 Coharie Loop
San Antonio FL 33576-4643
Ph: (978) 851-8283
www.fandm.edu/departments/
astronomy/miscell/astunit.html
E-mail: jwgbudd@earthlink.net

Bicycle Stamp Club
Norman Batho
358 Iverson Place
East Windsor NJ 08520
Ph: (609) 448-9547
members.tripod.com/~bicyclestamps
E-mail: normbatho@worldnet.att.net

Biology Unit
Alan Hanks
34 Seaton Dr.
Aurora, ON, Canada L4G 2K1
Ph: (905) 727-6993

Bird Stamp Society
Mrs. Rosie Bradley
31 Park View,
Chepsow, Gwent, United Kingdom
NP16 5NA
www.bird-stamps.org/bss
E-mail: bradley666@lycos.co.uk

Canadiana Study Unit
John Peebles
PO Box 3262, Station "A"
London, ON, Canada N6A 4K3
E-mail: john.peebles@sympatico.ca

Captain Cook Study Unit
Brian P. Sandford
173 Minuteman Dr.
Concord MA 01742-1923
www.captaincooksociety.com
E-mail: US@captaincooksociety.com/

Casey Jones Railroad Unit
Donald Kesler
709 NW 35th Place
Lawton OK 73505-5121
www.uqp.de/cjr/index.htm
E-mail: normaned@rochester.rr.com

Cats on Stamps Study Unit
Mary Ann Brown
3006 Wade Rd.
Durham NC 27705
www.catsonstamps.org
E-mail: mabrown@nc.rr.com

Chemistry & Physics on Stamps
   Study Unit
Dr. Roland Hirsch
20458 Water Point Lane
Germantown MD 20874
www.cpossu.org
E-mail: rfhirsch@cpossu.org

Chess on Stamps Study Unit
Anne Kasonic
7625 County Road #153
Interlaken NY 14847
E-mail: akasonic@capital.net

Christmas Philatelic Club
Linda Lawrence
312 Northwood Drive
Lexington KY 40505
www.hwcn.org/link/cpc
E-mail: stamplinda@aol.com

Christopher Columbus Philatelic
   Society
Donald R. Ager
PO Box 71
Hillsboro NH 03244-0071
http://ccps.maphist.nl/
Ph: (603) 464-5379
E-mail: meganddon@tds.net

Collectors of Religion on Stamps
Verna Shackleton
425 North Linwood Avenue #110
Appleton WI 54914
www://my.vbe.com/~cmfourl/
coros1.htm
E-mail: corosec@sbcglobal.net

Dogs on Stamps Study Unit
Morris Raskin
202A Newport Rd.
Monroe Township NJ 08831
Ph: (609) 655-7411
www.dossu.org
E-mail: mraskin@cellurian.com

Earth's Physical Features Study Group
Fred Klein
515 Magdalena Ave.
Los Altos CA 94024
epfsu.jeffhayward.com

Ebony Society of Philatelic Events
   and Reflections (African-
   American topicals)
Manuel Gilyard
800 Riverside Drive, Ste 4H
New York NY 10032-7412
www.esperstamps.org
E-mail: gilyardmani@aol.com

Embroidery, Stitchery, Textile Unit
http://www.caratexstamps.com/

Europa Study Unit
Donald W. Smith
PO Box 576
Johnstown PA 15907-0576
www.europanews.emperors.net
E-mail: eunity@aol.com or
donsmith65@msn.com

Fine & Performing Arts
Deborah L. Washington
6922 So. Jeffery Boulevard
#7 - North
Chicago IL 60649
E-mail: brasslady@comcast.net

Fire Service in Philately
Brian R. Engler, Sr.
726 1/2 W. Tilghman St.
Allentown PA 18102-2324
Ph: (610) 433-2782
www.firestamps.com

Gay & Lesbian History on Stamps
   Club
Joe Petronie
PO Box 190842
Dallas TX 75219-0842
www.glhsc.org
E-mail: glhsc@aol.com

Gems, Minerals & Jewelry Study Unit
George Young
PO Box 632
Tewksbury MA 01876-0632
Ph: (978) 851-8283
www.rockhounds.com/rockshop/
gmjsuapp.txt
E-mail: george-young@msn.com

Graphics Philately Association
Mark H Winnegrad
PO Box 380
Bronx NY 10462-0380
www.graphics-stamps.org
E-mail: indybruce1@yahoo.com

Journalists, Authors & Poets on
   Stamps
Ms. Lee Straayer
P.O. Box 6808
Champaign IL 61826
E-mail: lstraayer@dcbnet.com

Lighthouse Stamp Society
Dalene Thomas
8612 West Warren Lane
Lakewood CO 80227-2352
Ph: (303) 986-6620
www.lighthousestampsociety.org
E-mail: dalene@lighthousestampsociety.
org

Lions International Stamp Club
John Bargus
304-2777 Barry Rd. RR 2
Mill Bay, BC, Canada V0R 2P0
Ph: (250) 743-5782

Mahatma Gandhi On Stamps
   Study Circle
Pramod Shivagunde
Pratik Clinic, Akluj
Solapur, Maharashtra, India 413101
E-mail: drnanda@bom6.vsnl.net.in

Mask Study Unit
Carolyn Weber
1220 Johnson Drive, Villa 104
Ventura CA 93003-0540
E-mail: cweber@venturalink.net

Masonic Study Unit
Stanley R. Longenecker
930 Wood St.
Mount Joy PA 17552-1926
Ph: (717) 653-1155
E-mail: natsco@usa.net

Mathematical Study Unit
Estelle Buccino
5615 Glenwood Rd.
Bethesda MD 20817-6727
Ph: (301) 718-8898
www.math.ttu.edu/msu/
E-mail: m.strauss@ttu.edu

Medical Subjects Unit
Dr. Frederick C. Skvara
PO Box 6228
Bridgewater NJ 08807
E-mail: fcskvara@verizon.net

Mourning Stamps and Covers Club
John Hotchner
PO Box 1125
Falls Church VA 22041-0125
E-mail: jmhstamp@ix.netcom.com

Napoleonic Age Philatelists
Ken Berry
7513 Clayton Dr.
Oklahoma City OK 73132-5636
Ph: (405) 721-0044
www.nap-stamps.org
E-mail: krb2@earthlink.net

Old World Archeological Study Unit
Caroline Scannel
11 Dawn Drive
Smithtown NY 11787-1761
www.owasu.org
E-mail: editor@owasu.org

Petroleum Philatelic Society
   International
Dr. Chris Coggins
174 Old Bedford Road
Luton, England, LU2 7HW, United
Kingdom
E-mail: njav8t@verizon.net

Philatelic Computing Study Group
Robert de Violini
PO Box 5025
Oxnard CA 93031-5025
www.pcsg.org
E-mail: dviolini@adelphia.net

Philatelic Lepidopterists' Association
Alan Hanks
34 Seaton Dr.
Aurora, ON, Canada L4G 2K1
Ph: (905) 727-6933
E-mail: alan.hanks@sympatico.ca

Rotary on Stamps Unit
Gerald L. Fitzsimmons
105 Calla Ricardo
Victoria TX 77904
rotaryonstamps.org
E-mail: glfitz@suddenlink.net

Scouts on Stamps Society
   International
Lawrence Clay
PO Box 6228
Kennewick WA 99336
Ph: (509) 735-3731
www.sossi.org
E-mail: rfrank@sossi.org

Ships on Stamps Unit
Les Smith
302 Conklin Avenue
Penticton, BC, Canada, V2A 2T4
Ph: (250) 493-7486
www.shipsonstamps.org
E-mail: lessmith440@shaw.ca

Space Unit
Carmine Torrisi
PO Box 780241
Maspeth NY 11378
Ph: (718) 386-7882
stargate.1usa.com/stamps/
E-mail: ctorrisi1@nyc.rr.com

Sports Philatelists International
Margaret Jones
5310 Lindenwood Ave.
St. Louis MO 63109-1758
www.sportstamps.org

Stamps on Stamps Collectors Club
Alf Jordan
156 West Elm Street
Yarmouth ME 04096
Ph: (650) 234-1136
www.stampsonstamps.org
E-mail: ajordan1@maine.rr.com

Windmill Study Unit
Walter J. Hollien
PO Box 346
Long Valley NJ 07853-0346
Ph: (862) 812-0030
E-mail: whollien@earthlink.net

Wine On Stamps Study Unit
Bruce L. Johnson
115 Raintree Drive
Zionsville IN 46077
E-mail: indybruce@yahoo.com

Women on Stamps Study Unit
Hugh Gottfried
2232 26th St.
Santa Monica CA 90405-1902
E-mail: hgottfried@adelphia.net

Zeppelin Collectors Club
Cheryl Ganz
PO Box 77196
Washington DC 20013
www.americanairmailsociety.org

Expertizing Services

The following organizations will, for a fee, provide expert opinions about stamps submitted to them. Collectors should contact these organizations to find out about their fees andrequirements before submitting philatelic material to them. The listing of these groups here is not intended as an endorsement by Scott Publishing Co.

General Expertizing Services

American Philatelic Expertizing
  Service (a service of the
  American Philatelic Society)
100 Match Factory Place
Bellefonte PA 16823-1367
Ph: (814) 237-3803
Fax: (814) 237-6128
www.stamps.org
E-mail: ambristo@stamps.org
Areas of Expertise: Worldwide

B. P. A. Expertising, Ltd.
PO Box 137
Leatherhead, Surrey, United Kingdom
KT22 0RG
E-mail: sec.bpa@tcom.co.uk
Areas of Expertise: British
Commonwealth, Great Britain,
Classics of Europe, South America and
the Far East

Philatelic Foundation
70 West 40th St., 15th Floor
New York NY 10018
Ph: (212) 221-6555
Fax: (212) 221-6208
www.philatelicfoundation.org
E-mail:philatelicfoundation@verizon.net
Areas of Expertise: U.S. & Worldwide

Professional Stamp Experts
PO Box 6170
Newport Beach CA 92658
Ph: (877) STAMP-88
Fax: (949) 833-7955
www.collectors.com/pse
E-mail: pseinfo@collectors.com
Areas of Expertise: Stamps and
covers of U.S., U.S. Possessions,
British Commonwealth

Royal Philatelic Society Expert
  Committee
41 Devonshire Place
London, United Kingdom W1N 1PE
www.rpsl.org.uk/experts.html
E-mail: experts@rpsl.org.uk
Areas of Expertise: All

Expertizing Services Covering Specific Fields Or Countries

China Stamp Society Expertizing
  Service
1050 West Blue Ridge Blvd
Kansas City MO 64145
Ph: (816) 942-6300
E-mail: hjmesq@aol.com
Areas of Expertise: China

Confederate Stamp Alliance
  Authentication Service
Gen. Frank Crown, Jr.
PO Box 278
Capshaw AL 35742-0396
Ph: (302) 422-2656
Fax: (302) 424-1990
www.csalliance.org
E-mail: csaas@knology.net
Areas of Expertise: Confederate stamps
and postal history

Croatian Philatelic Society
  Expertizing Service
PO Box 696
Fritch TX 79036-0696
Ph: (806) 857-0129
E-mail: ou812@arn.net
Areas of Expertise: Croatia and other
Balkan areas

Errors, Freaks and Oddities
  Collectors Club
  Expertizing Service
138 East Lakemont Dr.
Kingsland GA 31548
Ph: (912) 729-1573
Areas of Expertise: U.S. errors, freaks
and oddities

Estonian Philatelic Society
  Expertizing Service
39 Clafford Lane
Melville NY 11747
Ph: (516) 421-2078
E-mail: esto4@aol.com
Areas of Expertise: Estonia

Hawaiian Philatelic Society
  Expertizing Service
PO Box 10115
Honolulu HI 96816-0115
Areas of Expertise: Hawaii

Hong Kong Stamp Society
  Expertizing Service
PO Box 206
Glenside PA 19038
Fax: (215) 576-6850
Areas of Expertise: Hong Kong

International Association of
  Philatelic Experts
  United States Associate members:

  Paul Buchsbayew
  119 W. 57th St.
  New York NY 10019
  Ph: (212) 977-7734
  Fax: (212) 977-8653
  Areas of Expertise: Russia, Soviet
  Union

  William T. Crowe
  (see Professional Stamp Experts)
  Areas of Expertise: United States

  John Lievsay
  (see American Philatelic Expertizing
  Service and Philatelic Foundation)
  Areas of Expertise: France

  Robert W. Lyman
  P.O. Box 348
  Irvington on Hudson NY 10533
  Ph and Fax: (914) 591-6937
  Areas of Expertise: British North
  America, New Zealand

  Robert Odenweller
  P.O. Box 401
  Bernardsville, NJ 07924-0401
  Ph and Fax: (908) 766-5460
  Areas of Expertise: New Zealand,
  Samoa to 1900

  Alex Rendon
  P.O. Box 323
  Massapequa NY 11762
  Ph and Fax: (516) 795-0464
  Areas of Expertise: Bolivia,
  Colombia, Colombian States

  Sergio Sismondo
  10035 Carousel Center Dr.
  Syracuse NY 13290-0001
  Ph: (315) 422-2331
  Fax: (315) 422-2956
  Areas of Expertise: British East
  Africa, Camerouns,
  Cape of Good Hope, Canada, British
  North America

International Society for Japanese
  Philately Expertizing Committee
32 King James Court
Staten Island NY 10308-2910
Ph: (718) 227-5229
Areas of Expertise: Japan and
related areas, except WWII Japanese
Occupation issues

International Society for
  Portuguese Philately Expertizing
  Service
PO Box 43146
Philadelphia PA 19129-3146
Ph: (215) 843-2106
Fax: (215) 843-2106
E-mail: s.s.washburne@worldnet.att.
net
Areas of Expertise: Portugal and
Colonies

Mexico-Elmhurst Philatelic Society
  International Expert Committee
PO Box 1133
West Covina CA 91793
Areas of Expertise: Mexico

Ukrainian Philatelic & Numismatic
  Society Expertizing Service
30552 Dell Lane
Warren MI 48092-1862
Ph: (810) 751-5754
Areas of Expertise: Ukraine, Western
Ukraine

V. G. Greene Philatelic Research
  Foundation
P.O. Box 204, Station Q
Toronto, ON, Canada M4T 2M1
Ph: (416) 921-2073
Fax: (416) 921-1282
E-mail: vggfoundation@on.aibn.com
www.greenefoundation.ca
Areas of Expertise: British North
America

Information on Catalogue Values, Grade and Condition

Catalogue Value

The Scott Catalogue value is a retail value; that is, an amount you could expect to pay for a stamp in the grade of Very Fine with no faults. Any exceptions to the grade valued will be noted in the text. The general introduction on the following pages and the individual section introductions further explain the type of material that is valued. The value listed for any given stamp is a reference that reflects recent actual dealer selling prices for that item.

Dealer retail price lists, public auction results, published prices in advertising and individual solicitation of retail prices from dealers, collectors and specialty organizations have been used in establishing the values found in this catalogue. Scott Publishing Co. values stamps, but Scott is not a company engaged in the business of buying and selling stamps as a dealer.

Use this catalogue as a guide for buying and selling. The actual price you pay for a stamp may be higher or lower than the catalogue value because of many different factors, including the amount of personal service a dealer offers, or increased or decreased interest in the country or topic represented by a stamp or set. An item may occasionally be offered at a lower price as a "loss leader," or as part of a special sale. You also may obtain an item inexpensively at public auction because of little interest at that time or as part of a large lot.

Stamps that are of a lesser grade than Very Fine, or those with condition problems, generally trade at lower prices than those given in this catalogue. Stamps of exceptional quality in both grade and condition often command higher prices than those listed.

Values for pre-1900 unused issues are for stamps with approximately half or more of their original gum. Stamps with most or all of their original gum may be expected to sell for more, and stamps with less than half of their original gum may be expected to sell for somewhat less than the values listed. On rarer stamps, it may be expected that the original gum will be somewhat more disturbed than it will be on more common issues. Post-1900 unused issues are assumed to have full original gum. From breakpoints in most countries' listings, stamps are valued as never hinged, due to the wide availability of stamps in that condition. These notations are prominently placed in the listings and in the country information preceding the listings. Some countries also feature listings with dual values for hinged and never-hinged stamps.

Grade

A stamp's grade and condition are crucial to its value. The accompanying illustrations show examples of Very Fine stamps from different time periods, along with examples of stamps in Fine to Very Fine and Extremely Fine grades as points of reference. When a stamp seller offers a stamp in any grade from fine to superb without further qualifying statements, that stamp should not only have the centering grade as defined, but it also should be free of faults or other condition problems.

FINE stamps (illustrations not shown) have designs that are quite off center, with the perforations on one or two sides very close to the design but not quite touching it. There is white space between the perforations and the design that is minimal but evident to the unaided eye. Imperforate stamps may have small margins, and earlier issues may show the design just touching one edge of the stamp design. Very early perforated issues normally will have the perforations slightly cutting into the design. Used stamps may have heavier than usual cancellations.

FINE-VERY FINE stamps will be somewhat off center on one side, or slightly off center on two sides. Imperforate stamps will have two margins of at least normal size, and the design will not touch any edge. For perforated stamps, the perfs are well clear of the design, but are still noticeably off center. *However, early issues of a country may be printed in such a way that the design naturally is very close to the edges. In these cases, the perforations may cut into the design very slightly.* Used stamps will not have a cancellation that detracts from the design.

VERY FINE stamps will be just slightly off center on one or two sides, but the design will be well clear of the edge. The stamp will present a nice, balanced appearance. Imperforate stamps will be well centered within normal-sized margins. *However, early issues of many countries may be printed in such a way that the perforations may touch the design on one or more sides. Where this is the case, a boxed note will be found defining the centering and margins of the stamps being valued.* Used stamps will have light or otherwise neat cancellations. This is the grade used to establish Scott Catalogue values.

EXTREMELY FINE stamps are close to being perfectly centered. Imperforate stamps will have even margins that are slightly larger than normal. Even the earliest perforated issues will have perforations clear of the design on all sides.

Scott Publishing Co. recognizes that there is no formally enforced grading scheme for postage stamps, and that the final price you pay or obtain for a stamp will be determined by individual agreement at the time of transaction.

Condition

Grade addresses only centering and (for used stamps) cancellation. *Condition* refers to factors other than grade that affect a stamp's desirability.

Factors that can increase the value of a stamp include exceptionally wide margins, particularly fresh color, the presence of selvage, and plate or die varieties. Unusual cancels on used stamps (particularly those of the 19th century) can greatly enhance their value as well.

Factors other than faults that decrease the value of a stamp include loss of original gum, regumming, a hinge remnant or foreign object adhering to the gum, natural inclusions, straight edges, and markings or notations applied by collectors or dealers.

Faults include missing pieces, tears, pin or other holes, surface scuffs, thin spots, creases, toning, short or pulled perforations, clipped perforations, oxidation or other forms of color changelings, soiling, stains, and such man-made changes as reperforations or the chemical removal or lightening of a cancellation.

Grading Illustrations

On the following two pages are illustrations of various stamps from countries appearing in this volume. These stamps are arranged by country, and they represent early or important issues that are often found in widely different grades in the marketplace. The editors believe the illustrations will prove useful in showing the margin size and centering that will be seen on the various issues.

In addition to the matters of margin size and centering, collectors are reminded that the very fine stamps valued in the Scott catalogues also will possess fresh color and intact perforations, and they will be free from defects.

Examples shown are computer-manipulated images made from single digitized master illustrations.

Stamp Illustrations Used in the Catalogue

It is important to note that the stamp images used for identification purposes in this catlaogue may not be indicative of the grade of stamp being valued. Refer to the written discussion of grades on this page and to the grading illustrations on the following two pages for grading information.

Fine-Very Fine

SCOTT
CATALOGUES
VALUE
STAMPS IN
THIS GRADE

Very Fine

Extremely Fine

Fine-Very Fine

SCOTT
CATALOGUES
VALUE
STAMPS IN
THIS GRADE

Very Fine

Extremely Fine

Fine-Very Fine →

SCOTT CATALOGUES VALUE STAMPS IN THIS GRADE

Very Fine →

Extremely Fine →

Fine-Very Fine →

SCOTT CATALOGUES VALUE STAMPS IN THIS GRADE

Very Fine →

Extremely Fine →

For purposes of helping to determine the gum condition and value of an unused stamp, Scott Publishing Co. presents the following chart which details different gum conditions and indicates how the conditions correlate with the Scott values for unused stamps. Used together, the Illustrated Grading Chart on the previous pages and this Illustrated Gum Chart should allow catalogue users to better understand the grade and gum condition of stamps valued in the Scott catalogues.

Gum Categories:	MINT N.H.	ORIGINAL GUM (O.G.)				NO GUM
	Mint Never Hinged *Free from any disturbance*	Lightly Hinged *Faint impression of a removed hinge over a small area*	Hinge Mark or Remnant *Prominent hinged spot with part or all of the hinge remaining*	Large part o.g. *Approximately half or more of the gum intact*	Small part o.g. *Approximately less than half of the gum intact*	No gum *Only if issued with gum*
Commonly Used Symbol:	★★	★	★	★	★	(★)
Pre-1900 Issues (Pre-1881 for U.S.)	*Very fine pre-1900 stamps in these categories trade at a premium over Scott value*			Scott Value for "Unused"		Scott "No Gum" listings for selected unused classic stamps
From 1900 to breakpoints for listings of never-hinged stamps	Scott "Never Hinged" listings for selected unused stamps	Scott Value for "Unused" (Actual value will be affected by the degree of hinging of the full o.g.)				
From breakpoints noted for many countries	Scott Value for "Unused"					

Never Hinged (NH; ★★): A never-hinged stamp will have full original gum that will have no hinge mark or disturbance. The presence of an expertizer's mark does not disqualify a stamp from this designation.

Original Gum (OG; ★): Pre-1900 stamps should have approximately half or more of their original gum. On rarer stamps, it may be expected that the original gum will be somewhat more disturbed than it will be on more common issues. Post-1900 stamps should have full original gum. Original gum will show some disturbance caused by a previous hinge(s) which may be present or entirely removed. The actual value of a post-1900 stamp will be affected by the degree of hinging of the full original gum.

Disturbed Original Gum: Gum showing noticeable effects of humidity, climate or hinging over more than half of the gum. The significance of gum disturbance in valuing a stamp in any of the Original Gum categories depends on the degree of disturbance, the rarity and normal gum condition of the issue and other variables affecting quality.

Regummed (RG; (★)): A regummed stamp is a stamp without gum that has had some type of gum privately applied at a time after it was issued. This normally is done to deceive collectors and/or dealers into thinking that the stamp has original gum and therefore has a higher value. A regummed stamp is considered the same as a stamp with none of its original gum for purposes of grading.

Understanding the Listings

On the opposite page is an enlarged "typical" listing from this catalogue. Below are detailed explanations of each of the highlighted parts of the listing.

1 **Scott number** — Scott catalogue numbers are used to identify specific items when buying, selling or trading stamps. Each listed postage stamp from every country has a unique Scott catalogue number. Therefore, Germany Scott 99, for example, can only refer to a single stamp. Although the Scott catalogue usually lists stamps in chronological order by date of issue, there are exceptions. When a country has issued a set of stamps over a period of time, those stamps within the set are kept together without regard to date of issue. This follows the normal collecting approach of keeping stamps in their natural sets.

When a country issues a set of stamps over a period of time, a group of consecutive catalogue numbers is reserved for the stamps in that set, as issued. If that group of numbers proves to be too few, capital-letter suffixes, such as "A" or "B," may be added to existing numbers to create enough catalogue numbers to cover all items in the set. A capital-letter suffix indicates a major Scott catalogue number listing. Scott uses a suffix letter only once. Therefore, a catalogue number listing with a capital-letter suffix will not also be found with the same letter (lower case) used as a minor-letter listing. If there is a Scott 16A in a set, for example, there will not also be a Scott 16a. However, a minor-letter "a" listing may be added to a major number containing an "A" suffix (Scott 16Aa, for example).

Suffix letters are cumulative. A minor "b" variety of Scott 16A would be Scott 16Ab, not Scott 16b.

There are times when a reserved block of Scott catalogue numbers is too large for a set, leaving some numbers unused. Such gaps in the numbering sequence also occur when the catalogue editors move an item's listing elsewhere or have removed it entirely from the catalogue. Scott does not attempt to account for every possible number, but rather attempts to assure that each stamp is assigned its own number.

Scott numbers designating regular postage normally are only numerals. Scott numbers for other types of stamps, such as air post, semipostal, postal tax, postage due, occupation and others have a prefix consisting of one or more capital letters or a combination of numerals and capital letters.

2 **Illustration number** — Illustration or design-type numbers are used to identify each catalogue illustration. For most sets, the lowest face-value stamp is shown. It then serves as an example of the basic design approach for other stamps not illustrated. Where more than one stamp use the same illustration number, but have differences in design, the design paragraph or the description line clearly indicates the design on each stamp not illustrated. Where there are both vertical and horizontal designs in a set, a single illustration may be used, with the exceptions noted in the design paragraph or description line.

When an illustration is followed by a lower-case letter in parentheses, such as "A2(b)," the trailing letter indicates which overprint or surcharge illustration applies.

Illustrations normally are 70 percent of the original size of the stamp. An effort has been made to note all illustrations not illustrated at that percentage. Virtually all souvenir sheet illustrations are reduced even more. Overprints and surcharges are shown at 100 percent of their original size if shown alone, but are 70 percent of original size if shown on stamps. In some cases, the illustration will be placed above the set, between listings or omitted completely. Overprint and surcharge illustrations are not placed in this catalogue for purposes of expertizing stamps.

3 **Paper color** — The color of a stamp's paper is noted in italic type when the paper used is not white.

4 **Listing styles** — There are two principal types of catalogue listings: major and minor.

Major listings are in a larger type style than minor listings. The catalogue number is a numeral that can be found with or without a capital-letter suffix, and with or without a prefix.

Minor listings are in a smaller type style and have a small-letter suffix or (if the listing immediately follows that of the major number) may show only the letter. These listings identify a variety of the major item.

Examples include perforation, color, watermark or printing method differences, multiples (some souvenir sheets, booklet panes and se-tenant combinations), and singles of multiples.

Examples of major number listings include 16, 28A, B97, C13A, 10N5, and 10N6A. Examples of minor numbers are 16a and C13Ab.

5 **Basic information about a stamp or set** — Introducing each stamp issue is a small section (usually a line listing) of basic information about a stamp or set. This section normally includes the date of issue, method of printing, perforation, watermark and, sometimes, some additional information of note. *Printing method, perforation and watermark apply to the following sets until a change is noted.* Stamps created by overprinting or surcharging previous issues are assumed to have the same perforation, watermark and printing method as the original. Dates of issue are as precise as Scott is able to confirm and often reflect the dates on first-day covers, rather than the actual date of release.

6 **Denomination** — This normally refers to the face value of the stamp; that is, the cost of the unused stamp at the post office at the time of issue. When a denomination is shown in parentheses, it does not appear on the stamp. This includes the non-denominated stamps of the United States, Brazil and Great Britain, for example.

7 **Color or other description** — This area provides information to solidify identification of a stamp. In many recent cases, a description of the stamp design appears in this space, rather than a listing of colors.

8 **Year of issue** — In stamp sets that have been released in a period that spans more than a year, the number shown in parentheses is the year that stamp first appeared. Stamps without a date appeared during the first year of the issue. Dates are not always given for minor varieties.

9 **Value unused and Value used** — The Scott catalogue values are based on stamps that are in a grade of Very Fine unless stated otherwise. Unused values refer to items that have not seen postal, revenue or any other duty for which they were intended. Pre-1900 unused stamps that were issued with gum must have at least most of their original gum. Later issues are assumed to have full original gum. From breakpoints specified in most countries' listings, stamps are valued as never hinged. Stamps issued without gum are noted. Modern issues with PVA or other synthetic adhesives may appear ungummed. Unused self-adhesive stamps are valued as appearing undisturbed on their original backing paper. Values for used self-adhesive stamps are for examples either on piece or off piece. For a more detailed explanation of these values, please see the "Catalogue Value," "Condition" and "Understanding Valuing Notations" sections elsewhere in this introduction.

In some cases, where used stamps are more valuable than unused stamps, the value is for an example with a contemporaneous cancel, rather than a modern cancel or a smudge or other unclear marking. For those stamps that were released for postal and fiscal purposes, the used value represents a postally used stamp. Stamps with revenue cancels generally sell for less.

Stamps separated from a complete se-tenant multiple usually will be worth less than a pro-rated portion of the se-tenant multiple, and stamps lacking the attached labels that are noted in the listings will be worth less than the values shown.

10 **Changes in basic set information** — Bold type is used to show any changes in the basic data given for a set of stamps. This includes perforation differences from one stamp to the next or a different paper, printing method or watermark.

11 **Total value of a set** — The total value of sets of three or more stamps issued after 1900 are shown. The set line also notes the range of Scott numbers and total number of stamps included in the grouping. The actual value of a set consisting predominantly of stamps having the minimum value of twenty cents may be less than the total value shown. Similarly, the actual value or catalogue value of se-tenant pairs or of blocks consisting of stamps having the minimum value of twenty cents may be less than the catalogue values of the component parts.

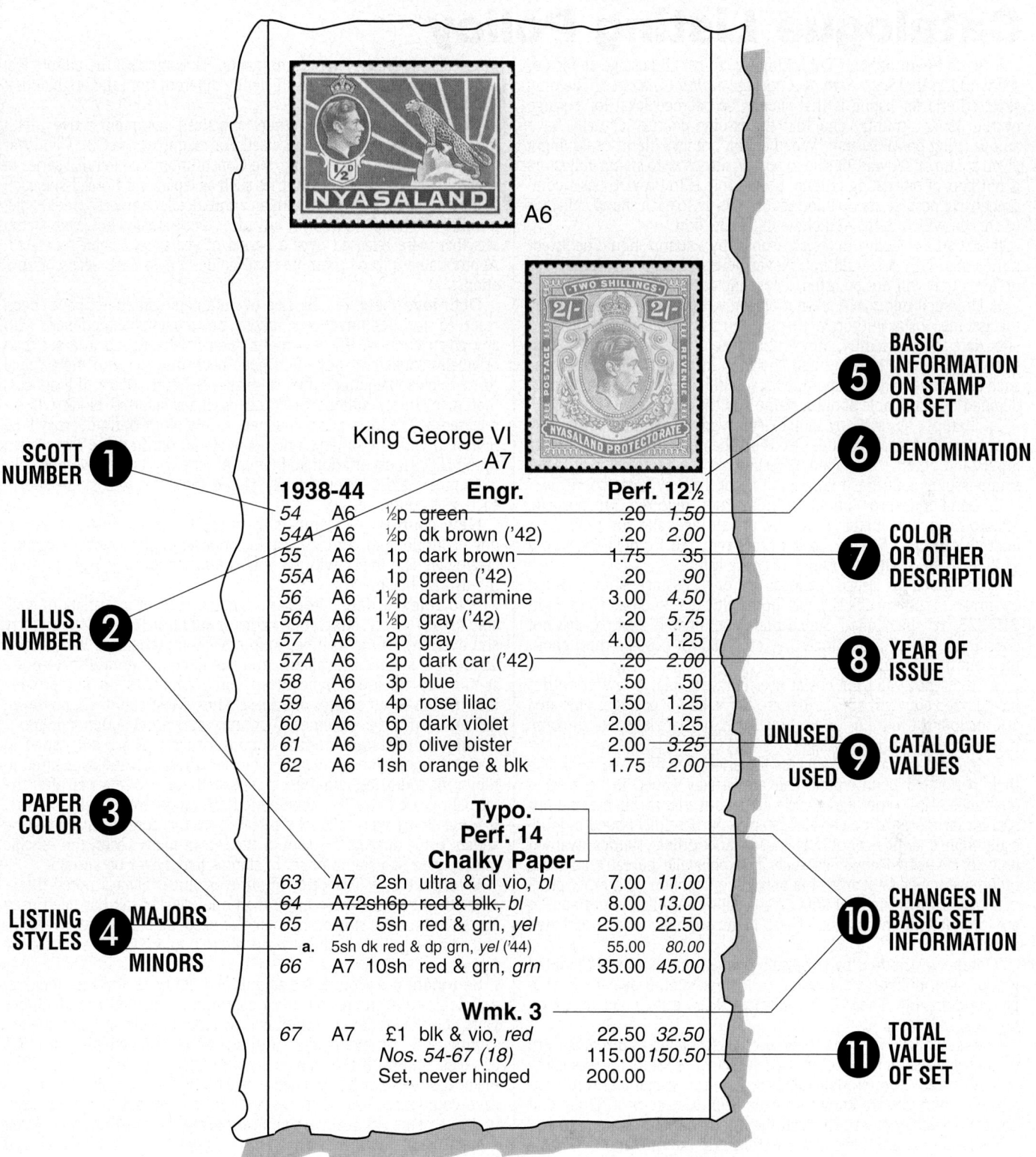

SCOTT NUMBER ❶

ILLUS. NUMBER ❷

PAPER COLOR ❸

LISTING STYLES ❹ MAJORS MINORS

A6

King George VI
A7

❺ BASIC INFORMATION ON STAMP OR SET

❻ DENOMINATION

❼ COLOR OR OTHER DESCRIPTION

❽ YEAR OF ISSUE

UNUSED ❾ CATALOGUE VALUES USED

❿ CHANGES IN BASIC SET INFORMATION

⓫ TOTAL VALUE OF SET

1938-44		Engr.		Perf. 12½	
54	A6	½p	green	.20	1.50
54A	A6	½p	dk brown ('42)	.20	2.00
55	A6	1p	dark brown	1.75	.35
55A	A6	1p	green ('42)	.20	.90
56	A6	1½p	dark carmine	3.00	4.50
56A	A6	1½p	gray ('42)	.20	5.75
57	A6	2p	gray	4.00	1.25
57A	A6	2p	dark car ('42)	.20	2.00
58	A6	3p	blue	.50	.50
59	A6	4p	rose lilac	1.50	1.25
60	A6	6p	dark violet	2.00	1.25
61	A6	9p	olive bister	2.00	3.25
62	A6	1sh	orange & blk	1.75	2.00

**Typo.
Perf. 14
Chalky Paper**

63	A7	2sh	ultra & dl vio, *bl*	7.00	11.00
64	A72	sh6p	red & blk, *bl*	8.00	13.00
65	A7	5sh	red & grn, *yel*	25.00	22.50
a.			5sh dk red & dp grn, *yel* ('44)	55.00	80.00
66	A7	10sh	red & grn, *grn*	35.00	45.00

Wmk. 3

67	A7	£1	blk & vio, *red*	22.50	32.50
		Nos. 54-67 (18)		115.00	150.50
		Set, never hinged		200.00	

Catalogue Listing Policy

It is the intent of Scott Publishing Co. to list all postage stamps of the world in the *Scott Standard Postage Stamp Catalogue*. The only strict criteria for listing is that stamps be decreed legal for postage by the issuing country and that the issuing country actually have an operating postal system. Whether the primary intent of issuing a given stamp or set was for sale to postal patrons or to stamp collectors is not part of our listing criteria. Scott's role is to provide basic comprehensive postage stamp information. It is up to each stamp collector to choose which items to include in a collection.

It is Scott's objective to seek reasons why a stamp should be listed, rather than why it should not. Nevertheless, there are certain types of items that will not be listed. These include the following:

1. Unissued items that are not officially distributed or released by the issuing postal authority. If such items are officially issued at a later date by the country, they will be listed. Unissued items consist of those that have been printed and then held from sale for reasons such as change in government, errors found on stamps or something deemed objectionable about a stamp subject or design.

2. Stamps "issued" by non-existent postal entities or fantasy countries, such as Nagaland, Occusi-Ambeno, Staffa, Sedang, Torres Straits and others. Also, stamps "issued" in the names of legitimate, stamp-issuing countries that are not authorized by those countries.

3. Semi-official or unofficial items not required for postage. Examples include items issued by private agencies for their own express services. When such items are required for delivery, or are valid as prepayment of postage, they are listed.

4. Local stamps issued for local use only. Postage stamps issued by governments specifically for "domestic" use, such as Haiti Scott 219-228, or the United States non-denominated stamps, are not considered to be locals, since they are valid for postage throughout the country of origin.

5. Items not valid for postal use. For example, a few countries have issued souvenir sheets that are not valid for postage. This area also includes a number of worldwide charity labels (some denominated) that do not pay postage.

6. Intentional varieties, such as imperforate stamps that look like their perforated counterparts and are usually issued in very small quantities. Also, other egregiously exploitative issues such as stamps sold for far more than face value, stamps purposefully issued in artificially small quantities or only against advance orders, stamps awarded only to a selected audience such as a philatelic bureau's standing order customers, or stamps sold only in conjunction with other products. All of these kinds of items are usually controlled issues and/or are intended for speculation. These items normally will be included in a footnote.

7. Items distributed by the issuing government only to a limited group, club, philatelic exhibition or a single stamp dealer or other private company. These items normally will be included in a footnote.

The fact that a stamp has been used successfully as postage, even on international mail, is not in itself sufficient proof that it was legitimately issued. Numerous examples of so-called stamps from non-existent countries are known to have been used to post letters that have successfully passed through the international mail system.

There are certain items that are subject to interpretation. When a stamp falls outside our specifications, it may be listed along with a cautionary footnote.

A number of factors are considered in our approach to analyzing how a stamp is listed. The following list of factors is presented to share with you, the catalogue user, the complexity of the listing process.

Additional printings — "Additional printings" of a previously issued stamp may range from an item that is totally different to cases where it is impossible to differentiate from the original. At least a minor number (a small-letter suffix) is assigned if there is a distinct change in stamp shade, noticeably redrawn design, or a significantly different perforation measurement. A major number (numeral or numeral and capital-letter combination) is assigned if the editors feel the "additional printing" is sufficiently different from the original that it constitutes a different issue.

Commemoratives — Where practical, commemoratives with the same theme are placed in a set. For example, the U.S. Civil War Centennial set of 1961-65 and the Constitution Bicentennial series of 1989-90 appear as sets. Countries such as Japan and Korea issue such material on a regular basis, with an announced, or at least predictable, number of stamps known in advance. Occasionally, however, stamp sets that were released over a period of years have been separated. Appropriately placed footnotes will guide you to each set's continuation.

Definitive sets — Blocks of numbers generally have been reserved for definitive sets, based on previous experience with any given country. If a few more stamps were issued in a set than originally expected, they often have been inserted into the original set with a capital-letter suffix, such as U.S. Scott 1059A. If it appears that many more stamps than the originally allotted block will be released before the set is completed, a new block of numbers will be reserved, with the original one being closed off. In some cases, such as the U.S. Transportation and Great Americans series, several blocks of numbers exist. Appropriately placed footnotes will guide you to each set's continuation.

New country — Membership in the Universal Postal Union is not a consideration for listing status or order of placement within the catalogue. The index will tell you in what volume or page number the listings begin.

"No release date" items — The amount of information available for any given stamp issue varies greatly from country to country and even from time to time. Extremely comprehensive information about new stamps is available from some countries well before the stamps are released. By contrast some countries do not provide information about stamps or release dates. Most countries, however, fall between these extremes. A country may provide denominations or subjects of stamps from upcoming issues that are not issued as planned. Sometimes, philatelic agencies, those private firms hired to represent countries, add these later-issued items to sets well after the formal release date. This time period can range from weeks to years. If these items were officially released by the country, they will be added to the appropriate spot in the set. In many cases, the specific release date of a stamp or set of stamps may never be known.

Overprints — The color of an overprint is always noted if it is other than black. Where more than one color of ink has been used on overprints of a single set, the color used is noted. Early overprint and surcharge illustrations were altered to prevent their use by forgers.

Se-tenants — Connected stamps of differing features (se-tenants) will be listed in the format most commonly collected. This includes pairs, blocks or larger multiples. Se-tenant units are not always symmetrical. An example is Australia Scott 508, which is a block of seven stamps. If the stamps are primarily collected as a unit, the major number may be assigned to the multiple, with minors going to each component stamp. In cases where continuous-design or other unit se-tenants will receive significant postal use, each stamp is given a major Scott number listing. This includes issues from the United States, Canada, Germany and Great Britain, for example.

Special Notices

Classification of stamps

The *Scott Standard Postage Stamp Catalogue* lists stamps by country of issue. The next level of organization is a listing by section on the basis of the function of the stamps. The principal sections cover regular postage, semi-postal, air post, special delivery, registration, postage due and other categories. Except for regular postage, catalogue numbers for all sections include a prefix letter (or number-letter combination) denoting the class to which a given stamp belongs. When some countries issue sets containing stamps from more than one category, the catalogue will at times list all of the stamps in one category (such as air post stamps listed as part of a postage set).

The following is a listing of the most commonly used catalogue prefixes.

Prefix... Category

C	Air Post
M	Military
P	Newspaper
N	Occupation - Regular Issues
O	Official
Q	Parcel Post
J	Postage Due
RA	Postal Tax
B	Semi-Postal
E	Special Delivery
MR	War Tax

Other prefixes used by more than one country include the following:

H	Acknowledgment of Receipt
I	Late Fee
CO	Air Post Official
CQ	Air Post Parcel Post
RAC	Air Post Postal Tax
CF	Air Post Registration
CB	Air Post Semi-Postal
CBO	Air Post Semi-Postal Official
CE	Air Post Special Delivery
EY	Authorized Delivery
S	Franchise
G	Insured Letter
GY	Marine Insurance
MC	Military Air Post
MQ	Military Parcel Post
NC	Occupation - Air Post
NO	Occupation - Official
NJ	Occupation - Postage Due
NRA	Occupation - Postal Tax
NB	Occupation - Semi-Postal
NE	Occupation - Special Delivery
QY	Parcel Post Authorized Delivery
AR	Postal-fiscal
RAJ	Postal Tax Due
RAB	Postal Tax Semi-Postal
F	Registration
EB	Semi-Postal Special Delivery
EO	Special Delivery Official
QE	Special Handling

New issue listings

Updates to this catalogue appear each month in the *Scott Stamp Monthly* magazine. Included in this update are additions to the listings of countries found in the *Scott Standard Postage Stamp Catalogue* and the *Specialized Catalogue of United States Stamps*, as well as corrections and updates to current editions of this catalogue.

From time to time there will be changes in the final listings of stamps from the *Scott Stamp Monthly* to the next edition of the catalogue. This occurs as more information about certain stamps or sets becomes available.

The catalogue update section of the *Scott Stamp Monthly* is the most timely presentation of this material available. Annual subscriptions to the *Scott Stamp Monthly* are available from Scott Publishing Co., Box 828, Sidney, OH 45365-0828.

Number additions, deletions & changes

A listing of catalogue number additions, deletions and changes from the previous edition of the catalogue appears in each volume. See Catalogue Number Additions, Deletions & Changes in the table of contents for the location of this list.

Understanding valuing notations

The *minimum catalogue value* of an individual stamp or set is 20 cents. This represents a portion of the cost incurred by a dealer when he prepares an individual stamp for resale. As a point of philatelic-economic fact, the lower the value shown for an item in this catalogue, the greater the percentage of that value is attributed to dealer mark up and profit margin. In many cases, such as the 20-cent minimum value, that price does not cover the labor or other costs involved with stocking it as an individual stamp. The sum of minimum values in a set does not properly represent the value of a complete set primarily composed of a number of minimum-value stamps, nor does the sum represent the actual value of a packet made up of minimum-value stamps. Thus a packet of 1,000 different common stamps — each of which has a catalogue value of 20-cents — normally sells for considerably less than 200 dollars!

The *absence of a retail value* for a stamp does not necessarily suggest that a stamp is scarce or rare. A dash in the value column means that the stamp is known in a stated form or variety, but information is either lacking or insufficient for purposes of establishing a usable catalogue value.

Stamp values in *italics* generally refer to items that are difficult to value accurately. For expensive items, such as those priced at $1,000 or higher, a value in italics indicates that the affected item trades very seldom. For inexpensive items, a value in italics represents a warning. One example is a "blocked" issue where the issuing postal administration may have controlled one stamp in a set in an attempt to make the whole set more valuable. Another example is an item that sold at an extreme multiple of face value in the marketplace at the time of its issue.

One type of warning to collectors that appears in the catalogue is illustrated by a stamp that is valued considerably higher in used condition than it is as unused. In this case, collectors are cautioned to be certain the used version has a genuine and contemporaneous cancellation. The type of cancellation on a stamp can be an important factor in determining its sale price. Catalogue values do not apply to fiscal, telegraph or non-contemporaneous postal cancels, unless otherwise noted.

Some countries have released back issues of stamps in canceled-to-order form, sometimes covering as much as a 10-year period. The Scott Catalogue values for used stamps reflect canceled-to-order material when such stamps are found to predominate in the marketplace for the issue involved. Notes frequently appear in the stamp listings to specify which items are valued as canceled-to-order, or if there is a premium for postally used examples.

Many countries sell canceled-to-order stamps at a marked reduction of face value. Countries that sell or have sold canceled-to-order stamps at *full* face value include United Nations, Australia, Netherlands, France and Switzerland. It may be almost impossible to identify such stamps if the gum has been removed, because official government canceling devices are used. Postally used copies of these items on cover, however, are usually worth more than the canceled-to-order stamps with original gum.

Abbreviations

Scott Publishing Co. uses a consistent set of abbreviations throughout this catalogue to conserve space, while still providing necessary information.

COLOR ABBREVIATIONS

amb .amber	crim .crimson	ol .....olive
anil ..aniline	cr .....cream	olvn .olivine
ap ....apple	dk ....dark	org ...orange
aqua.aquamarine	dl .....dull	pck...peacock
az.....azure	dp ....deep	pnksh pinkish
bis....bister	db ....drab	Prus .Prussian
bl .....blue	emer emerald	pur...purple
bld ...blood	gldn .golden	redsh reddish
blk ...black	grysh grayish	res....reseda
bril...brilliant	grn ...green	ros ...rosine
brn...brown	grnsh greenish	ryl ....royal
brnsh brownish	hel ...heliotrope	sal ....salmon
brnz .bronze	hn ...henna	saph .sapphire
brt....bright	ind ...indigo	scar ..scarlet
brnt..burnt	int....intense	sep ...sepia
car ...carmine	lav...lavender	sien ..sienna
cer ...cerise	lem ...lemon	sil .....silver
chlky chalky	lil .....lilac	sl ......slate
cham chamois	lt ......light	stl .....steel
chnt .chestnut	mag..magenta	turq..turquoise
choc.chocolate	man .manila	ultra.ultramarine
chr...chrome	mar ..maroon	Ven ..Venetian
cit ....citron	mv ...mauve	ver ...vermilion
cl .....claret	multi multicolored	vio ...violet
cob...cobalt	mlky milky	yel....yellow
cop...copper	myr ..myrtle	yelsh yellowish

When no color is given for an overprint or surcharge, black is the color used. Abbreviations for colors used for overprints and surcharges include: "(B)" or "(Blk)," black; "(Bl)," blue; "(R)," red; and "(G)," green.

Additional abbreviations in this catalogue are shown below:

Adm..............	Administration
AFL..............	American Federation of Labor
Anniv.	Anniversary
APS..............	American Philatelic Society
Assoc.	Association
ASSR............	Autonomous Soviet Socialist Republic
b.	Born
BEP..............	Bureau of Engraving and Printing
Bicent.	Bicentennial
Bklt..............	Booklet
Brit.	British
btwn.	Between
Bur.	Bureau
c. or ca........	Circa
Cat..............	Catalogue
Cent.............	Centennial, century, centenary
CIO..............	Congress of Industrial Organizations
Conf.............	Conference
Cong...........	Congress
Cpl..............	Corporal
CTO.............	Canceled to order
d.	Died
Dbl..............	Double
EKU	Earliest known use
Engr.	Engraved
Exhib.	Exhibition
Expo.	Exposition
Fed.	Federation
GB	Great Britain
Gen..............	General
GPO.............	General post office
Horiz............	Horizontal
Imperf..........	Imperforate
Impt.............	Imprint

Intl..............	International
Invtd............	Inverted
L.................	Left
Lieut., lt.	Lieutenant
Litho.	Lithographed
LL	Lower left
LR..............	Lower right
mm	Millimeter
Ms.	Manuscript
Natl..............	National
No.	Number
NY	New York
NYC.............	New York City
Ovpt.	Overprint
Ovptd...........	Overprinted
P.................	Plate number
Perf.............	Perforated, perforation
Phil.	Philatelic
Photo.	Photogravure
PO	Post office
Pr.	Pair
P.R.	Puerto Rico
Prec.	Precancel, precanceled
Pres.............	President
PTT..............	Post, Telephone and Telegraph
Rio	Rio de Janeiro
Sgt.	Sergeant
Soc..............	Society
Souv............	Souvenir
SSR	Soviet Socialist Republic, see ASSR
St................	Saint, street
Surch.	Surcharge
Typo.............	Typographed
UL	Upper left
Unwmkd......	Unwatermarked
UPU............	Universal Postal Union
UR	Upper Right
US..............	United States
USPOD	United States Post Office Department
USSR...........	Union of Soviet Socialist Republics
Vert.............	Vertical
VP	Vice president
Wmk...........	Watermark
Wmkd..........	Watermarked
WWI...........	World War I
WWII..........	World War II

Examination

Scott Publishing Co. will not comment upon the genuineness, grade or condition of stamps, because of the time and responsibility involved. Rather, there are several expertizing groups that undertake this work for both collectors and dealers. Neither will Scott Publishing Co. appraise or identify philatelic material. The company cannot take responsibility for unsolicited stamps or covers sent by individuals.

All letters, E-mails, etc. are read attentively, but they are not always answered due to time considerations.

How to order from your dealer

When ordering stamps from a dealer, it is not necessary to write the full description of a stamp as listed in this catalogue. All you need is the name of the country, the Scott catalogue number and whether the desired item is unused or used. For example, "Japan Scott 422 unused" is sufficient to identify the unused stamp of Japan listed as "422 A206 5y brown."

Basic Stamp Information

A stamp collector's knowledge of the combined elements that make a given stamp issue unique determines his or her ability to identify stamps. These elements include paper, watermark, method of separation, printing, design and gum. On the following pages each of these important areas is briefly described.

Paper

Paper is an organic material composed of a compacted weave of cellulose fibers and generally formed into sheets. Paper used to print stamps may be manufactured in sheets, or it may have been part of a large roll (called a web) before being cut to size. The fibers most often used to create paper on which stamps are printed include bark, wood, straw and certain grasses. In many cases, linen or cotton rags have been added for greater strength and durability. Grinding, bleaching, cooking and rinsing these raw fibers reduces them to a slushy pulp, referred to by paper makers as "stuff." Sizing and, sometimes, coloring matter is added to the pulp to make different types of finished paper.

After the stuff is prepared, it is poured onto sieve-like frames that allow the water to run off, while retaining the matted pulp. As fibers fall onto the screen and are held by gravity, they form a natural weave that will later hold the paper together. If the screen has metal bits that are formed into letters or images attached, it leaves slightly thinned areas on the paper. These are called watermarks.

When the stuff is almost dry, it is passed under pressure through smooth or engraved rollers - dandy rolls - or placed between cloth in a press to be flattened and dried.

Stamp paper falls broadly into two types: wove and laid. The nature of the surface of the frame onto which the pulp is first deposited causes the differences in appearance between the two. If the surface is smooth and even, the paper will be of fairly uniform texture throughout. This is known as *wove paper*. Early papermaking machines poured the pulp onto a continuously circulating web of felt, but modern machines feed the pulp onto a cloth-like screen made of closely interwoven fine wires. This paper, when held to a light, will show little dots or points very close together. The proper name for this is "wire wove," but the type is still considered wove. Any U.S. or British stamp printed after 1880 will serve as an example of wire wove paper.

Closely spaced parallel wires, with cross wires at wider intervals, make up the frames used for what is known as *laid paper*. A greater thickness of the pulp will settle between the wires. The paper, when held to a light, will show alternate light and dark lines. The spacing and the thickness of the lines may vary, but on any one sheet of paper they are all alike. See Russia Scott 31-38 for examples of laid paper.

Batonne, from the French word meaning "a staff," is a term used if the lines in the paper are spaced quite far apart, like the printed ruling on a writing tablet. Batonne paper may be either wove or laid. If laid, fine laid lines can be seen between the batons.

Quadrille is the term used when the lines in the paper form little squares. *Oblong quadrille* is the term used when rectangles, rather than squares, are formed. See Mexico-Guadalajara Scott 35-37 for examples of oblong quadrille paper.

Paper also is classified as thick or thin, hard or soft, and by color if dye is added during manufacture. Such colors may include yellowish, greenish, bluish and reddish.

Brief explanations of other types of paper used for printing stamps, as well as examples, follow.

Pelure — Pelure paper is a very thin, hard and often brittle paper that is sometimes bluish or grayish in appearance. See Serbia Scott 169-170.

Native — This is a term applied to handmade papers used to produce some of the early stamps of the Indian states. Stamps printed on native paper may be expected to display various natural inclusions that are normal and do not negatively affect value. Japanese paper, originally made of mulberry fibers and rice flour, is part of this group. See Japan Scott 1-18.

Manila — This type of paper is often used to make stamped envelopes and wrappers. It is a coarse-textured stock, usually smooth on one side and rough on the other. A variety of colors of manila paper exist, but the most common range is yellowish-brown.

Silk — Introduced by the British in 1847 as a safeguard against counterfeiting, silk paper contains bits of colored silk thread scattered throughout. The density of these fibers varies greatly and can include as few as one fiber per stamp or hundreds. U.S. revenue Scott R152 is a good example of an easy-to-identify silk paper stamp.

Silk-thread paper has uninterrupted threads of colored silk arranged so that one or more threads run through the stamp or postal stationery. See Great Britain Scott 5-6 and Switzerland Scott 14-19.

Granite — Filled with minute cloth or colored paper fibers of various colors and lengths, granite paper should not be confused with either type of silk paper. Austria Scott 172-175 and a number of Swiss stamps are examples of granite paper.

Chalky — A chalk-like substance coats the surface of chalky paper to discourage the cleaning and reuse of canceled stamps, as well as to provide a smoother, more acceptable printing surface. Because the designs of stamps printed on chalky paper are imprinted on what is often a water-soluble coating, any attempt to remove a cancellation will destroy the stamp. *Do not soak these stamps in any fluid.* To remove a stamp printed on chalky paper from an envelope, wet the paper from underneath the stamp until the gum dissolves enough to release the stamp from the paper. See St. Kitts-Nevis Scott 89-90 for examples of stamps printed on this type of chalky paper.

India — Another name for this paper, originally introduced from China about 1750, is "China Paper." It is a thin, opaque paper often used for plate and die proofs by many countries.

Double — In philately, the term double paper has two distinct meanings. The first is a two-ply paper, usually a combination of a thick and a thin sheet, joined during manufacture. This type was used experimentally as a means to discourage the reuse of stamps.

The design is printed on the thin paper. Any attempt to remove a cancellation would destroy the design. U.S. Scott 158 and other Banknote-era stamps exist on this form of double paper.

The second type of double paper occurs on a rotary press, when the end of one paper roll, or web, is affixed to the next roll to save time feeding the paper through the press. Stamp designs are printed over the joined paper and, if overlooked by inspectors, may get into post office stocks.

Goldbeater's Skin — This type of paper was used for the 1866 issue of Prussia, and was a tough, translucent paper. The design was printed in reverse on the back of the stamp, and the gum applied over the printing. It is impossible to remove stamps printed on this type of paper from the paper to which they are affixed without destroying the design.

Ribbed — Ribbed paper has an uneven, corrugated surface made by passing the paper through ridged rollers. This type exists on some copies of U.S. Scott 156-165.

Various other substances, or substrates, have been used for stamp manufacture, including wood, aluminum, copper, silver and gold foil, plastic, and silk and cotton fabrics.

Wove | Laid | Granite

Quadrille | Oblong Quadrille | Laid Batonne

Watermarks

Watermarks are an integral part of some papers. They are formed in the process of paper manufacture. Watermarks consist of small designs, formed of wire or cut from metal and soldered to the surface of the mold or, sometimes, on the dandy roll. The designs may be in the form of crowns, stars, anchors, letters or other characters or symbols. These pieces of metal - known in the paper-making industry as "bits" - impress a design into the paper. The design sometimes may be seen by holding the stamp to the light. Some are more easily seen with a watermark detector. This important tool is a small black tray into which a stamp is placed face down and dampened with a fast-evaporating watermark detection fluid that brings up the watermark image in the form of dark lines against a lighter background. These dark lines are the thinner areas of the paper known as the watermark. Some watermarks are extremely difficult to locate, due to either a faint impression, watermark location or the color of the stamp. There also are electric watermark detectors that come with plastic filter disks of various colors. The disks neutralize the color of the stamp, permitting the watermark to be seen more easily.

Multiple watermarks of Crown Agents and Burma

Watermarks of Uruguay, Vatican City and Jamaica

WARNING: Some inks used in the photogravure process dissolve in watermark fluids (Please see the section on Soluble Printing Inks). Also, see "chalky paper."

Watermarks may be found normal, reversed, inverted, reversed and inverted, sideways or diagonal, as seen from the back of the stamp. The relationship of watermark to stamp design depends on the position of the printing plates or how paper is fed through the press. On machine-made paper, watermarks normally are read from right to left. The design is repeated closely throughout the sheet in a "multiple-watermark design." In a "sheet watermark," the design appears only once on the sheet, but extends over many stamps. Individual stamps may carry only a small fraction or none of the watermark.

"Marginal watermarks" occur in the margins of sheets or panes of stamps. They occur on the outside border of paper (ostensibly outside the area where stamps are to be printed). A large row of letters may spell the name of the country or the manufacturer of the paper, or a border of lines may appear. Careless press feeding may cause parts of these letters and/or lines to show on stamps of the outer row of a pane.

Soluble Printing Inks

WARNING: Most stamp colors are permanent; that is, they are not seriously affected by short-term exposure to light or water. Many colors, especially of modern inks, fade from excessive exposure to light. There are stamps printed with inks that dissolve easily in water or in fluids used to detect watermarks. Use of these inks was intentional to prevent the removal of cancellations. Water affects all aniline inks, those on so-called safety paper and some photogravure printings - all such inks are known as *fugitive colors. Removal from paper of such stamps requires care and alternatives to traditional soaking.*

Separation

"Separation" is the general term used to describe methods used to separate stamps. The three standard forms currently in use are perforating, rouletting and die-cutting. These methods are done during the stamp production process, after printing. Sometimes these methods are done on-press or sometimes as a separate step. The earliest issues, such as the 1840 Penny Black of Great Britain (Scott 1), did not have any means provided for separation. It was expected the stamps would be cut apart with scissors or folded and torn. These are examples of imperforate stamps. Many stamps were first issued in imperforate formats and were later issued with perforations. Therefore, care must be observed in buying single imperforate stamps to be certain they were issued imperforate and are not perforated copies that have been altered by having the perforations trimmed away. Stamps issued imperforate usually are valued as singles. However, imperforate varieties of normally perforated stamps should be collected in pairs or larger pieces as indisputable evidence of their imperforate character.

PERFORATION

The chief style of separation of stamps, and the one that is in almost universal use today, is perforating. By this process, paper between the stamps is cut away in a line of holes, usually round, leaving little bridges of paper between the stamps to hold them together. Some types of perforation, such as hyphen-hole perfs, can be confused with roulettes, but a close visual inspection reveals that paper has been removed. The little perforation bridges, which project from the stamp when it is torn from the pane, are called the teeth of the perforation.

As the size of the perforation is sometimes the only way to differentiate between two otherwise identical stamps, it is necessary to be able to accurately measure and describe them. This is done with a perforation gauge, usually a ruler-like device that has dots or graduated lines to show how many perforations may be counted in the space of two centimeters. Two centimeters is the space universally adopted in which to measure perforations.

Perforation gauge

perce en arc   perce en lignes

perce en points   oblique roulette

perce en scie   perce serpentin

To measure a stamp, run it along the gauge until the dots on it fit exactly into the perforations of the stamp. If you are using a graduated-line perforation gauge, simply slide the stamp along the surface until the lines on the gauge perfectly project from the center of the bridges or holes. The number to the side of the line of dots or lines that fit the stamp's perforation is the measurement. For example, an "11" means that 11 perforations fit between two centimeters. The description of the stamp therefore is "perf. 11." If the gauge of the perforations on the top and bottom of a stamp differs from that on the sides, the result is what is known as *compound perforations*. In measuring compound perforations, the gauge at top and bottom is always given first, then the sides. Thus, a stamp that measures 11 at top and bottom and 10 1/2 at the sides is "perf. 11 x 10 1/2." See U.S. Scott 632-642 for examples of compound perforations.

Stamps also are known with perforations different on three or all four sides. Descriptions of such items are clockwise, beginning with the top of the stamp.

A perforation with small holes and teeth close together is a "fine perforation." One with large holes and teeth far apart is a "coarse perforation." Holes that are jagged, rather than clean-cut, are "rough perforations." *Blind perforations* are the slight impressions left by the perforating pins if they fail to puncture the paper. Multiples of stamps showing blind perforations may command a slight premium over normally perforated stamps.

The term *syncopated perfs* describes intentional irregularities in the perforations. The earliest form was used by the Netherlands from 1925-33, where holes were omitted to create distinctive patterns. Beginning in 1992, Great Britain has used an oval perforation to help prevent counterfeiting. Several other countries have started using the oval perfs or other syncopated perf patterns.

A new type of perforation, still primarily used for postal stationery, is known as microperfs. Microperfs are tiny perforations (in some cases hundreds of holes per two centimeters) that allows items to be intentionally separated very easily, while not accidentally breaking apart as easily as standard perforations. These are not currently measured or differentiated by size, as are standard perforations.

ROULETTING

In rouletting, the stamp paper is cut partly or wholly through, with no paper removed. In perforating, some paper is removed. Rouletting derives its name from the French roulette, a spur-like wheel. As the wheel is rolled over the paper, each point makes a small cut. The number of cuts made in a two-centimeter space determines the gauge of the roulette, just as the number of perforations in two centimeters determines the gauge of the perforation.

The shape and arrangement of the teeth on the wheels varies. Various roulette types generally carry French names:

Perce en lignes - rouletted in lines. The paper receives short, straight cuts in lines. This is the most common type of rouletting. See Mexico Scott 500.

Perce en points - pin-rouletted or pin-perfed. This differs from a small perforation because no paper is removed, although round, equidistant holes are pricked through the paper. See Mexico Scott 242-256.

Perce en arc and *perce en scie* - pierced in an arc or saw-toothed designs, forming half circles or small triangles. See Hanover (German States) Scott 25-29.

Perce en serpentin - serpentine roulettes. The cuts form a serpentine or wavy line. See Brunswick (German States) Scott 13-18.

Once again, no paper is removed by these processes, leaving the stamps easily separated, but closely attached.

DIE-CUTTING

The third major form of stamp separation is die-cutting. This is a method where a die in the pattern of separation is created that later cuts the stamp paper in a stroke motion. Although some standard stamps bear die-cut perforations, this process is primarily used for self-adhesive postage stamps. Die-cutting can appear in straight lines, such as U.S. Scott 2522, shapes, such as U.S. Scott 1551, or imitating the appearance of perforations, such as New Zealand Scott 935A and 935B.

Printing Processes

ENGRAVING (Intaglio, Line-engraving, Etching)

Master die — The initial operation in the process of line engraving is making the master die. The die is a small, flat block of softened steel upon which the stamp design is recess engraved in reverse.

Master die

Photographic reduction of the original art is made to the appropriate size. It then serves as a tracing guide for the initial outline of the design. The engraver lightly traces the design on the steel with his graver, then slowly works the design until it is completed. At various points during the engraving process, the engraver hand-inks the die and makes an impression to check his progress. These are known as progressive die proofs. After completion of the engraving, the die is hardened to withstand the stress and pressures of later transfer operations.

Transfer roll

Transfer roll — Next is production of the transfer roll that, as the name implies, is the medium used to transfer the subject from the master die to the printing plate. A blank roll of soft steel, mounted on a mandrel, is placed under the bearers of the transfer press to allow it to roll freely on its axis. The hardened die is placed on the bed of the press and the face of the transfer roll is applied to the die, under pressure. The bed or the roll is then rocked back and forth under increasing pressure, until the soft steel of the roll is forced into every engraved line of the die. The resulting impression on the roll is known as a "relief" or a "relief transfer." The engraved image is now positive in appearance and stands out from the steel. After the required number of reliefs are "rocked in," the soft steel transfer roll is hardened.

Different flaws may occur during the relief process. A defective relief may occur during the rocking in process because of a minute piece of foreign material lodging on the die, or some other cause. Imperfections in the steel of the transfer roll may result in a breaking away of parts of the design. This is known as a relief break, which will show up on finished stamps as small, unprinted areas. If a damaged relief remains in use, it will transfer a repeating defect to the plate. Deliberate alterations of reliefs sometimes occur. "Altered reliefs" designate these changed conditions.

Plate — The final step in pre-printing production is the making of the printing plate. A flat piece of soft steel replaces the die on the bed of the transfer press. One of the reliefs on the transfer roll is positioned over this soft steel. Position, or layout, dots determine the correct position on the plate. The dots have been lightly marked on

the plate in advance. After the correct position of the relief is determined, the design is rocked in by following the same method used in making the transfer roll. The difference is that this time the image is being transferred from the transfer roll, rather than to it. Once the design is entered on the plate, it appears in reverse and is recessed. There are as many transfers entered on the plate as there are subjects printed on the sheet of stamps. It is during this process that double and shifted transfers occur, as well as re-entries. These are the result of improperly entered images that have not been properly burnished out prior to rocking in a new image.

Modern siderography processes, such as those used by the U.S. Bureau of Engraving and Printing, involve an automated form of rocking designs in on preformed cylindrical printing sleeves. The same process also allows for easier removal and re-entry of worn images right on the sleeve.

Transferring the design to the plate

Following the entering of the required transfers on the plate, the position dots, layout dots and lines, scratches and other markings generally are burnished out. Added at this time by the siderographer are any required *guide lines*, *plate numbers* or other *marginal markings*. The plate is then hand-inked and a proof impression is taken. This is known as a plate proof. If the impression is approved, the plate is machined for fitting onto the press, is hardened and sent to the plate vault ready for use.

On press, the plate is inked and the surface is automatically wiped clean, leaving ink only in the recessed lines. Paper is then forced under pressure into the engraved recessed lines, thereby receiving the ink. Thus, the ink lines on engraved stamps are slightly raised, and slight depressions (debossing) occur on the back of the stamp. Prior to the advent of modern high-speed presses and more advanced ink formulations, paper had to be dampened before receiving the ink. This sometimes led to uneven shrinkage by the time the stamps were perforated, resulting in improperly perforated stamps, or misperfs. Newer presses use drier paper, thus both *wet* and *dry printings* exist on some stamps.

Rotary Press — Until 1914, only flat plates were used to print engraved stamps. Rotary press printing was introduced in 1914, and slowly spread. Some countries still use flat-plate printing.

After approval of the plate proof, older *rotary press plates* require additional machining. They are curved to fit the press cylinder. "Gripper slots" are cut into the back of each plate to receive the "grippers," which hold the plate securely on the press. The plate is then hardened. Stamps printed from these bent rotary press plates are longer or wider than the same stamps printed from flat-plate presses. The stretching of the plate during the curving process is what causes this distortion.

Re-entry — To execute a re-entry on a flat plate, the transfer roll is re-applied to the plate, often at some time after its first use on the press. Worn-out designs can be resharpened by carefully burnishing out the original image and re-entering it from the transfer roll. If the original impression has not been sufficiently removed and the transfer roll is not precisely in line with the remaining impression, the resulting double transfer will make the re-entry obvious. If the registration is true, a re-entry may be difficult or impossible to distinguish. Sometimes a stamp printed from a successful re-entry is identified by having a much sharper and clearer impression than its neighbors. With the advent of rotary presses, post-press re-entries were not possible. After a plate was curved for the rotary press, it was impossible to make a re-entry. This is because the plate had already been bent once (with the design distorted).

However, with the introduction of the previously mentioned modern-style siderography machines, entries are made to the preformed cylindrical printing sleeve. Such sleeves are dechromed and softened. This allows individual images to be burnished out and re-entered on the curved sleeve. The sleeve is then rechromed, resulting in longer press life.

Double Transfer — This is a description of the condition of a transfer on a plate that shows evidence of a duplication of all, or a portion of the design. It usually is the result of the changing of the registration between the transfer roll and the plate during the rocking in of the original entry. Double transfers also occur when only a portion of the design has been rocked in and improper positioning is noted. If the worker elected not to burnish out the partial or completed design, a strong double transfer will occur for part or all of the design.

It sometimes is necessary to remove the original transfer from a plate and repeat the process a second time. If the finished re-worked image shows traces of the original impression, attributable to incomplete burnishing, the result is a partial double transfer.

With the modern automatic machines mentioned previously, double transfers are all but impossible to create. Those partially doubled images on stamps printed from such sleeves are more than likely re-entries, rather than true double transfers.

Re-engraved — Alterations to a stamp design are sometimes necessary after some stamps have been printed. In some cases, either the original die or the actual printing plate may have its "temper" drawn (softened), and the design will be re-cut. The resulting impressions from such a re-engraved die or plate may differ slightly from the original issue, and are known as "re-engraved." If the alteration was made to the master die, all future printings will be consistently different from the original. If alterations were made to the printing plate, each altered stamp on the plate will be slightly different from each other, allowing specialists to reconstruct a complete printing plate.

Dropped Transfers — If an impression from the transfer roll has not been properly placed, a dropped transfer may occur. The final stamp image will appear obviously out of line with its neighbors.

Short Transfer — Sometimes a transfer roll is not rocked its entire length when entering a transfer onto a plate. As a result, the finished transfer on the plate fails to show the complete design, and the finished stamp will have an incomplete design printed. This is known as a "short transfer." U.S. Scott No. 8 is a good example of a short transfer.

TYPOGRAPHY (Letterpress, Surface Printing, Flexography, Dry Offset, High Etch)

Although the word "Typography" is obsolete as a term describing a printing method, it was the accepted term throughout the first century of postage stamps. Therefore, appropriate Scott listings in this catalogue refer to typographed stamps. The current term for this form of printing, however, is "letterpress."

As it relates to the production of postage stamps, letterpress printing is the reverse of engraving. Rather than having recessed areas trap the ink and deposit it on paper, only the raised areas of the design are inked. This is comparable to the type of printing seen by inking and using an ordinary rubber stamp. Letterpress includes all printing where the design is above the surface area, whether it is wood, metal or, in some instances, hardened rubber or polymer plastic.

For most letterpress-printed stamps, the engraved master is made in much the same manner as for engraved stamps. In this instance, however, an additional step is needed. The design is transferred to another surface before being transferred to the transfer roll. In this way, the transfer roll has a recessed stamp design, rather than one done in relief. This makes the printing areas on the final plate raised, or relief areas.

For less-detailed stamps of the 19th century, the area on the die not used as a printing surface was cut away, leaving the surface area raised. The original die was then reproduced by stereotyping or electrotyping. The resulting electrotypes were assembled in the required number and format of the desired sheet of stamps. The plate used in printing the stamps was an electroplate of these assembled electrotypes.

Once the final letterpress plates are created, ink is applied to the raised surface and the pressure of the press transfers the ink impression to the paper. In contrast to engraving, the fine lines of letterpress are impressed on the surface of the stamp, leaving a debossed surface. When viewed from the back (as on a typewritten page), the corresponding line work on the stamp will be raised slightly (embossed) above the surface.

PHOTOGRAVURE (Gravure, Rotogravure, Heliogravure)

In this process, the basic principles of photography are applied to a chemically sensitized metal plate, rather than photographic paper. The design is transferred photographically to the plate through a halftone, or dot-matrix screen, breaking the reproduction into tiny dots. The plate is treated chemically and the dots form depressions, called cells, of varying depths and diameters, depending on the degrees of shade in the design. Then, like engraving, ink is applied to the plate and the surface is wiped clean. This leaves ink in the tiny cells that is lifted out and deposited on the paper when it is pressed against the plate.

Gravure is most often used for multicolored stamps, generally using the three primary colors (red, yellow and blue) and black. By varying the dot matrix pattern and density of these colors, virtually any color can be reproduced. A typical full-color gravure stamp will be created from four printing cylinders (one for each color). The original multicolored image will have been photographically separated into its component colors.

Modern gravure printing may use computer-generated dot-matrix screens, and modern plates may be of various types including metal-coated plastic. The catalogue designation of Photogravure (or "Photo") covers any of these older and more modern gravure methods of printing.

For examples of the first photogravure stamps printed (1914), see Bavaria Scott 94-114.

LITHOGRAPHY (Offset Lithography, Stone Lithography, Dilitho, Planography, Collotype)

The principle that oil and water do not mix is the basis for lithography. The stamp design is drawn by hand or transferred from engraving to the surface of a lithographic stone or metal plate in a greasy (oily) substance. This oily substance holds the ink, which will later be transferred to the paper. The stone (or plate) is wet with an acid fluid, causing it to repel the printing ink in all areas not covered by the greasy substance.

Transfer paper is used to transfer the design from the original stone or plate. A series of duplicate transfers are grouped and, in turn, transferred to the final printing plate.

Photolithography — The application of photographic processes to lithography. This process allows greater flexibility of design, related to use of halftone screens combined with line work. Unlike photogravure or engraving, this process can allow large, solid areas to be printed.

Offset — A refinement of the lithographic process. A rubber-covered blanket cylinder takes the impression from the inked lithographic plate. From the "blanket" the impression is *offset* or transferred to the paper. Greater flexibility and speed are the principal reasons offset printing has largely displaced lithography. The term "lithography" covers both processes, and results are almost identical.

EMBOSSED (Relief) Printing

Embossing, not considered one of the four main printing types, is a method in which the design first is sunk into the metal of the die. Printing is done against a yielding platen, such as leather or linoleum. The platen is forced into the depression of the die, thus forming the design on the paper in relief. This process is often used for metallic inks.

Embossing may be done without color (see Sardinia Scott 4-6); with color printed around the embossed area (see Great Britain Scott 5 and most U.S. envelopes); and with color in exact registration with the embossed subject (see Canada Scott 656-657).

HOLOGRAMS

For objects to appear as holograms on stamps, a model exactly the same size as it is to appear on the hologram must be created. Rather than using photographic film to capture the image, holography records an image on a photoresist material. In processing, chemicals eat away at certain exposed areas, leaving a pattern of constructive and destructive interference. When the phororesist is developed, the result is a pattern of uneven ridges that acts as a mold. This mold is then coated with metal, and the resulting form is used to press copies in much the same way phonograph records are produced.

A typical reflective hologram used for stamps consists of a reproduction of the uneven patterns on a plastic film that is applied to a reflective background, usually a silver or gold foil. Light is reflected off the background through the film, making the pattern present on the film visible. Because of the uneven pattern of the film, the viewer will perceive the objects in their proper three-dimensional relationships with appropriate brightness.

The first hologram on a stamp was produced by Austria in 1988 (Scott 1441).

FOIL APPLICATION

A modern tecnique of applying color to stamps involves the application of metallic foil to the stamp paper. A pattern of foil is applied to the stamp paper by use of a stamping die. The foil usually is flat, but it may be textured. Canada Scott 1735 has three different foil applications in pearl, bronze and gold. The gold foil was textured using a chemical-etch copper embossing die. The printing of this stamp also involved two-color offset lithography plus embossing.

COMBINATION PRINTINGS

Sometimes two or even three printing methods are combined in producing stamps. In these cases, such as Austria Scott 933 or Canada 1735 (described in the preceding paragraph), the multiple-printing technique can be determined by studying the individual characteristics of each printing type. A few stamps, such as Singapore Scott 684-684A, combine as many as three of the four major printing types (lithography, engraving and typography). When this is done it often indicates the incorporation of security devices against counterfeiting.

INK COLORS

Inks or colored papers used in stamp printing often are of mineral origin, although there are numerous examples of organic-based pigments. As a general rule, organic-based pigments are far more subject to varieties and change than those of mineral-based origin.

The appearance of any given color on a stamp may be affected by many aspects, including printing variations, light, color of paper, aging and chemical alterations.

Numerous printing variations may be observed. Heavier pressure or inking will cause a more intense color, while slight interruptions in the ink feed or lighter impressions will cause a lighter appearance. Stamps printed in the same color by water-based and solvent-based inks can differ significantly in appearance. This affects several stamps in the U.S. Prominent Americans series. Hand-mixed ink formulas (primarily from the 19th century) produced under different conditions (humidity and temperature) account for notable color variations in early printings of the same stamp (see U.S. Scott 248-250, 279B, for example). Different sources of pigment can also result in significant differences in color.

Light exposure and aging are closely related in the way they affect stamp color. Both eventually break down the ink and fade colors, so that a carefully kept stamp may differ significantly in color from an identical copy that has been exposed to light. If stamps are exposed to light either intentionally or accidentally, their colors can be faded or completely changed in some cases.

Papers of different quality and consistency used for the same stamp printing may affect color appearance. Most pelure papers, for example, show a richer color when compared with wove or laid papers. See Russia Scott 181a, for an example of this effect.

The very nature of the printing processes can cause a variety of differences in shades or hues of the same stamp. Some of these shades are scarcer than others, and are of particular interest to the advanced collector.

Luminescence

All forms of tagged stamps fall under the general category of luminescence. Within this broad category is fluorescence, dealing with forms of tagging visible under longwave ultraviolet light, and phosphorescence, which deals with tagging visible only under shortwave light. Phosphorescence leaves an afterglow and fluorescence does not. These treated stamps show up in a range of different colors when exposed to UV light. The differing wavelengths of the light activates the tagging material, making it glow in various colors that usually serve different mail processing purposes.

Intentional tagging is a post-World War II phenomenon, brought about by the increased literacy rate and rapidly growing mail volume. It was one of several answers to the problem of the need for more automated mail processes. Early tagged stamps served the purpose of triggering machines to separate different types of mail. A natural outgrowth was to also use the signal to trigger machines that faced all envelopes the same way and canceled them.

Tagged stamps come in many different forms. Some tagged stamps have luminescent shapes or images imprinted on them as a form of security device. Others have blocks (United States), stripes, frames (South Africa and Canada), overall coatings (United States), bars (Great Britain and Canada) and many other types. Some types of tagging are even mixed in with the pigmented printing ink (Australia Scott 366, Netherlands Scott 478 and U.S. Scott 1359 and 2443).

The means of applying taggant to stamps differs as much as the intended purposes for the stamps. The most common form of tagging is a coating applied to the surface of the printed stamp. Since the taggant ink is frequently invisible except under UV light, it does not interfere with the appearance of the stamp. Another common application is the use of phosphored papers. In this case the paper itself either has a coating of taggant applied before the stamp is printed, has taggant applied during the papermaking process (incorporating it into the fibers), or has the taggant mixed into the coating of the paper. The latter method, among others, is currently in use in the United States.

Many countries now use tagging in various forms to either expedite mail handling or to serve as a printing security device against counterfeiting. Following the introduction of tagged stamps for public use in 1959 by Great Britain, other countries have steadily joined the parade. Among those are Germany (1961); Canada and Denmark (1962); United States, Australia, France and Switzerland (1963); Belgium and Japan (1966); Sweden and Norway (1967); Italy (1968); and Russia (1969). Since then, many other countries have begun using forms of tagging, including Brazil, China, Czechoslovakia, Hong Kong, Guatemala, Indonesia, Israel, Lithuania, Luxembourg, Netherlands, Penrhyn Islands, Portugal, St. Vincent, Singapore, South Africa, Spain and Sweden to name a few.

In some cases, including United States, Canada, Great Britain and Switzerland, stamps were released both with and without tagging. Many of these were released during each country's experimental period. Tagged and untagged versions are listed for the aforementioned countries and are noted in some other countries' listings. For at least a few stamps, the experimentally tagged version is worth far more than its untagged counterpart, such as the 1963 experimental tagged version of France Scott 1024.

In some cases, luminescent varieties of stamps were inadvertently created. Several Russian stamps, for example, sport highly fluorescent ink that was not intended as a form of tagging. Older stamps, such as early U.S. postage dues, can be positively identified by the use of UV light, since the organic ink used has become slightly fluorescent over time. Other stamps, such as Austria Scott 70a-82a (varnish bars) and Obock Scott 46-64 (printed quadrille lines), have become fluorescent over time.

Various fluorescent substances have been added to paper to make it appear brighter. These optical brightners, as they are known, greatly affect the appearance of the stamp under UV light. The brightest of these is known as Hi-Brite paper. These paper varieties are beyond the scope of the Scott Catalogue.

Shortwave UV light also is used extensively in expertizing, since each form of paper has its own fluorescent characteristics that are impossible to perfectly match. It is therefore a simple matter to detect filled thins, added perforation teeth and other alterations that involve the addition of paper. UV light also is used to examine stamps that have had cancels chemically removed and for other purposes as well.

Gum

The Illustrated Gum Chart in the first part of this introduction shows and defines various types of gum condition. Because gum condition has an important impact on the value of unused stamps, we recommend studying this chart and the accompanying text carefully.

The gum on the back of a stamp may be shiny, dull, smooth, rough, dark, white, colored or tinted. Most stamp gumming adhesives use gum arabic or dextrine as a base. Certain polymers such as polyvinyl alcohol (PVA) have been used extensively since World War II.

The *Scott Standard Postage Stamp Catalogue* does not list items by types of gum. The *Scott Specialized Catalogue of United States Stamps* does differentiate among some types of gum for certain issues.

Reprints of stamps may have gum differing from the original issues. In addition, some countries have used different gum formulas for different seasons. These adhesives have different properties that may become more apparent over time.

Many stamps have been issued without gum, and the catalogue will note this fact. See, for example, United States Scott 40-47. Sometimes, gum may have been removed to preserve the stamp. Germany Scott B68, for example, has a highly acidic gum that eventually destroys the stamps. This item is valued in the catalogue with gum removed.

Reprints and Reissues

These are impressions of stamps (usually obsolete) made from the original plates or stones. If they are valid for postage and reproduce obsolete issues (such as U.S. Scott 102-111), the stamps are *reissues.* If they are from current issues, they are designated as *second, third,* etc., *printing.* If designated for a particular purpose, they are called *special printings.*

When special printings are not valid for postage, but are made from original dies and plates by authorized persons, they are *official reprints. Private reprints* are made from the original plates and dies by private hands. An example of a private reprint is that of the 1871-1932 reprints made from the original die of the 1845 New Haven, Conn., postmaster's provisional. *Official reproductions* or imitations are made from new dies and plates by government authorization. Scott will list those reissues that are valid for postage if they differ significantly from the original printing.

The U.S. government made special printings of its first postage stamps in 1875. Produced were official imitations of the first two stamps (listed as Scott 3-4), reprints of the demonetized pre-1861 issues (Scott 40-47) and reissues of the 1861 stamps, the 1869 stamps and the then-current 1875 denominations. Even though the official imitations and the reprints were not valid for postage, Scott lists all of these U.S. special printings.

Most reprints or reissues differ slightly from the original stamp in some characteristic, such as gum, paper, perforation, color or watermark. Sometimes the details are followed so meticulously that only a student of that specific stamp is able to distinguish the reprint or reissue from the original.

Remainders and Canceled to Order

Some countries sell their stock of old stamps when a new issue replaces them. To avoid postal use, the *remainders* usually are canceled with a punch hole, a heavy line or bar, or a more-or-less regular-looking cancellation. The most famous merchant of remainders was Nicholas F. Seebeck. In the 1880s and 1890s, he arranged printing contracts between the Hamilton Bank Note Co., of which he was a director, and several Central and South American countries. The contracts provided that the plates and all remainders of the yearly issues became the property of Hamilton. Seebeck saw to it that ample stock remained. The "Seebecks," both remainders and reprints, were standard packet fillers for decades.

Some countries also issue stamps *canceled-to-order (CTO),* either in sheets with original gum or stuck onto pieces of paper or envelopes and canceled. Such CTO items generally are worth less than postally used stamps. In cases where the CTO material is far more prevalent in the marketplace than postally used examples, the catalogue value relates to the CTO examples, with postally used examples noted as premium items. Most CTOs can be detected by the presence of gum. However, as the CTO practice goes back at least to 1885, the gum inevitably has been soaked off some stamps so they could pass as postally used. The normally applied postmarks usually differ slightly from standard postmarks, and specialists are able to tell the difference. When applied individually to envelopes by philatelically minded persons, CTO material is known as *favor canceled* and generally sells at large discounts.

Cinderellas and Facsimiles

Cinderella is a catch-all term used by stamp collectors to describe phantoms, fantasies, bogus items, municipal issues, exhibition seals, local revenues, transportation stamps, labels, poster stamps and many other types of items. Some cinderella collectors include in their collections local postage issues, telegraph stamps, essays and proofs, forgeries and counterfeits.

A *fantasy* is an adhesive created for a nonexistent stamp-issuing authority. Fantasy items range from imaginary countries (Occusi-Ambeno, Kingdom of Sedang, Principality of Trinidad or Torres Straits), to non-existent locals (Winans City Post), or nonexistent transportation lines (McRobish & Co.'s Acapulco-San Francisco Line).

On the other hand, if the entity exists and could have issued stamps (but did not) or was known to have issued other stamps, the items are considered *bogus* stamps. These would include the Mormon postage stamps of Utah, S. Allan Taylor's Guatemala and Paraguay inventions, the propaganda issues for the South Moluccas and the adhesives of the Page & Keyes local post of Boston.

Phantoms is another term for both fantasy and bogus issues.

Facsimiles are copies or imitations made to represent original stamps, but which do not pretend to be originals. A catalogue illustration is such a facsimile. Illustrations from the Moens catalogue of the last century were occasionally colored and passed off as stamps. Since the beginning of stamp collecting, facsimiles have been made for collectors as space fillers or for reference. They often carry the word "facsimile," "falsch" (German), "sanko" or "mozo" (Japanese), or "faux" (French) overprinted on the face or stamped on the back. Unfortunately, over the years a number of these items have had fake cancels applied over the facsimile notation and have been passed off as genuine.

Forgeries and Counterfeits

Forgeries and counterfeits have been with philately virtually from the beginning of stamp production. Over time, the terminology for the two has been used interchangeably. Although both forgeries and counterfeits are reproductions of stamps, the purposes behind their creation differ considerably.

Among specialists there is an increasing movement to more specifically define such items. Although there is no universally accepted terminology, we feel the following definitions most closely mirror the items and their purposes as they are currently defined.

Forgeries (also often referred to as *Counterfeits*) are reproductions of genuine stamps that have been created to defraud collectors. Such spurious items first appeared on the market around 1860, and most old-time collections contain one or more. Many are crude and easily spotted, but some can deceive experts.

An important supplier of these early philatelic forgeries was the Hamburg printer Gebruder Spiro. Many others with reputations in this craft included S. Allan Taylor, George Hussey, James Chute, George Forune, Benjamin & Sarpy, Julius Goldner, E. Oneglia and L.H. Mercier. Among the noted 20th-century forgers were Francois Fournier, Jean Sperati and the prolific Raoul DeThuin.

Forgeries may be complete replications, or they may be genuine stamps altered to resemble a scarcer (and more valuable) type. Most forgeries, particularly those of rare stamps, are worth only a small fraction of the value of a genuine example, but a few types, created by some of the most notable forgers, such as Sperati, can be worth as much or more than the genuine. Fraudulently produced copies are known of most classic rarities and many medium-priced stamps.

In addition to rare stamps, large numbers of common 19th- and early 20th-century stamps were forged to supply stamps to the early packet trade. Many can still be easily found. Few new philatelic forgeries have appeared in recent decades. Successful imitation of well-engraved work is virtually impossible. It has proven far easier to produce a fake by altering a genuine stamp than to duplicate a stamp completely.

Counterfeit (also often referred to as *Postal Counterfeit* or *Postal Forgery*) is the term generally applied to reproductions of stamps that have been created to defraud the government of revenue. Such items usually are created at the time a stamp is current and, in some cases, are hard to detect. Because most counterfeits are seized when the perpetrator is captured, postal counterfeits, particularly used on cover, are usually worth much more than a genuine example to spe-

cialists. The first postal counterfeit was of Spain's 4-cuarto carmine of 1854 (the real one is Scott 25). Apparently, the counterfeiters were not satisfied with their first version, which is now very scarce, and they soon created an engraved counterfeit, which is common. Postal counterfeits quickly followed in Austria, Naples, Sardinia and the Roman States. They have since been created in many other countries as well, including the United States.

An infamous counterfeit to defraud the government is the 1-shilling Great Britain "Stock Exchange" forgery of 1872, used on telegraph forms at the exchange that year. The stamp escaped detection until a stamp dealer noticed it in 1898.

Fakes

Fakes are genuine stamps altered in some way to make them more desirable. One student of this part of stamp collecting has estimated that by the 1950s more than 30,000 varieties of fakes were known. That number has grown greatly since then. The widespread existence of fakes makes it important for stamp collectors to study their philatelic holdings and use relevant literature. Likewise, collectors should buy from reputable dealers who guarantee their stamps and make full and prompt refunds should a purchased item be declared faked or altered by some mutually agreed-upon authority. Because fakes always have some genuine characteristics, it is not always possible to obtain unanimous agreement among experts regarding specific items. These students may change their opinions as philatelic knowledge increases. More than 80 percent of all fakes on the philatelic market today are regummed, reperforated (or perforated for the first time), or bear forged overprints, surcharges or cancellations.

Stamps can be chemically treated to alter or eliminate colors. For example, a pale rose stamp can be re-colored to resemble a blue shade of high market value. In other cases, treated stamps can be made to resemble missing color varieties. Designs may be changed by painting, or a stroke or a dot added or bleached out to turn an ordinary variety into a seemingly scarcer stamp. Part of a stamp can be bleached and reprinted in a different version, achieving an inverted center or frame. Margins can be added or repairs done so deceptively that the stamps move from the "repaired" into the "fake" category.

Fakers have not left the backs of the stamps untouched either. They may create false watermarks, add fake grills or press out genuine grills. A thin India paper proof may be glued onto a thicker backing to create the appearance an issued stamp, or a proof printed on cardboard may be shaved down and perforated to resemble a stamp. Silk threads are impressed into paper and stamps have been split so that a rare paper variety is added to an otherwise inexpensive stamp. The most common treatment to the back of a stamp, however, is regumming.

Some in the business of faking stamps have openly advertised foolproof application of "original gum" to stamps that lack it, although most publications now ban such ads from their pages. It is believed that very few early stamps have survived without being hinged. The large number of never-hinged examples of such earlier material offered for sale thus suggests the widespread extent of regumming activity. Regumming also may be used to hide repairs or thin spots. Dipping the stamp into watermark fluid, or examining it under long-wave ultraviolet light often will reveal these flaws.

Fakers also tamper with separations. Ingenious ways to add margins are known. Perforated wide-margin stamps may be falsely represented as imperforate when trimmed. Reperforating is commonly done to create scarce coil or perforation varieties, and to eliminate the naturally occurring straight-edge stamps found in sheet margin positions of many earlier issues. Custom has made straight-edged stamps less desirable. Fakers have obliged by perforating straight-edged stamps so that many are now uncommon, if not rare.

Another fertile field for the faker is that of overprints, surcharges and cancellations. The forging of rare surcharges or overprints began in the 1880s or 1890s. These forgeries are sometimes difficult to detect, but experts have identified almost all. Occasionally, overprints or cancellations are removed to create non-overprinted stamps or seemingly unused items. This is most commonly done by removing a manuscript cancel to make a stamp resemble an unused example. "SPECIMEN" overprints may be removed by scraping and repainting to create non-overprinted varieties. Fakers use inexpensive revenues or pen-canceled stamps to generate unused stamps for further faking by adding other markings. The quartz lamp or UV lamp and a high-powered magnifying glass help to easily detect removed cancellations.

The bigger problem, however, is the addition of overprints, surcharges or cancellations - many with such precision that they are very difficult to ascertain. Plating of the stamps or the overprint can be an important method of detection.

Fake postmarks may range from many spurious fancy cancellations to a host of markings applied to transatlantic covers, to adding normally appearing postmarks to definitives of some countries with stamps that are valued far higher used than unused. With the increased popularity of cover collecting, and the widespread interest in postal history, a fertile new field for fakers has come about. Some have tried to create entire covers. Others specialize in adding stamps, tied by fake cancellations, to genuine stampless covers, or replacing less expensive or damaged stamps with more valuable ones. Detailed study of postal rates in effect at the time a cover in question was mailed, including the analysis of each handstamp used during the period, ink analysis and similar techniques, usually will unmask the fraud.

Restoration and Repairs

Scott Publishing Co. bases its catalogue values on stamps that are free of defects and otherwise meet the standards set forth earlier in this introduction. Most stamp collectors desire to have the finest copy of an item possible. Even within given grading categories there are variances. This leads to a controversial practice that is not defined in any universal manner: stamp *restoration*.

There are broad differences of opinion about what is permissible when it comes to restoration. Carefully applying a soft eraser to a stamp or cover to remove light soiling is one form of restoration, as is washing a stamp in mild soap and water to clean it. These are fairly accepted forms of restoration. More severe forms of restoration include pressing out creases or removing stains caused by tape. To what degree each of these is acceptable is dependent upon the individual situation. Further along the spectrum is the freshening of a stamp's color by removing oxide build-up or the effects of wax paper left next to stamps shipped to the tropics.

At some point in this spectrum the concept of *repair* replaces that of restoration. Repairs include filling thin spots, mending tears by reweaving or adding a missing perforation tooth. Regumming stamps may have been acceptable as a restoration or repair technique many decades ago, but today it is considered a form of fakery.

Restored stamps may or may not sell at a discount, and it is possible that the value of individual restored items may be enhanced over that of their pre-restoration state. Specific situations dictate the resultant value of such an item. Repaired stamps sell at substantial discounts from the value of sound stamps.

Terminology

Booklets — Many countries have issued stamps in small booklets for the convenience of users. This idea continues to become increasingly popular in many countries. Booklets have been issued in many sizes and forms, often with advertising on the covers, the panes of stamps or on the interleaving.

The panes used in booklets may be printed from special plates or made from regular sheets. All panes from booklets issued by the United States and many from those of other countries contain stamps that are straight edged on the sides, but perforated between. Others are distinguished by orientation of watermark or other identifying features. Any stamp-like unit in the pane, either printed or blank, that is not a postage stamp, is considered to be a *label* in the catalogue listings.

Scott lists and values booklet panes. Modern complete booklets also are listed and valued. Individual booklet panes are listed only when they are not fashioned from existing sheet stamps and, therefore, are identifiable from their sheet stamp counterparts.

Panes usually do not have a used value assigned to them because there is little market activity for used booklet panes, even though many exist used and there is some demand for them.

Cancellations — The marks or obliterations put on stamps by postal authorities to show that they have performed service and to prevent their reuse are known as cancellations. If the marking is made with a pen, it is considered a "pen cancel." When the location of the post office appears in the marking, it is a "town cancellation." A "postmark" is technically any postal marking, but in practice the term generally is applied to a town cancellation with a date. When calling attention to a cause or celebration, the marking is known as a "slogan cancellation." Many other types and styles of cancellations exist, such as duplex, numerals, targets, fancy and others. See also "precancels," below.

Coil Stamps — These are stamps that are issued in rolls for use in dispensers, affixing and vending machines. Those coils of the United States, Canada, Sweden and some other countries are perforated horizontally or vertically only, with the outer edges imperforate. Coil stamps of some countries, such as Great Britain and Germany, are perforated on all four sides and may in some cases be distinguished from their sheet stamp counterparts by watermarks, counting numbers on the reverse or other means.

Covers — Entire envelopes, with or without adhesive postage stamps, that have passed through the mail and bear postal or other markings of philatelic interest are known as covers. Before the introduction of envelopes in about 1840, people folded letters and wrote the address on the outside. Some people covered their letters with an extra sheet of paper on the outside for the address, producing the term "cover." Used airletter sheets, stamped envelopes and other items of postal stationery also are considered covers.

Errors — Stamps that have some major, consistent, unintentional deviation from the normal are considered errors. Errors include, but are not limited to, missing or wrong colors, wrong paper, wrong watermarks, inverted centers or frames on multicolor printing, inverted or missing surcharges or overprints, double impressions, missing perforations, unintentionally omitted tagging and others. Factually wrong or misspelled information, if it appears on all examples of a stamp, are not considered errors in the true sense of the word. They are errors of design. Inconsistent or randomly appearing items, such as misperfs or color shifts, are classified as freaks.

Color-Omitted Errors — This term refers to stamps where a missing color is caused by the complete failure of the printing plate to deliver ink to the stamp paper or any other paper. Generally, this is caused by the printing plate not being engaged on the press or the ink station running dry of ink during printing.

Color-Missing Errors — This term refers to stamps where a color or colors were printed somewhere but do not appear on the finished stamp. There are four different classes of color-missing errors, and the catalog indicates with a two-letter code appended to each such listing what caused the color to be missing. These codes are used only for the United States' color-missing error listings.

FO = A *foldover* of the stamp sheet during printing may block ink from appearing on a stamp. Instead, the color will appear on the back of the foldover (where it might fall on the back of the selvage or perhaps on the back of the stamp or another stamp). FO also will be used in the case of foldunders, where the paper may fold underneath the other stamp paper and the color will print on the platen.

EP = A piece of *extraneous paper* falling across the plate or stamp paper will receive the printed ink. When the extraneous paper is removed, an unprinted portion of stamp paper remains and shows partially or totally missing colors.

CM = A misregistration of the printing plates during printing will result in a *color misregistration*, and such a misregistraion may result in a color not appearing on the finished stamp.

PS = A *perforation shift* after printing may remove a color from the finished stamp. Normally, this will occur on a row of stamps at the edge of the stamp pane.

Overprints and Surcharges
— Overprinting involves applying wording or design elements over an already existing stamp. Overprints can be used to alter the place of use (such as "Canal Zone" on U.S. stamps), to adapt them for a special purpose ("Porto" on Denmark's 1913-20 regular issues for use as postage due stamps, Scott J1-J7) or to commemorate a special occasion (United States Scott 647-648).

A *surcharge* is a form of overprint that changes or restates the face value of a stamp or piece of postal stationery.

Surcharges and overprints may be handstamped, typeset or, occasionally, lithographed or engraved. A few hand-written overprints and surcharges are known.

Personalized Stamps
— In 1999, Australia issued stamps with se-tenant labels that could be personalized with pictures of the customer's choice. Other countries quickly followed suit, with some offering to print the selected picture on the stamp itself within a frame that was used exclusively for personalized issues. As the picture used on these stamps or labels vary, listings for such stamps are for *any* picture within the common frame (or any picture on a se-tenant label), be it a "generic" image or one produced especially for a customer, almost invariably at a premium price.

Precancels
— Stamps that are canceled before they are placed in the mail are known as precancels. Precanceling usually is done to expedite the handling of large mailings and generally allow the affected mail pieces to skip certain phases of mail handling.

In the United States, precancellations generally identified the point of origin; that is, the city and state. This information appeared across the face of the stamp, usually centered between parallel lines. More recently, bureau precancels retained the parallel lines, but the city and state designations were dropped. Recent coils have a service inscription that is present on the original printing plate. These show the mail service paid for by the stamp. Since these stamps are not intended to receive further cancellations when used as intended, they are considered precancels. Such items often do not have parallel lines as part of the precancellation.

In France, the abbreviation *Affranchts* in a semicircle together with the word *Postes* is the general form of precancel in use. Belgian precancellations usually appear in a box in which the name of the city appears. Netherlands precancels have the name of the city enclosed between concentric circles, sometimes called a "lifesaver." Precancellations of other countries usually follow these patterns, but may be any arrangement of bars, boxes and city names.

Precancels are listed in the Scott catalogues only if the precancel changes the denomination (Belgium Scott 477-478); if the precanceled stamp is different from the non-precanceled version (such as untagged U.S. precancels); or if the stamp exists only precanceled (France Scott 1096-1099, U.S. Scott 2265).

Proofs and Essays
— Proofs are impressions taken from an approved die, plate or stone in which the design and color are the same as the stamp issued to the public. Trial color proofs are impressions taken from approved dies, plates or stones in colors that vary from the final version. An essay is the impression of a design that differs in some way from the issued stamp. "Progressive die proofs" generally are considered to be essays.

Provisionals
— These are stamps that are issued on short notice and intended for temporary use pending the arrival of regular issues. They usually are issued to meet such contingencies as changes in government or currency, shortage of necessary postage values or military occupation.

During the 1840s, postmasters in certain American cities issued stamps that were valid only at specific post offices. In 1861, postmasters of the Confederate States also issued stamps with limited validity. Both of these examples are known as "postmaster's provisionals."

Se-tenant
— This term refers to an unsevered pair, strip or block of stamps that differ in design, denomination or overprint.

Unless the se-tenant item has a continuous design (see U.S. Scott 1451a, 1694a) the stamps do not have to be in the same order as shown in the catalogue (see U.S. Scott 2158a).

Specimens
— The Universal Postal Union required member nations to send samples of all stamps they released into service to the International Bureau in Switzerland. Member nations of the UPU received these specimens as samples of what stamps were valid for postage. Many are overprinted, handstamped or initial-perforated "Specimen," "Canceled" or "Muestra." Some are marked with bars across the denominations (China-Taiwan), punched holes (Czechoslovakia) or back inscriptions (Mongolia).

Stamps distributed to government officials or for publicity purposes, and stamps submitted by private security printers for official approval, also may receive such defacements.

The previously described defacement markings prevent postal use, and all such items generally are known as "specimens."

Tete Beche
— This term describes a pair of stamps in which one is upside down in relation to the other. Some of these are the result of intentional sheet arrangements, such as Morocco Scott B10-B11. Others occurred when one or more electrotypes accidentally were placed upside down on the plate, such as Colombia Scott 57a. Separation of the tete-beche stamps, of course, destroys the tete beche variety.

Currency Conversion

Country	Dollar	Pound	S Franc	Yen	HK $	Euro	Cdn $	Aus $
Australia	1.1488	2.2650	1.0380	0.0106	0.1472	1.6946	1.1470	—
Canada	1.0016	1.9748	0.9050	0.0092	0.1284	1.4775	—	0.8719
European Union	0.6779	1.3365	0.6125	0.0063	0.0869	—	0.6768	0.5901
Hong Kong	7.8025	15.383	7.0502	0.0719	—	11.510	7.7900	6.7919
Japan	108.46	213.84	98.003	—	13.901	159.99	108.29	94.412
Switzerland	1.1067	2.1820	—	0.0102	0.1418	1.6325	1.1049	0.9634
United Kingdom	0.5072	—	0.4583	0.0047	0.0650	0.7482	0.5064	0.4415
United States	—	1.9716	0.9036	0.0092	0.1282	1.4751	0.9984	0.8705

Country	Currency	U.S. $ Equiv.
Cambodia	riel	.0003
Cameroun	Community of French Africa (CFA) franc	.0023
Canada	dollar	.9984
Cape Verde	escudo	.0133
Cayman Islands	dollar	1.2195
Central African Republic	CFA franc	.0023
Chad	CFA franc	.0023
Chile	peso	.0020
China (Taiwan)	dollar	.0308
China (People's Republic)	yuan	.1375
Christmas Island	Australian dollar	.8705
Cocos Island	Australian dollar	.8705
Colombia	peso	.0005
Comoro Islands	franc	.0030
Congo Republic	CFA franc	.0023
Cook Islands	New Zealand dollar	.7654
Costa Rica	colon	.0020
Croatia	kuna	.2009
Cyprus	euro	1.4751
Czech Republic	koruna	.0565
Denmark	krone	.1980
Djibouti	franc	.0057
Dominica	East Caribbean dollar	.3724
Dominican Republic	peso	.0298
Ecuador	US dollar	1.00
Egypt	pound	.1814
Equatorial Guinea	CFA franc	.0023
Eritrea	nakfa	.0667
Estonia	kroon	.0943
Ethiopia	birr	.1087
Falkland Islands	pound	1.9716
Faroe Islands	krone	.1980
Fiji	dollar	.6472
Finland	euro	1.4751
Aland Islands	euro	1.4751
France	euro	1.4751
French Polynesia	Community of French Pacific (CFP) franc	.0123
French So. & Antarctic Terr.	euro	1.4751

*Source: **Wall Street Journal** Jan. 7, 2008. Figures reflect values as of Jan. 4, 2008.*

COMMON DESIGN TYPES

Pictured in this section are issues where one illustration has been used for a number of countries in the Catalogue. Not included in this section are overprinted stamps or those issues which are illustrated in each country.

EUROPA
Europa, 1956

The design symbolizing the cooperation among the six countries comprising the Coal and Steel Community is illustrated in each country.

Belgium	496-497
France	805-806
Germany	748-749
Italy	715-716
Luxembourg	318-320
Netherlands	368-369

Europa, 1958

"E" and Dove — CD1

European Postal Union at the service of European integration.

1958, Sept. 13

Belgium	527-528
France	889-890
Germany	790-791
Italy	750-751
Luxembourg	341-343
Netherlands	375-376
Saar	317-318

Europa, 1959

6-Link Enless Chain — CD2

1959, Sept. 19

Belgium	536-537
France	929-930
Germany	805-806
Italy	791-792
Luxembourg	354-355
Netherlands	379-380

Europa, 1960

19-Spoke Wheel CD3

First anniverary of the establishment of C.E.P.T. (Conference Europeenne des Administrations des Postes et des Telecommunications.) The spokes symbolize the 19 founding members of the Conference.

1960, Sept.

Belgium	553-554
Denmark	379
Finland	376-377
France	970-971
Germany	818-820
Great Britain	377-378
Greece	688
Iceland	327-328

Ireland	175-176
Italy	809-810
Luxembourg	374-375
Netherlands	385-386
Norway	387
Portugal	866-867
Spain	941-942
Sweden	562-563
Switzerland	400-401
Turkey	1493-1494

Europa, 1961

19 Doves Flying as One — CD4

The 19 doves represent the 19 members of the Conference of European Postal and Telecommunications Administrations C.E.P.T.

1961-62

Belgium	572-573
Cyprus	201-203
France	1005-1006
Germany	844-845
Great Britain	383-384
Greece	718-719
Iceland	340-341
Italy	845-846
Luxembourg	382-383
Netherlands	387-388
Spain	1010-1011
Switzerland	410-411
Turkey	1518-1520

Europa, 1962

Young Tree with 19 Leaves CD5

The 19 leaves represent the 19 original members of C.E.P.T.

1962-63

Belgium	582-583
Cyprus	219-221
France	1045-1046
Germany	852-853
Greece	739-740
Iceland	348-349
Ireland	184-185
Italy	860-861
Luxembourg	386-387
Netherlands	394-395
Norway	414-415
Switzerland	416-417
Turkey	1553-1555

Europa, 1963

Stylized Links, Symbolizing Unity — CD6

1963, Sept.

Belgium	598-599
Cyprus	229-231
Finland	419
France	1074-1075
Germany	867-868
Greece	768-769
Iceland	357-358
Ireland	188-189
Italy	880-881
Luxembourg	403-404
Netherlands	416-417
Norway	441-442
Switzerland	429
Turkey	1602-1603

Europa, 1964

Symbolic Daisy — CD7

5th anniversary of the establishment of C.E.P.T. The 22 petals of the flower symbolize the 22 members of the Conference.

1964, Sept.

Austria	738
Belgium	614-615
Cyprus	244-246
France	1109-1110
Germany	897-898
Greece	801-802
Iceland	367-368
Ireland	196-197
Italy	894-895
Luxembourg	411-412
Monaco	590-591
Netherlands	428-429
Norway	458
Portugal	931-933
Spain	1262-1263
Switzerland	438-439
Turkey	1628-1629

Europa, 1965

Leaves and "Fruit" CD8

1965

Belgium	636-637
Cyprus	262-264
Finland	437
France	1131-1132
Germany	934-935
Greece	833-834
Iceland	375-376
Ireland	204-205
Italy	915-916
Luxembourg	432-433
Monaco	616-617
Netherlands	438-439
Norway	475-476
Portugal	958-960
Switzerland	469
Turkey	1665-1666

Europa, 1966

Symbolic Sailboat — CD9

1966, Sept.

Andorra, French	172
Belgium	675-676
Cyprus	275-277
France	1163-1164
Germany	963-964
Greece	862-863
Iceland	384-385
Ireland	216-217
Italy	942-943
Liechtenstein	415
Luxembourg	440-441
Monaco	639-640
Netherlands	441-442
Norway	496-497
Portugal	980-982
Switzerland	477-478
Turkey	1718-1719

Europa, 1967

Cogwheels CD10

1967

Andorra, French	174-175
Belgium	688-689
Cyprus	297-299
France	1178-1179
Germany	969-970
Greece	891-892
Iceland	389-390
Ireland	232-233
Italy	951-952
Liechtenstein	420
Luxembourg	449-450
Monaco	669-670
Netherlands	444-447
Norway	504-505
Portugal	994-996
Spain	1465-1466
Switzerland	482
Turkey	B120-B121

Europa, 1968

Golden Key with C.E.P.T. Emblem CD11

1968

Andorra, French	182-183
Belgium	705-706
Cyprus	314-316
France	1209-1210
Germany	983-984
Greece	916-917
Iceland	395-396
Ireland	242-243
Italy	979-980
Liechtenstein	442
Luxembourg	466-467
Monaco	689-691
Netherlands	452-453
Portugal	1019-1021
San Marino	687
Spain	1526
Turkey	1775-1776

Europa, 1969

"EUROPA" and "CEPT" CD12

Tenth anniversary of C.E.P.T.

1969

Andorra, French	188-189
Austria	837
Belgium	718-719
Cyprus	326-328
Denmark	458
Finland	483
France	1245-1246
Germany	996-997
Great Britain	585
Greece	947-948
Iceland	406-407
Ireland	270-271
Italy	1000-1001
Liechtenstein	453
Luxembourg	474-475
Monaco	722-724
Netherlands	475-476
Norway	533-534
Portugal	1038-1040
San Marino	701-702
Spain	1567
Sweden	814-816

Switzerland	500-501
Turkey	1799-1800
Vatican	470-472
Yugoslavia	1003-1004

Europa, 1970

Interwoven Threads CD13

1970

Andorra, French	196-197
Belgium	741-742
Cyprus	340-342
France	1271-1272
Germany	1018-1019
Greece	985, 987
Iceland	420-421
Ireland	279-281
Italy	1013-1014
Liechtenstein	470
Luxembourg	489-490
Monaco	768-770
Netherlands	483-484
Portugal	1060-1062
San Marino	729-730
Spain	1607
Switzerland	515-516
Turkey	1848-1849
Yugoslavia	1024-1025

Europa, 1971

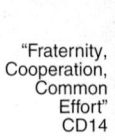

"Fraternity, Cooperation, Common Effort" CD14

1971

Andorra, French	205-206
Belgium	803-804
Cyprus	365-367
Finland	504
France	1304
Germany	1064-1065
Greece	1029-1030
Iceland	429-430
Ireland	305-306
Italy	1038-1039
Liechtenstein	485
Luxembourg	500-501
Malta	425-427
Monaco	797-799
Netherlands	488-489
Portugal	1094-1096
San Marino	749-750
Spain	1675-1676
Switzerland	531-532
Turkey	1876-1877
Yugoslavia	1052-1053

Europa, 1972

Sparkles, Symbolic of Communications CD15

1972

Andorra, French	210-211
Andorra, Spanish	62
Belgium	825-826
Cyprus	380-382
Finland	512-513
France	1341
Germany	1089-1090
Greece	1049-1050
Iceland	439-440
Ireland	316-317
Italy	1065-1066
Liechtenstein	504
Luxembourg	512-513
Malta	450-453
Monaco	831-832

Netherlands	494-495
Portugal	1141-1143
San Marino	771-772
Spain	1718
Switzerland	544-545
Turkey	1907-1908
Yugoslavia	1100-1101

Europa, 1973

Post Horn and Arrows CD16

1973

Andorra, French	219-220
Andorra, Spanish	76
Belgium	839-840
Cyprus	396-398
Finland	526
France	1367
Germany	1114-1115
Greece	1090-1092
Iceland	447-448
Ireland	329-330
Italy	1108-1109
Liechtenstein	528-529
Luxembourg	523-524
Malta	469-471
Monaco	866-867
Netherlands	504-505
Norway	604-605
Portugal	1170-1172
San Marino	802-803
Spain	1753
Switzerland	580-581
Turkey	1935-1936
Yugoslavia	1138-1139

Europa, 2000

CD17

2000

Albania	2621-2622
Andorra, French	522
Andorra, Spanish	262
Armenia	610-611
Austria	1814
Azerbaijan	698-699
Belarus	350
Belgium	1818
Bosnia & Herzegovina (Moslem)	358
Bosnia & Herzegovina (Serb)	111-112
Croatia	428-429
Cyprus	959
Czech Republic	3120
Denmark	1189
Estonia	394
Faroe Islands	376
Finland	1129
Aland Islands	166
France	2771
Georgia	228-229
Germany	2086-2087
Gibraltar	837-840
Great Britain (Guernsey)	805-809
Great Britain (Jersey)	935-936
Great Britain (Isle of Man)	883
Greece	1959
Greenland	363
Hungary	3699-3700
Iceland	910
Ireland	1230-1231
Italy	2349
Latvia	504
Liechtenstein	1178
Lithuania	668
Luxembourg	1035
Macedonia	187
Malta	1011-1012
Moldova	355
Monaco	2161-2162
Poland	3519
Portugal	2358
Portugal (Azores)	455
Portugal (Madeira)	208

Romania	4370
Russia	6589
San Marino	1480
Slovakia	355
Slovenia	424
Spain	3036
Sweden	2394
Switzerland	1074
Turkey	2762
Turkish Rep. of Northern Cyprus	500
Ukraine	379
Vatican City	1152

The Gibraltar stamps are similar to the stamp illustrated, but none have the design shown above. All other sets listed above include at least one stamp with the design shown, but some include stamps with entirely different designs. Bulgaria Nos. 4131-4132 and Yugoslavia Nos. 2485-2486 are Europa stamps with completely different designs.

PORTUGAL & COLONIES
Vasco da Gama

Fleet Departing CD20

Fleet Arriving at Calicut — CD21

Embarking at Rastello CD22 — Muse of History CD23

San Gabriel, da Gama and Camoens CD24 — Archangel Gabriel, the Patron Saint CD25

Flagship San Gabriel — CD26

Vasco da Gama — CD27

Fourth centenary of Vasco da Gama's discovery of the route to India.

1898

Azores	93-100
Macao	67-74
Madeira	37-44
Portugal	147-154
Port. Africa	1-8
Port. Congo	75-98
Port. India	189-196
St. Thomas & Prince Islands	170-193
Timor	45-52

Pombal
POSTAL TAX
POSTAL TAX DUES

Marquis de Pombal — CD28

Planning Reconstruction of Lisbon, 1755 — CD29

Pombal Monument, Lisbon — CD30

Sebastiao Jose de Carvalho e Mello, Marquis de Pombal (1699-1782), statesman, rebuilt Lisbon after earthquake of 1755. Tax was for the erection of Pombal monument. Obligatory on all mail on certain days throughout the year. Postal Tax Dues are inscribed "Multa."

1925

Angola	RA1-RA3, RAJ1-RAJ3
Azores	RA9-RA11, RAJ2-RAJ4
Cape Verde	RA1-RA3, RAJ1-RAJ3
Macao	RA1-RA3, RAJ1-RAJ3
Madeira	RA1-RA3, RAJ1-RAJ3
Mozambique	RA1-RA3, RAJ1-RAJ3
Nyassa	RA1-RA3, RAJ1-RAJ3
Portugal	RA11-RA13, RAJ2-RAJ4
Port. Guinea	RA1-RA3, RAJ1-RAJ3
Port. India	RA1-RA3, RAJ1-RAJ3
St. Thomas & Prince Islands	RA1-RA3, RAJ1-RAJ3
Timor	RA1-RA3, RAJ1-RAJ3

Vasco da Gama
CD34

Mousinho de
Albuquerque
CD35

Dam
CD36

Prince Henry
the Navigator
CD37

Affonso de
Albuquerque
CD38

Plane over
Globe
CD39

1938-39

Angola 274-291, C1-C9
Cape Verde 234-251, C1-C9
Macao....................... 289-305, C7-C15
Mozambique 270-287, C1-C9
Port. Guinea 233-250. C1-C9
Port. India 439-453, C1-C8
St. Thomas & Prince
  Islands ... 302-319, 323-340, C1-C18
Timor 223-239, C1-C9

Lady of Fatima

Our Lady of the
Rosary, Fatima,
Portugal — CD40

1948-49

Angola 315-318
Cape Verde 266
Macao........................... 336
Mozambique 325-328
Port. Guinea 271
Port. India 480
St. Thomas & Prince Islands 351
Timor 254

A souvenir sheet of 9 stamps was issued in 1951 to mark the extension of the 1950 Holy Year. The sheet contains: Angola No. 316, Cape Verde No. 266, Macao No. 336, Mozambique No. 325, Portuguese Guinea No. 271, Portuguese India Nos. 480, 485, St. Thomas & Prince Islands No. 351, Timor No. 254. The sheet also contains a portrait of Pope Pius XII and is inscribed "Encerramento do Ano Santo, Fatima 1951." It was sold for 11 escudos.

Holy Year

Church Bells and
Dove
CD41

Angel Holding
Candelabra
CD42

Holy Year, 1950.

1950-51

Angola 331-332
Cape Verde 268-269
Macao...........................339-340
Mozambique 330-331
Port. Guinea 273-274
Port. India...............490-491, 496-503
St. Thomas & Prince Islands ...353-354
Timor...........................258-259

A souvenir sheet of 8 stamps was issued in 1951 to mark the extension of the Holy Year. The sheet contains: Angola No. 331, Cape Verde No. 269, Macao No. 340, Mozambique No. 331, Portuguese Guinea No. 275, Portuguese India No. 490, St. Thomas & Prince Islands No. 354, Timor No. 258, some with colors changed. The sheet contains doves and is inscribed 'Encerramento do Ano Santo, Fatima 1951.' It was sold for 17 escudos.

Holy Year Conclusion

Our Lady of
Fatima — CD43

Conclusion of Holy Year. Sheets contain alternate vertical rows of stamps and labels bearing quotation from Pope Pius XII, different for each colony.

1951

Angola 357
Cape Verde 270
Macao........................... 352
Mozambique 356
Port. Guinea 275
Port. India 506
St. Thomas & Prince Islands 355
Timor 270

Medical Congress

CD44

First National Congress of Tropical Medicine, Lisbon, 1952. Each stamp has a different design.

1952

Angola 358
Cape Verde 287
Macao........................... 364
Mozambique 359
Port. Guinea 276
Port. India 516
St. Thomas & Prince Islands 356
Timor 271

Postage Due Stamps

CD45

1952

Angola J37-J42
Cape Verde J31-J36
Macao........................... J53-J58
Mozambique J51-J56
Port. Guinea J40-J45
Port. India J47-J52
St. Thomas & Prince Islands ... J52-J57
Timor J31-J36

Sao Paulo

Father Manuel
da Nobrega
and View of
Sao
Paulo — CD46

Founding of Sao Paulo, Brazil, 400th anniv.

1954

Angola 385
Cape Verde 297
Macao...........................382
Mozambique 395
Port. Guinea 291
Port. India...........................530
St. Thomas & Prince Islands 369
Timor...........................279

Tropical Medicine Congress

CD47

Sixth International Congress for Tropical Medicine and Malaria, Lisbon, Sept. 1958. Each stamp shows a different plant.

1958

Angola 409
Cape Verde 303
Macao........................... 392
Mozambique 404
Port. Guinea 295
Port. India 569
St. Thomas & Prince Islands 371
Timor 289

Sports

CD48

Each stamp shows a different sport.

1962

Angola 433-438
Cape Verde 320-325
Macao........................... 394-399
Mozambique 424-429
Port. Guinea 299-304
St. Thomas & Prince Islands ...374-379
Timor 313-318

Anti-Malaria

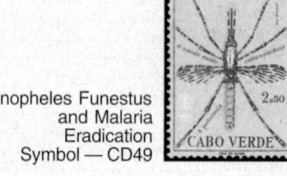

Anopheles Funestus
and Malaria
Eradication
Symbol — CD49

World Health Organization drive to eradicate malaria.

1962

Angola 439
Cape Verde 326
Macao........................... 400
Mozambique 430
Port. Guinea 305
St. Thomas & Prince Islands 380
Timor 319

Airline Anniversary

Map of Africa, Super
Constellation and Jet
Liner — CD50

Tenth anniversary of Transportes Aereos Portugueses (TAP).

1963

Angola 490
Cape Verde 327
Mozambique 434
Port. Guinea 318
St. Thomas & Prince Islands 381

National Overseas Bank

Antonio
Teixeira de
Sousa — CD51

Centenary of the National Overseas Bank of Portugal.

1964, May 16

Angola 509
Cape Verde 328
Port. Guinea 319
St. Thomas & Prince Islands 382
Timor 320

ITU

ITU Emblem and
the Archangel
Gabriel — CD52

International Communications Union, Cent.

1965, May 17

Angola 511
Cape Verde 329
Macao........................... 402
Mozambique 464
Port. Guinea 320
St. Thomas & Prince Islands 383
Timor 321

National Revolution

CD53

40th anniv. of the National Revolution. Different buildings on each stamp.

1966, May 28

Angola 525
Cape Verde 338
Macao........................... 403
Mozambique 465
Port. Guinea 329
St. Thomas & Prince Islands 392
Timor 322

Navy Club

CD54

Centenary of Portugal's Navy Club. Each stamp has a different design.

1967, Jan. 31

Angola	527-528
Cape Verde	339-340
Macao	412-413
Mozambique	478-479
Port. Guinea	330-331
St. Thomas & Prince Islands	393-394
Timor	323-324

Admiral Coutinho

CD55

Centenary of the birth of Admiral Carlos Viegas Gago Coutinho (1869-1959), explorer and aviation pioneer. Each stamp has a different design.

1969, Feb. 17

Angola	547
Cape Verde	355
Macao	417
Mozambique	484
Port. Guinea	335
St. Thomas & Prince Islands	397
Timor	335

Administration Reform

Luiz Augusto Rebello da Silva — CD56

Centenary of the administration reforms of the overseas territories.

1969, Sept. 25

Angola	549
Cape Verde	357
Macao	419
Mozambique	491
Port. Guinea	337
St. Thomas & Prince Islands	399
Timor	338

Marshal Carmona

CD57

Birth centenary of Marshal Antonio Oscar Carmona de Fragoso (1869-1951), President of Portugal. Each stamp has a different design.

1970, Nov. 15

Angola	563
Cape Verde	359
Macao	422
Mozambique	493
Port. Guinea	340
St. Thomas & Prince Islands	403
Timor	341

Olympic Games

CD59

20th Olympic Games, Munich, Aug. 26-Sept. 11. Each stamp shows a different sport.

1972, June 20

Angola	569
Cape Verde	361
Macao	426
Mozambique	504
Port. Guinea	342
St. Thomas & Prince Islands	408
Timor	343

Lisbon-Rio de Janeiro Flight

CD60

50th anniversary of the Lisbon to Rio de Janeiro flight by Arturo de Sacadura and Coutinho, March 30-June 5, 1922. Each stamp shows a different stage of the flight.

1972, Sept. 20

Angola	570
Cape Verde	362
Macao	427
Mozambique	505
Port. Guinea	343
St. Thomas & Prince Islands	409
Timor	344

WMO Centenary

WMO Emblem — CD61

Centenary of international meterological cooperation.

1973, Dec. 15

Angola	571
Cape Verde	363
Macao	429
Mozambique	509
Port. Guinea	344
St. Thomas & Prince Islands	410
Timor	345

FRENCH COMMUNITY
**Upper Volta can be found under Burkina Faso in Vol. 1
Madagascar can be found under Malagasy in Vol. 3
Colonial Exposition**

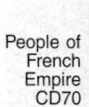

People of French Empire CD70

Women's Heads CD71

France Showing Way to Civilization CD72

"Colonial Commerce" CD73

International Colonial Exposition, Paris.

1931

Cameroun	213-216

Chad	60-63
Dahomey	97-100
Fr. Guiana	152-155
Fr. Guinea	116-119
Fr. India	100-103
Fr. Polynesia	76-79
Fr. Sudan	102-105
Gabon	120-123
Guadeloupe	138-141
Indo-China	140-142
Ivory Coast	92-95
Madagascar	169-172
Martinique	129-132
Mauritania	65-68
Middle Congo	61-64
New Caledonia	176-179
Niger	73-76
Reunion	122-125
St. Pierre & Miquelon	132-135
Senegal	138-141
Somali Coast	135-138
Togo	254-257
Ubangi-Shari	82-85
Upper Volta	66-69
Wallis & Futuna Isls.	85-88

Paris International Exposition
Colonial Arts Exposition

"Colonial Resources" CD74   CD77

Overseas Commerce CD75

Exposition Building and Women CD76

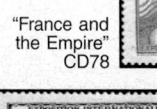

"France and the Empire" CD78

Cultural Treasures of the Colonies CD79

Souvenir sheets contain one imperf. stamp.

1937

Cameroun	217-222A
Dahomey	101-107
Fr. Equatorial Africa	27-32, 73
Fr. Guiana	162-168
Fr. Guinea	120-126
Fr. India	104-110
Fr. Polynesia	117-123
Fr. Sudan	106-112
Guadeloupe	148-154
Indo-China	193-199
Inini	41
Ivory Coast	152-158
Kwangchowan	132
Madagascar	191-197
Martinique	179-185
Mauritania	69-75
New Caledonia	208-214
Niger	72-83
Reunion	167-173
St. Pierre & Miquelon	165-171
Senegal	172-178
Somali Coast	139-145
Togo	258-264
Wallis & Futuna Isls.	89

Curie

Pierre and Marie Curie CD80

40th anniversary of the discovery of radium. The surtax was for the benefit of the Intl. Union for the Control of Cancer.

1938

Cameroun	B1
Cuba	B1-B2
Dahomey	B2
France	B76
Fr. Equatorial Africa	B1
Fr. Guiana	B3
Fr. Guinea	B2
Fr. India	B6
Fr. Polynesia	B5
Fr. Sudan	B1
Guadeloupe	B3
Indo-China	B14
Ivory Coast	B2
Madagascar	B2
Martinique	B2
Mauritania	B3
New Caledonia	B4
Niger	B1
Reunion	B4
St. Pierre & Miquelon	B3
Senegal	B3
Somali Coast	B2
Togo	B1

Caillie

Rene Caillie and Map of Northwestern Africa — CD81

Death centenary of Rene Caillie (1799-1838), French explorer. All three denominations exist with colony name omitted.

1939

Dahomey	108-110
Fr. Guinea	161-163
Fr. Sudan	113-115
Ivory Coast	160-162
Mauritania	109-111
Niger	84-86
Senegal	188-190
Togo	265-267

New York World's Fair

Natives and New York Skyline CD82

1939

Cameroun	223-224
Dahomey	111-112
Fr. Equatorial Africa	78-79
Fr. Guiana	169-170
Fr. Guinea	164-165
Fr. India	111-112
Fr. Polynesia	124-125
Fr. Sudan	116-117
Guadeloupe	155-156
Indo-China	203-204
Inini	42-43
Ivory Coast	163-164
Kwangchowan	121-122
Madagascar	209-210
Martinique	186-187
Mauritania	112-113
New Caledonia	215-216
Niger	87-88
Reunion	174-175
St. Pierre & Miquelon	205-206
Senegal	191-192
Somali Coast	179-180
Togo	268-269
Wallis & Futuna Isls.	90-91

French Revolution

Storming of
the Bastille
CD83

French Revolution, 150th anniv. The surtax was for the defense of the colonies.

1939

Cameroun	B2-B6
Dahomey	B3-B7
Fr. Equatorial Africa	B4-B8, CB1
Fr. Guiana	B4-B8, CB1
Fr. Guinea	B3-B7
Fr. India	B7-B11
Fr. Polynesia	B6-B10, CB1
Fr. Sudan	B2-B6
Guadeloupe	B4-B8
Indo-China	B15-B19, CB1
Inini	B1-B5
Ivory Coast	B3-B7
Kwangchowan	B1-B5
Madagascar	B3-B7, CB1
Martinique	B3-B7
Mauritania	B4-B8
New Caledonia	B5-B9, CB1
Niger	B2-B6
Reunion	B5-B9, CB1
St. Pierre & Miquelon	B4-B8
Senegal	B4-B8, CB1
Somali Coast	B3-B7
Togo	B2-B6
Wallis & Futuna Isls.	B1-B5

Plane over
Coastal
Area
CD85

All five denominations exist with colony name omitted.

1940

Dahomey	C1-C5
Fr. Guinea	C1-C5
Fr. Sudan	C1-C5
Ivory Coast	C1-C5
Mauritania	C1-C5
Niger	C1-C5
Senegal	C12-C16
Togo	C1-C5

Defense of the Empire

Colonial
Infantryman — CD86

1941

Cameroun	B13B
Dahomey	B13
Fr. Equatorial Africa	B8B
Fr. Guiana	B10
Fr. Guinea	B13
Fr. India	B13
Fr. Polynesia	B12
Fr. Sudan	B12
Guadeloupe	B10
Indo-China	B19B
Inini	B7
Ivory Coast	B13
Kwangchowan	B7
Madagascar	B9
Martinique	B9
Mauritania	B14
New Caledonia	B11
Niger	B12
Reunion	B11
St. Pierre & Miquelon	B8B
Senegal	B14
Somali Coast	B9
Togo	B10B

Colonial Education Fund

CD86a

1942

Cameroun	CB3
Dahomey	CB4
Fr. Equatorial Africa	CB5
Fr. Guiana	CB4
Fr. Guinea	CB4
Fr. India	CB3
Fr. Polynesia	CB4
Fr. Sudan	CB4
Guadeloupe	CB3
Indo-China	CB5
Inini	CB3
Ivory Coast	CB4
Kwangchowan	CB4
Malagasy	CB5
Martinique	CB3
Mauritania	CB4
New Caledonia	CB4
Niger	CB4
Reunion	CB4
St. Pierre & Miquelon	CB3
Senegal	CB5
Somali Coast	CB3
Togo	CB3
Wallis & Futuna	CB3

Cross of
Lorraine &
Four-motor
Plane
CD87

1941-5

Cameroun	C1-C7
Fr. Equatorial Africa	C17-C23
Fr. Guiana	C9-C10
Fr. India	C1-C6
Fr. Polynesia	C3-C9
Fr. West Africa	C1-C3
Guadeloupe	C1-C2
Madagascar	C37-C43
Martinique	C1-C2
New Caledonia	C7-C13
Reunion	C18-C24
St. Pierre & Miquelon	C1-C7
Somali Coast	C1-C7

Transport
Plane
CD88

Caravan
and Plane
CD89

1942

Dahomey	C6-C13
Fr. Guinea	C6-C13
Fr. Sudan	C6-C13
Ivory Coast	C6-C13
Mauritania	C6-C13
Niger	C6-C13
Senegal	C17-C25
Togo	C6-C13

Wallis & Futuna Isls. B7

Red Cross

Marianne
CD90

The surtax was for the French Red Cross and national relief.

1944

Cameroun	B28
Fr. Equatorial Africa	B38
Fr. Guiana	B12
Fr. India	B14
Fr. Polynesia	B13
Fr. West Africa	B1
Guadeloupe	B12
Madagascar	B15
Martinique	B11
New Caledonia	B13
Reunion	B15
St. Pierre & Miquelon	B13
Somali Coast	B13
Wallis & Futuna Isls.	B9

Eboue

CD91

Felix Eboue, first French colonial administrator to proclaim resistance to Germany after French surrender in World War II.

1945

Cameroun	296-297
Fr. Equatorial Africa	156-157
Fr. Guiana	171-172
Fr. India	210-211
Fr. Polynesia	150-151
Fr. West Africa	15-16
Guadeloupe	187-188
Madagascar	259-260
Martinique	196-197
New Caledonia	274-275
Reunion	238-239
St. Pierre & Miquelon	322-323
Somali Coast	238-239

Victory

Victory — CD92

European victory of the Allied Nations in World War II.

1946, May 8

Cameroun	C8
Fr. Equatorial Africa	C24
Fr. Guiana	C11
Fr. India	C7
Fr. Polynesia	C10
Fr. West Africa	C4
Guadeloupe	C3
Indo-China	C19
Madagascar	C44
Martinique	C3
New Caledonia	C14
Reunion	C25
St. Pierre & Miquelon	C8
Somali Coast	C8
Wallis & Futuna Isls.	C1

Chad to Rhine

Leclerc's Departure from
Chad — CD93

Battle at Cufra Oasis — CD94

Tanks in Action, Mareth — CD95

Normandy Invasion — CD96

Entering Paris — CD97

Liberation of Strasbourg — CD98

"Chad to the Rhine" march, 1942-44, by Gen. Jacques Leclerc's column, later French 2nd Armored Division.

1946, June 6

Cameroun	C9-C14
Fr. Equatorial Africa	C25-C30
Fr. Guiana	C12-C17
Fr. India	C8-C13
Fr. Polynesia	C11-C16
Fr. West Africa	C5-C10
Guadeloupe	C4-C9
Indo-China	C20-C25
Madagascar	C45-C50
Martinique	C4-C9
New Caledonia	C15-C20
Reunion	C26-C31
St. Pierre & Miquelon	C9-C14
Somali Coast	C9-C14
Wallis & Futuna Isls.	C2-C7

UPU

French Colonials, Globe and
Plane — CD99

Universal Postal Union, 75th anniv.

1949, July 4

Cameroun	C29
Fr. Equatorial Africa	C34
Fr. India	C17
Fr. Polynesia	C20
Fr. West Africa	C15
Indo-China	C26
Madagascar	C55
New Caledonia	C24
St. Pierre & Miquelon	C18
Somali Coast	C18
Togo	C18
Wallis & Futuna Isls.	C10

Tropical Medicine

Doctor Treating Infant CD100

The surtax was for charitable work.

1950

Cameroun	B29
Fr. Equatorial Africa	B39
Fr. India	B15
Fr. Polynesia	B14
Fr. West Africa	B3
Madagascar	B17
New Caledonia	B14
St. Pierre & Miquelon	B14
Somali Coast	B14
Togo	B11

Military Medal

Medal, Early Marine and Colonial Soldier — CD101

Centenary of the creation of the French Military Medal.

1952

Cameroun	332
Comoro Isls.	39
Fr. Equatorial Africa	186
Fr. India	233
Fr. Polynesia	179
Fr. West Africa	57
Madagascar	286
New Caledonia	295
St. Pierre & Miquelon	345
Somali Coast	267
Togo	327
Wallis & Futuna Isls.	149

Liberation

Allied Landing, Victory Sign and Cross of Lorraine — CD102

Liberation of France, 10th anniv.

1954, June 6

Cameroun	C32
Comoro Isls.	C4
Fr. Equatorial Africa	C38
Fr. India	C18
Fr. Polynesia	C22
Fr. West Africa	C17
Madagascar	C57
New Caledonia	C25
St. Pierre & Miquelon	C19
Somali Coast	C19
Togo	C19
Wallis & Futuna Isls.	C11

FIDES

Plowmen CD103

Efforts of FIDES, the Economic and Social Development Fund for Overseas Possessions (Fonds d' Investissement pour le Developpement Economique et Social). Each stamp has a different design.

1956

Cameroun	326-329
Comoro Isls.	43
Fr. Polynesia	181
Fr. West Africa	65-72
Madagascar	292-295
New Caledonia	303
Somali Coast	268
Togo	331

Flower

CD104

Each stamp shows a different flower.

1958-9

Cameroun	333
Comoro Isls.	45
Fr. Equatorial Africa	200-201
Fr. Polynesia	192
Fr. So. & Antarctic Terr.	11
Fr. West Africa	79-83
Madagascar	301-302
New Caledonia	304-305
St. Pierre & Miquelon	357
Somali Coast	270
Togo	348-349
Wallis & Futuna Isls.	152

Human Rights

Sun, Dove and U.N. Emblem CD105

10th anniversary of the signing of the Universal Declaration of Human Rights.

1958

Comoro Isls.	44
Fr. Equatorial Africa	202
Fr. Polynesia	191
Fr. West Africa	85
Madagascar	300
New Caledonia	306
St. Pierre & Miquelon	356
Somali Coast	274
Wallis & Futuna Isls.	153

C.C.T.A.

CD106

Commission for Technical Cooperation in Africa south of the Sahara, 10th anniv.

1960

Cameroun	335
Cent. Africa	3
Chad	66
Congo, P.R.	90
Dahomey	138

Gabon	150
Ivory Coast	180
Madagascar	317
Mali	9
Mauritania	117
Niger	104
Upper Volta	89

Air Afrique, 1961

Modern and Ancient Africa, Map and Planes — CD107

Founding of Air Afrique (African Airlines).

1961-62

Cameroun	C37
Cent. Africa	C5
Chad	C7
Congo, P.R.	C5
Dahomey	C17
Gabon	C5
Ivory Coast	C18
Mauritania	C17
Niger	C22
Senegal	C31
Upper Volta	C4

Anti-Malaria

CD108

World Health Organization drive to eradicate malaria.

1962, Apr. 7

Cameroun	B36
Cent. Africa	B1
Chad	B1
Comoro Isls.	B1
Congo, P.R.	B3
Dahomey	B15
Gabon	B4
Ivory Coast	B15
Madagascar	B19
Mali	B1
Mauritania	B16
Niger	B14
Senegal	B16
Somali Coast	B15
Upper Volta	B1

Abidjan Games

CD109

Abidjan Games, Ivory Coast, Dec. 24-31, 1961. Each stamp shows a different sport.

1962

Chad	83-84
Cent. Africa	19-20
Congo, P.R.	103-104
Gabon	163-164, C6
Niger	109-111
Upper Volta	103-105

African and Malagasy Union

Flag of Union CD110

First anniversary of the Union.

1962, Sept. 8

Cameroun	373
Cent. Africa	21
Chad	85
Congo, P.R.	105
Dahomey	155
Gabon	165
Ivory Coast	198
Madagascar	332
Mauritania	170
Niger	112
Senegal	211
Upper Volta	106

Telstar

Telstar and Globe Showing Andover and Pleumeur-Bodou — CD111

First television connection of the United States and Europe through the Telstar satellite, July 11-12, 1962.

1962-63

Andorra, French	154
Comoro Isls.	C7
Fr. Polynesia	C29
Fr. So. & Antarctic Terr.	C5
New Caledonia	C33
Somali Coast	C31
St. Pierre & Miquelon	C26
Wallis & Futuna Isls.	C17

Freedom From Hunger

World Map and Wheat Emblem CD112

U.N. Food and Agriculture Organization's "Freedom from Hunger" campaign.

1963, Mar. 21

Cameroun	B37-B38
Cent. Africa	B2
Chad	B2
Congo, P.R.	B4
Dahomey	B16
Gabon	B5
Ivory Coast	B16
Madagascar	B21
Mauritania	B17
Niger	B15
Senegal	B17
Upper Volta	B2

Red Cross Centenary

CD113

Centenary of the International Red Cross.

1963, Sept. 2

Comoro Isls.	55

Fr. Polynesia...................................205
New Caledonia................................328
St. Pierre & Miquelon....................367
Somali Coast...................................297
Wallis & Futuna Isls. 165

African Postal Union, 1963

UAMPT
Emblem,
Radio Masts,
Plane and
Mail
CD114

Establishment of the African and Malagasy Posts and Telecommunications Union.

1963, Sept. 8

Cameroun..C47
Cent. Africa C10
Chad...C9
Congo, P.R. C13
Dahomey C19
Gabon...C13
Ivory Coast C25
Madagascar.....................................C75
Mauritania C22
Niger C27
Rwanda 36
Senegal C32
Upper Volta C9

Air Afrique, 1963

Symbols of Flight — CD115

First anniversary of Air Afrique and inauguration of DC-8 service.

1963, Nov. 19

Cameroun...C48
Chad C10
Congo, P.R. C14
Gabon..C18
Ivory Coast C26
Mauritania C26
Niger C35
Senegal C33

Europafrica

Europe and Africa
Linked — CD116

Signing of an economic agreement between the European Economic Community and the African and Malagasy Union, Yaounde, Cameroun, July 20, 1963.

1963-64

Cameroun... 402
Chad C11
Cent. Africa C12
Congo, P.R. C16
Gabon..C19
Ivory Coast 217
Niger C43
Upper Volta C11

Human Rights

Scales of
Justice and
Globe
CD117

15th anniversary of the Universal Declaration of Human Rights.

1963, Dec. 10

Comoro Isls. 58
Fr. Polynesia...................................206
New Caledonia................................329
St. Pierre & Miquelon....................368
Somali Coast...................................300
Wallis & Futuna Isls. 166

PHILATEC

Stamp Album, Champs Elysees
Palace and Horses of Marly
CD118

Intl. Philatelic and Postal Techniques Exhibition, Paris, June 5-21, 1964.

1963-64

Comoro Isls. 60
France...1078
Fr. Polynesia...................................207
New Caledonia................................341
St. Pierre & Miquelon....................369
Somali Coast...................................301
Wallis & Futuna Isls. 167

Cooperation

CD119

Cooperation between France and the French-speaking countries of Africa and Madagascar.

1964

Cameroun................................... 409-410
Cent. Africa 39
Chad 103
Congo, P.R. 121
Dahomey 193
France 1111
Gabon 175
Ivory Coast 221
Madagascar.................................... 360
Mauritania 181
Niger 143
Senegal 236
Togo.. 495

ITU

Telegraph,
Syncom Satellite
and ITU Emblem
CD120

Intl. Telecommunication Union, Cent.

1965, May 17

Comoro Isls. C14
Fr. Polynesia...................................C33
Fr. So. & Antarctic Terr. C8
New Caledonia................................C40
New Hebrides...........................124-125
St. Pierre & Miquelon....................C29
Somali Coast...................................C36
Wallis & Futuna Isls. C20

French Satellite A-1

Diamant Rocket and Launching
Installation — CD121

Launching of France's first satellite, Nov. 26, 1965.

1965-66

Comoro Isls. C15-C16
France...................................1137-1138
Fr. Polynesia............................C40-C41
Fr. So. & Antarctic Terr. C9-C10
New Caledonia.........................C44-C45
St. Pierre & Miquelon.............C30-C31
Somali Coast............................C39-C40
Wallis & Futuna Isls. C22-C23

French Satellite D-1

D-1 Satellite in Orbit — CD122

Launching of the D-1 satellite at Hammaguir, Algeria, Feb. 17, 1966.

1966

Comoro Isls. C17
France...1148
Fr. Polynesia...................................C42
Fr. So. & Antarctic Terr. C11
New Caledonia................................C46
St. Pierre & Miquelon....................C32
Somali Coast...................................C49
Wallis & Futuna Isls. C24

Air Afrique, 1966

Planes and Air Afrique
Emblem — CD123

Introduction of DC-8F planes by Air Afrique.

1966

Cameroun...C79
Cent. Africa C35
Chad C26
Congo, P.R. C42
Dahomey C42
Gabon..C47
Ivory Coast C32
Mauritania C57
Niger C63
Senegal C47
Togo...C54
Upper Volta C31

African Postal Union, 1967

Telecommunications Symbols and Map
of Africa — CD124

Fifth anniversary of the establishment of the African and Malagasy Union of Posts and Telecommunications, UAMPT.

1967

Cameroun...C90
Cent. Africa C46
Chad C37
Congo, P.R. C57
Dahomey C61
Gabon..C58
Ivory Coast C34
Madagascar.....................................C85
Mauritania C65
Niger C75
Rwanda C1-C3
Senegal C60
Togo...C81
Upper Volta C50

Monetary Union

Gold Token of the
Ashantis, 17-18th
Centuries — CD125

West African Monetary Union, 5th anniv.

1967, Nov. 4

Dahomey 244
Ivory Coast 259
Mauritania 238
Niger 204
Senegal 294
Togo.. 623
Upper Volta 181

WHO Anniversary

Sun,
Flowers
and WHO
Emblem
CD126

World Health Organization, 20th anniv.

1968, May 4

Afars & Issas 317
Comoro Isls. 73
Fr. Polynesia 241-242
Fr. So. & Antarctic Terr. 31
New Caledonia 367
St. Pierre & Miquelon 377
Wallis & Futuna Isls. 169

Human Rights Year

Human Rights
Flame — CD127

1968, Aug. 10

Afars & Issas 322-323

Comoro Isls.	76
Fr. Polynesia	243-244
Fr. So. & Antarctic Terr.	32
New Caledonia	369
St. Pierre & Miquelon	382
Wallis & Futuna Isls.	170

2nd PHILEXAFRIQUE

CD128

Opening of PHILEXAFRIQUE, Abidjan, Feb. 14. Each stamp shows a local scene and stamp.

1969, Feb. 14

Cameroun	C118
Cent. Africa	C65
Chad	C48
Congo, P.R.	C77
Dahomey	C94
Gabon	C82
Ivory Coast	C38-C40
Madagascar	C92
Mali	C65
Mauritania	C80
Niger	C104
Senegal	C68
Togo	C104
Upper Volta	C62

Concorde

Concorde in Flight CD129

First flight of the prototype Concorde supersonic plane at Toulouse, Mar. 1, 1969.

1969

Afars & Issas	C56
Comoro Isls.	C29
France	C42
Fr. Polynesia	C50
Fr. So. & Antarctic Terr.	C18
New Caledonia	C63
St. Pierre & Miquelon	C40
Wallis & Futuna Isls.	C30

Development Bank

Bank Emblem — CD130

African Development Bank, fifth anniv.

1969

Cameroun	499
Chad	217
Congo, P.R.	181-182
Ivory Coast	281
Mali	127-128
Mauritania	267
Niger	220
Senegal	317-318
Upper Volta	201

ILO

ILO Headquarters, Geneva, and Emblem — CD131

Intl. Labor Organization, 50th anniv.

1969-70

Afars & Issas	337
Comoro Isls.	83
Fr. Polynesia	251-252
Fr. So. & Antarctic Terr.	35
New Caledonia	379
St. Pierre & Miquelon	396
Wallis & Futuna Isls.	172

ASECNA

Map of Africa, Plane and Airport CD132

10th anniversary of the Agency for the Security of Aerial Navigation in Africa and Madagascar (ASECNA, Agence pour la Securite de la Navigation Aerienne en Afrique et a Madagascar).

1969-70

Cameroun	500
Cent. Africa	119
Chad	222
Congo, P.R.	197
Dahomey	269
Gabon	260
Ivory Coast	287
Mali	130
Niger	221
Senegal	321
Upper Volta	204

U.P.U. Headquarters

CD133

New Universal Postal Union headquarters, Bern, Switzerland.

1970

Afars & Issas	342
Algeria	443
Cameroun	503-504
Cent. Africa	125
Chad	225
Comoro Isls.	84
Congo, P.R.	216
Fr. Polynesia	261-262
Fr. So. & Antarctic Terr.	36
Gabon	258
Ivory Coast	295
Madagascar	444
Mali	134-135
Mauritania	283
New Caledonia	382
Niger	231-232
St. Pierre & Miquelon	397-398
Senegal	328-329
Tunisia	535
Wallis & Futuna Isls.	173

De Gaulle

CD134

First anniversay of the death of Charles de Gaulle, (1890-1970), President of France.

1971-72

Afars & Issas	356-357
Comoro Isls.	104-105
France	1322-1325
Fr. Polynesia	270-271
Fr. So. & Antarctic Terr.	52-53
New Caledonia	393-394
Reunion	377, 380
St. Pierre & Miquelon	417-418
Wallis & Futuna Isls.	177-178

African Postal Union, 1971

UAMPT Building, Brazzaville, Congo — CD135

10th anniversary of the establishment of the African and Malagasy Posts and Telecommunications Union, UAMPT. Each stamp has a different native design.

1971, Nov. 13

Cameroun	C177
Cent. Africa	C89
Chad	C94
Congo, P.R.	C136
Dahomey	C146
Gabon	C120
Ivory Coast	C47
Mauritania	C113
Niger	C164
Rwanda	C8
Senegal	C105
Togo	C166
Upper Volta	C97

West African Monetary Union

African Couple, City, Village and Commemorative Coin — CD136

West African Monetary Union, 10th anniv.

1972, Nov. 2

Dahomey	300
Ivory Coast	331
Mauritania	299
Niger	258
Senegal	374
Togo	825
Upper Volta	280

African Postal Union, 1973

Telecommunications Symbols and Map of Africa — CD137

11th anniversary of the African and Malagasy Posts and Telecommunications Union (UAMPT).

1973, Sept. 12

Cameroun	574
Cent. Africa	194
Chad	294
Congo, P.R.	289
Dahomey	311
Gabon	320
Ivory Coast	361
Madagascar	500
Mauritania	304
Niger	287

Rwanda	540
Senegal	393
Togo	849
Upper Volta	297

Philexafrique II — Essen

CD138

CD139

Designs: Indigenous fauna, local and German stamps. Types CD138-CD139 printed horizontally and vertically se-tenant in sheets of 10 (2x5). Label between horizontal pairs alternately commemoratives Philexafrique II, Libreville, Gabon, June 1978, and 2nd International Stamp Fair, Essen, Germany, Nov. 1-5.

1978-1979

Benin	C285-C286
Central Africa	C200-C201
Chad	C238-C239
Congo Republic	C245-C246
Djibouti	C121-C122
Gabon	C215-C216
Ivory Coast	C64-C65
Mali	C356-C357
Mauritania	C185-C186
Niger	C291-C292
Rwanda	C12-C13
Senegal	C146-C147

BRITISH COMMONWEALTH OF NATIONS

The listings follow established trade practices when these issues are offered as units by dealers. The Peace issue, for example, includes only one stamp from the Indian state of Hyderabad. The U.P.U. issue includes the Egypt set. Pairs are included for those varieties issues with bilingual designs se-tenant.

Silver Jubilee

Windsor Castle and King George V CD301

Reign of King George V, 25th anniv.

1935

Antigua	77-80
Ascension	33-36
Bahamas	92-95
Barbados	186-189
Basutoland	11-14
Bechuanaland Protectorate	117-120
Bermuda	100-103
British Guiana	223-226
British Honduras	108-111
Cayman Islands	81-84
Ceylon	260-263
Cyprus	136-139
Dominica	90-93
Falkland Islands	77-80
Fiji	110-113
Gambia	125-128
Gibraltar	100-103
Gilbert & Ellice Islands	33-36

Gold Coast	108-111
Grenada	124-127
Hong Kong	147-150
Jamaica	109-112
Kenya, Uganda, Tanganyika	42-45
Leeward Islands	96-99
Malta	184-187
Mauritius	204-207
Montserrat	85-88
Newfoundland	226-229
Nigeria	34-37
Northern Rhodesia	18-21
Nyasaland Protectorate	47-50
St. Helena	111-114
St. Kitts-Nevis	72-75
St. Lucia	91-94
St. Vincent	134-137
Seychelles	118-121
Sierra Leone	166-169
Solomon Islands	60-63
Somaliland Protectorate	77-80
Straits Settlements	213-216
Swaziland	20-23
Trinidad & Tobago	43-46
Turks & Caicos Islands	71-74
Virgin Islands	69-72

The following have different designs but are included in the omnibus set:

Great Britain	226-229
Offices in Morocco	67-70, 226-229, 422-425, 508-510
Australia	152-154
Canada	211-216
Cook Islands	98-100
India	142-148
Nauru	31-34
New Guinea	46-47
New Zealand	199-201
Niue	67-69
Papua	114-117
Samoa	163-165
South Africa	68-71
Southern Rhodesia	33-36
South-West Africa	121-124

249 stamps

Coronation

Queen Elizabeth and King George VI CD302

1937

Aden	13-15
Antigua	81-83
Ascension	37-39
Bahamas	97-99
Barbados	190-192
Basutoland	15-17
Bechuanaland Protectorate	121-123
Bermuda	115-117
British Guiana	227-229
British Honduras	112-114
Cayman Islands	97-99
Ceylon	275-277
Cyprus	140-142
Dominica	94-96
Falkland Islands	81-83
Fiji	114-116
Gambia	129-131
Gibraltar	104-106
Gilbert & Ellice Islands	37-39
Gold Coast	112-114
Grenada	128-130
Hong Kong	151-153
Jamaica	113-115
Kenya, Uganda, Tanganyika	60-62
Leeward Islands	100-102
Malta	188-190
Mauritius	208-210
Montserrat	89-91
Newfoundland	230-232
Nigeria	50-52
Northern Rhodesia	22-24
Nyasaland Protectorate	51-53
St. Helena	115-117
St. Kitts-Nevis	76-78
St. Lucia	107-109
St. Vincent	138-140
Seychelles	122-124
Sierra Leone	170-172
Solomon Islands	64-66
Somaliland Protectorate	81-83
Straits Settlements	235-237

Swaziland	24-26
Trinidad & Tobago	47-49
Turks & Caicos Islands	75-77
Virgin Islands	73-75

The following have different designs but are included in the omnibus set:

Great Britain	234
Offices in Morocco	82, 439, 514
Canada	237
Cook Islands	109-111
Nauru	35-38
Newfoundland	233-243
New Guinea	48-51
New Zealand	223-225
Niue	70-72
Papua	118-121
South Africa	74-78
Southern Rhodesia	38-41
South-West Africa	125-132

202 stamps

Peace

King George VI and Parliament Buildings, London CD303

Return to peace at the close of World War II.

1945-46

Aden	28-29
Antigua	96-97
Ascension	50-51
Bahamas	130-131
Barbados	207-208
Bermuda	131-132
British Guiana	242-243
British Honduras	127-128
Cayman Islands	112-113
Ceylon	293-294
Cyprus	156-157
Dominica	112-113
Falkland Islands	97-98
Falkland Islands Dep.	1L9-1L10
Fiji	137-138
Gambia	144-145
Gibraltar	119-120
Gilbert & Ellice Islands	52-53
Gold Coast	128-129
Grenada	143-144
Jamaica	136-137
Kenya, Uganda, Tanganyika	90-91
Leeward Islands	116-117
Malta	206-207
Mauritius	223-224
Montserrat	104-105
Nigeria	71-72
Northern Rhodesia	46-47
Nyasaland Protectorate	82-83
Pitcairn Island	9-10
St. Helena	128-129
St. Kitts-Nevis	91-92
St. Lucia	127-128
St. Vincent	152-153
Seychelles	149-150
Sierra Leone	186-187
Solomon Islands	80-81
Somaliland Protectorate	108-109
Trinidad & Tobago	62-63
Turks & Caicos Islands	90-91
Virgin Islands	88-89

The following have different designs but are included in the omnibus set:

Great Britain	264-265
Offices in Morocco	523-524
Aden	
Kathiri State of Seiyun	12-13
Qu'aiti State of Shihr and Mukalla	12-13
Australia	200-202
Basutoland	29-31
Bechuanaland Protectorate	137-139
Burma	66-69
Cook Islands	127-130
Hong Kong	174-175
India	195-198
Hyderabad	51
New Zealand	247-257
Niue	90-93
Pakistan-Bahawalpur	O16
Samoa	191-194
South Africa	100-102
Southern Rhodesia	67-70

South-West Africa	153-155
Swaziland	38-40
Zanzibar	222-223

164 stamps

Silver Wedding

King George VI and Queen Elizabeth
CD304   CD305

1948-49

Aden	30-31
Kathiri State of Seiyun	14-15
Qu'aiti State of Shihr and Mukalla	14-15
Antigua	98-99
Ascension	52-53
Bahamas	148-149
Barbados	210-211
Basutoland	39-40
Bechuanaland Protectorate	147-148
Bermuda	133-134
British Guiana	244-245
British Honduras	129-130
Cayman Islands	116-117
Cyprus	158-159
Dominica	114-115
Falkland Islands	99-100
Falkland Islands Dep.	1L11-1L12
Fiji	139-140
Gambia	146-147
Gibraltar	121-122
Gilbert & Ellice Islands	54-55
Gold Coast	142-143
Grenada	145-146
Hong Kong	178-179
Jamaica	138-139
Kenya, Uganda, Tanganyika	92-93
Leeward Islands	118-119
Malaya	
Johore	128-129
Kedah	55-56
Kelantan	44-45
Malacca	1-2
Negri Sembilan	36-37
Pahang	44-45
Penang	1-2
Perak	99-100
Perlis	1-2
Selangor	74-75
Trengganu	47-48
Malta	223-224
Mauritius	229-230
Montserrat	106-107
Nigeria	73-74
North Borneo	238-239
Northern Rhodesia	48-49
Nyasaland Protectorate	85-86
Pitcairn Island	11-12
St. Helena	130-131
St. Kitts-Nevis	93-94
St. Lucia	129-130
St. Vincent	154-155
Sarawak	174-175
Seychelles	151-152
Sierra Leone	188-189
Singapore	21-22
Solomon Islands	82-83
Somaliland Protectorate	110-111
Swaziland	48-49
Trinidad & Tobago	64-65
Turks & Caicos Islands	92-93
Virgin Islands	90-91
Zanzibar	224-225

The following have different designs but are included in the omnibus set:

Great Britain	267-268
Offices in Morocco	93-94, 525-526
Bahrain	62-63
Kuwait	82-83
Oman	25-26
South Africa	106
South-West Africa	159

138 stamps

1949

Aden	32-35
Kathiri State of Seiyun	16-19
Qu'aiti State of Shihr and Mukalla	16-19
Antigua	100-103
Ascension	57-60
Bahamas	150-153
Barbados	212-215
Basutoland	41-44
Bechuanaland Protectorate	149-152
Bermuda	138-141
British Guiana	246-249
British Honduras	137-140
Brunei	79-82
Cayman Islands	118-121
Cyprus	160-163
Dominica	116-119
Falkland Islands	103-106
Falkland Islands Dep.	1L14-1L17
Fiji	141-144
Gambia	148-151
Gibraltar	123-126
Gilbert & Ellice Islands	56-59
Gold Coast	144-147
Grenada	147-150
Hong Kong	180-183
Jamaica	142-145
Kenya, Uganda, Tanganyika	94-97
Leeward Islands	126-129
Malaya	
Johore	151-154
Kedah	57-60
Kelantan	46-49
Malacca	18-21
Negri Sembilan	59-62
Pahang	46-49
Penang	23-26
Perak	101-104
Perlis	3-6
Selangor	76-79
Trengganu	49-52
Malta	225-228
Mauritius	231-234
Montserrat	108-111
New Hebrides, British	62-65
New Hebrides, French	79-82
Nigeria	75-78
North Borneo	240-243
Northern Rhodesia	50-53
Nyasaland Protectorate	87-90
Pitcairn Islands	13-16
St. Helena	132-135
St. Kitts-Nevis	95-98
St. Lucia	131-134
St. Vincent	170-173

Sarawak..............................176-179
Seychelles.........................153-156
Sierra Leone......................190-193
Singapore 23-26
Solomon Islands..................84-87
Somaliland Protectorate......112-115
Southern Rhodesia 71-72
Swaziland.............................50-53
Tonga...................................87-90
Trinidad & Tobago 66-69
Turks & Caicos Islands 101-104
Virgin Islands......................92-95
Zanzibar..........................226-229

The following have different designs but are included in the omnibus set:

Great Britain.....................276-279
Offices in Morocco................546-549
Australia..................................223
Bahrain.................................68-71
Burma..............................116-121
Ceylon.............................304-306
Egypt...............................281-283
India.................................223-226
Kuwait................................89-92
Oman.................................31-34
Pakistan-Bahawalpur   26-29, O25-O28
South Africa.....................109-111
South-West Africa 160-162

319 stamps

University

Arms of University College CD310 — Alice, Princess of Athlone CD311

1948 opening of University College of the West Indies at Jamaica.

1951

Antigua 104-105
Barbados 228-229
British Guiana....................250-251
British Honduras................141-142
Dominica..........................120-121
Grenada...........................164-165
Jamaica...........................146-147
Leeward Islands 130-131
Montserrat 112-113
St. Kitts-Nevis 105-106
St. Lucia..........................149-150
St. Vincent.......................174-175
Trinidad & Tobago 70-71
Virgin Islands......................96-97

28 stamps

Coronation

Queen Elizabeth II — CD312

1953

Aden......................................47
Kathiri State of Seiyun...................28
Qu'aiti State of Shihr and Mukalla .....
                                      28
Antigua 106
Ascension 61
Bahamas 157
Barbados 234
Basutoland................................45
Bechuanaland Protectorate...........153
Bermuda 142
British Guiana..........................252
British Honduras.......................143
Cayman Islands........................150

Cyprus 167
Dominica...............................141
Falkland Islands 121
Falkland Islands Dependencies 1L18
Fiji......................................145
Gambia.................................152
Gibraltar................................131
Gilbert & Ellice Islands 60
Gold Coast 160
Grenada................................170
Hong Kong 184
Jamaica.................................153
Kenya, Uganda, Tanganyika 101
Leeward Islands 132
Malaya
  Johore...............................155
  Kedah..................................82
  Kelantan...............................71
  Malacca................................27
  Negri Sembilan 63
  Pahang.................................71
  Penang.................................27
  Perak.................................126
  Perlis..................................28
  Selangor..............................101
  Trengganu..............................74
Malta.....................................241
Mauritius.................................250
Montserrat 127
New Hebrides, British 77
Nigeria....................................79
North Borneo............................260
Northern Rhodesia 60
Nyasaland Protectorate 96
Pitcairn 19
St. Helena 139
St. Kitts-Nevis 119
St. Lucia 156
St. Vincent..............................185
Sarawak.................................196
Seychelles...............................172
Sierra Leone............................194
Singapore 27
Solomon Islands..........................88
Somaliland Protectorate 127
Swaziland.................................54
Trinidad & Tobago 84
Tristan da Cunha 13
Turks & Caicos Islands 118
Virgin Islands............................114

The following have different designs but are included in the omnibus set:

Great Britain 313-316
Offices in Morocco................579-582
Australia..........................259-261
Bahrain...............................92-95
Canada.................................330
Ceylon..................................317
Cook Islands 145-146
Kuwait.............................113-116
New Zealand 280-284
Niue................................104-105
Oman................................52-55
Samoa..............................214-215
South Africa 192
Southern Rhodesia 80
South-West Africa 244-248
Tokelau Islands 4

106 stamps

Royal Visit 1953

Separate designs for each country for the visit of Queen Elizabeth II and the Duke of Edinburgh.

1953

Aden......................................62
Australia...........................267-269
Bermuda 163
Ceylon..................................318
Fiji.....................................146
Gibraltar................................146
Jamaica.................................154
Kenya, Uganda, Tanganyika 102
Malta.....................................242
New Zealand 286-287

13 stamps

West Indies Federation

Map of the Caribbean CD313

Federation of the West Indies, April 22, 1958.

1958

Antigua 122-124
Barbados 248-250
Dominica...........................161-163
Grenada...........................184-186
Jamaica...........................175-177
Montserrat 143-145
St. Kitts-Nevis 136-138
St. Lucia..........................170-172
St. Vincent.......................198-200
Trinidad & Tobago 86-88

30 stamps

Freedom from Hunger

Protein Food CD314

U.N. Food and Agricultural Organization's "Freedom from Hunger" campaign.

1963

Aden......................................65
Antigua 133
Ascension 89
Bahamas 180
Basutoland................................83
Bechuanaland Protectorate...........194
Bermuda 192
British Guiana..........................271
British Honduras.......................179
Brunei..................................100
Cayman Islands........................168
Dominica...............................181
Falkland Islands 146
Fiji.....................................198
Gambia.................................172
Gibraltar................................161
Gilbert & Ellice Islands 76
Grenada................................190
Hong Kong 218
Malta.....................................291
Mauritius.................................270
Montserrat 150
New Hebrides, British 93
North Borneo............................296
Pitcairn 35
St. Helena 173
St. Lucia 179
St. Vincent..............................201
Sarawak.................................212
Seychelles...............................213
Solomon Islands..........................109
Swaziland................................108
Tonga....................................127
Tristan da Cunha 68
Turks & Caicos Islands 138
Virgin Islands............................140
Zanzibar.................................280

37 stamps

Red Cross Centenary

Red Cross and Elizabeth II CD315

Red Cross Centenary.

1963

Antigua 134-135
Ascension 90-91
Bahamas 183-184
Basutoland..........................84-85
Bechuanaland Protectorate......195-196
Bermuda 193-194
British Guiana.....................272-273
British Honduras..................180-181
Cayman Islands...................169-170
Dominica..........................182-183
Falkland Islands 147-148
Fiji...............................203-204
Gambia............................173-174
Gibraltar..........................162-163
Gilbert & Ellice Islands...........77-78
Grenada...........................191-192
Hong Kong 219-220
Jamaica...........................203-204

Malta..............................292-293
Mauritius..........................271-272
Montserrat 151-152
New Hebrides, British 94-95
Pitcairn Islands....................36-37
St. Helena 174-175
St. Kitts-Nevis 143-144
St. Lucia..........................180-181
St. Vincent.......................202-203
Seychelles........................214-215
Solomon Islands..................110-111
South Arabia 1-2
Swaziland.........................109-110
Tonga.............................134-135
Tristan da Cunha...................69-70
Turks & Caicos Islands 139-140
Virgin Islands....................141-142

70 stamps

Shakespeare

Shakespeare Memorial Theatre, Stratford-on-Avon — CD316

400th anniversary of the birth of William Shakespeare.

1964

Antigua 151
Bahamas 201
Bechuanaland Protectorate............197
Cayman Islands........................171
Dominica...............................184
Falkland Islands 149
Gambia.................................192
Gibraltar................................164
Montserrat 153
St. Lucia 196
Turks & Caicos Islands 141
Virgin Islands..........................143

12 stamps

ITU

ITU Emblem CD317

Intl. Telecommunication Union, cent.

1965

Antigua 153-154
Ascension 92-93
Bahamas 219-220
Barbados 265-266
Basutoland.........................101-102
Bechuanaland Protectorate......202-203
Bermuda 196-197
British Guiana.....................293-294
British Honduras..................187-188
Brunei.............................116-117
Cayman Islands...................172-173
Dominica..........................185-186
Falkland Islands 154-155
Fiji...............................211-212
Gibraltar..........................167-168
Gilbert & Ellice Islands...........87-88
Grenada...........................205-206
Hong Kong 221-222
Mauritius..........................291-292
Montserrat 157-158
New Hebrides, British 108-109
Pitcairn Islands....................52-53
St. Helena 180-181
St. Kitts-Nevis 163-164
St. Lucia..........................197-198
St. Vincent.......................224-225
Seychelles........................218-219
Solomon Islands..................126-127
Swaziland.........................115-116
Tristan da Cunha...................85-86
Turks & Caicos Islands 142-143
Virgin Islands....................159-160

64 stamps

Intl. Cooperation Year

ICY Emblem CD318

1965

Antigua	155-156
Ascension	94-95
Bahamas	222-223
Basutoland	103-104
Bechuanaland Protectorate	204-205
Bermuda	199-200
British Guiana	295-296
British Honduras	189-190
Brunei	118-119
Cayman Islands	174-175
Dominica	187-188
Falkland Islands	156-157
Fiji	213-214
Gibraltar	169-170
Gilbert & Ellice Islands	104-105
Grenada	207-208
Hong Kong	223-224
Mauritius	293-294
Montserrat	176-177
New Hebrides, British	110-111
New Hebrides, French	126-127
Pitcairn Islands	54-55
St. Helena	182-183
St. Kitts-Nevis	165-166
St. Lucia	199-200
Seychelles	220-221
Solomon Islands	143-144
South Arabia	17-18
Swaziland	117-118
Tristan da Cunha	87-88
Turks & Caicos Islands	144-145
Virgin Islands	161-162

64 stamps

Churchill Memorial

Winston Churchill and St. Paul's, London, During Air Attack CD319

1966

Antigua	157-160
Ascension	96-99
Bahamas	224-227
Barbados	281-284
Basutoland	105-108
Bechuanaland Protectorate	206-209
Bermuda	201-204
British Antarctic Territory	16-19
British Honduras	191-194
Brunei	120-123
Cayman Islands	176-179
Dominica	189-192
Falkland Islands	158-161
Fiji	215-218
Gibraltar	171-174
Gilbert & Ellice Islands	106-109
Grenada	209-212
Hong Kong	225-228
Mauritius	295-298
Montserrat	178-181
New Hebrides, British	112-115
New Hebrides, French	128-131
Pitcairn Islands	56-59
St. Helena	184-187
St. Kitts-Nevis	167-170
St. Lucia	201-204
St. Vincent	241-244
Seychelles	222-225
Solomon Islands	145-148
South Arabia	19-22
Swaziland	119-122
Tristan da Cunha	89-92
Turks & Caicos Islands	146-149
Virgin Islands	163-166

136 stamps

Royal Visit, 1966

Queen Elizabeth II and Prince Philip CD320

Caribbean visit, Feb. 4 - Mar. 6, 1966.

1966

Antigua	161-162
Bahamas	228-229
Barbados	285-286
British Guiana	299-300
Cayman Islands	180-181
Dominica	193-194
Grenada	213-214
Montserrat	182-183
St. Kitts-Nevis	171-172
St. Lucia	205-206
St. Vincent	245-246
Turks & Caicos Islands	150-151
Virgin Islands	167-168

26 stamps

World Cup Soccer

Soccer Player and Jules Rimet Cup CD321

World Cup Soccer Championship, Wembley, England, July 11-30.

1966

Antigua	163-164
Ascension	100-101
Bahamas	245-246
Bermuda	205-206
Brunei	124-125
Cayman Islands	182-183
Dominica	195-196
Fiji	219-220
Gibraltar	175-176
Gilbert & Ellice Islands	125-126
Grenada	230-231
New Hebrides, British	116-117
New Hebrides, French	132-133
Pitcairn Islands	60-61
St. Helena	188-189
St. Kitts-Nevis	173-174
St. Lucia	207-208
Seychelles	226-227
Solomon Islands	167-168
South Arabia	23-24
Tristan da Cunha	93-94

42 stamps

WHO Headquarters

World Health Organization Headquarters, Geneva — CD322

1966

Antigua	165-166
Ascension	102-103
Bahamas	247-248
Brunei	126-127
Cayman Islands	184-185
Dominica	197-198
Fiji	224-225
Gibraltar	180-181
Gilbert & Ellice Islands	127-128
Grenada	232-233
Hong Kong	229-230
Montserrat	184-185
New Hebrides, British	118-119
New Hebrides, French	134-135
Pitcairn Islands	62-63
St. Helena	190-191
St. Kitts-Nevis	177-178
St. Lucia	209-210

St. Vincent	247-248
Seychelles	228-229
Solomon Islands	169-170
South Arabia	25-26
Tristan da Cunha	99-100

46 stamps

UNESCO Anniversary

"Education" — CD323

"Science" (Wheat ears & flask enclosing globe). "Culture" (lyre & columns). 20th anniversary of the UNESCO.

1966-67

Antigua	183-185
Ascension	108-110
Bahamas	249-251
Barbados	287-289
Bermuda	207-209
Brunei	128-130
Cayman Islands	186-188
Dominica	199-201
Gibraltar	183-185
Gilbert & Ellice Islands	129-131
Grenada	234-236
Hong Kong	231-233
Mauritius	299-301
Montserrat	186-188
New Hebrides, British	120-122
New Hebrides, French	136-138
Pitcairn Islands	64-66
St. Helena	192-194
St. Kitts-Nevis	179-181
St. Lucia	211-213
St. Vincent	249-251
Seychelles	230-232
Solomon Islands	171-173
South Arabia	27-29
Swaziland	123-125
Tristan da Cunha	101-103
Turks & Caicos Islands	155-157
Virgin Islands	176-178

84 stamps

Silver Wedding, 1972

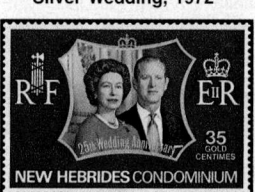

Queen Elizabeth II and Prince Philip — CD324

Designs: borders differ for each country.

1972

Anguilla	161-162
Antigua	295-296
Ascension	164-165
Bahamas	344-345
Bermuda	296-297
British Antarctic Territory	43-44
British Honduras	306-307
British Indian Ocean Territory	48-49
Brunei	186-187
Cayman Islands	304-305
Dominica	352-353
Falkland Islands	223-224
Fiji	328-329
Gibraltar	292-293
Gilbert & Ellice Islands	206-207
Grenada	466-467
Hong Kong	271-272
Montserrat	286-287
New Hebrides, British	169-170
Pitcairn Islands	127-128
St. Helena	271-272
St. Kitts-Nevis	257-258
St. Lucia	328-329
St.Vincent	344-345
Seychelles	309-310
Solomon Islands	248-249
South Georgia	35-36

Tristan da Cunha	178-179
Turks & Caicos Islands	257-258
Virgin Islands	241-242

60 stamps

Princess Anne's Wedding

Princess Anne and Mark Phillips — CD325

Wedding of Princess Anne and Mark Phillips, Nov. 14, 1973.

1973

Anguilla	179-180
Ascension	177-178
Belize	325-326
Bermuda	302-303
British Antarctic Territory	60-61
Cayman Islands	320-321
Falkland Islands	225-226
Gibraltar	305-306
Gilbert & Ellice Islands	216-217
Hong Kong	289-290
Montserrat	300-301
Pitcairn Island	135-136
St. Helena	277-278
St. Kitts-Nevis	274-275
St. Lucia	349-350
St. Vincent	358-359
St. Vincent Grenadines	1-2
Seychelles	311-312
Solomon Islands	259-260
South Georgia	37-38
Tristan da Cunha	189-190
Turks & Caicos Islands	286-287
Virgin Islands	260-261

44 stamps

Elizabeth II Coronation Anniv.

CD326   CD327

CD328

Designs: Royal and local beasts in heraldic form and simulated stonework. Portrait of Elizabeth II by Peter Grugeon. 25th anniversary of coronation of Queen Elizabeth II.

1978

Ascension	229
Barbados	474
Belize	397
British Antarctic Territory	71
Cayman Islands	404
Christmas Island	87
Falkland Islands	275
Fiji	384
Gambia	380
Gilbert Islands	312
Mauritius	464
New Hebrides, British	258
St. Helena	317
St. Kitts-Nevis	354
Samoa	472

Solomon Islands 368
South Georgia 51
Swaziland 302
Tristan da Cunha 238
Virgin Islands 337

20 sheets

Queen Mother Elizabeth's 80th Birthday

CD330

Designs: Photographs of Queen Mother Elizabeth. Falkland Islands issued in sheets of 50; others in sheets of 9.

1980

Ascension 261
Bermuda 401
Cayman Islands 443
Falkland Islands 305
Gambia 412
Gibraltar 393
Hong Kong 364
Pitcairn Islands 193
St. Helena 341
Samoa 532
Solomon Islands 426
Tristan da Cunha 277

12 stamps

Royal Wedding, 1981

Prince Charles and Lady Diana — CD331   CD331a

Wedding of Charles, Prince of Wales, and Lady Diana Spencer, St. Paul's Cathedral, London, July 29, 1981.

1981

Antigua 623-625
Ascension 294-296
Barbados 547-549
Barbuda 497-499
Bermuda 412-414
Brunei 268-270
Cayman Islands 471-473
Dominica.. 701-703
Falkland Islands 324-326
Falkland Islands Dep. 1L59-1L61
Fiji 442-444
Gambia 426-428
Ghana 759-761
Grenada... 1051-1053
Grenada Grenadines 440-443
Hong Kong 373-375
Jamaica 500-503
Lesotho.. 335-337
Maldive Islands 906-908
Mauritius 520-522
Norfolk Island 280-282
Pitcairn Islands 206-208
St. Helena 353-355
St. Lucia 543-545
Samoa 558-560
Sierra Leone 509-517
Solomon Islands 450-452
Swaziland 382-384
Tristan da Cunha 294-296
Turks & Caicos Islands 486-488
Caicos Island 8-10
Uganda 314-316
Vanuatu 308-310
Virgin Islands 406-408

Princess Diana

CD332

CD333

Designs: Photographs and portrait of Princess Diana, wedding or honeymoon photographs, royal residences, arms of issuing country. Portrait photograph by Clive Friend. Souvenir sheet margins show family tree, various people related to the princess. 21st birthday of Princess Diana of Wales, July 1.

1982

Antigua 663-666
Ascension 313-316
Bahamas 510-513
Barbados 585-588
Barbuda 544-546
British Antarctic Territory 92-95
Cayman Islands 486-489
Dominica... 773-776
Falkland Islands 348-351
Falkland Islands Dep. 1L72-1L75
Fiji 470-473
Gambia 447-450
Grenada... 1101A-1105
Grenada Grenadines 485-491
Lesotho.. 372-375
Maldive Islands 952-955
Mauritius 548-551
Pitcairn Islands 213-216
St. Helena 372-375
St. Lucia 591-594
Sierra Leone 531-534
Solomon Islands 471-474
Swaziland 406-409
Tristan da Cunha 310-313
Turks and Caicos Islands 530A-534
Virgin Islands 430-433

250th anniv. of first edition of Lloyd's List (shipping news publication) & of Lloyd's marine insurance.

CD335

Designs: First page of early edition of the list; historical ships, modern transportation or harbor scenes.

1984

Ascension 351-354
Bahamas 555-558
Barbados 627-630
Cayes of Belize 10-13
Cayman Islands 522-525
Falkland Islands 404-407
Fiji 509-512
Gambia 519-522
Mauritius 587-590
Nauru 280-283
St. Helena 412-415
Samoa 624-627
Seychelles 538-541
Solomon Islands 521-524
Vanuatu 368-371
Virgin Islands 466-469

Queen Mother 85th Birthday

CD336

Designs: Photographs tracing the life of the Queen Mother, Elizabeth. The high value in each set pictures the same photograph taken of the Queen Mother holding the infant Prince Henry.

1985

Ascension 372-376
Bahamas 580-584
Barbados 660-664
Bermuda 469-473
Falkland Islands 420-424
Falkland Islands Dep. 1L92-1L96
Fiji 531-535
Hong Kong 447-450
Jamaica 599-603
Mauritius 604-608
Norfolk Island 364-368
Pitcairn Islands 253-257
St. Helena 428-432
Samoa 649-653
Seychelles 567-571
Solomon Islands 543-547
Swaziland 476-480
Tristan da Cunha 372-376
Vanuatu 392-396
Zil Elwannyen Sesel 101-105

Queen Elizabeth II, 60th Birthday

CD337

1986, April 21

Ascension 389-393
Bahamas 592-596
Barbados 675-679
Bermuda 499-503
Cayman Islands 555-559
Falkland Islands 441-445
Fiji 544-548
Hong Kong 465-469
Jamaica 620-624
Kiribati 470-474
Mauritius 629-633
Papua New Guinea 640-644
Pitcairn Islands 270-274
St. Helena 451-455
Samoa 670-674
Seychelles 592-596
Solomon Islands 562-566
South Georgia 101-105
Swaziland 490-494
Tristan da Cunha 388-392
Vanuatu 414-418
Zambia 343-347
Zil Elwannyen Sesel 114-118

Royal Wedding

Marriage of Prince Andrew and Sarah Ferguson
CD338

1986, July 23

Ascension 399-400
Bahamas 602-603
Barbados 687-688
Cayman Islands 560-561
Jamaica 629-630
Pitcairn Islands 275-276
St. Helena 460-461
St. Kitts 181-182

Seychelles 602-603
Solomon Islands 567-568
Tristan da Cunha 397-398
Zambia 348-349
Zil Elwannyen Sesel................119-120

Queen Elizabeth II, 60th Birthday

Queen Elizabeth II & Prince Philip, 1947 Wedding Portrait — CD339

Designs: Photographs tracing the life of Queen Elizabeth II.

1986

Anguilla 674-677
Antigua 925-928
Barbuda 783-786
Dominica... 950-953
Gambia 611-614
Grenada... 1371-1374
Grenada Grenadines 749-752
Lesotho.. 531-534
Maldive Islands 1172-1175
Sierra Leone 760-763
Uganda 495-498

Royal Wedding, 1986

CD340

Designs: Photographs of Prince Andrew and Sarah Ferguson during courtship, engagement and marriage.

1986

Antigua 939-942
Barbuda 809-812
Dominica... 970-973
Gambia 635-638
Grenada... 1385-1388
Grenada Grenadines 758-761
Lesotho.. 545-548
Maldive Islands 1181-1184
Sierra Leone 769-772
Uganda 510-513

Lloyds of London, 300th Anniv.

CD341

Designs: 17th century aspects of Lloyds, representations of each country's individual connections with Lloyds and publicized disasters insured by the organization.

1986

Ascension 454-457
Bahamas 655-658
Barbados 731-734
Bermuda 541-544
Falkland Islands 481-484
Liberia.. 1101-1104
Malawi 534-537
Nevis 571-574
St. Helena 501-504
St. Lucia 923-926
Seychelles 649-652
Solomon Islands 627-630

South Georgia 131-134
Trinidad & Tobago 484-487
Tristan da Cunha...................439-442
Vanuatu 485-488
Zil Elwannyen Sesel 146-149

Moon Landing, 20th Anniv.

CD342

Designs: Equipment, crew photographs, spacecraft, official emblems and report profiles created for the Apollo Missions. Two stamps in each set are square in format rather than like the stamp shown; see individual country listings for more information.

1989

Ascension Is. 468-472
Bahamas 674-678
Belize....................................916-920
Kiribati..................................517-521
Liberia...................................1125-1129
Nevis.....................................586-590
St. Kitts 248-252
Samoa 760-764
Seychelles 676-680
Solomon Islands.....................643-647
Vanuatu 507-511
Zil Elwannyen Sesel 154-158

Queen Mother, 90th Birthday

CD343   CD344

Designs: Portraits of Queen Elizabeth, the Queen Mother. See individual country listings for more information.

1990

Ascension Is. 491-492
Bahamas 698-699
Barbados 782-783
British Antarctic Territory 170-171
British Indian Ocean Territory 106-107
Cayman Islands.......................622-623
Falkland Islands 524-525
Kenya....................................527-528
Kiribati..................................555-556
Liberia...................................1145-1146
Pitcairn Islands 336-337
St. Helena 532-533
St. Lucia 969-970
Seychelles 710-711
Solomon Islands.....................671-672
South Georgia 143-144
Swaziland 565-566
Tristan da Cunha.....................480-481
Zil Elwannyen Sesel 171-172

Queen Elizabeth II, 65th Birthday, and Prince Philip, 70th Birthday

CD345

CD346

Designs: Portraits of Queen Elizabeth II and Prince Philip differ for each country. Printed in sheets of 10 + 5 labels (3 different) between. Stamps alternate, producing 5 different triptychs.

1991

Ascension Is. 505-506
Bahamas 730-731
Belize....................................969-970
Bermuda................................617-618
Kiribati..................................571-572
Mauritius 733-734
Pitcairn Islands 348-349
St. Helena 554-555
St. Kitts 318-319
Samoa 790-791
Seychelles 723-724
Solomon Islands.....................688-689
South Georgia 149-150
Swaziland 586-587
Vanuatu 540-541
Zil Elwannyen Sesel 177-178

Royal Family Birthday, Anniversary

CD347

Queen Elizabeth II, 65th birthday, Charles and Diana, 10th wedding anniversary: Various photographs of Queen Elizabeth II, Prince Philip, Prince Charles, Princess Diana and their sons William and Henry.

1991

Antigua 1446-1455
Barbuda 1229-1238
Dominica................................1328-1337
Gambia 1080-1089
Grenada 2006-2015
Grenada Grenadines............1331-1340
Guyana 2440-2451
Lesotho 871-875
Maldive Islands.......................1533-1542
Nevis.....................................666-675
St. Vincent 1485-1494
St. Vincent Grenadines 769-778
Sierra Leone 1387-1396
Turks & Caicos Islands 913-922
Uganda 918-927

Queen Elizabeth II's Accession to the Throne, 40th Anniv.

CD348

CD349

Various photographs of Queen Elizabeth II with local Scenes.

1992 - CD348

Antigua 1513-1518
Barbuda 1306-1309
Dominica................................1414-1419
Gambia 1172-1177
Grenada 2047-2052
Grenada Grenadines............1368-1373

Lesotho 881-885
Maldive Islands...................1637-1642
Nevis.....................................702-707
St. Vincent 1582-1587
St. Vincent Grenadines 829-834
Sierra Leone 1482-1487
Turks and Caicos Islands 978-987
Uganda 990-995
Virgin Islands..........................742-746

1992 - CD349

Ascension Islands 531-535
Bahamas 744-748
Bermuda................................623-627
British Indian Ocean Territory 119-123
Cayman Islands.......................648-652
Falkland Islands 549-553
Gibraltar.................................605-609
Hong Kong 619-623
Kenya....................................563-567
Kiribati..................................582-586
Pitcairn Islands 362-366
St. Helena 570-574
St. Kitts 332-336
Samoa 805-809
Seychelles 734-738
Solomon Islands.....................708-712
South Georgia 157-161
Tristan da Cunha.....................508-512
Vanuatu 555-559
Zambia...................................561-565
Zil Elwannyen Sesel 183-187

Royal Air Force, 75th Anniversary

CD350

1993

Ascension 557-561
Bahamas 771-775
Barbados 842-846
Belize....................................1003-1008
Bermuda................................648-651
British Indian Ocean Territory 136-140
Falkland Is. 573-577
Fiji 687-691
Montserrat 830-834
St. Kitts 351-355

Royal Air Force, 80th Anniv.

Design CD350 Re-inscribed

1998

Ascension 697-701
Bahamas 907-911
British Indian Ocean Terr 198-202
Cayman Islands.......................754-758
Fiji 814-818
Gibraltar.................................755-759
Samoa 957-961
Turks & Caicos Islands 1258-1265
Tuvalu 763-767
Virgin Islands..........................879-883

End of World War II, 50th Anniv.

CD351

CD352

1995

Ascension 613-617
Bahamas 824-828
Barbados 891-895
Belize....................................1047-1050
British Indian Ocean Territory 163-167
Cayman Islands.......................704-708
Falkland Islands 634-638
Fiji 720-724
Kiribati..................................662-668
Liberia...................................1175-1179
Mauritius 803-805
St. Helena 646-654
St. Kitts 389-393
St. Lucia 1018-1022
Samoa 890-894
Solomon Islands.....................799-803
South Georgia & S. Sandwich Is. ....
198-200
Tristan da Cunha.....................562-566

UN, 50th Anniv.

CD353

1995

Bahamas 839-842
Barbados 901-904
Belize....................................1055-1058
Jamaica 847-851
Liberia...................................1187-1190
Mauritius 813-816
Pitcairn Islands 436-439
St. Kitts 398-401
St. Lucia 1023-1026
Samoa 900-903
Tristan da Cunha.....................568-571
Virgin Islands..........................807-810

Queen Elizabeth, 70th Birthday

CD354

1996

Ascension 632-635
British Antarctic Territory 240-243
British Indian Ocean Territory 176-180
Falkland Islands 653-657
Pitcairn Islands 446-449
St. Helena 672-676
Samoa 912-916
Tokelau 223-227
Tristan da Cunha.....................576-579
Virgin Islands..........................824-828

Diana, Princess of Wales (1961-97)

CD355

1998

Ascension	696
Bahamas	901A-902
Barbados	950
Belize	1091
Bermuda	753
Botswana	659-663
British Antarctic Territory	258
British Indian Ocean Terr.	197
Cayman Islands	752A-753
Falkland Islands	694
Fiji	819-820
Gibraltar	754
Kiribati	719A-720
Namibia	909
Niue	706
Norfolk Island	644-645
Papua New Guinea	937
Pitcairn Islands	487
St. Helena	711
St. Kitts	437A-438
Samoa	955A-956
Seycelles	802
Solomon Islands	866-867
South Georgia & S. Sandwich Islands	220
Tokelau	252B-253
Tonga	980
Niuafo'ou	201
Tristan da Cunha	618
Tuvalu	762
Vanuatu	719
Virgin Islands	878

Wedding of Prince Edward and Sophie Rhys-Jones

CD356

1999

Ascension	729-730
Cayman Islands	775-776
Falkland Islands	729-730
Pitcairn Islands	505-506
St. Helena	733-734
Samoa	971-972
Tristan da Cunha	636-637
Virgin Islands	908-909

1st Manned Moon Landing, 30th Anniv.

CD357

1999

Ascension	731-735
Bahamas	942-946
Barbados	967-971
Bermuda	778
Cayman Islands	777-781

Fiji	853-857
Jamaica	889-893
Kirbati	746-750
Nauru	465-469
St. Kitts	460-464
Samoa	973-977
Solomon Islands	875-879
Tuvalu	800-804
Virgin Islands	910-914

Queen Mother's Century

CD358

1999

Ascension	736-740
Bahamas	951-955
Cayman Islands	782-786
Falkland Islands	734-738
Fiji	858-862
Norfolk Island	688-692
St. Helena	740-744
Samoa	978-982
Solomon Islands	880-884
South Georgia & South Sandwich Islands	231-235
Tristan da Cunha	638-642
Tuvalu	805-809

Prince William, 18th Birthday

CD359

2000

Ascension	755-759
Cayman Islands	797-801
Falkland Islands	762-766
Fiji	889-893
South Georgia and South Sandwich Islands	257-261
Tristan da Cunha	664-668
Virgin Islands	925-929

Reign of Queen Elizabeth II, 50th Anniv.

CD360

2002

Ascension	790-794
Bahamas	1033-1037
Barbados	1019-1023
Belize	1152-1156
Bermuda	822-826
British Antarctic Territory	307-311
British Indian Ocean Territory	239-243
Cayman Islands	844-848
Falkland Islands	804-808
Gibraltar	896-900
Jamaica	952-956
Nauru	491-495
Norfolk Island	758-762
Papua New Guinea	1019-1023
Pitcairn Islands	552
St. Helena	788-792
St. Lucia	1146-1150
Solomon Islands	931-935
South Georgia & So. Sandwich Is.	274-278
Swaziland	706-710
Tokelau	302-306
Tonga	1059

Niuafo'ou	239
Tristan da Cunha	706-710
Virgin Islands	967-971

Queen Mother Elizabeth (1900-2002)

CD361

2002

Ascension	799-801
Bahamas	1044-1046
Bermuda	834-836
British Antarctic Territory	312-314
British Indian Ocean Territory	245-247
Cayman Islands	857-861
Falkland Islands	812-816
Nauru	499-501
Pitcairn Islands	561-565
St. Helena	808-812
St. Lucia	1155-1159
Seychelles	830
Solomon Islands	945-947
South Georgia & So. Sandwich Isls.	281-285
Tokelau	312-314
Tristan da Cunha	715-717
Virgin Islands	979-983

Head of Queen Elizabeth II

CD362

2003

Ascension	822
Bermuda	865
British Antarctic Territory	322
British Indian Ocean Territory	261
Cayman Islands	878
Falkland Islands	828
St. Helena	820
South Georgia & South Sandwich Islands	294
Tristan da Cunha	731
Virgin Islands	1003

Coronation of Queen Elizabeth II, 50th Anniv.

CD363

2003

Ascension	823-825
Bahamas	1073-1075
Bermuda	866-868
British Antarctic Territory	323-325
British Indian Ocean Territory	262-264
Cayman Islands	879-881
Jamaica	970-972
Kiribati	825-827
Pitcairn Islands	577-581
St. Helena	821-823
St. Lucia	1171-1173
Tokelau	320-322
Tristan da Cunha	732-734
Virgin Islands	1004-1006

Prince William, 21st

CD364

2003

Ascension	826
British Indian Ocean Territory	265
Cayman Islands	882-884
Falkland Islands	829
South Georgia & South Sandwich Islands	295
Tokelau	323
Tristan da Cunha	735
Virgin Islands	1007-1009

scott**mounts**

For stamp presentation unequaled in beauty and clarity, insist on ScottMounts. Made of 100% inert polystyrol foil, ScottMounts protect your stamps from the harmful effects of dust and moisture. Available in your choice of clear or black backs, ScottMounts are center-split across the back for easy insertion of stamps and feature crystal clear mount faces. Double layers of gum assure stay-put bonding on the album page. Discover the quality and value ScottMounts have to offer. ScottMounts are available from your favorite stamp dealer or direct from:

![SCOTT logo]

Scott Publishing Co.
1-800-572-6885
P.O. Box 828 Sidney OH 45365-0828
www.amosadvantage.com

Discover the quality and value ScottMounts have to offer.
For a complete list of ScottMount sizes call or write Scott Publishing Co.

AMOS
PUBLISHING
Publishers of:
Coin World, Linn's Stamp News and Scott Publishing Co.

British Commonwealth of Nations

Dominions, Colonies, Territories, Offices and Independent Members

Comprising stamps of the British Commonwealth and associated nations.

A strict observance of technicalities would bar some or all of the stamps listed under Burma, Ireland, Kuwait, Nepal, New Republic, Orange Free State, Samoa, South Africa, South-West Africa, Stellaland, Sudan, Swaziland, the two Transvaal Republics and others but these are included for the convenience of collectors.

1. Great Britain

Great Britain: Including England, Scotland, Wales and Northern Ireland.

2. The Dominions, Present and Past

AUSTRALIA

The Commonwealth of Australia was proclaimed on January 1, 1901. It consists of six former colonies as follows:

New South Wales	Victoria
Queensland	Tasmania
South Australia	Western Australia

The following islands and territories are, or have been, administered by Australia: Australian Antarctic Territory, Christmas Island, Cocos (Keeling) Islands, Nauru, New Guinea, Norfolk Island, Papua.

CANADA

The Dominion of Canada was created by the British North America Act in 1867. The following provinces were former separate colonies and issued postage stamps:

British Columbia and Vancouver Island	Newfoundland
	Nova Scotia
New Brunswick	Prince Edward Island

FIJI

The colony of Fiji became an independent nation with dominion status on Oct. 10, 1970.

GHANA

This state came into existence Mar. 6, 1957, with dominion status. It consists of the former colony of the Gold Coast and the Trusteeship Territory of Togoland. Ghana became a republic July 1, 1960.

INDIA

The Republic of India was inaugurated on January 26, 1950. It succeeded the Dominion of India which was proclaimed August 15, 1947, when the former Empire of India was divided into Pakistan and the Union of India. The Republic is composed of about 40 predominantly Hindu states of three classes: governor's provinces, chief commissioner's provinces and princely states. India also has various territories, such as the Andaman and Nicobar Islands.

The old Empire of India was a federation of British India and the native states. The more important princely states were autonomous. Of the more than 700 Indian states, these 43 are familiar names to philatelists because of their postage stamps.

CONVENTION STATES

Chamba	Jhind
Faridkot	Nabha
Gwalior	Patiala

NATIVE FEUDATORY STATES

Alwar	Jammu
Bahawalpur	Jammu and Kashmir
Bamra	Jasdan
Barwani	Jhalawar
Bhopal	Jhind (1875-76)
Bhor	Kashmir
Bijawar	Kishangarh
Bundi	Las Bela
Bussahir	Morvi
Charkhari	Nandgaon
Cochin	Nowanuggur
Dhar	Orchha
Duttia	Poonch
Faridkot (1879-85)	Rajpeepla
Hyderabad	Sirmur
Idar	Soruth
Indore	Travancore
Jaipur	Wadhwan

NEW ZEALAND

Became a dominion on September 26, 1907. The following islands and territories are, or have been, administered by New Zealand:

Aitutaki	Ross Dependency
Cook Islands (Rarotonga)	Samoa (Western Samoa)
Niue	Tokelau Islands
Penrhyn	

PAKISTAN

The Republic of Pakistan was proclaimed March 23, 1956. It succeeded the Dominion which was proclaimed August 15, 1947. It is made up of all or part of several Moslem provinces and various districts of the former Empire of India, including Bahawalpur and Las Bela. Pakistan withdrew from the Commonwealth in 1972.

SOUTH AFRICA

Under the terms of the South African Act (1909) the self-governing colonies of Cape of Good Hope, Natal, Orange River Colony and Transvaal united on May 31, 1910, to form the Union of South Africa. It became an independent republic May 3, 1961.

Under the terms of the Treaty of Versailles, South-West Africa, formerly German South-West Africa, was mandated to the Union of South Africa.

SRI LANKA (CEYLON)

The Dominion of Ceylon was proclaimed February 4, 1948. The island had been a Crown Colony from 1802 until then. On May 22, 1972, Ceylon became the Republic of Sri Lanka.

3. Colonies, Past and Present; ControlledTerritory and Independent Members of the Commonwealth

Aden	Bechuanaland
Aitutaki	Bechuanaland Prot.
Antigua	Belize
Ascension	Bermuda
Bahamas	Botswana
Bahrain	British Antarctic Territory
Bangladesh	British Central Africa
Barbados	British Columbia and
Barbuda	Vancouver Island
Basutoland	British East Africa
Batum	British Guiana

British Honduras
British Indian Ocean Territory
British New Guinea
British Solomon Islands
British Somaliland
Brunei
Burma
Bushire
Cameroons
Cape of Good Hope
Cayman Islands
Christmas Island
Cocos (Keeling) Islands
Cook Islands
Crete,
  British Administration
Cyprus
Dominica
East Africa & Uganda
  Protectorates
Egypt
Falkland Islands
Fiji
Gambia
German East Africa
Gibraltar
Gilbert Islands
Gilbert & Ellice Islands
Gold Coast
Grenada
Griqualand West
Guernsey
Guyana
Heligoland
Hong Kong
Indian Native States
  (see India)
Ionian Islands
Jamaica
Jersey

Kenya
Kenya, Uganda & Tanzania
Kuwait
Labuan
Lagos
Leeward Islands
Lesotho
Madagascar
Malawi
Malaya
  Federated Malay States
  Johore
  Kedah
  Kelantan
  Malacca
  Negri Sembilan
  Pahang
  Penang
  Perak
  Perlis
  Selangor
  Singapore
  Sungei Ujong
  Trengganu
Malaysia
Maldive Islands
Malta
Man, Isle of
Mauritius
Mesopotamia
Montserrat
Muscat
Namibia
Natal
Nauru
Nevis
New Britain
New Brunswick
Newfoundland
New Guinea

New Hebrides
New Republic
New South Wales
Niger Coast Protectorate
Nigeria
Niue
Norfolk Island
North Borneo
Northern Nigeria
Northern Rhodesia
North West Pacific Islands
Nova Scotia
Nyasaland Protectorate
Oman
Orange River Colony
Palestine
Papua New Guinea
Penrhyn Island
Pitcairn Islands
Prince Edward Island
Queensland
Rhodesia
Rhodesia & Nyasaland
Ross Dependency
Sabah
St. Christopher
St. Helena
St. Kitts
St. Kitts-Nevis-Anguilla
St. Lucia
St. Vincent
Samoa
Sarawak
Seychelles
Sierra Leone
Solomon Islands
Somaliland Protectorate
South Arabia
South Australia
South Georgia

Southern Nigeria
Southern Rhodesia
South-West Africa
Stellaland
Straits Settlements
Sudan
Swaziland
Tanganyika
Tanzania
Tasmania
Tobago
Togo
Tokelau Islands
Tonga
Transvaal
Trinidad
Trinidad and Tobago
Tristan da Cunha
Trucial States
Turks and Caicos
Turks Islands
Tuvalu
Uganda
United Arab Emirates
Victoria
Virgin Islands
Western Australia
Zambia
Zanzibar
Zululand

**POST OFFICES IN
FOREIGN COUNTRIES**
Africa
  East Africa Forces
  Middle East Forces
Bangkok
China
Morocco
Turkish Empire

Colonies, Former Colonies, Offices, Territories Controlled by Parent States

Belgium
Belgian Congo
Ruanda-Urundi

Denmark
Danish West Indies
Faroe Islands
Greenland
Iceland

Finland
Aland Islands

France
COLONIES PAST AND PRESENT, CONTROLLED TERRITORIES
Afars & Issas, Territory of
Alaouites
Alexandretta
Algeria
Alsace & Lorraine
Anjouan
Annam & Tonkin
Benin
Cambodia (Khmer)
Cameroun
Castellorizo
Chad
Cilicia
Cochin China
Comoro Islands
Dahomey
Diego Suarez
Djibouti (Somali Coast)
Fezzan
French Congo
French Equatorial Africa
French Guiana
French Guinea
French India
French Morocco
French Polynesia (Oceania)
French Southern & Antarctic Territories
French Sudan
French West Africa
Gabon
Germany
Ghadames
Grand Comoro
Guadeloupe
Indo-China
Inini
Ivory Coast
Laos
Latakia
Lebanon
Madagascar
Martinique
Mauritania
Mayotte
Memel
Middle Congo
Moheli
New Caledonia
New Hebrides
Niger Territory
Nossi-Be

Obock
Reunion
Rouad, Ile
Ste.-Marie de Madagascar
St. Pierre & Miquelon
Senegal
Senegambia & Niger
Somali Coast
Syria
Tahiti
Togo
Tunisia
Ubangi-Shari
Upper Senegal & Niger
Upper Volta
Viet Nam
Wallis & Futuna Islands

POST OFFICES IN FOREIGN COUNTRIES
China
Crete
Egypt
Turkish Empire
Zanzibar

Germany
EARLY STATES
Baden
Bavaria
Bergedorf
Bremen
Brunswick
Hamburg
Hanover
Lubeck
Mecklenburg-Schwerin
Mecklenburg-Strelitz
Oldenburg
Prussia
Saxony
Schleswig-Holstein
Wurttemberg

FORMER COLONIES
Cameroun (Kamerun)
Caroline Islands
German East Africa
German New Guinea
German South-West Africa
Kiauchau
Mariana Islands
Marshall Islands
Samoa
Togo

Italy
EARLY STATES
Modena
Parma
Romagna
Roman States
Sardinia
Tuscany
Two Sicilies
　Naples
　Neapolitan Provinces
　Sicily

FORMER COLONIES, CONTROLLED TERRITORIES, OCCUPATION AREAS
Aegean Islands
　Calimno (Calino)
　Caso
　Cos (Coo)
　Karki (Carchi)
　Leros (Lero)
　Lipso
　Nisiros (Nisiro)
　Patmos (Patmo)
　Piscopi
　Rodi (Rhodes)
　Scarpanto
　Simi
　Stampalia
Castellorizo
Corfu
Cyrenaica
Eritrea
Ethiopia (Abyssinia)
Fiume
Ionian Islands
　Cephalonia
　Ithaca
　Paxos
Italian East Africa
Libya
Oltre Giuba
Saseno
Somalia (Italian Somaliland)
Tripolitania

POST OFFICES IN FOREIGN COUNTRIES
"ESTERO"*
Austria
China
　Peking
　Tientsin
Crete
Tripoli
Turkish Empire
　Constantinople
　Durazzo
　Janina
Jerusalem
Salonika
Scutari
Smyrna
Valona
*Stamps overprinted "ESTERO" were used in various parts of the world.

Netherlands
Aruba
Netherlands Antilles (Curacao)
Netherlands Indies
Netherlands New Guinea
Surinam (Dutch Guiana)

Portugal
COLONIES PAST AND PRESENT, CONTROLLED TERRITORIES
Angola
Angra
Azores
Cape Verde
Funchal

Horta
Inhambane
Kionga
Lourenco Marques
Macao
Madeira
Mozambique
Mozambique Co.
Nyassa
Ponta Delgada
Portuguese Africa
Portuguese Congo
Portuguese Guinea
Portuguese India
Quelimane
St. Thomas & Prince Islands
Tete
Timor
Zambezia

Russia
ALLIED TERRITORIES AND REPUBLICS, OCCUPATION AREAS
Armenia
Aunus (Olonets)
Azerbaijan
Batum
Estonia
Far Eastern Republic
Georgia
Karelia
Latvia
Lithuania
North Ingermanland
Ostland
Russian Turkestan
Siberia
South Russia
Tannu Tuva
Transcaucasian Fed. Republics
Ukraine
Wenden (Livonia)
Western Ukraine

Spain
COLONIES PAST AND PRESENT, CONTROLLED TERRITORIES
Aguera, La
Cape Juby
Cuba
Elobey, Annobon & Corisco
Fernando Po
Ifni
Mariana Islands
Philippines
Puerto Rico
Rio de Oro
Rio Muni
Spanish Guinea
Spanish Morocco
Spanish Sahara
Spanish West Africa

POST OFFICES IN FOREIGN COUNTRIES
Morocco
Tangier
Tetuan

Dies of British Colonial Stamps

DIE A

DIE B

DIE I

DIE II

DIE A:

1. The lines in the groundwork vary in thickness and are not uniformly straight.
2. The seventh and eighth lines from the top, in the groundwork, converge where they meet the head.
3. There is a small dash in the upper part of the second jewel in the band of the crown.
4. The vertical color line in front of the throat stops at the sixth line of shading on the neck.

DIE B:

1. The lines in the groundwork are all thin and straight.
2. All the lines of the background are parallel.
3. There is no dash in the upper part of the second jewel in the band of the crown.
4. The vertical color line in front of the throat stops at the eighth line of shading on the neck.

DIE I:

1. The base of the crown is well below the level of the inner white line around the vignette.
2. The labels inscribed "POSTAGE" and "REVENUE" are cut square at the top.
3. There is a white "bud" on the outer side of the main stem of the curved ornaments in each lower corner.
4. The second (thick) line below the country name has the ends next to the crown cut diagonally.

DIE Ia.	DIE Ib.
1 as die II.	1 and 3 as die II.
2 and 3 as die I.	2 as die I.

DIE II:

1. The base of the crown is aligned with the underside of the white line around the vignette.
2. The labels curve inward at the top inner corners.
3. The "bud" has been removed from the outer curve of the ornaments in each corner.
4. The second line below the country name has the ends next to the crown cut vertically.

Wmk. 1
Crown and C C

Wmk. 2
Crown and C A

Wmk. 3
Multiple Crown
and C A

Wmk. 4
Multiple Crown
and Script C A

Wmk. 4a

Wmk. 314
St. Edward's Crown
and C A Multiple

Wmk. 373

Wmk. 384

British Colonial and Crown Agents Watermarks

Watermarks 1 to 4, 314, 373, and 384, common to many British territories, are illustrated here to avoid duplication.

The letters "CC" of Wmk. 1 identify the paper as having been made for the use of the Crown Colonies, while the letters "CA" of the others stand for "Crown Agents." Both Wmks. 1 and 2 were used on stamps printed by De La Rue & Co.

Wmk. 3 was adopted in 1904; Wmk. 4 in 1921; Wmk. 314 in 1957; Wmk. 373 in 1974; and Wmk. 384 in 1985.

In Wmk. 4a, a non-matching crown of the general St. Edwards type (bulging on both sides at top) was substituted for one of the Wmk. 4 crowns which fell off the dandy roll. The non-matching crown occurs in 1950-52 printings in a horizontal row of crowns on certain regular stamps of Johore and Seychelles, and on various postage due stamps of Barbados, Basutoland, British Guiana, Gold Coast, Grenada, Northern Rhodesia, St. Lucia, Swaziland and Trinidad and Tobago. A variation of Wmk. 4a, with the non-matching crown in a horizontal row of crown-CA-crown, occurs on regular stamps of Bahamas, St. Kitts-Nevis and Singapore.

Wmk. 314 was intentionally used sideways, starting in 1966. When a stamp was issued with Wmk. 314 both upright and sideways, the sideways varieties usually are listed also – with minor numbers. In many of the later issues, Wmk. 314 is slightly visible.

Wmk. 373 is usually only faintly visible.

CAMBODIA

kam-'bō-dē-ə

(Kampuchea)

(Khmer Republic)

LOCATION — Southern Indo-China
GOVT. — Republic
AREA — 69,898 sq. mi.
POP. — 11,626,520 (1999 est.)
CAPITAL — Phnom Penh

Before 1951, Cambodia used stamps of Indo-China. In October, 1970, the Kingdom of Cambodia became the Khmer Republic.
From 1978 to 1980 money was abolished.

100 Cents = 1 Piaster
100 Cents = 1 Riel (1955)

Imperforates
Most Cambodia stamps exist imperforate in issued and trial colors, and also in small presentation sheets in issued colors.

Catalogue values for all unused stamps in this country are for Never Hinged items.

Apsaras — A1   King Norodom Sihanouk — A3

Enthronement Hall — A2

1951-52		Unwmk. Engr.	Perf. 13	
1	A1	10c dk blue green	1.25	2.25
2	A1	20c cl & org brn	.75	1.00
3	A1	30c pur & indigo	.75	.50
4	A1	40c ultra & brt bl grn	1.00	.65
5	A2	50c dk grn & dk ol grn	.85	.40
6	A3	80c bl blk & dk bl grn	2.50	1.50
7	A2	1pi indigo & purple	2.00	.95
8	A3	1.10pi dp car & brt red	2.75	2.00
9	A3	1.50pi blk brn & red brn ('51)	2.75	1.00
10	A1	1.50pi dp car & cerise	2.75	1.50
11	A2	1.50pi indigo & dp ultra	2.75	1.25
12	A3	1.90pi indigo & dp ultra	4.75	4.75
13	A2	2pi dp car & org brn	3.75	1.25
14	A3	3pi dp car & org brn	5.25	2.50
15	A1	5pi indigo & purple	16.00	10.00
a.		Souvenir sheet of 1	50.00	
16	A2	10pi purple & indigo	18.00	15.00
a.		Souvenir sheet of 1	50.00	
17	A3	15pi dk pur & purple	42.50	30.00
a.		Souvenir sheet of 1	50.00	
		Nos. 1-17 (17)	110.35	76.50

Nos. 15a, 16a, 17a sold in a booklet.
Stamps with completely white gum and no toning sell for a premium.
For surcharges see Nos. B1-B4.

Phnom Daun Penh — A4

East Gate, Angkor Thom — A5

Arms of Cambodia — A6   Methods of Mail Transport — A7

1954-55		Unwmk.	Perf. 13	
18	A4	10c rose carmine	.20	.20
a.		Souvenir sheet of 5 ('55)	55.00	
19	A4	20c dark green	.20	.20
20	A4	30c indigo	.20	.20
21	A4	40c dark purple	.25	.25
22	A4	50c dk violet brn	.25	.25
23	A4	70c chocolate	.45	.75
a.		Souvenir sheet of 5 ('55)	55.00	
24	A5	1pi red violet	.55	.55
25	A5	1.50pi red	.50	.45
26	A6	2pi rose red	.85	.65
a.		Souvenir sheet of 5 ('55)	55.00	
27	A6	2.50pi green	1.25	.80
28	A7	2.50pi blue green	1.50	1.00
a.		Souvenir sheet of 5 ('55)	55.00	
29	A6	3pi ultra	1.75	1.50
30	A7	4pi black brown	1.90	1.50
31	A6	4.50pi purple	2.25	1.50
32	A7	5pi rose red	2.25	1.50
33	A6	6pi chocolate	2.75	1.75
34	A7	10pi purple	2.75	2.00
35	A7	15pi deep blue	4.00	3.75
36	A5	20pi ultra	8.00	4.75
37	A5	30pi blue green	12.00	8.50
		Nos. 18-37 (20)	43.85	32.05
		Nos. 18a/28a, Set of 4	200.00	

The 4 souvenir sheets each contain 5 stamps: #18a (10c, 20c, 30c, 40c, 50c); #23a (70c, 1pi, 1.50pi, 20pi, 30pi); #26a (2pi, 2.50pi green, 3pi, 4.50pi, 6pi); #28a (2.50pi blue green, 4pi, 5pi, 10pi, 15pi). Size of #18a, 26a and 28a: 120x120mm. Size of #23a: 160x92mm. Values are for very fine, unblemished sheets. Examples with toning and/or gum bends sell for less.
For overprints see Nos. 99-100.

King Norodom Suramarit — A8

King Norodom Suramarit and Queen Kossamak Nearirat Serey Vathana A9

Portraits: 50c (No. 39), 2.50r, 4r, 6r, 15r, Queen Kossamak Nearirat Serey Vathana.

Perf. 14x13(A8), 13(A9)

1955, Nov. 24		Engr.	Unwmk.	
38	A8	50c violet	.40	.40
39	A8	50c indigo	.40	.40
40	A8	1r car lake	.55	.50
41	A9	1.50r dk brown	.65	.50
42	A9	2r black & indigo	.65	.50
43	A8	2r dp ultra	.65	.65
44	A8	2.50r dk vio brn	.65	.65
45	A9	3r brn org & car	.85	.65
46	A8	4r dark green	1.40	1.00
47	A9	5r blk & dk grn	1.60	1.25
48	A8	6r deep plum	1.60	1.25
49	A8	7r dark brown	2.50	1.25
50	A9	10r brn car & vio	2.75	1.40
51	A8	15r purple	3.75	2.50
52	A8	20r deep green	5.50	3.25
		Nos. 38-52 (15)	23.90	16.15

Coronation of King Norodom Suramarit and Queen Kossamak Nearirat Serey Vathana. See #74-75. For surcharge see #122.

King Norodom Suramarit — A10   Prince Sihanouk, Globe and Flags — A11

Portrait: 3r, 5r, 50r, Queen Kossamak Nearirat Serey Vathana.

1956, Mar. 8			Perf. 13	
53	A10	2r dark red	2.00	2.00
54	A10	3r dark blue	2.75	2.75
55	A10	5r yellow green	4.00	4.00
56	A10	10r dark green	9.00	9.00
57	A10	30r dark violet	21.00	21.00
58	A10	50r rose lilac	40.00	40.00
		Nos. 53-58 (6)	78.75	78.75

Coronation of King Norodom Suramarit and Queen Kossamak Nearirat Serey Vathana.

1957, Mar. 1				
59	A11	2r green, ultra & car	1.40	.85
60	A11	4.50r ultra	1.40	.85
61	A11	8.50r carmine	1.40	.85
		Nos. 59-61 (3)	4.20	2.55

Admission to the UN, 1st anniv. (in 1956).

Type of Semi-Postal Stamps, 1957

1957, May 12		Unwmk.	Perf. 13	
62	SP1	1.50r vermilion	.90	.90
63	SP1	6.50r bluish violet	1.00	1.00
64	SP1	8r dark green	1.25	1.25
		Nos. 62-64 (3)	3.15	3.15

2500th anniv. of the birth of Buddha.

King Ang Duong A12

1958, Mar. 4				
65	A12	1.50r purple & brown	.40	.40
66	A12	5r olive gray & olive	.60	.60
67	A12	10r claret & dull brn	1.25	1.25
a.		Souvenir sheet of 3, #65-67	5.00	4.75
		Nos. 65-67 (3)	2.25	2.25

King Ang Duong (1795-1860).
No. 67a sold for 25r.

King Norodom I — A13

1958-59		Engr.	Perf. 12½x13	
68	A13	2r ultra & olive	.50	.50
69	A13	6r orange & sl grn	.70	.70
70	A13	15r green & ol gray	1.25	1.25
a.		Souv. sheet of 3, #68-70 ('59)	4.75	4.75
		Nos. 68-70 (3)	2.45	2.45

King Norodom I (1835-1904).
No. 70a sold for 32r.
Issued: #68-70, 11/3/58; #70a, 1/31/59.
For surcharge see No. 184.

Children of the World — A14

1959, Dec. 9		Unwmk.	Perf. 13	
71	A14	20c rose violet	.30	.30
72	A14	50c blue	.55	.55
73	A14	80c rose carmine	.90	.90
		Nos. 71-73 (3)	1.75	1.75

Issued to promote friendship among the children of the world.
For surcharges see Nos. 115, B8-B10.

Nos. 49 and 52 with Black Border

1960			Perf. 14x13	
74	A8	7r dk brown & blk	4.00	4.00
75	A8	20r dp green & blk	4.00	4.00

Death of King Norodom Suramarit.

Port of Sihanoukville, Prince Sihanouk and Serpent Naga — A15

20r (double size)

1960, Apr.			Perf. 13x12½	
76	A15	2r carmine & sepia	.50	.50
a.		Cambodian 20r	2.50	2.50
77	A15	5r ultra & dp brown	.50	.50
a.		Cambodian 20r	3.25	3.25
78	A15	20r lilac & dk blue	2.00	2.00
		Nos. 76-78 (3)	3.00	3.00

Opening of the port of Sihanoukville. By error the denomination in Cambodian on the 2r and 5r was engraved as 20r; it was corrected later.

Ceremonial Plow — A16

1960			Perf. 12	
79	A16	1r magenta	.50	.50
80	A16	2r brown	.75	.75
81	A16	3r bluish green	1.25	1.25
		Nos. 79-81 (3)	2.50	2.50

Feast of the Sacred Furrow.

Fight Against Illiteracy A17

Water Conservation, Dam at Chhouksar — A18

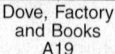

Dove, Factory
and Books
A19

Buddhist
Ceremony
A20

Works of Sangkum: 6r, Workman and
house. 10r, Woman in rice field.

1960, Sept. 1   Engr.   Perf. 13
82 A17 2r dk grn, brn & dk
              bl   .50   .40
  a.   Souvenir sheet of 3   5.00   5.00
83 A18 3r brown & green   .65   .40
  a.   Souvenir sheet of 3   5.00   5.00
84 A19 4r rose car, vio &
              grn   .65   .40
85 A17 6r brown, org & grn   .75   .45
86 A17 10r ultra, grn & bis   1.50   1.00
87 A20 25r dk car, red & mag   3.50   2.40
         Nos. 82-87 (6)   7.55   5.05

No. 82a contains one each of Nos. 82, 85
and 87, and sold for 42r. No. 83a contains one
each of Nos. 83, 84 and 86, and sold for 23r.
Nos. 82a-83a were issued Dec. 5, 1960.

Cambodian Flag
and Dove
A21

Frangipani
A22

1960, Dec. 24   Engr.   Perf. 13
Flag in Ultramarine and Red
88 A21 1.50r brown & green   .40   .25
89 A21 5r orange red   .60   .35
90 A21 7r green & ultra   1.25   1.00
  a.   Souvenir sheet of 3, #88-90 15.00 15.00
  b.   Souv. sheet of 3 (colors
           changed)   10.00 10.00
         Nos. 88-90 (3)   2.25   1.60

Peace propaganda. No. 90a sold for 16r.
No. 90b contains one of each denomination
with colors changed to: 1.50r orange red, 5r
green & ultramarine, 7r brown & green and
sold for 20r.

1961, July 1   Unwmk.   Perf. 13
91 A22 2r shown   .65   .65
92 A22 5r Oleander   1.10   1.10
93 A22 10r Amaryllis   2.50   2.50
  a.   Souvenir sheet of 3, #91-93 7.00   7.00
         Nos. 91-93 (3)   4.25   4.25

No. 93a sold for 20r.

Krishna in Chariot,
Khmer Frieze — A23

1961-63   Typo.   Perf. 14x13½
94   A23 1r lilac   .35   .20
94A A23 2r blue ('63)   2.75   1.40
95   A23 3r emerald   .90   .40
96   A23 6r orange   .90   .40
  a.   Souvenir sheet of 3   7.50   7.50
         Nos. 94-96 (4)   4.90   2.40

Issued to honor Cambodian armed forces.
No. 94A issued in coils. No. 96a contains
one each of Nos. 94, 95, 96. Sold for 12r.

Independence Monument — A24

1961, Nov. 9   Engr.   Perf. 13x12½
97 A24 2r green   .50   .50
98 A24 4r gray brown   .50   .50
  a.   Souvenir sheet of 2, #97-98 3.00   3.50
         Nos. 97-98,C15-C17 (5)   7.65   4.70

10th anniv. of Independence.
For surcharge see No. 116.

Nos. 27 and 31 Overprinted in Red:
"VIe CONFERENCE MONDIALE
BOUDDIQUE 12-11-1961"
1961, Nov. 11   Perf. 13
99   A6 2.50pi green   1.00   .55
100 A6 4.50pi purple   1.50   .90

Sixth World Conference of Buddhism.

Highway
(American
Aid) — A25

Foreign Aid: 2r, Power station (Czech aid).
4r, Textile factory (Chinese aid). 5r, Hospital
(Russian aid). 6r, Airport (French aid).

1961, Dec.   Engr.   Perf. 13
101 A25 2r org & rose car   .45   .30
102 A25 3r bl, grn & org brn   .45   .30
103 A25 4r dl bl, org brn & mag .45 .30
104 A25 5r dl grn & lil rose   .50   .35
105 A25 6r dk bl & org brn   .75   .55
  a.   Souvenir sheet of 5, #101-105 4.50 4.50
         Nos. 101-105 (5)   2.60   1.80

Malaria Eradication
Emblem — A26

1962, Apr. 7   Unwmk.   Perf. 13
106 A26 2r magenta & brown   .50   .40
107 A26 4r green & dk brown   .50   .40
108 A26 6r violet & olive bister .75   .45
         Nos. 106-108 (3)   1.75   1.25

WHO drive to eradicate malaria.
For surcharges see Nos. B11-B12.

Fruits
A27

1962, June 4   Engr.
109 A27 2r Turmeric   .60   .45
110 A27 4r Cinnamon   1.10   .75
111 A27 6r Mangosteens   1.10   .75
  a.   Souvenir sheet of 3, #109-111 5.50 5.50
         Nos. 109-111 (3)   2.80   1.95

Nos. 111a sold for 15r.

Pineapples — A28

1962   Unwmk.   Perf. 13
112 A28 2r shown   .75   .50
113 A28 5r Sugar cane   1.00   .75
114 A28 9r Sugar palms   1.75   .70
         Nos. 112-114 (3)   3.50   1.95

No. 73 Surcharged
1962, Nov. 9   Perf. 13
115 A14 50c on 80c rose car   .60   .40

No. 97 Surcharged with New Value
in Red and Overprinted in Black with
Two Bars and: "INAUGURATION / DU
/ MONUMENT"
1962
116 A24 3r on 2r green   .60   .40

Dedication of Independence Monument.
See No. C18.

Corn, Rice
and FAO
Emblem
A29

1963, Mar. 21   Engr.   Perf. 13
117 A29 3r multicolored   .70   .45
118 A29 6r org red, vio bl & ocher .70 .45

FAO "Freedom from Hunger" campaign.

Preah Vihear,
Ancient
Temple — A30

Tonsay
Lake — A31

1963, June 15   Perf. 12½x13
119 A30 3r claret, brown & sl
              grn   .45   .25
120 A30 6r org, sl grn & grnsh
              blk   .75   .50
121 A30 15r blue, choc & green 1.40 .80
         Nos. 119-121 (3)   2.60   1.55

Return by Thailand of Preah Vihear on the
Mekong River.
For overprint see No. 176.

No. 44 Surcharged with New Value
and Bars
1963   Engr.   Perf. 14x13
122 A8 3r on 2½r dk violet brn .80   .50

Perf. 12½x12½, 12½x12
1963, Aug. 1   Photo.

7r, Popokvil Falls. 20r, Beach, horiz.
123 A31 3r multicolored   .50   .30
124 A31 7r multicolored   .80   .70
125 A31 20r multicolored   2.25   1.10
         Nos. 123-125 (3)   3.55   2.30

UNESCO
Emblem,
Scales and
Globe
A32

1963, Dec. 10   Engr.   Perf. 13
126 A32 1r vio bl, rose cl & grn .35   .25
127 A32 3r yel grn, vio bl &
              rose cl   .60   .50
128 A32 12r rose cl, yel grn & vio
              bl   1.50   1.25
         Nos. 126-128 (3)   2.45   2.00

15th anniversary of the Universal Declaration of Human Rights.
For surcharge see No. 183.

Kouprey
A33

1964, Mar. 3   Unwmk.   Perf. 13
129 A33 50c grn, dk brn & org
              brn   .85   .40
130 A33 3r org, brn, dk brn &
              grn   1.10   .70
131 A33 6r blue, dk brn & grn   2.00   1.00
         Nos. 129-131 (3)   3.95   2.10

Black-billed
Magpie — A34

1964, May 2   Engr.   Perf. 13
132 A34 3r shown   1.10   .65
133 A34 6r Kingfisher   1.75   1.00
134 A34 12r Gray heron   3.25   2.00
         Nos. 132-134 (3)   6.10   3.65

For overprint & surcharge see #303, B16.

Emblem of
Royal
Cambodian
Airline
A35

1964   Unwmk.   Perf. 13x12½
135 A35 1.50r rose car & purple .40   .25
136 A35 3r ver & dk blue   .50   .25
137 A35 7.50r ultra & car   1.25   .60
         Nos. 135-137 (3)   2.15   1.10

8th anniv. of the Royal Cambodian Airline.

Prince Norodom
Sihanouk — A36

1964   Engr.   Perf. 12½x13
138 A36 2r purple   .40   .30
139 A36 3r red brown   .80   .50
140 A36 10r dark blue   1.60   .90
         Nos. 138-140 (3)   2.80   1.70

10th anniv. of the Sangkum (political party).
For overprints see Nos. 144-145.

A set of three stamps, imperf, showing clasped hands, was prepared for
International Cooperation Year but were
never issued. Value, $40.

Woman
Weaver
A37

Khmer Handicrafts: 3r, Metal worker. 5r,
Basket maker.

1965, Feb. 1   Perf. 13x12½
141 A37 1r multicolored   .30   .25
142 A37 3r red lil, red brn & gray
              ol   .60   .35
143 A37 5r green, dk brn & car 1.10   .70
         Nos. 141-143 (3)   2.00   1.30

Nos. 139-140 Overprinted in Black or Red:
"CONFERENCE / DES PEUPLES / INDOCHINOIS"

1965, Mar. 1   Perf. 12½x13
144 A36 3r red brown   .60 .40
145 A36 10r dark blue (R)   .90 .50
Conference of the people of Indo-China.

ITU Emblem, Old and New
Communication Equipment — A38

1965, May 17   Engr.   Perf. 13
146 A38 3r green & olive bister   .35 .30
147 A38 4r red & blue   .60 .40
148 A38 10r violet & rose lilac   .80 .70
     Nos. 146-148 (3)   1.75 1.40
Centenary of the ITU.

Cotton Plant — A39

3r, Peanut plant. 7.50r, Coconut palm.

1965, Aug. 2   Perf. 12½x13
149 A39 1.50r orange, sl grn &
            pur   .40 .35
150 A39 3r blue, yel, grn &
            brn   .70 .60
151 A39 7.50r orange brn & sl
            grn   1.40 1.00
     Nos. 149-151 (3)   2.50 1.95

Preah Ko Temple, Rolouoh — A40

Temples at Angkor: 5r, Baksei Chamkrong,
Rolouoh. 7r, Banteay Srei (Citadel of Women).
9r, Angkor Wat. 12r, Bayon, Angkor Thom.

1966, Feb. 1   Engr.   Perf. 13
152 A40 3r gray ol, sal & dl
            grn   1.25 .80
153 A40 5r lil, dk grn & redsh
            brn   1.50 .85
154 A40 7r dk grn, redsh brn
            & bis   2.00 1.60
155 A40 7r vio bl, pur & dk grn   2.50 2.10
156 A40 12r dk grn, rose car &
            ver   2.75 2.25
     Nos. 152-156 (5)   10.00 8.10
For overprints see Nos. 172-175, 177.

WHO Headquarters, Geneva — A41

1966, July 1   Photo.   Perf. 12½x13
WHO Emblem in Blue and Yellow
157 A41 2r black & pale rose   .35 .25
158 A41 3r black & yel grn   .45 .30
159 A41 5r black & lt bl   .70 .50
     Nos. 157-159 (3)   1.50 1.00
Inauguration of WHO Headquarters, Geneva.

Tree Planting — A42

UNESCO Emblem — A43

1966, July 22   Engr.   Perf. 12½x13
160 A42 1r brn, dull brn & brt grn   .25 .20
161 A42 3r org, dull brn & brt grn   .50 .30
162 A42 7r gray, dull brn & brt grn   .75 .40
     Nos. 160-162 (3)   1.50 .90
Issued for Arbor Day.

1966   Photo.   Perf. 13
163 A43 3r multicolored   .45 .25
164 A43 7r multicolored   .65 .35
20th anniv. of UNESCO.

Wrestlers and Games' Emblem A44

GANEFO Games (Games Emblem and): 3r,
Stadium, Phnom Penh. 7r, Swordsmen. 10r,
Indian club swingers. Bas-reliefs from Angkor
Wat.

1966, Nov. 25   Engr.   Perf. 13
165 A44 3r violet blue   .35 .20
166 A44 4r green   .40 .30
167 A44 7r dk car rose   .60 .40
168 A44 10r dark brown   .90 .60
     Nos. 165-168 (4)   2.25 1.50

Indian Wild Boar A45

Perf. 13x12½, 12½x13
1967, Feb. 20   Engr.
169 A45 3r shown   .80 .35
170 A45 5r Muntjac, vert.   1.25 .55
171 A45 7r Elephant   1.75 .80
     Nos. 169-171 (3)   3.80 1.70

Nos. 152-153, 155-156 and 121
Overprinted in Red: "ANNEE
INTERNATIONALE DU TOURISME
1967"

1967, Apr. 27   Engr.   Perf. 13
172 A40 3r multicolored   .85 .75
173 A40 5r multicolored   1.00 .75
174 A40 9r multicolored   1.40 1.25
175 A40 12r multicolored   1.75 1.50
176 A30 15r multicolored   2.10 1.75
     Nos. 172-176 (5)   7.10 6.00
International Tourist Year, 1967.

No. 154 Overprinted in Red:
"MILLENAIRE / DE BANTEAY SREI /
967-1967"

1967, Apr. 27
177 A40 7r multicolored   2.00 .75
Banteay Srei Temple at Angkor, millennium.

Royal Ballet Dancer — A46

Various Dancers

1967, June   Engr.   Perf. 13
178 A46 1r orange   .60 .60
179 A46 3r Prus blue   1.40 .80
180 A46 5r ultra   1.75 1.10
181 A46 7r carmine rose   2.75 1.60
182 A46 10r multicolored   3.50 2.10
     Nos. 178-182 (5)   10.00 6.10
Cambodian Royal Ballet.

Nos. 128 and 70 Surcharged in Red

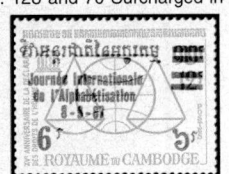

1967, Sept. 8   Engr.
183 A32 6r on 12r multi   .80 .40
184 A13 7r on 15r grn & olive gray 1.10 .60
Intl. Literacy Day, Sept. 8. The surcharge on
#184 is adapted to fit the shape of the stamp.

Symbolic Water Cycle — A47

1967, Nov. 1   Typo.   Perf. 13x14
185 A47 1r black, bl & org   .25 .20
186 A47 6r lilac, lt bl & org   .55 .30
187 A47 10r dk blue, emer & org   .80 .50
     Nos. 185-187 (3)   1.60 1.00
Hydrological Decade (UNESCO), 1965-74.

Royal University, Kompong Cham A48

6r, Engineering School, Phnom Penh. 9r,
University Center, Sangkum Reastr Niyum.

1968, Mar. 1   Engr.   Perf. 13
188 A48 4r violet bl & multi   .45 .30
189 A48 6r slate & multi   .65 .40
190 A48 9r Prus blue & multi   .90 .55
     Nos. 188-190 (3)   2.00 1.25

Vaccination and WHO Emblem A49

WHO, 20th Anniv.: 7r, Malaria control and
WHO emblem (man spraying DDT).

1968, July 8   Engr.   Perf. 13
191 A49 3r ultramarine   .60 .30
192 A49 7r deep blue   .90 .50

Stadium, Mexico City — A50

1968, Oct. 12   Engr.   Perf. 13
193 A50 1r shown   .30 .25
194 A50 2r Wrestling   .40 .30
195 A50 3r Bicycling   .65 .35
196 A50 5r Boxing, vert.   .85 .35
197 A50 7.50r Torch bearer, vert.   .95 .45
     Nos. 193-197 (5)   3.15 1.70
19th Olympic Games, Mexico City, 12/12-27.

Red Cross Team A51

1968, Nov. 1   Engr.   Perf. 13
198 A51 3r Prus bl, grn & red   .80 .35
Issued to honor the Cambodian Red Cross.

Prince Norodom Sihanouk A52

8r, Soldiers wading through swamp.

1968, Nov. 9
199 A52 7r emer, ultra & pur   .50 .30
200 A52 8r bl, grn & dp brn   .75 .55
15th anniversary of independence.

Human Rights Flame and Prince Sihanouk A53

1968, Dec. 10   Engr.   Perf. 13
201 A53 3r blue   .45 .25
202 A53 5r bright plum   .80 .35
203 A53 7r multicolored   1.00 .55
     Nos. 201-203 (3)   2.25 1.15
International Human Rights Year.

ILO Emblem A54

1969, May 1   Engr.   Perf. 13
204 A54 3r ultra   .35 .20
205 A54 6r dp carmine   .60 .30
206 A54 9r blue green   .80 .50
     Nos. 204-206 (3)   1.75 1.00
ILO, 50th anniversary.

Globe, Red Cross, Crescent, Lion and Sun Emblems A55

1969, May 8
207 A55 1r blue, red & yel   .20 .20
208 A55 3r sl grn, red & vio brn   .50 .35
209 A55 10r brt lil, red & brn   1.10 .60
     Nos. 207-209 (3)   1.80 1.15
50th anniv. of the League of Red Cross
Societies.

Papilio
Oeacus
A56

Butterflies: 4r, Papilio agamenon. 8r,
Danaus plexippus.

1969, Oct. 10   **Engr.**   *Perf. 13*
210	A56	3r lilac, blk & yel	5.00	1.25
211	A56	4r ver, blk & grn	8.50	2.00
212	A56	8r yel grn, dk brn & org	11.50	3.00
		Nos. 210-212 (3)	25.00	6.25

Map of
Cambodia
and Diesel
Engine
A57

Various railroad stations and trains.

1969, Nov. 27   **Engr.**   *Perf. 13*
213	A57	3r multicolored	1.00	.75
214	A57	6r slate grn & lt brn	2.00	1.50
215	A57	8r black	3.25	2.25
216	A57	9r dk green & blue	3.75	2.40
		Nos. 213-216 (4)	10.00	6.90

Issued to publicize the new rail link between
Phnom Penh and Sihanoukville.

Fish — A58

1970, Jan. 29   **Photo.**   *Perf. 13*
217	A58	3r Tripletail	2.40	1.40
218	A58	7r Sleeper goby	4.50	2.40
219	A58	9r Snakehead	5.25	3.00
		Nos. 217-219 (3)	12.15	6.80

Wat Maniratanaram — A59

Monasteries: 2r, Wat Tepthidaram, vert. 6r,
Wat Patumavati. 8r, Wat Unnalom.

1970, Apr. 29   **Photo.**   *Perf. 13*
220	A59	2r multicolored	.35	.30
221	A59	3r multicolored	.40	.30
222	A59	6r multicolored	.85	.35
223	A59	8r multicolored	1.60	.45
		Nos. 220-223 (4)	3.20	1.40

UPU Headquarters and Monument,
Bern — A60

1970, May 20
224	A60	1r green & multi	.30	.20
225	A60	3r scarlet & multi	.50	.20
226	A60	4r dp blue & multi	.60	.20
227	A60	10r brown & multi	1.10	.40
		Nos. 224-227 (4)	2.50	1.00

New UPU Headquarters in Bern.

Open Book and
Satellite Earth
Receiving
Station — A61

1970, May 17   **Photo.**   *Perf. 13*
228	A61	3r dk vio bl & multi	.25	.20
229	A61	4r sl grn & multi	.35	.25
230	A61	9r brn ol & multi	.85	.35
		Nos. 228-230 (3)	1.45	.80

World Telecommunications Day.

Nelumbium
Speciosum
A62

Flowers: 4r, Eichhornia crassipes. 13r,
Nymphea lotus.

1970, Aug. 17   **Photo.**   *Perf. 13*
231	A62	3r multicolored	.60	.30
a.		Cambodian and Arabic 3's transposed	15.00	20.00
232	A62	4r multicolored	1.40	.45
233	A62	13r multicolored	2.50	.70
		Nos. 231-233 (3)	4.50	1.45

Elephant
God, Bas
relief at
Banteay
Srei — A63

1970, Sept. 21   **Engr.**   *Perf. 13*
234	A63	3r lil rose & dp grn	.25	.25
235	A63	4r bl grn, grn & lil rose	.55	.25
236	A63	7r bl grn, dk brn & grn	.80	.40
		Nos. 234-236 (3)	1.60	.90

Issued for World Meteorological Day.

Khmer Republic

Globe,
Rocket,
Dove and
UN
Emblem
A64

1970, Nov. 9   **Photo.**   *Perf. 12½x12*
237	A64	3r black & multi	.30	.20
238	A64	5r brown red & multi	.45	.25
239	A64	10r dp violet & multi	.90	.50
		Nos. 237-239 (3)	1.65	.95

25th anniversary of the United Nations.

Education
Year
Emblem
A65

1970, Nov. 9   **Engr.**   *Perf. 13x12½*
240	A65	1r blue	.25	.20
241	A65	3r brt rose lilac	.30	.20
242	A65	8r blue green	.70	.45
		Nos. 240-242 (3)	1.25	.85

Issued for International Education Year.

Chuon-Nath — A66

1971, Jan. 27   **Photo.**   *Perf. 13*
243	A66	3r ol grn & multi	.30	.20
244	A66	8r purple & multi	.65	.30
245	A66	9r violet & multi	.90	.55
		Nos. 243-245 (3)	1.85	1.10

In memory of Chuon-Nath (1883-1969),
Cambodian language expert.
For surcharge see No. 322.

Soldiers in
Battle
A67

1971, Mar. 18   **Photo.**   *Perf. 13*
246	A67	1r gray & multi	.50	.20
247	A67	3r bister & multi	.50	.40
248	A67	10r blue & multi	4.00	.75
		Nos. 246-248 (3)	5.00	1.35

National territorial defense.
For overprint see No. 321.

UN
Emblem,
Men of
Four Races
A68

1971, Mar. 21
249	A68	3r blue & multi	.30	.20
250	A68	7r green & multi	.45	.30
251	A68	8r brt rose & multi	1.00	.50
		Nos. 249-251 (3)	1.75	1.00

Intl. year against racial discrimination.

General Post Office, Phnom
Penh — A69

1971, Apr. 19
252	A69	3r blue & multi	.20	.20
253	A69	9r lilac rose & multi	.55	.35
254	A69	10r black & multi	.70	.40
		Nos. 252-254 (3)	1.45	.95

Symbolic
Globe and
Waves
A70

Design: 7r, 8r, ITU emblem and waves.

1971, May 17   **Photo.**   *Perf. 13*
255	A70	3r green, blk & bl	.25	.20
256	A70	4r yellow & multi	.25	.20
257	A70	7r lilac, blk & red	.35	.25
258	A70	8r sal pink, blk & red	.50	.30
		Nos. 255-258 (4)	1.35	.95

3rd World Telecommunications Day.

Erythrina
Indica
A71

Wild Flowers: 3r, Bauhinia variegata. 6r,
Butea frondosa. 10r, Lagerstroemia floribunda, vert.

1971, July 5   *Perf. 13x12½, 12½x13*
259	A71	2r lt ultra & multi	.45	.45
260	A71	3r yel grn & multi	.55	.55
261	A71	6r blue & multi	1.10	1.10
262	A71	10r brown & multi	1.40	1.40
		Nos. 259-262 (4)	3.50	3.50

Khmer Coat of   Flag and Square
Arms — A72   of the
           Republic — A73

1971, Oct. 9   **Engr.**   *Perf. 13*
263	A72	3r brt grn & bis	.20	.20
264	A73	3r purple & multi	.20	.20
265	A73	4r dp claret & multi	.25	.20
266	A72	8r orange & bis	.45	.25
267	A72	10r lt brn & bis	.70	.30
a.		Souv. sheet of 3, #263, 266-267	2.75	2.75
268	A73	10r slate grn & multi	.70	.35
a.		Souv. sheet of 3, #264-265, 268	2.75	2.75
		Nos. 263-268 (6)	2.50	1.50

Republic, 1st anniv.
#267a sold for 25r, #268a for 20r.
For overprints and surcharges see Nos.
301-302, B13-B14.

UNICEF
Emblem — A74

1971, Dec. 11
269	A74	3r black brown	.30	.20
270	A74	5r ultra	.40	.25
271	A74	9r dk pur & brn red	.80	.45
		Nos. 269-271 (3)	1.50	.90

25th anniv. of UNICEF.
This set and others exist with overprint
"RPK," both with and without frame. Status
has not been determined.

Book Year
Emblem
A75

1972, Feb. 7
272	A75	3r blue, grn & vio	.40	.20
273	A75	8r violet, grn & bl	.60	.30
274	A75	9r emerald & multi	1.00	.50
a.		Souvenir sheet of 3, #272-274	2.25	2.25
		Nos. 272-274 (3)	2.00	1.00

Intl. Book Year. No. 274a sold for 23r.

Lion of St.
Mark
A76

Designs: 5r, Waves engulfing St. Mark's
Basilica. 10r, Bridge of Sighs, vert.

1972, Feb. 7   **Engr.**   *Perf. 13*
275	A76	3r lil rose & org brn	.50	.20
276	A76	5r yel grn & org brn	.75	.25
277	A76	10r org brn, bl & yel grn	1.25	.45
a.		Souvenir sheet of 3, #275-277	3.00	3.00
		Nos. 275-277 (3)	2.50	.90

UNESCO campaign to save Venice. No.
277a sold for 23r.

UN Emblem A77

1972, Mar. 28

278 A77 3r deep carmine .30 .20
279 A77 6r deep blue .50 .25
280 A77 9r deep orange .70 .45
a. Souvenir sheet of 3, #278-280 2.00 2.00
Nos. 278-280 (3) 1.50 .90

25th anniv. UN Economic Commission for Asia and the Far East (ECAFE). No. 280a sold for 23r.

Dancing Apsarases — A78

"UIT" A79

1972, May 5 Engr. *Perf. 13*

281 A78 1r golden brn .20 .20
282 A78 3r violet .30 .20
283 A78 7r rose claret .40 .30
284 A78 8r olive brn .50 .30
285 A78 9r blue grn .60 .30
286 A78 10r ultra .90 .30
287 A78 12r purple 1.10 .30
288 A78 14r Prus blue 1.40 .45
Nos. 281-288 (8) 5.40 2.35

1972, May 17 Litho.

289 A79 3r blk, yel & grnsh bl .30 .20
290 A79 9r blk, dp lil rose & bl grn .65 .30
291 A79 14r blk, brn & bl grn .95 .45
Nos. 289-291 (3) 1.90 .95

4th World Telecommunications Day.

"Human Environment" — A80

1972, June 5 Engr.

292 A80 3r org, plum & grn .35 .20
293 A80 12r brt grn & plum .50 .30
294 A80 15r plum & brt grn .75 .40
a. Souvenir sheet of 3, #292-294 3.25 3.25
Nos. 292-294 (3) 1.60 .90

UN Conf. on Human Environment, Stockholm, June 5-16. No. 294a sold for 35r.
For overprints and surcharges see Nos. 304-305, B15, B17.

Javan Rhinoceros A81

1972, Aug. 1 Engr. *Perf. 13*

295 A81 3r shown .45 .20
296 A81 4r Serow .55 .20
297 A81 6r Malayan sambar 1.00 .30
298 A81 7r Banteng 1.50 .30
299 A81 8r Water buffalo 1.75 .50
300 A81 10r Gaur 2.25 .60
Nos. 295-300 (6) 7.50 2.10

Nos. 263, 267, 134, 293, 294 Overprinted in Red

1972, Sept. 9 Engr. *Perf. 13*

301 A72 3r brt grn & bister .75 .30
302 A72 10r orange & bister 1.50 .60
303 A34 12r multicolored 1.50 .75
304 A80 12r brt grn & plum 1.60 .75
305 A80 15r plum & brt grn 2.10 .90
Nos. 301-305 (5) 7.45 3.30

20th Olympic Games, Munich, 8/26-9/11.

Raising Khmer Flag — A82

1972, Oct. 9 Photo. *Perf. 12½x13*

306 A82 3r multicolored .20 .20
307 A82 5r brt rose & multi .40 .30
308 A82 9r yel grn & multi .90 .30
Nos. 306-308 (3) 1.50 .80

2nd anniversary of the establishment of the Khmer Republic.
For surcharge see No. 323.

Stupa and Crest — A83

Apsaras — A84

1973, May 12 Engr. *Perf. 13*

309 A83 3r ocher & multi .30 .20
310 A83 12r yel grn & multi .30 .20
311 A83 14r blue & multi .50 .20
a. Souvenir sheet of 3, #309-311 2.50 2.50
Nos. 309-311 (3) 1.10 .60

New Constitution. No. 311a sold for 34r.

1973, July 23 Engr. *Perf. 13*

Sculptures from Angkor Wat: 8r, 10r, Devata, diff.

312 A84 3r brown black .60 .25
313 A84 8r Prus green 1.00 .30
314 A84 10r olive bister 1.50 .45
a. Souvenir sheet of 3, #312-314 2.50 2.25
Nos. 312-314 (3) 3.10 1.00

No. 314a sold for 25r.

INTERPOL Emblem — A85

Marshal Lon Nol — A86

1973, Oct. 2 Engr. *Perf. 13*

315 A85 3r green & multi .35 .20
316 A85 7r red brn & multi .45 .20
317 A85 10r olive & multi .60 .30
a. Souvenir sheet of 3, #315-317 2.75 2.75
Nos. 315-317 (3) 1.40 .70

50th anniv. of the Intl. Criminal Police Org. No. 317a sold for 30r.

1973, Oct. 9

318 A86 3r lt grn, blk & brn .40 .20
319 A86 8r brown, ol & blk .60 .30
320 A86 14r black & brn 1.00 .40
a. Souvenir sheet of 3 4.25 4.25
Nos. 318-320 (3) 2.00 .90

Marshal Lon Nol, 1st pres. of the Republic. No. 320a contains stamps similar to Nos. 318-320 in changed colors. Sold for 50r.

Nos. 248, 243 and 307 Surcharged with New Value, 2 Bars and Overprinted in Red or Silver: "4th ANNIVERSAIRE/DE LA REPUBLIQUE"

1974 Photo. *Perf. 13, 12½x13*

321 A67 10r multi (R) 1.00 .50
322 A66 50r on 3r multi 2.00 1.00
323 A82 100r on 5r multi 7.00 3.50
Nos. 321-323 (3) 10.00 5.00

4th anniversary of the Republic.

Copernicus and "Nerva" — A87

Copernicus, various spacecraft and events.

1974, Sept. 10 Litho. *Perf. 13*

324 A87 1r shown
325 A87 5r Mariner II
326 A87 10r Apollo
327 A87 25r Telstar
328 A87 50r Space walk
329 A87 100r Moon landing
330 A87 150r Separation of spaceship and module
Nos. 324-330 (7) 45.00
Nos. 324-330, C46-C47 (9) 55.00

500th anniversary of the birth of Nicolaus Copernicus (1473-1543), Polish astronomer.

Carrier Pigeon and UPU Emblem — A88

Design: 60r, Sailing ship and UPU emblem.

1974, Nov. 2

331 A88 10r multicolored .25 .20
332 A88 60r multicolored .75 .20
Nos. 331-332,C50 (3) 11.00 10.40

Cent. of UPU. A souvenir sheet containing one No. 332 exists.

A set of 9 stamps picturing musical instruments, overprinted and surcharged for use by the Khmer Republic just before the fall of the government in Apr. 1975, exists. Value, $1,100. Value for same set without surcharge, $500.

A89

1976 Summer Olympic Games, Montreal — A90

1r, 18th cent. swordsmen. 5r, Modern fencers. 10r, Ancient Olympic runner. 25r, Modern runner. 50r, Ancient rowers. 100r, Modern kayakers. 150r, Ancient horseman. 200r, Modern equestrian competitor. 250r, Buildings, Olympic flame.

1975, Jan. 2 Litho. *Perf. 13½*

333-341 A89 Set of 9 15.00

Litho. & Embossed

342 A90 1200r gold & multi *35.00*

Souvenir Sheets

343 A89 200r silver & multi *7.50*
344 A89 250r silver & multi *7.50*

Nos. 337-344 are airmail.
A number has been reserved for another souvenir sheet released with this set.

A91

1974 World Cup Soccer Championships — A92

Soccer players and arms of: 1r, Hamburg. 5r, Gelsenkirchen. 10r, Dortmund. 25r, Stuttgart. 50r, Dusseldorf. 100r, Hannover. 150r, Frankfurt. 200r, Munich. 250r, Berlin.

Litho. (#346-354, 356-357)
Litho. & Embossed (#355, 358)

1975, Feb. 13

346-354 A91 Set of 9 7.50
355 A92 1200r gold & multi *37.50*

Souvenir Sheets

356	A91	200r gold & multi	6.00
357	A91	250r gold & multi	6.00
358	A92	1200r gold & multi	13.00

Nos. 350-358 are airmail. Nos. 346-354 exist in imperforate souvenir sheets.

UPU, Cent. — A93

Designs: 15r, Letter carrier, pack mule. 20r, Biplane. 70r, Post coach. 160r, Biplane, Concorde. 180r, Steam-powered wagon. 235r, Postrider, tail of mailplane. 500r, Railway mail car. 1000r, Airship. 2000r, Caravel.

1975, Apr. 12

359-367	A93	Set of 9	10.00
366a		Souvenir sheet of 1	10.00
367a		Souvenir sheet of 1	10.00

Nos. 365-367 are airmail.

People's Republic of Kampuchea

Soldiers — A94

Designs, horiz.: 20c, People, flag. 50c, Fishermen. 1r, Soldiers passing flag.

1980, Apr. 10   Litho.   Perf. 11

368-371 A94 Set of 4   45.00 45.00

Soviet Union, 60th Anniv. — A95

Designs: 50c, Globe, Kremlin. 1r, Buildings, map of USSR.

1982, Dec. 30   Perf. 12x12½

372-373 A95 Set of 2   .75 .40

People's Republic of Kampuchea, 4th Anniv. — A96

Designs: 50c, Natl. arms, vert. 1r, shown. 3r, Map, stylized figures, vert. 6r, Temple, vert.

1983, Jan. 7   Litho.   Perf. 13

374-376	A96	Set of 3	3.50 1.10

Souvenir Sheet

377 A96 6r multicolored   4.75 2.25

1984 Summer Olympic Games, Los Angeles A97

Designs: 20c, Runner with torch. 50c, Javelin. 80c, Pole vault. 1r, Discus. 1.50r, Relay race. 2r, Swimming. 3r, Basketball. 20c-1r, 3r are vert.

1983, Jan. 20   Litho.   Perf. 13

378-384 A97 Set of 7   7.00 1.50

Souvenir Sheet

385 A97 6r Soccer   5.00 3.00

No. 385 contains one 32x40mm stamp.

Butterflies — A98

20c, Salatura genutia. 50c, Euploea althaea. 80c, Byasa polyeuctes. 1r, Stichophthalma howqua. 1.50r, Kallima inachus. 2r, Precis orithya. 3r, Catopsilia pomona.
20c, 50c, 1.50r, 2r, 3r are vert.

1983, Feb. 18   Perf. 13

386-392 A98 Set of 7   8.00 1.75

Khmer Culture A99

Designs: 20c, Ruins, Srah Srang. 50c, Temple, Bakong. 80c, Ta Son. 1r, North Gate, Angkor Thom. 1.50r, Two winged figures. 2r, Apsara, Angkor. 3r, Statue of Banteai Srei. 80c-3r are vert.

1983, Mar. 15   Set of 7   6.00 1.75

393-399 A99

Folk Dances A100

Various dances. Denominations 50c, 1r, 3r.

1983, Apr. 17   Litho.   Perf. 13

400-402 A100 Set of 3   3.75 1.25

Souvenir Sheet

403 A100 6r Native, "buffalo"   4.00 1.40

No. 403 contains one 32x40mm stamp.

Raphael (1483-1520) — A101

Parnassus (details): #404, 20c, Dante, Ennius, Homer. #406, 80c, Horace, Ovid, others. #409, 2r, The Muses. #410, 3r, Alcaeus, Petrarch, others.
School at Athens (details): #407, 1r, Euclid, disciples. #408, 1.50r, Telange, Pythagoras.
Details from: #405, 50c, Mass of Bolsena. 6r, Angels from Dispute of the Holy Sacrament, horiz.

1983, May 10   Litho.   Perf. 12½x13

404-410 A101 Set of 7   6.50 2.25

Souvenir Sheet   Perf. 13

411 A101 6r multicolored   5.00 1.40

No. 411 contains one 40x32mm stamp.

1st Hot Air Balloon Ascension, Bicent. A102

Designs: 20c, Montgolfier. 30c, Ville d'Orleans. 50c, Hydrogen balloon. 1r, Blanchard & Jeffries, 1785. 1.50r, Ascension in Arctic. 2r, Stratosphere balloon. 3r, Balloon race. 6r, Balloons over town.

1983, June 3   Perf. 12½

412-418 A102 Set of 7   5.50 2.00

Souvenir Sheet   Perf. 13

419 A102 6r multicolored   5.50 1.50

Reptiles — A103

Designs: 20c, Iguana. 30c, Cobra. 80c, Trionyx turtle. 1r, Chameleon. 1.50r, Boa constrictor. 2r, Crocodile. 3r, Turtle. 30c, 1r, 1.50r are vert.

1983, June 28

420-426 A103 Set of 7   6.00 2.00

Birds A104

Designs: 20c, Lorikeet. 50c, Swallow. 80c, Eagle. 1r, Vulture. 1.50r, Turtle dove. 2r, Magpie. 3r, Hornbill. 20c-50c, 2r-3r are vert.

1983, Sept. 20

427-433 A104 Set of 7   6.00 1.75

Flowers — A105

20c, Sunflower. 50c, Caprifoliacae. 80c, Bougainvillea. 1r, Renonculacae. 1.50r, Nyctaginaceae. 2r, Cockscomb. 3r, Roses.

1983, Oct. 18   Perf. 13

434-440 A105 Set of 7   5.00 1.75

1984 Winter Olympic Games, Sarajevo — A106

Designs: 1r, Luge. 2r, Biathlon. 4r, Ski jumping. 5r, Two-man bobsled. 7r, Hockey.

1983, Nov. 10   Perf. 12½

441-445 A106 Set of 5   8.50 2.75

Souvenir Sheet

446 A106 6r Cross-country skiing   4.50 1.75

No. 446 contains one 40x32mm stamp.

Fish A107

20c, 1.50r, 2r, 3r, Various Cyprinidae. 50c, Trout. 80c, Catfish. 1r, Moray eel.

1983, Nov. 16   Perf. 13

447-453 A107 Set of 7   7.00 2.00

Festival of Rebirth — A108

50c, Factory. 1r, Bull, tractor. 3r, Bridge, ship, train. 6r, Radio antenna. 50c, 3r, 6r vert.

Perf. 12½x13, 13x12½

1983, Dec. 2   Litho.

454-456 A108 Set of 3   3.25 1.00

Souvenir Sheet

457 A108 6r multicolored   4.25 1.40

No. 457 contains one 32x40mm stamp.

People's Republic of Kampuchea, 5th Anniv. — A109

Designs: 50c, Red Cross. 1r, Soldiers. 3r, People celebrating. 6r, Man carrying water.

1984, Jan. 7   Litho.   Perf. 13

458-460 A109 Set of 3   3.75 1.25

Souvenir Sheet

461 A109 6r multicolored   4.50 1.50

No. 461 contains one 32x40mm stamp.
For surcharges see Nos. 775-776.

1984 Winter Olympics, Sarajevo A110

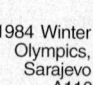

Designs: 20c, Speed skating. 50c, Hockey. 80c, Slalom skiing. 1r, Ski jumping. 1.50r, Biathlon. 2r, Cross-country skiing. 3r, Pairs figure skating. 6r, Women's figure skating.

1984, Jan. 6 **Litho.** **Perf. 13**
462-468 A110 Set of 7 6.00 2.00
Souvenir Sheet
469 A110 6r multicolored 4.50 1.40
No. 469 contains one 32x40mm stamp.

Birds — A111

Designs: 10c, Bubulcus ibis. 40c, Lanius schach. 80c, Psittacula himalayana. 1r, Chloropsis aurifrons. 1.20r, Clamator coromandus. 2r, Motacilla cinerea. 2.50r, Dendronanthus indicus.

1984, Feb. 2
470-476 A111 Set of 7 9.00 3.00

Intl. Peace in Southeast Asia Forum — A112

Background color: 50c, Green. 1r, Blue. 3r, Violet.

1984, Feb. 25 **Perf. 13x12½**
477-479 A112 Set of 3 3.75 1.00

Space Exploration — A113

Designs: 10c, Luna 1. 40c, Luna 2. 80c, Luna 3. 1r, Soyuz 6. 1.20r, Soyuz 7. 2r, Soyuz 8. 2.50r, Book, rocket, S.P. Koralev. 6r, Salyut space station.
1r-2.50r are vert.

1984, Mar. 8 **Perf. 12½**
480-486 A113 Set of 7 6.00 2.00
Souvenir Sheet
487 A113 6r multicolored 5.00 1.75
No. 487 contains one 40x32mm stamp.

1984 Summer Olympic Games, Los Angeles A114

Designs: 20c, Discus. 50c, Long jump. 80c, Hurdles. 1r, Relay race. 1.50r, Pole vault. 2r, Javelin. 3r, High jump. 6r, Sprint race.

1984, Apr. 20 **Perf. 13**
488-494 A114 Set of 7 5.00 1.75
Souvenir Sheet
495 A114 6r multicolored 5.00 1.75
No. 495 contains one 32x40mm stamp.

Souvenir Sheet

ESPAÑA '84, Madrid — A115

1984, Apr. 24 **Perf. 12½**
496 A115 5r 1933 Hispano-Suiza K6 5.00 1.50

Wild Animals A116

Designs: 10c, Canis latrans. 40c, Canis dingo. 80c, Lycaon pictus. 1r, Canis aureus. 1.20r, Vulpes vulpes. 2r, Chrysocyon brachyurus, vert. 2.50r, Canis lupus.

1984, May 5 **Perf. 13**
497-503 A116 Set of 7 6.00 1.60

Locomotives — A117

Designs: 10c, BB-1002, France, 1966. 40c, BB-1052, France, 1966. 80c, Franco-Belgian, 1945. 1r, #231-505, Franco-Belgian, 1929. 1.20r, #803, Germany, 1968. 2r, BDE-405, France, 1957. 2.50r, DS-01, France, 1979.

1984, June 15 **Litho.** **Perf. 12½**
504-510 A117 Set of 7 5.50 1.75

Flowers A118

Designs: 10c, Magnolia. 40c, Plumeria. 80c, Himenoballis. 1r, Peltophorum roxburghii. 1.20r, Couroupita guianensis. 2r, Lagerstroemia. 2.50r, Thevetia perubiana.

1984, July 10 **Litho.** **Perf. 13**
511-517 A118 Set of 7 6.00 2.00

Classic Automobiles — A119

Designs: 20c, Mercedes-Benz. 50c, Bugatti. 80c, Alfa Romeo. 1r, Franklin. 1.50r, Hispano-Suiza. 2r, Rolls Royce. 3r, Tatra. 6r, Mercedes Benz, diff.

1984, Sept. 15 **Perf. 13x12½**
518-524 A119 Set of 7 6.00 1.50
Souvenir Sheet
Perf. 12½
525 A119 6r multicolored 5.00 1.25
No. 525 contains one 40x32mm stamp.

Musical Instruments — A120

Designs: 10c, Sra Lai. 40c, Skor drum. 80c, Skor thom. 1r, Thro khmer. 1.20r, Raneat ek. 2r, Raneat kong. 2.50r, Thro khe.
10c, 80c are vert.

1984, Oct. 10 **Perf. 13**
526-532 A120 Set of 7 5.25 1.50

Wild Animals A121

Designs: 10c, Gazelle. 40c, Capreolus capreolus. 80c, Lepus. 1r, Cervus elaphus. 1.20r, Elephas maximus. 2r, Genet. 2.50r, Bibos sauveli.
10c-40c, 1r-1.20r are vert.

1984, Nov. 11 **Perf. 13**
533-539 A121 Set of 7 6.00 1.75

Correggio (1489-1534) — A122

Details from paintings: 20c, Rest on Flight into Egypt. 50c, Martyrdom of the Four Saints. 80c, Mystic Marriage of St. Catherine with Saints Francis and Dominic. 1r, Madonna & Child with Saints John the Baptist, Geminian, Peter Martyr and George. 1.50r, Mystic Marriage of St. Catherine. 2r, The Deposition. 2.50r, The Deposition, diff. 6r, Virgin Crowned by Christ.

1984, Dec. 10 **Perf. 12½x13**
540-546 A122 Set of 7 4.25 1.00
Souvenir Sheet
Perf. 12½
547 A122 6r multicolored 4.25 1.00
No. 547 contains one 40x32mm stamp.

Natl. Festival — A123

50c, Oxcart. 1r, Horse-drawn cart. 3r, Elephants. 6r, Oxcart with passengers, vert.

1985, Jan. 5 **Perf. 12½x12**
548-550 A123 Set of 3 4.25 1.00
Souvenir Sheet
Perf. 12½
551 A123 6r multicolored 4.25 1.00
No. 551 contains one 32x40mm stamp.

1986 World Cup Soccer Championships, Mexico — A124

Various soccer players; 20c, vert. 50c, vert. 80c, vert. 1r. 1.50r. 2r, vert. 3r, vert.

1985, Feb. 4 **Perf. 13**
552-558 A124 Set of 7 4.25 1.25
Souvenir Sheet
559 A124 6r multicolored 4.25 1.00
No. 559 contains one 40x32mm stamp.

Motorcycles — A125

20c, 1939 Eska-Mofa. 50c, 1939 Wanderer. 80c, 1929 Premier. 1r, 1939 Ardie. 1.50r, 1932 Jawa. 2r, 1983 Simson. 3r, 1984 CZ-125.

1985, Mar. 8 **Litho.** **Perf. 13**
560-566 A125 Set of 7 4.00 1.50
Souvenir Sheet
567 A125 6r 1984 MBA 4.00 1.50
No. 567 contains one 40x32mm stamp.

Mushrooms — A126

Designs: 20c, Gymnopilus spectabilis. 50c, Coprinus micaceus. 80c, Amanita panterina. 1r, Hebelona crustuliniforme. 1.50r, Amanita muscaria. 2r, Coprinus comatus. 3r, Amanita caesarea.
Nos. 569-574 are vert.

1985, Apr. 4 **Perf. 13**
568-574 A126 Set of 7 5.75 1.40

Soviet Space Achievements — A127

Designs: 20c, Sputnik. 50c, Yuri Gagarin, rocket. 80c, Valentina Tereshkova, Vostok 6. 1r, Cosmonaut walking in space. 1.50r, Soyuz 4 docked with Soyuz 5. 2r, Lunar rover. 3r, Apollo-Soyuz mission. 6r, Soyuz capsule.

1985, Apr. 12 **Perf. 13**
575-581 A127 Set of 7 4.25 1.25
Souvenir Sheet
582 A127 6r multicolored 4.25 1.00
No. 582 contains one 40x32mm stamp.

Traditional Dances — A128

Designs: 50c, Four dancers. 1r, Three dancers. 3r, One dancer, vert.

1985, Apr. 13   Litho.   Perf. 12½
583-585 A128   Set of 3
                              3.25 1.00

End of World War II, 40th Anniv. A129

Designs: 50c, Soldiers celebrating. 1r, Victory parade, Moscow. 3r, Tank battle.

1985, May 9   Litho.   Perf. 12x12½
586-588 A129   Set of 3
                              4.25 1.50

Cats — A130

Various cats: 20c, 50c, 80c, 1r, 1.50r, 2r, 3r.

1985, May 16   Litho.   Perf. 12x12½
589-595 A130   Set of 7
                              6.00 1.25

Flowers — A131

20c, Lilium Black Dragon. 50c, Iris delavayi. 80c, Crocus aureus. 1r, Cyclamen persicum, wild form. 1.50r, Primula malacoides. 2r, Viola tricolor. 3r, Crocus purpureus.

1985, June 5   Litho.   Perf. 13
596-602 A131   Set of 7
                              4.25 1.25

Intl. Music Year — A132

Paintings: 20c, Mezzetin, by Watteau. 50c, St. Cecilia and the Angel, by Saraceni. 80c, Still Life with Violin, Flute and Guitar, by Oudry, horiz. 1r, Three Musicians, by F. Leger. 1.50r, Opera Orchestra, by Degas. 2r, St. Cecilia, by Schedoni. 3r, Young Harlequin with Violin, by Caillard. 6r, The Fifer, by Manet.

1985, June 13   Perf. 13
603-609 A132   Set of 7
                              3.50 1.00
            Souvenir Sheet
610 A132 6r multicolored
                              3.25 1.00
No. 610 contains one 32x40mm stamp.

Lenin (1870-1924) A133

1r, Portrait. 3r, Lenin standing, map of Soviet Union.

1985, June 20   Litho.   Perf. 13
611-612 A133   Set of 2
                              3.50 .75

ARGENTINA '85 — A134

Birds: 20c, Xanthopsar flavus. 50c, Sicalis flaveola. 80c, Thraupis bonariensis. 1r, Amblyramphus holosericeus. 1.50r, Chiloroceryle amazona. 2r, Ramphastos toco. 3r, Turdus rufiventris.
20c-80c, 1.50r-2r are vert.

1985, July 5   Litho.   Perf. 12½
613-619 A134   Set of 7
                              4.25 1.25

Ships A135

Designs: 10c, River boat, 1942. 40c, River boat, 1948. 80c, Tugboat, Japan, 1913. 1r, Dredge. 1.20r, Tugboat, US. 2r, Freighter. 2.50r, Tanker, Panama.

1985, Aug. 8
620-626 A135   Set of 7
                              4.25 1.25

ITALIA 85 — A136

Paintings: 20c, The Flood, by Michelangelo. 50c, Virgin & St. Margaret, by Il Parmigianino (Filippo Mazzola). 80c, Martyrdom of St. Peter Martyr, by Domenichino. 1r, Spring, by Botticelli. 1.50r, Sacrifice of Abraham, by Veronese. 2r, Meeting of St. Joachim and St. Anne, by Giotto. 3r, Bacchus, by Caravaggio. 6r, Early train.

1985, Oct. 25
627-633 A136   Set of 7
                              4.00 1.10
            Souvenir Sheet
634 A136 6r multicolored
                              3.75 1.10
No. 634 contains one 32x40mm stamp.

Son Ngoc Minh — A137

1985, Dec. 2   Litho.   Perf. 12x12½
635-637 A137   Set of 3, 50c, 1r, 3r
                              3.50 1.25

Fish A138

20c, Barbus tetrazona. 50c, Ophiocephalus micropeltes. 80c, Carassius auratus. 1r, Trichogaster leeri. 1.50r, Puntius hexazona. 2r, Betta splendens. 3r, Datnioides microlepis.

1985, Dec. 28   Litho.   Perf. 13
638-644 A138   Set of 7
                              4.25 1.25

1986 World Cup Soccer Championships, Mexico — A139

Various soccer players: 20c, 50c, 80c, 1r, 1.50r, 2r, 3r.

1986, Jan. 29
645-651 A139   Set of 7
                              4.00 1.10
            Souvenir Sheet
652 A139 6r multicolored
                              3.50 .90
No. 652 contains one 32x40mm stamp.

Horses A140

Designs: 20c, Cob. 50c, Arabian. 80c, Australian pony. 1r, Appaloosa. 1.50r, Quarter horse. 2r, Vladimir heavy draft. 3r, Andalusian.

1986, Feb. 15
653-659 A140   Set of 7
                              4.50 1.50

27th Soviet Communist Party Congress A141

Designs: 50c, Space capsules. 1r, Lenin. 5r, Statue, rocket lift-off.

1986, Feb. 25   Perf. 12x12½
660-662 A141   Set of 3
                              3.25 1.00

Prehistoric Animals — A142

Designs: 20c, Edaphosaurus, horiz. 50c, Sauroctonus, horiz. 80c, Mastodonsaurus, horiz. 1r, Rhamphorhynchus. 1.50r, Brachiosaurus. 2r, Tarbosaurus. 3r, Indricotherium.

1986, Mar. 20   Perf. 12½
663-669 A142   Set of 7
                              8.00 3.00

Manned Space Flight, 25th Anniv. — A143

10c, Luna 16. 40c, Luna 3. 80c, Vostok. 1r, Alexei Leonov walking in space. 1.20r, Apollo-Soyuz mission. 2r, Soyuz capsule docking with Salyut station. 2.50r, Yuri Gagarin.

1986, Apr. 12   Perf. 12½
670-676 A143   Set of 7
                              6.00 2.00

Khmer Culture — A144

20c, Temple. 50c, Head of Buddha. 80c, Temple entrance. 1r, 1.50r, 2r, 3r, Various fans.

1986, Apr. 12   Perf. 13
677-683 A144   Set of 7
                              4.50 1.60

Mercedes-Benz Automobiles — A145

20c, 1885 3-wheel. 50c, 1935 sedan. 80c, 1907 open touring car. 1r, 1920 convertible. 1.50r, 1932 cabriolet. 2r, 1938 2-door. 3r, 1985 sedan.

1986, May 14   Perf. 13x12½
684-690 A145   Set of 7
                              4.50 1.25

Butterflies
A146

Designs: 20c, Danaus genutia. 50c, Graphium amtiphates. 80c, Papilio demoleus. 1r, Danaus sita. 1.50r, Idea blanchardi. 2r, Papilio polytes. 3r, Dabasa payeni.

1986, June 19   **Perf. 13**
691-697 A146 Set of 7   5.50 1.75

Ships
A147

20c, English cog. 50c, Cog. 80c, Nile barge. 1r, Galley. 1.50r, Viking long ship. 2r, Two-masted lateen-rigged ship. 3r, Cog, diff.

1986, July 7   **Perf. 13**
698-704 A147 Set of 7   4.25 1.50

Halley's
Comet — A148

Designs: 10c, Solar system, Copernicus, Galileo, Brahe. 20c, Comet above Adoration of the Magi in painting by Giotto. 50c, Comet, observatory. 80c, Edmond Halley. 1.20r, Giotto probe. 1.50r, Vega probe. 2r, Computer-enhanced images of comet. 6r, Vega probe, diff.

1986, July 21   Litho.   Perf. 12x12½
705-711 A148 Set of 7   3.50 1.25
Souvenir Sheet
Perf. 13
712 A148 6r multicolored   3.00 1.00
No. 712 contains one 32x40mm stamp.

STOCKHOLMIA 86 — A149

Chess masters: 20c, Ruy Lopez. 50c, Francois Philador. 80c, Adolph Anderssen. 1r, Wilhelm Steinetz. 1.50r, Emanuel Lasker. 2r, José Capablanca. 3r, Alexander Alekhine. 6r, Chess pieces.

1986, Aug. 28   Litho.   Perf. 12½
713-719 A149 Set of 7   4.00 1.10
Souvenir Sheet
Perf. 13
720 A149 6r multicolored   3.75 1.00
No. 720 contains one 40x32mm stamp.

Cactus — A150

Fruit — A151

20c, Parodia maasii. 50c, Rebutia marsoneri. 80c, Melocactus evae. 1r, Gymnocalycium valnicekianum. 1.50r, Discocactus silichromus. 2r, Neochilenia simulans. 3r, Weingartia chiqichuquensis.

1986, Sept. 25   **Perf. 13**
721-727 A150 Set of 7   4.25 1.25

1986, Oct. 4   **Perf. 12½**
Designs: 10c, Bananas. 40c, Papayas. 80c, Mangos. 1r, Breadfruit. 1.20r, Litchi. 2r, Pineapple. 2.50r, Grapefruit, horiz.
728-734 A151 Set of 7   3.25 1.25

Aircraft — A152

20c, Concorde. 50c, DC-10. 80c, 747. 1r, IL-62. 1.50r, IL-86. 2r, AN-124. 3r, A-300. Illustration reduced.

1986, Nov. 21
735-741 A152 Set of 7   4.25 1.25

Silverware — A153

Designs: 50c, Elephant, containers. 1r, Covered bowl. 3r, Serving dish.

1986, Dec. 2   **Perf. 13**
742-744 A153 Set of 3   4.00 1.40

World
Wildlife
Fund
A154

Designs: No. 745, 20c, Kouprey. No. 746, 20c, Gaur. 80c, Banteng. 1.50r, Buffalo.

1986, Dec. 30   Litho.   Perf. 13
745-748 A154 Set of 4   16.00 2.75

Tou Samouth
A155

Denominations and background colors: 50c, green. 1r, blue, 3r, yellow.

1987, Jan. 7   Litho.   Perf. 13
749-751 A155 Set of 3   3.00 1.00

1988 Winter Olympic Games,
Calgary — A156

Designs: 20c, Biathlon. 50c, Women's figure skating. 80c, Speed skating. 1r, Hockey. 1.50r, Luge. 2r, Two-man bobsled. 3r, Cross-country skiing. 6r, Slalom skiing.

1987, Jan. 14   **Perf. 13x12½**
752-758 A156 Set of 7   3.25 1.10
Souvenir Sheet
Perf. 12½
759 A156 6r multicolored   2.75 .90
No. 759 contains one 40x32mm stamp.

1988 Summer Olympic Games,
Seoul — A157

Designs: 20c, Weight lifting, vert. 50c, Archery. 80c, Fencing. 1r, Gymnastics, vert. 1.50r, Discus. 2r, Javelin, vert. 3r, Hurdles. 6r, Wrestling.

1987, Feb. 2   Perf. 12½x13, 13x12½
760-766 A157 Set of 7   3.50 1.25
Souvenir Sheet
Perf. 13
767 A157 6r multicolored   3.00 1.00
No. 767 contains one 40x32mm stamp.

Dogs
A158

Designs: 20c, shown. 50c, Greyhound. 80c, Great Dane. 1r, Doberman pinscher. 1.50r, Samoyed. 2r, Borzoi. 3r, Collie.

1987, Mar. 3   **Perf. 13**
768-774 A158 Set of 7   4.75 1.50

Nos. 458, 463 Surcharged

1987, Mar.   Litho.   Perf. 13
775 A110 35r on 50c #463   5.00
776 A109 50r on 50c #458   5.00

Soviet
Spacecraft
A159

Designs: 20c, Sputnik. 50c, Weather satellite. 80c, Proton. 1r, Vostok 1. 1.50r, Electron-2. 2r, Kosmos. 3r, Luna 2. 6r, Electron-4.

1987, Apr. 12   Litho.   Perf. 13
777-783 A159 Set of 7   4.00 1.40
Souvenir Sheet
784 A159 6r multicolored   3.25 1.00
No. 784 contains one 40x32mm stamp.

Silverware — A159a

Designs: 50c, Long-necked pot, vert. 1r, Box. 1.50r, Tea set. 3r, Sword.

1987, Apr. 13   **Perf. 13**
785-788 A159a Set of 4   3.00 .90

CAPEX 87 — A160

Birds: 20c, Merops nubicus. 50c, Upupa epops. 80c, Balearica pavonina. 1r, Tyto alba. 1.50r, Halcyon leucocephala. 2r, Pycnonotus jocosus. 3r, Ardea purpurea. 6r, Terpsiphone paradisi.
50c-1.50r, 3r are vert.

1987, May 5   **Perf. 13**
789-795 A160 Set of 7   4.00 1.25
Souvenir Sheet
796 A160 6r multicolored   3.50 1.25
No. 796 contains one 32x40mm stamp.

Early
Aircraft
Designs
A161

Designs by: 20c, Horatio F. Phillips, 1893. 50c, John Stringfellow, 1848. 80c, Thomas Moy, 1875. 1r, Leonardo da Vinci, 1490. 1.50r, Sir George Cayley, 1840. 2r, Sir Hiram Maxim, 1894. 3r, William S. Henson, 1842. 6r, Da Vinci, diff.

1987, Aug. 7   **Perf. 13**
797-803 A161 Set of 7   4.00 1.40
Souvenir Sheet
Perf. 12½
804 A161 6r multicolored   3.00 1.00
No. 804 contains one 32x40mm stamp.

Reptiles
A162

Designs: 20c, Testudo gigantea. 50c, Uromastix acanthinuros. 80c, Cyclura macleayi. 1r, Phrynosoma coronatum. 1.50r, Sauromalus obesus. 2r, Ophisaurus apodus. 3r, Thamnophis sirtalis.

1987, Sept. 9   **Perf. 13**
805-811 A162 Set of 7   5.00 1.50

HAFNIA 87 — A163

Helicopters: 20c, Kamov KA-15. 50c, Kamov KA-18. 80c, Westland Lynx WG-13. 1r, Sud Aviation Gazelle. 1.50r, Sud Aviation Puma. 2r, Boeing CH-47 Chinook. 3r, Boeing UTTAS. 6r, Fairey Rotodyne.

1987, Oct. 16   **Perf. 12½x12**
812-818 A163 Set of 7   4.00 1.40
Souvenir Sheet
Perf. 13
819 A163 6r multicolored   3.00 1.00
No. 819 contains one 40x32mm stamp.

Russian October Revolution, 70th Anniv. A164

1987   Litho.   Perf. 12x12¼
820 A164 2r Soldiers, horse   1.25 .30
821 A164 3r Soldiers   1.75 .45
822 A164 5r Lenin, aides   3.50 .80
Two additional stamps were issued in this set. The editors would like to examine them.

Fire Trucks
A165

1987, Nov. 24   Litho.   Perf. 13
823-829 A165 20c, 50c, 80c,
              1r, 1.50r, 2r, 3r,
              set of 7   6.50 2.00

Telecommunications — A166

50c, Dish antenna, vert. 1r, Broadcast center, vert. 3r, Dish antenna, broadcast center.

Perf. 13x12½, 12x12½, 12½x12
1987, Dec. 2
830-832 A166 Set of 3   3.00 1.00
No. 830 is 29x40mm. No. 831 is 28x44mm. No. 832 printed with se-tenant label.

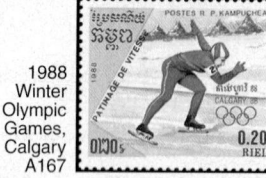

1988 Winter Olympic Games, Calgary A167

Designs: 20c, Speed skating. 50c, Hockey. 80c, Downhill skiing. 1r, Ski jumping. 1.50r, Biathlon. 2r, Pairs figure skating. 3r, Cross-country skiing. 6r, Four-man bobsled.

1988, Jan. 7   **Perf. 12½**
833-839 A167 Set of 7   3.00 1.00
Souvenir Sheet
Perf. 13
840 A167 6r multicolored   2.50 .75
No. 840 contains one 32x40mm stamp.

Water Projects
A168

Designs: 50c, Canal. 1r, Dam under construction. 3r, Dam, bridge.

1988, Jan. 7   Litho.   Perf. 13
841-843 A168 Set of 3   4.00 1.25

1988 Summer Olympic Games, Seoul — A169

Designs: 20c, Balance beam, vert. 50c, Uneven bars. 80c, Rhythmic gymnastics ribbon, vert. 1r, Rhythmic gymnastics hoop, vert. 1.50r, Rhythmic gymnastics clubs, vert. 2r, Rhythmic gymnastics ball. 3r, Floor exercise.

Perf. 12½x13, 13x12½
1988, Feb. 2   **Litho.**
844-850 A169 Set of 7   4.00 1.50
Souvenir Sheet
Perf. 12½
851 A169 6r Rhythmic gymnas-
              tics, diff.   3.00 1.50
No. 851 contains one 32x40mm stamp.

JUVALUX 88 A170

Various cats. Denominations: 20c, 50c, 80c, 1r, 1.50r, 2r, 3r. Nos. 853-854, 856-858 are vert.

1988, Mar. 15   **Perf. 12½**
852-858 A170 Set of 7   4.00 1.25
Souvenir Sheet
Perf. 13
859 A170 6r multicolored   4.00 1.25
No. 859 contains one 40x32mm stamp.

ESSEN 88 — A171

Ships: 20c, Passenger liner. 50c, Passenger liner, diff. 80c, Research ship. 1r, Communications ship. 1.50r, Tanker. 2r, Hydrofoil. 3r, Hovercraft.

1988, Apr. 14   Litho.   Perf. 12½
860-866 A171 Set of 7   3.50 1.25
Souvenir Sheet
Perf. 13
867 A171 6r Hydrofoil   3.25 1.10

Satellites — A172

Various satellites. Denominations: 20c, 50c, 80c, 1r, 1.50r, 2r, 3r. Nos. 868-870 are vert.

1988, Apr. 24   Perf. 12½x13, 13x12½
868-874 A172 Set of 7   4.00 1.50
Souvenir Sheet
Perf. 13
875 A172 6r multicolored   6.00 2.25
No. 875 contains one 40x32mm stamp.

FINLANDIA 88 — A173

Fish: 20c, Xiphophorus helleri. 50c, Hemigrammus ocellifer. 80c, Macropodus opercularis. 1r, Carassius auratus. 1.50r, Hyphessobrycon inesi. 2r, Corynopoma riisei. 3r, Mollienisia latipinna.
6r, Pterophyllum scalare.

1988, Jun 10   Litho.   Perf. 13x12½
876-882 A173 Set of 7   4.00 1.40
Souvenir Sheet
Perf. 12½
883 A173 6r multicolored   3.00 1.00
No. 883 contains one 32x40mm stamp.

Shells — A174

Designs: 20c, Helicostyla florida. 50c, Helicostyla marinduquensis. 80c, Helicostyla fulgens. 1r, Helicostyla woodiana. 1.50r, Chloraea sirena. 2r, Helicostyla mirabilis. 3r, Helicostyla limansauensis.

1988, Aug. 5   Litho.   Perf. 13x12½
884-890 A174 Set of 7   4.25 1.50

Insects — A175

Designs: 20c, Coccinellidae. 50c, Zonabride geminata. 80c, Carabus auronitens. 1r, Apis mellifera. 1.50r, Praying mantis. 2r, Odonata. 3r, Malachius aeneus.

1988, Sept. 6   Perf. 13x12½
891-897 A175 Set of 7   4.75 1.40

Orchids
A176

Designs: 20c, Cattleya aclandiae. 50c, Odontoglossum Royal Sovereign. 80c, Cattleya labiata. 1r, Ophrys apifera. 1.50r, Laelia anceps. 2r, Laelia pumila. 3r, Stanhopea tigrina, horiz.

1988, Oct. 10   Perf. 12½x13, 13x12½
898-904 A176 Set of 7   5.50 1.75

Reptiles — A177

Designs: 20c, Naja haje, vert. 50c, Iguana iguana, vert. 80c, Dryophis nasuta. 1r, Terrapene carolina. 1.50r, Cyclura macleayi. 2r, Bothrops bicolor. 3r, Naja naja, with hood spread, vert.

1988, Nov. 7   Perf. 12x12½, 12½x12
905-911 A177 Set of 7   5.50 1.75

Dance of the Peacock A178

50c, 3 dancers, vert. 1r, shown. 3r, 2 dancers.

1988, Dec. 2   **Perf. 13**
912-914 A178 Set of 3   4.00 1.25
For surcharges see Nos. 1195-1196.

Bridges — A179

1989   **Perf. 13x12½**
915-917 A179 50c, 1r, 3r, set of
              3   3.00 1.00

Decade of Progress — A180

3r, Telecommunications station. 12r, Central Electrical Plant No. 4. 30r, Cement plant, vert.

1989
918-920 A180 Set of 3   3.50 1.25

1990 World Cup Soccer Championships, Italy — A181

Various soccer players. Denominations: 2r, 3r, 5r, 10r, 15r, 20r, 35r.

1989   *Perf. 12½x13*
921-927 A181 Set of 7   4.50 1.50
Souvenir Sheet
Perf. 13
928 A181 45r multicolored   3.00 1.00
No. 928 contains one 32x40mm stamp.

Trains A182

Various locomotives. Denominations: 2r, 3r, 5r, 10r, 15r, 20r, 35r.

1989   *Perf. 13*
929-935 A182 Set of 7   4.25 1.50
Souvenir Sheet
Perf. 12½
936 A182 45r multicolored   3.25 1.00
No. 936 contains one 40x32mm stamp.

A183

A184

1989   *Perf. 13*
937 A183 12r red & black   1.00 .35
Cuban Revolution, 30th anniv.

1989
Birds: 20c, Ara macao. 80c, Kakatoe galerita. 3r, Psittacula krameri. 6r, Ara ararauna. 10r, Poicephalus robustus. 15r, Amazona aestiva. 25r, Pionus senilis, horiz.
45r, Cyanoramphus novaezelandiae.
938-944 A184 Set of 7   4.25 1.25
Souvenir Sheet
Perf. 12½
945 A184 45r multicolored   3.25 1.00
No. 945 contains one 40x32mm stamp.

1992 Winter Olympic Games, Albertville A185

2r, Slalom skiing. 3r, Biathlon. 5r, Cross-country skiing. 10r, Ski jumping. 15r, Speed skating. 20r, Hockey. 35r, Bobsled. 45r, Pairs figure skating.

1989, Mar. 30   *Perf. 13*
946-952 A185 Set of 7   4.50 1.50
Souvenir Sheet
Perf. 12½
953 A185 45r multicolored   2.75 .90
No. 953 contains one 32x40mm stamp.

Water Lilies A186

20c, Nymphaea capensis (pink). 80c, Nymphaea capensis (purple). 3r, Nymphaea lotus. 6r, Nymphaea Dir. Geo. T. Moore. 10r, Nymphaea Sunrise. 15r, Nymphaea Escarboncie. 25r, Nymphaea Cladstoniana. 45r, Nymphaea Paul Hariot.

1989   *Perf. 12½x13*
954-960 A186 Set of 7   4.25 1.25
Souvenir Sheet
Perf. 12½
961 A186 45r multicolored   3.25 1.00
No. 961 contains one 32x40mm stamp.

1992 Summer Olympic Games, Barcelona — A187

Designs: 2r, Wrestling. 3r, Pommel horse, vert. 5r, Shot put. 10r, Running, vert. 15r, Fencing. 20r, Canoeing, vert. 35r, Steeplechase, vert. 45r, Weight lifting, vert.

1989   *Perf. 13*
962-968 A187 Set of 7   4.50 1.50
Souvenir Sheet
Perf. 12½
969 A187 45r multicolored   4.00 1.50
No. 969 contains one 32x40mm stamp.

Mushrooms A188

Designs: 20c, Xerocomus subtomentosus. 80c, Inocybe patouillardii. 3r, Armillaria mellea. 6r, Agaricus campestris. 10r, Paxillus involutus. 15r, Coprinus comatus. 25r, Lepiota procera.

1989   *Perf. 12½x13*
970-976 A188 Set of 7   4.00 1.10

Horses — A189

Designs: 2r, Shire. 3r, Brabant. 5r, Bolounais. 10r, Breton. 15r, Vladimir heavy draft. 20r, Italian heavy draft. 35r, Freiberger. 45r, Horse-drawn cart.

1989   *Perf. 12½*
977-983 A189 Set of 7   4.25 1.50
Souvenir Sheet
984 A189 45r multicolored   3.25 1.10
Nos. 977-983 printed with se-tenant label. No. 984 contains one 40x32mm stamp.

Angkor Wat — A190

Denominations: 35r, 50r, 80r, 100r.

1989, May 15   *Litho.*   *Perf. 13¼*
985-988 A190 Set of 4   75.00 75.00

Cambodia

PHILEXFRANCE 89 — A191

Mail coaches: 2r, 17th cent. 3r, Paris-Lyon, 1720. 5r, 1793. 10r, 1805. 15r, Royal Mail. 20r, 1843. 35r, Paris-Lille, 1837, vert. 45r, 1815, vert.

1989   *Litho.*   *Perf. 13*
989-995 A191 Set of 7   4.50 1.50
Souvenir Sheet
Perf. 12½
996 A191 45r multicolored   3.00 1.50
No. 996 contains one 23x40mm stamp.

BRASILIANA 89 — A192

Butterflies: 2r, Papilio zagreus. 3r, Morpho catenarius. 5r, Morpho aega. 10r, Callithea sapphira. 15r, Catagramma sorana. 20r, Pierella nereis. 35r, Papilio brasiliensis. 45r, Thacia marsyas, horiz.

1989   *Perf. 13*
997-1003 A192 Set of 7   5.00 1.50
Souvenir Sheet
1004 A192 45r multicolored   4.50 1.50
No. 1004 contains one 40x32mm stamp.

Khmer Boats A193

Various pirogues. Denominations: 3r, 12r, 30r.

1989, Dec. 2   *Litho.*   *Perf. 12½*
1005-1007 A193 Set of 3   3.50 1.25

Natl. Organizations — A194

3r, Youth, vert. 12r, Labor. 30r, Natl. Front.

1990, Jan. 7   *Litho.*   *Perf. 13*
1008-1010 A194 Set of 3   3.50 .90

1990 World Cup Soccer Championships, Italy — A195

Various soccer players. Denominations: 2r, 3r, 5r, 10r, 15r, 20r, 35r.

1990, Jan. 5   *Litho.*   *Perf. 13*
1011-1017 A195 Set of 7   4.00 1.50
Souvenir Sheet
1018 A195 45r multicolored   2.75 1.00
No. 1018 contains one 32x40mm stamp. For surcharges see Nos. 1072, 1075.

STAMPWORLD LONDON 90 — A196

Various mail coaches. Denominations: 2r, 3r, 5r, 10r, 15r, 20r, 35r.
45r, Single horse van for rural deliveries.

12

1990
1019-1025 A196 Set of 7   4.00 1.25
Perf. 12½x12

Souvenir Sheet
Perf. 13
1026 A196 45r multicolored   2.50 .90
Nos. 1019-1025 are printed with se-tenant label. No. 1026 contains one 40x32mm stamp.

Rice — A197

Designs: 3r, Woman, rice. 12r, People hauling rice, horiz. 30r, Women threshing rice.

1990, June 19   Litho.   *Perf. 13*
1027-1029 A197 Set of 3   3.50 1.25

1992 Winter Olympic Games, Albertville A198

2r, 4-man bobsled. 3r, Speed skating. 5r, Pairs figure skating. 10r, Hockey. 15r, Biathlon. 20r, Luge. 35r, Ski jumping. 45r, Hockey goalie.

1990   Litho.   *Perf. 13*
1030-1036 A198 Set of 7   4.50 1.50
Souvenir Sheet
1037 A198 45r multicolored   2.50 .90
No. 1037 contains one 32x40mm stamp.

1992 Summer Olympic Games, Barcelona A199

Designs: 2r, Shooting. 3r, Shot put. 5r, Weight lifting. 10r, Boxing. 15r, Pole vault. 20r, Basketball. 35r, Fencing. 45r, Rhythmic gymnastics.

1990
1038-1044 A199 Set of 7   4.50 1.50
Souvenir Sheet
1045 A199 45r multicolored   2.50 .75
No. 1045 contains one 32x40mm stamp.

Khmer Culture A200

Designs: 3r, Facade, Bantey Srei. 12r, Relief. 30r, Ruins, Banon.

Perf. 12½, 12½x13 (#1048)
1990, Dec. 2   Litho.
1046-1048 A200 Set of 3   3.00 1.25
No. 1048 is 36x21mm.

Dogs A201

20c, Poodle. 80c, Shetland. 3r, Samoyed. 6r, Springer spaniel. 10r, Fox terrier. 15r, Afghan. 25r, Dalmatian. 45r, Bernese.

1990   Litho.   *Perf. 13*
1049-1055 A201 Set of 7   4.00 1.25
Souvenir Sheet
1056 A201 45r multicolored   3.00 1.00
No. 1056 contains one 40x32mm stamp.

Cacti — A202

Designs: 20c, Cereus hexagonus. 80c, Arthrocereus rondonianus. 3r, Matucana multicolor. 6r, Hildewintera aureispina. 10r, Opuntia retrosa. 15r, Erdisia tenuicula. 25r, Mamillaria yaquensis.

1990
1057-1063 A202 Set of 7   4.00 1.50

NEW ZEALAND 90 — A203

Butterflies: 2r, Zizina oxleyi. 3r, Cupha prosope. 5r, Heteronympha merope. 10r, Dodonidia helmsi. 15r, Argirophenga antipodum. 20r, Tysonotis danis. 35r, Pyrameis gonnarilla. 45r, Pyrameis itea.

1990   *Perf. 13*
1064-1070 A203 Set of 7   5.00 1.50
Souvenir Sheet
Perf. 12½
1071 A203 45r multicolored   3.25 1.00
No. 1071 contains one 40x32mm stamp.

Nos. 1012, 1013, 1015, 1016
Surcharged in Red
1990   Litho.   *Perf. 13*
1072 A195 200r on 3r #1012
1073 A195 300r on 5r multi
1075 A195 800r on 15r multi
1076 A195 1000r on 20r multi
Nos. are reserved for additions to this set.

Intl. Literacy Year — A204

Denominations: 3r, 12r, 30r.

1990   Litho.   *Perf. 13*
1077-1079 A204 Set of 3   3.50 1.25

Ships A205

Designs: 20c, English, 1200. 80c, Spanish galleon, 16th cent. 3r, Dutch ship, 1627. 6r, La Couronne, 1638. 10r, L'Astrolabe, 1826. 15r, French packet, Louisiana, 1864. 25r, Clipper ship, 1900, vert. 45r, Merchant ship, 1800.

1990   *Perf. 13*
1080-1086 A205 Set of 7   4.25 1.50
Souvenir Sheet
Perf. 12½
1087 A205 45r multicolored   3.00 1.00
No. 1087 contains one 32x40mm stamp.

Natl. Building Campaign — A206

3r, Railroad. 12r, Cargo ship, Kampong Som. 30r, Fishing boats, Kampong Som.

1990   Litho.   *Perf. 13*
1088-1090 A206 Set of 3   3.25 1.25

PARIS 90 — A207

Chess pieces and: 2r, Sacré Coeur. 3r, Equestrian statue. 5r, Winged Victory of Samothrace. 10r, Chateau, Azay le Riddeau. 15r, Sculpture, "The Dance." 20r, Eiffel Tower. 35r, Arc de Triomphe.
45r, Chess pieces, horiz.

1990, Nov. 15   Litho.   *Perf. 13*
1091-1097 A207 Set of 7   6.50 2.00
Souvenir Sheet
1098 A207 45r multicolored   4.25 1.50
No. 1098 contains one 40x32mm stamp.

Space Day — A208

Designs: 2r, Vostok. 3r, Soyuz. 5r, Artificial satellite. 10r, Luna 10. 15r, Mars 1. 20r, Venus 3. 35r, Mir. 45r, Energia, Buran.

1990   Litho.   *Perf. 13*
1099-1105 A208 Set of 7   4.75 1.50
Souvenir Sheet
1106 A208 45r multicolored   3.00 1.00
No. 1106 contains one 32x40mm stamp.
For surcharges see Nos. 1145-1151.

Discovery of America, 500th Anniv. (in 1992) — A209

Designs: 2r, Columbus. 3r, Queen Isabella's jewelry chest. 5r, Queen Isabella. 10r, Santa Maria. 15r, Juan de la Cosa. 20r, Columbus Monument. 35r, Pyramid, Yucatan. 45r, Columbus, diff.

1990, Oct. 12   Litho.   *Perf. 13*
1107-1113 A209 Set of 7   6.00 2.00
Souvenir Sheet
1114 A209 45r multicolored   3.75 1.25
No. 1114 contains one 32x40mm stamp.

Natl. Festival A210

Designs: 100r, Tire production. 300r, Rural infirmary. 500r, Fisherman.

Perf. 12½, 13 (#1117)
1991, Jan. 7   Litho.
1115-1117 A210 Set of 3   4.50 1.25
No. 1117 is 28x40mm.

1994 World Cup Soccer Championships, US — A211

Various soccer players. Denominations: 5r, 25r, 50r, 100r, 200r, 400r, 1000r.

1991, Feb. 15   Litho.   *Perf. 13*
1118-1124 A211 Set of 7   5.50 1.75
Souvenir Sheet
1125 A211 900r multicolored   3.00 1.10
No. 1125 contains one 32x40mm stamp.

1992 Winter Olympic Games, Albertville A212

Designs: 5r, Speed skating. 25r, Slalom skiing. 70r, Hockey. 100r, Bobsled. 200r, Freestyle skiing. 400r, Pairs figure skating. 1000r, Downhill skiing.
900r, Ski jumping.

1991, Mar. 30   Litho.   *Perf. 12½*
1126-1132 A212 Set of 7   6.00 2.00
Souvenir Sheet
Perf. 13
1133 A212 900r multicolored   3.00 1.00
No. 1133 contains one 32x40mm stamp.

Khmer Culture A213

Statues: 100r, Garuda, 10th cent. 300r, Torso of Vishnu reclining, 11th cent. 500r, Reclining Nandin, 7th cent.

1991, Apr. 13   Litho.   Perf. 12½
1134-1136   A213   Set of 3   3.50 1.25

1992 Summer Olympic Games, Barcelona A214

Designs: 5r, Pole vault. 25r, Table tennis. 70r, Women's running. 100r, Wrestling. 200r, Women's gymnastics. 400r, Tennis. 1000r, Boxing. 900r, Balance beam.

1991, Apr. 25   Litho.   Perf. 12½x13
1137-1143   A214   Set of 7   5.00 1.50
Souvenir Sheet
Perf. 13
1144   A214   900r multicolored   3.25 1.00
No. 1144 contains one 32x40mm stamp.

Nos. 1099-1103, 1105 Surcharged in Red

1991   Litho.   Perf. 13
1145   A208   100r on 2r #1099
1146   A208   150r on 3r #1100
1147   A208   200r on 5r #1101
1148   A208   300r on 10r #1102
1149   A208   500r on 15r #1103
1151   A208   2000r on 35r #1105

Number is reserved for surcharge on No. 1104.

Aircraft — A215

Designs: 5r, DC-10-30. 25r, MD-11. 70r, IL-96-300. 100r, A-310. 200r, YAK-42. 400r, TU-154. 1000r, DC-9

1991, June 15   Litho.   Perf. 13x12½
1152-1158   A215   Set of 7   5.25 1.75

ESPAMER 91 — A216

Pre-Columbian pottery: 5r, Catamarca. 25r, Catamarca, vert. 70r, Tucuman, vert. 100r, Santiago del Estero. 200r, Santiago del Estero, diff. 400r, Tucuman, diff., vert. 1000r, Catamarca, diff.
900r, Catamarca, diff.

1991, July 10   Perf. 13
1159-1165   A216   Set of 7   6.00 2.00
Souvenir Sheet
Perf. 12½
1166   A216   900r multicolored   4.00 1.25
No. 1166 contains one 40x32mm stamp.

Discovery of America, 500th Anniv. (in 1992) — A217

Designs: 5r, Pinta, vert. 25r, Niña, vert. 70r, Santa Maria, vert. 100r, Landing of Columbus. 200r, Encountering new cultures. 400r, First European settlement in Americas. 1000r, Native village.
900r, Columbus.

1991, Oct. 12   Perf. 12½x13, 13x12½
1167-1173   A217   Set of 7   6.00 2.00
Souvenir Sheet
Perf. 12½
1174   A217   900r multicolored   3.25 1.10
No. 1174 contains one 40x32mm stamp.

PHILANIPPON 91 — A218

Butterflies: 5r, Neptis pryeri. 25r, Papilio xuthus. 70r, Cyrestis thyodamas. 100r, Argynnis anadiomene. 200r, Lethe marginalis. 400r, Artopoetes pryeri. 1000r, Danaus chrysippus. 900r, Ochlodes subhyalina.

1991, Nov. 16   Perf. 13
1175-1181   A218   Set of 7   5.75 2.00
Souvenir Sheet
Perf. 12½
1182   A218   900r multicolored   3.50 1.25
No. 1182 contains one 40x32mm stamp.

Natl. Building Campaign A219

Designs: 100r, Fishing port. 300r, Preparing palm sugar, vert. 500r, Harvesting peppers.

1991, Dec. 2   Litho.   Perf. 12½
1183-1185   A219   Set of 3   4.50 1.25

Natl. Festival — A220

Traditional costumes: 150r, Chakdomuk. 350r, Longvek. 1000r, Angkor.

1992, Jan. 7   Perf. 13
1186-1188   A220   Set of 3   3.75 1.25

1992 Summer Olympic Games, Barcelona A221

5r, Wrestling. 15r, Soccer. 80r, Weight lifting. 400r, Archery. 1500r, Balance beam. 1000r, Equestrian.

1992, Jan.   Litho.   Perf. 13
1189-1193   A221   Set of 5   3.75 1.25
Souvenir Sheet
Perf. 12½
1194   A221   1000r multicolored   2.50 .80
No. 1194 contains one 32x40mm stamp.

Nos. 913-914 Surcharged in Red

1992, Jan.   Litho.   Perf. 13
1195   A178   200r on 3r #914
1196   A178   300r on 1r #913

Fish A222

Designs: 5r, Hyphessobrycon innesi. 15r, Betta splendens. 80r, Nematobrycon palmen. 400r, Colisa lalia. 1500r, Hoplosternum thoracatum.
1000r, Pterophyllum scalare.

1992, Feb. 8   Litho.   Perf. 12½
1197-1201   A222   Set of 5   4.50 1.50
Souvenir Sheet
1202   A222   1000r multicolored   2.75 1.00
No. 1202 contains one 40x32mm stamp.

1994 World Cup Soccer Championships, US — A223

Various soccer plays. Denominations: 5r, 15r, 80r, 400r, 1500r. Nos. 1203, 1205-1207 are vert.

1992, Mar. 6   Litho.   Perf. 12½
1203-1207   A223   Set of 5   4.25 1.50
Souvenir Sheet
1208   A223   1000r multicolored   2.75 .90
No. 1208 contains one 40x32mm stamp.

Khmer Culture — A224

19th cent. structures: 150r, Monument. 350r, Stupa. 1000r, Library of Mandapa.

1992, Apr. 13   Litho.   Perf. 12½
1209-1211   A224   Set of 3   4.25 1.40

Leonardo da Vinci (1452-1519) — A225

Designs: 5r, Automobile. 15r, Container ship. 80r, Helicopter. 400r, Scuba gear. 1500r, Parachute, vert.
1000r, Portrait.

1992, Apr. 15   Litho.   Perf. 12x12½
1212-1216   A225   Set of 5   4.50 1.50
Souvenir Sheet
Perf. 13
1217   A225   1000r multicolored   2.75 .80
Nos. 1212-1216 each printed with se-tenant labels showing Da Vinci's conceptions of the items shown on the stamps. No. 1217 contains one 32x40mm stamp.

EXPO 92, Seville A226

Inventors, builders: 5r, De la Cierva, autogyro. 15r, Edison, electric light bulb. 80r, Morse, telegraph. 400r, Monturiol, submarine. No. 1222, 1500r, Bell, telephone.
No. 1223, 1500r, Fulton, steamship.

1992, Apr. 23   Perf. 12½
1218-1222   A226   Set of 5   4.00 1.25
Souvenir Sheet
Perf. 13
1223   A226   1000r pink & black   2.75 .80
No. 1223 contains one 32x40mm stamp.

1992 Summer Olympic Games, Barcelona — A227

Designs: 5r, Weight lifting. 15r, Boxing. 80r, Basketball. 400r, Sprints. 1500r, Water polo. 1000r, Women's gymnastics.

1992, May 15   Perf. 13
1224-1228   A227   Set of 5   8.00 1.75
Souvenir Sheet
Perf. 12½
1229   A227   1000r multicolored   4.00 1.25
No. 1229 contains one 40x32mm stamp.

Environmental Protection — A228

Designs: 5r, Women filling water jars. 15r, Pagoda. 80r, Palm trees. 400r, Boy riding water buffalo. 1500r, Lake, swimmers. 1000r, Angkor Wat.

1992, June 16   Litho.   Perf. 12½
1230-1234   A228   Set of 5   6.00 1.75
Souvenir Sheet
Perf. 13
1235   A228   1000r multicolored   5.00 1.25
No. 1235 contains one 42x32mm stamp.

GENOA
92 — A229

Explorers, ship: 5r, Bougainville, Boudeuse.
15r, Cook, Endeavour. 80r, Darwin, Beagle.
400r, Cousteau, Calypso. 1500r, Heyerdahl,
Kon Tiki.
  1000r, Columbus.

1992, Aug. 1   Litho.   Perf. 12x12½
1236-1240 A229 Set of 5   4.50 1.50
Souvenir Sheet
Perf. 12½
1241 A229 1000r multicolored   2.75   .80
  No. 1241 contains one 32x40mm stamp.

Mushrooms
A230

Designs: 5r, Albatrellus confluens. 15r,
Boletus calopus. 80r, Stropharia aeruginosa.
400r, Telamonia armillata. 1500r, Cortinarius
traganus.

1992, Sept. 25   Perf. 13
1242-1246 A230 Set of 5   5.00 1.50

Seaplanes — A231

Designs: 5r, Bellanca Pacemaker, 1930.
15r, Canadair CL-215, 1965. 80r, G-21A
Goose, 1937. 400r, Sealand SA-6, 1947.
1500r, Short S-23, 1936.
  1000r, G-44 Widgeon, 1940.

1992, Oct. 16   Perf. 12½x12
1247-1251 A231 Set of 5   4.00 1.25
Souvenir Sheet
Perf. 13
1252 A231 1000r multicolored   2.75   .90
  No. 1252 contains one 32x40mm stamp.

Natl.
Development
A232

Designs: 150r, Dish antenna. 350r, Dish
antenna, flags. 1000r, Hotel Cambodiana.

1992, Dec. 2   Litho.   Perf. 12½
1253-1255 A232 Set of 3   4.00 1.25

Natl.
Festival
A233

Designs: 50r, Sociological Institute. 450r,
Motel Cambodiana. 1000r, Theater.

1993, Jan. 7   Litho.   Perf. 12½
1256-1258 A233 Set of 3   4.25 1.25

Dolphin, Bathyscaph — A234

Fauna, machine: 150r, shown. 200r, Falcon,
jet fighter. 250r, Beaver, dam. 500r, Bat, satellite. 900r, Hummingbird, helicopter.

1993, Feb. 5   Litho.   Perf. 13
Without Gum
1259-1263 A234 Set of 5   4.25 1.25

Flowers — A235

Designs: 150r, Datura suaveolens. 200r,
Convolvulus tricolor. 250r, Hippeastrum
hybrid. 500r, Camellia hybrid. 900r, Lilium
speciosum.
  1000r, Datura suaveolens, camellia, lilium
speciosum.

1993, Mar. 15   Perf. 13
Without Gum
1264-1268 A235 Set of 5   5.00 1.25
Souvenir Sheet
Perf. 12½
1269 A235 1000r multicolored   2.50   .85
  No. 1269 contains one 40x32mm stamp.

Khmer
Culture
A236

Designs: 50r, Statue of a Nandin. 450r,
Temple Vihear. 1000r, Man with offerings.

1993, Apr. 13   Litho.   Perf. 12½
1270-1272 A236 Set of 3   4.00 1.25

Wildlife — A237

  150r, Cynocephalus volans. 200r,
Petuarista petuarista. 250r, Ptychozoon
homalocephalum. 500r, Rhacophorus
nigropalmatus. 900r, Draco volans.

1993, May 4   Litho.   Perf. 12½x12
Without Gum
1273-1277 A237 Set of 5   4.25 1.25

BRASILIANA 93 — A238

Butterflies: 250r, Symbrenthia hypselis.
350r, Sithon nedymond. 600r, Geitoneura
minyas. 800r, Argyreus hyperbius. 1000r,
Argyrophenga antipodum.
  1500r, Pararge schakra.

1993, June 15   Perf. 12½x12
Without Gum
1278-1282 A238 Set of 5   5.25 1.50
Souvenir Sheet
Perf. 12½
1283 A238 1500r multicolored   3.50 1.25
  No. 1283 contains one 40x32mm stamp.

UN Transitional
Authority in
Cambodia
(UNTAC)
Pacification
Program
A239

  150r, Cambodian soldiers approaching UN
base. 200r, Cambodians entering camp. 250r,
Cambodians surrendering weapons to UN.
500r, Vocational training. 900r, Cambodians
re-entering society.
  1000r, Returning to homes and family.

1993, Aug. 4   Litho.   Perf. 12½
1284-1288 A239 Set of 5   5.50 1.50
Souvenir Sheet
Perf. 13
1289 A239 1000r blue & black   3.75 1.25
  No. 1289 contains one 32x40mm stamp.

Ships
A240

  150r, Venetian caravel. 200r, Phoenician
galley. 250r, Egyptian merchantman. 500r,
Genoese merchantman. 900r, English
merchantman.

1993, Aug. 27   Litho.   Perf. 13
Without Gum
1290-1294 A240 Set of 5   4.25 1.25

Alberto Santos-Dumont (1873-
1932) — A241

Designs: 150r, Portrait, Balloon, Eiffel
Tower, vert. 200r, 14-bis, 1906. 250r, Demoiselle. 500r, EMB-201A. 900r, EMB-111.

1993, Sept. 10   Perf. 13
Without Gum
1295-1299 A241 Set of 5   4.25 1.25

1994 World Cup Soccer
Championships, US — A242

Various soccer plays. Denominations: 250r,
350r, 600r, 800r, 1000r, vert.

1993, Sept. 23   Litho.   Perf. 12½
1300-1304 A242 Set of 5   5.25 1.75
Souvenir Sheet
1305 A242 1500r multicolored   4.50 1.50
  No. 1305 contains one 40x32mm stamp.

BANGKOK 93 — A243

Ducks: 250r, Anas penelope. 350r, Anas
formosa. 600r, Aix galericulata. 800r, Aix
sponsa. 1000r, Histrionicus histrionicus.
  1500r, Head of Air galericulata.

1993, Oct. 1   Litho.   Perf. 13
Without Gum
1306-1310 A243 Set of 5   5.50 1.75
Souvenir Sheet
1311 A243 1500r multicolored   3.25 1.10
  No. 1311 contains one 40x32mm stamp.

Vertical Take-Off Aircraft — A244

Designs: 150r, First helicopter model,
France, 1784, vert. 200r, Steam helicopter
model, 1863, vert. 250r, New York-Atlanta-
Miami autogyro flight, 1927. 500r, Sikorsky
helicopter, 1943. 900r, French VTOL jet.
  1000r, Juan de la Cierva's autogyro C-4,
1923.

Perf. 12x12½, 12½x12
1993, Nov. 6   Without Gum
1312-1316 A244 Set of 5   4.25 1.25
Souvenir Sheet
Perf. 12½
1317 A244 1000r multicolored   2.50   .90
  No. 1317 contains one 40x32mm stamp.

Insects — A245

Designs: 50r, Cnaphalocrosis medinalis.
450r, Cicadelle brune. 500r, Scirpophaga
incertulas. No. 1321, 1000r, Diopsis
macrophthlalma.
  No. 1322, Leptocorisa oratorius.

1993, Dec. 2   Perf. 13
1318-1321 A245 Set of 4   3.50 1.25
Souvenir Sheet
Perf. 12½
1322 A245 1000r multicolored   3.00   .80
  Issued without gum.
  No. 1322 contains one 32x40mm stamp.

Independence, 40th Anniv. — A246

Designs: 300r, Ministry of Posts and Telecommunications. 500r, Independence Monument, 1953, vert. 700r, Natl. flag.

1993   **Litho.**   **Perf. 12½**
1323-1325 A246   Set of 3   3.00 1.00

Hummel
Figurines
A247

Designs: 50r, Boy riding pony. 100r, Girl with baby carriage. 150r, Girl bathing doll. 200r, Girl holding doll. 250r, Boys playing. 300r, Girls pulling boy in cart. 350r, Girls playing ring-around-the-rosie. 600r, Boys with stick and drum.

1993   **Litho.**   **Perf. 12½**
1326-1333 A247   Set of 8   5.00 1.50

1994 Winter Olympic Games,
Lillehammer — A248

150r, Women's figure skating, vert. 250r, Two-man luge. 400r, Downhill skiing. 700r, Biathlon. 1000r, Speed skating, vert. 1500r, Curling, vert.

1994, Jan. 23   **Perf. 13**
1334-1338 A248   Set of 5   5.75 1.50
    Souvenir Sheet
1339 A248 1500r multicolored   3.50 1.25
No. 1339 contains one 32x40mm stamp.

Classic Automobiles — A249

Designs: 150r, 1924 Opel. 200r, 1901 Mercedes. 250r, 1927 Model T Ford. 500r, 1907 Rolls Royce. 1000r, 1908 Hutton. 1000r, 1931 Duesenberg.

1994, Feb. 20   **Perf. 13**
1340-1344 A249   Set of 5   5.00 1.50
    Souvenir Sheet
1345 A249 1000r multicolored   3.00 .90
No. 1345 contains one 32x40mm stamp.

1996 Summer
Olympic
Games,
Atlanta — A250

Designs: 150r, Women's gymnastics. 200r, Soccer. 250r, Javelin. 300r, Canoeing. 600r, Running. 1000r, Diving, horiz. 1500r, Equestrian.

1994, Mar. 20   **Perf. 13**
1346-1351 A250   Set of 6   5.00 1.50
    Souvenir Sheet
1352 A250 1500r multicolored   4.00 1.10
No. 1352 contains one 32x40mm stamp.

Khmer
Statues — A251

Designs: 300r, Siva and Uma. 500r, Vishnu. 700r, King Jayavarman VII.

1994, Apr. 13
1353-1355 A251   Set of 3   5.00 1.50

Intl. Olympic Committee,
Cent. — A252

Designs: 100r, Olympic Flag. 300r, Flag, Torch. 600r, Flag, Baron de Coubertin.

1994, Apr. 23   **Perf. 12½**
1356-1358 A252   Set of 3   3.00 1.00

Prehistoric Animals — A253

150r, Mesonyx. 250r, Doedicurus. 400r, Mylodon. 700r, Uintatherium. 1000r, Hyrachyus.

1994, May 10   **Perf. 12½**
1359-1363 A253   Set of 5   5.00 1.50

1994 World Cup
Soccer
Championships,
U.S. — A254

Various soccer plays. Denominations: 150r, 250r, 400r, 700r, 1000r.

1994, June 17   **Perf. 12½**
1364-1368 A254   Set of 5   5.00 1.50
    Souvenir Sheet
1369 A254 1500r multicolored   3.50 1.25
No. 1369 contains one 32x40mm stamp.

Statues
A255

Designs: 300r, shown. 500r, Soldiers in combat, vert. 700r, Lions, vert.

1994   **Perf. 13**
1370-1372 A255   Set of 3   3.75 1.25

Beetles
A256

Designs: 150r, Chlorophanus viridis. 200r, Chrysochroa fulgidissima. 250r, Lytta vesicatoria. 500r, Purpuricenus kaehleri. 900r, Dynastes hercules. 1000r, Timarcha tenebricosa.

1994, July 7   **Perf. 12½**
1373-1377 A256   Set of 5   4.50 1.25
    Souvenir Sheet
1378 A256 1000r multicolored   2.50 .90
No. 1378 contains one 40x32mm stamp.

Submarines — A257

Designs: 150r, Halley's diving bell, 1690, vert. 200r, Gimnote, 1886. 250r, Peral, 1888. 500r, Nuclear-powered Nautilus, 1954. 900r, Bathyscaphe Trieste, 1953. 1000r, Ictineo, 1885.

1994, Aug. 12   **Perf. 13**
1379-1383 A257   Set of 5   5.00 1.50
    Souvenir Sheet
    Perf. 12½
1384 A257 1000r multicolored   3.00 1.00
No. 1384 contains one 40x32mm stamp.

Chess Champions — A258

Designs: 150r, Francois-André Philador, 1795. 200r, Louis de la Bourdonnais, 1821. 250r, Adolph Anderssen, 1851. 500r, Paul Morphy, 1858. 900r, Wilhelm Steinitz, 1866. 1000r, Emanuel Lasker, 1894.

1994, Sept. 20   **Perf. 13**
1385-1389 A258   Set of 5   4.50 1.50
    Souvenir Sheet
1390 A258 1000r multicolored   3.00 1.00
No. 1390 contains one 32x40mm stamp.

Aircraft
A259

Designs: 150r, Sikorsky S-42 flying boat. 200r, Vought-Sikorsky VS-300A helicopter. 250r, Sikorsky S-37 biplane. 500r, Sikorsky S-35 biplane. 900r, Sikorsky S-43 amphibian. 1000r, 1st 4-engine bomber, Ilya Mourometz.

1994, Oct. 6   **Perf. 13**
1391-1395 A259   Set of 5   4.50 1.50
    Souvenir Sheet
    Perf. 12½
1396 A259 1000r multicolored   3.00 1.00
No. 1396 contains one 40x32mm stamp.

Birds
A260

Designs: 150r, Remiz pendulinus, vert. 250r, Panurus biarmicus. 400r, Emberiza rustica. 700r, Emberiza schoeniclus. 1000r, Regulus regulus. 1500r, Pitta angolensis.

1994, Nov. 20   **Perf. 12½**
1397-1401 A260   Set of 5   6.00 1.50
    Souvenir Sheet
    Perf. 13
1402 A260 1500r multicolored   3.75 1.25
No. 1402 contains one 32x40mm stamp.

Independence Festival — A261

Designs: 300r, Postal Service float. 500r, Soldiers marching. 700r, Army unit marching.

1994, Dec. 9   **Perf. 13**
1403-1405 A261   Set of 3   5.00 1.50

Natl. Development — A262

Designs: 300r, Chruoi Changwar Bridge. 500r, Olympic Commercial Center. 700r, Sakamony Chedei Temple.

1994, Dec. 10
1406-1408 A262   Set of 3   5.00 1.50

Prehistoric Animals — A263

100r, Psittacosaurus. 200r, Protoceratops. 300r, Montanoceraptors. 400r, Centrosaurus. 700r, Styracosaurus. 800r, Triceratops.

1995, Jan. 10
1409-1414 A263 Set of 6   6.50 1.50

100r, Anthocharis cardamines. 200r, Iphiclides podalirius. 300r, Mesoacidalia aglaja. 600r, Vanessa atalanta. 800r, Inachis io.

Butterflies A264

1995, Feb. 12
1415-1419 A264 Set of 5   5.00 1.50

1996 Summer Olympic Games, Atlanta A265

Designs: 100r, Swimming. 200r, Rhythmic gymnastics. 400r, Basketball. 800r, Soccer. 1000r, Cycling. 1500r, Running. 200r-1500r are vert.

1995, Mar. 9
1420-1424 A265 Set of 5   6.00 1.50
Souvenir Sheet
1425 A265 1500r multicolored   3.50 1.00
No. 1425 contains one 32x40mm stamp.

Mushrooms A266

Designs: 100r, Amanita phalloides. 200r, Cantharellus cibarius. 300r, Armillaria mellea. 600r, Agaricus campestris. 800r, Amanita muscaria.

1995, Mar. 23
1426-1430 A266 Set of 5   5.00 1.50

Statues — A267

Designs: 300r, Kneeling ascetic. 500r, Parasurama. 700r, Siva.

1995, Apr. 13   *Perf. 12½*
1431-1433 A267 Set of 3   4.25 1.10

Protected Wildlife — A268

Designs: 300r, Bos gaurus. 500r, Bos sauveli, vert. 700r, Grus antigone, vert.

1995, May 5   *Perf. 13*
1434-1436 A268 Set of 3   4.00 1.25

Parrots — A269

Designs: 100r, Lorus lory. 200r, Polytelis alexandrae. 400r, Eclectus voratus. 800r, Aramacao. 1000r, Melopsittacus undulatus. 1500r, Amazona ochrocephala.

1995, May 23   *Perf. 13*
1437-1441 A269 Set of 5   4.50 1.50
Souvenir Sheet
Perf. 12½
1442 A269 1500r multicolored   4.00 1.50
No. 1442 contains one 32x40mm stamp.

Tourism A270

Public gardens: 300r, Sculpture of Garuda. 500r, Fountain. 700r, Sculpture of mythological figures.

1995, July 15   *Perf. 12½*
1443-1445 A270 Set of 3   3.25 1.10

Locomotives — A271

100r, Richard Trevithick's steam locomotive, 1804. 200r, George Stephenson's Rocket, 1830. 300r, Stephenson's Locomotion, 1825. 600r, Lafayette, 1837. 800r, Best Friend of Charleston, 1830.
1000r, Stephenson, vert.

1995, Aug. 17
1446-1450 A271 Set of 5   5.00 1.50
Souvenir Sheet
1451 A271 1000r multicolored   3.00 .90
No. 1451 contains one 32x40mm stamp.

World War II Aircraft A272

100r, Bristol Blenheim II, vert. 200r, North American B-25. 300r, Avro Anson. 600r, Avro Manchester. 800r, Consolidated B-24. 1000r, Boeing B-17E.

Perf. 12x12½, 12½x12
1995, Sept. 15
1452-1456 A272 Set of 5   5.00 1.50
Souvenir Sheet
Perf. 12½
1457 A272 1000r multicolored   2.50 .90
No. 1457 contains one 32x40mm stamp.

FAO, 50th Anniv. A273

Designs: 300r, Separating rice plants. 500r, Transplanting rice. 700r, Model rice farm.

1995, Oct. 24   *Perf. 13*
1458-1460 A273 Set of 3   3.00 1.00

UN, 50th Anniv. A274

Designs: 300r, Bridge. 500r, People on bridge. 700r, Central spans of bridge.

1995, Oct. 24   *Perf. 12½*
1461-1463 A274 Set of 3   4.00 1.25

Queen Monineath A275

700r, shown. 800r, King Norodom Sihanouk.

1995, Nov. 9   *Perf. 12½x13*
1464-1465 A275 Set of 2   3.50 1.10

Fish A276

100r, Heniochus acuminatus. 200r, Chelmon rostratus. 400r, Amphiprion percula. 800r, Paracanthurus hepatus. 1000r, Holocanthus ciliaris.
1500r, Coris angulata, vert.

1995, Nov. 19   *Perf. 12½*
1466-1470 A276 Set of 5   6.00 1.50
Souvenir Sheet
1471 A276 1500r multicolored   4.00 1.00

Main Post Office, Cent. A277

Denominations: 300r, 500r, 700r.

1995, Dec. 2   *Perf. 12½*
1472-1474 A277 Set of 3   6.00 1.25

Admission to UN, 40th Anniv. — A278

300r, Independence Monument. 400r, Angkor Wat. 800r, Natl. flag, vert.

Perf. 12½x13, 13x12½
1995, Dec. 14   *Litho.*
1475-1477 A278 Set of 3   5.50 1.25

1996 Summer Olympic Games, Atlanta — A279

Designs: 100r, Tennis. 200r, Volleyball. 300r, Soccer. #1480A, 500r, Running. 900r, Baseball. 1000r, Basketball. 1500r, Windsurfing.

1996, Jan. 10 *Litho.* *Perf. 12½x13*
1478-1482 A279 Set of 6   6.00 1.50
Souvenir Sheet
Perf. 12½
1483 A279 1500r multicolored   3.50 1.00
No. 1483 contains one 32x40mm stamp.

A280

1996, Jan. 30   *Perf. 12½*
1484 A280 50r Kep State Chalet   .20 .20
1485 A280 100r Power station   .20 .20
1486 A280 200r Wheelchair   .30 .20
1487 A280 500r Wheelchair basketball   .60 .20
1488 A280 800r Making crutches, vert.   .85 .25
1489 A280 1000r Kep beach   1.00 .35
1490 A280 1500r Serpent Island   1.75 .45
Nos. 1484-1490 (7)   4.90 1.85

Wild Cats A281

100r, Felis libyca, vert. 200r, Felis silvestris. 300r, Felis caracal. 500r, Felis geoffroyi. 900r, Felis nigripes. 1000r, Felis planiceps.

1996, Feb. 8   *Perf. 13*
1491-1496 A281 Set of 6   6.00 2.00

1998 World Cup Soccer Championships, France — A282

Various soccer players. Denominations: 100r, 200r, 300r, 500r, 900r, 1000r. No. 1502 is horiz.

1996, Mar. 15   *Perf. 13*
1497-1502 A282   Set of 6   6.00 1.50
Souvenir Sheet
1503 A282 1500r multicolored   3.50 1.00
No. 1503 contains one 32x40mm stamp.

Khmer Culture — A283

100r, Tusmukh. 500r, Ream Iso. 900r, Isei.

1996, Apr. 13   Litho.   *Perf. 12½x13*
1504-1506 A283   Set of 3   2.50 .70

Locomotives — A284

100r, Pacific Type. 200r, Unidentified, 1902. 300r, Unidentified, 1930. 500r, Unidentified, 1914. 900r, LMS #6202, 1930. 1000r, Snake, 1864.
1500r, Canadian Pacific.

1996, Apr. 20
1507-1512 A284   Set of 6   4.50 1.50
Souvenir Sheet
1513 A284 1500r multicolored   2.25 .80
No. 1513 contains one 40x32mm stamp.
CAPEX 96 (#1513).

Birds A285

Designs: 100r, Kittacinela malabarica, vert. 200r, Leiothrix lutea. 300r, Parus varius, vert. 500r, Oriolus chinensis. 900r, Cettia diphone. 1000r, Cyanoptila cyanomelana, vert.

1996, May 7
1514-1519 A285   Set of 6   4.50 1.50

Olymphilex '96 — A286

Designs: 100r, Rhythmic gymnastics. 200r, Judo. 300r, High jump. 500r, Wrestling. 900r, Weight lifting. 1000r, Soccer. 1500r, Diving.

1996, June 14   Litho.   *Perf. 13x12½*
1520-1525 A286   Set of 6   3.75 1.25
Souvenir Sheet
Perf. 12½
1526 A286 1500r multicolored   2.10 .75
No. 1526 contains one 32x40mm stamp.

Early Aircraft — A287

100r, Douglas M-2, 1926. 200r, Pitcairn PA-5 Mailwing, 1928. 300r, Boeing 40 B, 1928. 500r, Potez 25, 1925. 900r, Stearman C-3MB, 1927. 1000r, De Havilland DH4, 1918. 1500r, Standard JR-1B, 1918.

1996, July 5   *Perf. 12½x12*
1527-1532 A287   Set of 6   4.50 1.50
Souvenir Sheet
Perf. 13
1533 A287 1500r multicolored   2.75 .90
No. 1533 contains one 40x32mm stamp.

Historic Sites — A288

50r, 100r, 200r, Diff. Apsaras, Tonle Bati. #1537, Statue, Angkor Wat. #1538, Statue of a Goddess. 500r, Carved wall, Tonle Bati. #1540, 1000r, #1543, Various structures, Tonle Bati. #1541, #1544, 1700r, 2500r, 3000r, Various views of Angkor Wat.
Nos. 1539, 1543, 1545-1547 are horiz.

1996-97   Litho.   *Perf. 12½*
1534 A288   50r black & yel org   .20 .20
1535 A288   100r black & blue   .20 .20
1536 A288   200r black & tan   .20 .20
1537 A288   300r blk & light bl   .20 .20
1538 A288   300r black & red   .20 .20
1539 A288   500r blk & bright bl   .30 .20
1540 A288   800r black & yel grn   .40 .20
1541 A288   800r black & yel grn   .40 .20
1542 A288   1000r black & green   .50 .20
1543 A288   1500r black & bister   .75 .25
1544 A288   1500r black & brown   .75 .25
1545 A288   1700r black & org brn   .90 .30
1546 A288   2500r black & blue   1.25 .40
1547 A288   3000r black & dk grn   1.50 .50
   Nos. 1534-1547 (14)   7.75 3.50

Issued: 50r, 100r, 200r, 500r, No. 1540, 1000r, No. 1543, 7/30/96; others, 3/26/97.
See Nos. 1686-1692, 1846-1852.

Dinosaurs — A289

No. 1548: a, 50r, Coelophysis. b, 100r, Euparkeria. c, 150r, Plateosaurus. d, 200r, Herrerasaurus.
No. 1549: a, 250r, Dilophosaurus. b, 300r, Tuojiangosaurus. c, 350r, Camarasaurs. d, 400r, Ceratosaurus.
No. 1550: a, 500r, Spinosaurus. b, 700r, Ouranosaurus. c, 800r, Avimimus. d, 1200r, Deinonychus.

1996, Aug. 8   Litho.   *Perf. 13*
Sheets of 4
1548 A289   #a.-d.   .80 .25
1549 A289   #a.-d.   2.10 .60
1550 A289   #a.-d.   5.25 1.50

Chess Champions A290

100r, José Raul Capablanca. 200r, Alexander Alekhine. 300r, Vassily Smyslov. 500r, Mikhail Tal. 900r, Bobby Fischer. 1000r, Anatoly Karpov. 1500r, Garry Kasparov.

1996, Sept. 10   *Perf. 13*
1551-1556 A290   Set of 6   4.50 1.50
Souvenir Sheet
Perf. 12½
1557 A290 1500r multicolored   2.75 .90
No. 1557 contains one 32x40mm stamp.

Wild Animals A291

Designs: 100r, Ursus arctos. 200r, Panthera leo. 300r, Tapirus indicus. 500r, Camelus ferus. 900r, Capra ibex. 1000r, Zalophus californianus.

1996, Oct. 3   *Perf. 13x12½*
1558-1563 A291   Set of 6   4.25 1.25

Dogs — A292

Designs: 200r, Collie. 300r, Labrador retriever. 500r, Doberman pinscher. 900r, German shepherd. 1000r, Boxer.

1996, Nov. 8   *Perf. 12½x13*
1564-1568 A292   Set of 5   4.25 1.25

Independence — A293

100, 500, 900r, Various water treatment plants.

1996, Nov. 9   *Perf. 13*
1569-1571 A293   Set of 3   3.00 .80

Ships A294

Designs: 200r, Chinese junk. 300r, Galley. 500r, Roman galley. 900r, Clipper ship, 19th cent. 1000r, Paddle steamer Sirius, 1838. 1500r, Great Eastern, 1858.

1996, Dec. 15   *Perf. 12½x13*
1572-1576 A294   Set of 5   4.25 1.25
Souvenir Sheet
Perf. 12½
1577 A294 1500r multicolored   2.75 .90
No. 1577 contains one 40x32mm stamp.

Cambodia's Admission to UPU, 45th Anniv. — A295

Denominations: 200r, 400r, 900r.

1996, Dec. 21   *Perf. 12½*
1578-1580 A295   Set of 3   2.10 .70

New Year 1997 (Year of the Ox) — A296

Paintings of oxen, attributed to Han Huang 723-87): a, Facing left. b, Looking right. c, Brown & white spotted. d, Facing left, head down.

1996, Dec. 28   *Perf. 13x12½*
1581 A296 500r Strip of 4, #a.-d.   + label   2.25 .75

UN Intl. Day of Volunteers — A297

Designs: 100r, Phnom Kaun Sat Dam. 900r, Chrey Krem Dam. 1500r, Angkrung Canal.

1996, Dec. 30
1582-1584 A297   Set of 3   3.25 .80

Greenpeace, 25th Anniv. — A298

Helicopter: 200r, Hovering over cargo. 300r, Hovering over ship. 500r, On helipad. 900r, Lifting cargo.
1000r, Close-up of helicopter.

1996, Dec. 30   *Perf. 12½x13*
1585-1588 A298   Set of 4   5.50 1.75
Souvenir Sheet
Perf. 12½
1589 A298 1000r multicolored   3.00 1.00
No. 1589 contains one 32x40mm stamp.

1998 World Cup Soccer Championships, France — A299

Various soccer plays. Denominations: 100r, 200r, 300r, 500r, 900r, 1000r.

1997, Jan. 6   Litho.   _Perf. 12½x13_
1590-1595 A299 Set of 6   4.50 1.50
Souvenir Sheet
Perf. 13
1596 A299 2000r multicolored   2.75   .90
No. 1596 contains one 40x32mm stamp.

Elephas Maximus — A300

World Wilflife Fund: a, 300r, Two walking. b, 500r, Three standing. c, 900r, Two fighting. d, 1000r, Adult, calf.

1997, Feb. 12   _Perf. 12½x12_
1597 A300 Strip of 4, #a.-d.   4.75 1.00

Birds — A301

600r, Bombycilla garrulus. 900r, Lanius excubitor. 1000r, Passer montanus. 2000r, Phoenicurus phoenicurus. 2500r, Emberiza schoeniclus. 3000r, Emberiza hortulana.

1997, Feb. 20   _Perf. 13x12½_
1598-1603 A301 Set of 6   12.50 4.50
Express mail service.

Fire Fighting Vehicles A302

Designs: 200r, English, 1731. 500r, Putnam, 1863. 900r, Merryweather, 1894. 1000r, Shand Mason Co., 1901. 1500r, Maxim Motor Co., Ford, 1949. 4000r, Merryweather, 1950. 5400r, Mack Truck Co., 1953.

1997, Mar. 11   _Perf. 12½x13_
1604-1609 A302 Set of 6   7.00 1.50
Souvenir Sheet
Perf. 13
1610 A302 5400r multicolored   4.00 1.10
No. 1610 contains one 40x32mm stamp.

Ducks A303

Designs: 200r, Polystieta stelleri. 500r, Alopochen aegyptiacus. 900r, Anas americana. 1000r, Anas falcata. 1500r, Melanitta perspicillata. 4000r, Anas discors. 5400r, Anas formosa, vert.

1997, Apr. 7   _Perf. 12½x13_
1611-1616 A303 Set of 6   4.50 1.50
Souvenir Sheet
Perf. 12½
1617 A303 5400r multicolored   3.25 1.10
No. 1617 contains one 32x40mm stamp.

Heinrich Von Stephan (1831-1897), Founder of UPU — A304

Denominations: 500r, 1500r, 2000r.

1997, Apr. 8   _Perf. 12½x13_
1618-1620 A304 Set of 3   3.25   .85

Khmer Culture — A305

Various views of Bantea Srei Temple. Denominations: 500r, 1500r, 2000r.

1997, Apr. 13   _Perf. 13x12½_
1621-1623 A305 Set of 3   3.25   .85

Cats — A306

Designs: 200r, Birman. 500r, Exotic short-hair. 900r, Persian. 1000r, Turkish. 1500r, American short-hair. 4000r, Scottish fold. 5400r, Sphinx.

1997, May 8   _Perf. 13x12½_
1624-1629 A306 Set of 6   11.00 2.00
Souvenir Sheet
Perf. 13
1630 A306 5400r multicolored   4.00 1.10
No. 1630 contains one 32x40mm stamp.

Trains A307

200r, 4-4-2T, #488. 500r, Frederick Smith 4-6-0. 900r, 0-8-0, #3131. 1000r, Transport #1, London #L44, 0-4-4. 1500r, 0-6-2, #1711. 4000r, 4-6-2, #60523. 5400r, North Yorkshire Moor (K1), 2-6-0, #2005.

1997, Jun 9   _Perf. 12½x12_
1631-1636 A307 Set of 6   4.75 1.50
Souvenir Sheet
Perf. 13
1637 A307 5400r multicolored   3.25 1.00
No. 1637 contains one 40x32mm stamp.

Dogs A308

Designs: 200r, Shar-pei. 500r, Tchin-tchin. 900r, Pekinese. 1000r, Chow-chow, vert. 1500r, Pug, vert. 4000r, Akita, vert. 5400r, Tufted Chinese, vert.

1997, July 4   _Perf. 12½x13, 13x12½_
1638-1643 A308 Set of 6   4.50 1.50
Souvenir Sheet
Perf. 12½
1644 A308 5400r multicolored   3.50 1.25
No. 1644 contains one 32x40mm stamp.

ASEAN, 30th Anniv. A309

Designs: 500r, Dunalom Wat. 1500r, Royal Palace. 2000r, Natl. Museum.

1997, Aug. 5   _Perf. 12½x13_
1645-1647 A309 Set of 3   3.00   .75

Ships A310

Designs: 200r, Caravelle, 15th cent. 500r, Spanish galleon, 16th cent. 900r, Galleon "Great Harry," 16th cent. 1000r, Galleon "Le Couronne," 17th cent. 1500r, Cargo ship, 18th cent. 4000r, Clipper ship, 19th cent. 5400r, HMS Victory.

1997, Sept. 10   _Perf. 12½x12_
1648-1653 A310 Set of 6   4.75 1.50
Souvenir Sheet
Perf. 13
1654 A310 5400r multicolored   3.25 1.10
No. 1654 contains one 40x32mm stamp.

A311

#1655-1658, Various public gardens. #1659-1661, Various dams. #1657 is vert.

1997, Sept. 30   _Perf. 12½_
1655 A311 300r black & yel grn   .25   .20
1656 A311 300r black & red   .25   .20
1657 A311 800r black & citron   .50   .20
1658 A311 1500r black & org brn   .90   .30
1659 A311 1700r blk & red brn   1.10   .35
1660 A311 2500r blk & grn bl   1.50   .50
1661 A311 3000r black & blue   1.75   .65
        Nos. 1655-1661 (7)   6.25 2.40

Mushrooms A312

Designs: 200r, Boletus satanas. 500r, Amanita regalis. 900r, Morchella semilibera. 1000r, Gomphus clavatus. 1500r, Hygrophorus hypothejus. 4000r, Albatrellus confluens. 5400r, Boletus chrysenteron.

1997, Oct. 5   _Perf. 12½x13_
1662-1667 A312 Set of 6   4.75 1.50
Souvenir Sheet
Perf. 12½
1668 A312 5400r multicolored   3.25 1.10
No. 1668 contains one 40x32mm stamp.

Fish A313

200r, Betta imbellis. 500r, Colisa fasciata. 900r, Puntius conchonius. 1000r, Macropodus concolor. 1500r, Epalzeorhynchos frenatus. 4000r, Capoeta tetrazona. 5400r, Rasbora heteromorpha.

1997, Nov. 8   _Perf. 12½x13_
1669-1674 A313 Set of 6   4.75 1.50
Souvenir Sheet
Perf. 13
1675 A313 5400r multicolored   3.25 1.00
No. 1675 contains one 40x32mm stamp.

Independence, 44th Anniv. — A314

Post Offices: 1000r, Kampot. 3000r, Prey Veng.

1997, Nov. 9   _Perf. 13_
1676-1677 A314 Set of 2   2.50   .70

Orchids — A315

200r, Orchis milicaris. 500r, Orchiaceras bivonae. 900r, Orchiaceras spuria. 1000r, Gymnadenia conopsea. 1500r, Serapias neglecta. 4000r, Pseudorhiza bruniana. 5400r, Dactylodenia wintonii.

1997, Dec. 12   _Perf. 13_
1678-1683 A315 Set of 6   10.00 2.00
Souvenir Sheet
1684 A315 5400r multicolored   4.75 1.10
No. 1684 contains one 32x40mm stamp.

Princess Diana (1961-97) A316

Designs: a, 100r, In dark blue jacket. b, 200r, In black dress. c, 300r, Holding hand to throat. d, 500r, Wearing face shield. e, 1000r, Watching mine clearing operation. f, 1500r, With Elizabeth Dole. g, 2000r, Holding land mine. h, 2500r, With members of Mother Teresa's Order.

1997, Dec. 30   _Perf. 12x12½_
1685 A316 Sheet of 8, #a.-h. +
            label   7.00 1.90

Historic Sites Type of 1996-97

Temples: 300r, Prasat Suorprat. 500r, Preah Kumlung, horiz. 1200r, Prasat Bapuon, horiz. 1500r, Palilai. 1700r, Prasat Prerup, horiz. 2000r, Prasat Preah Khan, horiz. 3000r, Prasat Bayon.

1998		Litho.		Perf. 12½
1686	A288	300r black & orange	.20	.20
1687	A288	500r black & pink	.30	.20
1688	A288	1200r black & buff	.70	.25
1689	A288	1500r black & buff	.90	.30
1690	A288	1700r black & blue	1.00	.35
1691	A288	2000r black & green	1.25	.45
1692	A288	3000r black & violet	1.75	.65
	Nos. 1686-1692 (7)		6.10	2.40

New Year 1998 (Year of the Tiger) A317

Various pictures of panthera tigris: 200r, vert., 500r, vert., 900r, vert., 1000r, 1500r, 4000r.
5400r, Tiger, vert.

1998				Perf. 13
1693-1698	A317	Set of 6	4.75	1.50

Souvenir Sheet
Perf. 12½

| 1699 | A317 | 5400r multicolored | 3.25 | 1.00 |

No. 1699 contains one 32x40mm stamp.

1998 World Cup Soccer Championships, France — A318

Designs showing portion of soccer player at left, various plays at right, stadium: 200r, 500r, 900r, 1000r, 1500r, 4000r.
5400r, Two players kicking ball.

1998				Perf. 13
1700-1705	A318	Set of 6	4.75	1.50

Souvenir Sheet

| 1706 | A318 | 5400r multicolored | 3.25 | 1.00 |

No. 1706 contains one 40x32mm stamp.

Domestic Cats A319

Designs: 200r, Scottish fold. 500r, Ragdoll. 900r, Welsh. 1000r, Devon rex. 1500r, American curl. 4000r, Sphinx.
5400r, Japanese bobtail.

1998				
1707-1712	A319	Set of 6	4.75	1.50

Souvenir Sheet

| 1713 | A319 | 5400r multi | 3.25 | 1.00 |

No. 1713 contains one 40x32mm stamp.

Italia '98, Intl. Philatelic Exhibition A320

Paintings: 200r, Baptism of Christ from triptych, Jean de Trompes, by Gerard David. 500r, The Virgin of Martin van Niuwenhoven, by Hans Memling. 900r, Baptism of Christ, by Hendrich Goltzius. 1000r, Christ Carrying the Cross, by Luis de Morales. 1500r, Angel in the

Desert, by Dirk Bouts. 4000r, The Virgin, by Petrus Christus.
5400r, The Immaculate Conception, by Bartolomé Esteban Murillo.

1998		Litho.		Perf. 12½x13
1714-1719	A320	Set of 6	4.75	1.50

Souvenir Sheet
Perf. 12½

| 1720 | A320 | 5400r multicolored | 3.25 | 1.00 |

No. 1720 contains one 40x32mm stamp.

Butterflies — A321

200r, Phyciodes tharos. 500r, Pararge mergera. 900r, Danaus plexippus. 1000r, Parnassius apollo. 1500r, Papilio machaon. 4000r, Eumenis semele.
5400r, Morpho rhetenor.

1998				Perf. 12½
1721-1726	A321	Set of 6	5.00	1.50

Souvenir Sheet

| 1727 | A321 | 5400r multicolored | 3.25 | 1.00 |

No. 1727 contains one 40x32mm stamp.

Mail Boxes — A322

Designs: 1000r, 1997. 3000r, 1951.

1998		Litho.		Perf. 13
1728-1729	A322	Set of 2	2.40	.85

Trains — A323

#1730a, 200r, Oakland, Antioch & Eastern. #1730b, 500r, New York, Westchester & Boston. #1731a, 900r, Spokane & Inland. #1731b, 1000r, International Railway. #1732a, 1500r, British columbia Electric Railway. #1732b, 4000r, Southern Pacific.
5400r, Storage battery locomotive.

1998, Mar. 2		Litho.		Perf. 12½
1730-1732	A323	Set of 3 pairs, #a.-b.	5.00	1.50

Souvenir Sheet

| 1733 | A323 | 5400r multicolored | 3.50 | 1.25 |

Dogs — A324

200r, Rottweiler. 500r, Beauceron. 900r, Boxer. 1000r, Siberian husky. 1500r, Welsh corgi (Pembroke). 4000r, Basset hound.
5400r, Schnauzer.

1998, Mar. 30		Litho.		Perf. 12¼
1734-1739	A324	Set of 6	4.75	1.50

Souvenir Sheet
Perf. 12½

| 1740 | A324 | 5400r multicolored | 3.25 | 1.00 |

Insects A325

200r, Lucanus cervus. 500r, Carabus auronitens. 900r, Rosalia alpina. 1000r, Geotrupes. 1500r, Megasoma elephas. 4000r, Chalcosoma.
5400r, Leptura rubra.

1998, Apr. 10		Litho.		Perf. 12½
1741-1746	A325	Set of 6	5.00	1.50

Souvenir Sheet

| 1747 | A325 | 5400r multicolored | 3.50 | 1.25 |

Khmer Culture A326

Designs: 500r, Prasat Prerup. 1500r, Prasat Bayon. 2000r, Angkor Wat.

1998, Apr. 13				Perf. 12¾
1748-1750	A326	Set of 3	3.25	1.10

Historic Ships A327

200r, Cutter. 500r, Steamship "Britannia." 900r, Viking ship. 1000r, Steamship "Great Britain." 1500r, Coaster. 4000r, Frigate.
5400r, Tartan.

1998, May 7		Litho.		Perf. 12¾
1751-1756	A327	Set of 6	4.75	1.50

Souvenir Sheet
Perf. 13

| 1757 | A327 | 5400r multicolored | 3.25 | 1.00 |

No. 1757 contains one 40x32mm stamp.

Turtles A329

200r, Platysternon megacephalum. 500r, Chelonia mydas. 900r, Trionyx spiniferus. 1000r, Eretmochelys imbricata. 1500r, Megalochelys gigantea. 4000r, Dermochelys coriacea.

1998, Nov. 8		Litho.		Perf. 12¾
1765-1770	A329	Set of 6	4.75	1.50

Souvenir Sheet
Perf. 13x13¼

| 1771 | A329 | 5400r Chelus fimbriatus | 3.25 | 1.00 |

No. 1771 contains one 40x32mm stamp.

Independence, 45th Anniv. — A330

Various dancers: 500r, 1500r, 2000r.

1998, Nov. 9		Litho.		Perf. 12½x12¼
1772-1774	A330	Set of 3	2.40	.85

Gemstones A331

Designs: 200r, Aquamarine. 500r, Cat's eye. 900r, Malachite. 1000r, Emerald. 1500r, Turquoise. 4000r, Ruby.
5400r, Diamond, horiz.

1998, Dec. 28		Litho.		Perf. 12¾
1775-1780	A331	Set of 6	4.75	1.50

Souvenir Sheet
Perf. 13

| 1781 | A331 | 5400r multi | 3.25 | 1.00 |

No. 1781 contains one 40x32mm stamp.

Wild Cats A332

Designs: 200r, Acinonyx juabatus. 500r, Panthera uncia. 900r, Felis pardalis. 1000r, Panthera pardus. 1500r, Felis serval. 4000r, Panthera onca.
5400r, Panthera tigris.

1998		Litho.		Perf. 12½x12¼
1782-1787	A332	Set of 6	4.75	1.50

Souvenir Sheet
Perf. 13

| 1788 | A332 | 5400r multi | 3.25 | 1.00 |

No. 1788 contains one 32x40mm stamp.

Flowers — A328

200r, Petasites japonica. 500r, Gentiana triflora. 900r, Doronicum cordatum. 1000r, Scabiosa japonica. 1500r, Magnolia sieboldii. 4000r, Erythronium japonica.
5400r, Callistephus chinensis.

1998		Litho.		Perf. 12¾
1758-1763	A328	Set of 6	4.75	1.50

Souvenir Sheet
Perf. 13

| 1764 | A328 | 5400r multicolored | 3.25 | 1.00 |

No. 1764 contains one 32x40mm stamp.

New Year 1999 (Year of the Rabbit) A333

Various rabbits: 200r, 500r, 900r, 1000r, 1500r, 4000r. 4000r is vert.

1999, Jan. 5   Litho.   Perf. 12¾
1790-1795   A333   Set of 6   4.75 1.50

Souvenir Sheet
Perf. 13
1796   A333   5400r   Rabbit, diff.   3.25 1.00
No. 1796 contains one 40x32mm stamp.

Trains — A334

Designs: 200r, Stourbridge Lion. 500r, Atlantic. 900r, 035. 100r, Iron Duke. 1500r, 4-6-0. 4000r, 4-4-2.

Perf. 12½x12¼
1999, Nov. 20   Litho.
1797-1802   A334   Set of 6   4.75 1.50

Souvenir Sheet
Perf. 12½
1803   A334   5400r   Firefly   3.25 1.00
No. 1803 contains one 40x32mm stamp.

Dogs A335

Designs: 200r, Shiba inu, vert. 500r, Shih tzu. 900r, Tibetan spaniel. 1000r, Ainu, vert. 1500r, Lhasa apso. 4000r, Tibetan terrier.

Perf. 12¼x12½ (200, 1000r), 12¾
1999, Feb. 3   Litho.
1804-1809   A335   Set of 6   5.00 1.50

Souvenir Sheet
Perf. 12½
1810   A335   5400r   Tosa inu, vert. 3.25 1.00
Size of Nos. 1804, 1807: 48x30mm. No. 1810 contains one 32x40mm stamp.

Antique Automobiles — A336

Designs: 200r, 1881 La Rapide. 500r, 1895 Duryea. 900r, 1898 Barbarou. 1000r, 1898 Panhard. 1500r, 1901 Mercedes-Benz. 4000r, 1915 Ford.
5400r, 1875 Siegfried Marcus.

1999, Mar. 5   Litho.   Perf. 13x12¾
1811-1816   A336   Set of 6   4.75 1.50

Souvenir Sheet
Perf. 13
1817   A336   5400r   multi   3.25 1.00
No. 1817 contains one 40x32mm stamp.

Cats — A337

Designs: 200r, Ragdoll. 500r, Russian blue. 900r, Bombay. 1000r, Snowshoe. 1500r, Oriental. 4000r, Somali.

1999, Mar. 30   Litho.   Perf. 13
1818-1823   A337   Set of 6   5.00 1.50

Souvenir Sheet
1824   A337   5400r   Egyptian mau   3.25 1.00
No. 1824 contains one 32x40mm stamp.

Butterflies A338

Designs: 200r, Araschnia levana. 500r, Vanessa cardui, horiz. 900r, Clossiana euphrosyne. 1000r, Coenonympha hero. 1500r, Parnassius apollo, horiz. 4000r, Plebejus argus.
5400r, Palaeochrysophanus hippothoe.

1999, Apr. 25   Perf. 12¾
1825-1830   A338   Set of 6   5.00 1.50

Souvenir Sheet
Perf. 12½
1831   A338   5400r   multi   3.25 1.00
No. 1831 contains one 32x40mm stamp.

Dinosaurs — A339

Designs: 200r, Saurornitholestes. 500r, Prenocephalus. 900r, Wuerhosaurus. 1000r, Muttaburrasaurus. 1500r, Shantungosaurus. 4000r, Microceratops.
5400r, Daspletosaurus.

1999, May 10   Litho.   Perf. 12¾
1832-1837   A339   Set of 6   4.75 1.50

Souvenir Sheet
Perf. 13
1838   A339   5400r   multi   3.25 1.00
No. 1838 contains one 40x32mm stamp.

Molluscs A340

Designs: 200r, Flabellina affinis. 500r, Octopus macropus. 900r, Helix hortensis. 1000r, Lima hians. 1500r, Arion empiricorum. 4000r, Anodonta cygnaea.
5400r, Eledone aldrovandii.

1999, May 31   Litho.   Perf. 12¾
1839-1844   A340   Set of 6   4.75 1.50

Souvenir Sheet
Perf. 12½
1845   A340   5400r   multi   3.25 1.00
No. 1845 contains one 32x40mm stamp.

Historic Sites Type of 1996-97
Designs: 100r, Prasat Neak Poan, horiz. 300r, Statue, Prasat Neak Poan, horiz. 500r, Prasat Banteay Srey. 1400r, Prasat Banteay Samré, horiz. 1600r, Prasat Banteay Srey, horiz. 1800r, Bas-relief, Angkor Wat. 1900r, Prasat Takeo, horiz.

1999   Litho.   Perf. 12½
Vignette Colors
1846   A288   100r   blue   .20   .20
1847   A288   300r   red   .20   .20
1848   A288   500r   olive green   .25   .20
1849   A288   1400r bright green   .85   .30
1850   A288   1600r pink   .95   .30
1851   A288   1800r violet   1.10   .35
1852   A288   1900r brown   1.10   .45
       Nos. 1846-1852 (7)   4.65 2.00

Khmer Culture A341

Designs: 500r, Dragon Bridge. 1500r, Temple with 100 columns, Kratie. 2000r, Krapum Chhouk stupa, Kratie.

1999, Apr. 13   Perf. 13
1853-1855   A341   Set of 3   2.40   .85

UPU, 125th Anniv. A342

1999   Litho.   Perf. 12½x12¼
1856   A342   1600r   multi   1.00   .30

Independence — A343

People and: 500r, Map. 1500r, Ship, airplane, dove, public works. 2000r, Buildings.

1999, Nov. 9   Perf. 12½
1857-1859   A343   Set of 3   2.40   .85

Snakes A344

Designs: 200r, Aspidelaps lubricus. 500r, Epicrates cenchria. 900r, Eunectes notaeus. 1000r, Diadophus punctatus. 1500r, Micrurus fulvius. 4000r, Telescopus semiannulatus.
5400r, Chondropython viridis.

1999, Dec. 6   Perf. 12¾
1860-1865   A344   Set of 6   4.75 1.50

Souvenir Sheet
Perf. 13
1866   A344   5400r   multi   3.25 1.00
No. 1866 contains one 39x31mm stamp.

Birds of Prey A345

Designs: 200r, Harpia harpyja. 500r, Terthopius ecaudatus, vert. 900r, Neophron pernopterus, vert. 1000r, Falco peregrinus, vert. 1500r, Buteo jamaicensis, vert. 4000r, Haliaetus leucocephalus.
5400r, Milvus milvus.

1999, Oct. 5   Litho.   Perf. 12¾
1867-1872   A345   Set of 6   4.75 1.50

Souvenir Sheet
Perf. 12½
1873   A345   5400r   multi   3.25 1.00
No. 1873 contains one 31x39mm stamp.

Philex France 99 — A346

Still life paintings by: 200r, Henri Fantin-Latour. 500r, Paul Cézanne. 900r, André Derain. 1000r, Henri Matisse. 1500r, Othon Friesz. 4000r, Matisse, diff.
5400r, Cézanne, diff.

1999, June 10   Litho.   Perf. 12½
1874-1879   A346   Set of 6   4.75 1.50

Souvenir Sheet
Perf. 13
1880   A346   5400r   multi   3.25 1.00

Souvenir Sheet

China 1999 World Philatelic Exhibition — A347

Pagodas: a, 200r, Tongzhou. b, 500r, Tianing Temple. c, 900r, Summer Palace. d, 900r, Temple of the Clouds. e, 1000r, Bei Hai. f, 1000r, Perfumed Hill. g, 1500r, Yunju. h, 4000r, Miaoying Temple.

Perf. 12¼x12½
1999, Aug. 12   Litho.
1881   A347   Sheet of 8, #a-h, +
              label   6.00 2.00

Orchids A348

Designs: 200r, Cymbidium insigne. 500r, Papillonanthe teres. 900r, Panisea uniflora. 1000r, Euanthe sanderiana. 1500r, Dendrobium trigonopus. 4000r, Vanda coerulea. 5400r, Paphiopedilum callosum.

1999, Aug. 5   Litho.   Perf. 12¾
1889-1894 A348   Set of 6   4.75 1.50
Souvenir Sheet
Perf. 12½
1895 A348 5400r multi   3.25 1.00
No. 1895 contains one 32x40mm stamp.

Birds
A349

Designs: 200r, Pyrrhula pyrrhula. 500r, Coccothraustes coccothraustes. 900r, Carduelis chloris. 1000r, Dendroica petechia. 1500r, Lanius excubitor. 4000r, Parus caeruleus. 5400r, Erithacus rubecula.

1999, Sept. 5   Litho.   Perf. 12¾
1896-1901 A349   Set of 6   4.75 1.50
Souvenir Sheet
Perf. 13
1902 A349 5400r multi   3.25 1.00
No. 1902 contains one 40x32mm stamp.

Fish
A350

Designs: 200r, Capoeta tetrazona. 500r, Epalzeorhynchus frenatus. 900r, Rasbora kalochroma. 1000r, Etroplus maculatus. 1500r, Betta imbellis. 4000r, Colisa sota. 5400r, Tetraodon biocellatus.

Perf. 12½x12¼
1999, Sept. 20   Litho.
1903-1908 A350   Set of 6   5.00 1.50
Souvenir Sheet
Perf. 13
1909 A350 5400r multi   3.25 1.00
No. 1909 contains one 40x32mm stamp.

Wildlife — A351

Designs: 200r, Ailuropada melanoleuca. 500r, Bos mutus. 900r, Hydropotes inermis. 1000r, Neomys fodiens, horiz. 1500r, Lutra lutra, horiz. 4000r, Panthera tigris, horiz. 5400r, Elaphurus davidianus, vert.

1999, Nov. 20   Litho.   Perf. 12¾
1910-1915 A351   Set of 6   4.75 1.50
Souvenir Sheet
Perf. 12½
1916 A351 5400r multi   3.25 1.00
No. 1916 contains one 32x40mm stamp.

Bangkok 2000 Stamp
Exhibition — A352

Turtle-shaped objects and turtles: 200r, Cuora amboinensis, vert. 500r, Cuora flavomarginata, vert. 900r, Geoemyda spengleri. 1000r, Manouria impressa. 1500r, Chinemys reevesi. 4000r, Heosemys spinosa. 4500r, Hieremys annandalei.

2000, Feb. 27   Perf. 12¾
1917-1922 A352   Set of 6   5.00 1.50
Souvenir Sheet
Perf. 13
1923 A352 4500r multi   3.00 .75
No. 1923 contains one 40x32mm stamp.

Dinosaurs — A353

Designs: 200r, Iguanodon. 500r, Euoplocephalus. 900r, Dilophosaurus. 1000r, Diplodocus. 1500r, Stegoceras. 4000r, Stegosaurus.
4500r, Brachiosaurus, vert.
Illustration reduced.

2000, Jan. 30   Litho.   Perf. 12½x12¼
1924-1929 A353   Set of 6   4.75 1.50
Souvenir Sheet
Perf. 12½
1930 A353 4500r multi   3.00 .75
No. 1930 contains one 32x40mm stamp.

Beetles
A354

Designs: 200r, Calosoma sycophanta. 500r, Oryctes nasicornis. 900r, Diochrysa fastuosa. 1000r, Blaps gigas. 1500r, Cincindela campestris. 4000r, Cissistes cephalotes. 4500r, Scarabeus aegyptiorum.

2000, Feb. 5   Litho.   Perf. 12¾
1931-1936 A354   Set of 6   5.00 1.50
Souvenir Sheet
Perf. 13
1937 A354 4500r multi   2.75 .75
No. 1937 contains one 40x32mm stamp.

New Year 2000
(Year of the
Dragon) — A355

Various dragons. Denominations: 200r, 500r, 900r, 1000r, 1500r, 4000r.

2000, Jan. 20   Litho.   Perf. 12¼x12½
1938-1943 A355   Set of 6   4.75 1.50
Souvenir Sheet
Perf. 13
1944 A355 4500r multi   2.75 .75
No. 1944 contains one 32x40mm stamp.

Bettas — A356

Designs: 200r, Unimaculata, Pugnax. 500r, Macrostoma, Taeniata. 900r, Foerschi, Imbellis. 1000r, Tessyae, Picta. 1500r, Edithae, Bellica. 4000r, Smaragdina.
4500r, Splendens.
Illustration reduced.

2000, Apr. 10   Litho.   Perf. 12½x12¼
1945-1950 A356   Set of 6   4.75 1.50
Souvenir Sheet
Perf. 13
1951 A356 4500r multi   2.75 .75
No. 1951 contains one 40x32mm stamp.

Mushrooms
A357

Designs: 200r, Amanita muscaria. 500r, Amanita pantherina. 900r, Clitocybe oleana. 1000r, Lactarius scrobiculatus. 1500r, Scleroderma vulgare. 4000r, Amanita verna. 4500r, Amanita phalloides.

2000, Mar. 20   Litho.   Perf. 12¾
1952-1957 A357   Set of 6   4.75 1.50
Souvenir Sheet
Perf. 13
1958 A357 4500r multi   2.75 .75
No. 1958 contains one 32x40mm stamp.

Khmer
Culture — A358

Designs: 500r, Srei Snam. 1500r, Srei Snam, diff. 2000r, Srei Krub Lakhna,

2000, Apr. 13   Litho.   Perf. 13
1959-1961 A358   Set of 3   2.40 .85

Growing
Rice — A359

Designs: 100r, Transporting seedlings. 300r, Harrowing. 500r, Threshing. 1400r, Winnowing. 1600r, Transplanting. 1900r, Plowing. 2200r, Harvesting.

2000   Perf. 12¼x12½
Vignette Color
1962 A359 100r brt yel grn   .20 .20
1963 A359 300r brt blue   .20 .20
1964 A359 500r brt pink   .30 .20
1965 A359 1400r brn orange   .85 .25
1966 A359 1600r dull blue   .95 .30
1967 A359 1900r bister brn   1.10 .35
1968 A359 2200r red   1.25 .40
    Nos. 1962-1968 (7)   4.85 1.90

Locomotives — A360

Designs: 200r, Jules Petiet. 500r, Longue Chaudiere. 900r, Les Grand Chocolats. 1000r, Glehn du Bousquet. 1500r, Le Pendule Français. 4000r, TGV 001.
4500r, Le Shuttle.

2000, Mar. 5   Litho.   Perf. 12½x12¼
1969-1974 A360   Set of 6   4.75 1.50
Souvenir Sheet
Perf. 13
1975 A360 4500r multi   2.75 .75
WIPA 2000 Philatelic Exhibition, Vienna (#1975). No. 1975 contains one 80x32mm stamp.

Birds
A361

Designs: 200r, Diomedea irrorata. 500r, Charadrius alexandrinus, vert. 900r, Sula nebouxii. 1000r, Sterna hirundo. 1500r, Larus argentatus, vert. 4000r, Chlidonia hybrida. 4500r, Sula bassana.

2000, May 8   Perf. 12¾
1976-1981 A361   Set of 6   4.75 1.50
Souvenir Sheet
Perf. 13
1982 A361 4500r multi   2.75 .75
No. 1982 contains one 40x32mm stamp.

Orchids — A362

Designs: 200r, Cypripedium macranthum. 500r, Vandopsis gigantea. 900r, Calypso bulbosa. 1000r, Vanda luzonica. 1500r, Paphiopedilum villosum. 4000r, Vanda merrillii. 4500r, Paphiopedilum victoria.

2000, May 30   Perf. 12¾
1983-1988 A362   Set of 6   4.75 1.50
Souvenir Sheet
Perf. 13
1989 A362 4500r multi   2.75 .75
No. 1989 contains one 32x40mm stamp.

Children's Stories — A363

Designs: 200r, The Courageous Little Tailor, vert. 500r, Tom Thumb, vert. 900r, Thumbelina, vert. 1000r, Pinocchio. 1500r, The Crayfish. 4000r, Peter Pan.
4500r, The Pied Piper, vert.

2000   **Litho.**   *Perf. 12¾*
1990-1995   A363   Set of 6   4.75   4.75
Souvenir Sheet
Perf. 12½
1996   A363   4500r multi   2.75   2.75
No. 1996 contains one 32x40mm stamp.

Water Festival and Tourism — A364

Designs: 500r, Men rowing canoe. 1500r, Men at canoe prow. 2000r, Temples, elephant, woman.

2000, June 1   **Litho.**   *Perf. 13*
1997-1999   A364   Set of 3   2.40   2.40

Fire Trucks — A365

Designs: 200r, Metz DLK 23-6. 500r, Iveco-Magirus SLF24/100. 900r, Metz SLF 7000 WS. 1000r, Iveco-Magirus TLF 24/50. 1500r, Saval-Kronenburg RFF 11000. 4000r, Metz TLF 24/50.
4500r, Metz TLF 16/25.

2000, July 30   *Perf. 12¾*
2000-2005   A365   Set of 6   4.75   4.75
Souvenir Sheet
Perf. 13
2006   A365   4500r multi   2.75   2.75
No. 2006 contains one 40x32mm stamp.

Independence, 47th Anniv. — A366

Flag, temple and: 500r, Flowers. 1500r, Dove. 2000r, People carrying torch.

2000, Nov. 9   *Perf. 12¾*
2007-2009   A366   Set of 3   2.40   2.40

Antique Automobiles — A367

Designs: 200r, 1912 Rover 12C. 500r, 1907, Austin 30CV. 900r, 1909 Rolls-Royce Silver Ghost. 1000r, 1929 Graham Paige Phaeton DC. 1500r, 1937 Austin 12. 4000r, 1957 Mercedes-Benz 300SL.
4500r, 1936 MG.

2000   *Perf. 12¾*
2010-2015   A367   Set of 6   4.75   4.75
Souvenir Sheet
Perf. 13
2016   A367   4500r multi   2.75   2.75
España 2000 Intl. Philatelic Exhibition (#2016). No. 2016 contains one 40x32mm stamp.

Dachshunds — A368

Designs: 200r, Smooth-haired dachshund. 500r, Wire-haired dachshund. 900r, Long-haired dachshund. 1000r, Two dachshunds. 1500r, Dachshund with pups. 4000r, Dachshunds resting.
4500r, Wire-haired dachshund, vert.

2000   *Perf. 13*
2017-2022   A368   Set of 6   4.75   4.75
Souvenir Sheet
Perf. 12½
2023   A368   4500r multi   2.75   2.75
No. 2023 contains one 32x40mm stamp.

Cats and Art — A369

Cat or cats and: 200r, Korean silk painting, 18th cent. 500r, Portuguese tile, 18th cent. 900r, Japanese ceramic cat. 1000r, Egyptian metallic cat. 1500r, Scandinavian engraving. 4000r, Japanese painting.
4500r, Cat on hind legs.

2000   *Perf. 12½x12¼*
2024-2029   A369   Set of 6   4.75   4.75
Souvenir Sheet
Perf. 13x13¼
2030   A369   4500r multi   2.75   2.75
No. 2030 contains one 40x32mm stamp.

Birds — A370

Designs: 200r, Creatophora cinerea. 500r, Sturnus vulgaris. 900r, Leiothrix lutea. 1000r, Rupicola rupicola. 1500r, Prunella collaris. 4000r, Panurus biarnicus.
4500r, Muscicapula pallipes, vert.

2000   *Perf. 13*
2031-2036   A370   Set of 6   4.75   4.75
Souvenir Sheet
2037   A370   4500r multi   2.75   2.75
No. 2037 contains one 32x40mm stamp.

Sports — A371

Designs: 200r, Weight lifting. 500r, Rhythmic gymnastics. 900r, Baseball. 1000r, Women's tennis. 1500r, Basketball. 4000r, Women's high jump.

2000   **Litho.**   *Perf. 12¾, 12½ (#2044)*
2038-2043   A371   Set of 6   4.75   4.75
Souvenir Sheet
2044   A371   4500r Runners   2.75   2.75
No. 2044 contains one 32x40mm stamp.

New Year 2001 (Year of the Snake) — A372

Various stylized snakes with background colors of: 200r, Beige. 500r, Dull bister. 900r, Light blue. 1000r, Greenish blue. 1500r, Dull green. 4000r, Blue.
5400r, Blue, horiz.

2001, Jan. 15   **Litho.**   *Perf. 12¼x12½*
2045-2050   A372   Set of 6   4.75   4.75
Souvenir Sheet
Perf. 13x13¼
2051   A372   5400r multi   3.25   3.25
No. 2051 contains one 40x32mm stamp.

Millennium — A373

Designs: 200r, Johannes Gutenberg, printers. 500r, Michael Faraday, electric motor. 900r, Samuel F. B. Morse, telegraph. 1000r, Alexander Graham Bell, telephone. 1500r, Enrico Fermi, nuclear energy. 4000r, Edward Roberts, computer.
No. 2058: a, Christopher Columbus, ships. b, Neil Armstrong, lunar module.

2001   **Litho.**   *Perf. 12¾*
2052-2057   A373   Set of 6   4.75   4.75
Souvenir Sheet
Perf. 12½
2058   A373   5400r Sheet of 2, #a-
     b + label   6.50   6.50
No. 2058 contains two 40x32mm stamps.

Fire and Rescue Equipment — A374

Designs: 200r, 1910 Sandou ladder wagon. 500r, 1899 Gallo cart. 900r, Merryweather pumper, 1950s. 1000r, 1940 Merryweather ambulance. 1500r, 1972 Man-Metz pumper. 4000r, Roman Diesel pumper, 1970s.
5400r, 1898 Metropolitan steam pumper.

2001   *Perf. 12¾*
2059-2064   A374   Set of 6   4.75   4.75
Souvenir Sheet
Perf. 13x13¼
2065   A374   5400r multi   3.25   3.25
No. 2065 contains one 40x32mm stamp.

Mushrooms — A375

Designs: 200r, Lycoperdon perlatum. 500r, Trametes versicolor. 900r, Hipholoma sublateritium. 1000r, Amanita muscaria. 1500r, Lycoperdon umbrinum. 4000r, Cortinarius orellanus.
5400r Amanita phalloides, vert.

2001   *Perf. 12¾*
2066-2071   A375   Set of 6   4.75   4.75
Souvenir Sheet
Perf. 12½
2072   A375   5400r multi   3.25   3.25
No. 2072 contains one 32x40mm stamp.

Belgica 2001 Intl. Stamp Exhibition, Brussels — A376

Butterflies: 200r, Nymphalis polychloros. 500r, Cethosia hypsea. 900r, Papilio palinurus. 1000r, Apatura ilia. 1500r, Parthenos sylvia. 4000r, Morpho grandensis.
5400r, Heliconius melpomene.

2001   *Perf. 12¾*
2073-2078   A376   Set of 6   4.75   4.75
Souvenir Sheet
Perf. 13x13¼
2079   A376   5400r multi   3.25   3.25

Film Personalities — A377

Designs: 200r, Gary Cooper. 500r, Marlene Dietrich. 900r, Walt Disney. 1000r, Clark Gable. 1500r, Jeanette MacDonald. 4000r, Melvyn Douglas.
No. 2086: a, Rudolph Valentino. b, Marilyn Monroe.

2001   **Litho.**   *Perf. 12¾*
2080   A377   200r multi   .20   .20
2081   A377   500r multi   .30   .30
2082   A377   900r multi   .55   .55
2083   A377   1000r multi   .60   .60
2084   A377   1500r multi   .90   .90
2085   A377   4000r multi   2.40   2.40
   Nos. 2080-2085 (6)   4.95   4.95
Souvenir Sheet
Perf. 13
2086   A377   5400r Sheet of 2,
     #a-b   6.50   6.50

Natl. Culture Day — A378

Sculptures: 500r, Angkor. 1500r, Bayon. 2000r, Bayon, diff.

2001   **Litho.**   *Perf. 12¾*
2087-2089   A378   Set of 3   2.40   2.40

Temples — A379

Designs: 200r, Preah Vihear. 300r, Thonmanom. 600r, Tasom. 1000r, Kravan. 1500r, Takeo. 1700r, Mebon. 2200r, Banteay Kdei.

2001   *Perf. 12¼x12½*
2090-2096   A397   Set of 7   4.50   4.50

...

Automobiles — A380

Designs: 200r, 1972 TVR Series M. 500r, 1958 Ferrari 410. 900r, 1995 Peugeot 405. 1000r, 1953 Fiat 8VZ. 1500r, 1997 Citroen Xsara. 4000r, 1997 Renault Espace. 5400r, 1963 Ferrari 250 GT SWB.

2001, June 5   **Litho.**   *Perf. 12¾*
2097-2102 A380   Set of 6   4.75 4.75
Souvenir Sheet
Perf. 13x13¼
2103 A380 5400r multi   3.25 3.25
No. 2103 contains one 40x32mm stamp.

Tourism A381

Designs: 500r, Sourire de Bayon. 1500r, Bayon. 2000r, Bayon, diff.

2001, June 5   *Perf. 12¾*
2104-2106 A381   Set of 3   2.40 2.40

Philanippon '01 — A382

Locomotives: 200r, 4-6-0. 500r, 4-6-4. 900r, 4-4-0. 1000r, 4-6-4, diff. 1500r, 4-6-2. 4000r, 4-8-2.
5400r, Undescribed locomotive.

2001, July 5   *Perf. 12½x12¼*
2107-2112 A382   Set of 6   4.75 4.75
Souvenir Sheet
Perf. 13x13¼
2113 A380 5400r multi   3.25 3.25
No. 2113 contains one 40x32mm stamp.

Penguins A383

Designs: 200r, Aptenodytes forsteri. 500r, Spheniscus demersus. 900r, Spheniscus humboldti. 1000r, Eudypes cristatus. 1500r, Aptenodytes patagonica. 4000r, Pygoscelis antarctica.
5400r, Pygoscelis papua.

2001, Aug. 5   *Perf. 12¾*
2114-2119 A383   Set of 6   4.75 4.75
Souvenir Sheet
Perf. 13x13¼
2120 A383 5400r multi   3.25 3.25
No. 2120 contains one 40x32mm stamp.

Cats A384

Designs: 200r, Singapura. 500r, Cymric. 900r, Exotic shorthair. 1000r, Ragdoll. 1500r, Manx. 4000r, Somali.
5400r, Egyptian Mau.

2001, Aug. 25   *Perf. 12½x12¼*
2121-2126 A384   Set of 6   4.75 4.75
Souvenir Sheet
Perf. 13x13¼
2127 A384 5400r multi   3.25 3.25
No. 2127 contains one 40x32mm stamp.

Kites A385

Designs: 300r, Khleng Chak. 500r, Khleng Kanton. 1000r, Khleng Phnong. 1500r, Khleng Kaun Morn. 3000r, Khleng Me Ambao.

2001, Sept. 7   *Perf. 12¾*
2128-2132 A385   Set of 5   3.75 3.75

Cacti — A386

Designs: 200r, Parodia cintiensis. 500r, Astrophytum astenas. 900r, Parodia faustiana. 1000r, Coryphantha sulcolanata. 1500r, Neochilenia hankena. 4000r, Mammilaria boolii.
5400r, Mammilaria swinglei.

2001, Sept. 15   *Perf. 12¾*
2133-2138 A386   Set of 6   4.75 4.75
Souvenir Sheet
Perf. 12½
2139 A386 5400r multi   3.25 3.25
No. 2139 contains one 32x40mm stamp.

Khmer Culture A387

Designs: 500r, Fish Dance. 1500r, Red Fish Ballet. 2000r, Apsara Ballet.

2001, Oct. 9   *Perf. 12¾*
2140-2142 A387   Set of 3   2.40 2.40

Wolves and Foxes A388

Designs: 200r, Canis lupus occidentalis. 500r, Canis lupus tundrorum, vert. 900r, Vulpes fulvas. 1000r, Canis latrans. 1500r, Vulpes zerda, vert. 4000r, Alopex lagopus.

5400r, Canis lupus signatus, vert.

2001, Oct. 15   *Perf. 12¾*
2143-2148 A388   Set of 6   4.75 4.75
Souvenir Sheet
Perf. 12½
2149 A388 5400r multi   3.25 3.25
No. 2103 contains one 32x40mm stamp.

Human Evolution — A389

Designs: 100r, Australopithecus anamensis. 200r, Australopithecus afarensis. 300r, Australopithecus africanus. No. 2153, 500r, Australopithecus rudolfensis. No. 2154, 500r, Australopithecus boisei. 1000r, Homo habilis. 1500r, Homo erectus. 4000r, Homo sapiens neanderthalensis.
5400r, Homo sapiens sapiens.

2001, Oct. 25   *Perf. 13*
2150-2157 A389   Set of 8   4.75 4.75
Souvenir Sheet
2158 A389 5400r multi   3.25 3.25
No. 2158 contains one 40x32mm stamp.

King Norodom Sihanouk, 80th Birthday (in 2002) A389a

Various photos: 100r, 200r, 300r, 400r, 500r, 600r, 700r, 800r, 900r, 1000r, 1500r, 2000r, 3000r.

2001, Oct. 31   **Litho.**   *Perf. 13*
2158A-2158M A389a   Set of 13   10.00 10.00

Chess A390

Designs: 200r, Rook. 500r, Pawn. 900r, King. 1000r, Bishop. 1500r, Queen. 4000r, Knight.
5400r, Pieces of Oriental chess-like game.

2001, Dec. 25   *Perf. 12¾*
2159-2164 A390   Set of 6   4.75 4.75
Souvenir Sheet
Perf. 13
2165 A390 5400r multi   3.25 3.25
No. 2165 contains one 40x32mm stamp.

Italian Soccer A391

Designs: 200r, 1934 World Cup championship team. 500r, 1938 World Cup championship team. 900r, 1968 European Cup championship team. 1000r, 1982 World Cup championship team. 1500r, 2002 World Cup team. 4000r, Italian soccer federation emblem.

2001   *Perf. 12¾*
2166-2171 A391   Set of 6   4.75 4.75

ASEAN Post, 10th Anniv A392

Temples: 500r, Prasat Preah Vihear. 1000r, Prasat Preah Ko. 1500r, Prasat Banteay Srei. 2500r, Prasat Bayon. 3500r, Prasat Angkor Wat.

2002, July 9   *Perf. 13*
2172-2176 A392   Set of 5   5.50 5.50

Sugar Palm — A393

Designs: 300r, Tree. 500r, Female flower. 700r, Male flower. 1500r, Fruit.

2003   **Litho.**
2177-2180 A393   Set of 4   5.75 5.75

Japanese Grant Aid — A394

Designs: 100r, Drawing of Bridge No. 26, Highway 6A. 200r, Bridge No. 26, Highway 6A. 400r, Chroy Changvar Bridge. 800r, Kizuna Bridge. 3500r, Monument, vert.

2003, Apr. 25   Set of 5   3.00 3.00
2181-2185 A394

Cambodian Red Cross — A395

Designs: 100r, Ox cart. 200r, Woman carrying rice bag, vert. 300r, Queen with Red Cross volunteers. 400r, Queen and women. 500r, Queen and elderly people. 700r, Queen and women, diff. 800r, Queen and Prime Minister's wife giving items to people. 1000r, Like 800r, diff. 1900r, Like 800r, diff., vert. 2100r, Like 800r, diff., vert. 4000r, Queen and Prime Minister's wife with baby.

2003, May 8
2186-2196 A395   Set of 11   7.25 7.25

Cambodia/People's Republic of China Diplomatic Relations, 50th Anniv. — A396

No. 2197: a, Angkor Wat. b, Great Wall of China.
Illustration reduced.

2003, July 19   *Perf. 12¼x12*
2197 A396 2000r Horiz. pair,
     #a-b   3.75 3.75

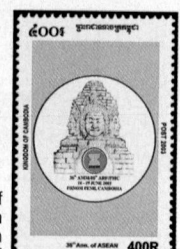

Association of South East Asian Nations, 36th Anniv. — A397

Designs: 400r, Conference emblem. 500r, Apsara dancer. 600r, Apsara dancer, diff. 1600r, Apsara dancers. 1900r, Temonorom dancers.

2003, Aug. 8　　　　　　　　　*Perf. 13*
2198-2202　A397　Set of 5　　　3.00　3.00

King Norodom Sihanouk — A398

Designs: 200r, Pointing at map. 400r, Meeting rural Cambodians, vert. 500r, Sitting in forest, vert. 800r, Pointing in forest, vert. 1000r, Saluting, vert. 2000r, Saluting, with flag and Independence Monument, vert. 5000r, With handicapped people.

2003, Nov. 9
2203-2209　A398　Set of 7　　　6.00　6.00

Khmer Culture A399

Sculptures: 100r, Bayon. 200r, Banteay Srei. 400r, Banteay Srei, diff. 800r, Bayon, vert. 3500r, Banteay Srei, vert. 2000r, Unattributed sculpture, vert.

2004, Apr. 3
2210-2214　A399　Set of 5　　　3.00　3.00
　　　　　　Souvenir Sheet
2215　A399　2000r multi　　　1.50　1.50

Rural Areas A400

Designs: 600r, Mill. 900r, House, field and cattle. 2000r, House and trees. 2000r, Ox cart and driver.

2004, Apr. 13
2216-2218　A400　Set of 3　　　3.00　2.00
　　　　　　Souvenir Sheet
2219　A400　2000r multi　　　1.50　1.50

Tepmonorum Dancers — A401

Dancers with: 400r, Yellow costumes. 1000r, Blue costumes. 2100r, Blue and yellow costumes.
2100r, Blue and yellow costumes, diff.

2004, May 5
2220-2222　A401　Set of 3　　　3.00　2.00
　　　　　　Souvenir Sheet
2223　A401　2000r multi　　　1.50　1.50

Flowers — A402

Designs: 600r, Cassia fistula. 700r, Butea monosperma. 900r, Couroupita quianensis. 1000r, Delonix regia, horiz. 1800r, Lagerstroemia floribunda.
2000r, Lagerstroemia floribunda, horiz.

2004, Aug. 25　　　Litho.　　*Perf. 13*
2224-2228　A402　Set of 5　　　3.75　3.75
　　　　　　Souvenir Sheet
2229　A402　2000r multi　　　1.75　1.75

Tourism — A403

Designs: 200r, Prasat Preah Khan. 500r, Prasat Preup. 600r, PrasatBanteay Samre. 1600r, Prasat Bayon. 1900r, Angkor Wat. 2000r, Prasat Bayon, vert.

2004, Sept. 27　　　Litho.　　*Perf. 13*
2230-2234　A403　Set of 5　　　3.00　3.00
　　　　　　Souvenir Sheet
2235　A403　2000r multi　　　1.50　1.50

Coronation of King Norodom Shiamoni A404

Various photos: 100r, 400r, 500r, 600r, 700r, 900r, 2100r, 2200r, 4000r. 700r-4000r are horiz.

2004, Oct. 29
2236-2244　A404　Set of 9　　　7.00　7.00

Ancient Fishing Tools A405

Various scoops and baskets: 100r, 200r, 800r, 1700r, 2200r. 1700r and 2200r are vert. 2000r, Child with basket, vert.

2004, Dec. 5
2245-2249　A405　Set of 5　　　3.00　3.00
　　　　　　Souvenir Sheet
2250　A405　2000r multi　　　1.50　1.50

Cambodian Red Cross, 50th Anniv. — A406

Designs: 400r, Emblem. 700r, Volunteers, horiz. 800r, Volunteers, diff., horiz. 1000r, Volunteers, diff., horiz. 2100r, Volunteers, diff. horiz. 2200r, Royalty on dais, horiz.

2005, Feb. 18
2251-2256　A406　Set of 6　　　4.75　4.75

Apsaras Dance — A407

Dancer with background color of: 800r, Pink. 900r, Light blue. 1400r, Green. 1600r, Rose. 2000r, Blue.
4000r, Brown.

2005, Apr. 12
2257-2261　A407　Set of 5　　　4.00　4.00
　　　　　　Souvenir Sheet
2262　A407　4000r multi　　　2.40　2.40

Khmer Culture A408

Designs: 500r, Banteay Kdei. 700r, Elephant Terrace. 1000r, Thommanon. 2000r, Ta Prohm. 2500r, Angkor Wat. 4000r, Ta Reach, vert.

2005, May 16
2263-2267　A408　Set of 5　　　4.00　4.00
　　　　　　Souvenir Sheet
2268　A408　4000r multi　　　2.40　2.40

Flowers — A409

Nymphaea lotus in: 100r, Purple. 500r, White. 1200r, Blue. 2000r, Yellow. 2500r, Red. 4000r, Red flowers in canoe, horiz.

2005, July 25　　　Litho.　　*Perf. 13*
2269-2273　A409　Set of 5　　　3.75　3.75
　　　　　　Souvenir Sheet
2274　A409　4000r multi　　　2.40　2.40

Fish A410

Designs: 700r, Pangasionodon gigas. 800r, Catlocarpio siamensis. 1000r, Mekongina erythrospila. 1900r, Probarbus labeaminor, vert. 2200r, Wallago leeri, vert.

2005, Sept. 5
2275-2279　A410　Set of 5　　　4.00　4.00

Coronation of King Norodom Sihamoni, 1st Anniv. — A411

Frame colors: 500r, Green. 1500r, Blue. 2200r, Red.

2005, Oct. 29　　　Litho.　　*Perf. 13*
2281-2283　A411　Set of 3　　　2.50　2.50

　　　　Miniature Sheet

Birds — A412

No. 2284: a, 200r, Great egret. b, 400r, Great-billed heron. c, 1000r, Painted stork. d, 1200r, Spot-billed pelican. e, 1800r, Sarus crane, horiz. f, 3500r, Greater adjutant, horiz.

2005, Dec. 5
2284　A412　Sheet of 6, #a-f　4.75　4.75

Khmer Culture A413

Women at work: 100r, Scooping dyes. 800r, Washing clothes. 1500r, Weaving. 2200r, Spinning thread. 3500r, Weaving, diff. 5400r, Weaving, diff.

2006, Jan. 26
2285-2289　A413　Set of 5　　　4.75　4.75
　　　　　　Souvenir Sheet
2290　A413　5400r multi　　　3.25　3.25

Marine Mammals — A414

Designs: 500r, Sousa chinensis. 900r, Neophocaena phocaenoides. 1400r, Dolphinus capensis tropicalis. 2100r, Stenella longirostris roseinventris. 3500r, Tursiops aduncus.
5400r, Neophocaena phocaenoides and boat.

2006, Mar. 9
2291-2295　A414　Set of 5　　　5.00　5.00
　　　　　　Souvenir Sheet
2296　A414　5400r multi　　　3.25　3.25

Reamker Legend — A415

Designs: 1000r, Jup Leak and Ream Leak. 1400r, Preah Ream, vert. 1600r, Neang Seda, vert. 1900r, Krong Reap, vert. 2100r, Hanuman, vert.
5400r, Two characters in water.

2006, Apr. 13
2297-2301 A415 Set of 5   5.00 5.00
Souvenir Sheet
2302 A415 5400r multi   3.25 3.25

Elephants — A416

Designs: 400r, Adult and juvenile elephant. 700r, Elephants in water. 1600r, Elephant, vert. 2200r, Elephant facing right. 3500r, Elephant facing left.
5400r, Elephants in water, diff.

2006, June 15 Litho. Perf. 13
2303-2307 A416 Set of 5   5.00 5.00
Souvenir Sheet
2308 A416 5400r multi   3.25 3.25

Dances — A417

Designs: 600r, Chhai Yaim dance. 1900r, Sacrifice of Buffalo dance. 2200r, Mouth Organ dance. 3500r, Rice Harvest dance.

2006, Aug. 17
2309-2312 A417 Set of 4   5.00 5.00

Birds
A418

Designs: 600r, Threskionis melanocephalus. 800r, Plegadis facinellus. 1500r, Houbaropsis bengalensis. 2100r, Pseudibis gigantea. 3500r, Pseudibis davisoni.
5400r, Pseudibis gigantea, vert.

2006, Nov. 8 Litho. Perf. 13
2313-2317 A418 Set of 5   4.25 4.25
Souvenir Sheet
2318 A418 5400r multi   2.75 2.75

Condom Use Program — A419

Designs: 300r, Man, woman, program emblem. 500r, Man, motorcycle, program

emblem. 2200r, Men on boat, flag with program emblem.

2006, Dec. 1 Litho. Perf. 13
2319-2321 A419 Set of 3   1.50 1.50
World AIDS Day.

SEMI-POSTAL STAMPS

Nos. 8, 12, 14 and 15 Surcharged in Black

1952, Oct. 20 Unwmk. Perf. 13
B1 A3 1.10pi + 40c   4.00 4.00
B2 A3 1.90pi + 60c   4.00 4.00
B3 A3 3pi + 1pi   4.00 4.00
B4 A1 5pi + 2pi   4.00 4.00
    Nos. B1-B4 (4)   16.00 16.00
For students assistance.

Preah Stupa — SP1

1957, Mar. 15 Engr. Perf. 13
B5 SP1 1.50r + 50c ind, ol & red   1.10 .90
B6 SP1 6.50r + 1.50r red lil, ol & red   1.75 1.50
B7 SP1 8r + 2r bl, ol & red   3.00 2.50
    Nos. B5-B7 (3)   5.85 4.90
Birth of Buddha, 1500th anniv. See #62-64.

Type of Regular Issue, 1959, with Red Typographed Surcharge

1959, Dec. 9
B8 A14 20c + 20c rose vio   .35   .35
B9 A14 50c + 30c blue   .40   .40
B10 A14 80c + 50c rose car   .90   .90
    Nos. B8-B10 (3)   1.65 1.65
The surtax was for the Red Cross.

Nos. 107-108 Surcharged and Overprinted in Red: "1863-1963 CENTENAIRE DE LA CROIX ROUGE"

1963, Oct. 1 Unwmk. Perf. 13
B11 A26 4r + 40c grn & dk brn   .70   .70
B12 A26 6r + 60c vio & ol bis   .90   .90
Centenary of International Red Cross.

Nos. 263, 267, 293-294, 134 Surcharged in Red

1972, Nov. 15 Engr. Perf. 13
B13 A72 3r + 2r multi   .25   .25
B14 A72 10r + 6r multi   .40   .35
B15 A80 12r + 7r multi   .60   .50
B16 A34 12r + 7r multi   .60   .50
B17 A80 15r + 8r multi   .90   .75
    Nos. B13-B17 (5)   2.75 2.35
Surtax was for war victims. Surcharge arranged differently on Nos. B15-B17.

AIR POST STAMPS

Kinnari — AP1

Unwmk.
1953, Apr. 16 Engr. Perf. 13
C1 AP1 50c deep green   .65   .60
  a. Souv. sheet of 4, #C1, C3, C5, C9   90.00 90.00
C2 AP1 3pi red brown   .85   .65
  a. Souv. sheet of 3, #C2, C4, C8   90.00 90.00
C3 AP1 3.30pi rose violet   1.00   .80
C4 AP1 4pi dk brn & dp bl   1.25   .85
C5 AP1 5.10pi brn, red & org   2.50 2.10
C6 AP1 6.50pi dk brn & lil rose   2.50 2.10
  a. Souv. sheet of 2, #C6-C7   90.00 90.00
C7 AP1 9pi lil rose & dp grn   3.75 3.25
C8 AP1 11.50pi multi   7.50 6.25
C9 AP1 30pi dk brn, bl grn & org   15.00 8.25
    Nos. C1-C9 (9)   35.00 24.85
#C1a sold for 50pi, #C2a for 25pi, #C6a for 20pi.
Souvenir sheets with completely white gum, no toning and no gum bends sell for a premium.

AP2

1957, Dec. 11
C10 AP2 50c maroon   .25   .20
C11 AP2 1r emerald   .40   .20
C12 AP2 4r ultra   1.25   .75
C13 AP2 50r carmine rose   5.75 4.00
C14 AP2 100r grn, bl & car   10.00 6.00
  a. Souv. sheet of 5, #C10-C14   30.00 30.00
    Nos. C10-C14 (5)   17.65 11.15
No. C14a sold for 160r.
See note after #C9.

Independence Type of 1961

1961, Nov. 9 Perf. 13x12½
C15 A24 7r multicolored   .65   .35
C16 A24 30r grn, car & ultra   2.50 1.10
C17 A24 50r ind, grn & ol   3.50 2.25
  a. Souv. sheet of 3, #C15-C17   10.00 10.00
    Nos. C15-C17 (3)   6.65 3.70

No. C15 Surcharged with New Value in Red and Overprinted in Black with Two Bars and: "INAUGURATION DU MONUMENT"

1962, Nov. 9
C18 A24 12r on 7r multi   1.75 1.10
Dedication of Independence Monument.

Hanuman, Monkey God — AP3

1964, Sept. 1 Engr. Perf. 13
C19 AP3 5r multicolored   .80   .35
C20 AP3 10r ol bis, lil rose & grn   1.10   .35
C21 AP3 20r vio, bl & ol bis   1.60   .75
C22 AP3 40r bl, ol bis & dk bl   3.50 1.40
C23 AP3 80r multicolored   5.75 3.50
    Nos. C19-C23 (5)   12.75 6.35

Nos. C19-C22 Surcharged in Red

1964, Oct.
C24 AP3 3r on 5r multi   .60   .55
C25 AP3 6r on 10r multi   .95   .85
C26 AP3 9r on 20r multi   1.25 1.10
C27 AP3 12r on 40r multi   1.90 1.60
    Nos. C24-C27 (4)   4.70 4.10
18th Olympic Games, Tokyo, Oct. 10-25.

1972 Summer Olympic Games, Munich — AP4

Designs: No. C28, shown. No. C29, Munich churches, Olympic emblem, vert.
Illustration reduced.

Litho. & Embossed
1972, Sept. 28 Perf. 13½
C28 AP4 900r gold & multi   19.00 19.00
C29 AP4 900r gold & multi   19.00 19.00
  a. Souvenir sheet of 2, #C28-C29   50.00
No. C29a exists imperf.

Apollo 16 AP5

Designs: No. C30, Astronauts in Lunar Rover. No. C31, Astronaut walking on moon.

1972, Sept. 28
C30 AP5 900r gold & multi   19.00 19.00
C31 AP5 900r gold & multi   19.00 19.00
  a. Souvenir sheet of 2, #C30-C31   50.00

Pres. Nixon's Visit to the People's
Republic of China — AP6

Nixon, Mao Zedong: No. C32, Large portraits (shown). No. C33, Small portraits.

1972, Sept. 28   *Perf. 12½*
C32 AP6 900r gold & multi   60.00 60.00
C33 AP6 900r gold & multi   60.00 60.00

Garuda, 12th
Century, Angkor
Thom — AP7

1973, Jan. 18   Engr.   *Perf. 13*
C34 AP7 3r carmine   .35   .20
C35 AP7 30r violet blue   1.50 .90
C36 AP7 50r dull purple   2.25 1.40
C37 AP7 100r dull green   4.50 2.50
   Nos. C34-C37 (4)   8.60 5.00

1972
Summer
Olympic
Games,
Munich
AP8

Gold medalists: No. C38, Heide Rosendahl.
No. C39, Mark Spitz.

Litho. & Embossed
1973, May 18   *Perf. 13½*
C38 AP8 900r gold & multi   19.00 19.00
C39 AP8 900r gold & multi   19.00 19.00

A souvenir sheet released with these
stamps exists.

Nos. C38-C39 Ovptd. with
"MUNICH 1974 / COUPE DE MONDE
DE FOOTBALL" and Emblem
1973, Nov. 19
C40 AP8 900r on C38   27.50 27.50
C41 AP8 900r on C39   27.50 27.50

An overprinted souvenir sheet exists.

1974 World Cup Soccer
Championships, Munich — AP9

Designs: No. C42, Trophy, players. No. C43,
Trophy, players, vert.

1973, Nov. 19   Litho. & Embossed
C42 AP9 900r gold & multi   30.00 30.00
C43 AP9 900r gold & multi   30.00 30.00

A souvenir sheet released with these
stamps exists.

John F. Kennedy, Apollo 11 — AP10

#C44, shown. #C45, Kennedy, Apollo 17.

1974, Feb. 18
C44 AP10 1100r gold & multi   30.00 30.00
C45 AP10 1100r gold & multi   30.00 30.00
  a. Souv. sheet of 2, #C44-C45   95.00

   Nos. C44-C45a exist imperf.

Copernicus Type of 1974 and

Copernicus, Sun — AP11

200r, Copernicus and Skylab III. 250r,
Copernicus, Concorde and solar eclipse. No.
C48, shown. No. C49, Moon, Skylab, hand
holding symbol of sun.

1974, Sept. 10   Litho.   *Perf. 13*
C46 A87 200r multi   5.00 2.50
C47 A87 250r multi   5.00 2.50

Litho. & Engraved
Perf. 13½
C48 AP11 1200r gold & multi 27.50 27.50

Souvenir Sheet of 1
C49 AP11 1200r gold & multi 27.50 27.50

   Nos. C46-C47 exist in perf or imperf souvenir sheets of 1.

UPU Type of 1974 and

AP12

700r, Rocket, globe and UPU emblem. No.
C51, UPU Headquarters. No. C52, US #1434-1435.

1974, Nov. 2   Litho.   *Perf. 13*
C50 A88 700r gold & multi   10.00 10.00

Litho. & Embossed
Perf. 13½
C51 AP12 1200r gold & multi 25.00 25.00

Souvenir Sheet
C52 AP12 1200r gold & multi 45.00

   Nos. C50-C51 exist in souvenir sheets of
one. Nos. C51-C52 exist imperf.

#C53-C54, UPU Centennial, 4/12/75.

Post Aerienne at
Right — AP14

Post Aerienne at
Left — AP15

Denominations: 5r, 10r, 15r, 25r.

1984, Feb. 1   Litho.   *Perf. 12x12½*
C55-C58 AP14 Set of 4   42.50 7.50

1986, Mar. 4   Litho.   *Perf. 12x12½*

Denominations: 5r, 10r, 15r, 25r.

C59-C62 AP15 Set of 4   37.50 7.50

POSTAGE DUE STAMPS

D1

Frieze, Angkor
Wat — D2

1957   Unwmk.   Typo.   *Perf. 13½*
Denomination in Black
J1 D1 10c ver & pale blue   .20   .20
J2 D1 50c ver & pale blue   .30   .30
J3 D1 1r ver & pale blue   .70   .70
J4 D1 3r ver & pale blue   .90   .90
J5 D1 5r ver & pale blue   1.40 1.40
   Nos. J1-J5 (5)   3.50 3.50

1974, Feb. 18   Engr.   *Perf. 12½x13*
J6 D2 2r ocher   .25   .25
J7 D2 6r green   .30   .30
J8 D2 8r deep carmine   .45   .45
J9 D2 10r violet blue   .55   .55
   Nos. J6-J9 (4)   1.55 1.55

CAMEROONS

ˌka-mə-ˈrün

LOCATION — West coast of Africa,
  north of equator
GOVT. — British Trust Territory
AREA — 34,081 sq. mi.
POP. — 868,637 (estimated)
CAPITAL — Buea

Prior to World War I, Cameroons
(Kamerun) was a German Protectorate.
It was occupied during the War by
Great Britain and France and in 1922
was mandated to these countries by the
League of Nations. Stamps of Nigeria
were used in the British part until 1960.
The northern section of the British
Cameroons became part of the inde-
pendent state of Nigeria in 1960, and
the southern section became a United
Kingdom Trust Territory. After a referen-
dum, this U.K.T.T. joined the indepen-
dent State of Cameroun to form the

Federal Republic of Cameroun, Oct. 1,
1961.

Stamps of the German Protectorate,
the French Mandate, the independent
state and the Cameroun Federal
Republic are listed under Cameroun.

> **Catalogue values for unused
> stamps in this country are for
> Never Hinged items.**

United Kingdom Trust Territory

Stamps and Type of Nigeria, 1953, Overprinted in Red

Perf. 13½, 14

1960, Oct. 1   Wmk. 4   Engr.
Size: 35½x22½mm
66 A17 ½p red org &
          black   .20   1.75
67 A17 1p ol gray &
          black   .20   .90
68 A17 1½p blue green   .20   .25
69 A17 2p gray (II)   .30   .50
70 A17 3p purple & black   .20   .20
71 A17 4p ultra & black   .25   1.75
72 A18 6p blk & org brn,
          perf. 14   .60   .25
  a. Perf. 13x13½ ('61)   .45   2.25
73 A17 1sh brown vio &
          blk   .25   .20
Size: 40½x24½mm
74 A17 2sh6p green & black 1.75   1.25
75 A17 5sh ver & black   2.50   4.50
76 A17 10sh red brn & blk   3.75   8.50
Size: 42x31½mm
77 A17 £1 violet & black   12.00 27.50
   Nos. 66-77 (12)   22.20 47.55

Nos. 66-77 were withdrawn in Northern
Cameroons on May 31, 1961, when that territory joined Nigeria and in Southern Cameroons Sept. 30, 1961, when that territory
joined the Cameroun Federal Republic.

CAMEROUN

ˌka-mə-'rün

(Kamerun)

LOCATION — On the west coast of Africa, north of the equator
GOVT. — Republic
AREA — 183,520 sq. mi.
POP. — 15,456,092 (1999 est.)
CAPITAL — Yaounde

Before World War I, Cameroun (Kamerun) was a German Protectorate. It was occupied during the war by Great Britain and France and in 1922 was mandated to these countries by the League of Nations. The French-mandated part became the independent State of Cameroon on January 1, 1960. The Southern Cameroons, a United Kingdom Trust Territory, joined this state to form the Federal Republic of Cameroun on October 1, 1961. The name was changed to United Republic of Cameroon on May 20, 1972.

Stamps of Southern Cameroons are listed under Cameroons.

100 Pfennig = 1 Mark
12 Pence = 1 Shilling
100 Centimes = 1 Franc

Catalogue values for unused stamps in this country are for **Never Hinged** items, beginning with Scott 296 in the regular postage section, Scott B29 in the semipostal section, Scott C8 in the airpost section, Scott J24 in the postage due section, and Scott M1 in the military stamp section.

Watermark

Wmk. 125 —
Lozenges

Wmk. 385

Issued under German Dominion

Stamps of Germany
Overprinted in Black

			Unwmk.	Perf. 13½x14½
1897				
1	A9	3pf yellow brn	11.00	16.00
a.		3pf red brown	50.00	150.00
b.		3pf dark brown	16.00	40.00
2	A9	5pf green	5.75	8.25
3	A10	10pf carmine	4.00	5.00
4	A10	20pf ultra	4.00	8.00
5	A10	25pf orange	20.00	40.00
6	A10	50pf red brown	16.00	29.00
		Nos. 1-6 (6)	60.75	106.25

A3

Kaiser's Yacht "Hohenzollern" — A4

1900		**Unwmk.**	**Typo.**	**Perf. 14**
7	A3	3pf brown	1.25	1.60
8	A3	5pf green	13.50	1.30
9	A3	10pf carmine	40.00	1.40
10	A3	20pf ultra	25.00	2.25
11	A3	25pf org & blk, yel	1.50	5.25
12	A3	30pf org & blk, sal	2.00	4.50
13	A3	40pf lake & blk	2.00	4.00
14	A3	50pf pur & blk, sal	2.00	6.00
15	A3	80pf lake & blk, rose	2.75	11.00

			Engr.	**Perf. 14½x14**
16	A4	1m carmine	67.50	75.00
17	A4	2m blue	5.25	75.00
18	A4	3m black vio	5.25	125.00
19	A4	5m slate & car	160.00	500.00
		Nos. 7-19 (13)	328.00	812.30

			Wmk. 125	**Typo.**
1905-18				
20	A3	3pf brown ('18)	.85	
21	A3	5pf green	.85	1.60
b.		Bklt. pane of 6, 2 #21 + 4 #22	62.50	
c.		Booklet pane of 5 + label	375.00	
22	A3	10pf carmine ('06)	2.00	1.40
b.		Booklet pane of 5 + label	500.00	
23	A3	20pf ultra ('14)	3.25	125.00
24	A4	1m carmine ('15)	10.00	
25	A4	5m slate & car ('13)	45.00	4,250.
		Nos. 20-25 (6)	61.95	4,378.

The 3pf and 1m were not placed in use.

Issued under British Occupation

Stamps of German Cameroun
Surcharged

		Wmk. Lozenges (125) (#54-56, 65);		
		Unwmk. (Other Values)		
1915			**Perf. 14, 14½**	
		Blue Surcharge		
53	A3	½p on 3pf brn	15.00	40.00
54	A3	½p on 5pf grn	4.00	16.50
a.		Double surcharge		1,000.
b.		Black surcharge	—	
55	A3	1p on 10pf car	4.00	16.50
a.		"1" with thin serifs	15.00	75.00
b.		Double surcharge	325.00	
c.		Black surcharge	20.00	82.50
d.		As "c," "1" with thin serifs	225.00	

		Black Surcharge		
56	A3	2p on 20pf ultra	6.50	29.00
57	A3	2½p on 25pf org & blk, yel	18.00	55.00
a.		Double surcharge	8,500.	
58	A3	3p on 30pf org & blk, sal	18.00	55.00
59	A3	4p on 40pf lake & blk	18.00	55.00
60	A3	6p on 50pf pur & blk, sal	18.00	55.00
61	A3	8p on 80pf lake & blk, rose	18.00	55.00
62	A4	1sh on 1m car	190.00	800.00
a.		"S" inverted	925.00	3,000.
63	A4	2sh on 2m bl	190.00	800.00
a.		"S" inverted	925.00	3,000.
64	A4	3sh on 3m blk vio	190.00	900.00
a.		"S" inverted	925.00	3,000.
b.		Double surcharge	10,500.	

65	A4	5sh on 5m sl & car	240.00	875.00
a.		"S" inverted	1,050.	3,250.
		Nos. 53-65 (13)	929.50	3,752.

The letters "C. E. F." are the initials of "Cameroons Expeditionary Force."

Numerous overprint varieties exist for #53-65.

Counterfeits exist of Nos. 54a, 54b.

See Cameroons for Nos. 66-77.

Issued under French Occupation

Gabon Nos. 37, 49-52, 54, 57-58, 60, 62-64, 66, 69-71 Overprinted

		1915	**Unwmk.**	**Perf. 13½x14**
		Inscribed "Congo Français"		
101	A10	10c red & car	22.50	15.00
		Inscribed "Afrique Equatoriale"		
102	A10	1c choc & org	75.00	30.00
103	A10	2c blk & choc	125.00	100.00
104	A10	4c vio & dp bl	125.00	100.00
105	A10	5c ol gray & grn	26.00	15.00
105A	A10	10c red & car	16,750.	18,000.
106	A10	20c ol brn & dk vio	150.00	150.00
107	A11	25c dp bl & choc	45.00	30.00
108	A11	30c gray blk & red	140.00	140.00
109	A11	35c dk vio & grn	47.50	30.00
a.		Double overprint	1,400.	
110	A11	40c choc & ultra	140.00	140.00
111	A11	45c car & vio	160.00	140.00
112	A11	50c bl grn & gray	160.00	140.00
113	A11	75c org & choc	210.00	150.00
114	A12	1fr dk brn & bis	190.00	160.00
115	A12	2fr car & brn	210.00	190.00
		Nos. 101-105,106-115 (15)	1,826.	1,530.

The overprint is vertical, reading up, on #101-106, 114-115, horizontal on #107-113.

Stamps of Middle Congo, Issue of 1907, Overprinted

		1916	**Unwmk.**	
116	A1	1c ol gray & brn	75.00	75.00
117	A1	2c violet & brn	75.00	75.00
118	A1	4c blue & brown	80.00	75.00
119	A1	5c dk green & blue	22.50	22.50
120	A2	35c violet brn & bl	87.50	60.00
121	A2	45c violet & red	62.50	55.00

The overprint is vert., reading down, on #120-121.

Same Overprint On Stamps of French Congo, 1900

Wmk. Branch of Thistle (122)

122	A4	15c dull vio & ol grn	75.00	75.00
a.		Inverted overprint	140.00	110.00

Wmk. Branch of Rose Tree (123)

123	A5	20c yellow grn & org	110.00	62.50
124a	A5	30c car rose & org	65.00	55.00
125	A5	40c org brn & brt grn	52.50	47.50
126	A5	50c gray vio & lil	70.00	55.00
127a	A5	75c red vio & org	70.00	55.00

Wmk. Branch of Olive (124)

128	A6	1fr gray lilac & ol	92.50	75.00
129	A6	2fr carmine & brn	92.50	75.00
		Nos. 116-129 (14)	1,030.	862.50

The overprint is horiz. on No. 122. The overprint is vert., reading down or up, on Nos. 123-129. Values are for the cheaper variety. See the *Scott Classic Specialized Catalogue of Stamps & Covers* for detailed listings.

Values are for copies centered in the grade of fine.

Counterfeits exist of Nos. 101-129.

Stamps of Middle Congo, Issue of 1907 Overprinted

		1916-17		**Unwmk.**
130	A1	1c ol gray & brn	.40	.30
131	A1	2c violet & brn	.45	.30
132	A1	4c blue & brn	.75	.35
133	A1	5c dk green & bl	.45	.30
134	A1	10c carmine & bl	.90	.50
135	A1	15c brn vio & rose ('17)	1.75	.50
136	A1	20c brown & bl	.75	.50
137	A2	25c blue & grn	.75	.35
a.		Triple overprint	550.00	
138	A2	30c scarlet & grn	.90	.50
a.		Double overprint	425.00	
139	A2	35c vio brn & bl	.75	.50
140	A2	40c dull grn & brn	2.00	.85
141	A2	45c violet & red	2.00	.85
142	A2	50c blue grn & red	2.00	1.00
143	A2	75c brown & blue	2.00	1.00
144	A3	1fr dp grn & vio	1.40	.80
145	A3	2fr vio & gray grn	7.50	4.25
146	A3	5fr blue & rose	10.50	6.50
		Nos. 130-146 (17)	35.25	19.35

Nos. 130-146 exist on ordinary paper and, with the exception of No. 135, on chalk surfaced paper. Nos. 137-146 are known with inverted "S" in "Francaise" and without period after "Francaise." See the *Scott Classic Specialized Catalogue of Stamps & Covers* for detailed listings.

On Nos. 137-146 there is 7mm between "Cameroun" and "Occupation."

Provisional French Mandate

Types of Middle Congo, 1907, Overprinted

		1921		
147	A1	1c ol grn & org	.20	.20
148	A1	2c brown & rose	.20	.20
149	A1	4c gray & lt grn	.40	.30
150	A1	5c dl red & org	.40	.30
a.		Double overprint	650.00	
151	A1	10c bl grn & lt grn	1.25	.45
152	A1	15c blue & grn	.40	.30
153	A1	20c red brn & ol	.85	.50
154	A2	25c slate & org	1.10	.50
155	A2	30c rose & ver	1.25	.45
156	A2	35c gray & ultra	.85	.45
157	A2	40c ol grn & grn	1.10	.50
158	A2	45c brown & rose	.85	.45
159	A2	50c blue & ultra	1.00	.45
160	A2	75c red brn & lt grn	1.10	.50
161	A3	1fr slate & org	2.25	1.10
162	A3	2fr ol grn & rose	6.50	3.25
163	A3	5fr dull red & gray	8.25	4.75
		Nos. 147-163 (17)	27.95	14.65

The 2c, 4c, 15c, 25c and 50c exist with overprint omitted. See the Scott Classic Catalogue.

Nos. 152, 162, 163, 158, 160 Surcharged with New Value and Bars

		1924-25		
164	A1	25c on 15c bl & org ('25)	.90	.90
165	A3	25c on 2fr ol grn & rose	1.25	1.25
166	A3	25c on 5fr red & gray	1.25	1.25
a.		Pair, one without new value and bars		
167	A2	65c on 45c brn & rose ('25)	1.40	1.40
168	A2	85c on 75c red brn & lt grn ('25)	2.00	2.00
		Nos. 164-168 (5)	6.80	6.80

French Mandate

Herder and Cattle Crossing Sanaga River — A5

Tapping Rubber Tree — A6

Rope Suspension Bridge A7

1925-38		Typo.	Perf. 14x13½	
170	A5	1c ol grn & brn vio, lav	.20	.20
171	A5	2c rose & grn, grnsh	.20	.20
172	A5	4c blue & blk	.20	.20
173	A5	5c org & red vio, lav	.20	.20
174	A5	10c red brn & org, yel	.35	.30
175	A5	15c sl grn & grn	.35	.30
176	A5	15c lilac & red ('27)	.80	.50

		Perf. 13½x14		
177	A6	20c ol brn & red brn	.50	.30
178	A6	20c green ('26)	.35	.30
179	A6	20c brn red & ol brn ('27)	.35	.35
180	A6	25c lt green & blk	.60	.35
181	A6	30c bluish grn & ver	.35	.20
182	A6	30c dk grn & grn ('27)	.60	.35
183	A6	35c brown & black	.75	.35
184	A6	35c dl grn & grn ('38)	1.90	1.00
185	A6	40c orange & vio	1.90	.85
186	A6	45c dp rose & cer	.60	.35
187	A6	45c vio & org brn ('27)	2.25	1.25
188	A6	50c lt green & car	.60	.20
189	A6	55c ultra & car ('38)	1.60	1.10
190	A6	60c red vio & blk	.60	.35
191	A6	60c brown red ('26)	.60	.35
192	A6	65c indigo & brn	1.10	.70
193	A6	75c indigo & dp bl	.60	.50
194	A6	75c org brn & red vio ('27)	1.25	.80
195	A6	80c carmine & brn ('38)	1.25	.80
196	A6	85c dp rose & bl	1.60	.85
197	A6	90c brn red & cer ('27)	2.50	.85

		Perf. 14x13½		
198	A7	1fr indigo & brn	1.10	.70
199	A7	1fr dull bl ('26)	.40	.35
200	A7	1fr ol brn & red vio ('27)	1.10	.50
201	A7	1fr grn & dk brn ('29)	2.50	.80
202	A7	1.10fr rose red & dk brn ('28)	4.75	3.75
203	A7	1.25fr gray & dp bl ('33)	5.50	2.75
204	A7	1.50fr dull bl ('27)	.65	.50
205	A7	1.75fr brn & org ('33)	1.60	1.00
206	A7	1.75fr dk bl & lt bl ('38)	2.50	1.00
207	A7	2fr dl grn & brn org	1.90	.75
208	A7	3fr ol brn & red vio ('27)	7.00	1.50
209	A7	5fr brn & blk, bluish	3.25	1.50
a.	Cliché of 2fr in plate of 5fr		1,050.	
210	A7	10fr org & vio ('27)	14.00	1.00
211	A7	20fr rose & ol grn ('27)	18.00	8.50
Nos. 170-211 (42)			88.40	42.65

Shades exist for several values.
For overprints and surcharge see Nos. 212, 264, 276, 278, 279, B7-B9, B21.

No. 199 Surcharged with New Value and Bars in Red

1926				
212	A7	1.25fr on 1fr dull blue	.80	.50

Common Design Types pictured following the introduction.

Colonial Exposition Issue
Common Design Types
Name of Country in Black

1931		Engr.	Perf. 12½	
213	CD70	40c deep green	5.25	2.50
214	CD71	50c violet	5.25	3.25
215	CD72	90c red orange	5.25	3.25
216	CD73	1.50fr dull blue	6.25	3.25
Nos. 213-216 (4)			22.00	12.25

Paris International Exposition Issue
Common Design Types

1937			Perf. 13	
217	CD74	20c deep violet	1.75	1.75
218	CD75	30c dark green	1.25	1.25
219	CD76	40c carmine rose	1.75	1.75
220	CD77	50c dark brown	1.75	1.75
221	CD78	90c red	1.75	1.75
222	CD79	1.50fr ultramarine	1.75	1.75
Nos. 217-222 (6)			10.00	10.00

French Colonial Art Exhibition
Common Design Type
Souvenir Sheet

1937			Imperf.	
222A	CD77	3fr org red & blk	7.50	6.50

New York World's Fair Issue
Common Design Type

1939			Perf. 12½x12	
223	CD82	1.25fr carmine lake	1.25	.85
224	CD82	2.25fr ultra	1.25	.85

For overprints and surcharges see Nos. 280-281, B14-B17, B23, B25.

Mandara Woman — A19

Falls on M'bam River near Banyo — A20

Elephants A21

Man in Yaré — A22

1939-40		Engr.	Perf. 13	
225	A19	2c black brn	.20	.20
226	A19	3c magenta	.20	.20
227	A19	4c deep ultra	.20	.20
228	A19	5c red brown	.20	.20
229	A19	10c dp bl grn	.20	.20
230	A19	15c rose red	.25	.20
231	A19	20c plum	.25	.20
232	A20	25c black brn	.60	.50
233	A20	30c dk red	.75	.45
234	A20	40c ultra	.75	.50
235	A20	45c slate green	2.40	1.60
236	A20	50c brown car	.80	.40
237	A20	60c pck blue	.75	.50
238	A20	70c plum	3.25	2.25
239	A21	80c Prus blue	2.40	1.75
240	A21	90c Prus blue	.90	.50
241	A21	1fr car rose	1.75	.75
242	A21	1fr choc ('40)	1.10	.60
243	A21	1.25fr car rose	4.00	2.40
244	A21	1.40fr org red	1.25	.75
245	A21	1.50fr chocolate	1.00	.75
246	A21	1.60fr black brn	2.40	1.60
247	A21	1.75fr bl blue	1.25	.75
248	A21	2fr dk green	.75	.60
249	A21	2.25fr dk blue	1.25	.75
250	A21	2.50fr brt red vio	1.10	.80
251	A21	3fr dk violet	1.10	.50
252	A22	5fr black brn	1.10	.65
253	A22	10fr brt red vio	1.75	1.25
254	A22	20fr dk green	3.50	2.10
Nos. 225-254 (30)			37.40	24.10

For overprints and surcharges see Nos. 255-263, 265-275, 277, 278A, 279A, B10-B13, B22, B24.

Stamps of 1925-40 Overprinted in Black or Orange
"CAMEROUN FRANCAIS 27.8.40."

1940		Perf. 14x13½, 13½x14, 13		
255	A19	2c blk brn (O)	1.00	.80
256	A19	3c magenta	.80	.65
257	A19	4c dp ultra (O)	.80	.65
258	A19	5c red brn	4.00	2.75
259	A19	10c dp bl grn (O)	.90	.75
260	A19	15c rose red	1.00	.75
260A	A19	20c plum (O)	11.00	8.00
261	A20	25c blk brn	.90	.75
b.	Inverted overprint		175.00	175.00
261A	A20	30c dk red	7.50	6.00
262	A20	40c ultra	4.75	4.00
263	A20	45c slate green	2.25	1.75
264	A6	50c lt grn & cer	1.50	1.00
a.	Inverted overprint		160.00	
265	A20	60c pck bl	5.50	4.00
266	A20	70c plum	1.50	1.10
267	A21	80c Prus bl (O)	4.75	3.50
268	A21	90c Prus bl (O)	1.50	1.00
269	A21	1.25fr car rose	1.50	1.00
270	A21	1.40fr org red	2.00	1.25
271	A21	1.50fr chocolate	1.00	.60
272	A21	1.60fr blk brn (O)	1.50	.90
273	A21	1.75fr dk bl (O)	2.00	1.25
274	A21	2.25fr dk bl (O)	1.00	.75
275	A21	2.50fr brt red vio	1.00	.80
276	A7	5fr brn & blk, bluish	16.00	12.50
277	A22	5fr black brn	20.00	11.00
278	A7	10fr org & vio	22.50	13.50
278A	A22	10fr brt red vio	45.00	23.00
279	A7	20fr rose & ol grn	47.50	32.50
279A	A22	20fr dk green	190.00	150.00

Same Overprint on Stamps of 1939
Perf. 12½x12

280	CD82	1.25fr car lake	5.50	5.50
281	CD82	2.25fr ultra	5.50	5.50
Nos. 255-281 (31)			411.65	297.50

Issued to note Cameroun's affiliation with General de Gaulle's "Free France" movement. Numerous overprint varieties exist.

Cattle Fording Sanaga River and Marshal Petain A22a

1941		Engr.	Perf. 12½x12	
281A	A22a	1fr green		.80
281B	A22a	2.50fr dark blue		.80

Nos. 281A-281B were issued by the Vichy government in France, but were not placed on sale in Cameroun.
For surcharges, see Nos. B25A-B25B.

Lorraine Cross and Joan of Arc Shield — A23

1941		Photo.	Perf. 14x14½	
282	A23	5c brown	.20	.20
283	A23	10c dk blue	.20	.20
284	A23	25c emerald	.20	.20
285	A23	30c dp orange	.20	.20
286	A23	40c dk slate green	.20	.20
287	A23	80c red brown	.40	.20
288	A23	1fr dp red lilac	.40	.35
289	A23	1.50fr brt red	.40	.20
290	A23	2fr gray black	.80	.35
291	A23	2.50fr brt ultra	.80	.35
292	A23	4fr dull violet	.80	.60
293	A23	5fr bister	.90	.70
294	A23	10fr dp brown	.90	.70
295	A23	20fr dp green	1.75	1.00
Nos. 282-295 (14)			8.15	5.60

For surcharges see Nos. 297A-303.

> Catalogue values for unused stamps in this section, from this point to the end of the section, are for Never Hinged items.

Eboue Issue
Common Design Type

1945		Unwmk.	Engr.	Perf. 13	
296	CD91	2fr black		.35	.30
297	CD91	25fr Prus green		1.25	.65

Nos. 282, 284, 291 Surcharged with New Values and Bars in Red, Carmine or Black

1946		Perf. 14x14½		
297A	A23	50c on 5c (R)	.40	.40
298	A23	60c on 5c (R)	.55	.55
a.	Inverted surcharge		110.00	
299	A23	70c on 5c (R)	.65	.65
300	A23	1.20fr on 5c (C)	.65	.65
301	A23	2.40fr on 25c	.60	.60
302	A23	3fr on 25c	.90	.90
302A	A23	4.50fr on 25c	1.10	1.10
303	A23	15fr on 2.50fr (C)	1.10	1.10
Nos. 297A-303 (8)			5.95	5.95

Zebu and Herder A25

Tikar Women — A26

Porters Carrying Bananas — A27

Bowman A28

Lamido Horsemen A29

Farmer — A30

1946		Engr.	Perf. 12½x12, 12x12½	
304	A25	10c blue grn	.25	.25
305	A25	30c brown org	.25	.25
306	A25	40c brt ultra	.25	.25
307	A26	50c olive brn	.25	.25
308	A26	60c dp plum	.45	.25
309	A26	80c chnt brn	.60	.40
310	A27	1fr org red	.25	.20
311	A27	1.20fr dp green	.75	.30
312	A27	1.50fr dk car	1.75	1.00
313	A28	2fr black	.25	.25
314	A28	3fr dk carmine	.45	.25
314A	A28	3.60fr red brn	1.25	.80
315	A28	4fr dp blue	.75	.25
316	A28	5fr brown car	.90	.40
317	A29	6fr ultra	.90	.35
318	A29	10fr slate green	1.25	.35
319	A30	15fr grnsh blue	1.75	.65

320	A30	20fr dk green	2.25	.65
321	A30	25fr black	2.40	1.00
		Nos. 304-321 (19)	16.95	8.05

Shades exist for most values.
For surcharges see Nos. 343-344, 346.

Imperforates

Most Cameroun stamps from 1952 onward exist imperforate in issued and trial colors, and also in small presentation sheets in issued colors.

Military Medal Issue
Common Design Type
Engraved and Typographed

1952		Unwmk.	Perf. 13
322	CD101	15fr multicolored	5.00 2.00

Porters Carrying Bananas — A32

Picking Coffee Beans — A33

1954			Engr.	
323	A32	8fr red vio, org brn & vio bl	.50	.20
324	A32	15fr brn red, yel & blk brn	1.00	.30
325	A33	40fr blk brn, org brn & lil rose	1.25	.30
		Nos. 323-325 (3)	2.75	.80

FIDES Issue
Common Design Type

Designs: 5fr, Plowmen. 15fr, Wouri bridge. 20fr, Technical instruction. 25fr, Mobile medical station.

1956		Unwmk.	Perf. 13	
326	CD103	5fr org brn & dk brn	1.00	.40
327	CD103	15fr aqua, slate & blk	1.25	.65
328	CD103	20fr grnsh bl & dp ultra	1.25	.65
329	CD103	25fr dp ultra	2.00	.85
		Nos. 326-329 (4)	5.50	2.55

For surcharges see Nos. 345, 347.

Coffee Issue

Coffee A35

1956		Engr.	Perf. 13
330	A35	15fr car & brt red	1.10 .25

For surcharge see No. 348.

Autonomous Government

Flag and Woman Holding Child A36

1958			
331	A36	20fr multicolored	1.00 .20

Anniv. of the installation of the 1st autonomous government of Cameroun.

Men Looking to the Sun — A37

1958

332	A37	20fr sepia & brn red	1.10 .25

10th anniv. of the signing of the Universal Declaration of Human Rights.

Flower Issue
Common Design Type
Design: 20fr, Randia malleifera.

1959		Photo.	Perf. 12½x12
333	CD104	20fr dp grn, yel & rose	.90 .20

Loading Bananas A38

Harvesting Bananas — A39

1959		Engr.	Perf. 13	
334	A38	20fr dk grn & org	.90	.20
335	A39	25fr maroon & slate grn	1.00	.20

For surcharge see No. 349.

Independent State

Map and Flag of Cameroun — A40

Prime Minister Ahmadou Ahidjo — A41

1960		Unwmk.	Engr.	Perf. 13
336	A40	20fr multicolored		.80 .20
337	A41	25fr blk, grn & pale lem		.85 .20

Declaration of independence, Jan. 1, 1960.
For surcharge see No. 350.

Uprooted Oak Emblem A42

1960

338	A42	30fr red brn, ultra & yel grn	1.10 .40

World Refugee Year, 7/1/59-6/30/60.
For surcharge see No. 351.

C.C.T.A. Issue
Common Design Type

1960			
339	CD106	50fr dull claret & slate	1.60 .40

UN Headquarters, NYC, and Flag — A43

1961, May 20			Perf. 13	

Flag in Green, Red and Yellow

340	A43	15fr grn, dk bl & brn	.60	.25
341	A43	25fr dk blue & grn	.75	.25
342	A43	85fr dk bl & vio brn	2.40	.80
		Nos. 340-342 (3)	3.75	1.30

Cameroun's admission to the UN, Sept. 20, 1960.

Federal Republic

Stamps of 1946-60 Surcharged in Red or Black:

Two types of 2sh6p:
I — Large figures. "2/6" measures 8x3¾mm.
II — Small figures. "2/6" measures 6x2½mm.

Perf. 12x12½, 13				
1961, Oct. 1			**Engr.**	
343	A27	½p on 1fr (#310)	.35	.20
344	A28	1p on 2fr (#313)	.45	.30
345	CD103	1½p on 5fr (#326)	.55	.35
346	A29	2p on 10fr (#318)	1.00	.45
347	CD103	3p on 15fr (#327)	1.40	.60
348	A35	4p on 15fr (Bk) (#330)	1.10	.70
349	A38	6p on 20fr (#334)	2.40	1.00
350	A41	1sh on 25fr (#337)	2.75	1.50
351	A42	2sh6p on 30fr (#338) (I)	5.00	5.00
a.		Type II	21.00	21.00
		Nos. 343-351 (9)	15.00	10.10

Issued for use in the former United Kingdom Trust Territory of Southern Cameroons.
The "Republique Federale" overprint is in one line on Nos. 345, 347-349, in two vertical lines on No. 350. See Nos. C38-C40.

President Ahidjo and Prime Minister Foncha A45

		Unwmk.		
1962, Jan. 1		**Engr.**	**Perf. 13**	
352	A45	20fr vio & choc	6.50	6.25
353	A45	25fr dk grn & brn	11.00	9.50
354	A45	60fr car & dl grn	32.50	29.00
		Nos. 352-354 (3)	50.00	44.75

Same Surcharged for Use in Southern Cameroons

355	A45	3p on 20fr	150.00	150.00
356	A45	6p on 25fr	150.00	150.00
357	A45	2sh6p on 60fr	150.00	150.00
		Nos. 355-357 (3)	450.00	450.00

Reunification of the former French and British Sections of Cameroun. It is reported that Nos. 352-357 were withdrawn after a few days and destroyed.

Mustache Monkey A46

Designs: 1fr, 4fr, Elephant, Ntem Falls. 1.50fr, 3fr, Buffon's kob, Dschang. 2fr, 5fr, Hippopotamus. 6fr, 15fr, Mustache monkey. 8fr, 30fr, Manatee, Lake Ossa. 10fr, 25fr, Buffalo, Batouri. 20fr, 40fr, Giraffes, Waza Reservation, vert.

1962		Unwmk. Engr.	Perf. 12	
358	A46	50c brn, brt grn & bl	.20	.20
359	A46	1fr gray brn, bl grn & org	.20	.20
360	A46	1.50fr brn, lt grn & sl grn	.20	.20
361	A46	2fr dk gray, grnsh bl & grn	.20	.20
362	A46	3fr brn, org & lil rose	.20	.20
363	A46	4fr brn, yel grn & bl grn	.25	.20
364	A46	5fr gray brn, grn & sal	.25	.20
365	A46	6fr brn, yel & bl	.45	.20
366	A46	8fr dk bl, red & grn	.90	.20
367	A46	10fr ol blk, org & brt bl	.70	.20
368	A46	15fr brn, Prus bl & bl	.90	.20
369	A46	20fr brn & gray	1.10	.20
370	A46	25fr red brn, grn & yel	2.75	.20
371	A46	30fr blk, org & bl	3.50	.25
372	A46	40fr dp cl, yel grn & blk	6.25	.40
		Nos. 358-372 (15)	18.05	3.25

See Nos. 396-397.

African and Malagasy Union Issue
Common Design Type

1962, Sept. 8		Photo.	Perf. 12½x12
373	CD110	30fr multicolored	2.00 .45

Village and Map of Cameroun A48

Designs: 20fr, 25fr, Sun rising over city. 50fr, Hands holding scroll.

1962, Oct. 1		Engr.	Perf. 13	
374	A48	9fr pur, olive & dk brn	.40	.20
375	A48	18fr grn, org brn & dk bl	.50	.20
376	A48	20fr lil rose, ol bis & ind	.50	.20
377	A48	25fr brn bl, red org & sep	.60	.20
378	A48	50fr dk red, sepia & bl	1.75	.50
		Nos. 374-378 (5)	3.75	1.30

1st anniv. of the reunification of Cameroun.

"School under the Trees" — A49

1962, Nov. 5   Photo.   Perf. 12x12½
379 A49 20fr ver, emerald & yel   1.00 .20
Literacy and popular education campaign.

Telstar and Globe A50

1963, Feb. 9   Engr.   Perf. 13
Size: 36x22mm
380 A50 1fr dk bl, olive & pur   .20 .20
381 A50 2fr dk bl, claret & grn   .20 .20
382 A50 3fr dk grn, ol & dp cl   .25 .20
383 A50 25fr grn, dp cl & brt bl   1.10 .40
   Nos. 380-383,C45 (5)   4.25 1.65
1st TV connection of the US and Europe through the Telstar satellite, July 11-12, 1962.

High Frequency Transmission Station, Mt. Bankolo — A51

Design: 20fr, Station and wiring plan.

1963, May 18   Photo.   Perf. 12x12½
384 A51 15fr multicolored   .45 .20
385 A51 20fr multicolored   .60 .20
   Nos. 384-385,C46 (3)   3.55 1.05
Issued to publicize the high frequency telegraph connection Douala-Yaounde.

"Yaoundé-Regional Center of Textbook Production" — A52

1963, Aug. 10   Unwmk.   Perf. 12½
386 A52 20fr emer, blk & red   .45 .20
387 A52 25fr org, blk & red   .55 .20
388 A52 100fr gold, blk & red   2.10 .60
   Nos. 386-388 (3)   3.10 1.00
UNESCO regional center for the production of school books at Yaounde.

Pres. Ahmadou Ahidjo and Flag — A53

Design: 18fr, Flag and map of Cameroun.

1963, Oct. 1   Perf. 12x12½
Flag in Green, Red and Yellow
389 A53 9fr grn, bl & dk brn   .45 .20
390 A53 18fr grn, bl & lil   .65 .20
391 A53 20fr grn, blk & yel grn   .70 .20
   Nos. 389-391 (3)   1.80 .60
Second anniversary of reunification.

Scales, Globe, UNESCO Emblem A54

1963, Dec. 10   Photo.   Perf. 12½x12
392 A54 9fr ultra, blk & sal   .35 .20
393 A54 18fr brt yel grn, blk & rose red   .45 .20
394 A54 25fr rose red, blk & brt yel grn   .60 .20
395 A54 75fr yel, blk & ultra   1.75 .50
   Nos. 392-395 (4)   3.15 1.10
Universal Declaration of Human Rights, 15th anniv.

Animal Type of 1962
Design: 10fr, 25fr, Lion, Waza National Park, North Cameroun.

1964, June 20   Engr.   Perf. 13
396 A46 10fr red brn, bis & grn   1.25 .20
397 A46 25fr green & bister   2.75 .20

Soccer Game in Stadium A55

18fr, Pile of sports equipment. 30fr, Stadium (outside), flags and map of Africa.

1964, July 11   Engr.   Perf. 13
398 A55 10fr grn, bl & red brn   .55 .20
399 A55 18fr car, grn & vio   .65 .20
400 A55 30fr blk, dk bl & org brn   1.10 .20
   Nos. 398-400 (3)   2.30 .60
Tropics Cup Games, Yaounde, July 11-19.

Europafrica Issue, 1964
Common Design Type and

Palace of Justice, Yaounde — A56

40fr, Emblems of Science, Agriculture, Industry and Education and two sunbursts.

1964, July 20   Photo.   Perf. 12x13
401 A56 15fr multicolored   1.25 .25
402 CD116 40fr multicolored   2.25 .60
1st anniv. of the economic agreement between the European Economic Community and the African and Malgache Union.

Hurdling and Olympic Flame — A57

Design: 10fr, Runners, vert.

1964, Oct. 10   Engr.   Perf. 13
403 A57 9fr red, yel grn & blk   1.50 .40
404 A57 10fr red, vio & ol gray   2.25 .40
   Nos. 403-404,C49 (3)   11.25 2.80
18th Olympic Games, Tokyo, Oct. 10-25.

Bamileke Dance Dress — A58   Ntem Falls, Ebolowa Region — A59

Designs: 18fr, Dance mask, Bamenda region. 25fr, Fulani horseman, North Cameroun, horiz.

1964   Unwmk.   Perf. 13
405 A58 9fr red, yel grn & bl   .55 .20
406 A58 18fr bl, red & brn   .70 .20
407 A59 20fr dk car, grn & ol   .90 .20
408 A58 25fr dk brn, org & car   1.40 .20
   Nos. 405-408,C50 (5)   4.55 1.15

Cooperation Issue
Common Design Type
1964, Nov. 7   Engr.
409 CD119 18fr dk bl, yel grn & dk brn   .80 .20
410 CD119 30fr red brn, bl grn & dk brn   1.60 .20

Memorial Stone — A60

Diesel Train A61

1965, Jan. 1   Engr.   Perf. 13
411 A60 12fr bl, indigo & grn   1.00 .20

Typo.   Perf. 14x13
412 A61 20fr rose car, yel & grn   2.50 .20
Laying of the 1st rail of the Mbanga-Kumba Railroad, Mar. 28, 1964.

Red Cross Station and Ambulance A62

50fr, Red Cross nurse and infant, vert.

1965, May 8   Engr.   Perf. 13
413 A62 25fr car, slate grn & ocher   .65 .20
414 A62 50fr gray, red & red brn   1.50 .30
Issued for the Cameroun Red Cross.

Coins Inserted in Map of Cameroun, and Bankbook — A63

Savings Bank Building — A64

Design: 20fr, Bankbook and coins inserted in cacao pod-shaped bank, vert.

1965, June 10
Size: 22x37mm
415 A63 9fr grn, red & org   .45 .20
Size: 48x27mm, 27x48mm
416 A64 15fr choc, ultra & grn   .55 .20
417 A63 20fr ocher, brt grn & brn   .65 .20
   Nos. 415-417 (3)   1.65 .60
Federal Postal Savings Banks.

Soccer Players and Africa Cup — A65

Unwmk.
1965, June 26   Engr.   Perf. 13
418 A65 9fr car, brn & yel   .55 .20
419 A65 20fr car, slate bl & yel   1.40 .20
Cameroun Oryx Club, winner of the club champions' Africa Cup, February 1965.

Symbolic Map of Europe and Africa — A66

40fr, Delegates around conference table.

1965, July 20   Photo.   Perf. 12x12½
420 A66 5fr car, blk & lilac   .30 .20
421 A66 40fr brn, buff, grn & ultra   1.50 .35
2nd, anniv. of the economic agreement between the European Economic Community and the African and Malgache Union.

UPU Monument, Bern A67

1965, July 26   Engr.   Perf. 13
422 A67 30fr black & red   .80 .25
Cameroun's admission to the UPU, 5th anniv.

ICY Emblem — A68

1965, Sept. 11   Unwmk.   Perf. 13
423 A68 10fr dk bl & car rose   .45 .20
Issued for the International Cooperation Year, 1964-65. See No. C57.

Pres. Ahidjo and Government
House — A69

Design: 9fr, 20fr, Pres. Ahidjo and Government House, vert.

Perf. 12x12½, 12½x12

1965, Oct. 1   Photo.   Unwmk.
424 A69 9fr multicolored   .25   .20
425 A69 18fr multicolored   .55   .20
426 A69 20fr multicolored   .65   .20
427 A69 25fr multicolored   .80   .20
         Nos. 424-427 (4)   2.25   .80
Reelection of Pres. Ahmadou Ahidjo.

National
Tourist
Office,
Yaoundé
A70

Designs: 9fr, Pouss Musgum houses. 18fr,
Great Calao's dance (North Cameroun). 20fr,
Gate of Sultan's Palace, Foumban, vert.

1965   Engr.   Perf. 13
428 A70 9fr grn, rose red & grn   .45   .20
429 A70 18fr brt bl, brn & grn   .65   .20
430 A70 20fr bl, brn & choc   1.00   .20
431 A70 25fr mar, emer & gray   .90   .20
         Nos. 428-431 (4)   3.00   .80
         See No. C58.

Mountain Hotel, Buea — A71

Designs: 20fr, Hotel of the Deputies,
Yaoundé. 35fr, Dschang Health Center.

1966
432 A71 9fr sl grn, rose cl &
          brn   .35   .20
433 A71 20fr brt bl, sl grn & blk   .45   .20
434 A71 35fr brn, sl grn & car   .80   .30
         Nos. 432-434,C63-C69 (10) 14.40 3.45

Bas-relief,
Foumban
A72

Designs: 18fr, Ekoi mask, vert. 20fr, Mother
and child, carving, Bamiléké, vert. 25fr, Ceremonial stool, Bamoun.

1966, Apr. 15   Unwmk.
435 A72 9fr red & blk   .55   .20
436 A72 18fr brt grn, org brn &
          choc   .65   .20
437 A72 20fr brt bl, red brn & pur 1.00   .20
438 A72 25fr pur & dk brn   1.10   .20
         Nos. 435-438 (4)   3.30   .80
Intl. Negro Arts Festival, Dakar, Senegal,
4/1-24.

New WHO Headquarters,
Geneva — A73

1966, May 3   Photo.   Perf. 12½x13
439 A73 50fr ultra, red brn & yel 1.40   .35

ITU Headquarters, Geneva — A74

1966, May 3   Photo.   Perf. 12½x13
440 A74 50fr ultra & yellow   1.40   .35

Phaeomeria   "6" and Men
Magnifica — A75   Dancing around
                    UN
                    Emblem — A76

Flowers: 18fr, Hibiscus (rose of China). 20fr,
Mountain rose.

1966, May 20   Perf. 12x12½
Flowers in Natural Colors
Size: 22x36mm
441 A75 9fr red brown   .55   .20
442 A75 18fr green   .70   .20
443 A75 20fr dark green   .70   .20
         Nos. 441-443,C70-C72 (6)   7.55 1.25
         See No. 469.

1966, Sept. 20   Engr.   Perf. 13
Design: 50fr, UN General Assembly, horiz.
444 A76 50fr ultra, grn & vio brn .90   .20
445 A76 100fr red brn, grn & ul-
          tra   2.00   .50
6th anniv. of Cameroun's admission to the
UN.

Prime Minister's Residence,
Buea — A77

Designs (Prime Minister's Residences):
18fr, at Yaoundé, front view. 20fr, at Yaoundé,
side view. 25fr, at Buea, front view.

1966, Oct. 1   Photo.
446 A77 9fr multicolored   .45   .20
447 A77 18fr multicolored   .65   .20
448 A77 20fr multicolored   .65   .20
449 A77 25fr multicolored   .80   .20
         Nos. 446-449 (4)   2.55   .80
5th anniversary of re-unification.

Learning to
Write and
UNESCO
Emblem
A78

#451, Children's heads & UNICEF emblem.

1966, Nov. 24   Engr.   Perf. 13
450 A78 50fr red lil, bl & brn   1.40   .30
451 A78 50fr red lil, blk & brt bl 1.40   .30
20th anniv. of UNESCO, 20th anniv. of
UNICEF.

Independence Proclamation — A79

1967, Jan. 1   Engr.   Perf. 13
452 A79 20fr grn, red & yel   2.00   .25
7th anniversary of independence.

Map of Africa
and
Madagascar,
Railroad Tracks
and
Symbols — A80

25fr, Map of Africa and Madagascar and
train.

1967, Feb. 21   Photo.   Perf. 13
453 A80 20fr multicolored   4.00   .20
454 A80 25fr multicolored   6.00   .20
5th Conf. of African and Madagascan Railroad Technicians.

Lions Emblem and Forest — A81

Design: 100fr, Lions emblem and palms.

1967, Mar. 3
455 A81 50fr multicolored   .90   .35
456 A81 100fr multicolored   2.10   .65
Lions International, 50th anniversary.

Jet and I.C.A.O.
Emblem — A82

Dove and
I.A.E.A.
Emblem
A83

Perf. 13x12½, 12½x13
1967, Mar. 15   Photo.
457 A82 50fr ultra, lt bl, brn & gold 1.25   .35
458 A83 50fr ultra & emer   1.25   .35
UN agencies: No. 457, the ICAO; No. 458,
the Intl. Atomic Energy Agency.

Rotary International Emblem — A84

1967, Apr. 17   Photo.   Perf. 12½
459 A84 25fr crim, vio bl & gold   1.25   .20
10th anniversary of the Douala, Cameroun,
branch of Rotary International.

Grapefruit — A85   Bird of Paradise
                    Flower — A86

1967, May 10   Photo.   Perf. 12x12½
460 A85 1fr shown   .20   .20
461 A85 2fr Papaya   .20   .20
462 A85 3fr Custard apple   .20   .20
463 A85 4fr Breadfruit   .20   .20
464 A85 5fr Coconut   .35   .20
465 A85 6fr Mango   .45   .20
466 A85 8fr Avacado   .90   .20
467 A85 10fr Pineapple   1.40   .20
468 A85 30fr Bananas   3.50   .20
         Nos. 460-468 (9)   7.40 1.80
For surcharges see Nos. 550, 593.

1967, June 22 Photo. Perf. 12x12½
Size: 22x36mm
469 A86 15fr lt blue & multi   .90   .20

Sanaga Falls and
ITY Emblem — A87

1967, Aug. 14 Photo. Perf. 13x12½
470 A87 30fr multicolored   .80   .20
Issued for International Tourist Year 1967.

Art of
Cameroun:
Coconut
Harvest
A88

Carved Bas-relief: 20fr, Lion hunt. 30fr,
Women carrying baskets. 100fr, Carved chest.

1967, Sept. 22   Perf. 12½x13
471 A88 10fr brn, bl & car   .35   .20
472 A88 20fr brn, yel & grn   .55   .20
473 A88 30fr emer, brn & car   .90   .20
474 A88 100fr red org, brn & em-
          er   2.25   .40
         Nos. 471-474 (4)   4.05 1.00

Coat of Arms
A89

1968, Jan. 1 Litho. Perf. 12½x13
475 A89 30fr gold & multi   1.00 .20

Spiny Lobster
A90

Designs (Fish and Crustaceans): 10fr, River crayfish. 15fr, Nile mouth-breeder. 20fr, Sole. 25fr, Common pike. 30fr, Crab. 40fr, Spadefish, vert. 50fr, Shrimp, vert. 55fr, African snakehead. 60fr, Threadfin.

1968, July 25 Engr. Perf. 13
476	A90	5fr brn, vio bl & dl grn	.20	.20
477	A90	10fr ultra, brn ol & slate	.20	.20
478	A90	15fr sal, red lil & sepia	.70	.20
479	A90	20fr red brn, dp bl & sep	.80	.20
480	A90	25fr lt brn, emer & slate	.90	.20
481	A90	30fr mag, dk bl & dk brn	1.10	.20
482	A90	40fr slate bl & org	1.60	.20
483	A90	50fr emer, gray & rose car	2.40	.20
484	A90	55fr lt brn, Prus bl & dk brn	3.25	.25
485	A90	60fr brn, bl grn & indigo	5.00	.35
		Nos. 476-485 (10)	16.15	2.20

Tanker, Refinery and Map of Area Served — A91

1968, July 30 Photo. Perf. 12½
486 A91 30fr multicolored   1.10 .20
Port Gentil (Gabon) Refinery opening, 6/12/68.

Human Rights Flame
A92

1968, Sept. 14 Photo. Perf. 12½x13
487 A92 15fr blue & salmon   .65 .20
Intl. Human Rights Year. See No. C110.

Pres. Ahmadou Ahidjo
A93

1969, Apr. 10 Photo. Perf. 12½x12
488 A93 30fr carmine & multi   .80 .20

Chocolate Vat — A94

Designs: 30fr, Chocolate factory. 50fr, Candy making, vert.

1969, Apr. 24 Engr. Perf. 13
489	A94	15fr red brn, ind & choc	.50	.20
490	A94	30fr grn, blk & red brn	.80	.20
491	A94	50fr brown & multi	1.10	.20
		Nos. 489-491 (3)	2.40	.60

Cameroun chocolate industry.

Fertility Symbol, Abbia — A95

Diesel Train on Bridge — A96

Art and Folklore from Abbia: 10fr, Two toucans, horiz. 15fr, Forest symbol. 30fr, Vulture attacking monkey, horiz. 70fr, Oliphant player.

1969, May 30 Engr. Perf. 13
492	A95	5fr ultra, Prus bl & brt rose lil	.25	.20
493	A95	10fr bl, ol gray & org	.35	.20
494	A95	15fr ultra, dk red & blk	.45	.20
495	A95	30fr brt bl, lem & grn	.80	.20
496	A95	70fr brt bl, dk grn & ver	1.75	.35
		Nos. 492-496 (5)	3.60	1.15

Perf. 12½x13, 13x12½

1969, July 11 Photo.
Design: 30fr, Kumba Railroad station, horiz.
497 A96 30fr blue & multi   1.00 .20
498 A96 50fr black & multi   2.50 .25
Opening of Mbanga-Kumba Railroad.

Development Bank Issue
Common Design Type
1969, Sept. 10 Engr. Perf. 13
499 CD130 30fr vio bl, grn & ocher   .80 .20
African Development Bank, 5th anniv.

ASECNA Issue
Common Design Type
1969, Dec. 12 Engr. Perf. 13
500 CD132 100fr slate green   2.00 .60

Red Sage — A99

Design: 30fr, Passionflower.

1970, Mar. 24 Photo. Perf. 12x12½
Size: 22x36½mm
501 A99 15fr yel grn & multi   .45 .20
502 A99 30fr multicolored   1.00 .20
    Nos. 501-502,C140-C141 (4) 5.60 1.05

UPU Headquarters Issue
Common Design Type
1970, May 20 Engr. Perf. 13
503 CD133 30fr blue, pur & grn   1.00 .20
504 CD133 50fr gray, red & bl   1.50 .20

Brewery A100

Design: 30fr, Cellar with barrels.

1970, July 9 Engr. Perf. 13
505 A100 15fr brn, gray & dk grn   .45 .20
506 A100 30fr bl grn, dk brn & brn red   .90 .20
Cameroun brewing industry.

Ozila Dancers — A101

Cameroun Doll — A102

Design: 50fr, Ozila dancer and drummer.

1970, Oct. 19 Engr. Perf. 13
507 A101 30fr multicolored   1.00 .20
508 A101 50fr red & multi   2.75 .20

1970, Nov. 2
Designs: 15fr, Doll in short skirt. 30fr, Doll with basket on back.
509 A102 10fr car & multi   .60 .20
510 A102 15fr dk grn & multi   .70 .20
511 A102 30fr brn red & multi 1.90 .20
    Nos. 509-511 (3)   3.20 .60

Cogwheels and Grain
A103

1970, Feb. 9 Photo. Perf. 13
512 A103 30fr multicolored   .80 .20
Europafrica Economic Conference.

Federal University, Yaoundé
A104

1971, Jan. 19 Engr.
513 A104 50fr multicolored   1.00 .20
Inauguration of Federal University at Yaoundé.

Presidents Ahidjo and Pompidou, Flags of Cameroun and France — A105

1971, Feb. 9 Photo. Perf. 13
514 A105 30fr multicolored   1.50 .35
Visit of Georges Pompidou, Pres. of France.

Young People, Globe, Map of Cameroun
A106

1971, Feb. 11
515 A106 30fr blue & multi   .80 .20
Fifth National Youth Festival, Feb. 11.

Gerbera Hybrida — A107

Men of Four Races — A108

Designs: 40fr, Opuntia polyantha (cactus). 50fr, Hemerocallis hybrida (lily).

1971, Mar. 14 Photo.
516 A107 20fr multicolored   .60 .20
517 A107 40fr green & multi   1.50 .20
518 A107 50fr blue & multi   2.10 .20
    Nos. 516-518 (3)   4.20 .60

1971, Mar. 21 Perf. 13x12½
Design: 30fr, Hands and globe.
519 A108 20fr green & multi   .55 .20
520 A108 30fr ultra & multi   .70 .20
Intl. year against racial discrimination.

Crowned Cranes at Waza Camp
A109

20fr, Canoe on Sanaga River. 30fr, Sanaga River.

1971, Apr. 9 Engr. Perf. 13
521 A109 10fr red, grn & blk   1.50 .20
522 A109 20fr dk grn, brn & red 1.00 .20
523 A109 30fr red, dk grn & brt bl   1.50 .20
    Nos. 521-523 (3)   4.00 .60

International Court, The Hague — A110

1971, June 14   Engr.   Perf. 13
524 A110 50fr ultra, org brn & sl grn   .90   .20

25th anniversary of the International Court in The Hague, Netherlands.

Liana Bridge — A111

Bamoun Horseman A113

Local Market A112

1971, Aug. 16   Photo.   Perf. 13
525 A111 40fr multicolored   1.25   .20
526 A112 45fr multicolored   1.50   .20

1971, Sept. 18

African Art: 15fr, Animal fetish statuette.

527 A113 10fr brown & yellow   .50   .50
528 A113 15fr dp brn & org yel   .50   .50

Communications Satellite and Globe — A114

1971, Oct. 14   Perf. 13x12½
529 A114 40fr Prus bl, sl grn & org   .80   .20

Pan-African telecommunications system.

UNICEF Emblem A115

50fr, UNICEF emblem and grain, vert.

1971, Dec. 11   Engr.   Perf. 13
530 A115 40fr sl grn, bl grn & plum   .95   .20
531 A115 50fr dp bl, dk red & lt grn   1.25   .25

25th anniv. of UNICEF.

Houses from South-Central Region — A116

Design: 15fr, Adamaua round houses.

1972, Jan. 15   Photo.   Perf. 13
532 A116 10fr dk blue & multi   .25   .20
533 A116 15fr black & multi   .55   .20

Giraffe — A117

Designs: 5fr, Home industries. 10fr, Smith, horiz. 15fr, Women carrying burdens.

Perf. 13x13½, 13½x13
1972, Feb. 18   Litho.
534 A117 2fr multicolored   .30   .20
535 A117 5fr black, org & red   .30   .20
536 A117 10fr multicolored   .30   .20
537 A117 15fr multicolored   .30   .20
Nos. 534-537 (4)   1.20   .80

Youth Day 1972.

Soccer Players and Field — A118

Designs: 20fr, African Soccer Cup, vert. 45fr, Team captains shaking hands, vert.

1972, Feb. 22   Perf. 13½
538 A118 20fr gray & multi   .55   .20
539 A118 40fr gray & multi   .95   .20
540 A118 45fr yellow & multi   1.50   .25
Nos. 538-540 (3)   3.00   .65

African Soccer Cup, Yaoundé, 2/23-3/5.

Government Building, Yaoundé, and Laurel — A119

1972, Apr. 6   Photo.   Perf. 12½x12
541 A119 40fr multicolored   .80   .20

110th session of Inter-Parliamentary Council, Yaoundé, Apr. 1972.

"Fantasia," North Cameroun A120

Bororo Woman — A121

40fr, Boat on Wouri River & Mt. Cameroun.

1972, Apr. 24   Perf. 13x12½, 12½x13
542 A120 15fr dk vio & multi   .35   .20
543 A121 20fr multicolored   .45   .20
544 A120 40fr multicolored   1.50   .20
Nos. 542-544 (3)   2.30   .60

Chemical Apparatus A122

1972, May 15   Engr.   Perf. 13
545 A122 40fr lilac, red & green   .80   .20
President Ahmadou Ahidjo Prize.

United Republic

Solanum Macranthum A123

Design: 45fr, Wax plant.

1972, July 20   Photo.   Perf. 13
546 A123 40fr multicolored   .95   .20
547 A123 45fr yellow & multi   1.25   .20

Charaxes Ameliae A124

Design: 45fr, Papilio tynderaeus.

1972, Aug. 20   Photo.   Perf. 13
548 A124 40fr bl, dk bl & gold   3.00   .20
549 A124 45fr lt grn, blk & gold   4.00   .20

No. 468 Surcharged

1972, Aug. 30   Photo.   Perf. 12x12½
550 A85 40fr on 30fr multicolored   1.00   .20

Resurrection Lily — A125

Great Blue Touraco — A126

Flowers: 45fr, Candlestick cassia. 50fr, Amaryllis.

1972, Sept. 16   Perf. 13
551 A125 40fr lt green & multi   1.00   .20
552 A125 45fr multicolored   1.50   .20
553 A125 50fr lt blue & multi   2.10   .20
Nos. 551-553 (3)   4.60   .60

Perf. 12½x13, 13x12½
1972, Nov. 20   Litho.

Design: 45fr, Red-faced lovebirds, horiz.

554 A126 10fr yellow & multi   1.75   .20
555 A126 45fr yellow & multi   3.75   .20

Cotton (North) — A127

10fr, Cacao (south central). 15fr, Logging (southeast & southern coast). 20fr, Coffee (west). 45fr, Tea (northwest & southwest).

1973, Mar. 26   Photo.   Perf. 12½x13
556 A127 5fr black & multi   .25   .20
557 A127 10fr black & multi   .25   .20
558 A127 15fr black & multi   .75   .20
559 A127 20fr black & multi   1.50   .20
560 A127 45fr black & multi   3.25   .20
Nos. 556-560 (5)   6.00   1.00

Third 5-Year Plan.
For surcharge see No. 568.

Flag and Map of Cameroun, Pres. Ahidjo and No. 331 — A128

Design: 20fr, Proclamation of independence, Pres. Ahidjo and No. 336.

1973, May 20   Engr.   Perf. 13
561 A128 10fr ultra & multi   .65   .20
562 A128 20fr multicolored   1.00   .20
Nos. 561-562, C200-C201 (4)   3.45   .85

United Republic of Cameroun, 1st anniv.

Bamoun Mask — A129

Dr. Hansen — A130

Designs: Various Bamoun masks.

1973, July 10   Engr.   Perf. 13
563 A129 5fr green, brn & blk   .20   .20
564 A129 10fr lilac, brn & blk   .25   .20
565 A129 45fr red, brn & blk   .75   .20
566 A129 100fr ultra, brn & blk   2.00   .40
Nos. 563-566 (4)   3.20   1.00

1973, July 25   Engr.   Perf. 13
567 A130 45fr multicolored   1.60   .20

Centenary of the discovery by Dr. Armauer G. Hansen of the Hansen bacillus, the cause of leprosy.

No. 556 Surcharged with New Value,
2 Bars, and Overprinted in
Ultramarine:
"SECHERESSE/SOLIDARITE
AFRICAINE"

1973, Aug. 16　Photo.　Perf. 12½x13
568　A127　100fr on 5fr multicolored　1.75　.40
African solidarity in drought emergency.

Dancers, South
West
Africa — A131

WMO
Emblem — A132

Designs: Southwest African dances.

1973, Aug. 17　　　　　Perf. 13
569　A131　10fr multicolored　　　.20　.20
570　A131　25fr multicolored　　　.55　.20
571　A131　45fr multicolored　　1.10　.20
　　　Nos. 569-571 (3)　　　1.85　.60

1973, Sept. 1　Engr.　Perf. 13
572　A132　45fr green & ultra　　1.60　.20
Cent. of intl. meteorological cooperation.

Garoua Party Headquarters — A133

1973, Sept. 1　　　　　Photo.
573　A133　40fr multicolored　　　.80　.20
7th anniv. of Cameroun National Union.

African Postal Union Issue, 1973
Common Design Type
1973, Sept. 12　　　　　Engr.
574　CD137　100fr brt bl, bl & sl grn　1.75　.40

Avocados — A135

1973, Sept. 20
575　A135　10fr shown　　　　.70　.20
576　A135　20fr Mangos　　　.80　.20
577　A135　45fr Plums　　　2.00　.20
578　A135　50fr Custard apple　2.50　.20
　　　Nos. 575-578 (4)　　　6.00　.80

Kirdi Village
A136

45fr, Mabas village. 50fr, Fishing village.

1973, Oct. 25　Engr.　Perf. 13
579　A136　15fr black, bis & grn　.25　.20
580　A136　45fr magenta, brn &
　　　　　　org　　　　　.90　.20
581　A136　50fr green, blk & org　1.25　.20
　　　Nos. 579-581 (3)　　　2.40　.60

Handshake on
Map of
Africa — A137

1974, May 15　Engr.　Perf. 12½x13
582　A137　40fr carmine & multi　.55　.20
583　A137　45fr indigo & multi　　.70　.20
Organization for African Unity, 10th anniv.

Spinning
Mill — A138

1974, May 25　Engr.　Perf. 13x12½
584　A138　45fr multicolored　　　.80　.20
CICAM Industrial Complex.

Carved
Panel from
Bilinga
A139

Cameroun Art (Carvings): 40fr, Detail from
Bubinga chair. 45fr, Detail Acajou Ngollon
panel.

1974, May 30
585　A139　10fr brt grn & ocher　.25　.20
586　A139　40fr red & brown　　.80　.20
587　A139　45fr blue & rose brn　1.10　.20
　　　Nos. 585-587 (3)　　　2.15　.60

Zebu — A140

1974, June 1　　　　　Perf. 13½
588　A140　40fr multicolored　　1.40　.20
North Cameroun cattle raising. See No.
C210.

Laying Rail
Section
A141

Designs: 5fr, Map showing line Yaoundé to
Ngaoundéré, vert. 40fr, Welding rail joint, vert.
100fr, Train on Djerem River Bridge.

Perf. 12½x13, 13x12½
1974, June 10　　　　　Engr.
589　A141　5fr multicolored　　　.65　.20
590　A141　20fr multicolored　　1.10　.20
591　A141　40fr multicolored　　1.75　.20
592　A141　100fr multicolored　3.00　.40
　　　Nos. 589-592 (4)　　　6.50　1.00
Opening of Yaoundé-Ngaoundéré railroad
line.
For surcharge see No. 596.

No. 466 Surcharged
1974, June 1　Photo.　Perf. 12x12½
593　A85　40fr on 8fr multi　　　.80　.20

UPU
Emblem,
Hands
Holding
Letters
A142

1974, Oct. 8　Engr.　Perf. 13
594　A142　40fr multicolored　　.90　.20
　　　Nos. 594,C218-C219 (3)　5.90　1.10
Cent. of the UPU.

Presidents and Flags of Cameroun,
CAR, Congo, Gabon and Meeting
Center — A143

1974, Dec. 8　Photo.　Perf. 13
595　A143　40fr gold & multi　　1.50　.20
10th anniversary of Central African Customs
and Economic Union (Union Douanière et
Economique de l'Afrique Centrale, UDEAC).
See No. C223.

No. 589
Surcharged in
Violet Blue

1974, Dec. 10　Engr.　Perf. 12½x13
596　A141　100fr on 5fr multi　　1.75　.45

Virgin of
Autun, 15th
Century
Sculpture
A144

Christmas: 45fr, Virgin and Child, by Luis de
Morales (c. 1509-1586).

1974, Dec. 20　Photo.　Perf. 13
597　A144　40fr gold & multi　　.95　.20
598　A144　45fr gold & multi　1.25　.20

Tropical
Plants — A145

1975, Mar. 10　Photo.　Perf. 13
599　A145　5fr Cockscomb　　　.25　.20
600　A145　40fr Costus spectabilis　1.40　.20
601　A145　45fr Mussaenda er-
　　　　　ythrophylla　　　1.75　.20
　　　Nos. 599-601 (3)　　　3.40　.60

Fishing by Night — A146

1975, Apr. 1　Engr.　Perf. 13
602　A146　40fr shown　　　　1.60　.20
603　A146　45fr Fishing by day　2.10　.20

Afo Akom Statue
and Chief's
Stool — A147

Tree
Fungus — A148

1975, Apr. 1　　　　　Photo.
604　A147　40fr multicolored　　.65　.20
605　A147　45fr multicolored　　.85　.20
606　A147　200fr multicolored　2.50　.75
　　　Nos. 604-606 (3)　　　4.00　1.15

1975, Apr. 14
607　A148　15fr shown　　　150.00　.20
608　A148　40fr Chrysalis　　90.00　.20

Ministry of Posts and
Telecommunications — A149

1975, July 21　Engr.　Perf. 13
609　A149　40fr brn, grn & Prus bl　.65　.20
610　A149　45fr Prus bl, brn & grn　.90　.20

Presbyterian Church, Elat — A150

Designs: No. 612, Foumban Mosque. 45fr,
Catholic Church, Ngaoundere.

1975, Aug. 20　Engr.　Perf. 13
611　A150　40fr multicolored　　.45　.20
612　A150　40fr multicolored　　.45　.20
613　A150　45fr multicolored　　.65　.20
　　　Nos. 611-613 (3)　　　1.55　.60

Plowing
A151

Design: No. 615, Corn harvest, vert.

Perf. 13x12½, 12½x13
1975, Dec. 15 Photo.
614 A151 40fr deep grn & multi .80 .20
615 A151 40fr deep grn & multi .80 .20
Green revolution.

Zamengoe Satellite Monitoring Station — A152

1976, May 20 Litho. **Perf. 13**
616 A152 40fr shown .60 .20
617 A152 100fr Radar, vert. 1.10 .40

Porcelain Rose — A153

Design: 50fr, Flower of North Cameroun.

1976, July 20 Litho. **Perf. 12½**
618 A153 40fr multicolored 1.00 .20
619 A153 50fr multicolored 1.40 .20

Leopard Dance — A154

Telephone Exchange A155

1976, Sept. 15 Litho. **Perf. 12**
620 A154 40fr gray & multi .80 .20
Nos. 620,C233-C234 (3) 2.55 .75

1976, Oct. 5 **Perf. 13**
621 A155 50fr multicolored .80 .20
Centenary of first telephone call by Alexander Graham Bell, Mar. 10, 1876.

Young Men Building House — A156

Design: 45fr, Young women working in field.

1976, Oct. 10 Litho. **Perf. 12**
622 A156 40fr multicolored .35 .20
623 A156 45fr multicolored .55 .20
10th National Youth Day.

Konrad Adenauer (1876-1967), German Chancellor, Cologne Cathedral A157

1976, Oct. 20
624 A157 100fr multicolored .90 .40

Party Headquarters, Douala — A158

No. 626, Party Headquarters, Yaoundé.

1976, Dec. 28 Litho. **Perf. 12**
625 A158 50fr orange & multi .45 .20
626 A158 50fr blue & multi .45 .20
10th anniv. of the Cameroun National Union.

Bamoun Copper Pipe — A159

Ostrich — A160

1977, Feb. 4 Litho. **Perf. 12½**
627 A159 50fr multicolored .70 .20
2nd World Black and African Festival, Lagos, Nigeria, 1/15-2/12. See No. C239.

1977, Mar. 20 Litho. **Perf. 12**
628 A160 30fr shown 2.25 .20
629 A160 50fr Crowned cranes 2.75 .20

Cameroun No. 609 and Switzerland No. 3L1 — A161

1977, June 5 Litho. **Perf. 12**
630 A161 50fr multicolored 1.00 .20
Nos. 630,C252-C253 (3) 4.35 .85
Juflex Philatelic Exhibition, Bern, Switzerland. See Nos. C252-C253.

Winter Olympics 1976, set of five, 40, 50fr, airmail 140, 200, 350fr, and airmail souv. sheet, 500fr, issued Aug. 10, 1977. Nos. 7701-7706. Value, set $7.50, souvenir sheet $5.

Apollo-Soyuz — A163

Designs: 40fr, Astronaut Thomas P. Stafford, Apollo lifting off. 60fr, Cosmonaut Alexei Leonov, Soyuz lifting off.

1977, Aug. 10 Litho. **Perf. 14x13½**
633 A163 40fr multicolored .45 .25
634 A163 60fr multicolored .70 .50
Nos. 633-634,C256-C258 (5) 7.55 6.60

No. 617 Overprinted in French and English in Red: "To the Welfare of the / families of martyrs and / freedom fighters of Palestine."
1977, Aug. 22 Litho. **Perf. 13**
635 A152 100fr multicolored .90 .40
Palestinian fighters and their families.

Chairman Mao and Great Wall A164

1977, Sept. 9 Engr. **Perf. 13**
636 A164 100fr olive & brown 3.00 .40
Mao Tse-tung (1893-1976), Chinese communist leader, first death anniversary.

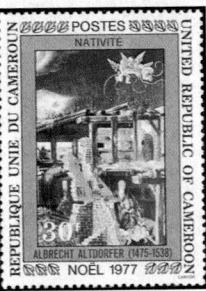
Nativity, by Albrecht Altdorfer A165

50fr, Madonna of the Grand Duke, by Raphael.
1977, Dec. 15 Litho. **Perf. 12½x12**
637 A165 30fr multicolored .55 .20
638 A165 50fr multicolored 1.10 .20
Nos. 637-638,C264-C265 (4) 7.65 2.40
Christmas 1977.

Gazelle and Rotary Emblem — A166

Pres. Ahidjo, Flag and Map of Cameroun A167

1978, Feb. 11 Litho. **Perf. 12**
639 A166 50fr orange & multi .70 .20
Rotary Club of Yaounde, 20th anniversary.

1978, Apr. 3 Litho. **Perf. 12½**
640 A167 50fr multicolored .90 .20
New flag of Cameroun. See No. C266.

Cardioglossa Escalerae — A168

Design: 60fr, Cardioglossa elegans.

1978, Apr. 5
641 A168 50fr multicolored 1.75 .20
642 A168 60fr multicolored 2.75 .25
Nos. 641-642,C267 (3) 8.25 .85

Jules Verne and "From Earth to Moon" — A169

1978, Oct. 10 Litho. **Perf. 12**
643 A169 250fr multicolored 2.25 1.40
Jules Verne (1828-1905), science fiction writer, birth sesquicentennial. See No. C276.

Hypolimnas Salmacis Drury — A170

Butterflies: 25fr, Euxanthe trajanus ward. 30fr, Euphaedra cyparissa cramer.

1978, Oct. 15
644 A170 20fr multicolored 2.00 .20
645 A170 25fr multicolored 2.25 .20
646 A170 30fr multicolored 3.75 .20
Nos. 644-646 (3) 8.00 .60

Men Planting Seedlings A171

Carved Bamun Drum A172

1978, Oct. 30
647 A171 10fr multicolored .25 .20
648 A171 15fr multicolored .35 .20

Green barrier against the desert.

1978, Nov. 20   Litho.   Perf. 12½
60fr, String instrument (Guéguérou), horiz.
649 A172 50fr multicolored .45 .20
650 A172 60fr multicolored .65 .25
Nos. 649-650,C277 (3) 2.20 .85

Pres. Ahidjo, Giscard D'Estaing, Flags of Cameroun and France — A173

1979, Feb. 8   Photo.   Perf. 13
651 A173 60fr multicolored 1.50 .25

Visit of Pres. Valery Giscard D'Estaing of France to Cameroun.

Human Rights Emblem, Globe, Scroll and African — A174

1979, Feb. 11   Litho.   Perf. 12x12½
652 A174 5fr multicolored .20 .20

Universal Declaration of Human Rights, 30th anniversary (in 1978). See No. C278. See No. 803.

Boy and Girl Greeting Sun — A175

1979, Aug. 15   Litho.   Perf. 12
653 A175 50fr multicolored .70 .20

International Year of the Child.

Protected Animals A176

Nos. 655, 658 vert.

1979, Sept. 20   Perf. 12½
654 A176 50fr Rhinoceros 1.50 .20
655 A176 60fr Giraffe 2.25 .25
656 A176 60fr Gorilla 2.25 .25
657 A176 100fr Leopard 3.50 .40
658 A176 100fr Elephant 3.50 .40
Nos. 654-658 (5) 13.00 1.50

Eugene Jamot, Map of Cameroun, Tsetse Fly — A177

1979, Nov. 5   Engr.   Perf. 13
659 A177 50fr multicolored 3.00 .20

Eugene Jamot (1879-1937), discoverer of sleeping sickness cure.

Annunciation, by Fra Filippo Lippi — A178

Paintings; 50fr, Rest During the Flight to Egypt, c. 1620. No. 622, Flight into Egypt, by Jan Joest, No. 663, Nativity, by Joest. 100fr, Nativity, by Botticelli.

1979, Dec. 6   Litho.   Perf. 12½x12
660 A178 10fr multicolored .20 .20
661 A178 50fr multicolored .60 .25
662 A178 60fr multicolored .75 .30
663 A178 60fr multicolored .75 .30
a.   Pair, #662-663 1.50 .65
664 A178 100fr multicolored 1.50 .40
Nos. 660-664 (5) 3.80 1.45

Christmas 1979.

Piper Capense A179

Medicinal Plants: 60fr, Bracken fern.

1979, Dec. 15   Litho.   Perf. 12½
665 A179 50fr multicolored 1.10 .20
666 A179 60fr multicolored 1.40 .25

Pres. Ahidjo, Cameroun Map, Arms and No. 331 A180

1980, Feb. 12   Litho.   Perf. 12½
667 A180 50fr multicolored .65 .20

Independence, 20th anniversary.

Congress Building, Bafoussam A181

1980, Feb. 12
668 A181 50fr multicolored .65 .20
Cameroun National Union, 3rd Ordinary Congress, Bafoussam, Feb. 12-17.

Rotary Emblem, Map of Cameroun A182

Rotary Intl., 75th Anniv.: #670, Anniv. emblem.

1980, Mar. 15   Litho.   Perf. 12½
669 A182 200fr multicolored 2.25 .80
670 A182 200fr multicolored 2.25 .80
a.   Souvenir sheet of 2, #669-670 5.00 1.60

Voacanga Medicinal Beans A183

1980, Dec. 3   Litho.   Perf. 12½
671 A183 50fr shown 1.00 .20
672 A183 60fr Voacanga tree, vert. 1.25 .25
673 A183 100fr Voacanga flower, vert. 1.75 .40
Nos. 671-673 (3) 4.00 .85

Violet Mellowstone A184

1980, Dec. 5
674 A184 50fr shown .70 .20
675 A184 60fr Patula 1.00 .25
676 A184 100fr Cashmere bouquet 1.60 .40
Nos. 674-676 (3) 3.30 .85

Occupation of Mecca by Mohammed, 1350th Anniversary — A185

1980, Dec. 9
677 A185 50fr multicolored 1.00 .30

African Slender-snouted Crocodile (Endangered Species) — A186

1980, Dec. 24
678 A186 200fr shown 3.25 .80
679 A186 300fr Buffon's antelope, vert. 4.25 1.20
See Nos. 888-889.

Bororo Girls and Roumsiki Peaks — A187

1980, Dec. 29
680 A187 50fr shown .55 .20
681 A187 60fr Dschang tourist center .55 .25

Banana Tree A188

1981, Feb. 5
682 A188 50fr shown .65 .30
683 A188 60fr Cattle, vert. .80 .40

Girl on Crutches — A189

1981, Feb. 20   Litho.   Perf. 12½
684 A189 60fr shown .55 .25
685 A189 150fr Boy in motorized wheelchair 1.25 .65

International Year of the Disabled.

Air Terminal, Douala Airport — A190

1981, Apr. 4   Litho.   Perf. 12½
686 A190 100fr shown .90 .55
687 A190 200fr Boeing 747 2.00 1.10
688 A190 300fr Douala Intl. Airport 2.75 1.60
Nos. 686-688 (3) 5.65 3.25

Cameroun Airlines, 10th anniv.

Pres. Ahidjo Presenting Trophy to Canon Soccer Team — A191

1981, Apr. 20
689 A191 60fr shown .90 .40
690 A191 60fr Union team captain .90 .40

1979 African Soccer Cup champions.

Scaly Anteater A192

Designs: Endangered species.

1981, July 20   **Litho.**   *Perf. 12½*
691 A192 50fr Moutourou   1.50 .20
692 A192 50fr Tortoise   1.50 .20
693 A192 100fr shown   3.00 .40
   Nos. 691-693 (3)   6.00 .80

Prince Charles and Lady Diana, St. Paul's Cathedral A193

1981, July 29   **Litho.**   *Perf. 12½*
694 A193 500fr shown   4.50 2.00
695 A193 500fr Couple, royal coach   4.50 2.00
   a.   Souvenir sheet of 2, #694-695   10.00 4.00
   Royal wedding.

Bafoussam-Bamenda Highway — A194

1981, Sept. 10   **Litho.**   *Perf. 12½*
696 A194 50fr multicolored   .55 .20

Freighter Cam Iroko (Cameroun Shipping Line) A195

1981, Sept. 25
697 A195 60fr multicolored   1.00 .40

20th Anniv. of Reunification — A196

1981, Oct. 10   *Perf. 12½x13*
698 A196 50fr multicolored   .65 .20

Medicinal Plants — A197

1981, Dec. 31   **Litho.**   *Perf. 12½*
699 A197 60fr Voacanga thouarsii   1.10 .25
700 A197 70fr Cassia alata   1.50 .30

Easter 1982 — A198

Paintings: 100fr, Christ in the Garden of Olives, by Delacroix. 200fr, Descent from the Cross, by Giotto. 250fr, Pieta in the Countryside, by Bellini.

1982, Apr. 10   **Litho.**   *Perf. 13*
701 A198 100fr multicolored   .90 .35
702 A198 200fr multicolored   1.75 .65
703 A198 250fr multicolored   2.25 .90
   Nos. 701-703 (3)   4.90 1.90

PHILEXFRANCE '82 Stamp Exhibition, Paris, June 11-21 — A199

1982, Apr. 25   *Perf. 12*
704 A199 90fr multicolored   2.10 .40

Snakeskin Handbag — A200

1982, Apr. 30   *Perf. 12½*
705 A200 60fr shown   .65 .25
706 A200 70fr Clay water jug   .70 .35

10th Anniv. of Republic — A201

1982, May 20   *Perf. 13*
707 A201 500fr multicolored   5.00 2.00

Town Hall, Douala — A202

1982, June 15   **Litho.**   *Perf. 12½*
708 A202 40fr shown   .45 .20
709 A202 60fr Yaounde   .65 .25
   See Nos. 730-731, 757-758, 790-791, 867.

1982 World Cup — A203

1982, July 10   *Perf. 13*
710 A203 100fr Natl. team   1.40 .40
711 A203 200fr Semi-finalists   2.75 .75
712 A203 300fr Players, vert.   4.50 1.25
713 A203 400fr Natl. team 2nd lineup   5.75 1.60
   a.   Souvenir sheet of 2, #713   14.50 3.50
   Nos. 710-713 (4)   14.40 4.00

Partridge — A204

1982   *Perf. 12½x13*
714 A204 10fr shown   2.75 .20
715 A204 15fr Turtle dove   3.00 .20
716 A204 20fr Swallow   4.50 .20
717 A204 200fr Bongo antelope   4.00 .80
718 A204 300fr Black colobus   6.25 1.25
   Nos. 714-718 (5)   20.50 2.65

Issued: 200fr, 300fr, July 20; others Aug. 10. See No. 804.

Scouting Year A205

1982, Sept. 30   **Litho.**   *Perf. 13x12½*
719 A205 200fr Campfire   2.25 .80
720 A205 400fr Baden-Powell   4.00 1.60

25th Anniv. of the Presbyterian Church in Cameroun — A206

1982, Oct. 30   *Perf. 13x12½, 12½x13*
721 A206 45fr Buea Chapel   .55 .20
722 A206 60fr Nyasoso Chapel, vert.   .65 .20

ITU Plenipotentiaries Conference, Nairobi, Sept. — A207

1982, Oct. 5   **Litho.**   *Perf. 12½x13*
723 A207 70fr multicolored   .70 .25

Italy's Victory in 1982 World Cup — A208

1982, Nov.   *Perf. 13*
724 A208 500fr multicolored   5.50 2.00
725 A208 1000fr multicolored   10.50 4.00

30th Anniv. of Customs Cooperation Council — A209

1983, Jan. 10   *Perf. 12½x13*
726 A209 250fr Emblem   2.25 .80
727 A209 250fr Headquarters, Brussels   2.25 .80

2nd Yaoundé Medical Conference — A210

1983, Jan. 23   **Litho.**   *Perf. 13*
728 A210 60fr grn & multi   .70 .20
729 A210 70fr brn & multi   .90 .25

City Hall Type of 1982

1983, Feb. 25   *Perf. 12½*
730 A202 60fr Bafoussam   .60 .25
731 A202 70fr Garoua   .70 .30

Homage to Women — A211

1983, Apr. 25   **Litho.**   *Perf. 12½*
733 A211 60fr Nurse   .70 .20
734 A211 70fr Lawyer   .70 .25

11th Anniv. of Independence — A212

Flag and Pres. Paul Biya.

1983, May 18   Litho.   Perf. 13
735 A212 60fr dk grn & multi   .55 .25
736 A212 70fr dk bl & multi   .70 .30

25th Anniv. of Intl. Maritime Org. A213

1983, May 23   Perf. 13x12½
737 A213 500fr multicolored   4.50 1.50

Eagle — A214

1983, June 15 Litho. Perf. 12½x13
738 A214 25fr shown   1.50 .20
739 A214 30fr Sparrowhawk   2.25 .20
740 A214 50fr Purple heron   4.25 .20
   Nos. 738-740 (3)   8.00 .60

See Nos. 798-800, 873, 882, 886.

A215

A216

1983, July 25   Litho.   Perf. 12
741 A215 60fr Pearl mask, by
    Wery-Nwen-Nto,
    1899   .70 .25
742 A215 70fr Basket with lid   .90 .30

1983, Aug. 20   Litho.   Perf. 12
743 A216 90fr Mobile Post Of-
    fice, horiz   .90 .20
744 A216 150fr Telegraph Opera-
    tor   1.40 .35
745 A216 250fr Tom-tom   2.75 .55
   Nos. 743-745 (3)   5.05 1.10

World Communications Year.

Endangered Species — A217

1983, Sept. 22   Perf. 12
746 A217 200fr Civet Cat   2.75 .40
747 A217 200fr Gorilla, vert   2.75 .40
748 A217 350fr Cobaya, vert   5.50 .80
   Nos. 746-748 (3)   11.00 1.60

See No. 887.

Lake Tizon — A218

1983, Nov. 25   Litho.   Perf. 13
749 A218 60fr shown   .55 .20
750 A218 70fr Mt. Cameroon   .70 .20

Human Rights Declaration, 35th Anniv — A219

1983, Dec. 20   Litho.   Perf. 12½x13
751 A219 60fr multicolored   .55 .20
752 A219 70fr multicolored   .70 .20

Christmas 1983 — A220

60fr, Christmas tree. 200fr, Stained glass window, Yaoundé Cathedral. #755, Rest during Flight into Egypt, by Philipp Otto Runge. #756, Angel of the Annunciation. 60fr, 200fr, #756 vert.

1983, Dec. 20   Litho.   Perf. 12½
753 A220 60fr multicolored   .45 .20
754 A220 200fr multicolored   1.75 .50
755 A220 500fr multicolored   4.50 1.25
756 A220 500fr multicolored   4.50 1.25
a. Souvenir sheet of 3, #754-
    756   11.50 3.25
   Nos. 753-756 (4)   11.20 3.20

City Hall Type of 1982

1984, Apr. 20   Litho.   Perf. 12½
757 A202 60fr Bamenda   .55 .20
758 A202 70fr Mbalmayo   .70 .25

Catholic Church, Zoetele — A221

1984, July 25   Litho.   Perf. 13
759 A221 60fr shown   .55 .25
760 A221 70fr Protestant Church,
    Yaounde   .70 .25

Endangered Species — A222

1984, Aug. 15
761 A222 250fr Wild pig   4.00 .65
762 A222 250fr Deer   4.00 .65

1984, Oct. 10   Litho.   Perf. 13½
763 A222 60fr Nightingale   5.00 5.00
764 A222 60fr Vultures   5.00 5.00

See No. 883.

Bamenda Farming Fair — A223

1984, Dec. 10   Litho.   Perf. 13
765 A223 60fr Corn   .60 .20
766 A223 70fr Cattle   .90 .25
767 A223 300fr Potatoes   3.50 .90
   Nos. 765-767 (3)   5.00 1.35

International Civil Aviation Organization, 40th Anniv. — A224

1984, Dec. 20   Litho.   Perf. 12½
768 A224 200fr Icarus   1.75 .60
769 A224 200fr ICAO emblem,
    vert.   1.75 .60
770 A224 300fr Boeing 747   2.75 .90
771 A224 300fr Solar Princess
    painting   3.25 .90
   Nos. 768-771 (4)   9.50 3.00

Olymphilex '85, Lausanne — A225

Wmk. 385
1985, Apr. 5   Photo.   Perf. 13
772 A225 150fr Wrestlers, exhibi-
    tion emblem   1.50 .40

Domestic Musical Instruments A226

1985, Apr. 23   Perf. 13½
773 A226 60fr Balafons (xylo-
    phone)   .65 .20
774 A226 70fr Guitar   .80 .20
775 A226 100fr Flute   1.10 .30
   Nos. 773-775 (3)   2.55 .70

INTELSAT Org., 20th Anniv. — A227

1985, May 8   Perf. 13
776 A227 125fr Intelsat V   1.60 .35
777 A227 200fr Intelcam, Yaoun-
    de   2.10 .60

New York Headquarters — A228

1985, May 30
778 A228 250fr multicolored   2.40 1.10
779 A228 500fr multicolored   4.50 2.25

UN, 40th anniv.

Pres. Mitterand, Biya — A229

1985, June 20
780 A229 60fr multicolored   1.40 .20
781 A229 70fr multicolored   1.60 .25

Visit of Pres. Mitterand of France.

UNICEF A230

UN Infant Survival Campaign A231

1985, July 15
782 A230 60fr multicolored   .55 .20
783 A231 300fr multicolored   2.75 1.00

Visit of Pope
John Paul II, Aug.
10-14 — A232

1985, Aug. 9   *Perf. 13x12½*
784 A232 60fr Pope, papal
arms   1.25   .40
785 A232 70fr Pope, crosier   1.75   .55

     Size: 55x38mm
786 A232 200fr Pres. Biya,
John Paul II   5.75   2.00
a.   Souv. sheet of 3, #784-786   9.50   6.00
    Nos. 784-786 (3)   8.75   2.95

Landscapes — A233

1985, July 25   Litho.   *Perf. 12½*
787 A233 60fr Lake Barumbi,
Kumba   .70   .20
788 A233 70fr Bonando Pygmy
Village, Doume   .70   .20
789 A233 150fr Cameroun River   1.40   .40
    Nos. 787-789 (3)   2.80   .80

    City Hall Type of 1982

1985, July 30
790 A202 60fr Ngaoundere   .55   .20
791 A202 60fr D'Ebolowa   .55   .20

Wildlife — A234

Wood Sculptures
A235

1985, Aug. 20   *Perf. 13½*
792 A234 125fr Porcupine   1.50   .40
793 A234 200fr Squirrel   2.50   .60
794 A234 350fr Hedgehog   4.00   1.10
    Nos. 792-794 (3)   8.00   2.10

1985, Sept. 15
795 A235 60fr Mask   .65   .20
796 A235 70fr Mask, diff.   .90   .25
797 A235 100fr Wood bas-relief,
horiz.   1.25   .30
    Nos. 795-797 (3)   2.80   .75

    Bird Type of 1983
  Inscribed Republic of Cameroon
1985, Nov. 10
798 A214 140fr Toucans   2.10   .50
799 A214 150fr Rooster   2.10   .55
800 A214 200fr Red-throated
bee-eater   3.00   .70
    Nos. 798-800 (3)   7.20   1.75

  See No. 873. For surcharge see No. 871.

American Peace Corps in Cameroun,
25th Anniv. — A237

1986, Jan. 1   Litho.   *Perf. 12½*
801 A237 70fr multicolored   .70   .25
802 A237 100fr multicolored   1.00   .30

  Stamps of 1979-1982 Redrawn
1986, Mar.   *Perf. 13, 13½*
803 A174 5fr multicolored   .35   .35
804 A204 10fr multicolored   .35   .35

  Nos. 803-804 inscribed "Republic of Cameroon" instead of "United Republic of Cameroon."

Easter — A238

Insects — A239

  Paintings: 210fr, Head of the Virgin, by Pierre-Paul Prud'Hon (1758-1823). 350fr, The Stoning of St. Steven, by Van Scorel (1495-1562).
1986, Apr. 15   *Perf. 13½*
805 A238 210fr multicolored   1.75   .60
806 A238 350fr multicolored   2.75   1.00

1986, Apr. 20
807 A239 70fr Honeybee   1.50   .40
808 A239 70fr Dragonfly   1.50   .40
809 A239 100fr Grasshopper   2.40   .55
    Nos. 807-809 (3)   5.40   1.35
    Nos. 808-809 horiz.

Flags, Conference Center — A240

1986, Apr. 25   Litho.   *Perf. 13*
810 A240 100fr Map, vert.   1.00   .30
811 A240 175fr shown   2.00   .60
  Conference of Ministers of the Economic Commission for Africa, Apr. 9-29.

Statues — A241

1986, July 5   Litho.   *Perf. 13½*
812 A241 70fr Bronze earth
mother   .85   .25
813 A241 100fr Wood funerary
figure   .95   .30
814 A241 130fr Wood equestrian
figure   1.60   .40
    Nos. 812-814 (3)   3.40   .95

Queen Elizabeth II, 60th
Birthday — A242

1986, July 15   Litho.   *Perf. 13*
815 A242 100fr Elizabeth   1.00   .40
816 A242 175fr Elizabeth, Pres.
Biya   1.40   .60
817 A242 210fr Elizabeth, diff.   2.00   .75
    Nos. 815-817 (3)   4.40   1.75

Natl. Democratic Party, 1st
Anniv. — A243

1986, July 25   *Perf. 12½*
818 A243 70fr Party headquarters, Bamenda   .70   .25
819 A243 70fr Pres. Biya, vert.   .70   .25
820 A243 100fr Presidential address, vert.   1.00   .35
    Nos. 818-820 (3)   2.40   .85

Kwem Mask
Dancers of the
Northeast — A244

1986, Aug. 1   *Perf. 13½*
821 A244 100fr multicolored   1.00   .35
822 A244 130fr multicolored   1.25   .45

Endangered Species — A245

1986, Aug. 20
823 300fr Varanus niloticus   3.50   1.00
824 300fr Panthera pardus   3.50   1.00
    For surcharge see No. 872.

A246

A247

  Intl. Peace Year: 175fr, 200fr, Desmond Tutu, South Africa, Nobel Peace Prize winner. 250fr, UN and IPY emblems.

1986, Sept. 7   Litho.   *Perf. 13½*
825 A246 175fr multicolored   1.60   1.10
826 A246 200fr multicolored   2.10   1.25
827 A246 250fr multicolored   2.75   1.50
    Nos. 825-827 (3)   6.45   3.85

1986, Oct. 30   Litho.   *Perf. 13½*
828 A247 70fr multicolored   .65   .25
  Natl. Fed. of Associations for the Handicapped.

A248

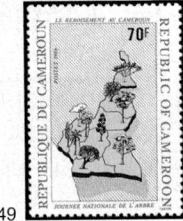

A249

1986, Nov. 9
829 A248 70fr Family under umbrella   .90   .25
830 A248 100fr Child immunization   1.10   .35
  African Vaccination Year.

1986, Dec. 20   Litho.   *Perf. 13½*
831 A249 70fr Afforestation map   .90   .25
832 A249 100fr Hands, seedling   1.10   .35
  Arbor Day.

Agricultural Development — A250

1986, Dec. 24
833 A250 70fr ONCPB seminar   .75   .40
834 A250 70fr Coconut farming,
Dibombari   .75   .40
835 A250 200fr Pineapple farm   2.00   1.10
    Nos. 833-835 (3)   3.50   1.90

Insects Destructive to Agriculture A251

1987, Sept. 25   Litho.   Perf. 13½
836 A251 70fr Antestiopsis
              lineaticollis intri-
              cata   1.50   .50
837 A251 100fr Distantiella theo-
              broma   2.00   .70

4th African Games, Nairobi — A252

1987, Oct. 1   Perf. 12½
838 A252 100fr Shot put   .90   .70
839 A252 140fr Pole vault   1.25   1.00

Maroua Agricultural Show — A253

1988, Jan. 6
840 A253 70fr Millet field   .90   .50
841 A253 100fr Cotton   1.10   .70
842 A253 150fr Cattle   1.60   1.10
        Nos. 840-842 (3)   3.60   2.30

World Wildlife Fund — A254

Baboons, *Papio leucophaeus.*

1988, Apr. 25   Litho.   Perf. 13
843 A254 30fr Adult   2.00   1.90
844 A254 40fr Adult grooming
              young   2.10   1.90
845 A254 70fr Baboon on
              branch   3.50   3.00
846 A254 100fr Adult carrying
              young   6.00   3.75
        Nos. 843-846 (4)   13.60 10.55

Interparliamentary Union, Cent. — A255

1989   Litho.   Perf. 13½
847 A255 50fr Natl. Assembly   .60   .30

World Cup Soccer Championships, Italy — A256

1990, Oct. 27   Litho.   Perf. 11½
Granite Paper
848 A256 200fr shown   1.75   1.00
849 A256 250fr Players, diff.   2.25   1.25
850 A256 250fr Goalkeeper, flags 2.25   1.25
851 A256 300fr Team   3.00   1.50
  a.   Souv. sheet of 4, #848-851   9.00   6.50
        Nos. 848-851 (4)   9.25   5.00

Roger Milla, World Cup Soccer Player A257

1990, July 4   Litho.   Perf. 11½
Granite Paper
852 A257 500fr multicolored   5.50   3.50
  a.   Souv. sheet of 1   9.00   6.00

Agriculture A258

70fr, Treating cacao plants. 100fr, Sheep.

1990, Dec. 1   Litho.   Perf. 13½
853 A258 70fr multicolored   1.25   .55
854 A258 100fr multicolored   1.75   .80
  a.   Sheet of 2, #853-854, perf. 12½   8.00   3.50

For surcharges see Nos. 894-895.

UN Development Program, 40th Anniv. — A259

1990, Dec. 31   Litho.   Perf. 13½
855 A259 50fr multicolored   .60   .40

Intl. Literacy Year A260

1990, Dec. 31
856 A260 200fr bl, blk, & lt bl 1.75   .75

Independence, 30th Anniv. — A261

1991, Jan. 1   Perf. 13
857 A261 150fr shown   1.60   1.25
858 A261 1000fr Flag, Pal-
              ace, #336   9.00   8.00
  a.   Souv. sheet of 2, #857-858   12.50 10.00

Fight Against AIDS A262

1991, Jan. 15
859 A262 15fr Hearts, map, vert. .20   .20
860 A262 25fr shown   .35   .20

See Nos. 884-885.

Birds A263

Designs: Nos. 861, 864, Pie grieche, vert. Nos. 862, 863, Picathartes chauve.

1991, May 3   Litho.   Perf. 13½
861 A263 70fr grn & multi   .60   .35
862 A263 70fr bl & multi   .60   .40
863 A263 300fr blk & multi   3.25   2.00
864 A263 350fr blk & multi   3.50   2.25
  a.   Souv. sheet of 2, #863-864   9.00   5.50
        Nos. 861-864 (4)   7.95   5.00

Wild Animals A264

1991, May 8   Perf. 13½
865 A264 125fr Elephant   1.60   1.00
866 A264 250fr Water buffalo   3.00   2.00
  a.   Souvenir sheet of 2, #865-866,
          perf. 12½   9.00   3.50

City Hall Type of 1982 Redrawn
1991   Perf. 13
867 A202 40fr multicolored   .60   .20

No. 867 inscribed "Republic of Cameroon" instead of "United Republic of Cameroon."

Cameroun Catholic Church, Cent. (in 1990) A265

1991, Dec. 8   Litho.   Perf. 13½
868 A265 125fr Mvolye church   1.25   .75
869 A265 250fr Akono church   2.25   1.75
  a.   Souvenir sheet of 2, #868-869,
          perf. 12½x13   4.00   3.00

Intl. Savings Banks Institute, 7th Meeting of the African Group A266

1991, Dec. 9
870 A266 250fr multicolored   2.40   1.60
  a.   Souv. sheet of 1, perf. 12½x13   3.00   2.00

Nos. 799 & 824 Surcharged

20 F

1992   Perf. 13½
871 A214 20fr on 150fr #799   1.75   .20
872 A245 70fr on 300fr #824   5.75   .55

Bird Type of 1983
1992   Litho.   Perf. 13½
873 A214 125fr like #800   1.40   .95
        Dated 1985.

Cameroun Soccer League A267

125fr, Mbappe Mbappe Samuel (1936-85), soccer player, vert. 250fr, Linafoote League emblem, vert. 400fr, Linafoote emblem, diff. 500fr, Stadium.

1992, Aug.   Perf. 11½
874 A267 125fr multicolored   1.25   .75
875 A267 250fr multicolored   2.40   1.75
876 A267 400fr multicolored   3.50   2.75
877 A267 500fr multicolored   5.50   3.50
        Nos. 874-877 (4)   12.65   8.75

See Nos. 896-896B.

Discovery of America, 500th Anniv. A268

Columbus and: 125fr, Fleet of ships. 250fr, Landing in New World. 400fr, Meeting with natives. 500fr, Map, ships.

1992, Aug.
878 A268 125fr multicolored   1.40   .75
879 A268 250fr multicolored   2.10   1.75
880 A268 400fr multicolored   3.50   2.75
881 A268 500fr multicolored   5.00   3.50
        Nos. 878-881 (4)   12.00   8.75

Types of 1983-84 Redrawn and Inscribed "Republic of Cameroon"
1992   Litho.   Perf. 13½
882 A214 200fr like #739   2.25   1.40
  a.   Booklet pane of 5
        Complete booklet, #882a
883 A222 350fr like #763   3.75   2.50

AIDS Type of 1991
1993   Litho.   Perf. 13½
884 A262 100fr like #859   1.10   .70
885 A262 175fr like #860   1.90   1.25

Types of 1983 Redrawn and Inscribed "Republic of Cameroon"
886 A214 370fr like #738   3.50   2.50
                                  Perf. 13
887 A217 410fr like #746   4.50   2.90

Wild Animal Type of 1980 Inscribed "Republique du Cameroun"
1993 Litho. Serpentine Die Cut 9½
Booklet Stamps
Self-Adhesive
888 A186 125fr Crocodile   1.40   .65
  a.   Booklet pane of 4   5.75
889 A186 250fr Buffon's ante-
              lope, vert.   2.75   1.25
  a.   Booklet pane of 4   11.50

By their nature, Nos. 888a, 889a are complete booklets. The peelable backing serves as a booklet cover.

1994 World Cup Soccer Championships, US — A270

Designs: 125fr, Pres. Paul Biya holding soccer ball, lion. 250fr, Logo, lion, player, map. 450fr, Players, globe, World Cup, flag. 500fr, US eagle, Cameroun lion, soccer ball.

1994, Mar. 28 **Litho.** *Perf. 13*
890 A270 125fr multicolored .75 .40
891 A270 250fr multicolored 1.50 .75
892 A270 450fr multicolored 2.75 1.50
893 A270 500fr multicolored 3.00 1.75
a. Min. sheet of 4, #890-893 90.00 90.00
Nos. 890-893 (4) 8.00 4.40

Nos. 853-854 Surcharged in Gold and Black

1993 **Litho.** *Perf. 13½*
894 A258 125fr on 70fr #853 —
895 A258 125fr on 100fr #854 —

Cameroun Soccer League Type of 1992

1992-93 **Litho.** *Perf. 11½*
896 A267 10fr like #876 — —
896A A267 25fr like #875 — —
896B A267 50fr like #874 — —

Nos. 896-896A dated 1993.
Issued: 50fr, 8/1/92; others, 1993.

Psittacus Erithacus — A271

1995 **Litho.** *Perf. 11½*
Granite Paper
897 A271 125fr multicolored 1.50 .50

Visit of Pope John Paul II A272

1995, Sept. 14 *Perf. 12½*
898 A272 55fr shown .35 .20
a. Souvenir sheet of 1
899 A272 125fr Pope, open text, cross .95 .50
a. Souvenir sheet of 1

UN, 50th Anniv. A273

1995, Oct. 24 *Perf. 11½*
900 A273 200fr shown 1.25 .60
901 A273 250fr "50," people 1.50 .80

Conf. of Heads of State & Govt., Yaounde A274

Perf. 12½, 14¾x14 (200fr, 250fr)
1996-97 **Litho.**
902 A274 125fr blue & multi —
902A A274 200fr lt grn & multi ('97) —
902B A274 250fr yel & multi ('97) —
903 A274 410fr pink & multi, vert. —

World Records Set at 1996 Summer Olympic Games, Atlanta A275

1996 *Perf. 11½*
904 A275 125fr Baily, M. Johnson .55 .45
905 A275 250fr Harrison, Galfione, Perec, vert. 1.00 .90

Universal Declaration of Human Rights, 50th Anniv. — A279

1998 **Litho.** *Perf. 14x14¾*
918 A279 370fr multi —

Additional stamps may have been released in this set. The editors would like to examine any examples.

1998 World Cup Soccer Championships, France — A280

Design: 125fr, Flag of Cameroun, World Cup trophy, vert.

1998 **Litho.** *Perf. 13*
922 A280 125fr multi —
923 A280 250fr multicolored —

The editors suspect that additional stamps were released with this stamp, and would like to examine them.

Shrike A281

1998 **Litho.** *Perf. 13x13¾*
926 A281 125fr multicolored —

The editors suspect that additional stamps were released with this stamp, and would like to examine them.

Economic and Monetary Community of Central Africa Week — A281a

Design: 125fr, Flags surrounding map of Africa.

1999 **Litho.** *Perf. 14½*
927 A281a 125fr multi — —
928 A281a 225fr multi — —

Flora & Fauna — A282

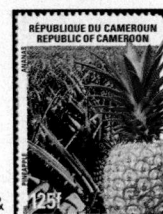

1998? **Litho.** *Perf. 14x14½*
929 A282 100fr Pineapple —
930 A282 125fr Pineapple —
930A A282 150fr Coffee beans —
930B A282 175fr Crowned crane —
931 A282 200fr Baboon —
932 A282 250fr Coffee beans —
934 A282 410fr Crowned crane —

The editors suspect that additional stamps may have been issued with this set and would like to examine any examples. Nos. 930-931 are dated 1998, but their earliest known use was in 2000.

Peace, Work, Country A283

2000 **Litho.** *Perf. 11¾*
935 A283 125fr multi — —

The editors suspect that additional stamps may have been issued in this set and would like to examine any examples.

Map and Scenes — A284   Airplane and Wildlife — A285

2000 **Litho.** *Perf. 11¾*
936 A284 200fr multi — —
937 A285 250fr multi — —

The editors suspect that additional stamps may have been issued in this set and would like to examine any examples.

Palais des Congrés, Yaounde A286

Perf. 11¾x11½
2001, Mar. 26 **Litho.**
938 A286 125fr multi —

Cameroun — People's Republic of China cooperation, 30th anniv.

Campaign Against AIDS — A287

Design: 125fr, Woman vaccinating child, Chantal Biya Foundation emblem. 250fr, Chantal Biya Foundation emblem, globe, ribbon, woman with fetus.

2001 **Litho.** *Perf. 13¼x13*
939 A287 125fr multi — —
941 A287 250fr multi — —

The editors suspect that additional stamps may have been issued in this set and would like to examine any examples.

2002 World Cup Soccer Championships, Japan and Korea — A287a

2002, June 20 **Litho.** *Perf. 13¾*
943 A287a 125fr multi — —

Two additional stamps exist in this set. The editors would like to examine any examples.

Indomitable Lions Soccer Team, 20th Anniv. of Success A288

2002 **Litho.** *Perf. 13x13¼*
944 A288 250fr multi — —

The editors suspect that additional stamps may have been issued in this set and would like to examine any examples.

Cooperation Between Cameroun and Japan — A290

2005 **Litho.** *Perf. 13*
948 A290 100fr multi — —

Seven additional stamps were released in this set. The editors would like to examine any examples.

SEMI-POSTAL STAMPS

Curie Issue
Common Design Type
1938 **Unwmk.** *Perf. 13*
B1 CD80 1.75fr + 50c brt ultra 10.00 10.00

French Revolution Issue
Common Design Type
Photogravure; Name and Value Typographed in Black
1939
B2 CD83 45c + 25c green 11.50 11.50
B3 CD83 70c + 30c brown 11.50 11.50
B4 CD83 90c + 35c red org 11.50 11.50
B5 CD83 1.25fr + 1fr rose pink 11.50 11.50
B6 CD83 2.25fr + 2fr blue 14.00 14.00
Nos. B2-B6 (5) 60.00 60.00

Stamps of 1925-33 Surcharged in Black

1940   *Perf. 14x13½*
B7 A7 1.25fr + 2fr gray & dp bl   16.00 12.00
B8 A7 1.75fr + 3fr brn & org   16.00 12.00
B9 A7   2fr + 5fr dl grn & brn
                                org   16.00 12.00
           Nos. B7-B9 (3)   48.00 36.00
The surtax was used for war relief work.

Regular Stamps of
1939 Surcharged in
Black

1940   *Perf. 13*
B10 A20 25c + 5fr blk brn   110.00 72.50
B11 A20 45c + 5fr slate grn   110.00 72.50
B12 A20 60c + 5fr peacock
                              bl   125.00 75.00
B13 A20 70c + 5fr plum   125.00 75.00
            Nos. B10-B13 (4)   470.00 295.00
The surtax was used to purchase Spitfire
planes for the Free French army.

Common Design Type and

Military
Doctor
SP2

Cameroun
Militiaman — SP4

1941   **Photo.**   *Perf. 13½*
B13A SP2   1fr + 1fr red   1.40
B13B CD86 1.50fr + 3fr maroon   1.40
B13C SP4 2.50fr + 1fr dk bl   1.40
            Nos. B13A-B13C (3)   4.20
Nos. B13A-B13C were issued by the Vichy
government in France, but were not placed on
sale in Cameroun.

New York World's Fair Stamps, 1939
Surcharged in Black

1941   *Perf. 12½x12*
B14 CD82 1.25fr + 10fr car
                        lake   110.00 67.50
B15 CD82 2.25fr + 10fr ultra   110.00 67.50

New York World's Fair Stamps, 1939,
Surcharged in Black or Blue

1941
B16 CD82 1.25fr + 10fr car
                lake (Bl)   21.00 16.00
B17 CD82 2.25fr + 10fr ultra
                     (Bk)   21.00 16.00
The surtax was used to purchase ambu-
lances for the Free French army.

Regular
Stamps of
1933-39
Surcharged
in Black

Valmy
+ 100 frs.

1943   *Perf. 14x13½, 13, 12½x12*
B21 A7 1.25fr + 100 gray &
                     dp bl   11.00 11.00
B22 A21 1.25fr + 100fr car
                      rose   11.00 11.00
B23 CD82 1.25fr + 100fr car
                      lake   11.00 11.00
B24 A21 1.50fr + 100fr choc   11.00 11.00
B25 CD82 2.25fr + 100fr ultra   11.00 11.00
            Nos. B21-B25 (5)   55.00 55.00

Nos. 281A-281B
Surcharged in Black or Red

ŒUVRES
+ 2f50
COLONIALES

1944   **Engr.**   *Perf. 12½x12*
B25A 50c + 1.50fr on 2.50fr
             deep blue (R)   .80
B25B   + 2.50fr on 1fr green   .80
Colonial Development Fund.
Nos. B25A-B25B were issued by the Vichy
government in France, but were not placed on
sale in Cameroun.

Red Cross Issue
Common Design Type
1944   **Photo.**   *Perf. 14½x14*
B28 CD90 5fr + 20fr rose   1.75 1.10
The surtax was for the French Red Cross
and national relief.

Catalogue values for unused stamps in this section, from this point to the end of the section, are for Never Hinged items.

Tropical Medicine Issue
Common Design Type
1950   **Engr.**   *Perf. 13*
B29 CD100 10fr + 2fr dk bl grn
                  & dk grn   5.00 5.00
The surtax was for charitable work.

Independent State

Map and
Flag — SP7

Unwmk.
1961, Mar. 25   **Engr.**   *Perf. 13*
B30 SP7 20fr + 5fr grn, car &
                     yel   1.00 1.00
B31 SP7 25fr + 10fr multi 1.25 1.25
B32 SP7 30fr + 15fr car, yel &
                     grn   1.75 1.75
            Nos. B30-B32 (3) 4.00 4.00
The surtax was for the Red Cross.

Federal Republic

Map of Cameroun, Lions Emblem and
Physician Helping Leper
SP8

1962, Jan. 28
B33 SP8 20fr + 5fr multi   .70   .40
B34 SP8 25fr + 10fr multi   .90   .50
B35 SP8 50fr + 15fr multi 1.75   .85
            Nos. B33-B35 (3) 3.35 1.75
Issued for leprosy relief work.

Anti-Malaria Issue
Common Design Type
1962, Apr. 7   *Perf. 12½x12*
B36 CD108 25fr + 5fr rose lilac 1.00 .45
WHO drive to eradicate malaria.

Freedom from Hunger Issue
Common Design Type
1963, Mar. 21   **Engr.**   *Perf. 13*
B37 CD112 18fr + 5fr multi 1.00 .35
B38 CD112 25fr + 15fr multi 1.25 .40

Antelopes — SP9

Designs: 125fr+10fr, Ourebia ourebi.
250fr+20fr, Kobus defassa.

1991, Apr. 30 **Litho.** *Perf. 13½x13*
B39 SP9 125fr + 10fr multi 2.00 1.10
B40 SP9 250fr + 20fr multi 3.00 2.25
  a. Souvenir sheet of 2, #B39-B40,
          perf. 12½   8.00 3.50

AIR POST STAMPS

Common Design Type
1942 **Unwmk. Photo.** *Perf. 14½x14*
C1 CD87   1fr dk orange   .25   .25
C2 CD87 1.50fr brt red   .25   .25
C3 CD87   5fr brown red   .55   .55
C4 CD87   10fr black   .70   .70
C5 CD87   25fr ultra   1.00 1.00
C6 CD87   50fr dk green   1.25 1.25
C7 CD87 100fr plum   1.50 1.50
            Nos. C1-C7 (7)   5.50 5.50

Types AP9 and AP10 without "RF" and

Plane Over
Coast
AP3

1943-44   **Photo.**   *Perf. 13, 13½*
C7A AP9   25c brown red   .20
C7B AP9   50c green   .20
C7C AP9   1fr brt violet   .25
C7D AP10   5fr red brown   .35
C7E AP10 10fr black   .45
C7F AP10 12fr orange   .50
C7G AP10 20fr crimson   .70
C7H AP10 50fr blue   .80
C7I AP3 100fr lilac brown   .80
            Nos. C7A-C7I (9) 4.25
Nos. C7A to C7I were issued by the Vichy
Government in France, but were not placed on
sale in Cameroun.
For Types AP9 and AP10 inscribed RF, see
Nos. C15-C24.

Catalogue values for unused stamps in this section are for Never Hinged items.

Victory Issue
Common Design Type
1946, May 8   **Engr.**   *Perf. 12½*
C8 CD92 8fr dk violet brn   .90   .90
European victory of the Allied Nations in
WWII.

Chad to Rhine Issue
Common Design Types
1946, June 6
C9 CD93 5fr dk blue grn   1.10 1.10
C10 CD94 10fr dk rose vio   1.25 1.25
C11 CD95 15fr red   1.60 1.60
C12 CD96 20fr brt blue   1.60 1.60

C13 CD97 25fr orange red   1.75 1.75
C14 CD98 50fr gray   2.10 2.10
            Nos. C9-C14 (6) 9.40 9.40

Plane and Map — AP9

Seaplane
Alighting
AP10

Plane and
Freighters
AP11

1946   **Photo.**   *Perf. 13, 13½*
C15 AP9 25c brown red   .20   .20
C16 AP9 50c green   .20   .20
C17 AP9   1fr brt violet   .60   .60
C18 AP10 2fr olive grn   .95   .95
C19 AP10 3fr chocolate   .95   .95
C20 AP10 4fr deep ultra   .95   .95
C21 AP10 6fr blue grn   .95   .95
C22 AP10 7fr brt violet 1.40 1.40
C23 AP10 12fr orange   7.25 7.25
C24 AP10 20fr crimson   2.40 2.40
C25 AP11 50fr dk ultra   3.50 3.50
            Nos. C15-C25 (11) 19.35 19.35
Nos. C15 to C25 were issued in 1941 in
France by the Vichy Government, but were not
sold in Cameroun until 1946.

Birds over Mountains — AP12

Cavalry and Plane — AP13

Warrior, Dance
Mask and Nose
of Plane — AP14

                     Perf. 12½
1947, Feb. 10 **Unwmk.**   **Engr.**
C26 AP12 50fr dk green   2.25   .70
C27 AP13 100fr brn red   3.75   .70
C28 AP14 200fr black   6.25 1.40
            Nos. C26-C28 (3) 12.25 2.80

UPU Issue
Common Design Type
1949, July   *Perf. 13*
C29 CD99 25fr multicolored 6.50 3.50

Rhumsiki
Peak — AP16

1953, Feb. 16
C30 AP16 500fr grnsh blk, dk
vio & vio bl   18.00   3.00

For surcharge see No. C40.

Edéa Dam and Sacred Ibis — AP17

1953, Nov. 18
C31 AP17 15fr choc, brn lake &
ultra   4.00   1.10
Dedication of Edea Dam on the Sanaga
River.

Liberation Issue
Common Design Type
1954, June 6
C32 CD102 15fr dk grnsh bl &
bl grn   5.50   3.50

Dr. Eugene Jamot, Research
Laboratory and Tsetse Flies — AP19

1954, Nov. 29
C33 AP19 15fr dk grn, ind & dk
brn   4.00   1.90
75th anniv. of the birth of Dr. Eugene Jamot.

Logging — AP20

100fr, Giraffes. 200fr, Port of Douala.

1955, Jan. 24
C34 AP20 50fr ol grn, brn &
vio brn   2.75   .50
C35 AP20 100fr grnsh bl, brn &
dk brn   6.25   1.25
C36 AP20 200fr dk grn, choc &
dp ultra   8.00   1.60
Nos. C34-C36 (3)   17.00   3.35
For surcharges see Nos. C38-C39.

Federal Republic
Air Afrique Issue
Common Design Type
Unwmk.
1962, Feb. 17   Engr.   Perf. 13
C37 CD107 25fr mar, pur & lt grn 1.00 .40

Nos. C35-C36 and C30 Surcharged in
Red with New Value, Bars and:
"REPUBLIQUE FEDERALE"

Two types of 5sh:
I — "5/-" measures 6½x4mm.

II — "5/" measures 3¾x3mm, No dash after
diagonal line.

Three types of 10sh:
I — "10/-" measures 9x3¾mm.
II — "10/-" measures 7x2½-3mm.
III — "1" of "10/" vertically in line with last "E"
of "FEDERALE".

Two types of £1:
I — "REPUBLIQUE / FEDERALE" 17¼mm
wide.
II — "REPUBLIQUE / FEDERALE" 22mm
wide.

1961, Oct. 1   Engr.   Perf. 13
C38 AP20 5sh on 100fr (I)   10.00   6.00
a.   Type II   32.50   18.00
C39 AP20 10sh on 200fr (I)   20.00   12.50
a.   Type II   75.00   42.50
b.   Type III   30.00   30.00
C40 AP16 £1 on 500fr (I)   32.50   21.00
a.   Type II   57.50   35.00
Nos. C38-C40 (3)   62.50   39.50

Issued for use in the former United Kingdom
Trust Territory of Southern Cameroons.

Kapsikis Mokolo — AP21

Designs: 50fr, Cocotieres Hotel, Douala.
100fr, Cymothoe sangaris butterflies. 200fr,
Ostriches, Waza Reservation.

1962, June 15
C41 AP21 50fr sl grn, bl & dl
red   .90   .25
C42 AP21 100fr multicolored   5.75   .60
C43 AP21 200fr dk grn, blk &
bis   8.00   1.40
C44 AP21 500fr vio brn, bl &
ocher   9.00   2.25
Nos. C41-C44 (4)   23.65   4.50

Telstar Type of Regular Issue
1963, Feb. 9
Size: 48x27mm
C45 A50 100fr dk grn & red brn 2.50 .65

Edéa Relay
Station — AP22

1963, May 18   Photo.   Perf. 12x12½
C46 AP22 100fr multicolored   2.50   .65
Issued to publicize the high frequency tele-
graph connection Douala-Yaoundé.

African Postal Union Issue
Common Design Type
1963, Sept. 8   Unwmk.   Perf. 12½
C47 CD114 85fr ultra, ocher &
red   2.25   1.00

Air Afrique Issue, 1963
Common Design Type
1963, Nov. 19   Perf. 13x12
C48 CD115 50fr pink, gray, blk &
grn   1.25   .40

Olympic Games Type of 1964
300fr, Greco-Roman wrestlers (ancient).

1964, Oct. 10   Engr.   Perf. 13
C49 A57 300fr red, dk brn & dl
grn   7.50   2.00
a.   Sheet of 3, #403-404, C49   13.50   4.25

Kribi Port — AP25

1964, Oct. 26   Unwmk.   Perf. 13
C50 AP25 50fr red brn, ultra &
grn   1.00   .35

Black Rhinoceros — AP26

1964, Dec. 15   Engr.   Perf. 13
C51 AP26 250fr brn red, grn &
dk brn   10.00   1.10

Pres. John F. Kennedy — AP27

1964, Dec. 8   Photo.   Perf. 12½
C52 AP27 100fr grn, yel grn &
brn   2.50   1.10
a.   Souvenir sheet of 4   10.00   4.50
Pres. John F. Kennedy (1917-63).

Abraham Lincoln — AP28

1965, Apr. 20   Unwmk.   Perf. 13
C53 AP28 100fr multicolored   2.50   .80
Abraham Lincoln, death centenary.

Syncom Satellite and ITU
Emblem — AP29

1965, May 17   Engr.
C54 AP29 70fr red, dk bl, & blk   1.60   .60
Cent. of the ITU.

Sir Winston
Spencer
Churchill,
Statesman and
World War II
Leader — AP30

Design: 18fr, Churchill, battleship and oak
leaves with acorns.

Perf. 13x12½
1965, May 28   Photo.   Unwmk.
C55 AP30 12fr multicolored   1.00   .50
C56 AP30 18fr multicolored   1.00   .50
a.   Strip of 2, #C55-C56 + label   2.75   1.40

ICY Type of Regular Issue
1965, Sept. 11   Engr.   Perf. 13
C57 A68 100fr dk red & dk bl   2.25   .70

Racing Boat, Sanaga River,
Edéa — AP31

1965, Oct. 27   Unwmk.   Perf. 13
C58 AP31 50fr brn, dk grn & sl   1.75   .35

Edward H. White Floating in Space
and Gemini IV — AP32

Designs: 50fr, Vostok 6. 200fr, Gemini V
and REP (rendezvous evaluation pod). 500fr,
Gemini VI & VII rendezvous.

1966, Mar. 30   Engr.   Perf. 13
C59 AP32 50fr car rose & dk
sl grn   .90   .35
C60 AP32 100fr red lil & vio bl   2.10   .65
C61 AP32 200fr ultra & dk pur   3.75   1.40
C62 AP32 500fr brt bl & indigo   9.00   3.00
Nos. C59-C62 (4)   15.75   5.40

Man's conquest of space.

Hotel Type of Regular Issue
18fr, Mountain Hotel, Buea. 25fr, Hotel
Akwa Palace, Douala. 50fr, Terminus Hotel,
Yaoundé. 60fr, Imperial Hotel, Yaoundé. 85fr,
Independence Hotel, Yaoundé. 100fr, Hunting
Lodge, Mora, vert. 150fr, Boukarous (round
huts), Waza Camp.

1966
C63 A71 18fr sl grn, brt bl &
blk   .45   .20
C64 A71 25fr car, ultra & sl   .55   .20
C65 A71 50fr choc, grn &
ocher   2.40   .35
C66 A71 60fr choc, grn & brt
bl   1.40   .35
C67 A71 85fr dk car rose, dl
bl & grn   1.75   .50
C68 A71 100fr brn, grn & sl   2.75   .50
C69 A71 150fr brn, dl bl &
ocher   3.50   .65
Nos. C63-C69 (7)   12.80   2.75

Issued: #C63-C64, 4/6; #C65-C69, 6/4.

Flower Type of Regular Issue
Flowers: 25fr, Hibiscus mutabilis. 50fr,
Delonix regia. 100fr, Bougainvillea.

1966, May 20   Photo.   Perf. 12½
Flowers in Natural Colors
Size: 26x45mm
C70 A75 25fr slate green   .75   .20
C71 A75 50fr brt grnsh bl   1.60   .20
C72 A75 100fr gold   3.25   .25
Nos. C70-C72 (3)   5.60   .65

Military Police — AP33

25fr, "Army," soldier, tanks & parachutes.
60fr, "Navy," & "Vigilante." 100fr, "Air Force,"
plane.

1966, June 21   Engr.   Perf. 13
C73 AP33 20fr vio bl, org brn &
                dl pur   .55   .20
C74 AP33 25fr dk grn, dl pur &
                brn   .55   .20
C75 AP33 60fr bl grn, bl & ind   1.60 .30
C76 AP33 100fr brn, Prus bl &
                car rose   2.75 .65
     Nos. C73-C76 (4)   5.45 1.35

Issued to honor Cameroun's armed forces.

Wembley Stadium, London — AP34

1966, July 20
C77 AP34 50fr shown   1.40   .25
C78 AP34 200fr Soccer   4.00 1.10

8th World Cup Soccer Championship, Wembley, England, July 11-30.

Air Afrique Issue, 1966
Common Design Type

1966, Aug. 31   Photo.   Perf. 13
C79 CD123 25fr red lil, blk & gray   .80 .20

Yaoundé Cathedral — AP35

18fr, Buea Cathedral. 30fr, Orthodox Church, Yaoundé. 60fr, Mosque, Garoua.

1966, Dec. 19   Engr.   Perf. 13
C80 AP35 18fr choc, bl & grn   .45 .20
C81 AP35 25fr brn, grn & brt vio   .55 .20
C82 AP35 30fr lil, grn & dl red   .70 .20
C83 AP35 60fr mar, brt grn & grn   1.40 .35
     Nos. C80-C83 (4)   3.10 .95

Pioneer A and Moon — AP36

1967, Apr. 30   Engr.   Perf. 13
C84 AP36 25fr shown   .45   .20
C85 AP36 50fr Ranger 6   .90   .35
C86 AP36 100fr Luna 9   2.10   .65
C87 AP36 250fr Luna 10   4.50 2.00
     Nos. C84-C87 (4)   7.95 3.20

"Conquest of the Moon."

Flower Type of Regular Issue

1967, June 22   Photo.   Perf. 12½
                    Size: 26x46mm
C88 A86 200fr Thevetia Peruvi-
                ana   4.50   .90
C89 A86 250fr Amaryllis   5.50 1.10

African Postal Union Issue, 1967
Common Design Type

1967, Sept. 9   Engr.   Perf. 13
C90 CD124 100fr red brn, Prus
                bl & brt lil   2.40 .65

Skis, Ice Skates, Olympic Flame and Emblem — AP38

1967, Oct. 11   Engr.   Perf. 13
C91 AP38 30fr ultra & sepia   1.60 .20

Issued to publicize the 10th Winter Olympic Games, Grenoble, Feb. 6-8, 1968.

Cameroun Exhibit, EXPO '67 — AP39

100fr, Bangwa house poles carved with ancestor figures. 200fr, Canadian Pavilions.

1967, Oct. 18
C92 AP39 50fr mag, ol & mar   .90   .25
C93 AP39 100fr dk grn, mar &
                dk brn   3.00   .55
C94 AP39 200fr brn, lil rose &
                sl grn   4.00 1.10
     Nos. C92-C94 (3)   7.90 1.90

EXPO '67, International Exhibition, Montreal, Apr. 28-Oct. 27, 1967.
See note after No. C116 regarding 1969 moon overprint.

Konrad Adenauer (1876-1967), Chancellor of West Germany (1949-63) and Cologne Cathedral AP40

70fr, Adenauer and Chancellery, Bonn.

1967, Dec. 1   Photo.   Perf. 12½
C95 AP40 30fr multi   .90   .20
C96 AP40 70fr multi   1.50   .40
  a.   Pair, #C95-C96 + label 3.50 .65

Pres. Ahidjo, King Faisal and View of Mecca — AP41

60fr, Pres. Ahidjo, Pope Paul VI & view of Rome.

1968, Feb. 18   Photo.   Perf. 12½
C97 AP41 30fr multi   .90   .20
C98 AP41 60fr multi   2.10   .30

Issued to commemorate President Ahidjo's Pilgrimage to Mecca and visit to Rome.

Earth on Television Transmitted by Explorer VI — AP42

30fr, Molniya spacecraft. 40fr, Earth on television screen transmitted by Molniya.

1968, Apr. 20   Engr.   Perf. 13
C99 AP42 20fr multi   .55   .20
C100 AP42 30fr multi   .80   .20
C101 AP42 40fr multi   1.10   .20
     Nos. C99-C101 (3)   2.45   .60

Telecommunication by satellite.

Forge — AP43

Boxing — AP44

#C103, Tea harvest. #C104, Trans-Cameroun railroad (diesel train emerging from tunnel). 40fr, Rubber harvest. 60fr, Douala Harbor, horiz.

1968, June 5   Engr.   Perf. 13
C102 AP43 20fr red brn, dk grn
                & ind   .65   .20
C103 AP43 30fr dk brn, grn &
                ultra   1.10   .20
C104 AP43 30fr ind, sl grn & bis
                brn   7.50   .20
C105 AP43 40fr ol bis, dk grn &
                bl grn   1.10   .20
C106 AP43 60fr ultra, dk brn &
                sl   3.00   .40
     Nos. C102-C106 (5)   13.35 1.20

Second Economic Development Five-Year Plan.

1968, Aug. 19   Engr.   Perf. 13
50fr, Long jump. 60fr, Athlete on rings.
C107 AP44 30fr brt grn, dk grn &
                choc   .65   .20
C108 AP44 30fr brt grn, brn red
                & choc   1.25   .30
C109 AP44 60fr brt grn, ultra &
                choc   1.50   .35
  a.   Min. sheet of 3, #C107-C109 4.00 1.50
     Nos. C107-C109 (3)   3.40   .85

19th Olympic Games, Mexico City, 10/12-27.

Human Rights Type of Regular Issue

1968, Sept. 14   Photo.   Perf. 12½x13
C110 A92 30fr grn & brt pink   .80   .20

Martin Luther King, Jr. — AP45

Portraits: No. C112, Mahatma Gandhi and map of India. 40fr, John F. Kennedy. 60fr, Robert F. Kennedy. No. C115, Rev. Martin Luther King, Jr. No. C116, Mahatma Gandhi.

1968, Dec. 5   Photo.   Perf. 12½
C111 AP45 30fr bl & blk   .55   .20
C112 AP45 30fr multi   .55   .20
C113 AP45 40fr pink & blk   .90   .25
C114 AP45 60fr bluish lil & blk 1.10 .40
C115 AP45 70fr yel grn & blk   1.25   .45
  a.   Souvenir sheet of 4,
                #C112-C115   8.00 2.00
C116 AP45 70fr multi   1.25   .50
     Nos. C111-C116 (6)   5.60 2.00

Issued to honor exponents of non-violence. The 2 King stamps (Nos. C111 and C115), the 2 Gandhi stamps (Nos. C112 and C116) and the 2 Kennedy stamps (Nos. C113-C114) are each printed as triptychs with a descriptive label between.

In 1969 Nos. C111-C116 and C94 were overprinted in carmine capitals: "Premier Homme / sur la Lune / 20 Juillet 1969" or "First Man / Landing on Moon / 20 July 1969". Values: on No. C94, $50; on #C111-C116, $275; on No. C115 (2 souvenir sheets, with both overprint types), $300.

PHILEXAFRIQUE Issue

The Letter, by Armand Cambon AP46

1968, Dec. 10
C117 AP46 100fr multi   3.25   .80

PHILEXAFRIQUE, Philatelic Exhibition in Abidjan, Feb. 14-23, 1969. Printed with alternating light green label.

2nd PHILEXAFRIQUE Issue
Common Design Type
Design: Cameroun #199 and Wouri Bridge.

1969, Feb. 14   Engr.   Perf. 13
C118 CD128 50fr multi   3.25   .55

Caladium Bicolor — AP47

Flowers: 50fr, Aristolochia elegans. 100fr, Gloriosa simplex.

1969, May 14   Photo.   Perf. 12½
C119 AP47 30fr lil & multi   .70   .20
C120 AP47 50fr grn & multi   1.40   .35
C121 AP47 100fr brn & multi   3.25   .55
     Nos. C119-C121 (3)   5.35 1.10

3rd Intl. Flower Show, Paris, Apr. 23-Oct. 5.

Douala Post Office — AP48

50fr, Buèa P.O. 100fr, Bafoussam P.O.

1969, June 19   Engr.   Perf. 13
C122 AP48 30fr grn, vio bl &
                brn   .55   .20
C123 AP48 50fr sl, emer & red
                brn   .90   .25
C124 AP48 100fr dk brn, brt grn
                & brn   1.75   .50
     Nos. C122-C124 (3)   3.20   .95

Coronation of Napoleon I, by Jacques
Louis David — AP49

Napoleon Crossing Saint Bernard,
after J. L. David — AP50

1969, July 4   Photo.   Perf. 12x12½
C125 AP49 30fr vio bl & multi 1.00   .20
Die-cut Perf. 10
Embossed on Gold Foil
C126 AP50 1000fr gold   45.00 16.00
     Bicentenary of birth of Napoleon I.

William E. B. Du
Bois (1868-1963),
American
Writer — AP51

15fr, Dr. Price Mars, Haiti (1876-1969).
#C128, Aimé Cesaire, Martinique (1913-).
#C130, Langston Hughes, US (1902-67).
#C131, Marcus Garvey, Jamaica (1887-1940).
100fr, René Maran, Martinique (1887-1960).

1969, Sept. 25   Photo.   Perf. 12½
C127 AP51 15fr lt bl & blk   .45   .20
C128 AP51 30fr lem & blk   .55   .20
C129 AP51 30fr rose brn & blk   .55   .20
C130 AP51 50fr gray & blk   .80   .25
C131 AP51 50fr emer & blk   .80   .25
C132 AP51 100fr yel & blk   2.00   .60
     a. Min. sheet of 6, #C127-C132 6.75 2.50
     Nos. C127-C132 (6)   5.15   1.70
     Issued to honor Negro writers.

ILO Emblem — AP52

1969, Oct. 29   Photo.   Perf. 13
C133 AP52 30fr blk, bl grn & gray .80   .20
C134 AP52 50fr blk, dp lil rose &
                gray   1.40   .25
     50th anniv. of the ILO.

Armstrong, Collins and Aldrin
Splashdown in the Pacific — AP53

Design: 500fr, Landing module and Neil A.
Armstrong's first step on moon.

1969, Nov. 29   Photo.   Perf. 12½
C135 AP53 200fr multi   5.00   1.25
C136 AP53 500fr multi   11.50   2.25
     See note after Algeria No. 427.

Pres. Ahidjo, Arms and Map of
Cameroun — AP54

Embossed on Gold Foil
1970, Jan. 1   Die-cut Perf. 10
C137 AP54 1000fr gold & multi 26.00   8.25
     10th anniversary of independence.

Hotel Mont Fébé, Yaoundé — AP55

1970, Jan. 15   Engr.   Perf. 13
C138 AP55 30fr lt brn, sl grn &
                gray   .80   .20

Lenin — AP56

1970, Jan. 25   Photo.   Perf. 12½
C139 AP56 50fr org & blk   2.00   .25

Plant Type of Regular Issue
Designs: 50fr, Cleome speciosa (caper).
100fr, Mussaenda erythrophylla (madder).

1970, Mar. 24   Photo.   Perf. 12½
Size: 26x46mm
C140 A99 50fr blk & multi   1.40   .25
C141 A99 100fr multi   2.75   .40

Map of Africa and Lions Emblem
Pinpointing Yaoundé — AP57

1970, May 2   Photo.   Perf. 12½
C142 AP57 100fr multi   2.25   .50
     13th Lions International Congress of District
13, Yaoundé, May 2, 1970.

UN Emblem and Doves — AP58

Design: 50fr, UN emblem and dove, vert.

1970, June 26   Engr.   Perf. 13
C143 AP58 30fr brn & org   1.00   .20
C144 AP58 50fr Prus bl & sl bl   1.25   .25
     25th anniversary of the United Nations.

Japanese Pavilion and EXPO
Emblem — AP59

Designs (EXPO Emblem and): 100fr, Map
of Japan, vert. 150fr, Australian pavilion.

1970, Aug. 1   Engr.   Perf. 13
C145 AP59 50fr ind, lt grn & ver .90   .25
C146 AP59 100fr bl, lt grn & red 2.00   .40
C147 AP59 150fr choc, bl & gray 3.25   .65
     Nos. C145-C147 (3)   6.15   1.30
     EXPO '70 International Exhibition, Osaka,
Japan, Mar. 15-Sept. 13.

Charles de
Gaulle — AP60

Pelé and
Team — AP61

Design: 200fr, de Gaulle in uniform.

1970, Aug. 27
C148 AP60 100fr grn, vio bl &
                ol brn   2.25   .50
C149 AP60 200fr ol brn, vio bl
                & grn   4.50   .90
     a. Pair, #C148-C149 + label 8.00   1.60
     Rallying of the Free French, 30th anniv.
For overprints see Nos. C159-C160.

1970, Oct. 14   Photo.   Perf. 12½
Designs: 50fr, Aztec Stadium, Mexico City,
horiz. 100fr, Mexican soccer team, horiz.

C150 AP61 50fr multi   .90   .25
C151 AP61 100fr multi   2.00   .50
C152 AP61 200fr multi   3.50   1.00
     Nos. C150-C152 (3)   6.40   1.75
     9th World Soccer Championships for the
Jules Rimet Cup, Mexico City, May 30-June
21, and the final victory of Brazil over Italy.

Ludwig van
Beethoven
(1770-1827),
Composer
AP62

1970, Nov. 23   Engr.   Perf. 13
C153 AP62 250fr multi   5.75   1.00

Christ at Emmaus, by
Rembrandt — AP63

150fr, The Anatomy Lesson, by Rembrandt.

1970, Dec. 5   Photo.   Perf. 12x12½
C154 AP63 70fr grn & multi   1.40   .25
C155 AP63 150fr multi   2.75   .60

Charles
Dickens — AP64

Designs: 50fr, Scenes from David Copperfield. 100fr, Dickens holding quill.

1970, Dec. 22   Perf. 13
C156 AP64 40fr blk & rose   .95   .20
C157 AP64 50fr bis & multi   1.00   .20
C158 AP64 100fr rose & multi   2.00   .40
     a. Strip of 3, #C156-C158   5.00   1.00
     Charles Dickens (1812-1870), English
novelist.

De Gaulle Type of 1970 Overprinted
with Black Border and: "IN
MEMORIAM / 1890-1970"

1971, Jan. 15   Engr.   Perf. 13
C159 AP60 100fr vio bl, emer
                & brn red   2.75   .40
C160 AP60 200fr brn red, em-
                er & vio bl   5.75   .80
     a. Pair, #C159-C160 + label 9.00   1.40
     In memory of Gen. Charles de Gaulle
(1890-1970), President of France.

Timber Storage, Douala — AP65

Industrialization: 70fr, ALUCAM aluminum plant, Edea, vert. 100fr, Mbakaou Dam.

1971, Feb. 14   Engr.   Perf. 13

C161	AP65	40fr dk red, bl grn & ol brn		
			.55	.20
C162	AP65	70fr ol brn, sl grn & brt bl		
			1.10	.25
C163	AP65	100fr Prus bl, yel grn & red brn		
			1.75	.40
	Nos. C161-C163 (3)		3.40	.85

Relay Race — AP66

50fr, Torch bearer, vert. 100fr, Discus.

1971, Apr. 24   Engr.   Perf. 13

C164	AP66	30fr dk brn, ver & ind		
			.65	.20
C165	AP66	50fr blk, bl & choc	.80	.25
C166	AP66	100fr multi	1.75	.35
	Nos. C164-C166 (3)		3.20	.80

75th anniv. of revival of Olympic Games.

Fishing Trawler — AP67

Designs: 40fr, Local fishermen, Northern Cameroun. 70fr, Fishing harbor, Douala. 150fr, Shrimp boats, Douala.

1971, May 14   Engr.   Perf. 13

C167	AP67	30fr lt brn, bl & grn	.70	.20
C168	AP67	40fr sl grn, bl & dk brn		
			.90	.20
C169	AP67	70fr dk brn, bl & red org		
			2.00	.25
C170	AP67	150fr multi	4.25	.60
	Nos. C167-C170 (4)		7.85	1.25

Cameroun fishing industry.

Cameroun No. 123 and War Memorial, Yaoundé — AP68

Designs (Cameroun Stamps): 25fr, No. C33 and Jamot memorial. 40fr, No. 431 and government buildings, Yaoundé. 50fr, No. 19 and Imperial German postal emblem. 100fr, No. 101 and World War II memorial.

1971, Aug. 1   Engr.   Perf. 13

C171	AP68	20fr grn, ocher & dk brn		
			.35	.20
C172	AP68	25fr dk brn, vio bl & sl grn		
			.55	.20
C173	AP68	40fr grn, mar & sl	.70	.20
C174	AP68	50fr dk brn, blk & ver		
			1.00	.20
C175	AP68	100fr mar, sl grn & org		
			1.75	.40
	Nos. C171-C175 (5)		4.35	1.20

PHILATECAM 1971 Philatelic Exhibition.

Cameroun Flag, Pres. Ahidjo and Reunification Highway — AP69

Typographed, Silk Screen, Embossed

1971, Oct. 1   Perf. 12½

C176	AP69	250fr gold & multi	5.75	2.00

PHILATECAM Philatelic Exhibition, Yaoundé-Douala.

African Postal Union Issue, 1971
Common Design Type

1971, Nov. 13   Photo.   Perf. 13x13½

C177	CD135	100fr bl & multi	2.00	.40

Annunciation, by Fra Angelico — AP71

Christmas (Paintings): 45fr, Virgin and Child, by Andrea del Sarto. 150fr, Christ Child with Lamb, detail from Holy Family, by Raphael, vert.

1971, Dec. 19   Perf. 13x13½, 13½x13

C178	AP71	40fr multi	.55	.20
C179	AP71	45fr multi	.70	.20
C180	AP71	150fr multi	3.25	.60
	Nos. C178-C180 (3)		4.50	1.00

Cameroun Airlines Emblem AP72

1972, Feb. 2   Photo.   Perf. 12½x12

C181	AP72	50fr lt bl & multi	.80	.20

Inauguration of Cameroun Airlines.

Doge's Palace, by Ippolito Caffi AP73

100fr, 200fr, Details from "Regatta on the Grand Canal," by School of Canaletto.

1972   Photo.   Perf. 13

C182	AP73	40fr gold & multi	.65	.20
C183	AP73	100fr gold & multi	1.75	.40
C184	AP73	200fr gold & multi	3.50	.80
	Nos. C182-C184 (3)		5.90	1.40

UNESCO campaign to save Venice.

Cosmonauts Patsayev, Dobrovolsky and Volkov — AP74

1972, May 1   Photo.   Perf. 13x13½

C185	AP74	50fr multi	1.00	.20

Salute-Soyuz 11 space mission, and in memory of the Russian cosmonauts Victor I. Patsayev, Georgi T. Dobrovolsky and Vladislav N. Volkov, who died during Soyuz 11 space mission, June 6-30, 1971.

UN Headquarters, Chinese Flag and Gate of Heavenly Peace — AP75

1972, May 19   Perf. 13

C186	AP75	50fr blk, scar & gold	3.25	.20

Admission of People's Republic of China to UN.

United Republic

Olympic Rings, Swimming AP76

Designs (Olympic Rings and): No. C188, Boxing, vert. 200fr, Equestrian.

1972, Aug. 1   Engr.   Perf. 13

C187	AP76	50fr lake & slate grn		
			.90	.20
C188	AP76	50fr choc & slate	.90	.20
C189	AP76	200fr cl, gray & dk brn		
			3.50	.70
a.	Min. sheet of 3		5.75	2.25
	Nos. C187-C189 (3)		5.30	1.10

20th Olympic Games, Munich, Aug. 26-Sept. 11. No. C189a contains stamps similar to Nos. C187-C189, but in changed colors. The 50fr (swimming) is Prussian blue, violet & brown; the 50c (boxing) lilac, Prussian blue & brown; the 200fr, Prussian blue & brown.

Nos. C187-C189 Overprinted in Red or Black

a

b

c

Madonna with Angels, by Cimabue AP77

Christmas: 140fr, Madonna of the Rose Arbor, by Stefan Lochner.

1972, Dec. 21   Photo.   Perf. 13

C193	AP77	45fr gold & multi	1.00	.20
C194	AP77	140fr gold & multi	2.75	.45

St. Teresa, the Little Flower — AP78

100fr, Lisieux Cathedral and St. Teresa.

1973, Jan. 2   Engr.

C195	AP78	45fr vio bl, pur & mar	.70	.20
C196	AP78	100fr mag, ultra & brn	1.75	.40

Centenary of the birth of St. Teresa of Lisieux (1873-1897), Carmelite nun.

African Unity Hall, Addis Ababa and Emperor Haile Selassie — AP79

1973, Mar. 14   Photo.   Perf. 13

C197	AP79	45fr yellow & multi	1.00	.20

80th birthday of Emperor Haile Selassie of Ethiopia.

Corn, Grain, Healthy and Starving People — AP80

1973, Apr. 10   Typo.   Perf. 13

C198	AP80	45fr multi	.80	.20

World Food Program, 10th anniversary.

1972, Oct. 23   Engr.   Perf. 13

C190	AP76(a)	50fr (R)	.90	.20
C191	AP76(b)	50fr	.90	.20
C192	AP76(c)	200fr	3.50	.80
	Nos. C190-C192 (3)		5.30	1.20

Gold Medal Winners in 20th Olympic Games: Mark Spitz, US, swimming (#C190); Dieter Kottysch, West Germany, light middleweight boxing (#C191); Richard Meade, Great Britain, 3-day equestrian (#C192).

Hearts and Blood
Vessels — AP81

Scout Emblem
and
Flags — AP82

1973, May 5   Engr.
C199 AP81 50fr dk car rose & dk
vio bl   1.00 .20

"Your Heart is Your Health" and for the 25th
anniv. of the WHO.

Type of Regular Issue

Designs: 45fr, Map of Cameroun, Pres.
Ahidjo and No. C176. 70fr, National colors
and commemorative inscriptions.

1973, May 20   **Perf. 13**
C200 A128 45fr grn & multi   .80 .20
C201 A128 70fr red & multi   1.00 .25

1973, July 31   Typo.   **Perf. 13**
C202 AP82 40fr multi   1.00 .20
C203 AP82 45fr multi   1.25 .20
C204 AP82 100fr multi   3.25 .40
    Nos. C202-C204 (3)   5.50 .80

Cameroun's admission to the World Scout
Conference, Mar. 26, 1971.

African Weeks Issue

Head and City
Hall,
Brussels — AP83

1973, Sept. 17   Engr.   **Perf. 13**
C205 AP83 40fr dp brn & rose
claret   .80 .20

African Weeks, Brussels, Sept. 15-30.

Map of Africa with Cameroun — AP84

1973, Sept. 29   Engr.   **Perf. 13**
C206 AP84 40fr blk, red & grn   .80 .20

Help for handicapped children.

Zamengoe
Radar
Station
AP85

1973, Dec. 8   Engr.   **Perf. 13**
C207 AP85 100fr bl, lt brn & grn   1.50 .40

Chancellor
Rolin
Madonna,
by Van
Eyck
AP86

Christmas: 140fr, Nativity, by Federigo
Barocei.

1973, Dec. 11   Photo.   **Perf. 13**
C208 AP86 45fr gold & multi   1.00 .20
C209 AP86 140fr gold & multi   2.75 .70

Zebu Type of 1974

1974, June 1   Litho.   **Perf. 13**
C210 A140 45fr Zebu herd   1.40 .20

Churchill
and Union
Jack
AP87

1974, July 10   Engr.   **Perf. 13**
C211 AP87 100fr blk, bl & red   1.60 .40

Winston Churchill (1874-1965).

Soccer, Arms of Frankfurt, Dortmund,
Gelsenkirchen and Stuttgart — AP88

100fr, Soccer & arms of Berlin, Hamburg,
Hanover & Düsseldorf. 200fr, Soccer cup &
game.

1974, Aug. 5   Photo.   **Perf. 13**
C212 AP88 45fr gray, sl & org   .65 .20
C213 AP88 100fr gray, sl & org   1.25 .40
C214 AP88 200fr org, slate & bl   2.50 .65
    a.   Strip of 3, Nos. C212-C214   5.00 1.40

World Cup Soccer Championship, Munich,
June 13-July 7.

**Nos. C212-C214 Overprinted in Dark
Blue: "7th JULY 1974 / R.F.A. 2
HOLLANDE 1 / 7 JUILLET 1974"**

1974, Sept. 16   Photo.   **Perf. 13**
C215 AP88 45fr multi   .65 .20
C216 AP88 100fr multi   1.25 .40
C217 AP88 200fr multi   2.40 .80
    a.   Strip of 3, Nos. C215-C217   5.50 1.50

World Cup Soccer Championship, 1974,
victory of German Federal Republic.

UPU Type of 1974

100fr, Cameroun #503. 200fr, Cameroun
#C29.

1974, Oct. 8   Engr.   **Perf. 13**
C218 A142 100fr blue & multi   1.75 .30
C219 A142 200fr red & multi   3.25 .60

Copernicus and Planets Circling
Sun — AP89

1974, Oct. 15   Engr.   **Perf. 13**
C220 AP89 250fr multi   3.50 1.00

500th anniversary of the birth of Nicolaus
Copernicus (1473-1543), Polish astronomer.

21st Chess
Olympiad, Nice,
France, June 6-
30 — AP90

1974, Nov. 3   Photo.   **Perf. 13x12½**
C221 AP90 100fr Chess pieces   4.50 .40

Mask and ARPHILA Emblem — AP91

1974, Nov. 30   Engr.   **Perf. 13**
C222 AP91 50fr choc & magenta   .65 .20

ARPHILA 75, Paris, June 6-16, 1975.

Presidents and Flags of Cameroun,
CAR, Gabon and Congo — AP92

1974, Dec. 8   Photo.
C223 AP92 100fr gold & multi   2.40 .40

See note after No. 595.

Man Landing on Moon — AP93

1974, Dec. 15   Engr.
C224 AP93 200fr brn, bl & car   3.25 .80

5th anniv. of man's 1st landing on the moon.

Charles de Gaulle and Félix
Eboué — AP94

1975, Feb. 24   Typo.   **Perf. 13**
C225 AP94 45fr multi   1.50 .20
C226 AP94 200fr multi   5.00 .80

Felix A. Eboué (1884-1944), Governor of
Chad, first colonial governor to join Free
French in WWII, 30th death anniversary.

Marquis de
Lafayette
AP95

American Bicentennial: 140fr, Washington
and soldiers. 500fr, Franklin and Independence Hall.

1975, Oct. 20   Engr.   **Perf. 13**
C227 AP95 100fr vio bl & multi   2.10 .40
C228 AP95 140fr brn & multi   2.25 .60
C229 AP95 500fr grn & multi   7.25 1.60
    Nos. C227-C229 (3)   11.60 2.60

The
Burning
Bush, by
Nicolas
Froment
AP96

Painting: 500fr, Adoration of the Kings, by
Gentile da Fabriano, horiz.

1975, Dec. 25   Photo.   **Perf. 13**
C230 AP96 50fr gold & multi   .90 .20
C231 AP96 500fr gold & multi   7.25 1.60

Christmas 1975.

Concorde and Route: Paris-Dakar-Rio
de Janeiro — AP97

1976, July 20   Litho.   **Perf. 13**
C232 AP97 500fr lt bl & multi   6.50 1.60
    a.   Souvenir sheet of 1   9.00 3.75

1st commercial flight of supersonic jet Con-
corde from Paris to Rio de Janeiro, Jan. 21.
No. C232a sold for 600fr.
For overprint see No. C263.

Dance Type of 1976

50fr, Dancers & drummer. 100fr, Woman
dancer.

1976, Sept. 15   Litho.   **Perf. 12**
C233 A154 50fr gray & multi   .65 .20
C234 A154 100fr gray & multi   1.10 .35

Virgin and Child, by Giovanni Bellini — AP98

Paintings: 30fr, Adoration of the Shepherds, by Le Brun. 60fr, Adoration of the Kings, by Rubens. 500fr, The Newborn, by Georges de la Tour.

1976, Dec. 15　Litho.　Perf. 12½
C235	AP98	30fr gold & multi	.70	.20
C236	AP98	60fr gold & multi	.90	.25
C237	AP98	70fr gold & multi	1.25	.25
C238	AP98	500fr gold & multi	9.00	1.60
a.		Souv. sheet of 4, #C235-C238	12.50	3.75
		Nos. C235-C238 (4)	11.85	2.30

Christmas 1976.

Festival Type of 1977
Traditional Chief on his throne, sculpture.

1977, Feb. 4　Litho.　Perf. 12½
C239	A159	60fr multi	1.10	.25

Crucifixion, by Matthias Grunewald — AP99

125fr, Christ on the Cross, by Velazquez, vert. 150fr, The Deposition, by Titian.

1977, Apr. 2　Litho.　Perf. 12½
C240	AP99	50fr gold & multi	.90	.20
C241	AP99	125fr gold & multi	1.75	.40
C242	AP99	150fr gold & multi	2.50	.55
a.		Souv. sheet of 3, #C240-C242, perf. 12	6.75	1.75
		Nos. C240-C242 (3)	5.15	1.15

Easter 1977. No. C242a sold for 350fr.

Lions Emblem, Map of Africa — AP100

1977, Apr. 29　Litho.　Perf. 12½
C243	AP100	250fr multi	3.00	1.00

Lions Club of Douala, 19th Cong., 4/29-30.

Rotary Emblem AP101

1977, May 18
C244	AP101	60fr multi	.70	.25

Rotary Club of Douala, 20th anniversary.

Antoine de Saint-Exupéry AP102

Charles Lindbergh and Spirit of St. Louis — AP103

Designs: 50fr, Jean Mermoz and his plane. 80fr, Maryse Bastié and her plane. 100fr, Sikorsky S-43. 300fr, Concorde.

1977, May 20　Engr.　Perf. 13
C245	AP103	50fr org & bl	.80	.20
C246	AP102	60fr mag & org	.95	.25
C247	AP103	80fr mag & bl	1.25	.30
a.		Souv. sheet, #C245-C247	3.25	1.10
C248	AP103	100fr grn & yel	1.50	.40
C249	AP103	300fr multi	5.50	1.25
C250	AP103	500fr multi	8.00	1.75
a.		Souv. sheet, #C248-C250	14.50	6.00
		Nos. C245-C250 (6)	18.00	4.15

Aviation pioneers and events. No. C247a sold for 200fr. No. C250a sold for 1000fr. For overprint see No. C262.

Sassenage Castle, Grenoble — AP104

1977, May 21　Litho.　Perf. 12½
C251	AP104	70fr multi	1.40	.25

10th anniv. of Intl. French Language Council.

Jufilex Type of 1977
Designs: 70fr, Switzerland (Zurich) No. 1L1 and Cameroun No. 16. 100fr, Switzerland (Geneva) No. 2L1 and Cameroun No. 254.

1977, June 5　Litho.　Perf. 12
C252	A161	70fr multi	1.25	.25
C253	A161	100fr multi	2.10	.40

Apollo-Soyuz Type
100fr, Astronaut Vance Brand, Apollo in orbit. 250fr, Apollo and Soyuz docking. 350fr, Cosmonaut Valery Kubasov, Soyuz in orbit. 500fr, Astronaut Donald Slayton, handshake.

1977, Aug. 10　Litho.　Perf. 14x13½
C256	A163	100fr multicolored	.90	.75
C257	A163	250fr multicolored	2.25	2.10
C258	A163	350fr multicolored	3.25	3.00
		Nos. C256-C258 (3)	6.40	5.85

Souvenir Sheet
C259	A163	500fr multicolored	5.00	4.25

Diseased Knee, WHO Emblem AP105

1977, Oct. 15　Engr.　Perf. 13
C260	AP105	70fr multi	.70	.25

World Rheumatism Year.

Nos. C249 and C232 Overprinted in Red: "PREMIER VOL PARIS-NEW YORK /FIRST FLIGHT PARIS-NEW YORK / 22 Nov. 1977-22nd Nov. 1977"

Engraved, Lithographed
1977, Nov. 22　　　　Perf. 13
C262	AP103	300fr multi	3.25	1.25
C263	AP97	500fr multi	5.00	2.00

Concorde, 1st commercial flight Paris to NY.

Christmas Type of 1977
Paintings: 60fr, Virgin and Child with 4 Saints, by Bellini, horiz. 400fr, Adoration of the Shepherds, by George de la Tour, horiz.

1977, Dec. 15　Litho.　Perf. 12x12½
C264	A165	60fr multi	1.00	.25
C265	A165	400fr multi	5.00	1.75

Flag Type of 1978
60fr, New flag, Pres. Ahidjo and spear.

1978, Apr. 3　Litho.　Perf. 12½
C266	A167	60fr multi	.55	.20

Frog Type of 1978
Design: 100fr, Cardioglossa trifasciata.

1978, Apr. 5
C267	A168	100fr multi	3.75	.40

L'Arlesienne, by Van Gogh — AP106

#C269, Burial of Christ, by Albrecht Dürer.

1978, May 15　Litho.　Perf. 12½
C268	AP106	200fr multi	3.00	1.10
C269	AP106	200fr multi	4.00	1.10

Leprosy Distribution on World Map, Raoul Follereau — AP107

1978, June 6　Litho.　Perf. 12
C270	AP107	100fr multi	1.00	.55

25th World Leprosy Day.

Capt. Cook and Siege of Quebec — AP108

Design: 250fr, Capt. Cook, Adventure and Resolution, map of voyages.

1978, July 26　Engr.　Perf. 13
C271	AP108	100fr multi	2.10	.55
C272	AP108	250fr multi	5.00	1.40

Capt. James Cook (1728-1779), explorer.

Argentine Soccer Team, Coat of Arms and Rimet Cup — AP109

200fr, Two soccer players, vert. 1000fr, Soccer ball illuminating world map, vert.

1978, Sept. 1　　　　Perf. 13
C273	AP109	100fr multi	1.00	.55
C274	AP109	200fr multi	1.75	1.10
C275	AP109	1000fr multi	10.00	5.50
		Nos. C273-C275 (3)	12.75	7.15

11th World Cup Soccer Championship, Argentina, June 1-25.

Jules Verne Type of 1978
Design: 400fr, Jules Verne and "20,000 Leagues Under the Sea," horiz.

1978, Oct. 10　　　　Perf. 12
C276	A169	400fr multi	4.00	2.00

Musical Instrument Type of 1978
Design: 100fr, Man playing Mvet zither.

1978, Nov. 20　Litho.　Perf. 12½
C277	A172	100fr multi	1.10	.40

Human Rights Type of 1979
1979, Feb. 11　Litho.　Perf. 12x12½
C278	A174	500fr multi	5.50	2.50

Lions Emblem, Map of District 403 — AP110

1979, Apr. 26　Litho.　Perf. 12½
C279	AP110	60fr multi	.70	.25

21st Congress of Lions Club of Yaoundé.

Penny Black, Hill, Cameroun No. 9 — AP111

1979, Oct. 10　Engr.　Perf. 13
C280	AP111	100fr multi	1.00	.40

Sir Rowland Hill (1795-1879), originator of penny postage.

"TELECOM 79" — AP112　　　Pope Paul VI — AP113

1979, Sept. 26　Litho.　Perf. 13x12½
C281	AP112	100fr multi	1.10	.40

3rd World Telecommunications Exhibition, Geneva, Sept. 20-26.

1979, Oct. 23 Engr. _Perf. 12½x13_
C282 AP113 100fr shown   2.25 .40
C283 AP113 100fr John Paul I   2.25 .40
C284 AP113 100fr John Paul II   2.25 .40
 Nos. C282-C284 (3)   6.75 1.20

"Double Eagle" over French Coastline AP114

Design: No. C286, Balloonists and balloon.

1979, Dec. 15 Litho. _Perf. 12½_
C285 AP114 500fr multi   5.00 2.25
C286 AP114 500fr multi   5.00 2.25

First Transatlantic balloon crossing.

100-Meter Race — AP115

Designs: 150fr, Figure skating pairs. 200fr, Javelin. 300fr, Wrestling.

1980, Dec. 18 Litho. _Perf. 12½_
C287 AP115 100fr yel brn & brn   .90 .50
C288 AP115 150fr bl & brn   1.25 .70
C289 AP115 200fr grn & brn   1.75 1.00
C290 AP115 300fr red & brn   2.50 1.40
 Nos. C287-C290 (4)   6.40 3.60

22nd Summer Olympic Games, Moscow, July 19-Aug. 3; 13th Winter Olympic Games, Lake Placid, Feb. 12-24 (150fr).

Alan Shepard and Freedom 7 — AP116

1981, Sept. 15 Litho. _Perf. 12½_
C291 AP116 500fr shown   6.00 4.00
C292 AP116 500fr Yuri Gagarin,
             Vostok I   6.00 4.00

Manned space flight, 20th anniv.

4th African Scouting Conference, Abidjan, June — AP117

1981, Oct. 5
C293 AP117 100fr Emblem, sa-
             lute, badge   .70 .40
C294 AP117 500fr Scout saluting 4.50 2.00

Guernica (detail), by Pablo Picasso (1881-1973) — AP118

#C296, Landscape, by Paul Cezanne (1839-1906).

1981, Nov. 10 Litho. _Perf. 12½_
C295 AP118 500fr multi   6.00 2.00
C296 AP118 500fr multi   6.00 2.00

Christmas 1981 — AP119

Designs: 50fr, Virgin and Child, by Froment, vert. 60f, San Zeno Altarpiece, by Mantegna, vert. 400fr, Flight into Egypt, by Giotto.

1981, Dec. 1 Litho. _Perf. 12½_
C297 AP119 50fr multi   .45 .25
C298 AP119 60fr multi   .65 .30
C299 AP119 400fr multi   3.50 2.00
 a. Souv. sheet of 3, #C297-
     C299, perf. 13x13½   9.00 2.75
 Nos. C297-C299 (3)   4.60 2.55

Still Life, by Georges Braque (1882-1963) — AP120

Paintings: No. C301, Olympia, by Edouard Manet (1832-1883).

1982, Dec. 5 Litho. _Perf. 13_
C300 AP120 500fr multi   5.00 2.00
C301 AP120 500fr multi   5.00 2.00

Pres. John F. Kennedy (1917-63) AP121

1983, Mar. 15 Litho. _Perf. 13_
C302 AP121 500fr multi   4.50 2.00

Lions District 403 (Douala), 2nd Convention, May — AP122

1983, May 5 Litho. _Perf. 12½_
C303 AP122 70fr multi   .55 .30
C304 AP122 150fr multi   1.25 .65

Jeanne of Aragon by Raphael AP123

No. C306, Massacre of Scio by Delacroix.

1983, Oct. 15 Litho. _Perf. 13_
C305 AP123 500fr multi   5.00 1.00
C306 AP123 500fr multi   5.00 1.00

Easter 1984 — AP124

200fr, Pieta, by G. Hernandez. 500fr, Martyrdom of St. John the Evangelist, by C. Le Brun.

1984, Mar. 30 Litho. _Perf. 13_
C307 AP124 200fr multi   1.75 .50
C308 AP124 500fr multi   4.50 1.40
 a. Souv. sheet of 2, #C307-
     C308   7.25 2.00

1984 Summer Olympics AP125

European Soccer Championship, June 12-27 — AP126

1984, Apr. 30 _Perf. 12½_
C309 AP125 100fr High jump   .90 .25
C310 AP125 150fr Volleyball   1.25 .30
C311 AP125 250fr Handball   2.25 .55
C312 AP125 500fr Bicycling   4.50 1.10
 Nos. C309-C312 (4)   8.90 2.20

See Nos. C321-C324.

1984, June 5 Litho. _Perf. 12½_
C313 AP126 250fr Player in
             red shorts   2.25 .65
C314 AP126 250fr Yellow
             shorts   2.25 .65
C315 AP126 500fr Players   4.50 1.25
 a. Souvenir sheet of 3   10.00 2.75
 Nos. C313-C315 (3)   9.00 2.55

No. C315a contains Nos. C313-C315 in changed panel colors.

Presidential Oath — AP127

1984 Litho. _Perf. 13_
C316 AP127 60fr French in-
             scription   .55 .20
 a. English inscription   .55 .20
C317 AP127 70fr French in-
             scription   .55 .20
 a. English inscription   .55 .20
C318 AP127 200fr French in-
             scription   1.75 .40
 a. English inscription   1.75 .40
 Nos. C316-C318 (3)   2.85 .80

Issue dates: French, Sept. 15; English, Nov.

Famous Men — AP128

#C316, Diana in the Bath, by Watteau (1684-1721). #C317, Portrait of Diderot (1713-1784).

1984, Sept. 20 Litho. _Perf. 13_
C319 AP128 500fr Watteau   5.00 1.00
C320 AP128 500fr Diderot, vert. 5.00 1.00

Nos. C309-C312 in Changed Colors with Added Inscriptions
100fr: MOEGENBURG (R.F.A.) 11-08-84
150fr: U.S.A. 11-08-84
250fr: YOUGOSLAVIE 9-08-84
500fr: GORSKI (U.S.A.) 3-08-84

1984, Sept. 25 Litho. _Perf. 12½_
C321 AP125 100fr multi   .90 .20
C322 AP125 150fr multi   1.25 .30
C323 AP125 250fr multi   2.25 .50
C324 AP125 500fr multi   4.50 1.00
 Nos. C321-C324 (4)   8.90 2.00

Moon Landing, 15th Anniv. — AP129

1984, Nov. 15 Litho. _Perf. 12½_
C325 AP129 500fr Neil Arm-
             strong   4.50 1.50
C326 AP129 500fr Apollo 12
             launching   4.50 1.50

Louis Pasteur (1822-1895), Chemist, Microbiologist — AP130

#328, Mourning Woman (detail), Mausoleum of Henri Claude d'Harcourt, by sculptor Jean Baptiste Pigalle (1714-1785).

1985, Oct. 10		Litho.		Perf. 13	
C327	AP130	500fr multi		6.00	1.75
C328	AP130	500fr multi		6.00	1.75

Christmas
AP131

250fr, Children's gifts. 300fr, Akono Church. 400fr, Holy Family & drummer boy. 500fr, The Virgin with the Blue Diadem, by Raphael.

1985, Dec. 20		Litho.	Perf. 13	
C329	AP131	250fr multi	2.25	.90
C330	AP131	300fr multi	2.50	1.10
C331	AP131	400fr multi	3.25	1.50
C332	AP131	500fr multi	5.00	2.00
	Nos. C329-C332 (4)		13.00	5.50

1986 World Cup Soccer
Championships, Mexico — AP132

1986			Perf. 13½	
C333	AP132	250fr Argentina, winner	2.75	1.40
C334	AP132	300fr Stadium	2.75	1.60
C335	AP132	400fr Mexican team	3.50	2.25
	Nos. C333-C335 (3)		9.00	5.25

Famous Men — AP133

#C336, Pierre Curie (1859-1906), chemist, atom, and elements. #C337, Jean Mermoz (1901-1936), aviator, and aircraft.

1986, Sept. 10		Litho.	Perf. 12½	
C336	AP133	500fr multi	6.25	2.00
C337	AP133	500fr multi	6.25	2.00

AIR POST SEMI-POSTAL STAMPS

Doctor Examining
Child — SPAP1

	Unwmk.			
1942, June 22		Engr.	Perf. 13	
CB1	SPAP1	1.50fr + 50c green		.80
CB2	SPAP1	2fr + 6fr brn & red brn		.80

Native children's welfare fund.

Nos. CB1-CB2 were issued by the Vichy government in France, but were not placed on sale in Cameroun.

Colonial Education Fund
Common Design Type

1942, June 22			
CB3	CD86a	1.20fr + 1.80fr blue & red	.80

No. CB3 was issued by the Vichy government in France, but was not placed on sale in Cameroun.

POSTAGE DUE STAMPS

Man Felling
Tree — D1

Perf. 14x13½

1925-27		Unwmk.		Typo.	
J1	D1	2c lt bl & blk		.30	.30
J2	D1	4c ol bis & red vio		.30	.30
J3	D1	5c vio & blk		.60	.60
J4	D1	10c red & blk		.60	.60
J5	D1	15c gray & blk		.70	.70
J6	D1	20c olive grn & blk		.70	.70
J7	D1	25c yel & blk		1.25	1.25
J8	D1	30c blue & org		1.25	1.25
J9	D1	50c brn & blk		1.90	1.90
J10	D1	60c bl grn & rose red		1.90	1.90
J11	D1	1fr dl red & grn, grnsh		1.90	1.90
J12	D1	2fr red & vio ('27)		4.00	4.00
J13	D1	3fr org brn & ultra ('27)		6.00	6.00
	Nos. J1-J13 (13)			21.40	21.40

Shades occur for several values.

Carved Figures — D2

1939		Engr.	Perf. 14x13	
J14	D2	5c brt red vio	.20	.20
J15	D2	10c Prus blue	.70	.70
J16	D2	15c car rose	.20	.20
J17	D2	20c blk brn	.20	.20
J18	D2	30c ultra	.45	.45
J19	D2	50c dk grn	.45	.45
J20	D2	60c brn vio	.85	.85
J21	D2	1fr dk vio	1.10	1.10
J22	D2	2fr org red	1.60	1.60
J23	D2	3fr dark blue	2.25	2.25
	Nos. J14-J23 (10)		8.00	8.00

Type D2 without "RF"

1944			
J23A	D2	10c Prussian blue	.50

No. J23A was issued by the Vichy government in France, but was not placed on sale in Cameroun.

> **Catalogue values for unused stamps in this section, from this point to the end of the section, are for Never Hinged items.**

D3

1947		Unwmk.	Perf. 13	
J24	D3	10c dark red	.20	.20
J25	D3	30c dp org	.20	.20
J26	D3	50c grnsh blk	.20	.20
J27	D3	1fr dark car	.35	.35
J28	D3	2fr dp yel grn	.50	.50
J29	D3	3fr dp red lil	.50	.50
J30	D3	4fr dp ultra	.60	.60
J31	D3	5fr red brn	.85	.85
J32	D3	10fr peacock bl	1.40	1.40
J33	D3	20fr sepia	2.25	2.25
	Nos. J24-J33 (10)		7.05	7.05

Federal Republic

Hibiscus
D4

Flowers: No. J35, Erythrina. No. J36, Plumeria lutea. No. J37, Ipomoea. No. J38, Hoodia gordonii. No. J39, Crinum. No. J40, Ochna. No. J41, Gloriosa. No. J42, Costus spectabilis. No. J43, Bougainvillea spectabilis. No. J44, Delonix regia. No. J45, Haemanthus. No. J46, Ophthalmophyllum. No. J47, Titanopsis. No. J48, Amorphophallus. No. J49, Zingiberaceae.

		Unwmk.			
1963, Apr. 10		**Engr.**		**Perf. 11**	
J34	D4	50c car, bl, grn & yel		.20	.20
J35	D4	50c car, bl, grn & yel		.20	.20
a.		Pair, #J34-J35		.25	.25
J36	D4	1fr mag, grn & yel		.20	.20
J37	D4	1fr mag, grn & yel		.20	.20
a.		Pair, #J36-J37		.25	.25
J38	D4	1.50fr dk grn, lil & yel		.20	.20
J39	D4	1.50fr dk grn, lil & yel		.20	.20
a.		Pair, #J38-J39		.25	.25
J40	D4	2fr org ver, yel & grn		.20	.20
J41	D4	2fr org ver, yel & grn		.20	.20
a.		Pair, #J40-J41		.25	.25
J42	D4	5fr mag, grn & yel		.20	.20
J43	D4	5fr mag, grn & yel		.20	.20
a.		Pair, #J42-J43		.25	.25
J44	D4	10fr crim, grn & yel		.45	.20
J45	D4	10fr crim, grn & yel		.45	.20
a.		Pair, #J44-J45		.90	.40
J46	D4	20fr grn, yel & lil		1.00	.45
J47	D4	20fr grn, yel & lil		1.00	.45
a.		Pair, #J46-J47		2.00	.90
J48	D4	40fr lilac & yel		1.75	.80
J49	D4	40fr lilac & yel		1.75	.80
a.		Pair, #J48-J49		3.50	1.60
	Nos. J34-J49 (16)			8.40	4.90

The pairs are se-tenant at the base.

MILITARY STAMPS

> **Catalogue values for unused stamps in this section are for Never Hinged items.**

M1

		Unwmk.		
1963, July 1		**Typo.**	**Perf. 13**	
M1	M1	rose claret	3.00	3.00

Type of 1963 Inscribed
"REPUBLIC UNIE DU CAMEROUN /
UNITED REPUBLIC OF CAMEROUN"

1982?		**Litho.**	**Perf. 13x13½**
M2	M1	rose claret	

CANADIAN PROVINCES

BRITISH COLUMBIA & VANCOUVER IS.

ˈbri-tish kə-ˈləm-bē-ə
and van-ˈkü-vər ˈī-lənd

LOCATION — On the northwest coast of North America
GOVT. — British Colony

AREA — 355,900 sq. mi.
POP. — 694,300

In 1871 the colony became a part of the Canadian Confederation and the postage stamps of Canada have since been used.

12 Pence = 1 Shilling
20 Shillings = 1 Pound
100 Cents = 1 Dollar (1865)

Values for unused stamps are for examples with original gum as defined in the catalogue introduction. Very fine examples of Nos. 2 and 5-18 will have perforations touching the design on at least one side due to the narrow spacing of the stamps on the plates. Stamps with perfs clear of the design on all four sides are extremely scarce and will command much higher prices.

Queen Victoria — A1

1860		Unwmk.	Typo.	Imperf.
1	A1	2½p dull rose		13,500.

No. 1 was not placed in use. It is ungummed and may be a proof or reprint.

			Perf. 14	
2	A1	2½p dull rose	450.00	250.00

VANCOUVER ISLAND

A2   A3

1865		Wmk. 1	Imperf.	
3	A2	5c rose	40,000.	11,000.
4	A3	10c blue	2,750.	1,150.

			Perf. 14	
5	A2	5c rose	340.00	225.00
6	A3	10c blue	300.00	215.00

BRITISH COLUMBIA

Seal of British
Columbia — A4

1865, Nov. 1				
7	A4	3p blue	120.00	100.00

Design A4 of 1865 Surcharged in
Various Colors

2c   5c - $1

1867-69			**Perf. 14**	
8		2c on 3p brown (Bk)	175.00	160.00
9		5c on 3p brt red (Bk) ('69)	230.00	200.00
10		10c on 3p lil rose (Bl)	1,600.	
11		25c on 3p org (V) ('69)	275.00	210.00

12	50c on 3p violet (R)	875.00	*1,150.*	
13	$1 on 3p green			
	(G)		1,500.	

Nos. 10 and 13 were not placed in use.

1869			**Perf. 12½**	
14	5c on 3p brt red			
	(Bk)	1,750.	1,350.	
15	10c on 3p lil rose			
	(Bl)	1,150.	1,000.	
16	25c on 3p orange			
	(V)	725.00	725.00	
17	50c on 3p violet (R)	1,050.	900.00	
18	$1 on 3p green			
	(G)	1,700.	1,700.	

NEW BRUNSWICK

'nü 'brənz-ˌwik

LOCATION — Eastern Canada, bordering on the Bay of Fundy and the Gulf of St. Lawrence.
GOVT. — British Province
AREA — 27,985 sq. mi.
POP. — 285,594 (1871)
CAPITAL — Fredericton

At one time a part of Nova Scotia, New Brunswick became a separate province in 1784. Upon joining the Canadian Confederation in 1867 its postage stamps were superseded by those of Canada.

12 Pence = 1 Shilling
100 Cents = 1 Dollar (1860)

Crown of Great Britain and Heraldic Flowers of the United Kingdom
A1

1851		Unwmk. Engr.		Imperf.
		Blue Paper		
1	A1	3p red	3,000.	550.
a.		3p dark red	3,100.	575.
b.		Half used as 1½p on cover		4,750.
2	A1	6p olive yellow	5,500.	1,150.
a.		6p orange yellow	5,500.	1,200.
b.		Half used as 3p on cover		3,500.
c.		Quarter used as 1½p on cover		30,000.
d.		6p mustard yellow	7,500.	1,350.
3	A1	1sh brt red violet	16,000.	6,000.
a.		Half used as 6p on cover		24,000.
b.		Quarter used as 3p on cover		24,000.
4	A1	1sh dull violet	20,000.	7,500.
a.		Half used as 6p on cover		24,000.
b.		Quarter used as 3p on cover		24,000.

The reprints are on stout white paper. The 3p is printed in orange and the 6p and 1sh in violet black. Value about $275 per set of 3.

Charles Connell — A2

1860			**Perf. 12**
5	A2	5c brown	12,000.

No. 5 was prepared for use but not issued. Most examples of No. 5 have creases or other faults. Value of an average example is about half that shown here.

Locomotive
A3

Victoria
A4

A5

A6

Steam and Sailing Ship — A7

Edward VII as Prince of Wales — A8

1860-63		**White Paper**	**Perf. 12**	
6	A3	1c red lilac	37.50	37.50
a.		1c brown violet	70.00	55.00
b.		Horiz. pair, imperf. vert.	700.00	
7	A4	2c orange ('63)	15.00	14.00
a.		Vertical pair, imperf. horiz.	750.00	
8	A5	5c yellow green	22.50	22.50
a.		5c blue green	22.50	22.50
b.		5c olive green	150.00	37.50
9	A6	10c vermilion	47.50	47.50
a.		Half used as 5c on cover		800.00
b.		Double impression	350.00	175.00
10	A7	12½c blue	77.50	77.50
11	A8	17c black	47.50	47.50
		Nos. 6-11 (6)	247.50	246.50

NEWFOUNDLAND

'nü-fən͜d‿-lənd

LOCATION — Island in the Atlantic Ocean off the coast of Canada, and Labrador, a part of the mainland
GOVT. — British Dominion
AREA — 42,734 sq. mi.
POP. — 321,177 (1945)
CAPITAL — St. John's

Newfoundland was a self-governing Dominion of the British Empire from 1855 to 1933, when it became a Crown Colony. In 1949 it united with Canada.

12 Pence = 1 Shilling
100 Cents = 1 Dollar (1866)

Values for unused stamps are for examples with original gum as defined in the catalogue introduction. However, very fine examples of Nos. 1-7, 9, 11, 13 and 15 without gum are often traded at values very close to those for examples with original gum.

Watermark

Wmk. 224
Coat of
Arms

As the watermark 224 does not show on every stamp in the sheet, pairs are found one with and one without watermark. This applies to all stamps with watermark 224.

Crown of Great Britain and Heraldic Flowers of the United Kingdom — A1

Rose, Thistle and Shamrock — A3

A2

A4

A5   A6

A7   A8

1857   Unwmk.   Engr.   Imperf.
Thick Porous Wove Paper with Mesh

1	A1	1p brown violet	120.00	190.00
a.		Half used as ½p on cover		15,000.
2	A2	2p scarlet ver	17,500.	5,500.
a.		Vert. half used as 1p on cover		19,000.
3	A3	3p green	475.00	475.00
4	A4	4p scarlet ver	11,500.	3,750.
a.		Half used as 2p on cover		20,000.
5	A1	5p brown violet	300.00	375.00
6	A5	6p scarlet ver	22,500.	4,750.
7	A6	6½p scarlet ver	4,500.	3,750.
8	A7	8p scarlet ver	375.00	475.00
a.		Half used as 4p on cover		6,000.
9	A8	1sh scarlet ver	25,000.	9,500.
a.		Half used as 6p on cover		20,000.

1860
Thin to Thick Wove Paper, No Mesh

11	A2	2p orange	375.00	475.00
11A	A3	3p green	77.50	105.00
12	A4	4p orange	3,000.	1,150.
b.		Half used as 2p on cover		15,000.
12A	A1	5p vio brown	77.50	135.00
13	A5	6p orange	3,750.	950.00
15	A8	1sh orange	30,000.	11,500.
b.		Half used as 6p on cover		17,500.

A 6½p orange exists as a souvenir item.
A 1sh exists in orange on horizontally or vertically laid paper. Most authorities consider these to be proofs. Value, $10,500.

1861-62

15A	A1	1p vio brown	160.00	225.00
16	A1	1p reddish brown		9,500.
17	A2	2p rose	160.00	175.00
18	A4	4p rose	35.00	70.00
a.		Half used as 2p on cover		—
19	A1	5p reddish brown	62.50	77.50
a.		5p orange brown	75.00	100.00
20	A5	6p rose	22.50	62.50
a.		Half used as 3p on cover		10,000.
21	A6	6½p rose	77.50	275.00
22	A7	8p rose	77.50	300.00
23	A8	1sh rose	37.50	275.00
a.		Half used as 6p on cover		18,000.

Some sheets of Nos. 11-23 are known with the papermaker's watermark "STACEY WISE 1858" in large capitals.
No. 16 was prepared but not issued.
False cancellations are found on Nos. 1, 3, 5, 8, 11, 11A, 12A, 17-23.
Forgeries exist of most or all of Nos. 1-23.

Codfish — A9

Harp Seal — A10

Prince Albert — A11

Victoria — A12

Fishing Ship — A13

Victoria — A14

1865-94   Perf. 12
White Paper (#24, 27, 28)
Thin Yellowish Paper (#25-26, 29-31)

24	A9	2c green	77.50	30.00
a.		Thin yellowish paper	95.00	40.00
b.		Half used as 1c on cover		4,000.
25	A10	5c brown	550.00	375.00
				5,250.
26	A10	5c black ('68)	325.00	150.00
27	A11	10c black	325.00	60.00
a.		Thin yellowish paper	375.00	115.00
				4,250.
28	A12	12c pale red brn	57.50	47.50
a.		Thin yellowish paper	500.00	190.00
b.		Half used as 6c on cover		3,250.
29	A12	12c brn, white ('94)	57.50	45.00
30	A13	13c orange	225.00	115.00
31	A14	24c blue, thin transluscent paper	52.50	30.00
a.		Thicker white paper ('70)	375.00	300.00

See Nos. 38, 40.

Edward VII as Prince of Wales
A15

Queen Victoria
A16

1868-94

32	A15	1c violet	75.00	60.00
32A	A15	1c brown lilac (re-engr. '71)	115.00	75.00
33	A16	3c ver ('70)	375.00	190.00
34	A16	3c blue ('73)	375.00	75.00
35	A16	6c dull rose ('70)	22.50	15.00
36	A16	6c car lake ('94)	37.50	22.50
		Nos. 32-36 (6)	1,000.	437.50

In the re-engraved 1c the top of the letters "N" and "F" are about ½mm from the ribbon with "ONE CENT." In No. 32 they are fully 1mm away. There are many small differences in the engraving.

1876-79   Rouletted

37	A15	1c brn lilac ('77)	160.00	52.50
38	A9	2c green ('79)	200.00	52.50
39	A16	3c blue ('77)	425.00	14.00
40	A10	5c blue	225.00	14.00
		Nos. 37-40 (4)	1,010.	133.00

A17

A19

A18

A20

1880-96   Perf. 12

41	A17	1c violet brown	42.50	11.50
42	A17	1c gray brown	42.50	11.50
43	A17	1c brown ('96)	90.00	57.50
44	A17	1c dp grn ('87)	19.00	3.75
45	A17	1c green ('97)	19.00	4.00
46	A19	2c yellow green	45.00	14.00
47	A19	2c green ('96)	77.50	27.50
48	A19	2c red org ('87)	30.00	9.50
a.		Imperf., pair	325.00	
49	A18	3c blue	45.00	6.50
51	A18	3c umber brn ('87)	37.50	4.75
52	A18	3c vio brown ('96)	115.00	90.00
53	A20	5c pale blue	375.00	9.00
54	A20	5c dark blue ('87)	160.00	7.50
55	A20	5c brt blue ('94)	45.00	6.50
		Nos. 41-55 (14)	1,143.	263.50

Newfoundland Dog — A21

Schooner — A22

1887-96

56	A21	½c rose red	9.50	7.25
57	A21	½c org red ('96)	75.00	45.00
58	A21	½c black ('94)	9.00	7.25
59	A22	10c black	120.00	67.50
		Nos. 56-59 (4)	213.50	127.00

Queen Victoria — A23

1890

60	A23	3c slate	25.00	1.50
a.		3c gray lilac	30.00	1.50
b.		3c brown lilac	50.00	1.50

c.		3c lilac	30.00	1.50
d.		3c slate violet	75.00	2.50
e.		Vert. pair, imperf. horiz.	625.00	

For surcharges see Nos. 75-77.

Victoria — A24

Cabot (John?) — A25

Cape Bonavista — A26

Caribou Hunting A27

Mining A28

Logging — A29

Fishing — A30

Cabot's Ship "Matthew" A31

Willow Ptarmigan A32

Seals — A33

Salmon Fishing — A34

Colony Seal — A35

Iceberg off St. John's — A36

Henry VII — A37

1897, June 24

61	A24	1c deep green	1.75	1.75
62	A25	2c carmine lake	2.20	1.35
63	A26	3c ultramarine	3.75	1.40
64	A27	4c olive green	5.25	2.75
65	A28	5c violet	9.00	2.75
66	A29	6c red brown	5.75	3.25
67	A30	8c red orange	17.50	14.00
68	A31	10c black brown	17.50	7.50
69	A32	12c dark blue	22.50	14.00
70	A33	15c scarlet	22.50	13.00
71	A34	24c gray violet	30.00	12.00
72	A35	30c slate	55.00	55.00

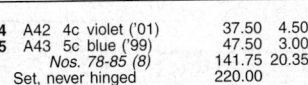

73	A36	35c red	120.00	60.00
74	A37	60c black	19.00	11.50
		Nos. 61-74 (14)	331.70	200.25
		Set, never hinged	525.00	

400th anniv. of John Cabot's discovery of Newfoundland; 60th year of Victoria's reign. The ship on the 10c was previously used by the American Bank Note Co. as the "Flagship of Columbus" on US No. 232. The portrait on the 2c, intended to be of John Cabot, is said to be a Holbein painting of his son, Sebastian.

For surcharges & overprints see #127-130, C2-C4.

No. 60a Surcharged with Bars and

No. 75

No. 76

No. 77

1897, Oct.

75	A23	1c on 3c gray lilac	60.00	25.00
a.		Double surch., one diag.	1,500.	
b.		Vert. pair, "ONE CENT" and lower bar omitted on bottom stamp	4,250.	
76	A23	1c on 3c gray lilac	225.00	190.00
77	A23	1c on 3c gray lilac	750.00	700.00
		Nos. 75-77 (3)	1,035.	915.00
		Set, never hinged	2,250.	

Most examples of Nos. 75-77 are poorly centered. Fine copies sell for about 60% of the values given. No. 75b is valued in the grade of fine.

Trial surcharges of Nos. 75-77 exist with red surcharge and with double surcharge, one in red and one in black, but these were not issued.

Edward VIII as a Child — A38

Victoria — A39

Edward VII as Prince of Wales — A40

Queen Alexandra as Princess of Wales — A41

Queen Mary as Duchess of York — A42

George V as Duke of York — A43

1897-1901   **Engr.**

78	A38	½c olive green	3.75	2.25
79	A39	1c carmine rose	4.75	4.75
80	A39	1c yel grn ('98)	4.50	.19
b.		Vert. pair, imperf. horiz.	500.00	
81	A40	2c orange	6.25	4.25
82	A40	2c ver ('98)	11.50	.60
b.		Pair, imperf. btwn.	475.00	
83	A41	3c orange ('98)	26.00	.75
a.		Vert. pair, imperf. horiz.	425.00	

84	A42	4c violet ('01)	37.50	4.50
85	A43	5c blue ('99)	47.50	3.00
		Nos. 78-85 (8)	141.75	20.35
		Set, never hinged	220.00	

No. 80b is valued in the grade of fine.

Imperf., Pairs

78a	A38	½c	475.00	
81a	A40	2c	—	400.00
82a	A40	2c	325.00	
83b	A41	3c	425.00	
84a	A42	4c	350.00	

Imperf., Pairs

Newfoundland imperforates virtually always are proofs on stamp paper or "postmaster's perquisites." Most part-perforate varieties also are "postmaster's perquisites." These items were not regularly issued, but rather were sold or given to favored persons.

Map of Newfoundland — A44

1908, Sept.

86	A44	2c rose carmine	45.00	1.90
		Never hinged	75.00	

Guy Issue

James I — A45

Arms of the London and Bristol Co. — A46

John Guy — A47

Lord Bacon — A50

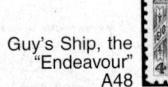
Guy's Ship, the "Endeavour" A48

View of Cupids — A49

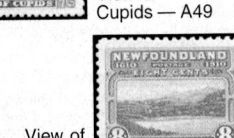
View of Mosquito — A51

Logging Camp — A52

Edward VII — A54

George V — A55

Paper Mills — A53

SIX CENT TYPES
I — "Z" of "COLONIZATION" reversed.
II — "Z" of normal.

1910, Aug. 15   **Litho.**   *Perf. 12*

87	A45	1c deep green, perf. 12x11	2.30	1.10
a.		Perf. 12	4.75	1.90
b.		Perf. 12x14	3.60	2.25
c.		Horiz. pair, imperf. btwn.	400.00	—
d.		Vert. pair, imperf. btwn.	350.00	
88	A46	2c carmine	7.50	1.15
a.		Perf. 12x14	6.25	.85
b.		As "a," horiz. pair, imperf. between	300.00	
c.		Perf. 12x11½	475.00	325.00
89	A47	3c brown olive	15.00	14.00
90	A48	4c dull violet	15.00	11.50
91	A49	5c ultramarine	15.00	4.50
a.		Perf. 12	22.50	7.50
92	A50	6c claret, type I	77.50	65.00
92A	A50	6c claret, type II	37.50	37.50
b.		Imperf., pair	350.00	
93	A51	8c pale brown	60.00	55.00
94	A52	9c olive green	60.00	55.00
95	A53	10c vio black	60.00	55.00
96	A54	12c lilac brown	60.00	55.00
a.		Imperf., pair	375.00	
97	A55	15c gray black	77.50	65.00
		Nos. 87-97 (12)	487.30	419.75
		Set, never hinged	950.00	

Tercentenary of the Colonization of Newfoundland.
On No. 87 printing flaws such as "NFW" and "JANES" exist.

1911   **Engr.**   *Perf. 14*

98	A50	6c brown vio	32.50	22.50
99	A51	8c bister brn	75.00	67.50
100	A52	9c olive grn	60.00	57.50
101	A53	10c violet blk	95.00	95.00
102	A54	12c red brown	75.00	75.00
103	A55	15c slate grn	75.00	75.00
b.		Horiz. pair, imperf. btwn.	325.00	
		Nos. 98-103 (6)	412.50	392.50
		Set, never hinged	750.00	

Nos. 100 and 103 are known with papermaker's watermark "E. TOWGOOD FINE."

Imperf., Pairs

98a	A50	6c	325.00
99a	A51	8c	325.00
100a	A52	9c	325.00
101a	A53	10c	325.00
102a	A54	12c	325.00
103a	A55	15c	325.00

Nos. 98a-103a were made with and without gum. Values the same.

Royal Family Issue

Queen Mary — A56

George V — A57

Prince of Wales (Edward VIII) — A58

Prince Albert (George VI) — A59

Princess Mary — A60

Prince Henry — A61

Prince George A62

Prince John A63

Queen Alexandra A64

Duke of Connaught A65

Seal of Colony — A66

1911, June 19   *Perf. 13½x14, 14*

104	A56	1c yellow grn	3.00	.25
105	A57	2c carmine	2.60	.80
106	A58	3c red brown	22.50	19.00
107	A59	4c violet	19.00	13.50
108	A60	5c ultra	7.50	1.75
109	A61	6c black	22.50	22.50
110	A62	8c blue (paper colored through)	75.00	65.00
a.		8c peacock blue	80.00	70.00
111	A63	9c bl violet	22.50	20.00
112	A64	10c dark green	40.00	37.50
113	A65	12c plum	37.50	37.50
114	A66	15c magenta	30.00	37.50
		Nos. 104-114 (11)	282.10	255.30
		Set, never hinged	500.00	

Coronation of King George V.

Imperf., Pairs
Without Gum

104a	A56	1c	325.00
105a	A57	2c	325.00
108a	A60	5c	325.00
113a	A65	12c	325.00
114a	A66	15c	125.00

Trail of the Caribou Issue

Caribou
A67   A68

1919, Jan. 2   *Perf. 14*

115	A67	1c green	2.25	.35
116	A68	2c scarlet	2.75	.50
117	A67	3c red brown	3.00	.30
118	A67	4c violet	4.50	1.40
119	A68	5c ultramarine	5.75	1.40
120	A67	6c gray	22.50	22.50
121	A68	8c magenta	22.50	19.00
122	A67	10c dark green	11.00	5.50
123	A68	12c orange	65.00	45.00
124	A67	15c dark blue	42.50	42.50
125	A67	24c red brown	45.00	42.50
126	A67	36c olive green	37.50	35.00
		Nos. 115-126 (12)	264.25	215.95
		Set, never hinged	425.00	

Services of the Newfoundland contingent in WWI.
Each denomination of type A67 is inscribed with the name of a different action in which Newfoundland troops took part.
For overprint & surcharge see #C1, C5.

Imperf., Pairs
Without Gum

115a	A67	1c	275.00
116a	A68	2c	275.00
117a	A67	3c	275.00
118a	A67	4c	275.00
119a	A68	5c	275.00
120a	A67	6c	275.00
121a	A68	8c	275.00
122a	A67	10c	275.00
123a	A68	12c	275.00
124a	A67	15c	275.00
125a	A67	24c	275.00
126a	A67	36c	275.00

No. 72 Surcharged in Black

1920 **Perf. 12**
127 A35 2c on 30c slate 5.75 5.50
  Never hinged 8.75
  a. Inverted surcharge 950.00

No. 127 with red surcharge is an unissued color trial. 25 examples are known. Value, $1,000.

Nos. 70 and 73 Surcharged in Black

THREE CENTS
Type I — Bars 10½mm apart.
Type II — Bars 13½mm apart.

128 A33 3c on 15c scar (I) 230.00 225.00
  Never hinged 330.00
  a. Inverted surcharge 2,300.
129 A33 3c on 15c scar (II) 19.00 11.00
  Never hinged 27.00
130 A36 3c on 35c red 11.50 9.50
  Never hinged 16.00
  a. Lower bar omitted 135.00 135.00
  b. Inverted surcharge —

The existence of No. 130b has been questioned by specialists. The editor would like to see authenticated evidence of the existence of this stamp.

All copies of the former No. 130c ("THREE" omitted) examined show part of the tops or bottoms of the letters. It is probable that no copies with "THREE" completely omitted exist.

Twin Hills, Tor's Cove — A70

South West Arm, Trinity — A71

War Memorial, St. John's A72

Humber River A73

Coast of Trinity — A74

Upper Steadies, Humber River — A75

Quidi Vidi, near St. John's — A76

Caribou Crossing Lake — A77

Humber River Canyon A78

Shell Bird Island A79

Mt. Moriah, Bay of Islands A80

Placentia, from Mt. Pleasant A82

Humber River near Little Rapids A81

Topsail Falls near St. John's A83

1923-24 **Engr.** **Perf. 14, 13½x14**
131 A70 1c gray green 1.90 .30
  a. Booklet pane of 8 450.00
132 A71 2c carmine 1.90 .25
  a. Booklet pane of 8 300.00
133 A72 3c brown 2.50 .25
134 A73 4c brn violet 2.75 1.80
135 A74 5c ultramarine 4.50 2.25
136 A75 6c gray black 5.25 5.25
137 A76 8c dull violet 4.50 4.25
138 A77 9c slate green 37.50 27.50
139 A78 10c dark violet 4.25 2.50
140 A79 11c olive green 7.00 7.00
141 A80 12c lake 7.50 7.50
142 A81 15c deep blue 9.50 8.00
143 A82 20c red brn ('24) 13.00 7.50
144 A83 24c blk brn ('24) 60.00 45.00
  Nos. 131-144 (14) 162.05 119.35
  Set, never hinged 250.00

For surcharge see No. 160.

Imperf., Pairs
131b A70 1c 200.00
132b A71 2c 200.00
134a A73 4c 200.00
135a A74 5c 200.00
136a A75 6c 200.00
137a A76 8c 200.00
138a A77 9c 200.00
139a A78 10c 200.00
140a A79 11c 200.00
141a A80 12c 200.00
142a A81 15c 160.00

Nos. 134a-139a, 141a-142a are without gum. Others are either with or without gum.

Map of Newfoundland A84

Steamship "Caribou" A85

Queen Mary, George V — A86

Prince of Wales — A87

Express Train — A88

Newfoundland Hotel, St. John's — A89

Heart's Content — A90

War Memorial, St. John's — A92

First Nonstop Transatlantic Flight, 1919 — A94

Cabot Tower, St. John's — A91

GPO, St. John's — A93

Colonial Building, St. John's — A95

Grand Falls, Labrador — A96

Perf. 14, 13½x13, 13x13½
1928, Jan. 3
145 A84 1c deep green 1.40 .75
146 A85 2c deep carmine 2.50 .70
  a. Imperf., pair 300.00
147 A86 3c brown 2.75 .50
148 A87 4c lilac rose 3.50 1.80
149 A88 5c slate green 10.00 4.25
150 A89 6c ultramarine 5.75 3.50
151 A90 8c lt red brown 7.25 4.50
152 A91 9c myrtle green 7.00 6.75
153 A92 10c dark violet 9.00 4.25
154 A93 12c brn carmine 5.50 4.00
155 A91 14c red brown 10.50 6.75
156 A94 15c dark blue 9.25 7.00
157 A95 20c gray black 11.50 6.00
158 A93 28c gray green 27.50 22.50
159 A96 30c olive brown 14.00 7.50
  Nos. 145-159 (15) 127.40 80.75
  Set, never hinged 215.00

See Nos. 163-182.

No. 136 Surcharged in Red or Black

THREE CENTS

Type I — 5mm between "CENTS" and bar.
Type II — 3mm between "CENTS" and bar.

1929 **Perf. 14x13½**
160 A75 3c on 6c gray black (II) (R) 4.25 4.25
  Never hinged 6.75
  a. Inverted surcharge (II) 950.00

The stamps with black surcharge, type I and II, were 1st or trial printings, and were not issued. There were 50 copies of each. Value, each $1,000.

Types of 1928 Issue
Re-engraved

1c — On No. 145 the lines of the engraving are thinner and the impression is clearer than on No. 163. On the former "C. BAULD" is above "C. NORMAN." On the latter these words are transposed.

2c — On the 1928 stamp the "D" of "NEW-FOUNDLAND" is 1mm from the scroll at the right; the flag at the stern is lower than the top of the boat davit. On the 1929 stamp the "D" is ½mm from the scroll and the flag rises above the davits.

3c — On the 1928 stamp the pearls at the top of the crown, the jewels of the tiara and the pillars flanking the portraits are all unshaded. On the reengraved stamp there are small curved lines inside the pearls, the jewels of the tiara are in solid color, and the pillars have vertical shading lines. On the 1928 stamps the

tablets with "THREE" and "CENTS" have a background of crossed lines (vertical and horizontal). On the 1929 stamp the background is of horizontal lines only.

4c — On the 1928 stamp the figures "4" have shading of horizontal and diagonal crossed lines. There are six circles at each side of the portrait.

On the 1929 stamp the "4s" have shading of horizontal lines only. There are five roses at each side of the portrait.

5c — The crossbars of the telegraph pole touch the frame at the left on the 1929 stamp but just clear it on the 1928 stamp. In the 1928 issue the foliate ornaments beside and below the figures "5" end in small scrolls and a small spur. These spurs are omitted on the 1929 stamp.

6c — On the re-engraved stamp the columns at right and left of the picture have heavy wavy outlines on the inner sides. There is no period after "JOHNS." The numerals in the lower corners are 1½mm wide instead of 1¼mm.

8c — The impression of the 1928 stamp is clear, that of 1931 is slightly blurred. The 1928 stamp has three horizontal lines above "EIGHT CENTS" and four berries on the laurel branch at the right side. On the 1931 stamp there are two horizontal lines and three berries.

10c — On the re-engraved stamp there is no period after "ST. JOHN'S." The letters of "TEN CENTS" are slightly larger and the numerals "10" slightly smaller than in 1928. Inside the "0" of "10" at the right there are two vertical lines instead of three. The clouds are fainter in 1929 and the cross upheld by the figure on the monument is more distinct. On the 1928 stamp the torch at the left side terminates in a single tongue of flame. On the 1929-30 stamp it terminates in two tongues.

15c — On the 1928 stamp the "N" of "NEW-FOUNDLAND" is 1½mm from the left frame, the "L" of "LEAVING" is under the first "A" of "AIRPLANE" and the apostrophe in "JOHN'S" breaks the first line above it.

On the 1929 stamp the "N" of "NEW-FOUNDLAND" is 1mm from the left frame, the "L" of "LEAVING" is below the "T" of "FIRST" and the apostrophe in "JOHN'S" does not touch the line above it.

20c — On the 1928 stamp the points of the "W" of "NEWFOUNDLAND" are truncated. The "O" is wide and nearly round. The columns that form the sides of the frame have a shading of evenly spaced horizontal lines at their inner sides.

On the 1929-31 stamp the points of the "W" form sharp angles. The "O" is narrow and has a small opening. Many lines have been added to the shading on the inner sides of the columns, making it almost solid.

30c — 1928 stamp. Size: 19¼x24½mm. At the outer side of the right column there are three strong and two faint vertical lines. Faint period after "FALLS."

1931 stamp. Size: 19x25mm. At the outer side of the right column there are two strong vertical lines and a fragment of the lower end of a faint one. Clear period after "FALLS." A great many of the small lines of the design have been deepened making the whole stamp appear darker.

1929-31 **Unwmk.** **Perf. 13½ to 14**
163 A84 1c green 2.25 .65
  a. Double impression 325.00
  b. Vert. pair, imperf. btwn. 210.00
164 A85 2c deep carmine 2.25 .35
165 A86 3c dp red brown 2.50 .35
166 A87 4c magenta 3.75 1.25
167 A88 5c slate green 7.25 1.60
168 A89 6c ultramarine 9.75 9.00
169 A92 10c dark violet 8.75 2.25
170 A94 15c deep blue ('30) 45.00 37.50
171 A95 20c gray blk ('31) 75.00 27.50
  Nos. 163-171 (9) 156.50 80.45
  Set, never hinged 250.00

Imperf., Pairs
163c A84 1c 120.00
164a A85 2c 145.00
165a A86 3c 120.00
166a A87 4c 145.00

Types of 1928 Issue
Perf. 13½x14
1931 **Re-engraved** **Wmk. 224**
172 A84 1c green, perf. 13½ 2.25 1.25
  a. Horiz. pair, imperf. btwn. 425.00
173 A85 2c red 5.50 1.30
174 A86 3c red brown 3.50 1.25
175 A87 4c rose 4.25 2.00
176 A88 5c grnsh gray 15.00 7.00
177 A89 6c ultramarine 22.50 16.00
178 A90 8c lt red brn 22.50 16.00
179 A92 10c dk violet 15.00 9.00
180 A94 15c deep blue 45.00 27.50
181 A95 20c gray black 57.50 17.50
182 A96 30c olive brown 45.00 25.00
  Nos. 172-182 (11) 238.00 123.80
  Set, never hinged 365.00

Codfish — A97

George V — A98

Queen Mary — A99

Prince of Wales — A100

Caribou A101

Princess Elizabeth A102

Salmon Leaping Falls — A103

Newfoundland Dog — A104

Harp Seal Pup — A105

Cape Race — A106

Sealing Fleet — A107

Fishing Fleet Leaving for "The Banks" — A108

FIVE CENT
Die I — Antlers even, or equal in height.
Die II — Antler under "T" higher.

1932-37   Engr.   Perf. 13½, 14

183	A97	1c green	2.25	.50
a.		Booklet pane of 4, perf. 13	75.00	
c.		Vert. pair, imperf. btwn.	200.00	
184	A97	1c gray black	.35	.20
a.		Bklt. pane of 4, perf. 13½	57.50	
b.		Booklet pane of 4, perf. 14	72.50	
185	A98	2c rose	2.25	.35
a.		Bklt. pane of 4, perf. 13	35.00	
b.		Booklet pane of 4, perf. 13	47.50	
186	A98	2c green	1.10	.25
a.		Bklt. pane of 4, perf. 13½	25.00	
b.		Booklet pane of 4, perf. 14	35.00	
d.		Horiz. pair, imperf. btwn.	160.00	
187	A99	3c orange brn	1.10	.35
a.		Bklt. pane of 4, perf. 13½	55.00	
b.		Booklet pane of 4, perf. 14	67.50	
c.		Booklet pane of 4, perf. 13	75.00	
e.		Vert. pair, imperf. btwn.	160.00	

188	A100	4c deep violet	5.50	1.60
189	A100	4c rose lake	.75	.35
b.		Vert. pair, imperf. btwn.	120.00	
c.		Horiz. pair, imperf. btwn.	120.00	
190	A101	5c vio brn, perf. 13½ (Die I)	9.50	1.25
191	A101	5c dp vio, perf. 13½ (Die II)	1.10	.20
a.		5c dp vio, perf. 13½ (Die I)	11.00	1.00
c.		Horiz. pair, imperf. btwn. (I)	240.00	
g.		Horiz. pair, imperf. btwn. (II)	240.00	
192	A102	6c dull blue	11.00	11.00
193	A103	10c olive black	1.40	.85
194	A104	14c int black	3.25	2.75
195	A105	15c magenta	2.50	2.25
196	A106	20c gray green	2.50	1.00
197	A107	25c gray	2.60	2.00
b.		Horiz. pair, imperf. btwn.	275.00	
c.		Vert. pair, imperf. btwn.	375.00	
198	A108	30c ultra	27.50	24.00
b.		Vert. pair, imperf. btwn.	475.00	
199	A108	48c red brn ('37)	11.00	5.25
		Nos. 183-199 (17)	85.65	54.15
		Set, never hinged	125.00	

Two dies were used for 2c green, one for 2c rose.
See Nos. 253-266.

Imperf., Pairs

183b	A97	1c	240.00
184c	A97	1c	47.50
185c	A98	2c	160.00
186c	A98	2c	47.50
187d	A99	3c	95.00
189a	A100	4c	60.00
190a	A101	5c	160.00
191b	A101	5c (II)	60.00
191d	A101	5c (I)	95.00
192a	A102	6c	145.00
193a	A103	10c	95.00
194a	A103	14c	120.00
195a	A103	15c	120.00
196a	A106	20c	160.00
197a	A107	25c	160.00
198a	A108	30c	550.00
199a	A108	48c	120.00

All with gum. Nos. 186c, 187d, 192a, 193a and 196a also made without gum; values about 10% less.

Queen Elizabeth when Duchess of York — A109

Corner Brook Paper Mills — A110

Loading Iron Ore at Bell Island — A111

1932

208	A109	7c red brown	1.40	1.25
a.		Imperf., pair	160.00	
b.		Horiz. pair, imperf. between	475.00	
209	A110	8c orange red	1.40	1.10
a.		Imperf., pair	120.00	
210	A111	24c light blue	2.75	2.75
a.		Imperf., pair	200.00	
b.		Double impression	1,200.	
		Nos. 208-210 (3)	5.55	5.10
		Set, never hinged	7.75	

No. 208a was made both with and without gum. Values about the same.
See Nos. 259, 264.

No. C9 Overprinted Bars and

1933, Feb. 9   Wmk. 224   Perf. 14

211	AP6	15c brown	11.00	9.50
		Never hinged	15.50	
a.		Pair, one without overprint	4,500.	
b.		Overprint reading up	4,500.	

"L. & S." stands for "Land and Sea."

Sir Humphrey Gilbert Issue

Sir Humphrey Gilbert — A112

Compton Castle, Home of the Gilbert Family — A113

Gilbert Coat of Arms — A114

Eton College — A115

Token from Queen Elizabeth I — A116

Sir Humphrey Receiving Royal Patents for Colonization A117

Sir Humphrey's Ships Leaving Plymouth, 1583 — A118

The Ships Arriving at St. John's — A119

Annexation of Newfoundland, Aug. 5, 1583 — A120

Coat of Arms of England A121

Sir Humphrey on the Deck of the "Squirrel" A122

Capt. John Mason's Map of Newfoundland, 1626 — A123

Queen Elizabeth I A124

Gilbert Statue at Truro A125

Perf. 13½, 14

1933, Aug. 3   Wmk. 224   Engr.

212	A112	1c gray black	1.10	.75
213	A113	2c green	1.10	.75
b.		Double impression	575.00	
214	A114	3c yellow brn	1.90	.75
215	A115	4c carmine	1.90	.75
216	A116	5c dull violet	2.75	1.10
217	A117	7c blue	19.00	12.50
218	A118	8c orange red	8.00	7.00
219	A119	9c ultramarine	8.00	7.50
220	A120	10c red brown	8.00	6.25
221	A121	14c black	16.00	14.00
222	A122	15c claret	14.00	14.00
223	A123	20c deep green	13.00	10.00
224	A124	24c vio brown	22.50	22.50
225	A125	32c gray	22.50	22.50
		Nos. 212-225 (14)	139.25	120.35
		Set, never hinged	205.00	

350th anniv. of annexation of Newfoundland to England, Aug. 5, 1583, by authority of Letters Patent issued by Queen Elizabeth I to Sir Humphrey Gilbert.

Imperf., Pairs

212a	A112	1c	47.50
213a	A113	2c	47.50
214a	A114	3c	240.00
215a	A115	4c	50.00
216a	A116	5c	280.00
219a	A119	9c	280.00
220a	A120	10c	280.00
221a	A120	14c	400.00
222a	A120	15c	200.00
224a	A124	24c	200.00

Common Design Types pictured following the introduction.

Silver Jubilee Issue
Common Design Type

1935, May 6   Wmk. 4   Perf. 11x12

226	CD301	4c bright rose	1.75	.70
227	CD301	5c violet	1.75	.85
228	CD301	7c dark blue	4.25	3.50
229	CD301	24c olive green	9.50	7.00
		Nos. 226-229 (4)	17.25	12.05
		Set, never hinged	24.00	

Coronation Issue
Common Design Type

1937, May 12   Perf. 11x11½

230	CD302	2c deep green	1.75	.70
231	CD302	4c carmine rose	1.75	.70
232	CD302	5c dark violet	3.50	1.40
		Nos. 230-232 (3)	7.00	2.80
		Set, never hinged	9.75	

Codfish A126

Map of Newfoundland — A127

Caribou A128

Corner Brook Paper Mills A129

Salmon
A130

Newfoundland Dog — A131

Harp Seal Pup
A132

Cape Race
A133

Loading Iron Ore at Bell Island
A134

Sealing Fleet
A135

Fishing Fleet Leaving for "The Banks"
A136

Two dies of the 3c
Die I — Fine impression; no lines on bridge of nose.
Die II — Coarse impression; lines on bridge of nose.

Perf. 13¼, 13½, 14

1937, May 12 **Wmk. 224**

233	A126	1c gray black	.40	.30
234	A127	3c org brn, die I	2.50	1.10
a.		Die II	1.75	1.10
b.		Vert. pair, imperf. btwn. (I)	575.00	
c.		Vert. pair, imperf. btwn. (II)	575.00	
d.		Horiz. pair, imperf. btwn. (I)	575.00	
e.		Horiz. pair, imperf. btwn. (II)	575.00	
f.		Imperf., pair	240.00	
235	A128	7c blue	2.50	2.50
236	A129	8c orange red	2.50	2.50
a.		Imperf., pair	275.00	
b.		Vert. pair, imperf. between	675.00	
c.		Horiz. pair, imperf. between	675.00	
237	A130	10c olive gray	4.25	4.25
a.		Double impression	280.00	
238	A131	14c black	3.50	3.50
a.		Imperf., pair	400.00	
239	A132	15c rose lake	3.50	3.50
a.		Vert. pair, imperf. between	550.00	
240	A133	20c green	2.75	2.25
a.		Vert. pair, imperf. between	850.00	
241	A134	24c turq blue	3.50	3.25
a.		Vert. pair, imperf. between	1,200.	
242	A135	25c gray	3.50	3.25
a.		Imperf., pair	200.00	
243	A136	48c dark violet	4.25	3.50
a.		Vert. pair, imperf. between	1,200.	
b.		Imperf., pair	240.00	
		Nos. 233-243 (11)	33.15	29.90
		Set, never hinged	45.00	

Imperfs are with gum. No. 243b also made without gum; value the same.

Princess Elizabeth — A139

Designs: 2c, King George VI. 3c, Queen Elizabeth. 7c, Queen Mother Mary.

1938, May 12 ***Perf. 13½***

245	A139	2c green	1.75	.20
246	A139	3c dark carmine	1.75	.20
247	A139	4c light blue	2.40	.20
248	A139	7c dark ultra	1.60	1.10
		Nos. 245-248 (4)	7.50	1.70
		Set, never hinged	9.50	

See Nos. 254-256, 258, 269.

Imperf., Pairs

245a	A139	2c	120.00	
246a	A139	3c	120.00	
247a	A139	4c	120.00	
248a	A139	7c	120.00	
		Set, never hinged	700.00	

George VI and Queen Elizabeth
A141

1939, June 17 **Unwmk.**

249	A141	5c violet blue	1.25	1.10
		Never hinged	1.60	

Visit of King George and Queen Elizabeth.

No. 249 Surcharged in Brown or Red

1939, Nov. 20

250	A141	2c on 5c vio blue (Br)	1.25	1.00
251	A141	4c on 5c vio blue (R)	1.10	1.00
		Set, never hinged	3.10	

There are many varieties of broken letters and figures in the settings of the surcharges.

Sir Wilfred Grenfell and "Strathcona II" — A142

1941, Dec. 1 **Engr.** ***Perf. 12***

252	A142	5c dull blue	.40	.30
		Never hinged	.50	

Grenfell Mission, 50th anniv.

Types of 1931-38

1941-44 **Wmk. 224** ***Perf. 12½***

253	A97	1c dark gray	.35	.20
a.		Imperf., pair	150.00	
254	A139	2c deep green	.35	.20
255	A139	3c rose carmine	.35	.20
256	A139	4c blue	.70	.30
257	A101	5c violet (Die I)	.70	.20
a.		Imperf., pair	175.00	
b.		Horiz. pair, imperf. vert.	475.00	
c.		Double impression	400.00	
258	A139	7c vio blue ('42)	1.20	1.00
259	A110	8c red	1.10	.65
260	A103	10c brownish blk	1.10	.60
261	A104	14c black	2.00	1.75
a.		Imperf., pair	240.00	
c.		Vert. pair, imperf. horiz.	240.00	
262	A105	15c pale rose vio	1.75	1.40
263	A106	20c green	1.70	1.10
264	A111	24c deep blue	2.25	2.00
265	A107	25c slate	2.25	2.00
266	A108	48c red brown ('44)	2.75	1.75
		Nos. 253-266 (14)	18.55	13.35
		Set, never hinged	24.00	

Nos. 254 and 255 are re-engraved.

Memorial University College
A143

Unwmk.

1943, Jan. 2 **Engr.** ***Perf. 12***

267	A143	30c carmine	1.40	1.00
		Never hinged	1.85	

No. 267 Surcharged in Black

1946, Mar. 21

268	A143	2c on 30c carmine	.30	.30
		Never hinged	.40	

Princess Elizabeth — A144

1947, Apr. 21 **Engr.** ***Perf. 12½***

269	A144	4c light blue	.30	.20
		Never hinged	.40	
a.		Imperf., pair	240.00	
b.		Horiz. pair, imperf. vert.	325.00	

Princess Elizabeth's 21st birthday.

Deck of the Matthew
A145

1947, June 23

270	A145	5c rose violet	.30	.25
		Never hinged	.40	
a.		Horiz. pair, imperf. between	1,200.	
b.		Imperf., pair	240.00	

Cabot's arrival off Cape Bonavista, 450th anniv.

AIR POST STAMPS

No. 117 Overprinted in Black

1919, Apr. 12 **Unwmk.** ***Perf. 14***

C1	A67	3c red brown	25,000.	16,000.
		Never hinged	37,500.	

No. 70 Surcharged in Black

1919, June 9 ***Perf. 12***

C2	A33	$1 on 15c scarlet	225.00	225.00
		Never hinged	375.00	
a.		Without comma after "Post"	240.00	275.00
b.		As "a," without period after "1919"	450.00	450.00

No. 73 Overprinted in Black

1921, Nov. 7

C3	A36	35c red	145.00	180.00
		Never hinged	250.00	
a.		Inverted overprint	6,000.	
b.		With period after "1921"	160.00	200.00
c.		As "b," inverted	6,250.	

No. C3 was printed in sheets of twenty-five, containing varieties of wide and narrow space

---

between "AIR" and "MAIL," date shifted to right, and with and without period after date.

No. 74 Overprinted in Red

1927, May 21

C4	A37	60c black	42,500.	17,500.
		Never hinged	57,500.	

No. 126 Surcharged in Black

1930, Sept. 25 ***Perf. 14***

C5	A67	50c on 36c ol grn	9,500.	9,500.
		Never hinged	13,750.	

Dog Sled and Airplane — AP6

First Transatlantic Mail Airplane and Packet Ship — AP7

Routes of Historic Transatlantic Flights — AP8

1931, Jan. 2 **Engr.** **Unwmk.**

C6	AP6	15c brown	11.00	7.50
a.		Horiz. pair, imperf. btwn.	950.00	
b.		Vert. pair, imperf. between	950.00	
c.		Imperf., pair	625.00	
C7	AP7	50c green	35.00	25.00
a.		Horiz. pair, imperf. btwn.	1,350.	825.00
b.		Vert. pair, imperf. between	1,350.	
c.		Imperf., pair	725.00	
C8	AP8	$1 blue	70.00	55.00
a.		Horiz. pair, imperf. btwn.	1,000.	
b.		Vert. pair, imperf. between	1,000.	
c.		Imperf., pair	725.00	
		Nos. C6-C8 (3)	116.00	87.50
		Set, never hinged	195.00	

1931 **Wmk. 224**

C9	AP6	15c brown	11.00	7.50
a.		Horiz. pair, imperf. between	950.00	
b.		Vert. pair, imperf. between	1,100.	
c.		Imperf., pair	600.00	
C10	AP7	50c green	45.00	35.00
a.		Horiz. pair, imperf. between	950.00	
b.		Vert. pair, imperf. between	950.00	
c.		Horiz. pair, imperf. vert.	950.00	
C11	AP8	$1 blue	110.00	90.00
a.		Vert. pair, imperf. between	1,000.	
c.		Horiz. pair, imperf. between	1,000.	
d.		Vert. pair, imperf. horiz.	1,000.	
e.		Imperf., pair	600.00	
		Nos. C9-C11 (3)	166.00	132.50
		Set, never hinged	280.00	

As the watermark 224 does not show on every stamp in the sheet, pairs are found one with and one without watermark.

For overprint and surcharge see Nos. 211, C12.

No. C11 Surcharged in Red

1932, May 19
C12 AP8 $1.50 on $1
blue   300.00 275.00
  Never hinged   450.00
a. Inverted surcharge   18,500.
  Never hinged   25,000.

A stamp of this design was produced in the US in 1932 by a private company under contract with Newfoundland authorities. The government canceled the contract and the stamp was not valid for prepayment of postage. Value, $35.

"Put to Flight" — AP9

"Land of Heart's Delight" AP10

"Spotting the Herd" AP11

"News from Home" AP12

"Labrador, The Land of Gold" AP13

Perf. 11½ (10, 60c), 14 (5, 30, 75c)
1933, June 9   Engr.
C13 AP9 5c lt brown   11.00   11.00
b.   Horiz. pair, imperf.
        btwn.   1,250.
c.   Vert. pair, imperf. btwn.   1,250.
C14 AP10 10c yellow   19.00   17.50
C15 AP11 30c blue   30.00   30.00
C16 AP12 60c green   60.00   57.50
C17 AP13 75c bister   60.00   57.50
b.   Horiz. pair, imperf.
        btwn.   1,250.
c.   Vert. pair, imperf. btwn.   1,250.
  Nos. C13-C17 (5)   180.00 173.50
  Set, never hinged   265.00

Beware of clever forgeries of Nos. C13b, C13c, C17b and C17c. Certificates of authenticity are highly recommended.

Imperf., Pairs

C13a AP9   5c   275.00
C14a AP10 10c   200.00
C15a AP11 30c   600.00
C16a AP12 60c   675.00
C17a AP13 75c   650.00
  Set, never hinged   3,150.

No. C17 Surcharged in Black

1933, July 24   **Perf. 14**
C18 AP13 $4.50 on 75c   400.00 375.00
  bis   575.00
  Never hinged
a. Inverted surcharge   120,000.
  Never hinged

Return flight from Chicago to Rome of the squadron of Italian seaplanes under the command of Gen. Italo Balbo.
No. C18a was not regularly issued. The $4.50 on No. C14, 10c yellow, is a proof.

View of St. John's AP14

1943, June 1 Unwmk.   Perf. 12
C19 AP14 7c bright ultra   .35   .30
  Never hinged   .45

POSTAGE DUE STAMPS

D1

Perf. 10-10½, Compound
1939-49 Litho.   Unwmk.
J1   D1   1c yellow green,
            perf. 11 ('49)   4.25   5.50
a.   Perf. 10-10½   7.25   5.50
J2   D1   2c vermilion   7.00   5.50
a.   Perf. 11x9 ('46)   7.00   5.50
J3   D1   3c ultramarine   7.00   5.50
a.   Perf. 11x9 ('49)   7.50   7.50
b.   Perf. 9   1,500.
J4   D1   4c yel org, perf.
            11x9 ('49)   9.50   9.50
a.   Perf. 10-10½   15.00 15.00
J5   D1   5c pale brown   15.00   4.25
J6   D1   10c dark violet   4.25   4.00
  Nos. J1-J6 (6)   47.00 34.25
  Set, never hinged   75.00

1949 Wmk. 224   Perf. 11
J7   D1   10c dark violet   11.00 14.00
  Never hinged   19.00
a.   Vert. pair, imperf. between   800.00

NOVA SCOTIA

ˌnō-və-ˈskō-shə

LOCATION — Eastern coast of Canada between the Gulf of St. Lawrence and the Atlantic Ocean
GOVT. — British Crown Colony
AREA — 21,428 sq. mi.
POP. — 386,500 (1871)
CAPITAL — Halifax

Nova Scotia joined the Canadian Confederation in 1867 and is now a province of the Dominion. Postage stamps of Canada are used.

12 Pence = 1 Shilling
100 Cents = 1 Dollar (1860)

Values for unused stamps are for examples with original gum as defined in the catalogue introduction except for Nos. 4-7, which are rarely found with original gum.

Queen Victoria — A1

Crown of Great Britain and Heraldic Flowers of the Empire — A2

1851-57   Unwmk. Engr.   Imperf.
Blue Paper
1   A1   1p red brown
           ('53)   3,250.   650.00
a.   Half used as ½p on
        cover
2   A2   3p bright blue   1,250.   240.00
a.   Half used as 1½p on
        cover   3,750.
b.   3p pale blue ('57)   1,250.   240.00
c.   As "b," half used as
        1½p on cover   3,750.
3   A2   3p dark blue   1,600.   300.00
a.   Half used as 1½p on
        cover   4,500.
4   A2   6p yellow
           green   4,750.   675.00
a.   Half used as 3p on
        cover   4,500.
5   A2   6p dark
           green   9,250. 1,900.
a.   Half used as 3p on
        cover   5,000.
b.   Quarter used as
        1½p on cover   47,500.
6   A2   1sh reddish
           pur ('57)   25,000. 5,250.
a.   Half used as 6p on
        cover   32,500.
b.   1sh deep purple   25,000. 5,250.
7   A2   1sh dull violet   25,000. 6,500.
a.   Half used as 6p on
        cover   47,500.
b.   Quarter used as 3p
        on cover   60,000.

Reprints are on thin hard white paper. 1p in brown, 3p in blue, 6p dark green, 1sh violet black. Value about $300 per set.
No. 6 was reproduced by the collotype process in a souvenir sheet distributed at the London International Stamp Exhibition 1950.

Queen Victoria — A3

A5

A6

1860-63   Perf. 12
White or Yellowish Paper
8   A3   1c black   12.00   7.50
a.   White paper   12.00   7.50
b.   Half used as ½c on cover   5,750.
c.   Horiz. pair, imperf. vert. 325.00
9   A3   2c lilac   12.00 10.00
a.   Yellowish paper   12.00 10.00
b.   Half used as 1c on cover   2,750.
10 A3   5c blue   400.00   9.00
a.   Yellowish paper   400.00   9.00
b.   Half used as 2½c on cover   —
11 A5   8½c green   12.00 16.00
a.   Yellowish paper   12.00 13.50
12 A5   10c vermilion   12.00 12.00
a.   Yellowish paper   12.00 12.00
b.   Half used as 5c on cover   1,200.
13 A6   12½c black   37.50 37.50
a.   White paper   37.50 37.50
  Nos. 8-13 (6)   485.50 92.00

The stamps of Nova Scotia were replaced by those of Canada.

PRINCE EDWARD ISLAND

ˈprin(t)s ˈed-wərd ˈī-lənds

LOCATION — In the Gulf of St. Lawrence, opposite the provinces of New Brunswick and Nova Scotia
GOVT. — British Crown Colony
AREA — 2,184 sq. mi.
POP. — 92,000 (estimated)
CAPITAL — Charlottetown

Originally annexed to Nova Scotia, Prince Edward Island was a separate colony from 1769 to 1873, when it became a part of the Canadian Confederation. Postage stamps of Canada are now used.

12 Pence = 1 Shilling
100 Cents = 1 Dollar (1872)

A1

A2

Queen Victoria — A3

1861, Jan. 1 Unwmk. Typo. Perf. 9
1   A1   2p dull rose   600.00 300.00
a.   2p deep rose   700.00 350.00
b.   Rouletted   22,500.
c.   Horiz. pair, imperf. be-
        tween   6,000.
d.   Diagonal half used as
        1p on cover   1,900.
2   A2   3p blue   1,150.   600.00
a.   Diagonal half used as
        1½p on cover   2,250.
b.   Double impression   3,500.
3   A3   6p yellow green 1,900. 1,150.

A4

A5

Perf. 11, 11½-12 and Compound
1862-65
White or Yellowish Paper
4   A4   1p yellow orange 37.50 35.00
a.   1p brown orange, perf. 11 37.50 35.00
b.   Imperf., pair   200.00
c.   Half used as ½p on cover   1,500.
5   A1   2p rose   7.50   7.50
a.   Yellowish paper   7.50   7.50
b.   Imperf., pair   72.50
c.   Horiz. pair, imperf. vert. 275.00
d.   Vert. pair, imperf. horiz. 375.00
e.   Diagonal half used as 1p
        on cover   1,900.
f.   "TWC" for "TWO"   60.00 30.00
6   A2   3p blue   11.00 15.00
a.   Yellowish paper   15.00 15.00
b.   Imperf., pair   85.00
c.   Vert. pair, imperf. horiz. 240.00
d.   Horiz. pair, imperf. vert. 240.00
e.   Diagonal half used as
        1½p on cover   250.00
7   A3   6p yellow green 115.00 95.00
a.   6p blue green   115.00 95.00
b.   Imperf.   —
c.   Diagonal half used as 3p
        on cover   3,000.
8   A5   9p violet   95.00 80.00
a.   Imperf., pair   300.00
b.   Horiz. pair, imperf. vert. 325.00
c.   Diagonal half used as
        4½p on cover   2,250.
  Nos. 4-8 (5)   266.00 232.50

A6

A7

Queen Victoria

1868
9   A6   4p black   9.50 19.00
a.   Yellowish paper   15.00 22.50
b.   Horiz. pair, imperf. vert. 190.00
c.   Diagonal half used as 2p
        on cover   2,250.

d.	Imperf., pair	115.00	
e.	Horiz. pair, imperf. between	160.00	

1870, June 1   Engr.   Perf. 12

10	A7	4½p brown	60.00	60.00

A8   A9

A10   A11

A12   A13

1872, Jan. 1   Typo.   Perf. 12, 12½

11	A8	1c brown orange	5.25	7.50
a.		Imperf., pair	240.00	
12	A9	2c ultra	24.00	30.00
a.		Imperf., pair	300.00	
b.		Diagonal half used as 1c on cover	—	
13	A10	3c rose	24.00	24.00
a.		Imperf., pair	240.00	
b.		Diagonal half used as 1½c on cover	—	
c.		Horiz. or vert. pair, imperf between	240.00	
14	A11	4c green	6.00	13.00
a.		Imperf., pair	240.00	
b.		Diagonal half used as 2c on cover		2,000.
15	A12	6c black	6.00	13.00
a.		Horiz. pair, imperf between	275.00	
b.		Half used as 3c on cover		900.00
16	A13	12c violet	7.75	30.00
a.		Imperf pair	240.00	
b.		Half used as 6c on cover		240.00
		Nos. 11-16 (6)	73.00	117.50

CANADA

ˈka-nə-də

LOCATION — Northern part of North American continent, except for Alaska

GOVT. — Self-governing dominion in the British Commonwealth of Nations

AREA — 3,851,809 sq. mi.

POP. — 28,846,761 (1996)

CAPITAL — Ottawa

Included in the dominion are British Columbia, Vancouver Island, Prince Edward Island, Nova Scotia, New Brunswick and Newfoundland, all of which formerly issued stamps.

12 Pence = 1 Shilling
100 Cents = 1 Dollar (1859)

> Catalogue values for unused stamps in this country are for Never Hinged items, beginning with Scott 268 in the regular postage section, Scott B1 in the semipostal section, Scott C9 in the air post section, Scott CE3 in the air post special delivery section, Scott CO1 in the air post official section, Scott E11 in the special delivery section, Scott EO1 in the special delivery official section, Scott J15 in the postage due section, and Scott O1 in the official section.

Values for unused stamps of #1-33 are for examples with partial original gum. Stamps without gum often trade at prices very close to those of stamps with partial gum. Examples with full original gum and lightly hinged are extremely scarce and generally sell for substantially more than the values listed.

Very fine examples of the perforated issues between Nos. 11-20 will have perforations touching the design or frameline on at least one side due to the narrow spacing of the stamps on the plates. Stamps with perfs clear of the designs on all four sides are extremely scarce and will command much higher prices.

Province of Canada

Beaver — A1   Prince Albert — A2

Queen Victoria — A3

1851   Unwmk.   Engr.   Imperf.
Laid Paper

1	A1	3p red	27,500.	1,150.
2	A2	6p slate violet	27,500.	1,850.
a.		Diag. half used as 3p on cover		32,500.
3	A3	12p black	110,000.	85,000.

On some stamps the laid lines of Nos. 1-3 are practically invisible.

1852-55
Wove Paper

4	A1	3p red	1,500.	240.
a.		3p brown red ('53)	1,600.	275.
b.		Diagonal half used as 1½p on cover		32,500.
c.		Ribbed paper	4,000.	575.
d.		Thin paper	1,500.	240.
5	A2	6p slate gray ('55)	25,000.	1,500.
a.		6p brownish gray	32,500.	2,000.
b.		6p greenish gray	25,000.	1,500.

c.	Diagonal half used as 3p on cover		17,500.
d.	Thick hard paper (gray vio)	27,500.	3,000.

Re-entries of the 3p are numerous. The main re-entry is distinguishable most easily by the line through "EE" and "PEN."

Most authorities believe the 12p black does not exist on wove paper.

Jacques Cartier — A4

1855

7	A4	10p blue	8,000.	1,750.
a.		Thick paper	9,000.	2,250.

Queen Victoria
A5   A6

1857

8	A5	½p rose	1,000.	700.
a.		Horizontally ribbed paper	9,500.	2,500.
b.		Vertically ribbed paper	9,750.	3,500.
9	A6	7½p green	8,500.	3,250.

Very Thick Soft Wove Paper

10	A2	6p reddish pur	17,500.	5,500.
a.		Half used as 3p on cover		22,500.

1858-59   Wove Paper   Perf. 12

11	A5	½p rose	3,250.	1,800.
12	A1	3p red	12,500.	1,000.
13	A2	6p brown vio ('59)	16,000.	6,750.
a.		6p gray violet	16,500.	7,250.
b.		Diagonal half used as 3p on cover		17,500.

Nos. 11-13 values are for copies with perfs touching the design.

A7   A8

A9   A10

A11   A12

1859

14	A7	1c rose	400.00	85.00
a.		Imperf., pair	5,000.	
b.		1c deep rose	550.00	125.00

15	A8	5c vermilion	525.00	37.50
a.		Imperf., pair	14,000.	
b.		Diagonal half used as 2½c on cover		6,000.
c.		5c brick red	625.00	42.50
16	A9	10c black	10,500.	5,500.
a.		Half used as 5c on cover		8,000.
17	A9	10c red lilac	1,050.	160.00
a.		10c violet	1,200.	165.00
b.		10c brown	1,050.	145.00
c.		Imperf., pair	11,000.	
d.		Diagonal half used as 5c on cover		3,750.
e.		10c deep red purple	3,250.	850.00
18	A10	12½c green	875.00	120.00
a.		12½c blue green	1,050.	125.00
b.		Imperf., pair	5,000.	
19	A11	17c blue	1,100.	190.00
a.		17c slate blue	1,100.	210.00
b.		Imperf., pair	4,750.	

No. 15b was used with a 10c for a 12½c rate.

Imperfs. are without gum.

Re-entries of the 5c are numerous. Many of them are slight and have only small premium value. The major re-entry has many lines of the design double, especially the outlines of the ovals and frame at left. Value, used, about $700.

Nos. 14-19 values are for copies with perfs touching the design.

1864

20	A12	2c rose	725.00	300.00
a.		2c deep claret rose	775.00	350.00
b.		Imperf., pair	3,500.	

Imperfs. are without gum.

Values are for copies with perfs touching the design.

Dominion of Canada

Queen Victoria
A13   A14

A15   A16

A17   A18

A19   A20

1868-76   Perf. 12, 11½x12 (5c)

21	A13	½c black	100.00	75.00
a.		Perf. 11½x12 ('73)	125.00	85.00
b.		Watermarked	18,500.	11,000.
c.		Thin paper	125.00	75.00
22	A14	1c brown red	600.00	110.00
a.		Watermarked	3,000.	450.00
b.		Thin paper	650.00	110.00
23	A14	1c yellow org	1,500.	190.00
a.		1c deep orange	2,250.	240.00
24	A15	2c green	750.00	95.00
a.		Watermarked	3,000.	375.00
b.		Thin paper	900.00	100.00
c.		Diag. half used as 1c on cover		4,000.
25	A16	3c red	1,900.	37.50
a.		Watermarked	4,750.	375.00
b.		Thin paper	2,000.	42.50
26	A17	5c ol grn ('75)	1,500.	190.00
a.		Perf. 12	3,250.	900.00
b.		Imperf., pair	12,000.	
27	A18	6c dark brown	2,000.	115.00
a.		6c yellow brown	1,750.	115.00
b.		Watermarked	6,250.	2,000.
c.		Thin paper	1,900.	160.00
d.		Diagonal half used as 3c on cover		3,000.
e.		Vert. half used as 3c on cover		—
f.		6c black brown, thin paper (Mar. '68, 1st printing)	2,750.	240.00
28	A19	12½c blue	1,100.	115.00
a.		Watermarked	4,000.	375.00
b.		Thin paper	1,000.	140.00
c.		Horiz. pair, imperf. vert.		—
d.		Vert. pair, imperf. horiz.		16,000.
29	A20	15c gray violet	95.00	55.00
a.		Perf. 11½x12 ('74)	1,600.	375.00
b.		15c red lilac	950.00	115.00
c.		Wmk. (Clutha Mills)	6,000.	1,150.
d.		Imperf., pair	1,250.	
e.		Thin paper	725.00	135.00
30	A20	15c gray	95.00	60.00
a.		Perf. 11½x12 ('73)	1,200.	375.00
b.		15c blue gray ('75)	115.00	65.00
c.		Very thick paper (dp vio)	4,750.	1,350.

d.		Script wmk., Perf. 11½x12, ('76)	22,500.	5,500.
e.		15c deep blue	1,650.	375.00

The watermark on Nos. 21b, 22a, 24a, 25a, 27b, 28a and 29c consists of double-lined letters reading: "E. & G. BOTHWELL CLUTHA MILLS." The script watermark on No. 30d reads in full: "Alexr. Pirie & Sons." Values for all these watermarked stamps are for fine examples. **Very fine examples are rare, seldom traded, and generally command premiums of about 100% over the values listed.**

No. 26a unused is valued in the grade of fine. No. 26b is a unique pair.

The existence of No. 28c has been questioned.

1868   Laid Paper

31	A14	1c brown red	22,500.	6,500.
32	A15	2c green		200,000.
33	A16	3c bright red	20,000.	2,000.

Only two examples of No. 32 are known, neither being very fine.

Montreal and Ottawa Printings

A21

A22

A23

A24

A25

A26

A27

1870-89   Wove Paper   Perf. 12

34	A21	½c black ('82)	15.00	10.00
a.		Imperf., pair	600.00	
b.		Horiz. pair, imperf. between	800.00	
35	A22	1c yellow	47.50	1.10
a.		1c orange ('70)	175.00	9.50
b.		Imperf., pair	475.00	
c.		Diagonal half used as ½c on cover		4,000.
36	A23	2c green ('72)	75.00	2.25
a.		Imperf., pair	725.00	
b.		Diagonal half used as 1c on cover		2,000.
c.		Vert. half used as 1c on cover		2,000.
d.		2c blue green ('89)	100.00	4.50
f.		Double impression	—	
37	A24	3c orange red ('73)	110.00	2.00
a.		3c rose ('71)	600.00	15.00
b.		3c copper red ('70)	1,400.	60.00
c.		3c dull red ('72)	120.00	3.00
38	A25	5c sl green ('76)	925.00	22.50
39	A26	6c yel brn ('72)	725.00	22.50
a.		Diagonal half used as 3c on cover		600.00
c.		Imperf., pair	2,750.	
40	A27	10c dull rose lilac ('77)	1,150.	75.00
a.		10c magenta ('80)	1,200.	80.00
b.		10c deep lilac rose	1,150.	75.00

No. 34a made with and without gum; values the same.

Copies of Nos. 36b and 36c postmarked "Halifax" are a private speculation.

1870   Perf. 12½

37d	A24	3c cop red (Ottawa)	9,500.	1,400.

1873-79   Perf. 11½x12

35d	A22	1c orange	300.00	18.50
36e	A23	2c green	475.00	22.50
37e	A24	3c red	275.00	11.00
38a	A25	5c slate green	1,100.	50.00
39b	A26	6c yellow brown	900.00	60.00
40c	A27	10c dull rose lilac	1,600.	240.00

The gum on Nos. 35d-40c is always dull and usually blotchy or streaky. It is distinct from the earlier clear, smooth gum and from the bright shiny gums of the later periods.

Nos. 38 and 40 were printed at Montreal. Printings of Nos. 34 to 37, and 39 were made at Ottawa or Montreal and can be separated only by differences in paper and gum.

Ottawa Printing

A28

A29

1888-93   Perf. 12

41	A24	3c brt vermilion	60.00	.80
a.		3c rose carmine	475.00	11.00
42	A25	5c gray	200.00	4.75
43	A26	6c red brown	200.00	11.00
a.		6c chocolate ('90)	240.00	30.00
44	A28	8c violet black ('93)	220.00	4.75
a.		8c blue gray	350.00	6.00
b.		8c slate	240.00	4.75
c.		8c gray	240.00	4.75
45	A27	10c brown red	625.00	55.00
a.		10c dull rose	600.00	50.00
b.		10c pink	600.00	55.00

46	A29	20c ver ('93)	475.00	115.00
47	A29	50c dp blue ('93)	475.00	85.00

Stamps of the 1870-93 issues are found on paper varying from very thin to thick, also occasionally on paper showing a distinctly ribbed surface.

The gum on Nos. 41-47 appears bright and shiny, often with a yellowish tint.

Imperf., Pairs

41b	A24	3c		475.00
42a	A25	5c		725.00
43b	A26	6c		600.00
44d	A28	8c		800.00
45c	A27	10c		600.00
46a	A29	20c		1,400.
47a	A29	50c		1,400.

Nos. 41b-45c made with and without gum. Values the same.

Imperforates and Part-Perforates

From 1859 through 1943 (Nos. 14a/262a), imperforate stamps were printed. These items are listed in this catalogue. The earliest imperforates through perhaps 1917 most likely were from imprimatur sheets (i.e. the first sheets from the approved plates, normally kept in government files) or proof sheets on stamp paper that once were in the post office archives. The imperforates from approximately 1927 to 1943 (often made both with and without gum) were specially created and traded for classic stamps needed for the post office museum, given as gifts to governmental or other dignitaries, or sold or given to favored persons.

The only imperforates from this entire period that were issued to the public were Nos. 90a and 136-138.

Similarly, almost all stamps that are known part-perforate (i.e. horizontal pairs imperforate vertically and vertical pairs imperforate horizontally) were specially made for trading purposes or as presentation items to be given to favored persons. These part-perforates are not listed here, but they are listed in the *Scott Classic Specialized Catalogue*. Part-perforate error stamps that

are believed to have been actually issued to the public are listed in this catalogue.

See the similar imperforates in the air post, Nos. CE1a and CE2a, special delivery, No. F2c (but not No. F1c which was an issued error), postage dues, and Nos. MR4b and MR4c.

Jubilee Issue

Queen Victoria, "1837" and "1897" — A30

1897, June 19   Unwmk.   Perf. 12

50	A30	½c black	120.00	115.00
	Never hinged		300.00	
51	A30	1c orange	24.00	9.00
	Never hinged		60.00	
52	A30	2c green	27.50	15.00
	Never hinged		67.50	
53	A30	3c bright rose	17.50	3.00
	Never hinged		45.00	
54	A30	5c deep blue	60.00	45.00
	Never hinged		150.00	
55	A30	6c yellow brown	240.00	190.00
	Never hinged		600.00	
56	A30	8c dark violet	110.00	65.00
	Never hinged		275.00	
57	A30	10c brown violet	115.00	120.00
	Never hinged		290.00	
58	A30	15c steel blue	260.00	190.00
	Never hinged		650.00	
59	A30	20c vermilion	275.00	190.00
	Never hinged		625.00	
60	A30	50c ultra	375.00	190.00
	Never hinged		775.00	
61	A30	$1 lake	900.00	750.00
	Never hinged		2,400.	
62	A30	$2 dk purple	1,350.	575.00
	Never hinged		3,750.	
63	A30	$3 yel bister	1,450.	1,100.
	Never hinged		4,000.	
64	A30	$4 purple	1,450.	1,100.
	Never hinged		4,000.	
65	A30	$5 olive green	1,450.	1,100.
	Never hinged		4,000.	
	Nos. 50-60 (11)		1,624.	1,132.
	Nos. 50-60, never hinged		3,838.	

60th year of Queen Victoria's reign.

Roller and smudged cancels on Nos. 61-65 sell for less.

A31   A32

1897-98

66	A31	½c black	11.00	6.50
	Never hinged		27.50	
67	A31	1c blue green	35.00	1.40
	Never hinged		87.50	
68	A31	2c purple	35.00	2.25
	Never hinged		87.50	
69	A31	3c carmine ('98)	55.00	1.00
	Never hinged		140.00	
70	A31	5c dk bl, *bluish*	150.00	9.00
	Never hinged		375.00	
71	A31	6c brown	130.00	35.00
	Never hinged		325.00	
72	A31	8c orange	250.00	12.50
	Never hinged		625.00	
73	A31	10c brown vio ('98)	500.00	90.00
	Never hinged		1,250.	
	Nos. 66-73 (8)		1,166.	157.65
	Nos. 66-73, never hinged		2,968.	

For surcharge see No. 87.

Imperf., Pairs

66a	A31	½c	400.
	Never hinged		750.
67a	A31	1c	400.
	Never hinged		750.
68a	A31	2c	400.
	Never hinged		750.
69a	A31	3c	800.
	Never hinged		1,450.
70a	A31	5c	400.
	Never hinged		750.
71a	A31	6c	800.
	Never hinged		1,450.
72a	A31	8c	600.
	Never hinged		1,100.
73a	A31	10c	600.
	Never hinged		1,100.

Nos. 66a, 67a, 68a and 70a made with and without gum. Without gum sell for about 95% of the unused hinged price.

1898-1902

TWO CENTS:
Type I — Frame of four very thin lines.
Type II — Frame of a thick line between two thin ones.

74	A32	½c black	7.50	2.25
	Never hinged		15.00	
75	A32	1c gray green	30.00	.35
	Never hinged		60.00	
76	A32	2c purple (I)	30.00	.35
	Never hinged		60.00	
a.	Thick paper ('99)		175.00	12.00
	Never hinged		350.00	
77	A32	2c car (I) ('99)	30.00	.35
	Never hinged		60.00	
a.	2c carmine (II)		40.00	.60
	Never hinged		80.00	
b.	Booklet pane of 6 (II) ('00)		1,600.	—
	Never hinged		3,000.	
78	A32	3c carmine	57.50	1.10
	Never hinged		115.00	
79	A32	5c blue, *bluish* ('99)	220.00	2.25
	Never hinged		440.00	
80	A32	6c brown	175.00	45.00
	Never hinged		350.00	
81	A32	7c olive yel ('02)	140.00	22.50
	Never hinged		280.00	
82	A32	8c orange	275.00	25.00
	Never hinged		550.00	
83	A32	10c brown vio	400.00	20.00
	Never hinged		800.00	
84	A32	20c olive grn ('00)	550.00	100.00
	Never hinged		1,100.	
	Nos. 74-84 (11)		1,915.	219.15
	Nos. 74-84, never hinged		3,830.	

For surcharges see Nos. 88-88C.

Imperf., Pairs

74a	A32	½c		475.
	Never hinged			775.
75a	A32	1c		1,200.
	Never hinged			1,900.
77c	A32	2c (I)		475.
	Never hinged			775.
77d	A32	2c (II)		1,800.
e.	As No. 77b, imperf., 2 panes tete beche			15,000.
79a	A32	5c		1,200.
	Never hinged			1,900.
80a	A32	6c		1,200.
	Never hinged			1,900.
81a	A32	7c		600.
82a	A32	8c		1,200.
	Never hinged			1,900.
83a	A32	10c		1,200.
	Never hinged			1,900.
84a	A32	20c		4,500.

Nos. 77d, 77e, 81a and 84a were made only without gum. No. 80a was made only with gum. Others either with or without gum and of these those without gum sell for about ⅔ of the values shown for unused hinged.

Imperial Penny Postage Issue

Map of British Empire on Mercator Projection A33

1898, Dec. 7   Engr. & Typo.

85	A33	2c black, lav & car	45.00	7.50
	Never hinged		90.00	
a.	Imperf., pair		550.00	
86	A33	2c black, bl & car	40.00	7.00
	Never hinged		80.00	
a.	Imperf., pair		550.00	

Imperfs. are without gum.

Nos. 69 and 78 Surcharged in Black

1899, July

87	A31	2c on 3c carmine	17.50	7.50
	Never hinged		45.00	
88	A32	2c on 3c carmine	27.50	6.00
	Never hinged		70.00	

No. 78 Surcharged in Blue or Violet

A32a

A32b

1899, Jan. 5

88B	A32a 1(c) on ⅓ of 3c, on cover (BI)		7,750.
88C	A32b 2(c) on ⅔ of 3c, on cover (V)		7,750.

Nos. 88B-88C were prepared and used at Port Hood, Nova Scotia, without official authorization.

King Edward VII — A34

1903-08   Engr.

89	A34	1c green	30.00	.20
	Never hinged		75.00	
90	A34	2c carmine	37.50	.20
	Never hinged		95.00	
b.	Booklet pane of 6		1,600.	1,250.
	Never hinged		2,750.	
91	A34	5c blue, *blue*	220.00	4.50
	Never hinged		550.00	
92	A34	7c olive bister	200.00	4.50
	Never hinged		500.00	
93	A34	10c brown lilac	400.00	10.00
	Never hinged		1,000.	
94	A34	20c olive green	675.00	40.00
	Never hinged		1,700.	
95	A34	50c purple ('08)	850.00	150.00
	Never hinged		2,100.	
	Nos. 89-95 (7)		2,412.	209.40
	Nos. 89-95, never hinged		6,020.	

Values for Nos. 94 and 95 used are for examples with contemporaneous circular datestamps. Stamps with heavy cancellations or parcel cancellations sell for much less.
Issued: 1c-10c, 7/1/03; 20c, 9/27/04; 50c, 11/19/08.

Imperf., Pairs

89a	A34	1c	725.00	
90a	A34	2c	45.00	45.00
	Never hinged		75.00	
c.	As No. 90b, imperf, 2 panes tete beche	14,500.	
91a	A34	5c	1,200.	
92a	A34	7c	800.00	
93a	A34	10c	1,200.	

All imperfs except No. 90a made without gum.

No. 90a issued to the public with gum; also made without gum from different plates distinguishable by experts. Value without gum, $350 with certificate of authenticity.

Quebec Tercentenary Issue

Prince and Princess of Wales, 1908 — A35

Jacques Cartier and Samuel de Champlain A36

Queen Alexandra and King Edward A37

Champlain's Home in Quebec A38

Generals Montcalm and Wolfe — A39

View of Quebec in 1700 — A40

Champlain's Departure for the West — A41

Arrival of Cartier at Quebec A42

1908, July 16

96	A35	½c black brown		5.75	5.00
		Never hinged		14.50	
97	A36	1c blue green		19.00	4.50
		Never hinged		47.50	
98	A37	2c carmine		32.50	2.00
		Never hinged		82.50	
99	A38	5c dark blue		70.00	50.00
		Never hinged		175.00	
100	A39	7c olive green		140.00	100.00
		Never hinged		350.00	

101	A40	10c dark violet		170.00	140.00
		Never hinged		425.00	
102	A41	15c red orange		200.00	130.00
		Never hinged		500.00	
103	A42	20c yel brn		250.00	175.00
		Never hinged		625.00	
		Nos. 96-103 (8)		887.25	606.50
		Nos. 96-103, never hinged		2,220.	

Imperf., Pairs

96a	A35	½c		650.00
97a	A36	1c		650.00
		Never hinged		1,150.
98a	A37	2c		650.00
		Never hinged		1,150.
99a	A38	5c		650.00
		Never hinged		1,150.
100a	A39	7c		650.00
		Never hinged		1,150.
101a	A40	10c		650.00
		Never hinged		1,150.
102a	A41	15c		650.00
		Never hinged		1,150.
103a	A42	20c		650.00
		Never hinged		1,150.

100 pairs of imperfs made, 50 with gum and 50 without. Due to demand, pairs without gum generally sell for 90-95% of the unused hinged price.

King George V — A43

Two dies of 1c.
Die I — The "N" of "ONE" is separated from the oval above it.
Die II — The "N" of "ONE" almost touches the oval above it.

Two dies of 3c carmine.
Die I — The "R" of "THREE" is separated from the oval above it. The bottom line of the vignette does not touch the heavy diagonal stroke at right.
Die II — The "R" of "THREE" almost touches the oval above it. The bottom horizontal line of the vignette touches the heavy diagonal stroke at right.

1911-25

104	A43	1c green		18.00	.20
		Never hinged		45.00	
a.		Booklet pane of 6		32.50	35.00
		Never hinged		65.00	
105	A43	1c org yel (I) ('22)		16.00	.20
		Never hinged		40.00	
a.		Booklet pane of 4 + 2 labels		55.00	55.00
		Never hinged		110.00	
b.		Booklet pane of 6		62.50	62.50
		Never hinged		125.00	
d.		1c orange yellow (II)		14.00	.20
		Never hinged		35.00	
106	A43	2c carmine		18.00	.20
		Never hinged		45.00	
a.		Booklet pane of 6		40.00	40.00
		Never hinged		80.00	
b.		2c pink		140.00	18.00
		Never hinged		350.00	
c.		2c rose carmine		18.00	.20
		Never hinged		45.00	
d.		As "c," booklet pane of 6		160.00	160.00
		Never hinged		320.00	
107	A43	2c yel green ('22)		15.00	.20
		Never hinged		37.50	
a.		Thin paper ('24)		15.00	2.50
		Never hinged		37.50	
b.		Booklet pane of 4 + 2 labels ('22)		65.00	70.00
		Never hinged		130.00	
c.		Booklet pane of 6 ('22)		300.00	325.00
		Never hinged		550.00	
108	A43	3c brown ('18)		16.00	.20
		Never hinged		40.00	
a.		Booklet pane of 4 + 2 labels		90.00	95.00
		Never hinged		180.00	
109	A43	3c car (I) ('23)		16.00	.20
		Never hinged		40.00	
a.		Booklet pane of 4 + 2 labels		70.00	75.00
		Never hinged		140.00	
c.		Die II ('24)		35.00	.20
		Never hinged		90.00	
110	A43	4c ol bis ('22)		45.00	3.25
		Never hinged		115.00	
111	A43	5c dk bl ('12)		135.00	1.00
		Never hinged		340.00	
112	A43	5c violet ('22)		35.00	.75
		Never hinged		87.50	
a.		Thin paper ('24)		30.00	7.50
		Never hinged		75.00	
113	A43	7c yel ocher ('12)		47.50	3.25
		Never hinged		120.00	

114	A43	7c red brown ('24)		22.50	11.00
		Never hinged		57.50	
115	A43	8c blue ('25)		35.00	11.00
		Never hinged		87.50	
116	A43	10c plum ('12)		275.00	3.00
		Never hinged		690.00	
117	A43	10c blue ('22)		47.50	2.25
		Never hinged		120.00	
118	A43	10c bis brn ('25)		42.50	2.25
		Never hinged		105.00	
119	A43	20c olive grn ('12)		110.00	2.00
		Never hinged		275.00	
120	A43	50c blk brn ('25)		85.00	3.00
		Never hinged		210.00	
a.		50c black ('12)		210.00	9.00
		Never hinged		525.00	
122	A43	$1 orange ('23)		100.00	10.00
		Never hinged		250.00	
		Nos. 104-122 (18)		1,079.	53.95
		Nos. 104-122, never hinged		2,705.	

For type A43 perforated 12x8 see No. 184.
For surcharges see Nos. 139-140.
Issued: #104, #106, 12/22/11; #105, 6/7/22; #108, 8/6/18; #109, 12/18/23; 4c, 7/7/22; #111, 1/17/12; #112, 2/2/22; #113, 116, 1/12/12; #114, 12/12/24; 8c, 9/1/25; #117, 2/20/22; #118, 8/1/25; 20c, 1/23/12; 50c, 1/26/12; $1, 7/22/23.

Imperf., Panes

105c		As No. 105b, imperf, 2 panes tete beche	12,500.
107d		As No. 107c, imperf, 2 panes tete beche	12,500.
109b		As No. 109a, imperf, 2 panes tete beche	12,500.

Imperf., Pairs

110a	A43	4c	2,000.
		Never hinged	3,600.
112b	A43	5c	2,000.
		Never hinged	3,600.
114a	A43	7c	2,000.
		Never hinged	3,600.
115a	A43	8c	2,000.
		Never hinged	3,600.
118a	A43	10c	2,000.
		Never hinged	3,600.
119a	A43	20c	2,000.
		Never hinged	3,600.
120b	A43	50c	2,400.
		Never hinged	4,250.
122a	A43	$1	2,000.
		Never hinged	3,600.

Nos. 105c and 109b made without gum, others with gum. About half of the No. 120b pairs have creases; value thus $500.

Coil Stamps

1912   **Perf. 8 Horizontally**

123	A43	1c dark green	105.00	60.00
		Never hinged	250.00	
124	A43	2c carmine	105.00	60.00
		Never hinged	250.00	

1912-24   **Perf. 8 Vertically**

125	A43	1c green	25.00	2.00
		Never hinged	50.00	
126	A43	1c orange yellow (II) ('23)	12.00	7.50
		Never hinged	24.00	
a.		Block of 4 (II)	60.00	50.00
		Never hinged	90.00	
b.		1c orange yellow (I)	25.00	11.00
		Never hinged	50.00	
c.		Block of 4 (I)	450.00	
		Never hinged	750.00	
127	A43	2c carmine	35.00	2.00
		Never hinged	70.00	
128	A43	2c green ('22)	16.00	1.10
		Never hinged	32.50	
a.		Block of 4	60.00	60.00
		Never hinged	90.00	
129	A43	3c brown ('18)	27.50	1.30
		Never hinged	55.00	
130	A43	3c carmine (I) ('24)	70.00	9.00
		Never hinged	140.00	
a.		Block of 4 (I)	950.00	750.00
		Never hinged	1,500.	
b.		Die II	85.00	10.00
		Never hinged	170.00	
		Nos. 125-130 (6)	185.50	22.90
		Nos. 125-130, never hinged	399.00	

Nos. 126a and 128a were issued to the public. Nos. 126c and 130a were issued "by favor" as were the various other imperf and part-perfs of this era.

Beware of fakes of No. 130a made from No. 138.

1915-24   **Perf. 12 Horizontally**

131	A43	1c dark green	7.50	6.50
		Never hinged	15.00	
132	A43	2c carmine	27.50	8.00
		Never hinged	55.00	
133	A43	2c yellow grn ('24)	75.00	60.00
		Never hinged	150.00	

134	A43	3c brown ('21)	11.00	6.50
		Never hinged	22.00	
		Nos. 131-134 (4)	121.00	81.00
		Nos. 131-134, never hinged	242.00	

"The Fathers of Confederation" — A44

1917, Sept. 15   **Perf. 12**

135	A44	3c brown	47.50	1.25
		Never hinged	120.00	
a.		Imperf., pair	600.00	

50th anniv. of the Canadian Confederation. Imperfs. are without gum.

1924   **Imperf.**

136	A43	1c orange yellow	35.00	35.00
		Never hinged	65.00	
		Pair	75.00	75.00
		Never hinged	135.00	
137	A43	2c green	35.00	35.00
		Never hinged	65.00	
		Pair	75.00	75.00
		Never hinged	135.00	
138	A43	3c carmine (I)	17.50	17.50
		Never hinged	32.50	
		Pair	37.50	37.50
		Never hinged	67.50	
		Nos. 136-138 (3)	87.50	87.50
		Nos. 136-138, never hinged	110.00	

No. 109 Surcharged:

      a   b

1926   **Perf. 12**

139	A43(a)	2c on 3c car (I)	60.00	60.00
		Never hinged	100.00	
a.		Pair, one without surcharge	350.00	
b.		Double surcharge	240.00	
c.		Die II	750.00	
140	A43(b)	2c on 3c carmine	30.00	26.00
		Never hinged	50.00	
a.		Double surcharge	240.00	
b.		Triple surcharge	240.00	
c.		Double surch., one invtd.	350.00	

Sir John A.   Sir Wilfrid
Macdonald   Laurier
A45   A48

"The Fathers of Confederation" — A46

Parliament Building at Ottawa A47

Map of Canada A49

1927, June 29

141	A45	1c orange	3.50	1.30
		Never hinged	6.50	
142	A46	2c green	1.90	.20
		Never hinged	3.50	
143	A47	3c brown carmine	10.00	6.50
		Never hinged	18.00	
144	A48	5c violet	4.50	3.50
		Never hinged	8.25	

145	A49	12c dark blue	25.00	6.50
		Never hinged	45.00	
		Nos. 141-145 (5)	44.90	18.00
		Nos. 141-145, never hinged	81.25	

60th year of the Canadian Confederation. Nos. 141-145 exist partly perforated.

Imperf., Pairs

141a	A45	1c	125.00
		Never hinged	180.00
142a	A46	2c	125.00
		Never hinged	180.00
143a	A47	3c	125.00
		Never hinged	180.00
144a	A48	5c	125.00
		Never hinged	180.00
145a	A49	12c	125.00
		Never hinged	180.00

Thomas d'Arcy McGee — A50

Laurier and Macdonald A51

Robert Baldwin and Sir Louis Hypolyte Lafontaine A52

1927, June 29

146	A50	5c violet	4.00	3.00
		Never hinged	7.25	
147	A51	12c green	10.00	5.50
		Never hinged	18.00	
148	A52	20c brown carmine	27.50	6.50
		Never hinged	50.00	
		Nos. 146-148 (3)	41.50	15.00
		Nos. 146-148, never hinged	75.25	

Nos. 146-148 were to have been issued in July, 1926, as a commemorative series, but were withheld and issued June 29, 1927. They exist partly perforated.

Imperf., Pairs

146a	A50	5c	125.00
		Never hinged	180.00
147a	A51	12c	125.00
		Never hinged	180.00
148a	A52	20c	125.00
		Never hinged	180.00

King George V — A53

Mt. Hurd from Bell-Smith's Painting "The Ice-crowned Monarch of the Rockies" A54

Quebec Bridge — A55

Harvesting Wheat A56

Schooner "Bluenose" A57

Parliament Building A58

1928-29

149	A53	1c orange	3.50	.35
		Never hinged	6.50	
a.		Booklet pane of 6	25.00	20.00
		Never hinged	35.00	
150	A53	2c green	1.90	.20
		Never hinged	3.50	
a.		Booklet pane of 6	25.00	20.00
		Never hinged	35.00	
151	A53	3c dk carmine	32.50	12.50
		Never hinged	60.00	
152	A53	4c bister ('29)	27.50	6.00
		Never hinged	50.00	
153	A53	5c dp violet	16.00	3.00
		Never hinged	30.00	
a.		Booklet pane of 6	160.00	140.00
		Never hinged	225.00	
154	A53	8c blue	19.00	7.50
		Never hinged	35.00	
155	A54	10c green	22.50	2.50
		Never hinged	42.50	
156	A55	12c gray ('29)	45.00	7.50
		Never hinged	85.00	
157	A56	20c dk car ('29)	60.00	12.00
		Never hinged	110.00	
158	A57	50c dk blue ('29)	220.00	65.00
		Never hinged	440.00	
159	A58	$1 olive grn ('29)	300.00	80.00
		Never hinged	600.00	
		Nos. 149-159 (11)	747.90	196.55
		#149-159, never hinged	1,463.	

Nos. 149 to 159 exist partly perforated.

Imperf., Panes

149c	As No. 149a, imperf, 2 panes tete beche	1,050.
	Never hinged	1,550.
150c	As No. 150a, imperf, 2 panes tete beche	1,050.
	Never hinged	1,550.
153c	As No. 153a, imperf, 2 panes tete beche	1,050.
	Never hinged	1,550.

Imperf., Pairs

149b	A53	1c	100.00
		Never hinged	140.00
150b	A53	2c	100.00
		Never hinged	140.00
151a	A53	3c	120.00
		Never hinged	170.00
152a	A53	4c	120.00
		Never hinged	170.00
153b	A53	5c	100.00
		Never hinged	140.00
154a	A53	8c	120.00
		Never hinged	170.00
155a	A54	10c	200.00
		Never hinged	280.00
156a	A55	12c	200.00
		Never hinged	280.00
157a	A56	20c	200.00
		Never hinged	280.00
158a	A57	50c	800.00
		Never hinged	1,150.
159a	A58	$1	725.00
		Never hinged	1,050.

Coil Stamps

1929   **Perf. 8 Vertically**

160	A53	1c orange	40.00	22.50
		Never hinged	75.00	
		Precanceled		17.50
161	A53	2c green	35.00	3.50
		Never hinged	65.00	

King George V A59

Library of Parliament A60

The Citadel at Quebec A61

Harvesting
Wheat
A62

Museum at
Grand Pré
and
Monument
to
Evangeline
A63

Mt. Edith
Cavell
A64

Two dies of 1c.
Die I — 3 thick and one thin colored lines between "P" at right and ornament above it.
Die II — 4 thick colored lines. Curved line in ball of ornament at right is longer than in die I.

Two dies of 2c.
Die I — The top of the letter "P" encloses a tiny dot of color.
Die II — The top of the "P" encloses a larger spot of color than in die I. The "P" appears almost like a "D."

1930-31			Perf. 11	
162	A59	1c orange	1.30	.60
		Never hinged	2.75	
163	A59	1c deep green (II)	2.25	.25
		Never hinged	4.75	
a.		Booklet pane of 4 + 2 labels (II)	120.00	110.00
		Never hinged	180.00	
b.		Die I	2.25	.20
		Never hinged	4.75	
c.		Booklet pane of 6 (I)	22.50	20.00
		Never hinged	35.00	
164	A59	2c dull green (I)	1.20	.20
		Never hinged	2.60	
a.		Booklet pane of 6	32.50	32.50
		Never hinged	47.50	
165	A59	2c deep red (I)	1.70	.20
		Never hinged	3.60	
a.		Die II	2.25	.20
		Never hinged	4.75	
b.		Booklet pane of 6 (I)	25.00	25.00
		Never hinged	37.50	
166	A59	2c dk brn (II) ('31)	2.25	.20
		Never hinged	4.75	
a.		Booklet pane of 4 + 2 labels (II)	130.00	130.00
		Never hinged	200.00	
b.		Die I	5.00	4.25
		Never hinged	10.50	
c.		Booklet pane of 6 (I)	57.50	57.50
		Never hinged	87.50	
167	A59	3c deep red ('31)	3.50	.25
		Never hinged	7.50	
a.		Booklet pane of 4 + 2 labels	40.00	40.00
		Never hinged	60.00	
168	A59	4c yel bister	14.00	7.50
		Never hinged	28.00	
169	A59	5c dull violet	8.50	5.00
		Never hinged	17.00	
170	A59	5c dull blue	5.50	1.25
		Never hinged	11.00	
171	A59	8c dark blue	27.50	13.50
		Never hinged	55.00	
172	A59	8c red orange	6.50	5.50
		Never hinged	13.00	
173	A60	10c olive green	14.00	1.30
		Never hinged	28.00	
174	A61	12c gray black	27.50	6.50
		Never hinged	55.00	
175	A62	20c brown red	42.50	1.40
		Never hinged	85.00	
176	A63	50c dull blue	200.00	14.00
		Never hinged	400.00	
177	A64	$1 dk ol green	200.00	27.50
		Never hinged	400.00	
		Nos. 162-177 (16)	558.20	85.15
		Nos. 162-177, never hinged	1,108.	

No. 169 was printed from both flat and rotary press plates.
See No. 201. For surcharge see No. 191. For overprint see No. 203.

Imperf., Pairs

163d	A59	1c (II)	1,600.
		Never hinged	2,400.
173a	A60	10c	1,600.
		Never hinged	2,400.
174a	A61	12c	725.
		Never hinged	1,050.
175a	A62	20c	725.
		Never hinged	1,050.
176a	A63	50c	1,000.
		Never hinged	1,500.
177a	A64	$1	1,000.
		Never hinged	1,500.

Coil Stamps

1930-31			Perf. 8½ Vertically	
178	A59	1c orange	15.00	9.00
		Never hinged	30.00	
179	A59	1c deep green	9.00	5.75
		Never hinged	18.00	
180	A59	2c dull green	6.00	3.00
		Never hinged	12.00	
181	A59	2c deep red	25.00	2.50
		Never hinged	50.00	
182	A59	2c dark brown ('31)	12.00	.70
		Never hinged	24.00	
183	A59	3c deep red ('31)	18.00	.70
		Never hinged	36.00	
		Nos. 178-183 (6)	85.00	21.65
		Nos. 178-183, never hinged	170.00	

George V Type of 1912-25

1931, June 24			Perf. 12x8	
184	A43	3c carmine	7.50	4.50
		Never hinged	18.50	

Sir Georges Etienne
Cartier — A65

1931, Sept. 30			Perf. 11	
190	A65	10c dark green	14.00	.20
		Never hinged	30.00	
a.		Imperf., pair	500.00	
		Never hinged	750.00	

Nos. 165, 165a
Surcharged

1932, June 21				
191	A59	3c on 2c dp red (II)	1.40	.20
		Never hinged	2.25	
a.		Die I	2.75	1.90
		Never hinged	4.50	

King George
V — A66

Edward,
Prince of
Wales — A67

Allegory of
British
Empire
A68

1932, July 12				
192	A66	3c deep red	1.40	.20
		Never hinged	2.75	
193	A67	5c dull blue	7.50	3.00
		Never hinged	15.00	
194	A68	13c deep green	10.50	7.00
		Never hinged	21.00	
		Nos. 192-194 (3)	19.40	10.20
		Nos. 192-194, never hinged	38.75	

Imperial Economic Conference, Ottawa.

Type of 1930 and

King George V — A69

Two dies of 3c.
Die I — Upper left tip of "3" level with horizontal line to its left.
Die II — Raised "3"; upper left tip of "3" is above horizontal line.

1932, Dec. 1				
195	A69	1c dark green	1.40	.20
		Never hinged	2.75	
a.		Booklet pane of 4 + 2 labels	80.00	80.00
		Never hinged	120.00	
b.		Booklet pane of 6	47.50	47.50
		Never hinged	72.50	

196	A69	2c black brown	1.50	.20
		Never hinged	3.00	
a.		Booklet pane of 4 + 2 labels	110.00	110.00
		Never hinged	165.00	
b.		Booklet pane of 6	70.00	70.00
		Never hinged	105.00	
197	A69	3c deep red (I)	1.40	.20
		Never hinged	2.75	
a.		Booklet pane of 4 + 2 labels	45.00	40.00
		Never hinged	67.50	
c.		Die II	1.40	.20
		Never hinged	2.75	
d.		As "a," die II	37.50	37.50
		Never hinged	57.50	
198	A69	4c ocher	50.00	7.00
		Never hinged	100.00	
199	A69	5c dark blue	14.00	.50
		Never hinged	28.00	
a.		Horiz. pair, imperf. vert.	1,600.	
			2,250.	
200	A69	8c red orange	45.00	3.50
		Never hinged	90.00	
201	A61	13c dull violet	45.00	3.50
		Never hinged	90.00	
		Nos. 195-201 (7)	158.30	15.10
		Nos. 195-201, never hinged	316.50	

Type A66 has at the foot of the stamp "OTTAWA-CONFERENCE 1932". This inscription does not appear on the stamps of type A69.

Imperf., Pairs

195c	A69	1c	240.00
		Never hinged	360.00
196c	A69	2c	240.00
		Never hinged	360.00
197b	A69	3c (I)	240.00
		Never hinged	360.00
197e	A69	3c (II)	2,000.
198a	A69	4c	240.00
		Never hinged	360.00
199b	A69	5c	240.00
		Never hinged	360.00
200a	A69	8c	240.00
		Never hinged	360.00
201a	A61	13c	800.00
		Never hinged	1,200.

No. 197e exists as one unused block of 4.

Government Buildings, Ottawa — A70

1933, May 18			Perf. 11	
202	A70	5c dark blue	10.00	3.75
		Never hinged	18.50	
a.		Imperf., pair	625.00	
		Never hinged	950.00	

Meeting of the Executive Committee of the UPU at Ottawa, May and June, 1933.

No. 175
Overprinted
in Blue

1933, July 24				
203	A62	20c brown red	45.00	14.00
		Never hinged	80.00	
a.		Imperf., pair	625.00	
		Never hinged	950.00	

World's Grain Exhibition and Conference at Regina.

Steamship Royal William — A71

1933, Aug. 17

204	A71	5c dark blue	10.00	3.75
		Never hinged	18.50	
a.		Imperf., pair	625.00	
		Never hinged	950.00	

Centenary of the linking by steam of the Dominion, then a colony, with Great Britain, the mother country. The Royal William's 1833 voyage was the first Trans-Atlantic passage under steam all the way.

George V Type of 1932
Coil Stamps

1933			**Perf. 8½ Vertically**	
205	A69	1c dark green	14.00	3.00
		Never hinged	24.00	
206	A69	2c black brown	17.50	1.10
		Never hinged	30.00	
207	A69	3c deep red	14.00	.40
		Never hinged	24.00	
		Nos. 205-207 (3)	45.50	4.50
		Nos. 205-207, never hinged	78.00	

Cartier's Arrival at Quebec — A72

1934, July 1 **Perf. 11**

208	A72	3c blue	4.50	1.40
		Never hinged	9.00	
a.		Imperf., pair	625.00	
		Never hinged	950.00	

Landing of Jacques Cartier, 400th anniv.

Group from Loyalists Monument, Hamilton, Ontario A73

1934, July 1

209	A73	10c olive green	28.00	7.50
		Never hinged	52.50	
a.		Imperf., pair	1,400.	
		Never hinged	2,100.	

Emigration of the United Empire Loyalists from the US to Canada, 150th anniv.

Seal of New Brunswick — A74

1934, Aug. 16

210	A74	2c red brown	3.25	2.25
		Never hinged	6.00	
a.		Imperf., pair	675.00	
		Never hinged	1,100.	

150th anniv. of the founding of the Province of New Brunswick.

Princess Elizabeth A75

Duke of York A76

King George V and Queen Mary — A77

Prince of Wales — A78

Windsor Castle A79

Royal Yacht Britannia A80

1935, May 4 **Perf. 12**

211	A75	1c green	.65	.35
		Never hinged	1.00	
212	A76	2c brown	1.00	.20
		Never hinged	1.50	
213	A77	3c carmine	2.00	.20
		Never hinged	3.25	
214	A78	5c blue	5.25	3.00
		Never hinged	8.50	
215	A79	10c green	8.00	3.00
		Never hinged	13.00	
216	A80	13c dark blue	9.00	6.50
		Never hinged	15.00	
		Nos. 211-216 (6)	25.90	13.25
		Nos. 211-216, never hinged	40.70	

25th anniv. of the accession to the throne of George V.

Imperf., Pairs

211a	A75	1c	275.00	
		Never hinged	425.00	
212a	A76	2c	275.00	
		Never hinged	425.00	
213a	A77	3c	275.00	
		Never hinged	425.00	
214a	A78	5c	275.00	
		Never hinged	425.00	
215a	A79	10c	275.00	
		Never hinged	425.00	
216b	A80	13c	275.00	
		Never hinged	425.00	

King George V — A81

Royal Canadian Mounted Police — A82

Confederation Conference at Charlottetown, 1864 — A83

Niagara Falls — A84

Parliament Buildings, Victoria, B.C. — A85

Champlain Monument, Quebec A86

1935, June 1 **Perf. 12**

217	A81	1c green	.30	.20
		Never hinged	.40	
a.		Booklet pane of 4 + 2 labels	70.00	70.00
		Never hinged	105.00	
b.		Booklet pane of 6	55.00	55.00
		Never hinged	32.50	
218	A81	2c brown	.45	.20
		Never hinged	.65	
a.		Booklet pane of 4 + 2 labels	70.00	70.00
		Never hinged	105.00	
b.		Booklet pane of 6	55.00	55.00
		Never hinged	82.50	
219	A81	3c dk carmine	.60	.20
		Never hinged	.90	
a.		Booklet pane of 4 + 2 labels	40.00	40.00
		Never hinged	60.00	
c.		Printed on gummed side	475.00	
220	A81	4c yel org	2.50	.55
		Never hinged	3.75	
221	A81	5c blue	3.25	.35
		Never hinged	5.00	
a.		Horiz. pair, imperf. vert.	225.00	
		Never hinged	340.00	
222	A81	8c dp orange	3.00	2.25
		Never hinged	4.50	
223	A82	10c car rose	7.00	.20
		Never hinged	10.50	
224	A83	13c violet	8.00	.75
		Never hinged	12.00	
225	A84	20c olive green	20.00	.75
		Never hinged	30.00	
226	A85	50c dull violet	30.00	6.00
		Never hinged	45.00	
227	A86	$1 deep blue	65.00	11.00
		Never hinged	100.00	
		Nos. 217-227 (11)	140.10	22.45
		Nos. 217-227, never hinged	212.70	

Imperf., Pairs

217c	A81	1c	150.00	
		Never hinged	220.00	
218c	A81	2c	150.00	
		Never hinged	220.00	
219b	A81	3c	150.00	
		Never hinged	220.00	
220a	A81	4c	150.00	
		Never hinged	220.00	
221b	A81	5c	150.00	
		Never hinged	220.00	
222a	A81	8c	150.00	
		Never hinged	220.00	
223a	A82	10c	225.00	
		Never hinged	340.00	
224a	A83	13c	225.00	
		Never hinged	340.00	
225a	A84	20c	225.00	
		Never hinged	340.00	
226a	A85	50c	225.00	
		Never hinged	340.00	
227a	A86	$1	300.00	
		Never hinged	450.00	

Coil Stamps

1935			**Perf. 8 Vertically**	
228	A81	1c green	15.00	3.25
		Never hinged	22.50	
229	A81	2c brown	19.00	1.00
		Never hinged	28.00	
230	A81	3c dark carmine	15.00	.60
		Never hinged	22.50	
		Nos. 228-230 (3)	49.00	4.85
		Nos. 228-230, never hinged	73.00	

George VI — A87

George VI and Queen Elizabeth A88

1937 **Perf. 12**

231	A87	1c green	.25	.20
		Never hinged	.40	
a.		Booklet pane of 4 + 2 labels	20.00	25.00
		Never hinged	30.00	
b.		Booklet pane of 6	7.50	20.00
		Never hinged	11.50	
232	A87	2c brown	.65	.20
		Never hinged	1.00	
a.		Booklet pane of 4 + 2 labels	20.00	22.50
		Never hinged	30.00	
b.		Booklet pane of 6	12.00	15.00
		Never hinged	18.00	

233	A87	3c carmine	.65	.20
		Never hinged	1.00	
a.		Booklet pane of 4 + 2 labels	7.00	14.00
		Never hinged	10.50	
234	A87	4c yellow	2.75	.20
		Never hinged	4.00	
235	A87	5c blue	3.50	.20
		Never hinged	5.00	
236	A87	8c orange	2.75	.45
		Never hinged	4.00	
		Nos. 231-236 (6)	10.55	1.45
		Nos. 231-236, never hinged	15.40	

Imperf., Pairs

231c	A87	1c	300.00	
		Never hinged	450.00	
232c	A87	2c	300.00	
		Never hinged	450.00	
233b	A87	3c	300.00	
		Never hinged	450.00	
234a	A87	4c	300.00	
		Never hinged	450.00	
235a	A87	5c	300.00	
		Never hinged	450.00	
236a	A87	8c	300.00	
		Never hinged	450.00	

1937, May 10

237	A88	3c carmine	.25	.20
		Never hinged	.35	
a.		Imperf., pair	625.00	

Coronation of King George VI and Queen Elizabeth.

George VI Types of 1937
Coil Stamps

1937			**Perf. 8 Vertically**	
238	A87	1c green	2.40	1.10
		Never hinged	3.60	
239	A87	2c brown	4.00	.40
		Never hinged	6.00	
240	A87	3c carmine	7.50	.20
		Never hinged	11.50	
		Nos. 238-240 (3)	13.90	1.70
		Nos. 238-240, never hinged	21.10	

Memorial Chamber, Parliament Building, Ottawa — A89

Entrance to Halifax Harbor A90

Fort Garry Gate, Winnipeg A91

Vancouver Harbor A92

Chateau de Ramezay, Montreal A93

1938 **Perf. 12**

241	A89	10c dk carmine	9.00	.20
		Never hinged	13.50	
a.		10c carmine rose	9.00	.20
		Never hinged	13.50	
242	A90	13c deep blue	12.00	.60
		Never hinged	18.00	
243	A91	20c red brown	16.00	.45
		Never hinged	24.00	
244	A92	50c green	40.00	6.00
		Never hinged	60.00	
245	A93	$1 dull violet	85.00	7.75
		Never hinged	125.00	
a.		Vert. pair, imperf. horiz.	4,750.	
		Nos. 241-245 (5)	162.00	15.00
		Nos. 241-245, never hinged	240.50	

Imperf., Pairs

241b	A89	10c dark carmine	450.00	
		Never hinged	675.00	

241c	A89	10c carmine rose	450.00
		Never hinged	675.00
242a	A90	13c	450.00
		Never hinged	675.00
243a	A91	20c	450.00
		Never hinged	675.00
244a	A92	50c	450.00
		Never hinged	675.00
245b	A93	$1	600.00
		Never hinged	900.00

Princess Elizabeth and Princess Margaret Rose — A94

War Memorial, Ottawa — A95

King George VI and Queen Elizabeth A96

Unwmk.

1939, May 15   Engr.   Perf. 12

246	A94	1c green & black	.25	.20
		Never hinged	.30	
247	A95	2c brown & black	.25	.20
		Never hinged	.30	
248	A96	3c dk car & black	.25	.20
		Never hinged	.30	
		Nos. 246-248 (3)	.75	.60
		Nos. 246-248, never hinged	.90	

Visit of George VI and Queen Elizabeth to Canada and the US.

Imperf., Pairs

246a	A94	1c	550.00
		Never hinged	800.00
247a	A95	2c	550.00
		Never hinged	800.00
248a	A96	3c	550.00
		Never hinged	800.00

A97

A98

King George VI A99

Grain Elevators A100

Farm Scene A101

Parliament Buildings A102

"Ram" Tank — A103

Corvette A104

Munitions Factory A105

Destroyer A106

1942-43   Engr.   Perf. 12

249	A97	1c green	.30	.20
		Never hinged	.40	
a.		Booklet pane of 4 + 2 labels	3.50	3.75
		Never hinged	5.25	
b.		Booklet pane of 6	5.00	5.50
		Never hinged	7.50	
c.		Booklet pane of 3	2.50	5.00
		Never hinged	3.75	
250	A98	2c brown	.40	.20
		Never hinged	.60	
a.		Booklet pane of 4 + 2 labels	7.00	8.00
		Never hinged	10.50	
b.		Booklet pane of 6	10.50	11.50
		Never hinged	16.00	
d.		Vert. strip of 3, imperf. horiz.	5,000.	
251	A99	3c dk carmine	.60	.20
		Never hinged	.90	
a.		Booklet pane of 4 + 2 labels	4.25	5.25
		Never hinged	6.50	
252	A99	3c rose violet ('43)	.40	.20
		Never hinged	.60	
a.		Booklet pane of 4 + 2 labels	3.25	4.50
		Never hinged	5.00	
b.		Booklet pane of 3	3.25	4.50
		Never hinged	4.75	
c.		Booklet pane of 6	3.50	4.00
		Never hinged	5.25	
253	A100	4c greenish black	1.25	.60
		Never hinged	1.90	
254	A98	4c dk car ('43)	.60	.20
		Never hinged	.90	
a.		Booklet pane of 6	5.25	10.00
		Never hinged	8.00	
b.		Booklet pane of 3	3.25	4.50
		Never hinged	4.75	
255	A97	5c deep blue	1.20	.20
		Never hinged	1.80	
256	A101	8c red brown	1.60	.50
		Never hinged	2.40	
257	A102	10c brown	4.50	.20
		Never hinged	6.75	
258	A103	13c dull green	5.00	3.60
		Never hinged	7.50	
259	A103	14c dull grn ('43)	6.50	.35
		Never hinged	9.75	
260	A104	20c chocolate	9.00	.20
		Never hinged	13.50	
261	A105	50c violet	35.00	1.75
		Never hinged	52.50	
262	A106	$1 deep blue	65.00	7.50
		Never hinged	100.00	
		Nos. 249-262 (14)	131.35	15.90
		Nos. 249-262, never hinged	199.50	

Canada's contribution to the war effort of the Allied Nations.

No. 250d totally imperf horiz. is unique. Beware of strips with blind perfs; these sell for much less.

For overprints see Nos. O1-O4.

Imperf., Pairs

249d	A97	1c	300.00
		Never hinged	450.00
250c	A98	2c	300.00
		Never hinged	450.00
251b	A99	3c	300.00
		Never hinged	450.00
252d	A99	3c	300.00
		Never hinged	450.00
253a	A100	4c	300.00
		Never hinged	450.00
254c	A98	4c	300.00
		Never hinged	450.00
255a	A97	5c	300.00
		Never hinged	450.00
256a	A100	8c	300.00
		Never hinged	450.00
257a	A102	10c	450.00
		Never hinged	675.00
258a	A103	13c	450.00
		Never hinged	675.00
259a	A103	14c	450.00
		Never hinged	675.00
260a	A104	20c	450.00
		Never hinged	675.00
261a	A105	50c	450.00
		Never hinged	675.00
262a	A106	$1	450.00
		Never hinged	675.00

Types of 1942
Coil Stamps

1942-43   Perf. 8 Vertically

263	A97	1c green ('43)	1.30	.55
		Never hinged	2.00	
264	A98	2c brown	2.00	1.10
		Never hinged	3.00	

265	A99	3c dark carmine	2.00	1.10
		Never hinged	3.00	
266	A99	3c rose violet ('43)	3.25	.40
		Never hinged	5.00	
267	A98	4c dk carmine ('43)	5.00	.30
		Never hinged	7.50	
		Nos. 263-267 (5)	13.55	3.45
		Nos. 263-267, never hinged	20.50	

See Nos. 278-281.

> **Catalogue values for unused stamps in this section, from this point to the end of the section, are for Never Hinged items.**

Farm Scene, Ontario A107

Great Bear Lake, Mackenzie A108

Hydroelectric Station, Saint Maurice River A109

Combine A110

Logging, British Columbia A111

Train Ferry, Prince Edward Island A112

1946, Sept. 16   Engr.   Perf. 12

268	A107	8c red brown	1.80	.60
269	A108	10c olive	2.40	.20
270	A109	14c black brown	4.00	.20
271	A110	20c slate black	5.50	.20

272	A111	50c dk blue green	24.00	1.50
273	A112	$1 red violet	47.50	3.00
		Nos. 268-273 (6)	85.20	5.70

For overprints see Nos. O6-O10, O21-O23, O25.

Alexander Graham Bell — A113

1947, Mar. 3

274	A113	4c deep blue	.30	.20

Birth centenary of Alexander Graham Bell.

Citizen of Canada — A114

1947, July 1

275	A114	4c deep blue	.30	.20

Issued on the 80th anniv. of the Canadian Confederation, to mark the advent of Canadian Citizenship.

Princess Elizabeth — A115

1948, Feb. 16

276	A115	4c deep blue	.25	.20

Marriage of Princess Elizabeth to Lieut. Philip Mountbatten, R. N., on Nov. 20, 1947.

Parliament Buildings Ottawa A116

1948, Oct. 1

277	A116	4c gray	.25	.20

Centenary of Responsible Government.

George VI Types of 1942
Coil Stamps

1948   *Perf. 9½ Vertically*

278 A97 1c green	6.00	2.00
279 A98 2c brown	20.00	8.50
280 A99 3c rose violet	10.00	2.00
281 A98 4c dark carmine	16.00	2.25
Nos. 278-281 (4)	52.00	14.75

John Cabot's Ship "Matthew" A117

1949, Apr. 1   **Engr.**   *Perf. 12*

282 A117 4c deep green   .25 .20

Entry of Newfoundland into confederation with Canada.

"Founding of Halifax, 1749" A118

1949, June 21   **Unwmk.**

283 A118 4c purple   .25 .20

200th anniv. of the founding of Halifax, Nova Scotia.

A119   A120

A121   A122

A123

1949, Nov. 15

284 A119 1c green	.25	.20
a. Booklet pane of 3 ('50)	.60	1.25
285 A120 2c sepia	.30	.20
286 A121 3c rose violet	.35	.20
a. Booklet pane of 3 ('50)	2.50	6.50
b. Booklet pane of 4 + 2 labels ('50)	3.25	3.75
287 A122 4c dk carmine	.60	.20
a. Booklet pane of 3 ('50)	12.50	12.50
b. Booklet pane of 6 ('50)	18.00	18.00
288 A123 5c deep blue	1.25	.30
Nos. 284-288 (5)	2.75	1.10

Stamps from booklet panes of 3 are imperf. on 2 or 3 sides.

"POSTES POSTAGE" Omitted
1950, Jan. 19

289 A119 1c green	.25	.20
290 A120 2c sepia	.30	.20
291 A121 3c rose violet	.30	.20
292 A122 4c dark carmine	.30	.20
293 A123 5c deep blue	1.40	1.00
Nos. 289-293 (5)	2.55	1.80

See Nos. 295-300, 305-306, 309-310. For overprints see Nos. O12-O20.

Oil Wells, Alberta A124

1950, Mar. 1   **Engr.**   *Perf. 12*

294 A124 50c dull green   11.00 1.40

Development of oil wells in Canada. For overprints see Nos. O11, O24.

Types of 1949
Coil Stamps
"POSTES POSTAGE" Omitted

1950   *Perf. 9½ Vertically*

295 A119 1c green	.70	.30
296 A121 3c rose violet	1.10	.60

With "POSTES POSTAGE"
Perf. 9½ Vertically

297 A119 1c green	.40	.20
298 A120 2c sepia	3.25	1.30
299 A121 3c rose violet	2.00	.20
300 A122 4c dark carmine	16.00	.70
Nos. 297-300 (4)	21.65	2.40

See note after No. 288.

Indians Drying Skins on Stretchers A125

1950, Oct. 2   *Perf. 12*

301 A125 10c black brown   .90 .20

Canada's fur resources. For overprint see No. O26.

Fishing A126

1951, Feb. 1   **Unwmk.**

302 A126 $1 bright ultra   50.00 11.00

Canada's fish resources. For overprint see No. O27.

Sir Robert Laird Borden A127   William L. Mackenzie King A128

1951, June 25   *Perf. 12*

303 A127 3c turquoise green	.25	.20
304 A128 4c rose pink	.30	.20

George VI Types of 1949

1951   *Perf. 12*

305 A120 2c olive green	.20	.20
306 A122 4c orange vermilion	.25	.20
a. Booklet pane of 3	5.25	2.75
b. Booklet pane of 6	5.00	5.00

For overprints see Nos. O28-O29.

Coil Stamps
Perf. 9½ Vertically

309 A120 2c olive green	1.40	.60
310 A122 4c orange vermilion	2.75	.70

Trains of 1851 and 1951 — A129

"Threepenny Beaver" of 1851 — A130

5c, Steamships City of Toronto and Prince George. 7c, Stagecoach and Plane.

1951, Sept. 24   **Unwmk.**   *Perf. 12*

311 A129 4c dark gray	.60	.20
312 A129 5c purple	1.80	1.25
313 A129 7c deep blue	1.10	.30
314 A130 15c bright red	1.20	.30
Nos. 311-314 (4)	4.70	2.05

Centenary of British North American postal administration.

Princess Elizabeth and Duke of Edinburgh A131

1951, Oct. 26   **Engr.**

315 A131 4c violet   .20 .20

Visit of Princess Elizabeth, Duchess of Edinburgh and the Duke of Edinburgh to Canada and the US.

Symbols of Newsprint Paper Production A132

1952, Apr. 1   **Unwmk.**   *Perf. 12*

316 A132 20c gray   1.70 .20

Canada's paper production. For overprint see No. O30.

Red Cross on Sun — A133

1952, July 26   **Engr. and Litho.**

317 A133 4c blue & red   .20 .20

18th Intl. Red Cross Conf., Toronto, July 1952.

Sir John J. C. Abbott A134   Alexander Mackenzie A135

1952, Nov. 3   **Engr.**

318 A134 3c rose lilac	.20	.20
319 A135 4c orange vermilion	.25	.20

Canada Goose A136

1952, Nov. 3

320 A136 7c blue   .40 .20

For overprint see No. O31.

Pacific Coast Indian House and Totem Pole — A137

1953, Feb. 2

321 A137 $1 gray   7.50 .90

For overprint see No. O32.

Natl. Wildlife Week — A138

1953, Apr. 1

322 A138 2c Polar bear	.20	.20
323 A138 3c Moose	.25	.20
324 A138 4c Bighorn sheep	.25	.20
Nos. 322-324 (3)	.70	.60

Elizabeth II — A139

1953, May 1

325 A139 1c violet brown	.20	.20
a. Booklet pane of 3	1.40	1.40
326 A139 2c green	.20	.20
327 A139 3c carmine rose	.20	.20
a. Booklet pane of 3	1.90	1.50
b. Booklet pane of 4 + 2 labels	1.40	1.75
328 A139 4c violet	.25	.20
a. Booklet pane of 3	1.90	1.75
b. Booklet pane of 6	1.60	1.60
329 A139 5c ultramarine	.25	.20
Nos. 325-329 (5)	1.10	1.00

Stamps from booklet panes of 3 are imperf. on 2 or 3 sides. See Nos. 331-333. For overprints see Nos. O33-O37.

Coronation Issue

Queen Elizabeth II — A140

1953, June 1

330 A140 4c violet   .20 .20

Coil Stamps

1953   *Perf. 9½ Vertically*

331 A139 2c green	1.40	.90
332 A139 3c carmine rose	1.40	.90
333 A139 4c violet	3.25	1.40
Nos. 331-333 (3)	6.05	3.20

See note after No. 329. Issued: 2c, 7/30; 3c, 7/27; 4c, 9/3.

Bobbin, Cloth and Spinning Wheel A141

1953, Nov. 2   *Perf. 12*

334 A141 50c light green   3.75 .25

For overprint see No. O38.

Walrus
A142

Beaver
A143

1954, Apr. 1
335 A142 4c gray .30 .20
336 A143 5c ultramarine .35 .20
a. Booklet pane of 5 + label 1.75 1.50

National Wildlife Week, 1954.

Elizabeth II
A144

Gannet
A145

1954-61
337 A144 1c violet brn .20 .20
a. Booklet pane of 5 + label
('56) 1.10 1.10
338 A144 2c green .20 .20
a. Pane of 25 ('61) 3.75 3.75
339 A144 3c carmine rose .20 .20
a. Horiz. pair, imperf. vert. 1,500.
340 A144 4c violet .25 .20
a. Booklet pane of 5 + label
('56) 1.50 1.50
b. Booklet pane of 6 ('55) 3.00 3.00
341 A144 5c bright blue .25 .20
a. Booklet pane of 5 + label 1.20 1.20
b. Pane of 20 (5 x 4) ('61) 7.00 7.00
c. Horiz. pair, imperf. vert. 6,000.
342 A144 6c orange .50 .20
343 A145 15c gray 1.50 .20
Nos. 337-343 (7) 3.10 1.40

Panes of 20 and 25 are imperf. on 4 sides.
Issued: 5c, 15c, 4/1; others, 6/10.
For overprints see Nos. O40-O44.

Luminescence

The overprinting of regular stamps with vertical luminescent bands began experimentally in 1962 when Nos. 337p-341p were released at Winnipeg. The bands are of varying number, position and chemical content.

Tagged varieties of stamps which were issued both untagged and with luminescent overprint are listed with suffix letter "p".

Tagged
1962, Jan. 13
337p A144 1c violet brown 1.30 .95
338p A144 2c green 1.30 .95
339p A144 3c carmine rose 1.30 .95
340p A144 4c violet 3.75 3.25
341p A144 5c bright blue 4.25 2.25
Nos. 337p-341p (5) 11.90 8.35

Coil Stamps
1954 **Perf. 9½ Vertically**
345 A144 2c green .55 .20
347 A144 4c violet 1.60 .25
348 A144 5c bright blue 2.25 .20
Nos. 345-348 (3) 4.40 .65

Issued: 2c, 9/9; 3c, 8/23; 4c, 7/6.

Sir John
Sparrow
David
Thompson
A146

Sir Mackenzie
Bowell
A147

1954, Nov. 1 **Perf. 12**
349 A146 4c violet .35 .20
350 A147 5c bright blue .35 .20

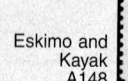

Eskimo and
Kayak
A148

1955, Feb. 21
351 A148 10c violet brown .40 .20

For overprint see No. O39.

Musk Ox — A149

Whooping
Cranes
A150

1955, Apr. 4
352 A149 4c purple .35 .20
353 A150 5c blue .40 .20

National Wildlife Week, April 10-16.

Torch, Dove and
Maple
Leaves — A151

1955, June 1 **Unwmk.**
354 A151 5c light blue .40 .20

ICAO, 10th anniversary.

Pioneer
Settlers
A152

1955, June 30 **Perf. 12**
355 A152 5c ultramarine .40 .20

50th anniv. of the founding of the provinces of Alberta and Saskatchewan.

Globe and
Scout
Emblem
A153

1955, Aug. 20 **Engr.**
356 A153 5c green & org brown .40 .20

8th Boy Scout World Jamboree, Niagara-on-the-Lake, Ont.

Richard
Bedford
Bennett
A154

Sir Charles
Tupper
A155

1955, Nov. 8
357 A154 4c violet .35 .20
358 A155 5c ultramarine .35 .20

Ice Hockey
Players
A156

1956, Jan. 23
359 A156 5c ultramarine .35 .20

Issued to publicize Canada's most popular winter sport.

Caribou
A157

Mountain
Goat
A158

1956, Apr. 12
360 A157 4c deep violet .40 .20
361 A158 5c ultramarine .40 .20

National Wildlife Week, 1956.

"Paper
Industry"
A159

"Chemical
Industry" — A160

1956, June 7 **Engr.**
362 A159 20c green 1.50 .20
363 A160 25c red 1.60 .20

For overprint see No. O45.

House on Fire — A161

1956, Oct. 9 **Unwmk.** **Perf. 12**
364 A161 5c gray & red .35 .20

Issued to emphasize the needless waste caused by preventable fires.

Canada's
Outdoor
Recreation
Facilities
A162

1957, Mar. 7
365 A162 5c Fishing .40 .20
366 A162 5c Swimming .40 .20
367 A162 5c Hunter and dog .40 .20
368 A162 5c Skiing .40 .20
a. Block of 4, #365-368 1.60 1.10

All four designs are printed alternating in sheet of 50, with various combinations possible.

Loon — A163

1957, Apr. 10 **Perf. 12**
369 A163 5c black .35 .20

David
Thompson
and Map of
Western
Canada
A164

1957, June 5 **Unwmk.**
370 A164 5c ultramarine .35 .20

David Thompson (1770-1857), explorer and geographer.

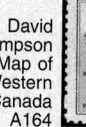

Parliament Building,
Ottawa — A165

Post Horn
and Globe
A166

1957, Aug. 14 **Perf. 12**
371 A165 5c dark blue .35 .20
372 A166 15c dark blue 2.25 1.90

UPU, 14th Congress, Ottawa, Aug. 1957.

Miner With Pneumatic
Drill — A167

1957, Sept. 5
373 A167 5c black .30 .20

Canada's mining industry; 6th Commonwealth Mining and Metallurgical Congress, Vancouver, Sept. 8-Oct. 8.

Elizabeth II and
Prince
Philip — A168

1957, Oct. 10 **Unwmk.**
374 A168 5c black .30 .20

Visit of Queen Elizabeth II and Prince Philip to Canada, Oct. 12-16.

Newspapers
and Symbols
of Industry
A169

1958, Jan. 22 **Engr.**
375 A169 5c black .35 .20

Canadian press; the importance of a free press.

Microscope and Globe — A170

1958, Mar. 5 *Perf. 12*
376 A170 5c blue .35 .20
Intl. Geophysical Year, 1957-1958.

Miner Panning Gold — A171

1958, May 8 **Unwmk.**
377 A171 5c bluish green .35 .20
Province of British Columbia, cent.

La Verendrye A172

1958, June 4 *Perf. 12*
378 A172 5c bright ultra .35 .20
Pierre Gaultier de Varenne, Sieur de la Verendrye, 18th century French explorer of Western Canada.

Champlain and View of Quebec A173

1958, June 26
379 A173 5c dk green & bis brn .35 .20
Founding of Quebec, 350th anniv.

Nurse — A174

1958, July 30 **Engr.**
380 A174 5c rose lilac .35 .20
Importance of health, both to the individual and to the nation.

Kerosene Lamp and Refinery — A175

1958, Sept. 10 *Perf. 12*
381 A175 5c olive & red .35 .20
Centennial of Canada's oil industry.

Speaker's Chair and Mace A176

1958, Oct. 2
382 A176 5c slate blue .35 .20
Bicentennial of the meeting of the first House of Representatives in Canada, Halifax, Oct. 2, 1758.

"Silver Dart" and Delta Wing Planes A177

1959, Feb. 23 *Perf. 12*
383 A177 5c blue & black .35 .20
50th anniv. of the 1st airplane flight in Canada near Baddeck, N. S., with J. A. D. McCurdy as pilot.

Globe and Dove — A178

1959, Apr. 2
384 A178 5c violet blue .35 .20
NATO, 10th anniversary.

Woman Tending Tree — A179

1959, May 13
385 A179 5c apple green & blk .35 .20
Associated Country Women of the World.

Elizabeth II — A180

1959, June 18
386 A180 5c dark carmine .35 .20
Visit of Queen Elizabeth and Prince Philip to Canada, June 18-Aug. 1.

Great Lakes, Maple Leaf and Eagle Emblems A181

1959, June 26 **Engr.**
387 A181 5c red & blue .35 .20
a. Center inverted 12,000. 10,000.
Opening of the St. Lawrence Seaway, June 26, 1959.
See United States No. 1131.

British Lion, Fleur-de-Lis and Maple Leaves A182

1959, Sept. 10 *Perf. 12*
388 A182 5c crim rose & dk green .35 .20
Bicentenary of the Battle of the Plains of Abraham.

Girl Guide Emblem — A183

1960, Apr. 20 **Unwmk.**
389 A183 5c brown org & ultra .35 .20
Canadian Girl Guides Assoc., 50th anniv.

Dollard des Ormeaux and Battle Scene — A184

1960, May 19
390 A184 5c ultra & bis brown .35 .20
Battle of the Long Sault, 300th anniv.

Compass Rose, Earth Mover and Surveyor A185

Emily Pauline Johnson A186

1961, Feb. 8 **Engr.** *Perf. 12*
391 A185 5c green & vermilion .35 .20
Development of Canada's Northland.

1961, Mar. 10
392 A186 5c green & red .35 .20
Emily Pauline Johnson (1861-1913), Mohawk princess and poet.

Arthur Meighen — A187

1961, Apr. 19
393 A187 5c ultramarine .35 .20
Arthur Meighen, Prime Minister of Canada, (1920-21, 1926).

Power Plant and Men Holding Blueprint A188

1961, June 28 **Unwmk.** *Perf. 12*
394 A188 5c lt red brn & blue .35 .20
10th anniv. of the Colombo Plan, initiated to assist underdeveloped countries by providing trained manpower and resources.

Natural Resources and Hands Holding Cogwheel — A189

1961, Oct. 12 **Engr.** *Perf. 12*
395 A189 5c brown & blue grn .35 .20
Canada's "Resources for Tomorrow Program" and to publicize the close link between industry and the country's renewable natural resources.

Young Adults and Education Symbols — A190

1962, Feb. 28 **Unwmk.** *Perf. 12*
396 A190 5c black & lt red brn .35 .20
a. Light red brown (symbols) omitted
Issued to stimulate public awareness of the importance of education.

Scottish Settler and Lord Selkirk A191

1962, May 3 *Perf. 12*
397 A191 5c lt green & vio brn .35 .20
150th anniv. of the Red River Settlement in Western Canada (Prairie Provinces).

Jean Talon Presenting Gifts to Young Farm Couple — A192

1962, June 13 **Unwmk.** *Perf. 12*
398 A192 5c dark blue .35 .20
Jean Talon, administrator of New France (Canada), 1665-1668.

British Columbia Legislative Building and Stamp of 1860 — A193

1962, Aug. 22 **Engr.** *Perf. 12*
399 A193 5c black & rose .35 .20
Centenary of Victoria as incorporated city.

Arms of the Provinces A194

1962, Aug. 31
400 A194 5c brown orange & black .35 .20
Official opening of the Trans-Canada Highway, Rogers Pass, Glacier National Park, Sept. 4.

Queen Elizabeth II and Wheat — A195

Designs (Symbol in upper left corner): 1c, Mineral crystals. 2c, Tree. 3c, Fish. 4c, Electric high tension tower.

1962-63   **Engr.**   **Perf. 12**
401 A195 1c dp brn ('63)   .20   .20
  a. Booklet pane of 5 + la-
    bel ('63)   3.00   3.00
402 A195 2c green ('63)   .20   .20
  a. Pane of 25 ('63)   8.00   8.00
403 A195 3c purple ('63)   .20   .20
404 A195 4c carmine ('63)   .20   .20
  a. Booklet pane of 5 + la-
    bel ('63)   3.00   3.00
  b. Pane of 25 ('63)   12.00   12.00
405 A195 5c violet blue   .25   .20
  a. Booklet pane of 5 + la-
    bel ('63)   3.00   3.00
  b. Pane of 20 ('63)   14.00   14.00
  c. Imperf., pair (#405b)   3,500.
  d. Vert. pair, imperf. horiz.   4,000.   575.00
  Nos. 401-405 (5)   1.05   1.00

Nos. 402a, 404b, and 405b are imperf. on four sides.
Used examples of No. 405d are canceled "Gonor, MB." Beware of examples with traces of blind perfs; a certificate of authenticity is recommended.
Issued: 5c, 10/3; 1c, 4c, 2/4/63; 2c, 3c, 5/2/63.
For overprints see Nos. O46-O49.

Tagged

1963
401p A195 1c deep brown   .20   .20
402p A195 2c green   .20   .20
403p A195 3c purple   .25   .20
404p A195 4c carmine   .80   .50
405p A195 5c violet blue   .50   .25
  q. Pane of 20   42.50   42.50
  Nos. 401p-405p (5)   1.95   1.35

See note after No. 343.

Coil Stamps

1962-63   **Perf. 9½ Horiz.**
406 A195 2c green   4.25   2.25
407 A195 3c purple   3.00   1.75
408 A195 4c carmine   4.25   2.25
  a. Pair, imperf between   3,000.
409 A195 5c violet blue   4.25   .90
  Nos. 406-409 (4)   15.75   7.15

No. 408a is valued in the grade of fine. Beware of dangerous fakes; a certificate of authenticity is necessary.
Issued: 5c, 10/3; 4c, 2/4/63; 2c, 3c, 5/2/63.

Sir Casimir Stanislaus Gzowski (1813-98), Engineer, Soldier and Educator — A196

1963, Mar. 5   Unwmk.   Perf. 12
410 A196 5c rose lilac   .30   .20

Export Crate and Mercator Map — A197

1963, June 14   Unwmk.   Perf. 12
411 A197 $1 rose carmine   10.00   2.25

Sir Martin Frobisher (1535-1594), Explorer and Discoverer of Frobisher Bay — A198

1963, Aug. 21   Engr.
412 A198 5c ultramarine   .30   .20

Postrider and First Land Mail Routes A199

1963, Sept. 25
413 A199 5c green & red brn   .30   .20
Bicentennial of the 1st regular postal service between Quebec, Three Rivers & Montreal.

Jet at Ottawa Airport — A200   Canada Geese — A201

1963-64
414 A200 7c blue ('64)   .50   .40
415 A201 15c deep ultra   1.80   .20
See No. 436. For surcharge see No. 430.

"Peace on Earth" — A202

1964, Apr. 8   Engr. & Litho.
416 A202 5c grnsh blue, Prus bl & ocher   .30   .20
Issued to promote world peace.

Three-Maple-Leaf Emblem (Canadian Unity) — A203

White Trillium and Arms of Ontario A204

#419, White garden lily and arms of Quebec. #420, Mayflower (trailing arbutus) and arms of Nova Scotia. #421, Purple violet and arms of New Brunswick. #422, Prairie crocus and arms of Manitoba. #423, Dogwood and arms of British Columbia. #424, Lady's slipper and arms of Prince Edward Island. #425, Prairie lily and arms of Saskatchewan. #426, Wild rose and arms of Alberta. #427, Pitcher plant and arms of Newfoundland. #428, Fireweed and arms of Yukon. #429, Mountain avens and arms of Northwest Territories. #429A, Maple leaf and arms of Canada.

1964-66   Engr. & Litho.   Perf. 12
417   A203 5c lt blue & dk car   .25   .20
418   A204 5c red brn, buff & green   .25   .20
419   A204 5c grn, yel & org   .25   .20
420   A204 5c blue, pink & grn   .25   .20
421   A204 5c car, green & vio   .25   .20
422   A204 5c red brn, lil & dl grn   .25   .20
423   A204 5c lilac, grn & bis   .25   .20
424   A204 5c vio, grn & dp rose   .25   .20
425   A204 5c sepia, org & grn   .25   .20
426   A204 5c dl grn, yel & car   .25   .20
427   A204 5c black, grn & car   .25   .20
428   A204 5c dk bl, rose & grn   .25   .20
429   A204 5c ol, yel & green   .25   .20
429A A204 5c dk blue & dp red   .25   .20
  Nos. 417-429A (14)   3.50   2.80

Issued: #417, 5/14/64; #418-419, 6/30/64; #420-421, 2/3/65; #422-423, 4/28/65; #424, 7/21/65; #425-426, 1/19/66; #427, 2/23/66; #428-429, 3/23/66; #429A, 6/30/66.

No. 414 Surcharged

1964, July 15   Engr.
430 A200 8c on 7c blue   .45   .25
  a. Pair, one without surcharge   12,000.
  b. Surcharge on reverse, inverted   4,000.
Nos. 430a and 430b are each unique.

Fathers of Confederation Memorial, Charlottetown — A205

1964, July 29   Engr.
431 A205 5c black   .30   .20
Centenary of the Charlottetown, P.E.I., Conference, Sept. 1-9, 1864, which led to the creation of the Canadian nation in 1867.

Maple Leaf and Hand Holding Quill Pen — A206

1964, Sept. 9   Unwmk.   Perf. 12
432 A206 5c dark brown & rose   .30   .20
Centenary of the Quebec Conference, Oct. 10-27, 1864, which led to the creation of the Canadian nation.

Elizabeth II   Family and Star
A207   of Bethlehem
                      A208

1964, Oct. 5   Engr.
433 A207 5c claret   .25   .20
Queen Elizabeth's visit, Oct. 6-13.

1964, Oct. 14   Perf. 12
434 A208 3c red   .20   .20
  a. Pane of 25   8.00   8.00
  p. Tagged   .70   .35
  q. As "a," tagged   12.50   12.50
435   A208 5c blue   .25   .20
  p. Tagged   1.20   .40
Panes of 25 are imperf. on four sides.

Jet Type of 1964

1964, Nov. 18   Unwmk.   Perf. 12
436 A200 8c blue   .40   .20

Maple Leaf and ICY Emblem A209

1965, Mar. 3   Engr.   Perf. 12
437 A209 5c slate green   .25   .20
International Cooperation Year.

Sir Wilfred Grenfell at Wheel of Hospital Ship Strathcona II — A210

1965, June 9   Engr.   Perf. 12
438 A210 5c Prussian blue   .25   .20
Sir Wilfred Grenfell, author, medical missionary and founder of the Grenfell Mission, birth cent.

Canada's Maple Leaf Flag, 1965 A211

1965, June 30   Unwmk.
439 A211 5c blue & red   .25   .20

Winston Churchill — A212

1965, Aug. 12   Litho.   Perf. 12
440 A212 5c brown   .25   .20
Sir Winston Spencer Churchill (1874-1965).

Peace Tower, Ottawa — A213

1965, Sept. 8   Engr.   Perf. 12
441 A213 5c slate green   .25   .20
Meeting of the Inter-Parliamentary Union, Ottawa, Sept. 8-17.

Parliament and Ottawa River A214

1965, Sept. 8
442 A214 5c brown   .25   .20
Centenary of the final selection of Ottawa as national capital.

Gifts of the Wise Men — A215

1965, Oct. 13   Engr.
443 A215 3c olive   .20   .20
  a. Pane of 25   6.50   6.50
  p. Tagged   .25   .20
  q. As "a," tagged   8.75   8.75
444   A215 5c violet blue   .20   .20
  p. Tagged   .35   .20
Christmas. Panes of 25 are imperf. on four sides.

Alouette II
Orbiting
Globe — A216

1966, Jan. 5   Unwmk.   Perf. 12
445 A216 5c dark violet blue   .25 .20

Launching (in California) of the Canadian satellite Alouette II, Nov. 28, 1965, as part of the Canadian-American program of space research.

La Salle, Map of 17th Century Canada, Ship, Canoe, Spyglass and Compass — A217

1966, Apr. 13   Engr.   Perf. 12
446 A217 5c blue green   .25 .20

Tercentenary of the arrival in Canada of Rene Robert Cavelier, Sieur de La Salle (1643-1687).

Traffic Signs — A218

1966, May 2
447 A218 5c black, blue & yel   .25 .20

Issued to publicize traffic safety.

House of Commons, Thames River and Canadian Delegates A219

1966, May 26
448 A219 5c brown   .25 .20

Centenary of the London Conf., Dec. 4, 1866, which resulted in the British North America Act.

Atomic Reactor, Heavy Water Atom Symbol and Microscope A220

1966, July 27   Engr.   Perf. 12
449 A220 5c deep ultra   .25 .20

Peaceful uses of atomic power. The design shows a stylized view of the Douglas Point Nuclear Power Station, Lake Huron, Ontario.

Parliamentary Library, Ottawa — A221

Praying Hands, by Albrecht Dürer — A222

1966, Sept. 8   Engr.   Perf. 12
450 A221 5c plum   .25 .20

12th General Conf. of the Commonwealth Parliamentary Assoc., Ottawa, Sept. 8-Oct. 5.

1966, Oct. 12   Engr.   Perf. 12
451 A222 3c carmine rose   .20 .20
  a. Pane of 25   4.00 4.00
  p. Tagged   .20 .20
  q. As "a," tagged   5.00 5.00
452 A222 5c orange   .20 .20
  p. Tagged   .45 .25

Christmas. Panes of 25 are imperf. on four sides.

Canadian Flag over Globe and Centennial Emblem — A223

1967, Jan. 11   Engr.   Perf. 12
453 A223 5c blue & red   .25 .20
  p. Tagged   .35 .30

Canada's centenary as a nation.

Northern Lights and Dog Team — A224

"Alaska Highway" by A. Y. Jackson A225

Two types of 6c black:

Type I   Type II

Designs: 2c, Totem pole (Pacific Area). 3c, Combine and oil rig (Prairie Region). 4c, Ship in lock (Central Canada). 5c, Lobster traps and boat (Atlantic Provinces). 6c, Transportation means. 10c, "The Jack Pine" by Tom Thomson. 15c, "Bylot Island" by Lawren Harris. 20c, "The Ferry, Quebec" by James Wilson Morrice. 25c, "The Solemn Land" by J. E. H. MacDonald. 50c, "Summer's Stores" by John Ensor (grain elevators). $1, Oilfield near Edmonton, by H. G. Glyde.

1967-72   Engr.   Perf. 12
454 A224 1c brown   .20 .20
  a. Booklet pane of 5 + label   .45 .45
  b. Bklt. pane, 1 #454d, 4 #459 + label, perf. 10 ('68)   3.00 2.50
  c. Bklt. pane, 5 #454d + 5 #457d, perf. 10 ('68)   1.75 1.75
  d. Perf. 10 ('68)   .25 .20
  e. Perf. 12½x12 ('71)   .20 .20
  f. Printed on gummed side   925.00
455 A224 2c green   .20 .20
  a. Bklt. pane, 4 #455, 4 #456 with gutter btwn. ('70) 1.60 1.60
456 A224 3c dull purple   .20 .20
  a. Perf. 12½x12 ('71)   .75 .30
457 A224 4c car rose   .20 .20
  a. Booklet pane of 5 + label   1.10 1.10
  b. Pane of 25 (5x5)   25.00 22.50
  c. Booklet pane of 25 + 2 labels, perf. 10 ('68)   8.00 7.50
  d. Perf. 10   .50 .20
458 A224 5c blue   .20 .20
  a. Booklet pane of 5 + label   5.25 5.25
  b. Pane of 20   35.00 32.50
  c. Bklt. pane of 20, perf. 10 ('68)   8.00 8.00
  d. Perf. 10   .60 .20
459 A224 6c org, perf. 10   .25 .20
  a. Bklt. pane of 25 + 2 labels, perf. 10 ('68)   8.00 8.00
  b. Perf. 12½x12 ('69)   .25 .20
460 A224 6c black (I), perf. 12½x12   .20 .20
  a. Bklt. pane of 25 + 2 labels (I), perf. 10 ('70)   12.00 8.00
  b. As "a," perf. 12½x12 16.00 13.00
  c. Type II, perf. 12½x12 .40 .20
  d. As "c," booklet pane of 4   3.50 3.25
  e. As "d," perf. 10 ('70)   11.00 6.50
  f. Type II, perf. 12 ('72)   .40 .20
  g. Type I, perf. 10   1.60 .30
  h. Type II, perf. 10   2.00 .65
  i. As "f," printed on gummed side   20.00
461 A225 8c violet brown   .25 .20
462 A225 10c olive green   .25 .20
463 A225 15c dull purple   .50 .20
464 A225 20c dark blue   .55 .20
465 A225 25c slate green   1.60 .20

465A A225 50c brown org   3.75 .20
465B A225 $1 carmine rose   6.00 .75
   Nos. 454-465B (14)   14.35 3.35

Nos. 454d, 454e, 456a, 457d, 458d, 460c, 460g and 460h are from booklet panes. Issued: #459, 11/1/68; #460, 1/7/70; others, 2/8/67.
  See Nos. 543-544, 549-550.

Tagged
454p A224 1c brown   .25 .20
  ep. Perf. 12½x12 ('71)   .30 .20
455p A224 2c green   .25 .20
456p A224 3c dull purple   .20 .20
457p A224 4c car rose   .60 .20
458p A224 5c blue   .60 .20
  bp. Pane of 20   60.00 50.00
459p A224 6c org, perf. 10   .60 .20
  bp. Perf. 12½x12 ('69)   .75 .30
460p A224 6c black (I), perf. 12½x12 .35 .20
  cp. Type II ('70)   .45 .50
  fp. As "cp," perf. 12 ('72)   .25 .20
462p A225 10c olive green   .90 .35
463p A225 15c dull purple   .90 .35
464p A225 20c dark blue   1.60 .55
465p A225 25c slate green   7.00 2.00
   Nos. 454p-465p (11)   13.25 4.65

Nos. 454ep and 460cp are from booklet panes Nos. 544q-544s. Issued: 1c-5c, 2/8/67; #459p, 11/1/68; #460p, 1/7/70; others, 12/9/69.
  See note after No. 343.

Coil Stamps
1967-70   Perf. 9½ Horiz.
466 A224 3c dull purple   3.75 .85
467 A224 4c carmine rose   1.10 .50
468 A224 5c blue   2.25 .65

Perf. 10 Horiz.
468A A224 6c orange   .50 .20
  c. Imperf., pair   325.00
468B A224 6c black, die II   .45 .20
  d. Imperf., pair   2,750.
   Nos. 466-468B (5)   8.05 2.40

Horizontal pairs or blocks of Nos. 468A and 468B may be found with a fine vertical score line between the stamps. These sell for little more than vertical pairs or strips.
  Issued: #468A, 1/69; #468B, 8/70; others, 2/8/67.

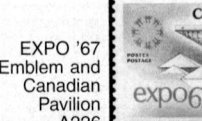

EXPO '67 Emblem and Canadian Pavilion A226

1967, Apr. 28   Engr.   Perf. 12
469 A226 5c blue & red   .25 .20

EXPO '67, Intl. Exhib., Montreal, Apr. 28-Oct. 27.

Symbolic Woman and Ballot — A227

1967, May 24   Litho.   Perf. 12
470 A227 5c black & rose lilac   .25 .20

50th anniversary of woman suffrage.

Elizabeth II — A228

1967, June 30   Engr.   Perf. 12
471 A228 5c deep org & purple   .25 .20

Centennial Year visit of Queen Elizabeth II and the Duke of Edinburgh.

Runner A229

1967, July 19   Engr.   Perf. 12
472 A229 5c red   .25 .20

Pan-American Games, Winnipeg, Manitoba, July 22-Aug. 7.

Globe and Flash A230

1967, Aug. 31   Unwmk.
473 A230 5c deep ultra   .25 .20

50th anniv. of the Canadian Press, news gathering and distributing service.

Georges Philias Vanier A231

Engr. & Litho.   Perf. 12
474 A231 5c black   .25 .20

Georges Philias Vanier (1888-1967), Governor General of Canada, 1959-1967.

Toronto in 1967 and Citizens of 1867 — A232

1967, Sept. 28   Engr.
475 A232 5c sl grn & sal pink   .25 .20

Centenary of Toronto as capital of Ontario.

Singing Children and Peace Tower, Ottawa — A233

1967, Oct. 11   Engr.   Perf. 12
476 A233 3c carmine   .20 .20
  a. Pane of 25   4.00 4.00
  p. Tagged   .20 .20
  q. As "a" tagged   4.50 4.50
477 A233 5c green   .20 .20
  p. Tagged   .30 .20

Christmas. Panes of 25 are imperf. on four sides.

Gray Jays — A234

1968, Feb. 15   Litho.
478 A234 5c green, blk & red   .45 .20

Weather Map and Composite of Instruments A235

1968, Mar. 13   **Perf. 11**
479 A235 5c dk & lt blue, yel & red   .25 .20
   200th anniv. of Canada's first long-term fixed point weather observations at Fort Prince of Wales, Churchill, by William Wales and Joseph Dymond.

Male Narwhal A236

1968, Apr. 10   Litho.   Perf. 11
480 A236 5c multicolored   .30 .20

Weighing Rain Gauge, World Map and Maple Leaf A237

1968, May 8   Litho.   Perf. 11
481 A237 5c multicolored   .25 .20
   Intl. Hydrological Decade, 1965-74.

The Nonsuch A238

Photo. & Engr.
1968, June 5   Perf. 10
482 A238 5c dk blue & multi   .25 .20
   300th anniv. of the voyage of the Nonsuch which opened the way to Canada's West through the fur trade.

Contemporary and Indian Lacrosse Players — A239

1968, July 3   Photo. & Engr.
483 A239 5c yel, black & red   .25 .20

George Brown, "Globe" Front Page and Legislature, Prince Edward Island A240

1968, Aug. 21   Perf. 10
484 A240 5c multicolored   .25 .20
   George Brown (1818-1880), founder of Toronto "Globe" and political leader.

Henri Bourassa and Newspaper Page — A241

Canadian Memorial, Near Vimy, France — A242

Litho. & Engr.
1968, Sept. 4   Perf. 12
485 A241 5c ver, buff & black   .25 .20
   Henri Bourassa (1868-1952), journalist and statesman.

1968, Oct. 15   Engr.   Perf. 12
486 A242 15c slate   2.00 1.25
   50th anniv. of the Armistice which ended WWI. The stamp shows "The Defenders and the Breaking of the Sword," a detail from the memorial designed by W. S. Allward.

John McCrae and "Flanders Fields" A243

1968, Oct. 15   Litho. & Engr.
487 A243 5c multicolored   .25 .20
   50th death anniv. of Lt. Col. John McCrae (1872-1918), author of "In Flanders Fields."

Eskimo Family, Carving — A244

1968, Nov.   Photo.   Perf. 12
   Eskimo soapstone carving: 6c, Mother and infant, by Munamee of Cape Dorset.

488 A244 5c brt blue & black   .20 .20
   a. Booklet pane of 10   3.25 3.25
   p. Tagged   .20 .20
   q. As "a," tagged   4.00 4.00
489 A244 6c dp bister & black   .20 .20
   p. Tagged   .25 .20

Christmas. Issued: 5c, Nov. 1; 6c, Nov. 15.

Curling A245

Photo. & Engr.
1969, Jan. 15   Perf. 10
490 A245 6c black, brt blue & car   .20 .20

Vincent Massey — A246

Litho. & Engr.
1969, Feb. 20   Perf. 12
491 A246 6c yel olive & dk brn   .25 .20
   Vincent Massey (1887-1967), 1st Canadian-born Gov. General of Canada, 1952-59.

Return from the Harvest Field, by Aurele de Foy Suzor-Cote A247

1969, Mar. 14   Photo.
492 A247 50c multicolored   3.50 2.50
   Aurele de Foy Suzor-Cote (1869-1937), painter.

Globe and Tools of Various Trades A248

1969, May 21   Engr.   Perf. 12x12½
493 A248 6c dk olive green   .25 .20
   50th anniv. of the ILO.

Vickers Vimy, 1919, and Map of the Atlantic A249

1969, June 13   Photo. and Engr.
494 A249 15c red brn, yel grn &
           lt ultra   1.75 1.50
   50th anniv. of the first non-stop Atlantic flight from Newfoundland to Ireland of Capt. John Alcock and Lt. Arthur Whitten Brown.

Sir William Osler — A250

1969, June 23   Perf. 12½x12
495 A250 6c dk blue & lt red brn   .25 .20
   Osler (1849-1919), physician, professor of physiology and pathology in Canada, US and England.

Ipswich Sparrow A251

1969, July 23   Litho.   Perf. 12
   Birds: 6c, White-throated sparrows, vert. 25c, Hermit thrush.

496 A251 6c multicolored   .35 .20
497 A251 10c ultra & multi   .70 .40
498 A251 25c black & multi   1.75 1.50
   Nos. 496-498 (3)   2.80 2.10

Map of Prince Edward Island A252

Photo. & Engr.
1969, Aug. 15   Perf. 12x12½
499 A252 6c ultra, org brn & black   .25 .20
   Bicentenary of Charlottetown as capital of Prince Edward Island.

Flags of Summer and Winter Canada Games — A253

Litho. & Engr.
1969, Aug. 15   Perf. 12
500 A253 6c ultra, brt green & red   .25 .20
   1st Canada Summer Games, Halifax and Dartmouth, N.S., Aug. 16-24.

Sir Isaac Brock and Memorial Queenston Heights — A254

1969, Sept. 12   Litho. and Engr.
501 A254 6c yel brown, brn & pale
           sal   .25 .20
   Major General Sir Isaac Brock (1769-1812), administrator of Upper Canada and leader in the war of 1812.

Children of Various Races — A255

1969, Oct. 8   Litho.   Perf. 12
502 A255 5c blue & mul-
           ti   .20 .20
   a. Booklet pane of 10   3.00 3.00
   p. Tagged   .25 .20
   q. As "a" tagged   4.00
503 A255 6c red & multi   .20 .20
   a. Black (inscriptions &
        frame line) omitted   2,250. 1,750.
   p. Tagged   .25 .20

Christmas.

Stephen Leacock, Comedy Mask and Mariposa View A256

Photo. & Engr.
1969, Nov. 12   Perf. 12x12½
504 A256 6c multicolored   .25 .20
   Stephen Butler Leacock (1869-1944), humorist, historian and economist.

Manitoba, Crossroads of Canada A257

1970, Jan. 27   Litho.   Perf. 12
505 A257 6c violet blue & multi   .25 .20
   p. Tagged   .35 .20
   Centenary of the province of Manitoba.

Enchanted Owl, by Kenojuak — A258

1970, Jan. 27 Engr. Perf. 12
506 A258 6c dark red & black .25 .20
Centenary of Nortwest Territories.

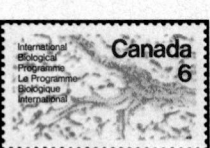

Microscopic View of Inside of Leaf A259

1970, Feb. 18 Photo. & Engr.
507 A259 6c green, lt org & blue .25 .20
Canada's participation in the Intl. Biological Program, 1967-1972.

Emblems of EXPO '67 and '70 — A260

EXPO '70 Emblem and Dogwood, British Columbia A261

Designs: No. 510, EXPO '70 emblem and white garden lily, Quebec. No. 511, EXPO '70 emblem and white trillium, Ontario.

1970, Mar. 18 Litho. Perf. 12
508	A260	25c red emblem		2.00	2.00
p.		Tagged		2.25	2.25
509	A261	25c violet emblem		2.00	2.00
p.		Tagged		2.25	2.25
510	A261	25c green emblem		2.00	2.00
p.		Tagged		2.25	2.25
511	A261	25c blue emblem		2.00	2.00
p.		Tagged		2.25	2.25
a.		Block of 4, #508-511		8.00	8.00
b.		As "a," tagged		10.00	10.00
		Nos. 508-511 (4)		8.00	8.00

EXPO '70 Intl. Exhibition, Osaka, Japan, Mar. 15-Sept. 13. Nos. 508-511 printed se-tenant in sheets of 50 (5x10), with various combinations possible.

Henry Kelsey A262

Photo. & Engr.
1970, Apr. 15 Perf. 12x12½
512 A262 6c multicolored .25 .20
300th birth anniv. of Henry Kelsey, explorer of Canada's western plains.

"A Divided World, with Energy Focused on Unification..." — A263

1970, May 13 Litho. Perf. 11
513	A263	10c blue		.70	.55
p.		Tagged		.85	.85
514	A263	15c lilac & dk red		1.10	.70
p.		Tagged		1.50	1.50

25th anniversary of the United Nations.

Louis Riel A264

Mackenzie Rock, Dean Channel A265

1970, June 19 Photo. Perf. 12½x12
515 A264 6c red & brt blue .25 .20
Louis Riel (1844-1885), Metis leader who became president of the Council of Assiniboin in 1870.

1970, June 25 Engr. Perf. 12
516 A265 6c brown .25 .20
Sir Alexander Mackenzie (1764-1820), Scottish explorer who in 1793 completed the first crossing of the North American continent north of Mexico.

Sir Oliver Mowat and Parliament, Ottawa A266

Photo. & Engr.
1970, Aug. 12 Perf. 12x12½
517 A266 6c red & black .25 .20
Sir Oliver Mowat (1820-1903), government leader and a Father of Confederation.

Isle of Spruce, by Arthur Lismer A267

1970, Sept. 18 Litho. Perf. 11
518 A267 6c multicolored .25 .20
50th anniv. of "The Group of Seven," Canadian landscape artists.

Santa Claus — A268

Christ Child — A269

Child in the Manger and Star-studded Sky — A270

Christmas: Designs by Canadian School Children.

1970, Oct. 7 Litho. Perf. 12
519	A268	5c	Santa Claus	.30	.20
520	A268	5c	Horse-drawn Sleigh	.30	.20
521	A268	5c	Nativity	.30	.20
522	A268	5c	Children Skiing	.30	.20
523	A268	5c	Snowmen and Christmas Tree	.30	.20
a.			Strip of 5, #519-523	2.75	2.25

524	A269	6c	Christ Child	.40	.20
525	A269	6c	Christmas Tree and Children	.40	.20
526	A269	6c	Toy Store	.40	.20
527	A269	6c	Santa Claus	.40	.20
528	A269	6c	Church	.40	.20
a.			Strip of 5, #524-528	3.25	2.50
529	A270	10c	Christ Child	.40	.35
530	A270	15c	Snowmobile and Trees	.90	.90
			Nos. 519-530 (12)	4.80	3.25

Tagged
519p	A268	5c multicolored		.35	.25
520p	A268	5c multicolored		.35	.25
521p	A268	5c multicolored		.35	.25
522p	A268	5c multicolored		.35	.25
523p	A268	5c multicolored		.35	.25
ap.		Strip of 5, #519p-523p		3.25	2.75
524p	A269	6c multicolored		.40	.25
525p	A269	6c multicolored		.40	.25
526p	A269	6c multicolored		.40	.25
527p	A269	6c multicolored		.40	.25
528p	A269	6c multicolored		.40	.25
ap.		Strip of 5, #524p-528p		4.50	3.00
529p	A270	10c multicolored		.50	.50
530p	A270	15c multicolored		1.10	1.10
		Nos. 519p-530p (12)		5.35	4.10

Christmas.
The sheets of 100 of both 5c and 6c contain all 5 designs, generally alternating, and arranged to permit vertical and horizontal pairs of each design in the two center vertical and horizontal rows. The center block of 4 is entirely of No. 522 (5c) and 525 (6c). The sheet may also be broken to provide 20 strips of 5, each stamp of different design.

Sir Donald Alexander Smith — A271

1970, Nov. 4 Litho. Perf. 12
531 A271 6c dk grn, yel & black .25 .20
Smith (1820-1914), railroad builder and Canadian High Commissioner, 1896-1914.

Big Raven, by Emily Carr — A272

1971, Feb. 12 Litho. Perf. 12
532 A272 6c multicolored .25 .20
Emily Carr (1871-1945), painter and writer.

Laboratory Equipment Used for Insulin Discovery — A273

1971, Mar. 3 Litho. Perf. 11
533 A273 6c multicolored .25 .20
Discovery of insulin by Dr. Frederick G. Banting and Dr. Charles H. Best, 50th anniversary.

A274

1971, Mar. 24 Litho. Perf. 11
534 A274 6c red, org & black .25 .20
Sir Ernest Rutherford (1871-1937), physicist, developer of theory of spontaneous disintegration of the atom.

Spring, Winged Maple Seed A275

Louis Joseph Papineau A276

1971 Litho. Perf. 11
535	A275	6c shown		.25	.20
a.		Imperf., pair		950.00	
536	A275	6c Summer		.25	.20
537	A275	7c Autumn		.25	.20
538	A275	7c Winter		.25	.20
		Nos. 535-538 (4)		1.00	.80

Issue dates: No. 535, Apr. 14; No. 536, June 16; No. 537, Sept. 3; No. 538, Nov. 19.

Litho. & Engr.
1971, May 7 Perf. 12½x12
539 A276 6c multicolored .25 .20
Louis Joseph Papineau (1786-1871), member of Legislative Assembly and leader of French Canadian Patriote party.

Map of Copper Mine River Basin A277

1971, May 7 Perf. 12x12½
540 A277 6c buff, red & brown .25 .20
Bicentenary of Samuel Hearne's expedition to the Copper Mine River.

Maple Leaves A278

1971, June 1
541 A278 15c blk, red org & yel 1.60 1.10
p. Tagged 2.25 2.25
Inauguration of new transmitters for Radio Canada International.

Computer Tape and Reels — A279

1971, June 1
542 A279 6c black, ultra & red .25 .20
Centenary of measured progress through census.

Migrating Phosphor
Canada's "Ottawa/General" tagging of engraved stamps printed March-October, 1972, used a phosphor which migrates onto or through other stamps, booklet covers and album pages. It fluoresces yellow under ultraviolet light.
This bleeding, contaminating "OP4" phosphor can be somewhat contained in mounts or envelopes of acetate, glassine or polyethylene, but it may leak or penetrate.
The migrating phosphor is found on all copies of Nos. 560p-561p, and on some of Nos. 544p, 544q, 544r, 544s, 562p-565p and 594-598.

Transportation Means — A280

Design: 8c, Library of Parliament.

1971-72   Engr.   Perf. 12½x12
543 A280 7c slate green   .35   .20
  a. Booklet pane of 5 + label
    (#454e, #456a + 3#543)   4.25 2.25
  b. Booklet pane of 20 (4 #454e, 4
    #456a, 12 #543)   8.00 7.00
  p. Tagged   .60   .25
544 A280 8c slate   .25   .20
  a. Booklet pane of 6 (3 #454e, 1
    #460e, 2 #544)   1.75   .80
  b. Booklet pane of 18 (6 #454e, 1
    #460e, 11 #544)   5.25 3.50
  c. Booklet pane of 10 (4 #454e, 1
    #460e, 5 #544 ('72)   2.25 2.25
  p. Tagged   .35   .20
  q. As "a," tagged   2.00 2.00
  r. As "b," tagged   4.00 4.00
  s. As "c," tagged   2.00 2.00

Coil Stamps

1971   *Perf. 10 Horiz.*
549 A280 7c slate green   .40   .20
  a. Imperf., pair   1,200.
550 A280 8c slate   .35   .20
  a. Imperf., pair   600.00
  p. Tagged   .50   .20
  q. As "p," imperf, pair   1,100.

  See note below No. 468B.
  Issued: 7c, 6/30/71; 8c, 12/30/71.

Abstract
"BC"
A282

1971, July 20   Litho.   Perf. 12
552 A282 7c multicolored   .25   .20
  Centenary of British Columbia's entry into
Canadian Confederation.

Indian Encampment on Lake Huron,
by Kane — A283

1971, Aug. 11   Perf. 12½
553 A283 7c multicolored   .40   .20
  Paul Kane (1810-1871), painter.

Snowflake   Pierre Laporte
A284   A285

1971, Oct. 6   Engr.   Perf. 12
Size: 24x30mm
554 A284 6c dark blue   .20   .20
  p. Tagged   .20   .20
  a. All color omitted (from foldover)   —
  b. Printed on gummed side (from
    foldover)   —
555 A284 7c bright green   .20   .20
  p. Tagged   .30   .20

Litho. and Engr.
Size: 30x30mm
556 A284 10c dp car & silver   .35   .30
  p. Tagged   .45   .30
557 A284 15c lt ultra, dp car &
    silver   .70   .65
  p. Tagged   .90   .75
    Nos. 554-557 (4)   1.45 1.35
    Christmas.

1971, Oct. 20   Engr.   Perf. 12½x12
558 A285 7c black   .25   .20
  Pierre Laporte (1921-1970), Minister of
Labor, kidnapped and killed.

Figure
Skating — A286

1972, Mar. 1   Litho.   Perf. 12
559 A286 8c deep red lilac   .25   .20
  World Figure Skating Championships, Calgary, Alberta, Mar. 6-12.

"Your Heart
is your
Health"
A287

1972, Apr. 7   Engr.   Perf. 12x12½
560 A287 8c red   .30   .20
  p. Tagged   .55   .35
  World Health Day, Apr. 7.

Frontenac,
by Philippe
Hébert and
Fort Saint
Louis,
Quebec
A288

Photo. and Engr.
1972, May 17   Perf. 12x12½
561 A288 8c red brown & multi   .25   .20
  p. Tagged   .65   .55
  Tercentenary of the appointment of Louis de
Buade, Count of Frontenac and Palluau (1622-
1698), as Governor of New France.

Indians of Canada

Buffalo
Chase, by
George Catlin
A289

Thunderbird,
Assiniboin
Pattern — A290

  In Nos. 562-581, the first two and last two
stamps of each annual set are printed checkerwise in same sheet of 50.

1972   Litho.   Perf. 12x12½
562 A289 8c shown   .40   .20
  p. Tagged   .55   .30
563 A289 8c Plains Indian arti-
    facts   .40   .20
  p. Tagged   .55   .30
  a. Pair, #562-563   .80   .50
  b. As "a," tagged   1.10   .75

Perf. 12½x12
Photo. & Engr.
564 A290 8c shown   .40   .20
  p. Tagged   .55   .30
565 A290 8c Ceremonial sun
    dance costume   .40   .20
  p. Tagged   .55   .30
  a. Pair, #564-565   .80   .50
  b. As "a," tagged   1.10   .75
  Plains Indians of Canada.
  Issued: #562-563, July 6; #564-565, Oct. 4.

Tagged (Nos. 566-581)
1973   Litho.   Perf. 12x12½
566 A289 8c Algonkian artifacts   .35   .20
567 A289 8c "Micmac Indians"   .35   .20
  a. Pair, #566-567   .70   .50

Perf. 12½x12
Photo. & Engr.
568 A290 8c Thunderbird and belt   .35   .20
569 A290 8c Algonkian man and
    woman   .35   .20
  a. Pair, #568-569   .70   .50
  Algonkian-speaking Indians of Canada
(Malecite, Micmac, Montagnais, Algonquin
and Ojibwa).
  Issued: #566-567, 2/21; #568-569, 11/28.

1974   Litho.   Perf. 12x12½
570 A289 8c Nootka Sound, house,
    inside   .35   .20
571 A289 8c Artifacts   .35   .20
  a. Pair, #570-571   .70   .50

Perf. 12½x12
Photo. & Engr.
572 A290 8c Chief wearing Chilkat
    blanket   .35   .20
573 A290 8c Thunderbird from
    Kwakiutl house   .35   .20
  a. Pair, #572-573   .70   .50
  Pacific Coast Indians of Canada (Haida,
Salish, Tsimshian, Chilkat and Kwakiutl).
  Issued: #570-571, 1/16; #572-573, 2/22.

1975, Apr. 4   Litho.   Perf. 13½
574 A289 8c Montagnais-Nas-
    kapi artifacts   .25   .20
575 A289 8c Dance of the
    Kutcha-Kutchin   .25   .20
  a. Pair, #574-575   .50   .50
  b. As "a," imperf. between   900.00

Perf. 12½
576 A290 8c Kutchin ceremonial
    costume   .25   .20

Litho. and Embossed
577 A290 8c Ojibwa thunderbird
    and Naskapi pat-
    tern   .25   .20
  a. Pair, #576-577   .50   .50
    Subarctic Indians.

1976, Sept. 17   Litho.   Perf. 13½
578 A289 10c Cornhusk mask,
    artifacts   .25   .20
579 A289 10c Iroquoian Encamp-
    ment, by George
    Heriot   .25   .20
  a. Pair, #578-579   .50   .50

Perf. 12½
Litho. & Embossed
580 A290 10c Iroquoian thunder-
    bird   .25   .20

Litho.
581 A290 10c Iroquoian man,
    woman   .25   .20
  a. Pair, #580-581   .50   .50
    Nos. 562-581 (20)   6.40 4.00
  Iroquois (Mohawk, Cayuga, Seneca,
Oneida, Onondaga and Tuscarora).

Geological
Fault — A291

1972, Aug. 2   Perf. 12
582 A291 15c shown   1.80 1.60
  p. Tagged   2.75 2.75
583 A291 15c Bird's eye view
    of town   1.80 1.60
  p. Tagged   2.75 2.75
584 A291 15c Aerial map pho-
    tography   1.80 1.60
  p. Tagged   2.75 2.75
585 A291 15c Contour lines   1.80 1.60
  p. Tagged   2.75 2.75
  a. Block of 4, #582-585   7.50 7.50
  b. As "a," tagged   11.00 11.00
    Nos. 582-585 (4)   7.20 6.40
  Earth sciences: 24th Intl. Geological Cong.
(#582); 22nd Intl. Geographical Cong. (#583);
12th Cong. of Intl. Soc. of Photogrammetry
(#584); 6th Cong. of Intl. Cartographic Assoc.
(#585).

Sir John A.   Elizabeth II
Macdonald   A292a
A292

Forest, Central
Canada — A293

Vancouver, B.C. — A294

  Designs: 2c, Sir Wilfrid Laurier. 3c, Sir Robert L. Borden. 4c, William Lyon Mackenzie
King. 5c, Richard Bedford Bennett. 6c, Lester
B. Pearson. 7c, Louis St. Laurent. 10c, Mountain sheep, Western Canada. 20c, Grain
fields, Prairie. 25c, Polar bears, North. 50c,
Seashore. $2, Quebec.

1972-76   Engr.   Perf. 12x12½
Tagged
586 A292 1c orange ('73)   .20   .20
  a. Booklet pane, 3 #586, 1
    #591, 2 #593 ('74)   1.20 1.00
  b. Bklt. pane, 6 #586, 1
    #591, 11 #593 ('74)   1.60 1.60
  c. Bklt. pane, 2 #586, 4
    #587, 4 #593Ac ('76)   1.20 1.00
  d. Printed on gummed side   600.00
587 A292 2c green ('73)   .20   .20
588 A292 3c brown ('73)   .20   .20
589 A292 4c black ('73)   .20   .20
590 A292 5c lilac ('73)   .20   .20
591 A292 6c dk red ('73)   .20   .20
  a. Printed on gummed side   200.00
592 A292 7c dk brn ('74)   .20   .20
593 A292a 8c ultra ('73)   .20   .20
  b. Perf. 13x13½ ('76)   .65   .20

Perf. 13x13½
593A A292a 10c dk car ('76)   .20   .20
  c. Perf. 12x12½   .35   .20

Perf. 12½x12
Photo. & Engr.
594 A293 10c multicolored   .30   .20
595 A293 15c multicolored   .45   .20
596 A293 20c multicolored   .45   .20
597 A293 25c multicolored   .50   .20
598 A293 50c multicolored   1.10   .20
599 A294 $1 multi ('73)   2.50   .50

Perf. 11
Litho. & Engraved
600 A294 $1 multicolored   5.75 1.60
601 A294 $2 multicolored   4.75 2.25
    Nos. 586-601 (17)   17.60 7.15

  No. 599 has engraved shading added in
some areas.
  Plates 1 and 2 of the scenic 10c differ in
impression and colors. Plate 1 has distinct
crosshatching of "Canada" background. On
plate 2, released in 1974, this area appears
solidly inked.
  A 1976 printing of the 15c shows the blue
trees on the hillside as solid color, while the
1972 printing shows clear detail on the trees.
  A 1974 printing of the 50c has darker shading and a deeper tone for the dark blue areas
of the photogravure impression.
  Nos. 600 and 601 are untagged.

1976-77   Photo. & Engr.   Perf. 13½
594a A293 10c multicolored   .30   .20
595a A293 15c multicolored   .45   .20
596a A293 20c multicolored   .60   .20
597a A293 25c multicolored   .65   .20
598a A293 50c multicolored   1.75   .20
599a A294 $1 multi ('77)   2.50   .20
    Nos. 594a-599a (6)   6.25 1.30

Coil Stamps
1974-76   Engr.   Perf. 10 Vert.
604 A292a 8c ultramarine   .25   .20
  a. Imperf., horiz. pair   160.00
605 A292a 10c dk carmine
    ('76)   .35   .20
  a. Imperf., horiz. pair   175.00
  See note below No. 468B. No. 604 also
exists in vertical multiples without score line.

Candles — A295

Candles and Fruit A296

Christmas: 8c, Like 6c. 15c, Candles, 15th century prayer book, boxes and brass vase.

1972, Nov. 1   Litho.   Perf. 12½x12
606 A295 6c red & multi   .20 .20
 p. Tagged   .30 .25
607 A295 8c vio blue & multi   .20 .20
 p. Tagged   .35 .45

Perf. 11
608 A296 10c green & multi   .45 .35
 p. Tagged   .65 .55
609 A296 15c yel bister & multi   .65 .65
 p. Tagged   1.20 1.20
     Nos. 606-609 (4)   1.50 1.40

"The Blacksmith's Shop," by Krieghoff — A297

1972, Nov. 29   Litho.   Perf. 12½
610 A297 8c multicolored   .30 .20
 p. Tagged   .35 .20

Cornelius Krieghoff (1815-1872), painter.

Tagged
From No. 611 onward, all stamps are tagged unless otherwise noted.

Monsignor de Laval — A298

1973, Jan. 31   Litho.   Perf. 11
611 A298 8c silver, ultra & gold .20 .20

Francois-Xavier de Montmorency-Laval de Montigny (1623-1708), 1st Bishop of Quebec and founder of many educational institutions; one of the builders of New France.

Commissioner G. A. French and Map of 1874 Trek — A299

10c, Spectrograph. 15c, R.C.M.P. Musical Ride.

1973, Mar. 9   Litho.   Perf. 11
612 A299 8c dk brn, org & red   .20 .20
613 A299 10c dk blue & multi   .35 .30
614 A299 15c yel grn & multi   .75 .50
 a. Imperf., pair   500.00
     Nos. 612-614 (3)   1.30 1.00

Royal Canadian Mounted Police, cent. Imperfs of No. 614 with a double impression and examples with 15c printed on 10c are from printer's waste.

Jeanne Mance A300

1973, Apr. 18
615 A300 8c multicolored   .20 .20

Jeanne Mance (1606-1673), first secular nurse in North America and founder of first hospital, the Hôtel-Dieu in Montreal settlement.

Joseph Howe — A301

1973, May 16
616 A301 8c gold & black   .20 .20

Joseph Howe (1804-1873), journalist, poet and Lieutenant-Governor of Nova Scotia.

Mist Fantasy, by James MacDonald A302

1973, June 8   Perf. 12½
617 A302 15c multicolored   .55 .50

Centenary of the birth of James E. H. MacDonald (1873-1932), painter.

Oaks on Shore A303

Photo. & Engr.
1973, June 22   Perf. 12x12½
618 A303 8c orange & red brn   .20 .20

Centenary of Prince Edward Island's entry into Confederation.

Scottish Settlers and "Hector" A304

1973, July 20   Litho.   Perf. 12x12½
619 A304 8c multicolored   .20 .20

Bicentenary of arrival of Scottish settlers at Pictou, N.S.

Queen Elizabeth II — A305

1973, Aug. 2   Photo. and Engr.
620 A305 8c silver & multi   .20 .20
621 A305 15c gold & multi   .60 .55

Visit to Ottawa of Elizabeth II and the Duke of Edinburgh, July 31-Aug. 4, and meeting of Commonwealth Heads of Government, Ottawa, Aug. 2-10.

Nellie McClung — A306

1973, Aug. 29   Litho.   Perf. 10½x11
622 A306 8c multicolored   .20 .20

Nellie McClung (1873-1951), leader of women's suffrage movement, social reformer and writer.

Montreal Olympic Games — A307

1973, Sept. 20   Perf. 12x12½
Size: 26x44mm
623 A307 8c silver & multi   .20 .20
624 A307 15c gold & multi   .55 .45

21st Olympic Games, Montreal, 1976. See Nos. B1-B3.

Ice Skate — A308

Santa Claus — A309

1973, Nov. 7   Litho.   Perf. 12½x12
625 A308 6c shown   .20 .20
626 A308 8c Dove   .20 .20

Perf. 10½
627 A309 10c shown   .25 .25
628 A309 15c Shepherd and star   .55 .55
     Nos. 625-628 (4)   1.20 1.20
         Christmas.

Children Diving from Dock — A310

1974, Mar. 22   Engr.   Perf. 12
629 A310 8c shown   .40 .20
630 A310 8c Joggers   .40 .20
631 A310 8c Bicycling family   .40 .20
632 A310 8c Hikers   .40 .20
 a. Block of 4, #629-632   1.60 .85

"Keep Fit." 21st Summer Olympic Games, Montreal, 1976. When stamps are observed at an angle the Montreal Olympic Games' emblem can be seen.

Main St. and Portage Ave., Winnipeg, 1872 — A311

Litho. & Engr.
1974, May 3   Perf. 12x12½
633 A311 8c multicolored   .20 .20

Winnipeg's incorporation as a city, cent.

Postmaster A312

1974, June 11   Litho.   Perf. 13½x13
634 A312 8c shown   .35 .30
635 A312 8c Mail collector and truck .35 .30
636 A312 8c Mail handler   .35 .30
637 A312 8c Mail sorters   .35 .30
638 A312 8c Mailman   .35 .30
639 A312 8c Rural mail delivery   .35 .30
 a. Block of 6, #634-639   2.25 2.25

Centenary of letter carrier delivery service. Printed in sheets of 50 (5x10).

Agricultural Education A313

1974, July 12   Perf. 12½x12
640 A313 8c multicolored   .20 .20

Ontario Agricultural College centenary.

Pedestal, Gallows Frame and Contempra Telephones A314

1974, July 26   Perf. 12½
641 A314 8c multicolored   .20 .20
 a. Imperf., pair   1,600.

Centenary of the idea for the telephone by Alexander Graham Bell while visiting Brantford, Canada.

Bicycle Wheel and Cycling Emblem A315

Photo. & Engr.
1974, Aug. 7   Perf. 12x12½
642 A315 8c black, red & silver   .20 .20

World Cycling Championships, Montreal, Aug. 14-25.

Mennonite Settlers A316

1974, Aug. 28   Litho.   Perf. 12x12½
643 A316 8c multicolored   .20 .20

Centenary of arrival of Mennonite settlers in Manitoba.

Snowshoeing
A317

1974, Sept. 23   Engr.   Perf. 13½
644 A317 8c shown   .35 .20
645 A317 8c Skiing   .35 .20
646 A317 8c Skating   .35 .20
647 A317 8c Curling   .35 .20
  a.   Block of 4, #644-647   1.40 1.40
  b.   Block or strip of 4, printed
         on gummed side   3,000.

"Keep Fit." 1976 Winter Olympic Games. When the stamps are observed at an angle the Montreal Olympic Games' emblem can be seen.
Warning: No. 647b must show each design; blocks exist that contain 2 No. 645 but no example of No. 647.

Mercury with Winged Horses, UPU Emblem
A318

Photo. & Engr.
1974, Oct. 9   Perf. 12x12½
648 A318 8c violet, red & blue   .20 .20
649 A318 15c violet, red & blue   .85 .70

Centenary of Universal Postal Union.

Nativity, by Jean Paul Lemieux
A319

Skaters at Hull, by Henri Masson — A320

Christmas (Paintings): 10c, The Ice Cone, Montmorency Falls, by Robert C. Todd. 15c, Village in the Laurentian Mountains, by Clarence A. Gagnon.

1974, Nov. 1   Litho.   Perf. 13½
650 A319 6c multicolored   .20 .20
651 A320 8c multicolored   .20 .20
652 A319 10c multicolored   .35 .30
653 A319 15c multicolored   .65 .55
     Nos. 650-653 (4)   1.40 1.25

Marconi and St. John's, Newfoundland, from Signal Hill — A321

1974, Nov. 15   Perf. 13
654 A321 8c multicolored   .20 .20

Guglielmo Marconi (1874-1937), Italian electrical engineer and inventor.

Merritt and Welland Canal
A322

Litho. & Engr.
1974, Nov. 29   Perf. 13x13½
655 A322 8c multicolored   .20 .20

Sesquicentennial of the start of construction of the Welland Canal between Lakes Ontario and Erie, a project conceived and supervised by William Hamilton Merritt (1793-1862). Portrait by Robert Whale.

The Sprinter — A323

The Plunger — A324

Designs: Sculptures by Robert Tait McKenzie, M.D. (1867-1938), and Montreal Olympic Games' emblem.

Perf. 12½x12, 12x12½
1975, Mar. 14   Litho.; Embossed
656 A323 $1 multicolored   2.25 2.25
657 A324 $2 multicolored   4.50 3.50

21st Olympic Games, Montreal, July 17-Aug. 1, 1976.

A325

No. 658, Anne of Green Gables. No. 659, Maria Chapdelaine.

1975, May 15   Litho.   Perf. 13
658   8c blue & multi   .20 .20
659   8c brown & multi   .20 .20
  a.   A325 Pair, #658-659   .40 .30

Birth centenary of Lucy Maud Montgomery (1874-1942), writer and author of "Anne of Green Gables"; Louis Hémon (1880-1913), writer and author of "Maria Chapdelaine." Nos. 658-659 printed checkerwise.

Marguerite Bourgeoys
A327

Alphonse Desjardins
A328

1975, May 30   Litho.   Perf. 12½x12
660 A327 8c red & multi   .20 .20
661 A328 8c red & multi   .20 .20

Marguerite Bourgeoys (1620-1700), founder of the Congrégation de Notre-Dame, Montreal, first girls' school in New France; Alphonse

---

Desjardins (1854-1920), journalist, founder of first credit union in North America.

A329

No. 662, Samuel Dwight Chown (1853-1933), Methodist minister, leader of temperance movement, founder of United Church. No. 663, Dr. John Cook (1805-92), 1st Moderator of the United Presbyterian Church in Canada.
Nos. 662-663 printed checkerwise.

Photo. & Engr.
1975, May 30   Perf. 12x12½
662   8c dk brown, yel & buff   .20 .20
663   8c dk brown, yel & buff   .20 .20
  a.   A329 Pair, #662-663   .40 .40

Pole Vaulting — A331

Hurdling — A332

Design: 25c, Marathon running and Montreal Olympic Games' emblem.

1975, June 11   Litho.   Perf. 12x12½
664 A331 20c dk blue & multi   .55 .45
665 A331 25c maroon & multi   .65 .50
666 A332 50c green & multi   1.40 1.00
     Nos. 664-666 (3)   2.60 1.95

21st Olympic Games, Montreal, July 17-Aug. 1, 1976.

"Untamed" (Wild Horse Race)
A333

1975, July 3
667 A333 8c gray & multi   .20 .20

Centenary of the founding of Calgary.

Female Symbol
A334

"Justice," by Walter S. Allward
A335

Photo. & Engr.
1975, July 14   Perf. 13
668 A334 8c dp yel, gray & black   .20 .20

International Women's Year.

1975, Sept. 2   Litho.   Perf. 12½
669 A335 8c multicolored   .20 .20

Supreme Court of Canada, centenary.

"Wm. D. Lawrence"
A336

Photo. & Engr.
1975, Sept. 24   Perf. 13
670 A336 8c shown   .35 .30
671 A336 8c "Beaver"   .35 .30
672 A336 8c "Neptune" .35 .30
673 A336 8c "Quadra"   .35 .30
  a.   Block of 4, #670-673   1.40 1.40

Coastal ships.

Santa Claus — A337

Child — A338

Trees — A339

Designs by Canadian School Children: "What Christmas Means to Me."

1975, Oct. 22   Litho.   Perf. 13½
674 A337 6c shown   .20 .20
675 A337 6c Skater   .20 .20
  a.   Pair, #674-675   .40 .30
676 A338 8c shown   .20 .20
677 A338 8c Family and Christ-
              mas tree   .20 .20
  a.   Pair, #676-677   .40 .35
678 A338 10c Gift box   .25 .20
679 A339 15c shown   .45 .45
     Nos. 674-679 (6)   1.50 1.45

Christmas. Stamps of same denomination printed checkerwise.

Legion Emblem and Bugle
A340

Photo. & Engr.

1975, Nov. 10			Perf. 13	
680	A340	8c gray & multi	.20	.20

Royal Canadian Legion, 50th anniversary.

Olympic Torch Ignited by Satellite in Canada — A341

Communication Arts — A342

High-rise Tower, Notre Dame Church, Montreal, and Games' Emblem — A343

Snowflake, Winter Olympics' Emblem — A344

Montreal Olympic Games' Emblem and: 20c, Canadian athletes carrying Olympic flag. 25c, Women athletes receiving Olympic medals.

1976, June 18			Litho.	Perf. 13	
681	A341	8c black & multi		.20	.20
682	A341	20c black & multi		.60	.55
683	A341	25c black & multi		.80	.60
		Nos. 681-683 (3)		1.60	1.35

1976 Olympic Games ceremonies.

1976, Feb. 6		Photo.	Perf. 12x12½	

25c, Handicraft tools. 50c, Performing arts.

684	A342	20c gray & multi	1.10	.50
685	A342	25c ocher & multi	1.40	.65
686	A342	50c blue & multi	2.00	1.10
		Nos. 684-686 (3)	4.50	2.25

Olympic Fine Arts and Cultural Program.

Photo. & Engr.

1976, Mar. 12			Perf. 13

Design: $2, Olympic Stadium, Velodrome, flags and emblem.

687	A343	$1 silver & multi	3.50	2.50
688	A343	$2 gold & multi	5.50	4.50

Nos. 681-688 were issued in commemoration of, or in connection with the 21st Olympic Games, Montreal, July 17-Aug. 1. Nos. 687-688 were issued in panes of 8.

Photo. and Embossed

1976, Feb. 6			Perf. 12½	
689	A344	20c multicolored	.85	.65

12th Winter Olympic Games, Innsbruck, Austria, Feb. 4-15.

Flower Growing from City — A345

1976, May 12		Litho.	Perf. 12x12½	
690	A345	20c multicolored	.50	.45

Habitat, UN Conference on Human Settlements, Vancouver, May 31-June 11.

Franklin and Map of North America, 1776 A346

Litho. & Engr.

1976, June 1			Perf. 13	
691	A346	10c multicolored	.35	.20

American Bicentennial; Benjamin Franklin (1706-1790), deputy postmaster general for the colonies (1753-1774). See US No. 1690.

Royal Military College, Kingston, Ont., Cent. — A347

No. 692, Color Parade, Memorial Arch. No. 693, Wing Parade, Mackenzie Building.

1976, June 1		Litho.	Perf. 12	
692		8c red & multi	.20	.20
693		8c red & multi	.20	.20
a.	A347 Pair, #692-693		.40	.30
b.	As "a," imperf.		2,250.	
c.	Block of 4, imperf. horiz.		650.00	
d.	As "a," double impression		4,000.	

A few used singles exist of Nos. 692-693 with double impression. Very rare.

Archer in Wheelchair A349

1976, Aug. 3			Perf. 12x12½	
694	A349	20c green & multi	.60	.50

Olympiad for the Physically Disabled (25th Stoke Mandeville Games), Toronto, Aug. 3-11.

A350

No. 695, The Cremation of Sam McGee. No. 696, The Outlander.

1976, Aug. 17			Perf. 13½	
695		8c multicolored	.20	.20
696		8c multicolored	.20	.20
a.	A350 Pair, #695-696		.40	.30

Robert W. Service (1874-1958), author of poem "The Cremation of Sam McGee"; Germaine Guevremont, author of "Le Survenant" (The Outlander).

Nativity, St. Michael's, Toronto — A352

Stained-glass windows: 10c, Nativity, St. Jude, London, Ontario. 20c, Nativity, by Yvonne Williams.

1976, Nov. 3		Litho.	Perf. 13½	
697	A352	8c multicolored	.20	.20
698	A352	10c multicolored	.20	.20
699	A352	20c multicolored	.40	.40
	Nos. 697-699 (3)		.80	.80

Christmas.

Inland Vessels A353

Litho. & Engr.

1976, Nov. 19			Perf. 12	
700	A353	10c Northcote	.35	.30
701	A353	10c Passport	.35	.30
702	A353	10c Chicora	.35	.30
703	A353	10c Athabasca	.35	.30
a.	Block of 4, #700-703		1.40	1.25

Elizabeth II A354

Litho. and Typo.

1977, Feb. 4			Perf. 12½x12	
704	A354	25c silver & multi	.65	.50

25th anniv. of the reign of Elizabeth II.

Bottle Gentian A355

Elizabeth II A356

Parliament, Ottawa A357

Trembling Aspen A358

Main Street, Prairie Town — A359

Fundy National Park — A359a

Designs: 2c, Western columbine. 3c, Canada lily. 4c, Hepatica. 5c, Shooting star. 10c, Franklin's lady's-slipper. No. 712, Jewelweed. No. 715, Parliament, Ottawa. No. 716, Queen Elizabeth II. 20c, Douglas fir. 25c, Maple. 30c, Red oak. 35c, White pine. 60c, Street scene, Ontario City. 75c, Old houses, eastern City Street. 80c, Street leading to the sea, Eastern Maritime Provinces. $2 Kluane National Park.

Litho. & Engr.

1977-82			Perf. 12x12½	
705	A355	1c multicolored	.20	.20
a.	Printed on gummed side, precanceled		950.00	
707	A355	2c multicolored	.20	.20
a.	Printed on gummed side		950.00	
708	A355	3c multicolored	.20	.20
709	A355	4c multicolored	.20	.20
a.	Printed on gummed side		300.00	
710	A355	5c multicolored	.20	.20
711	A355	10c multicolored	.20	.20
a.	Perf. 13x13½ ('78)		.20	.20

Photo. & Engr.
Perf. 13x13½

712	A355	12c multi ('78)	.30	.20
713	A356	12c blue & multi	.25	.20
a.	Perf. 12x12½		.35	.20

Engraved
Perf. 13x13½

714	A357	12c blue	.25	.20
a.	Printed on gummed side		300.00	
715	A357	14c red ('78)	.30	.20
a.	Printed on gummed side		37.50	
b.	All color omitted		400.00	

Photo. & Engr.
Perf. 13x13½

716	A356	14c red & blk ('78)	.30	.20
a.	Perf. 12x12½ ('78)		.30	.20
b.	As "a," booklet pane of 25 + 2 labels ('78)		6.00	
c.	Red omitted		1,600.	

Perf. 13½

717	A358	15c multi	.40	.20
718	A358	20c multi	.40	.20
719	A358	25c multi	.50	.20
720	A358	30c multi ('78)	.60	.20
721	A358	35c multi ('79)	.70	.20
723	A359	50c multi ('78)	1.10	.20
723A	A359	50c multi, litho. & engr. ('78)	1.00	.20
b.	Brown (all inscriptions, etc.) omitted		2,250.	
723C	A359	60c multi, litho. ('82)	1.20	.20
724	A359	75c multi ('78)	1.50	.25
725	A359	80c multi ('78)	1.60	.35

Lithographed and Engraved

726	A359a	$1 multi ('79)	2.00	.55
a.	Untagged		2.75	.65
b.	As "a," blk inscriptions omitted		750.00	600.00
727	A359a	$2 multi ('79)	4.00	1.40
a.	Silver inscriptions omitted		550.00	
	Nos. 705-727 (23)		17.60	6.35

On No. 715b, a strong embossed impression from the plate, without color, is evident.
On No. 723A license plate on yellow car reads "1978."
See Nos. 781-806, 934-937, 1084.

Coil Stamps

1977-78		Engr.	Perf. 10 Vert.	
729	A357	12c blue	.25	.20
a.	Imperf., pair		160.00	
730	A357	14c red ('78)	.30	.20
a.	Imperf., pair		175.00	

See note below No. 468B.

Eastern Cougar A360

1977, Mar. 30		Litho.	Perf. 12½	
732	A360	12c multicolored	.25	.20

Wildlife protection.

April in Algonquin Park, by Thomson — A361

#734, Autumn Birches, by Tom Thomson.

1977, May 26   *Perf. 12*
733 A361 12c black & multi   .25 .20
734 A361 12c ocher & multi   .25 .20
  a. Pair, #733-734   .50 .40
  Tom Thomson (1877-1917), landscape painter, birth centenary. Nos. 733-734 printed checkerwise.

Names of Governors General and Standard A362

1977, June 30   *Perf. 12½*
735 A362 12c vio blue & multi   .25 .20
  Honoring Canadian-born Governors General: Vincent Massey, Georges Philias Vanier, Daniel Roland Michener and Jules Léger.

Order of Canada A363

Litho. & Embossed
1977, June 30
736 A363 12c multicolored   .25 .20
  Order of Canada, 10th anniversary.

Peace Bridge, Canadian, US and UN Flags A364

1977, Aug. 4   *Litho.*
737 A364 12c blue & multi   .25 .20
  50th anniversary of the Peace Bridge, connecting Fort Erie, Ontario, with Buffalo, N.Y.

Joseph E. Bernier, CGS Arctic A365

Sandford Fleming, Railroad Bridge A366

1977, Sept. 16   *Engr.*   *Perf. 13*
738 A365 12c dark blue   .25 .20
739 A366 12c brown   .25 .20
  a. Pair, #738-739   .50 .40
  Joseph-Elzéar Bernier (1852-1934), explorer; Sandford Fleming (1827-1915), mapped route for Intercolonial Railway and designed Canada's first stamp. Nos. 738-739 printed checkerwise.

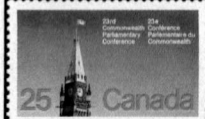

Peace Tower, Parliament, Ottawa A367

1977, Sept. 19   *Litho.*   *Perf. 12½*
740 A367 25c multicolored   .70 .60
  23rd Commonwealth Parliamentary Conference, Ottawa, Sept. 19-25.

Hunters Following Star — A368

Christmas: 12c, Angelic choir in northern light. 25c, Christ Child in Ring of Glory blessing chiefs from afar. Illustrations for Canada's first Christmas carol, written by Father Brébeuf, 1649.

1977, Oct. 26   *Perf. 13½*
741 A368 10c multicolored   .20 .20
  a. Horiz. pair, imperf between 1,250.
  b. Printed on gummed side   700.00
742 A368 12c multicolored   .20 .20
  a. Left margin block of 4, left
      vert. pair imperf, right
      pair part perf   1,900.
743 A368 25c multicolored   .50 .35
    Nos. 741-743 (3)   .90 .75

Pinky A369

  Designs: Canadian sailing ships.

Litho. and Engr.
1977, Nov. 18   *Perf. 12x12½*
744 A369 12c shown   .25 .20
745 A369 12c Tern schooner   .25 .20
746 A369 12c 5-masted schoon-
          er   .25 .20
747 A369 12c Mackinaw boat   .25 .20
  a. Block of 4, #744-747   1.00 .90
  b. As "a," #745, 747 imperf, #744,
      746 part perf   3,500.
    See Nos. 776-779.

Seal Hunter, Soapstone Sculpture A370

Disguised Caribou Hunter, Print — A371

  Inuit Art: #749, Spear fishing. #751, Walrus hunt. #749-751 are after stonecut prints.

1977, Nov. 18 *Litho.* *Perf. 12x12½*
748 A370 12c multicolored   .25 .20
749 A371 12c multicolored   .25 .20
  a. Pair, #748-749   .50 .40
  b. As "a," gray (inscriptions) omit-
      ted on No. 749   2,400.
750 A371 12c multicolored   .25 .20
751 A371 12c multicolored   .25 .20
  a. Pair, #750-751   .50 .40
    Nos. 748-751 (4)   1.00 .80
  Inuit hunting. Nos. 748-749 and Nos. 750-751 printed se-tenant checkerwise.

Peregrine Falcon A372

1978, Jan. 18
752 A372 12c multicolored   .25 .20
  Endangered wildlife.

Canada No. 3, 1851 — A373

1978   **Photo. & Engr.**   *Perf. 13½*
753 A373 12c shown   .25 .20
754 A373 14c No. 7   .30 .20
755 A373 30c No. 8   .60 .30

---

756 A373 $1.25 No. 2   2.50 1.00
  a. Souvenir sheet of 3   3.50
    Nos. 753-756 (4)   3.65 1.70
  CAPEX '78, Canadian Intl. Phil. Exhib., Toronto, June 9-18 (cent. of Canada's admission to UPU).
  No. 756a contains one each of Nos. 754-756 ($1.25 untagged). Value of No. 756 untagged, $2.75.
  Issue dates: 12c, Jan. 18; others, June 10.

Games' Emblem A374

Stadium A375

  Design: 30c, Badminton.

1978, Mar. 31 *Litho.*   *Perf. 12½*
757 A374 14c silver & multi   .30 .20
758 A374 30c silver & multi   .60 .45

1978, Aug. 3
#760, Running. #761, Alberta Legislature building, Edmonton. #762, Lawn bowling.
759 A375 14c silver & multi   .30 .20
760 A375 14c silver & multi   .30 .20
  a. Pair, #759-760   .60 .40
761 A375 30c silver & multi   .60 .50
762 A375 30c silver & multi   .60 .50
  a. Pair, #761-762   1.20 1.10
    Nos. 759-762 (4)   1.80 1.40
  Nos. 757-762 commemorate 11th Commonwealth Games, Edmonton, Aug. 3-12. #760a, 762a printed checkerwise.

A376

  No. 763, Capt. Cook, by Nathaniel Dance. No. 764, Nootka Sound, by John Webber.

1978, Apr. 26   *Perf. 13*
763   14c multicolored   .30 .20
764   14c multicolored   .30 .20
  a. A376 Pair, #763-764   .60 .40
  Capt. James Cook (1728-1779), explorer of Canada's East and West Coasts and bicentenary of his anchorage near Anchorage, June 1, 1778. Nos. 763-764 printed checkerwise.

Silver Mine, Cobalt Lake A378

Stripmining, Athabasca Tar Sands A379

1978, May 19   *Perf. 12½*
765 A378 14c multicolored   .30 .20
766 A379 14c multicolored   .30 .20
  a. Pair, #765-766   .60 .40
  Development of national resources. Nos. 765-766 printed checkerwise.

Prince's Gate A380

1978, Aug. 16
767 A380 14c multicolored   .30 .20
  Canadian National Exhibition, centenary.

Mère d'Youville and Miracle of Food — A381

1978, Sept. 21   *Perf. 13x13½*
768 A381 14c multicolored   .30 .20
  Marguerite d'Youville (1701-1771), founder of the Gray Nuns, beatified 1959.

Woman Walking, by Pitseolak A382

Migration, Soapstone by Joe Talurinili A383

  Works by Eskimo Artists: No. 771, Plane over village, stonecut and stencil print by Pudlo. No. 772, Dogteam and sled, ivory sculpture by Abraham Kingmeatook.

1978, Sept. 27   *Perf. 13½*
769 A382 14c multicolored   .30 .20
770 A383 14c multicolored   .30 .20
  a. Pair, #769-770   .60 .40
771 A382 14c multicolored   .30 .20
772 A383 14c multicolored   .30 .20
  a. Pair, #771-772   .60 .40
    Nos. 769-772 (4)   1.20 .80
  Travels of the Inuit. Printed checkerwise.

Madonna of the Flowering Pea, Cologne School — A384

  Renaissance Paintings in National Gallery of Canada: 14c, Virgin and Child, by Hans Memling. 30c, Virgin and Child, by Jacopo Di Cione.

1978, Oct. 20   *Perf. 12½*
773 A384 12c multicolored   .25 .20
774 A384 14c multicolored   .30 .20
  a. Black omitted   1,200.
775 A384 30c multicolored   .60 .25
    Nos. 773-775 (3)   1.15 .65
    Christmas.

Sailing Ships Type of 1977
Litho. & Engr.
1978, Nov. 15   *Perf. 13*
776 A369 14c "Chief Justice
          Robinson," 1842   .30 .25
777 A369 14c "St. Roch," 1928   .30 .25
778 A369 14c "Northern Light,"
          1928   .30 .25
779 A369 14c "Labrador," 1954   .30 .25
  a. Block of 4, #776-779   1.25 1.10
    Ice vessels.

Quebec
Carnival — A386

1979, Feb. 1   Litho.   Perf. 13½
780 A386 14c multicolored   .30 .20

Flower, Queen & Parliament Types

1c, Bottle gentian. 2c, Western columbine. 3c, Canada lily. 4c, Hepatica. 5c, Shooting star. 10c, Franklin's lady's-slipper. 15c, Canada violet. No. 789, Elizabeth II. No. 790, Parliament, Ottawa.

Photo. & Engr., Engr. (#790)

1977-83   Perf. 13x13½
781 A355 1c multi ('79)   .20 .20
  a.   Perf. 12x12½ ('77)   .20 .20
  b.   Bklt. pane, 2 #781a, 4
        #713a   1.50
782 A355 2c multi ('79)   .20 .20
  a.   Bklt. pane, 4 #782, 3 #716a
        + label   1.00
  b.   Perf. 12x12½ ('78)   .20 .20
783 A355 3c multi ('79)   .20 .20
784 A355 4c multi ('79)   .20 .20
785 A355 5c multi ('79)   .20 .20
786 A355 10c multi ('79)   .20 .20
787 A355 15c multi ('79)   .30 .20
789 A356 17c green & blk
           ('79)   .35 .20
  a.   Perf. 12x12½   .35 .20
  b.   Bklt. pane of 25 + 2 labels   7.00
  c.   Horiz. pair, imperf. btwn.
        and at left and bottom   2,000.
  d.   Black inscriptions omitted   1,000.
790 A357 17c slate green
           ('79)   .35 .20
  a.   Printed on gummed side   37.50
791 A356 30c multi ('82)   .60 .50
792 A356 32c multi ('83)   .65 .20
       Nos. 781-792 (11)   3.45 2.20

Nos. 781a, 782b, 789a are from booklet panes. No. 782b has one straight edge, others one or two.
No. 789d also shows the horiz. perfs. shifted.

Parliament Type of 1977
Booklet Stamps

1979, Mar. 28   Engr.   Perf. 12x12½
797 A357 1c slate blue   .50 .20
  a.   Bklt. pane, 1 #797, 3 #800, 2
        #789a   1.40
800 A357 5c violet brown   .20 .20

#797 has one straight edge, #800 has one or two.

Coil Stamp

1979, Mar. 8   Perf. 10 Vert.
806 A357 17c slate green   .35 .20
  a.   Imperf., pair   150.00

Endangered
Wildlife
A392

1979, Apr. 10   Litho.   Perf. 12½
813 A392 17c Soft-shelled turtle   .35 .20
814 A392 35c Bowhead whale   .70 .35

Ribbon Around
Woman's
Finger — A393

No. 816, String around man's finger.

1979, Apr. 10
815 A393 17c multicolored   .35 .20
816 A393 17c multicolored   .35 .20
  a.   Pair, #815-816   .70 .55

Use postal code. Printed checkerwise.

Fruits of the
Earth, by F.
P. Grove
A394

The Golden
Vessel, by
Emile Nelligan
A395

1979, May 3   Perf. 13x13½
817 A394 17c multicolored   .35 .20
818 A395 17c multicolored   .35 .20
  a.   Pair, #817-818   .70 .55
  c.   As "a," left margin block of 4,
        left vert. pair imperf, right
        pair part perf   2,000. —

Frederick Philip Grove (1879-1948), teacher and writer; Emile Nelligan (1879-1941), French-Canadian poet. Nos. 817-818 printed checkerwise.
Warning: horizontal pairs exist of No. 818a that appear to be imperforate. These actually are pairs made from No. 818c with normal perforations trimmed off the right edge.

A396

1979, May 11   Perf. 13½
819   17c De Salaberry   .35 .20
820   17c John By   .35 .20
  a.   A396 Pair, #819-820   .70 .55

Charles-Michel d'Irumberry de Salaberry (1778-1829), and John By (1779-1836), Canadian colonels. Printed checkerwise.

Flag of
Ontario
A398

Designs: Provincial and Territorial flags.

1979, June 15   Litho.   Perf. 13½
821 A398 17c shown   .35 .25
822 A398 17c Quebec   .35 .25
823 A398 17c Nova Scotia   .35 .25
824 A398 17c New Brunswick   .35 .25
825 A398 17c Manitoba   .35 .25
826 A398 17c British Columbia   .35 .25
827 A398 17c Prince Edward Is-
           land   .35 .25
828 A398 17c Saskatchewan   .35 .25
829 A398 17c Alberta   .35 .25
830 A398 17c Newfoundland   .35 .25
831 A398 17c Northwest Territo-
           ries   .35 .25
832 A398 17c Yukon Territory   .35 .25
  a.   Pane of 12, #821-832   4.50 4.00

White
Water
Kayak
Race
A399

1979, July 3   Perf. 12½
833 A399 17c multicolored   .35 .20

Canoe-Kayak (Slalom and Wild Water) World Championships, Jonquière and Desbiens, Quebec, June 30-July 8.

Women's
Field
Hockey
A400

1979, Aug. 16
834 A400 17c multicolored   .35 .20

Women's Field Hockey Championship, Vancouver, B.C., Aug. 16-30.

Summer Tent,
Print by
Kiakshuk
A401

Eskimos
Building Igloo,
by Abraham
of
Povungnituk
A402

Works by Eskimo Artists: No. 837, The Dance, print by Kalvak of Holman Island. No. 838, Two soapstone figures from Repulse Bay, by Madeleine Isserkut and Jean Mapsalak.

1979, Sept. 13   Litho.   Perf. 13½
835 A401 17c multicolored   .35 .20
836 A402 17c multicolored   .35 .20
  a.   Pair, #835-836   .70 .55
837 A401 17c multicolored   .35 .20
838 A402 17c multicolored   .35 .20
  a.   Pair, #837-838   .70 .55
       Nos. 835-838 (4)   1.40 .80

Inuit shelters and community. Printed checkerwise.

Painted
Wooden
Train
A403

Antique Toys: 17c, Horse, pull toy. 35c, Knitted doll, vert.

1979, Oct. 17   Litho.   Perf. 13
839 A403 15c multicolored   .30 .20
840 A403 17c multicolored   .35 .20
841 A403 35c multicolored   .70 .30
  a.   Gold (and tagging) omitted 1,400.
       Nos. 839-841 (3)   1.35 .70

Christmas.

Girl Watering Tree
of Life — A404

1979, Oct. 24
842 A404 17c multicolored   .35 .20

International Year of the Child.

Curtiss HS-
2L
A405

1979, Nov. 15   Litho.   Perf. 12½
843 A405 17c shown   .35 .20
844 A405 17c Canadair CL-215   .35 .20
  a.   Pair, #843-844   .70 .55
845 A405 35c Vickers Vedette   .70 .55
846 A405 35c Consolidated
           Canso   .70 .55
  a.   Pair, #845-846   1.40 1.25
       Nos. 843-846 (4)   2.10 1.50

Map of
Canada
Showing
Arctic Islands
A406

1980, Jan. 23   Litho.   Perf. 13½
847 A406 17c multicolored   .35 .20

Acquisition of the Arctic Islands, centenary.

Downhill
Skiing
A407

1980, Jan. 23
848 A407 35c multicolored   .70 .30

13th Winter Olympic Games, Lake Placid, NY, Feb. 12-24.

Meeting of
the School
Trustees, by
Robert Harris
A408

Royal Canadian Academy of Arts Centenary: No. 850, Inspiration, bronze sculpture, by Louis-Philippe Hebert (1850-1917). No. 851, Parliament Buildings, by Thomas Fuller (1822-1919). No. 852, Sunrise on the Saguenay, by Lucius O'Brien (1832-99).

1980, Mar. 6   Litho.
849 A408 17c multicolored   .35 .20
850 A408 17c multicolored   .35 .20
  a.   Pair, #849-850   .70 .55
851 A408 35c multicolored   .70 .55
852 A408 35c multicolored   .70 .55
  a.   Pair, #851-852   1.40 1.25
       Nos. 849-852 (4)   2.10 1.50

Printed checkerwise.

Atlantic
Whitefish
A409

Endangered wildlife. No. 854, Greater prairie chicken.

1980, May 6   Litho.   Perf. 12½
853 A409 17c multicolored   .35 .20
854 A409 17c multicolored   .35 .20

Garden — A410

1980, May 29   Litho.   Perf. 13½
855 A410 17c multicolored   .35 .20

Intl. Flower Show, Montreal, May 17-Sept. 1.

Helping
Hands — A411

Litho. & Embossed

1980, May 29   Perf. 12½
856 A411 17c ultra & gold   .35 .20
14th World Congress of Rehabilitation International, Winnipeg, June 22-27.

"O Canada"
Opening
Bars
A412

Composers
Lavallee,
Routhier,
Weir
A413

1980, June 6   Litho.   Perf. 12½
857 A412 17c multicolored   .35 .20
858 A413 17c multicolored   .35 .20
a.   Pair, #857-858   .70 .55
"O Canada" centenary. Printed checkerwise in sheets of 16.

John George
Diefenbaker
(1895-1979),
Prime Minister,
1956-63 — A414

1980, June 20   Engr.   Perf. 13½
859 A414 17c dark blue   .35 .20

Emma Albani
(1847-1930),
Soprano — A415

#861, Healey Willan (1880-1968), organist, composer. Printed checkerwise.

1980, July 4   Litho.   Perf. 13½
860 A415 17c multicolored   .35 .20
861 A415 17c multicolored   .35 .20
a.   Pair, #860-861   .70 .55

Ned Hanlan
(1855-1908),
Oarsman
A416

1980, July 4   Litho.
862 A416 17c multicolored   .35 .20

Wheat Fields,
Saskatchewan
A417

No. 864, Strip mining and town, Alberta.

1980, Aug. 27   Litho.   Perf. 13½
863 A417 17c multicolored   .35 .20
864 A417 17c multicolored   .35 .20
75th anniversary of Saskatchewan's and Alberta's creation as Provinces.

Uraninite
Molecular
Structure
A418

1980, Sept. 3
865 A418 35c multicolored   .70 .50
a.   Printed on gummed side   800.00
Discovery of uranium in Canada, 80th anniversary.

Sedna, by
Ashoona
Kiawak
A419

Return of the
Sun, Print by
Kenojouak
A420

Works by Eskimo Artists: No. 868, Bird Spirit, by Doris Hagiolok. No. 869, Shaman, print by Simon Tookoome.

1980, Sept. 25   Litho.   Perf. 13½
866 A419 17c multicolored   .35 .20
867 A420 17c multicolored   .35 .20
a.   Pair, #866-867   .70 .55
868 A419 35c multicolored   .70 .55
869 A420 35c multicolored   .70 .55
a.   Pair, #868-869   1.40 1.25
      Nos. 866-869 (4)   2.10 1.50
Inuit spirits. Printed checkerwise.

Christmas Morning,
by Frank Charles
Hennessey — A421

Christmas (Greeting Cards, 1931): 17c, Sleigh Ride, by Joseph Sydney Hallam. 35c, McGill Cab Stand, by Kathleen Morris.

1980, Oct. 22   Litho.   Perf. 12½x12
870 A421 15c multicolored   .30 .20
871 A421 17c multicolored   .35 .20
872 A421 35c multicolored   .70 .35
      Nos. 870-872 (3)   1.35 .75

Avro
Canada
CF-100,
1950
A422

Military Aircraft: No. 874, Avro Lancaster, 1941. No. 875, Curtiss JN-4 Canuck. No. 876, Hawker Hurricane, 1935.

1980, Nov. 10   Perf. 13x13½
873 A422 17c multicolored   .35 .20
874 A422 17c multicolored   .35 .20
a.   Pair, #873-874   .70 .55
875 A422 35c multicolored   .70 .55
876 A422 35c multicolored   .70 .55
a.   Pair, #875-876   1.40 1.25
      Nos. 873-876 (4)   2.10 1.50
Printed checkerwise.

Emmanuel-Persillier Lachapelle,
Caduceus — A423

1980, Dec. 5   Perf. 13½
877 A423 17c multicolored   .35 .20
Lachapelle (1845-1918), physician, founded Notre Dame Hospital, Montreal, 1880.

Mandora,
18th
Century
A424

1981, Jan. 19   Litho.   Perf. 12½
878 A424 17c multicolored   .35 .20
"The Look of Music" rare musical instrument exhibition, Vancouver, Nov. 2, 1980-Apr. 5, 1981.
No. 878 exists printed on gummed side with gold color and tagging omitted, from printer's waste.

Emily Stowe (1831-1903) and Toronto
General Hospital — A425

Designs: No. 880, Louise McKinney, (1868-1931) Alberta legislative building. No. 881, Idola Saint-Jean, (1875-1945) Quebec legislative building. No. 882, Henrietta Edwards, (1849-1931) clubwomen.

1981, Mar. 4   Litho.   Perf. 13x13½
879 A425 17c multicolored   .35 .20
880 A425 17c multicolored   .35 .20
881 A425 17c multicolored   .35 .20
882 A425 17c multicolored   .35 .20
a.   Block of 4, #879-882   1.40 1.40

Vancouver
Island
Marmot, by
Michael
Dumas
A426

Endangered Wildlife: 35c, Wood bison, by Robert Bateman.

1981, Apr. 6   Litho.
883 A426 17c multicolored   .35 .20
884 A426 35c multicolored   .70 .60

Kateri Tekakwitha
("Lily of the
Mohawks"), by Emile
Brunet — A427

Brunet Sculpture: #886, Marie de L'Incarnation.

1981, Apr. 24   Perf. 12½
885 A427 17c brown & pale grn   .35 .20
886 A427 17c lt blue & ultra   .35 .20
a.   Pair, #885-886   .70 .55
Beatification of Kateri Tekakwitha (1656-1680), first North American Indian saint, and Marie De L'Incarnation (1599-1672), founder of Ursuline Order.

At Baie Saint-Paul, by Marc-Aurele
Fortin (1888-1970) — A428

Paintings: No. 888, Self-portrait, by Frederick H. Varley (1881-1969). 35c, Untitled No. 6, by Paul-Emile Borduas (1905-60).

1981, May 22   Litho.   Perf. 12½
887 A428 17c multi   .35 .20
888 A428 17c multi, vert.   .35 .20
a.   Imperf, pair   1,600.

Photo.
Perf. 13
889 A428 35c multi, vert.   .70 .60
      Nos. 887-889 (3)   1.40 1.00

Map of
Canada
Showing
Provincial
Boundaries,
1867 — A429

1981, June 30   Litho.   Perf. 13½
890 A429 17c shown   .35 .20
891 A429 17c 1873   .35 .20
892 A429 17c 1905   .35 .20
893 A429 17c 1949   .35 .20
a.   Strip of 4, #890-893   1.40 1.40
Canada Day.

Frere Marie-
Victorin (1885-
1944)
Botanist — A430

Botanists: #895, John Macoun (1831-1920).

1981, July 22   Litho.   Perf. 12½
894 A430 17c multicolored   .35 .20
895 A430 17c multicolored   .35 .20
a.   Pair, #894-895   .70 .50

Montreal
Rose — A431

1981, July 22   Perf. 13½
896 A431 17c multicolored   .35 .20

A432

Photo. & Engr.
1981, July 31   Perf. 13½
897 A432 17c multicolored   .35 .20
Niagara-on-the-Lake (1st capital of Upper Canada).

A433

1981, Aug. 14   **Litho.**
898 A433 17c multicolored   .35 .20
Acadian Congress centenary.

A434

1981, Sept. 8
899 A434 17c multicolored   .35 .20
Aaron Mosher (1881-1959), Labor Congress founder.

A435

1981, Nov. 16   **Litho.**   **Perf. 13½**
900 A435 15c 1781   .30 .20
901 A435 15c 1881   .30 .20
902 A435 15c 1981   .30 .20
    Nos. 900-902 (3)   .90 .60
Christmas; bicentenary of 1st illuminated Christmas tree in Canada.

Canadair CL-41 Tutor A436

1981, Nov. 24   **Litho.**   **Perf. 12½**
903 A436 17c shown   .35 .20
904 A436 17c de Havilland Tiger
     Moth   .35 .20
   a.   Pair, #903-904   .70 .55
905 A436 35c Avro Canada C-
     102   .70 .55
906 A436 35c de Havilland Cana-
     da Dash-7   .70 .55
   a.   Pair, #905-906   1.40 1.25
    Nos. 903-906 (4)   2.10 1.50

A437

1981, Dec. 29   **Engr.**   **Perf. 13x13½**
907 A437 (30c) red   .85 .20
   a.   Printed on gummed side   800.00

Coil Stamp
        Perf. 10 Vert.
908 A437 (30c) red   .75 .20
   a.   Imperf., pair   400.00

See Nos. 923-924, 940, 943-946, 950-951.

Canada 30

CANADA '82 Intl. Philatelic Youth Exhibition, Toronto, May 20-24 — A438

1982   **Litho.**   **Perf. 13½**
909 A438 30c No. 1   .60 .20
910 A438 30c No. 102   .60 .20
911 A438 35c No. 223   .70 .50
912 A438 35c No. 155   .70 .50
913 A438 60c No. 158   1.20 .75
   a.   Souvenir sheet of 5, #909-913   4.00 3.50
    Nos. 909-913 (5)   3.80 2.15

Issued: #909, 911, 3/11; others, 5/20.

Jules Leger (1913-1980), 26th Governor General — A439

1982, Apr. 2   **Litho.**   **Perf. 13½**
914 A439 30c multicolored   .60 .20

Terry Fox (1958-1981), Marathon of Hope — A440

1982, Apr. 13   **Perf. 12½**
915 A440 30c multicolored   .60 .20

1982 Constitution — A441

1982, Apr. 16   **Litho.**   **Perf. 12x12½**
916 A441 30c multicolored   .60 .20

Types of 1979-81 and

Decoy A442

Parliament (Library) A443

Parliament (West Block) — A444

Parliament (East Block) — A445

Elizabeth II — A446

Designs: Artifacts, 18th and 19th cent.

1982-87   **Litho.**   **Perf. 14x13½**
917 A442 1c shown   .20 .20
   a.   Perf. 13x13½ ('85)   .20 .20
918 A442 2c Fishing spear   .20 .20
   a.   Perf. 13x13½ ('84)   .20 .20
   b.   Bottom margin block of 4,
       bottom pair imperf, top
       pair part perf   2,250.
   c.   As "a," printed on gummed
       side   60.00
919 A442 3c Stable lantern   .20 .20
   a.   Perf. 13x13½ ('85)   .20 .20
920 A442 5c Bucket   .20 .20
   a.   Perf. 13x13½ ('84)   .20 .20
921 A442 10c Weathercock   .20 .20
   a.   Perf. 13x13½ ('85)   .30 .20
922 A442 20c Ice skates   .40 .20
   a.   Brown omitted   400.00

Photo. & Engr.
Perf. 13x13½
923 A437 30c lt blue, bl, &
     red   .60 .20
   a.   Bklt. pane of 20, perf.
       12x12½   15.00
   b.   Perf. 12x12½   .75 .20
924 A437 32c beige, red &
     brn   .65 .20
   a.   Bklt. pane of 25, perf.
       12x12½   15.00
   b.   Perf. 12x12½   .75 .20
   c.   As #924, beige (and tag-
       ging) omitted   1,200.

Litho.
Perf. 13½x13
925 A443 34c multi   .70 .20
   a.   Booklet pane of 25   14.00
   b.   Perf. 13½x14 ('86)   .70 .20
   c.   Bklt. pane of 25, perf.
       13½x14   14.00

Photo. & Engr.
Perf. 13x13½
926 A446 34c lt bl & int bl   .70 .20
926A A446 36c plum   3.00 2.50
Perf. 13½x13
926B A443 36c multi   .70 .20
   c.   Booklet pane of 10
       #926Be   7.00
   d.   Booklet pane of 25
       #926Be   17.50
   e.   Perf. 13½x14 ('87)   .80 .20
   f.   Left margin block of 4, left
       vert. pair imperf, right
       pair part perf   1,600.

Litho.   **Perf. 12x12½**
Size A442: 26x20mm
927 A442 37c Wooden
     plow   .75 .20
928 A442 39c Settle-bed   .80 .20
929 A442 48c Cradle   .95 .30
930 A442 50c Sleigh   1.00 .25
932 A442 64c Wood
     stove   1.30 .40
933 A442 68c Spinning
     wheel   1.40 .35

Litho. & Engr.
Perf. 13½
934 A359a $1 Glacier
       Natl. Park   2.00 .45
   a.   Blue inscriptions omitted   1,000.
   b.   Imperf., pair   2,400.
935 A359a $1.50 Waterton
       Lakes
       Natl. Park   3.50 .55
   a.   Black omitted   2,400.
936 A359a $2 Moraine
       Lake,
       Banff
       Park   4.00 1.10
   a.   Bluish green inscriptions
       omitted   1,200.
937 A359a $5 Point Pe-
       lee Natl.
       Park   10.00 2.25
    Nos. 917-937 (22)   33.45 10.75

Issued:1c-20c, 10/19; 30c, 5/11; $1.50, 6/18; $5, 1/10/83; 32c, 2/10/83; 37c, 48c, 64c, 4/8/83; $1, 8/15/84; #925, $2, 6/21/85; #926, 7/12/85; 39c, 50c, 68c, 8/1/85; #926B, 3/30/87; #926A, 10/1/87.
For former No. 931, see new No. 723C.

Booklet Stamps
Perf. 12x12½ (A437), 12½x12
Engr.
938 A445 1c sage green ('87)   .20 .20
939 A444 2c myrtle grn ('85)   .20 .20
   a.   2c slate green ('89)   .20 .20
940 A437 5c deep claret   .20 .20
941 A445 5c dp brown ('85)   .25 .20
942 A444 6c henna brn ('87)   .20 .20
943 A437 8c dk blue ('83)   .45 .20
944 A437 10c dark green   .40 .25
945 A437 30c red   .75 .30
   a.   Bklt. pane of 4 + 2 labels (2
       #940, 944, 945)   1.20 1.40
946 A437 32c brown ('83)   .65 .20
   b.   Bklt. pane of 4 + 2 labels (2
       #940, 943, 946)   1.20 1.40
947 A443 34c dp slate bl ('85)   1.10 .55
   a.   Bklt. pane of 6 (3 #939, 2 #941,
       #947)   1.75 1.25

---

948 A443 36c dark lil rose ('87)   1.25 .55
   a.   Bklt. pane of 5 + label (2 #938,
       2 #942, #948)   1.75 1.25

Issued: #940, 10c, 30c, 3/1; 8c, 32c, 2/15/83; #941, 30c, 6/21/85; 1c, 6c, 36c, 3/30/87.

Coil Stamps
   Engr.   **Perf. 10 Vert.**
950 A437 30c red   .95 .20
   a.   Imperf., pair   350.00
951 A437 32c brown ('83)   .65 .20
   a.   Imperf., pair   175.00
     Perf. 10 Horiz.
952 A443 34c dull red brn ('85)   .70 .20
   a.   Imperf., pair   160.00
953 A443 36c dark red ('87)   .75 .20
   a.   Imperf., pair   300.00

Issued: 30c, 5/11; 32c, 2/10/83; 34c, 8/1/85; 36c, 5/19/87.

See #1080-1083, 1186-1188, 1194-1194A.

Centenary of Salvation Army in Canada A457

1982, June 25   **Litho.**   **Perf. 13**
954 A457 30c multicolored   .60 .20

Canada Day A458

Paintings: No. 955, The Highway near Kluana Lake, by A.Y. Jackson. No. 956, Montreal Street Scene, by Adrien Hebert. No. 957, Breakwater, by Christopher Pratt. No. 958, Along Great Slave Lake, by Rene Richard. No. 959, Tea Hill, by Molly Lamb. No. 960, Family and Rainstorm, by Alex Colville. No. 961, Brown Shadows, by Dorothy Knowles. No. 962, The Red Brick House, by David Milne. No. 963, Campus Gates, by Bruno Bobak. No. 964, Prairie Town—Early Morning, by Illingworth Kerr. No. 965, Totems at Ninstints, by Joe Plaskett. No. 966, Doc Snider's House, by Lionel LeMoine FitzGerald.

1982, June 30   **Perf. 12½x12**
955 A458 30c multicolored   .60 .60
956 A458 30c multicolored   .60 .60
957 A458 30c multicolored   .60 .60
958 A458 30c multicolored   .60 .60
959 A458 30c multicolored   .60 .60
960 A458 30c multicolored   .60 .60
961 A458 30c multicolored   .60 .60
962 A458 30c multicolored   .60 .60
963 A458 30c multicolored   .60 .60
964 A458 30c multicolored   .60 .60
965 A458 30c multicolored   .60 .60
966 A458 30c multicolored   .60 .60
   a.   Min. sheet of 12, #955-966   7.25 7.25

Regina Centenary A459

1982, Aug. 3   **Perf. 13½x13**
967 A459 30c multicolored   .60 .20

Centenary of Royal Canadian Henley Regatta, St. Catharines, Aug. 4-8 — A460

1982, Aug. 4
968 A460 30c multicolored   .60 .20

Fairchild
FC-2W1
A461

1982, Oct. 5   Litho.   Perf. 12½
969 A461 30c shown   .65   .20
970 A461 30c De Havilland Ca-
nada Beaver   .65   .20
  a. Pair, #969-970   1.30 1.00
971 A461 60c Noorduyn Norse-
man   1.20   .75
972 A461 60c Fokker Super Uni-
versal   1.20   .75
  a. Pair, #971-972   2.40 1.90
    Nos. 969-972 (4)   3.70 1.90

Christmas
A462

Designs: Creche figures.

1982, Nov. 3   Perf. 13½
973 A462 30c Holy Family   .60   .20
  a. All colors except black
    omitted   12,000.
  b. Printed on gummed side,
    black omitted   12,000.
974 A462 35c Shepherds   .70   .45
975 A462 60c Three Kings   1.20   .75
    Nos. 973-975 (3)   2.50 1.40

Nos. 973a and 973b are each unique and
were caused by a paper foldover.

World
Communications
Year — A463

1983, Mar. 10   Litho.   Perf. 12x12½
976 A463 32c multicolored   .65   .20

Commonwealth Day — A464

1983, Mar. 14
977 A464 $2 multicolored   8.00 3.50

Scene from
Angeline de
Montbrun, by
Laure Conan
(1845-1924),
Painted by
Rene
Milot — A465

Design: No. 979, Sea Gulls, by Edwin John
Pratt (1882-1966), woodcut by Claire Pratt.

1983, Apr. 22   Litho.   Perf. 13½
978 A465 32c multicolored   .65   .20
979 A465 32c multicolored   .65   .20
  a. Pair, #978-979   1.30 1.00
  b. As "a," all color missing   4,000.

No. 979b resulted from an extraneous piece
of paper receiving the colors. After removal,
the issued pane shows two vertical pairs without color plus six other stamps with only partial
color.

St. John
Ambulance
Centenary
A466

1983, June 3   Perf. 13½
980 A466 32c Emblem   .65   .20

World University
Games,
Edmonton, July 1-
11 — A467

1983, June 28   Perf. 13½
981 A467 32c multicolored   .65   .20
  a. Printed on gummed side   1,000.
982 A467 64c multicolored   1.30   .65

Canada Day — A468

#983, Fort Henry, Ontario. #984, Fort Wil-
liam, Ontario. #985, Fort Rodd Hill, British
Columbia. #986, Fort Wellington, Ontario.
#987, Fort Prince of Wales, Manitoba. #988,
Halifax Citadel, Nova Scotia. #989, Fort
Chambly, Quebec. #990, Fort No. 1, Point
Levis, Quebec. #991, Fort at Coteau-du-Lac,
Quebec. #992, Fort Beausejour, New Bruns-
wick. Sizes: #983, 988: 44x22mm; #984-985,
989-990, 36x22mm; #986-987, 991-992,
28x22mm.

1983, June 30   Perf. 12½x13
Booklet Stamps
983 A468 32c multicolored   .75   .65
984 A468 32c multicolored   .75   .65
985 A468 32c multicolored   .75   .65
986 A468 32c multicolored   .75   .65
987 A468 32c multicolored   .75   .65
988 A468 32c multicolored   .75   .65
989 A468 32c multicolored   .75   .65
990 A468 32c multicolored   .75   .65
991 A468 32c multicolored   .75   .65
992 A468 32c multicolored   .75   .65
  a. Booklet pane of 10, #983-992   7.50 7.50

Scouting
Year — A469

1983, July 6   Perf. 13½
993 A469 32c multicolored   .65   .20

Church Council
Emblem — A470

1983, July 22   Litho.
994 A470 32c tan & green   .65   .20

6th World Council of Churches Assembly,
Vancouver, July 24-Aug. 10.

Humphrey
Gilbert — A471

1983, Aug. 3   Litho.
995 A471 32c multicolored   .65   .20

400th anniv. of discovery of Newfoundland
by Sir Humphrey Gilbert (1537-1583).

Centenary
of
Discovery
of Nickel,
Sudbury,
Ontario
A472

Litho. & Typo.
1983, Aug. 12   Perf. 13
996 A472 32c multicolored   .65   .20
  a. Silver (and tagging) omitted   850.00

Beware of forgeries of No. 996a. A certificate of authenticity is mandatory.

Josiah Henson (1789-1883),
Preacher — A473

1983, Sept. 16   Litho.   Perf. 13x13½
997 A473 32c multicolored   .65   .20

Antoine
Labelle (1833-
1891), Deputy
Minister for
Settlement
A474

1983, Sept. 16   Perf. 13½
998 A474 32c multicolored   .65   .20

Locomotives — A475

1983, Oct. 3   Perf. 12½x13
999 A475 32c Toronto 4-4-0,
1853   .65   .30
1000 A475 32c Dorchester 0-4-0,
1836   .65   .30
  a. Pair, #999-1000   1.30   .90
1001 A475 37c Samson 0-6-0,
1838   .75   .60
1002 A475 64c Adam Brown 4-4-
0, 1860   1.30 1.10
    Nos. 999-1002 (4)   3.35 2.30

Dalhousie
Law School
Centenary
A476

1983, Oct. 28   Perf. 13
1003 A476 32c Arms   .65   .20

Christmas
A477

1983, Nov. 3   Litho.   Perf. 13½
1004 A477 32c Urban church   .65   .20
1005 A477 37c Family going to
church   .75   .45
1006 A477 64c Rural church   1.30   .75
    Nos. 1004-1006 (3)   2.70 1.40

Army Regiments,
Centenaries
A478

19th Cent. Uniforms: No. 1007, Royal Canadian Regiment, British Columbia Regiment.
No. 1008, Royal Winnipeg Rifles, Royal Canadian Dragoons.

1983, Nov. 10   Perf. 13½x13
1007 A478 32c shown   .65   .20
1008 A478 32c multicolored   .65   .20
  a. Pair, #1007-1008   1.30 1.00

Yellowknife, 50th
Anniv. — A479

1984, Mar. 15   Litho.   Perf. 13½
1009 A479 32c Gold mine   .65   .20

50th Anniv.
of Montreal
Symphony
Orchestra
A480

1984, Mar. 24   Litho.   Perf. 12½
1010 A480 32c multicolored   .65   .20

450th
Anniv. of
Cartier's
Landing in
Quebec
A481

1984, Apr. 20   Photo. & Engr.
1011 A481 32c multicolored   .65   .20

See France No. 1923.

Voyage of Tall
Ships, Saint-Malo,
France, to
Quebec
City — A482

1984, May 18   Litho.   Perf. 12x12½
1012 A482 32c multicolored   .65   .20

450th anniv. of Cartier's landing in Quebec.

Canadian Red
Cross Society,
75th
Anniv. — A483

1984, May 28   Litho.   Perf. 13
1013 A483 32c Meritorious Ser-
        vice Medal   .65 .20

New Brunswick,
Bicentenary
A484

Photo. & Engr.
1984, June 18   Perf. 13
1014 A484 32c Galleys   .65 .20

St. Lawrence Seaway, 25th
Anniv. — A485

1984, June 26   Litho.   Perf. 13
1015 A485 32c Seaway, Lake Su-
        perior   .65 .20

Canada
Day
A486

Provincial Landscapes by Jean Paul
Lemieux (b. 1904).

1984, June 29   Perf. 13
1016 A486 32c New Brunswick   .65 .35
1017 A486 32c British Columbia .65 .35
1018 A486 32c Yukon Territory .65 .35
1019 A486 32c Quebec   .65 .35
1020 A486 32c Manitoba   .65 .35
1021 A486 32c Alberta   .65 .35
1022 A486 32c Prince Edward Is-
        land   .65 .35
1023 A486 32c Saskatchewan   .65 .35
1024 A486 32c Nova Scotia, vert. .65 .35
1025 A486 32c Northwest Territo-
        ries   .65 .35
1026 A486 32c Newfoundland   .65 .35
1027 A486 32c Ontario, vert. .65 .35
  a. Min. sheet of 12, #1016-1027 8.00 8.00

Nos. 1018 and 1025 incorrectly inscribed.
No. 1018 shows Northwest Territories landscape; No. 1025, Yukon Territory church.

Loyalists, British Flag (1606-
1801) — A487

1984, July 3
1028 A487 32c multicolored .65 .20

United Empire Loyalists, American colonists
who remained loyal to British throne and emi-
grated to Canada during American Revolution.

Roman Catholic
Church in
Newfoundland
A488

1984, Aug. 17   Litho.   Perf. 13½
1029 A488 32c St. John's Basilica .65 .20

Papal Visit
A489

1984, Aug. 31   Litho.   Perf. 12½
1030 A489 32c multicolored   .65 .20
1031 A489 64c multicolored 1.30 .60

Lighthouses — A490

1984, Sept. 21   Litho.   Perf. 12½
1032 A490 32c Louisbourg, 1734 .65 .20
1033 A490 32c Fisgard, 1860   .65 .20
1034 A490 32c Ile Verte, 1809 .65 .20
1035 A490 32c Gibraltar Point,
        1808   .65 .20
  a. Block of 4, #1032-1035 2.60 1.30

Steam Locomotives — A491

1984, Oct. 25   Litho.   Perf. 12½x13
1036 A491 32c Scotia   .65 .20
1037 A491 32c Countess of Duf-
        ferin   .65 .20
  a. Pair, #1036-1037   1.30 1.00
1038 A491 37c Grand Trunk
        Class E3   .75 .65
1039 A491 64c Canadian Pacific
        D10a   1.30 1.10
  a. Souvenir sheet   3.25 3.25
   Nos. 1036-1039 (4)   3.35 2.15

#1039a contains #1036-1039 in changed
colors.
See #1071-1074, 1118-1121.

Christmas
A492

Paintings: 32c, The Annunciation, by Jean
Dallaire. 37c, The Three Kings, by Simone
Mary Bouchard. 64c, Snow in Bethlehem, by
David Milne.

1984, Nov. 2   Litho.   Perf. 13
1040 A492 32c multicolored   .65 .20
1041 A492 37c multicolored   .75 .50
1042 A492 64c multicolored 1.30 .65
   Nos. 1040-1042 (3)   2.70 1.35

Royal Canadian
Air Force — A493

1984, Nov. 9   Litho.   Perf. 12x12½
1043 A493 32c Pilots   .65 .20

Cent. of La
Presse — A494

1984, Nov. 16   Litho.   Perf. 13x13½
1044 A494 32c Treffle Berthiaume .65 .20

International Youth Year — A495

1985, Feb. 8   Litho.   Perf. 12½
1045 A495 32c Heart, arrow, jeans .65 .20

Canadians in
Space — A496

1985, Mar. 15   Litho.   Perf. 13½
1046 A496 32c Astronaut   .65 .20

Therese
Casgrain
(1896-1981),
Suffragist
A497

Emily Murphy
(1868-1933),
Writer
A498

1985, Apr. 17   Litho.
1047 A497 32c multicolored   .65 .20
1048 A498 32c multicolored   .65 .20
  a. Pair, #1047-1048   1.30 1.10

Gabriel Dumont (1837-1906), Metis
Leader — A499

1985, May 6   Litho.   Perf. 13
1049 A499 32c multicolored .65 .20

Centenary of the Northwest Rebellion.

Canada Day — A500

#1050, Lower Ft. Garry, Manitoba. #1051,
Ft. Anne, Nova Scotia. #1052, Ft. York, Onta-
rio. #1053, Castle Hill, Newfoundland. #1054,
Ft. Whoop Up, Alberta. #1055, Ft. Erie, Onta-
rio. #1056, Ft. Walsh, Saskatchewan. #1057,
Ft. Lennox, Quebec. #1058, York Redoubt,
Nova Scotia. #1059, Ft. Frederick, Ontario.
Sizes: #1050, 1055: 48x26mm. #1051-1052,
1056-1057: 40x26mm. #1053-1054, 1058-
1059, 32x26mm.

1985, June 28   Litho.   Perf. 12½x13
Booklet Stamps
1050 A500 34c multicolored 1.00 .65
1051 A500 34c multicolored 1.00 .65
1052 A500 34c multicolored 1.00 .65
1053 A500 34c multicolored 1.00 .65
1054 A500 34c multicolored 1.00 .65
1055 A500 34c multicolored 1.00 .65
1056 A500 34c multicolored 1.00 .65
1057 A500 34c multicolored 1.00 .65
1058 A500 34c multicolored 1.00 .65
1059 A500 34c multicolored 1.00 .65
  a. Bklt. pane of 10, #1050-
        1059   10.00 12.00

Intl. Pharmaceutical
Federation
Congress — A501

Design: Louis Hebert (1575-1627), 1st
French Apothecary in North America.

1985, Aug. 30   Litho.   Perf. 12½
1060 A501 34c multicolored .70 .20

Interparliamentary Union '85,
Ottawa — A502

1985, Sept. 3   Perf. 13½
1061 A502 34c multicolored .70 .20

A503

1985, Sept. 12   Photo.   Perf. 13½x13
1062 A503 34c Guide, brownie sa-
        luting   .70 .20

Natl. Girl Guides movement, cent.

Lighthouses
A504

1985, Oct. 3   Litho.   Perf. 13½
1063 A504 34c Sisters Islets .75 .30
1064 A504 34c Pelee Passage   .75 .30
1065 A504 34c Haut-fond Prince .75 .30

1066	A504	34c Rose Blanche	.75 .30
a.		Block of 4, #1063-1066	3.00 2.25
b.		Souv. sheet of 4, #1063-1066	4.50 4.50

Santa Claus
Parade
A505

Paintings by Barbara Carroll.

1985, Oct. 23   Litho.   Perf. 13½

1067	A505	34c Santa Claus	.70 .20
1068	A505	39c Horse-drawn coach	.80 .50
1069	A505	68c Christmas tree	1.35 1.00

Perf. 13½ on 3 Sides

1070	A505	32c Polar float	1.00 .50
a.		Booklet pane of 10	10.00
		Nos. 1067-1070 (4)	3.85 2.20

No. 1070 printed in booklets only.

Locomotives Type of 1984

1985, Nov. 7   Perf. 12½x13

1071	A491	34c Grand Trunk K2	.70 .20
1072	A491	34c Canadian Pacific P2a	.70 .20
a.		Pair, #1071-1072	1.40 1.00
1073	A491	39c Canadian Northern O10a	.80 .70
1074	A491	68c Canadian Govt. Railways H4D	1.35 1.10
		Nos. 1071-1074 (4)	3.55 2.20

1910 Gunner's
Mate, World War
II Officer, 1985
Woman
Recruit — A507

1985, Nov. 8   Perf. 13½x13

1075	A507	34c multicolored	.70 .20

Royal Canadian Navy, 75th anniv.

Old Holton House, Sherbrooke Street,
Montreal, by James Wilson Morrice
(1865-1924)
A508

1985, Nov. 15   Perf. 13½

1076	A508	34c multicolored	.70 .20

Montreal Museum of Fine Arts, 120th anniv.

Southwestern Alberta, Computer
Design Map — A509

1986, Feb. 13   Litho.   Perf. 12½x13

1077	A509	34c multicolored	.70 .20

1988 Winter Olympics, Calgary, Alberta,
Feb. 13-28.

EXPO '86,
Vancouver,
May 2-Oct.
13 — A510

1986, Mar. 7   Photo. & Engr.

1078	A510	34c Canada Pavilion	.70 .20
1079	A510	39c Communications	.80 .60

Heritage Artifacts Type of 1982

1987, May 6   Litho.   Perf. 14x13½

1080	A442	25c Butter stamp	.50 .30

Size: 20x26mm

Perf. 12x12½

1081	A442	42c Linen chest	1.10 .20
1082	A442	55c Iron kettle	1.45 .30
1083	A442	72c Hand-drawn cart	1.75 .40
		Nos. 1080-1083 (4)	4.80 1.20

Park Type of 1979

Litho. & Engr.

1986, Mar. 14   Perf. 13½

1084	A359a	$5 La Mauricie Natl. Park	10.00 2.25
a.		Dark blue inscriptions omitted	2,750. 1,600.

No. 1084a is valued in the grade of fine as
all known examples are centered thus.

Philippe Aubert
de Gaspe
(1786-1871),
Novelist
A511

Molly Brant (1736-
1796), Iroquois
Leader and Loyalist
A512

1986, Apr. 14   Litho.   Perf. 12½

1090	A511	34c multicolored	.70 .20

Perf. 13½

1091	A512	34c multicolored	.70 .20

EXPO '86 — A513

Photo. & Engr.

1986, Apr. 28   Perf. 13x13½

1092	A513	34c Expo Center, Vancouver	.70 .20
1093	A513	68c Transportation, horiz.	1.35 .65

Canadian
Forces Postal
Service, 75th
Anniv.
A514

1986, May 9   Litho.   Perf. 13½

1094	A514	34c multicolored	.70 .20

Indigenous
Birds — A515

1986, May 22

1095	A515	34c Great blue heron	.70 .30
1096	A515	34c Snow goose	.70 .30
1097	A515	34c Great horned owl	.70 .30
1098	A515	34c Spruce grouse	.70 .30
a.		Block of 4, #1095-1098	2.80 2.00

19th Intl. Ornithological Congress, Ottawa,
June 22-29.

Canada
Day — A516

Invention blueprints.

1986, June 27   Litho.

1099	A516	34c Rotary snowplow, 1869	.70 .25
1100	A516	34c Canadarm, 1986	.70 .25
1101	A516	34c Anti-gravity flight suit, 1938	.70 .25
1102	A516	34c Variable pitch propeller, 1923	.70 .25
a.		Block of 4, #1099-1102	2.80 2.00

Canadian Broadcasting Corp., 50th
Anniv. — A517

1986, July 23   Litho.   Perf. 12½

1103	A517	34c Emblem, map	.70 .20

Exploration
of Canada
A518

#1104, Siberian Indians discover and
inhabit America, 10,000 B.C. #1105, Viking
settlement, A.D. 1000. #1106, John Cabot
lands, 1498. #1107, Henry Hudson pioneers
Hudson Strait and Bay, 1610.

1986, Aug. 29   Litho.   Perf. 12½x13

1104	A518	34c multicolored	.70 .30
1105	A518	34c multicolored	.70 .30
1106	A518	34c multicolored	.70 .30
1107	A518	34c multicolored	.70 .30
a.		Block of 4, #1104-1107	2.80 2.50
b.		Souv. sheet of 4, #1104-1107	3.25 2.75

No. 1107b issued Oct. 1 for CAPEX '87.
See #1126-1129, 1199-1202, 1233-1236.

Peacemakers of the Frontier,
1870s — A519

Designs: No. 1108, Crowfoot (1830-1890),
Blackfoot Indian chief. No. 1109, James F.
Macleod (1836-1894), asst. commissioner of
Northwest Mounted Police.

1986, Sept. 5   Perf. 13x13½

1108	A519	34c scar, gray & ind	.70 .25
1109	A519	34c ind, gray & scar	.70 .25
a.		Pair, #1108-1109	1.40 1.10

Intl. Peace
Year — A520

Litho. & Embossed

1986, Sept. 16   Perf. 13½

1110	A520	34c multicolored	.70 .20

1988 Calgary
Winter
Olympics — A521

1986, Oct. 15   Litho.   Perf. 13½x13

1111	A521	34c Ice hockey	.70 .20
1112	A521	34c Biathlon	.70 .20
a.		Pair, #1111-1112	1.40 1.00

See #1130-1131, 1152-1153, 1195-1198.

Christmas
Angels — A522

1986, Oct. 29   Litho.   Perf. 12½

1113	A522	34c multicolored	.70 .20
1114	A522	39c multicolored	.80 .60
1115	A522	68c multicolored	1.35 .80

Booklet Stamps

Size: 72x26mm

Perf. 13½ Horiz.

1116	A522	29c multicolored	1.50 1.10
a.		Booklet pane of 10	15.00 14.00
b.		Perf. 12½ horiz.	8.00 3.25
c.		Bklt. pane of 10, #1116b	80.00 70.00
		Nos. 1113-1116 (4)	4.35 2.70

No. 1116 has bar code at left, for use on
covers with printed postal code matrix.

John Molson (1763-1836),
Entrepreneur — A523

1986, Nov. 4

1117	A523	34c multicolored	.70 .20

Locomotives Type of 1984

Locomotives, 1925-1945.

1986, Nov. 21   Perf. 12½x13

1118	A491	34c CN V1a	.70 .25
1119	A491	34c CP T1a	.70 .25
a.		Pair, #1118-1119	1.40 1.10
1120	A491	39c CN U2a	.85 .75
1121	A491	68c CP H1c	1.40 1.10
		Nos. 1118-1121 (4)	3.65 2.35

CAPEX
'87 — A524

1987   Litho. & Engr.   Perf. 13x13½

1122	A524	34c 1st Toronto P.O.	.70 .20
1123	A524	36c Nelson-Miramichi P.O.	.75 .25
1124	A524	42c Saint Ours P.O.	.85 .70
1125	A524	72c Battleford P.O.	1.45 1.10
		Nos. 1122-1125 (4)	3.75 2.25

Souvenir Sheet

Yellow Green Inscription

1125A		Sheet of 4	3.75 3.75
b.	A524	36c like #1122	.70 .70
c.	A524	36c like #1123	.70 .75
d.	A524	42c like #1124	.85 .85
e.	A524	72c like #1125	1.45 1.45

Issue dates: 34c, Feb. 16; others, June 12.

Exploration Type of 1986

Pioneers of New France: #1126, Etienne
Brule (c. 1592-1633), 1st European to see the
Great Lakes. #1127, Pierre Esprit Radisson
(c. 1636-1710) & Medard Chouart des Groseil-
liers (1625-98), British expedition to Hudson
Bay, 1668. #1128, Louis Jolliet (1645-1700) &
Fr. Jacques Marquette (1637-75) discovering

the Mississippi River, 1673. #1129, Recollet wilderness mission, 1615.

1987, Mar. 13 Litho. Perf. 12½x13
1126	A518	34c multicolored	.70	.30
1127	A518	34c multicolored	.70	.30
1128	A518	34c multicolored	.70	.30
1129	A518	34c multicolored	.70	.30
a.		Block of 4, #1126-1129	2.80	2.25

Olympics Type of 1986
1987, Apr. 3 Perf. 13½x13
1130	A521	36c Speed skating	.60	.20
1131	A521	42c Bobsledding	.75	.50

Volunteers Week — A525

1987, Apr. 13 Perf. 12½x13
1132	A525	36c multicolored	.70	.20

Law Day — A526

1987, Apr. 15 Perf. 14x13½
1133	A526	36c Coat of arms	.70	.20
a.		Imperf, pair	1,600.	

Canadian Charter of Rights and Freedoms, 5th anniv.

Engineering Institute of Canada, Cent. — A527

1987, May 19 Perf. 12½x13
1134	A527	36c multicolored	.70	.20

Canada Day — A528

Inventors & communications innovations: #1135, Reginald Aubrey Fessenden (1866-1932), AM radio, 1900. #1136, Charles Fenerty, newsprint, 1838. #1137, Georges-Edouard Desbarats and William Leggo, half-tone engraving, 1869. #1138, Frederick Newton Gisborne, No. America's 1st undersea cable, 1852, New Brunswick-Prince Edward Island.

1987, June 25 Litho. Perf. 13½
1135	A528	36c multicolored	.70	.30
1136	A528	36c multicolored	.70	.30
1137	A528	36c multicolored	.70	.30
1138	A528	36c multicolored	.70	.30
a.		Block of 4, #1135-1138	2.80	2.40

Steamships A529

1987, July 20 Perf. 13½x13
1139	A529	36c Segwun, 1887	.70	.30

51x22mm
1140	A529	36c Princess Marguerite, 1948	.70	.30
a.		Pair, #1139-1140	1.40	1.10

Shipwrecks A530

1987, Aug. 7
1141	A530	36c Hamilton & Scourge, 1813	.70	.30
1142	A530	36c San Juan, 1565	.70	.30
1143	A530	36c Breadalbane, 1853	.70	.30
1144	A530	36c Ericsson, 1892	.70	.30
a.		Block of 4, #1141-1144	2.80	2.40

Air Canada, 50th Anniv. — A531

1987, Sept. 1 Perf. 13½
1145	A531	36c multicolored	.70	.20

2nd Intl. Francophone Summit, Quebec, 9/2-4 — A532

1987, Sept. 2 Perf. 13x12½
1146	A532	36c multicolored	.70	.20

9th Commonwealth Meeting, Vancouver, Oct. 13-17 — A533

1987, Oct. 13
1147	A533	36c multicolored	.70	.20

Christmas A534

1987, Nov. 2 Litho. Perf. 13½
1148	A534	36c Poinsettia	.70	.20
1149	A534	42c Holly wreath	.85	.65
1150	A534	72c Mistletoe, Christmas tree	1.45	1.00

Size: 39x25mm
1151	A534	31c Gifts, Christmas tree	.65	.65
a.		Booklet pane of 10	6.50	8.00
		Nos. 1148-1151 (4)	3.65	2.50

No. 1151 has bar code at left, for use on covers with printed postal code matrix. Issued in booklets only.

Olympics Type of 1986
1987, Nov. 13 Perf. 13½x13
1152	A521	36c Cross-country skiing	.70	.25
1153	A521	36c Ski jumping	.70	.25
a.		Pair, #1152-1153	1.40	.75

75th Grey Cup, Vancouver, Nov. 29 — A535

1987, Nov. 20 Perf. 12½
1154	A535	36c multicolored	.70	.20

Types of 1982 and

 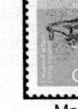

Elizabeth II A536 / Mammals A538

Parliament (Center Block) A537 A539

Architecture — A540

Flag and Clouds A541 / Flag A542

Natl. Flag, Deciduous Forest A543 / Flag and Mountains A544

1987-91 Litho. Perf. 13x13½
Sizes Vary on A536, A538
1155	A538	1c Flying squirrel	.20	.20
a.		Perf. 13x12½	4.00	.85
1156	A538	2c Prickly porcupine	.20	.20
1157	A538	3c Muskrat	.20	.20
1158	A538	5c Varying hare	.20	.20
a.		Imperf, pair	1,500.	
1159	A538	6c Red fox	.20	.20
a.		Horiz. pair, imperf	2,400.	
1160	A538	10c Skunk	.20	.20
a.		Perf. 13x12½	4.00	.40
1161	A538	25c Beaver	.50	.20

Perf. 13½x13
1162	A536	37c multicolored	.75	.20
1163	A537	37c multicolored	.75	.20
a.		Bklt. pane of 10, #1163c	7.50	
b.		Bklt. pane of 25, #1163c	19.00	
c.		Perf. 13½x14	.75	.20

Perf. 13x12½
1164	A536	38c multicolored	.75	.20
a.		Perf. 13x13½	.75	.25
b.		As "a," bklt. pane of 10 + 2 labels	7.50	
c.		Vert. block of 10, middle pair imperf, 2nd and 4th pairs part perf	1,200.	
d.		As "a," horiz. pair, imperf btwn.	1,000.	

e.		Bottom margin horiz. pair, imperf	—	

Perf. 13x13½ on 3 or 4 Sides
1165	A539	38c multicolored	.75	.20
a.		Bklt. pane of 10 + 2 labels	7.50	
b.		Bklt. pane of 25 + 2 labels	19.00	
c.		Printed on gummed side	120.00	
d.		Double impression of all litho colors except black	275.00	

Perf. 13½x13
1166	A541	39c multicolored	.80	.20
a.		Bklt. pane of 10 + 2 labels	8.00	
b.		Bklt. pane of 25 + 2 labels	22.50	
c.		Perf. 12½x13	12.00	.75

Perf. 13x13½
1167	A536	39c multicolored	.80	.20
a.		Bklt. pane of 10 + 2 labels	8.00	
b.		Perf. 13x13½	10.00	.75
1168	A536	40c multicolored	.80	.20
a.		Bklt. pane of 10 + 2 labels	8.00	

Perf. 13½x13
1169	A544	40c multicolored	.80	.20
a.		Bklt. pane of 25 + 2 labels	27.50	
b.		Bklt. pane of 10 + 2 labels	8.00	

Perf. 12x12½
1170	A538	43c Lynx	1.10	.40

Perf. 14½x14
1171	A538	44c Walrus	1.60	.20
a.		Perf. 12½x13	2.75	1.50
b.		As "a," bklt. pane of 5 + label	12.50	12.00
c.		Perf. 13½x13	450.00	47.50
1172	A538	45c Pronghorn	.90	.20
b.		As "f," bklt. pane of 5 + label	13.00	11.00
d.		Perf. 13	22.50	1.10
f.		Perf. 12½x13	2.60	.50
h.		Imperf., pair	950.00	

Perf. 13
1172A	A538	46c Wolverine	.95	.25
c.		Perf. 12½x13	1.25	.50
e.		As "c," bklt. pane of 5 + label	6.50	6.00
g.		Perf. 14½x14	5.50	.40

Perf. 12x12½
1173	A538	57c Killer whale	1.15	.35

Perf. 14½x14
1174	A538	59c Musk-ox	1.30	.35
a.		Perf. 13	12.00	7.00
1175	A538	61c Timber wolf	1.25	.40
a.		Perf. 13	77.50	5.75
1176	A538	63c Harbor porpoise	3.00	.40
a.		Perf. 13	12.50	4.75

Perf. 12x12½
1177	A538	74c Wapiti	1.90	.70

Perf. 14½x14
1178	A538	76c Grizzly bear	2.25	.55
a.		Perf. 12½x13	3.00	2.50
b.		As "a," bklt. pane of 5 + label	15.00	15.00
c.		Perf. 13	37.50	16.00
1179	A538	78c Beluga whale	2.40	.65
a.		As "c," bklt. pane of 5	15.00	15.00
b.		Perf. 13	35.00	6.00
c.		Perf. 12½x13	3.00	2.60
d.		Imperf, pair	950.00	

Perf. 13
1180	A538	80c Peary caribou	1.90	.70
a.		Perf. 12½x13	3.00	1.10
b.		As "a," bklt. pane of 5 + label	15.00	15.00
c.		Perf. 14½x14	6.00	2.25

Perf. 13½
Litho. & Engr.
1181	A540	$1 Runnymede Library, Toronto	2.00	.55
a.		Engr. inscriptions inverted	12,000.	
b.		Imperf, pair	1,600.	
1182	A540	$2 McAdam Railway Station	4.00	1.00
a.		Imperf., pair	1,200.	
1183	A540	$5 Bonsecours Market, Montreal	9.00	2.25
		Nos. 1155-1183 (30)	42.60	12.00

A later printing of No. 1182 has more intense and clearly defined green shading on the roofline and the deep orange background extends closer to the roofline.

Imperfs exist of Nos. 1155-1157 and 1160, from printer's waste.

Issued: 1c, 2c, 3c, 5c, 6c, 10c, 25c, 10/3/88; 37c, 12/30/87; 38c, 12/29/88; 43c, 57c, 74c, 1/18/88; 44c, 59c, 76c, 1/18/89; $1, $2, 5/5/89; #1166, 12/28/89; 45c, 61c, 78c, #1167, 1/12/90; $5, 5/28/90; 40c, 46c, 63c, 80c, 12/28/90.

Booklet Stamps
Perf. 13½x14 on 3 Sides
Litho.

1184	A542	1c shown	.20	.20
a.		Perf. 12½x13	12.00	12.00
1185	A542	5c multi	.20	.20
a.		Perf. 12½x13	8.00	8.00

Perf. 12½x12 on 2 or 3 sides
Engr.

1186	A445	6c dark purple	.65	.30
1187	A443	37c dark blue	.90	.75
a.		Bklt. pane of 4 + 2 labels		
		(#938, 2 #942, #1187)	1.25	1.25
1188	A443	38c dark blue	.80	.35
a.		Bklt. pane of 5 (3 #939a, #1186, #1188)	1.00	1.00

Perf. 13½x14 on 3 Sides
Litho.

1189	A542	39c multi	.90	.35
a.		Bklt. pane of 4 (#1184, 2 #1185, #1189)	1.10	1.10
b.		Perf. 12½x13	16.00	16.00
c.		As "a," perf. 12½x13	45.00	45.00
1190	A542	40c multi	1.60	.50
a.		Bklt. pane of 4 (2 #1184, #1185, #1190)	1.80	1.25
b.		As "a," imperf	*1,600.*	

Nos. 1190a, 1190c sold for 50c.

Issued: #1187, 2/3/88; #1188, 1/18/89; #1186, 1989; #1184-1185, 1189, 1/12/90; #1190, 12/28/90.

Self-Adhesives
Die Cut
Booklet Stamps

1191	A543	38c multicolored	1.50	.70
a.		Booklet of 12	18.00	
b.		Blue omitted	2,000.	
c.		Yellow omitted	1,000.	
1192	A543	39c Flag, field	1.25	.70
a.		Booklet of 12	15.00	
1193	A543	40c Flag, seacoast	1.25	.70
a.		Booklet of 12	15.00	

Issued: 38c, 6/30/89; 39c, 2/8/90; 40c, 1/11/91.

Issued on peelable paper backing serving as booklet cover. Nos. 1191a, 1192a sold for $5, No. 1193a for $5.25.

Coil Stamps
Perf. 10 Horiz.
Engr.

1194	A443	37c dark blue	.75	.20
d.		Imperf., pair	175.00	
1194A	A443	38c dark green	1.10	.20
e.		Imperf., pair	400.00	
1194B	A542	39c violet	.80	.20
f.		Imperf., pair	200.00	
1194C	A542	40c blue gray	.80	.20
g.		Imperf., pair	300.00	

Issued: 37c, 2/22/88; 38c, 2/1/89; 39c, 2/8/90; 40c, 12/28/90.

See #1356-1362, 1375-1376, 1388, 1394-1396, 1682-1683, 1687, 1703, 1705.

Olympics Type of 1986

1988, Feb. 12   Litho.   Perf. 12x12½

1195	A521	37c Alpine skiing	.75	.25
1196	A521	37c Curling	.75	.25
a.		Pair, #1195-1196	1.50	1.00
1197	A521	43c Figure skating	.85	.70
1198	A521	74c Luge	1.50	1.00
		Nos. 1195-1198 (4)	3.85	2.20

Exploration Type of 1986

18th Cent. explorers of the western territories: No. 1199, Anthony Henday, who traveled the Prairies in 1754 from the Hayes River to Red Deer, Alberta. No. 1200, George Vancouver (1757-1798), who circumnavigated Vancouver Is. and explored the Pacific Coast, 1792-94. No. 1201, Simon Fraser (1776-1862), fur trader who discovered and navigated the Fraser River. No. 1202, John Palliser (1807-1887), geographer who determined the topographical boundary between Canada and the US from Lake Superior to the Pacific Coast.

1988, Mar. 17   Litho.   Perf. 12½x13

1199	A518	37c multicolored	.75	.35
1200	A518	37c multicolored	.75	.35
1201	A518	37c multicolored	.75	.35
1202	A518	37c multicolored	.75	.35
a.		Block of 4, #1199-1202	3.00	2.50

The Young Reader, by Ozias Leduc A546

Photo. & Engr. with Foil Application
1988, May 20   Perf. 13x13½

1203	A546	50c multicolored	1.10	1.00

Masterpieces of Canadian art. Printed in sheets of 16.

See Nos. 1241, 1271, 1310, 1419, 1466, 1516, 1545, 1602, 1635, 1754, 1800, 1863, 1916.

Wildlife and Habitat Conservation A547

1988, June 1   Litho.   Perf. 13x13½

1204	A547	37c Duck landing	.75	.30
1205	A547	37c Moose at water hole	.75	.30
a.		Pair, #1204-1205	1.50	1.00

Grey Owl, born Archibald Belaney, (b. 1888), conservationist; Ducks Unlimited Canada, 50th anniv.

Science and Technology — A548

Inventions: No. 1206, Kerosene, invented by Abraham Gesner (1797-1864), patented in 1854. No. 1207, Marquis wheat, developed in 1908 by Charles Saunders. No. 1208, Electron microscope, developed in 1938 at the University of Toronto by James Hillier and Albert Prebus under the supervision of Eli Burton. No. 1209, Cobalt cancer therapy, introduced by Dr. Harold Johns and Atomic Energy of Canada, Ltd., in 1951.

1988, June 17   Perf. 12½x13

1206	A548	37c multicolored	.75	.35
1207	A548	37c multicolored	.75	.35
1208	A548	37c multicolored	.75	.35
1209	A548	37c multicolored	.75	.35
a.		Block of 4, #1206-1209	3.00	2.50

Intl. Entomology Congress, Vancouver A549

1988, July 4   Litho.   Perf. 12

1210	A549	37c Short-tailed swallowtail	.75	.35
1211	A549	37c Northern blue	.75	.35
1212	A549	37c Macoun's Arctic	.75	.35
1213	A549	37c Canadian tiger swallowtail	.75	.35
a.		Block of 4, #1210-1213	3.00	2.50

St. John's, Newfoundland, Cent. of Incorporation — A550

1988, July 22   Perf. 13½x13

1214	A550	37c Harbor entrance, skyline	.75	.20

Canadian 4-H Council, 75th Anniv. A551

1988, Aug. 5

1215	A551	37c Motto, farm, young scientists	.75	.20

Les Forges Du St. Maurice (1738-1883), Canada's 1st Industrial Complex — A552

Litho. & Engr.
1988, Aug. 19   Perf. 13½

1216	A552	37c multicolored	.75	.20

Canadian Kennel Club, Cent. A553

1988, Aug. 26   Perf. 12½x12

1217	A553	37c Tahltan bear dog	1.00	.40
1218	A553	37c Nova Scotia duck-tolling retriever	1.00	.40
1219	A553	37c Canadian Eskimo dog	1.00	.40
1220	A553	37c Newfoundland	1.00	.40
a.		Block of 4, #1217-1220	4.00	3.00

A554

1988, Sept. 14   Litho.   Perf. 13½x13

1221	A554	37c multicolored	.75	.20

Sesquicentennial of the 1st baseball game played in Canada, June 4, 1838 at Beachville, Upper Canada.

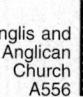

A555

1988, Oct. 27   Litho.   Perf. 13½

Christmas (Icons of the Eastern Church): 32c, Nativity. 37c, Conception. 43c, Virgin and Child. 74c, Virgin and Child, diff.

1222	A555	37c multicolored	.75	.20
1223	A555	43c multicolored	.85	.65
1224	A555	74c multicolored	1.50	1.00

Booklet Stamp
Size: 35½x21mm
Perf. 12½x13½

1225	A555	32c multicolored	1.00	.75
a.		Booklet pane of 10	10.00	
		Nos. 1222-1225 (4)	4.10	2.60

Millennium of Christianity in the Ukraine. No. 1225 has bar code at left; for use on covers with printed postal code matrix.

Inglis and Anglican Church A556

1988, Nov. 1   Perf. 12½x12

1226	A556	37c multicolored	.75	.20

Charles Inglis (1734-1816), Canada's 1st Anglican bishop and founder of the Kings-Edgehill School, Nova Scotia, and the University of King's College at Halifax, bicent.

Hopkins and Canoe Manned by Voyageurs A557

1988, Nov. 18   Perf. 13½x13

1227	A557	37c multicolored	.75	.35

Frances Ann Hopkins (1838-1918), painter.

The Bluenose and Capt. Walters — A558

1988, Nov. 18   Perf. 13½

1228	A558	37c multicolored	.75	.25

Angus Walters (1882-1968), mariner.

Small Craft A559

1989, Feb. 1   Litho.   Perf. 13½x13

1229	A559	38c Chipewyan canoe	.75	.35
1230	A559	38c Haida canoe	.75	.35
1231	A559	38c Inuit kayak	.75	.35
1232	A559	38c Micmac canoe	.75	.35
a.		Block of 4, #1229-1232	3.00	2.60

See Nos. 1266-1269, 1317-1320.

Exploration Type of 1986

Explorers of the North: No. 1233, Matonabbee (c. 1737-1782), Indian guide who led 1st overland European expedition to the Arctic Ocean. No. 1234, Relics of expedition led by Sir John Franklin (1786-1847) that proved the existence of the Northwest Passage. No. 1235, Relics of the discovery of the Alberta fossil bed by geologist Joseph Burr Tyrrell (1858-1957). No. 1236, Vilhjalmur Stefansson (1879-1962), American ethnologist who discovered the last uncharted islands in the Arctic Archipelago.

1989, Mar. 22   Litho.   Perf. 12½x13

1233	A518	38c multicolored	.75	.35
1234	A518	38c multicolored	.75	.35
1235	A518	38c multicolored	.75	.35
1236	A518	38c multicolored	.75	.35
a.		Block of 4, #1233-1236	3.00	2.60

Photography in Canada,
Sesquicentennial — A560

Photographers and their work: No. 1237, William Notman (1826-1891). No. 1238, W. Hanson Boorne (1859-1945). No. 1239, Alexander Henderson (1831-1913). No. 1240, Jules-Ernest Livernois (1851-1933).

1989, June 23 Litho.   Perf. 12½x12
1237	A560	38c multicolored	.75	.35
1238	A560	38c multicolored	.75	.35
1239	A560	38c multicolored	.75	.35
1240	A560	38c multicolored	.75	.35
a.		Block of 4, #1237-1240	3.00	2.60

Art Type of 1988

Ceremonial Frontlet (headpiece) Worn by Tsimshian Indian Chiefs, Early 20th Cent.

Litho. with Foil Application
1989, June 29   Perf. 12½x13
1241	A546	50c multicolored	1.10	.85

Masterpieces of Canadian Art and opening of the Museum of Civilization.

Poets — A562

1989, July 7   Litho.   Perf. 13½
1243	A562	38c Louis Frechette (1839-1908)	.75	.35
1244	A562	38c Archibald Lampman (1861-1899)	.75	.35
a.		Pair, #1243-1244	1.50	1.25

Mushrooms
A563

1989, Aug. 4
1245	A563	38c *Clavulinopsis fusiformis*	.75	.35
1246	A563	38c *Boletus mirabilis*	.75	.35
1247	A563	38c *Cantharellus cinnabarinus*	.75	.35
1248	A563	38c *Morchella esculenta*	.75	.35
a.		Block of 4, #1245-1248	3.00	2.60

Infantry Regiments, 75th Anniv. A564

#1249, Princess Patricia's Canadian Light Infantry. #1250, Royal 22nd Regiment.

Litho. & Engr.
1989, Sept. 8   Perf. 13
1249	A564	38c multicolored	.85	.40
1250	A564	38c multicolored	.85	.40
a.		Pair, #1249-1250	1.70	1.50

Intl. Trade
A565

1989, Oct. 2   Litho.   Perf. 13½x13
1251	A565	38c multicolored	.75	.30

Performing
Arts — A566

1989, Oct. 4   Perf. 13x13½
1252	A566	38c Dancers	.75	.35
1253	A566	38c Musicians	.75	.35
1254	A566	38c Camera, director	.75	.35
1255	A566	38c Youth and adult entertainers	.75	.35
a.		Block of 4, #1252-1255	3.00	2.60

Royal Winnipeg Ballet 50th anniv. (No. 1252), Vancouver Opera 30th anniv. (No. 1253), Natl. Film Board 50th anniv. (No. 1254), and Confederation Center of the Arts, Charlottetown, P.E.I., 25th anniv. (No. 1255).

A566a

A567

Winter landscapes: 33c, *Champ-de-Mars, Winter*, 1892, by William Brymner (1855-1925). 38c, *Bend in the Gosselin River, Arthabaska*, c. 1906, by Marc-Aurele de Foy Suzor-Cote (1869-1937). 44c, *Snow II*, 1915, by Lawren S. Harris (1885-1970). 76c, *Ste. Agnes*, c. 1925-30, by Albert H. Robinson (1881-1956). Nos. 1256-1258 vert.

1989, Oct. 26   Litho.   Perf. 13x13½
Size of 44c, 76c: 25x31mm
1256	A566a	38c multicolored	.75	.30
a.		Bklt. pane of 10, #1256b	47.50	
b.		Perf. 13x12½	4.75	

Perf. 13½
1257	A566a	44c multicolored	.90	.65
a.		Booklet pane of 5 + label	16.00	16.00
1258	A566a	76c multicolored	1.50	1.00
a.		Booklet pane of 5 + label	30.00	30.00

Booklet Stamp
Size: 35x21mm
Perf. 12½x13½
1259	A567	33c shown	1.25	1.25
a.		Booklet pane of 10	12.50	
b.		Horiz. pair, imperf btwn.	2,400.	
		Nos. 1256-1259 (4)	4.40	3.20

Christmas. No. 1259 has bar code at left; for use on covers with printed postal code matrix. Booklet panes separate easily.

Declaration of War, 1939 — A568

Political and military actions taken by Canada at the outbreak of World War II.

1989, Nov. 10   Perf. 13½
1260	A568	38c shown	.80	.55
1261	A568	38c Army mobilization	.80	.55
1262	A568	38c Navy convoy system	.80	.55
1263	A568	38c Commonwealth Air Training Plan	.80	.55
a.		Block of 4, #1260-1263	3.20	2.50

See Nos. 1298-1301, 1345-1348, 1448-1451, 1503-1506, 1537-1544.

Norman Bethune (1890-1939),
Surgeon — A569

Litho. & Engr.
1990, Mar. 2   Perf. 13x13½
1264	A569	39c In Canada	1.00	.35
1265	A569	39c In China	1.00	.35
a.		Pair, #1264-1265	2.00	1.25

See People's Republic of China Nos. 2263-2264.

Small Craft Type of 1989
1990, Mar. 15   Litho.   Perf. 13½x13
1266	A559	39c Dory	.80	.35
1267	A559	39c Pointer	.80	.35
1268	A559	39c York boat	.80	.35
1269	A559	39c North canoe	.80	.35
a.		Block of 4, #1266-1269	3.20	2.50

Multicultural
Heritage of
Canada
A570

Litho. & Engr.
1990, Apr. 5   Perf. 13
1270	A570	39c multicolored	.80	.20
a.		Black (inscriptions) omitted	1,200.	

Art Type of 1988

Painting: *The West Wind*, by Tom Thomson.

Litho. with Foil Application
1990, May 3   Perf. 12½x13
1271	A546	50c multicolored	1.10	1.00

Masterpieces of Canadian Art.

Mail Trucks
A571   A572

1990, May 3   Litho.   Perf. 13½
Booklet Stamps
1272	A571	39c multicolored	.90	.70
1273	A572	39c multicolored	.90	.70
a.		Bklt. pane of 8+printed margin (4 each #1272-1273)	7.25	
b.		Bklt. pane of 9+3 labels, printed margin (5 #1272, 4 #1273)	12.50	

Dolls
A573

1990, June 8   Litho.   Perf. 12½x12
1274	A573	39c Native	.80	.35
1275	A573	39c Settlers	.80	.35
1276	A573	39c 4 Commercial	.80	.35
1277	A573	39c 5 Commercial	.80	.35
a.		Block of 4, #1274-1277	3.20	2.75

Natl. Flag, 25th
Anniv. — A574

1990, June 29   Perf. 13x12½
1278	A574	39c Flag, fireworks	.80	.20
a.		Silver (inscriptions) omitted	2,000.	

Printed in sheets of 16.

Prehistoric
Life
A575

Litho. & Engr.
1990, July 12   Perf. 13x13½
1279	A575	39c Trilobite	.80	.35
1280	A575	39c Sea scorpion	.80	.35
1281	A575	39c Fossil algae	.80	.35
1282	A575	39c Soft invertebrate	.80	.35
a.		Block of 4, #1279-1282	3.20	2.75

See Nos. 1306-1309.

Canadian
Forests
A576

1990, Aug. 7   Litho.   Perf. 12½x13
1283	A576	39c Acadian	.80	.30
a.		Sheet of 4	10.00	8.00
1284	A576	39c Great Lakes-St. Lawrence	.80	.30
a.		Sheet of 4	10.00	8.00
1285	A576	39c Coast	.80	.30
a.		Sheet of 4	10.00	8.00
1286	A576	39c Boreal	.80	.30
a.		Block of 4, #1283-1286	3.20	2.75
b.		Sheet of 4	10.00	8.00

Sheets of four sold for $1 each through Petro-Canada gas stations, and for full face value through the philatelic bureau. Issue date: Sept. 7.

Weather Observations in Canada,
150th Anniv. — A577

1990, Sept. 5   Litho.   Perf. 12½x13½
1287	A577	39c multicolored	.80	.35

The left and right margin singles of No. 1287 differ slightly in design from stamps from columns 2-4, due to the nature of the continuous cloud design across the pane.

Intl. Literacy
Year — A578

1990, Sept. 7   Perf. 13½x13
1288	A578	39c multicolored	.80	.20

Legendary
Creatures
A579

1990, Oct. 1   Litho.   Perf. 12½x13½
1289	A579	39c Sasquatch	1.10	.75
1290	A579	39c Kraken	1.10	.75
1291	A579	39c Werewolf	1.10	.75

1292	A579	39c Ogopogo	1.10	.75
a.		Block of 4, #1289-1292	4.50	3.25
b.		As "a," imperf.	2,000.	

Perf. 12½x12

1289a	A579	39c	12.00	4.00
1290a	A579	39c	12.00	4.00
1291a	A579	39c	12.00	4.00
1292c	A579	39c	12.00	4.00
d.		Block of 4, #1289a-1292c	50.00	30.00

Agnes Campbell
Macphail (1890-
1954), First Woman
Member of
Parliament — A580

1990, Oct. 9   Litho.   Perf. 13x13½

1293	A580	39c multicolored	.80	.20

Virgin Mary with
Christ Child and
St. John the
Baptist by Norval
Morrisseau
A581

Rebirth by
Jackson
Beardy
A582

Indian Art: 45c, Sculpture of Mother and
Child by an Inuit artist. 78c, Children of the
Raven by Bill Reid.

1990, Oct. 25   Litho.   Perf. 13½

1294	A581	39c multicolored	.80	.20
a.		Booklet pane of 10	8.00	
1295	A581	45c multicolored	.90	.70
a.		Bklt. pane of 5 + label	4.50	4.50
1296	A581	78c multicolored	1.60	1.10
a.		Bklt. pane of 5 + label	8.00	7.00

Booklet Stamp
Perf. 12½x13 on 2 or 3 Sides

1297	A582	34c multicolored	.85	.40
a.		Booklet pane of 10	8.50	
		Nos. 1294-1297 (4)	4.15	2.40

Christmas. No. 1297 has bar code at left; for
use on covers with printed postal code matrix.

World War II Type of 1989
1990, Nov. 9   Perf. 12½x12

1298	A568	39c Home front	.90	.60
1299	A568	39c Communal war efforts	.90	.60
1300	A568	39c Food production	.90	.60
1301	A568	39c Science and war	.90	.60
a.		Block of 4, #1298-1301	3.60	3.25

A583

Physicians: No. 1302, Jennie Trout (1841-
1921), first licensed Canadian woman physician. No. 1303, Wilder Penfield (1891-1976),
neurosurgeon. No. 1304, Sir Frederick Banting
(1891-1941), discoverer of insulin. No. 1305,
Harold Griffith (1894-1985), anesthesiologist.

1991, Mar. 15   Litho.   Perf. 13½

1302	A583	40c multicolored	.80	.35
1303	A583	40c multicolored	.80	.35
1304	A583	40c multicolored	.80	.35
1305	A583	40c multicolored	.80	.35
a.		Block of 4, #1302-1305	3.20	2.75

Prehistoric Life Type of 1990
1991, Apr. 5   Litho.   Perf. 12½x13½

1306	A575	40c Microfossils	.80	.35
1307	A575	40c Early tree	.80	.35
1308	A575	40c Early fish	.80	.35
1309	A575	40c Land reptile	.80	.35
a.		Block of 4, #1306-1309	3.20	2.75

Art Type of 1988
Forest, British Columbia by Emily Carr.
Litho. with Foil Application
1991, May 7   Perf. 12½x13

1310	A546	50c multicolored	1.10	.90

Masterpieces of Canadian Art.

A584

1991, May 22   Litho.   Perf. 13x12½

Public Gardens: #1311, Butchart Gardens,
Victoria, B.C. #1312, Intl. Peace Garden, Bois-
sevain, Manitoba. #1313, Royal Botanical Gardens, Hamilton, Ontario. #1314, Montreal
Botanical Gardens. #1315, Halifax Public Gardens, Nova Scotia.

Booklet Stamps

1311	A584	40c multicolored	.85	.40
1312	A584	40c multicolored	.85	.40
1313	A584	40c multicolored	.85	.40
1314	A584	40c multicolored	.85	.40
1315	A584	40c multicolored	.85	.40
a.		Strip of 5, #1311-1315	4.25	3.75
b.		Bklt. pane, 2 each #1311-1315	8.50	

Canada
Day — A585

1991, June 28   Perf. 13½x13

1316	A585	40c multicolored	.80	.20

Small Craft Type of 1989
1991, July 18

1317	A559	40c Verchere rowboat	.80	.35
1318	A559	40c Touring kayak	.80	.35
1319	A559	40c Sailing dinghy	.80	.35
1320	A559	40c Cedar strip canoe	.80	.35
a.		Block of 4, #1317-1320	3.20	2.75

Canadian
Rivers — A586

1991, Aug. 20   Perf. 13x12½
Booklet Stamps

1321	A586	40c South Nahanni	.85	.35
1322	A586	40c Athabasca	.85	.35
1323	A586	40c Boundary Wa-ters-Voyageur Waterway	.85	.35
1324	A586	40c Jacques Cartier	.85	.35
1325	A586	40c Main	.85	.35
a.		Strip of 5, #1321-1325	4.25	3.25
b.		Bklt. pane, 2 each #1321-1325	8.50	

See #1408-1412, 1485-1489, 1511-1515.

Arrival of
Ukrainians,
Cent. — A587

Paintings by William Kurelek.

1991, Aug. 29   Perf. 13½x13

1326	A587	40c Leaving home-land	.80	.35
1327	A587	40c Winter in Canada	.80	.35
1328	A587	40c Clearing land	.80	.35
1329	A587	40c Growing wheat	.80	.35
a.		Block of 4, #1326-1329	3.20	2.75

Dangerous Public
Service
Occupations
A588

1991, Sept. 23   Perf. 13½

1330	A588	40c Ski patrol	1.10	.35
1331	A588	40c Police	1.10	.35
1332	A588	40c Fire fighters	1.10	.35
1333	A588	40c Search & Rescue	1.10	.35
a.		Block of 4, #1330-1333	4.40	2.75

Folktales
A589

1991, Oct. 1   Litho.   Perf. 13½x12½

1334	A589	40c Witched Canoe	.80	.35
1335	A589	40c Orphan Boy	.80	.35
1336	A589	40c Chinook Wind	.80	.35
1337	A589	40c Buried Treasure	.80	.35
a.		Block of 4, #1334-1337	3.20	2.75

Queen's
University,
Kingston, Ont.,
Sesqui. — A590

1991, Oct. 16   Litho.   Perf. 13x12½

1338	A590	40c multicolored	.80	.55
a.		Bklt. pane of 10 + 2 labels	8.00	

Santa
Claus
A592

1991, Oct. 23   Perf. 13½

1339	A591	40c At fireplace	.80	.20
a.		Booklet pane of 10	8.00	
1340	A591	46c With white horse, tree	.90	.50
a.		Bklt. pane of 5 + label	4.50	3.50
1341	A591	80c Sinterklaas, girl	1.60	1.00
a.		Bklt. pane of 5 + label	8.00	7.50

Booklet Stamp
Perf. 12½x13 on 2 or 3 Sides

1342	A592	35c With punchbowl	.75	.25
a.		Booklet pane of 10	7.50	
		Nos. 1339-1342 (4)	4.05	1.95

Christmas. No. 1342 has bar code at left; for
use on covers with printed postal code matrix.

Basketball,
Cent. — A593

1991, Oct. 25   Perf. 13x13½

1343	A593	40c multicolored	.80	.20

Souvenir Sheet

1344		Sheet of 3	5.25	5.25
a.	A593	40c like #1343	1.20	1.20
b.	A593	46c Player shooting, diff.	1.60	1.60
c.	A593	80c Player dribbling	2.40	2.40

No. 1344a has 3-line inscription.

World War II Type of 1989
1991, Nov. 8   Perf. 13½

1345	A568	40c Women's Armed Forces	.80	.55
1346	A568	40c War industry	.80	.55
1347	A568	40c Cadets and veter-ans	.80	.55
1348	A568	40c Defense of Hong Kong	.80	.55
a.		Block or strip of 4, #1345-1348	3.20	2.75

Types of 1987-91 and

Edible
Berries — A594

Hills — A595

Prairie
A596

Building
A597

Trees — A598

1991-98   Litho.   Perf. 13x13½

1349	A594	1c Blueberry	.20	.20
1350	A594	2c Wild strawberry	.20	.20
1351	A594	3c Black crowber-ry	.20	.20
1352	A594	5c Rose hip	.20	.20
1353	A594	6c Black raspber-ry	.20	.20
1354	A594	10c Kinnikinnick	.20	.20
a.		Horiz. pair, imperf at sides and bottom	1,000.	
1355	A594	25c Saskatoon ber-ry	.50	.20

Perf. 13½x13

1356	A595	42c multicolored	.85	.20
a.		Booklet pane of 10	8.50	
b.		Bklt. pane of 50 + 2 labels	95.00	80.00
c.		Bklt. pane of 25 + 2 labels	21.00	16.00
d.		Vert. pair, imperf between	1,000.	

Perf. 13x13½

1357	A536	42c multicolored	.85	.20
a.		Booklet pane of 10	8.50	7.50
1358	A536	43c multicolored	1.00	.20
a.		Booklet pane of 10	10.00	9.00

Perf. 13½x13

1359	A596	43c multicolored	.90	.20
a.		Booklet pane of 10	9.00	7.50
b.		Bklt. pane of 25 + 2 labels	22.50	
c.		Perf. 14½	1.10	.20
d.		As "c," bklt. pane of 10	11.00	9.00
e.		As "c," bklt. pane of 25 + 2 labels	27.50	25.00

f.	Vert. pair, imperf between (from #1359e)	900.00	

Perf. 13x13½

1360	A536 45c multicolored	.90	.20
a.	Booklet pane of 10	9.00	7.50
	Complete booklet, #1360a	9.50	

Perf. 14½

1361	A597 45c multicolored	.90	.20
a.	Booklet of 10	9.00	
	Complete booklet #1361a	9.50	
b.	Bkt. pane of 25+2 labels	30.00	
	Complete booklet, #1361b	30.00	
c.	Perf. 13½x13	.90	.20
d.	As "c," bklt. pane of 10	9.00	
	Complete booklet, #1361d	9.50	
e.	As "c," bklt. pane of 25 + 2 labels	20.00	
	Complete booklet #1361e	20.00	

Perf. 13x13½
Size: 16x20mm

1362	A597 45c multicolored	.90	.30
a.	Booklet pane of 10	9.00	
	Complete booklet, #1362a	9.50	
b.	Booklet pane of 30	27.50	
	Complete booklet, #1362b	27.50	

No. 1361 is 17x21mm.

Perf. 13

1363	A598 48c McIntosh apple	.95	.25
a.	Perf. 14½x14 on 3 sides	1.60	.40
b.	As "a," bklt. pane of 5 + label	8.00	7.00
1364	A598 49c Delicious apple	1.00	.25
a.	Perf. 14½x14	2.75	
b.	As "a," bklt. pane of 5 + 1 label	14.00	6.50
c.	Booklet pane of 5 + label	13.00	11.00
1365	A598 50c Snow apple	1.00	.30
a.	Booklet pane of 5 + label	7.00	5.75
b.	Perf. 14½x14	2.50	.45
c.	As "b," bklt. pane of 5 + label	14.00	12.50
1366	A598 52c Gravenstein apple	1.50	.40
a.	Booklet pane of 5+label	7.50	6.00
	Complete booklet, #1366a	8.00	
b.	Perf. 14½x14	2.50	.60
c.	As "b," bklt. pane of 5 + label	12.50	11.00
	Complete booklet, #1366c	13.00	
1367	A598 65c Black walnut	1.30	.40
1368	A598 67c Beaked hazelnut	1.35	.40
1369	A598 69c Shagbark hickory	1.40	.35
1370	A598 71c American chestnut	1.40	.35
a.	Perf. 14½x14	50.00	.85
1371	A598 84c Stanley plum	1.70	.40
a.	Perf. 14½x14 on 3 sides	2.50	.60
b.	As "a," bklt. pane of 5 + label	12.50	10.00
1372	A598 86c Bartlett pear	1.80	.60
a.	Perf. 14½x14	3.00	1.50
b.	As "a," bklt. pane of 5 + 1 label	15.00	12.50
c.	Booklet pane of 5 + label	17.50	16.00
1373	A598 88c Westcot apricot	1.75	.55
a.	Booklet pane of 5 + label	11.00	8.00
b.	Perf. 14½x14	4.25	2.25
c.	As "b," bklt. pane of 5 + label	22.50	15.00
1374	A598 90c Elberta peach	1.80	.45
a.	Booklet pane of 5+label	10.00	8.00
	Complete booklet #1374a	10.50	
b.	Perf. 14½x14	4.00	1.60
c.	As "b," bklt. pane of 5+label	20.00	14.00
	Complete booklet, #1374c	21.00	

Size: 48x40mm
Litho. & Engr.
Perf. 14½x14

1375	A540 $1 Court House, Yorkton	2.00	.60
a.	Dk bl (inscriptions) omitted	1,350.	
b.	Perf 13½x13	2.00	.60
c.	As "b," dk bl (inscriptions) omitted	1,350.	
1376	A540 $2 Provincial Normal School, Truro	4.00	1.10
a.	Dk grn (inscriptions) omitted	1,200.	
b.	Engr. inscriptions inverted	9,000.	
c.	Perf. 13½x13	4.00	1.10
d.	As "c," dk grn (inscriptions) omitted	1,400.	

Perf. 13½x13

1378	A540 $5 Carnegie Public Library, Victoria	9.00	2.50
	Nos. 1349-1378 (29)	39.95	11.80

Self-Adhesive
Die Cut
Imperf
Booklet Stamps

1388	A543 42c Flag, mountains	1.20	.80
a.	Booklet of 12	16.00	
1389	A543 43c Flag, estuary shore	1.20	.60
a.	Booklet pane of 12	16.00	

Nos. 1388a, 1389a issued on peelable paper backing serving as booklet cover and sold for $5.25.

Coil Stamps
Perf. 10 Horiz.
Engr.

1394	A542 42c red	.85	.20
a.	Imperf., pair	180.00	
1395	A542 43c olive green	.85	.20
a.	Imperf., pair	160.00	
1396	A542 45c blue green	.90	.20
a.	Imperf., pair	160.00	
	Nos. 1394-1396 (3)	2.60	.60

Nos. 1349-1363 are known imperf from printer's waste. Items exist imperf in wrong colors and with wrong denominations. These may be essays or printer's waste.

Issued: 1c-25c, 8/5/92; #1356-1357, 1394, 48c, 65c, 84c, 12/27/91; #1388, 1/28/92; #1358-1359, 1364, 1368, 1372, 1395, 12/30/92; #1389, 2/15/93; #1359c-1359e, 1/18/94; #1364c, 1372c, 1/7/94; 50c, 69c, 88c, 2/25/94; $1, $2, 2/21/94; #1375b, 1376c, 2/20/95; #1365c, 1373c, 3/27/95; #1360-1361, 1396, 52c, 71c, 90c, 7/31/95; $5, 2/29/96; #1362, 2/2/98.

1992 Winter Olympics, Albertville A601

1992, Feb. 7 Litho. Perf. 12½x13
Booklet Stamps

1399	A601 42c Ski jumping	.85	.40
1400	A601 42c Pairs figure skating	.85	.40
1401	A601 42c Hockey	.85	.40
1402	A601 42c Bobsledding	.85	.40
1403	A601 42c Alpine skiing	.85	.40
a.	Strip of 5, #1399-1403	4.25	3.75
b.	Bklt. pane, 2 each #1399-1403	8.50	8.50

See Nos. 1414-1418.

City of Montreal, 350th Anniv. — A602

Designs: No. 1404, City of Montreal, modern times. No. 1405, Early settlement of Montreal (Ville-Marie). 48c, Jacques Cartier's chart of Canada, snowshoe, ship's mast. 84c, World map, nocturnal and Aztec calendar stone.

1992, Mar. 25 Perf. 13½

1404	A602 42c multicolored	.85	.35
1405	A602 42c multicolored	.85	.35
a.	Pair, #1404-1405	1.70	1.25
1406	A602 48c multicolored	.95	.75
1407	A602 84c multicolored	1.70	1.00
a.	Souvenir sheet of 4, #1404-1407	4.00	4.00
	Nos. 1404-1407 (4)	4.35	2.45

Discovery of America, 500th Anniv. (#1407). Nos. 1404-1405 printed checkerwise. No. 1407a with engraved signatures in margin was produced in limited quantities for World Philatelic Youth Exhibition catalogue which sold for $12.

Canadian Rivers Type of 1991
1992, Apr. 22 Perf. 12½
Booklet Stamps

1408	A586 42c Margaree	.85	.40
1409	A586 42c West (Eliot)	.85	.40
1410	A586 42c Ottawa	.85	.40
1411	A586 42c Niagara	.85	.40
1412	A586 42c South Saskatchewan	.85	.40
a.	Strip of 5, #1408-1412	4.25	3.75
b.	Bklt. pane, 2 each #1408-1412	8.50	

Nos. 1408-1412 are horiz.

Alaska Highway, 50th Anniv. — A603

1992, May 15 Perf. 13½

1413	A603 42c multicolored	.85	.25

1992 Olympic Games Type
1992, June 15 Litho. Perf. 12½x13

1414	A601 42c Gymnastics	.85	.40
1415	A601 42c Running	.85	.40
1416	A601 42c Diving	.85	.40
1417	A601 42c Cycling	.85	.40
1418	A601 42c Swimming	.85	.40
a.	Strip of 5, #1414-1418	4.25	4.00
b.	Bkt. pane, 2 each #1414-1418	8.50	

1992 Summer Olympics, Barcelona. Stamps in bottom row of #1418b are in different sequence than those in #1418a.

Art Type of 1988
Painting: Red Nasturtiums, by David Milne.
Litho. with Foil Application

1992, June 29 Perf. 12½x13

1419	A546 50c multicolored	1.10	.75

Masterpieces in Canadian Art.

Miniature Sheet

Canada Day A604

1992, June 29 Litho. Perf. 12½x13

1420	A604 42c Nova Scotia	1.75	1.75
1421	A604 42c Ontario	1.75	1.75
1422	A604 42c Prince Edward Island	1.75	1.75
1423	A604 42c New Brunswick	1.75	1.75
1424	A604 42c Quebec	1.75	1.75
1425	A604 42c Saskatchewan	1.75	1.75
1426	A604 42c Manitoba	1.75	1.75
1427	A604 42c Northwest Territories	1.75	1.75
1428	A604 42c Alberta	1.75	1.75
1429	A604 42c British Columbia	1.75	1.75
1430	A604 42c Yukon	1.75	1.75
1431	A604 42c Newfoundland	1.75	1.75
a.	Sheet of 12, #1420-1431 + 13 labels	21.00	21.00

Canadian Folklore — A605

Legendary heroes: No. 1432, Jerry Potts, guide, interpreter. No. 1433, Captain William Jackman, rescuer. No. 1434, Laura Secord, patriot. No. 1435, Jos Monferrand, lumberjack.

1992, Sept. 8 Litho. Perf. 12½

1432	A605 42c multicolored	.85	.35
1433	A605 42c multicolored	.85	.35
1434	A605 42c multicolored	.85	.35
1435	A605 42c multicolored	.85	.35
a.	Block of 4, #1432-1435	3.40	2.75

Minerals A606

1992, Sept. 21 Perf. 12½

1436	A606 42c Copper	1.00	.40
1437	A606 42c Sodalite	1.00	.40
1438	A606 42c Gold	1.00	.40
1439	A606 42c Galena	1.00	.40
1440	A606 42c Grossular	1.00	.40
a.	Strip of 5, #1436-1440	5.00	4.50
b.	Bkt. pane, 2 each #1436-1440	10.00	

Canada in Space A607

1992, Oct. 1 Litho. Perf. 13

1441	A607 42c Anik E2 satellite	.85	.85
a.	Silver omitted	3,000.	2,000.

Size: 32x26mm

1442	A607 42c Earth, space shuttle	1.10	1.10
a.	Pair, #1441-1442	2.00	2.00
b.	As "a," hologram omitted on #1442	2,000.	

No. 1442 has a holographic image. Soaking in water may affect the hologram.

Natl. Hockey League, 75th Anniv. A608

Designs: No. 1443, Skates, stick, puck, photograph from the early years (1917-1942). No. 1444, Photograph, team emblems from the six-team years (1942-1967). No. 1445, Goalie's mask, gloves, photograph from the expansion years (1967-1992).

1992, Oct. 9 Litho. Perf. 13x12½
Booklet Stamps

1443	A608 42c multicolored	.90	.25
a.	Bkt. pane of 8 + 4 labels	7.25	
1444	A608 42c multicolored	.90	.25
a.	Bkt. pane of 8 + 4 labels	7.25	
1445	A608 42c multicolored	.90	.25
a.	Bkt. pane of 9 + 3 labels	8.00	
	Nos. 1443-1445 (3)	2.70	.75

A609

No. 1446, Order of Canada, 25th anniv. No. 1447, Daniel Roland Michener (1900-1991), Governor General.

1992, Oct. 21 Perf. 12½

1446	42c multicolored	.85	.25
1447	42c multicolored	.85	.35
a.	A609 Pair, #1446-1447	1.70	1.00

Nos. 1446-1447 printed in sheets of 25 containing 16 #1446 and 9 #1447.

World War II Type of 1989
1992, Nov. 10 Litho. Perf. 13½

1448	A568 42c War reporting	.85	.45
1449	A568 42c Newfoundland air bases	.85	.45
1450	A568 42c Raid on Dieppe	.85	.45
1451	A568 42c U-boats offshore	.85	.45
a.	Block or strip of 4, #1448-1451	3.40	2.50

A611

Santa Claus
A612

1992, Nov. 13　Litho.　Perf. 12½
1452 A611 42c Joulavana .85 .20
　　a. Perf. 13½ 1.10 .90
　　b. As "a," booklet pane of 10 11.00 6.75
Perf. 13½
1453 A611 48c La Befana 1.10 .75
　　a. Booklet pane of 5 + label 5.50 4.50
1454 A611 84c Weihnachtsmann 1.70 .75
　　a. Booklet pane of 5 + label 8.50 6.50
Booklet Stamp
Perf. 12½x13
1455 A612 37c Santa Claus .75 .75
　　a. Booklet pane of 10 7.50
　　Nos. 1452-1455 (4) 4.40 2.45

Christmas. No. 1455 has bar code at left; for use on covers with printed postal code matrix.

A613

Canadian Women: No. 1456, Adelaide Sophia Hoodless (1857-1910), founder of Victorian Order of Nurses. No. 1457, Marie-Josephine Gerin-Lajoie (1890-1971), founder of Notre-Dame du Bon Conseil Institute. No. 1458, Pitseolak Ashoona (c. 1904-83), Inuit graphic artist. No. 1459, Helen Alice Kinnear (1894-1970), first woman appointed King's Counsel and first federally appointed woman judge.

1993, Mar. 8　Litho.　Perf. 12½
1456 A613 43c multicolored .85 .35
1457 A613 43c multicolored .85 .35
1458 A613 43c multicolored .85 .35
1459 A613 43c multicolored .85 .35
　　a. Block or strip of 4, #1456-1459 3.40 2.50

Natl. Council of Women of Canada (NCWC), and Natl. office of YWCA, cent.

Stanley Cup,
Cent. — A614

1993, Apr. 16　Litho.　Perf. 13½
1460 A614 43c multicolored .85 .25

Handcrafted Textiles — A615

#1461, Coverlet, New Brunswick. #1462, Pieced quilt, Ontario. #1463, Doukhobor bedcover, Saskatchewan. #1464,

Kwakwaka'wakw ceremonial robe, British Columbia. #1465, Boutonne coverlet, Quebec.

Perf. 13x12½ on 3 Sides
1993, Apr. 30
Booklet Stamps
1461 A615 43c multicolored .85 .40
1462 A615 43c multicolored .85 .40
1463 A615 43c multicolored .85 .40
1464 A615 43c multicolored .85 .40
1465 A615 43c multicolored .85 .40
　　a. Strip of 5, #1461-1465 4.25 3.50
　　b. Bklt. pane, 2 ea #1461-1465 8.50

Stamps in bottom row of #1465b are in different sequence than those in #1465a.

Art Type of 1988
Painting: Drawing for The Owl, by Kenojuak Ashevak.
Litho. with Foil Application
1993, May 17　Perf. 12½x13½
1466 A546 86c multicolored 1.70 1.10

Intl. Year of Indigenous People.

Historic Canadian Pacific Railway Hotels
A616

#1467, Empress, Victoria, B.C. #1468, Banff Springs, Banff, Alberta. #1469, Royal York, Toronto, Ont. #1470, Chateau Frontenac, Quebec. #1471, Algonquin, St. Andrews, N.B.

Perf. 13½ on 3 Sides
1993, June 14　Litho.
Booklet Stamps
1467 A616 43c multicolored .85 .55
1468 A616 43c multicolored .85 .55
1469 A616 43c multicolored .85 .55
1470 A616 43c multicolored .85 .55
1471 A616 43c multicolored .85 .55
　　a. Strip of 5, #1467-1471 4.25 3.50
　　b. Booklet pane, 2 #1471a 8.50

Opening of Chateau Frontenac, cent.

Miniature Sheet

Canada Day
A617

Provincial and Territorial Parks: No. 1472, Algonquin, Ontario. No. 1473, De la Gaspesie, Quebec. No. 1474, Cedar Dunes, Prince Edward Island. No. 1475, Cape St. Mary's Seabird Ecological Reserve, Newfoundland. No. 1476, Mount Robson, British Columbia. No. 1477, Writing-On-Stone, Alberta. No. 1478, Spruce Woods, Manitoba. No. 1479, Herschel Island, Yukon. No. 1480, Cypress Hills, Saskatchewan. No. 1481, The Rocks, New Brunswick. No. 1482, Blomidon, Nova Scotia. No. 1483, Katannilik, Northwest Territories.

1993, June 30　Litho.　Perf. 13
1472 A617 43c multicolored 1.20 1.00
1473 A617 43c multicolored 1.20 1.00
1474 A617 43c multicolored 1.20 1.00
1475 A617 43c multicolored 1.20 1.00
1476 A617 43c multicolored 1.20 1.00
1477 A617 43c multicolored 1.20 1.00
1478 A617 43c multicolored 1.20 1.00
1479 A617 43c multicolored 1.20 1.00
1480 A617 43c multicolored 1.20 1.00
1481 A617 43c multicolored 1.20 1.00
1482 A617 43c multicolored 1.20 1.00
1483 A617 43c multicolored 1.20 1.00
　　a. Sheet of 12, #1472-1483 15.00 15.00

Algonquin Park, centennial.

City of Toronto, Bicent. — A618

1993, Aug. 6　Litho.　Perf. 13½x13
1484 A618 43c multicolored .85 .25

Canadian Rivers Type of 1991
1993, Aug. 10　Perf. 13x12½
Booklet Stamps
1485 A586 43c Fraser .85 .40
1486 A586 43c Yukon .85 .40
1487 A586 43c Red .85 .40
1488 A586 43c St. Lawrence .85 .40
1489 A586 43c St. John .85 .40
　　a. Strip of 5, #1485-1489 4.25 3.75
　　b. Bklt. pane, 2 each #1485-1489 8.50

Miniature Sheet

Historic Automobiles — A619

a, 1867 H.S. Taylor Steam Buggy. b, 1908 Russell Model L Touring Car. c, 1914 Ford Model T Open Touring Car. d, 1950 Studebaker Champion Deluxe Starlight Coupe. e, 1928 McLaughlin-Buick Model 28-496 Special Car. f, 1923-24 Gray-Dort 25-SM Luxury Sedan.

1993, Aug. 23　Litho.　Perf. 12½x13
1490 A619　Sheet of 6 7.50 7.50
　　a.-b. 43c any single, 35x22mm .85 .85
　　c.-d. 49c any single, 43x22mm 1.00 1.00
　　e.-f. 86c any single, 51x22mm 1.70 1.70

See Nos. 1527, 1552, 1604-1605.

Folk Songs
A620

Designs: No. 1491, The Alberta Homesteader, Alberta. No. 1492, Les Raftmans, Quebec. No. 1493, I'se the B'y That Builds the Boat, Newfoundland. No. 1494, Onkwa:ri tenhanonniahkwe, Kanien'kehaka (Mohawk).

1993, Sept. 7　Litho.　Perf. 12½
1491 A620 43c multicolored .85 .35
1492 A620 43c multicolored .85 .35
1493 A620 43c multicolored .85 .35
1494 A620 43c multicolored .85 .35
　　a. Block of 4, #1491-1494 3.40 2.50

Dinosaurs — A621

1993, Oct. 1　Litho.　Perf. 13½
1495 A621 43c Massospondylus .85 .35
1496 A621 43c Styracosaurus .85 .35
1497 A621 43c Albertosaurus .85 .35
1498 A621 43c Platecarpus .85 .35
　　a. Block or strip of 4, #1495-1498 3.40 2.50

See Nos. 1529-1532.

A622

Santa Claus
A623

1993, Nov. 4　Litho.　Perf. 13½
1499 A622 43c Swiety Mikolaj .85 .20
　　a. Booklet pane of 10 8.50 5.50
　　b. Horiz. pair, imperf between 1,750.
1500 A622 49c Ded Moroz 1.00 .45
　　a. Booklet pane of 5 + label 5.00 4.50
1501 A622 86c Father Christmas, Australia 1.70 .55
　　a. Booklet pane of 5 + label 8.50 7.00
Booklet Stamp
Perf. 13
1502 A623 38c Santa Claus .75 .60
　　a. Booklet pane of 10 7.50
　　Nos. 1499-1502 (4) 4.30 1.80

Christmas. No. 1502 has bar code at left; for use on covers with printed postal code matrix.

World War II Type of 1989
1993, Nov. 8　Litho.　Perf. 13½
1503 A568 43c Aid to Allies .85 .50
1504 A568 43c Bomber forces .85 .50
1505 A568 43c Battle of the Atlantic .85 .50
1506 A568 43c Italian campaign .85 .50
　　a. Block or strip of 4, #1503-1506 3.40 3.00

Greetings — A624

Design: No. 1508, "Canada" at right.

1994, Jan. 28　Litho.　Die Cut
1507 A624 43c multicolored 1.10 .70
1508 A624 43c multicolored 1.10 .70
　　a. Bklt pane, 5 ea #1507-1508 11.00

No. 1508a also contains 35 self-adhesive greetings labels in seven designs that complete the design when placed in the central circle of Nos. 1507-1508.
See Nos. 1568-1569, 1600-1601.

Jeanne Sauve (1922-93), Governor General — A625

1994, Mar. 8　Litho.　Perf. 12½x13
1509 A625 43c + label, multi .85 .30
　　a. Block or horiz. strip of 4 + 4 labels 3.40 2.75

No. 1509 issued se-tenant with label in sheets of 20 + 20 labels in four designs. In alternating rows, labels appear on left or right side of stamp.

T. Eaton Company, 125th Anniv. — A626

1994, Mar. 17   Litho.   Perf. 13½x13
1510 A626 43c multicolored   .85   .30
a.   Booklet pane of 10 + 2 labels   8.50

Canadian Rivers Type of 1991
1994, Apr. 22   Perf. 13½
Booklet Stamps
1511 A586 43c Saguenay   1.00   .50
1512 A586 43c French   1.00   .50
1513 A586 43c Mackenzie   1.00   .50
1514 A586 43c Churchill   1.00   .50
1515 A586 43c Columbia   1.00   .50
a.   Strip of 5, #1511-1515   5.00   4.00
b.   Bklt. pane, 2 ea #1511-1515   10.00   9.00

Art Type of 1988
Vera, by Frederick H. Varley (1881-1969).

Litho. with Foil Application
1994, May 6   Perf. 14x14½
1516 A546 88c multicolored   1.60   1.20

XV Commonwealth Games, Victoria, BC — A627

1994   Litho.   Perf. 14
1517 A627 43c Lawn bowls   .85   .25
1518 A627 43c Lacrosse   .85   .25
a.   Pair, #1517-1518   1.70   1.00
1519 A627 43c Wheelchair marathon   .85   .25
1520 A627 43c High jump   .85   .25
a.   Pair, #1519-1520   1.70   1.00
1521 A627 50c Diving   1.00   .75
a.   Gold ("CANADA 50") omitted   1,600.
1522 A627 88c Cycling   1.75   1.00
a.   Gold ("CANADA 88") omitted   2,000.
Nos. 1517-1522 (6)   6.15   2.75

Certificates of authenticity recommended for Nos. 1521a and 1522a.
Issued: #1517-1518, 5/20; #1519-1522, 8/5.

Souvenir Sheet

Intl. Year of the Family — A628

Designs: a, Mother and infant. b, Adults, children playing. c, Elderly woman, children. d, Adults, children in class. e, Judge, health care worker, child.

1994, June 2   Litho.   Perf. 14
1523 A628 Sheet of 5   4.25   4.25
a.-e.   43c any single   .85   .55

Canada Day A629

Maple trees: a, Big leaf. b, Sugar. c, Silver. d, Striped. e, Norway. f, Manitoba. g, Black. h, Douglas. i, Mountain. j, Vine. k, Hedge. l, Red.

1994, June 30   Litho.   Perf. 13x13½
1524 A629 Sheet of 12   11.00   11.00
a.-l.   43c any single   .85   .85

Design: No. 1526, Mary Travers, "La Bolduc" (1894-1941), folk singer.

1994, Aug. 12   Perf. 13
1525 A630 43c multicolored   .85   .35
1526 A630 43c multicolored   .85   .35
a.   Pair, #1525-1526   1.70   1.10

Historic Vehicles Type of 1993
Miniature Sheet
Designs: a, 1942 Ford F60L-AMB military ambulance. b, 1925 REO Speed Wagon Police Wagon. c, 1927 Sicard Snow Remover/Snowblower. d, 1936 Bickle Chieftain Fire Engine. e, 1894 Ottawa Car Company Streetcar. f, 1950 Motor Coach Industries Courier 50 Skyview bus.

1994, Aug. 19   Litho.   Perf. 12½x13
1527   Sheet of 6   7.50   7.50
a.-b.   A619 43c any single   .85   .85
c.-d.   A619 50c any single   1.00   1.00
e.-f.   A619 88c any single   1.75   1.75

ICAO, 50th Anniv. A632

1994, Sept. 16   Litho.   Perf. 13
1528 A632 43c multicolored   1.00   .25

Dinosaur Type of 1993
Prehistoric animals: No. 1529, Coryphodon. No. 1530, Megacerops. No. 1531, Short-faced bear. No. 1532, Woolly mammoth.

1994, Sept. 26
1529 A621 43c multicolored   .85   .30
1530 A621 43c multicolored   .85   .30
1531 A621 43c multicolored   .85   .30
1532 A621 43c multicolored   .85   .30
a.   Block or strip of 4, #1529-1532   3.40   2.50

Family Singing Carols A633

Soloist A634

1994, Nov. 3   Litho.   Perf. 13½
1533 A633 43c multicolored   .85   .20
a.   Booklet pane of 10   8.50
1534 A633 50c Choir, vert.   1.00   .55
a.   Booklet pane of 5 + label   5.00   4.25
1535 A633 88c Caroling, vert.   1.75   1.00
a.   Booklet pane of 5 + label   8.75   7.00

Booklet Stamp
Perf. 13
1536 A634 38c multicolored   .80   .45
a.   Booklet pane of 10   8.00
Nos. 1533-1536 (4)   4.40   2.20

Christmas. No. 1536 has bar code at left; for use on covers with printed postal code matrix.
Examples exist of 52c and 90c denominations with the same designs as Nos. 1534 (52c) and 1535 (90c). These were prepared in advance in anticipation of a rate increase that was not approved. Virtually all were destroyed, but a small quantity are known in private hands. None were regularly issued or sold at post offices.

World War II Type of 1989
1994, Nov. 7   Litho.   Perf. 13½
1537 A568 43c D-Day beachhead   .85   .35
1538 A568 43c Artillery-Normandy   .85   .35
1539 A568 43c Tactical Air Forces   .85   .35

1540 A568 43c Walcheren and the Scheldt   .85   .35
a.   Block or strip of 4, #1537-1540   3.40   2.50

1995, Mar. 20   Litho.   Perf. 13½
1541 A568 43c Veterans return home   .85   .35
1542 A568 43c Freeing the POW   .85   .35
1543 A568 43c Liberation of civilians   .85   .35
1544 A568 43c Crossing the Rhine   .85   .35
a.   Block or strip of 4, #1541-1544   3.40   2.50

Art Type of 1988
Painting: Floraison, by Alfred Pellan (1906-88).

Litho. with Foil Application
1995, Apr. 21   Perf. 13
1545 A546 88c multicolored   1.75   1.10
a.   Gold foil omitted   1,600.

Flag Over Lake — A635

1995, May 1   Litho.   Perf. 13½x13
1546 A635 (43c) multicolored   .85   .25
No. 1546 was valued at the first class domestic letter rate on day of issue.

Fortress of Louisbourg, 275th Anniv. — A636

#1547, Louisbourg Harbor, ships near Dauphin Gate. #1548, Walls, streets, buildings of Louisbourg. #1549, Museum behind King's Bastion. #1550, Drawing of King's Garden, Convent, Hospital and barracks. #1551, Partially eroded fortifications.

1995, May 5   Perf. 12½x13
1547 A636 (43c) 48x32mm   .85   .40
1548 A636 (43c) 32x32mm   .85   .40
1549 A636 (43c) 40x32mm   .85   .40
1550 A636 (43c) 56x32mm   .85   .40
1551 A636 (43c) 48x32mm   .85   .40
a.   Strip of 5, #1547-1551   4.25   3.75
b.   Booklet pane, 2 #1551a   8.50
Complete booklet, #1551b   8.75

Nos. 1547-1551 were valued at the first class domestic letter rate on day of issue. No. 1551a is a continuous design.

Historic Vehicles Type of 1993
Miniature Sheet
Farm, frontier vehicles: a, 1950 Cockshutt "30" farm tractor. b, 1970 Bombardier Ski-Doo Olympique 335 snowmobile. c, 1948 Bombardier B-12 CS multi-passenger snowmobile. d, 1924 Gotfredson model 20 farm truck. e, 1962 Robin-Nodwell RN 110 tracked carrier. f, 1942 Massey-Harris No. 21 self-propelled combine.

1995, May 26   Litho.   Perf. 12½x13
1552   Sheet of 6   7.50   7.50
a.-b.   A619 43c any single, 35x22mm   .85   .85
c.-d.   A619 50c any single, 43x22mm   1.00   1.00
e.-f.   A619 88c any single, 43x22mm   1.75   1.75

Golf in Canada A637

Designs: No. 1553, Banff Springs Golf Club. No. 1554, Riverside Country Club. No. 1555, Glen Abbey Golf Club. No. 1556, Victoria Golf Club. No. 1557, Royal Montreal Golf Club.

Perf. 13½x13 on 3 Sides
1995, June 6
Booklet Stamps
1553 A637 43c multicolored   1.00   .40
1554 A637 43c multicolored   1.00   .40
1555 A637 43c multicolored   1.00   .40
1556 A637 43c multicolored   1.00   .40
1557 A637 43c multicolored   1.00   .40
a.   Strip of 5, #1553-1557   5.00   4.00
b.   Booklet pane, 2 #1557a   10.00
Complete booklet, #1557b   10.50

Nat. Golf Week. Canadian Amateur Golf Championship, cent. Royal Canadian Golf Assoc., cent.

Lunenburg Academy, Cent. — A638

1995, June 29   Litho.   Perf. 13
1558 A638 43c multicolored   .85   .25

Souvenir Sheets

Group of Seven — A639

Painting, original members: No. 1559a, October Gold, by Franklin Carmichael. b, From the North Shore, Lake Superior, by Lawren Harris. c, Evening, Les Eboulements, Quebec, by A.Y. Jackson.
No. 1560a, Serenity, Lake of the Woods, by Frank H. Johnston. b, A September Gale, Georgian Bay, by Arthur Lismer. c, Falls, Montreal River, by J.E.H. MacDonald. d, Open Window, by Frederick Horsman Varley.
Painting, new members: No. 1561a, Mill Houses, by Alfred J. Casson. b, Pembina Valley, by Lionel LeMoine FitzGerald. c, The Lumberjack, by Edwin Headley Holgate.

1995, June 29
1559 A639 Sheet of 3   2.60   2.60
a.-c.   43c any single   .85   .85
1560 A639 Sheet of 4   3.50   3.50
a.-d.   43c any single   .85   .85
1561 A639 Sheet of 3   2.60   2.60
a.-c.   43c any single   .85   .85

Manitoba's Entry Into Confederation, 125th Anniv. — A640

1995, July 14   Perf. 13½x13
1562 A640 43c multicolored   .85   .30

Migratory Wildlife — A641

1995, Aug. 15   Litho.   Perf. 13x12½
1563 A641 45c Monarch butterfly   .90   .30
1564 A641 45c Belted kingfisher   .90   .40
1565 A641 45c Northern pintail   .90   .30
1566 A641 45c Hoary bat   .90   .30
a.   Block or strip of 4, #1563-1566   3.60   2.50

No. 1564 with Revised Inscription

1995, Sept. 26

1567	A641	45c like #1564	1.30	.90
a.		Block or strip of 4, #1563, 1565-1567	4.00	4.00

#1564 inscribed "aune," #1567 "Faune." See Mexico #1924.

Greetings Type of 1994

Designs: No. 1568, "Canada" at left. No. 1569, "Canada" at right.

1995, Sept. 1   *Die Cut*

Self-Adhesive

Size: 46x22mm

1568	A624	45c green & multi	1.00	.75
1569	A624	45c green & multi	1.00	.75
a.		Bklt. pane, 5 ea #1568-1569	10.00	

By its nature, No. 1569a is a complete booklet. The peelable backing serves as a booklet cover.

No. 1569a also contains 15 self-adhesive greetings labels in four designs that complete the design when placed in the central circle of Nos. 1568-1569.

No. 1569a exists with special cover and labels commemorating the Canadian Memorial Chiropractic College, Toronto, 50th anniv.

Bridges
A642

#1570, Quebec Bridge, Quebec. #1571, Highway 403-401-410 interchange, Ontario. #1572, Hartland Covered Wooden Bridge, New Brunswick. #1573, Alex Fraser Bridge, British Columbia.

1995, Sept. 1   *Perf. 12½x13*

1570	A642	45c multicolored	.90	.30
1571	A642	45c multicolored	.90	.30
1572	A642	45c multicolored	.90	.30
1573	A642	45c multicolored	.90	.30
a.		Block or strip of 4, #1570-1573	3.60	2.50

Canadian Arctic
A643

#1574, Polar bear, caribou. #1575, Arctic poppy, cargo canoe. #1576, Inuk man, igloo, sled dogs. #1577, Dog-sled team, ski plane. No. 1578, Children.

1995, Sept. 15   *Perf. 13x12½*

Booklet Stamps

1574	A643	45c multicolored	.90	.30
1575	A643	45c multicolored	.90	.30
1576	A643	45c multicolored	.90	.30
1577	A643	45c multicolored	.90	.30
1578	A643	45c multicolored	.90	.30
a.		Strip of 5, #1574-1578	4.50	3.50
b.		Bklt. pane, 2 #1578a	9.00	
		Complete booklet, #1578b	9.50	

Stamps in bottom row of #1578b are in different sequence.

Comic Book Characters
A644

1995, Oct. 2   Litho.   *Perf. 13x12½*

Booklet Stamps

1579	A644	45c Superman	1.10	.40
1580	A644	45c Johnny Canuck	1.10	.40
1581	A644	45c Nelvana	1.10	.40
1582	A644	45c Captain Canuck	1.10	.40
1583	A644	45c Fleur de Lys	1.10	.40
a.		Strip of 5, #1579-1583	5.50	5.00
b.		Booklet pane, 2 #1583a	11.00	
		Complete booklet, #1583b	11.50	

Stamps in the bottom row of No. 1583b are in different sequence.

UN, 50th Anniv. A645

1995, Oct. 24   Litho.   *Perf. 13½*

1584	A645	45c blue & multi	1.00	.25

No. 1584 printed in sheets of 10 with top label equal to 10 stamps. Label shows details of Canadian participation in UN activities. UN emblem on No. 1584 is stamped in blue foil.

Capital Sculptures, by Emile Brunet (1893-1977), Sainte-Anne-de-Deaupre Basilica — A646

Holly A647

1995, Nov. 2   Litho.   *Perf. 13½*

1585	A646	45c The Nativity	.90	.20
a.		Booklet pane of 10	9.00	
		Complete booklet, #1585a	9.50	
1586	A646	52c The Annunciation	1.00	.50
a.		Booklet pane of 5 + label	5.00	5.00
		Complete booklet, #1586a	5.25	
1587	A646	90c Flight to Egypt	1.80	.60
a.		Booklet pane of 5 + label	9.00	8.50
		Complete booklet, #1587a	9.50	

Booklet Stamp

Perf. 12½x13

1588	A647	40c multicolored	.80	.80
a.		Booklet pane of 10	8.00	10.00
		Complete booklet, #1588a	8.25	
		Nos. 1585-1588 (4)	4.50	2.10

Christmas. No. 1588 has bar code at left; for use on covers with printed postal code matrix.

La Francophonie's Agency for Cultural and Technical Cooperation, 25th Anniv. — A648

1995, Nov. 6   *Perf. 13x13½*

1589	A648	45c multicolored	.90	.25

End of the Holocaust, 50th Anniv. — A649

1995, Nov. 9   *Perf. 12½x13*

1590	A649	45c multicolored	.90	.25

Birds A650

#1591, American kestrel. #1592, Atlantic puffin. #1593, Pileated woodpecker. #1594, Ruby-throated hummingbird.

1996, Jan. 9   Litho.   *Perf. 13½*

1591	A650	45c multicolored	.90	.30
1592	A650	45c multicolored	.90	.30
1593	A650	45c multicolored	.90	.30
1594	A650	45c multicolored	.90	.30
a.		Strip of 4, Nos. 1591-1594	3.60	2.75

Issued in panes of 12 stamps, printed checkerwise, and in uncut sheets of 5 panes. See Nos. 1631-1634, 1710-1713, 1770-1777, 1839-1846, 1886-1889.

High Technology Industries — A651

Designs: No. 1595, Ocean technology. No. 1596, Aerospace technology. No. 1597, Information technology. No. 1598, Biotechnology.

Perf. 13½ on 3 Sides

1996, Feb. 15   Litho.

Booklet Stamps

1595	A651	45c multicolored	.90	.35
1596	A651	45c multicolored	.90	.35
1597	A651	45c multicolored	.90	.35
1598	A651	45c multicolored	.90	.35
a.		Booklet pane of 12, 3 each Nos. 1595-1598	11.00	8.00
		Complete booklet, No. 1598a	11.50	
		Nos. 1595-1598 (4)	3.60	1.40

Greetings Type of 1994

"Canada": #1600, at L. #1601, at R.

1996, Jan. 15   Litho.   *Die Cut*

Self-Adhesive

Size: 51x25mm

1600	A624	45c green & multi	1.50	1.00
1601	A624	45c green & multi	1.50	1.00
a.		Booklet pane, 5 ea #1600-1601	15.00	
b.		As "a," die cutting omitted	3,250.	

By its nature No. 1601a is a complete booklet. The peelable backing serves as a booklet cover.

No. 1601a also contains 35 self-adhesive greetings labels in seven designs that complete the design when placed in the central circle of Nos. 1600-1601.

Art Type of 1988

Sculpture: The Spirit of Haida Gwaii, by Bill Reid.

Litho. with Foil Application

1996, Apr. 30   *Perf. 12½x13*

1602	A546	90c multicolored	1.60	1.00

AIDS Awareness — A652

1996, May 8   Litho.   *Perf. 13½*

1603	A652	45c multicolored	.90	.20

Historic Vehicles Type of 1993

#1604: a, 1899 Still Motor Co. Ltd. Electric Van. b. 1914 Waterous Engine Works Road Roller. c, 1938 International D-35 Delivery Truck. d, 1936 Champion Road Grader. e, 1947 White Model WA 122 Tractor Trailer. f, 1975 Hayes HDX 45-115 Logging Truck.

#1605: a, like #1490a. b, like #1490b. c, like 1527a. d, like #1527b. e, like #1552b. f, like #1604a. g, like #1604b, h, like #1552a. i, like #1604c. j, like 1604d. k, like #1527e. l, like #1527f. m, like #1604e. n, like #1604f. o, like #1490c. p, like #1490d. q, like #1527d. r, like #1490e. s, like #1490f. t, like #1527c. u, like #1552c. v, like #1552d. w, like #1552f. x, like #1552f. y, 1975 Bricklin SV-1 Sports car.

1996   Litho.   *Perf. 12½x13*

1604	A619	Sheet of 6	7.50	7.50
a.-b.		45c any single	.90	.90
c.-d.		52c any single	1.00	1.00
e.-f.		90c any single	1.80	1.80

1605	A619	Sheet of 25	9.00	9.00
a.-j.		5c any single	.20	.20
k.-n.		10c any single	.35	.35
o.-x.		20c any single	.45	.45
y.		45c multicolored	1.00	1.00

Nos. 1604e-1604f, 1605k-1605n, 1605y are 51x22mm. Nos. 1605o-1605x are 43x21mm.

Yukon Gold Rush, Cent. A653

Designs: a, "Skookum" Jim Mason's discovery on Rabbit (Bonanza) Creek, 1896. b, Miners trekking to gold fields, boats on Lake Laberge. c, Supr. Sam Steele, North West Mounted Police, Alaska-Yukon border. d, Dawson, boom town, city of entertainment. e, Klondike gold fields.

1996, June 13   *Perf. 13½*

1606		Strip of 5	5.00	4.50
a.-e.	A653	45c any single	1.00	.50

CAPEX '96. #1606 was issued in sheets of 10 stamps.

Canada Day — A654

1996, June 28   Litho.   *Die Cut*

Self-Adhesive

1607	A654	45c multicolored	.90	.25
a.		Pane of 12	11.00	

Canadian Olympic Gold Medalists
A655

#1608, Ethel Catherwood, high jump, 1928. #1609, Etienne Desmarteau, 56 lb. weight throw, 1904. #1610, Fanny Rosenfeld, 100m, 400m relay, 1928. #1611, Gerald Ouellette, smallbore rifle, prone, 1956. #1612, Percy Williams, 100m, 200m, 1928.

Litho. & Typo.

1996, July 8   *Perf. 13x12½*

Booklet Stamps

1608	A655	45c gold, sep & silver	.90	.55
1609	A655	45c gold, sep & silver	.90	.55
1610	A655	45c gold, sep & silver	.90	.55
1611	A655	45c gold, sep & silver	.90	.55
1612	A655	45c gold, sep & silver	.90	.55
a.		Strip of 5, #1608-1612	4.50	3.25
b.		Booklet pane, 2 #1612a	9.00	
		Complete booklet, #1612b	9.50	

British Columbia's Entry Into Confederation, 125th Anniv. — A656

1996, July 19

1613	A656	45c multicolored	.90	.25

A657

1996, Aug. 19   Litho.   Perf. 12½x12
1614 A657 45c Canadian Heral-
            dry   .90   .25

Motion Pictures,
Cent. — A658

Film strips from motion pictures: No. 1615a,
L'arrivée d'un train en gare, Lumière cinema-
tography, 1896. b, Back to God's Country, Nell
& Ernest Shipman, 1919. c, Hen Hop, Norman
McLaren, 1942. d, Pour la suite du monde,
Pierre Perrault, Michel Brault, 1963. e, Goin'
Down the Road, Don Shebib, 1970.

No. 1616a, Mon oncle Antoine, Claude
Jutra, 1971. b, The Apprenticeship of Duddy
Kravitz, Ted Kotcheff, 1974. c, Les Ordres,
Michel Brault, 1974. d, Les Bons Débarras,
Francis Mankiewiez, 1980. e, The Grey Fox,
Philip Borsos, 1982.

1996, Aug. 22   Die Cut
Self-Adhesive
1615 A658 Sheet of 5   4.50   4.50
  a.-e. 45c Any single   .90   .60
1616 A658 Sheet of 5   4.50   4.50
  a.-e. 45c Any single   .90   .60

Edouard
Montpetit
(1881-1954),
Educator
A659

1996, Sept. 26   Litho.   Perf. 12½
1617 A659 45c multicolored   .90   .25

Winnie the
Pooh
A660

Designs: No. 1618, Winnie, Lt. Colebourne,
1914. No. 1619, Winnie, Christopher Robin,
1925. No. 1620, Milne and Shepard's Winnie
the Pooh, 1926. No. 1621, Winnie the Pooh at
Walt Disney World, 1996.

1996, Oct. 1   Litho.   Perf. 12½x13
1618 A660 45c multicolored   .90   .40
1619 A660 45c multicolored   .90   .40
1620 A660 45c multicolored   .90   .40
1621 A660 45c multicolored   .90   .40
  a. Block of 4, #1618-1621   3.60   2.50
  b. Souv. sheet of 4, #1618-1621 8.00 7.50
  c. Booklet pane of 16, 4 each
       #1618-1621   14.50
       Complete booklet, #1621c   15.00

No. 1621c was issued with the halves of the
booklet pane printed tete-beche. The booklet
pane of 16 was used as a cover for a souvenir
story booklet.
Walt Disney World, 25th anniv.

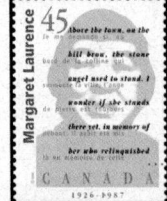

Authors — A661

#1622, Margaret Laurence (1926-87).
#1623, Donald G. Creighton (1902-79).
#1624, Gabrielle Roy (1909-83). #1625, Felix-
Antoine Savard (1896-1982). #1626, Thomas
C. Haliburton (1796-1865).

Perf. 13½x13 on 3 Sides
1996, Oct. 10   Litho. & Engr.
Booklet Stamps
1622 A661 45c multicolored   1.00   .40
1623 A661 45c multicolored   1.00   .40
1624 A661 45c multicolored   1.00   .40
1625 A661 45c multicolored   1.00   .40
1626 A661 45c multicolored   1.00   .40
  a. Strip of 5, #1622-1626   5.00   3.50
  b. Booklet pane, 2 #1626a   10.00   9.00
       Complete booklet, #1626b 10.50

A662

Christmas: 45c, Children on snowshoes,
sled. 52c, Santa Claus skiing. 90c, Children
skating.

**Perf. 13½ (#1627, 1629a), 12¾x12¼
(#1628, 1629), 13½x13 (#1627a,
1628a)**
1996, Nov. 1   Litho.
1627 A662 45c multicolored   .90   .20
  a. Booklet pane of 10   9.00   9.00
       Complete booklet, #1627a   9.50
1628 A662 52c multicolored   1.00   .25
  a. Booklet pane of 5 + label   5.00   5.00
       Complete booklet, #1628a   5.25
1629 A662 90c multicolored   1.60   .50
  a. Booklet pane of 5 + label   8.00   8.00
       Complete booklet, #1629a   8.50

UNICEF, 50th anniv.

New Year 1997
(Year of the
Ox) — A663

1997, Jan. 7   Litho.   Perf. 13x12½
1630 A663 45c multicolored   .90   .25
  a. Souvenir sheet of 2   2.75   2.75
  b. As No. 1630, gold omitted   4,000.

No. 1630a is fan shaped.
No. 1630a with Hong Kong 97 overprint was
sold as a limited edition only at the show.
Value $8.

Bird Type of 1996
#1631, Mountain bluebird. #1632, Western
grebe. #1633, Northern gannet. #1634, Scarlet tanager.

1997, Jan. 10   Litho.   Perf. 12½x13
1631 A650 45c multicolored   .90   .30
1632 A650 45c multicolored   .90   .30
1633 A650 45c multicolored   .90   .30
1634 A650 45c multicolored   .90   .30
  a. Block or strip of 4, #1631-1634 3.60 2.50

Nos. 1631-1634 were issued in sheets of
20, 5 each, printed checkerwise to contain 4
complete blocks or 5 strips.

Art Type of 1988
Painting: York Boat on Lake Winnipeg, by
Walter J. Phillips.

Litho. with Foil Application
1997, Feb. 17   Perf. 12½x13
1635 A546 90c gold & multi   1.80   1.10

Canadian
Tire, 75th
Anniv.
A664

1997, Mar. 3   Litho.   Perf. 13x13½
1636 A664 45c multicolored   .90   .25

Father Charles-
Emile Gadbois
(1906-81),
Musicologist
A665

1997, Mar. 20   Perf. 13½x13
1637 A665 45c multicolored   .90   .25

Québec en
Fleurs 97, Intl.
Horticultural
Exhibition
A666

Perf. 13x12½ on 3 Sides
1997, Apr. 4   Litho.
Booklet Stamp
1638 A666 45c Blue poppy   .90   .25
  a. Booklet pane of 12   11.00
       Complete booklet, #1638a 11.50

Victorian
Order of
Nurses for
Canada,
Cent.
A667

1997, May 12   Litho.   Perf. 12½x13
1639 A667 45c multicolored   .90   .25

Law Society of
Upper Canada,
Bicent. — A668

1997, May 23   Perf. 13½x13
1640 A668 45c multicolored   .90   .25

Salt
Water
Fish
A669

#1641, Great white shark. #1642, Pacific
halibut. #1643, Atlantic sturgeon. #1644, Bluefin tuna.

1997, May 30   Litho.   Perf. 12½x13
1641 A669 45c multicolored   .90   .30
1642 A669 45c multicolored   .90   .30
1643 A669 45c multicolored   .90   .30
1644 A669 45c multicolored   .90   .30
  a. Block or strip of 4, #1641-1644 3.60 2.50

Opening of the Confederation
Bridge — A670

1997, May 31
1645 A670 45c Lighthouse,
            bridge   .90   .25
1646 A670 45c Bridge, bird   .90   .25
  a. Pair, #1645-1646 + label   1.80   1.00

Gilles Villeneuve (1950-82), Formula
One Race Car Driver — A671

45c, Villeneuve winning race in Ferrari T-4.
90c, Close-up, racing in Number 12 Ferrari T-
3.

1997, June 12
1647 A671 45c multicolored   .90   .25
1648 A671 90c multicolored   1.80   1.00
  a. Pair, #1647-1648   2.70   2.50
  b. Sheet of 4 #1648a   11.00 10.00

John Cabot's Voyage to Canada,
500th Anniv.
A672

1997, June 24   Litho.   Perf. 12½x13
1649 A672 45c multicolored   .90   .25

See Italy No. 2162.

Scenic Canadian Highways — A673

Designs: No. 1650, Sea to Sky Highway,
British Columbia. No. 1651, The Cabot Trail,
Nova Scotia. No. 1652, The Wine Route, start-
ing in Ontario. No. 1653, The Big Muddy,
Saskatchewan.

1997, June 30   Perf. 12½x13
1650 A673 45c multicolored   .90   .50
1651 A673 45c multicolored   .90   .50
1652 A673 45c multicolored   .90   .50
1653 A673 45c multicolored   .90   .50
  a. Block or strip of 4, #1650-1653 3.60 2.50

See Nos. 1739-1742, 1780-1783.

Canadian Industrial Design — A674

1997, July 23
1654 A674 45c multicolored   .90   .25

No. 1654 was issued with se-tenant label in
sheets of 24 + 24 labels. The 12 different
labels each appear twice in different colors. In
alternating rows, labels appear on left or right
side of stamp.
Association of Canadian Industrial Designers, 50th anniv. and 20th Intl. Congress of Intl.
Council of Societies of Industrial Design.

Highland Games, Maxville,
Ontario — A675

1997, Aug. 1
1655 A675 45c multicolored .90 .25

Knights of Columbus
in Canada,
Cent. — A676

1997, Aug. 5 *Perf. 13*
1656 A676 45c multicolored .90 .25

28th World Congress of Postal,
Telegraph and Telephone Intl. Labor
Union, Montreal
A677

1997, Aug. 18 Litho. *Perf. 13*
1657 A677 45c multicolored .90 .25

Asia
Pacific
Year
A678

1997, Aug. 25 *Perf. 13½*
1658 A678 45c multicolored .90 .25

Canada-USSR Ice Hockey "Series of
the Century," 25th Anniv. — A679

Designs: No. 1659, Canadian players, Paul
Henderson, Yvan Cournoyer (No. 12), after
scoring winning goal in final game. No. 1660,
Canadian team members celebrating victory.

1997, Sept. 20 Litho. *Perf. 14x13*
Booklet Stamps
1659 A679 45c multicolored .90 .30
1660 A679 45c multicolored .90 .30
a. Bklt. pane, 5 ea #1659-1660 9.00
Complete booklet, #1660a 9.50

Famous
Politicians
A680

#1661, Martha Black (1866-1957). #1662,
Lionel Chevrier (1903-87). #1663, Judy
LaMarsh (1924-80). #1664, Réal Caouette
(1917-76).

1997, Sept. 26 *Perf. 13½x13*
1661 A680 45c multicolored .90 .35
1662 A680 45c multicolored .90 .35
1663 A680 45c multicolored .90 .35
1664 A680 45c multicolored .90 .35
a. Block or strip of 4, #1661-1664 3.60 2.50

Supernatural — A681

1997, Oct. 1 *Perf. 13x12½*
1665 A681 45c Vampire .90 .30
1666 A681 45c Werewolf .90 .30
1667 A681 45c Ghost .90 .30
1668 A681 45c Goblin .90 .30
a. Block of 4, #1665-1668 3.60 2.50

Christmas — A682

Stained glass windows: 45c, "Our Lady of
the Rosary," Holy Rosary Cathedral, Vancou-
ver. 52c, "Nativity Scene," United Church,
Leith, Ontario. 90c, Madonna and Child, St.
Stephen's Ukrainian Byzantine Rite Roman
Catholic Church, Calgary.

1997, Nov. 3 Litho. *Perf. 12½x13*
1669 A682 45c multicolored .90 .20
a. Booklet pane of 10 9.00 9.00
Complete booklet, #1669a 9.50
1670 A682 52c multicolored 1.00 .25
a. Booklet pane of 5 5.00 5.00
Complete booklet, #1670a 5.25
1671 A682 90c multicolored 1.80 .50
a. Booklet pane of 5 9.00 9.00
Complete booklet, #1671a 9.50
Nos. 1669-1671 (3) 3.70 .95

75th Royal
Agriculture
Winter Fair,
Toronto
A683

1997, Nov. 6
1672 A683 45c multicolored .90 .25

Types of 1987-98 and:

Traditional
Handiwork
A684

Maple Leaf
A685

Loon
A686

Moose — A687

Flag and
Inukshuk — A688

1997-2005 Litho. *Perf. 13x13½*
1673 A684 1c Bookbinding .20 .20
1674 A684 2c Ironwork .20 .20
1675 A684 3c Glass blowing .20 .20
1676 A684 4c Oyster farmer .20 .20
1677 A684 5c Weaving .20 .20
1678 A684 9c Quilting .20 .20
1679 A684 10c Artistic wood-
working .20 .20
a. Imperf, single —
b. Block of 4, top two stamps
imperf (cut between) —
1680 A684 25c Leatherwork-
ing .50 .20

Perf. 13
1681 A536 46c Queen Elizabeth II .90 .30
1682 A541 46c Flag over Ice-
bergs .90 .30
a. Booklet pane of 10 9.00
Complete booklet, #1682a 9.50

Perf. 13¼x13
1683 A536 47c multi .95 .30
a. Imperf, pair 725.00

Perf. 13
1684 A685 55c multicolored 1.10 .35
a. Booklet pane of 5 + label 5.50 5.00
Complete booklet, #1684a 5.75
1685 A685 73c multicolored 1.30 .30
1686 A685 95c multicolored 1.90 .65
a. Booklet pane of 5 + label 9.50 9.00
Complete booklet, #1686a 10.00

Litho. & Engr.
1687 A686 $1 Loon 2.00 .50
1688 A686 $1 White-tailed
deer ('05) 2.00 .60
1689 A686 $1 Atlantic wal-
rus ('05) 2.00 .60
a. Pair, #1688-1689 4.00 2.50
b. Souvenir sheet, 2 each
#1696-1697 8.00 8.00
1690 A686 $2 Polar bear 4.00 1.00
1691 A686 $2 Peregrine fal-
cons ('05) 4.00 1.00
1692 A686 $2 Sable Island
horses ('05) 4.00 1.00
a. Pair, #1691-1692 8.00 5.00
b. Souvenir sheet, 2 each
#1691-1692 16.00 16.00

Size 63x48mm
Perf. 12½x13
1693 A687 $5 Moose 10.00 2.00
a. Engraved colors (Moose,
etc.) omitted 6,000.
1694 A687 $8 Grizzly bear 15.00 4.50
Nos. 1673-1694 (22) 51.95 15.20

Coil Stamp
Engr.
Perf. 10 Horiz.
1695 A542 46c red .90 .30
a. Imperf, pair 175.00

Booklet Stamps
Self-Adhesive
Die Cut
1696 A685 45c multicolored 1.40 1.50
a. Booklet pane of 18 25.00

Typo. & Embossed
Die Cut Perf. 13
Self-adhesive
1697 A685 45c multicolored 1.10 .65

Litho.
Die Cut
1698 A541 46c Flag over Ice-
bergs .90 .65
a. Booklet pane of 30 27.00
b. Imperf, pair 325.00
1699 A685 46c multicolored 2.75 2.25
a. Booklet pane of 18 50.00

1700 A688 47c multi .95 .20
a. Booklet of 10 9.50
b. Booklet of 30 28.50

Nos. 1698a-1699a are complete booklets.
The peelable backing serves as a booklet
cover.

Issued: #1681, 1682, 1685-1687, 1695,
1698-1699, 12/28/98; $8, 10/15/97; Nos.
1690-1691, 4/14/98. No. 1688, 10/27/99;
1c-25c, 4/29/99; 47c, 12/28/00; Nos. 1689-
1690, 10/20/05; Nos. 1692-1693, 12/19/05.
The peelable paper backing of No. 1696a
serves as a booklet cover.

No. 1697 does not have the "POSTAGE /
POSTES" and copyright inscriptions found in
No. 1696. The gold on No. 1697 is embossed
and brighter than that on No. 1696.
See Nos. 1928-1930.

New Year
1998 (Year
of the
Tiger)
A690

1998, Jan. 8 Litho. *Perf. 13x12½*
1708 A690 45c multicolored .90 .25
a. Souvenir sheet of 2 1.80 1.25

No. 1708a overprinted exists. Value $2.50.

Provincial
Leaders
A691

Designs: a, John P. Robarts (1917-82),
Ontario. b, Jean Lesage (1912-80), Quebec.
c, John B. McNair (1889-1968), New Brunswick. d, Tommy Douglas (1904-86), Saskatchewan. e, Joseph R. Smallwood (1900-91),
Newfoundland. f, Angus L. MacDonald (1890-
1954), Nova Scotia. g, W.A.C. Bennett (1900-
79), British Columbia. h, Ernest C. Manning
(1908-95), Alberta. i, John Bracken (1883-
1969), Manitoba. j, J. Walter Jones (1878-
1954), Prince Edward Island.

1998, Feb. 18 Litho. *Perf. 13½*
1709 A691 Sheet of 10 11.00 7.50
a.-j. 45c any single 1.10 .40

Bird Type of 1996

#1710, Hairy woodpecker. #1711, Great
crested flycatcher. #1712, Eastern screech
owl. #1713, Gray-crowned rosy-finch.

1998, Mar. 13 Litho. *Perf. 13x13½*
1710 A650 45c multicolored .90 .30
1711 A650 45c multicolored .90 .30
1712 A650 45c multicolored .90 .30
1713 A650 45c multicolored .90 .30
a. Block or strip of 4, #1710-1713 3.60 2.50

Nos. 1710-1713 were issued in sheets of
20, 5 each, printed checkerwise to contain 4
complete blocks or 5 strips.

Fly Fishing in Canada — A693

Lure, type of fish: No. 1715, Coquihalla
orange, steelhead trout. No. 1716, Steelhead
bee, steelhead trout. No. 1717, Dark Montreal,
brook trout. No. 1718, Lady Amherst, Atlantic
salmon. No. 1719, Coho blue, coho salmon.
No. 1720, Cosseboom special, Atlantic
salmon.

1998, Apr. 16 *Perf. 12½x13*
1715 A693 45c multicolored .90 .45
1716 A693 45c multicolored .90 .45
1717 A693 45c multicolored .90 .45
1718 A693 45c multicolored .90 .45
1719 A693 45c multicolored .90 .45
1720 A693 45c multicolored .90 .45
a. Vertical strip of 6, #1715-
1720 5.50 5.00
b. Bklt. pane, 2 ea #1715-1720 11.00
Complete booklet, #1720a 11.50

Canadian Institute of Mining, Metallurgy and Petroleum, Cent. — A694

1998, May 4   Litho.   Perf. 12½
1721 A694 45c multicolored   .90 .25

Imperial Penny Post, Cent. A695

St. Edward's Crown, #86, Sir William Mulock.

1998, May 29   Perf. 12½x13
1722 A695 45c multicolored   .90 .25

#1722 was issued in sheets of 14 + 1 label.

Sumo Wrestling Tournament, Vancouver — A696

Rising sun, mapleleaf and: No. 1723, Two wrestlers. No. 1724, Sumo champion performing bow twirling ceremony.

1998, June 5   Litho. & Embossed
1723 A696 45c multicolored   .90 .25
1724 A696 45c multicolored   .90 .25
  a. Horiz. or Vert. Pair, #1723-
        1724 + 4 labels   1.80 1.20
  b. Souvenir sheet, #1723-1724 3.50 3.50

Nos. 1723-1724 were printed checkerwise in sheets of 20, 10 each, plus 40 labels.

Canals of Canada — A697

#1725, St. Peters Canal, Nova Scotia. #1726, St. Ours Canal, Quebec. #1727, Port Carling Lock, Ontario. #1728, Locks, Rideau Canal, Ontario. #1729, Peterborough lift lock, Trent-Severn Waterway, Ontario. #1730, Chambly Canal, Quebec. #1731, Lachine Canal, Quebec. #1732, Ice skating on Rideau Canal, Ottawa. #1733, Boat on Big Chute Marine Railway, Trent-Severn Waterway. #1734, Sault Ste. Marie Canal, Ontario.

1998, June 17   Litho.   Perf. 12½
Booklet Stamps
1725 A697 45c multicolored   1.00 .60
1726 A697 45c multicolored   1.00 .60
1727 A697 45c multicolored   1.00 .60
1728 A697 45c multicolored   1.00 .60
1729 A697 45c multicolored   1.00 .60
1730 A697 45c multicolored   1.00 .60
1731 A697 45c multicolored   1.00 .60
1732 A697 45c multicolored   1.00 .60
1733 A697 45c multicolored   1.00 .60
1734 A697 45c multicolored   1.00 .60
  a. Bklt. pane, #1725-1734 + 10
        labels   12.50
        Complete booklet, #1734a   15.00

Health Professionals A698

Litho. & Embossed with Foil Application
1998, June 25   Perf. 12½
1735 A698 45c multicolored   .90 .25

Royal Canadian Mounted Police, 125th Anniv. — A699

#1736, Male mountie, native, horse. #1737, Female mountie, helicopter, cityscape.

1998, July 3   Litho.   Perf. 12½x13
1736 A699 45c multicolored   .90 .25
1737 A699 45c multicolored   .90 .25
  a. Pair, #1736-1737 + 2 labels   1.80 1.80
  b. Souvenir sheet, #1736-1737 +
        1 label   1.80 1.80
  c. As "b," with signature   3.25 3.25
  d. As "b," with Portugal 98 em-
        blem   4.00 4.00
  e. As "b," with Italia 98 emblem 4.00 4.00

#1737c-1737e have added inscriptions in gold. Issued: #1737c, 7/3; #1737d, 9/4; #1737e, 10/23.

William James Roué (1879-1970), Naval Architect — A700

Litho. & Engr.
1998, July 24   Perf. 13
1738 A700 45c multicolored   .90 .25

Scenic Highway Type of 1997
Designs: No. 1739, Dempster Highway, Yukon. No. 1740, Dinosaur Trail, Alberta. No. 1741, River Valley Scenic Drive, New Brunswick. No. 1742, Blue Heron Route, Prince Edward Island.

1998, July 28   Litho.   Perf. 12½x13
1739 A673 45c multicolored   .90 .30
1740 A673 45c multicolored   .90 .30
1741 A673 45c multicolored   .90 .30
1742 A673 45c multicolored   .90 .30
  a. Block or strip of 4, #1739-1742 3.60 2.50

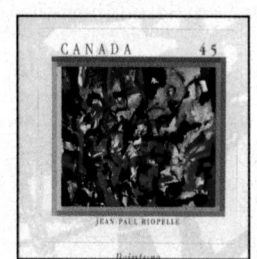

Publication of "Refus Global" by The Automatistes, 50th Anniv. — A701

Painting, artist: No. 1743, "Peinture," Jean-Paul Riopelle. No. 1744, "La dernière campagne de Napoléon," Fernand Leduc. No. 1745, "Jet fuligineux sur noir torturé," Jean-Paul Mousseau. No. 1746, "Le fond du garderobe," Pierre Gauvreau. No. 1747, "Joie lacustre," Paul-Emile Borduas. No. 1748, "Syndicat des gens de mer," Marcelle Ferron. No. 1749, "Le tumulte á la machoire crispée," Marcel Barbeau.

1998, Aug. 7   Die Cut
Self-Adhesive
Booklet Stamps
1743 A701 45c multicolored   1.10 .60
1744 A701 45c multicolored   1.10 .60
1745 A701 45c multicolored   1.10 .60
1746 A701 45c multicolored   1.10 .60
1747 A701 45c multicolored   1.10 .60
1748 A701 45c multicolored   1.10 .60
1749 A701 45c multicolored   1.10 .60
  a. Booklet pane, #1743-1749   8.00

No. 1746 is 34x48mm. No. 1749a is a complete booklet. The peelable paper backing serves as a booklet cover.

Legendary Canadians A702

#1750, Napoléon-Alexandre Comeau (1848-1923), outdoorsman, "King of the North Shore." #1751, Phyllis Munday (1894-1990), mountaineer, community service worker. #1752, Bill Mason (1929-88), film maker, canoe enthusiast. #1753, Harry "Red" Foster (1905-1985), founder of Canadian Special Olympics, sports enthusiast.

1998, Aug. 15   Perf. 13½
1750 A702 45c multicolored   .90 .30
1751 A702 45c multicolored   .90 .30
1752 A702 45c multicolored   .90 .30
1753 A702 45c multicolored   .90 .30
  a. Block or strip of 4, #1750-1753 3.60 2.50

Art Type of 1988
Painting: The Farmer's Family (detail), by Bruno Bobak.

Litho. with Foil Application
1998, Sept. 8   Perf. 12½x13
1754 A546 90c gold & multi   1.80 1.10

Housing in Canada A703

a, Native peoples. b, Settler. c, Regional. d, Heritage preservation. e, Multiple unit. f, Prefabricated. g, Veterans. h, Planned community. i, Innovative.

1998, Sept. 23
1755   Sheet of 9   10.00 10.00
  a.-i. A703 45c Any single   1.00 .75

University of Ottawa, 150th Anniv. — A704

1998, Sept. 25   Perf. 13
1756 A704 45c multicolored   .90 .25

The Circus — A705

Various circus clowns and: No. 1757, Elephant, bear performing tricks. No. 1758,

Woman standing on horse, aerial act. No. 1759, Lion tamer. No. 1760, Contortionists, acrobats.

Perf. 13 on 3 Sides
1998, Oct. 1   Litho.
Booklet Stamps
1757 A705 45c multicolored   .90 .30
1758 A705 45c multicolored   .90 .30
1759 A705 45c multicolored   .90 .30
1760 A705 45c multicolored   .90 .30
  a. Bklt. pane, 3 ea #1757-1760 11.00 11.00
        Complete booklet, #1760a   11.50
  b. Souvenir sheet, #1757-1760   4.50 4.60

Stamps in No. 1760b are perforated on all four sides.

John Peters Humphrey (1905-95), Author of Universal Declaration of Human Rights A706

1998, Oct. 7   Perf. 13
1761 A706 45c multicolored   .90 .25

Canadian Naval Reserve, 75th Anniv. — A707

1998, Nov. 4   Litho.   Perf. 12½x13
1762 A707 45c HMCS Sackville   .90 .25
1763 A707 45c HMCS Shawini-
              gan   .90 .25
  a. Pair, #1762-1763   1.80 1.60

Christmas — A708

Sculpted wooden angels: 45c, "Angel of Last Judgment" blowing trumpet. 52c, "Adoring Angel" raising hand. 90c, "Adoring Angel, Kneeling," by Thomas Baillairgé.

1998, Nov. 6   Perf. 13
1764 A708 45c multicolored   .90 .25
  a. Booklet pane of 10   35.00 35.00
        Complete booklet,
        #1764a   37.50
  b. Perf 13x13½   400.00 16.00
  c. As "b," booklet pane of
        10   14.00
        Complete booklet,
        #1764c   15.00

The values for No. 1764b are for singles perfed on all four sides from sheet format. These are extremely scarce. Single stamps from booklet pane No. 1764c have a straight edge on one side. Value, booklet single, unused $1.60, used $.30.

Perf. 13x13½
1765 A708 52c multicolored   1.00 .30
  a. Booklet pane of 5 + label   19.00 17.50
        Complete booklet,
        #1765a   20.00
  b. Perf 13   1.10 .50
  c. As "b," booklet pane of 5
        + label   5.50 5.00
        Complete booklet,
        #1765c   6.00
1766 A708 90c multicolored   1.80 .60
  a. Booklet pane of 5 + label   30.00 25.00
        Complete booklet,
        #1766a   30.00
  b. Perf 13   1.80 .90
  c. As "b," booklet pane of 5
        + label   9.00 8.00
        Complete booklet,
        #1766c   9.50
      Nos. 1764-1766 (3)   3.70 1.15

CANADA

96

New Year 1999
(Year of the
Rabbit)
A709

1999, Jan. 8   Litho.   Perf. 13½
1767 A709 46c multicolored   .90 .25

Souvenir Sheet
Perf. 12½x13
1768 A709 95c Sheet of 1   2.50 2.25
  a.   Single stamp   1.75 1.25

No. 1768 with China 99 overprint was sold only at the show. Value same as unoverprinted sheet.

Le Theatre du
Rideau Vert,
50th
Anniv. — A710

1999, Feb. 17   Litho.   Perf. 13x12½
1769 A710 46c multicolored   .90 .30

Bird Type of 1996
Designs: No. 1770, Northern goshawk. No. 1771, Red-winged blackbird. No. 1772, American goldfinch. No. 1773, Sandhill crane.

1999, Feb. 24   Litho.   Perf. 12½x13
1770 A650 46c multicolored   .90 .30
1771 A650 46c multicolored   .90 .30
1772 A650 46c multicolored   .90 .30
1773 A650 46c multicolored   .90 .30
  a.   Block or strip of 4, #1770-
        1773   3.60 2.00

Booklet Stamps
Self-Adhesive
Die Cut Perf. 11½
1774 A650 46c like #1770   1.20 .30
1775 A650 46c like #1771   1.20 .30
1776 A650 46c like #1772   1.20 .30
1777 A650 46c like #1773   1.20 .30
  a.   Booklet pane, 2 each #1774-
        1775, 1 each #1776-1777   7.25
  b.   Booklet pane, 2 each #1776-
        1777, 1 each #1774-1775   7.25
        Complete booklet, #1777a,
        #1777b   15.00

Nos. 1770-1773 were issued in sheets of 20, 5 each, printed checkerwise to contain 4 complete blocks or strips.
The peelable paper backing of Nos. 1777a, 1777b serves as the booklet cover.

Univ. of British Columbia's Museum of
Anthropology, 50th Anniv. — A711

1999, Mar. 9   Litho.   Perf. 13½
1778 A711 46c multicolored   .90 .30

Sailing Ship
Marco
Polo — A712

1999, Mar. 19   Litho.   Perf. 13x12½
1779 A712 46c multicolored   .90 .30
  a.   Sheet of 2, #1779 perf. 13,
        Australia #1631 perf. 13½   3.25 3.25

Australia '99 World Stamp Expo. See Australia #1631a.

Scenic Highway Type of 1997
#1780, Gaspé Peninsula, Highway 132, Quebec. #1781, Yellowhead Highway (PTH 16), Manitoba. #1782, Dempster Highway 8, Northwest Territories. #1783, Discovery Trail, Route 230N, Newfoundland.

1999, Mar. 31   Perf. 12½x13
1780 A673 46c multicolored   .90 .30
1781 A673 46c multicolored   .90 .30
1782 A673 46c multicolored   .90 .30
1783 A673 46c multicolored   .90 .30
  a.   Block or strip of 4, #1780-1783 3.60 2.50

Creation of the Nunavut
Territory — A713

1999, Apr. 1
1784 A713 46c multicolored   .90 .25

Intl. Year of Older Persons — A714

1999, Apr. 12   Litho.   Perf. 13½
1785 A714 46c multicolored   .90 .25

A715   A716

1999, Apr. 19   Perf. 13
1786 A715 46c multicolored   .90 .25
Baisakhi, Religious Holiday of Sikh Canadians, 300th Anniv.

1999, Apr. 27   Perf. 13x12½
Paintings (Canadian Orchids): No. 1787, Arethusa bulbosa, by Poon-Kuen Chow. No. 1788, Amerorchis rotundifolia, by Yakman Lai. No. 1789, Platanthera psycodes, by Lai. No. 1790, Cypripedium pubescens, by Chow.

Booklet Stamps
1787 A716 46c multicolored   .90 .30
1788 A716 46c multicolored   .90 .30
1789 A716 46c multicolored   .90 .30
1790 A716 46c multicolored   .90 .30
  a.   Bklt. pane, 3 ea #1787-1790 11.00
        Complete booklet, #1790a   11.50
  b.   Souvenir sheet, #1787-1790 3.75 3.75

China '99 World Philatelic Exhibition, Beijing. Designs of some stamps contained in No. 1790a extend into selvage of booklet pane. Issued: No. 1790b, 8/21/99.

Horses
A717

#1791, Northern Dancer, thoroughbred race horse. #1792, Kingsway Skoal, bucking horse. #1793, Big Ben, show horse. #1794, Armbro Flight, harness race horse.

1999, June 2   Litho.   Perf. 13x13½
1791 A717 46c multicolored   1.00 .35
1792 A717 46c multicolored   1.00 .35
1793 A717 46c multicolored   1.00 .35

1794 A717 46c multicolored   1.00 .35
  a.   Block or strip of 4, #1791-
        1794   4.00 3.00

Booklet Stamps
Self-Adhesive
Serpentine Die Cut 11½
1795 A717 46c like #1791   1.25 .35
1796 A717 46c like #1792   1.25 .35
1797 A717 46c like #1793   1.25 .35
1798 A717 46c like #1794   1.25 .35
  a.   Block of 4, #1795-1798   5.00
  b.   Complete booklet, 3 each
        #1795-1798   15.00

Nos. 1791-1794 were issued in sheets of 16, 4 each, printed checkerwise to contain 4 complete blocks or strips.

Quebec Bar
Assoc., 150th
Anniv. — A718

1999, June 3   Perf. 13½
1799 A718 46c multicolored   .90 .30

Art Type of 1988
Coq Licorne, by Jean Dallaire (1916-65).

Litho. with Foil Application
1999, July 3   Perf. 12½x13¼
1800 A546 95c multicolored   1.90 1.10
  a.   Silver omitted   1,150.

1999 Pan
American
Games,
Winnipeg
A719

Designs: No. 1801, Track & field. No. 1802, Cycling, weight lifting, gymnastics. No. 1803, Swimming, sailboarding, kayaking. No. 1804, Soccer, tennis, medal winners.

1999, July 12   Perf. 13¼
1801 A719 46c multicolored   .90 .30
1802 A719 46c multicolored   .90 .30
1803 A719 46c multicolored   .90 .30
1804 A719 46c multicolored   .90 .30
  a.   Block of 4, #1801-1804   3.60 2.50

Issued in sheets of 16 stamps.

23rd World Rowing Championships,
St. Catherines, Ont. — A720

1999, Aug. 22   Litho.   Perf. 12½x13
1805 A720 46c multicolored   .90 .30

UPU, 125th Anniv. — A721

1999, Aug. 26
1806 A721 46c multicolored   .90 .30

Airplanes — A722

No. 1807: a, Fokker DR-1, CT-114 Tutors. b, Tutors, H101 Salto sailplane. c, De Havilland DH100 Vampire MKIII. d, Stearman A-75.
No. 1808: a, De Havilland Mosquito FBVI. b, Sopwith F1 Camel. c, De Havilland Canada DHC-3 Otter. d, De Havilland Canada CC-108 Caribou. e, Canadair CL-28 Argus MK 2. f, North American F-86 Sabre 6. g, McDonnell Douglas CF-18 Hornet. h, Sopwith SF-1 Dolphin. i, Armstrong Whitworth Siskin IIIA. j, Canadian Vickers (Northrop) Delta II. k, Sikorsky CH-124A Sea King helicopter. l, Vickers-Armstrong Wellington MKII. m, Avro Anson MKI. n, Canadair (Lockheed) CF-104G Starfighter. o, Burgess-Dunne seaplane. p, Avro 504K.
Illustration reduced.

1999, Sept. 4   Litho.   Perf. 12½x13
1807 A722 Sheet of 4   4.50 4.50
  a.-d.   46c any single   1.10 .70
1808 A722 Sheet of 16   15.00 15.00
  a.-p.   46c any single   .90 .90
Canadian Intl. Air Show, 50th anniv. (#1807). Royal Canadian Air Force, 75th anniv. (#1808). Nos. 1808a-1808p are each 56x28mm.

NATO, 50th Anniv. — A723

1999, Sept. 21   Litho.   Perf. 12½x13
1809 A723 46c multicolored   .90 .30

Frontier
College,
100th
Anniv.
A724

1999, Sept. 24   Litho.   Perf. 13x13½
1810 A724 46c multicolored   .90 .30

Kites
A725

Designs: a, Master Control, sport kite by Lam Hoac (triagular). b, Indian Garden Flying Carpet, edo kite by Skye Morrison (trapezoidal). c, Gibson Girl, manufactured box kite (rectangular). d, Dragon centipede kite by Zhang tian Wei (oval).

Die cut in various patterns
1999, Oct. 1   Litho.
Self-Adhesive
1811   Complete booklet, 2
        each #a.-d.   8.75
  a.-d.   A725 46c any single   1.10 .35

A726

A727

Millennium
A728

1999, Oct. 12 Holography *Die Cut*
Self-Adhesive (46c)

1812	A726	46c silver	1.00	.45
		Pane of 4	4.00	4.00

Litho.
Perf. 13¼

1813	A727	55c multicolored	1.10	.75
		Pane of 4	4.50	4.50

Engr.
Perf. 12¾

1814	A728	95c brown	1.90	1.25
		Pane of 4	7.75	7.75
		Nos. 1812-1814 (3)	4.00	2.45

Nos. 1812-1814 each exist in souvenir sheets of 1 with decorative border.

Christmas — A729

1999, Nov. 4 Litho. Perf. 13¼

1815	A729	46c Angel, drum	.90	.25
a.		Booklet pane of 10	9.00	9.00
		Complete booklet	9.50	
1816	A729	55c Angel, toys	1.10	.35
a.		Booklet pane of 5 + label	5.50	5.50
		Complete booklet	6.00	
1817	A729	95c Angel, candle	1.90	.65
a.		Booklet pane of 5 + label	9.50	9.50
		Complete booklet	10.00	
		Nos. 1815-1817 (3)	3.90	1.25

Souvenir Sheets

Millennium — A730

No. 1818 — Media Technologies: a, IMAX movies. b, Softimage animation software. c, Ted Rogers, Sr. (1900-39) and radio tube. d, Invention of radio facsimile device for transmission of photographs for publishing by Sir William Stephenson (1896-1989).

No. 1819 — Canadian Entertainment: a, Calgary Stampede. b, Performers from Cirque du Soleil. c, Hockey Night in Canada. d, La Soiree du Hockey.

No. 1820 — Entertainers: a, Portia White (1911-68), singer. b, Glenn Gould (1932-82), pianist. c, Guy Lombardo (1902-77), band leader. d, Félix Leclerc (1914-88), singer, guitarist.

No. 1821 — Fostering Canadian Talent: a, Royal Canadian Academy of Arts (men viewing painting). b, Canada Council (sky, musical staff, "A"). c, National Film Board of Canada. d, Canadian Broadcasting Corporation.

No. 1822 — Medical Innovators: a, Sir Frederick Banting (1891-1941), co-discoverer of insulin, syringe and dog. b, Dr. Armand Frappier (1904-91), microbiologist, holding flask. c, Dr. Hans Selye (1907-82), endocrinologist, and molecular diagram. d, Maude Abbott (1869-1940), pathologist, and roses.

No. 1823 — Social Progress: a, Nun, doctor, hospital. b, Statue of woman holding decree. c, Alphonse Desjardins (1854-1920) and wife Dorimène (1858-1932), credit union founders, and credit union emblem. d, Father Moses Coady (1882-1959), educator of adults.

No. 1824 — Charity: a, Canadian International Development Agency (hands and tools). b, Dr. Lucille Teasdale (1929-96), hospital administrator in Uganda. c, Marathon of Hope inspired by Terry Fox (1958-81). d, Meals on Wheels program.

No. 1825 — Humanitarians and Peacekeepers: a, Raoul Dandurand (1861-1942), b, Pauline Vanier (1898-1991), Red Cross volunteer, and Elizabeth Smellie (1884-1968), head of various nursing services. c, Lester B. Pearson (1897-1972), prime minister, and Nobel Peace Prize winner, and dove. d, Amputee and shadow (Ottawa Convention on Land Mines).

No. 1826 — Canada's First People: a, Chief Pontiac (c. 1720-69). b, Tom Longboat (1887-1949), marathon runner. c, Inuit sculpture of shaman. d, Medicine man.

No. 1827 — Canada's Cultural Fabric: a, Norse boat, L'Anse aux Meadows. b, Immigrants on Halifax's Pier 21. c, Neptune Theater, Halifax (head of Neptune). d, Stratford Festival (actor and theater).

No. 1828 — Literary Legends: a, W. O. Mitchell (1914-98), novelist, and prairie scene. b, Gratien Gélinas (1909-99), actor and playwright, and stars. c, Le Cercle du Livre de France book club. d, Harlequin paperback books.

No. 1829 — Great Thinkers: a, Marshall McLuhan (1911-80), philosopher, and television set. b, Northrop Frye (1912-91), literary critic, and word "code." c, Roger Lemelin (1919-92), novelist, and cast of "The Plouffe Family" TV series. d, Hilda Marion Neatby (1904-75), historian, and farm scene.

No. 1830 — A Tradition of Generosity: a, Hart Massey (1823-96), Hart House, University of Toronto. b, Dorothy (1899-1965) and Izaak Killam (1885-1955), philanthropists, and molecular model. c, Eric Lafferty Harvie (1892-1975), philanthropist, and mountain scene. d, Macdonald Stewart Foundation.

No. 1831 — Engineering and Technological Marvels: a, Map of Rogers Pass, locomotive, tunnel diggers. b, Manic Dams. c, Canadian satellites, Remote Manipulator Arm. d, CN Tower.

No. 1832 — Fathers of Invention: a, George Klein (1904-92), gearwheels. b, Abraham Gesner (1797-1864), beaker of kerosene and lamp. c, Alexander Graham Bell (1847-1922), passenger-carrying kite, hydrofoil. d, Joseph-Armand Bombardier (1907-64), snowmobile.

No. 1833 — Food: a, Sir Charles Saunders (1867-1937), Marquis wheat. b, Pablum. c, Dr. Archibald Gowanlock Huntsman (1883-1973), marketer of frozen fish. d, Products of McCain Foods, Ltd., tractor.

No. 1834 — Enterprising Giants: a, Hudson's Bay Company (Colonist, Indian, canoe). b, Bell Canada Enterprises (earth, satellite, string of binary digits). c, Vachon Co. snack cakes. d, George Weston Limited (Baked goods, eggs).

1999-2000 Litho. Perf. 13¼

1818	A730	Sheet of 4	6.00	6.00
a.-d.		46c any single	1.40	.60
1819	A730	Sheet of 4	6.00	6.00
a.-d.		46c any single	1.40	.60
1820	A730	Sheet of 4	6.00	6.00
a.-d.		46c any single	1.40	.60
1821	A730	Sheet of 4	6.00	6.00
a.-d.		46c any single	1.40	.60
1822	A730	Sheet of 4	6.00	6.00
a.-d.		46c any single	1.40	.60
1823	A730	Sheet of 4	6.00	6.00
a.-d.		46c any single	1.40	.60
1824	A730	Sheet of 4	6.00	6.00
a.-d.		46c any single	1.40	.60
1825	A730	Sheet of 4	6.00	6.00
a.-d.		46c any single	1.40	.60
1826	A730	Sheet of 4	6.00	6.00
a.-d.		46c any single	1.40	.60
1827	A730	Sheet of 4	6.00	6.00
a.-d.		46c any single	1.40	.60
1828	A730	Sheet of 4	6.00	6.00
a.-d.		46c any single	1.40	.60
1829	A730	Sheet of 4	6.00	6.00
a.-d.		46c any single	1.40	.60
1830	A730	Sheet of 4	6.00	6.00
a.-d.		46c any single	1.40	.60
1831	A730	Sheet of 4	6.00	6.00
a.-d.		46c any single	1.40	.60
1832	A730	Sheet of 4	6.00	6.00
a.-d.		46c any single	1.40	.60
1833	A730	Sheet of 4	6.00	6.00
a.-d.		46c any single	1.40	.60

1834	A730	Sheet of 4	6.00	6.00
a.-d.		46c any single	1.40	.60
		Nos. 1818-1834 (17)	102.00	102.00

Issued: #1818-1821, 12/17; #1822-1825, 1/17/00; #1826-1830, 2/17/00; #1831-1834, 3/17/00.

Stamps similar to these were printed in a hardcover book produced by Canada Post Sept. 15, 1999 that sold for $59.99. Stamps from souvenir sheets show a distinct upward turn of the tails of the nines in the small 1999 date at upper left. The tails of the nines on stamps from the book are flat.

Millennium — A731

2000, Jan. 1 Litho. Perf. 13x12½

1835	A731	46c multicolored	.90	.30

New Year 2000 (Year of the Dragon) — A732

Litho. & Embossed
2000, Jan. 5 Perf. 12½x12¾

1836	A732	46c multicolored	.90	.25

Souvenir Sheet
Perf. 13¾x13¼

1837	A732	95c multicolored	1.90	1.90
a.		Orange and tagging omitted	1,600.	

No. 1837 has rounded corners and contains one 56x29mm stamp.

50th National Hockey League All-Star Game A733

Famous NHL players: a, Wayne Gretzky (Oilers jersey No. 99). b, Gordie Howe (Red Wings jersey No. 9). c, Maurice Richard (red, white and blue Canadiens jersey No. 9). d, Doug Harvey (Canadiens jersey No. 2). e, Bobby Orr (Bruins jersey No. 4). f, Jacques Plante (Canadiens jersey No. 1).

2000, Feb. 5 Litho. Perf. 12¾

1838	A733	Sheet of 6	5.50	5.50
a.-f.		46c any single	.90	.40

Bird Type of 1996

Designs: Nos. 1839, 1843, Canada warbler. Nos. 1840, 1844, Osprey. Nos. 1841, 1845, Pacific loon. Nos. 1842, 1846, Blue jay.

2000, Mar. 1 Litho. Perf. 12½x13¼

1839	A650	46c multi	.90	.35
1840	A650	46c multi	.90	.35
1841	A650	46c multi	.90	.35
1842	A650	46c multi	.90	.35
a.		Block or strip of 4	3.50	2.50

Booklet Stamps
Self-Adhesive
Die Cut 11½x11¼

1843	A650	46c multi	1.10	.35
1844	A650	46c multi	1.10	.35
1845	A650	46c multi	1.10	.35
1846	A650	46c multi	1.10	.35
a.		Booklet pane, 2 each #1843-1844, 1 each #1845-1846	6.75	
b.		Booklet pane, 2 each #1845-1846, 1 each #1843-1844	6.75	
		Complete bklt., #1846a, 1846b	13.50	

Nos. 1839-1842 were issued in sheets of 20, 5 each printed checkerwise to contain 4 complete blocks or strips.

Supreme Court, 125th Anniv. A734

2000, Apr. 10 Litho. Perf. 12½x13¼

1847	A734	46c multi	.90	.25

Ritual of the Calling of an Engineer, 75th Anniv. — A735

2000, Apr. 25

1848	A735	46c multi	.90	.25
a.		Tete-beche pair	1.80	1.20
b.		Silver ("CANADA 46") omitted	2,400.	

Decorated Rural Mailboxes — A736

Mailboxes with: No. 1849, Ship, fish, house designs. No. 1850, Flower, cow and church designs. No. 1851, Tractor design. No. 1852, Goose head, house designs.

Perf. 12½x13¼ on 3 sides
2000, Apr. 28
Booklet Stamps

1849	A736	46c multi	.90	.30
1850	A736	46c multi	.90	.30
1851	A736	46c multi	.90	.30
1852	A736	46c multi	.90	.30
a.		Block of 4, #1849-1852	3.50	3.00
b.		Bklt. pane, 3 ea #1849-1852	10.50	
		Complete booklet, #1852a	11.00	

Picture Frame A737

Serpentine Die Cut 11½
2000, Apr. 28 Litho.
Self-Adhesive

1853	A737	46c multi	1.00	.30
a.		Booklet pane of 5 + 5 different labels	5.00	
		Complete booklet, #1853a	5.00	
b.		Pane of 25	45.00	

No. 1853b sold for $24.95 each for one or two sheets, and $22.95 for three to ten sheets. Twenty-five self-adhesive, die cut address labels and reproductions of a photo sent in by the customer are on the reverse of No. 1853b. These panes were not available at post offices or through the philatelic bureau, but special orders from the printer, Ashton-Potter. The front cover of the booklet containing No. 1853a served as the order blank for No. 1853b.

See No. 1882.

A738

A739

A740

A741

A742

A743

A744

A745

A746

Fresh Waters — A747

Serpentine Die Cut 2½ Horiz.
2000, Feb. 23   **Litho.**
Self-Adhesive

1854	Complete booklet, #a.-e.	7.50	
a.	A738 55c multi	1.50	.75
b.	A739 55c multi	1.50	.75
c.	A740 55c multi	1.50	.75
d.	A741 55c multi	1.50	.75
e.	A742 55c multi	1.50	.75
1855	Complete booklet, #a.-e.	8.75	
a.	A743 95c multi	1.75	1.20
b.	A744 95c multi	1.75	1.20
c.	A745 95c multi	1.75	1.20
d.	A746 95c multi	1.75	1.20
e.	A747 95c multi	1.75	1.20

Queen Mother (b. 1900) A748

2000, May 23   **Litho.**   **Perf. 13x13¼**
1856   A748 95c multi   1.60   1.00

Boys and Girls Clubs of Canada, Cent. — A749

2000, June 1   **Perf. 13**
1857   A749 46c multi   .90   .25

World Session of Seventh Day Adventist Church, Toronto A750

2000, June 29   **Perf. 13½x13¼**
1858   A750 46c multi   .90   .25

Stampin' the Future Children's Stamp Design Contest Winners A751

Designs: No. 1859, Rainbow, space vehicle, astronauts, flag, by Rosalie Anne Nardelli. No. 1860, Three children in space vehicle, three children on ground, by Sarah Lutgen. No. 1861, Children and map of Canada, by Christine Weera. No. 1862, Two astronauts in space vehicle, planets, by Andrew Wright.

2000, July 1   **Perf. 13¼**

1859	A751 46c multi	.90	.30
1860	A751 46c multi	.90	.30
1861	A751 46c multi	.90	.30
1862	A751 46c multi	.90	.30
a.	Block or strip, #1859-1862	3.60	2.50
b.	Souvenir sheet, #1859-1862	3.60	3.60

Art Type of 1988
The Artist at Niagara, by Cornelius Krieghoff.

Litho. with Foil Application
2000, July 7   **Perf. 12½x13¼**
1863   A546 95c multi   1.60   .65

Tall Ships in Halifax Harbor — A752

Various ships: No. 1864, Denomination at L. No. 1865, Denomination at R.

Serpentine Die Cut 4¾x5
2000, July 19   **Litho.**
Booklet Stamps
Self-Adhesive

1864	A752 46c multi	.90	.40
1865	A752 46c multi	.90	.40
a.	Pair, #1864-1865	1.80	
b.	Booklet, 5 #1864a	9.00	

Dept. of Labor, Cent. — A753

2000, Sept. 1   **Litho.**   **Perf. 12½x13¼**
1866   A753 46c multi   .90   .30

Petro-Canada, 25th Anniv. — A754

2000, Sept. 13   **Litho.**   **Die Cut**
Self-Adhesive
Booklet Stamp

1867	A754 46c multi	1.00	.40
a.	Booklet pane of 12	12.00	
	Booklet, #1867a	12.50	
b.	Die cutting inverted (2 points jut at T, L)	8.50	8.50

No. 1867a is the cover of an informational booket about Petro-Canada. No. 1867b was issued in collector packs.

Cetaceans — A755

#1868, Monodon monoceros. #1869, Balaenoptera musculus. #1870, Balaena mysticetus. #1871, Delphinapterus leucas.

2000, Oct. 2   **Perf. 12½x13**

1868	A755 46c multi	.90	.30
1869	A755 46c multi	.90	.30
1870	A755 46c multi	.90	.30
1871	A755 46c multi	.90	.30
a.	Block of 4, #1868-1871	3.60	2.50

Christmas A756

Serpentine Die Cut 11¾
2000, Oct. 5
Booklet Stamp
Self-Adhesive

1872	A756 46c multi	1.00	.70
a.	Booklet pane of 5 + 5 labels	5.00	
	Booklet, #1872a	5.50	

See No. 1882e.

Christmas A757

Designs: 46c, Adoration of the shepherds. 55c, Creche. 95c, Flight into Egypt.

2000, Nov. 3   **Litho.**   **Perf. 13¼**

1873	A757 46c multi	.90	.25
a.	Booklet pane of 10	9.00	—
	Booklet, #1873a	9.50	
1874	A757 55c multi	1.10	.35
a.	Booklet pane of 6	6.50	—
	Booklet, #1874a	7.00	
1875	A757 95c multi	1.90	.70
a.	Booklet pane of 6	11.50	—
	Booklet, #1875a	12.00	
	Nos. 1873-1875 (3)	3.90	1.30

Regiments A758

No. 1876, Lord Strathcona's Horse Regiment. No. 1877, Les Voltigeurs de Quebec.

2000, Nov. 11   **Perf. 13¼x13**

1876	A758 46c multi	.90	.30
1877	A758 46c multi	.90	.30
a.	Pair, #1876-1877	1.60	.85

Maple Leaves A759

Animals A760

Serpentine Die Cut 8½ Horiz.
2000, Dec. 28   **Litho.**
Coil Stamps
Self-Adhesive

1878	A759 47c multi	.95	.20
1879	A760 60c Red fox	1.20	.25
a.	Booklet pane of 6	11.00	
1880	A760 75c Gray wolf	1.50	.35
1881	A760 $1.05 White-tailed deer	2.10	.40
a.	Booklet pane of 6	12.50	
	Nos. 1878-1881 (4)	5.75	1.20

Nos. 1879a and 1881a are complete booklets. See No. 1927.

Frame Type of 2000

No. 1882: a, Silver. b, Like #1853. c, Mahogany. d, Love (roses). e, Christmas.

Serpentine Die Cut 11¾
2000, Dec. 28   **Litho.**
Booklet Stamps
Self-Adhesive

1882	Bklt. pane of 5+5 labels	4.75	
a.-e.	A737 47c Any single	.95	.90
	Booklet, #1882	5.25	

New Year 2001 (Year of the Snake) A761

Litho. & Embossed
2001, Jan. 5   **Perf. 13¼**
1883   A761   47c green & multi   .95   .25
a.   Gold omitted   1,600.

Souvenir Sheet
1884   A761 $1.05 brown & multi   2.50   2.50

National Hockey League Stars A762

No. 1885: a, Jean Beliveau (Montreal Canadiens jersey No. 4). b, Terry Sawchuk (goalie in Detroit Red Wings uniform). c, Eddie Shore (Boston Bruins jersey No. 2). d, Denis Potvin (Islanders jersey No. 5). e, Bobby Hull (Chicago Black Hawks jersey No. 9). f, Syl Apps, Sr. (Toronto Maple Leafs jersey).

Perf. 12½x13 on 3 sides
2001, Jan. 18   **Litho.**
1885   Sheet of 6 + 3 labels   5.75   5.75
a.-f.   A762 47c Any single   .95   .50

Bird Type of 1996

Designs: Nos. 1886, 1890, Golden eagle. Nos. 1887, 1891, Arctic tern. Nos. 1888, 1892, Rock ptarmigan. Nos. 1889, 1893, Lapland longspur.

2001, Feb. 1   Litho.   Perf. 12½x13

1886	A650	47c multi	.95	.30
1887	A650	47c multi	.95	.30
1888	A650	47c multi	.95	.30
1889	A650	47c multi	.95	.30
a.		Block or strip of 4, #1886-1889	3.80	2.75

Booklet Stamps
Self-Adhesive
Die Cut Perf 11½x11¼

1890	A650	47c multi	1.10	.35
1891	A650	47c multi	1.10	.35
1892	A650	47c multi	1.10	.35
1893	A650	47c multi	1.10	.35
a.		Booklet pane, 2 each #1890-1891, 1 each #1892-1893	6.75	
b.		Booklet pane, 2 each #1892-1893, 1 each #1890-1891	6.75	
		Booklet, #1893a, 1893b	14.00	

Nos. 1886-1889 were issued in sheets of 20, 5 each printed checkerwise to contain 4 complete blocks or strips.

Games of La Francophonie, Ottawa and Hull — A763

2001, Feb. 28   Perf. 13¼

1894	A763	47c High jumper	.95	.30
1895	A763	47c Dancer	.95	.30
a.		Horiz. pair, #1894-1895	1.90	1.00

World Figure Skating Championships, Vancouver — A764

Designs: No. 1896, Pairs. No. 1897, Ice dancing. No. 1898, Men's singles. No. 1899, Women's singles.

2001, Mar. 19   Litho.   Perf. 13x12½

1896	A764	47c shown	.95	.30
1897	A764	47c multi	.95	.30
1898	A764	47c multi	.95	.30
1899	A764	47c multi	.95	.30
a.		Block of 4, #1896-1899	3.80	2.50

First Canadian Postage Stamps, 150th Anniv. — A765

Litho. & Engr.
2001, Apr. 6   Perf. 13

1900	A765	47c multi	.95	.30

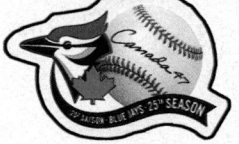

Toronto Blue Jays Baseball Team, 25th Anniv. A766

2001, Apr. 9   Litho.   Die Cut
Self-Adhesive

1901	A766	47c multi	1.10	.40
a.		Booklet pane of 8	9.00	

No. 1901a is a complete booklet.

Summit of the Americas, Quebec — A767

2001, Apr. 20   Perf. 13¼x13

1902	A767	47c multi	.95	.30

Tourist Attractions — A768

No. 1903: a, Butchart Gardens, British Columbia. b, Apple Blossom Festival, Nova Scotia. c, White Pass and Yukon Route. d, Sugar bushes, Quebec. e, Niagara-on-the-Lake, Ontario.

No. 1904: a, The Forks, Manitoba. b, Barkerville, British Columbia. c, Canadian Tulip Festival, Ontario. d, Auyuittuq National Park, Nunavut. e, Signal Hill National Historic Site, Newfoundland.

Die Cut Perf. 11x11¼
2001, May 11   Litho.
Self-Adhesive

1903		Booklet of 5	6.00
a.-e.	A768	60c Any single	1.20 .75
1904		Booklet of 5	10.50
a.-e.	A768	$1.05 Any single	2.10 1.25

Armenian Church, 1,700th Anniv. — A769

2001, May 16   Litho.   Perf. 13x12½

1905	A769	47c multi	.95	.30

Royal Military College of Canada, 125th Anniv. — A770

2001, June 1   Perf. 12½x13

1906	A770	47c multi	.95	.30

Eighth Intl. Amateur Athletic Federation World Championships, Edmonton A771

Perf. 12¾x12½
2001, June 25   Litho.

1907	A771	47c Pole vault	.95	.30
1908	A771	47c Runner	.95	.30
a.		Pair, #1907-1908	1.90	1.00

Pierre Elliott Trudeau (1919-2000), Prime Minister A772

2001, July 1   Perf. 13x12½

1909	A772	47c multi	.95	.30
a.		Souvenir sheet of 4	3.75	3.75

Roses — A773

Designs: Nos. 1910a, 1911, Morden Centennial. Nos. 1910b, 1912, Agnes. Nos. 1910c, 1913, Champlain. Nos. 1910d, 1914, Canadian White Star.
Illustration reduced.

2001, Aug. 1   Litho.   Perf. 12½x13
Souvenir Sheet

1910		Sheet of 4	5.25	5.25
a.-d.	A773	47c Any single	1.30	.75

Booklet Stamps
Die Cut

1911	A773	47c multi	.95	.30
1912	A773	47c multi	.95	.30
1913	A773	47c multi	.95	.30
1914	A773	47c multi	.95	.30
a.		Booklet pane, #1911-1914	3.80	
		Booklet, 3 #1914a	11.50	

Phila Nippon '01, Japan (No. 1910). Die-cutting on Nos. 1911-1914 has "thorn" at the center of each side, pointing outward at top and left and toward the design at bottom and right.

Great Peace of Montreal, 300th Anniv. — A774

2001, Aug. 3   Perf. 12½x13

1915	A774	47c multi	.95	.30

Art Type of 1988
Design: The Space Between Columns #21 (Italian), by Jack Shadbolt.

Litho. with Foil Application
2001, Aug. 24   Perf. 13x13¼

1916	A546	$1.05 multi	2.10	1.00

Shriners — A775

2001, Sept. 19   Litho.   Perf. 13¼x13

1917	A775	47c multi	.95	.30

Frame Type of 2000 Inscribed "Domestic Lettermail / Poste-lettres du régime intérieur"

No. 1918: a, Like #1882a. b, Like #1882b. c, Baby toys and flowers. d, Like #1882d. e, Like #1882e.

Serpentine Die Cut 11¾
2001, Sept. 21
Self-Adhesive

1918		Bklt. pane of 5 + 5 labels	4.75	
a.-e.	A737	(47c) Any single	.95	.95
		Booklet, #1918	5.25	

Theater Anniversaries — A776

Designs: No. 1919, Théâtre du Nouveau Monde, Montreal, 50th anniv. No. 1920, Grand Theater, London, Ont., cent.

2001, Sept. 28   Perf. 12½x12¾

1919	A776	47c multi	.95	.30
1920	A776	47c multi	.95	.30
a.		Horiz. pair, #1919-1920	1.90	1.00

Hot Air Balloons A777

Background colors: a, Green. b, Blue violet. c, Red violet. d, Olive.

2001, Oct. 1   Die Cut
Self-Adhesive

1921		Booklet, 2 each #a-d	8.00	
a.-d.	A777	47c Any single	1.00	.35

Christmas A778

Illuminated trees and: 47c, Horse-drawn sleigh. 60c, Skaters. $1.05, Children making snowman.

2001, Nov. 1   Litho.   Perf. 12½x13¼

1922	A778	47c multi	.95	.25
a.		Booklet pane of 10	9.50	
		Booklet, #1922a	10.00	
1923	A778	60c multi	1.20	.40
a.		Booklet pane of 6	7.25	
		Booklet, #1923a	7.75	
1924	A778	$1.05 multi	2.10	.70
a.		Booklet pane of 6	12.50	
		Booklet, #1924a	13.00	

YMCA in Canada, 150th Anniv. — A779

2001, Nov. 8　Litho.　Perf. 13¼
1925 A779 47c multi　　　　.95　.30

Royal Canadian Legion, 75th Anniv. — A780

2001, Nov. 11　　Perf. 12½x13
1926 A780 47c multi　　　　.95　.30

Maple Leaves Type of 2000, Traditional Handiwork Type of 1999 and

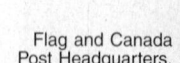

Flag and Canada Post Headquarters, Ottawa — A781

Designs: 65c, Jewelry making, horiz. 77c, Basket weaving, horiz. $1.25, Sculpture, horiz.

Serpentine Die Cut 8½ Horiz.
2002, Jan. 2　　　　　　Litho.
Self-Adhesive
Coil Stamps
1927	A759	48c multi	.95 .20
1928	A684	65c multi	1.30 .40
a.		Booklet of 6	7.75
1929	A684	77c multi	1.60 .40
1930	A684	$1.25 multi	2.50 .60
a.		Booklet of 6	15.00

Booklet Stamp
Serpentine Die Cut 8½
1931	A781	48c multi	.95 .30
a.		Booklet of 10	9.50 .20
b.		Booklet of 30	28.50
		Nos. 1927-1931 (5)	7.30 1.90

By separating the booklet along the columns of rouletting, No. 1931b could be broken up into three separately obtainable examples of No. 1931a. See No. 1991.

Reign of Queen Elizabeth II, 50th Anniv. A782

2002, Jan. 2　Litho.　Perf. 13¼x12½
1932 A782 48c multi　　　　.95　.30
a.　　Imperf, pair　　　　1,500.

New Year 2002 (Year of the Horse) — A783

Horse and: 48c, Bamboo leaves. $1.25, Peach blossoms.

Litho. & Embossed With Foil Application
2002, Jan. 3　　　　Perf. 13¼
1933 A783　48c multi　　　　.95　.30
Souvenir Sheet
1934 A783 $1.25 multi　　　　2.50 2.50

National Hockey League Stars A784

No. 1935: a, Tim Horton (Toronto Maple Leafs jersey No. 7). b, Guy Lafleur (Montreal Canadiens jersey No. 10). c, Howie Morenz (Canadiens jersey, with brown gloves). d, Glenn Hall (Chicago Black Hawks jersey No. 1). e, Red Kelly (Maple Leafs jersey No. 4). f, Phil Esposito (Boston Bruins jersey no. 7).

Perf. 12½x13 on 3 Sides
2002, Jan. 12　　　　　　Litho.
1935　　　Sheet of 6 + 3 labels　6.00 6.00
a.-f.　　A784 48c Any single　　1.00　.65

2002 Winter Olympics, Salt Lake City — A785

Designs: No. 1936, Short track speed skating. No. 1937, Curling. No. 1938, Freestyle aerial skiing. No. 1939, Women's hockey.

2002, Jan. 25　Litho.　Perf. 13¼x13
1936	A785	48c multi	1.00 .35
1937	A785	48c multi	1.00 .35
1938	A785	48c multi	1.00 .35
1939	A785	48c multi	1.00 .35
a.		Block or strip of 4, #1936-1939	4.00 3.25

Appointment of First Canadian Governor General, 50th Anniv. A786

2002, Feb. 1　Litho.　Perf. 13¼x12½
1940 A786 48c multi　　　　.95　.30

Universities — A787

Design: No. 1941, University of Manitoba, 125th anniv. No. 1942, Laval University, 150th anniv. No. 1943, University of Trinity College, 150th anniv. No. 1944, Saint Mary's University, Halifax, 200th anniv.

2002　　　Litho.　　　Perf. 13½
Booklet Stamp
1941	A787	48c multi	.95 .30
a.		Booklet pane of 8	7.50 —
		Booklet, #1941a	8.00
1942	A787	48c multi	.95 .30
a.		Booklet pane of 8	7.50 —
		Booklet, #1942a	8.00
1943	A787	48c multi	.95 .30
a.		Booklet pane of 8	7.50 —
		Booklet, #1943a	8.00
1944	A787	48c multi	.95 .30
a.		Booklet pane of 8	7.50 —
		Booklet, #1944a	8.00
		Nos. 1941-1944 (4)	3.80 1.20

Issued: No. 1941, 2/28. No. 1942, 4/4. No. 1943, 4/30. No. 1944, 5/27.

Art Type of 1988
Design: Church and Horse, by Alex Colville.

Litho. with Foil Application
2002, Mar. 22　　　Perf. 12½x13
1945 A546 $1.25 multi　　　2.50 1.10
a.　　Foil only (all other colors
　　　and tagging omitted)　　1,600.
b.　　Imperf, pair　　　　1,500.

Tulips — A788

Tulip varieties: a, City of Vancouver. b, Monte Carlo. c, Ottawa. d, The Bishop.

2002, May 3　　　　　Die Cut
Self-Adhesive
1946　　　Booklet pane of 4　　4.00
a.-d.　　A788 48c Any single　　1.00　.30
　　　　Booklet, 2 #1946　　　8.50

Tulips Type of 2002
Souvenir Sheet
No. 1947: a, Like #1946a. b, Like #1946b. c, Like #1946c. d, Like #1946d.

2002, Aug. 30　Litho.　Perf. 13x12½
1947　　　Sheet of 4　　　　4.50 4.50
a.-d.　　A788 48c Any single　1.10 1.00

Dendronepthea Giagantea and Dendronepthea Corals — A789

Tubastrea and Echinogorgia Corals — A790

North Atlantic Pink Tree, Pacific Orange Cup and North Pacific Horn Corals A791

North Atlantic Giant Orange Tree and Black Corals A792

2002, May 19　Litho.　Perf. 12½x13
1948	A789	48c multi	1.00 .35
1949	A790	48c multi	1.00 .35
1950	A791	48c multi	1.00 .35
1951	A792	48c multi	1.00 .35
a.		Block of 4, #1948-1951	4.00 3.00
b.		Souvenir sheet, #1948-1951, perf. 13¼x13	4.00 4.00

See Hong Kong Nos. 979-982.

Tourist Attractions Type of 2001

No. 1952: a, Yukon Quest, Yukon Territory. b, Icefields Parkway, Alberta. c, Agawa Canyon, Ontario. d, Old Port of Montreal, Quebec. e, Kings Landing, New Brunswick.
No. 1953: a, Northern Lights, Northwest Territories. b, Stanley Park, Vancouver, British Columbia. c, Head-Smashed-In Buffalo Jump,

Alberta. d, Saguenay Fjord, Quebec. e, Peggy's Cove, Nova Scotia.

2002, June 1　Die Cut Perf. 11x11¼
Self-Adhesive
1952		Booklet of 5	6.50
a.-e.	A768 65c Any single	1.30 .75
1953		Booklet of 5	12.50
a.-e.	A768 $1.25 Any single	2.50 1.10

Sculpture — A793

Designs: No. 1954, Embacle, by Charles Daudelin. No. 1955, Lumberjacks, by Leo Mol.

2002, June 10　Litho.　Perf. 13¼
1954	A793	48c multi	.95 .30
1955	A793	48c multi	.95 .30
a.		Horiz. or vert. pair, #1954-1955	1.90 1.00

Canadian Postmasters and Assistants Association, Cent. — A794

2002, July 5　　　Perf. 13¼x12½
1956 A794 48c multi　　　　.95　.30

Printed in sheets of 16 stamps + 12 labels.

17th World Youth Day, Toronto — A795

2002, July 23　　Litho.　　Die Cut
Booklet Stamp
Self-Adhesive
1957 A795 48c multi　　　　.95　.30
a.　　Booklet of 8　　　　8.00

Public Services International World Congress, Ottawa — A796

2002, Sept. 4　Litho.　Perf. 12½x13
1958 A796 48c multi　　　　.95　.30

Public Pensions, 75th Anniv. — A797

2002, Sept. 10　　　　Perf. 13¼
1959 A797 48c multi　　　　.95　.30

Souvenir Sheet

Intl. Year of Mountains — A798

No. 1960: a, Mt. Logan, Canada. b, Mt. Elbrus, Russia. c, Puncak Jaya, Indonesia. d, Mt. Everest, Nepal and China. e, Mt. Kilimanjaro, Tanzania. f, Vinson Massif, Antarctica. g, Mt. Aconcagua, Argentina. h, Mt. McKinley, Alaska.

2002, Oct. 1   Litho.   Die Cut
Self-Adhesive
1960	A798	Sheet of 8 + 8 labels	9.00 9.00
a.-h.		48c Any single	1.10 1.10

World Teachers' Day — A799

2002, Oct. 4   Litho.   Perf. 12½x13
1961	A799 48c multi	.95 .30

Toronto Stock Exchange, 150th Anniv. — A800

2002, Oct. 24   Litho.   Perf. 12½x13
1962	A800 48c multi	.95 .30

Communication Technology Centenaries — A801

Part of map of North America and: No. 1963, Sir Sandford Fleming (1827-1915), cable-laying ship . No. 1964, Guglielmo Marconi (1874-1937), radio and transmission towers.

2002, Oct. 31   Litho.   Perf. 13x12½
1963	48c multi	.95 .30
1964	48c multi	.95 .30
a.	A801 Horiz. pair, #1963-1964	1.90 1.20

Cent. of first telegraph message sent over transpacific cable (#1963); first transatlantic radio message (#1964).

Christmas
A802

Art by aboriginals: 48c, Genesis, by Daphne Odjig. 65c, Winter Travel, by Cecil Youngfox. $1.25, Mary and Child, sculpture by Irene Katak Angutitaq.

2002, Nov. 4   Perf. 12½x13
1965	A802 48c multi	.90 .25
a.	Booklet pane of 10	9.00
	Booklet, #1965a	9.50
1966	A802 65c multi	1.30 .40
a.	Booklet pane of 6	7.75
	Booklet, #1966a	8.25
1967	A802 $1.25 multi	2.50 .75
a.	Booklet pane of 6	15.00
	Booklet, #1967a	15.50
	Nos. 1965-1967 (3)	4.70 1.40

Quebec Symphony Orchestra, Cent.
A803

2002, Nov. 7
1968	A803 48c multi	.95 .30

New Year 2003
(Year of the Ram) — A804

Litho. & Embossed with Foil Application
2003, Jan. 3   Perf. 13
1969	A804 48c shown	.95 .30
a.	Gold omitted	400.00

Souvenir Sheet
Perf. 13¼
1970	A804 $1.25 Ram, diff.	2.50 2.50

No. 1970 contains one 33x58mm stamp. Slits replace perforations on the vertical sides of the stamps between the point of the acute angle made with the curving perforations and the point perpendicular to where the perforations on the opposite side form the obtuse angle with the curving perforations.

National Hockey League Stars
A805

Designs: Nos. 1971a, 1972a, Frank Mahovlich (orange panel). Nos. 1971b, 1972b, Raymond Bourque (lilac panel). Nos. 1971c, 1972c, Serge Savard (blue panel). Nos. 1971d, 1972d, Stan Mikita (red violet panel). Nos. 1971e, 1972e, Mike Bossy (bright pink panel). Nos. 1971f, 1972f, Bill Durnan (green panel).

Perf. 12½x13¼ on 3 Sides
2003, Jan. 18   Litho.
1971	Sheet of 6 + 3 labels	20.00 —
a.-f.	A805 48c Any single	3.00 1.20

Self-Adhseive
Die Cut
1972	Pane of 6	55.00 —
a.-f.	A805 48c Any single	6.50 2.00

Universities
A806

Design: No. 1973, Bishop's University, Lennoxville, Quebec, 150th anniv. No. 1974, University of Western Ontario, London, Ont., 125th anniv. No. 1975, St. Francis Xavier University, Antigonish, N. S., 150th Anniv. No. 1976, Macdonald Institute, Guelph, Ont., cent. No. 1977, University of Montreal, 125th anniv.

2003   Litho.   Perf. 13¼x13½
Booklet Stamps
1973	A806 48c multi	1.00 .30
a.	Booklet pane of 8	8.00
	Booklet, #1973a	8.50
1974	A806 48c multi	1.00 .30
a.	Booklet pane of 8	8.00
	Booklet, #1974a	8.50
1975	A806 48c multi	1.00 .30
a.	Booklet pane of 8	8.00
	Complete booklet, #1975a	8.50
1976	A806 48c multi	1.00 .30
a.	Booklet pane of 8	8.00
	Complete booklet, #1976a	8.50
1977	A806 48c multi	1.00 .30
a.	Booklet pane of 8	8.00
	Complete booklet, #1977a	8.50

Issued: No. 1973, 1/28. No. 1975, 4/4. No. 1976, 6/20. No. 1977, 9/4. No. 1974, 3/19. See Nos. 2033-2034.

Bird Paintings by John James Audubon — A807

Designs: No. 1979, Leach's storm petrel. No. 1980, Brant. No. 1981, Great cormorant. No. 1982, Common murre. 65c, Gyrfalcon, vert.

Perf. 13¼x12½
2003, Feb. 21   Litho.
1979	A807 48c multi	.95 .30
1980	A807 48c multi	.95 .30
1981	A807 48c multi	.95 .30
1982	A807 48c multi	.95 .30
a.	Block of 4, #1979-1982	3.80 2.75

Booklet Stamp
Self-Adhesive
Die Cut
1983	A807 65c multi	1.30 .55
a.	Booklet pane of 6	8.00
	Nos. 1979-1983 (5)	5.10 1.75

Canadian Rangers — A808

2003, Mar. 3   Perf. 12½x13¼
1984	A808 48c multi	.95 .30

American Hellenic Educational Progressive Association In Canada, 75th Anniv. — A809

Perf. 12½x13¼
2003, Mar. 25   Litho.
1985	A809 48c multi	.95 .30

Volunteer Firefighters A810

2003, May 30   Litho.   Perf. 13¼
1986	A810 48c multi	.95 .35

Coronation of Queen Elizabeth II, 50th Anniv. A811

2003, June 2   Perf. 13x12½
1987	A811 48c multi	.95 .35

Quebec City, Seal of Sovereign Council of New France, Signature of Pedro da Silva — A812

2003, June 6   Perf. 13x12¾
1988	A812 48c multi	.95 .35

Pedro da Silva, first courier in New France, 50th anniv. of Portuguese immigration to Canada.

Tourist Attractions Type of 2001

No. 1989: a, Wilberforce Falls, Nunavut. b, Inside Passage, B. C. c, Royal Canadian Mounted Police Depot Division, Regina, Sask. d, Casa Loma, Toronto, Ont. e, Gatineau Park, Que.
No. 1990: a, Dragon boat races, Vancouver, B. C. b, Polar bear watching, Man. c, Niagara Falls, Ont. d, Magdalen Islands, Que. e, Charlottestown, P. E. I.

2003, June 12   Die Cut Perf. 11¼
Self-Adhesive
1989	Booklet of 5	6.50
a.-e.	A768 65c Any single	1.30 .60
1990	Booklet of 5	12.50
a.-e.	A768 $1.25 Any single	2.50 1.10

Flag and Canada Post Headquarters Type of 2002 With "Vancouver / 2010" Added in Red
Serpentine Die Cut 8½
2003, July 11   Litho.
Booklet Stamp
Self-Adhesive
1991	A781 48c multi	1.70 1.20
a.	Booklet of 10	17.50
b.	Booklet of 30	50.00
c.	Die cutting omitted, pair	800.00

Selection of Vancouver as site of 2010 Winter Olympics. By separating the booklet along the columns of rouletting, No. 1991b could be broken up into three separately obtainable examples of No. 1991a.

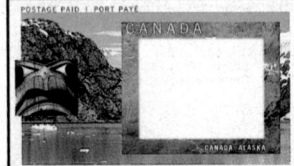

Canada-Alaska Cruise Scenes — A813

Mountains and: No. 1991C, Totem pole. No. 1991D, Whale's tail.

2003, July 19   **Litho.**   *Die Cut*
Self-Adhesive

1991C	A813	($1.25) multi	7.00 7.00
1991D	A813	($1.25) multi	7.00 7.00
e.		Horiz. pair, #1991C-1991D	14.00

Nos. 1991C-1991D were printed in sheets of 10 containing five of each stamp. The blank spaces in each stamp and the three stamp-like vignettes at the left of the sheet that lack die cutting and "Postage Paid / Port Payé" inscription could be personalized on cruise ships. Personalized sheets sold for $19.95 in US currency, while unpersonalized sheets sold for $12.50.

Lutheran World Federation, 10th Assembly, Winnipeg A814

2003, July 21   **Litho.**   *Perf. 12½x13*

1992	A814	48c multi	.95 .35

Korean War Armistice Agreement, 50th Anniv. — A815

2003, July 25   *Perf. 12¾*

1993	A815	48c multi	.95 .35

Authors A816

Designs: No. 1994, Anne Hébert (1916-2000). No. 1995, Hector de Saint-Denys Garneau (1912-43). No. 1996, Morley Callaghan (1903-90). No. 1997, Susanna Moodie (1803-85), and Catharine Parr Traill (1802-99).

2003, Sept. 8   **Litho.**   *Perf. 13¼x12½*
Booklet Stamps

1994	A816	48c multi	.95 .30
1995	A816	48c multi	.95 .30
1996	A816	48c multi	.95 .30
1997	A816	48c multi	.95 .30
a.		Block of 4, #1994-1997	3.80 2.75
b.		Booklet pane, 2 #1997a	7.75
		Complete booklet, #1997b	8.25

2003 Road Cycling World Championships, Hamilton, Ont. — A817

2003, Sept. 10   **Litho.**   *Perf. 12½x13*
Booklet Stamp

1998	A817	48c multi	.95 .55
a.		Booklet pane of 8	7.75 —
		Complete booklet, #1998a	8.25

Canadian Astronauts A818

No. 1999: a, Marc Garneau. b, Roberta Bondar. c, Steve MacLean. d, Chris Hadfield. e, Robert Thirsk. f, Bjarni Tryggvason. g, Dave Williams. h, Julie Payette.

Litho. With Foil Application
2003, Oct. 1   *Die Cut*
Self-Adhesive

1999		Sheet of 8	9.00
a.-h.	A818	48c Any single	1.00 .75

Trees of Canada and Thailand — A819

Designs: No. 2000, Acer saccharum leaves (Canada). No. 2001, Cassia fistula (Thailand).

2003, Oct. 4   **Litho.**   *Perf. 12¾x12½*

2000	A819	48c multi	.95 .30
2001	A819	48c multi	.95 .30
a.		Pair, #2000-2001	1.90 .80
b.		Souvenir sheet, #2000-2001	1.90 .80
c.		As "a," imperf	1,000.
d.		As "b," imperf	1,600.

Bangkok 2003 Intl. Philatelic Exhibition (#2001b).
See Thailand No. 2090.

L'Hommage à Rosa Luxemburg, by Jean-Paul Riopelle — A820

Painting details — No. 2002; a, Red and blue dots between birds at LR. b, Bird with yellow beak at center. c, Three birds in circle at R. d, Sun at UR. e, Birds with purple outlines at L. f, Bird with red outline in circle at R. $1.25, Pink bird in red circle at R.

2003, Oct. 7   **Litho.**   *Perf. 12½x13*

2002	A820	Sheet of 6	8.50 8.50
a.-f.		48c Any single	1.40 1.00

Souvenir Sheet
Perf. 12¾

2003	A820	$1.25 multi	3.00 3.00

Christmas A821

Gift boxes and: 48c, Ice skates. 65c, Teddy bear. $1.25, Toy duck.

2003, Nov. 4   *Die Cut*
Booklet Stamps
Self-Adhesive

2004	A821	48c multi	.95 .35
a.		Booklet pane of 6	5.75
		Complete booklet, 2 #2004a	11.50
b.		Pair, die cutting omitted	400.00
2005	A821	65c multi	1.30 .50
a.		Booklet pane of 6	7.75
b.		As "a," die cutting omitted	800.00
2006	A821	$1.25 multi	2.50 1.00
a.		Booklet pane of 6	15.00
		Nos. 2004-2006 (3)	4.75 1.85

Maple Leaf and Samara A822

Maple Leaf on Twig A823

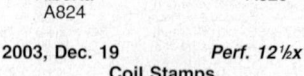

Flag Over Edmonton, Alberta A824

Queen Elizabeth II A825

2003, Dec. 19   *Perf. 12½x13*
Coil Stamps
Litho.
Self-Adhesive
Serpentine Die Cut 8 Horiz.

2008	A822	49c multi	1.00 .20

Serpentine Die Cut 8 Vert.

2009	A823	80c red & multi	1.60 .40
2010	A823	$1.40 grn & multi	2.80 .55

Booklet Stamps
Die Cut

2011	A824	49c multi	1.00 .20
a.		Booklet pane of 10	10.00
b.		Pair, die cutting omitted	160.00
2012	A825	49c multi	1.00 .20
a.		Booklet pane of 10	10.00
2013	A823	80c red & multi	1.60 .35
a.		Booklet pane of 6	9.50
2014	A823	$1.40 grn & multi	2.80 .50
a.		Booklet pane of 6	17.00
		Nos. 2008-2014 (7)	11.80 2.40

New Year 2004 (Year of the Monkey) — A826

Scenes from Chinese story *Journey to the West:* 49c, Monkey King. $1.40, Monkey King, Xuan Zang, Sandy, Pigsy and horse.

Litho. & Embossed with Foil Application
2004, Jan. 8   *Perf. 13x12½*

2015	A826	49c multi	1.00 .30

Souvenir Sheet

2016	A826	$1.40 multi	4.00 4.00
a.		As No. 2016, with 2004 Hong Kong Stamp Expo ovpt. in margin	5.50 5.50

No. 2016 has rouletted tab at right showing bar code.

National Hockey League Stars A827

Designs: Nos. 2017a, 2018a, Larry Robinson (blue background). Nos. 2017b, 2018b, Marcel Dionne (orange background). Nos. 2017c, 2018c, Ted Lindsay (red background). Nos. 2017d, 2018d, Johnny Bower (green background). Nos. 2017e, 2018e, Brad Park (brown background). Nos. 2017f, 2018f, Milt Schmidt (purple background).

Perf. 12½x13¼ on 3 Sides

2004, Jan. 24   **Litho.**

2017		Sheet of 6 + 3 labels	6.00 6.00
a.-f.	A827	49c Any single	1.00 .60

Self-Adhesive
Die Cut

2018		Pane of 6	6.00 6.00
a.-f.	A827	49c Any single	1.00 .35

Tourist Attractions Type of 2001

Design: No. 2019, Quebec Winter Carnival; No. 2020, St. Joseph's Oratory, Montreal, Quebec; No. 2021, International Jazz Festival, Montreal. No. 2022, Traversée Internationale du Lac St. Jean Swimming Marathon, Quebec; No. 2023, Canadian National Exhibition, Toronto.

2004, Jan. 29   **Litho.**   *Die Cut*
Self-Adhesive
Booklet Stamp

2019	A768	49c multi	1.00 .35
a.		Booklet of 6	6.00
2020	A768	49c multi	1.00 .35
a.		Booklet of 6	6.00
2021	A768	49c multi	1.00 .35
a.		Booklet of 6	6.00
2022	A768	49c multi	1.00 .35
a.		Booklet of 6	6.00
2023	A768	49c multi	1.00 .35
a.		Booklet of 6	6.00

Issued: No. 2019, 1/29; No. 2020, 4/2; No. 2021, 6/1; No. 2022, 6/18; No. 2023, 7/19.

Governor General Ramon John Hnatyshyn (1934-2002) — A828

2004, Mar. 16   **Litho.**   *Perf. 12½x13*

2024	A828	49c multi	1.00 .30

Royal Canadian Army Cadets, 125th Anniv. A829

2004, Mar. 26   **Litho.**   *Die Cut*
Booklet Stamp
Self-Adhesive

2025	A829	49c multi	1.00 .40
a.		Booklet pane of 4	4.00 .30
		Complete booklet, 2 #2025a	8.00

The Fram, Ship of Otto Sverdrup (1854-1930), Arctic Explorer — A830

Litho. & Engr.
2004, Mar. 26   *Perf. 13¼*

2026	A830	49c multi	1.00 .30

Souvenir Sheet

2027	A830	$1.40 multi + 2 labels	3.50 3.50

See Greenland No. 426, Norway Nos. 1398-1399.

Urban Transit and Light Rail Systems — A831

Train cars, station names and system emblems of: No. 2028, Toronto Transit Commission. No. 2029, TransLink SkyTrain, Vancouver. No. 2030, Société de Transport de Montréal. No. 2031, Calgary Transit Light Rail.

2004, Mar. 30   Litho.   Perf. 12½x13

2028	A831	49c multi	1.00	.30
2029	A831	49c multi	1.00	.30
2030	A831	49c multi	1.00	.30
2031	A831	49c multi	1.00	.30
a.		Vert. strip of 4, #2028-2031	4.00	2.25

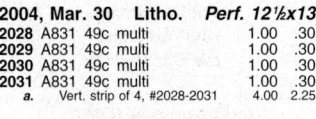

Home Hardware, 40th Anniv. — A832

Die Cut Perf. 11
2004, Apr. 19   Litho.
Self-Adhesive
Booklet Stamp

2032	A832	49c multi	1.00	.20
a.		Booklet pane of 10 + label	10.00	
		Complete booklet, #2032a	10.50	

No. 2032a is the inside front cover of the complete booklet. Fifteen self-adhesive seals are on the inside back cover of the complete booklet.

Universities Type of 2003

Designs: No. 2033, Sherbrooke University, Sherbrooke, Quebec, 50th anniv. No. 2034, University of Prince Edward Island, Charlottetown, bicent.

2004   Litho.   Perf. 13¼x13½
Booklet Stamps

2033	A806	49c multi	1.00	.30
a.		Booklet pane of 8	8.00	—
		Complete booklet, #2033a	8.50	
2034	A806	49c multi	1.00	.30
a.		Booklet pane of 8	8.00	—
		Complete booklet, #2034a	8.50	

Issued: No. 2033, 5/4; No. 2034, 5/8.

Montreal Children's Hospital, Cent. — A833

2004, May 6   Die Cut Perf. 9½x10¾
Self-Adhesive
Booklet Stamp

2035	A833	49c multi	1.00	.40
a.		Booklet pane of 4	4.00	
		Complete booklet, 2 #2035a	8.00	

Bird Paintings by John James Audubon A834

Designs: No. 2036, Ruby-crowned kinglet. No. 2037, White-winged crossbill. No. 2038, Bohemian waxwing. No. 2039, Boreal chickadee. 80c, Lincoln's sparrow.

2004, May 14   Perf. 12½x13

2036	A834	49c multi	1.00	.35
2037	A834	49c multi	1.00	.35
2038	A834	49c multi	1.00	.35
2039	A834	49c multi	1.00	.35
a.		Block of 4, #2036-2039	4.00	2.25

Self-Adhesive
Booklet Stamp
Die Cut

2040	A834	80c multi	1.60	.50
a.		Booklet pane of 6	10.00	
		Nos. 2036-2040 (5)	5.60	1.90

Pioneers of Transatlantic Mail Service — A835

Designs: No. 2041, Sir Samuel Cunard (1787-1865). No. 2042, Sir Hugh Allan (1810-82).

2004, May 28   Litho.   Perf. 13¼x12½
Self-Adhesive

2041	A835	49c multi	1.00	.35
2042	A835	49c multi	1.00	.35
a.		Horiz. pair, #2041-2042	2.00	1.20

D-Day, 60th Anniv. A836

2004, June 6   Litho.   Perf. 13x12½

2043	A836	49c multi	1.00	.35

Pierre Dugua de Mons, Leader of First French Settlement in Acadia, and Ship A837

Litho. & Engr.
2004, June 26   Perf. 13x12½

2044	A837	49c multi	1.00	.35

See France No. 3032.

Butterfly and Flower A838

Children on Beach A839

Rose A840

Dog A841

Serpentine Die Cut 11¾
2004, June   Litho.
Self-Adhesive
Booklet Stamps

2045	A838	(49c) multi	11.00	10.00
a.		Booklet pane of 2	22.00	
		Complete booklet, #2045a + phonecard in greeting card	26.00	
2046	A839	(49c) multi	11.00	10.00
a.		Booklet pane of 2	22.00	
		Complete booklet, #2046a + phonecard in greeting card	26.00	
2047	A840	(49c) multi	11.00	10.00
a.		Booklet pane of 2	22.00	
		Complete booklet, #2047a + phonecard in greeting card	26.00	
2048	A841	(49c) multi	11.00	10.00
a.		Booklet pane of 2	22.00	
		Complete booklet, #2048a + phonecard in greeting card	26.00	
		Nos. 2045-2048 (4)	44.00	40.00

Nos. 2045-2048, have a frame like No. 1918a, and are similarly inscribed "Domestic Lettermail" and "Poste-lettres du régime intérieur," but Nos. 2045-2048 have the vignettes printed on the stamps, while any vignettes found on No. 1918a are affixed stickers. Nos. 2045a-2048a are affixed to the insides of greeting cards that contain detachable phonecards valid for 15 minutes calling time on any touchtone phone in Canada or the United States. The stamps were available only in the greeting card, which sold for $5.99 along with a blank envelope for sending the greeting card.

2004 Summer Olympics, Athens — A842

Olympic rings and: No. 2049, Spyros Louis, 1896 Marathon gold medalist, diagram of track, "Athens" in Greek, and stylized runner. No. 2050, Soccer net inscribed "Canada," girls playing soccer.

2004, July 28   Perf. 12½x13¼

2049	A842	49c multi	1.00	.35
2050	A842	49c multi	1.00	.35
a.		Horiz. pair, #2049-2050	2.00	1.25

Canadian Open Golf Championship, Cent. — A843

Crowd, trophy and golfer: No. 2051, Finishing swing. No. 2052, Ready to putt.

Litho. & Embossed With Foil Application
2004, Aug. 12   Serpentine Die Cut
Self-Adhesive

2051	A843	49c multi	1.00	.35
2052	A843	49c multi	1.00	.35

Nos. 2051-2052 were issued in a sheet containing four of each stamp.

Maple Leaf Types of 2003
2004, Aug. 18   Litho.   Die Cut
Self-Adhesive
Coil Stamps

2053	A822	49c multi	1.00	.20

Serpentine Die Cut 8¼ Horiz.

2054	A823	80c red & multi	1.80	.40
2055	A823	$1.40 grn & multi	3.25	.75
a.		Die cutting omitted, pair		
		Nos. 2053-2055 (3)	6.05	1.45

Die cut gauges on Nos. 2054-2055 vary widely within the roll, from 8¼-8¾. Gauge 8¼ is the most common.

Montreal Heart Institute, 50th Anniv. — A844

Die Cut Perf. 13½
2004, Sept. 15   Litho.
Self-Adhesive
Booklet Stamp

2056	A844	49c multi	1.00	.35
a.		Booklet pane of 4	4.00	
		Complete booklet, 2 #2056	8.00	

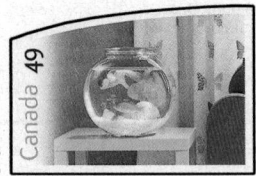

Pets A845

2004, Oct. 1   Litho.   Die Cut
Self-Adhesive
Booklet Stamps

2057	A845	49c Fish	1.00	.35
2058	A845	49c Cats	1.00	.35
2059	A845	49c Rabbit	1.00	.35
2060	A845	49c Dog	1.00	.35
a.		Booklet pane, #2057-2060	4.00	
		Complete booklet, 2 #2060a	8.00	

Nobel Laureates in Chemistry — A846

Designs: No. 2061, Gerhard Herzberg, 1971 laureate, and molecular structures. No. 2062, Michael Smith, 1993 laureate, and DNA double helix.

2004, Oct. 4   Perf. 12½x13

2061	A846	49c multi	1.00	.35
2062	A846	49c multi	1.00	.35
a.		Pair, #2061-2062	2.00	1.20

Ribbon Frame A847

Picture Album Frame A848

Serpentine Die Cut 12¾x13
2004, Oct. 8   Litho.
Self-Adhesive

2063	A847	(49c) multi	1.00	.50
2064	A848	(49c) multi	1.00	.50

Nos. 2063 and 2064 were each printed in sheets of 21 that sold for $9.80. These sheets were split by a row of rouletting in the center, with 20 stamps on one side and one on the other side. Sheets of 21 with vignettes that could be personalized by the customer were available for $24.95. Sheets of 40 stamps with personalized vignettes were also available for $39.95.

Victoria Cross, 150th Anniv. — A849

Designs: No. 2065, Victoria Cross. No. 2066, Design for Canadian Victoria Cross, approved with Queen Elizabeth II's signature.

Litho. & Embossed

2004, Oct. 21		Perf. 13x12½	
2065	A849 49c multi	1.00	.35

Litho.

2066	A849 49c multi	1.00	.35
a.	Pair, #2065-2066	2.00	1.20

Paintings by Jean Paul Lemieux — A850

Designs: 49c, Self-portrait. 80c, A June Wedding, horiz. (53x35mm). $1.40, Summer, horiz. (64x31mm).

2004, Oct. 22	Litho.	Perf. 13x13¼	
2067	A850 49c multi	1.00	.35
a.	Perf. 13	1.60	1.60

Souvenir Sheet

		Perf. 13	
2068	Sheet, #2067a, 2068a, 2068b	6.00	6.00
a.	A850 80c multi	1.60	1.60
b.	A850 $1.40 multi	2.80	2.80

Christmas — A851

Santa Claus and: 49c, Sleigh. 80c, Automobile. $1.40, Train.

Serpentine Die Cut 7¼ Horiz.

2004, Nov. 2

Booklet Stamps

Self-Adhesive

2069	A851 49c multi	1.00	.25
a.	Booklet pane of 6	6.00	
	Complete booklet, 2 #2069a	12.50	
2070	A851 80c multi	1.60	.50
a.	Booklet pane of 6	9.50	
2071	A851 $1.40 multi	2.80	.75
a.	Booklet pane of 6	17.00	

Queen Type of 2003 and

Red Calla Lilies A852

Flag and Saskatoon, Saskatchewan A853

Flag and Durrell, Newfoundland A854

Flag and Shannon Falls, British Columbia A855

Flag and Mont-Saint-Hilaire, Quebec — A856

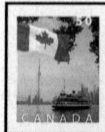

Flag and Toronto — A857

Designs: 85c, Yellow calla lily. $1.45, Dutch iris.

Serpentine Die Cut 6½-8¾ Horiz.

2004-05 Litho.

Self-Adhesive

Coil Stamps

2072	A852 50c multi	1.00	.25
a.	Serpentine die cut 6¾ horiz. ('05)	1.00	.20
2073	A852 85c multi	1.70	.30
a.	Serpentine die cut 6¾ horiz. ('05)	1.70	.30
2074	A852 $1.45 multi	2.90	.75
a.	Serpentine die cut 6¾ horiz. ('05)	4.00	1.60

The die cutting gauge on Nos. 2072-2074a will vary between stamps on a roll and between stamps on one roll and other rolls.

Issued: Nos. 2072, 2073, 2074, 12/20/04. Nos. 2072a, 2073a, 2074a, 2/2005. Die cuttings on these issues are variable. The editors are obtaining additional strips of the coils. Die cutting notes may change.

Booklet Stamps

Die Cut

2075	A825 50c multi	1.00	.20
a.	Booklet pane of 10	10.00	
2076	A853 50c multi	1.00	.20
2077	A854 50c multi	1.00	.20
2078	A855 50c multi	1.00	.20
2079	A856 50c multi	1.00	.20
2080	A857 50c multi	1.00	.20
a.	Booklet pane, 2 each #2076-2080	10.00	
2081	A852 85c multi	1.70	.40
a.	Booklet pane of 6	10.50	
b.	As "a," black inscriptions omitted	800.00	
2082	A852 $1.45 multi	2.90	.50
a.	Booklet pane of 6	17.50	
	Nos. 2072-2082 (11)	16.20	3.40

New Year 2005 (Year of the Cock) — A858

Rooster with: 50c, Red tail feathers. $1.45, Gold tail feathers.

Litho. & Embossed with Foil Application

2005, Jan. 7		Perf. 13¼	
2083	A858 50c multi	1.00	.30

Souvenir Sheet

		Perf. 12½x13	
2084	A858 $1.45 multi	3.00	3.00
a.	With dates, Canadian and Chinese flags added in sheet margin	4.50	4.50

Canada — People's Republic of China diplomatic relations, 35th anniv. (#2084a). No. 2084 contains one 40x40mm stamp.

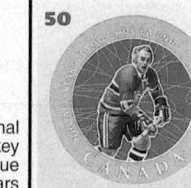

National Hockey League Stars A859

Designs: Nos. 2085a, 2086a, Henri Richard (blue background). Nos. 2085b, 2086b, Grant Fuhr (orange background). Nos. 2085c, 2086c, Allan Stanley (red background). Nos. 2085d, 2086d, Pierre Pilote (green background). Nos. 2085e, 2086e, Bryan Trottier (purple background). Nos. 2085f, 2086f, John Bucyk (yellow background).

Perf. 12½x13¼ on 3 Sides

2005, Jan. 29		Litho.	
2085	Sheet of 6 + 3 labels	6.00	6.00
a.-f.	A859 50c Any single	1.00	.40

Self-Adhesive

Die Cut

2086	Pane of 6	6.00	
a.-f.	A859 50c Any single	1.00	.35

Fishing Flies — A860

Designs: Nos. 2087a, 2088a, Alevin. Nos. 2087b, 2088b, Jock Scott. Nos. 2087c, 2088d, P. E. I. Fly. Nos. 2087d, 2088c, Mickey Finn.

2005, Feb. 4		Perf. 12½x13¼	
2087	A860 Sheet of 4	6.00	6.00
a.-d.	50c Any single	1.50	1.20

Self-Adhesive

Serpentine Die Cut 10 Syncopated

2088	A860 Booklet pane of 4	4.00	
a.-d.	50c Any single	1.00	.35
	Complete booklet, 2 #2088	8.00	

Universities Type of 2003

Design: Nova Scotia Agricultural College, cent.

Die Cut Perf. 12¾x13¼

2005, Feb. 14		Litho.	
Booklet Stamp			
Self-Adhesive			
2089	A806 50c multi	1.00	.35
a.	Booklet pane of 4	4.00	
	Complete booklet, 2 #2089a	8.00	

Expo 2005, Aichi, Japan — A861

2005, Mar. 4	Litho.	Perf. 13½	
2090	A861 50c multi	1.00	.35

Daffodils A862

Designs: Nos. 2091a, 2092, Yellow daffodils, green and yellow background. Nos. 2091b, 2093, White daffodils, red orange and yellow background.

2005, Mar. 10	Litho.	Perf. 13x13¼	
Souvenir Sheet			
2091	Sheet of 2	3.00	3.00
a.-b.	A862 50c Either single	1.50	.80

Booklet Stamps

Self-Adhesive

Die Cut Perf. 10

2092	A862 50c multi	1.00	.35
2093	A862 50c multi	1.00	.35
a.	Booklet pane, 5 each #2092-2093 + 10 stickers	11.00	

Pacific Explore 2005 World Stamp Expo, Sydney, Australia (#2091).

TD Bank Financial Group, 150th Anniv. — A863

2005, Mar. 18		Die Cut Perf. 11¼	
Self-Adhesive			
Booklet Stamp			
2094	A863 50c multi	1.00	.35
a.	Booklet pane of 10	10.00	
	Complete booklet, #2094a	12.50	

The booklet pane of 10 is the inside front cover of the booklet. Fifteen stickers are on inside back cover.

Bird Paintings by John James Audubon — A864

Designs: No. 2095, Horned lark. No. 2096, Piping plover. No. 2097, Stilt sandpiper. No. 2098, Willow ptarmigan. 85c, Double-crested cormorant.

2005, Mar. 23		Perf. 12½x13¼	
2095	A864 50c multi	1.00	.35
2096	A864 50c multi	1.00	.35
2097	A864 50c multi	1.00	.35
2098	A864 50c multi	1.00	.35
a.	Block of 4, #2095-2098	4.00	3.00

Booklet Stamp

Self-Adhesive

Size: 48x39mm

Die Cut

2099	A864 85c multi	1.70	.50
a.	Booklet pane of 6	10.50	

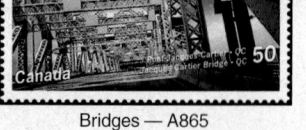

Bridges — A865

Designs: No. 2100, Jacques Cartier Bridge, Quebec. No. 2101, Souris Swinging Bridge, Manitoba. No. 2102, Angus L. Macdonald Bridge, Nova Scotia. No. 2103, Canso Causeway, Nova Scotia.

2005, Apr. 2	Litho.	Perf. 12½x13¼	
Self-Adhesive			
2100	A865 50c multi	1.00	.35
2101	A865 50c multi	1.00	.35
2102	A865 50c multi	1.00	.35
2103	A865 50c multi	1.00	.35
a.	Block or strip of 4, #2100-2103	4.00	3.25

Maclean's Magazine, Cent. A866

2005, Apr. 12			
2104	A866 50c multi	1.00	.30

Biosphere Reserves in Canada and
Ireland — A867

Designs: No. 2105, Saskatoon berries,
Waterton Lakes National Park, Canada. No.
2106, Deer, Killarney National Park, Ireland.

2005, Apr. 22
2105 A867 50c multi ... 1.00 .30
2106 A867 50c multi ... 1.00 .30
  a. Pair, #2105-2106 ... 2.00 1.25
  b. Souvenir sheet, #2106a ... 3.00 3.00
See Ireland Nos. 1611-1612.

Battle of the Atlantic, World War
II — A868

2005, Apr. 29
2107 A868 50c multi ... 1.00 .35

Opening of Canadian War Museum,
Ottawa — A869

Serpentine Die Cut 8x8½
Syncopated
2005, May 6 Litho.
Self-Adhesive
Booklet Stamp
2108 A869 50c multi ... 1.00 .40
  a. Booklet pane of 4 ... 4.00
  Complete booklet, 2 #2108a ... 8.00

Paintings by Homer Watson (1855-
1936) — A870

Designs: 50c, Down in the Laurentides. 85c,
The Flood Gate (54x40mm)

2005, May 27 Litho. *Perf. 13¼x13*
2109 A870 50c multi ... 1.00 .35
  a. Perf. 13½x13 ... 2.25 2.25
Souvenir Sheet
Perf. 13½x13
2110 Sheet, #2109a, 2110a ... 5.50 5.50
  a. A870 85c multi ... 3.25 3.25
Miniature Sheet

Search and Rescue — A871

No. 2111: a, Rescuer and dog at plane
crash. b, Rescuers at shipwreck. c, Helicopter,

airplane and rescuers. d, Mountainside
rescuers.

2005, June 13 *Perf. 13x13¼*
2111 A871 Sheet, 2 each #a-d ... 8.00 8.00
  a.-d. 50c Any single ... 1.00 .35
No. 2111 contains two horizontal strips, one
of which is inverted, so that a tete-beche pair
of No. 2111c and two tete-beche pairs containing Nos. 2111b and 2111d can be created.

Ellen Fairclough
(1905-2004), First
Female Cabinet
Minister — A872

2005, June 21 *Perf. 13x12½*
2112 A872 50c multi ... 1.00 .35

Diver Swimmer
A873 A874

2005, July 5 Litho. *Perf. 13¼*
2113 A873 50c multi ... 1.00 .35
2114 A874 50c multi ... 1.00 .35
  a. Horiz. pair, #2113-2114 ... 2.00 1.00
9th FINA World Championships, Montreal.
In No. 2114a, the denomination for one stamp
is on the opposite side of the pair from that of
the other stamp.

Founding of
Port-Royal,
Nova
Scotia,
400th
Anniv.
A875

Litho. & Engr.
2005, July 16 *Perf. 13x12½*
2115 A875 50c multi ... 1.00 .35

Province of
Alberta,
Cent. — A876

2005, July 21 Litho. *Perf. 12½x13*
Self-Adhesive
2116 A876 50c multi ... 1.00 .35
Printed in panes of 8 with each stamp having a different design on the backing.

Province of Saskatchewan,
Cent. — A877

2005, Aug. 2 Litho. *Perf. 13x12½*
2117 A877 50c multi ... 1.00 .35

Oscar Peterson,
Pianist, 80th
Birthday — A878

2005, Aug. 15
2118 A878 50c multi ... 1.00 .35
  a. Souvenir sheet of 4 ... 4.00 4.00

No. 176
and
Acadian
Flag
A879

2005, Aug. 15 Litho. *Perf. 13x12½*
2119 A879 50c multi ... 1.00 .35
Acadian Deportation, 250th anniv.

Children Playing and Leg
Braces — A880

2005, Sept. 2 *Perf. 12½x13*
2120 A880 50c multi ... 1.00 .35
Mass polio vaccinations in Canada, 50th
anniv.

Youth
Sports — A881

No. 2121: a, Wall climbing. b, Skateboarding. c, Mountain biking. d, Snowboarding.

2005, Oct. 1 Litho. *Die Cut*
Self-Adhesive
2121 Complete booket, 2 ...
  each #a-d ... 8.00
  a.-d. A881 50c Any single ... 1.00 .35

Wild Cats
A882

Designs: No. 2122, Puma concolor. No.
2123, Panthera pardus orientalis.

Perf. 13½x13¼ Syncopated
2005, Oct. 13
2122 A882 50c multi ... 1.00 .35
2123 A882 50c multi ... 1.00 .35
  a. Horiz. pair, #2122-2123 ... 2.00 .80
  b. Souvenir sheet, #2123a ... 2.25 .80
Diplomatic relations with People's Republic
of China, 35th anniv. (#2123b). The perforation column between the two stamps, which
gauges perf. 13½, has a maple leaf shaped
syncopation.
See People's Republic of China Nos. 3458-
3459.

Snowman — A883

Litho. with Hologram Applied
Serpentine Die Cut 8¼ Horiz.
2005, Nov. 2
Booklet Stamp
Self-Adhesive
2124 A883 50c multi ... 1.00 .35
  a. Booklet pane of 6 ... 6.00
  Complete booklet, 2 #2124a ... 12.00

A884 A885

Creche Figures, St.
Joseph's Oratory,
Montreal — A886

Serpentine Die Cut 6¾ Horiz.
2005, Nov. 2 Litho.
Booklet Stamps
Self-Adhesive
2125 A884 50c multi ... 1.00 .35
  a. Booklet pane of 6 ... 6.00
  Complete booklet, 2 #2125a ... 12.00
Serpentine Die Cut 6½ Horiz.
2126 A885 85c multi ... 1.70 .40
  a. Booklet pane of 6 ... 10.50
Serpentine Die Cut 6¾ Horiz.
2127 A886 $1.45 multi ... 3.00 .65
  a. Booklet pane of 6 ... 18.00

Flowers — A887

Designs: 51c, Red bergamot. 89c, Yellow
lady's slipper. $1.05, Pink fairy slipper. $1.49,
Himalayan blue poppy.

Serpentine Die Cut 7 to 7¾ Horiz.
2005, Dec. 19 Litho.
Coil Stamps
Self-Adhesive
2128 A887 51c multi ... 1.00 .20
2129 A887 89c multi ... 1.80 .30
2130 A887 $1.05 multi ... 2.10 .60
2131 A887 $1.49 multi ... 3.00 .60
Booklet Stamps
Die Cut
2132 A887 89c multi ... 1.80 .40
  a. Booklet pane of 6 ... 11.00
2133 A887 $1.05 multi ... 2.10 .65
  a. Booklet pane of 6 ... 12.50

2134 A887 $1.49 multi ... 3.00 .65
  a. Booklet pane of 6 ... 18.00
    Nos. 2128-2134 (7) ... 14.80 3.40

Flag and Houses, New Glasgow, Prince Edward Island A888

Flag and Bridge, Bouctouche, New Brunswick A889

Flag and Windmills, Pincher Creek, Alberta A890

Flag and Lower Fort Garry, Manitoba A891

Flag and Dogsled, Yukon Territory — A892

2005, Dec. 19   *Die Cut*
Booklet Stamps
Self-Adhesive
2135 A888 51c multi ... 1.00 .20
2136 A889 51c multi ... 1.00 .20
2137 A890 51c multi ... 1.00 .20
2138 A891 51c multi ... 1.00 .20
2139 A892 51c multi ... 1.00 .20
  a. Booklet pane, 2 each #2135-2139 ... 10.00
    Nos. 2135-2139 (5) ... 5.00 1.00

New Year 2006 (Year of the Dog) — A893

Litho. & Embossed With Foil Application
2006, Jan. 6   *Perf. 13¼*
2140 A893 51c shown ... 1.00 .35
Souvenir Sheet
2141 A893 $1.49 Dog and pup ... 3.25 3.25

Queen Elizabeth II, 80th Birthday A894

Serpentine Die Cut 10
2006, Jan. 12   Litho.
Booklet Stamp
Self-Adhesive
2142 A894 51c multi ... 1.00 .30
  a. Booklet pane of 10 ... 10.00
    See No. 2150.

2006 Winter Olympics, Turin, Italy A895

Designs: No. 2143, Team pursuit speed skating. No. 2144, Skeleton.

2006, Feb. 3   Litho.   *Perf. 12½x13*
2143 A895 51c multi ... 1.00 .30
2144 A895 51c multi ... 1.00 .30
  a. Horiz. pair, #2143-2144 ... 2.00 1.00

Gardens — A896

No. 2145: a, Shade garden and black-throated blue warbler. b, Flower garden and American painted lady butterfly. c, Water garden and green darner dragonfly. d, Rock garden and blue-spotted salamander.

Serpentine Die Cut 10
2006, Mar. 8   Litho.
Self-Adhesive
2145 Complete booklet, 2 each #a-d ... 8.00
  a.-d. A896 51c Any single ... 1.00 .45

Party Balloons A897

Serpentine Die Cut 6¾ Horiz.
2006, Apr. 3   Litho.
Self-Adhesive
Booklet Stamp
2146 A897 51c multi ... 1.00 .45
  a. Booklet pane of 6 ... 6.00

Paintings by Dorothy Knowles — A898

Designs: 51c, The Field of Rapeseed. 89c, North Saskatchewan River, vert. (42x51mm).

2006, Apr. 7   *Perf. 13¼x12½*
2147 A898 51c multi ... 1.00 .35
  a. Perf. 12¾x12½ ... 1.75 1.75
Souvenir Sheet
Perf. 13
2148 Sheet, #2147a, 2148a ... 3.50 3.50
  a. A898 89c multi ... 1.75 1.75

Canadian Labor Congress, 50th Anniv. — A899

2006, Apr. 20   *Perf. 13½x13¼*
2149 A899 51c multi ... 1.00 .35

Queen Elizabeth II, 80th Birthday Type of 2006
Souvenir Sheet
2006, Apr. 21   Litho.   *Perf. 12½x13*
2150 Sheet of 2 #2150a ... 6.00 6.00
  a. A894 149c multi, 36x28mm ... 3.00 3.00

McClelland & Stewart Publishing House, Cent. — A900

2006, Apr. 26   *Die Cut Perf. 11¼x11*
Self-Adhesive
Booklet Stamp
2151 A900 51c slate grn & sil ... 1.00 .35
  a. Booklet pane of 4 + 4 stickers ... 4.00
    Complete booklet, 2 #2151a ... 8.00

Northwest Coast Transformation Mask and Northwest Coast Exhibit — A901

Serpentine Die Cut 8 Horiz.
Syncopated
2006, May 11
Self-Adhesive
Booklet Stamp
2152 A901 89c multi ... 1.80 .70
  a. Booklet pane of 4 ... 7.25
    Complete booklet, 2 #2152a ... 14.50

Canadian Museum of Civilization, 150th anniv.

Canadians in Hollywood A903

Actors and actresses: Nos. 2153a, 2154a, John Candy (1950-94). Nos. 2153b, 2154c, Fay Wray (1907-2004). Nos. 2153c, 2154d, Lorne Greene (1915-87). Nos. 2153d, 2154b, Mary Pickford (1893-1979).

2006, May 26   *Perf. 13x12½*
2153 Souvenir sheet of 4 ... 5.00 5.00
  a.-d. A903 51c Any single ... 1.25 1.00
Self-Adhesive
Serpentine Die Cut 9¾x10
2154 Booklet pane of 4 + 4 stickers ... 4.00
  a.-d. A903 51c Any single ... 1.00 .35
    Complete booklet, 2 #2154 ... 8.00

Complete booklets were issued with four different covers depicting the featured actors or actresses.

A904

Exploration of Eastern Coast by Samuel de Champlain, 400th Anniv. — A905

Litho. & Engr.
2006, May 28   *Perf. 13x12½*
2155 A904 51c multi ... 1.00 .40
Souvenir Sheet
2156 A905 Sheet, 2 #2156a, 2 US #4074a ... 4.25 4.25
  a. A904 51c multi, perf. 11 ... 1.25 1.25

Washington 2006 World Philatelic Exhibition (#2156). No. 2156, sold only by Canada Post for $2, has bar code in sheet margin at lower left. United States No. 4074, sold only by the United States Postal Service, lacks this bar code.

Vancouver Aquarium, 50th Anniv. — A906

Serpentine Die Cut 9½
2006, June 15   Litho.
Self-Adhesive
Booklet Stamp
2157 A906 51c multi ... 1.00 .35
  a. Booklet pane of 5 ... 5.00
    Complete booklet, 2 #2157a ... 10.00

Canadian Forces Snowbirds Aerobatics Team — A907

Designs: No. 2158, Pilot in cockpit, two airplanes. No. 2159, Three airplanes.

Perf. 12½x13¼
2006, June 28   Litho.
2158 A907 51c multi ... 1.00 .40
2159 A907 51c multi ... 1.00 .40
  a. Horiz. pair, #2158-2159 ... 2.00 1.50
  b. Souvenir sheet, #2159a ... 2.50 2.50

James White, Dividers and Map of Canada — A908

2006, June 30   *Perf. 13¼x12½*
2160 A908 51c multi ... 1.00 .45

Atlas of Canada, cent. Printed in sheets of 16 + 4 labels.

World Lacrosse Championships, London, Ontario — A909

Serpentine Die Cut 11¾ Horiz.
2006, July 6
Self-Adhesive
Booklet Stamp

2161	A909 51c multi	1.00	.45
a.	Booklet pane of 8	8.00	

Alpine Club of Canada, Cent. — A910

2006, July 19   Die Cut Perf. 12½x13
Self-Adhesive
Booklet Stamp

2162	A910 51c multi	1.00	.45
a.	Booklet pane of 8	8.00	

Ducks and Duck Decoys A911

Designs: No. 2163, Barrow's goldeneyes. No. 2164, Mallards. No. 2165, American black ducks. No. 2166, Redbreasted mergansers.

2006, Aug. 3 Litho. Perf. 13¼x12½

2163	A911 51c blue & multi	1.00	.40
2164	A911 51c yel & multi	1.00	.40
2165	A911 51c red & multi	1.00	.40
2166	A911 51c grn & multi	1.00	.40
a.	Block of 4, #2163-2166	4.00	3.00
b.	Souvenir sheet, #2163-2166	4.50	4.50

Society of Graphic Designers of Canada, 50th Anniv. — A912

2006, Aug. 16   Perf. 12½x13

2167	A912 51c multi	1.00	.35

Canadian Wines A913

Canadian Cheeses A914

Designs: No. 2168, Three glasses of wine. No. 2169, Wine taster, barrels. No. 2170, Various cheeses. No. 2171, Woman with tray of cheeses and fruit.

2006, Aug. 23   Litho.   Die Cut
Booklet Stamps
Self-Adhesive

2168	A913 51c multi	1.00	.40
2169	A913 51c multi	1.00	.40
2170	A914 51c multi	1.00	.40
2171	A914 51c multi	1.00	.40
a.	Booklet pane, 2 each #2168-2171	8.00	
	Nos. 2168-2171 (4)	4.00	1.60

Universities Type of 2003
Design: Macdonald College, Sainte-Anne-de-Bellevue, Quebec, cent.

Die Cut Perf. 12⅜x13¼
2006, Sept. 26
Booklet Stamp
Self-Adhesive

2172	A806 51c multi	1.00	.35
a.	Booklet pane of 4	4.00	
	Complete booklet, 2 #2172a	8.00	

Endangered Animals — A915

Designs: Nos. 2173a, 2174, Newfoundland marten. Nos. 2173b, 2175, Blotched tiger salamander. Nos. 2173c, 2176, Blue racer snake. Nos. 2173d, 2177, Swift fox.

2006, Sept. 29   Litho.   Perf. 13¼

2173	Sheet of 4 + 4 labels	3.60	3.60
a.-d.	A915 51c Any single	.90	.45

Booklet Stamps
Self-Adhesive
Size: 47x24mm
Die Cut

2174	A915 51c multi	1.00	.40
2175	A915 51c multi	1.00	.40
2176	A915 51c multi	1.00	.40
2177	A915 51c multi	1.00	.40
a.	Block of 4, #2174-2177	4.00	
b.	Booklet pane, 2, #2177a	8.00	

Opera Singers — A916

Designs: No. 2178, Maureen Forrester. No. 2179, Raoul Jobin (1906-74). No. 2180, Léopold Simoneau (1916-2006) and Pierrette Alarie. No. 2181, Jon Vickers. No. 2182, Edward Johnson (1878-1959).

2006, Oct. 17   Litho.   Perf. 13½x13

2178	A916 51c multi	1.00	.40
2179	A916 51c multi	1.00	.40
2180	A916 51c multi	1.00	.40
2181	A916 51c multi	1.00	.40
2182	A916 51c multi	1.00	.40
a.	Vert. strip of 5, #2178-2182	5.00	4.00

Madonna and Child, by Antoine-Sébastien Falardeau A917

Christmas Card Art A918

Designs: No. 2184, Snowman, by Yvonne McKague Housser. 89c, Winter Joys, by J. E. Sampson. $1.49, Contemplation, by Edwin Holgate.

2006, Nov. 1   Litho.   Die Cut
Booklet Stamps
Self-Adhesive

2183	A917 51c multi	1.00	.35
a.	Booklet pane of 12	12.00	

Serpentine Die Cut 13¼ Horiz.

2184	A918 51c multi	1.00	.35
a.	Booklet pane of 12	12.00	
2185	A918 89c multi	1.80	.50
a.	Booklet pane of 6	11.00	
2186	A918 $1.49 multi	3.00	.75
a.	Booklet pane of 6	18.00	
	Nos. 2183-2186 (4)	6.80	1.95

Spotted Coralroot A919

Queen Elizabeth II A920

Flag and Sirmilik Natl. Park, Nunavut A921

Flag and Cliff Near Chemainus, British Columbia A922

Flag and Polar Bears Near Churchill, Manitoba A923

Flag and Bras d'Or Lake, Nova Scotia A924

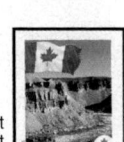

Flag and Tuktut Nogait Natl. Park, Northwest Territories — A925

2006, Nov. 16   Litho.
Coil Stamp
Self-Adhesive
Serpentine Die Cut 7½-9 Horiz.

2187	A919 P multi	1.00	.25

Booklet Stamps
Serpentine Die Cut 8 to 8½ Horiz.

2188	A920 P multi	1.00	.25
a.	Booklet pane of 10	10.00	
2189	A921 P multi	1.00	.25
2190	A922 P multi	1.00	.25
2191	A923 P multi	1.00	.25
2192	A924 P multi	1.00	.25
2193	A925 P multi	1.00	.25
a.	Booklet pane, 2 each #2189-2193	10.00	
b.	Booklet pane, 6 each #2189-2193	30.00	
	Nos. 2187-2193 (7)	7.00	1.75

Nos. 2187-2193 each sold for 51c on day of issue. On Nos. 2188a, 2193a and 2193b, adjacent stamps that are on both sides of the booklet fold have rouletting rather than die cutting between them. No. 2193b is sold folded into thirds. Each of the thirds has selvage surrounding the ten stamps on it, unlike No. 2193a.

Spotted Coralroot Type of 2006 and

Flat-leaved Bladderwort — A926

Designs: $1.10, Marsh skullcap. $1.55, Little larkspur.

2006, Dec. 19 Litho. Perf. 13¼x13

2194	Souvenir sheet of 4	8.25	8.25
a.	A919 P multi	1.00	.45
b.	A926 93c multi	1.85	.80
c.	A926 $1.10 multi	2.20	.95
d.	A926 $1.55 multi	3.10	1.40

Self-Adhesive
Coil Stamps
Serpentine Die Cut 7½-9

2195	A926 93c multi	1.85	.40
2196	A926 $1.10 multi	2.20	.60
2197	A926 $1.55 multi	3.10	.75

Booklet Stamps
Die Cut

2198	A926 93c multi	1.85	.40
a.	Booklet pane of 6	11.00	
2199	A926 $1.10 multi	2.20	.75
a.	Booklet pane of 6	13.00	
2200	A926 $1.55 multi	3.10	1.00
a.	Booklet pane of 6	18.50	
	Nos. 2195-2200 (6)	14.30	3.90

No. 2194a sold for 51c on day of issue.

New Year 2007 (Year of the Pig) A927

Pig facing: 52c, Left. $1.55, Right.

Litho. & Embossed with Foil Application
2007, Jan. 5   Perf. 13½x13

2201	A927 52c red & multi	1.00	.35

Souvenir Sheet

2202	A927 $1.55 grn & multi	3.00	3.00

Confetti and Streamers A928

Serpentine Die Cut 6¾ Horiz.
2007, Jan. 15   Litho.
Booklet Stamp
Self-Adhesive

2203	A928 52c multi	.90	.45
a.	Booklet pane of 6	5.50	

International Polar Year — A929

Designs: No. 2204, Somateria spectabilis. No. 2205, Crossota millsaeare.

Perf. 13½ Syncopated
2007, Feb. 12   Litho.

2204	A929 52c multi	.90	.45
2205	A929 52c multi	.90	.45
a.	Horiz. pair, #2204-2205	1.80	1.80
b.	Souvenir sheet, #2205a	1.80	1.80

Lilacs — A930

Color of lilacs: Nos. 2206a, 2207, White. Nos. 2206b, 2208, Purple.

2007, Mar. 1   Litho.   Perf. 12¾
Souvenir Sheet

2206	A930 Sheet of 2	1.75	1.75
a.-b.	52c Either single	.85	.45

Booklet Stamps
Self-Adhesive
Die Cut

2207	A930	52c multi	.85 .45
2208	A930	52c multi	.85 .45
a.		Booklet pane of 10, 5 each #2207-2208	8.50

Universities Type of 2003

Design: No. 2209, HEC Montreal, cent. No. 2210, University of Saskatchewan, cent.

2007 Litho. Die Cut Perf. 12¾x13¼
Booklet Stamp
Self-Adhesive

2209	A806	52c multi	.90 .45
a.		Booklet pane of 4	3.75
		Complete booklet, 2 #2209a	7.50
2210	A806	52c multi	.90 .45
a.		Booklet pane of 4	3.75
		Complete booklet, 2 #2210a	7.50

Issued: No. 2209, 3/12. No. 2210, 4/3.

Art by Mary Pratt — A931

Designs: 52c, Jelly Shelf. $1.55 Iceberg in the North Atlantic (58x36mm).

2007, Mar. 15 Litho. Perf. 13x12½

2211	A931	52c multi	.90 .45

Souvenir Sheet

2212		Sheet, #2211, 2212a	3.50 3.50
a.		A931 $1.55 multi	2.60 1.40

Selection of Ottawa as National Capital, 150th Anniv. — A932

Litho., Litho & Embossed with Foil Application (#2213b)
2007, May 3 Perf. 13¼

2213		Sheet of 2	3.75 3.75
a.		A932 52c multi	.95 .45
b.		A932 $1.55 multi	2.75 1.40

Booklet Stamp
Self-Adhesive
Serpentine Die Cut 7¼ Horiz.

2214	A932	52c multi	.95 .45
a.		Booklet pane of 4	3.80
		Complete booklet, 2 #2214a	7.75

Royal Architectural Institute of Canada, Cent. — A933

Buildings: No. 2215, University of Lethbridge, by Arthur Erickson. No. 2216, St. Mary's Church, by Douglas Cardinal. No. 2217, Ontario Science Centre, by Raymond Moriyama. No. 2218, National Gallery of Canada, by Moshe Safdie.

2007, May 9 Litho. Perf. 13

2215	A933	52c multi + label	.95 .45
2216	A933	52c multi + label	.95 .45
2217	A933	52c multi + label	.95 .45
2218	A933	52c multi + label	.95 .45
a.		Vert. strip of 4, #2215-2218, + 4 labels	3.80 1.80

Nos. 2215-2218 were printed in sheets containing two of each stamp. Labels flank the stamps, with labels on the left showing drawings of the buildings and the labels on the right showing the architect.

Capt. George Vancouver (1757-98), Explorer — A934

Litho. & Embossed
2007, June 22 Perf. 13x12½

2219	A934	$1.55 multi	3.00 1.50
a.		Souvenir sheet of 1, perf. 13	3.00 3.00

FIFA Under-20 World Soccer Championships, Canada — A935

2007, June 26 Litho. Perf. 12½x13

2220	A935	52c multi	1.00 .50

Popular Singers — A936

Designs: Nos. 2221a, 2222a, Gordon Lightfoot. Nos. 2221b, 2222b, Joni Mitchell. Nos. 2221c, 2222c, Anne Murray. Nos. 2221d, 2222d, Paul Anka.

2007, June 29 Perf. 12½x13

2221	A936	Sheet of 4	4.00 4.00
a.-d.		52c Any single	1.00 .50

Self-Adhesive
Serpentine Die Cut 13½

2222	A936	Booklet pane of 4	4.00
a.-d.		52c Any single	1.00 .50
		Complete booklet, 2 #2222	8.00

Complete booklets were issued with four different covers depicting the featured singers.

National Parks — A937

Designs: No. 2223, Terra Nova National Park, Newfoundland, 50th anniv. No. 2224, Jasper National Park, Alberta, cent.

2007 Serpentine Die Cut 13¼
Booklet Stamps
Self-Adhesive

2223	A937	52c multi	1.00 .50
a.		Booklet pane of 5	5.00
		Complete booklet, 2 #2223a	10.00
2224	A937	52c multi	1.00 .50
a.		Booklet pane of 5	5.00
		Complete booklet, 2 #2224a	10.00

Issued: No. 2223, 7/6; No. 2224, 7/20.

Scouting, Cent. A938

2007, July 25 Litho.
Booklet Stamp
Self-Adhesive

2225	A938	52c multi	1.00 .50
a.		Booklet pane of 4 + 4 labels	4.00
		Complete booklet, 2 #2225a	8.00

Henri Membertou, Grand Chief of Mi'kmaq Tribe — A939

2007, June 26 Engr. Perf. 13x12½

2226	A939	52c multi	1.00 .50

Law Society of Saskatchewan, Cent. — A940

2007, Sept. 13 Litho. Perf. 13

2227	A940	52c multi	1.00 .50

Printed in sheets of 8 + 8 labels.

Law Society of Alberta, Cent. A941

2007, Sept. 13 Perf. 12½x13

2228	A941	52c multi	1.00 .50

Endangered Animals Type of 2006

Designs: Nos. 2229a, 2230, North Atlantic right whale. Nos. 2229b, 2231, Northern cricket frog. Nos. 2229c, 2232, White sturgeon. Nos. 2229d, 2233, Leatherback turtle.

2007, Oct. 1 Litho. Perf. 13¼

2229		Sheet of 4 + 4 labels	4.50 4.50
a.-d.	A915	52c Any single	1.10 .55

Booklet Stamps
Self-Adhesive
Size: 47x24mm
Die Cut

2230	A915	52c multi	1.10 .55
2231	A915	52c multi	1.10 .55
2232	A915	52c multi	1.10 .55
2233	A915	52c multi	1.10 .55
a.		Block of 4, #2230-2233	4.50
b.		Booklet pane, 2 #2233a	9.00

Beneficial Insects — A942

Designs: 1c, Convergent lady beetle (Hippodamia convergens). 3c, Golden-eyed lacewing (Chrysopa oculata). 5c, Northern bumblebee (Bombus polaris). 10c, Canada darner (Aeshna canadensis). 25c, Cecropia moth (Hyalophora cecropia).

2007, Oct. 12 Litho. Perf. 13¼x13

2234	A942	1c multi	.20 .20
2235	A942	3c multi	.20 .20
2236	A942	5c multi	.20 .20
2237	A942	10c multi	.20 .20
2238	A942	25c multi	.55 .25
a.		Souvenir sheet, #2234-2238	.95 .95
		Nos. 2234-2238 (5)	1.35 1.05

Christmas
A943   A944

Designs: No. 2239, Reindeer and snowflakes. No. 2240, Holy Family. 93c, Angel over town. $1.55, Dove.

Litho. With Hologram Affixed
Serpentine Die Cut 8¼ Horiz.
2007, Nov. 1
Booklet Stamps
Self-Adhesive

2239	A943	(52c) multi	1.10 .55
a.		Booklet pane of 6	6.60
		Complete booklet, 2 #2239a	13.50

Litho.
Serpentine Die Cut 13½

2240	A944	(52c) multi	1.10 .55
a.		Booklet pane of 6	6.60
		Complete booklet, 2 #2240a	13.50
2241	A944	93c multi	2.00 1.00
a.		Booklet pane of 6	12.00
2242	A944	$1.55 multi	3.50 1.75
a.		Booklet pane of 6	21.00
		Nos. 2239-2242 (4)	7.70 3.85

Flowers Type of 2006 and

Odontioda Island Red Orchid — A945   Queen Elizabeth II — A946

Flag and Sambro Island Lighthouse, Nova Scotia A947   Flag and Point Clark Lighthouse, Ontario A948

Flag and Cap-des-Rosiers Lighthouse, Quebec — A949

Flag and Warren Landing Lighthouse, Manitoba A950   Flag and Pachena Point Lighthouse, British Columbia A951

Designs: 96c, Potinara Janet Elizabeth "Fire Dancer" orchid. $1.15, Laeliocattleya Memoria Evelyn Light orchid. $1.60, Masdevallia Kaleidoscope "Conni" orchid.

2007, Dec. 27 Litho. Perf. 13¼x13

2243		Sheet of 4	8.75 8.75
a.		A945 P multi	1.10 .55
b.		A926 96c multi	2.00 1.00
c.		A926 $1.15 multi	2.40 1.25
d.		A926 $1.60 multi	3.25 1.60

Self-Adhesive
Coil Stamps
Serpentine Die Cut 8½-9 Horiz.

2244	A945	P multi	1.10	.55
2245	A926	96c multi	2.00	1.00
2246	A926	$1.15 multi	2.40	1.25
2247	A926	$1.60 multi	3.25	1.60
	Nos. 2244-2247 (4)		8.75	4.40

Booklet Stamps
Serpentine Die Cut 13¼

2248	A946	P multi	1.10	.55
a.	Booklet pane of 10		11.00	
2249	A947	P multi	1.10	.55
2250	A948	P multi	1.10	.55
2251	A949	P multi	1.10	.55
2252	A950	P multi	1.10	.55
2253	A951	P multi	1.10	.55
a.	Booklet pane of 10, 2 each #2249-2253		11.00	

Die Cut

2254	A926	96c multi	2.00	1.00
a.	Booklet pane of 6		12.00	
2255	A926	$1.15 multi	2.40	1.25
a.	Booklet pane of 6		14.50	
2256	A926	$1.60 multi	3.25	1.60
a.	Booklet pane of 6		19.50	
	Nos. 2248-2256 (9)		14.25	7.15

Nos. 2243a, 2244, 2248-2253 each sold for 52c on day of issue.

New Year 2008 (Year of the Rat) — A952

Designs: 52c, Rat with umbrella. $1.60, Rat with fan.

Litho. & Embossed With Foil Application

2008, Jan. 8			***Perf. 13***	
2257	A952	52c multi	1.10	.55

Souvenir Sheet
2258	A952	$1.60 multi	3.25	3.25

No. 2257 printed in sheets of 25 + 20 labels.

Fireworks A953

Serpentine Die Cut 13½ Horiz.
2008, Jan. 15   **Litho.**

Self-Adhesive
Booklet Stamp

2259	A953	P multi	1.10	.55
a.	Booklet pane of 6		6.75	

No. 2259 sold for 52c on day of issue.

SEMI-POSTAL STAMPS

Olympic Type of 1973 and

SP1

SP2

1974, Apr. 17	**Litho.**		***Perf. 12½***	
	Size: 20x36mm			
B1	A307	8c + 2c multi	.40	.40
B2	A307	10c + 5c multi	.60	.60
B3	A307	15c + 5c multi	.80	.80
	Nos. B1-B3 (3)		1.80	1.80

1975, Feb. 5	**Litho.**		***Perf. 13***	
B4	SP1	8c + 2c Swimming	.40	.40
B5	SP1	10c + 5c Rowing	.60	.60
B6	SP1	15c + 5c Sailing	.80	.80
	Nos. B4-B6 (3)		1.80	1.80

1975, Aug. 6	**Litho.**		***Perf. 13***	
B7	SP2	8c + 2c Fencing	.40	.40
B8	SP2	10c + 5c Boxing	.60	.60
B9	SP2	15c + 5c Judo	.80	.80
	Nos. B7-B9 (3)		1.80	1.80

1976, Jan. 7				
B10	SP2	8c + 2c Basketball	.40	.40
B11	SP2	10c + 5c Vaulting	.60	.60
B12	SP2	20c + 5c Soccer	1.10	1.10
	Nos. B10-B12 (3)		2.10	2.10

21st Olympic Games, Montreal, July 17-Aug. 1. The surtax was for the Canadian Olympic Committee.

Literacy — SP3

1996, Sept. 9	**Litho.**		***Perf. 13x12½***	
B13	SP3	45c +5c multi	1.10	.50
a.	Booklet pane of 10		11.00	
	Complete booklet		11.50	

No. B13 has die cut opening in center to represent missing puzzle piece.
Surcharge donated to ABC CANADA literacy organization.

AIR POST STAMPS

Allegory of Flight — AP1

Unwmk.

1928, Sept. 21	**Engr.**		***Perf. 12***	
C1	AP1	5c brown olive	15.00	4.75
	Never hinged		27.50	
a.	Imperf., pair		275.00	
	Never hinged		375.00	

No. C1 is known imperforate horizontally and imperforate vertically.
For surcharge see No. C3.

Allegory-Air Mail Circles Globe AP2

1930, Dec. 4			***Perf. 11***	
C2	AP2	5c olive brown	85.00	27.50
	Never hinged		140.00	

For surcharge see No. C4.

No. C1 Surcharged

1932, Feb. 22			***Perf. 12***	
C3	AP1	6c on 5c brown olive	12.00	3.75
	Never hinged		21.00	
a.	Inverted surcharge		200.00	
	Never hinged		280.00	
b.	Double surcharge		675.00	
	Never hinged		950.00	
c.	Triple surcharge		400.00	
	Never hinged		550.00	
d.	Pair, one without surcharge		950.00	
	Never hinged		1,350.	

Counterfeit surcharges exist.
No. C3b is valued in the grade of fine.

No. C2 Surcharged in Dark Blue

1932, July 12			***Perf. 11***	
C4	AP2	6c on 5c olive brown	40.00	12.50
	Never hinged		70.00	

Daedalus AP3

1935, June 1	**Engr.**		***Perf. 12***	
C5	AP3	6c red brown	4.25	1.25
	Never hinged		6.00	
a.	Horiz. pair, imperf. vert.		6,000.	
b.	Imperf., pair		650.00	
	Never hinged		1,000.	

No. C5a is believed to be unique and is the result of a pre-perforating paper foldover.

For information on imperforate and part-perforate varieties, see note following No. 47a.

Mackenzie River Steamer and Seaplane AP4

1938, June 15				
C6	AP4	6c blue	3.50	.40
	Never hinged		5.00	
a.	Imperf., pair		650.00	
	Never hinged		950.00	

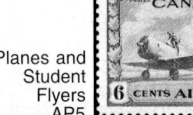

Planes and Student Flyers AP5

1942-43				
C7	AP5	6c deep blue	5.00	1.00
	Never hinged		7.25	
a.	Imperf., pair		650.00	
	Never hinged		950.00	

C8	AP5	7c deep blue ('43)	1.00	.20
	Never hinged		1.40	
a.	Imperf., pair		650.00	
	Never hinged		950.00	

Canada's contribution to the war effort of the Allied Nations.

Canada Geese in Flight — AP6

1946, Sept. 16				
C9	AP6	7c deep blue	1.10	.20
a.	Booklet pane of 4		3.25	3.25

For overprints see Nos. CO1, CO2.

AIR POST SPECIAL DELIVERY STAMPS

Trans-Canada Airplane and Aerial View of a City — APSD1

1942-43	**Unwmk.**	**Engr.**	***Perf. 12***	
CE1	APSD1	16c bright ultra	2.50	2.00
	Never hinged		3.50	
a.	Imperf., pair		650.00	
	Never hinged		950.00	
CE2	APSD1	17c brt ultra ('43)	3.25	3.00
	Never hinged		4.75	
a.	Imperf., pair		650.00	
	Never hinged		950.00	

Canada's contribution to the war effort of the Allied Nations.

DC-4 Transatlantic Mail Plane Over Quebec — APSD2

1946, Sept. 16				
CE3	APSD2	17c bright ultra	6.00	4.00

Circumflex accent on second "E" of "EXPRES."

Corrected Die

1946, Dec. 3				
CE4	APSD2	17c bright ultra	6.00	4.00

Grave accent on the 2nd "E" of "EXPRES."

AIR POST OFFICIAL STAMPS

No. C9
Overprinted
in Black

1949   **Unwmk.**   **Perf. 12**
CO1   AP6 7c deep blue   12.00   4.75
a.   No period after "S"   100.00   60.00

Same
Overprinted

1950
CO2   AP6 7c deep blue   17.50   15.00

SPECIAL DELIVERY

SD1

Unwmk.
1898, June 28   **Engr.**   **Perf. 12**
E1   SD1 10c blue green   110.00   11.00
   Never hinged   300.00

SD2

1922, Aug. 21
E2   SD2 20c carmine   90.00   9.00
   Never hinged   200.00

Five Stages of Mail
Transportation
SD3

1927, June 29
E3   SD3 20c orange   22.50   14.00
   Never hinged   45.00
a.   Imperf., pair   200.00
   Never hinged   275.00

No. E3 forms part of the Confederation
Commemorative issue. It is known imperforate
vertically and imperforate horizontally.

SD4

1930, Sept. 2   **Perf. 11**
E4   SD4 20c henna brown   60.00   15.00
   Never hinged   115.00

SD5

1933, Dec. 24
E5   SD5 20c henna brown   57.50   16.00
   Never hinged   110.00
a.   Imperf., pair   650.00
   Never hinged   950.00

Allegory of Progress — SD6

1935, June 1   **Perf. 12**
E6   SD6 20c dark carmine   10.00   7.50
   Never hinged   16.00
a.   Imperf., pair   650.00
   Never hinged   950.00

Arms of Canada — SD7

1938-39
E7   SD7 10c dk green ('39)   6.00   3.25
   Never hinged   8.75
a.   Imperf., pair   650.00
   Never hinged   950.00
E8   SD7 20c dark carmine   30.00   25.00
   Never hinged   47.50
a.   Imperf., pair   650.00
   Never hinged   950.00

No. E8 Surcharged in Black

1939, Mar. 1
E9   SD7 10c on 20c dk car   7.50   6.50
   Never hinged   11.00

Coat
of
Arms
and
Flags
SD8

1942, July 1   **Engr.**
E10   SD8 10c green   2.50   2.00
   Never hinged   3.50
a.   Imperf., pair   650.00
   Never hinged   950.00

Canada's contribution to the war effort of
the Allied Nations.

> **Catalogue values for unused
> stamps in this section, from this
> point to the end of the section, are
> for Never Hinged items.**

Arms of Canada — SD9

1946, Sept. 16
E11   SD9 10c green   2.75   1.10
   The laurel and olive branches symbolize
Victory and Peace.
   For overprints see Nos. EO1, EO2.

SPECIAL DELIVERY OFFICIAL STAMPS

> **Catalogue values for unused
> stamps in this section are for
> Never Hinged items.**

No. E11 Overprinted in Black

1950   **Unwmk.**   **Perf. 12**
EO1   SD9 10c green   17.50   15.00

Same Overprinted

EO2   SD9 10c green   25.00   20.00

REGISTRATION STAMPS

R1

1875-88   **Unwmk.**   **Engr.**   **Perf. 12**
F1   R1 2c orange   115.00   5.75
   Never hinged   225.00
a.   2c vermilion   170.00   15.00
   Never hinged   290.00
b.   2c rose carmine   340.00   110.00
   Never hinged   625.00
c.   As "a," imperf., pair   —
d.   Perf. 12x11½   525.00   100.00
   Never hinged   950.00
F2   R1 5c dark green   150.00   6.00
   Never hinged   300.00
a.   5c blue green ('88)   160.00   6.00
   Never hinged   325.00
b.   5c yellow green   240.00   7.50
   Never hinged   475.00
c.   Imperf., pair   1,200.
d.   Perf. 12x11½   1,300.   240.00
   Never hinged   1,700.
F3   R1 8c blue   450.00   325.00
   Never hinged   800.00
   Nos. F1-F3 (3)   715.00   336.75

POSTAGE DUE STAMPS

D1   D2

1906-28   **Unwmk.**   **Engr.**   **Perf. 12**
J1   D1 1c violet   15.00   4.75
   Never hinged   25.00
a.   Thin paper ('24)   32.50   7.50
   Never hinged   60.00
b.   Imperf., pair   400.00
J2   D1 2c violet   15.00   1.00
   Never hinged   25.00
a.   Thin paper ('24)   32.50   11.00
   Never hinged   60.00
b.   Imperf., pair   400.00
J3   D1 4c violet ('28)   65.00   22.50
   Never hinged   110.00
J4   D1 5c violet   15.00   2.00
   Never hinged   25.00
a.   Thin paper   12.50   7.50
   Never hinged   22.50
b.   Imperf., pair   400.00
J5   D1 10c violet ('28)   75.00   14.00
   Never hinged   140.00
   Nos. J1-J5 (5)   185.00   44.25
   Nos. J1-J5, never hinged   247.50

In 1924 there was a printing of Nos. J1, J2
and J4 on thin semi-transparent paper. Imperf
pairs are without gum.

1930-32   **Perf. 11**
J6   D2 1c dark violet   11.00   4.25
   Never hinged   20.00
J7   D2 2c dark violet   6.00   1.10
   Never hinged   11.50
J8   D2 4c dark violet   17.50   5.50
   Never hinged   32.50
J9   D2 5c dark violet   17.50   6.50
   Never hinged   32.50
J10   D2 10c dark violet ('32)   90.00   10.00
   Never hinged   170.00
a.   Vert. pair, imperf. horiz.   2,000.   —
   Never hinged   3,000.
   Nos. J6-J10 (5)   142.00   27.35
   Nos. J6-J10, never
   hinged   236.00

No. J10a is valued in the grade of fine.

D3   D4

1933-34
J11   D3 1c dark violet ('34)   12.00   6.50
   Never hinged   21.00
a.   Imperf., pair   400.00
   Never hinged   575.00
J12   D3 2c dark violet   6.00   1.25
   Never hinged   10.50
J13   D3 4c dark violet   12.00   8.00
   Never hinged   21.00
J14   D3 10c dark violet   25.00   6.50
   Never hinged   42.50
   Nos. J11-J14 (4)   55.00   22.25
   Nos. J11-J14, never hinged   95.00

> **Catalogue values for unused
> stamps in this section, from this
> point to the end of the section, are
> for Never Hinged items.**

1935-65   **Perf. 12**
J15   D4 1c dark violet   .30   .20
a.   Imperf., pair   200.00
J16   D4 2c dark violet   .30   .20
a.   Imperf., pair   200.00
J16B   D4 3c dark vio ('65)   2.00   1.50
J17   D4 4c dark violet   .35   .20
a.   Imperf., pair   200.00
J18   D4 5c dark vio ('48)   .40   .35
J19   D4 6c dark vio ('57)   2.25   1.75
J20   D4 10c dark violet   .40   .20
a.   Imperf., pair   200.00
   Nos. J15-J20 (7)   6.00   4.40

D5

1967, Feb. 8   **Litho.**   **Perf. 12**
      Size: 20x17mm

J21   D5 1c carmine rose   .20   .20
J22   D5 2c carmine rose   .20   .25
J23   D5 3c carmine rose   .20   .25
J24   D5 4c carmine rose   .25   .25
J25   D5 5c carmine rose   1.50   1.50
J26   D5 6c carmine rose   .25   .25
J27   D5 10c carmine rose   .40   .30
   Nos. J21-J27 (7)   3.00   3.00

1969-78   **Perf. 12**
      Size: 20x15¾mm

J28   D5 1c car rose ('70)   .45   .30
a.   Perf. 12½x12 ('77)   .20   .20
J29   D5 2c car rose ('72)   .25   .20
J30   D5 3c car rose ('74)   .25   .20
J31   D5 4c carmine rose   .40   .30
a.   Perf. 12½x12 ('77)   .20   .20

J32	D5	5c car rose, perf. 12½x12 ('77)	.20	.20
a.		Perf. 12	16.00	12.50
J33	D5	6c car rose ('72)	.20	.20
J34	D5	8c carmine rose	.20	.20
a.		Perf. 12½x12 (78)	.40	.30
J35	D5	10c carmine rose	.55	.20
a.		Perf. 12½x12 ('77)	.25	.20
J36	D5	12c carmine rose	.75	.60
a.		Perf. 12½x12 ('77)	1.50	.70
J37	D5	16c carmine rose ('74)	.40	.25

Perf. 12½x12

J38	D5	20c carmine rose ('77)	.55	.40
J39	D5	24c carmine rose ('77)	.65	.40
J40	D5	50c carmine rose ('77)	1.00	.75
		Nos. J28-J40 (13)	5.85	4.20

WAR TAX STAMPS

WT1   WT2

Unwmk.

1915, Mar. 25   Engr.   Perf. 12

MR1	WT1	1c green	21.00	.20
		Never hinged	50.00	
MR2	WT1	2c carmine	21.00	.25
		Never hinged	50.00	

In 1915 postage stamps of 5, 20 and 50 cents were overprinted "WAR TAX" in two lines. These stamps were intended for fiscal use, the war tax on postal matter being 1 cent. A few of these stamps were used to pay postage.

1916

TWO DIES:
Die I — There is a colored line between two white lines below the large letter "T."
Die II — The right half of the colored line is replaced by two short diagonal lines and five small dots.

MR3	WT2	2c + 1c car (I)	30.00	.20
		Never hinged	75.00	
a.		2c + 1c carmine (II)	150.00	4.50
		Never hinged	350.00	
MR4	WT2	2c + 1c brn (II)	17.50	.20
		Never hinged	42.50	
a.		2c + 1c brown (I)	600.00	10.00
		Never hinged	1,100.	
b.		Imperf., pair (I)	200.00	
c.		Imperf., pair (II)	1,600.	

#MR4b-MR4c were made without gum.

Perf. 12x8

MR5	WT2	2c + 1c car (I)	60.00	30.00
		Never hinged	140.00	

Coil Stamps

Perf. 8 Vertically

MR6	WT2	2c + 1c car (I)	140.00	9.00
		Never hinged	300.00	
MR7	WT2	2c + 1c brn (II)	32.50	1.10
		Never hinged	70.00	
a.		2c + 1c brown (I)	175.00	7.50
		Never hinged	400.00	

OFFICIAL STAMPS

With Perforated Initials O H M S

On March 28, 1939 the Treasury Board ruled that on and after June 30, 1939 all stamps used by government departments throughout the country should be perforated O H M S (On His Majesty's Service) and that "the Post Office Department is to make arrangements required to provide that all stamps sold to Government Departments are perforated with the letters O H M S." The sale of such perforated stamps was discontinued in 1948.

For listings see the *Scott Classic Specialized Catalogue.*

Catalogue values for unused stamps in this section are for Never Hinged items.

Nos. 249, 250, 252 and 254 Overprinted in Black

1949-50   Unwmk.   Perf. 12

O1	A97	1c green	2.00	1.75
a.		No period after "S"	90.00	65.00
O2	A98	2c brown	10.00	7.50
a.		No period after "S"	90.00	65.00
O3	A99	3c rose violet	2.25	1.25
O4	A98	4c dark carmine	2.75	.75

Nos. 269 to 273 Overprinted in Black

O6	A108	10c olive	3.50	.60
a.		No period after "S"	65.00	60.00
O7	A109	14c black brown	4.00	2.25
a.		No period after "S"	100.00	75.00
O8	A110	20c slate black	16.00	3.25
a.		No period after "S"	110.00	75.00
O9	A111	50c dk blue grn	200.00	110.00
a.		No period after "S"	600.00	500.00
O10	A112	$1 red violet	70.00	35.00
a.		No period after "S"	2,250.	1,750.
		Nos. O1-O4,O6-O10 (9)	310.50	162.35

It is recommended that a certificate of authenticity be acquired for No. O10a.

Same Overprint on No. 294

1950

O11	A124	50c dull green	40.00	25.00

Nos. 284 to 288 Overprinted in Black

1950

O12	A119	1c green	.40	.30
O13	A120	2c sepia	1.10	.75
O14	A121	3c rose violet	1.10	.50
O15	A122	4c dark carmine	1.10	.20
b.		No period after "S"	65.00	55.00
O15A	A123	5c deep blue	2.25	1.50
c.		No period after "S"	65.00	55.00
		Nos. O12-O15A (5)	5.95	3.25

Stamps of 1946-1950 Overprinted in Black

a

b

c

1950

O16	A119(a)	1c grn (#284)	.50	.20
O17	A120(a)	2c sepia (#285)	1.30	.90
O18	A121(a)	3c rose vio (#286)	1.30	.20
O19	A122(a)	4c dk car (#287)	1.30	.20
O20	A123(a)	5c dp bl (#288)	1.60	.90
O21	A108(b)	10c olive	2.50	.50
O22	A109(b)	14c black brn	6.50	2.00
O23	A110(b)	20c slate blk	14.00	1.00
O24	A124(b)	50c dull green	10.00	5.50
O25	A112(b)	$1 red violet	105.00	80.00
		Nos. O16-O25 (10)	144.00	91.40

Nos. 301-302 Overprinted Type "b"

1950-51

O26	A125	10c black brown	1.30	.20
a.		Pair, one without "G"	775.00	650.00
O27	A126	$1 brt ultra ('51)	100.00	90.00

It is recommended that a certificate of authenticity be acquired for No. O26a.

Nos. 305-306 Overprinted Type "a"

1951-52   Unwmk.   Perf. 12

O28	A120	2c olive green	.60	.20
O29	A122	4c orange ver ('52)	.95	.20

No. 316 Overprinted Type "b"

1952

O30	A132	20c gray	2.25	.20

Nos. 320-321 Overprinted Type "b"

1952-53

O31	A136	7c blue	4.00	1.25
O32	A137	$1 gray ('53)	17.50	11.00

Same Overprints on #325-329, 334

1953-61

O33	A139(a)	1c violet brown	.35	.20
O34	A139(a)	2c green	.35	.20
O35	A139(a)	3c carmine rose	.35	.20
O36	A139(a)	4c violet	.45	.20
O37	A139(a)	5c ultramarine	.45	.20
O38	A141(b)	50c light green	5.00	1.20
a.		Overprinted type "c" ('61)	5.00	2.00
		Nos. O33-O38 (6)	6.95	2.20

No. 351 Overprinted Type "b"

1955-62

O39	A148	10c violet brown	.90	.20
a.		Overprinted type "c" ('62)	1.90	1.25

#337-338, 340-341 Ovptd. Type "a"

1955-56

O40	A144	1c vio brown ('56)	.35	.30
O41	A144	2c green ('56)	.35	.20
O43	A144	4c violet ('56)	1.00	.20
O44	A144	5c bright blue	.60	.20
		Nos. O40-O44 (4)	2.30	.90

No. 362 Overprinted Type "b"

1956-62

O45	A159	20c green	1.75	.20
a.		Overprinted type "c" ('62)	7.00	.50

#401-402, 404-405 Ovptd. Type "a"

1963, May 15   Engr.   Perf. 12

O46	A195	1c deep brown	.75	.70
a.		Double overprint	750.00	
O47	A195	2c green	.75	.70
a.		Pair, one without "G"	750.00	
O48	A195	4c carmine	.80	.70
O49	A195	5c violet blue	.50	.50
		Nos. O46-O49 (4)	2.80	2.60

CAPE JUBY

'kāp 'jü-bē

LOCATION — Northwest coast of Africa in Spanish Sahara
GOVT. — Spanish administration
AREA — 12,700 sq. mi.
POP. — 9,836
CAPITAL — Villa Bens (Cape Juby)

By agreement with France, Spain's Sahara possessions were extended to include Cape Juby and in 1916 Spanish troops occupied the territory. It was attached for administrative purposes to Spanish Sahara.

100 Centimos = 1 Peseta

Stamps of Rio de Oro, 1914 Surcharged in Violet, Red or Green

		1916	**Unwmk.**	**Perf. 13**	
1	A6	5c on 4p rose (V)		175.00	19.00
2	A6	10c on 10p dl vio (R)		40.00	19.00
2E	A6	10c on 10p dl vio (V)		125.00	72.50
2G	A6	10c on 10p dl vio (B)		125.00	72.50
3	A6	15c on 50c dk brn (G)		52.50	30.00
4	A6	15c on 50c dk brn (R)		37.50	19.00
5	A6	40c on 1p red vio (G)		77.50	35.00
6	A6	40c on 1p red vio (R)		65.00	26.00
		Nos. 1-6 (8)		697.50	293.00
		Set, never hinged		1,100.	

For type II, inverted and double surcharges, see the *Scott Classic Catalogue.*
Very fine examples of Nos. 1-6 will be somewhat off center. Well centered examples are uncommon and will sell for more.

Stamps of Spain, 1876-1917, Overprinted in Red or Black

		1919		**Imperf.**	
7	A21	¼c bl grn (R)		.30	.30
			Perf. 13x12½, 14		
8	A46	2c dk brn (Bk)		.30	.30
a.		Double overprint		19.00	16.00
b.		Double overprint (Bk + R)		60.00	52.50
9	A46	5c grn (R)		.60	.60
a.		Double overprint		19.00	16.00
b.		Inverted overprint		30.00	47.50
10	A46	10c car (Bk)		.70	.70
a.		Double overprint (Bk + R)		60.00	60.00
11	A46	15c ocher (Bk)		3.00	3.00
b.		Double overprint		19.00	16.00
c.		Red control #		6.00	3.75
d.		As "c," inverted overprint		13.00	
12	A46	20c ol grn (R)		16.00	16.00
13	A46	25c dp bl (R)		3.00	3.00
a.		Double overprint		19.00	16.00
14	A46	30c bl grn (R)		3.00	3.00
15	A46	40c rose (Bk)		3.25	3.25
16	A46	50c sl bl (R)		3.50	3.50
17	A46	1p lake (Bk)		10.00	8.50
18	A46	4p dp vio (R)		37.50	32.50
19	A46	10p org (Bk)		52.50	42.50
		Nos. 7-19 (13)		133.65	117.15
		Set, never hinged		225.00	

Nos. 8-19 have blue control number on back. For imperfs, see the *Scott Classic Catalogue.*

Same on Stamps of Spain, 1920-21

		1922		**Imperf.**	
20	A47	1c blue green (R)		25.00	14.00
		Never hinged		42.50	

		Engr.		**Perf. 13x12½**	
		Blue Control Number on Back			
23	A46	20c violet		140.00	40.00
		Never hinged		200.00	

A 2c and a 15c exist, values $400 and $10, respectively, for unused, hinged copies, $600 and $15 for never hinged.

Same on Stamps of Spain, 1922-23

		1925		**Perf. 13½x13**	
25	A49	5c red vio		5.00	3.50
26	A49	10c bl grn		12.50	3.50
28	A49	20c violet		26.50	10.00
		Nos. 25-28 (3)		44.00	17.00
		Set, never hinged		65.00	

Exists on Spain No. 331, 2c olive green. Value $350 unused hinged and $575 never hinged.

Seville-Barcelona Exposition Issue
CABO JUBY
Stamps of Spain, 1929, Overprinted in Red or Blue

		1929		**Perf. 11**	
29	A52	5c rose lake (Bl)		.45	.45
30	A53	10c green (R)		.45	.45
31	A50	15c Prus bl (R)		.45	.45
32	A51	20c pur (R)		.45	.45
33	A50	25c brt rose (Bl)		.45	.45
34	A52	30c blk brn (Bl)		.45	.45
35	A53	40c dk bl (R)		.45	.45
36	A51	50c dp org (Bl)		.80	.80
37	A52	1p bl blk (R)		22.50	22.50
38	A53	4p dp rose (Bl)		29.00	29.00
39	A53	10p brn (Bl)		29.00	29.00
		Nos. 29-39 (11)		84.45	84.45
		Set, never hinged		125.00	

Stamps of Spanish Morocco, 1928-33, Overprinted in Black or Red

		1934		**Perf. 14**	
40	A7	1c brt rose (Bk)		.50	.50
41	A2	2c dk vio (R)		4.50	4.50
42	A2	5c dp bl (R)		5.00	5.00
43	A2	10c dk grn (Bk)		10.00	10.00
43A	A10	10c dk grn (R)		3.00	3.00
44	A2	15c org brn (Bk)		25.00	25.00
45	A7	20c sl grn (R)		8.75	8.75
46	A3	25c cop red (Bk)		4.75	4.75
47	A10	30c red brn (Bk)		8.75	8.75
48	A13	40c dp bl (R)		32.50	32.50
49	A13	50c red org (Bk)		60.00	60.00
50	A4	1p yel grn (Bk)		45.00	45.00
51	A3	2.50p red vio (Bk)		90.00	90.00
52	A6	4p ultra (R)		115.00	115.00

No. 43A and 1c, 20c, 30c, 40c, 50c, with control numbers.

Same Overprint in Black on Stamp of Spanish Morocco, 1932

		53	A2	1c car rose ("Ct")		2.10	2.10
				Nos. 40-53 (15)		414.85	414.85
				Set, never hinged		675.00	

Stamps of Spanish Morocco, 1933-35, Overprinted in Black, Blue or Red

		1935-36			
54	A8	2c grn (R)		.80	.80
55	A9	5c mag (Bk)		2.50	2.50
55A	A10	10c dk grn (R) ('36)		16.50	16.50
56	A11	15c yel (Bl)		6.50	6.50
57	A12	25c crim (Bk)		72.50	72.50
58	A8	1p grn (Bl)		10.00	10.00
59	A9	2.50p brn (Bl)		40.00	40.00
60	A11	4p yel grn (R)		67.50	67.50
61	A12	5p blk (R)		55.00	55.00
		Nos. 54-61 (9)		271.30	271.30
		Set, never hinged		425.00	

Same Overprint in Black or Red on Stamps of Spanish Morocco, 1935

		1935		**Perf. 13½**	
62	A14	25c vio (R)		4.00	4.00
63	A15	30c crim (Bk)		4.00	4.00
64	A14	40c org (Bk)		5.25	5.25
65	A15	50c brt bl (R)		9.50	9.50
66	A14	60c dk bl grn (R)		11.50	11.50
67	A15	2p brn blk (R)		62.50	62.50

Same Overprint on Stamps of Spanish Morocco, 1933

				Perf. 13½, 14	
68	A7	1c brt rose (Bk)		.30	.30

				Perf. 14	
69	A7	20c slate grn (R)		4.50	4.50
		Nos. 62-69 (8)		101.55	101.55
		Set, never hinged		160.00	160.00

Same Overprint on Stamps of Spanish Morocco, 1937

		1937		**Perf. 13½**	
70	A21	1c dk bl (Bk)		.45	.45
71	A21	2c org brn (Bk)		.45	.45
72	A21	5c cer (Bk)		.45	.45
73	A21	10c emer (Bk)		.45	.45
74	A21	15c brt bl (Bk)		.45	.45
75	A21	20c red brn (Bk)		.45	.45
76	A21	25c mag (Bk)		.45	.45
77	A21	30c red org (Bk)		.45	.45
78	A21	40c org (Bk)		1.10	1.10
79	A21	50c ultra (R)		1.10	1.10
80	A21	60c yel grn (Bk)		1.10	1.10
81	A21	1p bl vio (Bk)		1.10	1.10
82	A21	2p Prus bl (Bk)		70.00	70.00
83	A21	2.50p gray blk (R)		70.00	70.00
84	A21	4p dk brn (Bk)		70.00	70.00
85	A22	10p vio blk (R)		70.00	70.00
		Nos. 70-85 (16)		288.00	288.00
		Set, never hinged		450.00	

1st Year of the Revolution.

Same Overprint in Black on Types of Spanish Morocco, 1939

Designs: 5c, Spanish quarter. 10c, Moroccan quarter. 15c, Street scene, Larache. 20c, Tetuan.

		1939	**Photo.**	**Perf. 13½**	
86	A25	5c vermilion		.50	.50
87	A25	10c deep green		.50	.50
88	A25	15c brown lake		.50	.50
89	A25	20c bright blue		.50	.50
		Nos. 86-89 (4)		2.00	2.00
		Set, never hinged		2.75	

Same Overprint in Black or Red on Stamps of Spanish Morocco, 1940

		1940		**Perf. 11½x11**	
90	A26	1c dk brn (Bk)		.25	.25
91	A27	2c ol grn (R)		.25	.25
92	A28	5c dk bl (R)		.25	.25
93	A29	10c dk red lil (Bk)		.25	.25
94	A30	15c dk grn (R)		.25	.25
95	A31	20c pur (R)		.25	.25
96	A32	25c blk brn (R)		.25	.25
97	A33	30c brt grn (Bk)		.30	.30
98	A34	40c slate grn (R)		.60	.60
99	A35	45c org ver (Bk)		.60	.60
100	A36	50c brn org (Bk)		.65	.65
101	A37	70c saph (R)		1.90	1.90
102	A38	1p ind & brn (Bk)		4.00	4.00
103	A39	2.50p choc & dk grn (Bk)		10.00	10.00
104	A40	5p dk cer & sep (R)		10.50	10.50
105	A41	10p dk ol grn & brn org (Bk)		26.00	26.00
		Nos. 90-105 (16)		56.30	56.30
		Set, never hinged		85.00	

Imperfs exist. Value, set $250.

Stamps of Spanish Morocco, 1944. Overprinted in Black or Red

		1944, Oct. 2	**Unwmk.**	**Perf. 12½**	
106	A47	1c choc & lt bl		.25	.25
107	A48	2c slate grn & lt grn		.25	.25
108	A49	5c choc & grnsh blk (R)		.25	.25
109	A50	10c brt ultra & red org		.25	.25
110	A51	15c brt grn & lt grn		.25	.25
111	A52	20c dp cl & blk (R)		.25	.25
112	A53	25c lt bl & choc		.25	.25
113	A47	30c yel grn & brt ultra (R)		.25	.25
114	A48	40c choc & red org		.25	.25
115	A49	50c brt ultra, & red brn		.25	.25
116	A50	75c yel grn & brt ultra (R)		1.25	1.25
117	A51	1p brt ultra & choc		1.40	1.40
118	A52	2.50p blk & brt ultra (R)		3.25	3.25
119	A53	10p sal & gray blk (R)		25.00	25.00
		Nos. 106-119 (14)		33.40	33.40
		Set, never hinged		45.00	

Same Overprint on Stamps of Spanish Morocco, 1946

		1946, Mar.		**Perf. 10½x10**	
120	A54	1c pur & brn		.25	.25
121	A55	2c dk Prus grn & vio bl (R)		.25	.25
122	A54	10c dp org vio bl		.25	.25

123	A55	15c dk bl & bl grn		.25	.25
124	A54	25c yel grn & ultra		.25	.25
125	A56	40c dk bl & brn (R)		.30	.30
126	A55	45c blk & rose		.45	.45
127	A57	1p dk Prus grn & dp bl		1.60	1.60
128	A58	2.50p dp org & grnsh gray (R)		4.75	4.75
129	A59	10p dk bl & gray (R)		13.50	13.50
		Nos. 120-129 (10)		21.85	21.85
		Set, never hinged		30.00	

Same Overprint in Carmine, Black or Brown on Stamps of Spanish Morocco, 1948

		1948, Jan. 1		**Perf. 10, 10x10½**	
130	A64	2c pur & brn		.40	1.00
131	A65	5c dp claret & vio		.25	.25
132	A66	15c brt ultra & bl grn (Bk)		.25	.25
133	A67	25c blk & Prus grn		.25	.25
134	A65	35c brt ultra & gray blk		.25	.25
135	A68	50c red & vio (Br)		.25	.25
136	A66	70c dk gray grn & ultra (Bk)		.25	.25
137	A67	90c cer & dk gray grn (Bk)		.30	.30
138	A68	1p brt ultra & vio (Br)		.45	.45
139	A64	2.50p vio brn & sl grn (R)		1.60	1.60
140	A69	10p blk & dp ultra (R)		3.00	3.00
		Nos. 130-140 (11)		7.25	7.85
		Set, never hinged		12.00	

SEMI-POSTAL STAMPS

Types of Semi-Postal Stamps of Spain, 1926, Overprinted

		1926	**Unwmk.**	**Perf. 12½, 13**	
B1	SP1	1c orange		12.50	12.50
B2	SP2	2c rose		12.50	12.50
B3	SP3	5c blk brn		3.50	3.50
B4	SP4	10c dk grn		1.60	1.60
B5	SP4	15c dk vio		1.10	1.10
B6	SP4	20c vio brn		1.10	1.10
B7	SP5	25c dp car		1.10	1.10
B8	SP1	30c ol grn		1.10	1.10
B9	SP3	40c ultra		.45	.45
B10	SP2	50c red brn		.45	.45
B11	SP4	1p vermilion		.45	.45
B12	SP3	4p bister		1.60	1.60
B13	SP5	10p lt vio		3.50	3.50
		Nos. B1-B13 (13)		40.95	40.95
		Set, never hinged		65.00	

Nos. B12-B13 surcharged "Alfonso XIII" and new value are listed as Spain Nos. B68-B69. See Spain No. B6a.

AIR POST STAMPS

Spanish Morocco, Nos. C1 to C10 Overprinted "CABO JUBY" as on #54-61

		1938, June 1	**Unwmk.**	**Perf. 13½**	
C1	AP1	5c brown		.25	.25
C2	AP1	10c brt green		.25	.25
C3	AP1	25c crimson		.25	.25
C4	AP1	40c light blue		2.10	2.10
C5	AP2	50c brt mag		.25	.25
C6	AP2	75c dk bl		.25	.25
C7	AP1	1p sepia		.25	.25
C8	AP1	1.50p dp vio		1.90	1.90
C9	AP1	2p dp red brn		2.75	2.75
C10	AP1	3p brn blk		7.25	7.25
		Nos. C1-C10 (10)		15.50	15.50
		Set, never hinged		25.00	

Moroccan Views — AP3

Designs: 5c, Ketama landscape. 10c, Mosque, Tangier. 15c, Velez. 90c, Sanjurjo. 5p, Strait of Gibraltar

1942, Apr. 1	Photo.	Perf. 12½	
C11	AP3	5c deep blue	.25 .25
C12	AP3	10c org brn	.25 .25
C13	AP3	15c grnsh blk	.25 .25
C14	AP3	90c dk rose	.50 .50
C15	AP3	5p black	1.75 1.75
	Nos. C11-C15 (5)		3.00 3.00

SPECIAL DELIVERY STAMPS

Special Delivery Stamp of Spain
Ovptd. "CABO JUBY" as on #7-28

1919	Unwmk.	Perf. 14	
E1	SD1	20c red (Bk)	3.25 3.25
b.	Double overprint		27.50 13.00

Spanish Morocco #E4 Overprinted
"CABO JUBY" as on #40-52 in Red

1934			
E2	SD2	20c black	10.00 10.00

Spanish Morocco No. E5 Overprinted
"CABO JUBY" as on Nos. 54-61

1935			
E3	SD3	20c vermilion	3.50 3.50

Same Ovpt. on Spanish Morocco #E6

1937		Perf. 13½	
E4	SD4	20c bright carmine	1.10 1.10

1st Year of the Revolution.

Same Ovpt. on Spanish Morocco #E8

1940		Perf. 11½x11	
E5	SD5	25c scarlet	.55 .55

SEMI-POSTAL SPECIAL DELIVERY STAMP

Type of Semi-Postal Special Delivery
Stamp of Spain, 1926, Overprinted
"CABO-JUBY" as on Nos. B1-B13

1926	Unwmk.	Perf. 12½, 13	
EB1	SPSD1	20c ultra & black	3.50 3.50

CAPE OF GOOD HOPE

'kāp əv 'gud 'hōp

LOCATION — In the extreme southern
part of South Africa
GOVT. — Former British Colony
AREA — 276,995 sq mi. (1911)
POP. — 2,564,965 (1911)
CAPITAL — Cape Town

Cape of Good Hope joined with
Natal, the Transvaal and the Orange
River Colony in 1910, forming the Union
of South Africa.

12 Pence = 1 Shilling

Watermarks

Wmk. 15 —	Wmk. 16 —
Anchor	Anchor

"Hope"
Seated
A1

Printed by Perkins, Bacon & Co.
Wmk. 15

1853, Sept. 1	Engr.	Imperf.	
	Bluish Paper		
1	A1 1p brick red, bluish paper	3,500.	240.
a.	1p pale brick red, deeply blued paper	4,500.	350.
b.	1p deep brick red, deeply blued paper	6,000.	390.
2	A1 4p deep blue, lightly blued paper	1,550.	130.
a.	4p deep blue, deeply blued paper	2,750.	190.
b.	4p blue, bluish paper	1,700.	175.

Counterfeits exist.

1855-58

	White Paper		
3	A1 1p rose ('57)	540.00	240.00
a.	1p dull red	775.00	300.00
b.	1p brick red	6,000.	1,050.
4	A1 4p blue	575.00	60.00
a.	Half used as 3p on cover		42,000.
b.	4p deep blue	775.00	60.00
c.	4p bright blue	775.00	60.00
5	A1 6p pale lilac ('58)	950.00	240.00
a.	6p rose lilac	2,000.	350.00
b.	6p grayish lilac on bluish paper	5,000.	540.00
c.	6p slate purple on bluish paper	4,150.	1,200.
d.	Half used as 3p on cover		—
6	A1 1sh yellow grn ('58)	3,250.	210.00
a.	1sh dark green	325.00	600.00
b.	Half used as 6p on cover		—

Nos. 3-6 are known rouletted unofficially.
Counterfeits exist.
No. 4 was reproduced by the collotype process in an unwatermarked souvenir sheet distributed at the London Intl. Stamp Exhib. 1950.

A2

Printed by Saul Solomon & Co.

1861	Laid Paper	Unwmk.	Typo.
7	A2 1p vermilion	16,500.	2,650.
a.	1p carmine	28,500.	3,500.
b.	1p red	42,500.	5,000.
c.	1p milky blue (error)	175,000.	32,500.
d.	1p pale blue (error)		36,000.
9	A2 4p milky blue	24,000.	2,000.
a.	4p pale blue	25,000.	2,400.
b.	4p blue	29,500.	3,500.
c.	4p dark blue	112,500.	5,350.
d.	Right corner retouched		7,750.
f.	4p vermilion (error)	177,500.	65,000.
g.	4p carmine (error)		112,500.

Nos. 7 and 9 are usually called Wood
Blocks. The plates were made locally and
composed of clichés mounted on wood. The
errors were caused by a cliché of each value
being mounted in the plate of the other value.
In 1883 plate proofs of both values on white
paper, usually called "reprints," were made.
The 1p is in dull orange red; the 4p in dark
blue. These are known canceled, as a few
were misused as stamps. The proofs do not
include the errors.
Counterfeits exist.

Printed by De La Rue & Co.

1863-64	Wmk. 15	Engr.	
12	A1 1p dark carmine	200.00	270.00
a.	1p reddish brown	450.00	300.00
b.	1p brown red	450.00	275.00

13	A1 4p dark blue	200.00	65.00
a.	4p slate blue	2,400.	600.00
14	A1 6p purple	275.00	540.00
15	A1 1sh emerald	475.00	540.00
a.	1sh pale emerald	1,200.	

Nos. 12-15 can be distinguished from Nos.
3-6 not only by colors but because Nos. 12-15
often appear in a granular ink or with the background lightly printed in whole or part.
No. 12a, Wmk. 1, is believed to be a proof.
Counterfeits exist.

"Hope" and Symbols of
Colony
A3 A6
Frame Line Around Stamp

1864-65	Typo.	Wmk. 1	Perf. 14
16	A3 1p rose ('65)	95.00	30.00
17	A3 4p blue ('65)	120.00	4.25
a.	4p pale blue	120.00	4.25
b.	4p dull ultramarine	300.00	65.00
c.	4p deep blue ('72)	175.00	4.50
18	A3 6p bright violet	150.00	1.75
a.	6p dull violet	240.00	8.25
b.	6p pale lilac	130.00	26.00
19	A3 1sh yellow green	130.00	4.50
a.	1sh blue green	145.00	5.75
	Nos. 16-19 (4)	495.00	40.50

Imperf. stamps are believed to be proofs.
For surcharges see Nos. 20-21, N3.
For types A3 and A6 with manuscript
surcharge of 1d or overprints "G. W." or "G,"
see Griqualand West listings.

Stamps of 1864 Surcharged in Red or
Black:

a	b

1868-74		Red Surcharge	
20	A3(a) 4p on 6p	300.00	19.00
a.	"Peuce" for "Pence"	2,150.	900.00
b.	"Fonr" for "Four"		850.00
21	A3(b) 1p on 6p ('74)	600.00	115.00
a.	"E" of PENNY omitted		1,200.

Space between words and bars varies from
12½-16mm on #20, and 16½-18mm on #21.

1876		Black Surcharge	
22	A3 (b) 1p on 1sh green	100.00	65.00

Without Frame Line Around Stamp

1871-81		Perf. 14	
23	A6 ½p gray black ('75)	24.00	10.00
24	A6 1p rose ('72)	42.50	.70
25	A6 3p lilac rose ('80)	225.00	31.00
26	A6 3p claret ('81)	135.00	3.25
27	A6 4p blue ('76)	120.00	.90
a.	4p ultramarine	240.00	60.00
28	A6 5sh orange	425.00	19.00
	Nos. 23-28 (6)	971.50	64.85

For surcharges see Nos. 29-32, 39, 55.

No. 27 Surcharged in
Red

1879			
29	A6 3p on 4p blue	120.00	2.40
a.	"THE.EE"	2,400.	350.00
b.	"PENCB"	2,000.	275.00
c.	Double surcharge	10,750.	3,900.
d.	As "a," double surcharge	—	—

Type of 1871
Surcharged in Black

1880			
30	A6 3p on 4p lilac rose	82.50	2.40

No. 25 Surcharged in Black

e

f

31	A6(e) 3p on 3p lil rose	225.00	9.00
a.	Inverted surcharge	9,500.	1,200.
32	A6(f) 3p on 3p lil rose	90.00	2.10
a.	Inverted surcharge	1,100.	47.50

1882-83			Wmk. 2
33	A6 ½p gray black	27.50	3.00
34	A6 1p rose	72.50	2.00
35	A6 2p bister	115.00	.90
36	A6 3p claret	9.00	1.50
37	A3 6p bright violet	105.00	1.00
38	A6 5sh orange ('83)	950.00	275.00

For overprint see Rhodesia No. 49.

Nos. 26 and 36
Surcharged in Black

1882			Wmk. 1
39	A6 ½p on 3p claret	3,850.	150.00
a.	Hyphen omitted		3,750.

			Wmk. 2
40	A6 ½p on 3p claret	36.00	4.75
a.	"ENNY"	2,400.	825.00
b.	"PENN"	1,200.	725.00
c.	Hyphen omitted	775.00	425.00

1884-98			Wmk. 16
41	A6 ½p gray black ('86)	6.50	.20
42	A6 ½p yel grn ('96)	1.80	.60
43	A6 1p rose ('85)	7.75	.20
44	A6 2p bister	7.25	.20
45	A6 2p choc brown ('97)	2.35	1.20
46	A6 3p red violet ('98)	12.00	1.20
47	A6 4p blue ('90)	15.50	.60
48	A6 4p pale ol grn ('97)	6.00	3.00
49	A3 4p violet	14.00	.25
50	A3 1sh dull bluish green ('89)	115.00	.60

51	A6	1sh blue grn ('94)	77.50	6.00
52	A6	1sh yel buff ('96)	13.00	2.00
53	A6	5sh orange ('87)	115.00	7.25
54	A6	5sh brown org ('96)	90.00	4.25
		Nos. 41-54 (14)	483.65	27.55

For surcharges see Nos. 58, 162, 165-166.
For overprints see Rhodesia Nos. 43, 45-48.

Type of 1871
Surcharged in Black

1891, Mar.

55	A6	2½p on 3p dp mag	5.00	.25
a.		"1" of "½" has straight serif	65.00	37.50

Hope Seated — A13

1892-96

56	A13	2½p sage green	15.50	.20
57	A13	2½p ultra ('96)	7.25	.20

For surcharge see No. N4. For overprint see
Orange River Colony No. 55.

No. 44 Surcharged in
Black

1893, Mar.

58	A6	1p on 2p bister	4.25	.60
a.		Double surcharge		500.00
b.		No period after "PENNY"	65.00	15.50

Hope	Table
Standing	Mountain
A15	and Bay;
	Coat of
	Arms
	A16

1893-1902

59	A15	½p green ('98)	4.25	.20
60	A15	1p rose	1.50	.20
61	A15	3p red violet ('02)	5.25	1.00
		Nos. 59-61 (3)	11.00	2.40

For surcharges see Nos. 163-164, N2. For
overprints see Orange River Colony #54, 56,
Rhodesia #44, Transvaal #236-236A.

1900, Jan.

62	A16	1p carmine rose	4.25	.25

King Edward VII — A17

Various frames.

1902-04 **Wmk. 16**

63	A17	½p emerald	2.75	.20
64	A17	1p car rose	2.40	.20
65	A17	2p brown ('04)	15.50	.95
66	A17	2½p ultra ('04)	3.25	7.75
67	A17	3p red violet ('03)	9.50	1.20
68	A17	4p ol green ('03)	13.00	.80
69	A17	6p violet ('03)	21.00	.60
70	A17	1sh bister	16.50	.95
71	A17	5sh brown org ('03)	110.00	22.50
		Nos. 63-71 (9)	193.90	35.15

Imperf. stamps are proofs.

ISSUED IN MAFEKING

Excellent forgeries of Nos. 162-180
are known.

Stamps of Cape of
Good Hope Surcharged

1900, Mar. 24

162	A6	1p on ½p grn	240.	77.50
163	A15	1p on ½p grn	300.	90.00
164	A15	3p on 1p rose	275.	60.00
165	A6	6p on 3p red vio	42,500.	300.00
166	A6	1sh on 4p pale ol		
		green	7,750.	425.00

Stamps of
Bechuanaland
Protectorate Surcharged

1900 **Wmk. 30**

167	A54	1p on ½p ver	240.	77.50
a.		Inverted surcharge		6,500.
168	A40	3p on 1p lilac	1,000.	105.
a.		Double surcharge		30,000.
169	A56	6p on 2p grn & car	2,250.	90.
170	A58	6p on 3p vio, yel	6,600.	325.
a.		Inverted surcharge	—	36,000.
b.		Double surcharge		

The lettering of "Mafeking Besieged" shows
varying breaks in various letters, and may
have either a period or no punctuation after
"Mafeking."

On Stamps of Bechuanaland
Wmk. 29

171	A1	6p on 3p violet &		
		black	450.	80.

Wmk. 30

172	A59	1sh on 4p brn &		
		grn	1,650.	95.
a.		Double surch., one inverted	—	27,500.
b.		Triple surcharge	—	25,000.
c.		Inverted surcharge	—	25,000.
d.		Double surcharge	—	25,000.

Stamps of
Bechuanaland
Protectorate
Surcharged

173	A40	3p on 1p lilac	1,050.	90.
a.		Double surcharge		10,750.
174	A56	6p on 2p grn &		
		car	1,300.	90.
175	A62	1sh on 6p vio,		
		rose	7,250.	105.

On Stamps of Bechuanaland

176	A62	1sh on 6p vio,		
		rose	24,000.	825.
177	A65	2sh on 1sh green	14,500.	500.

Wmk. OCEANA FINE
Photographic Print

1900, Apr. **Perf. 12**

Laid Paper

178	M1	1p blue, blue	1,000.	425.00
a.		Imperf. pair	21,500.	

Sgt. Major
Goodyear
M1

Gen. Robert S.
S. Baden-
Powell
M2

179	M2	3p blue, blue,		
		18½mm wide	1,400.	425.00
a.		Horiz. pair, imperf btwn.	—	77,500.
b.		Double impression	—	20,000.
c.		Reversed design	77,500.	45,000.
180	M2	3p blue, blue,		
		21mm wide	10,750.	1,500.

The color of the paper varies from pale to
deep blue.
OCEANA FINE is a sheet watermark and
does not appear on every stamp.
Imperfs of No. 178 are proofs.
There is one used pair of No. 179a privately
owned. There are 2 unused and 6 used examples of No. 179c privately owned.
Issued: #179, Apr. 6; #178, 180, Apr. 10.

ISSUED IN VRYBURG

Under Boer Occupation

Cape of Good Hope
Stamps of 1884-96
Surcharged

Two Types of Surcharge:
Type I — Surcharge 10mm high. Space
between lines 5½mm.
Type II — Surcharge 12mm high. Space
between lines 7½mm.

1899, Nov. **Wmk. 16** **Perf. 14**

N1	A6	½p on ½p em-		
		er (I)	240.	95.
a.		Type II	2,000.	825.
N2	A15	1p on 1p rose		
		(I)	275.	120.
a.		Double surcharge		
b.		Type II	2,250.	950.
N3	A3	2p on 6p vio		
		(II)	2,500.	600.
N4	A13	2½p on 2½p ul-		
		tra (I)	2,000.	500.
a.		Type II	12,000.	5,000.

"Z.A.R." stands for Zuid Afrikaansche
Republiek (South African Republic).

Under British Occupation

Transvaal Stamps of
1895-96 Handstamped

1900 **Unwmk.** **Perf. 12½**

N5	A13	½p green	—	2,750.
N6	A13	1p rose & grn	10,750.	5,000.
N7	A13	2p brown & grn	—	36,000.
N8	A13	2½p ultra & grn	—	36,000.

CAPE VERDE

ˈkāp ˈvərd

LOCATION — A group of 10 islands
and five islets in the Atlantic Ocean,
about 500 miles due west of Senegal.
GOVT. — Republic
AREA — 1,557 sq. mi.
POP. — 405,748 (1999 est.)
CAPITAL — Praia

The Portuguese territory of Cape
Verde became independent on July 5,
1975.

1000 Reis = 1 Milreis
100 Centavos = 1 Escudo (1913)

Catalogue values for unused
stamps in this country are for
Never Hinged items, beginning
with Scott 268 in the regular postage section, Scott J31 in the postage due section, and Scott RA6 in
the postal tax section.

Crown of	King Luiz — A2
Portugal — A1	

Perf. 12½, 13½

1877 **Unwmk.** **Typo.**

1	A1	5r black	2.75	1.25
2	A1	10r yellow	27.50	7.00
3	A1	20r bister	2.50	1.00
4	A1	25r rose	1.40	.85
5	A1	40r blue	67.50	20.00
b.		Cliche of Mozambique in		
		Cape Verde plate, in pair		
		with #5	1,100.	1,100.
6	A1	50r green	125.00	65.00
7	A1	100r lilac	5.50	1.90
8	A1	200r orange	3.50	2.25
9	A1	300r brown	4.00	2.75
		Nos. 1-9 (9)	239.65	102.00

For expanded treatment of Nos. 1-9, see the
Scott Classic Catalogue.

1881-85

10	A1	10r green	1.75	1.25
11	A1	20r carmine ('85)	3.50	2.00
12	A1	25r violet ('85)	2.75	1.60
13	A1	40r yellow buff	1.75	1.00
a.		Imperf.		1.00
b.		Cliche of Mozambique in Cape		
		Verde plate, in pair with #13	70.00	62.50
c.		As "b," imperf.	35.00	
14	A1	50r blue	4.50	2.50
		Nos. 10-14 (5)	14.25	8.35

Reprints of the 1877-85 issues are on
smooth white chalky paper, ungummed, and
on thin white paper with shiny white gum. They
are perf 13½.
For expanded treatment of Nos. 10-14, see
the Scott Classic Catalogue.

1886 **Embossed** **Perf. 12½, 13½**
Chalk-Surfaced Paper

15	A2	5r black	3.75	1.60
16	A2	10r green	4.00	1.75
17	A2	20r carmine	5.00	2.75
18	A2	25r violet	4.50	3.25
19	A2	40r chocolate	6.50	2.00
20	A2	50r blue	5.50	2.00
21	A2	100r yel brown	5.50	2.75
22	A2	200r gray lilac	11.00	6.00
23	A2	300r orange	17.00	8.75
		Nos. 15-23 (9)	62.75	30.85

The 25r, 50r and 100r have been reprinted
in aniline colors with clean-cut Perf. 13½.
For expanded treatment of Nos. 15-19, see
the Scott Classic Catalogue.
For surcharges see Nos. 59-67, 184-187.

A3	King
	Carlos — A4

1894-95 Typo. Perf. 11½, 12½, 13½

24	A3	5r orange	.90	.75
25	A3	10r redsh violet	.90	.75
26	A3	15r chocolate	2.25	1.50
a.		Perf. 12½	90.00	67.50
27	A3	20r lavender	2.25	1.50
28	A3	25r dp green	1.90	1.40
a.		Perf. 12½	3.50	2.75
29	A3	50r lt blue	1.90	1.40
a.		Perf. 13½	8.00	3.00
30	A3	75r carmine ('95)	6.50	3.50
a.		Perf. 13½	17.50	10.50
31	A3	80r yel grn ('95)	7.75	4.50
a.		Perf. 13½	25.00	19.00
32	A3	100r brn, buff ('95)	5.50	2.75
a.		Perf. 12½	40.00	18.00
33	A3	150r car, rose ('95)	18.00	15.00
a.		Perf. 12½	110.00	90.00
b.		Perf. 11½	45.00	30.00
34	A3	200r dk blue, lt blue		
		('95)	18.00	15.00
a.		Perf. 12½	90.00	70.00
35	A3	300r dk blue, sal		
		('95)	20.00	9.50
		Nos. 24-35 (12)	85.85	57.55

For surcharges see Nos. 68-78, 137, 189-
193, 201-205.

1898-1903   *Perf. 11½*
Name and Value in Black except 500r

36	A4	2½r gray	.25	.20
37	A4	5r orange	.30	.20
38	A4	10r lt green	.40	.20
39	A4	15r brown	3.25	1.10
40	A4	15r gray grn ('03)	1.00	.75
41	A4	20r gray violet	1.00	.50
42	A4	25r sea green	2.00	.70
a.		*Perf. 12½*	35.00	20.00
43	A4	25r carmine ('03)	.60	.30
44	A4	50r dark blue	2.25	.80
45	A4	50r brown ('03)	2.00	1.40
46	A4	65r slate blue ('03)	40.00	*40.00*
47	A4	75r rose	4.75	*2.00*
48	A4	75r lilac ('03)	1.75	1.25
49	A4	80r violet	4.75	2.25
50	A4	100r dk blue, *blue*	1.75	1.00
51	A4	115r org brn, *pink* ('03)	12.00	13.50
52	A4	130r brn, *straw* ('03)	12.00	13.50
53	A4	150r brown, *straw*	8.00	6.75
54	A4	200r red vio, *pnksh*	2.50	1.60
55	A4	300r dk blue, *rose*	8.00	3.00
56	A4	400r dull blue, *straw* ('03)	10.00	6.00
57	A4	500r blk & red, *blue* ('01)	8.00	3.00
58	A4	700r vio, *yelsh* ('01)	16.00	10.00
		Nos. 36-58 (23)	142.55	110.00

For overprints and surcharges see Nos. 80-99, 139, 200.

Regular Issues Surcharged in Red or Black

Two spacing types of surcharge. See note above Angola No. 61.

On Issue of 1886
1902, Dec. 1   *Perf. 12½, 13½*

59	A2	65r on 5r black (R)	4.00	2.50
60	A2	65r on 200r gray lilac	4.00	2.50
61	A2	65r on 300r orange	4.00	2.50
62	A2	115r on 10r green	4.00	2.50
63	A2	115r on 20r rose	4.00	2.50
a.		*Perf. 13½*	27.50	19.00
64	A2	130r on 50r blue	4.00	2.50
65	A2	130r on 100r brown	4.00	2.50
66	A2	400r on 25r violet	2.00	1.50
67	A2	400r on 40r choc	4.00	2.50
a.		*Perf. 13½*	27.50	22.50

On Issue of 1894
Perf. 11½, 12½, 13½

68	A3	65r on 10r red violet	4.75	2.75
69	A3	65r on 20r lavender	4.50	2.50
70	A3	65r on 100r brown, *buff*	5.00	3.00
a.		*Perf 12½*	15.00	13.50
71	A3	115r on 5r orange	2.75	1.90
a.		*Inverted surcharge*	45.00	45.00
72	A3	115r on 25r blue grn	2.75	1.75
a.		*Perf. 11½*	45.00	25.00
73	A3	115r on 150r car, *rose*	4.75	3.75
a.		*Perf. 13½*	20.00	12.00
74	A3	130r on 75r car	2.75	2.00
a.		*Perf. 13½*	45.00	42.50
75	A3	130r on 80r yel grn	2.25	1.75
76	A3	130r on 200r dk blue, *blue*	3.00	1.75
77	A3	400r on 50r lt blue	3.25	2.25
a.		*Inverted surcharge*	65.00	55.00
b.		*Perf. 13½*	55.00	55.00
78	A3	400r on 300r dk blue, *sal*	1.75	1.10

On Newspaper Stamp of 1893

79	N1	400r on 2½r brown	1.25	1.10
a.		*Inverted surcharge*	27.50	
b.		*Perf. 12½*	45.00	42.50
		Nos. 59-79 (21)	72.75	46.85

Reprints of Nos. 59, 66, 67, and 77 have shiny white gum and clean-cut perforation 13½.
For overprint and surcharges see #137, 205-206.

Overprinted in Black On Nos. 39, 42, 44, 47

1902-03   *Perf. 11½*

80	A4	15r brown	1.50	.80
81	A4	25r sea green	1.50	.80
82	A4	50r blue ('03)	1.75	1.00
83	A4	75r rose ('03)	2.25	1.40
a.		*Inverted overprint*	42.50	42.50
		Nos. 80-83 (4)	7.00	4.00

For overprint see No. 139.

No. 46 Surcharged in Black

1905, July 1
84	A4	50r on 65r slate blue	2.50	1.75

Stamps of 1898-1903 Overprinted in Carmine or Green

1911, Aug. 20

85	A4	2½r gray	.20	.20
86	A4	5r orange	.20	.20
87	A4	10r lt green	.60	.50
88	A4	15r gray green	.35	.20
89	A4	20r gray violet	.65	.65
90	A4	25r carmine (G)	.65	.30
91	A4	50r brown	4.00	2.75
92	A4	75r red lilac	.85	.50
93	A4	100r dk blue, *blue*	.85	.60
94	A4	115r org brn, *pink*	.45	1.25
95	A4	130r brown, *straw*	.45	1.25
96	A4	200r red vio, *pnksh*	3.25	3.25
97	A4	400r dull bl, *straw*	1.25	1.25
98	A4	500r blk & red, *bl*	1.50	1.00
99	A4	700r violet, *straw*	1.50	1.10
		Nos. 85-99 (15)	16.75	15.00

King Manuel II — A5

Overprinted in Carmine or Green

1912   *Perf. 11½x12*

100	A5	2½r violet	.20	1.25
101	A5	5r black	.20	.20
102	A5	10r gray grn	.20	.20
103	A5	20r carmine (G)	1.25	.70
104	A5	25r vio brown	.25	.20
105	A5	50r dk blue	2.00	1.60
106	A5	75r bister brn	.45	.35
107	A5	100r brown, *lt grn*	.45	.35
108	A5	200r dk green, *sal*	.70	.60
109	A5	300r black, *azure*	.70	.60

Perf. 14½x15

110	A5	400r black & blue	2.00	1.60
111	A5	500r ol grn & vio brn	2.00	1.60
		Nos. 100-111 (12)	10.40	9.25

Common Design Types pictured following the introduction.

Vasco da Gama Issue of Various Portuguese Colonies

Common Design Types CD20-CD27 Surcharged

On Stamps of Macao
1913, Feb. 13   *Perf. 12½ to 16*

112	CD20	¼c on ½a blue grn	1.25	.75
113	CD21	½c on 1a red	.85	.75
114	CD22	1c on 2a red violet	.85	.75
115	CD23	2½c on 4a yel grn	.85	.75
116	CD24	5c on 8a dk blue	4.00	3.00
117	CD25	7½c on 12a vio brn	3.25	2.00
118	CD26	10c on 16a bister brn	1.40	1.25
119	CD27	15c on 24a bister	3.50	2.50
		Nos. 112-119 (8)	15.95	11.75

On Stamps of Portuguese Africa
Perf. 14 to 15

120	CD20	¼c on 2½r bl grn	.65	.55
121	CD21	½c on 5r red	.65	.55
122	CD22	1c on 10r red vio	.65	.55
123	CD23	2½c on 25r yel grn	.65	.55
124	CD24	5c on 50r dk blue	1.25	.90
125	CD25	7½c on 75r vio brn	1.90	1.60
126	CD26	10c on 100r bis brn	1.75	1.50
127	CD27	15c on 150r bister	1.75	1.50
		Nos. 120-127 (8)	8.75	7.30

On Stamps of Timor

128	CD20	¼c on ½a bl grn	.85	.75
129	CD21	½c on 1a red	.85	.75
130	CD22	1c on 2a red vio	.85	.75
131	CD23	2½c on 4a yel grn	.85	.75
132	CD24	5c on 8a dk blue	4.00	3.00
133	CD25	7½c On 12a vio brn	3.50	2.50
134	CD26	10c on 16a bis brn	1.40	1.25
135	CD27	15c on 24a bister	2.75	1.50
		Nos. 128-135 (8)	15.05	11.25
		Nos. 112-135 (24)	39.75	30.30

For surcharges see Nos. 197-198.

No. 75 Overprinted in Red

1913   *Perf. 11½, 12½, 13½*
137	A3	130r on 80r yel grn	3.25	2.50

Nos. 73 and 76 overprinted but not issued. Values, $15, $20.

Same Overprint on No. 83 in Green
1914   *Perf. 12*
139	A4	75r rose	3.25	2.50
a.		"PROVISORIO" double (G and R)	45.00	40.00

Ceres — A6

Perf. 11½, 12x11½, 15x14
1914-26   *Typo.*
Name and Value in Black

144	A6	¼c olive brn	.20	.20
a.		*Imperf.*		
145	A6	½c black	.20	.20
146	A6	1c blue grn	.85	.75
147	A6	1c yel grn ('22)	.20	.20
148	A6	1½c lilac brown	.20	.20
149	A6	2c carmine	.20	.20
150	A6	2c gray ('26)	.25	5.00
151	A6	2½c lt violet	.20	.20
152	A6	3c org ('22)	.30	.25
153	A6	4c rose ('22)	.20	1.60
154	A6	4½c gray ('22)	.20	5.00
155	A6	5c deep blue	.75	.45
156	A6	5c brt blue ('22)	.20	.20
157	A6	6c lilac ('22)	.20	2.75
158	A6	7c ultra ('22)	.20	2.75
159	A6	7½c yel brn	.20	1.00
160	A6	8c slate	.40	.30
161	A6	10c orange brn	.20	.20
162	A6	12c blue grn ('22)	.35	.20
163	A6	15c plum	4.00	3.00
164	A6	15c brn rose ('22)	.25	.20
165	A6	20c yel grn	.20	.20
166	A6	24c ultra ('26)	1.50	1.40
167	A6	25c choc ('26)	1.50	1.40
168	A6	30c brown, *grn*	3.00	3.00
169	A6	30c gray grn ('22)	.75	.20
170	A6	40c brown, *pink*	3.00	3.00
171	A6	40c turq blue ('22)	1.75	.25
172	A6	50c orange, *sal*	3.00	3.00
173	A6	50c violet ('26)	1.75	.30
174	A6	60c dk blue ('22)	1.75	.45
175	A6	60c rose ('26)	1.75	.45
176	A6	80c brt rose ('22)	2.00	1.10
177	A6	1e green, *blue*	3.00	3.00
178	A6	1e rose ('22)	7.00	2.25
179	A6	1e dp blue ('26)	9.00	1.50
180	A6	2e dk violet ('22)	10.00	4.00
181	A6	5e buff ('26)	25.00	12.00
182	A6	10e pink ('26)	90.00	40.00
183	A6	20e pale turq ('26)	125.00	50.00
		Nos. 144-183 (40)	300.70	152.45

For surcharge see No. 214.

Provisional Issue of 1902 Overprinted in Carmine

1915   *Perf. 11½, 12½, 13½*

184	A2	115r on 10r green	2.50	2.00
185	A2	115r on 20r rose	2.00	1.25
a.		*Perf. 13½*	15.00	15.00
186	A2	130r on 50r blue	2.00	1.10
187	A2	130r on 100r brown	1.50	.70

188	A3	115r on 5r orange	1.25	.40
a.		*Inverted overprint*	30.00	
189	A3	115r on 25r blue grn	1.50	.65
a.		*Perf. 11½*	15.00	15.00
190	A3	115r on 150r car, *rose*	1.00	.40
191	A3	130r on 75r carmine	2.00	.90
192	A3	130r on 80r yel grn	1.50	.70
a.		*Inverted overprint*	30.00	
193	A3	130r on 200r bl, *bl*	2.00	.90
a.		*Perf. 12½*	40.00	32.50
		Nos. 184-193 (10)	17.25	9.00

War Tax Stamps of Portuguese Africa Surcharged

1921, Feb. 3   *Perf. 15x14, 11½*

194	WT1	¼c on 1c green	.25	.25
195	WT1	½c on 1c green	.40	.30
a.		"1/2" instead of "½" as shown	10.00	10.00
196	WT1	1c green	.40	.30

Nos. 127 and 126 Surcharged

Perf. 14 to 15

197	CD27	2c on 15c on 150r	1.00	1.00
198	CD26	4c on 10c on 100r	1.25	1.00
a.		*On No. 118 (error)*	150.00	150.00

The 4c surcharge also exists on No. 134. Value, $500.

No. 50 Surcharged

Perf. 12

200	A4	6c on 100r dk bl, *bl*	1.25	1.25
a.		*No accent on "U" of surcharge*	12.50	8.00
		Nos. 194-200 (6)	4.55	4.10

No. 200 has an accent on the "U" of the surcharge.

Stamps of 1913-15 Surcharged

1922, Apr.   *Perf. 11½, 12½, 13½*
On No. 137
201	A3	4c on 130r on 80r	1.25	1.25

On Nos. 191-193
202	A3	4c on 130r on 75r	1.60	1.60
203	A3	4c on 130r on 80r	1.25	1.25
204	A3	4c on 130r on 200r	.90	.60
a.		*Perf. 12½*	15.00	15.00
		Nos. 201-204 (4)	5.00	4.70

Surcharge of Nos. 201-204 with smaller $ occurs once in sheet of 28. Value eight times normal.

Nos. 78-79 Surcharged

1925   *Perf. 13½, 11½*

205	A3	40c on 400r on 300r	.60	.55
206	N1	40c on 400r on 2½r	.60	.45

No. 176 Surcharged

1931, Nov.   *Perf. 12x11½*
214 A6 70c on 80c brt rose   2.75 1.40

Ceres — A7

1934, May 1			**Wmk. 232**	
215	A7	1c bister	.20	.20
216	A7	5c olive brown	.20	.20
217	A7	10c violet	.20	.20
218	A7	15c black	.20	.20
219	A7	20c gray	.20	.20
220	A7	30c dk green	.20	.20
221	A7	40c red org	.20	.20
222	A7	45c brt blue	1.40	.60
223	A7	50c brown	.65	.45
224	A7	60c olive grn	.65	.45
225	A7	70c brown org	.65	.45
226	A7	80c emerald	.65	.45
227	A7	85c deep rose	3.00	1.90
228	A7	1e maroon	2.10	.35
229	A7	1.40e dk blue	2.75	2.40
230	A7	2e dk violet	3.25	1.90
231	A7	5e apple green	14.50	3.75
232	A7	10e olive bister	24.00	14.00
233	A7	20e orange	45.00	18.00
Nos. 215-233 (19)			100.00	46.10

For surcharge see No. 256.

Vasco da Gama Issue
Common Design Types

1938		**Unwmk.**	*Perf. 13½x13*	
Name and Value in Black				
234	CD34	1c gray green	.20	.20
235	CD34	5c orange brn	.20	.20
236	CD34	10c dk carmine	.20	.20
237	CD34	15c dk vio brn	.70	.65
238	CD34	20c slate	.35	.20
239	CD35	30c rose vio	.35	.20
240	CD35	35c brt green	.35	.20
241	CD35	40c brown	.35	.20
242	CD35	50c brt red vio	.35	.20
243	CD36	60c gray blk	.35	.20
244	CD36	70c brown vio	.35	.20
245	CD36	80c orange	.30	.20
246	CD36	1e red	.50	.20
247	CD37	1.75e blue	1.25	.55
248	CD37	2e dk blue grn	2.50	1.50
249	CD37	5e ol grn	5.75	1.50
250	CD38	10e blue vio	9.75	2.00
251	CD38	20e red brown	30.00	4.00
Nos. 234-251 (18)			53.80	12.60

For surcharges see #255, 271-276, 288-292.

Outline Map of
Africa — A8

1939, June 23		**Litho.**	*Perf. 11½x12*	
252	A8	80c vio, *pale rose*	4.00	2.75
253	A8	1.75e blue, *pale bl*	32.50	25.00
254	A8	20e brown, *buff*	70.00	22.50
Nos. 252-254 (3)			106.50	50.25

Visit of the President of Portugal in 1939.

Nos. 239 and 221 Surcharged with
New Value and Bars in Black

1948		**Unwmk.**	*Perf. 13½x13*	
255	CD35	10c on 30c rose violet	1.25	.70

Perf. 12x11½
Wmk. 232
256 A7 25c on 40c red orange   1.25 .70

Machado Pt., Sao
Vicente — A9

Brava Creek,
Sao
Nicoláo — A10

Designs: 10c, Ribeira Grande. 1e, Harbor, Sao Vicente. 1.75e, Mindelo, distant view. 2e, Joao de Evora Beach. 5e, Mindelo. 10e, Volcano, Fire Island. 20e, Mt. Paul.

1948, Oct. 1		**Litho.**	*Perf. 14½*	
			Unwmk.	
257	A9	5c vio brn & bis	.25	.20
258	A9	10c ol grn & pale grn	.25	.20
259	A10	50c mag & lil rose	.45	.20
260	A10	1e brn vio & rose lil	1.60	.70
261	A10	1.75e ultra & grnsh bl	2.00	1.10
262	A10	2e dk brn & buff	4.50	1.25
263	A10	5e ol grn & yel	9.00	2.50
264	A10	10e red & cream	15.00	8.50
265	A10	20e dk vio & bis	37.50	16.00
Nos. 257-265 (9)			70.55	30.65

Lady of Fatima Issue
Common Design Type

1948, Dec.
266 CD40 50c dark blue   6.50 4.50

UPU Symbols —
A10a

1949, Oct.   *Perf. 14*
267 A10a 1e red vio & pink   5.00 2.50

UPU, 75th anniversary.

> Catalogue values for unused stamps in this section, from this point to the end of the section, are for Never Hinged items.

Holy Year Issue
Common Design Types

1950, May			*Perf. 13x13½*	
268	CD41	1e orange brown	.90	.45
269	CD42	2e slate	3.50	1.75

Holy Year Conclusion Issue
Common Design Type

1951, Oct.		**Unwmk.**	*Perf. 14*	
270	CD43	2e purple & lilac + label	1.40	1.25

Stamps without labels sell for less.

Nos. 240, 244-245, 247, 250
Surcharged with New Value and Bars
Perf. 13½x13

1951, May 21			**Unwmk.**	
271	CD35	10c on 35c	.70	.55
272	CD36	20c on 70c	.90	.65
273	CD36	40c on 70c	1.10	.65
274	CD36	50c on 80c	1.10	.65
275	CD37	1e on 1.75e	1.25	.65
276	CD38	2e on 10e	5.75	2.00
a.		1e on 10e	200.00	125.00
Nos. 271-276 (6)			10.80	5.15

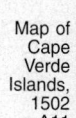

Map of
Cape
Verde
Islands,
1502
A11

Vicente
Dias and
Gonçalo de
Cintra
A12

Portraits: 30c, Diogo Alfonso and Alvaro Fernandes. 50c, Lançarote and Soeiro da Costa. 1e, Diogo Gomes and Antonio da Nola. 2e, Prince Fernando and Prince Henry the Navigator. 3e, Antao Gonçalves and Dinis Dias. 5e, Alfonso Goncalves Baldaia and Joao Fernandes. 10e, Dinis Eanes da Gra and Alvaro de Freitas. 20e, Map of Cape Verde Islands, 1502.

1952, Feb. 24			*Perf. 14*	
277	A11	5c multicolored	.20	.20
278	A12	10c multicolored	.20	.20
279	A12	30c multicolored	.20	.20
280	A12	50c multicolored	.20	.20
281	A12	1e multicolored	.20	.20
282	A12	2e multicolored	1.25	.20
283	A12	3e multicolored	10.50	1.50
284	A12	5e multicolored	3.50	.70
285	A12	10e multicolored	7.00	1.75
286	A11	20e multicolored	12.50	2.40
Nos. 277-286 (10)			35.75	7.55

Medical Congress Issue
Common Design Type

Design: Hypodermic Injection.

1952, June			*Perf. 13½*	
287	CD44	20c ol grn & dk brn	.70	.50

No. 247 Surcharged with New Values
and "X" in Black

1952, Jan. 25			*Perf. 13½x13*	
288	CD37	10c on 1.75e	1.40	1.10
289	CD37	20c on 1.75e	1.40	1.10
290	CD37	50c on 1.75e	5.75	5.00
291	CD37	1e on 1.75e	.70	.25
292	CD37	1.50e on 1.75e	.70	.25
Nos. 288-292 (5)			9.95	7.70

Facade of
Jeronymos
Convent
A13

Perf. 13½

1953, Jan.		**Unwmk.**	**Litho.**	
293	A13	10c brown & pale olive	.20	.20
294	A13	50c purple & fawn	.90	.40
295	A13	1e dark green & fawn	2.10	1.10
Nos. 293-295 (3)			3.20	1.70

Exhibition of Sacred Missionary Art held at Lisbon in 1951.

Stamp of Portugal
and Arms of
Colonies — A13a

1953			**Photo.**	
296	A13a	50c multicolored	1.75	1.10

Centenary of Portuguese stamps.

Sao Paulo Issue
Common Design Type

1954		**Litho.**	*Perf. 13½*	
297	CD46	1e green, cream & gray	.70	.60

Belem Tower,
Lisbon, and
Colonial
Arms — A14

Arms of
Praia — A15

1955, May 15		**Litho.**	*Perf. 13½*	
298	A14	1e multicolored	.50	.25
299	A14	1.60e buff & multi	.75	.60

Visit of Pres. Francisco H. C. Lopes.

1958, June 14			*Perf. 12x11½*	
300	A15	1e multicolored	.65	.45
301	A15	2.50e pink & multi	1.10	.90

Centenary of city of Praia.

Fair Emblem,
Globe and
Arms — A15a

1958			*Perf. 12x11½*	
302	A15a	2e multicolored	.90	.40

World's Fair, Brussels, Apr. 17-Oct. 19.

Tropical Medicine Congress Issue
Common Design Type

1958, Sept. 5			*Perf. 13½*	
303	CD47	3e Aloe vera	5.50	2.10

Prince
Henry — A16

Antonio da
Nola — A17

1960, June 25		**Litho.**	*Perf. 13½*	
304	A16	2e multicolored	.50	.25

500th anniv. of the death of Prince Henry the Navigator.

1960, Oct.   **Unwmk.**   *Perf. 14½*

Design: 2.50e, Diogo Gomes.

305	A17	1e multicolored	.75	.45
306	A17	2.50e multicolored	2.50	1.00

Discovery of Cape Verde, 500th anniv.

School
Children
A18

1960				
307	A18	2.50e multicolored	1.25	.65

10th anniv. of the Commission for Technical Cooperation in Africa South of the Sahara (C.C.T.A.).

Arms of
Praia — A19

Arms of various cities & towns of Cape Verde.

1961, July		**Litho.**	*Perf. 13½*	
308	A19	5c shown	.25	.20
309	A19	15c Nova Sintra	.25	.20
310	A19	20c Ribeira Brava	.25	.20
311	A19	30c Assomada	.25	.20
312	A19	1e Maio	.65	.20
313	A19	2e Mindelo	.65	.20
314	A19	2.50e Santa Maria	1.00	.20
315	A19	3e Pombas	1.60	.50
316	A19	5e Sal-Rei	1.60	.50
317	A19	7.50e Tarrafal	1.75	.90
318	A19	15e Maria Pia	2.40	.90
319	A19	30e San Felipe	6.50	2.50
Nos. 308-319 (12)			17.15	6.70

Sports Issue
Common Design Type

Sports: 50c, Javelin. 1e, Discus. 1.50e, Cricket. 2.50e, Boxing. 4.50e, Hurdling. 12.50e, Golf.

			Perf. 13½	
1962, Jan. 18				
320	CD48	50c lt brown	.25	.20
321	CD48	1e lt green	.75	.25
322	CD48	1.50e lt blue grn	5.00	2.00
323	CD48	2.50e pale vio bl	.75	.35
324	CD48	4.50e orange	1.10	.75
325	CD48	12.50e beige	2.40	1.60
		Nos. 320-325 (6)	10.25	5.15

Anti-Malaria Issue
Common Design Type

Design: Anopheles pretoriensis.

			Perf. 13½	
1962		**Litho.**		
326	CD49	2.50e multicolored	1.40	.90

Airline Anniversary Issue
Common Design Type

			Perf. 14½	
1963, Oct.		**Unwmk.**		
327	CD50	2.50e gray & multi	1.10	.70

National Overseas Bank Issue
Common Design Type

Design: 1.50e, Jose da Silva Mendes Leal.

			Perf. 13½	
1964, May 16				
328	CD51	1.50e multicolored	1.10	.75

ITU Issue
Common Design Type

			Perf. 14½	
1965, May 17		**Litho.**		
329	CD52	2.50e buff & multi	2.10	1.40

Militia Drummer, 1806 — A20

Designs: 1e, Soldier, Militia, 1806. 1.50e, Grenadier officer, 1833. 2.50e, Grenadier, 1833. 3e, Cavalry officer, 1834. 4e, Grenadier, 1835. 5e, Artillery officer, 1848. 10e, Drum major, infantry, 1856.

			Perf. 14½	
1965, Dec. 1		**Litho.**		
330	A20	50c multicolored	.25	.25
331	A20	1e multicolored	.45	.25
332	A20	1.50e multicolored	.45	.40
333	A20	2.50e multicolored	1.25	.35
334	A20	3e multicolored	2.50	.55
335	A20	4e multicolored	1.10	.55
336	A20	5e multicolored	1.25	.55
337	A20	10e multicolored	2.75	1.75
		Nos. 330-337 (8)	10.00	4.65

National Revolution Issue
Common Design Type

1e, Dr. Adriano Moreira School & Health Center.

			Perf. 12	
1966, May 28		**Litho.**		
338	CD53	1e multicolored	.60	.45

Navy Club Issue
Common Design Type

Designs: 1e, Capt. Fontoura da Costa and gunboat Mandovy. 1.50e, Capt. Carvalho Araujo and minesweeper Augusto Castilho.

			Perf. 13	
1967, Jan. 31		**Litho.**		
339	CD54	1e multicolored	.75	.50
340	CD54	1.50e multicolored	1.25	.90

Virgin Mary Statue — A21

Pres. Rodrigues Thomaz — A22

			Perf. 12½x13	
1967, May 13		**Litho.**		
341	A21	1e multicolored	.35	.25

50th anniv. of the apparition of the Virgin Mary to 3 shepherd children at Fatima.

			Perf. 13½	
1968, Feb. 9		**Litho.**		
342	A22	1e multicolored	.35	.25

Issued to commemorate the 1968 visit of Pres. Americo de Deus Rodrigues Thomaz.

Cabral Issue

Pedro Alvares Cabral — A23

1e, Cantino's world map, 1502, horiz.

			Perf. 14	
1968, Apr. 22		**Litho.**		
343	A23	1e multicolored	.85	.70
344	A23	1.50e multicolored	1.40	.75

See note after Angola No. 545.
For overprint see No. 365.

Sao Vicente Harbor — A24

Physic Nut — A25

Designs: 1.50e, Peanut plant. 2.50e, Castor-oil plant. 3.50e, Yams. 4e, Date palm. 4.50e, Guavas. 5e, Tamarind. 10e, Bitter cassava. 30e, Woman carrying fruit baskets.

			Perf. 14	
1968, Oct. 15		**Litho.**		
345	A24	50c multicolored	.25	.20
346	A25	1e multicolored	.40	.25
347	A25	1.50e multicolored	.40	.25
348	A25	2.50e multicolored	.40	.25
349	A25	3.50e multicolored	.45	.25
350	A25	4e multicolored	.45	.25
351	A25	4.50e multicolored	.70	.25
352	A25	5 multicolored	1.00	.30
353	A25	10e multicolored	1.25	.60
354	A25	30e multicolored	3.00	2.50
		Nos. 345-354 (10)	8.30	5.10

For overprint see No. 372.

Admiral Coutinho Issue
Common Design Type

Adm. Coutinho & map showing route of 1st flight from Lisbon to Rio de Janeiro.

			Perf. 14	
1969, Feb. 17		**Litho.**		
355	CD55	30c multi, vert.	.35	.25

For surcharge see No. 388.

Vasco da Gama — A26

King Manuel I — A27

Vasco da Gama Issue

			Perf. 14	
1969, Aug. 29		**Litho.**		
356	A26	1.50e multicolored	.35	.25

Vasco da Gama (1469-1524), navigator.

Administration Reform Issue
Common Design Type

			Perf. 14	
1969, Sept. 25		**Litho.**		
357	CD56	2e multicolored	.35	.25

King Manuel I Issue

			Perf. 14	
1969, Dec. 1		**Litho.**		
358	A27	3e multicolored	.55	.35

500th anniv. of the birth of King Manuel I.

Marshal Carmona Issue
Common Design Type

Design: 2.50e, Antonio Oscar Carmona in marshal's uniform.

			Perf. 14	
1970, Nov. 15		**Litho.**		
359	CD57	2.50e multi	.55	.35

Galleons on Sanaga River — A28

			Perf. 13	
1972, May 25		**Litho.**		
360	A28	5e lilac rose & multi	.65	.30

4th centenary of the publication of The Lusiads by Luiz Camoens.

Olympic Games Issue
Common Design Type

4e, Basketball & boxing, Olympic emblem.

			Perf. 14x13½	
1972, June 20				
361	CD59	4e multicolored	.65	.30

For surcharge see No. 371.

Lisbon-Rio de Janeiro Flight Issue
Common Design Type

Design: "Lusitania" landing at San Vicente.

			Perf. 13½	
1972, Sept. 20		**Litho.**		
362	CD60	3.50e multi	.65	.30

WMO Centenary Issue
Common Design Type

			Perf. 13	
1973, Dec. 15		**Litho.**		
363	CD61	2.50e ultra & multi	.65	.30

For overprint see No. 387.

Mindelo Desalination Plant — A29

			Perf. 13½	
1974		**Litho.**		
364	A29	4e multicolored	1.25	.85

Opening of the Mindelo desalination plant.
For surcharge see No. 371A.

Republic
No. 343 Overprinted:
"INDEPENDENCIA / 5-Julho-75"

			Perf. 14	
1975, Dec. 19		**Litho.**		
365	A23	1e multicolored	.35	.25

Proclamation of Independence.

Amilcar Cabral, Flag and Crowd — A30

1976, Jan. 20				
366	A30	5e multicolored	.55	.25

3rd anniv. of the assassination of Amilcar Cabral (1924-73), revolutionary leader.

Rising Sun, Coat of Arms, Liberated People — A31

			Perf. 14	
1976, July 5		**Litho.**		
367	A31	50c multicolored	.25	.20
368	A31	3e multicolored	.90	.20
369	A31	15e multicolored	2.00	.35
370	A31	50e multicolored	6.25	1.25
a.		Miniature sheet, #367-370	16.00	16.00
		Nos. 367-370 (4)	9.40	2.00

First anniversary of independence.

Nos. 351, 361, 364 Overprinted with Row of Stars and: "REPUBLICA / DE"

			Perf. 14	
1976		**Litho.**		
371	CD59	4e multi		—
371A	A29	4e multi	37.50	27.50
372	A25	4.50e multi	4.25	2.25

Amilcar Cabral, Map and Flag of Cape Verde A32

			Perf. 14	
1976, Sept. 19				
373	A32	1e multicolored	.45	.25

Party of Intl. Action (PAICC), 20th anniv.

Electronic Tree and ITU Emblem — A33

Ashtray — A34

1977, May 17   Litho.   Perf. 13½x13
374   A33   5.50e multi   .45   .25
World Telecommunications Day.

1977, July 5   Litho.   Perf. 14
Carved Coconut Shells: 30c, Bell on stand. 50c, Lamp with Adam and Eve. 1e, Hollow shell with Nativity. 1.50e, Desk lamp. 5e, Jar. 10e, Jar with hinged cover. 20e, Tobacco jar with palms. 30e, Stringed instrument.

375   A34   20c lilac & multi   .25   .20
376   A34   30c rose & multi   .25   .20
377   A34   50c salmon & multi   .25   .20
378   A34   1e lt green & multi   .35   .25
379   A34   1.50e orange yel & multi   .35   .25
380   A34   5e gray & multi   .75   .35
381   A34   10e lt blue & multi   1.25   .55
382   A34   20e yellow & multi   2.00 1.25
383   A34   30e rose lilac & multi   3.25 1.40
        Nos. 375-383 (9)   8.70 4.65

Cape Verde No. 1 and Coat of Arms — A35

Congress Emblem — A36

1977, Sept. 12   Litho.   Perf. 13½
384   A35   4e blue & multi   .40   .25
385   A35   8e lilac & multi   .80   .35
Centenary of Cape Verde stamps.

1977, Nov. 15   Perf. 14
386   A36   3.50e multi   .60   .25
African Party of Independence of Guinea-Bissau and Cape Verde (PAIGC), 3rd cong., Nov. 15-20.

No. 363 Overprinted

1978, May 1   Perf. 12
387   CD61   2.50e ultra & multi   .60   .25

No. 355 Surcharged with New Value and Bars

1978, May 1   Perf. 14
388   CD55   3e on 30c multi   2.25   .35

Antenna and ITU Emblem — A37

1978, May 17   Litho.   Perf. 14
389   A37   3.50e silver & multi   .55   .25
10th World Telecommunications Day.

Freighter Cabo Verde — A38

1978, June 25   Litho.   Perf. 14
391   A38   1e multicolored   .70   .20
First ship of Cape Verde merchant marine.

Map of Africa and Equality Emblem — A39

1978, June 21
392   A39   4.50e multi   .55   .25
Anti-Apartheid Year.

Human Rights Emblem — A40

1978, Dec. 10   Litho.   Perf. 14
393   A40   1.50e multicolored   .35   .25
394   A40   2e multicolored   .55   .35
Universal Declaration of Human Rights, 30th anniversary.

Children and Balloons, IYC Emblem — A41

IYC Emblem and Child's Drawing: 3.50e, Children and flowers.

1979, June 1   Litho.   Perf. 14
395   A41   1.50e multi   .65   .25
396   A41   3.50e multi   1.10   .35
International Year of the Child.

Pindjiguiti Massacre Monument — A42

Natl. Youth Week — A42a

1979, Aug. 3   Perf. 13
397   A42   4.50e multi   2.10   .25
Massacre of Pindjiguiti, 20th anniversary.

1979, Sept. 1   Litho.   Perf. 14
397A   A42a   3.50e Poster   1.10   .25

Centenary of Mindelo — A43

1980, Apr. 23   Litho.   Perf. 12½
398   A43   4e multicolored   .70   .25

Flag of Cape Verde — A44   Stylized Bird, "V" — A45

1980   Litho.   Perf. 12½
399   A44   4e multicolored   1.25   .25
400   A45   4e multicolored   .45   .25
401   A45   7e multicolored   .80   .35
402   A45   11e multicolored   1.10   .45
        Nos. 399-402 (4)   3.60 1.30
5th anniversary of independence.
Issued: No. 399, June 1; others July 5.

A45a

A46

1980, May 13
402A   A45a   3.50e multi   .55   .25
402B   A45a   4.50e multi   .70   .25
1980 Natl. census.

1980, June 6
403   A46   1e Running   .20   .20
404   A46   2.50e Boxing   .25   .20
405   A46   3e Basketball   .35   .25
406   A46   4e Volleyball   .50   .30
407   A46   20e Swimming   1.40   .90
408   A46   50e Tennis   4.00 1.75
        Nos. 403-408 (6)   6.70 3.60
            Souvenir Sheet
              Perf. 13
409   A46   30e Soccer, horiz.   18.00 18.00
22nd Summer Olympic Games, Moscow, July 19-Aug. 3.

Thunnus Alalunga A47

1980, Nov. 11   Litho.   Perf. 13
410   A47   50c shown   .25   .20
411   A47   4.50e Trachurus
              trachurus   .40   .20
412   A47   8e Muraena helena   .65   .25
413   A47   10e Corvina nigra   .75   .35
414   A47   12e Katsuwonus pe-
              lamis   1.10   .60
415   A47   50e Prionace glauca   4.00 1.90
        Nos. 410-415 (6)   7.15 3.50

Lochnera Rosea — A48

1980, Dec. 29
416   A48   50c shown   .25   .20
417   A48   4.50e Poinciana regia-
              bojer   .30   .25
418   A48   8e Mirabilis jalapa   .75   .45
419   A48   10e Nerium oleander   .95   .45
420   A48   12e Bougainvillia
              litoralis   1.10   .55
421   A48   30e Hibiscus   2.60 1.50
        Nos. 416-421 (6)   5.95 3.30

WHO Anti-smoking Campaign — A48a

1980, Sept. 19   **Perf. 12½**
421A	A48a	4e multicolored	.50	.25
421B	A48a	7e multicolored	1.10	.35

Arca
Verde
A49

1980, Nov. 30   **Litho.**   **Perf. 12½x12**
422	A49	3e shown	.30	.20
423	A49	5.50e Ilha do Maio	.50	.25
424	A49	7.50e Ilha de Komo	.95	.55
425	A49	9e Boa Vista	1.25	.75
426	A49	12e Santo Antao	1.40	.55
427	A49	30e Santiago	3.25	1.40
		Nos. 422-427 (6)	7.65	3.70

Hand-woven Bag, Map — A49a

Various hand-woven articles. 10e, vert.

1978, May 21   **Litho.**   **Perf. 14**
427A	A49a	50c multi	.25	.20
427B	A49a	1.50e multi	.25	.20
427C	A49a	2e multi	.55	.25
427D	A49a	3e multi	.55	.30
427E	A49a	10e multi	1.40	.70
		Nos. 427A-427E (5)	3.00	1.65

Desert Erosion Prevention
Campaign — A50

1981, Mar. 30   **Litho.**   **Perf. 13**
428	A50	4.50e multi	.60	.25
429	A50	10.50e multi	1.25	.50

6th Anniv. of
Constitution
A51

1981, Apr. 15
430	A51	4.50e multicolored	.60	.25

Souvenir Sheet

Austria No.
B336
A52

1981, May 18
431	A52	50e multicolored	6.50	6.50

WIPA '81 Philatelic Exhibition, Vienna, Austria, May 22-31.

Antenna — A53

1981, Aug. 25   **Litho.**   **Perf. 12½**
432	A53	4.50e shown	.65	.25
433	A53	8e Dish antenna	.95	.40
434	A53	20e Dish antenna, diff.	2.00	.95
		Nos. 432-434 (3)	3.60	1.60

Intl. Year
of the
Disabled
A54

1981, Dec. 25   **Litho.**   **Perf. 12½**
435	A54	4.50e multicolored	.65	.35

Purple
Gallinule
A55

1981, Dec. 30
436	A55	1e Egret, vert.	.60	.20
437	A55	4.50e Barn owl, vert.	1.25	.40
438	A55	8e Passerine, vert.	2.75	.55
439	A55	10e shown	3.00	.65
440	A55	12e Guinea fowl	3.75	.75
		Nos. 436-440 (5)	11.35	2.55

Souvenir Sheet
Perf. 13
441	A55	50e Razo Isld. lark	9.50	9.50

No. 441 contains 31x39mm one stamp.

CILSS Congress, Praia, Jan.
17 — A56

1982, Jan. 17   **Perf. 13x12½**
442	A56	11.50e multicolored	1.40	.65

Amilcar Cabral Soccer
Championship — A57

Designs: Soccer players and flags.

1982, Feb. 10   **Litho.**   **Perf. 12½**
443	A57	4.50e multicolored	.55	.25
444	A57	7.50e multicolored	.85	.40
445	A57	11.50e multicolored	1.40	.70
		Nos. 443-445 (3)	2.80	1.35

1982 World
Cup — A58

Designs: Soccer players and ball.

1982, Apr. 25
446	A58	1.50e multi	.25	.20
447	A58	4.50e multi	.50	.25
448	A58	8e multi	.85	.35
449	A58	10.50e multi	1.00	.45
450	A58	12e multi	1.25	.55
451	A58	20e multi	2.25	.90
		Nos. 446-451 (6)	6.10	2.70

Souvenir Sheet
452	A58	50e multi	6.25	6.25

First Anniv. of Women's
Organization — A59

1982, Apr. 15   **Litho.**   **Perf. 12½x12**
453	A59	4.50e Marching	.55	.25
454	A59	8e Farming	1.10	.40
455	A59	12e Child care	1.60	.70
		Nos. 453-455 (3)	3.25	1.35

Estaleiros Navais Port, St. Vincent
A59a

1982, July 5   **Litho.**   **Perf. 13x12½**
455A	A59a	10.50e multi	1.75	.60

Natl. independence, 7th anniv.

Return of Barque Morrissey-
Ernestina — A60

1982, July 5   **Litho.**   **Perf. 13**
456	A60	12e multi	1.40	.80

Butterflies — A61

1982, July 27   **Litho.**
457	A61	2e Hypolimnas misippus	.35	.20
458	A61	4.50e Melanitis lede	.70	.25
459	A61	8e Catopsilia florella	1.10	.25
460	A61	10.50e Colias electo	1.50	.40
461	A61	11.50e Danaus chrysippus	1.60	.60
462	A61	12e Papilio demodecus	2.75	.70
		Nos. 457-462 (6)	8.00	2.40

Francisco Xavier da Cruz (1905-1958),
Composer — A62

14e, Eugenio Tavares (1867-1930), poet.

1983, Feb. 20   **Litho.**   **Perf. 13**
463	A62	7e multi	.45	.30
464	A62	14e multi	1.90	.80

World Communications Year — A63

1983, Oct. 10   **Litho.**
465	A63	13e multicolored	1.60	.80

Local
Seashells — A64

1983, Nov. 30   **Perf. 13½**
466	A64	50c Conus ateralbus	.25	.20
467	A64	1e Conus decoratus	.25	.20
468	A64	3e Conus salreiensis	.35	.20
469	A64	10e Conus verdensis	1.50	.55
470	A64	50e Conus cuneolus	5.00	2.75
		Nos. 466-470 (5)	7.35	3.90

40th Anniv.
of Intl. Civil
Aviation
Org.
A65

Airplanes: 50c, Ogma-Auster D5/160, 1966. 2e, De Havilland DH-104 Dove, 1945. 10e, Hawker Siddeley 748-200, 1972. 13e, De Havilland Dragon Rapide, 1945. 20e, De Havilland Twin Otter, 1977. 50e, Britten-Norman Islander, 1971.

1984, Feb. 15   Litho.
471	A65	50c multicolored	.25	.20
472	A65	2e multicolored	.30	.25
473	A65	10e multicolored	1.10	.50
474	A65	13e multicolored	1.25	.85
475	A65	20e multicolored	1.90	1.25
476	A65	50e multicolored	4.50	2.50
		Nos. 471-476 (6)	9.30	5.55

Amilcar Cabral — A66   A67

1983, Jan. 17   Litho.   Perf. 14½
477	A66	7e multi	1.00	.50
478	A66	10.50e multi	1.50	.90
a.		Souvenir sheet of 2, #477-478	30.00	30.00

Amilcar Cabral Symposium, Jan. 17-20. No. 478a sold for 30e.

1983, Dec. 10   Photo.   Perf. 14½
479	A67	7e Cross overshadowing islands	1.10	.50

Christianity in Cape Verde, 450th anniv.

Natl. Solidarity Campaign A68

1984, Sept. 12   Perf. 13½
480	A68	6.50e multi	1.10	.25
481	A68	13.50e multi	2.10	.85

2nd Conference of Natl. Women's Orgs., Mar. 23-27 — A69

1985, Mar. 27   Litho.   Perf. 13½
482	A69	8e multicolored	1.10	.55

Miniature Sheet
483	A69	30e multicolored	70.00	70.00

Natl. Independence, 10th Anniv. — A70

1985, July 5   Litho.   Perf. 14
484	A70	8c multicolored	1.25	.55
485	A70	12e multicolored	1.90	.80

Intl. Youth Year — A71

1985, Sept. 12   Litho.   Perf. 14
486	A71	12e multicolored	2.50	.90

Vapor, by Hundertwasser A72

Photogravure and Engraved
1986, Apr. 25   Perf. 14
Black Surcharge
487	A72	30e on 10e multi	20.00	4.00

Souvenir Sheets
Background Color
488		Sheet of 4	140.00	
a.	A72	50e yellow & multi	15.00	15.00
489		Sheet of 4	140.00	
a.	A72	50e red & multi	15.00	15.00
490		Sheet of 4	140.00	
a.	A72	50e green & multi	15.00	15.00

No. 487 exists without surcharge. Value $27.50.

World Wildlife Fund — A73

Perf. 13½x14½
1986, June 15   Litho.
491	A73	8e Mabuya vaillanti	5.00	2.00
492	A73	10e Tarentola gigas brancoensis	6.50	2.75
493	A73	15e Tarentola gigas gigas	9.50	3.50
494	A73	30e Hemidactylus bouvieri	18.00	4.50
		Nos. 491-494 (4)	39.00	12.75

Souvenir Sheet
495		Sheet of 2	25.00	20.00
a.	A73	50e Mabuya vaillanti	12.00	9.00
b.	A73	50e Hemidactylus bouvieri	12.00	9.00

No. 495 printed with center label picturing progress union emblem. Nos. 495a-495b printed without WWF emblem.

World Food Day — A74

Intl. Peace Year — A75

1986, June 20   Perf. 14
496	A74	8e Cauldron	.50	.25
497	A74	12e Mortar & pestle	.80	.35
498	A74	15e Quern stone	1.40	.50
		Nos. 496-498 (3)	2.70	1.10

1986, Dec. 24   Litho.
499	A75	12e multicolored	.60	.25
500	A75	30e multicolored	2.10	1.40

Natl. Child Survival Campaign A76

1987, Mar. 27   Litho.   Perf. 14
501	A76	8e multicolored	.45	.20
502	A76	10e multicolored	.55	.25
503	A76	12e multicolored	.65	.35
504	A76	16e multicolored	.95	.50
505	A76	100e multicolored	4.50	2.75
		Nos. 501-505 (5)	7.10	4.05

Tourism A77

1987, May 17
506	A77	1e Bay, Mindelo	.20	.20
507	A77	2.50e Hill country	.20	.20
508	A77	5e Mountain peak	.25	.25
509	A77	8e Monument	.45	.25
510	A77	10e Mountain peaks	.65	.30
511	A77	12e Beached boats	.85	.40
512	A77	100e Harbor	5.25	3.00
		Nos. 506-512 (7)	7.85	4.60

For surcharge see No. 710.

Ships — A78

1987, Aug. 3   Perf. 13½x14½
513	A78	12e Carvalho, 1937	.75	.25
514	A78	16e Nauta, 1943	1.25	.25
515	A78	50e Maria Sony, 1911	3.75	1.25
		Nos. 513-515 (3)	5.75	1.75

Souvenir Sheet
516		Sheet of 2	9.00	9.00
a.	A78	60e Madalan, 1928	4.00	4.00

Crop Protection A80

1988, May 9   Litho.   Perf. 13½
518	A80	50c Identification of insect plague	.20	.20
519	A80	2e Use of insecticides	.20	.20
520	A80	9e Import of parasites	.50	.25
521	A80	13e Import of predators	.60	.25
522	A80	16e Locust	1.00	.40
523	A80	19e Estimation of crop loss	1.25	.60
		Nos. 518-523 (6)	3.75	1.90

Souvenir Sheet
524	A80	50e Agricultural Research Institute	5.00	5.00

Maps — A81

1988, July 5   Litho.   Perf. 14
525	A81	1e Dutch, 17th cent.	.20	.20
526	A81	2.50e Belgian, 18th cent.	.20	.20
527	A81	4.50e French, 18th cent.	.30	.20
528	A81	9.50e English, 18th cent.	.60	.25
529	A81	19.50e English, 19th cent.	1.25	.55
530	A81	20e French, 18th cent., vert.	1.40	.65
		Nos. 525-530 (6)	3.95	2.05

Churches A82

5e, St. Amaro Abade, Tarrafal, Santiago Is. 8e, Our Lady of the Light, Maio Is. 10e, Nazarene, Praia, Santiago Is. 12e, Our Lady of Rosa'rio, Sao Nicolau Is. 15e, Nazarene, Mindelo, Sao Vicente Is. 20e, Our Lady of Grace, Praia, Santiago Is.

1988, Aug. 15   Perf. 13½x14½
531	A82	5e multicolored	.20	.20
532	A82	8e multicolored	.45	.20
533	A82	10e multicolored	.55	.25
534	A82	12e multicolored	.60	.25
535	A82	15e multicolored	.85	.35
536	A82	20e multicolored	1.25	.45
		Nos. 531-536 (6)	3.90	1.70

Water Conservation — A83

1988, Sept. 26   Litho.   Perf. 14
537	A83	12e multicolored	.75	.35

Intl. Red Cross, 125th Anniv. — A84

1988, Oct. 20
538	A84	7e multi	.45	.25

3rd Communist Party (PAICV) Congress — A85

Portrait of Pres. Pereira, PAICV secretary-general, and: 7e, S. Jorginho Vocational Training Center. 10.50e, UN Secretary-General Perez de Cuellar. 30e, 100e, Star and text.

Perf. 14½x13½
1988, Nov. 25   Litho.
539 A85   7e multi   .40 .25
540 A85 10.50e multi   .60 .25
541 A85 30e multi   1.75 .75
    Nos. 539-541 (3)   2.75 1.25
Souvenir Sheet
542 A85 100e multi   6.25 6.25

1988 Summer Olympics, Seoul — A86

1988, Dec. 26
543 A86 12e shown   .60 .25
544 A86 15e Tennis   .90 .35
545 A86 20e Soccer   1.25 .50
546 A86 30e Boxing   1.75 .90
   Nos. 543-546 (4)   4.50 2.00
Souvenir Sheet
547 A86 50e Long jump   4.00 4.00

Roberto Duarte Silva (1837-89), Chemist A86a

1989, May 2   Litho.   **Perf. 14¼x14**
547A A86a 12.50e multi   .45 .25

2nd JAAC-CV Congress, Sept. 7-12 — A87

1989, Apr. 7   Litho.   **Perf. 14**
548 A87 30e Hot air balloon   1.10 .75

Liberty Guiding the People — A88

Relief, Arc de Triomphe — A89

1989, July 7   Litho.   **Perf. 14**
549 A88 20e multicolored   .85 .45
550 A88 24e multicolored   1.10 .55
551 A88 25e multicolored   1.25 .65
   Nos. 549-551 (3)   3.20 1.65
Souvenir Sheet
Perf. 14½x13½
552 A89 100e multicolored   5.50 5.50
   French revolution, bicent.

Interparliamentary Union, Cent. — A90

1989, Sept. 18   Litho.   **Perf. 14**
553 A90 2e shown   .20 .20
554 A90 4e Dove   .25 .20
555 A90 13e Natl. Assembly Bldg.   .45 .20
   Nos. 553-555 (3)   .90 .60

Traditional Ceramics A91

1989, Nov. 13   Litho.   **Perf. 13½**
Panel Colors
556 A91 13e lilac   .50 .25
557 A91 20e red, vert.   .70 .40
558 A91 24e brown   .90 .50
559 A91 25e orange, vert.   1.00 .55
   Nos. 556-559 (4)   3.10 1.70

Outdoor Toys — A92

1989, Dec. 23
560 A92 1e Yellow truck   .20 .20
561 A92 6e Car   .20 .20
562 A92 8e White truck   .35 .20
563 A92 11.50e Trucks   .45 .25
564 A92 18e Scooter   .75 .45
565 A92 100e Boat   4.00 2.25
   Nos. 560-565 (6)   5.95 3.55

Visit of Pope John Paul II — A93

1990, Jan. 25
566 A93 13e blue & multi   .40 .25
567 A93 20e purple & multi   .75 .40
Souvenir Sheet
568 A93 200e multi, diff.   10.00 10.00

Turtles A94

1990, May 17   Litho.   **Perf. 13½**
569 A94 50c Chelonia mydas   .20 .20
570 A94 1e Dermochelys coriacea   .20 .20
571 A94 5e Lepidochelys olivacea   .35 .20
572 A94 10e Caretta caretta   .60 .25
573 A94 42e Eretmochelys imbricata   2.75 .90
   Nos. 569-573 (5)   4.10 1.75

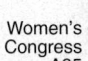

Women's Congress A95

1990, Aug. 13
574 A95 9e multicolored   .35 .20

A96

A97

Various drawings of soccer players in action.

1990, Aug. 7
575 A96 4e multicolored   .20 .20
576 A96 7.50e multicolored   .25 .20
577 A96 8e multicolored   .25 .20
578 A96 100e multicolored   3.50 2.10
   Nos. 575-578 (4)   4.20 2.70
Souvenir Sheet
579 A96 100e multi, diff.   4.50 4.50
World Cup Soccer Championships, Italy. For surcharges see Nos. 711-712.

1990, Oct. 15   **Perf. 11½**
Vaccinations: 5e, Emile Roux (1853-1933), diphtheria. 13e, Robert Koch (1843-1910), tuberculosis. 20e, Gaston Ramon (1886-1963), tetanus. 24e, Jonas Salk (1914-95), polio.
Granite Paper
580 A97 5e multicolored   .35 .20
581 A97 13e multicolored   1.00 .25
582 A97 20e multicolored   1.40 .40
583 A97 24e multicolored   1.75 .50
   Nos. 580-583 (4)   4.50 1.35

Intl. Literacy Year — A98

Designs: 3e, Adult literacy class. 15e, Teacher holding flash card, children. 19e, Teacher, student at blackboard.

1990, Sept. 28
Granite Paper
584 A98 2e shown   .20 .20
585 A98 3e multicolored   .20 .20
586 A98 15e multicolored   .50 .20
587 A98 19e multicolored   .75 .30
   Nos. 584-587 (4)   1.65 .95

Traditional Fairy Tales A99

1990, Dec. 20   Litho.   **Perf. 12½**
588 A99 50c shown   .20 .20
589 A99 2.50e Man catching mermaid   .25 .25
590 A99 12e Woman, snake   .50 .45
591 A99 25e Man, eggs, woman   1.00 .40
   Nos. 588-591 (4)   1.95 1.30

Fight Against AIDS A100

1991, Feb. 20   Litho.   **Perf. 14**
Granite Paper
592 A100 13e multicolored   .55 .25
593 A100 24e multi, diff.   1.00 .65

Fishing — A101

24e, Man removing hook from fish. 25e, Fishing boats. 50e, Two men long-line fishing.

1991, Apr. 23   Litho.   **Perf. 11½**
594 A101 10e multicolored   .35 .25
595 A101 24e multicolored   1.10 .60
596 A101 25e multicolored   1.25 .65
597 A101 50e multicolored   2.40 1.50
   Nos. 594-597 (4)   5.10 3.00

Medicinal Plants — A102

10e, Lavandula rotundifolia. 15e, Micromeria forbesii. 21e, Sarcostemma daltonii. 24e, Periploca chevalieri. 30e, Echium hypertropicum. 35e, Erysimum caboverdeanum.

1991, July 5   Litho.   **Perf. 11½**
598 A102 10e multicolored   .30 .20
599 A102 15e multicolored   .55 .25
600 A102 21e multicolored   .70 .30
601 A102 24e multicolored   .90 .35
602 A102 30e multicolored   1.10 .45
603 A102 35e multicolored   1.40 .55
   Nos. 598-603 (6)   4.95 2.10

Landmarks in Old Ribeira Grande on Santiago Island A103

12.50e, Church of Our Lady of the Rosary, 1495. 15e, Ruins of the Cathedral, 1556. 20e, Fortress of San Felipe, 1587. 30e, Ruins of the Convent of St. Francis, 1642. 100e, Pillory, 1520, vert.

1991, June 25   Litho.   **Perf. 11½**
604 A103 12.50e multicolored   .45 .25
605 A103 15e multicolored   .55 .25
606 A103 20e multicolored   .75 .45
607 A103 30e multicolored   1.10 .75
   Nos. 604-607 (4)   2.85 1.70
Souvenir Sheet
608 A103 100e multicolored   4.00 4.00

Musical Instruments — A104

1991, Oct. 9   Litho.   Perf. 11½
609 A104 10e 6-string guitar   .35   .20
610 A104 20e Violin   .85   .55
611 A104 29e 5-string guitar   1.40   .65
612 A104 47e Cimba   2.00 1.25
  Nos. 609-612 (4)   4.60 2.65

Souvenir Sheet
613 A104 60e Accordion, horiz.   3.00 3.00

Christmas
A105

1991, Dec. 20   Litho.   Perf. 11½
614 A105 31e Nativity scene   1.10   .50
615 A105 50e Nativity scene, diff.   1.75   .90

Discovery
of
America,
500th
Anniv.
A106

1992, Mar. 31   Litho.   Perf. 11½
616 A106 40e shown   2.00 1.10
617 A106 40e Columbus on ship   2.00 1.10
  a.   Pair, #616-617   4.50 4.50

Souvenir Sheet
618 A106 Sheet of 2   8.00 8.00

Stamps in No. 618 are smaller, without
white border and "Luis Duran" and
"Courvoisier" inscriptions. No. 618 was printed
in continuous design and sold for 150e.

Souvenir Sheet

Granada '92 — A107

Illustration reduced.

1992, Apr. 24   Perf. 11½
619 A107 50e multicolored   8.00 8.00
  No. 619 sold for 150e.

Tropical
Fruits
A108

1992, Feb. 29   Perf. 12x11½
620 A108 16e Syzygium jambos   .65   .30
621 A108 25e Mangifera indica   1.10   .50
622 A108 31e Anacardium oc-
                cidentale   1.40   .65
623 A108 32e Persea americana   1.60   .75
  Nos. 620-623 (4)   4.75 2.20

1992 Summer
Olympics,
Barcelona
A109

1992, June 30   Litho.   Perf. 13½
624 A109 16e Women's javelin   .60   .25
625 A109 20e Weight lifting   .75   .30
626 A109 32e Women's pole
                vault   1.40   .65

627 A109 40e Women's shot
                put   1.60   .85
  Nos. 624-627 (4)   4.35 2.05

Souvenir Sheet
628 A109 100e Women's gym-
                nastics   4.25 4.25

Sugar Cane Production — A110

Designs: 19e, Oxen, sugar cane. 20e, Oxen
yoked to press. 37e, Man placing cane inside
press. 38e, Refining process.

1992, Nov.   Litho.   Perf. 11
629 A110 19e multicolored   .65   .30
630 A110 20e multicolored   .65   .30
631 A110 37e multicolored   1.25   .60
632 A110 38e multicolored   1.40   .60
  Nos. 629-632 (4)   3.95 1.80

Domestic
Animals
A111

1992, Nov.   Perf. 13½
633 A111 16e Cat   .65   .40
634 A111 31e Chickens   1.10   .80
635 A111 32e Dog, vert.   1.25   .90
636 A111 50e Horse   2.00 1.25
  Nos. 633-636 (4)   5.00 3.35

Corals
A112

1993, Apr. 29   Litho.   Perf. 11½
637 A112   5e Tubastrea aurea   .20   .20
638 A112 31e Corallium rubrum   1.25   .80
639 A112 37e Porites porites   1.50 1.00
640 A112 50e Millepora alcicornis   2.00 1.25
  Nos. 637-640 (4)   4.95 3.25

Treaty of
Tordesillas,
500th
Anniv. (in
1994)
A113

Designs: No. 641, King Ferdinand, Queen
Isabella of Spain, Pope Alexander VI. No. 642,
Pope Julius II, King John II of Portugal. No.
643, Astrolabe, treaty signing. No. 644, Compass rose, map.

1993, Aug. 1   Litho.   Perf. 12x11½
641 A113 37e multicolored   1.40   .65
642 A113 37e multicolored   1.40   .65
  a.   Pair, #641-642   3.25 3.25
643 A113 38e multicolored   1.40   .65
644 A113 38e multicolored   1.40   .65
  a.   Pair, #643-644   3.25 3.25
  Nos. 641-644 (4)   5.60 2.60

Souvenir Sheet

Santiago Island, 1806 — A114

1993, July 30   Perf. 13½
645 A114 100e multicolored   4.25 4.25

Brasiliana '93.

Lobsters — A115

1993, Sept. 29   Litho.   Perf. 11½
646 A115   2e Palinurus
                charlestoni   .30   .20
647 A115 10e Panulirus
                echinatus   .60   .25
648 A115 17e Panulirus regius   1.10   .50
649 A115 38e Scyllarides latus   2.50 1.00
  Nos. 646-649 (4)   4.50 1.95

Souvenir Sheet
650 A115 100e Panulirus regius,
                diff.   6.00 6.00
  No. 650 contains one 51x36mm stamp.

Birds
A116

1993, Oct. 29   Litho.   Perf. 12x11½
651 A116 10e Calonectris ed-
                wardsii   .75   .25
652 A116 30e Sula leuco-
                gaster   2.25   .85
653 A116 40e Fregata
                magnificens   3.00 1.10
  a.   Souvenir sheet of 1   10.00 10.00
654 A116 41e Phaeton aether-
                eus   3.25 1.10
  Nos. 651-654 (4)   9.25 3.30

Hong Kong '94 (#653a).
No. 653a sold for 150e.

Flowers
A117

1993, Dec. 16   Litho.   Perf. 12x11½
655 A117   5e Rosa alexandra   .20
656 A117 30e Strelitzia reginae   1.10   .80
657 A117 37e Dianthus barbatus   1.50 1.00
  a.   Souvenir sheet of 1   6.50 6.50
658 A117 50e Dahlia   1.90 1.25
  Nos. 655-658 (4)   4.70 3.05

Singapore '95 (#657a). Issued 9/1/95.
No. 657a sold for 150e.

1994 World Cup Soccer
Championships, US — A118

Players, US flag, and: 1e, Giant's Stadium,
New Jersey. 20e, Rose Bowl Stadium,
Pasadena. 37e, Foxboro Stadium, Boston.
38e, Silverdome, Pontiac. 100e, RFK Stadium,
Washington DC.

1994, May 31   Litho.   Perf. 11½
659 A118   1e multicolored   .20   .20
660 A118 20e multicolored   .85   .50
661 A118 37e multicolored   1.50 1.00
662 A118 38e multicolored   1.60 1.10
  Nos. 659-662 (4)   4.15 2.80

Souvenir Sheet
663 A118 100e multicolored   4.25 4.25

Prince Henry the Navigator (1394-
1460) — A119

Illustration reduced.

1994, Mar. 4   Litho.   Perf. 12
664 A119 37e multicolored   2.00 1.00

See Brazil #2463, Macao #719, Portugal
#1987.

Sharks
A120

1994, June 27   Litho.   Perf. 12x11½
665 A120 21e Eugomphodus tau-
                rus   .85   .50
666 A120 27e Carcharhinus
                limbatus   1.10   .70
667 A120 37e Rhiniodon typus   1.50 1.00
668 A120 38e Etmopterus spinax   1.75 1.10
  Nos. 665-668 (4)   5.20 3.30

Bananas
A121

1994, Aug. 16   Litho.   Perf. 11½
669 A121 12e Prata, vert.   .40   .25
670 A121 16e Pao   .65   .40
671 A121 30e Ana roberta, vert.   1.25   .85
672 A121 40e Roxa, vert.   1.50 1.10
  Nos. 669-672 (4)   3.80 2.60

Souvenir Sheet
673 A121 100e Prata, diff., vert.   7.75 7.75

PHILAKOREA '94, SINGPEX '94 (#673).
No. 673 sold for 150e.

Lighthouses — A122

1994, Oct. 17   Perf. 12
674 A122   2e Fontes Pereira de
                Melo   .20   .20
675 A122 37e Morro Negro   1.50 1.00
676 A122 38e Amelia, vert.   1.50 1.10
677 A122 50e Maria Pia, vert.   2.00 1.40
  Nos. 674-677 (4)   5.20 3.70

Wilhelm Roentgen (1845-1923),
Discovery of the X-Ray, Cent. — A123

1995, Mar. 31   Litho.   Perf. 12
678 A123 20e yellow & multi   .80   .50
679 A123 37e blue & multi   1.50 1.00
  a.   Souvenir sheet of 2, #678-679 4.50 4.50

No. 679a sold for 100e.

A124

FAO, 50th
Anniv. — A125

1995, May 17   Litho.   Perf. 12
680 A124 37e multicolored   1.50 .90
681 A125 38e multicolored   1.50 .90

Dogs
A126

Dog, scene depicting story of dogs: 1e, Fox
terrier, Two foxhounds and fox terrier, by John
Emms. 10e, Cavalier King Charles, Shooting
over Dogs, by Richard Ansdell. 40e, Rough
collie, German shepherd. 50e, Braco, Hounds
at Full Cry, by Thomas Blinks.

1995, June 16   Litho.   Perf. 12x11½
682 A126 1e multicolored   .25 .20
683 A126 10e multicolored   .55 .25
684 A126 40e multicolored   2.25 1.25
685 A126 50e multicolored   2.75 1.10
    Nos. 682-685 (4)   5.80 2.80

Independence,
20th
Anniv. — A127

1995, July 20   Litho.   Perf. 12
686 A127 37e multicolored   1.90 1.25

Traditional
Festival
A128

Designs: 2e, Horse race. 10e, Horseman
leading parade. 37e, People singing, playing
drums. 40e, Playing game on horseback.

1995, Oct. 9   Perf. 12x11½
687 A128 2e multicolored   .20 .20
688 A128 10e multicolored   .45 .25
689 A128 37e multicolored   1.50 .85
690 A128 40e multicolored   1.75 1.00
    Nos. 687-690 (4)   3.90 2.30

Children's
Stories
A130

Designs: 10e, The cicadas making music,
ants. 25e, Cicada being exposed to light. 38e,
Cicada with guitar, ants working. 45e, Ants at
table making fun of cicada.

1995, Dec. 15   Litho.   Perf. 11½
692 A130 10e multicolored   .40 .55
693 A130 25e multicolored   .85 .85
694 A130 38e multicolored   1.40 1.10
695 A130 45e multicolored   1.60 1.00
    Nos. 692-695 (4)   4.25 3.50

Endangered
Plants — A131

20e, Sonchus daltonii. 37e, Echium vulca-
norum. 38e, Nauplius smithii. 50e, Campanula
jacobaea.

1996, Apr. 24   Litho.   Perf. 11½
696 A131 20e multicolored   .65 .40
697 A131 37e multicolored   1.20 .75
698 A131 38e multicolored   1.20 .75
699 A131 50e multicolored   1.60 1.10
    Nos. 696-699 (4)   4.65 3.00

1996
Summer
Olympic
Games,
Atlanta
A132

1996, June 30   Litho.   Perf. 11½
700 A132 1e Tennis   .20 .20
701 A132 37e Gymnastics   1.10 .75
702 A132 100e Athletics   3.25 2.10
    Nos. 700-702 (3)   4.55 3.05

UNICEF, 50th
Anniv. — A133

Water
Sports — A134

1996, Aug. 1   Litho.   Perf. 12
703 A133 20e Young girl   .90 .40
704 A133 40e Mother, child   1.75 .85

1996, Oct. 9   Litho.   Perf. 12
Designs: 2.50e, Fishing. 10e, Windsurfing.
22e, Jet skiing. No. 708, Surfing, horiz. No.
709, Diver's hand, pufferfish, horiz.
705 A134 2.50e multicolored   .20 .20
706 A134 10e multicolored   .35 .20
707 A134 22e multicolored   .70 .45
708 A134 100e multicolored   3.25 2.10
    Nos. 705-708 (4)   4.50 2.95
Souvenir Sheet
709 A134 100e multicolored   4.50 4.50
No. 709 contains one 80x61mm stamp.

Nos. 507, 575-576 Surcharged

a

b

1997   Litho.   Perf. 14
710 A77(a) 3e on 2.50e #507   .20 .20
    Perf. 13½
711 A96(b) 37e on 4e #575   1.25 .75
712 A96(a) 38e on 7.50e #576   1.25 .75
    Nos. 710-712 (3)   2.70 1.70

Natl.
Symbols
A135

1997   Perf. 12
713 A135 25e Arms   .80 .50
714 A135 37e Anthem   1.10 .75
715 A135 50e Flag   1.60 1.00
    Nos. 713-715 (3)   3.50 2.25

World
Wildlife
Fund
A136

Pristis pectinata: a, On seabed. b, Swimming, school of small fish. c, Swimming along
seabed, small fish. d, Two near seabed.

1997   Litho.   Perf. 11½
716 A136 15e Strip of 4, #a.-d.   9.00 9.00

Legends of
the
Sea — A137

a, Fish, dolphins. b, Merman, mermaid. c,
Fish swimming through portal, moray eel.

1997   Litho.   Perf. 11½
717 A137 45e Strip of 3, #a.-c.   4.00 4.00

Fish
A138

Designs: 13e, Thunnus albacares. 21e,
Thunnus obesus. 41e, Euthynnus alletteratus.
45e, Katsuwonus pelamis.

1997   Litho.   Perf. 12
718 A138 13e multicolored   .35 .30
719 A138 21e multicolored   .65 .60
720 A138 41e multicolored   1.40 1.25
721 A138 45e multicolored   1.60 1.50
    Nos. 718-721 (4)   4.00 3.65

1998 World Cup Soccer
Championships, France — A139

Designs: 30e, Soccer ball in net, vert. 45e,
Soccer player, ball, vert. 50e, Globe, ball,
World Cup trophy, fans in stadium.

1998   Litho.   Perf. 12x11½, 11½x12
722 A139 10e shown   .30 .25
723 A139 30e multicolored   .80 .80
724 A139 45e multicolored   1.25 1.25
725 A139 50e multicolored   1.50 1.40
    Nos. 722-725 (4)   3.85 3.70

Traditional
Cuisine
A140

5e, Boiled fish. 25e, Xerém com friginato.
35e, Cachupa. 40e, Molho de Saint-Nicholas.

1998   Litho.   Perf. 12x11½
726 A140 5e multicolored   .20 .20
727 A140 25e multicolored   .65 .65
728 A140 35e multicolored   1.00 1.00
729 A140 40e multicolored   1.10 1.10
    Nos. 726-729 (4)   2.95 2.95

Early
Exploration
A141

a, Quotation from Lusiadas, two men looking at maps. b, Man with sword, man &
woman. c, Compass, map, sailing ship, buildings on cliff.

1998   Perf. 11½
730 A141 50e Strip of 3, #a.-c.   4.00 4.00

Women's
Traditional
Costumes — A142

1998   Litho.   Perf. 12
731 A142 10e Brava   .25 .25
732 A142 18e Fogo   .50 .50
733 A142 30e Boa Vista   .80 .80
734 A142 50e Santiago   1.40 1.40
    Nos. 731-734 (4)   2.95 2.95

Butterflies
and Moths
A143

Designs: 5e, Byblia ilithyia. 10e, Aganais
speciosa. 20e, Utetheisia pulchella. 30e,
Vanessa cardui. 50e, Trichoplusia ni. 100e,
Grammodes congenita.

1999, Mar. 16   Litho.   Perf. 11¾
735 A143 5e multi   .20 .20
736 A143 10e multi   .25 .25
737 A143 20e multi   .50 .50
738 A143 30e multi   .80 .80
  a. Souvenir sheet, #737-738   4.00 4.00
739 A143 50e multi   1.25 1.25
740 A143 100e multi   2.60 2.60
    Nos. 735-740 (6)   5.60 5.60
No. 738a sold for 100e.

First
Concorde
Flight,
30th
Anniv.
A144

Concorde: 30e, In flight. 50e, On ground.

1999, June 14   Litho.   Perf. 12
741-742 A144   Set of 2   2.75 2.75

Famous People — A145

Design: 30e, Alain Gerbault (1893-1941), sailor, boats at dock. 50e, Roberto Duarte Silva (1837-89), chemist, Eiffel Tower.

1999, July 2　　Litho.　　Perf. 14½
743 A145 30e multi　　　　　2.00 2.00
744 A145 50e multi　　　　　3.25 3.25
744a　　Souvenir sheet,
　　　　#743-744　　　　　　6.50 6.50

Philex France 99 (#744a).

A146

UPU,
125th
Anniv.
A147

1999, Sept. 15　　Perf. 12x11¾
745 A146 30e shown　　　　　— —
746 A147 50e shown　　　　　— —
With Country Name Added
747 A146 30e multi　　　　　.65 .65
748 A147 50e multi　　　　　1.10 1.10
Nos. 745-748 (2)　　　　　1.75 1.75

Dance
A148

Designs: 10e, Colá Sanjon, vert. 30e, Contradança, vert. 50e, Desfile de tabanca. 100e, Batuque.

Perf. 11¾x12, 12x11¾
1999, Nov. 5　　　　　　Litho.
749-752 A148　　Set of 4　　5.00 5.00

Millennium — A149

Designs: 40e, Globe, hourglass and open antique book inscribed "2000," vert. 50e, "2000 Milenio."

2000, Jan. 31　Litho.　Perf. 11¾x11½
753-754 A149　　Set of 2　　2.50 2.50

SOS
Children's
Villages
A150

Emblem and child: 50e, Seated, vert. 100e, With arms outstretched.

smile **Perf. 11¾x12, 12x11¾**
2000, Apr. 28　　　　　　Litho.
755-756 A150　　Set of 2　　4.00 4.00

Independence, 25th Anniv. — A151

2000, July 5　　　　　　Perf. 11¾
757 A151 50e multi　　　　　1.25 1.25

2000
Summer
Olympics,
Sydney
A152

Designs: 10e, Women's gymnastics. 40e, Taekwondo. 50e, Women's hurdles.

2000, Sept. 15　　Litho.　　Perf. 11¾
758-760 A152　　Set of 3　　2.60 2.60
760a　　Souvenir sheet of 3, #758-
　　　760　　　　　　　　2.75 2.75

Dragoeiro
Tree — A153

2000, Oct. 9　Litho.　Perf. 11¾x11½
761 A153　5e green　　　　　.20 .20
762 A153　40e red　　　　　1.00 1.00
763 A153　60e brown　　　　1.60 1.60

Sao Nicolau Seminary and
School — A154

No. 764: a, Seminarians and students (denomination at LR, 27x26mm). b, Seminarians and students (denomination at LL, 29x26mm). c, José Alves Feijo, Dr. Julio Dias and Canon António Bouças (56x26mm).
Illustration reduced.

2000, Dec. 15　　Litho.　　Perf. 14½
764 A154 60e Horiz. strip of 3,
　　　#a-c　　　　　　　5.00 5.00

Fish
A155

Designs: 10e, Diplodus sargus lineatus. 22e, Diplodus prayensis. 28e, Lithognathus mormyrus. 48e, Diplodus fasciatus. 60e, Diplodus puntazzo.

2001, Apr. 24　　　　　　Perf. 12x11¾
765-769 A155　　Set of 5　　5.00 5.00

Spiders
A156

Designs: 13e, Thomisus onustus. 16e, Scytodes velutina. 40e, Hersiliola simoni. 100e, Loxosceles rufescens.

2001, May 28
770-773 A156　　Set of 4　　5.00 5.00

Trees —
A156a

Designs: 50e, Acacia albida. 60e, Ficus sycomorus.

2001, June 9　Litho.　Perf. 11¾x11½
773A-773B A156a　Set of 2　2.75 2.75

Souvenir Sheet

Belgica 2001 Intl. Stamp Exhibition,
Brussels — A157

Perf. 11¾x11½
2001, June 9　　　　　　Photo.
774 A157 100e multi　　　　2.75 2.75

Medicinal
Plants — A157a

Designs: 20e, Artimisia gorgonum. 27e, Globularia amygdalifolia. 47.50e, Sidereoxylon marginata, horiz. 50e, Umbilicus schmidtii, horiz. 60e, Verbascum cystolithicum. 100e, Limonium lobinii.

Perf. 11¾x12, 12x11¾
2001, Sept. 27　　　　　　Litho.
774A-774F A157a　Set of 6　8.00 8.00

Year of Dialogue
Among
Civilizations — A158

2001, Oct. 9　Litho.　Perf. 11¾x12
775 A158 60e multi　　　　　1.60 1.60

António Aurélio Gonçalves (1901-84),
Writer — A159

2001, Dec. 20　　　　　　Perf. 12¼
776 A159 100e multi　　　　2.75 2.75

Medicinal
Plants
A160

Designs: 10e, Euphorbia tuckeyna. 50e, Limonium sunding, vert. 60e, Aeonium gorgoneum, vert. 100e, Polycarpaea gayi, vert.

Perf. 12x11¾, 11¾x12
2002, Apr. 26　　　　　　Litho.
777-780 A160　　Set of 4　　5.75 5.75

2002 World Cup Soccer
Championships, Japan and
Korea — A161

Designs: 60e, Player heading ball towards goal. 100e, Player kicking ball towards goal.

2002, July 22　　　　　　Perf. 12x11¾
781-782 A161　　Set of 2　　4.00 4.00

Caretta
Caretta
A162

Designs: 10e, Pair mating. 20e, Female laying eggs, vert. 30e, Eggs hatching. 60e, Hatchlings heading for sea, vert. No. 787, 100e, Turtle swimming underwater. No. 788, 100e, Turtle on beach.

2002, Sept. 9　Perf. 12x11¾, 11¾x12
783-787 A162　　Set of 5　　6.50 6.50
Souvenir Sheet
788 A162 100e multi　　　　3.00 3.00

No. 788 contains one 80x60mm stamp.

Basketry
A163

Baskets and basket weavers from: 20e, Sao Nicolau Island. 33e, Santo Antao Island. 60e, Santiago Island. 100e, Boa Vista Island.

2002, Oct. 29　　　　　　Perf. 12x11¾
789-792 A163　　Set of 4　　6.50 6.50

Composers
and Poets
A164

Designs: 12e, Katcháss (1951-88), composer. 20e, Jorge Monteiro (1913-98), composer. 32e, Luis Rendall (1898-1986), composer. 47.50e, Jorge Barbosa (1902-71), poet. 60e, Januário Leite (1865-1930), poet. 100e, José Lopes (1872-1962), poet.

2003, Feb. 3
793-798 A164　　Set of 6　　7.50 7.50

Birds — A165

Designs: 10e, Ardea bournei. 27e, Ardea cinerea. 42e, Bubulcus ibis. 60e, Egretta garzeta.

2003, July 9　　　　　　Perf. 14x13¾
799-802 A165　　Set of 4　　4.00 4.00

Cesaria Evora, Singer
A166

Designs: 60e, Evora at left. 100e, Evora at right.
200e, Feet of Evora.

2003, May 26   *Perf. 13¾x14*
803-804 A166   Set of 2   4.50 4.50
Souvenir Sheet
Perf. 12¼x12
805 A166 200e multi + label   6.00 6.00
No. 805 contains one 50x38mm stamp.

Scouting in Cape Verde
A167

Emblem and scout of: 60e, Scouts Association of Cape Verde. 100e, Cape Verde Scouts Corps.

2003, Oct. 24 Litho. Perf. 13¾x14
806-807 A167   Set of 2   4.50 4.50

Whales
A168

Designs: 10e, Balaenoptera musculus. 20e, Physeter macrocephalus. 50e, Megaptera novaeangliae. 60e, Globicephala macrorhynchus.

2003, Nov. 25   *Perf. 12*
808-811 A168   Set of 4   4.00 4.00

First Dakar — Praia Seaplane Flight of Europe — Africa — South America Airmail Service, 75th Anniv. — A169

Seaplane and: 10e, Crew. 42e, Pilot Paulin Paris, map of South America — Africa route. 60e, Map of entire route.
100e, Like 10e.

2003, Dec. 11   *Perf. 14*
812-814 A169   Set of 3   3.25 3.25
Souvenir Sheet
815 A169 100e multi   3.00 3.00

Election of Pope John Paul II, 25th Anniv. — A170

Pope John Paul II and: 30e, Girl. 60e, Boats, horiz.
100e, Censer and crucifix.

2003, Dec. 29 Perf. 14x13¾, 13¾x14
816-817 A170   Set of 2   2.40 2.40
Souvenir Sheet
818 A170 100e multi   3.00 3.00

Trees
A171

Windmill
A172

Designs: 20e, Khaya senegalensis. 27e, Acacia nilotica. 60e, Ceiba pentandra. 100e, Phoenix atlantica.

2004, Jan. 25   *Perf. 14x13¾*
819-822 A171   Set of 4   5.50 5.50

2004, June 3   *Perf. 13¼x13*
Colors: 20e, Blue. 60e, Red. 100e, Green.
823-825 A172   Set of 3   4.75 4.75

2004 Summer Olympics, Athens — A173

Designs: 10e, Taekwondo. 60e, Rhythmic gymnastics. 100e, Boxing, horiz.

Perf. 13¼x13, 13x13¼
2004, Aug. 13   *Litho.*
826-828 A173   Set of 3   4.75 4.75

Lighthouses
A174

Designs: 10e, Ponta do Barril Lighthouse, Sao Nicolau Island. 30e, Ponta Jalunga Lighthouse, Brava Island. 40e, D. Luis Lighthouse, Passaros Islands, horiz. 50e, Ponta Preta Lighthouse, Santiago Island, horiz.

2004, Sept. 7
829-832 A174   Set of 4   4.00 4.00

Houses on Fogo Island
A175

Various houses: 20e, 40e, 50e, 60e.

2004, Oct. 9   *Perf. 13x13¼*
833-836 A175   Set of 4   4.75 4.75

Telephones — A176

Old telephones and: 10e, Switchboard. 40e, Operator. 60e, Telephone directory. 100e, Truck and telephone poles.

2004, Nov. 12
837-840 A176   Set of 4   5.50 5.50

Oral Stories and Legends
A177

Designs: 10e, Stória Stória. 20e, Era um Vez! 30e, Sapatinha Ribera Baxu. 60e, Quem ki Sabi Mas, Conta Midjor!, vert.

Perf. 13x13¼, 13¼x13
2005, Feb. 21   *Litho.*
841-844 A177   Set of 4   3.50 3.50

Amilcar Cabral (1924-73), Revolutionary Leader — A178

2005, June 30 Litho. Perf. 13¼x13
845 A178 60e multi   1.60 1.60
Independence, 30th anniv.

Shells
A179

Designs: 30e, Conus evorai. 40e, Harpa doris. 50e, Strombus lotus. 60e, Phyllonotus duplex.

2005, July 18   *Perf. 13x13¼*
846-849 A179   Set of 4   5.00 5.00

Birds — A180

Designs: 19e, Passer iagoensis. 42e, Estrilda astrild. 44e, Passer domesticus. 55e, Acrocephalus brevipennis.

2005, Aug. 8   *Perf. 13¼x13*
850-853 A180   Set of 4   4.25 4.25

World Summit on the Information Society, Tunis
A181

2005, Nov. 16 Litho. Perf. 13x13¼
854 A181 60e multi   1.60 1.60

Artifacts of the Slave Trade
A182

Designs: 5e, Pipe. 10e, Telescope. 30e, Cannon. 60e, Nautical instrument.

100e, Shackles.
2006, Jan. 31
855-858 A182   Set of 4   3.00 3.00
Souvenir Sheet
859 A182 100e multi   3.00 3.00
No. 859 contains one 80x60mm stamp.

AIR POST STAMPS

Common Design Type
Name and Value in Black
Perf. 13½x13
1938, July 26   Unwmk.
C1 CD39 10c red orange   .60 .50
C2 CD39 20c purple   .60 .50
C3 CD39 50c orange   .60 .50
C4 CD39 1e ultra   .60 .50
C5 CD39 2e lilac brown   1.40 .80
C6 CD39 3e dk green   1.75 1.40
C7 CD39 5e red brown   5.50 2.10
C8 CD39 9e rose carmine   9.00 3.75
C9 CD39 10e magenta   9.75 5.00
Nos. C1-C9 (9)   29.80 15.05
Set, never hinged

No. C7 exists with overprint "Exposicao Internacional de Nova York, 1939-1940" and Trylon and Perisphere.

POSTAGE DUE STAMPS

D1   D2

1904 Unwmk.   Typo.   *Perf. 12*
J1 D1 5r yellow grn   .40 .25
J2 D1 10r slate   .40 .25
J3 D1 20r yellow brn   .50 .40
J4 D1 30r red orange   1.25 .40
J5 D1 50r gray brown   .50 .35
J6 D1 60r red brown   9.25 4.25
J7 D1 100r lilac   1.75 1.25
J8 D1 130r dull blue   1.90 1.25
J9 D1 200r carmine   1.60 1.60
J10 D1 500r dull violet   5.00 3.00
Nos. J1-J10 (10)   22.55 13.00

Overprinted in Carmine or Green

1911
J11 D1 5r yellow grn   .30 .20
J12 D1 10r slate   .30 .20
J13 D1 20r yellow brn   .35 .20
J14 D1 30r orange   .35 .20
J15 D1 50r gray brown   .65 .40
J16 D1 60r red brown   .65 .40
J17 D1 100r lilac   .65 .40
J18 D1 130r dull blue   .75 .65
J19 D1 200r carmine (G)   2.00 1.50
J20 D1 500r dull violet   2.50 1.75
Nos. J11-J20 (10)   8.50 5.90

1921   *Perf. 11½*
J21 D2 ½c yellow grn   .30 .20
J22 D2 1c slate   .30 .20
J23 D2 2c red brown   .30 .20
J24 D2 3c orange   .30 .20
J25 D2 5c gray brown   .30 .20
J26 D2 6c lt brown   .30 .20
J27 D2 10c red violet   .30 .20
J28 D2 13c dull blue   .55 .40
J29 D2 20c carmine   .60 .50
J30 D2 50c gray   1.75 1.10
Nos. J21-J30 (10)   5.00 3.40

Catalogue values for unused stamps in this section, from this point to the end of the section, are for Never Hinged items.

Common Design Type
Photogravure and Typographed
1952   Unwmk.   Perf. 14
Numeral in Red, Frame Multicolored

J31	CD45	10c chocolate	.30	.25
J32	CD45	30c black brown	.30	.25
J33	CD45	50c dark blue	.30	.25
J34	CD45	1e dark blue	.40	.25
J35	CD45	2e red brown	.40	.30
J36	CD45	5e olive green	1.10	1.00
		Nos. J31-J36 (6)	2.80	2.30

NEWSPAPER STAMP

N1

1893   Typo.   Unwmk.   Perf. 11½

P1	N1	2½r brown	1.50	.60
a.		Perf. 12½	3.00	1.50
b.		Perf. 13½	6.50	3.00

For surcharges see Nos. 79, 206.

POSTAL TAX STAMPS

Pombal Issue
Common Design Types
1925   Unwmk.   Engr.   Perf. 12½

RA1	CD28	15c dull vio & blk	1.25	1.10
RA2	CD29	15c dull vio & blk	1.25	1.10
RA3	CD30	15c dull vio & blk	1.25	1.10
		Nos. RA1-RA3 (3)	3.75	3.30

St.
Isabel — PT1   PT2

1948   Litho.   Perf. 11

RA4	PT1	50c dark green	3.75	2.40
RA5	PT1	1e henna brown	7.50	3.00

> Catalogue values for unused stamps in this section, from this point to the end of the section, are for Never Hinged items.

No. RA5 Surcharged with New Value and Bars
1959

RA6	PT1	50c on 1e henna brown	1.40	1.10

Perf. 14

RA7	PT1	50c carmine rose	2.10	1.00
RA8	PT1	1e blue	2.10	1.00

St. Isabel Type Redrawn
1967-73   Litho.   Perf. 14

RA9	PT1	30c (blue panel)	.40	.40
RA9A	PT1	30c (orange panel)	.40	.40
RA10	PT1	50c (lilac rose panel)	.85	.85
RA11	PT1	50c (red panel) ('72)	.45	.45
RA12	PT1	1e (brn panel)	.90	.90
RA13	PT1	1e (red lilac panel) ('72)	.90	.90
		Nos. RA9-RA13 (6)	3.90	3.90

Nos. RA9-RA13 are inscribed "ASSISTENCIA" in large letters in bottom panel and "PORTUGAL" and "CABO VERDE" in small letters in upper left corner.

Revenue Stamps Surcharged in Green, Blue or Black
1967-72   Typo.   Perf. 12
Black "CABO VERDE" & Value
Pale Green Burelage

RA14	PT2	50c on 1c org (Bl) ('71)	1.40	.90
a.		Black surcharge ('68?)	15.00	14.50

RA15	PT2	50c on 2c org (Bk) ('69)	15.00	14.50
c.		Inverted surcharge	50.00	35.00
RA16	PT2	50c on 3c org (G) ('72)	1.10	.60
RA17	PT2	50c on 5c org (G)	1.10	.60
RA18	PT2	50c on 10c org (G) ('71)	1.25	1.00
RA19	PT2	1e on 1c org (Bk)	2.75	2.10
RA20	PT2	1e on 2c org (G) ('71)	1.90	1.75
a.		Blue surcharge ('71)	2.00	1.10
b.		Black surcharge	2.10	2.10
		Nos. RA14-RA20 (7)	24.50	21.45

POSTAL TAX DUE STAMPS

Pombal Issue
Common Design Types
1925   Unwmk.   Perf. 12½

RAJ1	CD28	30c dull vio & blk	.75	.70
RAJ2	CD29	30c dull vio & blk	.75	.70
RAJ3	CD30	30c dull vio & blk	.75	.70
		Nos. RAJ1-RAJ3 (3)	2.25	2.10

CAROLINE ISLANDS

ˈkar-ə-ˌlīn ˈī-lənds

LOCATION — A group of about 549 small islands in the West Pacific Ocean, north of the Equator.
GOVT. — German colony
AREA — 550 sq. mi.
POP. — 40,000 (approx. 1915)

100 Pfennig = 1 Mark

Watermark

Wmk. 125 —
Lozenges

#2   #2a

Stamps of Germany 1889-90
Overprinted in Black
Overprinted at 56 degree Angle
1900   Unwmk.   Perf. 13½x14½

1	A9	3pf dk brown	13.00	14.00
2	A9	5pf green	18.00	18.00
3	A10	10pf carmine	19.00	19.00
4	A10	20pf ultra	24.00	30.00
5	A10	25pf orange	55.00	65.00
6	A10	50pf red brown	55.00	65.00
		Nos. 1-6 (6)	184.00	211.00

1899
Overprinted at 48 degree Angle

1a	A9	3pf light brown	475.00	750.00
2a	A9	5pf green	525.00	575.00
3a	A10	10pf carmine	62.50	150.00
4a	A10	20pf ultra	62.50	150.00
5a	A10	25pf orange	1,650.	3,100.
6a	A10	50pf red brown	900.00	1,600.

A3

Kaiser's Yacht "Hohenzollern" — A4

1901, Jan.   Typo.   Perf. 14

7	A3	3pf brown	1.10	1.75
8	A3	5pf green	1.10	2.10
9	A3	10pf carmine	1.10	5.00
a.		Half used as 5pf on cover, back-stamped in Jaluit ('05)		110.00
10	A3	20pf ultra	1.25	9.00
a.		Half used as 10pf on cover ('10)		8,500.
11	A3	25pf org & blk, yel	1.60	14.50
12	A3	30pf org & blk, sal	1.60	14.50
13	A3	40pf lake & blk	1.60	16.50
14	A3	50pf pur & blk, sal	2.00	22.50
15	A3	80pf lake & blk, rose	3.00	25.00

Perf. 14½x14
Engr.

16	A4	1m carmine	4.50	62.50
17	A4	2m blue	7.25	85.00
18	A4	3m black violet	10.00	150.00
19	A4	5m slate & carmine	150.00	550.00
		Nos. 7-19 (13)	186.10	958.35

No. 9a is known as the "typhoon provisional" the stock of 5pf stamps having been destroyed during a typhoon. Covers (cards) without backstamp, value about $90.
Forged cancellations are found on #7-19.

No. 7 Handstamp
Surcharged

1910, July 12

20	A3	5pf on 3pf brown		5,500.
a.		Inverted surcharge		7,750.
b.		Double surcharge		11,000.

Values are for stamps tied to cover. Stamps on piece sell for about 40% less.

1915-19   Wmk. 125   Typo.

21	A3	3pf brown ('19)		.90
22	A3	5pf green		12.50

Engr.

23	A4	5m slate & carmine		35.00
		Nos. 21-23 (3)		48.40

Nos. 21-23 were not placed in use.

CASTELLORIZO

ˌkäs-tə-ˈlor-ə-ˌzō

(Castelrosso)

LOCATION — A Mediterranean island in the Dodecanese group lying close to the coast of Asia Minor and about 60 miles east of Rhodes.
GOVT. — Former Italian Colony
AREA — 4 sq. mi.
POP. — 2,238 (1936)

Formerly a Turkish possession, Castellorizo was occupied by the French in 1915 and ceded to Italy after World War I. In 1945 it became part of Greece.

25 Centimes = 1 Piaster
100 Centimes = 1 Franc

> Used values in italics are for postally used copies. Stamps with CTO cancels sell for about the same as hinged, unused stamps.

Issued under French Occupation

Stamps of French
Offices in Turkey
Overprinted

1920   Unwmk.   Perf. 14x13½

1	A2	1c gray	45.00	52.50
a.		Inverted overprint	200.00	200.00
b.		Double overprint	225.00	225.00
2	A2	2c vio brn	50.00	57.50
3	A2	3c red org	45.00	52.50
a.		Inverted overprint	225.00	225.00
4	A2	5c green	72.50	72.50
a.		Inverted overprint	240.00	240.00
5	A3	10c rose	82.50	82.50
6	A3	15c pale red	110.00	110.00
a.		Inverted overprint	400.00	400.00
7	A3	20c brn vio	110.00	100.00
8	A5	1pi on 25c blue	110.00	110.00
a.		Pair, one without overprint		800.00
9	A3	30c lilac	125.00	125.00

Overprint Reading Down

10	A4	40c red & pale bl	190.00	190.00
a.		Inverted ovpt (reading up)	825.00	825.00
11	A6	2pi on 50c bis brn & lav	210.00	225.00
a.		Inverted ovpt (reading up)	825.00	825.00
b.		Double overprint	1,100.	1,100.
12	A6	4pi on 1fr cl & ol grn	260.00	300.00
a.		Double overprint	1,100.	1,100.
b.		Inverted ovpt (reading up)	950.00	900.00
13	A6	20pi on 5fr dk bl & buff	600.00	650.00
a.		Double overprint	1,600.	1,600.
		Nos. 1-13 (13)	2,010.	2,127.

No. 1-9 were overprinted in blocks of 25. Position 4 had "CASTELLORIZO" inverted and Positions 8 and 18 had "CASTELLORISO." The later variety also occurred in the setting of the form for Nos. 10-13.
"B. N. F." are the initials of "Base Navale Francaise".

Overprinted in Black or
Red

1920
On Stamps of French Offices in Turkey

14	A2	1c gray	32.50	36.00
15	A2	2c vio brn	36.00	40.00
16	A2	3c red org	60.00	65.00
17	A2	5c green (R)	32.50	32.50
19	A3	10c rose	40.00	40.00
20	A3	15c pale red	65.00	65.00
21	A3	20c brn vio	92.50	92.50
22	A5	1pi on 25c bl (R)	60.00	60.00
23	A3	30c lilac (R)	67.50	67.50
24	A4	40c red & pale bl	65.00	65.00
25	A6	2pi on 50c bis brn & lav	60.00	60.00
26	A6	4pi on 1fr claret & ol grn	92.50	100.00
28	A6	20pi on 5fr dk bl & buff	360.00	360.00
		Nos. 14-28 (13)	1,063.	1,083.

On Nos. 25, 26 and 28 the two lines of the overprint are set wider apart than on the lower values.
"O.N.F." are the initials of "Occupation Navale Francaise."
"Casetllorizo" and "astellorizo" varieties are known on Nos. 14-23.
Overprint on 8pi on 2fr (#37), value $900 unused, $1,000 used.

On Stamps of France

30	A22	10c red	45.00	45.00
a.		Inverted overprint	200.00	200.00
31	A22	25c blue (R)	45.00	45.00
a.		Inverted overprint	200.00	200.00

This overprint exists on 8 other 1900-1907 denominations of France (5c, 15c, 20c, 30c, 40c, 50c, 1fr, 5fr). These are believed not to have been issued or postally used.

Stamps of France, 1900-1907, Handstamped in Black or Violet

1920

33	A22	5c green	160.00	160.00
34	A22	10c red	160.00	160.00
35	A22	20c vio brn	160.00	160.00
36	A22	25c blue	160.00	160.00
37	A18	50c bis brn & lav	900.00	900.00
38	A18	1fr cl & ol grn (V)	900.00	900.00
	Nos. 33-38 (6)		2,440.	2,440.

Nos. 1-38 are considered speculative.
Forgeries of overprints on Nos. 1-38 exist. They abound of Nos. 33-38.
Stamps of French Offices in Turkey hand-stamped "Occupation Francaise Castellorizo" were made privately.

Issued under Italian Dominion
100 Centesimi = 1 Lira

Italian Stamps of 1906-20 Overprinted

1922   Wmk. 140   Perf. 14

51	A48	5c green	5.00	19.00
52	A48	10c claret	2.25	19.00
53	A48	15c slate	3.00	19.00
54	A50	20c brn org	2.25	19.00
a.	Double overprint		275.00	
55	A49	25c blue	2.25	19.00
56	A49	40c brown	40.00	22.50
57	A49	50c violet	40.00	22.50
58	A49	60c carmine	40.00	35.00
59	A49	85c chocolate	5.00	40.00
	Nos. 51-59 (9)		139.75	215.00
	Set, never hinged		400.00	

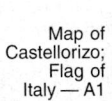

Map of Castellorizo; Flag of Italy — A1

1923

60	A1	5c gray green	3.00	18.00
61	A1	10c dull rose	3.00	18.00
62	A1	25c dull blue	3.00	18.00
63	A1	50c gray lilac	3.00	18.00
64	A1	1 l brown	3.00	18.00
	Nos. 60-64 (5)		15.00	90.00
	Set, never hinged		40.00	

Italian Stamps of 1901-20 Overprinted

1924

65	A48	5c green	1.50	24.00
66	A48	10c claret	1.50	24.00
67	A48	15c slate	1.50	30.00
68	A50	20c brn orange	1.50	30.00
a.	Double overprint		100.00	
69	A49	25c blue	1.50	24.00
70	A49	40c brown	1.50	24.00
71	A49	50c violet	1.50	30.00
72	A49	60c carmine	1.50	37.50
a.	Double overprint		300.00	
73	A49	85c red brown	1.500	45.00
74	A46	1 l brn & green	1.50	45.00
	Nos. 65-74 (10)		19.50	313.50
	Set, never hinged		40.00	

Ferrucci Issue
Types of Italian Stamps of 1930, Overprinted in Red or Blue

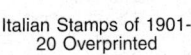

1930   Wmk. Crowns (140)

75	A102	20c violet	6.00	6.00
76	A103	25c dark green	6.00	15.00
77	A103	50c black	6.00	6.00
78	A103	1.25 l deep blue	6.00	15.00
79	A104	5 l + 2 l dp car (Bl)	22.50	52.50
	Nos. 75-79 (5)		46.50	94.50
	Set, never hinged		125.00	

Garibaldi Issue
Types of Italian Stamps of 1932, Overprinted like Nos. 75-79 in Red or Blue

1932

80	A138	10c brown	22.50	45.00
81	A138	20c red brn (Bl)	22.50	45.00
82	A138	25c dp grn	22.50	45.00
83	A138	30c bluish slate	22.50	45.00
84	A138	50c red vio (Bl)	22.50	45.00
85	A141	75c cop red (Bl)	22.50	45.00
86	A141	1.25 l dull blue	22.50	45.00
87	A141	1.75 l + 25c brn	22.50	45.00
88	A144	2.55 l + 50c org (Bl)	22.50	45.00
89	A145	5 l + 1 l dl vio	22.50	45.00
	Nos. 80-89 (10)		225.00	450.00
	Set, never hinged		650.00	

CAYMAN ISLANDS

kā-'man 'ī-lənds

LOCATION — Three islands in the Caribbean Sea, about 200 miles northwest of Jamaica
GOVT. — British Crown Colony, formerly a dependency of Jamaica
AREA — 100 sq. mi.
POP. — 39,335 (1999 est.)
CAPITAL — George Town, located on Grand Cayman

12 Pence = 1 Shilling
20 Shilling = 1 Pound
100 Cents = 1 Dollar (1969)

Watermark

Wmk. 362 — Basotho Hat Multiple

Catalogue values for unused stamps in this country are for Never Hinged items, beginning with Scott 112.

Victoria   Edward VII
A1   A2

1900   Typo.   Wmk. 2   Perf. 14

1	A1	½p pale green	7.00	22.50
2	A1	1p carmine rose	7.00	3.75

1901-03

3	A2	½p green ('02)	6.00	32.50
4	A2	1p car rose ('03)	13.00	11.50
5	A2	2½p ultramarine	13.00	16.00
6	A2	6p chocolate	40.00	77.50
7	A2	1sh brown orange	80.00	140.00
	Nos. 3-7 (5)		152.00	277.50

1905   Wmk. 3

8	A2	½p green	8.50	11.50
9	A2	1p carmine rose	17.00	22.50
10	A2	2½p ultramarine	8.50	4.25
11	A2	6p chocolate	20.00	50.00
12	A2	1sh brown orange	40.00	62.50
	Nos. 8-12 (5)		94.00	150.75

For surcharge see No. 17.

1907, Mar. 13

13	A2	4p brown & blue	40.00	75.00
14	A2	6p ol green & rose	40.00	87.50
15	A2	1sh violet & green	70.00	110.00
16	A2	5sh ver & green	240.00	375.00
	Nos. 13-16 (4)		390.00	647.50

Numerals of 4p, 1sh and 5sh of type A2 are in color on colorless tablet.
For surcharges see Nos. 18-20.

Nos. 9, 16, 13 Handstamped

#17   #18

#19   #20

1907-08

17	A2	½p on 1p	60.00	100.00
18	A2	½p on 5sh	350.00	575.00
a.	Inverted surcharge		45,000.	
b.	Double surcharge		12,750.	12,750.
c.	Dbl. surch., one inverted			
d.	Pair, one without surcharge		65,000.	
19	A2	1p on 5sh	375.00	575.00
a.	Double surcharge		21,000.	10,000.
b.	Inverted surcharge		150,000.	
20	A2	2½p on 4p	375.00	575.00
		('08)	2,000.	3,750.
a.	Double surcharge		45,000.	24,000.

No. 19b is unique. It exists on the upper left stamp in an upper left corner margin plate no. 1 block of four that is lightly hinged in the top margin only.
The 1p on 4p is a revenue stamp not authorized for postal use. Value about $300. Varieties exist.

A3   A4

1907-09   Perf. 14

21	A3	½p green	3.50	5.50
22	A3	1p carmine rose	2.10	1.10
23	A3	2½p ultramarine	4.75	5.25

Chalky Paper

24	A3	3p violet, *yellow*	4.50	9.75
25	A3	4p blk & red, *yel*	67.50	100.00
26	A3	6p violet	13.50	52.50
27	A3	1sh black, *grn*	11.00	32.50
28	A3	5sh grn & red, *yel*	52.50	90.00
	Nos. 21-28 (8)		159.35	296.60

Issued: ½p, 1p, 12/27; 2½p, 3p, 4p, 5sh, 3/30/08; 6d, 10/2/08; 1sh, 4/5/09.
Forged cancellations are found on No. 28.

1908, Mar. 30   Wmk. 2

29	A3	1sh black, *green*	85.00	125.00
30	A3	10sh grn & red, *grn*	225.00	400.00

Numerals of 3p, 4p, 1sh and 5sh of type A3 are in color on plain tablet.
Forged cancellations are found on No. 30.

1908   Wmk. 3

Ordinary Paper

31	A4	¼p brown	6.00	1.00

King George V
A5   A6

1912-20

32	A5	¼p brown ('13)	1.25	.50
33	A5	½p green	3.25	6.00
34	A5	1p carmine ('13)	4.00	3.00
35	A5	2p gray	1.25	12.50
36	A5	2½p ultra ('14)	8.50	13.50

Chalky Paper

37	A5	3p vio, *yel* ('13)	3.00	22.50
38	A5	4p blk & red, *yel* ('13)	1.25	12.50
39	A5	6p vio & red vio ('13)	4.50	9.00
40	A5	1sh blk, *grn* ('13)	4.25	32.50
41	A5	2sh vio & ultra, *bl*	14.50	57.50
42	A5	3sh green & vio	22.50	77.50

43	A5	5sh grn & red, *yel* ('14)	90.00	190.00
44	A5	10sh grn & red, *bl grn, olive* back ('18)	225.00	240.00
a.	10sh green & red, *grn* ('13)		150.00	240.00
	Nos. 32-44 (13)		383.25	677.00

The first printings of the 3p, 1sh and 10sh have a white back.
For surcharges see Nos. MR1-MR7.

1913, Nov. 19
Surface-colored Paper

45	A5	3p violet, *yel*	4.25	9.50
46	A5	1sh black, *green*	4.25	4.25
47	A5	10sh grn & red, *grn*	100.00	175.00
	Nos. 45-47 (3)		108.50	188.75

Numeral of ¼p, 2p, 3p, 4p, 1sh, 2sh, 3sh and 5sh of type A5 are in color on plain tablet.

1921-26   Wmk. 4   Perf. 14

50	A6	¼p yel brown	.60	1.75
51	A6	½p gray green	.60	.35
52	A6	1p rose red	1.75	1.00
53	A6	1½p orange brn	2.10	.35
54	A6	2p gray	2.10	4.75
55	A6	2½p ultramarine	.60	.60
56	A6	3p violet, *yel*	1.25	4.75
57	A6	4½p olive grn	2.75	3.75
58	A6	6p claret	6.50	37.50
59	A6	1sh black, *grn*	11.50	37.50
60	A6	2sh violet, *blue*	17.00	29.00
61	A6	3sh violet	27.50	19.00
62	A6	5sh green, *yel*	29.00	55.00
63	A6	10sh car, *green*	72.50	100.00
	Nos. 50-63 (14)		175.75	295.30

Issued: 1½p, 4/4/21; ¼p, ½p, 1p, 2p, 2½p, 6p, 2sh, 3sh, 4/1/22; 3p, 4½p, 6/29/23; 5sh, 2/15/25; 1sh, 5/15/25; 10sh, 9/5/26.

1921-22   Wmk. 3

64	A6	3p violet, *org*	1.75	9.50
65	A6	4p yel, *yel*	1.25	4.75
66	A6	1sh black, *green*	1.50	11.50
67	A6	5sh green, *yel*	19.00	85.00
68	A6	10sh car, *green*	72.50	125.00
	Nos. 64-68 (5)		96.00	235.75

Issued: 4p, 4/1/22; others, 4/4/21.

King William IV, King George V
A7

Perf. 12½

1932, Dec. 5   Wmk. 4   Engr.

69	A7	¼p brown	1.90	1.40
70	A7	½p green	3.25	10.50
71	A7	1p carmine	3.25	10.50
72	A7	1½p orange	3.25	3.75
73	A7	2p gray	3.25	4.75
74	A7	2½p ultramarine	3.25	2.00
75	A7	3p olive green	4.00	6.75
76	A7	6p red violet	11.50	30.00
77	A7	1sh brn & black	20.00	42.50
78	A7	2sh ultra & blk	55.00	100.00
79	A7	5sh green & blk	100.00	160.00
80	A7	10sh car & black	350.00	475.00
	Nos. 69-80 (12)		558.65	847.15
	Set, never hinged		1,225.	

Centenary of the formation of the Cayman Islands Assembly.

Common Design Types pictured following the introduction.

Silver Jubilee Issue
Common Design Type

1935, May 6   Perf. 13½x14

81	CD301	½p green & black	.30	1.50
82	CD301	2½p blue & brown	1.50	1.50
83	CD301	6p ol grn & lt bl	1.50	4.75
84	CD301	1sh brt vio & ind	10.50	10.00
	Nos. 81-84 (4)		13.80	17.75
	Set, never hinged		20.00	

King George V
A8

Catboat
A9

Red-footed
Boobies
A10

Conches and
Coconut
Palms — A11

Hawksbill
Turtles
A12

1935-36　　　　　**Perf. 12½**

85	A8	¼p brown & blk	.60	1.25
86	A9	½p yel grn & ultra	1.25	1.25
87	A10	1p car & ultra	5.00	3.00
88	A11	1½p org & black	1.75	2.40
89	A9	2p brown vio & ultra	4.50	1.50
90	A12	2½p dp blue & blk	4.00	1.60
91	A8	3p ol grn & blk	3.00	3.75
92	A12	6p red vio & blk	10.50	6.00
93	A9	1sh org & ultra	7.25	9.25
94	A10	2sh black & ultra	55.00	50.00
95	A12	5sh green & blk	60.00	70.00
96	A11	10sh car & black	125.00	140.00
		Nos. 85-96 (12)	277.85	290.00
		Set, never hinged	525.00	

Issued: #86, 2½p, 6p, 1sh, 1/1/36; others, 5/1/35.

Coronation Issue
Common Design Type

1937, May 13　　　　**Perf. 11x11½**

97	CD302	½p deep green	.20	1.50
98	CD302	1p dark carmine	.25	.25
99	CD302	2½p deep ultra	.55	.55
		Nos. 97-99 (3)	1.00	2.30
		Set, never hinged	2.25	

Beach
View,
Grand
Cayman
A13

Dolphin — A14

Hawksbill
Turtles — A16

Map of the
Islands
A15

Cayman
Schooner
A17

Perf. 12½; 11½x13 or 13x11½ (A14, #111); 14 (#104, 107)

1938-43　　　　　**Engr.**

100	A13	¼p red orange	.55	.75
a.		Perf. 13½x12½ ('43)	.20	.85
101	A14	½p yel green	.85	.75
a.		Perf. 14 ('43)	1.10	1.75
102	A15	1p carmine	.20	1.00
103	A13	1½p black	.20	.20
104	A16	2p dp violet ('43)	.50	.35
a.		Perf. 11½x13	2.50	.30
105	A17	2½p ultra	.30	.20
106	A15	3p orange	.30	.20
107	A16	6p dk ol grn ('43)	2.50	2.50
a.		Perf. 11½x13	7.25	5.25
108	A14	1sh reddish brown	5.75	2.00
a.		Perf. 14 ('43)	3.75	2.50
109	A13	2sh green	24.00	18.00
110	A17	5sh deep rose	27.50	19.00
111	A16	10sh dark brown	19.00	12.00
a.		Perf. 14 ('43)	19.00	12.00
		Nos. 100-111 (12)	81.65	56.95
		Never hinged	135.00	

See Nos. 114-115.

> **Catalogue values for unused stamps in this section, from this point to the end of the section, are for Never Hinged items.**

Peace Issue
Common Design Type

1946, Aug. 26　Wmk. 4　Perf. 13½

112	CD303	1½p black	.25	.20
113	CD303	3p orange	.25	.20

Types of 1938

1947, Aug. 25　　　　**Perf. 12½**

114	A17	2½p orange	3.50	.65
115	A15	3p ultramarine	3.50	.45

Silver Wedding Issue
Common Design Types

1948, Nov. 29　Photo.　Perf. 14x14½

116	CD304	½p dark green	.20	.65

Perf. 11½x11
Engr.; Name Typo.

117	CD305	10sh blue violet	18.00	18.00

UPU Issue
Common Design Types
Engr.; Name Typo. on #119, 120

1949, Oct. 10　Perf. 13½, 11x11½

118	CD306	2½p orange	.30	1.00
119	CD307	3p indigo	1.75	2.50
120	CD308	6p olive	.70	2.50
121	CD309	1sh red brown	.70	.40
		Nos. 118-121 (4)	3.45	6.40

Catboat
A18

Designs: ½p, Coconut grove. 1p, Green turtle. 1½p, Thatch rope industry. 2p, Caymanian seamen. 2½p, Map. 3p, Parrot fish. 6p, Bluff, Cayman Brac. 9p, George Town harbor. 1sh, Turtle "crawl". 2sh, Cayman schooner. 5sh, Boat-building. 10sh, Government offices.

Perf. 11½x11

1950, Oct. 2　Wmk. 4　Engr.

122	A18	¼p rose red & blue	.20	.80
123	A18	½p bl grn & red vio	.20	1.75
124	A18	1p dp blue & olive	.75	1.00
125	A18	1½p choc & bl grn	.45	1.00
126	A18	2p rose car & vio	1.75	2.00
127	A18	2½p sepia & aqua	1.75	.85
128	A18	3p bl & blue grn	2.10	2.00
129	A18	6p dp bl & org brn	2.50	1.75
130	A18	9p dk grn & rose red	10.50	2.50
131	A18	1sh red org & brn	4.50	3.75
132	A18	2sh red vio & vio	11.50	14.50
133	A18	5sh vio & olive	17.00	9.50
134	A18	10sh rose red & blk	22.50	19.00
		Nos. 122-134 (13)	75.70	60.40

Types of 1950 with Portrait of Queen Elizabeth II and

Lighthouse,
South
Sound — A20

Elizabeth II and
Turtles — A21

Perf. 11½x11, 11x11½

1953-59　　　　　**Engr.**

135	A18	¼p rose red & bl	1.40	.80
136	A18	½p bl grn & red vio	1.10	.75
137	A18	1p dp bl & olive	1.00	.70
138	A18	1½p choc & bl grn	.75	.35
139	A18	2p rose car & vio	3.50	1.40
140	A18	2½p black & aqua	4.25	1.25
141	A18	3p blue & bl grn	5.25	1.00
142	A20	4p dp blue & black	2.50	.70
143	A18	6p dp bl & red brn	2.10	.30
144	A18	9p dk green & rose red	8.50	.40
145	A18	1sh red org & brn	4.75	.40
146	A18	2sh red vio & vio	16.00	11.50
147	A18	5sh violet & olive	17.50	10.00
148	A18	10sh rose red & blk	19.00	11.50
149	A21	£1 bright blue	37.50	16.00
		Nos. 135-149 (15)	125.10	57.05

Issued: 4p, 3/2; 2p, 2½p, 9p, 6/2/54; ½p, 1p, 1½p, 6p, 7/7/54; ¼p, 3p, 1sh-10sh, 2/21/55; £1, 1/6/59.

Coronation Issue
Common Design Type

1953, June 2　　　　**Perf. 13½x13**

150	CD312	1p brt green & black	.40	1.00

Arms of
Cayman
Islands
A22

Perf. 12

1959, July 4　Wmk. 4　Photo.

151	A22	2½p dull blue & blk	.65	1.25
152	A22	1sh red orange & blk	.75	.50

Granting of a new constitution.

Cayman
Parrot — A23

Catboat
A24

1½p, Orchid. 2p, May of Islands. 2½p, Fisherman casting net. 3p, West Bay Beach. 4p, Green turtle. 6p, Cayman schooner. 9p, Angler with kingfish. 1sh, Iguana. 1sh3p, Swimming pool. Cayman Brac. 1sh9p, Girl and sailboat. 5sh, Fort George. 10sh, Coat of Arms. £1, Queen Elizabeth II.

Perf. 11x11½, 11½x11

1962, Nov. 28　Wmk. 314　Engr.

153	A23	¼p rose red & emer	1.00	1.50
154	A24	1p olive & black	.85	.40
155	A24	1½p purple & yel	4.25	1.25
156	A24	2p sepia & blue	1.10	.50
157	A24	2½p green & vio	.85	1.50
158	A24	3p car & blue	.40	.40
159	A24	4p pur & green	1.40	.95
160	A24	6p sepia & green	3.25	.55
161	A23	9p pur & vio bl	2.25	.85

162	A24	1sh rose & sepia	.85	.20
163	A24	1sh3p brn org & lt grn	3.75	3.50
164	A24	1sh9p vio & bl grn	15.00	2.25
165	A24	5sh grn & dl pur	11.50	9.50
166	A23	10sh blue & olive	21.00	13.00
167	A23	£1 blk & car rose	21.00	24.00
		Revenue cancel		.80
		Nos. 153-167 (15)	88.45	60.35

Freedom from Hunger Issue
Common Design Type

1963, June 4　Photo.　Perf. 14x14½

168	CD314	1sh9p car rose	.60	.30

Red Cross Centenary Issue
Common Design Type
Wmk. 314

1963, Sept. 2　Litho.　Perf. 13

169	CD315	1p black & red	.20	.20
170	CD315	1sh9p ultra & red	1.25	1.90

Shakespeare Issue
Common Design Type

1964, Apr. 23　Photo.　Perf. 14x14½

171	CD316	6p deep lilac rose	.40	.30

ITU Issue
Common Design Type

1965, May 17　Wmk. 314

172	CD317	1p ultra & red lil	.20	.20
173	CD317	1sh3p rose lil & grn	.90	.75

Intl. Cooperation Year Issue
Common Design Type

1965, Oct. 25　Wmk. 314　Perf. 14½

174	CD318	1p blue grn & claret	.20	.20
175	CD318	1sh lt vio & green	.65	.65

Churchill Memorial Issue
Common Design Type

1966, Jan. 24　Photo.　Perf. 14
Design in Black, Gold and Carmine Rose

176	CD319	¼p bright blue	.25	1.25
177	CD319	1p green	.50	.50
178	CD319	1sh brown	.95	.65
179	CD319	1sh9p violet	1.60	.90
		Nos. 176-179 (4)	3.30	3.30

Royal Visit Issue
Common Design Type

1966, Feb. 4　Litho.　Perf. 11x12

180	CD320	1p violet blue	.85	.20
181	CD320	1sh9p dk car rose	3.50	1.50

World Cup Soccer Issue
Common Design Type

1966, July 1　Litho.　Perf. 14

182	CD321	1½p multicolored	.20	.20
183	CD321	1sh9p multicolored	.65	.65

WHO Headquarters Issue
Common Design Type

1966, Sept. 20　Litho.　Perf. 14

184	CD322	2p multicolored	.75	.30
185	CD322	1sh3p multicolored	1.75	1.10

UNESCO Anniversary Issue
Common Design Type

1966, Dec. 1　Litho.　Perf. 14

186	CD323	1p "Education"	.20	.20
187	CD323	1sh9p "Science"	1.10	.35
188	CD323	5sh "Culture"	2.25	1.10
		Nos. 186-188 (3)	3.55	1.65

Telephone and Map of
Caymans — A25

Perf. 14½x14

1966, Dec. 5　Litho.　Wmk. 314

189	A25	4p multicolored	.20	.20
190	A25	9p multicolored	.30	.30

Linking of the Cayman telephone system with the intl. system.

BAC 1-11 Jet Liner over Schooner — A26

1966, Dec. 17
191 A26 1sh blue, ol & black .35 .35
192 A26 1sh9p ultra, grn & sepia .75 .75

Opening of the Grand Cayman Airport jet service.

Water Skiing and ITY Emblem A27

ITY Emblem and: 6p, Skin diving. 1sh, Sport fishing. 1sh9p, Sailing.

Perf. 14½x14
1967, Dec. 1   Photo.   Wmk. 314
193 A27 4p multi & gold .45 .20
  a. Gold omitted 110.00
194 A27 6p multi & gold .45 .45
195 A27 1sh multi & gold .45 .40
196 A27 1sh9p multi & gold .65 .75
    Nos. 193-196 (4) 2.00 1.60

International Tourist Year.

Human Rights Flame and Freed Slaves A28

1968, June 3   Photo.   Wmk. 314
197 A28 3p slate bl, grn & gold .20 .20
198 A28 9p lt brn, grn & gold .20 .20
199 A28 5sh ultra, grn & gold .70 .70
    Nos. 197-199 (3) 1.10 1.10

International Human Rights Year.

Long Jump A29

1968, Oct. 1   Litho.   Perf. 13½
200 A29 1sh multicolored .20 .20
201 A29 1sh3p multicolored .25 .25
202 A29 2sh yellow & multi .40 .40
    Nos. 200-202 (3) .85 .85

19th Olympic Games, Mexico City, 10/12-27.

Adoration of Shepherds, by Carel Fabritius — A30

Christmas: 1p, 8p, 2sh, Adoration of the Shepherds, by Rembrandt.

Perf. 14x14½
1968, Nov. 18   Photo.   Wmk. 314
203 A30 ¼p brown & multi .20 .20
  a. Gold omitted 200.00
204 A30 1p violet & multi .20 .20
205 A30 6p multicolored .20 .20
206 A30 8p car & multi .20 .20

207 A30 1sh3p multicolored .30 .30
208 A30 2sh gray & multi .45 .45
    Nos. 203-208 (6) 1.55 1.55

1969, Jan. 8   Unwmk.
209 A30 ¼p red lilac & multi .20 .20

Grand Cayman Thrush A31

1p, Brahman cattle. 2p, Blowholes on coast. 2½p, Map of Grand Cayman. 3p, Town scene in George Town. 4p, Royal poinciana. 6p, Map of Cayman Brac and Little Cayman. 8p, Motor vessels at berth. 1sh, Basket making. 1sh3p, Beach scene. 1sh6p, Rope making. 2sh, Barracudas. 4sh, Government House. 10sh, Coat of arms. £1, Queen Elizabeth II.

Unwmk.
1969, June 5   Litho.   Perf. 14
210 A31 ¼p multi .20 .90
211 A31 1p multi .20 .20
212 A31 2p multi .20 .20
213 A31 2½p multi .20 .20
214 A31 3p multi .20 .20
215 A31 4p multi .20 .20
216 A31 6p multi .20 .20
217 A31 8p multi .20 .20
218 A31 1sh multi .25 .20
219 A31 1sh3p multi .30 1.90
220 A31 1sh6p multi .40 1.90
221 A31 2sh multi 1.50 1.40
222 A31 4sh multi .70 1.40
223 A31 10sh multi, vert. 1.50 2.50
224 A31 £1 multi, vert. 3.50 3.50
    Nos. 210-224 (15) 9.75 15.10

See #262-276. For surcharges see #227-241.

1969, Aug. 11   Wmk. 314 Sideways
225 A31 ¼p multicolored .40 .40

Type of 1969 Surcharged

1969, Sept. 8   Wmk. 314   Perf. 14
227 A31 ¼c on ¼p multi .20 .85
228 A31 1c on 1p multi .20 .25
229 A31 2c on 2p multi .20 .25
230 A31 3c on 4p multi .20 .25
231 A31 4c on 2½p multi .20 .25
232 A31 5c on 6p multi .20 .25
233 A31 7c on 8p multi .20 .25
234 A31 8c on 3p multi .20 .25
235 A31 10c on 1s multi .35 .25
236 A31 12c on 1sh3p multi .50 1.90
237 A31 15c on 1sh6p multi .65 1.25
238 A31 20c on 2sh multi 2.25 2.10
239 A31 40c on 4sh multi .65 1.25
240 A31 $1 on 10sh multi 1.60 3.75
241 A31 $2 on £1 multi 2.50 4.50
    Nos. 227-241 (15) 10.10 17.60

The surcharge is arranged differently on various denominations.

"Noli me Tangere," by Titian — A33

Christmas: 1c, 7c, 20c, The Adoration of the Kings, by Jan Gossaert.

1969, Nov. 4   Photo.   Perf. 14
242 A32 ¼c blue & multi .20 .20
243 A32 ¼c emer & multi .20 .20
244 A32 ¼c red org & multi .20 .20
245 A32 ¼c brt pink & multi .20 .20
246 A32 1c vio blue & multi .20 .20
247 A32 5c red org & multi .20 .20
248 A32 7c dk green & multi .20 .20
249 A32 12c emer & multi .20 .20
250 A32 20c multicolored .20 .20
    Nos. 242-250 (9) 1.80 1.80

1970, Mar. 23   Litho.   Unwmk.
251 A33 ¼c dull grn & multi .20 .20
252 A33 ¼c dk car & multi .20 .20
253 A33 ¼c violet & multi .20 .20
254 A33 ¼c bister & multi .20 .20
255 A33 10c vio blue & multi .20 .20
256 A33 12c red brn & multi .25 .25
257 A33 40c brn vio & multi .60 .60
    Nos. 251-257 (7) 1.85 1.85

Easter.

Barnaby from "Barnaby Rudge" by Dickens (1812-70), English Novelist — A34

Characters from Charles Dickens: 12c, Sairey Gamp, from "Martin Chuzzlewit." 20c, Mr. Micawber and David, from "David Copperfield." 40c, The Marchioness from "The Old Curiosity Shop."

1970, June 17   Photo.   Perf. 14½x14
258 A34 1c ol green, yel & blk .20 .20
259 A34 12c red brn, brick red & black .20 .20
260 A34 20c dk ol bister, gold & black .35 .35
261 A34 40c dp ultra, lt bl & blk .75 .75
    Nos. 258-261 (4) 1.50 1.50

Type of Regular Issue 1969 Values in Cents and Dollars

Designs: ¼c, Grand Cayman thrush. 1c, Brahman cattle. 2c, Blowholes on coast. 3c, Royal poinciana. 4c, Map of Grand Cayman. 5c, Map of Cayman Brac and Little Cayman. 7c, Motor vessels at berth. 8c, Town scene in George Town. 10c, Basket making. 12c, Beach scene. 15c, Rope making. 20c, Barracudas. 40c, Government House. $1, Coat of arms, vert. $2, Queen Elizabeth II, vert.

Wmk. 314
1970, Sept. 8   Litho.   Perf. 14
262 A31 ¼c multicolored .60 .30
263 A31 1c multicolored .20 .20
264 A31 2c multicolored .20 .20
265 A31 3c multicolored .25 .20
266 A31 4c multicolored .25 .20
267 A31 5c multicolored .45 .20
268 A31 7c multicolored .40 .20
269 A31 8c multicolored .40 .20
270 A31 10c multicolored .40 .20
271 A31 12c multicolored 1.40 1.10
272 A31 15c multicolored 1.60 3.50
273 A31 20c multicolored 3.75 1.75
274 A31 40c multicolored 1.25 1.25
275 A31 $1 multicolored 1.60 5.75
276 A31 $2 multicolored 2.40 5.75
    Nos. 262-276 (15) 15.15 21.00

The Three Wise Men A35

Christmas: 1c, 10c, 20c, Nativity and globe.

1970, Oct. 8   Litho.   Perf. 14
277 A35 ¼c brt grn & yel grn .20 .20
278 A35 1c bl grn, yel grn & blk .20 .20
279 A35 5c dp claret & org .20 .20
280 A35 10c red org, yel & blk .20 .20
281 A35 12c ultra & lt grnsh bl .20 .20
282 A35 20c grn, yel grn & blk .25 .25
    Nos. 277-282 (6) 1.25 1.25

Grand Cayman Terrapin A36

Cayman Islands Turtles: 7c, Green turtle. 12c, Hawksbill turtle. 20c, Turtle farm.

1971, Jan. 28   Perf. 14x14½
283 A36 5c multicolored .70 .50
284 A36 7c multicolored .90 .50
285 A36 12c multicolored 2.00 .60
286 A36 20c multicolored 3.25 3.25
    Nos. 283-286 (4) 6.85 4.85

Dendrophylax Fawcetii — A37   Adoration of the Kings, 15th Century — A38

Wild Orchids of West Indies: 2c, Schomburgkia thomsoniana. 10c, Vanilla claviculata. 40c, Oncidium variegatum.

1971, Apr. 7   Wmk. 314   Perf. 14
287 A37 ¼c brown & multi .25 1.60
288 A37 2c ol green & multi .85 1.25
289 A37 10c gray bl & multi 3.25 1.00
290 A37 40c lt violet & multi 6.25 5.00
    Nos. 287-290 (4) 10.60 8.85

1971, Sept. 27   Perf. 14

Christmas: 1c, 15c, Nativity (detail), Paris, 14th cent. 5c, 20c, Adoration of the Kings (detail), Burgundian, 15th cent.

291 A38 ¼c gold & multi .20 .20
292 A38 1c gold & multi .20 .20
293 A38 5c gold & multi .20 .20
294 A38 12c gold & multi .20 .20
295 A38 15c gold & multi .30 .30
296 A38 20c gold & multi .40 .40
  a. Souvenir sheet of 6, #291-296 4.75 4.75
    Nos. 291-296 (6) 1.50 1.50

Underwater Cable, Turtle and Telephone — A39

1972, Jan. 10
297 A39 2c multicolored .20 .20
298 A39 10c multicolored .20 .20
299 A39 40c multicolored 1.00 1.00
    Nos. 297-299 (3) 1.40 1.40

Coaxial cable for world communications.

Courthouse — A40

Designs: 15c, 40c, Legislative Assembly Building, George Town.

1972, Aug. 15   **Perf. 13½x14**
300 A40 5c dp car & multi   .20 .20
301 A40 15c lilac rose & multi   .20 .20
302 A40 25c dull grn & multi   .30 .30
303 A40 40c dk blue & multi   .50 .50
a. Souvenir sheet of 4, #300-303   1.25 1.25
    Nos. 300-303 (4)   1.20 1.20

New Cayman Islands government buildings.

Silver Wedding Issue, 1972
Common Design Type

Design: Queen Elizabeth II, Prince Philip, hawksbill turtle and conch.

1972, Nov. 20 Photo.   Perf. 14x14½
304 CD324 12c vio black & multi   .25 .25
305 CD324 30c olive & multi   .50 .50

$1 Note and 1c Coin A41

6c, $5 note and 5c coin. 15c, $10 note and 10c coin. 25c, $25 note and 25c coin.

1973, Jan. 15
306 A41 3c emerald & multi   .20 .20
307 A41 6c yellow & multi   .30 .60
308 A41 15c lilac & multi   .75 .50
309 A41 25c orange & multi   1.50 .90
a. Souvenir sheet of 4, #306-309   5.25 5.25
    Nos. 306-309 (4)   2.75 2.20

First Cayman Islands coinage and bank notes, May 1, 1972.

Last Supper A42

Stained Glass Windows: 10c, Christ Carrying Cross, vert. 12c, Resurrection, vert. 30c, Crucifixion.

Perf. 14½x14, 14x14½
1973, Apr. 11   **Litho.**
310 A42 10c pink & multi   .20 .20
311 A42 12c yel green & multi   .20 .20
312 A42 20c lt blue & multi   .30 .30
313 A42 30c yellow & multi   .40 .40
a. Souvenir sheet of 4   1.60 1.60
    Nos. 310-313 (4)   1.10 1.10

Easter. No. 313a contains 4 stamps similar to Nos. 310-313 with simulated perforations.

Nativity — A43   White-winged Dove — A44

Christmas: 5c, 12c, 25c, Adoration of the Magi, from Breviary of Queen Isabella. 9c, 15c, Like 3c, Nativity from Sforza Book of Hours.

1973, Oct. 2   **Perf. 14½**
314 A43 3c dull green & multi   .20 .20
315 A43 5c dull pur & multi   .20 .20
316 A43 9c sepia & multi   .20 .20

317 A43 12c dk blue & multi   .20 .20
318 A43 15c dp rose & multi   .20 .20
319 A43 25c black & multi   .40 .40
    Nos. 314-319 (6)   1.40 1.40

Princess Anne's Wedding Issue
Common Design Type

1973, Nov. 14   Wmk. 314   Perf. 14
320 CD325 10c brt green & multi   .20 .20
321 CD325 30c lilac & multi   .30 .30

1974, Jan. 2   Litho.   Perf. 14x14½
322 A44 3c shown   2.75 .40
323 A44 10c Vitelline warblers   3.50 .40
324 A44 12c Greater Antillean
             grackles   3.50 .40
325 A44 20c West Indian red-
             bellied wood-
             pecker   5.75 1.00
326 A44 30c Stripe-headed
             tanagers   7.25 2.25
327 A44 50c Yucatan vireos   9.75 6.25
    Nos. 322-327 (6)   32.50 10.70

See Nos. 354-359.

One-room Schoolhouse — A45

Designs: 20c, New comprehensive school. 30c, Creative Arts Center, Mona, Jamaica.

1974, May 1   **Perf. 14**
328 A45 12c multicolored   .20 .20
329 A45 20c multicolored   .20 .20
330 A45 30c multicolored   .30 .30
    Nos. 328-330 (3)   .70 .70

25th anniv. of the University College of the West Indies.

Hermit Crab and Pirate Gold A46

Coat of Arms — A47   Elizabeth II — A48

Designs: 3c, Pirate, treasure chest and lion's paw. 4c, Spotted scorpionfish and crown. 5c, Flint-lock pistol and brain coral. 6c, Blackbeard on Grand Cayman and green turtle. 8c, 9c, Jeweled pomander and porkfish. 10c, Spiny lobster and gold coins. 12c, Jeweled sword, dagger and sea fan. 15c, Cabrit's murex and jeweled necklace. 20c, Queen conch, pistol and gold cup. 25c, Hogfish and pirate chest. 40c, Gold chalice and sea whip.

Wmk. 314 Upright, Sideways (#331-332, 336, 344-345)
1974-75   **Litho.**
Perf. 14
331 A46 1c multi ('75)   5.00 1.75
a. Wmk. upright   4.25 1.75
332 A46 3c multicolored   5.00 1.00
a. Wmk. upright   5.50 1.00
333 A46 4c multicolored   .70 .95
334 A46 5c multicolored   4.25 1.00
335 A46 6c multicolored   .50 3.25
336 A46 8c multicolored   3.50 11.50
337 A46 9c multicolored   5.25 12.50
338 A46 10c multicolored   6.25 1.10
339 A46 12c multicolored   .50 2.25
340 A46 15c multicolored   .65 1.75
341 A46 20c multicolored   5.00 4.00
342 A46 25c multicolored   .65 .95
343 A46 40c multicolored   5.75 1.75
344 A47 $1 multicolored   4.00 4.00
345 A48 $2 multicolored   10.50 9.00
    Nos. 331-345 (15)   57.50 57.25

Issued: #332, 11/12; 8c, 12/16; #331, 9/29; others, 8/1.

1976-77   **Wmk. 373**
332b A46 3c multicolored   1.40 5.50
333a A46 4c multi ('77)   1.75 6.50
334a A46 5c multi ('77)   9.00 8.25
336b A46 8c multicolored   10.50 7.25
338b A46 10c multicolored   4.00 5.50
341b A46 20c multicolored   4.50 4.25
344a A47 $1 multi ('77)   9.00 13.50
345b A48 $2 multicolored   10.00 9.25
    Nos. 332b-345b (8)   50.15 60.00

Issued: 3c, 8c, 10c, 20c, $2, 9/3; 4c, 5c, $1, 10/19.

Design Smaller
Size: 40x25mm
Wmk. 373 (Sideways on 1c-40c)
1978-80
346 A46 1c multicolored   1.50 2.25
346A A46 3c multicolored   1.25 .85
346B A46 5c multi ('79)   3.25 4.75
347 A46 10c multicolored   2.50 1.25
347A A46 20c multicolored   5.25 2.25
347B A46 40c multi ('79)   21.00 30.00
347C A47 $1 multi ('80)   26.00 11.00
348 A48 $2 multi ('80)   9.50 29.00
    Nos. 346-348 (8)   70.25 81.35

Issued: 1c, 3c, 3/16; 10c, 20c, 5/25; 5c, 12/11; $2, 4/3; $1, 7/30.

Sea Captain and Ship — A49

1974, Oct. 7   Wmk. 314   Perf. 14
349 A49 8c shown   .20 .20
350 A49 12c Thatch weaver   .25 .20
351 A49 20c Farmer   .55 .50
a. Miniature sheet of 3, #349-351 1.90 2.50
    Nos. 349-351 (3)   1.00 .90

Arms of Cinque Ports and Lord Warden's Flag — A50   Churchill Coat of Arms — A51

1974, Nov. 30
352 A50 12c multicolored   .20 .20
353 A51 50c multicolored   .70 .70
a. Souvenir sheet of 2, #352-353   1.10 1.25

Sir Winston Churchill (1874-1965).

Bird Type of 1974
Wmk. 314
1975, Jan. 1   Litho.   Perf. 14
354 A44 3c Yellow-shafted
             flicker   .75 .45
355 A44 10c West Indian tree
             duck   1.40 .45
356 A44 12c Yellow warblers   1.75 .70
357 A44 20c White-bellied
             dove   3.00 3.00
358 A44 30c Magnificent frig-
             ate bird   5.00 5.00
359 A44 50c Cayman ama-
             zon   6.00 11.50
a. Wmk. 362 (Lesotho)   600.00
    Nos. 354-359 (6)   17.90 21.10

Ivory Crosier with Crucifixion — A52

Design: 35c, Crucifixion, ivory and gilt. Designs show heads of 14th century French pastoral staffs.

Wmk. 314
1975, Mar. 24   Litho.   Perf. 14
360 A52 15c plum & multi   .20 .20
361 A52 35c gray & multi   .65 .65
a. Souvenir sheet of 2, #360-361   1.10 1.10

Easter. No. 361a exists imperf.
See Nos. 366-367.

Israel Hands A53

Designs: Pirates and various scenes.

1975, July 25   **Wmk. 314**
362 A53 10c shown   .60 .20
363 A53 12c John Fenn   .60 .20
364 A53 20c Thomas Anstis   .95 .45
365 A53 30c Edward Low   1.10 1.75
    Nos. 362-365 (4)   3.25 2.60

Easter Type of 1975

Designs after ivory carved pastoral staffs showing Virgin and Child with angels, French, 14th century.

Wmk. 373
1975, Oct. 31   Litho.   Perf. 14
366 A52 12c dk green & multi   .20 .20
367 A52 50c multicolored   .70 .70
a. Souvenir sheet of 2, #366-367   1.40 1.75

Christmas.

Registered Letter with Nos. 1-2; Cayman Brac Government House and Sub Post Office — A54

Cayman Islands 1st postage stamps, 75th anniv.: 20c, Cayman Islands #1 and cancelation used 1890-94; 30c, #2, 20; 50c, #1-2.

1976, Mar. 12   Litho.   Perf. 13½x14
368 A54 10c lt blue & multi   .20 .20
369 A54 20c pink & multi   .25 .25
370 A54 30c multicolored   .40 .40
371 A54 50c yellow & multi   .60 .60
a. Souvenir sheet of 4, #368-371   4.25 4.25
    Nos. 368-371 (4)   1.45 1.45

Seals of Georgia, Delaware and New Hampshire — A55

15c, Seals of SC, NJ, MD. 20c, Seals of VA, RI, MA. 25c, Seals of NY, CT, NC. 30c, Seal of PA, Liberty Bell and Great Seal of the US.

Wmk. 373
1976, May 29   Litho.   Perf. 14
372 A55 10c olive & multi   .40 .20
373 A55 15c blue & multi   .50 .20
374 A55 20c multicolored   .70 .30
375 A55 25c blue grn & multi   1.00 .60
376 A55 30c red brn & multi   1.25 .85
a. Souvenir sheet of 5 + label   7.25 7.25
    Nos. 372-376 (5)   3.85 2.15

American Bicentennial. Nos. 372-376 printed in sheets of 5. No. 376a contains one each of Nos. 372-376 and corner label inscribed "USA 200."

French Class 470 Racing Dinghies — A56

Queen Elizabeth II — A57

Design: 50c, One racing dinghy.

1976, Aug. 16   Litho.   Perf. 14
377	A56	20c multicolored	.70	.45
378	A56	50c multicolored	1.25	1.25

21st Olympic Games, Montreal, Canada, July 17-Aug. 1.

Perf. 14x13½, 13½x14
1977, Feb. 7   Litho.   Wmk. 373

8c, Prince Charles, 1973 visit. 50c, Preparation for anointing ceremony, horiz.

379	A57	8c multicolored	.20	.20
380	A57	30c multicolored	.35	.30
381	A57	50c multicolored	.55	.50
		Nos. 379-381 (3)	1.10	1.00

25th anniv. of the reign of Elizabeth II.

Scuba Diving A58

10c, Divers examining underwater wreck. 20c, Fairy basslets (fish). 25c, Sergeant majors (fish).

1977, July 25   Perf. 13½
382	A58	5c multicolored	.20	.20
383	A58	10c multicolored	.25	.25
384	A58	20c multicolored	.50	.50
385	A58	25c multicolored	.70	.65
a.		Souvenir sheet of 4	3.00	3.00
		Nos. 382-385 (4)	1.65	1.60

Tourist publicity. No. 385a contains one each of Nos. 382-385, perf. 14½.

Composia Fidelissima — A59

Butterflies: 8c, Heliconius charitonius. 10c, Danaus gilippus. 15c, Agraulis vanillae. 20c, Junonia evarete. 30c, Anartia jatrophae.

1977, Dec. 2   Wmk. 373   Perf. 14x13
386	A59	5c multicolored	1.25	.20
387	A59	8c multicolored	1.40	.30
388	A59	10c multicolored	1.50	.35
389	A59	15c multicolored	1.90	.55
390	A59	20c multicolored	2.10	.60
391	A59	30c multicolored	2.50	1.10
		Nos. 386-391 (6)	10.65	3.10

Cruise Ship "Southward" A60

Designs: 5c, "Renaissance." 30c, New harbor, vert. 50c, "Daphne," vert.

1978, Jan. 23   Litho.   Perf. 14
392	A60	3c multicolored	.45	.20
393	A60	5c multicolored	.45	.20
394	A60	30c multicolored	1.40	.65
395	A60	50c multicolored	1.90	.95
		Nos. 392-395 (4)	4.20	2.00

New harbor and cruise ships.

Crucifixion, by Dürer — A61

Explorers, Singing Game — A62

Etchings by Dürer: 15c, Christ at Emmaus. 20c, Entry into Jerusalem. 30c, Christ washing Peter's feet.

1978, Mar. 20   Litho.   Perf. 12
396	A61	10c multicolored	.35	.20
397	A61	15c multicolored	.50	.30
398	A61	20c multicolored	.65	.40
399	A61	30c multicolored	.75	.55
a.		Souvenir sheet of 4, #396-399	6.50	6.50
		Nos. 396-399 (4)	2.25	1.45

Easter; Albrecht Dürer (1471-1528). Nos. 396-399 issued in sheets of 6.

1978, Apr. 25   Litho.   Perf. 14

10c, Girls' Brigade presenting flag. 20c, Guides studying Bible, playing guitar, tennis and volleyball. 50c, Guides setting table.

400	A62	3c multicolored	.20	.20
401	A62	10c multicolored	.45	.40
402	A62	20c multicolored	.75	.70
403	A62	50c multicolored	1.60	1.60
		Nos. 400-403 (4)	3.00	2.90

3rd Intl. Council Meeting of Girls' Brigade.

Elizabeth II Coronation Anniversary Issue
Common Design Types
Souvenir Sheet

1978, June 2   Unwmk.   Perf. 15
404		Sheet of 6	2.50	3.00
a.	CD326	30c Yale of Beaufort	.40	.40
b.	CD327	30c Elizabeth II	.40	.40
c.	CD328	30c Screech owl	.40	.40

No. 404 contains 2 se-tenant strips of Nos. 404a-404c, separated by horizontal gutter with commemorative and descriptive inscriptions.

A63

A63a

A63: 1c, Trumpetfish. 3c, Nassau grouper. 5c, French angelfish. 10c, Schoolmaster snappers. 20c, Banded butterflyfish. 50c, Black-bar soldierfish.
A63a: 3c, Four-eyed butterflyfish. 5c, Grey angel fish. 10c, Squirrelfish. 15c, Parrotfish. 20c, Spanish hogfish. 30c, Queen angelfish.

1978-79   Wmk. 373   Litho.   Perf. 14
405	A63	1c multicolored	.20	.20
406	A63	3c multicolored	.40	.20
407	A63a	3c multicolored	.35	.20
408	A63a	5c multicolored	.40	.20
409	A63	5c multicolored	.35	.20
412	A63a	10c multicolored	.65	.20
413	A63	10c multicolored	.65	.20
414	A63	15c multicolored	.75	.35
415	A63	20c multicolored	1.00	.45
416	A63	20c multicolored	1.25	.45
417	A63a	30c multicolored	2.00	.70
418	A63	50c multicolored	3.00	1.10
		Nos. 405-418 (12)	11.00	4.45

Issued: design A63, 4/20/79; design A63a, 8/28/78.

Lockheed Lodestar — A64

Aircraft: 5c, Consolidated PBY. 10c, Vickers Viking. 15c, BAC1-11. 20c, Piper Cheyenne, HS 125 and Bell 47. 30c, BAC1-11.

1979, Feb. 5   Perf. 14½
420	A64	3c multicolored	.40	.20
421	A64	5c multicolored	.40	.20
422	A64	10c multicolored	.55	.20
423	A64	15c multicolored	1.00	.40
424	A64	20c multicolored	1.25	.45
425	A64	30c multicolored	1.75	.55
		Nos. 420-425 (6)	5.35	2.00

Opening of Owen Roberts Airport, 25th anniv.

Rowland Hill and No. 2 — A65

Sir Rowland Hill (1795-1879), originator of penny postage, and: 10c, Great Britain #132. 20c, Cayman Islands #149. 50c, Cayman Islands #20.

Perf. 13½x14½
1979, Aug. 15   Litho.
426	A65	5c multicolored	.20	.20
427	A65	10c multicolored	.20	.20
428	A65	20c multicolored	.60	.60
		Nos. 426-428 (3)	1.00	1.00

Souvenir Sheet
429	A65	50c multicolored	1.50	1.50

Flight into Egypt — A66

Christmas: 20c, Shepherds, Star of Bethlehem. 30c, Nativity. 40c, Three Kings, Star of Bethlehem.

1979, Nov. 20   Litho.   Perf. 13½
430	A66	10c multicolored	.20	.20
431	A66	20c multicolored	.25	.20
432	A66	30c multicolored	.40	.25
433	A66	40c multicolored	.70	.30
		Nos. 430-433 (4)	1.55	.95

Bonaventure House, Rotary Emblem — A67

Perf. 14x13½, 13½x14
1980, Feb. 14   Litho.   Wmk. 373
434	A67	20c shown	.30	.20
435	A67	30c Paul P. Harris, vert.	.50	.25
436	A67	50c Anniversary emblem, vert.	.80	.50
		Nos. 434-436 (3)	1.60	.95

Rotary International, 75th anniversary.

Mailman, London 1980 Emblem A68

1980, May 6   Litho.   Perf. 14
437	A68	5c shown	.20	.20
438	A68	10c Cat boat	.20	.20
439	A68	15c Mounted mailman	.25	.25
440	A68	30c Mail wagon	.50	.35
441	A68	40c Mailman on bicycle	.60	.45
442	A68	$1 Mail truck	1.25	.90
		Nos. 437-442 (6)	3.00	2.35

London '80 Intl. Stamp Exhib., May 6-14.

Queen Mother Elizabeth Birthday Issue
Common Design Type

1980, Aug. 4   Litho.   Perf. 14
443	CD330	20c multicolored	.40	.40

Spondylus Americanus A69

1980, Aug. 12   Perf. 14½x14
444	A69	5c shown	.90	.20
445	A69	10c Murex brevifrons	.90	.30
446	A69	30c Cymatium femorale	1.75	.65
447	A69	50c Vasum muricatum	2.00	1.25
		Nos. 444-447 (4)	5.55	2.40

See Nos. 502-505, 518-521.

Lantana — A70

1980, Oct. 21   Litho.   Perf. 14
448	A70	5c shown	.20	.20
449	A70	15c Bauhinia	.35	.20
450	A70	30c Hibiscus	.70	.30
451	A70	$1 Milk and wine lily	1.75	1.40
		Nos. 448-451 (4)	3.00	2.10

See Nos. 478-481.

Juvenile Tarpon and Fire Sponges — A71

1980, Dec. 9   Litho.   Perf. 13½x13

452 A71	3c shown	1.40	2.25
453 A71	5c Mangrove root oysters	1.60	1.10
a.	Wmk. 384	8.00	8.00
b.	Wmk. 384, perf. 14	6.75	7.00
454 A71	10c Mangrove crab	.65	1.10
a.	Wmk. 384, perf. 14	10.00	9.75
455 A71	15c Lizard, crescent spot butterfly	1.40	2.25
456 A71	20c Tricolored heron	1.90	2.75
457 A71	30c Red mangrove flower	.90	1.40
458 A71	40c Red mangrove seeds	.95	1.60
459 A71	50c Waterhouse's leaf-nosed bat	1.60	2.25
460 A71	$1 Black-crowned night heron	7.00	7.50
461 A71	$2 Cayman Isls. arms	2.75	5.50
462 A71	$4 Queen Elizabeth II	5.25	7.25
	Nos. 452-462 (11)	25.40	34.95

Nos. 452-462 also issued inscribed 1982 (Value, $45); 5c, 1984; 3c-$2, 1985. Other dates probably exist. No. 453a has large imprint date.

Issued: #453a, 4/86; #453b, 454a, 6/86.

Bread and Wine — A72

1981, Mar. 17   Wmk. 373   Perf. 14

463 A72	3c shown	.20	.20
464 A72	10c Crown of thorns	.20	.20
465 A72	20c Crucifix	.35	.35
466 A72	$1 Christ	1.00	1.10
	Nos. 463-466 (4)	1.75	1.85

Easter.

Wood Slave A73

1981, June 16   Litho.   Perf. 13½

467 A73	20c shown	.45	.45
468 A73	30c Cayman iguana	.70	.70
469 A73	40c Lion lizard	.95	.95
470 A73	50c Freshwater turtle	1.10	1.10
	Nos. 467-470 (4)	3.20	3.20

Royal Wedding Issue

Common Design Type

1981, July 22   Litho.   Perf. 14

471 CD331	20c Bouquet	.25	.25
472 CD331	30c Charles	.40	.40
473 CD331	50c Couple	1.00	1.00
	Nos. 471-473 (3)	1.65	1.65

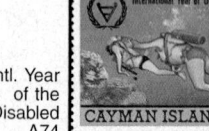

Intl. Year of the Disabled A74

1981, Sept. 29   Litho.   Perf. 14

474 A74	5c Scuba divers	.20	.20
475 A74	15c Old School for Handicapped	.25	.25
476 A74	20c New School for Handicapped	.35	.35
477 A74	$1 Beach scene	1.75	1.75
	Nos. 474-477 (4)	2.55	2.55

Flower Type of 1980

1981, Oct. 20   Litho.   Perf. 14

478 A70	3c Bougainvillea	.25	.20
479 A70	10c Morning glory	.25	.20
480 A70	20c Wild amaryllis	.55	.55
481 A70	$1 Cordia	3.00	3.00
	Nos. 478-481 (4)	4.05	3.95

TB Bacillus Centenary — A75

1982, Mar. 24   Litho.   Perf. 14½

482 A75	15c Koch, horizontal microscope	.35	.35
483 A75	30c Koch, vert.	.75	.75
484 A75	40c Microscope, vert.	.90	.90
485 A75	50c Koch, diff., vert.	1.25	1.25
	Nos. 482-485 (4)	3.25	3.25

Princess Diana Issue

Common Design Type

1982, July 1   Litho.   Perf. 13

486 CD333	20c Arms	.65	.40
487 CD333	30c Diana	1.10	.75
488 CD333	40c Wedding	1.25	.75
489 CD333	50c Portrait	4.00	1.50
	Nos. 486-489 (4)	7.00	3.40

Scouting Year A76

1982, Aug. 24   Wmk. 373   Perf. 14

490 A76	3c Pitching tent	.30	.20
491 A76	20c Cooking	.75	.75
492 A76	30c Troop	1.25	1.25
493 A76	50c Boating skills	1.75	1.75
	Nos. 490-493 (4)	4.05	3.95

Christmas 1982 — A77

Virgin and Child Paintings by Raphael.

1982, Oct. 26   Perf. 14½

494 A77	3c multicolored	.20	.20
495 A77	10c multicolored	.35	.35
496 A77	20c multicolored	.70	.70
497 A77	30c multicolored	1.00	1.00
	Nos. 494-497 (4)	2.25	2.25

Representative Govt. Sesquicentennial — A78

1982, Nov. 9   Litho.   Wmk. 373

498 A78	3c Mace	.20	.20
499 A78	10c Old Courthouse	.20	.20
500 A78	20c Commonwealth Parliamentary Assoc. arms	.45	.45
501 A78	30c Legislative Assembly building	.75	.75
	Nos. 498-501 (4)	1.60	1.60

Shell Type of 1980

1983, Jan. 11   Litho.   Perf. 13½

502 A69	5c Natica canrena	.20	.20
503 A69	10c Cassis tuberosa	.40	.40
504 A69	20c Strombus gallus	.90	.90
505 A69	$1 Cypraecassis testiculus	4.00	4.00
	Nos. 502-505 (4)	5.50	5.50

Visit of Queen Elizabeth II and Prince Philip A79

1983, Feb. 15   Litho.   Perf. 14

506 A79	20c Legislative Building, Cayman Brac	.60	.60
507 A79	30c Leg. Bldg., Grand Cayman	1.00	.90
508 A79	50c Prince Philip	1.75	1.50
509 A79	$1 Queen Elizabeth II	3.00	3.00
a.	Souvenir sheet of 4, #506-509	7.25	7.25
	Nos. 506-509 (4)	6.35	6.00

A80

1983, Mar. 14

510 A80	3c Globe	.30	.20
511 A80	15c Flags	.70	.60
512 A80	20c Fisherman	.80	.70
513 A80	40c Elizabeth II	1.25	.95
	Nos. 510-513 (4)	3.05	2.45

Commonwealth Day.

Manned Flight Bicentenary and Mosquito Research and Control Unit — A81

Airplanes.

1983, Oct. 10   Litho.   Perf. 14½

514 A81	3c MRCU Cessna	1.10	.70
515 A81	10c Consolidated Catalina PBY	1.25	.70
516 A81	20c Boeing 727	2.10	2.10
517 A81	40c Hawker Siddeley HS-748	3.00	3.75
	Nos. 514-517 (4)	7.45	7.25

Shell Type of 1980

1984, Jan. 18   Perf. 14x14½

518 A69	3c Natica floridana	1.50	.40
519 A69	10c Conus austini	1.75	.40
520 A69	30c Colubrania obscura	5.00	5.00
521 A69	50c Turbo cailletii	5.25	5.25
	Nos. 518-521 (4)	13.50	11.05

Lloyd's List Issue

Common Design Type

1984, May 16   Litho.   Perf. 14

522 CD335	5c Cruise ship	.75	.20
523 CD335	10c The Old Harbor	.85	.30
524 CD335	25c Ridgefield	1.60	1.60
525 CD335	50c Goldfield	3.25	3.25
	Nos. 522-525 (4)	6.45	5.35

Souvenir Sheet

526 CD335	$1 Goldfield, diff.	3.75	3.75

No. 525 Overprinted: "U.P.U. CONGRESS HAMBURG 1984"

1984, June 18

527 CD335	50c multicolored	1.50	1.60

Local Birds — A82

Snowy Egret Egretta thula

Perf. 14x14½

1984, Aug. 15   Litho.   Wmk. 373

528 A82	5c Snowy egret	1.40	.65
529 A82	10c Bananaquit	1.40	.65
530 A82	35c Kingfisher	4.75	3.25
531 A82	$1 Brown booby	8.50	9.50
	Nos. 528-531 (4)	16.05	14.05

Christmas — A83   Orchids — A84

#532a-532d, evening beach scenes. #533a-533d, daytime boating and beach scenes.

1984, Oct. 17   Litho.   Perf. 14

532	Strip of 4	5.00	5.00
a.-d.	A83 5c Any single	1.25	1.25
533	Strip of 4	6.00	5.00
a.-d.	A83 25c Any single	1.50	1.25

Souvenir Sheet

534	A83 $1 Bonfire, diff.	6.50	6.50

No. 534 contains one stamp 29x48mm.

1985, Mar. 13   Litho.   Perf. 14x13½

535 A84	5c Schomburgkia thomsoniana var.	1.75	.55
536 A84	10c Schomburgkia thomsoniana	1.75	.55
537 A84	25c Encyclia plicata	4.25	1.60
538 A84	50c Dendrophylax fawcetti	6.25	4.25
	Nos. 535-538 (4)	14.00	6.95

Shipwrecks A85

Unspecified shipwrecks found in Cayman waters.

1985, May 22   Perf. 14

539 A85	5c multicolored	1.50	.55
540 A85	25c multicolored	4.75	2.10
541 A85	35c multicolored	5.50	4.25
542 A85	40c multicolored	5.75	5.75
	Nos. 539-542 (4)	17.50	12.65

Intl. Youth Year — A86

5c, Natl. Athletic Assoc. track competition. 15c, High school students studying in Grand Cayman Campus Library. 25c, Amateur League Competition Football. 50c, Natl. Netball Assoc. competition.

1985, Aug. 14   Perf. 14½

543 A86	5c multicolored	.30	.25
544 A86	15c multicolored	.50	.40
545 A86	25c multicolored	1.10	.85
546 A86	50c multicolored	2.10	2.10
	Nos. 543-546 (4)	4.00	3.60

Telecommunications, 50th Anniv. — A87

Designs: 5c, Morse Code transmitter, 1935. 10c, Hand-cranked telephone, 1935. 25c, Tropospheric scatter dish, 1966. 50c, Earth dish receiver, 1979.

1985, Oct. 25   **Perf. 14**

547	A87	5c multicolored	.65	.65
548	A87	10c multicolored	.70	.70
549	A87	25c multicolored	1.90	1.10
550	A87	50c multicolored	3.25	4.00
		Nos. 547-550 (4)	6.50	6.45

Birds
A88

1986, Mar. 20   **Litho.**   **Wmk. 384**

551	A88	10c Magnificent fri-gatebird	2.50	1.10
552	A88	25c West Indian whistling duck	3.25	1.75
553	A88	35c La Sagra's fly-catcher	3.75	3.75
554	A88	40c Yellow-faced grassquit	4.50	4.50
		Nos. 551-554 (4)	14.00	11.10

Nos. 552-553 vert.

Queen Elizabeth II 60th Birthday
Common Design Type

Designs: 5c, As bridesmaid at wedding of Lady Mary Cambridge, 1931. 10c, Royal visit to Norway, 1955. 25c, Inspecting West Indian troop, royal tour, 1985. 50c, Gulf tour, 1979. $1, Visiting Crown Agents' offices, 1983.

1986, Apr. 21   **Perf. 14x14½**

555	CD337	5c scar, blk & sil	.20	.20
556	CD337	10c ultra, blk & sil	.25	.25
557	CD337	25c grn & multi	2.00	.95
558	CD337	50c vio & multi	1.00	1.10
559	CD337	$1 rose vio & multi	1.60	1.90
		Nos. 555-559 (5)	5.05	4.40

Royal Wedding Issue, 1986
Common Design Type

Designs: 5c, Informal portrait. 50c, Andrew in uniform, helicopter.

        Perf. 14½x14

1986, July 23   **Litho.**   **Wmk. 384**

560	CD338	5c multicolored	.35	.25
561	CD338	50c multicolored	1.50	1.90

Marine Life — A89

       Perf. 13½x13

1986, Sept. 15   **Wmk. 373**

562	A89	5c Rhynchocinetes rigeus	.80	.65
563	A89	10c Nemaster rubigi-nosa	.80	.65
a.		Wmk. 384, inscribed "1990"	2.75	3.00
564	A89	15c Calcinus tibicen	.70	.75
565	A89	20c Rhodactis sanc-tithomae	.70	.95
566	A89	25c Spirobranchus gi-gantea	.45	3.00
567	A89	35c Diodon hola-canthus	.70	3.25
568	A89	50c Pseudocorynactis aribbeorum	.80	5.00
569	A89	60c Astrophyton muri-catum	3.50	9.50
570	A89	75c Cyphoma gib-bosum	9.50	12.00
571	A89	$1 Conolylactis gi-gantea	2.25	3.25
572	A89	$2 Malacoctenus boehlkei	5.00	5.25
573	A89	$4 Lima scabra	10.00	8.25
		Nos. 562-573 (12)	35.20	52.50

Nos. 562-565, 571-573 exist inscribed "1987." Value $22. Nos. 562-566, 571-572 exist inscribed "1990." Value $38.

Tourism
A90

       Perf. 13x13½

1987, Jan. 26   **Wmk. 384**

574	A90	10c Golfing	3.00	1.00
575	A90	15c Sailing	3.25	1.00
576	A90	25c Snorkeling	3.25	1.50
577	A90	35c Parasailing	3.25	2.00
578	A90	$1 Fishing	7.25	9.75
		Nos. 574-578 (5)	20.00	15.25

Fruit — A91

1987, May 20   **Perf. 14½**

579	A91	5c Akee	.95	.95
580	A91	25c Breadfruit	2.10	.70
581	A91	35c Papaya	2.10	1.00
582	A91	$1 Soursop	5.75	6.75
		Nos. 579-582 (4)	10.90	9.40

Lizards — A92

1987, Aug. 26   **Litho.**   **Perf. 14**

583	A92	10c Lion lizard	2.40	.95
584	A92	50c Iguana	5.75	4.50
585	A92	$1 Anole	7.00	8.25
		Nos. 583-585 (3)	15.15	13.70

Flowers — A93   Herons — A95

Butterflies
A94

1987, Nov. 18   **Perf. 14½x14**

586	A93	5c Poinsettia	1.25	.55
587	A93	25c Periwinkle	3.00	.90
588	A93	35c Yellow allamanda	3.00	1.25
589	A93	75c Blood lily	5.25	6.00
		Nos. 586-589 (4)	12.50	8.70

1988, Mar. 29   **Wmk. 384**   **Perf. 14**

Designs: 5c, Hemiargus ammon erembis and Strymon martialis. 25c, Phocides pigmalion batabano. 50c, Anaea troglodyta cubana. $1, Papilio andraemon andraemon.

590	A94	5c multicolored	2.00	.65
591	A94	25c multicolored	4.25	1.40
592	A94	50c multicolored	6.50	5.25
593	A94	$1 multicolored	8.25	8.25
		Nos. 590-593 (4)	21.00	15.55

1988, Jan. 26   **Litho.**   **Perf. 14**

594	A95	5c Butorides striatus	2.50	.65
595	A95	25c Egretta tricolor	4.75	.90
596	A95	50c Nycticorax vio-laceus	6.00	6.00
597	A95	$1 Egretta caerulea	6.50	6.50
		Nos. 594-597 (4)	19.75	14.05

1988
Summer
Olympics,
Seoul — A96

1988, Sept. 21   **Perf. 14½**

598	A96	10c Cycling	2.25	.65
599	A96	50c Natl. team, pas-senger jet	3.75	2.75
600	A96	$1 Yachting	4.00	4.00
		Nos. 598-600 (3)	10.00	7.40

Souvenir Sheet
Wmk. 373

601	A96	$1 Tennis	7.00	7.00

No. 601 commemorates the 75th anniv. of the Intl. Tennis Federation.

Visit of Princess
Alexandra
A97

1988, Nov. 1   **Wmk. 373**   **Perf. 15**

602	A97	5c Portrait	2.75	1.25
603	A97	$1 Seated in garden	9.75	7.50

Cayman
Islands P.O.,
Cent. — A98

Designs: 5c, P.O., Georgetown, 1889, and Jamaica #24, canceled. 25c, S.S. Orinoco and Cayman Isls. #1. 35c, Grand Cayman G.P.O. and #442. $1, Cayman Airways mail plane and #191.

1989, Apr. 12   **Wmk. 384**   **Perf. 14½**

604	A98	5c multicolored	1.25	1.25
605	A98	25c multicolored	2.75	1.50
606	A98	35c multicolored	3.00	1.75
607	A98	$1 multicolored	11.00	11.00
		Nos. 604-607 (4)	18.00	15.50

A99   A100

Mutiny on the Bounty: a, Capt. Bligh. b, HMS Providence, two crewmen. c, HMS Assistant, transplanted breadfruit. d, Moving breadfruit on land, in longboat. e, Midshipman among casks and crates.

1989, May 24   **Perf. 14**

608		Strip of 5	32.50	32.50
a.-e.		A99 50c any single	6.50	6.50

       Perf. 14½x14

1989, Oct. 18   **Litho.**   **Wmk. 373**

609	A100	5c Panton House	.90	.90
610	A100	10c Town Hall	.90	.90
611	A100	25c Old Courts House	2.00	.80
612	A100	35c Elmslie Memori-al Church	2.10	1.10
613	A100	$1 Post office	5.00	5.25
		Nos. 609-613 (5)	10.90	8.95

Natl. Trust emblem & architecture, George Town.

Island
Surveys
A101

Maps or survey ships: 5c, Navigational instruments and George Gauld's map of 1773. 25c, Instruments and map created by surveyors aboard HMS Vidal, 1956. 50c, Mutine, 1914. $1, HMS Vidal.

1989, Nov. 15

614	A101	5c multicolored	1.75	1.40
615	A101	25c multicolored	4.50	1.75
616	A101	50c multicolored	7.00	5.25
617	A101	$1 multicolored	11.00	11.00
		Nos. 614-617 (4)	24.25	19.40

Angelfish
A102

1990, Apr. 25   **Wmk. 384**   **Perf. 14**

618	A102	10c French	2.10	.65
619	A102	25c Gray	3.75	1.40
620	A102	50c Queen	5.50	5.50
621	A102	$1 Rock beauty	9.00	9.00
		Nos. 618-621 (4)	20.35	16.55

Queen Mother, 90th Birthday
Common Design Types

1990, Aug. 4   **Wmk. 384**   **Perf. 14x15**

622	CD343	50c King, Queen Elizabeth, 1948	1.75	2.50

       Perf. 14½

623	CD344	$1 King, Queen with Churchill, 1940	3.75	4.25

Butterflies
A103

1990, Oct. 24   **Perf. 14½x14**

624	A103	5c Soldier	1.60	1.25
625	A103	25c Pygmy blue	3.50	2.40
626	A103	35c Cayman cres-cent spot	4.50	2.75
627	A103	$1 Gulf fritillary	10.50	10.50
		Nos. 624-627 (4)	20.10	16.90

Expo '90, International Garden and Greenery Exposition, Osaka, Japan.

Hurricane Awareness — A104

Designs: 5c, Goes weather satellite. 30c, Meteorologist tracks storm. 40c, Hurricane damage. $1, Lockheed WP-3D Orion flying in hurricane's eye.

1991, Aug. 8   **Perf. 14**

628	A104	5c multicolored	1.60	1.50
629	A104	30c multicolored	3.75	1.75
630	A104	40c multicolored	4.00	2.10
631	A104	$1 multicolored	9.50	9.50
		Nos. 628-631 (4)	18.85	14.85

Christmas
A105

Local flowers and Christmas scenes: 5c, Angel's trumpet, angels with trumpets. 30c,

Golden trumpet, Mary on donkey led by Joseph. 40c, Christmas flower, Adoration of the Magi. 60c, Tree of life, nativity scene.

1991, Nov. 6   **Wmk. 373**
632	A105	5c multicolored	1.00	1.00
633	A105	30c multicolored	3.00	.85
634	A105	40c multicolored	3.25	1.40
635	A105	60c multicolored	3.75	5.00
		Nos. 632-635 (4)	11.00	8.25

Island Scenes A106

Perf. 12½x13, 13x12½

1991, Dec. 11   **Litho.**   **Wmk. 373**
636	A106	5c Coconut tree, vert.	.75	.55
637	A106	15c Beach scene	1.60	.55
638	A106	20c Poincianas in bloom	.85	.70
639	A106	30c Blowholes	2.25	.90
640	A106	40c Police band	3.75	2.25
641	A106	50c Downtown scene, vert.	3.00	2.25
642	A106	60c The Bluff, Cayman Brac	2.50	3.50
643	A106	80c Coat of arms, vert.	2.25	3.75
644	A106	90c View of Hell	2.25	3.75
645	A106	$1 Sportfishing	4.50	3.75
646	A106	$2 Harbor scene, vert.	9.50	9.00
647	A106	$8 Queen Elizabeth II, vert.	22.50	25.00
		Nos. 636-647 (12)	55.70	55.95

No. 636 exists inscribed "1994." Value $1.

Queen Elizabeth II's Accession to the Throne, 40th Anniv.
Common Design Type
Wmk. 373, 384 (40c)

1992, Feb. 6   **Perf. 14**
648	CD349	5c multicolored	.45	.45
649	CD349	20c multicolored	1.60	.50
650	CD349	30c multicolored	1.75	.75
651	CD349	40c multicolored	1.75	1.40
652	CD349	$1 multicolored	3.25	4.00
		Nos. 648-652 (5)	8.80	7.10

1992 Summer Olympics, Barcelona A107

1992, Aug. 5   **Wmk. 373**
653	A107	15c Cyclist	2.25	.55
654	A107	40c Two cyclists	3.75	1.50
655	A107	60c Feet, pedals	4.50	4.50
656	A107	$1 Two cyclists, diff.	5.50	5.50
		Nos. 653-656 (4)	16.00	12.05

Island Heritage — A108

1992, Oct. 21
657	A108	5c Lady with donkey	.70	.70
658	A108	30c Making fish nets	1.75	1.00
659	A108	40c Maypole dancing	3.00	1.60
660	A108	60c Basket making	3.50	3.50
661	A108	$1 Cooking on caboose	4.25	4.25
		Nos. 657-661 (5)	13.20	11.05

Rays A109

Perf. 13½x14

1993, June 16   **Litho.**   **Wmk. 373**
662	A109	5c Yellow stingray	1.10	.85
663	A109	30c Southern stingray	2.75	1.60
664	A109	40c Spotted eagle ray	3.25	1.90
665	A109	$1 Manta ray	7.00	7.00
		Nos. 662-665 (4)	14.10	11.35

A110

A111

Tourism: No. 666a, Turtle, sailboats. b, Diver, coral, boats. c, Golf. d, Beach, tennis. e, Pirates, sailing ship.
No. 667: a, Cruise ship, boat, sailboat. b, City street scene. c, Submarines. d, Cyclist, scooters. e, Jet planes.

Perf. 14x13½

1993, Sept. 30   **Litho.**   **Wmk. 373**
666	A110	15c Strip of 5, #a.-e.	11.50	11.50
667	A110	30c Strip of 5, #a.-e.	12.50	12.50
f.		Booklet pane of 10, #666-667	30.00	

1993, Oct. 29   **Perf. 14**

Various views of Grand Cayman Parrot.
668	A111	5c green & multi	1.40	1.40
669	A111	5c red & multi	1.40	1.40
670	A111	30c yellow & multi	3.50	3.50
671	A111	30c blue & multi	3.50	3.50
		Nos. 668-671 (4)	9.80	9.80

Christmas A112

Christmas scenes, orchids: 5c, Manger, Ionopsis utricularioides. 40c, Shepherd, lamb, Encyclia cochleata. 60c, Magi, Vanilla pompona. $1, Virgin in prayer, Oncidium caymanense.

Perf. 13½x14

1993, Dec. 6   **Litho.**   **Wmk. 384**
672	A112	5c multicolored	1.40	.75
673	A112	40c multicolored	3.75	1.00
674	A112	60c multicolored	4.75	4.75
675	A112	$1 multicolored	6.25	6.25
		Nos. 672-675 (4)	16.15	12.75

Souvenir Sheet

Reef Life — A113

Designs: a, Holocanthus ciliaris. b, Bodianus pulchellus, anisotremus virginicus. c,

Holocanthus tricolor, gramma loreto. d, Pomacanthus paru, chaeton striatus.

Perf. 14½x13

1994, Feb. 18   **Litho.**   **Wmk. 373**
676	A113	60c Sheet of 4, #a.-d.	15.00	15.00

Hong Kong '94.

Royal Visit — A114

Designs: 5c, Cayman Islands, United Kingdom flags. 15c, Royal yacht Britannia. 30c, Queen Elizabeth II. $2, Queen, Prince Philip.

1994, Feb. 22   **Perf. 14½**
677	A114	5c multicolored	2.00	.95
678	A114	15c multicolored	3.75	1.60
679	A114	30c multicolored	3.75	1.40
680	A114	$2 multicolored	10.50	10.50
		Nos. 677-680 (4)	20.00	14.80

West Indian Whistling Duck A115

5c, One standing. 15c, Landing in water. 20c, Four ducks, various activities. 80c, One raising wings. $1, Adult, chick.

Wmk. 373

1994, Apr. 21   **Litho.**   **Perf. 14**
681	A115	5c multi, vert.	1.50	.80
682	A115	15c multi	2.25	.85
683	A115	20c multi	2.25	.90
684	A115	80c multi, vert.	5.00	5.50
685	A115	$1 multi, vert.	5.75	6.00
a.		Souvenir sheet of 1	13.00	13.00
		Nos. 681-685 (5)	16.75	14.05

No. 685a has a continuous design and contains Cayman Islands Natl. Trust emblem.

Butterflies A116

No. 686: a, Fulvous hairstreak. b, Atala butterfly.
No. 687: a, Barred sulphur. b, Dorantes skipper.

Wmk. 373

1994, Aug. 16   **Litho.**   **Perf. 13½**
686	A116	10c Pair, #a.-b.	3.00	3.25
687	A116	$1 Pair, #a.-b.	14.50	14.50

Wreck of the Ten Sail, Bicent. — A117

Perf. 13½x14

1994, Oct. 12   **Litho.**   **Wmk. 373**
688	A117	10c shown	.75	.75
689	A117	10c multicolored	.75	.75
690	A117	15c multicolored	1.25	.60
691	A117	20c multicolored	1.50	.70
692	A117	$2 multicolored	7.75	7.75
		Nos. 688-692 (5)	12.00	10.55

Sea Turtles A118

Wmk. 384

1995, Feb. 28   **Litho.**   **Perf. 14**
693	A118	10c Green	.85	.45
694	A118	20c Kemp's ridley	1.25	.55
695	A118	25c Hawksbill	1.40	.65
696	A118	30c Leatherback	1.60	.75
697	A118	$1.30 Loggerhead	5.75	5.75
698	A118	$2 Pacific ridley	7.25	7.25
a.		Souvenir sheet, #693-698	18.00	18.00
		Nos. 693-698 (6)	18.10	15.40

1995 CARIFTA & IAAF Games A119

1995, Apr. 15   **Litho.**   **Perf. 14**
699	A119	10c Running	1.00	.55
700	A119	20c Pole vault	1.50	1.10
701	A119	30c Javelin	2.10	1.25
702	A119	$1.30 Sailing	7.25	7.25
		Nos. 699-702 (4)	11.85	10.15

Souvenir Sheet
703	A119	$2 Medal winners	10.00	10.00

End of World War II, 50th Anniv.
Common Design Type

10c, Two soldiers, Cayman Home Guard. 25c, Freighter Comayagua torpedoed off Caymans, 5/14/42. 40c, Type IXc U-Boat U-125. $1, Navy airship L-3 used for U-boat patrol. $1.30, Reverse of War Medal 1939-45.

Wmk. 373

1995, May 8   **Litho.**   **Perf. 13½**
704	CD351	10c multicolored	1.50	.55
705	CD351	25c multicolored	3.00	.90
706	CD351	40c multicolored	3.50	2.25
707	CD351	$1 multicolored	6.50	6.50
		Nos. 704-707 (4)	14.50	10.20

Souvenir Sheet
Perf. 14
708	CD352	$1.30 multicolored	5.50	5.50

Souvenir Sheet

Queen Mother, 95th Birthday — A120

1995, Aug. 25   **Perf. 14½**
709	A120	$4 multicolored	13.50	13.50

Singapore '95.

A121

A122

Animals of the Nativity.

1995, Nov. 1   *Perf. 14*
710	A121	10c Ox	1.00	.30
711	A121	20c Sheep, lamb	1.50	.50
712	A121	30c Donkey	2.50	.60
713	A121	$2 Camels	9.00	10.50
a.		Souvenir sheet of 4, #710-713	14.00	14.00
		Nos. 710-713 (4)	14.00	11.90

Wmk. 384
1996, Mar. 21   Litho.   *Perf. 14*

Wild fruit.
714	A122	10c Sea grape	.70	.50
715	A122	25c Guava	1.50	.70
716	A122	40c West Indian cherry	2.25	1.25
717	A122	$1 Tamarind	4.50	5.75
		Nos. 714-717 (4)	8.95	8.20

Modern Olympic Games, Cent. — A123

     Perf. 14x13½
1996, June 19   Litho.   **Wmk. 384**
718	A123	10c Sailing	.65	.45
719	A123	20c Sailboarding	1.25	.55
720	A123	30c Sailing, diff.	1.60	.80
721	A123	$2 Running	6.50	6.50
		Nos. 718-721 (4)	10.00	8.30

Symbols of National Identity — A124

Designs: 10c, Guitar, music, natl. song. 20c, Boeing 737. 25c, Queen Elizabeth II opening Legislative Assembly. 30c, Seven Mile Beach. 40c, Scuba diver, stingrays. 60c, School children, Cayman Turtle Farm. 80c, Cayman parrot, natl. bird. 90c, Silver thatch palm, natl. tree. $1, Natl. flag. $2, Wild banana orchid, natl. flower. $4, Natl. arms. $6, Natl. currency.

Wmk. 373
1996, Sept. 26   Litho.   *Perf. 14*
722	A124	10c multicolored	.50	.45
		Complete booklet, 10 #722	5.25	
723	A124	20c multicolored	1.10	.85
724	A124	25c multicolored	1.25	.80
725	A124	30c multicolored	1.25	.80
		Complete booklet, 10 #725	13.00	
726	A124	40c multicolored	1.60	1.25
		Complete booklet, 10 #726	17.00	
727	A124	60c multicolored	2.25	1.60
728	A124	80c multicolored	3.75	3.00
a.		Souvenir sheet of 1	3.75	3.75
729	A124	90c multicolored	2.50	3.00
730	A124	$1 multicolored	4.00	3.25

731	A124	$2 multicolored	7.25	7.00
732	A124	$4 multicolored	13.00	16.00
733	A124	$6 multicolored	17.00	20.00
		Nos. 722-733 (12)	55.45	58.00

No. 728a for Hong Kong '97. Issued 2/3/97.
Nos. 723, 725, 727 exist dated "1999."
Value, set $6.

Christmas
A125

Designs: 10c, Christmas time on North Church Street. 25c, Santa "Gone Fishing." 30c, "Claus Encounters." $2, "Caymanian Christmas."

Wmk. 373
1996, Nov. 12   Litho.   *Perf. 14*
734	A125	10c multicolored	.65	.35
735	A125	25c multicolored	1.60	.90
736	A125	30c multicolored	2.00	1.25
737	A125	$2 multicolored	4.50	4.50
		Nos. 734-737 (4)	8.75	7.00

Queen Elizabeth II and Prince Philip, 50th Wedding Anniv. — A126

#738, Queen. #739, Royal Guard. #740, Young Prince riding horse. #741, Queen in blue, Prince in military attire in open carriage. #742 Prince holding horse's reins. #743, Queen looking at horses. $1, Queen, Prince in open carriage.

     Perf. 14x13½
1997, July 10   Litho.   **Wmk. 373**
738	A126	10c multicolored	1.25	1.25
739	A126	10c multicolored	1.25	1.25
a.		Pair, #738-739	2.50	2.50
740	A126	30c multicolored	2.00	2.00
741	A126	30c multicolored	2.00	2.00
a.		Pair, #740-741	4.00	4.00
742	A126	40c multicolored	2.40	2.40
743	A126	40c multicolored	2.40	2.40
a.		Pair, #742-743	5.00	5.00
		Nos. 738-743 (6)	11.30	11.30

Souvenir Sheet
744	A126	$1 multicolored	7.25	7.25

Telecommunications — A127

Designs: 10c, Children using the Internet. 25c, Cable and wireless ship. 30c, Children wearing numbers of new area code, "345." 60c, Cable and wireless satellite communications.

     Perf. 14x14½
1997, Oct. 10   Litho.   **Wmk. 384**
745	A127	10c multicolored	.45	.30
746	A127	25c multicolored	1.25	.80
747	A127	30c multicolored	1.40	.95
748	A127	60c multicolored	2.25	2.25
		Nos. 745-748 (4)	5.35	4.30

Christmas
A128

Santa Claus: 10c, Relaxing in hammock, Little Cayman. 30c, With children on bluff, Cayman Brac. 40c, Playing golf. $1, Diving with stingrays.

Wmk. 373
1997, Dec. 3   Litho.   *Perf. 13*
749	A128	10c multicolored	.40	.25
750	A128	30c multicolored	.85	.45
751	A128	40c multicolored	2.00	.80
752	A128	$1 multicolored	3.25	3.50
		Nos. 749-752 (4)	6.50	5.00

Diana, Princess of Wales (1961-97)
Common Design Type

Portraits: a, 10c. b, 20c. c, 40c. d, $1.

     Perf. 14½x14
1998   Litho.   **Wmk. 373**
752A	CD355	10c Like #753a	1.00	1.00
752B	CD355	20c Like #753b	2.00	2.00

Sheet of 4
753	CD355	#a.-d.	6.00	6.00

No. 753 sold for $1.70 + 30c, with surtax from international sales being donated to the Princess Diana Memorial Fund and surtax from national sales being donated to designated local charity.

Royal Air Force, 80th Anniv.
Common Design Type of 1993 Re-Inscribed

Designs: 10c, Hawker Horsley. 20c, Fairey Hendon. 25c, Hawker Siddeley Gnat. 30c, Hawker Siddeley Dominie.
No. 758: a, 40c, Airco DH-9. b, 60c, Spad 13 Scout. c, 80c, Airspeed Oxford. d, $1, Martin Baltimore.

Wmk. 373
1998, Apr. 1   Litho.   *Perf. 14*
754	CD350	10c multicolored	1.00	1.00
755	CD350	20c multicolored	1.40	1.40
756	CD350	25c multicolored	1.60	1.60
757	CD350	30c multicolored	2.00	2.00
		Nos. 754-757 (4)	6.00	6.00

Souvenir Sheet
758	CD350	Sheet of 4, #a.-d.	10.00	10.00

Birds — A129

Designs: 10c, West Indian whistling duck. 20c, Magnificent frigatebird. 60c, Red footed booby. $1, Grand Cayman parrot.

1998   Litho.   **Wmk. 373**   *Perf. 13½*
759	A129	10c multicolored	1.10	.60
760	A129	20c multicolored	2.00	.60
761	A129	60c multicolored	3.50	3.50
762	A129	$1 multicolored	4.25	4.25
		Nos. 759-762 (4)	10.85	8.95

Christmas
A130

Santa at various island locations: 10c, At Blowholes. 30c, Diving on wreck of MV Capt. Keith Tibbetts. 40c, Visiting Pedro Castle. 60c, Arriving at Little Cayman.

1998   *Perf. 14x14½*
763	A130	10c multicolored	.40	.40
764	A130	30c multicolored	1.10	.85
765	A130	40c multicolored	1.50	1.10
766	A130	60c multicolored	3.00	3.00
		Nos. 763-766 (4)	6.00	5.35

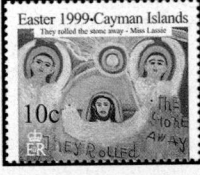

Easter
A131

Artworks by Miss Lassie (Gladwyn Bush): 10c, "They Rolled the Stone Away." 20c, "Ascension," vert. 30c, "The World Praying for Peace." 40c, "Calvary," vert.

Wmk. 373
1999, Mar. 26   Litho.   *Perf. 13*
767	A131	10c multicolored	.50	.50
768	A131	20c multicolored	.90	.90
769	A131	30c multicolored	1.40	1.40
770	A131	40c multicolored	1.50	1.50
		Nos. 767-770 (4)	4.30	4.30

Vision 2008
A132

Children's drawings: 10c, "Cayman House." 30c, "Coral Reef." 40c, "Fisherman on North Sound." $2, "Three Fish and A Turtle."

1999, June   *Perf. 13½*
771	A132	10c multicolored	.35	.35
772	A132	30c multicolored	1.25	1.25
773	A132	40c multicolored	1.40	1.40
774	A132	$2 multicolored	7.00	7.00
		Nos. 771-774 (4)	10.00	10.00

Wedding of Prince Edward and Sophie Rhys-Jones
Common Design Type

     Perf. 13¾x14
1999, June 16   Litho.   **Wmk. 384**
775	CD356	10c Separate portraits	.50	.50
776	CD356	$2 Couple	5.50	5.50

1st Manned Moon Landing, 30th Anniv.
Common Design Type

Designs: 10c, Coast Guard during launch. 25c, 3rd stage fires and puts rocket in orbit. 30c, Aldrin descends to lunar surface. 60c, Lander module sent back to moon. $1.50, Looking at earth from moon.

1999, July 20   *Perf. 14x13¾*
777	CD357	10c multicolored	.45	.45
778	CD357	25c multicolored	1.10	1.10
779	CD357	30c multicolored	1.25	1.25
780	CD357	60c multicolored	2.50	2.50
		Nos. 777-780 (4)	5.30	5.30

Souvenir Sheet
Perf. 14
781	CD357	$1.50 multicolored	5.50	5.50

No. 781 contains one circular stamp 40mm in diameter.

Queen Mother's Century
Common Design Type

Queen Mother: 10c, Looking at London's defenses, 1940. 20c, At Clarence House, 94th birthday. 30c, With Princes Charles and William. 40c, Reviewing the Chelsea Pensioners, 1986. $1.50, At her wedding.

Wmk. 384
1999, Aug. 18   Litho.   *Perf. 13¼*
782	CD358	10c multicolored	.45	.45
783	CD358	20c multicolored	.80	.80
784	CD358	30c multicolored	1.40	1.40
785	CD358	40c multicolored	1.75	1.75
		Nos. 782-785 (4)	4.40	4.40

Souvenir Sheet
786	CD358	$1.50 multicolored	4.75	4.75

Christmas — A133

Wmk. 373
1999, Nov. 17   Litho.   *Perf. 13¼*
787	A133	10c #242, vert.	.40	.35
788	A133	30c #532d, vert.	1.10	.90
789	A133	40c #749, vert.	1.50	1.25
790	A133	$1 #431	3.00	3.00
a.		Souv. sheet, #787-790, perf. 12	5.25	5.25
		Nos. 787-790 (4)	6.00	5.50

British Monarchs — A134

No. 792: a, Henry VIII. b, Mary I. c, Charles II. d, Anne. e, George IV. f, George V.

Wmk. 373

2000, Feb. 29		**Litho.**		**Perf. 14**
791	A134	10c Henry VII	.40	.40

Sheet of 6

792	A134	40c #a.-f.	8.00	8.00

The Stamp Show 2000, London.

Sesame Street — A135

Designs: 10c, Ernie. 30c, Big Bird. No. 795: a, Grover. b, Zoe. c, Oscar the Grouch. d, The Count. e, Like 30c. f, Cookie Monster. g, Like 10c. h, Bert. i, Elmo in pond. No. 796, Elmo collecting stamps.

Perf. 14½x14¾

2000, Mar. 15		**Litho.**	**Wmk. 373**	
793	A135	10c multi	.40	.40
794	A135	30c multi	1.10	1.10
795	A135	20c Sheet of 9, #a-i	6.25	6.25

Souvenir Sheet

796	A135	20c multi	1.90	1.90

Prince William, 18th Birthday
Common Design Type

10c, In checked shirt and in sweater and checked shirt. 20c, In white shirt and black bow tie. 30c, In blue casual shirt, vert. 40c, As child, with beret, vert. $1, As infant.

Perf. 14¼x13¾, 13¾x14¼

2000, June 21		**Litho.**	**Wmk. 373**	

Stamps With White Border

797	CD359	10c multi	.50	.40
798	CD359	20c multi	1.00	.95
799	CD359	30c multi	1.40	1.25
800	CD359	40c multi	1.90	1.90
		Nos. 797-800 (4)	4.80	4.50

Souvenir Sheet
Stamps Without White Border
Perf. 14¼

801		Sheet of 5	8.00	8.00
a.	CD359	10c multi	.35	.35
b.	CD359	20c multi	.75	.75
c.	CD359	30c multi	1.00	1.00
d.	CD359	40c multi	1.40	1.40
e.	CD359	$1 multi	4.00	4.00

Marine Life A136

10c, Green turtle. 20c, Queen angelfish. 30c, Parrotfish. $1, Green moray eel.

Wmk. 384

2000, Aug. 25		**Litho.**		**Perf. 14**
802-805	A136	Set of 4	8.25	8.25

National Drug Council A137

Various children's drawings. Denominations, 10c, 15c, 30c, $2.

2000, Aug. 25				
806-809	A137	Set of 4	12.00	12.00

Christmas A138

10c, Backing sand. 30c, Christmas dinner. 40c, Yard dance. 60c, Conch shell border.

Perf. 14½x14¼

2000, Nov. 14			**Wmk. 373**	
810-813	A138	Set of 4	9.00	9.00

UN Women's Human Rights Campaign — A139

Wmk. 373

2001, Mar. 8		**Litho.**		**Perf. 14**
814	A139	10c multi	.80	.80

Cayman Brac A140

Designs: 15c, Red mangrove. 20c, Peter's Cave. 25c, Bight Road stairway, vert. 30c, Westerly Pond. 40c, Aerial view. 60c, Marshes.

2001, Apr. 21				
815-820	A140	Set of 6	10.50	10.50

Non-profit Organizations — A141

Designs: Nos. 821, 826a, 15c, National Council of Voluntary Organizations. Nos. 822, 826b, 20c, Cayman Humane Society. Nos. 823, 826c, 25c, Red Cross/Red Crescent. Nos. 824, 826d, 30c, Cayman Islands Cancer Society, vert. Nos. 825, 826e, 40c, Lions Club of Tropical Gardens, vert.

Wmk. 373

2001, Aug. 15		**Litho.**		**Perf. 14**

Stamps With White Margins

821-825	A141	Set of 5	8.00	8.00

Souvenir Sheet
Stamps With Pink Margins

826	A141	Sheet of 5, #a-e	8.00	8.00

No. 826 sold for $1.80, 50c of which went to the various organizations honored.

Transportation — A142

Designs: No. 827, Walking home. No. 828, Boy on donkey. 20c, Bananas by canoe. 25c, Horse and buggy. 30c, Catboats. 40c, Schooner. 60c, Police bicycle, vert. 80c, Lady drivers. 90c, Launcing Cimboco, vert. $1, Seaplane. $4, Freighter. $10, Boeing 767.

Perf. 14¼x14½, 14½x14¼

2001, Sept. 29		**Litho.**	**Wmk. 373**	
827	A142	15c multi	.40	.40
828	A142	15c multi	.40	.40
829	A142	20c multi	.55	.55
830	A142	25c multi	.70	.70
831	A142	30c multi	.80	.80
832	A142	40c multi	1.10	1.10
833	A142	60c multi	1.60	1.60
834	A142	80c multi	2.25	2.25
835	A142	90c multi	2.50	2.50
836	A142	$1 multi	2.75	2.75
837	A142	$4 multi	11.00	11.00
838	A142	$10 multi	26.00	26.00
		Nos. 827-838 (12)	50.05	50.05

Christmas A143

Santa Claus: 15c, With children on dock. 30c, On eagle ray. 40c, In catboat. 60c, Parasailing.

Perf. 14¼x14½

2001, Nov. 21		**Litho.**	**Wmk. 373**	
839-842	A143	Set of 4	6.50	6.50

In Remembrance of Sept. 11, 2001 Terrorist Attacks — A144

Perf. 14x14¾

2002, Jan. 22		**Litho.**	**Wmk. 373**	
843	A144	$1 multi	4.75	4.75

Reign Of Queen Elizabeth II, 50th Anniv. Issue
Common Design Type

Designs: Nos. 844, 848a, 15c, Princess Elizabeth as child. Nos. 845, 848b, 20c, In 1976. Nos. 846, 848c, 30c, With Princess Margaret, 1942. Nos. 847, 848d, 80c, In 1996. No. 848e, $1, 1955 portrait by Annigoni (38x50mm).

Perf. 14¼x14½, 13¾ (#848e)

2002, Feb. 6		**Litho.**	**Wmk. 373**	

With Gold Frames

844-847	CD360	Set of 4	4.25	4.25

Souvenir Sheet
Without Gold Frames

848	CD360	Sheet of 5, #a-e	10.50	10.50

Peanuts Comic Strip Characters A145

Designs: 15c, Snoopy painting Woodstock at Cayman Brac Bluff. 20c, Charlie Brown and Sally at Hell Post Office. 25c, Peppermint Patty and Marcie at Little Cayman beach. 30c, Snoopy and Boeing 737-200. 40c, Linus and Snoopy at Point of Sand. 60c, Charlie Brown at Links Golf Course.

Wmk. 373

2002, Mar. 9		**Litho.**		**Perf. 14**
849-854	A145	Set of 6	9.50	9.50
854a		Souvenir sheet, #849-854	9.50	9.50

2002 World Cup Soccer Championships, Japan and Korea — A146

Denominations: 30c, 40c.

2002, Apr. 30				**Perf. 13¾**
855-856	A146	Set of 2	4.75	4.75

Queen Mother Elizabeth (1900-2002)
Common Design Type

Designs: 15c, Wearing hat (sepia photograph). 30c, Wearing dark blue hat. Nos. 859, 861a, 40c, Wearing hat (black and white photograph). Nos. 860, 861b, $1, Wearing tiara.

Perf. 13¾x14¼, 14¼ (#859-860)

2002, Aug. 5		**Litho.**	**Wmk. 373**	

With Purple Frames

857-860	CD361	Set of 4	8.75	8.75

Souvenir Sheet
Without Purple Frames
Perf. 14½x14¼

861	CD361	Sheet of 2, #a-b	8.75	8.75

Christmas A147

Designs: 15c, Hail Mary. 20c, Journey to Bethlehem. 30c, Her firstborn Son. 40c, I bring good tidings. 60c Star in the east.

Wmk. 373

2002, Oct. 18		**Litho.**		**Perf. 14**

Stamps + labels

862-866	A147	Set of 5	6.25	6.25
866a		Souvenir sheet of 5, #862-866 + 5 labels	6.75	6.75

Aviation in the Cayman Islands, 50th Anniv. A148

Designs: 15c, PBY Catalina Flying Boat. 20c, First landing at Grand Cayman Airport, 1952. 25c, Cayman Brac Airways AC 50. 30c, Cayman Airways B-737. 40c, Concorde at original airport, 1984. $1.30, Island Air DHC6.

2002, Nov. 8				
867-872	A148	Set of 6	11.50	11.50

Children's Games A149

Designs: 15c, Rope skipping. 20c, Maypole dancing. 25c, Gig. 30c, Hopscotch. $1, Marbles.

Wmk. 373

2003, May 27		**Litho.**		**Perf. 13¾**
873-877	A149	Set of 5	9.00	9.00

Head of Queen Elizabeth II
Common Design Type
Wmk. 373

2003, June 2	**Litho.**	**Perf. 13¾**	
878 CD362 $4 multi		20.00	20.00

Coronation of Queen Elizabeth II, 50th Anniv.
Common Design Type

Designs: Nos. 879, 15c, 881a, 20c, Queen wearing crown. Nos. 880, $2, 881b, $4, Queen holding symbols of office.

Perf. 14¼x14½

2003, June 2	**Litho.**	**Wmk. 373**	

Vignettes Framed, Red Background

879-880 CD363	Set of 2	8.75	8.75

Souvenir Sheet
Vignettes Without Frame, Purple Panel

881 CD363	Sheet of 2, #a-b	14.50	14.50

Prince William, 21st Birthday
Common Design Type

Color photographs: 15c, William with backpack at right. 40c, William in suit and tie at left
No. 884: a, William with hand on chin at right. b, William with white bow tie at left.

Wmk. 373

2003, June 21	**Litho.**	**Perf. 14¼**	
882 CD364 15c multi		.50	.50
883 CD364 40c multi		1.40	1.40
884	Horiz. pair	5.75	5.75
a. CD364 80c multi		2.50	2.50
b. CD364 $1 multi		3.25	3.25
Nos. 882-884 (3)		7.65	7.65

Discovery of the Cayman Islands, 500th Anniv. A150

Designs: 15c, Turtle hatchlings. No. 886, 20c, Old waterfront. No. 887, 20c, Turtle and ship of Christopher Columbus. 25c, Nassau grouper. 30c, Cayman Brac schooner "Kirk-B." 40c, George Town harbor. 60c, Musical instruments. 80c, Smokewood tree. 90c, Little Cayman Baptist Church. $1, Thatch rope. $1.30, Children's dance troupe. $2, Parliament in session.

Wmk. 373

2003, July 24	**Litho.**	**Perf. 13¾**	
885-896 A150	Set of 12	29.00	29.00
896a	Souvenir sheet, #885-896	29.00	29.00

Holiday Greetings A151

Various Christmas decorations and inscriptions of: 15c, Merry Christmas. 20c, Celebrate With Family. 30c, Happy New Year. 40c, Happy Holidays. 60c, Seasons Greetings.

Wmk. 373

2003, Nov. 4	**Litho.**	**Perf. 13¼**	
897-901 A151	Set of 5	8.50	8.50

Worldwide Fund for Nature (WWF) A152

Short-finned pilot whale: 15c, Adult and calf. 20c, Pod of four whales. 30c, Two whales at surface. 40c, One adult.

2003, Nov. 26		**Perf. 14**
902-905 A152	Set of 4	7.00 7.00
905a	Sheet, 4 each #902-905	30.00 30.00

Shipping Registry, Cent. — A153

Ships: 15c, Lady Slater. 20c, Seanostrum. 30c, Kirk Pride. $1, Boadicea.

Perf. 14x14¾

2004, Jan. 29	**Litho.**	**Wmk. 373**	
906-909 A153	Set of 4	9.75	9.75

Easter — A154

Designs: 15c, Jesus Carrying His Cross. 30c, The Ascension.

2004, Mar. 16		**Perf. 14¾x14**
910-911 A154	Set of 2	3.00 3.00

2004 Summer Olympics, Athens — A155

Designs: 15c, Swimmer. 40c, Runner. 60c, Long jumper. 80c, Swimmers.

Perf. 13½x13¼

2004, Aug. 23	**Litho.**	**Wmk. 373**	
912-915 A155	Set of 4	7.25	7.25

Blue Iguana A156

Designs: 15c, Adult on rocks. 20c, Eggs. 25c, Four juveniles. 30c, Juvenile on finger. 40c, Adult with open mouth. 90c, Eye.
No. 922: a, 60c, On rock facing right. b, 80c, On rock facing left.

2004, Oct. 26	**Litho.**	**Perf. 13¾**	
916-921 A156	Set of 6	8.25	8.25

Souvenir Sheet

922 A156	Sheet of 2, #a-b	6.75	6.75

No. 922 sold for $1.90.

Battle of Trafalgar, Bicent. — A157

Designs: 15c, HMS Victory. 20c, HMS Tonnant tangles into the bow of the Algesiras. 25c, Flint cannon lock and linstock. No. 926, 60c, Royal Navy boatswain's mate. $1, Adm. Horatio Nelson, vert. No. 928, $2, HMS Orion in action against the Intrepide.

No. 929, vert.: a, 60c, French gunship Pluton. b, $2, HMS Tonnant.

Wmk. 373, Unwmkd. (15c)

2005, June 8	**Litho.**	**Perf. 13¼**	
923-928 A157	Set of 6	14.50	14.50

Souvenir Sheet

929 A157	Sheet of 2, #a-b	8.25	8.25

No. 923 has particles of wood from the HMS Victory embedded in the areas covered by a thermographic process that produces a raised, shiny effect.

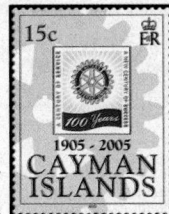

Rotary International, Cent. — A158

Designs: 15c, Centennial emblem. 30c, PolioPlus emblem.

2005, June 30	**Wmk. 373**	**Perf. 13¾**	
930-931 A158	Set of 2	2.00	2.00

Orchids A159

Designs: 15c, Myrmecophila albopurpurea. 20c, Prosthechea boothiana. 30c, Tolumnia calochila, vert. 40c, Encyclia phoenicia. 80c, Prosthechea cochleata, vert. $1.50, Encyclia kingsii.

2005, July 28		**Perf. 14**
932-936 A159	Set of 5	8.00 8.00

Souvenir Sheet

937 A159	$1.50 multi	6.50 6.50

Pope John Paul II (1920-2005) A160

2005, Aug. 18		
938 A160	30c multi	1.50 1.50

Butterflies A162

Designs: 15c, Queen. 20c, Mexican fritillary. 25c, Malachite. 30c, Cayman crescent spot. 40c, Cloudless sulphur. 90c, Swallowtail.

Wmk. 373

2005, Sept. 21	**Litho.**	**Perf. 14**
939 A161 15c multi		.55 .55
940 A161 20c multi		.70 .70
941 A161 25c multi		.80 .80
942 A161 30c multi		1.00 1.00
943 A161 40c multi		1.40 1.40
944 A161 90c multi		3.00 3.00
Nos. 939-944 (6)		7.45 7.45

Booklet Stamps
Self-Adhesive
Unwmk.
Serpentine Die Cut 9½x9

945 A162 15c multi		.60	.60
a. Booklet pane of 10		6.00	
946 A162 20c multi		.70	.70
a. Booklet pane of 6		4.20	
947 A162 30c multi		1.00	1.00
a. Booklet pane of 10		10.00	
Nos. 945-947 (3)		2.30	2.30

Christmas A163

Designs: 15c, Angels. 30c, Magi, horiz. 40c, Holy Family. 60c, Shepherds, horiz.

Perf. 14x14¾, 14¾x14

2005, Oct. 26			**Wmk. 373**
948-951 A163	Set of 4	4.00	4.00
951a	Souvenir sheet, #948-951, perf. 14¾	4.00	4.00

Trees and Blossoms — A164

Designs: 15c, Wash wood. 20c, Red mangrove. 30c, Ironwood. 60c, West Indian cedar. $2, Spanish elm.

Wmk. 373

2006, Feb. 23	**Litho.**	**Perf. 13¼**	

Stamp + Label

952-956 A164	Set of 5	8.00	8.00

Queen Elizabeth II, 80th Birthday A165

Designs: 15c, As child. 40c, Wearing uniform and cap. $1, Wearing tiara. $2, Wearing sunglasses.
No. 961: a, 40c, Like #958. b, $1, Like #959.

2006, Apr. 21		**Perf. 14**

With White Frames

957-960 A165	Set of 4	8.75 8.75

Souvenir Sheet
Without White Frames

961 A165	Sheet of 2, #a-b	3.50 3.50

A166

Marine Life — A167

Designs: Nos. 962, 967a, 968, Hawksbill turtle. Nos. 963, 967b, 969, Gray angelfish. Nos. 964, 967c, 970, Queen angelfish. Nos. 965, 967c, 971, Diamond blenny. Nos. 966, 967e, Juvenile spotted drum,vert. Nos. 964 and 967c are vert.

Wmk. 373

2006, July 18   **Litho.**   **Perf. 14**

With White Margins

962	A166	25c multi	.60	.60
963	A166	25c multi	.60	.60
964	A166	60c multi	1.50	1.50
965	A166	75c multi	1.90	1.90
966	A166	$1 multi	2.50	2.50
		Nos. 962-966 (5)	7.10	7.10

Souvenir Sheet

Without White Margin

967	A166	Sheet of 5, #a-e	7.25	7.25

Booklet Stamps

Self-Adhesive

Serpentine Die Cut 9½x9

Unwmk.

968	A167	25c multi	.60	.60
a.		Booklet pane of 10	6.00	
969	A167	25c multi	.60	.60
a.		Booklet pane of 10	6.00	
970	A167	60c multi	1.50	1.50
a.		Booklet pane of 10	15.00	
971	A167	75c multi	1.90	1.90
a.		Booklet pane of 10	19.00	
		Nos. 968-971 (4)	4.60	4.60

Birds
A168

Designs: 25c, Bananaquit. 50c, Vitelline warbler. 75c, Grand Cayman parrot. 80c, Caribbean dove. $1, Caribbean elaenia. $1.50, West Indian woodpecker. $1.60, Thick-billed vireo. $2, Northern flicker. $4, Cuban bullfinch. $5, Western spindalis. $10, Loggerhead kingbird. $20, Red-legged thrush.

Perf. 13½x13¾

2006, Oct. 9   **Litho.**   **Wmk. 373**

972	A168	25c multi	.60	.60
973	A168	50c multi	1.25	1.25
974	A168	75c multi	1.90	1.90
975	A168	80c multi	2.00	2.00
976	A168	$1 multi	2.50	2.50
977	A168	$1.50 multi	3.75	3.75
978	A168	$1.60 multi	4.00	4.00
979	A168	$2 multi	5.00	5.00
980	A168	$4 multi	9.75	9.75
981	A168	$5 multi	12.00	12.00
982	A168	$10 multi	24.00	24.00
983	A168	$20 multi	50.00	50.00
		Nos. 972-983 (12)	116.75	116.75

Booklet Stamps

Self-Adhesive

Unwmk.

983A	A168	25c multi	.60	.60
d.		Booklet pane of 10	6.00	
983B	A168	75c multi	1.90	1.90
e.		Booklet pane of 10	19.00	
983C	A168	80c multi	2.00	2.00
f.		Booklet pane of 10	20.00	
		Nos. 983A-983C (3)	4.50	4.50

Christmas
A169

Designs: 25c, "Faith," Magi. 75c, "Hope," Prophet with scroll. 80c, "Joy," angel. $1, "Love," Madonna and Child.

Perf. 12½x13¼

2006, Oct. 26   **Litho.**   **Wmk. 373**

984-987	A169	Set of 4	7.00	7.00

Island
Scenes
A170

Designs: 20c, Brac Reed dock. 25c, Waterfront buildings, Hog Sty Bay. 30c, East End blowholes, vert. 40c, Man in hammock, vert. 75c, Poinciana blooms. $1, Driftwood on Little Cayman.

Wmk. 373

2007, June 26   **Litho.**   **Perf. 13¾**

988-993	A170	Set of 6	7.25	7.25

Scouting,
Cent.
A171

Designs: 25c, Wolf Cubs and leaders, hands lashing rope. 75c, Cub Scouts and leaders, hands with trumpet. 80c, Scouts camping, hand with compass. $1, Scout Drill Team, poppies.

No. 998, vert.: a, 50c, Scouts marching. b, $1.50, Lord Robert Baden-Powell and dog.

2007, July 9

994-997	A171	Set of 4	7.00	7.00

Souvenir Sheet

998	A171	Sheet of 2, #a-b	5.00	5.00

Wedding of
Queen Elizabeth
II and Prince
Philip, 60th
Anniv. — A172

Designs: 50c, Couple and wedding coach. 75c, Elizabeth wearing bridal veil. 80c, Princess Elizabeth, Philip, Queen Mother Elizabeth, King George VI, Princess Margaret. $1, Wedding procession, Westminster Abbey. $2, Couple.

Wmk. 373

2007, Sept. 12   **Litho.**   **Perf. 13¾**

999-1002	A172	Set of 4	7.50	7.50

Souvenir Sheet

Perf. 14

1003	A172	$2 multi	5.00	5.00

No. 1003 contains one 42x57mm stamp.

Christmas
A173

Stained-glass windows from local churches: 25c, Nativity, Wesleyan Holiness Church. 50c, Jesus Praying, Elmslie Memorial Church. 75c, Jesus Calling First Disciples, St. George's Anglican Church. 80c, Dove, East End Adventist Church. $1, Orb, First Baptist Church of Grand Cayman. $1.50, Shepherd, Frank Sound Church of God.

2007, Oct. 22   **Perf. 15x14**

1004-1009	A173	Set of 6	12.00	12.00

WAR TAX STAMPS

No. 36 Surcharged:

a

b

1917, Feb. 26   **Wmk. 3**   **Perf. 14**

MR1	A5(a)	1½p on 2½p	11.00	13.50
a.		Fraction bar omitted	150.00	210.00
MR2	A5(b)	1½p on 2½p	2.10	7.25
a.		Fraction bar omitted	85.00	150.00

No. 1 exists with missing period. On No. 1 the distance between "WAR STAMP" and "1½" varies.

Surcharged

1917, Sept. 4

MR3	A5	1½p on 2½p ultra	1,000.	2,500.

Surcharged

1917, Sept. 4

MR4	A5	1½p on 2½p ultra	.30	.65

No. 33 Overprinted

1919, Feb. 4

MR5	A5	½p green	.70	3.00

The "brownish paper" variety comes from the interleaving used for shipment from England.

Type of 1912-16
Surcharged

1919, Feb. 4

MR6	A5	1½p on 2½p orange	.95	1.50

No. 35 Surcharged

1920, Mar. 10

MR7	A5	1½p on 2p gray	1.75	8.50

The "rose-tinted paper" variety comes from the interleaving used for shipment from England.

A surcharge in red was not issued.

CENTRAL AFRICAN REPUBLIC

ˈsen-trəl ˈa-fri-kə

LOCATION — Western Africa, north of equator
GOVT. — Republic
AREA — 241,243 sq. mi.
POP. — 3,444,951 (1999 est.)
CAPITAL — Bangui

The former French colony of Ubangi-Shari, a unit in French Equatorial Africa, proclaimed itself the Central African Republic Dec. 1, 1958. It became the Central African Empire Dec. 4, 1976. It

---

became the Central African Republic again in 1979.

100 Centimes = 1 Franc

Catalogue values for all unused stamps in this country are for Never Hinged items.

Watermark

Wmk. 385

Central African Republic

Premier Barthélemy
Boganda and
Flag — A1

Design: 25fr, Boganda and flag, horiz.

Unwmk.

1959, Dec. 1   **Engr.**   **Perf. 13**

1	A1	15fr multi	.40	.20
2	A1	25fr multi	.60	.20

1st anniv. of the Republic and honoring Premier Barthélemy Boganda (1910-59).
For overprints & surcharge see #12, 59, M1-M2.

Imperforates

Many stamps of Central African Republic exist imperforate in issued and trial colors, and also in small presentation sheets in issued colors.

Common Design Types pictured following the introduction.

C.C.T.A. Issue

Common Design Type

1960, May 21   **Unwmk.**   **Perf. 13**

3	CD106	50fr lt grn & dk bl	1.90	.65

Dactyloceras Widenmanni — A2

Designs: Various butterflies.

1960-61

4	A2	50c bl grn & dk red	.20	.20
5	A2	1fr multi	.20	.20
6	A2	2fr dk grn & brn	.20	.20
7	A2	3fr yel grn & dk red	.30	.20
8	A2	5fr multi	.35	.20
9	A2	10fr multi	.85	.35
10	A2	20fr multi	1.90	.50
11	A2	85fr multi	7.00	1.60
		Nos. 4-11 (8)	11.00	3.45

Issued: 50c-3fr, 6/10/61; others, 9/3/60.

No. 2 Overprinted:
"FETE NATIONALE 1-12-1960"

1960, Dec. 1

12	A1	25fr multi	1.60	1.60

National Holiday, Dec. 1, 1960.

Louis
Pasteur
and
Pasteur
Institute,
Bangui
A3

1961, Feb. 25   Unwmk.   Perf. 13
13   A3 20fr multi   1.25 .80
Opening of Pasteur Institute at Bangui.

Flag, Map,
and UN
Emblem
A4

1961, Mar. 4   Engr.
14   A4 15fr multi   .50   .30
15   A4 25fr multi   .60   .30
16   A4 85fr multi   1.75 1.00
      Nos. 14-16 (3)   2.85 1.60
Admission to the UN.

No. 15 Overprinted in Green: "FETE
NATIONALE 1-12-61" and Star
1961, Dec. 1
17   A4 25fr multi   2.25 2.25
National Holiday, Dec. 1.

No. 16 Surcharged in Red Brown:
"U.A.M. CONFERENCE DE BANGUI
25-27 Mars 1962"
1962, Mar. 25
18   A4 50fr on 85fr multi   1.90 1.90
Conf. of the African and Malgache Union at
Bangui, Mar. 25-27.

Abidjan Games Issue
Common Design Type
1962, July 21   Photo.   Perf. 12½x12
19   CD109 20fr Hurdling   .55   .30
20   CD109 50fr Bicycling   1.40   .80
      Nos. 19-20,C6 (3)   4.45 2.60

African-Malgache Union Issue
Common Design Type
1962, Sept. 8   Unwmk.
21   CD110 30fr multi   1.40 1.40
African and Malgache Union, 1st anniv.

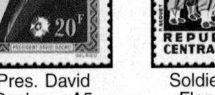

Pres. David   Soldiers with
Dacko — A5   Flag — A6

1962   Perf. 12
22   A5 20fr multi   .40   .20
23   A5 25fr multi   .60   .20
For surcharge see No. 60.

1963, Aug. 13   Photo.
24   A6 20fr blk & multi   .75   .35
National Army, third anniversary.

Waves
Around
Globe
A6a

Design: 100fr, Orbit patterns around globe.

1963, Sept. 19   Unwmk.   Perf. 12½
25   A6a 25fr plum & grn   .75   .55
26   A6a 100fr org, bl & grn   1.90 1.50
Issued to publicize space communications.

Young
Pioneers
A7

1963, Oct. 14   Engr.   Perf. 12½
27   A7 50fr grnsh bl, vio bl & brn 1.00 .55
Issued to honor Young Pioneers.

Boali Falls — A8

1963, Oct. 28   Perf. 13
28   A8 30fr bl, grn & red brn 1.00   .45

Colotis
Evippe
A9

Designs: Various butterflies.

1963, Nov. 18   Photo.   Perf. 12½x13
29   A9 1fr multi   .30   .20
30   A9 3fr multi   .75   .30
31   A9 4fr multi   1.10   .45
32   A9 60fr multi   6.50 3.25
      Nos. 29-32 (4)   8.65 4.20
For surcharge see No. 58.

UNESCO
Emblem,
Scales and
Tree — A9a

1963, Dec. 10   Perf. 13
33   A9a 25fr grn, ol & red brn 1.00 .55
15th anniversary of the Universal Declaration of Human Rights.

Leaves and
IQSY
Emblem
A10

1964, Apr. 20   Engr.   Perf. 13
34   A10 25fr org, Prus grn & bis 1.40 .80
International Quiet Sun Year, 1964-65.

Child — A11   "All Men Are
                     Men" — A12

Designs: Heads of Children.

1964, Aug. 13   Unwmk.   Perf. 13
35   A11 20fr multi   .40   .20
36   A11 25fr multi   .50   .30
37   A11 40fr multi   .65   .45
38   A11 50fr multi   .90   .45
a.   Miniature sheet of 4, #35-38 3.75 3.75
      Nos. 35-38 (4)   2.45 1.40

Cooperation Issue
Common Design Type
1964, Nov. 7   Engr.
39   CD119 25fr grn, mag & dk brn 1.00 .55

1964, Dec. 1   Litho.   Perf. 13x12½
40   A12 25fr multi   1.00   .45
Issued to publicize National Unity.

Putting
Yoke on
Oxen
A13

Designs: 50fr, Ox pulling harrow. 85fr,
Team of oxen in field. 100fr, Hay wagon.

1965, Apr. 28   Engr.   Perf. 13
41   A13 25fr sl grn, sep & rose .60 .30
42   A13 50fr sl grn, lt bl & brn 1.00 .45
43   A13 85fr bl, grn & red brn 1.40 .70
44   A13 100fr multi   1.90   .90
      Nos. 41-44 (4)   4.90 2.35
For surcharges see Nos. 63-64.

Telegraph Receiver by Pouget-
Maisonneuve — A14

ITU cent.: 30fr, Chappe telegraph, vert. 50fr,
Doignon regulator, vert. 85fr, Pouillet telegraph transcriber.

1965, May 17   Unwmk.
45   A14 25fr red, grn & ultra   .60   .40
46   A14 30fr lake & grn   .65   .40
47   A14 50fr car & vio   1.00   .60
48   A14 85fr red lil & slate   1.90 1.00
      Nos. 45-48 (4)   4.15 2.40

"Health"
A15

25fr, "Clothes;" shuttle, cloth & women. 60fr,
"Teaching;" student & school. 85fr, "Food;"
mother feeding child, tractor in wheat field.

1965, June 10   Engr.   Perf. 13
49   A15 25fr ultra, brt grn & brn .50 .30
50   A15 50fr ultra, brn & grn   .90   .45
51   A15 60fr grn, ultra & brn 1.00   .60
52   A15 85fr multi   1.40   .70
      Nos. 49-52 (4)   3.80 2.05
Issued to publicize the slogans and aims of
"M.E.S.A.N." (Mouvement d'Evolution Sociale
de l'Afrique Noire). See No. C30.

Caterpillars and
Moth on Coffee
Branch — A16

Designs: 3fr, Hawk moth and caterpillar on
coffee leaves, horiz. 30fr, Platyedra moth and
larvae on cotton plant.

1965, Aug. 25   Engr.   Perf. 13
53   A16 2fr dk pur, dp org & sl
          grn   .45   .20
54   A16 3fr blk, sl grn & red 1.25   .25
55   A16 30fr red lil, red & sl grn 7.25 .90
      Nos. 53-55 (3)   8.95 1.35
Issued to publicize plant protection.

Boy Scout,
Tents and
Animals
A17

Design: 25fr, Campfire and Scout emblem.

1965, Sept. 27   Unwmk.   Perf. 13
56   A17 25fr red org, bl & red lil 1.00 .25
57   A17 50fr brn & Prus bl   1.40   .60
Issued to honor the Boy Scouts.

Nos. 30, 1 and 22
Surcharged in Black
or Brown

Engraved; Photogravure
Perf. 13, 12, 12½x13
1965, Aug. 26   Unwmk.
58   A9 2fr on 3fr multi   5.75 5.75
59   A1 5fr on 15fr multi   4.50 4.50
60   A5 10fr on 20fr multi (Br) 6.25 6.25
      Nos. 58-60 (3)   16.50 16.50
The surcharges are adjusted to shape of
stamps.

UN
Emblem
and Wheat
A18

1965, Oct. 16   Engr.   Perf. 13
61   A18 50fr ocher, sl grn & brt bl 1.25 .70
FAO "Freedom from Hunger Campaign."

Diamond
Cutter
A19

1966, Mar. 14   Engr.   Perf. 13
62   A19 25fr car rose, dk pur &
          brn   1.40   .45

Nos. 43-44 Surcharged

1966, Feb.
63   A13 5fr on 85fr multi   .40   .40
64   A13 10fr on 100fr multi   .60   .60
Issue dates: 5fr, Feb. 17; 10fr, Feb. 15.

Statue of Mbaka Woman Porter — A20

WHO Headquarters, Geneva — A21

1966, Apr. 9   Photo.   Perf. 13x12½
65   A20   25fr multi   1.00   .45
   Intl. Negro Arts Festival, Dakar, Senegal, Apr. 1-24.

1966, May 3   Photo.   Unwmk.
66   A21   25fr pur, bl & yel   1.00   .45
   Inauguration of the WHO Headquarters, Geneva.

Eulophia Cucullata — A22

Orchids: 5fr, Lissochilus horsfalii. 10fr, Tridactyle bicaudata. 15fr, Polystachya. 20fr, Eulophia alta. 25fr, Microcelia macrorrhynchium.

1966, May 16   Photo.   Perf. 12x12½
Orchids in Natural Colors
67   A22   2fr dk red   .40   .20
68   A22   5fr brn org & vio   .95   .25
69   A22   10fr bl grn & blk   1.25   .40
70   A22   15fr lt grn & dk brn   1.75   .65
71   A22   20fr dk grn   2.75 1.00
72   A22   25fr lt ultra & brn   4.00 1.25
   Nos. 67-72 (6)   11.10 3.75
   For surcharge see No. 78.

Congo Forest Mouse A23

Rodents: 10fr, One-stripe mouse. 20fr, Dollman's tree mouse, vert.

1966, Sept. 15   Photo.   Perf. 12½x12
73   A23   5fr yel & multi   .70   .30
74   A23   10fr tan & multi   1.25   .45
75   A23   20fr lt grn & multi   2.40   .80
   Nos. 73-75 (3)   4.35 1.55

UNESCO Emblem — A24

Pres. Jean Bedel Bokassa — A25

1966, Dec. 5   Photo.   Perf. 13
76   A24   30fr multi   .75   .35
   20th anniv. of UNESCO.

1967, Jan. 1   Perf. 12x12½
77   A25   30fr yel grn, blk & bis brn   .75   .35

No. 72 Surcharged with New Value and "XX"
1967, May 8   Photo.   Perf. 12x12½
78   A22   10fr on 25fr multi   .55   .25
   See No. C43.

Central Market, Bangui A26

1967, Aug. 8   Photo.   Perf. 12½x13
79   A26   30fr multi   1.00   .40

Safari Hotel, Bangui A27

1967, Sept. 26   Photo.   Perf. 12½x13
80   A27   30fr multi   1.00   .40

Leucocoprinus Africanus — A28

Various Mushrooms

1967, Oct. 3   Photo.   Perf. 13
81   A28   5fr dk brn, ol & ocher   10.00   .80
82   A28   10fr dk brn, ultra & yel   15.00 1.25
83   A28   15fr dk brn, sl grn & yel   17.50 1.40
84   A28   30fr multi   50.00 4.00
85   A28   50fr multi   75.00 6.00
   Nos. 81-85 (5)   167.50 13.45

Map, Radio Tower, Projector and People A29

1967, Oct. 31   Engr.
86   A29   30fr emer, ocher & indigo   1.00   .45
   Radiovision service.

African Hair Style — A30

Various African Hair Styles.

1967, Nov. 7   Engr.   Perf. 13
87   A30   5fr ultra, dk brn & bis brn   .30   .20
88   A30   10fr car, dk brn & bis brn   .50   .25
89   A30   15fr dp grn, dk brn & bis brn .75   .40
90   A30   20fr org, dk brn & bis brn   .75   .40
91   A30   30fr red lil, dk brn & bis brn 1.40   .55
   Nos. 87-91 (5)   3.70 1.80

Nurse Vaccinating Children A31

1967, Nov. 14
92   A31   30fr dk red brn & brt grn   1.00   .55
   Vaccination campaign, 1967-70.

Douglas DC-3 A32

1967, Nov. 24
93   A32   1fr shown   .20   .20
94   A32   2fr Beechcraft Baron   .20   .20
95   A32   5fr Douglas DC-4   .20   .20
   Nos. 93-95,C47-C49 (6)   22.60 7.40

Pierced Stone, Kwe Tribe — A33

Designs: 30fr, Primitive dwelling at Toulou, horiz. 100fr, Megaliths, Bouar. 130fr, Rock painting (people), Toulou, horiz.

1967, Dec. 26   Engr.   Perf. 13
96   A33   30fr crim, ind & mar   .75   .20
97   A33   50fr ol brn, ocher & dk grn   1.50   .50
98   A33   100fr dk brn, brt bl & brn   3.00   .65
99   A33   130fr dk red, brn & dk grn   3.25   .65
   Nos. 96-99 (4)   8.50 2.00
   6th Pan-African Prehistoric Cong., Dakar.

Tanker, Refinery and Map of Area Served — A33a

1968, July 30   Photo.   Perf. 12½
100   A33a   30fr multi   1.00   .30
   Issued to commemorate the opening of the Port Gentil (Gabon) Refinery, June 12, 1968.

Bulldozer Clearing Land — A34

Designs: 10fr, Baoule cattle. 20fr, 15,000-spindle spinning machine. No. 104, Automatic Diederichs looms. No. 105, Bulldozer.

1968, Oct. 1   Engr.   Perf. 13
101   A34   5fr blk, grn & dk brn   .40   .20
102   A34   10fr blk, pale grn & bis brn .55   .30
103   A34   20fr grn, red brn & yel   .90   .30
104   A34   30fr brn, ol & ultra   1.40   .55
105   A34   30fr ind, red brn & sl grn   1.40   .55
   Nos. 101-105 (5)   4.65 1.90
   Issued to publicize "Operation Bokassa."

Bangui Mosque A35

1968, Oct. 14
106   A35   30fr grn, bl & ocher   .90   .40

Hunting Knife of Baya and Boufi Tribes A36

20fr, Hunting knife of Nzakara tribe. 30fr, Crossbow of Babinga & Babenzele (pygmy) tribes.

1968, Nov. 19   Engr.   Perf. 13
107   A36   10fr lem, Prus bl & ultra   .55   .25
108   A36   20fr ultra, dk ol & sl grn   .70   .30
109   A36   30fr sl grn, ultra & brn org 1.60   .40
   Nos. 107-109 (3)   2.85   .95

"Ville de Bangui," 1958 — A37

River Boats: 30fr, "J. B. Gouandjia," 1968. 50fr, "Lamblin," 1944.

1968, Dec. 10   Engr.   Perf. 13
Size: 36x22mm
110   A37   10fr mag, brt grn & vio bl   .65   .40
111   A37   30fr bl, grn & brn   1.10   .45
112   A37   50fr brn, sl & ol grn   1.90   .55
   Nos. 110-112,C62-C63 (5)   9.15 3.65

Woman Javelin Thrower — A38

1969, Mar. 18   Photo.   Perf. 13x12½
113   A38   5fr shown   .30   .20
114   A38   10fr Women runners   .30   .20
115   A38   15fr Soccer   .50   .25
   Nos. 113-115,C71-C72 (5)   4.45 1.55

BIT and ILO Emblems and Worker A39

1969, May 20   Photo.   Perf. 12½x13
116   A39   30fr dp bl, grn & ol brn   1.10   .40
117   A39   50fr dp car, grn & ol brn   1.60   .55
   50th anniv. of the ILO.

Pres. Bokassa — A40

Garayah — A41

1969, Dec. 1   Litho.   Perf. 13x13½
118   A40   30fr vermilion & multi   .65   .30

ASECNA Issue
Common Design Type

1969, Dec. 12 **Engr.** **Perf. 13**
119 CD132 100fr dp bl   2.25 .80

1970, Jan. 6 **Engr.** **Perf. 13**
Musical Instuments: 15fr, Ngombi (harp) horiz. 30fr, Xylophone, horiz. 50fr, Ndala (lute) horiz. 130fr, Gatta and babyon (drums).

120 A41 10fr yel grn, dk grn &
            ocher   .65 .25
121 A41 15fr bl grn, ocher & dk
            brn   .65 .25
122 A41 30fr mar, ocher & dk
            brn   1.10 .45
123 A41 50fr rose car & ind   1.60 .55
124 A41 130fr brt bl, brn & ol   5.25 .95
     Nos. 120-124 (5)   9.25 2.45

UPU Headquarters Issue
Common Design Type

1970, May 20 **Engr.** **Perf. 13**
125 CD133 100fr ultra, ver & red
            brn   1.90 .70

Loading Platform and Flour Storage Bins A42

50fr, Flour milling machinery. 100fr, View of mill.

1970, Feb. 24 **Litho.** **Perf. 14**
126 A42 25fr sl & multi   11.00 .70
127 A42 50fr lil & multi   26.50 1.50
128 A42 100fr red & multi   37.50 2.00
     Nos. 126-128 (3)   75.00 4.70

Inauguration of SICPAD (Société Industrielle Centrafricaine des Produits Alimentaires et Dérivés), a part of Operation Bokassa, 2/22/68.

Pres. Bokassa — A43

1970, Aug. 13 **Litho.** **Perf. 14**
129 A43 30fr multi   5.75 3.50
130 A43 40fr multi   7.50 4.25

Cheese Factory, Sarki — A44

Silk Worm — A45

10fr, M'Bali Ranch. 20fr, Zebu, vert.

Perf. 13x13½, 13½x13

1970, Sept. 15
131 A44 5fr red & multi   .55 .30
132 A44 10fr red & multi   6.50 4.25
133 A44 20fr red & multi   1.40 .55
134 A45 40fr red & multi   3.00 .95
     Nos. 131-134,C83 (5)   15.95 7.15

Issued to publicize Operation Bokassa, a national development plan.
Nos. 131-134 exist perf 10.

Gnathonemus Monteiri — A46

River Fish: 20fr, Mormyrus proboscirostris. 30fr, Marcusenius wilverthi. 40fr, Gnathonemus elephas. 50fr, Gnathonemus curvirostris.

1971, Apr. 6 **Photo.** **Perf. 12½**
135 A46 10fr multi   .40 .25
136 A46 20fr multi   .75 .30
137 A46 30fr multi   1.10 .60
138 A46 40fr multi   2.50 .70
139 A46 50fr multi   2.75 1.10
     Nos. 135-139 (5)   7.50 2.95

Berberati Cathedral A47

1971, July 20 **Litho.** **Perf. 13½**
140 A47 5fr grn & multi   .55 .25
New Roman Catholic Cathedral at Berberati.

Charles de Gaulle — A48

Gray Galago — A49

1971, Aug. 20 **Perf. 13½x13**
141 A48 100fr brt bl & multi   3.25 1.75
In memory of Gen. Charles de Gaulle (1890-1970), president of France.

1971, Oct. 25 **Photo.** **Perf. 13**
Designs: 40fr, Elegant galago. 100fr, Calabar potto, horiz. 150fr, Bosman's potto, horiz. 200fr, Oustalet's colobo, horiz.

142 A49 30fr pink & multi   .80 .60
143 A49 40fr lt bl & multi   1.10 .70
144 A49 100fr multi   3.25 1.50

---

145 A49 150fr multi   5.50 2.40
146 A49 200fr multi   6.75 3.00
     Nos. 142-146 (5)   17.40 8.20

Alan B. Shepard — A50

#148, Yuri Gagarin. #149, Edwin E. Aldrin, Jr. #150, Alexei Leonov. #151, Neil A. Armstrong on moon. #152, Lunokhod I on moon.

1971, Nov. 19 **Litho.** **Perf. 14**
147 A50 40fr vio & multi   .55 .30
148 A50 40fr vio & multi   .55 .30
149 A50 100fr multi   1.40 .45
150 A50 100fr multi   1.40 .45
151 A50 200fr red & multi   2.75 1.10
152 A50 200fr red & multi   2.75 1.10
     Nos. 147-152 (6)   9.40 3.70

Space achievements of US and Russia.

"Operation Bokassa" and Pres. Bokassa A51

1971, Dec. 1 **Photo.** **Perf. 13**
153 A51 40fr red & multi   .90 .45
12th anniversary of independence.

Racial Equality Emblem A52

1971, Dec. 6 **Litho.**
154 A52 50fr multi   .90 .45
Intl. Year Against Racial Discrimination.

Bokassa School Emblem and Cadets — A53

1972, Jan. 1 **Photo.**
155 A53 30fr gold & multi   .90 .45
J. B. Bokassa Military School.

Book Year Emblem — A54

1972, Mar. 11 **Photo.** **Perf. 12½x13**
156 A54 100fr red brn, gold &
            org   3.50 1.50
International Book Year 1972.

"Your Heart is your Health" A55

1972, Apr. 7 **Photo.** **Perf. 13x12½**
157 A55 100fr yel, blk & car   1.90 .95
World Health Day.

Red Cross Workers in Village — A56

1972, May 8 **Perf. 13**
158 A56 150fr multi   3.50 1.60
25th World Red Cross Day.

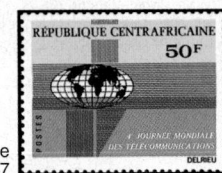

Globe A57

1972, May 17 **Litho.**
159 A57 50fr yel, blk & dp org   .90 .55
4th World Telecommunications Day.

Pres. and Mrs. Bokassa and Family — A58

1972, May 28 **Perf. 14**
160 A58 30fr yel & multi   .65 .30
Mother's Day. Mothers' gold medal awarded to Catherine Bokassa.

Pres. Bokassa Planting Cotton, Map of Africa — A59

1972, June 5 **Photo.** **Perf. 13**
161 A59 40fr yel & multi   .65 .40
Operation Bokassa, a natl. development plan.

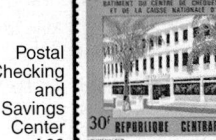

Postal Checking and Savings Center A60

1972, June 21
162 A60 30fr yel org & multi   .65 .40

Irrigated Rice Fields — A61

"Le Pacifique" Apartment House A62

25fr, Plowing rice field. #166, Swimming pool, Hotel St. Sylvestre. #167, Entrance, Hotel St. Sylvestre. #168, J. B. Bokassa University.

1972		Litho.	Perf. 13x13½	
163	A61	5fr multi	1.25	.25
164	A61	25fr multi	2.10	.30

		Engr.	Perf. 13	
165	A62	30fr multi	.40	.25
166	A62	30fr multi	.50	.30
167	A62	40fr multi	.60	.40
168	A62	40fr multi	.65	.40
		Nos. 163-168 (6)	5.50	1.90

Operation Bokassa. Issued: 5fr, 25fr, 11/10; #165, 6/27; #166-167, 12/9; #168, 8/26.

Bull Chasing Woman on Clock Face — A63

Scenes Painted on Clock Faces: 10fr, Men & open cooking fire. 20fr, Fishermen. 30fr, Palms, monkeys & giraffe. 40fr, Warriors.

1972, July 31		Photo.	Perf. 12½	
169	A63	5fr dk red & multi	.30	.30
170	A63	10fr brt bl & multi	.30	.30
171	A63	20fr grn & multi	.60	.30
172	A63	30fr yel & multi	.85	.45
173	A63	40fr vio & multi	1.25	.60
		Nos. 169-173 (5)	3.30	1.95

HORCEN Central African clock and watch factory.

Protestant Youth Center — A64

10fr, Postal runner carrying mail in cleft stick.

1972, Aug. 12			Perf. 13	
174	A64	10fr multi, vert.	.30	.30
175	A64	20fr multi	.50	.30
		Nos. 174-175,C95-C98 (6)	8.35	5.10

Centraphilex 1972, Central African Philatelic Exhibition, Bangui.

Mail Truck A65

1972, Oct. 23		Photo.	Perf. 13	
176	A65	100fr ocher & multi	1.90	.70

Universal Postal Union Day.

Mother Teaching Child to Write — A66

Central African Mothers: 10fr, Caring for infant. 15fr, Combing child's hair. 20fr, Teaching to read. 180fr, Nursing. 190fr, Teaching to walk.

1972, Dec. 27			Perf. 13½x13	
177	A66	5fr multi	.20	.20
178	A66	10fr lil & multi	.30	.20
179	A66	15fr dl org & multi	.30	.20
180	A66	20fr yel grn & multi	.50	.25
181	A66	180fr multi	2.75	1.25
182	A66	190fr pink & multi	2.75	1.25
		Nos. 177-182 (6)	6.80	3.35

Farmer Carrying Sheaf — A67

1973, May 30		Photo.	Perf. 13	
183	A67	50fr vio bl & multi	.90	.45

10th anniv. of the World Food Program.

Garcinia Punctata A68

African Flora: 20fr, Bertiera racemosa. 30fr, Corynanthe pachyceras. 40fr, Combretodendron africanum. 50fr, Xylopia Villosa, vert.

1973, June 8				
184	A68	10fr pale bl & multi	.55	.25
185	A68	20fr multi	.90	.30
186	A68	30fr lt gray & multi	1.10	.45
187	A68	40fr multi	1.75	.60
188	A68	50fr multi	2.25	.80
		Nos. 184-188 (5)	6.55	2.40

For surcharge see No. 193.

Pygmy Chameleon A69

1973, June 26		Photo.	Perf. 13	
189	A69	15fr multi	1.50	.40

Caterpillar — A70

Designs: Various caterpillars.

1973, Aug. 6		Photo.	Perf. 13	
190	A70	3fr multi	1.50	.30
191	A70	5fr multi	2.25	.40
192	A70	25fr multi	4.75	.60
		Nos. 190-192 (3)	8.50	1.30

For surcharge see No. 259.

No. 184 Surcharged with New Value, 2 Bars, and Overprinted in Red: "SECHERESSE SOLIDARITE AFRICAINE"

1973, Aug. 16				
193	A68	100fr on 10fr multi	1.75	1.00

African solidarity in drought emergency.

African Postal Union Issue
Common Design Type

1973, Sept. 12		Engr.	Perf. 13	
194	CD137	100fr dk brn, red org & ol	1.10	.55

Pres. Bokassa and CAR Flag — A71

1973, Nov. 30		Photo.	Perf. 12½	
195	A71	1fr brn & multi	.20	.20
196	A71	2fr pur & multi	.20	.20
197	A71	3fr vio bl & multi	.20	.20
198	A71	5fr ocher & multi	.20	.20
199	A71	10fr multi	.40	.20
200	A71	15fr org & multi	.40	.20
201	A71	20fr multi	.50	.25
202	A71	30fr dk grn & multi	.50	.25
203	A71	40fr dk brn & multi	.65	.40
		Nos. 195-203,C117-C118 (11)	5.40	3.30

INTERPOL Emblem A72

1973, Dec. 20			Perf. 13x12½	
204	A72	50fr yellow & multi	.90	.45

Intl. Criminal Police Organization, 50th anniv.

Catherine Bokassa Center A73

40fr, Ambulance in front of Catherine Bokassa Center.

1974, Jan. 24		Engr.	Perf. 13	
205	A73	30fr multi	.40	.25
206	A73	40fr multi	.50	.30

Catherine Bokassa Center for Mothers and Children.

Cigarette-making Machine — A74

10fr, Cigarette in ashtray, & factory. 30fr, Hand lighting cigarette, & Administration Building.

1974, Jan. 29				
207	A74	5fr slate grn & multi	.20	.20
208	A74	10fr slate grn & multi	.40	.25
209	A74	30fr slate grn & multi	.50	.25
		Nos. 207-209 (3)	1.10	.70

Publicity for Centra cigarettes.

"Communications" A75

1974, June 8		Photo.	Perf. 12½x13	
210	A75	100fr multi	1.75	.85

World Telecommunications Day. For surcharge see No. 280.

People and WPY Emblem A76

1974, June 20		Engr.	Perf. 13	
211	A76	100fr red, slate grn & brn	1.10	.55

World Population Year. For surcharge see No. 281.

Mother, Child, WHO Emblem — A77

1974, July 10				
212	A77	100fr multi	1.75	.70

26th anniv. of WHO. For surcharge see No. 282.

Hoeing — A78

Veterans' activities: 10fr, Battle scene ("yesterday"). 15fr, Pastoral scene ("today"). 20fr, Rice planting. 25fr, Storehouse. 40fr, Veterans Headquarters. Borders show tanks and tractors.

1974, Nov. 15		Litho.	Perf. 13	
213	A78	10fr multi	.20	.20
214	A78	15fr multi	.30	.20
215	A78	20fr multi	.30	.20
216	A78	25fr multi	.40	.25
217	A78	30fr multi	.40	.25
218	A78	40fr multi	.60	.25
		Nos. 213-218 (6)	2.20	1.35

For surcharges see Nos. 260, 265, 267.

Presidents and Flags of Cameroun, CAR, Congo, Gabon and Meeting Center — A79

1974, Dec. 8		Photo.	Perf. 13	
219	A79	40fr gold & multi	.65	.40

See #C126 and note after Cameroun #595. For surcharge see No. 272.

House in OCAM City — A80

Scenes in housing development, OCAM City.

1975, Feb. 1   **Photo.**   *Perf. 13*
220	A80	30fr multi	.40	.25
221	A80	50fr multi	.50	.30
222	A80	50fr multi	.60	.30
223	A80	100fr multi	1.00	.55
		Nos. 220-223 (4)	2.50	1.40

For surcharges see Nos. 269, 273.

1975, Feb. 22

Cottage scenes in J. B. Bokassa "pilot village."
224	A80	25fr multi	.30	.20
225	A80	30fr multi	.40	.25
226	A80	40fr multi	.50	.30
		Nos. 224-226 (3)	1.20	.75

For surcharges see Nos. 268, 270, 274.

Foreign Ministry A81

Television Station A82

1975, Feb. 28   *Perf. 13x12½*
227	A81	40fr multi	.65	.40

Perf. 13
228	A82	40fr multi	.65	.40

Public buildings, Bangui.
For surcharges see Nos. 275-276.

Bokassa's Saber — A83

Design: 40fr, Bokassa's baton.

1975, Feb. 22   **Photo.**   *Perf. 13*
229	A83	30fr dp bl & multi	.55	.30
230	A83	40fr vio bl & multi	.55	.30

Jean Bedel Bokassa, President for Life and Marshal of the Republic. See Nos. C127-C128. For surcharge see No. 286.

Traffic Signs A84

1975, Mar. 20
231	A84	5fr Do Not Enter	.20	.20
232	A84	10fr Stop	.20	.20
233	A84	20fr No parking	.30	.20
234	A84	30fr School	.50	.25
235	A84	Intersection	.75	.30
		Nos. 231-235 (5)	1.95	1.15

For surcharges see Nos. 261, 277.

Buffon's Kob — A85

1975, June 24   **Photo.**   *Perf. 13*
236	A85	10fr shown	.60	.30
237	A85	15fr Wart hog	1.40	.30
238	A85	20fr Waterbuck	2.00	.30
239	A85	30fr Lion	2.00	.45
		Nos. 236-239 (4)	6.00	1.35

For surcharges see Nos. 262-263, 266, 271.

Crane Lifting Log onto Truck A86

Designs: 10fr, Forest, vert. 15fr, Tree felling, vert. 100fr, Log pile. 150fr, Logs transported by raft. 200fr, Lumberyard.

1975, Nov. 28   **Engr.**   *Perf. 13*
240	A86	10fr multi	.20	.20
241	A86	15fr multi	.30	.20
242	A86	50fr multi	.55	.20
243	A86	100fr multi	1.50	.55
244	A86	150fr multi	1.75	1.00
245	A86	200fr multi	2.25	1.10
		Nos. 240-245 (6)	6.55	3.25

Promotion of Central African wood.
For surcharges see Nos. 264, 279.

Women's Heads and Various Occupations — A87

1975, Dec. 10   **Photo.**
246	A87	40fr multi	.50	.25
247	A87	100fr multi	1.40	.55

International Women's Year 1975.

Alexander Graham Bell — A88

1976, Mar. 25   **Litho.**   *Perf. 12½x13*
248	A88	100fr yel & blk	2.25	1.00

Centenary of first telephone call by Alexander Graham Bell, Mar. 10, 1876.
For surcharge see No. 283.

Satellite and ITU Emblem — A89

#250, UPU emblem, various forms of mail transport.

1976   **Engr.**   *Perf. 13*
249	A89	100fr vio bl, claret & grn	1.90	1.00
250	A89	100fr car, grn & ocher	1.60	.80

World Telecommunications Day (No. 249); Universal Postal Union Day (No. 250).

For surcharges see Nos. 284-285.

Soyuz on Launching Pad — A90

Design: 50fr, Apollo rocket.

1976, June 14   **Litho.**   *Perf. 14x13½*
251	A90	40fr multi	.65	.25
252	A90	50fr multi	1.00	.25
		Nos. 251-252,C135-C137 (5)	8.10	2.25

Apollo Soyuz space test project, Russo-American cooperation, launched July 15, link-up July 17, 1975.
For surcharges see Nos. 287, 290, C161, C168, C173, C177.

Drurya Antimachus — A91

Butterfly: 40fr, Argema mittrei, vert.

1976, Sept. 20   **Litho.**   *Perf. 12½*
253	A91	30fr ocher & multi	8.50	1.10
254	A91	40fr ultra & multi	12.00	1.10
		Nos. 253-254,C145-C146 (4)	46.00	5.05

For surcharge see #278.

Slalom, Piero Gros — A92

60fr, Karl Schnabel and Toni Innauer.

1976, Sept. 23   *Perf. 13½*
255	A92	40fr multi	.65	.25
256	A92	60fr multi	1.00	.30
		Nos. 255-256,C147-C149 (5)	8.05	2.45

12th Winter Olympic Games winners, Innsbruck.
For surcharges see Nos. 288, 291, C164, C170, C174, C178.

Viking Components A93

Design: 60fr, Viking take-off.

1976, Dec.
257	A93	40fr multi	.65	.25
258	A93	60fr multi	1.00	.30
		Nos. 257-258,C151-C153 (5)	8.05	2.40

Viking Mars project.
For surcharges and overprints see Nos. 289, 292, 391-392, C165, C171, C175, C179.

Central African Empire

Stamps of 1973-76 Overprinted with Bars and "EMPIRE CENTRAFRICAIN" in Black, Green, Violet Blue, Silver, Carmine, Brown or Red

Printing and Perforations as Before

1977, Mar.
259	A70	3fr (#190; B)	.30	.30
260	A78	10fr (#213;B)	.30	.30
261	A84	10fr (#232;VB)	.30	.30
262	A85	10fr (#236;C)	.30	.30
263	A85	15fr (#237;C)	.50	.50
264	A86	15fr (#241;B)	.30	.30
265	A78	20fr (#215;B)	.40	.40
266	A85	20fr (#238;C)	.50	.50
267	A78	25fr (#216;B)	.40	.40
268	A80	25fr (#224;B)	.40	.40
269	A80	30fr (#220;VB)	.50	.50
270	A80	30fr (#225;B)	.50	.50
271	A85	30fr (#239;C)	.60	.60
272	A79	40fr (#219;B)	.70	.70
273	A80	40fr (#221;VB)	.75	.75
274	A80	40fr (#226;B)	.70	.70
275	A81	40fr (#227;B & S)	.70	.70
276	A82	40fr (#228;B)	.75	.75
277	A84	40fr (#235;VB)	.75	.75
278	A91	40fr (#254;B)	.75	.75
279	A86	50fr (#242;Br)	1.00	1.00
280	A75	100fr (#210;B)	1.90	1.90
281	A76	100fr (#211;B)	1.90	1.90
282	A77	100fr (#212;G)	1.90	1.90
283	A88	100fr (#248;R)	1.90	1.90
284	A89	100fr (#249;B)	2.25	2.25
285	A89	100fr (#250;B)	2.50	2.50
		Nos. 259-285 (27)	23.75	23.75

Stamps of 1975-76 Overprinted "EMPIRE CENTRAFRICAIN" in Black on Silver Panel

1977, Apr. 1
286	A83	40fr multi (#230)	.90	.90
287	A90	40fr multi (#251)	.70	.70
288	A92	40fr multi (#255)	.70	.70
289	A93	40fr multi (#257)	.70	.70
290	A90	50fr multi (#252)	1.00	1.00
291	A92	60fr multi (#256)	.90	.90
292	A93	60fr multi (#258)	.90	.90
		Nos. 286-292 (7)	5.80	5.80

Pierre and Marie Curie — A94

Design: 60fr, Wilhelm C. Roentgen.

1977, Apr. 1   **Litho.**   *Perf. 13½*
293	A94	40fr multi	1.00	.30
294	A94	60fr multi	1.00	.40
		Nos. 293-294,C180-C182 (5)	8.00	3.45

Nobel Prize winners.

Italy No. C42 and Faustine Temple, Rome — A95

60fr, Russia #C12 & St. Basil's Cathedral, Moscow.

1977, Apr. 11   **Litho.**   *Perf. 11*
295	A95	40fr multi	1.00	.25
296	A95	60fr multi	1.10	.40
		Nos. 295-296,C184-C186 (5)	9.75	2.55

75th anniversary of the Zeppelin.

Lindbergh over Paris — A96

Designs: 60fr, Santos Dumont and "14 bis." 100fr, Bleriot and monoplane. 200fr, Roald Amundsen and "N24." 300fr, Concorde. 500fr, Lindbergh and Spirit of St. Louis.

		1977, Sept. 30 Litho.	Perf. 13½	
297	A96	50fr multi	.65	.20
298	A96	60fr multi	1.00	.25
299	A96	100fr multi	1.75	.40
300	A96	200fr multi	2.50	.55
301	A96	300fr multi	5.00	1.25
		Nos. 297-301 (5)	10.90	2.65

Souvenir Sheet

302	A96	500fr multi	6.00	2.00

History of aviation, famous fliers.

Shot on Goal A97

Designs: 60fr, Heading ball in net. 100fr, Backfield defense. 200fr, Argentina '78 poster. 300fr, Mario Zagalo and stadium. 500fr, Ferenc Puskas.

		1977, Nov. 18 Litho.	Perf. 13½	
303	A97	50fr multi	.50	.20
304	A97	60fr multi	.65	.25
305	A97	100fr multi	1.25	.30
306	A97	200fr multi	2.10	.55
307	A97	300fr multi	3.50	.90
		Nos. 303-307 (5)	8.00	2.20

Souvenir Sheet

308	A97	500fr multi	5.50	1.75

World Soccer Championships, Argentina, June 1-25, 1978.
For overprints see Nos. 370-375.

Emperor Bokassa I, Central African Flag — A98

		1977, Dec. 4 Litho.	Perf. 13½	
309	A98	40fr multi	.40	.20
310	A98	60fr multi	.55	.25
311	A98	100fr multi	1.00	.45
312	A98	150fr multi	1.40	.60
		Nos. 309-312,C188-C189 (6)	8.00	3.55

Coronation of Emperor Bokassa I, Dec. 4.

Lilium — A99

Electronic Tree, ITU Emblem — A100

		1977 Litho.	Perf. 13½x14	
313	A99	5fr shown	.55	.30
314	A99	10fr Hibiscus	1.10	.55

For overprints see Nos. 408-409.

1977

315	A100	100fr blk, org & brn	3.00	1.60

World Telecommunications Day.

Bible and People A101

		1977 Litho.	Perf. 14x13½	
316	A101	40fr multi	9.00	1.50

Bible Week.

People and Rotary Emblem A102

1977

317	A102	60fr multi	4.50	2.00

Rotary Club of Bangui, 20th anniversary.

Holy Family, by Rubens A103

Rubens Paintings: 150fr, Marie de Medicis. 200fr, Son of artist. 300fr, Neptune. 500fr, Marie de Medicis, diff.

		1978, Jan. 26		
318	A103	60fr multi	.60	.20
319	A103	150fr multi	1.50	.40
320	A103	200fr multi	2.40	.60
321	A103	300fr multi	3.50	.80
		Nos. 318-321 (4)	8.00	2.00

Souvenir Sheet

322	A103	500fr gold & multi	6.00	2.00

Peter Paul Rubens (1577-1640).

Rhinoceros — A104

Endangered Animals and Wildlife Fund Emblem: 50fr, Slender-nosed crocodile. 60fr, Leopard, vert. 100fr, Giraffe, vert. 200fr, Elephant. 300fr, Gorilla, vert.

		1978, Feb. 21 Litho.	Perf. 13½	
323	A104	40fr multi	1.50	.25
324	A104	50fr multi	2.40	.30
325	A104	60fr multi	2.50	.40
326	A104	100fr multi	4.50	.60
327	A104	200fr multi	11.00	.95
328	A104	300fr multi	13.50	1.60
		Nos. 323-328 (6)	35.40	4.10

Bokassa Sports Palace A105

Design: 60fr, Sports Palace, side view.

		1978	Perf. 14	
329	A105	40fr multi	.50	.25
330	A105	60fr multi	.65	.40

Automatic Telephone Exchange, Bangui A106

1978

331	A106	40fr multi	.50	.25
332	A106	60fr multi	.65	.40

Diligence and Satellite — A107

Designs (UPU Emblem and): 50fr, Steam locomotive and communications via satellite. 60fr, Paddle-wheel steamer and ship-to-shore communication via satellite. 80fr, Old mail truck and satellite.

		1978, May 17	Perf. 13½	
333	A107	40fr multi	.20	.20
334	A107	50fr multi	3.00	1.25
335	A107	60fr multi	.30	.20
336	A107	80fr multi	.40	.20
		Nos. 333-336,C191-C192 (6)	6.10	2.40

Posts and telecommunications, cent. of progress.

Mask — A108

Capt. Cook on "Endeavour" A109

Designs: 30fr, Mask. 60fr, Women dancers, horiz. 100fr, Men dancers, horiz.

		Perf. 13½x14, 14x13½		
		1978, July 11	Litho.	
337	A108	20fr blk & yel	.75	.30
338	A108	30fr blk & brt bl	.75	.30
339	A108	60fr blk & multi	1.90	.60
340	A108	100fr blk & multi	3.25	.95
		Nos. 337-340 (4)	6.65	2.15

Black-African World Arts Festival, Lagos.
For overprints see Nos. 411-412.

		1978, Aug. 30	Perf. 14½	

60fr, Resolution off Hawaii. 200fr, Hawaiians welcoming Capt. Cook. 350fr, Masked rowers in Hawaiian boat.

341	A109	60fr multi, horiz.	.75	.20
342	A109	80fr multi	1.25	.25
343	A109	200fr multi, horiz.	2.50	.70
344	A109	350fr multi, horiz.	4.50	1.25
		Nos. 341-344 (4)	9.00	2.40

Capt. James Cook (1728-1779), explorer.

Dürer, Self-portrait A110

Dürer Paintings: 80fr, The Four Apostles. 200fr, Virgin and Child. 350fr, Emperor Maximilian I.

		1978, Oct. 24 Litho.	Perf. 13½	
345	A110	60fr multi	.65	.25
346	A110	80fr multi	1.10	.55
347	A110	200fr multi	2.50	.85
348	A110	350fr multi	4.75	1.40
		Nos. 345-348 (4)	9.00	2.75

Albrecht Dürer (1471-1528), German painter.

Tutankhamen's Gold Mask — A111

Treasures of Tutankhamen: 60fr, King and Queen, gold back panel of throne. 80fr, Gilt folding chair. 100fr, King wearing crowns of Upper and Lower Egypt, painted wood sculpture. 120fr, Lion's head. 150fr, Tutankhamen, wood stature. 180fr, Gold throne. 250fr, Gold miniature coffin.

1978, Nov. 22

349	A111	40fr multi	.85	.30
350	A111	60fr multi	1.40	.40
351	A111	80fr multi	1.90	.55
352	A111	100fr multi	2.10	.55
353	A111	120fr multi	3.00	.60
354	A111	150fr multi	4.00	.70
355	A111	180fr multi	4.75	.85
356	A111	250fr multi	6.00	1.10
		Nos. 349-356 (8)	24.00	5.05

Tutankhamen, c. 1358 B.C., King of Egypt.

Lenin at Smolny Institute — A112

Soviet Union, 60th anniv.: 60fr, 200fr, 300fr, Various Lenin portraits. 100fr, Ulyanov family, horiz. 150fr, Lenin, Cruiser "Aurora" and flag, horiz. 500fr, "Aurora" and star.

		1978, Nov.	Perf. 14	
357	A112	40fr multi	.50	.30
358	A112	60fr multi	.60	.30
359	A112	100fr blk & gold	1.00	.45
360	A112	150fr blk, gold & red	1.90	.60

361	A112	200fr multi	3.00 1.00
362	A112	300fr multi	4.00 1.40
		Nos. 357-362 (6)	11.00 4.25

Souvenir Sheet

363	A112	500fr multi	6.00 4.00

Catherine Bokassa A113

Design: 60fr, Emperor Bokassa.

1978, Dec. 4   Litho.   Perf. 13

364	A113	40fr multi	.65 .25
365	A113	60fr multi	.90 .30

1st anniv. of coronation. See No. C202.

Rowland Hill, Letter Scale and G.B. No. 1 — A114

Rowland Hill and: 50fr, US #1, mailman on bicycle. 60fr, Austria #P4, 19th cent. mailman. 80fr, Switzerland #2L1, postilion and mailcoach.

1978, Dec. 9   Litho.   Perf. 13½

366	A114	40fr multi	.40 .20
367	A114	50fr multi	.50 .25
368	A114	60fr multi	.50 .30
369	A114	80fr multi	.65 .30
		Nos. 366-369,C203-C204 (6)	7.80 3.05

Sir Rowland Hill (1795-1879), originator of penny postage.

Nos. 303-307 Overprinted in Silver: "VAINQUEUR: ARGENTINE"

1978, Dec. 27

370	A97	50fr multi	.55 .25
371	A97	60fr multi	.65 .30
372	A97	100fr multi	1.00 .55
373	A97	200fr multi	2.25 1.00
374	A97	300fr multi	3.25 1.40
		Nos. 370-374 (5)	7.70 3.50

Souvenir Sheet

No. 308 Overprinted in Silver: "ARGENTINE-PAYS BAS 3-1 / 25 juin 1978"

375	A97	500fr multi	5.00 5.00

Argentina's victory in World Cup Soccer Championship 1978.

Children Painting and Dutch Portrait — A115

UNICEF, Eagle Emblems and: 50fr, Eskimo children skiing, ski jump. 60fr, Children with toy racing car, Carl Benz with early car model. 80fr, Children launching rocket, Intelsat.

1979, Mar. 6   Litho.   Perf. 13½

376	A115	40fr multi	.65 .20
377	A115	50fr multi	.75 .20
378	A115	60fr multi	.90 .20
379	A115	80fr multi	1.25 .30
		Nos. 376-379,C206-C207 (6)	7.70 1.95

International Year of the Child.

High Jump, Moscow '80 Emblem and "M" — A116

Designs (Moscow '80 Emblem, Various Sports and): 50fr, Bicycling and "O." 60fr, Weight lifting and "C." 80fr, Judo and "K."

1979, Mar. 16   Litho.   Perf. 13

380	A116	40fr multi	.55 .20
381	A116	50fr multi	.65 .20
382	A116	60fr multi	.75 .20
383	A116	80fr multi	1.10 .30
		Nos. 380-383,C209-C210 (6)	6.25 1.90

22nd Olympic Games, Moscow, July 19-Aug. 3, 1980. Background letters on Nos. 380-383, C209-C210 spell "Mockba." A 1500fr gold embossed stamp showing emblems and Discobolus exists.

Memorial, Bangui, Butterfly, Hibiscus — A117

Design: 150fr, Canoe, truck and letters.

1979, June 8   Litho.   Perf. 12x12½

384	A117	60fr multi	2.00 .80
385	A117	150fr multi	4.50 2.00

Philexafrique II, Libreville, Gabon, June 8-17. Nos. 384, 385 each printed in sheets of 10 with 5 labels showing exhibition emblem.

Schoolgirl A118

1979, July 25   Litho.   Perf. 12½x12

386	A118	70fr multi	.95 .40

Intl. Bureau of Education, Geneva, 50th anniv.

Chicken A119

1979, Aug.   Perf. 13

387	A119	10fr shown	1.90 1.10
388	A119	20fr Bull	1.90 1.10
389	A119	40fr Sheep	4.00 2.10
		Nos. 387-389,C211 (4)	13.55 6.30

National Husbandry Assoc.

Souvenir Sheet

Virgin and Child, by Dürer — A120

1979, Aug.   Perf. 13½

390	A120	500fr lt grn & dl red	5.50 1.60

Albrecht Dürer (1471-1528), German engraver and printer.

Central African Republic

Nos. 257-258 Overprinted "ALUNISSAGE/APOLLO XI/ JUILLET/1969" and Emblem

1979, Nov. 11   Litho.   Perf. 13½

391	A93	40fr multi	.65 .30
392	A93	60fr multi	.75 .40
		Nos. 391-392,C212-C214 (5)	7.05 3.35

Apollo 11 moon landing, 10th anniversary.

Girl and Rose A121

1979, Dec. 15

393	A121	30fr Butterfly and girl, vert.	.30 .20
394	A121	40fr shown	.50 .20
395	A121	60fr Hansel and Gretel, vert.	.55 .25
396	A121	200fr Cinderella	2.25 .70
397	A121	250fr Mermaid, vert.	2.75 .80
		Nos. 393-397 (5)	6.35 2.15

International Year of the Child.

Locomotive, U.S. Type A27, Hill — A122

Locomotives, Hill and Stamps: 100fr, France #1. 150fr, Germany type A11. 250fr, Great Britain #32. 500fr, CAR #2.

1979, Dec. 20

398	A122	60fr multi	.55 .20
399	A122	100fr multi	1.10 .30
400	A122	150fr multi	1.75 .45
401	A122	250fr multi	3.00 .95
		Nos. 398-401 (4)	6.40 1.90

Souvenir Sheet

402	A122	500fr multi	5.75 2.00

Sir Rowland Hill (1795-1879), originator of penny postage.

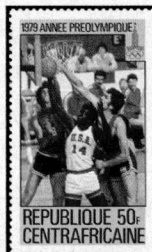

Basketball, Moscow '80 Emblem — A123

Pre-Olympic Year: Men's or women's basketball.

1979, Dec. 28   Litho.   Perf. 14½

403	A123	50fr multi	.50 .20
404	A123	125fr multi	1.10 .35
405	A123	200fr multi	1.90 .55
406	A123	300fr multi	3.25 .80
407	A123	500fr multi	5.00 1.40
		Nos. 403-407 (5)	11.75 3.30

For overprints see Nos. 425-429.

Nos. 313-314, 337-338 Overprinted "REPUBLIQUE CENTRAFRICAINE" in Black on Silver Panel and

Balambo Chair A124

Perf. 13½x14, 14x13½

1980, Mar. 20   Litho.

408	A99	5fr multi	.20 .20
409	A99	10fr multi	.20 .20
410	A124	20fr multi	.30 .20
411	A108	20fr multi	.30 .20
412	A108	30fr multi	.50 .25
		Nos. 408-412 (5)	1.50 1.05

Viking Satellite — A125

1980, Apr. 8   Perf. 13½

413	A125	40fr shown	.55 .20
414	A125	50fr Apollo-Soyuz	.65 .20
415	A125	60fr Voyager	.75 .20
416	A125	100fr European Space Agency emblem, flags	1.25 .30
		Nos. 413-416,C221-C222 (6)	6.70 1.85

Walking, Olympic Medal, Moscow '80 Emblem — A126

1980, July 25   Litho.   Perf. 13½

417	A126	30fr shown	.50 .20
418	A126	40fr Relay race	.55 .20
419	A126	70fr Running	.75 .20
420	A126	80fr High jump	.90 .25
		Nos. 417-420,C231-C232 (6)	5.30 1.50

For overprints see #462-465, C248-C250.

Fruit — A126a

1980, Aug. 1   Litho.   Perf. 13½

420A	A126a	40fr multicolored	— —
420B	A126a	70fr green & multi	— —

Agricultural
Development
A127

1980, Nov. 4   Litho.   Perf. 13½
421 A127 30fr shown   .30 .20
422 A127 40fr Telecommunica-
              tions   .50 .20
423 A127 70fr Engineering   .90 .25
424 A127 100fr Civil engineering 1.10 .40
  Nos. 421-424,C234-C235 (6)   6.20 2.15

Europe-Africa cooperation.

Nos. 403-407 Overprinted with Medal
and Country

1980, Nov. 12   Perf. 14½
425 A123 50fr multi   .55 .20
426 A123 125fr multi   1.10 .40
427 A123 200fr multi   1.90 .55
428 A123 300fr multi   3.60 .90
429 A123 500fr multi   5.00 1.60
  Nos. 425-429 (5)   12.15 3.65

Virgin and Child,
by
Raphael — A128

African Postal
Union, 5th
Anniversary
A129

Christmas: Virgin & Child paintings by
Raphael.

1980, Dec. 20   Perf. 12½
430 A128 60fr multi   .65 .25
431 A128 150fr multi   1.60 .60
432 A128 250fr multi   3.00 1.10
  Nos. 430-432 (3)   5.25 1.95

1980, Dec. 24   Photo.   Perf. 13½
433 A129 70fr multi   .75 .40

Peruvian Soccer Team, Soccer
Cup — A130

1981, Jan. 13   Litho.   Perf. 13½
434 A130 10fr shown   .20 .20
435 A130 15fr Scotland   .20 .20
436 A130 20fr Mexico   .20 .20
437 A130 25fr Sweden   .30 .20
438 A130 30fr Austria   .40 .20
439 A130 40fr Poland   .50 .20
440 A130 50fr France   .55 .20
441 A130 60fr Italy   .65 .20
442 A130 70fr Germany   .75 .25
443 A130 80fr Brazil   .90 .25
  Nos. 434-443,C237-C238 (12) 7.25 2.90
ESPANA '82 World Cup Soccer
Championship.

13th World Telecommunications
Day — A131

1981, May 17   Litho.   Perf. 12½
444 A131 150fr multi   1.40 .70

Apollo 15 Crew on Moon — A132

Space Exploration: Columbia space shuttle.

1981, June 10   Litho.   Perf. 14
445 A132 100fr multi   .90 .30
446 A132 150fr multi   1.50 .40
447 A132 200fr multi   2.10 .60
448 A132 300fr multi   3.50 1.00
  Nos. 445-448 (4)   8.00 2.30

Souvenir Sheet
449 A132 500fr multi   5.00 1.60

Family of
Acrobats
with
Monkey, by
Picasso
A133

Picasso Birth Cent.: 50fr, The Balcony. 80fr,
The Artist's Son as Pierrot. 100fr, The Three
Dancers.

1981, June 30   Perf. 13½
450 A133 40fr multi   .50 .20
451 A133 50fr multi   .65 .25
452 A133 80fr multi   1.10 .25
453 A133 100fr multi   1.40 .40
  Nos. 450-453,C245-C246 (6) 8.40 2.15

First Anniv. of Zimbabwe's
Independence — A134

1981, July 9   Litho.   Perf. 12½
454 A134 100fr multi   1.10 .45
455 A134 150fr multi   1.50 .55
456 A134 200fr multi   2.25 .70
  Nos. 454-456 (3)   4.85 1.70

Prince Charles
and Lady
Diana — A135

1981, July, 24   Perf. 14
457 A135 75fr Charles   .60 .25
458 A135 100fr Diana   .90 .30
459 A135 150fr St. Paul's Cathe-
              dral   1.50 .45
460 A135 175fr shown   1.90 .50
  Nos. 457-460 (4)   4.90 1.50

Souvenir Sheet
461 A135 500fr Couple   5.00 1.40

Royal Wedding.
For overprints see Nos. 529-533.

Nos. 417-420 Overprinted with Event,
Winner and Country in Gold

1981   Litho.   Perf. 13½
462 A126 30fr multi   .30 .20
463 A126 40fr multi   .40 .20
464 A126 70fr multi   .65 .30
465 A126 80fr multi   .75 .40
  Nos. 462-465,C248-C249 (6) 4.50 1.75

Prince Charles and Lady
Diana — A136

1981, Aug. 20   Litho.   Perf. 13½
466 A136 40fr shown   .50 .20
467 A136 50fr Crowned Prince
              of Wales   .50 .25
468 A136 80fr Diana   .85 .30
469 A136 100fr Naval training 1.10 .40
  Nos. 466-469,C251-C252 (6) 6.65 2.10

Royal wedding.

1906 Renault — A137

1981, Sept. 22   Litho.   Perf. 12½
470 A137 20fr shown   .30 .20
471 A137 40fr Mercedes-Benz,
              1937   .65 .20
472 A137 50fr Matra-Ford, 1969 .75 .20
473 A137 110fr Tazio Nuvolari,
              1927   1.50 .40
474 A137 150fr Jackie Stewart,
              1965   2.25 .55
  Nos. 470-474 (5)   5.45 1.55

Souvenir Sheet
Perf. 10
475 A137 450fr Finish line, 1914 6.00 6.00

Grand Prix of France, 75th anniv.

World Food
Day
A138

1981, Oct. 16
476 A138 90fr multi   .95 .30
477 A138 110fr multi   1.10 .40

Navigators and their Ships — A139

1981, Sept. 4   Litho.   Perf. 13½
478 A139 40fr C.V. Rietschoten .50 .30
479 A139 50fr M. Pajot   .55 .45
480 A139 60fr K. Jaworski   .75 .55
481 A139 80fr M. Birch   1.00 .60
  Nos. 478-481,C254-C255 (6) 6.30 4.00

Downfall
of Empire
A140

1981, Oct. 6
482 A140 5fr Bayonet through
              crown   .20 .20
483 A140 10fr like #482   .20 .20
484 A140 25fr Victory holding
              map   .30 .20
485 A140 60fr like #484   .75 .25
486 A140 90fr Toppled Bokassa
              statue   1.10 .40
487 A140 500fr like #486   4.75 2.00
  Nos. 482-487 (6)   7.30 3.25

Komba — A141

1981, Nov. 17
488 A141 50fr shown   .65 .20
489 A141 90fr Dodoro, horiz. 1.60 .25
490 A141 140fr Kaya, horiz.   2.75 .40
  Nos. 488-490 (3)   5.00 .85

Central
African
States
Bank
A142

1981, Dec. 12   Litho.   Perf. 12½x13
491 A142 90fr multi   1.00 .30
492 A142 110fr multi   1.10 .40

Christmas
1981 — A143

Virgin and Child Paintings.

1981, Dec. 24
493	A143	50fr Fra Angelico, 1430	1.00	.30
494	A143	60fr Cosimo Tura, 1484	1.10	.40
495	A143	90fr Bramantino	1.75	.45
496	A143	110fr Memling	2.25	.70

Nos. 493-496,C260-C261 (6)   13.10 3.00

Scouting Year — A144

1982, Jan. 13   *Perf. 12½*
497	A144	100fr Hiking	1.25	.40
498	A144	150fr Scouts, horiz.	1.90	.55
499	A144	200fr Hiking	2.75	.80
500	A144	300fr Salute, flag, vert.	3.75	1.25

Nos. 497-500 (4)   9.65 3.00

Souvenir Sheet
Perf. 13
501	A144	500fr Scout, Baden-Powell, vert.	6.25	1.60

Elephant
A145

1982, Jan. 22   *Perf. 13½*
502	A145	60fr shown	.90	.20
503	A145	90fr Giraffes	1.10	.30
504	A145	100fr Addaxes	1.25	.30
505	A145	110fr Okapi	1.50	.45

Nos. 502-505,C263-C264 (6)   13.50 3.30

Norman Rockwell Illustrations A146

1982, Feb. 17   *Perf. 13½x14*
506	A146	30fr Grandfather snowman	.30	.20
507	A146	60fr Croquet players	.55	.25
508	A146	110fr Women talking	1.25	.40
509	A146	150fr Searching	1.75	.55

Nos. 506-509 (4)   3.85 1.40

AT 16 Dirigible A147

1982, Feb. 27   *Litho.*   *Perf. 13½*
510	A147	5fr shown	.20	.20
511	A147	10fr Beyer-Garrat locomotive	.20	.20
512	A147	20fr Bugatti 24 "Royale," 1924	.30	.20
513	A147	110fr Vickers "Valentia," 1928	1.40	.40

Nos. 510-513,C266-C267 (6)   11.10 3.05

Bellvue Garden, by Edouard Manet — A148

Anniversaries: 400fr, Goethe, vert. #519-520, Princess Diana, 21st birthday, July 1, vert. 300fr, George Washington, vert.

1982, Apr. 6   *Litho.*   *Perf. 13*
517	A148	200fr multi	3.00	.60
517A	A148	300fr multi	3.00	.95
518	A148	400fr multi	4.00	1.25
519	A148	500fr multi	5.00	2.00

Nos. 517-519 (4)   15.00 4.80

Souvenir Sheet
520	A148	500fr multi	5.50	1.40

23rd Olympic Games, Los Angeles, 1984 — A149

1982, July 24   *Litho.*   *Perf. 13½*
521	A149	5fr Soccer	.20	.20
522	A149	10fr Boxing	.20	.20
523	A149	20fr Running	.30	.20
524	A149	110fr Long jump	1.00	.30

Nos. 521-524,C269-C270 (6)   9.70 3.10

21st Birthday of Princess Diana — A150

Portraits.

1982, July 20   *Litho.*   *Perf. 13½*
525	A150	5fr multi	.20	.20
526	A150	10fr multi	.20	.20
527	A150	20fr multi	.30	.20
528	A150	110fr multi	1.40	.30

Nos. 525-528,C272-C273 (6)   10.85 3.10

Nos. 457-461 Overprinted in Blue: "NAISSANCE ROYALE 1982"

1982, Aug. 20   *Perf. 14*
529	A135	75fr multi	.55	.25
530	A135	110fr multi	.75	.40
531	A135	150fr multi	1.40	.55
532	A135	175fr multi	2.25	.80

Nos. 529-532 (4)   4.95 2.00

Souvenir Sheet
533	A135	500fr multi	5.00	3.75

Birth of Prince William of Wales, June 21.

2nd UN Conference on Peaceful Uses of Outer Space, Vienna, Aug. 9-21 — A151

Various satellites and space scenes.

1982, Aug. 15   *Litho.*   *Perf. 13½*
534	A151	5fr multi	.20	.20
535	A151	10fr multi	.20	.20
536	A151	20fr multi	.30	.20
537	A151	110fr multi	1.00	.30

Nos. 534-537,C277-C278 (6)   9.70 3.10

Sakpa Basket A152

Baskets and bowls.

1982, Sept. 2   *Perf. 13*
538	A152	5fr shown	.20	.20
539	A152	10fr like 5fr	.20	.20
540	A152	25fr Ngbenda gourd, vert.	.30	.20
541	A152	60fr like 25fr	.75	.20
542	A152	120fr Ta ti ngou jugs	1.60	.40
543	A152	175fr Kangu bowls	2.25	.60
544	A152	300fr Kolongo bowls, vert.	4.50	1.25

Nos. 538-544 (7)   9.80 3.05

For surcharges see #792A-792B.

1982 World Cup Soccer Championships, Spain — A152a

Various soccer plays.

1982, Sept.   *Litho.*   *Perf. 13½x13*
Overprinted in Silver or Gold
545	A152a	60fr Italy, 1st, 2nd	.90	.25
546	A152a	150fr Poland, 3rd	1.75	.55
547	A152a	300fr France, 4th	3.75	1.25

Nos. 545-547 (3)   6.40 2.05

Souvenir Sheet
548	A152a	500fr Italy, 1st (G)	5.25	1.40

Not issued without overprint.

13th World UPU Day — A153

1982, Oct. 9
549	A153	60fr multi	.55	.25
550	A153	120fr multi	1.25	.45

Comb and Hairpins A154

1982, Oct. 20   *Perf. 13x12½*
551	A154	20fr multi	.20	.20
552	A154	30fr multi	.40	.25
553	A154	60fr multi	.75	.30
554	A154	80fr multi	1.10	.40
555	A154	120fr multi	1.50	.45

Nos. 551-555 (5)   3.95 1.60

Artist Pierre Ndarata and No.69 A155

1982, Oct.   *Perf. 13*
556	A155	40fr Jean Tubind at easel, vert.	.20	.20
557	A155	70fr shown	.45	.20
558	A155	90fr like 70fr	.55	.25
559	A155	140fr like 40fr	1.00	.35

Nos. 556-559 (4)   2.20 1.00

TB Bacillus Centenary A156

1982, Nov. 30   *Perf. 13½x13*
560	A156	100fr vio & blk	1.10	.30
561	A156	120fr red org & blk	1.40	.45
562	A156	175fr bl & blk	2.25	.80

Nos. 560-562 (3)   4.75 1.55

10th Anniv. of UN Conference on Human Environment A157

1982, Dec. 8
563	A157	120fr multi	1.10	.40
564	A157	150fr multi	1.40	.55
565	A157	300fr multi	3.00	1.00

Nos. 563-565 (3)   5.50 1.95

Granary A158

1982, Dec. 15   *Perf. 13*
566	A158	60fr multi	.55	.25
567	A158	80fr multi	.90	.40
568	A158	120fr multi	1.10	.65
569	A158	200fr multi	2.25	.90

Nos. 566-569 (4)   4.80 2.10

A159   A160

1982, Dec.
570	A159	100fr multi	1.00	.40
571	A159	120fr multi	1.40	.45

ITU Plenipotentiaries Conf., Nairobi, Sept.

1983, Jan. 31   *Litho.*   *Perf. 13½x13*
572	A160	5fr Modes of communication	.20	.20
573	A160	60fr like 5fr	.55	.30
574	A160	120fr Map, jet	1.40	.40
575	A160	175fr like 120fr	1.75	.55

Nos. 572-575 (4)   3.90 1.35

UN Decade for African Transportation and Communication, 1978-88.

Chess Champions — A161

Men and Chess Pieces: 5fr, Steinitz, first world champion, 1886. 10fr, Aaron Niemzovitch, castle. 20fr, Alexander Alekhine, knights. 110fr, Botvinnik. 300fr, Boris Spassky, glass pieces. 500fr, Bobby Fischer,

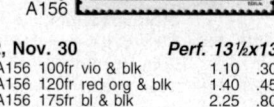

king, knight. 600fr, Korchnoi, Karpov, pawn. No. 582A, Bobby Fischer. No. 582B, Reti, Larsen, Petrossian, and Mecking, horiz.

1983, Jan. 15
576	A161	5fr multi	.20	.20
577	A161	10fr multi	.20	.20
578	A161	20fr multi	.20	.20
579	A161	110fr multi	1.40	.40
580	A161	300fr multi	3.25	.55
581	A161	500fr multi	5.50	1.40
	Nos. 576-581 (6)		10.75	2.75

Souvenir Sheet
582	A161	600fr multi	5.75	1.60

Litho. & Embossed
Perf. 13½
Size: 35x60mm
582A	A161	1500fr gold & multi	42.50	3.50

Souvenir Sheet
582B	A161	1500fr gold & multi	10.00	10.00

No. 582 contains one 56x33mm stamp, No. 582B one 35x60mm stamp. 300fr, 500fr, 600fr, Nos. 582A and 582B are airmail.

Marshal Tito (1892-1980) A162

1983, Jan. 22
583	A162	20fr George Washington	.20	.20
a.		Souvenir sheet	5.50	
584	A162	110fr shown	1.25	.30
a.		Souvenir sheet	5.50	—

1982 World Cup Soccer Championships, Spain — A162a

Trophy, flags, scores, players: 5fr, Hamilton, Pezzey. 10fr, Borovski, Boniek. 20fr, Littbarski, Zamora. 110fr, Zico, Passarella. 300fr, Rossi, Smolarek. 500fr, Rummenigge, Giresse. 600fr, Rossi, Rummenigge. No. 584I, Platini. No. 584J, Rossi.

1983, Feb. 8   Litho.   Perf. 13½
584B	A162a	5fr multi	.20	.20
584C	A162a	10fr multi	.20	.20
584D	A162a	20fr multi	.20	.20
584E	A162a	110fr multi	1.25	.30
584F	A162a	300fr multi	3.25	.70
584G	A162a	500fr multi	5.50	1.40
	Nos. 584B-584G (6)		10.60	3.00

Souvenir Sheet
584H	A162a	600fr multicolored	5.50	4.25

Litho. & Embossed
584I	A162a	1500fr gold & multi	35.00	6.50

Souvenir Sheet
584J	A162a	1500fr gold & multi	10.00	10.00

Nos. 584F-584J are airmail.

Easter 1983 A163

Rembrandt Paintings.

1983, Apr. 16
585	A163	100fr Entombment	1.00	.40
586	A163	300fr Crucifixion	2.50	1.25
587	A163	400fr Descent from the Cross	3.50	1.60
	Nos. 585-587 (3)		7.00	3.25

Vintage Cars and their Makers A164

A164a

Designs: 10fr, Emile Levassor, Rene Panhard, 1895 car. 20fr, Henry Ford, 1896 car. 30fr, Louis Renault, 1899 car. 80fr, Ettore Bugatti, type 37, 1925. 400fr, Enzo Ferrari, 815 sport, 1940. 500fr, Ferdinand Porsche, 356 coupe, 1951. 600fr, Karl Benz, velocipede, 1886. No. 594A, F.H. Royce and C.S. Rolls, 1911 Rolls-Royce Silver Ghost. No. 594B, G. Daimler, 1900 Mercedes 35CV.

1983, June 3   Litho.   Perf. 13½
588	A164	10fr multi	.20	.20
589	A164	20fr multi	.20	.20
590	A164	30fr multi	.30	.20
591	A164	80fr multi	1.00	.30
592	A164	400fr multi	4.50	1.10
593	A164	500fr multi	5.50	1.40
	Nos. 588-593 (6)		11.70	3.40

Souvenir Sheet
594	A164	600fr multi	5.75	1.60

Litho. & Embossed
594A	A164a	1500fr gold & multi	25.00	4.00

Souvenir Sheet
594B	A164a	1500fr gold & multi	10.00	6.00

Nos. 592-594B are airmail.

25th Anniv. of Intl. Maritime Org. — A165

1983, July 8   Litho.   Perf. 12½x13
595	A165	40fr multi	.50	.20
596	A165	100fr multi	1.00	.40

World Communications Year — A166

1983, July 22
597	A166	50fr multi	.50	.25
598	A166	130fr multi	1.40	.45

Pre-Olympics, Los Angeles A167

1984 Summer Olympics, Los Angeles A167a

1983, Aug. 3   Litho.   Perf. 13
599	A167	5fr Gymnast	.20	.20
600	A167	40fr Javelin throwing	.40	.20
601	A167	60fr Pole vault	.65	.25
602	A167	120fr Fencing	1.40	.30
603	A167	200fr Cycling	2.25	.40
604	A167	300fr Sailing	3.25	.80
	Nos. 599-604 (6)		8.15	2.15

Souvenir Sheet
605	A167	600fr Handball	5.00	1.60

Litho. & Embossed
Perf. 13½
605A	A167a	1500fr Shot put	35.00	3.50

Souvenir Sheet
605B	A167a	1500fr Dressage, horiz.	10.00	10.00

Nos. 603-605B are airmail.

Namibia Day — A168

1983, Sept. 16   Litho.   Perf. 13
606	A168	100fr multi	1.10	.40
607	A168	200fr multi	1.90	.80

Manned Flight Bicentenary — A169

A169a

Designs: 50fr, J. Montgolfier and his balloon, 1783. 100fr, J.P. Blanchard, English Channel crossing, 1785. 200fr, L.-J. Gay-Lussac, 4000-meter balloon ascent, 1804. 300fr, Giffard and his dirigible, 1852. 400fr, Santos Dumont, dirigible, Eiffel Tower. 500fr, A. Laquot, captive observation balloon, 1914. 600fr, J.A. Charles, first gas balloon; G. Tissandier, dirigible, 1883. No. 614, Marquis d'Arlandes and Jean Francois Pilatre de Rozier, Montgolfier balloon. No. 614B, Ferdinand von Zeppelin, Graf Zeppelin, horiz.

1983, Sept. 30   Litho.   Perf. 13½
608	A169	50fr multi	.50	.20
609	A169	100fr multi	1.10	.40
610	A169	200fr multi	2.50	.80
611	A169	300fr multi	3.25	1.10
612	A169	400fr multi	4.25	1.50
613	A169	500fr multi	5.75	1.90
	Nos. 608-613 (6)		17.35	5.90

Souvenir Sheet
614	A169	600fr multi	5.50	1.40

Litho. & Embossed
614A	A169a	1500fr gold & multi	37.50	4.00

Souvenir Sheet
614B	A169a	1500fr gold & multi	10.00	10.00

Nos. 612-614B are airmail.

Black Rhinoceros and World Wildlife Emblem — A170

Various black rhinoceroses.

1983, Nov. 14
615	A170	10fr multi	1.00	.20
616	A170	40fr multi	1.25	.20
617	A170	70fr multi	2.10	.40
618	A170	180fr multi	6.50	.75
	Nos. 615-618 (4)		10.85	1.55

Nos. 615-618 were issued in support of the World Wildlife Fund.
See Nos. C291A-C293.

UPU Day, World Communications Year — A171

1983, Nov. 2   Litho.   Perf. 13
619	A171	205fr multi	1.90	.90

2nd Anniv. of the Natl. Military Committee — A172

Gen. Andre Kolingba, head of state.

1983, Sept. 1   **Perf. 12½**
620 A172 65fr sil & multi   .55 .25
621 A172 130fr gold & multi   1.40 .45

Earth Satellite Receiving Station, Bangui M'Poko — A173

1983   **Perf. 13**
622 A173 130fr multi   1.40 .55

Natl. Day of the Handicapped and the Elderly — A174

1983, Dec. 20   **Engr.**   **Perf. 13x12½**
623 A174 65fr vio & org   .55 .30
624 A174 130fr ultra & org   1.10 .45
625 A174 205fr dk grn & org   1.75 .80
    Nos. 623-625 (3)   3.40 1.55

Fishing Resources A175

1983, Dec. 31   **Litho.**   **Perf. 12½**
626 A175 25fr Breeding tank   .20 .20
627 A175 65fr Net fishing   1.10 .25
628 A175 100fr Dam fishing   1.25 .40
629 A175 130fr Still life with fish   2.50 .70
630 A175 205fr Basket trap   2.75 .70
    Nos. 626-630 (5)   7.80 2.25

Wildlife Protection — A176

1984, Jan. 25   **Perf. 13**
631 A176 30fr Forest fire   3.50 .40
632 A176 130fr Hunters   5.00 1.10

CC-1500 Locomotive — A177

1984, July 16   **Litho.**   **Perf. 12½**
633 A177 110fr CC-1500 loco-
      motive   1.40 .30
634 A177 240fr PLM series
      210, 1868   3.00 .85
635 A177 350fr 231-726 loco-
      motive, 1937   4.25 1.10
636 A177 440fr Pacific S3/6,
      1908   5.75 1.25
637 A177 500fr Henschel 151
      series 45,
      1937   6.75 1.60
    Nos. 633-637 (5)   21.15 5.10

For overprints see Nos. 702, 704.

Packet Ship Pericles — A177a

1984, July 23   **Litho.**   **Perf. 12½**
638 A177a 65fr shown   .90 .30
639 A177a 120fr Three-master
      Pereire   1.40 .55
640 A177a 250fr Admella   3.00 1.10
641 A177a 400fr Royal William   5.50 1.90
642 A177a 500fr Great Britain   6.25 2.40
    Nos. 638-642 (5)   17.05 6.25

For overprints see Nos. 701, 703.

J. W. Goethe, Scene from Faust A178

Designs: 100fr, Henri Dunant, Red Cross Founder, Battle of Solferino, 125th anniv. 200fr, Alfred Nobel, Nobel Foundation headquarters. 300fr, Lord Baden-Powell, World Scouting Jamboree, Alberta, 1983. 400fr, John F. Kennedy, first man on the Moon, 1969. 500fr, 600fr, wedding of Prince and Princess of Wales.

1984, Feb. 25   **Litho.**   **Perf. 13½**
643 A178 50fr multi   .55 .20
644 A178 100fr multi   1.10 .40
645 A178 200fr multi   2.50 .55
646 A178 300fr multi   3.25 1.10
647 A178 400fr multi   4.50 1.10
648 A178 500fr multi   5.50 1.10
    Nos. 643-648 (6)   17.40 4.45

Souvenir Sheet
649 A178 600fr multi   5.00 1.40

Nos. 647-649 are airmail.

Old Masters A179

Paintings: 50fr, Madonna and Child, by Raphael. 100fr, Madonna with Pear, by Durer. 200fr, Aldobrandini Madonna, by Raphael. 300fr, Madonna with Carnation, by Durer. 400fr, Virgin and Child, by Correggio. 500fr, La Bohemienne, by Modigliani. 600fr, Madonna and Child on the Throne, by Raphael.

1984, Mar. 30   **Litho.**   **Perf. 13½**
650 A179 50fr multi   .60 .20
651 A179 100fr multi   1.10 .25
652 A179 200fr multi   2.50 .45
653 A179 300fr multi   3.50 .85
654 A179 400fr multi   4.75 1.90
655 A179 500fr multi   5.75 2.50
    Nos. 650-655 (6)   18.20 6.15

Miniature Sheet
656 A179 600fr multi   5.50 1.40

No. 656 contains 1 stamp, size 30x59mm.
Nos. 654-656 are airmail.

Space — A180

1984, Aug. 6   **Litho.**   **Perf. 13½**
657 A180 20fr Galileo, Ariane
      rocket   .30 .20
658 A180 70fr Piccard, X-15,
      balloon   .65 .25
659 A180 150fr Oberth, satellite   1.40 .45
660 A180 205fr Einstein, satel-
      lites   1.90 .55
661 A180 300fr Curie, Viking
      vehicle   3.25 .80
662 A180 500fr Merbold, Space-
      lab   5.00 1.00
    Nos. 657-662 (6)   12.50 3.25

Miniature Sheet
663 A180 600fr Armstrong,
      Apollo 11,
      horiz.   4.50 1.40

No. 663 contains 1 stamp, size: 42x36mm. 300fr, 500fr and 600fr are airmail.

Forestry Resources A181

UNICEF — A182

1984, Oct. 9   **Litho.**   **Perf. 13x12½**
664 A181 70fr Forest   1.00 .30
665 A181 130fr Logging   2.00 .55

1984, Oct. 27   **Litho.**   **Perf. 13x12½**
666 A182 10fr Weighing child   .20 .20
667 A182 30fr Vaccinating child   .40 .25
668 A182 65fr Giving liquids   .55 .30
669 A182 100fr Balancing diet   1.25 .55
    Nos. 666-669 (4)   2.40 1.30

Fishing Traps A183

1984, Nov. 6   **Litho.**   **Perf. 13**
670 A183 50fr Bangui-Kette   .75 .30
671 A183 70fr Mbres   1.10 .55
672 A183 150fr Bangui-Kette   1.90 .55
    Nos. 670-672 (3)   3.75 1.40

Mushrooms A184

1984, Nov. 15   **Litho.**   **Perf. 13½**
673 A184 5fr Leptoporus
      lignosus   .20 .20
674 A184 10fr Phlebopus
      sudanicus   .20 .20
675 A184 40fr Termitomyces
      letestui   .65 .20
676 A184 130fr Lepiota es-
      culenta   1.60 .30
677 A184 300fr Termitomyces
      aurantiacus   3.50 .80
678 A184 500fr Termitomyces
      robustus   6.25 1.25
    Nos. 673-678 (6)   12.40 2.95

Souvenir Sheet
679 A184 600fr Tricholoma-
      lobayensis   6.25 1.40

Nos. 677-679 are airmail.

1984 Winter Olympics, Sarajevo A184a

Gold medalists, communications satellite and events: 30fr, Gaetan Boucher, Canada, 1000 and 1500-meter speed skating. 90fr, W. Hoppe, R. Wetzig, D. Schauerhammer and A. Kirchner, German Democratic Republic, 4-man bobsled. 140fr, Paoletta Magoni, Italy, women's slalom. 200fr, Jayne Torvill and Christopher Dean, Great Britain, ice dancing. 400fr, Matti Nykaenen, Finland, 90-meter ski jumping. 500fr, USSR, ice hockey. 600fr, Bill Johnson, US, men's downhill.

1984, Nov. 30   **Litho.**   **Perf. 13½**
679A A184a 30fr multi   .30 .20
679B A184a 90fr multi   1.00 .30
679C A184a 140fr multi   1.50 .40
679D A184a 200fr multi   2.25 .55
679E A184a 400fr multi   4.00 1.00
679F A184a 500fr multi   5.25 1.25
    Nos. 679A-679F (6)   14.30 3.70

Souvenir Sheet
679G A184a 600fr multi   5.00 1.40

Nos. 679E-679G are airmail.

Flowers — A185

1984, Nov. 22   **Litho.**   **Perf. 13½**
680 A185 65fr Hibiscus   1.10 .40
681 A185 130fr Canna Indica   1.90 .50
682 A185 205fr Eichlornia Cras-
      sipes   3.00 1.00
    Nos. 680-682 (3)   6.00 1.90

Economic Campaign — A186

1984, Dec. 3   **Litho.**   **Perf. 13½**
683 A186 25fr Cotton planting   .40 .25
684 A186 40fr Selling cotton
      crop   .65 .40
685 A186 130fr Cotton market   1.70 .55
    Nos. 683-685 (3)   2.75 1.20

World Food Day A187

1984, Dec. 10   Litho.   *Perf. 13½*
686   A187   205fr Picking corn   2.50   .90

OLYMPHILEX '85 — A188

Publicity posters from previous Games and host city landmarks.

1985, Mar 18   Litho.   *Perf. 13½*
687   A188   5fr   Stockholm, 1912   .20   .20
688   A188   10fr   Paris, 1924   .20   .20
689   A188   20fr   London, 1948   .20   .20
690   A188   100fr   Tokyo, 1964   5.25   1.00
691   A188   400fr   Mexico   2.25   .45
692   A188   500fr   Munich, 1972   2.75   .55
    Nos. 687-692 (6)   10.85   2.60

Souvenir Sheet
693   A188   600fr   Athens, 1896, Baron Pierre de Coubertin   5.50   1.50

Nos. 691-693 are airmail. No. 693 contains one 60x30mm stamp.

Anniversaries and Events — A189

Queen Mother, 85th Birthday — A189a

Famous men: 50fr, Abraham Lincoln, American Civil War soldiers. 90fr, Auguste Piccard (1884-1962), inventor, bathyscaphe Trieste. 120fr, Gottlieb Daimler (1834-1900), 1938 Mercedes Type 540. 200fr, Louis Bleriot (1872-1936), inventor, plane. 350fr, Anatoly Karpov, world chess champion. 400fr, Jean Henri Dunant (1828-1910), Red Cross founder, worker caring for wounded soldier.

1984, Dec. 22   Litho.   *Perf. 13½*
694   A189   50fr multi   .55   .20
695   A189   90fr multi   1.00   .30
696   A189   120fr multi   1.60   .40
697   A189   200fr multi   2.50   .55
698   A189   350fr multi   3.75   .80
698A   A189   400fr multi   3.75   .90
    Nos. 694-698A (6)   13.15   3.15

Nos. 698-698A are airmail.

Souvenir Sheet
1984   Litho.   *Perf. 13½*
698B   A189a 600fr multi   5.00   1.40

Bangui Rotary Club and Water — A190

1984, Dec. 29
699   A190   130fr multi   1.90   .45
700   A190   205fr multi   2.75   .80

Nos. 635//641, C302A Overprinted with Exhibitions in Red

1985, Mar. 13   Litho.   *Perf. 12½*
701   A177   250fr Argentina '85, Buenos Aires (#640)   2.50   1.25
702   A177a 350fr Tsukuba Expo '85 (#635)   3.50   1.60
703   A177   400fr Italia '85, Rome (#641)   4.50   2.00
704   A177a 440fr Mophila '85, Hamburg (#636)   5.50   2.40
    Nos. 701-704 (4)   16.00   7.25

Souvenir Sheet
Perf. 13½x13
705   AP89 500fr Olymphilex '85, Lausanne   5.00   5.00

500fr airmail.

Beetles — A191

1985, Mar.   Litho.   *Perf. 13½*
706   A191   15fr Chelorrhina polyphemus   1.75   .20
707   A191   20fr Fornasinius russus   2.25   .20
708   A191   25fr Goliathus giganteus   2.50   .20
709   A191   65fr Goliathus meleagris   6.50   .30
    Nos. 706-709 (4)   13.00   .90

Audubon Birth Bicentenary — A192

Illustrations of North American bird species by John Audubon.

1985, Mar. 25   Litho.   *Perf. 13½*
710   A192   40fr Cyanocitta cristata   .90   .20
711   A192   80fr Caprimulgus carolinensis   1.25   .20
712   A192   130fr Campephilus principales   2.40   .25
713   A192   250fr Calocitta formosa   3.25   .55
714   A192   300fr Coccizus minor, horiz.   3.50   .60
715   A192   500fr Hirundo rustica, horiz.   5.75   1.10
    Nos. 710-715 (6)   17.05   2.90

Souvenir Sheet
716   A192 600fr Dryocopus pileatus, horiz.   7.75   2.50

Nos. 714-716 are airmail.

Intl. Youth Year A193

Famous children's book authors and scenes from their best-known novels: 100fr, The Jungle Book, 1894, by Kipling, vert. 200fr, Les Cavaliers, 1967, by Joseph Kessel (1898-1979). 300fr, Twenty-Thousand Leagues Under the Sea, 1873, by Verne. 400fr, The Adventures of Tom Sawyer, 1876, by Twain.

1985, Apr.   Litho.   *Perf. 13*
718   A193   100fr multi   1.10   .45
719   A193   200fr multi   2.40   .85
720   A193   300fr multi   3.00   1.25
721   A193   400fr multi   4.50   2.10
    Nos. 718-721 (4)   11.00   4.65

Philexafrica '85, Lome — A194

#722, UPU emblem, Postmen unloading parcel post van. #723, Exhibition emblem, scout troop.

1985, May 15   *Perf. 13x12½*
722   A194   200fr multi   2.50   .90
723   A194   200fr multi   2.50   .90
   a.   Pair, #722-723 + label   5.25   4.50

Rabies Vaccine Cent., Louis Pasteur (1822-95), Chemist, Microbiologist — A195

Anniversaries and events: 200fr, Battle of Solferino, founding of the Red Cross, 125th Anniv., founder Jean-Henri Dunant (1828-1910), horiz. 300fr, Girl Guides, 75th anniv. 450fr, Elizabeth, the Queen Mother, 85th birthday. 500fr, Statue of Liberty, cent.

1985, June   *Perf. 13*
724   A195   150fr multi   1.60   .70
725   A195   200fr multi   1.90   .90
726   A195   300fr multi   2.25   1.40
727   A195   450fr multi   3.75   2.25
728   A195   500fr multi   5.00   2.50
    Nos. 724-728 (5)   14.50   7.75

1986 World Cup Soccer Championships, Mexico — A196

Famous soccer players and match scenes.

1985, July 24   Litho.   *Perf. 13½*
730   A196   5fr   Pele   .20   .20
731   A196   10fr   Tony Schumacher   .20   .20
732   A196   20fr   Paolo Rossi   .20   .20
733   A196   350fr   Kevin Keegan   3.50   .90
734   A196   400fr   Michel Platini   4.00   .90
735   A196   500fr   Karl Heinz Rummenigge   5.00   1.10
    Nos. 730-735 (6)   13.10   3.50

Souvenir Sheet
736   A196 600fr Diego Armando Maradona   5.00   1.40

Nos. 734-736 are airmail.

Kotto Waterfalls A197

1985, July 27   Litho.   *Perf. 13½*
737   A197   65fr multi   1.00   .30
738   A197   90fr multi   1.10   .40
739   A197   130fr multi   1.75   .60
    Nos. 737-739 (3)   3.85   1.30

State Visit of Pope John Paul II — A198

Portraits.

1985, Aug. 14
740   A198   65fr multi   1.25   .40
741   A198   130fr multi   2.50   .80

Natl. Economic Development Campaign — A199

Designs: 5fr, Troops plowing. 60fr, Soldier preparing field for planting, vert. 130fr, Planting cotton seeds, vert.

1985, Sept. 1   *Perf. 13*
742   A199   5fr multi   .20   .20
743   A199   60fr multi   .75   .30
744   A199   130fr multi   1.50   .45
    Nos. 742-744 (3)   2.45   .95

Queen Mother, 85th Birthday — A200

1985, Sept. 16   Litho.   *Perf. 13½*
745   A200   100fr Age 4, with brother   .90   .25
746   A200   200fr Duchess of York, 1923   2.10   .35
747   A200   300fr Reviewing Irish Guards, 1928   3.25   .70
748   A200   350fr Family portrait, 1936   3.50   .75
749   A200   400fr George VI coronation, 1937   4.25   .90
750   A200   500fr Wedding anniv., 1948   5.50   1.00
    Nos. 745-750 (6)   19.50   3.95

Souvenir Sheet

751 A200 600fr Christening
Prince Charles,
1948 4.50 1.40

Nos. 749-751 are airmail.

Dr. Rene Labusquiere (1919-1977),
Promoter of Preventive
Medicine — A201

1985, Sept. 22   Litho.   Perf. 13½
752 A201 10fr multi .20 .20
753 A201 45fr multi .50 .20
754 A201 110fr multi .75 .45
Nos. 752-754 (3) 1.45 .85

Natl. Postal Service — A202

1985, Oct. 9   Perf. 12½
755 A202 15fr Loading mail van .20 .20
756 A202 60fr Bangui P.O., van .65 .25
757 A202 150fr Hdqtrs, Bangui,
and vans 1.60 .80
Nos. 755-757 (3) 2.45 1.25

Space Research — A203

Designs: 40fr, Yuri Gagarin, Soviet cosmonaut, and Sergei Korolev, rocket engineer.
110fr, Nicolaus Copernicus, Cassini probe.
240fr, Galileo, Viking orbiter. 300fr, Theodor
von Karman (1881-1963), American aeronau-
tical engineer, and space shuttle recovering
Palapa B satellite. 450fr, Percival Lowell
(1855-1916), American astronomer, and
Viking probe. 500fr, Dr. U. Merbold and orbiting space station project Colombo. 600fr,
Apollo 11 Project, first step on Moon by Neil
Armstrong.

1985, Oct. 31   Litho.   Perf. 13½
758 A203 40fr multi .25 .20
759 A203 110fr multi 1.00 .30
760 A203 240fr multi 2.75 .55
761 A203 300fr multi 3.50 .80
762 A203 450fr multi 5.50 1.00
763 A203 500fr multi 6.00 1.10
Nos. 758-763 (6) 19.00 3.95

Souvenir Sheet
Imperf

764 A203 600fr multi 5.00 1.40

Nos. 762-764 are airmail.

Solar
Energy
Apparatus,
Damara
A204

1985, Nov. 4   Litho.   Perf. 13½
765 A204 65fr multi .65 .30
766 A204 130fr multi 1.40 .55

Girl Guides Nature Study — A205

1985, Nov. 16   Perf. 13
767 A205 250fr shown 3.50 1.40
768 A205 250fr Quaka Sugar
Refinery 3.50 1.40
a. Pair, #767-768 + label 10.00 6.50

PHILEXAFRICA '85, Lome, Togo, 11/16-24.

State Visit of Pres. Mitterand of
France, Dec. 12-13 — A206

1985-86   Litho.   Perf. 13x12½
769 A206 65fr multi .75 .25
770 A206 130fr multi 1.50 .55
770A A206 160fr multi ('86) 2.10 .80
Nos. 769-770A (3) 4.35 1.60

Issued: #769-770, Dec. 12.

UN 40th Anniv.,
Central Africa
Admission, 25th
Anniv. — A207

1985, Dec. 18   Perf. 13½
771 A207 140fr multi 1.40 .55

Intl. Youth
Year
A208

Designs: 40fr, David, by Andrea del Ver-
rocchio; Madonna with the Carnation, 1470,
by Leonardo da Vinci. 80fr, Johann Sebastian
Bach. 100fr, St. John at Patmos, 1619, by
Velazquez. 250fr, The Erl King score, by
Franz Schubert. 400fr, Portrait of Vicente
Osorio de Moscoso, by Goya. 500fr, The
Young Mozart Playing in Paris, 1764. 600fr,
Woman in a Plumed Hat, 1901, by Picasso.

1985, Dec. 28
772 A208 40fr multi .40 .20
773 A208 80fr multi .90 .25
774 A208 100fr multi 1.25 .25
775 A208 250fr multi 2.50 .55
776 A208 400fr multi 4.50 .90
777 A208 500fr multi 5.00 1.10
Nos. 772-777 (6) 14.55 3.25

Souvenir Sheet
778 A208 600fr multi 5.25 1.40

Nos. 776-778 are airmail.

Halley's
Comet
A209

100fr, Edmond Halley, British astronomer.
200fr, Sir Isaac Newton's telescope & comet
sighting. 300fr, Halley & Newton observing
comet. 350fr, US probe. 400fr, Soviet probe
plotting comet's perihelion. 500fr, Isodensity
photograph of comet. 600fr, Comet, Earth,
Sun & probe.

1985, Dec. 31
779 A209 100fr multi .75 .25
780 A209 200fr multi 1.90 .40
781 A209 300fr multi 2.75 .45
782 A209 350fr multi 3.25 .80
783 A209 400fr multi 3.75 .85
784 A209 500fr multi 5.00 1.00
Nos. 779-784 (6) 17.40 3.75

Souvenir Sheet
785 A209 600fr multi 6.00 1.75

Nos. 783-785 are airmail.

Christopher Columbus — A210

Various events leading to the discovery of
America and beyond.

1986
786 A210 90fr Plotting course .90 .25
787 A210 110fr Receiving blessing 1.10 .25
788 A210 240fr Fleet in port 2.50 1.25
789 A210 300fr Trade with natives 3.25 .55
790 A210 400fr Storm at sea 4.50 2.00
791 A210 500fr Fleet at sea 5.50 2.40
Nos. 779-784 (6) 17.40 3.75

Souvenir Sheet
792 A210 600fr Portrait 6.50 1.75

Nos. 790-792 are airmail.

Nos. 543-544 Surcharged

30F ▬

1986, Apr. 1   Litho.   Perf. 13
792A A152 30fr on 175fr Kangu
bowls
792B A152 65fr on 300fr
Kolongo bowls

Hairstyles
A211

France- Central
Africa
Week — A212

1986, May 21   Litho.   Perf. 12½
793 A211 20fr multi .45 .20
794 A211 30fr multi .55 .25
795 A211 65fr multi .80 .40
796 A211 160fr multi 2.75 .70
Nos. 793-796 (4) 4.55 1.55

1986, May 26
797 A212 40fr Communications,
horiz. .40 .20
798 A212 60fr Youth, horiz. .55 .25
799 A212 100fr Basket maker .75 .40
800 A212 130fr Bicycling 1.60 .55
Nos. 797-800 (4) 3.30 1.40

Centrapalm
Palm
Oil — A213

25fr, 65fr, Refinery, Bossongo, and palm
tree. 120fr, 160fr, Refinery and palm tree.

1986, Aug. 12   Litho.   Perf. 13½
801 A213 25fr multi .30 .25
802 A213 65fr multi .75 .40
803 A213 120fr multi, vert. 1.40 .80
804 A213 160fr multi, vert. 1.90 .60
Nos. 801-804 (4) 4.35 2.05

Dogs
and
Cats
A214

1986, Sept. 9
805 A214 10fr Pointer .25 .20
806 A214 20fr Egyptian mau .50 .20
807 A214 200fr Newfoundland 3.00 .55
808 A214 300fr Borzoi 3.75 .60
809 A214 400fr Persian red 5.50 .85
Nos. 805-809 (5) 13.00 2.40

Souvenir Sheet
810 A214 500fr Spaniel, Bur-
mese-Malayan 7.00 1.75

Nos. 808-810 are airmail.

African Coffee Producers
Organization, 25th Anniv. — A215

1986, Sept. 25   Litho.   Perf. 13
811 A215 160fr multi 1.60 .55

1986 World Cup Soccer
Championships, Mexico — A216

Satellites, final scores, World Cup and athletes: 30fr, Muller, Socrates. 110fr, Scifo,
Ceulemans. 160fr, Stopyra, Platini. 350fr,
Brehme, Schumacher. 450fr, Maradona.
500fr, Schumacher, Burruchaga.

1986, Nov. 12   *Perf. 13½*
812	A216	30fr multi	.30	.20
813	A216	110fr multi	1.00	.25
814	A216	160fr multi	1.40	.30
815	A216	350fr multi	3.25	.80
816	A216	450fr multi	4.50	1.10
Nos. 812-816 (5)			10.45	2.65

Souvenir Sheet

817   A216   500fr multi   5.50   1.40

Nos. 816-817 are airmail.

US Anniversaries and Events A217

15fr, Judith Resnik. 25fr, Frederic Auguste Bartholdi. 70fr, Elvis Presley. 300fr, Ronald McNair. 450fr, Christa McAuliffe. 500fr, Challenger Astronauts: McAuliffe, Scobee, Smith, Resnik, Onizuka, McNair, Jarvis.

1986, Nov. 19
818	A217	15fr multi	.20	.20
819	A217	25fr multi	.40	.20
820	A217	70fr multi	1.90	.20
821	A217	300fr multi	3.00	.60
822	A217	450fr multi	4.50	1.10
Nos. 818-822 (5)			10.00	2.30

Souvenir Sheet

823   A217   500fr multi   6.25   1.50

US space shuttle Challenger explosion; Statue of Liberty, cent. #822-823 are airmail. For surcharges & overprint see #851-851B.

Flora and Fauna A218

1986, May 30   Litho.   *Perf. 13½*
824	A218	25fr Allamanda neri-		
		ifolia	.25	.20
825	A218	65fr Taurotragus		
		eurycerus	.90	.20
826	A218	160fr Plumieria		
		acuminata	2.10	.30
827	A218	300fr Acinonyx		
		jubatus	4.50	.80
828	A218	400fr Eulophia		
		erthoplata	4.75	.90
829	A218	500fr Leopard	6.50	1.10
Nos. 824-829 (6)			19.00	3.50

Souvenir Sheet

830   A218   600fr Derby's eland,
        eulophia cucul-
        lata   5.75   1.75

#824, 826, 828 vert. #828-830 are airmail. #830 contains one 51x30mm stamp.

Intl. Peace Year — A219

Air Africa, 25th Anniv. — A220

1986, Nov. 29
831   A219   160fr multi   1.60   .55

1986, Dec. 15
832   A220   200fr multi   1.90   .80

UNICEF, 40th Anniv. — A221

1986, Dec. 24
833	A221	15fr shown	.20	.20
834	A221	130fr Child immuniza-		
		tion	1.10	.55
835	A221	160fr Youth, food, map	1.25	.70
Nos. 833-835 (3)			2.55	1.45

German Railways Sesquicentenary — A222

Inventors and locomotives: 40fr, Alfred de Glehn, Prussian Railways DH2 Green Elephant. 70fr, Rudolf Diesel, S3/6 No. 1829 Rheingold. 160fr, Carl Golsdorf, Trans-Europe Express train Type 103. 300fr, Wilhelm Schmidt, Beyer Garratt locomotive. 400fr, Monsieur Du Bousquet, Series 3500 compound locomotive. 500fr, Werner von Siemens, 1980s electric locomotive.

1986, Dec. 31
836	A222	40fr multi	.55	.20
837	A222	70fr multi	1.00	.20
838	A222	160fr multi	2.25	.40
839	A222	300fr multi	3.75	.60
840	A222	400fr multi	4.50	1.10
Nos. 836-840 (5)			12.05	2.50

Souvenir Sheet

841   A222   500fr multi   5.00   1.40

Nos. 840-841 are airmail. No. 841 contains one 42x36mm stamp.

Agriculture Radio Project A223

1986, Dec. 27   Litho.   *Perf. 13½*
842	A223	170fr shown	2.25	.90
843	A223	265fr Satellite commu-		
		nication	3.25	1.40

Pan-African Telecommunications Union congress, Dec. 7, 1986.
No. 842 exists in souvenir sheet of one.

Space A224

Scientists and inventions: 25fr, Sir William Herschel (1738-1822), British astronomer, and Mariner Mark II. 65fr, Wernher von Braun (1912-1977), American engineer, and Mars rover. 160fr, Rudolf Hanel, Mariner Mark II and Titan. 300fr, Patrick Baudry, Hermes shuttle and Eureka platform. 400fr, U. Keller, Halley's Comet and Giotto probe. 500fr, Wubbo Ockels, Ulf Merbold and Columbus European Space Station. 600fr, Wilhelm Obers (1758-1840) and Mariner Mark II surveying asteroids. No. 850 horiz.

1987, Jan. 27
844	A224	25fr multi	.35	.20
845	A224	65fr multi	.75	.20
846	A224	160fr multi	1.75	.30
847	A224	300fr multi	3.00	.75
848	A224	400fr multi	3.25	.90
849	A224	500fr multi	4.00	1.25
Nos. 844-849 (6)			13.10	3.60

Souvenir Sheet

850   A224   600fr multi   6.25   1.75

Nos. 848-850 are airmail.

No. 820 Surcharged

1987, Feb. 20   Litho.   *Perf. 13½*
851   A217   485fr on 70fr Elvis
        Presley   7.75   2.00

Nos. 820 and 851 Ovptd. "Elvis PRESLEY / 1977-1987" in Black

1987, Feb. 20   Litho.   *Perf. 13½*
851A   A217   70fr multi   1.40   .40
851B   A217   485fr on 70fr multi   6.50   2.00

Overprint in red exists.

1992 Barcelona Olympics A225

Athletes and landmarks or sights: 30fr, Soccer player, Lady with Umbrella fountain. 150fr, Judo, Barcelona Cathedral. 265fr, Cyclist, Church of the Holy Family, by Gaudi. 350fr, Gymnast, Tomb of Columbus. 495fr, Runner, human tower. 500fr, Swimmer, Statue of Columbus.

1987, June 4
852	A225	30fr multi	.40	.20
853	A225	150fr multi	1.40	.45
854	A225	265fr multi	2.50	.80
855	A225	350fr multi	3.50	1.00
856	A225	495fr multi	5.50	1.40
Nos. 852-856 (5)			13.30	3.85

Souvenir Sheet

857   A225   500fr multi   4.50   1.40

Nos. 855-857 are airmail.

A226

1988 Winter Olympics, Calgary A227

1987, June 26
858	A226	20fr Two-man luge	.30	.20
859	A226	140fr Cross-country		
		skiing	1.40	.45
860	A226	250fr Women's figure		
		skating	2.25	.80
861	A226	300fr Hockey	3.00	.90
862	A226	400fr Men's slalom	3.75	1.10
Nos. 858-862 (5)			10.70	3.45

Souvenir Sheet

863   A227   500fr Downhill skiing   4.50   1.40

Nos. 861-863 are airmail.

Intl. Peace Year — A228

1987, July 20
864	A228	50fr dull ultra, sepia &		
		blk	.50	.25
865	A228	160fr lt ol grn, sep &		
		blk	1.40	.60

Intl. Decade of Drinkable Water — A228a

Designs: 5fr, Woman at village pump; 10fr, Two women at village pump; 200fr, Three women at village pump.

1987, Sept. 22   Litho.   *Perf. 13½*
865A	A228a	5fr multi	32.50	
865B	A228a	10fr multi	32.50	
865C	A228a	200fr multi	37.50	
Nos. 865A-865C (3)			102.50	

Butterflies A229

1987, Oct. 5   Litho.   *Perf. 13½*
866	A229	100fr Charaxes candi-		
		ope	2.00	.85
867	A229	120fr Graphium leoni-		
		das	2.75	.90
868	A229	130fr Charaxes brutus	3.00	.90
869	A229	160fr Salamis aetiops	3.25	1.10
Nos. 866-869 (4)			11.00	3.75

Pygmy Soccer Team from Nola — A230

1987, Nov. 30   Litho.   _Perf. 13_
870	A230	90fr multi	1.10	.60
871	A230	160fr multi	1.75	.90

Integration of the pygmy people into Central African society.

Dinosaurs — A231

Perf. 14x13½, 13½x14
1988, Mar. 19   Litho.
872	A231	50fr Brontosaurus	.45	.20
873	A231	65fr Triceratops	.80	.25
874	A231	100fr Ankylosaurus	1.10	.40
875	A231	160fr Stegosaurus	1.90	.60
876	A231	200fr Tyrannosaurus rex	2.00	.80
877	A231	240fr Corythosaurus	3.00	.90
878	A231	300fr Allosaurus	3.50	1.25
879	A231	300fr Brachiosaurus	4.25	1.50
	Nos. 872-879 (8)		17.00	5.90

Nos. 876-879 vert.

Anniversaries and Events A232

Designs: 40fr, Pres. James Madison and "We the People..." from the US Constitution. 160fr, Elizabeth II and Duke of Edinburgh . 200fr, Steffi Graf, tennis champion. 300fr, Garri Kasparov of Russia, 1985 world chess champion. 400fr, Boris Becker, 1985-86 Wimbledon champion. 500fr, Christoph Willibald Gluck (1714-87), composer. Nos. 880-884 vert.

1988, Feb. 15   _Perf. 13½_
880	A232	40fr multi	.40	.20
881	A232	160fr multi	1.50	.50
882	A232	200fr multi	1.90	.45
883	A232	300fr multi	3.00	.80
884	A232	400fr multi	3.50	1.25
	Nos. 880-884 (5)		10.30	2.95

Souvenir Sheet
885	A232	500fr multi	6.25	1.75

US Constitution bicentennial (40fr); 40th wedding anniv. of Elizabeth II and Prince Philip (160fr). Nos. 883-885 are airmail.

World Health Organization, 40th Anniv. — A233

1988, Apr. 7   Litho.   _Perf. 13½_
886	A233	70fr multi	.65	.40
887	A233	120fr multi	1.00	.55

Scout Ornithological Activities A234

Scouts and: 25fr, _Merops nubicus._ 170fr, _Euplectes hordeacea._ 300fr, _Ceryle rudis._ 400fr, _Estrilda bengala._ 450fr, _Kaupifalco monogrammicus._ 500fr, _Lamprotornis splendidus._

1988, July 1   Litho.   _Perf. 13½_
888	A234	25fr multi	.20	.20
889	A234	170fr multi	1.50	.70
890	A234	300fr multi	3.00	2.00
891	A234	400fr multi	4.25	2.00
892	A234	450fr multi	5.00	2.40
	Nos. 888-892 (5)		13.95	7.30

Souvenir Sheet
893	A234	500fr multi	6.25	1.75

Nos. 891-893 are airmail.
For surcharges see Nos. 921-924.

1988 Summer Olympics, Seoul A235

1988, Sept. 30
894	A235	150fr Running, vert.	1.25	.25
895	A235	300fr Judo, vert.	2.75	.70
896	A235	400fr Soccer, vert.	3.00	1.00
897	A235	450fr Tennis, vert.	3.50	1.10
	Nos. 894-897 (4)		10.50	3.05

Souvenir Sheet
898	A235	500fr Boxing	5.00	1.50

Nos. 896-898 are airmail.

1988 Winter Olympics, Calgary — A236

1988, Sept. 30   Litho.   _Perf. 13½_
899	A236	170fr Cross-country skiing	1.40	.30
900	A236	350fr Ice hockey	2.25	.60
901	A236	400fr Downhill skiing	3.00	.90
902	A236	450fr Freestyle	3.25	1.00
	Nos. 899-902 (4)		9.90	2.80

Souvenir Sheet
903	A236	500fr shown	5.50	1.50

Nos. 899-902 vert. Nos. 901-903 are airmail.

Natl. Arbor Day — A237

1988, July 16   Litho.   _Perf. 13½_
904	A237	50fr Students planting trees	.50	.25
905	A237	100fr like 50fr	1.00	.55
906	A237	130fr Forest (before and after)	1.40	.60
	Nos. 904-906 (3)		2.90	1.40

L'Amitie Hospital, 1st Anniv. A238

1988, Nov. 30
907	A238	5fr shown	.20	.20
908	A238	60fr Aerial view	.65	.40
909	A238	160fr Front gate	1.40	.80
	Nos. 907-909 (3)		2.25	1.40

Proclamation of Central African Republic, 30th Anniv. A238a

Design: 65fr, 160fr, Dove, map, flag, people. 240fr, Government buildings, horiz.

1988 (?)   Litho.   _Perf. 13½_
909A	A238a	65fr multi	52.50	—
909B	A238b	160fr multi	52.50	—
909C	A238a	240fr multi	52.50	—

A239

A240

Olympic Medalists, Seoul, 1988: 150fr, Kristine Otto, DDR, swimming. 240fr, Matt Biondi, US, swimming. 300fr, Florence Griffith-Joyner, US, running. 450fr, Pierre Durand, France, equestrian. 600fr, Carl Lewis, US, running.

1989, Apr. 1
910	A239	150fr multi	2.25	.55
911	A239	240fr multi	3.50	.80
912	A239	300fr multi	4.50	1.10
913	A239	450fr multi	7.50	1.75
_a._	_Souv. sheet of 4, #910-913_		17.50	
	Nos. 910-913 (4)		17.75	4.20

Souvenir Sheet
914	A239	600fr multi	5.75	2.00

Nos. 913-914 airmail. No. 914 contains one 37x43mm stamp.

1989, Apr. 10   Litho.   _Perf. 13½_

Transportation Innovations, Inventors: 20fr, Hebmuller and 1953 Volkswagen Beetle. 205fr, Werner von Siemens (1816-1892) and 1879 Locomotive B. 300fr, Dennis Conner, skipper of _Stars and Stripes_, winner of the 1988 America's Cup. 400fr, Andre Citroen (1878-1935) and 1955 Citroen-15 SIX. 450fr, Marc Seguin (1786-1875) and 1895 Decauville-Mallet 020-020. 750fr, Frederick S. Duesenberg (1876-1932), brother August, US flag and 1929 J Phaeton.
915	A240	20fr multi	.20	.20
916	A240	205fr multi	1.90	.55
917	A240	300fr multi	2.50	.60
918	A240	400fr multi	3.50	1.10
919	A240	450fr multi	4.50	1.25
	Nos. 915-919 (5)		12.60	3.70

Souvenir Sheet
920	A240	750fr multi	6.25	1.50

Nos. 919-920 airmail. No. 920 contains one 43x37mm stamp.
#915-919 exist in souvenir sheets of 1.

Nos. 889-892 Surcharged in Black or Silver

1988, Oct. 7   Litho.   _Perf. 13½_
921	A234	30fr on 170fr (B)	.40	.20
922	A234	70fr on 300fr	1.10	.55
923	A234	160fr on 400fr	1.90	.85
924	A234	200fr on 450fr	2.50	1.10
	Nos. 921-924 (4)		5.90	2.70

Nos. 923-924 are airmail.

PHILEXFRANCE '89, French Revolution Bicent. — A241

Designs: 200fr, Allegory in Honor of Liberty. 300fr, Declaration of Human Rights and Citizenship. 500fr, The Bastille, horiz.

1989, July 7   Litho.   _Perf. 13_
925	A241	200fr multi	1.90	.80
926	A241	300fr multi	4.00	1.25
_a._	Pair, #925-926 + label		6.50	6.50

Souvenir Sheet
927	A241	500fr multi	6.25	3.75

Souvenir Sheet

Statue of Liberty — A242

Designs: a, Crown and torch observatories lit at night. b, Working on statue's coiffure. c, Face and scaffolding. d, Workman sanding copper sheeting around the crown observatory. e, Re-opening ceremony, 1986. f, Crown observatory at night.

Wmk. 385
1989, July   Litho.   _Perf. 13_
928	Sheet of 6		11.00	11.00
_a.-c._	A242 150fr any single		1.60	.60
_d.-f._	A242 200fr any single		1.75	1.00

Statue of Liberty cent. (in 1986). Photograph of the statue is reversed.

M. Champagnat (1789-1840), Founder of the Marist Order — A243

1989   Litho.   _Perf. 13½_
929	A243	15fr Madonna and child, map	.20	.20
930	A243	50fr Cross, Earth	.45	.25
931	A243	160fr shown	1.40	.80
	Nos. 929-931 (3)		2.05	1.25

Nos. 929-930 vert.

Harvest Feast, Bambari A244

1989, Oct. 15
932	A244	100fr Produce	1.00	.55
933	A244	160fr Ox plow	1.50	.60

World Food Day A245

1989, Oct. 16
| 934 | A245 | 60fr Domestic animals | .55 | .30 |
| 935 | A245 | 240fr Arresting ivory poachers | 2.25 | 1.00 |

French Revolution, Bicent. — A246

Battle scenes and leaders: 160fr, Brig.-Gen. Francois-Christophe Kellermann (1735-1820), Battle of Valmy, Sept. 22, 1792. 200fr, Minister of War Charles-Francois du Perier Dumouriez (1739-1823), Battle of Jemappes, Nov. 7, 1792. 500fr, Gen. Jean-Charles Pichegru (1761-1804), capture of the Dutch fleet, Jan. 22, 1795. 600fr, Gen. Louis-Lazare Hoche (1768-97), Battle of Quiberon Bay, July 21, 1795. 1000fr, Napoleon at the Battle of Rivoli Veronese, Jan. 15, 1797. 1500fr, General Jean-Baptiste Jourdan.

1989, Dec. 5   Litho.   Perf. 13½
936	A246	160fr multicolored	1.40	.40
937	A246	200fr multicolored	1.75	.55
938	A246	500fr multicolored	5.50	1.10
939	A246	600fr multicolored	5.00	1.00
a.		Souvenir sheet of 4, #936-939	15.00	15.00
		Nos. 936-939 (4)	13.65	3.05

Souvenir Sheet
| 940 | A246 | 1000fr multicolored | 10.00 | 3.00 |

Litho. & Embossed
| 940A | A246 | 1500fr gold & multi | — | — |

PHILEXFRANCE '89. Nos. 938-940A are airmail.
No. 936 is incorrectly inscribed "Francois-Etienne." Jemappes is incorrectly spelled on No. 937. No. 940 is incorrectly inscribed "January 14."

1990 World Cup Soccer Championships, Italy — A247

Various athletes and Italian landmarks: 20fr, Bell tower, Palermo Cathedral. 120fr, Trinity of the Mount, Rome. 160fr, St. Francis Church apse, Bologna. 200fr, Palace, Florence. 1000fr, Milan Cathedral.

1989, Dec. 23
941	A247	20fr multicolored	.20	.20
942	A247	120fr multicolored	1.25	.40
943	A247	160fr multicolored	1.40	.40
944	A247	200fr multicolored	1.60	.55
		Nos. 941-944 (4)	4.45	1.55

Souvenir Sheet
| 945 | A247 | 1000fr multicolored | 9.25 | 2.00 |

Nos. 942 and 945 are airmail.

Save the Forests A247a

1989   Litho.   Perf. 13½
| 945A | A247a | 160fr multicolored | 1.40 | .60 |

Town of Bangui, Cent. A247b

Designs: 100fr, Governor's Palace, 1906. 160fr, Outpost. 200fr, A. Dolisie, founder of Bangui, vert. 1000fr, Signing of peace treaty between Michel Dolisie and Chief Gbembo, 1889, vert.

1989   Litho.   Perf. 13½
945B	A247b	100fr multi	1.25	.40
945C	A247b	160fr multi	1.75	1.00
945D	A247b	200fr multi	2.50	.95
945E	A247b	1000fr multi	10.50	4.25
		Nos. 945B-945E (4)	16.00	6.60

Championship Team from Central Africa, 1987 — A248

1990, Feb. 23   Litho.   Perf. 13½
946	A248	160fr Flag, players, trophy	1.40	.60
947	A248	240fr shown	2.25	.85
948	A248	500fr like 160fr	4.50	1.75
		Nos. 946-948 (3)	8.15	3.20

African Basketball Championships. Dated 1988. Nos. 946 and 948 vert.

A249

A250

1990, Feb. 23   Litho.   Perf. 13½
| 949 | A249 | 100fr multicolored | 1.00 | .40 |
| 950 | A249 | 130fr multicolored | 1.10 | .55 |

Central Africa, winner of the 1987 African Basketball Cup Championships, Tunis. Dated 1989.

1990, Mar. 12   Litho.   Perf. 13½
1992 Winter Olympics, Albertville: No. 955A, Slalom skier. No. 955B, Pairs figure skating.
951	A250	10fr Speed skating	.20	.20
952	A250	60fr Cross-country skiing	.55	.25
953	A250	500fr Slalom	4.50	1.00
954	A250	750fr Figure skating	6.25	1.40
		Nos. 951-954 (4)	11.50	2.85

Souvenir Sheet
| 955 | A250 | 1000fr Downhill skiing | 8.75 | 2.00 |

Litho. & Embossed
Souvenir Sheet
| 955A | A250 | 1500fr gold & multi | 12.00 | 3.50 |

Souvenir Sheet
| 955B | A250 | 1500fr gold & multi | 30.00 | 30.00 |

Nos. 953-955B are airmail. No. 955 contains one 36x42mm stamp. Nos. 951-954 exist in souvenir sheets of one.

Scout, *Euphaera eusemoides* — A251

Boy scouts and butterflies: 65fr, *Cymothoe beckeri.* 160fr, *Pseudacraea clarki.* 250fr, *Charaxes castor.* 300fr, *Euphaedra gausape.* 500fr, *Graphium ridleyanus.* 1000fr, *Euphaedra edwardsi.* No. 962A, *Antanartia delius.* No. 962B, Spotted flycatcher. No. 962C, *Cymothoe sangaris.*

1990, Mar. 26
956	A251	25fr multicolored	.30	.20
957	A251	65fr multicolored	.55	.20
958	A251	160fr multicolored	1.25	.25
959	A251	250fr multicolored	2.25	.55
960	A251	300fr multicolored	2.75	.60
961	A251	500fr multicolored	4.75	1.00
		Nos. 956-961 (6)	11.85	2.80

Souvenir Sheet
| 962 | A251 | 1000fr multicolored | 11.00 | 2.25 |

Litho. & Embossed
Perf. 12½
| 962A | A251 | 1500fr gold & multi | 13.75 | 4.00 |

Perf. 13½
| 962B | A251 | 1500fr gold & multi | 45.00 | 4.00 |

Souvenir Sheet
| 962C | A251 | 1500fr gold & multi | 12.00 | 12.00 |

Nos. 962A-962C are airmail. No. 962A exists in a souvenir sheet of 1.

1992 Summer Olympics, Barcelona A252

1990, Apr. 1   Litho.   Perf. 13½
963	A252	10fr Javelin	.20	.20
964	A252	40fr Runner	.40	.20
965	A252	130fr Tennis	1.10	.25
966	A252	240fr Hurdles	2.00	.55
967	A252	400fr Yachting	3.50	1.00
968	A252	500fr Soccer	4.50	1.10
		Nos. 963-968 (6)	11.70	3.30

Souvenir Sheet
| 969 | A252 | 1000fr Boxing | 9.75 | 2.00 |

Nos. 963-965 vert. Nos. 967-969 are airmail.

Pres. Gorbachev, Pres. Bush — A253

Pres. Gorbachev, Pope John Paul II — A254

1990, July 27   Litho.   Perf. 13½
| 970 | A253 | 120fr multicolored | .95 | .25 |
| 971 | A254 | 200fr multicolored | 1.50 | .30 |

Pope John Paul II-Gorbachev meeting Dec. 2, 1989. Bush-Gorbachev Summit Meeting Dec. 3, 1989. Nos. 970-971 exist in souvenir sheets of 1.

Great Britain No. 1, Sir Rowland Hill (1795-1879) — A255

1990, July 27
| 972 | A255 | 130fr multicolored | 1.00 | .25 |

No. 972 exists in a souvenir sheet of 1.

Events and Anniversaries — A256

Designs: 160fr, Galileo Probe to Jupiter. 240fr, Neil Armstrong, 1st man on moon. 250fr, Concorde, rapid-transit train, Rotary Intl. emblem.

1990, July 27   Litho.   Perf. 13½
973	A256	160fr multicolored	1.10	.40
974	A256	240fr multicolored	1.75	.50
975	A256	250fr multicolored	3.75	.50
		Nos. 973-975 (3)	6.60	1.40

Wildlife Protection A258

100fr, Declining elephant population, vert.

1991, Jan. 25   Litho.   Perf. 13½
976	A258	15fr gold & multi	.60	.20
977	A258	60fr multicolored	1.90	.40
978	A258	100fr multicolored	3.00	.55
		Nos. 976-978 (3)	5.50	1.15

Eutropius
A259

Design: 240fr, Distichodus.

1991, Jan. 26
979 A259 50fr multicolored .55 .25
980 A259 160fr gold & multi 2.10 .75
981 A259 240fr multicolored 3.50 1.50
Nos. 979-981 (3) 6.15 2.50

Fight Against AIDS
A260

Design: 120fr, Class speaker, vert.

1991, Jan. 24
982 A260 5fr gold & multi .45 .20
983 A260 70fr multicolored 1.40 .55
984 A260 120fr multicolored 1.90 .80
Nos. 982-984 (3) 3.75 1.55

Central African Diamonds
A260a

Designs: 65fr, Woman polishing diamond, 160fr, Map, diamond.

1991, Feb. 14 Litho. Perf. 11½
Granite Paper
984A A260a 65fr multicolored —
984B A260a 160fr multicolored —

Assumption of Power by Pres. Andre Kolingba, 10th Anniv. (in 1991) — A261

1992, Sept. 1 Litho. Perf. 13x13½
985 A261 160fr multicolored 1.60 .60

Anniversaries and Events — A262

Designs: 80fr, Maybach Zeppelin, zeppelin airship, Count Ferdinand Zeppelin. 140fr, Child being comforted, Jean-Henri Dunant. 160fr, Benetton-Ford B 192, Michael Schumacher. 350fr, Konrad Adenauer signing Constitution of German Republic. 500fr, Pope John Paul II, mother and child, map. 600fr, Wolfgang Amadeus Mozart. 1000fr, Columbus at La Rabida, sailing ship, and building in Seville, Spain.

1992, Sept. 22 Litho. Perf. 13½
986 A262 80fr multicolored .65 .20
987 A262 140fr multicolored 1.60 .25
988 A262 160fr multicolored 1.90 .40
989 A262 350fr multicolored 4.50 1.10

990 A262 500fr multicolored 6.25 1.40
991 A262 600fr multicolored 8.25 1.50
Nos. 986-991 (6) 23.15 4.85
Souvenir Sheet
992 A262 1000fr multicolored 8.25 2.00

Count Zeppelin, 75th anniv. of death (#986). Jean-Henri Dunant, first recipient of Nobel Peace Prize, 90th anniv. (in 1991) (#987). Grand Prix of Monaco (#988). Brandenburg Gate, bicent (#989). Visit of Pope John Paul II to Africa (#990). Wolfgang Amadeus Mozart, bicent. of death (in 1991) (#991). Discovery of America, 500th anniv. and Expo '92, Seville (#992).
Nos. 990-992 are airmail. Nos. 986-991 exist in souvenir sheets of 1.
For overprint see No. 1073.

A264

Elvis Presley (1935-1977)
A264a

Portrait of Presley, song or movie: 200fr, Heartbreak Hotel, 1956. 300fr, Love Me Tender, 1957. 400fr, Jailhouse Rock, 1957. 600fr, Harem Scarum, 1965.
1000fr, With guitar, at microphone. No. 1001A, Holding microphone. No. 1001B, Playing guitar.

1993, July 12 Litho. Perf. 13½
997 A264 200fr multi 2.40 .25
998 A264 300fr multi 3.50 .50
999 A264 400fr multi 4.25 .60
1000 A264 600fr multi 6.00 1.00
Nos. 997-1000 (4) 16.15 2.35
Souvenir Sheet
1001 A264 1000fr multi 9.50 2.40
Litho. & Embossed
1001A A264a 1500fr gold & multi 20.00 7.50
Souvenir Sheet
1001B A264a 1500fr gold & multi 13.00 8.00

Nos. 1000-1001B are airmail. Nos. 997-1000, 1001A exist imperf. and in souvenir sheets of one. Nos. 1001, 1001B exist imperf.

A265

Wedding of Japan's Crown Prince Naruhito and Masako Owada
A265a

Designs: 50fr, Princess Masako, parents. 65fr, Crown Prince Naruhito, parents. 160fr, Princess Masako, Harvard University 450fr, Crown Prince Naruhito, Oxford University. 750fr, Crown Prince, Princess.

1993, July 12 Litho. Perf. 13½
1002 A265 50fr multi .30 .20
1003 A265 65fr multi .65 .25
1004 A265 160fr multi 1.75 .25
1005 A265 450fr multi 4.50 1.00
Nos. 1002-1005 (4) 7.20 1.70
Souvenir Sheet
1006 A265 750fr multi 7.75 3.00
Litho. & Embossed
1006A A265a 1500fr gold & multi 26.00 4.00

Nos. 1005-1006A are airmail. Nos. 1002-1005, 1006A exist imperf. and in souvenir sheets of one. No. 1006 exists imperf.

A266

1994 World Cup Soccer Championships, US — A266a

Designs show winning team, scenes from: 40fr, Amsterdam, 1928; Montevideo, 1930. 50fr, Rome, 1934; Paris, 1938. 60fr, Rio, 1950; Berne, 1954. 80fr, Stockholm, 1958; Santiago, 1962. 160fr, London, 1966; Mexico City, 1970. 200fr, Munich, 1974; Buenos Aires, 1978. 400fr, Madrid, 1982; Mexico City, 1986. 500fr, Rome, 1990; emblem for US competition, 1994.
1000fr, 1990 German team; 1994 US team. No. 1015A, Pele, Brazil. No. 1015B, Gerd Muller, Germany.

1993, Oct. 9 Litho. Perf. 13½
1007 A266 40fr multi .40 .20
1008 A266 50fr multi .40 .20
1009 A266 60fr multi .50 .20
1010 A266 80fr multi .65 .20
1011 A266 160fr multi 1.40 .40
1012 A266 200fr multi 1.90 .70
1013 A266 400fr multi 3.50 .70
1014 A266 500fr multi 5.00 1.00
Nos. 1007-1014 (8) 13.75 3.60
Souvenir Sheet
1015 A266 1000fr multi 10.00 2.75
Litho. & Embossed
1015A A266a 1500fr gold & multi 26.00

Souvenir Sheet
1015B A266a 1500fr gold & multi 13.50

#1015 contains one 60x30mm stamp. #1007-1014 exist in souvenir sheets of one. Nos. 1015A-1015B are airmail.

Miniature Sheets

Modern Olympic Games, Cent. (in 1996) — A267

No. 1016: a, Ancient olympian. b, Baron de Coubertin, 1896. c, Charles Bennett, 1900. d, Etienne Desmarteau, 1904. e, Harry Porter, 1908. f, Patrick MacDonald, 1912. g, No games, 1916. h, Frank Loomis, 1920. i, Albert White, 1924.
No. 1017: a, El Ouafi, 1928. b, Eddie Tolan, 1932. c, Jesse Owens, 1936. d, No games, 1940. e, No games, 1944. f, Tapio Rautavaara, 1948. g, Jean Boiteux, 1952. h, Petrus Kasterman, 1956. i, Sante Gaiardoni, 1960.
No. 1018: a, Anton Geesink, 1964. b, Bob Beamon, 1968. c, Mark Spitz, 1972. d, Nadia Comaneci, 1976. e, Aleksandre Dityatin, 1980. f, J.F. Lamour, 1984. g, Pierre Durand, 1988. h, Michael Jordan, 1992. i, Soccer player, 1996.

1993 Litho. Perf. 13½
1016 A267 90fr Sheet of 9, #a.-i. 7.50 3.25
1017 A267 100fr Sheet of 9, #a.-i. 8.25 3.75
1018 A267 160fr Sheet of 9, #a.-i. 13.00 5.75

Miniature Sheet

Dinosaurs — A268

Designs: No. 1019a, 25fr, Saltoposuchus. b, 25fr, Rhamphorhynchus. c, 25fr, Dimorphodon. d, 25fr, Archaeopteryx. e, 30fr, Compsognathus longipes. f, 30fr, Cryptocleidus oxoniensis. g, 30fr, Stegosaurus. h, 30fr, Cetiosaurus. i, 50fr, Brontosaurus. j, 50fr, Corythosaurus casuarius. k, 50fr, Styracosaurus. l, 50fr, Gorgosaurus. m, 500fr, Scolosaurus. n, 500fr, Trachodon. o, 500fr, Struthiomimus. p, 500fr, Tarbosaurus.
No. 1020, Tylosaur.

1993, Dec. 3
1019 A268 Sheet of 16, #a.-p. 26.00 26.00
Souvenir Sheet
1020 A268 1000fr multicolored 10.50 2.75

No. 1020 is airmail and contains one 51x60mm stamp.

Biodiversity
A269

Various fauna surrounding: 100fr, Man planting tree. 130fr, Man with local fauna, vert.

1993, Oct. 20   Litho.   Perf. 13½
| 1021 | A269 | 100fr multicolored | 1.25 | .50 |
| 1022 | A269 | 130fr multicolored | 1.75 | .80 |

M'Bali
Dam — A270

1993, Jan. 14   Litho.   Perf. 13
| 1023 | A270 | 160fr shown | 1.60 | .30 |
| 1024 | A270 | 200fr Women, men with fish | 2.25 | .40 |

Cooperation Council, 40th
Anniv. — A271

1993, Jan. 26
| 1025 | A271 | 240fr multicolored | 2.50 | .50 |

Intl. Conference
on Nutrition,
Rome — A272

1993, Apr. 1
| 1026 | A272 | 90fr shown | .75 | .20 |
| 1027 | A272 | 140fr Fresh foods | 1.40 | .30 |

University
of Bangui
A273

1993, Apr. 8
| 1028 | A273 | 100fr multicolored | 1.00 | .25 |

Dated 1992.

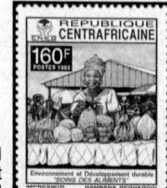

Environmental
Development
A274

Designs: 160fr, Woman with vegetables, fruit. 240fr, Woman cooking food.

1993, Oct. 27   Litho.   Perf. 13½
| 1029 | A274 | 160fr multicolored | 1.75 | .80 |
| 1030 | A274 | 240fr multicolored | 2.50 | .95 |

Miniature Sheets

1994 Winter
Olympics,
Lillehammer
A275

Past Winter Olympic champions: 1031a, Th. Haug, Nordic combined skiing, Chamonix, 1924. b, J. Heaton, 1-man sled, St. Moritz, 1928. c, B. Ruud, ski jumping, Lake Placid, 1932. d, I. Ballangrud, speed skating, Garmisch-Partenkirchen, 1936. e, G. Fraser, women's slalom skiing, St. Moritz, 1948. f, German 4-man bobsled, Oslo, 1952. g, USSR hockey team, Cortina D'Ampezzo, 1956. h, J. Vuarnet, downhill skiing, Squaw Valley, 1960.
No. 1032a, M. Goitschel, giant slalom, Innsbruck, 1964. b, Jean-Claude Killy, slalom skiing, Grenoble, 1968. c, U. Wehling, Nordic combined, Sapporo, 1972. d, Rodnina & Zaitsev, pairs figure skating, Innsbruck, 1976. e, E. Heiden, speed skating, Lake Placid, 1980. f, K. Witt, figure skating, Sarajevo, 1984. g, J. Mueller, luge, Calgary, 1988. h, E. Grospiron, freestyle skiing, Albertville, 1992. i, Speed skiing, Lillehammer, 1994.

1994, Jan. 14   Litho.   Perf. 13½
| 1031 | A275 | 100fr Sheet of 8, #a.-h. + label | 6.50 | 6.50 |
| 1032 | A275 | 200fr Sheet of 9, #a.-i. | 15.00 | 15.00 |

1994 Winter Olympics,
Lillehammer — A276

Design: 1500fr, Women figure skaters.

1994   Litho. & Embossed   Perf. 13½
| 1033 | A276 | 1500fr gold & multi | 12.00 | |

#1033 is airmail & exists in a souvenir sheet of 1. Value $24.

Flowers,
Vegetables,
Fruit, &
Mushrooms
A277

Flowers: No. 1034a, 25fr, Ansellia africana. b, 60fr, Polystachia bella. c, 90fr, Aerangis rhodosticta. d, 500fr, Angraecum eburneum.
Vegetables: No. 1035a, 30r, Yams. b, 65fr, Manioc. c, 100fr, Corn. d, 400fr, Sweet potato.
Fruits: No. 1036a, 40fr, Orange. b, 70fr, Banana. c, 160fr, Mango. d, 300fr, Coffee.
Mushrooms: No. 1037a, 50fr, Termitomyces schimperi. b, 80fr, Sympodia arborescens. c, 200fr, Phlebopus sudanicus. d, 600fr, Leucocoprinus africanus.

1994, Jan. 21   Litho.   Perf. 13½
1034	A277	Strip of 4, #a.-d.	5.50	2.50
1035	A277	Strip of 4, #a.-d.	5.00	2.25
1036	A277	Strip of 4, #a.-d.	4.50	2.00
1037	A277	Strip of 4, #a.-d.	8.75	3.75
e.		Sheet of 16, #1034-1037	24.50	11.00

Catholic
Church in
Africa,
Cent. — A278

Designs: 130fr, Monsignor Augouard, founder of mission, St. Paul of the Rapids. 160fr, Monsignor Grandin, Abbe Boganda, first sacred ordainment, 1938. 240fr, Father Louis Godart, House of Charity, Bangui.

1994, June 2   Litho.   Perf. 13½
1038	A278	130fr multicolored	.55	.25
1039	A278	160fr multicolored	.70	.30
1040	A278	240fr multicolored	1.00	.45
	Nos. 1038-1040 (3)		2.25	1.00

Relics from Early Civilizations,
Landmarks — A279

Designs: 10fr, Cabin-shaped cinerary urn, Rome. 25fr, Face of the secret denunciation, Venice, vert. 30fr, Statue of the Tetrarchs, Venice, vert. 50fr, Little cube-shaped building, Palermo, vert. 65fr, Frieze, The Alhambra, Granada, vert. 90fr, Grand Chateau, Bellinzona. 100fr, Museum D'Orsay, Paris, vert. 130fr, Granary, Galicia. 140fr, Mural, by Diego Rivera, Mexico, vert. 160fr, Guacamaya mask, Mexico, vert. 200fr, Ivory mask, Western Africa, vert. 240fr, La Sagrada Familia, Barcelona, vert. 260fr, Casbah of Amerhidil. 300fr, Gold aureus of Sulla, Rome, 82 BC. 400fr, Chimborazo volcano.

1994, June 2   Perf. 13
| 1041-1055 | A279 | Set of 15 | 10.50 | 4.50 |

D-Day, 50th Anniv. — A280

Pegasus Bridge, June 6: No. 1056a, British troops crossing bridge, piper. b, Glider, British and German soldiers. c, German soldiers.
Operation COBRA, July 24: a, Tank, monument, soldiers. b, Bombers, soldiers, gun barrel. c, Tank, soldiers up close.

1994, Oct. 25   Litho.   Perf. 13½
| 1056 | A280 | 600fr Strip of 3, #a.-c. | 10.00 | 3.75 |
| 1057 | A280 | 600fr Strip of 3, #a.-c. | 10.00 | 3.75 |

Nos. 1056b, 1057b are 30x46mm. Nos. 1056-1057 are continuous designs. See No. C359.

Anniversaries & Events — A281

No. 1058, 600fr — Characters from "Star Wars:" a, Han Solo, Chewbaca. b, Darth Vader, Princess Leia, Luke Skywalker, R2D2, C3PO. c, Obi Wan Kenobi.
No. 1059 — First manned moon landing, 25th anniv.: a, 400fr, Buzz Aldrin. b, 500fr, Neil Armstrong, Apollo 11 liftoff. c, 600fr, Michael Collins.
No. 1060: a, 400fr, Theodor von Karman. b, 500fr, Apollo 11 command module, Wernher

von Braun. c, 600fr, Hermes Rocket, Hermann Oberth.

1994, Oct. 25   Litho.   Perf. 13½
1058	A281	Strip of 3, #a.-c.	8.00	3.50
1059	A281	Strip of 3, #a.-c.	7.50	3.00
1060	A281	Strip of 3, #a.-c.	7.50	3.00

Motion Pictures, cent. (#1058).
Nos. 1058b, 1059b, 1060b are 60x51mm. Nos. 1058-1060 are continuous design and exist in a souvenir sheet of 1.

Natl.
Assembly
A282

1994, Dec. 8
| 1061 | A282 | 65fr blue & multi | .35 | .20 |
| 1062 | A282 | 430fr yel brn & multi | 1.90 | .90 |

Antoine de Saint-Exupery (1900-44),
Aviator, Author — A283

1994, Dec 16
| 1063 | A283 | 80fr Airplane | .35 | .20 |
| 1064 | A283 | 235fr Portrait, vert. | 1.00 | .50 |

Inauguration of
Pres. Ange-Felix
Patasse, 1st
Anniv. — A284

1994, Oct. 22
1065	A284	65fr blue & multi	.40	.20
1066	A284	300fr yellow & multi	1.60	.60
1067	A284	385fr green & multi	2.00	.75
	Nos. 1065-1067 (3)		4.00	1.55

A285

Intl. Olympic Committee,
Cent. — A286

1994, Oct. 25
| 1068 | A285 | 60fr bl grn & multi | .35 | .20 |
| 1069 | A285 | 405fr yel grn & multi | 1.75 | .80 |

Souvenir Sheet
| 1070 | A286 | 675fr Pierre de Coubertin | 3.00 | 1.40 |

No. 1070 is airmail.

Nos. 1031-1032 Ovptd. with Medalist & Country Name in Gold

Overprints on No. 1031: No. 1071a, "F.B. LUNDBERG / NORVEGE." b, "G. HACKL / ALLEMAGNE." c, "B. DAEHLIE / NORVEGE."

d, "J.O. KOSS / NORVEGE." e, "V. SCHNEI-DER / SUISSE." f, "MEDAILLE D'OR / ALLEMAGNE." g, "MEDAILLE D'OR / SUEDE." h, "T. MOE / U.S.A."
Overprints on No. 1032: No. 1072a, "M. WASMEIER / ALLEMAGNE." b, "T. STAN-GASSINGER / AUTRICHE." c, "MEDAILLE D'OR / PAR EQUIPES / JAPON." d, "Y. GORDEYEVA / S. GRINKOV / RUSSIE." e, "D. JANSEN / U.S.A." f, "O. BAYUL / UKRAINE." g, "G. HACKL / ALLEMAGNE." h, "J.-L. BRAS-SARO / CANADA." i, "K. SEIZINGER / ALLEMAGNE."

1994
1071 A275 100fr Sheet of 8, #a.-h. + label   6.50 3.00
1072 A275 200fr Sheet of 9, #a.-i.   15.00 7.00

No. 988 Overprinted in Silver
MICHAEL SCHUMACHER CHAMPION DU MONDE FORMULE I 1994

1994, Dec. 28   Litho.   Perf. 13½
1073 A262 160fr multicolored   10.00 4.50
No. 1073 also exists in souvenir sheet of 1.

1995 Boy Scout Jamboree, Holland — A287

Scout with mushrooms or butterflies: 300fr, Armillariela mellea. 385fr, Charaxes pleione. 405fr, Charaxes candiope. 430fr, Charaxes pollux. 500fr, Volvaria esculenta. 1000fr, Cortinarius.
2000fr, Euphaedra medon.

1995, May 24
1074-1079 A287 Set of 6   15.00 7.00
1077a Sheet, #1075-1077 10.00 2.75
1079a Sheet, #1074, #1078-1079 14.50 4.00
Souvenir Sheet
1080 A287 2000fr multicolored 18.00 4.25
Nos. 1074-1079 exist in souvenir sheets of 1. No. 1080 is airmail and contains one 39x57mm stamp.

1994 World Cup Soccer Championships, US — A288

Stadium: 300fr, Citrus Bowl, Orlando. 385fr, RFK Stadium, Washington, DC. 405fr, Soldier Field, Chicago. 430fr, Cotton Bowl, Dallas. 500fr, Giants Stadium, East Rutherford, NJ. 1000fr, Foxboro Stadium, Foxboro, MA.
2000fr, Rose Bowl, vert.

1995, July 14   Litho.   Perf. 13½
1081-1086 A288 Set of 6   14.00 6.50
Souvenir Sheet
1087 A288 2000fr multicolored 12.50 5.75
No. 1087 is airmail.

African Development Bank, 30th Anniv. — A289

1995, June 29
1088 A289 70fr multicolored   .35 .20
1089 A289 200fr multicolored 1.00 .45
Nos. 1088-1089 also exist in souvenir sheet of 1.

Fish A290

Designs, 25fr, 300fr, Auchenoglanis. 30fr, 50fr, Chrisicntys.

1995, June 22
1090-1093 A290 Set of 4   2.75 .90

Entertainers A291

Designs: 300fr, Freddie Mercury (Queen). 385fr, Jimi Hendrix. 430fr, Marilyn Monroe. 500fr, Michael Jackson. 600fr, Jerry Garcia (Grateful Dead). 800fr, Elvis Presley.
1500fr, Charlton Heston in "Planet of the Apes." 2000fr, Marilyn Monroe, diff.

1995, July 21
1094-1099 A291 Set of 6   15.00 6.50
Souvenir Sheets
1099B A291 1500fr multicolored 8.25 3.25
1100 A291 2000fr multicolored 10.50 4.25
Nos. 1094-1099 exist in souvenir sheets of 1. No. 1100 is airmail. No. 1099B contains one 51x60mm airmail stamp.

Volleyball, Cent. — A292

1995, Oct. 3   Litho.   Perf. 13½
1101 A292 300fr multicolored 1.40 .65
No. 1101 exists in a souvenir sheet of 1. Value $10.

Sports Figures A293

400fr, Andre Agassi, tennis. 500fr, Boris Becker, tennis. 700fr, Ayrton Senna (1960-94) race car driver. 800fr, Michael Schumacher, F-1 world driving champion.
2000fr, Michael Schumacher, diff.

1996, June 20   Litho.   Perf. 13½
1102-1105 A293 Set of 4   12.00 5.50
Souvenir Sheet
1106 A293 2000fr multicolored 10.00 4.50
#1102-1105 exist in souvenir sheets of 1. Value $30.

1996 Summer Olympic Games, Atlanta A294

Olympic athletes, sites in Atlanta: 170fr, Atlanta-Fulton County Stadium. 300fr, Martin Luther King Memorial. 350fr, Alexander H. Stephens Monument. 600fr, High Museum of Art.
2000fr, Pierre de Coubertin, runner.

1996, June 20
1107-1110 A294 Set of 4   7.50 3.25
Souvenir Sheet
1110A A294 2000fr multicolored 9.50 4.00
No. 1110A contains one 42x51mm stamp.

UN, 50th Anniv. (in 1995) A295

1996, July 15   Perf. 14
1111 A295 5fr "50," emblem, vert.   .20 .20
1112 A295 430fr shown 1.90 .90
#1111-1112 exist in souvenir sheets of 1.

1996 Summer Olympic Games, Atlanta A296

1900 Summer Olympics, Paris: 235fr, Alvin Kraenzlein, vert. 300fr, Paris Stadium. 385fr, Irving Baxter. 430fr, British soccer team.
Past Olympic medalists: No. 1117a, Miruts Yifter, 5,000-meters, 1980. b, Germany, team dressage, 1976. c, Bruce Jenner, decathlon, 1976. d, Mark Gorski, 1000-meter match sprint, 1984. e, Randy Williams, long jump, 1972. f, Shinodu Sekine, judo, 1972. g, Kiyomi Kato, wrestling, 1972. h, Mitsuo Tsukahama, gymnastics, 1976. i, Hartwig Steenken, Germany, 1972.
Each 1000fr: No. 1118, Betty Cuthbert, 100-meters, 1956. No. 1119, Gerhard Stock, javelin, 1936.

1996, July 19
1113-1116 A296 Set of 4   6.00 2.75

1117 A296 200fr Sheet of 9, #a.-i.   8.00 3.50
Souvenir Sheets
1118-1119 A296 Set of 2   8.75 4.00
Olymphilex '96 (#1113-1116, 1118-1119).

Francophonie, 25th Anniv. (in 1995) — A297

300fr, "25 ANS" surrounded by "1970-1995."

1996, July 22
1120 A297 235fr multicolored 1.00 .50
1121 A297 300fr multicolored 1.40 .60
#1120-1121 exist in souvenir sheets of 1.

FAO, 50th Anniv. (in 1995) A298

Designs: 10fr, Fish being lifted in net, vert. 385fr, Boy drinking water.

1996
1122 A298 10fr multicolored   .20 .20
1123 A298 385fr multicolored 1.60 .75
#1122-1123 exist in souvenir sheets of 1.

Queen Elizabeth II, 70th Birthday A299

a, Formal portrait. b, In blue suit. c, In red hat.
1000fr, Balmoral Castle.

1996, July 24   Perf. 13½x14
1124 A299 300fr Strip of 3, #a.-c.   3.75 1.75
Souvenir Sheet
1125 A299 1000fr multicolored 4.50 2.00
Nos. 1124 was issued in sheets of 9 stamps.

Pets — A300

1996   Litho.   Perf. 13½
1126 A300 250fr Dog   1.25 .60
1127 A300 600fr Cat   3.00 1.40
#1126-1127 exist in souvenir sheets of 1.

1998 World Cup Soccer
Championships, France — A301

Winning country, year, player: No. 1128a, Uruguay 1930, Pedro Cea (Argentina), Italy 1934. b, Italy 1938, Piola (Italy), Uruguay 1950. c, Germany 1954, Brazil 1958, Walter, (Germany). d, Amarildo, (Brazil), Brazil 1962, England 1966.
No. 1129: a, Brazil 1970, Pele (Brazil), Germany 1974. b, Kempes (Argentina), Argentina 1978, Italy 1982. c, Argentina 1986, Mattaus (Germany), Germany 1990. d, Platini (France), Brazil 1994.

			1996	Litho.	Perf. 13½
1128	A301	375fr	Sheet of 4, #a.-d.		7.25 3.25
1129	A301	425fr	Sheet of 4, #a.-d.		8.25 3.75

Dinosaur Eggs — A302

Denomination at: a, LR. b, LL.

1996, Apr. 28

1130	A302	140fr	Pair, #a.-b.	2.10 .65
	c.		Souv. Sheet, #1130a-1130b	3.00 .65

CHINA '96 (#1130c).

Scouting
A303

Raptors, butterflies, mushrooms: 175fr, Buzzard. 200fr, H. misippus. 300fr, Lepiota aspera. 350fr, Raptor with feathers ruffled. 450fr, Amanita caesarea. 500fr, Morpho portis-nymphalidae.

		1996	Litho.	Perf. 13½
1131-1136	A303	Set of 6		10.00 4.50

Nos. 1132-1133, 1135-1136 exist in souvenir sheets of 1.

Horses
A304

Great Nebula, Andromeda
A305

No. 1137, 235fr: a, Appaloosa. b, Arabian. c, Quarter horse. d, Belgian. e, Pure blood English. f, Mustang. g, Haflinger. h, Welsh pony.

No. 1138, 235fr: a, Pinto. b, Palomino. c, Welara. d, Morgan. e, Standard American. f, Norwegian fjord. g, Shetland. h, Shire. 1000fr, Saddlebred.

1996, Nov. 20   Perf. 14
Sheets of 8, #a-h

1137-1138	A304	235fr	Set of 2	16.00 7.50

Souvenir Sheet

1139	A304	1000fr	multicolored	4.50 2.25

1996, Nov. 22

Designs: b, Halley's Comet. c, Jupiter. d, Saturn. e, Moon. f, Mars.

1140	A305	300fr	Sheet of 6, #a.-f.	8.00 3.50

Wildlife — A306

Flowers: a, Bomax costatum. b, Clappertonia flcifolia. c, Canarina abyssinica. d, Kigelia africana. e, Adenium obesum. f, Oncoba spinosa. g, Orinum ornatum. h, Gloriosa simplex. i, Strophanthus gratus.
Bird: 1500fr, Sagittarius serpentarius.

1997, Feb. 6   Litho.   Perf. 14

1141	A306	205fr	Sheet of 9, #a.-i.	8.25 3.75

Souvenir Sheet

1142	A306	1500fr	multicolored	8.25 3.00

Intl. Express Mail Service A307

300fr, Globe, international express mail routes. 405fr, Emblem of hand holding letter.

		1996	Litho.	Perf. 13½
1143	A307	300fr	multicolored	1.40 .65
1144	A307	405fr	multicolored	1.90 .90

No. 1144 exists in a souvenir sheet of 1.

Human Rights Advocates A308

Designs: a, Dalai Lama. b, Martin Luther King. c, John F. Kennedy. d, Nelson Mandela. e, Mother Teresa. f, Mahatma Gandhi.

1996

1145	A308	175fr	Sheet of 6, #a.-f. + 2 labels	5.00 2.25

Red Cross and Red Crescent Societies — A309

Designs: a, Doctor with patient. b, Man sifting grain. c, Using stethoscope on patient. d, Wounded man. e, Bandaging patient. f, Aiding infant.

1996

1146	A309	250fr	Sheet of 6, #a.-f. + 2 labels	7.25 3.25

Boy Scouts — A310

Boy scout: a, With dog. b, Riding horse. c, Holding cat. d, Holding butterfly. e, On bicycle. f, Playing game.
Butterfly: 2000fr, Saturnidae, horiz.

1996   Litho.   Perf. 13½

1147	A310	300fr	Sheet of 6, #a.-f. + 2 labels	9.00 4.00

Souvenir Sheet

1148	A310	2000fr	multicolored	10.00 4.50

No. 1148 contains one 42x36mm stamp.

Lions Intl., Rotary Intl. — A311

Designs: a, Child drinking from cup. b, Child carrying sack. c, Girl holding sheaves of grain. d, Man breaking bread. e, Woman cooking over fire. f, Boy, corn stalk.

1996

1149	A311	500fr	Sheet of 6, #a.-f. + 2 labels	14.00 6.50

Flora and Fauna A312

15fr, Cucumis sativus, vert. 20fr, Phyllochistis citrella. 40fr, Cetonia aurata. 65fr, Nomadacris septemfasciata. 100fr, Crocodilus vulgaris. 140fr, Athyrium filix, vert. 405fr, Rhopalo ceres.

1996

1150-1156	A312	Set of 7		5.00 1.75

#1151, 1156 exist in sourvenir sheets of 1.

UN, UNICEF, 50th Anniv. — A313

Designs: a, Futuristic space vehicle. b, MIR space station. c, US space shuttle, space station. d, Woman carrying food. e, Child receiving vaccination. f, Baby being weighed.

1996

1157	A313	350fr	Sheet of 6, #a.-f. + 2 labels	10.00 4.50

Elizabeth Taylor, Actress — A314

Princess Diana — A315

Various portraits.

1997, Apr. 10   Litho.   Perf. 14

1158	A314	300fr	Sheet of 6, #a.-f.	8.00 3.50
1159	A315	300fr	Sheet of 6, #a.-f.	8.00 3.50

Souvenir Sheets

1160	A314	1500fr	multicolored	6.50 3.00
1161	A315	1500fr	multicolored	6.50 3.00

For overprints see Nos. 1181-1182.

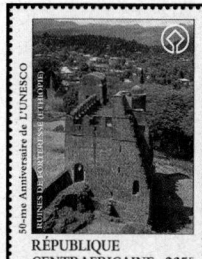

UNESCO, 50th Anniv. A316

No. 1162, 235fr: a, Fortress ruins, Ethiopia. b, Victoria Falls, Zambia. c, River during dry season, Zimbabwe. d, Nature Reserve, Niger. e, Pelican, Natl. Park, Mauritania. f, Native huts in village, Niokolo-Kobo Natl. Park, Senegal. g, M'Zab Valley, Algeria. h, Mosque, Morocco.
No. 1163, 235fr: a, c, Ruins of Roman Amphitheater, France. b, Split, Croatia. d, e, Quedlinberg, Germany. f, h, Tower of London, England. g, Olympic Natl. Park, US.
No. 1164, 235fr: a, Horyu-Ji, Japan. b, Waterfalls, Amazon River, Los Katios Natl. Park, Colombia. c, Abu Mena Church, Egypt. d, Boat on river, Fortress of Suomenlinna, Finland. e, Venice, Italy. f, Mural, Potala Palace, Lhasa, Tibet, China. g, Cathedral, town of Olinda, Brazil. h, Monastery, Mystras, Greece.
No. 1165, 1000fr, Jiuzhaigou Valley, China. No. 1166, 1000fr, Interior, Pilgrimage Church of Wies, Germany. No. 1167, 1000fr Ruins of Fountains Abbey, Studley Park, England.

1997, Apr. 30   Perf. 13½x14
Sheets of 8, #a-h + Label

1162-1164	A316	Set of 3	24.50 11.50

Souvenir Sheets

1165-1167	A316	Set of 3	13.00 6.00

UNICEF, 50th Anniv. — A317

No. 1168: a, 200fr, UN headquarters building. b, 250fr, Baby. c, 500fr, Danny Kaye seated inside vehicle. 1500fr, Child.

1997, Apr. 30   Perf. 14

1168	A317	Sheet of 3, #a.-c.	4.00 1.90

Souvenir Sheet

1169	A317	1500fr	multicolored	6.50 3.00

US Pres. Bill Clinton and His Cat, "Socks" — A318

Designs: a, b, c, e, g, h, i, Socks in various poses. d, f, Clinton, Socks.

1996
1170 A318 200fr Sheet of 9, #a.-i. 8.50 3.75

Conquest of Space — A319

Events in 1977: No. 1171: a, Voyager 1, US. b, Space Shuttle Enterprise, US. c, Meteosat 1, US. d, Salyut 6 Space Station, USSR.
Events in 1982: No. 1172: a, Salyut 7 Space Station, USSR. b, Landsat 4 Satellite, US. c, Venera 13, USSR. d, IRAS Infrared Telescope, US.
Events of 1967: No. 1173: a, Cosmos 186 & 188. b, Molnya satellite. c, Surveyor 3. d, Mariner 5.
Events in 1972: No. 1174: a, Copernicus probe, US. b, Pioneer 10, US. c, Apollo 16, US. d, Apollo 17, John F. Kennedy.
Events of 1962: No. 1175: a, Mariner 2, US. b, OSO 1, US. c, John Glenn. d, Mars 1, USSR.
Events of 1957: No. 1176: a, Vostok 1, Yuri Gagarin, USSR. b, Sputnik 2, USSR. c, Sputnik 1, USSR. d, Bell X15, US.
2000fr, Voyager, Pioneer 10, Apollo 11, US.

1997			**Perf. 13½**	
1171	A319	250fr Sheet of 4,		
		#a.-d.	4.50	2.00
1172	A319	350fr Sheet of 4,		
		#a.-d.	6.25	3.00
1173	A319	450fr Sheet of 4,		
		#a.-d.	8.00	3.75
1174	A319	500fr Sheet of 4,		
		#a.-d.	9.00	4.00
1175	A319	600fr Sheet of 4,		
		#a.-d.	10.50	5.00
1176	A319	800fr Sheet of 4,		
		#a.-d.	14.50	6.50

Souvenir Sheet
1177 A319 2000fr multicolored 9.00 4.00

No. 1177 contains one 60x30mm stamp.
No. 1173 exists imperf.

Marilyn Monroe (1926-62) — A320

Various portraits.

1997
1178 A320 375fr Sheet of 9, #a.-i. 14.00 6.50

John F. Kennedy (1917-63) — A321

Various portraits.

1997
1179 A321 300fr Sheet of 9, #a.-i. 11.00 5.00

Bruce Lee (1940-73), Actor — A322

Various portraits.

1997 **Litho.** **Perf. 13½**
1180 A322 200fr Sheet of 9, #a.-i. 7.50 3.25

Nos. 1159, 1161 Ovptd. "In Memoriam"

1997 **Perf. 14**
1181 A315 300fr Sheet of 6, #a.-f. 8.00 3.50

Souvenir Sheet
1182 A315 1500fr multicolored 6.50 3.00

Nos. 1181-1182 each contain "Diana, Princess of Wales (1961-1997) IN MEMORIAM" in sheet margin and on each stamp in No. 1181.

Dogs & Cats — A323

Dogs: No. 1183: a, Chinese crested. b, King Charles spaniel. c, Dachshund. d, Borzoi. e, Chow chow. f, Welsh springer. g, Rottweiler. h, Keeshond.
Cats: No. 1184: a, Birman. b, Black and white Persian. c, Siamese kitten. d, Red and black. e, American curl. f, Cornish rex. g, Silver shaded. h, White-footed cat.
1500fr, Pekingese. 2000fr, Somali.

1997 **Litho.** **Perf. 13½**
1183 A323 175fr Sheet of 8, #a.-h. 6.00 2.00
1184 A323 250fr Sheet of 8, #a.-h. 8.25 3.75

Souvenir Sheets
1185 A323 1500fr multicolored 7.00 2.75
1186 A323 2000fr multicolored 9.25 3.75

Nos. 1185-1186 each contain one 42x51mm stamp.

Return of Hong Kong to China — A324

No. 1187: a, Tung Chee-Hwa, taking down British flag. b, Raising Chinese flag, Chris Patten, British flag. c, Jiang Zemin, skyline at night. d, City lights, Queen Elizabeth II.
600fr, Tung Chee-Hwa.

1997
1187 A324 175fr Sheet of 4, #a.-d. 2.75 1.25

Souvenir Sheet
1188 A324 600fr multicolored 2.50 1.25

No. 1188 contains one 38x42mm stamp.

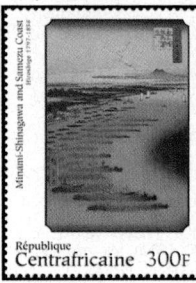

Paintings by Hiroshige (1797-1858) A325

No. 1189: a, Minami-Shinagawa and Samezu Coast. b, Plum Garden, Kamata. c, The Kawaguchi Ferry and Zenkoji Temple. d, Armor-Hanging Pine, Hakkeizaka. e, Robe-Hanging Pine, Senzoku Pond. f, Benten Shrine, Inokashira Pond.
No. 1190: a, A Little Brown Owl on a Pine Branch with a Crescent Moon Behind. b, Sparrows and Camellia in snow. c, Three Wild Geese Flying Downward across the Moon. d, A Blue Bird on a Yellow-flowered Hibiscus. e, Five Swallows in flight.
No. 1191: a, Sparrows and Wild Rose. b, Peonies. c, Morning Glory and Cricket. d, Blossoming Plum Tree. e, Kingfisher above a Yellow-flowered Water Plant.

No. 1192, 1500fr, Haneda Ferry and Benten Shrine. No. 1193, 1500fr, A Bird Clinging to a Tendril of Wisteria. No. 1194, 1500fr, Butterfly and Peony.

1998, Feb. 20 **Litho.** **Perf. 14**
1189 A325 300fr Sheet of 6, #a.-f. 6.75 3.00
1190 A325 430fr Sheet of 5, #a.-e. 8.25 3.75
1191 A325 500fr Sheet of 5, #a.-e. 9.25 4.25

Souvenir Sheets
1192-1194 A325 Set of 3 18.00 7.50

Nos. 1190-1191 each contain five 26x72mm stamps. Nos. 1192-1194 each contain one 26x72mm stamp.

Chinese Lunar New Year A326

Animals representing lunar year: a, Rat. b, Ox. c, Tiger. d, Hare. e, Dragon. f, Snake. g, Horse. h, Sheep. i, Monkey. j, Rooster. k, Dog. l, Boar.
1000fr, Tiger, diff.

1998 **Litho. & Typo.** **Perf. 14**
1195 A326 150fr Sheet of 12, #a.-l. 8.00 3.75

Souvenir Sheet
1196 A326 1000fr gold & multi 3.75 1.75

Intl. Scouting, 90th Anniv. A327

Insects: No. 1196A: b, Apis mellifica. c, Lucanus cervus. d, Oryctes nasicornis. e, Pseudacraea boisduvalii. f, Helictopleurus quadripunctatus, euchroea spininasuta. g, Bombus terrestris. h, Charaxes smaragdalis. i, Euchroea coelestis, mantis religiosa.
Wildlife — No. 1197: a, Coracias caudata, Otocyon megalotis. b, Gnu. c, Milvus aegyptus, pelecanus onocrotalus. d, Panthera leo. e, Loxondonta africana. f, Buffalo. g, Hippopotamus amphibius. h, Acinonyx jubatus.
Raptors — No. 1198: a, Buteo rufinus. b, Circus aeruginosus. c, Aquila verreauxii. d, Circaetus gallicus. e, Terathopius ecaudatus. f, Haliaeetus vocifer. g, Milvus milvus. h, Accipiter badius.

1997(?) **Litho.** **Perf. 13**
1196A A327 200fr Sheet of 8, #b.-i. 7.00 3.00
1197 A327 300fr Sheet of 8, #a.-h. 10.00 4.50
1198 A327 350fr Sheet of 8, #a.-h. 13.00 5.25

1998 World Cup Soccer Championships, France — A328

Player, country, vert: No. 1199, 300fr, Moore, England. No. 1200, 300fr, Rahn, Germany. No. 1201, 300fr, Paulao, Angola. No. 1202, 300fr, Shearer, England.
No. 1203: a, Seaman, England. b, Schillaci, Italy. c, Romario, Brazil. d, McCoist, Scotland. e, Makanaky, Angola. f, Moore, England. g, Muller, Germany. h, Schmeichel, Denmark.
No. 1204, 1500fr, Moore, England, diff. No. 1205, 1500fr, Pele, Brazil.

1998, June 2 **Perf. 13½x14, 14x13½**
1199-1202 A328 Set of 4 4.50 2.00

1203 A328 205fr Sheet of 8,
#a-h, + label   7.00   7.00

Souvenir Sheets

1204-1205 A328   Set of 2   12.00 12.00

Diana,
Princess of
Wales (1961-
97)
A329

Various portraits.

1998   **Perf. 13½**
1206 A329 200fr Sheet of 9, #a.-
i.   7.00 3.25
1207 A329 250fr Sheet of 9, #a.-
i.   9.00 4.00

Diana, Princess of Wales (1961-
97) — A330

Diana wearing gowns in one of four seasons: No. 1208, White gown, spring. No. 1209,
Blue gown, summer. No. 1210, Bridal gown,
fall. No. 1211, High-collared white gown,
winter.

1998   **Litho.**   **Perf. 13½**
Souvenir Sheets
1208 A330 1500fr multicolored   5.75 2.50
1209 A330 1500fr multicolored   5.75 2.50
1210 A330 2000fr multicolored   8.00 3.50
1211 A330 2000fr multicolored   8.00 3.50
Nos. 1208-1211 each contain one
50x60mm stamp.

Jacqueline
Kennedy
Onassis
(1929-94)
A331

Various portraits.

1997   **Litho.**   **Perf. 13½**
1212 A331 250fr Sheet of 9,
#a.-i.   10.50 4.25

1998 Winter Olympic Games,
Nagano — A332

Mirror images of vignette with different back-
grounds, denomination at — No. 1213: a, Bob-
sled, LR. b, Slalom skier, CL. c, Ski jumper,
CL. d, Bobsled, LL. e, Slalom skier, CR. f, Ski
jumper, CR.
No. 1214: a, Ice hockey, LR. b, Cross-coun-
try skier, CR. c, Speed skater, LR. d, Ice
hockey, LL. e, Cross-country skier, CL. f,
Speed skater, LL.
No. 1215: a, Snow boarding, UR. b, Down-
hill skier, CR. c, Pairs figure skating, CR. d,
Snow boarding, UL. e, Downhill skier, CL. f,
Pairs figure skating, CL.
No. 1216, Cross-country, freestyle skiers.

1998
1213 A332 180fr Sheet of 6,
#a.-f.   4.00 1.75
1214 A332 300fr Sheet of 6,
#a.-f.   7.00 3.00
1215 A332 350fr Sheet of 6,
#a.-f.   8.25 3.75

Souvenir Sheet
1216 A332 2000fr multicolored   9.25 3.50

Sports
A333

No. 1217 — Cyclists: a, Woman wearing
helmet. b, Woman in pink, white & black outfit.
c, Man in black & white outfit. d, Man in yellow
& black outfit.
No. 1218 — Female tennis players: a, Holding racket above head. b, Wearing black head
band. c, Wearing white head band. d, Wearing
dreadlocks.
No. 1219 — Male tennis players: a, Holding
racket with his right hand. b, In blue shirt,
shorts. c, Holding racket behind head. d,
Wearing cap backwards.
No. 1220 — Golfers: a, Completing swing.
b, Hitting ball in sand trap. c, In orange knick-
ers, argyle socks. d, Lining up putt.

1998   **Litho.**   **Perf. 13½**
1217 A333 350fr Sheet of 4, #a.-
d.   5.25 2.25
1218 A333 375fr Sheet of 4, #a.-
d.   5.75 2.50
1219 A333 450fr Sheet of 4, #a.-
d.   7.25 3.25
1220 A333 500fr Sheet of 4, #a.-
d.   8.00 3.50

Mickey
Mouse, 70th
Birthday
A334

Scenes from various Disney films drawn by
Floyd Gottfredson.
No. 1221: a, 10/78. b, 11/78. c, 3/79. d,
7/79. e, 9/79.
No. 1222: a, 10/79. b, 2/80. c, 4/80. d, 6/80.
e, 7/80.
No. 1223: a, 11/80. b, 3/81. c, 6/81. d, 9/81.
e, 3/82.
No. 1224: a, 5/82. b, 7/82. c, 10/82. d, 3/83.
e, 5/83.
No. 1225, 1500fr, Mickey with camera,
flashlight. No. 1226, 1500fr, Mickey with pearl
in box. No. 1227, 2000fr, Mickey and magic
lamp. No. 1228, 2000fr, Floyd Gottfredson.

Perf. 13½x14, 14x13½
1999, Feb. 10   **Litho.**
1221 A334 280fr Sheet of 5,
#a.-e., + label   5.25 2.25
1222 A334 365fr Sheet of 5,
#a.-e., + label   7.00 3.00
1223 A334 390fr Sheet of 5,
#a.-e., + label   7.50 3.25
1224 A334 440fr Sheet of 5,
#a.-e., + label   8.25 3.75
Souvenir Sheets
1225-1226 A334 1500fr Set of 2 11.00 5.00
1227-1228 A334 2000fr Set of 2 15.00 6.50

Birds of
Africa — A335   World Wildlife
Fund — A336

Designs: No. 1229, 500fr, Pandion
haliaetus. No. 1230, 500fr, Chaetops frenatus.
No. 1231, 500fr, Tachymarptis melba. No.
1232, 500fr, Ceratogymna bucinator. No.
1233, 500fr, Laniarius atrococcineus. No.
1234, 500fr, Coturnix coturnix.
No. 1235: a, Lamprotornis superbus. b,
Agapornis personatus. c, Coracias spatulata.
d, Euplectes jacksoni. e, Nectarinia violacea. f,
Emberiza schoeniclus. g, Pica pica. h,
Tauraco erythrolophus. i, Sitta europaea.
No. 1236: a, Merops apiaster. b, Coracias
garrulus. c, Cuculus canorus. d, Hirundo rustica. e, Motacilla flava. f, Ardea cinerea. g,
Falco tinnunculus. h, Tyto alba. i, Charadrius
hiaticula.
1500fr, Eremophila alpestris. 2000fr,
Delichon urbica.

1999, Mar. 10   **Litho.**   **Perf. 14**
1229-1234 A335   Set of 6   11.00 5.00
1235 A335 280fr Sheet of 9,
#a.-i.   9.25 4.25
1236 A335 490fr Sheet of 9,
#a.-i.   16.00 7.50

Souvenir Sheets
1237 A335 1500fr multicolored   5.50 2.50
1238 A335 2000fr multicolored   7.50 3.50

1999
Balaeniceps rex: a, Eating fish. b, Up close.
c, Standing. d, One in flight, one up close.
1239 A336 200fr Strip of 4, #a.-d. 5.00 2.25
No. 1239 was issued in sheets of 16 stamps.

Trains
A337

No. 1240: a, 40fr, 2-4-0 Steam locomotive.
b, 50fr, German Mallat. c, 60fr, Shunting locomotive. d, 260fr, Rhodesian 14A 2-6-2+2-6-2
Garrat. e, 280fr, Steam train. f, 390fr, Engine
No. 7, 0-6-0 Baldwin, 1920. g, 440fr, Amtrak
passenger train. h, 460fr, German TEE diesel.
i, 490fr, "Sir Nigel Gresley."
No. 1241: a, 40fr, Steam train. b, 50fr, 4-4-0,
LNWR, 1897. c, 60fr, 2-4-0 locomotive, Mid-
land. d, 260fr, Class XC. e, 280fr, 2-6-0T
Sernada and Aveiro, 1910. f, 390fr, East Dag-
gafontein Mines train, Great Britain. g, 440fr,
Union Pacific. h, 460fr, Engine No. 6, Baldwin.
i, 490fr, 4-4-2 aerodynamic train, Belgium,
1939.
No. 1242, 2000fr, Fairlie, Snake and Auck-
land, New Zealand, 1874. No. 1243, 2000fr,
Steam train arriving at the London-Brighton
Depot.

1999, Mar. 11
Sheets of 9
1240-1241 A337 Set of 2   22.50 8.50
Souvenir Sheets
1242-1243 A337 Set of 2   17.00 6.50

Prehistoric
Animals
A338

No. 1244: a, Archaeopteryx. b, Stegosaurus. c, Placerias. d, Rutiodon. e, Tyrannosaurus rex. f, Lystrosaurus.
No. 1245: a, Spinosaurus. b, Cynognathus.
c, Kuehneosaurus. c, Compsognathus. d,
Compsognathus. e, Triceratops. f,
Euoplocephalus.
2000fr, Desmatosuchus.

1998   **Litho.**   **Perf. 13½**
1244 A338 250fr Sheet of 6,
#a.-f.   6.25 2.75
1245 A338 300fr Sheet of 6,
#a.-f.   7.50 3.25
Souvenir Sheet
1246 A338 2000fr multicolored   8.50 3.75
No. 1246 contains one 51x36mm stamp.

Transportation
A339

No. 1247 — Antique automobiles: a, 1899
Fiat. b, First Chevrolet. c, Serpolet steam car-
riage. d, 130HP Fiat.
No. 1248 — Cyclists: a, Swiss rider. b, US
rider. c, Miguel Indurain (riding to right). d,
Jan. Ullrich (riding to left).
No. 1249 — Sports cars: a, Porsche Box-
ster. b, Corvette. c, Jaguar S-type. d, Maserati
3200 GT.
No. 1250 — High-speed trains: a, TGV
Atlantique. b, Shin Kansen. c, ETR X-500. d,
Advanced passenger train.
No. 1251 — Trains: a, Cornish Riviera
Express. b, Lancashire and Yorkshire Railway.
c, Type 230. d, Pacific Mallard.
No. 1252 — Fire trucks: a, 1916 Seagrave.
b, 1927 Ahrens-Fox Model JS-2. c, 1992 Die-
sel. d, 1958 Mack Bulldog, Type B-95.
No. 1253 — Space flight of John Glenn: a,
Portrait in business suit. b, In Project Mercury
spacesuit. c, In shuttle launch suit, 1998. d,
Orbiting earth, Space Shuttle.
No. 1254 — Supersonic airplanes: a, Boe-
ing 2707. b, Transatmospheric prototype. c,
Tupolev 144. d, Project of European Super-
sonic ESRP.

1998
1247 A339 300fr Sheet of 4,
#a.-d.   5.00 2.25
1248 A339 350fr Sheet of 4,
#a.-d.   5.75 2.50
1249 A339 400fr Sheet of 4,
#a.-d.   6.75 3.00
1250 A339 450fr Sheet of 4,
#a.-d.   7.50 3.25
1251 A339 500fr Sheet of 4,
#a.-d.   8.25 3.75
1252 A339 600fr Sheet of 4,
#a.-d.   10.00 4.50
1253 A339 800fr Sheet of 4,
#a.-d.   13.00 6.00
1254 A339 1000fr Sheet of 4,
#a.-d.   16.00 7.50

Scouting
A340

No. 1255 — Scouts with flowers: a, Vanilla
planifolia. b, Flamboyant. c, Angraecum
sesquipedale.
No. 1256 — Scouts with butterflies or bird:
a, Hesperie a bande. b, Philepitte souimanga.
c, Dryope.
No. 1257 — Scouts with dogs, cats, and
their young: a, Basenji. b, Egyptian mau cat. c,
White dog.
No. 1258 — Scouts with minerals: a, Tour-
maline. b, Jasper. c, Madagascar corundum.
No. 1259 — Scouts administrering Red
Cross aid: a, Girl Scout wiping child's tears. b,
Scout bandaging child. c, Scout kneeling to
help child.
No. 1260 — Scouts in leisure activities: a,
Playing table tennis. b, Playing chess. c, Rid-
ing horse.

1998   **Litho.**   **Perf. 13½**
1255 A340 400fr Sheet of 3,
#a.-c.   5.00 2.25
1256 A340 475fr Sheet of 3,
#a.-c.   6.50 2.50
1257 A340 500fr Sheet of 3,
#a.-c.   6.75 2.75
1258 A340 600fr Sheet of 3,
#a.-c.   7.50 3.25
1259 A340 700fr Sheet of 3,
#a.-c.   8.50 3.75
1260 A340 800fr Sheet of 3,
#a.-c.   10.00 4.50

Minerals
A341

No. 1261: a, Hematite (red). b, Challophyllite. c, Fer natif. d, Sylvanite. e. Hematite (specularite). f, Spodumene.
No. 1262: a, Amber. b, Opal. c, Struvite. d, Rhodochrosite. e, Polybasite. f, Silver.

1998   Litho.   Perf. 13½
1261 A341 400fr Sheet of 6,
　　　#a.-f.　　　　10.00　4.50
1262 A341 600fr Sheet of 6,
　　　#a.-f.　　　　14.50　6.75

A number has been reserved for a souvenir sheet to go with this set.

Mushrooms
A342

40fr, Jelly babies. 50fr, Herald of winter. 65fr, Dentate elf cup. 280fr, Pink wax cap. 345fr, Tripe fungus. 465fr, Funnel tooth. 485fr, Common white saddle. 600fr, False morel.
No. 1272: a, Parrot wax cap. b, Orange naval cap. c, Amethyst deceiver. d, Plums and custard. e, Blue legs. f, Tawny funnel cap. g, Goblet. h, Spindle-shank. i, Buttery tough shank.
No. 1273: a, Fetid mummy cap. b, Stainer. c, Lilac bonnet. d, Firm-fleshed brittle gill. e, Fly agaric. f, Arched bonnet. g, King bolete. h, Orange birch bolete. i, Dog stinkhorn.
1500fr, Hedgehog puffball. 2000fr, Striated earth star.

1999, June 11   Litho.   Perf. 14
1264-1271 A342　Set of 8　9.50　4.25
1272 A342 390fr Sheet of 9,
　　　#a.-i.　　　14.00　6.50
1273 A342 440fr Sheet of 9,
　　　#a.-i.　　　15.00　6.75
Souvenir Sheets
1274 A342 1500fr multicolored　5.75　2.50
1275 A342 2000fr multicolored　8.25　3.75

Birds
A343

No. 1276: a, Psittacula himalayama. b, Anodorhynchus hyacinthinus. c, Trichoglossus haematodus. d, Xipholena punicea. e, Chloebia gouldiae. f, Ramphastos tucanus.
No. 1277: a, Falco sparverius. b, Polyborus plancus. c, Terathopius ecaudatus. d, Tyto alba. e, Glaucidium passerinum. f, Speotyto cunicularia.

1999   Litho.   Perf. 13½
1276 A343 350fr Sheet of 6,
　　　#a.-f.　　　　8.25　3.75
1277 A343 500fr Sheet of 6,
　　　#a.-f.　　　　11.50　5.25

Dogs,
Cats, &
Horses
A344

Designs: 60fr, Doberman, vert. 280fr, Domestic cat, vert. No. 1280, Korat, vert. No. 1281, 390fr, Hanoverian, vert. 440fr, Ardennais. 490fr, Lhasa apso.
Dogs — No. 1284: a, Alaskan malamute. b, Musterlander. c, German shepherd. d, Borzoi. e, Afghan hound. f, Irish terrier. g, Komondor. h, Finnish spitz.

Cats — No. 1285: a, American bobtail. b, American curl. c, Singapura. d, Burmese. e, Tortoise shell. f, Scottish fold. g, British shorthair blue. h, Turkish van.
Horses — No. 1286: a, Shire. b, Clydesdale. c, Arabian. d, Soviet work horse. e, Finnish work horse. f, Percheron. g, Draco. h, North Swedish.
No. 1287, 2000fr, Beagle. No. 1288, 2000fr, Havana. No. 1289, 2000fr, Hanoverian.

1999, July 9   Litho.   Perf. 14
1278-1283 A344　Set of 6　9.75　3.50
1284 A344 465fr Sheet of 8,
　　　#a.-h.　　　14.50　6.50
1285 A344 485fr Sheet of 8,
　　　#a.-h.　　　15.00　6.75
1286 A344 515fr Sheet of 8,
　　　#a.-h.　　　15.00　7.00
Souvenir Sheets
1287-1289 A344　Set of 3　30.00 10.50
Nos. 1287-1289 each contain one 44x56mm stamp.

Butterflies
A345

Designs: 40fr, Heliconius melpomene. 65fr, Large oak blue. 280fr, Danaus chrysippus. 345fr, Aricia agestis. 485fr, Danis danis. 600fr, Plebejus argus.
No. 1296: a, Delias mysis. b, Ornithoptera priamus. c, Phoebis philea. d, Heliconius doris. e, Thecla coronata f, Lycaena dispar. g, Bematistes aganise. h, Pereute leucodrosime.
No. 1297: a, Colotis danae. b, Eueides isabella. c, Papilio cresphontes. d, Mimacraea marshalli. e, Parathyma nefte. f, Appias nero. g, Uraneis ucubis. h, Eurema brigitta.
No. 1298: a, Heliconius melpomene, diff. b, Mylothris chloris. c, Catopsilia florella. d, Hebomoia glaucippe. e, Palla ussheri. f, Papilio glaucus. g, Colias erytheme. h, Euploea corus.
No. 1299, 1500fr, Unnamed. No. 1300, 1500fr, Papilio, glaucus, vert.

1999, Dec.   Litho.   Perf. 14
1290-1295 A345　Set of 6　9.00　3.25
1296 A345 280fr Sheet of 8,
　　　#a.-h.　　　12.00　4.00
1297 A345 390fr Sheet of 8,
　　　#a.-h.　　　16.00　5.50
1298 A345 465fr Sheet of 8,
　　　#a.-h.　　　19.00　6.50
Souvenir Sheets
1299-1300 A345　Set of 2　15.00　6.00

Trains
A346

Designs: No. 1301, 280fr, Le Capitole, France. No. 1302, 390fr, Montreaux-Bern Line, Switzerland. No. 1303, 485fr, Zugspitzbahn, Switzerland. No. 1304, 485fr, Rhatische Bahn, Swizerland.
No. 1305: a, Schwebebahn, Germany. b, Reichsbahn Class 44, Germany. c, Rembrandt, Germany. d, Trans-Europe Express, Germany. e, Inter-city, Germany. f, Steam locomotive, Germany.
No. 1306: a, ETR300, Italy. b, Mistral, France. c, ER200, Russia. d, Pendoline, Italy. e, Class 1100, Netherlands. f, Rheingold Express, Germany.
No. 1307, 1500fr, TGV, France. No. 1308, 1500fr, Austrian train.

2000, Jan. 25
1301-1304 A346　Set of 4　8.50　3.00
1305 A346 280fr Sheet of 6,
　　　#a.-f.　　　　9.00　3.00
1306 A346 390fr Sheet of 6,
　　　#a.-f.　　　12.00　4.25
Souvenir Sheets
1307-1308 A346　Set of 2　17.50　5.00

Flowers — A347

No. 1309: a, Orchid. b, Water crinum. c, Flame lily. d, Narcissus poeticus. e, Belladonna lily. f, Table Mountain orchid. g, Upland cotton. h, Narcissus jonquilla.
No. 1310: a, Moore's crinum. b, Cyrtanthus brachyscyphus. c, Namaqualand daisy. d, "Narcissus poeticus," diff. e, Painted homeria. f, Helen O'Connor. g, Pink oxalis. h, Pink oxalis and pink arum.
No. 1311: a, Yellow wild iris. b, White arum lily (mountains in background). c, Blue tulip. d, Osteospermum. e, Table Mountain orchid, diff. f, White arum lily (with stems and leaves). g, Daisy. h, Meadow saffron.
No. 1312, 1500fr, Amaryllis belladonna, horiz. No. 1313, 1500fr, African tulip tree, horiz. No. 1314, 1500fr, Bird of paradise, horiz.

2000, Feb. 24
1309 A347 280fr Sheet of 8,
　　　#a.-h.　　　12.00　3.50
1310 A347 390fr Sheet of 8,
　　　#a.-h.　　　16.00　4.75
1311 A347 515fr Sheet of 8,
　　　#a.-h.　　　20.00　6.00
Souvenir Sheets
1312-1314 A347　Set of 3　22.50　8.00
Inscription on No. 1310d is incorrect.

Birds
A348

Designs: 100fr, Dendrocygna bicolor, vert. 150fr, Tockis flavirostris, vert. 200fr, Treron calva. 300fr, Ardeola ralloides. 450fr, Passer melanus, vert. 750fr, Sturnus vulgaris, vert.
No. 1321, vert.: a, Trachyphonus vaillantii. b, Polyhierax semitorquatus. c, Tockus nasutus. d, Estrilda astrild. e, Merops persicus. f, Amandava subflava. g, Guttera pucherani. h, Oriolus oriolus. i, Bycanistes brevis.
No. 1322: a, Butoides striatus. b, Limnocorax flavirostra. c, Terathopius ecaudatus. d, Mycteria ibis. e, Actophilornis africanus. f, Poicephalus rueppellii. g, Alopochen aegyptiacus. h, Morus capensis. i, Sagittarius serpentarius.
No. 1323: a, Gyps africanus. b, Tyto alba. c, Pelecanus onocrotalus. d, Ephippiorhynchus senegalensis. e, Ardea goliath. f, Sylvia communis. g, Buteo rufofuscus. h, Parus caeruleus. i, Dromas ardeola.
No. 1324, 2000fr, Buphagus africanus. No. 1325, 2000fr, Haliaeetus vocifer. No. 1326, 2000fr, Erythropgia coryphaeus, vert.

2000, Feb. 25
1315-1320 A348　Set of 6　8.50　3.00
1321 A348 390fr Sheet of 9,
　　　#a.-i.　　　16.00　5.25
1322 A348 440fr Sheet of 9,
　　　#a.-i.　　　18.00　6.00
1323 A348 485fr Sheet of 9,
　　　#a.-i.　　　18.00　6.50
Souvenir Sheets
1324-1326 A348　Set of 3　27.50 10.00

Aviation
A349

Designs: 280fr, Spirit of St. Louis. 345fr, Hindenburg. 465fr, Flight at Kitty Hawk. 485fr, AH-1 Cobra.
No. 1331: a, Fokker triplane. b, Spad XIII. c, Blériot XI. d, Nieuport 12. e, Sopwith Camel. f, 1920s US Mail plane. g, Otto Lilienthal's hang glider. h, Hydrogen-filled balloon of J. A. C. Charles.
No. 1332: a, Mitchell-B25. b, P-38E Lightning. c, Vought F-4U Corsair. d, Mitsubishi Zero. e, B-17 Flying Fortress. f, P-51 Mustang.

g, Flying Tiger plane. h, Messerschmitt Bf-109.
No. 1333: a, X-1. b, B-52C. c, Boeing 707. d, F-16C. e, Sabre jet. f, MiG-15. g, F-4 Phantom. h, F-117A Stealth.
No. 1334, 1500fr, Concorde. No. 1335, 1500fr, Space shuttle "Enterprise."

2000, Feb. 28
1327-1330 A349　Set of 4　7.50　2.40
1331 A349 345fr Sheet of 8,
　　　#a.-h.　　　13.00　4.25
1332 A349 390fr Sheet of 8,
　　　#a.-h.　　　14.50　4.75
1333 A349 515fr Sheet of 8,
　　　#a.-h.　　　19.00　6.25
Souvenir Sheets
1334-1335 A349 1500fr Set of 2 13.00　5.00

Chess Players — A350

No. 1336, 280fr: a, Otto IV of Brandenburg. b, Mme. de Verzu and Chevalier de Bourgogne. c, Chess Players by Estienne Porcher. d, Fresco by F. Pella.
No. 1337, 300fr: a, Two Nobles. b, Depiction from book of Jean Wauquelin. c, Girolamo de Cremona. d, Ashtapada.
No. 1338, 390fr: a, Ulysses and Palamedes. b, Christian cavalier and Muslim. c, Two Moorish women. d, Burzurgmikhr and Kannuja.
No. 1339, 465fr: a, Two men, 18th Cent. b, Napoleon and Cornwallis. c, Adolf Anderssen and Wilhelm Steinitz. d, Queen Victoria.
No. 1340, 485fr: a, Two women. b, Chess on an enlarged board. c, Xerxes. d, King Evil-Merodach.
No. 1341, 515fr: a, King Henry VIII of England. b, Queen Elizabeth I of England. c, King Charles I of England. d, Russian czarevitch.
Illustration reduced.

1999   Litho.   Perf. 13½
Sheets of 4, #a-d
1336-1341 A350　Set of 6　37.50 15.00

Cosmonauts and Astronauts — A351

No. 1342, 485fr: a, Vladimir Soloviev. b, Georgi Beregovoy. c, Alexei Leonov. d, Pavel Popovich. e, Yuri Gagarin. f, Valentina Tereshkova. g, Helena Kondakova. h, Gherman Titov. i, Alexander Volkov.
No. 1343, 515fr: a, Neil Armstrong. b, Edwin Aldrin. c, Michale Collins. d, Alan Bean. e, James Lovell. f, Alan Shepard. g, David Scott. h, John Young. i, Eugene Cernan.
2000fr, Armstrong and Gagarin, horiz.
Illustration reduced.

1999
Sheets of 9, #a-i
1342-1343 A351　Set of 2　35.00 14.00
Souvenir Sheet
1344 A351 2000fr multi　9.00　3.25
No. 1344 contains one 60x51mm stamp.

Millennium — A352

2000, Mar. 31   *Perf. 14*
1345 A352 515fr multicolored   2.50 1.00
            Issued in sheets of six.

2000 Summer Olympics,
Sydney — A353

No. 1346, 300fr: a, Individual dressage. b,
Rhythmic gymnastics. c, Women's 100-meter
hurdles. d, Cycling.
No. 1347, 485fr: a, Tennis. b, Diving. c, Soc-
cer. d, Pole vault.
No. 1348, 750fr: a, Long jump. b, Judo. c,
Basketball. d, Show jumping.
No. 1349, 800fr: a, Boxing. b, Table tennis.
c, Women's 200-meter sprint. d, Individual
three-day equestrian event.
Illustration reduced.

2000   *Perf. 13½*
            Sheets of 4, #a-d
1346-1349 A353 Set of 4   35.00 15.00

2002 Winter Olympics, Salt Lake
City — A354

No. 1350, 280fr: a, Freestyle skiing. b,
Cross-country skiing. c, Bobsled. d, Men's
slalom.
No. 1351, 390fr: a, Luge. b, Women's ski
relay. c, Downhill skiing. d, Short track skating.
No. 1352, 465fr: a, Women's figure skating.
b, Hockey. c, Ski jumping. d, Biathlon.
No. 1353, 515fr, a, Pairs figure skating. b,
Women's giant slalom. c, Speed skating. d,
Nordic combined.
Illustration reduced.

2000
            Sheets of 4, #a-d
1350-1353 A354 Set of 4   26.00 10.50

UPU, 125th Anniv. — A355

UPU emblem and various men: 280fr, 300fr,
390fr, 465fr, 485fr, 515fr, 750fr, 800fr.

2000, Sept. 8   *Litho.*   *Perf. 13¼*
1354-1361 A355 Set of 8   16.00 5.25

Millennium — A356

No. 1362: a, Roald Amundsen, first polar
exploration by dirigible, 1926. b, Vladimir
Zworykin, inventor of television camera, 1928.
c, Sir Alexander Fleming, discoverer of penicil-
lin, 1928.
No. 1363: a, Henri Dunant, 1901 Nobel
Peace prize winner. b, Wilbur and Orville
Wright, first airplane, 1903. c, Enrico Caruso,
opera singer.
No. 1364: a, Theodore Roosevelt, opening
of Panama Canal, 1914. b, Albert Einstein,
theory of general relativity, 1916. c, Battle of
Verdun, 1916.
No. 1365: a, Auguste Piccard, flight to strat-
osphere in balloon, 1931. b, Robert Goddard,
rocketry pioneer, 1935. c, Ferdinand von
Zeppelin and Graf Zeppelin, 1928-37.
No. 1366: a, Felix Eboue, governor of Chad,
1940. b, Mahatma Gandhi, independence of
India, 1947. c, Marilyn Monroe (1926-62),
actress.
No. 1367: a, Juan Manuel Fangio, race car
driver. b, James Dean (1931-55), actor. c,
Sputnik 1, 1957.
No. 1368: a, Charles De Gaulle (1890-
1970), French general and political leader. b,
Yuri Gagarin (1934-68), Soviet Cosmonaut. c,
Neil Armstrong (1930-), American Astronaut.
No. 1369: a, Elvis Presley (1935-77), Ameri-
can entertainer. b, Muhammed Ali (1942-),
American boxer. c, John Young (1930-), Amer-
ican Astronaut.
No. 1370: a, John Young, Space Shuttle,
1981. b, Mikhail Gorbachev, fall of the Berlin
Wall, 1989. c, Dalai Lama, 1989 Nobel Peace
prize winner.
No. 1371: a, Nelson Mandela, 1993 Nobel
Peace prize winner. b, Galileo probe reaches
Jupiter, 1995. c, Mars Pathfinder, 1998.

2000, Sept. 28   *Perf. 13¼*
1362 A356 100fr Sheet of 3,
                   #a-c   1.25   .60
1363 A356 280fr Sheet of 3,
                   #a-c   3.50   1.25
1364 A356 300fr Sheet of 3,
                   #a-c   4.25   1.50
1365 A356 390fr Sheet of 3,
                   #a-c   5.00   2.00
1366 A356 465fr Sheet of 3,
                   #a-c   6.00   2.25
1367 A356 485fr Sheet of 3,
                   #a-c   6.50   2.50
1368 A356 515fr Sheet of 3,
                   #a-c   6.00   3.00
1369 A356 750fr Sheet of 3,
                   #a-c   9.00   4.50
1370 A356 800fr Sheet of 3,
                   #a-c   10.50   3.75
1371 A356 1000fr Sheet of 3,
                   #a-c   12.50   4.75
      Nos. 1362-1371 (10)   64.50 26.10

Numbers have been reserved for two additional sheets.

Flora, Dinosaurs and
Mushrooms — A357

No. 1372 — Butterflies: a, Cymothoe lurida.
b, Charaxes lasti. c, Charaxes lactetinctus. d,
Charaxes opinatus. e, Charaxes subornatus. f,
Coelides hanno.
No. 1373 — Butterflies: a, Charaxes
cithaeron. b, Charaxes anticlea. c, Bebearia
plistonax. d, Charaxes jahlusa. e, Charaxes
acraeoides. f, Bebearia oxione.
No. 1374 — Dinosaurs: a, Compsognathus.
b, Kritosaurus. c, Nodosaurus. d, Tuoji-
angosaurus. e, Homalocephalus. f,
Tsintaosaurus.
No. 1375 — Birds: a, Veuve royale. b,
Travailleur cardinal. c, Gonolek a ventre rouge.
d, Touraco de Schalow. e, Touraco Pauline. f,
Souimanga orange.
No. 1376 — Dinosaurs: a, Monoclonius. b,
Dryosaurus. c, Anatosaurus. d,
Styracosaurus. e, Pinacosaurus. f,
Kentrosaurus.
No. 1377 — Birds: a, Bateleur de savanes.
b, Corbeau a nuque blanche. c, Corvinelle pie.
d, Cordon-bleu violace. e, Fauvette passer-
inette. f, Crombec a face rousse.
No. 1378 — Mushrooms: a, Lentinus sajor-
caju. b, Lentinus velutinus. c, Pleurotus
luteoalbus. d, Pluteus congolensis. e, Lentinus
crinitus. f, Leucoagaricus ferruginosus.
No. 1379 — Mushrooms: a, Lentinus squar-
rosulus. b, Phlebopus colossus. c, Lentinus
tuberregium. d, Phlebopus sudanicus. e,
Phlebopus silvaticus. f, Volvariella
congolensis.
No. 1380 — Dogs: a, Briard. b, Pyrenees
shepherd. c, Chow chow. d, Cocker spaniel. e,
Puli. f, Yorkshire terrier.
No. 1381 — Cats: a, American wirehair. b,
California spangled cat. c, Chinchilla. d, Exotic
shorthair. e, Selkirk Rex. f, Oriental.
No. 1382 — Dogs: a, Greenland dog. b,
Alaskan malamute. c, Samoyed. d, Siberian
husky.

2001, May 28   *Litho.*   *Perf. 13¼*
1372 A357 280fr Sheet of 6,
                   #a-f   7.25   2.25
1373 A357 300fr Sheet of 6,
                   #a-f   7.75   2.40
1374 A357 300fr Sheet of 6,
                   #a-f   7.75   2.40
1375 A357 350fr Sheet of 6,
                   #a-f   9.50   2.75
1376 A357 390fr Sheet of 6,
                   #a-f   9.50   3.25
1377 A357 390fr Sheet of 6,
                   #a-f   9.50   3.25
1378 A357 390fr Sheet of 6,
                   #a-f   9.50   3.25
1379 A357 465fr Sheet of 6,
                   #a-f   11.50   3.75
1380 A357 465fr Sheet of 6,
                   #a-f   11.00   3.75
1381 A357 485fr Sheet of 6,
                   #a-f   12.00   4.00
1382 A357 600fr Sheet of 4,
                   #a-d   10.00   3.25
      Nos. 1372-1382 (11)   105.25 34.30

Fauna
and Fish
A358

Designs: 280fr, Salamandra salamandra.
No. 1384, 300fr, Epiplatys annualatus. No.
1385, 350fr, Pseudotropheus zebra. 400fr,
Trichechus senegalensis. 450fr, Pelomedusa
subrufa. 500fr, Xenomystus nigri.
No. 1389, vert.: a, Damaliscus dorcas. b,
Manis temmincki. c, Hyaena brunnea. d,
Lycaon pictus. e, Diceros bicornis. f, Osteo-
laemis tetraspis. g, Cercocebus torquatus. h,
Bunologus monticularis. i, Myosciurus pumilia.
No. 1390: a, Plotosus lineatus. b, Protopterus dolloi. c, Calamoichthys calabaricus.
d, Malapterurus electricus. e, Discoglossus
pictus. f, Dugong dugon.
No. 1391, 1500fr, Julidochromis ornatus,
vert. No. 1392, 1500fr, Hippopotamus
amphibius, vert. No. 1393, 1500fr, Afropavo
congensis, vert.

        Perf. 13¼x13½, 13½x13¼
2001, July 12
1383-1388 A358 Set of 6   10.00 3.00
1389 A358 300fr Sheet of 9, #a-
                   i   12.50 3.50
1390 A358 350fr Sheet of 6, #a-
                   f   9.50 2.75
            Souvenir Sheets
1391-1393 A358 Set of 3   21.00 7.50

Reptiles and Amphibians — A359

No. 1394, 350fr: a, Boa arc-en-ciel. b,
Crapaud marine. c, Basilic vert. d, Grenouille
taureau. e, Tortue happante. f,
Pseudoeurycea leprosa.
No. 1395, 350fr: a, Trionix epinelix. b,
Iguane rhinoceros. c, Boa constrictor. d, Boa
canin. e, Tortue d'etang. f, Dermophis
mexicanus.
No. 1396, 1500fr, Serpent des arbres. No.
1397, 1500fr, Grenouille poison.

2001, July 12   *Perf. 13¼x13½*
            Sheets of 6, #a-f
1394-1395 A359 Set of 2   20.00 5.50
            Souvenir Sheets
1396-1397 A359 Set of 2   14.00 6.00

Butterflies — A360

No. 1398, 350fr, vert.: a, Papilio garamus. b,
Eunica orphise. c, Parides lysander. d, Julia
dryas iulia. e, Adelpha mythra. f, Thecla
coronata.
No. 1399, 350fr, vert.: a, Battus polydamas.
b, Mesene phareus. c, Anartia jatrophae. d,
Siproeta epaphus. e, Uraneis ucubis. f, Pereute leucodrosime.
No. 1400, 1500fr, Prepona meander. No.
1401, 1500fr, Morpho peleides. No. 1402,
1500fr, Pieris rapae. No. 1403, 1500fr, Hel-
conius melpomene.

2001, July 12   *Perf. 13½x13¼*
            Sheets of 6, #a-f
1398-1399 A360 Set of 2   20.00 6.00
            Souvenir Sheets
1400-1403 A360 Set of 4   27.50 10.00

Nos. 1398-1399 each contain six 28x42mm
stamps.

A361

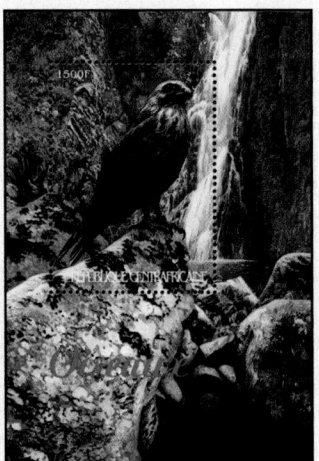

Birds — A362

Designs: 50fr, Macareux moine. 75fr, Harfang des neiges, vert. 100fr, Manchots, vert. 150fr, Fou à pieds bleus.

No. 1408, 325fr: a, Perruche soleil. b, Toucan de cuviée. c, Colibri. d, Ara hyacinthe. e, Pione à tete bleue. f, Perruche flavéolée. g, Pelican. h, Flamant rose. i, Toucan toco.

No. 1409, 325fr: a, Touraco à gros bec. b, Martin-chaseur à poitrine bleue. c, Faucon lanier. d, Inséparable masqué. e, Loriquet à tete bleue. f, Perroquet jaco. g, Perenoptere d'Egypte. h, Grue grise couronnée. i, Marabou.

No. 1410, 350fr: a, Colibri caraibe. b, Jaseur des cèdres. c, Colibri d'abeille. d, Bruant indigo. e, Tourterelle pleureuse. f, Talève pourprée.

No. 1411, 350fr, horiz.: a, Gros-bec bleu. b, Fauvette à gorge orangée. c, Pic flamboyant. d, Passerin nonpareil. e, Fauvette à capuchon. f, Bananaquit.

No. 1412, 1500fr, Cygne, vert. No. 1413, 1500fr, Pygargue à tete blanche, vert.

No. 1414, 1500fr, shown. No. 1415, 1500fr, Balbuzard.

Perf. 13¼x13½, 13½x13¼

2001, July 19
1404-1407	A361	Set of 4	3.75	1.50

Sheets of 9, #a-i
1408-1409	A361	Set of 2	26.50	8.25

Sheets of 6, #a-f
Perf. 13¼x13, 13x13¼
1410-1411	A362	Set of 2	20.00	6.00

Souvenir Sheets
Perf. 13½x13¼
1412-1413	A361	Set of 2	14.00	5.00

Perf. 13¼
1414-1415	A362	Set of 2	14.00	5.00

No. 1410 contains six 30x40mm stamps; No. 1411 contains six 40x30mm stamps.

Mushrooms A363

Designs: 550fr, Coltricia montagnei. 600fr, Inocybe fuscodisca. 650fr, Hydnum imbricatum. 700fr, Hygrophorus miniatus.

No. 1420: a, Coprinus picaceus. b, Crinipellis zonata. c, Naematoloma fasciculare. d, Cortinarius caerulescens. e, Amanita muscaria. f, Cortinarius obtusus. g, Entoloma serrulatum. h, Strobilomyces floccopus.

1500fr, Sarcosphaera crassa, horiz.

Perf. 13½x13¼, 13¼x13½

2001, July 26
1416-1419	A363	Set of 4	12.00	3.50
1420	A363	350fr Sheet of 8, #a-h	13.00	4.00

Souvenir Sheet
1421	A363	1500fr multi	7.00	2.50

Prehistoric Animals — A364

Designs: 50fr, Anatasaurus. 100fr, Apatosaurus. 150fr, Allosaurus. 200fr, Velociraptor.

No. 1426, 240fr: a, Rhamphorhynchus. b, Pteranodon. c, Tyrannosaurus rex. d, Deinonychus antirrhopus. e, Parasaurolophus. f, Corythosaurus. g, Patagosaurus. h, Triceratops. i, Brachylophosaurus. j, Europlocephalus. k, Dimetrodon. l, Leptoceratops.

No. 1427, 240fr: a, Perosaur. b, Albertosaurus. c, Dryptosaurus. d, Archaeopteryx. e, Ouranosaurus. f, Myahuera. g, Camptosaurus. h, Ichthyosaurus. i, Geosaurus. j, Trilobita. k, Plesiosaurus. l, Lewisiceras.

No. 1428, 1500fr, Herrerasaurus. No. 1429, 1500fr, Stegosaurus.

2001, July 31 **Perf. 12½**
1422-1425	A364	Set of 4	2.50	.70

Sheets of 12, #a-l, + 8 labels
1426-1427	A364	Set of 2	27.50	8.25

Souvenir Sheets
1428-1429	A364	Set of 2	14.00	4.25

Dinosaurs A365

Designs: 250fr, Apatosaurus. 300fr, Baryonyx. 325fr, Albertosaurus. 375fr, Dimetrodon.

No. 1434, 350fr: a, Triceratops. b, Ornithocherius. c, Brachiosaurus. d, Utahraptor. e, Tyrannosaurus rex. f, Stegosaurus.

No. 1435, 350fr: a, Diplodicus. b, Pachycephalosaurus. c, Archaeopteryx. d, Pteranodon. e, Herrerasaurus. f, Struthiomimus.

No. 1436, 1500fr, Rhamphorhynchus. No. 1437, 1500fr, Proleratops and Deinonychus.

2001, July 31 **Perf. 13¼x13½**
1430-1433	A365	Set of 4	6.00	1.75

Sheets of 6, #a-f
1434-1435	A365	Set of 2	20.00	6.00

Souvenir Sheets
1436-1437	A365	Set of 2	12.00	5.00

Belgica 2001 Intl. Stamp Exhibition, Brussels (#1434-1437).

2001 Catastrophes — A366

No. 1438: a, Jan. 26 earthquake, India. b, Sept. 11 terrorist attacks, US. c, Dec. 26 fires, Australia. d, Hurricane Michelle, Cuba, Oct. 27. e, July 4 tornado, Canada. f, July 24 eruption of Mt. Etna, Italy.

2002, July 23 **Perf. 13¼**
1438	A366	390fr Sheet of 6, #a-f	9.00	4.00

Each stamp in sheet exists in a souvenir sheet of 1.

Painters and Paintings — A367

No. 1439, 390fr: a, Claude Monet. b, Woman with an Umbrella, by Monet. c, Argenteuil, by Edouard Manet. d, Manet. e, Joseph Mallord William Turner. b, Mornings Amongst the Conniston Falls, Cumberland, by Turner.

No. 1440, 390fr: a, Girl with a Mandolin, by Pablo Picasso. b, Picasso. c, Georges Braque. d, The Musician, by Braque. e, Woman in Blue, by Fernand Leger. f, Leger.

2002, July 23
Sheets of 6, #a-f
1439-1440	A367	Set of 2	15.00	7.00

Chess — A368

No. 1441: a, Board from match between Garry Kasparov and Viswantathan Anand. b, Kasparov. c, Anand. d, Board from match between Anand and Shirov. e, Board from match between Ruslan Ponomariov and Vassily Ivanchuk. f, Ponomariov.

2002, July 23
1441	A368	605fr Sheet of 6, #a-f	13.00	5.50

Each horizontal pair in the sheet exists in a souvenir sheet of 2 stamps.

Cosmonauts — A369

No. 1442: a, Yuri Gagarin, Vostok 1. b, Pavel Vinogradov, Mir 24. c, Valentina Tereshkova, Vostok 6. d, Valeri Kubasov, Apollo-Soyuz. e, Alexei Leonov, Voskhod 2. f, Sergei Treschev, Intl. Space Station.

2002, July 23
1442	A369	605fr Sheet of 6, #a-f	13.00	5.50

Zeppelin NT and Concorde — A370

No. 1443: a, Zeppelin NT over Friedrichshafen, Germany. b, Concorde over Rio de Janeiro. c, Concorde over Alaska. d, Zeppelin NT over Lake Constance. e, Zeppelin NT over Orly Airport, Paris. f, Concorde over New York.

2002, July 23
1443	A370	665fr Sheet of 6, #a-f	15.00	6.00

Each stamp in sheet exists in a souvenir sheet of 1.

Famous People — A371

No. 1444: a, Paul Harris, founder of Rotary International. b, Princess Diana, Intl. Red Cross Ambassador against land mines. c, Pope John Paul II. d, Sir Alexander Fleming. e, Mother Teresa. f, Melvin Jones, founder of Lions Club International.

2002, July 23
1444 A371 665fr Sheet of 6, #a-
f   15.00 6.00
Each stamp in sheet exists in a souvenir sheet of 1.

Rotary and Lions Emblems and
Animals — A372

No. 1445, 390fr — Turtles: a, Eretmochelys imbricata. b, Lepidochelys olivacea. c, Natator depressa.
No. 1446, 600fr — Dinosaurs: a, Sauropelta. b, Chasmosaurus. c, Herrerasaurus.

2002, Dec. 23
Sheets of 3, #a-c
1445-1446 A372   Set of 2   11.00 4.75

Scouts — A373

No. 1447, 605fr — Orchids: a, Dactylorhiza markusii. b, Cephalanthera rubra. c, Neotinea maculata.
No. 1448, 665fr — Mushrooms: a, Agaricus ostreatus. b, Russula virescens. c, Lactarius deliciosus.
No. 1449, 815fr — Dinosaurs: a, Brachiosaurus. b, Sarcosuchus. c, Gigantosaurus carolinii.
No. 1450, 840fr — Minerals: a, Guilleminite. b, Torbernite. c, Bornite.

2002, Dec. 23
Sheets of 3, #a-c
1447-1450 A373   Set of 4   32.50 14.00
Each stamp in each sheet exists in a souvenir sheet of 1.

Famous
People
A374

Designs: No. 1453, 485fr, Christopher Columbus (1450-1506), explorer. No. 1454, 485fr, Admiral Horatio Nelson (1758-1805). No. 1455, 605fr, Jacques Cartier (1491-1557), explorer. No. 1456, 605fr, Vladimir Yourkevitch (1885-1964), naval designer. No. 1457, 665fr, Columbus, diff. No. 1458, 665fr, Sir Francis Drake (1540-96), explorer. No. 1459, 815fr, Jean-François Champollion (1790-1832), Egyptologist. No. 1460, 815fr, Queen Mother Elizabeth of England (1900-2002). No. 1461, 840fr, Marilyn Monroe (1926-62), actress. No. 1462, 840fr, Elvis Presley (1935-77), singer.

No. 1463, 1000fr, Pres. John F. Kennedy (1917-63). No. 1464, 1000fr, French President Charles de Gaulle (1890-1970).

2003, May 15   Litho.   Perf. 13½
1453-1464 A374   Set of 12   40.00 16.00
Dated 2002. Each stamp also exists in souvenir sheet of 1.

2004
Summer
Olympics,
Athens
A375

Designs: 390fr, Boxing. 485fr, Basketball. 605fr, Equestrian. 655fr, Tennis. 815fr, Table tennis.

2004, Mar. 3   Litho.   Perf. 13½
1465-1469 A375   Set of 5   14.00 5.75
Dated 2003. Each stamp also exists in souvenir sheet of 1.

_____

SEMI-POSTAL STAMPS

Anti-Malaria Issue
Common Design Type
Perf. 12½x12
1962, Apr. 7   Engr.   Unwmk.
B1 CD108 25fr + 5fr slate   1.40 1.40
WHO drive to eradicate malaria.

Freedom from Hunger Issue
Common Design Type
1963, Mar. 21   Perf. 13
B2 CD112 25fr + 5fr multi   1.25 1.25

Guinea
Fowl and
Partridge
SP1

Designs: 10fr+5fr, Yellow-backed duiker and snail. 20fr+5fr, Elephant, tortoise and hippopotamus playing tug-of-war. 30fr+10fr, Cuckoo and tortoise. 50fr+20fr, Patas monkey and leopard.

1971, Feb. 9   Photo.   Perf. 12½x12
B3 SP1 5fr + 5fr multi   4.50 2.00
B4 SP1 10fr + 5fr multi   5.75 2.50
B5 SP1 20fr + 5fr multi   7.50 2.75
B6 SP1 30fr + 10fr multi   10.00 7.00
B7 SP1 50fr + 20fr multi   16.00 12.00
    Nos. B3-B7 (5)   43.75 26.25

Lengué
Dancer — SP2

Dancers: 40fr+10fr, Le Lengué. 100fr+40fr, Teke. 140fr+40fr, Englabolo.

1971   Litho.   Perf. 13
B8 SP2 20fr + 5fr multi   .65   .25
B9 SP2 40fr + 10fr multi   1.10   .40
B10 SP2 100fr + 40fr multi   2.50 1.25
B11 SP2 140fr + 40fr multi   3.25 1.50
    Nos. B8-B11 (4)   7.50 3.40

_____

AIR POST STAMPS

Central African Republic

Abyssinian Roller — AP1

Birds: 200fr, Gold Coast touraco. 500fr, African fish eagle.

Unwmk.
1960, Sept. 3   Engr.   Perf. 13
C1 AP1 100fr vio bl, org brn &
        emer   2.50   .70
C2 AP1 200fr multi   4.75 2.00
C3 AP1 500fr Prus bl, emer &
        red brn   14.75 4.75
    Nos. C1-C3 (3)   22.00 7.45

French Equatorial Africa No. C37
Surcharged in Red

1960, Dec. 15   Perf. 13
C4 AP8 250fr on 500fr grnsh
        blk, blk & slate   8.25 8.25
17th Olympic Games, Rome, 8/25-9/11.

Air Afrique Issue
Common Design Type
1962, Feb. 17   Unwmk.   Perf. 13
C5 CD107 50fr vio, lt grn & red
          brn   1.00   .55
Founding of Air Afrique airline.

Pole
Vault — AP1a

1962, July 21   Photo.   Perf. 12x12½
C6 AP1a 100fr grn, yel, brn &
         blk   2.50 1.50
Abidjan games.

Red-faced Lovebirds — AP2

1962-63   Engr.   Perf. 13
C7 AP2 50fr Great blue touraco 2.50 .55
C8 AP2 250fr shown ('63)   7.50 2.50
Issued: 50fr, Nov. 15; 250fr, Mar. 11, 1963.

Runner with
Torch and Palm
Branch — AP3

1962, Dec. 24
C9 AP3 100fr gray grn, brn &
        car   2.75 1.50
Tropics Cup Games, Bangui, Dec. 24-31.

African Postal Union Issue
Common Design Type
1963, Sept. 8   Photo.   Perf. 12½
C10 CD114 85fr emer, ocher &
          red   1.90   .85

Sun Shining on Africa — AP4

1963, Nov. 9   Perf. 13x12
C11 AP4 25fr bl, yel & vio bl   .75   .40
Issued for African unity.

Europafrica Issue
Common Design Type
1963, Nov. 30   Perf. 12x13
C12 CD116 50fr ultra, yel & dk
          brn   2.75 2.00

Diesel Engine — AP5

Various Locomotives; 25fr, 50fr, vertical.

1963, Dec. 1   Engr.   Perf. 13
C13 AP5 20fr brn, cl & dk grn   .75   .75
C14 AP5 25fr brn, bl & choc   .90   .90
C15 AP5 50r brn, red lil &
         vio   3.00 3.00
C16 AP5 100fr brn, grn & dl
         red brn   4.00 4.00
a.   Min. sheet of 4, #C13-C16 13.50 13.50
    Nos. C13-C16 (4)   8.65 8.65
Bangui-Douala railroad project.

Bangui Cathedral — AP6

1964, Jan. 21   Unwmk.   Perf. 13
C17 AP6 100fr yel grn, org brn &
         bl   2.25 1.10

CENTRAL AFRICAN REPUBLIC

165

Radar Tracking Station and WMO
Emblem — AP7

1964, Mar. 23   Engr.   Perf. 13
C18 AP7 50fr org brn, bl & pur   1.25 1.25
World Meteorological Day.

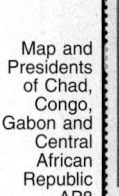

Map and
Presidents
of Chad,
Congo,
Gabon and
Central
African
Republic
AP8

1964, June 23   Photo.   Perf. 12½
C19 AP8 100fr multi   1.75 .80
5th anniversary of the Conference of Chiefs
of State of Equatorial Africa.

Javelin Throwers — AP9

Designs: 50fr, Basketball game. 100fr,
Four runners. 250fr, Swimmers, one in water.

1964, June 23   Engr.   Perf. 13
C20 AP9 25fr grn, dk brn & lt
    vio bl   .55 .30
C21 AP9 50fr blk, car & grn   1.10 .45
C22 AP9 100fr grn, vio bl & dk
    brn   2.50 .95
C23 AP9 250fr grn, blk & car   6.75 2.50
  a.   Min. sheet of 4, #C20-C23   18.00 18.00
    Nos. C20-C23 (4)   10.90 4.20
18th Olympic Games, Tokyo, 10/10-25/64.

John F.
Kennedy — AP10

1964, July 4   Photo.   Perf. 12½
C24 AP10 100fr lil, brn & blk   3.00 1.75
  a.   Min. sheet of 4   12.00 12.00

Industrial Symbols, Maps of Africa and
Europe — AP11

1964, Dec. 19   Unwmk.   Perf. 13x12
C25 AP11 50fr yel, org & grn   1.50 .85
See note after Cameroun No. 402.

International Cooperation Year
Emblem — AP12

1965, Jan. 2   Perf. 13
C26 AP12 100fr red brn, yel & bl   1.90 .80
International Cooperation Year.

Nimbus Weather Satellite — AP13

1965, Mar. 23   Engr.   Perf. 13
C27 AP13 100fr org brn, ultra &
    blk   1.90 .80
Fifth World Meteorological Day.

Lincoln and Statue of Liberty — AP14

1965, Apr. 15   Photo.   Perf. 13
C28 AP14 100fr bluish grn, ind &
    bis   1.90 .80
Centenary of death of Abraham Lincoln.

ITU Emblem and Relay
Satellite — AP15

1965, May 17   Engr.   Perf. 13
C29 AP15 100fr dk grn vio bl &
    brn   2.10 1.25
Centenary of the ITU.

"Housing," New Home in
Village — AP16

1965, June 10   Unwmk.
C30 AP16 100fr ultra, brn & sl grn 1.40 .80
See note after No. 52.

Europafrica Issue

Tractor, Cotton
Picker, Cotton,
Sun and
Emblem — AP17

1965, Nov. 7   Photo.   Perf. 12x13
C31 AP17 50fr multi   1.10 .80
See note after Chad No. C11.

Mercury by
Antoine
Coysevox
AP18

1965, Dec. 5   Engr.   Perf. 13
C32 AP18 100fr red brn, bl & blk 2.75 1.10
5th anniv. of Central African Republic's
admission to the UPU.

Father Holding
Sick
Child — AP19

1965, Dec. 12
Design: 100fr, Mother and child.
C33 AP19 50fr dk bl, car & blk   1.25 .45
C34 AP19 100fr red brn, red &
    brt grn   2.75 1.10
Issued to honor the Red Cross.

Air Afrique Issue
Common Design Type
1966, Aug. 31   Photo.   Perf. 13
C35 CD123 25fr bl, blk & lem   1.00 .40
For surcharge see No. C43.

Surveyor Spacecraft on Moon — AP20

Designs: No. C37, Luna 9 on Moon and
Earth. 200fr, Rocket take-off, Jules Verne's
"From the Earth to the Moon."

1966, Oct. 24   Photo.   Perf. 12x12½
C36 AP20 130fr multi   1.60 .95
C37 AP20 130fr multi   1.60 .95
C38 AP20 200fr multi   3.00 1.75
  a.   Souv. sheet of 3, #C36-C38   9.00 9.00
    Nos. C36-C38 (3)   6.20 3.65
Conquest of the Moon.
For surcharges see Nos. C58, C61.

Eugene A.
Cernan,
Gemini
9 and Agena
Rocket — AP21

No. C40, Pavel R. Popovich and rocket.

1966, Nov. 14   Photo.   Perf. 13
C39 AP21 50fr multi   1.25 .55
C40 AP21 50fr multi   1.25 .55
American and Russian astronauts.

Diamant Rocket, D-1 Satellite and
Globe with Map of Africa — AP22

1966, Nov. 14   Engr.
C41 AP22 100fr brt rose lil & brn 1.90 .95
Issued to commemorate the launching of
France's first satellite, Nov. 26, 1965, and the
launching of the D-1 satellite, Feb. 17, 1966.

Exchange of
Agricultural and
Industrial
Products between
Africa and
Europe — AP23

1966, Dec. 5   Photo.   Perf. 12x13
C42 AP23 50fr multi   1.40 .95
See note after Gabon No. C46.

No. C35 Surcharged

1967, May 8   Perf. 13
C43 CD123 5fr on 25fr multi   .55 .30
The surcharge obliterates the "2" of the orig-
inal 25fr denomination.

DC-8F Over M'Poko Airport,
Bangui — AP24

1967, July 3   Engr.   Perf. 13
C44 AP24 100fr sl, dk grn & brn 2.50 1.00

View of EXPO '67, Montreal — AP25

1967, July 17
C45 AP25 100fr vio bl, dk red brn
& dk grn   2.25 .80
International Exposition. EXPO '67, Montreal, Apr. 28-Oct. 27.

African Postal Union Issue, 1967
Common Design Type
1967, Sept. 9   Engr.   Perf. 13
C46 CD124 100fr brt grn, dk car
rose & plum   2.25 .85

Potez 25 TOE — AP26

1967, Nov. 24   Engr.   Perf. 13
C47 AP26 100fr shown   2.50 .80
C48 AP26 200fr Junkers 52   5.50 1.75
C49 AP26 500fr Caravelle 11R 14.00 4.25
  Nos. C47-C49 (3)   22.00 6.80
For surcharges see Nos. C59-C60.

Presidents Boganda and
Bokassa — AP27

1967, Dec. 1   Photo.   Perf. 12½
C50 AP27 130fr org, red, lt bl &
blk   2.50 1.25
9th anniversary of the republic.

Pres. Jean
Bedel
Bokassa
AP28

1968, Jan. 1   Perf. 12½x12
C51 AP28 30fr multi   1.00 .45

Human Rights Flame, Men and
Globe — AP29

1968, Mar. 26   Photo.   Perf. 13
C52 AP29 200fr brt grn, vio & ver 3.75 1.60
International Human Rights Year.

Man, WHO Emblem and Tsetse
Fly — AP30

1968, Apr. 8   Engr.
C53 AP30 200fr multi   4.00 2.00
20th anniv. of WHO.

Javelin
Thrower — AP31

1968, Apr. 16   Engr.   Perf. 13
C54 AP31 200fr shown   5.50 3.25
C55 AP31 200fr Downhill skier   5.50 3.25
The 1968 Olympic Games.

Space Probe
Landing on
Venus — AP32

1968, Apr. 23
C56 AP32 100fr ultra, dk & brt grn 1.75 .95
Venus exploration by Venus IV, 10/18/67.

Marie Curie and "Cancer
Destroyed" — AP33

1968, Apr. 30
C57 AP33 100fr vio, brt bl & brn 2.75 1.10
Marie Curie (1867-1934), scientist.

Nos. C36-C37 and C47-C48
Surcharged with New Value
Photogravure; Engraved
1968, Sept. 16   Perf. 12x12½, 13
C58 AP20 5fr on 130fr multi   .20 .20
C59 AP26 10fr on 100fr multi   .30 .20
C60 AP26 20fr on 200fr multi   .50 .30
C61 AP20 50fr on 130fr multi   1.10 .55
  Nos. C58-C61 (4)   2.10 1.25
On No. C58 the old denomination has been obliterated with "XIX," on No. C61 the obliteration is a rectangular bar. On Nos. C59-C60 the last zero of the old denomination has been obliterated with a black square.

River Boat Type of Regular Issue
Craft: 100fr, "Pie X," Bangui, 1894. 130fr, "Ballay," Bangui, 1891.
1968, Dec. 10   Engr.   Perf. 13
Size: 48x27mm
C62 A37 100fr bl, dk brn & ol   2.50 1.00
C63 A37 130fr brt pink, sl grn &
slate   3.00 1.25

PHILEXAFRIQUE Issue

Mme. de
Sévigné,
French
School,
17th
Century
AP34

1968, Dec. 17   Photo.   Perf. 12½
C64 AP34 100fr brn & multi   3.25 2.40
Issued to publicize PHILEXAFRIQUE, Philatelic Exhibition in Abidjan, Feb. 14-23. Printed with alternating brown label.

2nd PHILEXAFRIQUE Issue
Common Design Type
Design: 50fr, Ubangi-Shari No. J16, cotton field and Pres. Bokassa.
1969, Feb. 14   Engr.   Perf. 13
C65 CD128 50fr bis brn, blk & dk
grn   1.90 1.90

Holocerina Angulata Aur. — AP35

Butterflies and Moths: 20fr, Nudaurelia dione fabr. 30fr, Eustera troglophylla hamp., vert. 50fr, Aurivillius aratus west. 100fr, Epiphora albida druce.

1969, Feb. 25   Photo.
C66 AP35 10fr yel & multi   1.10 .35
C67 AP35 20fr vio & multi   1.60 .55
C68 AP35 30fr multi   3.75 1.00
C69 AP35 50fr multi   5.25 2.25
C70 AP35 100fr multi   9.00 3.25
  Nos. C66-C70 (5)   20.70 7.40

Boxing — AP36

1969, Mar. 18   Photo.   Perf. 13
C71 AP36 50fr shown   1.10 .30
C72 AP36 100fr Basketball   2.25 .60

Apollo 8 over Moonscape — AP37

1969, May 27   Photo.   Perf. 13
C73 AP37 200fr dp bl, gray & yel 3.75 1.75
US Apollo 8 mission, the 1st men in orbit around the moon, Dec. 21-27, 1968.
For overprint see No. C81.

Market Cross, Nuremberg, and
Toys — AP38

1969, June 3
C74 AP38 100fr blk, brt rose lil &
emer   2.25 .95
Intl. Toy Fair in Nuremberg, Germany.

Napoleon as First Consul, by Anne-Louis Girodet-Trioson — AP39

Designs: 130fr, Napoleon meeting Emperor Francis II, by Antoine Jean Gros, horiz. 200fr, The Wedding of Napoleon and Marie-Louise, by Georges Rouget, horiz.

1969, Nov. 4   Photo.   Perf. 12½
C75 AP39 100fr multi   2.25 1.25
C76 AP39 130fr brn & multi   3.25 1.50
C77 AP39 200fr multi   5.50 2.75
  Nos. C75-C77 (3)   11.00 5.50
Napoleon Bonaparte (1769-1821).

Pres. Bokassa,   Franklin Delano
Map of Africa and   Roosevelt — AP41
Flag — AP40

1970, Jan. 1   Die-cut; Perf. 10½
Embossed on Gold Foil
C78 AP40 2000fr gold   40.00 40.00

1970   Litho.   Perf. 13½x14
C79 AP41 100fr shown   2.25 1.00
C80 AP41 100fr Lenin   3.50 1.25
Roosevelt, 25th death anniv., Lenin, birth cent.
Issue dates: #C79, Apr. 29; #C80, Apr. 22.

No. C73 Overprinted in Red:

1970, June 1   Photo.   Perf. 13
C81 AP37 200fr multi   17.00 9.50
Moon landing mission of Apollo 12, 11/14-24/69.

AP42

1970, Sept. 15   Litho.   Perf. 10
C82 AP42   Pair + label   4.50 3.00
   a.   100fr Dancer   1.90   .55
   b.   100fr Still life   1.90   .55

Knokphila 70, 6th Intl. Phil. Exhib. at Knokke, Belgium, July 4-10. Imperf. between stamps and label.

Sericulture Type of Regular Issue
1970, Sept. 15   Perf. 10
C83 A45   140fr multi   4.50 1.10

C.A.R. Flag, EXPO Emblem and Pavilion
AP43

1970, Dec. 18   Litho.   Perf. 13½x13
C84 AP43   200fr red & multi   4.25 1.75

Intl. Exposition EXPO '70, Osaka, Japan.

Soccer — AP44

1970, Dec. 8   Perf. 13x13½
C85 AP44   200fr multi   4.00 1.60

World Soccer Championships, Mexico, May 30-June 21, 1970.

Dove — AP45

1970, Dec. 31
C86 AP45   200fr bl, yel & blk   4.00 1.60

25th anniversary of the United Nations.

Presidents Mobutu, Bokassa, and Tombalaye — AP46

1971, Jan. 10
C87 AP46   140fr multi   3.25 1.10

Return of Central African Republic to the United States of Central Africa which also includes Congo Democratic Republic and Chad.

Satellite over Globe — AP47

1971, May 17   Photo.   Perf. 12½
C88 AP47   100fr multi   2.25   .85

3rd World Telecommunications Day.

African Postal Union Issue, 1971
Common Design Type

Design: 100fr, Carved head and UAMPT building, Brazzaville, Congo.

1971, Nov. 13   Photo.   Perf. 13x13½
C89 CD135   100fr bl & multi   2.25   .85

Child and Education Year Emblem — AP48

1971, Nov. 11   Litho.   Perf. 13x13½
C90 AP48   140fr multi   2.25   .80

25th anniv. of UNESCO.

Fight Against Cancer — AP49

Gamal Abdel Nasser — AP50

1971, Nov. 20   Photo.   Perf. 12½
C91 AP49   100fr grn & multi   2.75 1.10

1972, Jan. 15
C92 AP50   100fr dk red, blk & bister   2.25   .85

In memory of Gamal Abdel Nasser (1918-1970), president of Egypt.

Olympic Rings and Boxing — AP51

No. C94, Track and Olympic rings, vert.

1972, May 26   Engr.   Perf. 13
C93 AP51   100fr brn org & sepia   1.75   .80
C94 AP51   100fr green & violet   1.75 1.10
   a.   Miniature sheet of 2   5.00 5.00

20th Olympic Games, Munich, Aug. 26-Sept. 10. No. C94a contains 2 stamps similar to Nos. C93-C94, but in changed colors. The boxing stamp is red lilac and green, the track stamp ocher and red lilac.
For overprints see Nos. C100-C101.

Tiling's Mail Rocket, 1931, and Mailman — AP52

Designs: 50fr, DC-3 and mailman riding camel, vert. 150fr, Sirio satellite and rocket, vert. 200fr, Intelsat 4 and rocket.

1972, Aug. 12
C95 AP52   40fr bl, org & indigo   .65   .45
C96 AP52   50fr bl, brn & org   .90   .55
C97 AP52   150fr brn, org & gray   2.50 1.25
C98 AP52   200fr brn, bl & org   3.50 1.25
   a.   Souv. sheet of 4, #C95-C98 9.25 9.25
      Nos. C95-C98 (4)   7.55 4.50

Centraphilex 1972, Central African Philatelic Exhibition, Bangui.

Europafrica Issue

Arrows with Symbols of Agriculture and Industry — AP53

1972, Nov. 17   Litho.   Perf. 13
C99 AP53   100fr multi   1.75   .80

Nos. C93-C94, C94a Overprinted
a. POIDS-MOYEN / LEMECHEV
    MEDAILLE D'OR
b. LONGUER / WILLIAMS
    MEDAILLE D'OR

1972, Nov. 24   Engr.
C100 AP51 (a) 100fr   1.75   .95
C101 AP51 (b) 100fr   1.75   .95
   a.   Miniature sheet of 2   3.75 3.75

Gold Medal Winners in 20th Olympic Games: Viatscheslav Lemechev, USSR, middleweight boxing; Randy Williams, US, broad jump.

Lunar Rover and Module — AP54

1972, Dec. 18   Engr.   Perf. 13
C102 AP54   100fr slate grn, bl & gray   1.75   .80

Apollo 16 US moon mission, 4/15-27/72.

Virgin and Child, by Francesco Pesellino
AP55

Christmas: 150fr, Adoration of the Child with St. John the Baptist and St. Romuald, by Fra Filippo Lippi.

1972, Dec. 25   Photo.
C103 AP55   100fr gold & multi   1.60   .85
C104 AP55   150fr gold & multi   2.75 1.25

Parthenon, Athens, Spyridon Louis, Marathon, 1896 — AP56

Olympic Rings and: 40fr, Arc de Triomphe, Paris, H. Barrelet, single scull, 1900. 50fr, Old Courthouse and Western Arch, St. Louis, Myer Prinstein, triple jump, 1904. 100fr, Tower, London, Henry Taylor, swimming, 1908. 150fr, City Hall, Stockholm, Greco-Roman wrestling, 1912.

1972, Dec. 28   Engr.
C105 AP56   30fr brt grn, mag & brn   .40   .25
C106 AP56   40fr vio bl, emer & brn   .50   .25
C107 AP56   50fr car rose, vio bl & Prus bl   .55   .40
C108 AP56   100fr sl, red lil & brn   1.10   .45
C109 AP56   150fr red lil, blk & Prus bl   1.75 1.10
      Nos. C105-C109 (5)   4.30 2.45

Olympic Games 1896-1912.

WHO Emblem, Surgeon and Nurse — AP57

1973, Apr. 7   Photo.   Perf. 13
C110 AP57   100fr multi   1.75   .80

WHO, 25th anniv.

AP58

AP58a

1973, May 17   Litho.   Perf. 12½
C111 AP58 200fr World map, arrows, waves   2.75 1.10
5th International Telecommunications Day.

1973, Sept. 17   Engr.   Perf. 13
Head and City Hall, Brussels.
C112 AP58a 100fr pur, ocher &
brn   1.40 .70
African Weeks, Brussels, Sept. 15-30, 1973.

Europafrica Issue

Map of Central African Republic with
Industry and Agriculture, Young
Man — AP59

1973, Sept. 28   Engr.   Perf. 13
C113 AP59 100fr sepia, grn & org 1.75 .80

Carrier Pigeon with Letter and UPU
Emblem — AP60

1973, Oct. 9   Photo.
C114 AP60 200fr multi   2.50 1.10
Universal Postal Union Day.

WMO Emblem, Weather Map — AP61

1973, Oct. 20   Engr.   Perf. 13
C115 AP61 150fr brt ultra & sl
grn   2.75 1.00
Cent. of intl. meteorological cooperation.

Copernicus, Heliocentric
System — AP62

1973, Nov. 2   Photo.
C116 AP62 100fr gold & multi   3.00 1.75
Copernicus (1473-1543), Polish astronomer.

Pres.
Bokassa
AP63

Pres.
Bokassa — AP64

Rocket Launch
and Apollo 17
Badge — AP65

1973, Nov. 30   Photo.   Perf. 12½
C117 AP63 50fr multi   .75 .40
C118 AP64 100fr multi   1.40 .70

1973, Dec. 15   Engr.   Perf. 13
65fr, Capsule over moonscape, horiz.
100fr, Moon landing, horiz. 150fr, Astronauts
on moon. 200fr, Splashdown with parachutes
and badge.
C119 AP65 50fr ver, gray grn &
brn   .55 .30
C120 AP65 65fr dk brn, brn red
& sl grn   .75 .40
C121 AP65 100fr ver, slate &
choc   1.10 .55
C122 AP65 150fr brn, ol & sl grn 1.75 .80
C123 AP65 200fr red, bl & sl grn 2.25 1.10
Nos. C119-C123 (5)   6.40 3.15
Apollo 17 US moon mission, 12/7-19/72.

St.
Teresa — AP66

UPU Emblem,
Letter — AP67

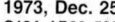

1973, Dec. 25
C124 AP66 500fr vio bl & grnsh
bl   6.75 3.50
St. Teresa of the Infant Jesus, the Little
Flower (1873-1897), Carmelite nun.

1974, Oct. 9   Engr.   Perf. 13
C125 AP67 500fr multi   7.50 4.00
Centenary of Universal Postal Union.
For surcharge see No. C159.

Presidents and Flags of Cameroun,
CAR, Gabon and Congo — AP68

1974, Dec. 8   Photo.   Perf. 13
C126 AP68 100fr gold & multi   1.40 .80
See note after Cameroun No. 595.
For surcharge see No. C155.

Marshal
Bokassa
AP69

100fr, Bokassa in Marshal's uniform with
cape.

1975, Feb. 22   Photo.   Perf. 13
C127 AP69 50fr tan & multi   .65 .40
C128 AP69 100fr tan & multi   1.40 .45
Jean Bedel Bokassa, President for Life and
Marshal of the Republic.

Mask, Map of
Africa, Arphila
Emblem — AP70

Albert Schweitzer
and Dugout,
Lambarene
AP71

1975, Aug. 25   Engr.   Perf. 13
C129 AP70 100fr brt bl, red brn &
red   1.40 .60
ARPHILA 75 International Philatelic Exhibi-
tion, Paris, June 6-16.
For surcharge see No. C156.

1975, Sept. 30   Engr.   Perf. 13
C130 AP71 200fr blk, ultra & ol 3.50 1.75
Dr. Albert Schweitzer (1875-1965), medical
missionary and musician.
For surcharge see No. C158.

Pres. Bokassa's Houseboat,
Bow — AP72

40fr, Pres. Bokassa's houseboat, stern.

1976, Feb. 22   Litho.   Perf. 13
C131 AP72 30fr multi   .65 .30
C132 AP72 40fr multi   .85 .45

Monument
to Franco-
CAR
Cooperation
AP73

Presidents
and Flags
of France
and CAR
AP74

1976, Mar. 5
C133 AP73 100fr multi   1.40 .80
C134 AP74 200fr multi   2.50 1.25
Official visit of Pres. Valery Giscard
d'Estaing to Central African Republic, 3/5-8.
For surcharge see No. C157.

Apollo Soyuz Type, 1976

Designs: 100fr, Soyuz space ship. 200fr,
Apollo space ship. 300fr, Astronauts and cosmonauts in cabin. 500fr, Apollo and Soyuz
after link-up.

1976, June 14   Litho.   Perf. 14x13½
C135 A90 100fr multi   1.10 .25
C136 A90 200fr multi   2.10 .55
C137 A90 300fr multi   3.25 .95
Nos. C135-C137 (3)   6.45 1.75

Souvenir Sheet

C138 A90 500fr multi   5.00 1.75
For surcharges see #C161, C168, C173,
C177.

French
Hussar
AP75

Uniforms: 125fr, Scottish "Black Watch."
150fr, German dragoon. 200fr, British grenadier. 250fr, American ranger. 450fr, American
dragoon.

1976, July 4   Perf. 13½
C139 AP75 100fr multi   .90 .30
C140 AP75 125fr multi   1.00 .45
C141 AP75 150fr multi   1.25 .45

C142	AP75	200fr multi	1.90	.55
C143	AP75	250fr multi	2.50	.95
	Nos. C139-C143 (5)		7.55	2.70

Souvenir Sheet

| C144 | AP75 | 450fr multi | 7.50 | 2.00 |

American Bicentennial.
For surcharges see Nos. C162, C166-C167, C169, C172, C176.

Acherontia Atropos — AP76

100fr, Papilio nireus & niocha marnois.

1976, Sept. 20   Litho.   Perf. 12½

| C145 | AP76 | 50fr multi | 8.50 | 1.10 |
| C146 | AP76 | 100fr multi | 17.00 | 1.75 |

For surcharges see Nos. C160, C163.

Olympic Winners Type, 1976

Designs: 100fr, Women's figure skating, Dorothy Hamill, vert. 200fr, Ice skating, Alexander Gorshkov and Ludmilla Pakhomova. 300fr, Men's figure skating, John Curry, vert. 500fr, Downhill skiing, Rosi Mittermaier, vert.

1976, Sept. 23   Litho.   Perf. 13½

C147	A92	100fr multi	.75	.70
C148	A92	200fr multi	2.40	.60
C149	A92	300fr multi	3.25	1.00
	Nos. C147-C149 (3)		6.40	1.90

Souvenir Sheet

| C150 | A92 | 500fr multi | 6.00 | 1.75 |

For surcharges see #C164, C170, C174, C178.

Viking Mars Type, 1976

Designs: 100fr, Phases of Mars landing. 200fr, Viking descending on Mars, horiz. 300fr, Viking probe. 500fr, Viking flight to Mars, horiz.

1976, Dec.

C151	A93	100fr multi	1.00	.30
C152	A93	200fr multi	2.40	.60
C153	A93	300fr multi	3.00	.95
	Nos. C151-C153 (3)		6.40	1.85

Souvenir Sheet

| C154 | A93 | 500fr multi | 5.50 | 1.75 |

For surcharges and overprints see Nos. C165, C171, C175, C179, C212-C215.

Central African Empire
Stamps of 1973-76 Overprinted with Bars and "EMPIRE CENTRAFRICAIN" in Black, Violet Blue or Gold
Printing and Perforations as Before

1977, Mar.

C155	AP68	100fr (#C126;B)	1.10	1.10
C156	AP70	100fr (#C129;VB)	1.10	1.10
C157	AP73	100fr (#C133;G)	1.10	1.10
C158	AP71	200fr (#C130;B)	3.25	1.50
C159	AP67	500fr (#C125;B)	10.00	10.00
	Nos. C155-C159 (5)		16.55	14.80

No bar on No. C159.

Stamps of 1976 Overprinted "EMPIRE CENTRAFRICAIN" in Black on Silver Panel

1977, Apr. 1

C160	AP76	50fr (#C145)	.55	.55
C161	A90	100fr (#C135)	1.10	1.10
C162	AP75	100fr (#C139)	1.10	1.10
C163	AP76	100fr (#C146)	1.10	1.10
C164	A92	100fr (#C147)	1.10	1.10
C165	A93	100fr (#C151)	1.10	1.10
C166	AP75	125fr (#C140)	1.40	1.40
C167	AP75	150fr (#C141)	1.60	1.60
C168	A90	200fr (#C136)	2.75	2.75
C169	AP75	200fr (#C142)	2.50	2.50
C170	A92	200fr (#C148)	2.25	2.25
C171	A93	200fr (#C152)	2.25	2.25
C172	AP75	250fr (#C143)	2.75	2.75
C173	A90	300fr (#C137)	3.50	3.50
C174	A92	300fr (#C149)	3.50	3.50
C175	A93	300fr (#C153)	3.50	3.50
	Nos. C160-C175 (16)		32.05	32.05

Souvenir Sheets

C176	AP75	450fr (#C144)	5.50	5.50
C177	A90	500fr (#C138)	8.00	8.00
C178	A92	500fr (#C150)	5.50	5.50
C179	A93	500fr (#C154)	5.50	5.50

Overprint on type AP75 is in upper and lower case letters.

Nobel Prize Type, 1977

Designs: 100fr, Rudyard Kipling. 200fr, Ernest Hemingway. 300fr, Luigi Pirandello. 500fr, Rabindranath Tagore.

1977, Apr. 1   Litho.   Perf. 13½

C180	A94	100fr multi	2.00	.40
C181	A94	200fr multi	4.00	.70
C182	A94	300fr multi	6.25	.95
	Nos. C180-C182 (3)		12.25	2.05

Souvenir Sheet

| C183 | A94 | 500fr multi | 6.00 | 1.75 |

Zeppelin Type of 1977

100fr, Germany #C42 and North Pole. 200fr, Germany #C44 and Science and Industry Building, Chicago. 300fr, Germany #C35 and Brandenburg Gate, Berlin. 500fr, US #C14 and US Capitol.

1977, Apr. 11   Litho.   Perf. 11

C184	A95	100fr multi	1.40	.30
C185	A95	200fr multi	2.75	.60
C186	A95	300fr multi	3.50	1.00
	Nos. C184-C186 (3)		7.65	1.90

Souvenir Sheet

| C187 | A95 | 500fr multi | 5.50 | 2.00 |

75th anniversary of Zeppelin.

Bokassa Type of 1977

1977, Dec. 4   Litho.   Perf. 13½

C188	A98	200fr multi	1.90	.80
C189	A98	300fr multi	2.75	1.25
a.	Souvenir sheet, 500fr		6.00	2.50

Coronation of Emperor Bokassa I, Dec. 4. No. C189a contains a horizontal stamp in similar design. A 2500fr gold embossed horizontal stamp in similar design exists. Value $25.

Vaccination AP77

1977   Litho.   Perf. 14x13½

| C190 | AP77 | 150fr multi | 4.00 | 1.25 |

World Health Day.

Communications Type of 1978

Designs: 100fr, Balloon and spaceships docking in space. 200fr, Hydrofoil and Concorde. 500fr, Tom-tom and Zeppelin. No. C193A, Early postman and rider, UPU emblem, Concorde. No. C193B, Mail coach, dove, satellites.

1978, May 17   Litho.   Perf. 13½

| C191 | A107 | 100fr multi | 1.10 | .25 |
| C192 | A107 | 200fr multi | 1.10 | .30 |

Souvenir Sheet

| C193 | A107 | 500fr multi | 5.75 | 2.25 |

Cent. of progress of posts and telecommunications. No. C193 contains one 53x35mm stamp.

**1978, Mar. 21   Litho. & Embossed
Size: 57x39mm**

| C193A | A107 | 1500fr gold & multi | 55.00 | 4.00 |

Souvenir Sheet

| C193B | A107 | 1500fr gold & multi | 15.00 | 4.75 |

Nos. C193A-C193B exist imperf. No. C193A exists in a souvenir sheet of one. No. C193B contains one 57x39mm stamp.

Clement Ader and his Plane — AP78

Designs: 50fr, Wilbur and Orville Wright and plane. 60fr, John W. Alcock, Arthur W. Brown and plane. 100fr, Alan Cobham and plane 150fr, Claude Dornier and hydroplane. 500fr, Wilbur and Orville Wright and plane.

1978, Sept. 19   Perf. 14

C194	AP78	40fr multi	.55	.20
C195	AP78	50fr multi	.55	.20
C196	AP78	60fr multi	.65	.20
C197	AP78	100fr multi	1.25	.40
C198	AP78	150fr multi	1.90	.60
	Nos. C194-C198 (5)		4.90	1.65

Souvenir Sheet

| C199 | AP78 | 500fr multi | 6.00 | 1.75 |

History of aviation.

**Philexafrique II-Essen Issue
Common Design Types**

#C200, Crocodile, #C3. #C201, Birds, Mecklenburg-Schwerin #1.

1978, Nov. 1   Litho.   Perf. 12½

C200	CD138	100fr multi	1.90	1.10
C201	CD139	100fr multi	1.90	1.10
a.	Pair, #C200-C201 + label		7.50	7.50

Bokassa Type of 1978

150fr, Catherine & Jean Bedel Bokassa.

1978, Dec. 4   Litho.   Perf. 13

| C202 | A113 | 150fr multi, horiz. | 1.90 | .70 |

First anniv. of coronation. A 1000fr gold embossed souvenir sheet showing Emperor Bokassa exists. Value $9.

Rowland Hill Type of 1978

Designs (Rowland Hill and): 100fr, Mailman and Tuscany No. 23. 200fr, Balloon and France No. 1. 500fr, Central Africa Nos. 1-2.

1978, Dec. 27

| C203 | A114 | 100fr multi | 4.00 | 1.40 |
| C204 | A114 | 200fr multi | 1.75 | .65 |

Souvenir Sheet

| C205 | A114 | 500fr multi | 5.50 | 1.75 |

Sir Rowland Hill (1795-1879), originator of penny postage. No. C205 contains one 37½x39mm stamp. 1500fr gold embossed stamp and souvenir sheet exist.

IYC Type of 1979

Designs (UNICEF, Eagle Emblems and): 100fr, Do-X flying boat, 1929. 200fr, Boys playing leapfrog, hurdler and Olympic emblem. 500fr, Child with abacus and Albert Einstein with his equation.

1979, Mar. 6   Perf. 13½

| C206 | A115 | 100fr multi | 1.40 | .40 |
| C207 | A115 | 200fr multi | 2.75 | .65 |

Souvenir Sheet

| C208 | A115 | 500fr multi | 5.50 | 1.75 |

International Year of the Child. No. C208 contains one 56x33mm stamp. 1500fr gold embossed stamp and souvenir sheet exist.

Olympic Type of 1979

Moscow '80 Emblem, various Sports and: 100fr, Hurdles & "B." 200fr, Broad jump & "A."

1979, Mar. 16   Litho.   Perf. 13

| C209 | A116 | 100fr multi | 1.10 | .35 |
| C210 | A116 | 200fr multi | 2.10 | .65 |

22nd Olympic Games, Moscow, July 19-Aug. 3, 1980. A 1500fr gold embossed souvenir sheet exists showing diver, runner and javelin.

National Husbandry Association Type

1979, Aug.   Litho.   Perf. 13

| C211 | A119 | 60fr Horse | 5.75 | 2.00 |

Central African Republic
Nos. C151-C154 Overprinted
"ALUNISSAGE/APOLLO XI/ JUILLET 1969" and Emblem in Black or Silver

1979, Oct.   Litho.   Perf. 14x13½

C212	A93	100fr multi	1.00	.55
C213	A93	200fr multi	1.90	.85
C214	A93	300fr multi	2.75	1.25
	Nos. C212-C214 (3)		5.65	2.65

Souvenir Sheet

| C215 | A93 | 500fr multi (S) | 5.50 | 5.50 |

Apollo 11 moon landing, 10th anniversary.

Ski Jump, Lake Placid '80
Emblem — AP79

1979, Nov. 11   Litho.   Perf. 13½

C216	AP79	60fr shown	.65	.20
C217	AP79	100fr Downhill skiing	1.10	.40
C218	AP79	200fr Hockey	2.25	.85
C219	AP79	300fr Bobsledding	3.25	1.25
	Nos. C216-C219 (4)		7.25	2.70

Souvenir Sheet

| C220 | AP79 | 500fr multi | 5.50 | 1.75 |

13th Winter Olympics Games, Lake Placid, NY, Feb. 12-24, 1980.
For overprints see Nos. C224-C228.

Space Type of 1980

1980, Apr. 8   Litho.   Perf. 13½

| C221 | A125 | 150fr Early satellites | 1.60 | .40 |
| C222 | A125 | 200fr Space shuttle | 1.90 | .55 |

Souvenir Sheet

| C223 | A125 | 500fr Apollo 11, Armstrong | 5.50 | 1.40 |

**Litho. & Embossed
Size: 51x57mm**

| C223A | A125 | 1500fr Armstrong, Apollo 11 | 50.00 | 3.00 |

Souvenir Sheet

| C223B | A125 | 1500fr Space shuttle, horiz. | 10.00 | |

C223A-C223B exist imperf. No. C223A exists in a souvenir sheet of one. Value $40. No. C223B contains one 57x51mm stamp.

Nos. C216-C220 Overprinted:

a
b. VAINQUEUR / MOSER-PROELL / AUTRICHE
c. VAINQUEUR / ETATS-UNIS
d. VAINQUEUR / STENMARK / SUEDE
e. VAINQUEURS / SCHAERER-BENZ / SUISSE

1980, May 12   Litho.   Perf. 13½

C224	AP79 (a)	60fr multi	.50	.20
C225	AP79 (b)	100fr multi	.75	.40
C226	AP79 (c)	200fr multi	1.90	.85
C227	AP79 (d)	300fr multi	2.75	1.25
	Nos. C224-C227 (4)		5.90	2.70

Souvenir Sheet

| C228 | AP79 (e) | 500fr multi | 5.00 | 5.00 |

World Telecommunications Day — AP80

1980, June 26   Litho.   Perf. 12½

| C229 | AP80 | 100fr multi | 1.10 | .55 |
| C230 | AP80 | 150fr multi, vert. | 1.40 | .80 |

Olympic Type of 1980

1980, July 25   Litho.   Perf. 13½

| C231 | A126 | 100fr Boxing | 1.00 | .25 |
| C232 | A126 | 150fr Hurdles | 1.60 | .40 |

Souvenir Sheet

| C233 | A126 | 250fr Long jump | 3.00 | .65 |

Litho. & Embossed

C233A	A126	1500fr	Relay race, diff.	35.00 4.00

Souvenir Sheet

C233B	A126	1500fr	Basketball, vert.	11.00 4.75

22nd Summer Olympic Games, Moscow, July 19-Aug. 3. #C233 contains one 39x36mm stamp.
For overprints see Nos. C248-C250B.

Europe-Africa Type of 1980

1980, Nov. 4		**Litho.**		**Perf. 13½**
C234	A127	150fr	Meteorology	1.50 .50
C235	A127	200fr	Aviation	1.90 .60

Souvenir Sheet

C236	A127	500fr	Concorde jet	5.50 1.60

No. C236 contains one 41½x29mm stamp.

Litho. & Embossed
Size: 42x39mm

C236A	A127	1500fr	Boy Scouts	15.00 4.00

Souvenir Sheet

C236B	A127	1500fr	Concorde	12.00 4.75

Nos. C236A-C236B exist imperf. No. C236B contains one 42x39mm stamp.
No. C236A exists in a souvenir sheet of one. Value $30.

Soccer Type of 1981

1981, Jan. 13		**Litho.**		**Perf. 13½**
C237	A130	100fr	Netherlands	1.00 .25
C238	A130	200fr	Spain	1.50 .55

Souvenir Sheet

C239	A130	500fr	Argentina	6.25 1.75

Litho. & Embossed
Size: 57x39mm

C239A	A130	1500fr	Players, trophy	24.00 5.50

Souvenir Sheet

C239B	A130	1500fr	Players, trophy, diff.	10.00 4.00

No. C239A exists with tabs for either Philexafrique II or Essen 78.
Nos. C239A-C239B exist imperf. No. C239A exists in a souvenir sheet of one. Value $38. No. C239B contains one 36x60mm stamp.

Jacob Wrestling with the Angel, by Rembrandt AP81

Rembrandt Paintings: 90fr, Christ during the Storm. 150fr, Jeremiah Mourning the Destruction of Jerusalem. 250fr, Tobit Accusing Anne of Theft of a Goat. 500fr, Belshazzar's Feast, horiz.

1981, Feb. 20				**Perf. 12½**
C240	AP81	60fr	multi	.55 .20
C241	AP81	90fr	multi	.90 .25
C242	AP81	150fr	multi	1.40 .55
C243	AP81	250fr	multi	2.50 .65
	Nos. C240-C243 (4)			5.35 1.65

Souvenir Sheet

C244	AP81	500fr	multi	5.50 1.75

Picasso Type of 1981

Paintings: 150fr, Woman in Mirror with Self-portrait. 200fr, Woman Sleeping, The Dream. 500fr, Portrait of Maia (the Artist's Daughter). No. C247A, Two Women and Glasses, Picasso. No. C247B, Woman with Handbag, statue of standing woman, vert.

1981, June 30		**Litho.**		**Perf. 13½**
C245	A133	150fr	multi	2.25 .45
C246	A133	200fr	multi	2.50 .60

Souvenir Sheet

C247	A133	500fr	multi	5.75 1.40

No. C247 contains one 42x46mm stamp.

Litho. & Embossed
Size: 57x39mm

C247A	A133	1500fr	gold & multi	15.00 4.00

Souvenir Sheet

C247B	A133	1500fr	gold & multi	12.00

Nos. C247A-C247B exist imperf. No. C247A exists in a souvenir sheet of one. Value $30. No. C247B contains one 39x58mm stamp.

Nos. C231-C233B Overprinted with Event, Winner and Country in Gold

1981		**Litho.**		**Perf. 13½**
C248	A126	100fr	multi	1.00 .25
C249	A126	150fr	multi	1.40 .40

Souvenir Sheet

C250	A126	250fr	multi	3.00 .65

Litho. & Embossed

C250A	A126	1500fr	on #C233A	14.00

Souvenir Sheet

C250B	A126	1500fr	on #C233B	15.00

No. C250A exists in a souvenir sheet of 1. Value $35.

Royal Wedding Type of 1981

1981, Aug. 20		**Litho.**		**Perf. 13½**
C251	A136	150fr	Prince of Wales arms	1.60 .40
C252	A136	200fr	Palace	2.10 .55

Souvenir Sheet

C253	A136	500fr	St. Paul's Cathedral	4.75 1.40

No. C253 contains one 60x32mm stamp.

Litho. & Embossed
Size: 51x42mm

C253A	A136	1500fr	Diana, Charles	15.00 4.00

Souvenir Sheet

C253B	A136	1500fr	Charles, Diana, ship	12.00

Nos. C253A-C253B exist imperf. No. C253A exists in a souvenir sheet of one. Value $21. No. C253B contains one 51x42mm stamp.

Navigator Type of 1981

1981, Sept. 4		**Litho.**		**Perf. 13½**
C254	A139	100fr	O. Kersauson	1.10 .70
C255	A139	200fr	Chichester	2.40 1.40

Souvenir Sheet

C256	A139	500fr	A. Colas	6.50 1.40

Litho. & Embossed
Size: 51x42mm

C256A	A139	1500fr	Riguidel	16.00 4.50

Souvenir Sheet

C256B	A139	1500fr	Tabarly	13.00

Nos. C256A-C256B exist imperf. No. C256A exists in a souvenir sheet of one. Value $40. No. C256B contains one 51x42mm stamp.

Lizard AP82

1981, Oct. 30				**Perf. 12½x13**
C257	AP82	30fr	shown	1.00 .25
C258	AP82	60fr	Snake	1.25 .30
C259	AP82	110fr	Crocodile	2.50 .45
	Nos. C257-C259 (3)			4.75 1.00

Christmas Type of 1981

1981, Dec. 24				**Perf. 13½**
C260	A143	140fr	Correggio	2.50 .45
C261	A143	200fr	Gentileschi, 1610	4.50 .70

Souvenir Sheet

C262	A143	500fr	Holy Family, by Cranach	6.75 1.75

No. C262 contains one 41x50mm stamp.

Litho. & Embossed
Size: 30x60mm

C262A	A143	1500fr	Hans Memling, c. 1470	15.00 4.50

Souvenir Sheet

C262B	A143	1500fr	Fra Angelico, 1438	11.00

Nos. C262A-C262B exist imperf. No. C262A exists in a souvenir sheet of one. Value $25. No. C262B contains one 30x60mm stamp.

Animal Type of 1982

1982, Jan. 22		**Litho.**		**Perf. 13½**
C263	A145	300fr	Mandrill	3.25 .65
C264	A145	500fr	Lion	5.50 1.40

Souvenir Sheet

C265	A145	600fr	Nile crocodiles	6.75 1.60

No. C265 contains one 47x38mm stamp.

Litho. & Embossed
Size: 51x57mm

C265A	A145	1500fr	Leopard, Rotary emblem	15.00 4.00

Souvenir Sheet

C265B	A145	1500fr	Emblem, eagle, horiz.	13.00

Nos. C265A-C265B exist imperf. No. C265A exists in a souvenir sheet of one. Value $42.50. No. C265B contains one 57x51mm stamp.

Transportation Type of 1982 and

AP82a

Designs: 300fr, Savannah cargo ship. 500fr, Columbia space shuttle. 600fr, Spirit of Locomotion emblem. No. C268A, Space shuttle launch, horiz. No. C268B, Shuttle, space telescope.

1982, Feb. 27		**Litho.**		**Perf. 13½**
C266	A147	300fr	multicolored	3.50 .65
C267	A147	500fr	multicolored	5.50 1.40

Souvenir Sheet

C268	A147	600fr	multicolored	5.50 1.60

Litho. & Embossed

C268A	AP82a	1500fr	gold & multi	15.00 4.50

Souvenir Sheet

C268B	AP82a	1500fr	gold & multi	11.50

No. C268 contains one 39x43mm stamp. No. C268B contains one 51x42mm stamp.
No. C268A exists in a souvenir sheet of 1. Value $50.

Olympic Type of 1982

1982, July 24		**Litho.**		**Perf. 13½**
C269	A149	300fr	Diving	3.00 .80
C270	A149	500fr	Equestrian	5.00 1.40

Souvenir Sheet

C271	A149	600fr	Basketball	5.50 1.60

No. C271 contains one 38x56mm stamp.

Diana Type of 1982

1982, July 20		**Litho.**		**Perf. 13½**
C272	A150	300fr	multi	3.25 .80
C273	A150	500fr	multi	5.50 1.40

Souvenir Sheet

C274	A150	600fr	multi	5.75 1.60

No. C274 contains one 56x32mm stamp.

Christmas 1982 AP83

Raphael Paintings.

1982, Dec.				**Perf. 13**
C275	AP83	150fr	Beautiful Gardener	1.75 .40
C276	AP83	500fr	Holy Family	5.50 1.40

Space Type of 1982

Designs: Various satellites and space scenes. No. C279A, European communications satellite, controller. No. C279B, Viking on Mars, vert.

1982, Aug. 15		**Litho.**		**Perf. 13½**
C277	A151	300fr	multi	3.00 .80
C278	A151	500fr	multi	5.00 1.40

Souvenir Sheet

C279	A151	600fr	multi	5.00 1.60

Litho. & Embossed
Size: 60x36mm

C279A	A151	1500fr	gold & multi	15.00 4.50

Souvenir Sheet

C279B	A151	1500fr	gold & multi	12.00

Nos. C279A-C279B exist imperf. No. C279A exists in a souvenir sheet of one. Value $55. No. C279B contains one 36x60mm stamp.

Birth of Prince William of Wales, June 21, 1982 — AP84

Designs: No. C281, Diana, William, Charles. No. 281B, Diana, William, vert.

1983, Jan. 22				
C280	AP84	500fr	Diana, William	5.50 1.40

Souvenir Sheet

C281	AP84	600fr	Family	5.50 4.00

Litho. & Embossed

C281A	AP84	1500fr	gold & multi	15.00 3.50

Souvenir Sheet

C281B	AP84	1500fr	gold & multi	10.00

No. C281A exists in a souvenir sheet of 1. Value $40.

Manned Flight Bicentenary AP85

1983, Apr.				
C282	AP85	65fr	Robert's & Hullin's balloon	1.00 .20
C283	AP85	130fr	John Wise's, 1859	1.50 .35
C284	AP85	350fr	Mail balloon, 1870	3.25 .90

C285 AP85 400fr Dirigible Un-
derberg 4.25 1.10
Nos. C282-C285 (4) 10.00 2.55
Souvenir Sheet
C286 AP85 500fr Montgolfiere,
1783 5.75 1.40

Pre-Olympics — AP86

Various equestrian events.

1983, July   Litho.   Perf. 13
C287 AP86 100fr multi 1.00 .40
C288 AP86 200fr multi 2.10 .60
C289 AP86 300fr multi 2.75 .80
C290 AP86 400fr multi 3.50 1.10
Nos. C287-C290 (4) 9.35 2.90
Souvenir Sheet
C291 AP86 500fr multi 5.75 1.40

Animal Type of 1983

Endangered Animals, Rotary Emblem

1983, Nov. 14   Litho.   Perf. 13½
C291A A170 400fr Black rhi-
noceros,
parrot, ze-
bra, scouts 7.00 1.25
C292 A170 500fr Lions, parrot,
antelope, el-
ephant, flag,
Rotary Int'l
emblem 8.25 1.40
Souvenir Sheet
C293 A170 600fr Leopard 6.00 1.50

15th World Scout Jamboree, Alberta (400fr).
No. C293 contains one 47x32mm stamp.

Christmas 1983 AP88

Paintings: 130fr, Annunciation, by da Vinci.
205fr, Virgin of the Rocks, by da Vinci. 350fr,
Adoration of the Shepherds, by Rubens.
500fr, Virgin and Child with Donor, by Rubens.

1984, Jan. 3   Litho.   Perf. 13
C294 AP88 130fr multi 1.00 .25
C295 AP88 205fr multi 1.60 .35
C296 AP88 350fr multi 2.75 .80
C297 AP88 500fr multi 4.50 1.00
Nos. C294-C297 (4) 9.85 2.40

1984 Summer Olympics — AP89

Various gymnastic and rhythmic gymnastic
events. 65fr, 100fr, 205fr, 350fr vert.

1984, Mar. 13   Litho.   Perf. 13
C298 AP89 65fr multi .55 .20
C299 AP89 100fr multi 1.10 .25
C300 AP89 130fr multi 1.40 .30
C301 AP89 205fr multi 2.10 .45
C302 AP89 350fr multi 3.50 .85
Nos. C298-C302 (5) 8.65 2.05

Souvenir Sheet
Perf. 13½x13
C302A AP89 500fr Rhythmic
formation 5.00 1.25

For overprint see No. 705.

Summer Olympics Winners AP90

1985, Jan. 7   Litho.   Perf. 14
C303 AP90 60fr 400 meter re-
lay .55 .25
C304 AP90 140fr 400 meter
hurdles 1.40 .30
C305 AP90 300fr 5000 meter
race 3.25 .80
C306 AP90 440fr Decathlon 4.50 1.00
Nos. C303-C306 (4) 9.70 2.35
Souvenir Sheet
C307 AP90 500fr 800 meter
race, horiz. 5.00 4.50

Christmas 1984 — AP91

Paintings by Titian: 130fr, Virgin and Infant
Jesus. 350fr, Virgin with Rabbit. 400fr, Virgin
and Child.

1985, Jan. 17   Litho.   Perf. 13
C308 AP91 130fr multi 1.25 .55
C309 AP91 350fr multi 2.75 1.10
C310 AP91 400fr multi 3.75 1.25
Nos. C308-C310 (3) 7.75 2.90

Audubon Bicentenary — AP92

1985, Jan. 25   Litho.   Perf. 13
C311 AP92 60fr Otus asio .80 .25
C312 AP92 110fr Coccizus mi-
nor, vert. 1.25 .45
C313 AP92 200fr Zenaidura
macroura,
vert. 2.10 1.00
C314 AP92 500fr Aix sponsa 5.25 2.50
Nos. C311-C314 (4) 9.40 4.20

Christmas 1985 AP93

Religious paintings: 100fr, Virgin with
Angels, by the Master of Burgo de Osma.
200fr, Nativity, by Louis Le Nain (1593-1648).

400fr, Virgin and Child with Dove, by Piero de
Cosimo (1462-1521).

1985, Dec. 24   Litho.   Perf. 13
C315 AP93 100fr multi 1.10 .40
C316 AP93 200fr multi 2.50 .85
C317 AP93 400fr multi 4.75 1.90
Nos. C315-C317 (3) 8.35 3.15

Halley's Comet — AP94

1986, Mar. 8
C318 AP94 110fr Edmond Hal-
ley 1.00 .25
C319 AP94 130fr Giotto probe 1.40 .25
C320 AP94 200fr Comet, planet 1.90 .45
C321 AP94 300fr Vega probe 2.75 .60
C322 AP94 400fr Space shuttle 4.50 1.00
Nos. C318-C322 (5) 11.55 2.55

Christmas AP95

Painting details: 250fr, Nativity, by Giotto.
440fr, Adoration of the Magi, by Botticelli, vert.
500fr, Nativity, by Giotto, diff.

1986, Dec. 24   Litho.   Perf. 13½
C323 AP95 250fr multi 2.50 1.10
C324 AP95 440fr multi 4.25 1.75
C325 AP95 500fr multi 5.25 2.10
Nos. C323-C325 (3) 12.00 4.95

Tennis at the 1988 Olympics — AP96

Various plays.

1986, Dec. 31   Perf. 12½
C326 AP96 150fr multi 1.60 .60
C327 AP96 250fr multi, vert. 3.00 .70
C328 AP96 440fr multi, vert. 3.75 1.25
C329 AP96 600fr multi 6.25 1.40
Nos. C326-C329 (4) 14.60 3.95

1988 Summer Olympics,
Seoul — AP97

1987, June 15   Litho.   Perf. 13
C330 AP97 100fr Triple jump,
vert. .90 .40
C331 AP97 200fr High jump 1.75 .80
C332 AP97 300fr Long jump 2.50 1.10
C333 AP97 400fr Pole vault, vert. 3.25 1.60
Nos. C330-C333 (4) 8.40 3.90
Souvenir Sheet
C334 AP97 500fr High jump, diff. 4.50 3.25

1988 Summer Olympics,
Seoul — AP98

Stamps on stamps and gymnasts: 90fr, No.
C94, balance beam, vert. 200fr, No. C21, balance beam, diff. 300fr, No. C22, pommel
horse. 400fr, No. C23, parallel bars. 500fr, No.
C93, rings.

1988, July 26   Litho.   Perf. 13
C335 AP98 90fr multi .65 .40
C336 AP98 200fr multi 1.40 .80
C337 AP98 300fr multi 2.10 1.10
C338 AP98 400fr multi 3.00 1.60
Nos. C335-C338 (4) 7.15 3.90
Souvenir Sheet
C339 AP98 500fr multi 3.75 2.75

1st Moon
Landing,
20th Anniv.
AP99

1989, Aug. 4   Litho.   Perf. 13
C340 AP99 40fr Apollo 11 .35 .25
C341 AP99 80fr Apollo 15 .65 .30
C342 AP99 130fr Apollo 16 1.25 .55
C343 AP99 1000fr Apollo 17 10.00 2.75
Nos. C340-C343 (4) 12.25 3.85

World Cup Soccer Championships,
Italy — AP100

1990, July 7   Litho.   Perf. 13
C344 AP100 5fr multicolored .20 .20
C345 AP100 30fr multi, diff. .30 .20
C346 AP100 500fr multi, diff. 4.25 1.00
C347 AP100 1000fr multi, diff. 9.25 1.60
Nos. C344-C347 (4) 14.00 3.00

Charles de Gaulle (1890-
1979) — AP101

1990, July 27   Perf. 13½
C348 AP101 500fr multicolored 3.75 .90

No. C348 exists in a souvenir sheet of 1.
For overprint see No. C360.

Don Mattingly, Baseball Player — AP102

Saturn V Rocket, Apollo 11 Astronauts AP103

Charles de Gaulle, Birth Cent. AP104

No. C352, De Gaulle and Cross of Lorraine.

1990, July 27　Litho.　Perf. 13½
C349 AP102 300fr multicolored　2.50　.80
Souvenir Sheet
C350 AP103 1000fr multicolored　8.25 1.75
Litho. & Embossed
C351 AP104 1500fr gold & multi 14.00 3.50
Souvenir Sheet
C352 AP104 1500fr gold & multi 11.00
No. C351 exists in souvenir sheet of 1. Value $14.
For overprints see Nos. C355-C356.

Visit of Pope John Paul II to Africa AP105

Pope John Paul II and: No. C353, Mother Theresa, portrait. No. C354, Papal arms, globe.

1993　Litho. & Embossed　Perf. 13½
C353 AP105 1500fr gold & multi 11.50 2.75
Souvenir Sheet
C354 AP105 1500fr gold & multi 20.00
No. C353 exists in a souvenir sheet of 1. Value $20.

No. C351 Ovptd. "6 JUIN / 1944"
No. C352 Ovptd. in Silver in Sheet Margin
Litho. & Embossed
1994, June 6　　　　Perf. 13½
C355 AP104 1500fr gold & multi 10.50 9.00
Souvenir Sheet
C356 AP104 1500fr gold & multi 10.50 9.00
Overprint on No. C356 contains map, soldiers and "50 eme ANNIVERSAIRE DU /DEBARQUEMENT."

No. C355 exists in souvenir sheet of 1. Value $12.

Souvenir Sheets

Japanese Exploration of Antarctica — AP106

1994, Oct. 25
C357 AP106 1200fr Nobu Shirase　4.75 4.75
C358 AP106 1200fr Schooner Kainman Maru, horiz. 4.75 4.75

D-Day, 50th Anniv. (in 1994) — AP107

Designs: a, Gliders over Pegasus Bridge, Sword beach. b, Fighter planes over Juno, Gold and Omaha beaches. c, Planes over Utah beach, St. Mere Eglise.

Litho. & Embossed
1995, Oct. 25　　　　Perf. 13½
C359 AP107 1000fr Strip of 3, #a.-c.　13.00 13.00
No. C359b is 60x45mm.

No. C348 Overprinted Souvenir Sheet
IN MEMORIAM
1970-1995

1995, Oct. 10　Litho.　Perf. 13½
C360 AP101 500fr multicolored 11.50 11.50

AIR POST SEMI-POSTAL STAMPS

Isis of Kalabsha SPAP1

Unwmk.
1964, Mar. 7　Engr.　Perf. 13
CB1 SPAP1 25fr + 10fr multi　1.40 1.40
CB2 SPAP1 50fr + 10fr multi　2.25 2.25
CB3 SPAP1 100fr + 10fr multi　3.50 3.50
Nos. CB1-CB3 (3)　　　7.15 7.15
UNESCO world campaign to save historic monuments in Nubia.

African Infants and Globe — SPAP2

1971, Dec. 11　Litho.　Perf. 13x13½
CB4 SPAP2 140fr + 50fr multi　3.25 1.75
25th anniv. of UNICEF, and Children's Day.

POSTAGE DUE STAMPS

Sternotomis Virescens — D1

Beetles: #J2, Sternotomis gama. #J3, Augosoma centaurus. #J4, Phosphorus virescens, ceroplesis carabarica. #J5, Cetoine scaraboidae. #J6, Ceroplesis S.P. #J7, Macrorhina S.P. #J8, Cetoine scaraboidae. #J9, Phryneta leprosa. #J10, Taurina longiceps. #J11, Monohamus griseoplagiatus. #J12, Jambonus trifasciatus.

Unwmk.
1962, Oct. 15　Engr.　Perf. 11
J1 D1 50c grn & dp org　.20　.20
J2 D1 50c grn & dp org　.20　.20
　a. Pair, #J1-J2　　　.30
J3 D1 1fr blk, brn & lt grn　.30　.30
J4 D1 1fr blk, brn & lt grn　.30　.30
　a. Pair, #J3-J4　　　.60
J5 D1 2fr blk, org & yel grn　.40　.40
J6 D1 2fr blk & red org　.40　.40
　a. Pair, #J5-J6　　　.80
J7 D1 5fr brn, org & grn　.55　.55
J8 D1 5fr brn, org, grn & red　.55　.55
　a. Pair, #J7-J8　　　1.10
J9 D1 10fr blk, grn & brn　1.00 1.00
J10 D1 10fr blk, grn & brn　1.00 1.00
　a. Pair, #J9-J10　　　2.10
J11 D1 25fr blk, bl grn & brn　2.40 2.40
J12 D1 25fr blk, brn & bl grn　2.40 2.40
　a. Pair, #J11-J12　　　4.75
　Nos. J1-J12 (12)　　9.70 9.70
Pairs se-tenant at the base.

Giant Anteater — D2

1985, Jan. 25　Litho.　Perf. 12½
J13 D2 5fr multi　　.50　.50
J14 D2 20fr multi　　.90　.90
J15 D2 30fr multi　　1.10 1.10
　Nos. J13-J15 (3)　　2.50 2.50

MILITARY STAMPS

No. 1 Overprinted

No. 1 Overprinted

Unwmk.
1962, Jan. 1　Engr.　Perf. 13
M1 A1 bl, car, grn & yel　15.00　—

1963
M2 A1 bl, car, grn & yel　16.00　—

OFFICIAL STAMPS

Central African Republic

Coat of Arms — O1

Imprint: "d'après G. RICHER SO.GE.IM."
Perf. 13x12½
1965-69　　Litho.　Unwmk.
Arms in Original Colors
O1 O1 1fr blk & brn org　.20　.20
O2 O1 2fr blk & violet　.20　.20
O3 O1 5fr blk & gray　.20　.20
O4 O1 10fr blk & green　.25　.20
O5 O1 20fr blk & red brn　.55　.25
O6 O1 30fr blk & emer ('69)　1.10　.55
O7 O1 50fr blk & dk bl　1.25　.70
O8 O1 100fr blk & bister　2.75 1.10
O9 O1 130fr blk & ver ('69)　4.25 2.25
O10 O1 200fr blk & claret　6.25 2.75
　Nos. O1-O10 (10)　17.00 8.40

Redrawn
Imprint: "d'après G. RICHER DELRIEU"
1971　　Photo.　Perf. 12x12½
Arms in Original Colors
O11 O1 5fr blk & gray　.20　.20
O12 O1 30fr blk & emer　.50　.25
O13 O1 40fr blk & dp claret　.65　.30
O14 O1 100fr blk & bister　1.50　.55
O15 O1 140fr blk & lt bl　2.75　.85
O16 O1 200fr blk & claret　3.25 1.40
　Nos. O11-O16 (6)　8.85 3.55

Empire
Nos. O11, O13-O16 Overprinted with Bar and "EMPIRE CENTRAFRICAIN"
1977　　Litho.　Perf. 12x12½
O17 O1 5fr multi　.20　.20
O18 O1 40fr multi　.40　.20
O19 O1 100fr multi　1.10　.45
O20 O1 140fr multi　1.50　.70
O21 O1 200fr multi　2.50 1.00
　Nos. O17-O21 (5)　5.70 2.55

Type of 1965 Inscribed: "EMPIRE CENTRAFRICAIN"
1978, July　　Litho.　Perf. 12½
O22 O1 1fr multi　.20　.20
O23 O1 2fr multi　.20　.20
O24 O1 5fr multi　.20　.20
O25 O1 10fr multi　.20　.20
O26 O1 15fr multi　.20　.20
O27 O1 20fr multi　.20　.20
O28 O1 30fr multi　.30　.25
O29 O1 40fr multi　.40　.25
O30 O1 50fr multi　.55　.30
O31 O1 60fr multi　.75　.40
O32 O1 100fr multi　1.00　.55
O33 O1 130fr multi　1.60　.95
O34 O1 140fr multi　1.75　.95
O35 O1 200fr multi　3.50 1.25
　Nos. O22-O35 (14)　11.05 6.10

CENTRAL LITHUANIA

'sen-trəl ˌli-thə-'wā-nē-ə

LOCATION — North of Poland and east of Lithuania
CAPITAL — Vilnius

At one time Central Lithuania was a grand duchy of Lithuania but at the end of the 18th Century it fell under Russian rule. After World War I, Lithuania regained her sovereignty but certain areas were occupied by Poland. During the Russo-Polish war this territory was seized by Lithuania whose claim was promptly recognized by the Soviet Government. Under the leadership of the Polish General Zeligowski the territory was recaptured and it was during this occupation the stamps of Central Lithuania came into being. Subsequently the territory became a part of Poland.

100 Fennigi = 1 Markka

Coat of Arms — A1

Perf. 11½, Imperf.

		Typo.	Unwmk.
1920-21			
1	A1	25f red	.30	.50
2	A1	25f dark grn ('21)	.30	.50
3	A1	1m blue	.30	.50
4	A1	1m dark brn ('21)	.30	.50
5	A1	2m violet	.30	.50
6	A1	2m orange ('21)	.30	.50
		Nos. 1-6 (6)	1.80	3.00

For surcharges see Nos. B1-B5.

Lithuanian Stamps of 1919 Surcharged in Blue or Black

Perf. 11½x12, 12½x11½, 14

				Wmk. 145
1920, Nov. 23				
13	A5	2m on 15sk lil	15.00	32.50
a.		Inverted surcharge	125.00	
14	A5	4m on 10sk red	21.00	27.50
a.		Inverted surcharge	125.00	
15	A5	4m on 20sk dl bl (Bk)	21.00	27.50
a.		Inverted surcharge	125.00	
16	A5	4m on 30sk buff	14.50	22.50
a.		Inverted surcharge	125.00	
17	A6	6m on 50sk lt grn	14.50	22.50
a.		4m on 50sk (error)	125.00	
b.		10m on 50sk (error)	125.00	
c.		Surcharge inverted		—
18	A6	6m on 60sk vio & red	27.50	42.50
a.		4m on 60sk (error)	125.00	
b.		10m on 60sk (error)	125.00	
19	A6	6m on 75sk bis & red	27.50	42.50
a.		4m on 75sk (error)	125.00	
b.		10m on 75sk (error)	125.00	
20	A8	10m on 1auk gray & red	24.00	37.50
a.		Inverted surcharge	190.00	
21	A8	10m on 3auk lt brn & red	575.00	975.00
22	A8	10m on 5auk bl grn & red	550.00	975.00
		Nos. 13-20 (8)	165.00	255.00
		Nos. 13-22 (10)	1,290.	2,205.

The overprint on Nos. 17-19 is down-reading, i.e., the top of the overprint is at the right of the original design, the bottom at the left. The inverted overprint on No. 17c is up-reading.
Reprints of Nos. 17a, 17b, 18a, 18b, 19a, 19b. Value, each $45.
Counterfeits of Nos. 21-22 exist.

Lithuanian Girl — A2

Warrior — A3

Holy Gate of Vilnius — A4

Tower and Cathedral, Vilnius — A5

Rector's Insignia — A6

Gen. Lucien Zeligowski — A7

Perf. 11½, Imperf.

		Litho.	Unwmk.
1920			
23	A2	25f gray	.20	.75
24	A3	1m orange	.20	.75
25	A4	2m claret	.30	1.00
26	A5	4m gray grn & buff	.70	1.50
27	A6	6m rose & gray	1.75	2.50
28	A7	10m brown & yellow	2.50	4.00
		Nos. 23-28 (6)	5.65	10.50

For surcharges see Nos. B13-B14, B17-B19.

St. Anne's Church, Vilnius — A8

St. Stanislas Cathedral, Vilnius — A9

White Eagle, White Knight Vytis — A10

Queen Hedwig and King Ladislas II Jagello — A11

Coat of Arms of Vilnius — A12

Poczobut Astronomical Observatory A13

Union of Lithuania and Poland — A14

Tadeusz Kosciuszko and Adam Mickiewicz A15

Perf. 14, Imperf.

1921				
35	A8	1m dk gray & yel	.60	1.00
36	A9	2m rose & green	.60	1.00
37	A10	3m dark green	.75	1.25
38	A11	4m brown & buff	.75	1.25
39	A12	5m red brown	.75	1.25
40	A13	6m slate & buff	.75	2.50
41	A14	10m red vio & buff	1.75	2.50
42	A15	20m blk brn & buff	1.75	2.50
		Nos. 35-42 (8)	7.70	13.25

Set, perf. 13½, $150.

Peasant Girl Sowing — A16

White Eagle and Vytis — A17

Great Theater at Vilnius — A18

Allegory: Peace and Industry — A19

Gen. Zeligowski Entering Vilnius — A20

Gen. Zeligowski — A21

Perf. 11½, Imperf.

1921-22				
53	A16	10m brown ('22)	6.50	10.00
54	A17	25m red & yel ('22)	6.75	12.00
55	A18	50m dk blue ('22)	7.00	14.00
56	A19	75m violet ('22)	7.50	16.00
57	A20	100m bl & bister	2.75	6.25
58	A21	150m ol grn & brn	2.75	6.25
		Nos. 53-58 (6)	33.25	64.50

Opening of the Natl. Parliament, Nos. 53-56; anniv. of the entry of General Zeligowski into Vilnius, Nos. 57-58.

SEMI-POSTAL STAMPS

Nos. 1-6 Surcharged in Black or Red

NA	
ŚLĄSK	
2 M.	

1921 **Unwmk.** **Perf. 11½, Imperf.**

B1	A1	25f + 2m red (Bk)	1.00	1.75
B2	A1	25f + 2m dk green	1.00	1.75
B3	A1	1m + 2m blue	1.75	2.25
B4	A1	1m + 2m dk brown	1.75	2.25
B5	A1	2m + 2m violet	1.50	2.25
B6	A1	2m + 2m orange	1.50	2.25
		Nos. B1-B6 (6)	8.50	12.50

The surcharge means "For Silesia 2 marks." The stamps were intended to provide a fund to assist the plebiscite in Upper Silesia.

Nos. 25, 26 Surcharged:

a

b

Perf. 11½, Imperf.

B13	A4 (a)	2m + 1(m) claret	2.75	10.00
B14	A5 (b)	4m + 1m gray green & buff	2.75	10.00

Nos. 25-26, 28 with inset

Perf. 11½, Imperf.

B17	A4	2m + 1m claret	.65	2.50
B18	A5	4m + 1m gray green & buff	.65	2.00
B19	A7	10m + 2m brn & yel	.90	3.75
		Nos. B13-B19 (5)	7.70	28.25

POSTAGE DUE STAMPS

University, Vilnius D1

Castle Hill, Vilnius D2

Castle Ruins, Troki — D3

Holy Gate, Vilnius — D4

St. Stanislas Cathedral D5

St. Anne's Church, Vilnius D6

1920-21 **Unwmk.** **Perf. 11½, Imperf.**

J1	D1	50f red violet	.35	.60
J2	D2	1m green	.35	.60
J3	D3	2m red violet	.45	.60
J4	D4	3m red violet	.65	1.25
J5	D5	5m red violet	.95	2.50
J6	D6	20m scarlet	2.25	4.00
		Nos. J1-J6 (6)	5.00	9.55

CEYLON
si-'län

LOCATION — An island in the Indian Ocean separated from India by the Gulf of Manaar
GOVT. — Independent republic within the British Commonwealth
AREA — 25,332 sq. mi.
POP. — 12,670,000 (est. 1971)
CAPITAL — Colombo

Ceylon changed its name to Republic of Sri Lanka on May 22, 1972.

12 Pence = 1 Shilling
100 Cents = 1 Rupee (1872)

Values for unused stamps are for examples with original gum as defined in the catalogue introduction except for Nos. 2, 5, 8-9 which seldom have any remaining trace of their original gum. Many unused stamps of Ceylon, especially between Nos. 59 and 274, have toned gum or tropical stains. Values quoted are for stamps with fresh gum. Toned stamps have lower values, and common stamps with toned gum are worth very little.

Very fine examples of Nos. 1-15 will be cut square, will have small margins, but will show an intact design. Inferior examples with the design partly cut away will sell for much less, and examples with large margins will command higher prices. Very fine examples of Nos. 17-58b will have perforations just cutting into the design on one or more sides due to the narrow spacing of the stamps on the plates and to imperfect perforating methods. Stamps with perfs clear on all four sides are extremely scarce and will command substantially higher prices.

> **Catalogue values for unused stamps in this country are for Never Hinged items, beginning with Scott 290 in the regular postage section and Scott B1 in the semi-postal section.**

Watermarks

Wmk. 1a —
22 ½mm high,
Oval Letters

Wmk. 1b —
21mm high,
Round Letters

Wmk. 6 — Large Star

Wmk. 290 —
Lotus and "Sri" Multiple

Queen Victoria
A1   A2

1857   Engr.   Wmk. 6   Imperf.
Blued Paper

1	A1	1p blue	—	260.00
2	A1	6p plum	10,000.	525.00

1857-59

White Paper

3	A1	1p deep turq	825.00	42.50
4	A1	2p deep green	190.00	72.50
a.		2p yellow green	600.00	105.00
5	A2	4p dl rose ('59)	72,500.	5,400.
6	A1	5p org brown	1,750.	175.00
6A	A1	6p plum	2,400.	160.00
7	A1	6p brown	7,750.	550.00
8	A2	8p brown ('59)	30,000.	1,750.
9	A2	9p lil brn ('59)	47,500.	1,050.
10	A1	10p vermilion	950.00	350.00
11	A1	1sh violet	5,500.	240.00
12	A2	1sh9p green ('59)	950.00	950.00
a.		1sh9p yellow green	5,000.	3,600.
13	A2	2sh blue ('59)	6,500.	1,400.

Stamps of type A2 frequently have repaired corners.
Nos. 3-4 exist unofficially rouletted. See the *Scott Classic Specialized Catalogue* for listings.
Beware of Nos. 17-57 trimmed to resemble Nos. 3-13. Values are for stamps with clear margins on all sides.
No. 5 was reproduced by the collotype process in a souvenir sheet distributed at the London International Stamp Exhibition 1950. The paper is unwatermarked.

A3

1857-58   Typo.   Unwmk.

14	A3	½p lilac ('58)	210.00	260.00
15	A3	½p lilac, *bluish*	4,200.	600.00

No. 14 exists unofficially rouletted.
Nos. 14-15, 38 are printed on surface-glazed paper. Values are for stamps without cracking of the surface, and examples showing cracking should be discounted.

Clean-Cut Perf. 14 to 15½
1861   Wmk. 6   Engr.

17	A1	1p blue	190.00	18.00
18	A1	2p yel green	240.00	29.00
b.		Vert. pair, imperf between		—
19	A2	4p dull rose	2,400.	350.00
20	A1	5p org brown	110.00	10.00
20A	A1	6p brown	2,700.	140.00
b.		6p bister brown		215.00
21	A2	8p brown	2,400.	600.00
22	A2	9p lilac brown	8,400.	275.00
23	A1	1sh violet	120.00	17.50
24	A2	2sh blue	3,600.	775.00

Rough Perf. 14 to 15½

25	A1	1p blue	150.00	10.00
b.		Blued paper	700.00	25.00
26	A1	2p yel green	500.00	95.00
27	A2	4p rose red	540.00	110.00
28	A2	6p olive brown	1,000.	120.00
a.		6p deep brown	1,100.	115.00
b.		6p bister brown	1,750.	160.00
29	A2	8p brown	1,750.	650.00
30	A2	8p yel brown	1,800.	400.00
31	A2	9p olive brown	700.00	80.00
32	A2	9p deep brown	110.00	90.00
33	A1	10p vermilion	300.00	25.00
a.		Imperf. vert., pair		—
34	A1	1sh violet	300.00	17.50
35	A2	1sh9p green	825.00	
36	A2	2sh blue	800.00	160.00

The 1sh9p green was never placed in use.

1863   Perf. 12½

37	A1	10p vermilion	260.00	18.00

1864   Typo.   Unwmk.

38	A3	½p lilac	260.00	210.00

See note following No. 15.

1863   Engr.   Perf. 13

39	A1	1p blue	160.00	7.00
40	A1	5p car brown	1,900.	175.00
41	A1	6p deep brown	210.00	32.50
42	A2	9p brown	1,400.	110.00
43	A1	1sh grayish violet	2,100.	95.00

Parts of the papermaker's sheet watermark, "T. H. SAUNDERS 1862," may be found on some copies of Nos. 39-43.

Perf. 12

44	A1	1p blue	1,600.	150.00
a.		Horiz. pair, imperf. btwn.		15,000.

Two Types of Watermark Crown and CC (1)

1863-67   Typo.   Wmk. 1a   Perf. 12½

45	A3	½p lilac	60.00	45.00
a.		½p reddish lilac	77.50	52.50

Engr.

46	A1	1p blue	150.00	7.50
a.		1p dark blue	150.00	7.50
c.		Perf. 11 ½	3,000.	375.00
47	A1	2p gray green	90.00	14.00
48	A1	2p emerald	175.00	115.00
48A	A1	2p yel green	10,000.	475.00
48B	A1	2p bottle green		4,000.
49	A1	2p olive	260.00	260.00
50	A2	4p rose	525.00	110.00
		4p carmine rose	825.00	200.00
51	A1	5p car brown	240.00	90.00
52	A1	5p olive green	875.00	275.00
e.		5p deep sage green	2,100.	450.00
53	A1	6p choc brown	190.00	7.50
		Perf. 13	1,900.	225.00
b.		6p black brown	200.00	12.00
c.		As "b," double impression		3,750.
d.		6p reddish brown	240.00	14.00
54	A2	8p red brown	125.00	60.00
55	A2	9p brown	350.00	52.50
c.		Perf. 13	5,000.	950.00
56	A1	10p vermilion	2,400.	70.00
		10p orange	5,000.	500.00
58	A2	2sh blue	325.00	45.00

The ½p, 1p blue, 2p olive, 4p and 5p green exist imperf.

Wmk. 1b

46d	A1	1p blue	210.00	15.00
e.		1p dark blue	200.00	12.00
49d	A1	2p orange yellow	110.00	7.00
e.		2p olive yellow	175.00	24.00
f.		2p olive green	175.00	30.00
50b	A2	4p rose	260.00	65.00
c.		4p carmine rose	125.00	40.00
52b	A1	5p myrtle green	120.00	19.00
c.		5p olive green	125.00	19.00
d.		5p bronze green>	47.50	60.00
53d	A1	6p chocolate brown	47.50	42.50
e.		6p brown	105.00	12.00
54a	A2	8p red brown	95.00	72.50
55a	A2	9p dark brown	65.00	7.00
b.		9p bister brown	550.00	37.50
56b	A1	10p orange brown	110.00	14.00
c.		10p orange red	65.00	18.00
d.		10p vermilion	3,900.	160.00
57	A1	1sh purple	110.00	10.00
a.		1sh reddish lilac	325.00	32.50
58a	A2	2sh deep blue	160.00	15.00
b.		2sh indigo	300.00	22.50

The 1p blue and 6p brown exist imperf.
For overprints see Nos. O2, O4-O7.

A4   A5

1866   Typo.   Wmk. 1   Perf. 12½

59	A5	3p rose	240.00	100.00
a.		Imperf., pair		900.00

For overprint see No. O3.

1868   Perf. 14

61	A4	1p blue	30.00	11.00
62	A5	3p rose	95.00	55.00

For overprint see No. O1.

A6   A7

A8   A9

A10   A11

A12   A13

A14   A15

A16

1872-80   Perf. 14

63	A6	2c brown	26.00	3.75
64	A7	4c gray	47.50	1.75
65	A7	4c lil rose ('80)	72.50	1.75
66	A8	8c orange	47.50	6.50
a.		8c orange yellow	35.00	7.00
67	A9	16c violet	110.00	3.25
68	A10	24c green	72.50	2.40
69	A11	32c slate bl ('77)	175.00	17.50
70	A12	36c blue	190.00	26.00
71	A13	48c rose	95.00	8.50
72	A14	64c red brn ('77)	350.00	85.00
73	A15	96c olive gray	260.00	30.00
		Nos. 63-73 (11)	1,446.	186.40

For surcharges see #83-84, 94A-110, 112-114. For types surcharged see #124-129.

1872   Perf. 12½

74	A6	2c brown	3,500.	225.00
75	A7	4c gray	2,000.	325.00

1879   Perf. 14x12½

77	A6	2c brown	425.00	77.50
78	A7	4c gray	1,900.	35.00
79	A8	8c orange	450.00	57.50

Perf. 12½x14

82	A16	2r50c claret	650.00	350.00

The 32c and 64c are known perf. 14x12 ½, but were not regularly issued.
No. 82, perf. 12 ½, was not regularly issued.
See Nos. 142, 158. For surcharges see Nos. 111, 115, 130. For types surcharged see Nos. 160-161.

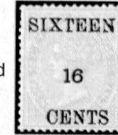

SIXTEEN
16
CENTS

Nos. 68, 72 Surcharged

1882   Perf. 14

83	A10	16c on 24c green	32.50	7.50
84	A14	20c on 64c red brn	13.00	7.50
a.		Double surcharge		1,400.

1883-99   Wmk. 2

85	A6	2c pale brown	72.50	2.50
86	A6	2c green ('84)	3.00	.20
a.		Perf. 12	5,000.	
87	A6	2c org brn ('99)	3.75	.40
88	A7	4c lilac rose	4.25	.35
89	A7	4c rose ('84)	7.50	14.00
a.		Perf. 12	5,000.	

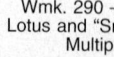

90	A7	4c brt rose ('98)	10.00	10.50
91	A7	4c yellow ('99)	3.50	3.25
92	A8	8c orange	6.00	11.00
93	A9	16c violet	2,000.	190.00
94	A10	24c purple brown	1,650.	
b.		Perf. 12	5,400.	

Nos. 86a, 89a, 94 and 94b were never placed in use. A 48c brown, perf. 12, was prepared but not issued.

For surcharges and overprints see Nos.116-123, 143-151D, 155-156. O8-O9.

Issues of 1872-82 Surcharged:

Postage & FIVE CENTS Revenue	TEN CENTS
a	b

Twenty-five Cents	One Rupee Twelve Cents
c	d

1885   Wmk. 1   Perf. 14

94A	A9 (a)	5c on 16c		3,500.
95	A10 (a)	5c on 24c	3,900.	130.00
96	A11 (a)	5c on 32c	77.50	20.00
a.		Inverted surcharge		2,250.
97	A12 (a)	5c on 36c	350.00	14.00
a.		Inverted surcharge		3,000.
98	A13 (a)	5c on 48c	1,900.	72.50
99	A14 (a)	5c on 64c	130.00	9.50
a.		Double surcharge		1,900.
100	A15 (a)	5c on 96c	600.00	85.00
101	A9 (b)	10c on 16c	7,750.	3,000.
102	A10 (b)	10c on 24c	540.00	140.00
103	A12 (b)	10c on 36c	450.00	225.00
104	A14 (b)	10c on 64c	500.00	210.00
105	A10 (b)	20c on 24c	72.50	21.00
106	A11 (c)	20c on 32c	90.00	72.50
107	A11 (c)	25c on 32c	21.00	5.25
108	A13 (c)	28c on 48c	47.50	9.00
a.		Double surcharge		2,250.
109	A12 (b)	30c on 36c	19.00	13.00
a.		Inverted surcharge	300.00	130.00
110	A15 (b)	56c on 96c	30.00	25.00

Perf. 12½

111	A16 (d)	1r12c on 2r50c	650.00	120.00

Perf. 14x12½

112	A11 (a)	5c on 32c	900.00	60.00
113	A14 (a)	5c on 64c	950.00	52.50
114	A14 (b)	10c on 64c	82.50	150.00
a.		Vert. pair, imperf. btwn.	4,200.	

Perf. 12½x14

115	A16 (d)	1r12c on 2r50c	130.00	52.50

Perf. 14
Wmk. 2

117	A7 (a)	5c on 4c rose	27.50	5.00
a.		Inverted surcharge		350.00
118	A8 (a)	5c on 8c org	95.00	10.00
a.		Inverted surcharge		3,000.
b.		Double surcharge		2,400.
119	A9 (a)	5c on 16c vio	140.00	15.00
a.		Inverted surcharge		260.00
120	A10 (a)	5c on 24c pur brn	—	600.00
121	A9 (b)	10c on 16c vio	7,750.	1,750.
122	A10 (b)	10c on 24c pur brn	17.50	9.00
123	A9 (b)	15c on 16c vio	14.00	10.00

A 5c on 4c lilac rose and a 5c on 24c green are known to exist and are considered to be forgeries.

Types of 1872-80 Surcharged

e

f

g

1885-87

124	A8 (e)	5c on 8c lilac	25.00	1.75
125	A10 (f)	10c on 24c pur brn	13.00	9.50
126	A9 (f)	15c on 16c org	72.50	14.00
127	A11 (f)	28c on 32c sl bl	30.00	3.00
128	A12 (f)	30c on 36c ol grn	32.50	16.00
129	A15 (f)	56c on 96c ol gray	60.00	17.50

Wmk. 1 Sideways

130	A16 (g)	1r12c on 2r50c cl	52.50	120.00
		Nos. 124-130 (7)	285.50	181.75

A23	A24

FIVE CENTS
Type I — Thin lines in background. Hair and curl clear.
Type II — Thicker lines in background. Heavier shading under chin.

1886   Wmk. 2

131	A23	5c lilac, type I	3.25	.20
a.		Type II	8.00	.20

For overprint see No. O12.

1886-1900

132	A24	3c org brn & green ('93)	4.25	.50
133	A24	3c green ('00)	3.75	.65
134	A24	6c rose & blk ('99)	1.75	.55
135	A24	12c ol grn & car ('00)	4.75	8.50
136	A24	15c olive green	7.50	1.75
137	A24	15c ultra ('00)	6.50	1.50
138	A24	25c brown	5.25	1.20
a.		25c brown, value in ol yel	140.00	90.00
139	A24	28c slate	26.00	1.60
140	A24	30c vio & org brown ('93)	5.00	2.60
141	A24	75c blk & org brown ('00)	7.25	8.50
		Nos. 132-141 (10)	72.00	27.35

Numeral tablet of 3c, 12c and 75c has lined background with colorless value and "c."
For surcharges & overprints see #152-154, 157, 159, O10-O11, O13-O17.

1887   Wmk. 1

142	A16	1r12c claret	32.50	27.50

For overprint see No. O18.

Issue of 1883-84 Surcharged

TWO CENTS

1888-90   Wmk. 2

143	A7	2c on 4c lilac rose	1.60	.95
a.		Inverted surcharge	25.00	24.00
b.		Double surcharge, one invtd.		325.00
144	A7	2c on 4c rose	2.50	.35
a.		Inverted surcharge	18.00	19.00
b.		Double surcharge		350.00

Surcharged

Two Cents

145	A7	2c on 4c lilac rose	.90	.35
a.		Inverted surcharge	37.50	37.50
b.		Double surcharge	95.00	95.00
c.		Double surcharge, one invtd.	77.50	77.50
146	A7	2c on 4c rose	7.50	.20
a.		Double surcharge, one invtd.	105.00	110.00
b.		Double surcharge	100.00	105.00
c.		Inverted surcharge	350.00	

Surcharged

2 Cents

147	A7	2c on 4c lilac rose	82.50	35.00
a.		Inverted surcharge	150.00	47.50
b.		Double surcharge, one inverted	190.00	
148	A7	2c on 4c rose	3.00	.90
a.		Inverted surcharge	17.50	10.00
b.		Double surcharge, one inverted	9.50	14.00
c.		Double surcharge	190.00	160.00

Surcharged

Two Cents

149	A7	2c on 4c lilac rose	65.00	27.50
a.		Inverted surcharge	190.00	35.00
150	A7	2c on 4c rose	3.00	1.25
a.		Inverted surcharge	17.50	7.00
b.		Double surcharge	140.00	130.00
c.		Double surcharge, one inverted	17.50	9.50

Surcharged

2 Cents

151	A7	2c on 4c rose	13.00	1.20
a.		Inverted surcharge	24.00	6.50
b.		Double surcharge	120.00	120.00
c.		Double surch., one invtd.	26.00	12.00
i.		"S" of "Cents" inverted	425.00	240.00
151D	A7	2c on 4c lilac rose	65.00	35.00
e.		Inverted surcharge	95.00	47.50
f.		Double surcharge		350.00
g.		Double surch., one invtd.	110.00	110.00
h.		"S" of "Cents" inverted		550.00

Counterfeit errors of surcharges of Nos. 143 to 151D are prevalent.

POSTAGE
Five Cents
REVENUE

No. 136 Surcharged

1890

152	A24	5c on 15c ol green	3.75	2.40
a.		"Five" instead of "Five"	140.00	100.00
b.		"REVENUE" omitted	200.00	190.00
c.		Inverted surcharge	60.00	65.00
d.		Double surcharge	120.00	140.00
e.		As "a," inverted surcharge	—	1,600.
f.		Inverted "s" in "Cents"	95.00	100.00
g.		As "f," inverted surcharge	2,000.	
h.		As "b," invtd. "s" in "Cents"	1,400.	

Nos. 138-139 Surcharged

FIFTEEN CENTS

1891

153	A24	15c on 25c brown	16.00	15.00
154	A24	15c on 28c slate	19.00	10.00

Nos. 88, 89 and 139 Surcharged

3 Cents

1892

155	A7	3c on 4c lilac rose	1.20	3.75
156	A7	3c on 4c rose	6.00	10.00
a.		Double surcharge, one invtd.		
157	A24	3c on 28c slate	5.25	5.00
a.		Double surcharge	175.00	
		Nos. 155-157 (3)	12.45	18.75

Type of 1879

1898

158	A16	2r50c violet, *red*	35.00	*62.50*

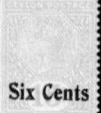

No. 136 Surcharged in Black

1899

159	A24	6c on 15c olive green	1.20	.85

Surcharged Type "g" in Black

1899   **Wmk. 1**

160	A16	1r50c on 2r50c gray	24.00	*52.50*
161	A16	2r25c on 2r50c yel	42.50	*95.00*

A35

1900   **Wmk. 1**

162	A35	1r50c car rose	29.00	*47.50*
163	A35	2r25c dull blue	42.50	*47.50*

King Edward VII
A36   A37

A38   A39

A40

1903-05   **Wmk. 2**

166	A36	2c org brown	2.40	.20
167	A37	3c green	2.40	1.20
168	A37	4c yel & blue	2.40	*4.50*
169	A38	5c dull lilac	1.75	.70
170	A39	6c car rose	11.00	1.75
171	A37	12c ol grn & car	6.00	*13.00*
172	A40	15c ultra	7.75	3.50
173	A40	25c bister	4.75	*9.50*
174	A40	30c vio & green	3.75	*4.75*
175	A37	75c bl & org ('05)	3.50	*24.00*
176	A40	1r50c gray ('04)	75.00	62.50
177	A40	2r25c brn & grn ('04)	82.50	60.00
		Nos. 166-177 (12)	203.20	185.60

For overprints see Nos. O19-O24.

1904-10   **Wmk. 3**

178	A36	2c orange brown	1.75	.20
a.		2c orange	1.75	.60
179	A37	3c green	1.75	.20
180	A37	4c yel & blue	2.75	1.75
181	A38	5c dull lilac	3.00	1.50
a.		Booklet pane of 12		
182	A39	6c car rose	3.25	.20
183	A40	10c ol grn & vio ('10)	3.00	2.75
184	A37	12c ol grn & car	1.75	*2.00*
185	A40	15c ultra	3.25	.70
186	A40	25c bister ('05)	7.25	4.50
187	A40	25c slate ('10)	3.00	2.10
188	A40	30c vio & grn ('05)	3.00	*3.50*
189	A40	50c brown ('10)	4.75	*9.00*
190	A37	75c bl & org ('05)	6.25	*9.50*
191	A40	1r vio, *yel* ('10)	9.00	*12.00*
192	A40	1r50c gray ('05)	32.50	12.00
193	A40	2r scar, *yel* ('10)	17.50	*32.50*
194	A40	2r25c brn & grn	26.00	*35.00*

195	A40	5r blk, *grn* ('10)	45.00	*85.00*
196	A40	10r blk, *red* ('10)	105.00	*210.00*
		Nos. 178-196 (19)	279.75	424.40

No. 181 exists on ordinary and chalky paper.

A41   A42

1908

197	A41	5c deep red violet	3.75	.20
a.		Booklet pane of 12		
198	A42	6c carmine rose	1.75	.20

1911, July 5

199	A40	3c green	1.10	.85

King George   King George
V — A44   V — A45

3 AND 6 CENTS
Type I — Small "c" after value, 2 ¼mm wide and 2mm high.
Type II — Large "c" after value, 2 ½mm wide and 2 ¼mm high.
1, 5 AND 9 CENTS are Type II, other denominations Type I.

Die I

For description of the dies, see back of this section of the Catalogue.

1912-25   **Wmk. 3**

200	A44	1c dp brn (Die Ib) ('20)	1.20	.20
201	A44	2c brown org	.35	.20
202	A44	3c dp grn (Die Ia, type II)	4.25	.50
a.		3c deep green, die I, type I	5.25	1.25
203	A44	5c red violet	1.20	.70
204	A44	6c car (Die Ib, type II)	1.50	1.00
a.		6c carmine, die I, type I	13.00	1.00
b.		As "a," bklt. pane of 6		
205	A44	10c olive green	3.50	2.00
206	A44	15c ultra	2.10	1.50

Chalky Paper

207	A44	25c yel & ultra	2.10	2.10
208	A44	30c green & vio	4.75	3.75
209	A44	50c black & scar	1.75	*2.10*
210	A44	1r violet, *yel*	5.00	4.25
211	A44	2r blk & red, *yel*	3.75	*15.00*
212	A44	5r blk, *green*	20.00	*35.00*
a.		5r black, *bl grn*, olive back	21.00	*45.00*
b.		5r blk, *emer* (Die II) ('20)	52.50	*120.00*
213	A44	10r vio & blk, *red*	85.00	*105.00*
a.		Die II ('20)	95.00	*165.00*
214	A44	20r blk & red, *bl*	165.00	*175.00*
215	A45	50r dull violet	500.00	
216	A45	100r gray black	2,000.	
217	A45	500r gray green	7,250.	
218	A45	1000r vio, *red* ('25)	26,000.	
		Nos. 200-214 (15)	301.45	*348.30*

Although Nos. 217 and 218 were theoretically available for postage it is not probable that they were ever used for other than fiscal purposes.
The 1r through 100r with revenue cancellations sell for minimal prices.
For surcharge & overprints see #223, MR1-MR3.

Die I
Surface-colored Paper

1913-14

220	A44	1r violet, *yellow*	5.00	*5.75*
221	A44	2r black & red, *yel*	3.25	*7.50*
222	A44	5r black, *green*	26.00	*37.50*
		Nos. 220-222 (3)	34.25	*58.25*

No. 203 Surcharged

1918

223	A44	1c on 5c red violet	.20	.30

For overprint see No. MR4.

Die I

1921-33   **Wmk. 4**
Ordinary Paper

225	A44	1c dp brn (Die Ib) ('27)	1.20	.40
226	A44	2c brn org (Die II)	.85	.30
227	A44	3c green (Die Ia, type I)	4.25	.90
228	A44	3c slate (Die Ia, type II) ('22)	.90	.20
229	A44	5c red vio (Die I)	.70	.20
230	A44	6c carmine (Die Ib, type II)	2.60	.90
231	A44	6c vio (Die Ib, type II) ('22)	1.75	.20
232	A44	9c red, *yel* (Die II) ('26)	1.50	.35
233	A44	10c olive green	1.60	.45
a.		Die II	2.10	.70
234	A44	12c scarlet, Die II	1.20	*2.60*
a.		Die I ('25)	6.00	6.50
235	A44	15c ultramarine	3.75	*14.00*
236	A44	15c green, *yel*, Die II	3.00	1.20
a.		Die I ('22)	3.00	1.50
237	A44	20c ultra, Die II ('24)	4.25	.50
a.		Die I ('22)	4.75	*7.25*
238	A44	25c yel & blue	2.40	2.25
a.		Die I	4.50	1.50

For surcharges see Nos. 248-249.

Chalky Paper

239	A44	30c green & violet	1.90	*4.25*
a.		Die II	5.00	1.50
240	A44	50c blk & scar (Die II)	1.90	.95
a.		Die I	65.00	*90.00*
241	A44	1r vio, *yel*, Die II	18.00	*32.50*
a.		Die I	22.50	*30.00*
242	A44	2r blk & red, *yel* (Die II)	8.50	*10.00*
243	A44	5r blk, *emer*, (Die II)	42.50	*70.00*
244	A44	20r blk & red, *bl*, (Die II)	210.00	*260.00*
245	A45	50r dull vio	600.00	*1,050.*
246	A45	100r gray black	2,100.	
247	A45	100r ultra & dl vio ('27)	1,600.	
		Nos. 225-244 (20)	312.75	*402.15*

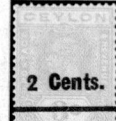

Nos. 228, 231 Surcharged

1926

248	A44	2c on 3c slate	.95	1.20
a.		Double surcharge	85.00	
b.		Bar omitted	90.00	*100.00*
249	A44	5c on 6c violet	.60	.45
a.		Double surcharge		

A46

1927-29   **Chalky Paper**   **Wmk. 4**

254	A46	1r red vio & dl vio ('28)	3.00	1.50
255	A46	2r car & green ('29)	4.50	3.25
256	A46	5r brn vio & grn ('28)	16.00	*24.00*
257	A46	10r org & green	47.50	*100.00*
258	A46	20r ultra & dl vio	150.00	*260.00*
		Nos. 254-258 (5)	221.00	*388.75*

Common Design Types pictured following the introduction.

Silver Jubilee Issue
Common Design Type
1935, May 6   Engr.   *Perf. 13½x14*

260	CD301	6c gray blk & ultra	.75	.35
261	CD301	9c indigo & green	.80	2.40
262	CD301	20c blue & brown	5.00	3.25
263	CD301	50c brt vio & ind	6.00	*8.00*
		Nos. 260-263 (4)	12.55	14.00
		Set, never hinged	22.50	

Tapping Rubber Tree — A47   Colombo Harbor — A49

Adam's Peak — A48

Picking Tea — A50   Coconut Palms — A53

Rice Terraces A51

River Scene A52

Temple of the Tooth, Kandy A54

Ancient Reservoir A55

Wild Elephants A56

View of Trincomalee A57

Perf. 11x11½, 11½x11; 11½x13, 13x11½ (A47, A48, A53); 14 (A56)

1935-36   Wmk. 4

264	A47	2c car rose & blk	.45 .55
a.		Perf. 14	12.00 .55
265	A48	3c olive & black	.50 .55
a.		Perf. 14	35.00 .55
266	A49	6c blue & black	.45 .40
267	A50	9c org red & ol grn	1.50 .90
268	A51	10c dk vio & blk	1.75 3.00
269	A52	15c grn & org brn	1.50 .70
270	A53	20c ultra & black	2.25 3.50
271	A54	25c choc & dk ultra	2.00 1.75
272	A55	30c green & lake	3.00 3.50
273	A56	50c dk vio & blk	12.00 2.50
274	A57	1r brown & vio	25.00 21.00
		Nos. 264-274 (11)	50.40 38.35
		Set, never hinged	97.50

Issued: 2c, 15c, 25c, 5/1/35; 10c, 6/1/35; 1r, 7/1/35; 30c, 8/1/35; 3c, 10/1/35; 6c, 9c, 20c, 50c, 1/1/36.

Coronation Issue
Common Design Type

1937, May 12   **Perf. 11x11½**

275	CD302	6c dark carmine	.75 .20
a.		Booklet pane of 10	3.00 6.00
276	CD302	9c deep green	3.00 6.00
a.		Booklet pane of 10	300.00
277	CD302	20c deep ultra	4.25 8.25
		Nos. 275-277 (3)	8.00 14.45
		Set, never hinged	16.00

Types of 1935 with "Postage & Revenue Removed" and Picturing George VI and:

Ancient Guard Stone — A68   George VI — A69

Sigiriya (Lion Rock) — A61

Perf. 11x11½, 11½x11; 12 (#286)

1938-52   Engr.   Wmk. 4

278	A47	2c car rose & blk ('44)	.45 .95
a.		Perf. 13½x13 ('38)	100.00 2.00
b.		Perf. 13½ ('38)	2.00 .20
c.		Perf. 12 ('49)	1.25 4.00
d.		Perf. 11½x13 ('38)	9.00 2.00
279	A48	3c dk grn & blk ('42)	.50 .20
a.		Perf. 13½x13 ('38)	225.00 10.00
b.		Perf. 14 ('41)	100.00 1.10
c.		Perf. 13½ ('38)	3.50 .20
d.		Perf. 12 ('46)	.70 .95
e.		Perf. 13x11½	8.00 .50
280	A49	6c blue & black	.20 .20
281	A61	10c blue & black	1.60 .20
282	A52	15c red brn & grn	1.25 .20
283	A50	20c dull bl & blk	2.25 .20
284	A54	25c choc & dk ultra	3.25 .25
285	A55	30c dk grn & rose car	8.00 2.25
286	A56	50c dk vio & blk ('46)	2.75 .20
a.		Perf. 14 ('42)	90.00 29.00
b.		Perf. 13x11½ ('38)	140.00 40.00
c.		Perf. 13x13½ ('38)	300.00 3.00
d.		Perf. 13½ ('38)	15.00 .35
e.		Perf. 11½x11 ('42)	4.00 4.00
287	A57	1r dk brn & bl vio	10.50 1.40
288	A68	2r dark car & blk	9.25 2.90

Perf. 14
Typo.

289	A69	5r brn vio & grn	27.50 4.00
289A	A69	10r yel org & dl grn ('52)	42.50 25.00
		Nos. 278-289A (13)	110.00 37.95

No. 289A differs from type A69 in having "REVENUE" inscribed vertically at either side of the frame. This revenue 10r was valid for postage Dec. 1, 1952-Mar. 14, 1954.
See #292, 295. For surcharges see #290-291.

> **Catalogue values for unused stamps in this section, from this point to the end of the section, are for Never Hinged items.**

No. 283 Surcharged in Black

1940, Nov. 5   **Perf. 11x11½**

290	A50	3c on 20c dull bl & blk	3.00 .75

No. 280 Surcharged with New Value and Bars

1941, May 10

291	A49	3c on 6c blue & black	.40 .20

Coconut Palms — A70

1943-47   Wmk. 4   Engr.   Perf. 12

292	A70	5c red org & ol grn ('47)	2.00 .35
a.		Perf. 13½ ('43)	.35 .20

Peace Issue
Common Design Type

1946, Dec. 10   **Perf. 13½x14**

293	CD303	6c deep blue	.20 .20
294	CD303	15c brown	.20 .20

Guard Stone Type of 1938

1947, Mar. 15   **Perf. 11x11½**

295	A68	2r violet & black	2.40 1.75

Parliament Building, Colombo — A71

Adam's Peak A72   Dagoba at Anuradhapura A74

Temple of the Tooth, Kandy A73

1947, Nov. 25   **Perf. 11x12, 12x11**

296	A71	6c deep ultra & black	.20 .20
297	A72	10c car, orange & black	.20 .20
298	A73	15c red vio & grnsh blk	.20 .20
299	A74	25c brt green & bister	.20 .20
		Nos. 296-299 (4)	.80 .80

New constitution of 1947.

National Flag A75   D. S. Senanayake A76

Engr., Flag Typo. (A75); Engr. (A76)
Perf. 12½x12, 12x12½, 13x12½

1949   Wmk. 4

300	A75	4c org brn, car & yel	.20 .20
301	A76	5c dark green & brn	.20 .20

Wmk. 290

302	A75	15c red org, car & yel	.60 .20
303	A76	25c dp blue & brown	.20 .50
		Nos. 300-303 (4)	1.20 1.10

Size of No. 302: 28x22¼mm.
1st anniv. of Ceylon's independence.
Issued: #300-301, Feb. 4; #302-303, Apr. 5.

A77

A78

Design: 15c, Lion Rock and UPU symbols.

Wmk. 290

1949, Oct. 10   Engr.   Perf. 12

304	A77	5c dk green & brown	.85 .20
305	A77	15c dark car & black	1.25 2.50
306	A78	25c ultra & black	1.25 1.25
		Nos. 304-306 (3)	3.35 3.95

75th anniv. of the UPU.

Kandyan Dancer A79   Kiri Vehera, Polonnaruwa A80

Vesak Orchid — A81   Sigiriya — A82

Ratmalana, Plane — A83

Vatadage Ruins at Madirigiriya A84

1950, Feb. 4   Perf. 12x12½

307	A79	4c bright red & choc	.20 .20
308	A80	5c green	.20 .20
309	A81	15c pur & blue green	2.50 .45
310	A82	30c carmine & yel	.35 .50

Perf. 11x11½, 11½x11

311	A83	75c red org & blue	7.25 .20
312	A84	1r red brn & dp blue	2.50 .45
		Nos. 307-312 (6)	13.00 2.00

See Nos. 340-345.

Coconut Palms — A85   Star Orchid — A86

1951-52   Unwmk.   Photo.   Perf. 11½

313	A85	10c gray & dark green	1.10 .75
314	A86	35c dk grn & rose brn ('52)	1.75 1.75
a.		Corrected inscription ('54)	7.00 .70

On No. 314a a dot has been added above the third character in the second line of the Tamil inscription.
Issue dates: 10c, Aug. 1; 35c, Feb. 1.
See No. 351.

Mace and Symbols of Industry A87

Perf. 12½x14

1952, Feb. 23   Wmk. 290

315	A87	5c green	.20 .20
316	A87	15c brt ultramarine	.40 .40

Colombo Plan Exhibition, February 1952.

Coronation Issue

Queen Elizabeth II — A88

1953, June 2   Engr.   Perf. 12x12½

317	A88	5c green	1.25 .20

Royal Procession A89

1954, Apr. 10   Perf. 13x12½

318	A89	10c deep blue	.35 .20

Visit of Queen Elizabeth II and the Duke of Edinburgh, 1954.

Sambar in Ruhuna National Park — A90   Rubber Trees — A91

Designs: 3c, Ancient guard stone. 6c and 10r, Harvesting rice. 25c, Sigiriya fresco. 50c, Outrigger fishing canoe. 85c, Tea Picker. 2r, Gal Oya dam. 5r, Bas-relief, "The Lovers."

1954 Unwmk. Photo. *Perf. 11½*
Size: 21x25½mm
319	A90	2c green & brown	.20	.20
320	A90	3c violet & black	.20	.20
321	A90	6c yel grn & blk brn	.20	.20
322	A90	25c vio bl, bl & brn orange		.20

Size: 25½x21mm
323	A91	40c black brown	5.25	1.00
324	A91	50c indigo	.40	.20

Size: 23x32½mm, 32½x23mm
325	A90	85c dk grn & gray	.60	.20
326	A91	2r blue & blk brn	7.25	1.25
327	A90	5r dp org & blk brn	5.00	1.40
328	A90	10r brown	42.50	11.00
	Nos. 319-328 (10)	61.80	15.85

See Nos. 346-356.
Issued: 25c, 50c, 5r, 10r, 3/15; others, 5/15. Nos. 327-328 with revenue cancellations sell for minimal prices.

King Coconuts — A92

Symbols of Agriculture A93

1954, Dec. 1
329 A92 10c brown & orange .30 .20
See No. 349.

Perf. 14x14½
1955, Dec. 10 Wmk. 290
330 A93 10c orange & brown .20 .20
Royal Agricultural and Food Exhibition.

House of Representatives — A94

1956, Mar. 26 Unwmk. *Perf. 11½*
Granite Paper
331 A94 10c deep green .20 .20
25th anniv. of Prime Minister Sir John Kotelawala's entry into the Ceylon Legislature.

Arrival of Vijaya in Ceylon — A95

Dharmachakra Encircling Globe — A96

1956, May 23 Granite Paper
332 A95 3c dull vio gray & saph .20 .20
333 A96 15c ultramarine .80 .20
Birth of Buddha, 2500th anniv. See #B1-B2.

Methods of Transportation — A97

35c, 85c, Ceylon's 1st stamp & coat of arms.

1957, Apr. 1 Photo. *Perf. 12½x13*
334 A97 4c blue green & ver .80 .45
335 A97 10c blue & vermilion .80 .20

Perf. 11½
Granite Paper
336 A97 35c blue, yel & brown .40 .55
337 A97 85c dull grn, yel & brn .85 1.50
Nos. 334-337 (4) 2.85 2.70
Ceylon's 1st postage stamps, cent.

Nos. B1-B2 Overprinted with Black Bars and Squares
1958, Jan. 15 Unwmk.
Granite Paper
338 SP1 4c dp blue & lt yel .20 .20
  a. Inverted overprint 12.50
  b. Double overprint 12.50
339 SP1 10c dk gray, yel & brt pink .20 .20
  a. Inverted overprint 20.00
The overprint obliterates the surtax and inscription at right.

Types of 1950-54 Redrawn
Perf. 12x12½
1958-59 Engr. Wmk. 290
340	A79	4c brt red & chocolate	.20	.20
341	A80	5c green	.20	1.00
342	A81	15c purple & blue grn	4.50	1.10
343	A82	30c car & yel ('59)	.20	1.50

Perf. 11½x11
344 A83 75c red org & bl ('59) 11.50 2.75

Perf. 11x11½
345 A84 1r red brn & dp blue .85 .20
Nos. 340-345 (6) 17.45 6.75
Issued: 4c, 5/14; 5c, 15c, 1r, 10/1; 30c, 75c, 5/1.
For surcharge see No. 368.

1958-59 Unwmk. Photo. *Perf. 11½*
Granite Paper
346	A90	2c green & brown	.20	.40
347	A90	3c violet & black	.20	.55
348	A90	6c yel grn & blk brn	.20	.50
349	A92	10c brown & orange	.20	.20
350	A90	25c vio bl, bl & brn orange	.20	.20
351	A86	35c dk grn & rose brn	7.75	.40
352	A91	50c indigo	.25	.20
353	A90	85c dark green & gray	4.50	4.50
354	A91	2r blue & blk brn	1.25	.25
355	A90	5r dp org & blk brn	4.75	.40
356	A90	10r brown	12.00	1.40
	Nos. 346-356 (11)	31.50	9.00

Designs and sizes of Nos. 340-356 remain as before, but wording has been changed to be predominantly Singhalese. "Ceylon" appears in small letters only in English and Tamil.
Nos. 355-356 with revenue cancellations sell for minimal prices.
Issue dates: 35c, 50c, July 15; 10c, Oct. 1; 85c, May 1, 1959; others, May 14, 1958.

Hands Reaching for UN Symbol A98

Perf. 13x12½
1958, Dec. 10 Photo. Unwmk.
357 A98 10c red brown & red .20 .20
358 A98 85c Prus green & red .55 .55
10th anniv. of the signing of the Universal Declaration of Human Rights.

Pirivena Universities and Founders A99

1959, Dec. 31
359 A99 10c brt ultra & dp org .40 .40
Institution of Pirivena Universities; founders Hikkaduwe Sri Sumangala Nayaka Thero and Ratmalane Sri Dharmaloka Nayake Thero.

Uprooted Oak Emblem A100 — Prime Minister Bandaranaike A101

1960, Apr. 7 Photo. *Perf. 11½*
Granite Paper
360 A100 4c chocolate & gold .20 .50
361 A100 25c vio blue & gold .20 .20
World Refugee Year, 7/1/59-6/30/60.

1961, Jan. 8 Granite Paper
Two types:
I — Gray hair at temple.
II — Dark hair at temple (redrawn).
362 A101 10c vio bl & gray bl (I) .40 .60
  a. Type II .90 .20
Solomon West Ridgeway Dias Bandaranaike, assassinated Sept. 26, 1959.

Badge of Singhalese Scouts — A102 — Malaria Eradication Emblem — A103

1962, Feb. 26 Unwmk. *Perf. 11½*
Granite Paper
363 A102 35c dark blue & ocher .35 .20
Boy Scouts of Ceylon, 50th anniv.

Perf. 14½x14
1962, Apr. 7 Photo. Wmk. 290
364 A103 25c lt sep, red org & brn .40 .40
WHO drive to eradicate malaria.

Monoplane 1938, and De Havilland Comet IV — A104

1963, Feb. 28 Unwmk. *Perf. 11½*
Granite Paper
365 A104 50c lt grnsh blue & blk .60 .60
25th anniv. of Ceylonese airmail service.

Stylized Vase and Wheat Emblem A105

1963, Mar. 21
Granite Paper
366 A105 5c blue & orange ver .75 2.50
367 A105 25c olive & brown 2.75 .75
FAO "Freedom from Hunger" campaign.

No. 340 Surcharged

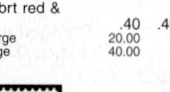

Perf. 12x12½
1963, June 1 Engr. Wmk. 290
368 A79 2c on 4c brt red & choc .40 .40
  a. Inverted surcharge 20.00
  b. Double surcharge 40.00

Rural Life — A106

1963, July 5 Photo. *Perf. 14x14½*
369 A106 60c dull red & black 1.25 .75
50th anniv. of the Cooperative Movement.

Landscape and Elephant A107

1963, Dec. 2 Wmk. 290
370 A107 5c blue & black .80 .45
National Conservation Week.

S.W.R.D. Bandaranaike A108 — Anagarika Dharmapala A109

Perf. 11½
1963, Sept. 26 Unwmk. Engr.
Granite Paper
371 A108 10c blue .40 .40

Redrawn
1964, July 1 Photo.
Granite Paper
372 A108 10c grnsh gray & bl vio .40 .40
Frame redrawn on No. 372; inscription in bottom panel replaced by ornament.
For surcharge see No. 389.

1964, Sept. 16 Unwmk. *Perf. 11½*
Granite Paper
373 A109 25c gray brn & dull yel .40 .40
Anagarika Dharmapala, Buddhist missionary, birth cent.

Ceylon Jungle Fowl — A110

Vatadage Ruins at Madirigiriya A111

Tea Picker — A112

Designs: 5c, Hill myna. 15c, Blue peafowl. 75c, Asiatic black-headed oriole. 5r, Girls, working in rice field. 10r, Map of Ceylon on scroll, showing agricultural development stations.

Wmk. 290, Unwmkd. (20c)
1964-69 Photo. Perf. 14, 11½ (20c)

374	A110	5c brt bl, blk, yel & grn	2.00	1.40
375	A110	15c yel, grn, blk, brt bl & rose	3.00	.25
376	A111	20c dk red brn, buff	.20	.25
377	A110	60c yel & multi	4.25	1.10
a.		Blue omitted	50.00	
b.		Red omitted	50.00	
378	A110	75c ol, blk, org & brn	3.00	.75
a.		Souvenir sheet of 4	10.00	
b.		As "a," overprinted	10.00	
379	A112	1r brown & grn	1.00	.25
c.		Brown omitted	125.00	
379A	A111	5r multicolored	6.00	4.00
379B	A110	10r brown & multi	22.50	3.50
		Nos. 374-379B (8)	41.95	11.50

No. 378a contains four imperf. stamps with simulated perforations similar to Nos. 374-375 and 377-378.

No. 378b is overprinted "First National Stamp Exhibition 1967" in two lines of black capitals.

No. 376 is on granite paper.

Issued: 20c, 1r, 10/1; 5c, 15c, 60c, 75c, 2/5/66; 5r, 8/15/69; 10r, 10/1/69.

See No. 325.

Exhibition Buildings, Cogwheels — A113

1964, Dec. 1 Unwmk. Perf. 11
"Industrial Exhibition" in Singhalese and English

380	A113	5c multicolored	.20	.50

"Industrial Exhibition" in Singhalese and Tamil

381	A113	5c multicolored	.20	.50
a.		Pair, #380-381	.25	1.00

1965 Industrial Exhibition.

Railroad Trains, 1864-1964 A114

Wmk. 290
1964, Dec. 21 Photo. Perf. 14
"Railway Centenary" in Singhalese and English

382	A114	60c lil rose, bl & yel grn	3.25	.55

"Railway Centenary" in Singhalese and Tamil

383	A114	60c lil rose, bl & yel grn	3.25	.55
a.		Vertical pair, #382-383	7.75	7.75

Centenary of Ceylonese railroads.

ITU Emblem, Old and New Communication Equipment — A115

1965, May 17 Perf. 14

384	A115	2c ultra & red	1.75	1.40
385	A115	30c brown & red	4.25	.55

ITU, centenary.

ICY Emblem A116

1965, June 26 Unwmk. Perf. 11½
Granite Paper

386	A116	3c rose car & dk bl	1.75	1.40
387	A116	50c gold, rose car & blk	4.25	.60

International Cooperation Year.

Municipal Council Building A117

1965, Oct. 29 Photo. Perf. 11½
Granite Paper

388	A117	25c gray & green	.40	.40

Centenary of Colombo Municipal Council.

No. 372 Surcharged

1965, Dec. 18 Photo. Perf. 11½

389	A108	5c on 10c	.40	.50

D. S. Senanayake — A118

1966, Mar. 22 Unwmk. Perf. 11½
Granite Paper

390	A118	10c bright green	.85	.20

D. S. Senanayake, first prime minister of Ceylon, 14th death anniv. See No. 418.

View and Arms of Kandy — A119

Perf. 14x13½
1966, June 15 Photo. Wmk. 290

391	A119	25c multicolored	.40	.40

Centenary of Kandy Municipal Council.

Opening of WHO Headquarters, Geneva A120

Unwmk.
1966, Oct. 8 Litho. Perf. 14

392	A120	4c multicolored	2.50	2.50
393	A120	1r multicolored	10.00	1.60

Rice, Map of Ceylon, FAO Emblem — A121

UNESCO Emblem A122

Design: 30c, Rice and globe.

1966, Oct. 25 Photo. Perf. 11½
Granite Paper

394	A121	6c dk green, org & brn	.20	.60
395	A121	30c brt blue, org & brn	.60	.20

Intl. Rice Year under sponsorship of the FAO.

1966, Nov. 3 Litho. Perf. 12

396	A122	3c tan & multi	4.00	4.00
397	A122	50c brt green & multi	7.75	1.60

20th anniv. of UNESCO.

Map of Ceylon and UNESCO Emblem — A123

Worshippers at Buddhist Shrine A124

1966, Dec. 1 Unwmk. Perf. 14

398	A123	2c yel brn, yel & blue	.45	1.00
399	A123	2r multicolored	1.75	2.25

Intl. Hydrological Decade (UNESCO), 1965-74.

1967, Jan. 2 Photo. Perf. 12

Designs: 20c, Muhintale Rock. 35c, Sacred Bo Tree. 60c, Adam's Peak.

400	A124	5c multicolored	.20	.40
401	A124	20c multicolored	.20	.20
402	A124	35c multicolored	.20	.20
403	A124	60c multicolored	.20	.20
		Nos. 400-403 (4)	.80	1.00

1st anniv. of the Poya Holiday System, Buddhist holiday replacing Sunday.

Dutch Ramparts, Clock Tower and Arms of Galle A125

1967, Jan. 5 Litho. Perf. 14x13½

404	A125	25c dk green & multi	.80	.20

Centenary of Galle Municipal Council.

Tea Research A126

40c, Tea tasting (cup & loose tea). 50c, Tea picking. 1r, Tea export (crate & freighter).

1967, Aug. 1 Unwmk. Perf. 13½

405	A126	4c multicolored	.70	.70
406	A126	40c multicolored	2.10	1.60
407	A126	50c multicolored	2.10	.40
408	A126	1r multicolored	2.10	.20
		Nos. 405-408 (4)	7.00	2.90

Centenary of the Ceylonese tea industry.

Elephant and ITY Emblem A127

1967, Aug. 15 Litho.

409	A127	45c multicolored	3.25	.85

Intl. Tourist Year.

Girl Guide, Jubilee Emblem and Flag — A128

1967, Sept. 19 Perf. 12x12½

410	A128	3c green & multi	.60	.20
411	A128	25c org yel & multi	.90	.20

Ceylon Girl Guide Assoc., 50th anniv.

Henry S. Olcott and Buddhist Flag A129

Perf. 13½
1967, Dec. 12 Unwmk. Litho.

412	A129	15c multicolored	.40	.20

Colonel Henry S. Olcott (1832-1907), an American who reorganized the Buddhist hierarchy and school system in Ceylon and was the first president of the Theosophical Society.

Independence Memorial, Colombo A130

Design: 1r, Flag of Ceylon and mace.

1968, Feb. 4 Wmk. 290 Perf. 14

413	A130	5c multicolored	.20	.50
414	A130	1r multicolored	.60	.20

20th anniversary of independence.

D. B. Jayatilaka — A131

1968, Feb. 14 Photo.

415	A131	25c brown	.40	.40

Sir Don Baron Jayatilaka (1868-1944), Buddhist leader and scholar.

Hygiene Institute, Kalutara A132

Perf. 11½x12

1968, Apr. 4   Litho.   Wmk. 290
416   A132   50c multicolored   .40   .40
WHO, 20th anniversary.

Jet over
Colombo
Terminal
A133

1968, Aug. 5   Perf. 13½
417   A133   60c org brn, dk bl &
                org   .55   .20
Opening of Colombo Airport.

D. S.
Senanayake — A134

1968, Sept. 23   Photo.   Perf. 14
418   A134   10c deep green   .20   .20
See No. 390.

Open Koran
A135

1968, Oct. 14   Photo.   Perf. 14
419   A135   25c org brn, blk, blue &
                emerald   .40   .40
1,400th anniversary of the Koran.

Human Rights
Flame
A136

Perf. 12½x13½

1968, Dec. 10   Unwmk.
420   A136   2c multicolored   .20   .20
421   A136   20c multicolored   .20   .20
422   A136   40c multicolored   .20   .20
423   A136   2r multicolored   .90 1.90
        Nos. 420-423 (4)   1.50 2.50
International Human Rights Year.

Ceylon Buddhist Headquarters,
Colombo — A137

1968, Dec. 19   Litho.   Perf. 13½
424   A137   5c multicolored   .40   .60
All-Ceylon Buddhist Cong., 50th anniv.
A multicolored 50c showing the Sri
Padmaya (Sacred Footprint) on Adam's Peak
was prepared but the issuance order was
countermanded on Dec. 18. Some were sold
in ignorance of the withdrawal order. Value
$65.

E. W.
Perera — A138

"Strength in
Saving" — A139

Wmk. 290

1969, Feb. 17   Photo.   Perf. 14
425   A138   60c brown   .40   .50
E. W. Perera, member of Legislative Council.

1969, Mar. 20
426   A139   3c blue, yel & black   .40   .40
National Savings Movement, 25th anniv.

A140

A141

4c, Seat of Enlightenment under Bodhi Tree.
6c, Buduresmala (disk symbolic of six-fold
Buddha rays).

Wmk. 290

1969, Apr. 10   Litho.   Perf. 15
427   A140   4c orange & multi   .20   .25
428   A140   6c gold & multi   .20   .25
429   A140   35c scarlet & multi   .20   .20
        Nos. 427-429 (3)   .60   .70
Vesak Day, which commemorates the birth,
enlightenment and death of Buddha.
For surcharges see Nos. 463, 466.

1969, Apr. 29   Photo.   Perf. 14x14½
430   A141   15c org yel & multi   .40   .40
Alexander Ekanayake Goonesingha (1891-
1967), trade unionist, political leader and
diplomat.

ILO, 50th
Anniv.
A142

1969, May 4   Perf. 14½x14
431   A142   5c grnsh bl & black   .20   .20
432   A142   25c car rose & black   .20   .20

Convocation
Hall,
University of
Ceylon
A143

Elephant Lamp (Ath
Pana) — A144

35c, "Lamp of Education," globe & flags.
50c, Uranium atom diagram. 60c, Symbols of
science education. 1r, Aerial view of Sigiriya
rock fortress.

Unwmk.
1969, Aug. 1   Litho.   Perf. 14
Inscribed: "SIYAWASA"
433   A143   4c yellow & multi   .20   .65
434   A143   6c multicolored   .40 1.25
435   A143   35c multicolored   .20   .20
436   A144   50c red & multi   .20   .20
437   A143   60c blue & multi   .20   .20
438   A144   1r yel & multi   .50   .20
        Nos. 433-438 (6)   1.70 2.70
Centenary of public education and archaeological research.
For surcharges see Nos. 464-467.

Wild Water
Buffalo
A145

15c, Slender loris. 50c, Axis deer. 1r,
Leopard.

Perf. 14x13½
1970, May 11   Litho.   Unwmk.
439   A145   5c lt blue & multi   .95 1.40
440   A145   15c buff & multi   1.50   .35
441   A145   50c salmon & multi   1.50 1.40
442   A145   1r gray & multi   1.50 1.90
        Nos. 439-442 (4)   5.45 5.05

Symbols of
Agriculture
and Industry
A146

1970, June 17
443   A146   60c multicolored   .40   .40
Asian Productivity Year.

Inauguration
of UPU
Headquarters,
Bern — A147

1970, Aug. 14   Litho.   Unwmk.
444   A147   50c org, black & blue   .75   .20
445   A147   1.10r red, black & blue 4.75   .60

Caduceus and
Oil
Lamp — A148

1970, Sept. 1   Perf. 13½x14
446   A148   5c multicolored   1.00 1.40
447   A148   45c gray & multi   1.00 1.10
Centenary of the Ceylon Medical School.

Victory March
and S.W.R.D.
Bandaranaike
A149

1970, Sept. 25   Perf. 14
448   A149   10c red & multi   .20   .20
For surcharge see No. 465.

UN Emblem
and
Dove — A150

Keppetipola
Dissawe — A151

1970, Oct. 24   Photo.   Perf. 12½x14
449   A150   2r dp orange & multi   3.00 3.00
25th anniversary of the United Nations.

1970, Nov. 26   Litho.   Perf. 14x14½
450   A151   25c multicolored   .40   .20
The 152nd anniversary of the execution of
Keppetipola Dissawe, leader of the Great
Rebellion of 1817-18.

Ola Leaf Manuscript and Education
Year Emblem — A152

1970, Dec. 21   Photo.   Perf. 13
451   A152   15c brown & multi   3.50 1.90
International Education Year.

Charles Henry
de
Soysa — A153

Edward Henry
Pedris — A154

1971, Mar. 3   Litho.   Perf. 14x13½
452   A153   20c orange & multi   .40   .50
de Soysa (1836-90), philanthropist who
founded hospitals and schools.

1971, July 8   Litho.   Perf. 14x14½
453   A154   25c blue & multi   .40   .40
Edward Henry Pedris (1888-1925), patriot.

A 5c stamp for the 10th Conf. of
World Fellowship of Buddhists, Ceylon,
May 9-13, was supposedly not issued
without "1972" overprint. See Sri Lanka
No. 471.

Lenin (1870-
1924)
A156

Cumaratunga
Munidasa
A157

1971, Aug. 31   Perf. 14½
455   A156   40c dp car & multi   .70   .70

1971, Oct. 29   Perf. 14
Poets and Philosophers: #457, Ananda
Coomaraswamy (1887-1947). #458, Rev. S.
Mahinda Thero (1905-51). #459, Ananda

Rajakaruna (1885-1957). #460, Arumuga
Navalar (1822-78).

456	A157	5c brown	.20	.20
457	A157	5c slate	.20	.20
458	A157	5c deep orange	.20	.20
459	A157	5c dp vio blue	.20	.20
460	A157	5c brown red	.20	.20
	Nos. 456-460 (5)		1.00	1.00

CARE
Package
A158

1971, Dec. 28   *Perf. 14x13*
461 A158 50c purple, blue & pink   .55 .35
25th anniv. of CARE, a US-Canadian Cooperative for American Relief Everywhere.

Map of
Ceylon,
Colombo
Plan
Emblem
A159

1971, Dec. 28 Litho. *Perf. 14x14½*
462 A159 20c multicolored   .40 .40
20th anniversary of the Colombo Plan.

Issues of 1969-70 Surcharged

a

b

c

d

e

Wmk. 290, Unwmkd.
1971, Dec. 5   *Perf. 15, 14*

463	A140 (a)	5c on 4c (#427)	7.50	2.50
464	A143 (b)	5c on 4c (#433)	.20	1.90
465	A149 (c)	15c on 10c (#448)	.20	.50
466	A140 (d)	25c on 6c (#428)	.80	.95
467	A144 (e)	25c on 6c (#434)	.80	3.25
	Nos. 463-467 (5)		9.50	9.10

Nos. 463-466 exist with surcharge inverted.

WHO Emblem
and
Heart — A160

1972, May 2 Unwmk. *Perf. 13x13½*
468 A160 25c multicolored   3.25 .90
"Your heart is your health," World Health
Day.

UN
Emblem,
Map
Showing
Asian
Highway
A161

1972, May 2   *Perf. 13x12½*
469 A161 85c lt blue & multi   6.50 3.25
Economic Commission for Asia and the Far
East (ECAFE), 25th anniversary.

SEMI-POSTAL STAMPS

Catalogue values for unused
stamps in this section are for
Never Hinged items.

Lamp and
Dharmachakra
SP1

Design: 10c+5c, Hand of Peace.

Perf. 11½
1956, May 10 Unwmk. Photo.
Granite Paper
B1 SP1 4c + 2c dp bl & lt yel   .35 .30
B2 SP1 10c + 5c dk gray, yel & brt
pink   .50 .40
2500th anniv. of the birth of Buddha. The
surtax went to the Buddha Jayanti Fund. For
overprints, see Nos. 338-339.

WAR TAX STAMPS

Nos. 201, 202, 202a
and 203 Overprinted

Die I
1918 Wmk. 3 *Perf. 14*

MR1	A44	2c brown orange	.25	.45
a.		Double overprint	35.00	47.50
b.		Inverted overprint	60.00	72.50
MR2	A44	3c dp grn (Die Ia,		
		type II)	2.60	.45
a.		3c dp green (Die I, type I)	.25	.60
b.		Double overprint (Die I)	95.00	105.00
MR3	A44	5c red violet	.60	.35
a.		Double overprint	52.50	65.00
b.		Inverted overprint	120.00	

Same Overprint on No. 223
MR4	A44	1c on 5c red violet	.20	.30
a.		Double overprint	210.00	
	Nos. MR1-MR4 (4)		3.65	1.55

OFFICIAL STAMPS

Regular Issues
Overprinted

1869 Wmk. 1 *Perf. 12½, 14*
Black Overprint

O1	A4	1p blue	85.00	
O2	A1	2p yellow	85.00	
O3	A5	3p rose	150.00	
O4	A2	8p red brown	85.00	
O5	A1	1sh gray lilac	190.00	

Red Overprint

O6	A1	6p brown	85.00	
O7	A2	2sh blue	140.00	
a.		Imperf.	1,000.	
	Nos. O1-O7 (7)		820.00	

Nos. O1-O7 were never placed in use.
The overprint measures 15mm on #O1, O3.

Regular Issues
Overprinted in Black or
Red

1895-1900 Wmk. 2 *Perf. 14*

O8	A6	2c green	13.00	.70
O9	A6	2c org brn ('00)	10.00	.70
O10	A24	3c org brn &		
		grn	12.00	1.50
O11	A24	3c green ('00)	11.00	3.75
O12	A23	5c lilac	4.75	.40
O13	A24	15c olive green	17.50	.60
O14	A24	15c ultra ('00)	24.00	.70
O15	A24	25c brown	13.00	2.00
O16	A24	30c vio & org		
		brn	15.00	.70
O17	A24	75c blk & org		
		brn (R)		
		('99)	6.50	7.50

Wmk. 1
O18	A16	1r12c claret	100.00	65.00
	Nos. O8-O18 (11)		226.75	83.55

1903-04   **Wmk. 2**

O19	A36	2c orange brown	17.50	1.20
O20	A37	3c green	12.00	2.40
O21	A38	5c dull lilac	26.00	1.75
O22	A40	15c ultramarine	37.50	3.25
O23	A40	25c bister	30.00	21.00
O24	A40	30c violet & green	17.50	1.75
	Nos. O19-O24 (6)		140.50	31.35

CHAD

'chad

(Tchad)

LOCATION — Central Africa, south of
Libya
GOVT. — Republic
AREA — 495,572 sq. mi.
POP. — 7,557,436 (1999 est.)
CAPITAL — N'Djamena

A former dependency of Ubangi-
Shari, Chad became a separate French
colony in 1920. In 1934, the colonies of
Chad, Gabon, Middle Congo and
Ubangi-Shari were grouped in a single
administrative unit known as French
Equatorial Africa, with the capital at

Brazzaville. The Republic of Chad was
proclaimed November 28, 1958.

100 Centimes = 1 Franc

Catalogue values for unused
stamps in this country are for
Never Hinged items, beginning
with Scott 64 in the regular postage section, Scott B1 in the semi-
postal section, Scott C1 in the air
post section, Scott CB1 in the air
post semi-postal section, Scott
J23 in the postage due section,
Scott M1 in the military stamp section, and Scott O1 in the officials
section.

See French Equatorial Africa No. 190
for stamp inscribed "Tchad."

Types of
Middle
Congo,
1907-17,
Overprinted

Perf. 14x13½, 13½x14
1922   **Unwmk.**

1	A1	1c red & violet	.40	.40
a.		Overprint omitted	225.00	
2	A1	2c ol brn & salmon	.50	.50
a.		Overprint omitted	250.00	
3	A1	4c ind & vio	1.10	1.10
4	A1	5c choc & grn	1.25	1.25
5	A1	10c dp grn & gray grn	2.25	2.25
6	A1	15c vio & red	2.50	2.50
7	A1	20c grn & vio	4.00	4.00
8	A2	25c ol brn & brn	9.00	9.00
9	A2	30c rose & pale rose	1.60	1.60
10	A2	35c dl bl & dl rose	2.75	2.75
11	A2	40c choc & grn	3.00	3.00
12	A2	45c vio & grn	2.25	2.25
13	A2	50c dk bl & pale bl	2.75	2.75
14	A2	60c on 75c vio, *pnksh*	3.75	3.75
a.		"TCHAD" omitted	275.00	
b.		"60" omitted	300.00	
15	A1	75c red & violet	3.00	3.00
16	A3	1fr indigo & salmon	11.00	11.00
17	A3	2fr indigo & violet	19.00	19.00
18	A3	5fr ind & olive brn	19.00	19.00
	Nos. 1-18 (18)		89.10	89.10

See Nos. 26a, 32a, 38a, 55a.

Stamps of 1922 Overprinted in Various
Colors:

Nos. 19-28

Nos. 29-50

1924-33

19	A1	1c red & vio	.30	.30
a.		"TCHAD" omitted	175.00	
b.		Double overprint	275.00	
c.		Violet omitted	225.00	
20	A1	2c ol brn & sal	.30	.30
a.		"TCHAD" omitted	160.00	
b.		Double overprint	190.00	
21	A1	4c ind & vio	.30	.30
a.		"TCHAD" omitted	750.00	
22	A1	5c choc & grn		
		(Bl)	1.00	1.00
a.		"TCHAD" omitted	160.00	
23	A1	5c choc & grn	.45	.45
a.		"TCHAD" omitted	190.00	
24	A1	10c dp grn & gray		
		grn (Bl)	1.00	.65
25	A1	10c dp grn & gray		
		grn	1.00	.65

26	A1	10c red org & blk ('25)	.45	.45
a.		"Afrique Equatoriale Fran-caise" omitted	175.00	
b.		"TCHAD" omitted	175.00	
27	A1	15c vio & red	.45	.45
28	A1	20c grn & vio	.70	.70
a.		"TCHAD" omitted	190.00	
b.		"Afrique Equatoriale Fran-caise" doubled	300.00	
29	A2	25c ol brn & brn	.45	.45
a.		"Afrique Equatoriale Fran-caise" doubled	125.00	
30	A2	30c rose & pale rose	.60	.60
31	A2	30c gray & bl (R) ('25)	.45	.45
32	A2	30c dk grn & grn ('27)	1.10	1.10
a.		"Afrique Equatoriale Fran-caise" omitted	300.00	
33	A2	35c ind & dl rose	.45	.45
34	A2	40c choc & grn	1.25	1.25
a.		Dbl. overprint (R + Bk)	225.00	
35	A2	45c vio & grn	.80	.80
a.		Dbl. overprint (R + Bk)	225.00	
36	A2	50c dk bl & pale bl	1.40	1.10
a.		Inverted overprint	140.00	
37	A2	50c grn & vio ('25)	1.10	1.10
38	A2	65c org brn & bl ('28)	1.90	1.90
a.		"Afrique Equatoriale Fran-caise" omitted	325.00	
39	A2	75c red & vio	1.40	1.10
40	A2	75c dp bl & lt bl (R) ('25)	.60	.60
a.		"TCHAD" omitted	225.00	
41	A2	75c rose & dk brn ('28)	2.40	2.40
42	A2	90c brn red & pink ('30)	6.50	6.50
43	A3	1fr ind & salmon	1.60	1.60
44	A3	1.10fr dl grn & bl ('28)	2.40	2.40
45	A3	1.25fr org brn & lt bl ('33)	7.00	7.00
46	A3	1.50fr ultra & bl ('30)	6.50	6.50
47	A3	1.75fr ol brn & vio ('33)	37.50	37.50
48	A3	2fr ind & vio	2.75	2.75
a.		Double impression of frame	525.00	
49	A3	3fr red vio ('30)	10.50	10.50
50	A3	5fr ind & ol brn	3.25	2.50
		Nos. 19-50 (32)	97.85	95.80

See No. 58a.

Types of 1922 Overprinted like Nos. 29-50 and Surcharged with New Values

1924-27

51	A2	60c on 75c dk vio, *pnksh*	.95	.95
a.		"60" omitted	200.00	
52	A3	65c on 1fr brn & ol grn ('25)	1.60	1.60
53	A3	85c on 1fr brn & ol grn ('25)	1.60	1.60
54	A2	90c on 75c brn red & rose red ('27)	1.40	1.40
55	A3	1.25fr on 1fr dk bl & ul-tra (R) ('26)	.70	.70
a.		"Afrique Equatoriale Francaise" omitted	175.00	
56	A3	1.50fr on 1fr ultra & bl ('27)	1.50	1.50
57	A3	3fr on 5fr org brn & dl red ('27)	5.00	5.00
58	A3	10fr on 5fr ol grn & cer ('27)	12.00	12.00
a.		"10fr" omitted	400.00	
59	A3	20fr on 5fr vio & ver ('27)	18.00	18.00
		Nos. 51-59 (9)	42.75	42.75

Common Design Types pictured following the introduction.

Colonial Exposition Issue
Common Design Types

1931		**Engr.**	**Perf. 12½**
Name of Country in Black			
60	CD70	40c deep green	5.00	*5.00*
61	CD71	50c violet	5.00	*5.00*
62	CD72	90c red orange	5.00	*5.00*
63	CD73	1.50fr dull blue	5.00	*5.00*
		Nos. 60-63 (4)	20.00	20.00

Catalogue values for unused stamps in this section, from this point to the end of the section, are for Never Hinged items.

Republic

"Birth of the Republic" A1　　"Solidarity of the Community" A2

1959		**Unwmk.**	**Engr.**	**Perf. 13**
64	A1	15fr ultra, grn & maroon	.80	.20
65	A2	25fr dk grn & dp claret	1.00	.20

1st anniv. of the proclamation of the Republic.

Imperforates

Most Chad stamps from 1959 onward exist imperforate in issued and trial colors, and also in small presentation sheets in issued colors.

C.C.T.A. Issue
Common Design Type

| **1960** | | | | |
| 66 | CD106 | 50fr rose lil & dk pur | 1.75 | .35 |

Flag and Map of Chad and UN Emblem — A3

Unwmk.
1961, Jan. 11		**Engr.**	**Perf. 13**
Flag in blue, yellow and carmine			
67	A3	15fr brn & dk bl	.60	.20
68	A3	25fr org brn & dk bl	.90	.20
69	A3	85fr slate grn & dk bl	2.50	.40
		Nos. 67-69 (3)	4.00	.80

Admission of Chad to United Nations.

Chari Bridge and Hippopotamus — A4

Abtouyoua Mountain and Ox — A5

Designs: 50c, Biltine and dorcas gazelle. 1fr, Logone and elephant. 2fr, Batha and lion. 3fr, Salamat and buffalo. 4fr, Ouaddai and Kudu. 15fr, Bessada and giant eland. 20fr, Tibesti mountains and mouflon. 25fr, Rocherg and antelope. 30fr, Kanem and cheetah. 60fr, Borkou and oryx. 85fr, Gorge of Archet and addax.

Perf. 13½x14, 14x13½			
1961-62			**Typo.**
70	A5	50c yel grn & dk grn ('62)	.20	.20
71	A5	1fr bl grn & dk bl grn ('62)	.20	.20
72	A5	2fr dk red brn & blk ('62)	.20	.20
73	A5	3fr ocher & dl grn ('62)	.20	.20
74	A5	4fr dk crim & blk ('62)	.20	.20
75	A4	5fr yellow & blk	.20	.20
76	A5	10fr pink & blk	.35	.20
77	A5	15fr lilac & blk ('62)	.70	.20
78	A5	20fr red & blk	.85	.20

79	A5	25fr blue & blk ('62)	.90	.20
80	A5	30fr ultra & blk ('62)	1.00	.20
81	A5	60fr yel & ol grn ('62)	2.25	.20
82	A5	85fr org & blk	2.75	.25
		Nos. 70-82 (13)	10.00	2.65

First anniversary of Independence.
For overprint see No. M1.

Abidjan Games Issue
Common Design Type
1962, July 21		**Photo.**	**Perf. 12½x12**
83	CD109	20fr Relay race	.80	.20
84	CD109	50fr High jump	2.00	.30
		Nos. 83-84,C8 (3)	6.30	1.25

African-Malgache Union Issue
Common Design Type
| **1962, Sept. 8** | | | **Unwmk.** |
| 85 | CD110 | 30fr dk bl, bluish grn, red & gold | 1.25 | .20 |

Pres. Ngarta Tombalbaye — A7

1963, Apr. 22			**Perf. 12x12½**
86	A7	20fr multi	.65	.20
87	A7	85fr multi	1.75	.30

For surcharge, see No. 125.

Space Communciations Issue

Waves Around Globe — A8

Design: 100fr, Orbit patterns around globe.

Perf. 12½			
1963, Sept. 19		**Unwmk.**	**Photo.**
88	A8	25fr grn & pur	1.00	.20
89	A8	100fr pink & ultra	3.00	.60

Ancestral Mask — A9

Excavated Sao Art: 5fr, Clay weight. 25fr, Ancestral clay statuette. 60fr, Gazelle, bronze. 80fr, Bronze pectoral.

1963, Dec. 2		**Engr.**	**Perf. 13**
90	A9	5fr brt grn & red brn	.20	.20
91	A9	15fr gray, dl cl & red	.45	.20
92	A9	25fr dk bl & org brn	1.10	.25
93	A9	60fr org brn & slate grn	2.75	.35
94	A9	80fr org red & olive	3.00	.40
		Nos. 90-94 (5)	7.50	1.40

UNESCO Emblem, Scales and Tree — A10

| **1963, Dec. 10** | | | |
| 95 | A10 | 25fr green & maroon | 1.00 | .20 |

15th anniv. of the Universal Declaration of Human Rights.

Potter A11

Perf. 12½			
1964, Feb. 5		**Unwmk.**	**Engr.**
96	A11	10fr shown	.35	.20
97	A11	30fr Boatmaker	.90	.20
98	A11	50fr Weaver	1.50	.25
99	A11	85fr Smiths	2.25	.35
		Nos. 96-99 (4)	5.00	1.00

Barograph and WMO Emblem A12

1964, Mar. 23 **Perf. 13**
100 A12 50fr red lil, pur & ultra　1.40　.25

Fourth World Meteorological Day.

Cotton A13

1964, Apr. 6		**Photo.**	**Perf. 12½x13**
101	A13	20fr shown	1.75	.35
102	A13	25fr Royal poinciana	2.00	.40

Co-operation Issue
Common Design Type
| **1964, Nov. 7** | | **Engr.** | **Perf. 13** |
| 103 | CD119 | 25fr ver, dk bl & dk brn | 1.00 | .25 |

National Guard and Map of Chad A14

Design: 25fr, Infantry, flag and map, vert.

Perf. 12½x13, 13x12½			
1964, Dec. 11			**Photo.**
104	A14	20fr multi	.85	.20
105	A14	25fr lt bl & multi	.95	.25

Issued to honor the army of Chad.

Aoudad or Barbary Sheep A15

10fr, Addax. 20fr, Oryx. 25fr, Derby's eland, vert. 30fr, Giraffe, buffalo & lion, Zakouma Park, vert. 85fr, Great kudu at water hole, vert.

Perf. 12½x12, 12x12½			
1965, Jan. 11			**Unwmk.**
106	A15	5fr dk brn, ultra & yel	.50	.20
107	A15	10fr ultra, org & blk	.75	.20
108	A15	20fr multi	1.50	.20
109	A15	25fr multi	1.75	.25
110	A15	30fr multi	2.50	.40
111	A15	85fr multi	5.00	.75
		Nos. 106-111 (6)	12.00	2.00

Olsen Perforator A16

Designs: 60fr, Mildé telephone, vert. 100fr, Distributor of Baudot telegraph.

1965, May 17   Engr.   Perf. 13
112 A16   30fr multi   .75   .20
113 A16   60fr multi   1.25   .45
114 A16 100fr multi   2.00   .60
    Nos. 112-114 (3)   4.00   1.25
Cent. of the ITU.

Motorized
Police
A17

Perf. 12½x12
1965, June 22   Photo.   Unwmk.
115 A17 25fr ol, dk grn, gold & brn .75 .25
Issued to honor the national police.

Guitar
A18

Musical Instruments from National Museum:
1fr, Drum and stool, vert. 3fr, Shoulder drums,
vert. 15fr, Viol. 60fr, Harp, vert.

1965, Oct. 26   Engr.   Perf. 13
Size: 22x36mm, 36x22mm
116 A18   1fr car, emer & brn   .20   .20
117 A18   2fr red, brt lil & brn   .20   .20
118 A18   3fr red & sepia   .20   .20
119 A18 15fr ocher & sl grn   .75   .20
120 A18 60fr maroon & slate grn   1.75   .60
    Nos. 116-120,C23 (6)   5.85   2.25

Head and   WHO
Bowl — A19   Headquarters,
                   Geneva — A20

Sao Art: 20fr, Head. 60fr, Head with crown.
80fr, Circlet with human head. From excavations at Bouta Kebira and Gawi.

1966, Apr. 1   Engr.   Perf. 13
121 A19 15fr ol, choc & ultra   .40   .20
122 A19 20fr dk red, brn & bl grn   .75   .20
123 A19 60fr brt bl, choc & ver   1.75   .50
124 A19 80fr brn org, grn & pur   2.50   .90
    Nos. 121-124 (4)   5.40   1.50
Issued to publicize the International Negro
Arts Festival, Dakar, Senegal, Apr. 1-24.

No. 86 Surcharged with New Value
and Two Bars in Orange

1966, Apr. 15   Photo.   Perf. 12x12½
125 A7 25fr on 20fr multi   .75   .30

1966, May 3
126 A20 25fr car, lt ultra & yel   .60   .20
127 A20 32fr emer, ultra & yel   .75   .20
New WHO Headquarters, Geneva.

Staff of
Mercury
and Map of
Africa
A21

1966, May 24   Perf. 12½x12
128 A21 30fr multi   .75   .25
Central African Customs and Economic
Union (Union Douaniere et Economique et
l'Afrique Centrale, UDEAC).

Soccer
Player — A22

Design: 60fr, Soccer player facing left.

1966, July 12   Engr.   Perf. 13
129 A22 30fr grn, bl grn & mar   .75   .25
130 A22 60fr dk bl, gray & car   1.40   .30
8th World Cup Soccer Championship, Wembley, England, July 11-30.

Young Men,
Flag and
Emblem
A23

1966, Aug. 11   Photo.   Perf. 12½x13
131 A23 25fr dk bl & multi   .75   .20
Chad Youth Movement.

Greek Columns and
UNESCO
Emblem — A24

1966, Aug. 23   Engr.   Perf. 13
132 A24 32fr sl bl, vio & car rose   .75   .20
20th anniv. of UNESCO.

Reconstructed Skull of
Chadanthropus — A25

1966, Sept. 20   Engr.   Perf. 13
133 A25 30fr gray, red & ocher   1.90   .50
Yves Coppens' discovery of Lake Chad man.

Stone
Axe — A26

Prehistoric Tools: 30fr, Flint arrow head.
85fr, Bone harpoon. 100fr, Sandstone mill-
stone with grinder.

1966, Dec. 11   Engr.   Perf. 13
134 A26 25fr dp bl, red & dk
              brn   .55   .20
135 A26 30fr brn, dp bl & blk   .80   .20
136 A26 85fr dk red, brt bl &
              brn   2.40   .50
137 A26 100fr Prus grn, dk brn
              & bis brn   2.75   .65
  a.   Miniature sheet of 4, #134-137 15.00 5.00
    Nos. 134-137 (4)   6.50   1.55

Map of Chad and
Various
Sports — A27

1967, Apr. 10   Photo.   Perf. 12x12½
138 A27 25fr multi   .75   .30
Issued for Sports Day, Apr. 10, 1967.

Colotis
Protomedia
A28

Various Butterflies.

1967, May 23   Photo.   Perf. 12½x12
139 A28   5fr blue & multi   1.75   .20
140 A28 10fr emerald & multi   4.25   .20
141 A28 20fr orange & multi   8.50   .40
142 A28 130fr red & multi   17.50   .70
    Nos. 139-142 (4)   32.00   1.50

WHO Headquarters,
Brazzaville — A29

1967, Sept. 23   Photo.   Perf. 12½x13
143 A29 30fr vio bl & multi   .75   .25
Opening of the Regional Office of the WHO,
Brazzaville.

Jamboree
Emblem
and Boy
Scouts
A30

32fr, Jamboree emblem and Boy Scout.

1967, Oct. 17   Photo.   Perf. 12½x13
144 A30 25fr multi   .80   .20
145 A30 32fr multi   .90   .20
12th Boy Scout World Jamboree, Farragut
State Park, Idaho, Aug. 1-9.

Great Mills
of Chad
A31

30fr, Lake reclamation project, grain fields.

1967, Nov. 14   Engr.   Perf. 13
146 A31 25fr brt bl, ind & sep   .70   .20
147 A31 30fr ultra, emer & ol brn   .90   .20
Economic development of Chad.

Woman and
Harp Player
A32

Rock Paintings: 30fr, Giraffes. 50fr, Camel
rider hunting ostrich.

1967, Dec. 19   Engr.   Perf. 13
Size: 36x22mm
148 A32 15fr bl, sal & mar   2.00   .20
149 A32 30fr grnsh bl, sal &
              mar   4.00   .40
150 A32 50fr emer, sal & mar   5.50   .55
    Nos. 148-150,C38-C39 (5)   28.50   3.60
Balloud expedition in the Ennedi Mountains.
See Nos. 163-166.

Rotary   Map of Chad,
Emblem — A33   WHO Emblem,
                Well, Physicians,
                Mother and
                Child — A34

1968, Jan. 9   Photo.   Perf. 13x12½
151 A33 50fr multi   1.40   .40
Rotary Club of Chad, 10th anniversary.

1968, Apr. 6   Perf. 13x12½
152 A34 25fr multi   .70   .20
153 A34 32fr multi   .90   .20
20th anniv. of WHO.

"Water"
Aiding
Agriculture
and
Industry
A35

1968, Apr. 23   Engr.   Perf. 13
154 A35 50fr grnsh bl, brn & brt
              grn   1.10   .25
Hydrological Decade (UNESCO), 1965-74.

National Administration School — A36

1968, Aug. 20   Engr.   Perf. 13
155 A36 25fr slate, brn red & rose
              vio   .70   .20

Boy
Learning to
Write
A37

1968, Sept. 10
156 A37 60fr dk bl, dk brn & blk   1.10   .30
Issued for National Literacy Day.

Cotton
Harvest
A38

Loom, Fort
Archambault
Factory — A39

Tiger
Moth — A40

1968, Sept. 24   Engr.   Perf. 13
157 A38 25fr Prus bl, choc & dk grn .80 .20
158 A39 30fr brt grn, ol & ultra   .90 .20

Issued to publicize the cotton industry.

1968, Oct. 1   Photo.

Moths: 30fr, Owlet. 50fr, Saturnid (Gynanisa maja). 100fr, Saturnid (Epiphora bauhiniae).

159 A40 25fr multi   5.25   .45
160 A40 30fr multi   6.25   .50
161 A40 50fr multi   9.50   .60
162 A40 100fr multi 11.00   .75
     Nos. 159-162 (4) 32.00 2.30

Rock Paintings Type of 1967

Rock Paintings: 2fr, Archers. 10fr, Costumes (4 women, 1 man). 20fr, Funeral vigil. 25fr, Dispute.

1968, Nov. 19   Engr.   Perf. 13
Size: 36x22mm
163 A32 2fr scar, salmon & brn   .65   .20
164 A32 10fr pur, salmon & dk
              red   1.60   .20
165 A32 20fr grn, salmon & mar   3.25   .50
166 A32 25fr bl, salmon & ma-
              roon   3.50   .60
     Nos. 163-166 (4)   9.00 1.50

Man and Human
Rights
Flame — A41

St. Paul — A42

1968, Dec. 10   Engr.   Perf. 13
167 A41 32fr grn, brt bl & red   .75   .20

International Human Rights Year.

1969, May 6   Litho.   Perf. 12½x13

Apostles: 1fr, St. Peter. 2fr, St. Thomas. 5fr, St. John the Evangelist. 10fr, St. Bartholomew. 20fr, St. Matthew. 25fr, St. James the Less. 30fr, St. Andrew. 40fr, St. Jude. 50fr, St. James the Greater. 85fr, St. Philip. 100fr, St. Simon.

168 A42 50c multi   .20   .20
169 A42 1fr multi   .20   .20
170 A42 2fr multi   .20   .20
171 A42 5fr multi   .20   .20
172 A42 10fr multi   .20   .20
173 A42 20fr multi   .30   .20
174 A42 25fr multi   .40   .20
175 A42 30fr multi   .50   .20
176 A42 40fr multi   .60   .20
177 A42 50fr multi   .70   .20
178 A42 85fr multi   1.10   .40
179 A42 100fr multi 1.25   .40
  a. Sheet of 12, #168-179 6.00 1.75

Jubilee Year of the Catholic Church in Chad.

Tractors and
Trucks — A43

1969, June 19   Engr.   Perf. 13
180 A43 32fr grn, red brn & ind   .75   .20

50th anniv. of the ILO.

Deborah
Meyer, US, 200
Meter Freestyle
A44

Woman with
Flowers, by
Veneto — A45

Winners of 1968 Olympic Games: #182, Roland Matthes, East Germany, 100m backstroke. #183, Klaus DiBiasi, Italy, springboard diving. #184, Bruno Cipolla, Primo Baran and Renzo Sambo, Italy, pair with coxswain. #185, Annemarie Zimmermann and Rosewitha Esser, West Germany, women's kayak tandem. #186, Sailing, G.B. #187, Pierre Trentin, France, 1000 meter bicycling. #188, Pier Franco Vianelli, Italy, 196k bicycle road race. #189, Daniel Morelon and Pierre Trentin, France, tandem.
#190, Daniel R. Rebillard, France, 4000m pursuit (bicycle). #191, Ingrid Becker, West Germany, pentathlon. #192, Jean J. Guyon, France, equestrian. #193, Olympic dressage team, West Germany. #194, Bernd Klinger, West Germany, small bore rifle. #195, Manfred Wolke, East Germany, welterweight. #196, Randy Matson, US, shot put. #197, Colette Besson, France, 400m run. #198, Mohammed Gammoudi, Tunisia, 5,000m run. #199, Tommie Smith, US, 200m run.
#200, David Hemery, G.B., 200m hurdles. #201, Willie Davenport, US, 110m hurdles. #202, Bob Beamon, US, long jump. #203, Sawao Kato, Japan, all around gymnastics. #204, Dick Fosbury, US, high jump.
Paintings: #206, Holy Family, by Murillo, horiz. #207, Adoration of the Magi, by Rubens. #208, Portrait of an African Woman, by Bezombes. #209, Three Black Men, by Rubens. #210, Mother and Child, by Gauguin.

1969, June 30   Litho.   Perf. 12½x13
181-204 A44 1fr set of 24   8.00   8.00

Perf. 12½x13, 13x12½
205-210 A45 1fr set of 6   1.90   1.90

Issued to stress the brotherhood of mankind.
For overprints see Nos. 244A-244F, 245A-245X.

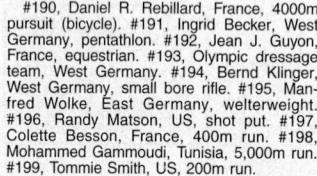

Cochlospermum
Tinctorium — A46

Flowers: 4fr, Parkia biglobosa. 10fr, Pancratium trianthum. 15fr, Morning glory.

1969, July 8   Photo.   Perf. 12½x13
211 A46 1fr pink, yel & blk   .60   .20
212 A46 4fr dk grn, yel & red   .90   .20
213 A46 10fr dk grn, yel & gray 1.10 .20
214 A46 15fr vio bl & multi   1.90 .20
     Nos. 211-214 (4)   4.50   .80

Meat
Freezer,
Farcha
A47

30fr, Cattle at Farcha slaughterhouse.

1969, Aug. 19   Engr.   Perf. 13
215 A47 25fr sl grn, ocher & red
              brn   .60   .20
216 A47 30fr red brn, sl grn & gray .75 .20

Economic development on Chad.

Development Bank Issue
Common Design Type
1969, Sept. 10
217 CD130 30fr dl red, grn & ocher .70 .20

Tilapia
Nilotica
A48

Fish: 3fr, Citharinus latus. 5fr, Tetraodon fahaka strigosus. 20fr, Hydrocyon forskali.

1969, Nov. 25   Engr.   Perf. 13
218 A48 2fr choc, grn & gray   .55   .20
219 A48 3fr gray, red & bl   1.10   .20
220 A48 5fr ocher, blk & yel   1.75   .20
221 A48 20fr blk, red & grn   4.75   .20
     Nos. 218-221 (4)   8.15   .80

ASECNA Issue
Common Design Type
1969, Dec. 12   Engr.   Perf. 13
222 CD132 30fr orange   .75   .25

Pres. François
Tombalbaye
A49

Lenin — A50

1970, Jan. 11   Litho.   Perf. 14
223 A49 25fr multi   .70   .20

1970, Apr. 22   Photo.   Perf. 11½
224 A50 150fr gold, blk & buff 3.25 1.10

Lenin (1870-1924), Russian communist leader.

UPU Headquarters Issue
Common Design Type
1970, May 20   Engr.   Perf. 13
225 CD133 30fr dk red, pur & brn .75 .25

During the 1970-73 period three different agents had entered into contracts to produce stamps with various officials of the Chad government, apparently including Pres. Tombalbaye.
In June 1973, Tombalbaye declared that some of the stamps produced by these agents were not recognized by the Chad government but might be put on sale at a later date, and that other stamps produced and shipped to Chad were refused by the government.
In July 1973, the Chad government announced that the stamps that were not recognized would be put on sale by the end of the year. We have no evidence that this actually happened.

Apollo
Program
A50a

Designs: 15fr, Apollo 11 in Lunar orbit. 25fr, Apollo 12 astronaut deploying lunar research equipment. 40fr, Astronaunt, lunar module on moon. 50fr, Astronauts Conrad and Bean in life raft after splashdown, horiz.

1970, June 12   Litho.   Perf. 12x12½
225A A50a Strip of 3, #b-d   6.00

Souvenir Sheet
Perf. 13½x13
225E A50a 50fr multicolored   10.00

No. 225E contains one 66x44mm stamp. 15fr, 25fr are airmail.

Expo '70,
Japan —
A50b

Japanese prints of women: 50c, by Kiyonaga. 1fr, by Utamaro. 2fr, from Heian period.

1970, June 12   Litho.   Perf. 12x12½
225F A50b Strip of 3, #a-c   13.50

For overprint see No. 239C.

Adult Education Class and UN
Emblem — A52

1970, June 16   Litho.   Perf. 14
226 A52 100fr blue & multi   1.75   .50

International Education Year.

Bull's Head, Symbols of Weather and Agriculture — A53

1970, July 22   Engr.   Perf. 13
227 A53 50fr org, gray & grn   1.00 .20
Issued for World Meteorological Day.

1970 World Cup Soccer Championships, Mexico City — A53a

Designs: 1fr, Three players, Italian flag. 4fr, Franz Beckenbauer, German flag. Nos. 227C, 227E, English players receiving World Cup trophy, 1966. No. 227D, Three players, Brazilian flag. No. 227F, Four players, "1970."

1970-71   Litho.   Perf. 12
227A A53a 1fr multicolored
227B A53a 4fr multicolored
227C A53a 5fr multicolored
227D A53a 5fr multicolored
   Nos. 227A-227D(3)   3.75
Embossed
Die Cut Perf 13
227E A53a 5fr gold   17.50
Souvenir Sheet
Litho.
Perf. 13½x13
227F A53a 15fr multicolored   6.25
No. 227F contains one 66x44mm stamp. Nos. 227D, 227F are airmail.
Issued: #227A-227D, 227F, 7/2; #227E, 11/1/71.
For overprints see Nos. 267A-267E.

Christmas
A53b

Virgin and Child by: 3fr, Solario. 25fr, Durer. 32fr, Fouquet.

1970, Aug. 19   Litho.   Perf. 12x12½
227G A53b 3fr multicolored
227H A53b 25fr multicolored
227I A53b 32fr multicolored
   Nos. 227G-227I (3)   13.50
   No. 227I is airmail.

Ahmed Mangue, Minister of Education — A54

1970, Sept. 15   Litho. & Engr.
228 A54 100fr gold, car & blk   1.50 .40

1972 Summer Olympics, Munich — A54a

Designs: No. 228A, 3fr, Horses pulling chariot. 8fr, Men running. 10fr, No. 228C, Woman hurdling. No. 228B, 20fr, Equestrian. 35fr, Woman diving. No. 228D, Woman diver in tuck position.

1970   Litho.   Perf. 12½x12
228A A54a Strip of 3, #a-c   4.00
   Perf. 12x12½
228B A54a Pair, #a-b + label   4.00
   Embossed
   Die Cut Perf 13
228C A54a 10fr gold   17.50
   Souvenir Sheet
   Litho.
   Perf. 13½x13
228D A54a 40fr multicolored   10.00
10fr, 35fr, Nos. 228C-228D are airmail. No. 228D contains one 66x43mm stamp. Issued: #228A-228B, 228D, Sept; #228C, 10/14.
For overprints see Nos. 239D-239F.

Tanner
A55

Designs: 2fr, Cloth dyer, vert. 3fr, Camel turning oil press. 4fr, Water carrier. 5fr, Copper worker.

1970, Oct. 10   Engr.   Perf. 13
229   A55 1fr ol brn, bl & brn   .20 .20
229A A55 2fr dk brn, ol & ind   .20 .20
229B A55 3fr pur, ol brn & rose car   .30 .20
229C A55 4fr choc, lem & bl grn   .40 .20
229D A55 5fr red, choc & sl grn   .50 .20
   Nos. 229-229D (5)   1.60 1.00

UN Emblem, Grain and Dove — A56

1970, Oct. 24   Photo.   Perf. 12x12½
230 A56 32fr dk bl & multi   .75 .25
25th anniversary of United Nations.

OCAM Headquarters, Map of Africa, Stars — A57

1971, Jan. 23   Photo.   Perf. 12½x12
231 A57 30fr dk grn & multi   .75 .20
OCAM (Organisation Commune Africaine, Malgache et Mauricienne) Summit Conference, N'djamena, Jan. 22-30.

Space Exploration — A57a

Illustration reduced.

1971, Feb. 16   Litho.   Perf. 13x13½
231A A57a 8fr shown   .60
231B A57a 10fr Apollo 11   .90
231C A57a 35fr Soviet space station   6.25
   Nos. 231A-231C (3)   7.75
   Embossed
   Die Cut Perf 13
231D A57a 8fr gold, like #231A   8.25
   f. Sheet of 1, Imperf.
   Souvenir Sheet
   Perf. 13½x13
231E A57a 40fr John F. Kennedy, Apollo spacecraft, vert.   10.00
Nos. 231C, 231E are airmail. No. 231Df contains one 73x45mm stamp with same size design as No. 231D. No. 231E contains one 33x50mm stamp.
Nos. 231D, 231Df probably were not available in Chad.

1972 Winter Olympics, Sapporo A57b

Paintings by Kiyonaga: 50c, Cherry Trees in Bloom, Tokyo. 1fr, Snowy Morning. 2fr, Sake Party.

1971   Litho.   Perf. 12x12½
231G A57b 50c multicolored   .80
231H A57b 1fr multicolored   1.40
231I A57b 2fr multicolored   2.25
   Nos. 231G-231I (3)   4.45
   Embossed
   Die Cut Perf 13
231J A57b 2fr gold, like #231I   17.50
   k. Sheet of 1, Imperf.   35.00
Issued: #231G-231I, 2/16; #231J-231Jk, 11/1. #231Jk contains one 43x54mm stamp with same size design as #231I.
For overprints see Nos. 246A-246C.
Nos. 231J-231Jk probably were not available in Chad.

Portraits of French Royalty — A57c

Designs: No. 232A, 25fr, The Dauphin (Louis XVII), by J.M. Vien the Younger. 32fr, Marie Antoinette, by E. Vigee-Lebrun. 60fr, Louis XVI, by J.S. Duplessis.
No. 232B, 25fr, Comtesse du Barry, by E. Vigee-Lebrun. 40fr, Louis XV, by M.Q. Delatour.
No. 232C, 40fr, Marie Antoinette, by Charpentier. 50fr, Louis XVI (Dauphin), by Michel Van Loo.
No. 232D, 35fr, Madame de Pompadour (detail), by Delatour. 70fr, Louis XV by Delatour.
No. 232E, 30fr, Madame de Pompadour (entire), by Delatour. 60fr, Marie Leszczynska, by Jean Marc Nattier. 80fr, Louis XV, by Van Loo.
No. 232F, 40fr, Duc D'Orleans as Regent, by 19th cent. French school. 200fr, Louis XIV, by H. Rigaud.
No. 232G, 100fr, Madame de Montespan, by Henry Gascard. 100fr, Madame de Maintenon, by Pierre Mignard.
No. 232H, 50fr, Colbert, by Claude Lefebvre. 200fr, Louis XIV, by J. Garnier.
No. 232J, 50fr, Marie Therese, by Mignard. 200fr, Louis XIV, by Marot.
No. 232K, 50fr, Marie de la Valliere, by English school. 200fr, Louis XIV, by French school.
No. 232L, 100fr, Giulio Cardinal Mazarin, by Mignard. 100fr, Anne of Austria, by Rubens.
No. 232M, 50fr, Vicomte de Turenne, by Champaigne. 200fr, Louis XIV as a Boy, by Mignard.
No. 232N, 100fr, Marquis de Cinq-Mars, by M. le Nain. 150fr, Cardinal Richelieu, by Champaigne.
No. 232P, 150fr, Anne of Austria, by Rubens. 250fr, Louis XIII (detail), by Simon Vouet.
No. 232Q, 150fr, Marriage of Marie de Medicis (looking right), by Rubens. 150fr, Mirror image.
No. 232R, 150fr, Duke of Sully, by Quesnel. 150fr, Mirror image.
No. 232S, 150fr, Henry IV, by Rubens. 150fr, Marie de Medicis, by Rubens.
No. 232T, 200fr, Gabrielle d'Estrees, by unknown artist. 250fr, Henry IV, by French school, c. 1595.
No. 232U, 150fr, Jeanne d'Albret, by Francois Clouet. 200fr, Marie de Medicis as a Girl, by Angelo Bronzino.
No. 232V, 200fr, Henry III, by Clouet. 250fr, Ambroise Pare, by 16th century French school.
No. 232W, 150fr, Catherine de Medicis, by Clouet. 250fr, Henry II, by Clouet.
No. 233A, 200fr, Elizabeth of Austria, by Clouet. 250fr, Charles IX, by Clouet.
No. 233B, 200fr, Mary Stuart, by 16th cent. Scottish school. 300fr, Diane de Poitiers, by Fontainbleu school.
No. 233C, 200fr, Elizabeth of Valois, by Alonso S. Coello. 250fr, Francis, Duke of Alencon, by Clouet.
No. 233D, 150fr, Marguerite d'Angouleme, by Clouet. 300fr, Francis I, by Clouet.
No. 233E, 200fr, Francis I, by Titian. 300fr, Francis I as Dauphin, by Corneille of Lyon.
No. 233F, 100fr, Anne of Austria, by Coello. 250fr, Louis XIII, by Champaigne.
No. 233G, 200fr, Marie de Medicis, by Rubens. 200fr, Marie de Medicis, Louis XIII, by Rubens.
No. 233H, 150fr, The Exchange of Princess Elizabeth of France and Princess Anne of Austria on the Andaye River, by Rubens. 250fr, Louis XIII of France and Navarre, by Vouet.
No. 233J, 250fr, Marie de Medicis, by Rubens. 250fr, Henry IV, by Rubens.
No. 233K, Louis XV and the Dauphin at Battle of Fontenoy. No. 233L, The Grand Dauphin and his Family, by Mignard. No. 233M, Madame de Montespan, horiz. No. 233N, Madame de la Valliere and her Children. No. 233P, The Birth of Louis XIII at Fontainebleau, by Rubens. No. 233Q, Reconciliation of the Queen and Louis XIII, by Rubens. No. 233R, Henry IV Entrusting Regency to Marie de Medici, by Rubens. No. 233S, The Majority of Louis XIII, by Rubens. No. 233T, The Apotheosis of Henry IV and the Proclamation of Regency, by Rubens. No. 233U, Felicity of the Regency, by Rubens.

1971-73   Litho.   Perf. 12½x13
232A A57c Strip of 3, #aa-ac   2.50
232B A57c Pair, #aa-ab   1.50
232C A57c Pair, #aa-ab   1.50
232D A57c Pair, #aa-ab   1.90

232E	A57c	Strip of 3, #aa-ac	3.75
232F	A57c	Pair, #aa-ab	3.75
232G	A57c	Pair, #aa-ab	2.50
232H	A57c	Pair, #aa-ab	3.75
232J	A57c	Pair, #aa-ab	3.75
232K	A57c	Pair, #aa-ab	3.75
232L	A57c	Pair, #aa-ab	2.50
232M	A57c	Pair, #aa-ab	3.75
232N	A57c	Pair, #aa-ab	3.75
232P	A57c	Pair, #aa-ab	6.00
232Q	A57c	Pair, #aa-ab	4.00
232R	A57c	Pair, #aa-ab	4.50
232S	A57c	Pair, #aa-ab	4.50
232T	A57c	Pair, #aa-ab	7.50
232U	A57c	Pair, #aa-ab	5.50
232V	A57c	Pair, #aa-ab	7.50
232W	A57c	Pair, #aa-ab	7.50
233A	A57c	Pair, #aa-ab	7.50
233B	A57c	Pair, #aa-ab	8.00
233C	A57c	Pair, #aa-ab	6.50
233D	A57c	Pair, #aa-ab	7.50
233E	A57c	Pair, #aa-ab	8.00
233F	A57c	Pair, #aa-ab	6.00
233G	A57c	Pair, #aa-ab	6.00
233H	A57c	Pair, #aa-ab	6.00
233J	A57c	Pair, #aa-ab	7.50
		Nos. 232A-233J (30)	148.65

Souvenir Sheets
Perf. 13x13½, 13½x13, 13½

233K	A57c	75fr multi	6.25
233L	A57c	100fr multi	5.50
233M	A57c	200fr multi	5.00
233N	A57c	300fr multi	5.00
233P	A57c	350fr multi	12.00
233Q	A57c	400fr multi	16.00
233R	A57c	400fr multi	10.00
233S	A57c	400fr multi	10.00
233T	A57c	400fr multi	6.00
233U	A57c	500fr multi	13.50
		Nos. 233K-233U (10)	89.25

Nos. 232A 60fr, 232B 40fr, 232C 50fr, 232D 70fr, 232E 80fr, 232F 200fr, 232G, 232H 200fr, 232J 200fr, 232K, 232L, 232M 200fr, 232N-233U are airmail.

Issued: 1971 — #232A, 2/24; #232B, 3/30; #232C, 3/4; #232D, 233K, 3/15; #232E, 4/12; #232F, 233L, 4/26; #232G, 8/10; #232H, 9/6; #232J, 9/23; #232K, 10/6; #232L, 10/26; #232M, 11/16; #232N, 11/20.
1972 — #232P, 233P, Jan.; #232Q, 233M-233N, Feb.; #233Q-233R, May; #232R, 233S, 6/15; #232S, 233T, 6/26; #232T, 8/8; #232U, 8/17; #232V, 8/30; #232W, 233U, 12/11; #233A, 12/18; #233B, 12/28.
1973 — #233C-233J.

Nos. 233K-233L, 233T-233U each contain one 37x62mm stamp. Nos. 233N, 233P each contain one 32x50mm stamp. No. 233M contains one 45x65mm stamp. Nos. 233Q-233R, 233U each contain one 65x45mm stamp.

Nos. 232Q-232V, 233G, 233J, 233R-233U and possibly 232P, 232W-233F, 233H probably were not available in Chad.

Symbolic Tree — A58

1971, Mar. 21   Engr.   Perf. 13
236 A58 40fr bl grn, dk red & grn   1.00 .20
Intl. year against racial discrimination.

Paintings of Flowers A58a

Designs: 1fr, The Three Graces (detail), by Rubens. 4fr, Imperial Bouquet, by Van Os. 5fr, Bouquet, by Jan Brueghel.

1971, Apr. 28   Litho.   Perf. 12x12½
236A A58a Strip of 3, #a-c   5.50
For overprint see No. 278A.

Summer Olympic Games — A58b

15fr, Swimming. 20fr, Women's relay races. 25fr, Swimming, medals. 50fr, Running.

Perf. 12x12½, 12½x12
1971, Apr. 28   Litho.
236B	A58b	15fr multi, vert.	1.75
236C	A58b	20fr multi, vert.	2.75
236D	A58b	25fr multi	3.50
		Nos. 236B-236D (3)	8.00

Embossed
Perf. 13
236E A58b 25fr gold, like No. 236D   17.50

Souvenir Sheet
Litho.
Die Cut Perf 13
236F A58b 50fr multicolored   10.00

Nos. 236D-236F are airmail. No. 236F contains one 62x36mm stamp.
Issued: #236B-236D, 236F, 4/28; #236E, 11/1.
For overprints see Nos. 251A-251D.
No. 236E probably was not available in Chad.

Map of Africa, Radar Antenna A59

Map of Africa and: 40fr, Communications tower. 50fr, Communications satellite.

1971, May 17   Engr.   Perf. 13
237	A59	5fr ultra, org & dk red	.20 .20
238	A59	40fr pur, emer & brn	.75 .20
239	A59	50fr dk red, blk & brn	1.00 .20
		Nos. 237-239 (3)	1.95 .60
3rd World Telecommunications Day.

Apollo 11 — A59a

1971, July 5   Embossed   Perf. 13
239A A59a 10fr gold   22.50
  b. Sheet of 1, imperf.   37.50
No. 239Ab contains one 73x45mm stamp with same size design as No. 239A.
Nos. 239A-239Ab probably were not available in Chad.

No. 225F Overprinted in Gold

1971, July 17   Litho.   Perf. 12x12½
239C A50b Strip of 3, #a-c   6.00
1972 Winter Olympics, Sapporo.

Nos. 228A-228B, 228D Ovptd. with "MUNICH 72" and Olympic Rings in Gold
Perf. 12½x12, 12x12½
1971, Nov. 1   Litho.
239D A54a Strip of 3, #a-c   10.00
239E A54a Pair, #a-b + label   6.00
Souvenir Sheet
Perf. 13½x13
239F A54a 40fr on #228D   20.00

UNICEF Emblem and Children — A60

1971, Dec. 11   Engr.   Perf. 13
240 A60 50fr Prus bl, emer & brt pink   1.10 .20
25th anniv. of UNICEF.

Gorane Nangara Dancers A61

Dancers: 15fr, Girls' initiation dance, Yondo. 30fr, Women of M'Boum, vert. 40fr, Men of Sara Kaba, vert.

1971, Dec. 18   Litho.   Perf. 13
241	A61	10fr blk & multi	.75 .20
242	A61	15fr brn org & multi	1.10 .20
243	A61	30fr bl & multi	1.50 .20
244	A61	40fr yel grn & multi	1.90 .20
		Nos. 241-244 (4)	5.25 .80

Nos. 205-210 Ovptd. in Gold

1971   Litho.   Perf. 12½x13, 13x12½
244A-244F A45 1fr on #205-210   4.50
Nos. 244A-244F probably were not available in Chad.

Presidents Pompidou and Tombalbaye, Map with Paris and Fort Lamy — A62

1972, Jan. 25   Photo.   Perf. 13
245 A62 40fr blue & multi   1.75 .20
Visit of Pres. Georges Pompidou of France, Jan. 1972.

Nos. 181-204 Ovptd. with "MUNICH 72" and Olympic Rings in Gold
1972, Feb. 7   Litho.   Perf. 12½x13
245A-245X A44 1fr on #181-204   16.00
Nos. 245A-245X probably were not available in Chad.

Nos. 231G-231I Ovptd. in Gold

a

b

1972, Feb.   Litho.   Perf. 12x12½
246A A57a 50c Pair, #d.-e.   1.50
246B A57b 1fr Pair, #f.-g.   2.25
246C A57b 2fr Pair, #h.-i.   2.75
Nos. 246A-246C probably were not available in Chad.

President Tombalbaye — A63

1972, Apr. 13   Litho.   Perf. 13
247 A63 30fr multi   .40 .20
247A A63 40fr multi   .60 .20
Nos. 247-247A,C112-C113 (4)   3.00 .80

Downhill Skiing — A64

75fr, Women's figure skating. 150fr, Luge.

1972, Apr. 13   Perf. 13½
248	A64	25fr multi	.30 .20
249	A64	75fr multi	.75 .25
250	A64	150fr multi	1.50 .45
		Nos. 248-250,C114-C115 (5)	6.45 1.95
11th Winter Olympic Games, Sapporo, Japan.

Heart — A65

Gorrizia Dubiosa — A66

1972, Apr. 25 Engr. Perf. 13
251 A65 100fr purple, bl & car 1.75 .20

"Your heart is your health," World Health Month.

Nos. 236B-236D, 236F Ovptd. with "MUNICH 72" and Olympic Rings in Gold

1972 Litho. Perf. 12x12½, 12½x12
251A A58b 15fr multicolored 3.25
251B A58b 20fr multicolored 5.00
251C A58b 25fr multicolored 7.75
Nos. 251A-251C (3) 16.00

Souvenir Sheet
Die Cut Perf 13
251D A58b 50fr multicolored 47.50
Nos. 251C-251D are airmail.

1972, May 6 Photo.
Insects and Spiders: 2fr, Spider (argiope sector). 3fr, Silk spider (nephila senegalense). 4fr, Beetle (oryctes boas). 5fr, Dragonfly (hemistigma albipunctata).
252 A66 1fr green & multi 1.40 .20
253 A66 2fr blue & multi 2.25 .20
254 A66 3fr car rose & multi 2.50 .20
255 A66 4fr yellow grn & multi 4.50 .25
256 A66 5fr dp green & multi 5.00 .30
Nos. 252-256 (5) 15.65 1.15

Trains — A66a

1972 Litho. Perf. 12
256A A66a 10fr Orient Express 1.00
256B A66a 40fr Osaka Express 2.25
256C A66a 50fr St. Germain 2.50
256D A66a 150fr Blue train 5.00
256E A66a 200fr Trans-Europe Express 9.25
Nos. 256A-256E (5) 20.00

Souvenir Sheet
256F A66a 300fr Rogers "Madison," 1855 14.00

No. 256F contains one 60x40mm stamp. See note before No. 225A.

Scout Greeting — A67

70fr, Mountain climbing. 80fr, Canoeing.
1972, May 15 Photo.
257 A67 30fr multi .75 .20
258 A67 70fr multi 1.40 .20
259 A67 80fr multi 1.75 .20
Nos. 257-259,C118-C119 (5) 8.40 1.30
Scout Jamboree.

Hurdles, Motion and Olympic Emblems A68

Motion and Olympic Emblems and: 130fr, Gymnast on rings. 150fr, Swimming. 300fr, Bicycling.
1972, June 9 Litho. Perf. 13½
260 A68 50fr blk & multi .75 .20
261 A68 130fr blk & multi 1.90 .25
262 A68 150fr blk & multi 2.25 .30
Nos. 260-262 (3) 4.90 .75

Souvenir Sheet
263 A68 300fr blk & multi 5.00 2.00
20th Olympic Games, Munich, Aug. 26-Sept. 10.

Ski Jump, Kasaya, Japan — A69

Designs: 75fr, Cross-country skiing, P. Tyldum, Sweden. 100fr, Figure-skating, pairs, L. Rodnina and A. Ulanov, USSR. 130fr, Men's speed skating, A. Schenk, Netherlands.
1972, June 15 Perf. 14½
264 A69 25fr gold & multi .40 .20
265 A69 75fr gold & multi 1.00 .25
266 A69 100fr gold & multi 1.50 .20
267 A69 130fr gold & multi 1.90 .40
Nos. 264-267,C130-C131 (6) 11.55 2.20
11th Winter Olympic Games, gold-medal winners. Nos. 264-267 exist se-tenant with label showing earth satellite.

Nos. 227A-227D, 227F Overprinted With Soccer Ball, "MUNICH 72" and Olympic Rings in Gold
1972 Perf. 12
267A A53a 1fr multicolored .95
267B A53a 4fr multicolored 1.20
267C A53a 5fr multicolored 1.90
267D A53a 5fr multicolored 1.90
Nos. 267A-267D (4) 5.95

Souvenir Sheet
Perf. 13½x13
267E A53a 15fr multicolored 9.00
Nos. 267D-267E are airmail.
Nos. 267A-267E probably were not available in Chad.

TV Tower and Weight-lifting — A70

Designs (TV Tower, Munich and): 40fr, Woman sprinter. 60fr, Soccer goalkeeper.
1972, Aug. 15 Litho. Perf. 14½
268 A70 20fr gold & multi .65 .20
269 A70 40fr gold & multi .80 .20
270 A70 60fr gold & multi 1.40 .20
Nos. 268-270,C135-C137 (6) 10.70 1.75
20th Summer Olympic Games, Munich. Nos. 268-270 exist se-tenant with label showing arms of Munich.

Domestic Animals A71

1972, Aug. 29 Engr. Perf. 13
271 A71 25fr Dromedary 1.75 .20
272 A71 30fr Horse 2.25 .20
273 A71 40fr Dog 3.25 .20
274 A71 45fr Goat 3.75 .20
Nos. 271-274 (4) 11.00 .80
For surcharge see No. 293.

Tobacco Cultivation A72

1972, Oct. 24 Engr. Perf. 13
275 A72 40fr shown .75 .20
276 A72 50fr Plowing 1.25 .20

Massa Warrior — A73

Design: 20fr, Moundang warrior.
1972, Nov. 15 Photo. Perf. 14x13
277 A73 15fr orange & multi .75 .20
278 A73 20fr yellow & multi 1.00 .20

No. 236A Overprinted "Noel 1972" in gold
1972 Litho. Perf. 12x12½
278A A58a Strip of 3, #a-c 5.50
No. 278A probably was not available in Chad.

King Faisal and Pres. Tombalbaye — A74

1972, Nov. 17 Litho. Perf. 13
279 A74 100fr gold & multi 2.50 .40
Visit of King Faisal of Saudi Arabia. See No. C143.

Gen. Gowon and Pres. Tombalbaye — A75

1972, Dec. 7
280 A75 70fr multi 1.00 .20
Visit of Gen. Yakubu Gowon of Nigeria.

Olympic Emblem and 100-meter Sprint, Valeri Borzov, USSR — A76

Designs (Olympic Emblem and): 20fr, Shotput, Komar, Poland. 40fr, Hammer throw, Bondartchuk, USSR. 60fr, Discus, Danek, Czechoslovakia.
1972, Dec. 22 Perf. 11
281 A76 10fr multi .55 .20
282 A76 20fr multi .55 .20
283 A76 40fr multi .70 .20
284 A76 60fr multi 1.15 .20
Nos. 281-284,C148-C149 (6) 10.15 2.10
20th Summer Olympic Games, winners.

Olympic Emblem and Fencing, Woyda, Poland — A77

Olympic Emblem and: 30fr, 3-day equestrian event, Richard Meade, Gt. Britain. 50fr, Two-man sculls, Brietzke-Mager, East Germany.
1972, Dec. 22
285 A77 20fr gold & multi .65 .20
286 A77 30fr gold & multi .65 .20
287 A77 50fr gold & multi 1.00 .20
Nos. 285-287,C151-C152 (5) 10.55 1.85
20th Summer Olympic Games, winners.

1972 Summer Olympics Gold Medalists — A77a

20fr, Teofilo Stevenson, boxing, Cuba. 25fr, Yugoslavia, team handball. 30fr, M. Peters, pentathlon, Great Britain. 40fr, basketball, USSR. No. 287E, W. Ruska, judo, Netherlands. No. 287F, Women's gymnastics, Ludmila Touristcheva, USSR. 75fr, Men's volleyball, Japan. No. 287H, A. Scalzone, shooting, Italy. No. 287I, Soccer, Poland. 130fr, J. Williams, archery, US. No. 287K, A. Nakayama, men's rings, Japan. No. 287L, Field hockey, West Germany. 200fr, Vassily Alexeiev, weight lifting, USSR. 250fr, D. Morelon, cycling, France.
1972, Dec. 22 Litho. Perf. 11½
287A A77a 20fr multicolored
287B A77a 25fr multicolored
287C A77a 30fr multicolored
287D A77a 40fr multicolored
287E A77a 50fr multicolored
287F A77a 50fr multicolored
287G A77a 75fr multicolored
287H A77a 100fr multicolored
287I A77a 100fr multicolored
287J A77a 130fr multicolored
287K A77a 150fr multicolored
287L A77a 150fr multicolored
Nos. 287A-287L (12) 19.00

Souvenir Sheets
Perf. 15
287M A77a 200fr multicolored   13.50
287N A77a 250fr multicolored   13.50

Nos. 287G-287N are airmail.

Soviet Flag and Shield — A78

1972, Dec. 30   Litho.   *Perf. 12*
288 A78 150fr red & multi   1.90 .40

50th anniversary of the Soviet Union.

High Jump — A79

Designs (Games Emblem and): 125fr, Running. 200fr, Shot put. 250fr, Discus.

1973, Jan. 17   Litho.   *Perf. 13½x13*
289 A79 50fr vio bl & multi   .75 .20
290 A79 125fr olive & multi   1.60 .40
291 A79 200fr lilac & multi   3.00 .65
   Nos. 289-291 (3)   5.35 1.25

Souvenir Sheet
292 A79 250fr brn & multi   3.75 2.25

2nd African Games, Lagos, Nigeria, 1/7-18.

Paintings with Musical Instruments — A79a

Details from Paintings: 30fr, Madeleine Playing her Lute, by unknown artist. 70fr, A Concert, by Lorenzo Costa. 100fr, Bass and Sheet Music, by Jean-Baptiste Oudry, horiz. 125fr, St. Cecilia and Angel, by Carlo Saraceni. 150fr, Woman Listening to Violinist, by Gabriel Metsu. 300fr, Still Life with Musical Instruments, by Pieter Claesz, horiz.

1973, Apr.   Litho.   *Perf. 11½*
292A A79a 30fr multicolored
292B A79a 70fr multicolored
292C A79a 100fr multicolored
292D A79a 125fr multicolored
292E A79a 150fr multicolored
   Nos. 292A-292E (5)   13.50

Souvenir Sheet
Perf. 15
292F A79a 300fr multicolored   13.50

Nos. 292D-292F are airmail.

No. 271 Surcharged with New Value, 2 Bars, and Overprinted in Red: "SECHERESSE SOLIDARITE AFRICAINE"

1973, Aug. 16   Engr.   *Perf. 13*
293 A71 100fr on 25fr multi   2.25 .40

African solidarity in drought emergency.

African Postal Union Issue
Common Design Type
1973, Sept. 17   Engr.   *Perf. 13*
294 CD137 100fr multicolored   1.75 .40

Easter A79b

Details from paintings: 40fr, Christ on the Cross, by Lucas Cranach. 60fr, Supper in Emmaus, by Titian, horiz. 120fr, The Crucifixion, by Durer. 150fr, The Tribute, by Titian. 250fr, The Pieta, by Botticelli. 400fr, Entombment of Christ, by Gaspard Isenmann, horiz.

1973   Litho.   *Perf. 11½*
294A A79b 40fr multicolored
294B A79b 60fr multicolored
294C A79b 120fr multicolored
294D A79b 150fr multicolored
294E A79b 250fr multicolored
   Nos. 294A-294E (5)   13.50

Souvenir Sheet
Perf. 15
294F A79b 400fr multicolored   13.50

Nos. 294A, 294D-294F are airmail.

Animals A79c

1973   Litho.   *Perf. 13½*
294G A79c 20fr Sheep
294H A79c 30fr Camels
294J A79c 100fr Cats
294K A79c 130fr Dogs
294L A79c 150fr Horses
   Nos. 294G-294L (5)   13.50

Nos. 294J-294L are airmail.
See note before No. 225A.

Christmas — A79d

30fr, The Virgin & Infant Surrounded by Saints, by Lorenzo Lotto. 40fr, Madonna and Child with St. Peter and a Martyred Saint, by Paolo Veronese (not Tintoretto), vert. 55fr, Nativity Scene, by Martin Schongauer, vert. 60fr, Nativity Scene, by Federico Barocci, vert. 250fr, Adoration of the Magi, by Stephan Lochner, vert. 400fr, Epiphany, by Hans Memling.

1973   Litho.   *Perf. 11½*
294M A79d 30fr multicolored
294N A79d 40fr multicolored
294P A79d 55fr multicolored
294Q A79d 60fr multicolored
294R A79d 250fr multicolored
   Nos. 294M-294R (5)   13.50

Souvenir Sheet
Perf. 15
294S A79d 400fr multicolored   13.50

Nos. 294Q-294S are airmail.
See note before No. 225A.

Dinothrombium Tinctorium A80   Rotary Emblem A81

1974, Sept. 3   Photo.   *Perf. 13*
295 A80 25fr *shown*   1.50 .20
296 A80 30fr *Bupreste sternocera*   2.25 .20
297 A80 40fr *Diptere hyperechia*   2.75 .20
298 A80 50fr *Chrysis*   3.25 .25
299 A80 100fr *Longicorn beetle*   4.75 .40
300 A80 130fr *Spider*   7.50 .55
   Nos. 295-300 (6)   22.00 1.80

1975, Apr. 11   Typo.   *Perf. 13*
301 A81 50fr multi   1.00 .20

Rotary International, 70th anniversary.

Craterostigma Plantagineum — A82

Flowers: 10fr, Tapinanthus globiferus. 15fr, Commelina forskalaei. 20fr, Adenium obesum. 25fr, Yellow hibiscus. 30fr, Red hibiscus. 40fr, Kigelia africana.

1975, Sept. 25   Photo.   *Perf. 13*
302 A82 5fr org & multi   .40 .20
303 A82 10fr gray bl & multi   .60 .20
304 A82 15fr yel grn & multi   .75 .20
305 A82 20fr lt brn & multi   1.00 .20
306 A82 25fr lil & multi   1.75 .20
307 A82 30fr bis & multi   1.90 .20
308 A82 40fr ultra & multi   3.00 .20
   Nos. 302-308 (7)   9.40 1.40

A. G. Bell, Satellite and Waves — A83

1976, June 10   Litho.   *Perf. 12½*
309 A83 100fr brn & ocher   1.40 .20
310 A83 125fr lt grn, brn & ocher   1.90 .25

Centenary of first telephone call by Alexander Graham Bell, Mar. 10, 1876.

Ice Hockey, USSR — A84

90fr, Ski jump, Karl Schnabl, Austria.

1976, June 21   *Perf. 14*
311 A84 60fr multi   .75 .20
312 A84 90fr multi   1.25 .20
   Nos. 311-312,C178-C179 (4)   8.25 1.65

12th Winter Olympic Games, winners. See No. C180.

High Hurdles A85

1976, July 12   Litho.   *Perf. 13½*
313 A85 45fr multi   .70 .20
   Nos. 313,C187-C189 (4)   8.70 1.65

21st Summer Olympic Games, Montreal, Canada.
See No. C190.

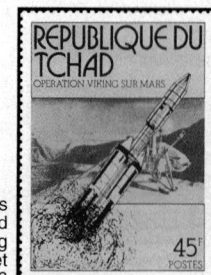

Mars Landing and Viking Rocket A86

Mars Landing and: 90fr, Viking trajectory, Earth to Mars.

1976, July 23   *Perf. 14*
314 A86 45fr multi   .50 .20
315 A86 90fr multi   1.00 .25
   Nos. 314-315,C191-C193 (5)   7.35 1.90

Viking Mars project.
For overprints see Nos. 379-380.

Robert Koch, Medicine — A87

Design: 90fr, Anatole France, literature.

1976, Dec. 15
316 A87 45fr multi   .75 .20
317 A87 90fr multi   1.50 .25
   Nos. 316-317,C196-C198 (5)   9.75 2.00

Nobel Prize winners.

Map and Flag of Chad, Clasped Hands A88

120fr, Map of Chad, people & occupations.

1976, Sept. 15   Litho.   Perf. 12½x13
318 A88   30fr multi   .60   .20
319 A88   60fr orange & multi   1.10   .20
320 A88   120fr brown & multi   2.25   .25
     Nos. 318-320 (3)   3.95   .65
        National reconciliation.

Freed Political Prisoners — A89

Designs: 60fr, Parade of cadets.

1976, Sept. 25   Litho.   Perf. 12½
321 A89   30fr blue & multi   .30   .20
322 A89   60fr black & multi   .75   .20
323 A89   120fr red & multi   1.40   .25
     Nos. 321-323 (3)   2.45   .65
     Revolution of Apr. 13, 1975, 1st anniv.

Decorated Calabashes — A90

Designs: Various pyrographed calabashes.

1976, Nov.   Litho.   Perf. 12½x13
324 A90   30fr multi   .40   .20
325 A90   60fr multi   .90   .20
326 A90   120fr multi   1.75   .25
     Nos. 324-326 (3)   3.05   .65

Germany No. C57 and
Friedrichshafen, Germany — A91

1977, Mar. 30   Perf. 14
327 A91   100fr multi   1.40   .25
     Nos. 327,C206-C209 (5)   11.55 1.90
        75th anniversary of the Zeppelin.

Elizabeth II in Coronation Regalia and
Clergy — A92

Design: 450fr, Elizabeth II and Prince Philip.

1977, June 15   Litho.   Perf. 14x13½
328 A92   250fr multi   3.25   .45
        Souvenir Sheet
329 A92   450fr multi   5.75 1.50
     25th anniv. of the reign of Elizabeth II.
     For overprints see Nos. 347-348.

Simon
Bolivar
A93

Famous Personalities: 175fr, Joseph J. Roberts. No. 332, Queen Wilhelmina of Netherlands. No. 333, Charles de Gaulle. 325fr, King
Baudouin and Queen Fabiola of Belgium.

1977, June 15   Perf. 13½x14
330 A93   150fr multi   1.50   .25
331 A93   175fr multi   2.25   .30
332 A93   200fr multi   3.00   .35
333 A93   200fr multi   3.00   .35
334 A93   325fr multi   4.00   .50
     Nos. 330-334 (5)   13.75 1.75

Post and Telecommunications
Emblem — A94

Map of Chad and
Waves — A95

Society
Emblem — A96

1977, Aug. 15   Litho.   Perf. 13
335 A94   30fr yel & blk   .50   .20
                      Perf. 12½
336 A95   60fr multi   .75   .20
                   Perf. 13½x13
337 A96   120fr multi   1.60   .40
     Nos. 335-337 (3)   2.85   .80
     Telecommunications (30fr); Natl. Telecom-
     munications School, 10th anniv. (60fr); Intl.
     Telecommunication Soc. of Chad (120fr).

WHO Emblem
and Man (Back
Pain) — A97

World Rheumatism Year (WHO Emblem
and): 60fr, Woman's head (neck pain), horiz.
120fr, Leg (knee pain).

Perf. 12½x13, 13x12½
1977, Nov. 10   Engr.
338 A97   30fr multi   .50   .20
339 A97   60fr multi   1.00   .20
340 A97   120fr multi   1.40   .40
     Nos. 338-340 (3)   2.90   .80

World Cup Emblems and Saving a
Goal — A98

Designs (Argentina '78, World Cup
Emblems and): 60fr, Heading the ball. 100fr,
Referee whistling a goal. 200fr, World Cup
poster. 300fr, Pelé. 500fr, Helmut Schoen and
Munich stadium.

1977, Nov. 25   Litho.   Perf. 13½
341 A98   40fr multi   .50   .20
342 A98   60fr multi   .75   .20
343 A98   100fr multi   1.10   .25
344 A98   200fr multi   2.50   .50
345 A98   300fr multi   3.75   .75
     Nos. 341-345 (5)   8.60 1.90
        Souvenir Sheet
346 A98   500fr multi   5.75 1.10
     World Cup Soccer Championship, Argentina
     '78.
     For overprints see Nos. 359-364.

Nos. 328-329 Overprinted in Silver:
"ANNIVERSAIRE DU
COURONNEMENT 1953-1978"

1978, Sept. 13   Perf. 14x13½
347 A92   250fr multi   3.00   .60
        Souvenir Sheet
348 A92   450fr multi   5.50 1.40
     25th anniv. of coronation of Elizabeth II.

Abraham and Melchisedek, by
Rubens — A99

Rubens Paintings: 120fr, Helene Fourment,
vert. 200fr, David and the Elders of Israel.
300fr, Anne of Austria, vert. 500fr, Marie de
Medicis, vert.

1978, Nov. 23   Litho.   Perf. 13½
349 A99   60fr multi   .75   .20
350 A99   120fr multi   1.75   .35
351 A99   200fr multi   3.00   .75
352 A99   300fr multi   4.50 1.25
     Nos. 349-352 (4)   10.00 2.55
        Souvenir Sheet
353 A99   500fr multi   6.75 2.50
        Peter Paul Rubens (1577-1640).

Dürer
Portrait
A100

Dürer Paintings: 150fr, Jacob Muffel. 250fr,
Young Woman. 350fr, Oswolt Krel.

1978, Nov. 23
354 A100   60fr multi   .60   .20
355 A100   150fr multi   1.75   .50
356 A100   250fr multi   3.00   .80
357 A100   350fr multi   4.50 1.25
     Nos. 354-357 (4)   9.85 2.75

Head, Village and
Fly — A101

1978, Nov. 28   Perf. 13
358 A101   60f multi   .75   .20
        National Health Day.

Nos. 341-346 Overprinted in Silver:
  a.   1962 BRESIL-TCHECOSLOVA-
QUIE / 3-1
  b.   1966 / GRANDE BRETAGNE / -
ALLEMAGNE (RFA) / 4-2
  c.   1970 BRESIL-ITALIE 4-1
  d.   1974 ALLEMAGNE (RFA)- / PAYS
BAS 2-1
  e.   1978 / ARGENTINE -/ PAYS BAS /
3-1
  f.   ARGENTINE -PAYS BAS / 3-1
1978, Dec. 30   Litho.   Perf. 13½
359 A98(a)   40fr multi   .50   .20
360 A98(b)   60fr multi   .75   .20
361 A98(c)   100fr multi   1.40   .30
362 A98(d)   200fr multi   2.50   .60
363 A98(e)   300fr multi   3.50   .95
     Nos. 359-363 (5)   8.65 2.25
        Souvenir Sheet
364 A98(f)   500fr multi   5.75 1.60
     World Soccer Championship winners.

UPU Emblems, Camel Caravan,
Satellites — A102

Design: 150fr, Obus woman and houses,
Massa Territory, hibiscus.

1979, June 8   Litho.   Perf. 12x12½
365 A102   60fr multi   3.00   .20
366 A102   150fr multi   5.00   .40
     Philexafrique II, Libreville, Gabon, June 8-
     17. Nos. 365, 366 each printed in sheets of 10
     with 5 labels showing exhibition emblem.

Wildlife Fund Emblem and
Gazelle — A103

Protected Animals.

1979, Sept. 15   Litho.   Perf. 14½
367 A103   40fr shown   1.90   .30
368 A103   50fr Addax   2.10   .50
369 A103   60fr Oryx antelope   2.50   .75
370 A103   100fr Cheetah   4.00 1.40
371 A103   150fr Zebra   5.50 1.90
372 A103   300fr Rhinoceros   11.00 3.00
     Nos. 367-372 (6)   27.00 7.85

Souvenir Sheet

Holy Family, by Dürer — A104

1979, Sept. 1   **Perf. 13½**
373 A104 500fr brown & dull red   6.75 1.60

Boy and Handpainted Doors — A105

IYC Emblem and: 75fr, Oriental girl. 100fr, Caucasian girl, doves. 150fr, African boys. 250fr, Pencil and outlines of child's hands.

1979, Sept. 19   Litho.   Perf. 13½
374 A105 65fr multi   .60   .20
375 A105 75fr multi   .75   .20
376 A105 100fr multi   1.00   .20
377 A105 150fr multi   1.50   .30
   Nos. 374-377 (4)   3.85   .90
Souvenir Sheet
378 A105 250fr multi   3.00   .50

Nos. 314-315 Overprinted
"ALUNISSAGE/APOLLO XI/JUILLET
1969" and Emblem
1979, Nov. 26   Perf. 13½x14
379 A86 45fr multi   .60   .20
380 A86 90fr multi   1.00   .30
   Nos. 379-380,C240-C242 (5)   7.45 2.20

Apollo 11 moon landing, 10th anniversary.

Ski Jump, Lake Placid '80
Emblem — A106

Lake Placid '80 Emblem and: 20fr, Slalom, vert. 40fr, Biathlon, vert. 150fr, Women's slalom, vert. 350fr, Cross-country skiing. 500fr, Downhill skiing.

1979, Dec. 18   Perf. 14½
381 A106 20fr multi   .30   .20
382 A106 40fr multi   .65   .20
383 A106 60fr multi   .80   .20
384 A106 150fr multi   1.75   .50
385 A106 350fr multi   3.00 1.40
386 A106 500fr multi   4.50 1.90
   Nos. 381-386 (6)   11.00 4.40

13th Winter Olympic Games, Lake Placid, NY, Feb. 12-24, 1980.

Jet over
Map of
Africa
A107

1980, Feb. 20   Litho.   Perf. 12½
387 A107 15fr yellow & multi   .20   .20
388 A107 30fr blue & multi   .40   .20
389 A107 60fr red & multi   .60   .20
   Nos. 387-389 (3)   1.20   .60

ASECNA (Air Safety Board), 20th anniv.

1982 World Cup Soccer
Championships, Spain — A108

1982   Litho.   Perf. 13½
390 A108 30fr Hungary   .30   .20
391 A108 40fr Italy   .40   .20
392 A108 50fr Algeria   .50   .20
393 A108 60fr Argentina   .60   .20
   Nos. 390-393,C258-C259 (6)   5.80 1.40

21st
Birthday
of
Princess
Diana
A109

1982, July 2   Litho.   Perf. 13½
395 A109 30fr 1961   .30   .20
396 A109 40fr 1965   .40   .20
397 A109 50fr 1967   .50   .20
398 A109 60fr 1975   .60   .20
   Nos. 395-398,C260-C261 (6)   5.80 2.00

For overprints see Nos. 413-419B.

A110

1984 Summer Olympics, Los
Angeles — A110a

#405A, Runner. #405B, Long jumper, vert.

1982, Aug. 2   Litho.   Perf. 13½
399 A110 30fr Gymnast   .30   .20
400 A110 40fr Equestrian   .40   .20
401 A110 50fr Judo   .50   .20
402 A110 60fr High jump   .60   .20
403 A110 80fr Hurdles   1.00   .25
404 A110 300fr Woman gymnast   3.00   .95
   Nos. 399-404 (6)   5.80 2.00
Souvenir Sheet
405 A110 500fr Relay race   5.50 1.50

For surcharge see No. C302.

1982, July 31   Litho. & Embossed
405A A110a 1500fr gold & multi 16.00
Souvenir Sheet
405B A110a 1500fr gold & multi 12.00

   No. 405 contains one 56x39mm stamp.
Nos. 403-405B airmail.
   No. 405A exists in a souvenir sheet of 1.
Value $47.50.

Scouting Year — A111

Boy Scouts,
75th Anniv.
A111a

Scouts from various countries. No. 412A, Lord Robert Baden-Powell. No. 412B, Scouts at campsite, Baden-Powell, horiz.

1982, July 15
406 A111 30fr West Germany   .30   .20
407 A111 40fr Upper Volta   .40   .20
408 A111 50fr Mali   .50   .20
409 A111 60fr Scotland   .60   .20
410 A111 80fr Kuwait   1.00   .25
411 A111 300fr Chad   3.00   .95
   Nos. 406-411 (6)   5.80 2.00
Souvenir Sheet
412 A111 500fr Chad, diff.   5.50 1.50
Litho. & Embossed
412A A111a 1500fr gold & multi 16.00
Souvenir Sheet
412B A111a 1500fr gold & multi 16.00

   No. 412 contains one 53x35mm stamp.
Nos. 410-412B airmail.
   No. 412A exists in a souvenir sheet of 1.
Value $40.
   For overprints see Nos. 466-472B.

Nos. 395-398, C260-C262B
Overprinted: "21 JUIN 1982 / WILLIAM
ARTHUR PHILIP LOUIS/ PRINCE DE
GALLES"
1982, Oct. 4   Litho.   Perf. 13½
413 A109 30fr multi   .30   .20
414 A109 40fr multi   .40   .20
415 A109 50fr multi   .50   .20
416 A109 60fr multi   .60   .20
417 A109 80fr multi   1.00   .25
418 A109 300fr multi   3.00   .95
   Nos. 413-418 (6)   5.80 2.00
Souvenir Sheet
419 A109 500fr multi   5.50 1.60
Litho. & Embossed
419A AP71b 1500fr on #C262A   16.00
Souvenir Sheet
419B AP71b 1500fr on #C262B   13.50

   Birth of Prince William of Wales, June 21.
Nos. 417-419B airmail.
   No. 419A exists in a souvenir sheet of 1.
Value $42.50.

A112

1982 World Cup Soccer
Championships, Spain — A112a

Various players and flags. No. 426A, Dino Zoff, Italy, holding World Cup trophy. No. 426B, Paolo Rossi, Italy, two players, trophy, horiz.

1982, Nov. 30
420 A112 30fr multi   .30   .20
421 A112 40fr multi   .40   .20
422 A112 50fr multi   .50   .20
423 A112 60fr multi   .60   .20
424 A112 80fr multi   1.00   .25
425 A112 300fr multi   3.00   .95
   Nos. 420-425 (6)   5.80 2.00
Souvenir Sheet
426 A112 500fr multi   5.50 1.60
Litho. & Embossed
426A A112a 1500fr gold & multi 16.00
Souvenir Sheet
426B A112a 1500fr gold & multi 16.00

   No. 426 contains one 56x32mm stamp.
Nos. 424-426B airmail.
   No. 426A exists in a souvenir sheet of 1.
Value $42.50.
   For surcharge see No. C306.

A113

Chess Champions — A113a

#433A, Bobby Fischer. #433B, William
Steinitz.

1982, Dec. 24
427 A113 30fr Philidor   1.00   .20
428 A113 40fr Paul Morphy   1.10   .20
429 A113 50fr Howard
              Staunton   1.25   .20
430 A113 60fr Capablanca   1.40   .20
431 A113 80fr Boris Spassky   2.10   .25
432 A113 300fr Anatoly Karpov   3.75   .75
   Nos. 427-432 (6)   10.60 1.80
Souvenir Sheet
433 A113 500fr Victor Korchnoi   9.00 1.60
Litho. & Embossed
433A A113a 1500fr gold &
              multi   17.50
Souvenir Sheet
433B A113a 1500fr gold &
              multi   12.00

   No. 433 contains one 53x35mm stamp.
Nos. 431-433B airmail.
   No. 433A exists in a souvenir sheet of 1.
Value $50.
   For overprints see Nos. 459-465.

2nd UN Conference on Peaceful Uses
of Outer Space, Vienna, Aug. 9-
21 — A114

A114a

Inventors and Satellites: 30fr, K.E. Tsiolkov-
sky, Soyuz. 40fr, R.H. Goddard, space telescope design. 50fr, Korolev, ultraviolet telescope. 60fr, von Braun, Columbia space
shuttle. 80fr, Esnault Pelterie, Ariana rocket.
300fr, H. Oberth, orbital space station. 500fr,
Pres. Kennedy, Apollo 11 badge, lunar rover.
No. 440A, Sir Bernard Lovell, Viking I & II. No.
440B, Sir Isaac Newton, satellite TDF 1.

1983, Feb. 1		**Litho.**	**Perf. 13½**	
434	A114	30fr multi	.30	.20
435	A114	40fr multi	.40	.20
436	A114	50fr multi	.50	.20
437	A114	60fr multi	.60	.20
438	A114	80fr multi	1.00	.25
439	A114	300fr multi	3.00	.95
	Nos. 434-439 (6)		5.80	2.00

Souvenir Sheet

440	A114	500fr multi	5.50	1.60

Litho. & Embossed

440A	A114a	1500fr gold & multi	16.00	

Souvenir Sheet

440B	A114a	1500fr gold & multi	12.00	

No. 440 contains one 42x50mm stamp.
Nos. 438-440B airmail.
No. 440A exists in a souvenir sheet of 1.
Value $50.

Bobsledding — A115

Woman
Figure
Skater
A115a

Design: No. 447B, Slalom skier, horiz.

1983, Apr. 25		**Litho.**	**Perf. 13½**	
441	A115	30fr shown	.30	.20
442	A115	40fr Speed skating	.40	.20
443	A115	50fr Cross-country		
		skiing	.50	.20
444	A115	60fr Hockey	.60	.25
445	A115	80fr Ski jumping	1.00	.30
446	A115	300fr Downhill skiing	3.00	1.10
	Nos. 441-446 (6)		5.80	2.25

Souvenir Sheet

447	A115	500fr Figure skating	5.50	1.60

Litho. & Embossed

447A	A115a	1500fr gold & multi	16.00	

Souvenir Sheet

447B	A115a	1500fr gold & multi	12.00	

14th Winter Olympic Games, Sarajevo,
Yugoslavia, Feb. 8-19, 1984.
Nos. 445-447B airmail.
No. 447A exists in a souvenir sheet of 1.
Value $45.
For surcharge see No. C298.

First
Manned
Balloon
Flight,
200th
Anniv.
A116

Designs: 25fr, Hot air balloon, Montgolfier
Brothers. 45fr, Captive balloon, Pilatre De
Rozier. 50fr, First parachute descent, Jacques
Garnerin. 60fr, Chelsea balloon, J.P.
Blanchard.

1983, May 30		**Litho.**	**Perf. 13½**	
448	A116	25fr multi	.30	.20
449	A116	45fr multi	.40	.20
450	A116	50fr multi	.50	.20
451	A116	60fr multi	.60	.20
	Nos. 448-451,C268-C269 (6)		5.80	1.45

Automobiles — A116a

Automobiles and their builders: 25fr, 1927
Mercedes Type S, Gottlieb Daimler and Karl
Benz. 45fr, 1913 Torpedo Martini Type GC 32-
2, 6L, Friedrich Martini. 50fr, 1926 Chrysler
"70," Walter P. Chrysler. 60fr, 1929 Alfa
Romeo 6C 1750 Grand Sport, Nicola Romeo.
80fr, 1934 Phantom II Continental, Stewart
Rolls and Henry Royce. 250fr, 1948 Talbot
Lago, Lord Shrewsbury and Talbot.

1983, July 15		**Litho.**	**Perf. 13½**	
451A	A116a	25fr multicolored		
451B	A116a	45fr multicolored		
451C	A116a	50fr multicolored		
451D	A116a	60fr multicolored		
451E	A116a	80fr multicolored		
451F	A116a	250fr multicolored		
	Nos. 451A-451F (6)		6.75	1.60

Nos. 451E-451F are airmail.

1984 Summer
Olympics, Los
Angeles
A117

A117a

1983, Nov. 15		**Litho.**	**Perf. 13½**	
452	A117	25fr Kayak	.30	.20
453	A117	45fr Long jump	.60	.20
454	A117	50fr Boxing	.70	.20
455	A117	60fr Discus	.75	.20
456	A117	80fr Running	1.00	.25
457	A117	350fr Equestrian	3.50	.75
	Nos. 452-457 (6)		6.85	1.80

Souvenir Sheet

458	A117	500fr Gymnastics	5.50	.80

Litho. & Embossed

458A	A117a	1500fr Hurdles	16.00	

Souvenir Sheet

458B	A117a	1500fr Equestrian,		
		vert.	12.00	

Nos. 456-458B are airmail.
No. 458A exists in a souvenir sheet of 1.
Value $47.50.

Pres. Hissein
Habre — A117b

Designs: Nos. 458D, 458H, Sources of food.
Nos. 458E, 458I, Dove of peace, different tribal groups, country map.

1983, Dec. 26		**Litho.**	**Perf. 13½**	
458C	A117b	50fr multicolored	.60	.20
458D	A117b	50fr multicolored	.60	.20
458E	A117b	50fr multicolored	.60	.20
458F	A117b	60fr multicolored	.70	.20
458G	A117b	80fr multicolored	.90	.25
458H	A117b	80fr multicolored	.90	.25
458I	A117b	80fr multicolored	.90	.25
458J	A117b	100fr multicolored	1.10	.35

Numbers have been reserved for 4 airmail
values in this set. The editors would like to see
these stamps.

Nos. 427-433 Overprinted: "60e
ANNIVERSAIRE FEDERATION /
MONDIALE D'ECHECS 1924-1984"

1983, Dec. 27		**Litho.**	**Perf. 13½**	
459	A113	30fr multi	.90	.20
460	A113	40fr multi	1.10	.20
461	A113	50fr multi	1.40	.20
462	A113	60fr multi	1.75	.20
463	A113	80fr multi	2.25	.30
464	A113	300fr multi	4.50	.75
	Nos. 459-464 (6)		11.90	1.85

Souvenir Sheet

465	A113	500fr multi	4.50	1.10

World Chess Fedn., 60th anniv.

Nos. 406-412B Ovptd. with Emblem
for the 15th World Scout Jamboree,
Alberta, Canada, 1983

1983, Dec. 27		**Litho.**	**Perf. 13½**	
466	A111	30fr multi	.30	.20
467	A111	40fr multi	.40	.20
468	A111	50fr multi	.50	.20
469	A111	60fr multi	.60	.20
470	A111	80fr multi	.70	.20
471	A111	300fr multi	3.00	.50
	Nos. 466-471 (6)		5.50	1.50

Souvenir Sheet

472	A111	500fr multi	6.00	1.10

Litho. & Embossed

472A	A111a	1500fr on #412A	16.00	

Souvenir Sheet

472B	A111a	1500fr on #412B	12.00	

Locomotive "Lady," 1879 — A118

1984, Mar. 15				
473	A118	50fr shown	.60	.20
474	A118	200fr Sailboat, Lake		
		Chad	2.40	.30
475	A118	300fr Graf Zeppelin	3.25	.45
476	A118	350fr Renault desert		
		transport, 1930	4.00	.55
477	A118	400fr Bloch 120 mon-		
		oplane	4.25	.75
478	A118	500fr Air Africa DC-8	5.50	1.10
	Nos. 473-478 (6)		20.00	3.35

Souvenir Sheet

479	A118	600fr Intelsat V satel-		
		lite	5.75	2.50

Nos. 477-479 airmail. For surcharge see
No. 579.

Liberation, 2nd
Anniv. — A119

Pres. Hissein
Habre — A120

1984, June 6			**Perf. 12½**	
480	A119	50fr multi	.60	.20

1984, June 18			**Perf. 12½x13**	
481	A120	125fr multi	1.50	.40

Anniversaries and Events — A121

Designs: 50fr, Pres. Habre, civil war martyrs. 200fr, Paul Harris, Rotary Intl. headquarters, Illinois. 300fr, Alfred Nobel, will establishing fund for Prizes. 350fr, Raphael, detail from
Virgin with Child and St. John the Baptist.
400fr, Rembrandt, detail from The Holy Family. 500fr, J.W. Goethe, scene from Faust.
600fr, Rubens, detail from Helene Fourment
and Her Two Children.

1984, Jan. 16		**Litho.**	**Perf. 13½**	
482	A121	50fr multi	.50	.20
483	A121	200fr multi	1.90	.30
484	A121	300fr multi	3.00	.45
485	A121	350fr multi	3.75	.55
486	A121	400fr multi	4.50	.60
487	A121	500fr multi	5.75	.70
	Nos. 482-487 (6)		19.40	2.80

Souvenir Sheet

488	A121	600fr multi	6.75	1.25

Nos. 486-488 are airmail.

Homage to Our
Martyred
Dead — A122

1984, Feb. 22		**Litho.**	**Perf. 13½**	
500	A122	50fr multi	.50	.20
501	A122	80fr multi	.75	.20
502	A122	120fr multi	1.10	.20
503	A122	200fr multi	1.90	.25
504	A122	250fr multi	2.50	.40
	Nos. 500-504 (5)		6.75	1.25

#503-504 airmail. For surcharge see #C303.

World Communications Year — A123

1984, Feb. 29   Litho.   Perf. 13½
505	A123	50fr sil & multi	.50	.20
506	A123	60fr sil & multi	.60	.20
507	A123	70fr sil & multi	.75	.20
508	A123	125fr sil & multi	1.10	.20
509	A123	250fr sil & multi	2.50	.40
		Nos. 505-509 (5)	5.45	1.20

#508-509 airmail. For surcharge see #C304.

Anniversaries and Events — A123a

50fr, Durer, detail from Madonna of the Rosary. 200fr, Henri Dunant, Red Cross founder, Battle of Solferino. 300fr, Early telephone, Goonhilly Downs Satellite Station, Britain. 350fr, J.F. Kennedy, Neil Armstrong's 1st step on Moon, 1969. 400fr, Europe-Africa Satellite infrared photograph. 500fr, Prince Charles & Lady Diana. 600fr, Wedding photograph of Prince Charles & Lady Diana.

1984
510	A123a	50fr multi	.50	.20
511	A123a	200fr multi	2.10	.30
512	A123a	300fr multi	3.00	.45
513	A123a	350fr multi	3.50	.50
514	A123a	400fr multi	3.75	.55
515	A123a	500fr multi	5.00	.80
		Nos. 510-515 (6)	17.85	2.80

Souvenir Sheet
| 516 | A121 | 600fr multicolored | 5.25 | |

A souvenir sheet of 6 containing #510-515 exists. Nos. 514-516 are airmail.
For surcharge see No. 578.

Development of Communications — A123b

Ships and locomotives.

1984, Aug. 1   Litho.   Perf. 12½
517	A123b	90fr Indiaman, East India Co.	1.10	.20
518	A123b	100fr Nord 701, 1885	1.10	.20
519	A123b	125fr Vera Cruz	1.75	.20
520	A123b	150fr Columbia, 1888	1.75	.20
521	A123b	200fr Carlisle Castle	2.50	.25
522	A123b	250fr Rete Mediterranea, 1900	3.00	.30
523	A123b	300fr Britannia	3.25	.35
524	A123b	350fr Mav 114	3.75	.50
		Nos. 517-524 (8)	18.20	2.20

Christmas — A124

1984, Dec. 28   Litho.   Perf. 13
525	A124	50fr lt bl & org brn	.50	.20
526	A124	60fr ver & org brn	.60	.20
527	A124	80fr emer & org brn	.75	.20
528	A124	85fr rose lil & org brn	.75	.20

529	A124	100fr org yel & org brn	1.00	.20
530	A124	135fr dp bl vio & org brn	1.25	.20
		Nos. 525-530 (6)	4.85	1.20

European Music Year — A125

Instruments.

1985, Apr. 30   Litho.   Perf. 12x12½
531	A125	20fr Guitar	.20	.20
532	A125	25fr Harp	.30	.20
533	A125	30fr Xylophone	.40	.20
534	A125	50fr Shoulder drum	.50	.20
535	A125	70fr like #534	.70	.20
536	A125	80fr like #532	.75	.20
537	A125	100fr like #531	1.00	.20
538	A125	250fr like #533	2.50	.30
		Nos. 531-538 (8)	6.35	1.70

Mushrooms A126

1985, May 15   Litho.   Perf. 12½
539	A126	25fr Chlorophyllum molybdites	.60	.20
540	A126	30fr Tulostoma volvulatum	.70	.20
541	A126	50fr Lentinus tuberregium	1.00	.20
542	A126	70fr like #541	1.40	.20
543	A126	80fr Podaxis pistillaris	1.60	.20
544	A126	100fr like #539	2.50	.35
		Nos. 539-544 (6)	7.80	1.35

Anniversaries and Events — A127

Designs: 25fr, Abraham Lincoln. 45fr, Henri Dunant, Geneva birthplace and red cross. 50fr, Gottlieb Daimler, 1887 Motor Carriage. 60fr, Louis Bleriot, Bleriot XI monoplane, 1909. 80fr, Paul Harris, Chicago site of Rotary Intl. founding. 350fr, Auguste Piccard, bathyscaphe Trieste, 1953. 600fr, Anatoly Karpov, 1981 world chess champion. 1500fr, Paul Harris.

1985, May 25   Litho.   Perf. 13½
545	A127	25fr multi	.30	.20
546	A127	45fr multi	.60	.20
547	A127	50fr multi	.75	.20
548	A127	60fr multi	1.00	.20
549	A127	80fr multi	1.10	.20
550	A127	350fr multi	4.00	.45
		Nos. 545-550 (6)	7.75	1.45

Souvenir Sheets
| 551 | A127 | 600fr multi | 6.75 | .85 |

Litho. & Embossed
| 551A | A127 | 1500fr Paul Harris on Medal | 14.50 | |

No. 551A contains one 130x90mm stamp. Nos. 548-551A are airmail.
Souvenir sheets of 1 exist for #545-551.

Intl. Youth Year — A128

1985, May 30   Litho.   Perf. 13
| 552 | A128 | 70fr Development levels, vert. | .70 | .20 |
| 553 | A128 | 200fr Globe | 1.75 | .25 |

A129

3rd Anniv. of the Republic A130

Perf. 13, 12½x13
1985, June 7   Litho.
554	A129	70fr Hand, claw	.70	.20
555	A129	70fr Hands, map	.70	.20
556	A130	70fr Pres. Hissein Habre	.70	.20
557	A129	110fr like #554	1.10	.20
558	A129	110fr like #555	1.25	.20
559	A130	110fr like #556	1.25	.20
		Nos. 554-559 (6)	5.70	1.20

Audubon Birth Bicent. — A131

1985, July 20   Engr.   Perf. 13
560	A131	70fr Stork	1.10	.20
561	A131	110fr Ostrich	1.60	.20
562	A131	150fr Marabou	2.25	.20
563	A131	200fr Snake eagle	3.00	.25
		Nos. 560-563 (4)	7.95	.85

Souvenir Sheet
| 564 | A131 | 500fr like 200fr | 6.75 | .70 |

Mammals A132

1985, Aug. 25
565	A132	50fr Waterbuck	.75	.20
566	A132	70fr Kudus, horiz.	1.00	.20
567	A132	250fr Shaggy mouflon	3.25	.40
		Nos. 565-567 (3)	5.00	.80

Souvenir Sheet
| 568 | A132 | 500fr White rhinoceros | 5.75 | .85 |

UN, 40th Anniv. — A133

1985, Nov. 24
| 569 | A133 | 200fr brt bl, red & brn | 2.25 | .25 |

Chad Admission to UN, 25th Anniv. — A134

1985, Nov. 24
| 570 | A134 | 300fr red, brt bl & yel | 3.25 | .50 |

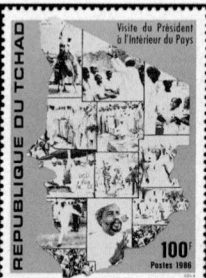

President's Visit to the Nation's Interior A135

1986, June 7   Litho.   Perf. 12½x13
571	A135	100fr multi	1.10	.20
572	A135	170fr multi	2.25	.35
573	A135	200fr multi	2.50	.45
		Nos. 571-573 (3)	5.85	1.00

Lions Club Intl. — A135a

1987   Litho.   *Perf. 14*

573A	A135a	30fr Like #573C		
573C	A135a	100fr Sick child		
573E	A135a	170fr Three children, horiz.		
573F	A135a	200fr Eye exam, horiz.		

There are two additional stamps in this. The editors would like to examine them.

World Wildlife Fund — A136

Various mouflons, *Ammotragus lervia.*

1988, Nov. 10   Litho.   *Perf. 13*

574	A136	25fr shown	2.50	.40
575	A136	45fr Adult, young	3.25	.60
576	A136	70fr Two adults, diff.	4.25	1.10
577	A136	100fr Adult, young	6.00	1.60
		Nos. 574-577 (4)	16.00	3.70

Nos. 512 and 475 Surcharged

1989   Litho.   *Perf. 13½*

578	A123a	170fr on 300fr #512	
579	A118	240fr on 300fr #475	

Liberation — A137

1989   *Perf. 11½x12*

580	A137	20fr multi	.20	.20
581	A137	25fr multi	.30	.20
582	A137	40fr multi	.50	.20
583	A137	100fr multi	1.10	.30
584	A137	170fr multi	1.75	.50
		Nos. 580-584 (5)	3.85	1.40

World Post Day — A137a

1989, Oct. 9   Photo.   *Perf. 12*
Granite Paper

584A	A137a	100fr grn bl & multi	
584B	A137a	120fr red & multi	
584C	A137a	170fr purple & multi	
584D	A137a	250fr olive & multi	
		Nos. 584A-584D (4)	160.00

Visit of Pope John Paul II — A138

Cathedral in Chad and: 20fr, 100fr, Pope holding crosier. 80fr, 170fr, Pope, diff.

1989, Dec. 20   Litho.   *Perf. 13*

585	A138	20fr multicolored	.35	.20
586	A138	80fr multicolored	1.10	.40
587	A138	140fr multicolored	1.40	.50
588	A138	170fr multicolored	2.25	1.10
		Nos. 585-588 (4)	5.10	2.20

Traditional Hair Styles — A139

1989, Oct. 9   Photo.   *Perf. 12*
Granite Paper

589	A139	100fr apple grn & multi	
590	A139	120fr purple & multi	
591	A139	170fr pink & multi	
592	A139	250fr org yel & multi	
		Nos. 589-592 (4)	160.00

Vaccinations A140

1991, Dec. 1   Photo.   *Perf. 11½*
Granite Paper

593	A140	30fr brown & multi	.30	.20
594	A140	100fr green & multi	1.00	.45
595	A140	170fr vio & multi	1.60	.75
596	A140	180fr blue & multi	1.75	.80
597	A140	200fr red & multi	1.90	.90
		Nos. 593-597 (5)	6.55	3.10

Liberty and Democracy Day — A141

1991, Dec. 1   Litho.

598	A141	10fr green & multi	.20	.20
599	A141	20fr lilac & multi	.20	.20
600	A141	40fr yellow & multi	.40	.20
601	A141	70fr blue & multi	.65	.30
602	A141	130fr tan & multi	1.25	.60
603	A141	200fr pink & multi	1.90	.90
		Nos. 598-603 (6)	4.60	2.40

Fight Against Insect Pests — A141a

1992, Sept. 1   Photo.   *Perf. 12*

603A	A141a	25fr multicolored	—	—
603B	A141a	45fr multicolored		
603C	A141a	100fr multicolored		
603D	A141a	130fr multicolored		
603E	A141a	170fr multicolored	—	—
		Nos. 603A-603E (5)	160.00	

A142

1992, Nov. 15   Litho.   *Perf. 11½*

604	A142	20fr bright yel & multi	.20	.20
605	A142	45fr golden yel & multi	.40	.20
606	A142	85fr pink & multi	.75	.35
607	A142	170fr blue & multi	1.50	.70
608	A142	300fr gray & multi	3.00	1.40
		Nos. 604-608 (5)	5.85	2.85

Doctors Without Borders, 20th anniv.

Campaign Against Illiteracy A143

1992, Nov. 30

609	A143	25fr yel grn & multi	.20	.20
610	A143	40fr golden yel & multi	.40	.20
611	A143	70fr pink & multi	.60	.30
612	A143	100fr lilac & multi	.75	.40
613	A143	180fr blue & multi	1.60	.60
614	A143	200fr gray & multi	1.75	.70
		Nos. 609-614 (6)	5.30	2.40

Intl. Conference on Nutrition, Rome — A144

1992, Dec. 15

615	A144	10fr yellow & multi	.20	.20
616	A144	60fr pink & multi	1.00	.25
617	A144	120fr yel grn & multi	1.75	.40
618	A144	500fr blue & multi	4.50	1.60
		Nos. 615-618 (4)	7.45	2.45

Palace of the People A145

1993, Apr. 15   Litho.   *Perf. 11½*

619	A145	80fr multi		
620	A145	100fr multi		
621	A145	130fr multi	—	
622	A145	400fr multi		
		Nos. 619-622 (4)	160.00	

Natl. Conference   OAU, 30th Anniv.
A146   A147

1993, Dec. 1   Litho.   *Perf. 11¾*
Granite paper

623	A146	55fr multi	.50	.35
624	A146	70fr multi	.70	.45
625	A146	110fr multi	1.10	.80
626	A146	125fr multi	1.10	.90
		Nos. 623-626 (4)	3.40	2.50

1993, Dec. 4   Litho.   *Perf. 11½x11¾*

627	A147	15fr multi	.20	.20
628	A147	30fr multi	.30	.20
629	A147	110fr multi	1.10	.80
630	A147	190fr multi	1.90	1.50
		Nos. 627-630 (4)	3.50	2.70

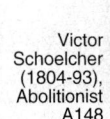

Victor Schoelcher (1804-93), Abolitionist A148

Perf. 11¾x11½

1993, Dec. 26   Litho.

631	A148	55fr multi	.40	.40
632	A148	105fr multi	1.10	.75
633	A148	125fr multi	1.40	1.10
634	A148	300fr multi	2.75	2.00

Tourism A149

Perf. 11¾x11½

1993, Dec. 27   Litho.

635	A149	15fr multi	37.50	20.00
636	A149	95fr multi	37.50	20.00
637	A149	100fr multi	37.50	20.00

An additional stamp was issued in this set. The editors would like to examine it.

Bank of Central African States A150

1994, June 22   Litho.   *Perf. 11½*

639	A150	20fr multicolored	.20	
640	A150	30fr pink & multi	.20	
641	A150	105fr blue & multi	.70	
642	A150	190fr lilac & multi	1.25	

Huts for Storing Grain A151

Designs: 75fr, Arabe, kim. 150fr, Sara, moundang. 300fr, Boulala, kotoko. 450fr, Ouaddai, kenga.

1995, Oct. 15   Litho.   *Perf. 14*

643	A151	75fr multicolored	.45	
644	A151	150fr multicolored	.80	
645	A151	300fr multicolored	1.50	
646	A151	450fr multicolored	2.50	

Souvenir Sheet

Chinese Post, Cent. — A151a

1996   Litho.   *Perf. 13¼*

646A	A151a	270fr multi	1.60	1.10

1996 Olympic Games, Atlanta —
A151b

No. 646B: e, Tennis. f, Equestrian. g, Soccer. h, Boxing.
No. 646C: i, Judo. j, Running. k, Cycling. l, Table tennis.
1500fr, Hurdler.

1996	Litho.		Perf. 13¼	
646B	A151b	250fr Sheet of 4, #e-h	4.00	4.00
646C	A151b	300fr Sheet of 4, #i-l	5.00	5.00

Souvenir Sheet

| 646D | A151b | 1500fr multi | 6.25 | 6.25 |

No. 646D contains one 39x57mm stamp.

1995 Boy Scout
Jamboree,
Holland — A152

Mushrooms: 150fr, Amanita phalloides. 170fr, Phallus impudicus. 200fr, Lyloperdon perlatum. 350fr, Hydne commun. 450fr, Agaricus bisporus. 800fr, Cortinarius orellanus.
1500fr, Pleurotus ostreatus.

1996, Apr. 15	Litho.		Perf. 13½
647-652	A152	Set of 6	9.25 4.75
a.		Souvenir sheet, #647-652	9.25 4.75

Souvenir Sheet

| 653 | A152 | 1500fr multicolored | 6.50 | 3.25 |

Nos. 647-652 exist in souvenir sheets of 1.

Butterflies, Mushrooms and Minerals
— A152a

No. 653A: g, Papilio zalmoxis. h, Anacridium melanorhodon. i, Otidea leporina. j, Haliaetus vocifer.
No. 653B: k, Amanita phalloides, Papilio dardanus. l, Papilio antimachus, Cortinarius praestans. m, Phallus impudicus, Chrysidia croesus. n, Papilio dardanus, Lycoperon perlatum.
No. 653C: o, Charaxes brutus. p, Epiphora albida. q, Euchloron megaera. r, Salamis duprei.
No. 653D: s, Disthene. t, Olivine. u, Sphene. v, Hemimorphite.
No. 653E, Argema mittrei. No. 653F, Zoisite.

1996	Litho.		Perf. 13¼	
653A	A152a	350fr Sheet of 4, #g-j	5.75	5.75
653B	A152a	400fr Sheet of 4, #k-n	6.50	6.50
653C	A152a	650fr Sheet of 4, #o-r	10.50	10.50

| 653D | A152a | 800fr Sheet of 4, #s-v | 13.00 | 13.00 |
| *Nos. 653B-653D (3)* | | | 30.00 | 30.00 |

Souvenir Sheets

| 653E | A152a | 2000fr multi | 8.25 | 8.25 |
| 653F | A152a | 2000fr multi | 8.25 | 8.25 |

A number has been reserved for an additional sheet in this set. Nos. 653E-653F each contain one 42x36mm stamp.

Greenpeace, 25th Anniv. — A153

No. 654: a, 170fr, Green coral, school of small fish. b, 200fr, Yellow & orange coral. c, 300fr, Red orange coral. d, 350fr, White coral. 1500fr, Diver, coral, vert.

1996, July 16

| 654 | A153 | Block of 4, #a.-d. | 5.00 | 5.00 |

Souvenir Sheet

| 655 | A153 | 1500fr multicolored | 6.50 | 6.50 |

Entertainers
A154

Designs: No. 656, 170fr, Bob Marley. No. 657, 170fr, Marilyn Monroe. No. 658, 200fr, Elvis Presley. No. 659, 200fr, Monroe. No. 660, 300fr, Monroe. No. 661, 350fr, Stevie Wonder. No. 662, 350fr, Presley. No. 663, 400fr, John Lennon. No. 664, 500fr, Presley. No. 665, 600fr, Lennon. No. 666, 700fr, Madonna. No. 667, 800fr, Presley. No. 668, 1000fr, Monroe.
No. 669, 1500fr, Tina Turner. No. 670, 1500fr, Clint Eastwood. No. 670A, 1500fr, Presley.

1996, May 15				
656-668	A154	Set of 13	25.00	12.50
665a		Sheet of 2, #663, 665	4.50	2.25
667a		Sheet of 4, #658, 662, 664, 667	8.00	3.75
668a		Sheet of 4, #657, 659-660, 668	7.00	3.50

Souvenir Sheets

| 669-670A | A154 | Set of 3 | 20.00 | 10.00 |

Nos. 656-668 exist in souvenir sheets of 1. No. 670A contains one 51x90mm stamp. See No. 674.

Pres. Bill Clinton — A155

No. 671: a, Shown. b, Elvis Presley in white jumpsuit.
No. 672: a, Pres. Richard Nixon. b, Presley in white shirt, black jacket.

1996, Dec. 17	Litho.		Perf. 13½	
671	A155	1500fr Sheet of 2, #a.-b.	16.00	8.00
672	A155	1500fr Sheet of 2, #a.-b.	16.00	8.00

Giant Panda
A156

No. 673: a, Holding branch, left claw out. b, Holding branch. c, Lying on back. d, Holding branch in mouth.

1996, Oct. 15

| 673 | A156 | 100fr Sheet of 4, #a.-d. | 1.90 | .90 |

Entertainers Type of 1996

1996	Litho.		Perf. 13½	
674	A154	500fr Jerry Garcia	2.50	1.25

No. 674 exists in a souvenir sheet of 1.

1998 World Cup Soccer
Championships, France — A157

1998 World Cup Soccer
Championships, France — A157a

Unidentified players, stadium: No. 675, 150fr, The Beaujoire, Nantes. No. 676, 200fr, Lescure Park, Bordeaux. No. 676A, 300fr, Municipal Stadium, Toulouse. No. 676B, 600fr, Felix Bollaert, Lens.
No. 677A: b, Player in white shirt. c, Player in red shirt.

1996, Dec. 17

| 675-676B | A157 | Set of 4 | 6.00 | 3.00 |

Souvenir Sheet

| 677 | A157a | 1500fr George Weah | 7.50 | 3.50 |
| 677A | A157a | 3000fr Sheet of 2, #b-c | — | — |

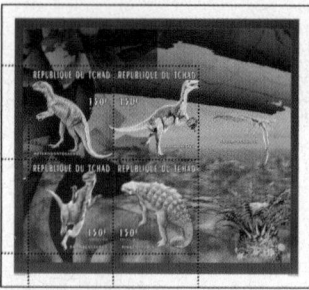

Dinosaurs, Dog & Cats, Butterflies &
Insects — A158

No. 678 — Dinosaurs: a, Heterodontosaurus. b, Ornitholestes. c, Dromaeosaurus. d, Pinacosaurus.
No. 679 — Dinosaurs: a, Corythosaurus. b, Ankylosaurides. c, Ornithomimus. d, Styracosaurus.
No. 680 — Dogs & cats: a, Artois. b, Bengal. c, Persian. d, Vendeen.
No. 681 — Butterflies & insects: a, Euphaedra zaddachi. b, Pseudacraea dolomena. c, Cicindela barbara. d, Goliath.

1996, Oct. 15

678	A158	150fr Sheet of 4, #a.-d.	3.00	1.50
679	A158	200fr Sheet of 4, #a.-d.	3.75	1.90
680	A158	250fr Sheet of 4, #a.-d.	5.00	2.50
681	A158	300fr Sheet of 4, #a.-d.	6.00	3.00

Ovptd. in Gold in Sheet Margin

1997	Litho.		Perf. 13½	
678e		Sheet of 4	2.50	1.25
679e		Sheet of 4	3.25	1.60
680e		Sheet of 4	4.75	2.25

Gold overprints on Nos. 678e-680e contain two-line inscription in Chinese and Hong Kong '97 exhibition emblem.

UNICEF, UN, 50th Anniv., Lions
Intl. — A159

No. 682 — UNICEF, 50th anniv.: a, 150fr, Girl, boy turtles. b, 400fr, Feeding small child.
No. 683 — UN, 50th anniv.: a, 170fr, Huygens probe, starving child. b, 500fr, Man with plant, Marsnet probe.
No. 684 — Lions Intl.: a, 200fr, Man carrying sack of grain. b, 800fr, Men examining plants, native man stirring kettle over fire.

1996, Oct. 15	Litho.		Perf. 13½	
682	A159	Pair, #a.-b. + label	2.75	1.40
683	A159	Pair, #a.-b. + label	3.25	1.60
684	A159	Pair, #a.-b. + label	5.00	2.50

Nos. 682-684 exist as souvenir sheets with colored margins.

1996 European Soccer
Championships — A160

No. 685: a, Oliver Bierhoff holding trophy. b, Two players. c, Two players, referee. d, Queen Elizabeth II, player holding trophy.

1996, Dec. 17

| 685 | A160 | 350fr Sheet of 4, #a.-d. | 6.75 | 3.25 |

Michael Schumacher, 1995 World
Driving Champion — A161

No. 686: a, Ferrari Formula-1 race car. b, Schumacher close-up. c, Schumacher in Benetton uniform. d, Benetton Formula-1 race car.
No. 687, Schumacher with arms raised. No. 687A, Winner of 1996 Italian Grand Prix.

1997, June 16

| 686 | A161 | 700fr Sheet of 4, #a.-d. | 13.50 | 6.75 |

Souvenir Sheets

| 687 | A161 | 2000fr multicolored | 10.00 | 5.00 |
| 687A | A161 | 2000fr multicolored | 10.00 | 5.00 |

No. 687 contains one 36x51mm stamp.

1998 Winter Olympic Games, Nagano, Japan — A162

Designs: 100fr, Women's figure skating. 170fr, Hockey. 350fr, Downhill skiing. 750fr, Speed skating. 1500fr, Slalom skiing.

1996, Dec. 17
688-691 A162 Set of 4   6.75 3.25
Souvenir Sheet
692 A162 1500fr multicolored   7.50 3.50

World Wildlife Fund — A163

No. 693 — Struthio camelus rothschildi: a, Female. b. Male. c, Chicks. d, Male, female up close.

1996, Dec. 17   Litho.   Perf. 13½
693 A163 200fr Block of 4, #a.-d.   15.50 3.25

Jacqueline Kennedy Onassis (1929-94) — A164

Various portraits.

1996, Dec. 17
694 A164 200fr Sheet of 9, #a.-i.   9.00 4.50

Intl. Red Cross, Rotary Intl., Scouts — A165

No. 695 — Intl. Red Cross: a, 100fr, Woman, airplane. b, 350fr, Man, train.
No. 696 — Rotary Intl.: a, 300fr, Boy, water coming through pipes. b, 700fr, Native boy and man, volunteers.
No. 697 — Scouts: a, 250fr, Boy scout holding book, hyena. b, 1000fr, Garry Kasparov, chess player, scout.

1996, Oct. 15   Litho.   Perf. 13½
695 A165 Pair, #a.-b. + label   2.25 1.10
696 A165 Pair, #a.-b. + label   5.00 2.50
697 A165 Pair, #a.-b. + label   6.00 3.00

Nos. 695-697 exist in souvenir sheets with colored margins.

Japanese Sumo Wrestling — A166

Various wrestlers in ring.

1996, Dec. 17   Litho.   Perf. 13½
698 A166 400fr Sheet of 4, #a.-d.   8.00 3.75

China '96 — A168

Various paintings showing mountains and trees.

1996
704 A168 100fr Sheet of 9, #a.-i.   4.50 2.25

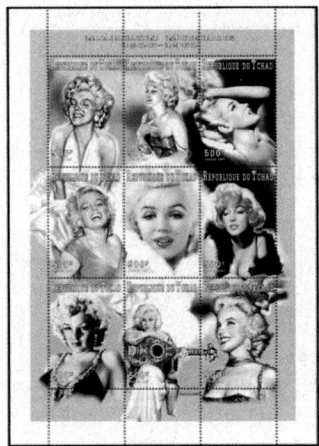

Marilyn Monroe — A168a

Various portraits.

1997   Litho.   Perf. 13¼
704J A168a 500fr Sheet of 9, #k-s   16.00 16.00

History of Space Travel — A169

No. 705: a, Lunar N1 rocket, USSR, Saturn 1, US, Apollo 1 crew, Grissom, White, Chaffee. b, Launch of Soyuz, USSR, V.M. Komarov. c, US Lunar Orbiter 4. d, Neil Armstrong, US, Molnya 1, USSR. e, Venera 4, USSR, Mariner, US. f, Surveyor 3, US.
No. 706: a, Ariane 1, Landsat 4, US. b, Spacelab & space shuttle, NASA, ESA, Thomas Mattingly, US. c, L-Sat Telecom Satelite, ESA. d, J.L. Chretien, Soviet Salyut 7, US Space Shuttle. e, Venera 13, USSR. f, Intelsat 6, US.
No. 707: a, John Glenn, Atlas rocket, Mercury capsule. b, Mariner 2, US. c, Scott Carpenter, US. d, Telstar, Tiros 6. e, Vostok capsule, USSR, Bell X15 airplane, US. f, Mars 1, USSR.
No. 708: a, "Sounds of Earth" record, Voyager 1 & 2, US. b, Himawari 1, MU-3H, Japan, Atlas Centaur, US. c, Soviet Salyut 6, Proton rocket, Galileo (1564-1642). d, Meteosat, SMS

Geos, Atlas EF, US. e, Boeing 747, space shuttle, US. f, ISEE, US.
No. 709: a, Saturn 5, US, OAO 3 Copernicus. b, Pioneer 10, US. c, Luna 20, USSR, John F. Kennedy. d, Landsat 1, US. e, Apollo 16, US astronauts Mattingly, Duke, Young. f, Lunar Rover, US Apollo 17 astronauts Schmitt, Evans, Cernan.
No. 710: a, RD 107 rocket, USSR, Vanguard rocket, US, Vanguard I, US. b, Aerobee, Goddard rockets, Robert H. Goddard. c, Laika, 1st dog in space, USSR. d, Theodor von Karman, V2A, Gird 09 rockets, USSR. e, Sputnik 1, USSR, Korolev airplane. f, Sanger, Bell X1 airplanes, US, Eugene Sanger.
No. 711, US Astronauts, Neil Armstrong, Michael Collins, Edwin E. Aldrin, Jr., USSR animals in space, Laika, Felix the cat.
Illustration reduced.

1997   Litho.   Perf. 13½
705 A169 150fr Sheet of 6, #a.-f.   3.50 1.75
706 A169 250fr Sheet of 6, #a.-f.   6.00 3.00
707 A169 300fr Sheet of 6, #a.-f.   7.50 3.75
708 A169 450fr Sheet of 6, #a.-f.   11.00 5.50
709 A169 475fr Sheet of 6, #a.-f.   11.50 5.75
710 A169 800fr Sheet of 6, #a.-f.   19.00 10.00
Souvenir Sheet
711 A169 2000fr multicolored   8.25 4.00
No. 711 contains one 80x85mm stamp.

Elvis Presley — A169a

Various portraits.

1997   Litho.   Perf. 13¼
711A A169a 300fr Sheet of 9, #b-j   12.00 12.00

Jacqueline Kennedy Onassis (1929-94) — A170

Various portraits.

1997, July 15   Litho.   Perf. 13½
712 A170 150fr Sheet of 9, #a.-i.   5.75 2.75

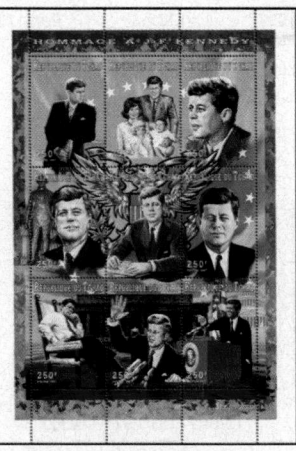

Pres. John F. Kennedy — A170a

No. 712J: k, Standing, looking right. l, With family. m, Looking left. n, With statue of George Washington. o, Seated, with Great Seal of the United States. p, Facing forward, with stars and arrows. q, In chair. r, With statue of Lincoln. s, Behind podium, with flag and Capitol.

1997   Litho.   Perf. 13¼
712J A170a 250fr Sheet of 9, #k-s   8.25 8.25

Diana, Princess of Wales (1961-97) — A171

Various portraits.

1997
713 A171 300fr Sheet of 9, #a.-i.   11.00 5.50
714 A171 450fr Sheet of 9, #a.-i.   16.00 8.25
Souvenir Sheet
715 A171 2000fr multicolored   8.25 4.00
No. 715 contains one 42x60mm stamp.

Deng Xiaoping and Bruce Lee — A171a

No. 715A — Deng and: c, Child. d, Chinese flag. e, Dancer. f, Boats in water. g, Farmers. h, Cityscape.
No. 715B — Lee and movie titles: i, Operation Dragon. j, La Fureur du Dragon. k, La Fureur de Vaincre. l, La Flute Silencieuse. m, Le Jeu de la Mort. n, Le Retour du Dragon. 1000fr, Deng and stars.

1997   Litho.   Perf. 13¼
715A A171a 75fr Sheet of 6,
                    #c-h   1.60 1.60
715B A171a 125fr Sheet of 6,
                    #i-n   2.75 2.75
Souvenir Sheet
715O A171a 1000fr multi   —   —

No. 715O contains one 36x41mm stamp.

Mahatma Gandhi (1869-1948), Mother
Teresa (1910-97) — A172

No. 716: a, Gandhi seated, dendrobium
speciosum. b, Mother Teresa with Indian people. c, Bulbophyllum umbellatum, Gandhi with
2 women.

1998, Feb. 5   Litho.   Perf. 13½
716 A172 150fr Sheet of 3, #a.-c. 1.90 .95

Famous
Men — A173

Designs: 300fr, Nelson Mandela, Pres. of
South Africa, diamond. 450fr, Albert Einstein
(1879-1955), physicist, satellite. 800fr, Robert
Barany (1876-1936), physician, Felix the
space cat.
2000fr, Alfred Nobel (1833-96).

1998, Feb. 5
717-719 A173 Set of 3   6.50 3.25
Souvenir Sheet
720 A173 2000fr multicolored   8.25 4.00

Nos. 717-719 exist in souvenir sheets of 1.
No. 720 contains one 41x60mm stamp.
See Nos. 729-734.

The Beatles — A174

No. 721: a-i, Various portraits of John
Lennon.
No. 722 — The Beatles: a, Paul McCartney.
b, Silhouettes. c, John Lennon. d, George Har-
rison, Lennon. e, Four faces. f, McCartney,
Ringo Starr. g, Starr. h, Four in Sgt. Pepper's
costumes. i, Harrison.
No. 723 — Life of John Lennon: a, Yoko
Ono. b, With McCartney. c, In profile. d, Wear-
ing suit. e, Wearing white shirt, tie. f, With
mother. g, Wearing dark glasses. h, With guru.
i, In white suit.
No. 724: Various portraits of Lennon,
McCartney, Harrison, Starr.
No. 724J, Beatles in suits and ties. No.
724K, Beatles in Sgt. Pepper uniforms.

1996   Litho.   Perf. 13½
721 A174 100fr Sheet of 9,
                    #a-f   3.25 3.25
722 A174 170fr Sheet of 9,
                    #a.-i.   5.50 2.75
723 A174 200fr Sheet of 9,
                    #a.-i.   6.75 3.50
724 A174 300fr Sheet of 9,
                    #a.-i.   10.50 5.25
Souvenir Sheets
724J A174 1500fr multi   5.50 5.50
724K A174 1500fr multi   5.50 5.50

Rotary Intl. — A175

Antelopes: a, 170fr, Damaliscus dorcas. b,
350fr, Oryx gazella. c, 500fr, Addax
nasomaculatus. d, 600fr, Aepyceros
melampus.

1996, Dec. 17
725 A175 Block of 4, #a.-d.   7.00 3.50
#725a-725d exist in souvenir sheets of 1.

No. 725 Overprinted in Gold

1996
726 A175 Block of 4, #a.-d.   7.00 3.50
#726a-726d exist in souvenir sheets of 1.

Marilyn Monroe (1926-1962) — A176

Various portraits.

1996
727 A176 250fr Sheet of 9,
                    #a.-i.   10.50 6.50
Souvenir Sheet
728 A176 1500fr multicolored   5.75 2.75

No. 728 contains one 51x90mm stamp.

Famous People Type of 1997

Nobel Prize winners: 100fr, Mother Teresa
(1910-97), humanitarian. 150fr, Martin Luther
King, Jr. (1929-68), civil rights leader. 475fr,
Otto Hahn (1879-1968), chemist, nuclear powered ship. 500fr, Ivan Pavlov (1849-1936),
physiologist, Russian space dog, Laika. 600fr,
Johannes van der Waals (1837-1923), physicist. 1000fr, Sir Edward Appleton (1892-1965),
physicist, Concorde jet.

1998, Feb. 5
729-734 A173 Set of 6   14.50 7.00

Nos. 729-734 exist in souvenir sheets of 1.

Scouting
A177

Wild animals: No. 735: a, Hyena. b,
Mongoose.
No. 736: a, Wildcat. b, Addax
nasomaculatus.
No. 737: a, Fennec. b, Hyena, diff.

1998, Feb. 6
735 A177 150fr Pair, #a.-b.   1.40   .65
736 A177 550fr Pair, #a.-b.   4.50 2.50
737 A177 600fr Pair, #a.-b.   5.25 2.75

Cats and Dogs — A178

No. 738: a, Maine coon. b, Singapore.
No. 739: a, Siberian husky. b, Malamute.
No. 740: a, Spitz. b, Eskimo.
No. 741: a, Siamese. b, Common cat.
No. 742, 1500fr, Abyssinian. No. 743,
1500fr, Samoyed.

1998, Feb. 6
738 A178 300fr Pair, #a.-b.   2.50 1.25
739 A178 450fr Pair, #a.-b.   3.75 1.90
740 A178 475fr Pair, #a.-b.   3.75 1.90
741 A178 475fr Pair, #a.-b.   4.00 2.00
Souvenir Sheets
742-743 A178 Set of 2   12.50 6.50

Nos. 742-743 each contain one 42x60mm
stamp.

Airplanes,
Ships, &
Trains
A179

No. 743A — Early aircraft: b, Latecoere 28,
France. c, D'Equeuilly, France. d, Liore et Oli-
vier Leo-213, France. e, Louis Bleriot monoplane. f, Graf Zeppelin LZ 127. g, Caproni CA
133, Italy.
No. 744 — Airplanes: a, Sikorsky VS-44A.
b, Short S25/V Sandringham 4. c, Bristol 167
Brabazon 1. d, Savoia S13 Bis. e, Curtiss CR-
3. f, Curtiss R3C-2.
No. 745 — Ships: a, Normandy, 1935. b,
Persia, 1856. c, Queen Elizabeth II, 1968. d,
Christian Radich, 1937. e, Amerigo Vespucci,
1933. f, Tovarich, 1933.
No. 745G — Classic sports cars: h, 1963-65
Porsche 356 SC. i, 1961-66 AC Cobra. j,
1960-61 Maserati Tipo 63 Birdcage. k, 1962-
63 Austin Healey 3000 MK11. l, 1959-62 Fer-
rari 250 GT Berlinetta SWB. m, 1958 Aston
Martin DB4.
No. 746 — Trains: a, BRB cog steam train.
b, AE 4/7 10969. c, Crocodile of Saint-Gothard
BE 6/8 111. d, RAE 2/4 1001. e, Steam train,
Spain. f, RE 6/6 11612 express.
No. 746G — High speed trains: h, ETR 470,
Italy. i, TGV Metro. j, Hikari, Japan. k,
TGV 001 turbotrain, France. l, Eurostar
3203/3204 Metro train, France, Germany,
Great Britain. m, 990 ICE train, Germany.
1500fr, Steam locomotive, C5/6 2978.
2000fr, TGV, France.

1998, Feb. 4
743A A179 150fr Sheet of 6,
                    #b.-g.   3.75 1.90
744   A179 200fr Sheet of 6,
                    #a.-f.   5.00 2.50
745   A179 250fr Sheet of 6,
                    #a.-f.   6.25 3.25
745G A179 300fr Sheet of 6,
                    #h.-m.   7.50 3.75
746   A179 350fr Sheet of 6,
                    #a.-f.   9.00 4.50
746G A179 400fr Sheet of 6,
                    #h.-m.   10.00 5.00
Souvenir Sheets
747 A179 1500fr multicolored   6.25 3.25
748 A179 2000fr multicolored   8.25 4.00

Nos. 747-748 contain one 36x42mm stamp.
Swiss rail service, 150th anniv. (#746-747).
Issued: #745G, 2/6.
See No. 758.

Diana,
Princess of
Wales (1961-
97)
A180

Various portraits.
2000fr, Portrait wearing high lace collar.

1997   Litho.   Perf. 13½
749 A180 250fr Sheet of 9,
                    #a.-i.   9.00 4.50
Souvenir Sheet
749J A180 2000fr multicolored   8.50 4.50

Literacy
Campaign
A181

Kellou
Dahalob — A182

1997, June 16
750 A181 150fr olive & multi   .55   .25
751 A181 300fr buff & multi   1.10   .50
752 A181 475fr salmon & multi   1.75   .80
    Nos. 750-752 (3)   3.40 1.55

1998, Apr. 8
753 A182   50fr pink & multi   .20   .20
754 A182 100fr blue & multi   .40   .20
755 A182 150fr green & multi   .65   .30
756 A182 300fr lilac & multi   1.10   .50
757 A182 400fr yellow & multi   1.50   .70
    Nos. 753-757 (5)   3.85 1.90

Transportation Type of 1997

No. 758 — Modern aircraft: a, SAT, France,
Germany. b, BAC/Aerospatiale Concorde. c,
X001, Japan. d, Bell X-2, US. e, Douglas X-3,
US. f, Aerospatiale STS 2000, France.

1998, Feb. 4   Litho.   Perf. 13½
758 A179 475fr Sheet of 6,
                    #a.-f.   12.00 6.25

Women — A183

Women: 50fr, 100fr, 150fr, Using grind-stone. 300fr, 450fr, 500fr, Kneeling.

1997, June 16

759	A183	50fr vio & multi, vert.	.20	.20
760	A183	100fr grn & multi, vert.	.40	.20
761	A183	150fr yel & multi, vert.	.55	.25
762	A183	300fr vio & multi	1.10	.50
763	A183	450fr grn & multi	1.75	.80
764	A183	500fr yel & multi	1.90	.85
		Nos. 759-764 (6)	5.90	2.80

Protect the Ozone Layer — A184

1998, June 20   Litho.   Perf. 13½

765	A184	150fr blue & multi	.60	.25
766	A184	300fr green & multi	1.25	.55
767	A184	475fr pink & multi	1.90	.85
768	A184	500fr blue green & multi	1.90	.85
		Nos. 765-768 (4)	5.65	2.50

Fauna — A185

No. 769 — Bats: a, Holding mouse, tree branch. b, Drinking. c, One in flight, bottom of mouse. d, One flying left. e, One flying right. f, Mouse on rock, bat landing.

No. 769G — Horses: h, Gray Arabian. i, Brown Arabian. j, Przewalski's. k, Australian brumbies. l, Camargue. m, Zebras.

No. 769N — Sea mammals: o-t, Various portraits of Trichechus senegalensis.

No. 770 — Gorillas & chimpanzees: a, Chimpanzee scratching head. b, Gorilla walking on all fours. c, Gorilla seated. d, Chimpanzee swinging from branch. e, Chimpanzee using stick. f, Two gorillas.

No. 771 — Raptors: a, Terathopius ecaudatus. b, Buteo buteo. c, Sagittarius serpentarius. d, Polemaetus belligosus. e, Circaetus allicus. f, Aquila chrysaetos.

No. 771G — Reptiles: h, Crocodylus niloticus. i, Drendroaspis angusticeps. j, Bitis nasicornis. k, Chamaeleo johnstoni. l, Naja nigricolis. m, Meroles cuneirostris.

No. 771N — Mushrooms: o, Coprinus atramentarius. p, Romaria botrytis. q, Aleuria aurantia. r, Amanita muscaria. s, Macrolepiota rhacodes. t, Helvella crispa.

No. 771U — Mushrooms: v, Morchella vulgaris. w, Tuber aestiuum. x, Tuber melanosporum. y, Mitrophora hybrida. z, Morchella conica. aa, Choeromyces meandriformis.

No. 772 — Butterflies: a, Charaxes jasius. b, Hamanumidia daedalus. c, Charaxes bohemani. d, Hallimoides rumia, denomination LL. e, Hallimoides rumia, denomination LR. f, Pseudacraea boisduuali.

1500fr, Coelogyne ovalis, palla ussheri. 2000fr, Baleniceps, Neurophyllum clauatum.

1998, June 20

769	A185	150fr Sheet of 6, #a.-f.	4.00	2.10
769G	A185	250fr Sheet of 6, #h.-m.	5.50	2.75
769N	A185	300fr Sheet of 6, #o.-t.	6.50	6.50
770	A185	300fr Sheet of 6, #a.-f.	8.00	4.00
771	A185	350fr Sheet of 6, #a.-f.	9.25	4.50
771G	A185	450fr Sheet of 6, #h.-m.	10.00	10.00
771N	A185	475fr Sheet of 6, #o.-t.	10.50	10.50
771U	A185	500fr Sheet of 6, #v.-aa.	11.00	11.00
772	A185	600fr Sheet of 6, #a.-f.	16.00	8.00

Souvenir Sheets

773	A185	1500fr multicolored	6.50	3.25
773A	A185	2000fr multicolored	7.50	3.75

Nos. 773-773A contain one 51x42mm stamp.

Bela Lugosi as Dracula — A185a

Lugosi in various poses.

1998, Dec. 11   Litho.   Perf. 13½

773B	A185a	250fr Sheet of 9, #d.-l.	8.50	8.50

Souvenir Sheet

773C	A185a	1500fr multi, horiz.	5.75	5.75

Diana, Princess of Wales — A186

No. 774 — Various portraits: a, 200fr. b, 250fr. c, 300fr. d, 400fr. e, 475fr. f, 500fr. g, 800fr. h, 900fr. i, 1000fr.

1999, Jan. 10   Litho.   Perf. 12½

774	A186	Sheet of 9, #a.-i.	17.50	9.00

Birds — A187

Designs: 75fr, Ibis ibis. 150fr, Ephippi-orhynchus senegalensis. 200fr, Phoen-icopterus ruber. 300fr, Leptoptilus crumeniferus. 400fr, Scopus umbretta. 475fr, Platalea alba.

1000fr, Balaeniceps rex.

1999, Jan. 15   Litho.   Perf. 12¾

775-780	A187	Set of 6	5.75	2.75

Souvenir Sheet

781	A187	1000fr multicolored	3.50	1.75

No. 781 contains one 32x40mm stamp.

Fire Trucks A188

Designs: 50fr, 1840 model. 150fr, 1920 Fiat. 200fr, 1915 Mack. 300fr, 1930 Renault. 400fr, Pegaso M 1090. 500fr, 1960 Jet Fire Power. 700fr, 1720 King George III Fire Company.

1998, Dec. 30

782-787	A188	Set of 6	5.75	2.75

Souvenir Sheet

788	A188	700fr multicolored	2.50	1.25

No. 788 contains one 35x28mm stamp.

Minerals — A188a

No. 788A: a, Opal. b, Cyanite. c, Chalcopyrite. d, Apatite. e, Celestite. f, Scorodite.

No. 788B: a, Agate. b, Wulfenite. c, Barytine. d, Tanzanite. e, Amazonite. f, Malachite.

1998, Nov. 12   Litho.   Perf. 13½

788A	A188a	475fr Sheet of 6, #a.-f.	11.00	5.50
788B	A188a	500f Sheet of 6, #a.-f.	11.50	5.75

Dinosaurs — A188b

No. 788C: a, Dilophosaurus. b, Argentinosaurus. c, Kritosaurus. d, Scutellosaurus. e, Ornithomimosaurus. f, Bactrosaurus.

No. 788D: a, Coelophysis. b, Kannemeyeria. c, Apatosaurus. d, Scipionyx. e, Lystrosaurus. f, Kentrosaurus.

No. 788E, Giganotosaurus, vert.

1998, Nov. 12   Litho.   Perf. 13¼

Sheets of 6

788C	A188b	400fr #a.-f.	9.25	4.75
788D	A188b	450fr #a.-f.	10.50	5.25

Souvenir Sheet

788E	A188b	2000fr multi	7.50	3.75

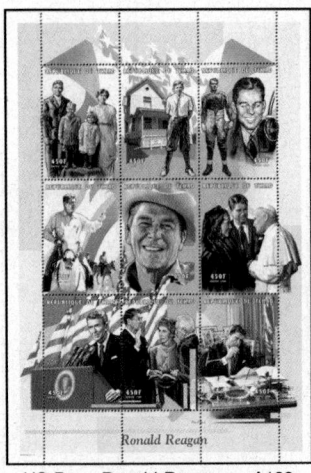

US Pres. Ronald Reagan — A189

No. 789: a, Family portrait as young boy. b, In front of family home. c, In football uniform, as radio announcer. d, Riding horse. e, Up close portrait. f, With Nancy, greeting Pope John Paul II. g, Making speech at podium. h, Being sworn in as president. i, At desk in Oval Office.

2000fr, At desk, White House.

1999, Feb. 2   Litho.   Perf. 13½

789	A189	450fr Sheet of 9, #a.-i.	16.00	8.00

Souvenir Sheet

790	A189	2000fr multicolored	8.00	3.75

American Railroads — A190

No. 791 — Train, railroad pioneer: a, "Alco" Santa Fe, 1945, Cyrus Holliday. b, Rio Grande, 1961, J.F. Stevens. c, Amtrak, 1976, Thomas Dehone Judah. d, 250 Gobernador, 1884, Mark Hopkins. e, Meeting of Central Pacific and Union Pacific at Promontory Point, 1869, Leland Stanford, Thomas Durant. f, Great Northern W1, 1947, Jim Hill. g, Union Pacific Railroad, 1951, G.M. Dodge. h, Pennsylvania GG1, 1934, S.M. Vauclain. i, 151 Santa Fe U.P., 1917, S. Barstow Strong.

1999, Feb. 2

791	A190	200fr Sheet of 9, #a.-i.	7.00	3.50

Fossils and Cave Paintings — A191

No. 792: a, Harlania enigmatica. b, Spirophyton. c, Fossils, dunes of Djourab. d, Chain of people, oxen, Bardai. e, Man of Gonoa. f, Oxen, Kozen, Borkou.

1998, Dec. 11

792	A191	150fr Sheet of 6, #a.-f.	3.50	1.75

Frank Sinatra — A191a

No. 792G — Sinatra with: h, Blonde actress. i, Green jacket. j, Ava Gardner. k, Striped suit. l, Actor. m, Gun. n, Dark green hat. o, Oscar statuette. p, Military cap.

1998, Dec. 30   Litho.   Perf. 13½
792G A191a 300fr Sheet of 9,
         #h.-p.   11.00 5.50

James Dean (1931-55), Actor — A192

Various portraits.

1999, Feb. 2
793 A192 200fr Sheet of 9, #a.-i. 7.00 3.50

Pope John Paul II — A193

Various portraits.

1999, Feb. 2
794 A193 300fr Sheet of 9,
         #a.-i.   10.50 5.25
Souvenir Sheet
795 A193 1500fr multicolored   6.00 3.00
No. 795 contains one 58x51mm stamp.

John Glenn's Return to Space — A194

Various portraits.

1999, Feb. 11   Litho.   Perf. 13½
796 A194 500fr Sheet of 9,
         #a.-i.   17.50 9.00
Souvenir Sheet
797 A194 2000fr multicolored   8.00 3.75
No. 797 contains one 57x51mm stamp.

Kofi Annan, UN Secretary-General — A195

Various portraits.

1999, Feb. 11
798 A195 150fr Sheet of 9, #a.-i. 5.25 2.75

Chess — A196

No. 798J: k, Paul Morphy. l, Chess board, Morphy-Anderssen, 1858. m, Adolf Anderssen. n, Emanuel Lasker. o, Chess board, Lasker-Capablanca, 1914. p, José Raul Capablanca. q, David Bronstein. r, Chess

board, Bronstein-Botvinnik, 1951. s, Mikhail Botvinnik.
a, Bobby Fischer. b, Chess board, Fischer-Tal, 1961. c, Mikhail Tal. d, Boris Spassky. e, Chess board, Spassky-Petrosian, 1969. f, Tigran Petrosian. g, Garry Kasparov. h, Chess board, Kasparov-Karpov, 1960. i, Anatoly Karpov.
No. 800, Margrave Othon IV of Brandenburg.
No. 800A, King Louis XVI playing chess, horiz.

1999, Feb. 20
798J A196 375fr Sheet of 9,
          #k.-s.   13.00 6.50
799 A196 500fr Sheet of 9,
          #a.-i.   17.50 9.00
Souvenir Sheets
800 A196 2000fr multi   7.75 3.75
800A A196 2000fr multi
Dated 1998. No. 800 contains one 58x51mm stamp. No. 800A contains one 58x51mm stamp. Sheets of 3 stamps, containing Nos. 798Jk-798Jm, 798Jn-798Jp, 798Jq-798Js, 799a-799c, 799d-799f, or 799g-799i exist.

Souvenir Sheets

France, 1998 World Cup Champions — A197

No. 801: a, Bikente Lizarazu. b, Christian Karembeu. c, Frank Leboeuf. d, Emmanuel Petit.
No. 802: a, Fabien Barthez. b, Marcel Desailly. c, Didier Deschamps. d, Christophe Dugarry.
No. 803: Youri Djorkaeff. b, Aime Jacquet. c, Lilian Thuram. d, Zinedine Zidane.
2000fr, Deschamps holding World Cup.

1999, Feb. 20   Litho.   Perf. 13½
801 A197 300fr Sheet of 4,
         #a.-d.   4.50 2.25
802 A197 400fr Sheet of 4,
         #a.-d.   6.25 3.00
803 A197 500fr Sheet of 4,
         #a.-d.   8.00 3.75
Perf. 13¼
804 A197 2000fr multicolored   8.00 3.75
No. 804 contains one 57x51mm stamp.

Hokusai Paintings A198

Designs: a, Voyagers Crossing the Oi River. b, Bird. c, On Totomi Mountain. d, Evening at Ueno. e, Higashimachi-matsuri-yatai-tenjou. f, Evening shower at Yoshiwara. g. Woman with Umbrella. h, Cascade. i, Courtesan.

1999, Sept. 10   Litho.   Perf. 13½
805 A198 475fr Sheet of 9,
         #a.-i.   17.50 9.00
Japex '99.

Millennium — A199

No. 806 — Highlights of 1000-1899: a, Commercial routes in West Africa. b, Crusades. c, Notre Dame Cathedral. d, Ming dynasty tombs. e, Discovery of America. f, Albrecht Dürer. g, Sir Isaac Newton. h, American Independence. i, Napoleon.
No. 807 — 1900-24: a, Return of Halley's Comet. b, Lord Baden-Powell founds Scouting movement. c, Sinking of the Titanic. d, 1st film in Technicolor. e, Marconi sends 1st message across Atlantic, birth of radio. f, Harry Houdini. g, Capablanca-Lasker chess matches. h, Pierre & Marie Curie win Nobel Prize. i, Theft of the Mona Lisa.
No. 808 — 1925-49: a, Birth of Marilyn Monroe. b, Discovery of Pluto. c, Laurel and Hardy. d, Independence of India. e, Alexander Fleming discovers penicillin. f, Introduction of Volkswagen Beetle & Vespa motor scooter. g, Opening of film "Dracula." h, World War II. i, Discovery of Lascaux cave drawings.
No. 809 — 1950-74: a, 1st flight of the Concorde, 7 original astronauts. b, Death of Buddy Holly. c, 1st Super Bowl. d, Death of Eva Peron. e, Art by Andy Warhol. f, The Beatles. g, Cultural Revolution in China. h, Assassination of Pres. John F. Kennedy. i, Cuban Revolution.
No. 810 — 1975-99: a, Death of Princess Diana. b, Death of Enzo Ferrari. c, Akira. d, Argentina, 1986 World Cup soccer champions. e, B. Lara breaks cricket records. f, France, 1998 World Cup Soccer champions. g, Explosion of the Space Shuttle Challenger. h, Pope John Paul II meets Lech Walesa. i, Deaths of Frank Sinatra, Freddie Mercury.

1999, Sept. 10
806 A199 150fr Sheet of 9,
         #a.-i.   5.25 2.50
807 A199 300fr Sheet of 9,
         #a.-i.   10.00 5.25
808 A199 450fr Sheet of 9,
         #a.-i.   15.00 7.75
809 A199 475fr Sheet of 9,
         #a.-i.   16.00 8.00
810 A199 500fr Sheet of 9,
         #a.-i.   16.00 8.25
    Nos. 806-810 (5)   62.25 31.75

Souvenir Sheet

PhilexFrance '99 — A200

Illustration reduced.

1999, Sept. 10
811 A200 1500fr multi   6.00 3.00

I Love Lucy — A201

No. 812: a, Lucy leaning against tree, Ricky. b, Lucy, Ricky kissing. c, Lucy pointing gun. d, Ricky falling to ground. e, Lucy in apartment. f, Ricky holding animal. g, Ricky drinking from canteen. h, Lucy, Ricky talking. i, Lucy behind bush.
No. 813, Lucy in grape vat. No. 814, Lucy, Ricky in bed.

1999, Feb. 20   Litho.   Perf. 13¼
812 A201 450fr Sheet of 9,
       #a.-i.   18.00 9.00
Souvenir Sheets
813 A201 1500fr multi   6.75 3.25
814 A201 2000fr multi   9.00 4.50
       Dated 1998.

Betty Boop — A202

No. 815: a, With cat and dog. b, In flowered dress. c, Looking back over shoulder. d, With hammer, dresser. e, As majorette. f, In red dress with fur collar. g, Holding paper. h, Holding blue dress. i, Holding telephone.
No. 816, With feathered hat. No. 817, In leopard-spotted blouse.

1999, Feb. 20   Litho.   Perf. 13¼
815 A202 450fr Sheet of 9,
       #a.-i.   18.00 9.00
Souvenir Sheets
816 A202 1500fr multi   6.75 3.25
817 A202 2000fr multi   9.00 4.50
       Dated 1998.

Antique Automobiles — A203

150fr, 1900 F.N. 300fr, 1906 Bianchi. 400fr, 1906 Renault. 500fr, 1919 Pierce-Arrow. 700fr, 1919 Citroen 5CV. 900fr, 1928 Ford. 1000fr, 1898 Renault.

1999   Litho.   Perf. 13x12¾
818-823 A203 Set of 6   14.00 6.75
Souvenir Sheet
    Perf. 13x13¼
824 A203 1000fr multi   5.00 2.50
No. 824 contains one 40x31mm stamp.

Locomotives — A204

Designs: 150fr, 0-4-4-0. 300fr, Red 0-4-0. 400fr, Green 0-6-0. 500fr, Brown 0-4-0. 700fr, Blue 0-4-0. 900fr, Blue 0-6-0. 1000fr, Electric locomotive.

1999   Perf. 12¾
825-830 A204 Set of 6   14.00 6.50
Souvenir Sheet
    Perf. 13x13¼
831 A204 1000fr multi   5.00 2.50
No. 831 contains one 36x28mm stamp.

Wonders of Forgotten Cultures — A205

Designs: 50fr, Easter Island. 150fr, Stonehenge. 300fr, Jericho. 400fr, Machu Picchu. 500fr, Valley of Statues. 700fr, Chichén Itzá. 900fr, Persepolis.

1999   Perf. 12¾
832-838 A205 Set of 7   15.00 7.00

Chad postal officials have declared the following items to be "not authorized:"
Set of six stamps of various denominations: New Year 2000 (Year of the Dragon)
Sheet of nine stamps of various denominations: Orchids
Sheet of nine 150fr stamps: Spanish Impressionist paintings
Sheet of nine 300fr stamps: Millennium (Composers), Van Gogh paintings
Sheet of nine 450fr stamps: Millennium (Marilyn Monroe), French Impressionist paintings
Sheet of nine 475fr stamps: Impressionist paintings
Sheet of nine 500fr stamps: Renoir nudes, Elvis Presley, Olympics
Souvenir sheets of one: Millennium (three 300fr, two 450fr, one 475fr, three 500fr, one 1500fr), New Year 2000 (1000fr), Palace of Versailles (1500fr, 2000fr), Hiroshige paintings (1500fr, 2000fr).

Minerals A206

Designs: 150fr, Wulfenite. 200fr, Argentite. 400fr, Siderite. 500fr, Dolomite and quartz. 700fr, Azurite. 900fr, Spinel and calcite. 1000fr, Cassiterite.

2000, Jan. 15   Litho.   Perf. 12¾
839-844 A206 Set of 6   14.00 14.00
Souvenir Sheet
845 A206 1000fr multi   5.00 5.00
       Dated 1999.

Elvis Presley — A207

No. 846: a, Playing guitar, wearing red jacket. b, Holding microphone and guitar, wearing red jacket. c, Holding guitar, wearing gold jacket. d, Playing guitar wearing black leather jacket. e, Playing guitar, wearing black jacket. f, Playing guitar, wearing blue jacket. g, Holding microphone, wearing blue shirt. h, Singing, wearing brown jacket. i, Holding microphone, wearing striped yellow jacket.

2000, Mar. 10   Perf. 13¼
846 A207 300fr Sheet of 9, #a-
       i   12.00 12.00
       Dated 1999.

Carl Benz and Mercedes-Benz Automobiles — A208

No. 847: a, 1934 W-25. b, 1934 500 K. c, 1964 230 SL. d, 1935 150. e, 1954 300 SL. f, 1971 280 SE.
2000fr, 1934 500 K, diff.

2000, Mar. 10
847 A208 250fr Sheet of 6, #a-f 7.00 7.00
Souvenir Sheet
848 A208 2000fr multi   9.00 9.00
No. 847 contains six 30x30mm stamps. Dated 1999.

Trains — A209

No. 849: a, FES 3228, European Union flag. b, TGV Duplex, French flag. c, 500 Series Unit W1, Japanese flag. d, AVE Class 100, Spanish flag. e, ICE3, German flag. f, ETR 500, Italian flag.
2000fr, TGC 001 V56, TGV Duplex, Etienne Chambron.

2000, Mar. 10
849 A209 600fr Sheet of 6,
       #a-f   11.50 11.50
Souvenir Sheet
850 A209 2000fr multi   6.50 6.50
No. 849 contains six 30x30mm stamps. Dated 1999.

French Rulers — A210

No. 851, 150fr: a, Charlemagne. b, King Charles VIII. c, King Francis I. d, King Henry II. e, Catherine de Medici. f, King Henry III.
No. 852, 200fr: a, King Louis XII. b, King Louis XIII. c, King Louis XIV. d, King Louis XV. e, King Louis XVI. f, King Louis XVIII.
No. 853, 300fr — Napoleon Bonaparte: a, Standing, wearing red cape. b, On horseback, wearing red cape. c, On horseback, with soldier at right. d, On horseback, with crowd at right. e, Standing with opter people. f, On white horse, leading battle.

2000, Mar. 10
    Sheets of 6, #a-f
851-853 A210 Set of 3   17.50 17.50
       Dated 1999.

Pope John Paul II — A211

No. 854 — Pope John Paul II and: a, Dalai Lama. b, Fidel Castro. c, King Hassan II of Morocco. d, Grand Rabbi Elio Toaff. e, Patriarch Bartholomew I. f, Mother Teresa.

2000, Mar. 10
854 A211 475fr Sheet of 6, #a-
       f   13.00 13.00
       Dated 1999.

Space — A212

No. 855: a, Sputnik, dog Laika. b, Yuri Gagarin, Vostok 1. c, Konstantin Feoktistov, Vladimir Komarov, Boris Yegorov, Voskhod 1. d, Luna 1, chimpanzee Ham. e, Neil Armstrong, Michael Collis, Edwin Aldrin, Apollo 11. f, Aldrin, splashdown of capsule.

2000, Mar. 10
855 A212 500fr Sheet of 6, #a-
       f   13.00 13.00
       Dated 1999.

Betty Boop Type of 1999
No. 856: a, Wearing red and violet striped leotard, kicking leg up. b, As cheerleader. c, At football field, holding pennant. d, At ice cream

shop. e, Wearing yellow and green striped leotard. f, Wearing baseball cap and orange shorts. g, Wearing baseball cap and checked shirt. h, Seated, drinking beverage. i, Wearing cut-off shorts.

No. 857, 1500fr, Riding bicycle. No. 858, 2000fr, Wearing glasses, elbow and knee pads.

2000, Mar. 30
856　A202　250fr Sheet of 9, #a-
　　　i　　　　　　　　　　　10.00 10.00
Souvenir Sheets
857-858　A202　Set of 2　　16.00 16.00

The Three Stooges — A213

No. 859, 250fr, horiz.: a, Larry, in surgeon's gown, and Curly. b, Curly, Moe, Larry around barrel. c, Moe, Larry and Curly on horse. d, Larry attacking man. e, Moe getting hair pulled. f, Moe with mallet. g, Curly, Moe and Larry in western outfits, outdoors. h, Larry, Curly and Moe in white doctor's jackets. i, Man looking at Moe.

No. 860, 300fr, horiz.: a, Larry grabbing Moe's chin. b, Moe and Larry holding scrolls. c, Moe, yellow background. d, Larry, blue background. e, Moe, Shemp and Larry. f, Shemp, blue background. g, Shemp, yellow background. h, Shemp pointing bellows at Larry. i, Moe and Larry in white.

No. 861, 1500fr, Moe in surgeon's gown. No. 862, 1500fr, Moe wearing hat. No. 863, 2000fr, Curly, Moe and Larry in western outfits, outdoors. No. 864, 2000fr, Larry with violin.

2000
Sheets of 9, #a-i
859-860　A213　Set of 2　　22.50 22.50
Souvenir Sheets
861-864　A213　Set of 4　　32.50 32.50

Issued: Nos. 859, 861, 863, 3/30; Nos. 860, 862, 864, 5/29.

I Love Lucy Type of 1999
No. 865: a, Lucy dancing, man in background. b, Lucy dancing, with knees bent and arms extended. c, Lucy in doorway. d, Lucy dancing behind sofa. e, Lucy kicking out leg. f, Lucy being caught by two men. g, Lucy with one arm extended. h, Lugy being sprayed with seltzer water. i, Lucy with leg on dance rail.

No. 866, 1500fr, Lucy looking at clown, horiz. No. 867, 2000fr, Lucy with clown costume and arms extended.

2000, May 29
865　A201　225fr Sheet of 9, #a-
　　　i　　　　　　　　　　　9.00 9.00
Souvenir Sheets
866-867　A201　Set of 2　　16.00 16.00

N'Djamena,
Cent.
A213a

Background colors: 150fr, Blue. 300fr, Red. 475fr, Green.

2000, May 29　Litho.　Perf. 13¼
867A-867C　A213a　Set of 3　　— —

Chadian Political History — A214

No. 868, 150fr: a, Louis Léon César Faidherbe. b, François Joseph Lamy. c, Henri Eugène Gouraud. d, Gustav Nachtigal. e, Head of Rabah on spike. f, Fernand Foureau.

No. 869, 300fr: a, Pierre Savorgnan de Brazza. b, Philippe Marie de Hautecloque Leclerc. c, Emile Gentil. d, Gabriel Lisette. e, Charles de Gaulle. f, Felix Eboué.

2000, May 29　　　　　Perf. 13½
Sheets of 6, #a-f
868-869　A214　Set of 2　　18.00 18.00

Wildlife, Map of Chad, Scouting Emblem — A215

No. 870, 150fr — Giraffa camelopardalis: a, Pair, one with head lowered. b, Pair, both with heads extended. c, Pair near forest. d, Trio.

No. 871, 200fr: a, Pair of Gazella granti in field. b, Gazella cuiveri. c, Gazella dorcas. d, Pair of Gazella granti at waterhole.

No. 872, 250fr — Addax nasomaculatus: a, View of head. b, Lying in grass. c, Standing. d, Grazing.

No. 873, 300fr — Ammotragus lervia: a, Pair. b, View of head. c, Standing on mountain ledge. d, Standing, with purple mountain in background

No. 874, 375fr — Diceros bicornis: a, View of head. b, Facing right, line of dark green foliage in background. c, Facing left. d, Facing right, with trees in background.

No. 875, 400fr — Panthera pardus: a, On tree branch. b, Lying in grass. c, Standing. d, View of head.

No. 876, 450fr: a, Head of Theropithecus gelada. b, Cercopithecus aethiops. c, Papio anubis. d, Adult and juvenile Thereopithecus gelada.

No. 877, 450fr — Hippopotamus amphibius: a, Pair laying in mud. b, With open mouth. c, Standing. d, Herd.

No. 878, 475fr — Oryx dammah: a, Facing right, green foliage in background. b, View of head. c, Pair. d, Grazing, mountain in background.

No. 879, 500fr — Panthera leo: a, Male on female. b, Females at waterhole. c, Female and cub. d, Female and male.

No. 880, 600fr — Loxodonta africana: a, With tree at right. b, Facing right. c, View of head. With tree and mountain in background.

No. 881, 750fr — Syncerus caffer: a, Juvenile, adult grazing. b, Adult in field. c, Pair lying on ground. d, With grass in mouth.

No. 882, 1000fr, Pair of Diceros bicornis. No. 883, 1000fr, Pair of Hippopotamus amphibius fighting. No. 884, 1500fr, Panthera leo with kill.

Illustration reduced.

2000, Aug. 1　　　　　Perf. 13¼
Horiz. Strips of 4, #a-d
870-881　A215　Set of 12　　90.00 90.00
Souvenir Sheets
882-884　A215　Set of 3　　16.00 16.00

Nos. 882-884 each contain one 36x51mm stamp.

Miniature Sheet

Baseball Player — A216

2000, Oct. 11　　Litho. & Embossed
885　A216　3000fr gold & multi　10.00 10.00
Exists with silver background.

High-five of Teenagers — A217

No. 886: a, Moon Hee-jun and Lee Jae-won. b, Jang Woo-hyuk and ear of Tony An. c, Tony an and Kang Ta. d, Jang Woo-hyuk. e, Entire group. f, Kang Ta. g, Moon Hee-jun. h, Lee Jae-won. i, Tony An.

2000　　　　　　　　　　Litho.
886　A217　150fr Sheet of 9, #a-i　4.50 4.50

Sports and Chess — A218

No. 887, 30fr — Dogs involved in sport activities: a, Sled dogs. b, Dog racing. c, Hunting dogs. d, Dogs and skier.

No. 888, 70fr — Various sports: a, Petanque. b, Rugby. c, Archery. d, Jai alai.

No. 889, 250fr — 2000 Summer Olympics, Sydney: a, Fencing. b, Judo. c, Tennis. d, Boxing.

No. 890, 300fr — 2000 Summer Olympics, Sydney: a, Cycling. b, Basketball. c, Beach volleyball. d, Baseball.

No. 891, 400fr — Soccer players: a, Zinedine Zidane. b, Lilian Thuram. c, Yuri Djorkaeff. d, Nicolas Anelka

No. 892, 475fr — 2000 Summer Olympics, Sydney: a, Table tennis. b, Equestrian. c, Swimming. d, Kayaking.

No. 893, 500fr — Golf: a, Man with white pants swinging club. b, Golfer analyzing putt. c, Man with black pants swinging club. d, Woman golfer.

No. 894, 750fr — Formula I race drivers: a, Michael Schumacher. b, Mikka Hakkinen. c, Ralf Schumacher. d, David Coulthard.

No. 895, 1000fr — Chess: a, Knight with shield. b, Knight on donkey. c, Knight with attendant. d, Horses and wheeled castle. 2000fr, Venus Williams.

2001, Jan. 31　　　　　Perf. 13¼
Sheets of 4, #a-d
887-895　A218　Set of 9　　67.50 67.50
Souvenir Sheet
896　A218　2000fr multi　　9.00 9.00

2000 Summer Olympics, Sydney (No. 896). No. 896 contains one 36x51mm stamp.

Trains — A219

No. 897, 200fr: a, Mallard, 1935. b, P8 Prussian, 1908. c, F2A, 1936. b, 240 P, 1940.

No. 898, 300fr: a, NSB No. 3641. b, New Zealand Railways Sereis EW. c, Series 277, Renfe. d, Series DF4 Vent d'Est IV Co-Co.

No. 899, 400fr: a, SNCF Series 9100 2-D-2, 1950. b, SNCF Series 72000 C-C, 1967. c, CC 21000, 1969. d, VL-80, 1963.

No. 900, 475fr: a, GNER Eurostar. b, Electric EMU ETR 500. c, DER OBB 1016 001. d, GNER train.

No. 901, 500fr: a, OL-49, 1951. b, Pacific Series 16E, 1935. c, Andaluces 030, 1877. d, Franco-Crosti Gr. 743, 1937.

No. 902, 500fr: a, JR West 8-car unit E4. b, TGV KTX. c, 300 Series unit J3. d, E3 Series unit R6.

No. 903, 600fr: a, 2D2 PO, 1926. b, Metropolitan BB Vickers, 1920. c, DB ET 491, 1935. d, Series D, 1925.

No. 904, 600fr: a, Electric EMU 490. b, Acela, 2001. c, CFF-FFS Electric EMU RABe 500. d, ICE-T Bavereihe 41.

No. 905, 750fr: a, Single Driver, 1870. b, Great Western Railway Castle, 1923. c, Schools Class, 1930. d, 230 Besa, 1905.

No. 906, 750fr: a, TGV Thalys. b, TGV Duplex. c, TGV La Poste. d, TGV Atlantique.

1500fr, SAR Series 26 2-D-2. 2000fr, TGV Sud-est.

2001, June 22　　　　　Litho.
Sheets of 4, #a-d
897-906　A219　Set of 10　　90.00 90.00
Souvenir Sheets
907-908　A219　Set of 2　　16.00 16.00

Nos. 907-908 each contain one 51x36mm stamp.

British Royalty — A220

No. 909, 300fr — Queen Mother: a, With King George VI. b, With young daughter. c, With Prince Charles. d, Waving. e, Wearing tiara and yellow dress. f, Wearing pink dress and hat. g, Wearing green dress and hat. h, Holding flowers. i, With dogs.

No. 910, 300fr — Prince William wearing: a, Black suit with lapel handkerchief. b, Suit with red and blue vest. c, Suit with gold vest. d, Sweater, looking right. e, Black suit and dark blue tie. f, Sweater, facing forward. g, Blue shirt with button. h, Dark blue shirt without button. i, Light blue suit.

2001, July 22   *Perf. 13¼*
Sheets of 9, #a-i
909-910 A220   Set of 2   24.00 24.00
No. 910 contains nine 36x51mm stamps.

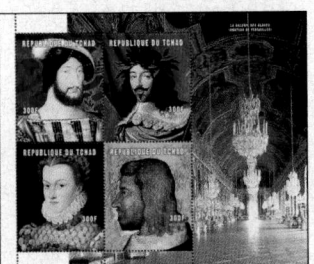

French Rulers — A221

No. 911, 300fr: a, King Francis I. b, King Louis XIII. c, Elizabeth of Austria, consort of King Charles IX. d, King John II the Good.
No. 912, 375fr: a, King Louis XIV. b, Francis I, diff. c, King Louis XVI. d, King Louis XVIII.
No. 913, 475fr: a, King Louis XV as child. b, King Louis XV as adult. c, Queen Marie Antoinette. d, King Charles VII.
No. 914, 500fr — Napoleon Bonaparte wearing: a, White tunic. b, Black jacket. c, Emperor's robes. d, Red tunic.

2001, July 22
Sheets of 4, #a-d
911-914 A221   Set of 4   30.00 30.00
Stamps of Nos. 911-913 exist in souvenir sheets of 1. Value, set $70.

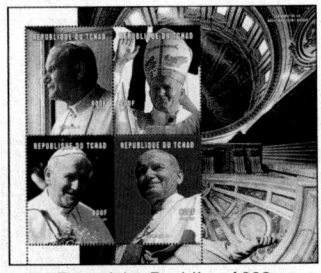

Pope John Paul II — A222

No. 915, 800fr: a, Standing in room, looking left. b, Waving. c, Holding flowers. d, With blue sky background.
No. 916, 1000fr: a, Wearing red hat. b, Wearing miter, waving. c, Bending to kiss ground. d, Wearing miter, holding crucifix.
4000fr, Wearing zucchetto.

2001   Litho.   *Perf. 13¼*
Sheets of 4, #a-d
915-916 A222   Set of 2   32.50 32.50
Miniature Sheet
Litho. & Embossed
917 A222 4000fr gold & multi   22.50 22.50
Issued: Nos. 915-916, 7/22; No. 917, 7/23. No. 917 contains one 60x90mm stamp and exists with a silver background. Stamps of Nos. 915-916 exist in souvenir sheets of 1. Value, set $60.

Famous Men — A223

Designs: 200fr, Charles Darwin (1809-82), naturalist. 250fr, Christopher Columbus (1451-1506), explorer. 300fr, Jacques-Yves Cousteau (1910-97), marine scientist. 350fr, Albert Schweitzer (1875-1965), missionary. 400fr, Juan Manuel Fangio (1911-95), race car driver. 450fr, Nicolaus Copernicus (1473-1543), astronomer. 500fr, Robert Stephenson

(1803-59), engineer. 550fr, Etienne Chambron, high speed rail pioneer. 600fr, Garry Kasparov, chess player. 750fr, Lord Robert Baden-Powell (1857-1941), founder of scouting. 800fr, Neil Armstrong, astronaut. 1000fr, Sir Alexander Fleming (1881-1955), bacteriologist.

2001, Oct. 30   Litho.
918-929 A223   Set of 12   29.00 29.00
Nos. 918-929 exist in souvenir sheets of 1. Value, set $115.

Fossils, Dinosaurs, Meteorites and Minerals — A224

No. 930, 300fr — Fossils: a, Stenosaurus bollensis. b, Rhamphorhynchus. c, Archaeopteryx lithographica. d, Keichousaurus hui.
No. 931, 375fr — Dinosaurs: a, Mesadactylus. b, Pteranodon. c, Tropeognathus. d, Quetzalcoatlus.
No. 932, 400fr — Meteorites found in: a, India. b, Nigeria. c, US. d, Australia.
No. 933, 500fr — Dinosaurs: a, Deinonychus. b, Seismosaurus. c, Pleurocoelus, Acrocanthosaur. d, Styracosaurus.
No. 934, 500fr — Minerals: a, Fluorite. b, Pyrite. c, Wulfenite. d, Merovingian scoria.
No. 935, 550fr — Meteorites found in: a, Antarctica. b, Libya. c, USSR. d, China.
No. 936, 600fr — Minerals: a, Magnetite. b, Kunzite. c, Apophyllite, Stilbite. d, Fluorite, diff.
No. 937, 750fr — Minerals: a, Quartz. b, Merovingian scoria, diff. c, Epidote. d, Amethyst, agate.
3000fr, Tyrannosaurus rex, vert.

2001, Dec. 27   Litho.
Sheets of 4, #a-d
930-937 A224   Set of 8   72.50 72.50
Miniature Sheet
Litho. & Embossed
938 A224 3000fr gold & multi   17.00 17.00
No. 938 contains one 60x90mm stamp and exists with silver background.

French Kings — A225

Designs: No. 939, 3000fr, Louis IX. No. 940, 3000fr, Francis I. No. 941, 3000fr, Henry IV. No. 942, 3000fr, Louis XIII. No. 943, 3000fr, Louis XV.

2002, Apr. 10   Litho. & Embossed
Gold & Multicolored
939-943 A225   Set of 5   50.00 50.00
Nos. 939-943 exist with silver background.

Egyptian Treasures A225a

Designs: No. 943A, 3000fr, Painted wooden box. No. 943B, 3000fr, Nekhbet vulture. No. 943C, 3000fr, Oushebti of Tutankhamen, vert. No. 943D, 3000fr, Pair of royal scepters, vert. No. 943E, 3000fr, Diadem, vert. No. 943F, 3000fr, Gold-plated throne, vert. No. 943G, 3000fr, Cynocephalic pectoral, vert. No. 943H, 3000fr, Coffin of Tutankhamen, vert. No. 943I, 3000fr, Statue of Ka, vert. No. 943J, 3000fr, Duck earring, vert. No. 943K, 3000fr, Lion-shaped vase, vert. No. 943L, 3000fr, Canopic dais and chapel, vert.

Embossed on Gold Paper
2002, Apr. 10   *Perf. 13¼*
943A-943L A225a   Set of 12   140.00 140.00

Artists and Their Paintings — A226

On Nos. 944-957, painting titles (in French) and artist's birth and death dates are in margins adjacent to each stamp. On Nos. 958-962 painting titles are not shown, but artist's name is in sheet margin.
No. 944, 150fr: a, Berthe Morisot (1841-95). b, Cache-cache. c, Le Berceau. d, Au bal. e, Jeune femme se poudrant. f, Paule Gobillard peignant.
No. 945, 200fr: a, Marc Chagall (1887-1985). b, Nature morte. c, Le violoniste vert. d, La maison bleue. e, Mariage. f, Le soldat ivre.
No. 946, 250fr: a, Camille Pissarro (1830-1903). b, Les chataigniers a Osny. c, Le verger. d, Le repos des glaneuses. e, Jeune paysanne prenant son cafe. f, La bergére.
No. 947, 300fr: a, Alfred Sisley (1839-99). b, Le pont de Villeneuve la Garenne. c, Allee de jardin a Louveciennes. d, Meule de foin bord du Loing. e, Moret sur Loing. f, Moulin a Moret.
No. 948, 325fr: a, Paul Delvaux (1897-1994). b, La voix publique. c, Nocturnes. d, Balgnade des Nymphes. e, Pygmalion. f, Jeunes femmes revant.
No. 949, 350fr: a, Edouard Manet (1832-83). b, Le Déjeuner sur l'herbe. c, Olympia. d, Le fifre. e, La serveuse de bocks. f, Le balcon.
No. 950, 375fr: a, Vincent van Gogh (1853-90). b, Champ de blé avec cypres. c, Rue a Auvers. d, La sieste. e, Chambre jaune a Arles. f, Rue de village.
No. 951, 400fr: a, Salvador Dali (1904-89). b, Cannibalisme en automne. c, Corpus Hypercubicus. d, Le sommeil. e, Le tentation de St. Antoine. f, Meditation sur harpe.
No. 952, 425fr: a, Paul Cézanne (1839-1906). b, Les baigneurs. c, Les grandes baigneuses (light blue background). d, Les grandes baigneuses, diff. (dark blue background). e, Les baigneueses. f, Les baigneurs au repos.
No. 953, 450fr: a, Pablo Picasso (1881-1973). b, Les demoiselles d'Avignon. c, Femme a l'eventail. d, La danse. e, La vie. f, La mere et son fils.
No. 954, 475fr: a, Amadeo Modigliani (1884-1920). b, Nu souche un divan. c, Nu debout. d, Cariatide debout. e, Nu allongé. f, Nu assis de dos.
No. 955, 500fr: a, Auguste Renoir (1841-1919). b, Diane chasseresse. c, Nu allongé. d, Baigneuses. e, Baigneuse assise. f, Nymphe au printemps.

No. 956, 550fr: a, Edgar Degas (1834-1917). b, Femme se coiffant. c, Aprés le bain (view of front of seated woman). d, Femme se peignant. e, Aprés le bain (view of back of woman). f, Aprés le bain (woman dressing).
No. 957, 600fr: a, Henri Matisse (1869-1954). b, Le nu bleu. c, Le genou levé. d, Nu assis un fauteuil. e, Odalisques. f, Nu allongé.
No. 958, 1500fr, Gustave Caillebotte. No. 959, 1500fr, Picasso, diff. No. 960, 1500fr, Auguste Renoir, diff. No. 961, 2000fr, Pablo Picasso, diff. No. 962, 2000fr, Van Gogh, diff.

2002, Apr. 10   *Perf. 12¾x13¼*
Sheets of 6, #a-f
944-957 A226   Set of 14   140.00 140.00
Souvenir Sheets
Perf. 13¼x12¾
958-962 A226   Set of 5   27.50 27.50
Nos. 944a-955a and 957a exist in souvenir sheets of 1 that are perf. 13¼x12¾. Value, set $92.50.

Miniature Sheet

Zeppelin NT — A227

No. 963: a, 475fr, Over Lake Constance. b, 500fr, Over Frankfurt. c, 600fr, Over Nürburgring, Germany. d, 750fr, At 2001 Salon du Bourget.

2002, Oct. 30   *Perf. 13¼*
963 A227   Sheet of 4, #a-d   11.00 11.00
Nos. 963a-963d exist in souvenir sheets of 1. Value, set $45.

Fauna and Mushrooms — A228

No. 964, 150fr: a, Hemichromis lifalili. b, Trichechus senegalensis. c, Synodontis nigriventris. d, Gnathonemus petersii. e, Ctenopoma ansorgii. f, Pseudocrenilabrus multicolor.
No. 965, 300fr, vert.: a, Nectarina venusta. b, Lamprotornis splendidus. c, Poicephalus meyeri. d, Halcyon leucocephala. e, Quelea quelea. f, Merops pusillus.
No. 966, 350fr, vert.: a, Terathopius ecaudatus. b, Gymnogyps californianus. c, Buteo jamaicensis. d, Lophaetus occipitalis. e, Aquila rapax. f, Melierax metabates.
No. 967, 375fr, vert.: a, Elanus caeruleus. b, Harpia harpyja. c, Gyps rueppellii. d, Milvus migrans. e, Torgos tracheliotus. f, Aquila chrysaetos.
No. 968, 550fr: a, Kallimoides rumia. b, Zophopetes dysmephila. c, Megalopalpus zymna. d, Coeliades forestan. e, Catopsilia florella. f, Anaphaesis aurota.
No. 969, 600fr: a, Amanita muscaria. b, Amanita rubescens. c, Cortinarius orellanus. d, Hygrophorus hypothejus. e, Leccinum piceinum. f, Strobilomyces strobilaceus.

2003, June 2   Litho.
Sheets of 6, #a-f
964-969 A228   Set of 6   55.00 55.00
Stamps of Nos. 965-969 exist in a set of twelve souvenir sheets of two, with each souvenir sheet of two containing adjacent stamps found in the sheet of six. Value, set $160.

Chad - Taiwan Cooperation — A229

Flags and: 50fr, Grain. 100fr, Surgeon's hands, Red Cross. 150fr, Bridge. 300fr, Handshake, maps.

2003, Dec. 1
970-973	A229	Set of 4	2.50	2.50
973a		Booklet pane, 2 each #970-973	5.00	—
		Complete booklet, #973a	5.00	
973b		Souvenir sheet, #970-973	2.50	2.50

AIDS Prevention
A230

Red ribbon and: 50fr, People under umbrella. 100fr, Man and woman. 150fr, Doctor. 300fr, "Prudence, Abstinence, Fidelité."

2004, July 7   Litho.   Perf. 13x12¾
974-977	A230	Set of 4	2.50	2.50

Opening of Petroleum Refinery, 1st Anniv. A231

Pres. Idriss Deby opening pipeline and: 150fr, Storage tank. 350fr, Storage tanks. 400fr, Refinery. 500fr, Tower, vert.

2004, Oct. 10   Perf. 12¾x13, 13x12¾
978-981	A231	Set of 4	6.50	6.50

Women's Hairstyles A232

Designs: 150fr, Figuerier. 350fr, Sakkindjala. 550fr, Kileskou. 575fr, Dabbou.

2005, Mar. 8   Perf. 13
982-985	A232	Set of 4	8.00	8.00

Toumai Skull A233

Color of skull: 25fr, Purple. 50fr, Green. 100fr, Gray. 150fr, Red. 1500fr, Gray.

2005, July 19   Litho.   Perf. 12¾x13
986-989	A233	Set of 4	1.40	1.40

Souvenir Sheet
990	A233	1500fr multi	5.75	5.75

SEMI-POSTAL STAMPS

> Catalogue values for unused stamps in this section are for Never Hinged items.

Anti-Malaria Issue
Common Design Type
Perf. 12½x12
1962, Apr. 7   Engr.   Unwmk.
B1	CD108	25fr + 5fr orange	1.00	.45

Freedom from Hunger Issue
Common Design Type
1963, Mar. 21   Perf. 13
B2	CD112	25fr + 5fr dk grn, dk bl & brn	1.00	.45

Red Cross, Mother and Children — SP1

1974, Oct. 2   Photo.   Perf. 12½x13
B3	SP1	30fr + 10fr multi	1.00	.20

Red Cross of Chad, first anniversary.

AIR POST STAMPS

> Catalogue values for unused stamps in this section are for Never Hinged items.

Olympic Games Issue
French Equatorial Africa No. C37
Surcharged in Red

Unwmk.
1960, Dec. 15   Engr.   Perf. 13
C1	AP8	250fr on 500fr grnsh blk, blk & slate	12.00	5.00

17th Olympic Games, Rome, Aug. 25-Sept. 11. Surcharge 46mm wide; illustration reduced.

Red Bishops — AP1

Discus Thrower — AP2

Birds in pairs: 100fr, Scarlet-chested sunbird. 200fr, African paradise flycatcher. 250fr, Malachite kingfisher. 500fr, Nubian carmine bee-eater.

1961-63   Unwmk.   Engr.   Perf. 13
C2	AP1	50fr dk grn, mag & blk	1.25	.35
C3	AP1	100fr multi	3.75	1.25
C4	AP1	200fr multi	6.50	1.90
C5	AP1	250fr dk bl, grn & dp org ('63)	10.00	3.00
C6	AP1	500fr multi	22.50	6.50
		Nos. C2-C6 (5)	44.00	13.00

Air Afrique Issue
Common Design Type
1962, Feb. 17   Unwmk.   Perf. 13
C7	CD107	25fr lt bl, org brn & blk	1.00	.20

Abidjan Games Issue
1962, July 21   Photo.   Perf. 12x12½
C8	AP2	100fr brn, lt grn & blk	3.50	.75

African Postal Union Issue
Common Design Type
1963, Sept. 8   Unwmk.   Perf. 12½
C9	CD114	85fr dk bl, ocher & red	2.40	.40

Air Afrique Issue, 1963
Common Design Type
1963, Nov. 19   Perf. 13x12
C10	CD115	50fr multi	2.40	.40

Europafrica Issue
Common Design Type
1963, Nov. 30   Photo.   Perf. 12x13
C11	CD116	50fr dp grn, yel & dk brn	1.75	.40

Mail Truck and Broussard Plane — AP4

Unwmk.
1963, Dec. 16   Engr.   Perf. 13
C12	AP4	100fr sl grn, ultra & red brn	4.00	.20

Chiefs of State Issue

Map and Presidents of Chad, Congo, Gabon and Central African Republic AP4a

1964, June 23   Photo.   Perf. 12½
C13	AP4a	100fr multi	2.40	.20

See note after Central African Republic No. C19.

Europafrica Issue, 1964

Globe and Emblems of Industry and Agriculture — AP5

1964, July 20   Perf. 13x12
C14	AP5	50fr brn, pur & dp org	1.75	.30

See note after Cameroun No. 402.

Soccer — AP6

Designs: 50fr, Javelin throw, vert. 100fr, High jump, vert. 200fr, Runners.

1964, Aug. 12   Engr.   Perf. 13
C15	AP6	25fr yel grn, sl grn & org brn	.75	.20
C16	AP6	50fr org brn, ind & brt bl	1.75	.30
C17	AP6	100fr blk, red & brt grn	3.50	.50
C18	AP6	200fr bis, blk & car	6.00	1.10
a.		Min. sheet of 4, #C15-C18	18.00	6.50
		Nos. C15-C18 (4)	12.00	2.10

18th Olympic Games, Tokyo, 10/10-25/64.

Communications Symbols — AP7

1964, Nov. 2   Litho.   Perf. 12½x13
C19	AP7	25fr lil, dk brn & lt red brn	1.00	.20

Pan-African and Malagasy Posts and Telecommunications Cong., Cairo, Oct. 24-Nov. 6.

President John F. Kennedy (1917-63) — AP8

1964, Nov. 3   Photo.   Perf. 12½
C20	AP8	100fr multi	2.40	.70
a.		Souvenir sheet of 4	12.00	6.00

ICY Emblem — AP9

1965, July 5   Photo.   Perf. 13
C21	AP9	100fr multi	1.50	.25

International Cooperation Year, 1965.

Abraham Lincoln — AP10

1965, Sept. 7   Unwmk.   Perf. 13
C22	AP10	100fr multi	2.25	.35

Centenary of death of Abraham Lincoln.

Musical Instrument Type
Design: 100fr, Xylophone (marimba).

1965, Oct. 26   Engr.   Perf. 13
Size: 48x27mm
C23 A18 100fr ocher, brt bl & vio bl   2.75   .85

Sir Winston Spencer Churchill (1874-1965) AP11

1965, Nov. 23   Engr.   Perf. 13
C24 AP11 50fr dk grn & blk   1.40   .20

Dr. Albert Schweitzer and Outstretched Hands — AP12

1966, Feb. 15   Photo.   Perf. 12½
C25 AP12 100fr multi   2.75   .25
Dr. Albert Schweitzer (1875-1965), medical missionary, theologian and musician.

Air Afrique Issue, 1966
Common Design Type

1966, Aug. 31   Photo.   Perf. 13
C26 CD123 30fr yel grn, blk & gray   .75   .20

White-throated Bee-eater — AP13

Birds: 50fr, Blue-eared glossy starling. 200fr, African pygmy kingfisher. 250fr, Red-throated bee-eater. 500fr, Little green bee-eater.

1966-67   Photo.   Perf. 13x12½
C27 AP13 50fr gold & multi   1.25   .20
C28 AP13 100fr bluish gray & multi   3.50   .30
C29 AP13 200fr grnsh gray & multi   6.75   .65
C30 AP13 250fr pale bl & multi   7.50   .80
C31 AP13 500fr pale sal & multi   14.00 1.75
   Nos. C27-C31 (5)   33.00 3.70
Issued: 100fr, 200fr, 500fr, 8/18/66; others, 3/21/67.
For surcharges see Nos. C67-C69.

Congress Hall — AP14

1967, Jan. 5   Photo.   Perf. 12½
C32 AP14 25fr multi   .75   .20
Opening of the new Congress Hall.

Breguet 19 Biplane — AP15

Planes: 30fr, Latécoère 631 hydroplane. 50fr, Douglas DC-3. 100fr, Piper Cherokee 6.

1967, Aug. 1   Engr.   Perf. 13
C33 AP15 25fr sky bl, sl grn & lt brn   .75   .20
C34 AP15 30fr sky bl, indigo & grn   1.00   .20
C35 AP15 50fr sky bl, ol bis & sl grn   1.75   .25
C36 AP15 100fr dk bl, sl grn & dk red   3.50   .35
   Nos. C33-C36 (4)   7.00 1.00
First anniversary of Air Chad.

African Postal Union Issue, 1967
Common Design Type

1967, Sept. 9   Engr.   Perf. 13
C37 CD124 100fr ol, brt pink & red brn   1.90   .40

Rock Painting Type of Regular Issue
1967, Dec. 19   Engr.   Perf. 13
Size: 48x27mm
C38 A32 100fr Masked dancers   8.00   .95
C39 A32 125fr Rabbit hunt   9.00 1.50

Downhill Skiing — AP16

1968, Feb. 5   Engr.   Perf. 13
C40 AP16 30fr shown   1.25   .20
C41 AP16 100fr Ski jump, vert.   3.25   .50
10th Winter Olympic Games, Grenoble, France, Feb. 6-18.

Konrad Adenauer (1876-1967), Chancellor of West Germany (1949-63) AP17

1968, Mar. 19   Photo.   Perf. 12½
C42 AP17 52fr grn, dk brn & lt lil   1.40   .30
   a.   Souvenir sheet of 4   6.00 2.40

The Snake Charmer, by Henri Rousseau — AP18

Design: 130fr, "War" by Henri Rousseau.

1968, May 14   Photo.   Perf. 13½
Size: 41x41mm
C43 AP18 100fr ultra & multi   3.50   .30
Size: 48x35mm
Perf. 12½
C44 AP18 130fr brn & multi   5.50   .40

Hurdlers — AP19

1968, Oct. 16   Engr.   Perf. 13
C45 AP19 32fr shown   1.00   .20
C46 AP19 80fr Relay race   2.75   .20
19th Olympic Games, Mexico City, 10/12-27.

PHILEXAFRIQUE Issue

The Actor Wolf (Bernard), by Jacques L. David AP20

1969, Jan. 15   Photo.   Perf. 12½
C47 AP20 100fr multi   3.75   .35
PHILEXAFRIQUE, Philatelic Exhib. in Abidjan, Feb. 14-23. Printed with alternating label.

2nd PHILEXAFRIQUE Issue
Common Design Type
50fr, Chad #J12 and Moundang Dancers.

1969, Feb. 14   Engr.   Perf. 13
C48 CD128 50fr red, brt bl, brn & grn   2.25   .30

Gustav Nachtigal and Tibesti Gorge, 1869 — AP21

#C50, Heinrich Barth & Lake Chad, 1851.

1969, Feb. 17
C49 AP21 100fr vio bl, dk brn & brn   2.40   .25
C50 AP21 100fr grn, pur & bl   2.40   .25
German explorers Gustav Nachtigal (1834-85) and Heinrich Barth (1821-65), and state visit of the Pres. of West Germany Heinrich Lubke.

Apollo 8, Earth and Moon — AP22

1969, Apr. 10   Photo.   Perf. 13
C51 AP22 100fr multi   2.10   .45
US Apollo 8 mission, the 1st men in orbit around the moon, Dec. 21-27, 1968.

Mahatma Gandhi — AP23

#C53, John F. Kennedy. #C54, Dr. Martin Luther King, Jr. #C55, Robert F. Kennedy.

1969, May 20   Photo.   Perf. 12½
C52 AP23 50fr blk & lt grn   1.25   .25
C53 AP23 50fr blk & tan   1.25   .25
C54 AP23 50fr blk & pink   1.25   .25
C55 AP23 50fr blk & lt vio bl   1.25   .25
   a.   Souvenir sheet of 4, #C52-C55   6.00 7.75
   Nos. C52-C55 (4)   5.00 1.00
Issued to honor exponents of non-violence.

Presidents Tombalbaye and Mobutu, Map and Flags of Chad and Congo — AP24

Embossed on Gold Foil
1969   Die-cut; Perf. 13½
C56 AP24 1000fr gold, dk bl & red   27.50 27.50
1st anniv. of the establishment of the Union of Central African States, comprising Chad, Congo Democratic Republic and Central African Republic.

Napoleon Visiting Hospital, by Alexandre Veron-Bellecourt — AP25

Paintings: 85fr, Battle of Wagram, by Horace Vernet. 130fr, Battle of Austerlitz, by Francois Pascal Gerard.

1969, July 23   Photo.   Perf. 12x12½
C57 AP25 30fr multi   1.10   .25
C58 AP25 85fr multi   2.40   .65
C59 AP25 130fr multi   4.25 1.25
   Nos. C57-C59 (3)   7.75 2.15
Bicentenary of birth of Napoleon I.

Apollo 11 Issue

Astronaut on Moon — AP26

Embossed on Gold Foil
1969, Oct. 17   Die-cut; Perf. 13½
C60 AP26 1000fr gold   27.50 19.00
See note after Algeria No. 427.

Village Life, by Goto Narcisse — AP27

No. 62, Women at the Market, by Iba N'Diaye. No. 63, Woman with Flowers, by Iba N'Diaye, vert.

1970 Photo. Perf. 12x12½, 12½x12
C61 AP27 100fr multi   3.25 .20
C62 AP27 250fr grn & multi   5.00 .35
C63 AP27 250fr brn & multi   5.00 .35
       Nos. C61-C63 (3)   13.25 .90

Issued: 100fr, Mar. 17; #C62-C63, Aug. 28.

Napoleon — AP27a

Designs: Nos. C63A, C63E, Napoleon II, Duke of Reichstadt, vert. No. C63B: g, 10fr, Crossing the Grand St. Bernard, by David. h, 25fr, Emperor Napoleon, by Gerard. i, 32fr, Marriage of Napoleon and Marie Louise, by Rouget. 40fr, Napoleon after return from Elba, vert.

Perf. 12x12½, 12½x12
1970-71   Litho.
C63A AP27a 10fr multicolored   4.00
C63B AP27a Strip of 3,
             #g.-i.   13.50

Embossed
Perf. 13
C63C AP27a 10fr gold   20.00
    f.   Sheet of 1, Imperf.   37.50

Souvenir Sheets
Litho.
Perf. 13x13½
C63D AP27a 40fr multicolored   10.00

Embossed
Imperf
C63E AP27a 10fr gold, like
             #C63A   37.50

#C63A is printed se-tenant with label. #C63D contains one 43x67mm stamp. #C63Cf contains one 53x42mm stamp with same size design as #C63Bg. #C63E contains one 43x104mm stamp with same size design as #C63A.
No. C63E probably was not available in Chad.
Issued: #C63B, 6/12; #C63A, C63D-C63E, 4/1971; #C63C, 11/1/71.

EXPO Emblem and Osaka Print — AP28

EXPO Emblem and: 100fr, Tower of the Sun. 125fr, Osaka print, diff.

1970, June 30   Engr.   Perf. 13
C64 AP28 50fr bl, red brn & sl
                       grn   .70 .20
C65 AP28 100fr red, yel grn &
                       Prus bl   1.40 .20
C66 AP28 125fr blk, dk red & bis   1.90 .20
       Nos. C64-C66 (3)   4.00 .65

Issued to publicize EXPO '70 International Exhibition, Osaka, Japan, Mar. 15-Sept. 13.

1968 Summer Olympics, 1970 World Cup Soccer Championships, Mexico AP28a

1970, July 1   Litho.   Perf. 12½x12
C66A AP28a 5fr Flags, soccer
                      players   1.40

Souvenir Sheet
Perf. 13½x13
C66C AP28a 15fr Olympic
             torch, soccer
             player   6.25

No. C66A printed in sheets of 2 + 2 labels. No. C66C contains one 66x43mm stamp. For overprints see Nos. C88A-C88B.

Nos. C28-C30 Surcharged in Carmine with New Value and Bars and Overprinted:
a. "APOLLO XI / 1er débarquement sur la lune/20 juillet 1969"
b. "APOLLO XII / Exploration de la lune / 19 Novembre 1969"
c. "APOLLO XIII / Exploit spatial / 11-17 avril 1970"

1970, July 9   Photo.   Perf. 13x12½
C67 AP13 (a) 50fr on 100fr   1.90 .25
C68 AP13 (b) 100fr on 200fr   3.25 .35
C69 AP13 (c) 125fr on 250fr   4.75 .50
       Nos. C67-C69 (3)   9.90 1.10

Space missions of Apollo 11, 12 and 13.

DC-8 "Fort Lamy" over Airport — AP29

1970, Aug. 5   Perf. 12½
C70 AP29 30fr dk sl grn & multi 1.10 .20

Souvenir Sheet

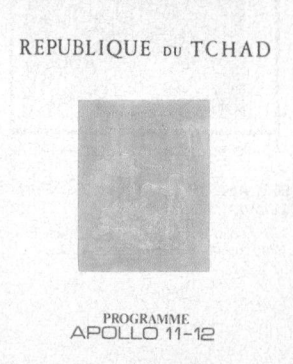

Apollo 12 — AP29a

1970, Sept.   Embossed   Imperf.
C70A AP29a 25fr gold   35.00

No. C70A probably was not available in Chad.

The Visitation, Venetian School, 15th Century AP30

Paintings, Venetian School: 25fr, Nativity, 15th century. 30fr, Virgin and Child, c. 1350.

1970, Dec. 15 Photo. Perf. 12½x12
C71 AP30 20fr gold & multi   .75 .20
C72 AP30 25fr gold & multi   1.10 .20
C73 AP30 30fr gold & multi   1.25 .20
       Nos. C71-C73 (3)   3.10 .60

Christmas 1970. See Nos. C105-C108.

Post Office Mauritius and Emblem AP31

1971, Jan. 23   Engr.   Perf. 13
C74 AP31 10fr shown   .20 .20
C75 AP31 20fr Tuscany #23   .40 .20
C76 AP31 30fr France #8   .60 .20
C77 AP31 60fr US #2   1.10 .20
C78 AP31 80fr Japan #8   1.50 .25
C79 AP31 100fr Saxony #1   1.90 .25
    a.   Souvenir sheet of 6, #C74-C79   8.00 3.25
       Nos. C74-C79 (6)   5.70 1.30

Publicity for PHILEXOCAM, philatelic exhibition, Fort Lamy, Jan. 23-30.

Gamal Abdel Nasser — AP32

1971, Feb. 16   Photo.   Perf. 12½
C80 AP32 75fr multi   1.10 .20

In memory of Gamal Abdel Nasser (1918-1970), President of Egypt.

Presidents Mobutu, Bokassa and Tombalbaye — AP33

1971, Apr. 28   Photo.   Perf. 13
C81 AP33 100fr multi   1.75 .20

Return of Central African Republic to the United States of Central Africa which also includes Congo Democratic Republic and Chad.

Map of Africa, Communications Network and Symbols — AP34

1971, May 17   Engr.   Perf. 13
C82 AP34 125fr ultra, sl grn & brn
                       red   2.25 .20

Pan-African telecommunications system.

Boys Around Campfire, Torii AP35

1971, Aug. 24   Photo.   Perf. 12½
C83 AP35 250fr multi   5.50 .40

13th Boy Scout World Jamboree, Asagiri Plain, Japan, Aug. 2-10.

White Egret — AP36

1971, Sept. 28 Photo. Perf. 13x12½
C84 AP36 1000fr blk, dk bl &
                   ocher   75.00 6.75

Greek Marathon Runners — AP37

45fr, Ancient Olympic Stadium. 75fr, Greek wrestlers. 130fr, Olympic Stadium, Athens, 1896.

1971, Oct. 5   Perf. 12½
C85 AP37 40fr multi   .75 .20
C86 AP37 45fr multi   1.00 .20
C87 AP37 75fr multi   1.75 .25
C88 AP37 130fr multi   1.90 .35
       Nos. C85-C88 (4)   5.40 1.00

75th anniv. of modern Olympic Games.

Nos. C66A, C66C Ovptd. in Gold

1971   Litho.   Perf. 12½x12
C88A AP28a 5fr on #C66A   2.50

Souvenir Sheet
Perf. 13½x13
C88B AP28a 15fr on #C66C   5.50

Overprint on No. C88B is 36mm long.

Duke Ellington — AP38

Charles de Gaulle — AP39

50fr, Sidney Bechet. 100fr, Louis Armstrong.

1971, Oct. 20   Litho.   Perf. 13
C89 AP38 50fr multi   2.00 .20
C90 AP38 75fr lt bl & multi   3.00 .30
C91 AP38 100fr multi   5.00 .40
     Nos. C89-C91 (3)   10.00 .90

Famous American jazz musicians.

Lithographed and Embossed
1971, Nov. 9   Perf. 12½

Design: No. C93, Félix Eboué.

C92 AP39 200fr grn, yel grn &
                    gold   8.00 2.75
C93 AP39 200fr bl, lt bl & gold   8.00 2.75
  a.   Souv. sheet, #C92-C93 + label 20.00 5.50

Charles de Gaulle (1890-1970), pres. of France.

African Postal Union Issue, 1971
Common Design Type

Design: 100fr, Sao antelope head and UAMPT building, Brazzaville, Congo.

1971, Nov. 13   Photo.   Perf. 13x13½
C94 CD135 100fr bl & multi   1.50 .20

Apollo 15 Rocket AP40

80fr, Apollo 15 capsule, horiz. 150fr, Lunar module on Moon, horiz. 250fr, Astronaut making tests. 300fr, Moon-buggy. #C100, Successful splashdown, horiz. #C101, Apollo 15 insignia.

1972, Jan. 5   Litho.   Perf. 13½
C95 AP40 40fr multi   .50 .20
C96 AP40 80fr multi   .90 .20
C97 AP40 150fr multi   1.50 .30
C98 AP40 250fr multi   2.50 .45
C99 AP40 300fr multi   3.00 .60
C100 AP40 500fr multi   5.50 1.40
     Nos. C95-C100 (6)   13.90 3.15

Souvenir Sheet
C101 AP40 500fr multi   8.00 1.25

Apollo 15 moon landing.

Soyuz 11 Link-up — AP41

Designs: 30fr, Soyuz 11 on launching pad, vert. 50fr, No. C108, Cosmonauts in uniform. 200fr, V. I. Patsayev. No. C106, V. N. Volkov. 400fr, G. L. Dobrovolsky. No. C109, Three cosmonauts.

1972, Jan. 5   Perf. 13½x13
C102 AP41 30fr multi   .25 .20
C103 AP41 50fr multi   .45 .20
C104 AP41 100fr multi   .80 .25
C105 AP41 200fr multi   2.00 .50
C106 AP41 300fr multi   3.25 .75
C107 AP41 400fr multi   4.25 1.10
     Nos. C102-C107 (6)   11.00 3.00

Souvenir Sheets
C108 AP41 300fr multi   3.50 1.00
C109 AP41 400fr multi   4.00 1.40

Soyuz 11 link-up project.

Bobsledding — AP42

Design: 100fr, Slalom.

1972, Feb. 24   Engr.   Perf. 13
C110 AP42 50fr Prus bl & rose
                    red   1.00 .20
C111 AP42 100fr red lil & slate
                    grn   1.90 .20

11th Winter Olympic Games, Sapporo, Japan, Feb. 3-13.

Pres. Tombalbaye Type, 1972

1972, Apr. 13   Litho.   Perf. 13
C112 AP63 70fr multi   .90 .20
C113 AP63 80fr multi   1.10 .20

11th Winter Olympic Type, 1972

130fr, Speed skating. #C115, Ice hockey. #C116, Ski jumping. 250fr, 4-man bobsled.

1972, Apr. 13   Perf. 13½
C114 A64 130fr multi   1.40 .45
C115 A64 200fr multi   2.50 .60

Souvenir Sheets
C116 A64 200fr multi   3.25 .75
C117 A64 250fr multi   4.25 1.10

Scout Jamboree Type, 1972

Designs: 100fr, Cooking preparation. 120fr, Lord Baden Powell. 250fr, Hiking.

1972, May 15
C118 A67 100fr multi   2.10 .30
C119 A67 120fr multi   2.40 .40

Souvenir Sheet
C120 A67 250fr multi   8.50 .75

Zebras — AP43

African wild animals: 30fr, Mandrills. 100fr, African elephants. 130fr, Gazelles. 150fr, Hippopotamuses. 200fr, Lion cub.

1972, May 15   Litho.   Perf. 13
C121 AP43 20fr multi   .35 .20
C122 AP43 30fr multi   .50 .20
C123 AP43 100fr multi   1.40 .35
C124 AP43 130fr multi   2.25 .50
C125 AP43 150fr multi   3.50 .75
     Nos. C121-C125 (5)   8.00 2.00

Souvenir Sheet
C126 AP43 200fr multi   35.00 4.00

View of Venice, by Caffi — AP44

Paintings by Ippolito Caffi: 40fr, Sailing ship and Doge's Palace, vert. 140fr, Grand Canal, vert.

1972, May 23   Photo.
C127 AP44 40fr gold & multi   1.10 .20
C128 AP44 45fr gold & multi   1.90 .20
C129 AP44 140fr gold & multi   3.50 .60
     Nos. C127-C129 (3)   6.50 1.00

UNESCO campaign to save Venice.

11th Winter Olympic Winners Type, 1972

Designs: 150fr, Slalom, B. Cochran, US. 200fr, Women's figure skating, B. Schuba, Austria. 250fr, Ice hockey, USSR. 300fr, 2-man bobsled. W. Zimmerer and P. Utzschneider, West Germany.

1972, June 15   Perf. 14½
C130 A69 150fr gold & multi   3.00 .45
C131 A69 200fr gold & multi   3.75 .55

Souvenir Sheets
C132 A69 250fr gold & multi   3.25 .80
C133 A69 300fr gold & multi   3.75 1.25

Nos. C130-C131 exist se-tenant with label showing earth satellite.

Daudet, "Tartarin de Tarascon," Book Year Emblem — AP45

1972, July 22   Engr.   Perf. 13
C134 AP45 100fr dk red, lil & dk
                    brn   1.90 .20

Intl. Book Year, 1972, and to honor Alphonse Daudet (1840-1897), French writer.

20th Summer Olympics Type, 1972

Designs (TV Tower, Munich and): 100fr, Gymnast. 120fr, Pole vault. 150fr, Fencing. 250fr, Hammer throw. 300fr, Boxing.

1972, Aug. 15
C135 A70 100fr gold & multi   2.10 .30
C136 A70 120fr gold & multi   2.50 .35
C137 A70 150fr gold & multi   3.25 .60
     Nos. C135-C137 (3)   7.85 1.15

Souvenir Sheets
C138 A70 250fr gold & multi   3.50 .90
C139 A70 300fr gold & multi   4.00 1.10

Nos. C135-C137 exist se-tenant with label showing arms of Munich.

Lunokhod on Moon — AP46

Russian moon missions: 100fr, Luna 16 on moon and rocket in flight, vert.

1972, Sept. 19
C140 AP46 100fr dk bl, pur & bis   1.90 .20
C141 AP46 150fr slate, brn & lil   2.50 .25

Farcha Laboratory, Cattle, Scientist — AP47

1972, Nov. 11   Photo.   Perf. 13
C142 AP47 75fr yellow & multi   1.40 .20

20th anniversary of the Farcha Laboratory for veterinary research.

King Faisal and Holy Kaaba, Mecca — AP48

1972, Nov. 17
C143 AP48 75fr multi   1.40 .25

Visit of King Faisal of Saudi Arabia.

Christmas Type of 1970

Christmas: 40fr, Virgin and Child, by Giovanni Bellini. 75fr, Virgin and Child, by Dall'Occhio. 80fr, Nativity, by Fra Angelico, horiz. 95fr, Adoration of the Kings, by Il Perugino.

1972, Dec. 15   Photo.   Perf. 13
C144 AP30 40fr gold & multi   .20 .20
C145 AP30 75fr gold & multi   1.75 .20
C146 AP30 80fr gold & multi   2.00 .20
C147 AP30 95fr gold & multi   2.00 .25
     Nos. C144-C147 (4)   5.95 .85

Summer Olympic Winners Type, 1972

Olympic Emblems and: 150fr, Pole vault, Nordwig, East Germany. 250fr, Hurdles, Milburn, US. 300fr, Javelin, Wolfermann, West Germany.

1972, Dec. 22
C148 A76 150fr multi   3.00 .50
C149 A76 250fr multi   4.25 .80

Souvenir Sheet
C150 A76 300fr multi   15.00 .95

Summer Olympic Winners Type, 1972

Olympic Emblem and: 150fr, Dressage, Mancinelli, Italy. #C152, Finn class sailing, Serge Maury, France. #C153, Swimming, Mark Spitz.

1972, Dec. 22   Litho.   Perf. 11
C151 A77 150fr gold & multi   3.25 .45
C152 A77 250fr gold & multi   5.00 .80

Souvenir Sheet
C153 A77 250fr multi   15.00 .80

Copernicus and Solar System — AP49

1973, Mar. 31   Engr.   Perf. 13
C154 AP49 250fr gray, mag &
                    brn   5.25 .70

500th anniversary of the birth of Nicolaus Copernicus (1473-1543), Polish astronomer.

Horses — AP49a

Details from paintings: 20fr, A Horse Frightened by Lightning, by Theodore Gericault. 60fr, The White Horse, by Paul Potter. 100fr, Mares and Foals, by George Stubbs. 150fr, Horse Head, by Theodore Gericault, vert. 500fr, The Carriage, by Vernet.

1973   **Litho.**   **Perf. 11½**
C154A AP49a 20fr multicolored
C154B AP49a 60fr multicolored
C154C AP49a 100fr multicolored
C154D AP49a 150fr multicolored
    Nos. C154A-C154D (4)   14.00
    Souvenir Sheet
    Perf. 15
C154E AP49a 500fr multicolored   15.00
    See note before No. 225A.

Airplanes — AP49b

1973   **Litho.**   **Perf. 12**
C154F AP49b 5fr Fokker F VII/3M
C154G AP49b 25fr DH 89A Rapide
C154H AP49b 70fr Viscount
C154J AP49b 150fr Boeing 747
C154K AP49b 200fr Concorde
    Nos. C154F-C154K (5)   14.00
    Souvenir Sheet
    Perf. 12
C154L AP49b 350fr Concorde, diff.   14.00
Nos. C154L contains one 60x40mm stamp. See note before No. 225A.

Skylab over Africa — AP50

1974, Aug. 6   **Engr.**   **Perf. 13**
C155 AP50 100fr shown   1.50   .25
C156 AP50 150fr Skylab   2.50   .35
Exploits of Skylab, US manned space station.

Soccer — AP51

125fr, 150fr, Soccer players; 125fr, vert.

1974, Oct. 22   **Engr.**   **Perf. 13**
C157 AP51 50fr dl red & choc   .75   .20
C158 AP51 125fr red & dp grn   1.75   .30
C159 AP51 150fr grn & rose red   2.50   .40
    Nos. C157-C159 (3)   5.00   .90
World Cup Soccer Championship, Munich, June 13-July 7.

Family and WPY Emblem — AP52

1974, Nov. 11
C160 AP52 250fr multi   3.75   .65
World Population Year.

Mail Delivery by Canoe — AP53

UPU Cent.: 40fr, Diesel train. 100fr, Jet. 150fr, Spacecraft.

1974, Dec. 20   **Engr.**   **Perf. 13**
C161 AP53 30fr car & multi   .60   .20
C162 AP53 40fr ultra & blk   1.00   .20
C163 AP53 100fr brn, ultra & blk   1.90   .30
C164 AP53 150fr grn, lil & ol   2.40   .45
    Nos. C161-C164 (4)   5.90   1.15

Women of Different Races, IWY Emblem — AP54

1975, June 25   **Photo.**   **Perf. 13**
C165 AP54 250fr bl & multi   4.50   .35
International Women's Year 1975.

Apollo and Soyuz Before Link-up — AP55

130fr, Apollo and Soyuz after link-up.

1975, July 15   **Engr.**   **Perf. 13**
C166 AP55 100fr ultra, choc & grn   1.50   .25
C167 AP55 130fr vio bl, brn & grn   2.00   .35
Apollo Soyuz space test project (Russo-American space cooperation), launching 7/15; link-up 7/17.
For overprints see Nos. C171-C172.

Soccer Player, View of Montreal — AP56

Olympic Rings, Montreal Skyline: 100fr, Discus thrower. 125fr, Runner.

1975, Oct. 14   **Engr.**   **Perf. 13**
C168 AP56 75fr car & slate grn   1.00   .25
C169 AP56 100fr car, choc & bl grn   1.40   .35
C170 AP56 125fr brn, bl & car   1.90   .50
    Nos. C168-C170 (3)   4.30   1.10
    Pre-Olympic Year 1975.

Nos. C166-C167 Overprinted: "JONCTION / 17 JUILLET 1975"

1975, Nov. 4   **Engr.**   **Perf. 13**
C171 AP55 100fr multi   1.75   .25
C172 AP55 130fr multi   2.10   .35
Apollo-Soyuz link-up in space, July 17.

Stylized British and American Flags, "200" — AP57

1975, Dec. 5   **Engr.**   **Perf. 13**
C173 AP57 150fr vio bl, car & ol bis   2.25   .50
American Bicentennial.

Adoration of the Shepherds, by Murillo — AP58

Christmas (Paintings): 75fr, Adoration of the Shepherds, by Georges de La Tour. 80fr, Virgin and Child with Bible, by Rogier van der Weyden, vert. 100fr, Holy Family, by Raphael, vert.

1975, Dec. 15   **Litho.**   **Perf. 13x12½**
C174 AP58 40fr yel & multi   .75   .20
C175 AP58 75fr yel & multi   1.25   .25
C176 AP58 80fr yel & multi   1.75   .25
C177 AP58 100fr yel & multi   2.75   .30
    Nos. C174-C177 (4)   6.50   1.00

12th Winter Olympic Winners Type, 1976

250fr, 4-man bobsled, West Germany. 300fr, Speed skating, J. E. Storholt, Norway. 500fr, Downhill skiing, F. Klammer, Austria.

1976, June 21   **Perf. 14**
C178 A84 250fr multi   2.75   .55
C179 A84 300fr multi   3.50   .70
    Souvenir Sheet
C180 A84 500fr multi   6.00   1.40

Paul Revere's Ride and Portrait by Copley — AP59

American Bicentennial: 125fr, Washington crossing Delaware. 150fr, Lafayette offering his services to America. 200fr, Rochambeau at Yorktown with Washington. 250fr, Franklin presenting Declaration of Independence. 400fr, Count de Grasse's victory at Cape Charles.

1976, July 4   **Litho.**   **Perf. 14**
C181 AP59 100fr multi   1.10   .30
C182 AP59 125fr multi   1.25   .35
C183 AP59 150fr multi   1.90   .40
C184 AP59 200fr multi   2.25   .50
C185 AP59 250fr multi   3.00   .55
    Nos. C181-C185 (5)   9.50   2.10
    Souvenir Sheet
C186 AP59 400fr multi   6.00   1.25

Summer Olympics Type, 1976

1976, July 12
C187 A85 100fr Boxing   1.50   .30
C188 A85 200fr Pole vault   2.50   .50
C189 A85 300fr muShot put   4.00   .65
    Nos. C187-C189 (3)   8.00   1.45
    Souvenir Sheet
C190 A85 500fr Sprint   6.00   1.25

Viking Mars Project Type, 1976

Mars Lander and: 100fr, Viking landing on Mars. 200fr, Capsule over Mars. 250fr, Lander over Mars. 450fr, Lander and probe.

1976, July 23   **Litho.**   **Perf. 14**
C191 A86 100fr multi   1.10   .30
C192 A86 200fr multi   2.25   .55
C193 A86 250fr multi   2.50   .60
    Nos. C191-C193 (3)   5.85   1.45
    Souvenir Sheet
C194 A86 450fr multi   7.50   1.75
    For overprints see Nos. C240-C243.

Concorde — AP60

1976, Oct. 15   **Litho.**   **Perf. 12½**
C195 AP60 250fr bl, blk & ver   6.00   .35
First commercial flight of supersonic jet Concorde, Jan. 21.

Nobel Prize Type, 1976

100fr, Albert Einstein, physics. 200fr, Dag Hammarskjold, peace. 300fr, Shinichiro Tomanaga, physics. 500fr, Alexander Fleming, medicine.

1976, Dec. 15
C196 A87 100fr multi   1.50   .30
C197 A87 200fr multi   2.50   .55
C198 A87 300fr multi   3.50   .70
    Nos. C196-C198 (3)   7.50   1.55
    Souvenir Sheet
C199 A87 500fr multi   8.00   .90

Adoration of the Shepherds, by Gerard van Honthorst — AP61

Christmas (Paintings): 30fr, Nativity, by Albrecht Altdorfer, vert. 60fr, Nativity, by Hans Holbein, vert. 150fr, Adoration of the Kings, by Gerard David.

1976, Dec. 22   Litho.   Perf. 12½

C200	AP61	30fr gold & multi	.50	.20
C201	AP61	60fr gold & multi	.75	.20
C202	AP61	120fr gold & blk	1.50	.35
C203	AP61	150fr gold & blk	2.25	.40
		Nos. C200-C203 (4)	5.00	1.15

Lesdiguières Bridge, by Jongkind — AP62

Design: 120fr, Sailing Ship and Boats, by Johan Barthold Jongkind (1819-1891).

1976, Dec. 27   Photo.   Perf. 13

C204	AP62	100fr multi	1.75	.20
C205	AP62	120fr multi	2.25	.20

Centenary of impressionism.

Zeppelin Type of 1977

125fr, Germany #C40, North Pole. 150fr, Germany #C45, Chicago department store. 175fr, Germany #C38 and scenes of NYC and London. 200fr, 500fr, US #C15, NYC.

1977, Mar. 30   Perf. 11

C206	A91	125fr multi	1.90	.30
C207	A91	150fr multi	2.25	.35
C208	A91	175fr multi	2.75	.45
C209	A91	200fr multi	3.25	.55
		Nos. C206-C209 (4)	10.15	1.65

Souvenir Sheet

C210	A91	500fr multi	8.00	1.25

Sassenage Castle, Grenoble — AP63

1977, May 21   Litho.   Perf. 12½

C211	AP63	100fr multi	1.00	.20

Intl. French Language Council, 10th Anniv.

Lafayette and Ships — AP64

American Bicentennial: 120fr, Abraham Lincoln, eagle and flags, vert. 150fr, James Madison and family.

1977, July 30   Engr.   Perf. 13

C212	AP64	100fr multi	1.40	.25
C213	AP64	120fr multi	1.75	.30
C214	AP64	150fr multi	2.25	.45
		Nos. C212-C214 (3)	5.40	1.00

Lindbergh and Spirit of St. Louis — AP65

100fr, Concorde. 150fr, 200fr, 300fr, Various Lindbergh portraits & Spirit of St. Louis.

1977, Sept. 27

C215	AP65	100fr multi	1.25	.30
C216	AP65	120fr multi	1.25	.35
C217	AP65	150fr multi	1.40	.50
C218	AP65	200fr multi	2.25	.60
C219	AP65	300fr multi	3.00	.75
		Nos. C215-C219 (5)	9.15	2.50

Charles A. Lindbergh's solo transatlantic flight from NY to Paris, 50th anniv., and 1st supersonic transatlantic flight of Concorde. For overprint see No. C227.

Mariner 10 — AP66

Spacecraft: 200fr, Lunokhod on moon, Luna 21. 300fr, Viking on Mars.

1977, Oct. 10   Engr.   Perf. 13

C220	AP66	100fr multi	1.25	.25
C221	AP66	200fr multi	2.00	.50
C222	AP66	300fr multi	2.75	.65
		Nos. C220-C222 (3)	6.00	1.40

Running — AP67

1977, Oct. 24   Engr.   Perf. 13

C223	AP67	30fr shown	.40	.20
C224	AP67	60fr Volleyball	.85	.20
C225	AP67	120fr Soccer	1.50	.25
C226	AP67	125fr Basketball	1.25	.35
		Nos. C223-C226 (4)	4.00	1.00

No. C215 Overprinted: "PARIS NEW-YORK / 22.11.77"

1977, Nov. 22

C227	AP65	100fr multi	3.25	.20

Concorde, 1st commercial flight Paris-NYC.

Virgin and Child, by Rubens AP68

Rubens Paintings: 60fr, Virgin and Child and Two Donors. 100fr, Adoration of the Shepherds. 125fr, Adoration of the Kings.

1977, Dec. 20   Litho.   Perf. 12½x12

C228	AP68	30fr multi	.75	.20
C229	AP68	60fr multi	1.10	.20
C230	AP68	100fr multi	1.50	.30
C231	AP68	125fr multi	1.90	.40
		Nos. C228-C231 (4)	5.25	1.10

Christmas 1977.

Antoine de Saint-Exupéry — AP69

50fr, Wilbur & Orville Wright & Flyer. 80fr, Hugo Junkers & his plane. 100fr, Gen. Italo Balbo & his plane. 120fr, Concorde. 500fr, Wilbur & Orville Wright & Flyer.

1978, Oct. 25   Litho.   Perf. 13½

C232	AP69	40fr multi	.60	.20
C233	AP69	50fr multi	.75	.20
C234	AP69	80fr multi	1.10	.25
C235	AP69	100fr multi	1.50	.30
C236	AP69	120fr multi	1.75	.40
		Nos. C232-C236 (5)	5.70	1.35

Souvenir Sheet

C237	AP69	500fr multi	6.75	2.00

History of aviation and 75th anniversary of 1st powered flight.

Philexafrique II-Essen Issue
Common Design Types

#C238, Rhinoceros & Chad #C6. #C239, Kingfisher & Mecklenburg-Strelitz #1.

1978, Nov. 1   Perf. 12½

C238	CD138	100fr multi	3.00	.30
C239	CD139	100fr multi	3.00	.30
a.		Pair, #C238-C239 + label	8.00	.75

Nos. C191-C194 Overprinted "ALUNISSAGE/APOLLO XI/ JUILLET 1969"

1979, Nov. 26   Litho.   Perf. 13½x14

C240	A86	100fr multi	1.10	.30
C241	A86	200fr multi	2.25	.60
C242	A86	250fr multi	2.50	.80
		Nos. C240-C242 (3)	5.85	1.70

Souvenir Sheet

C243	A86	450fr multi	5.50	1.10

Apollo 11 moon landing, 10th anniversary.

Hurdles, Moscow '80 Emblem — AP70

Emblem and: 30fr, Field hockey. 250fr, Swimming. 350fr, Running. 500fr, Yachting.

1979, Nov. 30   Perf. 13½

C244	AP70	15fr multi	.20	.20
C245	AP70	30fr multi	.30	.20
C246	AP70	250fr multi	1.90	.60
C247	AP70	350fr multi	3.00	1.10
		Nos. C244-C247 (4)	5.40	2.10

Souvenir Sheet

C248	AP70	500fr multi	5.75	1.75

Pre-Olympic Year.
For overprints see Nos. C254-C255.

Austria Jubilee Issue of 1910, Canoe, Hill — AP71

Hill, Stamps & Vessels: 100fr, US design A97, dhow. 200fr, France #21, Sidewheeler. 300fr, Holstein #16, ocean liner. 500fr, Chad #J13, ocean liner.

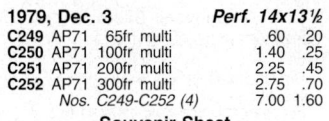

1979, Dec. 3   Perf. 14x13½

C249	AP71	65fr multi	.60	.20
C250	AP71	100fr multi	1.40	.25
C251	AP71	200fr multi	2.25	.45
C252	AP71	300fr multi	2.75	.70
		Nos. C249-C252 (4)	7.00	1.60

Souvenir Sheet

C253	AP71	500fr multi	5.75	1.75

Sir Rowland Hill (1795-1879), originator of penny postage.
For overprints see Nos. C256-C257.

Nos. C244-C245, C249-C250 Overprinted "POSTES 1981" in Red or Overprinted and Surcharged Silver on Red

Perf. 13½, 14x13½

1981, Nov. 15   Litho.

C254	AP70	30fr on 15fr multi	1.25	.20
C255	AP70	30fr multi	1.25	.20
C256	AP71	60fr on 65fr multi	2.25	.20
C257	AP71	60fr on 100fr multi	2.25	.20
		Nos. C254-C257 (4)	7.00	.80

Soccer Type of 1982 and

1982 World Cup Soccer Championships, Spain — AP71a

#C259C, Soccer players, ball, & trophy, vert.

1982   Litho.   Perf. 13½

C258	A108	80fr Brazil	1.00	.20
C259	A108	300fr W. Germany	3.00	.40

Souvenir Sheet

C259A	A108	500fr like 300fr	6.00	.70

Litho. & Embossed

C259B	AP71a	1500fr gold & multi	16.00

Souvenir Sheet

C259C	AP71a	1500fr gold & multi	14.00

No. C259A contains one 42x51mm stamp.
No. C259B exists in a souvenir sheet of 1. Value $42.50.
For surcharge see No. C305.

Diana Type of 1982 and

Princess Diana, 21st Birthday — AP71b

Design: No. C262A, Portrait, horiz.

1982, July 2   Litho.   Perf. 13½

C260	A109	80fr 1977	1.00	.25
C261	A109	300fr 1980	3.00	.95

Souvenir Sheet

C262	A109	500fr 1981	5.50	1.50

Litho. & Embossed

C262A	AP71b	1500fr gold & multi	16.00

Souvenir Sheet

C262B AP71b 1500fr gold & multi 16.00

No. C262A exists in a souvenir sheet of 1. Value $42.50.
For overprints see Nos. 419A-419B.

Manned Flight Bicentenary AP72

Balloons: 100fr, Charles' & Roberts', 1783. 200fr, J.P. Blanchard, Berlin, 1788. 300fr, Charles Green, London, 1837. 400fr, Modern blimp. 500fr, Montgolfiere, 1783.

1983, Apr.   Litho.   Perf. 13
C263 AP72 100fr multi, vert.   1.25   .25
C264 AP72 200fr multi, vert.   2.50   .40
C265 AP72 300fr multi   3.50   .60
C266 AP72 400fr multi   4.75   .75
    Nos. C263-C266 (4)   12.00 2.00

Souvenir Sheet

C267 AP72 500fr multi, vert.   5.75 1.40

Balloon Type and

First Balloon Ascension, Bicent. — AP72a

80fr, Steam Powered Airship, H. Giffard. 250fr, Graf Zeppelin; Airship L-1, 1st flight. 300fr, 1st Balloon Flight, Montgolfier & Rozier. #C270A, Airship Hindenburg, Count Ferdinand von Zeppelin. #C270B, Jean-Francois Pilatre de Rozier & Marquis d'Arlandes, 1st balloon ascension.

1983, May 30   Litho.   Perf. 13
C268 A116 80fr multi   1.00   .25
C269 A116 250fr multi   3.00   .40

Souvenir Sheet

C270 A116 300fr multi   3.75 1.00

Litho. & Embossed
Perf. 13½
C270A AP72a 1500fr gold & multi   16.00

Souvenir Sheet

C270B AP72a 1500fr gold & multi   12.00

No. C270A exists in a souvenir sheet of 1. Value $25.
For surcharge see No. C299.

1984 Summer Olympics — AP73

Various kayak scenes.

1984, Mar. 1   Litho.   Perf. 13
C271 AP73 100fr multi   1.00   .20
C272 AP73 200fr multi   2.00   .25
C273 AP73 300fr multi   3.00   .50
C274 AP73 400fr multi   4.00   .60
    Nos. C271-C274 (4)   10.00 1.55

Souvenir Sheet

C275 AP73 500fr multi   5.00   .70

Natl. Goals AP73a

#C276, C278, Peace & reconciliation. #C277, C279, Self-sufficiency in food production.

1983, Dec. 26   Litho.   Perf. 13½
C276 AP73a 150fr multi   1.50   .40
C277 AP73a 150fr multi   1.50   .40
C278 AP73a 200fr multi   2.25   .55
C279 AP73a 200fr multi   2.25   .55
    Nos. C276-C279 (4)   7.50 1.90

For surcharges see Nos. C300-C301.

Souvenir Sheet

Paul P. Harris (1868-1947), Founder of Rotary Intl. — AP73b

Litho. & Embossed
1984, Jan. 16   Perf. 13½
C279B AP73b 1500fr gold & multi   12.00

IYY, PHILEXAFRICA '85 — AP74

1985, May 2   Litho.   Perf. 13
C280 AP74 200fr Boy scout, tree   3.00   .25
C281 AP74 200fr Air Chad Fokker 27   3.00   .25
    a.   Pair, #C280-C281 + label   6.75   .50

IYY, PHILEXAFRICA Type of 1985

1985, Nov. 1   Litho.   Perf. 13x12½
C283 AP74 250fr Girl, Scout ceremony   3.00 .40
C284 AP74 250fr Communications and transportation   3.00 .40
    a.   Pair, #C283-C284 + label   6.75   .80

ASCENA Airlines, 25th Anniv. — AP75

1985, Aug. 25   Perf. 12½
C285 AP75 70fr bl & multi   .60   .20
C286 AP75 110fr org & multi   1.00   .20
C287 AP75 250fr yel & multi   2.25   .35
    Nos. C285-C287 (3)   3.85   .75

Victor Hugo (1802-1885), French Novelist — AP76

Scene from Les Miserables.

1985, Nov. 24   Engr.   Perf. 13
C288 AP76 70fr org brn, chlky bl & dp brn   .75   .20
C289 AP76 110fr lake, dk brn & dk grn   1.00   .20
C290 AP76 250fr brt org, blk & dk red   2.50   .40
C291 AP76 300fr dk red, cl & sl bl   2.75   .50
    Nos. C288-C291 (4)   7.00 1.30

Christmas 1985 — AP77

1985, Dec. 22   Litho.   Perf. 13½
C292   250fr Adoration of the Magi 2.25   .40

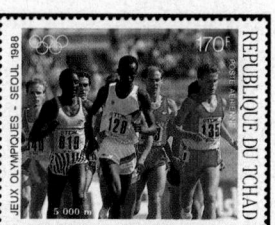

1988 Summer Olympics, Seoul — AP78

1988, June 1   Litho.   Perf. 13
C293 AP78 100fr 400-Meter hurdles, vert.   1.10   .30
C294 AP78 170fr 5000-Meter race   1.75   .55
C295 AP78 200fr Long jump   2.25   .65
C296 AP78 600fr Triple jump, vert.   5.75 2.00
    Nos. C293-C296 (4)   10.85 3.50

Souvenir Sheet

C297 AP78 750fr 10,000-Meter race, vert.   8.00 2.75

Stamps of 1982-84 Surcharged

1989   Perfs. as Before
C298 A115 100 on 300fr #446
C299 A116 100 on 250fr #C269
C300 AP73a 100 on 200fr #C278
C301 AP73a 100 on 200fr #C279
C302 A110 170 on 300fr #404
C303 A122 170 on 200fr #503
C304 A123 170 on 250fr #509
C305 A108 170 on 300fr #C259
C306 A112 240 on 300fr #425

AIR POST SEMI-POSTAL STAMPS

Catalogue values for unused stamps in this section are for Never Hinged items.

Ramses II Battling the Hittites (from Abu Simbel) — SPAP1

Unwmk.

1964, Mar. 9   Engr.   Perf. 13
CB1 SPAP1 10fr + 5fr multi   .60   .20
CB2 SPAP1 25fr + 5fr multi   1.10   .20
CB3 SPAP1 50fr + 5fr multi   2.25   .50
    Nos. CB1-CB3 (3)   3.95   .90

UNESCO world campaign to save historic monuments in Nubia.

Lions Emblem SPAP2

1967, July 5   Photo.   Perf. 13
CB4 SPAP2 50fr + 10fr multi   1.50   .20

50th anniv. of Lions Intl. and to publicize the Lions work for the blind.

POSTAGE DUE STAMPS

Postage Due Stamps of France Overprinted

1928   Unwmk.   Perf. 14x13½
J1 D2 5c light blue   .20   .20
J2 D2 10c gray brown   .20   .20
J3 D2 20c olive green   .55   .75
J4 D2 25c bright rose   .85   1.10
J5 D2 30c light red   .85   1.10
J6 D2 45c blue green   1.50   1.10
J7 D2 50c brown violet   2.00   2.50
J8 D2 60c yellow brown   2.00   2.50
J9 D2 1fr red brown   2.10   2.75
J10 D2 2fr orange red   4.75   6.50
J11 D2 3fr bright violet   4.00   5.50
    Nos. J1-J11 (11)   19.00 25.00

Huts — D3

Canoe — D4

1930   Typo.   Perf. 14x13½, 13½x14
J12 D3 5c dp bl & olive   .50   .40
J13 D3 10c dk red & brn   .50   .40
J14 D3 20c grn & brn   .80   .65
J15 D3 25c lt bl & brn   1.10   .90
J16 D3 30c bis brn & Prus bl   1.10   .90
J17 D3 45c Prus bl & olive   1.50   1.50
J18 D3 50c red vio & brn   2.25   3.00
J19 D3 60c gray lil & bl blk   3.00   4.25
J20 D4 1fr bis brn & bl blk   3.00   4.25
J21 D4 2fr vio & brn   6.25   8.50
J22 D4 3fr dp red & brn   35.00 50.00
    Nos. J12-J22 (11)   55.00 75.00

In 1934 stamps of Chad were superseded by those of French Equatorial Africa.

Catalogue values for unused stamps in this section, from this point to the end of the section, are for Never Hinged items.

Republic

Rhinoceros — D5

Tibesti Pictographs: #J24, Kudu. #J25, 2 antelopes. #J26, 3 antelopes. #J27, Ostrich. #J28, Horned bull. #J29, Bull. #J30, Wild swine. #J31, Elephant. #J32, Rhinoceros. #J33, Warrior with spear and shield. #J34, Masked archer.

Unwmk.

1962, Apr. 20   **Engr.**   **Perf. 13**

J23	D5	50c olive bister	.30	.20
J24	D5	50c brown red	.30	.20
a.		Pair, #J23-J24	.55	
J25	D5	1fr blue	.40	.20
J26	D5	1fr green	.40	.20
a.		Pair, #J25-J26	.75	
J27	D5	2fr vermilion	.50	.20
J28	D5	2fr maroon	.50	.20
a.		Pair, #J27-J28	1.00	
J29	D5	5fr slate green	.75	.20
J30	D5	5fr violet blue	.75	.20
a.		Pair, #J29-J30	1.50	
J31	D5	10fr brown	1.40	.30
J32	D5	10fr orange brown	1.40	.30
a.		Pair, #J31-J32	2.75	
J33	D5	25fr carmine rose	3.25	.75
J34	D5	25fr violet	3.25	.75
a.		Pair, #J33-J34	6.50	
		Nos. J23-J34 (12)	13.20	3.70

Dolls — D6

1969, Sept. 19   **Engr.**   **Perf. 14x13**

J35	D6	1fr Kanem	.20	.20
J36	D6	2fr Kotoko	.20	.20
J37	D6	5fr Leather	.20	.20
J38	D6	10fr Kotoko	.40	.20
J39	D6	25fr Guera	.40	.20
		Nos. J35-J39 (5)	1.40	1.00

MILITARY STAMPS

Catalogue values for unused stamps in this section are for Never Hinged items.

No. 78 Overprinted "F.M."

1965   **Typo.**   **Perf. 14x13½**

M1	A5	20fr red & black	300.00	250.00

Flag Bearer and Map of Chad — M1   1st Regiment Emblem — M2

1968   **Unwmk.**   **Litho.**   **Perf. 13x12½**

M2	M1	tan & multi	1.75	.50

1972, Jan. 21   **Photo.**   **Perf. 13**

M3	M2	blue & multi	1.00	.25

OFFICIAL STAMPS

Catalogue values for unused stamps in this section are for Never Hinged items.

Flag and Map of Chad — O1

Perf. 13½x14

1966-71   **Typo.**   **Unwmk.**
Flag in blue, yellow and carmine

O1	O1	1fr light blue	.20	.20
O2	O1	2fr gray	.20	.20
O3	O1	5fr black	.20	.20
O4	O1	10fr violet blue	.20	.20
O5	O1	25fr orange	.30	.20
O6	O1	30fr bright green	.50	.20
O7	O1	40fr carmine ('71)	.75	.20
O8	O1	50fr red lilac	.75	.20
O9	O1	85fr green	1.10	.30
O10	O1	100fr brown	1.75	.35
O11	O1	200fr red	3.00	.50
		Nos. O1-O11 (11)	8.95	2.75

Flag and Map Type of 1966-71
Redrawn with "N'Djamena" as Capital on Map

Perf. 13½x13¼, 11¾ (100fr)

1993-2000 ?   **Litho.**
Center Flag Stripe in Yellow Frame Color

O13	O1	100fr brown	—	—
O14	O1	200fr red	—	—

Nos. O13 and O14 have a large "F" in denomination, "POSTES" without serifs, and has printer's inscription of "COURVOISIER."

Center Flag Stripe in Orange Frame Color

O17	O1	50fr green	—	—
O18	O1	85fr orange	—	—
O19	O1	100fr red orange	—	—
O20	O1	150fr blue green	—	—
O21	O1	200fr green	—	—
O22	O1	250fr lilac	—	—
O23	O1	300fr blue	—	—
O24	O1	500fr red	—	—
O25	O1	1000fr dark green	—	—

Additional stamps may have been issued in this set. The editors would like to examine any examples. Numbers may change.

CHILE
'chi-lē

LOCATION — Southwest corner of South America
GOVT. — Republic
AREA — 284,520 sq. mi.
POP. — 14,973,843 (1999 est.)
CAPITAL — Santiago

100 Centavos = 1 Peso
1000 Milésimos = 100 Centésimos = 1 Escudo (1960)
100 Centavos = 1 Peso (1975)

Catalogue values for unused stamps in this country are for Never Hinged items, beginning with Scott 257 in the regular post-age section, Scott B3 in the semi-postal section, Scott C125 in the airpost section, and Scott CB1 in the airpost semi-postal section.

Pen cancellations are common on the 1862-67 issues. Such stamps sell for much less than the quoted values which are for those with handstamped postal cancellations.

Watermarks

a	b	c	d

e	f	g

Wmk. 215 — Small Star in Shield, Multiple

Christopher Columbus — A1

London Prints
1853   Wmk. b   Engr.   Imperf.
Blued Paper
1	A1	5c brown red	450.00	100.00
a.		White paper		110.00

Wmk. e
White Paper
2	A1	10c dp brt bl	600.00	150.00
a.		Blued paper		200.00
b.		Diag. half used as 5c on cover		550.00
c.		Horiz. half used as 5c on cover		550.00
d.		Vert. half used as 5c on cover		550.00

Santiago Prints
Impressions Fine and Clear
1854   Wmk. b and e
White Paper
3	A1	5c pale red brn	350.00	67.50
a.		5c deep red brown	350.00	67.50
b.		5c chestnut	575.00	100.00
e.		Double impression		275.00
4	A1	5c burnt sienna	1,400.	275.00
a.		5c dull chocolate	2,000.	1,100.
5	A1	10c deep blue	1,000.	190.00
a.		10c slate blue		190.00
b.		10c greenish blue		475.00
d.		Diag. half used as 5c on cover		450.00
e.		Horiz. half used as 5c on cover		450.00

---

f.		Vert. half used as 5c on cover		450.00
6	A1	10c lt dl bl	1,000.	190.00
a.		10c pale blue		190.00
b.		Diag. half used as 5c on cover		425.00
c.		Horiz. half used as 5c on cover		425.00
d.		Vert. half used as 5c on cover		425.00

Litho.
7	A1	5c pale brown	1,250.	325.00
a.		5c red brown	1,500.	300.00

London Print
1855   Blued Paper   Wmk. c   Engr.
8	A1	5c brown red	150.00	13.50
		Fiscal cancellation		2.75

Santiago Prints
Impressions Worn and Blurred
1856-62   Wmk. b and e
White Paper
9	A1	5c rose red ('58)	40.00	7.00
		Fiscal cancellation		1.40
a.		5c carmine red ('62)	90.00	20.00
b.		5c orange red ('61)	225.00	100.00
c.		5c dull redsh brn ('57)	250.00	27.50
f.		Printed on both sides	450.00	250.00
g.		Double impression	450.00	140.00
10	A1	10c sky blue ('57)	150.00	27.50
		Fiscal cancellation		1.75
a.		10c deep blue	125.00	27.50
b.		10c light blue ('59)	150.00	27.50
c.		10c indigo blue ('60)	175.00	50.00
k.		Printed on both sides		350.00
n.		Diag. half used as 5c on cover		165.00
o.		Horiz. half used as 5c on cover		200.00
p.		Vert. half used as 5c on cover		200.00

London Prints
1862   Wmk. a, f and g
11	A1	1c lemon yellow	67.50	5.00
		Fiscal cancellation		5.00
a.		Double impression, one inverted		200.00
12	A1	10c bright blue	40.00	15.00
		Fiscal cancellation		1.75
a.		10c deep blue	32.50	21.00
b.		Blued paper	—	17.50
c.		Wmkd. "20" (error)	5,000.	2,500.
d.		Diag. half used as 5c on cover		110.00
e.		Horiz. half used as 5c on cover		125.00
f.		Vert. half used as 5c on cover		125.00
13	A1	20c green	160.00	67.50
		Fiscal cancellation		6.75
		Nos. 11-13 (3)	267.50	122.50

No. 11a is only known fiscally used.

Santiago Print
1865   Wmk. d
14	A1	5c rose red	55.00	13.50
		Fiscal cancellation		1.50
a.		5c carmine red	55.00	13.50
b.		Printed on both sides	375.00	200.00
c.		Laid paper	—	90.00
d.		Double impression	—	160.00

The 5c rose red (shades) on unwatermaked paper, either wove or ribbed, and on paper watermarked Chilean arms in the sheet are reprints made about 1870.

No. 13 has been reprinted in the color of issue and in fancy colors, both from the origi-nal engraved plate and from lithographic trans-fers. The reprints are on paper without water-mark or with watermark CHILE and Star.

A2		A3	

1867   Unwmk.   Perf. 12
15	A2	1c orange	25.00	20.00
		Pen cancellation		.50
16	A2	2c black	35.00	40.00
		Pen cancellation		.65
17	A2	5c red	24.00	2.00
		Pen cancellation		.20
18	A2	10c blue	24.00	7.00
		Pen cancellation		.35
19	A2	20c green	35.00	3.50
		Pen cancellation		.45
		Nos. 15-19 (5)	143.00	72.50

Unused values for Nos. 15-19 are for stamps with original gum.

1877   Rouletted
20	A3	1c gray	2.50	1.90
21	A3	2c orange	13.00	5.50
22	A3	5c dull lake	15.00	.55

23	A3	10c blue	12.50	2.50
a.		Diagonal half used as 5c on cover		
24	A3	20c green	14.00	4.25
		Nos. 20-24 (5)	57.00	14.70

The panel inscribed "CENTAVO" is straight on No. 22.

A4	A5

Columbus — A6

1878-99   Rouletted
25	A4	1c green ('81)	1.00	.20
26	A4	2c rose ('81)	1.00	.20
27	A5	5c dull lake ('78)	7.25	.90
28	A5	5c ultra ('83)	1.90	.50
29	A5	10c orange ('85)	2.75	.35
a.		10c yellow	9.00	1.90
30	A5	15c dk grn ('92)	3.00	.55
31	A5	20c gray ('86)	3.00	.55
32	A5	25c org brn ('92)	3.00	.55
33	A5	30c rose car ('99)	2.75	3.75
34	A5	50c lilac ('78)	45.00	27.50
35	A5	50c violet ('85)	3.00	2.00
36	A6	1p dk brn & blk ('92)	19.00	2.75
a.		Imperf. horiz. or vert., pair	75.00	
		Nos. 25-36 (12)	97.15	39.80

For surcharge and overprint see Nos. 50, O16.

Columbus
A7	A8

1894   Re-engraved
37	A7	1c blue green	.90	.25
38	A7	2c carmine lake	.90	.25

In type A4 there is a small colorless orna-ment at each side of the base of the numeral, above the "E" and "V" of "CENTAVO." In type A7 these ornaments are missing, the figure "1" is broader than in type A4 and the head of the figure "2" is formed by a curved line instead of a ball.

1900-01

Type I — There is a heavy shading of short horzontal lines below "Chile" and the adjacent ornaments.
Type II — There is practically no shading below "Chile" and the ornaments.

Type I
39	A8	1c yel grn	.80	.20
40	A8	2c brn rose	1.25	.20
41	A8	5c dp bl	6.50	.35
42	A8	10c violet	6.50	.70
43	A8	20c gray	6.50	2.50
44	A8	30c dp org ('01)	6.50	2.50
45	A8	50c red brn	7.50	2.50
		Nos. 39-45 (7)	35.55	8.95

Type II
46	A8	1c yel grn ('01)	.85	.20
47	A8	2c rose ('01)	.85	.20
48	A8	5c dull blue ('01)	5.00	.30
a.		Printed on both sides		—
49	A8	10c vio ('01)	6.00	.85
		Nos. 46-49 (4)	12.70	1.55

For surcharge see No. 57.

No. 33 Surcharged in Black

1900
Black Surcharge
50	A5	5c on 30c rose car	1.25	.35
a.		Inverted surcharge	32.50	24.00
b.		Double surcharge	90.00	60.00
c.		Double surcharge, both invtd.	90.00	60.00
d.		Double surcharge, one invtd.	90.00	60.00

Columbus — A10

1901-02   Perf. 12
51	A10	1c green	.50	.20
52	A10	2c carmine	.65	.20
53	A10	5c ultra	1.50	.20
54	A10	10c red & blk	2.25	.35
55	A10	30c vio & blk	6.75	.85
56	A10	50c red org & blk	7.25	2.25
		Nos. 51-56 (6)	18.90	4.05

No. 44 Surcharged in Dark Blue

1903   Rouletted
57	A8	10c on 30c orange	1.90	.75
a.		Inverted surcharge	18.00	12.00
b.		Double surcharge	25.00	15.00
c.		Double surch., one inverted	25.00	15.00
d.		Double surch., both invtd.	25.00	15.00
e.		Stamp design printed on both sides		

Pedro de Valdivia — A11

Coat of Arms — A12

A13

Telegraph Stamps Surcharged or Overprinted in Black

Type I — Animal at left has neither mane nor tail.
Type II — Animal at left has mane and tail.

1904   Perf. 12
58	A11	1c on 20c ultra	.40	.30
a.		Imperf. horiz., pair	40.00	40.00
b.		Inverted surcharge	50.00	50.00
59	A13	2c yel brn, I	.35	.20
a.		Inverted overprint	20.00	20.00
b.		Pair, one without overprint	50.00	50.00
60	A13	5c red, I	.55	.20
a.		Inverted overprint	20.00	20.00
c.		Pair, one without overprint	50.00	50.00
61	A13	10c ol grn, I	1.50	.50
a.		Inverted overprint	50.00	50.00
		Nos. 58-61 (4)	2.80	1.20

Perf. 12½ to 16
62	A13	2c yel, brn, II	5.25	4.50
63	A11	3c on 5c brn red	37.50	32.50
a.		Inverted surcharge		
64	A12	3c on 1p brn, II	.45	.30
a.		Double surcharge	50.00	50.00
65	A13	5c red, II	6.25	5.50
a.		Inverted overprint		
66	A13	10c ol grn, II	14.50	10.00
67	A11	12c on 5c brn red	1.00	.45
a.		No star at left of "Centavos"	3.00	2.50
b.		Inverted surcharge	40.00	40.00
c.		Double surcharge	50.00	50.00
		Nos. 62-67 (6)	64.95	53.25

Counterfeits exist of the overprint and surcharge varieties of Nos. 57-67.
For overprint see No. O12.

A14

A15

Columbus — A16

1905-09 *Perf. 12*

68	A14	1c green	.25	.20
69	A14	2c carmine	.30	.20
70	A14	3c yel brn	.65	.30
71	A14	5c ultra	.70	.20
72	A15	10c gray & blk	1.10	.20
73	A15	12c lake & blk	5.50	2.25
74	A15	15c vio & blk	1.25	.20
75	A15	20c org brn & blk	2.25	.20
76	A15	30c bl grn & blk	3.50	.35
77	A15	50c ultra & blk	3.50	.40
78	A16	1p gold, grn & gray	16.00	11.00
		Nos. 68-78 (11)	35.00	15.50

A 20c dull red and black, type A15, was prepared but not issued. Value $125. "Specimen" copies of Nos. 74, 76-78 exist, punched to prevent postal use.

For surcharges and overprints see Nos. 79-82, O9, O11-O15.

Nos. 73, 78 Surcharged in Blue or Red

a

b

1910

79	A15 (a)	5c on 12c (Bl)	.50	.25
80	A16 (b)	10c on 1p (R)	1.10	.30
81	A16 (b)	20c on 1p (R)	1.60	.60
82	A16 (b)	1p (R)	3.00	1.10
		Nos. 79-82 (4)	6.20	2.25

The 1p is overprinted "ISLAS DE JUAN FERNANDEZ" only. The use of these stamps throughout Chile was authorized.

Independence Centenary Issue

Oath of Independence — A17

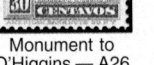
Monument to
O'Higgins — A26

Gen. Manuel
Blanco
Encalada — A29

Designs: 2c, Battle of Chacabuco. 3c, Battle of Roble. 5c, Battle of Maipu. 10c, Naval Engagement of "Lautaro" and "Esmeralda." 12c, Capturing the "Maria Isabel." 15c, First Sortie of Liberating Forces. 20c, Abdication of O'Higgins. 25c, Chile's First Congress. 50c, Monument to José M. Carrera. 1p, Monument to San Martin. 5p, Gen. José Ignacio Zenteno. 10p, Adm. Lord Thomas Cochrane.

1910 **Center in Black**

83	A17	1c dk green	.20	.25
a.		Center inverted	7,000.	

84	A17	2c lake	.20	.25
85	A17	3c red brown	1.10	.75
86	A17	5c dp blue	.45	.20
87	A17	10c gray brn	1.20	.30
88	A17	12c vermilion	2.50	1.00
89	A17	15c slate	1.90	.55
90	A17	20c red orange	2.50	.85
91	A17	25c ultra	3.25	2.00
92	A26	30c violet	3.25	1.40
93	A26	50c olive grn	6.75	2.25
94	A26	1p yel org	14.00	5.25
95	A29	2p red	14.00	5.25
96	A29	5p yel grn	37.50	37.50
97	A29	10p dk violet	35.00	16.00
		Nos. 83-97 (15)	123.80	53.80

Columbus
A32

De Valdivia
A33

Mateo de Toro
Zambrano
A34

Bernardo
O'Higgins
A35

Ramón
Freire — A36

F. A.
Pinto — A37

Joaquín
Prieto — A38

Manuel
Bulnes — A39

Manuel
Montt — A40

José Joaquín
Pérez — A41

Federico
Errázuriz
Zanartu — A42

José de
Balmaceda — A43

Designs: 1p Aníbal Pinto. 2p, Domingo Santa María. 10p, Federico Errázuriz Echaurren.

Outer backgrounds consist of horizontal and diagonal lines

1911 **Engr.** *Perf. 12*

98	A32	1c dp green	.25	.20
99	A33	2c scarlet	.25	.20
100	A34	3c sepia	.75	.25
101	A35	5c dk blue	.25	.20
102	A36	10c gray & blk	.75	.20
a.		Center inverted	800.00	600.00
103	A37	12c carmine & blk	1.00	.20
104	A38	15c violet & blk	.90	.20
a.		Center inverted	1,000.	
105	A39	20c org red & blk	1.75	.20
a.		Center inverted	50.00	50.00
106	A40	25c lt blue & blk	2.75	.60
107	A41	30c bis brn & blk	4.00	.30

108	A42	50c myr grn & blk	5.00	.30
109	A43	1p green & blk	9.00	.40
110	A43	2p ver & blk	17.50	1.75
111	A43	5p ol grn & blk	50.00	9.50
112	A43	10p org yel & blk	45.00	8.50
		Nos. 98-112 (15)	139.15	23.00

See Nos. 117, 121, 123, 127-128, 133-141, 143, 155A, 157-161, 165-169,171-172 and designs A47-A55, A57. For overprints see Nos. C6, C6B-C6D, C7-C8, C10-C11, C13-C21, O19-O22, O24-O27, O30-O34, O40.

Columbus
A47

Toro Zambrano
A48

Freire
A49

O'Higgins
A50

1912-13 **Engr.** *Perf. 12*

113	A47	2c scarlet	.20	.20
114	A48	4c black brn	.30	.20
115	A49	8c gray	1.00	.20
116	A50	10c blue & blk	1.00	.20
a.		Center inverted	500.00	400.00
b.		Imperf. horiz. or vert., pair	50.00	
117	A37	14c car & blk	1.50	.20
121	A38	40c violet & blk	5.75	.60
123	A40	60c lt blue & blk	14.00	1.75
		Nos. 113-123 (7)	23.75	3.35

See Nos. 125-126, 131, 164, 170, 173. For overprints see Nos. C6E, O18, O23, O28, O29.

Cochrane
A52

Columbus
A53

1915 **Engr.** *Perf. 13½x14*

124	A52	5c slate blue	.60	.35
a.		Imperf., pair	11.50	

See Nos. 155, 162-163. For overprints see Nos. O17, O37.

1918

125	A49	8c slate	17.50	.80

No. 125 is from a plate made in Chile to resemble No. 115. The top of the head is further from the oval, the spots of color enclosed in the figures "8" are oval instead of round, and there are many small differences in the design.

1921 **Worn Plate**

126	A49	8c gray	20.00	5.00

No. 126 differs from No. 125 in not having diagonal lines in the frame and only a few diagonal lines above the shoulders (due to wear), while No. 125 has diagonal lines in the oval up to the level of the forehead.

1915-25 **Typo.** *Perf. 13½ to 14½*

127	A32	1c gray green	.20	.20
128	A33	2c red	.20	.20
129	A53	4c brown ('18)	.25	.20

Frame Litho.; Head Engr.

131	A50	10c bl & blk	1.25	.20
a.		10c dark blue & black	1.25	.20
b.		Imperf., pair	110.00	
c.		Center inverted	325.00	
133	A38	15c vio & blk	.90	.20
134	A39	20c org red & blk	1.40	.20
a.		20c brown orange & blk	1.75	.20
135	A40	25c dl bl & blk	.55	.20
136	A41	30c bis brn & blk	1.75	.20
137	A42	50c dp grn & blk	1.75	.20

Perf. 14

138	A43	1p grn & blk	8.00	.20
139	A43	2p red & blk	9.75	.20
a.		2p vermilion & black	32.50	.60

140	A43	5p ol grn & blk ('20)	24.00	.60
141	A43	10p org & blk ('25)	25.00	1.75
		Nos. 127-141 (13)	75.00	4.55

The frames have crosshatching on the 15c, 20c, 30c, 2p, 5p and 10p. They have no crosshatching on the 10c, 25c, 50c and 1p.

Nos. 131a and 134a are printed from new head plates which give blacker and heavier impressions. No. 131a exists with; (a) frame litho., head engr.; (b) frame typo., head engr.; (c) frame typo., head litho. No. 134a is with frame typo., head engr.

A 4c stamp with portrait of Balmaceda and a 14c with portrait of Manuel de Salas were prepared but not placed in use. Both stamps were sent to the paper mill at Puente Alto for destruction. They were not all destroyed as some were privately preserved and sold.

Columbus
A54

Manuel Rengifo
A55

Types of 1915-20 Redrawn

1918-20 *Perf. 13½x14½*

143	A32	1c gray grn ('20)	.30	.20
144	A54	4c brown	.50	.20

No. 143 has all the lines much finer and clearer than No. 127. The white shirt front is also much less shaded.

1921

145	A55	40c dk vio & blk	2.00	.40

For overprints see Nos. C6A, C9.

Pan-American
Congress
Building — A56

Adm. Juan José
Latorre — A57

1923, Apr. 25 **Typo.** *Perf. 14½x14*

146	A56	2c red	.20	.20
147	A56	4c brown	.20	.20

Typo.; Center Engr.

148	A56	10c blue & blk	.20	.20
149	A56	20c orange & blk	.75	.25
150	A56	40c dl vio & blk	1.00	.30
151	A56	1p green & blk	1.25	.50
152	A56	2p red & blk	5.00	.60
153	A56	5p dk grn & blk	17.00	4.50
		Nos. 146-153 (8)	25.60	6.75

Fifth Pan-American Congress.

Typographed; Head Engraved

1927 *Perf. 13½x14½*

154	A57	80c dk brn & blk	2.00	.60

Types of 1915-25 Issues
Inscribed: "Chile Correos"

Perf. 13½x14½

1928-31 **Engr.** **Wmk. 215**

155	A52	5c slate blue	.90	.20

Frame Typo.; Center Engr.

155A	A38	15c violet & blk		350.00
156	A55	40c dk vio & blk	.40	.20
157	A42	50c dp grn & blk	1.75	.20

Perf. 14

158	A43	1p green & blk	.70	.20
159	A43	2p red & blk	3.25	.20
160	A43	5p ol grn & blk	6.50	.30
161	A43	10p orange & blk	6.50	1.25
		Nos. 155,156-161 (7)	20.00	2.55

Paper of #155-161 varies from thin to thick.

Types of 1915-25 Issues
Inscribed: "Correos de Chile"

1928 **Engr.** *Perf. 13½x14½*

162	A52	5c deep blue	.35	.20

1929   **Litho.**
163 A52   5c light green   .30   .20

Frame Litho.; Center Engr.
164 A50   10c blue & blk   1.25   .20
165 A38   15c violet & blk   1.50   .20
166 A39   20c org red & blk   3.50   .20
167 A40   25c blue & blk   .60   .20
168 A41   30c brown & blk   .45   .20
169 A42   50c dp grn & blk   .40   .20
   Nos. 163-169 (7)   8.00   1.40

Redrawn

1929   **Frame Typo.; Center Litho.**
170 A50   10c blue & blk   2.00   .20
171 A38   15c violet & blk   1.75   .20
172 A39   20c org red & blk   2.75   .20
   Nos. 170-172 (3)   6.50   .60

1931   **Unwmk.**
173 A50   10c blue & blk   .70   .20

In the redrawn stamps the lines behind the portraits are heavier and completely fill the ovals. There are strong diagonal lines above the shoulders. On #170 the head is larger than on #164, 173.

A58

Prosperity of Saltpeter Trade
A59   A60

Perf. 13½x14
1930, July 21   **Litho.**   **Wmk. 215**
Size: 20x25mm
175 A58   5c yellow grn   .60   .40
176 A58   10c red brown   .60   .30
177 A58   15c violet   .60   .30
178 A59   25c deep gray   1.90   .60
179 A60   70c dark blue   4.50   1.50

Perf. 14
Size: 24½x30mm
180 A60   1p dk gray grn   3.75   .75
   Nos. 175-180 (6)   11.95   3.85

Cent. of the 1st shipment of saltpeter from Chile, July 21, 1830.

Manuel Bulnes   Bernardo
A61   O'Higgins
            A62

1931   **Perf. 13½, 14**
181 A61   20c dark brown   1.00   .30

For overprints see Nos. O35, O39.

1932
182 A62   10c deep blue   1.10   .35

For overprints see Nos. O36, O38.

Mariano   Joaquin
Egana — A63   Tocornal — A64

1934   **Perf. 13½x14**
183 A63   30c magenta   .60   .20
Perf. 14
184 A64   1.20p bright blue   1.00   .20
   Centenary of the constitution.

José Joaquín
Pérez — A65

1934   **Perf. 13½x14**
185 A65   30c bright pink   1.60   .35

Atacama
Desert — A66

Designs: 10c, Fishing boats. 20c, Coquito palms. 25c, Sheep. 30c, Mining. 40c, Lonquimay forest. 50c, Colliery at Port Lota. 1p, Shipping at Valparaiso. 1.20p, Puntiagudo volcano. 2p, Diego de Almagro. 5p, Cattle. 10p, Mining saltpeter.

Wmk. 215
1936, Mar. 1   **Litho.**   **Perf. 14**
186 A66   5c vermilion   .60   .30
187 A66   10c violet   .30   .25
188 A66   20c magenta   .40   .25
189 A66   25c grnsh blue   3.00   .80
190 A66   30c lt green   .30   .25
191 A66   40c blk, *cream*   3.00   .85
192 A66   50c bl, *bluish*   1.50   .30

Engr.
193 A66   1p dk green   1.60   .50
194 A66   1.20p dp blue   1.75   .70
195 A66   2p dk brown   2.00   .80
196 A66   5p copper red   5.00   2.25
197 A66   10p dk violet   12.00   8.00
   Nos. 186-197 (12)   31.45   15.25

400th anniv. of the discovery of Chile by Diego de Almagro.

Laja   Fishing in
Waterfall — A78   Chiloé — A84

Designs: 10c, Agriculture. 15c, Boldo tree. 20c, Nitrate Industry. 30c, Mineral spas. 40c, Copper mine. 50c, Mining. 1.80p, Osorno Volcano. 2p, Mercantile marine. 5p, Lake Villarrica. 10p, State railways.

Perf. 13½x14
1938-40   **Litho.**   **Wmk. 215**
198 A78   5c brn car ('39)   .20   .20
199 A78   10c sal pink ('39)   .20   .20
200 A78   15c brn org ('40)   .20   .20
201 A78   20c light blue   .20   .20
202 A78   30c brt pink   .20   .20
203 A78   40c lt grn ('39)   .20   .20
204 A78   50c violet   .20   .20

Engr.   **Perf. 14**
205 A84   1p orange brn   .20   .20
206 A84   1.80p deep blue   .45   .40
207 A84   2p car lake   .20   .20
208 A84   5p dk slate grn   .35   .20
209 A84   10p rose vio ('40)   .90   .20
   Nos. 198-209 (12)   3.50   2.60

See Nos. 217-227. For surcharge and overprints see Nos. 253, O41-O66, O70-O71.

Map of the
Americas — A89

Unwmk.
1940, Sept. 11   **Litho.**   **Perf. 14**
210 A89   40c dl grn & yel grn   .35   .20
Pan American Union, 50th anniversary.

Camilo
Henríquez — A90

Founding
of
Santiago
A93

Designs: 40c, Pedro de Valdivia. 1.10p, Benjamin Vicuna Mackenna. 3.60p, Diego Barros Arana.

Perf. 14½x14, 14½
1941, Jan. 23   **Engr.**   **Wmk. 215**
211 A90   10c carmine lake   .20   .20
212 A90   40c green   .25   .20
213 A90   1.10p red   .90   .50
214 A93   1.80p blue   .90   .50
215 A90   3.60p indigo   2.75   2.00
   Nos. 211-215 (5)   5.00   3.40

400th anniversary of Santiago.

Types of 1938
Perf. 13½x14
1942-46   **Unwmk.**   **Litho.**
217 A78   10c sal pink ('43)   .20   .20
218 A78   15c brown org ('43)   .20   .20
219 A78   20c lt blue ('43)   .20   .20
220 A78   30c brt pink ('43)   .20   .20
221 A78   40c yellow grn   .80   .20
222 A78   50c violet ('43)   .20   .20

Engr.   **Perf. 14**
223 A84   1p brown orange   1.50   .20
225 A84   2p car lake ('43)   .20   .20
226 A84   5p dk sl grn ('43)   .50   .20
227 A84   10p rose violet ('46)   .90   .20
   Nos. 217-227 (10)   4.90   2.00

Valentin   University of
Letelier — A95   Chile — A98

Designs: 40c, Andrés Bello. 90c, Manuel Bulnes. 1.80p, Manuel Montt.

1942, Nov. 1   **Perf. 14x14½, 14 (1p)**
228 A95   30c rose red   .20   .20
229 A95   40c deep green   .20   .20
230 A95   90c rose violet   1.25   1.00
231 A98   1p deep brown   .70   .60
232 A95   1.80p dark blue   2.25   1.90
   Nos. 228-232 (5)   4.60   3.90

University of Chile cent. See No. C89.

Manuel
Bulnes — A100

Map Showing
Strait of
Magellan — A104

Designs: 30c, Juan Williams Wilson. 40c, Diego Duble Almeida. 1p, José Mardones.

1944, Mar. 1   **Litho.**   **Perf. 14**
233 A100   15c black   .20   .20
234 A100   30c deep rose   .20   .20
235 A100   40c yellow green   .20   .20
236 A100   1p brown carmine   .95   .20
237 A104   1.80p ultra   1.40   .95
   Nos. 233-237 (5)   2.95   1.75

100th anniversary of the occupation of the Strait of Magellan.

Red Cross and
Lamp of
Life — A105

Serpent and
Cup — A106

1944, Oct. 18   **Unwmk.**
238 A105   40c green, red & blk   .30   .20
239 A106   1.80p ultra & red   .90   .45

80th anniv. of the Intl. Red Cross Soc.

Bernardo
O'Higgins — A107

"Embrace of Maipú" (O'Higgins Joining San Martin) — A108

Designs: 40c, Abdication of O'Higgins. 1.80p, Battle of Rancagua.

1945   **Engr.**   **Perf. 14 (15c), 14½**
           Center in Black
240 A107   15c carmine   .30   .20
241 A108   30c brown   .30   .20
242 A108   40c deep green   .30   .20
243 A108   1.80p dark blue   1.40   .90
   Nos. 240-243 (4)   2.30   1.50

Death of Bernardo O'Higgins in 1842, cent.

A111

A112

Proposed Columbus lighthouse.

Wmk. 215
1945, Sept. 10   Litho.   Perf. 14
244 A111 40c light green   .50 .20

Issued in honor of the discovery of America by Columbus and the Memorial Lighthouse to be erected in his memory.

1946   Engr.
245 A112 40c dark green   .20 .20
246 A112 1.80p dark blue   .20 .20

80th anniv. of the death of Andrés Bello, poet and educator.

Map Showing Chile's Claims of Antarctic Territory A113

1947, May 12   Litho.   Perf. 14½
247 A113 40c carmine   .60 .30
248 A113 2.50p deep blue   1.60 .50

Eusebio Lillo and Ramon Carnicer A114

1947, Sept. 18   Engr.
249 A114 40c dark green   .20 .20

Centenary of national anthem.

Miguel de Cervantes Saavedra A115

1947, Oct. 11   Wmk. 215
250 A115 40c dk carmine   .20 .20

400th anniv. of the birth of Cervantes, novelist, playwright and poet.

Arturo Prat Chacón and Iquique Naval Battle A116

1948, Dec. 24   Perf. 14½
251 A116 40c deep blue   .20 .20

Centenary of the birth of Arturo Prat Chacón, Chilean naval hero.

Bernardo O'Higgins — A117

Perf. 13½x14
1948   Wmk. 215   Litho.
252 A117 60c black   .20 .20

See #262. For surcharges see #266-267.

No. 203 Surcharged in Black

VEINTE CTS.

1948
253 A78 20c on 40c lt grn   .20 .20

Chilean Pigeons — A118

FAUNA: a, Chilean Otter. c, Chilean pigeons. d, American skunk. f, Southern sea lions. g, Sugar-cane borer moth. h, Emperor penguins. i, Bat. j, Chinchilla. k, Grant's stag beetle. l, Trevally (fish). m, Chilean slender lizard. o, Crested caracara. q, Red-gartered coot. r, Chilean guemal (deer). s, Spiny rock lobster. u, Tilefish. v, Praying mantis. x, Torrent duck. y, Red conger.
FLORA: b, Araucarian pine (monkey puzzle tree). e, Evening primrose. n, Chilean red bell flower. p, Loxodon (flower). t, Boldo tree. w, Coquito palm trees.

Wmk. 215
1948, Dec. 6   Litho.   Perf. 14
254   A118 60c Block of 25   12.50
           Never hinged   17.50
  a.-y.   any single   .75 .45
255   A118 2.60p Block of 25 22.50
           Never hinged   27.50
  a.-y.   any single   1.50 .55

Issued in panes of 100.
Cent. (in 1944) of the publication of the 1st volume of Claudio Gay's Natural History of Chile. See No. C124.

Catalogue values for unused stamps in this section, from this point to the end of the section, are for Never Hinged items.

Benjamin Vicuna Mackenna — A121

1949, Mar. 22   Engr.   Perf. 13½x14
257 A121 60c deep blue   .30 .20

See No. C126.

Symbols of Arts and Crafts Education — A122

Heinrich von Stephan — A123

Design: 2.60p, Badge and book.

Unwmk.
1949, Nov. 11   Litho.   Perf. 14
258 A122 60c lilac rose   .20 .20
259 A122 2.60p violet blue   .40 .30
   Nos. 258-259,C127-C128 (4) 2.35 1.30

Cent. of the foundation of Chile's School of Arts and Crafts.

1950, Jan. 6   Engr.
260 A123 60c deep carmine   .20 .20
261 A123 2.50p deep blue   .40 .30
   Nos. 260-261,C129-C130 (4) 1.80 1.10

UPU, 75th anniv.

O'Higgins Type of 1948
1950   Litho.   Perf. 13x14
262 A117 60c black   .20 .20

For surcharge see No. 266.

San Martín — A124

Isabella I — A125

Wmk. 215
1951, Mar. 16   Engr.   Perf. 14
263 A124 60c deep blue   .30 .20

Cent. of the death of Gen. José de San Martin. See No. C165.

1952, Mar. 20
264 A125 60c brt blue   .35 .20

500th anniv. of the birth of Queen Isabella I of Spain. See No. C166.

Bernardo O'Higgins A126   Mateo de Toro Zambrano A127

1952 Unwmk. Litho.   Perf. 13½x14
265 A126 1p dk blue grn   .30 .20

See No. 275. For overprints see Nos. O67-O69.

#262, 252 Surcharged "40 Ctvs." in Red
1952, Sept.
266 A117 40c on 60c black   .35 .20
Wmk. 215
267 A117 40c on 60c black   .35 .20

1953, Mar. 13   Wmk. 215
268 A127 80c green   .20 .20

See No. 285.

Valdivia Arms — A128

Old Fort — A129

3p, Modern Valdivia. 5p, Street in ancient Valdivia.

1953, May   Perf. 14
269 A128 1p brt ultra   .40 .20
270 A129 2p dull rose vio   .40 .20
271 A129 3p blue green   .50 .20
272 A129 5p deep brown   .50 .20
   Nos. 269-272,C167 (5)   3.05 1.05

4th centenary of the founding of Valdivia, capital of Valdivia province.

José Toribio Medina (1852-1930), Historian and Bibliographer A130

1953, June   Engr.   Perf. 14½
273 A130 1p brown   .35 .20
274 A130 2.50p deep blue   .45 .20

O'Higgins Type of 1952
Perf. 13½x14
1953, Oct.   Wmk. 215   Litho.
275 A126 1p dk blue green   .35 .20

For overprint see No. O69.

A131

A132

1953, Oct. 15   Engr.   Perf. 14½
276 A131 1p Stamp of 1853   .50 .20

Centenary of Chile's first postage stamps.
Souvenir sheet including No. 276 is noted below No. C168.

1953, Nov. 5   Litho.   Perf. 13½x14
Census chart and map.
277 A132   1p blue green   .30 .20
278 A132 2.50p violet blue   .30 .20
279 A132   3p chocolate   .50 .20
280 A132   4p carmine   .50 .20
   Nos. 277-280 (4)   1.60 .80

12th general census of population and housing.

Arms of
Angol — A133

Ignacio
Domeyko — A134

1954, May 28   Unwmk.   Perf. 14
281 A133 2p deep carmine   .35 .20
400th anniversary of the founding of Angol,
capital of Malleco province.

1954, Aug. 16   Engr.   Perf. 13½x14
282 A134 1p greenish blue   .35 .20
150th anniversary of the birth of Ignacio
Domeyko (1802-89), mineralogist and educator. See No. C171.

Early Steam Locomotive — A135

1954, Sept. 10   Wmk. 215   Perf. 14½
283 A135 1p red   .60 .30
Centenary (in 1951) of the first South American railroad. See No. C172.

Adm. Arturo Prat
Chacón — A136

Arms of Viña del
Mar — A137

1954   Unwmk.   Litho.   Perf. 14
284 A136 2p dk violet blue   .35 .20
75th anniv. of the naval Battle of Iquique.

Toro Zambrano Type of 1953
1954, Nov. 6   Perf. 13½x14
285 A127 80c green   .30 .20

1955, Mar. 5   Wmk. 215   Perf. 14
Design: 2p, Arms of Valparaiso.
286 A137 1p violet blue   .35 .20
287 A137 2p carmine   .35 .20
1st Intl. Phil. Exhib., Valparaiso, Mar. 1955.

Dr. Alejandro del
Rio — A138

1955, May 24   Perf. 13½x14
288 A138 2p violet blue   .40 .20
14th Pan-American Sanitary Conference.

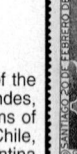

Christ of the
Andes,
Emblems of
Chile,
Argentina
A139

1955, Aug. 31   Unwmk.   Perf. 14½
289 A139 1p violet blue   .35 .20
Reciprocal visits of Presidents Juan D.
Peron and Carlos Ibanez del Campo. See No.
C173.

Manuel
Rengifo — A140

5p, Mariano Egana. 50p, Diego Portales.
1955-56   Unwmk.   Perf. 14x14½
290 A140 3p violet blue   .35 .20
291 A140 5p dk car rose   .35 .20
292 A140 50p rose lilac ('56)   1.90 .45
     Nos. 290-292 (3)   2.60 .85
Joaquin Prieto (1786-1854), soldier and
political leader; president, 1831-41. See No.
QRA1.

Jose M.
Carrera
A141

Ramón Freire
A142

Portraits: 5p, Manuel Bulnes. 10p, Pres.
Francisco A. Pinto. 50p, Manuel Montt.

Perf. 14x14½
1956-58   Unwmk.   Litho.
293 A141 2p purple   .30 .20
293A A142 3p lt violet blue   .25 .20
294 A141 5p redsh brn   .30 .20
     (19½x23mm)
  a. Size 19x22mm   .30 .20
295 A142 10p vio (19x22¼mm)   .30 .20
  a. Perf. 13½x14 (19¼x22½mm)
     ('58)   .55 .25
296 A141 50p rose red   .50 .20
     Nos. 293-296 (5)   1.65 1.00
Wmk. 215
297 A141 2p dull purple   .30 .20
298 A142 3p violet blue   .30 .20
#294 has yellow gum; #294a, white gum.
For overprints see Nos. O72-O76.

Federico Santa
Maria — A143

Gabriela
Mistral — A144

Unwmk.
1957, Jan. 31   Engr.   Perf. 14
299 A143 5p dk red brown   .30 .20
25th anniv. of the Federico Santa Maria
Technical University. See Nos. C190-C191.
Souvenir sheet including No. 299 is noted
below No. C191.

1958, Jan. 10
300 A144 10p red brown   .45 .20
Issued in honor of Gabriela Mistral, poet and
educator. See No. C192.

Arms of
Osorno — A145

Arms of
Santiago — A146

Design: 50p, Garcia Hdo. de Mendoza.
1958, Mar. 23   Litho.   Perf. 14
301 A145 10p carmine   .20 .20
Engr.
302 A145 50p green   .40 .20
400th anniversary of the founding of the city
of Osorno, capital of Osorno province.
Souvenir sheet including No. 302 in red
brown is noted below No. C193.

1958, Oct. 18   Unwmk.   Perf. 14
303 A146 10p dark violet   .30 .20
Natl. Philatelic Exposition, Santiago, Oct.
18-26.
Souvenir sheet including No. 303 in deep
red is noted below No. C194.

Symbolical
Savings
Bank — A147

Modern Map of
Antarctica — A148

1958, Dec. 18
304 A147 10p dark blue   .40 .20
Savings Bank for Public Employees, cent.
Souvenir sheet including No. 304 in violet is
noted below No. C195.

1958, Aug. 28   Unwmk.   Perf. 14
305 A148 40p rose carmine   .20 .20
IGY, 1957-1958. See No. C214.

Antarctic Map and
"La Araucana"
A149

Map of Strait of
Magellan,
1588 — A150

1958   Litho.   Perf. 14
310 A149 10p violet blue   .45 .20
Engr.
311 A150 200p dull purple   1.75 1.10
     Nos. 310-311,C199-C200 (4)   5.75 3.00
For overprint see No. O77.

Valdivia River
Bridge — A153

1959, Feb. 9   Engr.   Perf. 14
319 A153 40p green   .45 .20
Cent. of the German School in Valdivia and
to publicize the Valdivia Phil. Exhib., 2/9-18.
Souvenir sheet including No. 319 is noted
below No. C213.

Strait of
Magellan, Map
by Pedro
Sarmiento de
Gamboa, c.
1582 — A154

1959, Aug. 27   Litho.
320 A154 10p dull purple   .45 .20
Juan Ladrillero expedition to explore the
Strait of Magellan, 1557-58, 400th anniv. See
#C215.

Diego Barros
Arana — A155

Henri
Dunant — A156

1959, Aug. 27
321 A155 40p ultra   .45 .20
50th anniv. of the death of Diego Barros
Arana (1830-1907), historian. See No. C216.

1959, Oct. 6   Unwmk.   Perf. 14
322 A156 20p red & red brn   .45 .20
Cent. of the Red Cross idea. See No. C217.

Manuel Bulnes — A157

Francisco A. Pinto — A158

Choshuenco Volcano A159

#326, Choshuenco volcano, redrawn. 5c, Manuel Montt. 10c, Maule River Valley. 20c, 1e, Inca Lake.

1960-67   Litho.   Perf. 13x14
| 323 | A157 | 5m bluish grn | .20 | .20 |
| 324 | A158 | 1c carmine | .20 | .20 |

Perf. 14
Size: 29x25mm
| 325 | A159 | 2c ultra ('61) | .20 | .20 |

Perf. 14x13
Size: 23½x18mm
| 326 | A159 | 2c ultra ('62) | .20 | .20 |

Perf. 13x14
| 327 | A157 | 5c blue | .20 | .20 |

Perf. 14
Size: 29x25mm
328	A159	10c green ('62)	.20	.20
329	A159	20c Prus blue ('62)	.35	.20
329A	A159	1e bluish grn ('67)	.65	.25
		Nos. 323-329A (8)	2.20	1.65

On No. 325 "Volcan Choshuenco" is at upper left, below "Correos." On No. 326, it is at bottom, above "Centesimos."
For overprint and surcharge see #O79, RA1.

Refugee Family A160

1960, Apr. 7   Perf. 14½
| 330 | A160 | 1c green | .30 | .20 |

WRY, July 1, 1959-June 30, 1960. A souvenir sheet is noted below No. C218.

Type of Air Post Issue, 1962, and

Arms of Chile A161

José M. Carrera A162

#332, Palace of Justice. 5c, Natl. Memorial. 10c, Manuel de Toro y Zambrano and Martinez de Rozas. 20c, Manuel de Salas and Juan Egana. 50c, Manuel Rodriguez and Juan Mackenna.

Wmk. 215 (#331, 1e); Unwmk.
1960-65   Engr.   Perf. 14½
331	A161	1c maroon & sepia	.20	.20
332	A161	1c brn & claret ('62)	.20	.20
333	A162	5c grn & Prus grn ('61)	.20	.20
334	AP54	10c brn & vio brn ('64)	.40	.25
334A	AP54	20c ind & bl grn ('65)	.40	.25
335	AP54	50c red brn & mar ('65)	.70	.25
336	A162	1e gray ol & brn	1.25	.40
		Nos. 331-336,C218A-C220D (14)	6.60	3.45

150th anniv. of the formation of the 1st Natl. Government. A souvenir sheet is noted below No. C220B. See No. C285.

Family — A163

Design: 10c, Various buildings.

Unwmk.
1960, Jan. 18   Litho.   Perf. 14
| 337 | A163 | 5c green | .25 | .20 |
| 338 | A163 | 10c brt violet | .25 | .20 |

13th population census (No. 337) and 2nd housing census (No. 338).

Chamber of Deputies A164

1961, Aug. 14   Unwmk.   Perf. 14½
| 339 | A164 | 2c red brown | .65 | .20 |

150th anniv. of the 1st National Congress. See No. C245.

Soccer Players and Globe A165

Design: 5c, Goalkeeper and stadium, vert.

1962, May 30   Engr.   Perf. 14½
| 340 | A165 | 2c blue | .40 | .20 |
| 341 | A165 | 5c green | .55 | .20 |

World Soccer Championship, Chile, May 30-June 17. Note on souvenir sheet follows No. C247.

Mother and Child — A166

Centenary Emblem — A167

1963, Mar. 21   Litho.   Perf. 14
| 342 | A166 | 3c maroon | .35 | .20 |

FAO "Freedom from Hunger" campaign. See No. C248.

1963, Aug. 23   Unwmk.   Perf. 14
| 343 | A167 | 3c red & gray | .35 | .20 |

Cent. of the Intl. Red Cross. See #C249.

Fireman Carrying Woman — A168

Enrique Molina — A169

1963, Dec. 20   Unwmk.   Perf. 14
| 344 | A168 | 3c violet | .45 | .20 |

Centenary of the Santiago Fire Brigade. See No. C250.

1964, Nov. 14   Litho.   Perf. 14
Design: No. 346, Magr. Carlos Casanueva.
345	A169	4c bister brown	.35	.20
346	A169	4c rose claret	.35	.20
		Nos. 345-346,C257-C258 (4)	1.30	.80

Enrique Molina, founder of the University of Concepcion, and Msgr. Carlos Casanueva, rector of the Catholic University, 1920-53.

Easter Island Statue — A170

Copihue, National Flower — A171

Design: 30c, Robinson Crusoe.

1965-69   Litho.   Perf. 14x14½
| 347 | A170 | 6c rose lilac | .75 | .20 |
| 347A | A170 | 10c rose pink ('68) | .30 | .20 |

Perf. 14
| 348 | A171 | 15c yel grn & rose red | .75 | .20 |
| 348A | A171 | 20c yel grn & rose red ('69) | .35 | .20 |

Perf. 14x14½
| 349 | A170 | 30c rose claret | .55 | .20 |
| | | Nos. 347-349 (5) | 2.70 | 1.00 |

For surcharge see No. RA2.

Skier — A172

Lorenzo Sazie — A173

1965, Aug. 30   Perf. 14
| 350 | A172 | 4c blue green | .40 | .20 |

World Skiing Championships, Chile, 1966.

1966, Feb. 9   Litho.   Perf. 14x14½
| 351 | A173 | 1e green | .95 | .20 |

Cent. of the death of Dr. Lorenzo Sazie, dean of the Faculty of Medicine, University of Santiago.

German Riesco, President in 1901-1906 — A174

Portrait: 30c, Jorge Montt (1847-1922), president in 1891-1896.

1966   Unwmk.   Perf. 13x14
| 354 | A174 | 30c violet | .30 | .20 |
| 355 | A174 | 50c dull brown | .35 | .20 |

For surcharge see No. 450.

William Wheelwright and S.S. Chile — A175

1966, Aug. 2   Perf. 14½
| 358 | A175 | 10c ultra & lt bl | .35 | .20 |

125th anniv. (in 1965) of the arrival of the paddle steamers "Chile" and "Peru." See No. C268.

Learning to Read — A176

1966, Aug. 13   Litho.   Perf. 14
| 359 | A176 | 10c red brown | .35 | .20 |

Literacy campaign.

UN and ICY Emblems A177

1966, Oct. 28   Unwmk.   Perf. 14½
| 360 | A177 | 1e green & brown | 1.40 | .25 |

Intl. Cooperation Year, 1965. See No. C269.

Capt. Luis Pardo and Ship in
Antarctica — A178

1967, Jan.   Litho.   Perf. 14½
361 A178 20c turquoise blue   .45 .25
   Rescue of the Shackleton South Pole expedition by Capt. Luis Pardo of Chile, 50th anniv. See #C271.

Family — A179

Trees and
Mountains
A180

1967, Apr. 13   Unwmk.   Perf. 14
362 A179 10c magenta & blk   .35 .20
   8th Intl. Conf. for Family Planning, Santiago, Apr. 1967. See No. C272.

1967, June 9   Litho.   Perf. 14½
363 A180 10c blue grn & lt bl   .35 .20
   Reforestation Campaign. See No. C274.

Lions
Emblem — A181

1967, July 12   Litho.   Perf. 14
364 A181 20c Prus blue & yel   .35 .25
   Nos. 364,C275-C276 (3)   1.85 .80
   50th anniv. of Lions Intl.

Chilean
Flag
A182

1967, Oct. 20   Unwmk.   Perf. 14½
365 A182 80c crimson & ultra   .60 .25
   Natl. flag, 150th anniv. See No. C277.

José Maria
Cardinal
Caro — A183

1967, Dec. 4   Engr.   Perf. 14½
366 A183 20c deep carmine   .75 .35
   Cent. of the birth of José Maria Cardinal Caro, the first Chilean cardinal. See #C279.

San Martin and O'Higgins — A184

1968, Apr. 23   Litho.   Unwmk.
367 A184 3e blue   .65 .25
   Sesquicentennial of the Battles of Chacabuco and Maipu. See No. C280.

Farm
Couple — A185

1968, June 18   Perf. 14½
368 A185 20c black, org & grn   .40 .25
   Agrarian reforms. See No. C281.

Juan I.
Molina
A186

1968, Aug. 27   Litho.   Perf. 14½
369 A186 2e red lilac   .60 .25
   Issued to honor Juan I. Molina, educator and scientist. See No. C282.

Hand Holding
Cogwheel — A187

1968, Sept.   Perf. 14x14½
370 A187 30c deep carmine   .30 .25
   Fourth census of manufacturers.

Map of
Chiloé
Province,
Sailing
Ship and
Coastal
Vessel
A188

1968, Oct. 7   Perf. 14½
371 A188 30c ultra   .40 .25
   Anniversaries of the founding of five towns in Chiloé Province. See No. C283.

Automobile
Club Emblem
A189

1968, Nov. 10   Engr.   Perf. 14½x14
372 A189 1e carmine rose   .35 .25
   40th anniversary of the Automobile Club of Chile. See No. C284.

Francisco
Garcia
Huidobro
A190

Design: 5e, King Philip V of Spain.

1968, Dec. 31   Litho.   Perf. 14½
373 A190 2e pale rose & ultra   .40 .20
374 A190 5e brown & yel grn   .40 .20
   Nos. 373-374,C288-C289 (4)   1.40 .80
   225th anniv. of the founding of the State Mint (Casa de Moneda de Chile).

Satellite
and
Radar
Station
A191

1969, May 20   Litho.   Perf. 14½
375 A191 30c blue   .30 .25
   Inauguration of ENTEL-Chile, the 1st commercial satellite communications ground station, Longovilo.
   See #C290. For surcharges see #397, C308.

Red
Cross,
Crescent
and Lion
and Sun
Emblems
A192

1969, Sept.   Litho.   Perf. 14½
376 A192 2e violet blue & red   .40 .25
   50th anniversary of the League of Red Cross Societies. See No. C291.

Rapel Hydroelectric Plant — A193

1969, Nov. 18   Litho.   Perf. 14½
377 A193 40c green   .30 .25
   See No. C292.

Col. Rodriguez Monument — A194

1969, Nov. 24
378 A194 2e rose claret   .40 .25
   150th anniversary of the death of Col. Manuel Rodriguez. See No. C293.

EXPO '70
Emblem — A195

1969, Dec. 2   Litho.   Perf. 14
379 A195 3e blue   .55 .25
   EXPO '70 Intl. Exhibition, Osaka, Japan, Mar. 15-Sept. 13, 1970. See No. C294.

Open
Book
A196

1969, Dec. 3   Perf. 14½
380 A196 40c red brown   .40 .25
   Translation of the Bible into Spanish by Casiodoro de Reina, 400th anniv. See No. C295.

Globes
and ILO
Emblem
A197

1969, Dec. 17   Perf. 14½
381 A197 1e green & blk   .35 .25
   ILO, 50th anniv. See No. C296.

Human
Rights
Flame
A198

1969, Dec. 18
382 A198 4e blue & red   .60 .25
   Human Rights Year, 1968. See No. C297.

Policarpo
Toro and
Easter
Island
A199

1970, Jan. 26   Perf. 14½
383 A199 5e lilac   .90 .25
   80th anniversary of the acquisition of Easter Island. See No. C298.

Sailing
Ship and
Arms of
Valdivia
A200

1970, Feb. 4   Litho.   Perf. 14½
384 A200 40c dk carmine   .60   .25
  150th anniv. of the capture of Valdivia during Chile's war of independence by Thomas Cochrane (1775-1860), naval commander. See No. C299.

Paul Harris and
Rotary
Emblem — A201

1970, Mar. 18   Litho.   Perf. 14
385 A201 10e violet blue   1.10   .25
  Cent. of the birth of Paul Harris (1868-1947), founder of Rotary Intl. See No. C300.

Mahatma
Gandhi — A202

1970, Apr. 1   Litho.   Perf. 14½
386 A202 40c blue green   3.50   .30
  Mohandas K. Gandhi (1869-1948), leader in India's fight for independence, birth cent. See #C301. For surcharge see #449.

Santo Domingo
Church, Santiago,
Chile — A203

1970, Apr. 30   Engr.
  Designs: 2e, Casa de Moneda de Chile, horiz. 3e, Pedro de Valdivia. 5e, Bridge, horiz. 10e, Ambrosio O'Higgins.

387 A203 2e violet brown   .40   .20
388 A203 3e dark red   .40   .20
389 A203 4e dark blue   .30   .20
390 A203 5e brown   .30   .20
391 A203 10e green   .30   .20
    Nos. 387-391 (5)   1.70   1.00
  Exploration and development of Chile by Spanish explorers.
  A sheet containing imperf examples of Nos. 388, 390 and 391 exists. It was not valid for postage.

Education Year
Emblem — A204

Virgin and
Child — A205

1970, July 17   Litho.   Perf. 14½
392 A204 2e claret   .35   .25
  International Education Year. See No. C302.

1970, July 28
393 A205 40c green   .30   .25
  O'Higgins National Shrine at Maipu. See No. C303. For surcharge see No. 454.

Torch and
Snake — A206

Copper Symbol,
Chile
Arms — A207

1970, Aug. 11
394 A206 40c claret & light blue   .50   .25
  International Cancer Congress, Houston, Texas, May 22-29. See No. C304.

1970, Oct. 21   Litho.   Perf. 14½
395 A207 40c car & lt red brn   .35   .25
  Nationalization of the copper industry. See No. C305. For surcharge see No. 459.

Dove and
World
Map
A208

1970, Oct. 22
396 A208 3e rose magenta & pur   .40   .25
  25th anniv. of the UN. See No. C306.

No. 375 Surcharged in Red
1970, Dec. 24   Litho.   Perf. 14½
397 A191 52c on 30c blue   .45   .25

Freighter and
Ship's
Wheel — A209

1971, Jan. 18   Litho.   Perf. 14
398 A209 52c deep carmine   .35   .20
  Natl. Maritime Commission. See #C307.

Bernardo
O'Higgins
and Ship
A210

1971, Feb. 3   Perf. 14½
399 A210 5e grnsh bl & grn   .55   .20
  150th anniv. of the expedition to liberate Peru from Spanish rule. See No. C309.

Youth,
Girl and
UN
Emblem
A211

1971, Feb. 11   Litho.   Perf. 14½
400 A211 52c dk blue & brn   .35   .20
  1st meeting in Latin America of the Executive Council of UNICEF, Santiago, May 20-31, 1969. See No. C310.

Chilean Boy Scout
Emblem — A212

1971, Feb. 10   Perf. 14
401 A212 1e green & brn   .45   .20
  Founding of Chilean Boy Scouts, 60th anniversary. See No. C311.

Satellite
and
Radar
Station
A213

1971, May 25   Litho.   Perf. 14½
402 A213 40c dull green   .50   .20
  First commercial Chilean satellite communications ground station, Longovilo. See No. C312.

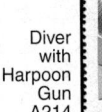

Diver
with
Harpoon
Gun
A214

1971, Sept. 1
403 A214 1.15e lt & dk green   1.10   .25
404 A214 2.35e vio bl & dp vio bl .40   .25
  10th World Championship of Underwater Fishing.

Ferdinand Magellan and Sailing
Ship — A215

1971, Nov. 3
405 A215 35c lt vio & brn vio   .35   .25
  450th anniv. of 1st trip through and discovery of the Strait of Magellan, Oct. 21-Nov. 28, 1520.

Dagoberto Godoy and Plane over
Andes — A216

1971, Nov. 4
406 A216 1.15e blue & grn   .40   .20
  First trans-Andean flight, Dec. 12, 1918.

Virgin of San
Cristobal — A217

Chilean
Flag and
Congress
Emblem
A218

  Congress Emblem and: 4.35e, Church of San Francisco. 9.35e, Central post office, horiz. 18.35e, La Posada (Inn) del Corregidor, horiz.

1971
407 A217 1.15e dk blue   .60   .30
408 A218 2.35e ultra & car   .60   .30
409 A217 4.35e brown red   .60   .30
410 A217 9.35e violet   .60   .30
411 A217 18.35e lilac rose   1.25   .30
    Nos. 407-411 (5)   3.65   1.50
  10th Cong. of the Postal Union of the Americas and Spain, Santiago.
  An imperf souvenir sheet containing #407-411 was not valid for postage. Value $11.
  Issued: 2.35e, 4.35e, Nov. 5; 1.15e, Nov. 11; 9.35e, Nov. 18; 18.35e, Nov. 19.

Observation Dome, Cerro el Tololo
Observatory — A219

1971, Dec. 18
412 A219 1.95e lt & dk blue   .35   .20

Boeing
707 over
Easter
Island
A220

1971, Dec. 18
413 A220 2.35e dk brn & yel   .45   .20
  Inauguration of regular flights: Santiago, Easter Island, Tahiti.

Alonso de Ercilla y
Zuniga — A221

1972, Mar. 20   Engr.   Perf. 14
414   A221   1e dark red   .40   .20
   4th centenary (in 1969) of "La Araucana," by
Alonso de Ercilla y Zuniga (1533-1596), Spanish author. See No. C313.

Map of Antarctica and Dog
Sled — A222

1972, Mar. 20   Litho.   Perf. 14½x15
415   A222   1.15e vio bl & blk   .65   .30
416   A222   3.50e blue grn & grn   1.10   .30
   10th anniversary (in 1971) of the Antarctic
Treaty pledging peaceful uses of and scientific
cooperation in Antarctica.
   For surcharge see No. 630.

"Your Heart is
your
Health" — A223

1972, Apr. 2   Litho.   Perf. 14½
417   A223   1.15e black & car   .40   .25
   World Health Month.
   For surcharge see No. 631.

People and Statement by Pres.
Allende — A224

Conference Hall and UN
Emblem — A225

1972, Apr. 13   Litho.   Perf. 14½
418   A224   35c dl grn & buff   .35   .25
419   A225   1.15e ultra & pur   .40   .20
420   A224   4e dk pur & pale
                rose   .60   .35
421   A225   6e orange & vio bl   .50   .20
      Nos. 418-421 (4)   1.85 1.00
   3rd UN Conf. on Trade and Development
(UNCTAD III), Santiago, Apr.-May 1972.
Design A224 is perf. horiz. in the middle.

Soldier,
1822,
Andes,
Military
College
Emblem
A226

1972, June 9
422   A226   1.15e blue & yel   .35   .25
   Sesquicentennial of Bernardo O'Higgins
Military College.

Miner Holding
Copper Ingot,
Chilean
Flag — A227

Sailing
Ship — A228

1972, July 11   Litho.   Perf. 15x14½
423   A227   1.15e blue & rose red   .35   .20
424   A227   5e blue, blk & rose
                red   .45   .20
   Nationalization of copper industry.

1972, Aug. 4
425   A228   1.15e violet brown   .55   .25
   Arturo Pratt Naval Training School, sesqui.

Mt. Calan Observatory — A229

1972, Aug. 31   Litho.   Perf. 14½
426   A229   50c ultra   .40   .25
   University of Chile Mt. Calan Observatory.

Carrier
Pigeon — A230

1972, Oct. 9   Litho.   Perf. 14½
427   A230   1.15e red lilac & vio   .40   .25
   Intl. Letter Writing Week, Oct. 9-15.

René Schneider and Army
Flag — A231

1972, Oct. 25   Perf. 14
428   A231   2.30e multi   .40   .30
   2nd anniv. of the death of Gen. René
Schneider.   No. 428 is perforated vertically in
the middle.

Book and
Young
People
A232

1972, Oct. 31   Perf. 14½
429   A232   50c black & dp org   .40   .25
   International Book Year 1972.

Guitar
and
Earthen
Jar
A233

   Designs: 2.65e, Fish and produce. 3.50e,
Stove, pots and rug, vert.

1972, Nov. 20   Litho.   Perf. 14½
430   A233   1.15e red & blk   .30   .20
431   A233   2.65e ultra & rose lake   .40   .20
432   A233   3.50e red & red brn   .40   .20
      Nos. 430-432 (3)   1.10   .60
   Tourism Year of the Americas.

José M. Carrera
Before Execution
A234

Map of
Antarctica, Flag
at Base — A235

1973, Feb. 1   Litho.   Perf. 14½
433   A234   2.30e lt ultra   .40   .25
   Sesquicentennial of the death of José
Miguel Carrera (1785-1821), Chilean revolutionist and dictator.

1973, Feb. 8
434   A235   10e ultra & red   .55   .20
   Bernardo O'Higgins Antarctic Base, 25th
anniv.

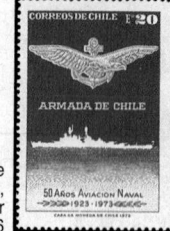

Naval Air Service
Emblem,
Destroyer
A236

La Silla
Observatory
A237

1973, Mar. 16   Litho.   Perf. 14½
435   A236   20e brt bl & ocher   .45   .25
   Chilean Naval Aviation, 50th anniversary.

1973, Apr. 25   Litho.   Perf. 14½
436   A237   2.30e ultra & blk   .40   .25

INTERPOL
Emblem
A238

   Designs: 50e, Fingerprint over globe.

1973, Sept. 23   Litho.   Perf. 14½
437   A238   30e bister & ultra   .65   .30
438   A238   50e black & red   .85   .30
   50th anniversary of International Criminal
Police Organization.

Grapes — A239

   Chilean wine export: 100e, Globe inscribed
"Chile Exporta Vino."

1973, Dec. 10   Litho.   Perf. 14½
439   A239   20e buff & lilac   .45   .20
440   A239   100e blue & claret   1.00   .25

UPU Headquarters, Bern — A240

1974, Apr. 4
441   A240   500e on 45c green   .75   .25
   UPU cent. No. 441 was not issued without
dark green surcharge and overprint.

Bernardo O'Higgins, Armed Forces Emblems — A241

1974, Apr. 11   Litho.   Perf. 14½
442 A241 30e shown   .30   .20
443 A241 30e Soldiers with mor-
                tar   .30   .20
444 A241 30e Navy anti-aircraft
                gunners   .30   .20
445 A241 30e Pilot in cockpit   .30   .20
446 A241 30e Mounted police-
                man   .30   .20
     Nos. 442-446 (5)   1.50 1.00
Honoring the Armed Forces.

Soccer Ball and Globe — A242

Traffic Police — A243

1000e, Soccer ball and stadium, horiz.

1974   Litho.   Perf. 14
447 A242 500e dk red & org   .60   .25
448 A242 1000e bl & indigo   1.25   .30
World Cup Soccer Championship, Munich, June 13-July 7.

A souvenir sheet contains 2 imperf. stamps similar to Nos. 447-448, with blue marginal inscription. Printed on thin card. Size: 90x119mm. Value, $12.

Nos. 386, 355 Surcharged
1974, June   Litho.   Perf. 14½
449 A202 100e on 40c bl grn   .35   .25
     Perf. 13x14
450 A174 300e on 50c dl brn   .40   .20

1974, June 20   Perf. 14½
451 A243 30e red brn & grn   .40   .20
Traffic safety.

Santiago-Australia Air Service — A244

1974, Sept. 5   Litho.   Perf. 14½x14
452 A244   Block of 4   4.00 2.50
a. 200e Easter Island turtle   .60   .25
b. 200e Polynesian dancer   .60   .25
c. 200e Map of Fiji Islands   .60   .25
d. 200e Kangaroo   .60   .25
Inauguration of air service by LAN (Chile's national airline) from Santiago to Easter Island, Tahiti, Fiji, Australia.

Globe Cut to Show Mantle and Core — A245

1974, Sept. 9   Perf. 14x14½
453 A245 500e red brn & org   1.00   .20
International Volcanology Congress, Santiago, Sept. 9-14.

No. 393 Surcharged in Brown

1974, Oct. 24   Litho.   Perf. 14½
454 A205 100e on 40c green   .40   .25
Inauguration of the O'Higgins National Shrine at Maipu, Oct. 24, 1974.

Juan Fernandez Archipelago — A246

1974, Nov. 22   Litho.   Perf. 14½x14
455 A246   Block of 4   3.50 2.00
a. 200e Robinson Crusoe Island   .75   .35
b. 200e Chonta palms   .75   .35
c. 200e Mountain goat   .75   .35
d. 200e Spiny rock lobster   .75   .35
400th anniversary of discovery of Juan Fernandez Archipelago.

O'Higgins and Bolivar A247

1974, Dec. 9   Perf. 14½
456 A247 100e red brn & buff   .30   .25
Sesquicentennial of the Battles of Junin and Ayacucho.

F. Vidal Gormaz and Institute Seal A248   Albert Schweitzer A249

1975, Jan. 22   Litho.   Perf. 14½
457 A248 100e rose claret & bl   .35   .25
Centenary of the Naval Hydrographic Institute; F. Vidal Gormaz was first commandant.

1975, Apr. 7   Litho.   Perf. 14x14½
458 A249 500e yel & red brn   .70   .25
Dr. Albert Schweitzer (1875-1965), medical missionary, birth centenary.

No. 395 Surcharged in Red

1975, Apr. 7   Perf. 14½
459 A207 70e on 40c car & lt red
                brn   .35   .25

Volunteer Lifeboat Service — A250

1975, Apr. 15   Litho.   Perf. 14½x14
460 A250   Block of 4   5.50 3.50
a. 150e Lighthouse   .80   .25
b. 150e Shipwreck   .80   .25
c. 150e Lifeboat   .80   .25
d. 150e Sailor reaching for life pre-
          server   .80   .25
Valparaiso Volunteer Lifeboat service, 50th anniversary.

Note: souvenir cards were issued by Chile starting in 1975 for various issues. They were printed on thin card. These are not souvenir sheets.

Frigate Lautaro A251

1975, May 21   Photo. & Engr.
461 A251 500e shown   .65   .25
462 A251 500e Corvette Ba-
              quedano   .65   .25
463 A251 500e Cruiser Cha-
              cabuco   .65   .25
464 A251 500e Brigantine
              Goleta Es-
              meralda   .65   .25
a. Block of 4, #461-464   5.25 5.25
465 A251 800e like #461   .85   .30
466 A251 800e like #462   .85   .30
467 A251 800e like #463   .85   .30

468 A251 800e like #464   .85   .30
a. Block of 4, #465-468   7.00 7.00
469 A251 1000e like #461   1.25   .40
470 A251 1000e like #462   1.25   .40
471 A251 1000e like #463   1.25   .40
472 A251 1000e like #464   1.25   .40
a. Block of 4, #469-472   9.25 9.25
     Nos. 461-472 (12)   11.00 3.80
Shipwreck of training frigate Lautaro, 30th anniversary. Se-tenant in sheets of 25 (5x5) with 7 Lautaro stamps and 6 each of the others.

Happy Mother, by Alfredo Valenzuela P. — A252

Diego Portales, Finance Minister — A253

Paintings: No. 474, Young Girl, by Francisco Javier Mandiola. No. 475, Lucía Guzman, by Pedro Lira Rencoret. No. 476, Woman, by Magdalena Mira Mena.

1975, Oct. 13   Litho.   Perf. 14½
473 A252 50c multicolored   .80   .25
474 A252 50c multicolored   .80   .25
475 A252 50c multicolored   .80   .25
476 A252 50c multicolored   .80   .25
     Nos. 473-476 (4)   3.20 1.00
International Women's Year 1975. Gray inscription on back, printed beneath gum, gives details about painting shown.

Inscribed D. Portales
1975-78   Litho.   Perf. 13x14
477 A253 10c gray grn   .30   .20
478 A253 20c violet ('76)   .30   .20
479 A253 30c orange ('76)   .30   .20
480 A253 50c lt brown   .30   .20
481 A253 1p blue   .30   .20
482 A253 1.50p ocher ('76)   .30   .20
483 A253 2p gray ('77)   .30   .20
483A A253 2.50p citron ('78)   .30   .20
483B A253 3.50p pnksh rose
              ('78)   .35   .20
484 A253 5p rose claret   .35   .20
     Nos. 477-484 (10)   3.10 2.00
See #635-639. For surcharge see #533.

Cochrane and Liberating Squadron, 1820 — A254

#486, Capture of Valdivia, 1820. #487, Capture of Three-master Esmeralda, 1820. #488, Cruiser Cochrane, 1874. #489, Destroyer Cochrane, 1962.

1976, Jan. 6   Perf. 14½
485 A254 1p multicolored   .70   .25
486 A254 1p multicolored   .70   .25
487 A254 1p multicolored   .70   .25
488 A254 1p multicolored   .70   .25
489 A254 1p multicolored   .70   .25
a. Strip of 5, #485-489   3.50 3.50
Lord Thomas Cochrane, first commander of Chilean Navy, birth bicentenary.

Flags of
Chile and
Bolivia
A255

1976, May 25   Litho.   Perf. 14½
490 A255 1.50p multicolored   1.50   .25
Sesquicentennial of Bolivia's independence.

Lake of
the Inca,
OAS
Emblem
A256

1976, June 11
491 A256 1.50p multicolored   1.25   .25
6th General Assembly of the Organization of
American States.

George
Washington
A257

1976, July 3
492 A257 5p multicolored   .80   .25
American Bicentennial.

Minerva
and
Academy
Emblem
A258

1976, July
493 A258 2.50p multicolored   .80   .25
Polytechnic Military Academy, 50th anniv.

Araucan
Indian — A259

Designs: 2p, Condor with broken chain. 3p,
Winged woman, symbolizing rebirth.

1976, Sept. 20   Litho.   Perf. 14½
494 A259 1p blue & multi   .30   .20
495 A259 2p blue & multi   1.50   .75
496 A259 3p yellow & multi   .60   .20
 a.   Strip of 3, #494-496   2.50   2.00
3rd anniversary of the Military Junta.

View, Antarctica — A260

1977, Feb. 10   Litho.   Perf. 14½
497 A260 2p multicolored   8.00   .45
Visit of President Augusto Pinochet to
Antarctica.

School Emblem,
Planted
Field — A261

Justice — A262

1977, Mar. 10   Perf. 14½
498 A261 2p multicolored   1.40   .30
Cent. of advanced agricultural education.

1977, Mar. 30   Litho.   Perf. 14½
499 A262 2p brown & slate   1.40   .30
Supreme Court of Justice, sesquicentennial.

Eye with Globe, Caduceus — A263

1977, Mar. 30   Litho.   Perf. 14½
500 A263 2p multicolored   1.60   .45
11th Pan-American Ophthalmological Cong.

Mounted
Policeman
A264

Designs: No. 502, Policewoman with children. No. 503, Paine Peaks and Osorno Volcano, crossed rifle emblem. No. 504, Crossed
rifle emblem, mounted and motorcycle police-
men, helicopter and automobile, horiz.

1977, Apr. 27
501 A264 2p multicolored   .45   .25
502 A264 2p multicolored   .45   .25
503 A264 2p multicolored   .45   .25
504 A264 2p multicolored   .45   .25
 Nos. 501-504 (4)   1.80   1.00
Chilean police organization, 50th anniv.

Intelsat Satellite
over
Globe — A265

1977, May 17   Litho.   Perf. 14½
505 A265 2p multi   .60   .25
World Telecommunications Day.

El Mercurio's First Front Page, Press
and Ship — A266

1977, July 5   Litho.   Perf. 14½
506 A266 2p multi   .40   .20
El Mercurio de Valparaiso, first Chilean
newspaper, 150th anniversary.

St. Francis, Birds
and
Cross — A267

Science and
Technology
A268

1977, July 26   Litho.   Perf. 14½
507 A267 5p multi   1.40   .25
St. Francis of Assisi, 750th death anniv.

1977, Aug. 26   Litho.   Perf. 14½
508 A268 4p multi   .55   .25

Young Mother
Weaving — A269

Diego de
Almagro — A270

#510, Handicapped boy in wheelchair &
nurse. #511, Children dancing in circle. #512,
Old man & home.

1977, Sept. 13   Litho.   Perf. 14½
509 A269 5p multi   .60   .20
510 A269 5p multi   .60   .20
511 A269 10p multi, horiz.   1.25   .25
512 A269 10p multi, horiz.   1.25   .25
 Nos. 509-512 (4)   3.70   .90
4th anniversary of Government Junta and
social services of armed forces.

1977, Oct. 31   Engr.   Perf. 14½
513 A270 5p rose & carmine   .40   .25
Diego de Almagro (1475-1538), leader of
Spanish expedition to Chile.

Bell,
Letters,
Dove and
Child
A271

1977, Dec. 12   Litho.   Perf. 14½
514 A271 2.50p multi   .40   .20
Christmas 1977.

Loading
Timber
A272

1978   Litho.   Perf. 15
515 A272 10p multi   1.25   .25
516 A272 20p multi   1.50   .35
No. 516 inscribed "CORREOS," ship is flying Chilean flag.

Papal Arms
and Globe
A273

University — A274

1978   Litho.   Perf. 14½
521 A273 10p multi   .85   .25
522 A274 25p multi   1.75   .60
World Peace Day (10p); Catholic University
of Valparaiso, 50th anniversary (25p). Issue
dates: 10p, July 28; 25p, July 31.

O'Higgins, by
Gil de
Castro — A275

1978, Aug. 20   Litho.   Perf. 15
523 A275 10p multi   .90   .30
Bernardo O'Higgins (1778-1842), soldier
and statesman.

Chacabuco Victory Monument A276

1978, Sept. 11
524 A276 10p multi .90 .30
160th anniv. of O'Higgins victory at Chacabuco, and 5th anniv. of military government.

Teacher Writing on Blackboard — A277

1978, Sept. 21
525 A277 15p multi 1.00 .25
10th anniversary and 9th Reunion of Interamerican Council for Education, Science and Culture (C.I.E.C.C.), Sept. 21-29.

First National Fleet, by Thomas Somerscales — A278

Design: 30p, Last Moments of Rancagua Battle, by Pedro Subercaseaux.

1978 **Litho.** **Perf. 15**
526 A278 20p multi 1.90 .45
527 A278 30p multi 2.10 .70
Bernardo O'Higgins (1778-1842), soldier and statesman.
Issue dates: 20p, Oct. 9; 30p, Oct. 2.

San Martin-O'Higgins Medal, by Rene Thenot, 1942 — A279

1978, Oct. 20
528 A279 7p multi .50 .25
José de San Martin and Bernardo O'Higgins, 200th birth anniversaries.

Council Emblem — A280

1978, Nov. 27 **Litho.** **Perf. 14½**
529 A280 50p multi 3.75 1.50
Intl. Council of Military Sports, 30th anniv.

Three Kings — A281

Virgin and Child — A282

1978, Dec. 14 **Litho.** **Perf. 14½**
530 A281 3p multi .75 .20
531 A282 11p multi 1.40 .40
Christmas 1978.

Philippi Brothers A283

1978, Dec. 29 **Litho.** **Perf. 14½x15**
532 A283 3.50p multi .40 .20
Bernardo E. Philippi (1811-1852) and Rodulfo A. Philippi (1808-1904), scientists and travelers.

No. 477 Surcharged in Bright Green
1979 **Litho.** **Perf. 13x14**
533 A253 3.50p on 10c gray grn .25 .20

Flags of Chile and Salvation Army — A284

1979, Mar. 17 **Litho.** **Perf. 14½**
534 A284 10p multi 1.25 .65
Salvation Army in Chile, 70th anniversary.

Pope Paul VI (1897-1978) — A285

1979, Mar. 30
535 A285 11p multi 1.25 .75

Battle of Maipu Monument — A286

1979, Apr. 17 **Litho.** **Perf. 14½**
536 A286 8.50p multi 1.40 .50
Bernardo O'Higgins (1778-1842), Liberator of Chile.

Naval Battles A287

1979, May 21 **Litho.** **Perf. 14½**
537 A287 3.50p Angamos .70 .25
538 A287 3.50p Iquique .70 .25
539 A287 3.50p Punta Gruesa .70 .25
Nos. 537-539 (3) 2.10 .75
Centenary of victorious naval battles against Peru.

1903 Ambulance and Red Cross — A288

1979, June 29 **Litho.** **Perf. 14½**
540 A288 25p multi 3.50 1.00
75th anniversary of Chilean Red Cross.

Diego Portales — A289

1979-86 **Litho.** **Perf. 13½**
542 A289 1.50p ocher .25 .20
543 A289 2p gray ('81) .25 .20
544 A289 3.50p red .30 .20
545 A289 4.50p bl grn ('81) .40 .20
546 A289 5p rose claret .50 .20
547 A289 6p emerald .60 .30
548 A289 7p yellow ('82) .55 .30
549 A289 10p blue ('82) .80 .30
550 A289 12p orange ('86) .35 .20
Nos. 542-550 (9) 4.00 2.10
1.50p, 3.50p, 5p and 6p inscribed "D. Portales."

People and Flag — A290

1979, Aug. 28 **Litho.** **Perf. 14½**
551 A290 10p multi .90 .60
Yugoslavian immigration, centenary.

Coat of Arms and Mt. Castillo A290a

1979, Oct. 12 **Litho.** **Perf. 14½**
552 A290a 20p multi 2.00 1.00
Coyhaique 50th anniv.

IYC Emblem, Playground — A291

IYC Emblem, Children's Drawings: 11p, Girl and shadow, vert. 12p, Dancing.

1979, Oct. 9 **Perf. 14½**
553 A291 9.50p multi .95 .60
554 A291 11p multi 1.10 .75
555 A291 12p multi 1.60 .85
Nos. 553-555 (3) 3.65 2.20
International Year of the Child.

Telecom 79 A292

1979, Oct. 26 **Litho.** **Perf. 14½**
556 A292 15p multi 1.50 .75
3rd World Telecommunications Exhibition, Geneva, Sept. 20-26.

Puerto Williams, 25th Anniversary — A293

1979, Nov. 21
557 A293 3.50p multi .60 .20

Adoration of the Kings A294

1979, Dec. 4 **Litho.** **Perf. 15**
558 A294 3.50p multi .60 .25
Christmas 1979.

Rafael Sotomayor, Minister of War — A295

Military heroes.

CHILE

1979, Dec. 29   *Perf. 13½*
559 A295 3.50p ocher & brn   .50 .25
560 A295 3.50p Erasmo Escala   .50 .25
561 A295 3.50p Emilio
    Sotomayor   .50 .25
562 A295 3.50p Eleuterio Rami-
    rez   .50 .25
   a.   Block of 4, #559-562   2.00 2.00

Bell UH-1 Rescue Helicopter at Tinguiririca Volcano, by S.O. Mococain — A296

Air Force, 50th Anniversary: No. 564, Flying boat Catalina Skua over Antarctic, by E.F. Alvarez. No. 565, F5-E Tiger II over Andes, by M.M. Barria.

1980, Mar. 21   Litho.   *Perf. 13½*
563 A296 3.50p shown   .50 .25
564 A296 3.50p Jet   .50 .25
565 A296 3.50p Sea plane   .50 .25
   Nos. 563-565 (3)   1.50 .75

The Death of Bueras, by Pedro Leon Carmona — A297

1980, Apr. 14   Litho.   *Perf. 13½*
566 A297 12p multi   1.00 .50
   Charge of Bueras, Battle of Maipo, 1818.

Rotary International, 75th Anniversary — A298

1980, Apr. 15
567 A298 10p multi   1.25 .45

Gen. Manuel Baquedano, by Pedro Subercaseaux A299

Gen. Pedro Lagos, Battle Scene, by Subercaseaux — A300

Battle of Morro de Arica Centenary (Subercaseaux Paintings): No. 570, Commander Juan J. San Martin, battle scene.

1980, June 7   Litho.   *Perf. 13½*
568 A299 3.50p multi   .40 .20
569 A300 3.50p multi   .40 .20
570 A300 3.50p multi   .40 .20
   Nos. 568-570 (3)   1.20 .60

Score and Perez's Silhouette — A301

1980, June 27   Litho.   *Perf. 13½*
571 A301 6p multi   .60 .30
   Osman Perez Freire (1880-1930), composer, and fragment from his song "Ay, Ay, Ay."

Mt. Gasherbrum II, Chilean Flag, Ice Pick — A302

1980, July 9
572 A302 15p multi   1.40 .60
   Chilean Himalayan expedition, June 1979.

"Charity," Stained-glass Window A303

1980, July 18
573 A303 10p multi   1.50 .35
   Daughters of Charity, 125th anniv. in Chile.

Condor, Colors of Chile — A304

1980, Sept. 11   Litho.   *Perf. 13½*
574 A304 3.50p multi   .40 .25
   17th anniversary of constitution.

Inca Child Mummy A305

Pablo Burchard, by Pedro Lira A306

1980, Sept. 14
575 A305 5p shown   .60 .20
576 A305 5p Claudio Gay   .60 .20
   a.   Pair, #575-576 + label   1.40 1.25
   Natl. Museum of Natural History (founded by Claudio Gay, 1800-73) sesqui.

1980, Sept. 27   Litho.   *Perf. 13½*
577 A306 3.50p multi   .40 .20
   Museum of Fine Art centenary (directed by Burchard, 1932).

Santiago International Fair — A307

1980, Oct. 30
578 A307 3.50p multi   .40 .20

Nativity — A308

Christmas 1980: 3.50p, Family, vert.

1980, Nov. 25   Litho.   *Perf. 13½*
579 A308 3.50p multi   .60 .25
580 A308 10.50p multi   1.25 .45

Infantryman 1879 — A309   Congress Emblem — A310

Pacific War period uniforms, 1879.

1980, Nov. 27
581 A309 3.50p shown   .75 .20
582 A309 3.50p Cavalry officer   .75 .20
583 A309 3.50p Artillery officer   .75 .20
584 A309 3.50p Engineer colonel   .75 .20
   a.   Block of 4, #581-584   4.00 4.00
   See Nos. 606-609.

1980, Dec. 1
585 A310 11.50p multi   1.25 .60
   23rd Intl. Cong. of Military Medicine & Pharmacy.

Eradication of Hoof and Mouth Disease A311

1981, Jan. 16   Litho.   *Perf. 13½*
586 A311 9.50p multi   .90 .25

Moai Statues, Easter Island — A312

1981, Jan. 28   Litho.   *Perf. 13½*
587 A312 3.50p shown   .35 .25
588 A312 3.50p Robinson Crusoe Island   .60 .25
589 A312 10.50p Penguins, Antarctic Territory   2.50 .75
   Nos. 587-589 (3)   3.45 1.25

National Heroine Javiera Carrera, by O.M. Pizarro, Birth Bicentenary — A313

1981, Mar. 20
590 A313 3.50p multi   .40 .20

UPU Membership Centenary A314

1981, Apr. 1
591 A314 3.50p multi   .40 .25

C130 Hercules Air Force Transport Plane Unloading Cargo — A315

1981, Apr. 21
592 A315 3.50p multi   1.00 .40
   Lieutenant Marsh Air Force Base, 1st anniv.

13th World Telecommunications Day — A316

1981, May 17   Litho.   *Perf. 13½*
593 A316 3.50p multi   .40 .20

Arturo
Prat
Naval
Base
A317

1981, June 23   Litho.   Perf. 13½
594 A317 3.50p multi   .75 .25

Capt. Jose
Luis Araneda
A318

1981, June 26
595 A318 3.50p multi   .40 .20
Battle of Sangrar centenary.

Philatelic
Society of
Chile, 90th
Anniv.
A319

1981, July 29   Litho.   Perf. 13½
596 A319 4.50p multi   .40 .20

Minister Recabarren and Chief
Conuepan Giving Speeches, by Hector
Robles Acuna — A320

1981, Aug. 7
597 A320 4.50p multi   .90 .25
Temuco city centenary.

Exports
A321

1981, Aug. 31   Litho.   Perf. 13½
598 A321 14p multi   .80 .35

Presidential Palace — A322

1981, Sept. 11
599 A322 4.50p multi   .80 .20
Natl. liberation, 8th anniv.

St. Vincent de
Paul, 400th
Birth Anniv.
A323

1981, Sept. 27   Litho.   Perf. 13½
600 A323 4.50p multi   .50 .25

Andres Bello,
Poet and
Sholar, Birth
Bicentenary
A324

1981, Sept. 29
601 A324 4.50p Coin   .40 .25
602 A324 9.50p Bust, books   .60 .30
603 A324 11.50p Statue, arms   1.00 .40
  Nos. 601-603 (3)   2.00 .95

2nd Congress
of South
American
Uniformed
Police
A325

1981, Oct. 15
604 A325 4.50p multi   .50 .20

World
Food
Day
A326

1981, Oct. 16
605 A326 5.50p multi   .50 .25

Uniform Type of 1980
1879 Parade Uniforms.

1981, Nov. 6   Perf. 13½
606 A309 5.50p Infantry private   .80 .25
607 A309 5.50p Cadet   .80 .25
608 A309 5.50p Cavalryman   .80 .25
609 A309 5.50p Artilleryman   .80 .25
  a.   Block of 4, #606-609   4.00 3.00

Intl. Year of
the Disabled
A327

1981, Nov. 11
610 A327 5.50p multi   1.00 .30

Christmas 1981 — A328

1981, Nov. 25
611 A328 5.50p Nativity   .50 .25
612 A328 11.50p Three Kings   1.00 .40

50th Anniv. of Federico Santa Maria
Technical University — A329

1981, Dec 1   Litho.   Perf. 13½
613 A329 5.50p multi   .40 .25

Dario Salas
(1881-1941),
Educator — A330

1981, Dec. 4
614 A330 5.50p multi   .45 .25

FIDA '82, 2nd Natl. Air Force
Fair — A331

1982, Mar. 6   Litho.   Perf. 13½
615 A331 4.50p multi   .50 .20

1980 Constitution — A332

1982, Mar. 11
616 A332 4.50p Cardinal Caro,
                   family   .50 .25
617 A332 11p Diego Portales   1.50 .40
618 A332 30p Bernardo
                   O'Higgins   2.50 .90
  Nos. 616-618 (3)   4.50 1.55

Panamerican
Institute of
Geography
and History,
12th General
Assembly
A333

1982, Mar. 22   Litho.   Perf. 13½
619 A333 4.50p multi   .50 .25

American Air Forces Cooperation
System — A334

1982, Apr. 12
620 A334 4.50p multi   .45 .20

Pedro   Fish
Montt — A335   Exports — A336

1982, Mar. 27
621 A335 4.50p light vio   .50 .20

1982, May 3   Litho.   Perf. 13½
622 A336 20p multi   2.00 .75

Scouting Year — A337

#623b, Robert Baden-Powell.

1982, May 21   Litho.   Perf. 13
623   Pair   40.00 32.50
  a.-b.   A337 4.50p, either single   15.00 8.00

Battle of
Concepcion
Centenary
A338

Chacabuco Regiment officers killed in
battle.

1982, June 18   Litho.   Perf. 13½
624   Block of 4   2.50 2.50
  a.   A338 4.50p I. Carrera Pinto   .50   .20
  b.   A338 4.50p A. Perez Canto   .50   .20
  c.   A338 4.50p J. Montt Salamanca .50   .20
  d.   A338 4.50p L. Cruz Martinez   .50   .20

UN World Assembly on Aging, July
26-Aug. 6 — A339

1982, Aug. 5
625   A339 4.50p multi   .40   .25

TB Bacillus
Centenary
A340

1982, Aug. 31
626   A340 4.50p multi   .40   .20

9th Anniv. of National
Liberation — A341

1982, Sept. 11   Litho.   Perf. 13½
627   A341 4.50p multi   .40   .20

Christmas 1982 — A342

Children's drawings.

1982, Nov. 2
628   A342 10p multi   1.00   .25
629   A342 25p multi, vert.   1.50   .60

Nos. 416-417 Surcharged in Green or
Black

1982, Nov.   Perf. 14½x15, 14½
630   A222 1p on 3.50p bl grn &
            grn (G)   .20   .20
631   A223 2p on 1.15p blk & car   .20   .20

Marist Alumni, 9th
World Congress
A342a

Virgin Mary & Marcellus Champagnat
(founder of Marist Brotherhood), stained glass
window, Church of the Sacred Heart of Jesus,
Barcelona.

1982, Nov. 11   Litho.   Perf. 13½
631A A342a 7p multi   1.40   .40

El Sur
Newspaper
Centenary
A342b

1982, Nov. 15
631B A342b 7p Wooden hand-
             press, mast-
             head   .50   .25

110th Anniv. of South American
Steamship Co. — A342c

1982, Dec. 20
631C A342c 7p Steamer Copiapo   .75   .30

60th Anniv. of
Radio Club of
Chile — A342d

1982, Dec. 29
631D A342d 7p multi   .50   .25

First Anniv. of Postal Agreement with
Order of Malta — A343

1983, Mar. 30   Litho.   Perf. 13½
632   25p Arms of Order of Malta   2.00   .40
633   50p Chile   4.00   .80
  a. Pair, #632-633   6.00 5.00

D.D. No. 20
This and similar inscriptions indicate
that the stamps would be sold at a discount if purchased in large quantities.

D. Portales Type of 1975 Inscribed
Diego Portales and:

Ramon Barros   Juan Luis
Luco   Sanfuentes
A344   A344a

1983-88   Litho.   Perf. 13½
634   A344   1p grnsh bl   .20   .20
635   A253   1p chalky bl   .20   .20
636   A253   1.50p ocher   .20   .20
637   A344   2p dl vio ('84)   .20   .20
638   A253   2p ol gray   .20   .20
639   A253   2.50p lemon   .20   .20
640   A253   5p red lilac   .35   .25
641   A344   5p crim rose   .20   .20
642   A344a 5p red ('84)   .20   .20
643   A344   7p ultra   .30   .20
644   A344a 9p brn ('84)   .25   .20

645   A344a   9p grn ('84)   .25   .20
646   A344   10p black   .25   .20
646A A344a 10p gray ('84)   .25   .20
647   A344a 15p ultra ('87)   .20   .20
  a. Booklet pane of 10   1.50
648   A344a 20p yel ('88)   .20   .20
  b. Booklet pane of 10   2.00
Nos. 644, 647, 648 inscribed "D.S. No. 20."
Issued: No. 640, 8/85.
For surcharge see No. 779.

50th Anniv. of
Bureau of
Investigation
A345

1983, June 19   Litho.   Perf. 13½
649   A345 20p multi   1.25   .50

Antonio Cardinal Samore (1905-
1983) — A346

1983, June 26
650   A346 30p multi   2.00   .60

Centenary of
Cliff Elevators
in Valparaiso
A347

1983, Aug. 19   Litho.   Perf. 13½
651   A347 40p multi   4.00   .45

Pucara de Quitor Settlement Ruins,
San Pedro de Atacama — A348

No. 653, Llamas, rock painting, Rio Ibanez,
Aisen. No. 654, Duck-shaped jug with human
head, Diaguita cultures. No. 655, Puoko Tangata carved stone head, Easter Isld.

1983, Aug. 26
652   A348 7p multi   .75   .30
653   A348 7p multi   .75   .30
654   A348 7p multi   .75   .30
655   A348 7p multi, vert.   .20   .20
    Nos. 652-655 (4)   2.45 1.10

10th Anniv. of National
Liberation — A349

1983, Sept. 11   Litho.   Perf. 13½
656   A349   7p Angel with broken
             chains   .60   .25
657   A349   7p Couple, flag   .60   .25
658   A349 10p Family, torch   .60   .25
659   A349 40p Coat of arms, "10"   2.00   .75
  a. Strip of 4, #656-659   5.00 3.50

For surcharges see Nos. 669-670.

Famous
Hondurans
A350

#660, Francisco Morazan (1792-1842),
Advocate of United Central America. #661,
Jose Cecilio Del Valle (1777-1834), Scholar
and Leader of Pan Americanism.

1983, Oct. 3   Litho.   Perf. 13½
660   A350 7p multi   .40   .20
661   A350 7p multi   .40   .20
  a. Pair, #660-661   .80   .80

World Communications Year — A351

1983, Oct. 13   Litho.   Perf. 13½
662   7p Central P.O.   .85   .25
663   7p Challenger spaceship   .85   .25
  a. A351 Pair, #662-663   1.75 1.75

Christmas 1983 — A353

Childrens' Drawings: 10p Chilean Peasant,
Hanny Chacon. 30p, Holy Family. Lucrecia
Cardenas, vert.

1983, Nov. 14   Litho.   Perf. 13
664   A353 10p multi   .50   .20
665   A353 30p multi   1.50   .40

Design descriptions printed on back on top
of gum.

State Railways Centenary — A354

Train Cars: a, Presidential coach, 1911. b,
Service coach, 1910; tender, 1929. c, Locomotive Type 80, 1929.

1984, Jan. 4   Litho.   Perf. 13½
666   Strip of 3   8.50 7.50
  a.-c. A354 9p, any single   2.00   .40

3rd Intl. Air Fair, Santiago, Mar. 3-11 — A355

1984, Jan. 31   Litho.   Perf. 13½
667 A355 9p Flags, plane   .90   .20

20th Anniv. of Nuclear Energy Commission — A356

1984, Apr. 16   Litho.   Perf. 13
668 A356 9p multi   .50   .25

Nos. 656-657 Surcharged in Purple
1984, June 11   Litho.   Perf. 13½
669 A349 9p on 7p #656   .45   .25
670 A349 9p on 7p #657   .45   .25
  a.   Pair, #669-670   1.00 .75

Antarctic Colonization — A357

1984, June 18
671 A357 15p Women's expedition   .75   .35
672 A357 15p Villa las Estrellas
             Station   .75   .35
673 A357 15p Scouts, flag, Air
             Force base   .75   .35
  a.   Strip of 3, #671-673   5.25 5.00

10th Anniv. of Regionalization — A358

Designs: a, Parinacota Church, Tarapaca. b, El Tatio geyser, Antofagasta. c, Copper mining, Atacama. d, Tololo Observatory, Coquimbo. e, Valparaiso Harbor, Valparaiso. f, Ahu Akivi head sculptures, Easter Isld. g, St. Francis Church, Santiago. h, El Hunique House, O'Higgins. i, Colburn Machicura Dam and Hydroelectric Power Station, Maule. j, Sta. Juana de Guadalcazar Fort, Bio-Bio. k, Indian woman, Araucania. l, Guar Isld. Church, Los Lagos. m, Main road, Gen. del Campo. n, Shepherds' Monument, Magellanes and Antarctic. o, Family, Villa las Estrellas Station, Antarctic.

1984, July 11
674   Sheet of 15   15.00 15.00
  a.-o.   A358 9p multi, any single .75   .40

Capt. Pedro Sarmiento de Gamboa, Map, 1584 — A359

1984, July 31   Litho.   Perf. 13
675 A359 100p multi   4.50 1.00

400th anniv. of Spanish presence in Straits of Magellan.

State Bank of Chile Centenary — A360

1984, Sept. 6   Litho.   Perf. 13½
676 A360 35p Founder Antonio
             Varas de la Bar-
             ra, coin   1.00 .45

11th Anniv. of Liberation — A361

1984, Sept. 11
677 A361 20p Monument to
             O'Higgins   1.10 .30

Circus Centenary — A362

1984, Sept. 28   Litho.   Perf. 13½
678 A362 45p Clown   1.50 .70

Endangered Species, World Wildlife Emblem — A363

1985, July   Litho.   Perf. 13½
679 A363 9p Chinchilla   8.00 2.25
680 A363 9p Blue whale   8.00 2.25
681 A363 9p Sea lions   8.00 2.25
682 A363 9p Chilean huemuls   8.00 2.25
  a.   Block of 4, #679-682   37.50 18.50

Christmas 1984 — A364

Children's drawings.

1984, Nov. 20   Litho.   Perf. 13½
683 A364 9p Shepherds   .40   .20
684 A364 40p Bethlehem   1.50 .40

Santiago University Planetarium Opening — A365

1984, Dec. 29
685 A365 10p multi   .70   .20

Flora and Fauna — A366

Wildlife: a, Conepatus chinga. b, Leucocoryne purpurea. c, Himantopus himantopus. d, Lutra felina. e, Balbisia peduncularis. f, Psittacus cyanalysias. g, Pudu pudu. h, Fuschia magellanica. i, Diuca diuca. j, Dusicyon griseus. k, Alstroemeria sierrae. l, Glaucidium nanum.

1985, Feb.
686   Block of 12   13.00 9.00
  a.-l.   A366 10p, Any single   .65   .35

American Airforces Cooperation System, 25th Anniv. A367

1985, Mar. 26
687 A367 45p Emblem, flags   2.00 1.10

Chile-Argentina Peace Treaty — A368

1985, May 2   Litho.   Perf. 13½
688 A368 20p Papal arms, flags   2.50 .50

Fr. Joseph Kentenich (1885-1968), Founder, Intl. Schonstatt Movement of Catholic Laymen A369

1985, May 19   Litho.   Perf. 13½
689 A369 40p Portrait, La Florida
             Sanctuary, Santia-
             go   .70   .40

Antarctic Treaty, 25th Anniv. — A370

Resources, research: 15p, Krill, pack ice, map. 20p, Seismological Station, O'Higgins' Base. 35p, Georeception Station, dish receiver.

1985, June 21
690 A370 15p multi   .65   .35
691 A370 20p multi   .85   .50
692 A370 35p multi   1.50 .75
        Nos. 690-692 (3)   3.00 1.60

Canis Fulvipes — A371

Endangered wildlife: b, Phoenicoparrus jamesi. c, Fulica gigantea. d, Lutra provocax.

1985, Aug. 9   Litho.   Perf. 13½
693   Block of 4   10.00 3.50
  a.-d.   A371 20p, any single   1.40   .30

Intl. Youth Year A372

UN, 40th Anniv. A373

1985, Aug. 31
694 A372 15p multi   .50   .25
695 A373 15p multi   .50   .25
  a.   Pair, #694-695   1.50 1.50

Gen. Jose Miguel Carrera Verdugo (1785-1821) — A374

1985, Oct. 8   Litho.   Perf. 13½
696 A374 40p multi   .90   .55

Farmer and Ox-drawn Hay Cart — A375

Folklore: b, Street photographer, wet plate camera. c, One-man band. d, Basket maker.

1985, Oct.
697   Block of 4   1.25   .90
  a.-d.   A375 10p, any single   .25   .20

For surcharges see Nos. 770-771.

Christmas
1985 — A376

Holy
Family — A376a

Winning children's drawings, 7th natl.
design contest.

1985, Nov. 4
698 A376 15p Nativity .55 .20
699 A376 100p Father Christmas,
vert. 3.75 1.00
Nos. 698-699 inscribed in black on gummed
side with child's name, age, school and region.

1985 Litho. Perf. 13½
699A A376a 10p buff & brn .30 .20
For surcharge see No. 768.

16th Armed Forces
Conference — A377

20p, Cavalryman, Directorial Escort, 1818.
35p, Officer, Grand Guard, 1813.

1985, Nov. 15 Litho. Perf. 13½
700 A377 20p multicolored .75 .25
701 A377 35p multicolored 1.00 .35

Halley's Comet — A378

1985, Nov. 29 Litho. Perf. 13½
702 A378 45p multicolored .75 .25
a. Souvenir sheet 17.50 17.50
No. 702a exists imperf. Value $27.50.

Natl. Solidarity Campaign — A379

1985
703 A379 5p red & blue .50 .50

Campaign for
Prevention of
Forest
Fires — A380

1985, Dec. 27
704 A380 40p Forest .75 .40
705 A380 40p Fire destruction .75 .40
a. Pair, #704-705 2.75 1.50
No. 705a has continuous design.

Dungeness Point Lighthouse, Straits of
Magellan — A381

1986, Jan. 26
706 A381 45p shown 1.40 .45
707 A381 45p Evangelistas Lighthouse 1.40 .45
a. Pair, #706-707 3.50 2.25
No. 707a continuous design.

View of Santiago, Mackenna — A382

1986, Jan. 28
708 A382 30p multi .45 .20
Benjamin Vicuna Mackenna (d. 1886),
municipal superintendent of Santiago, 1872-
1875.

Diego Portales, Natl. Crest,
Text — A382a

1986, Feb. Litho. Perf. 13½
708A A382a 12p on 3.50p multi .45 .20
No. 708A not issued without surcharge.

1986 World Cup Soccer
Championships, Mexico — A383

Host stadiums: 15p, Natl. Stadium, Chile,
1962. 20p, Aztec Stadium, Mexico, 1970.
35p, Maracana Stadium, Brazil, 1950. 50p,
Wembley Stadium, Great Britain, 1966.

1986, Feb. 18
709 A383 15p multi .40 .25
710 A383 20p multi .55 .25
711 A383 35p multi .80 .35
712 A383 50p multi 1.25 .50
Nos. 709-712 (4) 3.00 1.35

Environmental Conservation — A384

1986, Feb. 28
713 A384 20p Water .65 .20
714 A384 20p Air .65 .20
715 A384 20p Soil .65 .20
Nos. 713-715 (3) 1.95 .60

Sailing Ship
Santiaguillo,
Flags — A385

1986, Mar. 20
716 A385 40p multi .80 .45
Discovery of Valparaiso Bay, 450th anniv.

A386

1986, Apr. 9
717 A386 45p multi 1.00 .45
Interamerican Development Bank, 25th
anniv.

A387

1986, Apr. 30 Litho. Perf. 13½
718 A387 15p multi .65 .25
St. Rosa de Lima (1586-1617), sanctuary at
Pelequen.

Moai Statues,
Easter
Is. — A388

1986, May 15
719 A388 60p Raraku Volcano 1.50 .50
a. Souvenir sheet 10.50 10.50
720 A388 100p Tongariki Ruins 2.75 .85
a. Souvenir sheet 16.00 16.00

AMERIPEX '86 — A389

1986, May 23
721 A389 100p multi 2.50 1.10

Historic Naval Ships — A390

1986, May 30
722 A390 35p Schooner Ancud,
1843 .70 .35
723 A390 35p Armed merchantman Aguilar,
1830 .70 .35
724 A390 35p Corvette Esmeralda, 1856 .70 .35
725 A390 35p Frigate O'Higgins,
1834 .70 .35
a. Block of 4, #722-725 5.00 5.00
See Nos. 752-753.

Paintings by
Juan
Francisco
Gonzalez
(1853-1933)
A391

1986, June 24
726 A391 30p Rush and Chrysanthemums .75 .30
727 A391 30p Gate of La Serena .75 .30
a. Pair, #726-727 2.00 1.50

Exports — A392

Designs: a, Saltpeter. b, Iron. c, Copper. d,
Molybdenum.

1986 Litho. Perf. 13½
728 A392 Block of 4 1.60 1.25
a.-d. 12p, any single .25 .20

Antarctic Fauna — A393

a, Sterna vittata. b, Phalacrocorax atriceps.
c, Aptenodytes forsteri. d, Catharacta
lonnberg.

1986, July 16 Litho. Perf. 13½
729 Block of 4 6.50 4.00
a.-d. A393 40p, any single 1.00 .40

Writers — A394

No. 730, Pedro de Ona (1570-1643). No. 731, Vicente Huidobro (1893-1948).

1986, Aug. 19
730	A394	20p multi	.40	.25
731	A394	20p multi	.40	.25
a.		Pair, #730-731	1.50	.90

Has continuous design.

Military Academy, Cent. — A395

1986, Sept. 8   Litho.   Perf. 13½
732	A395	45p Major-General, 1878	.75	.40
733	A395	45p Major, 1950	.75	.40
a.		Pair, #732-733	1.75	1.10

Art A396

1986, Oct. 17   Perf. 13½
734	A396	30p Diaguita urn, duck jug	.50	.25
735	A396	30p Mapuche silver ornament, embroidery	.50	.25
a.		Pair, #734-735	2.00	1.50

Christmas — A397

8th Natl. design contest-winning children's drawings.

1986, Nov. 19   Litho.   Perf. 13½
736	A397	15p multi	.60	.20
737	A397	105p multi	2.40	.55

Nos. 736-737 inscribed in black on gummed side with child's name, age, school and region.

Christmas A397a

Design: Shepherds see star, Bethlehem.

1986, Nov.   Litho.   Perf. 13½
737A	A397a	12p multi	.35	.20

Intl. Peace Year — A398

1986, Nov. 26
738	A398	85p multi	1.50	.60

Natl. Women Volunteers — A399

1986, Dec. 15   Litho.   Perf. 13½
739	A399	15p multi	.35	.20

Crowning of Our Lady of Mt. Carmel, Patron of Chile, by Pius XI, 60th Anniv. — A400

1986, Dec. 19
740	A400	25p multi	.70	.25

Andean Railways Kitson-Meyer No. 59, 1907, Designed by Robert Sterling — A401

1987, Jan. 27   Litho.   Perf. 13½
741	A401	95p multi	2.75	1.10

Arturo Prat Naval Base, Greenwich Island, the Antarctic, 40th Anniv. — A402

Illustration reduced.

1987, Feb. 6
742		100p Storage and power supplies	4.50	2.00
743		100p Working and living quarters	4.50	2.00
a.		A402 Pair, #742-743	9.00	7.00

State Visit of Pope John Paul II, Apr. 1-6, 1987 A403

Pope John Paul II and: 20p, Christ the Redeemer statue. 25p, Votive Church, Maipu. 90p, Cross of the Seas, Straits of Magellan. 115p, Virgin of the Hill.

1987   Litho.   Perf. 13½
744	A403	20p multi	.30	.20
745	A403	25p multi	.40	.20
746	A403	90p multi	1.40	.60
747	A403	115p multi	1.90	.95
a.		Souv. sheet of one	4.75	4.75
747B	A403	115p multi	2.00	1.00
		Nos. 744-747B (5)	6.00	2.95

No. 747a sold for 250p.
No. 747B differs from No. 747 in that the Statue of the Virgin has a halo and Pope John Paul II is smiling.
Issue date: Nos. 744-747a, Apr. 6.

Los Carabineros (Natl. Guard), 60th Anniv. — A404

World Youth Soccer Championships A405

1987, Apr. 21
748	A404	50p Cavalry showmanship	.80	.35
749	A404	50p Air-sea rescue	.80	.35
a.		Pair, #748-749	2.40	2.00

1987, May 28

b, Concepcion Stadium, kick play. c, Antofagasta Stadium, dribbling the ball. d, Valparaiso Stadium, heading the ball.
750		Block of 4	3.50	3.50
a.-d.		A405 45p any single	.70	.50

Souvenir Sheet
751	A405	45p Four players	3.00	3.00

No. 751 sold for 150p.

Naval Ships Type of 1986

1987, May 29
752	A390	60p Battleship Almirante Latorre, 1913	1.00	.60
753	A390	60p Cruiser O'Higgins, 1936	1.00	.60
a.		Pair, #752-753	3.75	2.25

Diego Portales (1793-1837), Finance Minister — A406

1987, June 16
754	A406	30p multi	.50	.25

Public Works Ministry, Cent. — A407

1987, June 26
755	A407	25p multi	.55	.30

Infantry School, Cent. — A408

1987, July 9
756	A408	50p Entrance	.50	.25
757	A408	100p Soldiers, natl. flag	1.00	.50

Miniature Sheet

Flora and Fauna — A409

Designs: a, Chiasognathus granti. b, Calidris alba. c, Hippocamelus antisensis. d, Jubaea chilensis. e, Colias vauthieri. f, Pandion haliaetus. g, Cephalorhynchus commersonii. h, Austrocedrus chilensis. i, Jasus frontalis. j, Stephanoides fernandensis. k, Vicugna vicugna. l, Thyrsopteris elegans. m, Lithodes antarctica. n, Pterocnemia pennata. o, Lagidium viscacia. p, Cereus atacamensis.

1987, July 30
758		Sheet of 16	15.00	15.00
a.-p.		A409 25p any single	.55	.30

Intl. Year of Shelter for the Homeless A410

The Guitarist of Quinchamali A411

1987, Aug. 6
759	A410	40p multi	.60	.30

1987, July   Litho.   Perf. 13½

Legends and folk tales: b, El Caleuche. c, El Pihuychen. d, La Lola.
760		Block of 4	1.60	1.00
a.-d.		A411 15p any single	.20	.20

Nos. 760a-760d exist ovptd. "D.S. No 20." in golden brown on back. Value $2.50.
For surcharges see Nos. 812, 1104.

FISA '87, Santiago — A412

1987, Oct. 16   Litho.   Perf. 13½
761	A412	20p multi	.25	.20

25th Intl. agriculture and exports exhibition.

Rear Admiral Carlos Condell de la Haza (1843-1887), Naval Hero at the Battle of the Pacific — A413

1987, Nov. 7
762 A413 50p multi   1.10   .65

Christmas 1987 — A414

1987, Nov. 13
763 A414 30p multi   .60   .25
764 A414 100p multi   2.40   .75

1987, Nov. 23
765 A415 40p Foundry   2.10   .60
  a. Souv. sheet of one   2.50 2.50
     No. 765 sold for 150p.

Natl. Antarctic Exploration Commission, 25th Anniv. — A415a

1987, Dec. 11   Litho.   Perf. 13½
765B A415a 45p multi   1.10   .50

Ramon Freire Serrano (1787-1851), Chief of State A416

To Smoke Is To Contaminate A417

1987, Dec. 29   Perf. 13x13½
766 A416 20p pale lil & rose claret
                            .40   .30

1987, Dec.   Litho.   Perf. 13½
767 A417 15p blue & ver   .30   .20
Natl. Commission for the Control of Smoking.

No. 699A Surcharged in Green

1987   Litho.   Perf. 13½
768 A376a 12p on 10p buff & brn .30 .20

Christmas 1987 — A418

1987, Dec.
769 A418 15p ultra, org yel & blk .30 .20
  a. Bklt. pane of 10   4.00
No. 769a exists ovptd. "D.S. No 20." on back.

No. 697 Surcharged with New Value and 6 Bars in Rose Red and Black

1987, Dec.
770   Block of 4   1.10   .80
  a.-d. A375 12p on 10p, #697a-697d .25 .20
771   Block of 4   1.10   .80
  a.-d. A375 15p on 10p, #697a-697d .25 .20

St. John Bosco (1815-1888), Educator Canonized in 1934 — A419

1988, Jan. 29
772 A419 40p multi   .75   .30

20th Music Week, Frutillar — A420

1988, Jan. 27
773 A420 30p multi   .50   .25

FIDA '88, 5th Intl. Aviation Fair — A421

1988, Mar. 4   Litho.   Perf. 13½
774 A421 60p dark blue & blue .90 .60

1988 Summer Olympics, Seoul — A422

Flags of Chile and Korea, events: 50p, Shot put, pole vault, javelin. 100p, Swimming, cycling, running.

1988, Mar. 18   Perf. 13½
775 A422 50p multi   1.25   .60
776 A422 100p multi   2.50 1.00
  a. Souv. sheet of 2, #775-776 4.75 4.75
     No. 776a sold for 250p.

Natl. Agricultural Soc., 150th Anniv. — A423

1988, Apr. 8
777 A423 45p multi   1.40   .35

Intl. Red Cross and Red Crescent Organizations, 125th Annivs. — A424

1988, May 10
778 A424 150p multi   2.10   .65

No. 645 Surcharged

1988   Litho.   Perf. 13½
779 A344a 20p on 9p green   .25   .20

Easter Island Folk Art — A425

Designs: Nos. 780, 782, Carved wooden head from Kava Kava. Nos. 781, 783, Bird man stone carving from Tangata Manu.

1988, Apr. 1   Litho.   Perf. 13½
780 A425 20p brick red & blk .30 .20
781 A425 20p brick red & blk .30 .20
  a. Bklt. pane, 6 #780, 4 #781 2.00
  b. Pair, #780-781   .65   .65
782 A425 20p yel & blk   .30   .20
783 A425 20p yel & blk   .30   .20
  a. Bklt. pane, 6 #782, 4 #783 2.00
  b. Pair, #782-783   .65   .65
     Nos. 780-783 (4)   1.20   .80

Nos. 782-783 inscribed "D.S. No 20." For surcharges see Nos. 813-816, 955-956.

Merino, Biplane, Jet Passenger Plane and Supersonic Fighter Plane — A426

1988, May 17   Litho.   Perf. 13½
784 A426 35p multi   .90   .25
Commodore Arturo Merino Benitez (b. 1888), aviation pioneer.

Naval Tradition — A427

Designs: No. 785, Training ship *Esmeralda*. No. 786, Capt. Arturo Pratt, a stained-glass window in the Naval Museum, Valparaiso.

1988, May 23
785 50p multi   .90   .50
786 50p multi   .90   .50
  a. A427 Pair, #785-786   2.25 1.75

Pontifical Catholic University of Chile, Santiago, Cent. — A429

1988, June 21
787 A429 40p Papal & university arms .90 .25

Locomotives — A430

1988, July 22   Litho.   Perf. 13½
788 A430 60p Esslingen No. 3331 .55 .40
789 A430 60p North British No. 45 .55 .40
  a. Souv. sheet, #788-789, imperf 6.50 6.50
  b. Pair, #788-789   1.60 1.60
Arica-La Paz Railway, 75th anniv. (#788); Antofagasta Bolivia Railway, cent. (#789).

Jose Miguel Carrera Natl. Institute, 175th Anniv. — A431

1988, Aug. 10   Litho.   Perf. 13½
790 A431 45p multi   .60   .30

Annexation of Easter Is., Cent. — A432

1988, Sept. 9
791 A432 50p Ship, officer 1.00   .40
792 A432 50p Map, globe   1.00   .40
  a. Pair, #791-792   2.50 1.50
793 A432 100p Easter Is. folk dancers 1.50 .75
794 A432 100p Stone ruins   1.50   .75
  a. Souv. sheet of 4, #791-794, imperf. 7.00 6.50
  b. Pair, #793-794   5.00 3.00
     Nos. 791-794 (4)   5.00 2.30

Miniature Sheet

Flowers — A433

Designs: a, *Chloraea chrysantha.* b, *Lapageria rosea.* c, *Nolana paradoxa.* d, *Rhodophiala advena.* e, *Schizanthus hookeri.* f, *Acacia caven.* g, *Cordia decandra.* h, *Leontochir ovallei.* i, *Alstroemeria pelegrina.* j, *Copiapoa cinerea.* k, *Salpiglossis sinuata.* l, *Leucocoryne coquimbensis.* m, *Eucryphia glutinosa.* n, *Calandrinia longiscapa.* o, *Desfontainia spinosa.* p, *Sophora macrocarpa.*

1988, Aug. 23   Litho.   Perf. 13½
795   Sheet of 16   15.00 15.00
a.-p. A433 30p any single   .50   .25

First Domestic Airmail Route,
1919 — A434

1988, Oct. 11
796 A434 150p Clodomiro Figueroa Ponce's aircraft   1.90 1.00

Christmas 1988
A435   A436

Children's drawings: 35p, Nativity, by Paulette Thiers, age 8. 100p, Going to church, by Jose M. Lamas, age 9, horiz.

1988, Nov. 17
797 A435 20p rose lake & org yel   .45 .20
a.   Bklt. pane of 10   6.00
798 A435 20p rose lake & org yel   .45 .20
a.   Bklt. pane of 10   6.00
799 A436 35p multi   .65 .20
800 A436 100p multi   1.10 .40
     Nos. 797-800 (4)   2.65 1.00

No. 798 inscribed "D.S. No 20."

Artisans — A437

1988, Oct. 25   Litho.   Perf. 13½
801 A437 25p Potter   .40 .20
802 A437 25p Weaver   .40 .20
a.   Pair, #801-802   1.00 .75

No. 802a has continuous design.

Natl. Philatelic
Soc.,
Cent. — A438

1988, Nov. 24
803 A438 40p No. 38, cancellation   .60 .20

School Crossing Guards — A439

1988, Oct. 26
804 A439 45p multi   .60 .25

A440

Battle scenes and: #805, 807, Commanders. #806, 808, Servicemen.

1989, Jan. 12   Litho.   Perf. 13½
805   50p Manuel Bulnes (1799-1866)   .50 .25
806   50p Cavalryman   .50 .25
a.   A440 Pair, #805-806   1.75 .50
807   100p Roberto Simpson   .95 .50
808   100p Seaman   .95 .50
a.   A440 Pair, #807-808   3.25 1.25
     Nos. 805-808 (4)   2.90 1.50

Battles of 1839: Yungay (50p) and Casma (100p). Nos. 806a, 808a have continuous designs.

Municipal
Annivs.
A442

Municipal coats of arms and: 30p, San Ambrosio Church. 35p, Craftsman sculpting marble. 45p, Laja Spring and falls.

1989, Jan. 20
809 A442 30p multi   .25 .20
810 A442 35p multi   .35 .20
811 A442 45p multi   .40 .20
     Nos. 809-811 (3)   1.00 .60

Founding of Vallenar, 200th anniv. (30p); founding of Combarbala, 200th anniv. (35p); founding of Los Angeles, 250th anniv. (45p).

Nos. 760a-760d and 780-783
Surcharged

a

b

1989, Mar. 20   Litho.   Perf. 13½
812   Block of 4   1.25 .75
a.-d. A411(a) 25p on 15p #760a-760d, any single   .25 .20
813 A425(b) 25p on 20p #780   .25 .20
814 A425(b) 25p on 20p #781   .25 .20
815 A425(b) 25p on 20p #782   .20 .20
816 A425(b) 25p on 20p #783   .20 .20
     Nos. 812-816 (5)   2.15 1.55

Surcharge differs on Nos. 814, 816.
Issued: #812-814, 3/20. #815-816, 11/30.

Women
Beatified — A443

A444

1989, Mar. 21   Litho.   Perf. 13½
818 A443 40p Sr. Teresa de Los Andes   .50 .25
819 A443 40p Laura Vicuna   .50 .25
a.   Pair, #818-819   1.50 1.00

No. 819a has continuous design.

1989, Mar. 31
820 A444 100p Christopher Columbus   1.25 .60
821 A444 100p Galleons   1.25 .60
a.   Pair, #820-821   3.00 2.50
b.   Souvenir sheet of 2, #820-821   5.00 3.75
c.   Souvenir sheet of 2, #820-821   7.50 4.50

EXFINA '89, Santiago. No. 821a has continuous design. No. 821b margin pictures Columbus's coat of arms and the Order of the Great Admiralty, No. 821c margin Nos. 55, 69, 18, 76, 37, 1, 20 and 98.

CORFO Development Corp., 50th
Anniv. — A445

1989, Apr. 4
822 A445 60p Shipping   .60 .30
823 A445 60p Lumber   .60 .30
824 A445 60p Communication   .60 .30
825 A445 60p Coal   .60 .30
a.   Block of 4, #822-825   3.00 2.50

Gabriela Mistral (1889-1957),
Poet — A446

1989, Apr. 7   Litho.   Perf. 13½
826 A446 30p Poet, steeple   .50 .20
827 A446 30p Poet, children   .50 .20
828 A446 30p Poet working   .50 .20
829 A446 30p Receiving Nobel Prize, 1945   .50 .20
a.   Block of 4, #826-829   3.25 2.00

Exports — A447

#830, 832, Grapes. #831, 833, Apple.

1989, Apr. 19
830 A447 25p indigo & brt yel grn   .25 .20
831 A447 25p ver & brt yel grn   .25 .20
a.   Bklt. pane, 5 each #830-831   2.20
b.   Pair, #830-831   1.40 .75
832 A447 25p indigo & pale yel org   .25 .20
833 A447 25p ver & pale yel org   .25 .20
a.   Bklt. pane, 5 each #832-833   2.50
b.   Pair, #832-833   1.40 .75
     Nos. 830-833 (4)   1.00 .80

Nos. 832-833 inscribed "D.S. No 20."
See Nos. 861-864, 943-946. For surcharges see Nos. 956B-956C, 1085-1088.

Military Justice Department, 150th
Anniv. — A448

1989, Apr. 24   Litho.   Perf. 13½
834 A448 50p multicolored   .60 .25

Monument to the
Martyrs of
Carabineros de
Chile — A449

1989, Apr. 26
835 A449 35p multicolored   .50 .20

Surveyor and Penguins — A450

1989, May 29
836 A450 150p multi   2.25 .85

Antarctic Research Institute expeditions, 25th anniv.

Naval Engineers, Cent. — A451

#837, Naval school. #838, Seamen in boiler room. #839, Ship, helicopter, submarine. #840, *Aquiles* launch, Asmar-Talcahuano.

1989, May 31
837 A451 45p multicolored   .75 .25
838 A451 45p multicolored   .75 .25
839 A451 45p multicolored   .75 .25
840 A451 45p multicolored   .75 .25
a.   Block of 4, #837-840   3.00 3.00

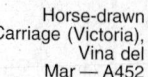

Horse-drawn
Carriage (Victoria),
Vina del
Mar — A452

Early transportation: 35p, Launch off Chiloe
Is., vert. 40p, Cart, Cautin. 45p, Ferry, Rio
Palena. 50p, Car transport, Lake Gral, Car-
retta. 60p, Incline railroad, Valparaiso. 100p,
Cable car (funicular), Santiago.

1989-92   Litho.   Perf. 13½
841	A452	30p black & orange	.30	.20
842	A452	60p black & lemon	.55	.25
843	A452	60p like No. 842	.45	.20
844	A452	100p black & brt yel grn	.90	.45

1989-91
845	A452	35p black & brt blue	.30	.20
846	A452	40p black & olive	.35	.20
847	A452	45p blk & pale blue grn	.35	.20
848	A452	45p black & lt ol grn	.35	.20
849	A452	50p black & scarlet	.45	.20
		Nos. 841-847 (7)	3.20	1.70

Nos. 843, 848 inscribed DS No. 20.
Issued: #841-842, 844, 4/22/89; #848,
2/1/91; #843, 1992; others, 8/1989.
#847 exists dated 1991; #847 dated 1992.
For surcharge see No. 1002.

Export Type of 1989

#861, 863, Grapes. #862, 864, Apple.

1989, May 22
861	A447	5p dark blue & gray	.20	.20
862	A447	5p brt red, dark blue & gray	.20	.20
a.		Pair, #861-862	.50	.50
863	A447	10p dark blue & gray	.20	.20
864	A447	10p brt red, dark blue & gray	.20	.20
a.		Pair, #863-864	.50	.50

A453

A454

1989, Aug. 25   Litho.   Perf. 13½
865	A453	250p multicolored	3.00	1.25
a.		Souvenir sheet of 1	8.00	8.00

World Stamp Expo '89.

1989, Oct. 12

UPAE emblem and pre-Columbian peoples:
30p, Atacamena potter. 150p, Selk'nam-onas
bow hunter.

866	A454	30p multicolored	.40	.20
867	A454	150p multicolored	2.10	.75

Drawing by Christina Lopez — A455

1989, Nov. 20   Litho.   Perf. 13½
868	A455	100p multicolored	1.25	.40

Christmas.

Christmas
Ornaments — A456

Nos. 869, 871, Balls. Nos. 870, 872, Bells.

1989
869	A456	25p dull green & org	.25	.20
870	A456	25p dull green & org	.25	.20
a.		Bklt. pane, 5 each Nos. 869-870	2.00	
b.		Pair, #869-870	.55	.40
871	A456	25p dull green & ver	.25	.20
872	A456	25p dull green & ver	.25	.20
a.		Bklt. pane, 5 each Nos. 871-872	2.00	
b.		Pair, #871-872	.55	.40
		Nos. 869-872 (4)	1.00	.80

Nos. 871-872 inscribed "D.S. No 20."

Miniature Sheet

Wildlife, Natl.
Parks — A457

Designs: a, Vicuna, Lauca Park. b, Chilean
flamingos, Salar de Surire. c, Cactus, La
Chimba Reserve. d, Guanaco, Pan de Azucar
Park. e, Song bird, Father Jorge Park. f, Terns,
Rapa Nui Park. g, Ferret, La Campana Park.
h, Duck, Rio Clarillo Park. i, Cypress tree, Rio
de Los Cipreses Reserve. j, Black-headed
swan, Laguna de Torca Reserve. k, Puma,
Laguna del Laja Park. l, Araucaria tree, Villar-
rica Park. m, Flower, Vicente Perez Rosales
Park. n, Lenga tree, Dos Lagunas. o, Sea lion,
Laguna San Rafael Park. p, Rhea, Torres del
Paine Park.

1990, Jan. 25
873		Sheet of 16	15.00 11.00
a.-p.		A457 35p any single	.65 .20

1990 World Cup Soccer
Championships, Italy — A458

1990, Feb. 23
874	A458	50p Cleated shoe	.60	.25
875	A458	50p Hand	.60	.25
876	A458	50p Soccer ball	.60	.25
877	A458	50p Athlete	.60	.25
a.		Block of 4, #874-877	2.50	2.00

Natl.
Air
Force
A459

Various aircraft: No. 878, Vickers Wibault.
No. 879, Curtiss O1E Falcon. No. 880, Pitts
S2A. No. 881, Extra 300.

1990, Mar. 16   Litho.   Perf. 13½
878	A459	40p multicolored	.50	.20
879	A459	40p multicolored	.50	.20
880	A459	40p multicolored	.50	.20
881	A459	40p multicolored	.50	.20
a.		Souvenir sheet of 4, #878-881	2.50	2.00
		Nos. 878-881 (4)	2.00	.80

FIDAE '90.

Discovery of America 500th Anniv. (in
1992) — A460

Maps and 16th cent. men: No. 882, Incan.
No. 883, Spanish infantryman.

1990, Apr. 20   Litho.   Perf. 13½
882		60p multicolored	.50	.20
883		60p multicolored	.50	.20
a.	A460	Pair, #882-883	2.00	1.50

Port
Cities
A462

1990, Apr. 27
884	A462	40p Valparaiso	.50	.20
885	A462	40p San Vicente	.50	.20
a.		Pair, #884-885	1.25	1.00

Democracy — A463

1990, June 8   Litho.   Perf. 13½
886	A463	20p Sunrise	.20	.20
887	A463	30p Peace dove	.30	.20
888	A463	60p Pleasure	.50	.25
889	A463	100p Star	.90	.45
a.		Souvenir sheet of 4, #886-889	3.00	3.00
		Nos. 886-889 (4)	1.90	1.10

Equality — A464

1990, June 8
890	A464	45p multicolored	.50	.25
a.		Souvenir sheet	1.00	1.00

No. 890a margin continues the design.

Naval Tradition — A465

#891, Transport ship Piloto Pardo. #892,
Oceanographic research ship Yelcho.

1990, May 30   Litho.   Perf. 13½
891	A465	50p multicolored	.60	.20
892	A465	50p multicolored	.60	.20
a.		Pair, #891-892	1.40	1.00

A466

A467

1990, June 12
893	A466	250p Sir Rowland Hill	3.00	1.40
a.		Souvenir sheet of 1	5.00	4.00

Penny Black, 150th anniv.
No. 893a margin continues the design.

1990, June 21
894	A467	150p multicolored	1.50	.65

Organization of American States, cent.

Marine Resources — A468

Designs: a, Scallop. b, Clam. c, Swordfish.
d, Crab. e, Fish. f, Baiting, processing.

1990, July 27   Litho.   Perf. 13½
895		Block of 6	4.00	3.00
a.-f.		A468 40p any single	.40	.20

Curimon
Convent
A469

1990, Aug. 1
896	A469	50p multicolored	.50	.20

250th anniversary of San Felipe.

Environmental
Protection — A470

1990, Sept. 1   Litho.   Perf. 13½
897	A470	35p Aerosol propellants	.25	.20
898	A470	35p Deforestation	.25	.20
899	A470	35p Smokestacks	.25	.20
900	A470	35p Oil slick, shore	.25	.20
901	A470	35p Forest fire	.25	.20
a.		Strip of 5, #897-901	1.50	.90
b.		Bklt. pane, 2 each #897-901	5.25	

Inscribed "D.S. No 20"
902	A470	35p Aerosol propellants	.25	.20
903	A470	35p Deforestation	.25	.20
904	A470	35p Smokestacks	.25	.20
905	A470	35p Oil slick, shore	.25	.20
906	A470	35p Forest fire	.25	.20
a.		Strip of 5, #902-906	1.50	.90
b.		Bklt. pane, 2 each #902-906	5.25	
		Nos. 897-906 (10)	2.50	2.00

See Nos. 988-997.

Presidents of
Chile — A471

1990, Sept. 4
912	A471	35p Salvador Allende	.25	.20
913	A471	35p Eduardo Frei	.25	.20
914	A471	40p Jorge Alessandri	.35	.20
915	A471	45p Gabriel Gonzalez V	.40	.20
916	A471	50p Juan Antonio Rios	.45	.25
917	A471	60p Pedro Aguirre Cerda	.50	.30
918	A471	70p Juan E. Montero	.60	.30
919	A471	80p Carlos Ibanez	.70	.35
920	A471	90p Emiliano Figueroa	.80	.40
921	A471	100p Arturo Alessandri	.85	.45
	Nos. 912-921 (10)		5.15	2.85

Nos. 914, 918, 920-921 exist dated 1992.

Rodeos — A472

Designs: a, Rodeo ring. b, Men on horses.
c, Man stopping horse. d, Men, horses, bull.

1990, Sept. 24
926	Block of 4	2.40	1.75
a.-d.	A472 45p any single	.40	.20

Discovery of America, 500th Anniv. (in
1992) — A473

1990, Oct. 12   Litho.   Perf. 13½
927	A473	30p Phoenicopterus chilensis	.50	.20
928	A473	150p Arctocephalus australis	2.10	.60

King and Queen of Spain's
Visit — A474

#930, Arms of King Juan Carlos I, Chilean
Arms.

1990, Oct. 18
929	A474	100p shown	.90	.45
930	A474	100p Denomination at LR	.90	.45
a.	Pair, #929-930		2.10	1.50

Malleco Bridge, Cent. — A475

Design: #932, Boy waving at train on bridge.

1990, Oct. 26   Litho.   Perf. 13½
931	A475	60p multicolored	1.00	.45
932	A475	60p multicolored	1.00	.45
a.	Pair, #931-932		2.50	1.75

Chilean Antarctic Territorial Claims,
50th Anniv. — A476

Design: #934, Penguins, helicopter, camp.

1990, Nov. 6   Perf. 13½
933	A476	250p multicolored	2.25	1.10
934	A476	250p multicolored	2.25	1.10
a.	Souvenir sheet of 2, #933-934		10.00	10.00

A477

Christmas — A478

1990, Nov. 20   Litho.   Perf. 13½
935	A477	35p lt green & bl grn	.40	.20
a.	Booklet pane of 10		3.00	
936	A477	35p dull org & bl grn	.25	.20
a.	Booklet pane of 10		2.50	
937	A478	35p shown	.25	.20
938	A478	150p Underwater dwelling	1.25	.65
	Nos. 935-938 (4)		2.15	1.25

No. 936 inscribed "D.S. No.20."

National Congress — A479

1990, Dec. 21   Litho.   Perf. 13½
939	A479	100p Congress chamber	.90	.40
940	A479	100p Early congressional session	.90	.40
a.	Pair, #939-940		1.90	1.25

City of Santiago, 450th Anniv. — A480

1991, Feb. 7
941	A480	100p Colorado House	.85	.40
942	A480	100p Skyline	.85	.40
a.	Pair, #941-942		1.90	1.25
b.	Souvenir sheet of 2, #941-942		2.50	2.50

Exports Type of 1989

Nos. 943, 945, Grapes. Nos. 944, 946,
Apple.

1991, Feb. 8   Perf. 13½ on 3 Sides
943	A447	45p indigo & brt pink	.35	.20
944	A447	45p ver & brt pink	.35	.20
a.	Bklt. pane, 5 each #943-944		6.00	
945	A447	45p indigo & yel	.35	.20
946	A447	45p ver & yel	.35	.20
a.	Bklt. pane, 5 each #945-946		6.00	
	Nos. 943-946 (4)		1.40	.80

Nos. 945-946 inscribed "D.S. No.20."
For surcharges see Nos. 1085-1088.

Historical Aircraft — A481

Designs: a, Voisin. b, S.E. 5a. c, Morane
Saulnier MS 35. d, Consolidated PBY-5A/OA-
10 Catalina. Illustration reduced.

1991, Mar. 21   Litho.   Perf. 13½
947	A481	150p Block of 4, #a.-d.	6.50	4.00

American Soccer Cup, Chile — A482

1991, Apr. 12   Litho.   Perf. 13½
948	A482	100p shown	1.00	.35
949	A482	100p Ball, goalie	1.00	.35
a.	Pair, #948-949		2.00	.90

Coal
Mining
A483

Design: #951, Miners dumping cart of coal.

1991, Apr. 18
950	A483	200p shown	1.40	.70
951	A483	200p multicolored	1.40	.70
a.	Pair, #950-951		4.00	2.75

Cultural Art — A484

Design: #953, Small sculptures, spurs, dish.

1991, Apr. 29
952	A484	90p shown	.65	.35
953	A484	90p multicolored	.65	.35
a.	Pair, #952-953		2.00	1.25

Chilean Scientific
Society,
Cent. — A485

1991, Apr. 29
954	A485	45p blue grn & blk	.50	.20

Nos. 782-783 Surcharged

a

b

1991, Apr. 30
955	A425(a)	45p on 20p, #782	.30	.20
956	A425(b)	45p on 20p, #783	.30	.20
a.	Pair, #955-956		1.00	.75

Nos. 832-833
Surcharged

1991, May 6   Litho.   Perf. 13½
956B	A447	45p on 25p, #832	.25	.20
956C	A447	45p on 25p, #833	.25	.20
d.	Pair, #956B-956C		1.00	.75

Santiago
Cathedral
A486

1991, May 9   Litho. & Engr.
957	A486	300p red brn, sal & blk	2.10	1.00

World Telecommunications
Day — A487

1991, May 17   Litho.
958	A487	90p multicolored	1.00	.30

A488   A489

1991, May 23
959	A488	100p Pope Leo XIII	.70	.30

Rerum Novarum Encyclical, cent.

1991, May 28   Litho.   Perf. 13½

Rescue of Shackleton Expedition, 75th
anniv.: a, Lt. Luis Pardo, Sir Ernest
Shackleton. b, Rescue ship, Yelcho. c, Sailor
pointing to survivors. d, Shackleton's ship,
Endurance.

960	A489	50p Block of 4, #a.-d.	2.00	1.50
e.	Miniature sheet, #960		2.50	2.50

21st General
Assembly of
Organization of
American States,
Santiago — A490

1991, June 5
961	A490	70p multicolored	.70	.25

New Carabinero School — A491

1991, June 12
962 A491 50p multicolored .60 .20

Natl. Merchant
Marine
Day — A492

1991, June 26
963 A492 45p black & red .50 .20

11th Pan American Games,
Havana — A493

1991, July 23
964 A493 100p Runners, torch,
          flags .90 .35
965 A493 100p Cycling, running,
          basketball .90 .35
a.   Pair, #964-965 2.00 1.50

Founding of the City of Los Andes,
Bicent. — A494

1991, July 29
966 A494 100p multicolored 1.00 .35

Miniature Sheet

Marine Life — A495

Designs: No. 967a, Octopus vulgaris. b,
Durvillaea antarctica. c, Paralichthys adspersus. d, Austromegabalanus psittacus. e, Concholepas concholepas. f, Cancer setosus. g,
Lessonia nigrescens. h, Loxechinus albus. i,
Homalaspis plana. j, Porphyra columbina. k,
Oplegnathus insignis. l, Chorus giganteus. m,
Rhynchocinetes typus. n, Engraulis ringens. o,
Graciaria spp. p, Pyura chilensis.

1991, Aug. 20   Litho.   Perf. 13½
967   Sheet of 16 10.50 5.00
a.-p. A495 50p any single .35 .20

1891 Revolution, Cent. — A496

Jose M. Balmaceda (1840-1891) and: No.
968, Machinery. No. 969, Teacher, students at
Valentin Letelier School of Medicine.

1991, Aug. 29
968 A496 100p multicolored .70 .35
969 A496 100p multicolored .70 .35
a.   Pair, #968-969 1.50 .90

Chilean
Art — A497

Paintings: 50p, Woman in Red, by Pedro
Reszka. 70p, The Traveler, by Camilo Mori.
200p, Head of Child, by Benito Rebolledo.
300p, Boy Wearing a Fez, by A. Valenzuela
Puelma.

1991, Sept. 26
970 A497 50p multicolored .50 .20
971 A497 70p multicolored .50 .25
972 A497 200p multicolored 2.00 .70
973 A497 300p multicolored 3.00 1.00
      Nos. 970-973 (4) 6.00 2.15

Antarctic Treaty, 30th Anniv. — A498

1991, Oct. 7   Litho.   Perf. 13½
974 A498 80p shown 1.10 .45
975 A498 80p Birds, sea life 1.10 .45
a.   Pair, #974-975 3.50 1.25

Intl.
Letter
Writing
Week
A499

1991, Oct. 9
976 A499 45p shown .35 .20
977 A499 70p Envelope filled
          with people .50 .25

America Issue — A500

UPAEP emblem, sailing ships and: 150p,
Navigator.

1991, Oct. 14
978 A500 50p multicolored .50 .20
979 A500 150p multicolored 1.50 .50

A501

A502

1991, Oct. 21
980 A501 45p blue hat .30 .20
981 A501 45p red hat .30 .20
a.   Pair, #980-981 1.00 .50
b.   Souvenir sheet of 2, #980-981 2.00 2.00

Pablo Neruda, (1904-1973), Nobel Prize
winner for literature, 1971. Nos. 981a has a
continuous design.

1991, Nov. 4
982 A502 45p Boy with stars .35 .20
983 A502 100p Girl with stars .70 .35

Christmas.

Christmas
A503   A504

1991, Nov. 18   Litho.   Perf. 13½
984 A503 45p violet & brt pink .30 .20
985 A504 45p violet & brt pink .30 .20
a.   Pair, #984-985 .60 .20
b.   Bklt. pane of 5 #985a 6.00
986 A503 45p violet & brt pink .30 .20
987 A504 45p violet & brt pink .30 .20
a.   Pair, #986-987 .60 .20
b.   Bklt. pane of 5 #987a 6.00
      Nos. 984-987 (4) 1.20 .80

Nos. 986-987 inscribed "D.S. No. 20."
For surcharges see Nos. 1016-1019.

Environmental Protection Type of 1990
1992, Jan. 28   Litho.   Perf. 13½
Lemon & Black
988 A470 60p like #897 .40 .20
989 A470 60p like #898 .40 .20
990 A470 60p like #899 .40 .20
991 A470 60p like #900 .40 .20
992 A470 60p like #901 .40 .20
a.   Strip of 5, #988-992 2.25 1.50
b.   Bklt. pane of 5 #988-992 4.50

Inscribed "D.S. No. 20"
Orange & Dark Green
993 A470 60p like #902 .40 .20
994 A470 60p like #903 .40 .20
995 A470 60p like #904 .40 .20
996 A470 60p like #905 .40 .20
997 A470 60p like #906 .40 .20
a.   Strip of 5, #993-997 2.25 1.50
b.   Bklt. pane, 2 each #993-997 4.50
      Nos. 988-997 (10) 4.00 2.00

Wolfgang Amadeus Mozart, Death
Bicent. (in 1991) — A505

1992, Jan. 31
998 A505 60p shown .35 .20
999 A505 200p Hands at piano 1.25 .65
a.   Sheet of 2, #998-999 2.50 2.50

FIDAE '92, Intl.
Air and Space
Fair — A506

1992, Mar. 5   Litho.   Perf. 13½
1000 A506 60p multicolored .60 .20

16th
Population
and Housing
Census
A507

1992, Mar.
1001 A507 60p multicolored .60 .20

No. 847
Surcharged in Red
Brown

1992, Mar.
1002 A452 60p on 45p .60 .20

Chilean Cities — A508

Cities' coat of arms and: 80p, Church of San
Jose de Maipo. 90p, People making pottery.
100p, Lircunlauta House. 150p, Wine and lumber industries. 250p, Huilquilemu cultural
center. Illustration reduced.

1992, Apr. 10   Litho.   Perf. 13½
1003 A508 80p multicolored .65 .25
1004 A508 90p multicolored .75 .25
1005 A508 100p multicolored .80 .30
1006 A508 150p multicolored 1.25 .45
1007 A508 250p multicolored 2.00 .75
      Nos. 1003-1007 (5) 5.45 2.00

80p, San Jose de Maipo, 200th anniv. 90p,
Melipilla, 250th anniv. 100p, San Fernando,
250th anniv. 150p, Cauquenes, 250th anniv.
250p, Talca, 250th anniv.

Expo
'92,
Seville
A509

1992, Apr. 23
1008 A509 150p Pavilion 1.25 .45
1009 A509 200p Iceberg 1.75 .60
a.   Sheet of 2, #1008-1009 3.75 3.75

A510

Easter Island A511

Marine life: No. 1010a, Morula praecipua, Strombus maculatus, Cypraea caputdraconis. b, Codium pocockiae. c, Myripristis tiki. d, Sargassum skottsbergii. e, Pseudolabrus fuentesi. f, Pocillopora danae. g, Panulirus pascuensis. h, Tripneustes gratilla.
No. 1011b, Natives, airplane, petroglyph.

1992, June 9   Litho.   Perf. 13½
1010 A510 60p Sheet of 8,
              #a.-h.   5.00 2.75
1011 A511 200p Pair, #a.-b.   4.00 1.50

Natl. Council of the Disabled — A512

Military Chiefs of Staff, 50th Anniv. — A513

1992, June 23
1012 A512 60p multicolored   .60 .20

1992, July 3
1013 A513 60p multicolored   .60 .20

Submarine Forces, 75th Anniv. — A514

Coat of arms and: 250p, Officer using periscope, control room.

1992, July 4
1014 A514 150p multicolored   1.50 .50
1015 A514 250p multicolored   2.25 .90

Nos. 984-987 Surcharged

1992, Aug. 11   Litho.   Perf. 13½
1016 A503 60p on 45p No. 984   .35 .20
1017 A504 60p on 45p No. 985   .35 .20
   a.   Pair, #1016-1017   1.40 .70
1018 A503 60p on 45p No. 986   .35 .20
1019 A504 60p on 45p No. 987   .35 .20
   a.   Pair, #1018-1019   1.40 .70
         Nos. 1016-1019 (4)   1.40 .80

Nos. 1018-1019 inscribed "D.S. No. 20."

Emperor Penguins — A515

1992, Sept. 28   Litho.   Perf. 13½
1020 A515 200p shown   1.50 .75
1021 A515 250p Adults with
              young   1.75 .90
   a.   Souv. sheet of 2, #1020-1021 5.00 5.00

Central Post Office, Santiago, 1772 — A516

1992, Oct. 9
1022 A516 200p multicolored   1.50 .60

Discovery of America, 500th Anniv. — A517

UPAEP emblem and: 200p, Calendar stone, astrolabe, Columbus. 250p, Church, map of Central and South America, sailing ship.

1992, Oct. 20
1023 A517 200p multicolored   1.50 .60
1024 A517 250p multicolored   2.00 .70

Radio Chile, 75th Anniv. — A518

Bernardo O'Higgins (1778-1842) A519

1992, Oct. 22
1025 A518 250p multicolored   1.75 .70

1992, Oct. 23
1026 A519 60p multicolored   .50 .20

Claudio Arrau, Pianist — A520

1992, Nov. 12   Litho.   Perf. 13½
1027 A520 150p As child   .90 .45
1028 A520 200p As adult   1.25 .60
   a.   Souv. sheet of 2, #1027-1028 3.00 3.00

Natl. Human Rights Day — A521

1992, Dec. 10
1029 A521 100p multicolored   .60 .30
   a.   Souvenir sheet of 1   1.10 1.10

Christmas — A522

Designs: Nos. 1030, 1032, Denomination at LR. Nos. 1031, 1033, Denomination at LL.

1992, Dec. 12   Litho.   Perf. 13½
1030 A522 60p buff & brown   .30 .20
1031 A522 60p buff & brown   .30 .20
   a.   Pair, #1030-1031   .65 .30
   b.   Booklet pane of 5 #1031a   3.50
1032 A522 60p buff & red   .30 .20
1033 A522 60p buff & red   .30 .20
   a.   Pair, #1032-1033   .65 .30
   b.   Booklet pane of 5 #1033a   3.25
         Nos. 1030-1033 (4)   1.20 .80

Nos. 1032-1033 inscribed "DS/20."

A523

A524

University of Chile, 150th Anniv.: a, Statue. b, Coat of arms, facade of building.

1992, Nov. 19   Litho.   Perf. 13½
1034 A523 200p Pair, #a.-b.   3.00 1.25
   c.   Souvenir sheet of 1, #1034   4.00 4.00

Nos. 1034a-1034b have a continuous design.

1992, Dec. 12
1035 A524 70p black & yellow   .60 .25

23rd meeting of Latin American Energy Ministers.

Churches of Chiloe — A525

#1036, 1038, Achao. #1037, 1039, Castro.

1993, Mar. 1   Litho.   Perf. 13½
1036 A525 70p black & pink   .45 .25
1037 A525 70p black & pink   .45 .25
   a.   Pair #1036-1037   .90 .90
   b.   Booklet pane of 5 #1037a   6.50

Inscribed "DS/20"

1038 A525 70p black & yellow   .45 .25
1039 A525 70p black & yellow   .45 .25
   a.   Pair, #1038-1039   .90 .90
   b.   Booklet pane of 5 #1039a   6.50
         Nos. 1036-1039 (4)   1.80 1.00

See Nos. 1053-1060, 1093-1098. For surcharges see Nos. 1129-1130.

Arrival of the Jesuits, 400th Anniv. — A526

Canonization of St. Teresa of the Andes, 1993 — A527

1993   Litho.   Perf. 13½
1040 A526 200p St. Ignatius of
              Loyola   1.50 .60
   a.   Souvenir sheet of 1   2.00 2.00
1041 A527 300p St. Teresa of the
              Andes   2.50 1.00

Issue dates: 200p, Mar. 15; 300p, Mar. 31. No. 1040a sold for 250p.

World Festival of Theatre of the Nations — A528

Second Space Conference of the Americas — A529

Clotario Blest
(1899-1990),
Syndicalist
A530

1993, Apr. 22
1042 A528 250p multicolored 2.00 .75

1993, Apr. 26
1043 A529 150p multicolored .90 .45
   a. Souvenir sheet of 1 2.10 2.10
    No. 1043a sold for 350p.

1993, Apr. 30
1044 A530 70p multicolored .50 .20
    Intl. Labor Day.

Vicente Huidobro,
Poet (1893-1948)
A531

1993, May 19   **Litho.**   **Perf. 13½**
1045 A531 100p shown .60 .30
1046 A531 100p Portrait, seated .60 .30
   a. Pair, #1045-1046 1.50 1.00

Antique Fire Engines — A532

#1047, 1902 Watterous Engineering Co.
Ltd., Canada. #1048, 1872 Merryweather,
England.

1993, June 30   **Litho.**   **Perf. 13½**
1047 A532 100p multicolored .80 .30
1048 A532 100p multicolored .80 .30
   a. Souv. sheet of 2, #1047-1048 2.50 2.50
    No. 1048a sold for 400p.

Aircraft — A533

Designs: No. 1049, Douglas B-26 Invader.
No. 1050, Mirage M50 Panther. No. 1051,
Sanchez Besa. No. 1052, Bell 47D1
helicopter.

1993, July 13
1049 A533 100p multicolored .55 .30
1050 A533 100p multicolored .55 .30
1051 A533 100p multicolored .55 .30
1052 A533 100p multicolored .55 .30
   a. Block of 4, #1049-1052 3.00 2.50

Church Type of 1993

Designs: 10p, Chonchi. 20p, Vilupulli. 30p,
Llau-llao. 40p, Dalcahue. 50p, Tenaun. 80p,
Quinchao. 90p, Quehui. 100p, Nercon.

1993, July   **Litho.**   **Perf. 13½**
1053 A525 10p green & black .20 .20
1054 A525 20p black & brown .20 .20
1055 A525 30p black & vermil-
          ion .20 .20
1056 A525 40p black & blue .25 .25
1057 A525 50p black & green
          blue .30 .30

1058 A525 80p black & buff .45 .45
   a. Booklet pane of 10 7.50
1059 A525 90p olive & black .50 .50
   a. Booklet pane of 10 7.50
    Complete booklet, #1059a 7.50
1060 A525 100p gray vio & blk .55 .55
   a. Booklet pane of 10 7.50
    Nos. 1053-1060 (8) 2.65 2.65

Issued: #1058a, 1/1/94; #1059a, 1995;
#1060a, 2/1/96.
No. 1058 exists dated 1994.
See No. 1093 for 80p black & violet.

Natl. Dance, "La
Cueca" — A534

Paintings — A535

1993, Sept. 15   **Litho.**   **Perf. 13½**
1061 A534 70p Cueca chilota .60 .20
1062 A534 70p Cueca central .60 .20
1063 A534 70p Cueca nortina .60 .20
    Nos. 1061-1063 (3) 1.80 .60

1993, Sept. 28

Designs: 80p, Tarde Amanecer, by Mario
Carreno, horiz. 90p, Summer, by Gracia Bar-
rios, horiz. 150p, Figura Protegida, by Roser
Bru. 200p, Tangueria-Valparaiso, by Nemesio
Antunez, horiz.

1064 A535 80p multicolored .55 .25
1065 A535 90p multicolored .60 .25
1066 A535 150p multicolored 1.00 .40
1067 A535 200p multicolored 1.40 .60
    Nos. 1064-1067 (4) 3.55 1.45

Chilean Mint,
250th Anniv.
A536

1993, Oct. 7   **Litho. & Engr.**
1068 A536 250p multicolored 1.75 .70
   a. Souvenir sheet of 1 2.50 2.50

A537

A538

1993, Oct. 19   **Litho.**
1069 A537 80p multicolored .70 .25
    Urban transportation system, 25th anniv.

1993, Oct. 12   **Litho.**   **Perf. 13½**
1070 A538 150p Cyanoliseus
         patagonus 1.00 .40
1071 A538 200p Hippocamelus
         bisulcus 1.50 .55
    America issue.

Chilean Possession of Straits of
Magellan, 150th Anniv. — A539

1993, Oct. 21
1072 A539 100p multicolored 3.00 .30

Naval Anniversaries — A540

1993, Oct. 27
1073 A540 80p Sailing ships .65 .25
1074 A540 80p Schooner .65 .25
1075 A540 80p Assault ship .65 .25
1076 A540 80p Patrol boat .65 .25
    Nos. 1073-1076 (4) 2.60 1.00
Sailing of first naval squadron (#1073),
Arturo Prat Naval Academy (#1074), Marine
Corps (#1075), 175th anniversaries. Alejandro
Navarette School for Cadets (#1076), 125th
anniv.

Intl. Year of Indigenous
Peoples — A541

1993, Nov. 24
1077 A541 100p multicolored .70 .30

Christmas
A542

Pygoscelis Adelie
A543

1993, Dec. 1   **Litho.**   **Perf. 13½**
1078 A542 70p tan & violet .55 .20
   a. Booklet pane of 10 6.00
1079 A542 70p green & blue .65 .20
   a. Booklet pane of 10 7.00
    No. 1079 inscribed "DS/20."
For surcharge see No. 1131.

1993, Dec. 3
1080 A543 200p Nesting 1.40
1081 A543 250p Adult, chicks 1.60 .65
   a. Souv. sheet of 2, #1080-1081,
      imperf. 3.50 3.50
    Chilean Antarctica.
No. 1081a has simulated perfs.

Chilean Cities — A544

1993, Dec. 15
1082 A544 80p Rancagua .60 .20
1083 A544 80p Curico .60 .20
1084 A544 80p Ancud .60 .20
    Nos. 1082-1084 (3) 1.80 .60
    Rancagua and Curico, 250th anniv. Ancud,
225th anniv.

Nos. 943-946
Surcharged

1993   **Litho.**   **Perf. 13½ on 3 Sides**
1085 A447 60p on 45p, #943 .35 .20
1086 A447 60p on 45p, #944 .35 .20
   a. Bklt. pane, 5 each #1085-1086 3.50
1087 A447 60p on 45p, #945 .35 .20
1088 A447 60p on 45p, #946 .35 .20
   a. Bklt. pane, 5 each #1087-1088 3.50
    Nos. 1085-1088 (4) 1.40 .80
Nos. 1087-1088 inscribed "D.S. No. 20."

Intl. Year of the
Family — A545

1994, Jan. 17   **Litho.**   **Perf. 13½**
1089 A545 100p multicolored .70 .25

Musical Instruments — A546

Designs: a, Violin. b, Cello.

1994, Jan. 27   **Litho.**   **Perf. 13½**
1091 A546 150p Pair, #a.-b. 2.50 2.50
    No. 1091 has a continuous design.

Church Type of 1993

Designs: 80p, Quinchao. 90p, Quehui.
#1097, 1098, Nercon.

1994-96   **Litho.**   **Perf. 13½**
1093 A525 80p black & violet .50 .25
1095 A525 90p red & black .50 .25
   a. Booklet pane of 10 4.75
    Complete booklet, #1095a 4.75
1097 A525 100p yellow & black .55 .30
   a. Booklet pane of 10 6.00
    Complete booklet, #1097a 6.00

1098 A525 100p gray vio & blk .60 .30
  a.   Booklet pane of 10 6.50
    Complete booklet, #1098a 6.50
  Nos. 1093-1098 (4) 2.15 1.10

Issued: 80p, 1/1/94; 90p, 1995; #1097-1098, 2/1/96.
Nos. 1093, 1095, 1097 inscribed "DS/20." This is an expanding set. Numbers may change.

Souvenir Sheet

Natl. Aviation Museum, 50th Anniv. — A547

Aircraft: a, Sukhoi SU-30 Flanker. b, Vought-Sikorsky OS-2U3 Kingfisher. c, Lockheed F-117A Nighthawk. d, Northrop F-5E Tiger III.

1994, Mar. 17   **Litho.**   ***Perf. 13***
1102 A547 300p Sheet of 4, #a.-d. + 2 labels 7.00 4.25

Intl. Air and Space Fair, FIDAE '94.
See No. 1159.

College of Agronomy, 50th Anniv. — A548

1994, Apr. 28   **Litho.**   ***Perf. 13***
1103 A548 220p multicolored 1.10 .55

No. 760 Surcharged

1994, May 1   **Litho.**   ***Perf. 13½***
1104   Block of 4 1.75 1.00
  a.-d. A411 80p on 15p any single .35 .20

Concepcion University, 75th Anniv. — A549

Sections of mural, by Jorge Gonzalez Camarena: No. 1105, Cactus plant, skeletons. No. 1106, Flags, pillars, nude woman, faces. No. 1107, Flags, bodies, woman, soldier in armor. No. 1108, Women's faces, pipelines.

1994, May 14   **Litho.**   ***Perf. 13***
1105 A549 250p multicolored 1.75 .75
1106 A549 250p multicolored 1.75 .75
1107 A549 250p multicolored 1.75 .75
1108 A549 250p multicolored 1.75 .75
  a.   Strip of 4, #1105-1108 + label 7.50 5.00

No. 1108a is a continuous design.

Chilean Antarctic Institute, 30th Anniv. — A550

Designs: No. 1109, Penguins, buildings. No. 1110, Buildings, coastal waters.

1994, May 31   ***Perf. 13***
1109 A550 300p multicolored 1.50 .85
1110 A550 300p multicolored 1.50 .85
  a.   Pair, #1109-1110 3.50 2.00

No. 1110a is a continuous design.

Antique Fire Engines — A551

#1111, Merryweather steam pumper, England, 1869. #1112, Western lever pumper, US, 1863. #1113, Mieusset steam pumper, France, 1905. #1114, Merryweather pumper, England, 1903.

1994, July 19   **Litho.**   ***Perf. 13***
1111 A551 150p multicolored .75 .35
1112 A551 150p multicolored .75 .35
1113 A551 150p multicolored .75 .35
1114 A551 150p multicolored .75 .35
  a.   Block of 4, #1111-1114 3.75 3.00

Javiera Carrera Girls' School, Cent. — A552

1994, Aug. 10
1115 A552 200p multicolored 1.00 .50

Arms, Sights from Chilean Cities — A553

Designs: 90p, Porvenir, cent. 100p, Villa Alemana, cent. 150p, Constitucion, bicent. 200p, Linares, bicent. 250p, Copiapo, 250th anniv. 300p, La Serena, 450th anniv.

1994, Aug. 26
1116 A553 90p multicolored .45 .20
1117 A553 100p multicolored .55 .25
1118 A553 150p multicolored .85 .35
1119 A553 200p multicolored 1.25 .50
1120 A553 250p multicolored 1.60 .60
1121 A553 300p multicolored 1.75 .75
  Nos. 1116-1121 (6) 6.45 2.65

Miniature Sheet of 8

Butterflies — A554

Designs: a, Vanessa terpsichore. b, Hypsochila wagenknechti. c, Battus polydamas. d, Polythysana apollina. e, Satyridae. f,

---

Tetraphloebia stellygera. g, Eroessa chilensis. h, Phoebis sennae.

1994, June 24   **Litho.**   ***Perf. 13***
1122 A554 100p #a.-h. 9.00 9.00

20th Intl. Conference on Data Bases — A555

1994, Sept. 21   **Litho.**   ***Perf. 13½***
1123 A555 100p multicolored .60 .30

America Issue — A556

Early postal transport vehicles: 80p, Van. 220p, DH-60-G, Gypsy Moth.

1994, Oct. 12
1124 A556 80p multicolored .65 .30
1125 A556 220p multicolored 1.60 .70

A557

A558

1994, Oct. 31   **Litho. & Engr.**
1126 A557 300p multicolored 1.60 .80

Beatification of Father Alberto Hurtado.

1994   **Litho.**   ***Perf. 13½***
1127 A558 80p multicolored .60 .25
  a.   Booklet pane of 10 6.00
    Complete booklet, #1127a 6.00

Inscribed "DS/20"
1128 A558 80p multicolored .60 .25
  a.   Booklet pane of 10 7.00
    Complete booklet, #1128a 7.00

Christmas.

Nos. 1036-1037, 1079 Surcharged

Perf. 13½ on 3 Sides
1994, Nov. 4   **Litho.**
1129 A525 80p on 70p #1036 .45 .25
1130 A525 80p on 70p #1037 .45 .25
  a.   Pair, #1129-1130 .90 .50
  b.   Booklet pane, 5 #1130a 7.00
    Complete booklet, #1130b 7.00

1131 A542 80p on 70p #1079 .45 .25
  a.   Booklet pane, 10 #1131 7.00
    Complete booklet, #1131a 7.00

Size and location of surcharge varies.

Miniature Sheet

Intl. Women's Day — A559

Designs: a, Star, "Women enriching the future." b, Moon, sun, "Women bringing harmony." c, Bird, "Women bringing peace." d, Earth, "Women changing the world."

1995, Mar. 8   **Litho.**   ***Perf. 13½***
1132 A559 90p Sheet of 4, #a.-d. 3.75 2.00

Ancud Seminary of Conciliation, 150th Anniv. — A560

1995, Apr. 27
1133 A560 200p multicolored 1.10 .55

Destroyer Admiral Williams A561

1995, Apr. 21
1134 A561 100p multicolored .70 .30

World Conference on Social Development A562

1995, Apr. 25
1135 A562 150p multicolored .85 .40

Order of St. Augustine in Chile, 400th Anniv. — A563

Stained glass, Cathedral of Santiago.

1995, Apr. 28
1136 A563 250p multicolored 1.40 .70

Petroglyphs — A564

Designs: a, Ceremonial mask, Buitre, Limari Province. b, Lamas, Taira Sector, El Loa Province. c, Harpooned whale, El Medano, Taltal Province. d, Two masks, Encanto, Ovalle.

1995, June 16 Litho. Perf. 13½
1137 A564 150p Block of 4, #a.-
d. 5.00 5.00

Miniature Sheet

Motion Pictures, Cent. — A565

Posters: a, Director's chair, camera. b, Charlie Chaplin in "The Kid." c, Lumiere brothers' 1895 Cinematographe. d, "Valparaiso, My Love", with Aldo Francia.

1995, June 21
1138 A565 100p Sheet of 4, #a.-
d. 5.00 2.50

City of Parral, Bicent. A566

1995, June 30 Litho. Perf. 13½
1139 A566 200p multicolored 1.10 .60

Miniature Sheet

Insects and Cacti — A567

a, Cheloderus childreni. b, Eulychnia acida. c, Chiasognathus grantii. d, Browningia candelaris. e, Copiapoa dealbata. f, Acanthinodera cummingi. g, Neoporteria subgibbosa. h, Semiotus luteipennis.

1995, Aug. 10 Litho. Perf. 13½
1140 A567 100p Sheet of 8,
#a.-h. 10.00 7.50

2nd World Congress of Police, Santiago — A568

1995, Oct. 2
1141 A568 200p multicolored 1.10 .55

Ministry of Housing and Urban Development, 30th Anniv. — A569

Design: Tower of Babel V, by Mario Toral.

1995, Oct. 5 Litho. Perf. 13½
1142 A569 200p multicolored 1.10 .60

Andres Bello (1781-1865), Scholar, Author A570

1995, Oct. 9 Litho. & Engr.
1143 A570 250p dk brn & blk 1.40 .70
Andres Bello Convenant, 25th anniv.

UNESCO, UN, FAO, 50th Anniv. — A571

Designs: a, Hands holding book, UNESCO emblem. b, Hands clasped between two globes, UN emblem. c, Hand holding seedling, FAO emblem.

1995, Oct. 10 Litho. Perf. 13½
1144 A571 100p Strip of 3, #a.-c. 1.75 .90
No. 1144 is a continuous design.

America Issue — A572

Children's drawings of environmental protection: 100p, Family in garden, trees, vert. 250p, Three people working with trees.

1995, Oct. 12 Litho. Perf. 13½
1145 A572 100p multicolored .60 .30
1146 A572 250p multicolored 1.50 .75

A573

A574

Chilean Soccer, Cent.: a, Carlos Dittborn. b, Hugo Lepe. c, Eladio Rojas. d, Honorino Landa.

1995, Nov. 13 Litho. Perf. 13½
1147 A573 100p Sheet of 4, #a.-
d. 2.25 1.10

1995, Oct. 24 Litho. Perf. 13½
1148 A574 250p multicolored 1.25 .75
51st World Congress of Cape Horn captains.

Gabriela Mistral (1889-1957), 50th Anniv. of Receiving Nobel Prize for Literature A575

Litho. & Engr.
1995, Nov. 15 Perf. 13½
1149 A575 300p blue black & blk 1.60 .80

Eudyptes Chrysolophus A576

1995, Nov. 22 Litho. Perf. 13½
1150 A576 100p shown 1.00 .40
1151 A576 250p Penguins, diff. 1.90 .90
a. Souv. sheet, #1150-1151 4.50 4.50
No. 1151a sold for 600p.

Chilean Export Assoc., 60th Anniv. — A577

Cargo ship and: a, Kiwi fruit. b, Grapes. c, Peaches. d, Apples.
Jet plane and: e, Various berries.

1995, Dec. 1
1152 A577 100p Strip of 5, #a.-e. 2.75 2.75

Christmas
A578 A579

1995, Nov. 13
Booklet Stamps
1153 A578 90p brt blue & blue .50 .25
1154 A579 90p brt blue & blue .50 .25
a. Bklt. pane, 5 ea #1153-1154 5.00
Complete booklet, #1154a 5.00
1155 A578 90p brt grn & brown .50 .25
1156 A579 90p brt grn & brown .50 .25
a. Bklt. pane, 5 ea #1155-1156 5.00
Complete booklet, #1156a 5.00
Nos. 1155-1156 inscribed "DS/20."

End of World War II, 50th Anniv. A580

1995, Dec. 20 Litho. Perf. 13½
1157 A580 200p multicolored 1.10 .55

Petroleum Production in Chile, 50th Anniv. — A581

Designs: a, Off-shore oil derrick, one main tower. b, Refinery, road trees, building. c, Refinery, up close. d, Off-shore oil derrick, four towers.

1995, Dec. 29
1158 A581 100p Block of 4, #a.-
d. 2.25 2.25

Aviation Type of 1994

Designs: a, Embraer EMB-145. b, Mirage M5M Elkan. c, DHC-6 Twin Otter Series 300. d, SAAB JAS 39, Gripen.

1996, Mar. 9 Litho. Perf. 13½
1159 A547 400p Sheet of 4,
#a.-d. 13.00 8.50
Intl. Air and Space Fair, FIDAE '96.

Men's High School, La Serena, 175th Anniv. — A582

1996, Apr. 12
1160 A582 100p multicolored .55 .30

Espamer '96, World Philatelic Exhibition — A583

Designs: No. 1161, Old Train Station, Cordoba. No. 1162, Lope de Vega Theater.

1996, Apr. 25
1161 A583 200p multicolored 1.10 .60
1162 A583 200p multicolored 1.10 .60
a. Pair, #1161-1162 2.25 2.25

Accident
Prevention
A584

Traffic safety: No. 1163a, Cross street at crosswalk. b, Respect traffic police. c, Obey traffic signals. d, Wait for ride on sidewalk. e, Don't cross street between parked cars. f, Never ride on side of bus. g, Walk beside road facing oncoming traffic. h, Pay attention to where you are walking. i, Don't play on streets. j, Obey traffic rules while riding a bicycle.

Safety in the home: No. 1164a, Extinguish matches after using. b, Be careful with boiling water. c, Curb sharp objects. d, Protect electrical outlets. e, Don't improvise electrical connections. f, Don't play radio or TV too loudly. g, Check all gas connections. h, Don't overload electrical outlets. i, Keep flammable materials away from furnace. j, Keep toys off floor.

Recreational safety: No. 1165a, Swim only in designated areas. b, Keep hands, head inside the car. c, Don't get a sunburn. d, Don't contaminate water with detergents. e, Don't litter. f, Extinguish camp fires. g, Don't bother others when swimming. h, Check car safety features. i, Keep kites away from electrical wires. j, Don't run in swimming pool area.

Safety in the workplace: No. 1166a, Use protective gear. b, Use only safe tools. c, Keep you mind on your work. d, Use proper tools. e, Avoid work accidents. f, Keep stairs free of objects. g, Don't carry objects that obstruct your view. h, Check ladder before using. i, Keep area clean, organized. j, Be aware of protruding nails.

Proper use of drugs and alcohol: No. 1167a, Don't drink and drive. b, Don't drink if you are pregnant. c, Don't encourage friends to drink. d, Alcohol and work don't mix. e, Drinking could destroy your family. f, Drugs can't make you happy. g, Drugs don't make you successful. h, Be happy without drugs. i, For your family say "no" to drugs. j, Drug free, happy and confident.

Safety in schools: No. 1168a, Keep calm in case of fire. b, Don't run along sides of buildings. c, Don't play dangerous jokes. d, Don't sit or stand in high dangerous places. e, Don't run on stairs. f, Don't walk and drink at the same time. g, Don't rock on chairs. h, Don't play with sharp objects. i, Don't open doors abruptly. j, Don't talk to strangers outside the school.

1996, May 2
1163	A584	50p Block of 10, #a.-j.		4.75	2.25
1164	A584	50p Block of 10, #a.-j.		4.75	2.25
1165	A584	50p Block of 10, #a.-j.		4.75	2.25
1166	A584	50p Block of 10, #a.-j.		4.75	2.25
1167	A584	50p Block of 10, #a.-j.		4.75	2.25
1168	A584	50p Block of 10, #a.-j.		4.75	2.25

No. 1 Dry Dock, Talcahuano,
Cent. — A585

1996, May 20
1169	A585	200p multicolored	1.10	.55

Sculptures — A586

#1170, Mariner's Compass, by Ricardo Mesa, vert. #1171, Friendship, by Francisca Cerda, vert. #1172, Andes Winds, by Benito Rojo. #1173, Memory, by Fernando Undurraga.

1996, June 20   Litho.   Perf. 13½
1170	A586	150p multicolored	1.00	.50
1171	A586	150p multicolored	1.00	.50
a.		Pair, #1170-1171	4.00	4.00
1172	A586	200p multicolored	1.50	.60
1173	A586	200p multicolored	1.50	.60
a.		Pair, #1172-1173	5.00	5.00
		Nos. 1170-1173 (4)	5.00	2.20

Intl. Day Against Use of Illegal Drugs
and Drug Trafficking — A587

1996, June 26
1174	A587	250p multicolored	1.40	.85

1996 Summer Olympic Games,
Atlanta — A588

Designs: a, Boxer's glove. b, Runner's shoe. c, Roller blade. d, Ball.

1996, July 3
1175	A588	450p Block of 4, #a.-d.		9.75	8.00

Order of Mother of God, 50th Anniv. of
Presence in Chile — A589

1996, Aug.   Litho.   Perf. 13½
1176	A589	200p multicolored	1.10	.55

Lyceum of San Fernando, 150th
Anniv. — A590

1996, Aug. 2
1177	A590	200p multicolored	1.10	.55

4th Intl. Congress
of Earth
Sciences — A591

Globe showing portions of continents, and: a, Forest fire. b, Smoke stacks creating air pollution. c, Cutting down trees. d, Surveying equipment, desert.

1996, Aug. 5   Litho.   Perf. 13½
1178	A591	200p Block of 4, #a.-d.		4.50	4.50

Minerals — A592

a, Kroehnkita. b, Lapis lazuli. c, Bornite. d, Azurite.

1996, Aug. 9
1179	A592	150p Block of 4, #a.-d.		4.00	3.50

German Immigration, 150th
Anniv. — A593

Designs: 250p, House, lake, mountain. 300p, Monument showing arrival on boat.

1996, Aug. 22
1180	A593	250p multicolored	1.40	.70
1181	A593	300p multicolored	1.60	.80

Aptenodytes
Patagonica
A594

1996, Sept. 9   Litho.   Perf. 13½
1182	A594	250p shown	2.00	1.00
1183	A594	300p Molting	2.10	1.10
a.		Souvenir sheet, #1182-1183	5.75	5.75

Castro
Fire
Dept.,
Cent.
A595

Designs: a, 1937 Italian pumper. b, 1940 Ford fire truck. c, Gorlitz G.A. Fischer manual 4-speed pumper. d, 1907 pumper.

1996, Sept. 14
1184	A595	200p Block of 4, #a.-d.		6.00	6.00

Ecotourism in National Parks — A596

Designs: a, River rafting. b, Horseback riding. c, Snow skiing. d, Hiking around cacti.

1996, Sept. 27
1185	A596	100p Sheet of 4, #a.-d.		2.25	2.25

Juan José Latorre
Benavente (1846-1912),
Admiral — A597

1996, Oct. 8
1186	A597	200p multicolored	1.10	.55

Historical Costumes — A598

America issue: No. 1187, Two women, child, dog, vert. No. 1188, Two men with horse, vert. 250p, Two men on horseback.

1996, Oct. 23
1187	A598	100p multicolored	.55	.30
1188	A598	100p multicolored	.55	.30
a.		Pair, #1187-1188	1.40	1.40
1189	A598	250p multicolored	1.40	.70

Church, City of Arica — A599

150p, Fauna, mountains, Parinacota Park.

1996, Nov. 18   Litho.   Perf. 13½
1190	A599	100p multicolored	.55	.30
1191	A599	150p multicolored	.80	.40

Christmas — A600

1996, Nov. 25
1192	A600	100p black & multi	.55	.25
a.		Booklet pane of 10	5.50	
		Complete booklet, #1192a	5.50	
1193	A600	100p orange & multi	.55	.25
a.		Booklet pane of 10	5.50	
		Complete booklet, #1193a	5.50	

No. 1193 is inscribed DS/20.

Mythology
A601   A602

1997, Feb. 12   Litho.   Perf. 13½
1194	A601	40p black & blue	.20	.20
1195	A602	110p black & green	.60	.30
a		Booklet pane of 10	6.00	
		Complete booklet, #1195a	6.00	
1196	A602	110p black & orange	.60	.30
a.		Booklet pane of 10	6.00	
		Complete booklet, #1196a	6.00	

No. 1195 inscribed DS/20.

Sixth Summit of Spanish-Americana Heads of State and Government — A603

Mural, Visual Memory of the Nation, by Mario Toral: No. 1198, Left half. No. 1199, Right half.

1996, Nov. 6
1198 A603 110p multicolored .60 .30
1199 A603 110p multicolored .60 .30
   a. Pair, #1198-1199 1.25 .60
   No. 1199a is a continuous design.

State Visit of King Carl XVI Gustaf, Queen Silvia of Sweden — A604

Design: Nobel Laureates Pablo Neruda, Gabriela Mistral, Nobel medal.

1996, Dec. 3
1200 A604 300p multicolored 1.60 .80

UNICEF, 50th Anniv. — A605

1996, Dec. 11
1201 A605 200p multicolored 1.10 .55

Frontier Region, Cent. — A606

#1202, Christian Alliance & Missionary Church, cent. #1203, Lonquimay municipality, cent.

1997
1202 A606 110p multicolored .60 .30
1203 A606 110p multicolored .60 .30
   Issued: #1202, 1/19; #1203, 1/25.

Arturo Prat Antarctic Naval Base, 50th Anniv. — A607

1997, Feb. 6 Litho. Perf. 13½
1204 A607 250p Aerial view, vert. 1.40 .70
1205 A607 300p shown 1.75 .85

Controller General of the Republic, 70th Anniv. — A608

1997, Mar. 26
1206 A608 110p multicolored 1.60 .35

Opening of Metro Line 5 — A609

1997, Apr. 2
1207 A609 200p multicolored 1.10 .55

Interamerican Masonic Confederation, 50th Anniv. — A610

1200p, Emblems, compass, square, book.

1997, Apr. 8
1208 A610 250p shown 1.40 .70
Souvenir Sheet
1209 A610 1200p multicolored 6.75 6.75
   No. 1209 contains one 48x60mm stamp.

Heinrich von Stephan (1831-97) A611

1997, Apr. 15
1210 A611 250p multicolored 1.40 .70

World Book and Copyright Day — A612

1997, Apr. 23
1211 A612 110p multicolored .60 .35

Details from "Death to the Invader," by David Alfaro Siqueiros (1896-1974), Muralist — A613

1997, June 26 Litho. Perf. 13½
1212 A613 150p shown 1.25 .35
1213 A613 200p Detail, diff. 1.50 .50
Souvenir Sheets
1214 A613 1000p like #1212 5.25 5.25
1215 A613 1000p like #1213 5.25 5.25
   #1214-1215 each contain one 48x36mm stamp.

Providencia, Cent. — A614

1997, July 17
1216 A614 250p multicolored 1.25 .70

A615   A616

1997, Sept. 1
1217 A615 300p multicolored 1.60 .90
   Diplomatic relations between Chile and Japan, cent. See Japan No. 2578.

1997, Oct. 1 Litho. Perf. 13½
1218 A616 110p Quality .60 .30

1st Radio Broadcast in Chile, 75th Anniv. — A617

1997 Litho. Perf. 13½
1219 A617 110p multicolored .60 .40

Chilean Opera Singers A618

Singer, opera: 120p, Carlo Morelli, "Rigoletto." 200p, Pedro Navia, "La Bohème." 250p, Renato Zanelli, "Faust." 300p, Rayèn Quitral, "The Magic Flute." 500p, Ramón Vinay, "Othello."

1997, Oct. 15
1220 A618 120p multicolored .65 .35
1221 A618 200p multicolored 1.10 .55
1222 A618 250p multicolored 1.40 .70
1223 A618 300p multicolored 1.60 .80
1224 A618 500p multicolored 2.75 1.40
   Nos. 1220-1224 (5) 7.50 3.80

America Issue — A619

Life of a postman: 110p, Delivering mail on bicycle. 250p, Delivering mail on horseback.

1997, Oct. 12 Litho. Perf. 13½
1225 A619 110p multicolored .60 .30
1226 A619 250p multicolored 1.40 .70

Christmas — A620

1997 Litho. Perf. 13½
1227 A620 110p multicolored .60 .30
   a. Booklet pane of 10 6.50
       Complete booklet, #1227a 7.00
1228 A620 110p multicolored .60 .30
   a. Booklet pane of 10 6.50
       Complete booklet, #1228a 7.00
   No. 1228 is inscribed D/S20 and was only issued in booklets.

Chilean Post, 250th Anniv. A621

Designs: 120p, Postman canceling letters. 300p, Man depositing letter into postbox.

1997, Dec. 22
| 1229 | A621 | 120p multicolored | .65 | .35 |
| 1230 | A621 | 300p multicolored | 1.60 | .80 |

Dogs

A622   A623

1998   **Litho.**   **Perf. 13½**
1231	A622	120p Great Dane	.60	.20
1232	A623	120p Dalmatian	.60	.20
a.		Pair, #1231-1232	1.25	1.00
b.		Booklet pane, 5 #1232a	7.00	
		Complete booklet, #1232b	7.00	
1233	A622	120p Great Dane	.60	.20
1234	A623	120p Dalmatian	.60	.20
a.		Pair, #1233-1234	1.25	1.00
b.		Booklet pane, 5 #1234a	7.00	
		Complete booklet, #1234b	7.00	

Nos. 1233-1234 are inscribed DS/20.

2nd Summit of the Americas, Santiago — A624

1998, Apr. 17   **Litho.**   **Perf. 13½**
| 1235 | A624 | 150p multicolored | .85 | .40 |

Souvenir Sheet
| 1236 | A624 | 1000p Logo, diff. | 10.00 | 10.00 |

No. 1236 contains one 26x42mm stamp.

Paintings — A625

350p, "Los Zambos de Calama," by Mauricio Moran. 400p, "Sandia Calada," by Roser Bru.

1998, May 14   **Litho.**   **Perf. 13½**
| 1237 | A625 | 350p multicolored | 1.75 | 1.00 |
| 1238 | A625 | 400p multicolored | 2.00 | 1.25 |

Capuchin Order in Chile, 150th Anniv. — A626

Designs: 150p, Native village, friar writing in book. 250p, Friar aiding injured man.

1998, May 18
| 1239 | A626 | 150p multicolored | .75 | .40 |
| 1240 | A626 | 250p multicolored | 1.25 | .60 |

1998 World Cup Soccer Championships, France — A627

Players and: 250p, Crowd. 350p, World Cup Trophy. 500p, Map of France. 700p, Chilean flag.
1500p, Player, vert.

1998, May 23
1241	A627	250p multicolored	1.25	.60
1242	A627	350p multicolored	1.75	.85
1243	A627	500p multicolored	2.50	1.25
1244	A627	700p multicolored	3.50	1.75
		Nos. 1241-1244 (4)	9.00	4.45

Souvenir Sheet
| 1245 | A627 | 1500p multicolored | 7.50 | 7.50 |

A628

A629

Antarctic Research: 250p, Scientific Committee on Antarctic Research, 25th meeting. 350p, Natl. Administrators of Antarctic Programs, 10th meeting.

1998, July 22
| 1246 | A628 | 250p Logo, penguin | 1.25 | .60 |
| 1247 | A628 | 350p Penguins, map, logo | 1.75 | .85 |

1998, Apr. 3
| 1248 | A629 | 120p multicolored | .60 | .30 |

Captain Arturo Prat Chacon, 150th birth anniv.

Army Veterinarian Service, Cent. — A630

350p, Veterinarian listening to horse's heartbeat.

1998, Apr. 20
| 1249 | A630 | 250p multicolored | 1.25 | .60 |
| 1250 | A630 | 350p multicolored | 1.75 | .85 |

Merchant Marine's Director General of Maritime Territory, 150th Anniv. — A631

1998, Aug. 31   **Litho.**   **Perf. 13½**
| 1251 | A631 | 500p multicolored | 3.00 | 1.25 |

Intl. Year of the Ocean.

Intl. Year of the Ocean A632

#1252, Nautical cartography. #1253, Iceberg. 500p, Silhouette of stone head, Easter Island.

1998, Sept. 10
1252	A632	400p multicolored	2.25	1.00
1253	A632	400p multicolored	2.25	1.00
1254	A632	500p multicolored	2.75	1.25
		Nos. 1252-1254 (3)	7.25	3.25

Folk Singers and Composers — A633

Designs: 200p, Clara Solovera Cortes (1909-92). 250p, Francisco Flores del Campo (1908-93). 300p, Victor Jara Martinez (1932-73). 350p, Violeta Parra Sandoval (1917-67).

1998, Sept. 14
1255	A633	200p multicolored	.95	.45
1256	A633	250p multicolored	1.25	.55
1257	A633	300p multicolored	1.40	.65
1258	A633	350p multicolored	1.75	.75
		Nos. 1255-1258 (4)	5.35	2.40

World Stamp Day A634

1998, Oct. 9   **Litho.**   **Perf. 13½**
| 1259 | A634 | 250p multicolored | 1.10 | .55 |

Francisco Bilbao (1823-65), Writer A635

Litho. & Engr.
1998, Oct. 29   **Perf. 13½**
| 1260 | A635 | 250p multicolored | 1.40 | .70 |

Chilean Painters — A636

Designs: 300p, Self-portrait, by Augusto Eguiluz (1894-1969), vert. 450p, Landscape, by Agustin Abarca (1882-1953).
1500p, "Two Nudes," by Henriette Petit (1894-1983).

1998, Nov. 3   **Litho.**
| 1261 | A636 | 300p multi | 1.40 | .75 |
| 1262 | A636 | 450p multi | 2.25 | 1.10 |

Souvenir Sheet
| 1262A | A636 | 1500p multicolored | 7.00 | 7.00 |

No. 1262A contains one 36x47mm stamp.

Catholic University of Valparaiso, 70th Anniv. — A637

1998, Nov. 18   **Litho.**   **Perf. 13½**
| 1263 | A637 | 130p multicolored | .60 | .30 |

Prominent Women from the University of Chile — A638

America Issue: 120p, Amanda Labarca, edcuator. 250p, Marta Brunet, writer.

1998, Nov. 19   **Litho.**   **Perf. 13½**
| 1264 | A638 | 120p multicolored | .60 | .35 |
| 1265 | A638 | 250p multicolored | 1.25 | .65 |

1999 World Scout Jamboree, Chile — A639

Scouting emblems and: 120p, Children of two races, stylized tents. 200p, Robert Baden-Powell. 250p, Stylized doves. 300p, Scout, stylized tents. 1000p, Scouts, leaders seated in semi-circle, vert.
3000p, Jamboree emblem over drawing of Jamboree site at Picarquin, emblems of past jamborees, Intl. Scouting Emblem.

1998, Dec. 27
1266	A639	120p multicolored	.55	.30
1267	A639	200p multicolored	.90	.45
1268	A639	250p multicolored	1.10	.55
1269	A639	300p multicolored	1.25	.65
1270	A639	1000p multicolored	4.50	2.25
		Nos. 1266-1270 (5)	8.30	4.20

Imperf
Size: 126x104mm
| 1270A | A639 | 3000p multicolored | 13.00 | 13.00 |

Birds — A640

Designs: 10p, Zonotrichia capensis. 20p, Curaeus curaeus.

1998, Nov. 29
1271 A640 10p multicolored .50 .20
1272 A640 20p multicolored .50 .20

Exist dated "2000."
See Nos. 1313-1314, 1385-1386.

World Equestrian High Jump Record, 50th Anniv. — A641

Captain Alberto Larraguibel and Huaso.

1999, Feb. 5 Litho. Perf. 13½
1273 A641 200p multicolored .85 .50

Temuco Fire Dept., Cent. — A642

Designs: 140p, 1900 pumper. 200p, 1929 Ford. 300p, 1955 Ford K tanker. 350p, 1967 Mercedes Benz hook and ladder truck. 1500p, Firefighter rescuing victim, vert.

1999, Feb. 18 Litho. Perf. 13½
1274 A642 140p multicolored .65 .30
1275 A642 200p multicolored .95 .40
1276 A642 300p multicolored 1.50 .60
1277 A642 350p multicolored 1.75 .70
Nos. 1274-1277 (4) 4.85 2.00
Souvenir Sheet
1278 A642 1500p multicolored 8.50 8.50

Chilean Chamber of Deputies, 1000th Session — A643

1999, Mar. 3 Perf. 13½
1279 A643 140p multicolored .60 .40

Sacred Heart College, 150th Anniv. — A644

1999, Mar. 15
1280 A644 250p multicolored 1.10 .75

Economic Development Corporation (CORFO), 60th Anniv. — A645

Pedro Aguirre Cerda, former president of Chile.

1999, Apr. 29 Perf. 13½
1281 A645 140p multicolored .65 .40

Chilean Insurance Assoc., Cent. — A646

1999, May 18 Litho. Perf. 13½
1282 A646 140p multicolored .65 .50

Chilean Antarctica A647

Designs: 360p, Leptonychotes weddellii. 450p, Pygoscelis antarctica. 1500p, Arctocephalus gazella, penguins.

1999, June 15
1283 A647 360p multicolored 1.75 .90
1284 A647 450p multicolored 3.00 1.00
Souvenir Sheet
1285 A647 1500p multicolored 8.50 8.50
No. 1285 contains one 35x48mm stamp.

Easter Island A648

1999, June 25
1286 A648 360p multicolored 2.00 2.00

Souvenir Sheet

Barcelona Soccer Club, Cent. — A649

Illustration reduced.

1999
1287 A649 1000p multicolored 5.00 5.00

University of Santiago, 150th Anniv. — A650

Designs: 140p, Monument, students in training room, School of Arts and Sciences, 1849. 250p, Technical equipment, building on campus, State Technical University, 1947. 300p, Student looking into microscope, computer, modern building, 1999.

1999, July 6 Litho. Perf. 13½
1288 A650 140p multicolored .60 .30
1289 A650 250p multicolored 1.00 .50
1290 A650 300p multicolored 1.40 .60
Nos. 1288-1290 (3) 3.00 1.40

Alexander von Humboldt (1769-1859), 200th Anniv. of Scientific Research in Latin America — A651

Face from monument and: 300p, Bust of Humboldt, wildlife, mountains. 360p, Portrait of Humboldt, penguins, sea.

1999, July 16
1291 A651 300p multicolored 1.25 .60
1292 A651 360p multicolored 1.50 .75

China '99, World Philatelic Exhibition, Beijing — A652

Chinese, Chilean flags and: 140p, Pagoda. 450p, Chinese junk. 1500p, Great Wall of China, Gate of Heavenly Peace.

1999, Aug. 10
1293 A652 140p multicolored .60 .30
1294 A652 450p multicolored 1.75 .90
Souvenir Sheet
1295 A652 1500p multicolored 7.00 4.50
No. 1295 contains one 60x48mm stamp.

City of Quilpue, Cent. — A653

1999, Aug. 20
1296 A653 250p multicolored 1.00 .50

A654 A655

140p, Raúl Cardinal Silva Henriquez (1907-99). 200p, Walking in street clothes, administering sacrament, face of Christ.

1999, Aug. 9
1297 A654 140p shown .60 .30
1298 A654 200p multicolored .80 .40

Holy Year 2000.

1999, Sept. 23 Litho. Perf. 13½
1299 A655 140p multicolored .60 .30

Red Cross blood donation campaign.

2000 World Congress of Authors & Composers, Santiago — A656

1999, Oct. 5
1300 A656 170p multicolored .70 .35

Intl. Year of Older Persons — A657

1999, Oct. 6
1301 A657 250p multicolored 1.00 .50

UPU, 125th Anniv. A658

1999, Oct. 9
1302 A658 300p Red mailbox 1.75 .60
1303 A658 360p Gold mailbox 1.75 .75
a. Pair, #1302-1303 + label 3.50 2.75

Nos. 1302-1303 printed in sheets of 16 pairs, with label in central column.

America Issue, A New Millennium Without Arms — A659

1999, Oct. 12
1304 A659 140p shown 1.00 .30
1305 A659 320p Broken bomb 1.50 .65

Labor Management, 75th Anniv. — A660

1999, Aug. 23
1306 A660 320p multicolored   1.25 .65

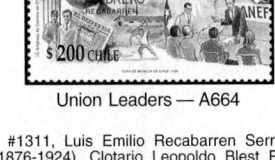

Interamerican Development Bank, 40th Anniv. — A661

1999, Oct. 29   Litho.   Perf. 13½
1307 A661 360p multicolored   1.50 .75

A662

1999, Dec. 1
1308 A662 450p multicolored   1.75 .90
    Holy Year 2000.

A663

1999, Dec. 1
1309 A663 170p multicolored   .70 .35

Inscribed "D.S. 20"
1310 A663 170p multicolored   .70 .35
  a.   Booklet pane of 10   7.50
    Complete booklet, #1310a   8.00
  b.   Booklet pane of 5   4.00
    Complete booklet, #1310b   4.50

Nos. 1309-1310 each were issued se-tenant with two labels that served as a lottery ticket and stub.

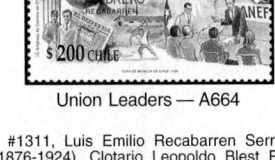

Union Leaders — A664

#1311, Luis Emilio Recabarren Serrano (1876-1924), Clotario Leopoldo Blest Riffo (1899-1990). #1312, Tucapel Jiménez Alfaro (1921-82), Manuel Bustos Huerta (1943-99).

1999, Dec. 29   Litho.   Perf. 13½
1311 A664 200p multi   .90 .50
1312 A664 200p multi   .90 .50
  a.   Pair, #1311-1312 + label   4.00 3.00

Bird Type of 1998

Designs: 50p, Campephilus magellanicus, vert. 100p, Falco peregrinus cassini, vert.

2000, Feb.   Perf. 13½
1313 A640 50p multi   .20 .20
1314 A640 100p multi   .40 .20

Discovery of Juan Fernández, Archipelago, 425th Anniv. — A665

a, Más Afuera (Alejandro Selkirk) Island, Santa Clara Island, tip of Más a Tierra (Robinson Crusoe) Island. b, Más a Tierra Island. c, Dendroseris litoralis. d, Rhaphythamnus venustus. e, Lobster. f, Lobster's antenna, boat. g, Boat, Gavilea insularis. h, Gavilea insularis.

2000, Feb. 29   Perf. 13¼
1315 A665 360p Sheet of 8,
    #a.-h.   16.00 16.00

Condorito, Cartoon Character by Rene Rios Boettiger Pepo — A666

Condorito: 150p, Celebrating millennium. 260p, As soccer player. 480p, As fire fighter. 980p, On horse.
2000p, With people.

2000, Mar. 20   Perf. 13½
1316 A666 150p multi   .75 .30
1317 A666 260p multi   1.50 .50
1318 A666 480p multi   2.50 .95
1319 A666 980p multi   5.25 2.00
    Nos. 1316-1319 (4)   10.00 3.75

Souvenir Sheet
1320 A666 2000p multi   11.00 11.00

Easter Island — A667

Designs: 200p, Dancer, stone weapon. 260p, Stone statue and carvings. 340p, Island native, stone statue. 480p, Female dancer, inscribed tablet, map of island.

2000, Apr. 27   Litho.   Perf. 13¼
1321 A667 200p multi   1.10 .60
1322 A667 260p multi   1.50 .70
1323 A667 340p multi   2.00 1.00
1324 A667 480p multi   2.75 1.40
    Nos. 1321-1324 (4)   7.35 3.70

Town of Carahue, Cent. (in 1998) — A668

Bridge and: No. 1325, Locomotive, pottery. No. 1326, Potatoes.

2000, May 5
1325 A668 220p multi   1.10 .55
1326 A668 220p multi   1.10 .55
  a.   Pair, #1325-1326   2.50 2.00

El Mercurio Newspaper, Cent. — A669

2000, June 1
1327 A669 370p multi   2.00 1.00

4th Natl. Masonic Convention — A670

2000, June 23
1328 A670 460p multi   2.50 1.25

Medicinal Plants — A671

Designs: 200p, Quillaja saponaria. 360p, Fabiana imbricata.

2000, July 3
1329 A671 200p multi   1.25 .60
1330 A671 360p multi   3.00 1.50

Discovery of Brazil, 500th Anniv. — A672

Designs: 260p, Map of Brazil, butterfly, girl. 1500p, Monkey, parrots, boy.

2000, July 10
1331 A672 260p multi   1.50 .75

Souvenir Sheet
1332 A672 1500p multi   8.50 8.50

No. 1332 contains one 48x36mm stamp.

Folklore A673

Religious festivals: 150p, Dancer in devil costume, La Tirana. 200p, Festival of San Pedro de Atacama. 370p, Candlemas Festival, Copiapo. 460p, Chinese dancers, Andacollo.

2000, July 13
1333 A673 150p multi   .80 .40
1334 A673 200p multi   1.10 .55
1335 A673 370p multi   2.00 1.00
1336 A673 460p multi   2.50 1.25
    Nos. 1333-1336 (4)   6.40 3.20

Prehistoric Animals — A674

No. 1337: a, Milodon. b, Titanosaurus. c, Plesiosaurus. d, Iguanodon.
Illustration reduced.

2000
1337 A674 150p Block of 4, #a-d   2.50 1.25

José de San Martín (1778-1850) — A675

2000, Aug. 25   Litho.   Perf. 13½
1338 A675 320p multi   1.40 .70

World Meteorological Organization, 50th Anniv. — A676

2000, Aug. 28
1339 A676 320p multi   1.40 .70

Antarctic Fauna — A677

450p, Sphenis magellanicus, vert. 650p, Megaptera novaeangliae. 940p, Orcinus orca.

2000, Sept. 15
1340-1342 A677 Set of 3   19.00 19.00

Souvenir Sheet
1343 A677 2000p Mirounga leonina, vert.   17.00 17.00

No. 1343 contains one 36x48mm stamp.

2000 Summer Olympics, Sydney — A678

Sydney Opera House, Olympic flag and: a, 290p, Chilean flag, tennis player, soccer player, sprinter. b, 290p, Australian flag, archer, high jumper, cyclist.
Illustration reduced.

2000, Sept. 20
1344 A678 Pair, #a-b   3.00 1.50

City of Concepcion, 450th Anniv. — A679

Mural by Gregorio De la Fuente: a, Indian holding stick. b, Soldier on white horse. c, Finger pointing upward. d, Seated figure, arms, horse-drawn carriage. e, Horse, statue, train. f, People and rainbow.

2000, Oct. 2
1345	Horiz. strip of 6	8.00	8.00
a.-f.	A679 250p Any single	1.25	.65

America Issue, World AIDS Day — A680

Designs: 150p, Heart, clasped hands of adult and child. 220p, Clasped hands.

2000, Oct. 12
1346-1347	A680 Set of 2	2.00	1.00

Penal Reform — A681

Designs: 150p, Flag, court proceedings. 2000p, People, doors of Justice Ministry.

2000, Nov. 16
1348	A681 150p multi	.70	.35

Souvenir Sheet
1349	A681 2000p multi	10.50	10.50

Christmas — A682

Designs: a, Star of Bethlehem. b, Santa Claus flying over town. c, Three Magi on camels. d, Star on top of Christmas tree. e, Boy at mailbox. f, Sleeping child. g, Two Magi, cow. h, Baby Jesus, cow. i, Mary, Joseph. j, Girl putting ornaments on tree.

2000, Nov. 20   **Perf. 13½**
1350	Block of 10	7.50	7.50
a.-j.	A682 150p Any single	.75	.40

Inscribed "DS/20"
Perf. 13½ on 3 sides
1351	Booklet pane of 10	9.00	
a.-j.	A682 150p Any single	.90	.45
	Booklet, #1351	9.00	

National Zoo, 75th Anniv. — A683

Various animals and birds, denomination in: a, LL. b, LR. c, UL. d, UR. Illustration reduced.

2001, Jan. 13   **Litho.**   **Perf. 13½**
1352	A683 160p Block of 4, #a-d	5.50	5.50

San Sebastian Festival, Yumbel — A684

2001, Jan. 18
1353	A684 210p multi	1.00	.50

Father Alberto Hurtado (1901-52) A685

Hurtado and: 160p, Truck. 340p, Children.

2001, Jan. 20
1354-1355	A685 Set of 2	2.50	1.25

Bird Type of 1998

No. 1356, vert.: a, Sephanoides fernandensis. b, Mimus thenca. c, Pteroptochos megapodius. d, Enicognathus leptorhynchus. Size of Nos. 1356a-1356d: 24x29mm.

2001, Jan. 29
1356	A640 160p Block of 4, #a-d	3.50	3.50

Assembly of Governors of Inter-American Development Bank and Investment Corporation — A686

2001, Mar. 16
1357	A686 230p multi	1.00	.50

Souvenir Sheet

Air Force Anniversaries — A687

No. 1358: a, Lockheed C-130 Hercules, map of Antarctica. b, Flugzeugbau Extra-300, acrobatic squadron. c, North American AT-6 Texan. d, Consolidated PBY-5A/OA-10 Catalina, map of Easter Island.

2001, Mar. 29
1358	A687 260p Sheet of 4, #a-d	5.50	5.50

Air Force presence in Antarctica, 50th anniv. (No. 1358a); Halcones acrobatic squadron, 20th anniv. (No. 1358b); Aviation Group No. 1, 75th anniv. (No. 1358c); First flight ot Easter Island, 50th anniv. (No. 1358d).

Nationalization of Copper Industry, 30th Anniv. — A688

Design: 2000p, Miner and equipment.

2001, Apr. 26   **Litho.**   **Perf. 13¼**
1359	A688 400p multi	2.00	1.00

Souvenir Sheet
1359A	A688 2000p multi	10.00	10.00

Organ Donation — A689

2001, May 3
1360	A689 160p multi	1.00	.40

Easter Island — A690

Designs: No. 1361, Stone carvings, map of island and: a, Compass rose. b, Bird and native. No. 1361C, Artifact and map of island. Illustration reduced.

2001, June 25
1361	A690 260p Horiz. pair, #a-b	2.50	2.50

Souvenir Sheet
1361C	A690 2000p multi	10.00	10.00

Lynchailurus Colocolo — A691

2001
1362	A691 100p multi	.50	.25

Endangered species.

Valparaiso Firefighting Corps, 150th Anniv. — A692

Firefighters and: 160p, Manuel Blanco Encalada. 260p, Old pumper, building on fire, modern fire truck. 350p, Flags, building. 490p, Helicopter, rail tank car.
2000p, Helicopter, modern fire truck.

2001, June 28   **Litho.**   **Perf. 13¼**
1363-1366	A692 Set of 4	6.00	3.00

Souvenir Sheet
1367	A692 2000p multi	10.00	10.00

Mushrooms A693

Designs: 300p, Macrolepiota rhacodes. 400p, Laccata ohiensis.

2001, July 25   **Litho.**   **Perf. 13¼**
1368-1369	A693 Set of 2	4.00	2.50

24th Conference of American Armies, Santiago — A694

2001, Aug. 13
1370	A694 350p multi	1.75	.85

Bernardo O'Higgins (1778-1842), Soldier and Statesman — A695

2001, Aug. 17
1371	A695 260p multi	1.25	.60

Chilean Antarctic Research — A696

Designs: 350p, Researcher, Leptonychotes weddellii. 700p, Researcher, Macronectes giganteus. 2000p, Chionis alba.

2001, Aug. 29
1372-1373	A696 Set of 2	4.75	2.40

Souvenir Sheet
1374	A696 2000p multicolored	9.00	9.00

America Issue — UNESCO World Heritage — A697

World Heritage Sites and stamps: 160p, Quinchao Church, #1058. 230p, Tenaun Church, #1057.

2001, Oct. 9   **Litho.**   **Perf. 13¼**
1375-1376	A697 Set of 2	6.75	2.25

Cape Horn A698

2001, Nov. 22
1377 A698 220p multi 1.00 .50

El Indice del Indice, by Roberto Matta (1911-2002) — A699

2001, Nov. 5 Litho. Perf. 13¼
1378 A699 300p multi 1.40 .70

Railroads in Chile, 150th Anniv. — A700

No. 1397 (50x29mm): a, Caldera Station, train cars. b, Locomotive and Copiapó Station. 220p, Train on bridge.

2001, Nov. 20
1379 A700 200p Horiz. pair, #a-b 2.25 1.25
1380 A700 220p multi 1.25 .65

Christmas — A701

Designs: a, Heads of three shepherds. b, Shepherd and cow. c, Joseph and Mary. d, Donkey and Magus. e, Cow and two Magi. f, Head of shepherd. g, Two sheep. h, Infant Jesus. i, Shepherd with staff. j, One sheep. Illustration reduced.

2001, Nov.
1381 A701 160p Block of 10, #a-j 8.00 8.00
Inscribed "DS/20"
1382 A701 160p Block of 10, #a-j 8.00 8.00
k. Booklet pane, #1382 with straight edge at right 9.50 —
Complete booklet, #1382k 9.50

Rotary Intl. Emblem, Map of Chile, Globe, Tropic of Capricorn Monument — A702

2001, Dec. 21
1383 A702 240p multi 1.25 .65
Antofagasta Rotary Club, 75th anniv.

Taxation Department, Cent. — A703

2002, Jan. 14
1384 A703 180p multi .80 .40

Bird Type of 1998
Designs: 10p, Turdus falcklandii. 20p, Sturnella loyca.

2002, Jan. 25
1385 A640 10p multi .25 .20
1386 A640 20p multi .25 .20

City of Valdivia, 450th Anniv. — A704

2002, Feb. 9
1387 A704 260p multi 1.25 .65

Carabinero Force, 75th Anniv. — A705

2002, Apr. 8
1388 A705 250p multi 1.25 .65

Ignacy Domeyko (1802-89), Mineralogist — A706

2002, Apr. 11
1389 A706 290p multi 1.40 .70

City of Villarrica, 450th Anniv. — A707

2002, Apr. 26
1390 A707 290p multi 1.25 .65

Town of Calbuco, 400th Anniv. — A708

2002, May 2
1391 A708 230p multi 1.10 .55

Barros Arana Natl. Boarding School — A709

2002, May 20
1392 A709 250p multi 1.25 .65

Abolition of Death Penalty, 1st Anniv. — A710

2002, May 29
1393 A710 240p multi 1.25 .65

Endangered Species Type of 2001
Designs: 10p, Oreailurus jacobita. 20p, Oncifelis geoffrovi.

2002, June 5
1394 A691 10p multi .25 .20
1395 A691 20p multi .25 .20

Easter Island A711

Map of Easter Island and: 250p, Toromiro sophora, moai. 450p, Bird, row of moai statues, native in traditional costume.
2000p, Toromiro sophora and bird.

2002, July 1
1396-1397 A711 Set of 2 3.00 1.50
Souvenir Sheet
1398 A711 2000p multi 9.00 9.00
No. 1398 contains one 47x47mm stamp.

World Heritage Sites — A712

Churches and stamps: 230p, Achao, #1036. 290p, Dalcahue, #1056.

2002, July 27
1399-1400 A712 Set of 2 2.25 1.10

America Issue — Youth, Education, and Literacy — A713

Designs: 230p, Adult students. 450p, Woman reading to child, teacher, boy at computer.

2002, Sept. 9
1401-1402 A713 Set of 2 3.00 1.50

Children's Toys — A714

Designs: 290p, Pinwheel. 380p, Kite, vert.

2002, Sept. 16
1403-1404 A714 Set of 2 3.00 1.50

Observatories — A715

Designs: 450p, Cerro-Tololo. 550p, Paranal. 2000p, Cerro-Tololo, diff.

2002, Sept. 27
1405-1406 A715 Set of 2 4.00 2.00
Souvenir Sheet
1407 A715 2000p multi 8.50 8.50
No. 1407 contains one 47x47mm stamp.

University of Chile Clinical Hospital, 50th Anniv. — A716

2002, Oct. 17
1408 A716 250p multi 1.10 .55

Forestry Education, 50th Anniv. — A717

2002, Oct. 22
1409 A717 250p multi 1.10 .55

12th Convention on International Trade in Endangered Species Conference — A718

Designs: 300p, Phoenicoparrus andinus. 450p, Vicugna vicugna. 2000p, Chinchilla lanigera.

2002, Oct. 29
1410-1411 A718 Set of 2 3.50 1.75
Souvenir Sheet
1412 A718 2000p multi 9.00 9.00
No. 1412 contains one 47x47mm stamp.

Protected Whales — A719

Designs: 250p, Eubalaena australis. 500p, Balaenoptera acutorostrata. 2000p, Physeter macrocephalus.

2002, Nov. 2
1413-1414 A719 Set of 2   3.50   1.50
Souvenir Sheet
1415 A719 2000p multi   10.00   10.00

Violence Against Women Prevention Day — A720

2002, Nov. 22
1416 A720 230p multi   1.00   .50

Town of Puerto Varas, 150th Anniv. A721

2002, Nov. 29
1417 A721 190p multi   .80   .40

Bird Type of 1998
Designs: 500p, Campephilus magellanicus, vert. 1000p, Falco peregrinus cassini, vert.

2003, Jan. 15   Litho.   Perf. 13¼
1418 A640 500p multi   2.10   .75
1419 A640 1000p multi   4.00   1.75

Puerto Montt, 150th Anniv. A722

2003, Feb. 13
1420 A722 240p multi   1.00   .45

Claudio Arrau (1903-91), Pianist — A723

2003, June 9   Litho.   Perf. 13¼
1421 A723 200p multi   .85   .30

First Chilean Postage Stamps, 150th Anniv. — A724

No. 1422 — Mailbox, building and: a, #1. b, #2.
2000p, Building, #1 and various other stamps.
Illustration reduced.

2003, July 1
1422 A724   300p Horiz. pair,
          #a-b   1.75   .85
Souvenir Sheet
1423 A724 2000p multi   8.00   3.00

America Issue — Flora and Fauna — A725

Designs: 240p, Trees, flowers, cactus. 300p, Frog, fox, butterfly, pudu, parrot.

2003, Oct. 12   Litho.   Perf. 13¼
1424-1425 A725   Set of 2   2.00   1.00

Supreme Court, 180th Anniv. — A726

2003, Nov. 5
1426 A726 200p multi   .85   .35

Chilean Red Cross, Cent. A727

2003, Nov. 18
1427 A727 200p black & red   .85   .35

Christmas — A728

2003, Nov. 28
1428 A728 190p multi   .80   .30
Inscribed "DS-20"
1429 A728 190p multi   .80   .30

Powered Flight, Cent. — A729

2003, Dec. 11
1430 A729 200p multi   .85   .35

Cristo Redentor Statue, Cent. A730

2004, Apr. 22   Litho.
1431 A730 200p multi   .85   .30

Seventh World Conference of Grand Masonic Lodges — A731

2004, May 5   Perf. 13¼
1432 A731 190p multi   .80   .30

Pablo Neruda (1904-73), Poet — A732

2004, June 11
1433 A732 300p multi   1.25   .45

Social Security, 80th Anniv. — A733

2004, Aug. 18
1434 A733 190p multi   .80   .30

America Issue — Environmental Protection — A734

Designs: 100p, Burnt forest, logs, field of flowers, puma, flower. 600p, Flower, wildlife, tanker truck, smokestacks.

2004, Sept. 27
1435-1436 A734   Set of 2   2.60   1.50

German Institute, Osorno, 150th Anniv. — A735

2004, Oct. 6
1437 A735 250p multi   1.10   .40

Tematica 2004 National Philatelic Exhibition A736

2004, Oct. 19
1438 A736 310p multi   1.25   .55

Naval Telecommunications, Cent. — A737

2004, Nov. 5
1439 A737 400p multi   1.75   .80

Electricity and Fuel Superintendency, Cent. — A738

2004, Dec. 7
1440 A738 240p multi   1.00   .40

Chilean Air Force, 75th Anniv. — A739

Illustration reduced.

2005, Mar. 15   Litho.   Perf. 13¼
1441 A739 230p multi   1.00   .40

Law No. 20,000 — A740

2005, May 4
1442 A740 220p multi .95 .40

Pope John Paul II (1920-2005) — A741

Pope John Paul II and: a, Child, condor, mountain. b, Crucifix, Chilean flag, mountain. c, Church, Chilean flag.

2005, May 13
1443 Horiz. strip of 3 3.25 1.75
a.-c. A741 230p Any single 1.00 .50

Rotary International, Cent. — A742

2005, June 30 Litho. Perf. 13¼
1444 A742 230p multi 1.00 .40

Treasury Building, Bicent. — A743

2005, June 30
1445 A743 230p multi 1.00 .40

Publication of Don Quixote, 400th Anniv. A744

No. 1446: a, Don Quixote on horseback. b, Windmill. c, Windmills. d, Miguel de Cervantes, author.

2005, July 14
1446 Horiz. strip of 4 .25 .20
a.-b. A744 10p Either single .20 .20
c.-d. A744 20p Either single .20 .20

El Teniente Copper Mine, Cent. — A745

2005, Aug. 3
1447 A745 390p multi 1.75 .75

Undersecretariat of Aviation, 75th Anniv. — A746

Illustration reduced.

2005, Aug. 19
1448 A746 400p multi 1.75 1.00

Valparaiso Customs House, 150th Anniv. — A747

2005, Sept. 1
1449 A747 390p multi 1.75 .75

Bicentennial Fountain, Santiago — A748

2005, Sept. 5
1450 A748 230p multi 1.00 .45

America Issue — Fight Against Poverty — A749

No. 1451: a, Denomination at right. b, Denomination at left.
Illustration reduced.

2005, Oct. 3 Litho. Perf. 13¼
1451 A749 250p Horiz. pair, #a-b 2.25 .95

Canonization of Father Alberto Hurtado (1901-52) — A750

2005, Oct. 13 Litho. Perf. 13¼
1452 A750 390p multi 1.75 .75

Expo Austral 2005 Philatelic Exhibition, Punta Arenas — A751

2005, Oct. 22
1453 A751 390p multi 1.75 .75

New Civil Matrimony Law — A752

2005, Nov. 18 Litho. Perf. 13¼
1454 A752 260p multi 1.10 .50

German Clinic, Cent. — A753

2005, Nov. 23
1455 A753 230p multi 1.00 .45

Restoration of Central Post Office, Santiago A754

2005, Nov. 30
1456 A754 230p multi 1.00 .45

Political Constitution A755

2005, Dec. 1
1457 A755 230p multi 1.00 .45

Department of Physical Education, Sports and Recreation, Cent. — A756

2006, Mar. 6 Litho. Perf. 13¼
1458 A756 230p multi 1.00 .45

Intl. Women's Day — A757

2006, Mar. 7
1459 A757 390p multi 1.75 .75

Wulff Castle, Cent. — A758

No. 1460 — Castle, arms of Vina del Mar and: a, Birds. b, Windmill.

2006, Mar. 21
1460 Horiz. pair + label 3.00 1.50
a. A758 230p multi 1.00 .55
b. A758 390p multi 1.75 .85

Tourism — A759

No. 1461: a, Morro de Arica. b, Moais, Easter Island. c, Palafittes, Castro. d, Torres del Paine. e, Penguins, Chilean Antarctic Territory.

2006, May 19
1461 Horiz. strip of 5 4.50 2.25
a.-e. A759 230p Any single .90 .45

Don Quixote Type of 2005

No. 1462: a, Building. b, Windmills. c, Windmill, country name at LR. d, Don Quixote and Sancho Panza.

2006, May 31
1462 Horiz. strip of 4 .20 .20
a.-d. A744 10p Any single .20 .20

Catholic University of the North, 50th Anniv. — A760

No. 1463: a, Students using computers, denomination at UR. b, Students, denomination at LL.

2006, June 9
1463   Horiz. pair + label   1.75   .85
a.-b.   A760 230p Either single   .85   .40

Citizenship Plaza, Santiago — A761

2006, July 7
1464   A761 390p multi   1.50   .75

World Quality Forum — A762

No. 1465: a, Building. b, Building and flags. Illustration reduced.

2006, Aug. 29   Litho.   Perf. 13¼
1465   A762 230p Horiz. pair, #a-b 1.75   .85

America Issue, Energy Conservation — A763

No. 1466: a, River and mountains. b, Clouds. c, Oil rigs in water. d, Windmill.

2006, Sept. 29
1466   A763 390p Block of 4, #a-d   6.00 3.00

Adventist University of Chile, Cent. — A764

No. 1467 — University emblem and: a, Building, 1906. b, Family and building, 1922. c, Building, 1960-70. d, Building, 2006.

2006, Oct. 20
1467   Horiz. strip of 4 + central label   4.00 2.00
a.-d.   A764 250p Any single   1.00   .50

Antarctic Wildlife — A765

No. 1468 — Chilean and Estonian flags and: a, Balaenoptera acutorostrata. b, Aptenodytes forsteri. Illustration reduced.

2006, Oct. 25   Perf. 13½
1468   A765 500p Horiz. pair, #a-b 4.00 2.00
       See Estonia No. 555.

Anniversaries — A766

No. 1469: a, Colonization of the Straits of Magellan area, 160th anniv. b, Fort Bulnes, 160th anniv. Illustration reduced.

2006, Dec. 7   Perf. 13¼
1469   A766 250p Horiz. pair, #a-b 1.90   .95

Gasco, 150th Anniv. — A767

No. 1470: a, San Borja facility. b, Gasco headquarters. Illustration reduced.

2006, Dec. 14
1470   A767 250p Horiz. pair, #a-b 1.90   .95

Federico Santa Maria Technical University, 75th Anniv. — A768

2006, Dec. 20
1471   A768 250p multi   .95   .45

Carabineros, 80th Anniv. — A769

No. 1472: a, Carabineros and mountains. b, Carabineros on horseback. Illustration reduced.

2007, Apr. 10   Litho.   Perf. 13¼
1472   A769 250p Horiz. pair, #a-b 1.90   .95

Tourism — A770

No. 1473: a, Valley of the Moon, Antofagasta Region. b, Easter Island, Valparaiso Region. c, Tourism emblem. d, Villarrica-Pucón Volcano, Araucania Region. e, Penguin in Chilean Antarctic.

2007, May 9
1473   Horiz. strip of 5   7.50 3.75
a.-e.   A770 390p Any single   1.50   .75

Church Centenaries — A771

No. 1474: a, Parinacota Church. b, San Pedro de Atacama Church. Illustration reduced.

Litho. With Foil Application
2007, June 29
1474   A771 250p Horiz. pair, #a-b 1.90   .95

Raul Cardinal Silva Henríquez (1907-99) — A772

No. 1475 — Color of portrait and panel: a, Blue violet. b, Red violet. c, Red orange. d, Green.

2007, Aug. 21   Litho.
1475   Horiz. strip of 4 + central label   4.00 2.00
a.-d.   A772 250p Any single   1.00   .50

A773

A774

A775

Sculptures by Marta Colvin (1907-95) — A776

2007, Aug. 24   Perf. 13¼
1476   Horiz. strip of 4 + central label   4.00 2.00
a.   A773 250p multi   1.00   .50
b.   A774 250p multi   1.00   .50
c.   A775 250p multi   1.00   .50
d.   A776 250p multi   1.00   .50

Las Condes, 106th Anniv. — A777

2007, Aug. 28
1477   A777 330p multi   1.25   .65

Museums in Santiago A778

Designs: 10p, Artequin Museum. 20p, National Museum of Fine Arts. 30p, National Museum of Natural History. 50p, Museum of Santiago.

2007, Aug. 31   Engr.
1478   A778 10p green   .20   .20
1479   A778 20p black   .20   .20
1480   A778 30p purple   .20   .20
1481   A778 50p red   .20   .20
       Nos. 1478-1481 (4)   .80   .80

Los Rios Region — A779

No. 1482: a, Lake Ranco. b, Huilo Huilo Waterfall. c, Bridge, Valdivia. d, Choshuenco Volcano.

2007, Oct. 2   Litho.
1482   Horiz strip of 4 + central label   6.25 3.25
a.-d.   A779 390p Any single   1.50   .75

Arica and Parinacota Region — A780

No. 1483: a, Morro de Arica. b, Parinacota Volcano. c, Anzota Caves. d, Vicunas.

2007, Oct. 8
1483   Horiz strip of 4 + central label   4.00 2.00
a.-d.   A780 250p Any single   1.00   .50

Chilean Postal Service, 260th Anniv. — A781

No. 1484: a, Half of original General Post Office, Santiago (denomination at UR). b, Half of modern General Post Office, Santiago (denomination at UL). c, Original and modern General Post Offices.
3000p, Statue of postal carrier on bicycle. Illustration reduced.

Litho. With Foil Application
2007, Oct. 9

1484	A781	390p Horiz. strip of 3, #a-c	4.75	2.40

Souvenir Sheet

1485	A781	3000p multi	12.00	6.00

SEMI-POSTAL STAMPS

S. S. Abtao and Captain Policarpo Toro SP1

S. S. Abtao and Brother Eugenio Eyraud SP2

Perf. 14½x15

1940, Mar. 1   Engr.   Unwmk.

B1	SP1	80c + 2.20p dk grn & lake	1.50	1.40
B2	SP2	3.60p + 6.40p lake & dk grn	1.50	1.40
a.		Pair, #B1-B2	5.50	4.50
		Set, never hinged	8.00	

50th anniv. of Chilean ownership of Easter Is. Surtax used for charitable institutions. Sheets containing 15 of each value, with 9 se-tenant pairs.

Catalogue values for unused stamps in this section, from this point to the end of the section, are for Never Hinged items.

Pedro de Valdivia — SP3

Portraits: 10c+10c, Jose Toribio Medina.

1961, Apr. 29   Photo.   Perf. 13x12½

B3	SP3	5c + 5c pale brn & sl	1.40	.45
B4	SP3	10c + 10c buff & vio blk	1.00	.35

Printed without charge by the Spanish Mint as a gift to Chile. The surtax was to aid the 1960 earthquake victims and to increase teachers' salaries. See Nos. CB1-CB2.

No. 402 Surcharged in Dark Green

1974, Mar. 25   Litho.   Perf. 14½

B5	A213	27e + 3e on 40c dl grn	.50	.25

Cent. of intl. meteorological cooperation. The 3e surtax of Nos. B5-B10 was for modernization of the postal system.

No. 412 Surcharged in Dark Blue

1974, Apr. 25   Litho.   Perf. 14½

B6	A219	27e + 3e on 1.95e	.50	.25

500th anniversary of the birth of Nicolaus Copernicus (1473-1534), Polish astronomer.

No. 329A Surcharged

1974, May 2   Litho.   Perf. 14

B7	A159	27e + 3e on 1e bluish grn	.40	.25

Centenary of the city of Vina del Mar.

#377 Surcharged in Blk, #395, 380 in Red

1974   Litho.   Perf. 14½

B8	A193	47e + 3e on 40c grn	.35	.25
B9	A207	67e + 3e on 40c multi	.40	.25
B10	A196	97e + 3e on 40c red brn	.35	.25
		Nos. B8-B10 (3)	1.10	.75

Issued: #B8, 6/7; #B9, 7/9; #B10, 6/20.

AIR POST STAMPS

Black Surcharge
Lithographed; Center Engraved
1927   Unwmk.   Perf. 13½x14
Black Brown & Blue

C1		40c on 10c	300.00	40.00
C2		80c on 10c	300.00	50.00
C3		1.20p on 10c	300.00	60.00
C4		1.60p on 10c	300.00	60.00
C5		2p on 10c	300.00	60.00
		Nos. C1-C5 (5)	1,500.	270.00

Issued for air post service between Santiago and Valparaiso. The stamps picture Bernardo O'Higgins and are not known without surcharge.

Regular Issues of 1915-28 Overprinted or Surcharged in Black, Red or Blue

Inscribed: "Chile Correos"
1928-29   Perf. 13½x14, 14

C6	A39	20c brn org & blk (Bk)	.30	.25
C6A	A55	40c dk vio & blk (R)	.30	.20
C6B	A43	1p grn & blk (Bl)	1.00	.50
C6C	A43	2p red & blk (Bl)	1.50	.30
f.		2p ver & blk (Bl)	65.00	15.00
C6D	A43	5p ol grn & blk (Bl)	2.40	.75
C6E	A50	6p on 10c dp bl & blk (R)	40.00	22.50

C7	A43	10p org & blk (Bk) ('29)	9.50	3.00
C8	A43	10p org & blk (Bl)	35.00	22.50
		Nos. C6-C8 (8)	90.00	50.00

On Nos. C6B to C6D, C7 and C8 the overprint is larger than on the other stamps of the issue.

Same Overprint or Surcharge on Nos. 155, 156, 158-161
Inscribed: "Chile Correos"
1928-32   Wmk. 215

C9	A55	40c vio & blk (R)	.55	.30
C10	A43	1p grn & blk (Bl)	1.50	.45
C11	A43	2p red & blk (Bl)	7.00	1.50
C12	A52	3p on 5c sl bl (R)	25.00	20.00
C13	A43	5p ol grn & blk (Bl)	6.00	1.50
C14	A43	10p org & blk (Bk)	27.50	7.25
		Nos. C9-C14 (6)	67.55	31.00

Same Overprint on Nos. 166-169, 172 and 158 in Black or Red
Inscribed: "Correos de Chile"
1928-30

C15	A39	20c (#166) ('29)	.75	.50
C16	A39	20c (#172) ('30)	.35	.20
C17	A40	25c bl & blk (R)	.45	.20
C18	A41	30c brn & blk	.20	.20
a.		Double ovpt., one inverted	250.00	250.00
C19	A42	50c dp grn & blk (R)	.25	.20
		Nos. C15-C19 (5)	2.00	1.30

Inscribed: "Chile Correos"
1932   Perf. 13½x14, 14

C21	A43	1p yel grn & blk (Bk)	2.75	1.50

Condor on Andes — AP1a

Airplane Crossing Andes — AP3

Los Cerrillos Airport — AP2

1931   Litho.   Perf. 13½x14, 14½x14

C22	AP1a	5c yellow grn	.25	.20
C23	AP1a	10c yellow brn	.25	.20
C24	AP1a	20c rose	.25	.20
C25	AP2	50c dark blue	1.25	.40
C26	AP3	50c black brn	.60	.20
C27	AP3	1p purple	.50	.20
C28	AP3	2p blue blk	.75	.25
a.		2p bluish slate	.90	.40
C29	AP2	5p lt red	2.50	.25
		Nos. C22-C29 (8)	6.35	1.90

For surcharges see Nos. C51-C53.

Airplane over City — AP4

Two Airplanes over Globe — AP9

Designs: 30c, 40c, 50c, Wings over Chile. 60c, Condor. 70c, Airplane and Star of Chile. 80c, Condor and Statue of Canpolican. 3p, 4p, 5p, Seaplane. 6p, 8p, 10p, Airplane. 20p, 30p, Airplane and Southern Cross. 40p, 50p, Airplane and symbols of space.

Perf. 13½x14

1934-39   Engr.   Wmk. 215

C30	AP4	10c yel grn ('35)	.25	.20
C31	AP4	15c dk grn ('35)	.35	.20
C32	AP4	20c dp bl ('36)	.20	.20
C33	AP4	30c blk brn ('35)	.20	.20
C34	AP4	40c indigo ('38)	.20	.20
C35	AP4	50c dk brn ('36)	.20	.20
C36	AP4	60c vio blk ('35)	.20	.20
C37	AP4	70c blue ('35)	.35	.20
C38	AP4	80c ol blk ('35)	.20	.20

Perf. 14

C39	AP9	1p slate blk	.20	.20
C40	AP9	2p grnsh bl	.20	.20
C41	AP9	3p org brn ('35)	.25	.20
C42	AP9	4p brn ('35)	.25	.20
C43	AP9	5p org red	.25	.20
C44	AP9	6p yel brn ('35)	.35	.20
a.		6p brown ('39)	2.50	1.75
C45	AP9	8p grn ('35)	.30	.20
C46	AP9	10p brn lake	.35	.20
C47	AP9	20p olive	.35	.20
C48	AP9	30p gray blk	.40	.20
C49	AP9	40p gray vio	1.00	.60
C50	AP9	50p brn vio	1.25	.60
		Nos. C30-C50 (21)	7.30	5.00

Nos. C30-C50 have been re-issued in slightly different colors, with white gum. The first printings are considerably scarcer. See Nos. C90-C107B, C148-C154.

Types of 1931 Surcharged in Black or Red

Perf. 13½x14, 14½x14

1940   Wmk. 215

C51	AP1a	80c on 20c lt rose	.50	.20
C52	AP2	1.60p on 5p lt red	4.00	.70
C53	AP3	5.10p on 2p sl bl (R)	1.80	1.10
		Nos. C51-C53 (3)	6.30	2.00

The surcharge on #C52 measures 21½mm.

Plane and Weather Vane — AP14

Plane and Caravel — AP23

Designs (Plane and): 20c, Globe. 30c, Chilean flag. 40c, Star of Chile and Southern Cross. 50c, Mountains. 60c, Tree. 70c, Lakes. 80c, Shore. 90c, Sunrise. 2p, Compass. 3p, Telegraph lines. 4p, Rainbow. 5p, Factory. 10p, Snow-capped mountain.

1941-42   Wmk. 215   Litho.   Perf. 14

C54	AP14	10c ol gray	.20	.20
C55	AP14	20c dp rose	.20	.20
C56	AP14	30c blue vio	.20	.20
C57	AP14	40c dl red brn	.20	.20
C58	AP14	50c red org ('42)	.35	.20
C59	AP14	60c dp green	.20	.20
C60	AP14	70c rose	.30	.25
C61	AP14	80c ultra ('42)	1.50	.45
C62	AP14	90c dk brown	.45	.25
C63	AP23	1p brt blue	.30	.20
C64	AP23	2p rose lake	.45	.30
C65	AP23	3p dk bl grn & yel grn	.65	.50
C66	AP23	4p bl vio & buff	1.00	.65
C67	AP23	5p dk org red ('42)	9.00	4.50
C68	AP23	10p gray grn & bl grn	5.00	3.50
		Nos. C54-C68 (15)	20.00	11.80

The 1p, dated "1541-1941", commemorates the 400th anniversary of Santiago.

1942-46   Unwmk.

C69	AP14	10c ultra ('43)	.20	.20
C70	AP14	10c rose lil ('45)	.20	.20
C71	AP14	20c dull grn ('43)	.20	.20
C72	AP14	20c cop brn ('45)	.20	.20
C73	AP14	30c dull vio ('44)	.20	.20
C74	AP14	30c ol blk ('45)	.20	.20
C75	AP14	40c red brn ('44)	.30	.20
C76	AP14	40c ultra ('45)	.20	.20
C77	AP14	50c rose ('43)	.20	.20
C78	AP14	50c org red ('45)	.20	.20
C79	AP14	60c orange	.20	.20
C79B	AP14	60c dp grn ('46)	.20	.20
C80	AP14	70c rose ('45)	.45	.35
C81	AP14	80c slate grn	.20	.20
C82	AP14	90c brown ('45)	.45	.35
C83	AP23	1p gray grn & lt bl ('43)	.25	.20
C84	AP23	2p org red ('43)	.20	.20
C85	AP23	3p dk pur & pale org ('43)	.45	.20
C86	AP23	4p bl grn & yel grn	.45	.35

C87 AP23 5p dk rose car ('43) .35 .20
  a. 5p dk car rose ('44) .20 .20
C88 AP23 10p sapphire ('43) .45 .35
  Nos. C69-C88 (21) 6.00 4.80

No. C83 is without dates "1541-1941."
See Nos. C109-C123. For surcharges see
Nos. C145-C147.

Coat of Arms and Plane AP29

1942, Nov. 5   **Engr.**   *Perf. 14½*
C89 AP29 100p car lake   25.00 20.00
University of Chile centenary.

Types of 1934-39
Perf. 13½x14

1944-55   **Unwmk.**   **Engr.**
C90 AP4 10c yel grn ('55) .25 .20
C92 AP4 20c deep blue .20 .20
C93 AP4 30c black brn .20 .20
C94 AP4 40c indigo .20 .20
C95 AP4 50c dk brn ('47) .20 .20
C96 AP4 60c slate vio .20 .20
C97 AP4 70c blue ('48) .20 .20
C98 AP4 80c olive blk .20 .20

Perf. 14
C99 AP9 1p slate blk .20 .20
C100 AP9 2p grnsh bl .25 .20
C101 AP9 3p org brn ('45) .20 .20
C102 AP9 4p brown .20 .20
C103 AP9 5p org red .35 .20
C104 AP9 6p yel brn ('46) .40 .20
C105 AP9 8p green .40 .20
C106 AP9 10p brn lake 1.10 .20
C107 AP9 20p ol gray ('45) .75 .20
  a. Imperf., pair 70.00
C107B AP9 50p rose vio ('50) 17.50 2.50
  Nos. C90-C107B (18) 23.00 5.90

Plane and Radio Tower — AP30

1945   **Unwmk.**   **Litho.**   *Perf. 14*
C108 AP30 1.60p brt violet .55 .25

See Nos. C118-C119.

Types of 1941-45

1946-48   **Wmk. 215**
C109 AP14 10c rose lil ('47) .20 .20
C110 AP14 20c dk red brn
    ('48) .20 .20
C111 AP14 20c dull grn ('48) 1.50 .30
C112 AP14 30c black ('48) .20 .20
C113 AP14 40c ultra ('48) .20 .20
C114 AP14 60c ol grn ('48) .20 .20
C115 AP14 80c ol blk ('48) .20 .20
C116 AP14 90c choc ('48) .20 .20
C117 AP23 1p gray grn & lt
    bl ('48) .20 .20
C118 AP30 1.60p brt violet .20 .20
C119 AP30 1.80p brt vio ('48) .20 .20
C119A AP23 2p org red .40 .20
C120 AP23 3p dk pur &
    pale org
    ('47) 1.50 .30
C121 AP23 4p bl grn & yel
    grn ('48) 1.10 .45
C122 AP23 5p rose car
    ('47) .80 .20
C123 AP23 10p sapphire
    ('47) 1.00 .20
  Nos. C109-C123 (16) 8.30 3.65

No. C117 is without dates "1541-1941."
For surcharges see Nos. C145, C147.

Flora and Fauna Type of 1948
1948
C124 A118 3p Block of 25 50.00
    Never hinged 60.00
  a.-y. any single 1.40 1.40

> Catalogue values for unused stamps in this section, from this point to the end of the section, are for Never Hinged items.

Air Line Emblem and Planes — AP32

1949   **Wmk. 215**   **Litho.**   *Perf. 14*
C125 AP32 2p ultra .45 .25

20th anniversary of the establishment of Chile's National Air Line.

Benjamin Vicuna Mackenna AP33

Factory, Badge and Book AP34

1949, Mar. 22   **Engr.**   *Perf. 13½x14*
C126 AP33 3p dk car rose .30 .20

Unwmk.
1949, Nov. 11   **Litho.**   *Perf. 14*
Design: 10p, Column and cogwheel.
C127 AP34 5p green .65 .35
C128 AP34 10p red brown 1.10 .45

Centenary of the founding of Chile's School of Arts and Crafts.

Plane and Globe — AP35

1950, Jan.   **Engr.**
C129 AP35 5p green .40 .20
C130 AP35 10p red brown .80 .40

75th anniv. of the UPU.

Plane over Snow-capped Mountain AP36

Araucarian Pine and Plane — AP38

Plane and: 40c, Coast and Sunrise. 60c, Over fishing boat. 2p, Chilean flag. 3p, Dock crane. 4p, Above river. 5p, Blast furnace. 10p, Mountain lake. 20p, Cable cars.

Imprint: "Especies Valoradas-Chile"
1950-54   **Wmk. 215**   **Litho.**   *Perf. 14*
C135 AP36 20c yel brn ('54) .30 .20
C136 AP36 40c purple ('52) .30 .20
C137 AP36 60c lt bl ('53) 1.40 .70
C138 AP38 1p dull green .30 .20
C139 AP38 2p brown red .30 .20
C140 AP38 3p violet bl .30 .20
C141 AP38 4p red org ('54) .30 .20
C142 AP38 5p violet .30 .20
C143 AP38 10p yel grn ('53) .30 .20
C144 AP38 20p red brn ('54) 1.00 .20
  Nos. C135-C144 (10) 4.30 2.50

See Nos. C155-C164, C207-C212.

Nos. C115, C81 and C116 Surcharged with New Value in Carmine or Black
1951-52   **Wmk. 215**
C145 AP14 40c on 80c ol blk (C)
    ('52) .25 .20

Unwmk.
C146 AP14 40c on 80c sl grn (C)
    ('52) 5.50 3.50
Wmk. 215
C147 AP14 1p on 90c choc .25 .20
  Nos. C145-C147 (3) 6.00 3.90

Types of 1934-39
1951-53   **Unwmk.**   **Engr.**   *Perf. 14*
C148 AP9 1p deep blue .20 .20
C149 AP9 2p blue .35 .20
C150 AP9 6p bis brn ('52) .45 .20
C151 AP9 30p dk gray ('53) 4.00 .60
C152 AP9 40p dk pur brn 12.00 1.60
C153 AP9 50p dark purple 20.00 6.50
  Nos. C148-C153 (6) 37.00 9.30

Wmk. 215
C154 AP9 50p dk pur ('52) .80 .40

Types of 1950-54
Designs as Before
Imprint: "Especies Valoradas-Chile"
1951-55   **Unwmk.**   **Litho.**   *Perf. 14*
C155 AP36 20c yel brn ('54) .20 .20
C156 AP36 40c purple .20 .20
C157 AP36 60c lt blue ('53) .25 .20
C158 AP38 1p dk bl grn ('55) .20 .20
C159 AP38 2p brown red .20 .20
C160 AP38 3p violet bl .20 .20
C161 AP38 4p red org ('52) .30 .20
C162 AP38 5p violet .30 .20
C163 AP38 10p emerald .30 .20
C164 AP38 20p brown .40 .20
  Nos. C155-C164 (10) 2.55 2.00

San Martin Crossing Andes AP40

Wmk. 215
1951, Mar. 16   **Engr.**   *Perf. 14½*
C165 AP40 5p red violet .40 .25

Gen. José de San Martín, death cent.

Isabella Type of Regular Issue, 1952
1952, Mar. 21   *Perf. 14*
C166 A125 10p carmine .50 .30

A souvenir card without franking value was issued for the Hispano-Chilean Philatelic Exhibition at Santiago, Oct. 12, 1969. It contains 2 imperf. stamps similar to Nos. 264 and C166-60c green and 10p rose red. Size: 115x137½mm.

Ancient Fortress AP42

1953, Apr. 28
C167 AP42 10p brown car 1.25 .25
4th centenary of the founding of Valdivia.

Stamp Centenary Type of 1953
1953, Oct. 15   **Engr.**   *Perf. 14½*
C168 A131 100p dp grnsh bl 2.75 1.00

An imperf. souvenir sheet contains one each of Nos. 276 and C168, with inscriptions in black at top and bottom center. Sheet measures 178x229mm. It is stated that this sheet was not valid for postage.

Early Plane and Stylized Modern Version — AP44

Unwmk.
1954, May 26   **Engr.**   *Perf. 14*
C170 AP44 3p deep blue .30 .20
25th anniversary of the founding of Chile's National Air Line.

Domeyko Type of Regular Issue, 1954.
1954, Aug. 16   *Perf. 13½x14*
C171 A134 5p orange brown .30 .20

Railroad Type of Regular Issue, 1954
1954, Sept. 10   **Wmk. 215**   *Perf. 14½*
C172 A135 10p dk purple 1.00 .20

An imperforate souvenir sheet contains one each of Nos. 283 and C172. Size: 174x232mm. Value, $200.

Presidential Visits Type of 1955
1955, May 24
C173 A139 100p red 1.50 1.25

Jet Plane in Clouds — AP48

Comet Air Liner — AP49

Designs: 2p, Helicopter over bridge. 10p, Oil derricks and plane. 50p, Control tower and plane. 200p, Beechcraft monoplane. 500p, Douglas DC-6.

Perf. 14½x14, 14x13½ (AP49)
1955-56   **Engr.**   **Wmk. 215**
C174 AP48 1p dp red lil ('56) .20 .20
C175 AP48 2p pale brn ('56) .20 .20
C176 AP48 10p bluish grn
    ('56) .20 .20
C177 AP48 50p rose ('56) .60 .20
C178 AP49 100p green .80 .20
C179 AP49 200p dp ultra 5.00 .70
C180 AP49 500p dk carmine 6.00 .70
  Nos. C174-C180 (7) 13.00 2.45

Stamps similar to type AP49, but inscribed in escudo currency, are listed as type AP58.

1956-58   **Unwmk.**
Designs: 5p, Train and plane. 20p, Jet plane and Easter Island statue.
C183 AP48 5p violet .20 .20
C184 AP48 10p grn ('57) .20 .20
C185 AP48 20p ultra .20 .20
C186 AP48 50p rose ('57) .20 .20
C187 AP49 100p bl grn ('57) .40 .20
  a. Lithographed ('60) .40 .20
C188 AP49 200p dp ultra ('57) .50 .20
C189 AP49 500p car ('58) .65 .20
  Nos. C183-C189 (7) 2.35 1.40

Symbols of University Departments — AP50

Design: 100p, View of the University.

1956, Dec. 15   **Unwmk.**   *Perf. 14*
C190 AP50 20p green .25 .20
C191 AP50 100p dk vio bl 1.00 .60

25th anniversary of the Federico Santa Maria Technical University, Valparaiso.

A souvenir sheet contains one each of Nos. 299, C190-C191, imperf. It was not issued for postal use, though some served postally. Size: 127x160mm. Value, $110.

Mistral Type of Regular Issue, 1958

1958, Jan. 10   Engr.   *Perf. 14*
C192 A144 100p green   .25 .20

Ambrosio O'Higgins — AP51

1958, Mar. 23
C193 AP51 100p lt blue   .25 .20

Founding of the city of Osorno, 500th anniv.

A souvenir sheet contains one each of Nos. 302 and C193, imperf. and printed in red brown. It was not issued for postal use, though some served postally. Size: 155x138mm. Value, $60.

Exhibition Type of Regular Issue

1958, Oct. 18   Unwmk.
C194 A146 50p dull green   .20 .20

A souvenir sheet contains one each of Nos. 303 and C194, imperf. and printed in deep red. It was not issued for postal use, though some served postally. Size: 188x220mm. Value, $48.

Bank Type of Regular Issue, 1958.

1958, Dec. 18   Engr.   *Perf. 14*
C195 A147 50p redsh brown   .20 .20

A souvenir sheet contains one each of Nos. 304 and C195, printed in dull violet, imperf. It was not issued for postal use, though some served postally. Value, $150.

Antarctic Types of Regular Issue

1958   Litho.   *Perf. 14*
C199 A149 20p violet   .30 .20
        Engr.
C200 A150 500p dark blue   3.25 1.50

Symbols of Various Religions AP52

Perf. 14½
1959, Jan. 23   Unwmk.   Engr.
C206 AP52 50p dk car rose   .30 .20

10th anniversary of the Universal Declaration of Human Rights.

Types of 1950-54.

Imprint: "Casa de Moneda de Chile."

Designs: 50p, Plane silhouette over shore. 100p, Plane over map of Antarctica. 200p, Plane over natural arch rock.

1959   Litho.   *Perf. 14*
C207 AP38 1p dk blue grn   .60 .35
  a.   Wmk. 215   30.00
C208 AP38 10p emerald   .40 .20
C209 AP38 20p red brown   .25 .20
C210 AP38 50p yellow grn   .25 .20
C211 AP38 100p car rose   .25 .20
C212 AP38 200p brt blue   .40 .20
    Nos. C207-C212 (6)   2.15 1.35

Carlos Anwandter AP53

1959, June 18   Engr.   *Perf. 14*
C213 AP53 20p rose carmine   .20 .20

Centenary of the German School in Valdivia, founded by Carlos Anwandter.

A souvenir sheet contains one each of Nos. 319 and C213, imperf. It was not issued for

postal use, though some served postally. Value, $60.

IGY Type of Regular Issue, 1958.

1959, Aug. 28   Unwmk.   *Perf. 14*
C214 A148 50p green   .30 .20

Ladrillero Type of Regular Issue

1959, Aug. 28   Litho.
C215 A154 50p green   .25 .20

Barros Arana Type of Regular Issue

1959, Aug. 28
C216 A155 100p purple   .40 .20

Red Cross Type of Regular Issue

1959, Oct. 6
C217 A156 50p red & blk   .25 .20

WRY Type of Regular Issue, 1960.

1960, Apr. 7   Unwmk.   *Perf. 14½*
C218 A160 10c violet   .25 .20

A souvenir sheet contains two stamps similar to Nos. 330 and C218, the 1c printed in blue, the 10c airmail in maroon. The sheet is imperf., printed on thin cardboard. Size: 160x204mm. Value, $110.

Type of Regular Issue, 1960-62, and

José Agustin Eyzaguirre and José Miguel Infante — AP54

Designs: 2c, Palace of Justice. 5c, National memorial. No. C220, Arms of Chile. No. C220A, José Gaspar Marin and J. Gregorio Argomedo. 50c, Archbishop J. I. Cienfuegos and Brother Camilo Henriquez. 1e, Bernardo O'Higgins.

1960-65   Unwmk.   Engr.   *Perf. 14½*
C218A AP54 2c mar & gray vio
             ('62)   .20 .20
C219 A162 5c vio bl & dl pur
             ('61)   .20 .20
          Wmk. 215
C220 A161 10c dk brn & red
             brn   .20 .20
          Unwmk.
C220A AP54 10c vio brn & brn
             ('64)   .40 .25
C220B AP54 20c dk bl & dl pur
             ('64)   .25 .20
C220C AP54 50c dl grn & ind
             ('65)   1.00 .25
C220D A162 1e dk red & red
             brn ('63)   1.00 .40
    Nos. C218A-C220D (7)   3.25 1.70

150th anniv. of the formation of the 1st Natl. Government.

A souvenir sheet contains two airmail stamps: a 5c brown similar to No. C219 (National Memorial) and a 10c green, type A161. The sheet is imperf., printed on heavy paper with papermaker's watermark. Size: 120x168mm. Value, $30.

Map and Rotary Emblem — AP55

1960, Dec. 1   Litho.   *Perf. 14*
C221 AP55 10c blue   .50 .20

South American Rotary Regional Conference, Santiago, 1960.

A souvenir sheet contains one 10c maroon, type AP55, with brown marginal inscription. Size: 118x158mm. Value, $60.

The souvenir sheet was overprinted in green "El Mundo Unida Contra la Malaria" and the outline of a mosquito, and released in October, 1962. Value, $30.

Plane over Mountain Lake — AP56

Designs: 1m, Araucarian pine and plane. 2m, Chilean flag and plane. 3m, Plane and dock crane. 4m, Plane above river (vignette like AP39). 5m, Blast furnace. 2c, Plane over cable cars. 5c, Plane silhouette over shore. 10c, Plane over map of Antarctica. 20c, Plane over natural arch rock.

Imprint: "Casa de Moneda de Chile."

1960-62   Litho.   *Perf. 14*
C222 AP56 1m orange   .20 .20
C223 AP56 2m yellow grn   .20 .20
C224 AP56 3m violet   .20 .20
C225 AP56 4m gray olive   .20 .20
C226 AP56 5m brt bl grn   .20 .20
C227 AP56 1c ultra   .20 .20
C228 AP56 2c red brn ('61)   .25 .20
C229 AP56 5c yel grn ('61)   1.25 .20
C230 AP56 10c car rose ('62)   .30 .20
C231 AP56 20c brt bl ('62)   .35 .20
    Nos. C222-C231 (10)   3.35 2.00

Oil Derricks and Douglas DC-6 — AP57

Beechcraft Monoplane AP58

5m, Train and plane. 2c, Jet plane & Easter Island statue. 5c, Control tower & plane. 10c, Comet airliner. 50c, Douglas DC-6.

Perf. 14x13½
1960-67   Unwmk.   Litho.
C234 AP57 5m red brown   .20 .20
C235 AP57 1c dull blue   .20 .20
C236 AP57 2c ultra ('62)   .20 .20
C237 AP57 5c rose red ('64)   .20 .20
C238 AP57 10c ultra ('67)   .20 .20
C239 AP58 20c car ('62)   .20 .20
C240 AP58 50c green ('63)   .20 .20
    Nos. C234-C240 (7)   1.40 1.40

Stamps similar to type AP58, but inscribed in peso ($) currency, are listed as type AP49.

Congress Type of Regular Issue.

1961, Oct. 5   *Perf. 14½*
C245 A164 10c gray green   .95 .60

Soccer Type of Regular Issue, 1962.

Designs: 5c, Goalkeeper and stadium, vert. 10c, Soccer players and globe.

1962, May 30   Unwmk.   Engr.
C246 A165 5c rose lilac   .20 .20
C247 A165 10c dk carmine   .25 .20

A souvenir sheet of four contains one each of Nos. 340-341, C246-C247, imperf., with light brown marginal inscriptions. Size: 123x194mm. Sold for 7.50 escudos (face value, 22 centavos). Value $12.

Hunger Type of Regular Issue.

20c, Mother with empty bowl, horiz.

1963, Mar. 21   Litho.   *Perf. 14*
C248 A166 20c green   .25 .20

Red Cross Type of Regular Issue.

Design: 20c, Centenary emblem and plane silhouette, horiz.

1963, Sept. 6   Unwmk.   *Perf. 14*
C249 A167 20c gray & red   .25 .20

Fire Engine of 1860's AP59

1963, Dec. 20   Litho.   *Perf. 14½*
C250 AP59 30c red   .50 .20

Centenary of the Santiago Fire Brigade.

Western Hemisphere AP60

1964, Apr. 9   Unwmk.   *Perf. 14½*
C254 AP60 4c ultra   .30 .20

Issued in memory of President John F. Kennedy and to honor the Alliance for Progress.

Battle of Rancagua — AP61

1965, May 7   Engr.   *Perf. 14½*
C255 AP61 5c dull grn & sepia   .30 .20

Battle of Rancagua, 10/7/14, 150th anniv.

ITU Emblem, Old and New Communication Equipment AP62

1965, May 7   Litho.   *Perf. 14½x14*
C256 AP62 40c red & maroon   .30 .20

ITU centenary.

Portrait Type of 1964

Portraits: No. C257, Enrique Molina. No. C258, Msgr. Carlos Casanueva.

1965, June   Litho.   *Perf. 14*
C257 A169 60c brt violet   .30 .20
C258 A169 60c green   .30 .20

See note after No. 346.

Skier Type of Regular Issue 1965

Design: 20c, Skier, horiz.

1965, Aug. 30   Unwmk.   *Perf. 14*
C259 A172 20c ultra   .30 .20

Fishing Boats, Angelmo Harbor AP63   Aviators' Monument AP64

1965
C260 AP63 40c brown   .30 .20
      Perf. 14x14½
C262 AP64 1e car rose   .30 .20

Andrés Bello (1780?-
1865), Venezuela-born
Writer and
Educator — AP65

1965, Nov. 29   Engr.   Unwmk.
C263 AP65 10c dk car rose   .20 .20

Skiers — AP66

Basketball
AP67

1966, Apr. 6   Litho.   Perf. 14
C264 AP66 4e dk bl & red brn   .60 .20

World Skiing Championships, Partillo, Aug. 1966.

1966, Apr. 28
C265 AP67 13c rose carmine   .30 .20

International Basketball Championships.

Slalom
AP68

Perf. 14½x15
1966, July 20   Litho.   Unwmk.
C266 AP68 75c rose car & lil   .40 .20
C267 AP68 3e ultra & lt bl   .40 .20

Intl. Skiing Championships, Partillo, August 1966. A souvenir sheet of 2 contains imperf. stamps similar to Nos. C266-C267. No gum. Size: 109x140mm. Value $36.

Ship Type of Regular Issue
1966   Litho.   Perf. 14½
C268 A175 70c Prus grn & yel grn .25 .20

See note below No. 358.

ICY Type of Regular Issue
1966, Oct. 28   Unwmk.   Perf. 14½
C269 A177 3e blue & carmine   .50 .25

A souvenir sheet of 2 contains imperf. stamps similar to Nos. 360 and C269. No gum. Size: 111x140mm. Value $7.50.

Chilean Flag and
Ships — AP69

1966, Nov. 21   Litho.   Perf. 14
C270 AP69 13c dull red brn   .30 .20

Centenary of the city of Antofagasta.

Pardo Type of Regular Issue

40c, Pardo & map of Chile's claim to Antarctica.

1967, Jan. 6   Unwmk.   Perf. 14½
C271 A178 40c ultra   .30 .20

See note below No. 361.

Family Type of Regular Issue
1967, Apr. 13   Litho.   Perf. 14
C272 A179 80c brt bl & blk   .25 .20

Ruben
Dario
and Title
Page of
"Azul"
AP70

1967, May 15   Engr.   Perf. 14½
C273 AP70 10c dark blue   .30 .20

Ruben Dario (pen name of Felix Ruben Garcia Sarmiento, 1867-1916), Nicaraguan poet, newspaper correspondent and diplomat.

Tree Type of Regular Issue
1967, June 9   Litho.
C274 A180 75c grn & pale rose   .25 .20

Lions Type of Regular Issue
1967   Litho.   Perf. 14
C275 A181 1e purple & yel   .40 .25
C276 A181 5e blue & yel   1.10 .30

A souvenir sheet without franking value contains 3 imperf. stamps, 20c, 1e and 5e, in violet blue and yellow. Size: 110x140mm. Value, $13.50.

Issue dates: 1e, July 12; 5e, Aug. 11.

Flag Type of Regular Issue
1967, Oct. 20   Unwmk.   Perf. 14½
C277 A182 50c ultra & crimson   .25 .20

ITY
Emblem
AP71

1967, Nov. 22   Litho.   Perf. 14½
C278 AP71 30c lt vio bl & blk   .25 .20

Issued for International Tourist Year, 1967.

Caro Type of Regular Issue, 1967.
1967, Dec. 4   Engr.   Perf. 14½
C279 A183 40c violet   .50 .25

Type of Regular Issue, 1968
1968, Apr. 23   Litho.   Perf. 14½
C280 A184 2e brt violet   .60 .25

Sesquicentennial of the Battles of Chacabuco and Maipu. A souvenir sheet of 2 contains imperf. stamps similar to Nos. 367 and C280. Value, $12. A second sheet exists with the 2e in green and the 3e in brown. Size: 139½x100mm. Value, $12.

Farm Type of Regular Issue
1968, June 18   Unwmk.
C281 A185 50c blk, org & grn   .25 .20

Juan I.
Molina,
Educator
and
Scientist
AP72

1968, Aug. 27   Litho.   Perf. 14½
C282 AP72 1e bright green   .30 .20

Map of Chiloé
Province — AP73

British Crown
and Map of
Chile — AP74

Perf. 14½
1968, Oct. 7   Unwmk.   Litho.
C283 AP73 1e rose claret   .20 .20

Anniversaries of the founding of five towns in Chiloé Province.

Auto Club Type of Regular Issue
1968, Nov. 10   Engr.   Perf. 14½x14
C284 A189 5e ultra   .25 .20

1968, Nov. 12   Litho.   Perf. 14½

50c, Chilean coat of arms (horiz.; similar to type A161). 3e, British coat of arms, horiz.

C285 AP74 50c green & brn   .25 .20
C286 AP74 3e bl & org brn   .40 .20

Engr.

C287 AP74 5e purple & mag   .60 .20
  Nos. C285-C287 (3)   1.25 .60

Visit of Queen Elizabeth II of Great Britain, Nov. 11-18. A souvenir sheet of 3 contains imperf., lithographed stamps similar to Nos. C285-C287. Size: 124½x190mm. The souvenir sheet also publicizes the British-Chilean Philatelic Exhibition. Value, $10.

First Coin
Minted in
Chile and
Coin
Press
AP75

Design: 1e, Chile No. 128.

1968, Dec. 31   Litho.   Perf. 14½
C288 AP75 50c ocher & vio brn   .30 .20
C289 AP75 1e lt bl & dp org   .30 .20

225th anniversary of the founding of the State Mint (Casa de Moneda de Chile). A souvenir sheet of 4 contains imperf. stamps similar to Nos. 373-374, C288-C289. Size: 150x119mm. Value, $10.

Satellite Type of Regular Issue
1969, May 20   Litho.   Perf. 14½
C290 A191 2e rose lilac   .30 .20

Red Cross Type of Regular Issue
1969, Sept.   Litho.   Perf. 14½
C291 A192 5e black & red   .50 .20

A souvenir card contains 2 imperf. stamps similar to Nos. 376 and C291, with red marginal inscription. Size: 109x140mm. Value $4.50.

Dam Type of Regular Issue
1969, Nov. 18   Litho.   Perf. 14½
C292 A193 3e blue   .30 .20

Rodriguez Type of Regular Issue
1969, Nov. 24
C293 A194 30c brown   .25 .20

EXPO '70 Type of Regular Issue
1969, Dec. 1   Litho.   Perf. 14
C294 A195 5e red   .25 .20

Bible Type of 1969
1969, Dec. 2   Perf. 14½
C295 A196 1e green   .30 .20

ILO Type of Regular Issue
1969, Dec. 17   Perf. 14½
C296 A197 2e rose lil & blk   .25 .20

Human Rights Year Type of 1969
1969, Dec. 18
C297 A198 4e brown & red   .25 .25

A souvenir sheet of 2 contains imperf. stamps similar to Nos. 382 and C297. Size: 110x140mm. Value, $9.

Easter Island Type of 1970
1970, Jan. 26
C298 A199 50c dull grnsh bl   .30 .20

Ship Type of Regular Issue
1970, Feb. 4   Litho.   Perf. 14½
C299 A200 2e deep ultra   .30 .20

Rotary Type of Regular Issue
1970, Mar. 18   Litho.   Perf. 14
C300 A201 1e rose claret   .35 .25

Gandhi Type of Regular Issue
1970, Apr. 1   Litho.   Perf. 14½
C301 A202 1e red brown   .40 .20

Education Year Type of 1970
1970, July 17   Litho.   Perf. 14½
C302 A204 4e red brown   .30 .25

National Shrine Type of 1970
1970, July 28   Litho.   Perf. 14½
C303 A205 1e ultra   .25 .20

Cancer Type of Regular Issue
1970, Aug. 11
C304 A206 2e brn & lt olive   .40 .20

A few copies are known inscribed "Correos de Chile" instead of "Correos Aereo Chile."

Copper Type of Regular Issue
1970, Oct. 21   Litho.   Perf. 14½
C305 A207 3e grn & lt red brn   .25 .20

United Nations Type of 1970
1970, Oct. 22
C306 A208 5e dk car & grn   .50 .20

Freighter Type of Regular Issue
1971, Jan. 18   Litho.   Perf. 14
C307 A209 5e lt red brown   .40 .20

No. C290 Surcharged in Red
1971, Jan. 21   Litho.   Perf. 14½
C308 A191 52c on 2e rose lil   .40 .20

Liberation Type of Regular Issue
1971, Feb. 3   Litho.   Perf. 14½
C309 A210 1e gray bl & brn   .40 .20

UNICEF Type of Regular Issue
1971, Feb. 11   Litho.   Perf. 14½
C310 A211 2e blue & grn   .30 .20

Boy Scout Type of Regular Issue
1971, Feb. 10   Perf. 14
C311 A212 5c dk car & ol   .40 .20

Satellite Type of Regular Issue
1971, May 25   Litho.   Perf. 14½
C312 A213 2e brown   .30 .20

De Ercilla Type of Regular Issue
1972, Mar. 20   Engr.   Perf. 14
C313 A221 2e Prussian blue   .30 .20

A souvenir card contains impressions of Nos. 414 and C313 with black marginal inscription commemorating España 75 Philatelic Exhibition. Size: 165x220mm.

AIR POST SEMI-POSTAL STAMPS

Catalogue values for unused stamps in this section are for Never Hinged items.

Type of Semi-Postal Stamps, 1961

Portraits: 10c+10c, Alonso de Ercilla. 20c+20c, Gabriela Mistral.

Perf. 13x12½

1961, Apr. 29		**Photo.**		**Unwmk.**
CB1	SP3	10c + 10c salmon &		
		choc	1.00	.30
CB2	SP3	20c + 20c gray & dp cl	1.00	.30

Printed without charge by the Spanish Mint as a gift to Chile. The surtax was to aid the 1960 earthquake victims and to increase teachers' salaries.

ACKNOWLEDGMENT OF RECEIPT STAMPS

AR1

1894		**Unwmk.**		**Perf. 11½**
H1	AR1	5c brown	.75	.50
a.	Imperf., pair		3.00	

The black stamp of design similar to AR1 inscribed "Avis de Paiement" was prepared for use on notices of payment of funds but was not regularly issued.

POSTAGE DUE STAMPS

D1   D2

Handstamped

1894		**Unwmk.**		**Perf. 13**
J1	D1	2c black, *straw*	11.00	5.00
J2	D1	4c black, *straw*	11.00	5.00
J3	D1	6c black, *straw*	11.00	5.00
J4	D1	8c black, *straw*	11.00	5.00
J5	D2	10c black, *straw*	11.00	5.00
J6	D1	16c black, *straw*	11.00	5.00
J7	D1	20c black, *straw*	11.00	5.00
J8	D1	30c black, *straw*	11.00	5.00
J9	D1	40c black, *straw*	11.00	5.00
		Nos. J1-J9 (9)	99.00	45.00
J1a	D1	2c black, *yellow*	45.00	42.50
J2a	D1	4c black, *yellow*	37.50	30.00
J3a	D1	6c black, *yellow*	27.50	25.00
J4a	D1	8c black, *yellow*	11.00	9.00
J5a	D2	10c black, *yellow*	11.00	9.00
J6a	D1	16c black, *yellow*	11.00	9.00
J7a	D1	20c black, *yellow*	11.00	9.00
J8a	D1	30c black, *yellow*	11.00	9.00
J9a	D1	40c black, *yellow*	11.00	9.00
		Nos. J1a-J9a (9)	176.00	151.50

Counterfeits exist.

D3

1895		**Litho.**		**Perf. 11**
J19	D3	1c red, *yellow*	5.00	2.00
J20	D3	2c red, *yellow*	5.00	2.00
J21	D3	4c red, *yellow*	4.25	2.00
J22	D3	6c red, *yellow*	5.00	2.00
J23	D3	8c red, *yellow*	3.25	2.00
J24	D3	10c red, *yellow*	3.25	3.00
J25	D3	20c red, *yellow*	3.25	1.50
J26	D3	40c red, *yellow*	3.25	2.00
J27	D3	50c red, *yellow*	3.25	2.00
J28	D3	60c red, *yellow*	6.50	3.00
J29	D3	80c red, *yellow*	6.50	4.25
J30	D3	1p red, *yellow*	11.00	9.00
		Nos. J19-J30 (12)	55.00	30.00

Nos. J19-J30 were printed in sheets of 100 (10x10) containing all 12 denominations. Counterfeits of Nos. J19-J42 exist.

1896				**Perf. 13½**
J31	D3	1c red, *straw*	.75	.35
J32	D3	2c red, *straw*	.75	.35
J33	D3	4c red, *straw*	1.00	.35
J34	D3	6c red, *straw*	2.00	.75
J35	D3	8c red, *straw*	1.00	.40
J36	D3	10c red, *straw*	.75	.40
J37	D3	20c red, *straw*	.75	.40
J38	D3	40c red, *straw*	12.00	10.00
J39	D3	50c red, *straw*	12.00	10.00
J40	D3	60c red, *straw*	12.00	10.00
J41	D3	80c red, *straw*	12.00	10.00
J42	D3	100c red, *straw*	25.00	21.00
		Nos. J31-J42 (12)	80.00	64.00

D4   D5

1898				**Perf. 13**
J43	D4	1c scarlet	.35	.30
J44	D4	2c scarlet	.90	.60
J45	D4	4c scarlet	.35	.30
J46	D4	10c scarlet	.35	.30
J47	D4	20c scarlet	.35	.30
		Nos. J43-J47 (5)	2.30	1.80

1924				**Perf. 11½, 12½**
J48	D5	2c blue & red	.75	.60
J49	D5	4c blue & red	.75	.60
J50	D5	8c blue & red	.75	.60
J51	D5	10c blue & red	.75	.60
J52	D5	20c blue & red	.75	.60
J53	D5	40c blue & red	.75	.60
J54	D5	60c blue & red	.75	.60
J55	D5	80c blue & red	.75	.60
J56	D5	1p blue & red	1.00	.75
J57	D5	2p blue & red	1.75	1.25
J58	D5	5p blue & red	1.75	1.25
		Nos. J48-J58 (11)	10.50	7.80

Nos. J48-J58 were printed in sheets of 150 containing all 11 denominations, and in sheets of 50 containing the five lower denominations, providing various se-tenants.

All values of this issue exist imperforate, also with center inverted, but are not believed to have been regularly issued. Those with inverted centers sell for about 10 times normal stamps.

OFFICIAL STAMPS

For Domestic Postage

O1

Single-lined frame
Control number in violet

1907		**Unwmk.**		**Imperf.**
O1	O1	dl bl, "CARTA" org	22.50	17.50
O2	O1	red, "OFICIO" bl	22.50	17.50
O3	O1	vio, "PAQUETE" red	22.50	17.50
O4	O1	org, bl, "EP" vio	22.50	17.50
		Nos. O1-O4 (4)	90.00	70.00

The diagonal inscription in differing color indicates type of usage: CARTA for letters of ordinary weight; OFICIO, heavy letters to 100 grams; PAQUETE, parcels to 100 grams; E P (Encomienda Postal), heavier parcels; C (Certificado), as on No. O8, registration including postage.

Varieties include CARTA, PAQUETE and E P inverted, OFICIO omitted, etc.

Double-lined frame
Large control number in black

				Perf. 11
O5	O1	bl, "CARTA" yel	8.00	7.00
O6	O1	red, "OFICIO" bl	8.00	5.25
O7	O1	brn, "PAQUETE"		
		grn	8.00	5.25
O8	O1	grn, "C" red	110.00	82.50
		Nos. O5-O8 (4)	134.00	100.00

Nos. O5-O8 exist in tête bêche pairs; with CARTA, OFICIO or PAQUETE double or inverted, and other varieties.

Counterfeits of Nos. O1-O8 exist.

For Foreign Postage

Regular Issues of 1892-1909 Overprinted in Red — a

On Stamps of 1904-09

1907				**Perf. 12**
O9	A14	1c green	7.50	7.50
a.	Inverted overprint		17.50	
O10	A12	3c on 1p brn	14.00	13.00
a.	Inverted overprint		52.50	
O11	A14	5c ultra	10.00	9.50
a.	Inverted overprint		35.00	
12	A15	10c gray & blk	10.50	10.50
O13	A15	15c vio & blk	14.00	13.00
O14	A15	20c org brn & blk	14.00	14.00
O15	A15	50c ultra & blk	45.00	45.00

On Stamp of 1892
Rouletted

O16	A6	1p dk brn & blk	110.00	87.50
		Nos. O9-O16 (8)	225.00	200.00

Counterfeits of Nos. O9-O16 exist.

Regular Issues of 1915-25 Overprinted in Red or Blue — b

1926				**Perf. 13½x14, 14**
O17	A52	5c slate bl (R)	2.50	.50
O18	A52	10c bl & blk (R)	4.00	.75
O19	A39	20c org red & blk (Bl)	2.00	.40
O20	A42	50c dp grn & blk (R)	2.00	.40
O21	A43	1p grn & blk (R)	2.75	.70
O22	A43	2p ver & blk (Bl)	4.00	1.00
		Nos. O17-O22 (6)	17.25	3.75

Nos. O21 and O22 are overprinted vertically at each side.
Nos. O17 to O22 were for the use of the Biblioteca Nacional.

Regular Issue of 1915-25 Overprinted in Red — c

1928				**Perf. 13½x14, 14**
O23	A50	10c bl & blk	6.50	2.00
O24	A39	20c brn org & blk	3.00	1.00
O25	A40	25c dl bl & blk	7.50	1.00
O26	A42	50c dp grn & blk	4.00	1.00
O27	A43	1p grn & blk	5.00	1.50
		Nos. O23-O27 (5)	26.00	6.50

The overprint on Nos. O23 to O26 is 16½mm high; on No. O27 it is 20mm.

Regular Issues of 1928-30 Overprinted in Red — d

On Stamp Inscribed: "Correos de Chile"

1930-31				
O28	A50	10c bl & blk	3.00	1.50

Wmk. 215
On Stamps Inscribed: "Correos de Chile"

O29	A50	10c bl & blk	6.00	3.00
O30	A39	20c org red & blk	.75	.50
O31	A40	25c bl & blk	.75	.50
O32	A42	50c dp grn & blk	1.50	.75

On Stamps Inscribed: "Chile Correos"

O33	A42	50c dp grn & blk	1.50	.75
O34	A43	1p grn & blk	1.50	.75
		Nos. O28-O34 (7)	15.00	7.75

Same Overprint on No. 181

1933				**Perf. 13½x14**
O35	A61	20c dk brn	.75	.25

Same Overprint in Red on No. 182

1935				**Wmk. 215**
O36	A62	10c deep blue	.75	.50

No. 163 Ovptd. Type "b" in Red
Inscribed: "Correos de Chile"

1934				
O37	A52	5c lt grn	.60	.50

Overprint "b" on No. 182

1935				
O38	A62	10c dp bl	.50	.50

Same Overprint in Black on No. 181

1936		**Wmk. 215**		**Perf. 13½x14**
O39	A61	20c dk brn	10.00	.50

Overprint "b" in Red on No. 158

1938				**Perf. 14**
O40	A43	1p grn & blk	2.50	1.00

Nos. 204 and 205 Overprinted Type "d" in Black

1939				**Perf. 13½x14, 14**
O41	A78	50c violet	4.00	2.50
O42	A84	1p org brn	5.00	4.00

Stamps of 1938-40 Overprinted Type "b" in Black, Red or Blue

1940-46				**Perf. 13½x14, 14**
O43	A78	10c sal pink ('45)	2.00	1.75
O44	A78	15c brn grn	1.00	.40
O45	A78	20c lt bl (R) ('42)	1.50	.60
O46	A78	30c brn pink (Bl)	.75	.40
O47	A78	40c lt grn	.75	.40
O48	A78	50c vio ('45)	4.00	.75
O49	A84	1p org brn ('42)	2.50	.75
O50	A84	1.80p dp bl (R) ('45)	10.00	6.00
O51	A84	2p car lake ('42)	2.00	1.25
		Nos. O43-O51 (9)	24.50	12.30

Overprint "b" in Black on Nos. 223, 225
Unwmk.

O58	A84	1p brn org	2.50	1.50
O59	A84	2p car lake ('46)	5.00	2.00

Regular Issues of 1938-43 Overprinted Diagonally in Carmine, Black or Blue — e

Wmk. 215, Unwmkd.

1948-54				**Perf. 13½x14, 14**
O60	A78	20c lt bl, #219 (C)	.75	.35
O61	A78	30c brt pink, #202 (Bl)		
		('54)	1.50	.50
O62	A78	40c brt grn, #203 ('54)	2.50	1.25
O63	A78	50c vio #222 ('49)	.75	.40
O64	A84	1p org brn, #205	2.50	1.00
O65	A84	2p car lake, #207		
		('54)	1.00	.50
O66	A84	5p dk sl grn, #208		
		(C) ('51)	1.75	1.00
		Nos. O60-O66 (7)	10.75	5.00

Overprint "e" Diagonally on Nos. 265 and 275 in Red or Black
Wmk. 215

1953-55				**Perf. 13½x14, 13x14**
O67	A126	1p dk bl grn, #265 (R)	1.00	.50
O68	A126	1p dk bl grn, #265		
		(Bk) ('55)	.75	.50
O69	A126	1p dk bl grn, #275 (R)		
		('55)	.75	.50
		Nos. O67-O69 (3)	2.50	1.50

Overprint "e" Horizontally on Nos. 207, 209 in Black or Blue

1955-56		**Wmk. 215**		**Perf. 14**
O70	A84	2p car lake ('56)	1.75	.75
O71	A84	10p rose vio (Bl)	2.75	1.75

Overprint "e" Horizontally on Nos. 293-295 and Types of 1956 Regular Issue in Black or Red

1956		**Unwmk.**		**Perf. 14x14½**
O72	A141	2p purple	1.00	.60
O73	A142	3p lt vio bl (R)	3.00	2.00
O74	A141	5p redsh brn	.75	.35
O75	A142	10p vio (19x22¼mm)		
		(R)	3.00	1.75
a.	Perf. 13½x14 (19½x22½mm)			
		('58)	.50	.40
O76	A141	50p rose red	2.50	1.00

No. 310 Overprinted in Red Vertically, Reading Down, Similar to Type "e"

Size of Overprint: 21x2½mm

1958	**Litho.**		**Perf. 14**
O77	A149	10p vio blue	200.00 30.00

Overprint "e" Horizontally on No. 327 in Red

1960	**Unwmk.**		**Perf. 13x14**
O79	A157	5c blue	1.75 .70

POSTAL TAX STAMPS

Talca Issue.

A 10c blue postal tax stamp, inscribed "Bicentenario de Talca" and picturing a coat of arms, was issued in 1942. It was sold only in Talca and was required for a time on all domestic letters sent from that city. The tax helped pay for Talca's bicentenary celebration. Value 20 cents.

Nos. 326 and 347 Surcharged

1970	**Unwmk.**	**Litho.**	**Perf. 14x13**
RA1	A159	10c on 2c ultra	.25 .20
		Perf. 14x14½	
RA2	A170	10c on 6c rose lil	.25 .20

Chilean Arms — PT1

		Perf. 14½x14	
1970, Apr. 23	**Litho.**		**Unwmk.**
RA3	PT1	10c blue	.25 .20

See No. RA6.

No. RA3 Surcharged in Red

a   b

1971-72			
RA4	PT1	(a) 15c on 10c bl	.25 .20
RA5	PT1	(b) 15c on 10c bl ('72)	.25 .20

	Type of 1970		
1972, July	**Litho.**		**Perf. 14½x14**
RA6	PT1	15c rose red	.25 .20

No. RA6 Surcharged in Ultramarine

1972-73			
RA7	PT1	20c on 15c rose red	.25 .20
RA8	PT1	50c on 15c rose red ('73)	.25 .20

No. RA8 has 9 bars instead of 8.

The surtax on Nos. RA1-RA8 was for modernization of postal system. Compulsory on all inland mail.

PARCEL POST POSTAL TAX STAMP

Pres. J. J. Prieto V. — PPT1

	Unwmk.		
1957, Apr. 8	**Litho.**		**Perf. 14**
QRA1	PPT1	15p green	.35 .30

The surtax aided the Prieto Foundation. No. QRA1 was required on parcel post entering or leaving Chile.

CHINA

'chī-nə

LOCATION — Eastern Asia
GOVT. — Republic
AREA — 2,903,475 sq. mi.
POP. — 462,798,093 (1948)

10 Candareen = 1 Mace
10 Mace = 1 Tael
100 Cents = 1 Dollar (Yuan) (1897)

Watermarks

Wmk. 103 — Yin-Yang Symbol

Wmk. 261 — Character Yu (Post) Multiple

Issues of the Imperial Maritime Customs Post

Imperial Dragon — A1

1878	**Unwmk.**	**Typo.**	**Perf. 12½**
	Thin Paper		
	Stamps printed 2½-3¼mm apart		
1	A1	1c green	375.00 300.00
a.		1c dark green	500.00 350.00
2	A1	3c brown red	500.00 225.00
a.		3c vermilion	600.00 275.00
3	A1	5c orange	600.00 225.00
a.		5c bister orange	900.00 350.00

Imperforate essays of Nos. 1-3 have an extra circle near the dragon's lower left foot. Copies with the circle completely or mostly removed are proofs or unfinished stamps.

1882			
	Thin or Pelure Paper		
	Stamps printed 4½mm apart		
4	A1	1c green	400.00 300.00
a.		1c dark green	425.00 325.00
5	A1	3c brown red	750.00 225.00
6	A1	5c orange yellow	9,750. 1,200.

1883	*Rough to smooth Perf. 12½*		
	Medium to Thick Opaque Paper		
	Stamps printed 2½ to 3¼mm apart		
7	A1	1c green	400.00 300.00
a.		1c dark green	475.00 350.00
b.		1c light green	450.00 400.00
c.		Vert. pair, imperf. between	25,000.
8	A1	3c brown red	525.00 225.00
a.		3c vermilion	900.00 250.00
b.		Vert. pair, imperf. between	25,000.
9	A1	5c yellow	900.00 275.00
a.		5c chrome yellow	1,000. 300.00
b.		Horiz. pair, imperf. btwn.	25,000.

Nos. 1-9 were printed from plates of 25, 20 or 15 individual copper dies, but only No. 5 exists in the 15-die setting. Many different printings and plate settings exist. All values occur in a wide variety of shades and papers. The effect of climate on certain papers has produced the varieties on so-called toned papers in Nos. 1-15.

Value for No. 8b is for a damaged copy.

Counterfeits, frequently with forged cancellations, occur in all early Chinese issues.

Imperial Dragon — A2

1885	**Wmk. 103**		**Perf. 12½**
10	A2	1c green	85.00 18.00
a.		Vert. pair, imperf. btwn.	13,000. 13,000.
b.		Horiz. pair, imperf. btwn.	—
11	A2	3c lilac	150.00 24.00
a.		Horiz. pair, imperf. btwn.	16,000. 16,000.
b.		Vert. pair, imperf. btwn.	18,000.
12	A2	5c grnsh yellow	150.00 27.50
a.		5c bister brown	175.00 35.00
b.		Vert. pair, imperf. btwn.	18,000. 18,000.
c.		Horiz. pair, imperf. btwn.	18,000.
		Nos. 10-12 (3)	385.00 69.50

1888			**Perf. 11½-12**
13	A2	1c green	35.00 17.50
14	A2	3c lilac	100.00 12.50
b.		Double impression	975.00
15	A2	5c grnsh yellow	160.00 37.50
b.		Horiz. pair, imperf. vert.	675.00
c.		Double impression	675.00 600.00
		Nos. 13-15 (3)	295.00 67.50

Nos. 10-15 were printed from plates made of 40 individual copper dies, arranged in two panes of 20 each. Several different settings exist of all values.

Imperforates of Nos. 13-15 are considered proofs by most authorities.

Stamps overprinted "Formosa" in English or Chinese are proofs.

For surcharges see Nos. 25-27, 75-77.

"Shou" and "Wu Fu" — A3   Dragon and Hydrangea Leaves — A4

"Pa Kua" Signs in Corners — A5   Dragon and Peony — A6

Carp, the Messenger Fish — A7

Dragon, "Pa Kua" and Immortelle A8   Dragons and "Shou" A9

Dragons and Giant Peony — A10

Junk on the Yangtse A11

1894		**Lithographed in Shanghai**		
16	A3	1c orange red	20.00	27.50
a.		Vert. pair, imperf. btwn.	1,900.	1,750.
b.		Horiz. pair, imperf. btwn.	3,750.	3,750.
c.		Vert. pair, imperf. horiz.	2,750.	2,750.
17	A4	2c green	32.50	16.00
a.		Horiz. pair, imperf. btwn.	2,750.	2,750.
18	A5	3c orange	24.00	10.00
a.		Vert. pair, imperf. btwn.	2,750.	2,750.
b.		Horiz. pair, imperf. btwn.	3,250.	3,250.
19	A6	4c rose pink	110.00	125.00
a.		Horiz. pair, imperf. btwn.	3,000.	
20	A7	5c dull orange	190.00	200.00
a.		Horiz. pair, imperf. btwn.	3,250.	3,250.
21	A8	6c dark brown	40.00	20.00
a.		Vert. pair, imperf. btwn.	6,000.	
b.		Horiz. pair, imperf. btwn.	6,000.	
22	A9	9c dark green	135.00	37.50
a.		Imperf., pair	1,750.	
b.		Horiz. pair, imperf. vert.	3,250.	3,250.
c.		Vert. pair, imperf. horiz.	3,250.	
d.		Vert. pair, imperf. btwn.	3,750.	3,750.
e.		Tete beche pair, vert.	1,100.	1,000.
f.		Tete beche pair, imperf. horiz.	4,500.	
g.		Tete beche pair, imperf. vert.	4,500.	4,500.
h.		Vert. strip of 3, imperf. btwn.	4,500.	
i.		Tete beche pair, imperf. horiz.	1,100.	1,200.
23	A10	12c orange	300.00	190.00
24	A11	24c carmine	425.00	160.00
a.		Vert. pair, imperf. btwn.	6,500.	
		Nos. 16-24 (9)	1,276.	786.00

60th birthday of Tsz'e Hsi, the Empress Dowager. All values exist in several distinct shades.

On Mar. 20, 1896, the Customs Post was changed, by Imperial Edict, effective Jan. 1, 1897, to a National Post and the dollar was adopted as the unit of currency.

Time was required to work out details of the Imperial Post and design new stamps. As a provisional measure, stocks of Nos. 16-24 were ordered surcharged with new values in dollars and cents. It is believed that only the Shanghai office stock of Nos. 16-24 (plus any reserve stock at the printers) was surcharged with small figures of value. Other post offices throughout China were instructed to return all unoverprinted stocks on receipt of the new surcharges.

Early in the year it was apparent that all stamps would be exhausted before the new issues were ready (Nos. 86-97), and since the stones from which Nos. 16-24 had been printed no longer existed, new stones were made from the original transfers. A printing from the new stones was made early in 1897 and surcharged with large figures of value spaced 2½mm below the Chinese characters. During the surcharging, sheets from the 1894 (original) printing were received from outlying post offices and surcharged as they arrived. A small quantity of the 1897 printing reached the public without surcharge (Nos. 16n-24n).

Additional stamps were still required and another printing was made from the new stones and surcharged with large figures, but in a new setting with 1½mm between the Chinese characters and the value. Additional sheets of the 1894 printing were received from the most distant post offices and were also surcharged with the 1½mm setting. Thus there are four different sets of the large-figure surcharges. All these stamps were regularly issued but no attempt was made by the post office to separate printings. Some values are difficult to distinguish as to printing, particularly in used condition.

See No. 73. For surcharges see Nos. 28-31, 74.

1897 Lithographed in Shanghai

16n	A3	1c pink	675.
17n	A4	2c olive green	1,000.
18n	A5	3c chrome yellow	675.
p.		3c yellow buff	900.
19n	A6	4c pale rose	800.
20n	A7	5c yellow	800.
21n	A8	6c red brown	1,000.
22n	A9	9c yellowish green	3,500.
p.		9c emerald green	
23n	A10	12c yellowish orange	3,500.
24n	A11	24c purplish red	2,000.

The colors of the 1897 printings are pale or dull; the gum is thin and white. The 1894 printing has a thicker, yellowish gum.

The set of 9 values on thick unwatermarked paper is a special printing of 5,000 sets ordered by P. G. von Mollendorf, a Customs official, for presentation purposes. Value, set $2,000.

For surcharges see Nos. 47-55, 65-72.

Issues of the Chinese Government Post

Preceding Issues Surcharged in Black

Small Numerals 2½mm Below Chinese Characters
Surcharged on Nos. 13-15

1897, Jan. 2   Perf. 11½-12

25	A2	1c on 1c	35.00	40.00
26	A2	2c on 3c	190.00	85.00
27	A2	5c on 5c	75.00	30.00
Nos. 25-27 (3)			300.00	155.00

Surcharged on Nos. 16-24

28	A5	½c on 3c	17.50	10.00
a.		"1" instead of "½"	350.00	350.00
b.		Horiz. pair, imperf. btwn.	3,000.	
c.		Vert. pair, imperf. horiz.	3,000.	2,250.
d.		Double surcharge	10,000.	10,000.
e.		Vert. pair, imperf. btwn.	3,000.	
f.		Horiz. pair, imperf. btwn.	2,000.	
29	A3	1c on 1c	14.50	11.00
a.		Inverted surcharge	9,000.	3,500.
30	A4	2c on 2c	17.50	7.50
a.		Horiz. pair, imperf. vert.	2,000.	
b.		Vert. pair, imperf. btwn.	2,000.	
c.		Double surcharge	7,500.	
d.		Inverted surcharge	—	15,000.
e.		Horiz. pair, imperf. btwn.	2,000.	
31	A6	4c on 4c	17.50	8.25
a.		Double surcharge	14,000.	14,000.
b.		Vert. pair, imperf. btwn.	3,000.	3,000.
c.		Horiz. pair, imperf. btwn.	3,000.	3,000.
32	A7	5c on 5c	19.00	7.00
a.		Vert. pair, imperf. btwn.	3,000.	3,000.
33	A8	8c on 6c	22.50	8.50
a.		Vert. strip of 3, imperf. btwn.	2,100.	2,100.
b.		Horiz. pair, imperf. btwn.	2,000.	2,000.
34	A8	10c on 6c	72.50	57.50
a.		Horiz. pair, imperf. btwn.	2,100.	2,100.
b.		Horiz. pair, imperf. vert.	2,400.	2,400.
35	A9	10c on 9c	375.00	95.00
a.		Double surcharge	40,000.	40,000.
b.		Inverted surcharge	15,000.	15,000.
36	A10	10c on 12c	325.00	140.00
a.		Vert. pair, imperf. horiz.	1,500.	
b.		Vert. pair, imperf. btwn.	1,500.	1,800.
37	A11	30c on 24c	400.00	175.00
a.		Vert. pair, imperf. btwn.	7,500.	
Nos. 28-37 (10)			1,281.	519.75

Small Numerals 4mm Below Chinese Characters

25a	A2	1c on 1c green	60.00	60.00
28f	A4	½c on 3c orange	50.00	50.00
29b	A3	1c on 1c vermilion	65.00	65.00
30f	A4	2c on 2c dark green	65.00	65.00
31d	A6	4c on 4c dark pink	45.00	45.00
32b	A7	5c on 5c dull orange	45.00	45.00
33d	A8	8c on 6c brown	32.50	32.50
35c	A9	10c on 9c dark green	325.00	325.00
37b	A11	30c on 24c dark red	450.00	450.00

Preceding Issues Surcharged in Black

Large Numerals
Numerals 2½mm below Chinese characters

1897, Mar.
Surcharged on Nos. 16-24

38	A5	½c on 3c	2,250.	800.
b.		Inverted surcharge		4,500.
39	A3	1c on 1c	600.	175.
40	A4	2c on 2c	325.	275.
41	A6	4c on 4c	400.	325.
b.		Horiz. pair, imperf. btwn.	11,000.	
42	A7	5c on 5c	175.	175.
43	A8	8c on 6c	1,400.	1,400.
44	A9	10c on 9c	525.	325.
45	A10	10c on 12c	35,000.	2,500.
46	A11	30c on 24c	1,000.	1,100.
b.		2mm spacing between "30" and "cents."	15,000.	

Same Surcharge on Nos. 16n-24n

47	A5	½c on 3c	17.50	30.00
a.		"cen" for "cent"	850.00	850.00
b.		Vert. pair, imperf. btwn.	1,500.	1,500.
c.		Vert. pair, imperf. horiz.	1,100.	1,100.
d.		As "a" and "c"	9,500.	9,500.
f.		As "a" and "b"	7,500.	7,500.
f.		Horiz. pair, imperf. btwn.	1,900.	1,900.
48	A3	1c on 1c	12.00	8.50
a.		Horiz. pair, imperf. btwn.		2,500.
49	A4	2c on 2c	11.00	6.50
50	A6	4c on 4c	17.50	12.00
a.		Horiz. pair, imperf. btwn.	3,250.	3,250.
b.		Vert. pair, imperf. btwn.		4,000.
51	A7	5c on 5c	30.00	11.00
52	A8	8c on 6c	400.00	225.00
53	A9	10c on 9c	140.00	67.50
a.		10c on 9c emerald	150.00	70.00
b.		Pair, one without surcharge	1,100.	
54	A10	10c on 12c	300.00	60.00
55	A11	30c on 24c	525.00	275.00
a.		2mm spacing btwn "30" and "cents"	1,250.	750.00
b.		Vert. pair, imperf. btwn.	6,250.	

All recorded unused copies of #45 are flawed.

Numerals 1½mm below Chinese characters

1897, May
Surcharged on Nos. 16-24

56	A5	½c on 3c org yel	450.	375.
57	A3	1c on 1c	300.	250.
58	A4	2c on 2c	—	3,500.
59	A6	4c on 4c	250.	200.
60	A7	5c on 5c	150.	140.
61	A8	8c on 6c	1,400.	1,150.
62	A9	10c on 9c	300.	225.
63	A10	10c on 12c	1,300.	950.
64	A11	30c on 24c	27,500.	—

Same Surcharge on Nos. 16n-24n

65	A5	½c on 3c	13.00	14.00
a.		Inverted surcharge	3,000.	3,000.
b.		1½mm spacing	1,500.	1,200.
66	A3	1c on 1c	14.50	8.50
67	A4	2c on 2c	16.50	9.50
a.		Inverted surcharge	8,750.	8,750.
b.		Vert. pair, imperf. btwn.		8,500.
68	A6	4c on 4c	250.00	150.00
a.		Inverted surcharge	1,300.	1,300.
69	A7	5c on 5c	250.00	125.00
70	A9	10c on 9c	160.00	42.50
a.		Inverted surcharge	1,000.	1,000.
71	A10	10c on 12c	325.00	85.00
72	A11	30c on 24c	13,000.	2,600.

Same Surcharge (1½mm Spacing) on Type A12, and

A12   A12a

Redrawn Designs
Printed from New Stones

1897

73	A12	½c on 3c yel	200.00	175.00
a.		½mm spacing	7,000.	7,000.
74	A12a	2c on 2c yel grn	47.50	20.00
a.		Horiz. pair, imperf. btwn.	6,000.	

Nos. 73 and 74 were surcharged on stamps printed from new stones, which differ slightly from the originals. On No. 73 the numeral "3" and symbols in the four corner panels have been enlarged and strengthened. On No. 74, the numeral "2" has a thick, flat base.

Surcharged on Nos. 13-15

75	A2	1c on 1c green	375.00	500.00
76	A2	2c on 3c lilac	800.00	775.00
77	A2	5c on 5c grnsh yel	200.00	350.00

Type A13 Surcharged in Black:

A13   a

b   c

d   e

f   g

1897   Unwmk.   Perf. 12 to 15

78	A13 (a)	1c on 3c red	325.00	200.00
a.		No period after "cent"	375.00	250.00
b.		Central character with large "box"	400.00	350.00
79	A13 (b)	2c on 3c red	600.00	350.00
a.		Inverted surcharge	7,500.	5,000.
b.		Inverted "S" in "CENTS"	700.00	475.00
c.		No period after "CENTS"	700.00	475.00
d.		Comma after "CENTS"	600.00	400.00
e.		Double surcharge	25,000.	25,000.
g.		Dbl. surch., both inverted	50,000.	
g.		Double surch. (blk & grn)	52,500.	
80	A13 (c)	2c on 3c red	400.00	250.00
81	A13 (d)	4c on 3c red	10,000.	7,500.
a.		Double surcharge (blk & vio)	67,500.	50,000.
82	A13 (e)	4c on 3c red	975.00	400.00
83	A13 (f)	$1 on 3c red	325,000.	—
a.		No period after "r"	—	
84	A13 (g)	$1 on 3c red	2,750.	1,250.
85	A13 (g)	$5 on 3c red	20,000.	15,000.
a.		Inverted surcharge	35,000.	22,000.

A few examples of the 3c red exist without surcharge; one canceled. No. 79 with green surcharge is a trial printing. Value for faulty upper left corner block, $190,000.

No. 79g is unique. The only canceled copy of #83 is in a museum.

Dragon — A14   Carp — A15

Wild Goose — A16

"Imperial Chinese Post"
Lithographed in Japan
Perf. 11, 11½, 12

1897, Aug. 16   Wmk. 103

86	A14	½c purple brn	3.75	3.50
a.		Horiz. pair, imperf. btwn.	475.00	
87	A14	1c yellow	5.00	3.00
88	A14	2c orange	4.25	1.75
a.		Vert. pair, imperf. horiz.	450.00	
89	A14	4c brown	8.00	2.75
a.		Horiz. pair, imperf. btwn.	750.00	
90	A14	5c rose red	9.00	3.00
91	A14	10c dk green	24.00	2.75
92	A15	20c maroon	55.00	14.00
93	A15	30c red	90.00	27.50
94	A15	50c yellow grn	65.00	37.50
a.		50c black green	400.00	
b.		50c blue green	725.00	
95	A16	$1 car & rose	210.00	150.00
96	A16	$2 orange & yel	1,250.	1,100.
97	A16	$5 yel grn & pink	875.00	825.00

The inner circular frames and outer frames of Nos. 86-91 differ for each denomination.

No. 97 imperforate was not regularly issued. Copies have been privately perforated and offered as No. 97. Shades occur in most values of this issue.

A17   A18

A19

"Chinese Imperial Post"
Engraved in London

1898		Wmk. 103	Perf. 12 to 16	
98	A17	½c chocolate	2.75	1.50
a.		Vert. pair, imperf. btwn.	700.00	425.00
b.		Horiz. pair, imperf. btwn.	700.00	425.00
99	A17	1c ocher	3.00	1.50
a.		Vert. pair, imperf. btwn.	200.00	200.00
b.		Horiz. pair, imperf. btwn.	300.00	300.00
100	A17	2c scarlet	4.75	1.50
a.		Vert. pair, imperf. btwn.	150.00	150.00
b.		Vert. pair, imperf. vert.	150.00	150.00
101	A17	4c orange brn	5.25	1.50
a.		Vert. pair, imperf. btwn.	300.00	
b.		Horiz. pair, imperf. vert.	225.00	225.00
c.		Horiz. pair, imperf. btwn.	525.00	525.00
d.		Horiz. strip of 3, imperf.	700.00	700.00
102	A17	5c salmon	7.50	1.75
a.		Vert. pair, imperf. btwn.	240.00	240.00
b.		Horiz. pair, imperf. btwn.	275.00	275.00
c.		Vert. pair, imperf. vert.	275.00	275.00
d.		5c pale reddish orange	14.00	3.00
e.		As "d," vert pair, imperf. btwn.	300.00	300.00
103	A17	10c dk blue grn	10.00	1.50
a.		Vert. or horiz. pair, imperf. btwn	—	—
104	A18	20c claret	52.50	7.50
a.		Horiz. pair, imperf. horiz.	600.00	600.00
b.		Vert. pair, imperf. btwn.	600.00	600.00
c.		Vert. pair, imperf. btwn.	675.00	675.00
105	A18	30c dull rose	40.00	10.00
a.		Horiz. pair, imperf. horiz.	675.00	
b.		Vert. pair, imperf. btwn.	675.00	
c.		Vert. pair, imperf. btwn.	675.00	
106	A18	50c lt green	60.00	14.00
a.		Vert. pair, imperf. btwn.	675.00	
107	A19	$1 red & pale rose	225.00	32.50
108	A19	$2 brn, red & yel	375.00	67.50
109	A19	$5 dp grn & sal	650.00	225.00
a.		Horiz. pair, imperf. btwn.		7,500.
b.		Vert. pair, imperf. btwn.		7,750.
		Nos. 98-109 (12)	1,435.	365.75

No. 98 surcharged "B. R. A.-5-Five Cents" in three lines in black or green, was surcharged by British military authorities shortly after the Boxer riots for use from military posts in an

occupied area along the Peking-Mukden railway. Usually canceled in violet.

See note following No. 122.

1900(?)-06		Unwmk.	Perf. 12 to 16	
110	A17	½c brown	1.75	1.50
a.		Horiz. pair, imperf. btwn.	275.00	275.00
b.		Vert. pair, imperf. btwn.	275.00	275.00
111	A17	1c ocher	1.75	1.50
a.		Horiz. pair, imperf. btwn.	190.00	190.00
b.		Vert. pair, imperf. btwn.	190.00	190.00
c.		Horiz. pair, imperf. horiz.	190.00	190.00
112	A17	2c scarlet	3.50	1.50
a.		Horiz. pair, imperf. btwn.	160.00	160.00
b.		Vert. pair, imperf. btwn.	160.00	160.00
c.		Horiz. pair, imperf. horiz.	160.00	160.00
d.		Horiz. pair, imperf. vert.	160.00	160.00
e.		Vert. strip of 3, imperf. btwn.	160.00	160.00
113	A17	4c orange brn	4.25	1.50
a.		Horiz. pair, imperf. btwn.	275.00	275.00
b.		Vert. pair, imperf. btwn.	275.00	275.00
114	A17	5c rose red	24.00	2.75
a.		Vert. pair, imperf. btwn.	260.00	260.00
b.		Horiz. pair, imperf. btwn.	225.00	225.00
115	A17	5c orange	20.00	3.50
a.		5c yellow	175.00	25.00
b.		Vert. pair, imperf. btwn.	300.00	300.00
c.		Horiz. pair, imperf. btwn.	300.00	300.00
116	A17	10c green	15.00	1.50
a.		Horiz. pair, imperf. btwn.	225.00	
b.		Vert. pair, imperf. btwn.	225.00	
c.		Horiz. pair, imperf. horiz.	225.00	
d.		Vert. strip of 3, imperf. btwn.	400.00	
117	A18	20c red brown	24.00	1.75
a.		Horiz. pair, imperf. btwn.	375.00	
b.		Vert. pair, imperf. btwn.	325.00	
c.		Horiz. pair, imperf. horiz.	325.00	
118	A18	30c dull red	24.00	1.50
a.		Vert. pair, imperf. btwn.	675.00	
119	A18	50c yellow grn	40.00	2.50
a.		Horiz. pair, imperf. btwn.	850.00	
120	A19	$1 red & pale rose ('06)	150.00	19.00
121	A19	$2 brn red & yel ('06)	350.00	45.00
122	A19	$5 dp grn & sal	550.00	200.00
		Nos. 110-122 (13)	1,208.	283.50

See #124-130. For surcharges and overprints see #123, 134-177, J1-J6, Offices in Tibet 1-11.

Diagonal Half of No. 112 Surcharged on Stamp and Envelope

Postage 1 Cent Paid

1903
123	A17	1c on half of 2c scarlet, on cover		1,500.

Used Oct. 22 to Oct. 24. Value is for cover mailed to post office other than sending office (Foochow) and bearing backstamp showing arrival date. Locally addressed or unaddressed covers without backstamps properly used are worth approximately $1,000. Others are worth less.

Forgeries are plentiful, particularly on pieces of cover. Certificates of authenticity are mandatory.

1905-10
124	A17	2c green ('08)	2.50	1.50
a.		Horiz. pair, imperf. btwn.	300.00	300.00
b.		Vert. pair, imperf. btwn.	300.00	300.00
c.		Vert. pair, imperf. vert.	300.00	300.00
d.		Horiz. strip of 4, imperf. btwn.	675.00	675.00
125	A17	3c slate grn ('10)	3.75	1.50
a.		Horiz. pair, imperf. btwn.	225.00	
b.		Vert. pair, imperf. btwn.	225.00	
126	A17	4c vermilion ('09)	5.00	1.40
127	A17	5c violet	6.50	1.50
a.		5c lilac	7.50	1.50
b.		Horiz. pair, imperf. btwn.	325.00	
c.		Vert. pair, imperf. btwn.	325.00	
d.		Vert. pair, imperf. vert.	275.00	
128	A17	7c maroon ('10)	12.50	7.50
129	A17	10c ultra ('08)	16.50	1.50
a.		Horiz. pair, imperf. btwn.	325.00	
b.		Vert. pair, imperf. btwn.	325.00	
c.		Vert. pair, imperf. btwn.	300.00	300.00
130	A18	16c olive grn ('07)	52.50	12.50
		Nos. 124-130 (7)	99.25	27.40

Temple of Heaven, Peking — A20

1909			Perf. 14	
131	A20	2c orange & green	5.25	7.00
132	A20	3c orange & blue	7.50	17.50
133	A20	7c orange & brn vio	11.00	8.50
		Nos. 131-133 (3)	23.75	33.00

1st year of the reign of Hsuan T'ung, who later became Henry Pu-yi and then Emperor Kang Teh of Manchukuo.

Stamps of 1902-10 Overprinted with Chinese Characters
Foochow Issue

Overprinted in Red or Black

立中臨時

1912			Perf. 12 to 16	
134	A17	3c slate grn (R)	250.	125.
135	A19	$1 red & pale rose	2,750.	2,500.
136	A19	$2 brn red & yel	4,000.	3,500.
137	A19	$5 dp grn & sal	5,000.	4,000.

The overprint "Ling Shih Chung Li" or "Provisional Neutrality," signified that the P.O. was conducted neutrally by agreement between the Manchu and opposing forces.

Nanking Issue

Overprinted in Red or Black

138	A17	1c ocher (R)	250.	160.
139	A17	3c slate grn (R)	225.	150.
140	A17	7c maroon	500.	350.
141	A18	16c olive grn (R)	2,250.	2,250.
142	A18	50c yellow grn (R)	2,250.	2,000.
143	A19	$1 red & pale rose	2,250.	1,750.
144	A19	$2 brn red & yel	4,250.	4,250.
145	A19	$5 dp green & sal	9,500.	9,500.

Vertical overprint reads: "Chung Hwa Min Kuo" (Republic of China).
Stamps of this issue were also used in Shanghai and Hankow.
Additional values were overprinted but not issued. Excellent forgeries of the overprints of Nos. 134-145 exist.

Issues of the Republic

Overprinted in Black or Red

Overprinted by the Maritime Customs Statistical Department, Shanghai

146	A17	½c brown	1.00	.80
a.		Inverted overprint	37.50	37.50
b.		Double overprint	95.00	
147	A17	1c ocher (R)	1.60	.80
a.		Vert. pair, imperf. horiz.	190.00	190.00
b.		Inverted overprint	150.00	95.00
c.		Double overprint	190.00	150.00
d.		Horiz. pair, imperf. btwn.	275.00	240.00
e.		Horiz. pair, imperf. vert.	140.00	
f.		Pair, one without overprint	140.00	
148	A17	2c green (R)	1.75	1.00
a.		Vert. pair, imperf. btwn.	190.00	190.00
149	A17	3c slate grn (R)	2.40	.75
a.		Inverted overprint	100.00	60.00
b.		Horiz. or vert. pair, imperf. btwn	275.00	275.00
d.		Horiz. pair, imperf. vert.	110.00	
150	A17	4c vermilion	3.75	.90
a.		Vert. pair, imperf. btwn.	750.00	
151	A17	5c violet (R)	5.00	.90
a.		Horiz. pair, imperf. btwn.		
152	A17	7c maroon	6.75	2.75
153	A17	10c ultra (R)	7.00	.90
a.		Double overprint	190.00	
b.		Pair, one without overprint	700.00	
c.		Brownish red overprint	20.00	8.50
d.		Inverted overprint	240.00	240.00
154	A18	16c olive grn (R)	17.50	6.50
155	A18	20c red brown	14.00	3.75
156	A18	30c rose red	18.50	4.50
157	A18	50c yel grn (R)	30.00	4.50
158	A19	$1 red & pale rose	225.00	22.50
a.		Inverted overprint		8,250.
159	A19	$2 brn red & yel	175.00	47.50
a.		Inverted overprint	400.00	400.00
160	A19	$5 dp grn & sal	425.00	400.00
		Nos. 146-160 (15)	934.25	498.05

Stamps with blue overprint similar to the preceding were not an official issue but were privately made by a printer in Tientsin.

Overprinted in Red

中華民國

Overprinted by the Commercial Press, Shanghai

This type differs in that the top character is shifted slightly to right and the bottom character is larger and has small "legs".

161	A17	1c ocher	5.50	1.00
a.		Inverted overprint	375.00	375.00
b.		Vert. pair, imperf. btwn.	450.00	
c.		Double overprint	450.00	
162	A17	2c green	32.50	2.25
a.		Inverted overprint	1,100.	900.00
b.		Vert. pair, imperf. btwn.	260.00	
c.		Horiz. pair, imperf. btwn.	300.00	
d.		Horiz. strip of 3, imperf.	475.00	

中華民國

Overprinted in Blue, Carmine or Black

Overprinted by Waterlow & Sons, London

163	A17	½c brown (Bl)	1.00	.80
a.		Vert. pair, imperf. btwn.	1,050.	1,050.
164	A17	1c ocher (C)	1.00	.80
a.		Horiz. pair, imperf. btwn.	190.00	
165	A17	2c green (C)	2.25	.90
166	A17	3c slate grn (C)	2.40	1.00
a.		Inverted overprint		1,600.
167	A17	4c vermilion (Bk)	4.00	1.00
168	A17	5c violet (C)	4.50	1.10
169	A17	7c maroon (Bk)	27.50	16.50
170	A17	10c ultra (C)	13.50	4.00
a.		Vert. pair, imperf. btwn.	525.00	525.00
171	A18	16c olive grn (R)	37.50	11.00
172	A18	20c red brn (Bk)	24.50	2.75
173	A18	30c dull red (Bk)	72.50	5.75
174	A18	50c yellow grn (R)	100.00	12.00
175	A19	$1 red & pale rose (Bk)	150.00	15.00
176	A19	$2 brn red & yel (Bk)	325.00	175.00
177	A19	$5 dp grn & sal (C)	500.00	475.00
		Nos. 163-177 (15)	1,265.	720.85

Due to instructions issued to postmasters throughout China at the time of the Revolution, a number of them prepared unauthorized overprints using the same characters as the overprints prepared by the government. While many were made in good faith, some, like the blue overprints from Tientsin, were bogus, and the status of certain others is extremely dubious.

Dr. Sun Yat-sen — A21

1912, Dec. 14			Perf. 14½	
178	A21	1c orange	2.25	2.75
179	A21	2c yellow grn	2.25	2.75
180	A21	3c slate grn	2.25	2.75
181	A21	5c rose lilac	4.00	3.25
182	A21	8c dp brown	4.00	3.25
183	A21	10c dull blue	4.00	3.25
184	A21	16c olive grn	13.00	12.00
185	A21	20c maroon	15.00	7.50
186	A21	50c dk green	50.00	25.00
187	A21	$1 brown red	130.00	40.00
188	A21	$2 yellow brn	375.00	250.00
189	A21	$5 gray	125.00	175.00
		Nos. 178-189 (12)	726.75	526.75

Honoring the leader of the Revolution.

President Yuan Shih-kai — A22

1912, Dec. 14				
190	A22	1c orange	1.25	1.25
191	A22	2c yellow green	1.25	1.25
192	A22	3c slate green	1.25	1.25
193	A22	5c rose lilac	1.40	1.40
194	A22	8c deep brown	5.75	3.25

195	A22	10c dull blue	4.25	2.00
196	A22	16c olive green	5.00	5.75
197	A22	20c maroon	4.00	4.00
198	A22	50c dark green	27.50	16.00
199	A22	$1 brown red	80.00	40.00
200	A22	$2 yellow brown	100.00	40.00
201	A22	$5 gray	325.00	250.00
		Nos. 190-201 (12)	556.65	366.15

Honoring the 1st pres. of the Republic.

Junk — A24

Reaping Rice — A25

Gateway, Hall of Classics, Peking — A26

DESIGN A24

London Printing: Vertical shading lines under top panel fine, junk with clear diagonal shading lines on sails, right pennant of junk usually long, lines in water weak except directly under junk.

Peking Printing: Vertical shading lines under top panel and inner vertical frame line much heavier, water and sails of junk more evenly and strongly colored, white wave over "H" of "CHINA" pointed upward, touching the junk.

DESIGN A25

London: Front hat brim thick and nearly straight, left foot touches shadow.

Peking: Front hat brim thin and strongly upturned, left foot and sickle clearly outlined in white, shadow of middle tree lighter than those of the right and left trees.

DESIGN A26

London: Light colored walk clearly defined almost to the doorway, figure in right doorway "T" shaped with strong horizontal cross-bar, white panel in base of central tower rectangular, vertical stroke in top left character uniformly thick at its base, tree to right of doorway ends in minute dots.

Peking: Walk more heavily shaded near doorway, especially at right; figure in right doorway more like a "Y", white panel at base of central tower is a long oval, right vertical stroke in top left character incurved near its base, tree at right has five prominent dots at top.

London Printing: By Waterlow & Sons, London, perf. 14 to 15.

Peking Printing: By the Chinese Bureau of Engraving and Printing, Peking, perf. 14.

London Printing

1913, May 5   **Perf. 14-15**

202	A24	½c black brn	.55	.35
a.		Horiz. or vert. pair, imperf. btwn.	190.00	
203	A24	1c orange	.55	.35
a.		Horiz. pair, imperf. btwn.	225.00	
b.		Vert. pair, imperf. btwn.	150.00	
c.		Horiz. strip of 5, imperf. btwn	600.00	
204	A24	2c yellow grn	1.75	.35
a.		Horiz. pair, imperf. btwn.	375.00	
205	A24	3c blue grn	4.75	.35
a.		Horiz. pair, imperf. btwn.	190.00	
b.		Vert. pair, imperf. btwn.		375.00
206	A24	4c scarlet	7.25	.60
207	A24	5c rose lilac	17.50	.50
208	A24	6c gray	3.25	.75
209	A24	7c violet	14.00	7.25
210	A24	8c brown org	27.50	1.75
211	A24	10c dk blue	24.00	.75
a.		Horiz. pair, imperf. btwn.	350.00	350.00
b.		Vert. pair, imperf. btwn.	375.00	275.00
212	A25	15c brown	21.00	4.75
213	A25	16c olive grn	10.00	1.50
214	A25	20c brown red	17.50	2.00
215	A25	30c brown vio	20.00	1.25
a.		Horiz. pair, imperf. btwn.	375.00	375.00
216	A25	50c green	37.50	2.75
217	A26	$1 ocher & blk	100.00	3.75
218	A26	$2 blue & blk	175.00	12.50
219	A26	$5 scarlet & blk	275.00	90.00
220	A26	$10 yel grn & blk	900.00	750.00
		Nos. 202-220 (19)	1,657.	881.50

First Peking Printing

1915   **Perf. 14**

221	A24	½c black brn	.45	.20
222	A24	1c orange	.45	.20
223	A24	2c yellow grn	.85	.20
224	A24	3c blue grn	.85	.20
225	A24	4c scarlet	9.25	.20
226	A24	5c rose lilac	3.75	.20
a.		Booklet pane of 4	110.00	
227	A24	6c gray	9.25	.25
228	A24	7c violet	11.00	3.75

229	A24	8c brown org	6.25	.25
230	A24	10c dk blue	7.25	.45
a.		Booklet pane of 4	110.00	
231	A25	15c brown	21.00	4.00
232	A25	16c olive grn	7.75	.45
233	A25	20c brown red	8.75	.45
234	A25	30c brown vio	7.75	.45
235	A25	50c green	22.00	.45
236	A26	$1 ocher & blk	75.00	.70
237	A26	$2 blue & blk	175.00	2.75
a.		Center inverted	20,000.	
238	A26	$5 scarlet & blk	450.00	27.50
239	A26	$10 yel grn & blk	700.00	200.00
		Nos. 221-239 (19)	1,516.	242.65

1919

240	A24	1½c violet	1.65	.40
241	A25	13c brown	4.00	.45
242	A26	$20 yellow & blk	2,750.	2,000.

Nos. 226 and 230 overprinted in red with five characters in vertical column were for postal savings use.

The higher values of the 1913-19 issues are often overprinted with Chinese characters, which are the names of various postal districts. Stamps were frequently stolen while in transit to post offices. The overprints served to protect them, since the stamps could only be used in the districts for which they were overprinted.

Compare designs A24-A26 with designs A29-A31. For surcharges and overprints see Nos. 247, 288, B1-B3, Sinkiang 1-38.

Yeh Kung-cho, Hsu Shi-chang and Chin Yun-peng A27

1921, Oct. 10

243	A27	1c orange	5.00 1.75
244	A27	3c blue green	5.50 1.50
245	A27	6c gray	6.50 3.50
246	A27	10c blue	7.50 3.00
		Nos. 243-246 (4)	24.50 9.75

National Post Office, 25th anniversary.
For overprints see Sinkiang Nos. 39-42.

No. 224 Surcharged in Red

1922

247	A24	2c on 3c blue green	3.00 .60
a.		Inverted surcharge	20,000.

Second Peking Printing

A29

A30

A31

Types of 1913-19 Issues Re-engraved

Type A29: Most of the whitecaps in front of the junk have been removed and the water made darker. The shading lines have been removed from the arabesques and pearls above the top inscription. The inner shadings at the top and sides of the picture have been cut away.

Type A30: The heads of rice in the side panels have a background of crossed lines instead of horizontal lines. The Temple of Heaven is strongly shaded and has a door. There are rows of pearls below the Chinese characters in the upper corners. The arabesques above the top inscription have been altered and are without shading lines.

Type A31: The curved line under the inscription at top is single instead of double. There are four vertical lines, instead of eight, at each side of the picture. The trees at the sides of

the temple had foliage in the 1913-19 issues, but now the branches are bare. There are numerous other alterations in the design.

1923   **Perf. 14**

248	A29	½c black brown	.90	.20
a.		Horiz. pair, imperf. btwn.	165.00	165.00
b.		Horiz. pair, imperf. vert.	140.00	140.00
249	A29	1c orange	.55	.20
a.		Imperf., pair	110.00	
b.		Horiz. pair, imperf. vert.	110.00	
c.		Booklet pane of 6	90.00	
d.		Booklet pane of 4	45.00	
250	A29	1½c violet	1.75	.70
251	A29	2c yellow grn	1.00	.20
252	A29	3c blue green	2.75	.20
a.		Booklet pane of 6	75.00	
253	A29	4c gray	12.50	.60
254	A29	5c claret	1.75	.35
a.		Booklet pane of 4	90.00	
255	A29	6c scarlet	4.00	.35
256	A29	7c violet	4.00	.35
257	A29	8c orange	8.00	.35
258	A29	10c blue	6.75	.25
a.		Booklet pane of 6	110.00	
b.		Booklet pane of 2	140.00	
259	A30	13c brown	14.00	.45
260	A30	15c dp blue	4.50	.45
261	A30	16c olive grn	5.50	.45
262	A30	20c brown red	4.00	.30
263	A30	30c purple	14.00	.30
264	A30	50c dp green	27.50	.45
265	A31	$1 org brn & sep	27.50	.55
266	A31	$2 blue & red brn	37.50	.80
267	A31	$5 red & slate	65.00	3.25
268	A31	$10 green & claret	325.00	22.50
269	A31	$20 plum & blue	600.00	125.00
		Nos. 248-269 (22)	1,168.	178.25

Nos. 249 and 275 exist with webbing watermark from experimental printing.

To prevent speculation and theft, the dollar denominations were overprinted with single characters in red for use in Kwangsi ($1-$20) and Kweichow ($1-$5).

See Nos. 275, 324. For surcharges and overprints see Nos. 274, 289, 311, 325, 330, 339-340, Szechwan 1-3, Yunnan 1-20, Manchuria 1-20, Sinkiang 47-69, 114, C1-C4.

Temple of Heaven, Peking — A32

1923, Oct. 17   **Perf. 14**

270	A32	1c orange	4.00 .95
271	A32	3c blue green	4.50 2.00
272	A32	4c red	9.00 2.25
273	A32	10c blue	14.00 2.75
		Nos. 270-273 (4)	31.50 7.95

Adoption of Constitution, October, 1923.
For overprints see Sinkiang Nos. 43-46.

No. 253 Surcharged in Red

1925

274	A29	3c on 4c gray	2.25 .30
a.		Inverted surcharge	22,500. 10,000.
b.		Vert. pair, imperf. btwn.	

Junk Type of 1923

1926

275	A29	4c olive green	1.25 .20
a.		Horiz. pair, imperf. vert.	175.00
b.		Horiz. pair, imperf. btwn.	175.00
c.		Horiz. strip of 3, imperf. btwn.	225.00

Marshal Chang Tso-lin — A34

President Chiang Kai-shek — A35

1928, Mar. 1   **Perf. 14**

276	A34	1c brown orange	1.10 1.25
277	A34	4c olive green	2.75 3.00
278	A34	10c dull blue	6.75 4.00
279	A34	$1 red	50.00 55.00
		Nos. 276-279 (4)	60.60 63.25

Assumption of office by Marshal Chang Tso-lin. The stamps of this issue were only available for postage in the Provinces of Chihli and Shantung and at the Offices in Manchuria and Sinkiang.

For overprints see Manchuria Nos. 21-24, Sinkiang 70-73.

1929, May

280	A35	1c brown orange	.85 .35
281	A35	4c olive green	1.25 .65
282	A35	10c dark blue	10.00 1.00
283	A35	$1 dark red	67.50 50.00
		Nos. 280-283 (4)	79.60 52.00

Unification of China.
For overprints see Yunnan Nos. 21-24, Manchuria 25-28, Sinkiang 74-77.

Sun Yat-sen Mausoleum, Nanking — A36

1929, May 30   **Perf. 14**

284	A36	1c brown orange	1.00 .75
285	A36	4c olive green	.90 1.25
286	A36	10c dark blue	5.50 2.25
287	A36	$1 dark red	62.50 30.00
		Nos. 284-287 (4)	69.90 34.25

The transfer of Dr. Sun Yat-sen's remains from Peiping to the mausoleum at Nanking.
For overprints see Yunnan Nos. 25-28, Manchuria 29-32, Sinkiang 78-81.

256

CHINA

Nos. 224 and 252
Surcharged in Red

1930
288 A24 1c on 3c blue green 1.10 2.00
289 A29 1c on 3c blue green .85 .35
a. No period after "Ct" 17.50 17.50

See Nos. 311, 325, 330.

Dr. Sun Yat-
sen — A37

Type I — Double-lined circle in the sun.
Type II — Heavy, single-lined circle in the
sun.

Printed by De la Rue & Co., Ltd.,
London
Perf. 11½x12½, 12½x13, 12½, 13½
1931, Nov. 12   Engr.
Type I
290 A37 1c orange .50 .30
291 A37 2c olive green .60 .40
292 A37 4c green 1.25 .30
293 A37 20c ultra 1.25 .30
294 A37 $1 org brn & dk brn 9.50 .50
295 A37 $2 blue & org brn 25.00 2.75
296 A37 $5 red & blk 37.50 4.50
Nos. 290-296 (7) 75.35 9.05

1931-37
Type II
297 A37 2c olive grn .35 .20
298 A37 4c green .60 .20
299 A37 5c green ('33) .35 .20
300 A37 15c dk green 4.00 1.25
301 A37 15c scarlet ('34) .40 .20
302 A37 20c ultra ('37) .75 .20
303 A37 25c ultra .40 .40
304 A37 $1 org brn & dk brn 10.00 .50
305 A37 $2 blue & org brn 18.00 .90
306 A37 $5 dull red & blk 37.50 4.50
Nos. 297-306 (10) 72.35 8.25

Stamps issued prior to 1933 were printed by
a wet-paper process, and owing to shrinkage
such stamps are 1-1½mm narrower than the
later dry-printed stamps.
Early printings are perf. 12½x13. Nos. 304,
305 and 306 were later perf. 11½x12½.
See #631-635. For surcharges and overprints see #341, 343, 678, 682, 684-685, 689-
691, 768, 843, 1N1, 2N1-2N5, 2N57-2N59,
2N83-2N84, 2N101-2N106, 2N116, 2N124-
2N126, 3N1-3N5, 4N1-4N5, 5N1-5N4, 6N1-
6N5, 7N1-7N4, 7N54, 8N2-8N3, 8N43-8N44,
8N54, 8N57, 8N69-8N71, 8N85, 9N1-9N5,
Taiwan 19, 21-22, Northeastern Provinces 44,
Szechwan 4-11, Yunnan 29-44, Sinkiang 82-
97.

"Nomads in the
Desert" — A38

1932   Unwmk.   Perf. 14
307 A38 1c deep orange 25.00 25.00
308 A38 4c olive green 25.00 25.00
309 A38 5c claret 25.00 25.00
310 A38 10c deep blue 25.00 25.00
Nos. 307-310 (4) 100.00 100.00

Northwest Scientific Expedition of Sven
Hedin. A small quantity of this issue was sold
at face at Peking and several other cities. The
bulk of the issue was furnished to Hedin and
sold at $5 (Chinese) a set for funds to finance
the expedition.

#252 Surcharged in Black Like #288
1932
311 A29 1c on 3c blue green 2.00 1.10

Martyrs Issue

Teng Keng   Ch'en Ying-shih
A39   A40

Chu Chih-hsin   Sung Chiao-
A45   jen A46

Huang Hsing   Liao Chung-
A47   kai A48

1932-34   Perf. 14
312 A39 ½c black brown .20 .20
313 A40 1c orange ('34) .20 .20
314 A39 2½c rose lilac ('33) .20 .20
315 A48 3c dp brown ('33) .20 .20
316 A45 8c brown orange .35 .20
317 A46 10c dull violet .40 .20
318 A45 13c blue green .50 .20
319 A46 17c brown olive .40 .20
320 A47 20c brown red .80 .20
321 A48 30c brown violet 1.25 .20
322 A47 40c orange .95 .20
323 A40 50c green ('34) 3.50 .50
Nos. 312-323 (12) 8.95 2.75

Perfs. 12 to 13 and compound and with
secret marks are listed as Nos. 402-439. No.
316 re-drawn is No. 485.
For overprints and surcharge see Nos. 342,
472, 474, 478-479, 486-487, 490, 531-536,
539-541, 544-549, 616, 619, 622-624, 647-
659, 662-665, 669, 672, 698, 704, 711,
713-715, 720-721, 831, 846-847, 867, 870,
872, 881-882, J120-J121, 1N14-1N15, 1N59,
2N6-2N9, 2N32-2N56, 2N60, 2N76-2N82,
2N85, 2N87-2N90, 2N107-2N115, 2N118,
2N121-2N123, 3N6-3N10, 3N34-3N55, 3N59,
4N6-4N9, 4N39-4N64, 4N69, 5N5-5N8, 5N34-
5N60, 5N65, 6N6-6N8, 6N35-6N61, 6N66,
7N5-7N7, 7N30-7N53, 7N55, 7N59, 8N1-8N4,
8N28-8N42, 8N45, 8N47-8N50, 8N60-8N61,
8N68, 8N73, 8N76-8N79, 8N89, 8N97, 8N99-
8N100, 8N103-8N104, 9N72-9N77, Taiwan
14-17, 20, 28A, 74, Northeastern Provinces 6-
8, 11, Szechwan 12-23, Yunnan 49-60, Sinkiang 102-113, 140-161, 197.

Junk Type of 1923 Issue
1933   Perf. 14
324 A29 6c brown 19.00 1.25

#275 Surcharged in Red Like #288
1933
325 A29 1c on 4c olive green 1.50 .30
a. No period after "Ct" 19.00 19.00

Tan Yuan-
chang — A49

1933, Jan. 9
326 A49 2c olive green 2.25 .35
327 A49 5c green 2.25 .35
328 A49 25c ultra 7.00 1.50
329 A49 $1 red 65.00 27.50
Nos. 326-329 (4) 76.50 29.70

Tan Yuan-chang, more commonly known as
Tan Yen-kai, a prominent statesman in China
since the revolution of 1912 and Pres. of the
Executive Dept. of the Natl. Government.
Placed on sale Jan. 9, 1933, the date of the
ceremony in celebration of the completion of
the Tan Yuan-chang Memorial Hall and Tomb
at Mukden.

For overprints see Yunnan Nos. 45-48, Sinkiang 98-101.

#251 Surcharged in Red Like #288
1935   Perf. 14
330 A29 1c on 2c yellow grn 2.25 .20

Emblem of New   Four Virtues of
Life Movement   New Life
A50   A51

Lighthouse — A52

1936, Jan. 1
331 A50 2c olive green .90 .75
332 A50 5c green 1.00 .25
333 A51 20c dark blue 5.00 .70
334 A52 $1 rose red 32.50 8.00
Nos. 331-334 (4) 39.40 9.70

"New Life" movement.

Methods of
Mail
Transportation
A53

Maritime
Scene — A54

Shanghai
General Post
Office — A55

Ministry of Communications,
Nanking — A56

1936, Oct. 10
335 A53 2c orange .40 .40
336 A54 5c green .50 .20
337 A55 25c blue 4.00 .45
338 A56 $1 dk carmine 25.00 7.00
Nos. 335-338 (4) 29.90 8.05

Founding of the Chinese PO, 40th anniv.

Nos. 260 and 261
Surcharged in Red

1936, Oct. 11
339 A30 5c on 15c dp blue 1.00 .35
340 A30 5c on 16c olive grn 3.00 .85

No. 298 Surcharged in
Red

1937
341 A37 1c on 4c green, type II 1.00 .40
a. Upper left character missing

Nos. 322 and 303
Surcharged in Black or
Red

1938   Perf. 12½, 14
342 A47 8c on 40c orange (Bk) 1.50 .75
343 A37 10c on 25c ultra (R) 1.00 .40

Dr. Sun Yat-
sen — A57

Type I — Coat button half circle. Six lines of
shading above head. Top frame partially
shaded with vertical lines.
Type II — Coat button complete circle. Nine
lines of shading above head. Top frame partially shaded with vertical lines.
Type III — Coat button complete circle. Nine
lines of shading above head. Top frame line
fully shaded with vertical lines.

Printed by the Chung Hwa Book Co.
1938   Unwmk.   Engr.   Perf. 12½
Type I
344 A57 $1 henna & dk brn 75.00 10.00
345 A57 $2 dp blue & org brn 14.00 3.50
346 A57 $5 red & grnsh blk 125.00 16.50
Nos. 344-346 (3) 214.00 30.00

1939
Type II
347 A57 $1 henna & dk brn 14.00 .75
348 A57 $2 dp blue & org brn 17.50 4.00

1939-43
Type III
349 A57 2c olive green .20 .20
350 A57 3c dull claret .20 .20
351 A57 5c green .20 .20
352 A57 5c olive green .20 .20
353 A57 8c olive green .20 .20
354 A57 10c green .20 .20
355 A57 15c scarlet 1.10 2.00
356 A57 15c dk vio brn ('43) 15.00 30.00
357 A57 16c olive gray 1.50 .40
358 A57 25c dk blue .35 .70
359 A57 $1 henna & dk brn 1.75 .70
360 A57 $2 dp blue & org brn 3.50 .50
a. Imperf., pair 275.00
361 A57 $5 red & grnsh blk 2.25 .50
362 A57 $10 dk green & dull pur 15.00 2.00
363 A57 $20 rose lake & dk blue 55.00 45.00
Nos. 349-363 (15) 96.65 83.00

Several values exist imperforate, but these
are not regularly issued. No. 361 imperforate
is printer's waste.
See Nos. 368-401, 506-524. For surcharges
and overprints see Nos. 440-448, 473, 475-
477, 480-481, 482-484, 489, 537-538, 615,
618, 620, 660-661, 664, 666-668, 673-676,
680-681, 686, 688, 699-703, 707-709, 717,
719, 830, J67-J68, M2, M11-M12, 1N2-1N13,
1N23-1N42, 1N57-1N58, 2N10-2N31, 2N61-
2N75, 2N86, 2N91-2N93, 2N117, 2N119-
2N120, 3N11-3N33, 3N56-3N58, 3N60-3N61,
4N10-4N38, 4N65-4N68, 4N70-4N71, 5N9-
5N33, 5N61-5N64, 5N66-5N68, 6N9-6N34,
6N62-6N65, 6N67-6N69, 7N8-7N29, 7N56-
7N58, 7N60-7N61, 8N5-8N27, 8N46, 8N51-
8N53, 8N55-8N56, 8N58-8N59, 8N62-8N67,
8N72, 8N74-8N75, 8N80-8N84, 8N86-8N88,
8N90, 8N95-8N96, 8N98, 8N101-8N102,
8N105-8N106, 9N6-9N71, 9N97, 9N99, Taiwan 78, 84, Northeastern Provinces 9-10, Sinkiang 135-139, 174-188, 196, 198.

Chinese and American Flags and Map
of China — A58

Printed by American Bank Note Co.
Frame Engr., Center Litho.
1939, July 4   Unwmk.   *Perf. 12*
Flag in Deep Rose and Ultramarine

364	A58	5c dark green	1.50	.50
365	A58	25c deep blue	1.75	.90
366	A58	50c brown	3.50	1.10
367	A58	$1 rose carmine	5.50	2.00
		Nos. 364-367 (4)	12.25	4.50

150th anniv. of the US Constitution.

Type of 1939-41 Issue
Re-engraved

2c, 1939-41   Re-engraved

8c, 1939-41

Re-engraved

1940   *Perf. 12½*

368	A57	2c olive green	.20	.20
369	A57	8c olive green	.20	.20

Type of 1938-41 Issue
1940   Unwmk.   *Perf. 14*
Type III

370	A57	2c olive green	2.50	1.00
371	A57	5c green	5.00	2.10
372	A57	$1 henna & dk brn	100.00	17.50
373	A57	$2 dp blue & org brn	20.00	5.00
374	A57	$5 red & grnsh blk	25.00	16.00
375	A57	$10 dk grn & dull pur	70.00	12.00
		Nos. 370-375 (6)	222.50	53.60

See surcharge note following No. 363.

Type of 1939-41
1940   Wmk. 261   *Perf. 12½*
Type III

376	A57	$1 henna & dk brn	6.50	8.50
377	A57	$2 dp blue & org brn	9.00	8.50
378	A57	$5 red & grnsh blk	9.00	18.00
379	A57	$10 dk green & dull pur	14.00	30.00
380	A57	$20 rose lake & dp blue	18.00	30.00
		Nos. 376-380 (5)	56.50	95.00

See surcharge note following No. 363.

Printed by the Dah Tung Book Co.
Type III with Secret Marks
Five Cent

Type III — Characters
joined

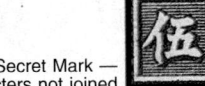

Secret Mark —
Characters not joined

Eight Cent

Type III —   Secret
Characters   Mark —
not joined   Characters
                     joined

Ten Cent

Type III —   Secret
Characters   Mark —
sharp and   Characters
well   coarse and
shaped   varying in
                     thickness

Dollar Values

Type III   Secret
                    Mark

1940   Unwmk.   *Perf. 14*

381	A57	5c green	.20	.20
382	A57	5c olive green	.20	.20
383	A57	8c olive green	.40	.20
a.		Without "star" in uniform button	1.50	2.50
384	A57	10c green	.20	.20
385	A57	30c scarlet	.35	.20
386	A57	50c dk blue	.45	.20
387	A57	$1 org brn & sepia	2.25	.20
388	A57	$2 dp blue & yel brn	.90	.35
389	A57	$5 red & slate grn	.90	.45
390	A57	$10 dk grn & dull pur	3.75	2.10
391	A57	$20 rose lake & dk blue	11.00	3.25
		Nos. 381-391 (11)	20.60	7.55

Type III with Secret Marks
1940   Wmk. 261   *Perf. 14*

392	A57	5c green	.20	.20
393	A57	5c olive green	.20	.20
394	A57	10c green	.35	.20
395	A57	30c scarlet	.20	.20
396	A57	50c dk blue	.55	.20
397	A57	$1 org brn & sepia	4.00	2.40
398	A57	$2 dp blue & yel brn	11.00	11.00
399	A57	$5 red & slate grn	10.00	10.00
400	A57	$10 dk grn & dull pur	14.00	15.00
401	A57	$20 rose lake & dk blue	22.50	18.00
		Nos. 392-401 (10)	63.00	57.40

Nos. 383, 384, 385, 397, 400 and 401 exist
perf. 12½, but were not issued with this
perforation.
See surcharge note following No. 363.

Types of 1932-34
Martyrs Issue with Secret Mark

1932-34 Issue. In the left
Chinese character in bottom
row, the two parts are not
joined.

Secret Mark, 1940-41
Issue. The two parts are
joined.

Perf. 12½, 13 and Compound
1940-41   Wmk. 261

402	A39	½c olive blk	.25	.20
403	A40	1c orange	.25	.20
404	A46	2c dp blue ('41)	.25	.20
405	A39	2½c rose lilac	.25	.20
406	A48	3c dp yellow brn	.25	.20
407	A39	4c pale vio ('41)	.25	.20
408	A48	5c dull red org ('41)	.25	.20
409	A45	8c dp orange	.25	.20
410	A46	10c dull violet	.25	.20
411	A45	13c dp yellow grn	.25	.20
412	A48	15c brown car	.25	.20
413	A46	17c brown olive	.25	.20
414	A47	20c lt blue	.25	.20
415	A45	21c olive brn ('41)	1.00	1.25
416	A40	25c red vio ('41)	.25	.20
417	A46	28c olive ('41)	.25	.20
418	A48	30c brown car	.25	.20
a.		Vert. pair, imperf. btwn.	125.00	
419	A47	40c orange	.25	.20
420	A40	50c green	.25	.20

Unwmk.

421	A39	½c olive black	.20	.20
422	A40	1c orange	.20	.20
a.		Without secret mark	2.25	2.25
b.		Horiz. pair, imperf. vert.	110.00	
423	A46	2c dp blue	.20	.20
a.		Horiz. pair, imperf. horiz.	100.00	
b.		Horiz. pair, imperf. between	160.00	
424	A39	2½c rose lilac	.20	.20
425	A48	3c dp yellow brn	.20	.20
426	A39	4c pale violet	.20	.20
427	A48	5c dull red org	.20	.20
428	A45	8c dp orange	.20	.20
429	A46	10c dull violet	3.00	.40
430	A45	13c dp yel grn	.20	.20
431	A48	15c brown car	.20	.20
432	A46	17c brn olive	.20	.20
433	A47	20c lt blue	.20	.20
a.		Vert. pair, imperf. horiz.	125.00	
b.		Horiz. pair, imperf. vert.	125.00	
434	A45	21c olive brn	.20	.20
435	A40	25c rose vio	.20	.20
436	A46	28c olive	.20	.20
437	A48	30c brown car	2.25	2.25
438	A47	40c orange	.20	.20
439	A40	50c green	3.00	.30
		Nos. 402-439 (38)	16.95	11.00

Several values exist imperforate, but they
were not regularly issued.
Used values are for favor cancels. Postally
used copies sell for more.
See surcharge note following No. 323.

Regional Surcharges.
The regional surcharges, Nos. 440-
448, 482-484, 486-491, 525-549, have
been listed according to the basic
stamps, with black or red surcharges.
The surcharges of the individual provinces, plus Hong Kong and Shanghai,
are noted in small type. The numeral
following each letter is the surcharge
denomination. These surcharges are
identified by the following letters:

a — Hong Kong		i — Kwangsi	
b — Shanghai		j — Kwangtung	
bx — Anhwei		k — Western Szechwan	
c — Hunan		l — Yunnan	
d — Kansu		m — Honan	
e — Kiangsi		n — Shensi	
f — Eastern Szechwan		o — Kweichow	
g — Chekiang		p — Hupeh	
h — Fukien			

Regional Surcharges on Stamps of
1939-40:

Hong Kong —   Shanghai —
a4   b3

Hunan — c3   Kansu — d3

Kiangsi — e3   Eastern
                      Szechwan —
                      f3

Chekiang — g3

1940-41   Unwmk.   *Perf. 12½, 14*
Carmine Surcharge

440	A57	4c on 5c ol grn (#382)	.55	.55
r.		Lower right character duplicated at left	30.00	32.50

Black Surcharge

441	A57	3c on 5c grn (#351) (b3)	1.10	1.25
442	A57	3c on 5c grn (#352) (c3, d3)	.60	1.60
443	A57	3c on 5c grn (#381) (b3)	.55	1.10
444	A57	3c on 5c grn (#382) (e3)	.65	.85
r.		Lower left character duplicated at right (Kiangsi)	42.50	42.50
		(b3) Shanghai	.65	1.40
		(f3) Eastern Szechwan	.65	1.60

The Kansu surcharges of #442 are of 6
types. Differences include formation of top
part of fen character (at left of "3"), fen with low
right hook, height of "3" (5-4mm), space
between upper and lower characters (6-9mm),
etc.

1940-41   Wmk. 261   *Perf. 14*

445	A57	3c on 5c grn (#392) (e3)	.55	1.25
r.		Lower left character duplicated at right (Kiangsi)	35.00	35.00
		(b3, c3) Shanghai, Hunan	.55	1.40
446	A57	3c on 5c ol grn (#393) (f3)	.65	1.60
		(b3) Shanghai	.85	1.60
r.		Lower left character duplicated at right (f3)	60.00	65.00

Red Surcharge

447	A57	3c on 5c grn (#392) (g3)	1.10	3.00
448	A57	3c on 5c ol grn (#393) (g3)	5.00	5.00

Dr. Sun Yat-
sen — A59

Printed by American Bank Note Co.
1941   Unwmk.   Engr.   *Perf. 12*

449	A59	½c sepia	.20	.30
450	A59	1c orange	.20	.20
451	A59	2c brt ultra	.20	.20
452	A59	5c green	.20	.20
453	A59	8c red orange	.20	.25
454	A59	8c turq green	.20	.20
455	A59	10c brt green	.20	.20
456	A59	17c olive	3.50	11.00
457	A59	25c rose violet	.20	1.00
458	A59	30c scarlet	.20	.25
459	A59	50c dk blue	.20	.20
460	A59	$1 brown & blk	.30	.20
461	A59	$2 blue & blk	.30	.20
a.		Center inverted	12,500.	
462	A59	$5 scarlet & blk	.50	.20
463	A59	$10 dk green & blk	3.75	1.00
464	A59	$20 rose vio & blk	2.10	5.00
		Nos. 449-464 (16)	12.45	20.60

For surcharges see Nos. 488, 491, 542-543,
617, 621, 670, 677, 687, 705-706, 712, 716,
718, M1, M3-M4, 1N16-1N22, 1N43-1N56,
9N78-9N96, 9N98, 9N100.

Industry and Agriculture — A60

1941, June 21   *Perf. 12½*

465	A60	8c green	.20	.20
466	A60	21c red brown	.20	.20
467	A60	28c dk olive grn	.20	.20
468	A60	33c vermilion	.90	1.50
469	A60	50c dp ultra	1.10	.85
470	A60	$1 dk violet	1.60	1.00
		Nos. 465-470 (6)	4.20	3.95

Souvenir Sheet
Imperf
Typo.

471		Sheet of 6	37.50	37.50
a.		A60 8c dull green	3.00	3.00
b.		A60 21c dark orange brown	3.00	3.00
c.		A60 28c dull yellow green	3.00	3.00
d.		A60 33c red	3.00	3.00
e.		A60 50c dull blue	3.00	3.00
f.		A60 $1 dark violet	3.00	3.00

The Thrift Movement and its aim to "Save for
Reconstruction."
Issued in sheets measuring 155x171mm,
without gum.

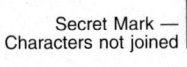

This sheet exists with additional blue marginal overprints in Russian, French and Chinese reading "Souvenir of the Exhibition of the Russian Philatelic Society in China, Shanghai, China, Feb. 28, 1943." Value, $65.

The overprinting was applied by the society, and when so overprinted this sheet had no franking power.

Stamps of 1939-41 Overprinted in Carmine or Blue

1941, Oct. 10   Perf. 12½, 14, 13

472	A40	1c dull orange	.20	.60
473	A57	2c olive grn (C)	.20	.60
474	A39	4c pale violet (C)	.20	.60
475	A57	8c ol grn (#369) (C)	.20	.60
476	A57	10c green (#354) (C)	.20	.60
477	A57	16c ol gray (#357) (C)	.20	.60
478	A45	21c olive brn (C)	.20	.60
479	A46	28c olive (C)	.55	1.65
480	A57	30c scarlet	.65	3.25
481	A57	$1 hn & dk brn (#359)	3.50	4.00
		Nos. 472-481 (10)	6.10	13.10

Chinese Republic, 30th anniversary.

 Kiangsi — e7

Eastern Szechwan — f7

 Chekiang — g7

 Fukien — h7

1941   Unwmk.   Perf. 12½, 14

482	A57	7c on 8c (#353) (g7, h7)	.55	1.10
483	A57	7c on 8c (#369) (f7)	.45	.55
484	A57	7c on 8c (#383) (h7)	.55	.90
		(e7) Kiangsi	.65	.90
		(g7) Chekiang	.65	1.10
r.		Without "star" in uniform button	65.00	

Type of 1932-34 Re-engraved

1941   Unwmk.   Perf. 14

485	A45	8c deep orange	11.50	57.50

The original stamps are 19½mm wide, the re-engraved 21mm.

Eleven other values of the Martyrs Issue and types A37 and A57 exist re-engraved, but were not issued.

 Hunan — c1

Kiangsi — e1

 Fukien — h1

Kwangsi — i1

Kwangtung — j1

1942
Red Surcharge

486	A39	1c on ½c blk brn (#312) (i1)	.85	1.75
	(c1)	Hunan	1.60	2.75
487	A39	1c on ½c ol blk (#421) (e1)	.45	1.60
	(c1)	Hunan	.55	2.00
	(i1)	Kwangsi	1.65	2.50
	(h1)	Fukien	5.00	8.00
488	A59	1c on ½c sepia (#449) (j1)	.85	1.60
	(c1)	Hunan	1.10	2.50

 Hunan — c40

 Eastern Szechwan — f40

 Western Szechwan — k40

 Yunnan — l40

Red Surcharge

489	A57	40c on 50c dk bl (#386) (f40)	.65	1.10
	(k40)	Western Szechwan	3.75	3.25
	(l40)	Yunnan	3.25	3.25
r.		Inverted surcharge (Yunnan)	110.00	

Wmk. 261

490	A40	40c on 50c grn (#420) (c40)	1.60	5.50

Unwmk.

491	A59	40c on 50c dk bl (#459) (c40)	2.75	7.50

 Dr. Sun Yat-sen — A62

Central Trust Printing
Perf. 10½-11, 11½-12½, 13 and Compounds

1942-43   Typo.

Without Gum

492	A62	10c dp green ('43)	.20	.35
493	A62	16c dull ol brn	12.50	45.00
a.		Perf 10½	500.00	325.00
494	A62	20c dk ol grn ('43)	.20	.20
a.		Perf. 11	10.00	10.00
495	A62	25c brown vio	.20	.20
496	A62	30c dull ver	.20	.20
a.		Perf. 11	2.75	2.75
497	A62	40c dk red brn ('43)	.20	.25
a.		Perf. 11x13	85.00	
b.		Perf. 11	12.00	12.00
498	A62	50c sage green	.20	.20
a.		Perf. 11	6.00	12.00
499	A62	$1 rose lake	.30	.20
a.		Perf. 11	35.00	35.00
500	A62	$1 dull grn ('43)	.30	.30
501	A62	$1.50 dp blue ('43)	.30	.30
a.		Perf. 11	275.00	275.00
502	A62	$2 dk blue grn	.30	.30
503	A62	$3 dk yel ('43)	.30	.30
504	A62	$4 red brown	.30	.30
505	A62	$5 cerise ('43)	.30	.30
		Nos. 492-505 (14)	15.80	48.40

Many shades and part-perforate varieties exist.

See Nos. 550 to 563 for other stamps of type A62 with secret mark and new values and colors. For surcharges and overprints see Nos. 525-530, 671, 683, 692-694, 696, 771, 773, 807-809, 811-820, 824-827, 832, 834-834A, 836, 848-850, 852-854, 857, 860-863, 876, 879, M5-M10, Taiwan 55, 86, 99, Kwangsi 6-7, Sinkiang 162-173, 194-195.

Type of 1938
Thin Paper Without Gum

1942-44   Unwmk.   Engr.   Imperf.

506	A57	$10 red brown	.35	.20
507	A57	$20 blue grn	.35	.30
508	A57	$20 rose red ('44)	4.75	1.50
509	A57	$30 dull vio ('43)	.35	.35
510	A57	$40 rose red ('43)	.45	.35
511	A57	$50 blue	1.00	.55
512	A57	$100 org brn ('43)	1.75	1.75

Rouletted

513	A57	$5 lilac gray ('44)	5.00	7.50
a.		Rouletted x perf. 12½	25.00	30.00
514	A57	$10 red brown	3.00	2.50
515	A57	$50 blue	3.00	2.50
a.		Rouletted x imperf.	2.50	
		Nos. 506-515 (10)	20.00	17.50

1942-45   Perf. 12½ to 15

516	A57	$4 dp blue ('43)	.30	.30
517	A57	$5 lil gray ('43)	.40	.30
518	A57	$10 red brown	.40	.30
519	A57	$20 blue grn ('43)	.40	.30
520	A57	$20 rose red ('43)	75.00	75.00
521	A57	$30 dull vio ('43)	.50	.35
522	A57	$40 rose ('43)	.50	.40
523	A57	$50 blue	.50	.40
524	A57	$100 org brn ('45)	80.00	80.00
		Nos. 516-524 (9)	158.00	157.25

Beware of Nos. 508 and 512 with faked perforations that are offered as Nos. 520 and 524. See surcharge note following No. 363.

 No. 493 Overprinted in Black or Red

1942

525	A62	(i) 16c (Bk)	75.00	85.00
	(c)	Hunan	450.00	
	(k)	Western Szechwan	175.00	175.00
	(m)	Honan	725.00	725.00
	(n)	Shensi	725.00	240.00
r.		Perf. 10½ (Kwangsi)	500.00	
s.		Inverted ovpt. (Shensi)	225.00	
526	A62	(d) 16c (R)	45.00	20.00
	(bx)	Anhwei	475.00	475.00
	(e)	Kiangsi	55.00	55.00
	(f)	Eastern Szechwan	110.00	70.00
	(h)	Fukien	275.00	200.00
	(j)	Kwangtung	575.00	600.00
	(l)	Yunnan	55.00	45.00
	(o)	Kweichow	200.00	200.00
	(p)	Hupeh, perf. 10½	825.00	725.00
r.		Perf. 10½ (E. Szechwan)	475.00	
s.		Horiz. pair, imperf. btwn (Yunnan)	600.00	
t.		Perf. 13 (Hupeh)	—	—

This overprint means "Domestic Ordinary Letter Surcharge Paid." It was applied in various sizes and types by 14 districts, 9 using red ink, 5 using black. (The Anhwei overprint comes in two types.) These overprinted stamps were briefly sold for $1.16 before the government ordered their sale suspended. The vertical bars and 50c surcharge of Nos. 527-528 were then applied.

 Anhwei — bx

 Hunan — c

 Kansu — d

 Kiangsi — e

 Eastern Szechwan — f

 Fukien — h

 Kwangsi — i

 Kwangtung — j

 Western Szechwan — k

Yunnan — l

 Honan — m

 Shensi — n

 Kweichow — o

Hupeh — p

Nos. 525-526 Surcharged "50 cents" and 2 Vertical Bars in Black or Red

1942   Unwmk.

527	A62	50c on 16c (Bk) (c,f)	2.40	2.50
	(i)	Kwangsi	5.00	5.00
	(k)	Western Szechwan	7.00	7.00
	(m)	Honan	7.00	7.00
	(n)	Shensi	4.00	4.0
r.		Inverted surch. (W. Szech.)	225.00	
s.		"k" surcharge on #493	325.00	
528	A62	50c on 16c (R) (p)	4.25	4.25
	(bx)	Anhwei	85.00	250.00
	(d)	Kansu	3.25	
	(e)	Kiangsi	5.00	9.50
	(h)	Fukien	6.00	6.50
	(j)	Kwangtung	6.00	5.00
	(l)	Yunnan	6.00	7.50
	(o)	Kweichow	3.25	6.00
r.		"o" surcharge inverted	250.00	
s.		"p" surch. on #526(f)	80.00	45.00

Many varieties of Nos. 527-528 exist, including narrow or wide spacing between the two top characters, or between the vertical bars, or both.

Surcharges on stamps perf. 10½ (basic No. 493a) usually sell at much higher prices.

 General Issue

 Hunan — c50

 Eastern Szechwan — f50

 Chekiang — g50

 Kwangsi — i50

 Kwangtung — j50

 Western Szechwan — k50

 Honan — m50

Shensi — n50   Kweichow — o50

No. 493 Surcharged in Black, Red or Carmine

1943 **Unwmk.**

529	A62	50c on 16c (Bk)		10.00	10.00
		(m50)		10.00	10.00
		(n50) Shensi		10.00	10.00
	r.	Perf. 11x13 (Shensi)		80.00	
530	A62	50c on 16c (C)		.90	1.60
		(c50) Hunan		2.75	5.50
		(f50) Eastern Szechwan		3.25	2.50
		(g50) Chekiang		37.50	40.00
		(i50) Kwangsi		6.00	7.00
		(j50) Kwangtung		4.50	6.50
		(k50) Western Szechwan		4.50	6.00
		(m50) Honan		7.50	8.00
		(o50) Kweichow		10.00	12.00
	r.	Inverted surch. (Hunan)		50.00	
	s.	"05" instead of "50" (Kweichow)		450.00	

Many varieties of Nos. 529-530 exist, such as narrow or wide spacing horizontally or vertically between the overprinted Chinese characters.

Surcharges on No. 493a (perf. 10½) usually sell at much higher prices.

The General Issue type, No. 530, was distributed to all head offices, which in turn supplied the post offices under their direction. It is surcharged in carmine; the other stamps listed under No. 530 are surcharged in red or carmine.

Hunan — c20   Kansu — d20

Kiangsi — e20   Eastern Szechwan — f20

Fukien — h20   Kwangsi — i20

Kwangtung — j20   Western Szechwan — k20

Yunnan — l20   Honan — m20

Shensi — n20   Kweichow — o20

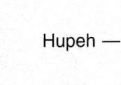

Hupeh — p20

1943 **Wmk. 261, Unwmkd.**

On No. 318

531	A45	20c on 13c (k20)	2.00	2.10
		(d20) Kansu		4.50
		(n20) Shensi	3.00	3.50
532	A45	20c on 13c (i20;R)	.70	2.40
		(c20) Hunan	1,000.	
		(d20) Kansu	250.00	
		(j20) Kwangtung	75.00	82.50
		(p20) Hupeh	1.75	3.50

On No. 411

533	A45	20c on 13c (n20)	2.00	3.75
		(d20) Kansu	1.50	6.75
		(k20) Western Szechwan	1.40	6.75
		(l20) Yunnan	20.00	12.00
		(m20) Honan	300.00	
534	A45	20c on 13c (p20;R)	1.50	4.75
		(c20) Hunan	2.25	1.60
		(i20) Kiangsi	8.00	1.90
		(f20) Eastern Szechwan	2.25	2.40
		(h20) Fukien	8.50	8.25
		(i20) Kwangsi	1.75	2.40
		(j20) Kwangtung	16.00	15.00
		(o20) Kweichow	3.25	3.00

On No. 430

535	A45	20c on 13c (l20)	2.00	4.25
		(d20) Kansu	2.00	2.40
		(k20) Western Szechwan	35.00	37.50
		(m20) Honan	8.50	8.25
		(n20) Shensi	3.00	4.75
536	A45	20c on 13c (f20;i20;R)		3.00
		(c20) Hunan	10.00	8.75
		(e20) Kiangsi	3.00	3.50
		(j20) Kwangtung	2.00	2.40
		(o20) Kweichow	2.00	9.00
		(p20) Hupeh	2.00	3.50

On No. 357

537	A57	20c on 16c (k20)	2.00	2.40
		(c20) Hunan	3.00	12.00
		(d20) Kansu	3.00	12.00
		(m20) Honan	10.00	16.00
		(n20) Shensi	3.00	12.00
538	A57	20c on 16c (e20, o20; R)	2.00	12.00
		(c20) Hunan	10.00	16.00
		(i20) Kwangsi	10.00	12.00
		(j20) Kwangtung	50.00	50.00

On No. 413

539	A46	20c on 17c (c20;R)	2.00	3.75
		(i20) Kwangsi	2.00	2.40
		(j20) Kwangtung	30.00	40.00

On No. 432

540	A46	20c on 17c (k20)	3.00	5.00
		(d20) Kansu	3.00	5.75
		(m20) Honan	35.00	45.00
541	A46	20c on 17c (e20;R)	2.00	5.00
		(j20) Kwangtung	3.25	11.00
		(o20) Kweichow	2.25	6.00

On No. 456

542	A59	20c on 17c (m20)	200.00	225.00
543	A59	20c on 17c (c20;R)	17.50	22.50

On No. 415

544	A45	20c on 21c (e20;R)	10.00	11.00

On No. 434

545	A45	20c on 21c (c20, k20)	1.00	3.50
		(d20) Kansu	2.25	6.00
		(l20) Yunnan	2.25	3.50
		(m20) Honan	2.25	8.25
546	A45	20c on 21c (f20;R)	1.00	3.75
		(e20) Kiangsi	1.50	5.00
		(h20) Fukien	2.25	4.25
		(i20) Kwangsi	2.50	3.50
		(j20) Kwangtung	3.25	4.50
		(o20) Kweichow	2.25	2.40
		(p20) Hupeh	2.25	5.00

On No. 417

547	A46	20c on 28c (e20;R)	750.00	650.00

On No. 436

548	A46	20c on 28c (l20)	1.10	5.75
		(d20) Kansu	15.00	21.00
		(k20) Western Szechwan	22.50	50.00
		(m20) Honan	35.00	40.00
549	A46	20c on 28c (e20;R)	1.00	3.00
		(c20) Hunan	1.50	4.25
		(h20) Fukien	3.25	4.25
		(i20) Kwangsi	4.25	4.25
		(j20) Kwangtung	3.75	5.75
		(o20) Kweichow	4.25	4.25

Many varieties of Nos. 531-549 exist, such as narrow or wide spacing between the overprinted Chinese characters, and "20" higher or lower than illustrated.

Type of 1942-43 Pacheng Printing

1944-46 **Unwmk.** **Perf. 12**
Without Gum

550	A62	30c chocolate	.40	12.50
551	A62	$1 green	3.00	3.50
552	A62	$2 dk vio brn	.20	.20
	a.	Imperf., pair	12.00	12.00
553	A62	$2 dk bl grn	.20	.20
	a.	Perf. 10½	35.00	26.00

554	A62	$2 deep blue	1.25	1.25
555	A62	$3 lt yellow	1.25	.75
556	A62	$4 violet brn	.20	.20
	a.	Imperf., pair	60.00	
557	A62	$5 car ('46)	.20	.20
	a.	Perf. 10½	60.00	60.00
558	A62	$6 gray vio ('45)	.20	.20
559	A62	$10 red brn ('45)	.20	.20
	a.	Imperf., pair	60.00	
560	A62	$20 dp ultra ('46)	.20	.20
561	A62	$50 dk green ('46)	3.25	.20
562	A62	$70 lilac ('46)	4.00	.20
563	A62	$100 lt brown ('46)	.20	.20
		Nos. 550-563 (14)	14.75	20.00

In the Pacheng printing of the Central Trust type stamps, the secret mark "C" has been added below the lower left foliate ornament beneath the sun emblem. On the $3, it is below the right ornament. New values also include a "P" at right of sun emblem on the $6 and $10, and at right of necktie on the $20. Some values of Pacheng printing exist on paper with elephant watermark in sheet.
See surcharge note following No. 505.

 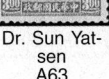

Dr. Sun Yat-sen A63   Allegory of Savings A64

1944-46 **Unwmk. Typo.** **Perf. 12½**
Without Gum

565	A63	40c brown red	.25	.25
566	A63	$2 gray brown	.25	.25
567	A63	$3 red	.25	.25
	a.	$3 orange red	2.50	3.00
568	A63	$3 lt red brown ('45)	.60	.60
569	A63	$6 pale lilac gray ('45)	.25	.25
570	A63	$10 dull lake ('45)	.25	.25
571	A63	$20 rose ('45)	.25	.25
	a.	Perf. 16	375.00	375.00
572	A63	$50 lt brown ('46)	.40	.40
573	A63	$70 rose violet ('46)	.40	.40
		Nos. 565-573 (9)	2.90	2.90

For surcharges see Nos. 772, 774, 828, 833, 835, 836A, 839, 842, 851, 864, 868, 873-875, 877, 880. Taiwan 81, 98, Sinkiang 200-201.

1944-45 **Engr.** **Perf. 13**
Without Gum

574	A64	$40 indigo ('45)	.20	.20
575	A64	$50 yellow grn ('45)	.20	.20
576	A64	$100 yellow brn	.20	.20
577	A64	$200 dk green ('45)	.20	.20
		Nos. 574-577 (4)	.80	.80

All four values were printed on thick paper; the first three were also printed on thin paper. For surcharges see Szechwan Nos. F1, F3.

A65   Dr. Sun Yat-sen — A66

1944, Dec. 25 **Litho.**
Without Gum

578	A65	$2 deep green	.50	.80
579	A65	$5 fawn	.50	.80
580	A65	$6 dull rose vio	.95	1.50
581	A65	$10 violet blue	1.90	2.50
582	A65	$20 carmine	4.25	6.00
		Nos. 578-582 (5)	8.10	11.60

50th anniversary of the Kuomintang.

1945, Mar. 12
Without Gum

583	A66	$2 gray green	.30	.80
584	A66	$5 red brown	.40	.80
585	A66	$6 dk vio blue	.45	1.25
586	A66	$10 lt blue	.70	1.25
587	A66	$20 rose	.95	1.50
588	A66	$30 buff	1.50	2.00
		Nos. 583-588 (6)	4.30	7.60

Death of Dr. Sun Yat-sen, 20th anniv.

Dr. Sun Yat-sen — A67

1945-46 **Without Gum** **Perf. 12½**

589	A67	$2 green	.25	.35
590	A67	$5 dull green	.25	.35
591	A67	$10 dk blue	.25	.35
	a.	Imperf., pair	70.00	
592	A67	$20 carmine ('46)	.25	.35
	a.	Imperf., pair	70.00	
		Nos. 589-592 (4)	1.00	1.40

For surcharges see Nos. 695, 697, 837, 855, Taiwan 58, 82, 87-88.

Statue of Liberty, Map of China, Flags of Great Britain, China and United States, and Chiang Kai-shek A68

Unwmk.
1945, July 7 **Engr.** **Perf. 12**
Flags in Dark Blue and Red

593	A68	$1 deep blue	.30	.20
594	A68	$2 dull green	.40	.35
595	A68	$5 olive gray	.40	.35
596	A68	$6 brown	1.00	1.00
597	A68	$10 rose lilac	5.00	5.00
598	A68	$20 carmine rose	5.00	5.00
		Nos. 593-598 (6)	12.10	11.90

Signing of a Treaty in 1943 between Great Britain, the US and China.

Pres. Lin Sen (1864-1943) A69   Pres. Chiang Kai-shek A70

1945, Aug. **Unwmk.** **Perf. 12**

599	A69	$1 dp ultra & blk	.25	.75
600	A69	$2 myrtle grn & blk	.25	.75
601	A69	$5 red & blk	.25	.75
602	A69	$6 purple & blk	.90	1.25
603	A69	$10 choc & blk	3.75	3.00
604	A69	$20 olive grn & blk	4.00	3.25
		Nos. 599-604 (6)	9.40	9.75

1945, Oct. 10
Flag in Rose Red and Violet Blue

605	A70	$2 green	.45	.50
606	A70	$4 dark blue	.45	.50
607	A70	$5 olive gray	.45	.50
608	A70	$6 bister brown	1.40	2.00
609	A70	$10 gray	3.75	2.50
610	A70	$20 red violet	4.50	3.50
		Nos. 605-610 (6)	11.00	9.50

Inauguration of Chiang Kai-shek as president, Oct. 10, 1943.

President Chiang Kai-shek — A71

1945, Oct. 10 **Typo.** **Perf. 13**
Without Gum
Flag in Carmine and Blue

611	A71	$20 green & blue	.25	.20
612	A71	$50 bister brn & bl	.50	.35
613	A71	$100 blue	.50	.35
614	A71	$300 rose red & blue	.50	.35
		Nos. 611-614 (4)	1.75	1.25

Victory of the Allied Nations over Japan.

C. N. C. Surcharges

The green surcharges on Nos. 615 to 621, and the surcharges on Nos. 647 to 721, and 768 to 774 represent Chinese National Currency and were applied at Shanghai.

Stamps of 1938-41 Surcharged in Black with Chinese Characters and New Value in Checkered Rectangle at Bottom, Resurcharged in Green

1945			*Perf. 12, 12½*	
615	A57	10c on $20 on 3c (#350)	.20	.20
616	A46	15c on $30 on 2c (#423)	.20	.35
a.	Horiz. pair, imperf. between		90.00	
b.	Vert. pair, imperf. between		85.00	
617	A59	25c on $50 on 1c (#450)	.20	.20
618	A57	50c on $100 on 3c (#350)	.20	.20
619	A40	$1 on $200 on 1c (#422)	.20	.20
a.	Horiz. pair, imperf. between		90.00	
620	A57	$2 on $400 on 3c (#350)	.20	.20
621	A59	$5 on $1000 on 1c (#450)	.20	.20
		Nos. 615-621 (7)	1.40	1.55

The black (first) surcharges on Nos. 615 to 621 represent Nanking puppet government currency.

In the green surcharge, the characters at the left express the new value and are either two or four in number.

Types of 1932-34, Re-engraved, and Surcharged in Green with Horizontal Bar and Four or Five Chinese Characters and Overprinted in Black:

		Perf. 14		
622	A47	$10 on 20c brown red	4.00	5.50
623	A47	$20 on 40c orange	21.00	24.00
a.	Green surcharge inverted		60.00	
624	A48	$50 on 30c violet brn	17.50	18.00
		Nos. 622-624 (3)	42.50	47.50

These provisional surcharges were applied in Honan in National currency to stamps of the Hwa Pei (North China) government. The black overprint reads: "Hwa Pei."

The two-character "Hwa Pei" overprint was applied to various stamps in 1941-43 by the North China puppet government. See Nos. 8N1-8N53, 8N60-8N84.

Dr. Sun Yat-sen
A72   A73

1945, Dec.		*Typo.*	*Perf. 12*	
		Without Gum		
625	A72	$20 dp carmine	.25	.25
626	A72	$30 dp blue	.25	.25
627	A72	$40 orange	.25	.25
628	A72	$50 green	.25	.25
629	A72	$100 dk brown	.25	.25
630	A72	$200 brown violet	.25	.25
		Nos. 625-630 (6)	1.50	1.50

For surcharges see Nos. 810, 829, 838, 865, J110-J119, Taiwan 75, Kwangsi F2, Szechwan F2, F4, Yunnan 66-67, 71.

Type of 1931-37

		Perf. 12½, 13x12½, 13½		
1946			**Unwmk.**	
631	A37	$1 dk violet	.30	.20
632	A37	$2 olive green	.30	.20
633	A37	$20 brt yellow grn	.30	.25
634	A37	$30 chocolate	.30	.25
635	A37	$50 red orange	.30	.20
		Nos. 631-635 (5)	1.50	1.10

$4 blue and $5 red values were prepared but not issued. Value $400.

For surcharges see Nos. 678, 684, 689-690, 768, 843.

1946-47		*Engr.*	*Perf. 14*	
		Without Gum		
636	A73	$20 carmine	.75	.25
637	A73	$30 dk blue ('47)	.20	.20
638	A73	$50 purple	.20	.20
639	A73	$70 red org ('47)	16.00	1.90
640	A73	$100 dk carmine	.20	.20
641	A73	$200 olive grn ('47)	.20	.20
642	A73	$500 brt bl grn ('47)	.20	.20
643	A73	$700 red brown ('47)	.20	.20
644	A73	$1000 rose lake	.35	.35
645	A73	$3000 blue	1.00	.40
646	A73	$5000 dp green & ver	1.00	.40
		Nos. 636-646 (11)	20.30	4.50

For surcharges see Nos. 679, 769, 775, 823, 837A, 844-845, 856, 866, 875A, 878, Taiwan 18, 23-28, 54, 76-77, 100, Northeastern Provinces 41-43, Fukien 5-6, Hunan 1, E1, F1, Kwangsi 11, F2, Szechwan F5-F8, Sinkiang 202-204, People's Republic of China 3L53, 3L67-3L68, 6L28.

Stamps of 1932-41 Surcharged in Black

		Perf. 12½, 13, 13x12, 14		
		Wmk. 261		
647	A45	$20 on 8c (#409)	.20	.65
648	A39	$30 on ½c (#402)	2,000.	
649	A45	$70 on 21c (#415)	.20	.20
650	A45	$70 on 13c (#411)	.20	.20
651	A46	$100 on 28c (#417)	.20	.65
		Unwmk.		
652	A39	$3 on 2½c (#424)	6.25	6.25
653	A48	$10 on 15c (#431)	6.25	6.25
654	A45	$20 on 8c (#428)	.20	.20
655	A47	$20 on 20c (#433)	.35	.35
656	A39	$30 on ½c (#421)	.20	.20
657	A45	$20 on 21c (#434)	.40	.55
657A	A45	$70 on 13c (#318)	140.00	140.00
658	A45	$70 on 13c (#430)	.40	.55
659	A46	$100 on 28c (#436)	.40	.40

Forgeries of No. 648 exist.

Stamps and Types of 1931-1946 Surcharged in Black or Carmine

		Perf. 12½, 13, 14		
1946-47			**Wmk. 261**	
660	A57	$50 on 5c green (#392)	.35	.85
661	A57	$50 on 5c ol grn (#393)	21.00	20.00
662	A48	$50 on 5c dl red org (#408)	.20	1.25
663	A40	$100 on 1c org (#403)	.20	1.10

		Perf. 12, 12½, 12½x13, 13, 14		
1946-47			**Unwmk.**	
664	A57	$20 on 3c (#350)	.20	.35
665	A45	$20 on 8c (#428)	.20	.20
666	A57	$50 on 3c (#350)	.20	.20
667	A57	$50 on 5c (#352)	.20	.20
668	A57	$50 on 5c (#382)	.95	1.75
669	A48	$50 on 5c (#427)	.20	.20
670	A59	$50 on 5c (#452)	.20	.20
671	A62	$50 on $1 (#500)	.20	.20
672	A40	$100 on 1c (#422)	.20	.20
a.	Without secret mark (#422a)		67.50	67.50
673	A57	$100 on 3c (#350)	.20	.20
674	A57	$100 on 8c (#428)	13.00	12.00
675	A57	$100 on 8c (#369)	2.00	.35
676	A57	$100 on 8c (#383)	.35	.35
a.	Without "star" in uniform button (No. 383a)		25.00	16.00
677	A59	$100 on 8c (#454)	.20	.20
678	A37	$100 on $1 (#631)	.20	.20

679	A73	$100 on $20 (#636)	.35	.35
680	A57	$200 on 10c (#354)	.75	.25
681	A57	$200 on 10c (#384)	.25	1.10
682	A37	$200 on $4 dl bl	.50	.20
a.	Double surcharge		16.00	
683	A62	$250 on $1.50 (#501)	.20	.20
a.	Perf. 11		250.00	250.00
684	A37	$250 on $2 (#632)	.50	.20
685	A37	$250 on $5 car	.50	.20
686	A57	$300 on 10c (#354)	.20	.20
687	A59	$300 on 10c (#455)	.20	.20
688	A57	$500 on 3c (#350)	.50	.20
689	A37	$500 on $20 (#633)	.20	.20
690	A37	$800 on $30 (#634)	.20	.20
691	A37	$1000 on 2c (#297)	.55	.35
692	A62	$1000 on $2 (#552)	.20	.20
a.	Imperf., pair		16.00	16.00
693	A62	$1000 on $2 (#553)	.20	.25
694	A62	$1000 on $2 (#554)	.20	.55
695	A67	$1000 on $2 (#589)	.20	.20
696	A62	$2000 on $5 (#557)	.20	.20
697	A67	$2000 on $5 dl grn (C) (#590)	.20	.20
		Nos. 664-697 (34)	24.65	22.25

Nos. 682 and 685 were not issued without surcharge. No. 682 is perf. 13x13½; No. 685, perf. 12x12½.

The characters at the left express the new value and vary in number.

Stamps of 1938-41 Surcharged in Black

		Perf. 12, 12½, 13, 14		
1946			**Wmk. 261**	
698	A45	$20 on 8c (#409)	175.00	175.00
699	A57	$50 on 5c (#392)	.20	.65
700	A57	$50 on 5c (#393)	.50	1.25
1946-48			**Unwmk.**	
700A	A57	$20 on 5c (#381)	1,000.	
701	A57	$20 on 8c (#353)	.20	.35
702	A57	$20 on 8c (#369)	.35	.35
703	A57	$20 on 8c (#383)	.20	.50
a.	Without "star" in uniform button (No. 383a)		4.50	4.50
b.	Inverted surcharge		20.00	
c.	Dbl. surch., one on back		32.50	32.50
d.	Double surcharge		32.50	
704	A45	$20 on 8c (#428)	.20	.20
a.	Double surcharge		22.50	
705	A59	$20 on 8c (#453)	.20	.20
706	A59	$20 on 8c (#454)	.20	.20
a.	Inverted surcharge		13.00	
b.	Double surcharge		13.00	
707	A57	$50 on 5c (#351)	7.25	6.75
708	A57	$50 on 5c (#352)	.20	.20
a.	Inverted surcharge		27.50	
709	A57	$50 on 5c (#381)	.70	.70
710	A57	$50 on 5c (#382)	.50	.35
711	A48	$50 on 5c (#427)	.20	.20
a.	Inverted surcharge		27.50	
712	A59	$50 on 5c (#452)	.50	.20
a.	Double surcharge		16.00	

Stamps of 1939-41 Surcharged in Blue or Red

1946		**Wmk. 261**	*Perf. 12½*	
713	A40	$10 on 1c org (#403)	.20	.20
a.	Inverted surcharge		40.00	
714	A48	$20 on 3c dp yel brn (#406)	750.00	750.00

Forgeries of No. 714 exist.

1946		**Unwmk.**	*Perf. 12, 12½, 13*	
715	A40	$10 on 1c org (#422)	.20	.20
a.	Without secret mark (#422a)		10.00	12.00
b.	Inverted surcharge		8.00	10.00
716	A59	$10 on 1c org (#450)	.20	.20
a.	Double surcharge		27.50	
717	A57	$20 on 2c ol grn (R) (#368)	.20	.20
718	A59	$20 on 2c brt ultra (R) (#451)	.20	.20
a.	Inverted surcharge		20.00	
b.	Double surcharge		16.00	
719	A57	$20 on 2c dl cl (#350)	.20	.20
a.	Double surcharge		22.50	
720	A48	$20 on 3c dp yel brn (#425)	.20	.35

721	A39	$30 on 4c pale vio (R) (#426)	.20	.25
a.	Inverted surcharge		9.00	
		Nos. 715-721 (7)	1.40	1.60

President Chiang Kai-shek — A74

		Perf. 10½-11½		
1946, Oct. 31		*Engr.*	**Unwmk.**	
722	A74	$20 carmine	.50	.55
723	A74	$30 green	.50	.55
724	A74	$50 vermilion	.50	.55
725	A74	$100 yellow grn	.50	.55
726	A74	$200 yellow org	.50	.55
727	A74	$300 magenta	.50	.55
		Nos. 722-727 (6)	3.00	3.30

60th birthday of Chiang Kai-shek.

Printed by Dah Yeh Printing Co.; the earlier ones are gumless, the later ones gummed. See Taiwan Nos. 29-34, Northeastern Provinces 30-35.

Printed by Dah Tung Book Co.
Without Gum

		Perf. 14		
722a	A74	$20 carmine	1.10	1.50
723a	A74	$30 green	1.10	1.50
724a	A74	$50 vermilion	1.10	1.50
725a	A74	$100 yellow green	1.10	1.50
726a	A74	$200 yellow orange	1.10	1.50
727a	A74	$300 magenta	1.10	1.50
		Nos. 722a-727a (6)	6.60	9.00

Assembly House, Nanking A75

1946, Nov. 15		*Litho.*	*Perf. 14*	
		Without Gum		
728	A75	$20 green	.60	.30
729	A75	$30 blue	.60	.30
730	A75	$50 dk brown	.60	.30
a.	Horiz. pair, imperf. between		70.00	70.00
731	A75	$100 carmine	.60	.30
		Nos. 728-731 (4)	2.40	1.20

Convening of National Assembly.

For surcharges see Taiwan Nos. 10-13, Northeastern Provinces 26-29.

Entrance to Dr. Sun Yat-sen Mausoleum — A76   Dr. Sun Yat-sen — A77

1947, May 5			*Engr.*	
732	A76	$100 dp green	.35	.20
733	A76	$200 deep blue	.35	.20
734	A76	$250 carmine	.35	.20
735	A76	$350 lt brown	.35	.20
736	A76	$400 dp claret	.35	.20
		Nos. 732-736 (5)	1.75	1.00

First anniversary of return of Chinese National Government to Nanking.

See Taiwan Nos. 35-39, Northeastern Provinces 36-40.

1947		*Perf. 12½, 11½x12½*		
737	A77	$500 olive green	.25	.20
738	A77	$1000 green & car	.25	.20
739	A77	$2000 dp blue & red brn	.25	.20
740	A77	$5000 org red & blk	.25	.20
		Nos. 737-740 (4)	1.00	.80

For surcharge see Szechwan No. 50.

Confucius
A78

Confucius'
Lecturing School
A79

Tomb of
Confucius
A80

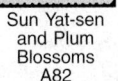

Temple of
Confucius
A81

1947, Aug. 27   Litho.   Perf. 14
Without Gum

741 A78 $500 carmine rose   .40   .25

Engr.

742 A79 $800 yellow brown   .40   .25
743 A80 $1250 blue green   .40   .25
744 A81 $1800 blue   .40   .25
     Nos. 741-744 (4)   1.60   1.00

Sun Yat-sen
and Plum
Blossoms
A82

Chinese Flag
and Map of
Taiwan
A83

1947-48   Engr.   Perf. 14
Without Gum

745 A82 $150 dk blue   .20   .25
746 A82 $250 dp lilac   .25   .20
747 A82 $500 blue grn   .20   .20
748 A82 $1000 red   .20   .20
749 A82 $2000 vermilion   .20   .20
750 A82 $3000 blue   .20   .20
751 A82 $4000 gray ('48)   .20   .20
752 A82 $5000 dk brown   .20   .20
753 A82 $6000 rose lilac
          ('48)   .20   .20
754 A82 $7000 lt red brn
          ('48)   .20   .20
755 A82 $10,000 dp blue & car   .85   .20
756 A82 $20,000 car & yel grn   .25   .20
757 A82 $50,000 grn & dk bl   .85   .20
758 A82 $100,000 dl yel & ol
          grn ('48)   1.50   .20
759 A82 $200,000 vio brn & dp
          bl ('48)   1.60   .45
760 A82 $300,000 sep & org
          brn ('48)   1.60   .45
761 A82 $500,000 dk Prus grn
          & sep ('48)   2.25   .45
     Nos. 745-761 (17)   10.95   4.20

See Nos. 788-799. For similar type see Formosa A1. For surcharges see Nos. 770, 804-
806, 821-822, 840-841, 858-859, 869, 871,
880A-880B, 885A-885E, 1025-1036, Taiwan
56-57, 59, 89, Fukien 1-4, 7-12, 19-23, Hunan
2-5, C1, Kiangsi 1-3, C1, E1, F1-F2, Kwangsi
8-10, 12-17, Shensi 1-2, C1, E1, Szechwan
24-49, Yunnan 61-62, 69, 205-207, People's
Republic of China 3L69-3L70, 3L76, 4L63-
4L64, 6L22, 6L27, 6L29, 6L32.

1947, Oct. 25
With Gum

762 A83 $500 carmine   .25   .25
763 A83 $1250 deep green   .25   .25

Restoration of Taiwan to China, 2nd anniv.

Mobile Post
Office — A84

Street-Corner Branch Post
Office — A85

1947, Nov. 5

764 A84 $500 carmine   .25   .20
765 A85 $1000 lilac   .25   .20
766 A85 $1250 green   .25   .20
767 A84 $1800 deep blue   .25   .20
     Nos. 764-767 (4)   1.00   .80

Stamps and Type of
1943-47 Surcharged in
Black or Green

1947-48   Unwmk.   Perf. 12½, 13, 14

768 A37 $500 on $20 brt yel
          grn (#633)   .20   .20
769 A73 $1250 on $70 red org
          (#639)   .20   .20
770 A82 $1800 on $350 yel org
          (#503)   .20   .20
771 A62 $2000 on $3 dk yel ('48)
          (#503)   .20   .20
772 A63 $2000 on $3 red (#567)   .20   .20
     a. On #567a   5.00   2.25
773 A62 $3000 on $3 lt yel ('48)
          (#555)   .20   .20
774 A63 $3000 on $3 lt red brn
          (G) ('48) (#568)   .20   .20
     Nos. 768-774 (7)   1.40   1.40

The characters at the left express the new
value and vary in number.

No. 640 Surcharged

1948, Aug.   Perf. 14

775 A73 $5000 on $100 dk car   6.00   40.00

No. 775 received its surcharge in Kwangsi
for use in that province.

Map of China
and Mail-
carrying
Vehicles
A86

Rural Mail
Delivery — A87

Early and
Modern Mail
Transportation
A88

1947, Dec. 16   Engr.   Perf. 12

776 A86 $100 violet   .25   .20
777 A87 $200 brt green   .25   .20
778 A87 $300 red brown   .25   .20
779 A88 $400 scarlet   .25   .20
780 A88 $500 brt vio blue   .25   .20
     Nos. 776-780 (5)   1.25   1.00

Chinese Postal Administration, 50th anniv.

National
Assembly
Building and
New
Constitution
A89

1947, Dec. 25   Perf. 14
Without Gum

781 A89 $2000 brt red   .25   .20
782 A89 $3000 blue   .25   .20
783 A89 $5000 deep green   .75   .60
     Nos. 781-783 (3)   1.75   .60

1st anniv. of the adoption of China's new
constitution, Dec. 25, 1946.

Chinese Stamps of 1947 and
1912 — A90

Perf. 14, Imperf.
1948, Mar. 20   Litho.
Without Gum

784 A90 $5000 dk car rose   .50   1.00
     a. Vert. pair, imperf. btwn   37.50
785 A90 $5000 dk green   .50   1.00
     a. Vert. pair, imperf. btwn   37.50

Stamp exhibitions at Nanking, Mar. 20 (No.
784), and at Shanghai, May 19 (No. 785).

Sun Yat-sen
Memorial Hall,
Taipei — A91

1948, Apr. 28   Engr.   Perf. 14

786 A91 $5000 violet   .20   1.00
787 A91 $10000 red   .20   1.00

Restoration of Formosa to China, 3rd anniv.

Sun Yat-sen Type of 1947-48

1948
Without Gum

788 A82 $20000 rose pink   .35   .20
789 A82 $30000 chocolate   .20   .20
790 A82 $40000 green   .20   .20
791 A82 $50000 dp blue   .20   .20
792 A82 $100000 dull grn   .20   .20
793 A82 $200000 brn vio   .55   .20
794 A82 $300000 yel grn   .85   .20
795 A82 $500000 lil rose   .85   .20
796 A82 $1000000 claret   .55   .20
797 A82 $2000000 vermilion   1.10   .20
798 A82 $3000000 ol bis   2.25   .25
799 A82 $5000000 ultra   4.50   .55
     Nos. 788-799 (12)   11.80   2.80

Zeros for "cents" omitted.
For surcharges see Nos. 841, 871, 880A-
880B, 885A-885E, 1025-1028, 1031-1036.

Early Ship and
Modern Hai
Tien — A92

Passenger Ship
Kiang
Ya — A93

1948, Aug. 16
Without Gum

800 A92 $20000 blue   .20   .20
801 A92 $30000 rose lilac   .20   .20
802 A93 $40000 yel brown   .20   .20
803 A93 $60000 vermilion   .20   .20
     Nos. 800-803 (4)   .80   .80

75th anniversary of the China Merchants'
Steam Navigation Company.

Type of 1947-48
Surcharged in Black

1948   Unwmk.   Perf. 14

804 A82 $4000 on $100 car   .20   .65
805 A82 $5000 on $100 car   .20   .20
806 A82 $8000 on $700 red brn   .20   .20
     Nos. 804-806 (3)   .60   1.05

Stamps of 1942-46
Surcharged in Black or
Red

1948   Perf. 12½, 13

807 A62 $5000 on $1 (#500)   .20   .20
808 A62 $5000 on $1 (#551)   18.00 18.00
809 A62 $5000 on $2 (#502)   .20   .20
810 A72 $10000 on $20 (#625)   .20   .20
811 A62 $20000 on 10c (#492)   .20   .20
812 A62 $20000 on 50c
          (#498;R)   .20   .20
813 A62 $30000 on 30c (#496)   .20   .20
     a. Perf. 10½   18.00 18.00
     Nos. 807-813 (7)   19.20 19.20

Nos. 492, 556 and
558 Surcharged in
Black or Carmine

1948

814 A62 $15,000 on 10c dp grn   .20   .20
815 A62 $15,000 on $4 vio brn   .20   .20
816 A62 $15,000 on $6 gray vio
          (C)   .20   .20
     Nos. 814-816 (3)   .60   .60

No. 498, 494 and 504
Surcharged in Black

1948   Unwmk.   Perf. 11½, 13

817 A62 $15,000 on 50c, perf.
          13   .20   .20
     a. Perf. 11½   10.00 10.00
818 A62 $40,000 on 20c dk ol
          grn   .20   .20
     a. Perf. 11   10.00   7.50
819 A62 $60,000 on $4 red
          brn   .20   .20
     Nos. 817-819 (3)   .60   .60

Gold Yuan Surcharges
(Nos. 820-885E)

Stamps of 1942-47
Surcharged in Black,
Carmine or Red

1948   Perf. 14, 13, 11

820 A62 ½c on 30c (#496)   .20   .20
821 A82 ½c on $500 (Bk)
          (#747)   .20   .20
822 A82 ½c on $500 (C) (#747)   .20   .20
823 A73 1c on $20 (#636)   .20   .20
824 A62 2c on $1.50 (R)
          (#501)   .20   .20
825 A62 3c on $5 (#505)   .20   .20
826 A62 4c on $1 (#499)   .20   .20

827 A62 5c on 50c (#498) .20 .20
a. Perf. 11 5.00 5.00
Nos. 820-827 (8) 1.60 1.60

On No. 820-827, the position of the surcharged denomination and "Gold Yuan" characters varies, the aim being to obliterate the original denomination.

Stamps of 1940-48 Surcharged in Black, Violet, Carmine, Blue or Green

Perf. 12, 12½, 13, 14, 12½x13

1948-49
828 A63 5c on $20 (#571) .20 .20
829 A72 5c on $30 (C) (#626) .20 .20
a. Double surcharge 16.00
830 A57 10c on 2c (#368) .20 .20
831 A39 10c on 2½c (#424) .20 .20
832 A62 10c on 25c (V) (#495) .20 .20
833 A63 10c on 40c (#565) .20 .20
834 A62 10c on $1 (#500) .20 .20
834A A62 10c on $1 (#551) 190.00 190.00
835 A63 10c on $2 (#566) .20 .20
836 A62 10c on $20 (C) (#560) .20 .20
836A A63 10c on $20 (#571) 150.00 150.00
837 A67 10c on $20 (#592) .20 .20
837A A73 10c on $20 (#636) .65 2.00
838 A72 10c on $30 (C) (#626) .20 .30
839 A63 10c on $70 (#573) .20 .20
a. Double surcharge 13.00
840 A82 10c on $7000 (#754) .20 .20
841 A82 10c on $20,000 (#788) .20 .20
842 A63 20c on $6 (#569) .20 .20
843 A37 20c on $30 (#634) .35 1.10
844 A73 20c on $30 (C) (#637) .20 .20
845 A73 20c on $100 (#640) .20 .20
a. Inverted surcharge 19.00
b. Double surcharge 14.00
846 A39 50c on ½c (#312) 60.00 60.00
847 A39 50c on ½c (#421) .20 .20
a. Inverted surcharge 27.50
848 A62 50c on 20c (#494) .20 .20
849 A62 50c on 30c (Bl) (#496) .20 .20
850 A62 50c on 40c (V) (#497) .20 .20
a. Perf. 11 6.50 7.25
851 A63 50c on 40c (V) (#565) .20 .20
852 A62 50c on $4 (#556) .20 .20
853 A62 50c on $4 (Bl) (#556) .20 .20
854 A62 50c on $20 (C) (#560) .20 .20
855 A67 50c on $20 (V) (#592) .20 .20
856 A73 50c on $20 (#636) .20 .20
857 A62 50c on $70 (C) (#562) .20 .20
858 A82 50c on $6000 (#753) .20 .20
859 A82 50c on $6000 (Bl) (#753) .20 .20
860 A62 $1 on 30c (#550) .20 .20
a. Perf. 11 20.00 20.00
861 A62 $1 on 40c (#497) .20 .20
a. Perf. 11 2.75 2.75
862 A62 $1 on $1 (#499) .20 .20
863 A62 $1 on $5 (#557) .20 .20
864 A63 $2 on $2 (R) (#566) .20 .20
865 A72 $2 on $20 (#625) .20 .20
866 A73 $2 on $100 (#640) .20 .20
867 A46 $5 on 17c (#432) .20 .20
868 A63 $5 on $2 (#566) .20 .20
869 A82 $5 on $3000 (C) (#750) .20 .20

870 A47 $8 on 20c (#433) .20 .20
871 A82 $8 on $30,000 (C) (#789) .20 .20
872 A47 $10 on 40c (#438) .20 .20
873 A63 $10 on $2 (G) (#566) .20 .20
874 A63 $10 on $2 (C) (#566) .20 .20
875 A63 $20 on $2 (C) (#566) .20 .20
875A A73 $20 on $20 (#636) 1.40 1.65
876 A62 $50 on 30c (#496) .20 .20
877 A63 $50 on $2 (Bl) (#566) .20 .20
878 A73 $80 on $20 (#636) .20 .20
879 A62 $100 on $1 (#551) .20 .20
a. Perf. 11 60.00 60.00
880 A63 $100 on $2 (C) (#566) .20 .20
880A A82 $50,000 on $20,000 (#788) .80 .35
880B A82 $100,000 on $30,000 (V) (#789) 2.00 .65

Wmk. 261
881 A39 10c on 2½c (#405) .40 4.00
882 A39 50c on ½c (#402) .20 .85
Nos. 828-882 (61) 416.00 420.90

Characters at left express the new value. Style of characters and numerals varies.

Nos. Q7 to Q9 Surcharged in Black or Carmine

1948 Unwmk. Perf. 12½
883 PP2 $200 on $3000 red org .20 .20
884 PP2 $500 on $5000 dk bl (C) .20 .20
885 PP2 $1000 on $10,000 vio .20 .20
Nos. 883-885 (3) .60 .60

Nos. 788-791 Surcharged in Gold Yuan in Red (Nos. 885A, 885D-885E) or Black (Nos. 885B-885C) at Foochow

1949, Apr. 30 Unwmk. Perf. 14
885A $20,000 on $40,000 14.00 15.00
885B $50,000 on $30,000 14.00 15.00
885C $100,000 on $20,000 14.00 15.00
885D $200,000 on $40,000 14.00 15.00
885E $200,000 on $50,000 14.00 15.00
Nos. 885A-885E (5) 70.00 75.00

Issued in Fukien Postal District.

Dr. Sun Yat-sen — A94

1949 Unwmk. Engr. Perf. 14
Without Gum
886 A94 $1 orange .35 .35
887 A94 $10 green .35 .35
888 A94 $20 vio brown .35 .35
889 A94 $50 dk Prus grn .35 .35
890 A94 $100 org brn .35 .35
891 A94 $200 red org .35 .35
892 A94 $500 rose lilac .35 .35
893 A94 $800 car rose .35 .45
894 A94 $1000 blue .35 .35

Redrawn
Engr.
Perf. 12½
895 A94 $10 green .35 2.25
a. Perf. 14 2.50 3.50
b. Perf. 13 .35 2.50
896 A94 $20 violet brn .35 .35
a. Perf. 14 .65 1.60
b. Perf. 13 .35 .35
Nos. 886-896 (11) 3.85 5.85

Small "T" at left of necktie on #895-896a.

Redrawn
1949 Litho. Perf. 12½
Without Gum
897 A94 $50 grnsh gray .20 1.40
898 A94 $100 dk org brn .20 .20
899 A94 $200 orange red .20 1.40
900 A94 $500 rose lilac .20 .20
901 A94 $1000 deep blue .20 .25
902 A94 $2000 violet .20 .20
903 A94 $5000 light blue .20 .20
904 A94 $10,000 sepia .20 .20
905 A94 $20,000 apple grn .20 .25
906 A94 $50,000 rose pink .20 .20
907 A94 $80,000 brn red .45 .65
908 A94 $100,000 bl grn .20 .20
Nos. 897-908 (12) 2.65 5.35

Diagonal lines have been added to the background of the redrawn design.
Zeros for "cents" omitted on No. 908.
See Nos. 973-981. For surcharges see Nos. 991-1006, 1057-1060, Fukien 13-17, Szechwan 51, Tsingtau 1-4, Yunnan 63-65, 68, 70, People's Republic of China 4L34-4L44, 4L48-4L60, 5L43-5L50, 5L54-5L59, 5L91-5L95, 6L1-6L16, 6L23-6L26, 6L30-6L31, 7L6-7L8, 7L13-7L16, 8L12-8L13, 8L48-8L51.

Gold Yuan Surcharge in Black or Other Colors on Revenue Stamps

Plane, Train and Ship — A95

Two types, 50c on $20:
I — Thick numerals in "20." Vertical stroke in lower right corner of vignette. (Dah Tung Book Co.)
II — Thin "20." No vertical stroke in corner. (Central Trust.)

Two types, $2 on $50, $10 on $30, $100 on $50 and $300 on $50:
III — "Y" in lower right corner of vignette. (Dah Yeh Printing Co.)
IV — No "Y" in corner. (Dah Tung, Central Trust or Chung Ming.)

Two types, $50 on $300 and $1000 on $100:
V — Projection on left frame column below foliate ornament. (Dah Yeh Printing Co.)
VI — No projection. (Dah Tung Book Co.)

Litho.; Nos. 923, 933, 935-936 Engr.
1949 Perf. 12½, 13, 14
Without Gum
913 A95 50c on $20 red brn, I .20 .20
a. 50c on $20 brown, II .20 .20
914 A95 $1 on $15 red org .20 .20
915 A95 $2 on $50 dk bl, IV (C) .25 .25
a. Type III .25 .25
916 A95 $3 on $50 dk bl (Bl) .20 .20
917 A95 $3 on $50 dk bl (Bl) .20 .20
918 A95 $5 on $500 brn .20 .20
919 A95 $10 on $30 dk vio, III (Bl) .20 .20
a. Type IV .45 .45
b. Double surcharge, IV
920 A95 $15 on $20 org brn (G) .20 .20
921 A95 $25 on $20 org brn (G) .20 .20
922 A95 $50 on $50 dk bl (R O) .20 .20
923 A95 $50 on $300 grn, VI (C) .20 .20
a. $50 on $300 yel grn, V (C) .20 .20
924 A95 $80 on $50 dk bl (Dk Br) .20 .20
925 A95 $100 on $50 dk bl, IV 1.00 .20
a. Type III 2.25 7.50
926 A95 $200 on $50 dk bl .20 .20
927 A95 $200 on $500 brn (Bl) .20 .20
928 A95 $300 on $50 dk bl, III (C) .20 .20
a. Type IV .65 1.10
929 A95 $300 on $50 dk bl (Br) 2.00 .60
930 A95 $500 on $15 red org (Bl) .25 .25
931 A95 $500 on $30 dk vio .25 .25
932 A95 $1000 on $50 dk bl (C) 8.00 5.00
933 A95 $1000 on $100 ol grn, V 1.00 2.25
a. Type VI 2.75 5.00
934 A95 $1500 on $50 dk bl (Bl) 2.50 1.50
935 A95 $2000 on $300 grn (Bl) .30 .30
a. Horiz. pair, imperf. between

936 A95 $5000 on $100 ol grn (C) 325.00
Nos. 913-936 (24) 343.30
Nos. 913-935 (23) 18.30 13.35

No. 936 was officially authorized, but never issued.

Key pattern of overprinted border inverted and in 2 or 3 detached sections at top and bottom in Blue, Black or Green

1949 Hankow Prints Litho.
Without Gum
Type A95
937 A95 $50 on $10 (Bk) 7.00 6.50
938 A95 $100 on $10 (Bk) 7.75 7.75
939 A95 $500 on $10 (Bk) 5.50 4.50
940 A95 $1000 on $10 4.50 4.50
941 A95 $5000 on $20 11.00 11.00
942 A95 $10,000 on $20 (Bk) 11.00 6.50
943 A95 $50,000 on $20 14.00 11.00
944 A95 $100,000 on $20 (Bk) 16.00 11.00
945 A95 $500,000 on $20 250.00 160.00
946 A95 $2,000,000 on $20 (G) 600.00 200.00
947 A95 $5,000,000 on $20 1,100. 600.00
Nos. 937-944 (8) 76.75 62.75

The $10 stamp is slate green, the $20 brown.
The basic revenue stamps of Nos. 915-947 were the work of several printers. There are three main types, differing in the bottom label. Nos. 922 and 925 are in a second type: Nos. 923 and 930 in a third. Varieties of paper, color and overprint exist.
Counterfeits exist of Nos. 945-947.
For surcharges and overprints see Nos. 960-970, C63, E13, F3, J122-J126, Hupeh 1-2, People's Republic of China 5L51-5L53, 6L17-6L21.

Redrawn Coarse Impression
1949 Litho.
Without Gum
Size: 18¼x20¾mm
951 A94 $50 green .40 24.00
952 A94 $1000 dp blue .50 2.00
953 A94* $5000 carmine .50 2.00
954 A94 $10,000 brown 4.00 5.00
955 A94 $20,000 orange 1.00 2.00
956 A94 $50,000 blue 3.00 3.00
957 A94 $200,000 violet 5.00 3.00
958 A94 $500,000 vio brn 5.00 3.00
Nos. 951-958 (8) 19.40 44.00

Zeros for "cents" omitted on Nos. 957-958.
See surcharge note following No. 900.

Locomotive and Ship — A96

1949, May 1 Litho. Perf. 12½
Without Gum
959 A96 orange 2.50 2.00
a. Rouletted 11.00 6.00

Nos. 959, C62, E12 and F2 were printed without denomination and sold at the daily rate of the yuan. This was necessitated by the gold yuan inflation.
For surcharges and overprints see Nos. 1130, 1213, Taiwan 97, Fukien 18, Kansu 1, People's Republic of China 24-29, 101-104, 4L31-4L33, 4L45-4L47, 4L61-4L62, 7L9-7L12, 8L52-8L54.

Revenue Stamps Overprinted in Black

1949, May   *Perf. 12½, 13, 14*
Without Gum
960 A95 $30 dark violet   75.00 55.00
Engr.
961 A95 $200 violet brown   10.00 6.00
962 A95 $500 dark green   14.00 10.00
Nos. 960-962 (3)   99.00 71.00

A similar overprint appears on #C63, E13, F3, differing in 2nd and 3rd characters of bottom row.

Silver Yuan Surcharge in Black or Other Colors

1949   **Litho.**
963 A95 1c on $5000 brn (G)   5.00 6.00
964 A95 4c on $100 ol grn (Bl)   2.25 2.00
965 A95 4c on $3000 org)   2.25 2.00
966 A95 10c on $50 dk bl (RV)   3.50 2.00
967 A95 10c on $1000 car   4.50 2.00
   a. Inverted surcharge   60.00
968 A95 20c on $1000 red (V)   5.00 3.00
   b. Inverted surcharge
968A A95 50c on $30 dk vio (C)   27.50 6.00
969 A95 50c on $50 dk bl (C)   6.00 2.00
970 A95 $1 on $50 dk bl   15.00 20.00
Nos. 963-970 (9)   71.00 45.00

Nos. 963-965 and 967 are engraved.

Sun Type of 1949 Redrawn Coarse Impression
1949   *Perf. 12½, 13 or Compound*
973 A94 1c apple green   16.00 6.00
974 A94 2c orange   3.50 4.00
975 A94 4c blue green   .20 2.00
976 A94 10c deep lilac   .20 2.00
977 A94 16c orange red   .45 3.00
978 A94 20c blue   .25 2.00
979 A94 50c dk brown   1.40 6.00
980 A94 100c deep blue   325.00 275.00
981 A94 500c scarlet   450.00 325.00
Nos. 973-981 (9)   797.00 625.00

For surcharges see Nos. 1057-1060.

Flying Geese Over Globe — A97   Pigeons, Globe and Wreath — A98

1949, May   **Litho.**   *Perf. 12½*
Without Gum
984 A97 $1 brown org   5.00 10.00
985 A97 $2 blue   40.00 16.00
986 A97 $5 car rose   40.00 20.00
987 A97 $10 blue grn   40.00 35.00
Nos. 984-987 (4)   125.00 81.00

Five other denominations — 10c, 16c, 50c, $20 and $50 — were also printed at Shanghai, but were not issued.

For surcharges see Nos. 1007-1011, 1042-1045, 1061-1063, People's Republic of China 49-56, 5LQ17-5LQ26, 7L17-7L18, 8L14-8L16.

Engraved and Typographed
1949, Aug. 1 Without Gum *Imperf.*
988 A98 $1 org red & blk   7.00 10.00
75th anniv. of the UPU.
Exists with black denomination omitted.

Summer Palace, Peiping — A99

Bronze Bull and Kunming Lake — A100

Engraved and Typographed
1949, Aug.   *Rouletted*
Without Gum
989 A99 15c org brn & grn   3.00 3.00
990 A100 40c dl grn & car   3.00 3.00
   a. 2nd and 3rd characters at top transposed   160.00 200.00

Silver Yuan Surcharge in Black on 1949 Sun Yat-sen Issues

1949   *Perf. 12½, 14*
991 A94 1c on $100 org brn (890)   9.25 10.00
992 A94 1c on $100 dk org brn (898)   9.25 10.00
993 A94 2½c on $500 rose lil (892)   11.00 11.00
   a. Inverted surcharge   35.00
994 A94 2½c on $500 rose lil (900)   12.50 12.00
995 A94 15c on $10 grn (887)   17.50 25.00
   a. Inverted surcharge   40.00
996 A94 15c on $20 vio brn (896)   27.50 35.00
Nos. 991-996 (6)   87.00 103.00

Silver Yuan Surcharge in Black or Carmine

997 A94 2½c on $50 grn (951)   1.60 3.50
998 A94 2½c on $50,000 bl (956)   4.50 3.50
999 A94 5c on $1000 dp bl (952) (C)   3.50 3.50
1000 A94 5c on $20,000 org (955)   2.25 3.00
1001 A94 5c on $200,000 vio (957) (C)   3.50 3.00
1002 A94 5c on $500,000 vio brn (958)   2.25 3.00
1003 A94 10c on $5000 car (953)   6.50 4.25
1004 A94 10c on $10,000 brn (954)   6.50 4.25
1005 A94 15c on $200 red org (891)   8.75 8.00
1006 A94 25c on $100 dk org brn (896)   17.50 17.50
Nos. 997-1006 (10)   56.85 53.50

REPUBLIC OF CHINA

ri-ˈpə-blik of ˈchī-nə

(Taiwan)

LOCATION — Taiwan (since 1949) (Formosa)
GOVT. — Republic
AREA — 13,970 sq. mi.
POP. — 22,113,250 (1999 est.)
CAPITAL — Taipei

Stamps issued and used in Taiwan after Communist forces occupied the Chinese mainland include Taiwan Nos. 91-96, 101-103, J10-J17.

Catalogue values for unused stamps in this country are for Never Hinged items, beginning with Scott 1124 in the regular postage section, Scott B17 in the semi-postal section, Scott C69 in the airpost section, and Scott J142 in the postage due section.

Watermarks

Wmk. 281 — Wavy Lines

Wmk. 323 — Seal Character (found with "Yu" in various arrangements)

Wmk. 368 — JEZ Multiple

Wmk. 370 — Geometrical Design

Type of 1949 with Value Omitted Surcharged in Various Colors

1950, Jan. 1   **Unwmk.**   *Perf. 12½*
1007 A97 $1 green (Bk)   150.00 7.00
1008 A97 $2 green (C)   175.00 14.00
1009 A97 $5 green (V)   1,600. 65.00
1010 A97 $10 green (Br)   1,500. 130.00
1011 A97 $20 green (Dk Bl)   3,500. 550.00
Nos. 1007-1011 (5)   6,925. 766.00

Two printings of the $1 and $2 show minor differences.

Cheng Ch'eng-kung (Koxinga) — A101

1950, June 26   **Typo.**   *Rouletted*
Without Gum
1012 A101 3c dk gray grn   3.50 .85
1013 A101 10c orange brn   2.50 .25
1014 A101 15c orange yel   12.00 2.00
1015 A101 20c emerald   2.50 .20
1016 A101 30c claret   45.00 11.00
1017 A101 40c red orange   2.50 .20
1018 A101 50c chocolate   8.00 1.00
1019 A101 80c carmine   5.50 2.00
1020 A101 $1 ultra   2.50 1.00
1021 A101 $1.50 green   32.50 2.00
1022 A101 $1.60 blue   15.00 1.00
1023 A101 $2 red violet   20.00 .75
1024 A101 $5 aqua   125.00 22.50
Nos. 1012-1024 (13)   276.50 44.80

Part perf pairs exist of the 10c, 20c, 80c. The 10c and 20c were reprinted from new plates. There are slight differences.
For surcharges see Nos. 1070-1072, 1105-1108, 1118-1119.

Nos. 751, 753, 788-791, 793, 795-799 Surcharged in Carmine or Black

1950   **Engr.**   *Perf. 14*
1025 A82 3c on $30,000   3.75 2.25
1026 A82 3c on $40,000 (C)   3.25 2.25
1027 A82 3c on $50,000 (C)   3.25 3.00
1028 A82 5c on $200,000   3.75 2.50
1029 A82 10c on $4000   32.50 4.00
1030 A82 10c on $6000   24.00 4.00
1031 A82 10c on $20,000   24.00 4.00
1032 A82 10c on $2,000,000   24.00 4.00
1033 A82 20c on $500,000   35.00 4.00
1034 A82 20c on $1,000,000   60.00 8.00
1035 A82 30c on $3,000,000   90.00 10.00
1036 A82 50c on $5,000,000 (C)   150.00 10.00
Nos. 1025-1036 (12)   453.50 58.00

Issued: #1025-1027, 3/6; #1028, 3/25; #1031, 6/10:#1029-1030, 1032, 1035-1036, 8/1; #1033-1034, 8/25.
Forgeries exist.

Inverted Surcharge
1029a A82 10c on $4000   160.00
1030a A82 10c on $6000   350.00
1031a A82 10c on $20,000   200.00
1032a A82 10c on $2,000,000   210.00
1033a A82 20c on $500,000   275.00
1034a A82 20c on $1,000,000   275.00

Allegory of Election A102

Perf. 12x12½, Imperf.
1951, Mar. 20   **Engr.**   **Unwmk.**
Without Gum
1037 A102 40c carmine   14.00 1.00
   a. Horiz. pair, imperf. btwn.   85.00
1038 A102 $1 dp blue   26.00 2.75
1039 A102 $1.60 purple   30.00 4.00
1040 A102 $2 brown   35.00 4.00
Nos. 1037-1040 (4)   105.00 11.75

Souvenir Sheet
Imperf
1041 A102 $2 dp blue grn   350.00 350.00

Adoption of local self-government in Taiwan.

Design A97 Surcharged A103

Farmer and Scroll Announcing Tax Reduction A104

Surcharge in Various Colors

1951, July 19   *Perf. 12½*
Without Gum

1042	A103	$5 green (R Br)	57.50	11.00
1043	A103	$10 green (Bk)	130.00	12.00
1044	A103	$20 green (R)	400.00	30.00
1045	A103	$50 green (P)	750.00	95.00
	Nos. 1042-1045 (4)		1,337.	148.00

1952, Jan. 1   *Perf. 14*
Without Gum

1046	A104	20c red orange	9.00	1.50
1047	A104	40c dk green	12.50	2.75
1048	A104	$1 brown	20.00	6.50
1049	A104	$1.40 dp blue	27.50	4.50
1050	A104	$2 dk gray	72.50	40.00
1051	A104	$5 brown car	95.00	16.00
	Nos. 1046-1051 (6)		236.50	71.25

Land tax reduction of 37.5% in Taiwan.
Value, imperf. set, $425.

Pres. Chiang Kai-shek, Flag and Followers A105

1952, Mar. 1   Unwmk.   *Perf. 14*
Without Gum
Flag in Violet Blue and Carmine

1052	A105	40c rose car	8.00	.50
a.		Vert. pair, imperf. btwn.	75.00	
1053	A105	$1 dp green	15.00	2.25
1054	A105	$1.60 brown org	30.00	1.10
a.		Horiz. pair, imperf. btwn.	160.00	
1055	A105	$2 brt blue	35.00	19.00
1056	A105	$5 violet brn	67.50	5.00
	Nos. 1052-1056 (5)		155.50	27.85

2nd anniv. of Chiang Kai-shek's return to the presidency.
Value, imperf. set, $300.
See Nos. 1064-1069.

Nos. 975-976, 978-979 Surcharged in Black

1952, Aug. 1   *Perf. 12½*

1057	A94	3c on 4c bl grn	4.50	3.00
1058	A94	3c on 10c dp lil	4.50	3.00
a.		Inverted surcharge		
1059	A94	3c on 20c blue	6.25	4.25
1060	A94	3c on 50c dk brn	7.25	5.00
	Nos. 1057-1060 (4)		22.50	15.25

Forgeries exist.

Geese Type of 1949 with Value Omitted Surcharged

1952, Dec. 8

1061	A97	$10 green (P)	95.00	16.00
1062	A97	$20 green (R)	275.00	27.50
1063	A97	$50 green (Bk)	2,000.	750.00
	Nos. 1061-1063 (3)		2,370.	793.50

Chiang Type of 1952
Redrawn
Perf. 12½

1953, Mar. 1   Engr.   Unwmk.
Without Gum
Flag in Dark Blue & Carmine

1064	A105	10c red orange	4.00	1.50
1065	A105	20c green	8.50	1.50
1066	A105	40c rose pink	12.00	2.00
1067	A105	$1.40 blue	35.00	3.00
1068	A105	$2 brown	90.00	6.00
1069	A105	$5 rose violet	140.00	16.00
	Nos. 1064-1069 (6)		289.50	30.25

Chiang Kai-shek's return to presidency, 3rd anniv.
Many differences in redrawn design. Value, imperf. set, $350.

Nos. 1020, 1014, 1016 and 1022 Surcharged in Various Colors

1953   *Rouletted*

1070	A101	3c on $1 ultra (C)	1.60	.35
1070A	A101	10c on 15c org yel (G) ('54)	5.75	.75
1071	A101	10c on 30c cl (Bl)	3.00	1.00
1072	A101	20c on $1.60 bl (Bk)	3.50	1.10
	Nos. 1070-1072 (4)		13.85	3.20

Chinese characters and ornamental device at bottom differ on each value.
Issued: #1071, 2/1; #1070, 5/25; #1072, 6/13; #1070A, 7/16.

Nurse & Patients — A106   Chiang Kai-shek — A107

1953, July 1   Litho.   *Perf. 12½*
Without Gum
Cross in Red, Burelage Color in Italics

1073	A106	40c brown, *buff*	12.50	1.50
1074	A106	$1.60 blue, *bl*	30.00	1.40
1075	A106	$2 green, *yel*	47.50	2.25
1076	A106	$5 red org, *org*	80.00	10.00
	Nos. 1073-1076 (4)		170.00	15.15

Chinese Anti-Tuberculosis Association.

1953, Oct. 31   Engr.
Without Gum

1077	A107	10c dk brown	4.75	.25
1078	A107	20c lilac	4.75	.25
1079	A107	40c dp green	4.75	.25
1080	A107	50c dp pink	6.50	.45
1081	A107	80c brown bis	17.50	2.00
1082	A107	$1 dp olive grn	8.25	.25
1083	A107	$1.40 dp blue	8.25	.25
1084	A107	$1.60 dp carmine	8.25	.25
1085	A107	$1.70 apple grn	8.25	1.10
1086	A107	$2 brown	9.75	.25
1087	A107	$3 dark blue	110.00	5.00
1088	A107	$4 aqua	9.75	.70
1089	A107	$5 red orange	15.00	.70
1090	A107	$10 dk green	65.00	3.25
1091	A107	$20 dk brn lake	85.00	10.00
a.		Souvenir folder	350.00	
	Nos. 1077-1091 (15)		365.75	24.95

67th birthday of Pres. Chiang Kai-shek.
#1091a contains #1077-1091 imperf, arranged in 3 sheets of 5 stamps each.

Silo Highway Bridge — A108

Forest of Evergreens — A109

$1.60 and $5, Silo bridge, side view.

1954, Jan. 28   Unwmk.   *Perf. 12½*
Without Gum
Various Frames

1092	A108	40c vermilion	17.50	1.00
1093	A108	$1.60 blue violet	80.00	1.75
1094	A108	$3.60 sepia	50.00	5.00
1095	A108	$5 magenta	125.00	9.00
a.		Souvenir folder	950.00	
	Nos. 1092-1095 (4)		272.50	16.75

Opening of Silo bridge, 1st anniversary.
No. 1095a contains one sheet of 4 containing Nos. 1092-1095 imperforate.

1954, Mar. 12   *Perf. 12x12½*
Without Gum

1096	A109	40c shown	15.00	1.00
1097	A109	$10 Nursery	110.00	5.00

Issued to publicize forest conservation.

Runner — A110   Globe, Bridge and Ship — A111

1954, Mar. 29
Without Gum

1098	A110	40c dp ultra	25.00	1.75
1099	A110	$5 carmine	75.00	9.50

11th Youth Day, Mar. 29, 1954.

1954, Oct. 21   *Perf. 12*
Without Gum

1100	A111	40c red orange	15.00	1.00
1101	A111	$5 deep blue	17.50	4.50

2nd Overseas Chinese Day, Oct. 21, 1954.

Ex-Prisoner with Broken Chains — A112

Designs: $1, Ex-prisoner with torch and flag, UN emblem. $1.60, Torch and date.

1955, Jan. 23

1102	A112	40c blue green	2.00	.65
a.		Vert. pair, imperf. btwn.	140.00	
1103	A112	$1 sepia	14.50	5.00
1104	A112	$1.60 lake	14.50	4.25
	Nos. 1102-1104 (3)		31.00	9.90

Honoring Chinese who fought on the side of the North Korean army, who, when released January 23, 1954, chose to return to the Republic of China.

Nos. 1019-1021, 1017 Surcharged in Brown, Blue or Green:

a   b

c

1955   *Rouletted*

1105	A101(a)	3c on $1 (Br)	2.00	.50
1106	A101(b)	10c on 80c (Bl)	2.75	.50
1107	A101(b)	10c on $1.50 (Bl)	2.75	.50
1108	A101(c)	20c on 40c (G)	3.25	.85
	Nos. 1105-1108 (4)		10.75	2.35

Issued: #1105, 1108, 2/18; #1106-1107, 8/1.

Hand Planting Evergreen Tree — A113

Chiang Kai-shek, Flags, Building A114

Design: $50, Seedling and map of Taiwan.

1955, Apr. 1   *Perf. 12*
Without Gum

1109	A113	$20 dp carmine	32.50	1.25
1110	A113	$50 blue	80.00	5.75

Issued to publicize forest conservation.

1955, May 20   Engr.   *Perf. 12*
Without Gum

1111	A114	20c olive	3.25	.30
1112	A114	40c blue green	3.00	.30
1113	A114	$2 car rose	8.00	.90
1114	A114	$7 dp ultra	12.50	1.50
a.		Souv. sheet of 4, #1111-1114, imperf.	150.00	150.00
	Nos. 1111-1114 (4)		26.75	3.00

First anniversary of Pres. Chiang Kai-shek's re-election.
No. 1114a is perf. 12 at right edge of sheet.
Value is for sheet with right selvage.

Armed Forces Emblem — A115

1955, Sept. 3
Without Gum

1115	A115	40c dk blue	3.50	.50
1116	A115	$2 org ver	12.50	1.50
1117	A115	$7 bl grn	20.00	1.75
a.		Sheet of 3, #1115-1117, imperf.	325.00	325.00
	Nos. 1115-1117 (3)		36.00	3.75

Armed Forces Day, Sept. 3.
No. 1117a is perf. 12 at right edge of sheet.
Value is for sheet with right selvage.

Nos. 1017, 1018 and C64 Surcharged in Magenta

1955, Sept. 16   Typo.   *Rouletted*

1118	A101	20c on 40c red org	4.00	.40
1119	A101	20c on 50c choc	4.00	.40
1120	AP6	20c on 60c dp blue	5.00	.50
	Nos. 1118-1120 (3)		13.00	1.30

Flags of UN and China A116

1955, Oct. 24   Engr.   *Perf. 11½*
Without Gum

1121	A116	40c dk blue	2.25	.50
1122	A116	$2 dk car rose	4.50	1.00
1123	A116	$7 slate green	7.75	1.75
	Nos. 1121-1123 (3)		14.50	3.25

10th anniv. of the UN, Oct. 24, 1955.

> **Catalogue values for unused stamps in this section, from this point to the end of the section, are for Never Hinged items.**

Pres. Chiang Kai-shek A117   Birthplace of Sun Yat-sen A118

1955, Oct. 31   Photo.   Perf. 13½

1124	A117	40c dk bl, red & brn	4.25	.50
1125	A117	$2 grn, red & dk bl	10.50	1.10
1126	A117	$7 brn, red & grn	14.00	2.25
a.		Souv. sheet of 3, #1124-1126, imperf.	140.00	140.00
		Nos. 1124-1126 (3)	28.75	3.85

69th birthday of Pres. Chiang Kai-shek.
No. 1126a is perf. 12 at right edge of sheet.
Value is for sheet with right selvage.

1955, Nov. 12   Engr.   Perf. 12
Without Gum

1127	A118	40c blue	1.75	.45
1128	A118	$2 red brown	6.00	1.00
1129	A118	$7 rose lake	10.00	2.00
		Nos. 1127-1129 (3)	17.75	3.45

90th anniversary, birth of Sun Yat-sen.

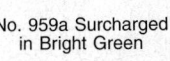

No. 959a Surcharged
in Bright Green

1956, Feb. 10   Litho.   Rouletted

1130	A96	20c on orange	.45	.20

See No. 1213.

China Map and
Transportation
Methods — A119

Wmk. 281
1956, Mar. 20   Engr.   Perf. 12
Without Gum

1131	A119	40c dk carmine	1.75	.25
1132	A119	$1 intense blk	3.50	.50
1133	A119	$1.60 chocolate	4.50	.35
1134	A119	$2 dk green	5.50	1.00
		Nos. 1131-1134 (4)	15.25	2.10

60th anniv. of the founding of the modern
Chinese postal system.

Souvenir Sheets
Imperf

1135	A119	$2 magenta	40.00	22.50
1136	A119	$2 red	40.00	22.50

Exhib. for the 60th anniv. of the modern Chinese postal system, Mar. 20, 1956.

Children at
Play — A120

Early and
Modern
Locomotives
A121

1956, Apr. 4   Unwmk.   Perf. 12
Without Gum

1137	A120	40c emerald	1.50	.25
1138	A120	$1.60 dk blue	3.00	.50
1139	A120	$2 dk carmine	3.50	.90
		Nos. 1137-1139 (3)	8.00	1.65

Children's Day, Apr. 4, 1956.

1956, June 9   Wmk. 281 Vert.
Without Gum

1140	A121	40c rose car	3.25	.40
1141	A121	$2 blue	6.50	.65
1142	A121	$8 green	8.00	1.40
		Nos. 1140-1142 (3)	17.75	2.45

75th anniversary of Chinese Railroads.

Pres. Chiang Kai-shek
A122   A123

A124

Various Portraits of Chiang
**Perf. 14½x13½, 14½ (A123),
13½x14½**
1956, Oct. 31   Photo.   Unwmk.

1143	A122	20c red orange	4.00	.20
1144	A122	40c carmine rose	6.25	.20
1145	A123	$1 brt ultra	8.25	.25
1146	A123	$1.60 red lilac	10.50	.20
1147	A124	$2 red brown	12.50	.30
1148	A124	$8 brt grnsh blue	21.00	.60
		Nos. 1143-1148 (6)	62.50	1.75

70th birthday of Pres. Chiang Kai-shek.

**Types of Special Delivery, Air Post and
Registration Stamps of 1949
Surcharged in Black or Maroon**

a   b

c

1956   Unwmk.   Litho.   Rouletted
Without Gum

1150	SD2(a)	3c red violet	1.25	.20
a.		Perf. 12½	2.75	
1151	AP5(b)	3c blue green (M)	1.25	.20
1152	R2(c)	10c bright red	1.25	.20
		Nos. 1150-1152 (3)	3.75	.60

Issued: #1150, 4/25; #1151, 11/11; #1152, 12/25.

Telecommunications
Emblem and Radio
Tower — A125

Wmk. 281
1956, Dec. 28   Engr.   Perf. 12
Without Gum

1153	A125	40c deep ultra	1.60	.20
1154	A125	$1.40 carmine	2.25	.20
1155	A125	$1.60 dark green	3.25	.20
1156	A125	$2 chocolate	4.25	.40
		Nos. 1153-1156 (4)	11.35	1.00

Chinese telegraph service, 75th anniv.

Map of China
A126

Mother
Instructing
Mencius
A127

Pin Perf., Perf. 12x12½
1957   Litho.   Wmk. 281
Without Gum

1157	A126	3c brt blue	.90	.20
1158	A126	10c violet	1.40	.20
1159	A126	20c red orange	.90	.20
1160	A126	40c rose red	1.75	.20

Unwmk.

1161	A126	$1 orange brown	2.50	.20
1162	A126	$1.60 green	3.75	.25
		Nos. 1157-1162 (6)	11.20	1.25

Map inscription reads: "Recovery of Mainland."
See Nos. 1177-1182.

Unwmk.
1957, May 12   Engr.   Perf. 12

Design: $3, Mother tattooing Yueh Fei.

Without Gum

1163	A127	40c green	1.50	.20
1164	A127	$3 redsh brown	2.75	.40

Issued to honor Mother's Day, 1957.

Badge of Chinese Boy Scouts — A128

1957, Aug. 11
Without Gum

1165	A128	40c lilac	.75	.20
1166	A128	$1 green	1.50	.35
1167	A128	$1.60 dk green	2.25	.25
		Nos. 1165-1167 (3)	4.50	.80

Cent. of the birth of Lord Baden-Powell and to publicize the World Scout Jubilee Jamboree, England, Aug. 1-12.

Globe, Radio
Tower and
Microphone
A129

1957, Sept. 16
Without Gum

1168	A129	40c vermilion	.60	.20
1169	A129	50c brt rose lilac	1.00	.20
1170	A129	$3.50 dark blue	1.50	.50
		Nos. 1168-1170 (3)	3.10	.90

30th anniv. of Chinese broadcasting.

Map of
Taiwan — A130

1957, Oct. 26
Without Gum

1171	A130	40c blue green	2.75	.35
1172	A130	$1.40 lt ultra	4.50	1.00
1173	A130	$2 gray	6.25	1.50
		Nos. 1171-1173 (3)	13.50	2.85

Start of construction on the Cross Island Highway, Taiwan.

Freighter "Hai Min" and River Boat
"Kiang Foo" — A131

1957, Dec. 16   Engr.   Perf. 12
Without Gum

1174	A131	40c deep ultra	.75	.25
1175	A131	80c rose lake	1.50	.95
1176	A131	$2.80 vermilion	2.25	1.40
		Nos. 1174-1176 (3)	4.50	2.60

85th anniv. of the establishment of the China Merchants Steam Navigation Co.

Type of 1957
Pin Perf., Perf. 12x12½
1957, Dec. 25   Typo.   Unwmk.
Without Gum
Dark Blue Frames

1177	A126	3c brt blue	.30	.20
1178	A126	10c violet	.55	.20
1179	A126	20c brick red	.85	.20
1180	A126	40c rose red	1.00	.20
1181	A126	$1 dp org brn	3.25	.25
1182	A126	$1.60 dp green	4.00	.30
		Nos. 1177-1182 (6)	9.95	1.35

Stamps with bars obliterating the face value are specimens.

Butterfly   Mme. Chiang
A132   Kai-shek Orchid
                  A133

Perf. 13½
1958, Mar. 20   Unwmk.   Photo.
Various Insects in Natural Colors

1183	A132	10c pale grn, grn & blk	1.25	.50
1184	A132	40c lem, pink, grn & blk	1.25	.50
1185	A132	$1 yel grn & mar	2.25	.60
1186	A132	$1.40 yel, org & blk	2.75	.75
1187	A132	$1.60 pale brn & dk pur	4.00	.90
1188	A132	$2 brt yel, org & blk	4.75	1.25
		Nos. 1183-1188 (6)	16.25	4.50

1958, Mar. 20

Orchids: 20c, Formosan Wilson, horiz. $1.40, Klotzsch. $3, Fitzgerald, horiz.

Orchids in Natural Colors

1189	A133	20c chocolate	2.00	.40
1190	A133	40c purple	2.25	.40
1191	A133	$1.40 dk vio brn	3.00	.60
1192	A133	$3 dark blue	4.25	1.10
		Nos. 1189-1192 (4)	11.50	2.50

World Health Organization
Emblem — A134

1958, May 28   Engr.   Perf. 12
Without Gum
1193 A134 40c dark blue   .50 .20
1194 A134 $1.60 brick red   .65 .20
1195 A134 $2 deep red lilac   .85 .40
Nos. 1193-1195 (3)   2.00 .80

10th anniv. of the WHO.

President's Mansion,
Taipei — A135

Wmk. 323
1958, Sept. 20   Engr.   Perf. 12
Without Gum
1196 A135 $10 blue green   8.00 .30
  a.   Granite paper   10.00 .30
1197 A135 $20 car rose   18.00 .50
  a.   Granite paper   18.00 .50
1198 A135 $50 red brown   55.00 2.00
1199 A135 $100 dk blue   85.00 4.75
Nos. 1196-1199 (4)   166.00 7.55

Issued: #1196a, 1197a, 5/24/63.
See #1349-1351. For surcharge see #J131.

Taiwan
Farm
Scene
A136

1958, Oct. 1   Unwmk.
Without Gum
1200 A136 20c emerald   1.25 .20
1201 A136 40c black   1.50 .20
1202 A136 $1.40 brt magenta   2.00 .25
1203 A136 $3 ultra   3.75 .75
Nos. 1200-1203 (4)   8.50 1.40

10th anniversary of the Joint Commission
on Rural Reconstruction.

Pres. Chiang
Kai-shek
A137

1958, Oct. 31   Photo.   Perf. 13½
1204 A137 40c multicolored   1.25 .45

Pres. Chiang Kai-shek on his 72nd birthday.

UNESCO
Building,
Paris
A138

1958, Nov. 3   Engr.   Perf. 12
Without Gum
1205 A138 20c dark blue   .30 .20
1206 A138 40c green   .40 .20
1207 A138 $1.40 orange ver   .60 .35
1208 A138 $3 red lilac   1.00 .50
Nos. 1205-1208 (4)   2.30 1.25

UNESCO Headquarters in Paris opening,
Nov. 3.

Flame from Liberty
Torch Encircling
Globe — A139

1958, Dec. 10   Unwmk.
Without Gum
1209 A139 40c green   .20 .20
1210 A139 60c gray brown   .30 .20
1211 A139 $1 carmine   .50 .20
1212 A139 $3 ultra   .75 .40
Nos. 1209-1212 (4)   1.75 1.00

10th anniversary of the signing of the Universal Declaration of Human Rights.

No. 959a Surcharged
in Bright Green

Rouletted
1958, Dec. 11   Litho.   Unwmk.
Without Gum
1213 A96 20c on orange   .55 .20

Ballot Box, Scales and
Constitution — A140

1958, Dec. 25   Engr.   Perf. 12
Without Gum
1214 A140 40c green   .90 .20
1215 A140 50c dull purple   1.25 .20
1216 A140 $1.40 car rose   1.50 .25
1217 A140 $3.50 dk blue   2.50 .75
Nos. 1214-1217 (4)   6.15 1.40

Adoption of the constitution, 10th anniv.

Chu Kwang Tower,
Quemoy — A141

1959-60   Wmk. 323   Litho.   Perf. 12
Without Gum
1218   A141   3c orange   .35 .20
1218A A141   5c lt yel grn
                ('60)   .40 .20
1219   A141 10c lilac   .50 .20
1220   A141 20c ultra   .65 .20
1221   A141 40c brown   .80 .20
1222   A141 50c bluish grn   1.00 .20
1223   A141 $1 rose red   1.10 .20
1224   A141 $1.40 yel grn   1.50 .20
1225   A141 $2 gray grn   2.00 .20
1226   A141 $2.80 rose pink   2.75 .25
1227   A141 $3 slate blue   3.00 .25
Nos. 1218-1227 (11)   14.05 2.30

See Nos. 1270-1283.

1959, June 15   Engr.   Perf. 12
Without Gum
1228 A142 40c blue   .30 .20
1229 A142 $1.60 dk brown   .40 .20
1230 A142 $3 brt blue grn   .50 .20
1231 A142 $5 orange ver   1.00 .50
Nos. 1228-1231 (4)   2.20 1.10

40th anniversary of the ILO.

Bugler
and Tents
A143

1959, July 8   Unwmk.
Without Gum
1232 A143 40c carmine   .95 .20
1233 A143 50c dark blue   1.10 .25
1234 A143 $5 green   1.90 .55
Nos. 1232-1234 (3)   3.95 1.00

10th World Boy Scout Jamboree, Makiling
National Park, Philippines, July 17-26.

Inscribed Stone,
Mt. Tai-wu,
Quemoy — A144

Map of
Taiwan
Straits
A145

1959, Sept. 3   Engr.   Perf. 12
Without Gum
1235 A144 40c brown   .75 .20
1236 A145 $1.40 ultra   .85 .20
1237 A145 $2 green   1.50 .20
1238 A144 $3 dark blue   1.75 .30
Nos. 1235-1238 (4)   4.85 .90

Defense of Quemoy and Matsu islands.
For overprints see Nos. 1258-1259.

Pigeons
Circling
Globe
A146

1959, Oct. 4
Without Gum
1239 A146 40c blue   .35 .20
1240 A146 $1 rose carmine   .60 .20
1241 A146 $2 gray brown   .85 .20
1242 A146 $3.50 red orange   1.00 .50
Nos. 1239-1242 (4)   2.80 1.10

Intl. Letter Writing Week, Oct. 4-10.

National Taiwan
Science Hall,
Taipei — A147

1959, Nov. 12   Photo.   Perf. 13x13½
1243 A147 40c shown   1.10 .20
1244 A147 $3 Front view   2.40 .70

Emblem
A148

1959, Dec. 7   Engr.   Perf. 12
Without Gum
1245 A148 40c blue green   .40 .25
1246 A148 $1.60 red lilac   .50 .25
1247 A148 $3 orange   .95 .60
Nos. 1245-1247 (3)   1.85 1.10

Intl. Confederation of Free Trade Unions,
10th anniv.

Sun Yat-
sen,
Lincoln
and
Flags
A149

Perf. 13½, 12
1959, Dec. 25   Photo.   Unwmk.
1248 A149 40c multicolored   .25 .25
1249 A149 $3 multicolored   1.00 .60

Issued to honor Sun Yat-sen and Abraham
Lincoln as "Leaders of Democracy."

Mailman on Motorcycle Delivering
Night Mail — A150

Postal
Launch
A151

1960, Mar. 20   Engr.   Perf. 11½
Without Gum
1250 A150 $1.40 dk violet brn 1.10 .25
1251 A151 $1.60 ultra   1.10 .25

Issued to publicize the Prompt Delivery
Service.

WRY Uprooted
Oak
Emblem — A152

1960, Apr. 7   Photo.   Perf. 13
1252 A152 40c blk, red brn & em-
              er   .50 .20
1253 A152 $3 blk, red org & grn .90 .35

World Refugee Year, 7/1/59-6/30/60.

Cross Island Highway, Taiwan — A153

Design: $1, $2, Road through tunnel, vert.

Perf. 11½
1960, May 9 Engr. Unwmk.
Without Gum

1254	A153	40c green	1.00	.20
1255	A153	$1 dk blue	1.75	.25
1256	A153	$2 brown vio	2.00	.30
1257	A153	$3 brown	3.00	.35
a.		Souv. sheet of 2, #1255, 1257, wmk. 323, imperf.	175.00	70.00
		Nos. 1254-1257 (4)	7.75	1.10

Opening of the Cross Island Highway, Taiwan.

Red Overprint on Nos. 1237-1238
Chinese and English: "Welcome U.S. President Dwight D. Eisenhower 1960"
1960, June 18 Unwmk. Perf. 12

1258	A145	$2 green	.90	.30
a.		Inverted overprint	2,250.	2,250.
1259	A144	$3 dk blue	1.40	.45

Eisenhower's visit to China, June 18, 1960.

Phonopost — A154

1960, June 27
Without Gum

1260	A154	$2 red orange	1.60	.40

Phonopost Service of the Chinese armed forces.

Two Horses and Groom, by Han Kan — A155

Paintings from Palace Museum, Taichung: $1, Two Riders, by Wei Yen. $1.60, Flowers and Birds by Hsiao Yung, vert. $2, Pair of Mandarin Ducks by Monk Hui Ch'ung.

1960, Aug. 4 Photo. Perf. 13

1261	A155	$1 ol gray, blk & brn	3.25	.55
1262	A155	$1.40 bis brn, blk & fawn	6.00	1.00
1263	A155	$1.60 multicolored	8.00	1.50
1264	A155	$2 beige, blk & gray grn	14.00	2.75
		Nos. 1261-1264 (4)	31.25	5.80

Chinese paintings, 7th-11th centuries. For other painting types with large straight numerals in the upper corners and large Chinese characters on the side see A186, A241 and A285.

Youth Corps Flag and Summer Activities A156

Reforestation A157

Design: $3, similar to 50c, horiz.

1960, Aug. 20 Engr. Perf. 12
Without Gum

1265	A156	50c slate green	.50	.20
1266	A156	$3 copper brown	1.10	.45

Summer activities of China Youth Corps.

1960, Aug. 29 Photo. Perf. 13½x13
$2, Protection of forest. $3, Timber industry.

1267	A157	$1 multicolored	1.25	.20
1268	A157	$2 multicolored	1.75	.25
1269	A157	$3 multicolored	2.50	.60
a.		Souvenir sheet of 3	25.00	17.50
		Nos. 1267-1269 (3)	5.50	1.05

Fifth World Forestry Congress, Seattle, Washington, Aug. 29-Sept. 10.
No. 1269a contains Nos. 1267-1269 assembled as a triptych, 65½x40mm and imperf., but with simulated black perforations.

Chu Kwang Tower, Quemoy — A158

Sports — A159

1960-61 Wmk. 323 Litho. Perf. 12
Without Gum

1270	A158	3c lt red brown	.50	.20
1271	A158	40c pale violet	.50	.20
1272	A158	50c orange ('61)	.80	.20
1273	A158	60c rose lilac	1.00	.20
1274	A158	80c pale green	1.10	.20
1275	A158	$1 gray grn ('61)	1.25	.20
1276	A158	$1.20 gray olive	1.25	.20
1277	A158	$1.50 ultra	1.50	.25
1278	A158	$2 car rose ('61)	1.75	.20
1279	A158	$2.50 pale blue	1.90	.25
1280	A158	$3 bluish green	2.00	.25
1281	A158	$3.20 lt red brown	1.75	.20
1282	A158	$3.60 vio blue ('61)	3.75	.30
1283	A158	$4.50 vermilion	7.00	.35
		Nos. 1270-1283 (14)	26.05	3.20

For surcharges see Nos. J132-J134.

1962-64
Granite Paper
Without Gum

1270a	A158	3c light red brown	.50	.20
1270B	A158	10c emerald ('63)	1.50	.20
1271a	A158	40c pale violet	.50	.20
1274a	A158	80c pale green	.50	.20
1275a	A158	$1 gray grn ('63)	8.00	.20
1278a	A158	$2 carmine rose	4.00	.20
1281a	A158	$3.20 red brn ('64)	10.00	.20
1282A	A158	$4 brt blue grn	10.00	.20
1283a	A158	$4.50 vermilion	15.00	.50
		Nos. 1270a-1283a (9)	50.00	2.10

Two types of No. 1271a: I. Seven lines in "0" of "40." II. Eight lines in "0."

Perf. 12½
1960, Oct. 25 Photo. Unwmk.

1284	A159	50c Diving	1.25	.20
1285	A159	80c Discus thrower	1.00	.20
1286	A159	$2 Basketball	2.50	.20
1287	A159	$2.50 Soccer	2.50	.40
1288	A159	$3 Hurdling	3.00	.40
1289	A159	$3.20 Runner	3.25	.60
		Nos. 1284-1289 (6)	13.50	2.00

Bronze Wine Container, 1751-1111 B.C. — A160

Flat Bowl, 1111-771 B.C. — A161

Ancient Chinese Art Treasures: $1, Cauldron, 1111-771 B.C. $1.20, Porcelain vase, 960-1126 A.D. $1.50, Perforated tube, 1111-771 B.C. $2, Jug in shape of monk's cap, 1368-1661 A.D. $2.50, Jade flower vase, 1368-1661, A.D.

1961 Photo. Perf. 13

1290	A160	80c lt ol, blk & dk vio	1.50	.20
1291	A160	$1 sal, bl & blk	1.90	.25
1292	A160	$1.20 yel, brn & ultra	2.75	.35
1293	A160	$1.50 lil, bl & sep	3.75	.60
1294	A160	$2 pale grn, dk grn & red	4.00	.60
1295	A160	$2.50 grnsh bl & dk vio	5.50	.70
			9.25	1.00
		Nos. 1290-1295 (6)	24.65	3.10

Issue dates: Nos. 1290, 1292, 1295, Feb. 1. Nos. 1291, 1293-1294, May 1.

1961
Designs: 80c, Palace perfumer, 1662-1911. $1, Corn vase, 770-221 B.C. $2, Jade tankard, 960-1126 A.D. $4, Glazed washer, 1127-1279 A.D. $4.50, Jade chimera, 8 B.C.-206 A.D.

1296	A160	80c pink, brn, bl & yel	1.50	.30
1297	A160	$1 cit, blk & brn	2.00	.60
1298	A161	$1.50 sal & ind	4.00	.70
1299	A160	$2 bl, blk & rose	4.00	.60
1300	A161	$4 red, blk & bluish gray	6.00	1.25
1301	A161	$4.50 grnsh bl, blk & brn	24.00	3.00
		Nos. 1296-1301 (6)	41.50	6.45

Issued: #1296-1298, 8/15; #1299-1301, 9/15.

1962
Designs: 80c, Topaz twin wine vessels, 1662-1911 A.D. $1, Squat pouring vase, 1751-1111 B.C. $2.40, Vase, 1368-1661 A.D. $3, Wine vase, 1751-1111 B.C. $3.20, Covered porcelain jar, 1662-1911 A.D. $3.60, Perforated disc, 206 B.C.-8 A.D.

1302	A160	80c crim, blk & ocher	1.00	.20
1303	A160	$1 blue & vio blk	1.25	.25
1304	A160	$2.40 hn brn, blk & bl	13.50	1.00
1305	A160	$3 blue, blk & pink	15.00	.90
1306	A160	$3.20 ultra, lt grn & red	13.00	.90
1307	A160	$3.60 yel, blk & brn	21.00	1.25
		Nos. 1302-1307 (6)	64.75	4.50

Issue dates: Nos. 1303-1304, 1307, Jan. 15. Nos. 1302, 1305-1306, Feb. 15.

Farmer with Mechanized Plow — A162

Madame Chiang Kai-shek and League Emblem — A163

1961, Feb. 4 Engr. Perf. 12
Without Gum

1308	A162	80c rose violet	1.40	.20
1309	A162	$2 green	2.50	.30
1310	A162	$3.20 vermilion	4.00	.30
		Nos. 1308-1310 (3)	7.90	.80

1961 agricultural census.

Unwmk.
1961, Mar. 8 Photo. Perf. 13
Portrait in Black

1311	A163	80c lt grn & car rose	2.10	.20
1312	A163	$1 yel grn & car rose	2.75	.60
1313	A163	$2 org brn & car rose	3.50	.70
1314	A163	$3.20 lil & car rose	4.25	1.00
		Nos. 1311-1314 (4)	12.60	2.50

10th anniversary of the Chinese Women's Anti-Aggression League.

Spiny Lobster and Mail Order Service Emblem — A164

Jeme Tien-yow and Pataling Tunnel — A165

1961, Mar. 20 Engr. Perf. 11½
Without Gum

1315	A164	$3 slate green	3.50	.35

Issued to publicize the mail order service for consumer goods.

1961, Apr. 26 Perf. 11½
Without Gum
$2, Jeme Tien-yow & 1909 locomotive.

1316	A165	80c lilac	1.40	.20
1317	A165	$2 black, horiz.	2.10	.50

Centenary of the birth of Jeme Tien-yow, builder of the Peking-Kalgan railroad.

Map of China inscribed: "Recovery of the Mainland" — A166

Pres. Chiang Kai-shek — A167

1961, May 20 Photo. Perf. 13½

1318	A166	80c multicolored	2.50	.25
1319	A167	$2 multicolored	4.00	1.10
a.		Souvenir sheet of 2	14.00	12.50

1st anniversary of Pres. Chiang Kai-shek's 3rd term inauguration.
No. 1319a contains one each of Nos. 1318-1319, imperf. with simulated perforations. Without gum.

Convair 880-M, Biplane of 1921 and Flag — A168

1961, July 1 Perf. 13x12½

1320	A168	$10 multicolored	3.00	1.10

40th anniversary of civil air service.

Sun Yat-sen and Chiang Kai-shek — A169

Flag and Map of China — A170

Perf. 13½
1961, Oct. 10   Unwmk.   Photo.

1321	A169	80c gray, lt brn & sl	1.60	.20
1322	A170	$5 gray, ultra, red & beige	3.25	1.40
a.		Souvenir sheet of 2	12.00	10.00

50th anniv. of the Republic of China. No. 1322a contains one each of Nos. 1321-1322, imperf. with simulated perforations. No gum.

Green Lake A171

Oil Refinery A173

Lotus Pond A172

Taiwan Scenery: $2, Sun-Moon Lake. $3.20, Wulai waterfalls.

Perf. 13½x14, 14x13½
1961, Oct. 31   Unwmk.

1323	A171	80c multicolored	4.00	.20
1324	A172	$1 multicolored	9.00	.50
1325	A172	$2 multicolored	9.00	.70
1326	A171	$3.20 multicolored	12.00	.90
		Nos. 1323-1326 (4)	34.00	2.30

1961, Nov. 14   Perf. 11½

Designs: $1.50, Steel works. $2.50, Aluminum plant. $3.20, Fertilizer plant, horiz.

1327	A173	80c multicolored	1.60	.20
1328	A173	$1.50 multicolored	3.25	.50
1329	A173	$2.50 multicolored	4.25	.55
1330	A173	$3.20 multicolored	5.00	.65
		Nos. 1327-1330 (4)	14.10	1.90

Chinese industrial development and the Golden Jubilee Convention of the Chinese Institute of Engineers, Nov. 13-16.

Atomic Reactor, Tsing-Hwa University A174

Atomic Reactor in Operation A175

Design: $3.20, Atomic symbol and laboratory, Tsing-Hwa, horiz.

1961-62   Photo.   Perf. 12½

1331	A174	80c multicolored	2.25	.20
1332	A175	$2 multicolored	4.50	1.40
1333	A175	$3.20 multicolored	4.25	.85
		Nos. 1331-1333 (3)	11.00	2.45

Inauguration on Apr. 13, 1961, of the 1st Chinese atomic reactor at the National Tsing-Hwa University Institute of Nuclear Science. Issued: 80c, 12/2; $2, $3.20, 3/20/62.

Microwave Reflector and Telegraph Wires — A176

Design: $3.20, Microwave parabolic antenna and mountains, horiz.

1961, Dec. 28   Perf. 12½

1334	A176	80c multicolored	1.25	.20
1335	A176	$3.20 multicolored	2.00	.80

80th anniv. of Chinese telecommunications.

Mechanical Postal Equipment and Twine Tying Machine — A176a

Wmk. 323
1962, Mar. 20   Engr.   Perf. 11½
Without Gum

1336	A176a	80c chocolate	1.10	.30

Yu Shan Observatory A177

Observation Balloon, Earth and Cumulus Clouds A178

Design: $1, Map showing route of typhoon Pamela, Sept. 1961, horiz.

1962
Without Gum

1337	A177	80c brown	.70	.20
1338	A178	$1 bluish black	1.40	.30
1339	A178	$2 green	1.90	.65
		Nos. 1337-1339 (3)	4.00	1.15

Issue dates: 80c, $2, Mar. 23; $1, May 7. World Meteorological Day, Mar. 23.

Child Receiving Milk, UN Emblem A179

1962, Apr. 4
Without Gum

1340	A179	80c rose red	.85	.20
1341	A179	$3.20 green	1.75	.50
a.		Souvenir sheet of 2	11.50	3.50

15th anniv. of UNICEF. No. 1341a contains one each of Nos. 1340-1341 imperf. with simulated perforations.

Malaria Eradication Emblem — A180

Unwmk.
1962, Apr. 7   Photo.   Perf. 13

1342	A180	80c dk bl, red & lt grn	.60	.20
1343	A180	$3.60 brn, pink & grn	1.10	1.00

WHO drive to eradicate malaria.

Yu Yu-jen — A181

Cheng Ch'eng-kung (Koxinga) — A182

1962, Apr. 24   Perf. 13

1344	A181	80c gray, blk & pink	1.60	.25

Issued to honor Yu Yu-jen, newspaper reporter, revolutionary leader and co-worker of Sun Yat-sen, on his 84th birthday.

1962, Apr. 29

1345	A182	80c deep claret	1.50	.20
1346	A182	$2 dark green	2.50	.55

300th anniversary (in 1961) of the recovery of Taiwan from the Dutch by Koxinga.

Emblem of Intl. Cooperative Alliance — A183

Clasped Hands Across Globe — A184

Wmk. 323
1962, July 7   Engr.   Perf. 12
Without Gum

1347	A183	80c brown	.70	.20
1348	A184	$2 violet	1.10	.45

Intl. Cooperative Movement and 40th Intl. Cooperative Day, July 7, 1962.

Mansion Type of 1958
1962, July 20
Without Gum

1349	A135	$5 gray green	2.00	.20
1350	A135	$5.60 violet	2.75	.20
1351	A135	$6 orange	2.40	.20
		Nos. 1349-1351 (3)	7.15	.60

1963
Granite Paper

1349a	A135	$5 gray green	2.50	.20
1350a	A135	$5.60 violet	3.00	.20
1351a	A135	$6 orange	4.00	.20
		Nos. 1349a-1351a (3)	9.50	.60

"Art and Science" — A185

$2, "Education," book and UNESCO emblem, horiz. $3.20, "Communications," globes, horiz.

1962, Aug. 28   Wmk. 323   Perf. 12
Without Gum

1352	A185	80c lilac rose	.60	.20
1353	A185	$2 rose claret	.95	.40
1354	A185	$3.20 yellow green	1.10	.30
		Nos. 1352-1354 (3)	2.65	.90

UNESCO activities in China.

Emperor T'ai Tsung, T'ang Dynasty, 627-649 A186

Emperors: $2, T'ai Tsu, Sung dynasty, 960-975. $3.20, T'ai Tsu, Yuan dynasty (Genghis Khan), 1206-27. $4, T'ai Tsu, Ming dynasty, 1368-98.

1962, Sept. 20   Photo.   Unwmk.

1355	A186	80c multicolored	10.00	2.25
1356	A186	$2 multicolored	27.50	7.00
1357	A186	$3.20 multicolored	47.50	7.50
1358	A186	$4 multicolored	60.00	19.50
		Nos. 1355-1358 (4)	145.00	36.25

Lions International Emblem A187

1962, Oct. 8   Perf. 13½

1359	A187	80c multicolored	1.10	.20
1360	A187	$3.60 multicolored	2.10	.80
a.		Souvenir sheet of 2	14.00	7.00

45th anniv. of Lions Intl. No. 1360a contains one each of Nos. 1359-1360, imperf. with simulated perforations.

Pole Vaulting — A188

Shooting A189

1962, Oct. 25   Unwmk.   Perf. 13

1361	A188	80c multicolored	.90	.20
1362	A189	$3.20 multicolored	2.10	.40

Sports meet.

Young Farmers and 4-H Emblem — A190

Flag, Liner of China Merchants' Steam Navigation Co. — A191

Design: $3.20, 4-H emblem and rice.

Wmk. 323
1962, Dec. 7   Engr.   Perf. 12
Without Gum

1363	A190	80c carmine	.60	.20
1364	A190	$3.20 green	1.90	.55
a.		Souvenir sheet of 2	13.00	9.00

10th anniv. of the 4-H Club in China. No. 1364a contains one each of Nos. 1363-1364, imperf. with simulated perforations.

Perf. 13½
1962, Dec. 16   Unwmk.   Photo.

Design: $3.60, Company's Pacific navigation chart and freighter, horiz.

1365	A191	80c multicolored	1.60	.20
1366	A191	$3.60 multicolored	2.50	.80

90th anniversary of the China Merchants' Steam Navigation Co., Ltd.

Farm Woman, Tractor and Plane Dropping Food over Mainland — A192

Perf. 12½
1963, Mar. 21   Unwmk.   Photo.

1367	A192	$10 multicolored	4.00	.70

FAO "Freedom from Hunger" campaign.

Torch, Young Couple and Martyrs' Monument, Canton A193

Wmk. 323
1963, Mar. 29   Engr.   Perf. 11½
Without Gum

1368	A193	80c purple	.75	.20
1369	A193	$3.20 green	1.50	.40

Issued for the 20th Youth Day.

Swallows, Pagoda and AOPU Emblem — A194

Designs: $2, Northern gannet, horiz. $6, Japanese crane and pine.

Unwmk.
1963, Apr. 1   Photo.   Perf. 13

1370	A194	80c multicolored	4.00	.55
1371	A194	$2 multicolored	5.50	.65
1372	A194	$6 multicolored	8.25	2.10
		Nos. 1370-1372 (3)	17.75	3.30

1st anniversary of the formation of the Asian-Oceanic Postal Union, AOPU.

Refugee Girl (Li Ying) and Map of China — A195

Refugees Fleeing Mainland A196

Wmk. 323
1963, June 27   Engr.   Perf. 11½
Without Gum

1373	A195	80c bluish black	1.00	.20
1374	A196	$3.20 dp claret	2.25	.30

1st anniv. of the evacuation of Chinese mainland refugees from Hong Kong to Taiwan. Designs from photographs of refugees.

Nurse and Red Cross A197

Design: $10, Globe and Red Cross.

Perf. 12½
1963, Sept. 1   Unwmk.   Photo.

1375	A197	80c black & carmine	5.25	.25
1376	A197	$10 slate, gray & car	6.25	2.25

Centenary of International Red Cross.

Basketball Player, Stadium and Asian Cup — A198

$2, Hands reaching for ball and Asian cup.

Wmk. 323
1963, Nov. 20   Engr.   Perf. 12
Without Gum

1377	A198	80c lilac rose	.90	.20
1378	A198	$2 violet	1.75	.60

The 2nd Asian Basketball Championship, Taipei, Nov. 20.

UN Emblem, Torch and Men — A199

Scales and Men of Various Races A200

1963, Dec. 10   Wmk. 323   Perf. 11½
Without Gum

1379	A199	80c brt green	.70	.30
1380	A200	$3.20 maroon	1.40	.65

Universal Declaration of Human Rights, 15th anniversary.

Village and Orchids A201

"Kindle the Fire of Conscience" A202

Perf. 13½x13
1963, Dec. 17   Photo.   Unwmk.

1381	A201	40c multicolored	2.50	.35
1382	A202	$4.50 multicolored	4.00	1.60

Contribution of the Good-People-Good-Deeds campaign to improve ethical standards.

Sun Yat-sen and Book, "Three Principles of the People" A203

1963, Dec. 25   Perf. 13

1383	A203	$5 blue & multi	6.75	1.00

"Land-to-the-Tillers" program, 10th anniv. An 80c was prepared but not issued.

Torch — A204

Hands Unchained — A205

Wmk. 323
1964, Jan. 23   Engr.   Perf. 11½
Without Gum

1384	A204	80c red orange	.60	.20
1385	A205	$3.20 indigo	1.90	.35

Liberty Day, 10th anniversary.

Broadleaf Cactus A206

Wu Chih-hwei A207

Designs: $1, Crab cactus. $3.20, Nopalxochia. $5, Grizzly bear cactus.

Perf. 12½
1964, Feb. 27   Unwmk.   Photo.
Plants in Original Colors

1386	A206	80c dp plum & fawn	2.50	.20
1387	A206	$1 dk blue & car	4.25	.90
1388	A206	$3.20 green	6.25	.20
1389	A206	$5 lilac & yellow	6.75	1.10
		Nos. 1386-1389 (4)	19.75	2.40

Wmk. 323
1964, Mar. 25   Engr.   Perf. 11½
Without Gum

1390	A207	80c black brown	1.40	.20

Centenary of the birth of Wu Chih-hwei (1865-1953), politician and leader of the Kuomintang.

Chu Kwang Tower, Quemoy — A208

Perf. 13x12½
1964-66   Wmk. 323   Litho.
Granite Paper; Without Gum

1391	A208	3c sepia	.25	.20
1392	A208	5c brt yel grn ('65)	.25	.20
1393	A208	10c yellow grn	.25	.20
1394	A208	20c slate grn ('65)	.25	.20
1395	A208	40c rose red	.25	.20
1396	A208	50c brown	.25	.20
1397	A208	80c orange ('65)	.25	.20
1398	A208	$1 violet ('65)	.25	.20

1399	A208	$1.50 brt lilac ('66)	2.25	.25
1400	A208	$2 lilac rose	.25	.20
1401	A208	$2.50 ultra ('65)	2.25	.25
1402	A208	$3 slate	2.25	.30
1403	A208	$3.20 brt blue	4.00	.20
1404	A208	$4 brt green	4.50	.25
		Nos. 1391-1404 (14)	17.50	3.05

Nurses Holding Candles A209

Florence Nightingale and Student Nurse — A210

1964, May 12   Engr.   Perf. 11½
Without Gum

1406	A209	80c violet blue	1.40	.25
1407	A210	$4 red	2.25	.50

Issued for Nurses Day.

Shihmen Reservoir A211

Designs: $1, Irrigation system. $3.20, Main dam and power plant. $5, Spillway.

Perf. 12½
1964, June 14   Unwmk.   Photo.

1408	A211	80c multicolored	1.75	.25
1409	A211	$1 multicolored	2.25	.45
1410	A211	$3.20 multicolored	6.25	.55
1411	A211	$5 multicolored	7.00	1.40
		Nos. 1408-1411 (4)	17.25	2.65

Completion of Shihmen Reservoir.

15th Century Ship, Modern Liner — A212

Wmk. 323
1964, July 11   Engr.   Perf. 11½
Without Gum

1412	A212	$2 orange	.80	.20
1413	A212	$3.60 brt green	1.25	.35

China's 10th Navigation Day.

Bananas A213

Unwmk.
1964, July 25   Photo.   Perf. 14

1414	A213	80c shown	8.50	.40
1415	A213	$1 Oranges	15.00	1.00
1416	A213	$3.20 Pineapple	18.00	1.00
1417	A213	$4 Watermelon	27.50	3.25
		Nos. 1414-1417 (4)	69.00	5.65

Artillery, Warships, Jet Fighters A214

Wmk. 323
1964, Sept. 3   **Engr.**   *Perf. 11½*
Without Gum

1418	A214	80c dk blue	1.10	.20
1419	A214	$6 violet brown	2.75	.50

Issued for the 10th Armed Forces Day.

Unisphere, Flags of
China and
U.S. — A215

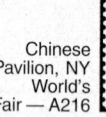

Chinese
Pavilion, NY
World's
Fair — A216

1964, Sept. 10   **Photo.**   **Unwmk.**

1420	A215	80c violet & multi	1.25	.25
1421	A216	$5 blue & multi	2.75	.90

NY World's Fair, 1964-65. See #1450-1451.

Cowboy Carrying
Calf, and
Ranch — A217

Bicycling — A218

Wmk. 323
1964, Sept. 24   **Engr.**   *Perf. 11½*
Without Gum

1422	A217	$2 brown lake	1.10	.20
1423	A217	$4 dark violet blue	2.25	.80

Animal Protection Week, Sept. 24-30.

1964, Oct. 10   **Without Gum**

Sports: $1, Runner. $3.20, Gymnast on
rings. $10, High jump.

1424	A218	80c violet blue	.80	.20
1425	A218	$1 rose red	1.40	.20
1426	A218	$3.20 dull blue grn	1.75	.25
1427	A218	$10 lilac	3.00	1.50
		Nos. 1424-1427 (4)	6.95	2.15

18th Olympic Games, Tokyo, Oct. 10-25.

Hsü Kuang-chi
A219

Pharmaceutical
Industry
A220

Textile
Industry
A221

1964, Nov. 8   **Engr.**   *Perf. 11½*
Without Gum

1428	A219	80c indigo	2.00	.20

Issued to honor Hsü Kuang-chi (1562-
1633), scholar and statesman.

1964, Nov. 11   **Photo.**   **Unwmk.**
$2, Chemical industry. $3.60, Cement
industry.

1429	A220	40c multi	2.25	.20
1430	A221	$1.50 multi	3.00	.70
1431	A220	$2 multi	4.50	.50
1432	A221	$3.60 multi	5.25	1.10
		Nos. 1429-1432 (4)	15.00	2.50

Dr. Sun Yat-
sen — A222

Eleanor Roosevelt
and Scales of
Justice — A223

1964, Nov. 24   **Engr.**   **Wmk. 323**
Without Gum

1433	A222	80c green	1.40	.30
1434	A222	$3.60 purple	3.75	.65

Founding of the Kuomintang by Sun Yat-
sen, 70th anniversary.

Unwmk.
1964, Dec. 10   **Photo.**   *Perf. 13*

1435	A223	$10 violet & brown	1.60	.40

Issued to honor Eleanor Roosevelt (1884-
1962) on the 16th anniversary of the Universal
Declaration of Human Rights.

Scales, Code
Book and Plum
Blossom
A224

Rotary Emblem
and Mainspring
A225

Wmk. 323
1965, Jan. 11   **Engr.**   *Perf. 11½*
Without Gum

1436	A224	80c carmine rose	.45	.20
1437	A224	$3.20 dull slate grn	.70	.40

The 20th Judicial Day.

1965, Feb. 23   **Wmk. 323**   *Perf. 11½*
Without Gum

1438	A225	$1.50 vermilion	.60	.20
1439	A225	$2 emerald	.70	.20
1440	A225	$2.50 blue	.90	.30
		Nos. 1438-1440 (3)	2.20	.70

Rotary International, 60th anniversary.

Double Carp
Design
A226

Madame Chiang
Kai-shek
A227

Wmk. 323
1965, Mar. 29   **Engr.**   *Perf. 11½*
Granite Paper; Without Gum

1441	A226	$5 purple	9.00	.95
1442	A226	$5.60 dp blue	15.00	1.60
1443	A226	$6 brown	13.50	.95
1444	A226	$10 lilac rose	22.50	.95
1445	A226	$20 rose car	26.00	1.60
1446	A226	$50 green	30.00	3.50
1447	A226	$100 crim rose	37.50	5.75
		Nos. 1441-1447 (7)	153.50	15.30

New dies used to reprint #1444-1447,
8/20/67. Remainders of #1441-1447 issued
with gum, 11/1/71.

1965, Apr. 17   **Photo.**   **Unwmk.**

1448	A227	$2 multicolored	12.50	.50
1449	A227	$6 salmon & multi	22.50	3.00

Chinese Women's Anti-Aggression League,
15th anniversary.

Unisphere and Chinese
Pavilion — A228

"100 Birds Paying Homage to Queen
Phoenix" and Unisphere — A229

1965, May 8

1450	A228	$2 blue & multi	12.00	1.25
1451	A229	$10 red, ocher & bis	14.00	2.00

New York World's Fair, 1964-65.

ITU Emblem,
Old and New
Communication
Equipment
A230

Design: $5, similar to 80c, vert.

Perf. 13½x13, 13x13½
1965, May 17   **Unwmk.**

1452	A230	80c multicolored	.60	.20
1453	A230	$5 multicolored	1.75	.55

Centenary of the ITU.

Red Sea
Bream
A231

Fish: 80c, White pomfret. $2, Skipjack, vert.
$4, Moonfish.

1965, July 1   *Perf. 13*

1454	A231	40c multicolored	1.60	.20
1455	A231	80c multicolored	2.50	.30
1456	A231	$2 multicolored	5.75	1.00
1457	A231	$4 multicolored	10.00	1.50
		Nos. 1454-1457 (4)	19.85	3.00

Issued for Fishermen's Day.

Confucius
A232

ICY Emblem
A233

Portraits: $2.50, Yueh Fei. $3.50, Wen Tien-
hsiang. $3.60, Mencius.

Wmk. 323
1965-66   **Engr.**   *Perf. 11½*
Without Gum

1458	A232	$1 deep carmine	3.00	.35
1459	A232	$2.50 black brown	2.00	.35
1460	A232	$3.50 dark red	4.50	.50
1461	A232	$3.60 dark blue	5.25	.60
		Nos. 1458-1461 (4)	14.75	1.80

The $2.50 and $3.50 have colored
background.
Forgeries of #1461 exist.
Issued: #1458, 1461, 9/28/65; #1459-1460,
9/3/66.

See Nos. 1507-1508, design A251.

Unwmk.
1965, Oct. 24   **Photo.**   *Perf. 13*
Design: $6, ICY emblem, horiz.

1462	A233	$2 brn, blk & gold	1.25	.20
1463	A233	$6 brt grn, red & gold	2.75	1.00

International Cooperation Year, 1965.

Street Crossing,
Traffic Light
A234

Sun Yat-sen
A235

Wmk. 323
1965, Nov. 1   **Engr.**   *Perf. 11½*
Without Gum

1464	A234	$1 brown violet	1.25	.25
1465	A234	$4 crimson rose	2.40	.80

Issued to publicize traffic safety.

Perf. 13½
1965, Nov. 12   **Unwmk.**   **Photo.**
Designs: $4, Dr. Sun Yat-sen, portrait at
right. $5, Sun Yat-sen and flags, horiz.

1466	A235	$1 multicolored	2.50	.20
1467	A235	$4 multicolored	7.75	.60
1468	A235	$5 multicolored	9.25	1.75
		Nos. 1466-1468 (3)	19.50	2.55

Children with New
Year's
Firecrackers
A236

Dragon Dance,
"Dragon Playing
Ball"
A237

1965, Dec. 1   **Photo.**   *Perf. 13*

1469	A236	$1 multi	3.50	.30
1470	A237	$4.50 multi	8.00	1.10

Lien Po from
"Marshal and Prime
Minister
Reconciled" — A238

Facial Paintings for Chinese Operas: $3,
Kuan Yü from "Reunion at Ku City." $4, Gen.
Chang Fei from "The Battle of Chang Pan Hill."
$6, Buddha from "The Flower-Scattering
Angel."

1966, Feb. 15   **Unwmk.**   *Perf. 11½*

1471	A238	$1 olive & multi	8.00	.50
1472	A238	$3 multicolored	13.50	1.00
1473	A238	$4 multicolored	24.00	1.50
1474	A238	$6 ver & multi	29.00	2.75
		Nos. 1471-1474 (4)	74.50	5.75

Labels with a similar appearance to these
stamps exist. These labels have the numbers
1 to 20 in the upper right corner, but lack the
"00."

Postal Service Emblem Held by Carrier Pigeon — A239

Stone, Mt. Tai-wu, Quemoy, and Mailman A240

postal service emblem and: $3, Postal Museum. $4, Mailman climbing symbolic slope.

1966, Mar. 20   Photo.   Perf. 12½
1475	A239	$1 green & multi	1.25	.20
1476	A240	$2 multicolored	2.50	.30
1477	A240	$3 multicolored	3.00	.40
1478	A239	$4 multicolored	6.25	1.25
	Nos. 1475-1478 (4)		13.00	2.15

China postal service, 70th anniversary.

Fishing on a Snowy Day, "Five Dynasties" (907-960) A241

Paintings from Palace Museum: $3.50, Calves on the Plain, Sung artist (960-1126). $4.50, Winter landscape, Sung artist (960-1126). $5, Magpies, by Lin Ch'un, Southern Sung dynasty (1127-1279).

1966, May 20   Photo.   Perf. 13
1479	A241	$2.50 blk, brn & red	2.50	.40
1480	A241	$3.50 bis brn, blk & gray	6.50	.60
1481	A241	$4.50 blk, buff & sl	9.00	1.50
1482	A241	$5 multicolored	12.00	2.25
	Nos. 1479-1482 (4)		30.00	4.75

Inauguration of Pres. Chiang Kai-shek for a 4th term.

Dragon Boat Race A242

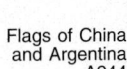

Lion Dance — A243

$4, Lady Chang O flying to the Moon.

1966   Unwmk.
1483	A242	$2.50 multi	1.75	.30
1484	A242	$4 multi	3.50	.40
1485	A243	$6 multi	5.75	.75
	Nos. 1483-1485 (3)		11.00	1.45

Dragon Boat, Mid-Autumn and Lunar New Year Festivals. Issued: $2.50, 6/23; $4, 9/29; $6, 11/26.

Flags of China and Argentina A244

1966, July 9   Photo.   Perf. 13
1486	A244	$10 multicolored	3.00	.50

Argentina's Independence. 150th anniv.

Lin Sen — A245

Flying Geese — A246

Wmk. 323
1966, Aug. 1   Engr.   Perf. 11½
Without Gum
1487	A245	$1 dk brown	1.60	.20

Centenary of the birth of Lin Sen (1867-1943), Chairman of the Nationalist Government of China (1931-43).

1966-67   Perf. 11½ Rough
Granite Paper; Without Gum
1496	A246	$3.50 brown	.85	.20
1497	A246	$4 vermilion	.80	.20
1498	A246	$4.50 brt green	1.40	.25
1499	A246	$5 rose lilac	.85	.20
1500	A246	$5.50 yel grn ('67)	1.60	.20
1501	A246	$6 brt blue	1.90	.30
1502	A246	$6.50 violet	1.60	.25
1503	A246	$7 black	.95	.20
1504	A246	$8 car rose ('67)	1.40	.20
	Nos. 1496-1504 (9)		11.35	2.00

The $4.50, $5, $6, $7 and $8 were reissued with gum in 1970-71.

Pres. Chiang Kai-shek in Chung San Robe — A247

$5, Chiang Kai-shek in marshal's uniform.

1966, Oct. 31   Photo.   Perf. 13
1505	A247	$1 multicolored	1.50	.25
1506	A247	$5 multicolored	4.75	1.25

Chiang Kai-shek's inauguration for a fourth term as president, May 20, 1966.

Famous Men Type of 1965-66 with Frame Line

Portraits: No. 1507, Tsai Yuan-pei (1868-1940), educator. No. 1508, Chiu Ching (1875-1907), woman educator and revolutionist.

1967   Wmk. 323   Engr.   Perf. 11½
Without Gum
1507	A232	$1 violet blue	1.60	.25
1508	A232	$1 black	1.60	.25

Issue dates: #1507, Jan. 11. #1508, July 15. No. 1507 is on granite paper.

Motorized Mailman and Microwave Station — A248

"Transportation" and Radar Weather Station — A249

Unwmk.
1967, Mar. 15   Photo.   Perf. 13
1511	A248	$1 multicolored	1.00	.25
1512	A249	$5 multicolored	1.75	.60

Issued to publicize the progress in communication and transportation services.

Pres. Chiang Kai-shek and Chinese Flag — A250

Chu Yuan, 332-295 B.C. — A251

Design: $4, Different frame.

1967, May 20   Litho.   Perf. 13
1513	A250	$1 multicolored	1.25	.20
1514	A250	$4 multicolored	2.25	.60

First anniversary of President Chiang Kai-shek's 4th-term inauguration.

Wmk. 323
1967, June 12   Engr.   Perf. 11½

Portraits: $2, Li Po (705-760). $2.50, Tu Fu (712-770). $3, Po Chu-i (772-846).

Granite Paper; Without Gum
1515	A251	$1 black	.85	.20
1516	A251	$2 brown	2.50	.20
1517	A251	$2.50 brown blk	3.50	.45
1518	A251	$3 grnsh black	5.25	.45
	Nos. 1515-1518 (4)		12.10	1.35

Issued for Poets' Day.
See design A232.

Hotei, Wood Carving — A252

World Map — A253

Handicrafts: $2.50, Vase and plate. $3, Dolls. $5, Palace lanterns.

Perf. 11½
1967, Aug. 12   Unwmk.   Photo.
1519	A252	$1 gray & multi	2.25	.40
1520	A252	$2.50 multi	3.00	.60
1521	A252	$3 multi	3.75	1.00
1522	A252	$5 multi	5.00	2.00
	Nos. 1519-1522 (4)		14.00	4.00

Taiwan handicraft industry.

Wmk. 323
1967, Sept. 25   Engr.   Perf. 11½
Granite Paper; Without Gum
1523	A253	$1 vermilion	.45	.20
1524	A253	$5 blue	1.10	.50

1st Conference of the World Anti-Communist League, WACL, Taipei, Sept. 25-29.

Players on Stilts: "The Fisherman and the Woodcutter" A254

Unwmk.
1967, Oct. 10   Photo.   Perf. 13
1525	A254	$4.50 multi	1.25	.35

Issued for the 56th National Day.

Maroon Oriole — A255

Formosan Birds: $1, Formosan barbet, vert. $2.50, Formosan green pigeon. $3, Formosan blue magpie. $5, Crested serpent eagle, vert. $8, Mikado pheasants.

1967, Nov. 25   Photo.   Perf. 11
Granite Paper
1526	A255	$1 multi	3.00	.25
1527	A255	$2 multi	4.00	.40
1528	A255	$2.50 multi	5.00	.50
1529	A255	$3 multi	6.00	.60
1530	A255	$5 multi	7.00	.70
1531	A255	$8 multi	8.50	1.25
	Nos. 1526-1531 (6)		33.50	3.70

Chung Hsing Pagoda — A256

Buddha, Changhua A257

Designs: $2.50, Seashore, Yeh Liu Park. $5, National Palace Museum, Taipei.

Unwmk.
1967, Dec. 10   Photo.   Perf. 13
1532	A256	$1 multi	1.10	.20
1533	A257	$2.50 multi	2.75	.40
1534	A257	$4 multi	3.50	.50
1535	A257	$5 multi	4.00	.75
	Nos. 1532-1535 (4)		11.35	1.85

Issued for International Tourist Year 1967.

China Park, Manila, and Flags — A258

1967, Dec. 30   Perf. 13½
1536	A258	$1 multicolored	.50	.20
1537	A258	$5 multicolored	1.75	.40

Sino-Philippine Friendship Year 1966-67.

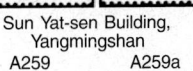

Sun Yat-sen Building, Yangmingshan
A259   A259a

Perf. 13x12½

1968-75 Litho. Wmk. 323
Granite Paper

1538	A259	5c lt brown	.45	.20
1539	A259	10c grnsh black	.45	.20
1540	A259	50c brt rose lilac	.45	.20
1541	A259	$1 vermilion	.45	.20
1542	A259	$1.50 emerald	.85	.25
1543	A259	$2 plum	.80	.20
1544	A259	$2.50 blue	.95	.20
1545	A259	$3 grnsh blue	1.00	.25
		Nos. 1538-1545 (8)	5.40	1.70

See Nos. 1702-1709. For overprints see Nos. 1723-1725.

Coil Stamps
Perf. 13 Horiz.
Photo. Unwmk.

1546	A259a	$1 carmine rose	.30	.25
1547	A259a	$1 vermilion	.30	.25

Issued: 50c, $1, $2.50, 1/23/68; #1546, 3/20/70; #1547, 1/28/75; others 7/11/68.

Inscription on No. 1546 is in color with white background. On No. 1547 it is white with colored background.

Harvesting Sugar Cane A260

Jade Cabbage, 1662-1911 A261

Unwmk.
1968, Mar. 1 Photo. Perf. 13

1548	A260	$1 olive & multi	1.40	.20
1549	A260	$4 multicolored	2.40	.45

1968, Mar. 29 Unwmk. Perf. 13

Ancient Art Treasures: $1.50, Jade battle axe. $2, Porcelain flower bowl, 960-1126 A.D., horiz. $2.50, Cloisonné enamel vase, 1723-1736 A.D. $4, Agate flower holder in shape of finger citrus, 1662-1911 A.D., horiz. $5, Sacrificial kettle, 1111-771 B.C.

1550	A261	$1 rose & multi	1.50	.20
1551	A261	$1.50 blue & multi	2.25	.50
1552	A261	$2 blue & multi	2.40	.20
1553	A261	$2.50 dull rose & multi	3.00	.50
1554	A261	$4 pink & multi	3.75	.60
1555	A261	$5 blue & multi	4.50	.70
		Nos. 1550-1555 (6)	17.40	2.70

For similar artifact designs inscribed "Republic of China," with single-color denominations in slanted numerals and the cents underlined, see types A276, A291, A323, A336, A372, A384, A395, A411. Artifact designs with denominations in outlined numerals begin with type A439.

View of City in Cathay (1) — A262

Views: No. 1557, City and wall of Forbidden City (2). No. 1558, Wall at right, bridge at left (3). No. 1559, Queen's ship landing at left (4). No. 1560, Palace (5). $5, City wall and gate. $8, Suburb around Great Bridge. Design from scroll "A City in Cathay," painted 1736.

1968, June 18 Photo. Perf. 13½
Size: 50x29mm

1556	A262	$1 multicolored	1.60	.30
1557	A262	$1 multicolored	1.60	.30
1558	A262	$1 multicolored	1.60	.30
1559	A262	$1 multicolored	1.60	.30
1560	A262	$1 multicolored	1.60	.30
a.		Strip of 5, #1556-1560	8.50	8.50

Size: 60x31mm
Perf. 13x13½

1561	A262	$5 multicolored	8.25	1.60
1562	A262	$8 multicolored	15.00	2.00
		Nos. 1556-1562 (7)	31.25	5.10

See Nos. 1610-1614. For similar designs see types A281, A299, A326, A343.

Entrance Gate, Taroko Gorge A263

$8, Sun Yat-sen Building, Yangmingshan.

1968, Feb. 12 Photo. Perf. 13

1563	A263	$5 multicolored	1.25	.25
1564	A263	$8 multicolored	2.40	.30

The 17th Annual Conference of the Pacific Area Travel Association.

Vice President Chen Cheng — A264

Flying Geese — A265

1968, Mar. 5

1565	A264	$1 brown & multi	1.25	.20

Vice President Chen Cheng (1898-1965).

Wmk. 323
1968, Mar. 20 Litho. Perf. 12
Granite Paper

1566	A265	$1 vermilion	9.00	.20

Souvenir Sheet
Imperf

1567	A265	$3 green	11.00	3.50

90th anniv. of Chinese postage stamps. No. 1567 contains one stamp with simulated perforations.

WHO Emblem and "20" — A266

Symbolic Water Cycle — A267

1968, Apr. 7 Engr. Perf. 12
Granite Paper

1568	A266	$1 green	.35	.20
1569	A266	$5 scarlet	.85	.45

20th anniv. of WHO.

Wmk. 323
1968, June 6 Litho. Perf. 11½
Granite Paper

1570	A267	$1 green & org	.45	.20
1571	A267	$4 brt blue & org	.90	.20

Hydrological Decade (UNESCO) 1965-74.

Broadcasting to Mainland China — A268

Dual Carriers for FM Broadcasting A269

Wmk. 323
1968, Aug. 1 Litho. Perf. 12
Granite Paper

1572	A268	$1 bl, vio bl & gray	.40	.20
1573	A269	$4 lt ultra & ver	.95	.25

40th anniv. of the Broadcasting Corp. of China, and the inauguration of frequency modulation broadcasting.

Human Rights Flame — A270

Crop Improvement and Extension Work — A271

1968, Sept. 3
Granite Paper

1574	A270	$1 multicolored	.45	.20
1575	A270	$5 multicolored	1.10	.20

International Human Rights Year 1968.

Wmk. 323
1968, Sept. 30 Litho. Perf. 12
Granite Paper

1576	A271	$1 yel, bister & dk brn	.30	.20
1577	A271	$5 yel, emer & dk grn	1.10	.50

Joint Commission on Rural Reconstruction, 20th anniversary.

Javelin — A272

Designs: $2.50, Weight lifting. $5, Pole vault, horiz. $8, Woman hurdling, horiz.

Unwmk.
1968, Oct. 12 Photo. Perf. 13

1578	A272	$1 multi	.40	.20
1579	A272	$2.50 multi	.60	.20
1580	A272	$5 multi	.90	.25
1581	A272	$8 pink & multi	1.40	.35
		Nos. 1578-1581 (4)	3.30	1.00

19th Olympic Games, Mexico City, 10/12-27.

Pres. Chiang Kai-shek and Whampoa Military Academy — A273

Designs: $2, Pres. Chiang Kai-shek reviewing forces of the Northern Expedition. $2.50, Suppression of bandits, reconstruction work and New Life Movement emblem. $3.50, Marco Polo Bridge near Peking and victory parade, Nanking. $4, Original copy of Constitution of Republic of China. $5, Nationalist Chinese flag flying over mainland China.

1968, Oct. 31 Perf. 11½x12

1582	A273	$1 multi	.55	.20
1583	A273	$2 multi	.75	.20
1584	A273	$2.50 multi	1.00	.30
1585	A273	$3.50 multi	1.25	.40

1586	A273	$4 multi	1.60	.65
1587	A273	$5 multi	2.75	.85
		Nos. 1582-1587 (6)	7.90	2.60

Chiang Kai-shek's achievements for China.

Cock — A274

Flag — A275

1968, Nov. 12 Litho. Perf. 12
Granite Paper

1588	A274	$1 pink & multi	13.00	1.00
1589	A274	$4.50 lilac & multi	29.00	3.50

Issued for use on New Year's greetings.

1968, Dec. 25 Wmk. 323 Perf. 12½
Granite Paper

1590	A275	$1 multicolored	.40	.20
1591	A275	$5 lt blue & multi	.85	.45

Constitution of the Republic of China, 20th anniversary.

Jade Belt Buckle, 1662-1911 A276

Ancient Art Treasures: $1.50, Yellow jade vase, 960-1126 A.D., vert. $2, Cloisonne enamel square teapot, 1662-1911 A.D. $2.50, Kuei, sacrificial bronze vessel, 722-481 B.C. $4, Heavenly ball vase, 1368-1661 A.D., vert. $5, Gourd-shaped vase, 1662-1911 A.D., vert.

Unwmk.
1969, Jan. 15 Photo. Perf. 13

1592	A276	$1 dl rose & multi	.95	.20
1593	A276	$1.50 rose & multi	1.60	.20
1594	A276	$2 brt rose & multi	2.00	.20
1595	A276	$2.50 lt blue & multi	2.25	.25
1596	A276	$4 tan & multi	2.40	.40
1597	A276	$5 pale blue & multi	2.50	.75
		Nos. 1592-1597 (6)	11.70	2.05

Servicemen and Savings Emblem A277

Wmk. 323
1969, Feb. 1 Engr. Perf. 12
Granite Paper

1598	A277	$1 dull red brown	.20	.20
1599	A277	$4 deep blue	.80	.35

Military Savings Program, 10th anniv.

Ti (Flute) A278

Musical Instruments: $2.50, Sheng (13 bamboo pipes connected at the base). $4, P'i p'a (lute). $5, Cheng (zither).

Unwmk.
1969, Mar. 16 Photo. Perf. 13

1600	A278	$1 buff & multi	.40	.20
1601	A278	$2.50 lt ap grn & multi	1.00	.25

1602	A278	$4 pink & multi	1.25	.30
1603	A278	$5 lt grnsh bl & multi	1.75	.40
		Nos. 1600-1603 (4)	4.40	1.15

Sun Yat-sen Building and Kuomintang Emblem A279

Double Carp Design — A280

1969, Mar. 29   Litho.   Perf. 13½

| 1604 | A279 | $1 multicolored | .50 | .20 |

10th Natl. Cong. of the Chinese Nationalist Party (Kuomintang), Mar. 29. A $2.50 stamp portraying Sun Yat-sen and Chiang Kai-shek was prepared but not issued.

Perf. 13½x12½

1974		**Engr.**		**Wmk. 323**
		Granite Paper		
1606	A280	$10 dark blue	1.40	.20
1607	A280	$20 dark brown	2.75	.20
1608	A280	$50 green	4.50	.40
1609	A280	$100 bright red	5.75	.60
		Nos. 1606-1609 (4)	14.40	1.40

1969

Perf. 11½

1606a	A280	$10	1.75	.20
1607a	A280	$20	2.40	.20
1608a	A280	$50	6.25	.25
1609a	A280	$100	9.50	.50
		Nos. 1606a-1609a (4)	19.90	1.15

The 1969 issue is 27mm high; 1974, 28mm. See No. 1980.

Bridal Procession — A281

Designs: No. 1610, Musicians and standard bearer from bridal procession. $2.50, Emigrant farm family in oxcart. $5, Art gallery. $8, Roadside food stands. Designs from scroll "A City in Cathay," painted in 1736.

Perf. 13½

1969, May 20		**Unwmk.**		**Photo.**
1610	A281	$1 multi	1.00	.35
1611	A281	$1 multi	1.00	.35
a.		Pair, #1610-1611	2.00	2.00
1612	A281	$2.50 multi	3.25	.60
1613	A281	$5 multi	3.50	.75
1614	A281	$8 multi	6.00	1.25
		Nos. 1610-1614 (5)	14.75	3.30

ILO Emblem A282

Wmk. 323

1969, June 15   Engr.   Perf. 11½

Granite Paper

| 1615 | A282 | $1 dark blue | .35 | .20 |
| 1616 | A282 | $8 dark carmine | 1.25 | .35 |

ILO, 50th anniversary.

Family at Dinner Table and Dressing A283

Pupils in Laboratory and Playing — A284

Designs: $2.50, Housecleaning and obeying traffic rules. $4, Recreation (music, fishing, basketball) and education.

Wmk. 323

1969, July 15   Engr.   Perf. 11½

1617	A283	$1 brick red	.20	.20
1618	A283	$2.50 blue	.45	.25
1619	A283	$4 green	.60	.25
		Nos. 1617-1619 (3)	1.25	.70

Model Citizen's Life Movement.

1969, Sept. 1   Wmk. 323   Perf. 11½

Design: $1, $5, Pupils with book and various school activities, horiz.

Granite Paper

1620	A284	$1 brt red	.20	.20
1621	A284	$2.50 brt green	.55	.20
1622	A284	$4 dk blue	.75	.30
1623	A284	$5 brown	1.00	.40
		Nos. 1620-1623 (4)	2.50	1.10

Free 9-year education system, 1st anniv.

Wild Flowers and Pheasants, by Lu Chih (Ming) A285

Paintings: $2.50, Bamboo and birds, Sung dynasty. $5, Flowers and Birds, Sung dynasty. $8, Cranes and Flowers, by G. Castiglione, S.J. (1688-1766).

1969, Oct. 9   Photo.   Perf. 13½

1624	A285	$1 multi	1.00	.35
1625	A285	$2.50 multi	2.50	.45
1626	A285	$5 multi	6.00	.75
1627	A285	$8 multi	8.00	1.10
		Nos. 1624-1627 (4)	17.50	2.65

Golden Scepter Rose — A286

Rocket and Radar Station — A287

Roses: $1, "Charles Mollerin," called black rose. $5, Peace. $8, Josephine Bruce.

1969, Oct. 31   Litho.   Perf. 14

1628	A286	$1 lt vio & multi	.75	.20
1629	A286	$2.50 lt bl & multi	2.40	.20
1630	A286	$5 dl org & multi	3.00	.25
1631	A286	$8 ap grn & multi	2.75	.55
		Nos. 1628-1631 (4)	8.90	1.20

Wmk. 323

1969, Nov. 21   Engr.   Perf. 11½

| 1632 | A287 | $1 rose claret | 1.10 | .20 |

The 30th Air Defense Day.

Symbol of International Cooperation A288

Pekingese — A289

1969, Nov. 25

| 1633 | A288 | $1 rose claret | .25 | .20 |
| 1634 | A288 | $5 green | .85 | .25 |

5th General Assembly of the Asian Parliamentary Union, Taipei, Nov. 24-28.

1969, Dec. 1   Litho.   Perf. 12

Granite Paper

| 1635 | A289 | 50c red & multi | 1.50 | .50 |
| 1636 | A289 | $4.50 green & multi | 7.00 | 2.00 |

Issued for use on New Year's greetings.

Satellite, Earth Station and Map of Taiwan A290

Unwmk.

1969, Dec. 28   Photo.   Perf. 13

1637	A290	$1 brown & multi	.35	.20
1638	A290	$5 vio blue & multi	1.25	.25
1639	A290	$8 purple & multi	1.60	.40
		Nos. 1637-1639 (3)	3.20	.85

Inauguration of the Communication Satellite Earth Station at Chin-Shan-Li, Dec. 28.

Agate Grinding Stone, 1662-1911 A291

Ancient Art Treasures: $1, Carved lacquer ware vase, 1662-1911, vert. $2, White jade Chin-li-chih melons, 1662-1911. $2.50, Black jade shepherd and ram, 206 B.C.-220 A.D. $4, Chien-lung twin porcelain vase, 1736-1796, vert. $5, Ju porcelain vase with 3 bulls, 960-1126, vert.

1970, Jan. 23

1640	A291	$1 lt grnsh bl & multi	.50	.20
1641	A291	$1.50 pale bl & multi	.90	.20
1642	A291	$2 green & multi	1.00	.20
1643	A291	$2.50 pink & multi	1.75	.25
1644	A291	$4 ol bis & multi	1.90	.30
1645	A291	$5 ultra & multi	2.50	.45
		Nos. 1640-1645 (6)	8.55	1.60

Hsuan Chuang — A292

Chu Hsi — A293

Design: $2.50, Hua To.

1970   Wmk. 323   Engr.   Perf. 11½

Granite Paper

1646	A292	$1 car rose	.55	.20
1647	A293	$2.50 blue grn	.80	.25
1648	A293	$4 blue	1.40	.30
		Nos. 1646-1648 (3)	2.75	.75

Issued in memory of Hsuan Chuang (602-664), who propagated Buddhism in China;

Chu Hsi (1130-1200), who developed Neo-Confucianism, and Hua To (3rd century A.D.) physician and surgeon.
Issued: $2.50, 3/17; others, 2/20.

EXPO '70 Pavilion, Emblem and Flags of Participants A294

Design: $5, Chinese pavilion, EXPO '70 emblem, exhibition and Chinese flags.

Unwmk.

1970, Mar. 13   Photo.   Perf. 13

| 1649 | A294 | $5 org red & multi | .60 | .25 |
| 1650 | A294 | $8 lt blue & multi | 1.25 | .40 |

EXPO '70 International Exhibition, Osaka, Japan, Mar. 15-Sept. 13.

Nimbus III and WMO Emblem A295

Design: $1, Agricultural meteorological station and tropical landscape, vert.

Perf. 14x13½, 13½x14

1970, Mar. 23   Litho.   Wmk. 323

Granite Paper

| 1651 | A295 | $1 green & multi | .25 | .20 |
| 1652 | A295 | $8 blue & multi | .85 | .40 |

10th Annual World Meteorological Day.

Martyrs' Shrine, Taipei A296

Shrine's Gate A297

Unwmk.

1970, Mar. 29   Photo.   Perf. 13

| 1653 | A296 | $1 multicolored | .45 | .20 |
| 1654 | A297 | $8 multicolored | 1.50 | .45 |

Completion of the Martyrs' Shrine in Northern Taipei, dedicated to the memory of 72 young revolutionaries who died Mar. 29, 1911.

Yueh Fei Fighting for Lost Territories A298

Characters from Chinese Operas: $2.50, Emperor Shun and stepmother. $5, The Lady Warrior Chin Liang-yu. $8, Kuan Yu and groom.

1970, May 4   Unwmk.   Perf. 13½

1655	A298	$1 multi	.80	.20
1656	A298	$2.50 multi	2.00	.30
1657	A298	$5 multi	2.75	.50
1658	A298	$8 multi	4.25	.65
		Nos. 1655-1658 (4)	9.80	1.65

— A299

Three Horses Playing — A300

Horses: #1659, Barren tree at right. #1660, Horse standing in river. #1661, Tree trunk in lower left corner. #1662, Trees in left background. #1663, shown. $8, Groom roping horses. Designs from scroll "One Hundred Horses" by Lang Shih-ning (Giuseppe Castiglione, 1688-1766).

Perf. 13½

				Photo.
1970, June 18		**Unwmk.**		
1659	A299	$1 multi	.60	.20
1660	A299	$1 multi	.60	.20
1661	A299	$1 multi	.60	.20
1662	A299	$1 multi	.60	.20
1663	A299	$1 multi	.60	.20
a.		Strip of 5, #1659-1663	5.00	5.00
1664	A300	$5 bister & multi	6.00	1.00
1665	A300	$8 dl yel & multi	7.00	1.40
		Nos. 1659-1665 (7)	16.00	3.40

Lai-tsu Amusing his Old Parents — A301

Chinese Fairy Tales: #1667, Man disguised as deer, and hunters. #1668, Boy cooling his father's bed. #1669, Boy fishing through ice. #1670, Son reunited with old mother. #1671, Emperor tasting mother's medicine. #1672, Boy saving oranges for mother. #1673, Boy saving father from tiger.

Wmk. 323

1970, July 10		**Litho.**		**Perf. 13½**
		Granite Paper		
1666	A301	10c red & multi	.20	.20
1667	A301	10c car rose & multi	.20	.20
1668	A301	10c lt vio & multi	.20	.20
1669	A301	10c gray & multi	.20	.20
1670	A301	10c emerald & multi	.20	.20
1671	A301	50c bister & multi	.20	.20
1672	A301	$1 sky blue & multi	.40	.20
1673	A301	$1 dp blue & multi	.40	.20
		Nos. 1666-1673 (8)	2.00	1.60

See Nos. 1726-1733.

Man's First Step onto Moon — A302

$1, Pres. Chiang Kai-shek's message brought to the moon. $5, Neil A. Armstrong, Michael Collins, Edwin E. Aldrin, Jr., and moon, horiz.

Perf. 13½x13, 13x13½

1970, July 21		**Photo.**		**Unwmk.**
1674	A302	$1 yellow & multi	.50	.20
1675	A302	$5 lt yel grn & multi	.85	.30
1676	A302	$8 blue & multi	1.40	.55
		Nos. 1674-1676 (3)	2.75	1.05

1st anniv. of man's 1st landing on the moon.

Asian Productivity Year Symbol A303

Wmk. 323

1970, Aug. 18		**Litho.**		**Perf. 13½**
		Granite Paper		
1677	A303	$1 emerald & multi		.30 .20
1678	A303	$5 blue & multi		1.00 .30

Issued to publicize Asian Productivity Year.

Flags of China and UN — A304

1970, Sept. 19	**Wmk. 323**		**Perf. 12**
	Granite Paper		
1679	A304	$5 blue, car & blk	1.40 .45

25th anniversary of the United Nations.

Postal Zone Map — A305

Postal Code Emblem A306

1970, Oct. 8			**Litho.**
1680	A305	$1 lt blue & multi	.35 .20
1681	A306	$2.50 green & multi	1.10 .30

Issued to publicize the postal code system.

Eleventh Month Scroll — A307

Designs: A scroll series, "Activities of the 12 Months," painted on silk by a group of painters of the Ch'ien Lung court (1736-1796). Chinese number in parenthesis at right of denomination tells month.

Jan., Feb., Mar.

(一) (二) (三)

Perf. 13½x13

1970-71		**Photo.**		**Unwmk.**
1682	A307	$1 multi	1.60	.30
1683	A307	$2.50 multi	3.50	.70
1684	A307	$5 multi	6.00	1.00

Apr., May, June

(四) (五) (六)

1685	A307	$1 multi	1.60	.30
1686	A307	$2.50 multi	3.50	.70
1687	A307	$5 multi	6.00	1.00

July, Aug., Sept.

(七) (八) (九)

1688	A307	$1 multi	1.60	.30
1689	A307	$2.50 multi	3.50	.70
1690	A307	$5 multi	6.00	1.00

Oct., Nov., Dec.

(十) (一十) (二十)

1691	A307	$1 multi	2.40	.45
1692	A307	$2.50 multi	5.25	1.00
1693	A307	$5 multi	10.00	2.00
		Nos. 1682-1693 (12)	50.95	9.45

Issued: 31691-1693, 10/21/70; #1682-1684, 1/14/71; #1685-1687, 4/26/71; #1688-1690, 8/27/71.

Family at Home A308

Piggy Bank — A309

$4, Family of 5 going on an excursion, vert.

Perf. 13½x14, 14x13½

1970, Nov. 11	**Litho.**		**Wmk. 323**
	Granite Paper		
1694	A308	$1 multicolored	.40 .20
1695	A308	$4 yel grn & multi	1.40 .35

Issued to publicize family planning.

1970, Dec. 1			**Perf. 12½x12**
	Granite Paper		
1696	A309	50c multi	1.00 .25
1697	A309	$4.50 blue & multi	4.00 .60

Issued for use on New Year's greetings.

Tibia Fusus Shells A310

Rare Taiwan Shells: $2.50, Harpeola kurodai. $5, Conus stupa kuroda. $8, Entemnotrochus rumphii.

1971, Feb. 25			**Perf. 13x13½**
1698	A310	$1 vio & multi	.25 .20
1699	A310	$2.50 multi	1.00 .25
1700	A310	$5 org & multi	1.25 .45
1701	A310	$8 grn & multi	1.75 .65
		Nos. 1698-1701 (4)	4.25 1.55

Sun Yat-sen Building, Yangmingshan A311

Passbook and Postal Savings Certificate A312

Perf. 13½x12½

1971		**Litho.**		**Wmk. 323**
		Granite Paper		
1702	A311	5c brown	.25	.20
1703	A311	10c dk gray	.25	.20
1704	A311	50c brt rose lilac	.70	.20
1705	A311	$1 vermilion	.75	.20
1706	A311	$1.50 ultra	.80	.25
1707	A311	$2 plum	.90	.20
1708	A311	$2.50 emerald	1.00	.20
1709	A311	$3 aqua	1.40	.30
		Nos. 1702-1709 (8)	6.05	1.75

Perf. 13½x14

1971, Mar. 20	**Litho.**		**Wmk. 323**

$4, People and hand dropping coin into bank.

1712	A312	$1 yel grn & multi	.35 .20
1713	A312	$4 ver & multi	1.40 .30

Publicizing Chinese Postal Savings Service.

Cooperation Emblem, Farmers — A313

Rock Monkey — A314

Design: $8, Chinese teaching rice farming to Africans, horiz.

Unwmk.

1971, May 20	**Photo.**		**Perf. 13**
1714	A313	$1 multicolored	.20 .20
1715	A313	$8 multicolored	1.25 .45

Sino-African Technical Cooperation Committee, 10th anniversary.

1971, June 25		**Perf. 11½**

Taiwan Animals: $2, White-face flying squirrel. $3, Chinese pangolin. $5, Formosan sika deer. $2, $3, $5 are horiz.

1716	A314	$1 gold & multi	.35	.20
1717	A314	$2 gold & multi	1.00	.20
1718	A314	$3 gold & multi	1.50	.30
1719	A314	$5 gold & multi	2.00	.50
		Nos. 1716-1719 (4)	4.85	1.20

Pitcher — A315

Designs: $2.50, Players at base, horiz. $4, Batter and catcher.

1971, July 29		**Photo.**		**Perf. 13**
1720	A315	$1 multi	.20	.20
1721	A315	$2.50 multi	.40	.20
1722	A315	$4 multi	.70	.25
		Nos. 1720-1722 (3)	1.30	.65

Pacific Regional competition for the 1971 Little League World Series.

Nos. 1541, 1544-1545 Overprinted in Magenta or Red

Perf. 13x12½

1971, Sept. 9   Litho.   Wmk. 323
Granite Paper

1723	A259	$1 vermilion (M)	.20	.20
1724	A259	$2.50 blue (R)	.40	.20
1725	A259	$3 grnsh blue (R)	.40	.25
		Nos. 1723-1725 (3)	1.00	.65

Chinese victory in 1971 Little League World Series, Williamsport, Pa., Aug. 24.

Fairy Tale Type of 1970

Chinese Fairy Tales (Filial Piety): No. 1726, Birds and elephant helping in rice field. No. 1727, Son gathering mulberries for mother. No. 1728, Son gathering firewood. No. 1729, Son, mother and bandits. No. 1730, Son carrying heavy burden. 50c, Son digging for bamboo shoots in winter. No. 1732, Man and wife working as slaves. No. 1733, Father, son and carriage.

1971, Sept. 22   Perf. 13½
Granite Paper

1726	A301	10c dp org & multi	.20	.20
1727	A301	10c lilac & multi	.20	.20
1728	A301	10c ocher & multi	.20	.20
1729	A301	10c dp car & multi	.20	.20
1730	A301	10c lt ultra & multi	.20	.20
1731	A301	50c multicolored	.25	.20
1732	A301	$1 emerald & multi	.50	.20
1733	A301	$1 lt red brn & multi	.50	.20
		Nos. 1726-1733 (8)	2.25	1.60

Flag of China, "Double Ten" and Anniversary Emblems — A316

Designs (Flag of China and): $2.50, National anthem. $5, Gen. Chiang Kai-shek. $8, Sun Yat-sen.

1971, Oct. 10   Photo.   Perf. 13

1734	A316	$1 orange & multi	.30	.20
1735	A316	$2.50 multi	.75	.20
1736	A316	$5 green & multi	.90	.30
1737	A316	$8 olive & multi	.95	.35
		Nos. 1734-1737 (4)	2.90	1.05

60th National Day.

Bird in Flight (AOPU Emblem) — A317

Perf. 13½x14

1971, Nov. 8   Litho.   Wmk. 323

1738	A317	$2.50 yellow & multi	.35	.20
1739	A317	$5 orange & multi	.80	.20

Asian-Oceanic Postal Union Executive Committee Session, Taipei, Nov. 8-15.

"White Frost Hawk," by Lang Shih-ning — A318

Dog Series I

Designs: $2, "Star-Glancing Wolf." $2.50, "Golden-Winged Face." $5, "Young Black Dragon." $8, "Young Gray Dragon."
Designs from painting named "Ten Prized Dogs," by Lang Shih-ning (Giuseppe Castiglione, 1688-1766).

Perf. 13½x13

1971, Nov. 16   Litho.   Unwmk.

1740	A318	$1 Facing left	.40	.20
1741	A318	$2 Lying down	.70	.20
1742	A318	$2.50 Scratching	1.00	.30
1743	A318	$5 Facing right	2.50	.50
1744	A318	$8 Looking back	3.50	1.00
		Nos. 1740-1744 (5)	8.10	2.20

Dog Series II

Designs: $1, "Black with Snow-white Paws." $2, "Yellow Leopard." $2.50, "Flying Magpie." $5, "Heavenly Lion." $8, "Mottled Tiger."

1972, Jan. 12

1745	A318	$1 Facing right	1.10	.20
1746	A318	$2 Walking	2.10	.20
1747	A318	$2.50 Sleeping	2.75	.30
1748	A318	$5 Facing left	7.50	.50
1749	A318	$8 Sitting	10.00	1.00
		Nos. 1745-1749 (5)	23.45	2.20

Squirrels — A319

Perf. 13½x12½

1971, Dec. 1   Wmk. 323

1750	A319	Block of 4	4.00	3.50
a.		50c in UL corner	.70	.25
b.		50c in UR corner	.70	.25
c.		50c in LL corner	.70	.25
d.		50c in LR corner	.70	.25
1751	A319	Block of 4	17.00	5.00
a.		$4.50 in UL corner	4.00	.60
b.		$4.50 in UR corner	4.00	.60
c.		$4.50 in LL corner	4.00	.60
d.		$4.50 in LR corner	4.00	.60

New Year 1972.

Flags of China and Jordan — A320

1971, Dec. 16   Perf. 13½
Granite Paper

1752	A320	$5 multicolored	1.25	.25

50th anniversary of the founding of the Hashemite Kingdom of Jordan.

Cargo Ship "Hai King" — A321

$7, Ocean liner & map of Pacific Ocean, vert.

1971, Dec. 16   Perf. 12½

1753	A321	$4 grn, dk bl & red	.50	.25
1754	A321	$7 ocher & multi	.85	.40

China Merchants Steam Navigation Co., cent.

Downhill Skiing, Olympic Rings — A322

$5, Cross-country skiing. $8, Giant slalom.

1972, Feb. 3   Perf. 13½

1755	A322	$1 org, blk & bl	.20	.20
1756	A322	$5 yel grn, dp org & blk	.40	.20
1757	A322	$8 red, gray & blk	.75	.25
		Nos. 1755-1757 (3)	1.35	.65

11th Winter Olympic Games, Sapporo, Japan, Feb. 3-13.

Vase, 18th Century — A323

Porcelain Series I

Porcelain Masterworks of Ching Dynasty: $2, Covered jar. $2.50, Pitcher. $5, Vase with 5 openings and dragon design. $8, Covered jar with children design.

Perf. 11½

1972, Mar. 20   Photo.   Unwmk.

1758	A323	$1 violet & multi	.50	.20
1759	A323	$2 plum & blue	1.00	.20
1760	A323	$2.50 org ver & bl	1.40	.25
1761	A323	$5 bis brn & bl	1.60	.45
1762	A323	$8 sl grn & multi	2.50	.45
		Nos. 1758-1762 (5)	7.00	1.55

See Nos. 1812-1821, 1864-1868.

Nine Flying Doves — A324

Perf. 13½x14

1972, Apr. 1   Litho.   Wmk. 323

1763	A324	$1 lt blue & blk	.35	.20
1764	A324	$5 lt violet & blk	1.00	.30

Asian-Oceanic Postal Union, 10th anniv.

"Dignity with Self-reliance" — A325

Perf. 13½x12½

1972-75   Litho.   Wmk. 323

1765	A325	5c brown & yel	.20	.20
1766	A325	10c blue & org	.20	.20
1767	A325	20c cl & yel grn ('75)	.20	.20
1768	A325	50c lil & lil rose	.20	.20
1769	A325	$1 red & brt bl	.30	.20
1770	A325	$1.50 yel & dk bl	.40	.20
1771	A325	$2 maroon & org	.60	.20
1772	A325	$2.50 emer & ver	.40	.20
1773	A325	$3 red & lt grn	.75	.20
		Nos. 1765-1773 (9)	3.25	1.80

Souvenir Sheet
Imperf

1775	A325	Sheet of 2	5.00	2.25

No. 1775 commemorates ROCPEX '72 Philatelic Exhibition, Taipei, Oct. 24-Nov. 2. It contains 2 stamps similar to Nos. 1771 and 1773 with simulated perforations.
Issued: $1, $1.50, $2, $3, 5/20/72; 5c, 10c, 50c, $2.50, #1775, 10/24/72; 20c, 1975.
For overprints see Nos. 1787-1790.

Emperor Shih-tsung's Procession — A326

Messengers on Horseback — A327

Designs from scrolls depicting Emperor Shih-tsung's (reigned 1522-1566) journey to and from tombs at Cheng-tien. No. 1776 shows land journey departure and is designed from right to left. No. 1779 shows return trip by boat and is designed from left to right. The 5 stamps of Nos. 1776 and 1780 are numbered 1 to 5 in Chinese (see illustrations with Nos. 1682-1686 for numerals).

1972   Photo.   Unwmk.   Perf. 13½

1776		Strip of 5	3.50	3.00
a.	A326	$1 shown (1)	.55	.35
b.	A326	$1 Seven carriages (2)	.55	.35
c.	A326	$1 Carriage drawn by 23 horses (3)	.55	.35
d.	A326	$1 Procession (4)	.55	.35
e.	A326	$1 Emperor under 2 canopies (5)	.55	.35
1777	A327	$2.50 shown	2.25	.50
1778	A327	$5 Guards with flags, fans & spears	3.00	.50
1779	A327	$8 Sedan chair carried by 28 men	6.00	.60
1780		Strip of 5	3.50	3.00
a.	A326	$1 Three barges (1)	.55	.35
b.	A326	$1 Procession, sedan chairs (2)	.55	.35
c.	A326	$1 Two barges with trunks (3)	.55	.35
d.	A326	$1 Procession on land (4)	.55	.35
e.	A326	$1 Procession, 2 sedan chairs (5)	.55	.35
1781	A326	$2.50 Courtiers at city welcoming Emperor	2.25	.40
1782	A327	$5 Orchestra on horseback	3.00	.40
1783	A326	$8 Barges	3.75	.50
		Nos. 1776-1783 (8)	27.25	8.90

Issue dates: No. 1776-1779, June 14; Nos. 1780-1783, July 12.

First Day Covers — A328

Magnifying Glass, Tongs, Gauge — A329

Design: $2.50, Sun Yat-sen stamp of 1971 (type A311) under magnifying glass.

Wmk. 323

1972, Aug. 9   Engr.   Perf. 12

1784	A328	$1 dk vio blue	.20	.20
1785	A328	$2.50 brt green	.25	.20
1786	A329	$8 scarlet	.55	.25
		Nos. 1784-1786 (3)	1.00	.65

Promotion of philately. Printed in sheets of 40. Each sheet contains 4 blocks of 10 stamps surrounded by margins with inscriptions.

Nos. 1768-1770, 1772 Overprinted in Dark Blue or Red

Perf. 13½x12½

1972, Sept. 9   Litho.   Wmk. 323

1787	A325	$1 red & brt bl (DB)	.20	.20
1788	A325	$1.50 yel & dk bl (R)	.25	.20
1789	A325	$2 mar & org (R)	.40	.20
1790	A325	$3 red & lt grn (DB)	.45	.20
		Nos. 1787-1790 (4)	1.30	.80

China's championship victories in the Little League World Series, Gary, Ind., and in the Senior League World Series, Williamsport, Pa., Aug. 1972.

Emperor Yao
(2357-2258
B.C.) — A330

Mountain
Climbing — A331

Rulers: $4, Emperor Shun (ruled 2255-2208 B.C.), $4.50, Yu, the Great (ruled 2205-2198 B.C.), $5, King T'ang (ruled 1783-1754 B.C.), $5.50, King Wen (ruled 1171-1122 B.C.), $6, King Wu (ruled 1121-1114 B.C.), $7, Chou Kung (died 1105 B.C.), $8, Confucius (551-479 B.C.).

1972-73   Engr.   Perf. 12
Granite Paper

1791	A330	$3.50 dk blue	.40	.20
1792	A330	$4 rose red	.60	.20
1793	A330	$4.50 bluish lil	.80	.20
1794	A330	$5 brt green	.40	.20
1795	A330	$5.50 dp claret ('73)	1.25	.25
1796	A330	$6 dp orgt ('73)	1.10	.20
a.		Perf. 13½x12½ ('76)	1.10	.30
1797	A330	$7 sepia ('73)	1.10	.20
a.		Perf. 13½x12½ ('76)	1.10	.30
1798	A330	$8 indigo ('73)	1.25	.20
a.		gray, perf. 13½x12½ ('76)	1.75	.35
		Nos. 1791-1798 (8)	6.90	1.65

In the first printing, Nos. 1791-1794, 1796-1798 measure 32mm high. In a 1974 reissue they are 33mm.

1972, Oct. 31   Unwmk.
**   Photo.   Perf. 12**

Designs (China Youth Corps emblem and): $2.50, Skiing (skiers forming circle). $4, Diving. $8, Parachute jumping.

1800	A331	$1 green & multi	.20	.20
1801	A331	$2.50 blue & multi	.40	.20
1802	A331	$4 orange & multi	.60	.20
1803	A331	$8 multicolored	1.00	.20
		Nos. 1800-1803 (4)	2.20	.85

China Youth Corps, 20th anniversary.

JCI Emblem
A332

1972, Nov. 12   Litho.   Wmk. 323

1804	A332	$1 multicolored	.20	.20
1805	A332	$5 orange & multi	.35	.20
1806	A332	$8 multicolored	.65	.40
		Nos. 1804-1806 (3)	1.20	.80

27th Junior Chamber International (JCI) World Congress, Taipei, Nov. 12-19.

Electronic Mail
Sorter — A333

Plane, Ship and
Pier — A334

Progress of Communications System on Taiwan: $5, Highway overpass over railroad.

**   Wmk. 323**
1972, Nov. 12   Engr.   Perf. 11½

1807	A333	$1 red	.20	.20
1808	A334	$2.50 blue	.50	.20
1809	A334	$5 dk violet brn	.55	.35
		Nos. 1807-1809 (3)	1.25	.75

Cow and Calf
(Parental
Love) — A335

1972, Dec. 1   Litho.   Perf. 12

1810	A335	50c red & blk	.75	.30
1811	A335	$4.50 yel, red & brn	4.25	.90

New Year 1973. Printed in sheets of 80, divided into 4 panes of 20, separated by vertical and horizontal gutters 2 rows wide. 20 red chops meaning "Happy New Year" are printed in the gutters.

Porcelain Type of 1972 and

Stem Bowl
with
Dragons
A336

Porcelain Series II

Porcelain Masterworks of Ming Dynasty: $1, Covered vase with fruits and flowers. $2, Vase with ornamental and floral design. $2.50, Vase imitating ancient bronze. $5, Flask with flowers of 4 seasons. $8, Garlic head vase.

1973   Photo.   Perf. 11½

1812	A323	$1 gray & multi	.70	.20
1813	A323	$2 lt brn & multi	1.00	.20
1814	A323	$2.50 brt grn & multi	1.40	.20
1815	A323	$5 ultra & multi	1.50	.35
1816	A323	$8 olive & multi	2.25	.60
		Nos. 1812-1816 (5)	6.85	1.55

Porcelain Series III

Ming Porcelain: $2, Refuse container with dragons. $2.50, Covered jar with lotus. $5, Covered jar with horses. $8, Bowl with figures of immortals.

1817	A336	$1 gray & multi	.70	.20
1818	A336	$2 lt vio & multi	1.00	.20
1819	A336	$2.50 dk red & multi	1.40	.20
1820	A336	$5 blue & multi	1.50	.35
1821	A336	$8 dp org & multi	2.25	.60
		Nos. 1817-1821 (5)	6.85	1.55

Issued: #1812-1816, 1/10; #1817-1821, 3/24. See Nos. 1864-1868.

Oyster Fairy and Fisherman's
Dance — A337

1973, Feb. 7   Photo.   Perf. 11½
Granite Paper

1822	A337	$1 Kicking shut-tlecock, vert.	.50	.20
1823	A337	$4 Shown	.80	.20
1824	A337	$5 Rowing boat over land	.90	.25
1825	A337	$8 Old man carrying young lady, vert.	1.00	.40
		Nos. 1822-1825 (4)	3.20	1.05

Chinese folklore popular entertainment.

Bamboo
Boat
A338

Taiwanese Handicrafts: $2.50, Painted marble vase, vert. $5, Painted glass plate. $8, Doll, bridegroom carrying bride on back, vert.

**   Perf. 13½x14½, 14½x13½**
1973, Mar. 9   Photo.

1826	A338	$1 multi	.20	.20
1827	A338	$2.50 multi	.60	.20
1828	A338	$5 multi	.85	.25
1829	A338	$8 multi	1.25	.40
		Nos. 1826-1829 (4)	2.90	1.05

Federation Emblem,
Cargo Hook,
Crane — A339

Emblem,
Tractor, New
Buildings
A340

**   Wmk. 323**
1973, Apr. 2   Litho.   Perf. 12½

1830	A339	$1 salmon & multi	.20	.20
1831	A340	$5 blue & blk	.70	.25

12th convention of International Federation of Asian and Western Pacific Contractors Association, Taipei, Apr. 2-10.

Pres. Chiang Kai-
shek, Flag of
China — A341

Lin Tse-
hsü — A342

Design: $4, like $1 with different border.

**   Unwmk.**
1973, May 20   Photo.   Perf. 12

1832	A341	$1 yellow & multi	.30	.25
1833	A341	$4 dk grn & multi	1.10	.50

First anniversary of Pres. Chiang Kai-shek's inauguration for a fifth term.

**   Wmk. 323**
1973, June 3   Engr.   Perf. 12

1834	A342	$1 sepia	.50	.20

Lin Tse-hsü (1785-1850), Governor of Hunan and Kwantung, who destroyed large quantity of opium at Humen, Kwantung, June 3, 1839.

Willows and Palace Gate in the
Morning — A343

Lady Watering
Peonies,
Stone
Ornament
A344

Design from scroll "Spring Morning in the Han Palace," by Chiu Ying. The five stamps of No. 1835 are numbered 1 to 5 and the five stamps of No. 1838 are numbered 6-10 in Chinese (see illustrations with Nos. 1682-1691 for numerals). The stamps are numbered and listed from right to left.

1973   Photo.   Unwmk.   Perf. 11½
Granite Paper

1835		Strip of 5	3.00	3.00
a.	A343	$1 shown (1)	.40	.20
b.	A343	$1 Ladies feeding peacocks (2)	.40	.20
c.	A343	$1 Lady watering peonies (3)	.40	.20
d.	A343	$1 Pear tree in bloom (4)	.40	.20
e.	A343	$1 Lady musicians (5)	.40	.20
1836	A344	$5 shown	2.25	.60
1837	A344	$8 Lady musicians	3.50	1.00
1838		Strip of 5	3.00	3.00
a.	A343	$1 Ladies playing go (6)	.40	.20
b.	A343	$1 Various games (7)	.40	.20
c.	A343	$1 Talking and playing music (8)	.40	.20
d.	A343	$1 Artist painting portrait (9)	.40	.20
e.	A343	$1 Sentries guarding wall (10)	.40	.20
1839	A344	$5 Ladies playing go	2.25	.60
1840	A344	$8 Girl chasing butterfly	3.50	1.00
		Nos. 1835-1840 (6)	17.50	9.20

Issued: #1835-1837, 6/20; #1838-1840, 7/18.

Fan, Bamboo Design, by Hsiang Te-
hsin — A345

Designs: Painted fans, Ming dynasty.

**   Perf. 12½x13**
1973, Aug. 15   Photo.   Wmk. 368

1841	A345	$1 bister & multi	.35	.20
1842	A345	$2.50 bister & multi	.70	.25
1843	A345	$5 bister & multi	1.25	.35
1844	A345	$8 bister & multi	1.90	.50
		Nos. 1841-1844 (4)	4.20	1.30

See Nos. 1934-1937.

Little League
Emblem — A346

INTERPOL
Emblem — A347

**   Wmk. 370**
1973, Sept. 9   Litho.   Perf. 13½

1845	A346	$1 yel, car & dk bl	.40	.20
1846	A346	$4 yel, grn & dk bl	1.40	.35

Chinese victory in Little League Twin Championships, Gary, Ind., and Williamsport, Pa.

**   Wmk. 370**
1973, Sept. 11   Litho.   Perf. 12

1847	A347	$1 blue & org	.20	.20
1848	A347	$5 green & org	.50	.20
1849	A347	$8 magenta & org	.75	.40
		Nos. 1847-1849 (3)	1.45	.85

Intl. Criminal Police Organization, 50th anniv.

Ch'iu Feng-
chia — A348

**   Wmk. 323**
1973, Oct. 5   Engr.   Perf. 11½

1850	A348	$1 violet black	.70	.25

2nd meeting of overseas Hakkas, Taipei, Oct. 5-7, and to honor Ch'iu Feng-chia (1864-1912), Hakka scholar, poet and revolutionist.

Tsengwen Reservoir A349

Tsengwen Dam — A350

Perf. 13½

1973, Oct. 31   Photo.   Unwmk.

1851	Strip of 3	.90	.70
a.	A349 $1 Upper shore	.25	.20
b.	A349 $1 shown	.25	.20
c.	A349 $1 Lower shore	.25	.20

Perf. 12x11½

1852	A350 $5 shown	.65	.30
1853	A350 $8 Spillway	1.00	.60
	Nos. 1851-1853 (3)	2.55	1.60

Inauguration of Tsengwen Reservoir. No. 1851 printed in sheets of 15.

Tiger — A351

Wmk. 370

1973, Dec. 1   Litho.   Perf. 12½

1854	A351 50c multi	.60	.20
1855	A351 $4.50 multi	1.75	.50

New Year 1974.

"Snow-dotted Eagle," by Lang Shih-ning — A352

#1857, "Comfortable Ride." #1858, "Red Flower Eagle." #1859, "Cloud-running Steed." #1860, "Sky-running steed." $2.50, "Red Jade Seat." $5, "Thunderclap Steed." $8, "Arabian Champion." Designs from painting series "Ten Prized Horses," by Lang Shih-ning (Giuseppe Castiglione, 1688-1766).

1973   Litho.   Unwmk.   Perf. 13

1856	A352 50c multi	.75	.20
1857	A352 $1 Pinto, blk tail	1.00	.35
1858	A352 $1 Facing left	1.00	.35
1859	A352 $1 Facing right	1.00	.35
1860	A352 $1 Pinto, white tail	1.00	.35
a.	Block of 4, #1857-1860	5.00	4.00
1861	A352 $2.50 Palomino	2.25	.60
1862	A352 $5 Grazing	3.75	1.00
a.	Souvenir sheet of 4	30.00	14.00
1863	A352 $8 Brown stallion	6.00	1.25
	Nos. 1856-1863 (8)	16.75	4.45

#1862a contains 4 stamps with simulated perforations similar to #1856-1857, 1861-1862.

Issued: 50c, $2.50, $5, 11/21; others 12/21.

Porcelain Types of 1972-73

Porcelain Series IV

Porcelain Masterworks of Sung Dynasty: $1, Vase. $2, Three-tiered vase. $2.50, Lotus-shaped bowl. $5, Incense burner. $8, Incense burner on stand.

1974, Jan. 16   Photo.   Perf. 11½

1864	A323 $1 ultra & multi	.40	.20
1865	A336 $2 multicolored	.80	.20
1866	A336 $2.50 red & multi	1.00	.20
1867	A336 $5 lilac & multi	1.10	.25
1868	A336 $8 green & multi	1.10	.50
	Nos. 1864-1868 (5)	4.40	1.35

Juggler — A353

Taroko Gorge, Hualien — A354

Design: $8, Magician producing dishes from his robe, horiz.

1974, Feb. 6   Photo.   Perf. 11½

1869	A353 $1 yellow & multi	.20	.20
1870	A353 $8 yellow & multi	1.25	.20

1974, Mar. 22   Photo.   Perf. 12

Designs: $2.50, Luce Chapel, Tunghai University. $5, Tzu En Pagoda, Sun Moon Lake. $8, Goddess of Mercy, Keelung.

1871	A354 $1 multi	.30	.20
1872	A354 $2.50 multi	.70	.20
1873	A354 $5 multi	.90	.20
1874	A354 $8 multi	1.25	.25
	Nos. 1871-1874 (4)	3.15	.85

Taiwan landmarks.

Fighting Cocks (Brass) A355

Designs: $2.50, Grapes and bowl with fruit (imitation jade). $5, Fisherman (wood carving), vert. $8, Basket with plastic roses, vert.

Perf. 13½x14½, 14½x13½

1974, Apr. 10

1875	A355 $1 bl grn & multi	.20	.20
1876	A355 $2.50 brown & multi	.50	.20
1877	A355 $5 crimson & multi	.70	.25
1878	A355 $8 multicolored	1.50	.40
	Nos. 1875-1878 (4)	2.90	1.05

Taiwanese handicraft products.

Sun Yat-sen Memorial Hall — A356

Taiwan landmarks: $2.50, Reaching-moon Tower, Cheng Ching Lake. $5, Orchid Island (boats). $8, Penghu Interisland Bridge.

1974, May 15   Photo.   Perf. 11½

Granite Paper

1879	A356 $1 blue & multi	.30	.20
1880	A356 $2.50 blue & multi	.70	.20
1881	A356 $5 blue & multi	.90	.20
1882	A356 $8 blue & multi	1.25	.25
	Nos. 1879-1882 (4)	3.15	.85

Pres. Chiang and Gate of Whampoa Military Academy A357

Marching Cadets and Entrance Gate — A358

Wmk. 323

1974, June 16   Engr.   Perf. 11½

1883	A357 $1 carmine rose	.20	.20
1884	A358 $14 violet blue	.70	.40

50th anniversary of the founding of the Whampoa Military Academy.

Long-distance Runner and Olympic Rings — A359

The Boy Wang Ch'i Fighting Invaders — A360

$8, Women's relay race, Olympic rings.

1974, June 23   Litho.   Perf. 12½

1885	A359 $1 blue, blk & red	.20	.20
1886	A359 $8 pink, blk & red	.80	.40

80th anniv. of Intl. Olympic Committee.

1974, July 15   Wmk. 370   Perf. 13½

Folk Tales: No. 1888, T'i Ying pleading for her father before the Emperor. No. 1889, Wen Yen-po flushing out ball caught in tree. No. 1890, Boy Wang Hua returning gold piece he found. No. 1891, Pu Shih, a rich sheep raiser and benefactor. No. 1892, K'ung Yung as a child choosing smallest pear. No. 1893, Tung Yu studying. No. 1894, Szu Ma-kuang saving playmate from drowning in water jar.

1887	A360 50c olive & multi	.20	.20
1888	A360 50c ultra & multi	.20	.20
1889	A360 50c ocher & multi	.20	.20
1890	A360 50c red brn & multi	.20	.20
a.	Block of 4, #1887-1890	.60	.60
1891	A360 $1 green & multi	.40	.40
1892	A360 $1 lilac & multi	.40	.40
1893	A360 $1 blue & multi	.40	.40
1894	A360 $1 car & multi	.40	.40
a.	Block of 4, #1891-1894	1.60	1.60
	Nos. 1887-1894 (8)	2.40	2.40

For similar designs see A380, A427, A456, A495.

Myrtle, by Wei Sheng — A361

Silk Fan Paintings, Sung Dynasty (960-1279 A.D.): $2.50, Cabbage and Insects, by Hsu Ti. $5, Hibiscus, Cat and Dog, by Li Ti. $8, Pomegranate and Birds, by Wu Ping. Fans from National Palace Museum.

Perf. 13x12½

1974, Aug. 14   Photo.   Wmk. 368

1895	A361 $1 multi	.20	.20
1896	A361 $2.50 multi	.60	.20
1897	A361 $5 multi	1.00	.40
1898	A361 $8 multi	1.40	.50
	Nos. 1895-1898 (4)	3.20	1.10

See Nos. 1950-1953.

Battle at Marco Polo Bridge, July 7, 1937 A362

Wmk. 370

1974, Sept. 3   Litho.   Perf. 13½

1899	A362 $1 multicolored	.25	.20

Souvenir Sheet

Wmk. 323

Without Gum; Granite Paper

1900	Sheet of 8	6.25	5.00
a.	A362 $1, single stamp	.55	.50

20th Armed Forces Day. No. 1900 commemorates Armed Forces Stamp Exhibition, Sun Yat-sen Memorial Hall, Sept. 3-9.

Chrysanthemum A363

Designs: Various chrysanthemums.

Unwmk.

1974, Sept. 30   Photo.   Perf. 12

Granite Paper

1901	A363 $1 lilac & multi	.20	.20
1902	A363 $2.50 multi	.50	.20
1903	A363 $5 orange & multi	.70	.25
1904	A363 $8 multi	1.25	.35
	Nos. 1901-1904 (4)	2.65	1.00

Rep. of China Pavilion, EXPO Emblem A364

Map of Fair Grounds, Chinese Flag A364a

Wmk. 370

1974, Oct. 10   Litho.   Perf. 13

1905	A364 $1 multi	.20	.20
1906	A364a $8 multi	.70	.40

EXPO '74, Spokane, Wash., May 4-Nov. 4. Theme, "Preserve the Environment."

Steel Mill, Kaohsiung A365

Taichung Harbor A366

Designs: $1, Taiwan North Link Railroad and map. $2, Oil refinery. $2.50, Electric train. $3.50, Taoyuan International Airport. $4, Taiwan North-South Highway and map. $4.50, Kaohsiung shipyard. $5, Su-ao Port.

Perf. 13x12½, 12½x13

1974, Oct. 31   Wmk. 323

1907	A365 50c lilac, yel & brn	.20	.20
1908	A365 $1 green & org	.20	.20
1909	A365 $2 blue & yel	.20	.20
1910	A365 $2.50 emer & org	.20	.20
1911	A366 $3 ocher & ultra	.20	.20
1912	A366 $3.50 sl grn & yel	.20	.20
1913	A366 $4 brown & yel	.20	.20
1914	A366 $4.50 ver & bl	.35	.20
1915	A366 $5 sepia & dk bl	.35	.20
	Nos. 1907-1915 (9)	2.10	1.80

Major construction projects.
See Nos. 2009-2017, 2068-2076. For overprints see Nos. 2064-2065, 2112-2113.

Agaricus
Bisporus
A367

Edible Mushrooms: $2.50, Pleurotus ostreatus. $5, Dictyophora indusiata. $8, Flammulina velutipes.

Perf. 11½

1974, Nov. 15	Unwmk.		Photo.	
1916	A367	$1 multi	.20	.20
1917	A367	$2.50 multi	.20	.20
1918	A367	$5 multi	1.00	.20
1919	A367	$8 multi	1.25	.30
	Nos. 1916-1919 (4)		2.65	.90

9th Intl. Scientific Congress on the Cultivation of Edible Fungi, Taipei, Nov. 1974.

Batters and
World
Map — A368

Pitcher and Championship
Banners — A369

Wmk. 323

1974, Nov. 24	Litho.		Perf. 13½	
1920	A368	$1 multicolored	.20	.20
1921	A369	$8 multicolored	.65	.35

China's victory in 1974 Little League Baseball World Series Triple Championships.

Rabbit — A370

Acrobat with Iron
Rod — A371

Wmk. 323

1974, Dec. 10	Photo.		Perf. 12½	
1922	A370	50c orange & multi	.30	.20
1923	A370	$4.50 brown & multi	1.60	.30

New Year 1975.

1975, Jan. 15   Unwmk.   Perf. 11½

$5, Two acrobats spinning tops, horiz.

Granite Paper

1924	A371	$4 yellow & multi	.60	.40
1925	A371	$5 yellow & multi	1.00	.45

Children Watching Puppet
Show — A372

Ceremonial New Year
Greetings — A373

Designs from scroll "Festivals for the New Year," by Ting Kuan-p'eng. Nos. 1926a-1926e are numbered 1-5 in Chinese.

1975, Feb. 25   Photo.   Perf. 11½
Granite Paper

1926		Strip of 5	3.00	2.50
a.		A372 $1 Ceremonial New Year Greetings (1)	.45	.20
b.		A372 $1 Man with trained monkey (2)	.45	.20
c.		A372 $1 Crowd and musicians (3)	.45	.20
d.		A372 $1 Picnic under a tree (4)	.45	.20
e.		A372 $1 shown (5)	.45	.20
1927	A373	$2.50 shown	2.00	.30
1928	A373	$5 Children buying firecrackers	2.50	.55
1929	A373	$8 Children and man with trained monkey	4.25	.90
	Nos. 1926-1929 (4)		11.75	4.25

Sun Yat-
sen
Memorial
Hall,
Taipei
A374

Sun Yat-sen's Handwriting — A375

Sun Yat-sen, Bronze
Statue in Memorial
Hall — A376

Sun Yat-sen Memorial Hall, St. John's
University, NY
A377

Perf. 13½x14, 14x13½

1975, Mar. 12			Litho.	
1930	A374	$1 green & multi	.20	.20
1931	A375	$4 yel grn & multi	.40	.20
1932	A376	$5 yellow & multi	.60	.20
1933	A377	$8 gray & multi	.80	.30
	Nos. 1930-1933 (4)		2.00	.90

Dr. Sun Yat-sen (1866-1925), statesman and revolutionary leader.

Fan Type of 1973 Inscribed
"Landscape" (1st Character, 2nd Row)

山水

Painted fans, Ming Dynasty. Second row of inscription gives design description.

Perf. 12½x13

1975, Apr. 16		Photo.	Wmk. 368	
1934	A345	$1 bister & multi	.20	.20
1935	A345	$2.50 bister & multi	.60	.20
1936	A345	$5 bister & multi	1.25	.35
1937	A345	$8 bister & multi	1.40	.55
	Nos. 1934-1937 (4)		3.45	1.30

Yuan-chin coin,
1122-221
B.C. — A378

Ancient Chinese Coins: $4, Pan-liang, 221-207 B.C. $5, Five chu, 206 B.C.-220 A.D. $8, Five chu, 502-557 A.D.

Wmk. 323

1975, May 20		Litho.	Perf. 13	
1938	A378	$1 salmon & multi	.20	.20
1939	A378	$4 yellow & multi	.70	.20
1940	A378	$5 dl yel & multi	.80	.20
1941	A378	$8 lt vio & multi	1.25	.25
	Nos. 1938-1941 (4)		2.95	.85

The Cloth-bag
Monk, by
Chang Hung
(1577-1668)
A379

Chinese Paintings: $4, Lao-tzu Riding Buffalo, by Chao Pu-chih (1053-1110). $5, Portrait of Shih-te, by Wang Wen (1497-1576). $8, Splashed-ink Immortal, by Liang K'ai (early 13th century).

Perf. 11½

1975, June 18		Photo.	Unwmk.	
		Granite Paper		
1942	A379	$2 blk, buff & ver	.60	.20
1943	A379	$4 blk, gray & red	1.40	.25
1944	A379	$5 blk, yel & ver	2.25	.40
1945	A379	$8 tan, red & blk	3.00	.60
	Nos. 1942-1945 (4)		7.25	1.45

Chu Yin Reading
by the Light of
Fireflies — A380

Folk Tales: No. 1947, Hua Mu-lan going to war for her father. No. 1948, King Kou Chien tasting gall. $5, Chou Ch'u killing tiger.

Perf. 14x13½

1975, July 16		Litho.	Wmk. 368	
1946	A380	$1 olive & multi	.20	.20
1947	A380	$2 bis brn & multi	.25	.20
1948	A380	$2 lt grn & multi	.25	.20
1949	A380	$5 blue & multi	.60	.20
	Nos. 1946-1949 (4)		1.30	.90
	See Nos. 2108-2111.			

Cherry-Apple
Blossoms, by
Lin
Ch'un — A381

Silk Fan Paintings, Sung Dynasty: $2, Spring Blossoms and Butterfly, by Ma K'uei. $5, Monkeys and Deer, by I Yüan-chih. $8, Tame Sparrow among Bamboo.

Perf. 13x12½

1975, Aug. 15		Litho.	Wmk. 323	
1950	A381	$1 multicolored	.20	.20
1951	A381	$2 multicolored	.70	.20
1952	A381	$5 multicolored	.90	.25
1953	A381	$8 multicolored	1.75	.50
	Nos. 1950-1953 (4)		3.55	1.15
	See Nos. 2001-2004.			

Gen. Chang Tzu-
chung (1891-1940)
A382

#1955, Maj. Gen. Kao Chih-hong (1908-37). #1956, Capt. Sha Shih-chiun (1896-1938). #1957, Maj. Gen. Hsieh Chin-yuan (1905-41). #1958, Lt. Yen Hai-wen (1916-37). #1959, Lt. Gen. Tai An-lan (1905-42).

Wmk. 323

1975, Sept. 3		Engr.	Perf. 12	
1954	A382	$2 carmine	.20	.20
1955	A382	$2 sepia	.20	.20
1956	A382	$2 dull green	.20	.20
1957	A382	$5 violet black	.30	.20
1958	A382	$5 violet blue	.30	.20
1959	A382	$5 dark blue	.30	.20
	Nos. 1954-1959 (6)		1.50	1.20

Martyrs of the resistance fight against Japan.

Lotus Pond with Willows, by Madame
Chiang — A383

Paintings by Madame Chiang Kai-shek: $5, Sun Breaks through Mountain Clouds. $8, A Pair of Pine Trees. $10, Fishing and Farming.

Perf. 13½

1975, Oct. 31		Litho.	Unwmk.	
1960	A383	$2 multicolored	.75	.20
1961	A383	$5 multicolored	1.60	.30
1962	A383	$8 multicolored	2.40	.40
1963	A383	$10 multicolored	3.25	.75
	Nos. 1960-1963 (4)		8.00	1.65

For similar design see type A404.

Cauldron
with
Phoenix
Handles,
481-221
B.C.
A384

Ancient Bronzes: $2, Rectangular cauldron, 1122-722 B.C., vert. $8, Flat jar, 481-221 B.C. $10, 3-legged wine vessel, 1766-1122 B.C., vert.

1975, Nov. 12   Photo.   Perf. 12

1964	A384	$2 pink & multi	.20	.20
1965	A384	$5 lt blue & multi	.65	.20
1966	A384	$8 yellow & multi	.85	.20
1967	A384	$10 lilac & multi	1.00	.30
	Nos. 1964-1967 (4)		2.70	.90

For similar design see type A395. No. 1964 has 7 Chinese characters at left, No. 2005 has 4. No. 1967 has 4 characters at left, No. 2008 has 5.

Dragon, Nine-Dragon Wall, Peihai — A385

Techi Dam — A386

Wmk. 323

1975, Dec. 1   Litho.   Perf. 12½
1968 A385 $2 orange & multi   .25 .20
1969 A385 $5 green & multi   1.25 .60

New Year 1976.

1975, Dec. 17   Unwmk.   Perf. 13½
Design: $10, Panoramic view of Techi Dam.
1970 A386 $2 green & multi   .20 .20
1971 A386 $10 blue & multi   .55 .45

Completion of Techi Dam, Tachia River.

Biathlon and Olympic Rings — A387

Olympic Rings and: $5, Luge. $8, Skiing.

1976, Jan. 15   Litho.   Perf. 13½
1972 A387 $2 blue & multi   .20 .20
1973 A387 $5 blue & multi   .35 .20
1974 A387 $8 blue & multi   .55 .25
    Nos. 1972-1974 (3)   1.10 .65

12th Winter Olympic Games, Innsbruck, Austria, Feb. 4-15.

Chin, Oldest Chinese Instrument A388

Musical Instruments: $5, Se, c. 2900 B.C. $8, Standing kong-ho (harp). $10, Sleeping kong-ho.

1976, Feb. 11   Unwmk.   Perf. 14
1975 A388 $2 yellow & multi   .25 .20
1976 A388 $5 orange & multi   .40 .20
1977 A388 $8 grnsh bl & multi   .55 .20
1978 A388 $10 multicolored   .80 .30
    Nos. 1975-1978 (4)   2.00 .90

For similar design see Type A407.

Double Carp Type of 1969
Perf. 13½x12½
1976, Dec. 15   Engr.   Unwmk.
1980 A280 $14 carmine rose   2.25 .30

Mail Collecting A389

Mail Sorting — A390

Postal Service, 80th Anniv.: $8, Mail transport. $10, Mail delivery.

Wmk. 323

1976, Mar. 20   Litho.   Perf. 13½
1984 A389 $2 yellow & multi   .20 .20
1985 A390 $5 green & multi   .35 .20
1986 A390 $8 blue & multi   .50 .20
1987 A389 $10 orange & multi   .60 .30
    a. Souv. sheet of 4, #1984-1987   9.00 6.50
    Nos. 1984-1987 (4)   1.65 .90

Pres. Chiang Kai-shek A391

People Paying Homage — A392

#1990, Pres. Chiang lying in state. #1991, Hearse leaving funeral chapel. $5, People along funeral route. $8, Spirit tablet in Tzuhu Guest House. $10, Tzuhu Guest House, Pres. Chiang's burial place.

1976, Apr. 4
1988 A391 $2 gray & multi   .20 .20
1989 A392 $2 gray & multi   .20 .20
1990 A392 $2 gray & multi   .20 .20
1991 A392 $2 gray & multi   .20 .20
1992 A392 $5 gray & multi   .40 .20
1993 A392 $8 gray & multi   .40 .25
1994 A392 $10 gray & multi   .50 .35
    Nos. 1988-1994 (7)   2.10 1.60

Pres. Chiang Kai-shek (1887-1975), first death anniversary.

Flags of China and US — A393

Wmk. 323

1976, May 29   Litho.   Perf. 13½
1995 A393 $2 multicolored   .20 .20
1996 A393 $10 yellow & multi   .60 .40

American Bicentennial.

Coin, 12th Century B.C. — A394

Cauldron, Shang Dynasty — A395

Bronze Shovel Coins (pu): $5, Pointed-feet coin, 481-221 B.C. $8, Round-feet coin, 722-481 B.C. $10, Square-feet coin, 3rd-2nd centuries B.C.

1976, June 16
1997 A394 $2 salmon & multi   .20 .20
1998 A394 $5 lt blue & multi   .50 .20
1999 A394 $8 gray & multi   .80 .20
2000 A394 $10 multicolored   1.25 .30
    Nos. 1997-2000 (4)   2.75 .90

Fan Painting Type of 1975

Silk Fan Paintings, Sung Dynasty: $2, Hibiscus, by Li Tung. $5, Lilies, by Lin Ch'un. $8,

---

Deer and Pine, by Mou Chung-fu. $10, Quail and Wild Flowers, by Li An-chung.

Perf. 13x12½
1976, July 14   Litho.   Wmk. 323
2001 A381 $2 multicolored   .45 .20
2002 A381 $5 multicolored   1.10 .20
2003 A381 $8 multicolored   1.40 .30
2004 A381 $10 multicolored   2.25 .40
    Nos. 2001-2004 (4)   5.20 1.10

1976, Aug. 25   Photo.   Perf. 11½
Granite Paper

Ancient Bronzes: $5, 3-legged cauldron, Chou Dynasty (1122-722 B.C.). $8, Wine container, Chou Dynasty. $10, Wine vessel with spout, Shang Dynasty (1766-1122 B.C.).

2005 A395 $2 rose & multi   .20 .20
2006 A395 $5 lt blue & multi   .70 .20
2007 A395 $8 yellow & multi   1.00 .20
2008 A395 $10 lilac & multi   1.10 .30
    Nos. 2005-2008 (4)   3.00 .90

Construction Types of 1974

Designs: $1, Taiwan North Link railroad and map. $2, Railroad electrification. $3, Taichung Harbor. $4, Taiwan North-South Highway and map. $5, Steel Mill, Kaohsiung. $6, Taoyuan International Airport. $7, Kao-hsiung shipyard. $8, Oil refinery. $9, Su-ao Port.

Perf. 13½x12½, 12½x13½
1976   Litho.   Wmk. 323
2009 A365 $1 carmine & grn   .20 .20
2010 A365 $2 orange & multi   .20 .20
2011 A366 $3 violet & multi   .20 .20
2012 A366 $4 carmine & multi   .20 .20
2013 A365 $5 green & brn   .20 .20
2014 A366 $6 brown & multi   .30 .20
2015 A366 $7 brown & multi   .35 .20
2016 A365 $8 carmine & grn   .45 .20
2017 A366 $9 olive & blue   .50 .20
    Nos. 2009-2017 (9)   2.60 1.80

Chiang Kai-shek and Mother A396

Sun Yat-sen and Chiang Kai-shek at Canton Station — A397

Design: $5, Chiang Kai-shek, portrait.

1976, Oct. 31   Litho.   Perf. 13½
2023 A396 $2 multicolored   .20 .20
2024 A396 $5 multicolored   .75 .20
2025 A397 $10 multicolored   .90 .40
    Nos. 2023-2025 (3)   1.85 .80

Pres. Chiang Kai-shek, 90th anniv. of birth.

Flags of Kuomintang and China A398

Sun Yat-sen and Chiang Kai-shek A399

1976, Nov. 12   Perf. 13½x14
2026 A398 $2 multicolored   .20 .20
2027 A399 $10 multicolored   .65 .45
    a. Souv. sheet of 2, #2026-2027   4.50 4.50

11th National Kuomintang Cong., Taipei.

Brazen Serpent — A400

1976, Dec. 15   Wmk. 323   Perf. 12½
2028 A400 $1 red, lilac & gold   .30 .20
2029 A400 $5 plum, yel & gold   1.50 .25

New Year 1977.

Bird and Plum Blossoms, by Ch'en Hung-shou A401

Chinese Paintings: $8, "Wintry Days" (pine), by Yang Wei-chen. $10, Rock and Bamboo, by Hsia Ch'ang.

Perf. 11½
1977, Jan. 12   Photo.   Unwmk.
Granite Paper
2030 A401 $2 multicolored   .60 .20
2031 A401 $8 multicolored   1.75 .25
2032 A401 $10 multicolored   2.25 .40
    Nos. 2030-2032 (3)   4.60 .85

Black-naped Orioles — A402

Birds of Taiwan: $8, Common Kingfisher. $10, Chinese pheasant-tailed jacana.

1977, Feb. 16   Litho.
2033 A402 $2 multicolored   .40 .20
2034 A402 $8 multicolored   1.00 .20
2035 A402 $10 multicolored   1.40 .35
    Nos. 2033-2035 (3)   2.80 .75

See Nos. 2163-2165.

Census Emblem, Industry and Commerce A403

Perf. 13½
1977, Mar. 16   Litho.   Unwmk.
2036 A403 $2 red & multi   .20 .20
2037 A403 $10 purple & multi   .60 .40

Industry and Commerce Census.

Green Mountains Rising into Clouds,
by Madame Chiang — A404

Landscapes, by Madame Chiang Kai-shek:
$5, Boat in the Beauty of Spring. $8, Scholar
beside Waterfall. $10, Water Rises to Meet the
Bridge.

Perf. 11½

1977, Mar. 31   Unwmk.   Photo.
Granite Paper

2038	A404	$2 multi	.40	.20
2039	A404	$5 multi	1.60	.25
2040	A404	$8 multi	2.00	.50
2041	A404	$10 multi	2.25	.60
	Nos. 2038-2041 (4)		6.25	1.55

League
Emblem — A405

Blood
Donation — A406

1977, Apr. 18   Litho.   Perf. 12½

| 2042 | A405 | $2 carmine & multi | .20 | .20 |
| 2043 | A405 | $10 green & multi | .50 | .40 |

10th World Anti-Communist League
Conference.

1977, May 5   Wmk. 323   Perf. 13½

Design: $2, Donating blood, horiz.

| 2044 | A406 | $2 red & black | .20 | .20 |
| 2045 | A406 | $10 red & black | .60 | .40 |

Blood donation movement.

San-hsien
A407

Musical Instruments: $5, Tung-hsiao (bam-
boo flute). $8, Yang-chin (butterfly harp-
sichord). $10, Pai-hsiao (pipes). Background
shows musician playing instrument.

Unwmk.

1977, June 21   Photo.   Perf. 14

2046	A407	$2 multicolored	.20	.20
2047	A407	$5 multicolored	.35	.20
2048	A407	$8 multicolored	.45	.20
2049	A407	$10 multicolored	.60	.30
	Nos. 2046-2049 (4)		1.60	.90

Idea
Leuconoe — A408

Protected Butterflies: $4, Hebomoia
glaucippe formosana. $6, Stichophthalma
howqua formosana. $10, Atrophaneura
horishana.

1977, July 20   Litho.   Perf. 13½

2050	A408	$2 ver & multi	.35	.20
2051	A408	$4 lt grn & multi	.75	.25
2052	A408	$6 lt bl & multi	1.10	.40
2053	A408	$10 yellow & multi	1.50	.50
	Nos. 2050-2053 (4)		3.70	1.35

National
Palace
Museum
A409

Temple — A410

Children's Drawings: $2, Sea Goddess Fes-
tival. $4, Boats on Shore of Lan-yu.

Wmk. 323

1977, Aug. 27   Litho.   Perf. 13½

2054	A409	$1 multicolored	.20	.20
2055	A409	$2 multicolored	.25	.20
2056	A409	$4 multicolored	.40	.20
2057	A410	$5 multicolored	.50	.20
	Nos. 2054-2057 (4)		1.35	.85

8th Exhib. of World School Children's Art.

Carved
Lacquer
Plate, Wan-li
Ware
A411

Ancient Carved Lacquer Ware: $5, Bowl,
Ching dynasty. $8, Round box, Ming dynasty.
$10, Four-tiered box, Ching dynasty.

Perf. 13x14

1977, Sept. 28   Photo.   Wmk. 368

2058	A411	$2 multicolored	.30	.20
2059	A411	$5 multicolored	.60	.20
2060	A411	$8 multicolored	1.25	.20
2061	A411	$10 multicolored	1.10	.30
	Nos. 2058-2061 (4)		3.25	.90

Lions International,
Emblem and
Activities — A412

Unwmk.

1977, Oct. 8   Litho.   Perf. 13

| 2062 | A412 | $2 multicolored | .20 | .20 |
| 2063 | A412 | $10 multicolored | .55 | .35 |

Intl. Association of Lions Clubs, 60th anniv.

Nos. 2069 and 2075
Overprinted in Claret

Perf. 13½x12½

1977, Sept. 9   Litho.   Unwmk.

| 2064 | A365 | $2 orange & multi | .20 | .20 |
| 2065 | A365 | $8 carmine & grn | .60 | .30 |

Little League baseball championship.

Chinese Quality
Mark — A413

Perf. 13x12½

1977, Oct. 14   Litho.   Unwmk.

| 2066 | A413 | $2 red & multi | .50 | .20 |
| 2067 | A413 | $10 blue & multi | 1.50 | .30 |

International Standardization Day.

Construction Types of 1974
Redrawn: Numerals Outlined

Designs as 1976 Issue.

Perf. 13½x12½, 12½x13½

1977   Litho.   Unwmk.
Granite Paper

2068	A365	$1 car & dp grn	.20	.20
2069	A365	$2 ver & multi	.20	.20
2070	A366	$3 violet & multi	.20	.20
2071	A366	$4 carmine & multi	.20	.20
2072	A365	$5 green & multi	.30	.20
2073	A366	$6 sepia & multi	.30	.20
2074	A367	$7 sepia & multi	.35	.20
2075	A365	$8 red lil & multi	.40	.20
2076	A366	$9 olive & multi	.40	.20
	Nos. 2068-2076 (9)		2.55	1.80

Numerals are in solid color on #1907-1915,
2009-2017; in outline on #2068-2076.
For overprints see #2064-2065, 2112-2113.

Man and
Heart — A414

White
Stallion — A415

Perf. 13½x12½

1977, Nov. 12   Litho.   Wmk. 323

| 2077 | A414 | $2 multicolored | .20 | .20 |
| 2078 | A414 | $10 multicolored | .55 | .40 |

Physical health, cardiac care.

Perf. 12½

1977, Dec. 1   Unwmk.   Litho.

New Year 1978: $5, Two horses, horiz.
Designs from painting "100 Horses," by Lang
Shih-ning.

| 2079 | A415 | $1 red & multi | .50 | .25 |
| 2080 | A415 | $5 emerald & multi | 1.50 | .55 |

First Page
of
Constitution
A416

Pres. Chiang Accepting Constitution,
1946 — A417

1977, Dec. 25   Litho.   Perf. 13½

| 2081 | A416 | $2 multicolored | .20 | .20 |
| 2082 | A417 | $10 multicolored | .55 | .30 |

30th anniversary of the Constitution.

Knife Coin with 3
Characters, 403-221
B.C. — A418

Designs: Ancient knife coins.

1978, Jan. 18   Wmk. 323   Perf. 13½

2083	A418	$2 salmon & multi	.30	.20
2084	A418	$5 lt blue & blk	.70	.20
2085	A418	$8 lt gray & multi	.80	.20
2086	A418	$10 tan & multi	1.00	.30
	Nos. 2083-2086 (4)		2.80	.90

China No. 1
and Flag of
China — A419

Designs: $5, No. 464 (Sun Yat-sen). $10,
No. 1204 (Chiang Kai-shek).

1978, Feb. 21   Litho.   Perf. 13½

2087	A419	$2 brown & multi	.20	.20
2088	A419	$5 blue & multi	.40	.25
2089	A419	$10 orange & multi	.70	.40
a.	Souv. sheet of 3, #2087-2089		7.75	3.50
	Nos. 2087-2089 (3)		1.30	.85

Centenary of Chinese postage stamps.

Sun Yat-
Sen
Memorial
Hall
A420

China Nos. 2079
and 2 — A421

Perf. 14x12½, 12½x14

1978, Mar. 20   Wmk. 323

| 2090 | A420 | $2 multicolored | .20 | .20 |
| 2091 | A421 | $10 multicolored | .50 | .35 |

ROCPEX '78 Phil. Exhib., Taipei, Mar. 20-29.

Chiang Kai-shek with Revolutionary
Army — A422

Pres. Chiang Kai-shek (1887-1975); $2, as
young man, 1912, vert. $8, Making speech at
Mt. Lu, July 17, 1937. $10, Reviewing Armed
Forces on National Day, 1956, and Chinese
flags, vert.

1978, Apr. 5   Wmk. 323   Perf. 13½

2092	A422	$2 violet & multi	.20	.20
2093	A422	$5 green & multi	.35	.20
2094	A422	$8 blue & multi	.55	.40
2095	A422	$10 vio blue & multi	.70	.50
	Nos. 2092-2095 (4)		1.80	1.30

Nuclear Reactor and Plant — A423

Poem by Wen Cheng-ming (1470-1559) A424

Perf. 13½x12½
1978, Apr. 26   **Unwmk.**
2096 A423 $10 multicolored   .70   .20

First nuclear power plant on Taiwan.

1978, May 20   Wmk. 323   Perf. 13½
Chinese Calligraphy: $2, Letter by Wang Hsi-chih (307-365). $4, Eulogy by Chu Sui-liang (596-658). $8, From Autobiography of Huai-su, Tang Dynasty. $10, Poem by Ch'ang Piao, Sung Dynasty.

2097	A424	$2 multicolored	.60	.20
2098	A424	$4 multicolored	2.40	.20
2099	A424	$4 multicolored	2.40	.50
2100	A424	$8 multicolored	2.75	.30
2101	A424	$10 multicolored	3.50	.55
		Nos. 2097-2101 (5)	11.65	1.75

Head and Dao Cancer Fund Emblem A425

Carved Lacquer Vase, Ming Dynasty A426

1978, June 15   Litho.   Perf. 13½
2102 A425 $2 red, org & ol   .20   .20
2103 A425 $10 dk & lt bl & grn   .55   .35

Cancer prevention.

1978, July 12
Ancient Carved Lacquer Ware: $2, Box with dragon and cloud design, Ch'ing dynasty, horiz. $5, Double box on legs, Ch'ing dynasty, horiz. $8, Round box with peonies, Ming dynasty, horiz.

2104	A426	$2 gray olive & multi	.25	.20
2105	A426	$5 gray olive & multi	.35	.20
2106	A426	$8 gray olive & multi	.50	.20
2107	A426	$10 gray olive & multi	.70	.30
		Nos. 2104-2107 (4)	1.80	.90

Tsu Ti Practicing with his Sword — A427

Folk Tales: No. 2109, Pan Ch'ao, diplomat and governor. No. 2110, Tien Tan's "Fire Bull Battle." $5, Liang Hung-yu, a general's wife, who served as drummer in battle.

Wmk. 323
1978, Aug. 16   Litho.   Perf. 13½
2108	A427	$1 multicolored	.25	.20
2109	A427	$2 bister & multi	.55	.20
2110	A427	$2 gray & multi	.55	.20
2111	A427	$5 multicolored	.85	.25
		Nos. 2108-2111 (4)	2.20	.85

For similar designs see types A456, A495.

Nos. 2071 and 2073 Overprinted in Red

1978, Sept. 9   Perf. 12½x13
2112 A366 $4 multicolored   .20   .20
2113 A366 $6 multicolored   .40   .30

Triple championships won by Chinese teams in Little League World Series. "1978" overprint on $4 at left, on $6 at right.

Ixias Pyrene A428

Protected Butterflies: $4, Euploea sylvestor swinhoei. $6, Cyrestis thyodamas formosana. $10, Byasa polyeuctes termessus.

1978, Sept. 20
2114	A428	$2 multicolored	.40	.20
2115	A428	$4 multicolored	.50	.20
2116	A428	$6 multicolored	.75	.30
2117	A428	$10 multicolored	1.90	.45
		Nos. 2114-2117 (4)	3.55	1.15

Scout Symbols — A429

Tropical Tomatoes — A430

1978, Oct. 5   Litho.   Perf. 13½
2118 A429 $2 multicolored   .20   .20
2119 A429 $10 multicolored   .35   .30

5th Chinese Boy Scout Jamboree, Cheng Ching Lake, Oct. 5-12.

1978, Oct. 23   Wmk. 323
Design: $10, Tropical tomatoes, horiz.
2120 A430 $2 multicolored   .30   .20
2121 A430 $10 multicolored   1.25   .40

International Symposium on Tropical Tomatoes, Taiwan, Oct. 23-28.

Sino-Saudi Bridge A431

Design: $6, Buttresses of bridge, flags of Taiwan and Saudi Arabia, horiz.

1978, Oct. 31
2122 A431 $2 multicolored   .35   .20
2123 A431 $6 multicolored   1.00   .30

Completion of Sino-Saudi Bridge over Cho-Shui River.

National Flag — A432

1978-80   Perf. 13½
2124	A432	$1 red & dk bl, I	.20	.20
a.		Bklt. pane of 16 ($5, $6, $8, $10, 3 $1, 9 $2)	7.75	
b.		Type II	.20	.20
2125	A432	$2 red & dk bl, I	.20	.20
a.		Bklt. pane of 15 + label	11.50	
b.		Type II	.20	.20
2126	A432	$3 yel grn & multi ('80)	.30	.20
2127	A432	$4 bis & multi ('80)	.35	.20
2128	A432	$5 dk grn & multi, I	.25	.20
a.		Type I	.25	
2129	A432	$6 brn org & multi	.30	.20
2130	A432	$7 dk brn & multi ('80)	.35	.20
2131	A432	$8 dk grn & multi, I	.45	.20
a.		Type II	.45	
2132	A432	$10 brt bl & multi ('79)	.60	.20
2133	A432	$12 brt rose lil & multi ('80)	.60	.25
		Nos. 2124-2133 (10)	3.60	2.05

Two types exist: I. Second line (red) below flag is same width as blue line. II. Second line is a hairline, notably thinner. The $3, $4, $7 and $12 were issued only in type II; $6, $10, Nos. 2134, 2124a, only in type I.

Nos. 2129-2133 have colorless inscriptions and denomination in a panel of solid color.

Nos. 2124a, 2125a have selvage inscribed in blue. 1980 printings are in green or red.

Coil Stamp
1980, Jan. 15   Perf. 12 Horiz.
2134 A432 $2 multicolored   .25   .20

See Nos. 2288-2300. For overprints see Nos. 2540-2541.

Three Rams, by Emperor Hsuan-tsung A433

Taoyuan International Airport A434

Wmk. 323
1978, Dec. 1   Litho.   Perf. 12½
2135 A433 $1 multicolored   .25   .20
2136 A433 $5 multicolored   1.40   .40

New Year 1979.

1978, Dec. 31   Perf. 13½
$10, Passenger terminal, control tower.
2137 A434 $2 multi   .20   .20
2138 A434 $10 multi, horiz.   .70   .40

Completion of Taoyuan Intl. Airport.

Oracle Bones and Inscription, 1766-1123 B.C. — A435

Antiquities and Inscriptions: $5, Lehchi cauldron, 722-481 B.C. $8, Small seal (turtle), 206 B.C.-8 A.D. $10, Inscribed stone tablet, 175-183 A.D.

1979, Jan. 17
2139	A435	$2 multicolored	.50	.20
2140	A435	$5 multicolored	1.00	.30
2141	A435	$8 multicolored	1.90	.50
2142	A435	$10 multicolored	1.90	.65
		Nos. 2139-2142 (4)	5.30	1.65

Origin and development of Chinese characters.

Chihkan Tower, 1653 A436

Taiwan Scenery: $5, Shrine of Confucius, 1665. $8, Shrine of Koxinga, 1661. $10, Eternal Castle and moat.

1979, Feb. 11   Litho.   Perf. 13½
2143	A436	$2 multicolored	.20	.20
2144	A436	$5 multicolored	.40	.20
2145	A436	$8 multicolored	.50	.20
2146	A436	$10 multicolored	1.00	.25
		Nos. 2143-2146 (4)	2.10	.85

Children Playing on Winter Day, Sung Dynasty — A437

1979, Mar. 8
2147	A437	Block of 4	9.50	6.50
a.		$5 in UL corner	2.40	.40
b.		$5 in UR corner	2.40	.40
c.		$5 in LL corner	2.40	.40
d.		$5 in LR corner	2.40	.40
e.		Souvenir sheet of 4, #2147, imperf.	22.00	12.00

No. 2147e has simulated perforations.

Lu Hao-tung — A438

Yellow Jade Brush Holder — A439

Perf. 13x12½
1979, Mar. 29   Engr.   Wmk. 323
2148 A438 $2 blue   .50   .20

Lu Hao-tung (1868-1895), revolutionist.

Unwmk.
1979, Apr. 12   Photo.   Perf. 12
Ancient Brush Washers: $5, White jade, Ming Dynasty. $8, Dark green jade, Ch'ing Dynasty. $10, Bluish jade, Ch'ing Dynasty. All horiz.

Granite Paper
2149	A439	$2 multicolored	.20	.20
2150	A439	$5 multicolored	.80	.25
2151	A439	$8 multicolored	1.10	.35
2152	A439	$10 multicolored	1.50	.50
		Nos. 2149-2152 (4)	3.60	1.30

For similar artifacts designs with single-color background and denominations in outlined numerals with the cents, see types A453, A469, A489, A523, A547, A582.

Plum Blossoms, Natl. Flower
A440   A440a

Perf. 13½x12½

1979-92		Engr.		Wmk. 323	
		Granite Paper			
2153	A440	$10 dk blue		1.60	.20
a.		Plain paper ('88)		2.50	.30
2154	A440	$20 brown		2.00	.20
b.		Plain paper ('87)		3.50	.60
2154A	A440	$40 brt car,			
			plain pa-		
			per ('85)	2.00	.20
2155	A440	$50 dull green		4.25	.25
a.		Plain paper ('87)		5.00	.55
2156	A440	$100 vermilion		6.00	.90
e.		Plain paper ('92)		6.00	3.25

Perf. 14x13½

2156A	A440a	$300 pur & red			
			org ('83)	16.00	3.25
c.		Plain paper ('91)		18.00	3.25
2156B	A440a	$500 ver & brn			
			('82)	24.00	5.50
d.		Plain paper ('91)		26.00	5.50
		Nos. 2153-2156B (7)		55.85	10.50

Issued: #2156Ac, 2156Bd, May 1; #2156e,
Jan. 7

City Houses and
Garden — A441

Design: $10, Rural landscape, horiz.

Perf. 13x12½, 12½x13

1979, June 5			Litho.	
2157	A441	$2 multicolored	.20	.20
2158	A441	$10 multicolored	.75	.35

Protection of the Environment.

Bankbook
and
Computer
Department
A442

Designs: $2, Children at counter, vert. $5,
People standing in line, vert. $10, Hand putting
coin in savings bank, symbolic tree.

1979, July 1		Wmk. 323	Perf. 13½	
2159	A442	$2 multicolored	.20	.20
2160	A442	$5 multicolored	.30	.20
2161	A442	$8 multicolored	.45	.20
2162	A442	$10 multicolored	.55	.25
		Nos. 2159-2162 (4)	1.50	.85

Postal savings, 60th anniversary.

Bird Type of 1977

Birds of Taiwan: $2, Swinoe's pheasant. $8,
Steere's babbler. $10, Formosan yuhina.

1979, Aug. 8			Perf. 11½	
2163	A402	$2 multicolored	.40	.20
2164	A402	$8 multicolored	1.00	.20
2165	A402	$10 multicolored	1.10	.35
		Nos. 2163-2165 (3)	2.50	.75

Rowland
Hill, Penny
Black
A443

Perf. 13½x13

1979, Aug. 27		Litho.	Wmk. 323	
2166	A443	$10 multicolored	.90	.25

Sir Rowland Hill (1795-1879), originator of
penny postage.

Jar with Rope
Design, Shang
Dynasty — A444

Ancient Chinese Pottery: $5, Two-handled
jar, Shang dynasty. $8, Red jar with "ears,"
Han dynasty. $10, Green glazed jar, Han
dynasty.

1979, Sept. 12			Perf. 13½	
2167	A444	$2 multicolored	.45	.20
2168	A444	$5 multicolored	.90	.20
2169	A444	$8 multicolored	1.50	.20
2170	A444	$10 multicolored	1.75	.30
		Nos. 2167-2170 (4)	4.60	.90

Children and IYC
Emblem — A445

1979, Sept. 28		Litho.	Perf. 13½	
2171	A445	$2 multicolored	.20	.20
2172	A445	$10 multicolored	.55	.35

International Year of the Child.

Trade
Symbols,
Competition
Emblem
A446

1979, Dec. 9		Litho.	Perf. 13½	
2173	A446	$2 blue & multi	.20	.20
2174	A446	$10 green & multi	.55	.35

10th National Vocational Training Competition, Taichung, Dec. 9.

Trees on a
Winter Plain,
by Li Ch'eng
A447

Paintings: $5, Bamboo, Wen T'ung. $8, Old
tree, bamboo and rock, by Chao Meng-fu. $10,
Twin Pines, by Li K'an.

1979, Nov. 21				
2175	A447	$2 multicolored	.45	.20
2176	A447	$5 multicolored	.90	.25
2177	A447	$8 multicolored	2.10	.40
2178	A447	$10 multicolored	3.00	.50
		Nos. 2175-2178 (4)	6.45	1.35

Monkey — A448

1979, Dec. 1			Perf. 12½	
2179	A448	$1 yellow & multi	.45	.20
2180	A448	$6 tan & multi	2.75	.50

New Year 1980.

Rotary
Emblem and
"75" — A449

Rotary Intl., 75th Anniv.: $12, Anniv.
emblem.

1980, Feb. 23		Litho.	Perf. 13½	
2181	A449	$2 multicolored	.20	.20
2182	A449	$12 multi, vert.	.75	.35

Mt. Hohuan
A450

Taiwan Landscapes (East-West Cross-
Island Highway): $2, Tunnel of Nine Turns,
vert. $12, Bridge, Tien Hsiang, vert.

1980, Mar. 1			Wmk. 323	
2183	A450	$2 multicolored	.20	.20
2184	A450	$8 multicolored	.70	.20
2185	A450	$12 multicolored	1.10	.35
		Nos. 2183-2185 (3)	2.00	.75

A451

1980, Mar. 29	Engr.	Perf. 13½x12½	
		Granite Paper	
2186	A451	$2 red brown	.25	.20

Shih Chien-Ju (1879-1900), revolutionist.

A452

1980, Apr. 4		Litho.	Perf. 13½	
2187	A452	$2 Chung-cheng		
		Memorial Hall	.20	.20
2188	A452	$8 Quotation	.35	.20
2189	A452	$12 Bronze statue	.45	.50
		Nos. 2187-2189 (3)	1.00	.90

Chiang Kai-shek (1887-1975).

Melon-shaped Jade Brush Washer,
Ming Dynasty — A453

Jade Pottery: $2, Jar with dragons, Sung
dynasty, vert. $8, Monk's alms bowl, Ch'ing
dynasty. $10, Yellow jade brush washer,
Ch'ing dynasty.

1980, May 20		Photo.	Perf. 12	
		Granite Paper		
2190	A453	$2 multicolored	.25	.20
2191	A453	$5 multicolored	.50	.20
2192	A453	$8 multicolored	.90	.20
2193	A453	$10 multicolored	1.10	.30
		Nos. 2190-2193 (4)	2.75	.90

Energy
Conservation
A454

1980, July 15		Litho.	Perf. 13½	
2194	A454	$2 multicolored	.20	.20
2195	A454	$12 multicolored	.60	.40

A455

A456

T'ang Dynasty pottery.

1980, Aug. 18		Litho.	Perf. 13½	
2196	A455	$2 Soldier	.30	.20
2197	A455	$5 Roosters	.90	.20
2198	A455	$8 Horse	1.25	.20
2199	A455	$10 Camel	1.40	.30
		Nos. 2196-2199 (4)	3.85	.90

Perf. 14x13½

1980, Sept. 23		Litho.	Wmk. 323	

Folk Tales: $1, Grinding mortar into a nee-
dle. No. 2201, Confucius Returning Lost Article (shown). No. 2202, Wen Tien-hsiang in jail.
$5, Sending coal in snow.

2200	A456	$1 multicolored	.20	.20
2201	A456	$2 multicolored	.30	.20
2202	A456	$2 multicolored	.30	.20
2203	A456	$5 multicolored	1.00	.30
		Nos. 2200-2203 (4)	1.80	.90

Railroad
Electrification
A457

1980, Oct. 10			Perf. 13½x14	
2204	A457	$2 shown	.50	.20
2205	A457	$2 Taichung Harbor	.40	.20
2206	A457	$2 Chiang Kai-shek		
		Airport	.40	.20
2207	A457	$2 Steel Mill	.40	.20
2208	A457	$2 Sun Yat-sen		
		Freeway	.40	.20
2209	A457	$2 Nuclear power		
		plant	.40	.20
2210	A457	$2 Petrochemical		
		plants	.40	.20
2211	A457	$2 Su-ao Harbor	.40	.20
2212	A457	$2 Kaohsiung ship-		
		yard	.40	.20
2213	A457	$2 North link rail-		
		road	.50	.20
a.		Souv. sheet of 10, #2204-		
		2213	9.50	9.50
b.		Block of 10, #2204-2213	4.50	4.50
		Nos. 2204-2213 (10)	4.20	2.00

Completion of major construction projects.

10th National
Savings
Day — A458

Wmk. 323
1980, Oct. 25   Litho.   Perf. 13½
2214 A458 $2 Ancient coin and
coin banks   .20 .20
2215 A458 $12 shown   1.00 .40

Landscape, by Ch'iu Ying, Ming
Dynasty — A459

1980, Nov. 12   Litho.   Perf. 13½
2216 A459 Block of 4   8.75 5.25
a. $5 in UL corner   1.90 .40
b. $5 in UR corner   1.90 .40
c. $5 in LL corner   1.90 .40
d. $5 in LR corner   1.90 .40
e. Souvenir sheet, imperf.   16.00 14.50

No. 2216e has simulated perforations.

Cock — A460

Faces, Flag,
Census
Form — A461

1980, Dec. 1   Perf. 12½
2217 A460 $1 multicolored   .50 .20
2218 A460 $6 multicolored   2.10 .35
a. Souv. sheet, 2 each #2217-
2218   8.50 8.50

New Year 1981.

1980, Dec. 13   Perf. 13½
2219 A461 $2 shown   .20 .20
2220 A461 $12 Buildings, horiz. .80 .40

1980 population and housing census.

TIROS-N
Satellite — A462

Design: $10, Central weather bureau, horiz.

1981, Jan. 28   Litho.   Perf. 13½
2221 A462 $2 multicolored   .20 .20
2222 A462 $10 multicolored   .80 .40
Completion of meteorological satellite
ground station, Taipei.

"Happiness"
A463

New Year 1981 (Calligraphy): No. 2224,
Wealth. No. 2225, Longevity. No. 2226, Joy.

1981, Feb. 3   Perf. 13½x12½
2223 A463 $5 multi, 5 at B   1.00 .20
2224 A463 $5 multi, 5 at R   1.00 .20
2225 A463 $5 multi, 5 at L   1.00 .20
2226 A463 $5 multi, 5 at T   1.00 .20
a. Block of 4, #2223-2226   4.50 1.75

International Year of the
Disabled — A464

1981, Feb. 19   Litho.   Perf. 13½
2227 A464 $2 multicolored   .20 .20
2228 A464 $12 multicolored   .60 .25

Mt. Ali — A465

1981, Mar. 1
2229 A465 $2 shown   .20 .20
2230 A465 $7 Oluanpi Beach   .70 .20
2231 A465 $12 Sun Moon Lake   1.10 .30
Nos. 2229-2231 (3)   2.00 .70

A $2 multicolored stamp for the 12th
National Kuomintang Congress at
Taipei was prepared for release Mar.
29, 1981, but not issued. It showed Sun
Yat-sen, Chiang Kai-shek, flags of
China and the Kuomintang and a map
of China.

Children in
Forest
A467

Children's Day: Drawings.

1981, Apr. 4
2233 A467 $1 multicolored   .20 .20
2234 A467 $2 multicolored   .20 .20
2235 A467 $5 multicolored   .25 .20
2236 A467 $7 multicolored   .30 .25
Nos. 2233-2236 (4)   .95 .85

Chiang Kai-shek
Memorial
Hall — A468

1981, Apr. 5   Perf. 12½x13½
2237 A468 20c bluish lilac   .20 .20
a. Photo. ('87)   .20 .20
2238 A468 40c crim rose   .20 .20
a. Photo. ('87)   .20 .20

2239 A468 50c dull red brn   .20 .20
a. Photo. ('88)   .20 .20
Nos. 2237-2239 (3)   .60 .60

Chiang Kai-shek (1887-1975).
See Nos. 2601-2603.

Cloisonne
Enamel
Brush
Washer,
15th Cent.
A469

Cloisonne Enamel: $5, Ritual vessel, 15th
cent., vert. $8, Plate, 17th cent. $10, Vase,
Ming Dynasty, vert.

1981, May 20   Photo.   Perf. 12
Granite Paper
2240 A469 $2 multicolored   .30 .20
2241 A469 $5 multicolored   .65 .20
2242 A469 $8 multicolored   .80 .25
2243 A469 $10 multicolored   1.00 .30
Nos. 2240-2243 (4)   2.75 .95

For similar enamelware stamps see Nos.
2318-2321, 2348-2351, 2410-2413.

Early & Modern   Linnaeus Crab
Locomotives   A471
A470

Wmk. 323
1981, June 9   Litho.   Perf. 12½
2244 A470 $2 shown   .20 .20
2245 A470 $14 Trains, horiz.   .80 .40

Railroad service centenary.

1981, June 14   Perf. 13½
2246 A471 $2 De Haan crab,
horiz.   .20 .20
2247 A471 $5 shown   .40 .20
2248 A471 $8 Miers crab, horiz. .60 .20
2249 A471 $14 Rathbun crab   1.10 .30
Nos. 2246-2249 (4)   2.30 .90

Central Weather
Bureau, 40th
Anniv. — A472

1981, July 1   Litho.   Perf. 13½
2250 A472 $2 multicolored   .30 .20
2251 A472 $14 multicolored   .80 .40

Scene from
The Cowherd
and the
Weaving
Maid — A473

Designs: Scenes from the Cowherd and the
Weaving Maid.

1981, Aug. 6   Litho.   Perf. 13½x14
2252 A473 $2 multicolored   .35 .20
2253 A473 $4 multicolored   .60 .20
2254 A473 $8 multicolored   1.10 .20
2255 A473 $14 multicolored   1.60 .50
Nos. 2252-2255 (4)   3.65 1.10

First Lasography
Exhibition — A474

Lasography Designs.

1981, Aug. 15   Perf. 13½
2256 A474 $2 multicolored   .20 .20
2257 A474 $5 multicolored   .25 .20
2258 A474 $8 multicolored   .50 .20
2259 A474 $14 multicolored   .85 .50
Nos. 2256-2259 (4)   1.80 1.10

Soccer Players — A475

1981, Sept. 9   Litho.   Perf. 13½
2260 $5 multicolored   .50 .20
2261 $5 multicolored   .50 .20
a. A475 Pair, #2260-2261   1.10 .65

Sports Day.

A477

70th Anniv. of Republic: No. 2263, Eastward
Expedition (soldiers on Hill). No. 2264, Northward Expedition (Chiang on horse). No. 2265,
Resistance War with Japan (Chiang, fist
raised). No. 2266, Suppression of Communist
Rebels (Battle scene). No. 2267, Counter-
offensive and unification. $8, Chiang Kai-shek.
$14, Sun Yat-sen.

1981, Oct. 10   Perf. 13½
2262 A477 $2 multicolored   .20 .20
2263 A477 $2 multicolored   .20 .20
2264 A477 $2 multicolored   .20 .20
2265 A477 $2 multicolored   .20 .20
2266 A477 $3 multicolored   .20 .20
2267 A477 $3 multicolored   .20 .20
2268 A477 $8 multicolored   .45 .25
2269 A477 $14 multicolored   1.00 .45
a. Souv. sheet of 8, #2262-2269 6.50 2.50
Nos. 2262-2269 (8)   2.65 1.90

No. 2269a issued Oct. 25.

ROCPEX TAIPEI
'81 Intl. Philatelic
Exhibition, Taipei,
Oct. 25-Nov. 2
A478

1981, Oct. 25
2270 A478 $2 multicolored   .20 .20
2271 A478 $14 multicolored   .50 .25

Nos. 2269a, 2270-2271 overprinted with
four characters meaning "Best of Show" were
not valid for postage. They were inserted in a
special "ROCPEX" book, edition of 10,000.

Boys Playing Games (#2272a) — A479

Designs: a.-j. "One Hundred Boys," Sung Dynasty scroll (each stamp is numbered from 1 to 10 in Chinese. See illustrations with Nos. 1682-1691 for numerals.) Two strips of 5 each in continuous design.

1981, Nov. 12
2272		Block of 10	14.50 14.50
a.-e.	A479	$2 single (top row)	1.25 .25
f.-j.	A479	$2 single (bottom row)	1.25 .25

New Year 1982 (Year of the Dog) — A480

Information Week, Dec. 6-12 — A481

Wmk. 323
1981, Dec. 1   Litho.   Perf. 12½
2273	A480	$1 multicolored	.40 .20
2274	A480	$10 multicolored	2.00 .40
a.		Souv. sheet, 2 ea #2273-2274	8.00 5.00

1981, Dec. 7   Perf. 14x13½
2275	A481	$2 multicolored	.30 .20

Telecommunications Centenary — A482

1981, Dec. 28   Perf. 14x13½, 13½x14
2276	A482	$2 Telephone, vert.	.20 .20
2277	A482	$3 Old, new phones	.25 .20
2278	A482	$8 Submarine cable	.40 .20
2279	A482	$18 Computers, vert.	.55 .30
		Nos. 2276-2279 (4)	1.40 .90

Floral Arrangement A483

Various floral arrangements in Ming vases.

Wmk. 323
1982, Jan. 23   Litho.   Perf. 13½
2280	A483	$2 multicolored	.20 .20
2281	A483	$3 multicolored	.25 .20
2282	A483	$8 multicolored	.55 .20
2283	A483	$18 multicolored	1.25 .50
		Nos. 2280-2283 (4)	2.25 1.10

Compare with designs A559, A584.

The Ku Cheng Reunion — A484

Designs: Opera scenes.

Wmk. 323
1982, Feb. 15   Litho.   Perf. 13½
2284	A484	$2 multicolored	.40 .20
2285	A484	$3 multicolored	1.25 .20
2286	A484	$4 multicolored	1.40 .25
2287	A484	$18 multicolored	2.50 .60
		Nos. 2284-2287 (4)	5.55 1.25

Flag Type of 1978
Value Colorless in Colored Panel
1981   Litho.   Perf. 13½
Panel Color
2288	A432	$1 dk blue	.20 .20
2289	A432	$1.50 lt olive	.20 .20
2290	A432	$2 dk olive bis	.20 .20
2291	A432	$3 red	.20 .20
2292	A432	$4 blue	.20 .20
2293	A432	$5 sepia	.20 .20
2294	A432	$6 orange	.25 .20
2295	A432	$7 green	.40 .20
2296	A432	$8 magenta	.50 .20
2297	A432	$9 olive grn	.60 .20
2298	A432	$10 dk purple	.70 .20
2299	A432	$12 lilac	.80 .25
2300	A432	$14 dk green	.75 .30
		Nos. 2288-2300 (13)	5.20 2.75

Second line (red) below flag is a hairline, notably thinner.
For overprints see Nos. 2540-2541.

Robert Koch A485

Cheng Shih-liang, Revolutionary A486

Wmk. 323
1982, Mar. 24   Litho.   Perf. 13½
2309	A485	$2 multicolored	.25 .20

Tubercle Bacillus centenary.

1982, Mar. 29 Engr. Perf. 13½x12½
Granite Paper
2310	A486	$2 carmine rose	.25 .20

Children's Day A487

Designs: Various children's drawings.

1982, Apr. 4   Litho.
2311	A487	$2 multi, vert.	.40 .20
2312	A487	$3 multicolored	.60 .20
2313	A487	$5 multicolored	.80 .20
2314	A487	$8 multicolored	.80 .20
		Nos. 2311-2314 (4)	2.60 .80

Dentists' Day A488

1982, May 4   Litho.   Perf. 13½
2315	A488	$2 Tooth, boy	.30 .20
2316	A488	$3 Flossing, brushing	.60 .20
2317	A488	$10 Examination	1.10 .30
		Nos. 2315-2317 (3)	2.00 .70

Champleve Enamel Cup and Saucer, 18th Cent. A489

Painted Enamelware: $5, Cloisonne gold-plated duck Ch'ien-lung period (1736-1795), vert. $8, Incense burner, K'ang-hsi period (1662-1722). $12, Cloisonne pitcher, Ch'ien-lung period, vert.

1982, May 20   Photo.   Perf. 12
Granite Paper
2318	A489	$2 multicolored	.40 .20
2319	A489	$5 multicolored	.80 .20
2320	A489	$8 multicolored	1.25 .20
2321	A489	$12 multicolored	2.10 .25
		Nos. 2318-2321 (4)	4.55 .85

See Nos. 2348-2351.

Poets' Day — A490

Tang Dynasty Poetry Illustrations (618-906): $2, Spring Dawn, by Meng Hao-Jan. $3, On Looking for a Hermit and Not Finding Him, by Chia Tao. $5, Summer Dying, by Liu Yu-Hsi. $18, Looking at the Snow Drifts on South Mountain, by Tsu Yung. Chinese characters are to the left of the denominations on Nos. 2322-2325, Nos. 2396-2399 have no characters to the left of the denominations.

Wmk. 323
1982, June 25   Litho.   Perf. 13½
2322	A490	$2 multicolored	1.75 .20
2323	A490	$3 multicolored	3.25 .35
2324	A490	$5 multicolored	5.00 .75
2325	A490	$18 multicolored	11.50 1.50
		Nos. 2322-2325 (4)	21.50 2.85

See Nos. 2352-2355.

5th World Women's Softball Championship, Taipei, July 1-12 — A491

1982, July 2
2326	A491	$2 lt grn & multi	.25 .20
2327	A491	$18 tan & multi	1.25 .40

Scouting Year A492

1982, July 18
2328	A492	$2 Crossing bridge, Baden-Powell	.20 .20
2329	A492	$18 Emblem, camp	.70 .40

Stamp in Tongs A493

1982, Aug. 9
2330	A493	$2 shown	.25 .20
2331	A493	$18 Album stamps magnified	1.10 .40

Carved Lion, Tsu Shih Temple — A494

Hsun Kuan Saving Hsiang-cheng City — A495

Tsu Shih Temple of Sanhsia Architecture: $3, Lion brackets, horiz. $5, Sub-lintels. $18, Tiled roof, horiz.

1982, Sept. 1   Litho.   Perf. 13½
2332	A494	$2 multicolored	.25 .20
2333	A494	$3 multicolored	.35 .20
2334	A494	$5 multicolored	.75 .20
2335	A494	$18 multicolored	1.10 .40
		Nos. 2332-2335 (4)	2.45 1.00

1982, Oct. 15   Perf. 14x13½
Designs: Scenes from The Thirty-Six Examples of Filial Piety, Folk Tale collection by Wu Yen-huan.
2336	A495	$1 multicolored	.20 .20
2337	A495	$2 multicolored	.50 .20
2338	A495	$3 multicolored	.70 .20
2339	A495	$5 multicolored	.80 .25
		Nos. 2336-2339 (4)	2.20 .85

30th Anniv. of China Youth Corps A496

1982, Oct. 31
2340	A496	$2 Riding	.20 .20
2341	A496	$3 Raising flag, vert.	.20 .20
2342	A496	$18 Mountain climbing	.60 .40
		Nos. 2340-2342 (3)	1.00 .80

Seated Lohan (Buddhist Saint) — A497

New Year 1983 (Year of the Boar) — A498

Paintings of Lohan, Hanging Scrolls by Liu Sung-nien, 13th cent.

Perf. 13x12½
1982, Nov. 12   Litho.   Wmk. 323

2343	A497	$2 multicolored	.85	.20
2344	A497	$3 multicolored	2.00	.20
2345	A497	$18 multicolored	5.25	.85
a.		Souv. sheet, #2343-2345	19.00	13.00
		Nos. 2343-2345 (3)	8.10	1.25

No. 2345a comes overprinted in red in the sheet margins. Value, unused $18, Used $12.

1982, Dec. 1   Perf. 12½

2346	A498	$1 multicolored	.60	.20
2347	A498	$10 multicolored	2.75	.45
a.		Souv. sheet, 2 ea #2346-2347	10.00	5.00

Enamelware Type of 1982

Designs: $2, Square basin, Ch'ing Dynasty (1644-1911). $3, Vase, Ch'ien-lung period (1736-1795). $4, Tea pot, Ch'ien-lung period. $18, Elephant vase, Ch'ing Dynasty.

1983, Jan. 5   Photo.   Perf. 12
Granite Paper

2348	A489	$2 multi	.35	.20
2349	A489	$3 multi, vert.	.50	.20
2350	A489	$4 multi	.90	.20
2351	A489	$18 multi, vert.	1.40	.50
		Nos. 2348-2351 (4)	3.15	1.10

Poetry Illustration Type of 1982

Sung Dynasty Poetry: $2, Seeing the Flowers Fade Away. $3, River. $5, Freckled with Clouds is the Azure Sky. $11, Yielding Fine Fragrance in the Snow. Nos. 2352-2355 vert.

Wmk. 323
1983, Feb. 10   Litho.   Perf. 13½

2352	A490	$2 multicolored	1.00	.25
2353	A490	$3 multicolored	3.75	.35
2354	A490	$5 multicolored	5.25	.50
2355	A490	$11 multicolored	7.75	.60
		Nos. 2352-2355 (4)	17.75	1.70

Mt. Jade, Taiwan — A499

1983, Mar. 1

2356	A499	$2 Wawa Valley, vert.	.50	.20
2357	A499	$3 University Pond, vert.	.75	.20
2358	A499	$18 shown	1.25	.50
		Nos. 2356-2358 (3)	2.50	.90

400th Anniv. of Arrival of Matteo Ricci (1552-1610), Italian Missionary A500

Perf. 14x13½
1983, Apr. 3   Litho.   Wmk. 323

2359	A500	$2 Globe	.30	.20
2360	A500	$18 Great Wall	1.00	.35

Mandarin Phonetic Symbols, 70th Anniv. — A501

Scenes from Lady White Snake Fairytale — A502

Wmk. 323
1983, May 22   Litho.   Perf. 13½

2361	A501	$2 Wu Ching-heng, inventor	.30	.20
2362	A501	$18 Children writing	1.00	.30

1983, June 15   Perf. 14x13½

2363	A502	$2 multicolored	.40	.20
2364	A502	$3 lt blue & multi	.75	.20
2365	A502	$3 orange & multi	.75	.20
2366	A502	$18 multicolored	.90	.50
		Nos. 2363-2366 (4)	2.80	1.10

A503

A504

Various bamboo carved objects. Nos. 2367-2369 Ch'ing dynasty.

Wmk. 323
1983, July 14   Litho.   Perf. 13½

2367	A503	$2 Bamboo jug	.55	.20
2368	A503	$3 Tao-t'ieh motif vase	.70	.20
2369	A503	$4 Landscape sculpture	.80	.20
2370	A503	$18 Brush holder, Ming dynasty	1.75	.40
		Nos. 2367-2370 (4)	3.80	1.00

Wmk. 323
1983, Aug. 5   Litho.   Perf. 13½

2371	A504	$2 Globe	.20	.20
2372	A504	$18 Emblem	.80	.35

World Communications Year.

Fishing Industry (Local Fish) A505

1983, Aug. 20

2373	A505	$2 Epinephelus tauvina	.20	.20
2374	A505	$18 Saurida undosquamis	.90	.35

40th Journalists' Day — A506

1983, Sept. 1

2375	A506	$2 multicolored	.25	.20

Views of Mongolia and Tibet — A507

1983, Sept. 15

2376	A507	$2 Village	.35	.20
2377	A507	$3 Potala Palace	.60	.20
2378	A507	$5 Sheep grazing	.70	.20
2379	A507	$11 Camel caravan	1.10	.40
		Nos. 2376-2379 (4)	2.75	1.00

2nd East Asian Bird Protection Conference, Oct. — A508

1983, Oct. 8   Litho.   Perf. 13½

2380	A508	$2 Lanius cristatus, vert.	.40	.20
2381	A508	$18 Butastur indicus	1.60	.40

A509

Plum Blossoms, photography by Hu Ch'unghsien.

1983, Oct. 31   Litho.   Perf. 14x13½

2382	A509	$2 multicolored	.25	.20
2383	A509	$3 multi, diff.	.45	.20
2384	A509	$5 multi, diff.	.50	.20
2385	A509	$11 multi, diff.	.70	.30
		Nos. 2382-2385 (4)	1.90	.90

A510

1983, Nov. 6   Perf. 13x13½, 13½x13

2386	A510	$2 JCI and Congress emblems	.25	.20
2387	A510	$18 Globe and emblems, horiz	.90	.40

Jaycees Intl., 38th World Congress, Taipei.

8th Asian-Pacific Cardiology Congress — A511

1983, Nov. 27   Litho.   Perf. 13½

2388	A511	$2 Electrocardiogram	.25	.20
2389	A511	$18 Electrocardiogram	.90	.40

New Year 1984 (Year of the Rat) — A512

1983, Dec. 1   Litho.   Perf. 12½

2390	A512	$1 multicolored	.90	.20
2391	A512	$10 multicolored	3.50	.45
a.		Souv. sheet, 2 each #2390-2391	22.00	7.50

Literacy Week A513

1983, Dec. 17   Litho.   Perf. 13½

2392	A513	$2 shown	.25	.20
2393	A513	$18 Modern family, vert.	.90	.35

World Freedom Day A514

1984, Jan. 23   Litho.   Perf. 13½

2394	A514	$2 Korean War Patriots	.25	.20
2395	A514	$18 Intl. support	1.00	.35

Drama Day — A515

Yuan Dynasty Poetry Illustrations by Tienshih Lin (Poems by): $2, Kuan Yun-shih. $3, Po Pu. $5, Chang Ko-chiu. $18, Shang Cheng-shu. (See note with Nos. 2322-2325.)

1984, Feb. 15   Litho.   Perf. 13½

2396	A515	$2 multicolored	1.50	.25
2397	A515	$3 multicolored	3.00	.35
2398	A515	$5 multicolored	5.00	.50
2399	A515	$18 multicolored	8.00	1.25
		Nos. 2396-2399 (4)	17.50	2.35

A516

A517

A518

Arbor Day — A519

1984, Mar. 12   Litho.   Perf. 13½x14
2400 A516 $2 multicolored   .70   .20
2401 A517 $2 multicolored   .70   .20
2402 A518 $2 multicolored   .70   .20
2403 A519 $2 multicolored   .70   .20
  a.   Block of 4, #2400-2403   3.50 2.25

Lin Chueh-min
A520

Central News
Agency, 60th
Anniv.
A521

1984, Mar. 29   Engr.   Perf. 13x12½
Granite Paper
2404 A520 $2 dark green   .25   .20

Perf. 14x13½
1984, Apr. 1   Litho.   Wmk.
2405 A521 $2 Emblem   .20   .20
2406 A521 $10 Emblem, satellite,
              dish antenna   .60   .30

God of
Longevity — A522

Ch'ing Dynasty
Enamelware
A523

Paintings by Chang Ta-chien (1899-1983):
$2, Five Auspicious Tokens. $18, Lotus Blossoms in Ink Splash.

Wmk. 323
1984, Apr. 20   Litho.   Perf. 11½
2407 A522 $2 multicolored   .95   .20
2408 A522 $5 multicolored   2.50   .20
2409 A522 $18 multicolored   3.75   .50
        Nos. 2407-2409 (3)   7.20   .90

1984, May 20   Photo.   Perf. 12
Granite Paper
2410 A523 $2 Cup, pot, plate,
              horiz.   .30   .20
2411 A523 $3 Wine jug   .60   .20
2412 A523 $4 Teapot   .90   .20
2413 A523 $18 Candle holder   1.25   .45
        Nos. 2410-2413 (4)   3.05 1.05

China
Airlines
World-wide
Service
inauguration
A524

1984, May 31   Litho.   Perf. 13½x14
2414 A524 $2 Jet circling globe   .20   .20
2415 A524 $7 Globe, jet   .35   .20
2416 A524 $11 New York City   .45   .30
2417 A524 $18 Amsterdam   .60   .45
        Nos. 2414-2417 (4)   1.60 1.15

30th
Navigation
Day
A525

Perf. 13½x13
1984, July 11   Litho.   Wmk. 323
2418 A525 $2 Container ship   .30   .20
2419 A525 $18 Oil tanker   2.10   .35

1984 Summer
Olympics — A526

Alpine
Plants — A527

Perf. 13½x14, 14x13½
1984, June 23
2420 A526 $2 Judo, horiz.   .20   .20
2421 A526 $5 Archery   .35   .20
2422 A526 $18 Swimming, horiz.   .70   .60
        Nos. 2420-2422 (3)   1.25 1.00

1984, Aug. 8   Perf. 13
$2, Gentiana arisanensis. $3, Epilobium
nankotaizanense. $5, Adenophora uehatae.
$18, Aconitum fukutomei.
2423 A527 $2 multi   .35   .20
2424 A527 $3 multi   .70   .20
2425 A527 $5 multi   .95   .20
2426 A527 $18 multi   1.50   .50
        Nos. 2423-2426 (4)   3.50 1.10

The Eighteen
Scholars,
Sung Dynasty
Hanging
Scroll — A528

Details.

Wmk. 323
1984, Aug. 20   Litho.   Perf. 13
2427 A528 $2 Playing instru-
              ments   1.50   .25
2428 A528 $3 Playing chess   3.00   .35
2429 A528 $5 Practicing callig-
              raphy   4.50   .50
2430 A528 $18 Painting   10.00 1.00
        Nos. 2427-2430 (4)   19.00 2.10

Athletics Day — A529

1984, Sept. 9
2431 $5 Two players   .60   .20
2432 $5 One player   .60   .20
  a.   'A529 Pair, #2431-2432   1.25   .90

A531   A532

1984, Sept. 9
2433 A531 $10 "20," map of Asia   .50   .20
Asian-Pacific Parliamentarians' Union, 20th
anniv.

1984, Oct. 10   Litho.   Perf. 12½
2434 A532 $2 No. 1458   .20   .20
2435 A532 $5 No. 296   .45   .20
2436 A532 $18 Museum   .65   .50
  a.   Souv. sheet of 3, #2434-2436 7.25 2.25
        Nos. 2434-2436 (3)   1.30   .90
        Postal Museum opening.

Flag, Alliance
Emblem — A533

Veteran's
Assistance
A534

1984, Oct. 16   Perf. 13½
2437 A533 $2 multicolored   .30   .20
Grand Alliance for China's Reunification
Under the Three Principles of the People Convention, Taipei, Oct. 16-17.

1984, Nov. 1   Litho.   Perf. 13½
2438 A534 $2 Vignettes   .30   .20

Pine Tree
A535

Bamboo
A535a

Plum Tree — A535b

1984-88
2439 A535 $2 multicolored   .20   .20
2440 A535a $8 multicolored   .55   .20
2441 A535b $10 pale yellow bister
              background   .65   .20
  a.   Grayish tan background   .45   .20
        Nos. 2439-2441 (3)   1.40   .60
Issued: #2439-2440, 2441a, 11/12;
#2441,1/12/88.
See #2495-2503, 3303.

A536   A537

1984, Dec. 1   Perf. 12x12½
2442 A536 $1 multicolored   .50   .20
2443 A536 $10 multicolored   2.50   .30
  a.   Min. sheet, 2 ea #2442-2443 7.00 3.50
New Year 1985 (Year of the Ox).

1985, Jan. 11   Litho.   Perf. 13½
2444 A537 $5 Scales, legal codes .45   .20
Judicial Day 1985.

Quemoy and
Matsu
Scenes
A538

1985, Jan. 23   Litho.   Perf. 13½x14
2445 A538 $2 Ku-kang Lake,
              Quemoy   .20   .20
2446 A538 $5 Kuang-hai Stone,
              Quemoy   .50   .20
2447 A538 $8 Sheng-li Reser-
              voir, Matsu   .65   .20
2448 A538 $10 Tung-chu Light-
              house, Matsu   .85   .25
        Nos. 2445-2448 (4)   2.20   .85

Sir Robert Hart
(1835-1911)
A539

1985, Feb. 15   Litho.   Perf. 14x13½
2449 A539 $2 No. 1   .30   .20
Inspector General of Chinese Customs,
1863-1908, and founder of the Chinese Postal
Service.

Lo Fu-hsing (1886-
1914)
A540

Tsou Jung (1882-
1905)
A541

1985, Feb. 24   Perf. 13x13½
2450 A540 $2 multicolored   .30   .20

1985, Mar. 29   Engr.   Perf. 13½x12½
Granite Paper
2451 A541 $3 green   .30   .20

Chung-cheng Memorial Hall Main
Gate — A542

1985, Apr. 5   Litho.   **Perf. 13**
2452 A542 $2 shown .20 .20
2453 A542 $8 Tzuhu Memorial .75 .25
2454 A542 $10 Chiang Kai-shek, vert. .90 .30
Nos. 2452-2454 (3) 1.85 .75

Tenth death anniv. of Chiang Kai-shek.

A543

A544

1985, May 8   Litho.   **Perf. 13½**
2455 A543 $2 Carnation .50 .20
2456 A543 $2 Day lily .50 .20
  a.   Pair, #2455-2456 1.60 .80

Mother's Day.

1985, May 18
2457 A544 $5 Tunnel to Chi-chin Island .45 .20

Kaohsiung Cross-Harbor Tunnel, 1st anniv.

Girl Scouts, 75th Anniv. — A545

Wmk. 323
1985, June 1   Litho.   **Perf. 13½**
2458 A545 $2 multicolored .25 .20
2459 A545 $18 multicolored .90 .30

The Book of Odes, Confucius A545a

1985, June 22   Litho.   **Wmk. 323**
2460 A545a $2 Spring .90 .20
2461 A545a $5 Summer 1.75 .20
2462 A545a $8 Fall 3.50 .30
2463 A545a $10 Winter 4.25 .50
Nos. 2460-2463 (4) 10.40 1.20

Fruit — A546

Perf. 13½x14
1985, July 5   Litho.   **Wmk. 323**
2464 A546 $2 Wax Jambo .50 .20
2465 A546 $3 Guava .85 .20
2466 A546 $5 Carambola 1.00 .20
2467 A546 $8 Litchi nut 1.10 .30
Nos. 2464-2467 (4) 3.45 .90

Ch'ing Dynasty (1644-1911) Ivory Carvings — A547

1985, July 18   Wmk. 323   **Perf. 13½**
2468 A547 $2 Dragon Boat .20 .20
2469 A547 $3 Landscape .45 .20
2470 A547 $5 Melon, water container .65 .20
2471 A547 $18 Brush holder, vert. .85 .35
Nos. 2468-2471 (4) 2.15 .95

T'ang Dynasty (618-907) Aristocrat — A548

Designs: $5, Sung Dynasty (960-1280) palace woman. $8, Yuan Dynasty (1280-1368) aristocrat. $11, Ming Dynasty (1368-1644) aristocrat.

1985, Aug. 1   Wmk. 323   **Perf. 13½**
2472 A548 $2 multicolored .40 .20
2473 A548 $5 multicolored 1.25 .20
2474 A548 $8 multicolored 1.75 .20
2475 A548 $11 multicolored 2.25 .30
Nos. 2472-2475 (4) 5.65 .90

4th Asian Conf. on Costume, Aug. 3.
In the 2 rows of Chinese characters above the denomination, the right row has 3 characters and a dot on #2472-2475, 4 characters and a dot on #2549-2552. #2605-2608, 2660-2663 have solid black numerals.
See #2549-2552, 2605-2608, 2660-2663, 2721-2724, 2794-2797.

Social Welfare Program A549

Perf. 13½x14
1985, Aug. 15   Wmk. 323
2476 A549 $2 Heart, bird feeding young .30 .20

Historic Sites A550

Wmk. 323
1985, Sept. 3   Litho.   **Perf. 13½**
2477 A550 $2 Taipei North Gate .20 .20
2478 A550 $5 San Domingo Fort, Tamsui .50 .20
2479 A550 $8 Lung Shun Temple, Lukang .65 .20
2480 A550 $10 Confucius Temple, Changhua .85 .25
Nos. 2477-2480 (4) 2.20 .85

Bonsai — A551

Trade Shows — A552

Perf. 13½x14
1985, Sept. 22   Wmk. 323
2481 A551 $2 Oak .20 .20
2482 A551 $5 Five-leaf pine .45 .20
2483 A551 $8 Lohan pine .60 .25
2484 A551 $18 Banyan .90 .50
Nos. 2481-2484 (4) 2.15 1.15

1985, Oct. 5   **Perf. 13½**
Taipei World Trade Center and show emblems: a, Sporting goods. b, Toys and gifts. c, Electronics. d, Machinery. Se-tenant in continuous design.
2485   Strip of 4 2.75 1.25
  a.-d.   A552 $2 any single .60 .20

Scenes of Modern Taiwan, Map, Flag A553

1985, Oct. 25
2486 A553 $2 shown .50 .20
2487 A553 $18 Chiang Kai-shek, Triumphal Arch 1.75 .40

Defeat of Japanese army, end of World War II, and return of Taiwan to control of the Republic, 40th anniv.

7th Asian Conference on Mental Retardation A554

Sun Yat-sen and Birthplace A555

1985, Nov. 8   **Perf. 14x13½**
2488 A554 $2 multicolored .40 .20
2489 A554 $11 multicolored .90 .30

1985, Nov. 12   **Perf. 13½**
2490 A555 $2 multicolored .40 .20
2491 A555 $18 multicolored 1.00 .40

Postal Life Insurance, 50th Anniv. — A556

New Year 1986 (Year of the Tiger) — A557

1985, Dec. 1
2492 A556 $2 multicolored .30 .20

1985, Dec. 1   **Perf. 12½**
2493 A557 $1 multicolored .60 .20
2494 A557 $10 multicolored 1.60 .35
  a.   Min. sheet, 2 ea #2493-2494 8.00 3.25

Flora Types of 1984
1986, Jan. 10   Litho.   **Perf. 13½**
2495 A535 $1 multicolored .20 .20
2496 A535a $11 multicolored .45 .20
2497 A535b $18 multicolored .65 .20

1988, Feb. 12
2498 A535 $1.50 multicolored .20 .20
2499 A535a $7.50 multicolored .40 .20
2500 A535b $16 multicolored 1.00 .30

#2500 has value expressed in dollars and cents.

1989, Feb. 24
2501 A535 $3 multicolored .20 .20
2502 A535a $16.50 multicolored 1.00 .30
2503 A535b $21 multicolored 1.10 .35
Nos. 2495-2503 (9) 5.20 2.15

Cultural Renaissance Movement — A558

Painting: Hermit Anglers on a Mountain Stream, Ming Dynasty, 1386-1644. Continuous design. (Each stamp is numbered from 1 to 5 in Chinese. See illustrations with Nos. 1682-1691 for numerals.)

1986, Jan. 28   Litho.   **Perf. 13½**
2507   Strip of 5 8.00 7.00
  a.-e.   A558 $2 any single 1.40 .25

See No. 2604.

Floral Arrangements A559

Wmk. 323
1986, Feb. 20   Litho.   **Perf. 13½**
2517 A559 $2 denom. UL .20 .20
2518 A559 $5 denom. UR .45 .20
2519 A559 $8 shown .50 .20
2520 A559 $10 denom. UL .75 .25
Nos. 2517-2520 (4) 1.90 .85

Compare with designs A483, A584.

Natl. Postal Service, 90th Anniv. A560

$2, Unloading express mail at airport. $5, Motorcycle delivery. $8, Technological innovations. $10, Electronic sorting machine.

1986, Mar. 20

2521	A560	$2 multi	.20	.20
2522	A560	$5 multi, vert.	.25	.20
2523	A560	$8 multi, vert.	.40	.20
2524	A560	$10 multi	.50	.25
a.		Souv. sheet of 4, #2521-2524	4.25	2.55
		Nos. 2521-2524 (4)	1.35	.85

Chen Tien-hua
(1875-1905),
Revolutionary
A561

1986, Mar. 29 Engr. Perf. 13½x12½
Granite Paper

2525	A561	$2 violet	.20	.20

Yushan
Natl. Park
A562

1986, Apr. 10   Litho.   Perf. 13½

2526	A562	$2 multicolored	.40	.20
2527	A562	$5 multi, diff.	1.00	.20
2528	A562	$8 multi, diff.	1.25	.20
2529	A562	$10 multi, diff.	1.50	.30
		Nos. 2526-2529 (4)	4.15	.90

Power
Plants
A563

1986, Apr. 29

2530	A563	$2 Hydro-electric	.20	.20
2531	A563	$8 Thermo-electric	.50	.20
2532	A563	$10 Nuclear	.70	.25
		Nos. 2530-2532 (3)	1.40	.65

Economic prosperity through energy development.

Paintings by P'u
Hsin-yu (1896-
1963)
A564

1986, May 22   Perf. 11½

2533	A564	$2 Bird	1.25	.20
2534	A564	$8 Landscape	2.50	.30
2535	A564	$10 Woman in forest	3.75	.35
		Nos. 2533-2535 (3)	7.50	.85

Asian Productivity Org., 25th
Anniv. — A565

1986, June 3   Perf. 13x13½

2536	A565	$2 multicolored	.20	.20
2537	A565	$11 multicolored	.75	.30

Natl. Productivity Center, 30th anniv.

Coral-reef
Fish
A566

Designs: a, Chrysiptera starcki. b, Chelmon rostratus. c, Chaetodon xanthurus. d, Chaetodon quadrimaculatus. e, Chaetodon meyeri. f, Genicanthus semifasciatus. g, Genicanthus semifasciatus. h, Pomacanthus annularis. i, Lienardella fasciata. j, Balistapus undulatus.

1986, June 27   Perf. 13½

2538		Block of 10	4.50 4.00
a.-j.		A566 $2 any single	.40 .20

Protection of
Intellectual Property
Rights — A567

1986, June 12

2539	A567	$2 Macaw	.75 .20

Nos. 2294, 2297
Surcharged

1986, July 9   Litho.   Perf. 13½

2540	A432	$2 on $6 multi	.20 .20
2541	A432	$8 on $9 multi	.45 .25

60th Anniv. of northward expedition by the national revolutionary army.

Bridges
A568

1986, July 30

2542	A568	$2 Tzu Mu, 1965	.30 .20
2543	A568	$5 Chang Hung, 1968	.75 .20
2544	A568	$8 Kuan Fu, 1977	1.00 .20
2545	A568	$10 Kuan Tu, 1983	1.40 .25
		Nos. 2542-2545 (4)	3.45 .85

Love between Liang
Shanpo and Chu
Yingtai, Folk
Tale — A569

Cartoons by Huang Mu-ts'un: a, Yingtai disguised to go to school. b, Yingtai and Shanpo meet in class. c, The friends at pond. d, Yingtai summoned home for arranged marriage. e, Yingtai and Shanpo ascend to heaven as butterflies (each stamp is numbered from 1 to 5 in Chinese. See illustrations with Nos. 1682-1691 for numerals.)

1986, Aug. 12   Perf. 12½

2546		Strip of 5	3.50 2.00
a.-e.		A569 $5 any single	.50 .20

Social
Awareness
Campaign
A570

1986, Sept. 12   Litho.   Perf. 13½

2547	A570	$2 Rainbow, children	.30	.20
2548	A570	$8 Children, adults	.60	.25

Folk
Costumes — A571

Designs: $2, Shang Dynasty (1766-1122 B.C.) aristocrat. $5, Warring States (403-221 B.C.) aristocrat. $8, Later Han Dynasty (A.D. 25-221) empress. $10, Flying ribbons gown, Wei and Tsin Dynasties (A.D. 221-420) aristocrat.

1986, Sept. 23   Litho.   Perf. 13½

2549	A571	$2 multicolored	.60	.20
2550	A571	$5 multicolored	1.00	.20
2551	A571	$8 multicolored	1.25	.20
2552	A571	$10 multicolored	1.90	.20
		Nos. 2549-2552 (4)	4.75	.80

Ch'ing
Dynasty Ju-i
Scepters
A572

1986, Oct. 10   Photo.   Perf. 14x14½

2553	A572	$2 White jade	.20	.20
2554	A572	$3 Red coral	.35	.20
2555	A572	$4 Redwood and gems	.45	.20
2556	A572	$18 Gilded wood	1.25	.40
		Nos. 2553-2556 (4)	2.25	1.00

See Nos. 2582-2585.

Chiang Kai-
shek
A573

Portrait and: $5, Map and flag. $8, Emblem. $10, Flags on globe.

1986, Oct. 31   Litho.   Perf. 13½

2557	A573	$2 multicolored	.20	.20
2558	A573	$5 multicolored	.60	.20
2559	A573	$8 multicolored	.80	.20
2560	A573	$10 multicolored	1.00	.25
a.		Souv. sheet of 4, #2557-2560	5.75	2.50
		Nos. 2557-2560 (4)	2.60	.85

Cultural
Heritage
A574

Architecture: $2, Chin-Kuang Fu land development and defense fund building, 1826. $5, Erh-sha-wan Gun Emplacement, Keelung, 1841, restored 1979. $8, Fort Hsi Tai, 1886. $10, Matsu Temple, Peng-hu, renovated 1563-1624.

1986, Nov. 14   Litho.   Perf. 13½

2561	A574	$2 multicolored	.30	.20
2562	A574	$5 multicolored	.70	.20
2563	A574	$8 multicolored	.80	.25
2564	A574	$10 multicolored	1.00	.30
		Nos. 2561-2564 (4)	2.80	.95

New Year 1987
(Year of the
Hare) — A575

1986, Dec. 1   Perf. 12½

2565	A575	$1 dl pink & multi	.50	.20
2566	A575	$10 pale grn & multi	1.75	.30
a.		Souv. sheet, 2 each #2565-2566	10.50	3.50

Kenting, 1st
Natl. Park
A576

1987, Jan. 8   Litho.   Perf. 13½

2567	A576	$2 Garden	.30	.20
2568	A576	$5 Shore rocks	.70	.20
2569	A576	$8 Shore and hill	.90	.20
2570	A576	$10 Shore and rocks, diff.	1.25	.30
		Nos. 2567-2570 (4)	3.15	.90

Folk Art — A577

Puppets: $2, Hand puppet. $5, Marionette. $18, Shadow puppet.

1987, Feb. 12   Litho.   Perf. 14x13½

2571	A577	$2 multicolored	.30	.20
2572	A577	$5 multicolored	.80	.20
2573	A577	$18 multicolored	1.40	.80
		Nos. 2571-2573 (3)	2.50	.80

Speedpost   Wu Yueh (1878-
A578   1905),
                        Revolutionary
                        A579

1987, Mar. 20   Litho.   Perf. 14x13½

2574	A578	$2 multicolored	.25	.20
2575	A578	$18 multicolored	.90	.40

Stamp Day.

1987, Mar. 29 Engr. Perf. 13½x12½

2576	A579	$2 orange	.50	.20

Landscapes Painted by Madame
Chiang Kai-shek — A580

$2, Singing Creek with Bamboo Orchestra. $5, Mountains Draped in Clouds. $8, Vista of Tranquility. $10, Mountains after a Snowfall.

1987, Apr. 10   Litho.   Perf. 13½

2577	A580	$2 blk, buff & ver	.30	.20
2578	A580	$5 blk, buff & ver	.75	.20
2579	A580	$8 blk, buff & ver	1.75	.30
2580	A580	$10 blk, buff & ver	2.40	.45
		Nos. 2577-2580 (4)	5.20	1.15

Stone
Sculptures — A581

Designs: a, Head of a Bodhisattva, sand-stone, Northern Wei Dynasty (386-534). b, Standing Buddha, limestone, Northern Ch'i Dynasty (550-577). c, Head of a Bodhisattva, sandstone, T'ang Dynasty (618-907). d, Seated Buddha, alabaster, T'ang Dynasty.

1987, Apr. 23

2581	Strip of 4	2.75	2.25
a.-d.	A581 $5 any single	.55	.30

No. 2581a shows seven Chinese characters at left; No. 2581c shows five.

Ju-i
Scepters,
Ch'ing
Dynasty
A582

1987, May 7   Photo.   Perf. 14x14½

2582	A582	$2 Silver and gems	.40	.20
2583	A582	$3 Gold and gems	1.00	.20
2584	A582	$4 Gilded, jade and inlaid gems	1.50	.20
2585	A582	$18 Gilded, inlaid malachite	2.10	.45
		Nos. 2582-2585 (4)	5.00	1.05

Feitsui
Reservoir
Inauguration
A583

1987, June 6   Litho.   Perf. 13½x14

2586	A583	$2 Reservoir	.35	.20
2587	A583	$18 Hsintien Stream, reservoir	1.25	.45

Flower
Arrangements by
Huang Yung-ch'uan
A584

Lions Club Intl.
70th Annual
Convention,
Taipei — A585

1987, June 19   Perf. 13½

2588	A584	$2 denom. LL	.20	.20
2589	A584	$5 denom. LL	.50	.20
2590	A584	$8 Flowers in brown vase	.65	.20
2591	A584	$10 denom. UR	.75	.25
		Nos. 2588-2591 (4)	2.10	.85

Compare with designs A483, A559.

1987, July 1

2592	A585	$2 multicolored	.30	.20
2593	A585	$18 multicolored	1.00	.50

Sino-Japanese
War, 50th
Anniv. — A586

1987, July 7   Perf. 14x13½

2594	A586	$1 Battle front	.20	.20
2595	A586	$2 Chiang Kai-shek giving speech	.30	.20
2596	A586	$5 Public donating funds	.35	.20
2597	A586	$6 Troops marching	.45	.20
2598	A586	$8 Signing of peace treaty	.65	.25
2599	A586	$18 Parade	.80	.40
		Nos. 2594-2599 (6)	2.75	1.45

Wang Yun-wu
(1888-1979),
Lexicographer
A587

1987, Aug. 14   Perf. 13½

2600	A587	$2 gray black	.25	.20

Memorial Hall Type of 1981
Perf. 12½x13½

1987, Sept. 24   Photo.

2601	A468	10c lake	.20	.20
2602	A468	30c brt green	.20	.20
2603	A468	60c brt blue	.20	.20
		Nos. 2601-2603 (3)	.60	.60

A588

Cultural Renaissance
Movement — A589

Scroll, 1543, by Weng Chen-ming (1470-1559), a copy of Chao Po-su's Red Cliff. Nos. 2604a-2604e and 2604f-2604j are printed in continuous designs. (Each stamp is numbered from 1 to 10 in Chinese. See illustrations with Nos. 1682-1691 for numerals.)

1987, Sept. 22   Engr.   Perf. 13½

2604		Block of 10	9.00	9.00
a.-e.	A588 $3 any single		.70	.25
f.-j.	A589 $3 any single		.70	.25

Folk
Costumes — A590

$1.50, Han woman, early Ch'ing Dynasty (1644-1911). $3, Wife of a Ch'ing Dynasty Manchu Bannerman. $7.50, Urban woman wearing Manchu ch'i-p'ao dress, c. 1912. $18, Short jacket over long skirt, c. 1920.

1987, Oct. 2   Litho.

2605	A590	$1.50 multicolored	.85	.20
2606	A590	$3 multicolored	1.10	.20
2607	A590	$7.50 multicolored	1.25	.20
2608	A590	$18 multicolored	1.50	.50
		Nos. 2605-2608 (4)	4.70	1.10

Nos. 2605-2608 have 3 groups of 2 smaller Chinese characters above denomination. Nos. 2660-2663 have 2 groups of 2 and 4 characters.

A591

A592

1987, Nov. 12   Perf. 13½x14

2609	A591	$3 Ta Chen Tian temple, Taichung	.30	.20
2610	A591	$18 Confucius	1.10	.55

Intl. Symposium on Confucianism, Taipei, Nov. 12-17.

1987, Dec. 1   Perf. 12½

2611	A592	$1.50 multicolored	.60	.20
2612	A592	$12 multicolored	1.60	.30
a.		Souv. sheet, 2 ea #2611-2612	8.00	2.50

New Year 1988 (Year of the Dragon).

Constitution, 40th Anniv. — A593

1987, Dec. 25   Litho.   Perf. 13½

2613	A593	$3 multicolored	.20	.20
2614	A593	$16 multi, diff.	.85	.55

Prevent
Hypertension
Campaign
A594

1988, Jan. 8   Perf. 12½x13½

2615	A594	$3 multicolored	.25	.20

Fruit Tree
Blossoms — A595

Wmk. 323

1988, Feb. 4   Litho.   Perf. 13½

2616	A595	$3 Prunus mume	1.10	.20
2617	A595	$7.50 Prunus armeniaca	1.25	.30
2618	A595	$12 Prunus persica	1.60	.50
a.		Min. sheet of 3, #2616-2618	17.00	17.00

Wmk. 323

1988, May 5   Litho.   Perf. 13½

2619	A595	$3 Paeonia suffruticosa	.30	.20
2620	A595	$7.50 Punica granatum	.90	.30

2621	A595	$12 Nelumbo nucifera	1.10	.50
a.		Min. sheet of 3, #2619-2621	9.00	9.00

Wmk. 323

1988, Aug. 9   Litho.   Perf. 13½

2622	A595	$3 Impatiens balsamina	.30	.20
2623	A595	$7.50 Osmanthus fragrans	.90	.30
2624	A595	$12 Chrysanthemum morifolium	1.10	.50
a.		Min. sheet of 3, #2622-2624	8.50	8.50

Wmk. 323

1988, Nov. 7   Litho.   Perf. 13½

2625	A595	$3 Hibiscus mutabilis	.30	.20
2626	A595	$7.50 Camellia japonica	1.25	.30
2627	A595	$12 Narcissus tazetta	1.50	.50
a.		Min. sheet of 3, #2625-2627	9.00	9.00
		Nos. 2616-2627 (12)	11.60	4.00

Tourism
Day — A596

Folk art: $3, Modeled dough figurines. $7.50, Blown sweet-malt sugar candy. $16, Sugar paintings.

Perf. 13½x14

1988, Mar. 2   Litho.   Wmk. 323

2628	A596	$3 multicolored	.55	.20
2629	A596	$7.50 multicolored	1.10	.30
2630	A596	$16 multicolored	2.00	.70
		Nos. 2628-2630 (3)	3.65	1.20

A597   A598

Perf. 13½x12½

1988, Mar. 29   Engr.   Wmk. 323

2631	A597	$3 brown	.40	.20

Hsu Hsi-lin (1873-1907), hero of the revolution.

1988   Litho.   Perf. 13½

2632	A598	$1.50 Biotechnology	.20	.20
2633	A598	$3 Energy resources	.25	.20
2634	A598	$7 Immunization	.35	.25
2635	A598	$7.50 Automation	.35	.25
2636	A598	$10 Telecommunications	.45	.40
2637	A598	$12 Laser technology	.50	.40
2638	A598	$16 Micro-optics	.75	.65
2639	A598	$16.50 Agricultural research	1.00	.65
		Nos. 2632-2639 (8)	3.85	3.00

Industrialization by technological development. Issued: $3, $7.50, $10, $16, Apr. 22; others, May 9.

Police Day
A599

Wmk. 323

1988, June 15   Litho.   Perf. 13½

2640	A599	$3 Traffic control	.20	.20
2641	A599	$12 Rescue operations	.50	.40

Amphibians
A600

1988, July 8   **Perf. 13½x14**
2642	A600	$1.50	Microhyla butleri	.80	.20
2643	A600	$3	Rana taipehensis	1.25	.20
2644	A600	$7.50	Microhyla inornata	1.60	.35
2645	A600	$16	Rhacophorus smaragdinus	2.10	.75

Nos. 2642-2645 (4) 5.75 1.50

China Broadcasting Corp. (BBC), 60th Anniv. — A601

Wmk. 323
1988, Aug. 1   **Litho.**   **Perf. 13½**
2646 A601 $3 multicolored .20 .20

Victory at the Battle of Kinmen, 30th Anniv. A602

Designs: $1.50, Chiang Kai-shek and artillery commander. $3, With troops. $7.50, Cannon. $12, Tanks.

1988, Aug. 23
2647	A602	$1.50	multicolored	.25	.20
2648	A602	$3	multicolored	.30	.20
2649	A602	$7.50	multicolored	.35	.25
2650	A602	$12	multicolored	.50	.40

Nos. 2647-2650 (4) 1.40 1.05

Sports Promotion — A603

#2651-2652, Basketball. #2653-2654, Baseball.

1988, Sept. 9
2651		$5	Players	.70	.25
2652		$5	Players	.70	.25
a.	A603	Pair, #2651-2652		1.40	1.10
2653		$5	Batter	.70	.25
2654		$5	Catcher	.70	.25
a.	A603	Pair, #2653-2654		1.40	1.10

Nos. 2651-2654 (4) 2.80 1.00

#2652a, 2654a have continuous designs.

Yangmingshan Natl. Park — A604

1988, Sept. 16
2655	A604	$1.50	Volcanic crater	.20	.20
2656	A604	$3	Lake	.35	.20
2657	A604	$7.50	Tatun Volcanic Range	.65	.25
2658	A604	$16	Dormant volcano	1.25	.55

Nos. 2655-2658 (4) 2.45 1.20

Lofty Mount Lu, a Hanging Scroll, 1467, By Shen Chou (1427-1509) — A605

Painting details: a, UL. b, UR. c, LL. d, LR.

Wmk. 323
1988, Oct. 19   **Litho.**   **Perf. 11½**
| 2659 | A605 | Block of 4 | 6.50 | 4.50 |
| a.-d. | | $5 any single | 1.50 | .35 |

Folk Costumes — A606

Designs: $2, Shang Dynasty (1766-1122 B.C.) nobleman. $3, Warring States (403-221) B.C.) ruler. $7.50, Wei-Chin Period (221-420) official. $12, Northern Dynasties (502-581) official.

Perf. 13½x14
1988, Nov. 23   **Litho.**   **Wmk. 323**
2660	A606	$2	multicolored	.40	.20
2661	A606	$3	multicolored	.70	.20
2662	A606	$7.50	multicolored	1.40	.35
2663	A606	$12	multicolored	2.00	.55

Nos. 2660-2663 (4) 4.50 1.30

Nos. 2721-2724 have groups of 2 and 6 Chinese characters above denomination; Nos. 2660-2663 groups of 2 and 4; #2794-2797 groups of 1 and 5.

A607   A608

1988, Dec. 1   **Perf. 12½**
2664	A607	$2	multicolored	.55	.20
2665	A607	$13	multicolored	4.25	.60
a.		Souv. sheet, 2 each #2664-2665	10.50	10.50

New Year 1989 (Year of the Snake).

Wmk. 323
1989, Jan. 4   **Litho.**   **Perf. 13½**
2666 A608 $3 black .40 .20

Tai Ch'uan-hsien (1890-1949), party leader.

Pres. Chiang Ching-kuo (1910-88) A609

1989, Jan. 13
2667	A609	$3	shown	.20	.20
2668	A609	$6	Suffrage	.30	.20
2669	A609	$7.50	Industry	.45	.30
2670	A609	$16	Children	.70	.65

Nos. 2667-2670 (4) 1.65 1.35

Ni Ying-tien (1884-1910), Revolution Leader — A610

Perf. 13½x12½
1989, Mar. 28   **Engr.**   **Wmk. 323**
2671 A610 $3 black .20 .20

Stop Smoking A611   Lighthouses A612

Perf. 13½x12½
1989, Apr. 7   **Litho.**   **Wmk. 323**
2672 A611 $3 multicolored .20 .20

1989-91   **Perf. 13½**
2673	A612	75c	Mu Tou Yu	.20	.20
2674	A612	$2	Lu Tao	.20	.20
2675	A612	$2.25	Pen Chia Yu	.20	.20
2676	A612	$3	Pitou Chiao	.25	.20
2677	A612	$4.50	Tungyin Tao	.30	.20
2678	A612	$6	Chilai Pi	.50	.25
2679	A612	$7	Fukwei Chiao	.60	.35
2680	A612	$7.50	Hua Yu	.65	.35
2681	A612	$9	Oluan Pi	.70	.25
2682	A612	$10	Kaohsiung	.80	.45
2683	A612	$10.50	Yuweng Tao	.85	.35
2683A	A612	$12	Tungchu Tao	1.00	.55
2683B	A612	$13	Yeh Liu	1.10	.45
2683C	A612	$15	Tungchi Yu	1.25	.80
2684	A612	$16.50	Chimei Yu	1.40	.75

Nos. 2673-2684 (15) 10.00 5.55

Issued: $7, $15, 5/19/90; $6, $12, 1/9/91; $2, $3, $7.50, $10, $16.50, 5/20/91; others, 1989.
See Nos. 2811-2823.

1st Natl. Wealth Survey A613

1989, May 18   **Litho.**   **Perf. 13½**
2685 A613 $3 multicolored .30 .20

Ch'u Ts'u Collection of Poems, 722-481 B.C. — A614

Excerpts: $3, "I once tended nine fields of orchids; Also I had planted a hundred rods of melilotus" (Li Sao). $7.50, "No grief is greater than parting of the living; No joy is more than making new friends" (Chiu Ko, shao ssu ming). $12, "Since my heart is straight and good, Why should I be chagrined at living remote and neglected?" (Chiu Chang, she chiang). $16, "The steed will not gallop itself into servitude; The phoenix has no appetite for slave food." (Chiu Pien).

1989, June 7   Photo.   Perf. 11½x12
Granite Paper
2686	A614	$3	Man overlooking fields	.35	.20
2687	A614	$7.50	Man, woman on path	.90	.45
2688	A614	$12	Man holding staff	1.60	.70
2689	A614	$16	Man, stallion, stone gate	2.00 1.00	2.35

Nos. 2686-2689 (4) 4.85 2.35

Compare with types A629, A663. Nos. 2686-2689 have two Chinese characters near denomination. Nos. 2725-2728 have groups of 3 and 4 characters.

Taipei Subway Inauguration — A615

1989, June 27   **Litho.**   **Perf. 13½**
| 2690 | A615 | $3 | Subway tunnel | .40 | .20 |
| 2691 | A615 | $16 | Entering underground | 1.10 | .90 |

A616

A616a

A616b

Butterflies A616c

$2, Graphium sarpedon connectens. $3, Papilo memnon heronus. $7.50, Princeps demoleus libanius. $9, Pachliopa aristolochiae interpositas.

Wmk. 323

1989, July 14   Litho.   Perf. 13½

2692	A616	$2 multicolored	.35	.25
2693	A616a	$3 multicolored	.65	.30
2694	A616b	$7.50 multicolored	1.50	.40
2695	A616c	$9 multicolored	2.00	.50
		Nos. 2692-2695 (4)	4.50	1.45

Compare with design A627.

Ch'ing Dynasty Teapots from I-Hsing of Kiangsu, 1644-1911 — A617

1989, July 28   Perf. 13½x14

2696	A617	$2 multicolored	.25	.20
2697	A617	$3 multi, diff.	.70	.20
2698	A617	$12 multi, diff.	1.75	.60
2699	A617	$16 multi, diff.	1.75	.70
		Nos. 2696-2699 (4)	4.45	1.60

For stamps with teapot designs and solid black denominations see Nos. 2760-2764.

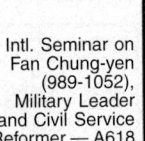

Intl. Seminar on Fan Chung-yen (989-1052), Military Leader and Civil Service Reformer — A618

Perf. 14x13½

1989, Sept. 1   Litho.   Wmk. 323

2700 A618 $12 multicolored   .90 .55

Autumn Colors on the Ch'iao and Hua Mountains, 14th Cent., by Ch'iao Meng-fu — A619

a, Right side of mountain, trees. b, Trees, left side of mountain. c, House, trees. d, shown.

Wmk. 323

1989, Oct. 5   Litho.   Perf. 13½

2701		Strip of 4	8.00	4.75
a.-d.	A619 $7.50 any single		1.90	.55

Social Welfare — A619a

1989, Nov. 3   Litho.   Perf. 13½

2701E A619a $3 multicolored   .25 .20

Taroko Natl. Park — A620   New Year 1990 (Year of the Horse) — A621

Designs: $2, Marble gorge, Liwu River. $3, Hohuan Mountain. $12, Waterfall, Cirque of Nanhu. $16, Chingshui Cliff.

Wmk. 323

1989, Nov. 28   Litho.   Perf. 13½

2702	A620	$2 multicolored	.20	.20
2703	A620	$3 multicolored	.25	.20
2704	A620	$12 multicolored	.55	.45
2705	A620	$16 multicolored	.70	.60
		Nos. 2702-2705 (4)	1.70	1.45

1989, Dec. 1   Perf. 12½

2706	A621	$2 multicolored	.45	.20
2707	A621	$13 multicolored	1.25	.60
a.	Souv. sheet, 2 ea #2706-2707		6.50	2.50

Yu Lu — A622

Men Shen, "guardian spirits" (likenesses of legendary beings placed on residence doors at the new year): No. 2708, Yu Lu. No. 2709, Shen Shu. No. 2710, Wei-ch'ih Ching-te. No. 2711, Ch'in Shu-pao.

Wmk. 323

1990, Jan. 19   Litho.   Perf. 13½

2708	A622	$3 shown	1.10	.20
2709	A622	$3 "$3" at LR	1.10	.20
a.	Pair, #2708-2709		2.25	2.00
2710	A622	$7.50 "$7.50" at LL	2.75	.50
2711	A622	$7.50 "$7.50" at LR	2.75	.50
a.	Pair, #2710-2711		5.50	5.00
		Nos. 2708-2711 (4)	7.70	1.40

Nos. 2709a, 2711a have continuous designs.

A623

Scenery — A624

Designs: $2, Lishan House, Pear Mountain. $18, Tayu Pass, Tayuling, vert.

Wmk. 323

1990, Feb. 10   Litho.   Perf. 13½

2712	A623	$2 multicolored	.20	.20
2713	A624	$18 multicolored	1.50	1.00

Labor Insurance System, 40th Anniv. — A625

1990, Mar. 1

2714 A625 $3 multicolored   .35 .20

Liquefied Natural Gas — A626

$3, Terminal, Yung-an Hsiang of Kaohsiung. $16, Container ship, map, refinery.

1990, Mar. 31   Litho.   Perf. 13½

2715	A626	$3 multi	.20	.20
2716	A626	$16 multi, vert.	.90	.65

A627

A627a

A627b

Butterflies — A627c

1990, Apr. 20

2717	A627	$2 Salatura genutia	.25	.20
2718	A627a	$3 Hypolimnas misippus	.25	.20
2719	A627b	$7.50 Pieris canidia	.70	.35
2720	A627c	$9 Precis almana	.90	.45
		Nos. 2717-2720 (4)	2.10	1.20

Compare with design A616.

Folk Costumes — A628

$2, Official, Sui & T'ang Dynasties (589-907). $3, Official, T'ang & Sung Dynasties (618-1280). $7.50, Royal guardsman, Chin & Yuan Dynasties (1115-1368). $12, Highest ranking civil official, Ming Dynasty (1368-1644).

1990, May 10   Litho.   Perf. 13½

2721	A628	$2 multicolored	.25	.20
2722	A628	$3 multicolored	.50	.20
2723	A628	$7.50 multicolored	1.00	.30
2724	A628	$12 multicolored	1.10	.55
		Nos. 2721-2724 (4)	2.85	1.25

See note after No. 2663.

Yueh Fu Classical Poetry — A629

Lyrics from Tzu-yeh folk songs, Six Dynasties (222-589): $3, Spring Song at Midnight. $7.50, Summer Song at Midnight. $12,

---

Autumn Song at Midnight. $16, Winter Song at Midnight.

Wmk. 323

1990, June 27   Litho.   Perf. 11½
Granite Paper

2725	A629	$3 shown	.30	.20
2726	A629	$7.50 Couple, river	.75	.35
2727	A629	$12 Washing clothes, river	1.75	.55
2728	A629	$16 River in winter	2.50	.80
		Nos. 2725-2728 (4)	5.30	1.90

Compare with designs A614 and A663.

Bonsai — A630

Designs: $3, Pinus thunbergii parl. $6.50, Ehretia microphylla lamk. $12, Buxus harlandii hance. $16, Celtis sinensis pers.

1990, July 20   Litho.   Perf. 13½

2729	A630	$3 multicolored	.20	.20
2730	A630	$6.50 multicolored	.45	.30
2731	A630	$12 multicolored	.65	.70
2732	A630	$16 multicolored	1.00	.80
		Nos. 2729-2732 (4)	2.30	2.00

Snuff Bottles — A631

1990, Aug. 9

2733	A631	$3 Bamboo stem shaped	.20	.20
2734	A631	$6 Peony motif	.35	.30
2735	A631	$9 Amber	.50	.45
2736	A631	$16 White jade	1.00	.80
		Nos. 2733-2736 (4)	2.05	1.75

Formosan Firecrest — A632

1990, Aug. 20   Litho.   Perf. 13½

2737	A632	$2 shown	.20	.20
2738	A632	$3 Laughing thrush	.20	.20
2739	A632	$7.50 White-eared sibia	.50	.25
2740	A632	$16 Yellow tit	1.10	.60
		Nos. 2737-2740 (4)	2.00	1.25

Sports — A633

1990, Sept. 8   Litho.   Perf. 13½

2741	A633	$2 Sprint	.20	.20
2742	A633	$3 Long jump	.20	.20
2743	A633	$7 Pole vault	.40	.30
2744	A633	$16 High hurdle	1.00	.60
		Nos. 2741-2744 (4)	1.80	1.30

Flying Tigers, 50th Anniv. A634

1990, Sept. 26   Litho.   Perf. 13½
2745 A634 $3 multicolored   .65 .20

Children's Drawings A635

1990, Oct. 9
2746 A635 $2 Cat   .20 .20
2747 A635 $3 Peacocks   .20 .20
2748 A635 $7.50 Chickens   .50 .30
2749 A635 $12 Cattle   .80 .50
Nos. 2746-2749 (4)   1.70 1.20

National Theater A636

Photo. & Engr.
1990, Oct. 30   Perf. 13½
2750 A636 $3 shown   .20 .20
2751 A636 $12 Natl. concert hall   .85 .40

A637   A638

Ancient money.

1990, Nov. 5   Litho.   Perf. 13x13½
2752 A637 $2 Shell   .20 .20
2753 A637 $3 Oyster   .20 .20
2754 A637 $6.50 Bone   .35 .35
2755 A637 $7.50 Jade   .40 .40
2756 A637 $9 Bronze   .50 .50
Nos. 2752-2756 (5)   1.65 1.65

1990, Dec. 1   Perf. 12½
2757 A638 $2 multicolored   .45 .20
2758 A638 $13 multicolored   1.75 .50
  a. Souv. sheet, 2 ea #2757-2758   6.25 2.25

New Year 1991 (Year of the Sheep).

Hu Shih (1891-1962), Educator — A639

Wmk. 323
1990, Dec. 17   Engr.   Perf. 13½
2759 A639 $3 purple   .20 .20

Teapots, Natl. Palace Museum A640

Teapots: $2, Blue phoenix, Ming Dynasty. $3, Dragon handle and spout, Ming Dynasty. $9, Blue landscape, flowered top, Ch'ing Dynasty. $12, Rectangular, passion flower motif, Ch'ing Dynasty. $16, Rectangular, flower motif, Ch'ing Dynasty.

1991, Jan. 18   Photo.   Perf. 12
Granite Paper
2760 A640 $2 yel, blk & blue   .20 .20
2761 A640 $3 brt yel grn & blk   .25 .20
2762 A640 $9 pink & multi   .65 .40
2763 A640 $12 violet & multi   .90 .55
2764 A640 $16 lt blue & multi   1.25 .85
Nos. 2760-2764 (5)   3.25 2.20

God of Happiness A641

God of Joy — A642

1991, Feb. 7   Litho.   Perf. 13½
2765 A641 $3 shown   .40 .20
2766 A641 $3 God of Wealth   .40 .20
2767 A642 $7.50 shown   .90 .30
2768 A642 $7.50 God of Longevity   .90 .30
Nos. 2765-2768 (4)   2.60 1.00

Perf. 13½ Vert.
2765a A641 $3   .70 .20
2766a A641 $3   .70 .20
2767a A642 $7.50   .70 .20
2768a A642 $7.50   .70 .20
  b. Bkt. pane of 8, 2 each #2765a-2768a + label   8.50

Native Plants A643

Designs: $2, Petasites formosanus. $3, Heloniopsis acutifolia. $7.50, Disporum shimadai. $9, Viola nagasawai.

1991, Mar. 12   Litho.   Perf. 13½
2769 A643 $2 multicolored   .20 .20
2770 A643 $3 multicolored   .20 .20
2771 A643 $7.50 multicolored   .50 .30
2772 A643 $9 multicolored   .60 .35

1991, June 12
Designs: $2, Gaultheria itoana. $3, Lysionotus montanus. $7.50, Leontopodium microphyllum. $9, Gentiana flavo-maculata.
2773 A643 $2 multicolored   .20 .20
2774 A643 $3 multicolored   .25 .20
2775 A643 $7.50 multicolored   .80 .30
2776 A643 $9 multicolored   1.00 .35

1991, Sept. 12
Designs: $3.50, Rosa transmorrisonensis. $5, Impatiens devolii. $9, Impatiens uniflora. $12, Impatiens tayemonii.
2777 A643 $3.50 multicolored   .25 .20
2778 A643 $5 multicolored   .45 .20
2779 A643 $9 multicolored   .80 .35
2780 A643 $12 multicolored   1.00 .45

1991, Dec. 12
Designs: $3.50, Kalanchoe garambiensis. $5, Pieris taiwanensis. $9, Pleione formosana. $12, Elaeagnus oldhamii.
2781 A643 $3.50 multicolored   .20 .20
2782 A643 $5 multicolored   .30 .20
2783 A643 $9 multicolored   .65 .40
2784 A643 $12 multicolored   .80 .45
Nos. 2769-2784 (16)   8.20 4.55

Hsiung Cheng-Chi (1887-1910), Revolutionary A644

1991, Mar. 28   Engr.   Perf. 13½x12½
2785 A644 $3 blue   .20 .20

Republic of China, 80th Anniv. A645

1991, Mar. 28   Litho.   Perf. 13½
2786 A645 $3 Agriculture   .20 .20
2787 A645 $7.50 Science & technology   .40 .30
2788 A645 $12 Cultural activities   .60 .40
2789 A645 $16 Transportation   .90 .55
Nos. 2786-2789 (4)   2.10 1.45

Children's Toys A646   Folk Costumes A647

1991, Apr. 20   Litho.   Perf. 13½
2790 A646 $3 Bamboo pony   .25 .20
2791 A646 $3 Woven-grass grasshopper   .25 .20
2792 A646 $3 Top   .25 .20
2793 A646 $3 Pinwheels   .25 .20
  a. Souv. sheet of 4, #2790-2793   4.50 2.00
Nos. 2790-2793 (4)   1.00 .80

See Nos. 2840-2843. Compare with designs A676, A696.

Perf. 13½ Vert.
2790a A646 $3   .75 .20
2791a A646 $3   .75 .20
2792a A646 $3   .75 .20
2793b A646 $3   .75 .20
  c. Bkt. pane, 2 each #2790a-2793b + label   7.00
Nos. 2790a-2793b (4)   3.00 .80

1991, June 29   Litho.   Perf. 13½
Ch'ing Dynasty (1644-1911): $2, Winter court hat, Mang robe. $3, Summer court hat, surcoat. $7.50, Winter overcoat. $12, Common hat, traveling robe.
2794 A647 $2 multicolored   .30 .20
2795 A647 $3 multicolored   .40 .20
2796 A647 $7.50 multicolored   1.00 .30
2797 A647 $12 multicolored   1.40 .45
Nos. 2794-2797 (4)   3.10 1.15

See note after No. 2663.
Nos. 2794-2797 have groups of one and five Chinese characters.

Traffic Safety Year A648

1991, July 17   Litho.   Perf. 13½
2798 A648 $3 shown   .30 .20
2799 A648 $7.50 Don't drink & drive   .90 .35

Cloisonne Enamel Lions, Ch'ing Dynasty (1644-1911) A649   A649a

1991, July 20   Litho.   Perf. 12½
2800 A649 yel grn & multi   .50 .25
2801 A649a violet & multi   2.00 .75
Nos. 2800-2801 (2)   2.50 2.00

#2800 paid basic domestic rate, #2801 paid basic express mail rate on date of issue.

Fruits — A650

Birds — A651

1991, Aug. 10   Litho.   Perf. 14x13½
2802 A650 $3 Strawberry   .20 .20
2803 A650 $7.50 Grapes   .35 .30
2804 A650 $9 Mango   .45 .35
2805 A650 $16 Sugar apple   .80 .60
Nos. 2802-2805 (4)   1.80 1.45

1991, Aug. 24   Perf. 13½
Designs: a, Myiophoneus insularis. b, Cinclus pallasii. c, Aix galericulata. d, Nycticorax nycticorax. e, Egretta garzetta. f, Rhyacornis fuliginosus. g, Enicurus scouleri. h, Motacilla cinerea. i, Alcedo atthis. j, Motacilla alba.
2806 Block of 10   3.50 2.40
  a.-j. A651 $5 any single   .30 .20

Outdoor Activities A652

Wmk. 323
1991, Sept. 27   Litho.   Perf. 13½
2807 A652 $2 Rock climbing   .20 .20
2808 A652 $3 Fishing   .25 .20
2809 A652 $7.50 Bird watching   .55 .35
2810 A652 $10 Playing in water   .80 .50
Nos. 2807-2810 (4)   1.80 1.25

Intl. Federation of Camping and Caravaning, 1991 Rally.

Lighthouse Type of 1989
Inscription Panel in Blue

1991-92   Perf. 13½
2811 A612 50c like #2683C   .20 .20
2812 A612 $1 like #2674   .20 .20
2813 A612 $3.50 like #2678   .20 .20
2814 A612 $5 like #2679   .30 .20
  a. Booklet pane of 10   4.00
2815 A612 $7 like #2676   .40 .25
2816 A612 $9 like #2681   .55 .35
2817 A612 $10 like #2682   .60 .40
2818 A612 $12 like #2683A   .75 .50
  a. $12 Bkt. pane of 5 + label   4.00
2819 A612 $13 like #2675   .75 .50
2820 A612 $19 like #2680   1.10 .80
2821 A612 $20 like #2683B   1.25 .80
2822 A612 $26 like #2683   1.60 1.10
2823 A612 $28 like #2684   1.60 1.10
Nos. 2811-2823 (13)   9.50 6.60

Issued: 50c, $3.50, $5, $12, 10/2; #2818a, 9/26/92; $1, $19, $20, 3/2/92; $26, $28, 5/20/92; $7, $9, $10, $13, 8/21/92.

Peacocks by Lan Shih-ning (Giuseppe Castiglione, 1688-1768) A653

$20, Peacock spreading tail feathers.

Perf. 12x11½

1991, Oct. 30   Photo.   Unwmk.
Granite Paper

2826	A653	$5 multicolored	.40	.20
2827	A653	$20 multicolored	1.60	.85
a.		Souvenir sheet of 1	4.00	2.75

New Year 1992 (Year of the Monkey) — A654

Wmk. 323

1991, Nov. 30   Litho.   Perf. 12½

2828	A654	$3.50 orange & multi	.25	.20
2829	A654	$13 tan & multi	.90	.60
a.		Souv. sheet, 2 ea #2828-2829	3.75	2.00

Chinese Books A655

Wmk. 323

1992, Jan. 17   Litho.   Perf. 13½

2830	A655	$3.50 Scroll	.20	.20
2831	A655	$5 Fold bindings	.35	.20
2832	A655	$9 Butterfly bindings	.60	.35
2833	A655	$15 String bindings	1.00	.65
		Nos. 2830-2833 (4)	2.15	1.40

Good Fortune and Satisfaction A656

Five Blessings Upon the House — A657

Nienhwa paintings: No. 2835, Peace in the Wake of Firecrackers. No. 2837, An Abundance for Every Year.

1992, Jan. 27   Litho.   Perf. 13½

2834	A656	$5 multicolored	.25	.25
2835	A656	$5 multicolored	.25	.25
2836	A657	$12 multicolored	.75	.60
2837	A657	$12 multicolored	.75	.60
a.		Bklt. pane, 2 each #2834-2837 + label	6.75	
		Nos. 2834-2837 (4)	2.00	1.70

Lunar New Year.

 A658   A659

Lunar New Year: a, like #2664. b, like #2611. c, like #2565. d, like #2493. e, like #2442. f, like #2390. g, like #2346. h, like #2273. i, like #2217. j, like #2828. k, like #2757. l, like #2706.

Wmk. 323

1992, Feb. 18   Litho.   Perf. 12½

2838	A658	$5 Block of 12, #a.-l., ver & multi	4.25	2.40
m.		Sheet of 12, #2838a-2838 l	4.50	2.50

1992, Mar. 12   Perf. 13½

Trees: a, Chamaecyparis formosensis. b, Chamaecyparis taiwanensis. c, Calocedrus formosana. d, Cunninghamia konishii. e. Taiwania crypto- merioides.

2839	A659	$5 Strip of 5, #a.-e.	1.75	.55

Children's Toys Type of 1991

1992, Apr. 29   Litho.   Perf. 13½

2840	A646	$5 Walking on iron pots	.40	.25
2841	A646	$5 Chopstick gun	.40	.25
2842	A646	$5 Hoop rolling	.40	.25
2843	A646	$5 Grass fighting	.40	.25
a.		Sheet of 4, #2840-2843	3.25	3.25
b.		As "a," imperf. (simulated perfs), red inscription in sheet margin	10.50	10.50
c.		Bklt. pane, 2 each #2840-2843 + label	5.25	
		Nos. 2840-2843 (4)	1.60	1.00

Issue date: No. 2843b, May 15.

 A660

 A661

Mother and son in: $3.50, Spring. $5, Summer. $9, Autumn. $10, Winter.

Wmk. 323

1992, May 9   Litho.   Perf. 13½

2844	A660	$3.50 multicolored	.20	.20
2845	A660	$5 multicolored	.40	.20
2846	A660	$9 multicolored	.70	.40
2847	A660	$10 multicolored	.80	.45
		Nos. 2844-2847 (4)	2.10	1.25

Parent-child relationships.

Wmk. 323

1992, June 25   Litho.   Perf. 13½

Glassware Decorated with Enamel - Vases: $3.50, Faceted, decorated with bats and longevity characters. $5, Double-lobed, with children at play. $7, Flowered. $17, Tutoring scene.

Background colors

2848	A661	$3.50 pink	.20	.20
2849	A661	$5 green	.30	.20
2850	A661	$7 bister	.45	.30
2851	A661	$17 blue	1.25	.70
		Nos. 2848-2851 (4)	2.20	1.40

Stone Lion of Lugouqiao A662

Various stone lions.

Wmk. 323

1992, July 7   Engr.   Perf. 13½

2852	A662	$5 olive grn & pur	.40	.20
2853	A662	$5 blue & brown	.40	.20
2854	A662	$12 org & olive grn	.90	.50
2855	A662	$12 purple & black	.90	.50
		Nos. 2852-2855 (4)	2.60	1.40

Compare with designs A614, A629, A663.

Ku Shih Classical Poetry — A663

Excerpts: $3.50, "Flesh and body are as closely linked as leaves to a tree." $5, "Once a man and woman get married, conjugal love will last forever without doubt." $9, "Man takes pains to uphold virtue." $15, "Tartar horses lean toward the northern wind."

1992, Aug. 8   Litho.

2856	A663	$3.50 Children playing near tree	.20	.20
2857	A663	$5 Man & woman	.45	.20
2858	A663	$9 Couple near stream	.75	.35
2859	A663	$15 Horse, tree	1.15	.60
		Nos. 2856-2859 (4)	2.55	1.35

Life in the Countryside A664

Scenes of temple fair: a, Two women, man beating drum, crowd. b, Vendor with basket. c, People playing musical instruments. d, Man with food cart. e, Women with umbrella, basket.

Wmk. 323

1992, Sept. 22   Litho.   Perf. 11½

2860	A664	$5 Strip of 5, #a.-e.	3.25	2.25

Silk Tapestries A665

Ming Dynasty Silk Tapestry Drawing on Life: $5, Two Birds Perched on a Red Camellia Branch. $12, Two Birds Playing on a Peach Branch.

1992, Oct. 9   Litho.   Perf. 11½
Granite Paper

2861	A665	$5 multicolored	.40	.20
2862	A665	$12 multicolored	1.10	.60
a.		Sheet of 2, #2861-2862	1.75	1.00

Chinese Opera A666

Actors, props: $3.50, Nin Hsiang-ju's carting to a party from "The General and Premier." $5, Hsao En rowing a boat from "The Lucky Pearl." $9, Wang Chao-chun making peace with the frontier from "Chao-chun Serves as an Envoy." $12, Scene with red sedan chair from "Escort to the Wedding."

Wmk. 323

1992, Oct. 21   Litho.   Perf. 13½

2863	A666	$3.50 multicolored	.20	.20
2864	A666	$5 multicolored	.40	.20
2865	A666	$9 multicolored	.65	.40
2866	A666	$12 multicolored	.90	.55
		Nos. 2863-2866 (4)	2.15	1.35

Alishan Forest Railway — A667

1992, Nov. 5   Perf. 11½

2867	A667	$5 Steam engine	.35	.20
2868	A667	$15 Diesel engine	1.10	.65

Endangered Mammals of Taiwan A668

Designs: a, Lutra lutra chinensis. b, Pteropus dasymallus formosus. c, Neofelis nebulosa brachyurus. d, Selenarctos thibetanus formosanus.

Perf. 11½x12

1992, Nov. 25   Photo.   Unwmk.
Granite Paper

2869	A668	$5 Block of 4, #a.-d.	2.00	1.10

New Year 1993 (Year of the Rooster) — A669

Design: $13, Rooster facing left.

Wmk. 323

1992, Dec. 1   Litho.   Perf. 12½

2870	A669	$3.50 red & multi	.25	.20
a.		Perf. 13½ vert.	.25	.20
2871	A669	$13 pur & multi	.70	.45
a.		Souv. sheet, 2 ea #2870-2871	2.25	2.25
b.		As "a" with added inscription in border	2.25	2.25
c.		Bklt. pane, 5 ea #2870-2871	5.25	
d.		Perf. 13½ vert.	.70	.50
e.		Booklet pane, 6 each #2870a, 2871d + label	5.75	

Inscription on No. 2871b reads "Philippine Stamp Exhibition 1992-Taipei" in English and Chinese.

Johann Adam Schall von Bell (1592-1666), Astronomer and Missionary — A670

1992 Dec. 10   **Perf. 11½**
2872 A670 $5 multicolored   .25 .20

Traditional Nienhwas of Window Frames — A671

Wmk. 323
1993, Jan. 7   **Litho.**   **Perf. 11½**
Background Color
2873 A671 $5 brt green   .25 .20
2874 A671 $5 red lilac   .25 .20
2875 A671 $12 yellow   .65 .40
2876 A671 $12 red   .65 .40
   Nos. 2873-2876 (4)   1.80 1.20

Lunar New Year.
Perf. 13½ Vert.
2873a A671 $5   1.00 .45
2874a A671 $5   1.00 .45
2875a A671 $12   1.00 .45
2876a A671 $12   1.00 .45
   b.   Booklet pane, 2 each
     #2873a-2876a + label   9.00

Nos. 2873a-2876a are 29x43mm.

Traditional Crafts A672

1993, Jan. 16
2877 A672 $3.50 Clip & paste
     moldings   .20 .20
2878 A672 $5 Lanterns   .25 .20
2879 A672 $9 Pottery jars   .50 .40
2880 A672 $15 Oil paper um-
     brella   .80 .65
   Nos. 2877-2880 (4)   1.75 1.45

Chinese Creation Story — A673

Designs: $3.50, Pan Gu's creation of the universe, vert. $5, Pan Gu transmitted himself into all creatures. $9, Nu Wa created human beings with pestled earth. $19, Nu Wa mended sky with smelted stone, vert.

1993, Feb. 6   **Perf. 12x11½, 11½x12**
2881 A673 $3.50 multicolored   .20 .20
2882 A673 $5 multicolored   .30 .20
2883 A673 $9 multicolored   .55 .40
2884 A673 $19 multicolored   1.10 .90
   Nos. 2881-2884 (4)   2.15 1.70

Lucky Animals A674

Water Plants A675

Wmk. 323
1993, Mar. 2   **Litho.**   **Perf. 13½**
2885 A674 $3.50 Mandarin duck   .20 .20
2886 A674 $5 Chinese uni-
     corn   .30 .25
2887 A674 $10 Deer   .60 .45
2888 A674 $15 Crane   .90 .70
   Nos. 2885-2888 (4)   2.00 1.60

See Nos. 2920-2923.

1993, Mar. 12   **Perf. 11½**
2889 A675 $5 Nymphaea x
     hybrida   .35 .20
2890 A675 $9 Nuphar shimadai   .65 .40
2891 A675 $12 Eichhornia cras-
     sipes   .85 .50
   Nos. 2889-2891 (3)   1.85 1.10

A676

1993   **Litho.**   **Wmk. 323**   **Perf. 11½**
2892 A676 $5 Sandbag tossing   .35 .20
2893 A676 $5 Bamboo dragonfly
     twisting   .35 .20
2894 A676 $5 Rubber band skip-
     ping   .35 .20
2895 A676 $5 Waist-strength du-
     eling   .35 .20
   a.   Souv. sheet, #2892-2895   2.25 2.25
   b.   As "a," with green & black in-
     scriptions in border   2.25 2.25
   c.   As "a," with red inscription in
     border   2.25 2.25
   Nos. 2892-2895 (4)   1.40 .80

Inscriptions on No. 2895b read "AUSTRA-LIAN STAMP EXHIBITION 1993-TAIPEI" in Chinese and English.
Inscription on No. 2895c reads "Chinese Stamp Exhibition-Thailand" in Chinese.
Nos. 2895b-2895c each have perforations extending into the margin at top (#2895c) or bottom (#2895b).
Issue dates: Nos. 2892-2895, 2895a, Apr. 20; No. 2895b, Apr. 23; No. 2895c, Apr. 30.

Perf. 13½ Vert.
2892a A676 $5   .65 .25
2893a A676 $5   .65 .25
2894a A676 $5   .65 .25
2895d A676 $5   .65 .25
   e.   Bkt. pane, 2 each #2892a-
     2894a, 2895d + label   5.50

Yangtze River A678

Designs: No. 2896, Source on Ching-Kang-Chang Plateau. No. 2897, Abrupt bend, Chinsha River. No. 2898, Narrow waterway, Roaring Tiger Gorge, Chinsha River. No. 2899, Sheer cliffs, Chutang Gorge. $9, Three Small Gorges (Dragon Gate, Pawu, and Titsui).

Perf. 13x13½
1993, May 15   **Litho.**   **Wmk. 323**
2896 A677 $3.50 shown   .20 .20
2897 A677 $3.50 multicolored   .20 .20
2898 A678 $5 shown   .35 .20

2899 A677 $5 multicolored   .35 .20
2900 A677 $9 multicolored   .65 .40
   Nos. 2896-2900 (5)   1.75 1.20

Environmental Protection A679   A680

Children's paintings: $5, No More Noise Pollution, by Yen Chao-min. $17, Clothing My Hometown with Green, by Hu Hui-chun.

Perf. 12½x13½, 13½x12½
1993, June 5
2901 A679 $5 multicolored   .30 .20
2902 A680 $17 multicolored   1.00 .80

Ch'eng-hua Porcelain, Natl. Palace Museum A681

Cups decorated in tou-ts'ai: $3.50, Human figures. $5, Chickens. $7, Flowers and fruits. $9, Dragon.

1993, June 30   **Perf. 12**
2903 A681 $3.50 multicolored   .20 .20
2904 A681 $5 multicolored   .35 .20
2905 A681 $7 multicolored   .50 .35
2906 A681 $9 multicolored   .60 .45
   Nos. 2903-2906 (4)   1.65 1.20

Vocational Training A682

Wmk. 323
1993, July 24   **Litho.**   **Perf. 12½**
2907 A682 $3.50 Graphic artist   .20 .20
2908 A682 $5 Computer oper-
     ator   .25 .20
2909 A682 $9 Carpenter   .50 .40
2910 A682 $12 Welder   .70 .60
   Nos. 2907-2910 (4)   1.65 1.40

Parent-Child Relationship A683

Silhouettes: $3.50, Adult carrying child on shoulders. $5, Father playing flute for daughter. $9, Father teaching daughter. $10, Father, adult son enjoying wildlife.

Wmk. 323
1993, Aug. 4   **Litho.**   **Perf. 11½**
Background Color
2911 A683 $3.50 tan   .20 .20
2912 A683 $5 green   .30 .20
2913 A683 $9 lilac   .60 .45
2914 A683 $10 red brown   .70 .55
   Nos. 2911-2914 (4)   1.80 1.40

Souvenir Sheet

Taipei '93, Asian Intl. Philatelic Exhibition — A684

Enjoying Antiques, by Tu Chin, 15th cent: a, Man carrying stick. b, Man selecting antiques from table. c, Man seated in chair. d, Two people at table.

Perf. 12x11½
1993, Aug. 14   **Photo.**   **Unwmk.**
Granite Paper
2915 A684 $5 Sheet of 4, #a.-d.   2.75 1.75

Persimmon A685   Loquat A686

1993, Sept. 10   **Litho.**   **Perf. 12½**
2916 A685 $5 shown   .25 .20
2917 A685 $5 Peach   .25 .20
2918 A686 $12 shown   .80 .60
2919 A686 $12 Papaya   .80 .60
   Nos. 2916-2919 (4)   2.10 1.60

Lucky Animals Type of 1993
Wmk. 323
1993, Sept. 29   **Litho.**   **Perf. 13½**
2920 A674 $1 Blue dragon   .20 .20
2921 A674 $2.50 White tiger   .20 .20
2922 A674 $9 Linnet   .60 .35
2923 A674 $19 Black tortoise   1.25 .80
   Nos. 2920-2923 (4)   2.25 1.55

Taiwan Area Games, Taoyuan — A687   Stone Lions — A688

Designs: a, Taekwondo. b, Pommel horse.

Wmk. 323
1993, Oct. 20   **Litho.**   **Perf. 12½**
2924 A687 $5 Pair, #a.-b.   .65 .60

1993, Oct. 30
Stone lions from: $3.50, Taipei New Park. $5, Hsinchu City Council. $9, Hsinchu City God Temple. $12, Fort Providentia, Tainan.
2925 A688 $3.50 multicolored   .20 .20
2926 A688 $5 multicolored   .30 .20
2927 A688 $9 multicolored   .55 .35
2928 A688 $12 multicolored   .75 .50
   Nos. 2925-2928 (4)   1.80 1.25

Syrmaticus Mikado A689

Designs: a, Hatchling. b, Mother with chicks. c, Immature female, male. d, Adult female, male (profile, showing plumage).

Perf. 11½
1993, Nov. 17   Photo.   Unwmk.
Granite Paper
2929 A689 $5 Strip of 4, #a.-d.   1.40 1.25

New Year 1994 (Year of the Dog) — A690

Design: $13, Dog facing left.

Wmk. 323
1993, Dec. 1   Litho.   Perf. 12½
2930 A690 $3.50 red & multi   .20   .20
  a.   Perf. 13½ vert.   .20   .20
  b.   As "a," bklt. pane of 12 + label   2.75
2931 A690 $13 green & multi   .90   .55
  a.   Souv. sheet, 2 ea #2930-2931   1.10   .75
  b.   As "a," overprinted in red   1.10   .75

No. 2931b is inscribed in Chinese for Kaohsiung Kuo-kuang Stamp Exhibition-1993, and has additional perforations extending into top and bottom margins.

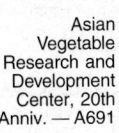

Asian Vegetable Research and Development Center, 20th Anniv. — A691

1993, Dec. 7
2932 A691 $5 shown   .30   .20
2933 A691 $13 Researchers in field   .90   .60

Formation of Constitutional Court — A692

Wmk. 323
1994, Jan. 11   Litho.   Perf. 12½
2934 A692 $5 multicolored   .30   .20

Paper Making — A693   Flowers — A694

Designs: No. 2935, Cutting bamboo. No. 2936, Cooking bamboo. No. 2937, Pouring syrup into wooden panel. No. 2938, Stacking panel. No. 2939, Drying paper.

1994, Jan. 24   Perf. 12x12½
2935 A693 $3.50 multicolored   .20   .20
2936 A693 $3.50 multicolored   .20   .20
2937 A693 $5 multicolored   .35   .20
2938 A693 $5 multicolored   .35   .20
2939 A693 $12 multicolored   .80   .50
    Nos. 2935-2939 (5)   1.90 1.30

See Nos. 2993-2997, 3071-3075, 3098-3102, 3174-3177.

1994, Feb. 17   Perf. 12½
2940 A694 $5 Clivia miniata   .30   .20
2941 A694 $12 Cymbidium sinense   .80   .50
2942 A694 $19 Primula malacoides   1.10   .85
    Nos. 2940-2942 (3)   2.20 1.55

Kinmen Wind Lion Lords — A695

Various Wind Lion Lords.
1994, Mar. 18   Litho.   Perf. 12½
2943 A695 $5 green & multi   .35   .20
2944 A695 $9 yellow & multi   .60   .35
2945 A695 $12 org yel & multi   .75   .50
2946 A695 $17 blue & multi   1.00   .65
    Nos. 2943-2946 (4)   2.70 1.70

Children at Play — A696

#2947, Playing with paper boat. #2948, Fighting with water gun. #2949, Throwing paper airplane. #2950, Playing "train" with rope.

Wmk. 323
1994, Apr. 2   Litho.   Perf. 12½
2947 A696 $5 multicolored   .30   .20
2948 A696 $5 multicolored   .30   .20
2949 A696 $5 multicolored   .30   .20
2950 A696 $5 multicolored   .30   .20
  a.   Souv. sheet, #2947-2950   1.40   .90
    Nos. 2947-2950 (4)   1.20   .80

Perf. 13½ Vert.
2947a A696 $5   .30   .20
2948a A696 $5   .30   .20
2949a A696 $5   .30   .20
2950b A696 $5   .30   .20
  c.   Bklt. pane, 2 ea #2947a-2949a, 2950b + label   3.00
    Nos. 2947a-2950b (4)   1.20   .80

A697   A698

Life in the countryside: $5, Playing chess. $10, Playing musical instruments. $12, Telling stories. $19, Drinking tea.

Wmk. 323
1994, Apr. 25   Litho.   Perf. 12½
2951 A697 $5 multicolored   .25   .20
2952 A697 $10 multicolored   .60   .35
2953 A697 $12 multicolored   .75   .50
2954 A697 $19 multicolored   1.10   .75
    Nos. 2951-2954 (4)   2.70 1.80

1994, May 7
Mother, baby birds: $5, Malay bittern. $7, Little tern, horiz. $10, Common noddy, horiz. $12, Muller's barbet.
2955 A698 $5 multicolored   .25   .20
2956 A698 $7 multicolored   .40   .25
2957 A698 $10 multicolored   .65   .40
2958 A698 $12 multicolored   .75   .45
    Nos. 2955-2958 (4)   2.05 1.30

A699   A700

Protection of Intellectual Property Rights: $5, Palm-shaped book. $15, Human head, computer disk.

Wmk. 323
1994, May 28   Litho.   Perf. 12½
2959 A699 $5 multicolored   .35   .25
2960 A699 $15 multicolored   1.00   .65

1994, June 11
Designs: $5, Care for Lost Children. $17, Care for the aged.
2961 A700 $5 multicolored   .30   .25
2962 A700 $17 multicolored   1.10   .75

Intl. Olympic Committee, Cent. — A701

1994, June 23
2963 A701 $5 shown   .35   .25
2964 A701 $15 Sporting events   1.00   .65

A702

A703

Shei-pa Natl. Park: $5, Tapachienshan. $7, Shei-san Landslide Scar. $10, Holy Ridge. $17, Shiah-tsuei Lake.

Wmk. 323
1994, July 1   Litho.   Perf. 12½
2965 A702 $5 multicolored   .35   .20
2966 A702 $7 multicolored   .45   .30
2967 A702 $10 multicolored   .70   .40
2968 A702 $17 multicolored   1.10   .75
    Nos. 2965-2968 (4)   2.60 1.65

1994, July 30   Perf. 11½x12
$5, Portrait of Chien Mu (b. 1895), educator.
2969 A703 $5 multicolored   .35   .20

Intl. Year of the Family A704

$5, Rainbow, window. $15, Globe, house.
1994, Aug. 25   Perf. 11½
2970 A704 $5 multicolored   .35   .25
2971 A704 $15 yel & multi   1.00   .65

Invention Myths — A705

Designs: $5, Sueirenjy digging wood to obtain fire. $10, Fushijy drawing Pa-Kua. $12, Shennungjy making agricultural tools. $15, Tsang-jier creating written characters.

1994, Sept. 17   Photo.   Perf. 11½
Granite Paper
2972 A705 $5 multicolored   .30   .20
2973 A705 $10 multicolored   .65   .40
2974 A705 $12 multicolored   .80   .55
2975 A705 $15 multicolored   1.00   .65
    Nos. 2972-2975 (4)   2.75 1.80

A706

A707

Design: $5, Dr. Lin Yutang, linguist, writer, 100th birthday.

Wmk. 323
1994, Oct. 8   Litho.   Perf. 12½
2976 A706 $5 multicolored   .35   .20

1994, Oct. 17
$5, Cheng Ho's ship. $17, Chart, ship, Cheng Ho.
2977 A707 $5 multicolored   .35   .25
2978 A707 $17 multicolored   1.00   .70

World Trade Week.

Sun Yat-sen, Founding of Kuomintang, Cent. — A708

Design: $19, Democratic elections, factories, economic development.

Wmk. 323
1994, Nov. 24   Litho.   Perf. 12½
2979 A708 $5 multicolored   .30   .20
2980 A708 $19 multicolored   1.10   .75

A709   A710

1994, Nov. 29
2981 A709 $3.50 Facing right   .25   .20
  a.   Perf. 13½ vert.   .25   .20
  b.   As "a," booklet pane of 6   1.60
    Complete booklet, 2 #2981b + label   3.25
2982 A709 $13 Facing left   .90   .60
  a.   Souv. sheet, 2 ea #2981-2982   2.25 1.50

New Year 1995 (Year of the Boar).

1994, Dec. 24   Litho.   Perf. 12½
2983 A710 $5 Portrait   .35   .25
2984 A710 $15 Greeting farm family   1.00   .65

Pres. Yen Chia-kan, 1st death anniv.

Traditional Architecture A711

Roof lines: #2985, Horse's back (shown). #2986, Swallow's tail. $12, Talisman (stove & bowl). $19, Cylinder-shaped brick.

Perf. 12½x12

1995, Jan. 10   Litho.   Wmk. 323

2985	A711	$5 multicolored	.30	.20
2986	A711	$5 multicolored	.30	.20
2987	A711	$12 multicolored	.80	.50
2988	A711	$19 multicolored	1.25	.85
	Nos. 2985-2988 (4)		2.65	1.75

See Nos. 3079-3082, 3113-3116, 3187-3190, 3235-3238.

Ancient Chinese Engravings — A712

Various floral designs.

1995, Jan. 24   Perf. 13½
Denomination in Black

2989	A712	$3.50 multicolored	.20	.20
2990	A712	$5 multicolored	.30	.20
2991	A712	$19 multicolored	1.25	.85
2992	A712	$26 multicolored	1.75	1.25
	Nos. 2989-2992 (4)		3.50	2.50

See Nos. 3018-3021, 3044-3047, 3076-3078, 3178-3181, 3221-3226, 3254-3256, 3299-3300.

Ancient Skills Type of 1994

Methods of irrigation: No. 2993, Water wheel. No. 2994, Gear-driven bucket lift. $5, Pedal-powered hoist. $12, Hand-cranked hoist. $13, Using pole with counter-weight to raise bucket.

Perf. 12x11½

1994, Feb. 14   Litho.   Wmk. 323

2993	A693	$3.50 multicolored	.20	.20
2994	A693	$3.50 multicolored	.20	.20
2995	A693	$5 multicolored	.30	.20
2996	A693	$12 multicolored	.80	.55
2997	A693	$13 multicolored	.90	.60
	Nos. 2993-2997 (5)		2.40	1.75

Beauties on an Outing, by Lee Gong-lin — A713

a, Two riders. b, Rider on black horse, woman with child on horse. c, Three riders. d, One rider.

Unwmk.
1995, Mar. 3   Photo.   Perf. 12
Granite Paper

2998	A713	$9 Strip of 4, #a.-d.	3.00	2.00
e.	Souv. sheet, #2998b-2998c		1.50	1.00

No. 2998 is a continuous design.

Natl. Health Insurance Plan — A714

Flowers — A715

Perf. 11½x12½

1995, Mar. 1   Litho.   Wmk. 323

2999	A714	$12 multicolored	.80	.50

1995, Mar. 20   Litho.   Perf. 12½

3000	A715	$5 Lilium speciosum	.25	.20
3001	A715	$12 Haemanthus mul-tiflorus	.60	.50
3002	A715	$19 Hyacinthus orientalis	1.25	.85
	Nos. 3000-3002 (3)		2.10	1.55

Chinese Calligraphy A716

Cold Food Observance, poem by Su Shih, red inscriptions at: a, Lower left. b, Middle. c, Upper right. d, Right half of design.

1995, Apr. 6   Perf. 13½

3003		Strip of 4	3.00	2.00
a.-d.	A716 $5 any single		.40	.30

Paintings by Tsou I Kuei's — A717

1995, May 5   Photo.   Die Cut
Self-Adhesive

3004	A717	$5 Red peony	.45	.25
3005	A717	$5 Pink peony	.45	.25
a.	Bklt. pane, 9 ea #3004-3005		8.00	

By its nature, No. 3005a is a complete booklet. The peelable backing serves as a booklet cover.

Campaign Against Illegal Drugs — A718

Wmk. 323
1995, June 1   Litho.   Perf. 12½

3006	A718	$5 shown	.30	.20
3007	A718	$15 Arm, hypodermic needle	.90	.60

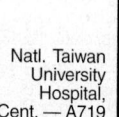

Natl. Taiwan University Hospital, Cent. — A719

Designs: $5, Medical treatment, old hospital. $19, Medical research, new hospital.

1995, June 20

3008	A719	$5 multicolored	.30	.25
3009	A719	$19 multicolored	1.25	.85

East Coast Scenes — A720

Designs: No. 3010, Green hills above Chichi Bay. No. 3011, Rocky promontory, Shihyuesan. $12, Hsiaoyehliu. $15, Changhong Bridge.

Wmk. 323
1995, July 1   Litho.   Perf. 12½

3010	A720	$5 multicolored	.30	.20
3011	A720	$5 multicolored	.30	.20
3012	A720	$12 multicolored	.90	.50
3013	A720	$15 multicolored	1.10	.65
	Nos. 3010-3013 (4)		2.60	1.55

Oncorhynchus Masou Formosanus A721

Designs: $5, Mating. $7, Female digging a spot to lay eggs. $10, Hatching of fry. $17, Fry swimming in river.

Perf. 14x14½

1995, July 27   Litho.   Unwmk.

3014	A721	$5 multicolored	.30	.20
3015	A721	$7 multicolored	.45	.30
3016	A721	$10 multicolored	.60	.45
3017	A721	$17 multicolored	1.10	.75
	Nos. 3014-3017 (4)		2.45	1.70

Ancient Chinese Engraving Type

Various pictures of birds on tree branches.

Wmk. 323
1995, Aug. 18   Litho.   Perf. 13½
Denomination in Black

3018	A712	$2.50 multicolored	.20	.20
3019	A712	$7 multicolored	.45	.25
3020	A712	$13 multicolored	.80	.55
3021	A712	$28 multicolored	1.90	1.10
	Nos. 3018-3021 (4)		3.35	2.10

Marine Life — A722

Louis Pasteur (1822-95) — A723

#3022, Tubastraea aurea. #3023, Chromodoris elizabethina. $5, Spirobranchus gigateus. $17, Himerometra magnipinna.

Wmk. 323
1995, Sept. 7   Litho.   Perf. 12½

3022	A722	$3.50 multicolored	.20	.20
3023	A722	$3.50 multicolored	.20	.20
3024	A722	$5 multicolored	.35	.20
3025	A722	$17 multicolored	1.00	.65
	Nos. 3022-3025 (4)		1.75	1.25

1995, Sept. 20

3026	A723	$17 multicolored	1.40	.65

Natl. Palace Museum, 70th Anniv. A724

Designs: No. 3027, Painting, "Strange Peaks and Myriad Trees." No. 3028, Greenish blue porcelain vase, vert. $5, Bronze X Fu-K'uei Ting vessel, vert. $26, Calligraphy of quatrain in seven-character verse, "The Fragrance of Flowers."

Perf. 12x11½, 11½x12

1995, Oct. 9   Photo.   Unwmk.

3027	A724	$3.50 multicolored	.20	.20
3028	A724	$3.50 multicolored	.20	.20
3029	A724	$5 multicolored	.30	.20
3030	A724	$26 multicolored	1.75	1.00
	Nos. 3027-3030 (4)		2.45	1.60

A725   A726

End of World War II, 50th Anniv.: $5, Chinese soldiers in battle. $19, Flag, outline map of Taiwan, presidential mansion.

Perf. 11½x12

1995, Oct. 24   Litho.   Wmk. 323

3031	A725	$5 multicolored	.30	.20
3032	A725	$19 multicolored	1.25	.65
a.	Souvenir sheet, #3031-3032		1.75	.90

Wmk. 323
1995, Nov. 10   Litho.   Perf. 12½

Sea Turtles: No. 3033, Chelonia mydas. No. 3034, Caretta caretta. No. 3035, Lepidochelys olivacea. No. 3036, Eretmochelys imbricata.

3033	A726	$5 multicolored	.35	.20
3034	A726	$5 multicolored	.35	.20
3035	A726	$5 multicolored	.35	.20
3036	A726	$5 multicolored	.35	.20
	Nos. 3033-3036 (4)		1.40	.80

Taiwan Agricultural Research Institute, Cent. — A727

Perf. 12x11½

1995, Nov. 22   Litho.   Wmk. 323

3037	A727	$5 In rice field	.35	.20
3038	A727	$28 In anthurium field	1.75	.90

New Year 1996 (Year of the Rat) — A728

Designs: $3.50, $13, Different stylized rats.

Wmk. 323
1995, Dec. 1   Litho.   Perf. 12½

3039	A728	$3.50 pink & multi	.20	.20
a.	Perf. 13½ vert.		.20	.20
b.	As "a," booklet pane of 6		1.40	
	Complete booklet, 2 #3039b + gutter		2.75	
3040	A728	$13 olive & multi	.90	.45
a.	Souv. sheet, 2 ea #3039-3040		2.25	1.10

Traditional Wedding Ceremony A729

Designs: $5, Escorting bride. $12, Kowtowing Heaven, Earth, and ancestors. $19, Seated in bridal chamber.

1996, Jan. 10

3041	A729	$5 multicolored	.35	.20
3042	A729	$12 multicolored	.95	.50
3043	A729	$19 multicolored	1.40	.75
	Nos. 3041-3043 (3)		2.70	1.45

Ancient Chinese Engraving Type of 1995

Various pictures of fruit.

Wmk. 323
1996, Jan. 25   Litho.   Perf. 13½
Denomination in Black

3044	A712	$9 multicolored	.65	.30
3045	A712	$12 multicolored	.90	.45
3046	A712	$15 multicolored	1.10	.55
3047	A712	$17 multicolored	1.25	.90
	Nos. 3044-3047 (4)		3.90	1.90

Scenic Dwelling at Chü-Ch'ü, by Wang Meng, Yüan Dynasty — A730

Denominations: a, UL. b, UR. c, LL. d, LR. Illustration reduced.

Perf. 12½x12

1996, Feb. 15   Litho.   Unwmk.
3048   A730   Block of 4, #a.-d.   3.50   2.50
a.-d. $5 any single   .50   .25

A731   A732

Flowers: $5, Bougainvillea spectabilis. $12, Wisteria sinensis. $19, Merremia tuberosa.

1996, Mar. 8   Unwmk.   Perf. 12½
3049   A731 $5 multicolored   .40   .20
3050   A731 $12 multicolored   .85   .45

Wmk. 323
3051   A731 $19 multicolored   1.25   .75
    Nos. 3049-3051 (3)   2.50   1.40

Wmk. 323

1996, Mar. 20   Litho.   Perf. 13½
Chinese Postal Service, Cent.: $5, Mailboxes. $9, Instruments of measurement. $12, Methods of mail transport. $13, Computers, plastic card.

3052   A732 $5 multicolored   .30   .20
3053   A732 $9 multicolored   .60   .30
3054   A732 $12 multicolored   .75   .45
3055   A732 $13 multicolored   .85   .50
a.   Souvenir sheet, #3052-3055   2.50   1.40
    Nos. 3052-3055 (4)   2.50   1.45

Natl. Chiao Tung University, Cent. — A733

Wmk. 323

1996, Apr. 8   Litho.   Perf. 12½
3056   A733 $19 multicolored   1.25   .70

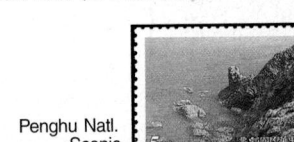

Penghu Natl. Scenic Areas — A734

#3057, Chimei Giant Lion. #3058, Chipei Beach. $12, Tungpan Yu. $17, Tingkou Yu.

1996, May 1
3057   A734 $5 multicolored   .35   .20
3058   A734 $5 multicolored   .35   .20
3059   A734 $12 multicolored   .80   .45
3060   A734 $17 multicolored   1.10   .65
    Nos. 3057-3060 (4)   2.60   1.50

Tzu-Chi Buddhist Compassionate Relief Foundation — A735

Wmk. 323

1996, May 11   Litho.   Perf. 13
3061   A735 $5 Hand holding people   .30   .20
3062   A735 $19 Lotus blossom, sick person   1.25   .70

First Democratic Presidential Election A736

New Pres., Vice Pres. and: $3.50, Natl. flag. $5, Presidential office building. $13, Development of Asia-Pacific Operations Hub project. $15, Greeting people at fair.

1996, May 20   Wmk. 323   Perf. 12½
3063   A736 $3.50 multicolored   .25   .20
3064   A736 $5 multicolored   .35   .20
3065   A736 $13 multicolored   .90   .50
3066   A736 $15 multicolored   1.00   .55
a.   Souvenir sheet, #3063-3066   2.50   1.40
    Nos. 3063-3066 (4)   2.50   1.45

South China Sea Archipelago A737

Outline map of region, Interior Dept. monuments on: $5, Pratas Isl. $17, Itu Aba Isl.

1996, June 5   Wmk. 323   Perf. 12½
3067   A737 $5 multicolored   .40   .20
3068   A737 $17 multicolored   1.25   .65
a.   Souvenir sheet #3067-3068   1.65   .85

Modern Olympic Games, Cent. — A738

Perf. 12½x12

1996, June 22   Litho.   Wmk. 323
3069   A738 $5 Gymnast, cyclist   .40   .20
3070   A738 $15 Early Greek athletes   1.10   .55

Ancient Skills Type of 1994

Manufacturing silk: #3071, Feeding silkworms. #3072, Picking out cocoons. $7, Reeling raw silk. $10, Degumming raw silk. $13, Weaving silk.

1996, July 5   Perf. 12
3071   A693 $5 multicolored   .35   .20
3072   A693 $5 multicolored   .35   .20
3073   A693 $7 multicolored   .45   .25
3074   A693 $10 multicolored   .70   .40
3075   A693 $13 multicolored   .90   .50
    Nos. 3071-3075 (5)   2.75   1.55

Ancient Chinese Engraving Type of 1995

1996, Aug. 5   Perf. 13½
Denomination in Black

3076   A712 $1 Bamboo   .20   .20
3077   A712 $10 Orchid   .75   .40
3078   A712 $20 Plum tree branch   1.50   .75
    Nos. 3076-3078 (3)   2.45   1.35

Traditional Architecture Type of 1995

Parts of column and beam construction.

Perf. 12x11½

1996, Aug. 22   Litho.   Wmk. 323
3079   A711 $5 Tou-kung (lion)   .40   .20
3080   A711 $5 Chiue-ti   .40   .20
3081   A711 $10 Bu-tong   .75   .40
3082   A711 $19 Dye-tou   1.40   .70
    Nos. 3079-3082 (4)   2.95   1.50

Motion Pictures, Cent. — A739

Chinese movies: No. 3083, Princess Iron Fan, first full-length animated film, 1941. No. 3084, Chin Shan Bi Xie, 1957. $5, Oyster Girl, 1964. $19, City of Sadness, 1989.

1996, Sept. 17   Litho.   Perf. 12½x12
3083   A739 $3.50 multicolored   .25   .20
3084   A739 $3.50 multicolored   .25   .20
3085   A739 $5 multicolored   .40   .20
3086   A739 $19 multicolored   1.40   .70
    Nos. 3083-3086 (4)   2.30   1.30

Winning Pictures from Children's Stamp Design Contest A740

Denomination triangle color, location: a, Red, LR. b, Red, LL. c, Green, LR. d, Green, LL. e, Pink, LL. f, Red, UR. g, Red, UL. h, Green, UR. i, Green, UL. j, Pink, UL. k, Purple, LR. l, Purple, LL. m, Tan, LR. n, Tan, LL. o, Pink, LR. p, Purple, UR. q, Purple, UL. r, Tan, UR. s, Tan, UL. t, Pink, UR.

Perf. 12½x12

1996, Oct. 9   Litho.   Unwmk.
3087   A740 $5 Sheet of 20, #a.-t.   8.00   4.00

A741   A742

Ancient Chinese paintings: $5, Autumn Scene with Wild Geese. $7, Reeds and Wild Geese. $13, Wild Geese Gathering on a Shore of Reeds. $15, Wild Geese on a Bank in Autumn.

1996, Oct. 21   Photo.   Perf. 12
Granite Paper

3088   A741 $5 multicolored   .40   .20
3089   A741 $7 multicolored   .50   .25
3090   A741 $13 multicolored   1.00   .50
3091   A741 $15 multicolored   1.10   .55
a.   Souv. sheet, #3088-3091   3.50   2.00
    Nos. 3088-3091 (4)   3.00   1.50

10th Asian Intl. Philatelic Exhib., Taipei '96.

Perf. 12½x12

1996, Nov. 1   Litho.   Wmk. 323
Designs: $5, Computerized letters, numbers, bar coding. $26, Globe, graph line.

3092   A742 $5 multicolored   .40   .20
3093   A742 $26 multicolored   2.00   1.00

Merchant's Day, 50th Anniv.

A743   A744

Caring for the Handicapped: $5, Woman in wheelchair working at computer. $19, Handicapped child painting picture.

Wmk. 323

1996, Nov. 15   Litho.   Perf. 12½
3094   A743 $5 multicolored   .40   .20
3095   A743 $19 multicolored   1.40   .75

1996, Dec. 2
3096   A744 $3.50 gray & multi   .30   .20
a.   Perf. 13½ vert.   .30   .20
b.   As "a," booklet pane of 6   1.80
    Complete booklet, 2 #3096b + gutter   3.60
3097   A744 $13 blue & multi   1.10   .55
a.   Souv. sheet, 2 ea #3096-3097   3.00   1.50
b.   As "a," overprinted   3.00   1.50

New Year 1997 (Year of the Ox). No. 3097b overprinted in red lilac in sheet margin with Chinese inscription for Kaohsiung Intl. Stamp Exhibition for Chinese Postal Service cent.

Ancient Skills Type of 1994

Making porcelain: No. 3098, Pounding stone, looking at bottom of bowl. No. 3099, Painting, shaping. $7, Painting. $10, Glazing. $13, Firing.

Perf. 11½x12

1997, Jan. 15   Litho.   Wmk. 323
3098   A693 $5 multicolored   .40   .20
3099   A693 $5 multicolored   .40   .20
3100   A693 $7 multicolored   .50   .25
3101   A693 $10 multicolored   .75   .40
3102   A693 $13 multicolored   1.00   .50
    Nos. 3098-3102 (5)   3.05   1.55

A745   A746

Carp encircled by dragons.

Perf. 13x12½

1997, Feb. 14   Engr.   Wmk. 323
3103   A745 $50 carmine   3.75   1.90
3104   A745 $60 dark blue   4.50   2.25
3105   A745 $70 red orange   5.25   2.75
3106   A745 $100 olive green   7.50   3.75
    Nos. 3103-3106 (4)   21.00   10.65

See Nos. 3131-3132, 3252-3253.

Perf. 12x11½

1997, Feb. 28   Litho.   Wmk. 323
3107   A746 $19 Memorial   1.40   .70

Feb. 28, 1947 Rebellion, 50th anniv.

Woody Plants — A747

$5, Rhododendron x mucronatum. $12, Hibiscus rosa-sinensis. $19, Hydrangea macrophylla.

Wmk. 323

1997, Mar. 12   Litho.   Perf. 12½
3108   A747 $5 multicolored   .40   .20
3109   A747 $12 multicolored   .85   .45
3110   A747 $19 multicolored   1.25   .70
    Nos. 3108-3110 (3)   2.50   1.35

Water Resource Protection A748   A749

1997, Mar. 22   Perf. 12½
3111   A748 $5 multicolored   .35   .20
3112   A749 $19 multicolored   1.25   .70

Architecture Type of 1995
Perf. 12x12½
1997, Apr. 9   Litho.   Wmk. 323

3113	A711	$5 Door, vert.	.40	.20
3114	A711	$5 Gable wall, vert.	.40	.20
3115	A711	$10 Carved brick, vert.	.80	.40
3116	A711	$19 Column dragon, vert.	1.40	.70
		Nos. 3113-3116 (4)	3.00	1.50

Insects — A750

Designs: $5, Dorcus formosanus. $7, Phyllophorina kotoshoensis. $10, Troides magellanus. $17, Megacrania tsudai.

1997, Apr. 25   Photo.   Perf. 11½
Granite Paper

3117	A750	$5 multicolored	.40	.25
3118	A750	$7 multicolored	.55	.35
3119	A750	$10 multicolored	.80	.45
3120	A750	$17 multicolored	1.40	.75
		Nos. 3117-3120 (4)	3.15	1.80

Minerals A751

Wmk. 323
1997, May 8   Litho.   Perf. 13

3121	A751	$5 Aragonite	.30	.20
3122	A751	$5 Alunite	.30	.20
3123	A751	$12 Enargite	.80	.40
3124	A751	$19 Hokutolite	1.10	.65
		Nos. 3121-3124 (4)	2.50	1.45

Nanyashan Outlook A752

1997, May 31   Perf. 12½

3125	A752	$5 shown	.40	.20
3126	A752	$5 Pitou coastline	.40	.20
3127	A752	$12 Stone pillars, Nanya	.90	.45
3128	A752	$19 Tsaoling trail	.90	.45
		Nos. 3125-3128 (4)	2.60	1.30

A753

Around-The-Island Railway System: $5, Cliffs at Chingshuei, Northern Loop Line. $28, Southbound train passing through tunnel, Central Mountain area.

Wmk. 323
1997, June 12   Litho.   Perf. 13½

3129	A753	$5 multicolored	.35	.20
3130	A753	$28 multicolored	1.25	.65

Carp Type
1997, July 3   Engr.   Perf. 13

3131	A745	$300 vio & dark blue	21.00	11.00
3132	A745	$500 dk red & mag	35.00	18.00

Electronic Industry's Use of Integrated Circuits A754

$5, Integrated circuit for computer & telecommunications industry. $26, Wafer linked to portable computer, cellular phone, electronic synthesizer.

1997, July 16   Litho.   Perf. 12½x12

3133	A754	$5 multicolored	.35	.20
3134	A754	$26 multicolored	1.90	.95

Chinese Martial Arts — A755

Various stances in martial arts.

Wmk. 323
1997, Aug. 8   Litho.   Perf. 13

3135	A755	$5 shown	.35	.20
3136	A755	$5 multi, vert.	.35	.20
3137	A755	$9 multicolored	.65	.30
3138	A755	$19 multi, vert.	1.25	.65
		Nos. 3135-3138 (4)	2.60	1.35

Chinese Classical (Yuan) Opera — A756

Designs: No. 3139, Chang Shen playing musical instrument, Tsuei Ying-ying listening outside, from "Hsi Hsiang Chi." No. 3140, Kuan Gung standing on ferry and holding large knife, enemies in distance, from "Dan Daw Huei." $12, Abduction of Wang Chao-juin on horseback, from "Han Guong Chiou." $15, Emperor Tang Ming Huang envisioning concubine, Makueibo, from "Wu Tong Yu."

1997, Aug. 22

3139	A756	$5 multicolored	.35	.20
3140	A756	$5 multicolored	.35	.20
3141	A756	$12 multicolored	.85	.40
3142	A756	$15 multicolored	1.00	.50
		Nos. 3139-3142 (4)	2.55	1.30

Sports — A757

1997, Sept. 9   Perf. 12½

3143	A757	$5 Badminton	.35	.20
3144	A757	$12 Bowling	.85	.40
3145	A757	$19 Tennis	1.25	.65
		Nos. 3143-3145 (3)	2.45	1.25

Ming Dynasty Novel "Journey to the West" — A758

Episodes from novel: No. 3146, "Palm of Buddha," man making inscription while holding pole. No. 3147, "The pilgrimage of T'ang Monk," characters traveling west, one on horse. $5, "The Flaming Mountain," people fighting, fire in background. $20, "The Cobweb Cave," man using pole to fight, spider in cobweb.

1997, Sept. 24   Photo.   Perf. 11½x12
Granite Paper

3146	A758	$3.50 multicolored	.25	.20
3147	A758	$3.50 multicolored	.25	.20
3148	A758	$5 multicolored	.35	.20
3149	A758	$20 multicolored	1.40	.70
		Nos. 3146-3149 (4)	2.25	1.30

Opening of Second Northern Freeway A759

Designs: $5, Bitan Bridge crossing, Shindian River. $19, Hsinchu interchange.

Wmk. 323
1997, Aug. 26   Litho.   Perf. 13

3150	A759	$5 multicolored	.35	.20
3151	A759	$19 multicolored	1.25	.65

Illustrations from Ching Dynasty Bird Manual A760

Various birds.

1997, Oct. 9   Photo.   Perf. 11½
Granite Paper

3152	A760	$5 Sheet of 20, #a.-t.	8.00	7.50

Compare with Nos. 3268-3269.

New Year 1998 (Year of the Tiger) — A761

Wmk. 323
1997, Dec. 1   Litho.   Perf. 12½

3153	A761	$3.50 pink & multi	.20	.20
a.		Perf. 14 vert.	.20	.20
b.		As "a," booklet pane of 6	1.50	
		Complete booklet, 2 #3153b + gutter	3.00	
3154	A761	$13 yellow & multi	.80	.45
a.		Souv. sheet, 2 ea #3153-3154	2.00	1.10

Pres. Chiang Ching-kuo (1910-88) A762

1998, Jan. 13   Engr.   Perf. 13½

3155	A762	$5 Portrait, vert.	.25	.20

Perf. 11½

3156	A762	$19 shown	1.00	.60

A763   A764

Common Chinese Expressions of Good Fortune, designs: No. 3157, "Happy Occasion of Abundance," fish, vase with pictures of sun and sea. No. 3158, "Harmonious Union as One," flower with two blooms. No. 3159, "Honor and Wealth," flowers growing in pot, vase of flowers. No. 3160, "All is Lucky," bowl of fruit, vase with branch of fruit blossoms.

Perf. 11½x12
1998, Jan. 23   Litho.   Wmk. 323
Background Color

3157	A763	$5 pink	.30	.20
3158	A763	$5 beige	.30	.20
a.		Pair, 3157-3158	.60	.30
3159	A763	$12 light yellow	.70	.35
3160	A763	$12 tan	.70	.35
a.		Pair, #3159-3160	1.40	.70
		Nos. 3157-3160 (4)	2.00	1.10

Wmk. 323
1998, Mar. 1   Litho.   Perf. 12½

Herbaceous Flowers: $5, Gaillardia pulchella. $12, Kalanchoe blossfeldiana. $19, Portulaca oleracea.

3161	A764	$5 multicolored	.30	.20
3162	A764	$12 multicolored	.70	.40
3163	A764	$19 multicolored	1.25	.60
		Nos. 3161-3163 (3)	2.25	1.20

Emperor Shih-tzu, on Hunting Expedition, by Liu Kuan-tao A765

$5, Horseman drawing bow. $19, Emperor Shih-tzu leading hunting party on horseback.

1998, Mar. 20   Photo.   Perf. 12
Granite Paper

3164	A765	$5 multicolored	.25	.20

Size: 64x40mm

3165	A765	$19 multicolored	1.25	.60
a.		Souvenir sheet, #3164-3165	2.00	1.25

No. 3165a is a continuous design.

Children's Folk Rhymes A766

#3166, "A Frog Has One Mouth." #3167, "A Little Mouse Climbs an Oil Lamp." $12, "Fireflies." $19, "Egrets."

Wmk. 323
1998, Apr. 4   Litho.   Perf. 11½

3166	A766	$5 multicolored	.30	.20
3167	A766	$5 multicolored	.30	.20
3168	A766	$12 multicolored	.70	.40
3169	A766	$19 multicolored	1.25	.60
		Nos. 3166-3169 (4)	2.55	1.40

Copyright Law in Taiwan, 70th Anniv. A767

1998, Apr. 30

3170	A767	$19 multicolored	1.25	.60

A768

Taiwan's Aboriginal Culture A784

Celebrations wearing traditional costumes: a, Dancing in row, mountain in background, Atayal Ancestor Festival. b, People wearing hip bells, Saisiat Festival of the Dwarfs. c, Standing arm in arm in circle, Bunun eight-part contrapuntal vocals. d, Row of people standing inside building, Tsou Victory Festival. e, Group outside before large display board, Rukai Harvest Festival. f, Holding bamboo poles in air, Paiwan "Maleveq" Bamboo Festival. g, Men walking while holding millet leaves in air, Puyuma Harvest Ceremony. h, Women dancing in row, tree in background, Ami Harvest Ceremony. i, Holding boat in air, Yami Boat Ceremony.

1999, Apr. 22   *Perf. 13*
Block of 9

3243　A784　$5　#a.-i. + label　3.50　3.25

No. 3243 was issued in sheets of 2 blocks + 2 labels. The labels contain the upper and lower halves of Taiwan. The lower block of 9 is in reverse order.

Intl. Council of Nurses, Cent. A785

1999, May 12   **Litho.**   *Perf. 11½*
3244　A785　$5　shown　　.40　.20
3245　A785　$17　Nurse, world map　1.25　.50

Chinese Classical Opera — A786

Legends of the Ming Dynasty: No. 3246, Fan Li watching Hsi-shih wash yarn, "Wuan Sha Chi.". No. 3247, Tsai Pochieh, Niu looking at moon, Chao Waniang with pipa (stringed instrument) on her back, "The Story of a Pipa." $12, Hung Funu surprising Li Ching, "The Story of Hung Fu." $15, Juelan setting up incense table, "Paiyueh Pavilion."

1999, May 27   *Perf. 13*
3246　A786　$5　multicolored　　.35　.20
3247　A786　$5　multicolored　　.40　.20
3248　A786　$12　multicolored　　.90　.35
3249　A786　$15　multicolored　　1.10　.45
  a.　Souvenir sheet, #3246-3249　2.50　1.75
  b.　As "a," imperf., with added inscription　　2.50　1.75
      Nos. 3246-3249 (4)　2.75　1.20

No. 3249b was issued 7/23 and is inscribed in sheet margin with exhibition emblem, two lines of Chinese text and "TAIPEI INTERNATIONAL STAMP EXHIBITION 1999 (INVITATIONAL)."

New Taiwan Dollar, 50th Anniv. A787

1999, June 15   *Perf. 11½*
3250　A787　$5　Coins　　.40　.20
3251　A787　$25　Currency　1.75　.75

Carp Encircled by Dragons Type of 1997 Redrawn With Denominations at Right

1999, July 1   **Engr.**   *Perf. 13½x12½*
3252　A745　$50　green　　3.75　1.60
3253　A745　$100　brown　6.75　3.25

Ancient Chinese Engravings Type of 1995
Redrawn With Chinese Inscription Reading Left to Right

1999, July 15   **Litho.**   **Unwmk.**
Denomination in Red

3254　A712　50c　like #3044　　.20　.20
3255　A712　$6　like #3045　　.50　.20
3256　A712　$25　like #3046　1.75　.75
      Nos. 3254-3256 (3)　2.45　1.15

Father's Day A788

Designs: $5, Children with large present, silhouette of their father. $25, Father teaching son how to ride bicycle, girl.

1999, Aug. 8   *Perf. 11½*
3257　A788　$5　multicolored　　.40　.20
3258　A788　$25　multicolored　1.75　.75

Chinese Gourmet Food A789

Dish, region: a, Peony lobster, Taiwan. b, "Buddha Jumps the Wall" steamed seafood (with blue & white teapot, bowl), Fukien. c, Hors d'oeuvres shaped as star, Canton. d, "Dongpo Pork" (on yellow plate, bowl), Kiangsu and Chekiang. e, "Stewed Fish Jaws" (surrounded by strawberries, pineapple), Shanghai. f, "Beggar's Chicken" (with napkin), Hunan. g, "Carp Jumping over Dragon's Gate," Szechwan. h, "Peking Duck" (in footed dish), Beijing.

Perf. 11½x11¼
1999, Aug 20   **Litho.**   **Unwmk.**
3259　A789　$5　Block of 8, #a.-h.　2.75　1.25

Outdoor Activities — A790

1999, Sept. 9   *Perf. 11¼x11½*
3260　A790　$5　Diving　　.40　.20
3261　A790　$6　Rafting　　.50　.20
3262　A790　$10　Surfing　　.75　.30
3263　A790　$25　Windsurfing　1.75　.80
      Nos. 3260-3263 (4)　3.40　1.50

Taiwanese Opera A791

1999, Oct. 15   **Litho.**   *Perf. 11½x11¼*
3264　A791　$5　Stage, audience　　.40　.20
3265　A791　$6　Dressing room　　.50　.20
3266　A791　$10　Actress, tents　　.75　.30
3267　A791　$25　Actress as clown　1.75　.80
      Nos. 3264-3267 (4)　3.40　1.50

Illustrations from Ching Dynasty Bird Manual A792

#3268, Yellow-headed parrot. #3269, Blue-winged parrotlet (4 characters at LL). $12, African gray parrot (5 characters at UL). $25, King parrot (5 characters at UL).

1999, Nov. 11   **Litho.**   *Perf. 11½*
3268　A792　$5　multicolored　　.40　.20
3269　A792　$5　multicolored　　.40　.20
3270　A792　$12　multicolored　1.00　.40
3271　A792　$25　multicolored　1.75　.80
      Nos. 3268-3271 (4)　3.55　1.60

Compare with No. 3152.

New Year 2000 (Year of the Dragon)
A793   A794

1999, Dec. 1   **Litho.**   *Perf. 12½*
3272　A793　$3.50　multicolored　　.30　.20
  a.　Perf. 13¼ vert.　　.30　.20
  b.　As "a," booklet pane of 6　1.60
    Complete booklet, 2 #3272b + gutter　3.50
3273　A794　$13　multicolored　1.00　.40
  a.　Souv. sheet, 2 ea #3272-3273　2.50　1.50

Millennium A795

#3274, ROCSAT-1. #3275, Deer. $12, Train. $15, Dove, St. Peter's Basilica.

1999, Dec. 31   **Litho.**   *Perf. 11½*
3274　A795　$5　multicolored　　.40　.20
3275　A795　$5　multicolored　　.40　.20
3276　A795　$12　multicolored　1.00　.40
3277　A795　$15　multicolored　1.25　.50
  a.　Souvenir sheet of 4, #3274-3277, perf. 12　　2.75　1.75
  b.　Souvenir sheet of 4, #3274-3277, imperf.　　2.75　1.75
      Nos. 3274-3277 (4)　3.05　1.30

Taipei 2000 Stamp Exhibition (No. 3277b). No. 3277b has simulated perforations.

Calligraphy Tools A796

Designs: No. 3278, "Colored Cloud Dragon" writing brushes of Ming Emperor Chia-Ching. No. 3279, "Imperial Dragon Fragrance" ink stick of Ming Emperor Lung-Ching, vert. $7, "Clear Heart House" calligraphic work by Tsai Hsiang, Sung Dynasty, vert. $26, Celadon toad inkstone, Sung Dynasty.

2000, Jan. 12   **Photo.**   *Perf. 11¾*
Granite Paper
3278　A796　$5　multicolored　　.40　.20
3279　A796　$5　multicolored　　.40　.20
3280　A796　$7　multicolored　　.65　.25
3281　A796　$26　multicolored　2.00　.85
      Nos. 3278-3281 (4)　3.45　1.50

Opening of Second Southern Freeway A797

Designs: $5, $25, Kaoping River bridge. $12, Interchange.

2000, Feb. 2   **Litho.**   *Perf. 13x13¼*
3282　A797　$5　multi　　.40　.20
3283　A797　$12　multi　1.20　.40

Souvenir Sheet
Perf. 12
3284　A797　$25　multi　　1.90　1.25
No. 3284 contains one 80x30mm stamp.

Seasons A798

Spring — No. 3285: a, Buds on tree. b, Farmer plowing. c, Cranes. d, Farmers planting. e, Basket of offerings to dead ancestors. f, Farmer's clothing.

Summer — No. 3286: a, Rice seedlings. b, Water wheel. c, Ripened rice. d, Cicada on tree. e, Palm leaf fan. f, Watermelons.

Autumn — No. 3287: a, Farmers in field. b, Granary. c, Dew on grass. d, Reddened maple leaves. e, Leafless tree. f, Hoarfrost on leaves.

Winter — No. 3288: a, Jar on table. b, Snow-covered pine trees. c, Snow-covered mountains. d, Bowl of rice balls. e, Snow-covered plum blossoms. f, House and village.

2000, Feb. 3   *Perf. 11¾*
3285　A798　$5　Strip of 6, #a-f　2.25　1.25
3286　A798　$5　Strip of 6, #a-f　2.25　1.25
3287　A798　$5　Strip of 6, #a-f　2.25　1.25
3288　A798　$5　Strip of 6, #a-f　2.10　1.00
      Nos. 3285-3288 (4)　8.85　4.75

Issued: #3285, 2/3; #3286, 5/5; #3287, 8/4; #3288, 11/3.

Soochow University, Cent. A799

Designs: $5 School gate. $25, Justice statue at Law School.

2000, Mar. 16   *Perf. 13x13¼*
3289　A799　$5　multi　　.40　.20
3290　A799　$25　multi　1.75　.80

Novel "The Romance of the Three Kingdoms" A800

#3291, Gathering of Liu Bei, Guan Yu and Chang Fei. #3292, Guan Yu reading. $5, Three visits to the thatched cottage. $20, Filling boats with straw for making arrows.

2000, Apr. 12   **Litho.**   *Perf. 11½*
3291　A800　$3.50　multi　　.30　.20
3292　A800　$3.50　multi　　.30　.20
3293　A800　$5　multi　　.40　.20
3294　A800　$20　multi　1.40　.70
  a.　Souv. sheet, #3291-3294, perf. 12　　2.50　1.50
      Nos. 3291-3294 (4)　2.40　1.30

Inauguration of New President and Vice-president — A801

a, Pres. Chen Shui-bian, Vice-pres. Lu Hsiu-lien. b, Presidential Office Building. Illustration reduced.

2000, May 20   **Litho.**   *Perf. 11¾*
3295　A801　$5　Pair, #a-b　　.75　.30
  c.　Souvenir sheet, 2 #3295　1.75　1.00

Tropic of Cancer Monuments A802

2000, June 21   **Perf. 13**

3296	A802	$5 Hsialiao	.40	.20
3297	A802	$12 Wuho	.90	.40
3298	A802	$25 Chingpu	1.75	.80
		Nos. 3296-3298 (3)	3.05	1.40

Ancient Chinese Engravings Type of 1995 Redrawn with Chinese Inscription Reading Left to Right

2000, July 5   **Litho.**   **Perf. 13½**

Denomination in Red

3299	A712	$32 like #3046	2.25	1.25
3300	A712	$34 like #3078	2.40	1.25

Sacred Trees — A803

Designs: $5, Taiwan Giant, Miaoli County. $39, Sleeping Moon, Chiayi County.

2000, July 20 Litho.   **Perf. 11¼x11½**

3301	A803	$5 multi	.40	.20
3302	A803	$39 multi	2.60	1.25

No. 2499 Surcharged in Red

2000, Aug. 24 Litho.   **Perf. 13½**

3303	A535a	$3.50 on $7.50 multi	.35	.20

Poisonous Plants — A804

Designs: No. 3304, $5, Lycoris radiata. No. 3305, $5, Cerbera manghas. $12, Abrus precatorius. $20, Nerium indicum.

2000, Sept. 8   **Litho.**   **Perf. 13**

3304-3307	A804	Set of 4	2.75	1.40

Sept. 21, 1999 Earthquake, 1st Anniv. — A805

Designs: $5, Map, seismograph reading. $12, Rescue workers. $25, Earthquake preparedness.

2000, Sept. 21   **Perf. 11¼x11½**

3308-3310	A805	Set of 3	3.00	1.40

Dragonflies A806

Designs: Nos. 3311, 3315a, $5, Lamelligomphus formosanus. Nos. 3312, 3315b, $5, Anotogaster sieboldii, vert. Nos. 3313, 3315c,

$12, Trithemis festiva, vert. Nos. 3314, 3315d, $12, Neurothemis ramburii.

2000, Oct. 11   **Perf. 13**

3311-3314	A806	Set of 4	2.75	1.40

Souvenir Sheet

Stamps Without White Margins

Perf. 11¾

3315	A806	Sheet of 4, #a-d	2.50	1.50

Bird Manual Type of 1999

#3316, $5, Corn bunting (2 characters at UR). #3317, $5, Brambling (3 characters at UL). $12, Bali mynah (3 characters at LR). $25, Indian grackle (2 characters at LR).

2000, Oct. 26   **Perf. 11½**

3316-3319	A792	Set of 4	3.25	1.60

Compare No. 3317 with No. 3378.

Tamkang University, 50th Anniv. A807

$5, Palace Lamp Boulevard, classroom buildings. $25, Maritime Museum, Scroll Plaza.

2000, Nov. 8   **Perf. 13**

3320-3321	A807	Set of 2	2.00	.95

A808   New Year 2001 (Year of the Snake) — A809

2000, Dec. 1   **Perf. 12½**

3322	A808	$3.50 multi	.25	.20
a.		Perf. 13¼ vert.	.25	.20
b.		As "a," booklet pane of 6	1.50	
		Booklet, 2 #3322b + gutter	3.00	
3323	A809	$13 multi	.90	.40
a.		Souv. sheet, 2 ea #3322-3323	2.50	1.50
b.		As "a," with added marginal inscription in red	2.50	1.50

Added marginal inscription of No. 3323b reads in Chinese "Turn-of-the-Century Intl. Stamp Exhibition, Kaohsiung / Dec. 25, 2000-Jan. 3, 2001" in red
Issued: No. 3323b, 12/25/00.

Establishment of Trade Links with People's Republic of China — A810

Ships in Taiwan Strait and: $9, Building. $25, Obelisk.

2001, Jan. 1   **Litho.**   **Perf. 11½**

3324-3325	A810	Set of 2	2.25	1.10

A811

Common Chinese expressions of good fortune: No. 3326, $5, "Marital bliss," twin lotus blossoms on one stalk (pink background). No. 3327, $5, "Success in one's career," longan, lichee and walnuts (light green background). No. 3328, $12, "Producing many offspring," split pomegranates (buff background). No.

3329, $12, "Growing old together with wealth and high position," bulbuls flying around peonies (light orange background).

2001, Jan. 2   **Perf. 11¾x12¼**

3326-3329	A811	Set of 4	2.25	1.10

Zodiac Signs A812

Designs: No. 3330, $5, Aquarius. No. 3331, $12, Gemini. No. 3332, $25, Libra. No. 3333, $5, Capricorn. No. 3334, $12, Taurus. No. 3335, $25, Virgo. No. 3336, $5, Aries. No. 3337, $12, Leo. No. 3338, $25, Sagittarius. No. 3339, $5, Pisces. No. 3340, $12, Cancer. No. 3341, $25, Scorpio.

2001   **Perf. 12**

3330-3341	A812	Set of 12	12.00	5.00

Values are for copies with surrounding selvage.
Issued: Nos. 3330-3332, 2/14. Nos. 3333-3335, 4/20. Nos. 3336-3338, 7/25. Nos. 3339-3341, 11/8.

Fruit — A813

2001-05   **Litho.**   **Perf. 12½x13¼**

3342	A813	$1 Plums	.20	.20
3343	A813	$3.50 Tangerines	.25	.20
a.		"Republic of China" 12½mm long ('05)	.25	.20
3344	A813	$5 Apples	.35	.20
3345	A813	$7 Pears	.50	.20
3346	A813	$12 Guavas	.80	.50
3347	A813	$20 Longans	1.25	.75
a.		"Republic of China" 12½mm long ('05)	1.25	.65
3348	A813	$25 Cantaloupes	1.50	.80
3349	A813	$40 Grapefruit	2.75	2.50
		Nos. 3342-3349 (8)	7.60	5.35

Issued: $5, $7, $12, $25, 2/23. $1, $3.50, $20, $40, 8/23. Nos. 3343a, 3347a, 5/16/05. "Republic of China" on Nos. 3343 and 3347 is 12mm long and is in taller letters.
See Nos. 3408-3411.

Mount Jade A814

Designs: No. 3350, $5, Main peak (shown). No. 3351, $5, Western peak, flowers in foreground. $12, Northern peak. $25, Eastern peak.

2001, Mar. 8 Litho.   **Perf. 11½x11¼**

3350-3353	A814	Set of 4	3.00	1.40

Compare Type A814 with Types A834-A837, A855-A858.

Children's Rhymes A815

Designs: No. 3354, $5, Little Ball (blue background). No. 3355, $5, Point to the Water Vat (pink background). $12, Pangolin. $25, Shake and Stamp.

2001, Apr. 4

3354-3357	A815	Set of 4	3.00	1.40

Buddhist Statues — A816

Designs: $5, Sakyamuni Buddha, Northern Wei Dynasty. $9, Seated Buddha, Tang Dynasty. $12, Mahavairocana Buddha, Sung Dynasty.

2001, May 11   **Perf. 11¼x11½**

3358-3360	A816	Set of 3	1.75	.75
3360a		Souvenir sheet #3358-3360, perf. 12	1.75	1.00

Agricultural Implements — A817

Designs: $5, Rice wind drum. $7, Plow. $10, Bamboo rice baskets. $25, Coir rainwear.

2001, May 25   **Perf. 11½x11¼**

3361-3364	A817	Set of 4	3.00	1.40

Dr. George Leslie Mackay (1844-1901) A818

2001, June 1   **Perf. 11¼x11½**

3365	A818	$25 multi	1.50	.70

2001 Kiwanis International Convention A819

Designs: $5, Girl, Earth. $25, Mother and child, map.

2001, June 22   **Perf. 13**

3366-3367	A819	Set of 2	2.00	.85

Kites — A820

No. 3368: a, Dragon. b, Phoenix. c, Tiger. d, Fish.

2001, July 13   **Perf. 11¼x11½**

3368		Horiz. strip of 4	1.50	1.00
a.-d.	A820	$5 Any single	.35	.20

Carp Encircled by Dragons Type of 1997 With Denominations at Right

2001, Aug. 3   **Engr.**   **Perf. 13**

Size: 25x33mm

3369	A745	$300 red vio & dk bl	20.00	10.00
3370	A745	$500 red & brown	32.50	17.50

Rapid Transit
A821

Designs: $5, Train, transit system emblem. $12, Passengers in station, fare card. $25, Chientan Station.

2001, Aug. 14	Litho.	Perf. 13		
3371-3372	A821	Set of 2	1.25	.50

Souvenir Sheet
Perf. 11¾

3373	A821	$25 multi	1.75	1.25

No. 3373 contains one 85x42mm stamp.

Fables — A822

Designs: No. 3374, $5, Now Three, Now Four (man and monkeys). No. 3375, $5, Selling the All-Penetrating Sword and Unyielding Shield (men watching man with sword and shield). $12, Waiting by the Tree for the Rabbit. $25, An Old Fool Moves Mountains.

2001, Sept. 6	Litho.	Perf. 11½		
3374-3377	A822	Set of 4	3.00	1.40

Bird Manual Type of 1999 and

Siberian
Rubythroat
A823

Designs: No. 3379, Waxwing (3 characters at UR). $12, White-rumped munia (2 characters at R). $25, Great barbet (3 characters at LL).

2001, Sept. 28	Litho.	Perf. 11½		
3378	A823	$5 shown	.35	.20
3379	A792	$5 multi	.35	.20
3380	A792	$12 multi	.75	.35
3381	A792	$25 multi	1.75	.75
Nos. 3378-3381 (4)			3.20	1.50

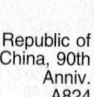

Republic of
China, 90th
Anniv.
A824

Designs: No. 3382, $5, Terminal, Chiang Kai-shek Intl. Airport. No. 3383, $5, Electronic products made in Republic of China. $12, Dancers at National Theater. $15, Dolphins.

2001, Oct. 9	Litho.	Perf. 11½		
3382-3385	A824	Set of 4	2.50	1.10

2001 National
Games — A825

Athletes and: $5, Torch. $25, Map.

2001, Oct. 18	Litho.	Perf. 12½		
3386-3387	A825	Set of 2	2.00	.85

34th
Baseball
World Cup
A826

Emblem, map and: No. 3388, $5, Pitcher. No. 3389, $5, Batter. $12, Catcher. $20, Runner sliding.

2001, Oct. 30		Perf. 11½		
3388-3391	A826	Set of 4	2.75	1.25
3391a		Souvenir sheet, #3388-3391, perf. 12	2.75	1.75

Puppet
Theater
A827

Designs: $5, Mozhaonu, from "Thunder Storm." $6, Taiyangnu, from "Rising Winds, Surging Clouds." $10, Kuangdao, from "Thunder Crazy Sword." $25, Chin Chia-chien, from "Thunder Golden Light."

2001, Nov. 16	Litho.	Perf. 11½		
3392-3395	A827	Set of 4	3.00	1.40

National
Defense
Medical
Center,
Cent. — A828

Designs: $5, Medical students, old medical school building. $25, Doctors, new medical school building.

2001, Nov. 23		Perf. 13		
3396-3397	A828	Set of 2	2.00	.85

New Year 2002 (Year
of the
Horse) — A829

Horse and: $3.50, Clouds. $13, Flowers.

2001, Dec. 3	Litho.	Perf. 12½		
3398	A829	$3.50 multi	.30	.20
a.		Perf. 13¾ vert.	.30	.20
b.		Booklet pane, 12 #3398a	2.50	—
		Booklet, #3398b	2.75	
3399	A829	$13 multi	.90	.35
a.		Souvenir sheet, 2 each #3398-3399	2.25	1.25

Paul Cardinal Yu
Pin (1901-
78) — A830

2001, Dec. 7		Perf. 11½		
3400	A830	$25 multi	1.75	.70
a.		Souvenir sheet of 1, perf. 12	1.75	1.25

Greetings
A831

No. 3401: a, Pink chrysanthemums, red background. b, White lilies, red background. c,

Pink flowers, yellow background. d, Red orange flowers, yellow background. e, Pink flowers, green background. f, Coral roses, blue green background. g, Star and wreath, blue background. h, Poinsettias, blue background. i, Red violet flowers, purple background. j, Yellow flowers, purple background.

2001, Dec. 12		Perf. 12½		
3401		Sheet of 10 + 10 labels	3.50	2.25
a.-j.	A831	$5 Any single	.35	.20

Labels could be personalized for an additional fee.
Sheets with blank (unprinted) labels were not released.

Fu Hsing
Kang
College,
50th Anniv.
A832

Designs: $5, Students with flags. $25, Tower, administration building, statue of students.

2002, Jan. 4		Perf. 11½		
3402-3403	A832	Set of 2	2.00	.85

Expressions of Good Fortune Type of 2001

Designs: No. 3404, $5, "Continuously produce good offspring," lotus and sweet osmanthus flowers in a vase (gradiated pink background). No. 3405, $5, "A high, moral gentleman," orchid and sweet osmanthus in containers (gradiated green background). No. 3406, $12, "A hall full of the rich and famous," flowering crabapple in a vase (gradiated orange background). No. 3407, $12, "Safe and peaceful in all seasons," roses in vase (gradiated purple background).

2002, Jan. 16		Perf. 11¾x12¼		
3404-3407	A811	Set of 4	2.25	1.00

Fruit Type of 2001

2002-05		Litho.	Perf. 12½x13¼		
3408	A813	$6 Avocados		.40	.20
3409	A813	$10 Lichees		.75	.30
a.		"Republic of China" 12½mm long ('05)		.65	.30
3410	A813	$17 Dates		1.25	.50
a.		"Republic of China" 12½mm long ('05)		1.10	.55
3411	A813	$32 Passion fruit		2.25	.90
a.		"Republic of China" 12½mm long ('05)		2.10	1.10
Nos. 3408-3411 (4)				4.65	1.90

Issued: Nos. 3408-3411, 2/8/02; 3409a, 3410a, 3411a, 5/16/05.
"Republic of China" on Nos. 3409-3411 is 12mm long and is in taller letters.

Folk Traditions
A833

Designs: No. 3412, $5, Release of sky lanterns (orange background). No. 3413, $5, Fireworks display (blue background). $10, Matsu procession (lilac background). $20, Dragon boat race (pink background).

2002, Feb. 26		Perf. 12½		
3412-3415	A833	Set of 4	2.50	1.10

See Nos. 3440-3443.

Winter,
Mount
Hsueh
A834

North
Ridge,
Mount
Hsueh
A835

Autumn,
Mount
Hsueh
A836

Glacial
Cirques,
Mount
Hsueh
A837

2002, Mar. 20		Perf. 11½		
3416	A834	$5 multi	.40	.20
3417	A835	$5 multi	.40	.20
3418	A836	$12 multi	.90	.35
3419	A837	$25 multi	1.60	.70
Nos. 3416-3419 (4)			3.30	1.45

Compare with Types A814, A855-A858.

Novel "The
Romance of
the Three
Kingdoms"
A838

Designs: No. 3420, $3.50, Three heroes battling Lu Bu (warriors on horseback). No. 3421, $3.50, To the rescue of his master's family (one warrior on horseback). $5, Scraping away the poison from the bone (medicinal bleeding). $20, Playing a lute to make the enemy retreat (horseman and gate).

2002, Apr. 4		Set of 4	2.25	.95
3420-3423	A838			
a.		Souvenir sheet, #3420-3423, perf. 12	2.25	2.25

Endangered Bird Thalasseus
Bernsteini — A839

No. 3424: a, Two birds in flight. b, Bird in flight heading left. c, Bird landing on rock carrying fish. d, Bird on rock with beak open. e, Adult feeding chick. f, Bird diving. g, Bird landing with bill open. h, Bird standing on rock, looking left. i, Adult with chick. j, Adult on nest. $25, Bird in flight.

2002, May 15	Litho.	Perf. 11½		
3424	A839	$5 Sheet of 10, #a-j	3.50	2.50

Souvenir Sheet
Perf. 12

3425	A839	$25 multi	1.75	1.50

No. 3424 contains ten 40x30mm stamps.

**Dragon & Carp Type of 1997
Redrawn With Denomination at
Right**

2002, June 5	Engr.	Perf. 13¼x12½		
3426	A745	$80 brown	5.25	2.75

Porcelain
Bowls
A840

Ching Dynasty bowls depicting: No. 3427, $5, Peacock (salmon background). No. 3428, $5, Lotus flowers (blue green background). $7, Peonies. $32, Sparrows and bamboo.

2002, June 21   Litho.   Perf. 11½
3427-3430 A840 Set of 4   3.50 1.50

Flowers — A841

Designs: $5, Matthiola incana. $12, Gardenia jasminoides. $25, Michelia figo.

2002, July 5   Perf. 13
3431-3433 A841 Set of 3   2.75 1.25

Cetaceans
A842

Designs: No. 3434, $5, Megaptera novaeangliae, whaling ship. No. 3435, $5, Tursiops truncatus, people on shore attracting cetacean. $10, Orcinus orca, boat following cetaceans. $25, Grampus griseus, people rescuing beached dolphin.

2002, July 25 Litho.   Perf. 11½x11¼
3434-3437 A842 Set of 4   3.50 1.40
a. Souvenir sheet, #3434-3437, perf. 12   3.50 2.50

Intl. Paralympic Committee World
Table Tennis Championships — A843

Player: No. 3438, $5, On crutches. No. 3439, $5, In wheelchair.

2002, Aug. 13   Perf. 11½x11¼
3438-3439 A843 Set of 2   .75   .30

Folk Traditions Type of 2002
Designs: No. 3440, $5, Launching of water lanterns (green background). No. 3441, $5, Snatching flags for good luck (yellow background). $10, Worship of the just (blue background). $20, Burning the Prince's boat (red orange background).

2002, Aug. 22   Perf. 12¼
3440-3443 A833 Set of 4   2.75 1.25

Republic of China — Vatican City Diplomatic Relations, 60th Anniv. A844

Designs: $5, Chinese and Vatican flags, Chinese Presidential building, St. Peter's Basilica. $17, Flags, doves, Celso Cardinal Costantini.

2002, Sept. 20   Perf. 11½x11¼
3444-3445 A844 Set of 2   1.50   .65

Bird Manual Type of 1999 and

White-rumped Munia — A845

Designs: No. 3446, $5, Vernal hanging parrot (3 characters at LL). $12, White-headed greenfinch (4 characters at LL). $25, Yunnan greenfinch (2 characters at UL).

2002, Oct. 9
3446 A792 $5 multi   .40   .20
3447 A845 $5 multi   .40   .20
3448 A792 $12 multi   .80   .35
3449 A792 $25 multi   1.60   .70
   Nos. 3446-3449 (4)   3.20 1.45

Taiwanese Opera A846

Designs: $5, Liang Shan-po and Chu Ying-tai. $6, Hsueh Ting-shan and Fan Li-hua. $10, Hsueh Ping-kuei and Wang Pao-chuan. $25, The Living Buddha Chikung.

2002, Oct. 25
3450-3453 A846 Set of 4   3.25 1.40

Koalas — A847

Designs: No. 3454, $5, Adult with cub. No. 3455, $5, Adult on branch. $9, Adult with head on branch. $21, Adult with cub, diff.

2002, Nov. 15   Perf. 11¼x11½
3454-3457 A847 Set of 4   2.75 1.25
a. Souvenir sheet, #3454-3457, perf. 12   2.75 2.25

Knots A848

Nos. 3458-3459 — Various knots (Denomination location, denomination color and background color): a, UL, orange, light orange. b, UL, purple, yellow. c, UL, green, light green. d, UL, yellow, light blue. e, UL, blue, pink. f, UR, orange, light orange. g, UR, red violet, yellow. h, UR, blue, light green. i, UR, yellow, light blue. j, UR, red violet, pink.
No. 3460 (yellow denominations, olive green background): a, Like #3458a. b, Like #3458b. c, Like #3458c, d, #3458d. e, Like #3458e. f, Like #3458f. g, Like #3458g. h, Like #3458h. i, Like #3458i. j, Like #3458j.

2002, Nov. 22   Litho.   Perf. 12½
3458   Block of 10   2.25 1.20
a.-j. A848 $3.50 Any single   .20   .20
k.   Sheet of 10 #3458f + 10 attached labels   12.00 12.00
l.   Sheet of 10 #3458g + 10 attached labels   12.00 12.00
m.   Sheet of 10 #3458h + 10 attached labels   12.00 12.00
n.   Sheet of 10 #3458i + 10 attached labels   12.00 12.00
o.   Sheet of 10 #3458j + 10 attached labels   12.00 12.00
p.   Sheet, #3458a-3458j + 10 attached labels   12.00 12.00
q.   Sheet, #3458a, 3458b, 3458d, 3458f, 3458g, 3458i + 6 attached labels ('04)   8.50 8.50
3459   Block of 10   3.50 1.75
a.-j. A848 $5 Any single   .35   .20
k.   Sheet of 10 #3459a + 10 attached labels   12.50 12.50
l.   *Sheet of 10 #3459b + 10 attached labels   12.50 12.50
m.   Sheet of 10 #3459c + 10 attached labels   12.50 12.50
n.   Sheet of 10 #3459d + 10 attached labels   12.50 12.50
o.   Sheet of 10 #3459e + 10 attached labels   12.50 12.50
p.   Sheet of 10 #3459f + 10 attached labels   12.50 12.50
q.   Sheet of 10 #3459g + 10 attached labels   12.50 12.50
r.   Sheet of 10 #3459h + 10 attached labels   12.50 12.50
s.   Sheet of 10 #3459i + 10 attached labels   12.50 12.50
t.   Sheet of 10 #3459j + 10 attached labels   12.50 12.50

3460   Block of 10   17.50 8.50
a.-j. A848 $25 Any single   1.75   .80
k.   Sheet of 10 #3460a + 10 attached labels   24.00 24.00
l.   Sheet of 10 #3460b + 10 attached labels   24.00 24.00
m.   Sheet of 10 #3460c + 10 attached labels   24.00 24.00
n.   Sheet of 10 #3460d + 10 attached labels   24.00 24.00
o.   Sheet of 10 #3460e + 10 attached labels   24.00 24.00
p.   Sheet, #3460a-3460j + 10 attached labels   24.00 24.00
   Nos. 3458-3460 (3)   23.25 11.45

Nos. 3458k-3458p sold for $185 each; Nos. 3459k-3459u for $200 each; Nos. 3460k-3460p for $400 each. Labels, which were personalized, were separated from stamps on Nos. 3458k-3458p, 3459k-3459u, 3460k-3460p by vertical rows of simulated perforations.
No. 3458q sold for $141 and has labels, which could be personalized, that are separated from the stamps by simulated perforations. Issued 9/30/04.

New Year 2003 (Year of the Ram) — A849

Designs: $3.50, Yellow ram. $13, Red ram.

2002, Dec. 2   Litho.   Perf. 12¼
3461 A849 $3.50 multi   .25   .20
a.   Perf. 12¼ Vert.   .25   .20
b.   As "a," booklet pane of 6   1.40
     Booklet, 2 #3461b   3.25
3462 A849 $13 multi   .90   .40
a.   Souvenir sheet, 2 each #3461-3462   2.25 1.50
b.   As "a," with Chinese text in red in L & R sheet margins   2.25 1.50

Issued: No. 3462b, 1/1/03. Chinese text in left and right sheet margins on No. 3462b commemorates the establishment of Chunghwa Post Co., Ltd.

Street Scene on a Summer Day, by Chen Cheng-po A850

Girl in the White Dress, by Li Mei-shu — A851

Courtyard with Banana Trees, by Liao Chi-chun — A852

Sunrise, by Kuo Po-chuan A853

Perf. 11½x11¼, 11¼x11½
2002, Dec. 6
3463 A850 $5 multi   .40   .20
3464 A851 $5 multi   .40   .20
3465 A852 $10 multi   .75   .30
3466 A853 $20 multi   1.25   .55
   Nos. 3463-3466 (4)   2.80 1.25

Admission to World Trade Organization, 1st Anniv. — A854

2003, Jan. 1   Litho.   Perf. 11½x11¼
3467 A854 $17 multi   1.25   .50

Spring on Wuyen Peak A855

Glacial Cirques, Mt. Nanhu A856

Mt. Nanhu A857

Snow on Mt. Chungyang Chien A858

2003, Jan. 23
3468 A855 $5 multi   .40   .20
3469 A856 $5 multi   .40   .20
3470 A857 $12 multi   .90   .35
3471 A858 $25 multi   1.60   .70
   Nos. 3468-3471 (4)   3.30 1.45

Compare with Types A814, A834-A837.

Fruit Type of 2001
2003-05   Litho.   Perf. 12½x13¼
3472 A813 $9 Rose apples   .60   .25
a.   "Republic of China" 12½mm long ('05)   .60   .60
3473 A813 $13 Kumquats   .90   .40
3474 A813 $15 Lemons   1.10   .45
a.   "Republic of China" 12½mm long ('05)   .95   .50
3475 A813 $34 Coconuts   2.00 1.00

Issued: Nos. 3472-3475, 2/14/03; 3472a, 3474a, 5/16/05.
"Republic of China" on Nos. 3472 and 3474 is 12mm long and in taller letters.

Love — A859

Hearts and: No. 3476, $5, Woman tending to man in wheelchair. No. 3477, $5, Family. $10, Landscape. $25, Girl and dogs.

2003, Mar. 20   Perf. 11¼x11½
3476-3479 A859 Set of 4   3.00 1.25

Puppet Theater A860

Designs: No. 3480, $5, *Journey to the West* performed on outdoor stage. No. 3481, $5, *Puppets on television.* $10, *Mysteries of the Wolf Castle* performed at the National Opera House. $25, *Screening of movie, Legend of the Sacred Stone.*

2003, Apr. 3   **Perf. 11½x11¼**
3480-3483 A860   Set of 4   3.00 1.25

Merops Philippinus A861

Designs: Nos. 3484, 3488a, $5, Foraging. Nos. 3485, 3488b, $5, Roosting. Nos. 3486, 3488c, $10, Bathing. Nos. 3487, 3488d, $20, Feeding chick.

2003, May 8   **Perf. 12½**
With White Frame
3484-3487 A861   Set of 4   2.75 1.25
Souvenir Sheet
Without White Frame
3488 A861   Sheet of 4, #a-d   2.75 1.25

No. 3488 contains four 33x25mm stamps.

Furniture — A862

Designs: No. 3489, $5, Wash basin stand. No. 3490, $5, Canopy bed. $12, Taishi chair. $20, Pahsien table.

2003, May 22   **Perf. 11¼x11½**
3489-3492 A862   Set of 4   2.75 1.25

Folktale "Eight Immortals Cross the Sea" — A863

Immortal: No. 3493, $5, Riding catfish. No. 3494, $5, On donkey. $10, Holding fan. $25, In brown robe.

2003, June 12
3493-3496 A863   Set of 4   3.00 1.25

Moths A864

Designs: No. 3497, $5, Antitrygodes divisaria perturbata. No. 3498, $5, Vamuna virilis. $12, Sinna extrema. $20, Thyas juno.

2003, June 26   **Perf. 11½x11¼**
3497-3500 A864   Set of 4   2.75 1.25

Dragonflies A865

Designs: Nos. 3501, 3505a, $5, Acisoma panorpoides panorpoides. Nos. 3502, 3505b, $5, Sympetrum eroticu ardens, vert. Nos. 3503, 3505c, $10, Anax parthenope julius. Nos. 3504, 3505d, $17, Rhyothemis variegata arria, vert.

2003, July 25   **Perf. 12½**
With White Frames
3501-3504 A865   Set of 4   2.75 1.25
Souvenir Sheet
Without White Frames
3505 A865   Sheet of 4, #a-d   2.75 1.25

Stamp size: Nos. 3505a, 3505c, 33x25mm; Nos. 3505b, 3505d, 25x33mm.

Greetings A866

No. 3506: a, Cranes. b, Wood carving and red plate. c, Fish and coin. d, Bamboo. e, Wood carving of bird.
No. 3507: a, Vase with tasseled rope. b, Like #3506a. c, Like #3506b. d, Three brown containers. e, Like #3508. f, Dragon. g, Like #3506c. h, Like #3506d. i, Horse and rider. j, Like #3506e.
No. 3508, Vase with flowers.

2003, Aug. 9   **Perf. 12½**
3506   Horiz. strip of 5   1.25   .65
 a.-e. A866 $3.50 Any single   .20   .20
 f.   Sheet of 10 #3506a+ 10 at-
        tached labels   12.00 12.00
 g.   Sheet of 10 #3506b+ 10 at-
        tached labels   12.00 12.00
 h.   Sheet of 10 #3506c + 10 at-
        tached labels   12.00 12.00
 i.   Sheet of 10 #3506d + 10 at-
        tached labels   12.00 12.00
 j.   Sheet of 10 #3506e + 10 at-
        tached labels   12.00 12.00
 k.   Sheet , 2 each #3506a-3506e
        + 10 attached labels   12.00 12.00
3507   Block of 10   3.50 1.75
 a.-j. A866 $5 Any single   .35   .20
 k.   Sheet of 10 #3507a + 10 at-
        tached labels   12.50 12.50
 l.   Sheet of 10 #3507b + 10 at-
        tached labels   12.50 12.50
 m.   Sheet of 10 #3507c + 10 at-
        tached labels   12.50 12.50
 n.   Sheet of 10 #3507d + 10 at-
        tached labels   12.50 12.50
 o.   Sheet of 10 #3507e + 10 at-
        tached labels   12.50 12.50
 p.   Sheet of 10 #3507f + 10 at-
        tached labels   12.50 12.50
 q.   Sheet of 10 #3507g + 10 at-
        tached labels   12.50 12.50
 r.   Sheet of 10 #3507h + 10 at-
        tached labels   12.50 12.50
 s.   Sheet of 10 #3507i + 10 at-
        tached labels   12.50 12.50
 t.   Sheet of 10 #3507j + 10 at-
        tached labels   12.50 12.50
 u.   Sheet, #3507a-3507j + 10 at-
        tached labels   12.50 12.50
 v.   Sheet, #3507c, 3507f,
        3507g, 3507h, 3507j + 6 at-
        tached labels ('04)   9.00 9.00
3508   A866 $12 multi   .85   .45
 a.   Sheet of 10 #3508 + 10 at-
        tached labels   17.00 17.00
        Nos. 3506-3508 (3)   5.60 2.85

Nos. 3506f-3506k sold for $185 each; Nos. 3507k-3507u for $200 each; No. 3508a for $270 each. Labels, which were personalized, were separated from stamps on Nos. 3506f-3506k, 3507k-3507u, 3508a by vertical rows of simulated perforations.
No. 3507v sold for $150 and has labels, which could be personalized, that are separated from the stamps by simulated perforations. Issued 5/30/04.

Bird Manual Type of 1999 and

White-throated Laughing Thrush — A867

Designs: No. 3510, Great mynah (2 characters at LR). $12, Yellow-legged buttonquail (3 characters at UL). $25, Crested lark (4 characters at L).

Perf. 11½x11¼
2003, Sept. 10   **Litho.**
3509 A867 $5 multi   .40   .20
3510 A792 $5 multi   .40   .20
3511 A792 $12 multi   .90   .35
3512 A792 $25 multi   1.75   .75
      Nos. 3509-3512 (4)   3.45 1.50

Chungshan Park, Taichung A868

Tourist attractions: No. 3514, $5, Dongshan River Bridge, Ilan. $11, Badlands, Tianliao. $20, Sansiantai, Chenggong.

2003, Oct. 28   Litho.   Perf. 11½
3513-3516 A868   Set of 4   3.00 1.25
Chungshan Park, cent. (#3513).

Veterans Day, 25th Anniv. A869

Veterans Affairs Commission insignia and: $5, Veterans building Central Cross-Island Highway. $25, Veterans, homes and hospital for veterans.

2003, Oct. 31
3517-3518 A869   Set of 2   2.00   .90

The Back Yard, by Lu Tie-jhou — A870

A Gold Mine Tower: Jioufen, by Lin Ke-gong — A871

Leisurely, by Chen Jin — A872

East Gate, by Li Ze-fan A873

2003, Nov. 20
3519 A870 $5 multi   .40   .20
3520 A871 $5 multi   .40   .20
3521 A872 $10 multi   .75   .30
3522 A873 $20 multi   1.50   .60
      Nos. 3519-3522 (4)   3.05 1.30

New Year 2004 (Year of the Monkey) — A874

Monkey holding fruit: $3.50. With tail. $13, In hand.

2003, Dec. 1   **Perf. 12¼**
3523-3524 A874   Set of 2   1.25   .60
3523a   Perf. 12¼ vert.   .30   .20
3524a   Sheet, 2 each #3523-3524   1.50
3523b   Booklet pane, 12 #3523a   5.75
          Complete booklet, #3523b   6.50

Springs A875

Designs: No. 3525, $5, Yangmingshan Hot Springs, fumaroles (light orange background). No. 3526, $5, Suao Cold Springs, Nanfangao Bridge (light blue background). $10, Guanziling Murky Hot Spring, Shuei Huo Tong Yuan. $25, Green Island Seabed Hot Springs, Green Island Lighthouse.

2003, Dec. 14   **Perf. 13**
3525-3528 A875   Set of 4   3.25 1.40
3528a   Souvenir sheet, #3525-3528   3.25 1.90

Completion of Highway 3 — A876

Designs: $5, Jhonggang Interchange. $25, Cingshuei Service Area. $20, Cingshuei Service Area, diff.

2004, Jan. 8   Litho.   Perf. 12½
3529-3530 A876   Set of 2   2.25   .90
Souvenir Sheet
Perf. 11½x11¼
3531 A876 $20 multi   1.50 1.25
No. 3531 contains one 80x30mm stamp.

Flowers — A877

Designs: No. 3532, $5, Lilium formosanum. No. 3533, $5, Hippeastrum x hybridum. $12, Fressia x hybrida.

2004, Jan. 17   **Perf. 12¼**
3532-3534 A877   Set of 3   1.75   .70
3534a   Souvenir sheet, #3532-3534,
          perf. 13   1.75 1.25
3534b   As "a," with Taiwan Flower Ex-
          po emblem and text added
          in margin   1.75 1.25

Eight Immortals Cross the Sea Type of 2003

Immortal: No. 3535, $5, With crane and flute. No. 3536, $5, With lotus flower. $10, Holding stick, wearing red robe. $25, Carrying flower basket.

2004, Feb. 25   **Perf. 11¼x11½**
3535-3538 A863   Set of 4   3.25 1.40

Red Cross Society, Cent. — A878

No. 3539: a, Heart, stylized people with arms raised. b, Heart, stylized people doing Red Cross activities.
Illustration reduced.

2004, Mar. 9   **Perf. 11¼x11½**
3539 A878 $5 Horiz. pair, #a-b   .75   .30

A Young Girl From Lu Kai, by Yan Shui-long
A879

Old Street in Taipei, by Yang San-lang
A880

Happy Farmers, by Lee Shih-chiao
A881

Fish Shop, by Liu Chi-hsiang
A882

Perf. 11¼x11½, 11½x11¼
2004, Mar. 25
3540 A879 $5 multi   .40   .20
3541 A880 $5 multi   .40   .20
3542 A881 $10 multi   .80   .30
3543 A882 $20 multi   1.40   .60
      Nos. 3540-3543 (4)   3.00 1.30

Butterflies A883

Designs: No. 3544, $5, Parantica sita niphonica. No. 3545, $5, Choaspes benjaminii formosanus. $17, Junonia almana. $20, Artipe eryx horiella.

2004, Apr. 21   **Perf. 11½x11¼**
3544-3547 A883 Set of 4   3.50 1.50

Yijhen Folk Art Performers
A884

Designs: No. 3548, $5, Eight Generals (buff background). No. 3549, $5, Song Jiang Battle Array (grayish blue background). $11, Drum Dance. $25, Stilt walkers.

2004, May 11
3548-3551 A884 Set of 4   3.25 1.40

Inauguration of Pres. Chen Shiu-bian and Vice-President Hsiu-lien Annette Lu — A885

No. 3552 — President, Vice-President and: a, Map of Taiwan, flag, crowd. b, Map of People's Republic of China and Taiwan, handshake, flowers. c, Buildings, crowd. d, Train, highway, buildings.
$12, President, Vice-President, buildings, train, highway.

2004, May 20   **Perf. 12½**
3552   Horiz. strip of 4   1.50   .60
  a.-d. A885 $5 Any single   .35   .20
       Souvenir Sheet
         Perf. 12
3553 A885 $12 multi   1.00   .75
No. 3553 contains one 80x30mm stamp.

Opening of Movie, *Harry Potter and the Prisoner of Azkaban* — A886

No. 3554: a, $5, Harry, messenger owl, Hedwig, with letter. b, $5, Hedwig, rose background. c, $5, Harry riding Hippogriff. d, $5, Hippogriff, green background. e, $5, Harry, Monster Book of Monsters. f, $25, Crookshanks the Cat.
No. 3555: a, $5, Harry playing quidditch. b, $5, Harry playing quidditch, Dementors. c, $5, Harry and Hermoine riding Hippogriff. d, $5, Harry holding wand, Hogwarts. e, $5, Harry practicing Patronus Charm to repel Dementors. f, $25, Harry thrusting wand.

2004, June 4   **Perf. 12**
      Sheets of 6, #a-f
3554-3555 A886 Set of 2   8.00 5.00
Nos. 3554-3555 were not sold directly to customers at foreign addresses but were made available abroad through Canada Post's philatelic agency.

Old Train Stations A887

Designs: No. 3556, $5, Keelung Station, rickshaws. No. 3557, $5, Taipei Station, automobile. $15, Hsinchu Station, ox and cart. $25, Taichung Station, wagons.

2004, June 9   **Perf. 13½x13¾**
3556-3559 A887 Set of 4   3.50 1.50
Compare Type A887 with Types A926-A929.

Iron Fort, Nangan Island A888

Cinbi, Beigan Island A889

Fujheng, Tungchu Island A890

Lienyuyikeng, Tungyin Island — A891

2004, July 1   **Litho.**   **Perf. 11½x11¼**
3560 A888 $5 multi   .40   .20
3561 A889 $5 multi   .40   .20
3562 A890 $9 multi   .65   .25
3563 A891 $25 multi   1.75   .75
      Nos. 3560-3563 (4)   3.20 1.40
Matsu National Scenic Area.

Crabs A892

Designs: No. 3564, $3.50, Uca formosensis. No. 3565, $3.50, Uca borealis. $5, Uca arcuata. $25, Uca lactea.

2004, July 21
3564-3567 A892 Set of 4   2.50 1.10

Souvenir Sheet

Listening to the Lute, Attributed to Li Sung — A893

No. 3568: a, $5, Lute player. b, $25, Scholar and woman.

2004, Aug. 6   **Perf. 12**
3568 A893 Sheet of 2, #a-b   2.00 1.40

Souvenir Sheet

Taipei 2005 Intl. Stamp Exhibition — A894

No. 3569: a, $5, Sun Moon Lake. b, $25, Mt. Ali.

2004, Aug. 27   **Perf. 11½x11¼**
3569 A894 Sheet of 2, #a-b   2.00 1.40

Intl. Day of Peace A895

2004, Sept. 21   **Perf. 12¼x11¾**
3570 A895 $15 multi   1.00   .45

Souvenir Sheets

Hello Kitty — A896

No. 3571, oval stamps: a, $5, Dear Daniel, donuts. b, $15, Hello Kitty, Taipei 101 Building. No. 3572, rectangular stamps: a, $5, Hello Kitty, bird, horiz. b, $15, Dear Daniel, Fisherman's Wharf, Danshuei.

2004, Sept. 24   **Perf.**
3571 A896 Sheet of 2, #a-b   1.50 1.00
      Perf. 12
3572 A896 Sheet of 2, #a-b   1.50 1.00

Sayings With Numbers Greeting Stamps

One Sea of Smooth Sailing A897

Two Lions
Bring
Good
Fortune
A898

Three Goats of
Auspiciousness — A899

Safety in
All Four
Seasons
A900

Five
Blessings
at the
Door
A901

Six is Silky
Smooth
A902

Married for
Seven
Lives
A903

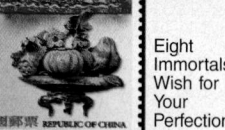

Eight
Immortals
Wish for
Your
Perfection
A904

Nine
Means
Success
A905

Ten is All
Around
Perfection
A906

2004, Oct. 10   **Perf. 12½**
3573   Block of 10   2.10 1.10
a. A897 $3.50 multi   .20 .20
b. A898 $3.50 multi   .20 .20
c. A899 $3.50 multi   .20 .20

---

d. A900 $3.50 multi   .20 .20
e. A901 $3.50 multi   .20 .20
f. A902 $3.50 multi   .20 .20
g. A903 $3.50 multi   .20 .20
h. A904 $3.50 multi   .20 .20
i. A905 $3.50 multi   .20 .20
j. A906 $3.50 multi   .20 .20

Changed Colors
3574   Block of 10   3.00 1.50
a. A897 $5 multi   .30 .20
b. A898 $5 multi   .30 .20
c. A899 $5 multi   .30 .20
d. A900 $5 multi   .30 .20
e. A901 $5 multi   .30 .20
f. A902 $5 multi   .30 .20
g. A903 $5 multi   .30 .20
h. A904 $5 multi   .30 .20
i. A905 $5 multi   .30 .20
j. A906 $5 multi   .30 .20
k. Sheet, #3574a-3574j + 10 at-
    tached labels ('04)   10.00 10.00

No. 3574k sold for $170 and has labels,
which could be personalized, that are separated from the stamps by simulated perforations. Issued 10/10/04.

Kaohsiung
Medical
University.
50th Anniv.
A907

Designs: No. 3575, $5, University gate and
buildings. No. 3576, $5, Building, researcher,
beaker, mosquito and snake.

2004, Oct. 16   **Perf. 12½**
3575-3576 A907   Set of 2   .75 .30

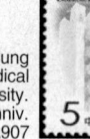

Main Peak,
Mt. Cilai
A908

North
Peak, Mt.
Cilai
A909

South
Peak, Mt.
Cilai
A910

Grasslands, Mt. Cilai — A911

2004, Oct. 16   **Perf. 11½x11¼**
3577 A908 $5 multi   .30 .20
3578 A909 $5 multi   .30 .20
3579 A910 $12 multi   .75 .35
3580 A911 $25 multi   1.50 .75
    Nos. 3577-3580 (4)   2.85 1.50

Sports In Which Taiwanese Athletes
Won Medals At 2004 Summer
Olympics
A912

Designs: No. 3581, $5, Women's
Taekwondo. No. 3582, $5, Men's Taekwondo,
vert. $9, Archery. $12, Athletes on winner's
platform, vert.

Perf. 11¼x11½, 11½x11¼
2004, Oct. 22
3581-3584 A912   Set of 4   2.00 .95

Platalea
Minor
A913

Designs: No. 3585, $2.50, Pair in flight. No.
3586, $2.50, Pair standing on one leg. $15,
With wings spread. $25, Foraging for food.
$20, Birds in water.

2004, Oct. 30   **Perf. 13½x13¼**
3585-3588 A913   Set of 4   3.00 1.40
Souvenir Sheet
3589 A913 $20 multi   1.50 1.00

No. 3589 contains one 80x30mm stamp.

Pres. Yen Chia-
kan (1905-93)
A914

2004, Nov. 5   **Perf. 13¼x13½**
3590 A914 $12 multi   .80 .35

New Year 2005
(Year of the
Cock) — A915

Designs: $3.50, Cock on lantern. $13, Lanterns, cock $5, Cock, hen and chick, horiz.

2004, Nov. 10   **Perf. 12¼x11¾**
3591-3592 A915   Set of 2   1.00 .50
Souvenir Sheet
Perf. 11¾x11¼
3593 A915 $5 multi   .50 .35

No. 3593 contains one 46x26mm stamp.

Prefectural
Hall,
Chiayi
A916

East Gate,
Chiayi
A917

2004, Nov. 20   **Perf. 13½x13¼**
3594 A916 $5 multi   .30 .20
3595 A917 $5 multi   .30 .20

Chiayi, 300th anniv.

Embroidered Squares for Ching
Dynasty Civil Official Court
Dresses — A918

Designs: No. 3596, $3.50, Manchurian
crane (orange background). No. 3597, $3.50,
Golden pheasant (green background). $5,
Peacock. $25, Goose.

2005, Jan. 20 Litho. Perf. 11½x11¼
3596-3599 A918   Set of 4   2.40 1.25

See Nos. 3727-3730.

Greetings
A919

No. 3600 — Cartoon balloon with various
keyboard characters creating faces and backgrounds with: a, Hands. b, Envelopes. c,
Hearts. d, Flowers.

2005, Jan. 31   **Perf. 12½**
3600   Horiz. strip of 4   1.25 .65
a.-d. A919 $5 Any single   .30 .20
e. Sheet, #3600a-3600d + 4 at-
    tached labels   9.00 9.00

No. 3600e sold for $140 and has labels,
which could be personalized, that are separated from the stamps by simulated perforations. Sheets exist with various arrangements
of stamps and positions of labels respective to
the stamps (at left, above or below).

Rotary International, Cent. — A920

Rotary emblem and: $5, Map of Taiwan.
$12, Dove.

2005, Feb. 23   **Perf. 13½x13¼**
3601-3602 A920   Set of 2   1.10 .55

Mangroves
A921

Designs: No. 3603, $3.50, Kandelia
obovata. No. 3604, $3.50, Rhizophora stylosa.
No. 3605, $5, Avicennia marina. No. 3606, $5,
Lumnitzera racemosa.

2005, Mar. 10   **Perf. 11½x11¼**
3603-3606 A921   Set of 4   1.10 .55

Longshan
Temple,
Mengjia
A922

Lin Ben Yuan Garden, Banciao A923

Designs: $13, Chaotain Temple, Beigang. $15, Fort Anping, Tainan.

2005, Mar. 18

3607	A922	$5 multi	.35	.20
3608	A923	$5 multi	.35	.20
3609	A923	$13 multi	.85	.40
3610	A923	$15 multi	.95	.45
	Nos. 3607-3610 (4)		2.50	1.25

Souvenir Sheet

Taipei 2005 Intl. Stamp Exhibition — A924

No. 3611: a, $5, Wood carving, Mandarin Ducks Playing in a Lotus Pond. b, $25, Hand puppets, horiz.

2005, Apr. 19 **Perf. 12**
3611 A924 Sheet of 2, #a-b 2.00 1.00

Coral Reef Fish A925

Designs: No. 3612, $5, Rhinomuraena quaesita. No. 3613, $5, Pomacanthus semicirculatus. $12, Forcipiger flavissimus. $25, Pterois volitans.

2005, May 16 **Perf. 11½x12**
3612-3615	A925	Set of 4	3.00	1.50
a.	Sheet, 2 each #3612-3615		6.00	6.00

Changhua Train Station, 1918 A926

Chiayi Train Station, 1933 A927

Tainan Train Station, 1936 A928

Kaohsiung Train Station, 1941 A929

2005, June 9 **Perf. 13½x13¾**
3616	A926	$5 multi	.35	.20
3617	A927	$5 multi	.35	.20
3618	A928	$15 multi	.95	.50
3619	A929	$25 multi	1.60	.80
	Nos. 3616-3619 (4)		3.25	1.70

Compare with type A887.

Novel "The Romance of the Three Kingdoms" A930

Designs: No. 3620, $3.50, Mayhem in the Fengyi Pavilion (man and woman near pavilion railing). No. 3621, $3.50, Deterring the Enemy in Changban (horse and rider on bridge). $5, Releasing Tsao Tsao (rider on horse near flag). $20, A Trick in the Bag (man in bed holding bag).

Perf. 11½x11¼
2005, June 23 **Litho.**
3620-3623	A930	Set of 4	2.10	1.10
3623a		Souvenir sheet, #3620-3623	2.10	1.10

Lifeline Suicide Prevention Hotline — A931

2005, July 1 **Perf. 12x11½**
3624 A931 $12 multi .75 .40

Albert Einstein's Theory of Relativity, Cent. — A932

2005, July 1
3625 A932 $15 multi .95 .45

Souvenir Sheets

Mickey Mouse — A933

No. 3626: a, $5, At ship's wheel, in *Steamboat Willie*. b, $25, As wizard, in *Fantasia*.

No. 3627: a, $5, Holding sword, in *The Prince and the Pauper*. b, $25. With Pluto, in *Mickey's Twice Upon a Christmas*.

2005, Aug. 3 **Perf. 12**
Sheets of 2, #a-b
3626-3627 A933 Set of 2 3.75 1.90

Rooster-shaped Wine Vessel — A934

2005, Aug. 19 **Perf. 11¼x11½**
3628	A934	$15 multi	.95	.45
a.	Sheet of 6, perf. 12		5.75	3.00

Taipei 2005 Intl. Stamp Exhibition.

Souvenir Sheets

A935

A936

A937

A938

A939

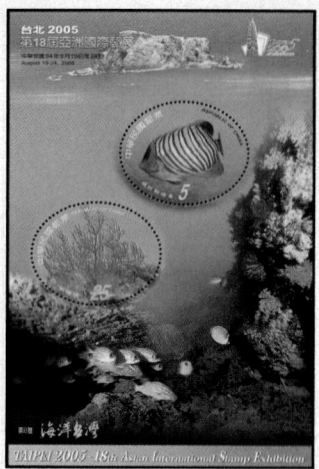

Taipei 2005 Intl. Stamp
Exhibition — A940

No. 3629: a, $5, Green Island and shoreline. b, $25, Formosan rock monkey.
No. 3630: a, $5, Microscope. b, $25, DNA double helices, vert.
No. 3631: a, $5, Flowers. $25, Fruit.
No. 3632: a, $5, Ear Shooting Ceremony, vert. b, $25, Dragon boat in race.
No. 3633: a, $5, Bowl of food and ladle. b, $25, Rice cakes.
No. 3634: a, $5, Royal empress angelfish. b, $25, Red horny coral.

2005				Perf.
3629	A935	Sheet of 2, #a-b	1.90	.95

Perf. 13½x13, 13x13½

| 3630 | A936 | Sheet of 2, #a-b | 1.90 | .95 |

Perf. 13½

| 3631 | A937 | Sheet of 2, #a-b | 1.90 | .95 |

Perf. 13¼x13½, 13½x13¼

| 3632 | A938 | Sheet of 2, #a-b | | .95 |

Perf. 12

| 3633 | A939 | Sheet of 2, #a-b | 1.90 | .95 |

Perf.

| 3634 | A940 | Sheet of 2, #a-b | 1.90 | .95 |
| | | Nos. 3629-3634 (6) | 11.40 | 5.70 |

Issued: No. 3629, 8/19; No. 3630, 8/20; No. 3631, 8/21; No. 3632, 8/22; No. 3633, 8/23; No. 3634, 8/24. No. 3629 contains two 38mm diameter stamps. No. 3634 contains two 43x33mm oval stamps.

Novel, "Journey
to the
West" — A941

Designs: No. 3635, $3.50, Stone Monkey (monkeys at waterfall). No. 3636, $3.50, Buddhist Baby in the River. $5, Making a Pass at Chang E. $20, Taming the Monster of the River of Flowing Sands.

2005, Sept. 15			Perf. 11¼x11½
3635-3638	A941	Set of 4	2.00 1.00

Souvenir Sheet

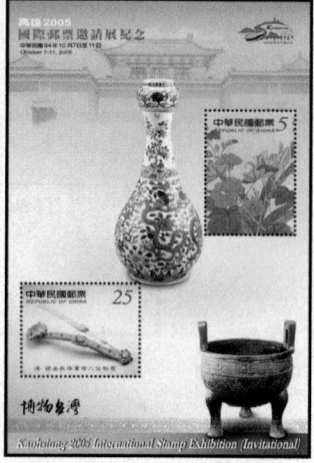

Kaohsiung 2005 Intl. Stamp
Exhibition — A942

No. 3639: a, $5, Loyalty and Filial Piety, by Cian Syuan, vert. b, Gilt scepter.

Perf. 13¼x13½, 13½x13¼

2005, Oct. 7			
3639	A942	Sheet of 2, #a-b	1.90 .95

Souvenir Sheets

A943

Opening of Movie, *Harry Potter and
the Goblet of Fire* — A944

No. 3640: a, $5, Triwizard Cup. b, $5, Harry and Hungarian Horntail. c, $5, Golden Egg. d, $5, Harry swimming. e, $5, Harry summoning Firebolt with wand. f, $25, Harry and Triwizard Cup.
No. 3641: a, $5, Hungarian Horntail. b, $5, Harry on Firebolt. c, $5, Voldemort's snake, Nagini. d, $5, Grindylows. e, $5, Dumbledore's phoenix, Fawkes. f, $25, Merchieftainess.

2005, Nov. 18			Perf. 12
3640	A943	Sheet of 6, #a-f	3.00 1.50
3641	A944	Sheet of 6, #a-f	3.00 1.50

New Year 2006
(Year of the
Dog) — A945

Designs: $3.50, Dog at left. $13, Dog at lower right.
$12, Three dogs, horiz.

2005, Dec. 1			Perf. 12¼x11¾
3642-3643	A945	Set of 2	1.00 .50

Souvenir Sheet
Perf. 11¾x11¼

| 3644 | A945 | $12 multi | .80 .40 |

No. 3644 contains one 46x26mm stamp.

Pets — A946

Designs: $3.50, Siberian husky. $5, Golden retriever. $12, Himalayan cat. $25, Scottish fold cat.

Perf. 13½x12½

2005, Dec. 22				Litho.
	Country Name in Green			
3645	A946	$3.50 multi	.25	.20
3646	A946	$5 multi	.30	.20
3647	A946	$12 multi	.75	.35
3648	A946	$25 multi	1.50	.75
	Nos. 3645-3648 (4)		2.80	1.50

See Nos. 3652-3655, 3685-3688.

Tea
Ceremony
A947

No. 3649: a, Preparation of tea set (dull orange panel). b, Placing of tea leaves in pot (lemon panel). c, Pouring hot water over pots and cups (light green panel). d, Drying of pot and pouring of tea (blue green panel). e, Smelling and drinking of tea (gray blue panel).

2006, Jan. 26		Perf. 13½
3649	Horiz. strip of 5	1.60 .80
a.-e.	A947 $5 Any single	.30 .20

Taipei 101
Building — A948

Designs: $5, In day. $12, At night.

2006, Mar. 23			Perf. 12
3650-3651	A948	Set of 2	1.10 .55

Pets Type of 2005

Designs: $2.50, Labrador retriever. $7, St. Bernard. $10, Siamese cat. $32, Persian cat.

2006, Mar. 8				Perf. 13½x12½
	Country Name in Blue			
3652	A946	$2.50 multi	.20	.20
3653	A946	$7 multi	.45	.20
3654	A946	$10 multi	.60	.30
3655	A946	$32 multi	2.00	1.00
	Nos. 3652-3655 (4)		3.25	1.70

See Nos. 3712-3715.

King Penguins
A949

Aptenodytes patagonicus: No. 3656, $5, Adult and juvenile. No. 3657, $5, Courtship. $9, Swimming and diving, horiz. $12, Gliding and preening, horiz.
$15, Colony, horiz.

Perf. 11¼x11½, 11½x11¼

2006, Mar. 26				
3656-3659	A949	Set of 4	1.90	.95

Souvenir Sheet
Perf. 12

| 3660 | A949 | $15 multi | .95 | .45 |

No. 3660 contains one 80x30mm stamp.

Miniature Sheet

Children's Art — A950

No. 3661 — Winning drawings in children's stamp design competition: a, Birds with black bills. b, People with red faces. c, Pheasants. d, Chinese celebration. e, Fishing boats and catch. f, People with large flowers and fruit. g, Man painting Chinese lantern. h, Bridge and ducks. i, Train. j, Bees and flowers. k, People with black faces. l, Boy on ladder. m, People and chickens. n, Ring of people around dancers and musicians. o, People and large lions. p, Two cats. q, People and cow. r, Whale and fish. s, People with white faces bending backwards. t, Bus.

2006, Apr. 4			Perf. 11½
3661	A950	$5 Sheet of 20, #a-t	6.25 3.25

Fireflies
A951

Designs: No. 3662, $5, Pyrocoelia analis. No. 3663, $5, Diaphanes citrinus. No. 3664, $5, Diaphanes niveus. No. 3665, $5, Diaphanes formosus.

2006, May 25			Perf. 13½x13¼
3662-3665	A951	Set of 4	1.25 .60

Souvenir Sheet

Completion of Nangang to Suao
Section of National Expressway
5 — A952

2006, June 16			Litho.	Perf. 11½
3666	A952	$12 multi		.75 .35

Souvenir Sheets

Winnie the Pooh — A953

No. 3667: a, $5, Winnie the Pooh pushing Piglet in wheelbarrow. b, $25, Winnie the Pooh, Piglet and Tigger floating in inner tube.
No. 3668: a, $5, Winnie the Pooh and Piglet running in autumn. b, $25, Winnie the Pooh and Tigger ice fishing.

2006, June 21			Perf. 12
	Sheets of 2, #a-b		
3667-3668	A953	Set of 2	3.75 1.90

Tourism
Greeting
Stamps
A954

Designs: Nos. 3669a, 3670a, Satchel and cliff. Nos. 3669b, 3670b, Camera and boat. Nos. 3669c, 3670c, Notebook, pen and bridge. No. 3669d, 3670d, Sailboat and rock. No. 3669e, 3670e, Heart and train.

				Perf. 12½
2006, June 30				
3669		Horiz. strip of 5	1.10	.55
a.-e.	A954 $3.50 Any single		.20	.20
3670		Horiz. strip of 5	1.60	.80
a.-e.	A954 $5 Any single		.30	.20

Fish
A955

Designs: No. 3671, $5, Amphiprion ocellaris. No. 3672, $5, Zanclus cornutus. No. 3673, $12, Coris gaimard. No. 3674, $12, Oxycirrhites typus.

				Perf. 11½
2006, July 14				
3671-3674	A955	Set of 4	2.10	1.10
3674a		Miniature sheet, 2 each #3671-3674, perf. 11½x12	4.25	4.25

A956

Sung Dynasty Calligraphy and
Painting — A957

Designs: $5, Poem by Huang T'ing-chien. $9, Calligraphy on silk, by Mi Fu. Nos. 3677, 3679a, $12, Detail of magpie in flight, from Magpies and Hare, by Ts'ui Po. Nos. 3678, 3679b, $15, Detail of magpie on branch, from Magpies and Hare.

				Perf. 11½
2006, Aug. 4				
Denominations in Black				
3675-3678	A956	Set of 4	2.50	1.25

Souvenir Sheet
Denominations in Black and Orange
Perf. 12½

3679	A957	Sheet of 2, #a-b	1.75	.85

Dragonflies
A958

Designs: Nos. 3680, 3684a, $5, Crocothemis servilia servilia. Nos. 3681, 3684b, $5, Orthetrum, pruinosum neglectum, vert. Nos. 3682, 3684c, $12, Diplacodes trivialis, vert. No. 3683, 3684d, $12, Orthetrum sabina sabina.

Perf. 13x13¼, 13¼x13
2006, Aug. 16
With White Frames

3680-3683	A958	Set of 4	2.10	1.10

Souvenir Sheet
Without White Frames
Perf. 11¾

3684	A958	Sheet of 4, #a-d	2.10	1.10

Pets Type of 2005
Designs: $1, Yorkshire terrier. $9, Pomeranian. $15, Abyssinian cat. $20, Norwegian Forest cat.

2006, Aug. 30			Perf. 13½x12½	
Country Name in Blue				
3685	A946	$1 multi	.20	.20
3686	A946	$9 multi	.55	.25
3687	A946	$15 multi	.90	.45
3688	A946	$20 multi	1.25	.60
	Nos. 3685-3688 (4)		2.90	1.50

Aerial
Activities — A959

Designs: No. 3689, $3.50, Paragliding. No. 3690, $3.50, Hang gliding, horiz. $12, Ultralight aircraft, horiz. $15, Parasailing.

2006, Sept. 15			Perf. 13½	
3689-3692	A959	Set of 4	2.10	1.10

Pitta
Nympha — A960

Designs: Nos. 3693, 3697a, $5, On branch. Nos. 3694, 3697b, $5, In flight, horiz. Nos. 3695, 3697c, $10, With young at nest, horiz. Nos. 3696, 3697d, $10, With insect in beak.

Perf. 13¼x13, 13x13¼
2006, Sept. 30
With White Frames

3693-3696	A960	Set of 4	1.90	.95

Souvenir Sheet
Without White Frames
Perf. 11¾

3697	A960	Sheet of 4, #a-d	1.90	.95

Cetaceans
A961

Designs: No. 3698, $5, Stenella attenuata. No. 3699, $5, Stenella longirostris. $10, Feresa attenuata. $15, Physeter macrocephalus.

Perf. 13x12 Syncopated				
2006, Oct. 18				Litho.
3698-3701	A961	Set of 4	2.10	1.10
3701a		Souvenir sheet, #3698-3701	2.10	1.10

Flowers
A962

Designs: No. 3702, $5, Ludwigia octovalvis. No. 3703, $5, Hygrophila pogonocalyx, vert. $12, Titanotrichum oldhamii, vert.

2006, Nov. 8			Perf. 11½	
3702-3704	A962	Set of 3	1.40	.70

Scenic Areas — A963

Designs: No. 3705, $5, Jhongshan Building, Yangmingshan National Park. No. 3706, $5, Taroko Gorge, vert. $9, Queen's Head Rock, vert. $12, Sun Moon Lake.

2006, Nov. 11			Perf. 12½	
3705-3708	A963	Set of 4	2.00	1.00

A964

New Year 2007 (Year of the
Pig) — A965

Designs: $3.50, Pig on drum. $13, Pig and drums.

2006, Dec. 1			Perf. 12¼x11¾	
3709-3710	A964	Set of 2	1.10	.55

Souvenir Sheet
Perf. 11½x11¼

3711	A965	$12 multi	.75	.35

Pets Type of 2005
Designs: 50c, Border collie. $13, Beagle. $17, American Shorthair cat. $34, Maine Coon cat.

2006, Dec. 18			Perf. 13½x12½	
Country Name in Green				
3712	A946	50c multi	.20	.20
3713	A946	$13 multi	.80	.40
3714	A946	$17 multi	1.10	.55
3715	A946	$34 multi	2.10	1.10
	Nos. 3712-3715 (4)		4.20	2.25

Inauguration of High Speed Rail
Line — A966

No. 3716: a, 700T Series train. b, Hsinchu Station.
Illustration reduced.

2006, Dec. 25			Perf. 11½	
3716	A966	$12 Horiz. pair, #a-b	1.50	.75

Orchids — A967

Designs: $3.50, Phaius tankervilleae. $5, Spiranthes sinensis. $12, Vanda x hybrida. $25, Cattleya sp.

2007, Jan. 10			Litho.	Perf. 13½x12½
3717	A967	$3.50 multi	.25	.20
3718	A967	$5 multi	.30	.20
3719	A967	$12 multi	.75	.35
3720	A967	$25 multi	1.50	.75
	Nos. 3717-3720 (4)		2.80	1.50

See Nos. 3751-3754, 3768-3771.

Ching
Dynasty
Jewelry
A968

Designs: No. 3721, $5, Earrings. No. 3722, $5, Hairpin. $12, Fingernail guard. $25, Ring.

2007, Jan. 17			Perf. 11½	
3721-3724	A968	Set of 4	3.00	1.50

Valentine's
Day — A969

Heart and faces in: $5, White. $20, Red.

2007, Feb. 6				
3725-3726	A969	Set of 2	1.50	.75

Embroidered Squares Type of 2005

Embroidered squares for Ching Dynasty military officials: No. 3727, $3.50, Cilin (light green background). No. 3728, $3.50, Lion (light orange background). $5, Leopard (bright orange background). $25, Tiger (light blue background).

2007, Feb. 16			Perf. 11½x11¼	
3727-3730	A918	Set of 4	2.25	1.10

Feb. 28,
1947
Massacre
Memorial
Museum
A970

2007, Feb. 28				
3731	A970	$5 multi	.30	.20

Bridges
A971

Designs: No. 3732, $5, Kanjin Bridge, Taoyuan (green panel). No. 3733, $5, Fusing

Bridge, Luofu (purple panel). $12, MacArthur Second Bridge, Taipei. $15, Dajhih Bridge, Taipei.

2007, Apr. 12   Litho.   Perf. 11½x12
3732-3735 A971   Set of 4   2.25 1.10

Lesser Panda
A972

Panda: No. 3736, $5, Eating bamboo. No. 3737, $5, Resting on rock. No. 3738, $10, Walking near tree, vert. No. 3739, $10, Scratching on rock, vert. $12, Two pandas, vert.

Perf. 11½x11¼, 11¼x11½
2007, Apr. 25
3736-3739 A972   Set of 4   1.90 .95
Souvenir Sheet
Perf. 12
3740 A972 $12 multi   .75 .35

No. 3740 contains one 40x50mm stamp.

Dharma Drum Mountain Intl. Buddhist Educational Complex — A973

Chung Tai Chan Monastery
A974

Fo Guang Shan Monastery
A975

Tzu Chi Foundation Building — A976

2007, May 24   Perf. 13¼x13
3741 A973 $5 multi   .30 .20
3742 A974 $5 multi   .30 .20
3743 A975 $5 multi   .30 .20
3744 A976 $5 multi   .30 .20
       Nos. 3741-3744 (4)   1.20 .80

Dahlia and Butterflies
A977

Iris and Butterfly
A978

Clematis and Ladybugs
A979

Tung Blossom and Butterflies
A980

Rose and Butterfly
A981

Sunflower and Insects — A982

Bird-of-Paradise Flower and Butterfly
A983

Lotus and Butterflies
A984

English Daisies and Dragonfly
A985

Balloon Flower and Dragonfly
A986

2007, May 28   Perf. 12½
3745   Block of 10   2.10 1.10
 a. A977 $3.50 multi   .20 .20
 b. A978 $3.50 multi   .20 .20
 c. A979 $3.50 multi   .20 .20
 d. A980 $3.50 multi   .20 .20
 e. A981 $3.50 multi   .20 .20
 f. A982 $3.50 multi   .20 .20
 g. A983 $3.50 multi   .20 .20
 h. A984 $3.50 multi   .20 .20
 i. A985 $3.50 multi   .20 .20
 j. A986 $3.50 multi   .20 .20

Changed Colors
3746   Block of 10   3.00 1.50
 a. A977 $5 multi   .30 .20
 b. A978 $5 multi   .30 .20
 c. A979 $5 multi   .30 .20
 d. A980 $5 multi   .30 .20
 e. A981 $5 multi   .30 .20
 f. A982 $5 multi   .30 .20
 g. A983 $5 multi   .30 .20
 h. A984 $5 multi   .30 .20
 i. A985 $5 multi   .30 .20
 j. A986 $5 multi   .30 .20

Food Preparation Implements — A987

Designs: No. 3747, $5, Rice bucket and shelf (light blue background). No. 3748, $5, Steamer (green background). No. 3749, $12, Rice baskets (tan background). No. 3750, $12, Dinnerware (lilac background).

2007, June 28   Perf. 11½x11¼
3747-3750 A987   Set of 4   2.10 1.10

Orchids Type of 2007 Inscribed "Taiwan" Instead of "Republic of China"

Designs: $1, Paphiopedilum sp. $2.50, Phalaenopsis aphrodite. $10, Dendrobium sp. $32, Oncidium x hybridum.

2007, July 12   Perf. 13½x12½
3751 A967 $1 multi   .20 .20
3752 A967 $2.50 multi   .20 .20
3753 A967 $10 multi   .60 .30
3754 A967 $32 multi   2.00 1.00
       Nos. 3751-3754 (4)   3.00 1.70

End of Martial Law, 20th Anniv. — A988

2007, July 15   Perf. 11¼x11½
3755 A988 $12 multi   .75 .35

Fish
A989

Designs: No. 3756, $5, Nemateleotris magnifica. No. 3757, $5, Balistoides conspicillum. $12, Paracanthurus hepatus. $25, Cetoscarus bicolor.

2007, July 27   Perf. 11½x11¼
3756-3759 A989   Set of 4   3.00 1.50

Chiang Wei-shui (1890-1931), Political and Social Leader — A990

2007, Aug. 6   Engr.   Perf. 11¼x11½
3760 A990 $25 brown   1.50 .75

Taiwan - African Heads of State Summit, Taipei
A991

2007, Sept. 9   Litho.   Perf. 11½x11¼
3761 A991 $12 multi   .75 .35

Miniature Sheet

Eighteen Scholars of T'ang, by Emperor Hui-tsung. — A992

No. 3762 — Various portions of painting numbered: a, (10-5), 36x30mm. b, (10-4), 51x30mm. c, (10-3), 43x30mm. d, (10-2), 45x30mm. e, (10-1), 43x30mm. f, (10-7), 43x30mm. g, (10-9), 51x30mm. h, (10-8), 43x30mm. i, (10-7), 45x30mm. j, (10-6), 36x30mm.

2007, Sept. 21   Perf. 13¼
3762 A992 Sheet of 10   3.00 1.50
 a.-j. $5 Any single   .30 .20

Doves — A993

2007, Sept. 28   Perf. 11¼x11½
3763 A993 $5 multi   .30 .20

Portions of the design were applied by a thermographic process producing a shiny, raised effect.

SEMI-POSTAL STAMPS

SP1

Red or Blue Surcharge
1920, Dec. 1   Unwmk.   Perf. 14, 15
B1 SP1 1c on 2c green   5.00 1.75
B2 SP1 3c on 4c scar (B)   7.50 2.90
B3 SP1 5c on 6c gray   12.00 5.00
       Nos. B1-B3 (3)   24.50 9.65

The surcharge represents the actual franking value. The extra cent helped victims of the 1919 Yellow River flood.

War Refugees
SP2

Black Surcharge
1944, Oct. 10   Engr.   Perf. 12
B4 $2 +$2 on 50c + 50c   1.50 1.50
B5 $4 +$4 on 8c + 8c   1.50 1.50
B6 $5 +$5 on 21c + 21c   2.00 2.00
B7 $6 +$6 on 28c + 28c   3.50 3.50
B8 $10 +$10 on 33c + 33c   4.50 4.50

B9	$20 +$20 on $1 + $1	5.50 5.50
a.	Sheet of 6, #B4-B9 (6)	40.00 40.00
	Nos. B4-B9 (6)	18.50 18.50

The borders of each stamp differ slightly in design. The surtax was for war refugees. Nos. B4-B8 exist without surcharge, but were not regularly issued.

Great Wall of China — SP4

Chinese Refugee Family — SP5

1948, July 5 Litho. Perf. 14, Imperf.
Without Gum
Cross in Carmine

B11	SP4 $5000 + $2000 vio	.40 1.75
B12	SP4 $10,000 + $2000 brn	.40 1.75
B13	SP4 $15,000 + $2000 gray	.40 1.75
a.	Cross omitted	
	Nos. B11-B13 (3)	1.20 5.25

The surtax was for anti-tuberculosis work. Fakes of B13a exist with cross chemically removed. No genuine used copies are known.

Republic of China (Taiwan)
1954, Oct. 1 Engr. Perf. 12
Without Gum

B14	SP5 40c + 10c dp bl	22.50 3.50
B15	SP5 $1.60 + 40c lil rose	62.50 22.50
B16	SP5 $5 + $1 red	115.00 100.00
	Nos. B14-B16 (3)	200.00 126.00

The surtax was used to aid in the evacuation of Chinese from North Viet Nam.

> **Catalogue values for unused stamps in this section, from this point to the end of the section, are for Never Hinged items.**

Sept. 21, 1999 Earthquake Relief SP6

a, Damaged buildings, map, rescue workers. b, Hands, heart, earthquake fault.

1999, Nov. 1 Litho. Imperf.
Sheet of 2

B17	SP6 $25 +$25, #a.-b.	9.00 9.00

No. B17 has simulated perforations.

AIR POST STAMPS

Curtiss "Jenny" over Great Wall (Bars of Republic flag on tail) — AP1

Unwmk.
1921, July 1 Engr. Perf. 14

C1	AP1 15c bl grn & blk	32.50 30.00
C2	AP1 30c scar & blk	32.50 30.00
C3	AP1 45c dull vio & blk	32.50 30.00
C4	AP1 60c dk blue & blk	39.00 35.00
C5	AP1 90c ol grn & blk	52.50 50.00
	Nos. C1-C5 (5)	189.00 175.00

(Nationalist sun emblem on tail) — AP2

1929, July 5

C6	AP2 15c blue grn & blk	4.00 .80
C7	AP2 30c dk red & blk	8.00 2.75
C8	AP2 45c dk vio & blk	16.00 7.25
C9	AP2 60c dk blue & blk	19.00 10.00
C10	AP2 90c ol grn & blk	17.00 16.50
	Nos. C6-C10 (5)	64.00 37.30

Junkers F-13 over Great Wall AP3

1932-37

C11	AP3 15c gray grn	.45 .45
C12	AP3 25c orange ('33)	.55 .45
C13	AP3 30c red	7.00 .45
C14	AP3 45c brown vio	1.00 .45
C15	AP3 50c dk brown ('33)	1.00 .45
C16	AP3 60c dk blue	1.00 .45
C17	AP3 90c olive blk	1.00 .45
C18	AP3 $1 yellow grn ('33)	1.25 .45
C19	AP3 $2 brown ('37)	2.25 1.50
C20	AP3 $5 brown car ('37)	4.50 4.00
	Nos. C11-C20 (10)	20.00 9.10

See #C21-C40. For surcharges and overprints see #C41-C52, C54-C60, 9N111-9N114, 9NC1-9NC7, Szechwan C1, C3-C6, Sinkiang C5-C19.

Type of 1932-37, with secret mark

1932-37 Issue. Lower part of left character joined

Secret Mark, 1940-41 Issue. Separated.

Perf. 12, 12½, 12½x13, 13
1940-41 Wmk. 261

C21	AP3 15c gray green	.50 .50
C22	AP3 25c yellow org	.50 .50
C23	AP3 30c red	.50 .50
a.	Vert. pair, imperf. between	200.00
C24	AP3 45c dull rose vio ('41)	.50 .50
C25	AP3 50c brown	.50 .50
C26	AP3 60c dp blue ('41)	.50 .50
C27	AP3 90c olive ('41)	.50 .50
C28	AP3 $1 apple grn ('41)	.50 .50
C29	AP3 $2 lt brown ('41)	.50 .50
C30	AP3 $5 lake	1.25 1.25
	Nos. C21-C30 (10)	5.75 5.75

Unwmk.
Perf. 12½, 13, 13½

C31	AP3 15c gray green ('41)	.45 .30
C32	AP3 25c lt orange ('41)	.45 .30
C33	AP3 30c lt red ('41)	.45 .30
C34	AP3 45c dl rose vio ('41)	.45 .30
C35	AP3 50c brown	.45 .30
C36	AP3 60c blue ('41)	.45 .30
C37	AP3 90c lt olive ('41)	.45 .30
C38	AP3 $1 apple grn ('41)	.65 .65
C39	AP3 $2 lt brown ('41)	1.50 1.50
C40	AP3 $5 lake ('41)	1.25 1.25
	Nos. C31-C40 (10)	6.55 5.50

For surcharges see note following No. C20.

Nos. C11 and C12 Surcharged

1946, May 2 Unwmk. Perf. 14

C41	AP3 $53 on 15c	1.00 2.00
C42	AP3 $73 on 25c	1,500. 1,400.

Forgeries of No. C42 exist.

On Nos. C23, C21, C22, C29 and C30
Perf. 13, 13x12, 12½
Wmk. 261

C43	AP3 $23 on 30c red	.50 .35
C44	AP3 $53 on 15c gray grn	17.50 20.00
C45	AP3 $73 on 25c yel org	.50 .35
C46	AP3 $100 on $2 lt brown	1.25 .50
C47	AP3 $200 on $5 lake	.50 .50
	Nos. C43-C47 (5)	20.25 21.70

On Nos. C33, C31, C32, C39 and C40
Perf. 13, 13x12, 13x12½, 12½
Unwmk.

C48	AP3 $23 on 30c lt red	.20 .25
a.	Inverted surcharge	100.00
b.	"2300" omitted	50.00
c.	Last character (kuo) of surch. omitted	65.00
C49	AP3 $53 on 15c gray grn	.20 .25
a.	Horiz. pair, imperf. btwn.	675.00
C50	AP3 $73 on 25c lt org	.20 .25
a.	Inverted surcharge	525.00
C51	AP3 $100 on $2 lt brn	.20 .20
C52	AP3 $200 on $5 lake	.20 .20
a.	Inverted surcharge	80.00
	Nos. C48-C52 (5)	1.00 1.15

The surcharges on #C41-C52 represent Chinese natl. currency and were applied at Shanghai.

Douglas DC-4 over Sun Yat-sen Mausoleum, Nanking — AP4

1946, Sept. 10 Litho. Perf. 14
Without Gum

C53	AP4 $27 blue	.35 .40

For surcharges see #C61, Szechwan C2.

No. C23 Surcharged in Black

Perf. 13x12
1948, May 18 Wmk. 261

C54	AP3 $10,000 on 30c red	.20 .35

Same, in Black or Carmine, on Nos. C33, C32, C37, C36, C18 and C38
Perf. 12½, 13x12½, 14
Unwmk.

C55	AP3 $10,000 on 30c lt red	.20 .20
C56	AP3 $20,000 on 25c lt org	.20 .20
C57	AP3 $30,000 on 90c lt ol (C)	.20 .20
C58	AP3 $50,000 on 60c blue (C)	.20 .20
C59	AP3 $50,000 on $1 yel grn (C) (#C57)	75.00 70.00
C60	AP3 $50,000 on $1 ap grn (C) (#C38)	.20 .20

No. C53 Surcharged in Black

Perf. 14

C61	AP4 $10,000 on $27 bl	.20 .55
	Nos. C54-C61 (8)	76.40 71.90

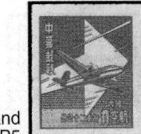

Douglas DC-4 and Arrow — AP5

Perf. 12½
1949, May 2 Unwmk. Litho.
Without Gum

C62	AP5 blue green	5.00 5.50
a.	Rouletted	7.00 8.00

See note after No. 959.
For overprints see Taiwan #C1, Fukien #C1, Kansu #C1, PRC #26, 102.

Revenue Stamp Overprinted in Blue

1949, May Engr. Perf. 14

C63	A95 $100 olive green	35.00 40.00

See note after No. 962.

Republic of China (Taiwan)

Cheng Ch'eng-kung (Koxinga) — AP6

Rouletted
1950, Sept. 26 Unwmk. Typo.
Without Gum

C64	AP6 60c deep blue	14.00 7.00

For surcharge see No. 1120.

Plane over City Gate, Taipei — AP7

Jet Planes above Chung Shan Bridge — AP8

Two Doves Near Koxinga Shrine — AP9

1954 Engr. Perf. 11½
Without Gum

C65	AP7 $1 dk brown	11.00 1.00
a.	Vert. pair, imperf. btwn.	200.00
C66	AP8 $1.60 olive blk	8.00 .80
a.	Vert. pair, imperf. btwn.	140.00
b.	Horiz. pair, imperf. btwn.	100.00 110.00
C67	AP9 $5 grnsh blue	20.00 1.75
	Nos. C65-C67 (3)	45.00 3.55

Issued: #C66, 8/14; #C65, C67, 9/1.

No. C67 Surcharged in Red
1958, Dec. 11
Without Gum

C68	AP9 $3.50 on $5 grnsh bl	3.50 1.40

> **Catalogue values for unused stamps in this section, from this point to the end of the section, are for Never Hinged items.**

Sea Gull
AP10

Sabre Jets in
Bomb Burst
Formation
AP11

1959, Mar. 20   Photo.   Perf. 13
C69 AP10 $8 blue, gray & blk   4.50   .30

1960, Feb. 29   Unwmk.   Perf. 13

Plane Formations: $2, Loop, horiz. $5, Diamond formation passing over grounded plane, horiz.

C70 AP11 $1 multicolored   5.00   .50
C71 AP11 $2 multicolored   6.00   .50
C72 AP11 $5 multicolored   10.00   .60
    Nos. C70-C72 (3)   21.00 1.60

Issued to honor the Chinese Air Force and the "Thunder Tiger" aerobatic team.

Jet Airliner
over Pitan
Bridge
AP12

Designs: $6, Jet over Tropic of Cancer monument, Kiai, vert. $10, Jet over Lion Head mountain, Sinchu, vert.

1963, Aug. 14   Photo.   Perf. 13
C73 AP12 $2.50 multi   4.25   .25
C74 AP12 $6 multi   6.50   .25
C75 AP12 $10 multi   8.25   .60
    Nos. C73-C75 (3)   19.00 1.05

Boeing 727 over
Chilin Pavilion,
Grand Hotel
AP13

Wild Geese
Flying over
Mountains
AP14

Design: $8, Boeing 727 over National Palace Museum, Taipei.

1967, Apr. 1   Unwmk.   Perf. 13
C76 AP13 $5 multicolored   2.50   .20
C77 AP13 $8 multicolored   4.00   .45

1969, Aug. 14   Photo.   Perf. 13

Wild Geese flying over: $5, The sea. $8, The land, horiz.

C78 AP14 $2.50 multicolored   1.75   .20
C79 AP14 $5 multicolored   3.25   .45
C80 AP14 $8 multicolored   4.75   .60
    Nos. C78-C80 (3)   9.75 1.25

Presidental
Palace and
Tzu-Ch'iang
Squadron
AP15

1980, June 18   Litho.   Perf. 13½
C81 AP15 $5 shown   .25   .20
C82 AP15 $7 China Airlines jet   .40   .25
C83 AP15 $12 China flag, jet   .70   .40
    Nos. C81-C83 (3)   1.35   .85

Civil Aeronautics Administration, 37th
Anniv. — AP16

Jet Airliners over: $7, Chiang Kai-shek Intl. Airport, vert. $11, Chung Cheng Memorial Hall. $18, Sun Yat-sen Memorial Hall.

Perf. 14x13½, 13½x14

1984, Jan. 20   Litho.
C84 AP16 $7 multicolored   .45   .20
C85 AP16 $11 multicolored   .60   .20
C86 AP16 $18 multicolored   .90   .35
    Nos. C84-C86 (3)   1.95   .75

Airplane
AP17

1987, Aug. 4   Litho.   Perf. 13½
C87 AP17 $9 multicolored   .50   .25
C88 AP17 $14 multicolored   .75   .50
C89 AP17 $18 multicolored   1.00   .60
    Nos. C87-C89 (3)   2.25 1.35

SPECIAL DELIVERY STAMPS

Design: Dragon in irregular oval.

Stamp 8x2½ inches, divided into four parts by perforation or serrate rouletting.

Values of Nos. E1-E8 are for used mailer's receipts. Complete unused strips of four are exceptionally scarce because the first section (#1) was to remain in the P.O. booklet.

The mailer received the righthand section (#4), usually canceled, as a receipt. The middle two sections were canceled and attached to the letter. Upon arrival at the destination P.O. they were canceled again, usually on the back, with the righthand copy (#3) retained by that P.O. The lefthand copy (#2) was signed by the recipient and returned to the original P.O. as evidence of delivery. Sections 2 and 3 usually are thin or badly damaged.

Unused strips of three (#2-4) can be found on Nos. E3-E8.

"Chinese Imperial Post Office" in lines, repeated to form the background which is usually lighter in color than the rest of the design.

Dragon's head facing downward
Background with period after
"POSTOFFICE."
No Date

1905   Unwmk.   Perf. 11
E1   10c grass green   475.00

Serrate Roulette in Black
E2   10c deep green   350.00

1907-10
Dragon's head facing forward
Background with no period after
"POSTOFFICE"
No Date

E3   10c light bluish green   225.00

1909-11
Background with date at bottom

E4   10c green (Feby 1909)   160.00
E5   10c bl grn (Jan. 1911)   160.00

1912
"IMPERIAL POST OFFICE" in
serifed letters repeated to form the
background.
No Date, No Border
Background of 30 or 28 lines

E6   10c green (30 lines)   75.00
 a.   28 lines   75.00

Background of 35 lines of sans-serif
letters
Colored Border

E8   10c green   150.00

On No. E8 the medallion in the third section has Chinese characters in the background instead of the usual English inscriptions. E6 and E8 occur with many types of four-character overprints reading "Republic of China," applied locally but unofficially at various post offices.

1913
Design: Wild Goose. Stamp 7½x2¾
inches, divided
into five parts.
"CHINESE POST OFFICE" in sans-
serif letters, repeated to form the
background of 28 lines. With
border.
Serrate Roulette in Black

E9   10c green   400.00 35.00

Unused values for Nos. E9-E10 are for complete strips of five parts. Used values are for single parts.

1914
"CHINESE POST OFFICE" in
antique
letters, forming a background of
29 or 30 lines. No border.
Serrate Roulette in Green

E10   10c green   95.00 4.00

On No. E9 the background is in sans-serif capitals, the Chinese and English inscriptions are on white tablets and the serial numbers are in black.

On No. E10 the background is in antique capitals and extends under the inscriptions. The serial numbers are in green.

NOTE:
In February, 1916, the Special Delivery Stamps were demonetized and became merely receipts without franking value. To mark this, four of the five sections of the stamp had the letters A, B, C, D either handstamped or printed on them.

SD1

1941   Unwmk.   Typo.   Rouletted
Without Gum
E11   SD1 ($2) car & yel   32.50 29.00

Motorcycle
Messenger — SD2

1949, July   Litho.   Perf. 12½
Without Gum
E12   SD2   red violet   7.00 14.00
 a.   Rouletted   8.00 15.00
    See note after No. 959.
For surcharge and overprints see Nos. 1150, Taiwan E1, Fukien E1.

Revenue Stamp
Overprinted in Purple
Brown

1949
Without Gum
E13   A95 $10 grnsh gray   20.00 20.00
    See note after No. 962.

REGISTRATION STAMPS

R1

1941   Unwmk.   Typo.   Rouletted
Without Gum
F1   R1 ($1.50) green & buff   21.00 15.00

Mountain Scene — R2

1949, July   Litho.   Perf. 12½
Without Gum
F2   R2   carmine   8.50 10.00
 a.   Rouletted   9.50 14.00
    See note after No. 959.
For surcharge and overprints see Nos. 1152, Taiwan F1, Fukien F1, PRC 103.

Revenue Stamp
Overprinted in
Carmine

1949
F3   A95 $50 dark blue   21.00 18.50
    See note after No. 962.

POSTAGE DUE STAMPS

Regular Issue of 1902-
03 Overprinted in
Black

1904   Unwmk.   Perf. 14 to 15
J1   A17 ½c chocolate   7.50 3.00
J2   A17 1c ocher   8.50 4.00
J3   A17 2c scarlet   9.50 5.00
J4   A17 4c red brn   11.00 6.00
J5   A17 5c salmon   20.00 9.50
J6   A17 10c dk blue grn   32.50 16.00
 a.   Vert. pair, imperf. btwn.   475.00
    Nos. J1-J6 (6)   89.00 43.50

D1

1904   Engr.
J7   D1   ½c blue   2.75 1.00
 a.   Horiz. pair, imperf. btwn. 350.00 325.00
J8   D1   1c blue   5.00 1.00
J9   D1   2c blue   3.50 1.00
 a.   Horiz. pair, imperf. btwn. 400.00 350.00
J10   D1   4c blue   6.50 1.00
J11   D1   5c blue   8.50 1.50
J12   D1   10c blue   8.75 2.25
J13   D1   20c blue   25.00 5.00
J14   D1   30c blue   32.50 27.50
    Nos. J7-J14 (8)   92.50 40.25

Arabic numeral of value at left on #J12-J14.

1911
J15   D1   1c brown   6.25 1.50
J16   D1   2c brown   13.00 13.00

The ½c, 4c, 5c and 20c in brown exist but were not issued as they arrived in China after the downfall of the Ching dynasty.

Issue of 1904 Overprinted in Red

1912

J19	D1	½c blue	475.	375.
J20	D1	4c blue	550.	500.
J21	D1	5c blue	625.	650.
J22	D1	10c blue	950.	950.
J23	D1	20c blue	2,000.	1,800.
J24	D1	30c blue	2,000.	1,800.

Nos. J15-J16 exist with this overprint, but were not regularly issued.

Nos. J25-J33

Nos. J34-J42

1912

Overprinted in Red

J25	D1	½c blue	.20	.20
J26	D1	1c brown	.30	.30
a.		Horiz. pair, imperf. btwn.	550.00	
b.		Inverted overprint	225.00	
J27	D1	2c brown	.35	.30
J28	D1	4c blue	2.75	3.00
J29	D1	5c blue	110.00	110.00
J30	D1	5c brown	1.25	.85
a.		Inverted overprint	225.00	175.00
J31	D1	10c blue	5.00	1.10
J32	D1	20c blue	11.00	10.00
J33	D1	30c blue	14.00	12.00
		Nos. J25-J33 (9)	144.85	137.75

1912

Overprinted in Black

J34	D1	½c blue	6.00	1.40
J35	D1	½c brown	.70	.30
J36	D1	1c brown	.65	.55
a.		Inverted overprint	350.00	175.00
J37	D1	2c brown	3.00	4.25
J38	D1	4c blue	5.00	5.50
J39	D1	5c brown	9.50	7.00
a.		Horiz. pair, imperf. btwn.	700.00	
J40	D1	10c brown	11.50	16.00
J41	D1	20c brown	30.00	35.00
J42	D1	30c brown	65.00	65.00
		Nos. J34-J42 (9)	131.35	135.00

D4 D5 D6

Printed by Waterlow & Sons

1913, May — Perf. 14, 15

J43	D4	½c blue	.60	.20
a.		Horiz. pair, imperf. btwn.	200.00	
J44	D4	1c blue	1.10	.20
J45	D4	2c blue	2.50	1.75
J46	D4	4c blue	2.00	.20
J47	D4	5c blue	3.00	.20
J48	D4	10c blue	6.00	4.25
J49	D4	20c blue	16.00	9.00
J50	D4	30c blue	20.00	6.00
		Nos. J43-J50 (8)	51.20	21.80

Printed by the Chinese Bureau of Engraving & Printing

1915 — Re-engraved — Perf. 14

J51	D4	½c blue	.50	.55
J52	D4	1c blue	1.25	.20
J53	D4	2c blue	1.25	.20
J54	D4	4c blue	1.25	.20
J55	D4	5c blue	2.50	.50
J56	D4	10c blue	3.00	.70
J57	D4	20c blue	9.00	2.00
J58	D4	30c blue	35.00	5.00
		Nos. J51-J58 (8)	53.75	9.35

In the upper part of the stamps of type D4 there is an ornament of five marks like the letter "V". Below this is a curved label with an inscription in Chinese characters. On the 1913 stamps there are two complete background lines between the ornament and the label. The

---

1915 stamps show only one unbroken line at this place. There are other minute differences in the engraving of the stamps of the two issues.

1932 — Perf. 14

J59	D5	½c orange	.20	.20
J60	D5	1c orange	.20	.20
J61	D5	2c orange	.20	.20
J62	D5	4c orange	.40	.20
J63	D5	5c orange	.40	.20
J64	D5	10c orange	.85	.45
J65	D5	20c orange	1.10	.55
J66	D5	30c orange	2.00	1.25
		Nos. J59-J66 (8)	5.35	3.25

See Nos. J69-J79. For surcharges see Nos. 1NJ1, 9NJ1-9NJ4.

Regular Stamps of 1939 Overprinted in Black or Red

1940

J67	A57	$1 henna & dk brn (Bk)	2.00	7.00
J68	A57	$2 dl bl & org brn (R)	2.00	7.00

Type of 1932
Printed by The Commercial Press, Ltd.
Perf. 12½, 12½x13, 13

1940-41 — Engr.

J69	D5	½c yellow orange	.20	.30
J70	D5	1c yellow orange	.20	.30
J71	D5	2c yellow orange ('41)	.20	.30
J72	D5	4c yellow orange	.20	.30
J73	D5	5c yellow orange ('41)	.55	.30
J74	D5	10c yellow orange ('41)	.20	.30
J75	D5	20c yellow orange ('41)	.20	.30
J76	D5	30c yellow orange	.20	.30
J77	D5	50c yellow orange	.35	.40
J78	D5	$1 yellow orange	.35	.60
J79	D5	$2 yellow orange	.60	.60
		Nos. J69-J79 (11)	3.25	4.00

For surcharge see No. 1NJ1.

Thin Paper Without Gum

1944 — Typo. — Perf. 13

J80	D6	10c bluish green	.20	.45
J81	D6	20c light chalky blue	.20	.45
J82	D6	40c dull rose	.20	.45
J83	D6	50c bluish green	.20	.40
J84	D6	60c dull blue	.20	.70
J85	D6	$1 dull rose	.20	.35
J86	D6	$2 lilac brown	.20	.35
		Nos. J80-J86 (7)	1.40	3.15

D7 D8

1945 — Without Gum — Unwmk.

J87	D7	$2 rose carmine	.20	.85
J88	D7	$6 rose carmine	.20	.85
J89	D7	$8 rose carmine	.20	.85
J90	D7	$10 rose carmine	.20	1.10
J91	D7	$20 rose carmine	.20	1.10
J92	D7	$30 rose carmine	.40	1.10
		Nos. J87-J92 (6)	1.40	5.85

For surcharges see Nos. J102-J109.

Thin Paper Without Gum

1947 — Litho. — Perf. 14

J93	D8	$50 plum	.20	.35
J94	D8	$80 plum	.20	.35
J95	D8	$100 plum	.20	.35
J96	D8	$160 plum	.20	.35
J97	D8	$200 plum	.20	.35
J98	D8	$400 violet brown	.20	.35
J99	D8	$500 violet brown	.20	.35
a.		Vert. pair, imperf. between	20.00	
J100	D8	$800 violet brown	.20	.35
J101	D8	$2000 violet brown	.20	.35
		Nos. J93-J101 (9)	1.80	3.15

Type of 1945, Redrawn
Surcharged with New Value in Black

1948 — Engr. — Perf. 13½x14
Without Gum
Deep claret

J102	D7	$1000 on $20	.20	.50
J103	D7	$2000 on $30	.20	.50
J104	D7	$3000 on $50	.20	.50
J105	D7	$4000 on $100	.20	.50
J106	D7	$5000 on $200	.20	.50
J107	D7	$10,000 on $300	.20	.55

J108	D7	$20,000 on $500	.20	.55
J109	D7	$30,000 on $1000	.20	.70
		Nos. J102-J109 (8)	1.60	4.30

There are many differences in the redrawn design.

No. 627 Surcharged in Black

1949 — Perf. 12

J110	A72	1 (c) on $40 orange	.20	.45
J111	A72	2 (c) on $40 orange	.20	.45
J112	A72	5 (c) on $40 orange	.20	.45
J113	A72	10 (c) on $40 orange	.20	.45
J114	A72	20 (c) on $40 orange	.20	.45
J115	A72	50 (c) on $40 orange	.20	.50
J116	A72	$1 on $40 orange	.20	.50
J117	A72	$2 on $40 orange	.20	.50
J118	A72	$5 on $40 orange	.20	.75
J119	A72	$10 on $40 orange	.20	.50
		Nos. J110-J119 (10)	2.00	5.00

Republic of China (Taiwan)

No. 438 Surcharged in Green or Black

1951 — Unwmk. — Perf. 12½

J120	A47	40c on 40c org (G)	17.50	24.00
J121	A47	80c on 40c org (Bk)	17.50	24.00

Revenue Stamps Surcharged in Various Colors

1953 — Unwmk. — Perf. 12½, 14
Without Gum

J122	A95	10c on $50 dk bl (O)	18.00	4.50
J123	A95	20c on $100 ol grn (Dk Br)	18.00	4.50
J124	A95	40c on $20 org brn	20.00	1.50
J125	A95	80c on $500 sl grn (Dk Bl)	30.00	2.50
J126	A95	$1 on $30 dk vio (G)	30.00	8.25
		Nos. J122-J126 (5)	116.00	21.25

D9 D10

D11

1956 — Unwmk. — Litho. — Perf. 12½
Without Gum

J127	D9	20c rose car, & lt bl	1.25	.20
J128	D9	40c green & buff	1.75	.20
J129	D9	80c brown & gray	3.50	.40
J130	D9	$1 ultra & pink	4.00	.40
		Nos. J127-J130 (4)	10.50	1.20

No. 1197 Surcharged in Dark Violet

Wmk. 323
1961, Dec. 28 — Engr. — Perf. 12
Without Gum

J131	A135	$5 on $20 car rose	1.75	.50

Nos. 1274, 1282-1283 Surcharged in Black, Carmine Rose or Blue

1964-65 — Litho.

J132	A158	10c on 80c pale grn	.20	.20
J133	A158	20c on $3.60 vio bl (CR) ('65)	.30	.20
J134	A158	40c on $4.50 ver (B) ('65)	.65	.20
		Nos. J132-J134 (3)	1.15	.60

1966-76 — Wmk. 323 — Perf. 12½
Granite Paper; Without Gum

J135	D10	10c dk brn & lil	.20	.20
J136	D10	20c blue & yel	.40	.20
J137	D10	50c vio bl & lt bl ('70)	.65	.20
J138	D10	$1 purple & sal	.50	.20
J139	D10	$2 grn & lt bl	.65	.20
J140	D10	$5 red & sal	1.25	.30
a.		$5 org red & pale yel	1.25	.30
J141	D10	$10 lil rose & pink ('76)	22.50	.75
		Nos. J135-J141 (7)	26.15	2.05

The 50c, $10 and No. J140a are gummed. The $1 and $2 were reissued with gum in 1968 and 1973 respectively. No. J140a and the $10 are on ordinary paper.

Catalogue values for unused stamps in this section, from this point to the end of the section, are for Never Hinged items.

1984-88 — Litho. — Perf. 12½

J142	D11	$1 rose & violet	.20	.20
J143	D11	$2 yellow & blue	.20	.20
J144	D11	$3 pale grn & brt rose lil	.25	.20
J145	D11	$5 blue & yellow	.25	.20
J146	D11	$5.50 rose lil & brt blue	.40	.35
J147	D11	$7.50 bister yel & dp violet	.60	.45
J148	D11	$10 yel & lil rose	.50	.30
J149	D11	$20 sky blue & citron	1.60	1.25
		Nos. J142-J149 (8)	4.00	3.15

Issued: $3, $5.50, $7.50, $20, Apr. 1, 1988; others, Mar. 15, 1984.

D12

1998, Sept. 30 — Litho. — Perf. 12½
Background Color

J150	D12	50c orange yellow	.20	.20
J151	D12	$1 pink	.20	.20
J152	D12	$2 deep pink	.20	.20
J153	D12	$5 yellow green	.30	.20
J154	D12	$10 blue	.60	.30
J155	D12	$20 green	1.25	.60
		Nos. J150-J155 (6)	2.75	1.70

PARCEL POST STAMPS

PP1 PP2

PP3

1945-48　Unwmk.　Engr.　*Perf. 13*
Without Gum

Q1	PP1	$500 green	11.50	.25
Q2	PP1	$1000 blue	11.50	.25
Q3	PP1	$3000 rose red	22.50	.25
Q4	PP1	$5000 brown	110.00	5.75
Q5	PP1	$10,000 lil gray	175.00	6.50
Q6	PP1	$20,000 red org	2,000.	
		Nos. Q1-Q5 (5)	330.50	13.00

No. Q6 was prepared but not issued.
For surcharges see People's Republic of China Nos. 5LQ1-5LQ2, 5LQ27-5LQ28.

Perf. 12½

Q7	PP2	$3000 red org	18.00	.60
Q8	PP2	$5000 dk blue	29.00	.60
Q9	PP2	$10,000 violet	29.00	.60
Q10	PP2	$20,000 dk red	29.00	.60

Perf. 13½

Q11	PP3	$1000 org yel	5.75	1.00
Q12	PP3	$3000 bl grn	6.00	1.00
Q13	PP3	$5000 org red	6.00	1.00
Q14	PP3	$7000 dl blue	6.00	1.00
Q15	PP3	$10,000 car rose	6.75	1.00
Q16	PP3	$30,000 olive	6.75	1.00
Q17	PP3	$50,000 indigo	6.75	1.00
Q18	PP3	$70,000 org brn	10.00	1.00
Q19	PP3	$100,000 dp plum	10.00	1.00

Denomination Tablet Without Inner Frame

Q20	PP3	$200,000 dk grn	13.00	2.00
Q21	PP3	$300,000 pink	13.00	2.00
Q22	PP3	$500,000 vio brn	13.00	2.50
Q23	PP3	$3,000,000 sl bl	14.00	3.25
Q24	PP3	$5,000,000 lilac	14.00	3.25
Q25	PP3	$6,000,000 ol gray	16.00	4.00
Q26	PP3	$8,000,000 scar	16.00	4.25
Q27	PP3	$10,000,000 sage grn	19.00	5.25
		Nos. Q11-Q27 (17)	182.00	35.50

Zeros for "cents" omitted on Nos. Q23-Q27.
See Taiwan Nos. Q1-Q5. For surcharges see Nos. 883-885, Northeastern Provinces Q1, Szechwan Q1, People's Republic of China 3LQ1-3LQ9, 5LQ3-5LQ16, 5LQ29-5LQ30.

#Q11-Q15, Q23-Q24 Surcharged in Black or Carmine (#Q35)

1949　Unwmk.　*Perf. 13½*

Q32	PP3	$10 on $3000	5.00	.20
Q33	PP3	$20 on $5000	5.00	.20
Q34	PP3	$50 on $10,000	5.00	.20
Q35	PP3	$100 on $3,000,000	6.00	.20
Q36	PP3	$200 on $5,000,000	12.00	.20
Q37	PP3	$500 on $1000	22.50	.20
Q38	PP3	$1000 on $7000	22.50	.30
		Nos. Q32-Q38 (7)	78.00	1.50

5 characters in each line on Nos. Q33-Q38.

MILITARY STAMPS

No. 454 Overprinted in Dull Red

1943-44　Unwmk.　*Perf. 12*

M1	A59	8c turquoise green	2.50	4.25

Nos. 383, 453-454 Overprinted in Red or Black

6mm between characters
Perf. 14, 12½

M2	A57	8c olive green	2.75	4.50
a.		8mm between characters	2.75	4.25
M3	A59	8c red orange (B)	290.00	
M4	A59	8c turquoise green	6.00	5.25

Forgeries of No. M3 abound.

No. 493 Overprinted in Red

Perf. 13

M5	A62	16c dull olive brn	5.50	3.50
a.		Perf. 10½-11	110.00	

No. M5 overprinted in black is a proof.

Stamps of 1942-44 Overprinted in Carmine or Black

M6	A62	50c sage green (C)	2.00	3.50
M7	A62	$1 rose lake	3.00	4.25
M8	A62	$1 dull green	3.00	4.25
M9	A62	$2 dk blue grn (C)	5.00	7.50
M10	A62	$2 dk vio brn ('44)	80.00	80.00
		Nos. M6-M10 (5)	93.00	99.50

Nos. 383 and 357 Overprinted in Red

1944　*Perf. 12, 14*

M11	A57	8c olive green	3.00	4.50
a.		Right character inverted	160.00	
M12	A57	16c olive gray	47.50	47.50

Anti-Aircraft Guns — M1

1945, Jan. 1　Typo.　*Perf. 12½*
Thin Paper Without Gum

M13	M1	rose	.75	4.50

For overprints see Northeastern Provinces Nos. M2-M3.

TAIWAN

(Formosa)
100 Sen = 1 Yen
100 Cents = 1 Dollar

Stamps and Types of Japan (Taiwan) Overprinted in Black

Values in Sen and Yen
Black Overprint

1945　Unwmk.　Litho.　*Imperf.*
Stamps Divided by Lines of Colored Dashes

1	A1	3s carmine	.60	.75
2	A1	5s blue grn	.65	.55
3	A1	10s pale blue	1.10	.55
a.		Inverted overprint	100.00	
b.		Double overprint	110.00	
4	A1	30s dk blue	3.75	5.00
5	A1	40s violet	3.50	4.00
6	A1	50s gray brn	3.75	3.75
7	A1	1y olive grn	4.50	4.75

Same Overprint on Types of Japan

8	A99	5y gray grn	18.00	18.00
9	A100	10y brown vio	24.00	24.00
a.		Inverted overprint	250.00	
		Nos. 1-9 (9)	59.85	61.35

The basic stamps of this issue were prepared by Japanese authorities for Taiwan use before the end of World War II when the island reverted to Chinese control. They are printed on crude buff or white wove paper. The overprint translates: "For Use in Taiwan, Chinese Republic."
A second overprinting of Nos. 2-3 was made with a different font.

China, Nos. 728-731, Surcharged in Black

1946　*Perf. 14*
Without Gum

10	A75	70s on $20 green	1.75	3.75
a.		Inverted surcharge	800.00	
11	A75	1y on $30 blue	2.40	4.00
12	A75	2y on $50 dk brn	2.25	4.25
13	A75	3y on $100 car	2.75	4.25
		Nos. 10-13 (4)	9.15	16.25

Convening of the Chinese Natl. Assembly.

China Issues and Types of 1940-1946 Surcharged in Black

a

Perf. 12½, 12½x13, 13, 13x12½, 14
1946-47

14	A46	2s on 2c dp bl	.20	.50
15	A48	5s on 5c dl red org	.20	.50
16	A39	10s on 4c pale vio	.20	.35
17	A48	30s on 15c brn car	.20	.30
18	A73	50s on $20 car	.30	.25
19	A37	65s on $20 brt yel grn	.35	1.60
20	A47	1y on 20c lt bl	.20	1.10
a.		Inverted surcharge	375.00	
21	A37	1y on $30 choc	.35	1.10
22	A37	2y on $50 red org	.40	.45
23	A73	3y on $100 dk car	.20	.25
24	A73	5y on $200 ol grn	.20	.25
25	A73	10y on $500 brt bl grn	.25	.35
26	A73	20y on $700 red brn	.70	.60
27	A73	50y on $1000 rose lake	1.25	1.25
28	A73	100y on $3000 blue	2.75	.90
		Nos. 14-28 (15)	7.75	9.75

The bottom line of the surcharge expresses the new value and consists of 2, 3 or 4 characters.
Nos. 14, 18-19, 21-28 issued in 1947.

Same Surcharge on China No. 412

1947　Wmk. 261　*Perf. 13*

28A	A48	30s on 15c brn car	70.00	100.00

Type of China, 1946, with additional inscription on both sides of head

1947　Unwmk.　Engr.　*Perf. 11, 11½*

29	A74	70c carmine	1.75	2.50
30	A74	$1 green	1.75	2.50
31	A74	$2 vermilion	1.75	2.50
32	A74	$3 yel grn	1.75	2.50
33	A74	$7 yel org	1.75	2.50
34	A74	$10 magenta	1.75	2.50
		Nos. 29-34 (6)	10.50	15.00

60th birthday of Chiang Kai-shek.

Type of China, 1947, with additional inscription above value

1947　*Perf. 14*

35	A76	50c deep green	1.90	2.50
36	A76	$3 deep blue	1.90	2.50
37	A76	$7.50 carmine	1.90	2.50
38	A76	$10 light brown	1.90	2.50
39	A76	$20 deep claret	1.90	2.50
		Nos. 35-39 (5)	9.50	12.50

First anniversary of return of Chinese National Government to Nanking.

Dr. Sun Yat-sen — A3

1947, July 10
Without Gum

40	A3	$1 dk brown	2.25	.25
41	A3	$2 org brn	.60	.25
42	A3	$3 blue grn	.60	.25
43	A3	$5 vermilion	.60	.25
44	A3	$9 deep blue	.60	.25
45	A3	$10 brt rose car	.60	.25
46	A3	$20 deep green	.60	.30
47	A3	$50 rose lilac	.60	.25
48	A3	$100 blue	.60	.60
49	A3	$200 dark red	.60	.60
		Nos. 40-49 (10)	7.65	3.25

The 30c gray and $7.50 orange were not regularly issued without surcharge. Value for the two stamps, $450.
See #63-68. For overprint and surcharges see #51-53, 69-73, 101-103, J10-J17.

Type of 1947 Surcharged in Black

b

1948　Unwmk.　*Perf. 14*

51	A3	$25 on $100 blue	1.10	1.65
52	A3	$500 on $7.50 org	1.10	.55
53	A3	$1000 on 30c gray	4.75	3.50
		Nos. 51-53 (3)	6.95	5.70

Stamps of China, 1943-48, Surcharged Type "a" in Black or Carmine

1948-49　*Perf. 12½, 14*

54	A73	$5 on $70 red org	.65	2.50
55	A62	$10 on $3 dk yel	1.75	2.75
56	A82	$10 on $150 dk bl (C)	.45	.70
57	A82	$20 on $250 dp lil (C)	1.10	.85
58	A67	$100 on $20 car	600.00	600.00
59	A82	$1000 on $20,000 rose pink ('49)	2.25	1.75
		Nos. 54-59 (6)	606.20	608.55

The bottom line of the surcharge expresses the new value and consists of 2 or 3 characters.
Forgeries of No. 58 abound.

Type of 1947

1949　Engr.　*Perf. 14*

63	A3	$25 olive grn	.70	.30
64	A3	$5000 ocher	7.25	.50
65	A3	$10,000 apple grn	8.50	2.00
66	A3	$20,000 ol bister	8.50	3.50
67	A3	$30,000 indigo	9.50	.70
68	A3	$40,000 violet brn	8.50	.60
		Nos. 63-68 (6)	42.95	7.60

For overprint and surcharges see #101, 103, J12.

No. 42 and Type of 1947 Surcharged Type "b" in Black, Carmine Violet or Red Violet

1949

69	A3	$300 on $3 bl grn	.65	.30
70	A3	$1000 on $3 bl grn (C)	3.00	.55
71	A3	$2000 on $3 bl grn (V)	5.00	.55
72	A3	$3000 on $3 bl grn (RV)	3.75	1.10
73	A3	$3000 on $7.50 org	57.50	1.90
		Nos. 69-73 (5)	69.90	4.40

For overprints see Nos. J10-J11.

Stamps of China, 1940-47, Surcharged Type "a" in Black or Carmine
Perf. 12½, 13x13½, 14

74	A39	$2 on 2½c rose lil (#424)	.55	2.00
75	A72	$5 on $40 org (#627)	.70	1.10
76	A73	$5 on $50 pur (C) (#638)	.70	.25
77	A73	$5 on $100 dk car (#640)	.70	.50
78	A57	$5 on 2c ol grn (#368)	.75	.75
81	A63	$100 on $20 rose (#571)	1.10	.50

82	A67 $200 on $10 dk bl (C) (#591)	1.75	1.10
84	A57 $500 on $30 dl vio (#521)	6.00	2.10
86	A62 $800 on $4 red brn (#504)	5.25	4.25
87	A67 $5000 on $10 dk bl (#591)	6.00	4.00
88	A67 $10,000 on $20 car (#592)	9.50	3.25
89	A82 $200,000 on $3000 bl (C) (#750)	350.00	24.00
	Nos. 74-89 (12)	383.00	43.80

Northeastern
Provinces No. 47,
Surcharged in Green,
Red Violet, Black or
Blue

1949-50

91	A2 2c on $44 (G)	35.00	6.00
92	A2 5c on $44 (RV) ('50)	32.50	7.00
a.	Violet surcharge	57.50	11.50
93	A2 10c on $44 (RV) ('50)	42.50	6.00
94	A2 20c on $44 (Bk) ('50)	55.00	7.00
a.	Double surcharge	100.00	
95	A2 30c on $44 (Bl) ('50)	62.50	14.00
96	A2 50c on $44 (Bl) ('50)	75.00	17.00
	Nos. 91-96 (6)	302.50	57.00

There were two printings of Nos. 91-93, with
minor differences.

China 959a,
Overprinted in Black

Overprint 15mm Wide

1949   Unwmk.   Rouletted 9½

97	A96 orange	1.10	.20

China Nos. 567, 498 and 640
Surcharged Type "a" in Black

1948-49   Unwmk.   Perf. 12½, 13, 14

98	A63 $20 on $3 red	2.25	1.40
99	A62 $50 on 50c sage grn	2.50	1.10
a.	Perf. 11	22.50	26.00
100	A73 $600 on $100 dk car	10.00	2.75
	Nos. 98-100 (3)	14.75	5.25

Botton line of surcharge consists of 3
characters.
No. 99 has two settings of surcharge: I.
Spacing 10mm between rows of characters. II.
Spacing 12mm.

#67, 47 and 68
Surcharged in
Violet (#101) or Black

1949   Perf. 14

101	A3 2c on $30,000 ind	35.00	20.00
102	A3 10c on $50 rose lil	35.00	4.50
103	A3 10c on $40,000 vio brn	80.00	20.00
	Nos. 101-103 (3)	150.00	44.50

Numerals slightly larger on Nos. 101-103.
For similar surcharges on China type A82
see China Nos. 1025-1036.

AIR POST STAMP

China No. C62a,
Overprinted in Black

Overprint 15mm Wide

1949   Unwmk.   Rouletted 9½

C1	AP5 blue green	4.50	4.50

SPECIAL DELIVERY STAMP

China No. E12a,
Overprinted in Black

Overprint 12½mm Wide

1950   Unwmk.   Rouletted 9½

E1	SD2 red violet	3.00	4.50

REGISTRATION STAMP

China No. F2a
Overprinted in Black

Overprint 12mm Wide

1950   Unwmk.   Rouletted 9½

F1	R2 carmine	2.25	4.50

TAIWAN POSTAGE DUE STAMPS

D1

Unwmk.

1948, Feb. 10   Litho.   Perf. 14

Without Gum

J1	D1 $1 blue	1.10	4.25
J2	D1 $3 blue	1.10	4.75
J3	D1 $5 blue	1.10	4.75
J4	D1 $10 blue	1.10	6.50
J5	D1 $20 blue	1.10	4.00
	Nos. J1-J5 (5)	5.50	24.25

Nos. J1-J4 Surcharged in
Carmine

1948, Dec. 4

J6	D1 $50 on $1 blue	7.75	11.00
J7	D1 $100 on $3 blue	7.75	11.00
J8	D1 $300 on $5 blue	7.75	11.00
J9	D1 $500 on $10 blue	7.75	11.00
	Nos. J6-J9 (4)	31.00	44.00

Nos. 70, 72 and 64
Handstamped in Violet

1949, Aug. 5

J10	A3 $1000 on $3 bl grn	19.00	19.00
J11	A3 $3000 on $3 bl grn	29.00	29.00
J12	A3 $5000 ocher	42.50	42.50
	Nos. J10-J12 (3)	90.50	90.50

No. 48 Surcharged in
Various Colors

1950

J13	A3 4c on $100 bl (Br)	12.00	10.00
J14	A3 10c on $100 bl (RV)	22.50	26.00
J15	A3 20c on $100 bl (Bk)	10.00	22.50
J16	A3 40c on $100 bl (C)	47.50	90.00
J17	A3 $1 on $100 bl (Bl)	35.00	47.50
	Nos. J13-J17 (5)	127.00	196.00

TAIWAN PARCEL POST STAMPS

Type of China, Parcel Post Stamps of
1945-48 With Added Inscription

1949   Unwmk.   Engr.   Perf. 14

Q1	PP3 $100 bluish grn	225.00	.60
Q2	PP3 $300 rose car	225.00	.60
Q3	PP3 $500 olive green	225.00	.60
Q4	PP3 $1000 slate	225.00	.60
Q5	PP3 $3000 deep plum	225.00	.60
	Nos. Q1-Q5 (5)	1,125.00	3.00

Chinese characters in lower corners have
colorless background; denomination tablet in
color.

OCCUPATION STAMPS

Issued Under Japanese Occupation

Canceled Stamps
Postally used stamps of the Japanese occupation generally have heavy,
smudgy cancels.

Kwangtung

China No. 297
Overprinted in Black

1942   Unwmk.   Perf. 12½

1N1	A37 2c olive green	8.00	8.00
a.	Inverted overprint	120.00	

**Same Overprint in Red or Black on
Stamps of China, 1939-41**

Perf. 12½, 14

1N2	A57 3c dl cl (#350)	2.75	2.75
1N3	A57 8c ol grn (#383)	2.75	2.75
1N4	A57 10c grn (#354) (R)	2.50	2.75
1N5	A57 10c grn (#384) (R)	3.50	3.50
1N6	A57 16c ol gray (#357)	4.75	7.25
1N7	A57 30c scar (#385)	4.00	2.75
1N8	A57 50c dk bl (#386) (R)	4.00	8.00
1N9	A57 $1 org brn & sep (#387)	7.25	9.25
1N10	A57 $2 dp bl & yel brn (#388)	8.00	9.50
1N11	A57 $5 red & sl grn (#389)	7.00	8.75
1N12	A57 $10 dk grn & dl pur (#390)	16.00	20.00
1N13	A57 $20 rose lake & dk bl (#391)	7.00	9.50

**Same Overprint on China Nos. 422
and 433**

Perf. 12½

1N14	A40 1c orange	1.90	2.40
a.	Inverted overprint	80.00	80.00
1N15	A47 20c lt blue	3.50	4.00

**Same Overprint on Stamps of
China, 1941**

Perf. 12

1N16	A59 1c orange	2.50	3.75
1N17	A59 5c green	2.50	3.75
1N18	A59 8c turq green	2.75	3.75
1N19	A59 10c brt green	3.25	3.75
1N20	A59 17c olive	3.25	3.75
1N21	A59 30c scarlet	3.25	3.75
1N22	A59 50c dark blue	3.25	3.75
	Nos. 1N1-1N22 (22)	103.65	127.40

Stamps of China,
1939-41 Overprinted
in Black

1942   Perf. 12½, 14

1N23	A57 2c olive grn (#368)	.65	.80
1N24	A57 3c dl claret (#350)	.65	.95
1N25	A57 5c olive grn (#352)	.65	1.25
1N26	A57 8c olive grn (#353)	300.00	—
1N27	A57 8c olive grn (#369)	.80	1.00
1N28	A57 10c green (#354)	1.00	1.25
1N29	A57 16c ol gray (#357)	1.25	1.25
1N30	A57 25c dk bl (#358)	1.25	2.75
1N31	A57 30c scarlet (#385)	.80	2.40
1N32	A57 50c dk blue (#386)	2.25	2.75
1N33	A57 $1 org brn & sep (#387)	6.50	8.00
1N34	A57 $2 dp bl & yel brn (#388)	8.00	9.50
1N35	A57 $5 red & sl grn (#389)	10.00	12.00
1N36	A57 $10 dk grn & dl pur (#390)	16.00	20.00
1N37	A57 $20 rose lake & dk bl (#391)	14.00	20.00
	Nos. 1N23-1N25,1N27-1N37 (14)	63.80	83.90

No. 1N26 is valued in fine condition.

**Same Overprint on China Nos. 397-
401**

1942   Wmk. 261   Perf. 14

1N38	A57 $1 org brn & sep	9.00	9.00
1N39	A57 $2 dp bl & yel brn	8.00	8.25
1N40	A57 $5 red & sl grn	11.00	13.00
1N41	A57 $10 dk grn & dl pur	17.50	20.00
1N42	A57 $20 rose lake & dk bl	22.50	24.00
	Nos. 1N38-1N42 (5)	68.00	74.25

**Same Overprint on Stamps of China,
1941**

1942   Unwmk.   Perf. 12

1N43	A59 2c brt ultra	.30	.50
1N44	A59 5c green	.30	.50
1N45	A59 8c red org	.35	.50
1N46	A59 8c turq grn	.35	.90
1N47	A59 10c brt green	.60	.65
1N48	A59 17c olive	.65	1.00
1N49	A59 25c rose vio	.65	1.00
1N50	A59 30c scarlet	.65	1.10
1N51	A59 50c dk blue	.65	1.10
1N52	A59 $1 brn & blk	4.75	8.00
1N53	A59 $2 bl & blk	6.00	8.75
1N54	A59 $5 scar & blk	4.75	4.75
1N55	A59 $10 grn & blk	9.00	13.00
1N56	A59 $20 rose vio & blk	11.00	20.00
	Nos. 1N43-1N56 (14)	40.00	61.75

China Nos. 354 and
369 Surcharged in
Black

1945   Unwmk.   Perf. 12½

1N57	A57 $200 on 10c grn	110.00	50.00
1N58	A57 $400 on 8c ol grn	110.00	60.00

China No. 422
Surcharged in Black

1945

1N59	A40 $400 on 1c org	750.00	600.00

Forgeries exist.

OCCUPATION POSTAGE DUE
STAMPS

China, No. J79
Surcharged Diagonally
with New Value Between
Parallel Lines in Black

1945   Unwmk.   Perf. 12½

1NJ1	D5 $100 on $2 yel org	750.00	700.00
a.	Inverted surcharge	1,100.	1,100.

MENG CHIANG (Inner Mongolia)

Nos. 297-298, 301-303 Overprinted

Characters 4mm High — I	Characters 5mm High — II

1941   Engr.   Unwmk.

2N1	A37	2c #297, I	1.25	2.00
a.		Type II	1.60	2.00
2N2	A37	4c #298, II	45.00	
a.		Type I	60.00	55.00
2N3	A37	15c #301, I	4.75	5.50
a.			4.50	6.00
2N4	A37	20c #302, II	8.75	8.75
a.		Type I	12.00	16.00
2N5	A37	25c #303, II	12.00	14.00
a.			92.50	92.50
		Nos. 2N1-2N5 (5)	71.75	30.25

For surcharge see No. 2N116.

On Nos. 312, 314, 318, 321

1941   Perf. 14

2N6	A39	½c #312, I	14.00	17.50
a.		Type II	20.00	
2N7	A39	2½c #314, II	3.75	3.75
a.		Type I	7.25	8.75
2N8	A45	13c #318, II	1.25	1.10
a.		Type I	110.00	110.00
2N9	A48	30c #321, II	72.50	72.50
		Nos. 2N6-2N9 (4)	91.50	94.85

On Stamps of 1939-41

1941   Perf. 12½

2N10	A57	2c #368, II	2.40	3.00
2N11	A57	3c #350, II	1.00	1.00
a.		Type I	1.25	1.25
2N12	A57	5c #352, II	2.10	2.50
a.		Type I	2.75	6.00
2N13	A57	8c #369, II	1.25	.85
a.		Type II	2.00	2.00
2N14	A57	8c #369, II	8.00	8.00
2N15	A57	10c #354, II	2.25	2.25
2N16	A57	16c #357, II	4.00	4.00
2N17	A57	$1 #359, II	9.50	9.50
a.		Type I	325.00	325.00
b.		#347, I	87.50	80.00
2N18	A57	$5 #361, II	65.00	65.00
		Nos. 2N10-2N18 (9)	95.50	96.10

For surcharges see Nos. 2N117, 2N119.

On Stamps of 1940 with Secret Marks

1941   Unwmk.   Perf. 14

2N19	A57	5c #382, I	1.60	1.75
2N20	A57	8c #383, I	3.25	3.25
a.		Type II	55.00	
2N21	A57	10c #384, II	2.25	2.00
a.		Type I	4.00	4.00
2N22	A57	30c #385, II	2.75	2.75
a.		Type I	4.75	5.00
2N23	A57	50c #386, I	7.25	7.25
a.		Type II	7.25	7.25
2N24	A57	$1 #387, I	11.00	12.00
a.		Type II	20.00	20.00
2N25	A57	$2 #388, I	12.00	14.00
a.		Type II	27.50	27.50
2N26	A57	$5 #389, I	30.00	30.00
a.		Type II	67.50	
2N27	A57	$10 #390, I	60.00	60.00
a.		Type I	70.00	70.00
2N28	A57	$20 #391, II	100.00	110.00
a.		Type I	100.00	110.00
		Nos. 2N19-2N28 (10)	230.10	243.00

For surcharge see No. 2N120.

On Stamps of 1940 with Secret Marks

1941   Wmk. 261   Perf. 14

2N29	A57	10c #394, II	4.50	4.50
2N30	A57	30c #395, II	4.75	4.75
a.		Type I	65.00	65.00
2N31	A57	50c #396, II	4.00	4.75
		Nos. 2N29-2N31 (3)	13.25	15.25

On Stamps of 1940-41 (Martyrs) with Secret Marks

Perf. 12½, 13 & Compound

1941   Wmk. 261

2N32	A39	½c #402, II	12.00	14.00
2N33	A40	1c #403, II	1.00	1.00
a.		Type I	3.50	3.50
2N34	A39	2½c #405, I	60.00	60.00
a.			80.00	80.00
2N35	A48	3c #406, II	3.50	3.50
2N36	A46	10c #410, II	12.50	12.50
a.			16.00	
2N37	A46	17c #413, II	47.50	
a.			80.00	80.00
2N38	A40	25c #416, II	3.50	3.50
2N39	A48	30c #418, II	60.00	60.00
a.			72.50	72.50
2N40	A47	40c #419, II	6.00	6.00
a.		Type I	8.00	8.00

2N41	A40	50c #420, I	12.00	12.00
a.		Type II	60.00	

Unwmk.

2N42	A39	½c #421, II	1.60	2.25
a.		Type I	5.00	5.00
2N43	A40	1c #422, I	1.60	1.40
a.		Type II	4.25	3.50
2N44	A46	2c #423, I	6.00	6.00
2N45	A48	3c #425, II	3.50	3.50
a.			4.00	4.00
2N46	A39	4c #426, II	2.00	1.75
2N47	A45	8c #428, II	16.00	
a.			80.00	
2N48	A46	10c #429, II	24.00	24.00
a.		Type II	72.50	
2N49	A45	13c #430, II	6.50	7.25
a.			24.00	
2N50	A48	15c #431, II	4.00	4.00
2N51	A46	17c #432, II	3.75	3.75
a.		Type I	4.75	4.75
2N52	A47	20c #433, II	2.25	3.00
a.		Type I	3.25	3.75
2N53	A45	21c #434, II	4.00	4.00
2N54	A40	25c #435, I	4.75	4.75
2N55	A46	28c #436, II	4.25	4.25
2N56	A40	50c #439, II	4.75	2.40
a.			7.75	7.75
		Nos. 2N42-2N56 (15)	88.95	72.30

For surcharges see Nos. 2N114-2N115, 2N118, 2N121-2N122.

China Nos. 297-298, 302 Surcharged in Black

1942   Unwmk.   Perf. 12½, 13

2N57	A37	1c on 2c ol grn	20.00	20.00
2N58	A37	2c on 4c grn	12.00	12.00
2N59	A37	10c on 20c ultra	32.50	32.50
		Nos. 2N57-2N59 (3)	64.50	64.50

Same, on China No. 313

Perf. 14

2N60	A40	½c on 1c org	20.00	20.00

Same, on Stamps of China, 1938-41

Perf. 12½

2N61	A57	1c on 2c (#368)	2.00	1.25
2N62	A57	4c on 8c (#353)	9.50	12.00
a.		Inverted surcharge	47.50	
2N63	A57	4c on 8c (#369)	1.25	1.25
2N64	A57	5c on 10c (#354)	1.00	.65
2N65	A57	8c on 16c (#357)	4.00	3.00
2N66	A57	8c on $1 (#359)	9.50	9.50
a.		On No. 347	47.50	47.50
b.		On No. 344	400.00	
2N67	A57	$1 on $2 (#360)	60.00	60.00
		Nos. 2N61-2N67 (7)	87.25	87.65

No. 2N66b was issued without gum.

Same, on Stamps of China, 1940

Perf. 14

2N68	A57	4c on 8c (#383)	.65	.65
2N69	A57	15c on 30c (#385)	7.25	10.00
a.		Inverted surcharge	55.00	55.00
2N70	A57	25c on 50c (#386)	7.00	8.00
2N71	A57	50c on $1 (#387)	6.00	7.25
2N72	A57	$1 on $2 (#388)	12.00	12.00
2N73	A57	$5 on $10 (#390)	45.00	45.00
2N74	A57	$10 on $20 (#391)	72.50	80.00
		Nos. 2N68-2N74 (7)	150.40	162.90

Same, on China No. 395

1942   Wmk. 261   Perf. 14

2N75	A57	15c on 30c scar	80.00	80.00

Same, on China Nos. 418 and 419

Perf. 12½, 13

2N76	A48	15c on 30c brn car	47.50	47.50
2N77	A47	20c on 40c org	9.50	11.00
		Nos. 2N75-2N77 (3)	137.00	138.50

Same, on Stamps of China, 1940-41

1942   Unwmk.

2N78	A40	½c on 1c org	.25	.35
2N79	A39	2c on 4c pale vio	6.00	6.00
2N80	A47	10c on 20c lt bl	6.00	6.00
2N81	A47	20c on 40c org	14.50	14.50
2N82	A40	25c on 50c grn	24.00	24.00
		Nos. 2N78-2N82 (5)	50.75	50.85

Same Surcharge on "New Peking" Prints

Perf. 14

2N83	A37	1c on 2c ol grn	12.00	20.00
2N84	A37	2c on 4c dl grn	.55	.65
2N85	A46	5c on 10c dl vio	4.00	7.25
2N86	A57	8c on 16c ol gray	1.60	2.40

2N87	A47	10c on 20c red brn	4.75	7.25
2N88	A48	15c on 30c brn car	1.75	2.75
2N89	A47	20c on 40c org	7.25	8.00
2N90	A40	25c on 50c grn	2.00	4.00
2N91	A57	50c on $1 org brn & sep	12.00	12.00
2N92	A57	$1 on $2 dp bl & org brn	30.00	35.00
2N93	A57	$5 on $10 dk grn & dl pur	65.00	65.00
		Nos. 2N83-2N93 (11)	140.90	164.30

The "New Peking" printings were made by the Chinese Bureau of Engraving and Printing for use in Japanese controlled areas of North China. They are on thin, poor quality paper, with dull gum or without gum and there are slight alterations in the designs.

Dragon-Carved Pillar and Doves — A1	Mining Coal — A2

Wmk. Characters in Circle in Sheet

1943   Engr.   Perf. 12xPin-perf. 12

2N94	A1	4f deep orange	.25	.80
2N95	A1	8f dark blue	.30	1.00

5th anniv. of the Inner Mongolia post and telegraph service.

The watermark, which is 40mm in diameter and covers four stamps, occurs three times in the sheet.

1943   Unwmk.   Photo.   Perf. 12

2N96	A2	4f Prus green	.25	1.00
2N97	A2	8f brown red	.30	1.25

2nd anniv. of the "Greater East Asia War."

Flying Horse — A3	Yun Wang — A4

1944   Perf. 12½x12, 12x12½

2N98	A3	4f rose	.20	1.00
2N99	A4	8f dull blue	.25	1.00

5th anniv. of the founding of the Federal Autonomous Government of Mongolia, Sept. 1, 1939.

Industrial Plant — A5

1944, Dec. 8   Photo.   Perf. 12x12½

2N100	A5	8f red brown	.25	1.75

3rd anniv. of the "Greater East Asia War" and to encourage production increase.

New Peking Printings of 1942 Overprinted in Black

1945   Unwmk.   Engr.   Perf. 14

Without Gum

2N101	A37	2c olive grn	9.50	—
2N102	A37	4c dull grn	16.00	—
2N103	A37	5c green	17.50	22.50
2N104	A57	$1 org brn & sep	2.75	3.50
2N105	A57	$2 dp bl & org brn	12.00	12.00
2N106	A57	$5 red & grnsh blk	40.00	40.00

Same Overprint on New Peking Printings of Martyrs Issue

2N107	A40	1c orange	.80	.80
2N108	A45	8c dp orange	.75	.75
2N109	A46	10c dl violet	.25	.35
2N110	A47	20c red brown	1.75	2.40
2N111	A48	30c brown car	.35	.35
2N112	A47	40c orange	.40	.40
2N113	A40	50c green	7.25	8.00

For surcharges see Nos. 2N123-2N127.

Stamps of Meng Chiang, 1941, Surcharged in Red or Black

50c

10c

$1

1945

2N114	A39	10c on ½c ol blk (#2N42, II, R)	2.00	2.25
a.		On #2N42a	6.00	7.25
2N115	A40	10c on 1c org (#2N43a, II, R)	1.00	1.25
a.		Without secret mark (China #422a)	40.00	40.00
b.		On #2N43, I	2.50	2.75
2N116	A37	50c on 2c ol grn (#2N1a, II, B)	24.00	30.00
b.		On #2N1, I	24.00	30.00
2N117	A57	50c on 2c ol grn (#2N10, II, B))	.80	1.50
2N118	A39	50c on 4c pale vio (#2N46, II, R)	.80	1.00
2N119	A57	50c on 5c ol grn (#2N12, II, R)	.55	1.25
a.		On #2N12a, I	10.50	10.50
2N120	A57	50c on 5c ol grn (#2N19, II, R)	1.00	1.75
		Nos. 2N114-2N120 (7)	30.15	39.00

Same Surcharge on #2N32, 2N33

1945   Wmk. 261

2N121	A39	10c on ½c ol blk, II (R)	20.00	24.00
2N122	A40	10c on 1c orange, II (R)	1.00	1.25
a.		On #2N33a, I	24.00	

Same Surcharge on Nos. 2N107, 2N101-2N103 and 2N108

1945   Unwmk.

2N123	A40	10c on 1c org (R)	.30	.60
2N124	A37	50c on 2c ol grn (Bk)	2.75	2.75
2N125	A37	50c on 4c dl grn (R)	4.00	4.00
2N126	A37	50c on 5c green	.40	.40
2N127	A45	$1 on 8c dp org (R)	.60	.60
		Nos. 2N123-2N127 (5)	8.05	8.35

NORTH CHINA
Honan

Nos. 297-298, 301-303 Overprinted

I	II

1941   Engr.   Unwmk.

3N1	A37	2c #297, II	7.25	7.25
a.		Type I	17.50	17.50
3N2	A37	4c #298, I	5.75	6.00
a.		Type II	27.50	27.50
3N3	A37	15c #301, I	1.75	2.00
a.		Type II	2.25	3.00

3N4	A37	20c #302, I	6.50	6.50
3N5	A37	25c #303, II	20.00	20.00
		Nos. 3N1-3N5 (5)	42.75	41.75

1941   *Perf. 14*

3N6	A39	½c #312, I	2.00	3.00
a.		Type II	32.50	—
3N7	A39	2½c #314, I	1.25	1.75
a.		Type II	1.75	2.40
3N8	A45	13c #318, II	1.25	1.25
a.		Type I	80.00	80.00
3N9	A48	30c #321, II	14.50	14.50
3N10	A47	40c #322, II	80.00	80.00
		Nos. 3N6-3N10 (5)	99.00	100.50

On Stamps of 1939-41

1941   *Perf. 12½*

3N11	A57	2c #368, II	1.25	1.25
3N12	A57	3c #350, I	.60	.60
a.		Type II	1.00	1.00
3N13	A57	5c #352, II	1.25	.65
a.		Type I	1.90	1.90
3N14	A57	8c #353, II	1.25	1.25
a.		Type I	1.25	1.25
3N15	A57	10c #354, II	2.40	3.50
3N16	A57	16c #357, II	1.40	2.40
3N17	A57	$1 #359, II	12.00	12.00
a.		Type I	250.00	250.00
b.		On #347, I	47.50	47.50
3N18	A57	$5 #361, II	65.00	65.00
		Nos. 3N11-3N18 (8)	85.15	86.65

For overprints see Nos. 3N56, 3N58, 3N61.

On Stamps of 1940 with Secret Marks

1941   **Unwmk.**   *Perf. 14*

3N20	A57	5c #382, II	2.00	1.60
3N21	A57	8c #383, II	.50	.50
3N22	A57	10c #384, II	1.60	1.25
3N23	A57	30c #385, I	6.50	7.25
a.		Type II	9.00	9.00
3N24	A57	50c #386, I	3.25	3.00
a.		Type II	14.00	14.00
3N25	A57	$1 #387, I	6.50	6.50
a.		Type II	60.00	60.00
3N26	A57	$2 #388, I	12.00	14.00
a.		Type II	20.00	20.00
3N27	A57	$5 #389, II	32.50	24.00
a.		Type I	47.50	47.50
3N28	A57	$10 #390, II	40.00	40.00
a.		Type I	125.00	125.00
3N29	A57	$20 #391, II	100.00	110.00
a.		Type I	100.00	110.00
		Nos. 3N20-3N29 (10)	204.85	208.10

On Stamps of 1940 with Secret Marks

1941   **Wmk. 261**   *Perf. 14*

3N30	A57	5c #392, II	20.00	12.00
3N31	A57	8c #393, II	9.50	6.00
3N32	A57	30c #395, I	20.00	20.00
a.		Type II	32.50	32.50
3N33	A57	50c #396, II	15.00	20.00
		Nos. 3N30-3N33 (4)	64.50	58.00

On Stamps of 1940-41 (Martyrs) with Secret Marks

Perf. 12½, 13 & Compound

1941   **Wmk. 261**

3N34	A39	½c #402, II	2.40	3.00
3N35	A40	1c #403, II	.60	.40
a.		Type I	1.60	1.60
3N36	A39	2½c #405, II	11.00	14.00
3N37	A46	10c #410, II	12.00	15.00
a.		Type I	27.50	27.50
3N38	A45	13c #411, II	3.50	3.50
3N39	A46	17c #413, II	3.50	3.50
a.		Type I	8.00	8.00
3N40	A46	25c #416, II	2.60	2.60
3N41	A47	40c #419, II	4.00	4.00
a.		Type I	14.50	14.50
		Nos. 3N34-3N41 (8)	39.60	46.00

Unwmk.

3N42	A39	½c #421, II	1.60	1.60
a.		Type I	3.50	3.50
3N43	A40	1c #422, I	2.00	2.00
a.		Type II	3.50	3.50
3N44	A46	2c #423, I	12.00	12.00
3N45	A48	3c #425, I	1.25	2.00
3N46	A39	4c #426, II	.70	.70
3N47	A46	10c #429, I	35.00	35.00
3N48	A45	13c #430, II	2.75	2.75
a.		Type I	16.00	16.00
3N49	A48	15c #431, II	3.50	3.50
3N50	A46	17c #432, II	3.50	3.50
a.		Type I	14.00	14.00
3N51	A47	20c #433, II	1.60	1.60
a.		Type I	50.00	40.00
3N52	A45	21c #434, II	3.50	3.50
3N53	A40	25c #435, II	4.00	4.00
3N54	A46	28c #436, II	3.50	3.50
		Nos. 3N42-3N54 (13)	74.90	75.65

For overprints see Nos. 3N55, 3N59.

Overprinted in Red

1942

3N55	A39	4c #3N46	2.75	3.75
3N56	A57	8c #3N14	20.00	27.50
3N57	A57	8c #3N57	4.75	8.00
		Nos. 3N55-3N57 (3)	27.50	39.25

The fall of Singapore.

Overprinted in Red

1942

3N58	A57	2c #3N11	8.00	12.00
3N59	A39	4c #3N46	14.00	20.00
3N60	A57	8c #369, II	35.00	40.00
3N61	A57	8c #3N14	27.50	30.00
		Nos. 3N58-3N61 (4)	84.50	102.00

Formation of Manchukuo, 10th anniv.

Hopei

Nos. 297-298, 301-303 Overprinted

	I			II

1941   **Engr.**   **Unwmk.**

4N1	A37	2c #297, II	1.10	.70
a.		Type I	3.50	2.75
4N2	A37	4c #298, I	3.75	3.75
a.		Type II	70.00	
4N3	A37	15c #301, II	2.40	2.40
a.		Type I	3.50	3.25
4N4	A37	20c #302, II	1.50	1.25
4N5	A37	25c #303, II	9.00	7.25
a.		Type I	80.00	75.00
		Nos. 4N1-4N5 (5)	17.75	15.35

On Nos. 312, 314, 318, 321

1941   *Perf. 14*

4N6	A39	½c #312, II	.35	.60
a.		Type I	.90	.90
4N7	A39	2½c #314, II	.50	.35
a.		Type I	.50	.60
4N8	A45	13c #318, II	1.25	1.10
a.		Type I	2.25	2.25
4N9	A48	30c #321, II	4.75	6.00
		Nos. 4N6-4N9 (4)	6.85	8.05

On Stamps of 1939-41

1941   *Perf. 12½*

4N10	A57	2c #368, II	1.00	.50
4N11	A57	2c #349, II	.65	.80
4N12	A57	3c #350, II	.35	.35
a.		Type I	1.60	1.60
4N13	A57	5c #352, II	.65	.50
a.		Type I	1.75	1.60
4N14	A57	8c #353, II	.35	.35
a.		Type I	1.40	1.25
4N15	A57	8c #369, II	3.00	3.00
4N16	A57	10c #354, II	.80	.65
4N17	A57	16c #357, II	2.00	.80
4N18	A57	$1 #359, II	8.00	8.00
a.		On #347, II	200.00	—
4N19	A57	$2 #360, II	10.00	10.00
a.		Type I	40.00	40.00
4N20	A57	$5 #361, I	40.00	40.00
a.		Type II	60.00	60.00
4N21	A57	$10 #362, II	160.00	160.00
4N22	A57	$20 #363, II	350.00	350.00
		Nos. 4N10-4N22 (13)	576.80	574.95

For overprints see Nos. 4N66-4N68, 4N70.

On Stamps of 1940 with Secret Marks

1941   **Unwmk.**   *Perf. 14*
Type II

4N24	A57	5c #382	.60	.50
4N25	A57	8c #383	1.25	1.25
4N26	A57	10c #384	1.00	.30
4N27	A57	30c #385	1.00	1.00
4N28	A57	50c #386	2.00	2.00
4N29	A57	$1 #387	4.00	3.50
4N30	A57	$2 #388	14.00	9.50
4N31	A57	$5 #389	35.00	35.00
4N32	A57	$10 #390	40.00	40.00
4N33	A57	$20 #391	60.00	72.50
		Nos. 4N24-4N33 (10)	158.85	165.55

For overprints see Nos. 4N65, 4N71.

Type I

4N24a	A57	5c	1.10	1.10
4N25a	A57	8c	52.50	52.50
4N26a	A57	10c	1.75	.80
4N28a	A57	50c	2.00	2.00
4N29a	A57	$1	6.00	4.00
4N30a	A57	$2	24.00	24.00

4N31a	A57	$5	40.00	40.00
4N32a	A57	$10	55.00	47.50
4N33a	A57	$20	80.00	80.00
		Nos. 4N24a-4N33a (9)	262.35	251.90

On Stamps of 1940 with Secret Marks

1941   **Wmk. 261**   *Perf. 14*

4N34	A57	5c #392, II	.40	.40
4N35	A57	5c #393, II	1.25	1.25
4N36	A57	10c #394, II	1.00	.50
4N37	A57	30c #395, II	1.25	1.25
a.		Type I	4.00	4.00
4N38	A57	50c #396, II	4.75	4.75
		Nos. 4N34-4N38 (5)	8.65	8.15

On Stamps of 1940-41 (Martyrs) with Secret Marks

Perf. 12½, 13 & Compound

1941   **Wmk. 261**

4N39	A39	½c #402, II	1.25	1.25
4N40	A40	1c #403, I	1.00	.70
a.		Type II	1.25	1.25
4N41	A46	2c #404, II	.80	.80
4N42	A39	2½c #405, II	1.00	1.40
4N43	A48	3c #406, II	1.60	2.40
4N44	A46	10c #410, II	2.40	2.40
a.		Type I	1.50	4.00
4N45	A45	13c #411, II	2.00	2.00
4N46	A46	17c #413, II	2.75	2.75
a.		Type I	3.50	3.50
4N47	A46	25c #416, II	2.60	2.60
4N48	A48	30c #418, II	10.00	10.00
a.		Type I	27.50	27.50
4N49	A47	40c #419, II	2.75	1.25
a.		Type I	4.75	4.75
		Nos. 4N39-4N49 (11)	28.15	27.55

Unwmk.

4N50	A39	½c #421, II	1.25	1.25
a.		Type I	1.75	1.75
4N51	A40	1c #422, II	1.75	1.25
a.		Type I	2.25	1.60
4N52	A46	2c #423	.40	.40
4N53	A48	3c #425, I	1.25	1.25
a.		Type II	2.75	3.50
4N54	A39	4c #426, II	1.00	1.00
4N55	A45	8c #428, II	1.25	1.50
a.		Type I	2.75	2.75
4N56	A46	10c #429, II	2.75	2.40
4N57	A45	13c #430, II	2.75	2.75
a.		Type II	3.75	3.75
4N58	A48	15c #431, II	4.75	4.75
4N59	A46	17c #432, II	2.75	2.75
a.		Type I	4.75	4.75
4N60	A47	20c #433, II	2.60	2.60
a.		Type I	3.25	3.25
4N61	A45	21c #434, II	4.00	4.00
4N62	A40	25c #435, I	4.00	4.00
a.		Type II	4.00	4.00
4N63	A46	28c #436, II	3.50	3.25
		Nos. 4N50-4N63 (14)	34.00	33.15

For overprints see Nos. 4N64, 4N69.

Honan Singapore Overprint in Red

1942

4N64	A39	4c #4N54	1.25	2.75
4N65	A57	8c #4N25	3.25	3.25
4N66	A57	8c #4N14	2.50	4.00
4N67	A57	8c #4N15	8.00	12.00
		Nos. 4N64-4N67 (4)	15.00	22.00

Honan Anniv. of Manchukuo Overprint in Red

1942

4N68	A57	2c #4N10	5.50	8.00
4N69	A39	4c #4N54	5.50	6.75
4N70	A57	8c #4N14	72.50	72.50
4N71	A57	8c #4N25	8.00	9.50
		Nos. 4N68-4N71 (4)	91.50	96.75

Shansi

Nos. 297-298, 301, 303 Overprinted

	I			II

1941   **Engr.**   **Unwmk.**

5N1	A37	2c #297, II	6.00	6.00
a.		Type I	6.00	6.00
5N2	A37	4c #298, I	55.00	55.00
a.		Type II	110.00	
5N3	A37	15c #301, II	4.75	6.00
a.		Type I	8.00	9.50
5N4	A37	25c #303, II	8.00	12.00
a.		Type I	55.00	60.00
		Nos. 5N1-5N4 (4)	73.75	79.00

On Nos. 312, 314, 318, 321

1941   *Perf. 14*

5N5	A39	½c #312, II	1.00	1.25
a.		Type I	1.75	3.00
5N6	A39	2½c #314, II	1.25	1.40
a.		Type I	1.75	1.60

5N7	A45	13c #318, II	2.00	2.00
a.		Type I	190.00	190.00
5N8	A48	30c #321, II	8.00	9.50
		Nos. 5N5-5N8 (4)	12.25	14.15

On Stamps of 1939-41

1941   *Perf. 12½*

5N9	A57	2c #368, II	.65	.65
5N10	A57	3c #350, II	1.00	1.00
a.		Type I	12.00	12.00
5N11	A57	5c #352, II	2.75	2.75
a.		Type I	4.00	4.00
5N12	A57	8c #353, II	1.25	1.25
a.		Type I	2.75	2.75
5N13	A57	8c #369, II	35.00	20.00
5N14	A57	10c #354, II	3.00	4.00
5N15	A57	16c #357, II	4.00	4.00
5N16	A57	$1 #359, II	10.00	10.00
5N17	A57	$2 #360, II	40.00	40.00
5N18	A57	$5 #361, II	47.50	47.50
		Nos. 5N9-5N18 (10)	145.15	131.15

For overprints see Nos. 5N62-5N64, 5N66-5N67.

On Stamps of 1940 with Secret Marks

1941   **Unwmk.**   *Perf. 14*

5N19	A57	5c #382, II	.65	.60
5N20	A57	8c #383, II	1.40	1.40
5N21	A57	10c #384, I	1.00	1.40
a.		Type II	4.00	4.00
5N22	A57	30c #385, II	1.75	1.75
a.		Type I	2.40	2.40
5N23	A57	50c #386, I	3.50	3.50
a.		Type II	4.75	4.75
5N24	A57	$1 #387, I	9.25	9.25
a.		Type II	30.00	30.00
5N25	A57	$2 #388, II	14.00	20.00
a.		Type I	16.00	16.00
5N26	A57	$5 #389, II	26.00	26.00
a.		Type I	80.00	80.00
5N27	A57	$10 #390, II	57.50	57.50
a.		Type I	60.00	60.00
5N28	A57	$20 #391, II	57.50	57.50
a.		Type I	100.00	110.00
		Nos. 5N19-5N28 (10)	172.55	178.90

For overprints see Nos. 5N61, 5N68.

On Stamps of 1940 with Secret Marks

1941   **Wmk. 261**   *Perf. 14*

5N29	A57	5c #392, II	1.25	1.25
5N30	A57	5c #393, II	1.00	1.00
5N31	A57	10c #394, II	2.40	2.40
5N32	A57	30c #395, II	65.00	65.00
5N33	A57	50c #396, I	6.00	6.75
		Nos. 5N29-5N33 (5)	75.65	76.40

On Stamps of 1940-41 (Martyrs) with Secret Marks

Perf. 12½, 13 & Compound

1941   **Wmk. 261**

5N34	A39	½c #402, II	1.25	1.25
5N35	A40	1c #403, II	.80	.80
a.		Type I	1.25	1.25
5N36	A46	2c #404, II	2.50	2.50
5N37	A39	2½c #405, I	7.25	9.50
5N38	A46	10c #410, II	8.00	8.00
5N39	A45	13c #411, II	3.75	3.75
5N40	A46	17c #413, II	27.50	27.50
5N41	A40	25c #416, II	3.25	3.25
5N42	A48	30c #418, II	125.00	125.00
a.		Type II	125.00	125.00
5N43	A47	40c #419, II	4.50	4.50
a.		Type I	30.00	30.00
5N44	A40	50c #420, II	6.00	6.00
a.		Type I	35.00	35.00
		Nos. 5N34-5N44 (11)	189.80	192.05

Unwmk.

5N45	A39	½c #421, II	2.40	3.00
a.		Type I	4.25	4.75
5N46	A40	1c #422, I	2.40	2.40
a.		Type II	2.40	2.40
5N47	A46	2c #423, II	.60	.60
5N48	A48	3c #425, I	7.25	7.25
5N49	A39	4c #426, I	1.00	1.00
5N50	A45	8c #428, I	12.00	12.00
a.		Type II	14.00	14.00
5N51	A46	10c #429, I	40.00	40.00
a.		Type II	47.50	47.50
5N52	A45	13c #430, I	16.00	16.00
a.		Type II	16.00	16.00
5N53	A48	15c #431, I	5.50	5.50
5N54	A46	17c #432, I	3.50	3.50
a.		Type II	4.50	4.50
5N55	A47	20c #433, I	2.60	2.60
a.		Type II	3.25	3.25
5N56	A45	21c #434, II	3.50	3.50
5N57	A40	25c #435, I	2.60	2.75
5N58	A46	28c #436, II	4.75	4.75
5N59	A40	50c #439, II	12.00	12.00
		Nos. 5N45-5N59 (15)	116.10	116.85

For overprints see Nos. 5N60, 5N65.

Honan Singapore Overprint in Red

1942

5N60	A39	4c #5N49	2.25	2.75
5N61	A57	8c #5N20	3.75	3.75
5N62	A57	8c #5N12	5.50	8.75
5N63	A57	8c #5N13	11.50	16.00
		Nos. 5N60-5N63 (4)	23.00	31.25

Honan Anniv. of Manchukuo Overprint
in Red

1942

5N64	A57	2c #5N9	9.50	14.00
5N65	A39	4c #5N49	11.00	14.00
5N66	A57	8c #5N12	40.00	47.50
5N67	A57	8c #5N13	60.00	67.50
5N68	A57	8c #5N20	32.50	32.50
Nos. 5N64-5N68 (5)			153.00	175.50

Shantung

Nos. 297-298, 301-303 Overprinted

I   II

1941   Engr.   Unwmk.

6N1	A37	2c #297, II	1.25	1.25
a.	Type I		3.25	3.25
6N2	A37	4c #298, II	6.00	5.50
a.	Type I		7.00	6.00
6N3	A37	15c #301, II	2.00	2.00
a.	Type I		2.75	2.75
6N4	A37	20c #302, II	3.75	3.75
6N5	A37	25c #303, II	5.50	5.50
a.	Type I		175.00	175.00
Nos. 6N1-6N5 (5)			18.50	18.00

On Nos. 312, 314, 318

1941   Perf. 14

6N6	A39	½c #312, II	1.00	1.00
a.	Type I		2.00	1.25
6N7	A45	2½c #314, II	1.25	1.75
a.	Type I		1.25	1.60
6N8	A45	13c #318, II	1.25	1.10
a.	Type I		19.00	19.00
Nos. 6N6-6N8 (3)			3.50	3.85

On Stamps of 1939-41

1941   Perf. 12½

6N9	A57	2c #349, II	.65	1.25
6N10	A57	2c #368, II	1.10	1.00
6N11	A57	3c #350, II	.60	.60
a.	Type I		1.25	1.25
6N12	A57	5c #352, II	1.10	1.10
a.	Type I		1.25	1.25
6N13	A57	8c #353, II	.65	.40
a.	Type I		.55	.55
6N14	A57	8c #369, II	.90	.65
6N15	A57	10c #354, II	.75	.65
6N16	A57	16c #357, II	4.50	6.00
6N17	A57	$1 #359, II	11.00	10.00
a.	Type I		350.00	350.00
b.	On No. 347, I		47.50	47.50
6N18	A57	$5 #361, II	40.00	40.00
Nos. 6N9-6N18 (10)			61.25	61.65

For overprints see Nos. 6N62, 6N64-6N65, 6N67-6N68.

On Stamps of 1940 with Secret Marks

1941   Unwmk.   Perf. 14

6N20	A57	5c #382, II	1.25	1.00
6N21	A57	8c #383, II	.30	.30
a.	Type I		1.25	1.25
6N22	A57	10c #384, II	1.25	1.00
6N23	A57	30c #385, II	1.60	1.25
a.	Type I		5.50	6.00
6N24	A57	50c #386, I	6.00	6.00
a.	Type I		7.25	6.50
6N25	A57	$1 #387, I	6.00	4.00
a.	Type I		14.00	14.00
6N26	A57	$2 #388, I	12.00	12.00
a.	Type I		20.00	20.00
6N27	A57	$5 #389, I	24.00	24.00
a.	Type I		32.50	32.50
6N28	A57	$10 #390, I	55.00	55.00
a.	Type I		60.00	60.00
6N29	A57	$20 #391, I	80.00	80.00
a.	Type I		80.00	90.00
Nos. 6N20-6N29 (10)			187.40	184.55

For overprints see Nos. 6N63, 6N69.

On Stamps of 1940 with Secret Marks

1941   Wmk. 261   Perf. 14

6N30	A57	5c #392, II	1.00	1.00
6N31	A57	5c #393, II	1.00	1.00
6N32	A57	10c #394, II	6.50	6.50
6N33	A57	30c #395, II	4.00	3.25
a.	Type I		20.00	20.00
6N34	A57	50c #396, II	3.50	3.50
a.	Type I		8.00	9.50
Nos. 6N30-6N34 (5)			16.00	15.25

On Stamps of 1940-41 (Martyrs) with
Secret Marks

Perf. 12½, 13 & Compound

1941   Wmk. 261

6N35	A39	½c #402, II	2.40	2.40
6N36	A40	1c #403, II	1.75	1.60
a.	Type I		2.25	1.90
6N37	A39	2½c #405, II	7.25	9.50
6N38	A46	10c #410, I	3.25	3.25

6N39	A45	13c #411, II	3.25	3.25
6N40	A46	17c #413, II	3.50	3.50
a.			8.00	8.75
6N41	A40	25c #416, II	3.50	3.50
6N42	A48	30c #418, I	27.50	27.50
6N43	A47	40c #419, I	3.50	3.50
a.	Type I		27.50	27.50
6N44	A40	50c #420, II	7.25	7.25
Nos. 6N35-6N44 (10)			63.15	65.25

Unwmk.

6N45	A39	½c #421, II	1.60	1.60
a.	Type I		3.50	3.50
6N46	A40	1c #422, II	1.60	1.25
a.	Type I		2.60	2.60
b.	On No. 422a, II		80.00	80.00
6N48	A46	2c #423, II	1.60	1.60
6N49	A48	3c #425, II	3.50	4.00
a.	Type I		4.00	5.50
6N50	A39	4c #426, II	1.00	.50
6N51	A45	4c #428, II	2.75	2.75
a.	Type I		32.50	32.50
6N52	A46	10c #429, I	12.00	12.00
6N53	A45	13c #430, I	3.75	3.75
a.	Type I		3.75	3.75
6N54	A48	15c #431, II	4.00	4.00
6N55	A46	17c #432, II	2.75	2.75
a.	Type I		4.00	4.00
6N56	A47	20c #433, II	3.75	3.75
a.			5.50	5.50
6N57	A45	21c #434, II	4.00	4.00
6N58	A40	25c #435, II	4.75	4.75
6N59	A46	28c #436, II	4.00	3.25
6N60	A40	50c #439, II	9.50	9.50
Nos. 6N45-6N60 (15)			60.55	59.45

For overprints see Nos. 6N61, 6N66.

Honan Singapore Overprint in Red

1942

6N61	A39	4c #6N50	2.00	2.75
6N62	A57	8c #6N13	20.00	24.00
6N63	A57	8c #6N21	20.00	20.00
6N64	A57	8c #6N14	3.25	3.25
Nos. 6N61-6N64 (4)			45.25	52.25

Honan Anniv. of Manchukuo Overprint
in Red

1942

6N65	A57	2c #6N10	2.75	4.00
6N66	A39	4c #6N50	4.00	4.25
6N67	A57	8c #6N13	16.00	20.00
6N68	A57	8c #6N14	40.00	47.50
6N69	A57	8c #6N21	3.25	4.00
Nos. 6N65-6N69 (5)			66.00	79.75

Supeh

Nos. 297-298, 301-302 Overprinted

I   II

1941   Engr.   Unwmk.

7N1	A37	2c #297, I	9.50	9.50
a.	Type II		12.50	12.50
7N2	A37	4c #298, I	47.50	47.50
a.	Type II		90.00	
7N3	A37	15c #301, II	2.75	2.75
a.	Type I		3.50	3.50
7N4	A37	20c #302, I	3.25	3.25
Nos. 7N1-7N4 (4)			63.00	63.00

On Nos. 312, 314, 318

1941   Perf. 14

7N5	A39	½c #312, I	3.50	3.50
7N6	A45	2½c #314, II	1.25	1.25
a.	Type I		1.25	1.25
7N7	A45	13c #318, II	1.25	1.25
a.	Type I		95.00	95.00
Nos. 7N5-7N7 (3)			6.00	6.00

On Stamps of 1939-41

1941   Perf. 12½

7N8	A57	2c #368, II	1.25	2.00
7N9	A57	3c #350, II	1.40	1.40
a.	Type I		20.00	20.00
7N10	A57	5c #352, II	1.25	1.75
a.	Type I		3.25	3.00
7N11	A57	8c #353, I	2.00	2.00
a.	Type II		2.75	2.75
7N12	A57	8c #369, II	32.50	27.50
7N13	A57	10c #354, II	3.00	4.00
7N14	A57	16c #357, II	1.25	2.00
7N15	A57	$1 #359, II	13.00	13.00
a.	On No. 347, I		160.00	160.00
Nos. 7N8-7N15 (8)			55.65	53.65

For overprints see Nos. 7N56-7N58, 7N60-
7N61.

On Stamps of 1940 with Secret Marks

1941   Unwmk.   Perf. 14

7N17	A57	5c #382, II	1.25	1.25
7N18	A57	8c #383, II	1.25	1.25
7N19	A57	10c #384, II	3.50	3.50
a.	Type II		3.50	3.50
7N20	A57	30c #385, I	2.75	3.25
a.			6.50	7.25
7N21	A57	50c #386, II	3.75	4.50
a.			4.00	4.00
7N22	A57	$1 #387, II	20.00	24.00
a.	Type II		32.50	32.50
7N23	A57	$2 #388, II	20.00	20.00
a.	Type II		27.50	32.50
7N24	A57	$5 #389, II	24.00	24.00
a.	Type II		65.00	65.00
7N25	A57	$10 #390, II	65.00	65.00
a.	Type II		72.50	72.50
7N26	A57	$20 #391, II	80.00	80.00
a.	Type I		80.00	90.00
Nos. 7N17-7N26 (10)			221.50	226.75

On Stamps of 1940 with Secret Marks

1941   Wmk. 261   Perf. 14

7N27	A57	10c #394, II	4.00	4.00
7N28	A57	30c #395, II	13.00	14.00
7N29	A57	50c #396, I	14.00	15.00
Nos. 7N27-7N29 (3)			31.00	33.00

On Stamps of 1940-41 (Martyrs) with
Secret Marks

Perf. 12½, 13 & Compound

1941   Wmk. 261

7N30	A39	½c #402, II	4.75	4.75
7N31	A40	1c #403, I	1.75	1.75
a.	Type II		2.75	2.75
7N32	A46	2c #404, II	1.60	1.60
7N33	A39	2½c #405, II	24.00	24.00
7N34	A46	10c #410, II	16.00	16.00
7N35	A45	13c #411, II	5.50	5.50
7N36	A46	17c #413, II	4.75	4.75
a.	Type I		80.00	80.00
7N37	A40	25c #416, II	4.75	4.75
7N38	A48	30c #418, I	12.00	12.00
7N39	A47	40c #419, II	4.75	4.75
7N40	A40	50c #420, II	80.00	80.00
a.			7.25	7.25
Nos. 7N30-7N40 (11)			159.85	159.85

Unwmk.

7N41	A39	½c #421, II	3.50	3.50
a.	Type I		4.75	4.75
7N42	A40	1c #422, II	1.60	1.60
7N43	A46	2c #423, I	12.00	12.00
7N44	A48	3c #425, I	3.50	3.50
7N45	A39	4c #426, II	1.00	1.00
7N46	A46	10c #429, I	40.00	40.00
7N47	A45	13c #430, I	5.50	6.00
7N48	A48	15c #431, II	6.00	6.00
7N49	A46	17c #432, II	3.75	3.75
a.			5.50	5.50
7N50	A47	20c #433, II	3.75	3.75
a.			5.50	5.50
7N51	A45	21c #434, II	4.00	4.00
7N52	A40	25c #435, II	5.25	5.25
a.	Type I		14.00	14.00
7N53	A46	28c #436, I	5.50	5.50
Nos. 7N41-7N53 (13)			95.35	95.85

For overprints see Nos. 7N55, 7N59.

Honan Singapore Overprint in Red

1942

7N54	A37	4c #298, II	40.00	47.50
7N55	A39	4c #7N45	5.00	5.50
7N56	A57	8c #7N11a	13.00	17.50
7N57	A57	8c #7N12	12.00	16.00
Nos. 7N54-7N57 (4)			70.00	86.50

Honan Anniv. of Manchukuo Overprint
in Red

1942

7N58	A57	2c #7N8	14.00	20.00
7N59	A39	4c #7N45	12.00	14.00
7N60	A57	8c #7N11a	60.00	67.50
7N61	A57	8c #7N12	72.50	80.00
Nos. 7N58-7N61 (4)			158.50	181.50

North China

**For use in Honan, Hopei, Shansi,
Shantung and Supeh (Northern
Kiangsu)**

Stamps of China,
1931-37 Surcharged
North China (Hwa Pei)
and Half of Original
Value

1942   Unwmk.   Perf. 14, 12½

8N1	A40	½c on 1c (#313)	1.60	2.00
8N2	A37	1c on 2c (#297)	.60	.35
8N3	A37	2c on 4c (#298)	1.25	1.00
8N4	A45	4c on 8c (#316)	125.00	

Same Surcharge on Stamps of
1938-41

Perf. 12½

8N5	A57	1c on 2c (#349)	4.00	6.00
8N6	A57	1c on 2c (#368)	.40	.25
8N7	A57	4c on 8c (#353)	1.75	1.00
8N8	A57	4c on 8c (#369)	.50	.30
8N9	A57	5c on 10c grn	.55	.40
8N10	A57	8c on 16c ol gray	1.60	.65
8N11	A57	50c on $1 (#359)	6.50	6.50
8N12	A57	50c on $1 (#344)	475.00	475.00
8N13	A57	50c on $1 (#347)	95.00	95.00
8N14	A57	$1 on $2 (#360)	10.00	10.00
8N15	A57	$1 on $2 (#345)	27.50	27.50
8N16	A57	$1 on $2 (#348)	125.00	125.00

No. 8N12 was issued without gum.
For overprint see No. 8N58.

Same Surcharge on China Nos. 383-
388, 390-391

Perf. 14

8N17	A57	4c on 8c ol grn	.55	.55
8N18	A57	5c on 10c grn	1.00	1.60
8N19	A57	15c on 30c scar	1.25	1.00
a.	Inverted surcharge		65.00	65.00
8N20	A57	25c on 50c dk bl	1.60	1.40
8N21	A57	50c on $1 org brn & sep	3.75	3.75
8N22	A57	$1 on $2 dp bl & yel brn	4.75	4.75
8N23	A57	$5 on $10 dk grn & dl pur	40.00	40.00
8N24	A57	$10 on $20 rose lake & dk bl	40.00	50.00
Nos. 8N17-8N24 (8)			92.90	103.05

For overprint see No. 8N55.

Same Surcharge on China Nos. 394-
396

Wmk. 261

8N25	A57	5c on 10c grn	.70	1.25
8N26	A57	15c on 30c scar	2.75	4.00
8N27	A57	25c on 50c dk bl	1.25	1.25
Nos. 8N25-8N27 (3)			4.70	6.50

Same Surcharge on Stamps of 1940-
41

1942   Wmk. 261   Perf. 12½, 13

8N28	A40	½c on 1c org	.25	.20
8N29	A46	1c on 2c dp bl	2.00	2.00
8N30	A46	4c on 8c dp grn	16.00	20.00
8N31	A46	5c on 10c dl vio	2.00	2.40
8N32	A48	15c on 30c brn car	8.00	8.00
8N33	A47	20c on 40c org	4.75	1.75
8N34	A47	25c on 50c grn	4.00	4.00
Nos. 8N28-8N34 (7)			37.00	38.35

Unwmk.

8N35	A40	½c on 1c org (#422)	.25	.20
a.	½c on 1c org (#422a)		30.00	30.00
8N36	A46	1c on 2c dp bl	1.10	1.10
8N37	A39	2c on 4c pale vio	.80	.70
8N38	A46	4c on 8c dp grn	2.40	2.40
8N39	A46	5c on 10c dl vio	2.40	2.40
8N40	A47	10c on 20c lt bl	3.00	.60
8N41	A47	20c on 40c org	3.25	.80
8N42	A40	25c on 50c grn	2.75	2.75
Nos. 8N35-8N42 (8)			14.55	10.15

Same Surcharge on "New Peking"
Prints

Perf. 14

8N43	A37	1c on 2c ol grn	.30	.20
8N44	A37	2c on 4c dl grn	.75	.20
a.	Inverted surcharge		35.00	
8N45	A47	4c on 8c dp org	.55	.20
8N46	A57	8c on 16c ol gray	.30	.20
8N47	A47	10c on 20c red brn	1.40	1.25
8N48	A48	15c on 30c brn car	.70	.70
8N49	A47	20c on 40c org	1.75	.25
a.	Inverted surcharge		45.00	
8N50	A40	25c on 50c grn	1.50	1.25
8N51	A57	50c on $1 org brn & sep	2.75	2.75
8N52	A57	$1 on $2 dp bl & org brn	4.75	2.75
8N53	A57	$5 on $10 dk grn & dl pur	20.00	20.00
Nos. 8N43-8N53 (11)			34.75	29.75

See note after No. 2N93. For overprints see
#8N54, 8N56-8N57, 8N59.

Nos. 8N44, 8N17 and
8N46 with Additional
Overprint in Red

1943   Unwmk.   Perf. 14

8N54	A37	2c on 4c dl grn	.25	.85
8N55	A57	4c on 8c ol grn	1.25	1.40
8N56	A57	8c on 16c ol gray	1.25	1.60
Nos. 8N54-8N56 (3)			2.75	3.85

Return of the Foreign Concessions to China.

Nos. 8N44, 8N8 and 8N46 with Additional Overprint in Red

1943, Aug. 15   **Perf. 14, 12½**
8N57	A37	2c on 4c dl grn	.35	.70
8N58	A57	4c on 8c ol grn	.35	.80
8N59	A57	8c on 16c ol gray	.40	.70
		Nos. 8N57-8N59 (3)	1.10	2.20

North China Postal Service, 5th anniv.

Stamps of China, 1934-41, Overprinted in Black

1943, Nov. 1
8N60	A40	1c org (#313)	.70	.70
8N61	A40	1c org (#422)	.70	.60
8N62	A57	10c grn (#354)	.40	.35
8N63	A57	$2 dp bl & yel brn (#388)	24.00	24.00
8N64	A57	$5 red & grnsh blk (#361)	16.00	16.00
8N65	A57	$5 red & sl grn (#389)	8.00	8.00
8N66	A57	$10 dk grn & dl pur (#390)	12.00	12.00
8N67	A57	$20 rose lake & dk bl (#391)	72.50	87.50
		Nos. 8N60-8N67 (8)	134.30	149.15

Same Overprint on "New Peking" Prints
8N68	A40	1c orange	.25	.20
8N69	A37	2c olive grn	.25	.60
8N70	A37	4c dull green	.25	1.25
8N71	A37	5c green	.50	.60
8N72	A57	9c olive grn	.30	.60
8N73	A46	10c dl violet	.30	.60
8N74	A57	16c olive gray	.25	.35
8N75	A57	18c olive gray	.25	.35
8N76	A47	20c henna	.40	.50
8N77	A48	30c brown car	.35	.35
8N78	A47	40c brt orange	.35	.60
a.		Inverted overprint	35.00	35.00
8N79	A40	50c green	2.00	2.00
8N80	A57	$1 org brn & sep	3.50	1.00
8N81	A57	$2 bl & org brn	2.00	.85
8N82	A57	$5 red & sl grn	4.00	6.00
8N83	A57	$10 dk grn & dl pur	7.25	7.25
8N84	A57	$20 rose lake & dk bl	8.50	10.00
		Nos. 8N68-8N84 (17)	30.70	33.00

See note after No. 2N93. For overprints see Nos. 8N85-8N90, 8N95-8N106.

Nos. 8N70 and 8N62 with Additional Overprint in Red

1944, Jan. 9
8N85	A37	4c dull green	.30	.85
8N86	A57	10c green	.30	.60

1st anniv. of the declaration of war against the Allies by North China.

Nos. 8N72, 8N75, 8N79 and 8N80 with Additional Overprint in Red

1944, Mar. 30
8N87	A57	9c olive green	.45	1.25
8N88	A57	18c olive gray	.80	2.40
8N89	A40	50c green	4.75	6.00
8N90	A57	$1 org brn & sepia	1.75	2.40
a.		Red overprint inverted	30.00	30.00
		Nos. 8N87-8N90 (4)	7.75	12.05

North China Political Council, 4th anniv.

Shanghai-Nanking Nos. 9N101-9N104 Surcharged North China (Hwa Pei) and New Value in Red or Black

    a   b

c

d

1944   **Perf. 12½x12, 12x12½**
8N91	OS1 (a)	9c on 50c org (R)	1.10	1.40
8N92	OS1 (b)	18c on $1 grn	1.25	1.75
a.		Double surcharge	30.00	30.00
8N93	OS2 (c)	36c on $2 dp bl (R)	1.40	1.75
8N94	OS2 (d)	90c on $5 car rose	1.75	2.00
		Nos. 8N91-8N94 (4)	5.50	6.90

Nos. 8N72, 8N75, 8N79 and 8N80 Overprinted in Red or Blue

1944, Aug. 15
8N95	A57	9c olive grn	.75	1.25
8N96	A57	18c olive gray	.75	2.40
8N97	A40	50c green	1.25	1.75
8N98	A57	$1 org brn & sep (Bl)	2.75	3.25
		Nos. 8N95-8N98 (4)	5.50	8.65

6th anniv. of the General P.O. Dept. of North China.

North China Nos. 8N76, 8N79-8N81 Overprinted in Blue or Black

1944, Dec. 5
8N99	A47	20c henna (Bl)	2.40	2.75
8N100	A40	50c green (Bl)	2.40	2.75
8N101	A57	$1 org brn & sep (Bl)	4.75	5.50
8N102	A57	$2 bl & org brn	1.40	1.40
		Nos. 8N99-8N102 (4)	10.95	12.40

Death of Wang Ching-wei, puppet ruler of China.

North China Nos. 8N76, 8N79-8N81 Overprinted in Red or Black

1945
8N103	A47	20c henna	2.40	3.25
8N104	A40	50c green (R)	7.25	7.25
8N105	A57	$1 org brn & sep	2.60	2.75
8N106	A57	$2 bl & org brn	1.75	1.60
		Nos. 8N103-8N106 (4)	14.00	14.85

2nd anniv. of the declaration of war.

Shanghai-Nanking Nos. 9N105-9N106 Surcharged in Red

1945   **Perf. 12x12½**
8N107	OS3	50c on $3 lt org	.55	.70
8N108	OS3	$1 on $6 blue	.55	.70

Return of the foreign concessions in Shanghai.

Dragon Pillar   Dr. Sun Yat-sen
OS1   OS2

Designs: $2, Long Bridge and White Pagoda. $5, Tower in Imperial City. $10, Marble Boat, Summer Palace.

1945   **Unwmk.**   **Litho.**   **Perf. 14**
Various Papers
8N109	OS1	$1 dull yellow	1.25	1.25
8N110	OS1	$2 deep blue	.25	1.25
8N111	OS1	$5 carmine	.85	.60
8N112	OS1	$10 dull green	.40	.90
		Nos. 8N109-8N112 (4)	2.75	4.00

North China Political Council, 5th anniv.

1945
Without Gum; Various Papers
8N113	OS2	$1 bister	.25	.20
8N114	OS2	$2 dark blue	.90	.20
8N115	OS2	$5 fawn	2.00	2.00
8N116	OS2	$10 sage green	2.00	.60
8N117	OS2	$20 dull violet	2.00	1.40
8N118	OS2	$50 brown	40.00	47.50
		Nos. 8N113-8N118 (6)	47.15	51.90

Nos. 8N113-8N118 without "Hwa Pei" overprint are proofs.

Wutai Mountain, Shansi — OS3

Designs: $10, Kaifeng Iron Pagoda. $20, International Bridge, Tientsin. $30, Taishan Mountain, Shantung. $50, General Post Office, Peking.

1945, Aug. 15
Without Gum; Various Papers
8N119	OS3	$5 gray green	.25	.85
8N120	OS3	$10 dull brown	.60	.85
8N121	OS3	$20 dull purple	.45	1.25
8N122	OS3	$30 slate blue	.90	1.25
8N123	OS3	$50 carmine	2.00	2.40
		Nos. 8N119-8N123 (5)	4.20	6.60

North China Postal Directorate, 7th anniv.

Shanghai and Nanking

China Nos. 299-303 Surcharged

    a   b

Overprinted Type "b"

1942-45   **Unwmk.**   **Perf. 12½, 13½**
9N1	A37	$6 on 5c green	.75	1.00
9N2	A37	$20 on 15c scar	.35	.75
9N3	A37	$500 on 15c dk grn	.25	1.00

9N4	A37	$1000 on 20c ultra	2.75	2.75
9N5	A37	$1000 on 25c ultra	2.75	2.75
		Nos. 9N1-9N5 (5)	6.85	8.25

A $1000 on 20c ultramarine, No. 293, exists.

Surcharged Type "a"
(Nos. 9N6-9N10)
or Type "b" (Nos. 9N11-9N40)
on Type A57 Stamps of 1939-41
Perf. 12½
9N6	25c on 5c (#352)	2.00	3.25
9N7	30c on 2c (#368)	.20	.25
9N8	50c on 3c (#350)	.25	.30
9N9	50c on 3c (#350)	.25	.25
9N10	50c on 8c (#353)	.25	.35
9N11	$1 on 8c (#353)	.25	.20
9N12	$1 on 8c (#369)	12.00	12.00
9N13	$1 on 15c (#356)	.25	.20
9N14	$1.30 on 16c (#357)	.25	.40
9N15	$1.50 on 3c (#350)	.25	.40
9N16	$2 on 5c (#352)	1.10	1.10
9N17	$2 on 10c (#354)	.25	.30
9N18	$3 on 15c (#356)	.25	.30
9N19	$4 on 16c (#357)	.40	.25
9N20	$5 on 15c (#356)	.25	.25
9N21	$6 on 5c (#351)	.60	1.40
a.	Perf. 14 (#371)	50.00	50.00
9N22	$6 on 5c (#352)	.25	.35
9N23	$6 on 8c (#353)	.40	1.00
9N24	$6 on 8c (#369)	800.00	800.00
9N25	$6 on 10c (#354)	.25	.25
9N26	$10 on 10c (#354)	.25	.30
9N27	$10 on 16c (#357)	.50	.25
9N28	$20 on 3c (#350)	.25	.40
9N29	$20 on 15c (#355)	1.10	2.40
9N30	$20 on 15c (#356)	.40	.40
9N31	$20 on $2 (#360)	1.40	2.75
9N32	$100 on 3c (#350)	.50	.40
9N33	$500 on 8c (#353)	2.40	4.50
9N34	$500 on 8c (#369)	35.00	47.50
9N35	$500 on 10c (#354)	2.40	3.50
9N36	$500 on 15c (#355)	1.25	2.40
9N37	$500 on 15c (#356)	1.00	2.00
9N38	$500 on 16c (#357)	1.25	4.00
9N39	$1000 on 25c (#358)	1.25	2.40
9N40	$1000 on $5 (#361)	1.40	2.40
	Nos. 9N1-9N23,9N25-9N40 (39)	76.90	106.65

Nos. 381-391 (Type A57) Surcharged with Type "b"
Perf. 14
9N41	$1 on 8c ol grn	.25	.30
9N42	$1.70 on 30c scar	.30	.60
a.	Perf. 12½	3.25	3.25
9N43	$2 on 5c ol grn	.40	1.25
9N44	$2 on $1 org brn & sep	1.00	2.40
9N45	$3 on 8c ol grn	.60	.60
a.	$3 on 8c olive green (#383a)	35.00	35.00
b.	"3" with flat top	.40	.40
9N46	$6 on 5c grn	.40	.50
9N47	$6 on 8c ol grn	.40	.80
9N48	$6 on 8c ol grn	.35	.70
9N49	$10 on 10c grn	.40	2.00
a.	Perf. 12½	2.00	6.00
9N50	$20 on $2 dp bl & yel brn	1.25	1.25
9N51	$50 on 30c scar	.75	.80
9N52	$50 on 50c dk bl	.65	.65
9N53	$50 on $5 red & sl grn	.95	.95
9N54	$50 on $20 rose lake & dk bl	2.00	2.40
9N55	$100 on $10 dk grn & dl pur	1.60	1.60
9N56	$200 on $20 rose lake & dk bl	.60	1.00
9N57	$500 on 8c ol grn	11.00	13.00
a.	$500 on 8c ol grn (#383a)	25.00	24.00
9N58	$500 on 10c grn	2.40	3.50
9N59	$1000 on 30c scar	2.00	2.75
9N60	$1000 on 50c dk bl	1.00	1.40
9N61	$1000 on $2 dp bl & yel brn	2.40	8.00
9N62	$2000 on $5 red & sl grn	1.25	1.60

China Nos. 392-395 and 399-401 (Type A57) Surcharged with Type "b"

1942-45   **Wmk. 261**   **Perf. 14**
9N63	$2 on $1 org brn & sep, perf. 12½	.80	1.40
9N64	$6 on 5c grn	.40	.85
9N65	$6 on 5c ol grn	1.10	1.60
9N66	$50 on $5 red & sl grn	.70	1.00
a.	Numeral tablet violet	.80	1.00
9N67	$100 on $10 dk grn & dl pur	.40	.60
9N68	$200 on $20 rose lake & dk bl	.50	.60
9N69	$500 on 10c grn	2.00	2.40
9N70	$1000 on 30c scar	2.75	3.25
9N71	$5000 on $20 grn & dl pur, perf. 12½	6.50	8.00
a.	Perf. 14	100.00	100.00
	Nos. 9N41-9N71 (31)	47.10	67.75

Nos. 9N63 and 9N71 were not issued without surcharge. A $50 on 30c scarlet exists.

Same Surch. on Stamps of 1940-41
Perf. 12½, 13
Wmk. 261

| 9N72 | A46 | $30 on 2c dp bl | 125.00 | 125.00 |

A $7.50 on ½c and a $15 on 1c are known.

Unwmk.

9N73	A39	$7.50 on ½c ol blk	1.25	2.40
9N74	A40	$15 on 1c org	.30	1.25
a.		Without secret mark	50.00	50.00
9N75	A46	$30 on 2c dp bl	1.10	1.60
9N76	A40	$200 on 1c org	.25	.30
9N77	A45	$200 on 8c dp org	.70	1.00
		Nos. 9N73-9N77 (5)	3.60	6.55

Surcharged Type "a" (Nos. 9N78-9N81)
or Type "b" (Nos. 9N82-9N96) on
Type A59 Stamps of 1941
Perf. 12

9N78	5c on ½c sepia	.20	.30
9N79	10c on 1c orange	.20	.30
9N80	20c on 1c orange	.20	.40
9N81	40c on 5c green	.20	.40
9N82	$5 on 5c green	.20	.30
9N83	$10 on 10c brt grn	.20	.30
9N84	$50 on ½c sepia	.20	.30
9N85	$50 on 1c orange	.35	.40
9N86	$50 on 17c olive	.35	.40
9N87	$200 on 5c green	.35	.40
9N88	$200 on 8c turq grn	.20	.25
9N89	$200 on 8c red org	.20	.60
9N90	$500 on $5 scar & blk	.40	.40
9N91	$1000 on 1c orange	.35	.55
9N92	$1000 on 25c rose vio	.40	.55
9N93	$1000 on 30c scarlet	1.00	.55
9N94	$1000 on $2 bl & blk	1.00	1.00
9N95	$1000 on $10 grn & blk	.40	.55
9N96	$2000 on $5 scar & blk	1.00	1.00
	Nos. 9N78-9N96 (19)	7.55	9.05

Stamps of China 1939-41 Surcharged in Red or Blue

1943　　Unwmk.　　Perf. 12, 12½

9N97	A57	25c on 5c green	.20	1.25
9N98	A59	50c on 8c red org (Bl)	.20	.50
9N99	A57	$1 on 16c ol gray	.20	1.40
9N100	A59	on 50c dk bl	.20	.50
		Nos. 9N97-9N100 (4)	.80	3.65

Return of the foreign concessions in Shanghai.

Wheat and Cotton — OS1

Purple Mountain, Nanking OS2

Perf. 12½x12, 12x12½

1944　　Engr.　　Unwmk.

9N101	OS1	50c orange	.20	.35
9N102	OS1	$1 green	.20	.35
9N103	OS2	$2 deep blue	.20	.40
9N104	OS2	$5 carmine rose	.20	.40
		Nos. 9N101-9N104 (4)	.80	1.50

Puppet government at Nanking, 4th anniv.
For surcharges see Nos. 8N91-8N94, 9N107-9N110.

Map of Foreign Concessions in Shanghai — OS3

1944　　　　　　Perf. 12x12½

| 9N105 | OS3 | $3 lt orange | .20 | .35 |
| 9N106 | OS3 | $6 blue | .20 | .35 |

1st anniversary of the return of the foreign concessions in Shanghai.
For surcharges see Nos. 8N107-8N108.

Nos. 9N101-9N104 Surcharged in Black with Type "b"

1945, Mar. 30

9N107	OS1	$15 on 50c orange	.20	.35
9N108	OS1	$30 on $1 green	.20	.35
9N109	OS2	$60 on $2 dp blue	.20	.35
9N110	OS2	$200 on $5 car rose	.20	.55
		Nos. 9N107-9N110 (4)	.80	1.60

China Nos. C31, C32, C36 and C38 Surcharged in Red, Green, Orange or Carmine

1945　　　　　　Perf. 12½, 13

9N111	AP3	$150 on 15c (R)	.20	.20
9N112	AP3	$250 on 25c (G)	.20	.35
9N113	AP3	$600 on 60c (O)	.20	.35
9N114	AP3	$1,000 on $1 (C)	.20	.35
		Nos. 9N111-9N114 (4)	.80	1.25

Issue as air raid precaution propaganda.

SHANGHAI AND NANKING AIR POST STAMPS

China Nos. C35 and C38 Surcharged in Black

The surcharges on Nos. 9NC1-9NC7 were in Japanese currency because all air mail then was carried by Japanese planes.

The surcharges translate: (10c) "Airmail fee for postcard within the nation has been paid." (20c) "Airmail fee for letter within the nation has been paid."

1941　　Unwmk.　　Perf. 12½

| 9NC1 | AP3 | 10(s) on 50c brown | .40 | .40 |
| 9NC2 | AP3 | 20(s) on $1 apple grn | .20 | .35 |

Two types of surcharge exist on No. 9NC1.

Similar Surcharge on No. C28

1941　　Wmk. 261　　Perf. 13

| 9NC3 | AP3 | 20(s) on $1 ap grn | 16.00 | 16.00 |

Nos. C37 and C39 Surcharged

The surcharges translate: (18c and 25c) "Airmail fee for postcard to Japan has been paid." (35c) "Airmail fee for letter to Japan has been paid."

1941　　Unwmk.　　Perf. 12½, 13

9NC4	AP3	18(s) on 90c lt olive	.20	.60
9NC5	AP3	25(s) on 90c lt olive	.20	.60
9NC6	AP3	35(s) on $2 lt brown	.20	.60
		Nos. 9NC4-9NC6 (3)	.60	1.80

No. 9NC6 with Additional Surcharge in Red

Perf. 12½

| 9NC7 | AP3 | 60(s) on 35(s) on $2 | .20 | .35 |

SHANGHAI AND NANKING POSTAGE DUE STAMPS

Postage Due Stamps of China 1932 Surcharged in Black

1945　　Unwmk.　　Perf. 14

9NJ1	D5	$1 on 2c org	.50	1.75
9NJ2	D5	$2 on 5c org	.50	1.75
9NJ3	D5	$5 on 10c org	.50	1.75
9NJ4	D5	$10 on 20c org	.90	3.00
		Nos. 9NJ1-9NJ4 (4)	2.40	8.25

Northeastern Provinces

With the end of World War II and the collapse of Manchukuo, the Northeastern Provinces reverted to China. In many Manchurian towns and cities, the Manchukuo stamps were locally hand-stamped in ideograms: "Republic of China," "China Postal Service" or "Temporary Use for China." A typical example is shown above.

Dr. Sun Yat-sen
A1　　　　A2
Black Surcharge

1946, Feb.　Unwmk.　Typo.　Perf. 14

1	A1	50c on $5 red	.20	.80
2	A1	50c on $10 green	.50	1.25
3	A1	$1 on $10 green	.20	1.00
4	A1	$2 on $20 brown vio	.20	.80
5	A1	$4 on $50 brown	.20	.65
		Nos. 1-5 (5)	1.30	4.50

The two characters at left express the new value.

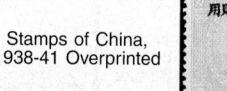

Stamps of China, 1938-41 Overprinted

1946, Apr.　　Perf. 12½, 13, 13½, 14

6	A40	1c org (#422)	.20	1.75
7	A48	3c dp yel brn (#425)	.20	1.75
8	A48	5c dl red org (#427)	.20	2.25
9	A57	10c grn (#354)	.20	1.75
10	A57	10c grn (#384)	.20	1.75
11	A47	20c lt bl (#433)	.20	1.75
a.		Horiz. pair, imperf. btwn		90.00
		Nos. 6-11 (6)	1.20	11.00

1946, July　　Engr.
Without Gum　　Perf. 14

12	A2	5c lake	.20	1.25
13	A2	10c orange	.20	.90
14	A2	20c yel grn	.20	2.50
15	A2	25c blk brn	.20	.75
16	A2	50c red org	.20	.85
17	A2	$1 blue	.20	.60
18	A2	$2 dk vio	.20	.60
19	A2	$2.50 indigo	.20	1.25
20	A2	$3 brown	.20	.60
21	A2	$4 org brn	.20	.70
22	A2	$5 dk grn	.20	.90
23	A2	$10 crimson	.20	.60
24	A2	$20 olive	.20	.60
25	A2	$50 blue vio	.20	.60
		Nos. 12-25 (14)	2.90	13.10

Two types of $4, $10, $20 and $50: I- Character kuo directly left of sun emblem is open at upper and lower left corners of "box." Diagonal

stroke from top center to lower right has no hook at bottom. II- Character is closed at left corners. Diagonal stroke has hook at bottom.
See Nos. 47-52, 61-63. For surcharges see Nos. M1, Taiwan 91-96, People's Republic of China 35-48, 3L37-3L52, 3L55-3L66, 3L71-3L75.

China Nos. 728-731 Surcharged in Black

1946

26	A75	$2 on $20 green	.20	.80
27	A75	$3 on $30 blue	.20	1.75
28	A75	$5 on $50 dark brown	.20	.85
29	A75	$10 on $100 carmine	.20	1.10
		Nos. 26-29 (4)	.80	4.50

Convening of Chinese National Assembly.

Type of China, 1946, with added inscriptions on both sides of head:

1947　　Engr.　　Perf. 11, 11½

30	A74	$2 carmine	.35	1.10
31	A74	$3 green	.45	1.25
32	A74	$5 vermilion	.45	1.40
33	A74	$10 yel grn	.60	1.25
34	A74	$20 yel org	.70	1.10
35	A74	$30 magenta	.70	1.00
		Nos. 30-35 (6)	3.25	7.35

60th birthday of Chiang Kai-shek.

Type of China, 1947, with additional inscription above value:

1947　　Unwmk.　　Engr.　　Perf. 14

36	A76	$2 deep green	.20	.50
37	A76	$4 deep blue	.20	.50
38	A76	$6 carmine	.20	.50
39	A76	$10 lt brown	.20	.60
40	A76	$20 deep claret	.20	.60
		Nos. 36-40 (5)	1.00	2.75

First anniversary of return of Chinese National Government to Nanking.

China Nos. 644 to 646 and 634 Surcharged in Black

1947　　　　　　Perf. 12½, 14

41	A73	$100 on $1000 rose lake	.35	1.25
42	A73	$300 on $3000 bl	.35	1.40
43	A73	$500 on $5000 dp grn & ver	.35	1.60
44	A37	$500 on $30 choc	1.10	1.75
		Nos. 41-44 (4)	2.15	6.00

Type of 1946

1947　　Engr.　　Perf. 14
Without Gum

47	A2	$44 dk car rose	25.00	35.00
48	A2	$100 dp green	.20	.35
49	A2	$200 rose brn	.20	.55
50	A2	$300 bluish grn	.20	1.25
51	A2	$500 rose car	.20	.35
52	A2	$1000 dp orange	.25	.35
		Nos. 47-52 (6)	26.05	37.85

For surcharges see note following No. 25.

Stamps and Types of 1946-47 Surcharged in Black or Red

1948   Unwmk.   *Perf. 14*

53	A2	$1500 on 20c yel grn	.55	2.60
54	A2	$3000 on $1 blue	.25	.55
55	A2	$4000 on 25c blk brn	.25	.55
		(R)		
56	A2	$8000 on 50c red org	.25	.85
57	A2	$10,000 on 10c org	.30	.55
58	A2	$50,000 on $109 dk		
		grn (R)	.60	3.75
59	A2	$100,000 on $65 dl grn	.55	3.75
60	A2	$500,000 on $22 gray		
		(R)	.90	3.75
		Nos. 53-60 (8)	3.65	16.35

Type of 1946

1947, Nov. 5   Without Gum

61	A2	$22 gray	40.00	
62	A2	$65 dull green	45.00	
63	A2	$109 dark green	55.00	
		Nos. 61-63 (3)	140.00	

For surcharges see note following No. 25.

POSTAGE DUE STAMPS

D1

1947   Unwmk.   Engr.   *Perf. 14*
Without Gum

J1	D1	10c dark blue	.20	5.00
J2	D1	20c dark blue	.20	5.00
J3	D1	50c dark blue	.20	4.00
J4	D1	$1 dark blue	.20	3.00
J5	D1	$2 dark blue	.20	4.00
J6	D1	$5 dark blue	.20	3.00
		Nos. J1-J6 (6)	1.20	24.00

Nos. J4-J6 are known on paper with the papermaker's watermark, "COSMOS BOND."

Nos. J1 to J3 Surcharged in Red

1948

J7	D1	$10 on 10c dark blue	.20	4.50
J8	D1	$20 on 20c dark blue	.20	4.50
J9	D1	$50 on 50c dark blue	.20	4.50
		Nos. J7-J9 (3)	.60	13.50

The surcharge reads "Changed to . . . dollars." Characters at the left express the new value and vary on each denomination.

MILITARY STAMPS

No. 16 Surcharged in Black

1947   Unwmk.   *Perf. 14*

M1	A2	$44 on 50c red org	6.00	12.00

The surcharge reads: "Army Post. Temporarily for 44 dollars."

China No. M13
Overprinted in Black

Thin Paper Without Gum
Perf. 12½

M2	M1	rose	1.00	1.00

China No. M13
Overprinted in Black

M3	M1	rose	47.50	47.50

PARCEL POST STAMP

China No. Q25
Surcharged in Black

1948   Unwmk.   Engr.   *Perf. 13½*
Without Gum

Q1	PP3	$500,000 on		
		$5,000,000		
		lil	90.00	

Used value is for CTO.

The use of this handstamp from Anhwei has not been verified.

Fukien Province

Stamps of China, 1945-49, Surcharged

1949   Engr.   *Perf. 14*
Without Gum

1	A82	1c on $500 bl grn	6.25	7.00
2	A82	1c on $7000 lt red brn	15.00	22.50
3	A82	2c on $2,000,000 ver	3.75	4.50
4	A82	2½c on $50,000 dp bl	22.50	22.50
5	A73	4c on $100 dk car	3.00	3.00
6	A73	10c on $200 ol grn	4.00	4.00
7	A82	10c on $3000 bl	2.50	3.00
8	A82	10c on $4000 gray	3.75	4.50
9	A82	10c on $6000 rose lil	3.75	4.25
10	A82	10c on $100,000 dl grn	3.75	4.25
11	A82	10c on $1,000,000 cl	3.75	4.25
12	A82	40c on $200,000 brn vio	5.00	5.50
		Nos. 1-12 (12)	77.00	89.50

The surcharge on No. 2 is handstamped and in slightly larger characters.
Issue dates: No. 2, May 10; others, June.

China Nos. 973, 975-978 Overprinted

1949, June   Litho.   *Perf. 12½, 13*

13	A94	1c apple grn	12.00	6.00
14	A94	4c blue green	6.00	1.25
15	A94	10c deep lilac	35.00	18.00
16	A94	16c orange red	7.00	18.00
17	A94	20c blue	35.00	18.00
		Nos. 13-17 (5)	95.00	61.25

Same Overprint on China No. 959

1949, July   Litho.   *Perf. 12½*

18	A96	orange	47.50	47.50

Same Overprint on Fukien Nos. 1, 3-4, 8, 11 in Black or Red

1949, June   Engr.   *Perf. 14*

19	A82	1c on $500 bl grn	100.00	100.00
20	A82	2c on $2,000,000 ver	35.00	35.00
21	A82	2½c on $50,000 dp bl	57.50	57.50
22	A82	10c on $4000 gray	25.00	25.00
23	A82	10c on $1,000,000 cl	92.50	87.50
		Nos. 19-23 (5)	310.00	305.00

AIR POST STAMP

China #C62 Overprinted as #13-17

1949, July   Litho.   *Perf. 12½*

C1	AP5	blue green	47.50	25.00

SPECIAL DELIVERY STAMP

China #E12 Overprinted as #13-17

1949, July   Litho.   *Perf. 12½*

E1	SD2	red violet	32.50	22.50

REGISTRATION STAMP

China #F2 Overprinted as #13-17

1949, July   Litho.   *Perf. 12½*

F1	R2	carmine	32.50	22.50

Hunan Province

China No. 640
Surcharged

1949, May   Engr.   *Perf. 14*

1	A73	on $100 dk car	9.00	5.50

The first printing of surcharge on No. 1 is in smaller characters.

China Nos. 797, 788, 750, 747
Surcharged

1949, May   Engr.   *Perf. 14*

2	A82	1c on $2,000,000 ver	18.00	18.00
3	A82	2c on $20,000 rose pink	18.00	18.00
4	A82	5c on $3000 rose	24.00	26.00
5	A82	10c on $500 blue grn	18.00	18.00
		Nos. 2-5 (4)	78.00	80.00

AIR POST STAMP

China No. 790
Surcharged

1949, May   Engr.   *Perf. 14*

C1	A82	On $40,000 green	14.00	16.00

SPECIAL DELIVERY STAMP

China No. 637 Surcharged as No. F1 in Red

1949, May   Engr.   *Perf. 14*

E1	A73	On $30 dark blue	18.00	18.00

REGISTRATION STAMP

China No. 754
Surcharged

1949, May   Engr.   *Perf. 14*

F1	A82	On $7000 lt red brn	18.00	18.00

Hupeh Province

China Type A95
Surcharged

1949, May   Litho.

1	A95	1c on $20 red brn	45.00	45.00
2	A95	10c on $20 red brn	45.00	45.00

Kansu Province

China No. 959
Handstamped in Purple

1949, Aug.   Litho.   *Perf. 12½*

1	A96	orange		1,100.

AIR POST STAMP

Same Handstamp Overprinted on China No. C62 in Red

1949, Aug.   Litho.   *Perf. 12½*

C1	AP5	blue green		1,100.

Counterfeits exist.

Kiangsi Province

China Nos. 789-791
Surcharged

1949   Engr.   *Perf. 14*

1	A82	On $30,000 choc	37.50	35.00
2	A82	On $40,000 green	37.50	35.00
3	A82	On $50,000 dp bl	37.50	35.00
		Nos. 1-3 (3)	112.50	105.00

AIR POST STAMP

Similar Surcharge on China No. 754

1949   Engr.   *Perf. 14*

C1	A82	On $7000 lt red brn	40.00	40.00

Third and fourth characters in right column of surcharge read "Air Mail" in Chinese on No. C1, "Registered" on Nos. F1-F2.

SPECIAL DELIVERY STAMP

Similar Surcharge on China No. 750

1949   Engr.   *Perf. 14*

E1	A82	On $3000 blue	45.00	30.00

See note below No. C1.

REGISTRATION STAMPS

Similar Surcharge on China Nos. 747
and 754

1949		**Engr.**	**Perf. 14**
F1	A82	On $500 bl grn	45.00 30.00
F2	A82	On $7000 lt red brn	45.00 30.00

Kwangsi Province

China Nos. 811 and
818 Also Surcharged
in Red

1949, May 21			**Typo.**
6	A62	5c on $20,000 on 10c dp grn	20.00 20.00
7	A62	5c on $40,000 on 20c dk ol grn	45.00 27.50

China Stamps of 1946-48 Surcharged
in Black or Red

a   b

1949		**Engr.**	**Perf. 14**
		Type "a" Surcharge	
8	A82	½c on $500,000 lil rose	26.00 19.00
9	A82	1c on $200,000 brn vio	22.50 7.75
10	A82	2c on $300,000 yel grn	77.50 47.50
11	A73	5c on $3000 blue	14.00 7.00
12	A82	5c on $3000 blue	11.50 7.00
13	A82	5c on $40,000 grn	22.50 13.00
		Type "b" Surcharge	
14	A82	13c on $50,000 dp bl (R)	17.00 9.50
15	A82	13c on $50,000 dp bl	62.50 17.00
16	A82	17c on $7000 lt red brn	17.50 11.50
17	A82	21c on $100,000 dl grn	21.00 14.00
		Nos. 8-17 (10)	292.00 153.25

Shensi Province

China Nos. 747, 750
Surcharged

1949, May		**Engr.**	**Perf. 14**
1	A82	On $500 bl grn	30.00 30.00
2	A82	On $3000 blue	30.00 30.00

AIR POST STAMP

Similar Surcharge on China No. 754

1949, May		**Engr.**	**Perf. 14**
C1	A82	On $7000 lt red brn	35.00 35.00

SPECIAL DELIVERY STAMP

Similar Surcharge on China No. 746 in
Red

1949, May		**Engr.**	**Perf. 14**
E1	A82	On $250 dp lil	40.00 40.00

REGISTRATION STAMPS

Similar Surcharge on China Nos. 626,
637 in Red

1949, May		**Typo.**	**Perf. 12**
F1	A72	on $30 bl	40.00 40.00
F2	A73	on $30 dk bl	35.00 35.00

Szechwan Province

Re-engraved Issue of
China, 1923,
Overprinted

1933		**Unwmk.**	**Perf. 14**
1	A29	1c orange	6.25 .60
2	A29	5c claret	6.25 .85
3	A30	50c deep green	19.00 4.00
		Nos. 1-3 (3)	31.50 5.45

The overprint reads "For use in Szechwan
Province exclusively."

Same on Sun Yat-sen Issue of 1931-
37
Type II

1933-34			**Perf. 12½**
4	A37	2c olive grn	.60 .60
5	A37	5c green	14.00 1.40
6	A37	15c dk green	4.50 1.75
7	A37	15c scar ('34)	4.00 7.00
8	A37	25c ultra	3.50 1.10
9	A37	$1 org brn & dk brn	12.00 2.40
10	A37	$2 bl & org brn	30.00 4.00
11	A37	$5 dl red & blk	77.50 22.50
		Nos. 4-11 (8)	146.10 40.75

Same on Martyrs Issue of 1932-34

1933			**Perf. 14**
12	A39	½c black brn	.50 .50
13	A40	1c orange	.75 .30
14	A39	2½c rose lilac	1.75 2.25
15	A48	3c deep brown	1.75 1.75
16	A45	8c brown org	1.10 .90
17	A46	10c dull violet	2.75 .30
18	A45	13c blue green	3.00 .60
19	A46	17c brown olive	3.25 .85
20	A47	20c brown red	5.00 .60
21	A48	30c brown violet	4.00 .60
22	A47	40c orange	8.25 .60
23	A40	50c green	22.50 1.25
		Nos. 12-23 (12)	54.60 10.50

Stamps of China,
1947-48, Surcharged

1949		**Engr.**	**Perf. 14**
24	A82	on $150 dk bl	47.50 35.00
25	A82	on $250 dp lil	47.50 35.00
26	A82	on $500 bl grn	14.00 8.50
27	A82	on $1000 red	35.00 27.50
28	A82	on $2000 ver	14.00 10.50
29	A82	on $3000 blue	14.00 10.50
30	A82	on $4000 gray	14.00 10.50
31	A82	on $5000 dk brn	35.00 40.00
32	A82	on $6000 rose lil	14.00 14.00
33	A82	on $7000 lt red brn	35.00 30.00
34	A82	on $10,000 dk bl & car	14.00 10.50
35	A82	on $20,000 rose pink	14.00 10.50
36	A82	on $30,000 choc	19.00 14.00
37	A82	on $50,000 grn & dk bl	19.00 17.00
38	A82	on $50,000 dp bl	19.00 14.00
39	A82	on $100,000 dl yel & ol	19.00 14.00
40	A82	on $100,000 dl grn	19.00 17.00
41	A82	on $200,000 vio brn & dp bl	19.00 14.00
42	A82	on $200,000 brn vio	19.00 14.00
43	A82	on $300,000 sep & org brn	26.00 18.00
44	A82	on $300,000 yel grn	26.00 18.00
45	A82	on $500,000 dk Prus grn & sep	19.00 14.00
46	A82	on $1,000,000 claret	35.00 18.00
47	A82	on $2,000,000 ver	19.00 17.00
48	A82	on $3,000,000 ol bis	19.00 17.00

49	A82	on $5,000,000 ultra	70.00 45.00
		Nos. 24-49 (26)	645.00 493.50

Several of Nos. 24-49 exist with inverted
surcharge and a few with bottom character of
left row repeated in right row, same position.
Counterfeits exist.

China No. 737
Surcharged in Black

1949			**Perf. 12½**
50	A77	2c on $500 ol grn	26.00 35.00

China No. 975
Handstamp
Surcharged in Purple

1949			**Litho.**
51	A94	2½c on 4c bl grn	22.50 27.50

SZECHWAN AIR POST STAMPS

China Nos. C55-C58, C60-C61
Surcharged

		Perf. 12½, 13x12½, 14	
1949, July			**Unwmk.**
C1	AP3	On $10,000 on 30c	6.00 6.00
a.		On #C54	500.00
C2	AP4	On $10,000 on $27	9.25 12.50
a.		Second surcharge inverted	250.00
b.		On #C53	125.00
C3	AP3	On $20,000 on 25c	9.25 10.50
C4	AP3	On $30,000 on 90c	7.25 10.50
C5	AP3	On $50,000 on 60c	85.00 100.00
C6	AP3	On $50,000 on $1	11.00 15.00
		Nos. C1-C6 (6)	127.75 154.50

SZECHWAN REGISTRATION STAMPS

Stamps of China,
1944-47, Surcharged

		Engraved; Typographed (A72)	
1949			**Perf. 12, 13, 14**
F1	A64	On $100 yel brn	50.00
F2	A72	On $100 dk brn	50.00
F3	A64	On $200 blue	100.00
F4	A72	On $200 brn vio	50.00
F5	A73	On $200 ol grn	35.00
F6	A73	On $500 brt bl grn	100.00
F7	A73	On $700 red brn	175.00
F8	A73	On $5000 dp grn & ver	75.00
		Nos. F1-F8 (8)	635.00

PARCEL POST STAMP

China No. Q10 Surcharged

1949		**Engr.**	**Perf. 12½**
Q1	PP2	1c on $20,000 dk red	

No. Q1 is also found with surcharged value
repeated in 5 characters at top of stamp.

Tsingtau Province

China Nos. 890, 903,
945, 894 Handstamp
Surcharged in Purple
(#1-2), Blue (#3) or
Red (#4)

		Engraved; Lithographed	
1949, May			**Perf. 14, 12½**
1	A94	1c on $100 org brn	67.50 60.00
2	A94	4c on $5000 lt bl	67.50 60.00
3	A94	6c on $500 rose lil	67.50 60.00
4	A94	10c on $1000 bl	67.50 60.00
		Nos. 1-4 (4)	270.00 240.00

Yunnan Province

Stamps of China,
1923-26, Overprinted

The overprint reads "For exclusive use in the
Province of Yunnan." It was applied to prevent
stamps being purchased in the depreciated
currency of Yunnan and used elsewhere.

1926		**Unwmk.**	**Perf. 14**
1	A29	½c blk brn	1.10 .20
2	A29	1c orange	1.10 .20
3	A29	1½c violet	2.40 2.40
4	A29	2c yellow grn	1.75 .30
5	A29	3c blue green	1.75 .30
6	A29	4c olive grn	2.25 .30
7	A29	5c claret	2.25 .30
8	A29	6c red	3.25 .70
9	A29	7c violet	3.50 1.10
10	A29	8c brown org	3.00 .80
11	A29	10c dark blue	1.90 .20
12	A30	13c brown	1.10 1.10
13	A30	15c dark blue	1.10 1.10
14	A30	16c olive grn	2.25 1.10
15	A30	20c brown red	5.25 1.90
16	A30	30c brown vio	3.25 3.25
17	A30	50c deep green	3.50 3.25
18	A31	$1 org brn & sep	13.00 8.00
19	A31	$2 blue & red brn	22.50 8.00
20	A31	$5 red & slate	150.00 150.00
		Nos. 1-20 (20)	226.20 184.40

Unification Issue of
China, 1929,
Overprinted in Red

1929			**Perf. 14**
21	A35	1c brown org	1.10 1.10
22	A35	4c olive grn	2.25 3.50
23	A35	10c dark blue	4.00 5.50
24	A35	$1 dark red	70.00 50.00
		Nos. 21-24 (4)	77.35 65.10

Similar Overprint in Black on Sun Yat-
sen Mausoleum Issue
Characters 15½-16mm apart

25	A36	1c brown orange	1.10 .85
26	A36	4c olive green	1.10 2.25
27	A36	10c dark blue	3.25 5.00
28	A36	$1 dark red	45.00 40.00
		Nos. 25-28 (4)	50.45 48.10

London Print Issue of China, 1931-37, Overprinted

1932-34 Unwmk. Perf. 12½
Type I (double circle)

29	A37	1c orange	2.50	1.75
30	A37	2c olive grn	3.00	3.50
31	A37	4c green	2.00	3.50
32	A37	20c ultra	2.00	2.00
33	A37	$1 org brn & dk brn	30.00	35.00
34	A37	$2 bl & org brn	50.00	55.00
35	A37	$5 dl red & blk	150.00	190.00
		Nos. 29-35 (7)	239.50	290.75

Type II (single circle)

36	A37	2c olive grn	17.00	17.00
37	A37	4c green	11.00	7.00
38	A37	5c green	10.00	6.75
39	A37	15c dk green	5.25	5.75
40	A37	15c scar ('34)	5.25	6.50
41	A37	25c ultra	7.00	7.50
42	A37	$1 org brn & dk brn	45.00	45.00
43	A37	$2 bl & org brn	77.50	77.50
44	A37	$5 dl red & blk	175.00	175.00
		Nos. 36-44 (9)	353.00	348.00

Nos. 36-39, 41-44 were overprinted in London as well as in Peking. The London overprints are 11mm in length; the Peking overprints are 12mm in length. There are other minor differences. Value of London overprints is significantly more than the Peking overprints, which are valued above.

Tan Yuan-chang Issue of China, 1933, Overprinted

1933 Perf. 14

45	A49	2c olive green	1.10	1.10
46	A49	5c green	1.90	1.50
47	A49	25c ultra	3.25	3.50
48	A49	$1 red	50.00	40.00
		Nos. 45-48 (4)	56.25	46.10

Martyrs Issue of China, 1932-34, Overprinted

1933

49	A39	½c blk brown	1.00	.90
50	A40	1c orange	2.00	1.50
51	A39	2½c rose lilac	2.25	2.50
52	A48	3c deep brown	3.50	1.25
53	A45	8c brown org	1.50	1.50
54	A46	10c dull vio	2.25	2.50
55	A45	13c blue grn	1.40	.60
56	A46	17c brn olive	7.00	7.00
57	A47	20c brown red	1.75	1.75
58	A48	30c brown vio	5.50	5.50
59	A47	40c orange	26.00	26.00
60	A40	50c green	26.00	26.00
		Nos. 49-60 (12)	80.15	77.00

China No. 324 was overprinted with characters arranged vertically, like Sinkiang No. 114, but was not issued.

China Stamps of 1945-49 Surcharged in Black or Blue

Engraved; Lithographed; Typographed
1949 Perf. 12, 12½, 14

61	A82	1c on $200,000 brn vio	12.50	12.50
62	A82	1.2c on $40,000 grn	12.50	14.00
63	A94	6c on $200 red org	12.50	12.50
64	A94	10c on $20,000 org	12.50	14.00
65	A94	12c on $50 dk Prus grn (Bl)	12.50	12.50

66	A72	12c on $50 grnsh gray (Bl)	12.50	12.50
67	A72	12c on $200 brn vio (Bl)	12.50	14.00
68	A94	30c on $20 vio brn	12.50	12.50
69	A82	$1.20 on $100,000 dl grn	20.00	22.50
		Nos. 61-69 (9)	120.00	127.00

China No. 888 and 630 Surcharged

1949 Engr. Perf. 14
70	A94	4c on $20 vio brn		225.00

Typo. Perf. 12
71	A72	12c on $200 brn vio		225.00

Manchuria

Kirin and Heilungkiang Issue
Stamps of China, 1923-26, Overprinted

The overprint reads: "For use in Ki-Hei District" the two names being abbreviated.

The intention of the overprint was to prevent the purchase of stamps in Manchuria, where the currency was depreciated, and their resale elsewhere.

1927 Unwmk. Perf. 14

1	A29	½c black brn	1.10	.20
2	A29	1c orange	1.10	.20
3	A29	1½c violet	1.50	1.10
4	A29	2c yellow grn	1.50	.20
5	A29	3c blue grn	1.00	.45
6	A29	4c olive grn	.50	.20
7	A29	5c claret	1.00	.20
8	A29	6c red	1.50	1.10
9	A29	7c violet	3.00	1.10
10	A29	8c brown org	2.00	1.10
11	A29	10c dk blue	1.10	.30
12	A30	13c brown	2.25	1.75
13	A30	15c dk blue	2.25	1.75
14	A30	16c olive grn	2.25	1.60
15	A30	20c brown red	3.50	1.90
16	A30	30c brown vio	5.00	2.00
17	A30	50c dp green	7.00	2.40
18	A31	$1 org brn & sep	15.00	5.00
19	A31	$2 bl & red brn	40.00	11.00
20	A31	$5 red & slate	190.00	190.00
		Nos. 1-20 (20)	282.55	223.55

Several values of this issue exist with inverted overprint, double overprint and in pairs with one overprint omitted. These "errors" were not regularly issued. Forgeries also exist.

Chang Tso-lin Stamps of 1928 Overprinted in Red or Blue

1928 Perf. 14

21	A34	1c brown org (R)	1.75	1.10
22	A34	4c olive grn (R)	1.10	1.10
23	A34	10c dull blue (R)	3.00	2.25
24	A34	$1 red (Bl)	30.00	27.50
		Nos. 21-24 (4)	35.85	31.95

Unification Issue of China, 1929, Overprinted in Red as in 1928

1929

25	A35	1c brown orange	1.25	1.25
26	A35	4c olive green	2.25	2.00
27	A35	10c dark blue	8.00	7.50
28	A35	$1 dark red	65.00	60.00
		Nos. 25-28 (4)	76.50	70.75

Similar Overprint in Black on Sun Yat-sen Mausoleum Issue of China Characters 15-16mm apart

1929 Perf. 14

29	A36	1c brown orange	1.40	1.60
30	A36	4c olive green	1.75	1.90
31	A36	10c dark blue	5.25	3.25
32	A36	$1 dark red	52.50	40.00
		Nos. 29-32 (4)	60.90	46.75

Sinkiang

Stamps of China, 1913-19, Overprinted in Black or Red

The first character of overprint is ½mm out of alignment, to the left, and the overprint measures 16mm.

1915 Unwmk. Perf. 14

1	A24	½c black brn	1.10	.60
2	A24	1c orange	1.10	.45
3	A24	2c yellow grn	1.50	.80
4	A24	3c slate grn	1.50	.40
5	A24	4c scarlet	3.00	.70
6	A24	5c rose lilac	2.25	.60
7	A24	6c gray	4.00	1.75
8	A24	7c violet	4.00	5.25
9	A24	8c brown orange	3.50	3.50
10	A24	10c dark blue	3.50	1.75
11	A25	15c brown	4.00	2.25
12	A25	16c olive grn	8.00	5.75
13	A25	20c brown red	8.00	4.50
14	A25	30c brown violet	9.00	7.00
15	A25	50c deep green	25.00	11.50
16	A26	$1 ocher & blk	90.00	40.00
a.		Second & third characters of overprint transposed	16,000.	
		Nos. 1-16 (16)	169.45	86.80

Stamps of China, 1913-19, Overprinted in Black or Red

The five characters of overprint are correctly aligned and measure 15½mm.

1916-19

17	A24	½c black brn	1.25	1.50
18	A24	1c orange	2.00	1.10
19	A24	1½c violet	2.75	2.50
20	A24	2c yellow grn	2.00	1.10
21	A24	3c slate grn	3.50	.45
22	A24	4c scarlet	3.50	.75
23	A24	5c rose lilac	3.50	.55
24	A24	6c gray	5.00	.75
25	A24	7c violet	5.00	7.00
26	A24	8c brown orange	5.50	5.25
27	A24	10c dark blue	5.50	.75
28	A25	13c brown	3.00	5.00
29	A25	15c brown	3.75	5.25
30	A25	16c olive grn	3.50	2.50
31	A25	20c brown red	2.75	1.90
32	A25	30c brown vio	4.25	3.75
33	A25	50c deep green	5.75	3.50
34	A26	$1 ocher & blk (R)	18.00	6.75
35	A26	$2 dk bl & blk (R)	17.50	7.50
36	A26	$5 scar & blk (R)	67.50	24.00
37	A26	$10 yel grn & blk (R)	175.00	110.00
38	A26	$20 yel & blk (R)	900.00	550.00
		Nos. 17-38 (22)	1,240.	741.85

For overprint see No. C4.

China Nos. 243-246 Overprinted

1921 Perf. 14

39	A27	1c orange	1.10	1.10
40	A27	3c blue green	2.25	2.25
41	A27	6c gray	8.50	6.00
42	A27	10c blue	50.00	50.00
		Nos. 39-42 (4)	61.85	59.35

Constitution Issue of China, 1923, Overprinted

1923

43	A32	1c orange	3.75	3.75
44	A32	3c blue green	4.25	4.25
45	A32	4c red	6.25	6.25
46	A32	10c blue	17.50	17.50
		Nos. 43-46 (4)	31.75	31.75

Stamps of China, 1923-26, Overprinted as in 1916-19, in Black or Red

1924 Re-engraved

47	A29	½c black brn	.90	1.75
48	A29	1c orange	.90	.70
49	A29	1½c violet	1.60	3.00
50	A29	2c yellow grn	2.50	.85
51	A29	3c blue grn	2.50	.19
52	A29	4c gray	2.50	4.00
53	A29	5c claret	.85	.60
54	A29	6c red	4.50	1.60
55	A29	7c violet	5.00	4.50
56	A29	8c org brn	10.00	9.00
57	A29	10c dark blue	4.00	1.10
58	A30	13c red brown	3.50	5.00
59	A30	15c deep blue	5.25	4.00
60	A30	16c olive grn	6.00	5.75
61	A30	20c brown red	5.00	3.75
62	A30	30c brown vio	5.75	4.00
63	A30	50c deep green	6.00	4.00
64	A31	$1 org brn & sep (R)	10.50	5.00
65	A31	$2 bl & red brn (R)	22.50	7.25
66	A31	$5 red & slate (R)	57.50	19.00
67	A31	$10 grn & claret (R)	175.00	100.00
68	A31	$20 plum & bl (R)	250.00	190.00
		Nos. 47-68 (22)	582.25	375.60

See #69, 114. For overprints see #C1-C3.

Same Overprint on China No. 275

1926

69	A29	4c olive green	2.50	2.50

Chang Tso-lin Stamps of China, 1928, Overprinted in Red or Blue

1928 Perf. 14

70	A34	1c brn org (R)	1.10	1.10
71	A34	4c ol grn (R)	1.75	1.75
72	A34	10c dull bl (R)	4.00	4.00
73	A34	$1 red (Bl)	35.00	30.00
		Nos. 70-73 (4)	41.85	36.85

Unification Issue of China, 1929, Overprinted in Red as in 1928

1929

74	A35	1c brown org	1.75	1.75
75	A35	4c olive grn	3.00	3.00
76	A35	10c dk blue	7.00	7.00
77	A35	$1 dk red	55.00	45.00
		Nos. 74-77 (4)	66.75	56.75

Similar Overprint in Black on Sun Yat-sen Mausoleum Issue of China Characters 15mm apart

1929 Perf. 14

78	A36	1c brown org	1.10	1.10
79	A36	4c olive grn	1.65	1.75
80	A36	10c dark blue	3.75	4.00
81	A36	$1 dark red	47.50	37.50
		Nos. 78-81 (4)	54.00	44.35

Stamps of Sun Yat-sen Issue of 1931-37 Overprinted

1932 Type I Perf. 12½

82	A37	1c orange	1.00	2.25
83	A37	2c olive grn	2.50	3.50
84	A37	4c green	1.50	3.75

85	A37	20c ultra	2.25	4.75
86	A37	$1 org brn & dk brn	7.00	11.50
87	A37	$2 bl & org brn	20.00	24.00
88	A37	$5 dl red & blk	22.50	35.00
		Nos. 82-88 (7)	56.75	84.75

No. 83 was overprinted in Shanghai in 1938. The overprint differs in minor details.

1932-38

Type II

89	A37	2c olive grn	.25	1.10
90	A37	4c green	.70	2.25
91	A37	5c green	.45	2.25
92	A37	15c dk green	.60	2.25
93	A37	15c scar ('34)	.60	2.25
93A	A37	20c ultra ('38)	.45	1.50
94	A37	25c ultra	.70	2.25
95	A37	$1 org brn & dk brn	5.25	6.00
96	A37	$2 bl & org brn	11.00	17.50
97	A37	$5 dl red & blk	22.50	35.00
		Nos. 89-97 (10)	42.50	72.35

Nos. 89, 90 and 94 were overprinted in London, Peking and Shanghai. Nos. 92, 95-97 exist with London and Peking overprints. Nos. 91 and 93 exist with Peking and Shanghai overprints. No. 93A is a Shanghai overprint. The overprints differ in minor details.

Tan Yuan-chang Issue of China, 1933, Overprinted as in 1928

1933   **Perf. 14**

98	A49	2c olive grn	2.40	2.40
99	A49	5c green	3.00	3.00
100	A49	25c ultra	9.50	9.50
101	A49	$1 red	47.50	40.00
		Nos. 98-101 (4)	62.40	54.90

Stamps of China
Martyrs Issue of 1932-
34 Overprinted

1933-34

102	A39	½c black brown	.20	1.25
103	A40	1c orange	1.10	1.50
104	A39	2½c rose lilac	.25	1.10
105	A48	3c deep brown	.25	1.10
106	A45	8c brown orange	.75	1.25
107	A46	10c dull violet	.25	1.10
108	A45	13c blue green	.25	1.60
109	A46	17c brown olive	.25	.90
110	A47	20c brown red	1.10	2.25
111	A48	30c brown violet	.40	1.60
112	A47	40c orange	.60	1.10
113	A40	50c green	.70	2.25
		Nos. 102-113 (12)	6.10	17.00

Nos. 102-113 were originally overprinted in Peking. In 1938, Nos. 103-105, 108-112 were overprinted in Shanghai. The two overprints differ in minor details. No. 105, Shanghai overprint, is scarce. Value $35.

China No. 324 Overprinted as in 1916-19

1936   **Perf. 14**

114	A29	6c brown	11.50	12.00

Stamps of China, 1939-40 Overprinted in Black

1940-45   Unwmk.   Perf. 12½

Type III

115	A57	2c olive green	.85	1.00
116	A57	3c dull claret ('41)	.20	1.50
117	A57	5c green	.20	1.50
118	A57	5c olive green	.20	1.50
119	A57	8c olive green ('41)	.20	.75
120	A57	10c green ('41)	.20	1.10
121	A57	15c scarlet	.55	2.50
122	A57	16c olive gray ('41)	.40	1.00
123	A57	25c dark blue	.55	2.75
124	A57	$1 hn & dk brn (type II)	6.25	11.00
125	A57	$2 dp bl & org brn (type I)	4.50	11.00
126	A57	$5 red & grnsh blk	26.00	32.50
		Nos. 115-126 (12)	40.10	68.10

Perf. 14

With Secret Marks

127	A57	8c ol grn (#383a)	1.10	1.65
a.		On #383	19.00	22.50
128	A57	10c green ('41)	10.00	13.00
129	A57	30c scarlet ('45)	.30	1.10
130	A57	50c dk blue ('45)	.55	1.75
131	A57	$1 org brn & sep	.55	2.25
132	A57	$2 dp bl & org brn	.55	2.25
133	A57	$5 red & sl grn	.65	3.75
134	A57	$10 dk grn & dl pur	1.90	2.75
135	A57	$20 rose lake & dk bl	3.50	5.50
		Nos. 127-135 (9)	19.10	34.00

Wmk. Character Yu (Post) (261)

Perf. 14

136	A57	5c olive green	.20	1.10
137	A57	10c green	.25	1.75
138	A57	30c scarlet	.25	2.25
139	A57	50c dark blue	.30	1.10
		Nos. 136-139 (4)	1.00	6.20

Martyrs Issue, 1940-41, Overprinted in Black

Perf. 12, 12½, 13, 13x12, 13½x13

1941-45   Wmk. 261

140	A40	1c orange	.20	.65
141	A39	2½c rose lilac	.20	1.25
142	A45	8c dp org ('45)	3.25	3.25
143	A46	10c dull vio	.25	.85
144	A45	13c dp yel grn	.55	1.50
145	A46	17c brown olive	.55	1.40
146	A45	25c red vio ('45)	1.10	2.00
147	A47	40c orange ('45)	1.90	2.50
		Nos. 140-147 (8)	8.00	13.40

Unwmk.

148	A39	½c olive blk	.20	.85
149	A40	1c orange ('45)	.20	.65
150	A45	2c dp blue ('45)	1.75	1.00
151	A48	3c dp yel brn	.20	1.25
152	A39	4c pale vio ('45)	.20	1.25
153	A45	8c dp orange	.20	1.50
154	A45	13c dp yel grn ('45)	.35	1.10
155	A48	15c brn car ('45)	.20	1.10
156	A46	17c brn ol ('45)	.55	1.25
157	A47	20c lt blue ('45)	.20	.90
158	A45	21c ol brn ('45)	.65	1.25
159	A46	28c olive ('45)	.80	1.50
160	A47	40c orange ('45)	1.65	3.75
161	A40	50c green ('45)	1.10	1.90
		Nos. 148-161 (14)	8.25	19.25

Stamps of China, 1942-43 Overprinted in Carmine, Black or Red

1944   Perf. 12½, 13

Without Gum

162	A62	10c dp grn (C)	1.10	2.75
163	A62	20c dk ol grn (C)	1.25	2.75
164	A62	25c violet brn	.20	2.75
165	A62	30c dk orange	.60	3.25
166	A62	40c red brown	.20	3.00
167	A62	50c sage green	.20	1.75
a.		Perf. 11	10.00	8.50
168	A62	$1 rose lake	2.25	1.75
169	A62	$1 dull green	.20	3.00
170	A62	$1.50 dp bl (C)	.20	3.25
171	A62	$2 dk bl grn (R)	1.50	2.50
172	A62	$3 yellow	.20	4.25
173	A62	$5 cerise	1.50	4.00
		Nos. 162-173 (12)	9.40	35.25

For surcharges see Nos. 194-195.

Same Overprint on Stamps of China, 1942-43, in Black

1944-46   Imperf.

174	A57	$10 red brown	50.00	67.50
175	A57	$20 rose red	1.90	7.25
176	A57	$30 dull vio	1.25	7.25
177	A57	$40 rose red	1.90	8.00
178	A57	$50 blue ('46)	625.00	675.00
179	A57	$100 orange brn	2.50	8.00

Perf. 13½

180	A57	$4 dp blue	.20	4.00
181	A57	$5 lilac gray	.30	4.50
182	A57	$10 red brn	.30	4.50
183	A57	$20 blue grn	.90	5.00
184	A57	$20 rose red	85.00	80.00
185	A57	$30 dull vio	1.25	5.50
186	A57	$40 rose	1.25	6.00
187	A57	$50 blue	1.60	5.00
188	A57	$100 orange brn	67.50	67.50
		Nos. 174-177,179-188 (14)	215.85	280.00

Beware of trimmed copies of Nos. 182 and 187 offered as Nos. 174 and 178.

Nos. 162 and 164
Surcharged in Black

1944, Aug. 1

194	A62	12c on 10c dp grn	1.40	3.50
195	A62	24c on 25c brn vio	2.00	3.25

Stamps of China, 1940-41, Overprinted in Black at Chengtu, Szechwan

1943

196	A57	10c green (#354)	15.00	30.00
197	A47	20c lt blue (#433)	15.00	30.00

Wmk. 261   Perf. 14

198	A57	50c dk blue (#396)	15.00	30.00

China Nos. 565 and 567 Overprinted in Black

1945   Unwmk.   Perf. 12½

200	A63	40c brown red	.30	.65
201	A63	$3 red	.30	.65

China Nos. 640-642, 788, 751, 753 Surcharged in Black or Red

1949   Engr.   Perf. 14

202	A73	1c on $100 dk car	19.00	22.50
203	A73	3c on $200 ol grn (R)	19.00	22.50
204	A73	5c on $500 brt bl grn (R)	19.00	22.50
205	A82	10c on $20,000 rose pink	16.00	20.00
206	A82	50c on $4000 gray (R)	62.50	62.50
207	A82	$1 on $6000 rose lil	72.50	72.50
		Nos. 202-207 (6)	208.00	222.50

AIR POST STAMPS

Sinkiang Nos. 53, 57, 59, 32 Overprinted in Red

1932-33   Unwmk.   Perf. 14

C1	A29	5c claret ('33)	165.00	90.00
C2	A29	10c dark blue ('33)	165.00	85.00
C3	A30	15c deep blue	1,000.	275.00
C4	A25	30c brown violet	400.00	325.00

Counterfeits exist of Nos. C1-C19.

Air Post Stamps of China, 1932-37 Handstamped in Dull Red

1942

C5	AP3	15c gray green	4.25	5.50
C6	AP3	25c orange	250.00	250.00
C7	AP3	30c red	10.00	16.00
C8	AP3	45c brown vio	6.25	10.50
C9	AP3	50c dk brown	26.00	32.50
C10	AP3	60c dk blue	6.25	13.00
C11	AP3	90c olive grn	35.00	47.50
C12	AP3	$1 yellow grn	7.25	11.50
		Nos. C5-C12 (8)	345.00	386.50

Same Handstamped Overprint on Air Post Stamps of China, 1940-41 in Dull Red

1942   Wmk. 261   Perf. 12½, 13, 13½

C13	AP3	15c gray green	3.25	4.00
C14	AP3	25c yellow orange	3.25	4.00

1942   Unwmk.

C15	AP3	25c light orange	2.75	2.75
C16	AP3	30c light red	4.00	4.00
C17	AP3	50c brown	5.50	5.50
C18	AP3	$2 light brown	26.00	26.00
C19	AP3	$5 lake	26.00	26.00
		Nos. C15-C19 (5)	64.25	64.25

Twelve values exist with this overprint in black. Their status has not been determined. Inverted overprints exist in both red and black.

Official Perforated Characters

For use on official mail, various Sinkiang stamps were perforated with an arrangement of four Chinese characters ("For Official Business Only"). These include Nos. 1-38, 47-69, 114.

_____

OFFICES IN TIBET

12 Pies = 1 Anna
16 Annas = 1 Rupee

Stamps of China, Issues of 1902-10, Surcharged

1911   Unwmk.   Perf. 12 to 16

1	A17	3p on 1c ocher	15.00	27.50
a.		Inverted surcharge	3,500.	
2	A17	½a on 2c grn	15.00	27.50
3	A17	1a on 4c ver	15.00	27.50
4	A17	2a on 7c mar	15.00	27.50
5	A17	2½a on 10c ultra	20.00	32.50
6	A18	3a on 16c ol grn	40.00	50.00
a.		Large "S" in "Annas"	1,250.	
7	A18	4a on 20c red brn	40.00	50.00
8	A18	6a on 30c rose red	60.00	72.50
9	A18	12a on 50c yel grn	175.00	250.00
10	A19	1r on $1 red & pale rose	475.00	600.00
11	A19	2r on $2 red & yel	900.00	1,200.
		Nos. 1-11 (11)	1,770.	2,365.

CHINA, PEOPLE'S REPUBLIC OF

'pē-pəls ri-'pə-blik of 'chī-nə

LOCATION — Eastern Asia
GOVT. — Communist Republic
POP. — 1,246,871,951 (1999 est.)
CAPITAL — Beijing (Peking)

The communists completed their conquest of all mainland China in 1949. They established the Central Government and General Postal Administration in Peking. They ordered all but two regions to stop selling regional issues by June 30, 1950, extending validity one year from that date. The Northeast and Port Arthur-Dairen regions were exempted because their currency had a different value. These two regions stopped using separate issues at the end of 1950. Thereafter unified issues were used throughout mainland China.

On July 1, 1997 Hong Kong returned to Chinese control as an administrative district. Hong Kong stamps issued under Chinese rule will continue to be listed under "Hong Kong."

Reprints

After currency revaluation Mar. 1, 1955, reprints were prepared and put on sale by the Philatelic Agency in order to supply stocks of exhausted issues for collectors. Minor differences in design or paper distinguish the reprints. They are of commemorative and special issues up to the gymnastics set of 1952. Reprints are less expensive. Values are for original issues. Reprint distinctions are footnoted.

Used Stamps

Most used stamps before 1970 exist primarily canceled to order. Postally used copies generally sell for ½ the unused value.

Beginning in 1987 the PRC stopped furnishing quantities of used stamps to the philatelic market. When available, used stamps of these issues sell for the same or more than unused copies.

PRC Issue Numbers

Commemorative issues, beginning in 1949, and special issues, beginning in 1951, bear 4 numbers in lower margin: 1. Issue number. 2. Total of stamps in set. 3. Position of stamp in set. 4. Cumulative number of stamp (usually in parenthesis). A fifth number, the year of issue, was added in 1952.

The numbering system varies at times, with all numbers omitted on Scott 938-1046.

In certain sets listings include parenthetically the position-in-set number. During some periods these parentheses in listings hold the stamp's cumulative number. Issue numbers are noted when one or more designs are not illustrated.

Gum

All stamps to the beginning of 1960 were issued without gum, except as noted. After that date, most stamps have gum, which is translucent and almost invisible. All issues are unwatermarked, unless otherwise noted.

100 fen = 1 yuan ($)

Catalogue values for unused stamps in this country are for Never Hinged items, beginning with Scott 487 in the regular postage section, Scott B1 in the semipostal section.

Syncopated Perforations

Type A (1st stamp #2880): On the two shorter sides, an oval hole equal in width to three holes is centered.

Lantern and Gate of Heavenly Peace — A1

Globe and Hand Holding Hammer — A2

1949, Oct. 8   Litho.   Perf. 12½

1	A1	$30 blue	2.25	1.75
2	A1	$50 rose red	2.25	1.75
3	A1	$100 green	2.25	1.75
4	A1	$200 maroon	2.25	1.75
		Nos. 1-4 (4)	9.00	7.00

1st session of Chinese People's Consultative Political Conference. See #1L121-1L124.

Original   Reprint

Reprints have altered ornament on lantern base. On originals, it is a full oval; in reprints, only a partial circle. Value, set: unused $3; used $1.25.

1949, Nov. 16

5	A2	$100 carmine	7.00	2.50
6	A2	$300 slate green	7.00	2.50
7	A2	$500 dark blue	7.00	2.50
		Nos. 5-7 (3)	21.00	7.50

Asiatic and Australasian Congress of the World Federation of Trade Unions, Peking. The $100, imperf., is of dubious status. See Nos. 1L133-1L135.

Original   Reprint

Reprints show heavier shading on index finger and thumb. Value, set $5.00 unused or $2.40 used.

Conference Hall, Peking — A3

Mao Tsetung on Rostrum A4

1950, Feb. 1   Engr.   Perf. 14

8	A3	$50 red	3.50	3.25
9	A3	$100 blue	3.50	3.25
10	A4	$300 red brown	3.50	3.00
11	A4	$500 green	3.50	3.50
		Nos. 8-11 (4)	14.00	13.00

Chinese People's Consultative Political Conference. See Nos. 1L136-1L139.

Original   Reprint

Nos. 8-9: First character in top inscription shows a square, reprints an oblong.
Nos. 10-11: Originals have heavy crosshatching and lines which touch back of head and top of rostrum. Reprints have lighter lines which do not touch head or top of rostrum. Reprints, value set $4.75.

Gate of Heavenly Peace (actual size) — A5

First Issue: Top line of shading broken at right.

1950, Feb. 10   Litho.   Perf. 12½

12	A5	$200 green	6.00	2.00
13	A5	$300 brown red	.20	2.00
14	A5	$500 red	.20	2.00
15	A5	$800 orange	70.00	2.00
16	A5	$1000 dull violet	1.25	2.00
17	A5	$2000 olive	8.00	2.00
18	A5	$5000 brt pink	.20	2.00
19	A5	$8000 blue	.20	20.00
20	A5	$10,000 brown	.60	2.00
		Nos. 12-20 (9)	86.65	36.00

1950, June 9   Typo.

Second Issue: Top line of shading extends to frame line at right.

21	A5	$1000 dull violet	1.10	1.50
22	A5	$3000 red brown	1.10	1.50
23	A5	$10,000 brown	1.10	1.50
		Nos. 21-23 (3)	3.30	4.50

Other Gate of Heavenly Peace issues are illustrated where they are listed. See A10, A13, A14 and A42 for similar designs.

For similar types with Chinese characters in upper right corner see Northeast China A28, A29, Port Arthur & Darien A11, North China A8.

China Nos. 959, C62, E12, F2 Surcharged in Blue, Black, Green or Red

Rouletted, Perf. 12½ (#27, 29)

1950, Mar.   Litho.

24	SD2	$100 on red vio (Bl)	.25	.85
a.		Perf. 12½	7.50	3.00
25	R2	$200 on red (Bk)	2.50	.60
a.		Perf. 12½	55.00	3.50
26	AP5	$300 on bl grn (Bk)	.25	.85
a.		Perf. 12½	1.00	1.00
27	A96	$500 on org (Bk)	.20	.30
a.		Perf. 14	67.50	60.00
28	A96	$800 on org (R)	2.50	.20
a.		Perf. 12½	22.50	2.50
b.		Perf. 14	900.00	70.00
29	A96	$1000 on org (Bk)	.20	.20
a.		Perf. 14	.20	.20
		Nos. 24-29 (6)	5.90	3.00

No. 27 exists with green surcharge.

Harvesters with Ox — A6

1950, May
30   A6 $20,000 on $10,000 red   475.00   95.00

No. 30 is surcharged on an unissued stamp of East China.

Flag, Mao Tsetung, Gate of Heavenly Peace — A7

1950, July 1   Perf. 14
Yellow Stars

31	A7	$800 green & red	35.00	8.00
32	A7	$1000 brn & red	42.50	8.00
33	A7	$2000 dk brn & red	55.00	8.00
34	A7	$3000 dk blue & red	75.00	11.00
		Nos. 31-34 (4)	207.50	35.00

Inauguration of the People's Republic, Oct. 1, 1949. See Nos. 1L150-1L153.

Original   Reprint

Originals have a single curved line in jacket button, reprints have an extra dot in button. Value, set $14.

Sun Yat-sen Stamps of Northeastern Provinces Surcharged in Red, Black or Blue

1950, July 1   Engr.

35	A2	$50 on 20c yel grn	3.50	8.00
36	A2	$50 on 25c blk brn	6.50	4.00
37	A2	$50 on 50c red org (Bk)	2.00	3.00
38	A2	$100 on $2.50 ind	1.90	3.00
39	A2	$100 on $3 brn (Bk)	2.10	2.00
40	A2	$100 on $4 org brn, Type II (Bl)	5.00	8.00
a.		Type I	800.00	125.00

41	A2	$100 on $5 dk grn (Bk)	2.10	2.00
42	A2	$100 on $10 crim, Type II (Bl)	20.00	12.00
a.		Type I	7,500.
43	A2	$400 on $20 ol, Type II (Bl)	50.00	50.00
a.		Type I	900.00	100.00
44	A2	$400 on $44 dk car rose (Bl)	1.10	8.00
45	A2	$400 on $65 dl grn	120.00	75.00
46	A2	$400 on $100 dp grn	30.00	10.00
47	A2	$400 on $200 rose brn (Bk)	80.00	20.00
48	A2	$400 on $300 bluish grn	80.00	25.00
		Nos. 35-48 (14)	404.20	230.00

Flying Geese Type of China Surcharged in Red, Blue, Green, Brown or Black

1950, Aug. 1   Perf. 12½, Imperf.

49	A97	$50 on 10c dk bl (R)	.20	.35
50	A97	$100 on 16c ol, imperf. (Bl)	.20	.35
51	A97	$100 on 50c dl grn, imperf. (Bl)	.20	.20
52	A97	$200 on $1 org (G)	.20	.20
53	A97	$200 on $2 bl (Br)	6.00	.80
54	A97	$400 on $5 car rose (Bk)	.20	.35
55	A97	$400 on $10 bl grn (Bk)	.20	1.00
56	A97	$400 on $20 pur (Bk)	.20	2.75
		Nos. 49-56 (8)	7.40	6.00

Dove of Peace, by Picasso — A8

Chinese Flag and "1" — A9

1950, Aug. 1   Engr.   Perf. 14

57	A8	$400 brown	11.00	4.00
58	A8	$800 green	11.00	4.00
59	A8	$2000 blue	14.00	4.00
		Nos. 57-59 (3)	36.00	12.00

World Peace Campaign. See #1L154-1L156.
Paper of originals appears bright under ultraviolet lamp. That of reprints looks dull. Value, set $3.

1950   Engr. & Litho.
Flag in Red & Yellow

60	A9	$100 purple	18.00	4.00
61	A9	$400 red brown	22.00	4.00
62	A9	$800 green	22.00	4.00
63	A9	$1000 lt olive	35.00	8.00
64	A9	$2000 blue	50.00	10.00
		Nos. 60-64 (5)	147.00	30.00

1st anniv. of the Chinese People's Republic.
Size of $800: 38x46mm; others 26x32mm.
Issue dates: No. 62, Oct. 1; others Oct. 31.
See Nos. 1L157-1L161.

$800

Original

Reprint

Reprints are a brighter red, leaves beside "1" are gray brown instead of reddish brown. On the $800 the arrangement of dots in background differs in relationship to large star. Value, set $4.

Gate of Heavenly Peace (actual size) — A10

Third Issue: Cloud almost touches character at upper left. Cloud breaks inner frame line at top.

1950   Litho.

65	A10	$100 lt grnsh bl	40.00	8.00
66	A10	$200 green	250.00	15.00
67	A10	$300 dk carmine	2.75	5.00
68	A10	$400 grnsh gray	1.00	3.00
69	A10	$500 carmine	.75	2.00
70	A10	$800 orange	7.00	1.00
71	A10	$2000 gray olive	1.50	1.00
		Nos. 65-71 (7)	303.00	35.00

Issued: $800, 10/8; $500, $2000, 12/1; others, 10/6.

"Communication" and Map of China — A11

1950, Nov. 1   Litho.

72	A11	$400 green & brn	10.00	4.00
73	A11	$800 carmine & grn	10.00	4.00

First All-China Postal Conference, Peking. See Nos. 1L162-1L163.

Original   Reprint

Originals have 3 lines below horizontal bar (2nd character); reprints have four. Value, set $1.75.

Stalin and Mao Tse-tung — A12

1950, Dec. 1   Engr.   Perf. 14

74	A12	$400 red	11.00	4.25
75	A12	$800 dp green	11.00	3.25
76	A12	$2000 dk blue	15.00	4.25
		Nos. 74-76 (3)	37.00	11.75

Signing of Sino-Soviet Treaty of Friendship, Alliance and Mutual Assistance. See Nos. 1L176-1L178.
Paper of originals appears bright under ultraviolet lamp. That of reprints looks dull. Value, set $3.75.

East China Issue of 1949 Surcharged in Red, Black, Brown or Blue

Train and Postal Runner — A12a

1950, Dec.   Litho.   Perf. 12½

77	A12a	$50 on $10 dp ultra (R)	.20	.20
78	A12a	$100 on $15 org ver (Bk)	.20	.20
a.		$100 on $15 red (Bk), perf. 14	.20	.20
79	A12a	$300 on $50 car (Bk)	.20	.20
80	A12a	$400 on $1600 vio bl (Br)	2.00	.20
81	A12a	$400 on $2000 brn vio (Bl)	.85	.20
		Nos. 77-81 (5)	3.45	1.00

East China Issue of 1949 Surcharged in Red or Black

Chairman Mao — A12b

1950, Dec.

82	A12b	$50 on $10 ultra (R)	.25	.20
83	A12b	$400 on $15 ver (Bk)	.25	.20
84	A12b	$400 on $2000 grn (Bk)	1.75	.20
		Nos. 82-84 (3)	2.25	.60

(actual size) — A13

(actual size) — A14

Fourth Issue: Similar to 3rd issue, but large cloud does not break inner frame line at top.

1950-51   Litho.

85	A13	$100 lt blue	1.60	1.00
86	A13	$200 dull green	1.75	2.00
87	A13	$300 dull lilac	.40	5.25
88	A13	$400 gray grn	.40	1.00
89	A13	$500 carmine	.20	1.10
90	A13	$800 orange	85.00	4.00
a.		Imperf., pair	—	
91	A13	$1000 violet	.50	1.00
92	A13	$2000 olive	240.00	6.00
93	A13	$3000 brown	.20	6.00
94	A13	$5000 pink	.20	6.00
		Nos. 85-94 (10)	330.25	33.35

Issued: $200, $300, $500, $800, $2000, $5000, 12/22/50; others 6/8/51.

1951, Jan. 18   Engr.   Perf. 14

Fifth Issue: Colored network on surface in salmon.

95	A14	$10,000 brown	1.40	10.00
96	A14	$20,000 olive	1.40	8.25
97	A14	$30,000 green	40.00	60.00
98	A14	$50,000 violet	90.00	17.00
99	A14	$100,000 scarlet	2,250.	250.00
100	A14	$200,000 blue	2,250.	250.00
		Nos. 95-100 (6)	4,632.	595.25

Unit Issue of China Surcharged

1951, May 2   Litho.   Perf. 12½

101	SD2	$5 on rose lilac	3.50	.50
102	AP5	$10 on brt grn	.25	.25
103	R2	$15 on red	.20	.25
104	A96	$25 on orange	.70	.25
		Nos. 101-104 (4)	4.65	1.25

Issued for use in Northeast China, but available for use throughout China. Nos. 101-104 rouletted were sold for philatelic purposes only. Value, set $2.75.

Chairman Mao Tse-tung — A15

1951, July 1   Engr.   Perf. 14

105	A15	$400 chestnut	4.50	1.25
106	A15	$500 deep green	4.50	1.25
107	A15	$800 crimson	4.50	1.25
		Nos. 105-107 (3)	13.50	3.75

Chinese Communist Party, 30th anniv.
Reprints are on whiter, thinner and harder paper. Value, set $3.50.

Picasso Dove — A16

1951, Aug. 15   Perf. 12½

108	A16	$400 orange brn	13.00	4.50
109	A16	$800 blue grn	13.00	4.50
110	A16	$1000 dull vio	13.00	4.50
		Nos. 108-110 (3)	39.00	13.00

Reprints are perf. 14. Value, set $12.

Remittance Stamp of China
Surcharged in Carmine or Black

(same size) — A17

Engraved, Commercial Press
1951, Sept. **Perf. 12½**
111 A17 $50 on $2 bl grn (C) .30 1.00

Typo., Kang Hwa Printing Co.
Rouletted 9½
112 A17 $50 on $2 gray bl (C) .85 7.00
113 A17 $50 on $5 red org (Bk) .20 1.00
114 A17 $50 on $50 gray (C) 8.00 4.00

Lithographed, Central Trust Co.
Perf. 13
115 A17 $50 on $50 gray blk (C) .20 .40

Lithographed, Chung Hwa Book Co.
Perf. 11½x10
116 A17 $50 on $50 gray (C) 2.00 .75
a. Perf. 11½ 1.00 1.00
Nos. 111-116 (6) 11.55 14.15

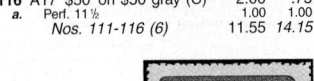

National
Emblem — A18

Engraved; Background Network
Lithographed in Yellow
1951, Oct. 1 **Perf. 14**
117 A18 $100 Prus blue 6.00 3.00
118 A18 $200 brown 6.00 3.00
119 A18 $400 orange 6.00 4.00
120 A18 $500 green 6.00 1.50
121 A18 $800 carmine 6.00 1.50
Nos. 117-121 (5) 30.00 13.00

Reprints exist but are difficult to distinguish; paper whiter, and colors slightly brighter. Value, set $6.

Rough Perfs
Rough perforations are normal on many early issues. These include Nos. 122-123, 136-140, 155-176, 239-240, 299-300, 453-456, 467-482, 629-634, 684-707, 737-745 and probably others.

Lu Hsun
and
Quotation
A19

1951, Oct. 19 **Litho.** **Perf. 12½**
122 A19 $400 lilac 3.75 3.00
123 A19 $800 green 5.25 1.50

15th anniversary of the death of Lu Hsun (1881-1936), writer.

Original

Reprint

Reprints have dot in triangle at lower right; no dot in original. Value, set 75 cents.

Peasant Uprising, Chintien — A20

Design: Nos. 126-127, Coin of Taiping Regime and decrees of peasant government.

1951, Dec. 15 **Engr.** **Perf. 14**
124 A20 $400 green 6.00 5.00
125 A20 $800 scarlet 6.00 3.00
126 A20 $800 orange 6.00 4.00
127 A20 $1000 deep blue 6.00 3.00
Nos. 124-127 (4) 24.00 15.00

Centenary of Taiping Peasant Rebellion.

Original

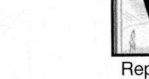
Reprint

Reprints of Nos. 124-125 have additional short stroke at upper left.

Original

Reprint

Reprints of Nos. 126-127 have two short strokes on scale near tail of right dragon on coin. Value, Nos. 124-127, $4.25.

Old and New Methods of
Agriculture — A21

1952, Jan. 1
128 A21 $100 scarlet 4.00 2.50
129 A21 $200 bright blue 4.00 2.50
130 A21 $400 deep brown 4.00 1.65
131 A21 $800 green 4.00 1.65
Nos. 128-131 (4) 16.00 8.30

Agrarian reform.

Original

Reprint

One short horizontal line between legs of plower; 2 lines in reprints. Value, set $1.10.

Potala Monastery, Lhasa — A22

Nos. 134-135, Farmer plowing with yaks.

1952, Mar. 15 **Perf. 12½**
132 A22 $400 vermilion 6.00 2.50
133 A22 $800 claret 6.00 2.50
134 A22 $800 blue grn 6.00 1.60
135 A22 $1000 dull vio 6.00 1.60
Nos. 132-135 (4) 24.00 8.20

Liberation of Tibet.
Reprints, perf 14, have a small Chinese character at lower left of the vignette which is missing in the original. Value, set $4.25.

Children of Four
Races
A23

Hammer and
Sickle on
Numeral 1
A24

1952, Apr. 12 **Litho.**
136 A23 $400 dull grn .45 .30
137 A23 $800 vio blue .45 .30

Intl. Child Protection Conf., Vienna.

1952, May 1

Labor Day: #139, Dove rising from worker's hand. #140, Dove, hammer, wheat & chimneys.

138 A24 $800 scarlet .20 .20
139 A24 $800 blue grn .20 .20
140 A24 $800 orange brn .50 .20
Nos. 138-140 (3) .90 .60

Physical Exercises — A25

Stamps printed in blocks of four for each color, each block representing a specific setting-up exercise; exercises coincided with a national radio program. Where exercise positions are identical within the block, the serial number (in parenthesis) is the only means of differentiation.

1952, June 20
141 A25 Block of 4 36.00 30.00
a. $400 vermilion (1) 5.00 1.75
b. $400 vermilion (2) 5.00 1.75
c. $400 vermilion (3) 5.00 1.75
d. $400 vermilion (4) 5.00 1.75
142 A25 Block of 4 36.00 30.00
a. $400 blue (5) 5.00 1.75
b. $400 blue (6) 5.00 1.75
c. $400 blue (7) 5.00 1.75
d. $400 blue (8) 5.00 1.75
143 A25 Block of 4 36.00 30.00
a. $400 brown red (9) 5.00 1.75
b. $400 brown red (10) 5.00 1.75
c. $400 brown red (11) 5.00 1.75
d. $400 brown red (12) 5.00 1.75
144 A25 Block of 4 36.00 30.00
a. $400 yellow green (13) 5.00 1.75
b. $400 yellow green (14) 5.00 1.75
c. $400 yellow green (15) 5.00 1.75
d. $400 yellow green (16) 5.00 1.75
145 A25 Block of 4 36.00 30.00
a. $400 red orange (17) 5.00 1.75
b. $400 red orange (18) 5.00 1.75
c. $400 red orange (19) 5.00 1.75
d. $400 red orange (20) 5.00 1.75

146	A25	Block of 4	36.00	30.00
a.		$400 dull blue (21)	5.00	1.75
b.		$400 dull blue (22)	5.00	1.75
c.		$400 dull blue (23)	5.00	1.75
d.		$400 dull blue (24)	5.00	1.75
147	A25	Block of 4	36.00	30.00
a.		$400 orange (25)	5.00	1.75
b.		$400 orange (26)	5.00	1.75
c.		$400 orange (27)	5.00	1.75
d.		$400 orange (28)	5.00	1.75
148	A25	Block of 4	36.00	30.00
a.		$400 dull purple (29)	5.00	1.75
b.		$400 dull purple (30)	5.00	1.75
c.		$400 dull purple (31)	5.00	1.75
d.		$400 dull purple (32)	5.00	1.75
149	A25	Block of 4	36.00	30.00
a.		$400 yellow bister (33)	5.00	1.75
b.		$400 yellow bister (34)	5.00	1.75
c.		$400 yellow bister (35)	5.00	1.75
d.		$400 yellow bister (36)	5.00	1.75
150	A25	Block of 4	36.00	30.00
a.		$400 sky blue (37)	5.00	1.75
b.		$400 sky blue (38)	5.00	1.75
c.		$400 sky blue (39)	5.00	1.75
d.		$400 sky blue (40)	5.00	1.75
		Nos. 141-150 (10)	360.00	300.00

Originals are on thin gray paper, colors darker. Reprints on thicker white paper, colors brighter. Value, set $16.50.

Hunting, Wei Dynasty, A.D. 386-580 — A26

Designs from Murals in Cave Temples at Tunhuang, Kansu Province: No. 152, Lady attendants, Sui Dynasty, 581-617 A.D. No. 153, Gandharvas (mythology), Tang Dynasty, 618-906. No. 154, Dragon, Tang Dynasty.

1952, July 1   **Engr.**

151	A26	$800 slate green (1)	.35	.25
152	A26	$800 chocolate (2)	.35	.25
153	A26	$800 indigo (3)	.35	.25
154	A26	$800 dk vio (4)	.35	.25
		Nos. 151-154 (4)	1.40	1.00

"Glorious Mother Country," 1st series.

Marco Polo Bridge, near Peking A27

Designs: No. 156, Cavalry passing through Great Wall. No. 157, Departure of New Fourth Army. No. 158, Mao Tse-tung and Gen. Chu Teh planning counter-attack.

1952, July 7   **Litho.**   **Perf. 14**

155	A27	$800 brt blue	.45	.30
156	A27	$800 blue grn	1.00	.70
157	A27	$800 plum	.45	.30
158	A27	$800 scarlet	.20	.20
		Nos. 155-158 (4)	2.10	1.50

15th anniversary of war against Japan.

Soldier and Tanks — A28

#159, Soldier, sailor & airman, vert. #161, Sailor & warships. #162, Airman & planes.

1952, Aug. 1   **Engr.**   **Perf. 12½**

159	A28	$800 carmine	.25	.20
160	A28	$800 deep green	.50	.30
161	A28	$800 purple	.25	.20
162	A28	$800 orange brown	.25	.20
		Nos. 159-162 (4)	1.25	.90

25th anniv. of People's Liberation Army.

Huai River Sluice Dam A29

#164, Train on the Chengtu-Chungking Railway. #165, Oil refinery and derricks in the Northwest. #166, Mechanized state farm.

1952, Oct. 1   **Perf. 14**

163	A29	$800 dk violet	.25	.20
164	A29	$800 red	.25	.20
165	A29	$800 dk vio brn	.40	.20
166	A29	$800 dp green	.40	.20
		Nos. 163-166 (4)	1.30	.80

"Glorious Mother Country," 2nd series.

Doves and Globe A30

Designs: Nos. 167-168, Picasso dove over Pacific, vert. $2500, as No. 169.

1952, Oct. 2   **Perf. 14**

167	A30	$400 maroon	.25	.25
168	A30	$800 red	.25	.25
169	A30	$800 brown orange	.25	.25
170	A30	$2500 deep green	.50	.50
		Nos. 167-170 (4)	1.25	1.25

Peace Conf. of the Asian and Pacific Regions.

Volunteers on the March — A31

#172, Chinese peasants loading supplies. #173, Volunteers attacking across river. #174, Meeting of Chinese & Korean troops.

1952, Oct. 25

171	A31	$800 blue green (1)	.25	.20
172	A31	$800 vermilion (2)	.25	.20
173	A31	$800 violet (3)	.35	.20
174	A31	$800 lake brown (4)	.50	.25
		Nos. 171-174 (4)	1.35	.85

2nd anniv. of Chinese Volunteers in Korea.

Woman Textile Worker A32

Design: No. 176, Farm woman with sickle.

1953, Mar. 10

175	A32	$800 carmine	.40	.20
176	A32	$800 emerald	.40	.20

International Women's Day.

Textile Worker — A33   Karl Marx — A34

$200, Shepherdess. $250, Stone lion. $800, Lathe operator. $1600, Coal miners. $2000, Corner tower of Forbidden City, Peking.

1953   **Litho.**   **Perf. 14, 12½ ($250)**

177	A33	$50 magenta	.80	.20
178	A33	$200 emerald	1.50	.40
179	A33	$250 ultra	4.00	2.00
180	A33	$800 blue grn	.70	.20
181	A33	$1600 gray	.80	.40
182	A33	$2000 red org	2.50	.20
		Nos. 177-182 (6)	10.30	3.40

Issued: #177-181, Mar. 25; #182, May 23.

1953, May 20   **Engr.**   **Perf. 14**

183	A34	$400 dk brown	.30	.20
184	A34	$800 slate grn	.60	.25

135th anniv. of the birth of Karl Marx.

Workers and Banners — A35

1953, June 25

185	A35	$400 Prus blue	.55	.20
186	A35	$800 carmine	.35	.20

7th All-China Trade Union Congress.

Picasso Dove — A36

1953, July 25

187	A36	$250 blue grn	.80	.20
188	A36	$400 orange brn	.40	.20
189	A36	$800 purple	.60	.20
		Nos. 187-189 (3)	1.80	.60

World Peace.

Groom, Wei Dynasty, 386-580 A37

Scenes from Tunhuang Murals: No. 191, Court Players, Wei Dynasty. No. 192, Battle Scene, Sui Dynasty, 581-617. No. 193, Ox-drawn palanquin, Tang Dynasty, 618-906.

1953, Sept. 1

190	A37	$800 dp green (1)	1.00	.20
191	A37	$800 red org (2)	.20	.20
192	A37	$800 Prus blue (3)	.45	.20
193	A37	$800 carmine (4)	.20	.20
		Nos. 190-193 (4)	1.85	.80

"Glorious Mother Country," 3rd series.

Stalin and Mao on Kremlin Terrace A38

Statue of Stalin at Volga-Don Canal — A39

Designs: No. 195, Lenin proclaiming Soviet power. No. 197, Stalin as orator.

1953, Oct. 5

194	A38	$800 green (1)	1.00	.45
195	A38	$800 carmine (2)	.45	.20
196	A39	$800 brt blue (3)	.40	.20
197	A39	$800 org brn (4)	.30	.20
		Nos. 194-197 (4)	2.15	1.05

Russian October Revolution, 35th anniv.
Stamps in same designs with two additional characters meaning "Soviet" in the single-line Chinese inscription, and in different colors, were unofficially released at several small post offices in Hunan, Fukien and Canton areas in February, 1953, but were withdrawn after only a small number had been sold. Value, set $7,250 unused, $2,000 canceled.

Compass, 3rd Century B.C. A40

#199, Seismoscope, later Han Dynasty. #200, Drum cart to measure distance, Chin Dynasty. #201, Armillary sphere, Ming Dynasty.

1953, Dec. 1

198	A40	$800 indigo (1)	.55	.20
199	A40	$800 dk green (2)	.20	.20
200	A40	$800 dk blue (3)	.30	.20
201	A40	$800 choc (4)	.30	.20
		Nos. 198-201 (4)	1.35	.80

Major inventions by ancient and medieval Chinese scientists.
"Glorious Mother Country," 4th series.

Francois Rabelais — A41   (same size) Gate of Heavenly Peace — A42

Designs: $400, Jose Marti, Cuban revolutionary. $800, Chu Yuan (350-275 B.C.), philosopher. $2200, Nicolaus Copernicus, astronomer.

1953, Dec. 30

202	A41	$250 slate grn (3)	.45	.25
203	A41	$400 brown blk (4)	.45	.25
204	A41	$800 indigo (1)	.45	.25
205	A41	$2200 choc (2)	.45	.25
		Nos. 202-205 (4)	1.80	1.00

1954, Apr. 16 Litho.

Sixth Issue: Inscription at upper right.

206	A42	$50 carmine	.20	.20
207	A42	$100 lt blue	.20	.20
208	A42	$200 green	.20	.20
209	A42	$250 ultra	3.00	.30
210	A42	$400 gray grn	.20	.20
211	A42	$800 orange	.20	.20
212	A42	$1600 gray	.20	.65
213	A42	$2000 olive	.20	.30
		Nos. 206-213 (8)	4.40	2.25

Textile Plant, Harbin — A43   Lenin — A44

Designs: $200, Tangku Harbor. $250, Tien-shui-Lanchow railroad bridge, Kansu Province. $400, Heavy machine-building plant, Taiyuan, Shansi. No. 218, Automatic blast, furnace, Anshan, Manchuria. No. 219, Fushun open-cut coal mine. $2000, Automatic power plant, Northeast. $3200, Prospecting in Tayeh district, Hupeh.

1954, May 1 Engr.

214	A43	$100 brown olive	.25	.20
215	A43	$200 blue green	.25	.20
216	A43	$250 violet	.20	.20
217	A43	$400 black	.25	.20
218	A43	$800 claret	.20	.20
219	A43	$800 indigo	.20	.20
220	A43	$2000 red	.20	.20
221	A43	$3200 dark brown	.45	.30
		Nos. 214-221 (8)	2.00	1.70

Economic progress.

1954, June 30 Engr.

$400, Lenin and Stalin Monument, Gorki, horiz. $2000, Lenin proclaiming Soviet power.

222	A44	$400 deep green	.55	.20
223	A44	$800 dark brown	.30	.20
224	A44	$2000 deep carmine	2.25	.30
		Nos. 222-224 (3)	3.10	.70

30th anniversary of the death of Lenin.

Pottery Vessels, Neolithic Period, 2000 B.C. — A45

Archeological Treasures: No. 226, Stone clime, Shang Dynasty, c. 1200 B.C. No. 227, Kuo Chi Tsu-pai bronze basin, Middle Chou Dynasty, 816 B.C. No. 228, Lacquered box and wine cup, Warring States Period, 403-221 B.C.

1954, Aug. 25

225	A45	$800 brown	.45	.20
226	A45	$800 indigo	.45	.20
227	A45	$800 Prus bl	.45	.20
228	A45	$800 dk car	.45	.20
		Nos. 225-228 (4)	1.80	.80

"Glorious Mother Country," 5th series.

Pipe Production, Anshan Steel Mill — A46   Stalin Statue, by Tomsky — A47

Design: $800, Rolling mill, Anshan.

1954, Oct. 1

229	A46	$400 Prus green	.55	.30
230	A46	$800 vio brown	.55	.30

1954, Oct. 15

Designs: $800, Stalin portrait. $2000, Stalin viewing hydroelectric plant.

Size: 21x45mm

231	A47	$400 black	1.60	.30

Size: 26x37mm

232	A47	$800 black brown	.35	.20

Size: 42x26mm

233	A47	$2000 deep red	.35	.20
		Nos. 231-233 (3)	2.30	.70

First anniversary of the death of Stalin.

Exhibition Building, Peking — A48

1954, Nov. 7

234	A48	$800 brown, *cream*	9.25	3.75
a.		Size: 53½x24mm	18.00	3.75

Russian Economic and Cultural Exhibition, Peking. No. 234 measures 52½x24½mm.

Apprentices and Lathe — A49

Progress in Technology: $800, Heavy machinery and workers.

1954, Dec. 15

235	A49	$400 dk olive grn	.40	.20
236	A49	$800 bright red	.25	.20

Woman Worker Voting — A50

People Celebrating Opening of Congress — A51

1954, Dec. 30

237	A50	$400 deep claret	.20	.20
238	A51	$800 bright red	.70	.20

First National Congress.

Flags, Worker and Woman Holding Constitution — A52

1954, Dec. 30

239	A52	$400 brown, *buff*	.45	.20
240	A52	$800 brt red, *yel*	.45	.20

Adoption of Constitution.

High-tension Pylon — A53

1955, Feb. 25

241	A53	$800 dk Prus bl	.90	.35

Development of electric power.

Factory Health Workers and Red Cross A54

1955, June 25 Engr.; Cross Typo.

242	A54	8f dp grn & red	7.25	2.00

50th anniversary of Chinese Red Cross.

Stalin and Mao in Kremlin A55

Soviet Specialist and Chinese Worker — A56

1955, July 25 Engr.

243	A55	8f brown red	7.25	.50
244	A56	20f olive blk	7.25	1.50

5th anniv. of Sino-Soviet Friendship Treaty.

Chang Heng (78-139), Astronomer — A57

Portraits of Scientists: No. 246, Tsu Chung-chih (429-500), mathematician. No. 247, Chang Sui (683-727), astronomer. No. 248, Li Shih-chen (1518-1593), physician and pharmacologist.

1955, Aug. 25 Perf. 14

245	A57	8f sepia, *buff*	2.00	.30
a.		Min. sheet, sepia, *white*	25.00	6.75
246	A57	8f dp grn, *buff*	2.00	.30
a.		Min. sheet, deep green, *white*	25.00	6.75
247	A57	8f black, *buff*	2.00	.30
a.		Min. sheet, blk, *white*	25.00	6.75
248	A57	8f claret, *buff*	2.00	.30
a.		Min. sheet, claret, *white*	25.00	6.75
		Nos. 245-248 (4)	8.00	1.20

Miniature sheets contain one imperf. stamp.

Steel Pouring Ladle A58

1955-56 Litho.

Position-in-set number in ( )

249	A58	8f shown (1)	.75	.20
250	A58	8f High tension line (2)	.75	.20
251	A58	8f Mechanized coal mining (3)	.75	.20
252	A58	8f Tank cars and derricks (4)	.75	.20
253	A58	8f Heavy machine shop (5)	.75	.20
254	A58	8f Soldier on guard (6)	.75	.20
255	A58	8f Spinning machine (7)	.75	.20

256 A58	8f Workers discussing 5-year plan (8)	.75	.20
257 A58	8f Combine harvester (9)	.75	.20
258 A58	8f Milk production (10)	.75	.20
259 A58	8f Dam (11)	.75	.20
260 A58	8f Pottery industry (12) ('56)	.75	.20
261 A58	8f Truck (13)	.75	.20
262 A58	8f Ship at dock (14)	.75	.20
263 A58	8f Geological survey (15)	.75	.20
264 A58	8f Higher education (16)	.75	.20
265 A58	8f Family (17)	.75	.20
266 A58	8f Workers' rest home (18) ('56)	.75	.20
	Nos. 249-266 (18)	13.50	3.60

1st 5 Year Plan. Issued: #249-257, 10/1; #258-259, 261-265, 12/15; #260, 266, 2/24/56.

Lenin — A59

Engels — A60

1955, Dec. 15   Engr.   Perf. 14

267 A59	8f dk blue grn	7.00	.25
268 A59	20f dk rose car	7.00	1.75

85th anniversary of the birth of Lenin.

1955, Dec. 15

269 A60	8f deep orange	6.75	.25
270 A60	20f brown	6.75	1.75

135th anniversary of the birth of Friedrich Engels (1820-1895), German socialist.

Storming Lu Ting Bridge — A61

Crossing Great Snow Mountains A62

1955, Dec. 30

271 A61	8f dark red	6.75	.35
272 A62	8f dark blue	6.75	1.60

Long March of Chinese Communist army, 20th anniversary.

Miner — A63   Gate of Heavenly Peace — A64

Designs: 1f, Machinist. 2f, Airman. 2½f, Nurse. 4f, Soldier. 8f, Steel worker. 10f, Scientist. 20f, Farm woman. 50f, Sailor.

1955-56   Litho.   Perf. 14

273 A63	½f orange brn	1.90	.20
274 A63	1f purple	1.90	.20
275 A63	2f green	1.90	.20
276 A63	2½f blue ('56)	1.90	.20
277 A63	4f gray olive	1.90	.45
278 A63	8f red org (Peking printing)	1.90	.65
a.	Perf. 12½ (Shanghai printing)	400.00	10.00
279 A63	10f claret ('56)	26.00	.20
280 A63	20f dp blue	6.75	.20
281 A63	50f gray	6.75	.20
	Nos. 273-281 (9)	50.90	2.50

Engr.

282 A64	$1 claret ('56)	.65	.25
283 A64	$2 sepia ('55)	1.10	.25
284 A64	$5 indigo ('56)	1.75	.40
285 A64	$10 dp org ('56)	5.50	4.25
286 A64	$20 gray vio ('56)	9.00	17.00
	Nos. 282-286 (5)	18.00	22.15

Nos. 282-286 are the 7th Gate Issue.

Trucks, Mountains, Highway Map — A65

Suspension Bridge over Tatu River — A66

#289, 1st truck arriving in Lhasa, & the Potala.

1956, Mar. 10   Engr.

287 A65	4f dp blue	.75	.20
288 A66	8f dk brown	.75	.20
289 A65	8f carmine	.75	.20
	Nos. 287-289 (3)	2.25	.60

Completion of Sikang-Tibet and Chinghai-Tibet Highways.

Summer Palace and Marble Boat A67

Famous Views of Imperial Peking: No. 291, Peihai Park with Jade Belt Marble Bridge. No. 292, Gate of Heavenly Peace. No. 293, Temple of Heaven. No. 294, Great Throne Hall, Forbidden City.

1956-57

290 A67	4f car rose (1)	2.25	.25
291 A67	4f blue grn (2)	2.25	.25
292 A67	8f red org (3) ('57)	2.25	.25
293 A67	8f Prus blue (4)	2.25	.25
294 A67	8f yellow brn (5)	2.25	.25
	Nos. 290-294 (5)	11.25	1.25

Issued: #292, 2/20/57; others, 6/15/56. No. 292 exists with sun rays in background.

Salt Making A68

Designs: No. 296, Dwelling of the Eastern Han period. No. 297, Duck hunting and harvesting. No. 298, Carriage crossing bridge.

1956, Oct. 1

295 A68	4f gray olive	.25	.20
296 A68	4f slate blue	.25	.20
297 A68	8f gray brown	.25	.20
298 A68	8f sepia	.25	.20
	Nos. 295-298 (4)	1.00	.80

Murals, Tung Han Dynasty, 250 B.C.-220 A.D., found near Chengtu.

Ancient Coins and "Save" A69

1956, Oct. 1

299 A69	4f yellow brown	5.25	.60
300 A69	8f rose red	5.25	.60

Promotion of saving.

Gate of Heavenly Peace — A70   Sun Yatsen — A71

1956, Nov. 10

301 A70	4f dk green	4.75	.40
302 A70	8f brt red	4.75	.40
303 A70	16f dk carmine	4.75	.80
	Nos. 301-303 (3)	14.25	1.60

8th National Congress of the Communist Party of China.

1956, Nov. 12

304 A71	4f brown, *cream*	6.75	.20
305 A71	8f dp blue, *cream*	6.75	1.25

90th anniversary of birth of Sun Yat-sen.

Weight Lifting — A72

1957, Mar. 20   Litho.   Perf. 12½
Hibiscus red and green; inscription brown

306 A72	4f Shot put (2)	1.10	.20
307 A72	4f shown (5)	1.10	.20
308 A72	8f Track (1)	1.10	.20
309 A72	8f Soccer (3)	1.10	.20
310 A72	8f Bicycling (4)	1.10	.20
	Nos. 306-310 (5)	5.50	1.00

First National Workers' Sports Meeting.

Truck Factory No. 1, Changchun — A73

China's truck industry: 8f, Trucks rolling off assembly line.

1957, May 1   Engr.   Perf. 14

311 A73	4f light brown	.45	.25
312 A73	8f slate green	.45	.25

Nanchang Uprising — A74

#314, Mao and Chu Teh at Chingkanshan. #315, Crossing Yellow River. #316, Liberation of Nanking, 4/23/49.

1957

313 A74	4f blk vio (1)	8.00	.70
314 A74	4f slate grn (2)	8.00	1.10
315 A74	8f red brn (3)	8.00	.45
316 A74	8f dp blue (4)	8.00	.45
	Nos. 313-316 (4)	32.00	2.70

People's Liberation Army, 30th anniv. Issued: #313, 315, 8/10; #314, 8/30; #316, 12/30.

Congress Emblem — A75

1957, Sept. 30

317 A75	8f chocolate	3.50	.40
318 A75	22f indigo	3.50	.60

4th Intl. Trade Union Cong., Leipzig, 10/4-15.

Yangtze River Bridge A76

20f, Road leading to and over bridge.

1957, Oct. 1

319 A76	8f scarlet	.55	.25
320 A76	20f slate blue	.55	.20

Completion of Yangtze River Bridge at Wuhan.

Fireworks over Kremlin — A77

Designs: 8f, Hammer and sickle over globe and broken chain. 20f, Stylized dove and olive branch. 22f, Hands of three races holding book with Marx and Lenin. 32f, Star and pylon.

1957, Nov. 7

321 A77	4f brt red	6.50	.35
322 A77	8f chocolate	6.50	.35
323 A77	20f dp green	6.50	.35
324 A77	22f red brown	6.50	.35
325 A77	32f dp blue	6.50	2.00
	Nos. 321-325 (5)	32.50	3.40

40th anniv. of Russian October Revolution.

Map of Yellow River Basin A78

#327, Sanmen Gorge dam & powerhouse. #328, ocean liner on Yellow River. #329, Dam, irrigation canals & tree-bordered fields.

1957, Dec. 30

326	A78	4f deep orange (1)	8.00	1.25
327	A78	4f deep blue (2)	8.00	1.65
328	A78	8f deep lake (3)	8.00	.60
329	A78	8f blue green (4)	8.00	.60
		Nos. 326-329 (4)	32.00	4.10

Yellow River control plan.

Old Man and
Young Drummer
A79

Crane, Dove and
Flowers
A80

1957, Dec. 30   **Litho.**

330	A79	8f shown (1)	.45	.20
331	A79	8f Plowman (2)	.45	.20
332	A79	8f Woman planting tree (3)	.45	.20
333	A79	8f Harvest (4)	.45	.20
		Nos. 330-333 (4)	1.80	.80

Agricultural cooperation.

1958, Jan. 30   **Engr.**

Designs (Congratulatory Banner and): 8f, Crane with hot ingots, cotton bolls and wheat. 16f, Train on bridge, ship and plane.

334	A80	4f emer, *cream*	.30	.20
335	A80	8f red, *cream*	.30	.25
336	A80	16f ultra, *cream*	.30	.20
		Nos. 334-336 (3)	.90	.65

Fulfillment of First Five-Year Plan.

Sungyu Pagoda,
Honan — A81

Trilobite,
Kaoli — A82

Ancient Pagodas: No. 338, Chienhsun Pagoda, Yunnan. No. 339, Sakyamuni Pagoda, Shansi. No. 340, Flying Rainbow Pagoda, Shansi.

1958, Mar. 15   **Engr.**

337	A81	8f sepia (1)	1.40	.20
338	A81	8f Prus blue (2)	1.40	.20
339	A81	8f maroon (3)	1.40	.20
340	A81	8f dp green (4)	1.40	.25
		Nos. 337-340 (4)	5.60	.85

1958, Apr. 15

Designs: 8f, Lufeng dinosaur. 16f, Choukoutien sino-megaceros.

341	A82	4f black	.65	.20
342	A82	8f sepia	.65	.25
343	A82	16f slate green	.65	.20
		Nos. 341-343 (3)	1.95	.65

Prehistoric animals of China.

Heroes
Monument
A83

1958, May 1

344	A83	8f scarlet	14.50	1.25
	a.	Souvenir sheet, imperf.	110.00	50.00

Unveiling of People's Heroes Monument, Peking. No. 344a issued May 30.

Karl Marx — A84

Cogwheels and
Factories — A85

Design: 22f, Marx Speaking to German Workers' Educational Association, London, painting by Zhukow.

1958, May 5

345	A84	8f chocolate	7.00	1.00
346	A84	22f dk green	7.00	2.00

Karl Marx (1818-83), 140th birth anniv.

1958, May 25

347	A85	4f brt grnsh bl	6.75	2.50
348	A85	8f red lilac	6.75	.60

8th All-China Trade Union Cong., Peking.

Dove over
Globe — A86

Mother and
Child — A87

1958, June 1

349	A86	8f violet blue	6.25	.25
350	A86	20f blue green	6.25	3.25

4th Congress of the Intl. Democratic Women's Federation, Vienna, June 1958.

1958, June 1   **Litho.**

Children's Day: No. 352, Watering sunflowers. No. 353, Playing hide-and-seek. No. 354, Sailing toy boat.

351	A87	8f green & multi (1)	10.00	1.60
352	A87	8f green & multi (2)	10.00	1.60
353	A87	8f green & multi (3)	10.00	1.60
354	A87	8f green & multi (4)	10.00	1.60
		Nos. 351-354 (4)	40.00	6.40

Kuan Han-ching
A88

Designs (Operas): 4f, "Dream of Butterflies." 20f, "The Riverside Pavilion."

1958, June 20   **Engr.**

355	A88	4f indigo, *cr*	7.50	3.50
356	A88	8f brown, *cr*	7.50	.60
357	A88	20f black, *cr*	7.50	.90
	a.	Souvenir sheet of 3, *ivory*	200.00	75.00
		Nos. 355-357 (3)	22.50	*5.00*

700th anniversary of publication of works of Kuan Han-ching (1210-1280), dramatist. No. 357a contains 3 imperf. stamps similar to Nos. 355-357. Size: 130x100mm. Issued June 28.

Planetarium
A89

20f, Telescope and stars over Peking.

1958, June 25

358	A89	8f dk green	4.00	.80
359	A89	20fr indigo	4.00	1.60

First Chinese planetarium, Peking.

Marx and
Engels — A90

Wild Goose and
Broadcasting
Tower — A91

8f, Cover of 1st edition of the Communist Manifesto.

1958, July 1

360	A90	4f dk red vio	6.75	3.25
361	A90	8f Prus blue	6.75	.25

110th anniversary of publication of the Communist Manifesto.

1958, July 10

362	A91	4f ultra	6.00	.75
363	A91	8f deep green	6.00	2.25

1st Conference of the Ministers of Posts and Telecommunications of Socialist Countries, Moscow, Dec. 3-17, 1957.

Peony and
Doves — A92

Bronze Weather
Vane — A93

8f, Olive branch with ribbon & clouds. 22f, Atomic energy symbol over factories.

1958, July 20

364	A92	4f red	8.50	.80
365	A92	8f green	8.50	5.50
366	A92	22f red brown	8.50	2.50
		Nos. 364-366 (3)	25.50	8.80

Congress for Disarmament and International Cooperation, Stockholm, July 17-22.

1958, Aug. 25

Designs: No. 368, Weather balloon. No. 369, Typhoon tower and weather map of Asia.

367	A93	8f yel bis & blk (1)	.65	.20
368	A93	8f blue & blk (2)	.65	.20
369	A93	8f brt grn & blk (3)	.65	.20
		Nos. 367-369 (3)	1.95	.60

Meteorological services in ancient and modern China.

"5" Encircling IUS
Emblem — A94

1958, Sept. 4

370	A94	8f rose lilac	5.50	.30
371	A94	22f dp blue grn	5.50	.90

Intl. Union of Students, 5th Cong., Peking, 9/4-13.
Copies exist with incorrect inscription.

Telegraph
Building,
Peking
A95

1958, Sept. 29

372	A95	4f greenish black	1.90	.60
373	A95	8f rose red	1.90	.60

Opening of Telegraph Building, Peking.

Exhibition
Emblem and
Exhortation
A96

Designs: No. 375, Dragon over clouds signifying "aiming high." No. 376, Flying horses, signifying "great leap forward" in production.

1958, Oct. 1

374	A96	8f slate grn (1)	5.00	.65
375	A96	8f rose car (2)	5.00	.65
376	A96	8f red brown (3)	5.00	2.50
		Nos. 374-376 (3)	15.00	3.80

National Exhibition of Industry and Communications, Peking.

Worker and
Excavator
A97

Design: 8f, Completed dam and pylon.

1958, Oct. 25

377	A97	4f dark brown	.60	.20
378	A97	8f deep Prussian blue	.70	.20

13 Ming Tombs Reservoir completion.

Sputnik over
Armillary
Sphere — A98

Designs: 8f, Sputnik 3 in orbit. 10f, Trajectories of 3 Sputniks over earth.

1958, Oct. 30

379	A98	4f scarlet	2.50	.25
380	A98	8f dp violet bl	2.50	.25
381	A98	10f dp green	2.50	1.60
		Nos. 379-381 (3)	7.50	2.10

Anniversary of first earth satellite launched by the USSR.

Chinese and North Korean Soldiers A99

Designs: No. 383, Chinese soldier embracing Korean woman. No. 384, Chinese girl presenting flowers to returning soldier.

1958, Nov. 20

382	A99	8f brt purple (1)	.90	.25
383	A99	8f chestnut (2)	.90	.20
384	A99	8f rose car (3)	.90	.20
		Nos. 382-384 (3)	2.70	.65

Return of the Chinese Volunteers from Korea.

Forest and Mountains — A100

Peony — A101

Afforestation: No. 386, Mounted forest patrol. No. 387, Mechanized lumbering, horiz. No. 388, Tree-planting: "Turning the Country Green," horiz.

1958, Dec. 15

385	A100	8f dp blue grn (1)	2.00	1.10
386	A100	8f slate grn (2)	2.00	.40
387	A100	8f dk purple (3)	2.00	.40
388	A100	8f indigo (4)	2.00	.70
		Nos. 385-388 (4)	8.00	2.60

1958, Sept. 25   Litho.

Designs: 3f, Lotus. 5f, Chrysanthemums.

389	A101	1½f lilac rose	4.75	.50
390	A101	3f blue grn	4.75	1.60
391	A101	5f dp orange	4.75	.35
		Nos. 389-391 (3)	14.25	2.45

Atomic Reactor A102

1958, Dec. 30   Engr.

| 392 | A102 | 8f shown | 6.50 | 2.75 |
| 393 | A102 | 20f Cyclotron | 6.50 | .50 |

Inauguration of China's first atomic reactor and cyclotron, Peking.

Children Launching Model Planes — A103

Camel Carrying Load — A104

8f, Gliders over trees. 10f, Parachutists descending. 20f, Small monoplanes in mid-air.

1958, Dec. 30

394	A103	4f carmine	.80	.20
395	A103	8f dp slate grn	.80	.20
396	A103	10f dk brown	.80	.20
397	A103	20f Prus blue	.80	.20
		Nos. 394-397 (4)	3.20	.80

Sports-aviation publicity.

1959, Jan. 1

Designs: No. 399, Pomegranates. No. 400, Rooster. No. 401, Theatrical figure.

398	A104	8f vio & blk (1)	6.00	.20
399	A104	8f dp bl grn & blk (2)	6.00	.50
400	A104	8f red & blk (3)	6.00	1.25
401	A104	8f dp bl & blk (4)	6.00	.50
		Nos. 398-401 (4)	24.00	2.45

Paper cut-outs (folk art).

Red Flag, Mao and Workers — A105

Women Workers and Atomic Model — A106

Designs: 8f, Traditional and modern blast furnaces. 10f, Steel works and workers.

1959

402	A105	4f brt red	4.50	1.40
403	A105	8f lake	4.50	1.40
404	A105	10f deep red	4.50	1.40
		Nos. 402-404 (3)	13.50	4.20

"Great Leap Forward" in steel production. Issue dates: 4f, 8f, Feb. 19; 10f, May 25.

1959, Mar. 8

Design: 22f, Chinese and Soviet women holding banners dated "3.8."

| 405 | A106 | 8f emerald, cr | .90 | .30 |
| 406 | A106 | 22f magenta, cr | .90 | .20 |

International Women's Day.

Natural History Museum A107

1959, Apr. 1

| 407 | A107 | 4f greenish blue | .55 | .20 |
| 408 | A107 | 8f olive brown | .55 | .20 |

Opening of Museum of Natural History, Peking.

Wheat — A108

Designs on Chinese Flag: No. 410, Rice. No. 411, Cotton bolls. No. 412, Soybeans, rapeseed and peanuts.

1959, Apr. 25

409	A108	8f red (1)	1.40	.30
410	A108	8f red (2)	1.40	.30
411	A108	8f red (3)	1.40	.30
412	A108	8f red (4)	1.40	.30
a.		Block of 4, #409-412	11.00	2.40

Successful harvest, 1958.

A109

A110

Designs: 4f, Marx, Lenin and workers. 8f, Black, yellow and white fists holding banner. 22f, Steel workers parading with banners dated "5.1."

1959, May 1

413	A109	4f ultra	4.50	1.40
414	A109	8f red	4.50	1.40
415	A109	22f emerald	4.50	1.40
		Nos. 413-415 (3)	13.50	4.20

International Labor Day.

1959, June 20

8f, Peking airport. 10f, Plane loading on runway.

| 416 | A110 | 8f lilac & blk | 8.00 | 1.00 |
| 417 | A110 | 10f ol gray & blk | 8.00 | .40 |

Opening of new Peking Airport.

Students with Marx-Lenin Banners A111

Design: 8f, Workers with banners of Mao.

1959, July 1   Photo.   Perf. 11x11½

| 418 | A111 | 4f gray, red & dk brn | 17.50 | 5.00 |
| 419 | A111 | 8f bis, red & dk brn | 17.50 | 5.00 |

40th anniv. of the May 4th students' uprising.

Frederick Joliot-Curie — A112

22f, Three races, dove and olive branch.

1959, July 25   Engr.   Perf. 11½

| 420 | A112 | 8f violet brn | 6.00 | 3.00 |
| 421 | A112 | 22f dk violet | 6.00 | .20 |

10th anniv. of the World Peace Movement.

Stamp Printing Plant, Peking A113

1959, Aug. 15   Perf. 11x11½

| 422 | A113 | 8f dp blue grn | 7.25 | 2.00 |

Sino-Czechoslovak cooperation in stamp production.

Table Tennis — A114

1959, Aug. 30   Litho.   Perf. 14

| 423 | A114 | 4f black & blue | 2.25 | .65 |
| 424 | A114 | 8f black & red | 2.25 | .45 |

25th World Table Tennis Championships, Dortmund, German Democratic Republic.

Soviet Space Rocket A115

Backyard Steel Production A116

1959, Sept. 10   Photo.   Perf. 11½

| 425 | A115 | 8f Prus bl, red & blk | 10.00 | 2.40 |

Launching of first Russian space rocket, Jan. 2, 1959.

1959, Sept. 25   Engr.

Designs: #426, Sun rising over "industry and agriculture." #428, Farming. #429, Trade. #430, Education. #431, Militia. #432, Communal dining. #433, Nursery. #434, Care for the aged. #435, Health services. #436, Flutist; culture and sports. #437, Flower symbolizing unity of industry, agriculture, trade, education and armed forces.

Position-in-set number in ( ).

426	A116	8f rose (1)	.75	.20
427	A116	8f violet brn (2)	.75	.20
428	A116	8f dp orange (3)	.75	.20
429	A116	8f slate grn (4)	.75	.20
430	A116	8f dp blue (5)	.75	.20
431	A116	8f olive (6)	.75	.20
432	A116	8f indigo (7)	.75	.20
433	A116	8f lilac rose (8)	.75	.20
434	A116	8f gray blk (9)	.75	.20
435	A116	8f emerald (10)	.75	.20
436	A116	8f dk violet (11)	.75	.20
437	A116	8f red (12)	.75	.20
		Nos. 426-437 (12)	9.00	2.40

First anniversary of Peoples' Communes.

Mao and Gate of Heavenly Peace — A117

National Emblem A118

Blast Furnaces — A119

Celebration at Gate of Heavenly Peace — A120

Mao Proclaiming Republic — A121

Designs: #439, Marx, Lenin and Kremlin. 22f, Dove over globe.

Perf. 11½ x 11

1959, Sept. 28   Photo.
With Gum
438 A117   8f lt brown & red   12.00 5.50
439 A117   8f dull blue & red   12.00 1.75
440 A117   22f blue grn & red   12.00 1.00
  Nos. 438-440 (3)   36.00 8.25

1959, Oct. 1   Litho.   Perf. 14
441 A118   4f pale grn, red &
                gold   10.00 4.25
442 A118   8f gray, red & gold   10.00 .40
443 A118   10f lt blue, red & gold 10.00 .40
444 A118   20f pale brn, red &
                gold   10.00 2.50
  Nos. 441-444 (4)   40.00 7.55

Engraved and Photogravure
1959, Oct. 1   Perf. 11½ x 11
#446, Large coal mine. #447, Planer, Wuhan heavy machinery plant. #448, Wuhan Yangtze River Bridge. #449, Combine harvester. #450, Hsinankiang hydroelectric station. #451, Spinning machine. #452, Kirin chemical fertilizer plant.

With Gum
445 A119   8f brown & rose red (1)   .90 .50
446 A119   8f brown & gray (2)   .90 .50
447 A119   8f brown & yel brn (3)   .90 .50
448 A119   8f brown & stl bl (4)   .90 .50
449 A119   8f brown & org (5)   .90 .50
450 A119   8f brown & ol (6)   .90 .50
451 A119   8f brown & bl grn (7)   .90 .50
452 A119   8f brown & vio (8)   .90 .50
  Nos. 445-452 (8)   7.20 4.00

1959, Oct. 1   Litho.   Perf. 14
Designs: 10f, Workers and factory, vert. 20f, People rejoicing, vert.
453 A120   8f cream & multi   4.50 1.60
454 A120   10f cream & multi   4.50 1.60
455 A120   20f cream & multi   4.50 1.60
  Nos. 453-455 (3)   13.50 4.80

1959, Oct. 1   Engr.
456 A121   20f deep carmine   22.50 11.00

Nos. 438-456 commemorate 10th anniversary of the Proclamation of the People's Republic of China.

A122   A123

Designs: No. 457, Pioneers' emblem. No. 458, Pioneer Bugler. No. 459, Schoolgirl. No. 460, Girl using rain gauge. No. 461, Boy planting tree. No. 462, Girl figure skater.

1959, Nov. 10   Photo.   Perf. 11½
457 A122   4f red yel & blk (1)   3.50 .50
458 A122   4f Prus bl & red (2)   3.50 .50
459 A122   8f brn & red (3)   3.50 .50
460 A122   8f dk bl & red (4)   3.50 .50
461 A122   8f red & grn (5)   3.50 .50
462 A122   8f mag & red (6)   3.50 .50
  Nos. 457-462 (6)   21.00 3.00

10th anniversary of the Young Pioneers. Black inscription on No. 457 engraved.

1959, Dec. 1   Engr.
4f, Exhibition emblem, communications symbols. 8f, Exhibition emblem & chimneys.
463 A123   4f dark blue   .45 .20
464 A123   8f red   .45 .20
Exhibition of Industry and Communications, Peking.

Palace of Nationalities A124

Engraved, Frame Lithographed
1959, Dec. 10   Perf. 14
465 A124   4f red & blk   3.50 .50
466 A124   8f brt grn & blk   3.50 .80
Inauguration of the Cultural Palace of Nationalities, Peking.

Athletes' Monument and Track — A125

#468, Parachuting. #469, Marksmanship. #470, Diving. #471, Table tennis. #472, Weight lifting. #473, High jump. #474, Rowing. #475, Track. #476, Basketball. #477, Traditional Chinese fencing. #478, Motorcycling. #479, Gymnastics. #480, Bicycling. #481, Horsemanship. #482, Soccer.

1959, Dec. 28   Litho.
467 A125   8f bis, blk & gray (1)   1.50 .25
468 A125   8f dl bl, blk & gray (2) 1.50 .25
469 A125   8f red brn & blk (3)   1.50 .25
470 A125   8f grn, blk & brn (4)   1.50 .25
471 A125   8f brt grn, blk, brn &
                gray (5)   1.50 .25
472 A125   8f gray, blk & brn (6)   1.50 .25
473 A125   8f dl bl, blk & brn (7) 1.50 .25
474 A125   8f Prus grn, blk & brn
                (8)   1.50 .25
475 A125   8f org, blk & brn (9)   1.50 .25
476 A125   8f dl vio, blk & brn
                (10)   1.50 .25
477 A125   8f lt ol, blk & brn (11) 1.50 .25
478 A125   8f bl, blk & gray (12)   1.50 .25
479 A125   8f gray bl, blk, grn, &
                bl (13)   1.50 .25
480 A125   8f gray, blk, brn, & vio
                (14)   1.50 .25
481 A125   8f red org, blk, brn, &
                gray (15)   1.50 .25
482 A125   8f lt gray, blk, brn, &
                red (16)   1.50 .25
  Nos. 467-482 (16)   24.00 4.00
First National Sports Meeting, Peking.

Wheat and Main Pavilion A126

Designs (Pavilion and): 8f, Meteorological symbols. 10f, Domestic animals. 20f, Fish.

1960, Jan. 20   Engr. & Litho.
Cream Background
483 A126   4f black & org   .75 .20
484 A126   8f black & dull bl   .75 .20
485 A126   10f black & org brn   .75 .20
486 A126   20f black & grnsh bl   .75 .30
  Nos. 483-486 (4)   3.00 .90
Opening of the National Agricultural Exhibition Halls, Peking.

With Gum
From No. 487 onward all stamps were issued with gum except as noted.

Catalogue values for unused stamps in this section, from this point to the end of the section, are for Never Hinged items.

Conference Hall, Tsunyi A127

Designs: 8f, Mao addressing conference. 10f, Crossing Chinsha River.

Engraved (4f, 10f); Photogravure (8f)
1960, Jan. 25   Perf. 11x11½
487 A127   4f violet & blue   9.00 .95
488 A127   8f red & multi   9.00 2.25
489 A127   10f slate green   17.50 .95
  Nos. 487-489 (3)   35.50 4.15
25th anniversary of the Communist Party Conference at Tsunyl.

Clara Zetkin (1857-1933) A128

Chinese and Russian Workers — A129

8f, Mother, child and dove. 10f, Woman tractor driver. 22f, Women of three races.

1960, Mar. 8   Photo.   Perf. 11½x11
490 A128   4f black & multi   1.60 .25
491 A128   8f black & multi   1.60 .55
492 A128   10f black & multi   1.60 .55
493 A128   22f black & multi   3.25 .25
  Nos. 490-493 (4)   8.05 1.60
50th anniv. of International Women's Day.

1960, Mar. 10
Designs: 8f, Chinese and Russian flags. 10f, Chinese and Russian soldiers.
494 A129   4f dk brown   5.00 2.25
495 A129   8f red, yel & blk   5.00 2.25
496 A129   10f dp blue   8.25 2.25
  Nos. 494-496 (3)   18.25 6.75
10th anniv. of Sino-Soviet Treaty of Friendship. Black inscription engraved on No. 495.

Flags of Hungary and China A130

Design: 8f, Parliament Building, Budapest.

1960, Apr. 4   Perf. 11 x 11½
497 A130   8f yel, blk, red & grn 10.00 2.10
498 A130   8f blue, red & blk   10.00 4.25
15th anniv. of the liberation of Hungary.

Lenin Speaking — A131

Lunik 2, Earth and Russian Arms — A132

Designs: 8f, Portrait of Lenin. 20f, Lenin talking with Smolny Palace guard.

Engraved (4f, 20f); Engraved and Photogravure (8f)
1960, Apr. 22   Perf. 11½ x 11
499 A131   4f violet brn   6.00 1.00
500 A131   8f org red & blk   10.00 4.00
501 A131   20f dk brown   19.00 2.00
  Nos. 499-501 (3)   35.00 7.00
90th anniversary of the birth of Lenin.

1960, Apr. 30   Engr.   Perf. 11½
Design: 10f, Lunik 3 over earth.
502 A132   8f red   2.75 .90
503 A132   10f green   3.50 .90
Russian space flights.

Pioneers and Flags of Czechoslovakia and China — A133

View of Prague with Charles Bridge A134

Perf. 11½x11; 11x11½
1960, May 9   Photo.
504 A133   8f yellow & multi   8.00 1.40
505 A134   8f deep green   8.00 2.75
Liberation of Czechoslovakia, 15th anniv.

Nostril Bouquet A135

Designs: Various goldfish.

1960, June 1   Perf. 11x11½
506 A135   4f shown (1)   30.00 4.00
507 A135   4f Black-back drag-
                on eye (2)   32.50 4.00
508 A135   4f Bubble eye (3)   32.50 4.50
509 A135   4f Red tiger head
                (4)   10.00 3.25
510 A135   8f Pearl scale (5)   50.00 6.00
511 A135   8f Blue dragon eye
                (6)   50.00 6.00
512 A135   8f Skyward eye (7)   10.00 3.00
513 A135   8f Red cap (8)   10.00 3.00
514 A135   8f Purple cap (9)   10.00 3.00
515 A135   8f Red head (10)   10.00 3.00
516 A135   8f Red and white
                dragon eye (11)   32.50 5.25
517 A135   8f Red dragon eye
                (12)   32.50 5.25
  Nos. 506-517 (12)   310.00 50.25

Sow with Litter A136

#519, Pig being inoculated. #520, Pigs. #521, Pig and mechanized feeding. #522, Pig and bales.

1960, June 15
518 A136   8f red & blk (1)   15.00 1.75
519 A136   8f dp grn & blk (2)   15.00 1.75
520 A136   8f lil rose & blk (3) 15.00 1.75
521 A136   8f lt yel grn & blk (4) 15.00 1.75
522 A136   8f org & blk (5)   20.00 4.75
  Nos. 518-522 (5)   80.00 11.75

Flag Inscribed "Serving the Workers" — A137

Flowers, Flags of North Korea and China — A138

Design: 8f, Inscribed stone seal.

1960, July 30 Photo. Perf. 11½x11
523 A137 4f lt grn, red, pink & brn 6.25 1.50

Photogravure & Engraved
524 A137 8f pale bl, red & bis 9.25 3.00

3rd Natl. Cong. for Literature and Arts, Peking.

1960, Aug. 15 Photo.
Design: 8f, Flying horse of Korea.
525 A138 8f red & multi 11.00 2.50
526 A138 8f ultra, red & indigo 11.00 4.50

15th anniversary of the liberation of Korea.

Railroad Station, Peking — A139

Design: 10f, Train arriving at station.

1960, Aug. 30 Perf. 11½
527 A139 8f blue, cream & brn 10.00 3.25
528 A139 10f bluish grn, cr & ind 14.00 4.00

Opening of new Peking Railroad Station.

Girls and Flags of North Viet Nam and China A140

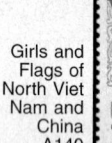

Lake of the Returning Sword, Hanoi A141

Worker and Fresh-air Installation A142

1960, Sept. 2 Perf. 11x11½, 11½x11
529 A140 8f red & multi 4.00 .95
530 A141 8f red, gray grn & gray 4.00 2.40

15th anniversary of the Democratic Republic of North Viet Nam.

1960, Sept. 10 Perf. 11½
Designs: No. 532, Exterminator. No. 533, Window cleaning. No. 534, Medical examination of child. No. 535, Physical exercise.
531 A142 8f black & orange (1) 1.60 .25
532 A142 8f indigo & slate (2) 1.60 .25
533 A142 8f brown & blue (3) 1.60 .25
534 A142 8f maroon & ocher (4) 1.60 .25
535 A142 8f indigo & brt grn (5) 1.60 .45
Nos. 531-535 (5) 8.00 1.45

National health campaign.

Great Hall of the People — A143

Design: 10f, Inside view.

1960, Oct. 1
536 A143 8f yellow & multi 10.00 2.50
537 A143 10f brown & multi 16.00 3.00

Completion of the Great Hall of the People, Peking.

Dr. Norman Bethune — A144

Engels Addressing Congress at The Hague — A145

No. 539, Dr. Bethune operating on a soldier.

Photo. (No. 538); Engr. (No. 539)
1960, Nov. 20 Perf. 11½x11
538 A144 8f red & multi 3.25 1.00
539 A144 8f sepia 3.25 .80

Dr. Norman Bethune (1890-1939), Canadian surgeon with 8th Army.

1960, Nov. 28 Engr.
540 A145 8f shown 6.00 1.25

Photo.
541 A145 10f Portrait of Engels 9.00 3.00

140th anniversary of the birth of Friedrich Engels (1820-1895), German Socialist.

"Hwang Shi Ba" A146

Freighter A147

1960-61 Photo.
Various Chrysanthemums in Natural Colors
542 A146 4f bl gray (1) 14.00 1.10
543 A146 4f pink (2) 27.50 1.10
544 A146 8f dk gray (3) 13.00 1.10
545 A146 8f dp blue (4) 13.00 1.10
546 A146 8f green (5) 13.00 1.10
547 A146 8f magenta (6) 13.00 1.10
548 A146 8f olive (7) 13.00 1.10
549 A146 8f grnsh bl (8) 47.50 1.10
550 A146 10f gray (9) 13.00 1.10

551 A146 10f choc (10) 13.00 1.10
552 A146 20f dp blue (11) 13.00 1.10
553 A146 20f brt red (12) 37.50 3.25
554 A146 22f olive bis (13) 25.00 7.00
555 A146 22f carmine (14) 47.50 11.00
556 A146 30f grnsh gray (15) 14.00 4.50
557 A146 30f brt pink (16) 14.00 4.50
558 A146 35f dp green (17) 20.00 4.50
559 A146 52f brt lilac rose (18) 21.00 8.75
Nos. 542-559 (18) 372.00 55.60

Issued: #548-550, 557-559, 12/10/60; #545-547, 554-556, 1/18/61; #542-544, 2/24/61.

1960, Dec. 15 Perf. 11½
Without Gum
560 A147 8f deep blue 3.50 1.40

1st 10,000-ton Chinese-built freighter, launching.

Pantheon, Paris — A148

Design: 8f, Proclamation of the Commune.

Engraved and Photogravure
1961, Mar. 18 Perf. 11½x11
561 A148 8f gray blk & red 9.50 3.00
562 A148 8f brown & red 9.50 3.00

90th anniversary of the Paris Commune.

Championship Symbol and Jasmine — A149

Designs: 10f, Table tennis racket and ball; Temple of Heaven. 20f, Table tennis match. 22f, Peking workers' gymnasium.

1961, Apr. 5 Photo. Perf. 11
563 A149 8f multicolored .80 .50
564 A149 10f multicolored 1.10 1.25
565 A149 20f multicolored 1.60 1.25
566 A149 22f multicolored 2.75 .50
a. Souv. sheet, #563-566 550.00 300.00
Nos. 563-566 (4) 6.25 3.50

26th World Table Tennis Championships, Peking.

Jeme Tien-yow — A150

Design: 10f, Train and tunnel, Peking-Changchow Railroad.

1961, June 20 Perf. 11½x11
567 A150 8f ol grn & blk 2.25 .65
568 A150 10f org brn & brn 4.00 2.00

Centenary of the birth of Jeme Tien-yow, railroad construction engineer.

Congress Building, Shanghai — A151

Designs: 8f, August 1st Building, Nanchang. 10f, Provisional Central Government Office, Juikin. 20f, Pagoda Hill, Yenan. 30f, Gate of Heavenly Peace, Peking.

1961, July 1 Perf. 11½
569 A151 4f gold, red & cl 10.00 .65
570 A151 8f gold, red & bl grn 10.00 2.00
571 A151 10f gold, red & yel brn 10.00 4.50
572 A151 20f gold, red & ultra 20.00 .65
573 A151 30f gold, red & org red 27.50 2.00
Nos. 569-573 (5) 77.50 9.80

40th anniv. of the Chinese Communist Party.

August 1 Building, Nanchang — A152

3f, 4f, 5f, Trees & Sha Cho Pa Building, Juikin. 8f, 10f, 20f, Pagoda Hill, Yenan. 22f, 30f, 50f, Gate of Heavenly Peace, Peking.

1961-62 Engr. Perf. 11
Without Gum
Size: 24x16mm
574 A152 1f vio blue 7.00 .25
575 A152 1½f maroon 13.00 .25
576 A152 2f indigo 7.00 .95
577 A152 3f dull vio 27.50 1.40
578 A152 4f green 2.40 .20
579 A152 5f gray 1.60 .20
580 A152 8f sepia 1.60 .20
581 A152 10f brt lil rose 4.50 .20
582 A152 20f grnsh bl 1.60 .20
583 A152 22f brown .80 .20
584 A152 30f blue 1.60 .20
585 A152 50f vermilion 1.60 .20
Nos. 574-585 (12) 70.20 4.50

Issued: 1f, 1½f, 5f, 7/20/62; others 7/20/61.
See Nos. 647-654, 1059-1064.

Flowers, Flags of Mongolia and China A153

Design: 10f, Parliament, Ulan Bator, and statue of Sukhe Bator.

1961, July 11 Photo. Perf. 11x11½
586 A153 8f crim, ultra & yel 11.00 1.60
587 A153 10f orange, blk & yel 18.00 7.25

40th anniv. of the Mongolian People's Republic.

Military Museum — A154

Photo. & Engr.
1961, Aug. 1 Perf. 11½
588 A154 8f gray bl, brn & grn 18.00 .85
589 A154 10f gray, blk & grn 15.50 1.40

Opening of the People's Revolutionary Military Museum.

Uprising at Wuchang A155

Sun Yat-
sen — A156

Perf. 11x11½, 11½x11
1961, Oct. 10   **Photo.**
590 A155   8f gray & blk   8.50 1.75
591 A156   10f tan & black   13.00   .90
50th anniversary of the 1911 Revolution.

Donkey — A157

Rejoicing
Tibetans — A158

Designs: 8f, 10f, 20f, 22f, Horses; 30f, 50f,
Camels. Ceramic statuettes from Tang
Dynasty (618-906) graves.

1961, Nov. 10   **Perf. 11½x11**
Statuettes in Original Colors
592 A157   4f dull blue   4.50   .65
593 A157   8f gray green   4.50   .65
594 A157   8f dp purple   4.50   .65
595 A157   10f dp blue   4.50   .65
596 A157   20f olive   9.00 2.00
597 A157   22f blue grn   14.00 2.75
598 A157   30f red brown   18.00 8.00
599 A157   50f slate   18.00 4.50
   Nos. 592-599 (8)   77.00 19.85

1961, Nov. 25
Designs: 8f, Woman sower. 10f, Celebration
of bumper crop. 20f, People's representatives.
30f, Tibetan children.

600 A158   4f brn & ocher   4.00   .80
601 A158   8f brn & lt bl grn   4.00   .80
602 A158   10f brn & yel   18.50 1.60
603 A158   20f brn & rose   27.50 2.40
604 A158   30f brn & bluish
              gray   47.50 3.25
   Nos. 600-604 (5)   101.50 8.85

Rebirth of the Tibetan people.

Lu Hsun — A159

1962, Feb. 26
605 A159   8f red brown & blk   1.60 .50
80th anniv. of the birth of Lu Hsun, writer.

An Chi Bridge, Chao Hsien — A160

Bridges of Ancient China: 8f, Pao Tai,
Soochow. 10f, Chu Pu, Kwan Hsien. 20f, Chen
Yang, San Kiang.

1962, May 15   **Perf. 11**
606 A160   4f dk gray blue   1.25   .20
607 A160   8f dp green   1.25   .20
608 A160   10f brown   2.00   .35
609 A160   20f grnsh blue   3.50   .70
   Nos. 606-609 (4)   8.00 1.45

Tu Fu — A161

Cranes and
Bamboo — A162

4f, Tu Fu memorial pavilion, Chengtu.

1962, May 25   **Perf. 11½x11**
610 A161   4f ol bis & blk   12.00   .80
611 A161   8f grnsh bl & blk   12.00 1.90

Poet Tu Fu, 1,250th anniversary of birth.

1962, June 10
10f, Two cranes in flight. 20f, Crane on rock.

612 A162   8f tan & multi   10.00 2.00
613 A162   10f blue & multi   15.00 3.00
614 A162   20f bister & multi 29.00 4.00
   Nos. 612-614 (3)   54.00 9.00

"The Sacred Crane," from paintings by Chen
Chi-fo.

Cuban
Soldier and
Flag
A163

Designs: 10f, Sugar cane worker. 22f, Militiaman and woman.

1962, July 10   **Perf. 11x11½**
615 A163   8f car, rose & blk 20.00 7.00
616 A163   10f green & blk   32.50 2.25
617 A163   22f ultra & blk   70.00 15.00
   Nos. 615-617 (3)   122.50 24.25

Support of Cuba.

Torch and Map of
Algeria — A164

Mei Lan-
fang — A165

Design: 22f, Algerian soldiers and flag.

1962, July 10   **Perf. 11½x11**
618 A164   8f dp brown & red org   .30   .25
619 A164   22f ocher & dp brn   1.50   .75

Support of Algeria.

1962   **Perf. 11½x11, 11x11½**
Designs (Mei Lan-fang in Women's Roles):
No. 621, Beating drum. No. 622, With fan. 10f,
Lady Yu with swords. 20f, With bag. 22f, Heavenly Maiden, horiz. 30f, With spinning wheel,
horiz. 50f, Kneeling, horiz. $3, Scene from
opera "Drunken Beauty."

620 A165   4f tan & multi   200.00 14.00
621 A165   8f tan & multi   40.00 6.00
622 A165   8f gray & multi   40.00 6.00
623 A165   10f gray & multi   40.00 7.00
624 A165   20f lt grn & multi 40.00 14.00
625 A165   22f cream & mul-
              ti   62.50 17.50
626 A165   30f lt blue & mul-
              ti   100.00 35.00
627 A165   50f buff & multi   90.00 27.50
   Nos. 620-627 (8)   612.50 127.00

Souvenir Sheet
Perf. 11
628 A165 $3 brown & mul-
              ti   6,000. 1,200.

Stage art of Mei Lan-fang, actor.
Issued: 4f, 8f, 10f, 8/8; $3, 9/15; others 9/1.
Nos. 620-627 exist imperf. Value, set
$3,000.
No. 628 contains one 48x58mm stamp and
almost always has some faults. Value above is
for fault-free examples. Value for No. 628 with
small faults, unused $2,500. Excellent forger-
ies exist.

Flower Drum
Dance,
Han — A166

Folk Dances: 8f, Ordos, Mongolia. 10f,
Catching shrimp, Chuang. 20f, Friend, Yi. 30f,
Fiddle dance, Tibet. 50f, Tambourine dance,
Uighur.
Cumulative numbers 246-251 at lower right.

1962, Oct. 15   Litho.   Perf. 12½
Without Gum
629 A166   4f cream & multi   .60   .35
630 A166   8f cream & multi   .60   .35
631 A166   10f cream & multi   .85   .35
632 A166   20f cream & multi   .85   .35
633 A166   30f cream & multi   1.75   .70
634 A166   50f cream & multi   3.50 1.40
   Nos. 629-634 (6)   8.15 3.50

See Nos. 696-707.

Soldiers Storming Winter
Palace — A167

Design: 8f, Lenin leading soldiers, vert.

1962, Nov. 7   Photo.   Perf. 11½
635 A167   8f black & red   13.00   .85
636 A167   20f slate grn & red 30.00 1.50

45th anniversary of the Russian Revolution.

Monument and
Map of
Albania — A168

Tsai Lun, Inventor
of Papermaking
A169

Design: 10f, Albanian flag and Girl Pioneer.

1962, Nov. 28   **Perf. 11½x11**
637 A168   8f Prus blue & sepia   1.40   .35
638 A168   10f red, yel, & blk   2.25 1.00

50th anniversary of Albanian independence.

1962, Dec. 1   **Perf. 11½x11**
Designs: No. 640, Paper making. No. 641,
Sun Szu-miao, physician. No. 642, Writing
medical treatise. No. 643, Shen Ko, geologist.
No. 644, Making field notes. No. 645, Kuo
Shou-chin, astronomer. No. 646, Astronomical
instrument.
Cumulative numbers 297-304 at lower right.

639 A169   4f multicolored   6.00   .20
640 A169   4f multicolored   2.75   .30
641 A169   8f multicolored   2.75   .30
642 A169   8f multicolored   2.75   .30
643 A169   10f multicolored   2.75   .30
644 A169   10f multicolored   3.50   .30
645 A169   20f multicolored   8.00   .90
646 A169   20f multicolored   8.00   .90
   Nos. 639-646 (8)   36.50 3.50

Scientists of ancient China.

Building Type of 1961
Designs: 1f, 2f, Building, Nanchang. 3f, 4f,
Trees and Sha Cho Pa Building. 8f, 10f, 20f,
Pagoda Hill, Yenan. 30f, Gate of Heavenly
Peace, Peking.

1962, Jan.   Litho.   Rough Perf. 12½
Size: 21x16mm
Without Gum
647 A152   1f ultra   .45   .20
648 A152   2f greenish gray   .45   .20
649 A152   3f violet gray   .45   .20
650 A152   4f green   .45   .20
651 A152   8f dk olive, perf. 14 .80 .20
   b. Perf. 11x11½   5.00
652 A152   10f brt rose lilac 1.25   .20
653 A152   20f slate blue   1.25   .20
654 A152   30f dull blue   1.75   .25
   Nos. 647-654 (8)   6.85 1.65

Tank
Monument,
Havana
A170

Crowd in Peking — A171

Designs: No. 656, Cuban revolutionaries.
No. 657, Crowd in Havana. No. 659, Cuban
soldier. No. 660, Castro and Cuban flag.

Perf. 11½, 11x11½
1963, Jan. 1   **Photo.**
655 A170   4f red & blk brn   32.50 1.90
656 A170   4f green & blk   22.00 1.90
657 A171   8f dull red & brn   22.00 1.90
658 A171   8f dull red & brn   65.00 12.00
659 A170   10f ocher & blk   65.00 5.50
660 A170   10f red, blue & blk 65.00 16.00
   Nos. 655-660 (6)   271.50 39.20

4th anniversary of the Cuban revolution.

Green
Dragontail — A172

Karl
Marx — A173

1963 **Without Gum** **Perf. 11**

661	A172	4f Tibetan clouded yellow (1)	12.50	5.00
662	A172	4f Tritailed glory (2)	12.50	.75
663	A172	4f Neumogeni jungle queen (3)	12.50	.75
664	A172	4f Washan swordtail (4)	12.50	.75
665	A172	4f Striped ringlet (5)	12.50	.75
666	A172	8f shown (6)	12.50	.75
667	A172	8f Dilunulated peacock (7)	12.50	.75
668	A172	8f Yamfly (8)	12.50	.75
669	A172	8f Golden kaiser-i-hind (9)	12.50	.75
670	A172	8f Mushaell hairstreak (10)	12.50	.75
671	A172	10f Yellow orangetip (11)	12.50	.75
672	A172	10f Great jay (12)	12.50	.75
673	A172	10f Striped punch (13)	12.50	.75
674	A172	10f Hainan violetbeak (14)	12.50	.75
675	A172	10f Omeiskipper (15)	12.50	.75
676	A172	20f Philippines birdwing (16)	12.50	3.50
677	A172	20f Richtofenis red apollo (17)	12.50	3.50
678	A172	22f Blue-banded king crow (18)	12.50	4.25
679	A172	30f Solskyi copper (19)	12.50	4.25
680	A172	50f Yunnan clipper (20)	12.50	5.50
		Nos. 661-680 (20)	250.00	40.00

Issued: #666-675, July 15; others Apr. 5.

1963, May 5 **Perf. 11½**

Designs: No. 682, "Workers of the World, Unite" on cover of first edition of Communist Manifesto. No. 683, Marx and Engels.

Without Gum

681	A173	8f black, gold & sal (1)	6.00	2.00
682	A173	8f gold & red (2)	6.00	2.00
683	A173	8f gold & choc (3)	6.00	2.00
		Nos. 681-683 (3)	18.00	6.00

145th anniversary of birth of Karl Marx (1818-1883), German political philosopher.

Child with
Top — A174

Child: #685, eating berries. #686, as traffic policeman. #687, with windmill. #688, listening to caged cricket. #689, with sword. #690, embroidering. #691, with umbrella. #692, playing with sand. #693, playing table tennis. #694, learning to add. #695, with kite.

1963, June 1 **Litho.** **Perf. 12½**

Without Gum

Multicolored Designs

684	A174	4f grnsh gray (1)	.75	.20
685	A174	4f tan (2)	.75	.20
686	A174	8f gray (3)	.75	.20
687	A174	8f blue (4)	.75	.20
688	A174	8f tan (5)	.75	.20
689	A174	8f dp gray (6)	.75	.20
690	A174	8f citron (7)	.75	.20
691	A174	8f gray (8)	.75	.20
692	A174	10f green (9)	1.50	.45
693	A174	10f violet (10)	1.50	.45
694	A174	20f bister (11)	3.50	1.00
695	A174	20f green (12)	3.50	1.00
		Nos. 684-695 (12)	16.00	4.50

Children's Day. Value, imperf set $125.

Dance Type of 1962

Folk Dances: 4f, Weavers' dance, Puyi. 8f, Kazakh. 10f, Olunchun. 20f, Labor dance, Kaochan. 30f, Reed pipe dance, Miao. 50f, Fan dance, Korea.
Cumulative numbers 261-266 at lower right.

1963, June 15 **Perf. 12½**

Without Gum

696	A166	4f cream & multi	.75	.35
697	A166	8f cream & multi	.75	.35
698	A166	10f cream & multi	1.25	.35
699	A166	20f cream & multi	1.25	.35
700	A166	30f cream & multi	2.75	.70
701	A166	50f cream & multi	2.75	.70
		Nos. 696-701 (6)	9.50	2.80

1963, June 30 **Without Gum**

Folk Dances: 4f, "Wedding Ceremony," Yu. 8f, "Encircling Mountain Forest," Pai. 10f, Long drum dance, Yao. 20f, Third day of the third month dance, Li. 30f, Knife dance, Kawa. 50f, Peacock dance, Thai.
Cumulative numbers 279-284 at lower right.

702	A166	4f cream & multi	.75	.35
703	A166	8f cream & multi	.75	.35
704	A166	10f cream & multi	1.10	.35
705	A166	20f cream & multi	1.10	.35
706	A166	30f cream & multi	2.75	.60
707	A166	50f cream & multi	4.00	1.00
		Nos. 702-707 (6)	10.45	3.00

Giant Panda
Eating
Apples — A175

Table Tennis
Player — A176

Designs: No. 709, Giant panda eating bamboo shoots. 10f, Two pandas, horiz.

1963, Aug. 5 **Photo.** **Perf. 11½x11**

Size: 28x38mm

708	A175	8f pale blue & blk	27.50	2.00
709	A175	8f pale blue & blk	27.50	6.25

Size: 50x29mm

Perf. 11½

710	A175	10f olive & blk	27.50	3.75
		Nos. 708-710 (3)	82.50	12.00

Value, imperf set $240.

1963, Sept. 10 **Engr.** **Perf. 11½**

No. 712, Trophies won by Chinese team.

711	A176	8f dk olive grn	13.00	.80
712	A176	8f brown	13.00	1.75

27th World Table Tennis Championships.

Snub-nosed
Langur — A177

Jade-green
Screen
Mountain — A178

Designs: 10f, Two monkeys playing. 22f, Two monkeys grooming.

1963, Sept. 23 **Photo.** **Perf. 11½x11**

713	A177	8f gray & multi	8.00	1.10
714	A177	10f gray & multi	8.00	1.10
715	A177	22f gray & multi	13.00	4.50
		Nos. 713-715 (3)	29.00	6.70

Value, imperf set $225.

Engraved and Photogravure

1963, Oct. 15 **Perf. 11½**

Hwang Shan Landscapes (Yellow Mountains), Anhwei Province. #724-731 horiz.

Design A178

716	4f shown (1)	14.00	1.25
717	4f "Guests Welcoming Pines" (2)	14.00	1.25
718	4f Pines and Rock Behind the Sea (3)	14.00	1.75
719	4f Terrace of Keeping Cool (4)	17.50	1.75
720	8f Mount of Heavenly Capital (5)	17.50	1.75
721	8f Mount of Scissors (6)	17.50	1.75
722	8f Forest of Ten Thousand Pines (7)	17.50	1.75
723	8f "Brush Blooming in Dream" (8)	20.00	1.75
724	10f Mount of Lotus Flower (9)	20.00	1.75
725	10f Cumulus Cloud over West Sea (10)	27.50	1.75
726	10f Old Pines of Hwang Shan (11)	32.50	1.75
727	10f "Watching the Clouds over West Sea" (12)	37.50	1.75
728	20f Mount of Stalagmites (13)	47.50	6.00
729	22f "Stone Monkey Watching the Sea" (14)	47.50	9.50
730	30f Forest of Lions (15)	72.50	45.00
731	50f Three Fairy Tales of Pen Lai (16)	60.00	17.50
	Nos. 716-731 (16)	477.00	98.00

Soccer
Player — A179

Athletes and Banners — A180

#733, Discus, women's. #734, Diving, men's. #735, Gymnastics, women's.

Engraved and Photogravure

1963, Nov. 17 **Perf. 11**

732	A179	8f gray, red & blk (1)	11.00	.80
733	A179	8f gray, ultra & blk (2)	11.00	.80
734	A179	8f lt grn, brn & blk (3)	11.00	.80
735	A179	8f gray, lil rose & blk (4)	11.00	.80

Photo. **Perf. 11½**

736	A180	10f red & multi (5)	11.00	3.25
		Nos. 732-736 (5)	55.00	6.45

Games of the Newly Emerging Forces, Djakarta.

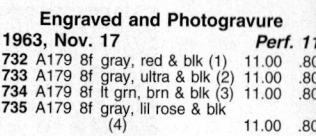

Clay Rooster
and
Goat — A181

Chinese Folk Toys: No. 738, Cloth camel. No. 739, Cloth tigers. No. 740, Clay ox and rider. No. 741, Cloth rabbit, wooden doll, clay roosters. No. 742, Straw rooster. No. 743, Cloth donkey and bird. No. 744, Clay lion. No. 745, Cloth tiger and tumbler doll.

1963, Dec. 10 **Litho.** **Perf. 11½**

Toys Multicolored; Without Gum

737	A181	4f bister (1)	.65	.20
738	A181	4f gray (4)	.65	.20
739	A181	4f lt blue (7)	.65	.20
740	A181	8f bister (2)	.65	.20
741	A181	8f gray (5)	.65	.20
742	A181	8f lt blue (8)	.65	.25
743	A181	10f bister (3)	.65	.25
744	A181	10f gray (6)	.65	.25
745	A181	10f lt blue (9)	.65	.25
		Nos. 737-745 (9)	5.85	2.00

Armed
Vietnamese
Family — A182

Flags of Cuba
and
China — A183

Liberation of South Viet Nam: No. 747, Militia with Vietnamese flag.

1963, Dec. 20 **Photo.** **Perf. 11½x11**

746	A182	8f tan, blk & red	2.75	.80
747	A182	8f red & multi	2.75	1.60

1964, Jan. 1

Design: No. 749, Boy waving Cuban flag.

748	A183	8f red, yel, bl & ind	9.00	.85
749	A183	8f multicolored	22.50	5.50

5th anniversary of the liberation of Cuba.

Woman Driving
Tractor — A184

Woman of the People's Commune: No. 751, harvesting. No. 752, picking cotton. No. 753, picking fruit. No. 754, reading book. No. 755, on guard duty.

1964, Mar. 8

750	A184	8f ol, pink & brn (1)	1.00	.20
751	A184	8f brn yel & org (2)	1.00	.20
752	A184	8f gray & multi (3)	1.00	.20
753	A184	8f black, org & bl (4)	1.25	.20
754	A184	8f green & multi (5)	1.25	.20
755	A184	8f lilac & multi (6)	1.25	.30
	Nos. 750-755 (6)		6.75	1.30

Chinese and African Men
A185

Design: No. 757, African drummer.

1964, Apr. 12   Photo.   *Perf. 11*

756	A185	8f red & multi	.90	.25
757	A185	8f black & dk brn	.90	.25

African Freedom Day.

Marx, Engels, Lenin and Stalin — A186

Design: No. 759, Banners and workers.

1964, May 1   *Perf. 11½*

758	A186	8f gold, red & blk	22.50	6.00
759	A186	8f gold, red & blk	8.00	2.00

Labor Day.

Orchard, Yenan
A187

Yenan, Shrine of the Chinese Revolution: No. 761, Central Auditorium, Yang Chia Ling. No. 762, Mao's office and residence. No. 763, Auditorium, Wang Chia Ping. No. 764, Border Region Assembly Hall. No. 765, Pagoda Hill and Bridge.

1964, July 1   Photo.   *Perf. 11x11½*

760	A187	8f multicolored (1)	22.50	1.50
761	A187	8f multicolored (2)	3.75	.60
762	A187	8f multicolored (3)	3.75	.60
763	A187	8f multicolored (4)	3.75	.60
764	A187	8f multicolored (5)	18.00	2.00
765	A187	52f multicolored (6)	12.50	4.00
	Nos. 760-765 (6)		64.25	9.30

Map and Flag of Viet Nam — A188

Alchemist's Glowing Crucible — A189

1964, July 20   *Perf. 11½*

766	A188	8f multicolored	16.00	5.00

Victory in South Viet Nam.

1964, Aug. 5   *Perf. 11½x11*

767	A189	4f shown (1)	6.00	1.00
768	A189	4f Night-shining jade (2)	6.00	1.00

769	A189	8f Purple Kuo's cap (3)	9.50	1.00
770	A189	8f Chao pink (4)	9.50	1.00
771	A189	8f Yao yellow (5)	9.50	1.00
772	A189	8f Twin beauty (6)	9.50	1.00
773	A189	8f Ice-veiled ruby (7)	9.50	1.40
774	A189	10f Gold-sprinkled Chinese ink (8)	11.50	1.40
775	A189	10f Cinnabar jar (9)	11.50	1.40
776	A189	10f Lan Tien jade (10)	13.50	2.10
777	A189	10f Imperial robe yellow (11)	14.00	2.10
778	A189	10f Hu red (12)	14.00	2.10
779	A189	20f Pea green (13)	29.00	5.00
780	A189	43f Wei purple (14)	40.00	17.50
781	A189	52f Intoxicated celestial peach (15)	57.50	20.00
	Nos. 767-781 (15)		250.50	59.00

Souvenir Sheet
Perf. 11½
Without Gum

782	A189	$2 Glorious crimson & great gold pink	1,200.	500.00

No. 782 contains one 48x59mm stamp.

Wine Cup — A190

Designs: Sacrificial bronze vessels of Yin dynasty, prior to 1050 B.C.

Engraved and Photogravure
1964, Aug. 25   *Perf. 11½x11*

783	A190	4f shown (1)	6.00	.90
784	A190	4f Ku beaker (2)	6.00	.90
785	A190	8f Kuang wine urn (3)	8.75	.90
786	A190	8f Chia wine cup (4)	9.50	.90
787	A190	10f Tsun wine vessel (5)	9.50	.90
788	A190	10f Yu wine urn (6)	9.50	.90
789	A190	20f Tsun wine vessel (7)	11.00	3.50
790	A190	20f Ceremonial cauldron (8)	11.00	3.50
	Nos. 783-790 (8)		71.25	12.40

1964, Sept. 26   Photo.

Grain Harvest — A191

Designs: #792, Students planting trees. #793, Study period. #794, Scientific experimentation.

791	A191	8f multicolored (1)	1.50	.25
792	A191	8f multicolored (2)	1.50	.25
793	A191	8f multicolored (3)	1.50	.25
794	A191	8f multicolored (4)	1.50	.25
	Nos. 791-794 (4)		6.00	1.00

Youth helping in agriculture.

Marx, Engels, Trafalgar Square, London — A192

People with Banners — A193

1964, Sept. 28   *Perf. 11½*

795	A192	8f red, gold & red brn	42.50	16.00

Centenary of the First International.

Gold Ink

Stamps with gold ink often show some tarnishing. Values are for untarnished gold color. Tarnished stamps will sell for less.

1964, Oct. 1

No. 797, Gate of Heavenly Peace and Chinese flag. No. 798, People with banners, facing left.

796	A193	8f cream & multi (1)	27.50	2.75
797	A193	8f cream & multi (2)	27.50	2.75
798	A193	8f cream & multi (3)	27.50	2.75
a.		Souvenir sheet of 3	1,900.	650.00
b.		Strip of 3, #796-798	140.00	15.00
	Nos. 796-798 (3)		82.50	8.25

15th anniv. of the People's Republic.
No. 798a contains No. 798b in continuous design without separating perfs. No. 798a almost always has disturbed gum, with interleaving paper sticking to it, or tarnished gilt. Such copies sell for considerably less than the very fine example valued above.
Values for No. 798b are for an unfolded strip.

Oil Derricks — A194

Oil industry: 4f, Geological surveyors and truck, horiz. 8f, "Christmas tree" and extraction accessories. 10f, Oil refinery. 20f, Tank cars, horiz.

1964, Oct. 1

799	A194	4f lt blue & multi	50.00	4.00
800	A194	8f lt blue & multi	22.50	1.75
801	A194	8f lilac & multi	22.50	1.75
802	A194	10f slate & multi	50.00	1.75
803	A194	20f brown & multi	100.00	23.50
	Nos. 799-803 (5)		245.00	32.75

Albanian and Chinese Flags
A195

10f, Enver Hoxha and Albanian coat of arms.

1964, Nov. 29   *Perf. 11x11½*

804	A195	8f red & multi	10.00	2.00
805	A195	10f red, yel & blk	15.00	8.00

20th anniv. of the liberation of Albania.

Power Dam Construction
A196

No. 807, Installation of turbogenerator rotor. No. 808, Main dam. 20f, Pylon.

1964, Dec. 15   *Perf. 11½*

806	A196	4f multicolored	60.00	2.25
807	A196	8f multicolored	20.00	.85
808	A196	8f multicolored	37.50	1.40
809	A196	20f multicolored	100.00	20.00
	Nos. 806-809 (4)		217.50	24.50

Hsin An Kiang Dam and hydroelectric power station.

Fertilizer Industry — A197

Chemical Industry: #811, Plastics. #812, Medicines. #813, Rubber. #814, Insecticides. #815, Industrial acids. #816, Industrial alkaloids. #817, Synthetic fibers.

1964, Dec. 30   Photo. & Engr.

810	A197	8f red & blk (1)	2.25	.25
811	A197	8f yel grn & blk (2)	2.25	.25
812	A197	8f brown & blk (3)	2.25	.25
813	A197	8f lilac rose & blk (4)	2.25	.25
814	A197	8f blue & blk (5)	2.25	.25
815	A197	8f orange & blk (6)	2.25	.25
816	A197	8f violet & blk (7)	2.25	.25
817	A197	8f brt green & blk (8)	2.25	.25
	Nos. 810-817 (8)		18.00	2.00

Mao Studying Map — A198

Mao Tsetung — A199

Design: No. 819, Victory at Lushan Pass.

1965, Jan. 31   Photo.   Perf. 11
818 A198 8f red & multi   40.00 4.25
819 A198 8f red & multi   22.50 4.25
Perf. 11½x11
820 A199 8f gold & multi   35.00 5.75
  Nos. 818-820 (3)   97.50 14.25
Tsunyi Conference, 30th anniversary.

Conference Hall, Bandung — A200

Lenin — A201

#822, Asians and Africans applauding.

1965, Apr. 18   Perf. 11½x11
821 A200 8f cream & multi   .90 .20
822 A200 8f cream & multi   .90 .20
10th anniversary of the Bandung, Indonesia, Conference, Apr. 1955.

1965, Apr. 25   Perf. 11½
823 A201 8f red, choc & salmon 20.00 5.00
95th anniversary of the birth of Lenin.

Chinese Player — A202

1965, Apr. 25   Perf. 11½
824 A202 8f shown (1)   .50 .20
825 A202 8f European woman (2)   .50 .20
826 A202 8f Chinese woman (3)   .50 .20
827 A202 8f European man (4)   .50 .20
  a.   Block of 4, #824-827   2.75 .80
28th World Table Tennis Championships, Ljubljana, Yugoslavia, Apr. 15-25.

Climbers on Mt. Minya Konka — A203

Marx and Lenin — A204

Mountain Climbers: No. 829, on Muztagh Ata. No. 830, on Mt. Jolmo Lungma (Mt. Everest). No. 831, Women camping on Kongur Tiubie Tagh. No. 832, on Shisha Pangma.

1965, May 25   Photo. & Engr.
828 A203 8f blue, blk & ol (1)   3.75 .75
829 A203 8f blue, blk & ol (2)   4.75 .75
830 A203 8f ultra, blk & gray (3)   4.75 .75
831 A203 8f lt bl, blk & yel gray (4)   4.75 .75
832 A203 8f ultra, blk & gray (5)   5.50 3.25
  Nos. 828-832 (5)   23.50 6.25
Chinese mountaineering achievements, 1957-64.

1965, June 21 Photo. Perf. 11½x11
833 A204 8f red, yel & blk   11.50 5.00
Postal Ministers' Congress, Peking.

Tseping Valley A205

Chingkang Mountains, Cradle of the Chinese Revolution.

1965, July 1   Perf. 11x11½
834 A205 4f shown (1)   8.00 1.00
835 A205 8f San Wan Tsun (2)   10.00 1.00
836 A205 8f Octagon Bldg., Mao Ping (3)   32.50 1.00
837 A205 8f River and Bridge at Lung Shih (4)   37.50 1.75
838 A205 8f Ta Ching Tsun (5)   16.00 2.75
839 A205 10f Bridge across the Lung Yuan (6)   16.00 4.00
840 A205 10f Hwang Yang Mountain (7)   13.50 5.00
841 A205 52f Chingkang peaks (8)   12.00 7.00
  Nos. 834-841 (8)   145.50 21.50

Soldiers with Books — A206

1965, Aug. 1   Perf. 11½
Without Gum
842 A206 8f shown (1)   20.00 2.00
843 A206 8f Soldiers reading Little Red Books (2)   20.00 2.00
844 A206 8f With shell and artillery (3)   20.00 2.00
845 A206 8f Rifle instruction (4)   20.00 2.00
846 A206 8f Sewing jacket (5)   20.00 2.00
847 A206 8f Bayonet charge (6)   20.00 6.00
848 A206 8f With Banner (7)   22.50 6.00
849 A206 8f Military band (8)   22.50 6.00
  Nos. 842-849 (8)   165.00 28.00
People's Liberation Army. Nos. 846-849 vertical.

"Welcome to Peking" — A207

#851, Chinese and Japanese young men. #852, Chinese and Japanese girls. #853, Musical entertainment. #854, Emblem of meeting.

1965, Aug. 25   Perf. 11½x11
850 A207 4f yellow & multi   1.25 .25
851 A207 4f pink & multi   1.25 .25
852 A207 8f multicolored   1.25 .25
853 A207 10f multicolored   1.75 .25
854 A207 22f lt blue & multi   3.00 .50
  Nos. 850-854 (5)   8.50 1.50
Chinese-Japanese Youth Meeting, Peking.

North Vietnamese Soldier — A208

Peoples of the World — A209

Designs: No. 856, Soldier with guns. No. 857, Soldier giving victory salute.

1965, Sept. 2   Perf. 11½x11
855 A208 8f red & red brn (1)   1.50 .35
856 A208 8f red & blk (2)   1.50 .35
857 A208 8f red & vio brn (3)   1.50 .35
Perf. 11½
858 A209 8f black & red (4)   1.50 .35
  Nos. 855-858 (4)   6.00 1.40
Struggle of the people of Viet Nam.

Mao Tse-tung at His Desk — A210

Crossing Yellow River A211

Victory Monument A212

Design: No. 862, Recruits in cart.

1965, Sept. 3   Perf. 11
859 A210 8f red & multi (1)   30.00 6.50
Perf. 11x11½, 11½x11
860 A211 8f red & dk grn (2)   10.00 .90
861 A212 8f red & dk brn (3)   10.00 .90
862 A211 8f red & dk grn (4)   10.00 .90
  Nos. 859-862 (4)   60.00 9.20
20th anniversary of victory over Japan.

2nd National Games — A213

National Games Opening Ceremonies — A214

Perf. 11½x11, 11 (A214)
1965, Sept. 28
863 A213 4f Soccer (1)   10.00 .85
864 A213 4f Archery (2)   10.00 .85
865 A213 8f Javelin (3)   10.00 .85
866 A213 8f Gymnastics (4)   10.00 .85
867 A213 8f Volleyball (5)   10.00 .85
868 A214 10f shown (6)   42.50 .85
869 A213 10f Bicyling (7)   60.00 .85
870 A213 20f Diving (8)   55.00 2.50
871 A213 22f Hurdles (9)   10.00 2.50
872 A213 30f Weight lifting (10)   10.00 5.50
873 A213 43f Basketball (11)   14.50 9.00
  Nos. 863-873 (11)   242.00 25.45

Government Building A215

Textile Workers A216

1 ½f, 5f, 22f, Gate of Heavenly Peace. 2f, 8f, 30f, People's Hall. 3f, 10f, 50f, Military Museum.

1965-66   Perf. 11½x11
Without Gum
874 A215 1f brown   .20 .20
875 A215 1½f red lilac   .20 .50
876 A215 2f green   .20 .20
877 A215 3f blue grn   .20 .20
878 A215 4f brt blue   .20 .20
879 A215 5f vio brn ('66)   .40 .20
880 A215 8f rose red   .40 .20
881 A215 10f gray olive   .80 .20
882 A215 20f violet   .80 .20
883 A215 22f orange   1.60 .25
884 A215 30f yellow grn   2.50 .30
885 A215 50f dp blue ('66)   7.50 1.50
  Nos. 874-885 (12)   15.00 4.15

1965, Nov. 30
886 A216 8f shown (1)   10.00 .80
887 A216 8f Machine shop (2)   10.00 .80
888 A216 8f Welder (3)   10.00 .80
889 A216 8f Students (4)   10.00 .80
890 A216 8f Militia (5)   10.00 3.00
  Nos. 886-890 (5)   50.00 6.20
Women workers.

Soccer — A217

Children's Sports: No. 892, Racing. No. 893, Tobogganing and skating. No. 894, Gymnastics. No. 895, Swimming. No. 896, Rifle practice. No. 897, Jumping rope. No. 898, Table tennis.

1966, Feb. 25   Perf. 11
891 A217 4f emerald & multi (1)   .50 .20
892 A217 4f yel brown & multi (2)   .50 .20
893 A217 8f blue & multi (3)   .50 .20
894 A217 8f yellow & multi (4)   .50 .20
895 A217 8f grnsh bl & multi (5)   .75 .20
896 A217 8f green & multi (6)   .75 .20
897 A217 10f orange & multi (7)   1.75 .40
898 A217 52f grnsh gray & multi (8)   3.00 1.25
  Nos. 891-898 (8)   8.25 2.85

Mobile Transformer A218

New Industrial Machinery: No. 900, Electron microscope, vert. No. 901, Lathe. No. 902, Vertical boring and turning machine, vert. No. 903, Gear-grinding machine. No. 904, Hydraulic press. No. 905, Milling machine. No. 906, Electron accelerator, vert.

Perf. 11x11½, 11½x11

1966, Mar. 30 **Photo. & Engr.**

899 A218 4f yellow & blk (1) 9.00 .90
900 A218 8f blk & lt ultra (2) 13.00 .90
901 A218 8f sal pink & blk (3) 13.00 .90
902 A218 8f olive & blk (4) 13.00 .90
903 A218 8f rose lil & blk (5) 13.00 .90
904 A218 10f gray & blk (6) 19.00 .90
905 A218 10f bl grn & blk (7) 19.00 3.50
906 A218 22f lilac & blk (8) 37.50 5.50
Nos. 899-906 (8) 136.50 14.40

Military and Civilian Workers A219

Women in Various Occupations: No. 908, Train conductor. No. 909, Red Cross worker. No. 910, Kindergarten teacher. No. 911, Road sweeper. No. 912, Hairdresser. No. 913, Bus conductor. No. 914, Traveling saleswoman. No. 915, Canteen worker. No. 916, Rural mail carrier.

1966, May 10 ***Perf. 11x11½***

907 A219 8f red & multi (1) .60 .25
908 A219 8f pale grn & multi (2) .60 .25
909 A219 8f yellow & multi (3) .60 .25
910 A219 8f green & multi (4) .60 .25
911 A219 8f salmon & multi (5) .60 .25
912 A219 8f pale bl & bl (6) .60 .25
913 A219 8f yellow & multi (7) .60 .25
914 A219 8f tan & multi (8) .60 .25
915 A219 8f yel grn & multi (9) .60 .25
916 A219 8f green & multi (10) .60 .25
Nos. 907-916 (10) 6.00 2.50

Statue "Thunderstorm" — A220

22f, Open book and association emblem.

1966, June 27 ***Perf. 11***

917 A220 8f red & black 2.00 .35
918 A220 22f red, gold & yel 6.00 .75

Afro-Asian Writers' Assoc. Conf., Peking.

Sun Yat-sen — A221

1966, Nov. 12 ***Perf. 11½x11***

919 A221 8f sepia & lt buff 60.00 9.00

Birth centenary of Sun Yat-sen.

Athletes Holding Portrait of Mao — A222

Two Women Athletes with Little Red Book A223

#921, Athletes holding Little Red Books. #923, Athletes reading Mao texts.

1966, Dec. 31 ***Perf. 11***

920 A222 8f red & multi (1) 27.50 7.00
921 A222 8f red & multi (2) 27.50 7.00

Perf. 11x11½

922 A223 8f blue & multi (3) 27.50 7.00
923 A223 8f blue & multi (4) 27.50 7.00
Nos. 920-923 (4) 110.00 28.00

1st Athletic Games of the New Emerging Nations.

Appreciation of Lu Hsun by Mao — A224

"Be Resolute ...," by Mao Tse-tung — A225

Designs: No. 925, Portrait of Lu Hsun. No. 926, Lu Hsun's handwriting (3 vert. rows).

Engr. & Photo.; Photo. (#925)

1966, Dec. 31 ***Perf. 11½***

924 A224 8f red & black (1) 62.50 13.00
925 A224 8f red & multi (2) 22.50 12.00
926 A224 8f red & black (3) 42.50 13.00
Nos. 924-926 (3) 127.50 38.00

Lu Hsun, Revolutionary writer (1881-1936).

Perf. 11½x11, 11½ (No. 928)

1967, Mar. 10 **Photo.**

Designs: No. 928, Drilling crew fighting natural gas fire, horiz. No. 929, Attempt to close fire-engulfed valve.

Sizes: Nos. 927, 929, 26x38mm; No. 928, 49x29mm

927 A225 8f red, gold & blk 24.50 12.50
928 A225 8f brick red & blk 27.50 6.00
929 A225 8f brick red & blk 27.50 6.00
Nos. 927-929 (3) 79.50 24.50

Heroic oil well firefighters.

Liu Ying-chun A226

1967, Mar. 25 ***Perf. 11½x11***

930 A226 8f shown (1) 25.00 7.75
931 A226 8f With book by Mao (2) 25.00 6.00
932 A226 8f Holding bridle of horse (3) 27.50 10.00
933 A226 8f With film slide (4) 27.50 6.00
934 A226 8f Lecturing (5) 27.50 5.25
935 A226 8f Fatal attempt to stop runaway horse (6) 27.50 5.25
Nos. 930-935 (6) 160.00 40.25

In memory of soldier Liu Ying-chun, hero.

Third 5-Year Plan — A227

Design: No. 936, Banners, 3 workers and male soldier facing right (industrial growth). No. 937, Banners, 3 workers and female militia member facing left (agricultural growth).

1967, Apr. 15 ***Perf. 11***

936 A227 8f red & multi 35.00 8.00
937 A227 8f red & multi 35.00 8.00

Third Five-Year Plan.

Mao Tse-tung — A228

Thoughts of Mao — A229

1967, Apr. 20 ***Perf. 11½***

938 A228 8f red & multi 35.00 17.50

Red & Gold

939 A229 8f 39 characters 75.00 17.50
940 A229 8f 50 characters 75.00 17.50
941 A229 8f 39 characters in 6 lines 75.00 17.50
942 A229 8f 53 characters 75.00 17.50
943 A229 8f 46 characters 75.00 17.50
a. Strip of 5, #939-943 1,100. 250.00

Gold & Red

944 A229 8f 41 characters 90.00 20.00
945 A229 8f 49 characters 90.00 20.00
946 A229 8f 35 characters 90.00 20.00
947 A229 8f 22 characters 90.00 20.00
948 A229 8f 29 characters 90.00 20.00
a. Strip of 5, #944-948 1,100. 250.00
Nos. 938-948 (11) 860.00 205.00

Thoughts of Mao Tse-tung.

Values for Nos. 943a and 948a are for unfolded strips without tarnishing.

No numbers appear below design on Nos. 938-1046.

Gate of Heavenly Peace and Text from C. C. P. Communique Praising Mao — A230

Mao and Lin Piao A231

#950, Mao and poem. #951, Mao among people of various races. #952, Mao facing left and Red Guards with books. #953, Mao with upraised right hand. #954, Mao leaning on rail, horiz. 10f, Mao and Lin Piao in discussion, horiz.

Engraved and Photogravure

1967 ***Perf. 11x11½***

Size: 36x56mm

949 A230 4f yel, red & mar 40.00 14.00

Photo.

950 A230 8f yel, brn, & red 50.00 14.00
951 A230 8f yel, red & multi 47.50 14.00
952 A230 8f yel, red & multi 65.00 14.00

Size: 36x50mm, 50x36mm

Perf. 11

953 A231 8f black & multi 40.00 14.00
954 A231 8f black & multi 160.00 30.00
955 A231 8f lt blue & multi 30.00 14.00
956 A231 10f black & multi 190.00 30.00
Nos. 949-956 (8) 622.50 144.00

"Mao Tse-tung Our Great Teacher." Issued: #949-953, 5/1; #954-956, 9/20.

Mao Text (4 lines) — A232

Parade of Supporters — A233

Design: No. 958, Mao text (5 lines).

Engraved and Photogravure
1967, May 23   **Perf. 11½**
957 A232 8f black, red & yel   175.00   35.00
958 A232 8f black, red & yel   225.00   45.00

Photo.   **Perf. 11**
959 A233 8f   225.00   45.00
Nos. 957-959 (3)   625.00   125.00

25th anniversary of Mao Tse-tung's "Talks on Literature and Art" in Yenan.

Mao Tse-tung — A234

1967   **Engr.**   **Perf. 11**
960 A234 4f brown   4.50   12.00
961 A234 8f carmine   190.00   10.00
962 A234 35f dk brown   4.50   12.00
963 A234 43f vermilion   4.50   12.00
964 A234 52f carmine   4.50   12.00
Nos. 960-964 (5)   208.00   58.00

46th anniv. of Chinese Communist Party. Issue dates: 8f, July 1; others Sept.

Mao, "Sun of the Revolution" — A235

No. 966, Mao and people of various races.

1967, Oct. 1   **Perf. 11½x11**
965 A235 8f multicolored   6.00   11.00
966 A235 8f multicolored   62.50   13.00

People's Republic of China, 18th anniv.

"September 9" — A236

"Huichang"
A237

"Peitaiho"
A238

Reply to Comrade Kuo Mo-jo — A239

Mao Tse-tung Writing Poems — A240

Poems by Mao: #967, "The Long March." #968, "Liupanshan." #969, shown. #970, "The Cave of the Fairies." #971, "Snow." #972, "Lushan Pass." #975, "Conquest of Nanking." #976, "The Yellow Crane Pavilion." #977, "Swimming." #979, "Changsha."

1967-68   **Photo.**   **Perf. 11**
Size: 79x18½mm
967 A236 4f 9 charac-
           ters, UL
           panel   11.00   17.50
968 A236 4f 11 charac-
           ters, UL
           panel   10.00   17.50
Size: 60x24mm
Perf. 11½
969 A236 8f shown, 10
           characters
           in UL panel   90.00   20.00
970 A236 8f 21 charac-
           ters in UL
           panel   80.00   20.00
971 A236 8f 11 charac-
           ters in UL
           panel   90.00   22.00
972 A236 8f 9 characters
           in UL panel   90.00   22.00
Size: 29x50mm
973 A237 8f shown   175.00   45.00
974 A238 8f shown   450.00   50.00
975 A238 8f 3 rows in
           bottom
           panel   175.00   40.00
976 A238 8f 2 rows in
           bottom
           panel   260.00   35.00
Size: 52x38mm
Perf. 11
977 A239 8f 3 short vert.
           rows, at left
           of poem   260.00   30.00
978 A239 10f shown   10.00   17.50
979 A239 10f undivided
           text   11.00   17.50
980 A240 10f red, yel &
           multi   12.00   17.50
Nos. 967-980 (14)   1,724.   371.50

Issued: #969-970, 980, 10/1; #973-974, 977, 5/20/68; others 7/20/68.

Lin Piao's Epigram on Mao Tse-tung A241

1967, Dec. 26 Photo. Perf. 11x11½
981 A241 8f red & gold   14.00   7.50

Mao and Parade of Artists — A242

"Raid on White Tiger Regiment" — A243

"Red Detachment of Women" — A244

1968   **Perf. 11½x11; 11 (983, 990)**
982 A242 8f shown
           (56x36mm)   50.00   12.00
983 A242 8f "The Red Lan-
           tern," vert.   50.00   12.00
984 A243 8f "Shachiapang"   50.00   14.00
985 A243 8f "Shachiapang"
           (women & sol-
           dier)   50.00   14.00
986 A243 8f "On the Dock"   50.00   14.00
987 A243 8f "Taking Bandits'
           Fort"   50.00   14.00
988 A244 8f shown   50.00   14.00
989 A244 8f "The White-
           haired Girl"   50.00   14.00
990 A242 8f Mao with
           Orchestra &
           Chorus
           (50x36mm)   75.00   17.50
Nos. 982-990 (9)   475.00   125.50

Mao's direction for revolutionary literature and art. Issued: #982-987, Jan. 30; #988-990, May 1.

"Unite still more closely . . ." — A245

1968, May 31 Photo. Perf. 11
991 A245 8f red, gold & red
           brn   95.00   20.00

Mao Tse-tung's statement of support of Afro-Americans.

Statement about Cultural Revolution A246

Directives of Chairman Mao: No. 993, Experiences of Revolutionary Committee. No.

994, Leadership role of Revolutionary Committee. No. 995, Basic principle of reform. No. 996, Purpose of Cultural Revolution.

1968, July 20   Photo.   Perf. 11½
No. of Lines Over Signature
992 A246 8f shown   100.00   37.50
993 A246 8f 5   100.00   37.50
994 A246 8f 4½   100.00   37.50
995 A246 8f 4   100.00   37.50
996 A246 8f 8   100.00   37.50
a. Strip of 5, #992-996   3,000.   600.00
Nos. 992-996 (5)   500.00   187.50

Value for No. 996a is for an unfolded strip.

Lin Piao's Statement, July 26, 1965 — A247

1968, Aug. 1   Engr. & Photo.
997 A247 8f red, gold & blk   10.50   5.50

Chinese People's Liberation Army, 41st anniv.

Mao Tse-tung Going to An Yuan, 1921 A248

1968, Aug. 1   Perf. 11x11½
998 A248 8f multicolored   75.00   8.00

Shade varieties include varying amount of red in clouds.

Directive of Chairman Mao — A249

1968, Nov. 30   Perf. 11½
999 A249 8f red & blk brn   90.00   25.00

China Map, Worker, Farmer and Soldier A249a

1968, Nov.   Photo.   Perf. 11½x11
999A A249a 8f red, bl &
           bis   20,000.   15,000.

Map inscribed: "The entire nation is red." Issued in Canton and quickly withdrawn because Taiwan appears white instead of red. No. 999A most often is found repaired. Values are for sound, unrepaired examples. Counterfeits exist.

Woman, Miner and Soldier Holding Little Red Book
A250

1968, Dec. 26   *Perf. 11x11½*
1000 A250 8f multicolored   25.00   3.75

Canceled-to-order
From about this point on stamps are valued postally used.

Yangtze Bridge, Nanking
A251

Road across Bridge — A252

No. 1003, Side view. 10f, Aerial view.

Lithographed, *Perf. 11½x11* (A251);
Photogravure, *Perf. 11½* (A252)

1969
Without Gum
1001 A251 4f multicolored   4.50   2.25
1002 A252 8f multicolored   18.00   6.75
1003 A252 8f multicolored   12.50   6.75
1004 A251 10f multicolored   4.50   2.25
   Nos. 1001-1004 (4)   39.50   18.00

Inauguration of Yangtze Bridge at Nanking on Dec. 29, 1968.

Singer and Pianist
A253

(Piano Music from the Opera, "The Red Lantern"): #1006, Woman singer and pianist.

1969, Aug.   **Photo.**   *Perf. 11x11½*
Without Gum
1005 A253 8f multicolored   10.00   7.50
1006 A253 8f multicolored   52.50   11.00

Harvest
A254

1969, Oct.
Without Gum
1007 A254 4f shown   5.00   2.25
   a.   Brown omitted   20.00   20.00
1008 A254 8f Two harvesters   10.00   1.50
1009 A254 8f Harvesters with Little Red Books   60.00   9.00
1010 A254 10f Red Cross Worker examining baby   5.25   2.50
   Nos. 1007-1010 (4)   80.25   15.25

Agriculture students.

Armed Forces and Slogan — A255

Guarding the Coast — A256

Designs: No. 1013, 43f, Snow patrol, vert.

1969, Oct.   *Perf. 11½*
Without Gum
1011 A255 8f red & multi   27.50   10.00
   a.   Bayonets omitted   80.00   40.00
1012 A256 8f blue & multi   4.50   3.50
1013 A256 8f blue & multi   4.50   3.50
1014 A256 35f black & multi   4.50   3.50
1015 A256 43f black & multi   4.50   3.50
   Nos. 1011-1015 (5)   45.50   24.00

Defense of Chen Pao-tao (Damansky Islands) in Ussuri River.

Farm Woman
A257

Designs: 8f, Foundry worker. 10f, Soldier.

1969, Dec.   *Perf. 10; 11½*
Without Gum
1016 A257 4f ver & dk pur   .50   .40
   a.   Perf 11½   1.75   1.10
1017 A257 8f ver & dk brn   1.00   .60
   a.   Perf 11½   1.75   1.10
1018 A257 10f ver & blk   2.00   1.10
   a.   Perf 11½   1.75   1.10
   Nos. 1016-1018 (3)   3.50   2.10

Perforation
Nos. 1016-1018 and some succeeding issues bear two kinds of perforation: clean (Peking) and rough (Shanghai).

Building — A258

Communist Party Building, Shanghai
A259

Agriculture Building, Canton — A260

Foundry Worker — A261

Two types of 8f Gate of Heavenly Peace:

I — Strong, definite halo around sun.
II — Halo missing, white shades gradually into red.

1969-72   **Photo.**   *Perf. 10, 11½*
Without Gum
1019 A258 1f shown   .20   .20
1020 A259 1½f shown   .65   .70
   a.   Perf. 11½   5.50   4.00
1021 A260 2f shown   .20   .20
1022 A260 3f 1929 Party Day House, Pu Tien   .20   .20
1023 A260 4f Mao's Home and Office, Yunnan   .20   .20
1024 A261 5f Woman Tractor Driver   1.75   .75
1025 A260 8f Gate of Heavenly Peace, type II   .65   .35
   a.   Type I   2.50   1.25
1026 A259 8f Heroes Monument   1.25   .70
   a.   Perf. 11½   4.50   3.00
1027 A260 8f Pagoda Hill, Yenan   1.25   *3.50*
1028 A260 8f Gate of Heavenly Peace (no sun)   .20   .20
1029 A260 10f Monument, Tsu Ping   .30   .20
1030 A259 20f Conference Hall, Tsunyi   1.90   1.40
   a.   Perf. 11½   6.00   4.50
1031 A260 20f Highway ('72)   .40   .20
1032 A260 22f Shao Shan Village, Birthplace of Mao   .75   .35
1033 A260 35f Conference Hall   1.00   .35
1034 A260 43f Chingkang Peaks   1.50   .35
1035 A259 50f as 4f, different view   1.50   1.40
1036 A260 52f People's Hall, Peking   2.25   .35
1037 A261 $1 shown ('70)   5.00   2.75
   Nos. 1019-1037 (19)   21.15   14.35

Kin Hsün-hua
A262

Mounted Patrol — A263

1970, Jan.   **Without Gum**   *Perf. 11½*
1045 A262 8f red & black   21.00   16.00
   a.   8f red & gray brown   23.00   12.00

Death of Kin Hsün-hua in Kirin border flood.

1970, Aug. 1
Without Gum
1046 A263 8f yel grn & multi   7.00   6.00

People's Liberation Army, 43rd anniv.

Commemorative stamps from Nos. 1047 to 1142 and 1211-1214, carry a cumulative number in parenthesis at lower left and the year at lower right. Where such numbers help to identify, they are quoted in parenthesis.

Cpl. Yang Tse-jung — A264

Ensemble
A265

1970, Aug. 1   *Perf. 11½x11, 11x11½*
Without Gum
1047 A264 8f shown (1)   32.50   8.00
1048 A264 8f Armed guards (2)   3.50   2.50
1049 A264 8f Yang leaping through forest (3)   3.50   2.50
1050 A265 8f shown (4)   27.50   8.00
1051 A265 8f Yang in folk costume (5)   3.50   2.50
1052 A265 8f Four actors (6)   21.00   8.00
   Nos. 1047-1052 (6)   91.50   31.50

Scenes from opera "Taking Tiger Mountain by Strategy." Nos. 1048, 1052, horizontal.

Frontier Guard
A266

1971, Jan.   **Litho.**   *Perf. 10*
Without Gum
1053 A266 4f multicolored   2.00   1.50
   a.   Perf. 11½   2.10   1.10
   b.   Perf. 11½x10   3.00
   c.   Perf. 10x11½   4.00

Banner of the Commune
A267

Street Battle, Paris, 1871
A268

10f, Proclamation of the Commune. 22f, Rally.

Perf. 11½x11, 11x11½
1971, Mar. 18   **Litho. & Engr.**
Without Gum
1054 A267 4f sal & multi   25.00   8.00
1055 A268 8f ver, pink & brn   160.00   25.00
1056 A267 10f ver, pink & dk brn   9.00   8.00
1057 A268 22f ver, pink & dk brn   3.50   *8.00*
   Nos. 1054-1057 (4)   197.50   49.00

Centenary of the Paris Commune.

Redrawn Building Type of 1961

Designs: 2f, 3f, August 1 building, Nanchang. 4f, 52f, Gate of Heavenly Peace, Peking. 10f, 20f, Pagoda Hill, Yenan.

1971, July 1   Litho.   Perf. 11x11½
Size: 21x16mm
Without Gum

1059	A152	2f slate green	1.50	.75
1060	A152	3f sepia	2.00	1.25
1061	A152	4f brt pink	2.00	1.25
1062	A152	10f brt rose lil	4.75	1.25
1063	A152	20f dk blue grn	2.75	1.25
1064	A152	52f orange	1.50	1.25
		Nos. 1059-1064 (6)	14.50	7.00

Paper of Nos. 1059-1064 is white. That of Nos. 647-654 is toned.

Communist Party Building, Shanghai — A269

People and Factories — A270

Designs: No. 1068, Peasant Movement Training Institute. No. 1069, Ching Kang Peaks. No. 1070, Conference Building, Tsunyi. No. 1071, Pagoda Hill, Yenan. No. 1073, People and People's Hall, Peking. No. 1074, People and Pagoda Hill, Yenan. 22f, Gate of Heavenly Peace, Peking.

1971, July 1   Photo.   Perf. 11½
Red and Gold Frame
Without Gum

1067	A269	4f vermilion (12)	5.00	1.25
1068	A269	4f brt grn (13)	5.00	1.25
1069	A269	8f grnsh bl & red (14)	4.00	1.25
1070	A269	8f ol blk (15)	4.00	1.25
1071	A269	8f bis, grn & red (16)	15.00	2.75
1072	A270	8f yel, red & multi (18)	15.00	2.75
1073	A270	8f yel, red & multi (19)	15.00	2.75
1074	A270	8f yel, red & multi (20)	15.00	2.75
a.		Strip of 3, #1072-1074	95.00	40.00
1075	A269	22f red, gold & brn (17)	35.00	3.00
		Nos. 1067-1075 (9)	113.00	19.00

50th anniv. of the Chinese Communist Party. No. 1074a has a continuous design and is valued as an unfolded strip.

Chinese Welcome A271

Enver Hoxha — A272

#1077, Chinese & African players. #1078, Chinese & African girl players. 43f, Games' emblem.

1971, Nov. 3   Litho.   Perf. 11½
Without Gum

1076	A271	8f lil rose & multi	7.00	1.75
1077	A271	8f lt yellow & multi	7.00	1.75
1078	A271	8f dk grn & multi	7.00	1.75
1079	A271	43f grn, gold & org	4.00	1.75
		Nos. 1076-1079 (4)	25.00	7.00

Afro-Asian Table Tennis Games, Peking.

1971, Nov. 3   Photo.   Perf. 11

#1081, Party's birthplace. #1082, Albanian flag. 52f, Albanian partisans, horiz.

Without Gum

1080	A272	8f Prus blue & multi	8.50	5.00
1081	A272	8f buff & multi	6.75	3.00
1082	A272	8f red, yel & multi	6.75	3.00
1083	A272	52f lt blue & multi	7.75	5.00
		Nos. 1080-1083 (4)	29.75	16.00

30th anniversary of the founding of Albanian Communist Party.

Yenan Pagoda and 1942 Meeting House A273

1972, May 23   Photo.   Perf. 11
Without Gum

1084	A273	8f shown (33)	6.00	2.00
1085	A273	8f Uniformed choir (34)	6.00	2.00
1086	A273	8f "Brother & Sister" (35)	7.00	2.00
1087	A273	8f Outdoor performance (36)	7.00	2.00
1088	A273	8f "The Red Signal Lantern" (37)	7.00	2.00
1089	A273	8f Dancer from "The Red Company of Women" (38)	7.00	2.00
		Nos. 1084-1089 (6)	40.00	12.00

30th anniversary of the publication of the Discussions on Literature and Art at the Yenan Forum.

Various Ball Games — A274

Workers' Gymnastics A275

1972, June 10

1090	A274	8f shown (39)	7.50	1.25
1091	A275	8f shown (40)	7.50	1.25
1092	A275	8f Tug of war (41)	7.50	1.25
1093	A275	8f Mountain climbers and tents (42)	7.50	1.25
1094	A275	8f Children diving & swimming (43)	7.50	1.25
		Nos. 1090-1094 (5)	37.50	6.25

10th anniversary of Mao Tse-tung's edict on physical culture.

Ocean Freighter Fenglei — A276

1972, July 10   Photo.   Perf. 11½
Without Gum

1095	A276	8f shown (29)	16.00	2.50
1096	A276	8f Tanker Taching No. 30 (30)	16.00	2.50
1097	A276	8f Cargo-passenger ship Changzeng (31)	16.00	2.50
1098	A276	8f Dredger Xienfeng (32)	16.00	2.50
		Nos. 1095-1098 (4)	64.00	10.00

Table Tennis Players' Welcome A277

1972, Sept. 2   Perf. 11½x11, 11x11½
Without Gum

1099	A277	8f Championship emblem, vert. (45)	3.00	1.00
1100	A277	8f shown (46)	3.00	1.00
1101	A277	8f Table tennis (47)	3.00	1.00
1102	A277	22f Women from different countries, vert. (48)	7.00	3.00
		Nos. 1099-1102 (4)	16.00	6.00

First Asian table tennis championships.

Wang Chin-hsi — A278

Workers on Cliffs along Canal — A279

Engraved and Photogravure
1972, Dec. 25   Perf. 11½x11

1103	A278	8f multicolored (44)	10.00	2.00

Wang Chin-hsi, the Iron Man, fighter for the working class.

1972, Dec. 30

#1105, Canal flowing through tunnel. #1106, Bridge. #1107, Canal along cliffs.

1104	A279	8f multicolored (49)	2.25	1.00
1105	A279	8f multicolored (50)	2.25	1.00
1106	A279	8f multicolored (51)	2.25	1.00
1107	A279	8f multicolored (52)	2.25	1.00
		Nos. 1104-1107 (4)	9.00	4.00

Construction of Red Flag Canal, Linhsien county, Honan.

Giant Panda — A280

Woman Coal Miner — A281

Designs: Pandas in various positions. The 8f stamps are horizontal.

Perf. 11½x11, 11x11½
1973, Jan. 15   Photo.
Designs in Black and Red

1108	A280	4f lt yel grn (61)	2.00	2.50
1109	A280	8f buff (59)	2.00	2.50
1110	A280	8f lt tan (60)	2.00	2.50
1111	A280	10f pale green (58)	80.00	20.00
1112	A280	20f pale bl gray (57)	55.00	20.00
1113	A280	43f pale lilac (62)	8.50	9.50
		Nos. 1108-1113 (6)	149.50	57.00

1973, Mar. 8   Photo.   Perf. 11½x11

1114	A281	8f shown (63)	2.25	1.50
1115	A281	8f Committee member (64)	2.25	1.50
1116	A281	8f Telephone line worker (65)	2.25	1.50
		Nos. 1114-1116 (3)	6.75	4.50

Intl. Working Women's Day. Designs are after paintings from an exhib. for 30th anniv. of the Yenan Forum on Literature and Art.

Dancing Girl — A282

1973, June 1   Photo.   Perf. 11

1117	A282	8f shown (86)	1.50	1.25
1118	A282	8f Musician, boy (87)	1.50	1.25
1119	A282	8f Girl with scarf (88)	1.50	1.25
1120	A282	8f Boy with tambourine (89)	1.50	1.25
1121	A282	8f Girl with drum (90)	1.50	1.25
a.		Strip of 5, #1117-1121	9.50	6.25
		Nos. 1117-1121 (5)	7.50	6.25

Values for No. 1121a are for an unfolded strip.

Tournament Emblem — A283

1973, Aug. 25   Photo.   Perf. 11½

#1123, Visitors from Asia, Africa and Latin America arriving by plane. #1124, Woman player. 22f, African, Asian & Latin American women.

1122	A283	8f multicolored (91)	2.25	.90
1123	A283	8f multicolored (92)	2.25	.90
1124	A283	8f multicolored (93)	2.25	.90
1125	A283	22f multicolored (94)	1.10	.90
		Nos. 1122-1125 (4)	7.85	3.60

Asian, African and Latin American Table Tennis Friendship Invitational Tournament.

The White-haired Girl — A284

Designs: Scenes from the ballet "The White-haired Girl." Nos. 1126, 1129 vert.

1973, Sept. 25   Photo.   Perf. 11½

1126	A284	8f multicolored (53)	3.00	1.10
1127	A284	8f multicolored (54)	3.00	1.10
1128	A284	8f multicolored (55)	3.00	1.10
1129	A284	8f multicolored (56)	3.00	1.10
		Nos. 1126-1129 (4)	12.00	4.40

Fair Building, Canton — A285

1973, Oct. 15   Photo.   Perf. 11

1130	A285	8f multicolored (95)	4.25	2.25

Export Commodities Fall Fair, Canton.

Teapot with Blue Phoenix Design — A286

Excavated Works of Art: No. 1132, Silver pot with horse design. No. 1133, Black pottery horse. No. 1134, Woman, clay figurine. No. 1135, Carved stone pillar base. No. 1136, Galloping bronze horse. No. 1137, Bronze inkwell (toad). No. 1138, Bronze lamp, Chang Hsin Palace. No. 1139, Bronze tripod. No. 1140, Square bronze pot. 20f, Bronze wine vessel. 52f, Painted red clay tripod.

1973, Nov. 20   Perf. 11½

1131	A286	4f ol bis & multi (66)	1.50	1.00
1132	A286	4f ver & multi (67)	1.50	1.00
1133	A286	8f yel grn & multi (68)	1.10	.50
1134	A286	8f brt rose & multi (69)	1.10	.50
1135	A286	8f lt vio & multi (70)	.80	.50
1136	A286	8f yel bis & multi (71)	.80	.50
1137	A286	8f lt bl & multi (72)	.80	.50
1138	A286	8f gray & multi (73)	.80	.50
1139	A286	10f yel bis & multi (74)	.35	.50
1140	A286	10f dp org & multi (75)	.35	.50
1141	A286	20f lil & multi (76)	1.50	1.25
1142	A286	52f grn & multi (77)	1.50	2.00
		Nos. 1131-1142 (12)	12.10	9.25

Marginal Markings

Marginal inscriptions on stamps of 1974-91 start at lower left with "J" for commemoratives and "T" for "special issues," followed by three numbers indicating (a) set sequence for the year, (b) total of stamps in set, and (c) number of stamp within set. At right appears the year date. Listings include the "c" number parenthetically. The "a" number is included only when it will help identify stamps not illustrated.

Example: T26 (6-3), the 3rd stamp of 6 from the 26th special set. Set numbers and or positions will be shown only when they help identify a stamp. An illustrated single stamp set will not have these numbers in the listings.

Woman Gymnast — A287

Designs: No. 1144, Gymnast on rings. No. 1145, Aerial split over balance beam, woman. No. 1146, Gymnast on parallel bars. No. 1147,

Uneven bars, woman. No. 1148, Gymnast on horse. T.1.

1974, Jan. 1   Photo.   Perf. 11½x11

1143	A287	8f lt grn & multi (1)	8.00	3.00
1144	A287	8f lt vio & multi (2)	8.00	3.00
1145	A287	8f lt blue & multi (3)	8.00	3.00
1146	A287	8f sal & multi (4)	8.00	3.00
1147	A287	8f yel & multi (5)	9.00	4.00
1148	A287	8f lil rose & multi (6)	9.00	4.00
		Nos. 1143-1148 (6)	50.00	20.00

Girls Twirling Bamboo Diabolos — A288

Designs: No. 1149, Lion Dance, vert. No. 1150, Handstand on chairs, vert. No. 1152, Men balancing jar. No. 1153, Plate spinning, vert. No. 1154, Twirling umbrella, vert. T.2.

1974, Jan. 21   Perf. 11

1149	A288	8f brn & multi (1)	5.75	2.75
1150	A288	8f Prus bl & multi (2)	5.75	2.75
1151	A288	8f lilac & multi (3)	5.75	2.75
1152	A288	8f dull bl & multi (4)	7.00	2.75
1153	A288	8f ol grn & multi (5)	7.00	2.75
1154	A288	8f gray & multi (6)	7.00	2.75
		Nos. 1149-1154 (6)	38.25	16.50

Traditional acrobatics.

Shao Shan — A289

Transportation by Railroad — A290

1½f, Site of 1st National Communist Party Congress. 2f, Peasant Movement Institute, Kwangchow. 3f, Headquarters of Nanchang Uprising. 4f, Great Hall of the People, Peking. 5f, View of Wen Chia Shih. 8f, Tien An Men. 10f, Tzeping in Chingkang Mountains. 20f, Site of Kutien Meeting. 22f, Tsunyi Conference site. 35f, Yenan (bridge). 43f, Hsi Pai Ho, Communist Party meeting site. 50f, Fairy Cave, Lushan. 52f, Monument to People's Heroes. $2, Trucks on mountain road.

1974   Litho.   Perf. 11
Without Gum

1163	A289	1f sl grn & pale grn	.50	.20
1164	A289	1½f car & buff	.50	.20
1165	A289	2f dk blue & pale grn	.50	.20
1166	A289	3f dk ol & yel	.50	.20
1167	A289	4f red & yel	.50	.20
1168	A289	5f brn & lt yel	.50	.20
1169	A289	8f dull mag & buff	.50	.20
a.		Perf. 11½x12	8.00	
1170	A289	10f blue & pink	.50	.20
1171	A289	20f dk red & buff	1.25	.20
1172	A289	22f vio & lt yel	1.90	.25
1173	A289	35f mar & lt yel	2.50	.75
1174	A289	43f red brn & buff	3.25	1.25
1175	A289	50f dk blue & pink	3.75	2.00
1176	A289	52f sepia & buff	5.00	2.50

Photogravure & Engraved

1177	A290	$1 multicolored	1.25	.20
1178	A290	$2 multicolored	2.50	.40
		Nos. 1163-1178 (16)	25.40	9.15

Capital Stadium — A290a

Design: 8f, Hotel Peking.

"Veteran Secretary" — A291   Well Diggers — A292

Designs: Nos. 1183-1186 horizontal. T.3.

1974, Apr. 20   Photo.   Perf. 11

1181	A291	8f shown (1)	1.60	1.10
1182	A292	8f shown (2)	1.60	1.10
1183	A291	8f Spring hoeing (3)	1.60	1.10
1184	A291	8f Farmers (4)	1.60	1.10
1185	A292	8f Farm (5)	2.40	1.10
1186	A291	8f Bumper crops (6)	2.40	1.10
		Nos. 1181-1186 (6)	11.20	6.60

Paintings by farmers of Huhsien County, shown at exhibition in Peking.

Mailman on Motorcycle — A293

1974, May 15   Photo.   Perf. 11

1187	A293	8f shown (1)	6.25	3.50
1188	A293	8f People of the world (2)	6.25	3.50
1189	A293	8f Great Wall (3)	6.25	3.50
		Nos. 1187-1189 (3)	18.75	10.50

Centenary of the UPU. J.1.

Barefoot Doctor Inoculating Children A294

Designs (Barefoot Doctors): No. 1191, Crossing stream at night to reach patient, vert. No. 1192, Gathering herbs, vert. No. 1193, Acupuncture treatment for farmer in the field.

Perf. 11x11½, 11½x11

1974, June 26   Photo.

1190	A294	8f multicolored (82)	1.40	1.00
1191	A294	8f multicolored (83)	1.40	1.00
1192	A294	8f multicolored (84)	1.40	1.00
1193	A294	8f multicolored (85)	1.40	1.00
		Nos. 1190-1193 (4)	5.60	4.00

Steel Worker Wang Chin-hsi — A295

#1195, Workers studying Mao's writings around campfire. #1196, Drilling for oil in winter. #1197, Scientific industrial management. #1198, Oil derricks and farms. T.4.

1974, Sept. 30   Photo.   Perf. 11

1194	A295	8f multicolored (5-1)	1.25	.90
1195	A295	8f multicolored (5-2)	1.25	.90
1196	A295	8f multicolored (5-3)	1.25	.90

1974, Dec. 1   Photo.   Perf. 11
Without Gum

1179	A290a	4f black & yel grn	.20	.20
1180	A290a	8f black & ultra	.30	.20

1197	A295	8f multicolored (5-4)	1.25	.90
1198	A295	8f multicolored (5-5)	1.25	.90
		Nos. 1194-1198 (5)	6.25	4.50

Workers of Taching as examples of achievement.

Members of Tachai Commune — A296

#1200, Farmers leveling mountains and fields in winter. #1201, Scientific farming. #1202, Trucks carrying surplus harvest. #1203, Young workers with banner. T.5.

1974, Sept. 30

1199	A296	8f multi (5-1)	1.75	.80
1200	A296	8f multi (5-2)	.90	.80
1201	A296	8f multi (5-3)	1.75	.80
1202	A296	8f multi (5-4)	.90	.80
1203	A296	8f multi (5-5)	.90	.80
		Nos. 1199-1203 (5)	6.20	4.00

Farmers of Tachai as examples of achievement.

Arms of Republic and Members of Ethnic Groups — A297

1974, Oct. 1

1204	A297	8f multi (1-1)	6.00	3.50

Taching Steel Worker — A298

Designs: No. 1206, Tachai farm woman. No. 1207, Soldier, planes and ships. J.3.

1974, Oct. 1

1205	A298	8f multi (3-1)	1.75	1.50
1206	A298	8f multi (3-2)	1.75	1.50
1207	A298	8f multi (3-3)	1.75	1.50
a.		Strip of 3, #1205-1207	6.00	5.25

People's Republic of China, 25th anniv. Values for No. 1207a are for an unfolded strip.

Export Commodities Fair Building, Canton — A299

1974, Oct. 15

1208	A299	8f multicolored	3.50	1.50

Chinese Export Commodities Fair, Canton.

Guerrillas' Monument, Permet, Albania — A300

Albanian Patriots and Coat of Arms — A301

1974, Nov. 29 Photo.   *Perf. 11½x11*

1209	A300	8f multicolored	3.75	1.50
1210	A301	8f multicolored	3.75	1.50

Albania's liberation, 30th anniversary.

Water-cooled Generator — A302

Industrial Products: No. 1212, Motorized rice sprouts transplanter. No. 1213, Universal cylindrical grinding machine. No. 1214, Open-air rock drill, vert. All dated 1973.

Photogravure and Engraved
1974, Dec. 23   *Perf. 11*

1211	A302	8f vio & multi (78)	37.50	6.00
1212	A302	8f yel grn & multi (79)	37.50	6.00
1213	A302	8f ver & multi (80)	37.50	6.00
1214	A302	8f blue & multi (81)	37.50	6.00
		Nos. 1211-1214 (4)	150.00	24.00

Congress Delegates — A303

Designs: No. 1216, Red flags, constitution and flowers. No. 1217, Worker, farmer and soldier, agriculture and industry.

1975, Jan. 25 Photo.   *Perf. 11½*

1215	A303	8f gold & multi (3-1)	5.00	1.75
1216	A303	8f gold & multi (3-2)	5.00	1.75
1217	A303	8f gold & multi (3-3)	5.00	1.75
		Nos. 1215-1217 (3)	15.00	5.25

Fourth National People's Congress, Peking.

Teacher Studying Revolutionary Works — A304

#1219, Teacher, children and horse. #1220, Outdoors class. #1221, Class held in boat. T.9.

1975, Mar. 8 Photo.   *Perf. 11*

1218	A304	8f multi (4-1)	9.00	3.00
1219	A304	8f multi (4-2)	9.00	3.00
1220	A304	8f multi (4-3)	9.00	3.00
1221	A304	8f multi (4-4)	9.00	3.00
		Nos. 1218-1221 (4)	36.00	12.00

Rural women teachers and for International Working Women's Day.

"Broadsword," Encounter Position — A305

#1223, Exercise with 2 swords (woman). #1224, Graceful boxing (woman). #1225, Man leaping with spear. #1226, Woman holding fighting staff. 43f, 2 women with spears against man with 3-section staff.

1975, June 10 Photo.   *Perf. 11x11½*
Size: 39x29mm

1222	A305	8f (6-1)	4.50	3.00
1223	A305	8f (6-2)	4.50	3.00
1224	A305	8f (6-3)	4.50	3.00
1225	A305	8f (6-4)	4.50	3.00
1226	A305	8f (6-5)	4.50	3.00

Size: 59x29mm

1227	A305	43f red & multi (6-6)	4.50	6.00
		Nos. 1222-1227 (6)	27.00	21.00

Wushu ("Kung Fu"), self-defense exercises. Tête bêche in sheets of 50 (5x10).

Mass Judgment and Criticisms — A306

No. 1229, Brigade leader writing wall news-paper. No. 1230, Study and criticism on battle-field, horiz. No. 1231, Former "slave" led into battle by criticism of Lin Piao and Confucius, horiz. T.8.

Perf. 11½x11, 11x11½
1975, Aug. 20   **Photo.**

1228	A306	8f red & multi (4-1)	6.50	2.50
1229	A306	8f red & multi (4-2)	6.50	2.50
1230	A306	8f red & multi (4-3)	6.50	2.50
1231	A306	8f red & multi (4-4)	6.50	2.50
		Nos. 1228-1231 (4)	26.00	10.00

Campaign to encourage criticism of Lin Piao and Confucius.

Athletes Studying Theory of Dictatorship of Proletariat — A307

3rd National Sports Meet: No. 1232, Women athletes leading parade, vert. No. 1234, Women volleyball players. No. 1235, Runner, soldier, farmer and worker, vert. No. 1236, Young athlete and various sports. No. 1237, Athletes of various races and horse race. 35f, Children and diving tower, vert. J.6.

1975, Sept. 12 Photo.   *Perf. 11½*

1232	A307	8f multi (7-1)	1.25	.85
1233	A307	8f multi (7-2)	1.25	.85
1234	A307	8f multi (7-3)	1.25	.85
1235	A307	8f multi (7-4)	1.25	.85
1236	A307	8f multi (7-5)	1.25	.85
1237	A307	8f multi (7-6)	1.25	.85
1238	A307	35f multi (7-7)	4.25	4.25
		Nos. 1232-1238 (7)	11.75	9.35

Mountaineers A308

Mt. Everest A309

Design: No. 1240, Mountaineers raising Chinese flag on summit, horiz. T.15.

Agricultural Workers with Book — A310

#1243, Workers carrying load. #1244, Woman driving harvester combine. J.7.

1975, Oct. 1   *Perf. 11½*

1242	A310	8f multi (3-1)	3.75	1.25
1243	A310	8f multi (3-2)	3.75	1.25
1244	A310	8f multi (3-3)	3.75	1.25
		Nos. 1242-1244 (3)	11.25	3.75

National Conference to promote learning from Tachai's achievements in agriculture.

Girl Giving Boy Red Scarf — A311

Designs (Children): No. 1246, Putting up wall posters criticizing Lin Piao and Confucius. No. 1247, Studying. No. 1248, Harvesting. 52f, Physical training. T.14.

1975, Dec. 1 Photo.   *Perf. 11½*

1245	A311	8f multi (5-1)	1.25	1.00
1246	A311	8f multi (5-2)	1.25	1.00
1247	A311	8f multi (5-3)	1.25	1.00
1248	A311	8f multi (5-4)	1.25	1.00
1249	A311	52f multi (5-5)	5.75	3.50
		Nos. 1245-1249 (5)	10.75	7.50

Moral, intellectual and physical progress of Chinese children.

Woman Plowing Rice Field A312

#1251, Mechanized rice planting. #1252, Drainage and irrigation. #1253, Woman spraying insecticide over cotton field. #1254, Combine. T.13.

1975, Dec. 15   *Perf. 11*

1250	A312	8f multi (5-1)	2.10	1.25
1251	A312	8f multi (5-2)	2.10	1.25
1252	A312	8f multi (5-3)	2.10	1.25
1253	A312	8f multi (5-4)	2.10	1.25
1254	A312	8f multi (5-5)	2.10	1.25
		Nos. 1250-1254 (5)	10.50	6.25

Priority program of farm mechanization.

Farmland and Irrigation Canal — A313

Designs of Nos. 1255-1270 numbered J.8.

1976, Feb. 20 Photo.   *Perf. 11½*

1255	A313	8f shown (16-1)	3.50	2.00
1256	A313	8f Irrigation canal (16-2)	3.50	2.00
1257	A313	8f Fertilizer plant (16-3)	3.50	2.00

1975 Photo.   *Perf. 11½x11, 11x11½*

1239	A308	8f multi (3-2)	.65	.35
1240	A308	8f multi (3-3)	.65	.35
1241	A309	43f multi (3-1)	.95	.75
		Nos. 1239-1241 (3)	2.25	1.45

Chinese Mt. Everest expedition.

1258	A313	8f Textile plant (16-4)	3.50	2.00
1259	A313	8f Anshan Iron and Steel Co. (16-5)	3.50	2.00

Nos. 1255-1270 commemorate fulfillment of 4th Five-year Plan.

1976, Apr. 9

1260	A313	8f Coal freight trains (16-6)	3.75	2.00
1261	A313	8f Hydroelectric station (16-7)	3.75	2.00
1262	A313	8f Ship building (16-8)	3.75	2.00
1263	A313	8f Oil industry (16-9)	3.75	2.00
1264	A313	8f Pipe line and port (16-10)	3.75	2.00

1976, June 12

1265	A313	8f Train on viaduct (16-11)	5.00	2.00
1266	A313	8f Scientific research (16-12)	5.00	2.00
1267	A313	8f Classroom (16-13)	5.00	2.00
1268	A313	8f Health Center (16-14)	5.00	2.00
1269	A313	8f Apartment houses (16-15)	5.00	2.00
1270	A313	8f Department store (16-16)	5.00	2.00
		Nos. 1255-1270 (16)	66.25	32.00

Heart Surgery with Acupuncture Anesthesia — A314

Operating Room and: #1272, Man driving tractor with severed arm restored. #1273, Man exercising broken arm in cast. #1274, Patient threading needle after cataract operation. T.12.

1976, Apr. 9 Photo.   *Perf. 11½*

1271	A314	8f brn & multi (4-1)	3.00	1.00
1272	A314	8f yel grn & multi (4-2)	3.00	1.00
1273	A314	8f bl grn & multi (4-3)	3.00	1.00
1274	A314	8f vio bl & multi (4-4)	3.00	1.00
		Nos. 1271-1274 (4)	12.00	4.00

Achievements in medical and health services.

Students in May 7 School — A315

Designs: No. 1276, Students as farm work-ers. No. 1277, Production brigade. J.9.

1976, May 7 Photo.   *Perf. 11½*

1275	A315	8f multi (3-1)	1.75	1.40
1276	A315	8f multi (3-2)	1.75	1.40
1277	A315	8f multi (3-3)	1.75	1.40
		Nos. 1275-1277 (3)	5.25	4.20

Chairman Mao's May 7 Directive, 10th anniv.

Mass Training in Swimming — A316

No. 1279, Swimmers crossing Yangtze River. No. 1280, Swimmers walking into the surf. J.10.

1976, July 16 Photo.   *Perf. 11½*
Size: 47x27mm

1278	A316	8f multi (3-1)	1.75	1.10

Size: 35x27mm

1279	A316	8f multi (3-2)	1.75	1.10
1280	A316	8f multi (3-3)	1.75	1.10
		Nos. 1278-1280 (3)	5.25	3.30

Chairman Mao's swim in Yangtze River, 10th anniversary.

Workers, Peasants and Soldiers Going to College — A317

#1282, Classroom. #1283, Instruction on construction site. #1284, Computer room. #1285, Graduates returning home. T.18.

1976, Sept. 6   Photo.   Perf. 11½

1281	A317	8f multi (5-1)	2.50	1.10
1282	A317	8f multi (5-2)	2.50	1.10
1283	A317	8f multi (5-3)	2.50	1.10
1284	A317	8f multi (5-4)	2.50	1.10
1285	A317	8f multi (5-5)	2.50	1.10
		Nos. 1281-1285 (5)	12.50	5.50

Success of proletarian education system.

Power Line Repair by Woman — A318

#1287, Insulator repair. #1288, Cherry picker. #1289, Transformer repair. T.16.

1976, Sept. 15

1286	A318	8f multi (4-1)	1.50	1.40
1287	A318	8f multi (4-2)	1.50	1.40
1288	A318	8f multi (4-3)	3.00	1.40
1289	A318	8f multi (4-4)	3.00	1.40
		Nos. 1286-1289 (4)	9.00	5.60

Maintenance of high power lines.

Lu Hsun A319

#1291, Lu Hsun sick, writing in bed. #1292, Lu Hsun with worker, soldier and peasant. J.11.

Photo. & Engr.

1976, Oct. 19   Perf. 11x11½

1290	A319	8f multi (3-1)	4.50	1.75

Photo.

1291	A319	8f multi (3-2)	4.50	1.75
1292	A319	8f multi (3-3)	4.50	1.75
		Nos. 1290-1292 (3)	13.50	5.25

Lu Hsun (1881-1936), writer and revolutionary leader.

Old Farmer Tying Towel on Student's Head — A320

Designs: No. 1294, Student teaching farm woman, horiz. No. 1295, Students climbing mountain for new water resources. No. 1296, Student testing wheat. 10f, Student feeding lamb. 20f, Frontier guards, horiz. T.17.

1976, Dec. 22   Photo.   Perf. 11½

1293	A320	4f multi (6-1)	.75	.45
1294	A320	8f multi (6-2)	.75	.45
1295	A320	8f multi (6-3)	.75	.45
1296	A320	8f multi (6-4)	.75	.45
1297	A320	10f multi (6-5)	2.25	1.00
1298	A320	20f multi (6-6)	4.50	2.00
		Nos. 1293-1298 (6)	9.75	4.80

Students' efforts to help poor country people.

Mao's Home, Shaoshan — A321

Shaoshan, Mao's birthplace: No. 1300, School building. No. 1301, Farmers' Association building. 10f, Railroad station. T.11.

1976, Dec. 26   Perf. 11

1299	A321	4f multi (4-1)	.80	.75
1300	A321	8f multi (4-2)	1.25	.75
1301	A321	8f multi (4-3)	1.25	.75
1302	A321	10f multi (4-4)	2.00	1.75
		Nos. 1299-1302 (4)	5.30	4.00

Chou En-lai — A322

#1304, Chou giving report at 10th Party Congress. #1305, Chou with Wang Chin-hsi, famous oil worker, horiz. #1306, Chou with people of Tachai, 1973, horiz. J.13.

1977, Jan. 8   Photo.   Perf. 11½

1303	A322	8f multi (4-1)	.70	.70
1304	A322	8f multi (4-2)	.70	.70
1305	A322	8f multi (4-3)	.70	.70
1306	A322	8f multi (4-4)	5.00	.70
		Nos. 1303-1306 (4)	7.10	2.80

Premier Chou En-lai (1898-1976), a founder of Chinese Communist Party, 1st death anniversary.

Liu Hu-lan, an Inspiration A323

Liu Hu-lan, Chinese heroine: No. 1307, Liu Hu-lan monument. No. 1308, Mao Tse-tung quotation: "A great life-a glorious death." J.12.

1977, Jan. 31

1307	A323	8f multi (3-1)	6.00	2.50
1308	A323	8f multi (3-2)	2.25	1.75
1309	A323	8f multi (3-3)	2.25	1.75
		Nos. 1307-1309 (3)	10.50	6.00

Uprising in Taiwan A324

Design: 10f, Gate of Heavenly Peace, Peking; Sun Moon Lake, Taiwan, Taiwanese people holding PRC flag. J.14.

1977, Feb. 28   Photo.   Perf. 11

1310	A324	8f multi (2-1)	.90	.70
1311	A324	10f multi (2-2)	2.25	1.40

Uprising of the people of Taiwan, 2/28/47.

Sharpshooters — A325

Militia Women: No. 1313, Women horseback riders. No. 1314, Underground defense tunnel. T.10.

1977, Mar. 8   Perf. 11½

1312	A325	8f multi (3-1)	4.25	2.75
1313	A325	8f multi (3-2)	4.25	2.75
1314	A325	8f multi (3-3)	4.25	2.75
		Nos. 1312-1314 (3)	12.75	8.25

Forestry — A326

Designs: 1f, Coal mining. 1½f, Sheepherding. 2f, Export (loading railroad car onto ship). 4f, Hydroelectric station. 5f, Fishery. 8f, Combine in field. 10f, Radio tower and mail truck. 20f, Steel production. 30f, Trucks on mountain road. 40f, Textiles. 50f, Tractor assembly line. 60f, Offshore oil rigs and birds, setting sun. 70f, Railroad bridge, Yangtze Gorge. No numbers.

1977   Photo.   Perf. 11½

1315	A326	1f yel grn, red & blk	.20	.20
1316	A326	1½f bl grn, yel grn & brn	.20	.20
1317	A326	2f org, bl & blk	.20	.20
1318	A326	3f ol & dk grn	.20	.20
1319	A326	4f lil, org & blk	.20	.20
1320	A326	5f lt ol & ultra	.20	.20
1321	A326	8f red & yel	.20	.20
1322	A326	10f lt grn, org & bl	.25	.20
1323	A326	20f org, yel & brn	.30	.20
1324	A326	30f bl, lt grn & blk	.30	.20
1325	A326	40f multicolored	.40	.20
1326	A326	50f cit, red & blk	.50	.20
1327	A326	60f pur, yel & org	.60	.25
1328	A326	70f blue & multi	.90	.30
		Nos. 1315-1328 (14)	4.65	2.95

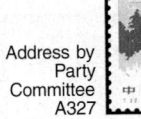

Address by Party Committee A327

Designs: No. 1330, Planting new rice fields. No. 1331, Farmers reading wall newspaper. No. 1332, Land reclamation. T.22.

1977, Apr. 9   Perf. 11x11½

1329	A327	8f multi (4-1)	.90	.75
1330	A327	8f multi (4-2)	.90	.75
1331	A327	8f multi (4-3)	.90	.75
1332	A327	8f multi (4-4)	.90	.75
		Nos. 1329-1332 (4)	3.60	3.00

Building Tachai-type communities throughout China.

Worker at Microphone — A328

Designs: No. 1334, Drilling for oil during snowstorm. No. 1335, Crowd advancing under Red banner. No. 1336, Workers, industrial complex, rocket blast-off. J.15.

1977, Apr. 25   Perf. 11

1333	A328	8f multi (4-1)	1.50	1.10
1334	A328	8f multi (4-2)	1.50	1.10
1335	A328	8f multi (4-3)	1.50	1.10
1336	A328	8f multi (4-4)	1.50	1.10
		Nos. 1333-1336 (4)	6.00	4.40

Conference on learning from Taching workers in industry.

Mongolians Hailing Anniversary A329

10f, Iron and steel complex, iron ore train. 20f, Cattle grazing in improved pasture. J.16.

1977, May 1   Perf. 11x11½

1337	A329	8f multi (3-1)	.40	.20
1338	A329	10f multi (3-2)	.40	.30
1339	A329	20f multi (3-3)	1.50	.95
		Nos. 1337-1339 (3)	2.30	1.45

30th anniversary of Inner Mongolian Autonomous Region.

1877 Flag of Romania and Oak Leaves — A330 / Mihai Viteazu Memorial (16th Century Hero) — A331

10f, Battle of Smirdan, by N. Grigorescu. J.17.

1977, May 9   Photo.   Perf. 11

1340	A330	8f multi (3-1)	.75	.60
1341	A331	10f multi (3-2)	.75	.60
1342	A331	20f multi (3-3)	2.10	1.75
		Nos. 1340-1342 (3)	3.60	2.95

Centenary of Romanian independence.

Yenan "Let 100 Flowers Bloom" A332

#1344, Hammer, sickle, gun & flowers; "Proletarian revolutionary literature will prosper." J.18.

1977, May, 23

1343	A332	8f grn, red & gold	.90	.55
1344	A332	8f lt brn, red & gold	.90	.55

Yenan Forum on Literature & Art, 35th anniv.

Zhu De — A333

Designs: No. 1346, Zhu De, last address to Congress. No. 1347, Zhu De at his desk, horiz. No. 1348, Zhu De on horseback as commander of Red Army. J.19.

1977, July 6   Photo.   Perf. 11½
1345	A333	8f multi (4-1)	.65 .35
1346	A333	8f multi (4-2)	.65 .35
1347	A333	8f multi (4-3)	.65 .35
1348	A333	8f multi (4-4)	.65 .35
		Nos. 1345-1348 (4)	2.60 1.40

Zhu De (1886-1976), Commander of Red Army, Chairman of National People's Congress.

Military under Mao's Banner — A334

#1350, Red Flag, Soldiers, Chingkang Mountains. #1351, Guerrilla fighters returning to base. #1352, Guerrillas crossing Yangtze. #1353, National defense. J.20.

1977, Aug. 1
1349	A334	8f multi (5-1)	1.75 1.10
1350	A334	8f multi (5-2)	1.75 1.10
1351	A334	8f multi (5-3)	1.75 1.10
1352	A334	8f multi (5-4)	1.75 1.10
1353	A334	8f multi (5-5)	1.75 1.10
		Nos. 1349-1353 (5)	8.75 5.50

Liberation Army Day, 50th anniversary of People's Army.

Gate of Heavenly Peace, People and Red Flags — A335

Designs: No. 1355, People marching under Red Flag with Mao's portrait. No. 1356, People marching under Red Flag with hammer and sickle. J.23.

1977, Aug. 22   Photo.   Perf. 11½x11
1354	A335	8f multi (3-1)	4.25 2.75
1355	A335	8f multi (3-2)	4.25 2.75
1356	A335	8f multi (3-3)	4.25 2.75
		Nos. 1354-1356 (3)	12.75 8.25

11th National Congress of the Communist Party of China.

Chairman Mao — A336

Designs (Mao Portraits): No. 1358, as young man in Shansi. No. 1359, addressing Communist Party in Plenary Session. No. 1360, Proclaiming People's Republic at Gate of Heavenly Peace. No. 1361, at airport with Chou En-lai and Zhu De, horiz. No. 1362, Reviewing Army as old man. J.21.

1977, Sept. 9   Photo.   Perf. 11½
1357	A336	8f multi (6-1)	1.10 .90
1358	A336	8f multi (6-2)	1.10 .90
1359	A336	8f multi (6-3)	1.10 .90
1360	A336	8f multi (6-4)	1.10 .90
1361	A336	8f multi (6-5)	1.10 .90
1362	A336	8f multi (6-6)	1.10 .90
		Nos. 1357-1362 (6)	6.60 5.40

Mao-Tse-tung (1893-1976), first death anniversary.

Mao Memorial Hall — A337

Completion of Mao Memorial Hall: No. 1364, Chairman Hua's inscription. J.22.

1977, Sept. 9
1363	A337	8f ultra & multi	2.25 1.50
1364	A337	8f lt grn, tan & gold	2.25 1.50

Tractors Moving Drilling Tower — A338

#1366, Shui Pow Tsi oil well and women workers. #1367, Construction of oil pipe line, Taching, and silos. #1368, Tung Fang Hung oil refinery, Peking. #1369, Taching oil loaded into tanker in harbor. 20f, Off-shore drilling platform "Pohai No. 1." T.19.

1978, Jan. 31   Photo.   Perf. 11
1365	A338	8f multi (6-1)	.35 .40
1366	A338	8f multi (6-2)	.35 .40
1367	A338	8f multi (6-3)	.35 .40
1368	A338	8f multi (6-4)	.35 .40
1369	A338	8f multi (6-5)	.35 .40
1370	A338	20f multi (6-6)	1.90 .90
		Nos. 1365-1370 (6)	3.65 2.90

Development of Chinese oil industry.

"Army Teaching Militia" — A339

#1372, "Army helping with rice planting." T.23.

1978, Feb. 5   Photo.   Perf. 11
1371	A339	8f multi (2-1)	1.40 1.10
1372	A339	8f multi (2-2)	1.40 1.10

Army and people working as a family.

Red Flags, Mao Tse-tung — A340

Constitution and Red Flags — A341

#1375, Atom symbol over symbols of agriculture & industry. All designs include Great Hall of the People, Peking, & flowers. J.24.

1978, Feb. 26
1373	A340	8f multi (3-1)	.90 .75
1374	A341	8f multi (3-2)	.90 .75
1375	A340	8f multi (3-3)	.90 .75
		Nos. 1373-1375 (3)	2.70 2.25

5th National People's Congress.

Mao's Eulogy for Lei Feng — A342

Lei Feng, Studying Mao's Works — A343

#1377, Chairman Hua's thoughts (5 lines). J.26.

1978, Mar. 5
1376	A342	8f gold & red (3-1)	1.40 1.10
1377	A342	8f gold & red (3-2)	1.40 1.10
1378	A343	8f multicolored (3-3)	1.40 1.10
		Nos. 1376-1378 (3)	4.20 3.30

Lei Feng (1940-1962), communist fighter; 15th anniversary of Chairman Mao's eulogy "Learn from Comrade Lei Feng."

Hsiang Ching-yu — A344

Yang Kai-hui — A345

1978, Mar. 8
1379	A344	8f multi (2-1)	.95 .75
1380	A345	8f multi (2-2)	.95 .75

Hsiang Ching-yu, pioneer of Women's Movement, executed 1928; Yang Kai-hui, communist fighter, executed 1930. J.27.

A346

A346a

A346b

#1381, Conference emblem. #1382, Banners symbolizing industry, agriculture, defense & science. #1383, Red flag, atom symbol & globe. J.25.

1978, Mar. 18   Litho.   Perf. 11½x11
1381	A346	8f gold & red (3-1)	.90 .70
1382	A346a	8f multi (3-2)	.90 .70
1383	A346b	8f multi (3-3)	.90 .70
a.		Souvenir sheet of 3	325.00 250.00
		Nos. 1381-1383 (3)	2.70 2.10

Natl. Science Conf. #1383a contains #1381-1383 with simulated perforations. Sold for 50f.

Release of Weather Balloon A347

Weather Observations: No. 1385, Radar station, typhoon watch. No. 1386, Computer, weather maps. No. 1387, Local weather observers. No. 1388, Rockets intercepting hail clouds. T.24.

1978, Apr. 25   Photo.   Perf. 11x11½
1384	A347	8f multi (5-1)	.60 .50
1385	A347	8f multi (5-2)	.60 .50
1386	A347	8f multi (5-3)	.60 .50
1387	A347	8f multi (5-4)	.60 .50
1388	A347	8f multi (5-5)	.60 .50
		Nos. 1384-1388 (5)	3.00 2.50

Galloping Horse — A348   Children Playing Soccer — A349

Designs: Galloping Horses, by Hsu Peihung (1895-1953). 40f, 50f, 60f, 70f, $5, horiz. T.28.

1978, May 5   Perf. 11½x11, 11x11½
1389	A348	4f multi (10-1)	.85 .75
1390	A348	8f multi (10-2)	.85 .75
1391	A348	8f multi (10-3)	.85 .75
1392	A348	10f multi (10-4)	.85 .75
1393	A348	20f multi (10-5)	3.50 .75
1394	A348	30f multi (10-6)	2.50 .75
1395	A348	40f multi (10-7)	2.50 1.50
1396	A348	50f multi (10-8)	3.50 1.50
1397	A348	60f multi (10-9)	2.50 3.00
1398	A348	70f multi (10-10)	3.50 4.25
		Nos. 1389-1398 (10)	21.40 14.75

Souvenir Sheet
1399	A348	$5 multicolored	275.00 150.00

No. 1399 contains one stamp showing 4 horses, size: 89x39mm.

1978, June 1   Perf. 11½

Designs: No. 1401, Children on the beach. No. 1402, Little girls dancing. No. 1403, Children taking long walks. 20f, Children exercising for good health. T.21.

Size: 22x27mm
1400	A349	8f multi (5-2)	.45 .40
1401	A349	8f multi (5-3)	.45 .40
1402	A349	8f multi (5-4)	.45 .40
1403	A349	8f multi (5-5)	.45 .40

Size: 48x28mm
1404	A349	20f multi (5-1)	.90 .70
		Nos. 1400-1404 (5)	2.70 2.30

Build up your health while young.

Synthetic Fiber Feeder A350

Designs: No. 1406, Drawing out threads. No. 1407, Weaving. No. 1408, Dyeing and printing. No. 1409, Finished products. T.25.

1978, June 15 Photo. Perf. 11½

1405	A350	8f multi (5-1)	.60	.50
1406	A350	8f multi (5-2)	.60	.50
1407	A350	8f multi (5-3)	.60	.50
1408	A350	8f multi (5-4)	.60	.50
1409	A350	8f multi (5-5)	.60	.50
a.		Strip of 5, #1405-1409	3.50	3.00
		Nos. 1405-1409 (5)	3.00	2.50

Chemical fiber industry. No. 1409a has continuous design.

Conference Emblem A351

"Develop Economy and Ensure Supplies" A352

1978, June 20 Perf. 13

1410	A351	8f multi (2-1)	.40	.30
1411	A352	8f multi (2-2)	.40	.30

Natl. Conf. on Learning from Taching and Tachai in Finance and Trade. J.28.

New Pastures, Mongolia — A353

Designs: No. 1413, Kazakh shepherds selecting sheep for breeding. No. 1414, Mechanized shearing of sheep, Tibet, T.27.

1978, June 30 Photo. Perf. 11½

1412	A353	8f multi (3-1)	1.10	.55
1413	A353	8f multi (3-2)	1.10	.55
1414	A353	8f multi (3-3)	1.10	.55
		Nos. 1412-1414 (3)	3.30	1.65

Learning from Tachai in developing animal husbandry and new pastoral areas.

Coke Oven — A354

Iron and Steel Industry: No. 1416, Iron furnace. No. 1417, Pouring steel. No. 1418, Steel rolling. No. 1419, Finished iron and steel products. T.26.

1978, July 22

1415	A354	8f multi (5-1)	.70	.45
1416	A354	8f multi (5-2)	.70	.45
1417	A354	8f multi (5-3)	.70	.45
1418	A354	8f multi (5-4)	.70	.45
1419	A354	8f multi (5-5)	.70	.45
		Nos. 1415-1419 (5)	3.50	2.25

Iron Fist to Prevent Revisionism A355

Jug in Shape of Sheep — A356

#1421, "Carrying forward revolutionary tradition." #1422, "Strenuous training in military skills to wipe out enemy." T.32.

1978, Aug. 1 Photo. Perf. 11½

1420	A355	8f multi (3-1)	.90	.45
1421	A355	8f multi (3-2)	.90	.45
1422	A355	8f multi (3-3)	.90	.45
		Nos. 1420-1422 (3)	2.70	1.35

"Learn from Hard-boned 6th Company." (A military unit since 1939).

1978, Aug. 26

Arts and Crafts: 4f, Giant lion (toy; horiz.). No. 1425, Rhinoceros (lacquer ware; horiz.). 10f, Cat (embroidery). 20f, Bag (weaving; horiz.). 30f, Teapot in shape of peacock (cloisonné). 40f, Plate with lotus, and swan-shaped box (lacquer ware; horiz.). 50f, Dragon flying in sky (ivory). 60f, Sun rising (jade; horiz.). 70f, Flight to human world (ivory). $3, Flying fairies (arts and crafts; horiz.). T.29.

1423	A356	4f multi (10-1)	.45	.25
1424	A356	8f multi (10-2)	.45	.25
1425	A356	8f multi (10-3)	.45	.25
1426	A356	10f multi (10-4)	.45	.40
1427	A356	20f multi (10-5)	.45	.40
1428	A356	30f multi (10-6)	.45	.40
1429	A356	40f multi (10-7)	.90	.75
1430	A356	50f multi (10-8)	1.75	1.00
1431	A356	60f multi (10-9)	1.75	1.00
1432	A356	70f multi (10-10)	1.75	1.25
		Nos. 1423-1432 (10)	8.85	5.95

Souvenir Sheet

1433	A356	$3 multi	250.00	160.00

No. 1433 contains one 85x36mm stamp.

Women, Atom Symbol, Rocket and Wheat A357

1978, Sept. 8 Photo. Perf. 11

1434	A357	8f multicolored	1.40	.90

4th National Women's Congress.

Ginseng — A358

Flag, Wheat, Cogwheel, Plane, Atom Symbols — A359

Medicinal Plants: No. 1436, Horn of plenty. No. 1437, Blackberry lily. No. 1438, Balloon-flower. 55f, Rhododendron dauricum. T.30.

1978, Sept. 15

1435	A358	8f multi (5-1)	.45	.25
1436	A358	8f multi (5-2)	.45	.25
1437	A358	8f multi (5-3)	.45	.25
1438	A358	8f multi (5-4)	.45	.25
1439	A358	55f multi (5-5)	1.75	.80
		Nos. 1435-1439 (5)	3.55	1.80

1978, Oct. 11 Photo. Perf. 11

1440	A359	8f multicolored	2.25	1.75

9th National Trade Union Congress.

Youth League Emblem A360

1978, Oct. 16

1441	A360	8f multicolored	1.75	1.10

10th Natl. Communist Youth League Cong.

Chinese and Japanese Girls Exchanging Gifts A361

Great Wall and Mt. Fuji A362

1978, Oct. 22

1442	A361	8f multicolored	.65	.40
1443	A362	55f multicolored	1.75	1.50

Signing of Sino-Japanese Peace and Friendship Treaty.

Moslem, Chinese and Mongolian People — A363

Chinsha River Bridge, West Szechuan A364

#1445, Loading coal at Holan Mountain. 10f, Irrigated rice fields & boxthorn. J.29.

1978, Oct. 25

1444	A363	8f multi (3-1)	.90	.75
1445	A363	8f multi (3-2)	.90	.75
1446	A363	10f multi (3-3)	.90	.75
		Nos. 1444-1446 (3)	2.70	2.25

20th anniversary of founding of Ningsia Moslem Autonomous Region.

1978, Nov. 1 Photo. Perf. 11½x11

Highway Bridges: No. 1448, Hsinhong bridge, Wuhsi. No. 1449, Chiuhsikou bridge, Fengdu. No. 1450, Chinsha River bridge, West

Szechuan. 60f, Shangyeh bridge, Sanmen. $2, Hsiang-kiang River bridge. T.31.

1447	A364	8f multi (5-1)	.45	.30
1448	A364	8f multi (5-2)	.45	.30
1449	A364	8f multi (5-3)	.45	.30
1450	A364	8f multi (5-4)	.45	.30
1451	A364	60f multi (5-5)	2.50	1.25
		Nos. 1447-1451 (5)	4.30	2.45

Souvenir Sheet

1452	A364	$2 multi	250.00	140.00

No. 1452 contains one 86x37mm stamp.

Mechanical Transplanting of Rice Seedlings A365

Paintings: No. 1454, Spraying fields. No. 1455, Seed selection. No. 1456, Trade. No. 1457, Delivery of public grain in city. T.34.

1978, Nov. 30 Perf. 11½

1453	A365	8f multi (5-1)	5.00	2.50
1454	A365	8f multi (5-2)	5.00	2.50
1455	A365	8f multi (5-3)	5.00	2.50
1456	A365	8f multi (5-4)	5.00	2.50
1457	A365	8f multi (5-5)	5.00	2.50
a.		Strip of 5, #1453-1457	29.00	15.00

Agricultural progress. No. 1457a has a continuous design.

Dancers and Fireworks — A366

Designs: No. 1459, Industry, vert. 10f, Agriculture, vert. J.33.

1978, Dec. 11 Photo. Perf. 11

1458	A366	8f multi (3-1)	2.00	.60
1459	A366	8f multi (3-2)	2.00	.60
1460	A366	10f multi (3-3)	1.00	1.00
		Nos. 1458-1460 (3)	5.00	2.20

20th anniversary of Kwangsi Chuang Autonomous Region.

Miners with Pneumatic Drill A367

Mine Development: 4f, Old Tibetan peasant reporting to surveyor. 10f, Open-cut mining with power shovel. 20f, Loaded electric train in pit. T.20.

1978, Dec. 29 Photo. & Engr.

1461	A367	4f multi (4-1)	.55	.30
1462	A367	8f multi (4-2)	.55	.30
1463	A367	10f multi (4-3)	1.25	1.00
1464	A367	20f multi (4-4)	1.25	1.10
		Nos. 1461-1464 (4)	3.60	2.70

A368

A369

Golden Pheasants: 4f, Roosting on rock. 8f, In flight. 45f, Seeking food. T.35.

1979, Jan. 25　Photo.　Perf. 11½
1465	A368	4f multi (3-1)	1.10	1.00
1466	A368	8f multi (3-2)	3.25	1.00
1467	A368	45f multi (3-3)	2.25	2.00
		Nos. 1465-1467 (3)	6.60	4.00

1979, Mar. 14　Photo.　Perf. 11½x11
1468	A369	8f Albert Einstein, equation	2.25	1.75

Phoenix Battling Monster, Praying Woman
A370

60f, Man riding dragon to heaven. Designs from silk paintings found in Changsha tomb, Warring States Period (475-221 B.C.). T.33.

1979, Mar. 29　　　Perf. 11
1469	A370	8f multi (2-1)	2.40	.75
1470	A370	60f multi (2-2)	1.60	1.50

Summer Palace — A371

Photo., Photo. & Engr. ($5)
1979-80　　　　　　　Perf. 13
1471	A371	$1 Pagoda ('80)	.60	.20
1472	A371	$2 Shown	1.25	.50
1473	A371	$5 Temple, Beihai Park	4.00	1.10
		Nos. 1471-1473 (3)	5.85	1.80

Issued: $2, June 16, 1979.

Hammer and Sickle "51" and Bars from "International" — A372

1979, May 1　Photo.　Perf. 11
1474	A372	8f multicolored	.90	.75

International Labor Day, 90th anniv.

"Tradition of May 4th Movement"
A373

Young Woman, Rocket, Antenna, Nuclear Reactor
A374

1979, May 4
1475	A373	8f multicolored	.65	.50
1476	A374	8f multicolored	.65	.50

60th anniversary of May 4th Movement.

IYC Emblem, Children Holding Balloons — A375

Children of Three Races, IYC Emblem — A376

1979, May 25　　　　　Perf. 11½
1477	A375	8f multicolored	1.00	.65
1478	A376	60f multicolored	7.00	5.25

International Year of the Child.

Great Wall in Spring
A377

Designs (The Great Wall): No. 1480, in summer. No. 1481, in autumn. 60f, in winter. $2, Guard tower. T.38.

1979, June 25　Photo.　Perf. 11
1479	A377	8f multi (4-1)	1.00	.80
1480	A377	8f multi (4-2)	1.00	.80
1481	A377	8f multi (4-3)	1.00	.80
1482	A377	60f multi (4-4)	5.75	4.75
		Nos. 1479-1482 (4)	8.75	7.15

Souvenir Sheet
1483	A377	$2 multi	125.00	75.00

For overprint see No. 1492.

Roaring Tiger — A379

Manchurian Tiger: 8f, Two young tigers. 60f, Tiger at rest. T.40.

1979, July 20　　　Perf. 11½x11
1484	A379	4f multi (3-1)	1.50	1.00
1485	A379	8f multi (3-2)	1.50	1.00
1486	A379	60f multi (3-3)	4.00	2.00
		Nos. 1484-1486 (3)	7.00	4.00

Mechanical Harvesting — A380

Work of the Communes: No. 1488, Forestry. No. 1489, Raising ducks. No. 1490, Women weaving baskets. 10f, Fishing. T.39.

1979, Aug. 10　　　　Perf. 11½
1487	A380	4f multi (5-1)	.50	.40
1488	A380	8f multi (5-2)	1.00	.90
1489	A380	8f multi (5-3)	1.00	.90
1490	A380	8f multi (5-4)	1.00	.90
1491	A380	10f multi (5-5)	2.00	1.25
		Nos. 1487-1491 (5)	5.50	4.35

No. 1483 Overprinted with Gold Inscription and "1979"
Souvenir Sheet

1979, Aug. 25　Photo.　Perf. 11
1492	A377	$2 multicolored	400.00

31st International Stamp Exhibition, Riccione, Italy. J41 (1-1).
Forged overprints exist.

Games Emblem, Sports — A381

#1494, Soccer, badminton, high jump, speed skating. #1495, Fencing, skiing, gymnastics, diving. #1496, Motorcycling, table tennis, basketball, archery. #1497, Emblem only. J.43.

1979, Sept. 15　　　Perf. 11½x11
1493	A381	8f multi (4-1)	.50	.40
1494	A381	8f multi (4-2)	.50	.40
1495	A381	8f multi (4-3)	.50	.40
1496	A381	8f multi (4-4)	.50	.40
a.		Block of 4, #1493-1496	2.75	2.50

Souvenir Sheet
Perf. 11½
1497	A381	$2 multi, vert.	40.00	25.00

4th National Games. Size of stamp in No. 1497: 22x26mm.

Flag and Rainbow — A382

Design: No. 1499, Flag and mountains.

1979, Oct. 1　Photo.　Perf. 11½
1498	A382	8f multicolored	1.60	1.25
1499	A382	8f multicolored	1.60	1.25

National Emblem — A383

Dancers — A384

1979, Oct. 1　Photo.　Perf. 11½
1500	A383	8f multicolored	2.00	1.00

Souvenir Sheet
1501	A383	$1 multicolored	40.00	25.00

1979, Oct. 1　Photo.　Perf. 11½
Designs: #1503-1505, various dances. J.47.
1502	A384	8f multi (4-1)	.60	.30
1503	A384	8f multi (4-2)	.60	.30
1504	A384	8f multi (4-3)	.60	.30
1505	A384	8f multi (4-4)	.60	.30
a.		Block of 4, #1502-1505	2.75	2.25

Tractor, Aerial Crop Spraying, Irrigation — A385

#1507, Gear, computers. #1508, Rocket, submarine, jets. #1509, Atom symbol. J.48.

1979, Oct. 1　Photo.　Perf. 11½
1506	A385	8f multi (4-1)	.65	.55
1507	A385	8f multi (4-2)	.65	.55
1508	A385	8f multi (4-3)	.65	.55
1509	A385	8f multi (4-4)	.65	.55
		Nos. 1506-1509 (4)	2.60	2.20

National Anthem
A386

1979, Oct. 1　Engr.　Perf. 11
1510	A386	8f multicolored	2.75	2.75

Exhibition Emblem — A387

Children Flying Model Planes — A388

1979, Oct. 3
1511	A387	8f multicolored	.90	.55

Junior National Scientific and Technological Exhibition.

1979, Oct. 3

#1513, Girls and microscope. #1514, Children and telescope. #1515, Boy catching butterflies. #1516, Girl taking meteorological readings. #1517, Boys sailing model boat. #1518, Girl with book. T.41.

1512	A388	8f multi (6-1)	.50	.40
1513	A388	8f multi (6-2)	.50	.40
1514	A388	8f multi (6-3)	.50	.40
1515	A388	8f multi (6-4)	.50	.40
1516	A388	8f multi (6-5)	.50	.40
1517	A388	60f multi (6-6)	2.75	1.75
		Nos. 1512-1517 (6)	5.25	3.75

Souvenir Sheet
Perf. 11
1518	A388	$2 multi	825.00	425.00

Study Science from Childhood. No. 1518 contains one stamp, size: 90x40mm.

Yu Shan Mountain
A389

Taiwan Landscapes: No. 1520, Sun and Moon Lake. No. 1521, Chihkan Tower. No. 1522, Suao-Hualien Highway. 55f, Tian Xiang Falls. 60f, Banping Mountain. T.42.

1979, Oct. 20   Photo.   *Perf. 11x11½*

1519	A389	8f multi (6-1)	.80	.65
1520	A389	8f multi (6-2)	.80	.65
1521	A389	8f multi (6-3)	.80	.65
1522	A389	8f multi (6-4)	.80	.65
1523	A389	55f multi (6-5)	2.40	1.40
1524	A389	60f multi (6-6)	3.25	2.75
		Nos. 1519-1524 (6)	8.85	6.75

Arts Symbols A390

8f, Seals and modernization symbols. J.39.

1979, Oct. 30

1525	A390	4f multicolored	.55	.45
1526	A390	8f multicolored	1.25	.70

4th Natl. Cong. of Literary and Art Workers.

Train in Tunnel A391

Railroads: No. 1528, Mountain bridge. No. 1529, Freight train. T.36.

1979, Oct. 30   Photo. & Engr.

1527	A391	8f multi (3-1)	.90	.75
1528	A391	8f multi (3-2)	.90	.75
1529	A391	8f multi (3-3)	.90	.75
		Nos. 1527-1529 (3)	2.70	2.25

Chrysanthemum Petal — A392

Camellias: No. 1531, Lion head. No. 1532, Camellia chryantha. 10f, Small osmanthus leaf. 20f, Baby face. 30f, Cornelian. 40f, Peony camellia. 50f, Purple gown. 60f, Dwarf rose. 70f, Willow leaf spinel pink. $2, Red jewelry. T.37.

1979, Nov. 10   Photo.   *Perf. 11x11½*

1530	A392	4f multi (10-1)	.80	.50
1531	A392	8f multi (10-2)	.80	.50
1532	A392	8f multi (10-3)	.80	.50
1533	A392	10f multi (10-4)	.80	.50
1534	A392	20f multi (10-5)	1.60	1.00
1535	A392	30f multi (10-6)	3.25	1.00
1536	A392	40f multi (10-7)	2.40	1.00
1537	A392	50f multi (10-8)	2.40	1.00
1538	A392	60f multi (10-9)	1.60	1.00
1539	A392	70f multi (10-10)	1.60	1.00
		Nos. 1530-1539 (10)	16.05	8.00

Souvenir Sheet
Perf. 11½x11

1540	A392	$2 multi	*125.00*	80.00

No. 1540 contains one 86x36mm stamp.

No. 1540 Overprinted and Numbered in Gold in Margin
Souvenir Sheet

1979, Nov. 10

1541	A392	$2 multicolored	*250.00*

People's Republic of China Phil. Exhib., Hong Kong, 1979. J.42 (1-1). Forged overprints exist.

Norman Bethune Treating Soldier — A393

Design: 70f, Bethune statue.

1979, Nov. 12

1542	A393	8f multi (2-2)	2.25	1.50
1543	A393	70f multi (2-1)	.45	.30

Dr. Norman Bethune, 40th death anniv. J.50.

Central Archives Hall A394

Intl. Archives Weeks: No. 1545, Gold archive cabinet, vert. 60f, Pavilion. J.51.

Perf. 11x11½, 11½x11

1979, Nov. 26   Photo.

1544	A394	8f multi (3-1)	.40	.35
1545	A394	8f multi (3-2)	.40	.35
1546	A394	60f multi (3-3)	5.25	2.00
		Nos. 1544-1546 (3)	6.05	2.70

Monkey King in Waterfall Cave — A395

Monkey King, Scenes from Pilgrimage to the West (Novel): No. 1548, Fighting Necha, son of Prince Li. No. 1549, In Mother Queen's peach orchard. No. 1550, In the alchemy furnace. 10f, Subduing the white bone demon. 20f, With palm leaf fan. 60f, In cobweb cave. 70f, Walking on scripture-seeking route. T.43.

1979, Dec. 1   *Perf. 11½x11*

1547	A395	8f multi (8-1)	1.60	1.40
1548	A395	8f multi (8-2)	1.60	1.40
1549	A395	8f multi (8-3)	1.60	1.40
1550	A395	8f multi (8-4)	1.60	1.40
1551	A395	10f multi (8-5)	4.75	1.40
1552	A395	20f multi (8-6)	4.75	1.40
1553	A395	60f multi (8-7)	7.75	4.00
1554	A395	70f multi (8-8)	7.75	4.00
		Nos. 1547-1554 (8)	31.40	16.40

Stalin Delivering Speech A396

Joseph Stalin (1879-1953): No. 1555, Portrait of Stalin, vert. J.49.

Perf. 11x11½, 11½x11

1979, Dec. 21   Engr.

1555	A396	8f brown (2-1)	1.10	.90
1556	A396	8f black (2-2)	1.10	.90

A397

A398

1980   Photo.   *Perf. 11½*

1557	A397	4f Peony (16-1)	.75	.65
1558	A397	4f Squirrels and grapes (16-2)	.75	.65
1559	A397	8f Crabs candle and wine (16-3)	.75	.65

1560	A397	8f Tadpoles in mountain spring (16-4)	.75	.65
1561	A397	8f Chicks (16-5)	.75	.65
1562	A397	8f Lotus (16-6)	.75	.65
1563	A397	8f Red plum (16-7)	.75	.65
1564	A397	8f Kingfisher (16-8)	.75	.65
1565	A397	10f Bottle gourd (16-9)	1.50	.65
1566	A397	20f Voice of autumn (16-10)	1.50	.65
1567	A397	30f Wisteria (16-11)	1.50	1.10
1568	A397	40f Chrysanthemums (16-12)	1.50	1.10
1569	A397	50f Shrimp (16-13)	3.00	1.50
1570	A397	55f Litchi (16-14)	3.75	1.90
1571	A397	60f Cabbages, mushrooms (16-15)	5.25	3.75
1572	A397	70f Peaches (16-16)	6.00	5.50
		Nos. 1557-1572 (16)	30.00	21.35

Souvenir Sheet

1573	A397	$2 Hyacynth	*135.00*	55.00

Qi Baishi paintings. Issued: #1557-1560, 1569-1572, 1/15; others, 5/20. #1573 contains one 37½x61mm stamp. T. 44.

1980, Jan. 25   *Perf. 11½x11*

Opera Masks: No. 1574, Meng Liang Mask from Hongyang Cave Opera. No. 1575, Li Kui, from Black Whirlwind. No. 1576, Huang Gai, from Meeting of Heroes. No. 1577, 10f, Lu Zhishen, from Wild Boar Forest. 20f, Lian Po, from Reconciliation between the General and Minister. 60f, Zhang Fei, from Reed Marsh. 70f, Dou Erdun, from Stealing the Emperor's Horse. T. 45.

1574	A398	4f multi (8-1)	.90	.75
1575	A398	4f multi (8-2)	3.50	.75
1576	A398	8f multi (8-3)	1.75	.75
1577	A398	8f multi (8-4)	1.75	.75
1578	A398	10f multi (8-5)	3.50	1.75
1579	A398	20f multi (8-6)	3.50	1.75
1580	A398	60f multi (8-7)	7.25	3.50
1581	A398	70f multi (8-8)	9.00	5.25
		Nos. 1574-1581 (8)	31.15	15.25

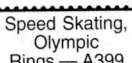

Speed Skating, Olympic Rings — A399

Monkey, New Year — A400

Olympic Rings and: No. 1582, Chinese flag. No. 1584, Figure skating. 60f, Downhill skiing. J.54.

1980, Feb. 13

1582	A399	8f multi (4-1)	.45	.30
1583	A399	8f multi (4-2)	.45	.30
1584	A399	8f multi (4-3)	.45	.30
1585	A399	60f multi (4-4)	4.75	1.75
		Nos. 1582-1585 (4)	6.10	2.65

13th Winter Olympic Games, Lake Placid, NY, Feb. 12-24.

Engraved and Photogravure
1980, Feb. 15   *Perf. 11½*

1586	A400	8f multicolored	*475.00*	95.00

Clara Zetkin — A401

Photogravure & Engraved
1980, Mar. 8   *Perf. 11½x11*

1587	A401	8f black & yellow	1.10	.90

International Working Women's Day, 70th anniv., founded by Clara Zetkin (1857-1933).

Orchard A402

Afforestation: 8f, Trees lining highway. 10f, Aerial seeding. 20f, Trees surrounding factory. T.48.

1980, Mar. 12   *Perf. 11x11½*

1588	A402	4f multi (4-1)	.45	.25
1589	A402	8f multi (4-2)	.45	.25
1590	A402	10f multi (4-3)	.90	.50
1591	A402	20f multi (4-4)	.90	.50
		Nos. 1588-1591 (4)	2.70	1.50

Apsaras, Symbols of Modernization — A403

1980, Mar. 15   Photo.   *Perf. 11½*

1592	A403	8f multicolored	1.75	1.25

2nd National Conference of the Scientific and Technical Association of China.

Mail Transport (T.49) — A404

1980, Mar. 20   *Perf. 11x11½*

1593	A404	2f Ship (4-1)	1.00	1.00
1594	A404	4f Bus (4-2)	1.00	1.00
1595	A404	8f Train (4-3)	2.00	1.00
1596	A404	10f Jet (4-4)	3.00	2.00
		Nos. 1593-1596 (4)	7.00	5.00

Forgeries exist.

Lungs, Heart, Cigarette, WHO Emblem — A405

Statue of Chien Chen (688-763) — A406

1980, Apr. 7   *Perf. 11½x11*

1597	A405	8f shown (2-1)	.80	.45
1598	A405	60f Faces (2-2)	5.00	2.75

Fight against cigarette smoking. J.56.

1980, Apr. 13   *Perf. 11x11½, 11½x11*

Loan to China by Japan of statue of Chien Chen (Jian Zhen), Buddhist missionary to Japan (754-763): No. 1600, Chien Chen Memorial Hall, Yangchou, horiz. 60f, Chien Chen's ship, horiz. His name in Japan is Ganjin. J.55.

1599	A406	8f multi (3-1)	2.40	.85
1600	A406	8f multi (3-2)	2.40	.85
1601	A406	60f multi (3-3)	15.00	6.75
		Nos. 1599-1601 (3)	19.80	8.45

Lenin's 110th Birthday — A407

Swallow Chick Kite — A408

Photogravure and Engraved
1980, Apr. 22   **Perf. 11½x11**
1602 A407 8f multicolored   1.40   .90

1980, May 10   **Photo.**   **Perf. 11½**
Designs: Kites. T.50.

1603	A408	8f shown (4-1)	2.50	1.10
1604	A408	8f Slender-swallow (4-2)	2.50	1.10
1605	A408	8f Semi-slender swallow (4-3)	2.50	1.10
1606	A408	70f Dual swallows (4-4)	10.00	4.50
		Nos. 1603-1606 (4)	17.50	7.80

Hare Running from Fallen Papaya A409

1980, June 1   **Photo.**   **Perf. 11x11½**
1607		Strip of 4 + label	7.25	6.00
a.	A409	8f shown (4-1)	1.40	1.25
b.	A409	8f Hare fox, monkey running away (4-2)	1.40	1.25
c.	A409	8f Lion instructing animals (4-3)	1.40	1.25
d.	A409	8f Discovery of fallen papaya (4-4)	1.40	1.25

Gu Dong fairy tale. T.51.

Terminal Building, Jets — A410

1980, June 20   **Perf. 11½**
1608	A410	8f Shown (2-1)	1.10	1.00
1609	A410	10f Runways, jets (2-2)	1.60	1.00

Peking Intl. Airport opening. T.47.

Sika Stag — A411

White Lotus — A412

1980, July 18   **Photo.**   **Perf. 11½**
1610	A411	4f Shown (3-1)	1.25	1.25
1611	A411	8f Doe and fawn (3-2)	1.25	1.25
1612	A411	60f Herd (3-3)	6.00	5.00
		Nos. 1610-1612 (3)	8.50	7.50

T.52.

1980, Aug. 4
1613	A412	8f Shown (4-1)	3.25	1.25
1614	A412	8f Rose-tipped snow (4-2)	2.25	1.25
1615	A412	8f Buddha's seat (4-3)	2.25	1.25
1616	A412	70f Variable charming face (4-4)	17.00	7.50
		Nos. 1613-1616 (4)	24.75	11.25

Souvenir Sheet
1617	A412	$1 Fresh lotus on rippling water	150.00

#1617 contains one 48x88mm stamp. T.54.

Pearl Cave, Sword-cut Stone Sculptures — A413

Guilin Landscapes: No. 1619, Three mountains, distant views. No. 1620, Nine-horse fresco hill. No. 1621, Egrets around aged banyan. No. 1622, Western hills at sunset, vert. No. 1623, Moonlight on Lijiang River, vert. 60f, Springhead, ancient ferry, vert. 70f, Scenic path, Yangshue, vert. T.53.

1980, Aug. 30   **Photo.**   **Perf. 11½**
1618	A413	8f multi (8-1)	1.25	.60
1619	A413	8f multi (8-2)	1.25	.60
1620	A413	8f multi (8-3)	1.25	.60
1621	A413	8f multi (8-4)	1.25	.60
1622	A413	8f multi (8-5)	1.25	.60
1623	A413	8f multi (8-6)	1.25	.60
1624	A413	60f multi (8-7)	9.00	3.50
1625	A413	70f multi (8-8)	10.00	4.75
		Nos. 1618-1625 (8)	26.50	11.85

Entrance Gate and Good Fairies A414

Great Wall, Symbols of Chicago, San Francisco and New York A415

1980, Sept. 13   **Photo.**   **Perf. 11x11½**
1626	A414	8f multicolored	.80	.70
1627	A415	70f multicolored	5.50	2.75

Exhibitions of the People's Republic of China in San Francisco, Chicago and New York, Sept.-Dec. Sheets of 12 were sold only at the US exhibitions at increasing prices. Retail value of set of two sheets of 12, approximately $500.

Romanian Flag, Warrior and Scroll — A416

1980, Sept. 20   **Photo.**   **Perf. 11½x11**
1628	A416	8f multicolored	1.75	1.25

2050th anniv. of Dacia, 1st independent Romanian state.

UNESCO Exhibition of Drawings and Paintings (J.60) — A417

1980, Oct. 8   **Perf. 11½**
1629	A417	8f Sea of Clouds, by Liu Haisu (3-1)	1.25	.55
1630	A417	8f Oriole and Magnolia, by Yu Feian, vert., (3-2)	1.25	.55
1631	A417	8f Camels, by Wu Zuoren (3-3)	1.25	.55
		Nos. 1629-1631 (3)	3.75	1.65

Scenes from Tarrying Garden (T.56) — A418

1980, Oct. 25   **Photo.**   **Perf. 11½**
1632	A418	8f Quxi Tower (4-1)	5.00	3.00
1633	A418	8f Yuancui Pavilion (4-2)	5.00	3.00
1634	A418	10f Hanbi Shanfang (4-3)	5.00	3.00
1635	A418	60f Guanyun Peak (4-4)	45.00	15.00
		Nos. 1632-1635 (4)	60.00	24.00

Xu Guangpi (1562-1633), Agronomist A419

Shooting, Olympic Rings — A420

Scientists of Ancient China: No. 1637, Li Bing, hydraulic engineer, 3rd century B.C. No. 1638, Jia Sixie, agronomist, 5th century. 60f, Huang Daopo, textile expert, 13th century. J.58.

Photogravure and Engraved
1980, Nov. 20   **Perf. 11½x11**
1636	A419	8f multi (4-1)	1.75	.85
1637	A419	8f multi (4-2)	1.75	.85
1638	A419	8f multi (4-3)	1.75	.85
1639	A419	60f multi (4-4)	11.00	5.00
		Nos. 1636-1639 (4)	16.25	7.55

1980, Nov. 26   **Photo.**
1640	A420	4f shown (5-1)	.45	.20
1641	A420	8f Gymnastics (5-2)	.90	.25
1642	A420	8f Diving (5-3)	.90	.25
1643	A420	10f Volleyball (5-4)	1.40	.60
1644	A420	60f Archery (5-5)	3.50	1.75
		Nos. 1640-1644 (5)	7.15	3.05

Return to International Olympic Committee, 1st anniversary. J.62.

Chinese River Dolphin A421

Photogravure & Engraved
1980, Dec. 25   **Perf. 11x11½**
1645	A421	8f shown (2-1)	1.25	.50
a.		Booklet pane of 6	16.00	
1646	A421	60f Dolphins (2-2)	5.00	1.50
a.		Booklet pane of 1	16.00	

Stamps from No. 1645a have straight edges on top or bottom.

Cock — A422

Photogravure & Engraved
1981, Jan. 5   **Perf. 11½**
1647	A422	8f multicolored	5.50	2.75
a.		Booklet pane of 12	35.00	

New Year 1981.
Stamps from booklet pane have straight edges on top or bottom.

Early Morning in Xishuang Bana (T.55) A423

Perf. 11x11½, 11½x11
1981, Jan. 20   **Photo.**
1648	A423	4f shown (6-1)	.90	.60
1649	A423	4f Dai mountain village (6-2)	.90	.60
1650	A423	8f Rainbow over Lanchang River (6-3)	1.60	.60
1651	A423	8f Ancient temple vert. (6-4)	1.60	.60
1652	A423	8f Moonlit night, vert. (6-5)	1.60	.60
1653	A423	60f Phoenix tree, vert. (6-6)	7.00	4.00
		Nos. 1648-1653 (6)	13.60	7.00

Flower Basket Palace Lantern — A424

Designs: Palace lanterns. T.60.

1981, Feb. 19   **Photo.**   **Perf. 11½**
1654	A424	4f multi (6-1)	1.60	.90
1655	A424	8f multi (6-2)	1.60	.90
1656	A424	8f multi (6-3)	1.60	.90
1657	A424	8f multi (6-4)	1.60	.90
1658	A424	20f multi (6-5)	4.00	3.50
1659	A424	60f multi (6-6)	9.50	7.00
		Nos. 1654-1659 (6)	19.90	14.10

Crossing River, Scene from Marking the Gunwale A425

Scenes from Marking the Gunwale fable. T.59.

1981, Mar. 10 Photo.   Perf. 11x11½
1660	A425	8f Text (5-1)	1.25	1.00
1661	A425	8f shown (5-2)	1.25	1.00
1662	A425	8f Dropping sword in water (5-3)	1.25	1.00
1663	A425	8f Marking gunwale (5-4)	1.25	1.00
1664	A425	8f Searching for sword (5-5)	1.25	1.00
a.		Bklt. pane, 2 each #1660-1664	21.00	
b.		Strip of 5, #1660-1664	8.00	6.50

Chinese Juniper A426

Designs: Miniature landscapes. T.61.

1981, Mar. 31   Perf. 11½
1665	A426	4f Chinese elm, vert. (6-1)	.75	.65
1666	A426	8f Juniper, vert. (6-2)	.75	.65
1667	A426	8f Maidenhair tree, vert. (6-3)	.75	.65
1668	A426	10f shown (6-4)	.75	.65
1669	A426	20f Persimmon (6-5)	1.50	1.25
1670	A426	60f Juniper (6-6)	4.50	3.00
		Nos. 1665-1670 (6)	9.00	6.85

Vase with Tiger-shaped Handles — A427

Cizhou Kiln Ceramic Pottery: 4f, Vase with 2 tigers, Song Dynasty. #1672, Black glazed jar, Jin Dynasty. #1673, Amphora. #1674, Jar with 2 phoenixes (Yuan Dynasty). 10f, Flat flask, Yuan Dynasty. T.62.

1981, Apr. 15 Photo.   Perf. 11½x11
1671	A427	4f multi, vert. (6-1)	.35	.30
1672	A427	8f multi (6-2)	.75	.70
1673	A427	8f multi, vert. (6-3)	.75	.70
1674	A427	8f multi (6-4)	.75	.70
1675	A427	10f multi (6-5)	1.50	.70
1676	A427	60f multi (6-6)	3.25	2.75
		Nos. 1671-1676 (6)	7.35	5.85

Panda and Colored Stamps — A428

1981, Apr. 29 Photo.   Perf. 11½x11
1677	A428	8f shown (2-1)	.25	.25
1678	A428	60f Boat, bird (2-2)	2.50	1.40
a.		Booklet pane (8 #1677, souv. sheet with 1677-1678)	9.00	

Qinchuan Steer A429

Cattle Breeds: #1680, Binhu buffalo. #1681, Yak. #1682, Black and white dairy cows. 10f, Pasture red cow. 55f, Simmental cross-breed. T.63.

1981, May 5   Perf. 11x11½
1679	A429	4f multi (6-1)	.35	.30
1680	A429	8f multi (6-2)	.35	.55
1681	A429	8f multi (6-3)	.35	.55
1682	A429	8f multi (6-4)	.35	.55
1683	A429	10f multi (6-5)	.75	.55
1684	A429	55f multi (6-6)	4.50	2.10
		Nos. 1679-1684 (6)	6.65	4.60

Mail Delivery Slogan — A430

13th World Telecommunications Day — A431

1981, May 9   Perf. 11
| 1685 | A430 | 8f multicolored | .70 | .20 |

1981, May 17   Perf. 11½x11
| 1686 | A431 | 8f multicolored | .70 | .20 |

Construction Worker — A432

Telephone Building, Peking — A433

1981, May 20   Perf. 11½
1687	A432	8f shown (4-1)	.55	.45
1688	A432	8f Miner (4-2)	.55	.45
1689	A432	8f Children crossing street (4-3)	.55	.45
1690	A432	8f Farm worker (4-4)	.55	.45
		Nos. 1687-1690 (4)	2.20	1.80

National Safety Month. J.65.

1981, June 5 Engr.   Perf. 11½x11
| 1691 | A433 | 8f violet brown | .90 | .55 |

Swaythling Cup, Men's Team Table Tennis — A434

36th World Table Tennis Championships Victory — #1692: a, St. Bride Vase, men's singles (7-3). b, Iran Cup, men's doubles (7-4). c, G. Geist Prize, women's singles (7-5). d, W.J. Pope Trophy, women's doubles (7-6). e, Heydusek Prize, mixed doubles (7-7). #1694, Marcel Corbillon Cup, women's team. #1693-1694 printed in sheets of 16 (8 each) + 2 labels. J.71.

1981, June 30 Photo.   Perf. 11½x11
1692		Strip of 5	1.60	1.50
a.-e.		A434 8f multi	.20	.20
1693	A434	20f multi (7-1)	.80	.75
1694	A434	20f multi (7-2)	.80	.75

Chinese Communist Party, 60th Anniv. A435

1981, July 1 Photo.   Perf. 11x11½
| 1695 | A435 | 8f multicolored | .55 | .30 |

Hanpo Pass, Lushan Mountains (T.67) A436

Photogravure & Engraved
1981, July 20   Perf. 12½x12
1696		8f Five-veteran Peak, vert. (7-1)	.85	.60
1697		8f shown (7-2)	.85	.60
1698		8f Yellow Dragon Pool, vert. (7-3)	.85	.60
1699		8f Sunlit Peak (7-4)	.85	.60
1700		8f Three-layer Spring, vert. (7-5)	.85	.60
1701		8f Stone and pines (7-6)	.85	.60
1702		60f Dragon-head Cliff, vert. (7-7)	7.25	4.00
		Nos. 1696-1702 (7)	12.35	7.60

Tremella Fuciformis A437

Designs: Edible mushrooms. T.66.

1981, Aug. 6 Photo.   Perf. 11½
1703	A437	4f shown (6-1)	.30	.25
1704	A437	8f Dictyophora indusiata (6-2)	.60	.40
1705	A437	8f Hericium erinaceus (6-3)	.60	.40
1706	A437	8f Russula rubra (6-4)	.60	.40
1707	A437	10f Lentinus edodes (6-5)	.90	.40
1708	A437	70f Agaricus bisporus (6-6)	2.50	1.60
		Nos. 1703-1708 (6)	5.50	3.45

Quality Month (J.66) — A438

Lunan Stone Forest, Yunn — A439

1981, Sept. 1 Photo.   Perf. 11½x11
| 1709 | A438 | 8f Silver medal (2-1) | .45 | .40 |
| 1710 | A438 | 8f Gold medal (2-2) | .45 | .40 |

1981, Sept. 18   Perf. 11½
Designs: Views of limestone formations, Lunan Stone Forest. #1711-1713 horiz. T.64.
1711	A439	8f multi (5-1)	.75	.50
1712	A439	8f multi (5-2)	.75	.50
1713	A439	8f multi (5-3)	.75	.50
1714	A439	10f multi (5-4)	.75	.50
1715	A439	70f multi (5-5)	3.75	4.00
		Nos. 1711-1715 (5)	6.75	6.00

Lu Xun, Writer, Birth Centenary (J.67) A440

1981, Sept. 25
| 1716 | A440 | 8f shown (2-1) | .70 | .40 |
| 1717 | A440 | 20f Portrait (diff.) (2-2) | 1.10 | 1.00 |

Sun Yat-sen and Text A441

70th Anniv. of 1911 Revolution: No. 1719, 72 Martyrs Grave, Huang Hua Gang. No. 1720, Hubei Provincial Government Headquarters, 1911. J.68.

1981, Oct. 10 Photo.   Perf. 11x11½
1718	A441	8f multi (3-1)	.55	.35
1719	A441	8f multi (3-2)	.55	.35
1720	A441	8f multi (3-3)	.55	.35
		Nos. 1718-1720 (3)	1.65	1.05

Asian Conference of Parliamentarians on Population and Development, Peking, Oct. 27 (J.73) — A442

1981, Oct. 27 Perf. 11½x11, 11x11½
| 1721 | A442 | 8f Tree, vert. (2-1) | .20 | .20 |
| 1722 | A442 | 70f shown (2-2) | .70 | .60 |

Huang Guo Shu
Falls — A443

Cowrie Shell and
Shell-shaped
Coin — A444

Nos. 1731-1739 are horizontal.

**Perf. 11¼, 13x13¼ (#1726, 1729),
13¼x13 (#1731)**

1981-83				**Engr.**
1723	A443	1f	Xishuang Banna	.20 .20
1724	A443	1½f	Mt. Hua	.20 .20
1725	A443	2f	Mt. Tai	.20 .20
1726	A443	3f	shown	.20 .20
1727	A443	4f	Hainan Isld.	.20 .20
b.		Perf. 11½x11		10.00 10.00
1728	A443	5f	Tiger Hill, Suzhou	.20 .20
1729	A443	8f	Great Wall	.20 .20
1730	A443	10f	Immense Forest	.20 .20
1731	A443	20f	Mt. Tian	.25 .20
1732	A443	30f	Grassland, Inner Mongolia	.25 .20
1733	A443	40f	Stone Forest	.35 .20
1734	A443	50f	Banping Mountain	.45 .25
1735	A443	70f	Mt. Qomolangma	.55 .40
1736	A443	80f	Seven-Star Crag	.55 .50
1737	A443	$1	Three Gorges, Changjiang River	.75 .55
1738	A443	$2	Guilin landscape	.90 1.10
1739	A443	$5	Mt. Huangshan	2.40 2.00
		Nos. 1723-1739 (17)		8.05 7.00

Issued: #1737-1739, 10/9/82; #1726, 1734-1736 4/1/83.

Photo.
Perf. 11½

1726a	A443	3f		.20 .20
1727a	A443	4f		.20 .20
1729a	A443	8f		.30 .25
1730a	A443	10f		.40 .35
1731a	A443	20f		.80 .70
		Nos. 1726a-1731a (5)		1.90 1.70

Nos. 1727a, 1729a, 1730a exist tagged.
Values 10-15% higher.

Photogravure and Engraved
1981, Oct. 29   Perf. 11½x11

Ancient Coins. T.65.

1740	A444	4f	shown (8-1)	.30 .25
1741	A444	4f	Shovel (8-2)	.30 .25
1742	A444	8f	Shovel, diff. (8-3)	.60 .25
1743	A444	8f	Shovel, diff. (8-4)	.60 .25
1744	A444	8f	Knife (8-5)	.60 .25
1745	A444	8f	Knife (8-6)	.60 .25
1746	A444	60f	Knife, diff. (8-7)	1.90 1.10
1747	A444	70f	Gong (8-8)	3.00 1.90
		Nos. 1740-1747 (8)		7.90 4.50

See Nos. 1765-1772.

A445

A446

1981, Nov. 10   Photo.   Perf. 11½x11
1748 A445   8f multicolored   .35 .20

Intl. Year of the Disabled.

1981-82   Photo.   Perf. 11

Twelve Beauties, from The Dream of Red
Mansions, by Cao Xueqin.

1749	A446	4f	Daiyu (12-1)	1.00 .70
1750	A446	4f	Baochai (12-2)	1.00 .70
1751	A446	8f	Yuanchun (12-3)	1.00 .75
1752	A446	8f	Yingchun (12-4)	1.00 .75

1753	A446	8f	Tanchun (12-5)	1.00 .75
1754	A446	8f	Xichun (12-6)	1.00 .75
1755	A446	8f	Xiangyuh (12-7)	1.00 .75
1756	A446	10f	Liwan (12-8)	1.75 .75
1757	A446	20f	Xifeng (12-9)	2.00 .80
1758	A446	30f	Sister Qiao (12-10)	3.00 .90
1759	A446	40f	Keqing (12-11)	4.00 2.75
1760	A446	80f	Miaoyu (12-12)	7.25 4.00
		Nos. 1749-1760 (12)		25.00 14.35

Souvenir Sheet
1761 A446 $2 Baoyu, Daiyu   110.00 50.00

No. 1761 contains one 59x39mm stamp.
Issued: #1749, 1751, 1753, 1755, 1757, 1759,
1761, 11/20/81; others, 4/24/82. T.69.

A447   A448

1981, Dec. 21   Photo.
1762 A447   8f Girl playing (2-1)   .20 .20
1763 A447   20f Girl holding trophy
(2-2)   .60 .45

Women's team victory in 3rd World Cup Volleyball Championship (J.76).

Photogravure & Engraved
1982, Jan. 5   Perf. 11½
1764 A448   8f multicolored   3.50 2.10
a.   Booklet pane of 10 + label   13.50

New Year 1982 (Year of the Dog).
Stamps from No. 1764a have straight edges
at top or bottom.

Coin Type of 1981
1982, Feb. 12

1765	A444	4f	Guilian mask (8-1)	.60 .45
1766	A444	4f	Shu shovel (8-2)	.60 .45
1767	A444	8f	Xia zhuan shovel (8-3)	.60 .45
1768	A444	8f	Han Dan shovel (8-4)	.60 .45
1769	A444	8f	Knife (8-5)	.60 .45
1770	A444	8f	Ming knife (8-6)	.60 .60
1771	A444	70f	Jin hua knife (8-7)	1.10 .90
1772	A444	80f	Yi Liu Hua coin (8-8)	2.25 2.00
		Nos. 1765-1772 (8)		6.95 5.75

T.71.

Nie Er (1912-1935), Natl. Anthem
Composer — A449

1982, Feb. 15   Perf. 11x11½
1773 A449   8f multicolored   .30 .20

Intl. Drinking
Water and
Sanitation
Decade, 1981-
1990
A450

1982, Mar. 1   Perf. 11½x11
1774 A450   8f multicolored   .30 .20

TB Bacillus
Centenary
A451

1982, Mar. 24   Perf. 11x11½
1775 A451   8f multicolored   .30 .20

Fire Control
(T.76) — A452

1982, May 8   Photo.   Perf. 11½x11
1776 A452   8f Water hoses (2-1)   .45 .20
1777 A452   8f Chemical extinguisher
(2-2)   .45 .20

Syzygy of the Nine Planets, Mar. 10
and May 16 — A453

1982, May 16   Perf. 11½
1778 A453   8f multicolored   .60 .25

Medicinal
Herbs — A454

Soong Ching
Ling (1893-
1981), Sun Yatsen's
Widow — A455

1982, May 20   Perf. 11½x11

1779	A454	4f	Hemerocallis flava (6-1)	.40 .35
1780	A454	8f	Fritillaria unibracteata (6-2)	.40 .35
1781	A454	8f	Aconitum carmichaeli (6-3)	.40 .35
1782	A454	10f	Lilium brownii (6-4)	.40 .35
1783	A454	20f	Arisaema (6-5)	.75 .50
1784	A454	70f	Paeonia lactiflora (6-6)	2.25 1.00
		Nos. 1779-1784 (6)		4.60 2.90

Souvenir Sheet
1785 A454 $2 Iris tectorum
maxim   11.00 8.50

No. 1785 contains one 89x39mm stamp.
Nos. 1779-1784 numbered T.72.

1982, May 29   Perf. 11½
1786 A455   8f Addressing Consultative Conf.
(2-1)   .40 .35
1787 A455   20f Portrait (2-2)   1.25 1.10

J.82.

Sable
(T.68)
A456

1982, June 20   Photo.   Perf. 11½
1788 A456   8f shown (2-1)   .65 .45
1789 A456   80f Sable, diff. (2-2)   3.75 3.00
a.   Bkt. pane of 8, 6 8f plus
sheetlet of 2 (8f, 80f)   10.50

A457

1982, June 30   Perf. 11½x11
1790 A457   8f multicolored   .20 .20

Natl. census, July 1.

A458

1982, July 25   Photo.   Perf. 11½x11
1791 A458   8f multicolored   .20 .20

2nd UN Conference on Peaceful Uses of
Outer Space, Vienna, Aug. 9-21.

Strolling in Autumn Woods, by Shen
Zhou, Ming Dynasty — A459

Fan Paintings (Ming or Qing Dynasty): No.
1793, Jackdaw on Withered Tree, by Tang Yin.
No. 1794 Bamboo and Sparrows, by Zhou
Zhimian. 10f, Writing Poem under Pine, by
Chen Hongshou and Bai Han. 20f, Chrysanthemums, by Yun Shouping, Qing. 70f, Birds,
Crape Myrtle and Chinese Parasol, by Wang
Wu, Qing. T.77.

1982, July 31   Perf. 11½

1792	A459	4f	multi (6-1)	.40 .30
1793	A459	8f	multi (6-2)	.80 .60
1794	A459	8f	multi (6-3)	.80 .60
1795	A459	10f	multi (6-4)	.80 .60
1796	A459	20f	multi (6-5)	1.10 .60
1797	A459	70f	multi (6-6)	2.25 1.75
		Nos. 1792-1797 (6)		6.15 4.45

A460

A461

1982, Aug. 25   *Perf. 11½x11*
1798   A460   8f multicolored   .20   .20

60th anniv. of Chinese Geological Society.

1982, Aug. 25   **Photo.**   *Perf. 11½x11*
1799   A461   4f Orpiment (4-1)   .20   .20
1800   A461   8f Stibnite (4-2)   .20   .20
1801   A461   10f Cinnabar (4-3)   .40   .20
1802   A461   20f Wolframite (4-4)   .65   .45
    Nos. 1799-1802 (4)   1.45   1.05
       T.73.

Souvenir Sheet

Messenger, Tomb Mural, Jiayu Pass,
Wei-Jin Period — A462

1982, Aug. 25
1803   A462 $1 multicolored   10.00   7.50

All-China Philatelic Federation, 1st Cong.

12th Natl.
Communist Party
Congress
A463

Hoopoe — A464

1982, Sept. 1   *Perf. 11½*
1804   A463   8f multicolored   .20   .20

1982, Sept. 10   *Perf. 11½x11*
1805   A464   8f shown (5-1)   .65   .30
1806   A464   8f Swallows (5-2)   .65   .30
1807   A464   8f Oriole (5-3)   .65   .30
1808   A464   20f Chickadees (5-4)   1.00   .50
1809   A464   70f Woodpecker (5-5)   2.75   2.50
    Nos. 1805-1809 (5)   5.70   3.90
Souvenir Sheet
1810   A464 $2 Cuckoos   22.50

#1810 contains one 56x36mm stamp. T.79.

Japan-China
Relations
Normalization, 10th
Anniv. — A465

World Food
Day — A466

Flower Paintings: 8f, Plum blossoms, by
Guan Shanyue. 70f, Hibiscus, by Xiao
Shufang. J.84.

1982, Sept. 29   *Perf. 11*
1811   A465   8f multi (2-1)   .35   .20
1812   A465   70f multi (2-2)   .65   .55

1982, Oct. 16   *Perf. 11½*
1813   A466   8f multicolored   .20   .20

Guo Morou (1892-
1978), Acad. of
Sciences Pres.
A467

Bodhisattva, 11th
Cent. Sculpture
A468

Designs: Portraits. J.87.

1982, Nov. 16   **Photo.**   *Perf. 11½x11*
1814   A467   8f multi (2-1)   .20   .20
1815   A467   20f multi (2-2)   .30   .25

1982, Nov. 19   *Perf. 11*
Liao Dynasty Buddha Sculptures, Lower
Huayan Monastery. T.74.

1816   A468   8f multi (4-1)   .40   .30
1817   A468   8f multi (4-2)   .40   .30
1818   A468   8f multi (4-3)   .40   .30
1819   A468   70f multi (4-4)   3.25   2.25
    Nos. 1816-1819 (4)   4.45   3.15
Souvenir Sheet
Perf. 11½x11½
1820   A468 $2 multicolored   20.00   9.00

No. 1820 contains one 36x55mm stamp.

Dr. D.S.
Kotnis,
Indian
Physician in
8th Army
(J.83)
A469

Perf. 11½x11, 11x11½
1982, Dec. 9   **Photo.**
1821   A469   8f Portrait, vert. (2-1)   .45   .20
1822   A469   70f Riding horse (2-2)   1.75   1.25

11th
Communist
Youth
League
Natl.
Congress
A470

1982, Dec. 20   *Perf. 11x11½*
1823   A470   8f multicolored   .20   .20

Bronze Wine
Container — A471

Western Zhou Dynasty Bronze (1200-771
B.C.): No. 1825, Three-legged cooking pot.
No. 1826, Food bowl. No. 1827, Three-legged
cooking pot (diff.). No. 1828, Animal-shaped
wine container. 10f, Wine container with lid.
20f, Round food bowl. 70f, Square wine
container. T.75.

Photogravure & Engraved
1982, Dec. 25   *Perf. 11*
1824   A471   4f multi (8-1)   .85   .55
1825   A471   4f multi (8-2)   .85   .55
1826   A471   8f multi (8-3)   .85   .55
1827   A471   8f multi (8-4)   .85   .55
1828   A471   8f multi (8-5)   .85   .55
1829   A471   10f multi (8-6)   1.75   .55
1830   A471   20f multi (8-7)   1.75   1.10
1831   A471   70f multi (8-8)   6.00   2.10
    Nos. 1824-1831 (8)   13.75   6.50

A472

1983, Jan. 5   *Perf. 11½*
1832   A472   8f multicolored   4.00   3.50
   a.   Booklet pane of 12   18.00

New Year 1983 (Year of the Pig).
Stamps from No. 1832a have straight edges
at top or bottom.

A473

A474

Stringed Instruments (T.81).

1983, Jan. 20   *Perf. 11½x11, 11x11½*
1833   A473   4f Konghou (5-1)   1.40   .70
1834   A473   8f Ruan (5-2)   1.40   .70
1835   A473   8f Qin, horiz. (5-3)   1.40   .70
1836   A473   10f Piba (5-4)   1.40   .70
1837   A473   70f Sanxian (5-5)   12.00   3.50
    Nos. 1833-1837 (5)   17.60   6.30

1983, Feb. 7   **Photo.**   *Perf. 11½x11*
1838   A474   8f Memorial Tower,
           Zhengzhou (2-1)   .40   .30
1839   A474   8f Monument, Jiangan
           (2-2)   .40   .30
60th Anniv. of Peking-Hankow Railroad
Workers' Strike (J.89).

The
Western
Chamber,
Traditional
Opera, by
Wang Shifu
(1271-1368)
A475

Scenes from the opera.

1983, Feb. 21   **Photo.**   *Perf. 11x11½*
1840   A475   8f multi (4-1)   1.50   .80
1841   A475   8f multi (4-2)   1.50   .80
1842   A475   10f multi (4-3)   3.00   1.60
1843   A475   80f multi (4-4)   12.00   4.50
    Nos. 1840-1843 (4)   18.00   7.70
Souvenir Sheet
Photogravure and Engraved
Perf. 12
1844   A475 $2 multicolored   70.00   30.00

#1844 contains one 27x48mm stamp. T.82.

Karl Marx (1818-
1883)
(J.90) — A476

Photogravure & Engraved
1983, Mar. 14   *Perf. 11½x11*
1845   A476   8f Portrait (2-1)   .20   .20
1846   A476   20f Making speech (2-2)   .50   .25

Tomb of the
Yellow
Emperor
(T.84)
A477

Photogravure & Engraved
1983, Apr. 5   *Perf. 11½*
1847   A477   8f Tomb, vert. (3-1)   .90   .40
1848   A477   10f Hall of Founder of
           Chinese Culture
           (3-2)   1.40   .40
1849   A477   20f Cypress tree, vert.
           (3-3)   2.25   .80
    Nos. 1847-1849 (3)   4.55   1.60

World Communications Year — A478

1983, Apr. 28   **Photo.**   *Perf. 11½*
1850   A478   8f multicolored   .45   .20

Male Chinese Alligator (T.85) — A479

Photogravure & Engraved
1983, May 24 **Perf. 11**
1851 A479 8f shown (2-1) .80 .40
1852 A479 20f Female, hatching
eggs (2-2) 1.60 .70

Kitten, by Tan
Arxi — A480

Various children's drawings. T.86.

1983, June 1 **Perf. 11½x11**
1853 A480 8f multi (4-1) .25 .20
1854 A480 8f multi (4-2) .25 .20
1855 A480 8f multi (4-3) .25 .20
1856 A480 8f multi (4-4) .25 .20
Nos. 1853-1856 (4) 1.00 .80

6th Natl.
People's
Congress
(J.94)
A481

1983, June 6 **Perf. 11x11½**
1857 A481 8f Hall (2-1) .20 .20
1858 A481 20f Natl. anthem
score (2-2) .75 .35

Terra Cotta
Figures,
Qin
Dynasty
(221-207
BC)
A482

1983, June 30
1859 A482 8f Soldiers (4-1) .80 .60
1860 A482 8f Heads (4-2) .80 .60
1861 A482 10f Soldiers, horses (4-3) .80 .60
1862 A482 70f Excavation site
(4-4) 4.75 2.75
a. Bkt. pane of 8 (#1859, 3
#1860, 3 #1861, #1862) 57.50 27.50
Nos. 1859-1862 (4) 7.15 4.55

Souvenir Sheet
1863 A482 $2 Soldier leading
horse 55.00 21.00
a. Booklet pane 55.00
#1863 contains one 59x39mm stamp. T.88.

A483

A484

Female roles in Peking opera (T.87).

1983, July 20 **Photo.** **Perf. 11**
Design A483
1864 4f Sun Yujiao (8-1) .75 .35
1865 8f Chen Miaochang (8-
2) .75 .35
1866 8f Bai Suzhen (8-3) .75 .35
1867 8f Sister Thirteen (8-4) .75 .35
1868 10f Qin Xianglian (8-5) .75 .35
1869 20f Yang Yuhuan (8-6) 2.25 .75
1870 50f Cui Yingying (8-7) 4.50 1.60
1871 80f Mu Guiying (8-8) 5.75 2.00
Nos. 1864-1871 (8) 16.25 6.10

1983, Aug. 10 **Photo.** **Perf. 11½**
Paintings by Liu Lingcang.
1872 A484 8f Li Bai (4-1) .55 .25
1873 A484 8f Du Fu (4-2) .55 .25
1874 A484 8f Han Yu (4-3) .55 .25
1875 A484 70f Liu Zongyuan (4-
4) 3.25 2.25
Nos. 1872-1875 (4) 4.90 3.00
Poets and philosophers of ancient China
(J.92).

5th Natl. Women's Congress — A485

1983, Sept. 1 **Photo.** **Perf. 11½**
1876 A485 8f multicolored .20 .20

5th National
Games
(J.93) — A486

1983, Sept. 16 **Photo.** **Perf. 11½**
1877 A486 4f Emblem (6-1) .45 .25
1878 A486 8f Gymnast (6-2) .45 .25
1879 A486 8f Badminton (6-3) .45 .25
1880 A486 8f Diving (6-4) .45 .25
1881 A486 20f High jump (6-5) .80 .70
1882 A486 70f Wind surfing (6-6) 2.00 1.75
Nos. 1877-1882 (6) 4.60 3.45

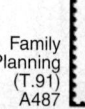

Family
Planning
(T.91)
A487

1983, Sept. 19 **Perf. 11x11½**
1883 A487 8f One child (2-1) .20 .20
1884 A487 8f Cultivated land (2-2) .20 .20

10th Intl. Trade Union
Congress — A488

1983, Oct. 18 **Litho.** **Perf. 11½**
1885 A488 8f multicolored .20 .20

Swans
(T.83)
A489

Perf. 11x11½ on 3 sides
1983, Nov. 18 **Photo.**
1886 A489 8f (4-1) .30 .30
1887 A489 8f (4-2) .30 .30
1888 A489 10f (4-3) .55 .30
1889 A489 80f (4-4) 2.00 1.50
a. Booklet pane, 7 #1886, 1
each #1887-1889 10.00
Nos. 1886-1889 (4) 3.15 2.40

A490

A491

Various photos. J.96.

1983, Nov. 24 **Photo.** **Perf. 11½**
1890 A490 8f multi (4-1) .40 .35
1891 A490 8f multi (4-2) .40 .35
1892 A490 8f multi (4-3) .40 .35
1893 A490 8f multi (4-4) .40 .35
Nos. 1890-1893 (4) 1.60 1.40
85th birth anniv. of Liu Shaoqi, political
leader.

1983, Nov. 29 **Photo.** **Perf. 11½**
1894 A491 8f No. 117 (2-1) .20 .20
1895 A491 20f No. 4L1 (2-2) .50 .25
CHINAPEX '83 Natl. Philatelic Exhibition
(J.99).

A492

A493

Various portraits. J.97.

1983, Dec. 26 **Photo.** **Perf. 11½**
1896 A492 8f 1925 (4-1) .20 .20
1897 A492 8f 1945 (4-2) .20 .20
1898 A492 10f 1952 (4-3) .45 .20
1899 A492 20f 1961 (4-4) 1.00 .90
Nos. 1896-1899 (4) 1.85 1.55
90th birth anniv. of Mao Tse-tung.

Photogravure and Engraved
1984, Jan. 5 **Perf. 11½**
1900 A493 8f multicolored 2.50 1.10
a. Booklet pane of 12 16.00
New Year 1984 (Year of the Rat).
Stamps from No. 1900a have straight edge
at top or bottom.

Beauties Wearing Flowers — A494

Portions of painting by Zhou Fang (Tang
Dynasty). T.89.

1984, Mar. 24 **Photo.** **Perf. 11**
1901 A494 8f multi (3-1) .80 .30
1902 A494 10f multi (3-2) .80 .30
1903 A494 70f multi (3-3) 4.00 2.25
Nos. 1901-1903 (3) 5.60 2.85

Souvenir Sheet
1904 A494 $2 Entire painting 110.00 50.00
No. 1904 contains one 162x40mm stamp.

Chinese Roses
(T.93) — A495

Ren Bishi (1904-
50), Statesman
A496

1984, Apr. 20 **Photo.** **Perf. 11½**
1905 A495 4f Spring of Shang-
hai (6-1) .35 .20
1906 A495 8f Rosy Dawn of
Pujiang River (6-
2) .35 .20
1907 A495 8f Pearl (6-3) .35 .20
1908 A495 10f Black whirlwind
(6-4) .35 .25
1909 A495 20f Yellow flower in
battlefield (6-5) .65 .35
1910 A495 70f Blue Phoenix (6-
6) 1.75 1.10
Nos. 1905-1910 (6) 3.80 2.30

1984, Apr. 30 **Perf. 11½x11**
1911 A496 8f multicolored .20 .20

Crested
Ibis (T.94)
A497

1984, May 15 **Photo.** **Perf. 11x11½**
1912 A497 8f Flying (3-1) .50 .20
1913 A497 8f Wading (3-2) .50 .20
1914 A497 80f Perching (3-3) 1.50 1.25
Nos. 1912-1914 (3) 2.50 1.65

Chinese Red Cross Society, 80th
Anniv. — A498

1984, May 29   **Perf. 11½**
1915 A498 8f multicolored   .20 .20

Gezhou Dam, Yangtze River
(T.95) — A499

1984, June 15   **Photo.**
1916 A499 8f Dam (3-1)   .25 .25
1917 A499 10f Bridge, vert. (3-2)   .30 .25
1918 A499 20f Lock Gate #2 (3-
        3)   .60 .50
     Nos. 1916-1918 (3)   1.15 1.00

Zhuo Zheng
Garden, Suzhou
(T.96) — A500

Photogravure & Engraved
1984, June 30   **Perf. 11½x11**
1919 A500 8f Inverted Image
        Tower (4-1)   .60 .35
1920 A500 8f Loquat Garden (4-
        2)   .60 .35
1921 A500 10f Water Court, Xiao
        Cang Lang (4-3)   .60 .35
1922 A500 70f Yuanxiang Hall,
        Yiyu Study (4-4)   1.75 1.40
     Nos. 1919-1922 (4)   3.55 2.45

1984
Summer
Olympics
A501

1984, July 28   Photo.   Perf. 11½
1923 A501 4f Shooting (6-1)   .20 .20
1924 A501 8f High jump (6-2)   .20 .20
1925 A501 8f Weight lifting (6-3)   .20 .20
1926 A501 10f Gymnastics (6-4)   .25 .20
1927 A501 20f Volleyball (6-5)   .25 .25
1928 A501 80f Diving (6-6)   1.00 .35
     Nos. 1923-1928 (6)   2.10 1.40

Souvenir Sheet
1929 A501 $2 Athletes, rings   4.50
#1929 contains one 61x38mm stamp. J.103.

Calligraphy
A502

Luanhe River
Water Diversion
Project (T.97)
A503

Artworks by Wu Changshuo. T.98.

1984, Aug. 27   Photo.   Perf. 11½
1930 A502 4f shown (8-1)   .40 .25
1931 A502 4f A Pair of Peaches
        (8-2)   .40 .25
1932 A502 8f Lotus (8-3)   .40 .25
1933 A502 8f Wisteria (8-4)   .40 .25
1934 A502 8f Peony (8-5)   .40 .25
1935 A502 10f Chrysanthemum
        (8-6)   .80 .45
1936 A502 20f Plum Blossom (8-
        7)   .80 .45
1937 A502 70f Seal Cutting (8-8)   2.00 1.60
     Nos. 1930-1937 (8)   5.60 3.75

Perf. 11½x11, 11 (#1939)
1984, Sept. 11   **Photo.**
1938 A503 8f multi (3-1)   .20 .20
1939 A503 10f multi, horiz. (3-2)   .20 .20
1940 A503 20f multi (3-3)   .30 .25
     Nos. 1938-1940 (3)   .70 .65

Chinese-Japanese Youth
(J.104) — A504

1984, Sept. 24   Photo.   Perf. 11½
1941 A504 8f Neighbors (3-1)   .20 .20
1942 A504 20f Planting tree (3-2)   .20 .20
1943 A504 80f Dancing (3-3)   .60 .50
     Nos. 1941-1943 (3)   1.00 .90

People's
Republic, 35th
Anniv.
(J.105) — A505

1984, Oct. 1   Photo.   Perf. 11½x11
Size: 26x35mm
1944 A505 8f Engineer (5-1)   .20 .20
1945 A505 8f Farm woman (5-
        2)   .20 .20
1946 A505 8f Scientist (5-4)   .20 .20
1947 A505 8f Soldier (5-5)   .20 .20
Size: 36x48mm
Perf. 11
1948 A505 20f Cranes (5-3)   .30 .25
     Nos. 1944-1948 (5)   1.10 1.05

110th Birth
Anniv. of
Chen
Jiageng
(J.106)
A506

1984, Oct. 21   Photo.   Perf. 12½x12
1949 A506 8f Chen Jiageng (2-
        1)   .20 .20
1950 A506 80f Jimei School (2-2)   .45 .30

The
Maiden's
Study
A507

Scenes from The Peony Pavilion, by Tang
Xianzu. T.99.

Photogravure & Engraved
1984, Oct. 30   **Perf. 11**
1951 A507 8f shown (4-1)   .45 .35
1952 A507 8f In the dream-
        land (4-2)   .45 .35
1953 A507 20f Du Liniang
        drawing self-
        portrait (4-3)   .80 .65
1954 A507 70f Married to Liu
        Mengmai (4-4)   2.50 2.50
     Nos. 1951-1954 (4)   4.20 3.85

Souvenir Sheet
Perf. 11½
1955 A507 $2 Playing in the
        garden   24.00 12.00
No. 1955 contains one 90x60mm stamp.

Emei Shan Mountain Scenery
(T.100) — A508

1984, Nov. 16   **Perf. 11**
1956 A508 4f Baoguo Temple
        (6-1)   .45 .25
1957 A508 8f Leiyin Temple (6-
        2)   .45 .30
1958 A508 8f Hongchun Lawn
        (6-3)   .45 .30
1959 A508 10f Elephant bath (6-
        4)   .45 .40
1960 A508 20f Woyun Temple (6-
        5)   1.00 .90
1961 A508 80f Shining Cloud
        Sea at Jinding
        (6-6)   3.75 2.40
     Nos. 1956-1961 (6)   6.55 4.55

A509   A510

Portraits.

1984, Dec. 15   Photo.   Perf. 11½x11
1962 A509 8f During the Long
        March (3-1)   .20 .20
1963 A509 10f At 7th Natl. Party
        Congress (3-2)   .20 .20
1964 A509 20f In motorcade (3-3)   .25 .20
     Nos. 1962-1964 (3)   .65 .60
Former party secretary Ren Bishi (1904-50).

1984, Dec. 25   **Perf. 11**
1965 A510 8f Flower arrangement   .20 .20
Chinese insurance industry.

New Year 1985
(Year of the
Ox) — A511

Photogravure & Engraved
1985, Jan. 5   **Perf. 11½**
1966 A511 8f T.102   .40 .30
     a. Bklt. pane of 4 + 8 plus label 13.50
Stamps from No. 1966a have straight edge
at top or bottom.

Zunyi Meeting, 50th Anniv. — A512

Paintings: 8f, The Zunyi Meeting, by Liu
Xiangping. 20f, The Red Army Successfully
Arrived in Northern Shaanxi, by Zhao Yu.
J.107.

1985, Jan. 15   Photo.   Perf. 11x11½
1967 A512 8f multi (2-1)   .25 .25
1968 A512 20f multi (2-2)   .60 .50

A513

A514

Lantern Folk Festival: No. 1969, Lotus of
Good Luck. No. 1970, Auspicious dragon and
phoenix. No. 1971, A hundred flowers blossoming. 70f, Prosperity and affluence. T.104.

1985, Feb. 28   **Perf. 11½**
1969 A513 8f multi (4-1)   .40 .20
1970 A513 8f multi (4-2)   .40 .20
1971 A513 8f multi (4-3)   .40 .20
1972 A513 70f multi (4-4)   2.10 1.10
     Nos. 1969-1972 (4)   3.30 1.70

1985, Mar. 8
1973 A514 20f multicolored   .20 .20
UN Decade for Women (1976-85).

Mei (Prunus mume)
(T.103) — A515

1985, Apr. 5   *Perf. 11*
1974 A515 8f Green calyx (6-
                  1)   .20 .20
1975 A515 8f Pendant mei (6-
                  2)   .20 .20
1976 A515 8f Contorted drag-
                  on (6-3)   .20 .20
1977 A515 10f Cinnabar (6-4)   .30 .20
1978 A515 20f Versicolor mei
                  (6-5)   .45 .25
1979 A515 80f Apricot mei (6-6)   2.00 .90
        Nos. 1974-1979 (6)   3.35 1.95

Souvenir Sheet
Perf. 11½
1980 A515 $2 Duplicate and
                  condensed fra-
                  grance mei   16.00

No. 1980 contains one 93x52mm stamp.

A516   A518

A517

1985, May 1   Photo.   *Perf. 11*
1981 A516 8f Huizo Guild Hall,
                  Guangzhou   .20 .20

All-China Fed. of Trade Unions.

1985, May 4   Photo.
1982 A517 20f multicolored   .20 .20

Intl. Youth Year.

1985, May 24   *Perf. 11½*
Paintings of giant pandas: 8f, 20f, 50f, 80f,
by Han Meilin; $3, by Wu Zuoren. T.106.
1983 A518 8f multi (4-1), vert.   .25 .25
1984 A518 20f multi (4-2)   .25 .25
1985 A518 50f multi (4-3), vert.   .35 .30
1986 A518 80f multi (4-4)   .50 .45
        Nos. 1983-1986 (4)   1.35 1.20

Souvenir Sheet
Perf. 11x11½
1987 A518 $3 multi, vert.   3.25
     a.   Ovptd. in sheet margin   6.00

No. 1987 contains one 39x59mm stamp.
No. 1987a ovptd. in sheet margin with
panda hologram, PJZ-4 and horizontal Chinese inscription in gold. Issued 10/9/96.
No. 1987a was sold in a mount affixed to a
small card.

Xian Xinghai
(1905-1945),
Composer
A519

Agnes Smedley,
1892-1950 (3-
1) — A520

Design: Bust, by Cao Chongen and music
from The Yellow River Cantata.

1985, June 13   Photo. *Perf. 11½x11*
1988 A519 8f multicolored   .20 .20

1985, June 25
American journalists: 20f, Anna Louise
Strong, 1885-1970 (3-2). 80f, Edgar Snow,
1905-1972 (3-3). J.112.
1989 A520 8f multicolored   .20 .20
1990 A520 20f multicolored   .20 .20
1991 A520 80f multicolored   .55 .35
        Nos. 1989-1991 (3)   .95 .75

Zheng He's West
Seas Expedition,
580th
Anniv. — A521

#1992, Portrait of the navigator. #1993,
Peace envoy. 20f, Trade, cultural exchange.
80f, Honored for navigational feats. J.113.

1985, July 11   *Perf. 11½*
1992 A521 8f multi (4-1)   .20 .20
1993 A521 8f multi (4-2)   .20 .20
1994 A521 20f multi (4-3)   .35 .30
1995 A521 80f multi (4-4)   1.10 .60
        Nos. 1992-1995 (4)   1.85 1.30

Xu
Beihong,
1895-1953,
Painter
(J.114)
A522

1985, July 19 *Perf. 11½x11, 11x11½*
1996 A522 8f Self-portrait (2-1),
                  vert.   .20 .20
1997 A522 20f shown (2-2)   .55 .20

A523   A524

Designs: 8f, Lin Zexu, 1785-1850, statesman, patriot. 80f, Burning opium at Humen,
bas-relief.

1985, Aug. 30   *Perf. 11*
1998 A523 8f multi (2-1)   .20 .20
Size: 51x22mm
1999 A523 80f multi (2-2)   .35 .25
Lin Zexu's ban of the opium trade catalyzed
the Anglo-Chinese Opium Wars. J.115.

1985, Sept. 1   *Perf. 11½x11*
2000 A524 8f Prosperity (3-1)   .20 .20
2001 A524 10f Celebration (3-2)   .20 .20
2002 A524 20f Abundant Harvest
                  (3-3)   .45 .45
        Nos. 2000-2002 (3)   .85 .85
Tibet Autonomous Region, 20th anniv.
(J.116).

End of
World War
II, 40th
Anniv. —
A525

Woodcuts by Wu Biduan: 8f, The Chinese
Army Rose Against the Japanese Agressors
at Logouqiao (2-1). 80f, The Eighth Route
Army and Militia Fought Around the Great Wall
(2-2). J.117.

1985, Sept. 3   *Perf. 11*
2003 A525 8f multi   .20 .20
2004 A525 80f multi   .25 .20

2nd Natl.
Worker's
Games,
Sept. 8-15,
Beijing
A526

Competitors from various events and: 8f,
Men's bicycling (2-1). 20f, Women hurdlers (2-
2). J.118.

1985, Sept. 8   *Perf. 11x11½*
2005 A526 8f multi   .60 .50
2006 A526 20f multi   .80 .75

Xinjiang
Uygur
Autonomous
Region, 30th
Anniv.
(J.119)
A527

1985, Oct. 1   Photo.   *Perf. 11½*
2007 A527 8f Oasis in the Gobi,
                  woman (3-1)   .20 .20
2008 A527 10f Oil field, Lake
                  Tianchi (3-2)   .20 .20
2009 A527 20f Tianshan pasture,
                  woman (3-3)   .20 .20
        Nos. 2007-2009 (3)   .60 .60
     Size of No. 2008, 60x30mm.

1st Natl. Youth
Games, Oct. 6-
15, Zhengzhou
(J.121) — A528

1985, Oct. 6   *Perf. 11½x11*
2010 A528 8f Girls' track & field
                  (2-1)   .20 .20
2011 A528 20f Boys' basketball (2-
                  2)   .30 .30

Forbidden City Main Buildings — A529

1985, Oct. 10   *Perf. 11½*
2012 A529 8f multi (4-1)   .20 .20
2013 A529 8f multi (4-2)   .20 .20
2014 A529 20f multi (4-3)   .20 .20
2015 A529 80f multi (4-4)   .45 .45
     a.   Vert. strip of 4, #2012-2015 .90 .90
Palace Museum, 60th anniv. J.120.

Zou Taofen
(1895-1935),
Journalist
(J.122) — A530

1985, Nov. 5   *Perf. 11½x11*
2016 A530 8f Portrait (2-1)   .20 .20
2017 A530 20f Epitaph by Zhou En-
                  lai (2-2)   .20 .20
     a.   Pair, #2016-2017   .30 .30

December 9th
Revolution, 50th
Anniv. — A531

1985, Dec. 9   *Perf. 11½*
2018 A531 8f Memorial Pavilion   .20 .20

New Year   Natl. Space
1986 — A532   Industry — A533

Photogravure & Engraved
1986, Jan. 5   *Perf. 11½*
2019 A532 8f multicolored   .40 .40
     a.   Bklt. pane of 4 + 8 with label
            btwn   5.50

1986, Feb. 1   Photo.
4f, 1st experimental satellite. #2021, Recov-
erable satellite. #2022, Underwater rocket
launch. 10f, Rocket launch. 20f,Earth satellite
receiver. 70f, Satellite trajectory diagram.
T.108.
2020 A533 4f multi (6-1)   .20 .20
2021 A533 8f multi (6-2)   .20 .20
2022 A533 8f multi (6-3)   .20 .20
2023 A533 10f multi (6-4)   .20 .20
2024 A533 20f multi (6-5)   .20 .20
2025 A533 70f multi (6-6)   .60 .30
        Nos. 2020-2025 (6)   1.60 1.30

Dong Biwu (1886-
1975), Party
Founder
(J.123) — A534

Lin Boqu (1886-
1960), Party
Leader
(J.124) — A535

Photogravure and Engraved
1986, Mar. 5   *Perf. 11½x11*
2026 A534 8f 1975 (2-1)   .20 .20
2027 A534 20f 1945 (2-2)   .20 .20

1986, Mar. 20
2028 A535 8f shown (2-1)   .20 .20
2029 A535 20f Lin standing (2-2)   .20 .20

Marshal He Long (1896-1969),
Revolution Leader (J.126) — A536

1986, Mar. 22   *Perf. 11x11½*
2030 A536 8f shown (2-1)   .20 .20
2031 A536 20f On horseback (2-2)   .20 .20

Halley's Comet — A537

1986, Apr. 11 Photo. *Perf. 11½*
2032 A537 20f dk bl & gray .20 .20

White Crane (T.110) A538

1986, May 22 *Perf. 11x11½, 11½x11*
2033 A538 8f Two cranes (3-1) .20 .20
2034 A538 10f One flying (3-2), vert. .20 .20
2035 A538 70f Four cranes (3-3), vert. .45 .20
Nos. 2033-2035 (3) .85 .60

Souvenir Sheet
2036 A538 $2 Flock 5.50
No. 2036 contains one 116x25mm stamp.

Li Weihan (1896-1984), Party Leader (J.127) — A539

1986, June 2 *Perf. 11x11½*
2037 A539 8f Portrait (2-1) .20 .20
2038 A539 20f Writing (2-2) .20 .20

Intl. Peace Year A540

1986, June 16 *Perf. 11*
2039 A540 8f multi .20 .20

Mao Dun (1896-1981), Writer (J.129) — A541

1986, July 4 *Perf. 11x11½*
2040 A541 8f Portrait (2-1) .20 .20
2041 A541 20f Portrait, diff. (2-2) .20 .20

Wang Jiaxiang (1906-1974), Party Leader (J.130) — A542

1986, Aug. 15
2042 A542 8f Portrait (2-1) .20 .20
2043 A542 20f Portrait, diff. (2-2) .20 .20

Teacher's Day A543

1986, Sept. 10 *Perf. 11*
2044 A543 8f multi .20 .20

Magnolia Liliflora (T.111) A544

1986, Sept. 23 *Perf. 11x11½*
2045 A544 8f Blossom (3-1) .30 .30
2046 A544 8f Two blossoms (3-2) .30 .30
2047 A544 70f Blossom, diff. (3-3) 2.10 2.10
Nos. 2045-2047 (3) 2.70 2.70

Souvenir Sheet
2048 A544 $2 Three blossoms 9.00
No. 2048 contains one 132x70mm stamp.

Folk Houses — A545

Perf. 13x13½, 11x11½, (1½f, 3f, #2057-2062)

1986, Apr. 1 Photo.
2049 A545 1f Inner Mongolia .20 .20
2050 A545 1½f Tibet .20 .20
2051 A545 2f Northeastern China .20 .20
2052 A545 3f Hunan .20 .20
2053 A545 4f So. Yangtze River .20 .20
2054 A545 8f Beijing .20 .20
2055 A545 10f Yunnan .20 .20
2056 A545 20f Shanghai .20 .20
2057 A545 30f Anhui .25 .20
2058 A545 40f No. Shaanxi .35 .25
2059 A545 50f Sichuan .40 .35
2060 A545 90f Taiwan .70 .50
2061 A545 $1 Fujian .75 .60
2062 A545 $1.10 Zhejiang .80 .70
Nos. 2049-2062 (14) 4.85 4.20

Issue dates: 3f, Dec. 25; 4f, $1, Oct. 15; 20f, 50f, Sept. 10; 40f, Nov. 15; others, Apr. 1.
Postal forgeries of No. 2056 exist.
See Nos. 2198-2207.

1989-90 Photo.
2055a Perf. 11x11½ ('89) .25 .20
2056a Perf. 11x11½ ('89) .35 .25
2057a Perf. 13x13½ ('90) .65 .35
2058a Perf. 13x13½ .85 .45
2059a Perf. 13x13½ ('89) 1.10 .60
2061a Perf. 13x13½ ('90) 2.25 1.25
Nos. 2055a-2061a (6) 5.45 3.10

Souvenir Sheet

All-China Philatelic Federation, 2nd Congress — A546

1986, Oct. 17 Litho. *Perf. 11½*
2063 A546 $2 Jade lion 3.25

Leaders of the 1911 Revolution (J.132) A547

1986, Oct. 10 Photo. *Perf. 11x11½*
2064 A547 8f Sun Yat-sen (3-1) .20 .20
2065 A547 10f Huang Xing (3-2) .20 .20
2066 A547 40f Zhang Taiyan (3-3) .90 .90
Nos. 2064-2066 (3) 1.30 1.30

Souvenir Sheet

Sun Yat-sen (1866-1925) — A548

1986, Nov. 12 *Perf. 11½*
2067 A548 $2 multicolored 6.25

Marshal Zhu De (1886-1976) (J.134) — A549

Designs: 20f, Orating.

1986, Dec. 1 Engr. *Perf. 11½x11*
2068 A549 8f sepia (2-1) .20 .20
2069 A549 20f myrtle grn (2-2) .30 .20

Sports of Ancient China A550

Stone carvings. T.113.

Perf. 11½x11, 11x11½
1986, Dec. 20 Photo.
2070 A550 8f Archery (4-1), vert. .25 .20
2071 A550 8f Weiqi (4-2) .25 .20
2072 A550 10f Golf (4-3) .35 .25
2073 A550 50f Soccer (4-4), vert. 2.75 1.75
Nos. 2070-2073 (4) 3.60 2.40

A551   A552

Photogravure & Engraved
1987, Jan. 5 *Perf. 11½*
2074 A551 8f blk, dk pink & yel grn .20 .20
a. Bklt. pane of 4 + 8 + label 4.50
New Year 1987 (Year of the Hare).

1987, Feb. 20 Photo. *Perf. 11½*
2075 A552 8f Traveling (3-1) .35
2076 A552 20f Cave writing (3-2) 1.60
2077 A552 40f Mountain climbing (3-3) 3.25
Nos. 2075-2077 (3) 5.20

Xu Xiake (1587-1621), Ming Dynasty geographer (J.136).

Birds of Prey (T.114) — A553

1987, Mar. 20
2078 A553 8f Kite (4-1) .25 .20
2079 A553 8f Sea eagle (4-2), vert. .25 .20
2080 A553 10f Vulture (4-3), vert. .35 .20
2081 A553 90f Buzzard (4-4) 4.50 1.00
Nos. 2078-2081 (4) 5.35 1.60

Liao Zhongkai (1877-1925), National Party Leader (J.137) — A554

1987, Apr. 23 *Perf. 11½x11*
2082 A554 8f shown (2-1) .20
2083 A554 20f Liao, He Xiangning (2-2) .25

Kites (T.115) — A555

A556

1987, Apr. 1

2084	A555	8f Hawk (4-1)	.40	
2085	A555	8f Dragon (4-2)	.40	
a.		Pair, #2084-2085	.80	
2086	A555	30f Symbolic octagon (4-3)	1.50	
2087	A555	30f Phoenix (4-4)	1.50	
a.		Pair, #2086-2087	3.00	
		Nos. 2084-2087 (4)	3.80	

Nos. 2085a, 2087a have continuous designs.

1987, Apr. 28

Portraits of Ye Jianying (1897-1986), central committee vice chairman (J.138).

2088	A556	8f multi (3-3)	.25	.25
2089	A556	10f multi (3-2)	.35	.35
2090	A556	30f multi (3-1)	1.60	1.60
		Nos. 2088-2090 (3)	2.20	2.20

Caves of the Thousand Buddhas, Dunhuang, Gansu Province — A557

Wall Paintings: 8f, Worshipping Bodhisattvas, Northern Liang Dynasty. 10f, Deer King Jatka, Northern Wei Dynasty. 20f, Heavenly Musicians, Northern Wei Dynasty. 40f, Flying Devata, Northern Wei Dynasty. $2, Mahasattva Jataka. T.116.

1987, May 20   **Perf. 11½**

2091	A557	8f multi (4-1)	.35	.20
2092	A557	10f multi (4-2)	.40	.25
2093	A557	20f multi (4-3)	1.10	.60
2094	A557	40f multi (4-4)	2.25	1.10
		Nos. 2091-2094 (4)	4.10	2.15

Souvenir Sheet

| 2095 | A557 | $2 multi | 20.00 | |

No. 2095 contains one 92x73mm stamp. See Nos. 2149-2152, 2283-2286, 2407-2411, 2505-2508, 2704-2707.

Children's Day Festival A558

Children's drawings: No. 2096, Happy Holiday, by Yan Qinghui, age 7. No. 2097, Peace and Happiness, by Liu Yuan, age 7. T.117.

1987, June 1   **Perf. 12½x12**

| 2096 | A558 | 8f shown (2-1) | .20 | .20 |
| 2097 | A558 | 8f multi, vert. (2-2) | .20 | .20 |

Rural Development   Postal Savings
A559   Bank
                           Inauguration
                           A560

1987, June 25   **Perf. 11½**

2098	A559	8f Village, southeast China (4-1)	.35	.35
2099	A559	8f Market (4-2)	.35	.35
2100	A559	10f Dairy industry (4-3)	.50	.50
2101	A559	20f Theater (4-4)	1.00	1.00
		Nos. 2098-2101 (4)	2.20	2.20

Nos. 2099-2100 horiz. T.118.

1987, July 1

| 2102 | A560 | 8f multicolored | .20 | .20 |

Esperanto Language Movement, Cent. — A561

1987, July 26

| 2103 | A561 | 8f lt olive grn, blk & brt blue | .20 | |

People's Liberation Army, 60th Anniv. (J.140) A562

1987, Aug. 1   **Perf. 11**

2104	A562	8f Flag, Great Wall (4-1)	.30	
2105	A562	8f Rocket launch, soldier, village (4-2)	.30	
2106	A562	10f Submarine, sailor (4-3)	.40	
2107	A562	30f Aircraft, pilot (4-4)	1.10	
		Nos. 2104-2107 (4)	2.10	

Intl. Year of Shelter for the Homeless A563

1987, Aug. 20   **Perf. 11**

| 2108 | A563 | 8f gray, dk car rose & blk | .20 | |

Chinese Art Festival, Sept. 5-25, Beijing — A564

1987, Sept. 5   **Perf. 11**

| 2109 | A564 | 8f brt red, gold & blk | .20 | |

1987, Sept. 25   **Perf. 11½**

4f, Pan Gu inventing the universe. #2111, Nu Wa creating man. #2112, Yi shooting nine suns. 10f, Chang'e flying to the moon. 20f, Kua Fu pursuing the sun. 90f, Jing Wei filling the sea. T.120.

Fairy Tales — A565

2110	A565	4f multi (6-1)	.20	.20
2111	A565	8f multi (6-2)	.25	.20
2112	A565	8f multi (6-3)	.25	.20
2113	A565	10f multi (6-4)	.35	.20
2114	A565	20f multi (6-5)	.60	.30
2115	A565	90f multi (6-6)	2.50	1.10
		Nos. 2110-2115 (6)	4.15	2.20

Communist Party of China, 13th Natl. Congress A566

1987, Oct. 25   **Perf. 11**

| 2116 | A566 | 8f multicolored | .20 | .20 |

Yellow Crane Tower (T.121) A567

1987, Oct. 30

2117	A567	8f shown (4-1)	.30	.20
2118	A567	8f Yue Yang Tower (4-2)	.30	.30
2119	A567	10f Teng Wang Pavilion (4-3)	.35	.35
2120	A567	90f Peng Lai Pavilion (4-4)	3.25	3.25
a.		Min. sheet of 4, #2117-2120	12.00	
		Nos. 2117-2120 (4)	4.20	4.10

No. 2120a sold for $1.50.

6th Natl. Games (J.144) — A568

1987, Nov. 20   **Perf. 11½x11**

2121	A568	8f Pole vault (4-1)	.20	
2122	A568	8f Softball (4-2)	.20	
2123	A568	30f Weight lifting (4-3)	.50	
2124	A568	50f Diving (4-4)	.90	
		Nos. 2121-2124 (4)	1.80	

Souvenir Sheet

Bronze Bells from the Tomb of Marquis Yi of the Zeng State (c. 433 B.C.), Hubei Province — A569

1987, Dec. 10   **Litho.**   **Imperf.**

| 2125 | A569 | $3 multicolored | 6.25 | |

Classic Literature — A570

Outlaws of the Marsh: 8f, Shi Jin practicing martial arts. 10f, Sagacious Lu, the "Tattooed Monk," uprooting a willow tree. 30f, Lin Chong seeking shelter from snow storm at the Mountain Spirit Temple. 50f, Song Jiang helps Ward Chief Chao Gai flee. $2, Outlaws of the Marsh capture treasures. T.123.

1987, Dec. 20   **Photo.**   **Perf. 11**

2126	A570	8f multi (4-1)	.35	
2127	A570	10f multi (4-2)	.45	
2128	A570	30f multi (4-3)	1.50	
2129	A570	50f multi (4-4)	2.00	
		Nos. 2126-2129 (4)	4.30	

Souvenir Sheet

Perf. 11½x11

| 2130 | A570 | $2 multi | 16.00 | |

No. 2130 contains one 90x60mm stamp. See Nos. 2216-2219, 2373-2377, 2449-2452, 2822-2826, 2889-2893.

New Year 1988   Cai Yuanpei (1868-
(Year of the   1940), Education
Dragon) — A571   Reformer
                       ((J.145) — A572

Photo. & Engr.

1988, Jan. 5   **Perf. 11½**

| 2131 | A571 | 8f multicolored | .20 | |
| a. | | Bklt. pane of 4 + 8 with label between | 5.50 | |

1988, Jan. 11   Photo.   Perf. 11½x11

| 2132 | A572 | 8f shown (2-1) | .20 | |
| 2133 | A572 | 20f Seated (2-2) | .20 | |

Tao Zhu (1908-1969), Party Leader (J.146) — A573

1988, Jan. 16   **Perf. 11x11½**

| 2134 | A573 | 8f shown (2-1) | .20 | |
| 2135 | A573 | 20f Tao, diff. (2-2) | .20 | |

Folklore (T.125) A574

1988, Feb. 10

2136	A574	8f shown (4-1)	.20	
2137	A574	10f multi, diff. (4-2)	.20	
2138	A574	20f multi, diff. (4-3)	.40	
2139	A574	30f multi, diff. (4-4)	.65	
		Nos. 2136-2139 (4)	1.45	

A575

A576

1988, Mar. 25   **Photo.**   **Perf. 11½**

| 2140 | A575 | 8f multicolored | .20 | |

7th Natl. People's Congress.

1988, Apr. 20 Photo. *Perf. 11½*
2141 A576 8f Wuzhi Mountain (4-1) .20
2142 A576 10f Wanquan River (4-2) .20
2143 A576 30f "End of the Earth" (4-3) .20
2144 A576 $1.10 "Deer Turning Its Head" (4-4) .50
Nos. 2141-2144 (4) 1.10
Establishment of Hainan Province (J.148).

Modern Scientists A577

Designs: 8f, Li Siguang, geologist. 10f, Zhu Kezhen, meteorologist and geographer. 20f, Wu Youxun, physicist. 30f, Hua Luogeng, mathematician. J.149.

1988, Apr. 28 *Perf. 11x11½*
2145 A577 8f multi (4-1) .20
2146 A577 10f multi (4-2) .20
2147 A577 20f multi (4-3) .20
2148 A577 30f multi (4-4) .25
Nos. 2145-2148 (4) .85

Wall Paintings Type of 1987
Caves of the Thousand Buddhas, Dunhuang, Gansu Province: No. 2149, Hunting, Western Wei Dynasty. No. 2150, Fishing, Western Wei Dynasty. 10f, Farming, Northern Zhou Dynasty. 90f, Building a Pagoda, Northern Zhou Dynasty. T.126.

1988, May 25 *Perf. 11½x11*
2149 A557 8f multi (4-1) .20
2150 A557 8f multi (4-2) .20
2151 A557 10f multi (4-3) .25
2152 A557 90f multi (4-4) 2.00
Nos. 2149-2152 (4) 2.65

Environmental Protection — A578

1988, June 5 Photo. *Perf. 11*
2153 A578 8f Soil (4-1) .20
2154 A578 8f Air (4-2) .20
2155 A578 8f Water (4-3) .20
2156 A578 8f Prevent noise pollution (4-4) .20
a. Block of 4, #2153-2156 .55

Souvenir Sheet

China Nos. 1-3 — A579

Photo. & Engr.
1988, July 2 *Perf. 13*
2157 A579 $3 multicolored 4.25
Postage stamps of China, 110th anniv.

11th Asian Games (in 1990), Beijing (J.151) A580

1988, July 20 Photo. *Perf. 11x11½*
2158 A580 8f Emblem (2-1) .20 .20
2159 A580 30f Character trademark (2-2) .20 .20
See No. 2300a.

Signing of the Sino-Japanese Peace Treaty, 10th Anniv. (J.152) — A581

1988, Aug. 12 Photo. *Perf. 11*
2160 A581 8f Peony (2-1) .20
2161 A581 $1.60 Sakura (2-2) .80
a. Pair, #2160-2161 .90

Achievements in Construction — A582

Designs: 8f, Coal-loading wharf, Ch'inhuang-tao Port. 10f, Ethylene refinery, Qilu. 20f, Pao-shan steel plant, Shanghai. 30f, Central Television Broadcasting Station. T.128.

1988, Sept. 2 Photo. *Perf. 11*
2162 A582 8f multi (4-1) .20
2163 A582 10f multi (4-2) .20
2164 A582 20f multi (4-3) .20
2165 A582 30f multi (4-4) .20
Nos. 2162-2165 (4) .80

See #2221-2224, 2279-2282, 2354-2357.

Mt. T'ai Shan, Shantung Province (T.130) — A583

1988, Sept. 14 **Photo. & Engr.**
2166 A583 8f T'ai Shan Temple (4-1) .25
2167 A583 10f Ladder to Heaven (4-2) .35
2168 A583 20f Daguang peak (4-3) .65
2169 A583 90f Sun-watching peak (4-4) 2.75
Nos. 2166-2169 (4) 4.00

Liao Chengzhi (1908-1983), Party Leader (J.153) — A584

1988, Sept. 25 Photo. *Perf. 11½x11*
2170 A584 8f shown (2-1) .20
2171 A584 20f Writing (2-2) .20

Marshal Peng Dehuai (1898-1974), Party Leader (J.155) — A585

1988, Oct. 24 Photo. *Perf. 11x11½*
2172 A585 8f shown (2-1) .20
2173 A585 20f Peng in uniform (2-2) .20

1st Natl. Farmers' Games (J.154) A586

1988, Oct. 9 Photo. *Perf. 11½*
2174 A586 8f Cycling (2-1) .20
2175 A586 20f Javelin (2-2) .20

Literary Masterpieces — A587

The Romance of the Three Kingdoms, by Luo Guanzhong, 14th cent.: No. 2176, Three heroes' sworn brotherhood (4-1). No. 2177, Battle between Lu Bu and the heroes, vert. (4-2). No. 2178, Struggle between man and woman at Fengyi Pavilion (4-3). No. 2179, Two noblemen, vert. (4-4). No. 2180, Guan Yu's battle through five passes. T.131.

Perf. 11½x11, 11x11½
1988, Nov. 25 Photo.
2176 A587 8f multicolored .30
2177 A587 8f multicolored .30
2178 A587 30f multicolored .80
2179 A587 50f multicolored 1.40
Nos. 2176-2179 (4) 2.80

Souvenir Sheet
Perf. 11
2180 A587 $3 multicolored 16.00
See #2310-2313, 2403-2406, 2539-2543.

A588   A589

1988, Dec. 5 Photo. *Perf. 11*
2181 A588 20f multicolored .20
Intl Volunteers' Day.

1988, Dec. 20 Photo. *Perf. 11½x11*
Milu, *Elaphurus davidianus* (T.132).
2182 A589 8f Buck (2-1) .25
2183 A589 40f Herd (2-2) 1.10
Exist imperf. Value, pairs each $5.50.

Orchids (T.129) — A590

1988, Dec. 25 *Perf. 12*
2184 A590 8f Da yi pin (4-1) .20
2185 A590 10f Dragon (4-2) .25
2186 A590 20f Large phoenix tail (4-3) .40
2187 A590 50f Silver-edged black (4-4) 1.00
a. Strip of 4, #2184-2187 1.90
Nos. 2184-2187 (4) 1.85

Souvenir Sheet
Perf. 11½x11
2188 A590 $2 Red lotus petal 13.00
No. 2188 contains one 55x37mm stamp.

A591   A592

Grotto Statuary: $2, Buddha. $5, Warrior, Longmen Grotto, Henan. $10, Goddess. $20, Woman and birds.

Photo. & Engr.
1988-89 *Perf. 11½x11*
2189 A591 $2 buff & reddish blk .45 .25
2190 A591 $5 buff & grnh blk 1.10 .55
2191 A591 $10 buff & brn blk 2.40 1.10
a. Souv. sheet of 1, buff & sep 17.00
2192 A591 $20 buff & indigo 5.00 2.25
Nos. 2189-2192 (4) 8.95 4.15

Issued: $2, 11/30; $5, 8/10; $10, 10/15; $20, 10/20.
No. 2191a released on Oct. 12, 1989, for the China Natl. Philatelic Exhibition and the 40th anniv. of the People's Republic.
Nos. 2189-2192, 2191a are almost always found with small ink spots on the stamps. Values are for stamps in this condition.

Photo. & Engr.
1989, Jan. 5 *Perf. 11½*
2193 A592 8f multicolored .25
a. Bklt. pane of 4+8 with label between 4.50
New Year 1989 (Year of the Snake).

Qu Qiubai (1899-1935), Party Leader (J.157) — A593

1989, Jan. 29 Photo. *Perf. 11x11½*
2194 A593 8f multi (2-1) .20
2195 A593 20f multi, diff. (2-2) .20

Brown-eared Pheasant, *Crossoptilon mantchuricum* (T.134) — A594

1989, Feb. 21 *Perf. 11½*
2196 A594 8f multi (2-1) .20
2197 A594 50f multi, diff. (2-2) .30

Folk Houses Type of 1986
1989-91 Photo. *Perf. 13x13½*
2198 A545 5f Shandong .20 .20
2199 A545 15f Guangxi .20 .20
2200 A545 25f Ningxia .20 .20
2201 A545 80f Shanxi .40 .25
2202 A545 $1.30 Qinghai .50 .30
2203 A545 $1.60 Guizhou .65 .35
2204 A545 $2 Jiangxi .65 .35
Nos. 2198-2204 (7) 2.80 1.85

Issued: 5f, 6/10/91; 15f, 11/25/90; 25f, 11/10/90; 80f, 9/20/90; $1.30, $1.60, 3/10/89; $2, 4/25/91.

Silk Painting Excavated from Han
Tomb No. 1 at Mawangdui, Changsha
(T.135)
A595

1989, Mar. 25   Photo.   Perf. 11½
2208 A595 8f In the Heavens
              (3-1)   .20
2209 A595 20f On the Earth,
              vert. (3-2)   .20
2210 A595 30f In the Nether-
              world, vert. (3-3)   .20
    Nos. 2208-2210 (3)   .60
Textured Paper, Without Gum
Size: 90x165mm
Imperf
2211 A595 $5 Entire painting   4.00

Prevention and
Resistance of
Cancer
(T.136) — A596

1989, Apr. 7   Litho.   Perf. 12
2212 A596 8f shown (2-1)   .20
2213 A596 20f Woman's thermo-
              gram (2-2)   .20

May Fourth
Movement,
70th Anniv.
(J.158)
A597

1989, May 4   Photo.   Perf. 11
2214 A597 8f Bas-relief   .20

Interparliamentary Union,
Cent. — A598

1989, June 29 Photo. Perf. 11x11½
2215 A598 20f multi   .20

Literature Type of 1987
Outlaws of the Marsh: 8f, Wu Song slaying a
tiger on Jingyang Ridge. 10f, Qin Ming dodg-
ing arrows. 20f, Hua Rong shooting a wild
goose on Mt. Liangshan. $1.30, Li Kui fighting
Zhang Shun from a junk. T.138.

1989, July 25   Perf. 11
2216 A570 8f multi (4-1)   .20
2217 A570 10f multi (4-2)   .20
2218 A570 20f multi (4-3)   .25
2219 A570 $1.30 multi (4-4)   1.50
    Nos. 2216-2219 (4)   2.15

Asia-Pacific Telecommunity, 10th
Anniv. — A599

1989, Aug. 4   Litho.   Perf. 12
2220 A599 8f multi   .20

Type of 1988
Achievements in Engineering and Construc-
tion: 8f, Beijing Intl. Telecommunications Build-
ing, vert. 10f, Xi Qu Coal Mine, Gu Jiao,
Shanxi Province. 20f, Long Yang Gorge
Hydroelectric Power Station, Qinghai Prov-
ince. 30f, Da Yao Shan Tunnel of the
Guangzhou-Heng Yang Railway. T.139.

1989, Aug. 10   Photo.   Perf. 11
2221 A582 8f multi (4-1)   .20
2222 A582 10f multi (4-2)   .20
2223 A582 20f multi (4-3)   .20
2224 A582 30f multi (4-4)   .20
    Nos. 2221-2224 (4)   .80

Mt. Huashan — A601

Designs: 8f, Five prominent peaks. 10f,
View from atop Huashan. 20f, 1000-foot preci-
pice. 90f, Blue Dragon Ridge. T.140.

1989, Aug. 25   Photo. & Engr.
2225 A601 8f multi (4-1)   .20
2226 A601 10f multi (4-2)   .20
2227 A601 20f multi (4-3)   .30
2228 A601 90f multi (4-4)   .90
    Nos. 2225-2228 (4)   1.60

Modern Art — A602

Paintings: 8f, *The Fable of the White Snake*,
by Ye Qianyu. 20f, *Li River in Fine Rain*, by Li
Keran. 50f, *Marching Together*, by Wu Zuoren.
T.141.

1989, Sept. 1   Photo.
2229 A602 8f multi (3-1)   .20
2230 A602 20f multi (3-2)   .25
2231 A602 50f multi (3-3)   .55
    Nos. 2229-2231 (3)   1.00

People's Political
Conference
A603

1989, Sept. 21   Perf. 12
2232 A603 8f No. 2   .20

A604

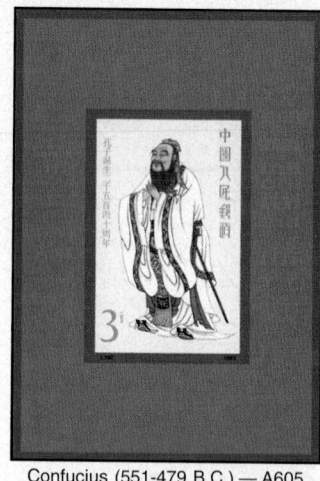

Confucius (551-479 B.C.) — A605

Designs: 8f, The lecture in the Apricot Temple, Qufu. $1.60, Confucius riding in an ox
cart. J.162.

1989, Sept. 28   Photo.   Perf. 11
2233 A604 8f shown (2-1)   .20
2234 A604 $1.60 multi (2-2)   .70

Souvenir Sheet
Litho.   Imperf.
Without Gum
2235 A605 $3 multicolored   3.25

A606

Gate of Heavenly Peace — A607

1989, Oct. 1   Photo.   Perf. 11x11½
2236 A606 8f shown (4-1)   .20
2237 A606 10f Flowers (4-2)   .20
2238 A606 20f Five stars (4-3)   .20
2239 A606 40f Construction (4-4)   .25
    Nos. 2236-2239 (4)   .85

Souvenir Sheet
Litho.   Imperf.
Without Gum
2240 A607 $3 shown   1.75
    PRC, 40th anniv. J.163.

Photography,
Sesquicentennial — A608

1989, Oct. 15   Photo.   Perf. 11
2241 A608 8f multicolored   .20

Li Dazhao (1889-1927), Party Leader
(J.164) — A609

1989, Oct. 29   Photo.   Perf. 11½
2242 A609 8f Li, soldiers (2-1)   .20
2243 A609 20f Li, text (2-2)   .20

Positron
Collider
Produced
in Beijing
A610

1989, Nov. 1   Perf. 11
2244 A610 8f multicolored   .20

Rocket
Defense
A611

Designs: 4f, Transporting 3 rockets. 8f, Dis-
assembled rocket on transport. 10f, Launch,
vert. 20f, Stage separation in space. T.143.

1989, Nov. 15   Litho.   Perf. 12
2245 A611 4f multicolored (4-1)   .20
2246 A611 8f multicolored (4-2)   .20
2247 A611 10f multicolored (4-3)   .20
2248 A611 20f multicolored (4-4)   .20
    Nos. 2245-2248 (4)   .80

A612

Views of West Lake (T.144) — A613

1989, Nov. 25 Photo. Perf. 11x11½
2249 A612 8f multi (4-1)   .20
2250 A612 10f multi, diff. (4-2)   .20
2251 A612 30f multi, diff. (4-3)   .25
2252 A612 40f multi, diff. (4-4)   .35
    Nos. 2249-2252 (4)   1.00
Souvenir Sheet
Perf. 11½x11
2253 A613 $5 multicolored   3.50

11th Asian
Games
A614

Various stadiums. J.165.

1989, Dec. 15   Perf. 11x11½
2254 A614 8f multi (4-1)   .20
2255 A614 10f multi (4-2)   .20
2256 A614 30f multi (4-3)   .20
2257 A614 $1.60 multi (4-4)   .30
    Nos. 2254-2257 (4)   .90

    See Nos. 2295-2300.

A615

Narcissus
(T.147) — A616

Photo & Engr.
1990, Jan. 5   **Perf. 11½**
2258 A615 8f multicolored   .40   .20
   a.   Bklt. pane of 12 + 4 labels   8.00
New Year 1990 (Year of the Horse).

1990, Feb. 10   **Photo.**   **Perf. 11x11½**
2259 A616   8f multi (4-1)   .20
2260 A616   20f multi, diff. (4-2)   .20
2261 A616   30f multi, diff. (4-3)   .20
2262 A616 $1.60 multi, diff. (4-4)   .40
   Nos. 2259-2262 (4)   1.00

Norman Bethune (1890-1939),
Surgeon (J.166) — A617

Litho. & Engr.
1990, Mar. 3   **Perf. 11x11½**
2263 A617   8f In Canada (2-2)   .20
2264 A617 $1.60 In China (2-1)   .50
   a.   Pair, #2263-2264   .65

     See Canada #1264-1265.

Intl. Women's
Day — A618

1990, Mar. 8   **Photo.**   **Perf. 11½x11**
2265 A618 20f multicolored   .20

Afforestation (T.148) — A619

1990, Mar. 12   **Perf. 11**
2266 A619   8f Bird, flora (4-1)   .20
2267 A619   10f Buildings (4-2)   .20
2268 A619   20f Great Wall, forest, (4-3)   .20
2269 A619   30f Bushes, evergreens (4-4)   .20
   Nos. 2266-2269 (4)   .80

Pottery
(T.149) — A620

1990, Apr. 10   **Litho.**   **Perf. 12**
2270 A620   8f multi (4-1)   .20
2271 A620   20f multi (4-2)   .20
2272 A620   30f multi (4-3)   .20
2273 A620   20f multi (4-4)   .20
   Nos. 2270-2273 (4)   .80

Li Fuchun (1900-1975), Party Leader
(J.168) — A621

1990, May 22   **Photo.**   **Perf. 11x11½**
2274 A621   8f shown   .20
2275 A621   20f In uniform (2-2)   .20

Bronze
Head — A622

Bronze treasures from Emperor Qin Shi
Huang Mausoleum: 50f, Horse head. $5,
Chariots. T.151.

1990, June 20   **Photo.**   **Perf. 11½x11**
2276 A622   8f shown (2-1)   .20
2277 A622   50f multicolored (2-2)   .35
Miniature Sheet
Size: 141x79mm
2278 A622 $5 multicolored   4.75

Achievements Type of 1988
Designs: 8f, 2nd automobile factory. 10f,
Yizheng Joint Corporation of Chemical Fiber
Industry. 20f, Shengli Oil Field. 30f, Qinshan
Nuclear Power Station. T.152.

1990, June 30   **Litho.**   **Perf. 12**
2279 A582   8f shown (4-1)   .20
2280 A582   10f multicolored (4-2)   .20
2281 A582   20f multicolored (4-3)   .20
2282 A582   30f multicolored (4-4)   .20
   Nos. 2279-2282 (4)   .80

Wall Paintings Type of 1987
8f, Flying Devatas. 10f, Worshipping
Bodhisatva. 30f, Savior Avolokitesvara. 50f,
Indra. T.150.

1990, July 10   **Perf. 11½x11**
2283 A557   8f multi (4-1)   .20
2284 A557   10f multi, vert. (4-2)   .20
2285 A557   20f multi, vert. (4-3)   .40
2286 A557   50f multi (4-4)   .70
   Nos. 2283-2286 (4)   1.50

Snow
Leopard
(Uncia
Uncia)
(T.153)
A624

1990, July 20   **Photo.**   **Perf. 11½**
2287 A624   8f multicolored (2-1)   .20
2288 A624   50f multicolored (2-2)   .25

Chinese
Soviet Post
Stamp of
1931
A625

Design: 20f, Chinese Red Post issue of
West Fukien, 1929. J.169.

1990, Aug. 1   **Litho.**   **Perf. 12**
2289 A625   8f multi (2-1)   .20
2290 A625   20f multi, diff. (2-2)   .20

Zhang Wentian (1900-1990)
(J.170) — A626

1990, Aug. 30   **Perf. 11x11½**
2291 A626   8f shown (2-1)   .20
2292 A626   20f multi, diff. (2-2)   .20

Intl. Literacy
Year — A627

Chinese
Films — A628

1990, Sept. 8   **Perf. 11½x11**
2293 A627 20f multicolored   .20

1990, Sept. 21   **Litho.**   **Perf. 11**
2294 A628 20f multicolored   .20

11th Asian
Games,
Beijing
(J.172)
A629

1990, Sept. 22   **Perf. 11x11½**
2295 A629   4f Running (6-1)   .20
2296 A629   8f Gymnastics (6-2)   .20
2297 A629   10f Karate (6-3)   .20
2298 A629   20f Volleyball (6-4)   .20
2299 A629   30f Swimming (6-5)   .20
2300 A629 $1.60 Shooting (6-6)   .60
   a.   Souv. sheet of 12, #2158-2159, 2254-2257, 2295-2300   8.00
   Nos. 2295-2300 (6)   1.60

Souvenir Sheet

Sportphilex '90, Beijing — A629a

1990, Sept. 21   **Litho.**   **Perf. 11½**
2300B A629a $10 multicolored   14.50

Modern
Scientists
A630

Designs: 8f, Lin Qiaozhi, obstetrician. 10f,
Zhang Yuzhe, astronomer. 20f, Hou Debang,
chemist. 30f, Ding Ying, agronomist. J.173.

1990, Oct. 10   **Litho.**   **Perf. 12**
2301 A630   8f multicolored (4-1)   .20
2302 A630   10f multicolored (4-2)   .20
2303 A630   20f multicolored (4-3)   .20
2304 A630   30f multicolored (4-4)   .25
   Nos. 2301-2304 (4)   .85

Mt. Hengshan — A631

Designs: 8f, Towering Temple. 10f, South
Sacred Mountain. 20f, Forested mountainside.
50f, Imposing Zhurong Peak. T.155.

Photo. & Engr.
1990, Nov. 5   **Perf. 11**
2305 A631   8f multicolored (4-1)   .20
2306 A631   10f multicolored (4-2)   .20
2307 A631   20f multicolored (4-3)   .20
2308 A631   50f multicolored (4-4)   .40
   Nos. 2305-2308 (4)   1.00

   See Nos. 2342-2345. 2628-2631.

Souvenir Sheet

China Philatelic Federation, 3rd
Congress — A632

1990, Nov. 28   **Perf. 11½x11**
2309 A632 $2 multicolored   4.75

Two types of No. 2309 exist. Either two or
three of the horizontal bars in seventh character from top right are connected at left side.

Literature Type of 1988
Romance of the Three Kingdoms by Luo
Guanzhong: No. 2310, Night Attack on
Wuchao. No. 2311, Making Three Calls at the
Thatched Cottage. 30f, Rescuing the Master
Single-handedly. 50f, Turning the Changban
Bridge Upside Down. T.157.

1990, Dec. 10   **Photo.**   **Perf. 11½x11**
2310 A587   20f multicolored (4-1)   .20
2311 A587   20f multi, vert. (4-2)   .20
2312 A587   30f multicolored (4-3)   .25
2313 A587   50f multi, vert. (4-4)   .45
   Nos. 2310-2313 (4)   1.10

Han Xizai's Night Revels by Gu
Hongzhong — A633

Designs: a, Guests enjoying food, music (5-1). b, Music and dance (5-2). c, Hand washing
(5-3). d, Musicians (5-4). e, Guests departing
(5-5). T.158. (Illustration reduced).

1990, Dec. 20   **Litho.**   **Perf. 12**
2314   Strip of 5   2.75
   a.-e.   A633 50f any single   .55

New Year 1991 (Year of the Sheep) — A634

Photo. & Engr.

1991, Jan. 5		**Perf. 11½**
2315	A634 20f multicolored	.35
a.	Bklt. pane of 12 + label	4.50

Dujiangyan Irrigation Project — A635

Designs: 20f, Yuzui, flood control. 50f, Feishayan, drainage. 80f, Baopingkou, water volume control. T.156.

1991, Feb. 20 Photo.		**Perf. 11½x11**
2316	A635 20f multicolored	.20
2317	A635 50f multicolored	.30
2318	A635 80f multicolored	.50
	Nos. 2316-2318 (3)	1.00

A636

A637

1991, Mar. 18

2319	A636 20f multicolored	.20

Paris Commune, 120th anniv.

1991, Apr. 20 Photo.		**Perf. 10**
2320	A637 20f multi (2-1)	.20
a.	Perf. 11½x11	1.40
	Perf. 11½x11	
2321	A637 50f Child & adult hands (2-2)	.20

Family planning (T.160).

Horned Animals (T.161) A638

1991, May 10		**Perf. 11x11½**
2322	A638 20f Saiga tatarica (4-1)	.20
2323	A638 20f Budorcas taxicolor (4-2)	.20
2324	A638 50f Ovis ammon (4-3)	.20
2325	A638 $2 Capra ibex (4-4)	.50
	Nos. 2322-2325 (4)	1.10

A639

A640

1991, May 23 Photo.		**Perf. 11**
2326	A639 25f Song and dance (2-1)	.20
2327	A639 50f Golden bridge (2-2)	.20
	Souvenir Sheet	
2328	A639 $2 No. 132, cranes	4.50

Occupation of Tibet, 40th anniv. (J.176).

1991, June 22		**Perf. 11½x11**
2329	A640 20f multicolored	.20

Antarctic Treaty, 30th anniv.

Rhododendrons — A641

Varieties of rhododendrons. T.162.

1991, June 25 Litho.		**Perf. 12**
2330	A641 10f Delavayi (8-1)	.20
2331	A641 15f Molle (8-2)	.20
2332	A641 20f Simsii (8-3)	.20
2333	A641 20f Fictolacteum (8-4)	.20
2334	A641 50f Agglutinatum, vert. (8-5)	.40
2335	A641 80f Fortunei, vert. (8-6)	.65
2336	A641 90f Giganteum, vert. (8-7)	.75
2337	A641 $1.60 Rex, vert. (8-8)	1.25
	Nos. 2330-2337 (8)	3.85
	Souvenir Sheet	
	Perf. 11½	
2338	A641 $5 Wardii	9.50

No. 2338 contains one 80x40mm stamp.

Chinese Communist Party, 70th Anniv. (J.178) A642

1991, July 1 Photo.		**Perf. 11x11½**
2339	A642 20f shown (2-1)	.20
2340	A642 50f Hammer and sickle (2-2)	.20

Peasant Uprising, 209B.C. A643

1991, July 7

2341	A643 20f brown	.20

Mt. Hengshan Type of 1990

Designs: No. 2342, Monastery on mountainside. No. 2343, Snow-covered mountain top. 55f, Inscription carved into mountainside. 80f, Hidden monastery. T.163.

Photo. & Engr.

1991, July 20		**Perf. 11**
2342	A631 20f multi (4-1)	.20
2343	A631 20f multi (4-2)	.20
2344	A631 55f multi (4-3)	.45
2345	A631 80f multi (4-4)	.65
	Nos. 2342-2345 (4)	1.50

Intl. Union for Quaternary Research, 13th Conf. A644

1991, Aug. 2 Photo.		**Perf. 11x11½**
2346	A644 20f multicolored	.20

Chengde Mountain Resort — A645

Ch'ing Dynasty Royal Gardens: 15f, Pine valleys. 20f, Mid-lake pavilion. 90f, Islet, maple trees. $2, Chengde Royal Summer Resort. T.164.

1991		**Perf. 11½x11**
2347	A645 15f multi (3-1)	.20
2348	A645 20f multi (3-2)	.20
2349	A645 90f multi (3-3)	.60
	Nos. 2347-2349 (3)	1.00
	Souvenir Sheet	
2350	A645 $2 multicolored	5.75

No. 2350 contains one 90x40mm stamp. Issue dates: $2, Aug. 19; others, Aug. 10.

A646

A647

Chen Yi, (b. 1901), party leader (J.181).

1991, Aug. 26 Photo.		**Perf. 11½x11**
2351	A646 20f shown (2-1)	.20
2352	A646 50f Verse (2-2)	.20
1991, Sept. 14		
2353	A647 80f Disaster relief	.30

Achievements Type of 1988

20f, Luoyang glassworks. 25f, Urumchi chemical fertilizer project. 55f, Dalian expressway, Shenyang. 80f, Xichang satellite launching center. T.165.

1991, Sept. 20 Litho.		**Perf. 12**
2354	A582 20f multi (4-1)	.20
2355	A582 25f multi (4-2)	.20
2356	A582 55f multi (4-3)	.20
2357	A582 80f multi (4-4)	.20
	Nos. 2354-2357 (4)	.80

Revolutionary Heroes — A648

Designs: No. 2358, Xu Xilin (1873-1907). No. 2359, Qiu Jin (1879-1907). No. 2360, Song Jiaoren (1882-1913). J.182.

1991, Oct. 10 Photo.		**Perf. 10**
2358	A648 20f multi (3-1)	.20
a.	Perf. 11x11½	5.00
	Perf. 11x11½	
2359	A648 20f multi (3-2)	.20
2360	A648 20f multi (3-3)	.20

Jingdezhen Chinaware A649

Designs: 15f, Glazed wine pot and warming bowl, Song Dynasty, vert. No. 2362, Porcelain vase, Yuan Dynasty, vert. No. 2363, Jar, Ming Dynasty. 25f, Porcelain vase, Ch'ing Dynasty, vert. 50f, Modern underglazed plate, vert. $2, Modern octagonal eggshell bowl, T.166.

	Perf. 11¼x11½, 11½x11¼ (#2363, 2366)	
1991, Oct. 11		**Photo.**
2361	A649 15f multi (6-1)	.20
2362	A649 20f multi (6-2)	.20
2363	A649 20f multi (6-3)	.20
2364	A649 25f multi (6-4)	.20
2365	A649 50f multi (6-5)	.20
2366	A649 $2 multi (6-6)	.50
	Nos. 2361-2366 (6)	1.50
	Perf. 11¼x11, 11x11¼ (#2363a, 2366a)	
1991		
2361a	15f multi	.20
2362a	20f multi	.20
2363a	20f multi	.20
2364a	25f multi	.20
2365a	50f multi	.20
2366a	$2 multi	.50
	Nos. 2361a-2366a (6)	1.50

Tao Xingzhi, Educator, Birth Cent. (J.183) — A650

1991, Oct. 18 Litho.		**Perf. 12**
2367	A650 20f shown (2-1)	.20
2368	A650 50f Wearing robe (2-2)	.20

Xu Xiangqian, Revolutionary Leader, 90th Birth Anniv. (J.184) — A651

1991, Nov. 8		**Perf. 11½x11**
2369	A651 20f shown (2-1)	.20
2370	A651 50f In uniform (2-2)	.20

1st Women's Soccer World Championships, Guangdong Province (J.185) — A652

Designs: 50f, Woman kicking soccer ball.

1991, Nov. 16		**Perf. 11½x11**
2371	A652 20f red & multi (2-1)	.20
2372	A652 50f grn & multi (2-2)	.20

Literature Type of 1987

Outlaws of the Marsh: 20f, Dai Zong sends a false letter from Liangshan Marsh. No. 2374, Ten feet of steel alone captures Stumpy Tiger Wang. No. 2375, Mistress Gu breaks open the jail in Dengzhou to rescue the Xie Brothers.

90f, Sun Li offers a plan to attack Zhu Family manor. $3, Mount Liangshan gallants raid the execution grounds. T.167.

1991, Nov. 19   **Perf. 11**

2373 A570	20f multi (4-1)		.20
2374 A570	25f multi (4-2)		.20
2375 A570	25f multi (4-3)		.20
2376 A570	90f multi (4-4)		.90
	Nos. 2373-2376 (4)		1.50

Souvenir Sheet
Perf. 11x11½

2377 A570	$3 multicolored		6.75

No. 2377 contains one 60x90mm stamp.

Beginning with No. 2378 stamps are inscribed "CHINA" and are numbered chronologically with the year followed by the number of the set. Additional numbers in parentheses indicate the number and position of each stamp in a set. We will note these only when helpful in identifying stamps.

New Year 1992, Year of the Monkey
A653   A654

Photo. & Engr.
1992, Jan. 25   **Perf. 11½**

2378 A653	20f Monkey, peach		.20
2379 A654	50f Magpies, plum branches		.20

Storks — A655

Conifers — A656

1992, Feb. 20   **Photo.**   **Perf. 11x11½**

2380 A655	20f Ciconia nigra		.20
2381 A655	$1.60 Ciconia ciconia		.70

1992, Mar. 10   **Litho.**   **Perf. 12½**

Designs: 20f, Metasequoia glyptostroboides. 30f, Cathaya argyrophylla. 50f, Taiwania flousiana. 80f, Abies beshanzuensis.

2382 A656	20f multicolored		.20
2383 A656	30f multicolored		.20
2384 A656	50f multicolored		.20
2385 A656	80f multicolored		.30
	Nos. 2382-2385 (4)		.90

Marine Life — A660

1992, Apr. 15   **Photo.**   **Perf. 11**

2386 A660	20f Pagrosomus major		.20
2387 A660	25f Penaeus chinesis		.20
2388 A660	50f Chlamys farreri		.20
2389 A660	80f Laminaria japonica		.20
	Nos. 2386-2389 (4)		.80

Publication of "Discussions on Literature and Art at the Yenan Forum," 50th Anniv. — A661

1992, May 23   **Photo.**   **Perf. 11½x11**

2390 A661	20f org, blk & red		.20

A662

A663

1992, June 5   **Litho.**   **Perf. 12**

2392 A662	20f multicolored		.20

UN Conf. on Human Development, 20th anniv.

1992, June 28

Insects: 20f, Coccinella septempunctata. 30f, Sympetrum croceolum. 50f, Chrysopa septempunctata. $2, Tenodera aridifolia sinensis.

2393 A663	20f multicolored		.20
2394 A663	30f multicolored		.20
2395 A663	50f multicolored		.25
2396 A663	$2 multicolored		.80
	Nos. 2393-2396 (4)		1.45

1992 Summer Olympics, Barcelona A664

1992, July 25   **Photo.**   **Perf. 11**

2397 A664	20f Basketball, vert.		.20
2398 A664	25f Women's gymnastics		.20
2399 A664	50f Women's diving		.20
2400 A664	80f Weight lifting, vert.		.30
	Nos. 2397-2400 (4)		.90

Souvenir Sheet

2401 A664	$5 Runners		2.50

No. 2401 contains one 54x40mm stamp.

Intl. Space Year — A665

1992, Aug. 18   **Litho.**   **Perf. 12**

2402 A665	20f multicolored		.20

Literature Type of 1988

Romance of the Three Kingdoms by Luo Guanzhong: 20f, Verbal battle with scholars. 30f, Goading Sun Quan with sarcasm, vert. 50f, Jiang Gan stealing the letter. $1.60, Gathering arrows with straw-covered boats, vert.

Perf. 11½x11, 11x11½

1992, Aug. 25			**Photo.**
2403 A587	20f multi		.20
2404 A587	30f multi		.20
2405 A587	50f multi		.20
2406 A587	$1.60 multi		.40
	Nos. 2403-2406 (4)		1.00

Wall Paintings Type of 1987

20f, Bodhisattva, vert. 25f, Musical performance, vert. 55f, Flight of a dragon. 80f, Envoy to the western regions. $5, Avalokitesvara-Bodhisattva, vert.

1992, Sept. 15   **Perf. 11**

2407 A557	20f multicolored		.20
2408 A557	25f multicolored		.20
2409 A557	55f multicolored		.25
2410 A557	80f multicolored		.35
	Nos. 2407-2410 (4)		1.00

Souvenir Sheet
Perf. 11½

2411 A557	$5 multicolored		3.00

No. 2411 contains one 52x70mm stamp.

Normalization of Diplomatic Relations Between China and Japan, 20th Anniv. — A666

20f, Cranes, Great Wall of China, Mt. Fuji. $2, Japanese, Chinese children, dove.

1992, Sept. 29   **Photo.**   **Perf. 11x11½**

2412 A666	20f multicolored		.20
2413 A666	$2 multicolored		.75

A667

A667a

Statue of Mazu, Chinese Goddess of the Sea.

1992, Oct. 4   **Litho.**   **Perf. 12**

2414 A667	20f multicolored		.20

1992, Oct. 12   **Photo.**   **Perf. 11½x11**

2414A A667a	20f multicolored		.20

14th Chinese Communist Party Congress.

Jiao Yulu (1922-1964), Communist Party Leader — A668

1992, Oct. 28   **Litho.**   **Perf. 12**

2415 A668	20f multicolored		.20

Famous Men A669

Designs: 20f, Xiong Qinglai, mathematician. 30f, Tang Feifan, microbiologist. 50f, Zhang Xiaoqian, physician. $1, Liang Sicheng, architect.

1992, Nov. 20

2416 A669	20f multicolored		.20
2417 A669	30f multicolored		.20
2418 A669	50f multicolored		.20
2419 A669	$1 multicolored		.20
	Nos. 2416-2419 (4)		.80

Luo Ronghuan, Leader of People's Army, 90th Anniv. of Birth A670

1992, Nov. 26   **Photo.**   **Perf. 11x11½**

2420 A670	20f In dress uniform		.20
2421 A670	50f In field uniform		.20

Constitution of the People's Republic of China, 10th Anniv. — A671

1992, Dec. 4   **Perf. 11½x11**

2422 A671	20f multicolored		.20

Liu Bocheng, Leader of People's Army, Birth Cent. A672

Designs: 20f, In dress uniform. 50f, During period of Long March, vert.

1992, Dec. 4   **Perf. 11x11½, 11½x11**

2423 A672	20f multicolored		.20
2424 A672	50f multicolored		.20

Quingtian Stone Carvings — A673

1992, Dec. 15   **Litho.**   **Perf. 12**

2425 A673	10f Spring		.20
2426 A673	20f Chinese sorghum		.20
2427 A673	40f Harvest		.20

2428 A673 $2 Blooming flowers,
full moon   .40
Nos. 2425-2428 (4)   1.00

New Year 1993 (Year of the
Rooster)
A674   A675

Photo. & Engr.

1993, Jan. 5   *Perf. 11½*
2429 A674 20f red & black   .25
2430 A675 50f red, white & blk .25

Madam
Song
Quingling,
Chinese
Communist
Leader,
Birth Cent.
A676

1993, Jan. 20   Photo.   Perf. 11x11½
2431 A676 20f Portrait   .20
2432 A676 $1 With children   .30

Camelus
Bactrianus
Ferus
A677

1993, Feb. 20   Litho.   Perf. 12
2433 A677   20f shown   .20
2434 A677 $1.60 Adult, young   .45

8th Natl.
People's
Congress
A678

1993, Mar. 15   Litho.   Perf. 12
2435 A678 20f multicolored   .20

A679

1993, Apr. 30   Litho.   Perf. 12
2436 A679   20f multi   .20
2437 A679 $1.60 multi   .40

1993, May 15   Litho.   Perf. 12

20th Cent. Revolutionaries: 20f, Li Jishen (1885-1959), horiz. 30f, Zhang Lan (1872-

A680

Game of Weiqi (Go): 20f, Painting of players of ancient times. $1.60, Game board showing Chinese-style position.

1955). 50f, Shen Junru (1875-1963). $1, Huang Yanpei (1878-1965), horiz.

2438 A680 20f multi   .20
2439 A680 30f multi   .20
2440 A680 50f multi   .20
2441 A680 $1 multi   .20
    Nos. 2438-2441 (4)   .80
    See Nos. 2483-2486.

A681

1993, May 9   Photo.   Perf. 12
2442 A681 50f Runner (2-1)   .20
2443 A681 50f Mascot (2-2)   .20
    a. Pair, #2442-2443   .40

First East Asian Games. No. 2443a printed in continuous design.

A682

1993, June 15   Litho.   Perf. 12½

Bamboo: 20f, Phyllostachys nigra. 30f, Phyllostachys aureosulcata spectabilis. 40f, Bambusa ventricosa. $1, Pseudosasa amabilis. $5, Phyllostachys heterocycla pubescens, horiz.

2444 A682 20f multi   .20
2445 A682 30f multi   .20
2446 A682 40f multi   .20
2447 A682 $1 multi   .20
    Nos. 2444-2447 (4)   .80

Souvenir Sheet
Photo.
Perf. 11
2448 A682 $5 multicolored   2.75
    a. As #2448, added inscription 4.00

No. 2448 contains one 54x40mm stamp. No. 2448a is inscribed in sheet margin with hologram of panda at left, Chinese inscription for CHINA '96 and PJZ-3 at bottom, and flag and tagged security emblem at right. Soaking in water may affect the hologram. Issued: May 10, 1996.

Literature Type of 1987

Outlaws of the Marsh: 20f, Chai Jin is trapped in Gaotang. 30f, Shi Qian steals armor. 50f, Xu Ning teaches how to use barbed lance. $2, Shi Xiu leaps from building to rescue condemned man from execution.

1993, Aug. 20   Photo.   Perf. 11
2449 A570 20f multi   .20
2450 A570 30f multi   .20
2451 A570 50f multi   .20
2452 A570 $2 multi   .60
    Nos. 2449-2452 (4)   1.20

Changbai Mountains — A683

1993, Sept. 3   Perf. 11½x11
2453 A683 20f Tianchi   .20
2454 A683 30f Alpine tundra   .20
2455 A683 50f Waterfall   .20
2456 A683 $1 Mixed forest   .20
    Nos. 2453-2456 (4)   .80

Seventh Natl.
Games — A684

Longmen
Grottoes — A685

1993, Sept. 4
2457 A684 20f multicolored   .20

1993, Sept. 5   Litho.   Perf. 12

Designs: 20f, Rocana, Ancestor Worshipping Temple. 30f, Sakyamuni, Middle Binyang Cave, Northern Wei. 50f, Maharaja, devas treading on Yaksha. $1, Bodhisattva at the left side of Rocana, Guyang Cave, Northern Wei. $5, Ancestor Worshipping Temple.

2458 A685 20f multi   .20
2459 A685 30f multi   .20
2460 A685 50f multi   .20
2461 A685 $1 multi   .20
    Nos. 2458-2461 (4)   .80

Souvenir Sheets
2462 A685 $5 multicolored   2.75
    a. Overprinted in gold   9.00
    b. Overprinted in silver   5.00

No. 2462 contains one 120x40mm stamp. Overprint in margin of No. 2462a includes Chinese characters and "PJZ-1." Bangkok '95 (#2462a). No. 2462a sold for $6.
No. 2462a exists with serial number inscribed in sheet margin. The same number is inscribed on Thailand No. 1615b. These were sold as a set. Value for the two sheets with matching numbers, $26.50.
Sheet margin of No. 2462b contains silver lettering in Chinese for Thailand stamp exhibition and "PJZ-7." No. 2462b exists with serial number inscribed in sheet margin. Value: $11.50.
Issued: No. 2462a, 8/95; No. 2462b, 12/5/97.

Honey Bees
A686

1993, Sept. 21   Photo.   Perf. 11½
2463 A686 10f Queen and two
bees   .20
2464 A686 15f Extracting nectar .20
2465 A686 20f Two Zhonghua
bees   .20
2466 A686 $2 Two bees in flight .35
    Nos. 2463-2466 (4)   .95

Lacquerware — A687

1993, Oct. 20   Photo.   Perf. 12
2467 A687 20f Bowl   .20
2468 A687 30f Duck   .20
2469 A687 50f Round tray   .20
2470 A687 $1 Lidded box   .20
    Nos. 2467-2470 (4)   .80

Paintings, by Zheng Banqiao — A688

Designs: 10f, Bamboo, rock on fan. No. 2472, Orchard. No. 2473, Orchard, bamboo, rock on scroll, vert. 30f, Bamboo, rock on scroll, vert. 50f, Vase and chrysanthemums. $1.60, Chinese calligraphy on fan.

1993, Nov. 22   Litho.   Perf. 12½
2471 A688   10f multi (6-1)   .20
2472 A688   20f multi (6-2)   .20
2473 A688   20f multi (6-3)   .20
2474 A688   30f multi (6-4)   .20
2475 A688   50f multi (6-5)   .20
2476 A688 $1.60 multi (6-6)   .50
    Nos. 2471-2476 (6)   1.50

A689

1993, Nov. 26   Perf. 12
2477 A689 20f multicolored   .20

Yang Hucheng, birth cent.

A690

1993   Photo.   Perf. 11½

Mao Tse-tung (1893-1976).

2478 A690 20f shown   .20
2479 A690 $1 Portrait, seated .20

Souvenir Sheet
2480 A690 $5 Standing by Great
Wall   2.00
    a. Overprinted in gold in margin 2.00 2.00

No. 2480 contains one 48x58mm stamp. No. 2480a sold for $8.
Issued: $5, 11/16; 20f, $1, 12/26; #2480a, 4/9/99.

New Year 1994 (Year of the Dog)
A691   A692

1994, Jan. 5   Photo.   Perf. 11½
2481 A691 20f multi   .20
2482 A692 50f yel, red & blk   .20

20th Cent. Revolutionaries Type

Designs: No. 2483, Chen Qiyou, horiz. No. 2484, Chen Shutong. No. 2485, Ma Xulun. No. 2486, Xu Deheng, horiz.

1994, Feb. 25   Litho.   Perf. 12
2483 A680 20f blk & brn (4-1) .20
2484 A680 20f blk & brn (4-2) .20
2485 A680 50f blk & brn (4-3) .20
2486 A680 50f blk & brn (4-4) .20
    Nos. 2483-2486 (4)   .80

Sturgeon — A693

20f, Huso dauricus. 40f, Acipenser sinensis. 50f, Psephurus gladius. $1, Acipenser dabryanus.

1994, Mar. 18   Litho.   Perf. 12½
2487 A693 20f multi   .20
2488 A693 40f multi   .20
2489 A693 50f multi   .20
2490 A693 $1 multi   .20
        Nos. 2487-2490 (4)   .80

Afforestation Campaign — A694

Designs: 15f, Sand dunes. 20f, Flowers on sand dune. 40f, Forest of poplars. 50f, Oasis.

1994, Apr. 21   Litho.   Perf. 12
2491 A694 15f multi   .20
2492 A694 20f multi   .20
2493 A694 40f multi   .20
2494 A694 50f multi   .20
        Nos. 2491-2494 (4)   .80

Teapots — A695

Style of teapot: 20f, Round, three-legged. 30f, Square, four-legged. 50f, Eight diagrams. $1, Round-eared.

1994, May 5   Litho.   Perf. 12
2495 A695 20f multi   .20
2496 A695 30f multi   .20
2497 A695 50f multi   .20
2498 A695 $1 multi   .20
        Nos. 2495-2498 (4)   .80

Huangpu Military School, 70th Anniv. — A696

1994, June 16   Litho.   Perf. 12
2499 A696 20f multicolored   .20

Intl. Olympic Committee, Cent. — A697

1994, June 23
2500 A697 20f multicolored   .20

Ancient Chinese Writers — A698

Designs: 20f, Tao Yuanming holding basket of flowers. 30f, Cao Zhi holding sword at side. 50f, Si Maqian writing on scroll. $1, Qu Yuan walking away with sword under arm.

1994, June 25
2501 A698 20f multi   .20
2502 A698 30f multi   .20
2503 A698 50f multi   .20
2504 A698 $1 multi   .20
        Nos. 2501-2504 (4)   .80

Wall paintings Type of 1987

10f, Flying Devata. 20f, Vimalakirti. 50f, Z. Yichao on the march. $1.60, Sorceresses.

1994, July 16   Photo.   Perf. 11
2505 A557 10f multi   .20
2506 A557 20f multi   .20
2507 A557 50f multi   .20
2508 A557 $1.60 multi   .40
        Nos. 2505-2508 (4)   1.00

Zhaojun's Marriage to Xiongnu — A699

1994, Aug. 25   Photo.   Perf. 11½x11
2509 A699 20f Zhaojun   .20 .20
2510 A699 50f Leaving home   .20 .20
Souvenir Sheet
Perf. 11½
2511 A699 $3 Wedding   3.00 3.00
No. 2511 contains one 85x46mm stamp.

Sixth Far East and South Pacific Games for the Disabled, Beijing — A700

1994, Sept. 4   Litho.   Perf. 12
2512 A700 20f multicolored   .20 .20

Wulingyuan State Forest Park — A701

20f, South Gate to Heaven. 30f, Shentangwan. 50f, No. One Bridge. $1, Writing-brush Peak. $3, Picturesque corridor.

1994, Sept. 25   Litho.   Perf. 12
2513 A701 20f multi, vert.   .20
2514 A701 30f multi, vert.   .20
2515 A701 50f multi   .20
2516 A701 $1 multi   .20
        Nos. 2513-2516 (4)   .80
Souvenir Sheet
Perf. 11½x12
2517 A701 $3 multicolored   3.00
No. 2517 contains one 50x36mm stamp.

Wuyi Mountains — A702

Designs: a, Jade-girl Peak (4-1). b, Nine-bend Brook (4-2). c, Guadun Village (4-3). d, Alpine Grassland (4-4).

1994, Sept. 30   Perf. 12
2518   Strip of 4   1.00
  a.-d. A702 50f any single   .25

Listening to the Rapids, by Fu Baoshi (1904-65) A703

Paintings: No. 2520, Appreciating a Painting. No. 2521, Dadi's Thatched Hut. 40f, Playing the Ruan. 50f, At Hupao. $1, The Road to Shanyin.

1994, Oct. 5
2519 A703 10f multi (6-1)   .20
2520 A703 20f multi (6-2)   .20
2521 A703 20f multi (6-3)   .20
2522 A703 40f multi (6-4)   .20
2523 A703 50f multi (6-5)   .20
2524 A703 $1 multi (6-6)   .20
        Nos. 2519-2524 (6)   1.20

Cranes — A704

Photo. & Engr.
1994, Oct. 9   Perf. 11x11½
2528 A704 20f Whooping crane   .20 .20
2529 A704 $2   Black-necked
                  crane   .45 .45
See US Nos. 2867-2868.

Souvenir Sheet

UPU, 120th Anniv. — A705

Illustration reduced.

1994, Oct. 9   Litho.   Perf. 12
2530 A705 $3 multicolored   3.00
  a.   Ovptd. in sheet margin   3.00
No. 2530a ovptd. in sheet margin with UPU hologram, vertical Chinese inscription in gold. Issued: July 18, 1996.

Gorges of Yangtze River — A706

Designs: 10f, Baidicheng. No. 2532, Qutang Gorge. No. 2533, Wuxia Gorge. 30f, Goddess Peak. 50f, Xiling Gorge. $1, Qu Yuan Memorial Temple. $5, The Three Gorges.

1994, Nov. 4   Photo.   Perf. 12
2531 A706 10f multi (6-1)   .20
2532 A706 20f multi (6-2)   .20
2533 A706 20f multi (6-3)   .20
2534 A706 30f multi (6-4)   .20
2535 A706 50f multi (6-5)   .20
2536 A706 $1 multi (6-6)   .20
        Nos. 2531-2536 (6)   1.20
Souvenir Sheet
Perf. 11½x11
2537 A706 $5 multicolored   3.25
No. 2537 contains one 116x35mm stamp.

Souvenir Sheet

All-China Philatelic Federation, 4th Congress — A707

Illustration reduced.

1994, Nov. 17   Litho.   Perf. 11
2538 A707 $3 multicolored   2.00

Literature Type of 1988

Romance of the Three Kingdoms by Luo Guanzhong: 20f, Composing a poem with a lance in hands. 30f, Liu Bei's marriage, vert. 50f, Overwhelming Xiaoyaojin with prowess. $1, Campsites burned, vert. $5, Fierce battle at Chibi.

Perf. 11½x11, 11x11½
1994, Nov. 24   Photo.
2539 A587 20f multicolored   .20
2540 A587 30f multicolored   .20
2541 A587 50f multicolored   .20
2542 A587 $1 multicolored   .20
        Nos. 2539-2542 (4)   .80
Souvenir Sheet
Perf. 11
2543 A587 $5 multicolored   5.00
No. 2543 contains one 158x36mm stamp.

Special Economic Zones A708

Designs: a, Shenzhen (5-1). b, Zhuhai (5-2). c, Shantou (5-3). d, Xiamen (5-4). e, Hainan (5-4).

1994, Dec. 10   Litho.   Perf. 12
2544 A708 50f Strip of 5, #a.-e.   .60

Pagodas of Ancient China — A709

Designs: No. 2545, Dayan Pagoda, Cien Temple. No. 2546, Zhenguo Pagoda, Kaiyuan Temple. 50f, Liuhe Pagoda, Kaihua Temple. $2, Youguo Temple.

Photo. & Engr.

1994, Dec. 15　　　　　　　Perf. 11½x11

2545	20f	tan, brn & blk (4-1)	.20
2546	20f	tan, brn & blk (4-2)	.20
2547	50f	tan, brn & blk (4-3)	.20
2548	$2	tan, brn & blk (4-4)	.20
a.		Souvenir sheet of 4, #2545-2548	7.00
		Nos. 2545-2548 (4)	.80

No. 2548a sold for $5.

New Year 1995 (Year of the Boar)
A711　　　　　　A712

Photo. & Engr.

1995, Jan. 5　　　　　　　　Perf. 11½

2550	A711	20f multicolored	.20
2551	A712	50f multicolored	.20

Winter Scenes A713

Designs: 20f, Snow willows, Cold River. 50f, Ice & snow on jade trees, vert.

1995, Jan. 12　　Litho.　　Perf. 12

2552	A713	20f multicolored	.20
2553	A713	50f multicolored	.20

Mt. Dinghushan — A714

Designs: 15f, Topographical map. No. 2555, Stream flowing down from mountain. No. 2556, Buildings on mountain side. $2.30, Silver pheasants.

1995, Feb. 15　　Litho.　　Perf. 12½

2554	A714	15f multi (4-1)	.20
2555	A714	20f multi (4-2)	.20
2556	A714	20f multi (4-3)	.20
2557	A714	$2.30 multi (4-4)	.20
		Nos. 2554-2557 (4)	.80

World Summit for Social Development, Copenhagen — A715

1995, Mar. 6　　Photo.　　Perf. 11x11½

2558	A715	20f multicolored	.20

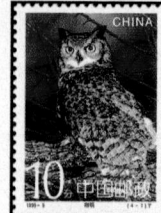

Owls — A716

1995, Mar. 22　　Photo.　　Perf. 11½

2559	A716	10f Eagle owl	.20
2560	A716	20f Long-eared owl	.20
2561	A716	50f Snowy owl	.20
2562	A716	$1 Grass owl	.20
		Nos. 2559-2562 (4)	.80

Sweet Osmanthus A717

1995, Apr. 14　　Litho.　　Perf. 12

2563	A717	20f Thunbergii (4-1)	.20
2564	A717	20f Latifolius (4-2)	.20
2565	A717	50f Aurantiacus (4-3)	.20
2566	A717	$1 Semperflorens (4-4)	.20
		Nos. 2563-2566 (4)	.80

A souvenir sheet of 4, #2563-2566, exists, both perf and imperf. Value, perf $5., imperf. $75.

43rd World Table Tennis Championships, Tianjin — A718

1995, May 1　　Litho.　　Perf. 12

2567	A718	20f Athlete	.20
2568	A718	50f Arena	.20
a.		Souv. sheet of 2, #2567-2568	22.50

No. 2568a sold for $7. Issued 8/14/95.

Spring Outing — A719

Designs: No. 2569, Group riding horses. No. 2570, Three riding horses.

1995, May 23　　Litho.　　Perf. 12

2569	A719	50f multi (2-1)	.25
2570	A719	50f multi (2-2)	.25
a.		Pair, #2569-2570	.50

No. 2570a is a continuous design.

Shadow Play — A720

Various costumed characters.

1995, June 8　　Photo.　　Perf. 12x12½

2571	A720	20f multi (4-1)	.20
2572	A720	40f multi (4-2)	.20
2573	A720	50f multi (4-3)	.20
2574	A720	50f multi (4-4)	.20
		Nos. 2571-2574 (4)	.80

Highway Interchanges, Beijing — A721

1995, June 20　　Photo.　　Perf. 11½x11

2575	A721	20f Siyuan	.20
2576	A721	30f Tianningsi	.20
2577	A721	50f Yuting	.20
2578	A721	$1 Anhui	.20
		Nos. 2575-2578 (4)	.80

Diplomatic Relations Between China & Thailand, 20th Anniv. — A722

#2579, Elephants walking right into water. #2580, Elephants walking left into water.

1995, July 1

2579	A722	$1 multi (2-1)	.25
2580	A722	$1 multi (2-2)	.25
a.		Pair, #2579-2580	.50

No. 2580a is a continuous design.

Taihu Lake A723

Lake scenes: No. 2581, Yellow trees. No. 2582, Structures on bank, boats, hills. No. 2583, Structures across inlet. No. 2584, Red trees, home. 230f, Winter scene. 500f, Houses on cliff, lighthouse.

1995, July 20　　Photo.　　Perf. 11½

2581	A723	20f multi (5-1)	.20
2582	A723	20f multi (5-2)	.20
2583	A723	50f multi (5-3)	.20
2584	A723	50f multi (5-4)	.20
2585	A723	230f multi (5-5)	.20
		Nos. 2581-2585 (5)	1.00

Souvenir Sheet

Perf. 11

2586	A723	500f multicolored	3.25
a.		Ovptd. in sheet margin	8.00

No. 2586 contains one 90x60mm stamp with continuing design.

No. 2586a issued 3/24/97. Gold overprint in sheet margin contains an emblem, Chinese inscription saying "Hong Kong Returns to China" and "PJZ-5."

Posts of Ancient China A724

1995, Aug. 17　　Photo.　　Perf. 12

2587	A724	20f Yucheng	.20
2588	A724	50f Jimingshan	.20

Shaolin Temple, 1500th Anniv. A725

1995, Aug. 30

2589	A725	20f Entrance (4-1)	.20
2590	A725	20f Pagoda Forest (4-2)	.20
2591	A725	50f Martial arts (4-3)	.20
2592	A725	100f Historical rescue (4-4)	.20
		Nos. 2589-2592 (4)	.80

Cultural Relics of Tibet — A726

1995, Sept. 1

2593	A726	20f Jar	.20
2594	A726	30f Casque	.20
2595	A726	50f Celestial motion chart	.20
2596	A726	100f Pearl mandala	.20
		Nos. 2593-2596 (4)	.80

Wildlife A727

1995, Sept. 1　　　　　　　Perf. 11x11½

2597	A727	20f Koalas	.20
2598	A727	$2.90 Pandas	.60

See Australia No. 1459.

End of World War II, 50th Anniv. A728

10f, July 7th event. #2600, Victory at Taier village. #2601, Soldier, hundred-regiment battle. #2602, Guerrilla war. #2603, Troops on parade, joining forces at Mangyo. 60f, Aircraft donated by Chinese living abroad. #2605, Taiwan recovered. #2606, Japanese surrender aboard USS Missouri.

1995, Sept. 3

2599	A728	10f multi (8-1)	.20
2600	A728	20f multi (8-2)	.20
2601	A728	20f multi (8-3)	.20
2602	A728	50f multi (8-4)	.20
2603	A728	50f multi (8-5)	.20
2604	A728	60f multi (8-6)	.20
2605	A728	100f multi (8-7)	.20
2606	A728	100f multi (8-8)	.20
		Nos. 2599-2606 (8)	1.60

4th World Conference on Women, Beijing A729

Symbols of: 15f, Equality. 20f, Development. 50f, Peace. 60f, Friendship.

1995, Sept. 4　　　　　　　　Perf. 12

2607	A729	15f multi	.20
2608	A729	20f multi	.20
2609	A729	50f multi	.20
2610	A729	60f multi	.20
		Nos. 2607-2610 (4)	.80

The Great Wall — A730

Jiuhua Mountains — A731

1995, Oct. 5   **Photo.**   *Perf. 12½*
2611 A730 60f shown .20
2612 A730 230f Shanhaiguan Pass .60
2613 A730 290f Jinshanling .80
  Nos. 2611-2613 (3) 1.60

See Nos. 2755, 2792-2795, 2907-2910, 2934-2941, 2952-2955.

1995, Oct. 9   **Perf. 12**
10f, Sunrise at Peak Terrace, horiz. #2615, Hall of Meditation. #2616, Temple of Bodhisattva, horiz. #2617, Sunset at Zhiyuan, horiz. #2618, Great Rock. #2619, Phoenix Pine, horiz.

2614 A731 10f multi (6-1) .20
2615 A731 20f multi (6-2) .20
2616 A731 20f multi (6-3) .20
2617 A731 50f multi (6-4) .20
2618 A731 50f multi (6-5) .20
2619 A731 290f multi (6-6) .50
  Nos. 2614-2619 (6) 1.50

Motion Pictures, Cent. A732

Projector and: 20f, Black and white film. 50f, Color film.

1995, Oct. 13
2620 A732 20f blue & black .20
2621 A732 50f multicolored .20

UN, 50th Anniv. A733

Designs: 20f, UN flag, Headquarters. 50f, Stylized flags, UN emblem, "50."

1995, Oct. 24   **Litho.**
2622 A733 20f multi .20
2623 A733 50f multi .20

Sanqing Mountains — A734

#2624, Good Fortune Land. #2625, Sichun Goddess. 50f, Bodhisattva Enjoys Music. 100f, Huge Boa out of Mountain.

1995, Nov. 1   **Photo.**   *Perf. 12*
2624 A734 20f multi (4-1) .20
2625 A734 20f multi (4-2) .20
2626 A734 50f multi, vert. (4-3) .20
2627 A734 100f multi, vert. (4-4) .20
  Nos. 2624-2627 (4) .80

Mt. Hengshan Type of 1990
Songshan Mountains: 20f, Ancient Temple of Mount Song. 50f, Moon waiting at Songmen Gate. 60f, Shaolin Temple. $1, Panorama view of Mt. Song.

Photo. & Engr.
1995, Nov. 10   *Perf. 11*
2628 A631 20f multi .20
2629 A631 50f multi .20
2630 A631 60f multi .20
2631 A631 $1 multi .20
  Nos. 2628-2631 (4) .80

Scenic Views of Hong Kong — A735

Designs: 20f, Victoria Harbor. 50f, Central Plaza at night. 60f, Hong Kong Cultural Center. 290f, Repulse Bay.

1995, Nov. 28   **Photo.**   *Perf. 12*
2632 A735 20f multi .20
2633 A735 50f multi .20
2634 A735 60f multi .20
2635 A735 290f multi .50
  Nos. 2632-2635 (4) 1.10

Sun Zi's Art of War — A736

Drawings depicting: No. 2637, Discussing strategy. 30f, Capturing Ying. 50f, Battle at Ailing. 100f, Meeting of sovereigns, Huangchi.

1995, Dec. 4   *Perf. 11x11½*
2636 A736 20f multi (5-1) .20
2637 A736 20f multi (5-2) .20
2638 A736 30f multi (5-3) .20
2639 A736 50f multi (5-4) .20
2640 A736 100f multi (5-5) .20
  Nos. 2636-2640 (5) 1.00

New Year 1996 (Year of the Rat)
A737   A738

Photo. & Engr.
1996, Jan. 5   *Perf. 11½*
2641 A737 20f multi .20
2642 A738 50f multi .20

3rd Asian Winter Games A739

#2643, Speed skating. #2644, Ice hockey. #2645, Figure skating. #2646, Skiing.

1996, Feb. 4   **Litho.**   *Perf. 12*
2643 A739 50f multi (4-1) .20
2644 A739 50f multi (4-2) .20
2645 A739 50f multi (4-3) .20
2646 A739 50f multi (4-4) .20
  a. Block of 4, #2643-2646 .50

China/Korea Submarine Fiber Optic Cable System — A740

1996, Feb. 8   **Litho.**   *Perf. 12*
2647 A740 20f multicolored .20
First day covers are dated 12/15/95.
See Korea No. 1863.

Shenyang Imperial Palace — A741

Designs: No. 2648, Buildings, denomination UL. No. 2649, Buildings, denomination LR.

1996, Mar. 18   **Photo.**   *Perf. 12*
2648 A741 50f multi (2-1) .20
2649 A741 50f multi (2-2) .20
  a. Pair, Nos. 2648-2649 .30

China Post, Cent. A742

Post Office buildings: 10f, Tianjin Posts Bureau. 20f, Beijing Postal Administration. 50f, Directorate of Posts of China. 100f, Beijing postal hub.
  500f, China #78-85.

1996, Mar. 20   *Perf. 11½*
2650 A742 10f multi .20
2651 A742 20f multi .20
2652 A742 50f multi .20
2653 A742 100f multi .20
  Nos. 2650-2653 (4) .80

Souvenir Sheet
Perf. 11
2654 A742 500f multicolored 5.00
No. 2654 contains one 89x59mm stamp.

Huang Binhong, Artist — A743

#2655, Calligraphy. #2656, Landscape. 40f, Qingcheng Mts. #2658, View from Xiing. #2659, Colored landscape. 230f, Flowers.

1996, Apr. 5   *Perf. 11½*
2655 A743 20f multi (6-1) .20
2656 A743 20f multi (6-2) .20
2657 A743 40f multi (6-3) .40
2658 A743 50f multi (6-4) .50
2659 A743 50f multi (6-5) .50
2660 A743 230f multi (6-6) 2.25
  Nos. 2655-2660 (6) 4.05

Aircraft — A744

1996, Apr. 17   *Perf. 12*
2661 A744 20f F-8 (4-1) .20
2662 A744 50f A-5 (4-2) .20
2663 A744 50f Yun-7 (4-3) .20
2664 A744 100f Yun-12 (4-4) .20
  Nos. 2661-2664 (4) .80

Potted Landscapes — A745

#2665-2666, Lijing & Divine Peak. #2667-2668, Melting Snow & Eagle Rock. #2668-2669, Manch & Rosy Clouds.

1996, Apr. 18
2665 A745 20f multi (6-1) .20
2666 A745 20f multi (6-2) .20
  a. Pair, #2665-2666 .40
2667 A745 50f multi (6-3) .20
2668 A745 50f multi (6-4) .20
  a. Pair, #2667-2668 .60
2669 A745 100f multi (6-5) .20
2670 A745 100f multi (6-6) .20
  a. Pair, #2669-2670 1.25
  Nos. 2665-2670 (6) 1.20

Iron Trees — A746

#2671, Cycas revoluta. #2672, Cycas panzhihuaensis. 50f, Cycas pectinata. 230f, Cycas multipinnata.

1996, May 2   **Litho.**   *Perf. 12*
2671 A746 20f multi (4-1) .20
2672 A746 20f multi (4-2) .20
2673 A746 50f multi (4-3) .20
2674 A746 230f multi (4-4) .35
  Nos. 2671-2674 (4) .95

China-San Marino Relations, 25th Anniv. A747

1996, May 6   **Photo.**   *Perf. 12*
2675 A747 100f Great Wall of China (2-1) .30
2676 A747 100f Mt. Titano (2-2) .30
  a. Pair, #2675-2676 .60
See San Marino Nos. 1356-1357.

Artifacts from Hemudu Ruins — A748

Designs: 20f, Agricultural tool. 50f, Pile to support building. 100f, Paddles for boats. 230f, Bird and sun carved in wood.

1996, May 12	Litho.	Perf. 12
2677 A748	20f multi	.20
2678 A748	50f multi	.20
2679 A748	100f multi	.20
2680 A748	230f multi	.50
Nos. 2677-2680 (4)		1.10

Souvenir Sheet

CHINA '96, 9th Asian Intl. Philatelic
Exhibition — A749

1996, May 18		Perf. 11½x12
2681 A749	500f multicolored	6.00
a.	Overprinted in gold	7.75

No. 2681 exists imperf. Value, $16.
Overprint in margin of No. 2681a includes
Chinese characters, Shanghai '97 exhibition
emblem, and "PJZ-6." Issued in 1998.

Children's
Activities
A750

Designs: 20f, Singing, playing musical
instruments. 30f, Pushing child in wheelchair,
holding umbrella. 50f, Placing flag on South
Pole, penguins. 100f, Planting tree.

1996, June 1		Perf. 12
2682 A750	20f multi	.20
2683 A750	30f multi	.20
2684 A750	50f multi	.20
2685 A750	100f multi	.20
Nos. 2682-2685 (4)		.80

Modern Olympic
Games,
Cent. — A751

1996, June 23	Photo.	Perf. 12
2686 A751 20f multicolored		.20

Protection
of Land
A752

Stylized designs representing: 20f, Making
use of land. 50f, Protection of farmland.

1996, June 25		Perf. 11x11½
2687 A752	20f multi	.20
2688 A752	50f multi	.20

A753

Military
Terraces — A754

1996, July 9	Litho.	Perf. 12
2689 A753	20f multi	.20
2690 A754	50f multi	.20

Vehicles — A755

#2691, Red Flag, 4-door limousine. #2692,
Dongfeng, stake truck. 50f, Jiefang, 4-door
truck. 100f, Beijing, canvas-topped jeep.

1996, July 15	Photo.	Perf. 12
2691 A755	20f multi (4-1)	.20
2692 A755	20f multi (4-2)	.20
2693 A755	50f multi (4-3)	.25
2694 A755	100f multi (4-4)	.40
Nos. 2691-2694 (4)		1.05

New Tangshan Built Following 1976
Earthquake — A756

1996, July 28		Perf. 11½
2695 A756	20f Farm cottages (4-1)	.20
2696 A756	50f Factory (4-2)	.20
2697 A756	50f Street (4-3)	.20
2698 A756	100f Port (4-4)	.20
Nos. 2695-2698 (4)		.80

30th Intl. Geological
Conference — A757

1996, Aug. 4	Litho.	Perf. 12
2699 A757 20f multicolored		.20

Tianchi Lake, Tianshan
Mountains — A758

20f, High mountain lake. #2701, Splendid
Waterfalls. #2702, Snow-capped peaks. 100f,
Lakeside scenery.

1996, Aug. 8		
2700 A758	20f multi (4-1)	.20
2701 A758	50f multi, vert. (4-2)	.20
2702 A758	50f multi, vert. (4-3)	.20
2703 A758	100f multi (4-4)	.40
Nos. 2700-2703 (4)		1.00

Wall Paintings Type of 1987

10f, Illustration of Mount Wutai. 20f, King of
Khotan, vert. 50f, Savior Avalokitesvara. 100f,
Worshipping Bodhisattvas.
$5, Thousand Arm Avalokitesvara.

1996, Aug. 15	Photo.	Perf. 11
2704 A557	10f multi, vert.	.20
2705 A557	20f multi	.20
2706 A557	50f multi	.20
2707 A557	100f multi	.20
Nos. 2704-2707 (4)		.80

Souvenir Sheet

2708 A557 500f multicolored		6.00

No. 2708 contains one 46x102mm stamp.

Mausoleums of
Western
Xia — A759

Designs: No. 2709: Mausoleum terrace. No.
2710, Ornament on Divine Gate. 50f, Stele.
100f, Stele remnant, Shouling.

1996, Aug. 22	Photo.	Perf. 11½
2709 A759	20f multi (4-1)	.20
2710 A759	20f multi (4-2)	.20
2711 A759	50f multi (4-3)	.20
2712 A759	100f multi (4-4)	.40
Nos. 2709-2712 (4)		1.00

Railways in China — A760

Designs: 15f, Datong-Quinhuangdao Railway. 20f, Lanzhou-Xinjiang Two-Track Railway. 50f, Beijing-Kowloon Railway. 100f, Beijing Western Railway Station

1996, Sept. 1		
2713 A760	15f multi	.20
2714 A760	20f multi	.20
2715 A760	50f multi	.20
2716 A760	100f multi	.20
Nos. 2713-2716 (4)		.80

A761

A762

Chinese Archives: No. 2717, Archives on
tortoise shells, Shang Dynasty. No. 2718,
Archives on wood slips, Han Dynasty. 50f, Iron
scrolls, Ming Dynasty. 100f, Books of Ch'ing
Dynasty.

1996, Sept. 2	Litho.	Perf. 12
2717 A761	20f multi (4-1)	.20
2718 A761	20f multi (4-2)	.20
2719 A761	50f multi (4-3)	.20
2720 A761	100f multi (4-4)	.20
Nos. 2717-2720 (4)		.80

1996, Sept. 10		Perf. 12
2721 A762	20f Portrait	.20
2722 A762	50f In uniform	.20

Ye Ting (1896-1946), co-founder of Chinese
People's Liberation Army.

96th Conference of Inter-Parliamentary
Union — A763

1996, Sept. 16		Perf. 11½
2723 A763 20f multi		.30

Shanghai — A764

Photo. & Engr.

1996, Sept. 21		Perf. 11½
2724 A764	10f Communication (6-1)	.20
2725 A764	20f Lujiazui (6-2)	.20
2726 A764	20f Jinqiao (6-3)	.20
2727 A764	50f Zhanghiang (6-4)	.20
2728 A764	60f Waigaoqiao (6-5)	.20
2729 A764	100f Residential (6-6)	.20
Nos. 2724-2729 (6)		1.20

Souvenir Sheet
Perf. 11

2730 A764	500f Panoramic view	6.00
a.	Margin ovptd.	14.00 —

No. 2730 contains one 90x45mm stamp.
No. 2730a issued 10/20/01. It is inscribed in
margin with multicolored emblems and gold
"PJZ-14," "APEC CHINA 2001," and Chinese
characters.

Space Navigation — A765

1996, Oct. 7	Litho.	Perf. 12
2731 A765	20f Rocket lift-off	.25
2732 A765	100f Satellite in orbit	.40

Singapore Waterfront — A766

Design: 290f, Panmen, Suzhou, China.

1996, Oct. 9	Photo.	Perf. 11½
2733 A766	20f multi	.20
2734 A766	290f multi	.75

See Singapore Nos. 768-769.

Victory of Long March, 60th
Anniv. — A767

Designs: 20f, Red Army through Marshland.
50f, Reunion of Three Armies.

1996, Oct. 22   Litho.   Perf. 12
2735 A767 20f multi   .30   .20
2736 A767 50f multi   .70   .20

Colored
Sculpture
of Tianjin
A768

Designs: 20f, The Two Immortals. No. 2738,
Making Candy. No. 2739, Returning from
Fishing. 100f, Xi Chun in Painting.

1996, Nov. 5   Photo.   Perf. 11½
2737 A768 20f multi (4-1)   .20
2738 A768 50f multi (4-2)   .20
2739 A768 50f multi (4-3)   .20
2740 A768 100f multi (4-4)   .20
    Nos. 2737-2740 (4)   .80

Hong
Kong
A769

20f, Bank of China. 40f, Container Terminal.
60f, Kai Tak Airport. 290f, Stock Exchange.

1996, Dec. 19   Litho.   Perf. 12
2741 A769 20f multi (4-1)   .20
2742 A769 40f multi (4-2)   .20
2743 A769 60f multi (4-3)   .20
2744 A769 290f multi (4-4)   .45
    Nos. 2741-2744 (4)   1.05

A770   A771

1997, Jan. 1
2745 A770 50f Visit China   .20

1997, Jan. 1
2746 A771 50f multicolored   .20
    First natl. agricultural census.

New Year 1997 (Year of the Ox)
A772   A773

Photo. & Engr.
1997, Jan. 5   Perf. 11½
2747 A772 50f multi (2-2)   .20
2748 A773 150f multi (2-1)   .40

Paintings by
Pan
Tianshou
(1897-1971)
A774

#2749, Pines on the Yellow Mountain.
#2750, Rosy Clouds of Dawn. #2751, Clearing
Up after Mould Rains. #2752, Chrysanthemum
and Bamboo. #2753, Sleeping Cat. #2754, A
Corner of Lingyan Brook.

1997, Mar. 14   Photo.   Perf. 11½
2749 A774 50f multi (6-1)   .30
2750 A774 50f multi (6-2)   .30
2751 A774 100f multi (6-3)   .65
2752 A774 100f multi (6-4)   .65
2753 A774 150f multi (6-5)   1.00
2754 A774 150f multi (6-6)   1.00
    Nos. 2749-2754 (6)   3.90

Great Wall Type of 1995
1997, Apr. 1   Photo.   Perf. 13x12
2755 A730 50f multicolored   .20

A776

A777

Tea: No. 2756, People forming circle beside
tea tree. No. 2757, Statue of tea sage. No.
2758, Tea utensils, horiz. No. 2759, Painting of
tea party, horiz.

1997, Apr. 8   Litho.   Perf. 12
2756 A776 50f multi (4-1)   .20
2757 A776 50f multi (4-2)   .20
2758 A776 150f multi (4-3)   .45
2759 A776 150f multi (4-4)   .45
    Nos. 2756-2759 (4)   1.30

1997, May 1   Photo.   Perf. 11½
Stylized designs depicting: No. 2760, Celebration. No. 2761, Unity (group of people),
horiz. 200f, Advance (horses running), horiz.

2760 A777 50f multi (3-1)   .20
2761 A777 50f multi (3-2)   .20
2762 A777 200f multi (3-3)   .80
    Nos. 2760-2762 (3)   1.20

Inner Mongolia Autonomous Region, 50th
anniv.

Pheasants
A778

Designs: 50f, Chinese copper pheasant.
540f, Common pheasant.

Litho. & Engr.
1997, May 9   Perf. 11½x11
2763 A778 50f multi (2-1)   .20
2764 A778 540f multi (2-2)   1.10
    See Sweden Nos. 2225-2226.

Dong Architecture
A779

Maiji
Grottoes — A780

#2765, Zengchong Drum Tower. #2766,
Bai'er Drum Tower. #2767, Wind and Rain
Bridge over the River, horiz. #2768, Wind and
Rain Bridge in the Field, horiz.

1997, June 2   Litho.   Perf. 12
2765 A779 50f multi (4-1)   .20
2766 A779 50f multi (4-2)   .20
    a. Pair, #2765-2766   .30
2767 A779 150f multi (4-3)   .45
2768 A779 150f multi (4-4)   .45
    a. Pair, #2767-2768   .90
    Nos. 2765-2768 (4)   1.30

1997, June 13
Statues: No. 2769, Buddha and Xieshi
Bodhisattva. No. 2770, Xieshi Bodhisattva and
his disciple. 100f, Maid. No. 2772, Buddha.
No. 2773, Xieshi Bodhisattva. 200f, Provider.

2769 A780 50f multi (6-1)   .20
2770 A780 50f multi (6-2)   .20
2771 A780 100f multi (6-3)   .25
2772 A780 150f multi (6-4)   .35
2773 A780 150f multi (6-5)   .35
2774 A780 200f multi (6-6)   .45
    Nos. 2769-2774 (6)   1.80

A780a

A781

Texts surrounded by flowers: 50f, Sino-Brit-
ish Joint Declaration. 150f, Basic Law of the
Hong Kong Special Adminstrative Region.
800f, Deng Xiaoping.

1997, July 1   Litho.   Perf. 12
2774A A780a 50f multi (2-1)   .30
2774B A780a 150f multi (2-2)   .80

Souvenir Sheets
2774C A781 800f multi   2.75
    d. Overprinted in sheet
       margin   3.25

Litho. (stamp) & Embossed (margin)
Perf. 13½
2775 A781 $50 gold &
            multi   32.50
    a. Overprinted in margin   45.00 45.00
    Deng Xiaoping (1904-97), return of Hong
Kong to China.

No. 2775 was released in special souvenir
folder.
No. 2774d contains gold Chinese inscription for Hong Kong's Return Exhibition Tour,
emblem, and "PJZ-8" in sheet margin. Issued:
6/19/98.
Overprint in margin on No. 2775a is Chinese inscription, "2000-1" and "(2-1)J." Issued:
1/1/00.

Ancient Temples of Wutai
Mountain — A782

Designs: 40f, Taihuai Township. No. 2777,
Nanchan Temple. No. 2778, Foguang Temple.
No. 2779, Xiantong Temple. No. 2780, Bodhi-
sattva Summit. 200f, Zhenhai Temple.

1997, July 26   Litho.   Perf. 12
2776 A782 40f multi (6-1)   .20
2777 A782 50f multi (6-2)   .20
2778 A782 50f multi (6-3)   .20
2779 A782 150f multi (6-4)   .35
2780 A782 150f multi (6-5)   .35
2781 A782 200f multi (6-6)   .45
    Nos. 2776-2781 (6)   1.75

Chinese People's Liberation Army,
70th Anniv. — A783

#2782, Land Force. #2783, Naval Force.
#2784, Air Force. #2785, Strategic Missile
Troops. 200f, Joint military maneuvers.

1997, Aug. 1
2782 A783 50f multi (5-1)   .20
2783 A783 50f multi (5-2)   .20
2784 A783 50f multi (5-3)   .20
2785 A783 50f multi (5-4)   .20
2786 A783 200f multi (5-5)   .50
    Nos. 2782-2786 (5)   1.30

Shoushan
Stone
Carvings
A784

Designs: No. 2787, "Rhythm of Autumn,"
vert. No. 2788, "Rhinoceros under Sunshine,"
vert. No. 2789, "Jade's Fragrance," (basket of
fruit). No. 2790, "Drunken Joy."
800f, Qianlong's Chain Seals.

1997, Aug. 17   Litho.   Perf. 12
2787 A784 50f multi (4-1)   .20
2788 A784 50f multi (4-2)   .20
2789 A784 150f multi (4-3)   .45
2790 A784 150f multi (4-4)   .45
    Nos. 2787-2790 (4)   1.30

Souvenir Sheet
2791 A784 800f multi   5.00
    No. 2791 contains one 60x60mm stamp.

Great Wall Type of 1995
Gates: 30f, Huangyaguan. 100f, Badaling.
150f, Joyongguan. 200f, Zijingguan.

1997, Sept. 1   Photo.   Perf. 13x12
2792 A730 30f yellow & black   .20
2793 A730 100f vermilion & black   .25
2794 A730 150f green & black   .40
2795 A730 200f red & black   .50
    Nos. 2792-2795 (4)   1.35

Communist Party of China, 15th Natl. Congress A785

1997, Sept. 12   Litho.   Perf. 12
2796 A785 50f multicolored   .50

A786

#2797, China Rose. #2798, New Zealand Monthly Rose.

1997, Oct. 9   Photo.   Perf. 11½
2797   150f multi (2-1)   .50
2798   150f multi (2-2)   .50
a.   A786 Pair, #2797-2798   1.00

See New Zealand Nos. 1469-1470.

Eighth Natl. Games A788

1997, Oct. 12   Litho.   Perf. 12
2799 A788 50f Athletes (2-1)   .20
2800 A788 150f Stadium)2-2)   .45
a.   Souv. sheet, #2799-2800   5.00

No. 2800a sold for 300f.

Temple of Heaven, Beijing — A789

#2801, Hall of Prayers for Bumper Harvests. #2802, Imperial Vault of Heaven. #2803, Circular Mound Altar. #2804, Fasting Palace.

1997, Oct. 16   Litho.   Perf. 12
2801 A789 50f multi (4-1)   .20
2802 A789 50f multi (4-2)   .20
a.   Pair, #2801-2802   .25
2803 A789 150f multi (4-3)   .40
2804 A789 150f multi (4-4)   .40
a.   Pair, #2803-2804   .80
    Nos. 2801-2804 (4)   1.20

Mt. Huangshan — A790

a, Mt. Huangshan at sunrise (8-1). b, Xihai Peaks (8-2). c, Flying Rock in surging clouds (8-3). d, Beihai in drifting clouds (8-4). e, Yuping Peak (8-5). f, Mystical stone (8-6). g, Tiandu Peak over clouds (8-7). h, Fabled Abode of Immortals (8-8).

1997, Oct. 20   Photo.   Perf. 11½
Sheet of 8 + Label
2805 A790 200f #a.-h.   10.00

Nos. 2805d, 2805e are each 36x46mm. 22nd UPU Congress, Beijing, 1999.

City Wall of Xi'an A791

Designs: No. 2806, Surrounding tower. No. 2807, Arrow Tower. No. 2808, Watch Tower. No. 2809, Corner Tower.

1997, Oct. 24   Litho.   Perf. 12
2806 A791 50f multi (4-1)   .20
2807 A791 50f multi (4-2)   .20
2808 A791 150f multi (4-3)   .40
2809 A791 150f multi (4-4)   .40
    Nos. 2806-2809 (4)   1.20

Three Gorges Dam Project on Yangtze River — A792

#2810, New channel being opened to navigation. #2811, Damming Yangtze River.

1997, Nov. 8   Photo.   Perf. 11½
2810 A792 50f multi (2-1)   .20
2811 A792 50f multi (2-2)   .20
a.   Pair, #2810-2811   .25

Macao Landmarks — A793

50f, Ma Kok Temple. 100f, Lin Fong Temple. 150f, St. Paul's Ruins. 200f, Guia Lighthouse.

1997, Nov. 11   Litho.   Perf. 12
2812 A793 50f multi (4-1)   .20
2813 A793 100f multi (4-2)   .25
2814 A793 150f multi (4-3)   .35
2815 A793 200f multi (4-4)   .50
    Nos. 2812-2815 (4)   1.30

Steel Production Exceeds 100 Million Tons in 1996 A794

50f, Ancient method of producing steel. 150f, Modern mill, pouring steel from smelter.

1997, Nov. 25
2816 A794 50f multi (2-1)   .20
2817 A794 150f multi (2-2)   .45

Telecommunications — A795

Stylized designs: #2818, Digital transmissions. #2819, Computer, "X-changing" data. #2820, Computer receiving signals, Chinese landmarks. #2821, Cellular phone transmission, man's head.

1997, Dec. 10
2818 A795 50f multi (4-1)   .20
2819 A795 50f multi (4-2)   .20
2820 A795 150f multi (4-3)   .35
2821 A795 150f multi (4-4)   .35
    Nos. 2818-2821 (4)   1.10

Literature Type of 1987
Outlaws of the Marsh: 40f, Huyan Zhuo coaxes Guan Sheng in a moonlit night. No. 2823, Lu Junyi captures Shi Wengong. No. 2824, Yan Qing defeats sky supporting pillar. 150f, Thunderbolt defeats Imperial Army. 800f, Heroes of Mount Liangshan take seats in order of rank.

1997, Dec. 22   Photo.   Perf. 11
2822 A570 40f multi (4-1)   .20
2823 A570 50f multi (4-2)   .20
2824 A570 50f multi (4-3)   .20
2825 A570 150f multi (4-4)   .60
    Nos. 2822-2825 (4)   1.20

Souvenir Sheet
2826 A570 800f multicolored   3.25

No. 2826 contains one 60x90mm stamp.

New Year 1998 (Year of the Tiger) A796   A797

Photo. & Engr.
1998, Jan. 5   Perf. 11½
2827 A796 50f multi (2-1)   .20
2828 A797 150f multi (2-2)   .35

Gardens of Lingnan — A798

1998, Jan. 18   Litho.   Perf. 12
2829 A798 50f Keyaun (4-1)   .20
2830 A798 50f Liangyuan (4-2)   .20
2831 A798 100f Qinghui (4-3)   .25
2832 A798 200f Yuyin Villa (4-4)   .50
    Nos. 2829-2832 (4)   1.15

Deng Xiaoping (1904-97) — A799

#2833, At middle age. #2834, During Liberation War. #2835, With Mao Tse-tung. 100f, As Chairman of Central Military Commission. 150f, Making speech on 35th anniversary of People's Republic. 200f, Making speech, hand raised, 1992.

1998, Feb. 19   Photo.   Perf. 11½
2833 A799 50f multi (6-1)   .20
2834 A799 50f multi (6-2)   .20
2835 A799 50f multi (6-3)   .20
2836 A799 100f multi (6-4)   .25
2837 A799 150f multi (6-5)   .35
2838 A799 200f multi (6-6)   .50
    Nos. 2833-2838 (6)   1.70

Chinese People's Police — A800

Designs: 40f, Golden shield. No. 2840, Blitz operation. No. 2841, Cooperation between police and people. 100f, Traffic control. 150f, Fire police. 200f, Border guards.

1998, Feb. 28   Litho.   Perf. 12
2839 A800 40f multi (6-1)   .20
2840 A800 50f multi (6-2)   .20
2841 A800 50f multi (6-3)   .20
2842 A800 100f multi (6-4)   .25
2843 A800 150f multi (6-5)   .35
2844 A800 200f multi (6-6)   .50
    Nos. 2839-2844 (6)   1.70

A801

A802

1998, Mar. 5
2845 A801 50f multi (1-1)   .20   .20
Ninth Natl. People's Congress, Beijing.

1998, Mar. 5   Photo.   Perf. 11½
Chou En-lai (1898-1976), Communist Party leader: No. 2846, In military uniform on horse. No. 2847, As First Premier, walking. No. 2848, As diplomat wearing lei. No. 2849, Standing and applauding.

2846 A802 50f multi (4-1)   .20
2847 A802 50f multi (4-2)   .20
2848 A802 150f multi (4-3)   .30
2849 A802 150f multi (4-4)   .30
    Nos. 2846-2849 (4)   1.00

Nine-Village Valley — A803

Designs: No. 2850, Fangcao Lake. No. 2851, Wuhua Lake. No. 2852, Shuzheng Waterfalls. No. 2853, Nuorilang Waterfalls.

1998, Mar. 26   Litho.   Perf. 12
2850 A803 50f multi (4-1)   .20
2851 A803 50f multi (4-2)   .20
2852 A803 150f multi (4-3)   .30
2853 A803 150f multi (4-4)   .30
    Nos. 2850-2853 (4)   1.00

Souvenir Sheet
2854 A803 800f Long Lake   3.00

No. 2854 contains one 93x52mm stamp.

Dai Architecture — A804

#2855, Building on stilts. #2856, Well. #2857, Pavilion. #2858, Pagoda.

1998, Apr. 12   Photo.   Perf. 11½
2855 A804 50f multi (4-1)   .20
2856 A804 50f multi (4-2)   .20
2857 A804 150f multi (4-3)   .30
2858 A804 150f multi (4-4)   .30
    Nos. 2855-2858 (4)   1.00

Construction, Hainan Special Economic Zone — A805

#2859, Urban construction, Haikou. #2860, Economic development zone, Yangpu. #2861, Phoenix Intl. Airport, Sanya. #2862, Natl. tourism and resort zone, Yalongwan.

1998, Apr. 13   Litho.   Perf. 12
2859	A805	50f multi (4-1)	.20
2860	A805	50f multi (4-2)	.20
a.		Pair, #2859-2860	.40
2861	A805	150f multi (4-3)	.30
2862	A805	150f multi (4-4)	.30
a.		Pair, #2861-2862	.60
		Nos. 2859-2862 (4)	1.00

Ancient Academies — A806

Designs: No. 2863, Yingtian. No. 2864, Songyang. No. 2865, Yuelu. No. 2866, Bailu.

1998, Apr. 29
2863	A806	50f multi (4-1)	.20
2864	A806	50f multi (4-2)	.20
2865	A806	150f multi (4-3)	.30
2866	A806	150f multi (4-4)	.30
		Nos. 2863-2866 (4)	1.00

Beijing University, Cent. A807

1998, May 4   Litho.   Perf. 12
2867	A807	50f multicolored	.20

22nd UPU Congress, Beijing A808

1998, May 15   Litho.   Perf. 12
2868	A808	50f Emblem (2-1)	.20
2869	A808	540f Emblem, vert. (2-2)	1.50

Shennongjia Nature Reserve — A809

#2870, Mountain peaks. #2871, River, gorge. #2872, Primitive forest. #2873, Grasslands.

1998, June 6
2870	A809	50f multi (4-1)	.20
2871	A809	50f multi (4-2)	.20
2872	A809	150f multi (4-3)	.40
2873	A809	150f multi (4-4)	.40
		Nos. 2870-2873 (4)	1.20

Chongqing — A810

1998, June 18   Litho.   Perf. 12
2874	A810	50f Great Hall (2-1)	.20
2875	A810	150f Port (2-2)	.40

Xilinguole Grassland — A811

Designs: No. 2876, Sheep grazing, sheep herders. No. 2877, Cattle grazing, flowers. 150f, Poplar and birch forest, deer. 800f, Xilinguole River Bend.

1998, June 24
2876	A811	50f multi (3-1)	.20
2877	A811	50f multi (3-2)	.20
2878	A811	150f multi (3-3)	.40
		Nos. 2876-2878 (3)	.80

Souvenir Sheet
2879	A811	800f multicolored	2.75

No. 2879 contains one 56x36mm stamp.

Paintings, by He Xiangning (1878-1972) — A812

Perf. 12½ Syncopated Type A (2 Sides)

1998, June 27   Photo.
2880	A812	50f Tiger (3-1)	.25
2881	A812	100f Lion, vert. (3-2)	.30
2882	A812	150f Plum blossom, vert. (3-3)	.45
		Nos. 2880-2882 (3)	1.00

Jingpo Lake — A813

Views of lake: No. 2883, Bridge, houses on cliff, boat. No. 2884, Islands, boats at shore. No. 2885, Boat, island. No. 2886, Waterfalls.

1998, Aug. 15   Litho.   Perf. 12
2883	A813	50f multi (4-1)	.20
2884	A813	50f multi (4-2)	.20
2885	A813	50f multi (4-3)	.20
2886	A813	50f multi (4-4)	.20
a.		Strip of 4, #2883-2886	.55

Würzburg Palace — A814

Puning Temple, Chengde — A815

1998, Aug. 20   Litho.   Perf. 12
2887	A814	50f multi (2-1)	.20	.20
2888	A815	540f multi (2-2)	1.25	1.25

See Germany Nos. 2012-2013.

Literature Type of 1987

Romance of the Three Kingdoms: No. 2889, Liu Bei finds a guardian for his heir at Baidi City. No. 2890, Zhuge Liang leads his army home, vert. 100f, Death of Zhuge Liang. 150f, Three Kingdoms united under the reign of Jin, vert.
800f, The Stratagem of Empty City.

1998, Aug. 26   Photo.   Perf. 11½
2889	A570	50f multi (4-1)	.20	.20
2890	A570	50f multi (4-2)	.20	.20
2891	A570	100f multi (4-3)	.25	.25
2892	A570	150f multi (4-4)	.45	.45
		Nos. 2889-2892 (4)	1.10	1.10

Souvenir Sheet
2893	A570	800f multicolored	4.00	3.50

No. 2893 contains one 158x37mm stamp.

Flood Victims Relief — A816

1998, Sept. 10   Photo.   Perf. 13x13½
2894	A816	50f + 50f label	.30	.30

The Louvre, France A817

Design: 200f, Hall of Heavenly Peace, Imperial Palace, China.

1998, Sept. 12   Photo.   Perf. 13x13½
2895	A817	50f multi (2-1)	.20	.20
2896	A817	200f multi (2-2)	.50	.50

See France Nos. 2669-2670.

Cliff Paintings of Helan Mountains — A818

1998, Sept. 23   Litho.   Perf. 12
2897	A818	50f Human face (3-1)	.20	.20
2898	A818	100f Hunting (3-2)	.25	.25
2899	A818	150f Ox (3-3)	.35	.35
		Nos. 2897-2899 (3)	.80	.80

Longquan Pottery and Porcelain — A819

Designs: No. 2900, Vase with five spouts. No. 2901, Vase with phoenix ears. No. 2902, Double gourd vase. 150f, Ewer.

1998, Oct. 13
2900	A819	50f multi (4-1)	.20	.20
2901	A819	50f multi (4-2)	.20	.20
2902	A819	50f multi (4-3)	.20	.20
2903	A819	150f multi (4-4)	.40	.40
		Nos. 2900-2903 (4)	1.00	1.00

Mausoleum of Yandi A820

Designs: 50f, Meridian Gate. 100f, Saluting Pavilion. 150f, Tomb.

1998, Oct. 28   Litho.   Perf. 12
2904	A820	50f multi (3-1)	.20	.20
2905	A820	100f multi (3-2)	.25	.25
2906	A820	150f multi (3-3)	.35	.35
a.		Souvenir sheet, #2904-2906	1.75	1.50
		Nos. 2904-2906 (3)	.80	.80

Great Wall Type of 1995

10f, Jiumenko Pass. 300f, Niagziguan Pass. 420f, Pianguan Pass. 500f, Bianjing Tower.

1998, Nov. 1   Photo.   Perf. 13x12
2907	A730	10f apple green & black	.20	.20
2908	A730	300f olive & black	.75	.75
2909	A730	420f brn org & blk	1.00	1.00
2910	A730	500f blue, black & brown	1.25	1.25
		Nos. 2907-2910 (4)	3.20	3.20

Major Campaigns in Liberation War — A821

#2911, Making plans. #2912, Conquering Jinzhou. #2913, Battle in Huaihai. #2914, Liberating Beijing. 150f, People moving supplies.

1998, Nov. 14   Litho.   Perf. 12
2911	A821	50f red & multi (5-1)	.20	.20
2912	A821	50f gray & multi (5-2)	.20	.20
2913	A821	50f org yel & multi (5-3)	.20	.20
2914	A821	50f orange & multi (5-4)	.20	.20
2915	A821	150f brn org & multi (5-5)	.35	.35
		Nos. 2911-2915 (5)	1.15	1.15

Liu Shaoqi (1898-1969), Communist Party Leader — A822

Various portraits.

1998, Nov. 24   Photo.   Perf. 11½
2916	A822	50f multi (4-1), vert.	.20	.20
2917	A822	50f multi (4-2), vert.	.20	.20
2918	A822	50f shown (4-3)	.20	.20
2919	A822	150f multi (4-4)	.35	.35
		Nos. 2916-2919 (4)	.95	.95

Chillon Castle, Lake Geneva
A823

Bridge 24, Slender West Lake, Yangzhou
A824

1998, Nov. 25   **Perf. 11x11½**
2920 A823 50f multi (2-1)   .20   .20
2921 A824 540f multi (2-2)   1.30   1.30
See Switzerland Nos. 1037-1039.

Lingqu Canal — A825

#2922, Dam. #2923, Bridge over canal, vert. 150f, Boat approaching lock, vert.

1998, Dec. 1   **Litho.**   **Perf. 12**
2922 A825 50f multi (3-1)   .20   .20
2923 A825 50f multi (3-2)   .20   .20
2924 A825 150f multi (3-3)   .35   .35
    Nos. 2922-2924 (3)   .75   .75

Buildings in Macao — A826

Designs: 50f, Building complex, Nanwan. 100f, Friendship Bridge. 150f, Macao Stadium. 200f, Macao Intl. Airport.

1998, Dec. 12   **Litho.**   **Perf. 12**
2925 A826 50f multi (4-1)   .20   .20
2926 A826 100f multi (4-2)   .25   .25
2927 A826 150f multi (4-3)   .35   .35
2928 A826 200f multi (4-4)   .55   .55
    Nos. 2925-2928 (4)   1.35   1.35

11th Communist Party Congress, 20th Anniv. — A827

1998, Dec. 18
2929 A827 50f Deng Xiaoping (2-1)   .20   .20
2930 A827 150f Handbill, buildings (2-2)   .35   .35

Fish of the Coral Reef
A828

a, Pomacanthus imperator (8-1). b, Plectropomus maculatus (8-2). c, Chaetodon plebeius (8-3). d, Chaetodon chrysurus (8-4), vert. e, Heniochus acuminatus (8-5), vert. f, Lutjanus sebae (8-6). g, Balistoides conspicillum (8-7). h, Pygoplites diacanthus (8-8).

1998, Dec. 22   **Photo.**   **Perf. 11½**
         Sheet of 8
2931 A828 200f #a.-h. + label   5.00   5.00
  i.   As No. 2931, with margin ovptd. in gold   6.00   6.00

UPU, 22nd Congress, Beijing '99 World Philatelic Exhibition.
Nos. 2931d-2931e are each 40x49mm. No.2931i issued 7/15/00. No. 2931i inscribed in margin in gold "PJZ-12" , "1997-1999" and Chinese characters. Inscription for best philatelic item from 1997-99.

New Year 1999 (Year of the Rabbit)
A829   A830

Photo. & Engr.
1999, Jan. 5   **Perf. 11½**
2932 A829 50f Stylized rabbit (2-1)   .20   .20
2933 A830 150f Symbol for rabbit (2-2)   .35   .35

Great Wall Type of 1995

5f, Hushan Section. 20f, Shanhaiguan Pass. 40f, Jinshanling Section. 80f, Mutianyu Section. 270f, Pingxingguan Pass. 320f, Desheng Pass. 440f, Yanmen Pass. 540f, Zhenbei Tower.

1999, Mar. 1   **Photo.**   **Perf. 13x12**
2934 A730 5f bl, blk & bl grn   .20   .20
2935 A730 20f vio & blk   .20   .20
2936 A730 40f pink & blk   .20   .20
2937 A730 80f grn, blk & ol   .20   .20
2938 A730 270f grn, blk & brn   .65   .65
2939 A730 320f vio, blk & bwn   .75   .75
2940 A730 440f red brn, blk & bwn   1.10   1.10
2941 A730 540f blue & black   1.25   1.25
    Nos. 2934-2941 (8)   4.55   4.55

Stone Carvings of the Han Dynasty
A831

#2942, Plowing fields with oxen. #2943, Group weaving. #2944, Three figures dancing in front of fire. #2945, Horses, carriage. #2946, Group in assassination attempt. #2947, Goddess Chang'e.

1999, Mar. 16   **Perf. 12**
2942 A831 50f dark green & blk   .20   .20
2943 A831 50f brown & blk   .20   .20
2944 A831 50f dark blue & blk   .20   .20
2945 A831 150f dark brown & blk   .35   .35
2946 A831 150f brown olive & blk   .35   .35
2947 A831 150f dark purple & blk   .35   .35
    Nos. 2942-2947 (6)   1.65   1.65

A832

A833

Chinese Ceramics (Porcelain from the Jun Kiln): 80f, Halberd-shaped cup. 100f, Cup. 150f, Dual-handled stove. 200f, Dual-handled vase with base.

1999, Apr. 8   **Photo.**   **Perf. 11½**
2948 A832 80f multi (4-1)   .20   .20
2949 A832 100f multi (4-2)   .25   .25
2950 A832 150f multi (4-3)   .35   .35
2951 A832 200f multi (4-4)   .50   .50
    Nos. 2948-2951 (4)   1.30   1.30

Great Wall Type of 1995

Designs: 60f, Huanghua Tower. $10, Huama section. $20, Sanguankou Pass. $50 Jiayuguan Pass.

1999, May 1   **Photo.**   **Perf. 13x12**
2952 A730 60f multicolored   .30   .30
      Size: 28x22mm
      Perf. 11½
      Photo. & Engr.
2953 A730 $10 multicolored   3.00   3.00
2954 A730 $20 multicolored   5.75   5.75
2955 A730 $50 multicolored   14.50   14.50
    Nos. 2952-2955 (4)   23.55   23.55

1999, May 1   **Litho.**   **Perf. 12**
2956 A833 80f shown (2-1)   .20   .20
2957 A833 200f Tree (2-2)   .50   .50

Kunming World Horticultural Fair.

Red Deer
A834

1999, May 18   **Litho.**   **Perf. 11x11½**
2958 A834 80f Bucks   .20   .20
2959 A834 80f Does   .20   .20
  a.   Pair, #2958-2959   .45   .45

See Russia No. 6514.

Beauty of Putuo Mountain — A835

1999, June 3   **Litho.**   **Perf. 12**
2960 A835 30f Puji Temple (6-1)   .20   .20
2961 A835 60f Nantian Gate, vert. (6-2)   .20   .20
2962 A835 60f 100-step Sand (6-3)   .20   .20
2963 A835 80f Pantuo Rock (6-4)   .20   .20
2964 A835 80f Fanyin Cave, vert. (6-5)   .20   .20
2965 A835 280f Fayu Temple (6-6)   .65   .65
    Nos. 2960-2965 (6)   1.65   1.65

Fang Zhimin (1899-1935), Revolutionary
A836

1999, Aug. 21   **Photo.**   **Perf. 11¼**
2966 A836 80f Close-up (2-1)   .30   .30
2967 A836 80f Standing (2-2)   .30   .30

      Souvenir Sheet

China 1999 World Philatelic Exhibition — A837

Illustration reduced.

1999, Aug. 21   **Perf. 11½x11¼**
2968 A837 800f multicolored   3.25   3.25

Exists overprinted in upper corners in gold. Value, $10.

A838

22nd UPU Congress — A839

Congress sites: 80f, 1st, Bern. 540f, 22nd, Beijing.
800f, Inscription by Pres. Jiang Zemin. A839 illustration reduced.

1999, Aug. 23   **Litho.**   **Perf. 12**
2969 A838 80f multi (2-1)   .20   .20
2970 A838 540f multi (2-2)   1.25   1.25
      Souvenir Sheet
      Perf. 12¼
2971 A839 800f multicolored   2.75   2.75

UPU, 125th Anniv. — A840

Intl. Year of the Elderly — A841

1999, Sept. 7   **Litho.**   **Perf. 12**
2972 A840 80f multicolored   .30   .30

1999, Sept. 9
2973 A841 80f multicolored   .20   .20

Chinese People's Political Consultative Conference, 50th Anniv. — A842

1999, Sept. 21
2974 A842 60f Building (2-1) .20 .20
2975 A842 80f Mao Zedong, vert. (2-2) .20 .20

Ethnic Groups in China — A843

Designs (stamp number following "56-" at LR): a, Han (1). b, Mongols (2). c, Hui (3). d, Tibetans (4). e, Uygurs (5) f, Miao (6). g, Yi (7). h, Zhuang (8). i, Bouyei (9). j, Koreans (10). k, Manchu (11). l, Dongs (12). m, Yao (13). n, Bai (14). o, Tujia (15). p, Hani (16). q, Kazak (17). r, Dai (18). s, Li (19). t, Lisu (20). u, Va (21). v, She (22). w, Gaoshan (23). x, Lahu (24). y, Shui (25). z, Dongxiang (26). aa, Naxi (27). ab, Jingpo (28). ac, Kirgiz (29). ad, Tu (30). ae, Daur (31). af, Mulam (32). ag, Qiang (33). ah, Blang (34). ai, Salas (35). aj, Maonan (36). ak, Gelao (37). al, Xibe (38). am, Achang (39). an, Pumi (40). ao, Tajiks (41). ap, Nu (42). aq, Uzbeks (43). ar, Russians (44). as, Ewenki (45). at, De'ang (46). au, Bonan (47). av, Yugur (48). aw, Jing (49). ax, Tartars (50). ay, Drung (51). az, Oroqen (52). ba, Hezhe (53). bb, Moiba (54). bc, Lhoba (55). bd, Jino (56).

1999, Oct. 7 Photo. Perf. 13¼
2976 A843 80f Sheet of 56, #a.-bd. 15.00 15.00

Mountains — A844

1999, Oct. 5 Perf. 11½x11¼
2977 A844 80f Lushan (2-1) .20 .20
2978 A844 80f Kuryongyon (2-2) .20 .20

Project Hope, 10th Anniv. — A845

Li Lisan (1899-1967), Minister of Labor — A847

Scientific and Technological Achievements — A846

1999, Oct. 30 Photo. Perf. 11½
2979 A845 80f multi .20 .20

1999, Nov. 1 Litho. Perf. 12
Designs: No. 2980, Cambrian era fossil. No. 2981, Underwater robot. No. 2982, Best result of Goldbach conjecture, vert. No. 2983, 2.16m telescope, vert.

2980 A846 80f multi (4-1) .20 .20
2981 A846 80f multi (4-2) .20 .20
  a. Pair, #2980-2981 .45 .45
2982 A846 80f multi (4-3) .20 .20
2983 A846 80f multi (4-4) .20 .20
  a. Pair, #2982-2983 .45 .45
  Nos. 2980-2983 (4) .80 .80

1999, Nov. 19 Photo. Perf. 11½
2984 A847 80f As young man (2-1) .20 .20
2985 A847 80f Wearing glasses (2-2) .20 .20

Return of Macao to China — A848

Designs: 80f, Sino-Portuguese declaration, flower. 150f, Basic Law of Macao Special Administrative Region, Great Wall. 800f, $50, Deng Xiaoping.

1999-2000 Photo. Perf. 11¾x11½
2986 A848 80f multi (2-1) .20 .20
2987 A848 150f multi (2-2) .35 .35

Souvenir Sheets Perf. 13
2988 A848 800f multi 3.50 3.50

Litho. (stamp) & Embossed (margin) Perf. 12
2989 A848 $50 multi 24.00 24.00
  a. Overprinted in margin 37.50 37.50

No. 2988 contains one 60x50mm stamp with star-shaped perforations in the corners. Overprint in margin on No. 2989a is Chinese inscription "2000-1" and "(2-2)J." Issued: No. 2989a, 1/1/00; others, 12/20/99.

Nie Rongzhen (1899-1992), Military Leader — A849

New Year 2000 (Year of the Dragon) — A851

Millennium — A850

1999, Dec. 29 Litho. Perf. 12
2990 A849 80f In uniform (2-1) .20 .20
2991 A849 80f Seated (2-2) .20 .20

1999, Dec. 31 Litho. Perf. 12
No. 2992, Sun Yat-sen, #590. No. 2993, #2214. No. 2994, #2339. No. 2995, #2601.

No. 2996, Mao Zedong, #456. 200f, #2248. 260f, #2730. 280f, Deng Xiaoping, #2774C.

2992 A850 60f multi (8-1) .20 .20
2993 A850 60f multi (8-2) .20 .20
2994 A850 80f multi (8-3) .20 .20
2995 A850 80f multi (8-4) .20 .20
2996 A850 80f multi (8-5) .20 .20
2997 A850 200f multi (8-6) .45 .45
2998 A850 260f multi (8-7) .60 .60
2999 A850 280f multi (8-8) .65 .65
  Nos. 2992-2999 (8) 2.70 2.70

Photo. & Engr.
2000, Jan. 5 Perf. 11½x11¾
3000 A851 80f Dragon (2-1) .20 .20
3001 A851 $2.80 Rising sun (2-2) .60 .60

A852

Spring Festival: No. 3002, Welcoming the Spring Festival. No. 3003, Bidding farewell to outgoing year. $2.80, Offering sacrifices to god of land.
$8, Family reunion, horiz.

2000, Jan. 29 Photo. Perf. 11¼
3002 A852 80f multi (3-1) .20 .20
3003 A852 80f multi (3-2) .20 .20
3004 A852 $2.80 multi (3-3) .65 .65
  Nos. 3002-3004 (3) 1.05 1.05

Souvenir Sheet Perf. 11¼x11
3005 A852 $8 multi 5.00 5.00
  a. Ovptd. in sheet margin 7.50 7.50

No. 3005 contains one 90x60mm stamp. No. 3005a contains gold Chinese inscription for New Century Philatelic Exhibition, "2000," and "PJZ-11" in sheet margin. Issued: 4/28.

A853

2000, Feb. 25 Photo. Perf. 13¼x13
Wildlife.
3006 Sheet of 10 + 2 labels 6.00 6.00
  a. A853 30f Nipponia nippon .20 .20
  b. A853 60f Teinopalpus aureus .20 .20
  c. A853 80f Ailuropoda melanoleuca .20 .20
  d. A853 $1 Crossoptilon manichuricum .20 .20
  e. A853 $1.50 Acipenser sinensis .30 .30
  f. A853 $2 Rhinopithecus roxellanae .40 .40
  g. A853 $2.60 Lipotes vexillifer .55 .55
  h. A853 $2.80 Grus japonensis .60 .60
  i. A853 $3.70 Panthera tigris .80 .80
  j. A853 $5.40 Alligator sinensis 1.25 1.25

Cultural Relics — A854

Designs; 60f, Neolithic Age jade dragon. No. 3008, Dragon-shaped ornament. No. 3009, Carved tile with dragon. No. 3010, Copper mirror with dragon. No. 3011, Bronze dragon. $2.80, Dragon on sandalwood throne.

2000, Mar. 7 Litho. Perf. 12
3007 A854 60f multi (6-1) .20 .20
3008 A854 80f multi (6-2) .20 .20
3009 A854 80f multi (6-3) .20 .20
3010 A854 80f multi (6-4) .20 .20
3011 A854 80f multi (6-5) .20 .20
3012 A854 $2.80 multi (6-6) .60 .60
  Nos. 3007-3012 (6) 1.60 1.60

Yangtze River Highway Bridges — A855

2000, Mar. 26 Litho. Perf. 12
3013 A855 80f Wanxian (4-1) .20 .20
3014 A855 80f Huangshi (4-2) .20 .20
3015 A855 80f Tongling (4-3) .20 .20
3016 A855 $2.80 Jiangyin (4-4) .60 .60
  Nos. 3013-3016 (4) 1.20 1.20

Landscapes in Dali — A856

Designs: No. 3017, Cangshan Mountain and Erhai Lake. No. 3018, Pagodas at Chongsheng Temple. No. 3019, Jizu Mountain. $2.80, Shibao Mountain.

Perf. 11¾x11½
2000, Apr. 19 Photo.
3017 A856 80f multi (4-1) .20 .20
3018 A856 80f multi (4-2) .20 .20
3019 A856 80f multi (4-3) .20 .20
3020 A856 $2.80 multi (4-4) .65 .65
  Nos. 3017-3020 (4) 1.25 1.25

Legend of Mulan — A857

Mulan: No. 3021, Weaving cloth. No. 3022, Joining army. No. 3023, On expedition. No. 3024, Returning home.

2000, Apr. 30 Litho. Perf. 12
3021 A857 80f multi (4-1) .20 .20
3022 A857 80f multi (4-2) .20 .20
3023 A857 80f multi (4-3) .20 .20
3024 A857 80f multi (4-4) .20 .20
  a. Strip, #3021-3024 2.00 2.00

Taer Lamasery A858

#3025, Good Luck Treasure Pagoda. #3026, Big Golden Tile Palace. #3027, Big Scripture Hall. $2.80, Banqen residence.

2000, May 5
3025 A858 80f multi (4-1) .20 .20
3026 A858 80f multi (4-2) .20 .20
3027 A858 80f multi (4-3) .20 .20
3028 A858 $2.80 multi (4-4) .65 .65
  Nos. 3025-3028 (4) 1.25 1.25

Cai Chang
and Li
Fuchun
A859

2000, May 22
3029 A859 80f multi　　　　　　.20　.20

Stampin' the Future Children's Stamp
Design Contest Winners — A860

Various children's drawings: #3030, 30f, (8-
1). #3031, 60f, (8-2). #3032, 60f, (8-3). #3033,
80f, (8-4). #3034, 80f, (8-5). #3035, 80f, (8-6).
$2.60, (8-7). $2.80, (8-8).

Perf. 11½x11¼
2000, June 1　　　　　　　　　**Photo.**
3030-3037 A860 Set of 8　　　　2.25 2.25

Chen Yun (1905-
95), Statesman
A861

#3038, 80f, As a young man (4-1). #3039,
80f, In uniform, vert. (4-2). #3040, 80f, In black
jacket, vert. (4-3). $2.80, As old man (4-4).

Perf. 13x13¼, 13¼x13
2000, June 13
3038-3041 A861 Set of 4　　　　1.25 1.25

Pots
A862

Designs: No. 3042, 80f, Wine vessel (2-1).
No. 3042, 80f, Horse milk pot (2-2).

2000, June 28　　**Litho.**　　**Perf. 12**
3042-3043 A862 Set of 2　　　　.40　.40

See Kazakhstan No. 305.

Laoshan Mountain — A863

#3044, 80f, Huge Peak (4-1). #3045, 80f,
Yangkou Bay (4-2). #3046, 80f, Beijiu Lake (4-
3). $2.80, Taiqing Palace (4-4).

Perf. 11½x11¼
2000, July 15　　　　　　　　　**Photo.**
3044-3047 A863 Set of 4　　　　1.50 1.50
3047a　　　Souvenir sheet, #3044-3047　6.00 6.00

Souvenir Sheet

All-China Philatelic Federation, Fifth
Congress — A864

Illustration reduced.

2000, July 18　　**Litho.**　　**Perf. 12**
3048 A864 $8 multi　　　　　　4.75 4.75
a.　　Margin ovptd. in gold　　　5.25　—

No. 3048a issued 9/21/01. It is inscribed in
margin in gold "PJZ-13," "2001," with Chinese
characters and Nanjing 2001 Philatelic Exhibition mascot.

Small Carp Leap
Through Dragon
Gate
Legend — A865

No. 3049: a, Grandma Carp tells a story (5-
1). b, Small Carp look for Dragon Gate (5-2).
c, Help from Uncle Crab (5-3). d, Small Carp
leap through Dragon Gate (5-4). e, Aunt Swallow passes on a letter (5-5).

2000, Aug. 8　　**Photo.**　　**Perf. 11½**
3049 A865 80f Horiz. strip of 5,
　　　　　　#a-e　　　　　　　2.00 2.00
f.　　Booklet pane, #3049 + 2 la-
　　　bels, perf. 12　　　　　　10.00
　　　Booklet, #3049f　　　　　1.00

Shenzhen Special Eonomic
Zone — A866

No. 3050: a, 80f, Financial Center district (5-
1). b, 80f, China Intl. Exhibition Center (5-2). c,
80f, Yantian Harbor area (5-3). d, 80f,
Shenzhen Bay tourist area (5-4). e, $2.80,
Shekou industrial district (5-5).

2000, Aug. 26　　**Litho.**　　**Perf. 12**
3050 A866　Horiz. strip of 5,
　　　　　　#a-e　　　　　　　1.50 1.50

2000 Summer Olympics,
Sydney — A867

Illustration reduced.

2000, Sept. 15　**Photo.**　**Perf. 13¼x13**
3051 A867 $8 multi　　　　　3.75 3.75
a.　　Sheet of 2　　　　　　40.00 40.00

No. 3051a issued 10/31/00.

Beaches — A868

---

a, Coconuts Bay, PRC (2-1). b, Varadero
Beach, Cuba (2-2).

2000, Sept. 26　　**Litho.**　　**Perf. 12**
3052 A868　Pair　　　　　　.40　.40
a.-b.　　80f Any single　　　　.20　.20

See Cuba Nos. 4108-4109.

Masks and
Puppets
A869

No. 3053, Tan background (2-1). No. 3054,
Violet blue background (2-2).

2000, Oct. 9　　**Photo.**　　**Perf. 13x13½**
3053-3054 A869 80f Set of 2　　.40　.40

See Brazil Nos. 2767-2768.

Relics from the
Tomb of Prince Jing
of
Zhongshan — A870

#3055, 80f, Eternal Fidelity palace lamp (4-
1). #3056, 80f, Bronze pot (4-2). #3057, 80f,
Boshan incense burner (4-3). $2.80, Cup (4-
4).

2000, Oct. 20　　　　　**Perf. 13½x13¼**
3055-3058 A870　Set of 4　　　1.25 1.25

Ancient
Thinkers — A871

#3059, 60f, Confucius (6-1). #3060, 80f,
Mencius (6-2). #3061, 80f, Lao Zi (6-3).
#3062, 80f, Zhuang Zi (6-4). #3063, 80f, Mo Zi
(6-5). $2.80, Xun Zi (6-6).

Photo. & Engr.
2000, Nov. 11　　　　　　**Perf. 11¼x11**
3059-3064 A871　Set of 6　　　1.60 1.60

Test of Shenzhou Spacecraft, 1st
Anniv. — A872

No. 3065: a, Launch (2-1). b, In orbit (2-2).
Illustration reduced.

2000, Nov. 20　　**Photo.**　　**Perf. 11½**
3065 A872　Pair　　　　　　1.75 1.75
a.-b.　　80f Any single　　　　.20　.20
c.　　Sheet, 6 #3065　　　35.00 35.00

World Meteorological Organization,
50th Anniv. — A873

Designs: No. 3066, 80f, Weather satellite (4-
1). No. 3067, 80f, Weather measuring equipment on Qinghai-Tibetan Plateau (4-2). No.
3068, 80f, Weather-predicting computer (4-3).
$2.80, Airplane for cloud seeding (4-4).

2000, Nov. 22　　**Litho.**　　**Perf. 12**
3066-3069 A873　Set of 4　　　1.25 1.25

Flowers — A874

#3070, 80f, Scarlet kaffir lily (4-1). #3071,
80f, Noble clivia (4-2). #3072, 80f, Golden striated lily (4-3). $2.80, White kaffir lily (4-4).

Perf. 11¼x11½
2000, Dec. 12　　　　　　　　　**Photo.**
3070-3073 A874　Set of 4　　　1.25 1.25
3073a　　　Souv. sheet, #3070-3073　6.00 6.00

Ancient
Bells — A875

#3074, 80f, Jingshu bell (4-1). #3075, 80f,
Su chime bell (4-2). #3076, 80f, Jingyun bell
(4-3). $2.80, Qianlong bell (4-4).

2000, Dec. 31　　　　　　**Perf. 11¼x11½**
3074-3077 A875　Set of 4　　　1.25 1.25

Advent of New
Millennium
A876

Designs: 60f, Sun, moon, date, time, building (5-1). No. 3079, 80f, Dove, Earth (5-2). No.
3080, 80f, Map, leaf, infant's hands (5-3). No.
3081, 80f, Circuitboard, head, Earth, horiz. (5-
4). $2.80, Moon, stars, sundial (5-5).

2001, Jan. 1　　**Litho.**　　**Perf. 12**
3078-3082 A876　Set of 5　　　1.40 1.40

New Year 2001
(Year of the
Snake) — A877

Snake and: 80f, Flower (2-1). $2.80, Chi-
nese character for snake (2-2).

Photo. & Engr.
2001, Jan. 5　　　　　**Perf. 11½x11¾**
3083 A877 80f multi　　　　　.20　.20
a.　　Sheet of 6　　　　　　6.00 6.00
3084 A877 $2.80 multi　　　　.70　.70
a.　　Sheet of 6　　　　　20.00 20.00

Clown Roles in Peking Opera — A878

Designs: No. 3085, 80f, Tang Qin (6-1). No. 3086, 80f, Lin Lihua (6-2). No. 3087, 80f, Gao Lishi (6-3). No. 3088, 80f, Jiang Gan (6-4). No. 3089, 80f, Yang Xiangwu (6-5). $2.80, Shi Qian (6-6).

2001, Feb. 15   Photo.   Perf. 11½x11
3085-3090 A878   Set of 6   1.60 1.60

Wildlife — A879

2001, Mar. 16   Perf. 13¼x13
3091   Sheet of 10 + 2 labels   9.00 9.00
  a.   A879 30f Budorcas taxicolor   .20   .20
  b.   A879 60f Psephurus gladius   .40   .40
  c.   A879 60f Elaphurus davidianus   .40   .40
  d.   A879 80f Acipenser dabryanus   .50   .50
  e.   A879 80f Capra ibex   .50   .50
  f.   A879 80f Haliaeetus pelagicus   .50   .50
  g.   A879 80f Camelus bactrianus   .50   .50
  h.   A879 $1 Uncia uncia   .65   .65
  i.   A879 $2.60 Martes zibellina   1.75 1.75
  j.   A879 $5.40 Saiga tatarica   3.50 3.50

Ancient Towns — A880

Designs: No. 3092, 80f, Zhouzhuang, Kunshan (6-1). No. 3093, 80f, Tongli, Wujiang (6-2). No. 3094, 80f, Wuzhen, Tongxiang (6-3). No. 3095, 80f, Nanxun, Huzhou (6-4). No. 3096, 80f, Luzhi, Wuxian (6-5). $2.80, Xitang, Jiashan (6-6).

2001, Apr. 7   Photo.   Perf. 11½x11¼
3092-3097 A880   Set of 6   2.10 2.10
3097a   Booklet pane, #3092-3097
           + 6 labels   8.75
           Booklet, #3097a   8.75

Strange Stories From a Chinese Studio, by Pu Songling — A881

Designs: 60f, Ying Ning (4-1). No. 3099, 80f, A Bao (4-2). No. 3100, 80f, Mask of Evildoer (4-3). $2.80, Stealing Peach (4-4).
$8, Taoist Priest from Laoshan.

2001, Apr. 21   Perf. 11½
3098-3101 A881   Set of 4   1.60 1.60
Souvenir Sheet
Perf. 13½x13
3102 A881 $8 multi   10.00 10.00
No. 3102 contains one 90x60mm stamp.

Yongle Temple Murals A882

No. 3103: a, Lady Queen Mother (4-1). b, Jade Lady Presenting Treasure (4-2). c, Celestial Worthy of the East (4-3). d, Venus and Mercury (4-4).

2001, May 5   Litho.   Perf. 12
3103   Horiz. strip of 4   1.60 1.60
  a.   A882 60f multi   .20   .20
  b.-c. A882 80f Any single   .25   .25
  d.   A882 $2.80 multi   .90   .90

Mount Wudang — A883

Designs: 60f, Nanyan Hall (3-1). No. 3105, 80f, Zixiao Temple (3-2). No. 3106, 80f, Taizi Slope (3-3).
$8, Golden Crown in spring.

Perf. 11¼x11½
2001, May 26   Photo.
3104-3106 A883   Set of 3   .65   .65
Souvenir Sheet
Perf. 12¼x12½
3107 A883 $8 multi + label   7.00 7.00
No. 3107 contains one 47x71mm stamp.

Ancient Chinese Receptacles A884

Designs: No. 3108, 80f, Earthenware vase. No. 3109, 80f, Porcelain coffee pot.

2001, June 12   Perf. 11¼x11½
3108-3109 A884   Set of 2   .40   .40
See Belgium Nos. 1858-1859.

Dragon Boat Festival A885

Designs: No. 3110, Dragon boat race (3-1). No. 3111, Making Zongzi (3-2). $2.80, Expelling five poisons (3-3).

2001, June 25   Photo.   Perf. 13x13½
3110 A885   80f multi   .20   .20
  a.   Sheet of 9   8.00
3111 A885   80f multi   .20   .20
  a.   Sheet of 9   8.00
3112 A885 $2.80 multi   .70   .70
  a.   Sheet of 9   30.00
       Nos. 3110-3112 (3)   1.10 1.10
Nos. 3110-3112 each issued in sheets of 40.

Early Leaders of the Communist Party — A886

Designs: No. 3113, 80f, Wang Jinmei (5-1). No. 3114, 80f, Zhao Shiyan (5-2). No. 3115, 80f, Deng Enming (5-3). No. 3116, 80f, Cai Hesen (5-4). No. 3117, 80f, He Shuheng (5-5).

2001, June 28   Perf. 11¼x11
3113-3117 A886   Set of 5   1.00 1.00

Communist Party, 80th Anniv. A887

2001, July 1   Photo.   Perf. 13x13¼
3118 A887 80f multi   .25   .25
  a.   Sheet of 8   14.00
No. 3118 issued in sheets of 40.

Emblem of 2008 Summer Olympics, Beijing — A888

2001, July 14   Perf. 13x13¼
3119 A888 80f multi + label   .25   .25
  a.   Sheet of 36 + 39 labels   40.00   —
No. 3119 printed in sheets of 12 stamp + label pairs with one large central label. See Hong Kong No. 940, Macao No. 1067.
No. 3119a contains 12 each of No. 3119, Hong Kong No. 940 (with different adjacent label), and Macao No. 1067 (with different adjacent label).

Waterfalls A889

Designs: No. 3120, 80f, Yinlianzhuitan (3-1). No. 3121, 80f, Doupotang, horiz. (3-2). No. 3122, 80f, Dishuitan (3-3).
$8, Huangguoshu.

Perf. 12¼x12, 12x12¼
2001, July 22   Litho.
3120-3122 A889   Set of 3   .60   .60
Souvenir Sheet
Perf. 12
3123 A889 $8 multi   5.00 5.00
No. 3123 contains one 40x60mm stamp.

Beidaihe Beach — A890

Designs: 60f, Pigeon Nest (4-1). No. 3125, 80f, Zhonghai Beach (4-2). No. 3126, 80f, Lianfeng Hill (4-3). $2.80, Tiger Stone (4-4).

2001, Aug. 5   Litho.   Perf. 12
3124-3127 A890   Set of 4   1.40 1.40

21st Universiade A891

Emblem, "2001" and: 60f, Concentric circles (3-1). 80f, Runners (3-2). $2.80, Hemispheres of globe (3-3).

2001, Aug. 22   Litho.
3128-3130 A891   Set of 3   1.10 1.10
3129a   Sheet of 20 + 20 labels   20.00
No. 3129a exists with different margin designs.
Sheets of four No. 3129 plus four labels were not placed on sale but were included with 2001 year sets. Uncut sheets containing two of these sheets also exist.

Datong River Diversion Project — A892

Designs: No. 3131, 80f, Sluice gates (4-1). No. 3132, 80f, Xianming Gorge water pipeline (4-2). No. 3133, 80f, Tunnel (4-3). $2.80, Zhuanglang River Aqueduct (4-4).

2001, Aug. 26
3131-3134 A892   Set of 4   1.40 1.40

Wuhu Bridge — A893

View from: 80f, Shore (2-1). $2.80, Roadway (2-2).

Photo. & Engr.
2001, Sept. 20   Perf. 11½x11¼
3135-3136 A893   Set of 2   1.00 1.00

Orchids A894

Designs: No. 3137, 80f, Paphiopedilum malipoense (4-1). No. 3138, 80f, Paphiopedilum dianthum (4-2). No. 3139, 80f, Paphiopedilum markianum (4-3). $2.80, Paphiopedilum appletonianum (4-4).

2001, Sept. 28   Photo.   Perf. 12½
3137-3140 A894   Set of 4   1.40 1.40
3140a   Souvenir sheet, #3137-
           3140   5.75

Ancient Gold Masks — A895

Designs: No. 3141, 80f, Mask of San Xing Dui (2-1). No. 3142, 80f, Funerary mask of King Tutankhamun, Egypt (2-2).

2001, Oct. 12   *Perf. 11¾x11½*
3141-3142 A895   Set of 2   .60   .60
See Egypt Nos. 1807-1808.

People's Republic of China as 2001 Asia-Pacific Economic Cooperation Head
A896

2001, Oct. 20   Litho.   *Perf. 12*
3143 A896 80f multi   .25   .25

Souvenir Sheet

Ertan Hydroelectric Plant — A897

2001, Oct. 20   Litho.   *Perf. 12¼*
3144 A897 $8 multi   3.00   3.00

Horses, Zhaoling Mausoleum
A898

Horse: a, Facing right, galloping (6-1). b, Facing right, galloping, diff. (6-2). c, Facing right, walking (6-3). d, With attendant (6-4). e, Facing left, walking (6-5). f, Facing left, galloping (6-6).

2001, Oct. 28   Photo.   *Perf. 12*
Fawn Background
3145   Horiz. strip of 6   1.75   1.75
a.   A898 60f multi   .20   .20
b.-e. A898 80f multi   .20   .20
f.   A898 $2.80 multi   .75   .75
g.   Sheet, 2 each #3145a-3145c, white background, photo. & embossed   16.00   —
h.   Sheet, 2 each #3145d-3145f, white background, photo. & embossed   16.00   —

Sailing Ships — A899

No. 3146: a, Chinese junk, 13th cent. (2-1). b, Portuguese caravel, 15th cent. (2-2). Illustration reduced.

2001, Nov. 8   *Perf. 13x13¼*
3146 A899 80f Horiz. pair, #a-b   .45   .45
See Portugal No. 2454.

9th Natl. Games — A900

No. 3147: a, 80f, Diving (2-1). b, $2.80, Volleyball (2-2).

2001, Nov. 11   Litho.   *Perf. 12*
3147 A900 Horiz. pair, #a-b   1.00   1.00
c.   Souvenir sheet, #3147   3.75   3.75

Liupan Shan Mountains — A901

Various landscapes: No. 3148, 80f (4-1). No. 3149, 80f (4-2). No. 3150, 80f (4-3). $2.80, (4-4).

Photo. & Engr.
2001, Nov. 24   *Perf. 11¼x11½*
3148-3151 A901   Set of 4   1.60   1.60

Xiu Xian and the White Snake — A902

Designs: No. 3152, Women, umbrella (4-1). No. 3153, Three men (4-2). No. 3154, Man with sword, man with bowl (4-3). $2.80, Women on bridge (4-4).

Perf. 11½, 11½x11 (#3153-3154)
2001, Dec. 5   **Photo.**
3152 A902 80f multi   .20   .20
a.   Booklet pane of 1   1.00   —
3153 A902 80f multi   .20   .20
a.   Booklet pane of 1   1.00   —
3154 A902 80f multi   .20   .20
a.   Booklet pane of 1   1.00   —
3155 A902 $2.80 multi   .75   .75
a.   Booklet pane of 1   3.75   —
       Booklet, #3152a-3155a   6.75
       Nos. 3152-3155 (4)   1.35   1.35

Admission to World Trade Organization
A903

2001, Dec. 11   Photo.   *Perf. 13¼x13*
3156 A903 80f multi   1.25   1.25

Koxinga's Recovery of Taiwan from the Dutch, 340th Anniv. — A904

Koxinga and: No. 3157, 80f, Warriors, ships (3-1). No. 3158, 80f, Warriors, horse (3-2). $2.80, People, trees (3-3).

Perf. 11½x11¼
2001, Dec. 13   **Photo.**
3157-3159 A904   Set of 3   1.50   1.50

Souvenir Sheet

Qinhai - Tibet Railway — A905

2001, Dec. 29   *Perf. 13¼*
3160 A905 $8 multi   5.00   5.00

New Year 2002 (Year of the Horse) — A906

Designs: 80f, Ceramic horse (2-1). $2.80, Flowers, Chinese symbol for horse (2-2).

Photo. & Engr.
2002, Jan. 5   *Perf. 11½*
3161-3162 A906   Set of 2   .90   .90
Nos. 3161-3162 each exist in a miniature sheet of six. Value, each $10.

Art of Badashanren (1626-1705) A907

Designs: 60f, Two Eagles (6-1). No. 3164, 80f, Pine Tree (6-2). No. 3165, 80f, Lotus Flowers (6-3). No. 3166, 80f, Chysanthemum in Vase (6-4). $2.60, Two Magpies on a Rock (6-5). $2.80, Landscape After Dong Yuan (6-6).

Perf. 11¼x11½
2002, Jan. 20   **Photo.**
3163-3168 A907   Set of 6   2.10   2.10

Environmental Protection — A908

Designs: 5f, Keeping birth rate low. 10f, Forest conservation. 30f, Conservation of mineral resources. 60f, Preventing air pollution. 80f, Conservation of water. $1.50, Conservation of ocean resources.

Perf. 12¾x13¼ Syncopated
2002   **Photo.**
3169 A908 5f multi   .20   .20
3170 A908 10f multi   .20   .20
3171 A908 30f multi   .20   .20
3172 A908 60f multi   .20   .20
3173 A908 80f multi   .20   .20
3174 A908 $1.50 multi   .35   .35
       Nos. 3169-3174 (6)   1.35   1.35
Issued: 10f, 60f, 2/1; others, 4/1.

Birds — A909

Designs: 80f, Yellow-bellied tragopan. $1, Biddulph's ground jay. $2, Taiwan blue magpies. $4.20, Alashan redstart. $5.40, Kozlov's bunting.

2002   *Perf. 13¼*
3175 A909 80f multi   .20   .20
a.   Booklet pane of 10 +2 labels   2.00
       Booklet, #3175a   2.00
3176 A909 $1 multi   .30   .30
3177 A909 $2 multi   .60   .60
3178 A909 $4.20 multi   1.25   1.25
3179 A909 $5.40 multi   1.50   1.50
       Nos. 3175-3179 (5)   3.85   3.85
Issued: 80f, $1, $2, 2/1; Nos. 3178, 3179, 4/1. No. 3175a, 12/7.

Flowers — A910

No. 3180: a, Camellia nitidissima (2-1). b, Couroupita guianensis (2-2).

2002, Feb. 5   *Perf. 13¼x13*
3180 A910 80f Horiz. pair, #a-b   .40   .40
See Malaysia Nos. 861-864.

Musical Instruments A911

Designs: 60f, Yaqin (5-1). No. 3182, 80f, Erhu (5-2). No. 3183, 80f, Banhu (5-3). No. 3184, 80f, Satar (5-4). $2.80, Matouqin (5-5).

2002, Feb. 23   Litho.   *Perf. 12*
3181-3185 A911   Set of 5   1.40   1.40

Souvenir Sheet

The Royal Carriage, by Yan Liben — A912

2002, Mar. 16   **Photo.**
3186 A912 $8 multi   1.90   1.90

Song Dynasty Pottery and Porcelain from Ruyao Kilns A913

Designs: 60f, Wine vessel (4-1). No. 3188, 80f, Three-legged basin (4-2). No. 3189, 80f, Bowl (4-3). $2.80, Dish (4-4).

2002, Mar. 30   **Litho.**
3187-3190 A913   Set of 4   1.25   1.25

Strange Stories from a Chinese Studio, by Pu Songling — A914

No. 3191: a, 60f, Xi Fangping (4-1). b, 80f, Pianpian (4-2).
No. 3192: a, 80f, Tian Qilang (4-3). b, $2.80, Bai Qiulian (4-4).

2002, Apr. 21   Photo.   Perf. 11½
3191 A914 Vert. pair, #a-b   .40 .40
3192 A914 Horiz. pair, #a-b   .95 .95

Qianshan Mountain — A915

No. 3193: a, Wuliang Taoist Temple (4-1). b, Maitreya Peak (4-2). c, Longquan Temple (4-3). d, Terrace of Immortals (4-4).

2002, Apr. 26   Perf. 12
3193   Horiz. strip of 4   1.25 1.25
a.-c. A915 80f Any single   .20   .20
d.   A915 $2.80 multi   .65   .65

Ancient City of Lijiang — A916

Designs: No. 3194, 80f, Sifang Street (3-1). No. 3195, 80f, Stream, vert. (3-2). $2.80, House of Naxi people (3-3).

2002, May 1   Perf. 11½
3194-3196 A916 Set of 3   1.10 1.10
a. Souvenir sheet, #3194-3196 1.60 1.60
No. 3196a sold for $6.60.

Ruyi (Good Luck Symbol) — A917

2002, May 10   Litho.   Perf. 12
3197 A917 80f multi + label   .20   .20
Exists in miniature sheet of 4 + 4 vert. labels and in sheet of 16 + 16 horiz. labels.

Stamps with Attached Labels

Starting with No. 3197, stamps listed as having attached labels are known to have been issued in dozens of different sheets having various margin and label designs, various numbers of stamps and labels in the sheets, and different stamp and label combinations. Little information has been made available about these sheets, and all seem to have been sold for prices significantly above face value. Labels on these sheets do not seem to have been personalizable with personal photos but have illustrations with approved designs.

2002 World Cup Soccer Championships, Japan and Korea — A918

No. 3198: a, 80f, Player (2-1). b, $2.80, Players (2-2).
Illustration reduced.

2002, May 16   Photo.   Perf. 12¼
3198 A918 Horiz. pair, #a-b   .65   .65
A souvenir sheet containing People's Republic of China No. 3198, Hong Kong Nos. 978a-978b and Macao 1091a-1091b exists, and sold for premium over face value.

Lighthouses A919

Nautical charts and: No. 3199, 80f, Maota Pagoda Lighthouse (5-1). No. 3200, 80f, Jiangxin Pagoda Lighthouses (5-2). No. 3201, 80f, Huaniaoshan Lighthouse (5-3). No. 3202, 80f, Laotieshan Lighthouse (5-4). No. 3203, 80f, Lin'gao Lighthouse (5-5).

Photo. & Engr.
2002, May 18   Perf. 11½x11
3199-3203 A919 Set of 5   1.00 1.00

Yellow River Dams A920

Designs: No. 3204, 80f, Lijia Gorge (4-1). No. 3205, 80f, Liujia Gorge (4-2). No. 3206, 80f, Qingtong Gorge (4-3). No. 3207, 80f, Sanmen Gorge (4-4). $8, Xiaolangdi, vert.

2002, June 8   Photo.   Perf. 12
3204-3207 A920 Set of 4   1.00 1.00
Souvenir Sheet
Perf. 13x13¼
3208 A920 $8 multi   1.90 1.90
No. 3208 contains one 40x60mm stamp.

Dazu Stone Carvings — A921

Designs: No. 3209, 80f, Avalokitesvara of the Sun and Moon, North Mountain (4-1). No. 3210, 80f, Samantabhadra, North Mountain (4-2). No. 3211, 80f, Three Avatamasaka Sages, Holy Summit Mountain (4-3). No. 3212, 80f, Statue in Cave of the Three Emperors, Stone Gate Mountain (4-4).
$8, Avalokitesvara of a Thousand Hands, Holy Summit Mountain.

2002, June 18   Litho.   Perf. 12
3209-3212 A921 Set of 4   .80 .80
Souvenir Sheet
Photo.
Perf. 13x13¼
3213 A921 $8 multi   1.90 1.90
No. 3213 contains one 40x60mm stamp.

Desert Flowers A922

No. 3214: a, Ammopiptanthus mongolicus (4-1). b, Calligonum rubicandum (4-2). c, Hedysarum scoparium (4-3). d, Tamarix leptostachys (4-4).

2002, June 29 Photo. Perf. 13x13¼
3214   Vert. strip of 4   1.25 1.25
a.-c. A922 80f Any single   .20   .20
d.   A922 $2 multi   .50   .50

Antarctic Scenes A923

Designs: No. 3215, 80f, Penguins (3-1). No. 3216, 80f, Aurora Australis (3-2). $2, Bird, Grove Mountains (3-3).

2002, July 15   Litho.   Perf. 12
3215-3217 A923 Set of 3   .90 .90

Qinghai Lake — A924

Designs: No. 3218, 80f, Lake shore (3-1). No. 3219, 80f, Birds on rock (3-2). $2.80, View of lake and birds (3-3).

2002, July 20
3218-3220 A924 Set of 3   1.10 1.10

Early Communist Party Leaders — A925

Designs: No. 3221, 80f, Huang Gonglue (1898-1931) (5-1). No. 3222, 80f, Xu Jishen (1901-31) (5-2). No. 3223, 80f, Cai Shengxi (1906-32) (5-3). No. 3224, 80f, Wei Baqun (1894-1932) (5-4). No. 3225, 80f, Liu Zhidan (1903-36) (5-5).

2002, Aug. 1   Photo.
3221-3225 A925 Set of 5   1.00 1.00

Scientists of Ancient China — A926

Designs: No. 3226, 80f, Bian Que (4-1). No. 3227, 80f, Liu Hui (4-2). No. 3228, 80f, Su Song (4-3). No. 3229, 80f, Song Yingxing (4-4).

Photo. & Engr.
2002, Aug. 20   Perf. 11¼x11
3226-3229 A926 Set of 4   .80 .80

Yandangshan Mountain — A927

Designs: No. 3230, 80f, Xianshengmen Gate (4-1). No. 3231, 80f, Dalongqui Pond (4-2). No. 3232, 80f, Beidou Cave, horiz. (4-3). No. 3233, 80f, Guanyin Peak, horiz. (4-4).

2002, Sept. 7   Litho.   Perf. 12¾
3230-3233 A927 Set of 4   1.00 1.00

Mid-Autumn Festival — A928

Designs: No. 3234, 80f, Family reunion (3-1). No. 3235, 80f, People looking at Moon (3-2). $2, The Moon as a matchmaker (3-3).

2002, Sept. 21   Perf. 12
3234-3236 A928 Set of 3   .90 .90
Each printed in sheets of 20. Sheets of nine containing three of each stamp exist with a decorative border and a border with Chinese text for the Beijing 2002 Stamp Exhibition.

Peng Zhen (1902-97) — A929

Designs: No. 3237, 80f, Head of Peng Zhen (2-1). No. 3238, 80f, Peng Zhen standing (2-2).

2002, Oct. 12   Perf. 11¾x12
3237-3238 A929 Set of 2   .40 .40

Architecture in Slovakia and China — A930

No. 3239: a, Bojnice Castle, Slovakia (2-1). b, Handan Congtai Pavilion, China (2-2).

Photo. & Engr.

2002, Oct. 12   *Perf. 11¼x11*
3239 A930 80f Horiz. pair, #a-b   .40   .40
See Slovakia No. 410.

Dong Yong and Lady — A931

No. 3240: a, Dong Yong's filial love moves immortals (5-1). b, Dong Yong marries seventh immortal maiden (5-2). c, Immortal maiden weaving brocade (5-3). d, Dong Yong returns home (5-4). e, Everlasting love (5-5).

2002, Oct. 26   Litho.   Perf. 13¼x13
3240   Horiz. strip of 5   1.25   1.25
  a.-d. A931 80f Any single   .20   .20
  e.   A931 $2 multi   .45   .45

Nos. 3240a-3240e exist in booklet panes of one that made up a booklet that had limited distribution to people with standing order accounts.

Flower — A932

2002, Nov. 8   Litho.   Perf. 12
3241 A932 80f multi + label   .25   .25
Exists in a miniature sheet of 4 + 4 labels.

Souvenir Sheet

Hukou Waterfall — A933

Photo. (Margin Photo. & Embossed)
2002, Nov. 8   Perf. 13¼x13
3242 A933 $8 multi   1.90   1.90

Museums — A934

Designs: No. 3243, 80f, Shanxi History Museum (5-1). No. 3244, 80f, Shanghai Museum (5-2). No. 3245, 80f, Henan Museum (5-3). No. 3246, 80f, Tibet Museum (5-4). No. 3247, 80f, Tianjin Natural Museum.

2002, Nov. 9   Photo.   Perf. 12¾
3243-3247 A934   Set of 5   1.00   1.00

Martial Arts
A935

No. 3248: a, Kung Fu (2-1). b, Taekwondo (2-2).

2002, Nov. 20   Photo.   Perf. 12
3248 A935 80f Vert. pair, #a-b   .40   .40
No. 3248 is a joint issue with South Korea No. 2109.

Gibbons — A936

Designs: No. 3249, 80f, Hylobates lar (4-1). No. 3250, 80f, Hylobates leucogenys (4-2). No. 3251, 80f, Hylobates concolor (4-3). $2, Hylobates hoolock (4-4).

Photo. & Engr.
2002, Dec. 7   Perf. 11¼x11
3249-3252 A936   Set of 4   1.10   1.10

New Year 2003 (Year of the Ram) — A937

Designs: 80f, Ram (2-1). $2, Chinese symbol (2-2).

Photo. & Engr.
2003, Jan. 5   Perf. 11½
3253-3254 A937   Set of 2   .70   .70
Sheets of 8 + central label of Nos. 3253-3254 exist. Value, each $8.

Yangliuqing New Year Woodprints A938

Designs: No. 3255, 80f, Five boys wrestling for a lotus (4-1). No. 3256, 80f, Zhong Kui, vert. (4-2). No. 3257, 80f, Steaing the herb of immortality (4-3). $2, Wealth in a jade hall (4-4).

2003, Jan. 25   Photo.   Perf. 12
3255-3258 A938   Set of 4   1.10   1.10
A sheetlet containing two each #3255-3258 exists. Value $11.

Seal Characters
A939

Designs: No. 3259, 80f, 24 characters (2-1). No. 3260, 80f, 12 characters (2-2).

2003, Feb. 3   Litho.
3259-3260 A939   Set of 2   .40   .40
A sheetlet exists containing four each Nos. 3259-3260. Value $11.

Knot
A940

2003, Feb. 22
3261 A940 80f multi + label   .30   .30
Exists in sheets of 4 stamps + 4 labels. Value $20.
Perf 12¾ examples come from a sheetlet containing four examples with labels below the stamps that also contain four #3375. The sheetlet sold for $15.

Lilies
A941

Designs: 60f, Lilium taliense (4-1). No. 3263, 80f, Lilium lankongense (4-2). No. 3264, 80f, Lilium distichum (4-3). $2, Lilium lophophorum (4-4). $8, Lilium leucanthum.

2003, Mar. 5   Photo.   Perf. 13x13¼
3262-3265 A941   Set of 4   1.25   1.25

Souvenir Sheet
Perf. 13¼
3266 A941 $8 multi   2.50   2.50
Nos. 3262-3265 each exist in sheetlets of 10. Value, set of 4, $22.
No. 3266 contains one 75x53mm stamp.

Arch Bridges — A942

Designs: No. 3267, 80f, Maple Bridge (4-1). No. 3268, 80f, Xiaoshang Bridge (4-2). No. 3269, 80f, Lugouqiao Bridge (4-3). No. 3270, 80f, Double Dragon Bridge (4-4).

Photo. & Engr.
2003, Mar. 29   Perf. 11½
3267-3270 A942   Set of 4   1.00   1.00
A sheetlet of 8 exists for each of Nos. 3267-3270. Value, set of 2, $22.

Chinese and Iranian Buildings A943

Designs: No. 3271, 80f, Bell Tower, Xian, China (2-1). No. 3272, 80f, Mosque, Isfahan, Iran (2-2).

2003, Apr. 15   Photo.   Perf. 13x13¼
3271-3272 A943   Set of 2   .50   .50
See Iran No. 2856.
A sheetlet exists containing 4 each Nos. 3271-3272. Value $13.

Souvenir Sheet

Leshan Giant Buddha — A944

Photo. & Engr.
2003, Apr. 28   Perf. 12
3273 A944 $8 multi   2.50   2.50

Gulangyu Island — A945

No. 3274: a, Eight Diagram Building (3-1). b, Sunlight Rock (3-2). c, Shuzhuang Park (3-3).

2003, May 2   Photo.   Perf. 12
3274   Horiz. strip of 3   1.00   1.00
  a.-b. A945 80f Either single   .20   .20
  c.   A945 $2 multi   .50   .50
  d.   Souvenir sheet, #3274   1.40   1.40
A souvenir sheet exists containing three No. 3274. Value $13.

Campaign to Combat Epidemic of Severe Acute Respiratory Syndrome — A946

2003, May 19   Perf. 13¼x13
3275 A946 80f multi   3.00   3.00

Strange Stories from a Chinese Studio, by Pu Songling A947

Designs: 10f, Xiang Yu (6-1). 30f, Tiger of Zhaocheng (6-2). 60f, Huanniang (6-3). 80f, Ah Xiu (6-4). $1.50, Wang Gui'an (6-5). $2, Goddess (6-6).
$8, Princess of Dongting Lake, horiz.

2003, May 16   Perf. 12
3276-3281 A947   Set of 6   3.00   3.00

Souvenir Sheet
Perf. 13¼x13
3282 A947 $8 multi   4.50   4.50
No. 3282 contains one 90x60mm stamp.
Sheetlets exist containing 4 each of Nos. 3276-3277, 3278-3279 and 3280-3281. Value, set $16.

1976 Meteorite Shower Over Jilin — A948

Designs: No. 3283, 80f, Meteorites falling (3-1). No. 3284, 80f, Dispersal of meteorites (3-2). $2, Meteorite (3-3).

2003, June 21   **Litho.**
3283-3285 A948   Set of 3   1.00 1.00

A sheetlet exists containing 3 each of Nos. 3283-3285. Value $13.

Master-of-Nets Garden, Suzhou — A949

No. 3286: a, 80f, Late Spring Cottage (4-1). b, 80f, Pavilion Greeting the Moon and Breeze (4-2). c, 80f, Veranda of Bamboo (4-3). d, $2, Hall of Ten Thousand Volumes (4-4). Illustration reduced.

2003, June 29   **Photo.**   **Perf. 12¾**
3286 A949   Horiz. strip of 4, #a-d   1.25 1.25

Tibetan Antelopes A950

Designs: 80f, Antelopes and mountain (2-1). $2, Antelope's head, adult with young (2-2).

Photo. & Engr.

2003, July 20   **Perf. 11x11¼**
3287-3288 A950   Set of 2   .90 .90

Kongtong Mountain — A951

No. 3289: a, 80f, Town of Huangcheng (4-1). b, 80f, Gorge of Playing the Zither (4-2). c, 80f, Pagoda Courtyard (4-3). d, $2, Peak of Thunder (4-4). Illustration reduced.

2003, July 26   **Litho.**   **Perf. 12**
3289 A951   Block of 4, #a-d   1.25 1.25

Sailing Ship — A952

2003, Aug. 5
3290 A952   80f multi + label   1.00 1.00

Exists in sheets of 4 stamps + 4 labels. Value $6.

Powered Flight, Cent. — A953

Designs: 80f, Foreign airplanes (2-1). $2, Chinese airplanes (2-2).

2003, Aug. 9   **Photo.**   **Perf. 12¾**
3291-3292 A953   Set of 2   .90 .90

Jinci Temple Painted Statues — A954

Designs: No. 3293, 80f, Ruyi maid (4-1). No. 3294, 80f, Maid holding a towel (4-2). No. 3295, 80f, Maid carrying a royal seal (4-3). $2, Maid singing and dancing (4-4).

2003, Aug. 16   **Perf. 11¾x12**
3293-3296 A954   Set of 4   1.25 1.25

Sheetlets exist containing four each of Nos. 3293-3294 and 3295-3296. Value $16.

Three Gorges Project — A955

Designs: No. 3297, 80f, Dam and reservoir (3-1). No. 3298, 80f, Ship locks (3-2). $2, Power plant and high tension wire towers (3-3).

2003, Aug. 20   **Litho.**   **Perf. 12**
3297-3299 A955   Set of 3   1.00 1.00

Traditional Sports of Ethnic Minorities A956

Designs: No. 3300, 80f, Wrestling (4-1). b, No. 3301, 80f, Archery (4-2). No. 3302, 80f, Horse racing (4-3). No. 3303, 80f, Swinging (4-4).

2003, Sept. 5   **Photo.**   **Perf. 13x13½**
3300-3303 A956   Set of 4   .90 .90
3303a   Souvenir sheet, #3300-3303   1.40 1.40

No. 3303a sold for $5. Sheets exist containing four each of No. 3300-3301 and 3302-3303. Value set, $16.

Tienanmen Gate, Beijing — A957

2003, Sept. 10   **Litho.**   **Perf. 12**
3304 A957   80f multi + label   .30 .30

Two different sheets each containing four examples of No. 3304 were included in a souvenir folder sold only at the International Stamp and Coin Expo in Beijing in 2004.

General Yue Fei (1103-42) — A958

Designs: No. 3305, 80f, Mother tattooing "Loyalty to the Country" on Yue Fei's back (3-1). No. 3306, 80f, Yue Fei standing with sword (3-2). $2, Yue Fei seated (3-3).

2003, Sept. 25
3305-3307 A958   Set of 3   1.00 1.00

Souvenir Sheet

Water Diversion Projects — A959

2003, Sept. 26   **Photo.**   **Perf. 12¾**
3308 A959 $8 multi   2.25 2.25

Book Printing — A960

Designs: No. 3309, 80f, Ritual of Zhou, China (2-1). No. 3310, 80f, Hungarian Illuminated Chronicle, 1473 (2-2).

2003, Sept. 30   **Litho.**   **Perf. 12**
3309-3310 A960   Set of 2   .50 .50

Nos. 3309-3310 have large perforation holes at the stamp corners. See Hungary Nos. 3863-3864.

Double Ninth Festival — A961

Designs: No. 3311, 80f, Climbing mountain (3-1). No. 3312, 80f, Enjoying the beauty of chrysanthemums (3-2). $2, Playing chess and drinking wine (3-3).

2003, Oct. 4   **Photo.**   **Perf. 11½**
3311-3313 A961   Set of 3   1.00 1.00

Launch of First Manned Chinese Spacecraft A962

No. 3314: a, 80f, Astronaut, Shenzhou spacecraft (2-1). b, $2, Yang Liwei, flag (2-2).

2003, Oct. 16   **Perf. 13x13¼**
3314 A962   Pair, #a-b   .90 .90

A booklet containing No. 3314, Hong Kong No. 1062 and Macao Nos. 1128a-1128b exists. The booklet sold for a premium over face value.

Folktale of Liang Shanbo and Zhu Yingtai — A963

Designs: No. 3315, 80f, Zhu Yingtai, disguised as a man, and Liang Shanbo become sworn brothers at Caoqiao (5-1). No. 3316, 80f, Classmates for three years (5-2). No. 3317, 80f, Bidding farewell (5-3). No. 3318, 80f, Sad parting on the terrace (5-4). $2, Turning into butterflies (5-5).

2003, Oct. 18   **Perf. 12**
3315-3319 A963   Set of 5   1.40 1.40

A booklet containing booklet panes of one of each of Nos. 3315-3319 exists.

China 2003 Intl. Stamp Exhibition, Mianyang A964

2003, Nov. 20   **Photo.**   **Perf. 13¼**
3320 A964   80f multi   .30 .30

World AIDS Day — A965

2003, Dec. 1   **Perf. 11¼x11**
3321 A965   80f multi   .30 .30

Mao Zedong (1893-1976) — A966

Mao: No. 3322, 80f, Seated in folding chair (4-1). No. 3323, 80f, Standing (4-2). No. 3324, 80f, Seated on bench (4-3). No. 3325, 80f, Seated at desk (4-4).

Litho. & Engr.

2003, Dec. 6   **Perf. 12**
3322-3325 A966   Set of 4   1.00 1.00

Bronze Objects of Eastern Zhou Dyansty — A967

Designs: No. 3326, 60f, Square plate with turtle and fish patterns (8-1). No. 3327, 60f, Gui of the Duke of Qin (handled bowl with lid) (8-2). No. 3328, 80f, Iron-footed tripod of the King of Zhongshan (8-3). No. 3329, 80f, Gourd-shaped ladle of Yi, the Marquis of Zeng (8-4). No. 3330, 80f, Divine animal wine vessel, vert. (8-5). No. 3331, 80f, Wine vessel with phoenix pattern, vert. (8-6). $1, Square pot with lotus and cranes design, vert. (8-7). $2, Tripod with a dragon-shaped handle, vert. (8-8).

Perf. 11½x11¼, 11¼x11½

2003, Dec. 13   **Photo. & Engr.**
3326-3333 A967   Set of 8   2.40 2.40

Environmental Protection Type of 2002

Designs: 50f, Prevention and control of desertification. $4.50, Protection of biodiversity.

Perf. 12¾x13¼ Syncopated

2004, Jan. 1			Photo.	
3334	A908	50f multi	.30	.30
3335	A908	$4.50 multi	1.25	1.25

Bird Type of 2002

Designs: $5, Yellow-bellied tit. $6, Yunnan nuthatch.

2004, Jan. 1			Perf. 13¼	
3336	A909	$5 multi	1.50	1.50
3337	A909	$6 multi	1.75	1.75

New Year 2004 (Year of the Monkey) A968

2004, Jan. 5		Perf. 13 Syncopated	
3338	A968	80f multi	1.00 1.00
a.		Booklet pane of 10	4.75 —
		Complete booklet, #3338a	6.00

Sheets of 4 and sheets of 6 exist.

Taohuawu New Year Pictures — A969

Designs: No. 3339, 80f, Feelings of Pipa (4-1). No. 3340, 80f, Kylin Bringing a Son (4-2). No. 3341, 80f, Liu Hai Playing with the Golden Toad (4-3). $2, Ten Beauties Playing Football (4-4).

2004, Jan. 14		Litho.	Perf. 12	
3339-3342	A969	Set of 4	1.25	1.25
3342a		Souvenir sheet, #3339-3342	3.00	3.00

Deng Yingchao (1904-92), Communist Party Leader — A970

No. 3343: a, Holding book. b, Portrait.

2004, Feb. 4		Litho. & Engr.	
3343	A970	80f Vert. pair, #a-b	1.00 1.00

Suzhou Industrial Park, 10th Anniv. A971

2004, Mar. 1		Photo.	Perf. 13x13¼	
3344	A971	80f multi	.30	.30

See Singapore No. 1084.

Red Cross Society, Cent. — A972

2004, Mar. 10			Perf. 11¼x11	
3345	A972	80f multi	.30	.30

Stories Explaining Chinese Idioms A973

Idioms: No. 3346, 80f, Trying to learn the Handan walk (4-1). No. 3347, 80f, Lord Ye's love for dragon (4-2). No. 3348, 80f, Filling a position in a Yu band (4-3). No. 3349, 80f, When the snipe and the clam grapple (4-4).

Perf. 12½x13¼ Syncopated

2004, Apr. 2				
3346-3349	A973	Set of 4	1.10	1.10

Peacocks — A974

Designs: No. 3350, 80f, Blue peacock (2-1). No. 3351, 80f, Albino peacock, vert. (2-2). $6, Green peacocks.

2004, Apr. 13			Perf. 12¾	
3350-3351	A974	Set of 2	.50	.50

Souvenir Sheet

Perf. 13¼x13

3352	A974	$6 multi	2.00	2.00

No. 3352 contains one 60x40mm stamp.

Nanxi River — A975

No. 3353: a, River and mountain (4-1). b, Tree and boat in foreground, mountains in background (4-2). c, Rocks, boat in river (4-3). d, Boat, spit of land with trees (4-4).

2004, Apr. 24		Photo.	Perf. 12¾	
3353		Horiz. strip of 4	1.25	1.25
a.		A975 60f multi	.25	.25
b.-c.		A975 80f Either single	.25	.25
d.		A975 $2 multi	.50	.50

Danxia Mountain — A976

Designs: 60f, Sengmao Peak (4-1). No. 3355, 80f, Xianlong Lake (4-2). No. 3356, 80f, Chahu Peak (4-3). $2, Jinjiang River (4-4).

2004, May 1		Litho. & Engr.	Perf. 12	
3354-3357	A976	Set of 4	1.25	1.25

Economic and Technological Development Zones, 20th Anniv. — A977

2004, May 4			Litho.	
3358	A977	80f multi	.30	.30

Exists in a sheet of 8 stamps + 8 labels.

Hometowns of Returned Chinese — A978

Designs: No. 3359, 80f, Xinglong Overseas Chinese Farm (4-1). No. 3360, 80f, Jinan University (4-2). No. 3361, 80f, Fuqing Rongqiao Development Zone (4-3). No. 3362, 80f, Kaiping (4-4).

2004, May 15		Photo.	Perf. 11x11¼	
3359-3362	A978	Set of 4	1.00	1.00

Sima Guang Breaking the Vat — A979

Designs: No. 3363, 80f, Sima Guang falling into water (3-1). No. 3362, 80f, Breaking vat (3-2). No. 3363, $2, Rescued (3-3).

2004, June 1			Perf. 12	
3363-3365	A979	Set of 3	1.10	1.10

Scenes of Villages of Southern Anhui Province A980

Designs: No. 3366, 80f, Archway (4-1). No. 3367, 80f, Old buildings (4-2). No. 3368, 80f, Buildings on South Lake (4-3). No. 3369, 80f, Moon Pond (4-4).

Photo. & Engr.

2004, June 25			Perf. 11x11¼	
3366-3369	A980	Set of 4	1.00	1.00

Liu Yi Delivering a Letter — A981

Designs: No. 3370, 80f, Dragon Princess asking Liu Yi to deliver a letter (4-1). No. 3371, 80f, Delivering letter to Dongting Lake (4-2). No. 3372, 80f, Family reunion (4-3). $2, Couple embracing (4-4).

2004, July 17		Photo.	Perf. 13¼x13	
3370	A981	80f multi	.25	.25
a.		Booklet pane of 1	.30	
3371	A981	80f multi	.25	.25
a.		Booklet pane of 1	.30	
3372	A981	80f multi	.25	.25
a.		Booklet pane of 1	.30	

3373	A981	$2 multi	.55	.55
a.		Booklet pane of 1	.75	
		Complete booklet, #3370a-3373a	1.90	
		Nos. 3370-3373 (4)	1.30	1.30

Complete booklet sold for $6.

Souvenir Sheet

Eight Immortals Crossing the Sea — A982

2004, July 30		Perf. 12 Syncopated	
3374	A982	$6 multi	2.25 2.25

Peony — A983

2004, July 31		Litho.	Perf. 12¾	
3375	A983	80f multi + label	.30	.30

Perf 12¾ examples come from a sheetlet containing four examples with labels below the stamps that also contain four #3261. The sheetlet sold for $15.

2004 Summer Olympics, Athens — A984

Olympic rings and: No. 3376, 80f, Parthenon, Athens (2-1). No. 3377, 80f, Hall of Good Harvest, Temple of Heaven, Beijing.

2004, Aug. 13		Photo.	Perf. 12¾	
3376-3377	A984	Set of 2	.50	.50

Perf 12¾ examples come from a sheetlet containing four examples with labels below the stamps that also contain four #3261. The sheetlet sold for $15. See Greece Nos. 2124-2125.

Deng Xiaoping (1904-97), Chinese Leader — A985

Designs: No. 3378, 80f, Walking (2-1). No. 3379, 80f, Saluting, horiz. (2-2). $6, Seated.

2004, Aug. 22		Perf. 12 Syncopated	
3378-3379	A985	Set of 2	.50 .50

Souvenir Sheet

Perf. 13 Syncopated

3380	A985	$6 multi	2.25 2.25

No. 3380 contains one 47x57mm stamp.

South China Tiger A986

Designs: 80f, Head (2-1). $2, Adult and young (2-2).

2004, Aug. 23   Litho.   Perf. 12
3381-3382 A986   Set of 2   .85   .85

People's Congress, 50th Anniv. — A987

Designs: No. 3383, 80f, Congress members arriving at Huairentang Hall of Zhongnanhai (2-1). No. 3384, 80f, Interior of Great Hall of the People (2-2).

2004, Sept. 15   Perf. 13¼
3383-3384 A987   Set of 2   .50   .50

A sheet containing 3 pairs of Nos. 3383-3384 exists.

Bloodstone Seals A988

No. 3385: a, 80f, Seal of Emperor Qianlong (2-1). b, $2, Seal of Emperor Jiaqing (2-2).

Litho. & Embossed
2004, Sept. 17   Perf. 13x13¼
3385 A988   Pair, #a-b   .90   .90

Celery Wormwood A989

Designs: No. 3386, 80f, Purple flowers (4-1). No. 3387, 80f, Blue flowers (4-2). No. 3388, 80f, Red flowers (4-3). $2, Yellow flowers (4-4).

2004, Sept. 19   Photo.   Perf. 13¼x13
3386-3389 A989   Set of 4   1.40   1.40

A sheet containing 2 strips of 3386-3389 exists.

Chinese and Romanian Handicrafts A990

Designs: No. 3390, 80f, Drum with tigers and birds, China (2-1). No. 3391, 80f, Cucuteni pottery jar, Romania (2-2).

2004, Sept. 22   Perf. 13 Syncopated
3390-3391 A990   Set of 2   .50   .50

A sheet containing 4 pairs of Nos. 3390-3391 exists.
See Romania No. 4668.

National Symbols A991

Designs: No. 3392, 80f, Flag (2-1). No. 3393, 80f, Arms, vert. (2-2).

Perf. 13¼x13 Syncopated, 13x13¼ Syncopated
2004, Sept. 30
3392-3393 A991   Set of 2   .50   .50

A sheet of 4 self-adhesive examples of both Nos. 3392 and 3393 was included in a souvenir folder sold only at the International Stamp and Coin Expo in Beijing in 2004.

Landscapes of Chinese Borderlands — A992

Designs: No. 3394, 80f, Forest, Xing'an Mountains (12-1). No. 3395, 80f, Lake in Yalu River Basin (12-2). No. 3396, 80f, Reefs in Yellow Sea (12-3). No. 3397, 80f, Zhoushan Archipelago (12-4). No. 3398, 80f, Coast of Taiwan (12-5). No. 3399, 80f, Xisha Islands (12-6). No. 3400, 80f, Karst landscape, Southern Guangxi (12-7). No. 3401, 80f, Rain forest, Southern Yunnan (12-8). No. 3402, 80f, Mt. Qomolangma (12-9). No. 3403, 80f, Pamirs (12-10). No. 3404, 80f, Badain Jaran Desert (12-11). No. 3405, 80f, Hulun Buir Steppe (12-12).

2004, Oct. 1   Perf. 12¾
3394-3405 A992   Set of 12   2.75   2.75
3405a   Sheet of 12, #3394-3405 + central label   3.00   3.00

Buildings in China and Spain — A993

Designs: No. 3406, 80f, Jinmao Tower, China (2-1). No. 3407, 80f, Park Guell, Spain.

2004, Oct. 8   Perf. 13¼x13
3406-3407 A993   Set of 2   .50   .50

See Spain Nos. 3319-3320.

Miniature Sheet

The Festival of Pure Brightness on the River, by Zhang Zeduan — A994

No. 3408 — Various details from painting: a, 60f, Trees (9-1). b, 80f, Trees, people on horseback (9-2). c, 80f, Buildings, boats on river (9-3). d, 80f, Buildings, boats on river, diff. (9-4). e, 80f, Bridge (9-5). f, 80f, Buildings, boats on river (9-6). g, 80f, Buildings (9-7). h, $1, Tower (9-8). i, $2, Intersection (9-9).

Litho. & Engr.
2004, Oct. 18   Perf. 12
3408 A994   Sheet of 9, #a-i   2.10   2.10

Phoenix — A995

2004, Nov. 1   Litho.   Perf. 12¾
3409 A995 80f multi + label   .20   .20

A sheet of 10 serpentine die cut 12¼ self-adhesive stamps like No. 3409 + 10 labels depicting Snoopy for 25 yuan.

Pavilions — A996

Designs: No. 3410, 80f, Aiwan (4-1). No. 3411, 80f, Pipa (4-2). No. 3412, 80f, Lan (4-3). No. 3413, 80f, Zuiweng (4-4).

2004, Nov. 6   Photo.   Perf. 13¼x13
3410-3413 A996   Set of 4   .80   .80

Ancient Calligraphy A997

Designs: No. 3414, 80f, Yiying stele (4-1). No. 3415, 80f, Zhangqian stele (4-2). No. 3416, 80f, Caoquan stele (4-3). No. 3417, 80f, Shimen song (4-4).

Photo. & Engr.
2004, Dec. 5   Perf. 11¼x11
3414-3417 A997   Set of 4   .80   .80

New Year 2005 (Year of the Rooster) A998

Perf. 13 Syncopated
2005, Jan. 5   Photo.
3418 A998 80f multi   .20   .20
a.   Booklet pane of 10   2.00
       Complete booklet, #3418a   2.00

No. 3418 exists in a sheet of 4.

Tarim-Baihe Gas Pipeline — A999

No. 3419: a, 80f, Derrick (2-1). b, $3, Pipes (2-2).
Illustration reduced.

2005, Jan. 8   Litho.   Perf. 12
3419 A999   Horiz. pair, #a-b   .95   .95

Historic Structures in Taiwan A1000

No. 3420: a, North Gate, Taipei City Wall (5-1). b, Confucian Temple (5-2). c, Longshan Temple, Lugang (5-3). d, Erkunshen Cannon Fort, Tainan (5-4). e, Matsu Temple, Penghu (5-5).

Perf. 13 Syncopated
2005, Jan. 30   Litho. & Engr.
3420   Vert. strip of 5   1.25   1.25
a.-d.   A1000 80f Any single   .20   .20
e.   A1000 $1.50 multi   .40   .40

Yangjiabu New Year Woodprints A1001

Designs: No. 3421, 80f, Door God (4-1). No. 3422, 80f, Abundance for year (4-2). No. 3423, 80f, Good news on New Year's Day (4-3). No. 3424, 80f, Goddess strewing flowers from heaven (4-4).

2005, Feb. 1   Litho.   Perf. 13¼x13
3421-3424 A1001   Set of 4   .80   .80
3424a   Souvenir sheet, #3421-3424   1.25   1.25

No. 3424a sold for $4.80. A miniature sheet containing 2 of each stamp exists.

Magnolias A1002

Designs: No. 3425, 80f, Magnolia dennudata (4-1). No. 3426, 80f, Magnolia delavayi (4-2). No. 3427, 80f, Magnolia grandiflora (4-3). No. 3428, 80f, Magnolia liliflora (4-4).

2005, Mar. 5   Photo.   Perf. 13x13¼
3425-3428 A1002   Set of 4   .80   .80

Great Wall of China — A1003

2005, Apr. 1   Litho.   Perf. 12¾
3429 A1003 80f multi + label   .20   .20

Earth Day — A1004

2005, Apr. 22   Photo.   Perf. 13¼
3430 A1004 80f multi   .20   .20

A ring of syncopated perforations surrounds the vignette.

Jigong Mountains A1005

No. 3431: a, Mountain at daybreak (4-1). b, Garden in clouds (4-2). c, Moon Pond (4-3). d, Black Dragon Waterfall (4-4).

Perf. 12½ Syncopated

2005, Apr. 28   **Litho.**
3431   Horiz. strip of 4   .80   .80
a.-d.   A1005 80f Any single   .20   .20

All-China Federation of Trade Unions, 80th Anniv. — A1006

2005, May 1   **Perf. 12**
3432   A1006 80f multi   .20   .20

Paintings of Flower Arrangements A1007

Designs: No. 3433, 80f, Magnolia Flowers, by Chen Hongshou (2-1). No. 3434, 80f, Flower Vase in a Window Niche, by Ambrosius Bosschaert the Elder (2-2).

Perf. 12½ Syncopated

2005, May 18   **Photo.**
3433-3434 A1007 Set of 2   .40   .40

See Liechtenstein Nos. 1315-1316.

Dalian Bay Area Views — A1008

No. 3435: a, Tiger Beach (4-1). b, Bangchui Island (4-2). c, Golden Pebble Beach (4-3). d, Lushunkou (4-4).

2005, May 21 Perf. 12¾ Syncopated
3435   Horiz. strip of 4   .80   .80
a.-d.   A1008 80f Any single   .20   .20

Fudan University, Cent. A1009

Litho., Engr. & Embossed

2005, May 27   **Perf. 12**
3436   A1009 80f multi   .20   .20

Hans Christian Andersen (1805-75), Author A1010

No. 3437 — Fairy tales by Andersen: a, The Emperor's New Clothes (5-1). b, The Little Mermaid (5-2). c, Thumbelina (5-3). d, The Little Match Girl (5-4). e, The Ugly Duckling (5-5).

Perf. 13¼ Syncopated

2005, June 1   **Photo.**
3437   Horiz. strip of 5   1.00   1.00
a.-e.   A1010 80f Any single   .20   .20
f.   Booklet pane of 1, #3437a   .30   —
g.   Booklet pane of 1, #3437b   .30   —
h.   Booklet pane of 1, #3437c   .30   —
i.   Booklet pane of 1, #3437d   .30   —
j.   Booklet pane of 1, #3437e   .30   —
            Complete booklet, #3437f-3437j 1.50

The complete booklet sold for $6.
A sheet of ten serpentine die cut 10 self-adhesive stamps containing two of each of the designs of Nos. 3437a-3437e and ten labels exists.

Voyages of Admiral Zheng He, 600th Anniv. — A1011

No. 3438: a, Admiral Zheng He (3-1). b, Building, map of voyages (3-2). c, Compass, drawing of ship (3-3)
$6, Ship, horiz.

2005, June 28   **Litho.**
3438   Horiz. strip of 3   .60   .60
a.-c.   A1011 80f Any single   .20   .20
            Souvenir Sheet
3439   A1011 $6 multi   1.50   1.50
No. 3439 contains one 70x50mm stamp.

Nantong Museum — A1012

No. 3440: a, Southern Hall (2-1). b, Central Hall (2-2).
Illustration reduced.

Photo. & Engr.
2005, June 16   **Perf. 12½x12¾**
3440   A1012 80f Horiz. pair, #a-b   .40   .40

Xianghai National Nature Reserve — A1013

Designs: No. 3441, 80f, Red-crowned cranes in nest (4-1). No. 3442, 80f, Three birds in flight, trees (4-2). No. 3443, 80f, Birds at lake (4-3). No. 3444, 80f, Eagles flying above steppe (4-4).

2005, July 30   **Photo.**   **Perf. 12¾**
3441-3444 A1013 Set of 4   .80   .80

Miniature Sheet

People's Army Generals — A1014

No. 3445: a, Yang Jingyu (5-1). b, Zuo Quan (5-2). c, Peng Xuefeng (5-3). d, Luo Binghui (5-4). e, Guan Xiangying (5-5).

2005, Aug. 1   **Perf. 12**
3445   A1014 80f Sheet of 10, 2
            each #a-e   2.00   2.00

End of World War II, 60th Anniv. — A1015

No. 3446: a, Soldiers with machine guns (4-1). b, Bugler (4-2). c, Soldier holding gun, troops landing in Normandy (4-3). d, Conquering Berlin (4-4).
$6, Dove, vert.
Illustration reduced.

Perf. 12¾ Syncopated

2005, Aug. 15   **Litho.**
3446   A1015 80f Block of 4, #a-d   .80   .80
            Souvenir Sheet
            Photo.
            Perf. 12¾
3447   A1015 $6 multi   1.50   1.50

Tibet Autonomous Region, 40th Anniv. — A1016

2005, Aug. 26   **Photo.**   **Perf. 13¼**
3448   A1016 80f multi   .20   .20

Chinese Motion Pictures, Cent. — A1017

2005, Aug. 28 Litho.   Perf. 12¾x13
3449   A1017 80f multi   .20   .20

Exists in a sheet of 8 stamps + 8 labels.

"Five Happinesses Arrive" — A1018

2005, Sept. 16   **Perf. 12¾**
3450   A1018 80f multi + label   .20   .20

Fanjing Mountain Nature Reserve A1019

No. 3451: a, Golden Summit (4-1). b, Mushroom Rock (4-2). c, Forest (4-3). d, Heiwan River (4-4).

2005, Sept. 18 Photo. Perf. 13x13¼
3451   Horiz. strip of 4   .80   .80
a.-d.   A1019 80f Any single   .20   .20

Farm Technology A1020

Sheep and: No. 3452, 80f, Chinese water wheel (2-1). No. 3453, 80f, Dutch windmill (2-2).

2005, Sept. 22   **Perf. 12**
3452-3453 A1020   Set of 2   .40   .40

See Netherlands Nos. 1203-1204.

Miniature Sheet

People's Liberation Army Generals — A1021

No. 1021: a, Su Yu (10-1). b, Xu Haidong (10-2). c, Huang Kecheng (10-3). d, Chen Geng (10-4). e, Tan Zheng (10-5). f, Xiao Jinguang (10-6). g, Zhang Yunyi (10-7). h, Luo Ruiqing (10-8). i, Wang Shusheng (10-9). j, Xu Guangda (10-10).

Litho. & Engr.
2005, Sept. 27   **Perf. 13¼x13**
3454   A1021 80f Sheet of 10, #a-j 2.00 2.00

Miniature Sheet

Goddess of the River Luo, by Gu Kaizhi — A1022

Various painting details with width of: a, 50mm (10-1). b, 50mm (10-2). c, 60mm (10-3). d, 40mm (10-4). e, 60mm (10-5). f, 60mm (10-6). g, 60mm (10-7). h, 50mm (10-8). i, 40mm (10-9). j, 50mm (10-10).

2005, Sept. 28   **Perf. 12**
3455   A1022 80f Sheet of 10, #a-j 2.00 2.00

Xinjiang Uygur Autonomous Region, 50th Anniv. — A1023

No. 3456: a, Male dancers and musicians (3-1). b, Male and female dancers (3-2). c, Women carrying plates of food (3-3).

Perf. 12x12½ Syncopated

2005, Oct. 1 **Litho.**
3456   Horiz. strip of 3   .60 .60
a.-c. A1023 80f single   .20 .20

Souvenir Sheet

10th National Games, Jiangsu Province — A1024

2005, Oct. 12   Photo.   Perf. 12¾
3457 A1024 $6 multi   1.50 1.50

Wild Cats
A1025

Designs: No. 3458, 80f, Panthera pardus orientalis (2-1). No. 3459, 80f, Puma concolor (2-2).

2005, Oct. 13 Photo.   Perf. 13x13¼
3458-3459 A1025 Set of 2   .40 .40

See Canada Nos. 2122-2123.

"Be Safe Every Year" — A1026

Illustration reduced.

2005, Nov. 6   Litho.   Perf. 13¼
3460 A1026 80f red & blk + label .20 .20

Relics From Chengtoushan Archaeological Site — A1027

2005, Nov. 6   Photo.   Perf. 12½
3461 A1027 80f multi   .20 .20

"Beam With Delight" — A1028

2005, Nov. 11   Litho.   Perf. 12¾
3462 A1028 80f multi + label   .20 .20

2008 Summer Olympics, Beijing — A1029

Designs: No. 3463, Beijing Olympics emblem, Olympic rings (6-1).
No. 3464 — Beijing Olympic mascots with emblem on chest: a, Beibei (6-2). b, Jingjing (6-3). c, Huanhuan (6-4). d, Yingying (6-5). e, Nini (6-6).

2005, Nov. 12 Photo. Perf. 13¼x13
3463 A1029 80f multi   .20 .20
3464 A1029 80f Horiz. strip of 5,
          #a-e   1.00 1.00

Beijing Olympics Type of 2005

No. 3465: a, Like #3463. b, Like #3464a. c, Like #3464b. d, Like #3464c. e, Like #3464d. f, Like #3464e.

Serpentine Die Cut 11¾

2005, Nov. 12   Photo.
Self-Adhesive
3465 A1029 80f Sheet, 2 each
          #a-f   2.40 2.40

New Year 2006 (Year of the Dog) A1030

Perf. 13 Syncopated

2006, Jan. 5   Photo.
3466 A1030 80f multi   .20 .20
  a.   Sheet of 6   3.75 3.75
  b.   Booklet pane of 10 2.00 —
        Complete booklet, #3466b 2.00

A sheet of 4 exists that was a giveaway for standing order customers.

Wuqiang New Year Woodprints A1031

Designs: No. 3467, 80f, Being Safe All Year Round (4-1). No. 3468, 80f, Five Blessings Approach Your Door (4-2). No. 3469, 80f, Flower of Prosperity Blossoms (4-3). No. 3470, 80f, Lion Rolling the Embroidered Ball (4-4).

Litho. & Engr.

2006, Jan. 22   Perf. 12
3467-3470 A1031   Set of 4   .80 .80
3470a   Souvenir sheet, #3467-
        3470   .80 .80
3470b   Souvenir sheet, 2 each
        #3467-3470   1.60 1.60

Lanterns A1032

Designs: No. 3471, 80f, Fish lantern (5-1). No. 3472, 80f, Chinese white cabbage lantern (5-2). No. 3473, 80f, Lotus lantern (5-3). No. 3474, 80f, Dragon and phoenix lantern (5-4). $1.50, Butterfly lantern (5-5).

2006, Feb. 12   Photo. Perf. 13¼x13
3471-3475 A1032   Set of 5   1.25 1.25
3475a   Sheet, 2 each #3471-3475 2.50 2.50

Abolition of Agricultural Tax — A1033

Perf. 13½ Syncopated
2006, Feb. 22
3476 A1033 80f multi   .20 .20

Lijiang River — A1034

No. 3477: a, Yangdi (4-1). b, Langshi (4-2). c, Huangbu (4-3). d, Xingping (4-4).

2006, Feb. 25   Perf. 12¾
3477   Horiz. strip of 4   .80 .80
a.-d. A1034 80f Any single   .20 .20

Relic Plants — A1035

Designs: No. 3478, 80f, Ginkgo biloba (4-1). No. 3479, 80f, Glyptostrobus pensilis (4-2). No. 3480, 80f, Davidia involucrata (4-3). No. 3481, 80f, Liriodendron chinense (4-4).

Perf. 12x12¼ Syncopated
2006, Mar. 12   Litho.
3478-3481 A1035   Set of 4   .80 .80

Dogs A1036

Designs: Nos. 3482, 3486a, 80f, Pekingese (4-1). Nos. 3483, 3486b, 80f, Pug, vert. (4-2). Nos. 3484, 3486c, 80f, Chow chow (4-3). Nos. 3485, 3486d, 80f, Tibetan mastiff, vert. (4-4).

Perf. 13¼ Syncopated
2006, Mar. 19   Litho. & Engr.
3482-3485 A1036   Set of 4   .80 .80
Self-Adhesive
Serpentine Die Cut 11¾ on 2 Sides
3486 A1036 80f Sheet, 2 each
        #3486a-3486d   1.60 1.60

Qingcheng Mountain A1037

Designs: 60f, Remote mountain gate (4-1). No. 3488, 80f, Winding path (4-2). No. 3489, 80f, Ancient temple (4-3). No. 3490, 80f, Spring (4-4).

2006, Apr. 12 Perf. 13¼ Syncopated
3487-3490 A1037   Set of 4   .75 .75

Statues in Yungang Grottoes A1038

Designs: No. 3491, 80f, Sakyamuni (4-1). No. 3492, 80f, Bodhisattva (4-2). No. 3493, 80f, Head of Bodhisattva (4-3). No. 3494, 80f, Xieshi Bodhisattva (4-4).
$6, Sakyamuni, diff.

Perf. 13¼x13½ Syncopated
2006, Apr. 13   Photo.
3491-3494 A1038   Set of 4   .80 .80
Souvenir Sheet
Perf. 13 Syncopated
3495 A1038 $6 multi   1.50 1.50

No. 3495 contains one 40x60mm stamp.

Tianzhu Mountain — A1039

Designs: 60f, Green Dragon Mountain Stream (4-1). No. 3497, 80f, Taoist Practice Terrace (4-2). No. 3498, 80f, Sanzu Temple (4-3). No. 3499, 80f, Qingtian Peak (4-4).

2006, Apr. 22   Perf. 11½x11¼
3496-3499 A1039   Set of 4   .75 .75

Scientists A1040

Designs: No. 3500, 80f, Liang Xi (1883-1958), forester (4-1). No. 3501, 80f, Mao Yisheng (1896-1989), civil engineer (4-2). No. 3502, 80f, Yan Jici (1900-96), physicist (4-3). No. 3503, 80f, Zhou Peiyuan (1902-93), physicist (4-4).

Litho. & Engr.
2006, May 13   Perf. 12
3500-3503 A1040   Set of 4   .80 .80

Lighthouses
A1041

No. 3504: a, Dagu Lighthouse (4-1). b, Guishan Island Lighthouse (4-2). c, Wusongkou Lighthouse (4-3). d, Mulantou Lighthouse (4-4).

2006, May 22   Photo.   Perf. 12¾
3504   Horiz. strip of 4   .80   .80
  a.-d.   A1041 80f Any single   .20   .20

Chinese Space Program, 50th
Anniv. — A1042

No. 3505: a, Geospace Double Star Exploration (2-1). b, Shenzhou 6 (2-2). Illustration reduced.

Perf. 12x11¼ Syncopated
2006, June 8   Litho.
3505   A1042 80f Horiz. pair, #a-b   .40   .40

Silver and Gold
Objects — A1043

Designs: No. 3506, 80f, Jeeweled Qing Dynasty cup, China (2-1). No. 3507, 80f, Tankard with Biblical designs, by Peter Rohde, Poland.

2006, June 20   Photo.   Perf. 13¼x13
3506-3507 A1043   Set of 2   .40   .40
  See Poland No. 3829.

Olympic Rings and Emblem of 2008
Summer Olympics, Beijing — A1043a

2006, June 23   Photo.   Perf. 12
3507A   A1043a 80f multi + label   .20   .20
  Printed in sheets of 15 stamps + 15 labels, sheets of 4 stamps + 4 labels to right of stamps, sheets of 4 stamps + 4 labels below stamps, and sheets of 8 stamps + 8 labels.

Early Communist
Leaders
A1044

Designs: No. 3508, 80f, Gao Junyu (1896-1925) (5-1). No. 3509, 80f, Wang Hebo (1882-1927) (5-2). No. 3510, 80f, Su Zhaozheng (1885-1929) (5-3). No. 3511, 80f, Peng Pai

(1896-1929) (5-4). No. 3512, 80f, Deng Xhongxia (1894-1933) (5-5).

2006, June 30   Litho. & Engr.
3508-3512 A1044   Set of 5   1.00   1.00

Opening of Qinghai-Tibet
Railway — A1045

Designs: No. 3513, 80f, Bridge across Kekexili, antelopes (3-1). No. 3514, 80f, Train crossing Danggula Mountains, cattle (3-2). No. 3515, 80f, Lhasa Railway Station, birds (3-3).

Perf. 12½x12 Syncopated
2006, July 1   Litho.
3513-3515 A1045   Set of 3   .60   .60

Kanasi Nature Reserve — A1046

Designs: No. 3516, 80f, Kanasi Lake (4-1). No. 3517, 80f, Crouching Dragon Bend (4-2). No. 3518, 80f, Celestial Bend (4-3). No. 3519, 80f, Moon Bend (4-4).

2006, July 8   Photo.   Perf. 12¾
3516-3519 A1046   Set of 4   .80   .80

Earthquake
Protection and
Damage
Mitigation
A1047

2006, July 26   Perf. 13½x13
3520   A1047 80f multi   .20   .20

2008 Summer
Olympics,
Beijing — A1048

Designs: Nos. 3521, 3525a, 60f, Basketball (4-1). Nos. 3522, 3525b, 80f, Fencing (4-2). Nos. 3523, 3525c, Sailing (4-3). Nos. 3524, 3525d, $3, Gymnastics (4-4).

2006, Aug. 8   Photo.   Perf. 13½x13
3521-3524 A1048   Set of 4   1.40   1.40

Self-Adhesive
Serpentine Die Cut 11¾
3525   A1048   Sheet of 8, 2 each
                      #a-d   3.00   3.00
  Portions of the designs of Nos. 3525a-3525d were applied by a thermographic process, producing a shiny, raised effect.

Treasures of the
Study — A1049

Designs: No. 3526, 80f, Brushes (4-1). No. 3527, 80f, Ink (4-2). No. 3528, 80f, Paper (4-3). No. 3529, 80f, Ink stone (4-4).

Perf. 12½x12½ Syncopated
2006, Sept. 10   Litho.
3526-3529 A1049   Set of 4   .80   .80

All-China
Federation
of
Returned
Overseas
Chinese,
50th Anniv.
A1050

Perf. 12½x12 Syncopated
2006, Sept. 25
3530   A1050 80f multi   .20   .20

Musical Instruments — A1051

Designs: No. 3531, 80f, Seven-stringed qin, China (2-1). No. 3532, 80f, Bösendorfer piano, Austria (2-2).

Perf. 13x12½ Syncopated
2006, Sept. 26   Litho.
3531-3532 A1051   Set of 2   .40   .40
  See Austria Nos. 2066-2067.

Chinese Export Commodities
Fair — A1052

Perf. 13½x13¼ Syncopated
2006, Oct. 15   Photo.
3533   A1052 80f multi   .20   .20

Long March, 70th Anniv. — A1053

Designs: No. 3534, 80f, Setting Out (4-1). No. 3535, 80f, Zunyi Conference (4-2). No. 3536, 80f, Speedily Occupy the Luding Bridge (4-3). No. 3537, 80f, The Red Army Through the Marshland (4-4). $6, Reunion.

2006, Oct. 22   Perf. 13x13¼
3534-3537 A1053   Set of 4   .80   .80

Souvenir Sheet
3538   A1053 $6 multi   1.60   1.60
  No. 3538 contains one 80x50mm stamp.

Dialogue
With
ASEAN,
15th Anniv.
A1054

Perf. 12½x12 Syncopated
2006, Oct. 30   Litho.
3539   A1054 80f multi   .20   .20

"Enjoying
Prosperity
Year After
Year"
A1055

"Happy New
Year" —
A1055a

Perf. 12¾ Syncopated
2006, Nov. 1   Photo.
3540   A1055 80f multi   .20   .20
3541   A1055a $3 multi   .80   .80

Beijing Summit of Forum on China-
Africa Cooperation — A1056

2006, Nov. 3   Litho.   Perf. 13¼
3542   A1056 80f multi   .20   .20

Buildings
Associated With
Dr. Sun Yat-sen
(1826-1925)
A1057

Designs: No. 3543, 80f, Sun Yat-sen Villa (4-1). No. 3544, 80f, Mausoleum (4-2). No. 3545, 80f, Sun Yat-sen Memorial Hall (4-3). No. 3546, 80f, Sun Yat-sen University (4-4).

Perf. 13¼ Syncopated
2006, Nov. 12   Litho. & Engr.
3543-3546 A1057   Set of 4   .85   .85

Birds Type of 2002
Designs: 40f, Chinese monal pheasant. $1.20, Taiwan yuhinas.

Perf. 13½ Syncopated
2006, Nov. 15   Photo.
3547   A909   40f multi   .20   .20
3548   A909 $1.20 multi   .30   .30

Heavenly Steed, Silk Roll
Painting — A1058

No. 3549: a, Horse and rider. b, People looking at horse.
Illustration reduced.

2006, Dec. 3   Photo.   Perf. 12¾
3549 A1058 $1.20 Horiz. pair,
#a-b   .60 .60

Wu Lanfu (1906-
88), Politician
A1059

2006, Dec. 23   Perf. 13¼x13
3550 A1059 $1.20 multi   .30 .30

Trains — A1060

Designs: No. 3551, $1.20, Locomotive, blue background (4-1). No. 3552, $1.20, Locomotive, red brown background (4-2). No. 3553, $1.20, Box car (4-3). No. 3554, $1.20, Log cars and gateway (4-4).
$6, Locomotive and city skyline.

2006, Dec. 28   Perf. 13x13¼
3551-3554 A1060 Set of 4   1.25 1.25
Souvenir Sheet
Perf. 13¼x13
3555 A1060 $6 multi   1.50 1.50

No. 3555 contains one 90x40mm stamp.

China Post, 110th Anniv. — A1061

Perf. 12x11½ Syncopated
2006, Dec. 30   Litho.
3556 A1061 $1.20 multi   .30 .30

New Year
2007 (Year of
the
Pig) — A1062

Perf. 13 Syncopated
2007, Jan. 5   Photo.
3557 A1062 $1.20 multi   .30 .30
a.   Souvenir sheet of 6   1.80 1.80
b.   Booklet pane of 10   3.00
        Complete booklet, #3557b 3.00

6th Asian Winter
Games — A1063

Perf. 12x12½ Syncopated
2007, Jan. 28   Litho.
3558 A1063 $1.20 multi   .30 .30

Shiwan Pottery
Figurines
A1064

Designs: No. 3559, $1.20, Ta Xue Xun Mei (2-1). No. 3560, $1.20, Wang Zhaojun Chu Sai (2-2).

2007, Feb. 3   Photo.   Perf. 13¼x13
3559-3560 A1064 Set of 2   .60 .60
3560a   Miniature sheet, 4 each
           #3559-3560   2.40 2.40

"Divine Birds of the Sun" — A1065

2007, Feb. 9   Litho.   Perf. 12
3561 A1065 $1.20 multi + label   .30 .30

Mianzhu New
Year Woodcuts
A1066

Designs: No. 3562, $1.20, Zuo Zuo Ti Dao (4-1). No. 3563, $1.20, Mu Guiying (4-2). No. 3564, $1.20, Shuang Xi Tong Zi (4-3). No. 3565, $1.20, Zhang Xian She Gou (4-4).

Perf. 12x11½ Syncopated
2007, Feb. 10   Litho. & Engr.
3562-3565 A1066 Set of 4   1.25 1.25
3565a   Souvenir sheet of 4,
           #3562-3565   1.25 1.25
3565b   Miniature sheet of 8, 2
           each #3562-3565   2.50 2.50

A lithographed sheet similar to No. 3565b on a textured silk-faced paper exists.

Beijing
Opera — A1067

Designs: 80f, Lin Xiangru (6-1). No. 3567, $1.20, Song Shijie (6-2). No. 3568, $1.20, Zhou Yu (6-3). No. 3569, $1.20, Xu Xian (6-4). No. 3570, $1.20, Gao Chong (6-5). No. 3571, $1.20, Ren Tanghui (6-6).

2007, Mar. 10   Photo.   Perf. 13¼x13
3566-3571 A1067 Set of 6   1.75 1.75

Postal Savings Bank — A1068

2007, Mar. 20   Perf. 12¾
3572 A1068 $1.20 multi   .30 .30
a.   Miniature sheet of 8   2.40 2.40

Writings of
Li Keran
A1069

Designs: No. 3573, $1.20, Man viewing waterfall (6-1). No. 3574, $1.20, Mountains with red-leaved trees (6-2). No. 3575, $1.20, People looking at scroll (6-3). No. 3576, $1.20, Crane flying above man under tent (6-4). No. 3577, $1.20, Cattle and driver in pond (6-5). No. 3578, $1.20, Raining in Jiangnan (6-6).

Perf. 13x13¼ Syncopated
2007, Mar. 26
3573-3578 A1069 Set of 6   1.90 1.90

Modern
Chinese
Drama,
Cent.
A1070

Perf. 13 Syncopated
2007, Apr. 6   Litho.
3579 A1070 $1.20 multi   .30 .30

Yangzhou Garden — A1071

No. 3580: a, He Garden (3-1). b, Ge Garden (3-2). c, Xu Garden (3-3).

Perf. 12x11½ Syncopated
2007, Apr. 8
3580   Horiz. strip of 3   .90 .90
a.-c. A1071 $1.20 Any single   .30 .30

Dances — A1072

Designs: No. 3581, $1.20, Dragon dance (2-1). No. 3582, $1.20, Lion dance (2-2).

2007, Apr. 13   Litho.   Perf. 12¾x13
3581-3582 A1072 Set of 2   .65 .65
See Indonesia No. 2100.

Torch Relay for 2008 Summer
Olympics, Beijing — A1073

2007, Apr. 27   Perf. 12
3583 A1073 $1.20 multi + label   .35 .35

Inner Mongolia Autonomous Region,
60th Anniv. — A1074

Designs: No. 3584, $1.20, Horsemen, wrestlers, archer (2-1). No. 3585, $1.20, Seven women (2-2).

Perf. 12½x12 Syncopated
2007, May 1
3584-3585 A1074 Set of 2   .65 .65
3585a   Souvenir sheet, #3584-
           3585   .65 .65

Mausoleums of
Qing Emperors
A1075

Designs: No. 3586, $1.20, Zhaoling Mausoleum (3-1). No. 3587, $1.20, Xiaoling Mausoleum (3-2). No. 3588, Tailing Mausoleum (3-3).

2007, May 12   Photo.   Perf. 12¾
3586-3588 A1075 Set of 3   .95 .95

Tongji
University,
Cent.
A1076

2007, May 20   Perf. 12½ Syncopated
3589 A1076 $1.20 multi   .35 .35

Kong Rong and Pears — A1077

Nos. 3590 and 3591: a, Denomination at LL (2-1). b, Denomination at LR (2-2).

2007, June 1   Perf. 13¼x13
3590 A1077 $1.20 Horiz. pair,
#a-b   .65 .65

Self-Adhesive
Booklet Stamps
Serpentine Die Cut 11¾

3591 A1077 $1.20 Horiz. pair,
#a-b   .65 .65
c.   Booklet pane, 4 #3591   2.60

Chongqing — A1078

No. 3592: a, City skyline (2-1). b, City and
highway interchange (2-2).
Illustration reduced.

Perf. 12x11½ Syncopated
2007, June 8   Litho.
3592 A1078 $1.20 Horiz. pair,
    #a-b   .65   .65

Wudalianchi Natl. Park — A1079

No. 3593: a, Heilong Mountain (3-1). b,
Sanchi Pool (3-2). c, Sea of Rock (3-3).

2007, June 19 Photo.   **Perf. 12¾**
3593   Horiz. strip of 3   .95   .95
a.-c.   A1079 $1.20 Any single   .30   .30

Return
of Hong
Kong,
10th
Anniv.
A1080

Designs: No. 3594, $1.20, Flags of People's
Republic of China and Hong Kong, doves,
monument (3-1). No. 3595, $1.20, "CEPA" and

stylized buildings (3-2). No. 3596,
$1.20, Hong Kong buildings, bridge (3-
3).

Perf. 13¼x12¾ Syncopated
2007, July 1
3594-3596 A1080 Set of 3   .95   .95
A souvenir sheet containing Nos. 3594-
3596 and Hong Kong No. 1275 sold for $12.95
in Hong Kong currency.

Pres. Yang
Shangkun (1907-
98)
A1081

Designs: No. 3597, $1.20, Standing in uni-
form (2-1). No. 3598, $1.20, Seated at desk,
horiz. (2-2).

Perf. 11½x11, 11x11½
2007, July 5   Photo. & Engr.
3597-3598 A1081   Set of 2   .65   .65

Nanji Islands Marine
Reserve — A1082

Shells and: No. 3599, $1.20, Sanpanwei (3-
1). No. 3600, $1.20, Longchuanjiao (3-2), No.
3601, $1.20, Dashaao (3-3).

Perf. 12¾x12½ Syncopated
2007, July 10   Photo.
3599-3601 A1082   Set of 3   .95   .95

Emblem of People's Liberation
Army — A1083

2007, July 15   Litho.   **Perf. 12**
3602 A1083 $1.20 multi + label   .35   .35

Souvenir Sheet

All-China Philatelic Federation, 6th
Congress — A1084

Perf. 12½ Syncopated
2007, July 28   Litho. & Engr.
3603 A1084 $6 multi   1.60   1.60

People's
Liberation Army,
80th
Anniv. — A1085

Designs: No. 3604, $1.20, Soldiers saluting
(4-1). No. 3605, $1.20, Soldier carrying sack
(4-2). No. 3606, $1.20, Soldier with rifle (4-3).
No. 3607, $1.20, Soldiers wearing UN
Peacekeeper berets (4-4).

Perf. 13¼x12½ Syncopated
2007, Aug. 1   Photo.
3604-3607 A1085   Set of 4   1.25   1.25

Olympic
Sports — A1086

Designs: Nos. 3608, 3614a, $1.20, Diving
(6-1). Nos. 3609, 3614b, $1.20, Shooting (6-
2). Nos. 3610, 3614c, $1.20, Athletics (6-3).
Nos. 3611, 3614d, $1.20, Volleyball (6-4).
Nos. 3612, 3614e, $1.20, BMX bicycling (6-5).
Nos. 3613, 3614f, $1.20, Weight lifting (6-6).

2007, Aug. 8 Photo.   Perf. 13¼x13
3608-3613 A1086   Set of 6   1.90   1.90
Self-Adhesive
Serpentine Die Cut 11¾
3614   Miniature sheet of 12,
      2 each #a-f   4.00
a.-f.   A1086 $1.20 Any single   .30   .30

Tengchong Volcano Area — A1087

Designs: No. 3615, $1.20, Rehai (3-1). No.
3616, $1.20, Volcanoes, vert. (3-2). No. 3617,
$1.20, Shenzhu Valley, vert. (3-3).

**Perf. 12x12½ Syncopated, 12½x12
Syncopated**
2007, Aug. 18
3615-3617 A1087   Set of 3   .95   .95
Nos. 3615-3617 were printed together in a
sheet of 15 stamps + a horizontal label. The
first row consists of the label and 2 #3615; the
second row, 3 #3615; the third row, 5 #3616;
and the fourth row, 5 #3617.

Jin Hu — A1088

No. 3618: a, Da Chibi (2-1). b, Maoer Mountain (2-2).
Illustration reduced.

Perf. 12¾ Syncopated
2007, Sept. 2   Litho.
3618 A1088 $1.20 Horiz. pair,
   #a-b   .65   .65

2007
Women's
Soccer World
Cup,
People's
Republic of
China
A1089

2007, Sept. 10 Photo.   Perf. 13¼
3619 A1089 $1.20 multi   .35   .35
Values are for stamps with surrounding
selvage.

2007 World Summer Special
Olympics, Shanghai — A1090

2007, Oct. 2   **Perf. 13¼**
3620 A1090 $1.20 multi   .35   .35

Historic Sites in Three Gorges
Reservoir Area — A1091

Designs: No. 3621, $1.20, Zhang Fei Tem-
ple (4-1). No. 3622, $1.20, Shibaozhai Village,
vert. (4-2). No. 3623, $1.20, Ancient Dachang,
vert. (4-3). No. 3624, $1.20, Quyuan's Grave
(4-4).

Perf. 13¼ Syncopated
2007, Oct. 13   Litho. & Engr.
3621-3624 A1091   Set of 4   1.40   1.40

17th Natl. Communist Party
Congress — A1092

Designs: No. 3625, $1.20, Memorial for First
Natl. Communist Party Congress (2-1). No.
3626, $1.20, Site of Second Plenary Session
of the Seventh Central Committee.
$6, Dove and monument.

Perf. 13¼x13 Syncopated
2007, Oct. 15   Photo.
3625-3626 A1092   Set of 2   .65   .65
Souvenir Sheet
Perf. 13¼x13
3627 A1092 $6 multi   1.60   1.60
No. 3627 contains one 60x40mm stamp.

SEMI-POSTAL STAMPS

Catalogue values for unused
stamps in this section are for
Never Hinged items.

Girl Holding
Ball — SP1

Hands Reading Braille — SP2

1984, Feb. 16   Photo.   Perf. 11½

B1	SP1	8f + 2f shown (2-1)	.25	.20
B2	SP1	8f + 2f Boy, panda (2-2)	.25	.20

Surtax for China Children's Fund. T.92.

1985, Mar. 15   Photo.   Perf. 11½

B3	SP2	8f + 2f shown (4-1)	1.00	.60
B4	SP2	8f + 2f Sign language, lip reading (4-2)	1.00	.60
B5	SP2	8f + 2f Artificial limb (4-3)	1.00	.60
B6	SP2	8f + 2f Handicapped person in wheel-chair (4-4)	1.00	.60
		Nos. B3-B6 (4)	4.00	2.40

Surtax for China Welfare Fund. T.105.

Children (T.137) SP3

1989, June 1   Litho.   Perf. 12

B7	SP3	8f +4f Friends (4-1)	.20	.20
B8	SP3	8f +4f Penguins (4-2)	.20	.20
B9	SP3	8f +4f Bird, Moon, Sun (4-3)	.20	.20
B10	SP3	8f +4f Girl, boy playing ball (4-4)	.20	.20
a.		Strip of 4, #B7-B10	.50	.50

Intl Children's Day, 40th anniv., and 10th Intl. Year of the Child. Surtax for China Children's Fund.

AIR POST STAMPS

Mail Plane and Temple of Heaven — AP1

1951, May 1   Engr.   Perf. 12½
Without Gum

C1	AP1	$1000 carmine	.20	.20
C2	AP1	$3000 green	.30	.20
C3	AP1	$5000 orange	.20	.20
C4	AP1	$10,000 vio brn & grn	.25	.25
C5	AP1	$30,000 dk bl & brn	8.50	1.25
		Nos. C1-C5 (5)	9.45	2.10

Planes at Airport — AP2

Designs: 28f, Plane over winding mountain highway. 35f, Plane over railroad yard. 52f, Plane over ship.

1957-58   Perf. 14
Without Gum

C6	AP2	16f indigo	10.00	.25
C7	AP2	28f olive black	10.00	.25
C8	AP2	35f slate	10.00	5.00
C9	AP2	52f Prus blue ('58)	10.00	.75
		Nos. C6-C9 (4)	40.00	6.25

POSTAGE DUE STAMPS

Grain and Cogwheel — D1

D2

1950, Sept. 1   Typo.   Perf. 12½
Without Gum

J1	D1	$100 steel blue	.20	.20
J2	D1	$200 steel blue	.20	.20
J3	D1	$500 steel blue	.20	.20
J4	D1	$800 steel blue	27.50	.20
J5	D1	$1000 steel blue	.45	.40
J6	D1	$2000 steel blue	.45	.40
J7	D1	$5000 steel blue	.30	.60
J8	D1	$8000 steel blue	.30	1.00
J9	D1	$10,000 steel blue	.60	2.00
		Nos. J1-J9 (9)	30.20	5.20

1954, Aug. 18   Litho.   Perf. 14
Without Gum

J10	D2	$100 red	2.00	.20
J11	D2	$200 red	.60	.20
J12	D2	$500 red	2.00	.20
J13	D2	$800 red	.20	.20
J14	D2	$1600 red	.20	.20
		Nos. J10-J14 (5)	5.00	1.00

MILITARY STAMP

Red Star, 8-1 in Center — M1

1953, Aug.   Litho.   Perf. 14
Without Gum

M1	M1	$800 yel, org & red	85.00	27.50

This stamp also was printed in deep purple, orange & red, and blue, orange & red. These were not issued.

While it has been assumed for many years that each color was for a separate branch of the armed forces (army, air force and navy), there is no documentation to support that theory. Quantities printed also do not correspond to the number of servicemen in each branch.

M2

1995   Litho.   Perf. 12

M4	M2	20f multicolored	8.00

NORTHEAST CHINA

The Northeast Liberation Area included the provinces of Liaoning, Kirin, Jehol and Heilungkiang, the area generally known as Manchuria under the Japanese. The first post war issues were local overprints on stamps of Manchukuo. In early 1946, a Ministry of Posts and Telegraphs served the areas already liberated, and in August, 1946, a Communications Committee of the Political Council was established. In June, 1947, these postal services were subordinated to the Harbin General Post Office, and this was extended to

Changchun on Oct. 22, 1948, and to Mukden on Nov. 4, 1948. It was rapidly extended to cover all Manchuria.

Rough Perfs
Rough perforations are normal on most regional issues.

All Stamps Issued without Gum

Mao Tse-tung

A1   A2

1946, Feb.   Unwmk.   Litho.   Perf. 11

1L1	A1	$1 violet	20.00	10.00
1L2	A2	$2 vermilion	1.50	1.00
1L3	A2	$5 orange	1.75	1.00
1L4	A2	$10 blue	2.00	1.25
a.		Booklet pane of 6	250.00	
		Booklet pane of 6	250.00	
		Nos. 1L1-1L4 (4)	25.25	13.25

Value, imperf set $125.
For surcharges see Nos. 1L20-1L23, 1L49-1L50, 1L89, 1L91, 1L93.

Map of China, Lion, Hyena and Chiang Kai-shek — A3

1946, Dec. 12   Perf. 10½

1L5	A3	$1 violet	2.00	1.50
1L6	A3	$2 orange	2.00	1.50
1L7	A3	$5 org brn	7.00	7.00
1L8	A3	$10 lt grn	10.00	10.00
a.		Imperf., pair	60.00	
		Nos. 1L5-1L8 (4)	21.00	20.00

10th anniversary of the capture of Chiang Kai-shek at Sian.

Railroad Workers, Chengchow A4

1947, Feb. 7   Perf. 10½

1L9	A4	$1 pink	1.00	1.10
1L10	A4	$2 dull grn	1.00	1.10
1L11	A4	$5 pink	1.75	1.60
1L12	A4	$10 dull grn	3.75	3.75
		Nos. 1L9-1L12 (4)	7.50	7.55

24th anniversary of the Chengchow railroad workers' strike and massacre.

Women (Worker, Soldier and Farmer) — A5

Wmk. Chinese Characters in Sheet
1947, Mar. 8   Perf. 10½x11

1L13	A5	$5 brick red	1.00	1.00
1L14	A5	$10 brown	1.00	1.00

International Women's Day, March 8. Exists imperf.

Same Overprinted in Green ("Northeast Postal Service")

1947, Mar. 18

1L15	A5	$5 brick red	3.00	4.50
1L16	A5	$10 brown	3.00	4.50

Exists imperf.

Children Carrying Banner — A6

1947, Apr. 4   Perf. 11x10½
Granite Paper

1L17	A6	$5 rose red	1.50	2.25
1L18	A6	$10 lt green	3.25	3.00
1L19	A6	$30 orange	5.00	4.00
		Nos. 1L17-1L19 (3)	9.75	9.25

Children's Day.

Nos. 1L1-1L2 Surcharged in Red, Brown, Black, Blue or Green

1947, Apr.   Unwmk.   Perf. 11

1L20	A1	$50 on $1 vio (R)	24.00	25.00
a.		Brown surcharge	24.00	25.00
1L21	A2	$50 on $2 ver	24.00	25.00
a.		Brown surcharge	24.00	25.00
1L22	A1	$100 on $1 vio	24.00	25.00
a.		Green surcharge	24.00	25.00
1L23	A2	$100 on $2 ver (Bl)	24.00	25.00
a.		Green surcharge	24.00	25.00
		Nos. 1L20-1L23 (4)	96.00	100.00

Farmer and Worker — A7

Ax Severing Chain — A8

Wmk. Chinese Characters in Sheet
1947, May 1   Perf. 10½x11
Granite Paper

1L24	A7	$10 orange red	2.25	2.25
1L25	A7	$30 ultra	2.75	2.75
1L26	A7	$50 gray green	4.25	4.25
		Nos. 1L24-1L26 (3)	9.25	9.25

Labor Day. Value, imperf. pairs, set $425.

1947, May 4   Perf. 11

1L27	A8	$10 brt green	2.50	2.50
1L28	A8	$30 brown	2.50	2.50
1L29	A8	$50 violet	3.00	3.00
		Nos. 1L27-1L29 (3)	8.00	8.00

28th anniversary of the students' revolt at Peking University against the 1918 peace treaty. Value, imperf. pairs, set $525.

Workers with Banner: "Oppose Imperialist Aggression" — A9

1947, May 30   Perf. 10½x11
Banner in Red

1L30	A9	$2 brt lilac	2.25	3.00
1L31	A9	$5 brt green	2.25	3.00
1L32	A9	$10 yellow	2.75	3.00
1L33	A9	$20 violet	2.75	3.00
1L34	A9	$30 red brown	2.75	3.00
1L35	A9	$50 dk blue	4.75	3.00
1L36	A9	$100 brown	6.75	3.00
a.		Souvenir sheet of 7	150.00	
		Nos. 1L30-1L36 (7)	24.25	21.00

22nd anniversary of the Shanghai-Nanking Road incident. No. 1L36a is on granite paper and contains 7 imperf. stamps similar to Nos.

1L30-1L36. Size: 215x158mm. Value, imperf. pairs, ordinary paper, set $1,300.

Mao and Communist Flag — A10

1947, July 1   **Perf. 10½x11**
1L37	A10	$10 red	9.50	11.00
1L38	A10	$30 brt lilac	9.50	11.00
1L39	A10	$50 rose brn	20.00	26.00
1L40	A10	$100 vermilion	25.00	29.00
		Nos. 1L37-1L40 (4)	64.00	77.00

26th anniversary of the founding of the Chinese Communist Party.

Hand Holding Rifle — A11

1947, July 7   **Perf. 10½**
1L41	A11	$10 orange	3.75	4.75
1L42	A11	$30 green	3.75	4.75
1L43	A11	$50 dull blue	5.75	5.75
1L44	A11	$100 brown	8.00	8.00
a.		Souvenir sheet of 4	160.00	175.00
		Nos. 1L41-1L44 (4)	21.25	23.25

10th anniversary of the start of Sino-Japanese War. No. 1L44a contains 4 imperf. stamps similar to Nos. 1L41-1L44. Size: 149x107mm.
Exist imperf. Value, set of pairs $1,100.

White Mountain and Black Water, Northeast China — A12

Wmk. Zigzag Lines (141)
1947, Aug. 15   **Perf. 10½**
1L45	A12	$10 brown org	3.00	7.50
1L46	A12	$30 lt ol grn	3.00	7.50
1L47	A12	$50 blue grn	12.00	13.00
1L48	A12	$100 sepia	21.00	18.00
		Nos. 1L45-1L48 (4)	39.00	46.00

2nd anniversary of the reoccupation of Northeast China and the surrender of Japan.
Exist imperf. Value, set of pairs $700.

Nos. 1L1-1L2 Surcharged in Black, Red, Green or Blue

1947, Aug. 29   Unwmk.   Perf. 11
1L49	A1	$5 on $1 vio	22.50	22.50
a.		Red surcharge	22.50	22.50
b.		Green surcharge	22.50	22.50
1L50	A2	$10 on $2 ver	22.50	22.50
a.		Blue surcharge	22.50	22.50
b.		Green surcharge	22.50	22.50

Map of Manchuria — A13

1947, Sept. 18   Unwmk.
White Paper
1L51	A13	$10 gray green	4.50	8.75
1L52	A13	$20 rose lilac	4.50	8.75
1L53	A13	$30 black brown	8.75	8.75
1L54	A13	$50 carmine	8.75	8.75
		Nos. 1L51-1L54 (4)	26.50	35.00

16th anniversary of Japanese attack on Mukden, Sept. 18, 1931.

Northeast Political Council Offices — A14

Mao Tse-tung (Value figures repeated) — A15

1947, Oct. 10   **Perf. 10½**
1L55	A14	$10 yel orange	30.00	30.00
1L56	A14	$20 rose red	30.00	30.00
1L57	A14	$100 brown	77.50	77.50
		Nos. 1L55-1L57 (3)	137.50	137.50

35th anniversary of the founding of the Chinese Republic.

1947, Oct. 10   White Paper   Perf. 11
1L58	A15	$1 brown	.35	1.50
1L59	A15	$5 gray green	2.00	1.50
1L60	A15	$10 brt green	8.00	8.00
1L61	A15	$15 bluish lilac	8.00	8.00
1L62	A15	$20 brt rose	.80	1.50
1L63	A15	$30 green	.80	2.00
1L64	A15	$50 black brown	15.00	12.00
1L65	A15	$90 blue	4.50	4.00
		Nos. 1L58-1L65 (8)	39.45	38.50

Newsprint
1L66	A15	$100 red		.70
a.		White paper	7.00	4.00
1L67	A15	$500 red orange	27.50	16.00
a.		White paper	27.50	25.00

Type A22 resembles A15, but has "YUAN" at upper right.
The $1, $90 were also printed on newsprint. See footnote following No. 1L72.
See Nos. 1L68-1L72. For surcharges see Nos. 1L84-1L88, 1L90, 1L92, 1L94.

1947, Nov.   Redrawn
White Paper
1L68	A15	$50 lt grn	1.00	1.50
1L69	A15	$150 red org, wmkd.		
		Chinese characters	2.25	1.50
a.		Unwatermarked	2.75	
1L70	A15	$250 bluish lil	.90	1.50
a.		Wmkd. Chinese characters	1.25	1.50

Nos. 1L69 and 1L69a exist in same sheet.

1947, Dec.   Unwmk.
Newsprint
1L71	A15	$300 green	52.50	27.50
1L72	A15	$1000 yellow	1.50	1.50
a.		White paper	1.50	1.50
		Nos. 1L68-1L72 (5)	58.15	33.50

Panel below portrait 8½x3mm on Nos. 1L68-1L70; 7x3mm on No. 1L58-1L67. Nos. 1L68-1L70 have different ornamental border. Nos. 1L71-1L72 without zeros for cents.
For surcharges see Nos. 1L90, 1L92, 1L94.

Hand Holding Torch — A16

1947, Dec. 12   Unwmk.   Perf. 11
White Paper
1L73	A16	$30 rose red	6.00	8.50
1L74	A16	$90 dk bl	8.00	8.50
1L75	A16	$150 green	12.00	8.50
		Nos. 1L73-1L75 (3)	26.00	25.50

11th anniversary of the capture of Chiang Kai-shek at Sian.

Tomb of Gen. Li Chao-lin — A17

Globe and Banner — A18

1948, Mar. 9   Unwmk.   Perf. 10½x11
1L76	A17	$30 green	12.00	12.00
1L77	A17	$150 vio gray	12.00	12.00
a.		Granite paper, wmkd.	12.00	12.00

2nd anniversary of the assassination of Gen. Li Chao-lin, Commander of 3rd Army.

Wmk. Chinese Characters in Sheet
1948, May 1   Perf. 11x10½
1L78	A18	$50 red	8.00	12.00
1L79	A18	$150 green	3.00	18.00
1L80	A18	$250 lilac	3.00	35.00
		Nos. 1L78-1L80 (3)	14.00	65.00

Labor Day.

Student, Torch and Banner — A19

1948, May 4   Unwmk.   Perf. 10½x11
Granite paper
1L81	A19	$50 green	8.00	7.00
1L82	A19	$150 brown	8.00	11.00
1L83	A19	$250 red	15.00	17.00
		Nos. 1L81-1L83 (3)	31.00	35.00

Youth Day, May 4.

Nos. 1L58, 1L61, 1L59, 1L63, 1L65, 1L2-1L4, 1L68-1L69, 1L71 Surcharged in Black, Blue, Red or Green

1948-49			**Perf. 11**
1L84	A15	$100 on $1	75.00	90.00
a.		Blue surcharge	50.00	50.00
1L85	A15	$100 on $15	18.00	17.50
a.		Blue surcharge	50.00	50.00
1L86	A15	$300 on $5 (R)	55.00	25.00
1L87	A15	$300 on $30 (R)	6.00	10.00
1L88	A15	$300 on $90 (R)	6.00	10.00
1L89	A2	$500 on $2	6.00	8.00
1L90	A15	$500 on $5 brn, '49	27.50	20.00
1L91	A2	$1500 on $5 (Bl)	6.00	7.50
1L92	A15	$1500 on $150 (G; '49)	22.50	15.00
a.		Blue surcharge	50.00	50.00
1L93	A2	$2500 on $10 (R)	7.50	9.00
1L94	A15	$2500 on $300 ('49)	9.00	12.00
		Nos. 1L84-1L94 (11)	238.50	222.00

Crane Operator — A20

Wmk. Chinese Characters in Sheet
1948, May   **Perf. 11**
1L95	A20	$100 red & pink	1.25	1.00
1L96	A20	$300 vio brn & yel	1.50	1.50
1L97	A20	$500 bl & grn	2.00	2.00
		Nos. 1L95-1L97 (3)	4.75	4.50

6th All-China Labor Conference, Harbin.

Farmer, Worker and Soldier Saluting — A21

Mao Tse-tung ("YUAN" at upper right) — A22

1948, Dec. 3   Unwmk.   Perf. 11x10½
White paper
1L98	A21	$500 vermilion	8.00	8.00
1L99	A21	$1500 brt grn	12.00	12.00
1L100	A21	$2500 brown	21.00	21.00
		Nos. 1L98-1L100 (3)	41.00	41.00

Liberation of Northeast China.
Values for Nos. 1L98-1L100 are for fine stamps.

1949, Feb.   **Perf. 11**
1L101	A22	$300 olive	.50	1.00
1L102	A22	$500 orange	1.50	1.75
1L103	A22	$1500 bl grn	.50	1.00
1L104	A22	$4500 brown	.50	1.00
1L105	A22	$6500 dk bl	.50	1.00
		Nos. 1L101-1L105 (5)	3.50	5.75

See type A15. For surcharges see Nos. 1L126-1L129, 1L131-1L132.

Workers, Globe and Flag — A23

Fields and Factories — A24

1949, May 1   **Perf. 11½**
1L106	A23	$1000 red & dl bl	.35	.65
1L107	A23	$1500 red & pale bl	.35	.65
1L108	A23	$4500 rose & ol brn	.50	1.00
1L109	A23	$6500 dl org & grn	.50	1.00
1L110	A23	$10,000 mar & ultra	.60	1.40
		Nos. 1L106-1L110 (5)	2.30	4.70

Labor Day.

1949   **Perf. 10, 11**
1L111	A24	$5000 Prus bl	4.50	3.25
1L112	A24	$10,000 org brn	.35	1.60
1L113	A24	$50,000 green	.45	2.40
1L114	A24	$100,000 violet	.90	12.00
		Nos. 1L111-1L114 (4)	6.20	19.25

Production in agriculture and industry.

Workers with Flags — A25

Heroes' Monument, Harbin — A26

1949, July 1   **Perf. 11**
1L115	A25	$1500 vio, lt bl & red	.50	.65
1L116	A25	$4500 dk brn, lt bl & ver	.50	.65
1L117	A25	$6500 gray, lt bl & rose red	.90	1.25
		Nos. 1L115-1L117 (3)	1.90	2.55

28th anniversary of the founding of the Chinese Communist Party.

1949, Aug. 15   **Perf. 11½x11**
1L118	A26	$1500 brick red	.90	1.20
1L119	A26	$4500 yel grn	.90	1.20
1L120	A26	$6500 lt blue	1.00	1.20
	Nos. 1L118-1L120 (3)	2.80	3.60

4th anniversary of the Reoccupation, and the surrender of Japan.

"Northeast Postal Service"

The following commemorative issues are similar to those of the People's Republic of China, with the 4 characters shown added in different sizes and various arrangements. Reprints were also issued similar to those of the PRC.

Chinese Lantern Type of PRC, 1949

1949, Sept. 12   **Litho.**   **Perf. 12½**
1L121	A1	$1000 dp blue	3.00	5.00
1L122	A1	$1500 scarlet	4.00	5.00
1L123	A1	$3000 green	6.00	6.50
1L124	A1	$4500 maroon	7.00	7.50
	Nos. 1L121-1L124 (4)	20.00	24.00

Reprints exist. Value, set $1.10.

Factory — A27

1949, Oct.   **Perf. 11x10½**
1L125	A27	$1500 orange	.90	1.25

For surcharge see No. 1L130.

Nos. 1L101, 1L103-
1L105, 1L125
Surcharged in Black
or Green

1949, Nov. 20
1L126	A22	$2000 on $300	22.50	4.25
1L127	A22	$2000 on $4500		
		(G)	47.50	32.50
1L128	A22	$2500 on $1500	.70	5.00
1L129	A22	$2500 on $6500	24.00	32.50
1L130	A27	$5000 on $1500	.60	1.75
1L131	A22	$20,000 on $4500	.40	5.00
1L132	A22	$35,000 on $300	.50	6.75
	Nos. 1L126-1L132 (7)	96.20	87.75

Globe and Hammer Type of PRC

1949, Nov. 15   **Perf. 12½**
1L133	A2	$5000 crimson	150.00	60.00
1L134	A2	$20,000 dp green	250.00	70.00
1L135	A2	$35,000 vio blue	350.00	90.00
	Nos. 1L133-1L135 (3)	750.00	220.00

Reprints, value; #1L133-1L134, each $1.50;
#1L135, $175.

Mao and Conference Hall Types of PRC

1950, Feb. 1   **Perf. 14**
1L136	A3	$1000 vermilion	10.00	13.00
1L137	A3	$1500 dp blue	10.00	13.00
1L138	A4	$5000 dk vio brn	20.00	14.00
1L139	A4	$20,000 green	20.00	20.00
	Nos. 1L136-1L139 (4)	60.00	60.00

Reprints exist. Value, set $4.

Gate of Heavenly
Peace — A28

1950   **Perf. 10½**
Narrow horizontal shading
1L140	A28	$500 olive	1.50	.55
1L141	A28	$1000 orange	1.75	.55
1L142	A28	$1000 lil rose	4.00	.55
1L143	A28	$2000 gray grn	1.25	.30
1L144	A28	$2500 yellow	4.50	.30
1L145	A28	$5000 dp org	20.00	.30

1L146	A28	$10,000 brn org	2.25	.55
1L147	A28	$20,000 vio brn	1.25	.30
1L148	A28	$35,000 dp blue	1.25	.40
1L149	A28	$50,000 brt grn	20.00	.80
	Nos. 1L140-1L149 (10)	57.75	4.60

See A29.

Flag and Mao Type of PRC

1950, July 1   **Perf. 14**
Yellow Stars
1L150	A7	$5000 grn & red	57.50	52.50
1L151	A7	$10,000 brn & red	72.50	52.50
1L152	A7	$20,000 dk brn & red	80.00	52.50
1L153	A7	$30,000 dk vio bl & red	110.00	72.50
	Nos. 1L150-1L153 (4)	320.00	230.00

Reprints exist. Value, set $7.

Picasso Dove Type of PRC

1950, Aug. 1   **Engr.**   **Perf. 14**
1L154	A8	$2500 brown	10.00	18.00
1L155	A8	$5000 green	15.00	18.00
1L156	A8	$20,000 blue	20.00	18.00
	Nos. 1L154-1L156 (3)	45.00	54.00

Reprints exist. Value, set $4.75.

Flag Type of PRC

1950, Oct. 1   **Engr. & Litho.**
Flag in Red & Yellow
1L157	A9	$1000 purple	35.00	27.50
1L158	A9	$2500 org brn	52.50	35.00
1L159	A9	$5000 dp grn	60.00	45.00
1L160	A9	$10,000 olive	80.00	45.00
1L161	A9	$20,000 blue	125.00	72.50
	Nos. 1L157-1L161 (5)	352.50	225.00

Size of #1L159: 38x47mm, others 26x33mm.
Reprints exist. Value, set $7.

Postal Conference Type of PRC

1950, Nov. 1   **Litho.**
1L162	A11	$2500 grn & dp org	12.00	9.50
1L163	A11	$5000 car & grn	12.00	9.50
	Nos. 1L162-1L163 (2)		

Reprints exist. Value, set, $5.

Gate of Heavenly
Peace — A29

1950-51   **Perf. 10½**
Wide horizontal shading
1L164	A29	$5000 orange	6.00	6.25
1L165	A29	$30,000 scarlet	2.25	15.00
1L166	A29	$100,000 violet	10.00	16.00

Wmk. Zigzag Lines (141)
1L167	A29	$250 brown	.90	1.50
1L168	A29	$500 olive	.90	1.50
1L169	A29	$1000 lil rose	1.25	2.50
1L170	A29	$2000 dl grn ('51)	2.00	2.50
1L171	A29	$2500 yellow	.90	2.50
1L172	A29	$5000 orange	2.25	2.50
1L173	A29	$10,000 brn org		
		('51)	1.60	2.50
1L174	A29	$12,500 maroon	.90	2.50
1L175	A29	$20,000 dp brn		
		('51)	1.75	5.00
	Nos. 1L164-1L175 (12)	30.70	60.25

A $50,000 green was prepared, but not issued. Value $150.

Stalin and Mao Tse-tung Type of PRC
Unwmk.

1950, Dec. 1   **Engr.**   **Perf. 14**
1L176	A12	$2500 red	20.00	10.00
1L177	A12	$5000 dp green	25.00	10.00
1L178	A12	$20,000 dk blue	25.00	10.00
	Nos. 1L176-1L178 (3)	70.00	30.00

Reprints exist. Value, set $2.75.

NORTHEAST CHINA PARCEL POST STAMPS

Locomotive — PP1

1951   **Litho.**   **Perf. 10½**
1LQ1	$100,000 purple	200.00	

Imperf
1LQ2	$300,000 brown	400.00	
1LQ3	$500,000 grnsh bl	700.00	
1LQ4	$1,000,000 ver	1,100.	

Value, Nos. 1LQ2-1LQ4 perf. 10½, $2,650.
For similar type see North China PP1.

PORT ARTHUR AND DAIREN

The Liaoning Postal Administration was established on April 1, 1946, in accordance with the Sino-Soviet Treaty, but was renamed one week later the Port Arthur and Dairen Postal Administration. On Apr. 3, 1947, it was combined with telecommunications and renamed the Kwantung Post and Telegraph General Administration.

On May 1, 1949, the name was again changed to Port Arthur and Dairen Post and Telegraph Administration. Postal tariffs were based on local currency and both Manchukuo and Japanese stamps were overprinted for use.

Gum
#2L1-2L55 were issued with gum.

Manchukuo Nos. 162
and 94 Handstamp
Surcharged in Violet
("Liaoning Post")

1946, Mar. 15
2L1	A19	20f on 30f buff	72.50	72.50
2L2	A18	1y on 12f org	37.50	37.50

Same Surcharge on Japan Nos. 260,
337, 195, 244, 263, 342 in Violet, Red
or Black

1946, Apr. 1
2L3	A85	20f on 3s grn (V)	19.50	21.00
2L4	A151	1y on 17s gray vio (R)	16.00	18.00
2L5	A57	5y on 6s car	29.00	27.50
2L6	A57	5y on 6s crim	29.00	27.50
2L7	A88	5y on 6s org	22.00	20.00
2L8	A154	15y on 40s dk vio	110.00	125.00
	Nos. 2L1-2L8 (8)	335.50	349.00

Surcharge sideways on Nos. 2L5-2L6.

Japan Nos. 260 and
263 Surcharged

1946, Apr.
2L9	A85	1y on 3s grn	—	
2L10	A88	5y on 6s org	—	

Sha Ho Kow (suburb of Dairen) issue.
The status of this issue is in question.

Manchukuo Nos. 84,
88 and 98 Handstamp
Surcharged in Green,
Red or Black

1946, May 1
2L11	A16	1y on 1f red brn		
		(G)	18.00	24.00
2L12	A18	5y on 4f lt ol grn		
		(R)	24.00	32.50
2L13	A19	15y on 30f chnt brn	52.50	62.50
	Nos. 2L11-2L13 (3)	94.50	119.00

Transfer of postal administration and Labor Day.

Manchukuo Nos. 159,
86 and 94 Surcharged
in Green, Red or Black

1946, July 7
2L14	A17	1y on 6f crim rose (G)	11.50	20.00
2L15	A17	5y on 2f lt grn (R)	52.50	85.00
2L16	A18	15y on 12f dp org	110.00	110.00
	Nos. 2L14-2L16 (3)	174.00	215.00

Outbreak of war with Japan, 9th anniv.

Manchukuo Nos. 94,
84 and 158
Surcharged in Black,
Green or Red

1946, Aug. 15
2L17	A18	1y on 12f dp org	22.50	27.50
2L18	A16	5y on 1f red brn		
		(R)	52.50	50.00
2L19	A10	15y on 5f gray blk	110.00	100.00
	Nos. 2L17-2L19 (3)	185.00	177.50

Surrender of Japan, first anniversary.

Manchukuo Nos. 159,
94 and 86 Surcharged
in Green, Black or Red

1946, Oct. 10
2L20	A17	1y on 6f crim rose (G)	32.50	30.00
2L21	A18	5y on 12f dp org	57.50	55.00
2L22	A17	15y on 2f lt grn	110.00	100.00
	Nos. 2L20-2L22 (3)	200.00	185.00

35th anniversary of Chinese revolution.

Manchukuo Nos. 84,
159 and 94
Surcharged in Black,
Green or Blue

1946, Oct. 19
2L23	A16	1y on 1f red brn	47.50	45.00
2L24	A17	5y on 6f crim rose (G)	87.50	85.00
2L25	A18	15y on 12f dp org (Bl)	125.00	125.00
	Nos. 2L23-2L25 (3)	260.00	255.00

10th anniversary of the death of Lu Hsun (1881-1936), writer.

Manchukuo Nos. 86,
159 and 95
Surcharged in Red,
Green or Black

1947, Feb. 20
2L26	A17	1y on 2f lt grn (R)	80.00	77.50
2L27	A17	5y on 6f crim rose (G)	160.00	150.00
2L28	A18	15y on 13f dk red brn	325.00	300.00
	Nos. 2L26-2L28 (3)	565.00	527.50

29th anniversary of the Red (USSR) Army.

Manchukuo Nos. 86, 159 and 162 Surcharged in Red, Green or Black

1947, May 1
2L29	A17	1y on 2f lt grn (R)	24.00	24.00
2L30	A17	5y on 6f crim rose (G)	67.50	65.00
2L31	A19	15y on 30f buff	110.00	100.00
Nos. 2L29-2L31 (3)			201.50	189.00

Labor Day.

Manchukuo Nos. 86, 88, 98 and 162 Surcharged ("Kwantung Postal Service, China")

1947, Sept. 15
2L32	A17	5y on 2f lt grn	40.00	40.00
2L33	A18	15y on 4f lt ol grn	65.00	62.50
2L34	A19	20y on 30f red brn	100.00	95.00
2L35	A19	20y on 30f buff	110.00	100.00
Nos. 2L32-2L35 (4)			315.00	297.50

Manchukuo Nos. 86 and 159 Surcharged in Red and Green

Sacred Golden Kite (same size) — A1

1948, Feb. 20
2L36	A17	10y on 2f lt grn (R)	140.00	140.00
2L37	A17	20y on 6f crim rose (G)	175.00	175.00
2L38	A1	100y on bl & red brn	725.00	725.00

30th anniversary of the Red (USSR) Army. No. 2L38 is on an ungummed label for the 2600th anniv. of the Japanese Empire.

Japan No. 260 and Manchukuo Nos. 84, 86 and 88 Surcharged in Red, Blue or Black

1948, July
2L39	A85	5y on 3s grn (R)	125.00	125.00
2L40	A16	10y on 1f red brn (Bl)	225.00	250.00
2L41	A17	50y on 2f lt grn	500.00	475.00
2L42	A18	100y on 4f lt ol grn (R)	875.00	900.00

Smaller Characters on Bottom Line
2L43	A17	10y on 2f lt grn (R)	300.00	225.00
2L44	A16	50y on 1f red brn	350.00	300.00

Stamps of Manchukuo Nos. 84, 86 and 88 Surcharged in Blue, Red or Black

---

1948, Nov. 1
2L45	A16	10y on 1f red brn (Bl)	275.00	600.00
2L46	A17	50y on 2f lt grn (R)	450.00	600.00
2L47	A18	100y on 4f lt ol grn	1,100.	600.00

31st anniversary of the Russian Revolution.

Manchukuo Nos. 86 and 161 Surcharged in Red or Green

1948, Nov. 15
2L48	A17	10y on 2f lt grn	1,050.	1,050.
2L49	A17	50y on 20f brn (G)	1,200.	1,200.

Kwantung Agricultural and Industrial Exhibition.

Manchukuo Nos. 86, 88 and 161 Surcharged in Red, Black or Green

1949, Jan.
2L50	A17	20y on 2f lt grn (R)	500.00	
2L51	A18	50y on 4f lt ol grn	700.00	
2L52	A17	100y on 20f brn (G)	700.00	

Without Gum
From No. 2L56 onward all stamps were issued without gum except as noted.

Farmer and Worker — A2

Train and Ship — A3

Ship at Dock (No. 2L55) — A4

(No. 2L56)

1949　　Litho.　　Perf. 11, 11½
2L53	A2	5y pale grn	2.25	4.00
2L54	A3	10y orange	12.00	11.00
2L55	A4	50y vermilion	17.50	16.00
2L56	A4	50y red (redrawn)	24.00	24.00
Nos. 2L53-2L56 (4)			55.75	55.00

Issue dates: #2L56, July 7; others Apr. 1. For surcharges see Nos. 2L62-2L66.

Worker, Flag and Means of Transport A5

1949, May 1　　　　Perf. 11
2L57	A5	10y rose pink	17.50	18.00
a.		10y vermilion	75.00	75.00

Labor Day. #2L57a is from a worn plate.

Mao Tse-tung and Red Flag — A6

Heroes Monument, Dairen — A7

1949, July 1
2L59	A6	50y red	32.50	35.00

28th anniversary of the founding of the Chinese Communist Party.

1949, Sept.
2L60	A7	10y red, bl & olive	16.00	13.00
a.		10y red, blue & pale blue	100.00	85.00

4th anniversary of victory over Japan and opening of the Dairen Industrial Fair.

Nos. 2L53-2L54 Surcharged in Red or Black

a　　　　　　b

c

1949, Sept.　　　　With Gum
2L62	A2(a)	7y on 5y (R)	37.50	32.50
2L63	A2(a)	7y on 5y	35.00	32.50
2L64	A2(b)	50y on 5y (R)	90.00	80.00
2L65	A3(b)	100y on 10y	450.00	350.00
2L66	A3(c)	500y on 10y (R)	600.00	400.00
Nos. 2L62-2L66 (5)			1,212.	895.00

Size of surcharge on No. 2L63: 16x19mm.
A 500y on 5y, red surcharge "c," and a 500y on 10y orange, surcharge "b" were prepared but not issued.

Stalin and Lenin — A8

1949, Nov. 7　　　Perf. 11x11½
2L68	A8	10y dl bl grn (shades)	15.00	16.00

32nd anniversary of the Russian Revolution.

Workers Saluting Mao, Star and Flag — A9

1949, Nov. 16　　　　Perf. 11
2L69	A9	35y dk bl, red, & yel	20.00	20.00

Founding of the People's Republic of China.

Stalin — A10

(same size) Gate of Heavenly Peace — A11

1949, Dec. 20　　　　Perf. 11½
2L70	A10	20y dull magenta	37.50	40.00
2L71	A10	35y rose red	37.50	40.00

70th birthday of Stalin.

1950, Mar. 10　　Typo.　　Perf. 10½
2L72	A11	10y Prus blue	210.00	85.00
2L73	A11	20y dull grn	110.00	110.00
2L74	A11	35y red	22.50	22.50
2L75	A11	50y deep pur	16.00	16.00
2L76	A11	100y lilac rose	22.50	22.50
Nos. 2L72-2L76 (5)			381.00	256.00

NORTH CHINA

The North China Liberation Area included the provinces of Hopeh, Chahar, Shansi and Suiyuan. The original postal service, begun in the Shansi-Hopeh-Chahar Border Area in December, 1937, became the North China Postal and Telegraph Administration in May, 1949.

All Stamps Issued without Gum
Except as Noted
Large Victory Issue

Cavalry Man Holding Nationalist Flag — A1

Wmk. Wavy Lines
1946, Mar.　　　　Perf. 10½
Granite Paper
Size: 34½x42mm
3L1	A1	$1 red brown	1.25	1.40
a.		Newsprint	10.00	12.00
3L2	A1	$2 gray grn	1.25	1.25
3L3	A1	$4 vermilion	1.40	1.25
3L4	A1	$5 vio brn	4.25	1.25
3L5	A1	$8 vio bl	1.25	1.25
3L6	A1	$10 dp car	1.40	1.25
3L7	A1	$12 yellow	4.00	4.50
3L8	A1	$20 lt green	8.50	8.00
Nos. 3L1-3L8 (8)			26.30	20.15

Defeat of Japan.

Small Victory Issue
Perf. 10½x10, 9½ rough
1946, May　　　　Unwmk.
Granite paper
Size: 20x21mm
3L9	A1	$1 red org	1.50	2.00
3L10	A1	$2 green	2.40	2.00
3L11	A1	$3 lt lilac	4.50	8.00
3L12	A1	$5 dull pur	6.00	.35
3L13	A1	$8 dk blue	12.50	16.00
3L14	A1	$10 rose red	2.40	4.00
3L15	A1	$15 purple	50.00	40.00
3L16	A1	$20 green	4.50	6.00
3L17	A1	$30 brt grnsh bl	3.75	7.00
3L18	A1	$40 brt rose lilac	4.50	3.00
3L19	A1	$50 brown	26.00	.70
3L20	A1	$60 myrtle green	50.00	4.00

Wmk. Wavy Lines
3L21	A1	$100 orange	1.60	4.00
3L22	A1	$200 dull blue	1.60	4.00
3L23	A1	$500 rose	47.50	50.00
Nos. 3L9-3L23 (15)			218.75	148.55

North China Postal and Telegraph Administration

Charging Infantrymen A2 — Agriculture and Industry A3

1949, Jan.   Unwmk.   Imperf.
White Paper

3L24	A2	50c brown lake	1.10	1.10
3L25	A2	$1 Prussian blue	1.10	1.10

Newsprint

3L26	A2	$2 apple green	1.10	1.10
3L27	A2	$3 dull violet	1.10	1.10
3L28	A2	$5 brown	1.10	1.10
3L29	A3	$6 deep rose	1.10	1.10
a.		White paper	1.10	1.10
3L30	A2	$10 blue grn	.40	.50
3L31	A2	$12 dp car	1.25	1.25
		Nos. 3L24-3L31 (8)	8.25	8.35

No. 3L29 issued in Peking, others in Tientsin.

Remittance Stamps of China Surcharged

A4

壹
$1

叁
$3

1949, Jan.   Engr.   Perf. 13
Small Central Characters

3L32	A4	50c on $50 brn blk	3.25	3.50
3L33	A4	$1 on $50 gray blk	2.25	2.75
3L34	A4	$3 on $50 gray	2.50	2.50

Large Central Characters

3L35	A4	50c on $50 blk	1.60	1.60
3L36	A4	$6 on $20 dk vio brn	1.60	1.60
		Nos. 3L32-3L36 (5)	11.20	11.95

Issued in Tientsin.
For surcharges see Nos. 3LQ10-3LQ21.

Sun Yat-sen Type A2 of Northeastern Provinces and China No. 640 Surcharged in Black, Red, Green or Blue

#3L37-3L45, 3L47-3L50, 3L52 — #3L46, 3L51, 3L53

c

Type "b," bottom character of left vertical row (yuan) differs. Type "c," top character of right vertical row differs.

1949, Mar. 7   Perf. 14

3L37	A2	50c on 5c lake	.45	2.40
3L38	A2	$1 on 10c org	.45	1.90
3L39	A2	$2 on 20c yel grn	42.50	22.50
3L40	A2	$3 on 50c red org	.45	1.50
3L41	A2	$4 on $5 dk grn	4.75	1.90
3L42	A2	$6 on $10 crim	1.50	1.90
3L43	A2	$10 on $300 blu-ish grn	3.00	3.75
3L44	A2	$12 on $1 bl	1.25	2.75

3L45	A2	$18 on $3 brn	1.25	1.40
3L46	A2	$20 on 50c red	1.50	1.25
3L47	A2	$20 on $20 ol, II	3.00	4.00
a.		Type I	12.00	13.50
3L48	A2	$30 on $2.50 ind (R)	3.00	3.75
3L49	A2	$40 on 25c blk brn (R)	4.50	5.75
3L50	A2	$50 on $109 dk grn (R)	9.50	7.75
3L51	A2	$80 on $1 bl (R)	12.50	4.00
3L52	A2	$100 on $65 dl grn (R)	16.00	7.75
3L53	A73	$100 on $100 dk car, surch. 16mm wide (Bl)	20.00	2.75
a.		Surcharge 14mm wide	20.00	10.00

1949, Apr.

3L55	A2 (c)	$2 on 20c yel grn	1.50	2.75
3L56	A2 (c)	$3 on 50c red org	.75	1.90
3L57	A2 (c)	$4 on $5 dk grn	6.00	3.75
3L58	A2 (c)	$6 on $10 crim, I	4.25	3.75
a.		Type II	15.00	10.00
3L59	A2 (c)	$12 on $1 blue	1.50	1.50

d

e

1949, Apr.
Type "d"

3L60	A2	$1 on 25c blk grn (G)	.45	1.10
3L61	A2	$10 on $300 bluish grn (R)	9.50	5.25
3L62	A2	$20 on 50c red org (G)	18.00	22.50
3L63	A2	$20 on $20 ol (R)	6.50	3.75
3L64	A2	$40 on 25c blk brn (R)	6.50	4.50
3L65	A2	$50 on $109 dk grn, surch. 15mm wide (R)	9.50	11.50
a.		Surcharge 13mm wide	30.00	30.00
3L66	A2	$80 on $1 bl (R)	6.50	5.75

Type "d" On Stamps on China

3L67	A73	$100 on $100 dk car (G)	52.50	30.00
3L68	A73	$300 on $700 red brn (R)	11.00	11.00
3L69	A82	$500 on $500 bl grn (R)	8.00	3.75
3L70	A82	$3000 on $3000 bl (R)	12.00	7.50

Type "e" On Stamps of Northeastern Provinces

1949, Aug.

3L71	A2	$10 on $10 crim, II (Bl)	6.50	3.00
a.		Type I	12.50	12.00
3L72	A2	$30 on 20c yel grn (R)	6.50	1.90
3L73	A2	$50 on $44 dk car rose (Bl)	6.50	1.00
3L74	A2	$100 on $3 brn (Bl)	12.00	5.75
3L75	A2	$200 on $4 org brn, II (Bl)	30.00	19.00
a.		Type I	1,100.	450.00

On China No. 754 in Blue

3L76	A82	$10 on $7000 lt red brn	11.00	7.75
		Nos. 3L37-3L76 (39)	352.55	235.65

Overprints on Nos. 3L71 and 3L76 have 2 characters in center row.

Farmer and Worker on Globe — A5

1949, May 1   Engr.   Perf. 14

3L77	A5	$20 crimson	1.75	.65
3L78	A5	$40 dark blue	1.75	.80
3L79	A5	$60 brown org	1.75	.65

3L80	A5	$80 dk green	1.75	1.00
3L81	A5	$100 purple	1.75	1.00
		Nos. 3L77-3L81 (5)	8.75	4.10

Labor day. Exists imperf. Value, set $12.50. Also issued in blocks of 4, imperf between. Value, unused or used, $13.50.

Mao Tse-tung (Chinese Numeral) — A6

Mao Tse-tung (Arabic Numeral) — A7

1949, July 1   Perf. 14

3L82	A6	$10 red	.80	.60
3L83	A7	$20 dk blue	.80	.60
3L84	A6	$50 orange	5.00	1.00
3L85	A7	$80 dk green	1.00	1.00
3L86	A6	$100 purple	5.00	1.00
3L87	A7	$120 olive	.70	1.00
3L88	A6	$140 vio brn	5.00	1.00
		Nos. 3L82-3L88 (7)	18.30	5.80

28th anniv. of the founding of the Chinese Communist Party. Value, imperf, set $40.

Gate of Heavenly Peace — A8 — Farmers and Factory — A9

1949, Nov. 26   Litho.   Perf. 12½

3L89	A8	$50 orange	.30	3.50
3L90	A8	$100 crimson	.30	1.00
3L91	A8	$200 green	.70	1.00
3L92	A8	$300 rose brn	9.00	2.25
3L93	A8	$400 blue	9.00	2.25
3L94	A8	$500 brown	9.00	1.25
3L95	A8	$700 violet	3.25	3.50
		Nos. 3L89-3L95 (7)	31.55	14.75

1949, Dec.   Engr.   Perf. 14

3L96	A9	$1000 orange	2.75	1.50
3L97	A9	$3000 dark blue	.30	1.25
3L98	A9	$5000 crimson	.30	2.40
3L99	A9	$10,000 red brown	.30	4.75
		Nos. 3L96-3L99 (4)	3.65	9.90

NORTH CHINA PARCEL POST STAMPS

Parcel Post Stamps of China Nos. Q23-Q27 (Type PP3) Surcharged in Red, Black (#3LQ6-3LQ9) or Blue (#3LQ2)

a   b

1949, June
Surcharged Type "a"

3LQ1		$300 on $6,000,000	55.00	
3LQ2		$400 on $8,000,000	55.00	
3LQ3		$500 on $10,000,000	55.00	
3LQ4		$800 on $5,000,000	55.00	
3LQ5		$1000 on $3,000,000	75.00	

Surcharged Type "b"

3LQ6		$500 on $3,000,000	75.00	
3LQ7		$1000 on $5,000,000	90.00	
3LQ8		$3000 on $8,000,000	225.00	
3LQ9		$5000 on $10,000,000	300.00	
		Nos. 3LQ1-3LQ9 (9)	985.00	

Nos. 3LQ8-3LQ9 have large numerals unboxed.

Remittance Stamps of China (like North China Type A4) Surcharged in Black or Red

a   b

Peking Surcharge "a"

1949, June   Litho.   Perf. 13

3LQ10		$6 on $5 ver	11.00	3.50
3LQ11		$20 on $50 gray	11.00	3.50
3LQ12		$50 on $20 dk vio brn	11.00	3.50
3LQ13		$100 on $10 ol grn	11.00	7.00

Tientsin Surcharge "b"

Engr.   Perf. 14

3LQ14		$20 on $1 brn org	13.00	6.00
a.		Perf. 12½	22.50	7.50
3LQ15		$30 on $2 dk grn	13.00	5.00
a.		Red surcharge	22.50	11.00
3LQ16		$30 on $10 ol grn	100.00	42.50
3LQ17		$100 on $10 gray grn (R)	13.00	6.00

Litho.   Perf. 13

3LQ18		$50 on $5 red	13.00	6.00

Engr.   Perf. 14

3LQ19		$20 on $1 org brn	37.50	17.00

Perf. 12½

3LQ20		$100 on $10 yel grn (R)	62.50	30.00

Typo.   Roulette 9½

3LQ21		$30 on $2 bl grn (R)	47.50	20.00

The surcharge on No. 3LQ19 is without first and last lines.
Nos. 3LQ14, 3LQ14a, 3LQ15, 3LQ15a, 3LQ16-3LQ17, 3LQ19-3LQ20 issued with gum.

Locomotive — PP1

1949, Nov.   Engr.   Perf. 14

3LQ22	PP1	$500 crimn	9.00	13.00
3LQ23	PP1	$1000 dp bl	65.00	22.50
3LQ24	PP1	$2000 green	65.00	32.50
3LQ25	PP1	$5000 dp ol	100.00	70.00
3LQ26	PP1	$10,000 or-ange	175.00	130.00
3LQ27	PP1	$20,000 red brn	350.00	325.00
3LQ28	PP1	$50,000 brn pur	750.00	625.00
		Nos. 3LQ22-3LQ28 (7)	1,493.	1,206.

NORTHWEST CHINA

The Northwest China Liberation Area consisted of the provinces of Sinkiang, Tsinghai, Ningsia and the western part of Shensi. The area was first established as the Shensi-Kansu-Ningsia Border Area in October, 1936, after the Long March to Yenan. Remote Sinkiang was not included until late 1949.

All Stamps Issued without Gum

Pagoda on Yenan Hill — A1

1945, Mar.		**Litho.**	**Imperf.**
4L1	A1	$1 green	23.00
4L2	A1	$5 dk blue	125.00
4L3	A1	$10 rose red	19.00
4L4	A1	$50 dull pur	24.00
4L5	A1	$100 yel org	45.00
		Nos. 4L1-4L5 (5)	236.00

Rouletted 9

4L1a	A1	$1	82.50
4L2a	A1	$5	125.00
4L3a	A1	$10	82.50

First issue; denomination in Chinese and Arabic. Heavy shading at top of vignette. Columns at sides.

See types A2, A3 and A4. For surcharges see Nos. 4L6-4L10, 4L23.

Nos. 4L1-4L2 Surcharged in Red:

a   b

c   d

1946, Nov.			
4L6	A1	(a) $30 on $1 grn	25.00
4L7	A1	(b) $30 on $1 grn	125.00
a.		Rectangular lower left character	1,000.
4L8	A1	(c) $30 on $1 grn	15.00
4L9	A1	(b) $60 on $1 grn	2,500.
4L10	A1	(d) $90 on $5 dk bl	24.00

Surcharge on Nos. 4L7a is type "b" as illustrated. Surcharge on No. 4L7 differs from "b," having lower left character as in type "a."

Surcharge on No. 4L9 the upper left surcharge character differs from that shown in "b."

A2

Pagoda on Yenan Hill (same size) — A3

1948, June			
4L11	A2	$100 buff	160.00
4L12	A2	$300 rose pink	6.00
4L13	A2	$500 red	6.00
4L14	A2	$1000 blue	6.00
4L15	A2	$2000 yel grn	20.00
4L16	A2	$5000 dull pur	18.00
		Nos. 4L11-4L16 (6)	216.00

Second issue; denominations in Chinese only. Many shades and proofs exist.

For surcharge see No. 4L24.

1948, Dec.			
4L17	A3	10c yel org	1.75
4L18	A3	20c lemon	1.75
4L19	A3	$1 dk blue	1.75
4L20	A3	$2 vermilion	1.75
4L21	A3	$5 pale bl grn	9.50
4L22	A3	$10 violet	14.50
		Nos. 4L17-4L22 (6)	31.00

Third issue; ornamental border at sides. Many shades exist.

Nos. 4L2 and 4L13 Surcharged in Red or Black

1949, Jan.			
4L23	A1	$1 on $5 dk bl	40.00
4L24	A2	$2 on $500 red	25.00

Pagoda on Yenan Hill — A4

1949, May 1				
4L25	A4	50c yel to olive	.50	.45
4L26	A4	$1 dl bl to indigo	.50	.45
4L27	A4	$3 ol yel to org yel	.50	.45
4L28	A4	$5 blue green	1.75	.50
a.		Upper left character as on #4L25		
4L29	A4	$10 vio to dp vio	4.50	5.50
4L30	A4	$20 pink to rose red	9.00	12.00
		Nos. 4L25-4L30 (6)	16.75	19.35

Fourth issue; light shading at top of vignette, columns without ornaments at sides. Many shades exist.

China Nos. 959, F2 and E12 Overprinted ("People's Post, Shensi")

1949, June 13		**Engr.**	**Perf. 12½**
4L31	A96	orange	16.00 16.00
4L32	R2	carmine	29.00 29.00
4L33	SD2	red vio	29.00 29.00
		Nos. 4L31-4L33 (3)	74.00 74.00

Stamps of China, Sun Yat-sen Type A94 of 1949, Overprinted in Black or Red ("People's Post, Shensi")

Lithographed; Engraved

1949, July 1			**Perf. 14, 12½**	
4L34		$10 green (887)	1.25	1.25
4L35		$20 vio brn (888)	1.25	2.25
4L36		$20 vio brn (896)	1.25	1.25
4L37		$50 dk Prus grn (889; R)	6.00	5.25
4L38		$50 grn (951)	6.00	5.25
4L39		$100 org brn (890)	14.50	6.25
4L40		$500 ros lil (892)	20.00	6.25
4L41		$1000 dp bl (952; R)	27.50	15.00
4L42		$2000 vio (902;R)	27.50	18.00
4L43		$5000 car (953)	40.00	37.50
4L44		$10,000 (954)	75.00	75.00
		Nos. 4L34-4L44 (11)	220.25	173.25

Kansu-Ningsia-Tsinghai Area, Lanchow Overprints

China Nos. 959a, F2 and E12 Overprinted ("People's Post, Kansu")

1949, Oct.		**Engr.**	**Rouletted**
4L45	A96	orange	16.00 10.00
		Perf. 12½	
4L46	R2	carmine	20.00 17.00
4L47	SD2	red vio	20.00 20.00
		Nos. 4L45-4L47 (3)	56.00 47.00

Stamps of China, Sun Yat-sen Type A94 of 1949, Overprinted ("People's Post, Kansu")

Engraved; Lithographed

1949, Oct.			**Perf. 14, 12½**	
4L48		$10 grn (887)	2.25	2.25
4L49		$20 vio brn (888)	2.25	3.25
4L50		$50 dk Prus grn (889)	5.25	8.25
4L51		$100 org brn (890)	3.50	3.25
4L52		$100 dk org brn (898)	5.25	6.00
4L53		$200 red org (891)	6.50	5.25
4L54		$500 rose lil (892)	6.50	5.25
4L55		$1000 blue (894)	3.50	3.25
4L56		$1000 dp bl (901)	6.50	7.50
4L57		$2000 vio (902)	11.00	15.00
4L58		$5000 lt bl (903)	22.00	27.50
4L59		$10,000 sepia (904)	30.00	37.50
4L60		$20,000 ap grn (905)	60.00	72.50
		Nos. 4L48-4L60 (13)	164.50	196.75

No. 4L54-4L60 exist with wider spaced overprints.

China Nos. 959, F2 and 791-792 Surcharged in Black or Red ("People's Post, Sinkiang")

1949, Oct.			
4L61	A96	$1 on org	10.00 11.00
4L62	R2	$3 on car	16.00 19.00
4L63	A82	10c on $50,000 dp bl (R)	30.00 30.00
4L64	A82	$1.50 on $100,000 dl grn (R)	60.00 60.00
		Nos. 4L61-4L64 (4)	116.00 120.00

Northwest People's Post

Mao Tse-tung — A5   Great Wall — A6

1949, Oct. 15		**Litho.**	**Imperf.**
4L65	A5	$50 rose	1.75 2.50
a.		$200 cliche in $50 plate	200.00
4L66	A6	$100 dark blue	1.00 1.10
4L67	A6	$200 orange	1.00 4.00
4L68	A6	$400 sepia	3.50 4.00
		Nos. 4L65-4L68 (4)	7.25 11.60

EAST CHINA

The East China Liberation Area included the provinces of Shantung, Kiangsu, Chekiang, Anhwei and Fukien. The original postal service established in Shantung in 1941, became the East China Posts and Telegraph General Office in July, 1948.

All Stamps Issued without Gum

Mao Tse-tung — A1

Transportation and Tower — A2

1948, Mar.		**Litho.**	**Perf. 10½**	
5L1	A1	$50 yel org	1.60	1.50
5L2	A1	$100 dp rose	4.25	2.50
5L3	A1	$200 dk vio bl	4.25	2.50
5L4	A1	$300 brt grn	5.25	2.50
5L5	A1	$500 dp blue	2.00	2.50
5L6	A1	$800 vermilion	5.25	1.75
5L7	A1	$1000 dk blue	8.00	8.00
5L8	A1	$5000 rose	18.00	18.00
5L9	A1	$10,000 dp car	45.00	45.00
		Nos. 5L1-5L9 (9)	93.60	84.25

Many varieties, including unissued imperforates exist.

Perf. 9 to 11 and compound

1949, Apr.			**Litho.**	
5L10	A2	$1 yel grn	.25	.20
5L11	A2	$2 blue grn	.25	.20
5L12	A2	$3 dull red	.25	.20
5L13	A2	$5 pale brn (ovpt. 4x4mm)	.25	.20
a.		Without overprint	65.00	65.00
b.		Overprint 3x3mm	1.25	1.00
c.		As "b," purple overprint	65.00	
5L14	A2	$10 ultra	.25	.20
5L15	A2	$13 brt vio	.25	.20
5L16	A2	$18 brt blue	.25	.20
5L17	A2	$21 vermilion	.25	.20
5L18	A2	$30 gray	.25	.30
5L19	A2	$50 crimson	.40	.55
5L20	A2	$100 olive	16.00	9.50
		Nos. 5L10-5L20 (11)	18.65	11.95

Seventh anniv. of Shantung Communist Postal Administration. The overprint on the $5, character "yu" meaning "Posts," obliterates Japanese flag on tower, erroneously included in design. Value, imperfs. of Nos. 5L10-5L12, 5L13c, 5L14-5L20 on different paper, set $125.

Train and Postal Runner (1949.2.7) — A3

Mao, Soldiers, Map — A4

1949, Apr.		**Litho.**	**Perf. 8 to 11**	
5L21	A3	$1 brt emer	.20	.20
5L22	A3	$2 blue grn	.20	.20
5L23	A3	$3 dk red	.20	.20
5L24	A3	$5 brown	.25	.25
5L25	A3	$10 ultra	.45	.25
5L26	A3	$13 brt vio	.25	.25
5L27	A3	$18 brt blue	.25	.25
5L28	A3	$21 vermilion	.25	.25
5L29	A3	$30 slate	.25	.35
5L30	A3	$50 crimson	.35	.35
5L31	A3	$100 olive	.75	.70
		Nos. 5L21-5L31 (11)	3.40	3.25

7th anniv. of Shantung P. O., Feb. 7. Imperf. sets were sold by the Philatelic Dept., Tientsin P.O. Value $40. See Nos. 5L69-5L76. For surcharges see People's Republic of China Nos. 77-81.

Perf. 9½ to 11 and comp.

1949, Apr.				
5L32	A4	$1 brt emer	.20	.20
5L33	A4	$2 blue grn	.20	.20
5L34	A4	$3 dull red	.20	.20
5L35	A4	$5 brown	.20	.20
5L36	A4	$10 ultra	.25	.25
5L37	A4	$13 brt vio	.25	.25
5L38	A4	$18 brt blue	.25	.25
5L39	A4	$21 vermilion	.25	.25
5L40	A4	$30 gray	.25	.25
5L41	A4	$50 crimson	.25	.25
5L42	A4	$100 olive	2.25	2.25
		Nos. 5L32-5L42 (11)	4.55	4.50

Victory of Hwai-Hai (Hwaiying and Haichow). Imperf. sets were sold by the Philatelic Dept., Tientsin P.O. Value, set $100.

Stamps of China, Sun Yat-sen Type of 1949, Surcharged in Red or Black

(Nanking) — a   (Wuhu) — b

1949, May 4   Engr.   Perf. 12½

5L43	A94 (a)	$1 on $10 grn (895, R)	.55	.50
a.	Perf. 13		3.25	3.00
5L44	A94 (a)	$3 on $20 vio brn (896)	.55	.55
a.	Perf. 13		.75	2.25
b.	Perf. 14		5.75	5.50
c.	Surcharge inverted		200.00	

Sun Yat-sen Type A94 Surcharged Type "b"

Lithographed, Engraved

1949, May   Perf. 12½, 14

5L45		$30 on $1000 dp bl (901)	8.00	6.00
5L46		$30 on $1000 bl (894)	8.00	6.00
5L47		$50 on $200 org red (899)	8.00	6.00
5L48		$100 on $5000 lt bl (903, R)	16.00	16.00
5L49		$300 on $10,000 sep (904)	50.00	50.00
5L50		$500 on $200 org red (899)	75.00	75.00
		Nos. 5L45-5L50 (6)	165.00	159.00

Many varieties exist.

China Nos. 913a and 913 Surcharged in Blue, Green, Black or Red

(East China)

1949, May   Litho.   Perf. 12½

5L51	A95	$5 on 50c on $20 brn, II (B)	14.00	13.00
a.	Green surcharge		100.00	100.00
5L52	A95	$10 on 50c on $20 brn, II	14.00	14.00
5L53	A95	$20 on 50c on $20 red brn, II (R)	14.00	14.00
a.	Type I (R)		21.00	21.00
		Nos. 5L51-5L53 (3)	42.00	41.00

Stamps of China, Sun Yat-sen Type of 1949, Surcharged in Black or Red

(Hangchow)

Engr., Litho. (No. 5L57)

1949, June 25   Perf. 14, 12½

5L54	A94	$1 on $1 org (886)	1.50	1.60
5L55	A94	$3 on $20 vio brn (896, R)	.80	.80
5L56	A94	$5 on $100 org brn (890)	4.00	4.00
5L57	A94	$5 on $100 dk org brn (898)	1.90	1.50
5L58	A94	$10 on $50 dk Prus grn (889, R)	13.00	13.00
5L59	A94	$13 on $10 grn (895)	1.00	1.00
		Nos. 5L54-5L59 (6)	22.20	21.90

East China Liberation Area

Maps of Shanghai and Nanking — A5

1949, May 30   Litho.   Perf. 8½ to 11

5L60	A5	$1 orange ver	.20	.30
5L61	A5	$2 blue green	.20	.30
5L62	A5	$3 brt violet	.25	.25
5L63	A5	$5 violet brn	.25	.25
5L64	A5	$10 ultra	.25	.25

5L65	A5	$30 slate	.25	.30
5L66	A5	$50 carmine	.25	.60
5L67	A5	$100 olive	.25	.45
5L68	A5	$500 orange	4.00	2.25
		Nos. 5L60-5L68 (9)	5.90	4.95

Liberation of Shanghai and Nanking. Many shades, paper and perforation varieties and imperfs. exist.

Train and Postal Runner Type Dated "1949"

1949, July-1950, Feb.   Perf. 12½, 14

5L69	A3	$10 dp ultra	.25	.25
5L70	A3	$15 orange ver	.25	.45
a.	$15 red, perf. 14		.50	.30
5L71	A3	$30 slate green	.25	.25
a.	Perf. 12½		.50	.30
5L72	A3	$50 carmine	.25	.50
5L73	A3	$60 bl grn, perf. 14	.25	1.00
5L74	A3	$100 ol, perf. 14	2.50	.50
5L75	A3	$1600 vio bl ('50)	.60	3.00
5L76	A3	$2000 brn vio ('50)	.75	3.00
		Nos. 5L69-5L76 (8)	5.10	8.95

Chu Teh, Mao, Troops with Flags — A7   Mao Tse-tung — A8

1949, Aug. 17   Perf. 12½

5L77	A7	$70 orange	.20	.25
5L78	A7	$270 crimson	.20	.25
5L79	A7	$370 emerald	.35	.35
5L80	A7	$470 vio brn	.55	.45
5L81	A7	$570 blue	.25	.40
		Nos. 5L77-5L81 (5)	1.55	1.70

22nd anniv. of the People's Liberation Army. For similar type see Southwest China A1.

1949, Oct.

5L82	A8	$10 dk blue	2.25	3.00
5L83	A8	$15 vermilion	2.75	3.75
5L84	A8	$70 brown	.25	.20
5L85	A8	$100 vio brn	.25	.20
5L86	A8	$150 orange	.25	.25
5L87	A8	$200 grnsh gray	.25	.25
5L88	A8	$500 gray bl	.25	.25
5L89	A8	$1000 rose	.25	.25
5L90	A8	$2000 emerald	.25	.25
		Nos. 5L82-5L90 (9)	6.75	8.40

For surcharges see People's Republic of China Nos. 82-84.

Stamps of China, Sun Yat-sen Type of 1949 Surcharged in Black or Red

1949, Nov.   Litho.   Perf. 12½

5L91	A94	$400 on $200 org red (899)	22.50	1.50
5L92	A94	$1000 on $50 grnsh gray (897, R)	2.25	.70
5L93	A94	$1200 on $100 dk org brn (898)	.30	1.50
5L94	A94	$1600 on $20,000 ap grn (905)	.30	3.00
5L95	A94	$2000 on $1000 dp bl (952,R)	.30	.75
a.	Perf. 14		45.00	25.00
		Nos. 5L91-5L95 (5)	25.65	7.45

EAST CHINA PARCEL POST STAMPS

Parcel Post Stamps of China 1945-48 Surcharged

(Shantung)

1949, Aug. 1   Engr.   Perf. 13

5LQ1	PP1	$200 on $500 grn	8.00	8.00
5LQ2	PP1	$500 on $1000 bl	18.00	18.00

	Type PP3		Perf. 13½

5LQ3	$200 on $200,000 dk grn		16.00	16.00
5LQ4	$200 on $10,000,000 sage grn		14.00	14.00
5LQ5	$500 on $7000 dl bl		40.00	40.00
5LQ6	$500 on $50,000 indigo		10.00	10.00
5LQ7	$1000 on $10,000 car rose		10.00	10.00
5LQ8	$1000 on $100,000 dk rose brn		18.00	18.00
5LQ9	$1000 on $300,000 pink		10.00	10.00
5LQ10	$1000 on $500,000 vio brn		52.50	45.00
5LQ11	$1000 on $8,000,000 org ver		12.00	12.00
5LQ12	$2000 on $5,000,000 dl vio		30.00	30.00
5LQ13	$2000 on $6,000,000 brn blk		35.00	35.00
5LQ14	$3000 on $30,000 ol		35.00	35.00
5LQ15	$3000 on $70,000 org brn		24.00	24.00
5LQ16	$5000 on $3,000,000 dl bl		52.50	52.50
	Nos. 5LQ1-5LQ16 (16)		385.00	377.50

China Type A97, No. 987 Surcharged

紙印裹包 圓萬壹	圖百贰 $200	圖百伍 $500	
政郵東華	圓什壹 $1000	圓什贰 $2000	
圓什伍 $5000	圓萬壹 紙印裹包 $10,000		

1949, Sept. 7   Litho.   Perf. 12½

5LQ17		$200 on $10	35.00	15.00
5LQ18		$500 on $10	35.00	15.00
5LQ19		$1000 on $10	35.00	15.00
5LQ20		$2000 on $10	50.00	30.00
5LQ21		$5000 on $10	75.00	45.00
5LQ22		$10,000 on $10	150.00	60.00
		Nos. 5LQ17-5LQ22 (6)	380.00	180.00

Flying Geese Type of China, 1949, and China Nos. 984-986 Surcharged in Red or Black

1950, Jan. 28

5LQ23	A97	$5000 on 10c bl vio (R)	30.00	25.00
5LQ24	A97	$10,000 on $1 brn org	45.00	40.00
5LQ25	A97	$20,000 on $2 bl	75.00	70.00
5LQ26	A97	$50,000 on $5 car rose	130.00	130.00
		Nos. 5L23-5L26 (4)	280.00	265.00

Parcel Post Stamps of China Type PP3, Nos. Q1-Q2, Q12-Q13 Surcharged in Red or Black

1950, Jan. 28   Engr.   Perf. 13, 13½

5LQ27		$5000 on $500 grn (R)	.60	15.00
5LQ28		$10,000 on $1000 bl (R)	75.00	60.00
5LQ29		$20,000 on $3000 bl grn	125.00	100.00
5LQ30		$50,000 on $5000 org red	7.50	75.00
		Nos. 5L27-5L30 (4)	208.10	250.00

CENTRAL CHINA

The Central Chinese Liberation Area included the provinces of Honan, Hupeh, Hunan and Kiangsi. The area was established between August and September, 1949, following the occupation of Hankow by Red Army forces.

All Stamps Issued without Gum
Hupeh Postal and Telegraph Administration

Stamps of China, Sun Yat-sen Type A94 of 1949, Surcharged ("Chinese P.O., Temporary Use")

Engraved; Lithographed

1949, June 4   Perf. 14, 12½

Thin parallel lines

6L1		$1 on $200 red org (891)	.85	1.25
6L2		$6 on $10,000 sep (904)	.85	1.25
6L3		$15 on $1 org (886)	.85	1.25
6L4		$30 on $100 org brn (890)	4.00	2.50
6L5		$30 on $100 dk org brn (898)	.85	1.25
6L6		$50 on $20 vio brn (896)	18.00	11.00
6L7		$80 on $1000 dp bl (901)	2.40	1.25

Thick parallel lines

6L8		$1 on $200 red org (891)	3.75	3.50
6L9		$3 on $5000 lt bl (903)	.65	1.50
6L10		$10 on $500 rose lil (892)	.65	1.50
6L11		$10 on $500 rose lil (900)	3.75	3.50
6L12		$50 on $20 vio brn (888)	3.75	3.50
6L13		$50 on $20 vio brn (896)	1.25	3.00
6L14		$80 on $1000 bl (894)	4.00	3.75
6L15		$80 on $1000 dp bl (901)	20.00	12.00
6L16		$100 on $50 dk Prus grn (903)	1.75	3.75
		Nos. 6L1-6L16 (16)	67.35	55.75

Kiangsi Postal and Telegraph Administration.

Central Trust Revenue Stamps of China Surcharged ("People's Post, Kiangsi")

(same size) — A1

$30 $60

1949, June 20   Engr.   Perf. 12½

6L17	A1	$3 on $30 pur	1.25	1.25
6L18	A1	$15 on $15 red org	1.25	1.25
6L19	A1	$30 on $50 dk bl	1.25	1.25
6L20	A1	$60 on $50 dk bl	1.25	1.25
6L21	A1	$130 on $15 red org	1.25	1.25

The $15 surcharge has 3 characters in left vertical row, the $130 surcharge has 5.

Same Surcharge on Sun Yat-sen Issues of China, 1945-49
Engraved, Lithographed
Perf. 14, 12½

6L22	A82	$1 on $250 dp lil (746)	3.25	3.25
6L23	A94	$5 on $1000 dp bl (901)	3.25	3.25
6L24	A94	$5 on $2000 vio (902)	3.25	3.25
6L25	A94	$5 on $5000 lt bl (903)	1.25	1.25
6L26	A94	$10 on $1000 bl (894)	3.25	3.25
6L27	A94	$20 on $4000 org	1.25	1.25
6L28	A73	$30 on $100 dk car	3.25	3.25
6L29	A82	$30 on $20,000 rose pink	1.25	1.25
6L30	A94	$80 on $5000 rose lil (900)	1.25	1.25
6L31	A94	$100 on $1000 dp bl (901)	1.25	1.25
6L32	A82	$200 on $250 dp lil	2.25	2.25
		Nos. 6L17-6L32 (16)	31.00	31.00

Central China Posts and Telegraph Administration

Farmer, Soldier and Worker
A2   A3

I — Top white line of square character (yuan) at upper left does not touch left vertical stroke. No gap in shading between soldier's feet.
II — Top line connects with left vertical stroke. Gap in shading between feet.

Perf. 10 to 11½ & Comp.

1949				Litho.
6L33	A2	$1 orange	7.50	2.25
6L34	A2	$3 brn org	2.75	2.25
6L35	A2	$6 emerald	3.00	2.25
6L36	A3	$7 yel brn	.50	2.25
6L37	A2	$10 bl grn	.25	.35
6L38	A3	$14 org brn	15.00	14.00
6L39	A2	$15 ultra	.40	.50
6L40	A2	$30 grn, type I	.25	.40
a.		Type II	.30	.30
6L41	A3	$35 gray bl	10.00	16.00
6L42	A3	$50 rose vio	8.50	12.00
6L43	A3	$70 dp grn	.25	.25
6L44	A2	$80 pink	.55	.90
6L45	A3	$100 bl grn	.40	.95
6L46	A2	$220 rose red	3.50	.75
		Nos. 6L33-6L46 (14)	52.85	55.10

For surcharges & overprints see #6L63-6L65, 6L66-6L73, 6L75, 6L90-6L98, 6L100-6L108.

Star Enclosing Map of Hankow Area — A4

Two types of $500:
I — Thick numerals of "500." No period after "500."
II — Thin numerals and period.

Two types of $1000:
I — No period after "1000."
II — Period after "1000."

1949, July				
6L48	A4	$110 org brn	.30	1.25
6L49	A4	$130 violet	4.00	2.00
6L50	A4	$200 dp org	.25	.50
6L51	A4	$290 brown	1.60	.50
6L52	A4	$370 dk bl	1.60	1.25
6L53	A4	$500 lt bl, I	4.00	.60
a.		$500 blue, II	18.00	7.00
6L54	A4	$1000 dull red, II	18.00	1.50
a.		$1000 dark red, I	25.00	8.00
6L55	A4	$5000 brown	.85	3.00
6L56	A4	$10,000 brt pink	1.75	6.00
		Nos. 6L48-6L56 (9)	32.35	16.60

For surcharges and overprints see Nos. 6L74, 6L76-6L81, 6L99, 6L109.

Hankow River Customs Building A5

River Wall, Wuchang — A6

Design: $290, $370, River scene, Hanyang.

1949, Aug. 16			**Perf. 11**	
6L57	A5	$70 green	1.40	.90
6L58	A5	$220 crimson	1.40	1.25
6L59	A5	$290 brown	1.40	1.25
6L60	A5	$370 brt blue	1.40	1.25

6L61	A6	$500 purple	1.40	1.75
6L62	A6	$1000 vermilion	1.25	1.75
		Nos. 6L57-6L62 (6)	8.25	8.15

Liberation of Hankow, Wuchang and Hanyang.
Exist imperf. About the same value.
For overprints see Nos. 6L82-6L87.

Nos. 6L35, 6L39 and 6L40 Surcharged in Red ("Honan Renminbi Currency")

1949, July				
6L63	A2	$7 on $6 emer	3.00	4.00
6L64	A2	$14 on $15 ultra	4.50	6.00
6L65	A2	$70 on $30 grn	7.50	10.00
		Nos. 6L63-6L65 (3)	15.00	20.00

Surcharge is for $70. The $7 has 5 characters in left column and no bottom line.

Issues of 1949 Overprinted ("Honan Renminbi Currency")

1949, Aug.				
6L66	A2	$3 brn org	.95	.90
6L67	A3	$7 yel brn	.95	.90
6L68	A2	$10 bl grn	1.90	1.90
6L69	A2	$14 org brn	1.90	3.00
6L70		$30 yel grn		
		(6L40a)	2.00	3.00
6L71	A3	$35 gray bl	.95	5.00
6L72	A2	$50 rose vio	7.00	5.00
6L73	A3	$70 dp grn	2.00	3.75
6L74	A4	$110 org brn	7.00	7.00
6L75	A3	$220 rose red	6.00	6.00
6L76	A4	$290 brown	6.00	6.00
6L77	A4	$370 blue	10.00	10.00
6L78	A4	$500 bl, II	12.00	14.00
6L79	A4	$1000 dk red, I	25.00	30.00
6L80	A4	$5000 brown	100.00	110.00
6L81	A4	$10,000 brt pink	200.00	225.00
		Nos. 6L66-6L81 (16)	383.65	431.45

Width of the overprint varies slightly.

Nos. 6L57-6L62 Overprinted ("Honan Renminbi Currency")

1949, Aug.			**Perf. 11**	
6L82	A5	$70 green	2.00	2.50
6L83	A5	$220 crimson	3.50	3.75
6L84	A5	$290 brown	3.50	3.75
6L85	A5	$370 brt bl	5.50	6.00
6L86	A5	$500 purple	5.50	6.00
6L87	A6	$1000 vermilion	7.50	8.00
		Nos. 6L82-6L87 (6)	27.50	30.00

Width of overprint on Nos. 6L82-6L85, 7mm; on Nos. 6L86-6L87, 12mm.
Exist imperf. About the same value.

Changchow Issue Surcharged in Red ("Honan Renminbi Currency")

(same size) Mao Tse-tung — A7

1949, Sept.			**Perf. 10**	
6L88	A7	$290 on $30 yel grn	35.00	40.00
6L89	A7	$370 on $30 yel grn	52.50	57.50

Issues of 1949 Surcharged

1950, Jan.				
6L90	A2	$200 on $1	.55	1.75
6L91	A2	$200 on $3	3.00	1.60
6L92	A2	$200 on $6	.55	1.75
6L93	A3	$200 on $7	3.00	1.60
6L94	A3	$200 on $14	3.00	1.60
6L95	A3	$200 on $35	3.25	2.40
6L96	A3	$200 on $70	3.00	1.60
6L97	A2	$200 on $80	3.00	1.60
6L98	A3	$200 on $220	3.00	1.60
6L99	A4	$200 on $370	.50	1.75
6L100	A3	$300 on $70	.50	2.50
6L101	A2	$300 on $80	.50	1.75
6L102	A3	$300 on $220	.25	1.75
6L103	A2	$1200 on $3	27.50	22.50
6L104	A3	$1200 on $7	5.75	5.00
6L105	A3	$1500 on $14	8.25	6.75
6L106	A2	$2100 on $1	37.50	22.50
6L107	A2	$2100 on $6	37.50	22.50
6L108	A3	$2100 on $35	12.00	9.75
6L109	A4	$5000 on $370	5.00	5.00
		Nos. 6L90-6L109 (20)	157.60	117.25

Two types of surcharge exist, differing in spacing of characters in top row.

CENTRAL CHINA PARCEL POST STAMPS

Star and Map of Hankow — PP1

1949, Nov.		Litho.	**Perf. 11, 11½**	
6LQ1	PP1	$5000 brown	2.00	3.75
6LQ2	PP1	$10,000 scarlet	9.50	9.00
6LQ3	PP1	$20,000 dk sl grn	4.50	11.00
6LQ4	PP1	$50,000 vermilion	2.00	32.50
		Nos. 6LQ1-6LQ4 (4)	18.00	56.25

SOUTH CHINA

The South China Liberation Area included the provinces of Kwangtung and Kwangsi and Hainan Island. The South China Postal and Telegraph Administration was organized on or about Nov. 4, 1949.

All Stamps Issued without Gum

Pearl River Bridge, Canton — A1

1949, Nov. 4			Litho.	**Imperf.**
7L1	A1	$10 green	.30	.25
7L2	A1	$20 sepia	.30	.25
7L3	A1	$30 violet	.30	.25
7L4	A1	$50 carmine	.30	.25
7L5	A1	$100 ultramarine	.50	.25
		Nos. 7L1-7L5 (5)	1.70	1.25

For surcharges see Nos. 7L19-7L23.

China Nos. 993-995 With Additional Overprint in Red ("Liberation of Swatow")

1949, Nov. 9				
7L6	A94	2½c on $500 röse lil (993)	16.00	16.00
a.		Handstamped	40.00	40.00
7L7	A94	2½c on $500 rose lil (994)	20.00	20.00
a.		Handstamped	47.50	47.50

7L8	A94	15c on $10 grn (995)	24.00	24.00
a.		Handstamped	90.00	90.00

On Unit Issues of China, 1949

7L9	A96	org (959)	19.00	12.50
7L10	AP5	bl grn (C62)	24.00	27.50
7L11	SD2	red vio (E12)	24.00	27.50
7L12	R2	car (F2)	20.00	27.50

On Sun Yat-sen and Flying Geese Issues of China

7L13	A94	2c org (974)	150.00	175.00
7L14	A94	4c bl grn (975)	300.00	375.00
7L15	A94	10c dp lil (976)	13.50	20.00
7L16	A94	20c bl (978)	22.50	32.50
7L17	A97	$1 brn org (984)	37.50	25.00
7L18	A97	$10 vio (987)	450.00	375.00
		Nos. 7L6-7L18 (13)	1,120.	1,157.

Forgeries exist of #7L13-7L14, 7L18.

Nos. 7L1-7L3 Surcharged in Red or Green

1950, Jan.				
7L19	A1	$300 on $30 vio (R)	3.25	1.00
7L20	A1	$500 on $20 brn (R)	3.25	1.25
7L21	A1	$800 on $30 vio (G)	3.50	2.00
7L22	A1	$1000 on $10 gray grn (R)	4.25	3.00
7L23	A1	$1000 on $20 brn (R)	4.25	2.25
		Nos. 7L19-7L23 (5)	18.50	9.50

SOUTHWEST CHINA

The Southwest China Liberation Area included the provinces of Kweichow, Szechwan, Yunnan, Sikang and Tibet. The Southwest Postal and Telegraph Administration was organized on or about Nov. 15, 1949 after the liberation of Kweiyang, capital of Kweichow Province.

All Stamps Issued without Gum

Chu Teh, Mao and Troops — A1

1949, Dec.			Litho.	**Perf. 12½**
8L1	A1	$10 deep blue	2.50	3.75
8L2	A1	$20 rose claret	.40	1.25
8L3	A1	$30 dp org	.55	1.25
8L4	A1	$50 gray grn	.55	1.25
8L5	A1	$100 carmine	.90	.75
8L6	A1	$200 blue	1.25	1.00
8L7	A1	$300 bl vio	1.50	1.50
8L8	A1	$500 dk gray	2.75	2.25
8L9	A1	$1000 pale pur	7.50	6.00
8L10	A1	$2000 green	17.50	20.00
8L11	A1	$5000 orange	55.00	60.00
		Nos. 8L1-8L11 (11)	90.40	99.00

For surcharges and overprints see Nos. 8L21-8L29, 8L40-8L47, 8L55.

China Nos. 974-975, 984, 986-987 Surcharged ("Kweichow People's Post")

1949, Dec. 1			**Perf. 12½**	
8L12	A94	$20 on 2c org	3.50	4.50
8L13	A94	$50 on 4c bl grn	5.00	5.00
8L14	A97	$100 on $1 brn org	10.00	7.25
8L15	A97	$400 on $5 car rose	16.00	22.50
8L16	A97	$2000 on $10 bl	62.50	57.50
		Nos. 8L12-8L16 (5)	97.00	96.75

Map of China,
Flag Planted in
Southwest
A2

1950, Jan.   Litho.   Perf. 9 to 11½

8L17	A2	$20 dark blue	.40	.65
8L18	A2	$30 green	.40	.65
8L19	A2	$50 red	.40	.95
8L20	A2	$100 brown	.40	.95
	Nos. 8L17-8L20 (4)		1.60	3.20

Liberation of the Southwest.
For surcharges see #8L30-8L39, 8L56-8L59.

Nos. 8L5-8L6
Surcharged

Perf. 12½

8L21	A1	$300 on $100 car	3.50	4.00
8L22	A1	$500 on $100 car	3.50	4.00
8L23	A1	$1200 on $100 car	7.00	7.00
8L24	A1	$1500 on $200 bl	7.00	7.00
8L25	A1	$2000 on $200 bl	11.00	10.00
	Nos. 8L21-8L25 (5)		32.00	32.00

Nos. 8L5-8L6
Overprinted
("East
Szechwan")

1950, Jan.

8L26	A1	$100 carmine	6.00	7.50
8L27	A1	$200 blue	6.00	7.50

Nos. 8L5-8L6
Handstamp
Surcharged

1950, Jan.

8L28	A1	$1200 on $100 car	15.00	27.50
8L29	A1	$1500 on $200 bl	40.00	27.50

Many varieties, including wide and narrow
settings, exist.

Nos. 8L17-8L20 Surcharged in Black
or Red

$3000   改作 $5000

$10,000 $20,000 $50,000

$60

$300

1950   Perf. 9 to 11½

8L30	A2	$60 on $30	20.00	9.00
8L31	A2	$150 on $30	20.00	9.00
8L32	A2	$300 on $20 (R)	2.00	4.00
8L33	A2	$300 on $100	8.00	9.00
8L34	A2	$1500 on $100	32.50	22.50
8L35	A2	$5000 on $50	7.75	22.50
8L36	A2	$5000 on $50	3.50	22.50
8L37	A2	$10,000 on $50	60.00	42.50
8L38	A2	$20,000 on $50	4.00	42.50
8L39	A2	$50,000 on $50	5.75	60.00
	Nos. 8L30-8L39 (10)		175.50	243.50

Nos. 8L5-8L7
Overprinted
("West
Szechwan")

1950, Jan.   Perf. 12½

8L40	A1	$100 carmine	10.50	11.00
8L41	A1	$200 pale blue	17.00	18.50
8L42	A1	$300 blue violet	26.00	28.00
	Nos. 8L40-8L42 (3)		53.50	57.50

Nos. 8L4-8L7 Surcharged

1950, Jan.

8L43	A1	$500 on $100	8.75	8.75
a.	Narrow spacing		70.00	60.00
8L44	A1	$800 on $100	8.75	8.75
8L45	A1	$1000 on $50	11.00	11.00
8L46	A1	$2000 on $200	22.50	27.50
8L47	A1	$3000 on $300	35.00	45.00
	Nos. 8L43-8L47 (5)		86.00	101.00

Two lines of surcharge 7mm apart on No.
8L43, 4mm on No. 8L43a.

China Nos. 975 and 977 Surcharged

Perf. 12½, 13 or Compound
1950, Jan.

8L48	A94	$100 on 4c	13.50	13.50
8L49	A94	$200 on 4c	24.00	22.50
8L50	A94	$800 on 16c	67.50	67.50
8L51	A94	$1000 on 16c	300.00	375.00
	Nos. 8L48-8L51 (4)		405.00	478.50

Unit Issue of China
Overprinted
("Southwest People's
Post")

1950, Jan.   Engr.   Rouletted

8L52	A96	orange	150.00	175.00
a.	Perf. 12½		225.00	250.00

Perf. 12½

8L53	SD2	red violet	225.00	250.00
8L54	R2	carmine	225.00	250.00
	Nos. 8L52-8L54 (3)		600.00	675.00

On No. 8L54, space between overprint columns is 3mm and right column is raised to
height of left.

Nos. 8L3, 8L17-8L20 Surcharged in
Black or Red

1950, Mar.   Perf. 12½, 9 to 11½

8L55	A1	$800 on $30	42.50	40.00
8L56	A2	$1000 on $50	9.00	12.00
8L57	A2	$2000 on $100	12.50	18.00
8L58	A2	$4000 on $20 (R)	35.00	37.50
8L59	A2	$5000 on $30	55.00	55.00
	Nos. 8L55-8L59 (5)		154.00	162.50

CHRISTMAS ISLAND

ˈkris-məs ˈī-lənd

LOCATION — In the Indian Ocean, 230
miles south of Java
GOVT. — A territory of Australia
AREA — 52 sq. mi.
POP. — 2,373 (1999 est.)

Australia took over Christmas Island
from Singapore in 1958.

Catalogue values for all unused
stamps in this country are for
Never Hinged items.

 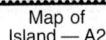

Queen
Elizabeth II — A1

**Engr.; Name and Value Typo. in
Black**

1958, Oct. 15   Unwmk.   Perf. 14½

1	A1	2c yellow orange	.90	1.90
2	A1	4c brown	.95	.75
3	A1	5c lilac	.95	.75
4	A1	6c dull blue	2.50	.75
5	A1	8c gray brown	5.00	1.25
6	A1	10c violet	3.50	.75
7	A1	12c carmine rose	5.25	4.25
8	A1	20c ultramarine	3.50	4.25
9	A1	50c yellow green	6.00	4.25
10	A1	$1 greenish blue	6.25	4.25
	Nos. 1-10 (10)		34.80	23.15
	Set, hinged		13.00	

Map of
Island — A2

Island
Scene — A3

4c, Moonflower. 5c, Robber crab. 8c,
Phosphate train. 10c, Crane loading
phosphate. 12c, Flying fish cove. 20c, Loading
ship. 50c, Frigate bird. $1, Yellow-billed tropic
bird.

Perf. 14x14½, 14½x14

1963, Aug. 28   Engr.

11	A2	2c orange	.80	.70
12	A2	4c red brown	.45	.30
13	A2	5c rose lilac	.45	.40
14	A3	6c slate	.40	.70
15	A2	8c black	2.50	.70
16	A2	10c violet	.40	.30
17	A3	12c dull red	.40	.40
18	A3	20c dark blue	.95	.40
19	A3	50c green	1.25	.40

Size: 35x21mm

20	A3	$1 orange yellow	2.40	.70
	Nos. 11-20 (10)		10.00	5.10

"Simpson and His
Donkey" by Wallace
Anderson — A3a

1965, Apr. 14   Photo.   Perf. 13½x13

21	A3a	10c brt grn, sepia & blk	.75	1.00

ANZAC issue. See note after Australia No.
387.

Moorish
Goddess
A4

Fish: 1c, Golden striped grouper. 3c, For-
ceps fish. 4c, Queen triggerfish. 5c, Regal
angelfish. 9c, Surgeonfish. 10c, Turkeyfish.
15c, Saddleback butterflyfish. 20c, Clown butterflyfish. 30c, Ghost pipefish. 50c, Lined
surgeonfish. $1, Meyer's butterflyfish.

1968-70   Photo.   Perf. 13½

22	A4	1c multicolored	.75	1.25
23	A4	2c multicolored	1.00	.55
24	A4	3c multicolored	1.00	.85
25	A4	4c multicolored	1.00	.55
26	A4	5c multicolored	1.00	.55
27	A4	9c multicolored	1.00	1.10
28	A4	10c multicolored	1.00	.55
29	A4	15c multicolored	14.50	7.00
30	A4	20c multicolored	2.75	1.50
31	A4	30c multicolored	14.50	7.00
32	A4	50c multicolored	3.50	4.25
33	A4	$1 multicolored	3.50	5.50
	Nos. 22-33 (12)		45.50	30.65

Issued: 15c, 30c, 12/14/70; others, 5/6/68.

Christmas Issues

"Hark the Herald
Angels Sing" — A5

1969, Nov. 10   Photo.   Perf. 13½

34	A5	5c dk blue, gold, buff & red	.40	.40

A6   A7

3c, The Ansidei Madonna, by Raphael. 5c,
Virgin and Child, by Morando.

1970, Oct. 26   Photo.   Perf. 14x14½

35	A6	3c gold & multi	.20	.20
36	A6	5c silver & multi	.25	.25

1971, Oct. 4

5c, Adoration of the Shepherds, Seville
School. 20c, Adoration of the Shepherds, by
Guido Reni.

37	A7	6c black & multi	.75	.50
38	A7	20c dark blue & multi	1.60	1.25

"Flying Fish,"
1887 — A8

Ships and Map of Christmas Island: 1c, "Eagle," 1714. 2c, "Redpole," 1890. 3c, "Hoi Houw," 1959. 4c, "Pigot," 1771. 5c, "Valetta," 1968. 7c, "Asia," 1805. 8c, "Islander," 1929-60. 9c, "Imperieuse," 1888 (incorrectly inscribed "Imperious"). 10c, "Egeria," 1887. 20c, "Thomas," 1615. 25c, "Gordon," 1864. 30c, "Cygnet," 1688. 35c, "Triadic," 1958. 50c, "Amethyst," 1857. $1, "Royal Mary," 1643.

1972-73   Photo.   Perf. 14½x13½

39	A8	1c yel green & multi	.30	.60
40	A8	2c lt red brn & multi	.35	.70
41	A8	3c dp rose & multi	.35	.70
42	A8	4c multicolored	.50	.75
43	A8	5c multicolored	.50	.75
44	A8	6c lilac & multi	.50	.75
45	A8	7c lt green & multi	.50	.75
46	A8	8c blue & multi	.55	.75
47	A8	9c org & multi	.80	.60
48	A8	10c lem & multi	.65	.70
49	A8	20c tan & multi	.85	.90
50	A8	25c multicolored	.90	1.50
51	A8	30c multicolored	.90	.90
52	A8	35c tan & multi	.90	.90
53	A8	50c ultra & multi	.90	1.50
54	A8	$1 yellow & multi	1.25	1.75
		Nos. 39-54 (16)	10.70	14.50

Issued: 6c, 7c, 8c, 20c, 2/5/72; 1c, 2c, 3c, $1, 6/5/72; 4c, 5c, 9c, 50c, 2/6/73; 10c, 25c, 30c, 35c, 6/4/73.

A9   A9a
"Peace"   "Joy"

1972, Oct. 2   Litho.   Perf. 14½

55	A9	3c black & multi	.65	.40
56	A9a	3c black & multi	.65	.40
a.		Pair, #55-56	1.40	1.40
57	A9	7c black & multi	.85	.75
58	A9a	7c black & multi	.85	.75
a.		Pair, #57-58	1.75	1.75
		Nos. 55-58 (4)	3.00	2.30

Mother and Child, Christmas Island Map — A10

1973, Oct. 2   Photo.   Perf. 14½x13½

59	A10	7c blue & multi	1.00	.60
60	A10	25c brt green & multi	3.00	2.25

Christmas.

Mother and Child with Star and Cross — A11

1974, Oct. 2   Photo.   Perf. 13½x14½

61	A11	7c black & lilac rose	.75	.60
62	A11	30c black & yellow	2.25	2.25

Christmas.

Flight into Egypt — A12

1975, Oct. 2   Photo.   Perf. 14½x13½

63	A12	10c gold, black & yel	.70	.40
64	A12	35c gold, vio blk & rose	1.40	1.60

Christmas.

Star of Bethlehem and Dove
A13   A14

1976, Oct. 2   Photo.   Perf. 13½

65	A13	10c red & multi	.65	.40
66	A14	10c red & multi	.65	.40
a.		Pair, #65-66	1.40	1.40
67	A13	35c blue & multi	.85	.75
68	A14	35c blue & multi	.85	.75
a.		Pair, #67-68	1.75	1.75
		Nos. 65-68 (4)	3.00	2.30

Christmas.

Andrew Clunies-Ross (first settler) A15

Famous Visitors: 1c, William Dampier, explorer, buccaneer. 2c, Capt. Willem de Vlamingh, Dutch explorer. 3c, Vice Adm. John F. L. P. Maclear, Royal Navy. 4c, John Murray, oceanographer, scientist. 5c, Adm. Pelham Aldrich and crew collecting specimen. 7c, Joseph Jackson Lister, naturalist, and arenga listeri plant. 8c, Adm. William Henry May. 9c, Henry Nicholas Ridley, botanist. 10c, George Clunies-Ross, pioneer phosphate miner. 20c, Capt. Joshua Slocum. 45c, Charles William Andrews, zoologist, and frigate birds. 50c, Karl Richard Hanitsch, zoologist, and fruit pigeon. 75c, Victor W. W. Saunders Purcell, Sinologist. $1, Fam Choo Beng, educator. $2, Harold Spencer-Jones, astronomer.

1977-78   Photo.   Perf. 14x13½

69	A15	1c multicolored	.20	.80
70	A15	2c multicolored	.20	.80
71	A15	3c multicolored	.25	.80
72	A15	4c multicolored	.30	.90
73	A15	5c multicolored	.30	.35
74	A15	6c multicolored	.30	.65
75	A15	7c multicolored	.30	.40
76	A15	8c multicolored	.35	.70
77	A15	9c multicolored	.40	2.00
78	A15	10c multicolored	.35	.60
79	A15	20c multicolored	.45	.75
80	A15	45c multicolored	.85	.45
81	A15	50c multicolored	1.00	2.00
82	A15	75c multicolored	.90	1.60
83	A15	$1 multicolored	.90	1.60
84	A15	$2 multicolored	1.50	2.50
		Nos. 69-84 (16)	8.55	16.90

Issued: 1c, 6c, 9c, $1, 4/30/77; 2c, 3c, 4c, $2, 2/22/78; 5c, 7c, 45c, 50c, 5/31/78; 8c, 10c, 20c, 75c, 9/1/78.

Australian Arms, Map of Christmas Island — A16

1977, June 2   Litho.   Perf. 14½x13½

85	A16	45c multicolored	.80	.80

25th anniv. of reign of Elizabeth II.

Souvenir Sheet

Partridge in a Pear Tree — A17

Twelve Days of Christmas: a, Partridge in a pear tree. b, 2 turtle doves. c, 3 French hens. d, 4 calling birds. e, 5 gold rings. f, 6 geese. g, 7 swans. h, 8 maids a-milking. i, 9 ladies dancing. j, 10 lords a-leaping. k, 11 pipers piping. l, 12 drummers drumming.

Unwmk.
1977, Oct. 20   Litho.   Perf. 14

86		Sheet of 12	1.90	2.25
a.-l.		A17 10c, single stamp	.20	.20
m.		Wmk. 373 ('78)	2.50	3.50

Christmas.

Common Design Types pictured following the introduction.

Elizabeth II Coronation Anniversary
Common Design Types
Souvenir Sheet

1978, Apr. 21   Litho.   Perf. 15

87		Sheet of 6	4.25	4.25
a.		CD326 45c White swan of Bohun	.70	.90
b.		CD327 45c Elizabeth II	.70	.90
c.		CD328 45c Abbott's booby	.70	.90

No. 87 contains 2 se-tenant strips of Nos. 87a-87c, separated by horizontal gutter with commemorative and descriptive inscriptions.

Souvenir Sheet

Christ Child — A18

Song of Christmas: a, Christ Child. b, Herald angels. c, Redeemer. d, Israel. e, Star. f, Three Wise Men. g, Manger. h, "All He stands for." i, "Shepherds came."

1978, Oct. 2   Litho.   Perf. 14

88	A18	Sheet of 9	1.75	2.00
a.-i.		10c single stamp	.20	.20

Christmas. Each stamp design incorporates one letter of "Christmas."

IYC Emblem, Oriental Children — A19

Design: IYC emblem and children of different races holding hands, continuous design.

1979, Apr. 20   Litho.   Perf. 14

89		Strip of 5	1.90	2.00
a.		A19 20c single stamp	.35	.50

International Year of the Child.

Rowland Hill and No. 25 A20

Sir Rowland Hill (1795-1879), originator of penny postage, and Christmas Island stamps: a, #1. b, #11. c, #21. d, #25. e, #34.

1979, Aug. 27   Litho.   Perf. 13x13½

90		Strip of 5	1.40	1.50
a.-e.		A20 20c any single	.20	.30

Three Kings Bearing Gifts — A21

Christmas: 55c, Virgin and Child, globe.

1979, Oct. 22   Litho.   Perf. 14x14½

91	A21	20c multicolored	.25	.25
92	A21	55c multicolored	.60	.50

25 Years of Golf — A22

1980, Feb. 12   Litho.   Perf. 14½x14

93	A22	20c shown	.40	.45
94	A22	55c Clubhouse	1.00	1.25

Surveyor, Phosphate Industry A23

1980, May 5   Litho.   Perf. 14x14½

95	A23	15c shown	.30	.40
96	A23	22c Drilling for samples	.30	.40
97	A23	40c Sample analysis	.35	.45
98	A23	55c Mine planning	.55	.65

1980, July 14

99	A23	15c Jungle clearing	.30	.30
100	A23	22c Overburden removal	.30	.30
101	A23	40c Open cut mining	.35	.45
102	A23	55c Restoration	.55	.65

1981, Feb. 9

103	A23	22c Screening and stockpiling	.30	.30
104	A23	28c Loading train	.40	.40
105	A23	40c Rail transport	.50	.50
106	A23	60c Drying	.60	.60

1981, May 4

107	A23	22c Crushing	.30	.30
108	A23	28c Pipeline	.40	.45
109	A23	40c Bulk storage	.50	.55
110	A23	60c Loading ship	.60	.65
		Nos. 95-110 (16)	6.60	7.20

Souvenir Sheet

Virgin and Child — A24

1980, Oct. 6   Litho.   Perf. 13½x13

111		Sheet of 6	2.25	2.40
a.		A24 15c Angel	.20	.20
b.		A24 22c shown	.25	.25
c.		A24 60c Angel	.35	.35
d.		A24 15c Angel holding soldier	.20	.20
e.		A24 22c Kneeling woman and man	.25	.30
f.		A24 60c Chinese, Indian, European children	.35	.35

Christmas. No. 111 contains 2 strips of 3 (Nos. 111a-111c and 111d-111f) with gutter between.

Cryptoblepharus Egeriae — A25

Designs: Reptiles.

1981, Aug. 10   Litho.   Perf. 13x13½

112	A25	24c shown	.30	.30
113	A25	30c Emoia nativitata	.50	.50
114	A25	40c Lepidodactylus listeri	.60	.60
115	A25	60c Cyrtodactylus nov.	.75	.75
		Nos. 112-115 (4)	2.15	2.15

Souvenir Sheet

Nativity A26

1981, Oct. 19   Litho.   Perf. 14½x14
116	Sheet of 4	1.60 1.75
a.	A26 18c Angels, star	.20 .25
b.	A26 24c shown	.25 .30
c.	A26 40c Children praying to Jesus	.50 .55
d.	A26 60c Children praying	.60 .70

Christmas.

Reef Heron
A27

1982-83   Litho.   Perf. 14
117	A27	1c shown	.70 .20
118	A27	2c Noddies	.70 .20
119	A27	3c Glossy swiftlet	.70 .20
120	A27	4c Imperial pigeon	.70 .70
121	A27	5c Christmas Isld. silvereyes	.85 .85
122	A27	10c Thrush	.70 .70
123	A27	25c Silver bosunbird	1.25 .70
124	A27	30c Christmas Isld. emerald doves	.75 .60
125	A27	40c Brown boobies	.75 .60
126	A27	50c Red-footed boobies	.75 .60
127	A27	65c Christmas Isld. frigatebird	.75 .60
128	A27	75c Golden bosunbirds	.90 .80
129	A27	80c Nankeen kestrel, vert.	1.25 1.75
130	A27	$1 Christmas Isld. hawk owl, vert.	2.75 1.75
131	A27	$2 Goshawk, vert.	2.00 4.25
132	A27	$4 Abbott's boobies, vert.	3.25 3.25
	Nos. 117-132 (16)		18.75 18.40

Issued: 1c, 2c, 25c $4, 3/8; 3c, 4c, 10c, $2, 6/14; 40c, 50c, 65c, 75c, 8/23; 5c, 30c, 80c, $1, 2/21/83.

Christmas — A28   25th Anniv. of Boat Club — A29

Paper sculptures.

1982, Oct. 18   Litho. & Embossed
135	A28	27c Joseph	.40 .40
136	A28	50c Angel	.55 .55
137	A28	75c Mary, Baby Jesus	.80 .80
a.	Strip of 3, #135-137		1.75 1.75

Perf. 14x14½, 14½x14

1983, May 2   Litho.

Designs: Various boating activities.
138	A29	27c multicolored	.50 .50
139	A29	35c multicolored	.50 .50
140	A29	50c multi, horiz.	.60 .75
141	A29	75c multi, horiz.	.65 .75
	Nos. 138-141 (4)		2.25 2.50

25th Anniv. of Australian Territory A30

1983, Oct. 1   Litho.   Perf. 14
142	A30	24c Maps. golden bosun bird, kangaroo	.65 .40
143	A30	30c Map, flag	.75 .75
144	A30	85c Boeing 727, maps	1.50 1.50
	Nos. 142-144 (3)		2.90 2.65

Christmas — A31

Designs: Christmas candles.

1983, Oct. 31   Litho.   Perf. 13½x13
145	A31	24c multicolored	.30 .30
146	A31	30c multicolored	.45 .50
147	A31	85c multicolored	1.10 1.40
	Nos. 145-147 (3)		1.85 2.20

Red Land Crab — A32

1984, Feb. 20   Litho.   Perf. 14x14½
148	A32	30c Feeding	.65 .65
149	A32	40c Migration	.75 .75
150	A32	55c Developmental stages	.75 .75
151	A32	85c Adult female, young	1.10 1.10
	Nos. 148-151 (4)		3.25 3.25

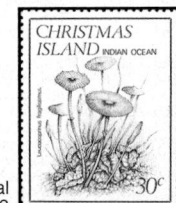

Local Fungi — A33

1984, Apr. 30   Perf. 13½x14½
152	A33	30c Leucocoprinus fragilissimus	.60 .60
153	A33	40c Microporus xanthopus	.75 .75
154	A33	45c Trogia anthidepas	.90 .90
155	A33	55c Haddowia longipes	1.00 1.00
156	A33	85c Phillipsia domingensis	1.25 1.25
	Nos. 152-156 (5)		4.50 4.50

Cricket on Christmas Isld., 25th Anniv. A34

1984, July 23   Litho.   Perf. 14
157	A34	30c Runout	.70 .85
158	A34	40c Catch at point	.75 1.10
159	A34	55c Batsman	.80 1.50
160	A34	85c Batsman hitting	1.00 1.75
	Nos. 157-160 (4)		3.25 5.20

Souvenir Sheet

Christmas; Ausipex '84 — A35

1984, Sept. 21   Litho.   Perf. 13½
161	Sheet of 3 + 3 labels	3.00 3.00
a.	A35 30c Father Christmas arriving	.50 .50
b.	A35 55c Distributing gifts	1.00 1.00
c.	A35 85c Waving good-bye	1.40 1.40

Crabs A36

1985   Litho.   Perf. 13x13½
162	A36	30c Birgus latro	1.00 .80
163	A36	33c Cardisoma hirtipes	1.00 .80
164	A36	33c Gecarcoidea natalis	1.10 .90
165	A36	40c Ocypode ceratophthalma	1.10 .90
166	A36	45c Ceonobita rugosa	1.10 1.10
167	A36	45c Metasesarma rousseauxi	1.40 1.40
168	A36	55c Coenobita brevimana	1.40 1.40
169	A36	60c Geograpsus stormi	1.75 1.75
170	A36	60c Grapsus tenuicrustatus	2.25 2.25
171	A36	85c Geograpsus grayi	2.50 2.50
172	A36	90c Ocypode cordimana	2.50 3.50
173	A36	90c Geograpsus crinipes	3.00 4.00
	Nos. 162-173 (12)		20.10 21.30

Issued: 30c, 40c, 55c, 85c, 1/30; #163, 166, 169, 172, 4/29; #164, 167, 170, 173, 7/22.

Once in Royal David's City — A37

Songs: 33c, While Shepherds Watched Their Flocks by Night. 45c, Away in a Manger. 60c, We Three Kings of Orient Are. 90c, Hark! The Herald Angels Sing.

1985, Oct. 28   Litho.   Perf. 14x14½
174	A37	27c multicolored	.90 1.10
175	A37	33c multicolored	1.00 1.25
176	A37	45c multicolored	1.25 1.40
177	A37	60c multicolored	1.40 1.50
178	A37	90c multicolored	1.50 1.60
a.	Strip of 5, #174-178		7.50 8.00

Christmas.

Halley's Comet — A38

1986, Apr. 30   Litho.   Perf. 14
179	A38	33c Over island	.60 .65
180	A38	45c Edmond Halley	.80 1.00
181	A38	60c Over phosphate shipping	1.10 1.90
182	A38	90c Over Flying Fish Cove	1.75 2.25
	Nos. 179-182 (4)		4.25 5.80

Indigenous Flowers — A39

1986, June 30   Litho.   Perf. 14
183	A39	33c Ridley's orchid	1.50 .55
184	A39	45c Hanging flower	.95 .90
185	A39	60c Hoya	.95 1.60
186	A39	90c Sea hibiscus	1.25 2.25
	Nos. 183-186 (4)		4.65 5.30

Royal Wedding Issue, 1986
Common Design Type

Designs: 33c, Couple in Buckingham Palace garden. 90c, Andrew operating helicopter.

1986, July 23   Litho.   Perf. 14½x14
187	CD338	33c multicolored	.60 .50
188	CD338	90c multicolored	1.40 1.60

Christmas A40

Santa Claus at Christmas Island.

1986, Sept. 30   Litho.   Perf. 13x13½
189	A40	30c Speedboating	.90 .70
190	A40	36c At the beach	1.00 .70
191	A40	55c Fishing	1.50 1.50
192	A40	70c Golfing	2.50 3.75
193	A40	$1 Sleeping in hammock	2.50 4.25
	Nos. 189-193 (5)		8.40 10.90

Visiting Ships, Cent. A41

1987, Jan. 21   Perf. 14½
194	A41	36c Flying Fish	1.25 .75
195	A41	90c Egeria	2.25 2.25

Wildlife A42

1987-89   Litho.   Perf. 14
196	A42	1c Blind snake	.55 .90
197	A42	2c Blue-tailed skink	.55 .90
198	A42	3c Insectivorous bat	1.00 .90
199	A42	5c Green cricket	1.00 .90
200	A42	10c Christmas Is. fruit bat	1.00 .90
201	A42	25c Gecko	1.25 1.00
202	A42	30c Praying mantis	1.50 1.25
203	A42	36c Hawk owl	3.25 2.00
204	A42	40c Bull-mouth helmet shell	2.00 1.75
204A	A42	41c Nudibranch ('89)	1.50 .80
205	A42	50c Textile cone shell	2.25 2.00
206	A42	65c Brittle-stars	1.50 1.25
207	A42	75c Royal angelfish	1.50 1.75
208	A42	90c Christmas Is. white butterfly	4.50 4.00
209	A42	$1 Mimic butterfly	4.50 4.00
210	A42	$2 Shrew	4.50 7.50
211	A42	$5 Green turtle	5.50 8.00
a.	Sheet of 16, #196-204, 205-211		52.50 52.50
	Nos. 196-211 (17)		37.85 39.80

Issued: 1c, 2c, 25c, $5, 3/25; 3c, 10c, 36c, $2, 6/24; 40c, 50c, 65c, 75c, 8/26; 5c, 30c, 90c, $1, 3/1/88; 41c, 9/1/89.
Stamps contained in No. 211a inscribed "1988" at bottom.
For overprint see Nos. 246-247.

Souvenir Sheet

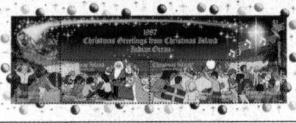

Santa Claus Delivering Presents — A43

Illustration reduced.

1987, Oct. 7   Litho.   Perf. 13½
212	A43 Sheet of 4	5.75 5.75
a.	30c multicolored	.60 .60
b.	37c multicolored	.65 .65
c.	90c multicolored	1.75 1.75
d.	$1 multicolored	1.90 1.90

Christmas. Nos. 212a-212d printed in a continuous design.

Australia
Bicentennial
A44

Designs: a, First Fleet sighted by 5 Aboriginals on land. b, Four Aboriginals on land, one in canoe. c, Ships entering bay, kangaroos. d, Europeans land. e, Flag raising.

1988, Jan. 26   Litho.   Perf. 13
| 213 | Strip of 5 | 8.00 | 8.00 |
| a.-e. | A44 37c any single | 1.50 | 1.50 |

Nos. 213a-213e printed in a continuous design. See Cocos Islands No. 172.

Annexation of the
Island,
Cent. — A45

1988, June 8   Litho.   Perf. 14½
214	A45	37c Capt William Henry May	.75	.75
215	A45	53c Annexation ceremony	1.00	1.00
216	A45	95c HMS Imperieuse	1.75	1.75
217	A45	$1.50 Building cairn of stones	2.25	2.25
		Nos. 214-217 (4)	5.75	5.75

Settlement of
Christmas
Is.,
Cent. — A46

Transportation: 37c, Horse and cart, 1910. 55c, Phosphate mining, 1910. 70c, Steam locomotive, 1914. $1, Arrival of first aircraft, 1957.

1988, Aug. 24   Litho.   Perf. 14½
218	A46 37c multicolored	.85	.50
219	A46 55c multicolored	1.25	.65
220	A46 70c multicolored	1.75	.95
221	A46 $1 multicolored	2.00	1.50
	Nos. 218-221 (4)	5.85	3.60

Christmas
Presents — A47

1988, Nov. 15   Perf. 14x14½
222	A47 32c Bucket, shovel, boat	.65	.65
223	A47 39c Snorkeling equipment	.80	.80
224	A47 90c Toy soldier, doll, stuffed animals	1.75	1.75
225	A47 $1 Race car, truck, plane	2.00	2.00
	Nos. 222-225 (4)	5.20	5.20

Chinese
New
Year — A48

1989, Jan. 31   Perf. 14½
226	A48 39c Good harvest	.75	.65
227	A48 70c Prosperity	1.40	1.25
228	A48 90c Good fortune	1.90	1.50
229	A48 $1 Progress	2.10	1.75
	Nos. 226-229 (4)	6.15	5.15

Sir John Murray (1841-1914),
Oceanographer — A49

1989, Mar. 16   Perf. 14½x14
230	A49 39c Portrait	.75	.75
231	A49 80c Murray Hill (map)	1.40	1.40
232	A49 $1 Murray's equipment	1.75	1.75
233	A49 $1.10 HMS Challenger	2.10	2.10
	Nos. 230-233 (4)	6.00	6.00

Malay-Hari Raya
Folk
Celebration — A50

1989, May 31   Perf. 14
234	A50 39c Children	.65	.60
235	A50 55c Tambourine player	1.00	.85
236	A50 80c Girl	1.50	1.50
237	A50 $1.10 Minaret	2.10	1.90
	Nos. 234-237 (4)	5.25	4.60

Ferns
A51

Christmas
A52

1989, Aug. 16
238	A51	41c Huperzia phlegmaria	.90	.90
239	A51	65c Asplenium polydon	1.25	1.25
240	A51	80c Davallia denticulata	1.50	1.25
241	A51	$1.10 Asplenium nidus	2.10	2.10
		Nos. 238-241 (4)	5.75	5.50

1989, Oct. 4   Litho.   Perf. 14½x15

Biblical scenes: 36c, Joseph. 41c, Manger. 80c, Shepherds see star. $1.10, Magi riding camels.

242	A52 36c multi	.70	.50
243	A52 41c multi	.75	.55
244	A52 80c multi	1.90	.80
245	A52 $1.10 multi	2.00	1.10
	Nos. 242-245 (4)	5.35	2.95

Nos. 204A
and 209
Overprinted

1989, Oct. 18   Litho.   Perf. 14
| 246 | A42 41c multicolored | 1.25 | .55 |
| 247 | A42 $1 multicolored | 4.25 | 1.25 |

STAMPSHOW '89, Melbourne.
No. 247 is dated "1989."

1st Sighting of
Christmas Is., 375th
Anniv. — A53

Sightings of the island: 41c, John Milward, master of the British East India ship *Thomas*, 1615. $1.10, William Mynors, captain of *Royal Mary*, 1643.

1990, Jan. 31   Litho.   Perf. 14x15
| 248 | A53 | 41c multicolored | 2.00 | .60 |
| 249 | A53 | $1.10 multicolored | 2.50 | 1.60 |

Transport
Through the
Ages — A55

Perf. 14x13½, 13½x14
1990		Litho.	Unwmk.	
254	A55	1c Phosphate transport	.25	.25
255	A55	2c Phosphate train	.50	.50
256	A55	3c Rail car, vert.	.35	.35
257	A55	5c Road train	.55	.55
258	A55	10c Trishaw, vert.	.45	.45
259	A55	15c Terex	1.10	.95
260	A55	25c Long bus	.45	.45
261	A55	30c Passenger rake, vert.	.45	.45
262	A55	40c Passenger barge, vert.	.55	.45
263	A55	50c Kolek canoe	.75	.55
264	A55	65c Flying doctor, ambulance	5.00	2.10
265	A55	75c Tradestore van	2.40	2.40
266	A55	90c Vintage truck	2.40	2.40
267	A55	$1 Water tanker	2.75	2.40
268	A55	$2 Traction engine	3.50	3.50
269	A55	$5 Steam locomotive, flat car	4.75	6.25
		Nos. 254-269 (16)	26.20	24.00

Issued: 1c, 3c, 10c, 25c, 30c, 40c, 50c, $5, Apr. 18; others, Aug. 22.

World Wildlife
Fund — A56

Abbott's boobies *(Sula abbotti)*: 20c, Adult (facing left). 29c, Adult (facing right). No. 273, Adults, nest, hatchling. No. 274a, Adult landing on tree branch. No. 274b, Adult resting on branch. No. 274c, Adult, young in nest.

Perf. 14x14½
1990, June 6		Litho.	Unwmk.	
270	A56	10c shown	1.75	1.75
271	A56	20c multicolored	2.25	2.25
272	A56	29c multicolored	2.50	2.50
273	A56	41c multicolored	3.25	3.25
		Nos. 270-273 (4)	9.75	9.75

Souvenir Sheet
Perf. 14½
274	Sheet of 3	10.00	10.00
a.-c.	A56 41c any single	3.25	3.25
d.	Overprinted in purple	14.00	14.00
e.	Overprinted in green	20.00	20.00

No. 274d overprint reads "WORLD STAMP EXHIBITION / AUCKLAND, NEW ZEALAND, 24 AUGUST-2 SEPTEMBER 1990."
No. 274e overprint reads "BIRDPEX '90 National Philatelic Exhibition / University of Canterbury Christchurch NZ 6-9 Dec 1990 / In Conjunction / With The 20th International Ornithological Congress" and Bird's head.
Issued: #274d, Aug. 24; #274e, Dec. 6.

Centenary of Visit by Botanist Henry
Ridley — A57

1990, July 11   Litho.   Perf. 14½
| 275 | A57 41c No. 77 | 1.50 | .80 |
| 276 | A57 75c Ridley, vert. | 2.25 | 2.00 |

Christmas
A58

Flowers.

1990, Oct. 3   Litho.   Perf. 14½
294	A58	38c Corymborkus veratrifolia	1.00	.90
295	A58	43c Hoya aldrichii	1.25	1.00
296	A58	80c Quisqualis indica	2.00	2.00
297	A58	$1.20 Barringtonia racemosa	3.00	3.50
		Nos. 294-297 (4)	7.25	7.40

1st Phosphate
Mining Lease,
Cent. — A59

1991, Feb. 13   Litho.   Perf. 14½
298	A59	43c Freighter	1.25	1.25
299	A59	43c Loading rail cars	1.25	1.25
300	A59	85c Shay locomotive	1.50	1.50
301	A59	$1.20 Bucket shovel	2.00	2.00
302	A59	$1.70 Reforestation	2.50	2.50
a.		Strip of 5, #298-302	9.00	9.00

Island Police
Force — A60

1991, Apr. 17   Litho.   Perf. 14½
303	A60	43c Community relations	1.75	1.75
304	A60	43c Traffic control	1.75	1.75
305	A60	90c Customs and quarantine	2.50	2.50
306	A60	$1.20 Search and rescue	3.25	3.25
a.		Souvenir sheet of 4, #303-306	9.50	8.00
		Nos. 303-306 (4)	9.25	9.25

Maps — A61

1991, June 19   Litho.   Perf. 14
307	A61	43c 1991	1.25	1.25
308	A61	75c Goos Atlas, 1666	2.25	2.00
309	A61	$1.10 Apres De Manevillette, 1745	2.75	2.75
310	A61	$1.20 Comberford, 1667	3.00	3.00
		Nos. 307-310 (4)	9.25	9.00

Trees
A62

1991, Aug. 21   Litho.   Perf. 14
311	A62	43c Bruguiera gymnorrhiza	1.50 1.50
312	A62	70c Syzygium operculatum	2.00 2.00
313	A62	85c Ficus microcarpa	2.25 2.25
314	A62	$1.20 Arenga listeri	2.50 2.50
		Nos. 311-314 (4)	8.25 8.25

Christmas
A63

Drawings of "What Christmas Means to Me" by: No. 315a, S'ng Yen Luiw. b, Liew Ann Nee. c, Foo Pang Chuan. d, Too Lai Peng. e, Jesamine Wheeler. 43c, Ho Puay Ha. $1, Ng Hooi Hua. $1.20, Yani Kawi.

1991, Oct. 2   Litho.   Perf. 14½
315		Strip of 5	5.00 5.00
a.-e.		A63 38c any single	.90 .90
316	A63	43c multicolored	1.00 .85
317	A63	$1 multicolored	2.25 2.25
318	A63	$1.20 multicolored	2.50 2.50
		Nos. 315-318 (4)	10.75 10.60

A64   Shells — A65

War Time Evacuation, 50th Anniv.: No. 319, Conference to decide upon evacuation. No. 320, Europeans awaiting barge. $1.05, Barge approaching waiting ship. $1.20, Remaining population waving to TSS Islander.

1992, Feb. 19   Litho.   Perf. 14½
319	A64	45c multicolored	1.25 1.25
320	A64	45c multicolored	1.25 1.25
321	A64	$1.05 multicolored	2.75 2.75
322	A64	$1.20 multicolored	3.00 3.00
		Nos. 319-322 (4)	8.25 8.25

1992   Litho.   Perf. 15x14½
326	A65	5c Cypraea tigris	.65 .90
327	A65	10c Cypraea caputserpentis	.95 .90
328	A65	15c Lambis scorpius	1.25 .90
329	A65	20c Chlamys pallium	1.25 .90
330	A65	25c Engina mendicaria	1.25 .90
331	A65	30c Drupa ricinus	1.25 .90
332	A65	40c Distorsio reticulata	1.25 1.00
333	A65	45c Turbo petholatus	1.60 1.00
334	A65	50c Cantharus pulcher	1.60 1.00
335	A65	60c Conus capitaneus	2.00 1.10
336	A65	70c Turbo lajonkairii	2.00 1.25
337	A65	80c Lambis chiragra	2.50 1.40
338	A65	90c Angaria delphinus	2.50 1.60
339	A65	$1 Vasum ceramicum	2.50 1.90
340	A65	$2 Tonna perdix	1.90 2.75
341	A65	$5 Drupa rubusidaea	4.75 4.50
		Nos. 326-341 (16)	29.20 22.90

Issued: 10c, 20c, 30c, 45c, 60c, 80c, $1, $2, 4/15; 5c, 15c, 25c, 40c, 50c, 70c, 90c, $5, 8/19.

For overprint see No. 348.

Sinking of Eidsvold and Nissa Maru, 50th Anniv. A66

Designs: 45c, Eidsvold hit by torpedo. 80c, Eidsvold sinking. $1.05, Nissa Maru hit by torpedo. $1.20, Nissa Maru sinking.

1992, June 17   Litho.   Perf. 14x13½
343	A66	45c multicolored	1.75 1.25
344	A66	80c multicolored	2.50 2.50
345	A66	$1.05 multicolored	3.00 3.00
346	A66	$1.20 multicolored	3.00 3.00
		Nos. 343-346 (4)	10.25 9.75

Christmas — A67

Coastline, booby birds: a, 40c, Plants on shore, birds. b, 40c, Birds, rocks offshore. c, 45c, Birds on shore. d, $1.05, Birds in flight, coastline. e, $1.20, Forest, rocky coastline.

1992, Oct. 7   Litho.   Perf. 14½
347	A67	Strip of 5, #a.-e.	7.75 8.50

No. 341 Ovptd. in Red Violet

1992, Sept. 1   Litho.   Perf. 15x14½
348	A65	$5 on #342	12.00 8.00

Kuala Lumpur Philatelic Exhibition.

Starting with No. 349, Christmas Island stamps are valid for postage on items mailed in Australia and Australian stamps are valid on items posted on Christmas Island.

Seabirds — A68

Designs: a, Abbott's booby. b, Christmas Island frigatebird. c, Common noddy. d, Golden bosunbird. e, Brown booby.

1993, Mar. 4   Litho.   Perf. 14½x14
349	A68	45c Strip of 5, #a.-e.	4.25 4.50
f.		Souvenir sheet of 5, #a.-e.	5.00 5.00
g.		As "f," overprinted	10.00 10.00
h.		As "f," overprinted	8.00 8.00

No. 349g Ovptd. in Gold in sheet margin with Taipei '93 emblem and: "ASIAN INTERNATIONAL INVITATION STAMP EXHIBITION / TAIPEI '93" in Chinese and English.

No. 349h Ovptd. in Gold in Sheet Margin with "INDOPEX '93 / 6TH ASIAN INTERNATIONAL PHILATELIC EXHIBITION 1993 / PAMERAN INTERNASIONAL PENGUMPUL-AN / KEENAM DI ASIA TAHUN 1993" and show emblem.

Issued: #349g, 4/93; #349h, 5/29/93.

Scenic Views — A69

1993, June 1   Perf. 14x14½
350	A69	85c Dolly Beach	1.75 1.75
351	A69	95c Blow holes	2.00 2.00
352	A69	$1.05 Merrial Beach	2.25 2.25
353	A69	$1.20 Rain forest	2.50 2.50
		Nos. 350-353 (4)	8.50 8.50

Christmas — A70

1993, Sept. 2   Litho.   Perf. 14½x14
354	A70	40c Turtle on beach	1.25 1.25
355	A70	45c Crabs, wave	1.25 1.25
356	A70	$1 Frigatebird, rainforest	2.75 2.75
		Nos. 354-356 (3)	5.25 5.25

Naming of Christmas Island, 350th Anniv. — A71

1993, Dec. 1   Litho.   Perf. 14x14½
357	A71	$2 multicolored	4.00 4.00

New Year 1994 (Year of the Dog) — A72

1994, Jan. 20   Litho.   Perf. 14x14½
358	A72	45c shown	1.40 1.50
359	A72	45c Pekingese	1.40 1.50
a.		Pair, #358-359	3.00 3.75
b.		Souvenir sheet of 1, #359a	4.25 4.25
c.		As "b," overprinted	4.50 4.50
d.		As "b," overprinted	7.50 7.50
e.		As "b," overprinted	4.50 4.50
f.		As "b," overprinted	12.50 12.50

No. 359c Ovptd. in gold in sheet margin with dog and "Melbourne / STAMP & COIN SHOW / 11-13 February 1994;" No. 359d with "HONG KONG '94 STAMP EXHIBITION" and show emblem; No. 359e with "Canberra /Stamp Show '94 / 19-21 March / 1994" and show emblem; No. 359f with "QUEENSLAND STAMP & COIN SHOW 1994 / JUNE 11, 12, 13."

Issued: #359c, 2/11/94; #359d, 2/18/94; #359e, 3/19/94; #359f, 1995.

Christmas Island Railway Steam Locomotives A73

1994, May 19   Litho.   Perf. 14x14½
360	A73	85c Locomotive No. 4	2.00 1.75
361	A73	95c Locomotive No. 9	2.25 1.75
362	A73	$1.20 Locomotive No. 1	2.75 2.00
		Nos. 360-362 (3)	7.00 5.50

Orchids — A74

---

a, Brachypeza archytas. b, Thelasis capitata. c, Corymborkis veratrifolia. d, Flickingeria nativitatis. e, Dendrobium crumenatum.

1994, Aug. 16   Litho.   Perf. 14½x14
363	A74	45c Strip of 5, #a.-e.	7.00 7.00

Christmas
A75

1994, Sept. 8   Litho.   Perf. 14x14½
364	A75	40c Angel	1.10 .80
365	A75	45c Wise man	1.25 .80
366	A75	80c Bethlehem	1.75 1.50
		Nos. 364-366 (3)	4.10 3.10

New Year 1995 (Year of the Boar) — A76

Design: 85c, Stylized boar, diff.

1995, Jan. 12   Litho.   Perf. 14x14½
367	A76	45c shown	.90 .85
368	A76	85c multicolored	1.60 1.40
a.		Souvenir sheet, #367-368	3.25 3.25
b.		As "a," overprinted	6.00 6.00

No. 368b ovptd. in gold in sheet margin with outline of boar and: "STAMP & COIN FAIR / ROYAL EXHIBITION BUILDING / MELBOURNE VIC. 3000 . 10-12 FEB 1995."

Christmas Island Golf Course, 40th Anniv. — A77

1995, May 11   Litho.   Perf. 14
369	A77	$2.50 multicolored	7.50 7.50

Christmas A78

Santa Claus riding great frigatebird: 40c, Reading map. 45c, Dropping presents. 80c, Waving.

1995, Sept. 14   Litho.   Perf. 14x14½
370	A78	40c multicolored	1.00 .85
371	A78	45c multicolored	1.10 .85
372	A78	80c multicolored	1.75 1.40
		Nos. 370-372 (3)	3.85 3.10

End of World War II, 50th Anniv. — A79

#373a, RAAF reconnaissance flight, 1945. #373b, Arrival of HMS Rother, 1945.

Litho. & Engr.

1995, Oct. 12   Perf. 14x14½
373		Pair	3.00 3.00
a.-b.		A79 45c any single	1.40 1.40

Angelfish
A80

1995, Oct. 12   Litho.
374 A80 75c Lemonpeel   1.60 1.60
375 A80 $1 Emperor   2.00 2.00

New Year
1996 (Year of
the Rat)
A81

1996, Jan. 9   Litho.   Perf. 14x14½
376 A81 45c Facing right   1.10 1.10
377 A81 45c Facing left   1.10 1.10
    a.   Pair, #376-377   2.25 2.25
    b.   Souvenir sheet, #377a   2.50 2.50
    c.   As "b," overprinted   3.25 3.25

No. 377c overprinted in gold in sheet margin "STAMP AND COIN FAIR / MELBOURNE / 23-25 February 1996."

Fish — A82

1996-97   Litho.   Perf. 14x14½
381 A82 20c Pinktail trigger-
           fish   .55   .55
382 A82 30c Longnose file-
           fish   .70   .70
383 A82 45c Princess
           anthias   .90   .90
384 A82 85c Green moon
           wrasse   1.50 1.50
385 A82 90c Spotted boxfish   1.75 1.75
386 A82 95c Moorish idol   1.75 1.75
387 A82 $1.20 Glass bigeye   2.25 1.90
     Nos. 381-387 (7)   9.40 9.05

Issued: 20c, 30c, 45c, 90c, 4/18/96; 85c, 95c, $1.20, 7/17/97.

Birds — A83

1996, July 11   Litho.   Perf. 14½x14
399 A83 45c White-eye   1.25 1.25
400 A83 85c Hawk-owl   2.00 2.00

Christmas
A84

Sailing ships, words from Christmas carol: 40c, "I Saw Three Ships." 45c, "Come sailing in." 80c, "On Christmas day in the morning."

1996, Sept. 12   Litho.   Perf. 14
401 A84 40c multicolored   1.00   .70
402 A84 45c multicolored   1.10   .80
403 A84 80c multicolored   1.75 1.40
     Nos. 401-403 (3)   3.85 2.90

Exploration of
Australian Coast
& Christmas
Island by Willem
de Vlamingh,
300th
Anniv. — A85

"Portrait of a Dutch Navigator," by Jan Verkolje.

1996, Oct. 27   Litho.   Perf. 14
404 A85 45c multicolored   1.50 1.50

No. 404 was issued se-tenant with Australia No. 1571 (No. 1571a).

New Year
1997 (Year of
the
Ox) — A86

Constellation and: No. 405, Ox facing right. No. 406, Ox facing left.

1997, Jan. 6   Litho.   Perf. 14x14½
405 A86 45c multicolored   1.10 1.10
406 A86 45c multicolored   1.10 1.10
    a.   Pair, #405-406   2.40 2.40
    b.   Souvenir sheet, #405-406   2.75 3.00

Christmas
A87

Santa on Christmas Island: 40c, Reading letters. 45c, Making toys. 80c, In sleigh.

1997, Sept. 11   Litho.   Perf. 14x14½
407 A87 40c multicolored   .90   .85
408 A87 45c multicolored   .95   .90
409 A87 80c multicolored   2.10 1.75
     Nos. 407-409 (3)   3.95 3.50

New Year
1998 (Year of
the
Tiger) — A88

1998, Jan. 5   Litho.   Perf. 14x14½
410 A88 45c shown   1.25 1.25
411 A88 45c Looking backward   1.25 1.25
    a.   Pair, #410-411   2.75 2.75
    b.   Souvenir sheet of 2, #410-411   3.25 3.50

Marine
Life — A89

Designs: a, 5c, Frigatebird. b, 5c, Ambon chromis, denomination LR. c, 5c, Ambon chromis, denomination LL. d, 5c, Pink anemonefish, denomination, UR. e, 5c, Pink anemonefish, denomination LL. f, 10c, Eastern reef egret. g, 10c, Whitelined cod. h, 10c, Pyramid butterfly fish. i, 10c, Dusky parrotfish. j, 10c, Spotted garden eel. k, 25c, Sooty tern. l, 25c, Scissortail sergeant. m, 25c, Thicklip wrasse. n, 25c, Blackaxil chromis. o, 25c, Orange anthias. p, 45c, Brown booby. q, 45c, Green turtle. r, 45c, Pink anemonefish. s, 45c, Blue sea star. t, 45c, Kunie's chromodoris.

1998, Mar. 12   Litho.   Perf. 14
412 A89   Sheet of 20, #a.-t.   10.00 10.00

Tree Flowers of
Christmas — A90

1998, Sept. 3   Litho.   Perf. 14½x14
413 A90 40c Orchid tree   .80   .80
414 A90 80c Flame tree   1.75 1.75
415 A90 95c Sea hibiscus   1.90 1.90
     Nos. 413-415 (3)   4.45 4.45

New Year
1999 (Year of
the Rabbit)
A91

1999, Jan. 14   Litho.   Perf. 14x14½
416 A91 45c shown   1.25 1.25
417 A91 45c Rabbit looking left   1.25 1.25
    a.   Pair, #416-417   2.75 2.75
    b.   Souvenir sheet, #417a   3.00 3.00

Festivals on
Christmas
Island — A92

Children's drawings: No. 418, Carrying balloons in parade, by Fong Jason. No. 419, Giant crab, by Siti Zanariah Zainal. 85c, Children at night, by Tan Diana, vert. $1.20, Green mosque, tree, by Anwar Ramian, vert.

1999, July 15   Litho.   Perf. 14x14½
418 A92   45c multicolored   .90   .80
419 A92   45c multicolored   .90   .80
    a.   Pair, #418-419   1.90 1.90
               Perf. 14½x14
420 A92   85c multicolored   1.40 1.40
421 A92 $1.20 multicolored   2.00 2.00
     Nos. 418-421 (4)   5.20 5.00

Christmas
A93

Designs: 40c, Santa Claus in hammock. 45c, Santa, birds, crab, lizard, cake. 95c, Santa, booby-drawn sleigh.

1999, Sept. 9   Litho.   Perf. 14x14½
422 A93 40c multicolored   .95   .80
423 A93 45c multicolored   1.10   .95
424 A93 95c multicolored   1.75 1.75
     Nos. 422-424 (3)   3.80 3.50

New Year
2000 (Year of
the Dragon)
A94

2000, Jan. 13   Litho.   Perf. 14x14½
425 A94 45c shown   1.25 1.25
426 A94 45c Dragon facing left   1.25 1.25
    a.   Pair, #425-426   2.75 2.75
    b.   Souvenir sheet, #426a   3.00 3.25

Faces of Christmas
Island — A95

Ordinary people: a, Yeow Jian Min, without shirt. b, Ida Chin, with blue shirt. c, Ho Tak Wah, old man. d, Thomas Faul and James Neill. e, Siti Sanniah Kawi, with striped blouse.

2000, Apr. 13   Litho.   Perf. 14½x14
427 A95 45c Strip of 5, #a.-e.   5.00 5.50

Christmas — A96

No. 428: a, We three kings of Orient are. b, Bearing gifts we traverse afar. 45c, Star of wonder, star of night.

2000, Sept. 5   Litho.   Perf. 14½x14
428   1.60 1.60
    a.-b.   A96 40c Any single   .80   .70
429 A96 45c multi   .80   .70

New Year
2001 (Year of
the Snake)
A97

Snake color: 45c, Green. $1.35, Silver.

Litho. with Foil Application
2001, Jan. 8   Perf. 14x14½
430-431 A97   Set of 2   3.00 3.00
    a.   Souvenir sheet, #430-431   4.00 4.50

Fungi — A98

Designs: $1, Chaetocalathus semisupinus. $1.50, Pycnoporus sanguineus.

2001, Oct. 25   Litho.   Perf. 14x14½
432-433 A98   Set of 2   4.00 4.25

New Year
2002 (Year of
the
Horse) — A99

Zodiac
Animals and
Their
Chinese
Characters
A100

Designs: 45c, Purple horse. $1.35, Gold horse.
No. 436: a, Rat. b, Ox. c, Tiger. d, Rabbit. e, Dragon. f, Snake. g, Horse. h, Sheep. i, Monkey. j, Cock. k, Dog. l, Boar.

Litho. With Gold Foil Application
2002, Jan. 8   Perf. 14x14½
434-435 A99   Set of 2   3.25 3.25
    a.   Souvenir sheet, #434-435   4.00 4.00
436   Sheet of 14, #a-l,
           #435a   10.00 10.00
    a.-d.   A100 5c Any single   .45   .45
    e.-h.   A100 15c Any single, orange
           background   .50   .50
    i.-l.   A100 25c Any single, orange
           background   .55   .55

See No. 442.

Worldwide Fund for
Nature
(WWF) — A101

Christmas Island birds - No. 437: a, Imperial pigeon. b, Hawk owl. $1, Goshawk. $1.50, Thrush.

2002, May 1   Litho.   *Perf. 14½x14*
437	A101	45c Horiz. pair, #a-b	1.50	1.50
438	A101	$1 multi	1.50	1.50
439	A101	$1.50 multi	2.50	2.50
		Nos. 437-439 (3)	5.50	5.50

Zodiac Animals Type of 2002 and

New Year 2003 (Year of the Ram)
A102

Designs: 50c, Yellow and orange ram. $1.50, Blue ram.
No. 442: a, Rat. b, Ox. c, Tiger. d, Rabbit. e, Dragon. f, Snake. g, Horse. h, Sheep. i, Monkey. j, Cock. k, Dog. l, Boar.

Litho. With Gold Foil Application
2003, Jan. 7   *Perf. 14x14½*
440-441	A102	Set of 2	3.50	3.50
a.		Souvenir sheet, #440-441	4.00	4.00
442		Sheet of 14, #a-l, #441a	10.00	10.00
a.-d.		A100 10c Any single, red violet background	.40	.40
e.-h.		A100 15c Any single, red violet background	.50	.50
i.-l.		A100 25c Any single, red violet background	.60	.60

Christmas — A103

Designs: 45c, Arrival of Santa Claus on whale shark. 50c, Santa giving gifts to red crabs.

2003, Oct. 31   Litho.   *Perf. 14½x14*
443-444	A103	Set of 2	2.25	2.25

Zodiac Animals Type of 2002 and

New Year 2004 (Year of the Monkey)
A104

Designs: 50c, Yellow and orange monkey. $1.45, Red orange monkey, lotus flower.
No. 447: a, Rat. b, Ox. c, Tiger. d, Rabbit. e, Dragon. f, Snake. g, Horse. h, Sheep. i, Monkey. j, Cock. k, Dog. l, Boar.

Litho. With Gold Foil Application
2004, Jan. 6   *Perf. 14x14½*
445-446	A104	Set of 2	4.00	4.00
446a		Souvenir sheet, #445-446	5.00	5.00
447		Sheet of 14, #a-l, #446a	10.00	10.00
a.-d.		A100 10c Any single, light and dark blue background	.40	.40
e.-h.		A100 15c Any single, light and dark blue background	.50	.50
i.-l.		A100 25c Any single, light and dark blue background	.60	.60

No. 446a exists with a 2004 Hong Kong Stamp Expo overprint in sheet margin in red. This sheet was sold at the show, but not on Christmas Island.

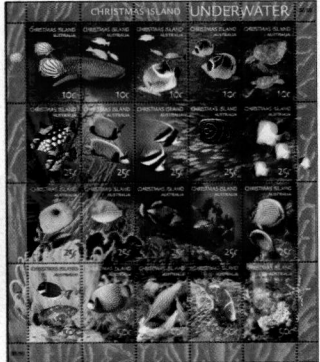

Marine Life — A105

No. 448: a, Two butterflyfish, rear of whale shark. b, Three striped fish, front of whale shark. c, Four fish. d, Two fish. e, Two green turtles. f, Two triggerfish (polka dots), red coral at LL. g, Two fish with thin horizontal stripes with yellow tails. h, Two fish with thick vertical stripes. i, Black and white fish. j, Three fish. k, Yellow fish with black spot, blue fish, red coral, yellow coral. l, Striped fish, clam. m, Black fish, small red fish. n Red fish, divers. o, Two striped fish, red coral under denomination. p, Blue and yellow fish, red and white spotted fish, yellow coral. q, Blue and yellow fish, yellow coral, sea anemones. r, Three blue fish with orange spots. s, Sea anemone and two anemonefish. t, Nudibranch, red coral and starfish.

2004, July 13   Litho.   *Perf. 14½x14*
448	A105	Sheet of 20	9.50	9.50
a.-e.		10c Any single	.20	.20
f.-o.		25c Any single	.40	.40
p.-t.		50c Any single	.85	.85

Zodiac Animals Type of 2002 and

New Year 2005 (Year of the Cock)
A106

Designs: 50c, Cock, spirals at right. $1.45, Cock, spirals at right.
No. 451: a, Rat. b, Ox. c, Tiger. d, Rabbit. e, Dragon. f, Snake. g, Horse. h, Sheep. i, Monkey. j, Cock. k, Dog. l, Boar.

Litho. With Gold Foil Application
2005, Jan. 4   *Perf. 14x14½*
449-450	A106	Set of 2	4.00	4.00
450a		Souvenir sheet, #445-446	4.00	4.00
451		Sheet of 14, #a-l, #450a	10.00	10.00
a.-d.		A100 10c Any single, red and yellow background	.35	.35
e.-h.		A100 15c Any single, red and yellow background	.35	.35
i.-l.		A100 25c Any single, red and yellow background	.55	.55

Christmas
A107

Santa Claus, birds and: 45c, Palm tree, presents. 90c, Sleigh, crabs.

2005, Nov. 1   Litho.   *Perf. 14½x14*
452	A107	45c multi	.75	.75
a.		Booklet pane of 4	3.50	
453	A107	90c multi	1.60	1.60

No. 452a exists with two different margins. These two panes were issued in a booklet that also contained three examples of Australia No. 2423a. The entire booklet sold for $9.95.

Zodiac Animals Type of 2002 and

New Year 2006 (Year of the Dog)
A108

Designs: 50c, Purple dog. $1.45, Copper dog.
No. 456: a, Rat. b, Ox. c, Tiger. d, Rabbit. e, Dragon. f, Snake. g, Horse. h, Sheep. i, Monkey. j, Cock. k, Dog. l, Boar.

Litho. With Copper Foil Application
2006, Jan. 5   *Perf. 14x14½*
454-455	A106	Set of 2	3.00	3.00
455a		Souvenir sheet, #454-455	3.00	3.00
456		Sheet of 14, #a-l, #455a	6.00	6.00
a.-d.		A100 10c Any single, brown and yellow background	.20	.20
e.-h.		A100 15c Any single, brown and yellow background	.20	.20
i.-l.		A100 25c Any single, brown and yellow background	.35	.35

Buildings — A109

Designs: 50c, Mosque. $1.45, Tai Jin House.
No. 458: a, Tai Pak Kong Temple. b, Soon Tian Temple.

2006, June 13   Litho.   *Perf. 14½x14*
457	A109	50c multi	.75	.75
458	A109	$1 Horiz. pair, #a-b	3.00	3.00
459	A109	$1.45 multi	2.25	2.25
		Nos. 457-459 (3)	6.00	6.00

Zodiac Animals Types of 1996-2006 and

New Year 2007 (Year of the Boar)
A110

Zodiac Animals
A111

Designs: Nos. 460, 463l, 50c, Boar facing right. $1.45, Boar facing left.
No. 462: a, Rat. b, Ox. c, Tiger. d, Rabbit. e, Dragon. f, Snake. g, Horse. h, Sheep. i, Monkey. j, Cock. k, Dog. l, Boar.

Litho. With Copper Foil Application
2007, Jan. 9   *Perf. 14x14½*
460-461	A110	Set of 2	3.25	3.25
461a		Souvenir sheet, #460-461	3.25	3.25
462		Sheet of 14, #a-l, #461a	6.50	6.50
a.-d.		A100 10c Any single, multicolored background	.20	.20
e.-h.		A100 15c Any single, multicolored background	.20	.20
i.-l.		A100 25c Any single, multicolored background	.40	.40

Self-Adhesive
Serpentine Die Cut 12¼ Syncopated (#463a-463l), Serpentine Die Cut (#463m)
463		Sheet of 13	11.50	
a.	A81	50c Like #376	.80	.80
b.	A86	50c Like #405	.80	.80
c.	A88	50c Like #410	.80	.80
d.	A91	50c Like #416	.80	.80
e.	A94	50c Like #416	.80	.80
f.	A97	50c Like #430	.80	.80
g.	A99	50c Like #434	.80	.80
h.	A102	50c Like #440	.80	.80
i.	A104	50c Like #445	.80	.80
j.	A106	50c Like #449	.80	.80
k.	A108	50c Like #454	.80	.80
l.	A110	50c Like #460	.80	.80
m.	A111	$1 multi	1.60	1.60
n.		Booklet pane, 2 each #463a-463b	3.50	
o.		Booklet pane, 2 each #463c-463d	3.50	
p.		Booklet pane, 2 each #463e-463f	3.50	
q.		Booklet pane, 2 each #463g-463h	3.50	
r.		Booklet pane, 2 each #463i-463j	3.50	

---

s.	Booklet pane, 2 each #463k-463l	3.50	
	Complete booklet, #463n-463s	21.00	

Complete booklet sold for $12.95.

Christmas
A112

Santa Claus: 45c, In boat. 50c, Hoisted by crane. $1.10, On beach.

2007, Nov. 1   Litho.   *Perf. 14x14½*
464-466	A112	Set of 3	3.75	3.75

CILICIA

sə-'li-sh.ē-.ə

LOCATION — A territory of Turkey, in Southeastern Asia Minor
GOVT. — Former French occupation
AREA — 6,238 sq. mi.
POP. — 383,645
CAPITAL — Adana

British and French forces occupied Cilicia in 1918 and in 1919 its control was transferred to the French. Eventually part of Cilicia was assigned to the French Mandated Territory of Syria but by the Lausanne Treaty of 1923 which fixed the boundary between Syria and Turkey, Cilicia reverted to Turkey.

40 Paras = 1 Piaster

Issued under French Occupation

The overprint on Nos. 2-93 is often found inverted, double, etc.
Numbers in parentheses are those of basic Turkish stamps.

Turkish Stamps of 1913-19 Handstamped

Perf. 11½, 12, 12½, 13½
1919   Unwmk.
On Pictorial Issue of 1913
2	A24	2pa red lil (254)	2.00	1.50
3	A25	4pa dk brn (255)	1.75	1.25
4	A27	6pa dk bl (257)	20.00	10.00
5	A32	1¾pi sl & red brn (262)	3.00	1.75

On Issue of 1915
6	A17	1pi bl (300)	1.50	1.25
7	A21	20pa car rose (318)	1.50	1.25
9	A22	20pa car rose (330)	5.00	3.00

On Commemorative Issue of 1916
9A	A41	5pa green (345)	110.00	70.00
10	A41	20pa ultra (347)	2.50	1.00
11	A41	1pi vio & blk (348)	3.00	1.25
12	A41	5pi yel brn & blk (349)	3.50	1.25

On Issue of 1916-18
13	A44	10pa grn (424)	3.00	1.50
14	A47	50pa ultra (428)	10.00	3.50
15	A51	25pi car, *straw* (434)	3.50	2.00
16	A52	50pi car (437)	3.00	1.50
17	A52	50pi ind (438)	20.00	13.00

On Issue of 1917
18	A53	5pi on 2pa Prus bl (547)	10.00	4.50

On Issue of 1919

19	A47	50pa ultra (555)	15.00	3.75
20	A48	2pi org brn & ind (556)	5.00	2.00
21	A49	5pi pale bl & blk (557)	17.50	4.00

On Newspaper Stamp of 1916

22	A10	5pa on 10pa gray grn (P137)	4.00	1.25

On Semi-Postal Stamps of 1915

22A	A21	20pa car rose (B8)	90.00	55.00
22B	A21	1pi ultra (B9)	1,500.	1,100.
22C	A21	1pi ultra (B13)	1,100.	750.00

On Semi-Postal Stamps of 1916

23	A17	1pi bl (B19)	3.00	1.00
24	A21	20pa car rose (B28)	2.50	1.00
25	A21	1pi ultra (B29)	8.00	5.50

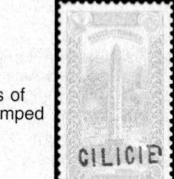

Turkish Stamps of 1913-18 Handstamped

CILICIE

1919

On Pictorial Issue of 1913

31	A24	2pa red lil (254)	2.00	1.00
32	A25	4pa dk brn (255)	3.00	1.75

On Issue of 1915

33	A17	1pi blue (300)	3.00	1.50
34	A22	20pa car rose (330)	3.00	1.50

On Commemorative Issue of 1916

35	A41	20pa ultra (347)	3.00	1.25
36	A41	1pi vio & blk (348)	2.00	1.25

On Issue of 1917

40	A53	5pi on 2pa Prus bl (547)	4.00	1.25

On Newspaper Stamp of 1916

41	A10	5pa on 10pa gray grn (P137)	4.00	1.75

On Semi-Postal Stamp of 1915

41A	A21	20pa car rose (B8)	160.00	110.00

On Semi-Postal Stamps of 1916

42	A17	1pi blue (B19)	4.00	2.00
43	A21	20pa car rose (B28)	3.50	1.25

Turkish Stamps of 1913-19 Handstamped

Cilicie

1919

On Pictorial Issue of 1913

51	A24	2pa red lil (254)	3.00	1.25
52	A25	4pa dk brn (255)	3.00	1.25

On Issue of 1915

53	A17	1pi blue (300)	3.00	1.00
55	A22	5pa ocher (328)	8.00	4.00
56	A22	20pa car rose (330)	3.00	1.50

On Commemorative Issue of 1916

57	A41	20pa ultra (347)	2.00	1.75
58	A41	1pi vio & blk (348)	2.00	1.75
59	A41	5pi yel brn & blk (349)	2.50	2.25

On Issue of 1916

59A	A17	1pi blue (372)	80.00	55.00

On Issue of 1916-18

60	A43	5pa org (421)	8.00	5.00
61	A46	1pi dl vio (426)	4.00	2.00
63	A52	50pi grn, straw (439)	30.00	15.00

On Issue of 1917

64	A53	5pi on 2pa Prus bl (547)	10.00	4.00

On Newspaper Stamp of 1916

65	A10	5pa on 10pa gray grn (P137)	3.00	1.25

On Semi-Postal Stamp of 1915

65A	A21	20pa car rose (B8)	850.00	675.00

On Semi-Postal Stamps of 1916

66	A17	1pi blue (B19)	8.00	2.50
67	A19	20pa car (B26)	9.00	4.00
68	A21	20pa car rose (B28)	125.00	67.50
69	A21	20pa car rose (B31)	7.50	2.50

Turkey No. 424 Handstamped

T.E.O.
Cilicie

1919

71	A44	10pa green	4.00 2.50

"T.E.O." stands for "Territoires Ennemis Occupés."

Turkish Stamps of 1913-19 Overprinted in Black, Red or Blue

T.E.O.
Cilicie

In this setting there are various broken and wrong font letters and the letter "i" is sometimes replaced by a "t."

1919   **On Pictorial Issue of 1913**

75	A30	1pi blue (R) (260)	3.00	.90

On Issue of 1915

76	A21	20pa car rose (318)	5.00	2.25

On Commemorative Issue of 1916

76A	A41	5pa green (345)	150.00	75.00
77	A41	20pa ultra (347)	3.00	1.40
78	A41	1pi vio & blk (348)	3.50	1.00

On Issue of 1916-18

79	A43	5pa org (Bl) (421)	2.00	.60
80	A44	10pa green (424)	2.00	.60
81	A45	20pa dp rose (Bk) (425)	9.00	6.00
82	A45	20pa dp rose (Bl) (425)	2.00	.60
83	A48	2pi org brn & ind (429)	3.00	1.00
83C	A49	5pi pale bl & blk (R) (430)	3.50	1.25
84	A51	25pi car, straw (434)	9.00	5.00
85	A52	50pi grn, straw (439)	105.00	65.00

On Issue of 1917

85A	A53	5pi on 2pa Prus bl (547)	—	
86	A53	5pi on 2pa Prus bl (548)	8.00	5.00

On Newspaper Stamps of 1916-19

87	A10	5pa on 10p gray grn (P137)	3.00	2.00
88	A21	5pa on 2pa ol grn (P173)	1.75	.60

On Semi-Postal Stamps of 1915-17

90	A21	20pa car rose (B28)	3.50	1.75
91	A41	10pa car (B42)	2.00	.65
92	A11	10pa on 20pa vio brn (B38)	2.50	1.00
93	SP1	10pa red vio (B46)	3.00	1.25

It is understood that the newspaper and semi-postal stamps overprinted "Cilicie" were used as ordinary postage stamps.

A1

1920   Blue Surcharge   Perf. 11½

98	A1	70pa on 5pa red	2.50	.60
a.		Double surcharge	30.00	30.00
b.		Triple surcharge	200.00	

99	A1	3½pi on 5pa red	3.50	2.00
a.		Se-tenant with No. 98, horiz. pair		90.00
b.		As "a," inverted surcharge		200.00
c.		As "a," double surcharge	9.00	32.50

Nos. 98-99 exist with surcharge misspelled "OCCUPTTION," "OCCCPATION," "OCCUPITION". Value $9 each.

T.E.O.
20
PARAS

French Offices in Turkey No. 26 Surcharged

1920   Perf. 14x13½

100	A3	20pa on 10c rose red	2.50	1.00
a.		"PARAS" omitted	25.00	25.00
b.		Surcharged on back	22.50	22.50

Three types of "20" exist on No. 100.

O.M.F.
Cilicie
5 PARAS

Stamps of France, 1900-17, Surcharged

1920

101	A16	5pa on 2c vio brn	1.00	.85
102	A22	10pa on 5c green	1.50	1.00
a.		Inverted surcharge	17.50	22.50
103	A22	20pa on 10c red	2.00	1.75
104	A22	1pi on 25c blue	2.75	2.25
105	A20	2pi on 15c gray grn	6.00	5.00
106	A18	5pi on 40c red & gray bl	9.25	8.00
107	A18	10pi on 50c bis brn & lav	10.50	9.50
108	A18	50pi on 1fr cl & ol	125.00	125.00
109	A18	100pi on 5fr dk bl & buff	625.00	625.00
		Nos. 101-109 (9)	783.00	778.35

Nos. 106 to 109 surcharged in four lines. "O.M.F." stands for "Occupation Militaire Francaise."

O.M.F.
Cilicie
SAND. EST
5 PARAS

Stamps of France, 1917, Surcharged

1920

110	A16	5pa on 2c vio brn	6.50
111	A22	10pa on 5c green	6.50
112	A22	20pa on 10c red	5.50
113	A22	1pi on 25c blue	5.50
114	A20	2pi on 15c gray grn	16.00
115	A18	5pi on 40c red & gray bl	55.00
116	A18	20pi on 1fr cl & ol grn	75.00
a.		"O.M.F. Cilicie" omitted	300.00
b.		Double surcharge	240.00
		Nos. 110-116 (7)	

On Nos. 115 and 116 "SAND. EST" is placed vertically. "Sand. Est" is an abbreviation of Sandjak de l'Est (Eastern County). Nos. 110-116 were prepared for use, but never issued.

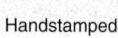

O.M.F.
Cilicie
5 PARAS

Stamps of France, 1900-17, Surcharged

1920

117	A16	5pa on 2c vio brn	1.75	.75
a.		Inverted surcharge	12.50	12.50
b.		Double surcharge	20.00	21.00
c.		"Cililie"	10.00	10.00
d.		Surcharge 5pi (error)	25.00	26.00
119	A22	10pa on 5c green	1.75	.75
a.		Inverted surcharge	12.50	12.50
b.		Surch. 5pa (grn), invtd.	37.50	30.00
c.		Surch. 5pa (error), upright	27.50	26.00
121	A22	20pa on 10c red	1.75	.75
a.		Inverted surcharge	12.50	12.50
b.		Surch. 10pa (error), invtd.	37.50	30.00
c.		Surch. 10pa (error), upright	27.50	26.00
d.		Double surcharge	22.50	21.00
122	A22	1pi on 25c blue	1.25	.75
a.		Double surcharge	47.50	47.50
b.		Inverted surcharge	12.50	12.50

123	A20	2pi on 15c gray grn	1.75	1.00
a.		Double surcharge	17.50	17.50
b.		Inverted surcharge	12.50	12.50
124	A18	5pi on 40c red & gray bl	2.50	1.50
a.		Double surcharge	37.50	37.50
b.		Inverted surcharge	12.50	12.50
c.		"PIASRTES"	27.50	27.50
125	A18	10pi on 50c bis brn & lavender	3.00	2.00
a.		"PIASRTES"	27.50	27.50
b.		Double surcharge	37.50	37.50
c.		Inverted surcharge	24.00	22.50
126	A18	50pi on 1fr claret & ol grn	7.50	3.50
a.		"PIASRTES"	37.50	37.50
b.		Inverted surcharge	32.50	26.00
127	A18	100pi on 5fr dk bl & buff	17.50	17.50
a.		"PIASRTES"	72.50	72.50
b.		Inverted surcharge	72.50	70.00
		Nos. 117-127 (9)	38.75	28.55

This surcharge has "O.M.F." in thicker letters than the preceding issues.

There were two printings of this surcharge which may be distinguished by the space of 1 or 2mm between "Cilicie" and the numeral. For overprints see Nos. C1-C2.

AIR POST STAMPS

POSTE PAR AVION

Nos. 123 and 124 Handstamped

Perf. 14x13½

1920, July 15   Unwmk.

C1	A20	2pi on 15c gray grn	6,000.
C2	A18	5pi on 40c red & gray bl	6,000.
a.		"PIASRTES"	

A very limited number of Nos. C1 and C2 were used on two air mail flights between Adana and Aleppo. At a later date impressions from a new handstamp were struck "to oblige" on stamps of the regular issue of 1920 (Nos. 123, 124, 125 and 126) that were in stock at the Adana Post Office. Counterfeits exist.

POSTAGE DUE STAMPS

Turkish Postage Due Stamps of 1914 Handstamped

Handstamped

CILICIE

1919   Unwmk.   Perf. 12

J1	D1	5pa claret	7.00	1.75
J2	D2	20pa red	7.00	1.75
J3	D3	1pi dark blue	9.00	3.50
J4	D4	2pi slate	9.00	3.50
		Nos. J1-J4 (4)	32.00	10.50

Handstamped

CILICIE

J5	D1	5pa claret	6.50	1.75
J6	D2	20pa red	6.50	1.75
J7	D3	1pi dark blue	9.50	4.50
J8	D4	2pi slate	9.50	4.50
		Nos. J5-J8 (4)	32.00	12.50

Handstamped

J9	D1	5pa claret	6.00	1.75
J10	D2	20pa red	6.00	1.75
J11	D3	1pi dark blue	11.00	3.50
J12	D4	2pi slate	11.00	4.50
		Nos. J9-J12 (4)	34.00	11.50

Postage Due Stamps of France Surcharged

1921

J13	D2	1pi on 10c choc	7.25	4.00
J14	D2	2pi on 20c olive grn	7.25	4.00
J15	D2	3pi on 30c red	9.00	4.50
J16	D2	4pi on 50c vio brn	9.00	4.50
		Nos. J13-J16 (4)	32.50	17.00

COCHIN CHINA

'kō-chən 'chī-nə

LOCATION — The southernmost state of French Indo-China in the Cambodian Peninsula.
GOVT. — French Colony
AREA — 26,476 sq. mi.
POP. — 4,615,968
CAPITAL — Saigon

100 Centimes = 1 Franc

Values for unused stamps are for examples without gum, as most stamps were issued in that condition.

Surcharged in Black on Stamps of French Colonies:

a   b

c

1886-87   Unwmk.   Perf. 14x13½

1	A9(a)	5c on 25c yel, straw	160.00	120.00
2	A9(b)	5c on 2c brn, buff	24.00	24.00
3	A9(b)	5c on 25c yel, straw	26.00	26.00
4	A9(c)	5c on 25c blk, rose ('87)	40.00	40.00
a.		Dbl. surch., one of type b	3,100.	1,800.
b.		Triple surch., two of type b	—	—
c.		Inverted surcharge	—	—
		Nos. 1-4 (4)	250.00	210.00

1888

5	A9	15c on half of 30c brn, bis	57.50

No. 5 was prepared but not issued. The so-called Postage Due stamps were never issued.

Stamps of Cochin China were superseded by those of Indo-China in 1892.

COCOS ISLANDS

'kō-kəs 'ī-lənds

(Keeling Islands)

LOCATION — Indian Ocean, 1,330 miles northwest of Australia, 580 miles southwest of Java
GOVT. — A territory of Australia
AREA — 6 sq. mi.
POP. — 670 (1994)

Of 27 small coral islands making up two atolls, two islands are inhabited. Cocos Islands stamps are also valid within Australia.

12 Pence = 1 Shilling
100 Cents = 1 Dollar (1969)

Catalogue values for all unused stamps in this country are for Never Hinged items.

Copra Industry — A1

Super Constellation A2

Map of Islands — A3

Designs: 1sh, Coco palms. 2sh, Sailboat (dukong). 2sh3p, Fairy tern.

Perf. 14½

1963, June 11   Unwmk.   Engr.

1	A1	3p dk red brown	1.40	1.25
2	A2	5p vio blue	1.75	1.00
3	A3	8p red	3.75	1.75
4	A1	1sh green	3.75	1.00
5	A3	2sh dull purple	7.00	3.75
6	A2	2sh3p green	25.00	5.25
		Nos. 1-6 (6)	42.65	14.00
		Set, hinged	18.00	

"Simpson and His Donkey" by Wallace Anderson — A3a

1965, Apr. 14   Photo.   Perf. 13½x13

7	A3a	5p brt grn, sepia & blk	1.00	.85

ANZAC issue. See note after Australia No. 387.

Turbo Lajonkairii — A4   Blenny — A5

Designs: 2c, Tridacna crocea (shell). 3c, Tridacna derasa (shell). 5c, Porites cocosensis (coral). 6c, Flyingfish. 10c, Banded rail (bird). 15c, Java sparrow. 20c, Red-tailed tropic bird. 30c, Sooty tern. 50c, Eastern reef heron. $1, Great frigate bird.

Perf. 13½

1969, July 9   Unwmk.   Photo.

Size: 21½x27mm, 26½x22mm

8	A4	1c multicolored	.25	.50
9	A4	2c multicolored	.90	.65
10	A5	3c multicolored	.35	.20
11	A5	4c multicolored	.25	.40
12	A5	5c multicolored	.30	.25
13	A5	6c multicolored	.75	.70
14	A5	10c multicolored	1.10	.55
15	A5	15c multicolored	1.10	.55
16	A5	20c multicolored	1.10	.40
17	A5	30c multicolored	1.10	.45
18	A5	50c multicolored	1.10	.45

Size: 21½x34mm

19	A4	$1 multicolored	3.00	1.40
		Nos. 8-19 (12)	11.30	6.70

"Dragon" — A6

"Juno" — A7

Perf. 13½x13, 13x13½

1976, Mar. 29   Photo.

20	A6	1c shown	.40	.40
21	A7	2c shown	.40	.40
22	A7	5c "Beagle"	.40	.40
23	A7	10c "Sydney"	.45	.45
24	A7	15c "Emden"	.85	.85
25	A7	20c "Ayesha"	.85	.85
26	A6	25c "Islander"	.85	.85
27	A6	30c "Cheshire"	.85	.85
28	A7	35c "Jukung"	.85	.85
29	A7	40c "Scotia"	.85	.85
30	A6	50c "Orontes"	.85	.85
31	A6	$1 Royal Yacht "Goth-ic"	1.50	1.50
		Nos. 20-31 (12)	9.10	9.10

Historic ships.

Flag, Southern Cross, Islands' Map — A8

Council Emblem, Sailboat A9

1979, Sept. 3   Litho.   Perf. 15½

32	A8	20c multicolored	.35	.30
33	A9	50c multicolored	.55	.70

Inauguration of Cocos Islands' postal service (20c), and establishment of Cocos Islands Council (50c).

Forcipiger Flavissimus A10

Fish: 2c, Chaetodon ornatissimus. 5c, Anthias. 10c, Meyer's coralfish. 15c, Halichoeres. 20c, Amphiprion clarkii. 22c, Balistapus undulatus. 25c, Maori wrasse. 28c, Macropharyngodon meleagris. 30c, Chaetodon madagascariensis. 35c, Centropyge colini. 40c, Bodianus axillaris. 50c, Corisgaimardi. 55c, Spotted wrasse. 60c,

---

Epinepnelus tauvina. $1, Paracanthurus hepatus. $2, Striped butterflyfish.

1979-80   Litho.   Perf. 15½

34	A10	1c multicolored	.20	.90
35	A10	2c multicolored	.20	.30
36	A10	5c multicolored	.40	.95
37	A10	10c multi ('80)	.20	.90
38	A10	15c multicolored	.35	.30
39	A10	20c multicolored	.45	.30
40	A10	22c multi ('80)	.40	.30
41	A10	25c multi ('80)	.45	.90
42	A10	28c multi ('80)	.40	.30
43	A10	30c multicolored	.55	.40
44	A10	35c multi ('80)	.65	1.40
45	A10	40c multicolored	.70	.50
46	A10	50c multicolored	.95	.70
47	A10	55c multi ('80)	.85	1.10
48	A10	60c multi ('80)	.75	.70
49	A10	$1 multicolored	1.10	2.75
50	A10	$2 multi ('80)	2.25	3.00
		Nos. 34-50 (17)	10.85	15.70

Sailboats in Lagoon A11

Christmas: 25c, Yachts and seagulls, vert.

1979, Oct. 22   Litho.   Perf. 15½

51	A11	25c multicolored	.35	.25
52	A11	55c multicolored	.55	.65

Star of Bethlehem, Map of Cocos Islands A12

Christmas (Map of Cocos Islands and): 28c, Three kings. 60c, Nativity.

1980, Oct. 22   Litho.   Perf. 13½x13

53	A12	15c multicolored	.20	.20
54	A12	28c multicolored	.25	.25
55	A12	60c multicolored	.80	.80
		Nos. 53-55 (3)	1.25	1.25

Flag and Arms of Great Britain — A13

Australian Territory Status, 25th Anniv. (British Flag and Arms of Past Administrators): No. 57, Ceylon, 1878, 1942-1946. No. 58, Straits Settlements, 1886. No. 59, Singapore, 1946. No. 60, Australia (flag), 1955.

1980, Nov. 24   Litho.   Perf. 13½x13

56	A13	22c multicolored	.30	.30
57	A13	22c multicolored	.30	.30
58	A13	22c multicolored	.30	.30
59	A13	22c multicolored	.30	.30
60	A13	22c multicolored	.30	.30
a.		Strip of 5, Nos. 56-60	1.75	1.75

Eye of the Wind, Map of Cocos Islands — A14

1980, Dec. 18   Perf. 13x13½, 13½x13

61	A14	22c shown	.45	.45
62	A14	28c Expedition routes, horiz.	.45	.45
63	A14	35c Francis Drake, Golden Hinde	.45	.45
64	A14	60c Prince Charles, Eye of the Wind	.75	.75
		Nos. 61-64 (4)	2.10	2.10

Operation Drake circumnavigation.

Livestock in
Quarantine
A15

1981, May 12　Litho.　Perf. 13½x13
65　A15　22c　Aerial view of sta-
　　　　tion　　　　　　.35　.35
66　A15　45c　shown　　　　.50　.50
67　A15　60c　Livestock, diff.　.85　.85
　　　Nos. 65-67 (3)　　　1.70　1.70

West Island Quarantine Station opening.

Catalina
Guba II
A16

Inauguration of Air Service to Indian Ocean:
No. 69, Avro Lancastrian. No. 70, Douglas
DC4 Skymaster, Lockheed Constellation. No.
71, Lockheed Electra. No. 72, Boeing 727.

1981, June 23　Litho.　Perf. 13½x13
68　A16　22c　multicolored　　.40　.40
69　A16　22c　multicolored　　.40　.40
70　A16　22c　multicolored　　.40　.40
71　A16　22c　multicolored　　.40　.40
72　A16　22c　multicolored　　.40　.40
　　a.　Strip of 5, #68-72　2.25　2.25

Prince
Charles and
Lady
Diana — A17

1981, July 29　Litho.　Perf. 13½x13
73　A17　24c　multicolored　　.35　.35
74　A17　60c　multicolored　　.90　.90

Royal Wedding.

Angels We
Have Heard
on
High — A18

Christmas: Carols.

1981, Oct. 22　Photo.　Perf. 13½x13
75　A18　18c　shown　　　　.35　.35
76　A18　30c　Shepherds Why this
　　　　Jubilee　　　　.50　.50
77　A18　60c　Come to Bethlehem
　　　　and See Him　　.70　.70
　　　Nos. 75-77 (3)　　1.55　1.55

Sesquicentennial of Charles Darwin's
Visit — A19

1981, Dec. 28　Litho.　Perf. 13½x13
78　A19　24c　Coral　　　　.35　.35
79　A19　45c　Darwin, coral　.50　.50
80　A19　60c　Beagle, coral　.75　.75
　　　Nos. 78-80 (3)　　1.60　1.60

Souvenir Sheet
81　　Sheet of 2　　　1.25　1.25
　　a.　A19　24c Atoll　　.60　.60
　　b.　A19　24c Atoll, diff.　.60　.60

125th Anniv.
of Annexation
to the British
Dominions
A20

1982, Mar. 31　Litho.　Perf. 13½x14
82　A20　24c　Queen Victoria　.40　.40
83　A20　45c　British flag　　.75　.75
84　A20　60c　Capt. Fremantle　.85　.85
　　　Nos. 82-84 (3)　　2.00　2.00

Scouting
Year — A21

Perf. 13½x14, 14x13½
1982, July 21　　　　　Litho.
85　A21　27c　Baden-Powell　.55　.55
86　A21　75c　Emblem, map, vert.　1.10　1.10

Macroglossum Corythus — A22

1982, Sept. 6
87　A22　1c　Presic villida,
　　　　vert.　　　　1.25　.70
88　A22　2c　Cephonodes
　　　　picus　　　　.45　.45
89　A22　5c　shown　　1.90　.80
90　A22　10c　Chasmina
　　　　candida, vert.　.45　.45
91　A22　20c　Nagia linteola　.45　.55
92　A22　25c　Eublemma rivula,
　　　　vert.　　　　.45　.65
93　A22　30c　Eurrhyparodes
　　　　tricoloralis, vert.　.45　.55
94　A22　35c　Hippotion
　　　　boerhaviae　2.00　.85
95　A22　40c　Euploea core
　　　　corinna, vert.　.45　.70
96　A22　45c　Psara hipponalis　.60　.70
97　A22　50c　Danaus chrysip-
　　　　pus　　　　.70　1.25
98　A22　55c　Hypolimas misip-
　　　　pus, vert.　.70　.80
99　A22　60c　Spodoptera litura,
　　　　vert.　　　.75　1.75
100　A22　$1　Achaea janata,
　　　　vert.　　　3.50　3.25
101　A22　$2　Hippotion velox　2.50　3.25
102　A22　$3　Utetheisa pulchel-
　　　　loides　　3.50　3.25
　　　Nos. 87-102 (16)　20.10　19.95

Christmas
A23

1982, Oct. 25　　　　Perf. 13x13½
104　A23　21c　Holy Family　.30　.20
105　A23　35c　Angel　　.45　.30
106　A23　75c　Flight into Egypt　1.25　1.25
　　　Nos. 104-106 (3)　2.00　1.75

Christmas
A24

Cocos-Malay
Culture
A25

The Birth of Christ: a, God Will Look After
Us; b, Our Baby King Jesus; c, Your Saviour is
Born; d, Wise Men Followed the Star; e, And
Worship the Lord.

1983, Oct. 31　Litho.　Perf. 14x13½
107　　Strip of 5　　1.75　1.75
　　a.-e.　A24 24c any single　.30　.30

1984, Jan. 27　Litho.　Perf. 14x13½
Festive Occasions.
108　A25　45c　Hari Raya　.65　.45
109　A25　75c　Melenggok dance　1.00　.65
110　A25　85c　Wedding　1.25　.75
　　　Nos. 108-110 (3)　2.90　1.85

75th Anniv.
of Barrel Mail
(1909-1955)
A26

Designs: 35c, Mail distribution, Direction
Isld. 55c, Jukongs retrieving barrels from
ocean liner. 70c, Morea receiving outgoing
barrel mail, 1909. $1, Barrel mail recovery.

1984, Apr. 20　Litho.　Perf. 13½x14
111　A26　35c　multicolored　.60　.60
112　A26　55c　multicolored　1.00　1.00
113　A26　70c　multicolored　1.10　1.10
　　　Nos. 111-113 (3)　2.70　2.70

Souvenir Sheet
114　A26　$1　multicolored　2.50　2.50

375th Anniv. of
Islands'
Discovery — A27

1984, July 10　Litho.　Perf. 14x13½
115　A27　30c　Capt. William
　　　　Keeling　.75　.50
116　A27　65c　The Hector　1.50　1.10
117　A27　95c　Astrolabe　1.90　1.50
118　A27　$1.10　Map, 1666　2.10　1.75
　　　Nos. 115-118 (4)　6.25　4.85

AUSIPEX
'84 — A28

45c, Malay Settlement, Home Island. 55c,
West Island Air Strip, settlement. $2, Jukong
ships racing, Melbourne Exhibition Center.

1984, Sept. 21　Litho.　Perf. 13½
119　A28　45c　multicolored　.70　.50
120　A28　55c　multicolored　.80　.65

Souvenir Sheet
121　A28　$2　multicolored　3.25　3.25

Christmas
A29

1984, Oct. 31　Litho.　Perf. 13½
122　A29　24c　Fish　.45　.45
123　A29　35c　Butterfly　.70　.70
124　A29　55c　Bird　1.10　1.10
　　　Nos. 122-124 (3)　2.25　2.25

Souvenir Sheet

Act of Self-Determination — A30

Integration with Australia: a, Australians welcoming Cocos islanders. b, Australian flag
over the islands.

1984, Nov. 30　Litho.　Perf. 13½x14
125　　Sheet of 2　3.00　3.00
　　a.-b.　A30 30c any single　1.25　1.25

Crafts — A31

1985, Jan. 30　　　　Perf. 14x13½
126　A31　30c　Boat building　.60　.30
127　A31　45c　Blacksmith　.90　.45
128　A31　55c　Woodcarving　1.25　.75
　　　Nos. 126-128 (3)　2.75　1.50

Cable-laying
Ships — A32

1985, Apr. 24　　　　Perf. 13½x14
129　A32　33c　Scotia　1.60　.90
130　A32　65c　Anglia　2.50　1.50
131　A32　80c　Patrol　2.50　2.50
　　　Nos. 129-131 (3)　6.60　4.90

Birds
A33

1985, July 17　　　　Perf. 13½
132　A33　33c　Redfooted booby,
　　　　vert.　2.75　2.75
133　A33　60c　Nankeen night
　　　　heron　3.25　3.25
134　A33　$1　Buff-banded rail　3.50　3.50
　　a.　"Block" of 3, #132-134　11.00　11.00

Nos. 132-134 printed in a continuous design.

Seashells
A34

1985-86　Litho.　Perf. 13½x14
135　A34　1c　Trochus macu-
　　　　latus　.70　1.00
136　A34　2c　Smaragdia rangi-
　　　　ana　.70　1.00
137　A34　3c　Chama　.70　1.00
138　A34　4c　Cypraea moneta　1.25　1.00
139　A34　5c　Drupa morum　.70　1.00
140　A34　10c　Conus miles　.80　2.10
141　A34　15c　Terebra maculata　2.40　1.75
142　A34　20c　Fragum fragum　2.40　2.00
143　A34　30c　Turbo lajonkairii　2.40　2.00
144　A34　33c　Mitra fissurata　2.50　2.00
145　A34　40c　Lambis lambis　2.50　2.00
146　A34　50c　Tridacna
　　　　squamosa　2.50　2.75
147　A34　60c　Cypraea histrio　2.50　3.00
148　A34　$1　Phillidia varicosa　3.75　4.00
149　A34　$2　Halgerda tessel-
　　　　lata　4.00　5.00
150　A34　$3　Harminoea
　　　　cymbalum　5.00　6.00
　　　Nos. 135-150 (16)　34.80　37.60

Issue dates: 1c, 5c, 33c, $1, Sept. 18. 2c,
3c, 10c, $3, Jan. 29, 1986. 15c-30c, 40c, Apr.
30, 1986. 4c, 50c, 60c, $2, July 30, 1986.
For surcharges see #225, 228-229, 231-
233.

Souvenir Sheet

Christmas
A35

a, Star LR. b, Star LL. c, Star UR. d, Star
UL.

1985, Oct. 30　　　　Perf. 13½x14
151　　Sheet of 4　3.00　3.00
　　a.-d.　A35 27c any single　.70　.70

Darwin's Visit to the Islands — A36

1986, Apr. 1   Litho.   Perf. 14x13½
152 A36 33c Charles Darwin   1.00 .70
153 A36 60c Map of voyage   1.75 1.90
154 A36 $1 HMS Beagle   2.50 3.00
   Nos. 152-154 (3)   5.25 5.60

Christmas A37

1986, Oct. 20   Litho.   Perf. 13½x14
155 A37 30c Coconut palm, holly   .75   .75
156 A37 90c Shell, ornament   2.75 2.75
157 A37 $1 Tropical fish, bell   2.75 2.75
   Nos. 155-157 (3)   6.25 6.25

Sailboats A38

a, Jukong. b, Ocean racers. c, Sarimanok. d, Ayesha. #158 has a continuous design.

1987, Jan. 28
158   Strip of 4   6.00 6.00
   a.-d. A38 36c any single   1.10 1.10

Island Views — A39

1987, Apr. 8
159 A39 70c Direction Is.   1.50 1.40
160 A39 90c West Is.   1.75 2.00
161 A39 $1 Golf course, Cocos   2.50 2.75
   Nos. 159-161 (3)   5.75 6.15

Communications — A40

1987, July 29   Litho.   Perf. 13½x14
162 A40 70c Radio   1.40 1.40
163 A40 75c Air service   1.50 1.50
164 A40 90c Satellite   1.75 1.75
165 A40 $1 Airmail   2.00 2.00
   Nos. 162-165 (4)   6.65 6.65

Industries A41

1987, Sept. 16
166 A41 45c Batik printing   1.40 1.40
167 A41 65c Boat building   1.90 1.90
168 A41 75c Copra production   2.25 2.25
   Nos. 166-168 (3)   5.55 5.55

Industrial activities of the Cocos Malay people.

Christmas — A42

1987, Oct. 28   Perf. 14x13½
169 A42 30c Peace on Earth   .55   .55
170 A42 90c Unity   1.50 1.50
171 A42 $1 Goodwill Towards
           All   2.00 2.00
   Nos. 169-171 (3)   4.05 4.05

Australia Bicentennial A43

Arrival of the First Fleet, Sydney Cove, Jan. 1788: a, Five aboriginals on shore. b, Four aboriginals on shore, one in canoe. c, Ships entering bay, kangaroos. d, Europeans land, white cranes. e, Flag raising.

1988, Jan. 26   Litho.   Perf. 13
172   Strip of 5   9.00 9.00
   a.-e. A43 37c any single   1.10 1.10

No. 172 has a continuous design. See Christmas Is. No. 213.

Life Cycle of the Coconut — A44

1988, Apr. 13   Litho.   Perf. 14x13½
173 A44 37c Flower   .75   .70
174 A44 65c Small nut stage   1.40 1.40
175 A44 90c Mature nuts   1.60 1.75
176 A44 $1 Seedlings   2.00 2.00
   a.   Souvenir sheet of 4, #173-176   7.00 7.00
   Nos. 173-176 (4)   5.75 5.85

For surcharge see No. O1.

Cocos Postage Stamps, 25th Anniv. A45

Litho. & Engr.
1988, June 15   Perf. 15x14
177 A45 37c No. 1   1.25   .90
178 A45 55c No. 4   1.60 1.25
179 A45 65c No. 2   1.75 1.75
180 A45 70c No. 3   1.90 1.75
181 A45 90c No. 5   2.25 2.75
182 A45 $1 No. 6   2.40 2.75
   Nos. 177-182 (6)   11.15 11.15

For overprint and surcharge see #216, 236.

Flowering Plants — A46

1988-89   Litho.   Perf. 14x13½
183 A46 1c Pisonia grandis   .70   .90
184 A46 2c Cocos nucifera   .70   .90
185 A46 5c Morinda citrifolia   1.40 1.00
186 A46 10c Cordia sub-
            cordata   .95   1.00
189 A46 30c Argusia argentea   1.40 1.50
190 A46 37c Calophyllum in-
            ophyllum   2.00 1.25
191 A46 40c Barringtonia
            asiatica   1.40 1.50
192 A46 50c Caesalpinia
            bonduc   1.75 3.25
194 A46 90c Terminalia catap-
            pa   2.40 4.75
195 A46 $1 Pemphis acidula   2.40 2.75
197 A46 $2 Scaevola sericea   3.00 3.00
198 A46 $3 Hibiscus tiliaceus   4.75 4.25
   Nos. 183-198 (12)   22.85 26.05

Issued: 1c, 5c, 37c, $3, 7/29; 2c, 10c, 30c, $2, 1/18/89; 40c, 50c, 90c, $1, 4/19/89.
For self-adhesive sheet of 3 see No. 217.

Souvenir Sheet
1988, July 30
199 A46 $3 like No. 198   8.50 8.50

SYDPEX '88.

Christmas A47

1988, Oct. 12   Litho.   Perf. 13½x14
200 A47 32c multicolored   1.00 1.00
201 A47 90c multicolored   2.25 2.25
202 A47 $1 multicolored   2.75 2.75
   Nos. 200-202 (3)   6.00 6.00

1st Aerial Survey of the Indian Ocean Air Route, 50th Anniv.— A48

40c, P.G. Taylor, pilot. 70c, Guba II seaplane and crew. $1, Guba II landing off Direction Island. $1.10, Unissued 5sh stamp of Australia, 1939.

1989, July 19   Litho.   Perf. 14x13½
203 A48 40c multicolored   1.00 1.00
204 A48 70c multicolored   1.60 1.60
205 A48 $1 multicolored   2.25 2.25
206 A48 $1.10 multicolored   2.50 2.50
   Nos. 203-206 (4)   7.35 7.35

Jukong, Traditional Sailing Vessel of the Cocos Malay People — A49

1989, Oct. 18   Litho.   Perf. 14x13½
207 A49 35c multicolored   .95   .90
208 A49 80c multicolored   2.25 2.25
209 A49 $1.10 multicolored   3.00 3.00
   Nos. 207-209 (3)   6.20 6.15

Christmas.

Naval Engagement of the HMAS Sydney and the German Raider SMS Emden, 75th Anniv.— A50

Designs: 40c, HMAS Sydney. 70c, SMS Emden. $1, Steam launch belonging to the Emden. $1.10, HMAS Sydney and naval crest.

1989, Nov. 9   Litho.   Perf. 13½x14
210   Strip of 4 + label   7.25 7.50
   a.   A50 40c multicolored   .65   .65
   b.   A50 70c multicolored   1.25 1.25
   c.   A50 $1 multicolored   1.75 1.75
   d.   A50 $1.10 multicolored   1.90 1.90
   e.   Souvenir sheet of 4, #210a-210d 9.00 9.00

Crabs — A52

1990, May 31   Litho.   Perf. 14½
212 A52 45c Xanthid   1.25 1.25
213 A52 75c Ghost   2.25 2.25
214 A52 $1 Red-backed mud
           crab   2.50 2.50
215 A52 $1.30 Coconut, vert.   3.00 3.00
   Nos. 212-215 (4)   9.00 9.00

No. 180 Overprinted in Red

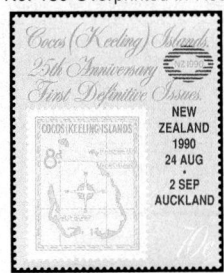

Litho. & Engr.
1990, Aug. 24   Perf. 15x14
216 A45 70c gray, black & red   7.50 7.50

Flowering Plants Type of 1988
1990, Aug. 24   Photo.   Rouletted 9½
Self-Adhesive
217   Sheet of 3   10.50 10.50
   a.   A46 10c like No. 186   .40   .40
   b.   A46 90c like No. 194   2.75 2.75
   c.   A46 $2 like No. 197   6.25 6.25

World Stamp Exhibition, New Zealand 1990. Nos. 217a-217c inscribed 1990.

Explorers and Their Ships A54

45c, Capt. Keeling, Hector, 1609. 75c, Capt. Fitzroy, Beagle, 1836. $1, Capt. Belcher, Samarang, 1846. $1.30, Capt. Fremantle, Juno, 1857.

1990, Aug. 24   Litho.   Perf. 14½
218 A54 45c violet brown   1.75 1.60
219 A54 75c pale bl & vio
            brn   3.00 3.50
220 A54 $1 pale yel & vio
            brn   3.50 4.50
221 A54 $1.30 buff & vio brn   5.50 6.75
   a.   Souv. sheet of 4, #218-221,
        imperf.   12.00 12.00
   Nos. 218-221 (4)   13.75 16.35

Christmas — A55

1990, Dec. 12   Litho.   Rouletted 5
222 A55 40c Star at left   1.00 1.00
   a.   Bklt. pane of 10 + 2 labels 15.00
223 A55 70c Star in center   2.00 2.00
   a.   Bklt. pane, 4 #222, 2 #223 + 6
        labels   20.00
224 A55 $1.30 Star at right   3.50 3.50
   Nos. 222-224 (3)   6.50 6.50

Nos. 140, 141, 143, 146-147, 179
Surcharged
in Blue or Black

Litho., Litho. & Engr.
1990-91   **Perf. 13½x14, 15x14**

225	A34	(1c) on 30c #143	14.00	5.00
228	A34	(43c) on 10c #140	24.00	27.50
229	A34	(43c) on 10c #140	17.50	9.75
231	A34	70c on 60c #147		
		(bk)	5.50	5.00
232	A34	80c on 50c #146		
		(bk)	5.50	5.00
233	A34	$1.20 on 15c #141		
		(bk)	5.50	5.00
236	A45	$5 on 65c #179	52.50	35.00
		Nos. 225-236 (7)	124.50	92.25

Obliterator consists of diagonal lines on No. 228, crosshatched lines on No. 229.

Additional text in surcharges reads: "MAINLAND / POSTAGE PAID" (Nos. 228-229), "ZONE 1 / POSTAGE PAID" (No. 231), "ZONE 2 / POSTAGE PAID" (No. 232), "ZONE 5 / POSTAGE PAID" (No. 233).

Issued: #236, 11/11; #228, 12/18; #225, 229, 231-233, 1/1991.

Beaded Sea Star — A56

1991, Feb. 28   Litho.   Perf. 14½

237	A56	45c shown	1.10	1.10
238	A56	75c Feather star	1.75	1.75
239	A56	$1 Slate pencil urchin	2.40	2.40
240	A56	$1.30 Globose sea urchin	3.25	3.25
		Nos. 237-240 (4)	8.50	8.50

Hari Raya — A57

1991, Mar.   Litho.   Perf. 14½

241	A57	45c multicolored	1.25	1.25
242	A57	75c multi, diff.	2.00	2.00
243	A57	$1.30 multi, diff.	3.50	3.50
		Nos. 241-243 (3)	6.75	6.75

Christmas — A58

1991, Nov. 6   Litho.   Perf. 15½

244	A58	38c Child praying	.80	.80
245	A58	43c Child sleeping	1.00	1.00
246	A58	$1 Child singing	2.25	2.25
247	A58	$1.20 Child in wonder	2.75	2.75
		Nos. 244-247 (4)	6.80	6.80

Souvenir Sheet

248		Sheet of 4	8.00	8.00
a.	A58	38c Two children	.75	.75
b.	A58	43c Three girls	.95	.95
c.	A58	$1 Boy, two girls	2.25	2.25
d.	A58	$1.20 Boy, girl	2.75	2.75

Nos. 248a-248d are in a continuous design depicting a children's choir.

Crustaceans A59

Designs: 5c, Lybia tessellata. 10c, Pilodius areolatus. 20c, Trizopagurus strigatus. 30c, Lophozozymus pulchellus. 40c, Thalamitoides quadridens. 45c, Calcinus elegans, vert. 50c, Clibarius humilis. 60c, Trapezia rufopunctata, vert. 80c, Pylopaguropsis magnimanus, vert. $1, Trapezia ferruginea, vert. $2, Trapezia guttata, vert. $3, Trapezia cymodoce, vert.

1992   Litho.   Perf. 14½

249	A59	5c multicolored	1.25	1.60
250	A59	10c multicolored	1.25	1.60
251	A59	20c multicolored	1.25	1.60
252	A59	30c multicolored	1.40	2.75
253	A59	40c multicolored	1.50	2.75
254	A59	45c multicolored	1.60	2.75
255	A59	50c multicolored	1.60	3.75
256	A59	60c multicolored	1.90	3.75
257	A59	80c multicolored	2.25	3.75
258	A59	$1 multicolored	3.00	3.75
259	A59	$2 multicolored	6.00	6.00
260	A59	$3 multicolored	9.25	9.25
		Nos. 249-260 (12)	32.25	43.30

Issued: 10c, 30c, 50c, 80c, $1, $2, 8/11; others, 2/28.

Discovery of America, 500th Anniv. — A60

1992, May 22   Litho.   Perf. 14½

261	A60	$1.05 multicolored	3.50	3.50

Buff-banded Rail — A61

No. 262: a, 10c, Bird looking for food. b, 15c, Adult with chick. c, 30c, Two adults eating. d, 45c, Adult with eggs, hatchling.

No. 263: a, 45c, Two birds, one in water. b, 85c, Chick in nest. c, $1.20, Bird's head.

1992, June 18   Litho.   Perf. 14

262	A61	Strip of 4, #a.-d.	6.00	6.00

Souvenir Sheet

263	A61	Sheet of 3, #a.-c.	7.50	7.50

World Wildlife Fund (#262).

World War II, 50th Anniv. — A62

45c, Royal Air Force Spitfire fighters. 85c, Japanese bombing of Kampong. $1.20, Sunderland reconnaissance flying boat.

1992, Oct. 13   Litho.   Perf. 14½

264	A62	45c multicolored	1.50	1.50
265	A62	85c multicolored	2.75	2.75
266	A62	$1.20 multicolored	3.75	3.75
		Nos. 264-266 (3)	8.00	8.00

Festive Season — A63   Corals — A64

40c, Storm waves on reef edge. 80c, Direction Island. $1, Moorish idols among coral.

1992, Nov. 10   Litho.   Perf. 15x14½

267	A63	40c multicolored	1.25	1.25
268	A63	80c multicolored	2.25	2.25
269	A63	$1 multicolored	3.00	3.00
		Nos. 267-269 (3)	6.50	6.50

1993, Jan. 28   Litho.   Perf. 14½

270	A64	45c Lobophyllia hemprichii	.90	.90
271	A64	85c Pocillopora eydouxi	1.60	1.60
272	A64	$1.05 Fungia scutaria	2.25	2.25
273	A64	$1.20 Sarcophyton sp.	2.75	2.75
		Nos. 270-273 (4)	7.50	7.50

A65   A66

Island Currency Tokens: 45c, 5r token, 1968. 85c, Island scene token, 1968. $1.05, 150r token, 1977. $1.20, Token, 1910.

1993, Mar. 30   Litho.   Perf. 15x14½

274	A65	45c multicolored	.90	.90
275	A65	85c multicolored	1.60	1.60
276	A65	$1.05 multicolored	2.25	2.25
277	A65	$1.20 multicolored	2.75	2.75
		Nos. 274-277 (4)	7.50	7.50

1993, June 1   Litho.   Perf. 14½

Education: 5c, Primary classroom activities. 45c, Secondary studies. 85c, Crafts, traditional basket weaving. $1.05, Office staff, higher education. $1.20, Marine officers, coxswain's training.

278	A66	5c multicolored	.75	.75
279	A66	45c multicolored	1.25	1.25
280	A66	85c multicolored	2.10	2.10
281	A66	$1.05 multicolored	2.40	2.40
282	A66	$1.20 multicolored	2.75	2.75
		Nos. 278-282 (5)	9.25	9.25

Air-Sea Rescue Service A67

45c, Men in lifeboat. 85c, Westwind Seascan. $1.05, R.J. Hawke inter-island ferry.

1993, Aug. 17   Litho.   Perf. 14½

283	A67	45c multicolored	1.25	1.25
284	A67	85c multicolored	2.00	2.00
285	A67	$1.05 multicolored	2.75	2.75
a.		Souvenir sheet of 3, #283-285	8.50	8.50
		Nos. 283-285 (3)	6.00	6.00

A limited printing exists of No. 285a with Taipei '95 overprint. Value, $60.

Festive Season — A68

1993, Oct. 24   Litho.   Perf. 14½

286	A68	40c pink & multi	1.00	1.00
287	A68	80c blue & multi	2.00	2.00
288	A68	$1 yellow & multi	3.00	3.00
		Nos. 286-288 (3)	6.00	6.00

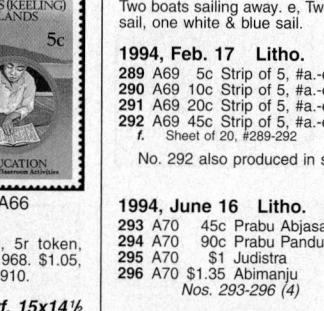

Map and Reef Life — A69   Puppets — A70

Reef triggerfish — No. 289: a, Two fish, purple coral (b). b, Three fish. c, Two fish. d, Two fish, red coral (e). e, One fish.

Green turtles — No. 290: a, Eggs, turtles. b, Two turtles (c). c, Group of baby turtles. d, Baby turtle. e, Fish, large turtle.

Pyramid butterflyfish — No. 291: a, Three fish. b, Two small, one large fish, coral (c). c, One small, one large fish, coral (d). d, Three fish, coral (e). e, Coral, one fish.

Junkongs sailing craft — No. 292: a, One boat, red sail. b, Two boats, one blue & white sail, one red sail. c, One boat, yellow sail. d, Two boats sailing away. e, Two boats, one red sail, one white & blue sail.

1994, Feb. 17   Litho.   Perf. 14½x14

289	A69	5c Strip of 5, #a.-e.	1.25	1.60
290	A69	10c Strip of 5, #a.-e.	1.60	2.00
291	A69	20c Strip of 5, #a.-e.	2.00	2.75
292	A69	45c Strip of 5, #a.-e.	4.75	5.25
f.		Sheet of 20, #289-292	10.00	13.00

No. 292 also produced in sheets of 20.

1994, June 16   Litho.   Perf. 14½x14

293	A70	45c Prabu Abjasa	.85	.85
294	A70	90c Prabu Pandu	1.60	1.60
295	A70	$1 Judistra	1.75	1.75
296	A70	$1.35 Abimanju	2.25	2.25
		Nos. 293-296 (4)	6.45	6.45

Christmas A71

1994, Oct. 31   Litho.   Perf. 14x14½

297	A71	40c Angel	.75	.75
298	A71	45c Wise man	.95	.95
299	A71	80c Bethlehem	1.50	1.50
		Nos. 297-299 (3)	3.20	3.20

Seabirds A72

45c, White-tailed tropicbird, masked booby. 85c, Great frigatebird, white tern.

1995, Mar. 16   Litho.   Perf. 14x14½

300	A72	45c multicolored	.75	.75
301	A72	85c multicolored	1.50	1.50
a.		Souvenir sheet of 2, #300-301	2.75	2.75
b.		As "a," overprinted	7.00	7.00

No. 301b ovptd. in gold in sheet margin with Jakarta '95 exhibition emblem and: "8th Asian International Philatelic Exhibition / PAMERAN FILATELI INTERNASIONAL ASIA VIII."

No. 301b issued 8/19/95.

Insects — A73

#302a, Yellow crazy ant. b, Aedes mosquito. c, Hawk moth. d, Scarab beetle. e, Lauxaniid fly.

$1.20, Common eggfly butterfly.

1995, July 13   Litho.   Perf. 14½x14
302	A73	45c Strip of 5, #a.-e.	5.50	5.50
303	A73	$1.20 multicolored	2.50	2.50

Fish — A74

Designs: 5c, Redspot wrasse. 30c, Gilded triggerfish. 40c, Saddled butterflyfish. 45c, Ringeyed hawkfish. 75c, Orangespine unicornfish. 80c, Blue tang. 85c, Humpback wrasse. 90c, Threadfin butterflyfish. $1, Bluestripe snapper. $1.05, Longnosed butterflyfish. $1.20, Freckled hawkfish. $2, Powder blue surgeonfish.

1995-97   Litho.   Perf. 14x14½
304	A74	5c multicolored	.35	.35
305	A74	30c multicolored	.55	.55
306	A74	40c multicolored	.85	.85
307	A74	45c multicolored	1.00	1.00
308	A74	75c multicolored	1.50	1.50
309	A74	80c multicolored	1.60	1.60
310	A74	85c multicolored	1.60	1.60
311	A74	90c multicolored	1.90	1.90
312	A74	$1 multicolored	2.10	2.10
313	A74	$1.05 multicolored	2.10	2.10
314	A74	$1.20 multicolored	2.75	2.75
315	A74	$2 multicolored	4.75	4.75
		Nos. 304-315 (12)	21.05	21.05

Issued: 40c, 80c, $1.05, 11/1/95; 30c, 45c, 85c, $2, 8/8/96; 5c, 75c, 90c, $1, $1.20, 8/14/97.

See Nos. 327-329.

Festive Season — A75

Designs: 45c, Greeting others, asking forgiveness. 75c, Drum beaters celebrate Hari Raya Puasa. 85c, Sharing food with friends.

1996, Feb. 19   Litho.   Perf. 14
316	A75	45c multicolored	.75	.75
317	A75	75c multicolored	1.75	1.75
318	A75	85c multicolored	2.00	2.00
		Nos. 316-318 (3)	4.50	4.50

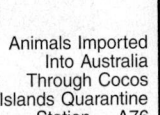

Animals Imported Into Australia Through Cocos Islands Quarantine Station — A76

1996, June 13   Litho.   Perf. 14½x14
319	A76	45c Black rhinoceros	1.00	1.00
320	A76	50c Alpacas	1.25	1.25
321	A76	$1.05 Boran cattle	2.25	2.25
322	A76	$1.20 Ostrich	3.25	3.25
		Nos. 319-322 (4)	7.75	7.75

A77

A78

Festive Season: 45c, Tambourine, dancing on shore, bird. 75c, Woman clapping, sailboats racing. 85c, Fish, night scene on beach.

1997, Jan. 6   Litho.   Perf. 14x14½
323	A77	45c multicolored	.85	.85
324	A77	75c multicolored	1.40	1.40
325	A77	85c multicolored	1.75	1.75
		Nos. 323-325 (3)	4.00	4.00

1998, Jan. 22   Litho.   Perf. 14

Children's drawings: a, Gift package. b, Mosque. c, Cocos Malay woman. d, Island scene. e, Two dancers.

326	A78	45c Strip of 5, #a.-e.	4.75	4.75

Festive Season.

Marine Life Type of 1995

Designs: 70c, Crowned squirrelfish. 95c, Sixstripe wrasse. $5, Goldback anthias.

1998, Aug. 13   Litho.   Perf. 14x14½
327	A74	70c multicolored	1.10	1.10
328	A74	95c multicolored	1.40	1.40
329	A74	$5 multicolored	7.50	7.50
		Nos. 327-329 (3)	10.00	10.00

Jukong Boats, Hari Raya Festival — A79

a, Women placing items in leaves, people along beach. b, Two women, boats along beach. c, Flowers, man in boat. d, Palm trees, two men, man in boat. e, Two people in boat.

1999, Feb. 11   Litho.   Perf. 14½x14
330	A79	45c Strip of 5, #a.-e.	4.25	4.25

Flora and Fauna — A80

a, 45c, Two birds on tree branch. b, 25c, Bird in flight. c, 10c, Sailboat with sail down. d, 5c, Sailboat with red sails. e, 45c, Two birds in flight. f, 25c, Butterflies. g, 10c, School of fish. h, 5c, School of fish swimming left, coral. i, 45c, Red hibiscus flower. j, 25c, Three birds in flight. k, 10c, Two moorish idols. l, 5c, Turtles. m, 45c, Butterfly, flowers. n, 25c, Moth with wings folded, flowers. o, 10c, Two gold fish. p, 5c, Various fish swimming right. q, 45c, Yellow hibiscus. r, 25c, Butterfly on flowers. s, 10c, Two birds in flight. t, 5c, Large fish, coral.

1999, June 17   Litho.   Perf. 14x14½
331	A80	Sheet of 20, #a.-t.	15.00	15.00

Faces of Cocos Islands A81

Ordinary people: a, Ratma Anthoney, with white shirt. b, Nakia Haji Dolman, with multicolored head covering. c, Muller Eymin, with white head covering. d, Courtney Press, with flowered outfit. e, Mhd Abu-Yazid, with blue shirt with stripes.

2000, Apr. 13   Litho.   Perf. 14x14½
332	A81	45c Strip of 5, #a.-e.	4.50	4.50

Worldwide Fund for Nature — A82

#333: a, Purple crab. b, Little nipper crab. #334: a, Horn-eyed ghost crab. b, Smoothbanded ghost crab.

Illustration reduced.

2000, June 20   Litho.   Perf. 14x14¾
333	A82	5c Pair, #a-b	1.00	1.00
334	A82	45c Pair, #a-b	2.00	2.00

Fish Type of 1995

No. 335: a, Wideband fusilier. b, Striped surgeonfish. c, Orangeband surgeonfish. d, Indo-Pacific sergeant.

2001, Feb. 8   Litho.   Perf. 14x14½
335		Block of 4	5.00	5.00
a.-d.	A74 45c Any single		.90	.85

Turtles — A83

No. 336: a, Loggerhead. b, Hawksbill. c, Leatherback. d, Green.
Illustration reduced.

2002, Oct. 1   Litho.   Perf. 14x14½
336	A83	Block of 4	5.00	5.00
a.-d.	45c Any single		.90	.90

Shore Birds — A84

No. 337: a, Eastern reef egret. b, Sooty tern. c, Ruddy turnstone. d, Whimbrel.

2003, June 17   Litho.   Perf. 14x14½
337		Horiz. strip of 4	6.00	6.00
a.-d.	A84 50c Any single		1.10	1.10

Royal Visit, 50th Anniv. — A85

Queen Elizabeth II and: No. 338a, Cocos Malay musicians. No. 338b, Royal Yacht Gothic. $1, Clunies Ross (Oceania) House. $1.45, Dignitary presenting model of Malay jukong.

2004, Mar. 16   Litho.   Perf. 14x14½
338	A85	50c Horiz. pair, #a-b	2.25	2.25
339	A85	$1 multi	2.25	2.25
340	A85	$1.45 multi	3.50	3.50
a.	Souvenir sheet, #338a, 338b, 339, 340		8.25	8.25
b.	As "a," with 2004 World Stamp Championship emblem ovptd. in gold in margin		9.00	9.00
	Nos. 338-340 (3)		8.00	8.00

No. 340b issued 8/28.

Worldwide Fund for Nature (WWF) A86

Designs: No. 341a, Blacktip reef shark. No. 341b, Gray reef sharks. $1, Blacktip reef sharks. $1.45, Gray reef shark.

2005, June 21   Litho.   Perf. 14½x14
341	A86	50c Horiz. pair, #a-b	2.00	2.00
342	A86	$1 multi	2.00	2.00
343	A86	$1.45 multi	3.00	3.00
		Nos. 341-343 (3)	7.00	7.00

Miniature Sheet

Wildlife — A87

No. 344: a-e, Various birds. f-t, Various fish and marine life.

2006, June 13   Litho.   Perf. 14¾x14
344	A87	Sheet of 20	10.00	10.00
a.-e.	10c Any single		.25	.25
f.-o.	25c Any single		.40	.40
p.-t.	50c Any single		.90	.90

Mollusks A88

Designs: No. 345a, Oriental moonsnail. No. 345b, Pearly nautilus. $1, Partridge tun. $1.45, Giant clam.

2007, Mar. 20   Litho.   Perf. 14x14½
345	A88	50c Horiz. pair, #a-b	1.60	1.60
346	A88	$1 multi	1.60	1.60
347	A88	$1.45 multi	2.40	2.40
		Nos. 345-347 (3)	5.60	5.60

OFFICIAL STAMP

No. 175 Ovptd. and Surcharged in Dark Blue

1991, Jan. 25   Litho.   Perf. 14x13½
O1	A44	(43c) on 90c multi	120.00

No. O1 was not sold to the public unused. Used value is for a canceled-to-order example. Mint examples exist in the marketplace. Value the same as used.

COLOMBIA

kə-'ləm-bē-ə

LOCATION — On the northwest coast of South America, bordering on the Caribbean Sea and the Pacific Ocean
GOVT. — Republic
AREA — 456,535 sq. mi.
POP. — 39,309,422 (1999 est.)
CAPITAL — Bogota

In 1810 the Spanish Viceroyalty of New Granada gained its independence and with Venezuela and Ecuador formed the State of Greater Colombia. In 1832 this state split into three independent units as Venezuela, Ecuador and the Republic of New Granada. The name of the country has been, successively, Granadine Confederation (1858-61), United States of New Granada (1861), United States of Colombia (1861-65), and the Republic of Colombia (1885 to date).

100 Centavos = 1 Peso

Catalogue values for unused stamps in this country are for Never Hinged items, beginning with Scott 594 in the regular postage section, Scott B1 in the semi-postal section, Scott C200 in the airpost section, Scott CE1 in the airpost special delivery section, Scott E2 in the special delivery section, and Scott RA33 in the postal tax section.

In the earlier days many towns did not have handstamps for canceling and stamps were canceled with pen and ink. Pen cancellations, therefore, do not indicate fiscal use. (Postage stamps were not used for revenue purposes.) Used values for Nos. 1-128 are for stamps with illegible manuscript cancels or handstamp cancels of Bogota or Medellin. Stamps with legible manuscript or other handstamped town-name cancels sell for more.

Fractions of many Colombian stamps of both early and late issues are found canceled, their use to pay postage having been tolerated even though forbidden by the postal laws and regulations. Many are known to have been made for philatelic purposes.

Watermarks

Wmk. 116 — Crosses and Circles

Wmk. 127 — Quatrefoils

Wmk. 194 — Multiple Curvilinear Triangles

Wmk. 229 — Wavy Lines

Wmk. 255 — Wavy Lines and C Multiple

Wmk. 331 — REPUBLICA DE COLOMBIA

Wmk. 334 — Rectangles

Wmk. 346 — Parallel Curved Lines

Stamps inscribed "Colombia" that show the Panama Canal area were used in Panama and can be found in Vol. 5.

Granadine Confederation

A1

A2
Coat of Arms

Type A1 — Asterisks in frame. Wavy lines in background.
Type A2 — Diamond-shaped ornaments in frame. Straight lines in background. Numerals larger.

1859   Unwmk.   Litho.   Imperf.

Wove Paper

1	A1	2½c green	95.00	95.00
a.		2½c yellow green	95.00	95.00
2	A1	5c blue	110.00	75.00
a.		Tête bêche pair	3,500.	5,750.
b.		"50" instead of "5"		7,500.
3	A1	5c violet	300.00	95.00
a.		Tête bêche pair	5,000.	6,000.
b.		"50" instead of "5"		7,500.
4	A1	10c red brown	110.00	65.00
a.		10c buff	110.00	65.00
6	A1	20c blue	95.00	55.00
a.		20c gray blue	95.00	55.00
b.		Se-tenant with 5c		
c.		Tête bêche pair	25,000.	25,000.

7	A1	1p carmine	70.00	100.00
a.		1p rose	85.00	125.00
8	A1	1p rose, *bluish*	350.00	

The 10c green is an essay.
Reprints of No. 7 are in brown rose or brown red. Wavy lines of background are much broken; no dividing lines between stamps.

1860

Laid Paper

9	A2	5c lilac	250.00	175.00

Wove Paper

10	A2	5c gray lilac	65.00	50.00
a.		5c lilac	65.00	50.00
11	A2	10c yellow buff	65.00	45.00
a.		Tête bêche pair	7,000.	
12	A2	20c blue	160.00	110.00

United States of New Granada

Arms of New Granada — A3

1861

13	A3	2½c black	1,100.	300.00
14	A3	5c yellow	325.00	140.00
a.		5c buff	325.00	140.00
16	A3	10c blue	950.00	140.00
17	A3	20c red	400.00	190.00
18	A3	1p pink	950.00	300.00

There are 54 varieties of the 5c, 20c, and 1 peso.
Forgeries exist of Nos. 13-18.

United States of Colombia

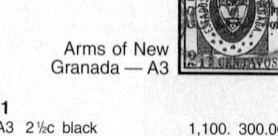

Coat of Arms
A4   A5   A6

1862

19	A4	10c blue	200.00	100.00
20	A4	20c red	3,600.	600.00
21	A4	50c green	200.00	140.00
22	A4	1p red lilac	475.00	140.00
23	A4	1p red lil, *bluish*	4,250.	1,450.

No. 23 is on a thinner, coarser wove paper than Nos. 19-22.

1863

24	A5	5c orange	80.00	52.50
a.		Star after "Cent"	90.00	60.00
25	A5	10c blue	160.00	19.00
a.		Period after "10"	180.00	25.00
26	A5	20c red	175.00	62.50
a.		Star after "Cent"	200.00	70.00
b.		Transfer of 50c in stone of 20c	14,000.	4,500.

Bluish Paper

28	A5	10c blue	140.00	27.50
a.		Period after "10"	150.00	30.00
29	A5	50c green	175.00	62.50
a.		Star after "Cent"	175.00	70.00

Ten varieties of each.

1864

Wove Paper

30	A6	5c orange	57.50	30.00
a.		Tête bêche pair	350.00	325.00
31	A6	10c blue	42.50	12.50
a.		Period after 10	42.50	12.50
32	A6	20c scarlet	80.00	45.00
33	A6	50c green	65.00	45.00
34	A6	1p red violet	275.00	140.00

Two varieties of each.

Arms of Colombia
A7   A9

A8

1865

35	A7	1c rose	8.00	8.00
a.		bluish pelure paper	22.50	17.50
36	A8	2½c black, *lilac*	16.00	11.00
37	A9	5c yellow	35.00	16.00
a.		5c orange	35.00	16.00
38	A9	10c violet	52.50	3.50
39	A9	20c blue	52.50	16.00
40	A9	50c green	92.50	42.50
41	A9	50c grn (small figures)	92.50	42.50
42	A9	1p vermilion	100.00	15.00
a.		1p rose red	100.00	15.00
b.		Period after "PESO"	120.00	17.50

Ten varieties of each of the 5c, 10c, 20c, and 50c, and six varieties of the 1 peso. No. 36 was used as a carrier stamp.

A10   A11   A12

A13

A14

A15

A16

1866

White Wove Paper

45	A10	5c orange	55.00	22.50
46	A11	10c lilac	13.00	4.25
a.		Pelure paper	17.50	10.00
47	A12	20c light blue	32.50	17.50
a.		Pelure paper	50.00	42.50
48	A13	50c green	13.00	10.00
49	A14	1p rose red, *bluish*	72.50	26.00
a.		1p vermilion	72.50	26.00
51	A15	5p blk, *green*	400.00	175.00
52	A16	10p blk, *vermilion*	275.00	160.00

There are several varieties of the 1 peso having the letters "U," "N," "S" and "O" smaller.

A17

A18

A19

A20

A21

TEN CENTAVOS:
Type I — "B" of "COLOMBIA" over "V" of "CENTAVOS."
Type II — "B" of "COLOMBIA" over "VO" of "CENTAVOS."
ONE PESO:
Type I — Long thin spear heads. Diagonal lines in lower part of shield.
Type II — Short thick spear heads. Horizontal and a few diagonal lines in lower part of shield.
Type III — Short thick spear heads. Crossed lines in lower part of shield. Ornaments at each side of circle are broken. (See No. 97.)

1868

53	A17	5c orange	55.00	42.50
54	A18	10c lilac (I)	3.25	.90
a.		10c red violet (I)	3.25	.90
b.		10c lilac (II)	3.25	.90
c.		10c red violet (II)	3.25	.90
d.		Printed on both sides	6.25	2.00
55	A19	20c blue	2.25	1.00
56	A20	50c yellow green	2.75	2.00
57	A21	1p ver (II)	3.25	1.75
a.		Tête bêche pair	110.00	85.00
b.		1p rose red (I)	45.00	22.50
c.		1p rose red (II)	3.00	1.75
		Nos. 53-57 (5)	66.50	48.15

See Nos. 83-84, 96-97.
Counterfeits or reprints.
10c — There is a large white dot at the upper left between the circle enclosing the "X" and the ornament below.
50c — There is a shading of dots instead of dashes below the ribbon with motto. There are crossed lines in the lowest section of the shield instead of diagonal or horizontal ones.
1p — The ornaments in the lettered circle are broken. There are crossed lines in the lowest section of the shield. These counterfeits, or reprints, are on white paper, wove and laid, on colored wove paper and in fancy colors.

A22
Two varieties

1869-70
Wove Paper

59	A22	2½c black, *violet*	3.50	2.10
a.		Laid paper ('70)	250.00	210.00
b.		Laid batonné paper ('70)	22.50	19.00

Nos. 59, 59a, 59b were used as carrier stamps.
Counterfeits, or reprints, are on magenta paper wove or ribbed.

A23   A24

1870
Wove Paper

62	A23	5c orange	1.60	1.10
a.		5c yellow	1.60	1.10
63	A24	25c black, *blue*	13.00	11.00

See No. 89.
In the counterfeits, or reprints, of No. 63, the top of the "2" of "25" does not touch the down stroke. The counterfeits are on paper of various colors.

A25   A26

5 pesos — The ornament at the left of the "C" of "Cinco" cuts into the "C," and the shading of the flag is formed of diagonal lines.
10 pesos — The stars have extra rays between the points, and the central part of the shield has some horizontal lines of shading at each end.

1870
Surface Colored, Chalky Paper

64	A25	5p blk, *green*	80.00	55.00
65	A26	10p blk, *vermilion*	92.50	55.00

See Nos. 77-79, 125-126.

A29

TEN CENTAVOS:
Type I — "S" of "CORREOS" 2½mm high. First "N" of "NACIONALES" small.
Type II — "S" of "CORREOS" 2mm high. First "N" of "NACIONALES" wide.

1871-74
Thin Porous Paper

66	A27	1c green ('72)	2.75	2.75
67	A27	1c rose ('73)	2.75	2.75
a.		1c carmine ('73)	2.75	2.75
68	A28	2c brown	1.25	1.25
a.		2c red brown	1.25	1.25
69	A29	10c vio (I) ('74)	2.00	1.60
a.		10c lilac (I) ('74)	2.00	1.60
b.		10c violet (II) ('74)	2.00	1.60
c.		10c lilac (II) ('74)	2.00	1.60
d.		Laid paper ('72)	110.00	110.00
e.		As "b," laid paper ('72)	110.00	110.00
		Nos. 66-69 (4)	8.75	8.35

Counterfeits or reprints.
1c — The outer frame of the shield is broken near the upper left corner and the "A" of "Colombia" has no cross-bar.
2c — There are scratches across "DOS" and many white marks around the letters on the large "2." The counterfeits, or reprints, are on white wove and bluish white laid paper.

Condor — A30

Liberty Head
A31   A32

5 pesos, redrawn — The ornament at the left of the "C" only touches the "C," and the shading of the flag is formed of vertical and diagonal lines.
10 pesos, redrawn — The stars are distinctly five pointed, and there is no shading in the central part of the shield.

1877
Wove Paper

73	A30	5c purple	5.50	1.75
a.		5c lilac	5.50	1.75
74	A31	10c bister brown	2.75	.75
a.		10c red brown	2.75	.75
b.		10c violet brown	2.75	.75
75	A32	20c blue	3.25	1.10
a.		20c violet blue	6.50	2.75
77	A26	10p blk, *rose*	92.50	57.50
78	A25	5p blk, *lt grn,* redrawn	32.50	27.50
79	A26	10p blk, *rose,* redrawn	13.00	2.25
a.		10p blk, *dark rose,* redrawn	13.00	2.25
		Nos. 73-79 (6)	149.50	90.85

Stamps of the issues of 1871-77 are known with private perforations of various gauges, also with sewing machine perforations.
In the counterfeits, or reprints, of the 5 pesos the ornament at the left of the "C" of "Cinco" is separated from the "C" by a black line.
In the counterfeits, or reprints, of the 10 pesos the outer line of the double circle containing "10" is broken at the top, below "OS" of "Unidos," and the vertical lines of shading contained in the double circle are very indistinct. There is a colorless dash below the loop of the "P" of "Pesos."

1876-79
Laid Paper

80	A30	5c lilac	65.00	52.50
81	A31	10c brown	35.00	2.25
82	A32	20c blue	80.00	55.00
83	A20	50c green ('79)	77.50	52.50
84	A21	1p pale red (II) ('79)	50.00	12.50
		Nos. 80-84 (5)	307.50	174.75

1879
Wove Paper

89	A24	25c green	26.00	26.00

1881
Blue Wove Paper

93	A30	5c violet	16.00	10.50
a.		5c lilac	16.00	10.50
94	A31	10c brown	9.25	2.10
95	A32	20c blue	9.25	2.10
96	A20	50c yellow green	9.50	6.00
97	A21	1p ver (III)	13.00	6.00
		Nos. 93-97 (5)	57.00	26.70

For types of 1p, see note over No. 53.
Reprints of the 10c and 20c are much worn. On the 10c the letters "TAVOS" of "CENTA-VOS" often touch. On the 20c the letters "NT" of "VEINTE" touch and the left arm of the "T" is too long. Reprints of the 25c, 50c and 1p have the characteristics previously described. The reprints are on white wove or laid paper, on colored papers, and in fancy colors. Stamps on green paper exist only as reprints.

A34   A35

A36

1 centavo — The period before "UNION" is round and there are rays between the stars and the condors.
2 centavos — The "2's" and "C's" in the corners are placed upright.
5 centavos — The last star at the right almost touches the frame.
10 centavos — The letters of the inscription are thin; there are rays between the stars and the condor.

1881
White Wove Paper   *Imperf.*

103	A34	1c green	3.75	3.25
104	A35	2c vermilion	1.60	1.25
a.		2c rose	1.90	1.40
106	A34	5c blue	4.50	1.40
a.		Printed on both sides		
107	A36	10c violet	3.25	1.00
108	A34	20c black	3.50	1.00
		Nos. 103-108 (5)	16.60	8.50

The stamps of this issue are found with perforations of various gauges, also sewing machine perforations, all of which are unofficial.
See Nos. 112, 114-115.

Liberty
Head — A37   A37a

1881   *Imperf.*

109	A37	1c blk, *green*	2.50	4.00
110	A37	2c blk, *lilac rose*	2.50	4.00
111	A37	5c blk, *lilac*	6.50	1.50
		Nos. 109-111 (3)	11.50	9.50

Nos. 109 to 111 are found with regular or sewing machine perforation, unofficial.
Reprints:
1c — The top line of the stamp and the top frame extend to the left. 2c — There is a curved line over the scroll below the "AV" of "CENTAVOS."
5c — There are scratches across the "5" in the upper left corner. All three values were reprinted on the three colors of paper of the originals.

Redrawn

1 centavo — The period before "UNION" is square and the rays between the stars and the condor have been wholly or partly erased.
2 centavos — The "2's" and "C's" in the corners are placed diagonally.
5 centavos — The last star at the right touches the wing of the condor.
10 centavos — The letters of the inscription are thick; there are no rays under the stars; the last star at the right touches the wing of the condor and this wing touches the frame.

1883   *Imperf.*

112	A34	1c green	4.75	4.25
113	A37a	2c rose	1.60	1.40
114	A34	5c blue	4.00	1.00
a.		5c ultramarine	4.00	1.00
b.		Printed on both sides, reverse ultra	25.00	20.00
115	A36	10c violet	5.00	1.40
		Nos. 112-115 (4)	15.35	8.05

The stamps of this issue are found with regular or sewing machine perforations, privately applied.

A38   A39

1883   *Perf. 10½, 12, 13½*

116	A38	1c gray grn, *grn*	.80	.80
a.		Imperf., pair	4.00	4.00
117	A39	2c red, *rose*	.80	1.10
a.		2c org red, *rose*	.80	1.10
b.		2c red, *buff*	10.00	10.00
c.		Imperf., pair (No. 117 or 117a)	6.50	6.50
d.		"DE LOS" in very small caps	12.50	12.50
118	A38	5c blue, *bluish*	2.00	1.25
a.		5c dk bl, *bluish*	2.00	.90
b.		5c blue	2.75	2.00
c.		Imperf., pair (No. 118 or 118a)	6.50	6.50
d.		As "b," imperf., pair	10.00	10.00
119	A39	10c org, *yel*	1.00	1.10
a.		"DE LOS" in large caps	45.00	20.00
b.		Imperf., pair	13.00	13.00
120	A39	20c vio, *lilac*	1.10	1.10
a.		Imperf., pair	13.00	13.00
122	A38	50c brn, *buff*	2.25	2.50
a.		Perf. 12	2.25	2.50
123	A38	1p claret, *bluish*	4.25	1.60
a.		Imperf., pair	13.00	13.00
		Nos. 116-123 (7)	12.20	9.45

Redrawn Types of 1877

1883 (?)   *Perf. 10½, 12*

125	A25	5p orange brown	6.00	6.00
126	A26	10p black, *gray*	6.50	7.25

1886   *Perf. 10½, 11½, 12*

127	A38	5p brown, *straw*	8.00	4.75
a.		Imperf., pair	26.00	26.00
128	A38	10p black, *rose*	8.00	4.75
a.		Imperf., pair	26.00	26.00

Republic of Colombia

A40   Simón Bolívar — A41

Pres. Rafael Núñez — A42

1886   *Perf. 10½ and 13½*

129	A40	1c grn, *grn*	1.25	.60
a.		Imperf., pair	5.50	5.50
130	A41	5c blue, *bl*	1.25	.35
a.		5c ultra, *blue*	1.25	.35
b.		Imperf., pair (#130)	5.50	5.50
131	A42	10c orange	2.75	.60
a.		Imperf., pair	7.50	7.50
b.		Pelure paper	3.50	.85
		Nos. 129-131 (3)	5.25	1.55

Gen. Antonio Jose de Sucre y Alcala
A43

Gen. Antonio Nariño
A44

1887

133	A43	2c org red, *rose*	1.75	.85
a.		2c orange red, *yellowish*	4.50	4.50
b.		2c orange red	5.25	5.25
c.		Imperf., pair (No. 133)	8.00	8.00

134 A44 20c pur, *grysh*   2.25 .85
a.   Imperf., pair   6.50 6.50
b.   Pelure paper   2.75 1.75

Impressions of No. 134 on white, blue or greenish blue paper were not regularly issued.

Arms — A45   Nariño — A46

1888
135 A45 50c brn, *buff*   1.40 *1.50*
a.   Imperf., pair   4.75 4.75
136 A45 1p claret, *bluish*   6.00 1.75
137 A45 1p claret   2.50 1.25
138 A45 5p org brn   6.50 5.50
139 A45 5p black   11.00 8.00
140 A45 10p black, *rose*   16.00 5.50
   Nos. 135-140 (6)   43.40 23.50

See Nos. 154, 156-157.

1889
141 A46 20c pur, *grayish*   1.50 1.00
a.   Imperf., pair   7.50 7.50

Impressions on white, blue or greenish blue paper were not regularly issued.

A47   A48

A49   A50

A51

1890-91   *Perf. 10½, 13½, 11*
142 A47 1c grn, *grn*   1.50 1.25
143 A48 2c org red, *rose*   .75 .75
144 A49 5c bl, *grnsh bl*   1.10 .35
a.   5c deep blue, *blue*   1.10 .35
b.   Imperf., pair   4.50 4.50
146 A50 10c brn, *yel*   .80 .35
a.   10c brown, *buff*   .80 .35
147 A51 20c vio, pelure paper   2.75 *3.50*
   Nos. 142-147 (5)   6.90 6.20

A52   A52a

A53   A53a

A54

Perf. 10½, 12, 13½, 14 to 15½
1892-99
Ordinary Paper
148 A47 1c red, *yel*   .65 .35
149 A52 2c red, *rose*   32.50 32.50
150 A52 2c green   .40 .25
a.   2c yellow green   .40 .25
151 A49 5c blk, *buff*   10.00 .30
152 A52a 5c org brn, *pale buff*   .85 .25
a.   5c red brown, *salmon ('97)*   .85 .25
153 A50 10c bis brn, *rose*   .60 .35
a.   10c brown, *brownish*   1.60 1.25
154 A53 20c brn, *bl*   .60 .35
a.   20c red brown, *blue*   .60 .35
b.   20c yel brn, *grnsh bl ('97)*   4.50 11.00
c.   20c brown, *buff ('97)*   15.00 11.00
155 A45 50c vio, *vio*   1.00 .60
156 A53a 50c red vio, *vio ('99)*   1.25
157 A54 1p bl, *grnsh*   1.60 .75
a.   1p blue, *buff*   1.60 .75
158 A45 5p red, *pale rose*   6.00 2.75
159 A45 10p blue   12.50 2.75
a.   Thin, pale rose paper   22.50 6.00
   Nos. 148-159 (12)   67.95
   Nos. 148-155,157-159 (11)   41.20

Type A53a is a redrawing of type A45. The letters of the inscriptions are slightly larger and the numerals "50" slightly smaller than in type A45.

The 20c brown on white paper is believed to be a chemical changeling.

Nos. 148, 150-152a, 153-155, 157, 159 exist imperf. Value per pair, $5-$7.50.

A56

1899
162 A56 1c red, *yellow*   .55 .30
163 A56 5c red brn, *sal*   .55 .30
164 A56 10c brn, *lil rose*   1.60 .80
165 A56 50c blue, *lilac*   1.10 1.00
   Nos. 162-165 (4)   3.80 2.40

Cartagena Issues

A57

1899   **Blue Overprint**   *Imperf.*
167 A57 5c red, *buff*   24.00 24.00
a.   Sewing machine perf.   24.00 24.00
168 A57 10c ultra, *buff*   24.00 24.00
a.   Sewing machine perf.   24.00 24.00

Nos. 168 and 168a differ slightly from the illustration.

Bolivar No. 55 Overprinted with 7 Parallel Wavy Lines and:

A58   A59

A60   A61

Perf. 14 (No. 169), Sewing Machine Perf.
1899   **Purple Overprint**
169 A18 1c black   50.00 50.00
170 A58 1c brn, *buff*   17.00 17.00
a.   Altered from 10c   25.00 25.00
171 A59 2c blk, *buff*   17.00 17.00
a.   Altered from 10c   25.00 25.00
172 A60 5c mar, *grnsh bl*   15.00 15.00
a.   Perf. 12   15.00 15.00
b.   Without overprint   8.75 8.75

---

173 A61 10c red, *sal*   15.00 15.00
a.   Perf. 12   15.00 15.00
   Nos. 169-173 (5)   114.00 114.00

Types A58 and A59 illustrate Nos. 170a and 171a, which were made from altered plates of the 10c (No. 168). Nos. 170 and 171 were made from altered plate of the 5c denomination (No. 167), show part of the top flag of the "5" and differ slightly from the illustrations.

Nos. 170-173 exist imperf. Values about same as perf.

A62

1900   *Imperf.*
Purple Overprint
174 A62 5c red   20.00 20.00
a.   Perf. 12   27.50 27.50

A63   A64

"Gobierno Provisorio" at Top
1900   **Litho.**   *Perf. 12 Vertically*
175 A63 1c (ctvo) blk, *bl grn*   35.00 6.50
a.   "cvo."   92.50 12.00
b.   "cvos."   35.00 6.50
c.   "centavo"   42.50 40.00
176 A63 2c black   25.00 4.00
177 A63 5c blk, *pink*   25.00 4.00
a.   Name at side (V)   50.00 7.50
178 A63 10c blk, *pink*   25.00 4.00
a.   Name at side (V)   50.00 7.50
179 A63 20c blk, *yellow*   35.00 6.50
a.   Name at side (G)   75.00 10.00
   Nos. 175-179 (5)   145.00 25.00

"Gobierno Provisional" at Top
Name at Side in Black or Green
180 A64 1c (ctvo.) blk, *bl grn*   35.00 5.00
a.   "centavo"   100.00 40.00
181 A64 2c blk, *bl grn*   20.00 5.00
182 A64 5c blk (G)   20.00 5.00
a.   "ctvos." smaller   40.00 7.50
183 A64 10c blk, *pink*   20.00 5.00
184 A64 20c blk, *yel* (G)   35.00 7.50
   Nos. 180-184 (5)   130.00 27.50

Issues of the rebel provisional government in Cucuta.

A65   A66

1901   *Sewing Machine Perf.*
Purple Overprint
185 A65 1c black   .85 .85
a.   Without overprint   1.90 1.90
b.   Double overprint   2.00 2.00
c.   Imperf., pair   2.00 2.00
d.   Inverted overprint   1.00 1.00
186 A66 2c blk, *rose*   .85 .85
a.   Imperf., pair   2.00 2.00
b.   Without overprint   1.90 1.90
c.   Double overprint   2.00 2.00

A67   A68

1901
Rose Overprint
187 A67 1c blue   .85 .85
a.   Imperf., pair   3.00 3.00

---

188 A68 2c brown   .85 .85
a.   Imperf., pair   3.00 3.00
b.   Without overprint   .85 .85

A69   A70

Sewing Machine or Regular Perf. 12, 12½

1902
Magenta Overprint
189 A69 5c violet   1.75 1.75
a.   Without overprint   1.75 1.75
b.   Double overprint   1.75 1.75
c.   Imperf., pair   3.75 3.75
190 A70 10c yel brn   1.75 1.75
a.   Double overprint   1.75 1.75
b.   Imperf., pair   3.75 3.75
c.   Without overprint   1.75 1.75
d.   Printed on both sides   2.50 2.50

A71   A72

1902
Magenta Overprint
191 A71 5c yel brn   1.75 1.75
a.   Without overprint   1.60 1.60
b.   Imperf., pair   5.00 5.00
192 A71 10c black   1.25 1.25
a.   Without overprint   1.00 1.00
b.   Imperf., pair   7.50 7.50
193 A72 20c maroon   4.00 2.50
b.   Imperf., pair   12.50 12.50
   Nos. 191-193 (3)   7.00 5.50

Nos. 191-193 exist tête bêche. Value of 10c and 20c, each $12.50.

Washed examples of Nos. 167-174, 185-193 are offered as "without overprint."

Barranquilla Issues

Magdalena   Iron Quay at
River — A75   Sabanilla — A76

La Popa
Hill — A77

1902-03   *Imperf.*
194 A75 2c green   1.25 1.25
195 A75 2c dk bl   1.25 1.25
196 A75 2c rose   18.00 18.00
197 A76 10c scarlet   .85 .85
198 A76 10c orange   10.00 10.00
199 A76 10c rose   1.25 1.25
200 A76 10c maroon   1.40 1.40
201 A76 10c claret   1.40 1.40
202 A77 20c violet   2.75 2.75
a.   Laid paper   7.50
203 A77 20c dl bl   7.50 7.50
204 A77 20c dl bl, *pink*   110.00 110.00
205 A77 20c car rose   16.00 16.00
   Nos. 194-205 (12)   171.65 171.65

Sewing Machine Perf. and Perf. 12
194a A75 2c green   7.50 7.50
195a A75 2c dark blue   7.50 7.50
196a A75 2c carmine   35.00 35.00
197a A76 10c scarlet   3.50 3.50
198a A76 10c orange   27.50 27.50
199a A76 10c rose   5.50 5.50
200a A76 10c maroon   5.50 5.50
201a A76 10c claret   5.00 5.00
202b A77 20c purple   .55 .55
c.   20c lilac   .55 .55
203a A77 20c dull blue   7.50 7.50
204a A77 20c dull blue, *rose*   140.00 140.00
205b A77 20c carmine rose   55.00 55.00
   Nos. 194a-205b (12)   300.05 300.05

See Nos. 240-245.

Cruiser
"Cartagena" — A78

Bolívar — A79

General Próspero
Pinzón — A80

A81   A82

1903-04 — Imperf.

209	A78	5c blue	2.10	2.10
210	A78	5c bister	3.50	3.50
211	A79	50c yellow	3.00	3.00
212	A79	50c green	3.50	3.50
213	A79	50c scarlet	3.50	3.50
214	A79	50c carmine	3.50	3.50
a.		50c rose	3.50	3.50
215	A79	50c pale brown	3.50	3.50
216	A80	1p yellow brn	1.25	1.25
217	A80	1p rose	2.00	2.00
218	A80	1p blue	2.00	2.00
219	A80	1p violet	20.00	10.00
220	A81	5p claret	4.25	4.25
221	A81	5p pale brown	6.50	6.50
222	A81	5p blue green	6.00	6.00
223	A82	10p pale green	6.25	6.25
224	A82	10p claret	20.00	20.00
		Nos. 209-224 (16)	90.85	90.85

Nos. 216 and 217 measure 20½x26½mm and No. 218, 18x24mm. Stamps of this issue exist with forged perforations.

Perf. 12

209a	A78	5c blue	7.50	7.50
210a	A78	5c bister	7.50	7.50
211a	A79	50c yellow	12.50	12.50
b.		50c orange	20.00	20.00
212a	A79	50c green	20.00	20.00
213a	A79	50c scarlet	9.00	9.00
214a	A79	50c rose	9.00	9.00
215a	A79	50c pale brown	9.00	9.00
216a	A80	1p yellow brown	4.00	4.00
217a	A80	1p rose	6.00	6.00
218a	A80	1p blue	7.50	6.00
219a	A80	1p violet	50.00	50.00
220a	A81	5p claret	16.00	16.00
221a	A81	5p pale brown	18.00	18.00
222a	A81	5p blue green	18.00	18.00
223a	A82	10p pale green	25.00	25.00
224a	A82	10p claret	60.00	60.00
		Nos. 209a-224a (16)	279.00	277.50

Laid Paper — Imperf.

240	A76	10c dk bl, *lil*	5.00	5.00
241	A76	10c dk bl, *bluish*	3.00	3.00
242	A76	10c dk bl, *brn*	3.00	3.00
243	A76	10c dk bl, *sal*	7.50	7.50
244	A76	10c dk bl, *grnsh bl*	4.00	4.00
245	A76	10c dk bl, *dp rose*	3.00	3.00
		Nos. 240-245 (6)	25.50	25.50

Perf. 12

240a	A76	10c dk bl, *lilac*	10.50	10.50
241a	A76	10c dk bl, *bluish*	7.50	7.50
242a	A76	10c dk bl, *brn*	7.50	7.50
243a	A76	10c dk bl, *salmon*	55.00	55.00
244a	A76	10c dk bl, *grnsh bl*	16.00	16.00
245a	A76	10c dk bl, *deep rose*	7.50	7.50
		Nos. 240a-245a (6)	104.00	104.00

A82a

Imperf., Sewing Machine Perf.
1902 — Typeset

255	A82a	10c black, *rose*	3.50	3.50
256	A82a	20c blk, *orange*	2.50	2.50

This issue was printed in either Cali or Popayan.

Medellin Issue

A83

1902

257	A83	1c grn, *straw*	.25	.40
258	A83	2c salmon, *rose*	.25	.40
259	A83	5c dp bl, *grnsh*	.25	.40
260	A83	10c pale brn, *straw*	.25	.40
261	A83	20c pur, *rose*	.35	.40
262	A83	50c dl rose, *grnsh*	1.75	2.50
263	A83	1p blk, *yellow*	3.50	5.25
264	A83	5p slate, *blue*	27.50	27.50
265	A83	10p dk brn, *rose*	17.50	17.50
		Nos. 257-265 (9)	51.60	54.75

For overprint see No. L8.

Imperf., Pairs

257a	A83	1c	8.50	8.50
258a	A83	2c	8.50	8.50
259a	A83	5c	8.50	8.50
260a	A83	10c	8.50	8.50
261a	A83	20c	8.50	8.50
262a	A83	50c	22.50	22.50
263a	A83	1p	62.50	62.50
264a	A83	5p	50.00	50.00
265a	A83	10p	50.00	50.00

Regular Issue

A84

A85

A86   A87

A88

A89

A90

A91

A92

1902 — Imperf.

266	A84	2c blk, *rose*	.20	.20
267	A85	4c red, *grn*	.20	.20
268	A86	5c grn, *bl*	.20	.20
269	A87	10c blk, *pink*	.20	.20
c.		10c blk, *rose*	.75	.75
270	A88	20c brn, *buff*	.20	.20
271	A89	50c dk grn, *rose*	1.10	1.10
272	A90	1p pur, *buff*	.45	.45
273	A91	5p grn, *bl*	3.25	3.25
274	A92	10p grn, *pale grn*	10.00	5.00
		Nos. 266-274 (9)	15.80	10.80

For overprint see No. H13.

Sewing Machine Perf.

266a	A84	2c blk, *rose*	1.50	1.50
267a	A85	4c red, *grn*	1.25	1.25
268a	A86	5c grn, *blue*	1.50	1.50
269a	A87	10c blk, *pink*	1.50	1.50
270a	A88	20c brn, *buff*	2.50	2.00
271a	A89	50c dk grn, *rose*	5.00	4.00
272a	A90	1p pur, *buff*	6.00	5.00
273a	A91	5p grn, *blue*	27.50	27.50
274a	A92	10p grn, *pale grn*	50.00	50.00
		Nos. 266a-274a (9)	96.75	94.25

1903 — Perf. 12

266b	A84	2c blk, *rose*	1.10	1.10
269b	A87	10c blk, *pink*	1.25	1.25
270b	A88	20c brn, *buff*	1.25	1.25
272b	A90	1p pur, *buff*	2.50	2.50
273b	A91	5p grn, *blue*	22.50	22.50
274b	A92	10p grn, *pale grn*	40.00	35.00
•		*Nos. 266b-274b (6)*	68.60	63.60

1903 — Imperf.

284	A85	4c blue, *grn*	.25	.25
285	A86	5c blue, *blue*	.25	.25
286	A88	20c blue, *buff*	.25	.25
288	A89	50c blue, *rose*	1.40	1.40
		Nos. 284-288 (4)	2.15	2.15

Sewing Machine Perf.

284a	A85	4c blue, *grn*	1.75	1.40
285a	A86	5c blue, *blue*	1.75	1.40
286a	A88	20c blue, *buff*	2.50	2.00
288a	A89	50c blue, *rose*	5.00	4.50
		Nos. 284a-288a (4)	11.00	9.30

Perf. 12

284b	A85	4c blue, *grn*	2.00	2.00
285b	A86	5c blue, *blue*	2.00	2.00
286b	A88	20c blue, *buff*	2.75	2.75
288b	A89	50c blue, *rose*	7.50	7.50
		Nos. 284b-288b (4)	14.25	14.25

A93

1904 — Pelure Paper — Imperf.

303	A93	½c yellow brn	1.00	1.00
304	A90	1c blue green	1.00	1.00
a.		1c yellow green	1.00	1.00
306	A84	2c blue	.90	.60
307	A86	5c carmine	1.00	1.00
308	A87	10c violet	1.00	.90
		Nos. 303-308 (5)	4.90	4.50

For overprint see No. H13.

1904 — Perf. 13

303a	A93	½c yellow brown	3.00	3.00
304b	A90	1c blue green	4.00	3.50
c.		1c yellow green	5.00	4.50
306a	A84	2c blue	2.50	2.50

Perf. 12

307a	A86	5c carmine	2.25	2.25
308a	A87	10c violet	2.25	2.25
		Nos. 303a-308a (5)	14.00	13.50

A94

A95

Pres. José Manuel
Marroquín — A96

Imprint: "Lit. J.L.Arango Medellin. Col."

1904 — Wove Paper — Perf. 12

314	A94	½c yellow	.65	.20
315	A94	1c green	.65	.20
316	A94	2c rose	.65	.20
317	A94	5c blue	1.00	.20
318	A94	10c violet	1.40	.20
319	A94	20c black	1.40	.25
320	A95	1p brown	15.00	2.50
321	A96	5p red & blk, *yel*	45.00	45.00
322	A96	10p bl & blk, *grnsh*	45.00	45.00
		Nos. 314-322 (9)	110.75	93.75

Redrawn

314a	A94	½c	.65	.20
315a	A94	1c	.65	.20
316a	A94	2c	.65	.20
317a	A94	5c	1.00	.20
319a	A94	20c	1.40	.20
		Nos. 314a-319a (5)	4.35	1.00

Imperf., Pairs

314b	A94	½c	2.50	2.50
315b	A94	1c	2.00	2.00
316b	A94	2c	2.50	2.50
317b	A94	5c	2.50	2.50
318a	A94	10c	3.25	3.25
319b	A94	20c	6.00	6.00
320a	A95	1p	50.00	50.00
		Nos. 314b-320a (7)	68.75	68.75

On the redrawn types, the imprint is close to the base of the design instead of being spaced from it. On the redrawn 2c and 5c, the lower end of the vertical white line below "OR" of "CORREOS" forms a hook which turns to the right instead of to the left as in the originals.

See Nos. 325-330. For surcharges see Nos. 351-354, L1-L7, L9-L13, L15-L25.

A97

100p has different frame.

1903 — Imperf.

323	A97	50p org yel, *pale pink*	75.00	75.00
324	A97	100p dk bl, *dk rose*	60.00	60.00

Imprint: "Lit. Nacional"
Perf. 10, 13, 13½ and Compound
1908

325	A94	½c orange	.60	.20
a.		½c yellow	.60	.20
b.		Imperf., pair	2.00	1.50
c.		Without imprint	4.00	4.00
326	A94	1c yel grn	.60	.20
a.		Without imprint	.60	.20
d.		Imperf., pair	3.00	2.50
327	A94	2c red	.60	.20
a.		2c carmine	.60	.20
b.		Imperf., pair	3.00	2.50
328	A94	5c blue	.50	.20
a.		Imperf., pair	5.00	4.00
329	A94	10c violet	40.00	.70
330	A94	20c gray blk	40.00	.50
		Nos. 325-330 (6)	82.30	2.00

The above stamps may be easily distinguished from those of 1904 by the perforation, by the height of the design, 24mm instead of 23mm, and by the "Lit. Nacional" imprint.

Camilo Torres
A99

Policarpa
Salavarrieta
A100

Bolívar Demanding
Liberation of
Slaves — A105

Designs: 2c, Nariño. 5c, Bolívar. 10c, Francisco José de Caldas. 20c, Francisco de Paula Santander. 10p, Bolívar Resigning.

1910, Aug. — Engr. — Perf. 12

331	A99	½c violet & blk	.50	.25
a.		Center inverted	425.00	425.00
332	A100	1c deep green	.40	.25
333	A100	2c scarlet	.40	.25
334	A100	5c deep blue	1.25	.45
335	A100	10c plum	10.00	5.00
336	A100	20c black brn	15.00	5.50
337	A100	1p dk violet	65.00	20.00
338	A105	10p claret	250.00	200.00
		Nos. 331-338 (8)	342.55	231.70

Colombian independence centenary.

Caldas
A107

Monument to
Battle of
Boyacá
A113

View of
Cartagena
A114

Coat of Arms
A118

Designs: 1c, Torres. 2c, Narino. 4c, Santander. 5c, Bolivar. 10c, Jose Maria Cordoba. 1p, Sucre. 2p, Rufino Cuervo. 5p, Antonio Ricaurte y Lozano.

1917		**Engr.**		**Perf. 14**	
339	A107	½c bister		.35	.20
340	A107	1c green		.30	.20
341	A107	2c car rose		.30	.20
342	A107	4c violet		.90	.30
343	A107	5c dull blue		2.25	.20
344	A107	10c gray		2.25	.20
345	A113	20c red		1.25	.20
346	A114	50c carmine		1.50	.20
347	A107	1p brt blue		11.00	.40
348	A107	2p orange		12.00	.45
349	A107	5p gray		30.00	8.50
350	A118	10p dk brown		35.00	10.00
	Nos. 339-350 (12)			97.10	21.05

The 1c, 5c, 10c, 50c, 2p, 5p and 10p also exist perf. 11½ and 11½ compounded with 14.
Litho. varieties of Nos. 343, 345 and 346 are counterfeits made to defraud the government. Imperforate examples of Nos. 339-350 are not known to have been regularly issued.
See Nos. 373-374, 400-405. For overprints and surcharges see Nos. 369-370, 377, 409-410, 440, C1, O3, O5-O9.

Nos. 318-319, 329-330
Surcharged in Red

1918

On Issue of 1904

351	A94	½c on 20c black	1.00	.25
352	A94	3c on 10c violet	2.50	.50

On Issue of 1908

353	A94	½c on 20c gray blk	8.00	5.00
354	A94	3c on 10c violet	12.00	4.25
	Nos. 351-354 (4)		23.50	10.00

Nos. 351-354 inclusive exist with surcharge reading up or down. On one stamp in each sheet the letter "S" in "Especie" is omitted. All denominations exist with a small zero before the decimal in the surcharge.

A119   A120

1918		**Litho.**	**Perf. 13½**	
358	A119	3c red	.50	.20
a.	Imperf., pair		4.00	4.00

1920		**Engr.**	**Perf. 14**	
359	A120	3c red, *org*	.30	.20
a.	Imperf., pair		3.00	3.00

See Nos. 371-372. For surcharge see No. 453.

A121

A122

A123

Perf. 10, 13½ and Compound

1920-21			**Litho.**	
360	A121	½c yellow	.50	.25
361	A121	1c green	.85	.20
362	A121	2c red	.65	.20
363	A122	3c green	.65	.20
a.	3c yellow green		.65	.20
364	A121	5c blue	.95	.25
365	A121	10c violet	3.00	1.50
366	A121	20c deep green	8.00	3.50
367	A123	50c dark red	8.00	3.50
	Nos. 360-367 (8)		22.60	9.60

The tablet with "PROVISIONAL" was added separately to each design on the various lithographic stones and its position varies slightly on different stamps in the sheet. For some values there were two or more stones, on which the tablet was placed at various angles.
Nos. 360-366 exist imperf.
See No. 375.

No. 342 Surcharged in Red

a   (15mm wide)
                             — b

1921				
369	A107 (a)	3c on 4c violet	.80	.25
a.	Double surcharge		13.00	
370	A107 (b)	3c on 4c violet	3.50	2.00
	See No. 377.			

Types of 1917-21

1923-24		**Engr.**	**Perf. 13½**	
371	A120	1½c chocolate	1.00	.50
372	A120	3c blue	.50	.20
373	A120	5c claret ('24)	2.00	.20
374	A107	10c blue	7.50	.40

		Litho.		
375	A121	10c dark blue	10.00	6.00
	Nos. 371-375 (5)		21.00	7.30

No. 342 Surcharged in Red

(18mm wide)

1924				
377	A107	3c on 4c vio	3.00	1.25
a.	Double surcharge		12.00	
b.	Double surch., one invtd.		12.00	
c.	With added surch. "3cs." in red			

A124

1924-25	**Litho.**	**Perf. 10, 10x13½**		
379	A124	1c red	.70	.20
380	A124	3c dp blue ('25)	.70	.20

Nos. 379-380 exist imperf. Value, each pair $5.

A125

A126

Black, Red or Green Surch. & Ovpt.
Imprint of Waterlow & Sons

1925			**Perf. 14, 14½**	
382	A125	1c on 3c bis brn	.30	.20
383	A126	4c violet (R)	.40	.20
a.	Inverted surcharge		7.00	7.00

Imprint of American Bank Note Co.
Perf. 12

384	A125	1c on 3c bis brn	6.00	5.00
a.	Inverted surcharge		15.00	15.00
385	A126	4c violet (G)	.40	.30
a.	Inverted overprint		7.50	5.70
	Nos. 382-385 (4)		7.10	5.70

Correos
Provisional

Revenue stamps of basic types A125 and A126 were handstamped as above in violet or blue by the Cali post office in 1925, but were not authorized by the government. Denominations so overprinted are 1c, 2c, 3c, 4c and 5c.

A127

A128

Perf. 10, 13½x10

1926		**Litho.**	**Wmk. 194**	
395	A127	1c gray green	.40	.20
396	A128	4c deep blue	.45	.20

Nos. 395-396 exist imperf. Value, each pair $4.

Types of 1917 and

Sabana
Station — A129

1926-29	**Unwmk.**	**Engr.**	**Perf. 14**	
400	A107	4c deep blue	.40	.20
401	A118	8c dark blue	.50	.20
402	A107	30c olive bister	4.75	.60
403	A129	40c brn & yel brn	7.50	1.00
404	A107	5p violet	7.50	.70
a.	Perf. 11 ('29)		12.00	1.00
405	A118	10p green	12.00	2.00
a.	Perf. 11 ('29)		25.00	4.00
	Nos. 400-405 (6)		32.65	4.70

For surcharges & overprint see Nos. 409-410, O4.

Death of
Bolívar
A130

1930, Dec. 17		**Perf. 12½**		
408	A130	4c dk blue & blk	.60	.35

Cent. of the death of Simón Bolívar. See Nos. C80-C82.

Nos. 400 and 402
Surcharged in Red or
Dark Blue

1932, Jan. 20			**Perf. 14**	
409	A107	1c on 4c dp bl (R)	.30	.20
a.	Inverted surcharge		5.25	5.25
410	A107	20c on 30c ol bis	8.00	.70
a.	Inverted surcharge		17.50	
b.	Double surcharge		17.50	

Emerald
Mine — A131

Oil
Wells — A132

Coffee Cultivation
A133

Platinum
Mine — A134

Gold
Mining — A135

Christopher
Columbus — A136

Imprint: "Waterlow & Sons Ltd. Londres"

1932		**Wmk. 229**	**Perf. 12½**	
411	A131	1c green	.50	.20
412	A132	2c red	.50	.20
413	A133	5c brown	.60	.20
414	A134	8c blue blk	3.75	.20
415	A135	10c yellow	2.75	.20
416	A136	20c dk blue	8.00	.35
	Nos. 411-416 (6)		16.10	1.65

See Nos. 441-442, 464-466a, 517. For surcharges see Nos. 455, 527, O1, O10-O11, O13, RA30.

Pedro de
Heredia — A137

Coffee
Picking — A138

Perf. 11½
1934, Jan. 10   Unwmk.   Litho.
417 A137 1c dark green   2.40 .70
418 A137 5c chocolate   3.25 .60
419 A137 8c dark blue   2.40 .70
   Nos. 417-419 (3)   8.05 2.00

Cartagena, 400th anniv. See Nos. C111-C114.

1934, Dec.   Engr.   Perf. 12
420 A138 5c brown   3.00 .20

Discus Thrower — A139   Post and Telegraph Building — A145

Allegory of Olympic Games at Barranquilla — A140

Foot Race A141

Tennis A142

Pier at Puerto Colombia A143

View of the Bay A144

Designs: 2c, Soccer. 10c, Hurdling. 15c, Athlete in stadium. 18c, Baseball. 24c, Swimming. 50c, View of Barranquilla. 2p, Monument to Flag. 5p, Coat of Arms. 10p, Condor.

1935, Jan. 26   Litho.   Perf. 11½
421 A139 2c bluish grn & buff   1.25 .40
422 A139 4c deep green   1.25 .40
423 A140 5c dk brn & yel   1.25 .40
   a.   Horiz. pair, imperf. btwn.   200.00
424 A141 7c dk carmine   2.50 1.50
425 A142 8c blk & pink   2.00 2.00
426 A141 10c brown & bl   2.75 1.50
427 A143 12c indigo   3.25 2.50
428 A141 15c bl & red brn   5.50 4.25
429 A141 18c dk vio & buff   8.00 6.50
430 A144 20c purple & grn   6.50 5.50
431 A144 24c bluish grn & ultra   6.50 5.25
432 A144 50c ultra & buff   10.00 8.50
433 A145 1p drab & blue   92.50 50.00
434 A145 2p dull grn & gray   110.00 90.00
435 A145 5p pur blk & bl   350.00 275.00
436 A145 10p black & gray   425.00 400.00
   Nos. 421-436 (16)   1,028. 853.70

3rd Natl. Olympic Games, Barranquilla. Counterfeits of 10p exist.

Oil Wells — A155   Gold Mining — A157

Imprint: "American Bank Note Co."
1935, Mar.   Unwmk.   Engr.   Perf. 12
437 A155 2c carmine rose   .35 .20
439 A157 10c deep orange   20.00 .20

See Nos. 468, 470, 498, 516. For surcharge and overprints see Nos. 496, 596, O2.

No. 347 Surcharged in Black

1935, Aug.   Perf. 14
440 A107 12c on 1p brt bl   3.50 1.50

Types of 1932
Imprint: "Lit. Nacional Bogotá"
1935-36   Litho.   Perf. 11, 11½, 12½
441 A131 1c lt green   .20 .20
   a.   Imperf., pair   3.50
442 A133 5c brown ('36)   .55 .20
   a.   Imperf., pair   4.00 4.00

For surcharge see No. 527.

Bolívar A159   Tequendama Falls A160

Wmk. Wavy Lines. (229)
1937   Engr.   Perf. 12½
443 A159 1c deep green   .20 .20
   a.   Perf. 14
444 A160 12c deep blue   3.25 1.10

See No. 570. For surcharges and overprints see Nos. 454, 456, C231, C326, O12.

Soccer Player — A161   Runner — A163

Discus Thrower — A162

1937, Jan. 4   Photo.   Unwmk.
445 A161 3c lt green   1.40 .85
446 A162 10c carmine rose   3.00 1.75
447 A163 1p black   27.50 24.00
   Nos. 445-447 (3)   31.90 26.60

National Olympic Games, Manizales. For surcharge see No. 452.

Exposition Palace — A164

Stadium at Barranquilla A165   Monument to the Colors A166

1937, Jan. 4
448 A164 5c violet brown   2.50 .40
449 A165 15c blue   6.50 4.50
450 A166 50c orange brn   18.00 9.75
   Nos. 448-450 (3)   27.00 14.65

Barranquilla National Exposition.

Stamps of 1926-37 Surcharged in Black

1937-38   Unwmk.   Perf. 12½
452 A161 1c on 3c lt grn   .75 .75
   a.   Inverted surcharge   1.75 1.75
453 A118 5c on 8c dk bl   .40 .35
   a.   Inverted surcharge   1.75 1.75
Wmk. 229
454 A160 2c on 12c dp bl   .40 .35
455 A134 5c on 8c bl blk   .45 .55
   a.   Invtd. surcharge   1.50 1.50
456 A160 10c on 12c dp bl ('38)   4.25 .85
   a.   Dbl. surcharge   8.50 8.50
   Nos. 452-456 (5)   6.25 2.85

Calle del Arco — A168   Entrance to Church of the Rosary — A169

Arms of Bogotá A170   Gonzálo Jiménez de Quesada A171

Bochica A172   Santo Domingo Convent A173

Mass of the Conquistadors — A174

1938, July 27   Unwmk.   Perf. 12½
457 A168 1c yellow green   .20 .20
458 A169 2c scarlet   .20 .20
459 A170 5c brown blk   .25 .20
460 A171 10c brown   .60 .30
461 A172 15c brt blue   3.00 1.25

462 A173 20c brt red vio   3.00 1.25
463 A174 1p red brown   40.00 22.50
   Nos. 457-463 (7)   47.25 25.90

Bogotá, 400th anniversary.

Types of 1932
Imprint: "Litografia Nacional Bogotá"
1938, Dec. 5   Litho.   Perf. 10½, 11
464 A132 2c rose   .80 .30
465 A135 10c yellow   2.00 .30
466 A136 20c dull brown   8.00 1.00
   a.   20c dark blue, perf. 12½ ('44)   50.00 5.00
   Nos. 464-466 (3)   10.80 1.60

Types of 1935 and

Bolívar A175   Coffee Picking A176

Arms of Colombia A177   Christopher Columbus A178

Caldas A179   Sabana Station A180

Imprint: "American Bank Note Co."
Wmk. 255
1939, Mar. 3   Engr.   Perf. 12
467 A175 1c green   .20 .20
468 A155 2c car rose   .20 .20
469 A176 5c dull brown   .20 .20
470 A157 10c deep orange   .40 .20
471 A177 15c dull blue   1.25 .20
472 A178 20c violet blk   14.00 .20
473 A179 30c olive bister   4.25 .30
474 A180 40c bister brn   13.00 2.75
   Nos. 467-474 (8)   33.50 4.25

See Nos. 497-499, 515, 518, 574. For surcharges and overprints see Nos. 506-507, 520-522, 596, RA26, RA47.

Gen. Santander A181   Allegory A182

Gen. Santander A183   Statue at Cúcuta A184

Birthplace of Santander A185   Church at Rosario A186

Paya — A187

Bridge at Boyacá — A188

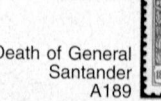

Death of General Santander A189

Invasion of the Liberators A190

Perf. 13x13½, 13½x13

1940, May 6	Engr.		Wmk. 229	
475	A181	1c olive green	.20	.20
476	A182	2c dk carmine	.40	.25
477	A183	5c sepia	.20	.20
478	A184	8c carmine	1.50	1.50
479	A185	10c orange yel	.65	.50
480	A186	15c dark blue	1.75	1.10
481	A187	20c green	2.25	1.75
482	A188	50c violet	5.25	5.00
483	A189	1p deep rose	17.00	17.00
484	A190	2p orange	55.00	55.00
		Nos. 475-484 (10)	84.20	82.50

Death of General Francisco Santander, cent.

Tobacco Plant — A194

Gen. Santander A195

Garcia Rovira A196

R. Galan — A197

Antonio Sucre — A198

1940-43	Engr.		Wmk. 255	Perf. 12	
488	A194	8c rose car & grn	1.00	.55
489	A195	15c dp blue ('43)	1.10	.25
490	A196	20c gray blk ('41)	3.50	.40
491	A197	40c brown bis ('41)	2.10	.40
492	A198	1p black	6.75	.50
		Nos. 488-492 (5)	14.45	2.10

See Nos. 500, 554. For overprint see No. RA28.

Arms of Palmira — A199

Unwmk.

1942, July 4	Litho.	Perf. 11	
493	A199 30c claret	4.25	.60

8th Natl. Agricultural Exposition, held at Palmira.

Paradise of Isaacs, Palmira — A200

Signing Treaty of the Wisconsin A201

1942, July 4
494	A200 50c lt blue grn	4.25	.85

Issued in honor of the writer, Jorge Isaacs.

1942, Nov. 21		Perf. 10½	
495	A201 10c dull orange	3.00	.50
a.	"2. XI.1902" instead of "21. XI. 1902"	17.50	20.00
b.	Perf. 12	5.00	5.00

40th anniv. of the signing of the Treaty of the Wisconsin, Nov. 21, 1902.

No. 470 Surcharged in Black

1944		Wmk. 255	Perf. 12	
496	A157 5c on 10c dp org	.20	.20

Counterfeits exist of No. 496 with inverted or double surcharge.

Types of 1935-41 and

National Shrine — A202

San Pedro Alejandrino A203

Imprint: "Columbian Bank Note Co."

1944-45	Unwmk.	Engr.	Perf. 11	
497	A175	1c green	.20	.20
498	A155	2c rose	.20	.20
499	A176	5c dull brown	.20	.20
500	A196	20c gray black	3.00	.75
501	A202	30c dl ol grn ('45)	1.75	.95
502	A203	50c rose	1.75	.95
		Nos. 497-502 (6)	7.10	3.25

No. 499 Surcharged in Black

1944, Oct.
506	A176 1c on 5c dull brn	.20	.20
507	A176 2c on 5c dull brn	.20	.20

Nos. 506 and 507 exist with inverted or double surcharge, created by favor.

Flag — A204

Arms — A205

Murillo Toro — A206

Hospital of St. John of God A207

Virrey Solis A208

1944, Oct. 10			Litho.	
508	A204	2c ultra & bis	.30	.30
a.		Sheet of 18	15.00	
b.		Imperf., pair	15.00	
509	A205	5c ultra & bis	.45	.45
a.		Sheet of 22	18.00	
b.		Imperf., pair	15.00	
510	A206	20c blk & bluish grn	1.50	1.50
a.		Sheet of 8	16.00	
b.		Imperf., pair	22.50	
511	A207	40c blk & red	6.25	6.25
a.		Sheet of 4	26.00	
512	A208	1p blk & red	14.00	14.00
a.		Sheet of 2	30.00	
		Nos. 508-512 (5)	22.50	22.50

Souvenir Sheet
Perf. 11x11½ All Around, Stamps Imperf.

513	Sheet of 5, #508-512	25.00	25.00

75th anniv. of Gen. Benevolent Assoc. of Cundinamarca.
Nos. 508-513 were printed in composite sheets containing one each of Nos. 508a, 509a, 510a, 511a and 512a, and two of 513. Fifty of these were presented to government officials.

Murillo Toro — A210

San Pedro Alejandrino — A211

1944, Nov. 10		Perf. 11	
514	A210 5c lt brown	.30	.20

Types of 1932-39 and A211
Imprint: "Litografia Nacional Bogota"

1944		Litho.	Perf. 12½	
515	A175	1c dp green	.35	.20
a.		1c olive green	.35	.20
b.		Imperf., pair	1.75	1.75
516	A155	2c dk carmine	.40	.20
a.		Imperf., pair	1.75	1.75
517	A135	10c yellow org	2.75	.45
518	A179	30c gray olive	7.50	3.50
a.		Imperf., pair	27.50	
519	A211	50c rose	8.00	3.75
		Nos. 515-519 (5)	19.00	8.10

No. 469 Overprinted in Green, Blue or Red

Wmk. 255
1945, July 19	Engr.		Perf. 12	
520	A176	5c dull brn (G)	.40	.25
521	A176	5c dull brn (R)	.40	.25
522	A176	5c dull brn (Bl)	.40	.25
		Nos. 520-522 (3)	1.20	.75

Portraits are Joseph Stalin, Franklin D. Roosevelt and Winston Churchill.
Nos. 520-522 exist with overprint inverted. Value, $20 each.

Clock Tower, Cartagena — A212

1945, Nov. 15
523	A212 50c olive black	4.25	1.50

For overprints see Nos. 543-544.

Sierra Nevada of Santa Marta A213

Designs: 30c, Seaplane Tolima. 50c, San Sebastian Fort, Cartagena.

Unwmk.
1945, Dec. 14	Litho.		Perf. 11	
524	A213	20c light green	2.00	1.25
525	A213	30c pale blue	2.00	1.25
526	A213	50c salmon pink	2.00	1.25
		Nos. 524-526 (3)	6.00	3.75

25th anniv. of the 1st airmail service in America, according to the inscription, but earlier services are known to have existed.

No. 442 Surcharged in Black

1946, Mar. 8		Perf. 11x11½, 12½	
527	A133 1c on 5c brown	.20	.20
a.	Inverted surcharge		.90

Gen. Antonio Jose de Sucre — A216

Wmk. 255
1946, Apr. 16	Engr.		Perf. 12	

Size: 19x26½mm

528	A216	1c brn & turq grn	.20	.20
529	A216	2c vio & rose car	.20	.20

Size: 23x31mm

530	A216	5c sepia & blue	.20	.20
531	A216	9c dk grn & red	.85	.85
532	A216	10c ultra & org	.65	.65
533	A216	20c blk & dp org	.65	.65
534	A216	30c brn red & grn	.90	.35
535	A216	40c ol blk & red vio	.90	.40
536	A216	50c dp brn & vio	.90	.40
		Nos. 528-536 (9)	5.45	3.90

No. 470 Surcharged in Black

5 Centavos

Map of South America — A217

National Observatory A218

Unwmk.
1946, June 7   Litho.   Perf. 11
537 A217 15c ultra   .50 .30
  a. Imperf., pair   4.00

1946, Aug.
538 A218 5c fawn   .30 .20
  a. Imperf., pair   6.00

See No. 565.

Andrés Bello — A219

Joaquín de Cayzedo y Cuero — A220

Wmk. 255
1946, Sept. 3   Engr.   Perf. 12
539 A219 3c sepia   .25 .20
540 A219 10c orange   .60 .30
541 A219 15c slate black   .75 .35
  Nos. 539-541,C145 (4)   1.80 1.05

Bello (1781-1865), poet and educator.

1946, Sept. 20   Wmk. 229   Perf. 12½
542 A220 2p bluish green   4.50 1.25

See No. 568. For surcharge see No. 613.

Type of 1945, Overprinted in Black or Green

1946, Dec. 6   Wmk. 255   Perf. 12
543 A212 50c red (Bk)   4.00 2.25
  a. Double overprint   25.00
544 A212 50c red (G)   4.00 2.25
  a. Double overprint   25.00

5th Central American and Caribbean Championship Games.

Coffee — A221

Engraved and Lithographed
1947, Jan. 10   Wmk. 229   Perf. 12½
545 A221 5c multicolored   .40 .20

Colombian Orchid: Masdevallia Nycterina A222

Designs (Orchids): 2c, Miltonia vexillaria. No. 548, Cattleya chocoensis. No. 549, Odontoglossum crispum. No. 550, Cattleya dowiana aurea. 10c, Cattleya labiata trianae.

1947, Feb. 7   Wmk. 255   Perf. 12
546 A222 1c multicolored   .50 .20
547 A222 2c multicolored   .50 .20
548 A222 5c multicolored   1.50 .20
549 A222 5c multicolored   1.50 .20
550 A222 5c multicolored   1.50 .20
551 A222 10c multicolored   2.25 .35
  Nos. 546-551 (6)   7.75 1.35

Antonio Nariño — A228

Alberto Urdaneta y Urdaneta — A229

Perf. 12½
1947, May 9   Litho.   Unwmk.
552 A228 5c blue, grnsh   .25 .20
553 A229 10c red brn, grnsh   .30 .20
  Nos. 552-553,C146-C147 (4)   1.40 1.05

4th Pan-American Press Congress, 1946.

Sucre Type of 1940
1947   Wmk. 255   Engr.   Perf. 12
554 A198 1p violet   2.50 1.00

José Celestino Mutis and José Jerónimo Triana A230

Miguel A. Caro and Rufino J. Cuervo — A231

1947   Wmk. 229   Perf. 12½
555 A230 25c olive green   .75 .30
556 A231 3p dark purple   4.50 3.50

See Nos. 567, 569. For surcharge see No. 610.

Metropolitan Cathedral, Plaza Bolívar, Bogotá — A232

National Capitol A233

Ministry of Foreign Affairs A234

A235

1948, Apr. 2
557 A232 5c black brown   .20 .20
558 A233 10c orange   .55 .55
559 A234 15c dark blue   .55 .55
  Nos. 557-559,C148-C149 (5)   2.40 2.40

Miniature Sheet
Imperf
560 A235 50c slate   2.00 1.60

9th Pan-American Conf., Bogotá.

No. RA5A Overprinted in Black

1948   Unwmk.   Perf. 12½
Without Gum
561 PT3 1c yellow orange   .20 .20

The letter "C" is the initial of "CORREOS."

Nos. RA33, RA24 and RA25 Overprinted in Black

1948   Wmk. 255   Perf. 12.
562 PT6 1c olive   .20 .20
563 PT6 2c green   .20 .20
564 PT6 20c brown   .20 .20
  Nos. 562-564 (3)   .60 .60

Nos. 561-564 exist with inverted and double overprints.

Observatory Type of 1946
Unwmk.
1948, June 30   Litho.   Perf. 11
565 A218 5c blue   .20 .20

Simón Bolívar — A236

Carlos Martinez Silva — A237

Wmk. 255
1948, May 29   Engr.   Perf. 12
566 A236 15c green   .40 .20

Types of 1946-47
1948   Unwmk.   Perf. 12½
567 A230 25c green   .30 .20
568 A220 2p dp green   .55 .20
569 A231 3p dp red violet   .70 .20
  Nos. 567-569 (3)   1.55 .60

Falls Type of 1937
1948   Wmk. 229
570 A160 10c red   .20 .20

For overprints see Nos. C231, C326.

Perf. 13½
1948, Dec. 21   Unwmk.   Litho.
571 A237 40c carmine   .40 .25

Juan de Dios Carrasquilla A238

1949, May 20   Wmk. 229   Perf. 12½
572 A238 5c bister   .20 .20

75th anniv. of the foundation of the Colombian Soc. of Agriculture.

Julio Garavito Armero A239

Arms of Colombia A240

Wmk. 229
1949, Apr. 24   Engr.   Perf. 12
573 A239 4c green   .35 .20

Issued to honor Julio Garavito Armero (1865-1920), mathematician.

Coffee Type of 1939.
Imprint: "American Bank Note Co."
1949, Aug. 4   Wmk. 255
574 A176 5c blue   .20 .20

1949, Oct. 7   Unwmk.   Perf. 13
575 A240 15c blue   .20 .20

Issued to honor the new Constitution. See Nos. C164-C165.

Shield and Tree — A241

Francisco Javier Cisneros — A242

1949, Oct. 13   Wmk. 229   Perf. 12½
576 A241 5c olive   .20 .20

4th anniv. of Colombia's 1st Forestry Cong. and propaganda for the government's reforestation program.

1949, Dec. 15   Photo.   Unwmk.
577 A242 50c red vio & yel   1.00 .60
578 A242 50c green & vio   1.00 .60
579 A242 50c brown & lt bl   1.00 .60
  Nos. 577-579 (3)   3.00 1.80

50th anniv. (in 1948) of the death of Francisco Javier Cisneros.

Masdevallia Chimaera A243

Odontoglossum Crispum — A244

71702

Eastern Hemisphere — A245

Designs: 3c, Cattleya labiata trianae. 4c, Masdevallia nycterina. 5c, Cattleya dowiana aurea. 11c, Miltonia vexillaria. 18c, Santo Domingo post office.

1950, Aug. 22   Photo.   Perf. 13
580	A243	1c brown	.20	.20
581	A244	2c violet	.20	.20
582	A243	3c rose lilac	.20	.20
583	A243	4c emerald	.25	.20
584	A243	5c red orange	.65	.20
585	A244	11c red	1.50	1.50
586	A244	18c ultra	2.50	.50
	Nos. 580-586 (7)		5.50	3.00

Miniature Sheet
Imperf
587	A245	50c orange yel	1.40	1.40

75th anniv. (in 1949) of the UPU. See No. C199. For surcharge see No. C232.

Antonio Baraya — A246

Perf. 12½
1950, Nov. 27   Unwmk.   Engr.
588	A246	2c red	.20	.20

Colombian Farm A247

1950, Dec. 28   Photo.   Perf. 11½
589	A247	5c dp car & buff	.20	.20
590	A247	5c bl grn & gray	.20	.20
591	A247	5c vio bl & gray	.20	.20
	Nos. 589-591 (3)		.60	.60

Issued to publicize rural life.

Arms of Bogotá A248

Arms of Colombia A249

Perf. 12x12½
1950, Dec. 28   Engr.   Wmk. 255
592	A248	5p deep green	2.50	1.25
593	A249	10p red orange	7.50	1.75

> **Catalogue values for unused stamps in this section, from this point to the end of the section, are for Never Hinged items.**

Map and Badge A250

Guillermo Valencia A251

Perf. 12½x13
1951, Jan. 30   Photo.   Unwmk.
594	A250	20c red, yel & bl	.45	.25

60th anniversary (in 1947) of the formation of the Colombian Society of Engineers.

1951, Oct. 20   Engr.   Perf. 13x13½
595	A251	25c black	.90	.25

Issued to honor Guillermo Valencia (1873-1943), newspaper founder, governor of Cauca, presidential candidate, author.

No. 468 Overprinted in Black

1951, Dec. 11   Wmk. 255   Perf. 12
596	A155	2c carmine rose	.30	.20

Issued to publicize the reversion of the Mares oil concession to Colombia.

Nicolas Osorio — A252

No. 598, Pompilio Martinez. No. 599, Ezequiel Uricoechea. No. 600, Jose M. Lombana.

Perf. 11½
1952, Aug. 6   Unwmk.   Engr.
Various Frames
597	A252	1c deep blue	.25	.20
598	A252	1c deep blue	.25	.20
599	A252	1c deep blue	.25	.20
600	A252	1c deep blue	.25	.20
	Nos. 597-600 (4)		1.00	.80

Nos. 597-600 were printed in a single sheet containing four panes of twenty-five each, separated by double rows of ornamental tabs. Although inscribed "sobretasa," the stamps were for ordinary postage.

Types of Postal Tax Stamps of 1945-50 and

Communications Building   A253a
A253

1952   Perf. 12
601	A253	5c ultra	.30	.25

Wmk. 255
602	PT10	20c brown	8.00	4.00
603	PT6	25c dk gray	32.50	32.50
604	PT10	25c blue green	.85	.25
605	A253a	50c orange yel	21.00	12.50
606	A253a	1p rose carmine	2.00	.30

607	A253a	2p lilac rose	21.00	8.50
608	A253a	2p violet	2.25	.60
	Nos. 601-608 (8)		87.90	58.90

Although inscribed "sobretasa," Nos. 601-608 were issued for ordinary postage.
For surcharges see Nos. 612, RA48.

Cathedral of Manizales — A254

Perf. 11½
1952, Oct. 10   Photo.   Unwmk.
609	A254	23c blue & gray blk	.45	.25

Centenary of city of Manizales.
For surcharge see No. 619.

No. 555 Surcharged in Blue

1952, Oct. 30   Wmk. 229   Perf. 12½
610	A230	15c on 25c olive green	.45	.25

Latin American Siderurgical Conf., 1952. See No. C226.

Queen Isabella I and Monument A255

Perf. 12½
1953, Mar. 10   Unwmk.   Engr.
611	A255	23c blue & black	.75	.55

5th cent. of the birth of Queen Isabella I of Spain.
For surcharge see No. 693.

Nos. 606 and 568 Surcharged with New Values in Dark Blue

1953, Oct. 19   Wmk. 255
612	A253a	40c on 1p rose car	1.40	.25
613	A220	50c on 2p dp green	1.40	.25

Manuel Ancizar A256

Portraits: 23c, José Jeronimo Triana. 30c, Manuel Ponce de Leon. 1p, Agustin Codazzi.

Perf. 12½x13
1953, Nov.   Engr.   Unwmk.
Frames in Black
614	A256	14c rose red	.50	.50
615	A256	23c ultra	.40	.25
616	A256	30c chocolate	.35	.25
617	A256	1p emerald	.35	.25
	Nos. 614-617 (4)		1.60	1.25

Cent. (in 1950) of the establishment of the Chorographic Commission. For surcharges and overprint see Nos. 620, 687, 690, 692, C284.

Murillo Toro and Map — A257

Engraved and Lithographed
1953, Dec. 12   Wmk. 255   Perf. 12
Black Surcharge
618	A257	5c on 5p multi		.35	.20

2nd Natl. Phil. Exhib., Bogotá, Dec. 1953. See No. C237.

Nos. 609 and 614 Surcharged with New Value or New Value and Ornaments

1953   Unwmk.   Perf. 11½, 12½x13
619	A254	5c on 23c (C)	.35	.20
620	A256	5c on 14c (Bk)	.35	.25

No. 614 surcharged "CINCO" in blue is listed as No. 687.

Symbolical of St. Francis Receiving Christ's Wounds — A258

1954, Apr. 23   Photo.   Perf. 11½
621	A258	5c sepia & green	.35	.20

400th anniversary of the establishment of Colombia's first Franciscan community.

Soldier, Map and Arms A259

1954, June 13   Engr.   Perf. 13
622	A259	5c dull blue	.25	.20

1st anniv. of the assumption of the presidency by Gen. Gustavo Rojas Pinilla. See Nos. C255, 637a.

Sports Emblem — A260

Design: 10c, Stadium and athlete holding arms of Colombia.

1954, July 18   Unwmk.
623	A260	5c deep blue	.40	.20
624	A260	10c red	.75	.20
	Nos. 623-624,C256-C257 (4)		3.05	.95

7th Natl. Athletic Games, Cali, July 1954.

History Academy Seal — A261

1954, July 24
625 A261 5c ultra & green .25 .20

50th anniversary (in 1952) of the Colombian Academy of History.

Convent and Cell of St. Peter Claver — A262

1954, Sept. 9
627 A262 5c dark green .25 .20
a. Souvenir sheet 4.50 4.50

300th anniv. of the death of St. Peter Claver. No. 627a contains one stamp similar to No. 627, but printed in greenish black. Sheet size: 121x129½mm. See Nos. C258-C258a.

Mercury — A263

1954, Oct. 29
628 A263 5c orange .50 .25
Nos. 628,C259-C260 (3) 1.20 .65

1st Intl. Fair and Exhibition, Bogota, 1954.

Tapestry Madonna A264

College Cloister A265

Designs: 10c, Brother Cristobal de Torres. 20c, College chapel and arms.

Perf. 12½x11½, 11½x12½
1954, Dec. 6
629 A264 5c orange & blk .35 .20
630 A264 10c blue .35 .20
631 A265 15c violet brn .40 .20
632 A265 20c black & brn .80 .35
a. Souvenir sheet 7.50 7.50
Nos. 629-632,C263-C266 (8) 4.25 2.15

Founding of the Senior College of Our Lady of the Rosary, Bogota, 300th anniv. (in 1953). No. 632a contains four stamps similar to Nos. 629-632, but printed in different colors: 5c yellow and black, 10c green, 15c dull violet, 20c black and light-blue.

Steel Mill — A266   José Marti — A267

1954, Dec. 12   **Perf. 12½x13**
633 A266 5c ultra & blk .25 .20

Issued to mark the opening of the Paz del Rio steel mill, October 1954. See No. C267.

1955, Jan. 28   **Perf. 13½x13**
634 A267 5c deep carmine .25 .20

Centenary of the birth of José Marti (1853-1895), Cuban patriot. See No. C268.

Arms, Flags and Soldiers Building Bridge A268

1955, Mar. 23   **Perf. 12½**
635 A268 10c claret .30 .20

Issued to honor Colombian soldiers who served in Korea, 1951-53. See Nos. 637a, C269.

Fleet Emblem — A269

M. S. City of Manizales and New York Skyline A270

1955, Apr. 12   **Unwmk.**
636 A269 15c deep green .20 .20
637 A270 20c violet .40 .20
a. Souvenir sheet 7.50 7.50
Nos. 636-637,C270-C271 (4) 1.45 .90

Grand-Colombian Merchant Fleet. No. 637a contains four stamps similar to Nos. 622, 635-637, but printed in different colors: 5c blue, 10c dark carmine, 15c green, 20c purple.

Hotel Tequendama and Church of San Diego — A271

1955, May 16   **Photo.**   **Perf. 11½x12**
638 A271 5c blue .25 .20

See No. C273.

Bolivar's Country Estate, Bogotá A272

1955, Sept. 28   **Engr.**   **Perf. 12½**
639 A272 5c deep ultra .25 .20

50th anniv. of Rotary Intl. See No. C274.

Belalcazar, Jiménez de Quesada and Balboa A273

Caravels and Columbus A274

5c, San Martin, Bolivar and Washington.

Engraved and Photogravure
1955, Oct. 29   **Perf. 13x12½**
640 A273 2c yel grn & brn .40 .25
641 A273 5c brt bl & brn .40 .25
642 A273 23c lt ultra & blk .45 .25
a. Souvenir sheet 17.50 17.50
Nos. 640-642,C275-C280 (9) 18.50 12.30

7th Cong. of the Postal Union of the Americas and Spain, Bogota, Oct. 12-Nov. 9, 1955. No. 642a contains one each of Nos. 640-642, printed in slightly different shades.

José Eusebio Caro — A275

1955, Nov. 29 Engr.   **Perf. 13½x13**
643 A275 5c brown .25 .20

José Eusebio Caro (1817-53), poet. See No. C281.

Departmental Issue

Map — A276

View of San Andres Harbor — A277

Cattle at Waterhole A278

Designs: 2c, Docks, Atlantico. 3c, "Industry," Antioquia. 4c, Cartagena Harbor, Bolivar. #647, Steel Mill, Boyaca. #648, Cattle, Cordoba. #649, Map. #650, San Andres Harbor. #651, Cacao picker, Cauca. 10c, Coffee picker, Caldas. 15c, Salt Mine Chapel, Zipaquira, Cundinamarca. 20c, Tropical plants and map, Choco. 23c, Harvester, Huila. 25c,

Banana Plantation, Magdalena. 30c, Gold mining, Nariño. 40c, Tobacco plantation, Santander. 50c, Oil wells, North Santander. 60c, Cotton plantation, Tolima. 1p, Sugar industry, Cauca. 3p, Amazon river at Leticia, Amazonas. 5p, Windmills and panoramic view, La Guajira. 10p, Rubber plantation, Vaupes.

Perf. 13½x13, 13x13½, 13
Engr.; Engr. & Litho.
1956   **Unwmk.**
Various Frames
644 A277 2c car & grn .20 .20
645 A277 3c brn vio & blk .20 .20
646 A277 4c grn & blk .20 .20
647 A276 5c dk brn & bl .20 .20
648 A277 5c ol & dk vio brn .30 .20
649 A276 5c bl & blk .25 .20
650 A277 5c car & grnsh bl .20 .20
651 A277 5c ol grn & red brn .20 .20
652 A276 10c org & blk .40 .20
653 A277 15c ultra & blk .25 .20
654 A276 20c dk brn & bl .25 .20
655 A277 23c ultra & ver .30 .20
656 A277 25c ol grn & blk .30 .20
657 A277 30c ultra & brn .25 .20
658 A277 40c dl pur & red brn .25 .20
659 A277 50c dk grn & blk .25 .20
660 A277 60c pale brn & grn .25 .20
661 A278 1p mag & grnsh bl 1.60 .20
662 A278 2p grn & red brn 2.40 .25
663 A278 3p car & blk 2.75 .45
664 A277 5p brn & lt ultra 5.00 1.00
665 A276 10p red brn & grn 14.00 6.00
Nos. 644-665 (22) 30.00 11.30

Nos. 645, 647, 649, 652-654 measure 27x32mm, No. 665 27x37mm. See Nos. 681-684, 685, 688-689. For surcharges and overprints see Nos. 685, 688-689, C289, C312.

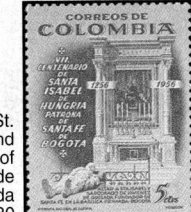

Columbus and Proposed Lighthouse A279

1956, Oct. 12   **Photo.**   **Perf. 12**
666 A279 3c gray black .50 .25

Issued in honor of Christopher Columbus. See Nos. C285, C306.

Altar of St. Elizabeth and Tomb of Jimenez de Quesada A280

1956, Nov. 19   **Unwmk.**
667 A280 5c red lilac .25 .20

7th cent. of St. Elizabeth of Hungary, patron saint of Sante Fé de Bogotá. See No. C286.

St. Ignatius of Loyola — A281

Javier
Pereira — A282

1956, Nov. 26   Engr.   Perf. 12½x13
668 A281 5c blue   .25 .20
    400th anniv. of the death of St. Ignatius of
Loyola. See No. C287. For overprint see No.
C324.

1956, Dec. 28   Unwmk.   Perf. 12
669 A282 5c blue   .25 .20
    Issued to honor 167-year-old Javier Pereira.
See No. C288.

Emblem
and Dairy
Farm
A283

Designs: 2c, Emblem and tractor. 5c,
Emblem, coffee and corn.

1957, Mar. 5   Photo.   Perf. 14x13½
670 A283 1c lt ol grn   .25 .20
671 A283 2c lt brn   .25 .20
672 A283 5c lt bl   .25 .20
    Nos. 670-672,C292-C296 (8)   2.85 1.80
    Agrarian Savings Bank of Colombia, 25th
anniv.
    For overprint see No. C322.

Arms of
Military
Academy
and Gen.
Rafael
Reyes
A284

Design: 10c, Arms and Academy.

1957, July 20   Engr.   Perf. 12½
673 A284 5c blue   .20 .20
674 A284 10c orange   .30 .20
    a. Souv. sheet of 2   16.00 16.00
    Nos. 673-674,C299-C300 (4)   .95 .80
    50th anniv. of the Colombian Military
Academy.
    No. 674a contains one each of Nos. 673-
674 in slightly different shades.
    For overprints see Nos. C328, C312.

Statue of José
Matias
Delgado — A285

1957, Sept. 16   Photo.   Perf. 12
675 A285 2c rose brn   .25 .20
    Issued in honor of Jose Matias Delgado, lib-
erator of El Salvador. See No. C301.

Santo Michelena, Marcos V. Crespo,
P. Alcantara Herran and UPU
Monument
A286

1957, Oct. 10   Unwmk.
676 A286 5c green   .20 .20
677 A286 10c gray   .30 .20
    Nos. 676-677,C302-C303 (4)   .90 .80
    Intl. Letter Writing Week and 14th UPU
Cong.

St. Vincent de Paul
and Children — A287

1957, Oct. 18
678 A287 1c dark olive green   .25 .20
    Colombian Society of St. Vincent de Paul,
cent. See No. C304. For overprint see No.
C323.

Fencer
A288

1957, Nov. 22   Photo.   Perf. 12
679 A288 4c lilac   .25 .20
    3rd South American Fencing Championship.
See No. C305. For overprint see No. C332.

Francisco José de Caldas and
Hypsometer — A289

1958, May 12   Unwmk.   Perf. 12
680 A289 10c black   .25 .20
    Nos. 680,C309-C310 (3)   1.05 .60
    International Geophysical Year, 1957-58.

Departmental Issue
Type of 1956
Designs as before.

1958   Engr.   Perf. 13
681 A276 3c ultra & brn   .25 .20
682 A276 3c ol grn & pur   .25 .20
683 A276 10c grn & brn   .25 .20
684 A276 10c dk bl & brn   .25 .20
    Nos. 681-684 (4)   1.00 .80

    Nos. 646, C291, 614, 653, 655, 616,
C308, 615 and 611 Surcharged with
New Value, and Old Value Obliterated,
or Overprinted in Dark Blue or Green

Perf. 12½, 12½x13, 13
1958-59   Unwmk.
685 A277 2c on 4c grn & blk   .25 .20
686 AP48 5c dp plum & multi
               ('59)   .25 .20
687 A256 5c on 14c blk & rose
               red ("CINCO")
               ('59)   .30 .30
688 A276 5c on 15c ultra & blk   .25 .20
689 A277 5c on 23c ultra & ver
               (G)   .25 .20
690 A256 5c on 30c blk & choc   .25 .20
691 AP40 10c on 25c rose vio   .25 .20
692 A256 20c on 23c blk & ultra
               (G) ('59)   .30 .20
693 A255 20c on 23c bl & blk
               ('59)   .30 .20
    Nos. 685-693 (9)   2.40 1.90
    On No. 686 the words "Correo Extra
Rapido" are obliterated in dark blue.

Father Rafael
Almanza and
Church of
San Diego,
Bogota
A290

1958, Oct. 23   Photo.   Perf. 14x13
695 A290 10c purple   .25 .20
    Nos. 695,C313-C314 (3)   .70 .60
    For overprint see No. C336.

Msgr. R. M.
Carrasquilla
and Church
A291

1959, Jan. 22   Perf. 14x13
696 A291 10c dk red brn   .25 .20
    Nos. 696,C315-C316 (3)   1.05 .60
    Cent. of the birth of Msgr. R. M. Carrasquilla
(1857-1930), rector of Our Lady of the Rosary
Seminary, Bogotá. For overprints see Nos.
C335, C341.

Miss Universe
1959 — A292

Jorge Eliecer
Gaitan — A293

1959, June 26   Photo.   Perf. 11½
697 A292 10c multi   .70 .25
    Nos. 697,C317-C318 (3)   42.10 38.85
    Luz Marina Zuluaga, Miss Universe, 1959.
    For overprint see No. C342.

1959, July 28   Engr.   Perf. 12x13½
698 A293 10c on 3c gray bl (Bl)   .25 .20
699 A293 30c rose vio   .45 .25
    Nos. 698-699,C319-C320 (4)   3.50 2.95
    Issued in honor of Jorge Eliecer Gaitan
(1898-1948), lawyer and politician.
    No. 698 exists without blue surcharge.

Gen. Francisco de
Paula
Santander — A294

Designs: Nos. 701, 703, Simon Bolivar.

1959   Litho.   Wmk. 331   Perf. 12½
700 A294 5c brown & yel   .25 .20
701 A294 5c ultra & bl   .25 .20
702 A294 10c gray & grn   .25 .20
703 A294 10c gray & red   .25 .20
    Nos. 700-703,C389 (5)   4.00 1.20

Capitol,
Bogota
A295

1959
704 A295 2c dk bl & red brn   .25 .20
705 A295 3c blk brn & lilac   .25 .20

Stamp of 1859
and Mail
Transport by
Mule — A296

Two-Toed
Sloth — A297

Designs (various stamps of 1859 and): 10c,
Mail boat on the Magdalena river. 15c, as 5c.
25c, Train.

Unwmk.
1959, Dec. 1   Photo.   Perf. 12
709 A296 5c org & grn   .20 .20
710 A296 10c rose cl & bl   .20 .20
711 A296 15c car rose & grn   .40 .40
712 A296 25c bl & red brn   .50 .50
    Nos. 709-712,C351-C354 (8)   5.00 3.30
    Centenary of Colombian postage stamps.

1960, Feb. 12   Perf. 12
    Designs: 10c, Alexander von Humboldt.
20c, Spider monkey.
713 A297 5c grnsh bl & brn   .30 .20
714 A297 10c blk & dp car   .40 .20
715 A297 20c cit & gray brn   .30 .20
    Nos. 713-715,C357-C359 (6)   6.65 4.30
    Cent. of the death of Alexander von Hum-
boldt (1769-1859), German naturalist and
geographer.
    For overprint and surcharge see Nos. C411,
C413.

Anthurium
Andreanum
A298

Lincoln Statue,
Washington
A299

Flower: 20c, Espeletia grandiflora.

1960, May 10
716 A298 5c multi   .60 .25
717 A298 20c brn, yel & gray
               ol   .60 .25
    Nos. 716-717,C360-C370 (13)   13.95 15.20
    See Nos. C420-C425. For overprint see No.
C412.

Wmk. 331
1960, June 10   Litho.   Perf. 10½
718 A299 20c rose lil & blk   .30 .25
    Nos. 718,C375-C376 (3)   1.40 1.05

Florero
House,
Cradle of
the
Republic
A300

Arms of Santa Cruz
de Mompox — A301

Design: 5c, First coins of Republic.

Unwmk.
1960, July 19   Photo.   Perf. 12
719 A301 5c grn & ocher   .25 .20
720 A300 20c ol bis & mar   .25 .20
721 A301 20c multi   .25 .20
    Nos. 719-721,C377-C385 (12)   6.25 4.90
    Colombia's independence, 150th anniv.

St. Isidore and Farm Animals — A302

Design: 20c, Nativity by Gregorio de Arce Vasquez y Ceballos.

1960, Sept. 26   *Perf. 12*
722 A302 10c multi   .20 .20
723 A302 20c multi   .25 .20
    Nos. 722-723,C387 (3)   .70 .60

St. Isidore the Farmer, patron saint of the rural people.
See Nos. 747, C388, C439-C440.

UN Headquarters and Emblem A303

    Wmk. 331
1960, Oct. 24   **Litho.**   *Perf. 11*
724 A303 20c blk & pink   .25 .20
    Souvenir Sheet
    Imperf
725 A303 50c dk brn, brt grn & blk   3.50 3.50

15th anniversary of the United Nations.

Pan-American Highway through Colombia — A304

Alfonso Lopez — A305

1961, Mar. 7   **Unwmk.**   *Perf. 10½x11*
726 A304 20c brn & grnsh bl   .75 .70
    Nos. 726,C390-C393 (5)   2.75 2.70

8th Pan-American Highway Congress, Bogota, May 20-29, 1960.

1961, Mar. 22   **Photo.**   *Perf. 12½*
727 A305 10c brt rose & brn   .25 .20
728 A305 20c vio & brn   .25 .20
    Nos. 727-728,C394-C395 (4)   1.20 .80

Alfonso Lopez (1886-1959), President of Colombia. See No. C396.

Cauca River Bridge, Cali A306

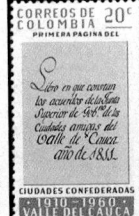

Page from Resolutions of Confederated Cities — A307

1961-62   *Perf. 12½x13, 13½x13*
729 A306 10c red brn, bl, grn & red ('62)   .25 .20
730 A307 20c pale brn & blk   .25 .20
    Nos. 729-730,C397-C401 (7)   3.00 2.05

50th anniversary (in 1960) of the Department of Valle del Cauca.

View of Cucuta and Arms A308

No. 732, Arms of Ocana and Pamplona.

1961, Aug. 29   *Perf. 13x13½*
731 A308 20c bl, blk, yel & red   .25 .20
732 A308 20c ocher, ultra & red   .25 .20
    Nos. 731-732,C402-C403 (4)   1.30 .80

50th anniv. (in 1960) of the Department of North Santander.

Arms of Popayan A309

Basketball A310

Designs: No. 734, Arms of Barranquilla. No. 735, Arms of Bucaramanga.

    Perf. 12½x13
1961, Oct. 10   **Unwmk.**
    Arms in Multicolor
733 A309 10c blue & silver   .25 .20
734 A309 20c blue & yellow   .25 .20
735 A309 20c blue & gold   .25 .20
    Nos. 733-735,C404-C408 (8)   2.75 1.60

Issued to honor Atlantico Department.

1961, Dec. 16   **Litho.**   *Perf. 13½x14*
736 A310 20c shown   .25 .20
737 A310 20c Runners   .25 .20
738 A310 20c Boxers   .40 .25
739 A310 25c Soccer   .25 .20
    Nos. 736-739,C414-C418 (9)   3.75 2.20

4th Bolivarian Games, Barranquilla, 1961.

Colombian Anti-Malaria Emblem — A311

Engineers Society Emblem — A312

Design: 50c, Malaria eradication emblem and mosquito in swamp.

1962, Apr. 12   **Unwmk.**   *Perf. 12*
740 A311 20c lt bis & red   .25 .20
741 A311 50c bis & ultra   .30 .20
    Nos. 740-741,C426-C428 (5)   4.80 4.50

1962, June 12   **Photo.**   *Perf. 11½x12*
742 A312 10c multi   .25 .25
    Nos. 742,C429-C432 (5)   2.40 2.35

Colombian Society of Engineers, 75th anniv.

Flags of American Nations A313

Woman Casting Ballot and Statue of Policarpa Salavarrieta A314

1962, June 28   *Perf. 13*
    Flags in National Colors
743 A313 25c blk & org ver   .25 .20
    Souvenir Sheet
744 A313 2.50p blk & yel   5.00 5.00

70th anniv. of the founding of the Organization of American States.
See No. C433.

    Perf. 12x12½
1962, July 20   **Litho.**   **Wmk. 229**
745 A314 10c lt bl, gray & blk   .25 .20

Issued to publicize women's political rights. See Nos. 752, C434, C448-C450.

Scouts at Campfire and Tents A315

Railroad Map of Colombia A316

    Perf. 11½x12
1962, July 28   **Photo.**   **Unwmk.**
746 A315 10c brt grnsh bl & brn   .35 .30
    Nos. 746,C435-C438 (5)   5.60 4.80

Colombian Boy Scouts, 30th anniv.

    St. Isidore Type of 1960 Redrawn
1962, Aug. 28   *Perf. 12*
747 A302 10c pink & multi   .25 .20
    Nos. 747,C439-C440 (3)   4.20 3.90

The frame on No. 747 is solid color with white inscription similar to type AP82.

1962, Sept. 28   *Perf. 12½*
748 A316 10c blk, gray, grn & red   .20 .20
    Nos. 748,C441-C444 (5)   5.75 4.55

Progress of Colombian railroads and the completion of the Atlantic Line from Santa Marta to Bogota.

Post Horn — A317

    Perf. 13½x14
1962, Oct. 18   **Litho.**   **Wmk. 346**
749 A317 20c gold, dl gray vio & blk   .25 .20
    Nos. 749,C445-C446 (3)   .80 .60

50th anniv. of the founding of the Postal Union of the Americas and Spain, UPAE.

"Virgin of the Rock" A318

Red Cross Centenary Emblem A319

1963, Mar. 11   **Wmk. 346**
750 A318 60c multi   .25 .20

Vatican II, the 21st Ecumenical Council of the Roman Catholic Church. See No. C447.

1963, May 1   *Perf. 12x12½*
751 A319 5c olive bister & red   .25 .20

Centenary of International Red Cross.

    Women's Rights Type of 1962
1963, July 11   **Wmk. 346**
752 A314 5c org, gray & blk   .25 .20
    Nos. 752,C448-C450 (4)   1.05 .80

Manuel Mejia J. and Flag of National Coffee Growers Assn. A320

    Perf. 12½x13
1965, Feb. 10   **Engr.**   **Unwmk.**
753 A320 25c rose & blk   .25 .20
    Nos. 753,C464-C466 (4)   4.60 .95

Manuel Mejia J. (1887-1958), banker and manager of the National Coffee Growers Association.

Julio Arboleda (1817-62), Writer, Soldier and Statesman A321

1966, Mar. 9   **Litho.**   *Perf. 14x13½*
754 A321 5c lt brn, lt yel grn & blk   .30 .20

Spanish Galleon, 16th Century A322

History of Maritime Mail: 15c, Rio Hacha brigantine, 1850. 20c, Uraba canoe. 40c, Magdalena River steamship and barge, 1900. 50c, Modern motor ship and sea gull.

1966, June 16   **Photo.**   **Unwmk.**
755 A322 5c org & multi   .35 .20
756 A322 15c car rose, blk & brn   .35 .20
757 A322 20c brt grn, org & blk   .35 .20
758 A322 40c dp bl & multi   .50 .20
759 A322 50c pale bl & multi   1.00 .40
    Nos. 755-759 (5)   2.55 1.20

Plumed Hogfish A323

Design: 10p, Bat ray and brittle starfish.

1966, Aug. 25   **Photo.**   *Perf. 12½x13*
760 A323 80c multi   .25 .20
761 A323 10p multi   7.50 5.00
    Nos. 760-761,C481-C483 (5)   23.35 17.30

Arms of
Venezuela,
Colombia
and Chile
A324

1966, Oct. 11 Litho. Perf. 14x13½
762 A324 40c yel & multi   .25   .20
     Nos. 762,C484-C485 (3)   .70   .60

Visits of Eduardo Frei and Raul Leoni, presidents of Chile and Venezuela.

Camilo Torres,
1766-1816,
Lawyer — A325

Portraits: 60c, Jorge Tadeo Lozano (1771-1816), naturalist. 1p, Francisco Antonio Zea (1776-1822), naturalist and politician.

Perf. 13½x14
1967, Jan. 18 Litho. Unwmk.
763 A325 25c vio & bis   .25   .20
764 A325 60c dk red brn & bis   .25   .20
765 A325 1p grn & bis   .35   .25
     Nos. 763-765,C486-C487 (5)   1.30 1.05

Issued to honor famous men of Colombia.

Map of
South
America
and Arms
A326

1967, Feb. 2 Litho. Perf. 14x13½
766 A326 40c multi   .25   .20
767 A326 60c multi   .25   .20
     Nos. 766-767,C488 (3)   .85   .60

Declaration of Bogota for cooperation and world peace, signed by Colombia, Chile, Ecuador, Peru and Venezuela.

Monochaetum Orchid and
Bee — A327

Orchid: 2p, Passiflora vitifolia and butterfly.

1967, May 23 Litho. Perf. 14
768 A327 25c multi   .25   .20
769 A327 2p multi   4.25 2.75
     Nos. 768-769,C489-C491 (5)   14.70 4.40

1st Natl. Orchid Exhib. and the Topical Phil. Flora and Fauna Exhib., Medellin, Apr. 1967.

Lions
Emblem — A328

SENA
Emblem — A329

1967, July 12 Litho. Perf. 13½x14
770 A328 10p multi   3.00 2.00

50th anniv. of Lions Intl. See No. C492.

Lithographed and Embossed
1967, Sept. 20 Unwmk.
771 A329 5p gold, brt grn & blk   1.40 .25

10th anniv. of Natl. Apprenticeship Service, SENA. See No. C494.

Gold Diadem in
Calima
Style — A330

Radar Installation
A331

Pre-Columbian Art: 3p, Gold statuette, ornamental globe and bird, horiz.

Perf. 13½x14, 14x13½
1967, Oct. 13 Photo.
772 A330 1.60p brt rose lil,   gold & brn   .80   .25
773 A330 3p dk bl, gold &   brn   1.25   .35
     Nos. 772-773,C495-C497 (5)   12.25 9.35

Meeting of the UPU Committee of Postal Studies, Bogota, Oct., 1967.

1968, May 14 Litho. Perf. 13½x14

1p, Map of communications network.
774 A331 50c brt yel grn, blk &   org brn   .20   .20
775 A331 1p multi   .30   .20
     Nos. 774-775,C498-C499 (4)   1.00   .80

20th anniv. of the National Telecommunications Service (TELECOM).

The
Eucharist — A332

St. Augustin, by
Gregorio
Vasquez — A333

1968, June 6 Litho. Perf. 13½x14
776 A332 60c multi   .25   .20
     Nos. 776,C500-C501 (3)   .75

39th Eucharistic Cong., Bogotá, 8/18-25.

1968, Aug. 13 Photo. Perf. 13

Designs: 60c, The Gathering of Manna, by Gregorio Vasquez. 1p, The Marriage of the Virgin, by Baltazar de Figueroa. 5p, Jeweled

monstrance, c. 1700. 10p, Pope Paul VI, painting by Roman Franciscan nuns.
777 A333 25c multicolored   .20   .20
778 A333 60c multicolored   .20   .20
779 A333 1p multicolored   .20   .20
780 A333 5p multicolored   .65   .20
781 A333 10p multicolored   1.25   .45
    a.   Souvenir sheet of 2   2.75 2.75
     Nos. 777-781,C502-C506 (10)   7.95 4.05

39th Eucharistic Congress. Bogotá, Aug. 18-25. No. 781a contains two imperf. stamps similar to Nos. 780-781.

Pope Paul
VI — A334

Arms of National
University — A335

1968, Aug. 22 Litho. Perf. 13½x14
782 A334 25c multi   .25   .20
     Nos. 782,C507-C509 (4)   .95   .80

Visit of Pope Paul VI to Colombia, 8/22-24.

1968, Oct. 29 Litho. Perf. 13½x14
783 A335 80c multi   .35   .25

Centenary of the founding of the National University. See No. C510.

Stamp of
Antioquia,
1868 — A336

Institute
Emblem — A337

1968, Nov. 20 Litho. Perf. 12x12½
784 A336 30c emer & bl   .30   .20

Souvenir Sheet
785 A336 5p lt olive & blue   5.00 5.00

Cent. of the 1st postage stamps of Antioquia and the 7th Natl. Phil. Exhib., Medellin, Nov. 20-29.

1969, Mar. 5 Litho. Perf. 13½x14
786 A337 20c multi   .35   .25

25th anniv. (in 1967) of the Inter-American Agricultural Sciences Institute. See No. C511.

Battle of Boyaca (Detail), by José
Maria Espinosa — A338

Design: 30c, Army of liberation crossing Pisba Pass, by Francisco Antonio Caro.

1969, July 24 Litho. Perf. 13½x14
787 A338 20c gold & multi   .35   .25
788 A338 30c gold & multi   .35   .25
     Nos. 787-788,C517 (3)   1.70   .85

Fight for independence, sesquicentennial.

"Poverty"
A339

1970, Mar. 1 Litho. Perf. 14
789 A339 30c bl & multi   .35   .25

Colombian Institute for Family Welfare and 10th anniv. of the Children's Rights Law.

Greek Mask and Pre-Columbian
Symbol of Literary Contest — A340

1970, Sept. 12 Litho. Perf. 14x13½
790 A340 30c dk brn, red org &   ocher   .25   .20

3rd Latin American Theatrical Festival of the Universities, Manizales, Sept. 12-20.

Colombian
Stamps,
Envelope
and
Emblem
A341

1970, Sept. 24 Litho. Perf. 14x13½
791 A341 2p brt bl & multi   .30   .25

Issued to publicize Philatelic Week.

Arms of
Ibague and
Discobolus
A342

1970, Oct. 13
792 A342 80c buff, emer & sepia   .25   .20

9th National Games in Ibague.

St. Theresa, by
Baltazar de
Figueroa — A343

1970, Oct. 28 Litho. Perf. 13½x14
793 A343 2p multi   .40   .25

Elevation of St. Theresa (1515-1582), to Doctor of the Church. See No. C568. For overprint see No. C568.

Casa Cural
A344

1971, May 20 Litho. Perf. 14x13½
794 A344 1.10p multi   .30 .20
  Fourth centenary (in 1970) of the founding of Guacari, Valle. See No. 809.

Dancers and Music, Currulao — A345

1p, Chicha Maya dancers and music.

1971 Litho. Perf. 13½x14
795 A345 1p pink & multi   .35 .25
796 A345 1.10p lt bl & multi   .35 .25
Souvenir Sheets
Imperf
797   Sheet of 3   3.50 3.50
  a. A345 2.50p Napanga   .35 .35
  b. A345 2.50p Joropo   .35 .35
  c. A345 5p Guabina   .70 .70
798   Sheet of 3   3.50 3.50
  a. A345 4p Bambuco   .55 .55
  b. A345 4p Cumbia   .55 .55
  c. A345 4p Currulao   .55 .55
  Issued: No. 795, 12/20; No. 796, 8/5; Nos. 797-798, 8/10.

Constitutional Assembly, by Delgado A346

1971, Oct. 2 Perf. 14
801 A346 80c multi   .25 .20
  Sequicentennial of Gran Colombian Constitutional Assembly in Rosario del Cucuta. See No. C589. For overprint see No. C589.

Arrows Emblem — A347

1972, Feb. 24 Perf. 13½x14
802 A347 60c blk & gray   .30 .20
  Inter-Governmental Committee on European Migration, 20th anniversary.

Student and World Map A348

1972, Mar. 15 Perf. 14x13½
803 A348 1.10p lt grn & brn   .25 .20
  20th anniv. of ICETEX, an organization which furnishes financial help for educational purposes and for technical studies abroad.

UN Emblem, Soldier and Frigate A349

1972, Apr. 7
804 A349 1.20p lt bl & multi   .25 .20
  Colombian Battalion in Korea, 20th anniv.

Mother Francisca Josefa del Castillo — A350

1972, Apr. 6 Perf. 13½x14
805 A350 1.20p brn & multi   .25 .20
  Tercentenary (in 1971) of the birth of Mother Francisca Josefa del Castillo, Poor Clare abbess and writer.

1972, Apr. 11
806 A351 1.10p multi   .35 .20
  Nos. 806,C569-C571 (4)   1.55 .85
  Colombian artisans.

Handicraft A351

Maxillaria Triloris — A352

1972, Apr. 20
807 A352 20p green & multi   6.50 .75
  10th Natl. Phil. Exhib., Medellin.

Emeralds — A353

1972, June 16 Litho. Perf. 13½x14
808 A353 1.10p multi   1.00 .20

Type of 1971
Design: Antonio Nariño House.
1972, June 17 Perf. 14x13½
809 A344 1.10p multi   .50 .25
  4th centenary, town of Leyva.

San Andres and Providencia Islands — A354

1972, June 24 Perf. 13½x14
810 A354 60c bl & multi   .25 .20
  Sesquicentennial of annexation by Colombia of San Andres and Providencia Islands.

Postal Service Emblem A355

1972, Nov. 15 Litho. Perf. 12½x12
811 A355 1.10p emerald   .25 .20

Family A356

1972, Nov. 23
812 A356 60c orange   .25 .20
  Social progress.

Radio League Emblem A357

Human Figure, Tamalameque A358

1973, Apr. 6 Litho. Perf. 12x12½
813 A357 60c lt bl, ultra & red   .25 .20
  40th anniversary of the Colombian Radio Amateurs' League.

1973, June 15 Litho. Perf. 13½x14
  Excavated Ceramic Artifacts: 1p, Winged urn, Tairona. 1.10p, Jug, Muisca.
814 A358 60c lt bl & multi   .35 .25
815 A358 1p org & multi   .70 .25
816 A358 1.10p vio bl & multi   .40 .25
  Nos. 814-816,C583-C586 (7)   4.60 2.50

Antonio Nariño, by José M. Espinosa — A359

Child — A360

1973, Dec. 13 Litho. Perf. 13½x14
817 A359 60c multi   .25 .20
  Sesquicentennial of the death of General Antonio Nariño (1765-1823).

1973, Dec. 17
818 A360 1.10p multi   .25 .20
  National Campaign for Children's Welfare.

Symbols of Financial Controls A361

1973, Dec. 20 Litho. Perf. 14x13½
819 A361 80c ultra, ocher & blk   .25 .20
  50th anniv. of Comptroller-general's Office.

Mother Laura Montoya — A362

1974, June 18 Litho. Perf. 13½x14
820 A362 1p multi   .25 .20
  Mother Laura Montoya (1874-1949), founder and Mother Superior of the Missionaries of Mary Immaculata and St. Catherine of Siena.

Runner and Games' Emblem A363

1974, July 18 Litho. Perf. 14x13½
821 A363 2p ver, yel & brn   .35 .20
  10th National Games, Pereira.

José Rivera A364

1974, Aug. 3 Litho. Perf. 14x13½
822 A364 10p grn & multi   1.25 .20
  50th anniv. of the publication of "La Voragine" (The Whirlpool) by José Eustasio Rivera.

Abstract
Pattern — A365

Train Emerging from
Tunnel — A366

1974, Oct. 24   Litho.   Perf. 13½x14
823   A365   1.10p multi   .25   .20
Cent. of Natl. Insurance Co. See No. C610.

1974, Nov. 27   Litho.   Perf. 13½x14
824   A366   1.10p multi   .25   .20
    Centenary of the Antioquia railroad.

Boy, Puppy and
Soccer
Ball — A367

Christmas: 1p, Girl with racket and kitten.

1974, Dec. 9
825   A367   80c multi   .25   .20
826   A367   1p multi   .25   .20

A368

1975, Apr. 11   Litho.   Perf. 14x13½
827   A368   80c Gold Animal   .40   .25
828   A368   1.10p Gold necklace   .40   .25
   Nos. 827-828,C621-C622 (4)   6.45   1.30
    Pre-Columbian Sinu culture artifacts.
For surcharge see No. 840.

Guglielmo
Marconi — A369

Santa Marta
Cathedral — A370

1975, June 2   Litho.   Perf. 13½x14
829   A369   3p multi   .30   .20
    Birth centenary of Guglielmo Marconi
(1874-1937), Italian electrical engineer and
inventor.

1975, July 26
830   A370   80c multi   .30   .20
    400th anniv. of Santa Marta City. See No.
C623.

Rafael
Nuñez — A371

Arms of
Medellin — A372

1975, Sept. 28   Litho.   Perf. 13½x14
831   A371   1.10p multi   .30   .20
    Rafael Nunez (1825-1894), philosopher,
poet, political leader, birth sesquicentenary.
For surcharge see No. 848.

1975-79   Perf. 13½x14, 12 (1.20p)
832   A372   1p shown   .35   .20
833   A372   1.20p Ibagué   .30   .20
834   A372   1.20p Tunja   .20   .20
835   A372   1.50p Cucuta   .50   .20
836   A372   1.50p Cartagena   .20   .20
836A   A372   4p Sogamoso   .90   .20
837   A372   5p Popayan   .45   .20
838   A372   5p Barranquilla   .45   .20
839   A372   10p San Gil   .90   .20
839A   A372   10p Socorro   .90   .20
   Nos. 832-839A (10)   5.15   2.00

    1p for the tercentenary of Medellin; No. 835,
the cent. of Cucuta's reconstruction.
    Issued: 1p, 11/4; No. 835, 11/29; No. 836,
2/10/76; No. 833, 7/30/76; No. 834, 12/2076;
No. 837, 8/30/77; No. 838, 9/20/77; 10p,
8/9/79; 4p, 9/14/79.
    See Nos. 905-913, C818. For surcharge see
No. 849.

No. 827 Surcharged

1975   Perf. 14x13½
840   A368   1.20p on 80c multi   .25   .20

Purace Indians,
Cauca — A373

1976, Nov. 10   Litho.   Perf. 13½x14
841   A373   1.50p multi   .25   .20

Callicore
A374

5p, Morpho (butterfly). 20p, Anthurium.

1976, Nov. 17   Perf. 12
842   A374   3p multicolored   .85   .20
843   A374   5p multicolored   1.25   .20
844   A374   20p multicolored   3.75   .75
   Nos. 842-844 (3)   5.85   1.15

Rotary
Emblem — A375

1976, Dec. 3   Litho.   Perf. 12
845   A375   1p multicolored   .25   .20
    Rotary Club of Colombia, 50th anniversary.

Declaration of Independence, by John
Trumbull — A376

1976, Dec. 21   Litho.   Perf. 12
846   A376   Strip of 3   9.00   10.50
   a.-c.   30p any single   2.75   2.00
    American Bicentennial. No. 846 printed in
sheets of 4 triptychs.

Policeman with
Dog — A377

1976, Dec. 29   Perf. 13½x14
847   A377   1.50p multicolored   .25   .20
    Honoring the National Police.
For surcharge see No. 850.

Nos. 831, 834, 847 Surcharged in
Light Brown
1977, June   Litho.   Perf. 13½x14, 12
848   A371   2p on 1.10p multi   .40   .20
849   A372   2p on 1.20p multi   .20   .20
850   A377   2p on 1.50p multi   .25   .20
   Nos. 848-850 (3)   .85   .60

Souvenir Sheet

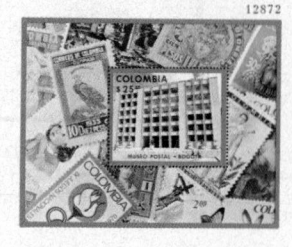

Postal Museum, Bogota — A378

1977, July 27   Litho.   Perf. 14
855   A378   25p multi   2.50   2.50
    Postal Museum, Bogota.

Mother and
Child — A379

1977-78   Litho.   Perf. 12
856   A379   2p multi   .20   .20
857   A379   2.50p multi ('78)   1.50   .20
    National good nutrition plan.
Issue dates: 2p, Aug. 30; 2.50p, Jan. 26.

Jacana and
Eichhornia
A380

Fidel Cano, by
Francisco
Cano — A381

20p, Mayan cotinga and pyrostegia venusta.

1977, Sept. 6   Litho.   Perf. 14
858   A380   10p multicolored   2.25   .25
859   A380   20p multicolored   3.75   .45
   Nos. 858-859,C644-C647 (6)   9.20   1.50

1977, Sept. 16   Perf. 14
860   A381   4p multicolored   .25   .20
    90th anniversary of El Espectador, newspa-
per founded by Fidel Cano.

Abacus and
Alphabet
A382

Cattleya
Triannae
A383

1977, Sept. 16   Perf. 13½x14
861   A382   3p multicolored   .25   .20
    Popular education.

1978-79   Litho.   Perf. 12
862   A383   2.50p multi   .75   .20
863   A383   3p multi ('79)   .75   .20
    Issue dates: 2.50p, Apr. 18. 3p, May 10.

Sprinting and Games Emblem A384

Sports: a, sprinting. b, basketball. c, baseball. d, boxing. e, bicycling. f, fencing. g, soccer. h, gymnastics. i, judo. j, weight lifting. k, wrestling. l, swimming. m, tennis. n, target shooting. o, volleyball. p, water polo.

1978, June 27   Litho.   Perf. 14
868   Sheet of 16   22.50 22.50
    a.-p. A384 10p, any single   1.00   .20
13th Central American and Caribbean Games, Medellin.

"Sigma 2" by Alvaro Herrán A385

1978, June 30
869 A385 8p multicolored   .45 .20
Chamber of Commerce, Bogota, centenary.

Gen. Tomás Cipriano de Mosquera (1778-1878), Statesman A386

1978, Oct. 6   Litho.   Perf. 12
870 A386 6p multicolored   .45 .20

Anthurium Narinenses — A387

1979, July 23   Perf. 12
871 A387 3p red & multi   .25 .20
872 A387 3p purple & multi   .25 .20
873 A387 3p rose & purple   .25 .20
874 A387 3p white & multi   .25 .20
    a.   Block of 4, #871-874   1.75 1.75

Gen. Rafael Uribe, by Acevedo Bernal — A388

1979, Oct. 31   Litho.   Perf. 12
875 A388 8p multicolored   .40 .20
Gen. Uribe, statesman, 60th death anniv.

Village, by Leonor Alarcon — A389

1979, Nov. 22   Perf. 14
876 A389 15p multicolored   1.00 .35
Community Work Boards, 20th anniversary.

Introduction of Color Television A390

1980, Mar. 4   Litho.   Perf. 14
877 A390 5p multicolored   .50 .20

Bullfight, Arms of Cali A391

1980, Mar. 25
878 A391 5p multicolored   .70 .20
Cali Tourist Festival, 12/25/79-1/2/80.

"Learn to Write" — A392

a, shown. b, "a." c, "b." d, "c." e, "ch." f, "d." g, "e." h, "f." i, "g." j, "h." k, "i." l, "j." m, "k." n, "l." o, "ll." p, "m." q, "n." r, "ñ." s, "o." t, "p." u, "q." v, "r." w, "s." x, "t." y, "u." z, "v." aa, "w." ab, "x." ac, "y." ad, "z."

1980, Apr. 25   Litho.   Perf. 12½
879   Block of 30   25.00 25.00
    a.-ad. A392 4p, any single   .75   .20
Each stamp shows letter of alphabet and corresponding animal or subject. Issued in sheets of 90 (10x9).

Villavicencio Festival — A393

Design: 9p, Vallenato festival.

1980   Litho.   Perf. 14
880 A393 5p multicolored   .45 .20
881 A393 9p multicolored   .45 .20
    Issue dates: 5p, July 15; 9p, June 17.

Gustavo Uribe Ramirez and Tree A394

1980, Aug. 5   Litho.   Perf. 12
882 A394 10p multicolored   .90 .20
Gustavo Uribe Ramirez (1893-1968), ecologist.

Narino Palace (Former Presidential Residence) — A395

1980, Sept. 19   Litho.   Perf. 14
883 A395 5p multicolored   .60 .20

Monument to First Pioneers of 1819, Armenia A396

1980, Oct. 14
884 A396 5p multicolored   .50 .20

11th National Games, Neiva — A397

1980, Nov. 28   Perf. 13½x14
885 A397 5p multicolored   .45 .20

Fight against Cancer — A398

1980, Dec. 9
886 A398 10p multicolored   .40 .20

Xavier University Law Faculty, 50th Anniversary A399

1980, Dec. 16   Litho.   Perf. 14½
887 A399 20p multicolored   .60 .20

Death of Bolivar — A400

1980, Dec. 17   Perf. 12
888 A400 25p multicolored   1.00 .60
Simon Bolivar, death sesquicentennial. See No. C696.

José Maria Obando, President of Colombia A401

115th Anniv. of Constitution (Former Presidents): b, Jose Hilario Lopez. c, Manuel Murillo Toro. d, Santiago Perez. e, Rafael Reyes. f, Carlos E. Restrepo. g, Jose Vicente Concha. h, Miguel Abadia Mendez. i, Eduardo Santos. j, Mariano Ospina Perez.

1981, June 9   Litho.   Perf. 12
889   Strip of 10   6.00
    a.-j. A401 5p multicolored   .50 .20

1981, Sept. 23   Litho.   Perf. 12
Designs: a, Rafael Nunez (1825-94). b, Marco Fidel Suarez (1855-1927). c, Pedro Nel Ospina (1858-1927). d, Enrique Olaya Herrera (1880-1937). e, Alfonso Lopez Pumarejo (1886-1959). f, Aquileo Parra (1825-1900). g, Santos Gutierrez (1820-72). h, Tomas Cipriano de Mosquera (1789-1878). i, Mariano Ospina Rodriguez. j, Pedro Alcantara Herran (1800-72).

890   Strip of 10   50.00
    a.-j. A401 7p multicolored   3.50 .50

1981, Aug. 11   Litho.   Perf. 12
Designs like No. 889.
891   Strip of 10   50.00
    a.-j. A401 7p multicolored   4.00 1.00

1981, Nov. 11   Litho.   Perf. 12
Designs: a, Manuel Maria Mallarino. b, Santos Acosta. c, Eustorgio Salgar. d, Julian Trujillo. e, Francisco Javier Zaldua. f, Guillermo Leon Valencia. g, Laureano Gomez. h, Manuel A. Sanclemente. i, Miguel Antonio Caro. j, Jose Eusebio Otalora.

892   Strip of 10   30.00
    a.-j. A401 7p multicolored   2.50 .40

1981, Dec. 15   Litho.   Perf. 12
Designs: a, Ruben Piedrahita Arango. b, Jorge Holguin. c, Ramon Gonzalez Valencia. d, Jose Manuel Marroquin. e, Carlos Holguin. f, Bartolome Calvo. g, Sergio Camargo. h, Jose Maria Rojas Garrido. i, J.M. Campo Serrano. j, Eliseo Payan.

893   Strip of 10   25.00
    a.-j. A401 7p multicolored   1.75 .30

1982, May 3   Perf. 12
Designs: a, Simon Bolivar. b, Francisco de Paula Santander. c, Joaquin Mosquera. d, Domingo Caicedo. e, Jose Ignacio de Marquez. f, Roberto Urdaneta Arbelaez. g, Carlos Lozano y Lozano. h, Guillermo Quintero Calderon. i, Jose de Obaldia. j, Juan de Dios Aranzazu.

894   Strip of 10   13.50
    a.-j. A401 7p multicolored   1.25 .20
        See No. 1110.

Jose Maria Villa and West Bridge over Cauca River A404

1981, Nov. 25   Litho.   Perf. 14x13½
895 A404 60p multicolored   1.40 .30

Agrarian, Mineral and Industrial Credit Bank, 50th Anniv. — A405

1981, Dec. 9 Litho. **Perf. 14**
896 A405 15p multicolored .35 .20

Los Nevados Park — A406

1981, Dec. 10 Litho. **Perf. 13½x14**
897 A406 20p multicolored .60 .20

Girl Sitting on Fence — A407

1982, Feb. 22 Litho. **Perf. 12½x12**
898 Strip of 3 4.50 4.50
a. A407 30p shown 1.00 .35
b. A407 30p Girl, basket 1.00 .35
c. A407 30p Boy, wheelbarrow 1.00 .35

Floral Bouquet — A408

Hipotecario Bank, 50th Anniv. — A409

Various floral arrangements (background): a, Flowers in vase (gray). b, Roses (red). c, Daisies (green). d, Roses (blue). e, Assorted (red). f, Yellow & orange flowers (green). g, Assorted (lilac). h, Roses (gray). i, Pink flowers (green). j, Flowers in basket (gray).

1982, July 28
900 Strip or block of 10 15.00 15.00
a.-j. A408 7p, any single 1.50 .30

1982, July 29 **Perf. 14**
901 A409 9p black & green .35 .20

St. Thomas Aquinas (1225-1274) A410

Paintings by Zurbaran.

1982 Litho. **Perf. 12**
902 A410 5p multicolored .25 .20
903 A410 5p St. Teresa of Avila .25 .20
904 A410 5p St. Francis of Assisi .25 .20
Nos. 902-904 (3) .75 .60

Issued: No. 902, 8/6; No. 903, 9/28; No. 904, 10/4.

Arms Type of 1975
1982-90 Litho. **Perf. 14, 12 (50p)**
905 A372 10p Buga .35 .20
906 A372 10p San Juan de Pasto 1.10 .20
907 A372 16p Rionegro .60 .20
908 A372 20p Santa Fe de Bogota .90 .20
909 A372 20p Santiago de Cali .25 .20
910 A372 23p Honda .65 .25
911 A372 50p Cartago .60 .20
912 A372 55p Antioquia ('86) .90 .25
Nos. 905-912 (8) 5.35 1.70

Issued: 16p, 23p, No. 905, 12/7; No. 908, 3/1/83; No. 906, 4/12/83; No. 909, 7/25/86; 55p, 8/5/86; 50p, 5/30/90.
See No. C818.

Gabriel Marquez, 1982 Nobel Prize, Literature — A412

1982, Dec. 10 **Perf. 13½x14**
917 A412 7p gray & green .25 .20
See Nos. C731-C732.

Public Education Bicentenary (Society of Mary for Education) A413

1983, May 6
918 A413 9p gold & blk .35 .20

José Maria Espinosa Prieto, Painter — A414

250th Anniv. of City of Cucuta — A415

1983, June 3 **Perf. 12**
919 A414 9p Self-portrait, 1860 .30 .20

1983, June 23 Litho. **Perf. 12**
920 A415 9p multicolored .25 .20

Porfirio Barba-Jacob (1883-1942), Poet — A416

1983, July 29 Litho. **Perf. 13½x14**
921 A416 9p Portrait .25 .20

Simon Bolivar, 200th Birth Anniv. A417

1983, July 24 **Perf. 12**
922 A417 9p multicolored .25 .20
See Nos. C736-C737.

Royal Spanish Botanical Expedition, 200th Anniv. — A418

1983, Aug. 18 **Perf. 14**
923 A418 9p Cinchona lancefolia .25 .20
924 A418 9p Passiflora laurifolia .25 .20
925 A418 60p Cinchona cordiflora 1.75 .50
Nos. 923-925,C738-C740 (6) 6.25 1.70

Dawn in the Andes, by Alejandro Obregon A420

1983, Oct. 5 Litho. **Perf. 12**
928 A420 20p multicolored .45 .20
See No. C741.

Francisco de Paula Santander (1792-1840), General — A421

1984, Mar. 6 Litho. **Perf. 14½x14**
929 A421 12p light olive green .25 .20
930 A421 12p pale carmine .25 .20
931 A421 12p light ultra .25 .20
Nos. 929-931 (3) .75 .60

Admiral Jose Prudencio Padilla (1784-1831) — A423

1984, May 17 Litho. **Perf. 12**
933 A423 10p multicolored .30 .20

Luis Antonio Calvo (1882-1945) Composer — A424

1984, July 26
934 A424 18p multicolored .30 .20

Diego Fallon (1834-1905), Educator, Musician, Poet — A425

1984, Aug. 31 **Perf. 12**
935 A425 20p multicolored .45 .20

Candelario Obeso (1849-1884), Writer — A426

1984, Sept. 4 **Perf. 14x13½**
936 A426 20p multicolored .45 .20

Site of Marandua, Future City A427

1984, Sept. 28 **Perf. 12**
937 A427 15p multicolored .30 .20
See No. C744.

Christmas 1984 A428

Nativity and Children Playing, by Jose Uriel Sierra, Age 7.

1984, Dec. 14
938 A428 12p multicolored .30 .20
See No. C746.

Dr. Luis Eduardo Lopez, Education Minister A429

1984, Dec. 21
939 A429 22p multicolored .35 .20

Maria Concepcion Loperena de Fernandez de Castro, Independence War Heroine — A430

1985, Jan. 6
940 A430 12p multicolored .25 .20

Gonzalo Mejia (1885-1956) — A431

1985, Feb. 25
941 A431 12p Portrait, biplane, camera .35 .20

Aviation, motion picture and meat exporting industrialist.

Self-portrait with Wife — A432

1985, Feb. 25
942 A432 37p multicolored .65 .30

Pedro Nel Gomez (1899-1984), painter. See No. C748.

Fauna A433

1985 **Perf. 14**
943 A433 12p Hydrochaeris hydrochaeris .45 .30

Perf. 13
944 A433 15p Felis pardalis .45 .25
945 A433 15p Tremarctos ornatus, vert. .45 .25
946 A433 20p Tapirus pinchaque .75 .30
Nos. 943-946, C758 (5) 3.60 1.35

Carlos Gardel (1890-1935), Entertainer A434

Camina Literacy Program — A435

1985, June 23 **Perf. 14**
947 A434 15p Portrait, Fokker F-31 Trimotor .25 .20

1985, Nov. 25 **Perf. 13½x14**
948 A435 15p Tree, alphabet .30 .20

Christmas 1985 A436

1985, Dec. 4 **Litho.** **Perf. 13**
949 A436 15p multicolored .35 .20

Rafael Pombo Children's Foundation. See No. C755.

Eduardo Carranza (b. 1913), Poet — A437

Colombian Free University, Cent. — A438

1986, Feb. 13
950 A437 18p multicolored .25 .20

1986, Feb. 14
951 A438 18p multicolored .30 .20

Gen. Antonio Ricaurte (b. 1786), Liberator A439

1986, May 7 **Litho.** **Perf. 13**
952 A439 18p Leiva birthplace .25 .20

Jose Asuncion Silva (1865-1896), Poet, and Scene from Nocturno — A440

1986, May 30 **Litho.** **Perf. 12**
953 A440 18p multicolored .25 .20

Fernando Gomez Martinez (1897-1985), Journalist — A441

1986, June 19
954 A441 24p multicolored .30 .20

Santiago de Cali, 450th Anniv. A442

1986, July 25 **Litho.** **Perf. 13**
955 A442 25p La Merced .30 .20

A443

A444

Monsignor Jose Vicente Castro Silva (1885-1968), rector of the Mayor del Rosario School: portrait by Ricardo Gomez.

1986, Aug. 4 **Litho.** **Perf. 12**
956 A443 20p multicolored .25 .20

1986, Oct. 14 **Litho.** **Perf. 12**
957 A444 40p Natl. University .45 .20

Faculties: Fine Arts, cent., and Architecture, 50th anniv.

Rafael Maya (1897-1980), Poet, and Salamanca University Entrance — A445

1986, Oct. 15
958 A445 25p multicolored .30 .20

See No. C772.

Condor in Flight — A446

Inia goefrenis A446a

No. 962, Inia goefrenis. No. 963, Procyon cancrivorus. No. 964, Monachus tropicalis. No. 965, Pteronura brasiliensis. No. 966, Trichechus manatus. No. 967, Odocoileus virginianus. No. 968, Trogon personatos personatos. Nos. 962-968 horiz.

1986-89 **Litho.** **Perf. 12**
959 A446 20p ultra .25 .20
960 A446 25p ultra ('87) .30 .20

Perf. 14½x14, 14x14½
961 A446a 30p grn ('87) .45 .20
962 A446a 30p dull vio ('87) .45 .20

Engr.
Wmk. 334
963 A446a 35p chest brn ('88) .65 .20
964 A446a 35p dark grn ('88) .65 .20
965 A446a 40p deep org ('88) .65 .20
966 A446a 40p gray ('88) .75 .20

967 A446a 40p tan ('89) .75 .20
968 A446a 45p dark vio ('88) .75 .20
Nos. 959-968 (10) 5.65 2.00

Issued: 20p, 11/6; 25p, 5/25; No. 961, 6/8; No. 962, 12/24; No. 963, 8/6; No. 964, 9/20; No. 965, 9/20; No. 966, 11/29; No. 967, 4/29; No. 968, 12/16.
See Nos. 996, 1000, C778-C781.

A447

A448

1987, Jan. 29 **Unwmk.** **Perf. 12**
969 A447 25p multicolored .45 .20

Pedro Uribe Mejia (1886-1972), pioneer of Colombian coffee industry.

1987, May 3 **Perf. 13½x13**
970 A448 500p Santa Barbara Church 5.50 1.75

Mompox, 450th anniv.

Writers A449

Portraits and scenes from works: 70p, Jorge Isaacs (1837-1895), novelist, and scene from *Maria*. 90p, Aurelio Martinez Mutis (1884-1954), poet, and scene from *La Epopeya del Condor*.

1987 **Perf. 12**
971 A449 70p multicolored .75 .25
972 A449 90p multicolored 1.10 .40

Issue dates: 70p, July 28. 90p, Sept. 2.

A450

A451

Social Security & Communications.

1987 **Litho.** **Perf. 13½x13**
973 A450 35p multicolored .40 .20

1988, May 25   Litho.   Perf. 12

Natl. Anthem, Cent.: Score, lyricist Rafael Nunez and composer Oreste Sindici. Dated 1987.

974 A451 70p multicolored   .65 .25

Human Rights — A452

Perf. 14½x14, 14x14½

1988-89   Engr.
975 A452 30p Life   .30 .20
976 A452 35p Suffrage   .30 .20
977 A452 40p Association, horiz.   .40 .20
978 A452 45p Culture, horiz.   .30 .20
    Nos. 975-978 (4)   1.30 .80

Issued: 30p, 35p, 5/12; 40p, 7/1; 45p, 10/27/89.
See Nos. C797, C807.

Pasto, 450th Anniv. A453

1988, May 20   Litho.   Perf. 12
979 A453 60p Cathedral, Pasto   .60 .20
    Dated 1987.

Bogota Aqueduct and Sewage System, Cent. — A454

1988, May 20
980 A454 100p Waterfall   1.10 .30

Maria Currea de Aya (1888-1985), Women's Rights Activist — A455

1988, May 27
981 A455 80p multicolored   .85 .25

A456

A457

Sailfish, *Istiaophorus Americanus.*

Perf. 14x13½
1988, July 19   Engr.   Wmk. 334
982 A456 (A) dark blue   4.25 2.25
983 A456 (B) Prus blue   1.25   .40

At the time of issue, No. 982 was sold for 400p and No. 983 for 100p. See type A486.

Unwmk.
1988, Aug. 10   Litho.   Perf. 12
984 A457 120p multicolored   1.10   .35

San Bartolome College, founded in 1604.

Jorge Alvarez Lleras (1885-1952), Engineer and Director of the Natl. Astronomical Observatory — A458

1988, Aug. 17
985 A458 90p multicolored   .80 .35

Pres. Eduardo Santos (1888-1974) A459

1988, Aug. 30
986 A459 80p multicolored   .70 .20

Andres Bello Seminary A460

Unwmk.
1988, Dec. 27   Litho.   Perf. 12
987 A460 115p multicolored   .95 .20

Adpostal, 25th Anniv. A461

1989, May 3
988 A461 45p multicolored   .35 .20

Military Leaders — A462

Bolivar and Santander at the Los Llanos Campaign — A463

1989   Litho.   Perf. 12
989 A462 40p Santander   .50 .25
990 A462 40p Bolivar   .50 .25
991 A463 45p multicolored   .50 .25
    Nos. 989-991 (3)   1.50 .75

Liberation campaign, 170th anniv.
Issued: No. 989, 8/25; No. 990, 7/25; 45p, 8/7.

From Boyaca to Santa Fe — A464

1989, Aug. 7   Litho.   Perf. 12
992   45p multicolored   1.50 .45
993   45p multicolored   1.50 .45
 a. A464 Pair, #992-993   4.00 2.00

Liberation campaign, 170th anniv.

Liberation Campaign Triptych — A466

Designs: a, Gen. Santander, liberation force. b, Simon Bolivar riding mount. c, Insurgent cavalry.

Unwmk.
1989, Aug. 7   Litho.   Perf. 13
994 A466 Strip of 3   3.50 1.50
 a.-c.   45p any single   1.00   .35

Liberation Campaign, 170th anniv.

Tunja, 450th Anniv. A467

1989, Aug. 8   Perf. 12
995 A467 45p multicolored   .35 .20

Fauna Type of 1988

Designs: No. 996, Harpia harpyja, horiz. No. 997, Urocyon cinereoargenteus. No. 998, Dendrobates histrionicus. No. 1000, Phenacosaurus indenenae. No. 1001, Cebuella pygmaea. No. 1002, Eurypyga helias, horiz.

Perf. 14½x14, 14x14½
1989-90   Engr.   Wmk. 334
996   A446a 45p black   1.00 .20
997   A446a 50p blue gray   .50 .20
998   A446a 50p deep claret   .30 .20
999   A446a 55p red brown   .75 .20
1000 A446a 60p brown   .50 .20
1001 A446a 60p org brown   .50 .20
    Nos. 996-1001 (6)   3.55 1.20

Issued: 45p, 9/7; Nos. 997, 1000, 3/1/90; No. 998, 4/25; 55p, 8/18; No. 1001, 8/6.

A468

A469

1989, Aug. 30   Unwmk.   Perf. 12
1011 A468 135p multicolored   1.10   .75

City of Armenia, cent.

1990, Mar. 28   Litho.   Perf. 12
1012 A469 60p Espeletia hartwegi-
             ana   .35   .20

Gen. Francisco De Paula Santander (1792-1840) — A470

1990, May 6   Perf. 14x13½
1013 A470 50p multicolored   .35   .20
    Nos. 1013,C823-C827 (6)   3.75 2.50
    See Nos. 1046-1047.

General Santander Police Academy, 50th Anniv. — A471

1990, May 16   Perf. 12
1014 A471 60p multicolored   .35   .20

Department of La Guajira A473

1990, July 1   Perf. 12
1016 A473 60p multicolored   .55   .20

Ceiba Pentandra A474

1990, July 15   Litho.   Perf. 12
1017 A474 60p multicolored   .35   .20

A475

A476

1990, Aug. 8 **Litho.** *Perf. 12*
1018 A475 70p Tibouchina
lepidota .65 .25

Unwmk.
1990, Aug. 28 **Litho.** *Perf. 14*
1019 A476 70p Ceroxylon
quindiuense .40 .20

A477

A478

1990, Sept. 28 *Perf. 12*
1020 A477 60p St. John Bosco .45 .20

Salesian Order in Colombia, cent.

1991, Mar. 28 **Litho.** *Perf. 12*
1021 A478 70p multicolored .40 .20

Miraculous Christ, Pilgrimage Church of Buga.

Moths and
Butterflies
A479

1991, Apr. 18 **Litho.** *Perf. 14*
1022 A479 70p Callithea philo-
tima .65 .20
1023 A479 70p Anaea syene,
vert. .65 .20
1024 A479 80p Thecla
coronata, vert. .80 .20
1025 A479 80p Agrias amydon .85 .20
1026 A479 170p Morpho rhetenor 1.75 .30
1027 A479 190p Heliconius lon-
garenus 2.00 .30
Nos. 1022-1027 (6) 6.70 1.40

Nos. 1025-1027 are airmail.

New
Constitution
A480

1991, July 4 **Litho.** *Perf. 14*
1028 A480 70p multicolored .35 .20

A481

A482

1991, July 19 *Perf. 12*
1029 A481 80p multicolored .40 .20

Pres. Dario Echandia Olaya (1897-1989).
See No. 1042.

1991, Aug. 7
1030 A482 70p multicolored .35 .20

Col. Antanasio Girardot (1791-1813).

A483

A484

1991, Aug. 15 **Litho.** *Perf. 14*
1031 A483 80p multicolored .40 .20

Luis Carlos Galan Sarmiento (1943-1989),
political reformer.

1991, Aug. 24 *Perf. 12*

Pre-Columbian Artifacts: 80p, Statue of cat
god. No. 1033, Pitcher from tomb of high official. No. 1034, Statue with two heads. 210p,
Flying fish, horiz.

1032 A484 80p multicolored .55 .20
1033 A484 90p multicolored .75 .20
1034 A484 90p multicolored .75 .20
1035 A484 210p multicolored 1.75 .30
Nos. 1032-1035 (4) 3.80 .90

Nos. 1034-1035 are airmail.

Colonial
Architecture
A485

80p, Cloister of St. Augustine, Tunja. No.
1037, Community Bridge, Chia. No. 1038,
Roadside Chapel, Pamplona. 190p, Church of
Immaculate Conception, Bogota.

1991 **Litho.** *Perf. 12*
1036 A485 80p multi .55 .20
1037 A485 90p multi .90 .20
1038 A485 90p multi, vert. .75 .20
1039 A485 190p multi, vert. 1.50 .25
Nos. 1036-1039 (4) 3.70 .85

Issue dates: No. 1037, Sept. 9; others, Sept.
27. Nos. 1038-1039 are airmail.

Istiaphorus
Americanus
A486

1991, Sept. 3 *Perf. 14*
1040 A486 830p multicolored 5.50 1.40

Colombian
Police
Force,
Cent.
A487

1991, Oct. 12 *Perf. 12*
1041 A487 80p multicolored .45 .20

President Type of 1991

Pres. Alberto Lleras Camargo (1906-1990)

1991, Nov. 5
1042 A481 80p multicolored .40 .20

A489

A490

1991, Dec. 17 **Litho.** *Perf. 12*
1043 A489 80p Sogamoso City
Hall .45 .20

1992 **Litho.** *Perf. 14*

Designs: No. 1044, Diana Turbay Quintero
(1950-91), journalist. No. 1045, Indalecio
Lievano Aguirre (1917-82), diplomat.

1044 A490 80p multicolored .40 .20
1045 A490 80p multicolored .40 .20

Issued: No. 1044, Jan. 24; No. 1045, Apr.
21.

Santander Type of 1990 and

Battle of Boyaca — A491a

1992, Apr. 2 *Perf. 14*
Size: 26x37mm
1046 A470 80p Monument .40 .30
1047 A470 190p Portrait 1.00 .65

Souvenir Sheet
Perf. 13½x14
1047A A491a 950p multicolored 5.50 5.50

Nos. 1047-1047A are airmail. Gen. Francisco de Paula Santander, bicent. of birth.

A492

A493

Ministers of Justice: 100p, Enrique Low
Murtra (1939-91). 110p, Rodrigo Lara Bonilla
(1946-84).

1992, Apr. 30 **Litho.** *Perf. 12*
1048 A492 100p multicolored .40 .20
1049 A492 110p multicolored .50 .20

1992, May 18 *Perf. 14*
1050 A493 110p multicolored .60 .30

15th natl. games, Barranquilla.

Wildlife — A494

1992, Apr. 14 **Litho.** *Perf. 12*
1051 A494 (B) Oroaetus icidori 1.50 .60
1052 A494 (A) Tremarctos
ornatus 8.00 2.50

Nos. 1051-1052 had face values of 200p
and 950p respectively on date of issue.

Endangered
Species
A495

1992, Aug. 4
1053 A495 100p Crocodylus
acatus 1.00 .35
1054 A495 100p Vultur gryphus,
vert. 1.00 .35

A496

A497

1992, Aug. 24   Litho.   Perf. 14
1055 A496 100p multicolored   .45   .30
1056 A496 110p multicolored   .45   .30

Maria Lopez de Escobar, founder of the House of the Mother and Child. No. 1056 is airmail.

1992, Sept. 23   Litho.   Perf. 12
1057 A497 100p multicolored   .45   .30

Conference of First Ladies of the Americas and Caribbean, Cartagena.

Recycling — A498

1992, Oct. 9   Litho.   Perf. 12
1058 A498 100p multicolored   .45   .30

Discovery of America, 500th Anniv. — A499

Paintings: 100p, Zenaida, by Ana Mercedes Hoyos. No. 1060, Estudio Para 1/500, by Beatriz Gonzalez. No. 1061, Blue Eagle, by Alejandro Obregon. 230p, Cantileo, by Luis Luna. 260p, Corn, by Antonio Caro. 400p, Grand Curtain, by Luis Caballero. 440p, Homage to Guatavita, by Alejandro Obregon.

1992, Oct. 5   Litho.   Perf. 13½x14
1059 A499 100p multicolored   .40   .30
1060 A499 110p multicolored   .45   .30
1061 A499 110p multicolored   .45   .30
1062 A499 230p multicolored   .95   .70
1063 A499 260p multicolored   1.10   .80
     Nos. 1059-1063 (5)   3.35   2.40

Souvenir Sheets
Perf. 12
1064 A499 400p multicolored   2.00   2.00
1065 A499 440p multicolored   2.00   2.00

Nos. 1061-1063 are airmail.

World Post Day — A500

1992, Oct. 19   Litho.   Perf. 12
1066 A500 (B) multicolored   .95   .65

No. 1066 had face value of 200p on day of issue.

Christmas — A501

Children's paintings of: 100p, Nativity scene. 110p, Adoration of the Magi.

1992, Nov. 20   Litho.   Perf. 12
1067 A501 100p multicolored   .45   .30
1068 A501 110p multicolored   .45   .30

No. 1068 is airmail.

Three Musicians, by Fernando Botero A502

1993, Feb. 5   Litho.   Perf. 12
1069 A502 (B) multicolored   .95   .65

No. 1069 had a face value of 250p on day of issue.

Lions Intl. Campaign Against Amblyopia A503

1993, Mar. 26   Perf. 14
1070 A503 100p multicolored   .40   .30

Holy Week in Popayan A504

1993, Apr. 5   Perf. 14x13½
1071 A504 (B) multicolored   .95   .65

No. 1071 had a face value of 250p on day of issue.

A505

A506

1993, Apr. 7   Perf. 12
1072 A505 (B) multicolored   .95   .65

Pan American Health Org., 90th anniv. No. 1072 had a face value of 250p on day of issue.

1993, Apr. 14
1073 A506 (B) multicolored   .95   .65

Franciscans of Mary Immaculate, cent. No. 1073 had a face value of 250p on day of issue.

A507

A508

1993, Apr. 22   Litho.   Perf. 14
1074 A507 (B) multicolored   .90   .60

EXFILBO '93, 18th Natl. Philatelic Exhibition. No. 1074 had a face value of 250p on day issue.

1993, July 2   Litho.   Perf. 12
1075 A508 250p Guillermo Cano, writer   1.00   .65

Human Rights A509

Rights: a, 150p, Of prisoners. b, 150p, Of the elderly. c, 200p, Of the infirm. d, 200p, Of children. e, 220p, Of women. f, 220p, Of the poor. g, 460p, To clean environment. h, 520p, Of indigenous people.
Painting: 800p, Peace, Rights, and Freedom, by Alfredo Vivero, vert.

1993, June 10   Perf. 14
1076 A509 Block of 8, #a.-h.   10.00   7.00

Souvenir Sheet
1077 A509 800p multicolored   5.00   5.00

Nos. 1076e-1076h are airmail.

Amazon Region of Colombia — A510

No. 1078a, Parrot. No. 1078b, Anaconda. No. 1079a, Victoria regia. No. 1079b, Flor ipecacuana. 880p, Map, native, horiz.

1993   Litho.   Perf. 12
1078 A510 150p Pair, #a.-b.   1.25   .75
1079 A510 220p Pair, #a.-b.   1.75   1.00

Souvenir Sheet
1080 A510 880p multicolored   4.00   4.00

Nos. 1079-1080 are airmail.

Famous People — A511

Designs: a, 150p, Alberto Pumarejo (1893-1970). b, 150p, Lorencita Villegas de Santos (1892-1960). c, 200p, Meliton Rodriguez (1875-1942). d, 200p, Tomas Carrasquilla (1858-1940).

1993   Litho.   Perf. 14x13½
1081 A511 Block of 4, #a.-d.   2.50   1.60

Christmas A512

1993, Nov. 30   Perf. 12
1082 A512 200p Holy Family   .90   .50
1083 A512 220p Shepherd   1.50   1.00

No. 1083 is airmail.

Tourism A513

Designs: No. 1084a, San Andres Providence. b, Cocuy Natl. Park. c, Lake Cocha. d, Waterfalls, Serrania de la Macarena. 250p, Lake Otun. No. 1086a, Chicamocha River. b, Sierra Nevada de Santa Marta mountains. 520p, Penol Reservoir.

1993, Dec. 1   Litho.   Perf. 12
1084 A513 220p Block of 4, #a.-d.   4.00   3.00
1085 A513 250p multicolored   1.10   .55
1086 A513 460p Pair, #a.-b.   4.00   3.00
1087 A513 520p multicolored   2.40   1.50
     Nos. 1084-1087 (4)   11.50   8.05

Nos. 1084, 1086-87 are airmail.

A514

A515

1993, Dec. 21   Litho.   Perf. 14
1088 A514 150p multicolored   .50   .35
Natl. Museum, 170th anniv.

1994, Jan. 25   Litho.   Perf. 14
1089 A515 300p Marie Poussepin   1.10   .70

A516

A517

Birds: 180p, Ognorhynchus icterotis. 240p, Rallus semiplumbeus. 270p, Semnornis ramphastinus. 560p, Anas cyanoptera.

1994, Mar. 4
1090 A516 180p multi   1.25   .40
1091 A516 240p multi   1.50   .55
1092 A516 270p multi, horiz.   1.75   .65
1093 A516 560p multi, horiz.   3.50   1.25
   Nos. 1090-1093 (4)   8.00   2.85
Nos. 1092-1093 are airmail.

1994, Apr. 11   Litho.   Perf. 14
1094 A517 300p multicolored   1.25   .80
Air Force, 75th anniv.

Latin American Presidential Summit, Cartagena
A518

1994, June 14   Litho.   Perf. 14
1095 A518 300p shown   .95   .60
1096 A518 630p Flags   2.00   1.40
No. 1096 is airmail.

1994 World Cup Soccer Championships, US — A519

World Cup Trophy and: 180p, Soccer player, Colombian flag. 270p, Two players with ball. 560p, Soccer ball, Colombian flag, vert. 1110p, Soccer player offering hand to another.

1994, May 26   Perf. 12
1097 A519 180p multicolored   .60   .40
1098 A519 270p multicolored   .90   .55
1099 A519 560p multicolored   2.00   1.25
   Nos. 1097-1099 (3)   3.50   2.20
Souvenir Sheet
1100 A519 1110p multicolored   5.00   5.00
Nos. 1098-1099 are airmail.

Ricardo Rendon (1894-1931), Artist — A520

1993 Census — A521

1994, June 30   Litho.   Perf. 12
1101 A520 240p black   .90   .45

1994, Aug. 12   Perf. 14
1102 A521 240p multicolored   .80   .45

Ministry of Communications Inravision, 30th Anniv. — A522

1994, Aug. 3
1103 A522 180p multicolored   .65   .30

Intl. Year of the Family
A523

1994, Sept. 1   Litho.   Perf. 14
1104 A523 300p multicolored   1.00   .65

America Issue — A524

Methods of mail delivery: 270p, Horse, bicycle. 300p, Men holding stamps showing truck, ship, plane.

1994, Oct. 18   Litho.   Perf. 13
1105 A524 270p multicolored   1.00   .60
1106 A524 300p multicolored   1.50   .65
No. 1105 is airmail.

Colombian Society of Engineers, Cent.
A525

1994, Oct. 20   Litho.   Perf. 12
1107 A525 180p multicolored   .60   .40

Christmas
A526

1994, Nov. 22   Litho.   Perf. 13½x13
1108 A526 270p Magi   .90   .60
1109 A526 300p Holy family   1.00   .65
No. 1108 is airmail.

Former President Type of 1981
Miniature Sheet of 20

Designs: a, Jose Miguel Pey. b, Jorge Tadeo Lozano. c, Antonio Narino. d, Camilo Torres. e, Jose Fernandez Madrid. f, Jose Maria del Castillo y Rada. g, Custodio Garcia Rovira. h, Antonio Villavicencio. i, Liborio Mejia. j, Rafael Urdaneta. k, Juan Garcia del Rio. l, Jose Maria Melo. m, Tomas Herrera. n, Froilan Largacha. o, Salvador Camacho Roldan. p, Ezequiel Hurtado. q, Dario Echandia Olaya. r, Alberto Lleras Camargo. s, Gustavo Rojas Pinilla. t, Carlos Lleras Restrepo.

1995, Apr. 4   Litho.   Perf. 12
1110 A401 270p #a.-t.   35.00   35.00

World Offroad Bicycle Championships, Melgar — A527

1995, Mar. 30   Perf. 14
1111 A527 400p multicolored   1.40   .90

A528

A529

1995, Oct. 12   Litho.   Perf. 12
1112 A528 220p multicolored   .65   .30
Gen. Jose Maria Obando (1795-1861), President.

1995, Nov. 28   Perf. 14
1113 A529 400p Clean air   1.10   .55
1114 A529 400p Clean water   1.10   .55
Preserve the environment. America issue.

Christmas
A530

Stained glass windows: 220p, Flight into Egypt. 330p, Nativity.

1995, Dec. 18   Perf. 12
1115 A530 220p multicolored   .75   .30
1116 A530 330p multicolored   1.10   .55
No. 1116 is airmail.

Bogotá to Boyacá World Cycling Championship — A531

1995, Oct. 4   Litho.   Perf. 12
1117 A531 400p multicolored   1.25   .65

León De Greiff (1895-1976), Poet — A532

1996, May 2   Litho.   Perf. 12
1118 A532 400p black   1.40   .40

Mosquera Courtyard, Natl. Capitol
A533

1996, July 18   Litho.   Perf. 14
1119 A533 400p multicolored   1.10   .40

Medellin Rapid Transit System
A534

1996, July 2   Perf. 12
1120 A534 500p multicolored   1.75   .90

A535

A536

1996, June 20
1121 A535 500p multicolored 1.40 .50
Community of St. John of God in Colombia, 400th anniv.

1996, June 25
Arms: a, Santa Maria la Antigua del Darien. b, San Sebastian de Mariquita. c, Villa de la Marinilla. d, Villa of Santa Cruz of Mompox.
1122 A536 400p Block of 4, #a.-
  d. 4.25 3.00
  e. As "d," inscribed AEREO 10.00
  f. Block of 4, #1122a-1122c, 1122e 12.00

Issued in sheets of 16 stamps.

1996 Summer Olympic Games, Atlanta — A537

1996, July 16
1123 A537 500p multicolored 1.40 .50

SAYCO (Colombian Authors and Composers Society), 50th Anniv. — A538

1996, Aug. 17 Litho. Perf. 12
1124 A538 400p multicolored 1.25 .50

Exfilbo '96, 20th Natl. Philatelic Exhibition A539

Jewelry from Gold Museum, Bogotá.

1996, Oct. 19 Litho. Perf. 12
1125 A539 400p multicolored 1.25 .50

Souvenir Sheet

Founders Theater, Manizales, 30th Anniv. — A540

Drop curtain: a, Eagle, people watching man drawing on ground, vert. b, People, animals on hillside.

1996, Oct. 28 Perf. 14
1126 A540 4000p #a.-b. 20.00 20.00

Christmas A541

Designs: No. 1127, Mailman handing woman letter. No. 1128, Woman reading letter, mailman holding bundle of mail.

1996, Nov. 22
1127 A541 400p multicolored 1.10 .40
1128 A541 400p multicolored 1.10 .40
No. 1128 is airmail.

America Issue — A542

1996, Nov. 29 Perf. 12
1129 A542 500p Men's costume 1.40 .50
1130 A542 500p Women's costume 1.40 .50

Historical Landmarks — A543

a, Cemetery, Santa Cruz of Mompox. b, Carved face, San Agustin Archaelogical Park. c, Entrance, Palace of the Inquisition, Cartagena de Indias. d, Inside ruins, Tierradentro Archaelogical Park.

1996, Dec. 6 Perf. 14
1131 A543 400p Block of 4,
  #a.-d. 10.00 10.00

Alvaro Gomez Hurtado (1919-95), Politician, Writer — A544

1997, Mar. 18 Litho. Perf. 12
1132 A544 400p multicolored 1.00 .40

Bogotá Journalists Assoc., 50th Anniv. A545

1997, July 10 Litho. Perf. 12
1133 A545 400p multicolored 1.00 .40

Natl. Festival of Porro — A546

1997, June 26 Perf. 13½x14
1134 A546 400p multicolored 1.00 .40

Pres. Virgilio Barco (1921-97) — A547

1997, Nov. 27 Litho. Perf. 14
1135 A547 500p multicolored 1.25 .40

Colombia in Peace A548

1997, Dec. 30 Litho. Perf. 12
1136 A548 500p Children playing 1.10 .40
1137 A548 1100p Children dancing 2.50 .90
No. 1137 is airmail.

America Issue A549

1997, Dec. 30
1138 A549 500p Postman by
  day 1.25 .45
1139 A549 1100p Postman by
  night 2.75 1.00
No. 1139 is airmail.

Jorge Eliecer Gaitan (1903-48), Politician — A550

1998, Apr. 24 Litho. Perf. 14
1140 A550 500p multicolored 1.10 .40

Free University, 75th Anniv. A551

1998, July 1 Litho. Perf. 14
1141 A551 500p black & red 1.00 .35

Santander Industrial University, 50th Anniv. — A552

1998, May 14 Perf. 12
1142 A552 500p multicolored 1.10 .35

City of Manizales, 150th Anniv. — A553

1998, July 24 Litho. Perf. 12
1143 A553 500p multicolored 1.00 .40

A554

A555

Pre-Columbian art, agency: a, Tairona, Bank of the Republic. b, Malagana, Controller General. c, Quimbaya, Bank Superintendent.

1998, July 24
1144 A554 500p Strip of 3, #a.-c. 3.00 2.00
Natl. financial agencies, 70th anniv.

1998, Aug. 21 Perf. 14
1145 A555 500p multicolored 1.00 .40
Pres. Misael Pastrana Borrero (1923-97).

University of the Andes, 50th Anniv. A556

1998, Sept. 28
1146 A556 500p multicolored   .80 .40

Christmas A557

Designs: 500p, Woman kneeling down to get water with bowl, cherubs in sky. No. 1148a, Magi. No. 1148b, Nativity scene.

1998, Nov. 19   **Litho.**   **Perf. 14**
1147 A557 500p multicolored   1.00 .50
1148 A557 1000p Pair, #a.-b.   4.00 3.00
No. 1148 is airmail.

A558

A559

Emblems of Colombian Academies: a, Language. b, Medicine. c, Law. d, History. e, Science. f, Ecomonics. g, Religion.

1998, Dec. 15   **Perf. 12**
Sheet of 7 + Label
1149 A558 500p #a.-g.   13.50 13.50

1999, Apr. 16   **Perf. 14**
1150 A559 1000p multicolored   1.25 .60
Gen. José Hilario López.

Famous Women — A559a

America Issue: 600p, Soledad Román de Nuñez. 1200p, Bertha Herández de Ospina.

1999, Mar. 25   **Litho.**   **Perf. 12**
1151 A559a 600p multicolored   1.50 .40
1152 A559a 1200p multicolored   2.75 .70
No. 1152 is airmail.

Turtles — A560

a, Chelonia mydas. b, Dermochelys coriacea. c, Eretmochelys imbricata.

1999, Apr. 16   **Perf. 14**
1153 A560 1300p Strip of 3, #a.-c.   10.00 10.00

Dr. Eduardo Zuleta Angel, Diplomat (b. 1899) — A561

1999, Sept. 9   **Litho.**   **Perf. 12**
1154 A561 600p multicolored   1.25 .35

Pamplona, 450th Anniv. A562

1999   **Litho.**   **Perf. 12**
1155 A562 1000p multicolored   2.25 .60

Sovereign Military Order of Malta, 900th Anniv. — A563

1999, June 24   **Perf. 14**
1156 A563 1200p multicolored   3.00 .85

Japanese Immigration to Colombia — A564

Designs: a, Red at right. b, Red at left.

1999, May 12   **Perf. 13½x14**
1157 A564 1300p Pair, #a.-b.   5.00 5.00

Pan American Games, Winnipeg, Manitoba A565

Designs: a, Flag, Olympic rings. b, Runner facing right. c, Weight lifter facing left. d, Cyclist facing right. e, Shooter facing left. f, Roller skater facing right. g, Runner facing left. h, Weight lifter facing right. i, Cyclist facing left. j, Shooter facing right. k, Roller skater facing left. l, Like "a," with lilac line under "12."

1999, July 23   **Litho.**   **Perf. 14**
1158 A565 1200p Sheet of 12, #a.-l.   30.00 30.00

Luis A. Robles (b. 1849) — A566

1999, Oct. 27
1159 A566 600p multi   .95 .40

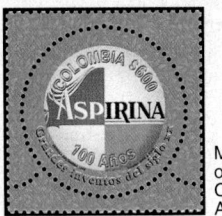

Manufacture of Aspirin, Cent. A567

1999, Dec. 1   **Perf. 12¾**
1160 A567 600p multi   .95 .40
Value is for stamp with surrounding selvage.

UPU, 125th Anniv. A568

1999, Oct. 29   **Perf. 14¼**
1161 A568 1000p "125"   1.50 .65
1162 A568 1300p "1874-1999"   2.50 .85

Inter-American Development Bank, 40th Anniv. — A569

Abstract art: a, "Colombia" in yellow. b, "Colombia" in red.

1999, Nov. 19   **Perf. 14x14¼**
1163 A569 1000p Pair, #a.-b.   3.25 1.40

America Issue, A New Millennium Without Arms — A570

a, Stylized hands. b, Large flower at LR.

1999, Nov. 9   **Perf. 14**
1164 A570 1200p Pair, #a.-b.   4.00 1.75

Christmas — A571

a, Holy Family, animals. b, Angel, Magi.

1999, Nov. 29   **Perf. 13½x14**
1165 A571 600p Pair, #a.-b.   2.00 .80

Millennium — A572

Designs: a, Nude man, flag, dove. b, Globe, rainbow, "2000."

2000, Jan. 3   **Perf. 14**
1166 A572 1000p Pair, #a.-b.   3.00 3.00

University of Medellin, 50th Anniv. A573

2000   **Litho.**   **Perf. 14**
1167 A573 1000p multi   1.25 .55

Father José Rafael Faría Bermúdez (1896-1979) A574

2000, Mar. 6   **Litho.**   **Perf. 14**
1168 A574 1300p multi   1.50 .75

2000 Summer Olympics, Sydney A575

2000, Apr. 21
1169 A575 1000p multi   1.50 .65

Popayán Religious Music Festival A576

2000, July 7
1170 A576 1000p multi   1.90 .65

America Issue, Campaign Against AIDS
A577

2000 Litho. Perf. 14x13½
1171 A577 1000p multi   3.00 1.25

Radio Station HJCK, 50th Anniv. — A578

2000, Sept. 28 Litho. Perf. 14
1172 A578 1000p multi   1.25 .55

Birth Registration A579

2000 Litho. Perf. 14¼
1173 A579 1000p multi   1.10 .50

Paintings A580

No. 1174: a, Archangel, by Fernando Botero. b, Gypsy Woman With Tamourine, by Jean-Baptiste-Camille Corot. c, Vera Sergine Renoir, by Renoir. d, Man on Horse, by Botero. e, Mother Superior, by Botero. f, A Town, by Botero. g, Flowers, by Botero. h, Cézanne, by Botero. i, Patio, by Botero. j, Absinthe Drinker in Grenelle, by Toulouse-Lautrec. k, A Little Valley, by Corot. l, The Studio, by Botero.

2000 Perf. 12
1174   Sheet of 12   12.00 12.00
a.-l. A580 650p Any single   .75 .35

Children's Day — A581

2001, Mar. 15 Litho. Perf. 14
1175 A581 1100p multi   2.75 1.00

Abolition of Slavery, 150th Anniv. — A582

2001, May 21 Litho. Perf. 14¼x14
1176 A582 1100p multi   2.75 1.00

Discovery of Magdalena River, 500th Anniv. — A583

2001, June 13 Litho. Perf. 14
1177 A583 1100p multi   2.75 1.00

Copa America Soccer Tournament A584

2001, July 18 Litho. Perf. 12¾
1178 A584 1900p multi   3.00 1.25

Values are for examples with surrounding selvage.

America Issue — Los Katios Natl. Park, UNESCO World Heritage Site — A585

2001, Aug. 17 Perf. 13¾x14
1179 A585 2100p multi   3.00 1.25

Year of Dialogue Among Civilizations A586

2001, Oct. 9 Perf. 14
1180 A586 650p multi   1.75 .60

Reclining Woman, by Fernando Botero — A587

2001 Perf. 14¼
1181 A587 1100p multi   2.75 1.00

Christmas A588

2001 Perf. 14
1182 A588 1100p multi   2.75 1.00

National Beauty Pageant — A589

Flag, Miss Colombia Vanesa A. Mendoza Bustos and: a, Cartagena de Indias. b, St. Francis of Assisi Cathedral, Quibdo.
Illustration reduced.

2002, Jan. 22 Perf. 14x14¼
1183 A589 800p Horiz. pair, #a-b 2.00 .80

Natural Riches of Colombia — A590

Parts of map of Colombia, various wildlife and/or natives and: a, Bird and clouds at left. b, Turtle at upper left. c, Fish and whales at left. d, Man on horse at center. e, Volcano at upper left. f, Red and blue parrots at right. g, Flamingos at left. h, Snake at upper left.

2002, Feb. 1 Perf. 14¼x14
1184 A590 2300p Sheet of 8,
    #a-h   25.00 25.00

Children's Day — A591

2002, Feb. 18 Perf. 12
1185 A591 1400p multi   1.75 .75

New Emblem of Adpostal — A592

2002, Mar. 7 Perf. 14
1186 A592 800p multi   1.10 .40

7th South American Games A593

2002
1187 A593 2100p multi   2.50 1.10

Oxyura Jamaicensis A594

2002, Apr. 30 Litho. Perf. 12
1188 A594 3900p multi   5.00 2.25

Souvenir Sheet

Frogs — A595

No. 1189: a, 7200p, Hyla crepitans. b, 7600p, Dendrobates histrionicus.

2002, Apr. 30 Perf. 13¾x14
1189 A595   Sheet of 2, #a-b   20.00 20.00

Souvenir Sheet

Butterflies — A596

No. 1190: a, Dryas iulia. b, Dryadula phaetusa, vert.

2002, Apr. 30 Perf. 12
1190 A596 13,700p Sheet of 2,
    #a-b   35.00 35.00

Foundation for Reconstructive Surgery, 25th Anniv. — A597

2002, May 24 Perf. 14
1191 A597 1000p multi   1.25 .50

Pre-Columbian Art — A598

No. 1192, 800p: a, Nariño pectoral. b, Nariño disc.
No. 1193, 1400p: a, Calima diadem. b, Calima pectoral.
No. 1194, 2100p: a, Anthropomorphic Tairona pectoral. b, Round Tairona pectoral.
Illustration reduced.

2002, June 7 **Perf. 13½x14**
Horiz. Pairs, #a-b
1192-1194 A598 Set of 3 12.00 12.00

Surgical Society of Bogota San José
Hospital, Cent. — A599

No. 1195: a, Early doctors and nurse. b,
Hospital.

2002, July 22 **Perf. 14**
1195 A599 800p Horiz. pair, #a-b 2.00 2.00

Consuelo Araújo Noguera (1940-
2001), Assassinated Former Minister
of Culture — A600

2002, Aug. 1
1196 A600 1400p multi 2.00 .80

Union Network
International
A601

2002, Aug. 12
1197 A601 1000p multi 1.25 .50

America Issue — Youth, Education
and Literacy — A602

No. 1198: a, Person reading book. b, Letters
amd words.

2002, Oct. 9
1198 A602 2500p Horiz. pair,
#a-b 5.50 4.50

Christmas
A603

2002, Nov. 6 **Litho.** **Perf. 14x13¾**
1199 A603 800p multi 1.25 .50

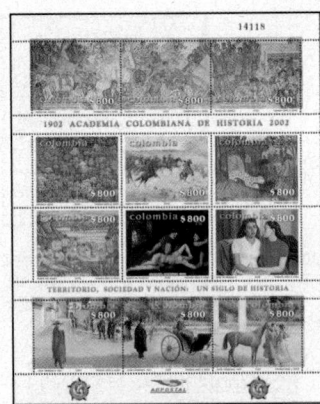

Colombian History Academy,
Cent. — A604

No. 1200: a, Mural scene with Simon Bolivar
at UR. b, Mural scene with horsemen at top. c,
Mural scene with man with outstretched arms
at UL. d, Cafetal, 1956. e, Batalla de
Palonegro, 1905. f, Tigre Cazando Sabanera,
1963. g, El Barqueo, 1936. h, Colombia
Asesinada, 1902. i, Dos Mujeres, 1951. j,
Bearded man at left, Plaza de Santander. k,
Carriage, Plaza de Santander. l, Horse, man
and woman, Plaza de Santander.

2002, Nov. 19 **Perf. 13¾x14**
1200 A604 800p Sheet of 12,
#a-l 21.00 21.00

Peace
Treaty
Ending War
of 1,000
Days, Cent.
A605

2002, Nov. 21 **Perf. 14x13¾**
1201 A605 1600p multi 3.00 .90

Carnival
A606

No. 1202: a, shown. b, Participants holding
masks on sticks. c, Participants on float.

2003, Jan. 4 **Perf. 14**
1202 Horiz. strip of 3 5.50 5.50
a.-b. A606 1000p Either single 1.10 1.10
c. A606 1200p multi 1.40 1.40

Printed in sheets of 3 horizontal strips and 2
horiz. strips of 3 labels.

Articulated
Bus, Bogota
A607

2003, Mar. 13 **Perf. 12**
1203 A607 1000p multi 1.10 .45

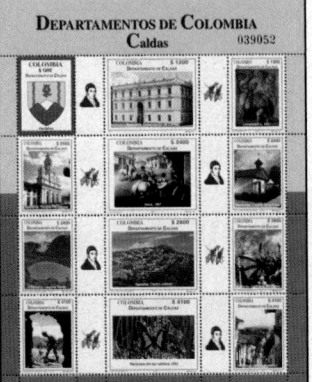

Departments — A608

No. 1204 — Caldas Department: a, 1200p,
Arms. b, 1200p, Government office building,
Manizales, horiz. c, 1200p, Campesinos,
1957. d, 2400p, Church, Salamina. e, 2400p,
Neira, 1997, horiz. f, 2400p, Enea Chapel,
Manizales. g, 2800p, Laguna Verde, Vil-
lamaria. h, 2800p, Aguadas, horiz. i, 2800p,
Devil's carnival, Riosucio. j, 4100p, Miner,
Marmato. k, 4100p, Mariposas del Eje
Cafetero, 2001, horiz. l, 4100p, Pacora.
No. 1205, 1000p — Huila Department: a,
Arms. b, Government office building, Neiva,
horiz. c, La Gaitana. d, Bordones Waterfall,
Isnos. e, San Agustín World Heritage
Archaeological Park, horiz. f, Lavapatas
Spring, San Agustín. g, La Tatacoa Desert,
Villavieja. h, Liberty tree, Gigante, horiz. i,
Sombrero maker, Suaza. j, Nuestra Señora de
los Dolores Church, Aipe. k, Paisaje, horiz. l,
Dancers.
No. 1206 — 2400p: a, Historic center of
Barichara. b, Ophthalmologic Foundation of
Santander, Bucaramanga, horiz. c, Girón. d,
Santander Industrial University Intl. Piano Fes-
tival, 20th anniv. emblem. e, Petroleum Christ
Statue, refinery, Barrancabermeja, horiz. f,
Church, San Andrés. g, Gustavo Cote Uribe
(1918-94), writer. h, Chamber of Commerce,
Bucaramanga, horiz. i, Carnival of Eastern
Colombia, Bucaramanga. j, Historic center of
Albania. k, Chicamocha River Canyon, Cepitá,
horiz. l, Entreguerras.

2003 **Perf. 12**
Sheets of 12, #a-l, + 8 labels
1204 A608 Caldas 37.50 37.50
1205 A608 Huila 15.00 15.00
1206 A608 Santander 25.00 25.00

Issued: No. 1204, Apr. 11. No. 1205, June
29. No. 1206, June 22. Size of horiz. stamps:
46x37mm.
See Nos. 1224-1226, 1246, 1265-1267,
1273.

Fish and Coral of
the Rosario
Islands — A609

2003, Jan. 16 **Litho.** **Perf. 12**
1207 A609 1000p multi 2.25 .60

Hapalopsittaca
Fuertesi — A610

2003, June 13
1208 A610 1000p multi 2.25 .60

Souvenir Sheets

Orchids — A611

No. 1209 — 2400p: a, Masdevallia ignea. b,
Miltoniopsis vexillaria, horiz.
No. 1210 — 2800p: a, Odontoglossum cris-
pum, horiz. b, Masdevallia macrura.
No. 1211 — 5000p: a, Cimbidium. b, Oncid-
ium obryzatum.
No. 1212 — 7000p: a, Cattleya dowiana. b,
Cattleya trianaei (49x49mm).

Perf. 14¼, 13¾x14 (#1212b)
2003, June 13
Sheets of 2, #a-b
1209-1212 A611 Set of 4 45.00 45.00

Tejo,
National
Sport
A612

No. 1213: a, Players, tree in foreground
(49x39mm). b, Players, light poles
(49x39mm). c, Cacique Turmeque.

2003, July 25 **Perf. 12**
1213 Horiz. strip of 3 9.00 9.00
a.-c. A612 2400p Any single 2.10 1.25

America Issue — A613

Flora and fauna: a, Denomination at UR. b,
Denomination at LR.

2003, Oct. 9 **Litho.** **Perf. 12**
1214 A613 1600p Vert. pair, #a-b 4.00 4.00

Printed in sheets of four pairs and four
labels.

Souvenir Sheet

Colombia Libraries National Reading Plan — A614

No. 1215: a, 1200p, Building. b, 4100p, Building, diff.

2003, Oct. 30   Litho.   Perf. 12
1215 A614   Sheet of 2, #a-b   7.00 7.00

General Ramón Arturo Rincón Quiñones (1922-75) — A615

2003, Oct. 31
1216 A615 1000p multi   1.50 .40

Souvenir Sheet

Administrative Security Deparment, 50th Anniv. — A616

2003, Oct. 31
1217 A616 4100p multi   6.00 6.00

Armed Forces A617

No. 1218 — Arms and mottos (#a-d): a, General Command of Military Forces. b, National Army. c, National Navy. d, Air Force. e, Colombian Forces in Korea, 50th anniv.

2003, Nov. 7
1218   Vert. strip of 5   7.50 7.50
a.-e. A617 1200p Any single   1.00 .50

Christmas — A618

No. 1219: a, Good Shepherd, sheep. b, Tree, comet, airplane, rabbit. c, Rabbits, dog. d, Automobile, angel, reindeer, horse. e, Sheep, woman with basket, swan, house. f, Branch with leaves, horse and rider, duck, Indian with bow and arrow.

2003, Dec. 2   Litho.   Perf. 12
1219   Block of 6   8.00 8.00
a.-f. A618 1000p Any single   .95 .55

Colombia and the Eldorado Legend — A619

No. 1220: a, Print of Eldorado ceremony, by Teodoro De Bry, 1595. b, Watercolor painting of Lake Guatavita, by M. María Paz, 1855. c, Watercolor painting of Lake Guatavita, by Gonzalo Ariza, 1984. d, Print of Lake Guatavita, by A. Humboldt Thibault and F. Schoell, 1813. e, Photo of Lake Guatavita, by Fernando Urbina Rangel, 1983. f, Print of Lake Guatavita, by Eustacio Barreto, 1883.
No. 1221 — Muisca raft: a, 1700p, Front. b, 2000p, Back, vert.

2004, Mar. 10
1220 A619 2800p Sheet of 6,
#a-f, + 3 la-
bels   13.00 13.00

Souvenir Sheet

1221 A619   Sheet of 2, #a-b   3.00 3.00

Locomotives — A620

No. 1222, 1100p: a, 2-8-2. b, 4-8-0.
No. 1223, 1300p: a, 2-6-2. b, 4-6-2.
Illustration reduced.

2004, Mar. 19
Horiz. Pairs, #a-b
1222-1223 A620   Set of 2   12.00 12.00
Nos. 1222-1223 each printed in sheets of four pairs and two pairs of labels.

Departments Type of 2003

No. 1224, 1100p — Nariño Department: a, Galeras Volcano, San Juan de Pasto, horiz. b, Statue of Gen. Antonio Nariño. c, Nariño Government Building, San Juan de Pasto, horiz. d, Farm, Catambuco, horiz. e, Nuestra Señora de las Lajas Sanctuary, Ipiales. f, Sandoná city center, horiz. g, Gallery of Mirrors, horiz. h, Barnizadores de Pasto Chorography Commission. i, Golden palms, horiz. j, El Morro, Tumaco, horiz. k, Virgen de la Playa Sanctuary, San Pablo. l, Festival of Whites and Blacks, horiz.
No. 1225, 2000p — Tolima Department: a, Nevado del Tolima, horiz. b, Tolima arms. c, Ambalema, horiz. d, Bowls, La Chamba, horiz. e, Natural Bridge, Icononzo. f, Hermitage, Mariquita, horiz. g, Matachos, horiz. h, Prison, Ibagué. i, Alberto Castilla Conservatory Room, horiz. j, Fishermen, Magdalena River, horiz. k, Cacique Calarcá. l, Tolima Art Museum, Ibagué.
No. 1226, 3000p — Chocó Department: a, Coat of Arms. b, Quibdó skyline, horiz. c, Indian girls. d, San Pacho Fiesta. e, Carrasquilla College, Quibdó, horiz. f, Houses, Nóvita. g, Canoe on San Juan River. h, Women grinding corn meal, horiz. i, Nuestra Senora del Rosario Church, Condoto. j, Utría Bay. k, Bellavista Church, Bojayá, horiz. l, Goldsmith, Acandi.
Horiz. stamps are 46x37mm.

2004		Litho.	Perf. 13¾x14

Sheets of 12, #a-l, +8 labels

1224	A608	Nariño	10.50 10.50
1225	A608	Tolima	18.00 18.00
1226	A608	Chocó	30.00 30.00
	Nos. 1224-1226 (3)		58.50 58.50

Issued: No. 1224, 8/5; No. 1225, 4/16. No. 1226, 11/17

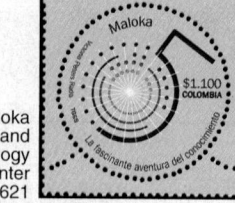

Maloka Science and Technology Center A621

2004, June 6   Litho.   Perf. 12¾
1227 A621 1100p multi   .80 .80
Values are for stamps with surrounding selvage.

2004 Summer Olympics, Athens — A622

2004, Aug. 5   Perf. 13¾x14
1228 A622 4400p multi   3.50 3.50

Natl. Association of Contractors, 60th Anniv. — A623

No. 1229: a, Denomination in white. b, Denomination in black.

2004, Aug. 5   Perf. 14x13¾
1229   Pair   4.50 4.50
a.-b. A623 2800p Either single   2.25 2.25
Printed in sheets containing 6 pairs and one large central label.

FIFA (Fédération Internationale de Football Association), Cent. — A624

2004, Aug. 25   Perf. 13¼x14
1230 A624 3500p multi   2.75 2.75

Women's Citizenship, 50th Anniv. — A625

2004, Sept. 24   Perf. 14
1231 A625 15,000p multi   12.00 12.00

Fair and Expositions Corporation, 50th Anniv. — A626

2004, Oct. 14   Perf. 13½x13
1232 A626 1300p multi   1.10 1.10

Colombian Radio Announcers Association, 50th Anniv. — A627

2004, Oct. 21   Perf. 14
1233 A627 1700p multi   1.50 1.50

17th National Games — A628

Illustration reduced.

2004, Dec. 10   Litho.   Perf. 12¾
1234 A628 7000p multi + label   5.75 5.75
Printed in sheets of 4 + 5 labels.

America Issue — Environmental Conservation — A629

Designs: No. 1235, 5000p, Whale, Gorgona National Nature Park. No. 1236, 5000p, Hammerhead sharks, Malpelo Flora and Fauna Sanctuary.

2004, Dec. 14   Perf. 14
1235-1236 A629   Set of 2   8.50 8.50

Miniature Sheet

Christmas — A630

No. 1237 — Inscriptions: a, Jesús en la mansion de su padre. b, Eterna sumision a Dios. c, Jesús desciende al seno de su madre. d, Aceptacion de milagro divino. e, La ilusion de Maria. f, Voluntad divina en manos del emperador. g, Paciencia, expectativa y anhelo. h, Belén: Humilde hospedaje. i, Nacimiento, la faz de Dios encarnado.

2004, Dec. 15
1237 A630 2800p Sheet of 9, #a-i 22.00 22.00

Pre-Columbian Gold Artifacts From Gold Museum — A631

No. 1238, 1200p: a, Tumaco ear covering. b, Zenú nose ring.
No. 1239, 1800p: a, Cauma nose ring. b, Tierradentro bracelet.
Illustration reduced.

2005 *Perf. 12x12½*
Pairs, #a-b
1238-1239 A631 Set of 2 5.25 5.25
Issued: No. 1238, 1/21; No. 1239, 3/28.

Rotary International, Cent. — A632

2005, Feb. 23 *Perf. 13½x14*
1240 A632 3100p multi 2.75 2.75

Souvenir Sheet

Butterflies — A633

No. 1241: a, Protographium tyastes panamensis. b, Dismorphia zaela laura. c, Actinote ozomene.

2005 *Litho.* *Perf. 14¼*
1241 A633 4600p Sheet of 3, #a-c 12.50 12.50

FENALCO (Natl. Federation of Retailers), 60th Anniv. A634

2005 *Perf. 14*
1242 A634 1200p multi 1.10 1.10

Souvenir Sheets

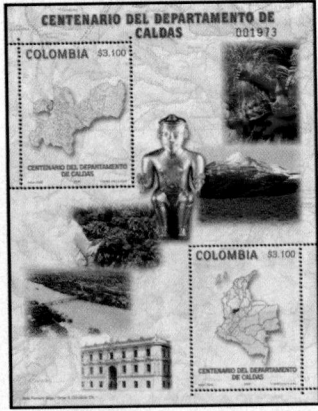

Department Centenaries — A635

No. 1243, 3100p: a, Map of Caldas Department. b, Map of Colombia highlighting Caldas.
No. 1244, 3700p: a, Map of Huila Department. b, Map of Colombia highlighting Huila.
No. 1245, 4200p: a, Map of Atlantico Department. b, Map of Colombia highlighting Atlantico.

2005 *Perf. 14x13½*
Sheets of 2, #a-b
1243-1245 A635 Set of 3 19.50 19.50

Departments Type of 2003
No. 1246 — San Andrés y Providencia Department: a, Aerial view of San Andrés, horiz. b, Arms. c, Aerial view of Johnny Cay, horiz. d, Cayo Cangrejo, horiz. e, Artisan. f, Culture House, San Andrés, horiz. g, Morgan Head, Santa Catalina Island, horiz. h, Island view. i, Ensenada, San Andrés, horiz. j, Island architecture, horiz. k, Baptist Church, San Andrés. l, Aerial view of Providencia and Santa Catalina Islands.
Horiz. stamps are 46x37mm.

2005 *Perf. 13¾x14*
1246 A608 1200p Sheet of 12, #a-l 13.00 13.00

Bogota Botanical Gardens — A636

2005 *Perf. 14*
1247 A636 1400p multi 1.25 1.25

15th Bolivarian Games — A637

2005 *Perf. 13¾x14*
1248 A637 3500p multi 3.25 3.25

Association of Graduates of the University of the Andes, 50th Anniv. A638

2005 *Perf. 14*
1249 A638 2000p multi 1.75 1.75

Intl. Day of Ozone Layer Protection A639

2005
1250 A639 2000p multi 1.75 1.75

Souvenir Sheet

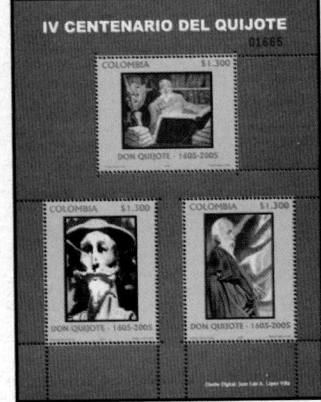

Publication of Don Quixote, 400th Anniv. — A640

No. 1251 — Paintings of Miguel de Cervantes by: a, Ricardo Rendón Bravo. b, Eduardo Ramírez Villamizar, vert. c, Santiago Martínez Delgado, vert.

Perf. 13½x14 (#1251a), 14x13½
2005
1251 A640 1300p Sheet of 3, #a-c 3.50 3.50

Colpatria Bank, 50th Anniv. A641

2005 *Perf. 14x13½*
1252 A641 1200p multi 1.10 1.10

Arms of City of Facatativá A642

2005 *Litho.* *Perf. 14*
1253 A642 1800p multi 1.75 1.75

Latin Union, 50th Anniv. — A643

2005 *Perf. 13½x14*
1254 A643 5000p multi 4.75 4.75
Printed in sheets of 4.

Souvenir Sheet

America Issue, Fight Against Poverty — A644

2005 *Perf. 14x13½*
1255 A644 Sheet of 2 #1255a 9.50 9.50
a. 5000p Single stamp 4.75 4.75

Souvenir Sheet

Escuela de Lanceros (Military School), 50th Anniv. — A645

2005 *Perf. 14*
1256 A645 Sheet of 2 #1256a 19.00 19.00
a. 10,000p Single stamp 9.50 9.50

Christmas A646

2005 *Perf. 14*
1257 A646 3100p multi 3.00 3.00
Printed in sheets of 7.

Colombian Journalism A647

2006 *Litho.*
1258 A647 2000p multi 1.90 1.90

St. Francis
Xavier
(1506-52)
A648

2006
1259 A648 4500p multi　　　　　3.75 3.75

Pope John Paul
II (1920-2005)
A649

2006
1260 A649 4800p multi　　　　　3.75 3.75

Souvenir Sheet

Frederic Chopin
(1810-49),
Composer
A650

2006　　　　　　　　　　*Perf. 13½x13*
1261 A650 5300p multi　　　4.25 4.25
Printed in sheets of 4.

Gold Artifacts Type of 2005

No. 1262: a, Quimbaya striated lime receptacle with handles. b, Quimbaya thin lime receptacle.

2006　　　　　　　　　　*Perf. 12x12½*
1262 A631 1500p Horiz. pair, #a-
　　　　　b　　　　　　　　2.50 2.50

Italian Cultural Institute of Bogota,
50th Anniv. — A651

No. 1263: a, Lute at lower left. b, Violin at lower right.
Illustration reduced.

2006　　　　　　　　　　*Perf. 14*
1263 A651 1300p Horiz. pair, #a-
　　　　　b　　　　　　　　2.25 2.25

Souvenir Sheet

Rayo Museum, 25th Anniv. — A652

No. 1264: a, Artwork in blue, white, red, yellow and black. b, Artwork in white, blue, tan and black.

2006　　　　　　　　　　*Perf. 13½x13*
1264 A652　Sheet, 2 each #a-b　4.50 4.50
a.-b.　1300p Either single　　1.10 1.10

Departments Type of 2003

No. 1265 — Valle del Cauca Department: a, Mapping Commission drawing of Cali, horiz. b, Arms of Valle del Cauca. c, Arms and panoramic view of Sevilla, horiz. d, Calima Lake, El Darién, horiz. e, La Ermita, Santiago de Cali. f, Port of Buenaventura, horiz. g, Railroad station, Palmira, horiz. h, Sugar cane. i, Salsa dancers, Cali, horiz. j, El Paraiso Museum, El Cerrito, horiz. k, Basilica, Buga. l, Aerial view of Valle del Cauca, horiz.

No. 1266 — Boyacá Department: a, Plaza de Bolivar, Tunja, horiz. b, Arms of Boyacá. c, Mapping Commission drawing of Campo de Boyacá, horiz. d, Bolivar Monument, Campo de Boyacá, horiz. e, Altar of the Virgin of Chiquinquirá. f, Panoramic view of Garagoa, horiz. g, Plaza de los Libertadores, Duitama, horiz. h, Emeralds. i, Plaza Mayor, Villa de Leyva, horiz. j, Sierra Nevada del Cocuy, horiz. k, Temple of the Sun, Sogamoso. l, El Salitre Farm, Paipa, horiz.

No. 1267 — Quindío Department: a, Quindío Pass, 1836, horiz. b, Quimbaya culture sculpture. c, Coffee plantation house, Quimbaya, horiz. d, Coffee bean picker, Pijao, horiz. e, Valle de Cocora, Salento. f, Botanical Gardens, Calarca, horiz. g, La Estación Metropolitan Cultural Center, Armenia, horiz. h, Monument and government building, Armenia. i, Free Cemetery, Circasia, horiz. j, Aerial view of Buenavista, horiz. k, San José Temple, Génova. l, Founding of Armenia, horiz.

Horizontal stamps are 46x37mm.

2006　　　　　　　　　*Perf. 13½x14*
Sheets of 12, #a-l, + 8 labels
1265 A608 1300p Valle del
　　　　　　　Cauca　　　　13.00 13.00
1266 A608 2000p Boyacá　　20.00 20.00
1267 A608 3300p Quindío　32.50 32.50
　　Nos. 1265-1267 (3)　　　65.50 65.50

20th
Central
American
and
Caribbean
Games
A653

2006　　　*Litho.*　　　*Perf. 14*
1268 A653 2000p multi　　　1.75 1.75

Pres. Alberto Lleras Camargo (1906-
90) — A654

Denominations: a, 1300p. b, 3300p.
Illustration reduced.

2006　　　*Litho.*　　*Perf. 14x13¾*
1269 A654　Horiz. pair, #a-b +
　　　　　　alternating labels　4.25 4.25

Souvenir Sheet

America Issue, Energy
Conservation — A655

No. 1270: a, Left hand. b, Right hand.

2006　　　　　　　　　　*Perf. 12*
1270 A655 5000p Sheet of 2, #a-
　　　　　b　　　　　　　　9.00 9.00

Christmas — A656

Denominations: a, 1300p. b, 3300p.

2006, Dec. 13　　　*Perf. 13¾x14*
1271 A656　Vert. pair, #a-b　4.25 4.25

General José
Maria Cordova
Military School,
Cent. — A657

2007, May 30　　　　　*Perf. 14*
1272 A657 10,000p multi　11.00 11.00

Departments Type of 2003

No. 1273 — Sucre Department: a, Coat of arms. b, St. Francis of Assisi Cathedral, Sincelejo, horiz. c, Palm trees, Tolú. d, Cattle, Sucre. e, Bull ring, Sincelejo, horiz. f, Church, Corozal. g, Musical score of "Fiesta en Corraleja." h, Painting of fandango dancers, horiz. i, Fisherman, Caimito. j, Palm trees, Sincelejo. k, Cane weaver, Sampués, horiz. l, Hammocks, Morroa.

Horizontal stamps are 46x37mm.

2007, May 30　　　　　*Perf. 12*
Sheet of 12, #a-l, + 8 Labels
1273 A608 3300p Sucre　42.50 42.50

Miniature Sheet

Scouting, Cent. — A658

No. 1274: a, International and Colombian Scouting emblems, Scouts with Lord Robert Baden-Powell. b, Emblem of 21st World Scout Jamboree, Colombian Scouting emblem, children's drawing of Colombian scout. c, Scouting emblem, Lord Robert Baden-Powell. d, International and Colombian Scouting emblems, animal track.

2007, June 26　　　　　*Perf. 14*
1274 A658 1500p Sheet of 8,
　　　　　2 each #a-
　　　　　d, + central
　　　　　label　　　　　12.50 12.50

Souvenir Sheet

El Espectador Newspaper, 120th
Anniv. — A659

No. 1275: a, Newspaper from 1887. b, Paperboy, horiz.

2007, June 28　　　　　*Perf. 12*
1275 A659 4500p Sheet of 2, #a-
　　　　　b　　　　　　　　9.25 9.25

Pan American
Games, Rio de
Janeiro — A660

2007, July 9　　　　　*Perf. 14*
1276 A660 3700p multi　　3.75 3.75

Fourth Spanish Language Intl.
Congress — A661

2007
1277 A661 5300p multi + label　5.25 5.25

SEMI-POSTAL STAMP

Catalogue values for unused stamps in this section are for Never Hinged items.

Girl Giving First
Aid — SP1

　　　　　　　　　Perf. 13½x14
1966, Apr. 26　*Litho.*　*Unwmk.*
B1　SP1 5c + 5c multicolored　.25 .20
　　Issued for the Red Cross.

AIR POST STAMPS

No. 341 Overprinted

1919 Unwmk. Perf. 14

C1	A107	2c car rose	3,250.	1,600.
a.		Numerals "1" with serifs	6,500.	4,000.

Used for the first experimental flight from Barranquilla to Puerto Colombia, 6/18/19. Values are for faulty stamps.

Issued by Compania Colombiana de Navegacion Aerea

From 1920 to 1932 the internal airmail service of Colombia was handled by the Compania Colombiana de Navegacion Aerea (1920) and the Sociedad Colombo-Alemana de Transportes Aéreos, known familiarly as "SCADTA" (1920-1932).

These organizations, under government contracts, operated and maintained their own post offices and issued stamps which were the only legal franking for airmail service during this period, both in the internal and international mails. All letters had to bear government stamps as well.

Woman and Boy Watching Plane — AP1

Designs: No. C3, Clouds and small biplane at top. No. C4, Tilted plane viewed close-up from above. No. C5, Flier in plane watching biplane. No. C6, Lighthouse. No. C7, Fuselage and tail of biplane. No. C8, Condor on cliff. No. C9, Plane at rest; pilot foreground. No. C10, Ocean liner.

1920, Feb. Unwmk. Litho. Imperf. Without Gum

C2	AP1	10c multicolored	2,750.	1,750.
C3	AP1	10c multicolored	3,500.	1,750.
C4	AP1	10c multicolored	4,250.	1,750.
C5	AP1	10c multicolored	3,250.	1,750.
C6	AP1	10c multicolored	2,750.	1,750.
C7	AP1	10c multicolored	10,000.	3,500.
C8	AP1	10c multicolored	5,500.	2,750.
C9	AP1	10c multicolored	3,250.	1,750.
C10	AP1	10c multicolored	4,250.	2,500.

Nos. C2-C10 were overprinted on the nine lighter-colored varieties of a set of 18 publicity labels produced by the Curtis Co. for inclusion with packs of cigarettes. These labels were printed se-tenant, in panes of 18 (3x6). Value for the set of 18 values without overprint: $4,000.

Flier in Plane Watching Biplane — AP2

1920, Mar.

C11	AP2	10c green	50.00 85.00

Four other 10c stamps, similar to No. C11, have two designs showing plane, mountains and water. They are printed in deep green or light brown red. Some authorities state that these four were not used regularly.

Issued by Sociedad Colombo-Alemana de Transportes Aereos (SCADTA)

Seaplane over Magdalena River — AP3

1920-21 Litho. Perf. 12

C12	AP3	10c yellow ('21)	35.00	30.00
C13	AP3	15c blue ('21)	40.00	32.50
C14	AP3	30c blk, rose	22.50	13.00
C15	AP3	30c rose ('21)	35.00	27.50
C16	AP3	50c pale green	35.00	30.00
	Nos. C12-C16 (5)		167.50	133.00

For surcharges see Nos. C17-C24, C36-C37.

No. C16 Handstamp Surcharged in Violet or Black:

(Illustrations of types "a" to "e" are reduced in size.)

VALOR 10 CENTAVOS
a

VALOR 10 CENTAVOS
b

Valor 10 Centavos
c

d

30¢   30¢
e

f

$030¢
g

1921

C17	AP3 (a)	10c on 50c	900.	850.
C18	AP3 (b)	10c on 50c	900.	850.
C19	AP3 (c)	10c on 50c	900.	850.
C20	AP3 (b)	30c on 50c	700.	600.
C21	AP3 (d)	30c on 50c	700.	600.
C22	AP3 (e)	30c on 50c	1,100.	1,100.
C23	AP3 (f)	30c on 50c	1,300.	1,100.
C24	AP3 (g)	30c on 50c	1,300.	1,100.

Plane over Magdalena River — AP4

Plane over Bogota Cathedral AP5

1921 Perf. 11½

C25	AP4	5c orange yellow	3.00	3.00
C26	AP4	10c slate green	1.25	1.00
C27	AP4	15c orange brown	1.25	1.10
C28	AP4	20c red brown	3.00	1.40
a.		Horiz. pair, imperf. vert.	140.00	
C29	AP4	30c green	1.40	.70
C30	AP4	50c blue	2.40	.75
C31	AP4	60c vermilion	50.00	22.50
C32	AP5	1p gray black	14.00	3.75
C33	AP5	2p rose	26.00	14.00
C34	AP5	3p violet	80.00	52.50
C35	AP5	5p olive green	225.00	210.00
	Nos. C25-C35 (11)		407.30	310.70

Nos. C25-C35 exist imperf. For surcharge see No. C52.

Nos. C16 and C12 Handstamp Surcharged

Illustration of type "h" is reduced in size.

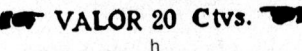

VALOR 20 Ctvs.
h

30 cent.
i

1921-22 Perf. 12

C36	AP3 (h)	20c on 50c	2,250.	1,700.
C37	AP3 (i)	30c on 10c	575.	—

Seaplane over Magdalena River — AP6

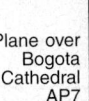

Plane over Bogota Cathedral AP7

1923-28 Wmk. 116 Perf. 14x14½

C38	AP6	5c orange yellow	1.00	.20
C39	AP6	10c green	1.00	.20
C40	AP6	15c carmine	1.00	.20
C41	AP6	20c gray	1.00	.20
C42	AP6	30c blue	1.00	.20
C43	AP6	40c purple ('28)	8.00	5.50
C44	AP6	50c green	1.25	.20
C45	AP6	60c brown	2.10	.20
C46	AP6	80c olive grn ('28)	21.00	20.00
C47	AP7	1p black	9.00	2.00
C48	AP7	2p red orange	13.00	4.00
C49	AP7	3p violet	27.50	17.50
C50	AP7	5p olive green	45.00	24.00
	Nos. C38-C50 (13)		131.85	74.40

For surcharges and overprints see Nos. C51, C53-C54, CF1.

Nos. C41 and C31 Surcharged in Carmine and Dark Blue:

No. C51	No. C52

1923

C51	AP6	30c on 20c gray (C)	60.00 40.00
C52	AP4	30c on 60c ver	52.50 27.50

Nos. C41-C42 Overprinted in Black

1928 Wmk. 116 Perf. 14x14½

C53	AP6	20c gray	42.50 40.00
C54	AP6	30c blue	42.50 40.00

Goodwill flight of Lt. Benjamin Mendez from New York to Bogota.

Magdalena River and Tolima Volcano AP8

Columbus' Ship and Plane AP9

1929, June 1 Wmk. 127 Perf. 14

C55	AP8	5c yellow org	.65	.20
C56	AP8	10c red brown	.65	.20
C57	AP8	15c deep green	.65	.20
C58	AP8	20c carmine	.65	.20
C59	AP8	30c gray blue	.65	.20
C60	AP8	40c dull violet	.65	.25
C61	AP8	50c dk olive grn	1.25	.25
C62	AP8	60c orange brown	2.10	.25
C63	AP8	80c green	5.50	2.25
C64	AP9	1p blue	6.50	1.75
C65	AP9	2p brown orange	9.75	4.25
C66	AP9	3p pale rose vio	24.00	14.00
C67	AP9	5p olive green	60.00	26.00
	Nos. C55-C67 (13)		113.00	50.00

For surcharges and overprints see Nos. C80-C95, CF2, CF4.

For International Airmail

AP10   AP11

1929, June 1 Wmk. 127 Perf. 14

C68	AP10	5c yellow org	3.50	4.25
C69	AP10	10c red brown	.65	1.75
C70	AP10	15c deep green	.65	1.75
C71	AP10	20c carmine	.65	2.10
C72	AP10	25c violet blue	.65	.35
C73	AP10	30c gray blue	.65	.55
C74	AP10	50c dk olive grn	.65	1.00
C75	AP10	60c brown	1.50	1.75
C76	AP11	1p blue	3.00	4.25
C77	AP11	2p red orange	4.50	5.75
C78	AP11	3p violet	60.00	60.00
C79	AP11	5p olive green	80.00	90.00
	Nos. C68-79 (12)		156.40	173.50

This issue was sold abroad for use on correspondence to be flown from coastal to interior points of Colombia. Cancellations are those of the country of origin rather than Colombia.

For overprint see No. CF3.

Nos. C63, C66 and C64 Surcharged in Black:

m

n

1930, Dec. 15

C80	AP8(m)	10c on 80c	4.25	4.25
C81	AP9(n)	20c on 3p	8.25	9.00
C82	AP9(n)	30c on 1p	10.00	9.00
	Nos. C80-C82 (3)		22.50	22.25

Simon Bolivar (1783-1830).

Colombian Government Issues
Nos. C55-C67 Overprinted in Black:

o

p

Wmk. 127

1932, Jan. 1   **Typo.**   *Perf. 14*

C83	AP8(o)	5c yellow org	8.00	8.00
C84	AP8(o)	10c red brown	1.75	.50
C85	AP8(o)	15c deep green	3.00	.50
C86	AP8(o)	20c carmine	1.50	.30
C87	AP8(o)	30c gray blue	1.50	.50
C88	AP8(o)	40c dull violet	2.00	1.00
C89	AP8(o)	50c dk ol grn	4.00	3.00
C90	AP8(o)	60c orange brn	3.25	3.00
C91	AP8(o)	80c green	14.00	14.00
C92	AP9(p)	1p blue	11.00	9.00
C93	AP9(p)	2p brown org	30.00	27.50
C94	AP9(p)	3p pale rose vio	60.00	52.50
C95	AP9(p)	5p olive green	100.00	110.00
	Nos. C83-C95 (13)		240.00	232.30

Coffee   Gold
AP12   AP16

Designs: 10c, 50c, Cattle. 15c, 60c, Petroleum. 20c, 40c, Bananas. 3p, 5p, Emerald.

1932-39 Wmk. 127 Photo.   *Perf. 14*

C96	AP12	5c org & blk brn	.90	.25
C97	AP12	10c lake & blk	1.00	.20
C98	AP12	15c bl grn & vio blk	.45	.20
C99	AP12	15c ver & vio blk ('39)	2.50	.20
C100	AP12	20c car & ol blk	.70	.20
C101	AP12	20c turq grn & ol blk ('39)	3.50	.30
C102	AP12	30c dk bl & blk brn	1.60	.20
C103	AP12	40c dk vio & ol bis	.85	.20
C104	AP12	50c dk grn & brnsh blk	3.50	1.25
C105	AP12	60c dk brn & blk vio	1.00	.25
C106	AP12	80c grn & blk brn	5.50	2.00
C107	AP16	1p dk bl & ol bis	9.00	1.25
C108	AP16	2p org brn & ol bis	10.00	2.25
C109	AP16	3p dk vio & emer	17.00	6.25
C110	AP16	5p gray blk & emer	47.50	20.00
	Nos. C96-C110 (15)		105.00	35.00

For overprint see No. CF5.

Nos. C104, C106-C108 Surcharged:

a

b

1934, Jan. 5

C111	AP12(a)	10c on 50c	3.50	3.50
C112	AP12(a)	15c on 80c	4.75	4.75
C113	AP16(b)	20c on 1p	5.25	5.25
C114	AP16(b)	30c on 2p	5.75	5.75
	Nos. C111-C114 (4)		19.25	19.25

400th anniversary of Cartagena.

Nos. C100 and C103 Surcharged in Black or Carmine:

1939, Jan. 15

C115	AP12	5c on 20c (Bk)	.35	.35
C116	AP12	5c on 40c (C)	.35	.25
C117	AP12	15c on 20c (Bk)	1.50	.50
a.	Double surcharge		12.00	
b.	Pair, one with dbl. surch.		14.00	
c.	Inverted surcharge		12.00	12.00

No. CF5 Surcharged in Black

C118	AP12	5c on 20c	.70	.70
	Nos. C115-C118 (4)		2.90	1.80

Nos. C102-C103
Surcharged in Black or
Red

1940, Oct. 20

C119	AP12	15c on 30c	1.25	.50
a.	Inverted surcharge		12.00	
C120	AP12	15c on 40c (R)	2.00	.75
a.	Double surcharge		12.00	

Pre-Columbian
Monument — AP18

Proclamation of
Independence — AP22

Designs: 10c, 40c, Symbol of Legend of El Dorado. 15c, 50c, Spanish Fortifications, Cartagena. 20c, 60c, Colonial Bogotá. 2p, 5p, National Library, Bogota.

Unwmk.

1941, Jan. 28   **Engr.**   *Perf. 12*

C121	AP18	5c gray black	.20	.20
C122	AP18	10c yellow org	.20	.20
C123	AP18	15c carmine rose	.20	.20
C124	AP18	20c yellow grn	.35	.20
a.	Horiz. pair, imperf. vert.		87.50	
C125	AP18	30c deep blue	.35	.20
C126	AP18	40c rose lake	.70	.20
C127	AP18	50c turq green	.70	.20
C128	AP18	60c sepia	.70	.20
C129	AP18	80c olive blk	1.90	.40
C130	AP22	1p blue & blk	3.25	.50
C131	AP22	2p red org & blk	5.25	2.00
C132	AP22	3p violet & blk	14.00	5.00
C133	AP22	5p lt green & blk	27.50	17.50
	Nos. C121-C133 (13)		55.30	27.00

See Nos. C151-C163, C217-C225. For overprints see Nos. C175-C198, C200-C216, C226, C290.

San Sebastian Fort,
Cartagena — AP24

National
Capitol,
Bogotá
AP27

Designs: 5c, 20c, 50c, San Sebastian Fort, Cartagena. 10c, 30c, 60c, Tequendama Waterfall. 15c, 40c, 80c, Bay of Santa Maria.

Unwmk.

1945, Nov. 3   **Litho.**   *Perf. 11*

C134	AP24	5c blue gray	.20	.20
C135	AP24	10c yellow org	.20	.20
C136	AP24	15c rose	.20	.20
C137	AP24	20c lt yel grn	.30	.20
C138	AP24	30c ultra	.30	.20
C139	AP24	40c claret	.50	.20
C140	AP24	50c bluish grn	.55	.20
C141	AP24	60c lt vio brn	2.25	.80

C142	AP24	80c dk slate grn	3.50	.80
C143	AP27	1p dk blue	5.00	.75
C144	AP27	2p red orange	7.00	2.50
	Nos. C134-C144 (11)		20.00	6.25

Part-perforate varieties exist for all denominations except 80c.

Imperf., Pairs

C134a	AP24	5c	8.50
C135a	AP24	10c	8.50
C136a	AP24	15c	8.50
C137a	AP24	20c	8.50
C138a	AP24	30c	8.50
C139a	AP24	40c	8.50
C140a	AP24	50c	8.50
C141a	AP24	60c	8.50
C142a	AP24	80c	10.50
C143a	AP27	1p	17.50
C144a	AP27	2p	60.00

Bello Type of Regular Issue, 1946
Wmk. 255

1946, Sept. 3   **Engr.**   *Perf. 12*

C145	A219	5c deep blue	.20	.20

Francisco José de   Manuel del
Caldas   Socorro
AP29   Rodriguez
                AP30

Perf. 12½

1947, May 9   **Litho.**   **Unwmk.**

C146	AP29	5c dp bl, grnsh	.35	.20
C147	AP30	10c red org, grnsh	.50	.45

4th Pan-American Press Congress (1946).

Chancellery Patio — AP31

Capitol,
Patio
Rafael
Nunez
AP32

38586

AP33

1948, Apr. 2   **Engr.**   **Wmk. 229**

C148	AP31	5c dark brown	.20	.20
C149	AP32	15c deep blue	.90	.90

Miniature Sheet
Imperf

C150	AP33	50c brown	1.90	1.90

9th Pan-American Conference, Bogotá.

Types of 1941

1948, July 21   **Unwmk.**   *Perf. 12*

C151	AP18	5c orange yel	.20	.20
C152	AP18	10c scarlet	.20	.20
C153	AP18	15c deep blue	.20	.20
C154	AP18	20c violet	.20	.20
C155	AP18	30c yellow grn	.35	.20
C156	AP18	40c gray	.40	.20
C157	AP18	50c rose lake	.40	.20
C158	AP18	60c olive gray	.70	.20
C159	AP18	80c red brn	.85	.20

C160	AP22	1p ol grn & vio brn	1.50	.30
C161	AP22	2p dp grn & brt bl	2.50	.68
C162	AP22	3p rose car & blk	5.50	3.75
C163	AP22	5p lt brn & turq grn	14.00	7.00
	Nos. C151-C163 (13)		27.00	13.50

"Air Week" 5c Blue
The War and Air Department issued a 5c blue stamp in May, 1949, to publicize Air Week (Semana de Aviacion). This stamp had no franking value and its use was optional during May 16-23.

Justice and   Wing
Liberty   AP35
AP34

Design: 10c, Liberty holding tablet of laws.

1949, Oct. 7   **Unwmk.**   *Perf. 13*

C164	AP34	5c blue green	.20	.20
C165	AP34	10c orange	.20	.20

Issued to honor the new Constitution.

For Domestic Postage

1950, June 22   **Litho.**   *Perf. 12*

C166	AP35	5c orange yellow	.25	.25
C167	AP35	10c brown red	.35	.30
C168	AP35	15c lt blue	.40	.40
C169	AP35	20c lt green	.60	.65
C170	AP35	30c lilac gray	1.50	2.00
C171	AP35	60c chocolate	1.90	2.50

With Network as in Parenthesis

C172	AP35	1p gray (buff)	14.00	16.00
C173	AP35	2p bl (pale grn)	14.00	16.00
C174	AP35	5p red brn (red brn)	40.00	45.00
	Nos. C166-C174 (9)		73.00	83.00

No. C172 was issued both with and without network.

Nos. C151-C157 and
C160-C163
Overprinted in Black

1950, July 18

C175	AP18	5c orange yel	.20	.20
C176	AP18	10c scarlet	.20	.20
C177	AP18	15c deep blue	.20	.20
C178	AP18	20c violet	.20	.20
C179	AP18	30c yellow green	.30	.20
C180	AP18	40c gray	.80	.20
C181	AP18	50c rose lake	.40	.25
C182	AP22	1p ol grn & vio brn	2.50	2.25
C183	AP22	2p dp grn & brt bl	3.75	3.25
C184	AP22	3p rose car & blk	11.00	11.00
C185	AP22	5p lt brn & turq grn	24.00	24.00
	Nos. C175-C185 (11)		43.55	42.00

Nos. C151-C163
Overprinted in Black

1950, July 12

C186	AP18	5c orange yel	.20	.20
C187	AP18	10c scarlet	.20	.20
C188	AP18	15c deep blue	.20	.20
C189	AP18	20c violet	.20	.20
C190	AP18	30c yellow green	.20	.20
C191	AP18	40c gray	.40	.20
C192	AP18	50c rose lake	.40	.20
C193	AP18	60c olive gray	.70	.20
C194	AP18	80c red brown	1.00	.40
C195	AP22	1p ol grn & vio brn	1.10	.50
C196	AP22	2p dp grn & brt bl	3.00	1.40
C197	AP22	3p rose car & blk	7.25	6.50
C198	AP22	5p lt brn & turq grn	16.00	14.00
		Nos. C186-C198 (13)	30.85	24.40

On Nos. C175-C198, "L" stands for LANSA, "A" for AVIANCA.

UPU Type
Miniature Sheet
Unwmk.

1950, Aug. 22		**Photo.**		***Imperf.***
C199	A245	50c gray	1.00	1.00

75th anniv. (in 1949) of the UPU.

Catalogue values for unused stamps in this section, from this point to the end of the section, are for Never Hinged items.

Types of 1941 Overprinted at Lower Right in Black

Unwmk.

1951, Sept. 15		**Engr.**		***Perf. 12***
C200	AP18	40c orange yel	1.50	1.25
C201	AP18	50c ultra	1.50	1.25
C202	AP18	60c gray	1.50	1.25
C203	AP18	80c car rose	1.10	.95
C204	AP22	1p red org & red brn	3.75	3.00
C205	AP22	2p rose car & bl	4.00	3.00
C206	AP22	3p choc & emer	10.00	8.00
C207	AP22	5p org & gray	30.00	30.00
		Nos. C200-C207 (8)	53.35	48.70

Types of 1941 Overprinted at Lower Right in Black

1951-54

C208	AP18	40c orange yel	3.25	.55
C209	AP18	50c ultra	4.00	.60
C210	AP18	60c gray	3.00	.45
a.		Overprint centered	2.00	.50
C211	AP18	80c car rose	.85	.30
C212	AP22	1p red org & red brn	3.25	.50
C213	AP22	1p ol grn & vio brn ('54)	4.00	.75
C214	AP22	2p rose car & bl	3.25	.55
C215	AP22	3p choc & emer	5.00	1.40
C216	AP22	5p org & gray	10.00	1.90
		Nos. C208-C216 (9)	36.60	7.00

All values except the 2p and 3p exist without overprint.

Types of 1941

1952, May 10			**Engr.**	
C217	AP18	5c ultra	.45	.20
C218	AP18	10c ultra	.45	.20
C219	AP18	15c ultra	.45	.20
C220	AP18	20c ultra	.90	.25
C221	AP18	30c ultra	2.25	.55

Color Change

C222	AP18	5c car rose	.45	.20
C223	AP18	10c car rose	.45	.20
C224	AP18	20c car rose	.85	.20
C225	AP18	30c car rose	1.75	.30
		Nos. C217-C225 (9)	8.00	2.30

Type of 1941 Surcharged in Blue

1952, Oct. 30

C226	AP18	70c on 80c car rose	1.50	.70

Latin American Siderurgical Conf., 1952.

Type of Postal Tax Stamps, 1948-50, Nos. 602 and 604 Surcharged or Overprinted in Black

1953		**Wmk. 255**		***Perf. 12***
C227	PT10	5c on 8c blue	.20	.20
C228	PT10	15c on 20c brown	.25	.20
C229	PT10	15c on 25c bl grn	1.00	.20
C230	PT10	25c blue green	.55	.20
		Nos. C227-C230 (4)	2.00	.80

Many varieties of overprint or surcharge exist on Nos. C227-C231.

No. 570 Overprinted "AEREO" in Blue

1953, Aug.		**Wmk. 229**		***Perf. 12½***
C231	A160	10c red		.25 .20

"Extra Rapido"

Stamps inscribed "Extra Rapido" are for use on domestic airmail carried by airlines other than AVIANCA.

No. 585 Surcharged and Overprinted "Extra Rapido" in Dark Blue

1953		**Unwmk.**		***Perf. 13***
C232	A244	5c on 11c red	.50	.35

Capitol and Arms — AP37

Revenue Stamps Overprinted "Correo Extra-Rapido"
Gray Security Paper

1953		**Wmk. 255**	**Engr.**	***Perf. 12***
C233	AP37	1c on 2c green	.25	.20
C234	AP37	50c red orange	.25	.20

AP38

Real Estate Tax Stamps Ovptd. "Correo Extra-Rapido" in Black or Carmine

1953				
C235	AP38	5c red orange	.25	.20
C236	AP38	20c brown (C)	.30	.20

On 20c, overprint is at bottom of stamp and two lines of ornaments cover real estate tax inscription at top.

Castillo y Rada and Map — AP39

Real Estate Tax Stamp Surcharged "Correo Aereo, II Exposicion Filatelica Nacional, Bogota Dicbre 1953, 15 Centavos"

1953, Dec. 12		**Engr. & Litho.**	
C237	AP39	15c on 10p multi	.40 .20

2nd Natl. Philatelic Exhib., Bogota, Dec. 1953.

No. RA45 Overprinted in Black

1953				
C238	PT10	10c purple	.25	.20

Galeras Volcano — AP40

Retreat of San Diego — AP41

Designs: No. C241, Las Lajas Shrine, Narino. No. C242, 50c, Bolivar monument. 20c, 80c, Ruiz mountain, Manizales. 40c, George Isaacs monument, Cali. 60c, Monkey Fountain, Tunja. 1p, Stadium, Medellin. 2p, Pastelillo Fort, Cartagena. 3p, Santo Domingo University gate. 5p, Las Lajas Shrine. 10p, Map of Colombia.

Perf. 13½x13, 13

1954, Jan. 15				**Unwmk.**
C239	AP40	5c dp red vio	.20	.20
C240	AP41	10c black	.20	.20
C241	AP40	15c red orange	.20	.20
C242	AP40	15c car rose	.20	.20
C243	AP40	20c brown	.20	.20
C244	AP40	30c brown org	.20	.20
C245	AP40	40c blue	.20	.20
C246	AP40	60c dk violet brn	.20	.20
C247	AP40	60c dk brown	.25	.20
C248	AP40	80c red brown	.30	.20

Size: 37x27mm
Center in Black

C249	AP41	1p deep blue	2.25	.20
C250	AP41	2p dark green	3.50	.30
C251	AP41	3p carmine rose	7.50	1.10

Size: 38x32mm, 32x38mm

C252	AP41	5p dk grn & red brn	9.50	2.90
C253	AP40	10p gray grn & red org	12.50	6.00
		Nos. C239-C253 (15)	37.40	12.50

See Nos. C307-C308. For surcharges and overprints see Nos. 691, C321, C325, C330, C333-C334, C343-C346.

Condor Carrying Shield AP42

Inscribed: "Correo Extra-Rapido"

1954, Apr. 23		**Litho.**	***Perf. 12½***
C254	AP42	5c lilac rose	.60 .30

For overprint see No. RA53.

Soldier-Map-Arms Type

1954, June 13		**Engr.**	***Perf. 13***
C255	A259	15c carmine	.30 .20

See No. C271a.

Games Type

Design: 20c, Stadium and Athlete holding arms of Colombia.

1954, July 18

C256	A260	15c chocolate	.65	.20
C257	A260	20c deep blue green	1.25	.35

Church of St. Peter Claver, Cartagena AP45

1954, Sept. 9

C258	AP45	15c deep blue	1.25	.20
a.		Souvenir sheet	3.50	3.00

St. Peter Claver, 300th death anniv. No. C258a contains one stamp similar to No. C258, but printed in red brown.

Mercury Type

1954, Oct. 29				
C259	A263	15c deep blue	.35	.20

Inscribed "Extra Rapido"

C260	A263	50c scarlet	.35	.20

Archbishop Manuel José Mosquera, Death Cent. — AP47

Inscribed: "Correo Extra-Rapido"

1954, Nov. 17

C261	AP47	2c yellow green	.25	.20

Virgin of Chiquinquira — AP48

Inscribed: "Correo Extra-Rapido"

1954, Dec. 4		**Engr. & Litho.**	
C262	AP48	5c org brn & multi	.25 .20

See No. C291. For overprint see No. 686.

College Types

Designs: 20c, Brother Cristobal de Torres. 50c, College chapel and arms.

Perf. 12½x11½, 11½x12½				
1954, Dec. 6		**Engr.**		**Unwmk.**
C263	A264	15c orange & blk	.25	.20
C264	A264	20c ultra	.35	.20
C265	A265	25c dark brown	.50	.20
C266	A265	50c black & car	1.25	.60
a.		Souvenir sheet	4.75	4.75
		Nos. C263-C266 (4)	2.35	1.20

No. C266a contains four stamps similar to Nos. C263-C266, but printed in different colors: 15c red and black, 20c pale purple, 25c brown, 50c black and olive green.

Steel Mill Type

1954, Dec. 12			***Perf. 12½x13***
C267	A266	20c green & blk	1.00 .60

Marti Type

1955, Jan. 28			***Perf. 13½x13***
C268	A267	15c deep green	.30 .20

Korean Veterans Type

1955, Mar. 23			***Perf. 12½***
C269	A268	20c dark green	.50 .20

Merchant Fleet Types

1955, Apr. 12			***Perf. 12½***
C270	A269	25c black	.30	.20
C271	A270	50c dark green	.55	.30
a.		Souvenir sheet	6.00	5.25

No. C271a contains 4 stamps similar to Nos. C255, C269-C271, but printed in different colors; 15c lilac red, 20c olive, 25c bluish black, 50c bluish green.

Marco Fidel Suarez (1855-1927), Pres. 1918-21 — AP56

Inscribed: "Correo Extra Rapido"

1955, April 23   *Perf. 13*
C272 AP56 10c deep blue   .25 .20

Hotel-Church Type
1955, May 16   Photo.   Perf. 11½x12
C273 A271 15c rose brown   .25 .20

Rotary Type
Unwmk.
1955, Oct. 17   Engr.   Perf. 13
C274 A272 15c dk carmine rose   .25 .20

Atahualpa, Tisquesuza and Montezuma AP59

Ferdinand the Catholic and Queen Isabella I AP60

Designs: 15c, O'Higgins, Santander and Sucre. 20c, Marti, Hidalgo and Petion. 1p, Artigas, Solano Lopez and Murillo. 2p, Abdon Calderon, Baron de Rio Branco and José de La Mar.

1955, Oct. 12   Engr. & Photo.
Inscribed: "Extra Rapido"
C275 AP59 2c dull brn & blk   .25 .20
C276 AP60 5c dk brn & yel   .25 .20

Regular Air Post
C277 AP59 15c rose car & blk   .30 .20
C278 AP59 20c pale brn & blk   .45 .20
a.   Souvenir sheet of 2   12.50 7.50

Inscribed: "Extra Rapido"
C279 AP60 1p ol gray & brn   10.00 6.00
C280 AP60 2p violet & blk   6.00 4.75
  Nos. C275-C280 (6)   17.25 11.55

7th Cong. of the Postal Union of the Americas and Spain, Bogota, Oct. 12-Nov. 9, 1955. No. C278a contains one each of Nos. C277-C278 printed in different shades.

Caro Type
1955, Nov. 29   Engr.   Perf. 13½x13
C281 A275 15c gray green   .25 .20

University of Salamanca AP62

Inscribed: "Extra Rapido"

1955, Nov. 29   Unwmk.   Perf. 13
C282 AP62 20c dark brown   .25 .20

University of Salamanca, 7th centenary.

Type of Postal Tax Stamp of 1948-50 Surcharged

1956   Wmk. 255   Engr.   Perf. 12
C283 PT10 2c on 8c blue   .25 .20

No. 617 Overprinted in Black

1956   Unwmk.   Perf. 12½x13
C284 A256 1p black & emerald   .25 .20

Columbus Type
1956, Oct. 11   Photo.   Perf. 12
C285 A279 15c intense blue   .55 .20
   See No. C306.

St. Elizabeth Type
1956, Nov. 19
C286 A280 15c red brown   .30 .20

St. Ignatius Type
1956, Nov. 26   Engr.   Perf. 12½x13
C287 A281 5c brown   .25 .20

Javier Pereira — AP63

1956, Dec. 28   Unwmk.   Perf. 12
C288 AP63 20c rose carmine   .25 .20

Issued to honor 167-year-old Javier Pereira.

No. 649 and Type of 1941 Overprinted in Red "EXTRA RAPIDO"
1957   Perf. 13½x13
C289 A276 5c blue & black   6.00 2.50
     Perf. 12
C290 AP22 5p orange & gray   6.50 5.00
  The overprint measures 14mm.

Virgin Type of 1954
Engraved and Lithographed
1957, May 23   Unwmk.   Perf. 13
C291 AP48 5c dp plum & multi   .25 .20

Bank Type
No. C292, 20c, Emblem & dairy farm. 10c, Emblem & tractor. 15c, Emblem, coffee & corn. No. C293, Emblem, cow, horse & herd.
1957   Photo.   Perf. 14x13½
C292 A283 5c chocolate   .20 .20
C293 A283 5c orange   .20 .20
C294 A283 10c green   .55 .40
C295 A283 15c black   .35 .20
C296 A283 20c dull red   .80 .20
  Nos. C292-C296 (5)   2.10 1.20

No. C292 is inscribed "Extra Rapido." Issued: No. C292, 3/5; others 5/23.

Cyclist AP64

1957, July 6   Unwmk.   Perf. 12
C297 AP64 2c brown   .20 .20
C298 AP64 5c ultra   .25 .20

Seventh Bicycle Tour of Colombia.

Academy Type
Designs: 15c, Coat of arms and Gen. Rafael Reyes. 20c, Coat of arms and Academy.

1957, July 20   Engr.   Perf. 12½
C299 A284 15c rose carmine   .20 .20
C300 A284 20c brown   .25 .20

Delgado Type
1957, Sept. 15   Photo.   Perf. 12
C301 A285 10c slate blue   .25 .20

UPU Type
1957, Oct. 10
C302 A286 15c dark red brown   .20 .20
C303 A286 25c dark blue   .20 .20

St. Vincent de Paul Type
1957, Oct. 18
C304 A287 5c rose brown   .25 .20

Fencing Type
1957, Nov. 23   Perf. 12
C305 A288 20c dark red brown   .25 .20

Columbus Type Inscribed "Extra Rapido"
1958, Jan. 8   Unwmk.   Perf. 12
C306 A279 3c dark green   .25 .20

Scenic Type
Design: 25c, Las Lajas Shrine.
1958, June 20   Engr.   Perf. 13
C307 AP40 25c dark blue   .30 .20
C308 AP40 25c rose violet   .30 .20

IGY Type
1958, May 12   Photo.   Perf. 12
C309 A289 25c green   .30 .20

Inscribed "Extra Rapido"
C310 A289 1p purple   .50 .20

No. 659 Overprinted "AEREO" in Carmine
1958, Oct. 16   Engr.   Perf. 13
C312 A277 50c dk green & blk   .40 .20

Almanza Type
1958, Oct. 23   Photo.   Perf. 14x13
C313 A290 25c dark gray   .25 .20

Inscribed "Extra Rapido"
C314 A290 10c olive green   .20 .20

Carrasquilla Type
1959, Jan. 22   Photo.   Perf. 14x13
C315 A291 25c carmine rose   .20 .20
C316 A291 1p dark blue   .60 .20

Miss Universe Type
1959, June 26   Unwmk.   Perf. 11½
C317 A292 1.20p multicolored   1.40 1.10
C318 A292 5p multicolored   40.00 37.50

Gaitan Type Inscribed "Extra Rapido" and Surcharged in Black or Blue
1959, July 28   Engr.   Perf. 12x13½
C319 A293 2p on 1p black   1.40 1.25
C320 A293 2p on 1p black (Bl)   1.40 1.25

The 1p black, type A293, exists without surcharge.

No. C247 Surcharged with New Value in Dark Blue; Old Value Obliterated
1959, Aug. 24   Unwmk.   Perf. 13
C321 AP40 50c on 60c dk brown   1.25 .40

Regular and Air Post Issues of 1948-59 Overprinted in Black or Red

1959-60
C322 A283 5c orange   .35 .25
C323 A287 5c rose brn   ('60)   .50 .50
C324 A281 5c brown (R)   .40 .30
C325 AP41 10c black   .25 .20
a.   Double overprint   2.50 2.50
C326 A160 10c red, #C231   .40 .20
a.   Double overprint   1.40 1.40
C328 A284 15c rose car   .25 .20
a.   Inverted overprint   3.00 3.00
C330 AP40 20c brown   .25 .20
a.   Double overprint   1.40 1.40

C331 A284 20c brown   .25 .20
C332 A288 20c dk red brn   ('60)   .25 .20
C333 AP40 25c rose vio   ('60)   .25 .20
C334 AP40 25c dark blue   .25 .20
C335 A291 25c car rose   .25 .20
C336 A290 25c dark gray   .25 .20
C338 AP40 30c brown org   .25 .20
C340 AP40 50c on 60c dk brn   .40 .20
C341 A291 1p dark blue   .95 .20
a.   Double overprint   2.50 2.50
C342 A292 1.20p brn, ultra, car & ol   1.50 .80
C343 AP41 2p dk grn & blk   2.00 .20
C344 AP41 3p car rose & blk   6.00 1.00
a.   Double overprint   10.00 10.00
C345 AP41 5p dk grn & red brn   8.00 1.10
a.   Double overprint   10.00 10.00
b.   Inverted overprint   10.00 10.00
C346 AP40 10p gray grn & red org   10.00 2.25
  Nos. C322-C346 (21)   33.00 8.50

Issued following agreement between the Colombian government and AVIANCA to unify the air postage used on all mail carried by AVIANCA.
Vertical overprint on Nos. C342 and C346.

Airmail Stamp of 1919 and Planes AP66

60c, Nos. C349a, C350a, Planes of 1919 and 1959. Nos. C349b, C350b, Stamp of 1919 and Planes.

Unwmk.
1959, Dec. 5   Photo.   Perf. 12
C347 AP66 35c lt bl, blk & red   .40 .20
C348 AP66 60c yel grn & gray   .60 .35

Souvenir Sheets
C349   Sheet of 2   7.50 6.75
a.   AP66 1p orange & gray   1.50 1.00
b.   AP66 1p lilac, gray & red   1.50 1.00

Inscribed "Extra Rapido"
1960, May 17
C350   Sheet of 2   7.50 6.75
a.   AP66 1.50p red orange & gray   1.50 1.25
b.   AP66 1.50p olive, gray & rose   1.50 1.25

Nos. C347-C350 for the 40th anniv. of air post service and of the AVIANCA company.

Type of Regular Issue and

1859 Stamp and Seaplane AP67

Tête Bêche 5c Stamps of 1859 — AP68

Designs (various stamps of 1859 and): 10c, Map of Colombia. 25c, Pres. Mariano Ospina. 1.20p, Plane over mountains.

1959, Dec. 1   Photo.   Perf. 12
C351 A296 25c choc & red   .50 .20
C352 AP67 50c ver & ultra   1.00 .50
C353 AP67 1.20p yel grn & car   2.00 1.10

Inscribed "Extra Rapido"
C354 A296 10c lemon & vio   .20 .20
  Nos. C351-C354 (4)   3.70 2.00

Souvenir Sheet
Wmk. 331
1959, Dec. 23   Litho.   *Imperf.*
C355 AP68   5p blue, *pink*   19.00 19.00

Cent. of Colombian postage stamps.
No. C355 exists with inscription "VALOR
$5.10" instead of "VALOR $5."

Eldorado
Airport,
Bogota
AP69

1960, Jan. 5   Wmk. 331   *Perf. 12½*
C356   AP69 35c black & ocher   .50   .20
C356A AP69 60c ver & gray   .65   .35

Inscribed "Extra Rapido"
C356B AP69 1p Prus bl & gray   .85   .50
    Nos. C356-C356B (3)   2.00 1.05

Ant Bear
AP70

1.30p, Armadillo. 1.45p, Parrot fish.

Unwmk.
1960, Feb. 12   Photo.   *Perf. 12*
C357 AP70 35c sepia   1.25   .20
C358 AP70 1.30p rose car & dk
      brn   2.40 2.25
C359 AP70 1.45p lt bl, bl & yel   2.00 1.25
    Nos. C357-C359 (3)   5.65 3.70

Alexander von Humboldt, German naturalist
and geographer (1769-1859).

Flower Type
Nos. C360, C362, C366, Passiflora mollissima. Nos. C361, C364, C367, Odontoglossum luteo purpureum. Nos. C363, C369,
Anthurium andreanum. Nos. C365, C370,
Stanhopea tigrina. No. C368, Espeletia
grandiflora.

1960, May 10   Photo.   *Perf. 12*
Flowers in Natural Colors
C360 A298   5c dark blue   .20   .20
C361 A298   35c maroon   .40   .20
C362 A298   60c dark blue   .75   .55
C363 A298   1.45p dark brown   1.00   .85

Inscribed "Extra Rapido"
C364 A298   5c maroon   .20   .20
C365 A298   10c brown   .20   .20
C366 A298   1p dark blue   2.00 2.50
C367 A298   1p maroon   2.00 2.50
C368 A298   1p brown   2.00 2.50
C369 A298   1p brown   2.00 2.50
C370 A298   1p brown   2.00 2.50
    Nos. C360-C370 (11)   12.75 14.70

See Nos. C420-C425.

Fleeing
Family and
Uprooted Oak
Emblem
AP71

Perf. 10, 11
1960, May 24   Litho.   Wmk. 331
C371 AP71 60c bl grn & gray   .30   .20

World Refugee Year, 7/1/59-6/30/60.

Souvenir Sheet

Pan-American Highway Through
Colombia — AP72

1960, May 28   Litho.   *Imperf.*
C372 AP72 2.50p brn & aqua   5.00 5.00

8th Pan-American Highway Congress,
Bogota, May 20-29.

Lincoln Type
1960, June 6   *Perf. 10½*
C375 A299 40c dl red brn & blk   .85   .60
C376 A299 60c rose red & blk   .25   .20

Type of Regular Issue and

Joaquin Camacho, Jorge Tadeo
Lozano and Jose Miguel Pey
AP73

Flag, Coins and Arms of Mompox and
Cartagena — AP74

No. C378, Arms of Cartagena. 35c, 1.45p,
Colombian flag. 60c, Andres Rosillo, Antonio
Villavicencio and Joaquin Caicedo. 1p,
Manuel de Bernardo Alvarez and Joaquin
Gutierrez. 1.20p, Jose Antonio Galan statue.
1.30p, Front page of newspaper La Bagatela,
1811. 1.65p, Antonia Santos, Jose Acevedo y
Gomez and Liborio Mejia.

Unwmk.
1960, July 20   Photo.   *Perf. 12*
C377 AP73 5c lilac & brn   .20   .20
C378 A301 5c dp bl grn &
      multi   .20   .20
C379 AP73 35c multicolored   .20   .20
C380 AP73 60c red brn & grn   .40   .20
C381 AP73 1p ver & sl grn   .85   .60
C382 A301 1.20p ultra & ind   .85   .60
C383 AP73 1.30p orange & blk   .85   .60
C384 AP73 1.45p multicolored   1.10   .85
C385 AP73 1.65p green & brn   .85   .85
    Nos. C377-C385 (9)   5.50 4.30

Souvenir Sheet
Stamps Inscribed "Extra Rapido"
C386 AP74   Sheet of 4   4.00 4.00
    a.   50c deep claret & multi   .65   .65
    b.   50c green & multi   .65   .65
    c.   1p brown olive, yel, blue & car   .65   .65
    d.   1p lilac & gray   .65   .65

150th anniv. of Colombia's independence.

St. Isidore Type
Designs: 35c, No. C388a, St. Isidore and
farm animals. No. C388b, Nativity.

Unwmk.
1960, Sept. 26   Photo.   *Perf. 12*
C387 A302 35c multicolored   .25   .20

Souvenir Sheet
Stamps Inscribed "Extra Rapido"
C388 A302   Sheet of 2   6.00 6.00
    a.   1.50p multicolored   2.00 2.00
    b.   1.50p multicolored   2.00 2.00

See Nos. C439-C440.

Type of Regular Issue, 1959
Wmk. 331
1960, Nov. 23   Litho.   *Perf. 12½*
C389 A294 35c Bolivar   3.00   .40

Pan-American Highway Type
1961, Mar. 7   Unwmk.   *Perf. 10½x11*
C390 A304 10c rose lil & emer   .50   .50
C391 A304 20c ver & lt bl   .50   .50
C392 A304 30c black & emer   .50   .50

Inscribed "Extra Rapido"
C393 A304 10c dk blue & emer   .50   .50
    Nos. C390-C393 (4)   2.00 2.00

8th Pan-American Highway Congress,
Bogota, May 20-29, 1960.

Lopez Type
1961, Mar. 22   Photo.   *Perf. 12½*
C394 A305 35c blue & brown   .50   .20

Inscribed "Extra Rapido"
C395 A305 10c emerald & brn   .20   .20

Souvenir Sheet
C396 A305 1p lilac & brn   4.00 3.50

Brother
Damian
and San
Francisco
Church,
Cali
AP75

Designs: 10c, View of Cali, vert. No. 398,
Emblem of University del Valle, vert. 1.30p,
Fine Arts School, Cali. 1.45p, Agricultural Col-
lege, Palmira.

Perf. 13x13½, 13½x13
1961, Aug. 17   Photo.   Unwmk.
C397 AP75 35c vio brn & ol   .30   .20
C398 AP75 35c olive & grn   .30   .20
C399 AP75 1.30p sepia & pink   .85   .45
C400 AP75 1.45p multicolored   .85   .60

Inscribed: "Extra Rapido"
C401 AP75 10c brn & yel grn   .20   .20
    Nos. C397-C401 (5)   2.50 1.65

50th anniv. (in 1960) of the department of
Valle del Cauca.

View of
Cucuta
AP76

10c, Church of the Rosary, Cucuta, vert.

1961, Aug. 29
C402 AP76 35c brn ol & grn   .60   .20

Inscribed: "Extra Rapido"
C403 AP76 10c dk brn & gray grn   .20   .20

50th anniv. (in 1960) of the department of
North Santander.

Old and New
Ships of
Barranquilla
AP77

Arms and
View of San
Gil — AP78

Hotel, Popayan
AP79

Statue of Christ
in Procession
AP80

Design: 1.45p, View of Velez.

Perf. 12½x13, 13x12½
1961, Oct. 10   Photo.   Unwmk.
C404 AP77 35c gold & bl   .45   .20
C405 AP78 35c bl grn, yel &
      red   .45   .20
C406 AP79 35c car & brn   .45   .20
C407 AP78 1.45p brown & grn   .45   .20

Inscribed: "Extra Rapido"
C408 AP80 10c brown & yel   .20   .20
    Nos. C404-C408 (5)   2.00 1.00

Types of Regular and Air Post
Souvenir Sheets
Designs, No. C409: 35c, Barranquilla arms.
40c, Popayan arms. c, Arms and view of San
Gil. d, Holy Week in Popayan.
No. C410: a, Old and new ships at Barranquilla. b, Hotel, Popayan. c, Bucaramanga
arms. d, Holy Week in Popayan.

C409   Sheet of 4   6.00 6.00
    a.   A309 35c gold & multi   .55   .55
    b.   A309 40c gold & multi   .55   .55
    c.   AP78 1p blue, yellow & red   1.10   1.10
    d.   AP80 1p car rose & yellow   1.10   1.10

Stamps Inscribed: "Extra Rapido"
C410   Sheet of 4   6.00 6.00
    a.   AP77 50c gold & car rose   .85   .85
    b.   AP79 50c gold & blue   .85   .85
    c.   A309 50c pink & multi   .85   .85
    d.   AP80 50c blue & yellow   .85   .85

Nos. C404-C408 are in honor of the Atlantico Department. Nos. C409-C410 are in
honor of the Departments of Atlantico, Cauca
and Santander.

Nos. 713, 716 and
715 Overprinted and
Surcharged

1961, Sept.   *Perf. 12*
C411 A297 5c grnsh bl & brn   .20   .20
C412 A298 5c on 20c cit &
C413 A297 10c on 20c cit &
      gray brn   .20   .20
    Nos. C411-C413 (3)   .60   .60

"Aereo" in script on No. C412.
See Nos. C420-C425.

Sports Type
Designs: No. C414, Women divers. No.
C415, Tennis, mixed doubles. 1.45p, No.
C419b, Baseball. No. C417, Torch bearer.
Nos. C418, C419a, Bolivar statue and flags of
six participating nations. No. C419c, Soccer.
No. C419d, Basketball.

1961, Dec. 16   Litho.   *Perf. 13½x14*
C414 A310 35c ultra, yel & brn   .60   .20
C415 A310 35c car, yel & brn   .60   .20
C416 A310 1.45p Prus grn, yel &
      brn   1.00   .55

Inscribed: "Extra Rapido"
C417 A310 10c car lake, yel &
      brn   .20   .20
C418 A310 10c ol, yel, bl & red   .20   .20
    Nos. C414-C418 (5)   2.60 1.35

Souvenir Sheet
Stamps Inscribed: "Extra Rapido"
Imperf
C419   Sheet of 4   6.00 6.00
    a.   A310 50c multi   .40   .40
    b.   A310 50c multi   .40   .40
    c.   A310 1p multi   .85   .85
    d.   A310 1p multi   .85   .85

Flower Type of 1960
5c, Passiflora mollissima. 10c, Espeletia
grandiflora. 20c, 2p, Odontoglossum luteo

purpureum. 25c, Stanhopea tigrina. 60c, Anthurium Andreanum.

Unwmk.
1962, Jan. 30   Photo.   *Perf. 12*
Flowers in Natural Colors
C420	A298	5c gray	.20	.20
C421	A298	10c gray blue	.20	.20
C422	A298	20c rose lilac	.20	.20
C423	A298	25c citron	.30	.20
C424	A298	60c light brown	.30	.20

Inscribed "Extra Rapido"
C425	A298	2p salmon pink	2.75	1.25
		Nos. C420-C425 (6)	3.95	2.25

Anti-Malaria Type
Designs: 40c, Colombian anti-malaria emblem. 1p, 1.45p, Malaria eradication emblem and mosquito in swamp.

1962, Apr. 12   Litho.   *Perf. 12*
C426	A311	40c yellow & red	.25	.20
C427	A311	1.45p gray & ultra	.50	.40

Inscribed "Extra Rapido"
C428	A311	1p yel grn & ultra	3.50	3.50
		Nos. C426-C428 (3)	4.25	4.10

WHO drive to eradicate malaria.

Type of Regular Issue, 1962 and

Abelardo Ramos and Engineering School, Cauca — AP81

Designs: 10c, Miguel Triana, Andres A. Arroyo and Monserrate shrine with cable cars. 15c, Diodoro Sanchez and first meeting place of Engineers Society. 2p, Engineers Society emblem.

1962, June 12 Photo. *Perf. 11½x12*
C429	AP81	5c blue & dp rose	.20	.20
C430	AP81	10c green & sepia	.20	.20
C431	AP81	15c lilac & sepia	.20	.20

Inscribed: "Extra Rapido"
C432	A312	2p blk, yel, red & bl	1.50	1.50
		Nos. C429-C432 (4)	2.15	2.10

75th anniv. of the founding of the Colombian Soc. of Engineers and 6th Natl. Cong. of Engineers.

American States Type
1962, June 28   Photo.   *Perf. 13*
Flags in National Colors
C433	A313	35c black & blue	.35	.20

Women's Rights Type
Perf. 12x12½
1962, July 20   Litho.   Wmk. 229
C434	A314	35c buff, gray & blk	.25	.20

See Nos. C448-C450.

Scout Type
Designs: 15c, No. C438, Scouts at campfire and tents. 40c and No. C437, Girl Scouts.

Perf. 11½x12
1962, July 26   Photo.   Unwmk.
C435	A315	15c brown & rose	.20	.20
C436	A315	40c dp cl & pink	.25	.20
C437	A315	1p blue & buff	.80	.35

Inscribed "Extra Rapido"
C438	A315	1p purple & yel	4.00	3.75
		Nos. C435-C438 (4)	5.25	4.50

Nos. C435 and C438 for 30th anniv. of the Colombian Boy Scouts. Nos. C436 and C437 for the 25th anniv. of the Girl Scouts.

Nativity by Gregorio Vasquez AP82

Design: 2p, St. Isidore, similar to type A302.

Inscribed "Extra Rapido"
Unwmk.
1962, Aug. 28   Photo.   *Perf. 12*
C439	AP82	10c gray & multi	.20	.20
C440	AP82	2p gray & multi	3.75	3.50

See Nos. C387-C388.

Type of Regular Issue, 1962 and

Pres. Aquileo Parra and Magdalena River Bridge AP83

Design: 5c, Locomotives of 1854 and 1961. 10c, Railroad map of Colombia.

1962, Sept. 28 Photo. *Perf. 12½*
C441	AP83	5c sep & slate grn	.20	.20
C442	A316	10c multicolored	.20	.20

Engr.
C443	AP83	1p dull pur & brn	1.40	.20

Inscribed: "Extra Rapido."
C444	AP83	5p bl, brn & dl grn	3.75	3.75
		Nos. C441-C444 (4)	5.55	4.35

Progress of Colombian railroads and completion of the Atlantic Line from Santa Maria to Bogota.

UPAE Type
Designs: 50c, Map of Americas and carrier pigeon. 60c, Post horn.

Perf. 13½x14
1962, Oct. 18   Litho.   Wmk. 346
C445	A317	50c slate grn & gold	.30	.20
C446	A317	60c gold & plum	.25	.20

Pope John XXIII AP84

1963, Mar. 11
C447	AP84	60c gold, red brn, buff & red	.25	.20

Vatican II, the 21st Ecumenical Council of the Roman Catholic Church.

Women's Rights Type of 1962
1963-64   *Perf. 12x12½*
C448	A314	5c sal, gray & blk ('64)	.20	.20
C449	A314	45c pale grn, gray & blk	.30	.20
C450	A314	45c brt pink, gray & blk	.30	.20
		Nos. C448-C450 (3)	.80	.60

Games Emblem — AP85

1963, Aug. 12   *Perf. 13x14*
C451	AP85	20c gray & multi	.20	.20
C452	AP85	80c buff & multi	.25	.20

South American Athletic Championships (22nd for men, 12th for women), Cali, June 30-July 7.

Bolivar Statue by Arenas-Betancourt — AP86

Perf. 14x13½
1963, Aug. 30   Unwmk.
C453	AP86	1.90p olive bis & blue	.25	.20

Centenary of the city of Pereira.
For surcharge see No. C574.

Tennis Player — AP87

1963, Oct. 11   *Perf. 13½x14*
C454	AP87	55c multicolored	.25	.20

30th South American Tennis Championships, Medellin, Oct. 3-13.

Pres. John F. Kennedy and Alliance for Progress Emblem AP88

1963, Dec. 17   Litho.   *Perf. 14x13½*
C455	AP88	10c multicolored	.40	.20

President John F. Kennedy (1917-1963).

Church of the True Cross, National Pantheon, Bogota — AP89

2p, Christ of the Martyrs, bell and tomb.

Perf. 13½x14
1964, Mar. 10   Photo.   Unwmk.
C459	AP89	1p multicolored	.20	.20
C460	AP89	2p multicolored	.35	.20

View of Cartagena AP90

1964, Mar. 18   Litho.   *Perf. 14x13½*
C461	AP90	3p vio, bl, ocher & brn	1.40	.60

Cartagena's independence in 1811, Simon Bolivar's visit in 1812 and the siege of 1815.

Eleanor Roosevelt AP91

1964, Nov. 10   Photo.   *Perf. 12*
C462	AP91	20c ol & dl red brn	.25	.20

Eleanor Roosevelt (1884-1962).

Alberto Castilla and Score of "El Bunde" AP92

1964, Nov. 10   Unwmk.
C463	AP92	30c ol bis & Prus grn	.25	.20

Department of Tolima and Maestro Alberto Castilla (1878-1937) who in 1906 founded the Tolima Conservatory of Music in Ibague.

Mejia Type
Mejia portrait and: 45c, Women picking coffee. 5p, Mules carrying coffee bags. 10p, Loading coffee on freighter "Manuel Mejia."

1965, Feb. 10   Engr.   *Perf. 12½x13*
C464	A320	45c brown & blk	.20	.20
C465	A320	5p gray grn & blk	1.75	.25
C466	A320	10p ultra & blk	2.40	.30
		Nos. C464-C466 (3)	4.35	.75

ITU Emblem AP93

1965, Oct. 25   Photo.   *Perf. 12*
C467	AP93	80c Prus bl, lt bl & red	.25	.20

Cent. of the ITU.

Cattleya Truanae — AP94

1965, Oct. 3   Litho.   *Perf. 13½x14*
C468	AP94	20c yellow & multi	.25	.20

Fifth Philatelic Exhibition.

Cent. of the Telegraph in Colombia — AP95

1965, Nov. 1   *Perf. 13½x14, 14x13½*
No. C469, Pres. Manuel Murillo Toro statue, telegraph and orbits. No. C470, Telegraph and satellites over South America, horiz.
C469	AP95	60c multicolored	.25	.20
C470	AP95	60c multicolored	.25	.20

Junkers F-13 Seaplane, 1920 AP96

History of Colombian Aviation: 10c, Dornier Wal, 1924. 20c, Dornier Mercur, 1926. 50c, Trimotor Ford, 1932. 60c, De Havilland biplane, 1930. 1p, Douglas DC-4, 1947. 1.40p, Douglas DC-3, 1944. 2.80p, Superconstellation 1049, 1951. 3p, Boeing 720B jet, 1961.

Perf. 14x13½
1965-66   Photo.   Unwmk.
C471	AP96	5c multicolored	.20	.20
C472	AP96	10c multicolored	.20	.20
C473	AP96	20c multicolored	.20	.20
C474	AP96	50c multicolored	.20	.20
C475	AP96	60c multicolored	.40	.20

C476	AP96	1p multicolored	.75	.20
C477	AP96	1.40p multicolored	.90	.20
C478	AP96	2.80p multicolored	1.60	.60
C479	AP96	3p multicolored	2.40	.85
		Nos. C471-C479 (9)	6.85	2.85
		Nos. C471-C479,CE4 (10)	7.20	3.05

Issued: 5c, 60c, 3p, 12/13/65; 10c, 1p, 1.40p, 7/15/66; 20c, 50c, 2.80p, 12/14/66.

Automobile Club Emblem and Car on Road AP97

1966, Feb. 16   Litho.   Perf. 14x13½

C480	AP97	20c multicolored	.25	.20

25th anniv. (in 1965) of the Automobile Club of Colombia.

Fish Type

Fish: 2p, Flying fish. 2.80p, Queen angelfish. 20p, King mackerel.

1966, Aug. 25   Photo.   Perf. 12½x13

C481	A323	2p multicolored	.50	.20
C482	A323	2.80p multicolored	1.10	.90
C483	A323	20p multicolored	14.00	11.00
		Nos. C481-C483 (3)	15.60	12.10

Coat of Arms Type

1966, Oct. 11   Litho.   Perf. 14x13½

C484	A324	1p ultra & multi	.25	.20
C485	A324	1.40p red & multi	.20	.20

Portrait Type

80c, Father Felix Restrepo Mejia, S.J. (1887-1965), theologian, scholar. 1.70p, José Joaquin Casas (1866-1951), educator, diplomat.

Perf. 13½x14

1967, Jan. 18   Litho.   Unwmk.

C486	A325	80c dk bl & bis	.20	.20
C487	A325	1.70p blk & bis	.25	.20

Declaration of Bogota Type

1967, Feb. 2   Litho.   Perf. 14x13½

C488	A326	3p multicolored	.35	.20

See note after No. 767.

Orchid Type

Orchids: 1p, Cattleya dowiana aurea, vert. 1.20p, Masdevallia coccinea, vert. 5p, Catasetum macrocarpum and bee.

1967, May 23   Litho.   Perf. 14

C489	A327	1p multicolored	1.60	.30
C490	A327	1.20p multicolored	1.10	.25
C491	A327	5p multicolored	7.50	.90
a.		Souv. sheet of 3, #C489-C491	25.00	25.00
		Nos. C489-C491 (3)	10.20	1.45

Lions Type

1967, July 12   Litho.   Perf. 13½x14

C492	A328	25c multicolored	.25	.20

"First Caesarean Section" by Grau AP98

Perf. 14x13½

1967, Sept. 7   Litho.   Unwmk.

C493	AP98	80c multicolored	.25	.20

Issued to publicize the 6th Congress of Colombian Surgeons, Bogota, Sept. 25.

SENA Type

Lithographed and Embossed
1967, Sept. 20   Perf. 13½x14

C494	A329	2p gold, ver & blk	.50	.20

Pre-Columbian Art Type

Designs: 30c, Bird pectoral. 5p Ornamental pectoral. 20p, Pitcher.

1967, Oct. 13   Photo.   Perf. 13½x14

C495	A330	30c ver, gold & brn	.20	.20
C496	A330	5p red, gold & brn	1.75	.30
a.		Souvenir sheet of 2	2.25	2.25
C497	A330	20p vio, gold & brn	8.25	8.25
		Nos. C495-C497 (3)	10.20	8.75

No. C496a also commemorates the 6th Natl. Phil. Exhib. No. C496a contains 2 imperf. stamps in changed colors similar to Nos. C495-C496 (30c has green background and 5p maroon background).

Telecommunications Type

Designs: 50c, Signal lights. 1p, Early Bird satellite, Southern Cross and radar.

Perf. 13½x14

1968, May 14   Litho.   Unwmk.

C498	A331	50c blk, ver & emer	.20	.20
C499	A331	1p ultra, yel & gray	.30	.20

Eucharist Type

1968, June 6   Litho.   Perf. 13½x14

C500	A332	80c rose lil, red, yel & blk	.20	.20
C501	A332	3p bl, red, yel & blk	.30	.20

Eucharistic Congress Type

Designs: 80c, The Last Supper, by Gregorio Vasquez, horiz. 1p, St. Francis Xavier Preaching, by Gregorio Vasquez. 2p, The Dream of the Prophet Elias, by Gregorio Vasquez. 3p, Monstrance, c. 1700. 20p, Pope Paul VI, painting by Roman Franciscan nuns.

1968, Aug. 13   Photo.   Perf. 13

C502	A333	80c multicolored	.20	.20
C503	A333	1p multicolored	.25	.20
C504	A333	2p multicolored	.35	.20
C505	A333	3p lil & multi	.65	.20
C506	A333	20p gold & multi	4.00	2.00
		Nos. C502-C506 (5)	5.45	2.80

Shrine of the Eucharist, Bogota AP99

1.20p, Pope Paul VI giving blessing and Papal arms. 1.80p, Cathedral of Bogota.

Perf. 14x13½, 13½x14

1968, Aug. 22   Litho.

C507	AP99	80c multi	.20	.20
C508	AP99	1.20p multi, vert.	.20	.20
C509	AP99	1.80p multi, vert.	.30	.20
		Nos. C507-C509 (3)	.70	.60

Visit of Pope Paul VI to Colombia.

Computer Symbols — AP100

1968, Oct. 29   Litho.   Perf. 13½x14

C510	AP100	20c buff, car & grn	.25	.20

Cent. of the Natl. University and the 1st Data Processing Cong. in 1967 at the University.

Agriculture Institute Type

1968, Mar. 5   Litho.   Perf. 13½x14

C511	A337	1p gray & multi	.25	.20

Microscope and Pen — AP101

1969, Mar. 24   Litho.   Perf. 14

C512	AP101	5p blk, yel, ver & pur	2.40	.35

20th anniv. (in 1968) of the University of the Andes.

Alexander von Humboldt and Andes AP102

1969, May 3   Litho.   Perf. 14x13½

C513	AP102	1p grn & brn	.65	.35

Alexander von Humboldt (1769-1859), German naturalist and traveler.

Map of Colombia, Amphibian Plane and Letter AP103

Design: 1.50p, No. C516b, Globe, letter, and jet of Avianca airlines.

1969, June 18   Litho.   Perf. 14x13½

C514	AP103	1p multi	.45	.20
C515	AP103	1.50p multi	.65	.25

Souvenir Sheet
Imperf

C516		Sheet of 2	7.50	7.50
a.		AP103 5p green & multi	1.00	1.00
b.		AP103 5p violet & multi	1.00	1.00

50th anniv. of the 1st air post flight in Colombia. No. C516 also for 8th Natl. Philatelic Exhibition, EXFILBA 69, Barranquilla, June 18-22. No. C516 contains 2 stamps in the designs of the 1p and 1.50p.

Independence Type

2.30p, Simon Bolivar, José Antonio Anzoategui, Francisco de Paula Santander and victorious army entering Bogota, 9/18/1819; painting by Ignacio Castillo Cervantes.

1969, July 24   Litho.   Perf. 13½x14

C517	A338	2.30p gold & multi	1.00	.35

Social Security Emblem — AP104

Neurosurgeons' Congress Emblem — AP105

1969, Oct. 29   Litho.   Perf. 13½x14

C518	AP104	20c emer & blk	.25	.20

20th anniv. of the Colombian Institute of Social Security.

1969, Oct. 29

C519	AP105	70c vio, red & yel	.50	.30

Issued to publicize the 13th Congress of Latin-American Neurosurgeons, Bogota.

Junkers F-13 AP106

Nos. C521, C522b, Globe with airlines from Bogota & Boeing jet. No. C522a, like No. C520.

1969, Nov. 28   Litho.   Perf. 14x13½

C520	AP106	2p grn & multi	.75	.25
C521	AP106	3.50p ultra & multi	1.40	.50

Souvenir Sheet
Imperf

C522		Sheet of 2	7.50	7.50
a.		AP106 3.50p lt grn & multi	.75	.75
b.		AP106 5p ultra & multi	1.00	1.00

50th anniv. of AVIANCA; No. C522 also publicizes the 1st Interamerican Phil. Exhib., Bogota, Nov. 28-Dec. 7.
No. C522 contains 2 imperf. stamps.

Child Mailing Letter — AP107

Christmas: 1.50p, Praying child and gifts.

1969, Dec. 16   Litho.   Perf. 13½x14

C523	AP107	60c ocher & multi	.80	.20
C524	AP107	1p multicolored	.85	.25
C525	AP107	1.50p multicolored	1.10	.25
		Nos. C523-C525 (3)	2.75	.70

Radar Station and Pre-Columbian Head — AP108

1970, Mar. 25   Litho.   Perf. 14x13½

C526	AP108	1p dl grn, blk & brick red	.30	.20

Issued to publicize the opening of the communications satellite earth station at Chocontá in Cundinamarca Province.

Emblem of Colombian Youth Sports Institute — AP109

Art Exhibition Emblem — AP110

2.30p, Games' emblem (dove and 3 rings).

1970, Apr. 6   Litho.   Perf. 13½x14
C527 AP109 1.50p dk ol grn, yel & blk   .30 .20
C528 AP109 2.30p red & multi   .40 .20
9th Natl. Youth Games, Ibague, July 10-20.

1970, Apr. 30   Litho.   Perf. 13½x14
C529 AP110 30c multicolored   .25 .20
2nd Biennial Art Exhib., Medellin, 6/1-7/14.

Eduardo Santos, Rural and Urban Buildings AP111

1970, June 18   Litho.   Perf. 14x13½
C530 AP111 1p grn, yel & blk   .25 .20
Issued to commemorate the founding (in 1939) of the Territorial Credit Institute.

UN Emblem, Scales and Dove — AP112

EXFILCA Emblem — AP113

1970, June 26   Perf. 13½x14
C531 AP112 1.50p dk bl, lt bl & yel   .25 .20
25th anniversary of United Nations.

1970, Nov.   Litho.   Perf. 13½x14
C532 AP113 10p bl, gold & blk   3.50 .25
EXFILCA 70, 2nd Interamerican Philatelic Exhib., Caracas, Venezuela, Nov. 27-Dec. 6.

Mother Juana Ruperta in Napanga Costume and Music by Efrain Orozco — AP114

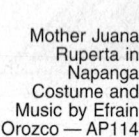

Designs: 1p, Dancers from Eastern Plains and music by Alejandro Wills. No. C535, Guabina man, woman and folk song. No. C536, Bambuco man and woman, and music. No. C537, Man and woman dancing the Cumbia, and music.

1970-71   Litho.   Perf. 13½x14
C533 AP114 60c dp lil rose & multi   .50 .20
C534 AP114 1p ultra & multi   .40 .20
C535 AP114 1.30p bl & multi   .55 .20
C536 AP114 1.30p emer & multi ('71)   .60 .20
C537 AP114 1.30p lil & multi ('71)   .40 .20
Nos. C533-C537 (5)   2.45 1.00

Athlete and Games Emblem — AP115

Design: 2p, Games emblem.

1971, Mar. 11
C542 AP115 1.50p multicolored   .90 .90
C543 AP115 2p blk, org & grn   .80 .55
6th Pan-American Games, Cali, 7/30-8/13.

Gilberto Alzate Avendano AP116

1971, Apr. 29   Litho.   Perf. 14x13½
C544 AP116 1p bl & multi   .40 .25
Avendano (1910-60), journalist, popular leader.

Commemorative Medal — AP117

Lithographed and Embossed
1971, June 21   Perf. 14x13½
C545 AP117 1p slate grn & gold   .55 .30
Centenary (in 1970) of the Bank of Bogota.

Olympic Center — AP118

Soccer — AP119

Designs (Games Emblem and): Nos. C546-C546C, Olympic Center. No. 547, Soccer. No. C548, Wrestling. No. C549, Bicycling. No. C550, Volleyball. No. C551, Diving (women). No. C552, Fencing. No. C553, Sailing. No. C554, Equestrian. No. C555, Jumping. No. C556, Rowing. No. C557, Cali emblem. No. C558, Basketball (women). No. C559, Stadium. No. C560, Baseball. No. C561, Hockey. No. C562, Weight lifting. No. C563, Medals. No. C564, Boxing. No. C565, Gymnastics (women). No. C566, Sharpshooting.

1971, July 16   Litho.   Perf. 13½x14
Multicolored and Emblem Color:
C546 AP118 1.30p yellow   1.25 .30
C546A AP118 1.30p green   1.25 .30
C546B AP118 1.30p blue   1.25 .30
C546C AP118 1.30p carmine   1.25 .30
C547 AP119 1.30p emerald   1.25 .30
C548 AP119 1.30p lilac   1.25 .30
C549 AP119 1.30p blue   1.25 .30
C550 AP119 1.30p carmine   1.25 .30
C551 AP119 1.30p blue   1.25 .30
C552 AP119 1.30p carmine   1.25 .30
C553 AP119 1.30p blue   1.25 .30
C554 AP119 1.30p gray   1.25 .30
C555 AP119 1.30p green   1.25 .30
C556 AP119 1.30p blue   1.25 .30
C557 AP118 1.30p orange   1.25 .30
C558 AP119 1.30p carmine   1.25 .30
C559 AP118 1.30p light blue   1.25 .30
C560 AP119 1.30p plum   1.25 .30
C561 AP119 1.30p yel grn   1.25 .30
C562 AP119 1.30p pink   1.25 .30
C563 AP118 1.30p deep org   1.25 .30
C564 AP119 1.30p plum   1.25 .30
C565 AP119 1.30p lilac rose   1.25 .30
C566 AP119 1.30p green   1.25 .30
a.   Sheet of 25, #C546-C566   35.00 35.00
6th Pan American Athletic Games, Cali. No. C546B appears twice in sheet.

Battle of Carabobo, by Martin Tovar y Tovar — AP120

1971, Nov. 25   Litho.   Perf. 13½x14
C567 AP120 1.50p multicolored   1.00 .20
Sesquicentennial of the Battle of Carabobo.

St. Theresa Type Overprinted "AEREO"
1972   Litho.   Perf. 13½x14
C568 A343 2p multicolored   .30 .20
See note after No. 793.

Vendor — AP121

Designs: 50c, Woman wearing shawl, and woven shawl. 3p, Fruit vendor (puppet).

1972, Apr. 11   Litho.   Perf. 13½x14
C569 AP121 50c multicolored   .35 .20
C570 AP121 1p multicolored   .35 .20
C571 AP121 3p multicolored   .50 .25
Nos. C569-C571 (3)   1.20 .65
Colombian artisans.

Mormodes Rolfeanum AP122

1972, Apr. 20   Perf. 14x13½
C572 AP122 1.30p multicolored   .45 .20
7th World Orchidology Congress, Medellin.

Congo Grande Dancer — AP123

Laureano Gomez, by Rodriguez Cubillos — AP124

1972, June 21   Litho.   Perf. 13½x14
C573 AP123 1.30p multicolored   .50 .20
International Carnival of Barranquilla.

No. C453 Surcharged in Brown

1972, Oct. 5   Litho.   Perf. 14x13½
C574 AP86 1.30p on 1.90p   .55 .20

1972   Perf. 13½x14
1.30p (#C576), Guillermo Leòn Valencia Muñoz.
C575 AP124 1.30p multicolored   .25 .20
C576 AP124 1.30p multicolored   .25 .20
Laureano Gomez (1898-1966), Guillermo Leon Valencia Munoz (1909-71), Presidents of Colombia.
Issued: No. C575, 10/17; No. C576, 11/28.

Benito Juarez — AP125

Rebecca Fountain AP126

1972, Dec. 12   Perf. 13½x14
C577 AP125 1.50p multicolored   .25 .20
Benito Juarez (1806-1872), revolutionary leader and president of Mexico.

1972, Dec. 19   Litho.
C578 AP126 80c multicolored .50 .45
C579 AP126 1p multicolored .45 .20

"Bucaramanga" — AP127

1972, Dec. 22   *Perf. 14x13½*
C580 AP127 5p multicolored .85 .20
Founding of Bucaramanga, 350th anniv.

Xavier University AP128

1973, May 8   Litho.   *Perf. 14x13½*
C581 AP128 1.30p lt grn & sep .25 .20
C582 AP128 1.50p lt bl & sep .25 .20
350th anniversary of the founding of Xavier University in Bogotá.

Ceramic Type

Excavated Ceramic Artifacts: 1p, Winged urn, Tairona. 1.30p, Woman and child, Sinu. 1.70p, Two-headed figure, Quimbaya. 3.50p, Man, Tumaco.

1973   Litho.   *Perf. 13½x14*
C583 A358 1p multicolored 1.00 1.00
C584 A358 1.30p multicolored .50 .20
C585 A358 1.70p multicolored .55 .25
C586 A358 3.50p multicolored 1.10 .30
    Nos. C583-C586 (4) 3.15 1.75
Issue dates: 1p, Oct. 11; others, June 15.

Battle of Maracaibo, by Manuel F. Rincon AP129

1973, July 24   Litho.   *Perf. 14x13½*
C587 AP129 10p bl & multi 2.00 .20
Battle of Maracaibo, sesquicentennial.

Bank Emblem AP130

1973, Oct. 1   Litho.   *Perf. 14x13½*
C588 AP130 2p multicolored .25 .20
50th anniv. of the Bank of the Republic.

No. 801 Overprinted "AEREO"

1973, Oct. 11   *Perf. 14*
C589 A346 80c multicolored .30 .20

Pres. Pedro Nel Ospina, by Coroleano Leudo — AP131

Arms of Toro — AP132

1973, Nov. 9   *Perf. 13½x14*
C590 AP131 1.50p multicolored .25 .20
50th anniversary of the Ministry of Communications founded under Pres. Ospina.

1973, Dec. 1
C591 AP132 1p multicolored .25 .20
Founding of Toro, Valle del Cauca, 4th cent.

Bolivar, Battle of Bombona AP133

1973, Dec. 7   Litho.   *Perf. 14x13½*
C592 AP133 1.30p multicolored .25 .20
Sesquicentennial (in 1972) of the Battle of Bombona.

Nicolaus Copernicus AP134

Andes, Map of South America AP135

1974, Feb. 19   Litho.   *Perf. 13½x14*
C593 AP134 2.50p multicolored .55 .20
500th anniversary of the birth of Nicolaus Copernicus (1473-1543), Polish astronomer.

1974, May 11   Litho.   *Perf. 14*
C594 AP135 2p multicolored .50 .20
Meeting of Communications Ministers of Members of the Andean Group, Cali, May 7-11, 1974.

Television Set AP136

1974, July 16   Litho.   *Perf. 14x13½*
C595 AP136 1.30p org, blk & brn .25 .20
20th anniversary of Colombian television and 10th anniversary of INRAVISION, the National Institute of Radio and Television.

Championship Emblem — AP137

1974, Aug. 5   Litho.   *Perf. 14x13½*
C596 AP137 4.50p multicolored .30 .20
2nd World Swimming Championships, Cali.

Condor — AP138

1974, Aug. 28   *Perf. 14*
C597 AP138 1.50p multicolored .25 .20
Bank of Colombia centenary.

UPU Envelope AP139

1974, Sept. 9   Litho.   *Perf. 14*
C598 AP139 20p multicolored 2.50 .30
Centenary of Universal Postal Union.

Symbol of Flight — AP140

1974, Sept.   *Perf. 12x12½*
C599 AP140 20c olive .25 .20

Gen. José Maria Cordoba — AP141

1974, Oct. 14   Litho.   *Perf. 13½x14*
C609 AP141 1.30p multicolored .25 .20
Sesquicentennial of the Battles of Junin and Ayacucho.

Insurance Type

Design: 3p, Abstract pattern.

1974, Oct. 24   Litho.   *Perf. 13½x14*
C610 A365 3p multicolored .30 .20

White-tailed Trogon, Letter — AP142

Perf. 13½x14, 14x13½
1974, Nov. 14
Designs (UPU Letter and): 1.30p, Keelbilled Toucan, horiz. 2p, Peruvian cock-of-the-rock, horiz. 2.50p, Scarlet macaw.

C611 AP142 1p multicolored .75 .20
C612 AP142 1.30p multicolored .75 .20
C613 AP142 2p multicolored 1.00 .20
C614 AP142 2.50p multicolored 1.00 .20
    Nos. C611-C614 (4) 3.50 .80
Centenary of Universal Postal Union.
For surcharge see No. C656.

Forest No. 1, by Roman Roncancio — AP143

Boy with Thorn in Finger, by Gregorio Vazquez AP144

Paintings: 3p, Women Fruit Vendors, by Miguel Diaz Vargas (1886-1956). 5p, Annunciation, Santafereña School, 17th-18th cent.

Perf. 13½x14, 14x13½
1975, Mar. 12   Litho.
C615 AP143 2p multicolored .75 .20
C616 AP144 3p multicolored .50 .20
C617 AP144 4p multicolored .65 .20
C618 AP144 5p multicolored 1.10 .25
    Nos. C615-C618 (4) 3.00 .85
Modern and Colonial Colombian paintings.

Trees and Lake AP145

Design: 6p, Victoria regia, Amazon River.

1975, Mar. 12   *Perf. 14x13½*
C619 AP145 1p yellow & multi .20 .20
C620 AP145 6p yellow & multi .60 .20
Nature conservation of trees and Amazon Region.

Gold Treasure Type

Designs: 2p, Nose pendant. 10p, Alligator-shaped staff ornament.

1975, Apr. 11   Litho.   *Perf. 14x13½*
C621 A368 2p grn, gold & brn .90 .20
C622 A368 10p multicolored 4.75 .60

El Rodadero, Santa Maria AP146

1975, July 26   Litho.   *Perf. 14x13½*
C623 AP146 2p multicolored .25 .20
400th anniversary of Santa Marta City.

AP147

AP148

1975, Aug. 31   Litho.   Perf. 13½x14
C624 AP147 4p multicolored   .25 .20

Intl. Women's Year 1975. Maria de Jesus Paramo de Collazos founded 1st normal school for women in Bucaramanga in 1875.

1976, Mar. 12   Litho.   Perf. 13½x14
C625 AP148 5p "Sugar Cane"   .85 .30

4th Congress of Latin-American and Caribbean sugar-exporting countries, Cali, 3/8-12.

View of Bogota — AP149

1976, July 2   Litho.   Perf. 12
C626 AP149 10p shown   1.25 .90
C627 AP149 10p Barranquilla   1.25 .90
C628 AP149 10p Cali   1.25 .90
C629 AP149 10p Medellin   1.25 .90
  a.   Block of 4, #C626-C629   6.00 6.00

Habitat, UN Conf. on Human Settlements, Vancouver, Canada, May 31-June 11.

University Emblem and "90" — AP150

1976, Aug. 6   Litho.   Perf. 13½x14
C630 AP150 5p lt blue & multi   .50 .20

Univ. of Colombia day school, 90th anniv.

Miguel Samper — AP151

Telephone, 1895 — AP152

1976, Oct. 29   Litho.   Perf. 13½x14
C631 AP151 2p multicolored   .25 .20

Samper (1825-99), economist and writer.

1976, Nov. 2
C632 AP152 3p multicolored   .25 .20

Centenary of first telephone call by Alexander Graham Bell, Mar. 10, 1876.

747 Jumbo Jet AP153

1976, Dec. 3   Litho.   Perf. 12
C633 AP153 2p multicolored   .25 .20

Inauguration of 747 jumbo jet service by Avianca.
For surcharge see No. C636.

Convent, Church and Plaza de San Francisco — AP154

1976, Dec. 29   Litho.   Perf. 14
C634 AP154 6p multicolored   .50 .20

150th anniv. of the Congress of Panama.

Souvenir Sheet

Bank of the Republic Emblem — AP155

1977, June 6   Litho.   Perf. 14
C635 AP155 25p multicolored   11.00 11.00

Opening of Philatelic Museum of Medellin under auspices of Banco de la Republica.

No. C633 Surcharged in Light Brown
1977, June   Litho.   Perf. 12
C636 AP153 3p on 2p multi   .25 .20

Coffee AP156

Coffee Grower, Pack Mule AP157

1977-78   Litho.   Perf. 12½
C640 AP156 3p multi   .50 .20
C641 AP156 3.50p multi ('78)   .50 .20

Colombian coffee.

1977, Aug. 9   Litho.   Perf. 13½x14
C642 AP157 10p multicolored   .50 .20

National Federation of Coffee Growers, 50th anniversary.

Beethoven and 9th Symphony AP158

Games' Emblem AP159

1977, Aug. 17
C643 AP158 8p multicolored   .75 .20

Sesquicentennial of the death of Ludwig van Beethoven (1770-1827).

Bird Type

Tropical Birds and Plants: No. C644, Woodpecker and Meriania. C645, Purple gallinule and water lilies. No. C646, Xipholaena punicea and Cochlospermum orinocense. No. C647, Crowned flycatcher and Jacaranda copaia.

1977, Sept. 6   Litho.   Perf. 14
C644 A380 5p multicolored   .70 .20
C645 A380 5p multicolored   .70 .20
C646 A380 10p multicolored   .90 .20
C647 A380 10p multicolored   .90 .20
  Nos. C644-C647 (4)   3.20 .80

1977, Sept. 9   Perf. 12x12½
C648 AP159 6p multicolored   .25 .20

13th Central American and Caribbean Games, Medellin, 1978.

La Cayetana, by Enrique Grau AP160

No. C650, Water Nymphs, by Beatriz Gonzalez.

1977, Sept. 13   Perf. 14x13½
C649 AP160 8p multicolored   .45 .20
C650 AP160 8p multicolored   .45 .20

Women's suffrage, 20th anniversary.

Judge Francisco Antonio Moreno, by Joaquin Gutierrez AP161

Design: 25p, Viceroy Manuel de Guirior.

1977, Sept. 13   Perf. 12
C651 AP161 20p multicolored   1.25 .75
C652 AP161 25p multicolored   1.75 1.10

Bicentenary of National Library.

Federico Lleras Acosta — AP162

Cauca University Arms — AP163

1977, Sept. 27   Litho.   Perf. 14
C653 AP162 5p multicolored   .30 .20

Dr. Federico Lleras Acosta, veterinarian and bacteriologist; birth centenary.

1977, Oct. 14
C654 AP163 5p multicolored   .30 .20

Sesquicentennial of the University of Cauca.

CUDECOM Building, Bogota AP164

1977, Oct. 14
C655 AP164 1.50p multicolored   .25 .20

Colombian Society of Engineers, 90th anniv.

No. C612 Surcharged with New Value and Bars in Brown
1977, Dec. 3   Litho.   Perf. 14x13½
C656 AP142 2p on 1.30p multi   .30 .20

Lost City, Tayrona Culture AP165

Creator of Energy, by Arenas Betancourt AP166

1978, Apr. 18   Litho.   Perf. 12½
C657 AP165 3.50p multicolored   .25 .20

1978, Apr. 25   Perf. 12
C658 AP166 4p blue & multi   .25 .20
Sesquicentennial of Antioquia University Law School.

Column of the Slaves — AP167

Statue of Catalina, Cartagena AP168

1978, May 9
C659 AP167 2.50p multicolored   .25 .20
Sesquicentennial of Ocana Convention (meeting of various political groups).

1978, May 30   Litho.   Perf. 12
C660 AP168 4p blk & lt bl   .25 .20
Sesquicentennial of University of Cartagena.

Gold Pendant, Tolima — AP169

1978, July 11   Litho.   Perf. 12x12½
C661 AP169 3.50p multicolored   .25 .20

Apotheosis of Spanish Language, by Luis Alberto Acuña — AP170

1978, Aug. 9   Perf. 14
C662 AP170 Strip of 3   4.75 4.75
a.-c.   11p, any single   1.10 1.10
Millennium of Spanish language.

Presidential Guard AP171

Figure, Muisca Culture AP172

1978, Aug. 16   Perf. 13½x14
C663 AP171 9p multicolored   .45 .45
Presidential Guard Battalion, 50th anniv.

1978, Sept. 12   Litho.   Perf. 12½
C664 AP172 3.50p multicolored   .30 .20

Apse of Carmelite Church — AP173

1978, Oct. 12   Perf. 13
C665 AP173 30p multicolored   2.50 .40
Souvenir Sheet
Perf. 13½x14
C666 AP173 50p multicolored   3.50 3.50
ESPAMER '78 Philatelic Exhibition, Bogota, Oct. 12-21.

Owl, Gold Ornament, Calima AP174

Virgin and Child, by Gregorio Vasquez AP175

No. C669, Gold frog, Quimbaya culture. No. C670, Gold nose pendant, Tairona, horiz.

1978-80   Litho.   Perf. 12½
C667 AP174 3.50p multi   .40 .20
C668 AP174 4p multi ('79)   .25 .20
C669 AP174 4p multi ('79)   .40 .20
C670 AP174 5p multi ('80)   .60 .20
Nos. C667-C670 (4)   1.65 .80

1978, Nov. 28   Perf. 13½x14
C671 AP175 2.50p multicolored   .25 .20
Christmas 1978.

Bull Ring, Cathedral, Manizales AP176

1979, Jan. 6   Litho.   Perf. 14
C672 AP176 7p multicolored   .60 .20
Manizales Fair.

Children Playing Hopscotch, and IYC Emblem — AP177

No. C674, Child at blackboard and UNESCO emblem. No. C675, The Paper Collector, by Omar Gordillo, and UN emblem.

1979, July 19   Perf. 13½x14, 14x13½
C673 AP177 8p multi   .40 .30
C674 AP177 12p multi, horiz.   .55 .45
C675 AP177 12p multi   .55 .45
Nos. C673-C675 (3)   1.50 1.20
International Year of the Child.

Rio Prado Hydroelectric Station — AP178

1979, Aug. 24   Perf. 13½x14
C676 AP178 5p multicolored   .50 .20

Tomb, 6th Century — AP179

1979, Sept. 25   Litho.   Perf. 14
C677 AP179 8p multicolored   .55 .35
San Augustin Archaeological Park.

Gonzalo Jimenez de Quesada, by C. Leudo AP180

1979, Oct. 11   Perf. 12
C678 AP180 20p multicolored   1.50 .50
Gonzalo Jimenez de Quesada (1500-1579), Spanish conquistador.

Hill, Penny Black, Colombia No. 1 — AP181

1979, Oct. 23   Perf. 13½x14
C679 AP181 15p multicolored   .60 .20
Sir Rowland Hill (1795-1879), originator of penny postage.

Amazon Region — AP182

Tourism: 14p, San Fernando Fortress.

1979   Litho.   Perf. 13½x14
C680 AP182 7p multicolored   .40 .20
C681 AP182 14p multicolored   1.10 .60
Issue dates: 7p, Nov. 16; 14p, Nov. 9. See Nos. C717-C719.

Nativity — AP183

Creche Sculptures: No. C682, Three Kings and soldiers. No. C684, Shepherds.

1979, Nov. 30   Perf. 12
C682 AP183 3p multicolored   .35 .35
C683 AP183 3p multicolored   .35 .35
C684 AP183 3p multicolored   .35 .35
a.   Strip of 3, #C682-C684   1.40 1.40
Christmas 1979.

AP184

AP185

Magdalena Bridge, Avianca emblem.

1979, Dec. 5   Perf. 14
C685 AP184 15p multicolored   .60 .20
Barranquilla, 350th anniversary; Avianca National Airline, 60th anniversary.

1980, Feb. 15   Perf. 13½x14
Boy Playing Flute, by Judith Leyster.
C686 AP185 6p multicolored   .45 .20
2nd Intl. Music Competition, Ibague, Dec. 1979.

Gen. Antonio José de Sucre, 150th Death Anniversary AP186

1980, Feb. 15   Litho.   Perf. 12½x12
C687 AP186 12p multicolored   .45 .20

The Watchman, by Edgar Negret AP187

1980, Feb. 26   **Perf. 12x12½**
C688 AP187 25p multicolored   1.75 .80

Virgin Mary, by Real del Sarte, 1929 AP188

1980, May 23   **Litho.**   **Perf. 14x13½**
C689 AP188 12p multicolored   .30 .20
Apparition of the Virgin Mary to Sister Catalina Labouri Gontard, 150th anniv.

San Gil Produce Market, by Luis Roncancio — AP189

1980, May 27   **Perf. 13½x14**
C690 AP189 12p multicolored   .50 .25

Pres. Enrique Olaya Herrera, by Miguel Diaz Vargas — AP190

1980, Oct. 28   **Litho.**   **Perf. 12**
C691 AP190 20p multicolored   1.00 .40
Enrique Olaya Herrera (1880-1936), president, 1930-1934.

The Boy Fishing in a Bucket AP191

Christmas (Christmas Stories by Rafael Pombo): No. C693, The Frog and the Mouse. No. C694, The Seven Lives of the Cat.

1980, Nov. 21   **Litho.**   **Perf. 14½**
C692 AP191 4p multicolored   .20 .20
C693 AP191 4p multicolored   .20 .20
C694 AP191 4p multicolored   .20 .20
   Nos. C692-C694 (3)   .60 .60

28th World Golf Cup, Cajica — AP192

1980, Dec. 9   **Litho.**   **Perf. 13½x14**
C695 AP192 30p multicolored   3.75 .50

Bolivar Type

Simon Bolivar Death Sesquicentennial: 6p, Portrait, last words to Colombia, vert.

1980, Dec. 17   **Perf. 12**
C696 A400 6p multicolored   .60 .45

St. Peter Claver Holding Cross AP193

1981, Jan. 13   **Perf. 14½**
C697 AP193 15p multicolored   .50 .20
St. Peter Claver (1580-1654), helped American Indians.

Sculptured Bird, San Augustin AP194

Archaeological Finds: No. C699, Funeral chamber, Tierradentro. No. C700, Chamber hallway, Tierradentro. No. C701, Statue of man, San Augustin.

1981, May 12   **Litho.**   **Perf. 14**
C698 AP194 7p multicolored   1.00 .20
C699 AP194 7p multicolored   1.00 .20
C700 AP194 7p multicolored   1.00 .20
C701 AP194 7p multicolored   1.00 .20
   a.   Block of 4, #C698-C701   5.00 5.00
See Nos. C707-C710D.

Child with Hobby Horse, by Fernando Botero — AP195

4th Biennial Arts show, Medellin: 20p, Square Abstract, by Omar Rayo. 25p, Flowers, by Alejandro Obregon.

1981, May 15   **Perf. 12**
C702 AP195 20p multicolored   .85 .20
C703 AP195 25p multicolored   1.00 .30
C704 AP195 50p multicolored   1.75 .75
   Nos. C702-C704 (3)   3.60 1.25

8th South American Swimming Championships, Medellin — AP196

1981, June 5
C705 AP196 15p multicolored   .50 .25

Santamaria Bull Ring, 50th Anniv. — AP197

1981, June 9   **Litho.**   **Perf. 12**
C706 AP197 30p multicolored   2.00 1.25

Quimbaya Culture — AP197a

1981, Sept. 23   **Litho.**   **Perf. 14**
Yellow Background
C707 9p Man   1.00 .20
C708 9p Seated man   1.00 .20
C709 9p Seal, print   1.00 .20
C710 9p Jug   1.00 .20
   e.   AP197a Block of 4, #C707-C710   5.00 3.50

Calima Culture — AP197b

1981, Dec. 17
White Background
C710A 9p Anthropomorphic container   1.25 .20
C710B 9p Jar   1.25 .20
C710C 9p Anthropomorphic jar   1.25 .20
C710D 9p Urn   1.25 .20
   f.   AP197b Block of 4, #C710A-C710D   6.00 4.50

Fruit AP198

1981, Nov. 3   **Litho.**   **Perf. 14**
C711   Block of 6   22.50 20.00
   a.-f.   AP198 25p, any single   3.00 .80

Revolt of the Comuneros, 200th Anniv. — AP199

1981, Nov. 21   **Litho.**   **Perf. 12**
C712 AP199 20p multicolored   .55 .30

Jose Manuel Restrepo, Historian, 1775?-1860? AP200

Andres Bello, 1780?-1865 AP201

1981, Dec. 1   **Litho.**   **Perf. 12**
C713 AP200 35p multicolored   1.00 .35

1981, Dec. 11   **Litho.**   **Perf. 12**
C714 AP201 18p multicolored   .50 .20

Colombia's Admission to UPU, 100th Anniv. AP202

30p, No. 103. 50p, Hemispheres, Nos. 104-108.

1981   **Litho.**   **Perf. 12**
C715 AP202 30p multicolored   1.00 .35
Size: 100x70mm
Imperf
C716 AP202 50p multicolored   3.00 3.00
Issued: No. C715, Dec. 18. No. C716, Dec. 28.

Tourism Type of 1979
1982   **Litho.**   **Perf. 12**
C717 AP182 20p Solano Bay   .50 .20
C718 AP182 20p Tota Lake, Boyaca   .50 .20
C719 AP182 20p Corrales, Boyaca   .50 .20
   Nos. C717-C719 (3)   1.50 .60
Issued: No. C717, 6/2; others, 6/16.

1982 World
Cup — AP202a

Players and team emblems: a, "America." b,
"A. B." c, "Cali." d, "C." e, "C/D." f, "Junior
F.B.C." g, "D/M." h, Stadium. i, "M." j, "Club
Atletico Nacional." k, "D/P." l, "Quindio." m,
"Santa Fe." n, "T." o, "Santa Marta."

1982, June 21   *Perf. 14*
C720   Sheet of 15   10.00 6.75
  a.-o. AP202a 9p, any single   .70 .30

Bogota
Gun Club
Centenary
AP202b

1982, July 16   *Perf. 12*
C721 AP202b 20p multicolored   .50 .20

Gold
Crocodile
Figure,
Tairona
Culture
AP202c

Tairona Culture Exhibit, Gold Museum: Various figures. Nos. C723-C727 vert.

1982, July 28
Gold, Black and:
C722 AP202c 25p light brown   1.60 .45
C723 AP202c 25p bright pink   1.60 .45
C724 AP202c 25p green   1.60 .45
C725 AP202c 25p dark blue   1.60 .45
C726 AP202c 25p violet   1.60 .45
C727 AP202c 25p red   1.60 .45
  Nos. C722-C727 (6)   9.60 2.70

Government Buildings,
Pereira — AP203

1982, Aug. 4   *Litho.*   *Perf. 12*
C728 AP203 35p multicolored   1.00 .40

Biplane in
Flight, by
Edgar
Antonio
Bustos
AP204

1982, Aug. 5   *Perf. 14*
C729 AP204 18p multicolored   .50 .20
American Air Forces Cooperation System.

Magdalena
River
AP205

1982, Oct. 21   *Litho.*   *Perf. 12*
C730 AP205 30p multicolored   1.25 .35

Marquez Type
1982, Dec. 10   *Perf. 13½x14*
C731 A412 25p gray & blue   .60 .20
C732 A412 30p gray & brown   .85 .20

San Andres Archipelago — AP206

1983, Apr. 9   *Litho.*   *Perf. 12*
C733 AP206 25p Liberty Fort   .50 .20

Opening of Las Gaviotas (The
Seagulls) Ecological Center,
Bogota — AP207

1983, June 1   *Litho.*
C734 AP207 12p multicolored   .30 .20

50th Anniv.
of Radio
Amateurs
League
AP208

1983, June 11   *Perf. 14x13½*
C735 AP208 12p multicolored   .30 .20

Bolivar Type
1983, July 24   *Perf. 12*
C736 A417 30p multicolored   .60 .20
C737 A417 100p multicolored   2.00 1.50

Botanical Exhibition Type
1983, Aug. 18   *Perf. 14*
C738 A418 12p Begonia
   guaduensis   .55 .20
C739 A418 12p Chinchona
   ovaliflora   .55 .20
C740 A418 40p Begonia urticae   2.90 .40
  Nos. C738-C740 (3)   4.00 .80

Cartagena, 450th Anniv. — AP208a

1983, Sept. 9   *Litho.*   *Perf. 12*
C740A AP208a 12p Customs
   Square   .35 .20
C740B AP208a 35p Historic
   sites, Car-
   tagena   .90 .30

Painting Type
1983, Oct. 5   *Litho.*   *Perf. 12*
C741 A420 30p multicolored   .50 .20

Scouting Year
AP209

Coffee Beans
AP210

1983, Oct. 24
C742 AP209 12p multicolored   .25 .20

1984, Mar. 28   *Litho.*   *Perf. 14½x14*
C743 AP210 14p multicolored   .25 .20

Marandua City Type
1984, Sept. 28   *Perf. 12*
C744 A427 30p multicolored   .50 .20

AP211

AP212

1984, Nov. 2
C745 AP211 45p multicolored   .70 .25
45th Cong. of Americanists, Bogota, 1985.

Christmas Type
1984, Dec. 14
C746 A428 14p multicolored   .30 .20

1985, Feb. 15
  Design: Dove, map and flags of Colombia,
Mexico, Costa Rica and Venezuela.
C747 AP212 40p multicolored   .70 .30
  Contadora Group of Latin American
countries.

Gomez Type
1985, Feb. 25
C748 A432 40p multicolored   .70 .30

Birds — AP213

AP214

1985
C749 AP213 14p Dryocopus
   lineatus
   nuperus   .70 .25
C750 AP213 20p Xiphorhynchus
   picus   1.40 .25
C751 AP213 50p Eriocnemis
   cupreoventris   3.00 .30
C752 AP213 55p Momotus
   momota   3.75 .30
  Nos. C749-C752 (4)   8.85 1.10
Issued: 14p, 4/12; 20p, 50p, 8/6; 55p, 8/29.

1985, July 15
C753 AP214 20p multicolored   .30 .20
Admiral Padilla Naval School, 50th anniv.

1985
Census
AP215

1985, Oct. 15   *Perf. 12*
C754 AP215 20p multicolored   .40 .20

Christmas Type
1985, Dec. 4   *Litho.*   *Perf. 13*
C755 A436 20p Girl, Christmas
   tree   .30 .20

Alfonso Lopez
Pumarejo (1886-
1959), President,
1934-38, 1942-
45 — AP216

1986, Jan. 31
C756 AP216 24p multicolored   .30 .20

Coffee
Berries,
Natl.
Cycling
Team
AP217

1986, Feb. 4
C757 AP217 60p multicolored   1.00 .60
Natl. Coffee Producers Assoc. sponsorship
of natl. cycling team, 25th anniv.

Fauna Type of 1985
1986, Feb. 18
C758 A433 50p Pudu mephis-
   tophiles   1.50 .25

World
Communications
Day — AP218

Intl. Peace
Year — AP219

1986, May 17   **Litho.**   **Perf. 13**
C759 AP218 50p multicolored   .65   .25

1986, June 13   **Litho.**   **Perf. 13**
C760 AP219 55p multicolored   .65   .25

AP220

AP221

1986, July 1   **Litho.**   **Perf. 13**
C761 AP220 24p Portrait, papal
     arms   1.50   .20
C762 AP220 55p Portrait, Me-
     dellin cathe-
     dral, horiz.   1.50   .25
C763 AP220 60p Blessing
     crowd, horiz.   1.50   .25
    Nos. C761-C763 (3)   4.50   .70

Souvenir Sheet
C764 AP220 200p Praying, Ma-
     donna of Bo-
     gota   3.00 3.00

Visit of Pope John Paul II.
Nos. C762-C763 each printed in sheets of
20 with se-tenant labels picturing religious
symbols.

1986, July 15   **Perf. 12**
C765 AP221 25p multicolored   .30   .20

Enrique Santos Montejo (1886-1971),
journalist.

Bach,
Handel and
Schutz,
Composers
AP222

1986, July 17   **Perf. 13**
C766 AP222 70p Bach   1.50   .40
C767 AP222 100p Text, music   2.00   .55

Salesian
Order
Education
in
Colombia,
Cent.
AP223

1986, July 23   **Perf. 12**
C768 AP223 25p De La Salle,
     founder   .30   .20

Completion
of Coal
Mining
Complex,
El Cerrejon
AP224

1986, July 29   **Litho.**   **Perf. 12**
C769 AP224 55p multi   .80   .20

AP225

Natl. Constitution, Cent. — AP226

25p, The Five Signators, by R. Vasquez,
detail, & Bogota Cathedral. 200p, Pres. Nunez
& Miguel Antonio Caro, Natl. Council of Delegates chairman, & Presidential Palace,
constitution.

1986, Aug. 5   **Litho.**   **Perf. 14**
C770 AP225 25p multi   .30   .20

Souvenir Sheet
Perf. 12
C771 AP226 200p multi   2.25 2.25

Poet Type

Federico Garcia Lorca (1898-1936), poet,
and birthplace, Fuentevaqueros, Granada,
Spain.

1986, Sept. 26   **Litho.**   **Perf. 12**
C772 A445 60p multi   .70   .25

Gratitude
for Intl. Aid
after the
Armero
Mudslide
Disaster
AP227

1986, Nov. 13
C773 AP227 50p multi   .55   .20

Christmas
AP228

Wood sculpture: Virgin Mestiza, Nerina.

1986, Dec. 19   **Litho.**   **Perf. 12**
C774 AP228 25p multi   .30   .20

The Apotheosis of Popayan, by
Ephrain Martinez Zambrano (1898-
1956) — AP229

1987, Jan. 13
C775   100p Popayan riding horse 1.50   .75
C776   100p Onlookers   1.50   .75
  a. AP229 Pair, #C775-C776   3.50 3.50

AP230

AP231

1987, Mar. 16   **Litho.**   **Perf. 12**
C777 AP230 30p multi   .40   .20

The Conversion of St. Augustine of Hippo,
1600th anniv.

Type of 1987

30p, Phoenicopterus ruber. 35p,
Pseudemys scripta, horiz. No. C780, Crax
alberti. No. C781, Symphysodon aequifas-
ciatum, horiz.

Perf. 14½x14, 14x14½
1987-89   **Wmk. 334**
C778 A446a 30p lake   .35   .20
C779 A446a 35p dark red brn   .40   .20
C780 A446a 45p dark blue gray   .30   .20
C781 A446a 45p blue   .30   .20
    Nos. C778-C781 (4)   1.35   .80

Issue dates: 30p, June 8. 35p, Dec. 24. No.
C780, Dec. 6, 1988. No. C781, June 23, 1989.

Perf. 13½x13
1987, Apr. 10   **Unwmk.**
C783 AP231 25p multi   .30   .20

Natl. University School of Mining, Medellin,
cent.

Purebred
Horses
AP232

1987, June 17   **Perf. 12**
C784 AP232 60p White horse   1.00   .25
C785 AP232 70p Black horse   1.00   .30

El Espectador
Newspaper,
Cent.
AP233

Design: Frontispieces from 1887, 1915,
1948, 1974 and portraits of founder Don Fidel
Cano, editors Don Luis Cano, Luis Gabriel
Cano Isaza and Alfonso Cano Isaza.

1987, July 24   **Perf. 12½x12**
C786 AP233 60p multi   .75   .25

Intl. Year of
Shelter for the
Homeless
AP234

1987, Sept. 21   **Perf. 14**
C787 AP234 60p multi   1.10   .25

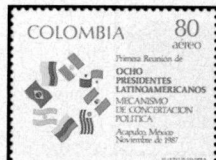

Flags
AP235

1987, Nov. 27   **Litho.**   **Perf. 13x13½**
C788 AP235 80p multi   .80   .30

Ist Meeting of the eight Latin-American
Presidents, Acapulco, Nov.

Christmas
AP236

1987, Dec. 8   **Litho.**   **Perf. 14**
C789 AP236 30p multi   .45   .20

Rural
Telephone
System
AP237

1988, Feb. 4   **Litho.**   **Perf. 14**
C790 AP237 70p multi   .80   .30

Founding of
Bogota, 450th
Anniv. — AP238

1988, Apr. 11   **Litho.**   **Perf. 12**
C791 AP238 70p multi   .75   .25

Bogota, 450th Anniv. AP238a

Unwmk.

1988, July 1   Litho.   Perf. 12
C792 AP238a 80p Modern district, vert. .75 .25
C793 AP238a 90p Colonial district .85 .30

Gold Artifacts AP239

Artifacts in the Gold Museum: 70p, Mask. 80p, Two-headed human figure inside a circle, Muisca tribe. 90p, Ritual figure of the Quimbaya.

1988   Perf. 12
C794 AP239 70p multi .65 .30
C795 AP239 80p multi .75 .25
C796 AP239 90p multi 1.00 .35
Nos. C794-C796 (3) 2.40 .90

Issue dates: 70p, May 13; 80p, 90p, Oct. 7.

Human Rights Type
Perf. 14x14½
1988, July 1   Engr.   Wmk. 334
C797 A452 40p Communication, horiz. .40 .20

AP240

AP241

1988, Sept. 28   Litho.   Perf. 12
C798 AP240 80p multi .70 .20

Zipa Tisquesusa (d. 1538), Chibcha Indian leader during revolt against Spanish Conquistadors.

1988, Nov. 23   Litho.   Perf. 12
C799 AP241 40p multi .50 .20
Christmas.

Agustin Nieto Caballero (1889-1975), Educator — AP242

Unwmk.
1989, Mar. 18   Litho.   Perf. 12
C800 AP242 100p multi .75 .25

Pres. Laureano Gomez (1889-1965) AP243

1989, Mar. 29
C801 AP243 45p multi .30 .20

Intl. Coffee Organization — AP244

1989, Apr. 3
C802 AP244 110p multi .90 .30

12th Session of the UN Commission on Human Rights — AP245

1989, Apr. 28
C803 AP245 100p multi .90 .25

French Revolution, Bicent. AP246

1989, June 29   Litho.   Perf. 12
C804 AP246 100p multi .75 .25

PHILEXFRANCE '89 — AP247

a, Bananas, tropical fruits. b, Fruits, flowers. c, Birds, animals. d, Precious gems, metals and mineral resources. e, View of fields, Colombian carrying produce basket. f, Waterfall. g, Fish, coast. Illustration reduced.

1989   Litho.   Perf. 14
C805   AP247   Pane of 7   17.50 17.50
a.-g.   110p any single   1.75 .40
No. C805 printed in sheets containing panes of 7, rouletted between.

Souvenir Sheet

Los Lanceros, by R. Arenas Betancur — AP248

1989   Litho.   Perf. 12
C806 AP248 250p multicolored 1.75 1.25

Human Rights Type
Perf. 14½x14
1989, Aug. 18   Engr.   Wmk. 334
C807 A452 55p Family .40 .20

Natl. Anti-Drugs Campaign AP249

Unwmk.
1989, Aug. 23   Litho.   Perf. 12
C808 AP249 115p multicolored .90 .25

America Issue AP250

UPAE emblem and artifacts or customs of pre-Columbian peoples: 115p, Quimbaya, Calima or Tolima gold smiths. 130p, Potter and Sinu ceramic figurine.

1989   Perf. 12
C809 AP250 115p multicolored 1.00 .25
C810 AP250 130p multicolored 1.10 .30
Issue dates: 115p, Oct. 12; 130p, Aug. 23.

Joaquin Quijano Mantilla (1878-1944), Journalist — AP251

1989, Sept. 29   Perf. 12
C811 AP251 170p multicolored 1.20 .40

Arts and Crafts in Barro-Raquira AP252

1989   Litho.   Perf. 12
C812 AP252 55p multicolored .40 .20
Christmas.

Boeing 767 AP253

1989, Dec. 5   Litho.   Perf. 12
C813 AP253 130p multicolored .90 .30

Bolivar Installed at the Congress of Angostura, by Tito Salas — AP254

1989, Dec. 12
C814 AP254 130p multicolored .90 .30
Creation of the Republic, 1819.

Fathers of the Nation Leaving the Constitutional Convention AP255

1989, Dec. 12
C815 AP255 130p shown .90 .30
C816 AP255 130p Arms .90 .30
C817 AP255 130p Temple of the Rosary .90 .30
Nos. C815-C817 (3) 2.70 .90
Constitution of the Republic, 1821.

Arms Type of Regular Issue, 1982
1990, Mar. 1   Litho.   Perf. 12
C818 A372 60p Velez .30 .20

Presidential Summit, Cartagena AP256

1990, Feb. 15   Litho.   Perf. 12
C819 AP256 130p Plaza de la Aduana .55 .20

Colombian National Radio, 50th Anniv. — AP257

1990, Feb. 16   Litho.   Perf. 12
C820 AP257 150p multicolored 1.00 .20

Teresa Cuervo Borda (1889-1976), Art Historian — AP258

1990, Mar. 28   **Litho.**   *Perf. 12*
C821 AP258 60p multicolored   .35   .20

Second Latin American Theater Festival, Bogota — AP259

1990, Apr. 10
C822 AP259 150p buff, tan & gold   .80   .25

Santander Type

No. C823, Santander holding the Constitution. No. C824, Central Cemetery, Bogata and National Pantheon. No. C825, Santander, as organizer of public education. No. C826, "Postman of New Granada" (Man and burro) by Joseph Brown and Jose Maria del Castillo, horiz. 500p, Santander on death bed.

1990, May 6   *Perf. 14x13½*
C823 A470 60p multicolored   .30   .20
C824 A470 60p multicolored   .30   .20
C825 A470 70p multicolored   .40   .20
C826 A470 70p multicolored   .40   .20
    Nos. C823-C826 (4)   1.40   .80
Souvenir Sheet
Perf. 12
C827 A470 500p multi   2.00 1.50
No. C827 contains one 54x40mm stamp.

First Postage Stamp, 150th Anniv. AP260

1990, May 6   *Perf. 14*
C828 AP260 150p multicolored   .80   .25

Trans-Caribbean Fiber Optic Cable — AP261

1990, May 19   *Perf. 12*
C829 AP261 150p multicolored   .80   .25

Institute of Industrial Development, 25th Anniv. — AP262

1990, May 22
C830 AP262 60p multicolored   .40   .20

Souvenir Sheet

World Cup Soccer Championships, Italy — AP263

1990, June 8
C831 AP263 500p multicolored   3.00 2.25

AP264

1990, June 27
C832 AP264 130p multicolored   .60   .20
Organization of American States, cent.

AP265

1990, July 26
C833 AP265 170p multicolored   .80   .25
Museum of Gold, 50th Anniv.

Dolphins, Marine Birds AP266

1990, Oct. 12   **Litho.**   *Perf. 12*
C834 AP266 150p shown   1.50   .20
C835 AP266 170p Jungle fauna, vert.   1.50   .25

AP267

AP268

1990, Nov. 16   **Litho.**   *Perf. 12*
C836 AP267 70p multicolored   .40   .20
Monastery of Our Lady of Las Lajas..

1991, Feb. 8   **Litho.**   *Perf. 12*
C837 AP268 170p multicolored   .80   .30
Newspaper Publishing, 200th Anniv.

AP269

AP270

1990, Nov. 1   **Litho.**   *Perf. 12*
C838 AP269 70p multicolored   .40   .20
Christmas.

1991, May 31   **Litho.**   *Perf. 14*

Whales and Dolphins: 80p, Megaptera novaeangliae, breaching. 170p, Megaptera novaeangliae, diving. 190p, Inia geoffrensis, Sotalia fluviatilis, horiz.

C839 AP270 80p multicolored   .90   .20
C840 AP270 170p multicolored   1.90   .30
C841 AP270 190p multicoloed   2.10   .30
    Nos. C839-C841 (3)   4.90   .80

America Issue AP271

1991, Oct. 11   **Litho.**   *Perf. 14*
C842 AP271 90p shown   .45   .20
C843 AP271 190p Ship arriving in New World   .85   .25

Adoration of the Magi — AP272

1991, Dec. 20   **Litho.**   *Perf. 14*
C844 AP272 90p multicolored   .45   .20
Christmas.

AP273

AP274

1991, Dec. 2
C845 AP273 190p Country flags   .85   .25
Fifth summit of Latin American presidents.

1992, Feb. 8   **Litho.**   *Perf. 12*
C846 AP274 210p multicolored   1.00   .30
8th UNCTAD Conference, Cartagena.

Proclamation of New Constitution, July 4, 1991 — AP275

1991, Nov. 27   **Litho.**   *Perf. 14*
C847 AP275 90p multicolored   .40   .20

Export Products AP276

Copyright Protection AP277

1992, Mar. 11   *Perf. 12*
C848 AP276 90p Flowers   .40   .20
C849 AP276 210p Fruits, vegetables, horiz.   1.10   .30

1992, Apr. 13   **Litho.**   *Perf. 12*
C850 AP277 190p multicolored   .85   .25

1992 Summer Olympics AP278

1992, June 4   **Litho.**   *Perf. 14*
C851 AP278 110p multicolored   .75   .30

Earth
Summit '92
AP279

a, Tree, mountain landscape. b, Birds in tree.

1992, June 2   Litho.   Perf. 14
C852 A279 230p Pair, #a.-b.   2.10 1.40

America
Issue
AP280

Paintings: 230p, Discovery of America by Christopher Columbus, by Salvador Dali. 260p, Magical America, Myth and Legend, by Alfredo Vivero.

1992, July 22   Perf. 14x13½
C853 AP280 230p multicolored   1.00 .70
C854 AP280 260p multicolored   1.10 .75

McDonnell
Douglas
MD83
AP281

1992, Sept. 22   Litho.   Perf. 12
C855 AP281 110p multicolored   .50 .30

Curtain of
Colon
Theatre
AP282

1992, Oct. 12   Litho.   Perf. 12
C856 AP282 230p multicolored   1.00 .65

AP283

AP284

1992, Nov. 27   Litho.   Perf. 12
C857 AP283 230p Gloria Lara,
1938-82   1.00 .65

1993, June 7   Litho.   Perf. 12
C858 AP284 220p multicolored   .95 .60
1993 American Soccer Cup, Ecuador.

Intl. Year of
Indigenous
People — AP285

1993, July 1   Perf. 14
C859 AP285 460p multicolored   2.00 1.25

South American Eliminations for 1994
World Cup Soccer Championships,
US — AP286

1993, July 31   Litho.   Perf. 12
C860 AP286 220p multicolored   .95 .50

AP287

AP288

America Issue (Endangered species): a, 220p, Saguinus oedipus. b, 220p, Porphyrula martinica. c, 460p, Rupicola peruviana. d, 520p, Trichecus manatus.

1993, Oct. 19   Litho.   Perf. 12
C861 AP287 Block of 4, #a.-d.   7.50 7.50

1994, Mar. 21   Litho.   Perf. 12
C862 AP288 630p multicolored   2.25 1.40
Intl. Decade for Natural Disaster Reduction.

Beatification of Josemaria Escriva de
Balaguer — AP289

1994, May 17   Litho.   Perf. 13½x14
C863 AP289 560p multicolored   1.90 1.25

First
Airmail
Delivery,
75th Anniv.
AP290

Design: 270p, William Knox Martin, airplane over Port Colombia, 1919.

1994, July 29   Litho.   Perf. 14
C864 AP290 270p multicolored   1.00 .55

Natl.
Institute of
Medical
Law &
Forensic
Sciences,
80th Anniv.
AP291

1994, Oct. 27   Litho.   Perf. 12
C865 AP291 560p multicolored   1.90 1.25

Sociedad Colombo-Alemana de
Transportes Aereos (SCADTA), 75th
Anniv. — AP292

1995, Jan. 2   Litho.   Perf. 12
C866 AP292 330p No. C15   1.10 .50

Flora and Fauna — AP293

Iguana iguana: No. C867a, Facing right. b, Facing left.
Rain forest: No. C868a, Nuts on branch, flowers. b, Waterfall, hanging red flower.

1995, Jan. 17
C867 AP293 650p Pair, #a.-b.   4.50 3.00
C868 AP293 750p Pair, #a.-b.   5.50 4.00
Nos. C867-C868 are continuous designs.

SCADTA,
75th Anniv.
AP294

1995, Mar. 30   Litho.   Perf. 14
C869 AP294 330p No. C9   1.50 .75

FAO, 50th
Anniv.
AP295

1995, Apr. 25   Litho.   Perf. 13x13½
C870 AP295 750p multicolored   2.25 1.25

Andres Bello
Organization,
25th
Anniv. — AP296

Colombian
Firefighters,
Cent. — AP297

1995, Apr. 27   Perf. 13½x13
C871 AP296 650p multicolored   2.00 .85

1995, May 5   Perf. 12
C872 AP297 330p multicolored   1.10 .45

Fenalco, 50th
Anniv. — AP298

UN, 50th
Anniv. — AP299

1995, May 25   Perf. 13½
C873 AP298 330p multicolored   1.10 .45

1995, June 21   Perf. 12
C874 AP299 750p multicolored   1.50 1.00

First Pacific
Ocean
Games — AP300

1995, June 23
C875 AP300 750p multicolored   2.25 1.25

11th Summit of Non-Aligned
Countries, Cartagena — AP302

1995, Oct. 13   Litho.   Perf. 12
C877 AP302 650p multicolored   1.50   .90

Motion
Pictures,
Cent.
AP303

Design: 330p, Charlie Chaplin and Jackie
Coogan in "The Kid," Estela López Pomareda
in "Maria," first Colombian feature length film.

1995, Oct. 19   Perf. 14
C878 AP303 330p black & sepia   .90   .45

AP304

AP305

1995, Nov. 23   Perf. 12
C879 AP304 650p multicolored   1.90   .90
Andes Development Corporation (CAF),
25th Anniv.

1995, Nov. 21   Perf. 14
Fight against illegal drug trafficking: No.
C880, Locating illegally grown plants. No.
C881, Hands in handcuffs, horiz.

C880 AP305 330p multicolored   .70   .45
C881 AP305 330p multicolored   .70   .45

Miniature Sheet of 16

Myths and Legends — AP306

Madre-Monte: a.-d.
La Llorna: e.-h.
El Mohán: i.-l.
Hombre Caimán: m.-p.
Background color changes from top to bot-
tom rows. Top row is blue. Row 2 is blue

green. Row 3 is green. Row 4 is lilac. Each
design comes in all four colors.

1995, Dec. 6
C882 AP306 750p #a.-p.   27.50 27.50
See No. C886.

José
Asunción
Silva (1865-
96), Poet
AP307

1996, Apr. 23   Litho.   Perf. 12
C883 AP307 400p multicolored   .90   .40

Isla de
Providencia
AP308

Policarpa
Salavarrieta
(1796-1817),
Patriot — AP309

1996, Apr. 25   Perf. 14
C884 AP308 800p multicolored   2.25   .80

1996, Apr. 26
C885 AP309 900p multicolored   2.50   .85

Myths and Legends Type
Designs: a, Kogui Creation. b, Yonna Wayu.
c, Jaguar Man. d, Master of the Animals.

1996, Aug. 12   Litho.   Perf. 13½x14
C886 AP306 900p Block of 4,
#a.-d.   13.00 13.00

Metropolitan
Basilica, Medellin
AP310

1996, July 12
C887 AP310 400p multicolored   1.10   .55

National
Archives
Building
AP311

1996, July 30   Litho.   Perf. 14
C888 AP311 400p multicolored   1.10   .40

CERLALC,
25th Anniv.
AP312

1996, Aug. 16   Litho.   Perf. 12
C889 AP312 800p multicolored   2.10 1.00
UNESCO.

Pioneers in Petroleum
Industry — AP313

a, Jorge Isaacs, pumping oil. b, Francisco
Burgos Rubio, refinery at night. c, Diego Martí-
nez Camargo, derrick. d, Prisciliano Cabrales
Lora, off-shore drilling. e, Manuel María Pala-
cio, oil tanker loading offshore. f, Roberto De
Mares, refinery, lake. g, General Virgilio Barco
Maldonado, men positioning equipment. h,
Roustabout, "ECOPETROL" emblem.

1996, Sept. 5   Litho.   Perf. 13½x14
C890 AP313 800p Block of 8,
#a.-h.   20.00 20.00

Colombian
Golf
Federation,
50th Anniv.
AP314

1996, Sept. 19   Litho.   Perf. 12
C891 AP314 400p multicolored   1.25   .50

Covenant for the
Children
AP315

1997, Feb. 28   Litho.   Perf. 14
C892 AP315 400p multicolored   1.40   .55

AP316

AP317

1997, Apr. 25   Perf. 12
C893 AP316 800p multicolored   1.75 1.40
Motion pictures in Colombia, cent.

1997, May 13   Litho.   Perf. 12
C894 AP317 400p multicolored   1.50   .50
Social Security Institute, 50th anniv.

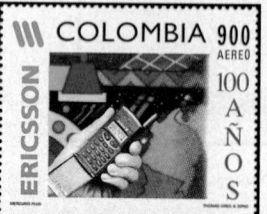

Ericsson in Colombia, Cent. — AP318

1997, May 22   Perf. 13½x14
C895 AP318 900p multicolored   2.50 1.40

Bogatá Colonial Bldg., Home of Natl.
Mint and Numismatic
Museum — AP319

1997, July 10   Perf. 12
C896 AP319 800p multicolored   2.50 1.40

Phytelephas Seemannii — AP320

1997, July 23   Perf. 13½x14
C897 AP320 900p multicolored   3.00   .90

Cordoba
Cattle Fair
AP321

1997, June 21   Perf. 14
C898 AP321 400p multicolored   1.25   .45

Personalities — AP322

No. C899: a, Cacique Gaitana, 16th cent., Indian resistance leader. b, Josefa Acevedo de Gómez (1803-61), writer. c, Domingo Bioho (d. 1621), black leader. d, Soledad Acosta de Samper (1831-1913), historian. e, Maria Cano Márquez (1897-1967), popular leader. f, Manuel Quintín Lame (1880-1967), native leader. g, Ezequiel Uricoechea (1834-80), linguist, naturalist. h, Juan Rodríguez Freyle (1566-1642), colonial reporter. i, Gerardo Reichel-Dolmatoff (1912-94), archaeologist. j, Ramón de Zubiría (1922-95), writer, educator. k, Esteban Jaramillo (1874-1947), economist. l, Pedro Fermín de Vargas (1762-c. 1810), economist.

No. 900: a, Luis Carlos "el turerto" López (1879-1950), poet. b, Aurelio Arturo (1906-74), poet. c, Enrique Pérez Arbeláez (1896-1972), botanist. d, José Maria González Benito (1843-1903), mathematician, astronomer. e, José Manuel Rivas Sacconi (1917-91), diplomat. f, Eduardo Lemaitre Román (1914-94), historian. g, Diójenes Arrieta (1848-93), politician. h, Gabriel Turbay Abunader (1901-47), politician, diplomat. i, Guillermo Echavarría Misas (1888-1985), aviation pioneer. j, Juan Friede Alter (1901-90), historian. k, Fabio Lozano Torrijos (1865-1947), diplomat. l, Lino de Pombo (1797-1862), engineer, diplomat.

1997, Dec. 19   Litho.   Perf. 13½x14
Sheets of 12
C899   AP322 500p #a.-l.   22.50   22.50
C900   AP322 500p #a.-l.   22.50   22.50

Colombian Society of Orthopedic Surgery and Traumatology, 50th Anniv. — AP323

1997   Perf. 12
C901   AP323 1000p multicolored   3.00   1.00

AP324

AP325

1998, Apr. 30   Litho.   Perf. 14
C902   AP324 1000p multicolored   3.00   .80
Organization of American States, 50th anniv.

1998, May 22
C903   AP325 1000p bl & org   3.00   .80
4th Bolivar Philatelic Exhibition, Santa Fe de Bogota.

World Health Organization, 50th Anniv. — AP326

1998, Apr. 7   Perf. 12
C904   AP326 1100p multicolored   3.00   1.00

1998 World Cup Soccer Championships, France — AP327

Stylized designs: a, Foot. b, Soccer ball. c, Hand.

1998, June 9   Litho.   Perf. 14
C905   AP327 1100p Strip of 3,
#a.-c.   9.00   9.00

Intl. Year of the Ocean — AP328

1998, May 22   Perf. 12
C906   AP328 1100p ARC Gloria   3.50   .95

Myths and Legends — AP329

Designs: a, Bochica. b, Chimingagua. c, Bachue and Huitica.

Perf. 13¼x12¾
1998, Nov. 27   Litho.
C907   AP329 1000p Strip of 3,
#a.-c.   15.00   15.00

AIR POST SPECIAL DELIVERY STAMPS

Catalogue values for unused stamps in this section are for Never Hinged items.

Post Horn and Wings APSD1

Unwmk.
1958, May 19   Litho.   Perf. 12
CE1   APSD1 25c dk bl & red   .40   .20

Same Overprinted Vertically in Red

1959
CE2   APSD1 25c dk bl & red   .50   .20

Jet Plane and Envelope — APSD2

1963, Oct. 4   Perf. 14
CE3   APSD2 50c red & blk   .25   .20

Aviation Type
80c, Boeing 727 jet, 1966.

Perf. 14x13½
1966, Dec. 14   Photo.   Unwmk.
CE4   AP96 80c crim & multi   .35   .20

AIR POST REGISTRATION STAMPS

Issued by Sociedad Colombo-Alemana de Transportes Aereos (SCADTA)

No. C41 Overprinted in Red

1923   Wmk. 116   Perf. 14x14½
CF1   AP6 20c gray   2.50   1.10

No. C58 Overprinted in Black

1929   Wmk. 127   Perf. 14
CF2   AP8 20c carmine   4.50   1.10
Same Overprint on No. C71
CF3   AP10 20c carmine   6.50   6.00

Colombian Government Issues
Same Overprint on No. C86
1932
CF4   AP8 20c carmine   6.50   6.00

No. C100 Overprinted

CF5   AP12 20c car & ol blk   4.50   1.25
For surcharge see No. C118.

SPECIAL DELIVERY STAMPS

Special Delivery Messenger — SD1

1917   Unwmk.   Engr.   Perf. 14
E1   SD1 5c gray green   25.00   75.00

Catalogue values for unused stamps in this section, from this point to the end of the section, are for Never Hinged items.

SD2

1987, July 31   Litho.   Perf. 14
E2   SD2 25p emerald & ver   .30   .30
E3   SD2 30p emerald & ver   .35   .35

REGISTRATION STAMPS

R1   R2

1865   Unwmk.   Litho.   Imperf.
F1   R1 5c black   80.00   40.00
F2   R2 5c black   75.00   40.00

R3   R4

1870

White Paper
Vertical Lines in Background
F3   R3 5c black   2.25   1.90
F4   R4 5c black   2.25   1.90
Horizontal Lines in Background
F5   R3 5c black   7.50   6.50
F6   R4 5c black   2.25   1.90
Nos. F3-F6 (4)   14.25   12.20

Reprints of Nos. F3 to F6 show either crossed lines or traces of lines in background.

R5

R6

1881 — Imperf.

F7	R5 10c violet	47.50 40.00
a.	Sewing machine perf.	55.00 47.50
b.	Perf. 11	60.00 50.00

1883 — Perf. 12, 13½

F8	R6 10c red, *orange*	1.50 1.90

R7

1889-95 — Perf. 12, 13½

F9	R7 10c red, *grysh*	5.25 2.50
F10	R7 10c red, *yelsh*	5.25 2.50
F11	R7 10c dp brn, *rose buff* ('95)	1.50 1.25
F12	R7 10c yel brn, *lt buff* ('92)	1.50 1.25
	Nos. F9-F12 (4)	13.50 7.50

Nos. F9-F12 exist imperf. Values same as for perf.

R9

1902 — Imperf.

F13	R9 20c red brown, *blue*	1.40 1.40
a.	Sewing machine perf.	3.75 3.75
b.	Perf. 12	3.75 3.75

Medellin Issue

R10

1902 — Perf. 12

Laid Paper

F16	R10 10c blk vio	12.50 12.50
a.	Wove paper	17.50 17.50

Regular Issue

1903 — Imperf.

F17	R9 20c blue, *blue*	1.40 1.40
a.	Sewing machine perf.	4.00 4.00
b.	Perf. 12	4.00 4.00

R11

1904 — Pelure Paper — Imperf.

F19	R11 10c purple	3.00 3.00
a.	Sewing machine perf.	4.00 3.00
b.	Perf. 12	5.00 4.00

R12

Imprint: "J. L. Arango"

1904 — Perf. 12

Wove Paper

F20	R12 10c purple	2.00 .50
a.	Imperf., pair	6.25 6.25

Imprint: "Lit. Nacional"

1909 — Perf. 10, 14, 10x14, 14x10

F21	R12 10c purple	2.25 .70
a.	Imperf., pair	5.00 5.00

For overprints see Nos. LF1-LF4.

Execution at Cartagena in 1816 — R13

1910, July 20 — Engr. — Perf. 12

F22	R13 10c red & black	17.50 75.00

Centenary of National Independence.

Pier at Puerto Colombia — R14

Tequendama Falls — R15

Perf. 11, 11½, 14, 11½x14

1917, Aug. 25

F23	R14 4c green & ultra	.50 2.50
a.	Center inverted	575.00 575.00
F24	R15 10c deep blue	1.90 .60

R16

1925 — Litho. — Perf. 10x13½

F25	R16 (10c) blue	3.50 1.50
a.	Imperf., pair	12.00 10.00
b.	Perf. 13½x10	6.00 4.00

ACKNOWLEDGMENT OF RECEIPT STAMPS

AR1   AR2

1893 — Unwmk. — Litho. — Perf. 13½

H1	AR1 5c ver, *blue*	4.25 4.25

1894 — Perf. 12

H2	AR1 5c vermilion	3.50 4.00

1902-03 — Imperf.

H3	AR2 10c blue, *blue*	2.75 4.00
a.	10c blue, *greenish blue*	2.75 4.00
b.	Sewing machine perf.	2.75 4.00
c.	Perf. 12	2.75 4.00

The handstamp "AR" in circle is believed to be a postmark.

AR2a

Purple Handstamp

1903 — Imperf.

H4	AR2a 10c black, *pink*	20.00 20.00

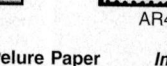

AR3   AR4

1904 — Pelure Paper — Imperf.

H12	AR3 5c pale blue	10.50 10.50
a.	Perf. 12	10.50 10.50

No. 307 Overprinted in Black, Green or Violet   **A R**

H13	A86 5c carmine	17.50 17.50

1904 — Perf. 12

H16	AR4 5c blue	3.25 2.75
a.	Imperf., pair	8.75 8.75

For overprints see Nos. LH1-LH2.

General José Acevedo y Gómez — AR5

1910, July 20 — Engr.

H17	AR5 5c orange & green	5.75 16.00

Centenary of National Independence.

Sabana Station   Map of
AR6   Colombia
            AR7

1917 — Perf. 14

H18	AR6 4c bister brown	1.75 2.00
H19	AR7 5c orange brown	1.50 1.75
a.	Imperf., pair	11.00

LATE FEE STAMPS

LF1   LF2

1886 — Unwmk. — Litho. — Perf. 10½

I1	LF1 2½c blk, *lilac*	3.25 2.50
a.	Imperf., pair	12.00 12.00

1892 — Perf. 12, 13½

I2	LF2 2½c dk bl, *rose*	2.75 2.00
a.	Imperf., pair	12.00
I3	LF2 2½c ultra, *pink*	2.75 2.00

LF3   LF4

1902 — Imperf.

I4	LF3 5c purple, *rose*	.85 .85
a.	Perf. 12	1.75 1.75

1914 — Perf. 10, 13½

I6	LF4 2c vio brown	4.00 4.00
I7	LF4 5c blue green	4.00 3.25

Retardo   Refardo 1921

Overprints illustrated above are unauthorized and of private origin.

POSTAGE DUE STAMPS

These are not, strictly speaking, postage due stamps but were issued to cover an additional fee, "Sobreporte," charged on mail to foreign countries with which Colombia had no postal conventions.

D1   D2

D3

1866 — Unwmk. — Litho. — Imperf.

J1	D1 25c black, *blue*	65.00 45.00
J2	D2 50c black, *yellow*	45.00 65.00
J3	D3 1p black, *rose*	140.00 110.00
	Nos. J1-J3 (3)	250.00 220.00

DEPARTMENT STAMPS

These stamps are said to be for interior postage, to supersede the separate issues for the various departments.

Regular Issues Handstamped in Black, Violet, Blue or Green — a

On Stamps of 1904

1909 — Unwmk. — Perf. 12

L1	A94 ½c yellow	2.00 2.00
a.	Imperf., pair	6.00 6.00
L2	A94 1c yel grn	3.00 2.00
L3	A94 2c red	4.50 3.00
a.	Imperf., pair	12.50 12.50
L4	A94 5c blue	5.00 3.25
L5	A94 10c violet	7.00 7.00
L6	A94 20c black	11.00 10.00
L7	A95 1p brown	18.00 17.00

On Stamp of 1902

L8	A83 10p dk brn, *rose*	20.00 20.00
	Nos. L1-L8 (8)	70.50 64.25

On Stamps of 1908

Perf. 10, 13, 13½ and Compound

L9	A94 ½c orange	2.00 2.00
a.	Imperf., pair	6.00 6.00
L10	A94 1c green	4.00 3.25
a.	Without imprint	5.00 5.00
L11	A94 2c red	4.50 3.25
a.	Imperf., pair	6.00 6.00
L12	A94 5c blue	4.50 3.25
a.	Imperf., pair	12.50 12.50
L13	A94 10c violet	6.00 6.00

On Tolima Stamp of 1888

Perf. 10½

L14	A23 1p red brn	12.50 12.50
	Nos. L9-L14 (6)	33.50 30.25

Regular Issues Handstamped — b

On Stamps of 1904
Perf. 12

L15	A94	½c yellow	2.00	2.00
L16	A94	1c yellow grn	3.50	3.00
L17	A94	2c red	6.00	5.00
L18	A94	5c blue	6.00	5.00
L19	A94	10c violet	8.00	6.00
L20	A94	20c black	11.00	11.00
L21	A94	1p brown	20.00	20.00
		Nos. L15-L21 (7)	56.50	52.00

On Stamps of 1908
Perf. 10, 13, 13½

L22	A94	½c orange	2.25	2.25
L23	A94	1c yellow grn	6.25	6.25
L24	A94	2c red	5.00	5.00
a.		Imperf., pair	12.50	12.50
L25	A94	5c light blue	6.00	5.00
		Nos. L22-L25 (4)	19.50	18.50

The handstamps on Nos. L1-L25 are, as usual, found inverted and double.

DEPARTMENT OF REGISTRATION STAMPS

Registration Stamps Handstamped like Nos. L1-L25
On Registration Stamp of 1904

1909   Unwmk.   Perf. 12

LF1	R12 (a)	10c purple	25.00	25.00
LF2	R12 (b)	10c purple	25.00	25.00

On Registration Stamp of 1909
Perf. 10, 13

LF3	R12 (a)	10c purple	25.00	25.00
LF4	R12 (b)	10c purple	25.00	25.00
		Nos. LF1-LF4 (4)	100.00	100.00

Nos. LF1-LF4 exist imperf. Value per pair, $100.

DEPARTMENT ACKNOWLEDGMENT OF RECEIPT STAMPS

Acknowledgment of Receipt Stamp of 1904 Handstamped like Nos. L1-L25

1909   Unwmk.   Perf. 12

LH1	AR4 (a)	5c blue	25.00	25.00
a.		Imperf., pair	100.00	
LH2	AR4 (b)	5c blue	25.00	25.00
a.		Imperf., pair	100.00	

LOCAL STAMPS FOR THE CITY OF BOGOTA

A1

Pelure Paper

1889   Unwmk.   Litho.   Perf. 12

LX1	A1	½c black	.95	.95
a.		Imperf., pair	6.00	6.00

Impressions on bright blue and blue-gray paper were not regularly issued.

A2

A3

White Wove Paper

1896   Perf. 12, 13½

LX2	A2	½c black	.95	.95

1903   Imperf.

LX3	A3	10c black, *pink*	6.00	1.25
a.		Perf. 12	6.00	1.25

OFFICIAL STAMPS

Stamps of 1917-1937 Overprinted in Black or Red:

a

b

1937   Unwmk.   Perf. 11, 12, 13½

O1	A131 (a)	1c green	.20	.20
O2	A157 (a)	10c dp org	.20	.20
O3	A107 (b)	30c olive bis	1.75	1.00
O4	A129 (b)	40c brn & yel		
		brn	1.50	.80
O5	A114 (b)	50c car	1.00	.50
O6	A107 (b)	1p lt bl	5.00	4.00
O7	A107 (b)	2p org	10.00	6.50
O8	A107 (b)	5p gray	37.50	27.50
O9	A118 (b)	10p dk brn	110.00	100.00

Wmk. 229
Perf. 12½

O10	A132 (a)	2c red	.20	.20
O11	A133 (a)	5c brn	.20	.20
O12	A160 (b)	12c dp bl (R)	1.00	.50
O13	A136 (b)	20c dk bl (R)	1.60	.60
		Nos. O1-O13 (13)	170.15	142.20

Tall, wrong font "I's" in OFICIAL exist on all stamps with "a" overprint.

POSTAL TAX STAMPS

"Greatest Mother" PT1

Perf. 11½

1935, May 27   Unwmk.   Litho.

RA1	PT1	5c olive blk & scar	2.50	.75

Required on all mail during Red Cross Week in 1935 (May 27-June 3) and in 1936.

Mother and Child — PT2

Perf. 10½, 10½x11

1937, May 24   Unwmk.

RA2	PT2	5c red	1.50	.60

Required on all mail during Red Cross Week. The tax was for the Red Cross.

PT3

Ministry of Posts and Telegraphs Building — PT4

1939-45   Litho.   Perf. 10½, 12½

RA3	PT3	¼c dp bl	.20	.20
RA3A	PT3	¼c dk vio brn ('45)	.20	.20
RA4	PT3	½c pink	.20	.20
RA5	PT3	1c violet	.20	.20
RA5A	PT3	1c yel org ('45)	1.50	.60
RA6	PT3	2c pck grn	.40	.20
RA7	PT3	20c lt brn	3.50	1.25
		Nos. RA3-RA7 (7)	6.30	2.85

Obligatory on all mail. The tax was for the construction of the new Communications Building.
The 25c of type PT3 and PT4 were not usable on postal matter.
For overprint see No. 561.

Perf. 12½x13

1940, Jan. 20   Engr.   Wmk. 229

RA8	PT4	¼c ultra	.20	.20
RA9	PT4	½c carmine	.20	.20
RA10	PT4	1c violet	.20	.20
RA11	PT4	2c bl grn	.25	.20
RA12	PT4	20c brown	1.00	.20
		Nos. RA8-RA12 (5)	1.85	1.00

See note after No. RA7. See No. RA18.

"Protection" — PT5

1940, Apr. 25   Wmk. 255   Perf. 12

RA13	PT5	5c rose carmine	.25	.20

See No. RA17.

Postal Tax Stamps of 1939 Surcharged in Black

1943   Unwmk.   Perf. 10½

RA14	PT3	½c on 1c violet	.20	.20
a.		Inverted surcharge	1.50	
RA15	PT3	½c on 2c pck grn	.20	.20
RA16	PT3	½c on 20c lt brn	.20	.20
		Nos. RA14-RA16 (3)	.60	.60

Types of 1940
Imprint: "Litografia Colombia Bogota S.A."

1944   Litho.   Perf. 11

RA17	PT5	5c dark rose	.35	.20

Imprint: "Lito-Colombia Bogota-Colombia"

RA18	PT4	¼c ultra	.20	.20

Ministry of Posts and Telegraphs Building — PT6

1945-48   Wmk. 255   Engr.   Perf. 12

RA19	PT6	¼c ultra	.20	.20
RA20	PT6	¼c sepia ('46)	.20	.20
RA21	PT6	½c car rose	.20	.20
RA22	PT6	½c dp mag ('46)	.20	.20
RA23	PT6	1c vio ('46)	.20	.20
RA23A	PT6	1c red org ('46)	.20	.20
RA24	PT6	2c grn ('46)	.20	.20
RA25	PT6	20c brn ('46)	.90	.25
a.		20c red brown ('48)	.60	.20
		Nos. RA19-RA25 (8)	2.30	1.65

These stamps were obligatory on all mail. The surtax was for the construction of the new Communications Building. See Nos. 603, RA33. For overprints see Nos. 562-564.

No. 469 Overprinted in Carmine

1946, May 25

RA26	A176	5c dull brown	.35	.20

The surtax was for the Red Cross.

Ministry of Posts and Telegraphs Building — PT7

1946   Unwmk.   Litho.   Perf. 11

RA27	PT7	3c blue	.20	.20

No. 490 Overprinted in Carmine

1947   Wmk. 255   Perf. 12

RA28	A196	20c gray black	3.75	1.25

Arms of Colombia and Red Cross — PT8

PT9

Perf. 12½

1947, Sept.   Unwmk.   Engr.

RA29	PT8	5c car lake	.25	.20

The surtax of Nos. RA29 and RA40 was for the Red Cross. See No. RA40.

No. 466 Overprinted Like No. RA28 in Carmine

RA30	A136	20c dark blue	15.00	12.50

> Catalogue values for unused stamps in this section, from this point to the end of the section, are for Never Hinged items.

Type of 1945

1947   Wmk. 255   Engr.   Perf. 12

RA33	PT6	1c olive bister	.30	.20

Black Surcharge

1948   Unwmk.   Litho.   Perf. 11

RA36	PT9	1c on 5c lt brn	.30	.20
RA37	PT9	1c on 10c lt vio	.30	.20
RA38	PT9	1c on 25c red	.30	.20
RA39	PT9	1c on 50c ultra	.30	.20
		Nos. RA36-RA39 (4)	1.20	.80

Type of 1947

1948   Perf. 10½

RA40	PT8	5c vermilion	.25	.20

Ministry of Posts and Telegraphs Building — PT10

Mother and Child — PT11

1948-50   Wmk. 255   Engr.   Perf. 12

RA41	PT10	1c rose car ('49)	.30	.20
RA42	PT10	2c green ('50)	.30	.20
RA43	PT10	3c blue	.30	.20
RA44	PT10	5c gray	.30	.20
RA45	PT10	10c purple	.30	.20
		Nos. RA41-RA45 (5)	1.50	1.00

A 25c stamp of type PT10 was for use on telegrams, later for regular postage. See Nos. 602, 604. For overprints and surcharge see Nos. C227-C230, C238, C283, RA51.

Unwmk.

1950, May 25   **Litho.**   *Perf. 11*

Dark Blue Surcharge

RA46 PT11 5c on 2c gray, red, blk & yel   1.00   .30
- a.   "195" instead of "1950"   2.00   2.00
- b.   Top bar and "19" of "1950" omitted   2.00   2.00

Marginal perforations omitted, creating 26 straight-edged stamps in each sheet of 44. Surtax for Red Cross.

No. 574 Overprinted in Black

1950, May 26   **Wmk. 255**   *Perf. 12*

RA47 A176 5c blue   .25 .20
- a.   Inverted overprint   1.25

Telegraph Stamp Surcharged in Black

RA48 A253a 8c on 50c org yel   .25 .20

Fiscal stamps of type A253a were available for postal use after May 9, 1952. See Nos. 605-608.

Arms and Cross — PT12   Bartolome de Las Casas Aiding Youth — PT13

Perf. 12½

1951, May   **Unwmk.**   **Engr.**

RA49 PT12 5c red   .30 .20
RA50 PT13 5c carmine   .30 .20

The surtax was for the Red Cross.

No. RA43 Surcharged with New Value in Black

1951   **Wmk. 255**   *Perf. 12*

RA51 PT10 1c on 3c blue   .25 .20

Type of 1951

Engraved; Cross Lithographed

1953   **Unwmk.**   *Perf. 12½*

RA52 PT13 5c grn & car   .30 .20

Surtax of Nos. RA52-RA60 for the Red Cross.

No. C254 Overprinted with Cross and Bar in Carmine

1954

RA53 AP42 5c lilac rose   .60 .50

St. Peter Claver Offering Gifts to Slaves — PT14

Engraved; Cross Typographed

1955, May 2   **Unwmk.**   *Perf. 13*

RA54 PT14 5c dp plum & red   .30 .20

Death of St. Peter Claver, 300th anniv.

Jean Henri Dunant and Santiago Samper Brush PT15

Photo.; Red Cross & "Cruz Roja" Engr.

1956, June 1   **Unwmk.**   *Perf. 13*

RA55 PT15 5c brown & red   .30 .20

Nurses and Ambulances PT16

1958, June 2   **Photo.**   *Perf. 12*

RA56 PT16 5c gray & red   .30 .20

St. Louisa de Marillac and Church PT17

No. RA58, Henri Dunant and battle scene.

1960, Sept. 1   **Litho.**   *Perf. 11*

RA57 PT17 5c brown & rose   .25 .20
RA58 PT17 5c vio blue & rose   .25 .20

No. RA57 for 3rd cent. of the Sisters of Charity. No. RA58 for cent. (in 1959) of the Red Cross idea.

Manuelita de la Cruz — PT18   Red Cross Worker, Patient — PT19

1961, Nov. 2   **Engr.**   *Perf. 13*

RA59 PT18 5c dull pur & red   .25 .20
RA60 PT18 5c brown & red   .25 .20

Issued in memory of Red Cross Nurse Manuelita de la Cruz, who died in the line of duty during the floods of 1955. Obligatory on domestic mail for a month.

1965, Apr. 30   **Photo.**   *Perf. 12*

RA61 PT19 5c blue gray & red   .25 .20

Obligatory on domestic mail during May.

Nurse's Cap — PT20

Red Cross — PT21

1967, June 1   **Litho.**   *Perf. 12*

RA62 PT20 5c brt bl & red   .25 .20

1969, July 1   **Litho.**   *Perf. 12x12½*

RA63 PT21 5c vio bl & red   .25 .20

Child Care — PT22

1970, July 1   **Litho.**   *Perf. 12½x12*

RA64 PT22 5c light bl & red   .25 .20

ANTIOQUIA

ˌant-ē-'ō-kē-ə

Originally a State, now a Department of the Republic of Colombia. Until the revolution of 1885, the separate states making up the United States of Colombia were sovereign governments in their own right. On August 4, 1886, the National Council of Bogotá, composed of two delegates from each state, adopted a new constitution which abolished the sovereign rights of states, which then became departments with governors appointed by the President of the Republic. The nine original states represented at the Bogotá Convention retained some of their previous rights, as management of their own finances, and all issued postage stamps until as late as 1904. For Panama's issues, see Panama Nos. 1-30.

Coat of Arms
A1   A2

A3   A4

Wove Paper

1868   **Unwmk.**   **Litho.**   *Imperf.*

1 A1 2½c blue   1,000.   750.
2 A2 5c green   750.   575.
3 A3 10c lilac   3,000.   1,000.
4 A4 1p red   675.   750.

Reprints of Nos. 1, 3 and 4 are on a bluish white paper and all but No. 3 have scratches across the design.

A5   A6

A7   A8

A9   A10

1869

5 A5 2½c blue   3.25   2.75
6 A6 5c green   5.00   4.50
7 A7 5c green   5.00   4.50
8 A8 10c lilac   6.25   3.25
9 A9 20c brown   6.25   3.25
10 A10 1p rose red   12.50   11.00
- a.   1p vermilion   25.00   22.50
Nos. 5-10 (6)   38.25   29.25

Reprints of Nos. 7, 8 and 10 are on a bluish white paper; reprints of Nos. 5 and 10a on white paper. The 10c blue is believed to be a reprint.

A11   A12

A13   A14

A15   A16

A17   A18

1873

12 A11 1c yellow grn   4.50   3.50
- a.   1c green   4.50   3.50
13 A12 5c green   7.50   5.50
14 A13 10c lilac   22.50   19.00
15 A14 20c yellow brn   7.50   6.50
- a.   20c dark brown   7.50   6.50
16 A15 50c blue   1.75   1.50
17 A16 1p vermilion   3.25   2.75
18 A17 2p black, *yellow*   7.75   7.00
19 A18 5p black, *rose*   55.00   47.50

A19   A20

Liberty Head
A21   A22

Pedro Justo
Berrio — A23

1875-85
20	A19	1c blk, *grn*, unglazed ('76)	1.60	1.40
a.		Glazed paper	2.25	1.90
b.		1c blk, *lt grn*, laid paper ('85)	3.75	3.50
21	A19	1c black ('76)	1.10	1.00
a.		Laid paper	140.00	100.00
22	A19	1c bl grn ('85)	2.25	1.90
23	A19	1c red lil, laid paper ('85)	2.25	1.90
24	A20	2½c blue	2.25	1.90
a.		Pelure paper ('78)	1,500.	1,100.
25	A21	5c green	15.00	12.50
a.		Laid paper	140.00	80.00
26	A22	5c green	15.00	12.50
a.		Laid paper	140.00	80.00
27	A23	10c lilac	22.50	19.00
a.		Laid paper	140.00	110.00
28	A20	10c vio, pelure paper ('78)	900.00	675.00

Arms — A24   Liberty — A25

A26   A27

1878-85
29	A24	2½c blue, pelure paper	2.50	2.25
30	A24	2½c green ('83)	2.25	1.90
a.		Laid paper ('83)	70.00	47.50
31	A24	2½c blk, *buff* ('85)	6.25	5.50
32	A25	5c green ('83)	3.75	3.25
a.		Pelure paper	30.00	25.00
b.		Laid paper ('82)	37.50	11.00
33	A25	5c violet ('83)	8.75	6.50
a.		5c blue violet ('83)	8.75	6.50
34	A26	10c vio, laid paper ('82)	160.00	55.00
35	A26	10c scar ('83)	2.25	1.90
a.		Tete beche pair	50.00	45.00
36	A27	20c brown ('83)	3.75	3.25
a.		Laid paper ('82)	5.00	4.50

A28   A29

Liberty — A30   Coat of Arms — A31

1883-85
37	A28	5c brown	4.50	3.00
a.		Laid paper	190.00	75.00
38	A28	5c green ('85)	125.00	40.00
a.		Laid paper ('85)	140.00	65.00
39	A28	5c yel, laid paper ('85)	5.00	4.00
40	A29	10c bl grn, laid paper	5.00	4.50

41	A29	10c bl, *bl* ('85)	5.00	4.00
42	A29	10c lil, laid paper ('85)	9.50	6.50
a.		Wove paper ('85)	100.00	40.00
43	A30	20c bl, laid paper ('85)	4.50	4.00

1886   **Wove Paper**
55	A31	1c grn, *pink*	.55	.50
56	A31	2½c blk, *orange*	.55	.50
57	A31	5c ultra, *buff*	1.75	1.60
a.		5c blue, *buff*	3.25	2.75
58	A31	10c rose, *buff*	1.60	1.40
a.		Transfer of 50c in stone of 10c	75.00	65.00
59	A31	20c dk vio, *buff*	1.60	1.40
61	A31	50c yel brn, *buff*	2.75	2.50
62	A31	1p yel, *grn*	4.50	4.00
63	A31	2p green, *vio*	4.50	4.00
		Nos. 55-63 (8)	17.80	15.90

1887-88
64	A31	1c red, *vio*	.45	.40
65	A31	2½c lil, *pale lil*	.45	.55
66	A31	5c car, *buff*	.60	.55
67	A31	5c red, *grn*	3.25	1.60
68	A31	10c brn, *grn*	.65	.80
		Nos. 64-68 (5)	5.40	3.90

Medellin Issue

A32   A33

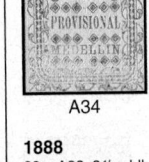

A34   A35

1888   **Typeset**
69	A32	2½c blk, *yellow*	14.00	12.50
70	A33	5c blk, *yellow*	7.50	6.75
71	A34	5c red, *yellow*	4.50	4.00
		Nos. 69-71 (3)	26.00	23.25

Two varieties of No. 69, six of No. 70 and ten of No. 71.

1889
72	A35	2½c red	7.00	6.00

Ten varieties including "eentavos."

Regular Issue

Coat of Arms
A36   A37

A38   A39

A40   A41

1889   **Litho.**   **Perf. 13½**
73	A36	1c blk, *rose*	.25	.25
74	A36	2½c blk, *blue*	.25	.25
75	A36	5c blk, *yellow*	.30	.30
76	A36	10c blk, *green*	.30	.30
		Nos. 73-76 (4)	1.10	1.10

1890
78	A37	20c blue	1.25	1.25
79	A38	50c vio brn	2.50	2.50
a.		Transfer of 20c in stone of 50c	82.50	82.50
80	A38	50c green	2.00	2.00
81	A39	1p red	1.75	1.75
82	A40	2p blk, *mag*	12.50	12.50
83	A41	5p blk, *org red*	20.00	20.00
		Nos. 78-83 (6)	40.00	40.00

Nos. 73-76, 82-83 exist imperf.
The so-called "errors" of Nos. 73 to 76, printed on paper of wrong colors, are essays or, possibly, reprints. They exist perforated and imperforate.
See No. 96.

A42   A43

A44   A45

1890   **Typeset**   **Perf. 14**
84	A42	2½c blk, *buff*	2.00	2.00
85	A43	5c blk, *orange*	2.00	2.00
86	A44	10c blk, *buff*	6.00	6.00
87	A44	10c blk, *rose*	7.50	7.50
88	A45	20c blk, *orange*	7.50	7.50
		Nos. 84-88 (5)	25.00	25.00

20 varieties of the 5c, 10 each of the other values.

A46   A47

1892   **Litho.**   **Perf. 13½**
89	A46	1c brn, *brnsh*	.35	.35
90	A46	2½c pur, *lil*	.35	.35
92	A46	5c blk, *gray*	1.00	.50
a.		Transfer of 2½c in stone of 5c	150.00	
		Nos. 89-92 (3)	1.70	1.20

1893
93	A46	1c blue	.25	.25
94	A46	2½c green	.35	.35
95	A46	5c vermilion	.25	.25
96	A36	10c pale brown	.25	.25
		Nos. 93-96 (4)	1.10	1.10

1896   **Perf. 14**
97	A47	2c gray	.25	.25
98	A47	2c lilac rose	.25	.25
99	A47	2½c brown	.25	.25
100	A47	2½c steel blue	.25	.25
101	A47	3c orange	.25	.25
102	A47	3c olive grn	.25	.25
103	A47	5c green	.25	.25
104	A47	5c yellow buff	.30	.30
105	A47	10c brown vio	.55	.55
106	A47	10c violet	.55	.55
107	A47	20c brown org	1.25	1.25
108	A47	20c blue	1.25	1.25
109	A47	50c gray brn	1.25	1.25
110	A47	50c rose	1.10	1.10
111	A47	1p blue & blk	16.00	16.00
112	A47	1p rose red & blk	16.00	16.00
113	A47	2p orange & blk	47.50	47.50
114	A47	2p dk grn & blk	47.50	47.50
115	A47	5p red vio & blk	82.50	82.50
116	A47	5p purple & blk	82.50	82.50
		Nos. 97-116 (20)	300.00	300.00

Nos. 115-116 with centers omitted are proofs.

General José María Córdoba — A48

1899   **Perf. 11**
117	A48	½c grnsh bl	.20	.20
118	A48	1c slate blue	.20	.20
119	A48	2c slate brown	.20	.20
120	A48	3c red	.20	.20
121	A48	4c bister brown	.20	.20
122	A48	5c green	.20	.20
123	A48	10c scarlet	.20	.20
124	A48	20c gray violet	.20	.20
125	A48	50c olive bister	.20	.20
126	A48	1p greenish blk	.20	.20
127	A48	2p olive gray	.20	.20
		Nos. 117-127 (11)	2.20	2.20

Numerous part-perf. and imperf. varieties of Nos. 117-127 exist.

A49   A50

A50a

1901   **Typeset**   **Perf. 12**
128	A49	1c red	.20	.20
129	A50	1c ultra	.60	.60
130	A50	1c bister	.60	.60
130A	A50a	1c dull red	.60	.60
130B	A50a	1c ultra	4.00	4.00
		Nos. 128-130B (5)	6.00	6.00

Eight varieties of No. 128, four varieties of Nos. 129-130B.

A51   A52

Atanasio Girardot
A53
Dr. José Félix Restrepo
A54

1902   **Litho.**   **Wove Paper**
131	A51	1c brt rose	.20	.20
a.		Laid paper	.60	.60
b.		Imperf., pair	2.50	
132	A51	2c blue	.20	.20
a.		Transfer of 3c in stone of 2c	5.00	5.00
133	A51	3c green	.20	.20
a.		Imperf., pair	4.00	
134	A51	4c dull violet	.20	.20
135	A52	5c rose red	.20	.20
136	A53	10c rose lilac	.20	.20
a.		Small head	5.00	5.00
b.		10c rose	.20	.20
137	A53	20c gray green	.20	.20
138	A53	30c brt rose	.20	.20
139	A53	40c blue	.20	.20
140	A53	50c brn, *yel*	.20	.20

Laid Paper
141	A54	1p purple & blk	.70	.70
142	A54	2p rose & blk	.70	.70
143	A54	5p sl bl & blk	1.25	1.25
		Nos. 131-143 (13)	4.65	4.65

1903   **Wove Paper**
143A	A51	1c blue	.20	.20
144	A51	2c violet	.20	.20
a.		Imperf.	2.50	

A55　　　　A56

A57

Designs: 1p, Francisco Antonio Zea. 2p, Custodio Garcia Rovira. 3p, La Pola (Policarpa Salavarrieta). 4p, J. M. Restrepo. 5p, José Fernández Madrid. 10p, Juan del Corral.

1903-04
145	A55	4c yellow brn	.20	.20
146	A55	5c blue	.20	.20
147	A56	10c yellow	.20	.20
148	A56	20c purple	.20	.20
149	A56	30c brown	.60	.60
150	A56	40c green	.60	.60
151	A56	50c rose	.20	.20
152	A57	1p olive gray	.60	.60
153	A57	2p purple	.60	.60
154	A57	3p dark blue	.60	.60
155	A57	4p dull red	1.00	1.00
156	A57	5p red brown	3.00	1.50
157	A57	10p scarlet	6.50	3.50
		Nos. 145-157 (13)	14.50	10.00

Nos. 145-146, 151, 153-157 exist imperf. Value of pairs, $3 to $4.

Manizales Issue

Stamps of these designs are local private post issues.

OFFICIAL STAMPS Stamps of 1903-04 with overprint "OFICIAL" were never issued.

REGISTRATION STAMPS

R1

1896　Unwmk.　Litho.　Perf. 14
F1	R1	2½c rose	1.10	1.10
F2	R1	2½c dull blue	1.10	1.10

Córdoba
R2

R3

R4

1899　　　　Perf. 11
F3	R2	2½c dull blue	.25	.25
F4	R3	10c red lilac	.25	.25

1902　　　　Perf. 12
F5	R4	10c purple, *blue*	.30	.30
a.		Imperf.		

ACKNOWLEDGMENT OF RECEIPT STAMPS

AR1

1902-03　Unwmk.　Litho.　Perf. 12
H1	AR1	5c black, *rose*	.90	.90
H2	AR1	5c slate ('03)	.30	.30

LATE FEE STAMPS

Córdoba — LF1

1899　Unwmk.　Litho.　Perf. 11
I1	LF1	2½c dark green	.25	.25
a.		Imperf., pair		2.75

LF2　　　　LF3

1901　　Typeset　　Perf. 12
I2	LF2	2½c red violet	.50	.50
a.		2½c purple	.50	.50

1902　　　　Litho.
I3	LF3	2½c violet	.20	.20

City of Medellin

Stamps of the designs shown were not issued by any governmental agency but by the Sociedad de Mejoras Publicas.

BOLIVAR

bə-'lē-ˌvär

Originally a State, now a Department of the Republic of Colombia. (See Antioquia.)

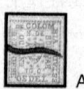

A1

1863-66　Unwmk.　Litho.　Imperf.
1	A1	10c green	1,100.	550.00
a.		Five stars below shield	2,400.	2,200.
2	A1	10c red ('66)	25.00	27.50
a.		Diagonal half used as 5c on cover		55.00
b.		Five stars below shield	75.00	67.50
3	A1	1p red	6.25	7.25

Fourteen varieties of each. Counterfeits of Nos. 1 and 1a exist.

Coat of Arms
A2　　　　A3

A4　　　　A5

1873
4	A2	5c blue	7.00	7.00
5	A3	10c violet	7.00	7.00
6	A4	20c yellow green	30.00	30.00
7	A5	80c vermilion	60.00	60.00
		Nos. 4-7 (4)	104.00	104.00

A6　　　　A7

A8　　　　Bolívar — A9

1874-78
8	A6	5c blue	25.00	12.50
9	A7	5c blue ('78)	7.75	7.00
10	A8	10c violet ('77)	3.75	3.50
		Nos. 8-10 (3)	36.50	23.00

Dated "1879"

1879　White Wove Paper　Perf. 12½
11	A9	5c blue	.25	.25
a.		Imperf., pair	.80	
12	A9	10c violet	.20	.20
13	A9	20c red	.25	.25
a.		20c green (error)	10.00	10.00

Bluish Laid Paper
15	A9	5c blue	.30	.30
a.		Imperf., pair	2.00	
16	A9	10c violet	1.60	1.60
a.		Imperf., pair	4.00	
17	A9	20c red	.40	.40
a.		Imperf., pair	1.75	
		Nos. 11-17 (6)	3.00	3.00

Stamps of 80c and 1p on white wove paper and 1p on bluish laid paper were prepared but not placed in use.

Dated "1880"

1880　White Wove Paper　Perf. 12½
19	A9	5c blue	.25	.25
a.		Imperf., pair	1.60	
20	A9	10c violet	.35	.35
a.		Imperf., pair	1.60	
21	A9	20c red	.35	.35
a.		20c green (error)	13.00	13.00

23	A9	80c green	2.25	2.25
24	A9	1p orange	2.50	2.50
a.		Imperf., pair	5.50	
		Nos. 19-24 (5)	5.70	5.70

Bluish Laid Paper
25	A9	5c blue	.25	.25
a.		Imperf., pair	1.25	
26	A9	10c violet	2.25	2.25
27	A9	20c red	.35	.35
a.		Imperf., pair	2.75	
28	A9	1p orange	400.00	
a.		Imperf.	450.00	

A11　　　　A12

A13　　　　A15

A16

Dated "1882"
White Wove Paper

1882　　　　Perf. 12, 16x12
29	A11	5c blue	.35	.35
30	A12	10c lilac	.25	.25
31	A13	20c red	.35	.35
33	A15	80c green	.65	.65
34	A16	1p orange	.65	.65
		Nos. 29-34 (5)	2.25	2.25

Nos. 29, 30 and 34 are known imperforate. They are printer's waste and were not issued through post offices.

A17　　　　A18

1882　　Engr.　　Perf. 12
35	A17	5p blue & rose red	.60	.60
a.		Imperf., pair	4.75	
b.		Perf. 16	7.50	6.25
c.		Perf. 16	6.25	6.25
36	A17	10p brown & blue	1.60	1.60
a.		Imperf., pair	8.00	
b.		Perf. 16	7.00	5.00
c.		Rouletted	8.00	8.00

Dated "1883"

1883　Litho.　Perf. 12, 16x12
37	A11	5c blue	.20	.20
a.		Imperf., pair	.80	
b.		Perf. 12	3.00	1.00
38	A12	10c lilac	.25	.25
39	A13	20c red	.25	.25
41	A15	80c green	.30	.30
42	A16	1p orange	.60	.60
a.		Perf. 16x12	2.00	2.00
		Nos. 37-42 (5)	1.60	1.60

Dated "1884"

1884
43	A11	5c blue	.30	.30
a.		Perf. 12	10.00	9.25
44	A12	10c lilac	.20	.20
45	A13	20c red	.20	.20
a.		Perf. 12	4.25	4.25
47	A15	80c green	.25	.25
a.		Perf. 12	2.00	2.00
48	A16	1p orange	.30	.30
		Nos. 43-48 (5)	1.25	1.25

Dated "1885"

1885
49	A11	5c blue	.20	.20
50	A12	10c lilac	.20	.20
51	A13	20c red	.20	.20
53	A15	80c green	.25	.25
54	A16	1p orange	.30	.30
		Nos. 49-54 (5)	1.15	1.15

The note after No. 34 will also apply to imperforate stamps of the 1884-85 issues.

1891   *Perf. 14*
55	A18	1c black	.30	.30
56	A18	5c orange	.30	.30
a.		Imperf., pair	.80	
57	A18	10c carmine	.30	.30
58	A18	20c blue	.60	.60
59	A18	50c green	.90	.90
60	A18	1p purple	.90	.90
		Nos. 55-60 (6)	3.30	3.30

For overprint see Colombia No. 169.

Bolívar
A19

José
Fernández
Madrid
A20

Manuel
Rodriguez
Torices
A21

José María
García de
Toledo
A22

1903   **Laid Paper**   *Imperf.*
62	A19	50c dk bl, *pink*	.60	.60
a.		Bluish paper	.60	.60
63	A19	50c sl grn, *pink*	.60	.60
a.		Rose paper	2.00	2.00
b.		Greenish blue paper	3.00	3.00
c.		Yellow paper	4.00	4.00
d.		Brown paper	4.00	4.00
e.		Salmon paper	7.50	7.50
64	A19	50c pur, *pink*	2.00	2.00
a.		White paper	4.00	4.00
b.		Brown paper	4.00	4.00
c.		Greenish blue paper	4.00	4.00
d.		Lilac paper	4.00	4.00
e.		Rose paper	3.50	3.50
f.		Yellow paper	4.00	4.00
g.		Salmon paper	6.00	6.00
h.		As "a," wove paper	9.00	9.00
65	A20	1p org, *sal*	.60	.60
a.		Yellow paper	4.50	4.50
b.		Greenish blue paper	15.00	15.00
66	A20	1p gray grn, *lil*	1.40	1.40
a.		Yellow paper	6.50	6.50
b.		Salmon paper	7.50	7.50
c.		Green paper	7.50	7.50
d.		White wove paper	10.00	
67	A21	5p car rose, *lil*	.60	.60
a.		Brown paper	1.10	1.10
b.		Yellow paper	1.10	1.10
c.		Greenish blue paper	4.50	4.50
d.		Bluish paper	6.00	6.00
e.		Salmon paper	7.50	7.50
f.		Rose paper	9.00	9.00
68	A22	10p dk bl, *bluish*	1.25	1.25
a.		Greenish blue paper	1.25	1.25
b.		Rose paper	7.50	7.50
c.		Salmon paper	7.50	7.50
d.		Yellow paper	7.50	7.50
e.		Brown paper	8.50	8.50
f.		Lilac paper	10.00	10.00
g.		White paper	9.00	9.00
69	A22	10p pur, *grnsh bl*	3.50	3.50
a.		Bluish paper	7.50	7.50
b.		Rose paper	6.75	6.75
c.		Yellow paper	7.50	7.50
d.		Brown paper	7.50	7.50
		Nos. 62-69 (8)	10.55	10.55

Sewing Machine Perf.
Laid Paper
70	A19	50c dk bl, *pink*	1.00	1.00
a.		Bluish paper	1.00	1.00
71	A19	50c sl grn, *pink*	2.00	2.00
72	A19	50c pur, *grnsh bl*	4.00	4.00
a.		White paper	4.00	4.00
b.		White wove paper	7.50	
73	A20	1p org, *sal*	2.00	2.00
74	A20	1p gray grn, *lil*	9.00	9.00
a.		Yellow paper	9.00	9.00
75	A21	5p car rose, *yel*	1.60	1.60
a.		Lilac paper	4.00	4.00
b.		Brown paper	4.00	4.00
c.		Bluish paper	5.50	5.50
d.		White wove paper	9.00	

76	A22	10p dk bl, *grnsh bl*	4.50	4.50
a.		Bluish paper	7.00	7.00
b.		Yellow paper	9.00	9.00
c.		As "b," wove paper	10.00	
77	A22	10p pur, *grnsh bl*	7.00	7.00
a.		Bluish paper	11.00	11.00
b.		Rose paper	8.00	8.00
c.		Yellow paper	11.00	11.00
		Nos. 70-77 (8)	31.10	31.10

José María del
Castillo y
Rada — A23

Manuel
Anguiano — A24

Pantaleón C.
Ribón — A25

1904   **Sewing Machine Perf.**
89	A23	5c black	.25	.25
90	A24	10c brown	.25	.25
91	A25	20c red	.30	.30
92	A25	20c red brown	.60	.60
		Nos. 89-92 (4)	1.40	1.40

Imperf., pairs
89a	A23	5c black	3.50	3.50
90a	A24	10c brown	2.75	2.75
91a	A25	20c red	6.50	6.50
92a	A25	20c red brown	6.50	6.50

A26

A27

A28

1904   *Imperf.*
93	A26	½c black	.65	.65
a.		Tête bêche pair	3.50	3.50
94	A27	1c blue	1.10	1.10
95	A28	2c purple	1.25	1.25
		Nos. 93-95 (3)	3.00	3.00

REGISTRATION STAMPS

Simón Bolívar
R1   R2
White Wove Paper
Perf. 12½, 16x12

1879   **Unwmk.**   **Litho.**
F1	R1	40c brown	.70	.70

Bluish Laid Paper
F2	R1	40c brown	.70	.70
a.		Imperf., pair	3.25	

Dated "1880"

1880

White Wove Paper
F3	R1	40c brown	.30	.30

Bluish Laid Paper
F4	R1	40c brown	.65	.65
a.		Imperf., pair	3.50	

Dated "1882" to "1885"
White Wove Paper
1882-85   *Perf. 16x12*
F5	R2	40c brown (1882)	.30	.30
F6	R2	40c brown (1883)	.25	.25
F7	R2	40c brown (1884)	.25	.25
F8	R2	40c brown (1885)	.30	.30
		Nos. F5-F8 (4)	1.10	1.10

                                Perf. 12
F5a	R2	40c	18.00	
F6a	R2	40c	9.25	
F7a	R2	40c	9.50	
F8a	R2	40c	2.50	
		Nos. F5a-F8a (4)	39.25	

R3

Laid Paper

1903   *Imperf.*
F9	R3	20c orange, *rose*	.60	.60
a.		Salmon paper	1.10	1.10
b.		Greenish blue paper	6.00	6.00

Sewing Machine Perf.
F10	R3	20c orange, *rose*	2.50	2.50
a.		Salmon paper	2.50	2.50
b.		Greenish blue paper	6.00	6.00

R4

1904

Wove Paper
F11	R4	5c black	3.25	3.25

ACKNOWLEDGMENT OF RECEIPT STAMPS

AR1   AR2

1903   **Unwmk.**   **Litho.**   *Imperf.*
Laid Paper
H1	AR1	20c org, *rose*	2.50	2.50
a.		Yellow paper	1.25	1.25
b.		Greenish blue paper	5.00	5.00
H2	AR1	20c dk bl, *yel*	2.00	2.00
a.		Brown paper	3.50	3.50
b.		Rose paper	2.50	2.50
c.		Salmon paper	7.00	7.00
d.		Greenish blue paper	7.00	7.00

Sewing Machine Perf.
H3	AR1	20c org, *grnsh bl*	6.25	6.25
a.		Yellow paper	7.25	7.25
H4	AR1	20c dk bl, *yel*	7.25	7.25
a.		Lilac paper	7.25	7.25
		Nos. H1-H4 (4)	18.00	18.00

1904

Wove Paper
H5	AR2	2c red	1.10	1.10

LATE FEE STAMPS

LF1

1903 **Unwmk.** **Litho.** *Imperf.*
Laid Paper
I1	LF1	20c car rose, *bluish*	.60	.60
I2	LF1	20c pur, *bluish*	.55	.55
a.		Rose paper	2.00	2.00
b.		Brown paper	2.00	2.00
c.		Lilac paper	2.00	2.00
d.		Yellow paper	6.25	6.25

Sewing Machine Perf.
I3	LF1	20c car rose, *bluish*	3.50	3.50
I4	LF1	20c pur, *bluish*	3.50	3.50
a.		Rose paper	6.00	6.00
b.		Lilac paper	6.00	6.00
c.		Yellow paper	10.00	10.00
		Nos. I1-I4 (4)	8.15	8.15

BOYACA

Originally a State, now a Department of the Republic of Colombia. (See Antioquia.)

Diego Mendoza
Pérez — A1

1902 **Unwmk.** **Litho.** *Perf. 13½*
Wove Paper
1	A1	5c blue green	.70	.70
a.		Bluish paper	90.00	90.00
b.		Imperf., pair	12.50	

Laid Paper
Perf. 12
2	A1	5c green	100.00	100.00

Coat of Arms
A2   A3

Gen. Próspero
Pinzón — A4   A5

Monument of
Battle of
Boyacá — A6

President José
Manuel
Marroquin — A7

BOYACA

1903		Litho.		Imperf.	
4	A2	10c dark gray		.25	.25
5	A3	20c red brown		.30	.30
6	A5	1p red		3.00	3.00
a.		1p claret		3.50	3.50
8	A6	5p black, *rose*		1.10	1.10
a.		5p black, *buff*		11.00	11.00
9	A7	10p black, *buff*		1.10	1.10
a.		10p black, *rose*		11.00	11.00
b.		Tête bêche pair		15.00	
		Nos. 4-9 (5)		5.75	5.75

		Perf. 12			
10	A2	10c dark gray		.30	.30
11	A3	20c red brown		.35	.35
12	A4	50c green		.30	.30
13	A4	50c dull blue		2.00	2.00
14	A5	1p red		.30	.30
a.		1p claret		3.00	3.00
16	A6	5p black, *rose*		11.00	11.00
		5p black, *buff*		9.50	9.50
17	A7	10p black, *buff*		1.10	1.10
		10p black, *rose*		11.00	11.00
b.		Tête bêche pair		12.00	12.00
		Nos. 10-17 (7)		15.35	15.35

Statue of Bolívar — A8

1904					
18	A8	10c orange		.25	.25
a.		Imperf., pair		3.50	3.50

CAUCA

Stamps of these designs were issued by a provincial post between 1879(?) and 1890.

Stamps of this design are believed to be of private origin and without official sanction.

Items inscribed "No hay estampillas" (No stamps available) and others inscribed "Manuel E. Jiménez" are considered by specialists to be receipt labels, not postage stamps.

CUNDINAMARCA

¸kün-di-nə-'mär-kə

Originally a State, now a Department of the Republic of Colombia. (See Antioquia.)

Coat of Arms
A1   A2

1870		Unwmk.	Litho.	Imperf.	
1	A1	5c blue		4.75	4.75
2	A2	10c red		15.00	15.00

The counterfeits, or reprints, show traces of the cuts made to deface the dies.

A3   A4

A5   A6

1877-82					
3	A3	10c red ('82)		3.25	3.25
a.		Laid paper ('77)		4.25	4.25
4	A4	20c green ('82)		7.00	7.00
a.		Laid paper ('77)		11.00	11.00
7	A5	50c purple ('82)		7.75	7.75
8	A6	1p brown ('82)		11.00	11.00
		Nos. 3-8 (4)		29.00	29.00

A7

1884					
10	A7	5c blue		.75	.75
11	A7	5c blue (redrawn)		.75	.75
a.		Tête bêche pair		75.00	75.00

The redrawn stamp has no period after "COLOMBIA."

A8

A9

A10

E. U. DE COLOMBIA
E.S.DE CUNDINAMARCA
SELLO PROVISORIO
CORREOS DEL ESTADO
VALE DOS REALES

A11

1883			Typeset	
13	A8	10c black, *yellow*	12.50	12.50
14	A9	50c black, *rose*	12.50	12.50
15	A10	1p black, *brown*	35.00	35.00
16	A11	2r black, *green*	2,000.	

Typeset varieties exist: 4 of the 10c, 2 each of 50c and 1p.

Some experts doubt that No. 16 was issued. The variety without signature and watermarked "flowers" is believed to be a proof. Forgeries exist.

       A12

1886			Litho.	
17	A12	5c blue	.75	.75
18	A12	10c red	4.50	4.50
19	A12	10c red, *lilac*	2.50	2.50
20	A12	20c green	3.75	3.75
a.		20c yellow green	4.50	4.50
21	A12	50c purple	5.00	5.00
22	A12	1p orange brown	5.25	5.25
		Nos. 17-22 (6)	21.75	21.75

Nos. 17 to 22 have been reprinted. The colors are aniline and differ from those of the original stamps. The impression is coarse and blurred.

A13   A14

A15   A16

A17   A18

A19   A20

A21

1904			Perf. 10½, 12		
23	A13	1c orange		.25	.25
24	A14	2c gray blue		.25	.25
25	A15	3c rose		.35	.35
26	A15	5c olive grn		.35	.35
27	A16	10c pale brn		.35	.35
28	A17	15c pink		.35	.35
29	A18	20c blue, *grn*		.35	.35
30	A18	20c blue		.60	.60
31	A19	40c blue		.60	.60
32	A19	40c blue, *buff*		17.50	17.50
33	A20	50c red vio		.60	.60
34	A21	1p gray grn		.45	.45
		Nos. 23-34 (12)		22.00	22.00

			Imperf		
23a	A13	1c orange		.75	.75
24a	A14	2c blue		.75	.75
b.		2c slate		6.00	6.00
25a	A15	3c rose		.90	.90
26a	A15	5c olive green		1.50	1.50
27a	A16	10c pale brown		2.00	2.00
28a	A17	15c pink		.50	.50
29a	A18	20c blue, green		2.00	2.00
30a	A18	20c blue		2.00	2.00
31a	A19	40c blue		.70	.70
32a	A19	40c blue, *buff*		17.50	17.50
33a	A20	50c red violet		.70	.70
34a	A21	1p gray green		.70	.70
		Nos. 23a-34a (12)		30.00	30.00

REGISTRATION STAMPS

R1

1883		Unwmk.		Imperf.	
F1	R1	black, *orange*		15.00	16.00

R2

1904				**Perf. 12**	
F2	R2	10c bister		.80	.80
a.		Imperf.		3.50	3.50

Magdalena

Items inscribed "No hay estampillas" (No stamps available) are considered by specialists to be not postage stamps but receipt labels.

Panama

Issues of Panama as a state and later Department of Colombia are listed with the Republic of Panama issues (Nos. 1-30).

SANTANDER

¸sän-¸tän-'de͜ə r

Originally a State, now a Department of the Republic of Colombia. (See Antioquia.)

Coat of Arms
A1   A2

1884		Unwmk.	Litho.	Imperf.	
1	A1	1c blue		.30	.30
		1c gray blue		.50	.50
2	A2	5c red		.50	.50
3	A2	10c bluish purple		1.75	1.75
a.		Tête bêche pair			
		Nos. 1-3 (3)		2.55	2.55

No. 2 exists unofficially perforated 14.

A3   A4

1886   *Imperf.*

4	A3	1c blue	.90	.90
5	A3	5c red	.30	.30
6	A3	10c red violet	.50	.50
a.		10c deep violet	.50	.50
b.		Inscribed "CINCO CENTAVOS"	25.00	25.00
		Nos. 4-6 (3)	1.70	1.70

The numerals in the upper corners are omitted on No. 5, while on No. 6 there are no numerals in the side panels. No. 6 exists unofficially perforated 12.

1887

7	A4	1c blue	.25	.25
a.		1c ultramarine	1.60	1.60
8	A4	5c red	1.60	1.60
9	A4	10c violet	5.00	5.00
		Nos. 7-9 (3)	6.85	6.85

A5   A6

A7

1889   *Perf. 11½ and 13½*

10	A5	1c blue	.30	.30
11	A6	5c red	1.25	1.25
12	A7	10c purple	.45	.45
a.		Imperf., pair	16.00	
		Nos. 10-12 (3)	2.00	2.00

A8   A9

1892   *Perf. 13½*

13	A8	5c red, *rose buff*	1.00	1.00

1895-96

14	A9	5c brown	.70	.70
15	A9	5c yel grn ('96)	.70	.70

A10   A11

A12

1899   *Perf. 10*

16	A10	1c black, *green*	.35	.35
17	A11	5c black, *pink*	.35	.35

               Perf. 13½

18	A12	10c blue	.70	.70
a.		Perf. 12	1.00	1.00
		Nos. 16-18 (3)	1.40	1.40

A13

1903   *Imperf.*

19	A13	50c red	.55	.55
a.		50c rose	.55	.55
b.		"SANTENDER"	2.50	2.50
c.		"Corrcos"	2.50	2.50
d.		"Corceos"	2.50	2.50
e.		Tête bêche pair	4.75	4.75
f.		Pair, one without overprint	2.75	2.75

The overprint "Correos de Departmento Bucaramanga" on the 50c red revenue stamp has been proved to be a cancellation.

A14   A15

Arms   Locomotive
A16   A17

A18   A19

A20

1904   *Imperf.*

22	A14	5c dark green	.25	.25
a.		5c yellow green	.40	.40
24	A15	10c rose	.20	.20
25	A16	20c brown violet	.20	.20
26	A17	50c yellow	.20	.20
27	A18	1p black	.20	.20
28	A19	5p dark blue	.35	.35
29	A20	10p carmine	.40	.40
		Nos. 22-29 (7)	1.80	1.80

1905

30	A14	5c pale blue	.40	.40
31	A15	10c red brown	.40	.40
32	A16	20c yellow green	.40	.40
33	A17	50c red violet	.60	.60
34	A18	1p dark blue	.60	.60
35	A19	5p pink	.60	.60
36	A20	10p red	1.60	1.60
		Nos. 30-36 (7)	4.60	4.60

A21

1907   *Imperf.*

37	A21	½c on 50c rose	.55	.55

City of Cucuta

A6   A7

Stamps of these and similar designs on white and yellow paper, with and without surcharges of ½c, 1c or 2c, are believed to have been produced without government authorization.

TOLIMA

tə-lē-mə

Originally a State, now a Department of the Republic of Colombia. (See Antioquia.)

A1

1870   **Unwmk.**   **Typeset**   *Imperf.*
White Wove Paper

1	A1	5c black	50.00	50.00
2	A1	10c black	75.00	75.00
a.		Vert. se-tenant pair	1,500.	1,500.

Printed from two settings. Setting I, ten types of 5c. Setting II, six types of 5c and four types of 10c.

Blue Laid Batonné Paper

3	A1	5c black	950.00	

Buff Laid Batonné Paper

4	A1	5c black	150.00	100.00

Blue Wove Paper

5	A1	5c black	70.00	45.00

Blue Vertically Laid Paper

6	A1	5c black	100.00	75.00
a.		Paper with ruled blue vertical lines		

Blue Horizontally Laid Paper

7	A1	5c black	200.00	150.00

Blue Quadrille Paper

8	A1	5c black	100.00	75.00

Ten varieties each of Nos. 3-5 and 7; 20 varieties each of Nos. 6 and 8.

Official imitations were made in 1886 from new settings of the type. There are only 2 varieties of each value. They are printed on blue and white paper, wove, batonné, laid, etc.

A2   A3

A4   A5

Yellowish White Wove Paper

1871   **Litho.**   *Imperf.*

9	A2	5c deep brown	2.25	2.25
a.		5c red brown	2.25	2.25
b.		Value reads "CINGO"	37.50	37.50
10	A3	10c blue	6.00	6.00
11	A4	50c green	7.75	7.75
12	A5	1p carmine	12.00	12.00
		Nos. 9-12 (4)	28.00	28.00

The 5p stamps, type A2, are bogus varieties made from an altered die of the 5c.

The 10c, 50c and 1 peso stamps have been reprinted on bluish white wove paper. They are from new plates and most examples show traces of fine lines with which the dies had been defaced. Reprints of the 5c have a large cross at the top. The 10c on laid batonné paper is known only as a reprint.

A6   A7

A8   A9

1879
Grayish or White Wove Paper

14	A6	5c yellow brown	.45	.45
a.		5c purple brown	.45	.45
15	A7	10c blue	.50	.50
16	A8	50c green, *bluish*	.50	.50
a.		White paper	1.60	1.60
17	A9	1p vermilion	2.25	2.25
a.		1p carmine rose	9.00	9.00
		Nos. 14-17 (4)	3.70	3.70

A10   Coat of
          Arms — A12

1883   *Imperf.*

18	A6	5c orange	.45	.45
19	A7	10c vermilion	.90	.90
20	A10	20c violet	1.40	1.40
		Nos. 18-20 (3)	2.75	2.75

1884   *Imperf.*

23	A12	1c gray	.20	.20
24	A12	2c rose lilac	.20	.20
a.		2c slate	.20	.20
25	A12	2½c dull orange	.20	.20
26	A12	5c brown	.20	.20
27	A12	10c blue	.35	.35
a.		10c slate	.25	.25
28	A12	20c lemon	.35	.35
a.		Laid paper	5.00	5.00
29	A12	25c black	.30	.30
30	A12	50c green	.30	.30
31	A12	1p vermilion	.40	.40
32	A12	2p violet	.60	.60
a.		Value omitted	27.50	27.50
33	A12	5p yellow	.40	.40
34	A12	10p lilac rose	1.10	1.10
a.		Laid paper	30.00	30.00
b.		10p gray	160.00	
		Nos. 23-34 (12)	4.60	4.60

A13   A14

Condor with Long Wings
Touching Flagstaffs
A15   A16

1886   **Litho.**   *Perf. 10½, 11*
White Paper

36	A13	5c brown	1.25	1.25
a.		5c yellow brown	1.25	1.25
b.		Imperf., pair	16.00	
37	A14	10c blue	3.50	3.50
a.		Imperf., pair	16.00	
38	A15	50c green	3.00	3.00
a.		Imperf., pair	16.00	
39	A16	1p vermilion	2.50	2.50
a.		Imperf., pair	24.00	
		Nos. 36-39 (4)	10.25	10.25

No. 38 has been reprinted in pale gray green, perforated 10½, and No. 39 in bright vermilion, perforated 11½. The impressions show many signs of wear.

Lilac Tinted Paper

36c	A13	5c orange brown	12.00	12.00
37b	A14	10c blue	12.00	12.00
38b	A15	50c green	9.00	9.00
39b	A16	1p vermilion	8.00	8.00
		Nos. 36c-39b (4)	41.00	41.00

Items similar to A15 and A16 but with condor with long wings and upper flagstaffs omitted are forgeries.

A17

A18

A19

A20

Condor with Short Wings

1886		White Paper		Perf. 12	
44	A19	1c gray		6.25	6.25
45	A17	2c rose lilac		6.50	6.50
46	A18	2½c dull org		19.00	19.00
47	A19	5c brown		8.50	8.00
48	A20	10c blue		8.00	8.00
49	A20	20c lemon		6.50	6.50
a.		Tête bêche pair		225.00	225.00
50	A20	25c black		6.25	6.25
51	A20	50c green		3.50	3.00
52	A20	1p vermilion		5.00	4.25
53	A20	2p violet		7.25	7.25
b.		Tête bêche pair		175.00	175.00
54	A20	5p orange		13.00	13.00
55	A20	10p lilac rose		7.25	7.25
		Nos. 44-55 (12)		97.00	95.25

Imperf., Pairs

44a	A19	1c	16.00	
47a	A19	5c	27.50	
48a	A20	10c	27.50	
52a	A20	1p	20.00	
53a	A20	2p	25.00	
54a	A20	5p	32.50	
55a	A20	10p	16.00	

A23

1888			Perf. 10½	
62	A23	5c red	.20	.20
63	A23	10c green	.30	.30
64	A23	50c blue	.75	.75
65	A23	1p red brown	1.75	1.75
		Nos. 62-65 (4)	3.00	3.00

For overprint see Colombia No. L14.

1895			Perf. 12, 13½	
66	A23	1c blue, rose	.25	.25
67	A23	2c grn, lt grn	.25	.25
68	A23	5c red	.20	.20
69	A23	10c green	.50	.50
70	A23	20c blue, yellow	.30	.30
71	A23	1p brown	2.00	2.00
		Nos. 66-71 (6)	3.50	3.50

Imperf., Pairs

62a	A23	5c	2.75	
63a	A23	10c	3.25	
64a	A23	50c	4.75	4.75
65a	A23	1p	7.25	
66a	A23	1c	7.25	
67a	A23	2c	7.25	
70a	A23	20c	8.00	

"No Hay Estampillas"
Items inscribed "No hay estampillas" (No stamps available) are considered by specialists to be not postage stamps but receipt labels.

"Honda Issue"
This item seems to be of private origin.

A24

A25

A26

A27

A28

A29

A30

A31

1903-04		Sewing Machine or Regular Perf. 12			
				Litho.	
79	A24	4c black, green		.25	.25
80	A25	10c dull blue		.25	.25
81	A26	20c orange		.50	.50
82	A27	50c black, rose		.25	.25
a.		50c black, buff		.20	.20
84	A28	1p brown		.20	.20
85	A29	2p gray		.20	.20
86	A30	5p red		.20	.20
a.		Tête bêche pair		5.00	5.00
87	A31	10p black, blue		.25	.25
a.		10p black, light green		.25	.25
b.		10p black, grn, glazed		3.50	3.50
		Nos. 79-87 (8)		2.10	2.10

Imperf

79a	A24	4c black, green	.25	.25
80a	A25	10c dull blue	.20	.20
81a	A26	20c orange	1.10	1.10
82b	A27	50c black, rose	1.50	1.50
c.		50c black, buff	1.50	1.50
84a	A28	1p brown	.20	.20
85a	A29	2p gray	.25	.25
86b	A30	5p red	.25	.25
87c	A31	10p black, blue	2.25	2.25
d.		Tête bêche pair		
e.		10p black, light green	3.50	3.50
f.		10p black, green, glazed	18.00	18.00
		Nos. 79a-87c (8)	6.00	6.00

COMORO ISLANDS

ˈkä-mə-ˌrō ˈī-lənds

LOCATION — In Mozambique Channel between Madagascar and Mozambique
GOVT. — Republic
AREA — 838 sq. mi.
POP. — 562,723 (1999 est.)
CAPITAL — Moroni

The Comoro Archipelago consists of the islands of Mayotte, Anjouan, Grand

Comoro (Grande Comore) and Moheli, which issued their own stamps as French protectorates or colonies from 1887-1914. The archipelago was attached to Madagascar from 1914 to 1946, when it became a separate French territory. In July 1975, Anjouan, Grand Comoro and Moheli united to declare independence as the State of Comoro. Mayotte remained French.

100 Centimes = 1 Franc

Catalogue values for all unused stamps in this country are for Never Hinged items.

Anjouan Bay — A2

Comoro Woman Grinding Grain — A3

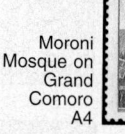
Moroni Mosque on Grand Comoro A4

1950		Unwmk.	Engr.	Perf. 13	
30	A2	10c blue		.30	.30
31	A2	50c green		.30	.30
32	A2	1fr dk ol brn		.30	.30
33	A3	2fr brt grn		.70	.55
34	A3	5fr purple		1.10	.90
35	A3	6fr vio brn		1.40	1.00
36	A4	7fr red		1.40	1.00
37	A4	10fr dk grn		1.40	1.00
38	A4	11fr dp ultra		1.50	1.25
		Nos. 30-38 (9)		8.40	6.60

Imperforates
Most Comoro Islands stamps exist imperforate in issued and trial colors, and also in small presentation sheets in issued colors.

Common Design Types pictured following the introduction.

Military Medal Issue
Common Design Type

1952		Engraved and Typographed		
39	CD101	15fr multi		50.00	32.50

Mosque of Ouani, Anjouan — A5

Coelacanth A6

1952-54			Engr.	
40	A5	15fr dark brown	2.25	2.00
41	A5	20fr red brown	3.75	3.50
42	A6	40fr aqua & indigo ('54)	26.00	15.00
		Nos. 40-42 (3)	32.00	20.50

FIDES Issue
Common Design Type

1956		Unwmk.	Perf. 13x12½	
43	CD103	9fr dp vio	1.75	1.00

Human Rights Issue
Common Design Type

1958		Engr.	Perf. 13	
44	CD105	20fr ol grn & dk bl	11.00	11.00

Flower Issue
Common Design Type

1959		Photo.	Perf. 12½x12	
45	CD104	10fr Colvillea	5.50	3.50

View of Dzaoudzi and Radio Symbol A8

Comoro radio station: 25fr, Radio tower and radio waves over Islands.

1960, Dec. 23		Engr.	Perf. 13	
46	A8	20fr maroon, vio bl & grn	1.60	.90
47	A8	25fr ultra, brn & grn	2.00	1.00

Harpa Conoidalis — A9

Sea Shells: 50c, Cypraecassis rufa. 2fr, Murex ramosus. 5fr, Turbo marmoratus. 20fr, Pterocera scorpio. 25fr, Charonia tritonis.

1962, Jan. 13			Photo.	
		Shells in Natural Colors		
48	A9	50c lilac & brn	1.25	1.25
49	A9	1fr yel & red	1.25	1.25
50	A9	2fr pale grn & pink	2.75	2.75
51	A9	5fr yel & grn	4.25	4.25
52	A9	20fr salmon & brn	11.50	11.50
53	A9	25fr bister & pink	14.00	14.00
		Nos. 48-53,C5-C6 (8)	81.00	70.50

Wheat Emblem and Globe A10

1963, Mar. 21		Engr.	Perf. 13	
54	A10	20fr choc & dk grn	5.50	3.50

FAO "Freedom from Hunger" campaign.

Red Cross Centenary Issue
Common Design Type

1963, Sept. 2		Unwmk.	Perf. 13	
55	CD113	50fr emer, gray & car	9.00	6.00

Human Rights Issue
Common Design Type

1963, Dec. 10			Engr.	
56	CD117	15fr dk red & yel grn	9.00	6.00

Tobacco Pouch — A13

Grand Comoro Canoe — A14

Designs: 4fr, Censer. 10fr, Carved lamp.

1963, Dec. 27   **Perf. 13**
Size: 22x36mm
57 A13 3fr multi .95 .95
58 A13 4fr org, dp cl & sl grn 1.00 1.00
59 A13 10fr org brn, dk red brn & grn 1.90 1.90
Nos. 57-59,C8-C9 (5) 18.85 10.60

Philatec Issue
Common Design Type
1964, Mar. 31
60 CD118 50fr dk bl, red & grn 4.50 4.50

1964, Aug. 7 Photo. Perf. 13x12½
Design: 30fr, Boutre felucca.
Size: 22x37mm
61 A14 15fr multi 3.50 3.50
62 A14 30fr lt grn & multi 5.50 5.50
Nos. 61-62,C10-C11 (4) 20.50 12.50

Spiny Lobster — A15

Designs: 12fr, Hammerhead shark, horiz. 20fr, Turtle, horiz. 25fr, Merou fish.

1965, Dec. 20 Engr. Perf. 13
63 A15 1fr grn, lil & ocher .90 .50
64 A15 12fr org red, slate & gray 2.10 1.25
65 A15 20fr org, red & bl grn 4.25 2.10
66 A15 25fr bl grn, dk brn & red 6.75 2.50
Nos. 63-66 (4) 14.00 6.35

Hotel Itsandra, Moroni A16

Design: 15fr, Lake Salé, Grand Comoro.

1966, Dec. 19 Photo. Perf. 12½x13
67 A16 15fr multi 1.10 .60
68 A16 25fr multi 1.40 .80
Nos. 67-68,C18-C19 (4) 16.50 9.40

Comoro Sunbird A17

Birds: 10fr, Malachite kingfisher. 15fr, Rothschild's fody. 30fr, Cuckoo-roller.

1967, June 20 Photo. Perf. 12½x13
Size: 36x23mm
69 A17 2fr ocher & multi 1.90 1.90
70 A17 10fr lil & multi 5.25 4.00
71 A17 15fr yel grn & multi 6.25 5.00
72 A17 30fr pink & multi 12.00 12.00
Nos. 69-72,C20-C21 (6) 47.65 34.90
For surcharge see No. 133.

WHO Anniversary Issue
Common Design Type
1968, May 4 Engr. Perf. 13
73 CD126 40fr grn, vio & dp car 2.50 1.90

Surgeonfish A19

Design: 25fr, Imperial angelfish.

1968, Aug. 1 Engr. Perf. 13
Size: 36x22mm
74 A19 20fr vio bl, yel & red brn 3.50 2.50
75 A19 25fr Prus bl, dk bl & org 4.25 4.25
Nos. 74-75,C23-C24 (4) 25.75 14.00
For surcharge & overprint see #C52, C74.

Human Rights Year Issue
Common Design Type
1968, Aug. 10 Engr. Perf. 13
76 CD127 60fr brn, grn & org 3.50 3.50

Msoila Prayer Rug and Praying Man — A20

Each stamp shows a different prayer position.

1969, Feb. 27 Engr. Perf. 13
77 A20 20fr bl grn, rose red & pur 1.25 .60
78 A20 30fr pur, rose red & bl grn 1.60 1.10
79 A20 45fr rose red, pur & bl grn 2.75 1.50
Nos. 77-79 (3) 5.60 3.20

Vanilla Flower A21

Design: 15fr, Flower of ylang-ylang tree. 25fr, Poinsettia (country name at upper left).

1969-70 Photo. Perf. 12½x13
Size: 36x23mm
80 A21 10fr multi 1.75 .60
81 A21 15fr multi 2.10 .80
82 A21 25fr multi ('70) 3.25 1.50
Nos. 80-82,C26-C28 (6) 27.10 13.65
Issue dates: #80-81, Mar. 20. #82, Mar. 5.

ILO Issue
Common Design Type
1969, Nov. 24 Engr. Perf. 13
83 CD131 5fr org, emerald & gray 1.40 .80

UPU Headquarters Issue
Common Design Type
1970, May 20 Engr. Perf. 13
84 CD133 65fr pur, bl grn & red brn 5.50 2.10

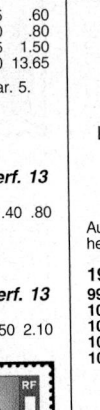

Chiromani Costume, Anjouan — A22

Friday Mosque — A23

25fr, Bouiboui costume, Grand Comoro.

1970, Oct. 30 Photo. Perf. 12½x13
85 A22 20fr grn, yel & red 1.40 .90
86 A22 25fr brn, yel & dk bl 1.90 .95

1970, Dec. 18 Engr. Perf. 13
87 A23 5fr rose car, grn & grnsh bl .75 .75
88 A23 10fr dk lil, grn & vio 1.00 1.00
89 A23 40fr cop red, grn & dp brn 1.75 1.75
Nos. 87-89 (3) 3.50 3.50

Great White Egret — A24

Pyrostegia Venusta — A25

Birds: 10fr, Comoro pigeon. 15fr, Green-backed heron. 25fr, Comoro blue pigeon. 35fr, Humbolt's flycatcher. 40fr, Allen's gallinule.

1971, Mar. 12 Photo. Perf. 12½x13
90 A24 5fr multi 1.50 .50
91 A24 10fr yel & multi 2.00 .50
92 A24 15fr bl & multi 3.25 1.40
93 A24 25fr org & multi 4.75 1.60
94 A24 35fr yel grn & multi 6.50 2.00
95 A24 40fr gray & multi 8.00 2.75
Nos. 90-95 (6) 26.00 8.75
For overprint see No. 145.

1971, July 19 Photo. Perf. 13
Flowers: 3fr, Dogbane, horiz. 20fr, Frangipani.
Size: 22x36mm, 36x22mm
96 A25 1fr ver & grn .90 .60
97 A25 3fr yel, grn & red 1.40 .90
98 A25 20fr ver & grn 3.50 2.10
Nos. 96-98,C37-C38 (5) 17.30 9.35
For surcharges see Nos. 131-132, C75, C83.

Lithograph Cone A26

Sea Shells: 10fr, Pacific lettered cone. 20fr, Aulicus cone. 35fr, Polita nerita. 60fr, Snakehead cowrie.

1971, Oct. 4
99 A26 5fr lt ultra & multi 1.00 .80
100 A26 10fr multi 1.40 1.00
101 A26 20fr vio & multi 3.25 1.75
102 A26 35fr lt bl & multi 7.25 2.10
103 A26 60fr lt vio & multi 8.50 3.00
Nos. 99-103 (5) 21.40 8.65
For surcharge see No. 150.

De Gaulle Issue
Common Design Type
Designs: 20fr, Gen. de Gaulle, 1940. 35fr, Pres. de Gaulle, 1970.
1971, Nov. 9 Engr. Perf. 13
104 CD134 20fr dk car & blk 3.50 2.50
105 CD134 35fr dk car & blk 4.50 3.25

Louis Pasteur, Slides, Microscope A27

1972, Aug. 2
106 A27 65fr indigo, org, & ol brn 5.00 3.50
Sesquicentennial of the birth of Louis Pasteur (1822-1895), chemist.

Type of Air Post Issue 1971
Designs: 10fr, View of Goulaivoini. 20fr, Bay, Mitsamiouli. 35fr, Gate and fountain, Foumbouni. 50fr, View of Moroni.
1973, June 28 Photo. Perf. 13
107 AP10 10fr bl & multi .85 .50
108 AP10 20fr grn & multi 1.40 .80
109 AP10 35fr bl & multi 2.00 1.25
110 AP10 50fr bl & multi 2.25 1.75
Nos. 107-110,C53 (5) 16.00 8.55
For overprint see No. 143.

Bank of Madagascar and Comoros — A28

Buildings in Moroni: 15fr, Post and Telecommunications Administration. 20fr, Prefecture.
1973, July 10 Photo. Perf. 13x12½
111 A28 5fr multi .55 .35
112 A28 15fr multi .80 .65
113 A28 20fr multi 1.25 .95
Nos. 111-113 (3) 2.60 1.95
For surcharge see No. 134.

Salimata Hamissi Mosque A29

20fr, Zaouiyat Chaduli Mosque, vert.
Perf. 12½x13, 13x12½
1973, Oct. 20 Photo.
114 A29 20fr multi 1.25 .75
115 A29 35fr multi 1.90 1.00
For surcharges see Nos. 135, 138.

Cheikh Mausoleum A30

Design: 50fr, Mausoleum of President Said Mohamed Cheikh (different view).
1974, Mar. 16 Engr. Perf. 13
116 A30 35fr grn, ol brn & blk 1.60 1.10
117 A30 50fr grn, ol brn & blk 2.25 1.50
For surcharge see No. 140.

Koran Stand, Anjouan A31

Designs: 15fr, Carved combs, vert. 20fr, 3-legged table, vert. 75fr, Sugar press.

1974, May 10 Photo. Perf. 12½x13

118	A31	15fr emer & multi	1.25	.90
119	A31	20fr grn & multi	1.60	.90
120	A31	35fr multi	2.25	1.50
121	A31	75fr multi	4.25	2.60
	Nos. 118-121 (4)		9.35	5.90

For overprints and surcharge see #137, 141, 149.

UPU Emblem, Symbolic Postmark A32

1974, Oct. 9 Engr. Perf. 13x12½

122	A32	30fr multi	1.75	1.75

Centenary of Universal Postal Union.
For surcharge see No. 155.

Bracelet A33

1975, Feb. 28 Engr. Perf. 13

123	A33	20fr shown	1.00	.75
124	A33	35fr Diadem	1.75	1.10
125	A33	120fr Saber	4.75	3.00
126	A33	135fr Dagger	7.00	3.50
	Nos. 123-126 (4)		14.50	8.35

For surcharges see Nos. 136, 142, 151, 154.

Mohani Village, Moheli — A34

50fr, Djoezi Village, Moheli. 55fr, Chirazi tombs.

1975, May 26 Photo. Perf. 13

127	A34	30fr vio bl & multi	1.60	1.10
128	A34	50fr Prus bl & multi	2.75	1.50
129	A34	55fr grn & multi	4.00	2.50
	Nos. 127-129 (3)		8.35	5.10

For overprints and surcharge see #139, 146, 148.

Scuba Diver Photographing Coelacanth — A35

1975, June 27 Engr. Perf. 13

130	A35	50fr multi	8.25	5.25

1975 coelacanth expedition.
For overprint see No. 147.

STATE OF COMORO

In 1978 the islands' name became the Federal and Islamic Republic of the Comoros.

Issues of 1971-75 Surcharged and Overprinted with Bars and: "ETAT COMORIEN" in Black, Silver or Red.

Tambourine Player — A36

#153, Women dancers & tambourine players.

Printing & Perforations as Before, Photogravure (A36)

1975 Perf. 13 (A36)

131	A25	5fr on 1fr	1.00	.20
132	A25	5fr on 3fr	1.00	.20
133	A17	10fr on 2fr	1.00	.30
134	A28	15fr on 20fr (R)	.20	.20
135	A29	15fr on 20fr (S)	.20	.20
136	A33	15fr on 20fr	.20	.20
137	A31	20fr	.20	.20
138	A29	25fr on 35fr	.20	.20
139	A34	30fr	.40	.25
140	A30	30fr on 35fr	.80	.25
141	A31	30fr on 35fr	.80	.25
142	A33	30fr on 35fr	.40	.25
143	AP10	35fr	.40	.25
144	SP2	35fr on 35fr + 10fr	.40	.25
145	A24	40fr	2.50	.30
146	A34	50fr	.50	.40
147	A35	50fr	3.75	.40
148	A34	50fr on 55fr (S)	.90	.40
149	A31	75fr	2.10	.60
150	A26	75fr on 60fr (S)	3.75	.60
151	A33	100fr on 120fr	2.10	.80
152	A36	100fr bl & multi	6.75	.80
153	A36	100fr on 150fr (S)	6.75	.80
154	A33	200fr on 135fr	5.00	2.00
155	A32	500fr on 30fr	8.75	5.00
	Nos. 131-155 (25)		50.05	15.40

Nos. 152-153 exist without overprint or surcharge. Value, each $75.
No. 155 exists with red surcharge.

Litho. & Embossed "Gold Foil" Stamps
These stamps generally are of a different design format than the rest of the issue. Since there is a commemorative inscription tieing them to the issue a separate illustration is not being shown.

Apollo-Soyuz — A37

Spacecraft and astronauts: 10fr, Soyuz lift-off, Alexei A. Leonov and Valeri N. Kubasov, vert. 30fr, Apollo lift-off, Thomas P. Stafford, Vance D. Brand, Donald K. Slayton, vert. 50fr, Meeting in space. 100fr, Chairman Brezhnev, President Ford talking with astronauts and cosmonauts. 200fr, Spacecraft preparing to dock. 400f, Return to Earth. 500fr, Spacecraft, mission emblems. 1500fr, Apollo-Soyuz crew. No. 164, Preparing to dock, diff.

1975, Dec. 15 Litho. Perf. 13½

156	A37	10fr multicolored	.20	.20
157	A37	30fr multicolored	.50	.25
158	A37	50fr multicolored	.80	.55
159	A37	100fr multicolored	1.40	.60
160	A37	200fr multicolored	2.75	1.25
161	A37	400fr multicolored	5.00	2.50
	Nos. 156-161 (6)		10.65	5.35

Litho. & Embossed
Size: 45x45mm

162	A37	1500fr gold & multi	17.50	—

Souvenir Sheets
Litho.

163	A37	500fr multicolored	5.50	1.75

Litho. & Embossed

164	A37	1500fr gold & multi	17.50	—

Nos. 159-164 are airmail. No. 163 contains one 64x44mm stamp. No. 164 contains one 45x45mm stamp.
No. 162 exists in a souvenir sheet of 1. Value $50.
For overprints see Nos. 477-478.

A38

American Revolution, Bicent. — A39

Designs: 15fr, Lewis and Clark, Blackfoot Indian. 25fr, John C. Fremont, Kit Carson, Indian dancer. 35fr, Daniel Boone, Buffalo Bill Cody, wagon train. 40fr, Richard E. Egan, Johnny Frey, Pony Express. 75fr, Henry Wells, William G. Fargo, stagecoach. 400fr, Frontiersman, Indian. 500fr, Leland Stanford, Thomas C. Dunant, transcontinental railroad. 1000fr, George Washington, winter at Valley Forge. 1500fr, John Paul Jones, ship.

1976, Jan. 15 Litho.

165	A38	15fr multicolored	.20	.20
166	A38	25fr multicolored	.45	.25
167	A38	35fr multicolored	.75	.35
168	A38	40fr multicolored	.85	.45
169	A38	75fr multicolored	1.50	.60
170	A38	500fr multicolored	6.25	2.50
	Nos. 165-170 (6)		10.00	4.35

Litho. & Embossed

171	A39	1000fr gold & multi	13.50	—

Souvenir Sheets
Litho.

172	A38	400fr multicolored	5.50	1.75

Litho. & Embossed

173	A39	1500fr gold & multi	16.50	—

Nos. 170-173 are airmail. See Nos. 230, 232 and note after No. 479.
No. 171 exists in a souvenir sheet of 1. Value $55.

1976 Winter Olympics, Innsbruck — A40

1976, Mar. 30 Litho.

174	A40	5fr Women's figure skating	.20	.20
175	A40	30fr Slalom skiing	.25	.20
176	A40	35fr Speed skating	.35	.20
177	A40	50fr Downhill skiing	.60	.35
178	A40	200fr Ski jumping	2.10	1.00
179	A40	400fr Cross country skiing	4.50	1.25
	Nos. 174-179 (6)		8.00	3.20

Litho. & Embossed
Size: 56x35mm

180	A40	1000fr Downhill skier, hockey	13.00	—

Souvenir Sheets
Litho.

181	A40	500fr Hockey	5.50	1.75

Litho. & Embossed

182	A40	1000fr Olympic Rings	11.00	—

Nos. 178-182 are airmail. Nos. 181-182 contain one 58x35mm stamp. For overprint see No. 471.
No. 162 exists in a souvenir sheet of 1. Value $45.

1976 Summer Olympics, Montreal — A41

1976, Mar. 30 Litho.

183	A41	20fr Runner, Athens, 1896	.20	.20
184	A41	25fr Sprints	.25	.20
185	A41	40fr High jump, Paris, 1900	.45	.20
186	A41	75fr High jump	1.00	.45
187	A41	100fr Women stretching, St. Louis, 1904	1.10	.50
188	A41	500fr Uneven parallel bars	6.00	1.75
	Nos. 183-188 (6)		9.00	3.30

Souvenir Sheet

189	A41	400fr Olympic Stadium, Montreal	4.50	1.25

Nos. 187-189 are airmail.
For overprint see No. 476.

Fairy Tales — A42

1976, June 28

190	A42	15fr Hansel & Gretel	.20	.20
191	A42	30fr Alice in Wonderland	.50	.20
192	A42	35fr Pinocchio	.65	.25
193	A42	40fr Good Little Henry	.65	.25
194	A42	50fr Peter and the Wolf	1.00	.25
195	A42	400fr Thousand and One Nights	6.50	2.00
	Nos. 190-195 (6)		9.50	3.10

#195 is airmail. #190-191, 193, 195 are vert.

Invention of Telephone, Cent. — A43

Designs: 10fr, A. G. Bell, 1st telephone. 25fr, Charles Bourseul, Paris-London phone service, 1891. 75fr, Philipp Reis, telephone operators. 100fr, Earth to Moon to Earth communications. 200fr, Satellite. 400fr, Ship-to-Satellite communications. No. 201, Satellite in orbit, antenna. No. 203, Global communications.

1976, July 1

196	A43	10fr multicolored	.20	.20
197	A43	25fr multicolored	.25	.20
198	A43	75fr multicolored	.75	.30
199	A43	100fr multicolored	1.00	.20
200	A43	200fr multicolored	2.25	.90
201	A43	500fr multicolored	5.50	1.75
	Nos. 196-201 (6)		9.95	3.85

Souvenir Sheets

202	A43	400fr multicolored	4.50	1.25
203	A43	500fr multicolored	5.50	1.75

Nos. 199-203 are airmail. Nos. 202-203 contain a 73x44mm stamp. For overprint see No. 472.

Comoro Flag, Map and Government
Buildings — A44

1976, Nov. 18   Litho.   Perf. 13½
204	A44	30fr multi	.75	.30
205	A44	50fr multi	1.25	.30

1st anniversary of independence.
For overprints and surcharges see Nos.
353-372.

Viking Probe to
Mars — A45

Designs: 5fr, Nicolaus Copernicus, rocket
launch. 10fr, Albert Einstein, Carl Sagan,
Thomas Young, horiz. 25fr, Viking probe orbiting Mars. 35fr, Discovery of America by Vikings, horiz. 100fr, Flag, Viking landing on
Mars. 500fr, Viking emblem, surface of Mars,
horiz. 400fr, Viking probe. No. 212, Wagon
train, frontiersman, rocket launch. No. 214,
Viking on Martian surface, robotic shovel.

1976, Nov. 23
206	A45	5fr multicolored	.20	.20
207	A45	10fr multicolored	.20	.20
208	A45	25fr multicolored	.25	.30
209	A45	35fr multicolored	1.10	.30
210	A45	100fr multicolored	1.75	.40
211	A45	500fr multicolored	10.50	1.50
		Nos. 206-211 (6)	14.00	2.90

Litho. & Embossed
Size: 57x39mm
212	A45	1500fr gold & multi	14.00	—

Souvenir Sheets
Litho.
213	A45	400fr multicolored	5.00	1.50

Litho. & Embossed
214	A45	1500fr gold & multi	15.00	—

American Revolution, bicentennial. Nos.
211-214 are airmail. No. 213 contains one
60x42mm stamp.
No. 212 exists in a souvenir sheet of 1.
Value $50.

UN Postal Administration, 25th
Anniv. — A46

Designs: 15fr, UN #24, irrigating field. 30fr,
UN #43, doctor, nurse. 50fr, UN #162, mother
holding child. 75fr, UN #42, communications
satellite in orbit. 200fr, UN #32, Concorde,
Zeppelin. 400fr, UN #18, cargo plane. 500fr,
People passing letters around globe.

1976, Nov. 25   Litho.
215	A46	15fr multicolored	.20	.20
216	A46	30fr multicolored	.30	.20
217	A46	50fr multicolored	.60	.30
218	A46	75fr multicolored	.80	.30
219	A46	200fr multicolored	2.50	.50
220	A46	400fr multicolored	5.00	1.50
		Nos. 215-220 (6)	9.40	3.00

Souvenir Sheet
221	A46	500fr multicolored	5.00	2.00

Nos. 219-221 are airmail. No. 221 contains
one 57x40mm stamp. For overprints see Nos.
282-284, 473.

Comoro Flag, UN Headquarters and
Emblem — A47

1976, Nov. 25
222	A47	40fr multi	1.40	.30
223	A47	50fr multi	1.90	.40

1st anniv. of UN membership.

Type of 1976 and

US Bicentennial — A48

Civil War Battles: 10fr, Fort Sumter, Lincoln.
30fr, Bull Run, Gen. P.G.T. Beauregard, vert.
50fr, Antietam, Gen. Joseph E. Johnston.
100fr, Gettysburg, Gen. Meade. 200fr, Chatta-
nooga, Gen. Sherman, vert. 400fr, Appomat-
tox, Gen. Pickett. 500fr, Surrender at Appo-
mattox, Generals Lee and Grant. 1000fr,
Lincoln, battlefield. No. 230, Pres. Kennedy,
lunar lander.

1976, Dec. 30   Litho.
224	A48	10fr multicolored	.20	.20
225	A48	30fr multicolored	.30	.20
226	A48	50fr multicolored	.65	.25
227	A48	100fr multicolored	1.10	.45
228	A48	200fr multicolored	2.50	.80
229	A48	400fr multicolored	5.00	1.50
		Nos. 224-229 (6)	9.75	3.40

Litho. & Embossed
Size: 61x51mm
230	A39	1500fr gold & multi	17.00	—

Souvenir Sheets
Litho.
231	A48	500fr multicolored	6.50	1.75

Litho. & Embossed
232	A39	1000fr gold & multi	9.50	—

American Revolution bicentennial. Nos.
227-232 are airmail. No. 231 contains one
60x42mm stamp.
No. 230 exists in a souvenir sheet of 1.
Value $50.

Endangered Species — A49

1976, Dec. 30   Litho.
233	A49	15fr Andean condor, vert.	.30	.20
234	A49	20fr Australian tiger cat	.45	.20
235	A49	35fr Leopard, vert.	1.00	.20
236	A49	40fr White rhinocer-os	1.25	.45
237	A49	75fr Nyala, vert.	3.00	.55
238	A49	400fr Orangutan	8.00	1.50
		Nos. 233-239 (7)	21.00	4.85

Souvenir Sheet
239	A49	500fr Lemur, vert.	7.00	1.75

Nos. 238-239 airmail. No. 239 contains one
40x58mm stamp.
See note after No. 479.

Endangered Species — A50

1977, Apr. 14
240	A50	10fr Wolf	.20	.20
241	A50	30fr Aye-aye	.45	.20
242	A50	40fr Cephalopus ze-bra	.85	.20
243	A50	50fr Giant tortoise	1.00	.25
244	A50	200fr Ocelot	3.25	.75
245	A50	400fr Penguin	6.25	1.50
		Nos. 240-245 (6)	12.00	3.15

Souvenir Sheet
246	A50	500fr Sumatran tiger	8.50	1.50

Nos. 244-246 airmail. No. 246 contains one
58x40mm stamp.

Giffard
Airship, 1851
and Paris-St.
Germain
Train, 1837,
France — A51

Airships & Locomotives: 25fr, Santos-
Dumont's airship, 1906, Brazilian Tander
120FIN, Brazil. 50fr, Astra, 1914, Trans-Sibe-
rian Express, 1905, Russia. 75fr, R.34, 1919,
Southern Belle, 1910, Great Britain. 200fr,
Navy airship, Pacific Class locomotive, 1930,
US. No. 252, Hindenburg, Rheingold Express,
1933, Germany. No. 253, Graf-Zeppelin,
1928, Nord-Express Type 231, 1925,
Germany.

1977, Apr. 14
247	A51	20fr multicolored	.30	.20
248	A51	25fr multicolored	.30	.20
249	A51	50fr multicolored	.75	.25
250	A51	75fr multicolored	1.10	.25
251	A51	200fr multicolored	2.75	.60
252	A51	500fr multicolored	6.25	1.60
		Nos. 247-252 (6)	11.45	3.10

Souvenir Sheet
253	A51	500fr multi, horiz.	6.00	2.00

Nos. 251-253 are airmail. No. 253 contains
one 58x39mm stamp.

Nobel Prize, 75th Anniv. — A52

Nobel Prize winners: 30fr, Medicine. 40fr,
Physics. 50fr, Literature. 100fr, Physics. 200fr,
Chemistry. 400fr, Peace.

1977, July 7
254	A52	30fr multicolored	.75	.20
255	A52	40fr multicolored	.75	.20
256	A52	50fr multicolored	1.25	.25
257	A52	100fr multicolored	3.25	.25
258	A52	200fr multicolored	5.50	.75
259	A52	400fr multicolored	12.50	1.25
		Nos. 254-259 (6)	24.00	2.90

Souvenir Sheet
260	A52	500fr Nobel medal	5.50	1.75

Nos. 258-260 are airmail. No. 260 contains
one 58x39mm stamp.
See note after No. 479.

Peter Paul
Rubens,
400th Birth
Anniv. — A53

Portraits: 20fr, Portrait of the Artist's Daughter, Clara. 25fr, Suzanne Fourment. 50fr, Toilet
of Venus, (detail). 75fr, Ceres (detail). 200fr,
Young Woman with Blonde Braided Hair. No.
266, Helene Fourment in her Wedding Dress.
No. 267, Self-portrait.

1977, July 7
261	A53	20fr multicolored	.20	.20
262	A53	25fr multicolored	.30	.20
263	A53	50fr multicolored	.65	.25
264	A53	75fr multicolored	1.10	.30
265	A53	200fr multicolored	2.50	.60
266	A53	400fr multicolored	6.25	1.50
		Nos. 261-266 (6)	11.00	3.05

Souvenir Sheet
267	A53	500fr multicolored	5.50	1.75

Nos. 265-267 are airmail.
See note after No. 479.

Fish
A54

1977, Nov. 21
268	A54	30fr Swordfish	.50	.20
269	A54	40fr Gaterin	1.00	.20
270	A54	50fr Sea scorpion	1.75	.20
271	A54	100fr Chaetodon lu-nula	3.25	.45
272	A54	200fr Amphiprion	4.00	.75
273	A54	400fr Tetrodon	7.50	1.50
		Nos. 268-273 (6)	18.00	3.30

Souvenir Sheet
274	A54	500fr Coelacanth	8.00	2.00

Nos. 272-274 airmail. No. 274 contains one
52x47mm stamp.

Space Exploration — A55

1977, Nov. 21
275	A55	30fr Jupiter lander	.30	.20
276	A55	50fr Voyager probe, Uranus, vert.	.60	.20
277	A55	75fr Pioneer probe, Venus	1.00	.25
278	A55	100fr Space shuttle, vert.	1.10	.40
279	A55	200fr Viking III, Mars	2.50	.60
280	A55	400fr Apollo-Soyuz, vert.	5.00	1.25
		Nos. 275-280 (6)	10.50	2.90

Souvenir Sheet
281	A55	500fr Allegory of the Sun	5.00	1.75

Nos. 279-281 are airmail. No. 281 contains one
52x42mm stamp.

No. 219 Overprinted in One Line in
Gold, Silver or Red
"Paris-New-York - 22 Nov. 1977"

1977, Nov. 22
282	A46	200fr multicolored	5.00	2.75
283	A46	200fr multicolored (S)	30.00	—
284	A46	200fr multicolored (R)	10.00	—
		Nos. 282-284 (3)	45.00	2.75

Birds — A56

1978, Feb. 6

285	A56	15fr Porphyrula alleni	.35	.20
286	A56	20fr M. superciliosus	.60	.20
287	A56	35fr Alcedo vintsioides johannae	.95	.20
288	A56	40fr Terpsiphone	1.25	.25
289	A56	75fr Nectarinia comorensis	2.10	.40
290	A56	400fr Egretta alba	10.75	1.50
		Nos. 285-290 (6)	16.00	2.65

Souvenir Sheet

291	A56	500fr Foudia eminentissima, horiz.	7.50	1.75

Nos. 290-291 are airmail. For overprint and surcharges see Nos. 444-448.

World Cup Soccer Championships, Argentina — A57

Designs: 30fr, Greece, 5th. cent. B.C. 50fr, Brittany, 19th cent. 75fr, London, 14th cent. 100fr, Italy, 18th cent. 200fr, England, 19th cent. 400fr, English Cup match, 1891. 500fr, English Cup final, 1962. No. 298, Player, satellite. No. 300, Players.

1978, Feb. 6

292	A57	30fr multicolored	.30	.20
293	A57	50fr multicolored	.60	.20
294	A57	75fr multicolored	.75	.30
295	A57	100fr multicolored	1.10	.40
296	A57	200fr multicolored	2.50	.60
297	A57	400fr multicolored	5.00	1.25
		Nos. 292-297 (6)	10.25	2.95

Litho. & Embossed
Size: 60x42mm

298	A57	1000fr gold & multi	11.00	—

Souvenir Sheets
Litho.

299	A57	500fr multicolored	6.00	1.75

Litho. & Embossed

300	A57	1000fr gold & multi	10.00	4.00

Nos. 296-300 are airmail. No. 300 contains one 60x42mm stamp.
No. 298 exists in a souvenir sheet of 1. Value \$50.
For overprints and surcharges see Nos. 402-408, 449-453.

Composers — A58

1978, Apr. 5 **Litho.**

301	A58	30fr J.S. Bach	.90	.20
302	A58	40fr W.A. Mozart	1.10	.20
303	A58	50fr Berlioz	1.50	.30
304	A58	100fr Verdi	3.00	.30
305	A58	200fr Tchaikovsky	4.50	.60

306	A58	400fr George Gershwin	9.00	1.25
		Nos. 301-306 (6)	20.00	2.85

Souvenir Sheet

307	A58	500fr Beethoven	9.00	1.75

Nos. 305-307 are airmail. For overprints and surcharges see Nos. 454-458.

Albrecht Durer, 450th Death Anniv. — A59

Portraits: 20fr, Oswolt Krel. 25fr, Elspeth Tucher. 50fr, Hieronymus Holzschuher. 75fr, Young Woman. 200fr, Emperor Maximilian I. No. 313, Young Woman, (detail). No. 314, Self-portrait.

1978, Apr. 5

308	A59	20fr multicolored	.20	.20
309	A59	25fr multicolored	.30	.20
310	A59	50fr multicolored	.65	.30
311	A59	75fr multicolored	1.00	.30
312	A59	200fr multicolored	2.50	.60
313	A59	500fr multicolored	6.00	1.60
		Nos. 308-313 (6)	10.65	3.20

Souvenir Sheet

314	A59	500fr multicolored	5.50	1.75

Nos. 312-314 airmail. No. 314 contains one 42x52mm stamp. See note after No. 479.

Issues Not Valid for Postage

The government changed in May 1978. A number of sets that had not been issued seem to have been invalid for postage until they were overprinted with the new country name. These are a set of 9 for the 25th anniv. of Elizabeth's coronation, a set of 7 for butterflies, a set of 6 for the 10th Intl. Communications Year, a set of 7 for the history of aviation, a set of 9 for Rubens, and a set of 9 for Durer.

These sets, unoverprinted, exist both mint and cancelled to order. They are no scarcer than the previous listed issues.

See note after No. 479.

Islamic Republic
Nos. 204-205 Surcharged and Overprinted with 3 Lines and: "République / Fédérale / et Islamique / des Comores"

1978, July 24 **Litho.** **Perf. 13½**

353	A44	30fr multi	.30	—
354	A44	40fr on 30fr multi	.30	—
355	A44	50fr multi	.50	—
356	A44	100fr on 50fr multi	.90	—
		Nos. 353-356 (3)	1.50	

Nos. 353 and 355 were also overprinted to commemorate World Cup Soccer winner; Albrecht Durer; Railroad anniversary; Voyager I and II; 1980 Olympic Games; World Cup Soccer, Espana '82.

Nos. 353, 355 Overprinted

1978, July 25 **Litho.** **Perf. 13½**

357	A44	30fr multi	9.00	—
358	A44	50fr multi	13.00	—

Coronation of Queen Elizabeth II, 25th anniv.

Nos. 353, 355 Overprinted

1978, July 26 **Litho.** **Perf. 13½**

359	A44	30fr multi	6.00	—
360	A44	50fr multi	9.00	—

Birth of Capt. James Cook, 250th anniv.

Nos. 353, 355 Overprinted

1978, July 31 **Litho.** **Perf. 13½**

365	A44	30fr multi	8.00	—
366	A44	50fr multi	12.00	—

Intl. Civil Aviation Organization.

Nos. 353, 355 Overprinted

1978, Aug. 3 **Litho.** **Perf. 13½**

371	A44	30fr multi	7.50	—
372	A44	50fr multi	7.50	—

Intl. Year of the Child (in 1979).

Europe-Africa A66

Various satellites or spacecraft.

1978, Dec. 16

386	A66	10fr multicolored	.20	.20
387	A66	25fr multicolored	.20	.20
388	A66	35fr multicolored	.40	.20
389	A66	75fr multicolored	.65	.20
390	A66	100fr multicolored	1.10	.60
391	A66	500fr multicolored	5.50	1.25
		Nos. 386-391 (6)	8.05	2.65

Souvenir Sheet

392	A66	500fr multicolored	5.50	1.75

Nos. 390-392 airmail. No. 392 contains one 61x40mm stamp.

Sir Rowland Hill — A67

1978, Dec. 16

393	A67	20fr Saxony #1	.20	.20
394	A67	30fr Netherlands #1	.30	.20
395	A67	40fr Great Britain #2	.60	.20
396	A67	75fr US #2	.75	.30
397	A67	200fr France #33	2.10	.60
398	A67	400fr Basel #3L1	4.50	1.25
		Nos. 393-398 (6)	8.45	2.75

Litho. & Embossed
Size: 39x58mm

399	A67	1500fr British Guiana #13	13.00	

Souvenir Sheets
Litho.

400	A67	500fr Moheli, Mayotte, Anjouan, Grand Comoro #1	5.50	1.75

Litho. & Embossed

401	A67	1500fr Hill, Mauritius #3	13.00	

Nos. 397-401 are airmail. No. 400 contains one 57x49mm stamp. No. 401 contains one 58x39mm stamp.
No. 399 exists in a souvenir sheet of 1. Value \$40.

Nos. 292-297 Ovptd. with New Country Name in Black on Silver and
1 ARGENTINE
2 HOLLANDE
3 BRESIL

1978, Dec. 16

402	A57	30fr multicolored	.30	.20
403	A57	50fr multicolored	.60	.20
404	A57	75fr multicolored	.90	.20
405	A57	100fr multicolored	1.10	.45
406	A57	200fr multicolored	2.25	.60
407	A57	400fr multicolored	4.75	1.25
		Nos. 402-407 (6)	9.90	2.90

Souvenir Sheet

408	A57	500fr multicolored	5.50	1.25

Nos. 406-407 are airmail.

Exists with Country name in red on silver. Value approx. triple those of overprints in black.

Galileo and Voyager I — A68

Exploration of Solar System: 30fr, Kepler and Voyager II. 40fr, Copernicus and Voyager I, 100fr, Huygens and Voyager II. 200fr, William Herschel and Voyager II. 400fr, Urbain Leverrier and Voyager II. 500fr, Voyagers I and II, symbolic solar system.

1979, Feb. 19 **Litho.** **Perf. 13**

409	A68	20fr multi	.20	.20
410	A68	30fr multi	.30	.20
411	A68	40fr multi	.50	.20
412	A68	100fr multi	1.10	.20
413	A68	200fr multi	1.90	.50
414	A68	400fr multi	4.00	1.00
		Nos. 409-414 (6)	8.00	2.35

Souvenir Sheet

415	A68	500fr multi	5.00	1.50

Nos. 413-415 airmail.

Philidor, Anderssen, Steinitz and King — A69

100fr, Chess pieces and board, Venetian chess player. 500fr, Chess Grand Masters Alekhine, Spassky, Fischer, and bishop.

1979, Feb. 19

416	A69	40fr multi	.50	.20
417	A69	100fr multi	1.10	.20
418	A69	500fr multi	5.00	1.50
		Nos. 416-418 (3)	6.60	1.90

Chess Grand Masters. No. 418 airmail.

Nos. 419-425 are reserved for Summer Olympics set of 6 with one souvenir sheet, released Mar. 28, 1979.

Charaxes Defulvata — A71

Birds: 50fr, Leptosomus discolor. 75fr, Bee eater.

1979, Apr. 10   Litho.   Perf. 12½

426	A71	30fr multi	1.50	.30
427	A71	50fr multi	3.75	.60
428	A71	75fr multi	6.25	1.00
		Nos. 426-428 (3)	11.50	1.90

Otto Lilienthal and Glider — A72

History of Aviation: No. 430, Wright brothers and Flyer A. No. 431, Louis Bleriot and Bleriot XI. 100fr, Claude Dornier and Dornier-Wal hydrofoil. 200fr, Charles Lindbergh and Spirit of St. Louis.

1979, May 2   Perf. 13
Black Overprint and Surcharge

429	A72	30fr multi	.50	.50
430	A72	50fr multi	.80	.80
431	A72	50fr on 75fr multi	.80	.80
432	A72	100fr multi	1.60	1.60
433	A72	200fr multi	2.50	2.50
		Nos. 429-433 (5)	6.20	6.20

No. 433 airmail.
For unoverprinted stamps see note after No. 314.

Papilio Dardanus Cenea A73

Butterflies: 15fr, Papilio dardanus. 30fr, Chrysiridia croesus. 50fr, Precis octavia. 75fr, Bunaea alcinoe.

1979, May 2
Black Overprint and Surcharge

434	A73	5fr on 20fr multi	.20	.20
435	A73	15fr multi	.35	.20
436	A73	30fr multi	.70	.45
437	A73	50fr multi	1.40	.95
438	A73	75fr multi	2.25	1.50
		Nos. 434-438 (5)	4.90	3.30

For unoverprinted stamps see note after No. 314.

Man Reading Proclamation — A74

1979, May 2   Litho.   Perf. 13½
Black Surcharge and Overprint

439	A74	5fr on 25fr coronation coach	.20	.20
440	A74	10fr Drummer	.30	.30
441	A74	50fr on 40fr with crown, orb, scepter	.70	.70
442	A74	50fr on 200fr shown	1.10	1.10
443	A74	100fr St. Edward's Crown	1.40	1.40
		Nos. 439-443 (5)	3.70	3.70

No. 442 is airmail.
For unoverprinted stamps see note after No. 314.

Nos. 285-289 Overprinted or Surcharged like A72-A74

1979, May 2   Litho.   Perf. 13

444	A56	15fr multi	.30	.30
445	A56	30fr on 35fr multi	.70	.70
446	A56	50fr on 20fr multi	1.25	1.25
447	A56	50fr on 40fr multi	1.25	1.25
448	A56	200fr on 75fr multi	4.00	4.00
		Nos. 444-448 (5)	7.50	7.50

Nos. 292-296 Overprinted or Surcharged like A72-A74

1979, May 2   Litho.   Perf. 13

449	A57	1fr on 100fr multi	.20	.20
450	A57	2fr on 75fr multi	.20	.20
451	A57	3fr on 30fr multi	.20	.20
452	A57	50fr multi	.90	.55
453	A57	200fr multi	2.25	2.25
		Nos. 449-453 (5)	3.75	3.40

No. 453 airmail.

Nos. 301-305 Overprinted or Surcharged like A72-A74

1979, May 2   Perf. 13½

454	A58	5fr on 100fr multi	.20	.20
455	A58	30fr multi	1.25	1.25
456	A58	40fr multi	1.75	1.75
457	A58	50fr multi	2.25	2.25
458	A58	50fr multi	3.50	3.50
		Nos. 454-458 (5)	8.95	8.95

No. 458 airmail.

Nos. 459-465 are reserved for Intl. Year of the Child set of 6 with one souvenir sheet, released May 30, 1979.

Litchi Nuts — A76

Basketball Players — A77

1979, June 15   Litho.   Perf. 12½

466	A76	60fr shown	1.00	.30
467	A76	70fr Papayas	1.25	.45
468	A76	100fr Avocados	1.40	.55
469	A76	125fr Bananas	1.90	.90
		Nos. 466-469 (4)	5.55	2.20

For surcharges see Nos. 515, 533.

1979, Aug. 28   Litho.   Perf. 13

470	A77	200fr multi	2.50 1.40

Indian Ocean Olympics.

Nos. 176, 198, 218, 187, 159-160 and Type A78 Overprinted in Black

Nimbus Weather Satellite — A78

No. 475, Apollo-Soyuz. No. 479, Molniya.

Printing & Perfs. as Before, Litho. (A78)

1979, Sept. 15   Perf. 13 (A78)

471	A40	35fr multi	.70	.70
472	A43	75fr multi	1.50	1.50
473	A46	75fr multi	1.50	1.50
474	A78	75fr multi	1.50	1.50
475	A78	100fr multi	2.10	2.10
476	A41	100fr multi	2.10	2.10
477	A37	100fr multi	2.10	2.10
478	A37	200fr multi	4.25	4.25
479	A78	200fr multi	4.25	4.25
		Nos. 471-479 (9)	20.00	20.00

Nos. 476-479 airmail.
For type A78 see note after No. 314.

Nos. 166-167, 169, 235-236, 257, 262, 309, 311, the unissued Rubens set (4 values) and Durer set (5 values) exist with this overprint, supposedly also issued Sept. 15.

Dugout on Beach A80

Anjouan Puppet — A81

1980, Jan. 4   Litho.   Perf. 13

498	A80	60fr multi	1.00	.25
499	A81	100fr multi	1.50	.45

For surcharge see No. 534.

Sultan Said Ali — A82

1980, Feb. 20   Perf. 12½x13

500	A82	40fr shown	.60	.20
501	A82	60fr Sultan Ahmed	.75	.25

Sherlock Holmes, Doyle — A83

1980, Feb. 25   Perf. 12½

502	A83	200fr multi	4.75 1.75

Sir Arthur Conan Doyle (1859-1930), writer.
For surcharge see No. 513.

Grand Mosque, Holy Ka'aba, Mecca — A84

1980, Mar. 12   Perf. 13x12½

503	A84	75fr multi	1.00 .40

Hegira, 1500th anniv.
For surcharge see No. 514.

Year of the Holy City of Jerusalem A85

1980, Mar. 12   Perf. 13x13½

504	A85	60fr multi	.75 .40

Kepler, Copernicus and Pluto — A86

1980, Apr. 30   Litho.   Perf. 12½

505	A86	400fr multi	4.50 2.25

Discovery of Pluto, 50th anniversary.
For surcharge see No. 531.

Muscle System, Avicenna — A87

1980, Apr. 30   Engr.   Perf. 13

506	A87	60fr multi	.75 .40

Avicenna, Arab physician, birth millennium.

Soccer Players — A88

World Cup Soccer 1982; Various soccer scenes. 60fr, 150fr, 500fr, vert.

1981, Feb. 20   **Litho.**   **Perf. 12½**
507	A88	60fr multi	.65	.20
508	A88	75fr multi	.75	.20
509	A88	90fr multi	1.25	.25
510	A88	100fr multi	1.10	.45
511	A88	190fr multi	1.90	.60
		Nos. 507-511 (5)	5.65	1.70

Souvenir Sheet
512	A88	500fr multi	5.00	1.50

For overprints & surcharge see #532, 555-560.

Nos. 502-503, 469 Surcharged and

Merops Superciliosus A89

Perf. 12½, 13x12½ (No. 514)
1981, Feb.   **Litho.**
Red, Black or Blue Surcharge
513	A83	15fr on 200fr multi	.50	.50
514	A84	20fr on 75fr multi	.50	.50
515	A76	40fr on 125fr multi (Bk)	1.50	1.50
516	A89	60fr on 75fr multi (Bl)	3.00	3.00
		Nos. 513-516 (4)	5.50	5.50

A90

Space Exploration: 50fr, Apollo program, vert. 75fr, 100fr, 500fr, Columbia space shuttle.

1981, July 13   **Litho.**   **Perf. 14**
517	A90	50fr multi	.60	.20
518	A90	75fr multi	.75	.20
519	A90	100fr multi	1.25	.30
520	A90	450fr multi	6.00	1.50
		Nos. 517-520 (4)	8.60	2.20

Souvenir Sheet
521	A90	500fr multi	5.00	1.50

For overprints and surcharges see Nos. 599, 804F.

Prince Charles and Lady Diana, Buckingham Palace — A91

1981, Sept. 1   **Litho.**   **Perf. 14½**
522	A91	125fr shown	1.10	.30
523	A91	200fr Highwood House	1.75	.60
524	A91	450fr Carnarvon Castle	3.75	1.25
a.		Souvenir sheet of 3	6.75	2.00
		Nos. 522-524 (3)	6.60	2.15

Royal wedding. No. 524a contains Nos. 522-524 in changed colors.
For overprints see Nos. 551-553.

Official Stamp Flag Type
1981, Oct.   **Litho.**   **Perf. 13**
526	O1	5fr multi	.20	.20
527	O1	15fr multi	.20	.20
528	O1	25fr multi	.30	.20
529	O1	35fr multi	.40	.20
530	O1	75fr multi	.75	.35
		Nos. 526-530 (5)	1.85	1.15

Nos. 505, 509, 468, 499 Surcharged
1981, Nov.   **Litho.**   **Perf. 12½**
531	A86	5fr on 400fr multi	.40	.40
532	A88	20fr on 90fr multi	.80	.80
533	A76	45fr on 100fr multi	2.00	.20
534	A81	45fr on 450fr multi	2.00	.20
		Nos. 531-534 (4)	5.20	1.60

75th Anniv. of Grand Prix — A92

Designs: Winners and their Cars.

1981, Dec. 28   **Litho.**   **Perf. 12½**
535	A92	20fr Mercedes, 1914	.30	.20
536	A92	50fr Delage, 1925	.65	.20
537	A92	75fr Rudi Caracciola, 1926	.90	.25
538	A92	90fr Stirling Moss, 1955	1.10	.35
539	A92	150fr Maserati, 1957	1.60	.45
		Nos. 535-539 (5)	4.55	1.45

Souvenir Sheet
Perf. 13
540	A92	500fr Changing wheels, vert.	6.00	1.75

For overprint see No. 600.

Scouting Year — A93

1982, Jan. 5   **Perf. 12½**
541	A93	50fr Climbing rocks	.60	.20
542	A93	75fr Boating	.85	.25
543	A93	250fr Sailing	3.00	.90
544	A93	350fr Sailing, diff.	3.75	1.10
		Nos. 541-544 (4)	8.20	2.45

Souvenir Sheet
Perf. 13
545	A93	500fr Baden-Powell	6.50	1.75

For overprint see No. 601.

21st Birthday of Princess of Wales — A94

Various portraits of Princess Diana.

1982, July 1   **Litho.**   **Perf. 14**
546	A94	200fr multi	2.50	.60
547	A94	300fr multi	3.25	.90

Souvenir Sheet
548	A94	500fr multi	5.50	1.50

Johannes von Goethe (1749-1832) A95

1982, July
549	A95	75fr multi	.75	.25
550	A95	350fr multi	3.75	.90

Nos. 522-524a Overprinted in Blue: "NAISSANCE ROYALE 1982"
1982, July 31   **Perf. 14½**
551	A91	125fr multi	1.50	.60
552	A91	200fr multi	2.50	.90
553	A91	450fr multi	4.50	2.00
a.		Souvenir sheet of 3	8.75	8.75
		Nos. 551-553 (3)	8.50	3.50

Birth of Prince William of Wales, June 21.

Nos. 507-512 Overprinted with Finalists and Score in Red
1982, Sept. 20   **Perf. 12½**
555	A88	60fr multi	.65	.25
556	A88	75fr multi	.75	.35
557	A88	90fr multi	1.00	.45
558	A88	100fr multi	1.10	.45
559	A88	150fr multi	1.40	.60
		Nos. 555-559 (5)	4.90	2.10

Souvenir Sheet
560	A88	500fr multi	5.00	1.50

Italy's victory in 1982 World Cup.

Paintings by Norman Rockwell A96

1982, Oct. 11   **Litho.**   **Perf. 14**
561	A96	60fr 1931	.65	.25
562	A96	75fr 1925	.70	.25
563	A96	100fr 1922	1.25	.25
564	A96	150fr 1919	1.40	.55
565	A96	200fr 1924	2.00	.60
566	A96	300fr 1918	3.50	1.00
		Nos. 561-566 (6)	9.50	2.90

Sultans of Anjouan — A97

1982, Dec.   **Perf. 12½x13, 13x12½**
567	A97	30fr Said Mohamed Sidi, vert.	.40	.20
568	A97	60fr Ahmed Abdallah, vert.	.75	.25
569	A97	75fr Salim	1.00	.25
570	A97	300fr Sidi, Abdallah	3.50	1.40
		Nos. 567-570 (4)	5.65	2.10

Landscapes — A98

1983, Sept. 30   **Litho.**   **Perf. 13**
571	A98	60fr D'Ziani Lake	.75	.30
572	A98	100fr Sunset	1.25	.45
573	A98	175fr Anjouan, vert.	2.00	.75
574	A98	360fr Itsandra	4.00	1.25
575	A98	400fr Anjouan, diff.	5.00	1.60
		Nos. 571-575 (5)	13.00	4.35

For surcharge see No. 815S.

Woman from Moheli A99

1983, Oct. 17   **Litho.**   **Perf. 12½x13**
576	A99	30fr shown	.40	.20
577	A99	45fr Woman, diff.	.55	.20
578	A99	50fr Man from Mayotte	.55	.20
		Nos. 576-578 (3)	1.50	.60

Horses — A100

1983, Nov. 30   **Litho.**   **Perf. 13**
579	A100	75fr Arabian	.70	.25
580	A100	100fr Anglo-Arabian	1.25	.30
581	A100	125fr Lippizaner	1.50	.40
582	A100	150fr Tennessee	1.75	.50
583	A100	200fr Appaloosa	2.00	.70
584	A100	300fr Pure English	3.50	1.00
585	A100	400fr Clydesdale	4.75	1.25
586	A100	500fr Andalusian	6.50	1.50
		Nos. 579-586 (8)	21.95	5.90

Double Portrait, by Raphael A101

1983, Dec. 30   **Litho.**   **Perf. 13**
587	A101	100fr shown	1.25	.45
588	A101	200fr Girl, fresco detail	2.50	.80
589	A101	300fr St. George Killing Dragon	3.25	.90
590	A101	400fr Balthazar Castiglione	5.50	1.25
		Nos. 587-590 (4)	12.50	3.40

For surcharges see Nos. 703, 800E, 815M.

Ships and Automobiles — A102

1984, Oct. 9   **Litho.**   **Perf. 12½**
591	A102	100fr William Fawcett	1.25	.30
592	A102	100fr De Dion, 1885	1.50	.30
593	A102	150fr Lightning	1.90	.45
594	A102	150fr Benz Victoria, 1893	2.25	.60
595	A102	200fr Rapido	2.50	.75

596	A102	200fr Columbia Electric, 1901		3.00	.75
597	A102	350fr Sindia		4.50	1.00
598	A102	350fr Fiat, 1902		5.00	1.10
		Nos. 591-598 (8)		21.90	5.25

For surcharge see No. 812Q.

Souvenir Sheets
Nos. 521, 540, 545, C126, C131
Ovptd. with Exhibition in Black, Blue, Red or Gold

1985, Mar. 11   *Perf. 14, 13*

599	A90	500fr '85 / HAMBOURG (Bk)		5.00	5.00
600	A92	500fr TSUKUBA EXPO '85 (Bl)		5.00	5.00
601	A93	500fr ARGENTINA '85/BUENOS AIRES (R)		5.00	5.00
602	AP31	500fr Rome, ITALIA '85 emblem (R)		5.00	5.00
603	AP32	500fr OLYM-PHILEX/ '85 / LAUSANNE (G)		5.00	5.00
		Nos. 599-603 (5)		25.00	25.00

Nos. 602-603 airmail.

Victor Hugo (1802-1885), Author, Pantheon, Paris — A103

Anniversaries and events: 200fr, IYY, Jules Verne (1828-1905), author. 300fr, IYY, Mark Twain (1835-1910), author. 450fr, Queen Mother, 85th birthday, vert. 500fr, Statue of Liberty, cent., vert.

1985, May 27   **Litho.**   *Perf. 13*

604	A103	100fr multi		1.25	.30
605	A103	200fr multi		2.25	.60
606	A103	300fr multi		3.50	.90
607	A103	450fr multi		5.00	1.25
608	A103	500fr multi		6.00	1.50
		Nos. 604-608 (5)		18.00	4.55

For surcharges see Nos. 704, 800A.

Sea Shells — A104

1985, Oct. 23   *Perf. 14*

609	A104	75fr Lambis chiragra		1.00	.20
610	A104	125fr Strombe lentifinosum		1.50	.35
611	A104	200fr Tonna gala		2.50	.60
612	A104	300fr Cymbium glans		4.00	.90
613	A104	450fr Lambis crocata		6.00	1.40
		Nos. 609-613 (5)		15.00	3.45

Comoros Admission to UN, 10th Anniv. — A105

1985, Nov. 12   **Litho.**   *Perf. 13x12½*

614	A105	5fr multi		.20	.20
615	A105	30fr multi		.30	.20
616	A105	75fr multi		.90	.25

617	A105	125fr multi		1.40	.50
618	A105	400fr multi		4.50	1.50
		Nos. 614-618 (5)		7.30	2.65

For surcharge see No. 800F.

Moroni Rotary Club, 20th Anniv. — A106

1985, Nov. 30   *Perf. 13*

619	A106	25fr multi		.30	.20
620	A106	75fr multi		.90	.40
621	A106	125fr multi		1.40	.45
622	A106	500fr multi		5.00	2.00
		Nos. 619-622 (4)		7.60	3.05

Mushrooms — A107

1985, Dec. 24   *Perf. 13½*

623	A107	75fr Boletus edulis		1.00	.30
624	A107	125fr Sarcoscypha coccinea		1.50	.45
625	A107	200fr Hypholoma fasciculare		2.50	.60
626	A107	350fr Astraeus hygrometricus		4.00	.90
627	A107	500fr Armillariella mellea		7.00	1.50
		Nos. 623-627 (5)		16.00	3.75

For surcharge see No. 815R.

Health Year A108

1986, Oct. 2   **Litho.**   *Perf. 15x14½*

628	A108	25fr Pediatric examination		.30	.20
629	A108	100fr Weighing child		1.25	.60
630	A108	200fr Immunization		2.50	1.25
		Nos. 628-630 (3)		4.05	2.05

For surcharge see No. 705.

Musical Instruments A109

1986, Dec. 24   **Litho.**   *Perf. 13*

631	A109	75fr Ndzoumara		.90	.40
632	A109	125fr Ndzedze		1.25	.60
633	A109	210fr Gaboussi		2.10	.90
634	A109	500fr Ngoma		6.00	1.75
		Nos. 631-634 (4)		10.25	3.65

For surcharges see Nos. 796P, 796T, 800L, 815A.

Role of Women in National Development — A110

1987, Mar. 7   **Litho.**   *Perf. 13*

635	A110	75fr Working fields		.80	.30
636	A110	125fr Harvesting crops, vert.		1.40	.45
637	A110	1000fr Basketweaving		11.00	3.00
		Nos. 635-637 (3)		13.20	3.75

Service Organizations — A111

Emblems and activities: 75fr, Nos. 642, Kiwanis or 643c, Rotary Intl. for child survival. 125fr, Nos. 641, Kiwanis or 643b, Lions Intl. for aid to the handicapped. 210fr, No. 643a, Kiwanis helping poor and homeless children.

1988   **Litho.**   *Perf. 13½*

638	A111	75fr dk bl, lt bl & multi		.75	.30
639	A111	125fr dk brn, lt brn & multi		1.40	.45
640	A111	210fr org, yel & multi		2.25	.75
641	A111	425fr red, pink & multi		4.50	1.75
642	A111	500fr bl, yel & multi		6.00	2.00
643		Strip of 3		13.00	6.00
a.	A111	210fr grn, lt grn & multi		2.10	.75
b.	A111	425fr pur, pink & multi		4.50	1.75
c.	A111	500fr red, orange & multi		6.00	2.00
		Nos. 638-643 (6)		27.90	11.25

For surcharges see Nos. 654-656, 815B, 815W.

A112

1988 Olympics, Calgary and Seoul — A113

1988   **Litho.**   *Perf. 13½*

644	A112	75fr Women's figure skating		.65	.20
645	A112	100fr Running		1.00	.30
646	A112	125fr Women's speed skating		1.00	.40
647	A112	150fr Equestrian		1.50	.50
648	A112	350fr Two-man luge		3.25	.90
649	A112	400fr Biathlon		4.00	1.40
650	A112	500fr Pole vault		4.00	1.25
651	A112	600fr Soccer		6.00	1.50
		Nos. 644-651 (8)		21.40	6.45

Souvenir Sheets

652	A113	750fr Women's downhill skiing, satellite		7.75	1.50
653	A113	750fr Track, satellite		7.75	1.50

Nos. 649 and 651-653 are airmail.
For surcharges see Nos. 800C, 800M, 815V.

No. 643 and Service Organization Types Surcharged
No. 655, like #643b. No. 656, like #643c.

1988, July 18   **Litho.**   *Perf. 13½*

654		Strip of 3		5.50	5.00
a.	A111	75fr on 210fr #643a		.65	.45
b.	A111	200fr on 425fr #643b		1.75	.90
c.	A111	300fr on 500fr #643c		2.75	1.25
655	A111	125fr on 425fr pur, lt pur & multi, blk letters		1.10	.60

656	A111	400fr on 500fr car, pink & multi		3.75	2.00
		Nos. 654-656 (3)		10.35	7.60

Nos. 655-656 not issued without surcharge.

Discovery of America, 500th Anniv. (in 1992) — A114

Designs: 75fr, Christopher Columbus, *Santa Maria.* 125fr, Martin Alonzo Pinzon (c. 1441-1493), *Pinta.* 150fr, Vicente Yanez Pinzon (c. 1460-1523), *Nina.* 250fr, Search for Cipango, legendary rich islands off the coast of Asia. 375fr, *Santa Maria* shipwrecked. 450fr, Preparing for 4th voyage. 750fr, Samana Cay landing.

1988, Apr. 18   **Litho.**   *Perf. 13½*

657	A114	75fr multi		.65	.20
658	A114	125fr multi		1.10	.30
659	A114	150fr multi		1.50	.45
660	A114	250fr multi		2.10	.75
661	A114	375fr multi		3.75	1.00
662	A114	450fr multi		4.50	1.25
		Nos. 657-662 (6)		13.60	3.95

Souvenir Sheet

663	A114	750fr multi, horiz.		7.75	1.50

Nos. 661-663 airmail. No. 663 contains one 42x30mm stamp.
For surcharges see Nos. 702, 815D.

1992 Summer Olympics, Barcelona A115

1988, Apr. 18   **Litho.**   *Perf. 13½*

664	A115	75fr Discus, vert.		.60	.20
665	A115	100fr shown		.90	.30
666	A115	125fr Cycling		1.75	.45
667	A115	150fr Wrestling		2.25	.50
668	A115	375fr Basketball, vert.		5.25	1.00
669	A115	600fr Tennis, vert.		8.25	1.25
		Nos. 664-669 (6)		19.00	3.70

Souvenir Sheet

670	A115	750fr Marathon, vert.		7.75	1.50

Nos. 668-670 are airmail.

Famous Men — A116

Rotary Intl. — A117

150fr, Yuri Gagarin (1934-68), USSR, cosmonaut. 300fr, Jean-Henri Dunant, Red Cross founder. 400fr, Roger Clemens, baseball player. 500fr, Gary Kasparov, USSR, 1985 world chess champion. 600fr, Paul Harris, US, Rotary founder. 750fr, Neil Armstrong walking on the Moon, John F. Kennedy. #678, The Thinker by Rodin, Rotary Intl. emblem.

1988, Dec. 6   **Litho.**   *Perf. 13½*

671	A116	150fr multi		1.75	.50
672	A116	300fr multi		1.75	.50
673	A116	400fr multi		1.75	.50

674	A116	500fr multi	1.75	.50
675	A116	600fr multi	1.75	.50
a.		Souv. sheet of 5, #671-675 + label	10.00	—
		Nos. 665-669 (5)	18.40	3.50

Litho. & Embossed

676	A117	1500fr gold & multi	15.00	—

Souvenir Sheets
Litho.

677	A116	750fr multi	7.75	1.50

Litho. & Embossed

678	A117	1500fr gold & multi	15.00	—

Intl. Red Cross, 125th anniv. (300fr), Rotary Intl. (600fr, Nos. 676, 678). Nos. 674-678 are airmail.
#672-673 exist in souv. sheets of 1.
No. 676 exists in a souvenir sheet of 1. Value $42.50.

Inventors and Sportsmen
A118

Portraits and modes of transportation: Designs: 75fr, Alain Prost, F-1 MacLaren-Honda. 125fr, George Stephenson and locomotive *Borsig* of 1935. 500fr, Ettore Bugatti (1881-1947), 1939 Bugatti Aravis Type 57. 600fr, Rudolf Diesel (1858-1913) and V200 BB diesel-electric locomotive. 750fr, Dennis Conner, captain of the *Stars and Stripes*, winner of the 1987 America's Cup. No. 684, Michael Fay, patron of the *New Zealand*, an entry in the America's Cup. No. 685, Enzo Ferrari and 1989 Ferrari Formula 1, horiz.

1988, Dec. 27   Litho.   Perf. 13½

679	A118	75fr multi	.75	.45
680	A118	125fr multi	1.25	.25
681	A118	500fr multi	5.00	1.25
682	A118	600fr multi	6.00	1.25
683	A118	750fr multi	7.00	1.25
684	A118	1000fr multi	10.00	1.25
		Nos. 679-684 (6)	30.00	5.70

Souvenir Sheet

685	A118	1000fr multi	10.00	1.50

Nos. 683-685 are airmail.
#679-684 exist in souv. sheets of 1.

Scouts, Butterflies and Birds — A119

Scouts involved in various activities and species: 50fr, Gathering specimens, *Papilio nireus aristophontes oberthur* female. 75fr, Studying specimen and male. 150fr, Cooking out, *Charaxes fulvescens separanus poulton*. 375fr, Picking mushrooms, *Lonchura cucullatus*. 450fr, Examining specimen, *Charaxes castor comoranus rothschild*. 500fr, Identifying specimen, *Zosterops maderaspatana*. 750fr, Studying specimens, *Foudia omissa* and *Charaxes paradoxa lathy* female. No. 692, Photographing specimen, *Junonia rhadama*. No. 694, Examining specimen, *Agapornis cana cana*.

1989   Litho.

686	A119	50fr multi	.50	.20
687	A119	75fr multi	.60	.20
688	A119	150fr multi	1.40	.30
689	A119	375fr multi	4.00	.75
690	A119	450fr multi	4.75	1.00
691	A119	500fr multi	5.75	1.25
		Nos. 686-691 (6)	17.00	3.70

Litho. & Embossed

692	A119	1500fr gold & multi	13.00	—

Souvenir Sheets
Litho.

693	A119	750fr multi	12.00	1.50

Litho. & Embossed

694	A119	1500fr gold & multi	13.00	—

Nos. 690-694 are airmail. Issue dates: Nos. 692, 694, May 15; others, Mar. 15.
No. 692 exists in a souvenir sheet of 1. Value $42.50.
For surcharges see Nos. 800D, 815T.

Gold Medalists of the 1988 Summer Olympics
A120

Communication satellites, various equestrians and their mounts: 75fr, Nicole Uphoff, West Germany, individual dressage, and Aussat K3. 150fr, Pierre Durand, France, individual jumping, and Brazilsat. 375fr, Janos Martinek, Hungary, individual modern pentathlon, and ECS 4. 600fr, Mark Todd, New Zealand, individual three-day event, and Olympus. 750fr, Team jumping, West Germany, and satellite. No. 699, Pierre Durand, France, individual show jumping. No. 701, Nicole Uphoff, West Germany, individual dressage.

1989, Apr. 10   Litho.   Perf. 13½

695	A120	75fr multi	.65	.20
696	A120	150fr multi	1.25	.35
697	A120	375fr multi	3.00	.75
698	A120	500fr multi	5.00	1.25
		Nos. 695-698 (4)	9.90	2.55

Litho. & Embossed

699	A120	1500fr gold & multi	13.00	—

Souvenir Sheets
Litho.

700	A120	750fr multi	6.75	1.50

Litho. & Embossed

701	A120	1500fr gold & multi	13.00	—

No. 701 contains one 39x38mm stamp.
Nos. 698-701 are airmail.
No. 699 exists in a souvenir sheet of 1. Value $45.
For surcharges see Nos. 796Q, 804I.

Nos. 660, 588, 605 and 630
Surcharged

1989   Litho.   Perfs. as Before

702	A114	25fr on 250fr #660	.20	.20
703	A101	150fr on 200fr #588	1.25	.50
704	A103	150fr on 200fr #605	1.25	.50
705	A108	150fr on 200fr #630	1.25	.50
		Nos. 702-705 (4)	3.95	1.70

1992 Summer Olympics, Barcelona
A121

1989, Apr. 26   Litho.   Perf. 13½

706	A121	75fr Running	.65	.20
707	A121	150fr Soccer	1.25	.40
708	A121	300fr Tennis	2.50	.60
709	A121	375fr Baseball	3.25	.80
710	A121	500fr Pommel horse	4.00	1.00
711	A121	600fr Table tennis	5.00	1.25
		Nos. 706-711 (6)	16.65	4.25

Souvenir Sheet

712	A121	750fr Equestrian	6.75	1.50

Nos. 710-712 are airmail.
For surcharges see Nos. 796J, 796K, 800J, 812R.

Dr. Joseph-Ignace Guillotin (1738-1814) — A122

French Revolution, Bicent.: 150fr, French artillery, Gen. Francois-Christophe Kellerman (1735-1820). 375fr, Royalist insurgents & leader, Jean Cotterau (1757-94). 600fr, King Louis XVI (1774-92), troops. 1000fr, Storming of the Bastille & Jacques Necker, statesman (1732-1804). #717, Lafayette, Mounier, Sieyes & Declaration of the Rights of Man and Citizen. #719, Robespierre & St. Just before the Convention on 9 Thermidor.

1989, Oct. 25   Litho.   Perf. 13½

713	A122	75fr multicolored	.70	.20
714	A122	150fr multicolored	1.25	.35
715	A122	375fr multicolored	3.00	.60
716	A122	600fr multicolored	5.00	1.25
		Nos. 713-716 (4)	9.95	2.40

Litho. & Embossed

717	A122	1500fr gold & multi	13.00	—

Souvenir Sheets
Litho.

718	A122	1000fr multicolored	8.50	1.75

Litho. & Embossed

719	A122	1500fr gold & multi	13.00	—

Philexfrance 1989. Nos. 716-719 are airmail.
No. 714 incorrectly inscribed "Francois-Etienne."
Nos. 713-716 exist in souvenir sheets of 1.
No. 717 exists in a souvenir sheet of 1. Value $22.
For surcharges see Nos. 796B, 800W, 804J.

Airport Pavilion
A124

Designs: 10fr, 25fr, Airport pavilion. 50fr, 75fr, 150fr, Federal Assembly.

1990, Apr. 1   Litho.   Perf. 13

722	A124	5fr brn, org & brt red	.20	.20
723	A124	10fr brn, org & brt bl	.20	.20
724	A124	25fr brn, org & brt grn	.20	.20
725	A124	50fr blk & brt red	.45	.20
726	A124	75fr blk & brt bl	.75	.30
727	A124	150fr blk & grn	1.40	.60
		Nos. 722-727 (6)	3.20	1.70

World Cup Soccer Championships, Italy — A125

Players from: 50fr, Brazil. 75fr, England. 100fr, Federal Republic of Germany. 150fr, Belgium. 375fr, Italy. 600fr, Argentina. 750fr, Argentina and Italy.

1990   Litho.   Perf. 13½

728	A125	50fr multicolored	.45	.20
729	A125	75fr multicolored	.65	.30
730	A125	100fr multicolored	.80	.35
731	A125	150fr multicolored	1.10	.45
732	A125	375fr multicolored	3.00	1.00
733	A125	600fr multicolored	5.00	1.25
		Nos. 728-733 (6)	11.00	3.55

Litho. & Embossed

734	A125	1500fr gold & multi	13.00	5.00

Souvenir Sheets
Litho.

735	A125	750fr multicolored	6.75	1.50

Litho. & Embossed

736	A125	1500fr gold & multi	13.00	—

Nos. 732-736 are airmail.
No. 734 exists in a souvenir sheet of 1. Value $22.50.
For surcharges see Nos. 796L, 796O, 804K.

Telecom '91
A125a

1990, Oct. 29   Litho.   Perf. 13½

736A	A125a	75fr Emblem, vert.	.75	.60
736B	A125a	150fr shown	1.60	1.25

Nos. 736A-736B exist imperf.

A126

Designs: 75fr, Hubble Space Telescope placed in orbit. 150fr, Pope John Paul II, Pres. Gorbachev meet Dec. 3, 1989. 200fr, Kevin Mitchell, San Francisco Giants, Natl. League Most Valuable Player, 1989. 250fr, De Gaulle, France, and Adenauer, West Germany, meet in Sept. 1962. 300fr, Cassini probe to Titan, 2002. 375fr, Bullet train and Concorde, France. 450fr, Gary Kasparov, World Chess Champion. 500fr, Paul Harris (1868-1947), founder of Rotary Intl.

1990, Nov. 26   Litho.   Perf. 13½

737	A126	75fr sil & multi	.75	.25
738	A126	150fr sil & multi	1.50	.40
739	A126	200fr sil & multi	2.00	.40
740	A126	250fr sil & multi	2.50	.40
741	A126	300fr sil & multi	3.00	.50
742	A126	375fr sil & multi	3.75	.60
743	A126	450fr sil & multi	4.50	1.00
744	A126	500fr sil & multi	5.25	.75
		Nos. 737-744 (8)	23.25	4.35

Nos. 743-744 are airmail.
#738, 744 exist in souv. sheets of 1.
For surcharges see Nos. 796A, 796R, 800I, 804A, 804L, 815E, 815U.

A127

A128

Winter Olympics participants: 75fr, Edi Reinalter, Switzerland, slalom, 1948. 100fr, Canadian hockey team, 1924. 375fr, Gratia Van der Oye, women's slalom, Holland, 1936. 600fr, Heikki Hasu, Finland, combined cross country and ski jumping, 1948. 750fr, Helene Engelman & Alfred Berger, Austria, pairs figure skating, 1924. No. 751, Speed skater, horiz. No. 751A, Luge, horiz.

1990, Dec. 10

746	A127	75fr multicolored	.60	.20
747	A127	100fr multicolored	.75	.30
748	A127	375fr multicolored	3.50	1.00
749	A127	600fr multicolored	6.00	1.25
		Nos. 746-749 (4)	10.85	2.75

Souvenir Sheet

750	A127	750fr multicolored	8.25	1.50

Litho. & Embossed

751	A127	1500fr gold & multi	16.00	—

Souvenir Sheet

751A	A127	1500fr gold & multi	15.00	—

1992 Winter Olympics, Albertville. Nos. 748-751A are airmail. No. 750 contains one 36x41mm stamp.
No. 751 exists in a souvenir sheet of 1. Value $22.
For surcharges see Nos. 796M, 800K, 804M, 812S.

1991, May 17   Litho.   Perf. 13½

Ground station, Moroni Volo-Volo.

752	A128	75fr multicolored	1.00	.20
753	A128	150fr multicolored	1.60	.45
754	A128	225fr multicolored	2.40	.75
755	A128	300fr multicolored	3.50	1.00
756	A128	500fr multicolored	5.50	1.25
		Nos. 752-756 (5)	14.00	3.65

For surcharge see 815N.

Indian Ocean Conference — A129

1991, June 17

757	A129	75fr multicolored	.30	.20
758	A129	150fr multicolored	.90	.75
759	A129	225fr multicolored	1.40	1.00
		Nos. 757-759 (3)	2.60	1.95

World War II,
50th Anniv.
A130

Actors, Films: 150fr, Errol Flynn, Objective Burma. 300fr, Henry Fonda, The Longest Day. 450fr, Humphrey Bogart, Sahara.

1991, Aug. 5

760	A130	150fr sil & multi	1.75	.45
761	A130	300fr sil & multi	3.25	.75
762	A130	450fr sil & multi	5.00	.90
		Nos. 760-762 (3)	10.00	2.10

No. 762 is airmail. Nos. 760-762 exist in souvenir sheets of 1.
For surcharges see Nos. 796D, 800H, 804B, 804G.

A131

Charles de
Gaulle
A132

De Gaulle and: 125fr, Battle of Koufra. 375fr, Battle of Britain. 500fr, Battle of Monte Cassino. 1000fr, Airplanes. 1500fr, De Gaulle at podium.

1991, Aug. 5   Litho.   Perf. 13½

763	A131	125fr multi	1.25	.30
764	A131	375fr multi	2.75	.75
765	A131	500fr multi	4.50	.90
		Nos. 763-765 (3)	8.50	1.95

Souvenir Sheet

766	A131	1000fr multi	12.00	2.00

Litho. & Embossed

767	A132	1500fr gold & multi	16.00	—

Nos. 765-767 are airmail. No. 767 exists in souvenir sheet of 1. Value $20.
For surcharges see Nos. 796G, 804N, 816I.

Anniversaries and Events — A133

Designs: 100fr, Satellite Columbus in polar orbit. 150fr, Gandhi. 250fr, Jean-Henri Dunant. 300fr, Wolfgang Amadeus Mozart. 375fr, Brandenburg Gate. 400fr, Konrad Adenauer. 450fr, Elvis Presley. 500fr, Ferdinand von Zeppelin.

1991, Nov. 18   Litho.   Perf. 13½

768	A133	100fr multicolored	1.25	.30
769	A133	150fr multicolored	1.60	.35
770	A133	250fr multicolored	2.50	.60
771	A133	300fr multicolored	3.25	.60
772	A133	375fr multicolored	4.50	.90
773	A133	400fr multicolored	4.50	.90
774	A133	450fr multicolored	5.50	1.00
a.		Souv. sheet, #771, 774	—	
775	A133	500fr multicolored	5.50	1.00
a.		Souv. sheet, #772-773, 775	—	
		Nos. 768-775 (8)	28.60	5.65

Nobel Peace Prize, 90th anniv. (#770). Mozart, bicent. of death (#771). Brandenburg Gate, bicent. (#772). Konrad Adenauer, 25th anniv. of death (#773). Elvis Presley, 15th anniv. of death (in 1992) (#774). Count Zeppelin, 75th anniv. of death (in 1992) (#775).
Nos. 774-775 are airmail. Nos. 768-775 exist in souvenir sheets of 1. Value, set $50.
For surcharges see Nos. 796F, 796H, 800G, 804C, 804O, 815F, 815O, 816J.

Mushrooms — A134

1992, Mar. 23   Litho.   Perf. 13½

776	A134	75fr Cepe comestible	.80	.40
777	A134	150fr Geastre en etoile	1.90	.60
778	A134	600fr Pezize ecarlate	8.25	1.50
		Nos. 776-778 (3)	10.95	2.50

No. 778 is airmail. Nos. 776-778 exist imperf. and in souvenir sheets of one.

Shells
A135

1992, Mar. 23

779	A135	125fr Conus textile	1.60	.50
780	A135	150fr Cypraecassis rufa	2.10	.65
781	A135	500fr Leporicypraea mappa	6.50	1.90
		Nos. 779-781 (3)	10.20	3.05

Souvenir Sheet

782	A135	750fr Nautilus pompilius	10.50	2.00

Nos. 781-782 are airmail. Nos. 779-781 exist imperf. and in souvenir sheets of one. No. 782 exists imperf.
For surcharges see Nos. 800N, 816K.

Space
Programs
A136

Designs: 75fr, Mercury rocket, chimpanzee Ham, US. 125fr, Mars Observer, US. No. 785, Veronica rocket, cat Felix, France. No. 786, Mars rover, US, Mars car, USSR. 500fr, Phobos project, USSR. 600fr, Sputnik II, dog Laika, USSR. 1000fr, Viking, US, vert.

1992, Mar. 30   Litho.   Perf. 13½

783	A136	75fr multicolored	1.25	.25
784	A136	125fr multicolored	1.75	.30
785	A136	150fr multicolored	2.25	.70
786	A136	150fr multicolored	2.10	.70
787	A136	500fr multicolored	6.50	1.25
a.		Souv. sheet, #784, 786-787	7.75	1.40
788	A136	600fr multicolored	7.75	1.40
a.		Souv. sheet, #783, 785, 788		
		Nos. 783-788 (6)	21.60	4.60

Souvenir Sheet

789	A136	1000fr multicolored	13.00	2.25

Nos. 787-789 are airmail. Nos. 783-788 exist imperf. and in souvenir sheets of one. No. 789 contains one 30x42mm stamp.
For surcharges see Nos. 800O, 804Q.

Voyages
of
Discovery
A137

Designs: 75fr, Space shuttle Endeavour, sailing ship Endeavour, Capt. Cook. 100fr, Satellite, sailing ship Golden Hinde, Sir Francis Drake. 150fr, ISO observation satellite, sailing ship Susan Constant, John Smith. 225fr, Probe B, sailing ship Discovery, Robert F. Scott. 375fr, Magellan probe over Venus, sailing ship, Ferdinand Magellan. 500fr, Newton probe, sailing ship Sao Gabriel, Vasco da Gama.
1000fr, Hermes-Columbus space shuttle, Columbus and his fleet.

1992, May 28   Litho.   Perf. 13½

790	A137	75fr multicolored	1.25	.25
791	A137	100fr multicolored	1.40	.30
792	A137	150fr multicolored	2.25	.45
793	A137	225fr multicolored	2.75	.75
794	A137	375fr multicolored	5.25	1.00

795	A137	500fr multicolored	6.00	1.25
a.		Souvenir sheet of 6, #790-795	15.00	7.00
		Nos. 790-795 (6)	18.90	4.00

Souvenir Sheet

796	A137	1000fr multicolored	13.00	2.25

Nos. 794-796 are airmail. Nos. 790-795 exist imperf. in souvenir sheets of one.
For surcharges see Nos. 796E, 800P, 804P.

Various Stamps Surcharged

a — (Obliterator
of dots)

Methods and Perfs as Before

1992-95

796A	A126	10fr on 300fr #741	
796B	A122	15fr on 375fr #715	
796C	AP41	25fr on 210fr #C164	
796D	A130	25fr on 300fr #761	
796E	A137	25fr on 375fr #794	
796F	A133	35fr on 400fr #773	
796G	A131	50fr on 375fr #764	
796H	A133	50fr on 375fr #772	
796I	AP34	50fr on 475fr #C138	
796J	A121	75fr on 300fr #708	
796K	A121	75fr on 375fr #709	
796L	A125	75fr on 375fr #732	
796M	A127	75fr on 375fr #748	
796N	AP42	75fr on 600fr #C170	
796O	A125	100fr on 375fr #732	
796P	A109	150fr on 210fr #633	
796Q	A120	150fr on 375fr #697	
796R	A126	150fr on 375fr #742	
796S	AP40	150fr on 450fr #C162	
796T	A109	150fr on 500fr #634	
796U	AP42	150fr on 500fr #C169	

No. 796J exists with quadruple surcharge.
No. 796Q exists with inverted surcharge and with double surcharge, one inverted.

Organization of
African Unity,
30th
Anniv. — A138

1993, Feb. 15   Litho.   Perf. 13½x13

797	A138	25fr blue & multi	.20	.20
798	A138	50fr pink & multi	.50	.20

Perf. 12

799	A138	75fr green & multi	1.40	.45
800	A138	150fr vermilion & multi	2.25	1.00
		Nos. 797-800 (4)	4.35	1.85

Various Stamps Surcharged

b — (Bar
obliterator)

Methods and Perfs as Before

1992-95

800A	A103	50fr on 450fr #607	
x.		Zero in surcharge thin at top and bottom	
800B	AP47	75fr on 800fr #C192	
800C	A112	100fr on 350fr #648	
f.		Zero in surcharge thin at top and bottom	—

800D	A119 100fr on 375fr #689	
g.	Zero in surcharge thin at top and bottom	—
y.	150fr on 375fr #689 (error)	
800E	A101 100fr on 400fr #590	
800F	A105 100fr on 400fr #618	
h.	Zero in surcharge thin at top and bottom	—
800G	A133 100fr on 400fr #773	
i.	Zero in surcharge thin at top and bottom	—
800H	A130 125fr on 450fr #762	
800I	A126 150fr on 250fr #740	
j.	Zero in surcharge thin at top and bottom	—
800J	A121 150fr on 375fr #709	
z.	Zero in surcharge thin at top and bottom	—
800K	A127 150fr on 375fr #748	
a.	Zero in surcharge thin at top and bottom	—
800L	A109 150fr on 500fr #634	
k.	Zero in surcharge thin at top and bottom	—
800M	A112 150fr on 500fr #650	
b.	Zero in surcharge thin at top and bottom	—
800N	A115 150fr on 500fr #781	
800O	A136 150fr on 500fr #787	
800P	A137 150fr on 500fr #795	
800Q	AP41 150fr on 500fr #C165	
d.	Zero in surcharge thin at top and bottom	—
800R	AP44 150fr on 500fr #C177	
l.	Zero in surcharge thin at top and bottom	—
m.	Denomination above obliterator	
n.	As "m," denomination above obliterator	
800S	AP45 150fr on 500fr #C181	
e.	Zero in surcharge thin at top and bottom	—
800T	AP42 150fr on 500fr #C185	
o.	Zero in surcharge thin at top and bottom	—
800U	AP47 150fr on 500fr #C191	
800V	AP50 150fr on 500fr #C212	
t.	Zero in surcharge thin at top and bottom	—
800W	A122 150fr on 600fr #716	

Surcharge on No. 800W is sideways reading top to bottom. Nos. 800B and 800F exist with inverted surcharge, Nos. 800R and 800W exist with misplaced surcharge.
No. 800F exists with zeros in surcharge in different sizes.

1994 World Cup Soccer Championships, U.S. — A139

Intl. Telecommunications Day — A140

1993, May 12   Litho.   Perf. 13x12½

801	A139	25fr red & multi	.20	.20
802	A139	75fr brown & multi	.65	.30
803	A139	100fr blue & multi	1.40	.40
804	A139	150fr green & multi	1.60	.60
		Nos. 801-804 (4)	3.85	1.50

Various Stamps Surcharged Type "b" in Black or Red
Methods and Perfs as Before
1992-95

804A	A126 200fr on 300fr #741	
s.	Zero in surcharge thin at top and bottom	—
804B	A130 200fr on 300fr #761	
804C	A133 200fr on 300fr #771	
w.	Zero in surcharge thin at top and bottom	—
804D	AP45 200fr on 300fr #C180	
x.	Zero in surcharge thin at top and bottom	—

804E	AP47 200fr on 300fr #C190	
t.	Zero in surcharge thin at top and bottom	—
804F	A90 200fr on 400fr #520	
u.	Overprint right side up	
y.	Overprint right side up, zero in surcharge thin at top and bottom	—
804G	A130 200fr on 450fr #762	
a.	Zero in surcharge thin at top and bottom	—
b.	As "a," two obliterators	
804H	AP40 200fr on 450fr #C162	
c.	Zero in surcharge thin at top and bottom	—
804I	A120 225fr on 375fr #697	
804J	A122 225fr on 375fr #715	
804K	A125 225fr on 375fr #732	
804L	A126 225fr on 375fr #742	
804M	A127 225fr on 375fr #748	
v.	"f" in surcharge omitted	
804N	A127 225fr on 375fr #764	
804O	A133 225fr on 375fr #772	
804P	A137 225fr on 375fr #794	
804Q	A136 225fr on 375fr #787	

Red Surcharge

804R	AP40 200fr on 300fr #C161	

Surcharge on No. 804F is inverted.
No. 804D exists with "020fr" surcharge and with zeroes in surcharge in different sizes. Nos. 804D and 804F exists with zeroes in surcharge in different sizes.

1993, May 17

805	A140	50fr red & multi	.40	.20
806	A140	75fr blue & multi	.65	.30
807	A140	100fr green & multi	1.10	.40
808	A140	150fr black & multi	1.60	.60
		Nos. 805-808 (4)	3.75	1.50

Miniature Sheet

Prehistoric Animals A141

Designs: a, 75fr, Edaphosaurus. b, 75fr, Moschops. c, 75fr, Sauroctonus. d, 75fr, Ornitholestes. e, 75fr, Kentrosaurus. f, 75fr, Compsognathus. g, 75fr, Styracosaurus. h, 75fr, Acantholphis. i, 150fr, Edmontonia. j, 150fr, Struthiomimus. k, 150fr, Dromiceiomimus. l, 450fr, Iguanodon. m, 150fr, Diatryma. n, 150fr, Uintatherium. o, 525fr, Synthetoceras. p, 525fr, Euryapteryx. 1200fr, Tyrannosaurus rex.

1994, Apr. 5   Litho.   Perf. 13½

809	A141	Sheet of 16, #a.-p.	22.50	9.00

Souvenir Sheet

810	A141	1200fr multicolored	13.00	3.00

No. 810 is airmail and contains one 42x60mm stamp.

Miniature Sheets

Flora — A142

Orchids: No. 811a, 75fr, Hibiscus syriacus. 150fr, Pyrostegia venusta. 525fr, Allamanda cathartica.
Vegetables: No. 811b, 75fr, Anacardier. 150fr, Manioc. 525fr, Cacao.
Mushrooms: No. 811c, 75fr, Suillus lutens. 150fr, Lycogala epidendron. 525fr, Clathrus ruber.
Butterflies, insects: No. 812a, 75fr, Colotis zoe. b, 150fr, Acherontia atropos. c, 450fr, Danaus chrysippus. d, 75fr, Charaxes comoranus. e, 150fr, Euchloron megaera. f, 450fr, Papilio phorbanta. g, 75fr, Hypurgus ova. h, 150fr, Onthophagus catta. i, 450fr, Echinosoma bolivari.

1994, May 24   Litho.   Perf. 13½

811	A142	Sheet of 9	16.00	5.50
a.		Strip of 3	4.25	1.50
b.		Strip of 3	4.25	1.50
c.		Strip of 3	4.25	1.50
d.		Souvenir sheet of 3, #811a	16.00	5.00
e.		Souvenir sheet of 3, #811b	16.00	5.00
f.		Souvenir sheet of 3, #811c	16.00	5.00
812	A142	Sheet of 9, #a.-i.	15.00	5.00
j.		Souv. sheet of 3, #812a-812c	16.00	5.00
k.		Souv. sheet of 3, #812d-812f	16.00	5.00
l.		Souv. sheet of 3, #812g-812i	16.00	5.00

For surcharges see No. 826F.

Independence, 20th Anniv. — A142a

Designs: 100fr, 200fr, 300fr, Maps of Grand Comoro, Moheli, Mayotte and Anjouan.

1995 (?)   Litho.   Perf. 13x12¾

812M	A142a 100fr multi		—
812N	A142a 200fr multi		—
812O	A142a 300fr multi		—

For surcharge see No. 826M.

Various Stamps Surcharged in Gold

c — (Wide numerals, obliterator of small sqares in grid)

Methods and Perfs as Before
1996, Dec.

812P	AP40 200fr on 300fr #C161	
812Q	A102 200fr on 350fr #598	
812R	A121 200fr on 375fr #709	
v.	"2" same size as "0"	
812S	A127 200fr on 375fr #748	
812T	AP31 200fr on 400fr #C125	
812U	AP44 200fr on 500fr #C177	

Size of numerals and obliteration grids varies.

A143   A144

Diana, Princess of Wales (1961-97): Various portraits.

1997, Dec. 15   Litho.   Perf. 14

813	A143	150fr Sheet of 12, #a.-l.	10.00	4.00
814	A143	375fr Sheet of 6, #a.-f.	12.00	5.00

Souvenir Sheet

815	A143	1000fr multicolored	5.50	2.25

Various Stamps Surcharged Type "c" in Black
Methods and Perfs as Before
1996, Dec.

815A	A109 200fr on 210fr #633	
815B	A111 200fr on 210fr #640	
815C	AP41 200fr on 210fr #C164	
815D	A114 200fr on 250fr #660	
815E	A126 200fr on 250fr #740	
815F	A133 200fr on 250fr #770	
815G	AP30 200fr on 250fr #C116	
815H	AP38 200fr on 250fr #C151	
815I	AP38 200fr on 250fr #C152	
x.	Pair, #815H-815I + label	
815J	AP42 200fr on 250fr #C168	
815K	AP42 200fr on 250fr #C184	
815L	AP28 200fr on 260fr #C110	
815M	A101 200fr on 300fr #589	
y.	With gold obliterator over old value	
815N	A128 200fr on 300fr #755	
815O	A133 200fr on 300fr #771	
815P	AP31 200fr on 300fr #C124	
815Q	AP37 200fr on 300fr #C150	
815R	A107 200fr on 350fr #626	
815S	A98 200fr on 360fr #574	
815T	A119 200fr on 375fr #689	
815U	A126 200fr on 375fr #742	
815V	A112 200fr on 400fr #649	
815W	A111 200fr on 425fr #641	

Size of surcharge numerals and obliteration grid varies. Black surcharge on No. 815My is misplaced. No. 815Q exists with misplaced surcharge that is faintly tripled, a surcharge with thinner zeroes, and a pair containing No. C150 next to No. 815Q with misplaced surcharge that is faintly tripled and has thinner zeroes. No. 815W exists with an inverted surcharge and with a double surcharge, one inverted.

1997, Dec. 15   Litho.   Perf. 14

816	A144	200fr Mother Teresa (1910-97)	1.50	.45

No. 816 was issued in sheets of 9.

Aromatic Plants A144a

Designs: 25fr, 50fr, 1000fr, Piper nigrum. 100fr, 125fr, 200fr, Cinnamomum ceylanicum. 300fr, Syzygium aromaticum. 500fr, Myristica fragrans.

1997, Dec. 15   Litho.   Perf. 14

816A	A144a 25fr multi	
816B	A144a 50fr multi	
816C	A144a 100fr multi	
816D	A144a 125fr multi	
816E	A144a 200fr multi	
816F	A144a 300fr multi	
816G	A144a 500fr multi	
816H	A144a 1000fr multi	

Various Stamps Surcharged Type "c" in Black
Methods and Perfs as Before
1996, Dec.

816I	A131 200fr on 500fr #765	
816J	A133 200fr on 500fr #775	
816K	A135 200fr on 500fr #781	
816L	AP42 200fr on 500fr #C169	
816M	AP42 200fr on 500fr #C185	
816N	AP42 200fr on 600fr #C170	
816O	AP42 200fr on 600fr #C186	

Size of surcharge and obliteration grid varies.

Vertical Pairs from No. B4 Surcharged with Silver Bar to Obliterate Surtax
Methods and Perfs as before.
1996, Dec.

816P	Surcharged pair of #B4a, B4e	
t.	SP3 200fr on 200fr+10fr Galileo	
u.	SP3 200fr on 210fr Planet A & 3 stars	
816Q	Surcharged pair of #B4b, B4f	
v.	SP3 200fr on 200fr+10fr Copernicus	
w.	SP3 200fr on 200fr+10fr ICE	

816R Surcharged pair of
#B4c, B4g
x. SP3 200fr on 200fr+10fr Kepler
y. SP3 200fr on 200fr+10fr Planet
A & 5 stars
816S Surcharged pair of
#B4d, B4h
z. SP3 200fr on 200fr+10fr Halley
aa. SP3 200fr on 200fr+10fr Vega

A full sheet of Nos. 816P-816S is not known
to exist.

Cats
A145

Designs, vert: 75fr, Silver banded. 150fr,
Lac de Van. No. 819, 200fr, European short
hair. No. 820, 200fr, Somali. No. 821, 375fr,
Japanese bobtail. No. 822, 375fr, Egyptian
mau.
No. 823, each 375fr: a, Poupée de chiffon.
b, Maine coon. c, Norwegian forest cat. d, Persian. e, Droop-eared. f, Marbled American
short hair.
No. 824, each 375fr: a, Manx. b, Cashmere.
c, British shorthair. d, Cornish rex. e, American curl. f, Ocicat.
No. 825, 1500fr, Silver-chocolate Somali.
No. 826, 1500fr, Chocolate Persian, vert.

1998, June 3	Litho.	Perf. 14
817-822 A145	Set of 6	7.50 7.50
Sheets of 6		
823-824 A145	Set of 2	24.00 24.00
Souvenir Sheets		
825-826 A145	Set of 2	17.50 6.00

**No. C215D Surcharged Type "c" in
Red or Black**

Methods and Perfs as Before

1997 (?)
826A AP52a 100fr on 225fr
826B AP52a 200fr on 225fr
826C AP52a 200fr on 225fr (Bk)
826D AP52a 500fr on 225fr
826E AP52a 600fr on 225fr

Size of surcharge numerals varies. No.
826B exists with inverted surcharge, No. 826C
exists with double surcharge.

No. 811 Surcharged on Six Stamps

d — (Obliterator of Triangles and
Wavy Lines)

Methods and Perfs as Before

1998 (?)
826F Sheet of 9
g. A142 200fr on 150fr Pyrostegia
venusta
h. A142 200fr on 150fr Manioc
i. A142 200fr on 150fr Lycogala epidendron
j. A142 200fr on 525fr Allamanda
cathartica
k. A142 200fr on 525fr Cacao
l. A142 200fr on 525fr Clathrus
ruber

The three 75fr stamps on the sheet received
no surcharge.

No. 8120 Surcharged

e — (Obliterator of Bars, Dots, and
Semicircles)

Methods and Perfs as Before

1998 (?)
826M A142a 100fr on 300fr

Size of surcharge numerals varies.

Marine
Life
A146

No. 827, each 150fr: a, Pomacanthus imperator. b, Cephalopholis miniatus. c, Diver. d,
Nautilus pompilius. e, Sphyraena barracuda. f,
Manta birostris. g, Lutjanus sebae. h,
Chaetodonplus duboulayi. i, Amphiprion
bicinctus.
No. 828, vert , each 150fr: a, Istiophorus
platypterus. b, Sterna fuscata. c, Larus pipix-
can. d, Hippocampus kuda. e, Amphiprion
ocellaris (2 fish). f, Octopus vulgaris. g, Chaetodon striatus. h, Actini aquina. i, Acanthurus
leucosternon.
No. 829: a, Diomedea exulans. b, Delphinus
delphis. c, Sailboat. d, Sphyrna zygaena. e,
Loligo forbesi. f, Galeocerdo cuvieri. g, Pomacanthus imperator, diff. h, Amphiprion ocellaris
(1 fish). i, Forcipiger flavissimus. j, Electropho-
rus electricus. k, Dermochelys coriaoea. l,
Asterias rubens.
No. 830, 1500fr, Mastigias papua, vert. No.
831, 1500fr, Sepia officinalis. No. 832, 1500fr,
Zancius canescens.

1998, Aug. 10	Litho.	Perf. 14
Sheets of 9 or 12		
827-828 A146	Set of 2	13.00 13.00
829 A146	200fr #a.-l.	12.00 12.00
Souvenir Sheets		
830-832 A146	Set of 3	22.50 22.50

Nos. 830-832 each contain one 51x38mm
or 38x51mm stamp.

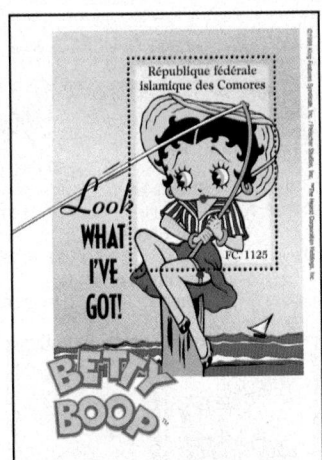

Betty Boop — A146a

No. 832A: b, Wearing hula skirt, dancing. c,
With dog, wearing blue dress, in pink heart. d,
Wearing polka dot dress. e, In bathtub. f, Face
in red heart. g, Holding top hat. h, With flamingos. i, With dog, Wearing red dress, blue
ribbon. j, Wearing hula skirt, on surf board.
1125fr, With fishing pole.

1998	Litho.	Perf. 13¼
832A A146a	300fr Sheet of 9, #b-j	— —
Souvenir Sheet		
832K A146a	1125fr multi	— —

No. 832A contains nine 35x41mm stamps.

Popeye — A146b

No. 832L: m, Wimpy. n, Popeye, Olive Oyl,
ship's wheel. o, Swee'Pea. p, Head of Popeye.
q, Popeye. r, Head of Olive Oyl. s, Jeep. t,
Olive Oyl. u, Brutus.
No. 832V, 1125fr, Popeye with spinach can.
No. 832W, 1125fr, Like #832Ln, horiz.

1998
832L A146b 450fr Sheet of 9,
#m-u   — —
Souvenir Sheets
832V-832W A146b Set of 2   — —

No. 832L contains nine 35x51mm stamps,
No. 832W contains one 60x50mm stamp.

Coelacanth — A147

World Wildlife Fund: a, Swimming right,
colored background. b, Swimming right, white
background. c, In net. d, Swimming left.
No. 833E: f, Like #833a. g, Like #833d. h,
Like #833c. i, Like #833b.

1998
833 A147 200fr Strip of 4, #a-
d   6.00 6.00
833E A147 375fr Sheet of 4, #f-i 37.50

No. 833 was issued in sheets of 3 vertical
strips.
No. 833E exists imperf.

I Love Lucy — A147a

No. 833F, vert. — Lucy: g, With black ribbon
in hair. h, Wearing burlap sack. i, With trapeze
in mouth. j, With one arm raised. k, On telephone. l, Wearing red and white apron. m,
Wearing bright green dress. n, Wearing blue
dress. o, With fishing gear.
1125fr, With Ricky, with fishing gear.

1998	Litho.	Perf. 13¼
833F A147a	250fr Sheet of 9, #g-o	— —
Souvenir Sheet		
833P A147a	1125fr multi	— —

No. 833F contains nine 35x51mm stamps.

Diana,
Princess of
Wales (1961-
97)
A148

Nos. 834-835, 835J, Various portraits.
No. 836, 1125fr, Wearing scarf, green
dress. No. 837, 1125fr, Wearing black and
white hat and outfit.

1998	Litho.	Perf. 13½
Sheets of 9		
834 A148	250fr #a.-i.	13.00 13.00
835 A148	350fr #a.-i.	18.00 18.00
835J A148	450fr #k.-s.	24.00 24.00
Souvenir Sheets		
836-837 A148	Set of 2	13.00 13.00

Nos. 835, 835J contain 42x51mm stamps.
Nos. 836-837 each contain one 42x60mm
stamp.

Entertainers
A149

#838: Various portraits of Grace Kelly (Prin-
cess Grace of Monaco) (1929-92).
#839: Various portraits of Frank Sinatra
(1915-98).

1998
Sheets of 9		
838 A149	300fr #a.-i.	16.00 16.00
839 A149	500fr #a.-i.	26.50 26.50

Classic Automobiles — A150

No. 840, each 150fr: a, 1936 Jaguar SS. b,
1939 Lincoln Continental. c, 1903 Mercedes.
d, 1936 MG-TA. e, 1946 Oldsmobile Custom
Cruiser 98. f, 1933 Pontiac. g, 1940 Rolls-
Royce Silver Ghost 40/50. h, 1950 Studebaker
Starlight Coupe. i, 1932 Ford V8.
No. 841, each 150fr: a, 1927 Alfa Romeo
RLSS. b, 1933 DuPont Model G. c, Bentley
Speed Six. d, 1932 Cadillac 355. e, 1955 Cor-
vette. f, 1934 Chrysler Airflow. g, Buick Coupe
deVille. h, Model T Ford. i, 1920 Duesenberg
Model A.
No. 842, 1500fr, Rolls-Royce Phantom II
Continental. No. 843, 1500fr, 1927 Daimler
Double Six.

1998, Oct. 29	Litho.	Perf. 14
Sheets of 9		
840-841 A150	Set of 2	13.00 13.00
Souvenir Sheets		
842-843 A150	Set of 2	17.00 17.00

Birds — A151

No. 844, 75fr, Macareux moine. No. 845, 75fr, Calliste à tête verte. No. 846, 150fr, Soutmanga de la reine Christine. No. 847, 150fr, Rale d'eau. No. 848, 200fr, Lophophore replendissant. No. 849, 200fr, Francolin noir. No. 850, 375fr, Mesia â oreillonis argentes. No. 851, 375fr, Mérion splendide.

No. 852: a, Canard plongeur austral. b, Garrot a ceil d'or. c, Harle huppé. d, Canard colvert. e, Canard branchu. f, Sarcelle elegante.

No. 853: a, Emérillon. b, Nyctale de tengmalm. c, Aigle royal d, Kétoupa malais. e, Caracara. f, Chouette à lunettes

No. 854, Jacana du mexique. No. 855, Toucan de cuvier.

1999, Jan. 23   Litho.   Perf. 14
844-851 A151 Set of 8   8.50 8.50
Sheets of 6, #a-f
852-853 A151 375fr Set of 2   22.50 22.50
Souvenir Sheets
854-855 A151 1500fr Set of 2   16.00 16.00

Fauna
A152

No. 856, vert, each 150fr: a, Giraffa camaloprdalis. b, Macaca fusata. c, Loxodonta africana. d, Ovis dalli. e, Phoenicopterus ruber. f, Orcinus orca. g, Ursus horribilis. h, Lemur catta.

No. 857, vert, each 150fr: a, Pongo pygmaeus. b, Ceratotherium simum. c, Ailuropoda melanoleuca. d, Tursiops truncartus. e, Felis caracel. g, Eudyptes chrysocome. h, Bison bison. i, Panthera uncia.

No. 858, vert, each 150fr: a, Phascolarctos cinereus. b, Ammotragus levia. c, Hippopatamus amphibius. d, Saimiri boliviensis. e, Acinonyx jubatus. f, Gorilla gorilla. g, Branta sandvicensis. h, Thalarctos maritimus.

No. 859, each 150fr: a, Panthera tigris. b, Phoca groenlandica. c, Acipenser sturio. d, Lepidochelys kempii. e, Ailuropoda melanoleuca. f, Isurus oxyrinchus. g, Chelydra serpentina. h, Eretmochelys imbricata.

Each 1500fr: No. 860: Pan troglodytes, vert. No. 861, Panthera tigris altaica, vert. No. 862, Oryx gazella, vert. No. 863, Hippotigris zebra. No. 864, Diceros bicornis. No. 865, Panthera leo. No. 866, Amazona viridgenalis. No. 867, Pygoscelis papua, vert.

1999, Jan. 25
Sheets of 8
856-859 A152 Set of 4   25.00 25.00
Souvenir Sheets
860-867 A152 Set of 8   65.00 65.00

Fish
A153

No. 868, 75fr, Pomacantus imperator. No. 869, 75fr, Heniochus intermedium. No. 870, 150fr, Mirolaprichthys. No. 871, 150fr, Pomacanthus paru. No. 872, 375fr, Ostzacion tuberculatus. No. 873, 375fr, Colisa calia.

No. 874, each 150fr: a, Coris aygula. b, Chromis caeruleys. c, Euxiphipops navarchus. d, Pseudobalistes fuscus. e, Zebrasoma flavescens. f, Mycteroperca urba. g, Epinephelus flavocaeruleus. h, Equetus lanceolatus. i, Acanthurus leucostemon.

No. 875, each 150fr: a, Chaetodon tinkeri. b, Ostzaciidae. c, Seatophagus argus. d, Adioryx coruscus. e, Pygoplites diacanthus. f, Paracanthurus hepatus. g, Chaetodon plebius. h, Lythrypnus dalli. i, Myrichthys oculatus.

Each 1500fr: No. 876, Amphipzion percula. No. 877, Cymnothorne undulatus.

1998, Oct.-Nov.   Litho.   Perf. 14
868-873 A153 Set of 6   7.00 7.00
Sheets of 9
874-875 A153 Set of 2   14.00 14.00
Souvenir Sheets
876-877 A153 Set of 2   16.00 16.00

Marine Life — A154

No. 878, 75fr, Tubastrea aurea. No. 879, 75fr, Condylachtis gigantea. No. 880, 150fr, Paracanthurus hepatus. No. 881, 150fr, Balistoides conspicillum. No. 882, 200fr, Diodon holocanthus. No. 883, 200fr, Sebastes rubrivintus. No. 884, 375fr, Trygonorhina fasciata. No. 885, 375fr, Phocoenoides dalli.

No. 886, each 150fr: a, Epinephelus guttatus. b, Diademichthys lineatus. c, Plotosus lineatus. d, Rhinomuraena quaesita. e, Zanclus cornutus. f, Persephona punctata. g, Murex pecten. h, Tetrosomus gibbosus.

No. 887, each 150fr: a, Lythrpnus dalli. b, Premnas biacilleatus. c, Psendathias tuka. d, Capros aper. e, Balistoides conspicillum. f, Oreaster reticulatus. g, Octopus joubini. h, Fasciolaris tulipa.

Each 1500fr: No. 888, S. picturatus. No. 889, Megaptera novaeangliae.

1999
878-885 A154 Set of 8   8.50 8.50
Sheets of 8
886-887 A154 Set of 2   17.00 17.00
Souvenir Sheets
888-889 A154 Set of 2   19.00 19.00

Prehistoric Animals — A155

No. 890, each 150fr: a, Meganeura. b, Archaeopteryx. c, Peteinosaurus. d, Eudimorphodon. e, Brachiosaurus. f, Gallimimus. g, Tarbosaurus. h, Parasaurolophus. i, Sauropelta. j, Herrarasaurus. k, Stegosaurus. l, Lambeosaurus.

No. 891, each 150fr: a, Ramphorhinchus. b, Quetzalcoatlus. c, Pterodactylus. d, Pteranodon. e, Dimorphodon. f, Camarasaurus. g, Tenontosaurus. h, Protoceratops. i, Coelurosaurus. j, Mixosaurus. k, Ceresiosaurus. l, Sharovipteryx.

Each 1500fr: No. 892, Ceratosaurus. No. 893, Mesosaurus. No. 894, Megazostrodon. No. 895, Diatryma.

1999
Sheets of 12
890-891 A155 Set of 2   19.00 19.00
Souvenir Sheets
892-895 A155 Set of 4   32.50 32.50

Prehistoric Animals, Lemurs and Butterflies — A156

Prehistoric animals — No. 895A — Prehistoric sea creatures: b, Eurhinodelphis. c, Stenopterygius. d, Ichthyosaurus. e, Pakicetus. f, Xenacanthus. g, Zygorhiza. h, Basilosaurus. i, Mesosaurus. j, Cetotherium. No. 896: a, Elasmosaurus (b). b, Quetzalcoatl (c). c, Mesadactyl (b). d, Dimorphodon (e). e, Rhamphorhynchus (c, d, f, i). f, Pteranodon (c, i). g, Pterodactylus (h). h, Eudimorphodon (i). i), Ornithodesmus (g, h).

Lemurs — No. 897: a, Haplorhinien primitif. b, Aye aye (c, e, f). c, Lemur vari. d, Indri. e,

Makis varis (f, i). f, Potto. g, Lemur catta. h, Lemur macaos. i, Microcebe souris.

Butterflies — No. 898: a, Charaxes nobilis. b, Charaxes eupale. c, Charaxes brutus. d, Lobobunea turlini. e, Papilio nobilis. f, Athletes gigas. g, Papilio antimachus. h, Epiphora albida. i, Papilio zalmoxis.

1998   Perf. 13¼x13½
Sheets of 9
895A A156 150fr Sheet of 9,
                       #b-j   6.50   6.50
896   A156 200fr #a.-i.   9.75   9.75
897   A156 250fr #a.-i.   12.00 12.00
898   A156 300fr #a.-i.   14.50 14.50
See Nos. 928-933.

A157

Endangered Species — A157a

Designs: 75fr, Galago crassicaudatus. 150fr, Vulpes vulpes. 200fr, Anomalurus pusillus. 375fr, Loxodonta africana, vert.

Primates, vert: Nos. 903a-903c, Various views of Pan troglodytes. Nos. 903d-903f, Various views of gorilla gorilla. Nos. 903g-903i, Various views of pongo pygmaeus.

No. 904, each 375fr: a, Tragelaphus strepsiceros. b, Capra hircus. c, Egretta alba. d, Tockus flavirostris.

No. 905, each 375fr: a, Ursus maritimus. b, Megaptera novaeangliae. c, Phoca vitulina. d, Aptenodytes forsteri.

No. 906, each 375fr: a, Pelecanus occidentalis. b, Orcinus orca. c, Delphinus delphis. d, Iguana iguana.

No. 907: a, Panthera tigris altaica. b, Camelus bactrianus. c, Canus lupus. d, Cuon alpinus. e, Rangifer tarandus dawsoni. f, Gulo gulo.

Each 1500fr: No. 908, Loxodonta africana, vert. No. 909, Ursus thibetanus.

Perf. 14, 14½x14 (#904-906)
1999, Jan. 25   Litho.
899-902 A157 Set of 4   4.50 4.50
903   A157 150fr Sheet of 9,
                  #a.-i.   8.00 8.00
Sheets of 4
904-906 A157a Set of 3   24.00 24.00
Sheet of and 6
907   A157 375fr #a.-f.   12.00 12.00
Souvenir Sheets
908-909 A157 Set of 2   16.00 16.00

Mushrooms
A158   A159

No. 910, 75fr, Russula xerampelina. No. 911, 75fr, Catathelasma imperiale. No. 912, 150fr, Cortinarius violaceus. No. 913, 150fr, Cortinarius camphoratus. No. 914, 200fr, Rozites caperata. No. 915, 200fr, Coprinus picaceus. No. 916, 375fr, Coprinus cromatus. No. 917, 375fr, Russula cavipes.

No. 918, each 150fr: a, Boletus edulis. b, Suillus grevillei. c, Boletinus cavipes. d,

Morchella esculenta. e, Morchella conica. f, Clitocybe dealbata. g, Hygrocybe nigrescens. h, Clitocybe geotropa. i, Lepiota cristata.

No. 919, each 150fr: a, Amanita citrina. b, Amanita phalloides. c, Cortinarius praestans. d, Phallus impudicus. e, Cortinarius bicolor. f, Cortinarius renidens. g, Lactarius torminosus. h, Boletus satanas. i, Cystolepiota bucknalii.

No. 920, each 375fr: a, Amanita muscaria. b, Coprinus comatus. c, Clitocybe odora. d, Cantharellus cibarius. e, Mycena epipterygia. f, Marasmius oreades.

No. 921, each 375fr: a, Boletus edulis. b, Laccaria laccata. c, Agaricus campestris. d, Hypholoma fasciculare. e, Lepiota procera. f, Russula aurata.

Each 1500fr: No. 922, Ramaria aurea, horiz. No. 923, Panellus serotinus. No. 924, Macrolepiota procera. No. 925, Amanita muscaria. No. 926, Hebeloma crustuliniforme. No. 927, Lepiota molybdites.

1999   Litho.   Perf. 14
910-917 A158 Set of 8   8.50 8.50
Sheets of 9
918-919 A158 Set of 2   14.00 14.00
Sheets of 6
920-921 A159 Set of 2   24.00 24.00
Souvenir Sheets
922-925 A158 Set of 4   32.50 32.50
926-927 A159 Set of 2   16.00 16.00

Raptors — A160

No. 927A — Birds: b, Souimanga royal. c, Martin-pecheur huppe. d, Pie-grieche. e, Barbican a tete roughe. f, Beau-marquet. g, Rollier a poitrine lilas. h, Pintade vulturine. i, Grenadier. j, Outarde korhaon.

No. 928: a, Sparrow hawk. b, Red-tailed buzzard. c, Dark kite. d, African fish eagle. e, Bald eagle. f, Fawn-colored vulture. g, Peregrine falcon. h, Osprey. i, Harpie eagle.

Dinosaurs — No. 929: a, Dilophosaurus. b, Megalosaurus. c, Ceratosaurus. d, Coelophysis. e, Tyrannosaurus. f, Deinonychus. g, Allosaurus. h, Stegosaurus. i, Albertosaurus.

Gems — No. 930: a, Ruby. b, Liroconite. c, Emerald. d, Euclase. e, Diamond. f, Chrysoberyl. g, Plancheite. h, Kasolite. i, Indigolite.

Meteorites — No. 931: a, Martian. b, Antarctic. c, C2 Chondrite. d, Archondrite. e, Octaedrite moyenne. f, Iron. g, Tektite. h, Chondrite olivine. i, Iron, diff.

Mushrooms — No. 932: a, Paxillus atrotomentosus. b, Craterellus cornucopioides. c, Boletus satanas. d, Clavaria truncata. e, Phallus impudicus. f, Scleroderma aurantiacum. g, Amanita citrina. h, Catathe lasma. i, Inocybe fastigiata.

1125fr, Wulfenite.

1998   Perf. 13¼x13½
Sheets of 9
927A A160 175fr Sheet of 9,
                  #b-j   8.00   8.00
928   A160 200fr #a.-i.   9.75   9.75
929   A160 250fr #a.-i.   11.50 11.50
930   A160 375fr #a.-i.   17.50 17.50
931   A160 400fr #a.-i.   19.00 19.00
932   A160 400fr #a.-i.   19.00 19.00
Souvenir Sheet
933   A160 1125fr multicolored 5.75   5.75
No. 933 contains one 36x51mm stamp. Captions on Nos. 928e and 928h are transposed.
See Nos. 896-898.

"Illegal" Stamps

Comoro Islands postal officials have declared as "illegal" the following items: Muhammad Ali, sheet of nine 300fr stamps (previously No. 934); Muhammad Ali, 1125fr souvenir sheet (previously No. 935); Babe Ruth, sheet of nine 375fr stamps; Babe Ruth, two 1125fr souvenir sheets; Ocean Life, sheet of nine stamps with values of 100, 150, 250, 300, 350, 400, 450, and 500fr; Horses, sheet of nine stamps with values of 100, 150, 250, 300, 350, 400, 450, and 500fr; Pandas, sheet of nine stamps with values of 100, 150, 250, 300, 350, 400, 450, and 500fr; Flora and Fauna: 25fr Harpe costata, 25fr Hibiscus, 50fr Volute lapponica, 50fr Tournesol de Comoros, 100fr Ghetonia mydas, 125fr Octopus vulgaris, 150fr Ylang ylang, 300fr Coelacanth, 300fr Tellina variegata. Famous People: 250fr, Willy Messerschmitt, Messerschmitt BF-109G-6/R6. 300fr, Louis Pasteur, rabies vaccine administered to Joseph Meister. 350fr, Dr. Albert Schweitzer. 400fr, Ferdinand von Zeppelin, flying Zeppelin. 475fr, Henri Dunant, Nobel Prize. 500fr, Albert Einstein, Gravity Probe B. 550fr, Ayrton Senna, race car. 600fr, Pope John Paul II. 750fr, Iranian Pres. Mohammad Khatami, Pope John Paul II. 800fr, Crew of Apollo 11. 1125fr souvenir sheet, Lindbergh, Spirit of St. Louis.

Submarines — A161

No. 934: a, USS Salt Lake City, US. b, Le Terrible, France. c, Amethyste, France.

1999 Litho. Perf. 13¼
934 A161 150fr Sheet of 3, #a-c 3.00 3.00

Automobiles — A161a

No. 935: a, Cadillac Eldorado, Cadillac Series 62, US. b, Aston Martin DB2 IV Mark III, Austin Healey. c, Alfa Romeo Superlegera, Alfa Romeo Giuletta. 1125fr, Aston Martin DB5.

1999
935 A161a 200fr Sheet of 3, #a-c 3.50 3.50
Souvenir Sheet
935D A161a 1125fr multi 7.00 7.00
No. 935D contains one 51x30mm stamp.

Motorcycles — A162

No. 935E: f, Honda NR. g, Christian Leliard and motorcycle. h, Joe S. Wright and motorcycle.

1999
935E A162 250fr Sheet of 3, #f-h 4.50 4.50

Helicopters — A162a

No. 936: a, Westland Wessex. b, MIL MI-8. c, Sikorsky 5-76 Spirit.

1999
936 A162a 300fr Sheet of 3, #a-c 5.50 5.50

Dogs and Sleds A163

No. 937: a, Alaskan malamute, US. b, Greenlandic. c, Siberian husky.

1999
937 A163 400fr Sheet of 3, #a-c 7.00 7.00

Airplanes A164

No. 938: a, Tupolev Tu-160. b, Lockheed F-117A. c, Rafale C.01.
No. 939: a, Ilyshin Il-76. b, Boeing E-3. c, Concorde. 1125fr, Concorde, diff.

1999 Litho. Perf. 13¼
Sheets of 3
938 A164 375fr #a.-c. 6.50 6.50
939 A164 450fr #a.-c. 8.00 8.00
Souvenir Sheet
940 A164 1125fr mulicolored 7.00 7.00
No. 940 contains one 50x30mm stamp.

Trains A165

No. 941: a, Series E. b, Series 9100. c, Kitson-Still I-C-I.
No. 942: a, HST 125. b, TGV. c, RTG. 1125fr, Sereis DD40AX.

1999 Litho. Perf. 13¼
Sheets of 3
941 A165 400fr #a.-c. 7.25 7.25
942 A165 500fr #a.-c. 9.00 9.00
Souvenir Sheet
943 A165 1125fr mulicolored 7.00 7.00
No. 943 contains one 50x30mm stamp.

Space Achievements — A166

#944: a, Shuttles Discovery, Buran. b, Ariane V. c, John Glenn, Saturn V.
#945: a, Valentina Tereshkova, Soyuz 4. b, Dogs Laika, Bielka. c, Yuri Gagarin, Vostok 1.

1999 Litho. Perf. 13¼
Sheets of 3
944 A166 500fr #a.-c. 9.00 9.00
945 A166 600fr #a.-c. 11.00 11.00
Space Achievements Type of 1999
Souvenir Sheet
1125fr, Space Shuttle Discovery, John Glenn.
946 A166 1125fr multi 7.00 7.00
No. 946 contains one 51x30mm stamp.

Teams in 1998 World Cup Soccer Tournament — A167

Players in 1998 World Cup Soccer Tournament — A168

No. 947, 150fr: a, Italy. b, Chile, c, Cameroun. d, Austria. e, Netherlands. f, Belgium. g, South Korea. h, Mexico.
No. 948, 250fr: a, Brazil. b, Scotland. c, Morocco. d, Norway. e, Spain. f, Nigeria. g, Paraguay. h, Bulgaria.
No. 949, 300fr: a, France. b, South Africa. c, Saudi Arabia. d, Denmark. e, Germany. f, United States. g, Yugoslavia. h, Iran.
No. 950, 500fr: a, England. b, Colombia. c, Romania. d, Tunisia. e, Argentina. f, Croatia. g, Jamaica. h, Japan.
No. 951, 350fr: a, Desailly, French flag. b, Ronaldo, Brazilian flag. c, Suker, Croatian flag. d, Kluivert, Netherlands flag. e, French players, World Cup trophy. f, Brazilian player (yellow and green shirt). g, Croatian player (checked shirt). h, Netherlands player (orange shirt).
Illustrations reduced.

1998 Litho. Perf. 13x13½
Sheets of 8, #a-h
947-950 A167 Set of 4 50.00 50.00
951 A168 multi 14.50 14.50

Trucks — A169

No. 952: a, Truck with ornamentation over cab. b, Blue truck. c, Green truck. d, Yellow truck.

1999 Litho. Perf. 13¼
952 A169 350fr Sheet of 4, #a-d — —

Automobile Racing, Chess, Tennis and Table Tennis, Fishing and Diving — A170

No. 953, 250fr — Automobile racing: a, Giuseppe Farina and Alfa 1500. b, Juan Fangio and Mercedes 2.5L. c, Jack Brabham and Cooper Climax 2.5L. d, Jim Clark and Lotus Climax 1.5L.

No. 954, 300fr — Chess players: a, Garry Kasparov. b, Akiba Rubinstein. c, Max Euwe. d, Mikhail Botvinnik.
No. 955, 375fr — Fishing and diving: a, Shark fishing. b, Sport fishing. c, Diver, back half of shark. d, Diver, front half of shark.
No. 956, 500fr — Chess players: a, Bent Larsen. b, José Raúl Capablanca. c, Boris Spassky. d, Bobby Fischer.
No. 957, 600fr — Tennis and table tennis: a, Female tennis player. b, Male table tennis player. c, Female table tennis player. d, Male tennis player.
No. 958, 1125fr — Chess players: a, Samuel Reshevsky. b, Vassili Smyslov.
No. 959, 1125fr — Fishing and diving: a, Sport fishing, diff. b, Divers and marine life.
No. 960, 1125fr — Tennis and table tennis: a, Male table tennis player, diff. b, Women tennis players.

1999 Perf. 13¼
Sheets of 4, #a-d
953-957 A170 Set of 5 47.50 47.50
Souvenir Sheets of 2, #a-b
958-960 A170 Set of 3 21.00 21.00

Nos. 816E, 816G Surcharged

Methods and Perfs. As Before
2001, June 16
963 A144a 100fr on 500fr multi — —
964 A144a 125fr on 200fr multi — —

Traditional Costumes A171

Designs: 125fr, Woman. No. 966, 150fr, No. 969, 300fr, Woman, diff. No. 967, 150fr, No. 968, 300fr, Man.

2002, Apr. 8 Litho. Perf. 13¼x13
965-969 A171 Set of 5 8.50 8.50

Flowers — A172

Designs: 50fr, Cananga odorata. 600fr, Vanilla planifolia.

2003, Oct. 9
970-971 A172 Set of 2 5.25 5.25

Marine Mammals A173

Designs: 75fr, Peponocephala electra. 1000fr, Megaptera novaeangliae.

2003, Oct. 9 Perf. 13x13¼
972-973 A173 Set of 2 9.00 9.00

Wood
Handicrafts
A174

Designs: 100fr, Carved door. 300fr, Candleholder.

2003, Oct. 9		**Perf. 13¼x13**	
974-975	A174	Set of 2	3.25 3.25

Orchids — A175

Orchid color: 50fr, White. 75fr, Yellow. 100fr, Mauve. 600fr, Red.

2003, Oct. 9			
976-979	A175	Set of 4	6.50 6.50

Diplomatic Relations Between Comoro
Islands and People's Republic of
China, 30th Anniv. — A176

No. 980: a, 125fr, Chinese President Hu Jintao and Comoro Islands President Azali Assoumani, country flags. b, 125fr, Coelacanth, Worldwide Fund for Nature emblem, country arms. c, 300fr, Comoros Islands Broadcasting Center, country arms. d, 600fr, Comoros Islands People's Palace, country flags.
Illustration reduced.

2006, Jan. 1		**Litho.**	**Perf. 12**
980	A176	Block of 4, #a-d	5.75 5.75

SEMI-POSTAL STAMPS

Anti-Malaria Issue
Common Design Type
Perf. 12½x12

1962, Apr. 7		**Engr.**	**Unwmk.**
B1	CD108	25fr + 5fr brt pink	4.00 4.00

WHO drive to eradicate malaria.

Nurse Feeding
Infant — SP1

Mother and
Child — SP2

1967, July 3		**Engr.**	**Perf. 13**
B2	SP1	25fr + 5fr multi	3.25 3.25

For the Red Cross.

1974, Aug. 10		**Engr.**	**Perf. 13**
B3	SP2	35fr + 10fr red & dk brn	2.50 2.50

For the Red Cross.
For surcharge see No. 144.

Miniature Sheet

Space
Achievements
SP3

World Philatelic Programs emblems (stamp collecting or Halley's Comet) and astronomer or satellite: a, Galileo. b, Copernicus. c, Kepler. d, Halley. e, *Planet A*, Japan, and 3 stars. f, *ICE*, US. g, *Planet A*, 5 stars. h, *Vega*, USSR.

1988		**Litho.**	**Perf. 13½**
B4		Sheet of 8	15.00 15.00
a.-h.	SP3	200fr +10fr multi	1.50 1.50

See No. C193.
For surcharges see Nos. 816P-816S.

AIR POST STAMPS

Comoro Village — AP1

Comoro Men and Moroni
Mosque — AP2

Design: 200fr, Mosque of Ouani, Anjouan.

1950-54		**Unwmk. Engr.**	**Perf. 13**
C1	AP1	50fr grn & red brn	3.50 1.25
C2	AP2	100fr dk brn & red	6.00 1.25
C3	AP1	200fr dk grn, rose brn	
		& pur ('54)	21.00 8.00
		Nos. C1-C3 (3)	30.50 10.50

Liberation Issue
Common Design Type

1954, June 6			
C4	CD102	15fr sepia & red	30.00 18.00

Madrepora
Fructicosa
AP3

100fr, Coral, shells and sea anemones.

1962, Jan. 13		**Photo.**	**Perf. 12½x13**
C5	AP3	100fr multi	16.00 16.00
C6	AP3	500fr multi	30.00 19.50

Telstar Issue
Common Design Type

1962, Dec. 5		**Engr.**	**Perf. 13**
C7	CD111	25fr dp vio, dl pur &	
		red lil	5.00 2.75

Type of Regular Issue
Unwmk.

1963, Dec. 27		**Engr.**	**Perf. 13**
		Size: 26½x48mm	
C8	A13	65fr Baskets	5.00 2.75
C9	A13	200fr Pendant	10.00 4.00

Boat Type of Regular Issue

1964, Aug. 7		**Photo.**	**Perf. 13**
		Size: 27x48mm	
C10	A14	50fr Mayotte pirogue	4.50 1.25
C11	A14	85fr Schooner	7.00 2.25

Olympic Torch
and
Boxers — AP4

Order of Star of
Grand
Comoro — AP5

1964, Oct. 10		**Engr.**	**Perf. 13**
C12	AP4	100fr red brn, dk brn &	
		gray grn	7.50 5.75

18th Olympic Games, Tokyo, Oct. 10-25.

1964, Dec. 10		**Photo.**	**Perf. 13**
C13	AP5	500fr multi	20.00 20.00

ITU Issue
Common Design Type

1965, May 17		**Engr.**	**Perf. 13**
C14	CD120	50fr gray, grnsh bl	
		& ol	24.00 15.00

French Satellite A-1 Issue
Common Design Type

Designs: 25fr, Diamant rocket and launching installations. 30fr, A-1 satellite.

1966, Jan. 17			**Perf. 13**
C15	CD121	25fr dk pur & ultra	4.00 4.00
C16	CD121	30fr dk pur & ultra	4.50 4.50
a.		Strip of 2, #C15-C16 + label	11.00 11.00

French Satellite D-1 Issue
Common Design Type

1966, May 16		**Engr.**	**Perf. 13**
C17	CD122	30fr dk grn, org &	
		brn	4.00 4.00

Old Gun Battery, Dzaoudzi — AP6

200fr, Ksar Castle, Mutsamudu, vert.

1966, Dec. 19		**Photo.**	**Perf. 13**
C18	AP6	50fr multi	5.00 2.25
C19	AP6	200fr multi	9.00 5.75

Bird Type of Regular Issue

Birds: 75fr, Madagascar paradise flycatchers. 100fr, Blue-cheeked bee eaters.

1967, June 20		**Photo.**	**Perf. 13**
		Size: 27x48mm	
C20	A17	75fr yel grn & multi	9.25 5.50
C21	A17	100fr lt bl & multi	13.00 6.50

Woman
Skier — AP7

1968, Apr. 29		**Engr.**	**Perf. 13**
C22	AP7	70fr brt grn, lt bl & choc	5.50 4.00

10th Winter Olympic Games, Grenoble, France, Feb. 6-18, 1968.

Fish Type of Regular Issue

50fr, Moorish idol. 90fr, Diagramma lineatus.

1968, Aug. 1		**Engr.**	**Perf. 13**
		Size: 47½x27mm	
C23	A19	50fr plum blk & yel	8.00 3.25
C24	A19	90fr brt grn, yel & gray	
		grn	10.00 4.00

For surcharge & overprint see #C52, C74.

Swimmer, Butterfly Stroke — AP8

1969, Jan. 27		**Photo.**	**Perf. 12½**
C25	AP8	65fr ver, grnsh bl & blk	5.00 3.00

19th Olympic Games, Mexico City, 10/12-27.

Flower Type of Regular Issue

50fr, Heliconia sp. 85fr, Tuberose. 200fr, Orchid (angraecum eburneum).

1969, Mar. 20		**Photo.**	**Perf. 13**
		Size: 27x48mm	
C26	A21	50fr multi, vert.	4.00 2.75
C27	A21	85fr multi, vert.	5.00 3.25
C28	A21	200fr multi, vert.	11.00 4.75
		Nos. C26-C28 (3)	20.00 10.75

Concorde Issue
Common Design Type

1969, Apr. 17		**Engr.**	
C29	CD129	100fr pur & brn	
		org	22.50 11.50

View of EXPO, Globe and Moon — AP9

90fr, Geisha, map of Japan & EXPO emblem.

1970, Sept. 13   Photo.   Perf. 13
C30 AP9 60fr slate & multi   3.50 1.75
C31 AP9 90fr multi   4.50 2.10

EXPO '70 International Exposition, Osaka, Japan, Mar. 15-Sept. 13.

Sunset over Mutsamudu — AP10

Map of Archipelago — AP11

Designs: 20fr, Sada Village, Mayotte. 65fr, Old Iconi Palace, Grand Comoro. 85fr, Nioumatchoua Island, Moheli.

1971, May 3   Photo.   Perf. 13
C32 AP10 15fr dk bl & multi   .85   .45
C33 AP10 20fr multi   1.40 .65
C34 AP10 65fr grn & multi   3.50 1.50
C35 AP10 85fr bl & multi   4.50 2.25

Engr.
C36 AP11 100fr brn red, grn &
                vio bl   6.75 4.00
     Nos. C32-C36 (5)   17.00 8.85

See #107-110, C45-C49, C53, C62-C64. For overprints & surcharges see #143, C69, C71, C73, C76-C77, C79-C80, C82, C84.

Flower Type of Regular Issue

Flowers: 60fr, Hibiscus schizopetalus. 85fr, Acalypha sanderii.

1971, July 19   Photo.   Perf. 13
Size: 27x48mm
C37 A25 60fr grn, ver & yel   5.00 1.75
C38 A25 85fr grn, red & yel   6.50 4.00

For surcharge see No. C75.

Mural, Moroni Airport — AP12

Designs: 85fr, Mural in Arrival Hall, Moroni Airport. 100fr, View of Moroni Airport.

1972, Mar. 30   Photo.   Perf. 13
C39 AP12 65fr gray & multi   2.00 .60
C40 AP12 85fr gray & multi   2.25 .95

Engr.
C41 AP12 100fr brn, bl & slate
                grn   3.25 1.75
     Nos. C39-C41 (3)   7.50 3.30
     New airport in Moroni.

Eiffel Tower and Moroni Telephone Exchange — AP13

75fr, Frenchman and Comoro Islander talking on telephone, radio tower and beacons.

1972, Apr. 24
C42 AP13 35fr dl red & gray   1.25 .60
C43 AP13 75fr dk car, vio & bl   2.25 .80

First radio-telephone connection between France and Comoro Islands.

Underwater Spear-fishing — AP14

1972, July 5   Engr.   Perf. 13
C44 AP14 70fr vio bl, brt grn &
                mar   8.00 4.25

For surcharge see No. C78.

Types of 1971
1972, Nov. 15   Photo.

Designs: 20fr, Cape Sima. 35fr, Bambao Palace. 40fr, Domoni Palace. 60fr, Gomajou Peninsula. 100fr, Map of Anjouan Island.

C45 AP10 20fr brn & multi   .70   .50
C46 AP10 35fr dk grn & multi   1.10 .65
C47 AP10 40fr bl & multi   1.60 .80
C48 AP10 60fr grnsh blk &
                multi   2.25 1.25

Engr.
C49 AP11 100fr mar, bl & sl
                grn   12.00 5.00
     Nos. C45-C49 (5)   17.65 8.20

Pres. Said Mohamed Cheikh (1904-70) AP15

1973, Mar. 16   Photo.   Perf. 13
C50 AP15 20fr multi   1.00 .60
C51 AP15 35fr multi   1.50 .80

For overprints see Nos. C70, C72.

No. C24 Surcharged

1973, Apr. 30   Engr.   Perf. 13
C52 A19 120fr on 90fr multi   11.00 5.75
     Intl. Commission for Coelacanth Studies.

Map of Grand Comoro AP16

1973, June 28   Engr.   Perf. 13
C53 AP16 135fr vio, bl & dk brn   9.50 4.25

See Nos. C65, C68. For surcharges see Nos. C90-C92.

Karthala Volcano AP17

1973, July 16   Photo.   Perf. 13x12½
C54 AP17 120fr multi   7.50 3.50

Eruption of Karthala, Sept. 1972. For surcharge see No. C89.

Armauer G. Hansen — AP18

Design: 150fr, Nicolaus Copernicus (1473-1543), Polish astronomer.

1973, Sept. 5   Engr.   Perf. 13
C55 AP18 100fr brn, dk bl & sl
                grn   7.50 2.50
C56 AP18 150fr grnsh bl, vio bl &
                choc   7.00 4.00

Cent. of the discovery of the Hansen bacillus, the cause of leprosy.
     For overprint & surcharge see #C81, C93.

Pablo Picasso (1881-1973) — AP19

1973, Sept. 30   Photo.
C57 AP19 200fr blk & multi   10.00 6.50
Souvenir Sheet
C58 AP19 100fr blk & multi   14.00 14.00
     For overprint see No. C87.

Order of the Star of Anjouan — AP20

Said Omar ben Soumeth — AP21

1974, Jan. 7   Photo.   Perf. 13
C59 AP20 500fr brn, bl & gold   13.00 7.25
     For overprint see No. C95.

1974, Jan. 31   Perf. 13x13½, 13½x13

135fr, Grand Mufti Said Omar, horiz.

C60 AP21 135fr blk & multi   4.25 2.10
C61 AP21 200fr blk & multi   5.25 3.00

For overprint & surcharge see #C85, C88.

Types of 1971-73

Designs (Views on Mayotte): 20fr, Moya Beach. 35fr, Chiconi. 90fr, Port Mamutzu. 120fr, Map of Mayotte.

1974, Aug. 31   Photo.   Perf. 13
C62 AP10 20fr bl & multi   .95   .65
C63 AP10 35fr grn & multi   3.50 2.00
C64 AP10 90fr multi   6.25 3.50

Engr.
C65 AP16 120fr ultra & grn   7.00 4.25
     Nos. C62-C65 (4)   17.70 10.40

Jet Take-off — AP22

1975, Jan. 10   Engr.   Perf. 13
C66 AP22 135fr multi   7.00 3.50

First direct route Moroni-Hahaya-Paris. For surcharge see No. C86.

Rotary Emblem, Meeting House, Map — AP23

1975, Feb. 23   Photo.   Perf. 13
C67 AP23 250fr multi   8.50 5.75

Rotary Intl., 70th anniv., Moroni Rotary Club, 10th anniv.
For surcharge see No. C94.

Map Type of 1973

Design: 230fr, Map of Moheli, horiz.

1975, May 26   Engr.   Perf. 13
C68 AP16 230fr ocher, ol grn &
                bl   10.00 5.75

STATE OF COMORO

Issues of 1968-75 Surcharged and Overprinted with Bars and: "ETAT COMORIEN" in Black, Silver, Red or Orange

1975		Printing & Perfs. as Before		
C69	AP10	10fr on 20fr #C62	.30	.20
C70	AP15	20fr (S)	.30	.20
C71	AP10	30fr on 35fr (R) #C63	.35	.20
C72	AP15	35fr (S)	.40	.25
C73	AP10	40fr (O)	.50	.25
C74	A19	50fr	.55	.30
C75	A25	75fr on 60fr	.80	.45
C76	AP10	75fr on 60fr	.80	.45
C77	AP10	75fr on 65fr (O)	.80	.45
C78	AP14	75fr on 70fr	.80	.45
C79	AP11	100fr #C36	1.00	.60
C80	AP11	100fr #C49	1.00	.60
C81	AP18	100fr	1.00	.60
C82	AP10	100fr on 85fr (O)	1.00	.60
C83	A25	100fr on 85fr	1.00	.60
C84	AP10	100fr on 90fr	1.00	.60
C85	AP21	100fr on 135fr (S)	1.00	.60
C86	AP22	100fr on 135fr	1.00	.60
C87	AP19	200fr (S)	2.10	1.25
C88	AP21	200fr (S)	2.10	1.25
C89	AP17	200fr on 120fr	2.10	1.25
C90	AP16	200fr on 120fr	2.10	1.25
C91	AP16	200fr on 135fr	2.10	1.25
C92	AP16	200fr on 230fr	2.10	1.25
C93	AP18	400fr on 150fr	4.75	2.50
C94	AP23	400fr on 250fr	4.75	2.50
C95	AP20	500fr	5.25	3.25
		Nos. C69-C95 (27)	40.95	23.75

See postage section for airmail stamps that are part of joint postage/airmail sets.

Rotary Emblem, Landscape AP26

1979, July 31　Litho.　Perf. 13x12½
C107　AP26 400fr multi　　7.00 3.00

Rotary International.

IYC Emblem, Mother and Child — AP27

1979, July 31　　Perf. 13x13½
C108　AP27 250fr multi　　3.50 3.50

Intl. Year of the Child. See No. CB1. For surcharges see Nos. C121, C202.

Dimadjou Dispensary, Map of Southern Africa, Emblem AP28

1980, Feb. 23　Litho.　Perf. 12½
C109　AP28 100fr shown　　1.25　.40
C110　AP28 260fr Globe, Concorde, emblem 3.00 1.00

Rotary International, 75th anniv. and Moroni Rotary Club, 15th anniv. (100fr).
For surcharges see Nos. 815L, C119-C120.

First Transatlantic Flight, 50th Anniversary — AP29

1980, May 30　Litho.　Perf. 13
C111　AP29 200fr multi　　2.50 1.25

No. C111 Surcharged in Blue

1981, Feb.　Litho.　Perf. 13
C112　AP29 30fr on 200fr multi　1.00　.35

The Dove and the Rainbow, by Picasso — AP30

Picasso Birth Centenary: 70fr, Still Life on a Sideboard. 150fr, Studio with Plaster Head. 250fr, Bowl and Pot, vert. 500fr, The Red Tablecloth.

1981, June 30　Litho.　Perf. 12½
C113	AP30	40fr multi	.55	.20
C114	AP30	70fr multi	.95	.20
C115	AP30	150fr multi	1.90	.50
C116	AP30	250fr multi	3.25	.70
C117	AP30	500fr multi	6.25	1.50
		Nos. C113-C117 (5)	12.90	3.10

For surcharges see Nos. 815G, C118.

#C114, C109-C110, CB1 Surchd.

1981, Nov.　Litho.　Perf. 12½, 13
C118	AP30	10fr on 70fr multi	.40	.40
C119	AP28	10fr on 100fr multi	.80	.80
C120	AP28	50fr on 260fr multi	2.00	.20
C121	AP27	50fr on 200fr+30fr multi	2.00	.20
		Nos. C118-C121 (4)	5.20	1.60

Manned Flight Bicentenary — AP31

Balloons. 100fr, 200fr, 300fr, 500fr vert.

1983, Apr. 20　Litho.　Perf. 13
C122	AP31	100fr Montgolfiere, 1783	1.00	.30
C123	AP31	200fr Lunardi, 1784	1.90	.50
C124	AP31	300fr Blanchard and Jeffries, 1785	3.25	.90
C125	AP31	400fr Giffard, 1852	4.50	1.25
		Nos. C122-C125 (4)	10.65	2.95

Souvenir Sheet
C126　AP31 500fr Paris Siege. 1870　5.50 1.50

For overprints and surcharges see Nos. 602, 812T, 815P.

Pre-Olympic Year Sailing — AP32

1984 Summer Olympics — AP33

1983, June 30　Litho.　Perf. 13
C127	AP32	150fr Type 470	1.50	.40
C128	AP32	200fr Flying Dutchman	2.25	.50
C129	AP32	300fr Type 470, diff.	3.25	.90
C130	AP32	400fr Finn	4.75	1.00
		Nos. C127-C130 (4)	11.75	2.80

Souvenir Sheet
C131　AP32 500fr Soling　5.50 1.50

For overprint and surcharge see Nos. 603, C206.

1984, July 10　Litho.　Perf. 13
C132	AP33	60fr Basketball	.50	.20
C133	AP33	100fr Basketball, diff.	.90	.40
C134	AP33	165fr Basketball, diff.	1.50	.65
C135	AP33	175fr Baseball, horiz.	1.60	.65
C136	AP33	200fr Baseball, horiz.	1.90	.80
		Nos. C132-C136 (5)	6.40	2.70

Souvenir Sheet
C137　AP33 500fr Basketball, diff.　8.00 1.50
　Nos. C132-C134 vert.

Development Conference AP34

1984, July 2　Litho.　Perf. 13
C138　AP34 475fr Tools for development　5.50 2.00

For surcharge see No. 796I.

Audubon Bicentenary — AP35

1985, Jan. 15　Litho.　Perf. 13
C139	AP35	100fr Hirundo rustica, vert.	1.25	.40
C140	AP35	125fr Icterus galbula, vert.	1.50	.50
C141	AP35	150fr Buteo lineatus	2.00	.60
C142	AP35	500fr Sphyropieus varius	5.25	2.00
		Nos. C139-C142 (4)	10.00	3.50

Moroni Port Missile Defense — AP36

No. C146, Ngome Ntsoudjini Scout troop.

1985, May 20　Litho.　Perf. 13x12½
C145　AP36 200fr multi　　3.25 1.25
C146　AP36 200fr multi　　3.25 1.25
　a.　Pair, #C145-C146 + label　6.75 6.75

PHILEXAFRICA '85, Lome.
For surcharges see Nos. C207-C208.

Natl. Flag, Sun, Outline Map of Islands — AP37

1985, July 6
C147	AP37	10fr multi	.30	.20
C148	AP37	15fr multi	.30	.20
C149	AP37	125fr multi	2.25	.60
C150	AP37	300fr multi	5.50	1.50
		Nos. C147-C150 (4)	8.35	2.50

Natl. independence, 10th anniv.
For surcharge see No. 815Q.

Runners — AP38

1985, Nov. 12
C151　AP38 250fr shown　2.75 1.75
C152　AP38 250fr Mining　2.75 1.75
　a.　Pair, #C151-C152 + label　6.00 6.00

PHILEXAFRICA '85, Lome, Togo, 11/16-24. For surcharges see Nos. 815H-815I, C204-C205.

Air Transport Union, UTA, 50th Anniv. — AP39

1985, Dec. 30　Litho.　Perf. 13
C153	AP39	25fr F-AOUL seaplane	.20	.20
C154	AP39	75fr Camel driver, DC-8	.75	.30
C155	AP39	100fr Noratlas and Heron DC-4s	1.10	.40
a.		Souv. sheet of 3, #C153-C155, perf. 12½	3.50	2.25
C156	AP39	125fr UTA cargo plane	1.40	.60

Size: 40x52mm
Perf. 12½x13
C157	AP39	1000fr Aircraft, 1935-1985	12.00	6.00
a.		Souv. sheet of 2, #C156-C157, perf. 12½	13.00	8.00
		Nos. C153-C157 (5)	15.45	7.50

Halley's Comet — AP40

Comets, astronomers and probes.

1986, Mar. 7   *Perf. 13*
C158	AP40	125fr Edmond Halley, Giotto probe	1.25 .45
C159	AP40	150fr Giacobini-Zinner, 1959	1.50 .50
C160	AP40	225fr Encke, 1961	2.50 .90
C161	AP40	300fr Bradfield, 1980	3.00 1.25
C162	AP40	450fr Planet A probe	5.00 1.75
		Nos. C158-C162 (5)	13.25 4.85

For surcharges see Nos. 796S, 804H, 804R, 812P.

1986 World Cup Soccer
Championships, Mexico — AP41

Various soccer plays.

1986, June 11   Litho.   *Perf. 13*
C163	AP41	125fr multi	1.25 .45
C164	AP41	210fr multi	2.25 .80
C165	AP41	500fr multi	5.50 2.00
C166	AP41	600fr multi	6.00 2.25
		Nos. C163-C166 (4)	15.00 5.50

For surcharges see Nos. 796C, 800Q, 815C.

Tennis at the
1988 Summer
Olympics — AP42

Various players.

1987, Jan. 28   Litho.   *Perf. 13½*
C167	AP42	150fr multi	1.75 .45
C168	AP42	250fr multi	3.00 .75
C169	AP42	500fr multi	5.50 1.50
C170	AP42	600fr multi	6.75 1.75
		Nos. C167-C170 (4)	17.00 4.45

For overprints and surcharges see Nos. 796N, 796U, 815J, 816L, 816N, C183-C186, C203.

World Wildlife Fund — AP43

Various pictures of the mongoose lemur.

1987, Feb. 18   *Perf. 13*
C171	AP43	75fr multi, vert.	2.50 .50
C172	AP43	100fr multi	3.50 .75
C173	AP43	125fr multi	5.50 1.00
C174	AP43	150fr multi	6.50 1.25
		Nos. C171-C174 (4)	18.00 3.50

1988
Winter
Olympics,
Calgary
AP44

1987, Apr. 10   Litho.   *Perf. 13½*
C175	AP44	150fr Slalom	1.25 .45
C176	AP44	225fr Ski jumping	2.25 .75
C177	AP44	500fr Women's giant slalom	5.50 1.60
C178	AP44	600fr Luge	6.00 2.25
		Nos. C175-C178 (4)	15.00 5.05

For surcharges see Nos. 800R, 812U.

AP45

Aviation
History
AP46

Designs: 200fr, Inventors Didier Daurat and Raymond Vanier with 1935 Air Blue F-ANR1. 300fr, Farman biplane, 1st scheduled airmail delivery, Paris-LeMans-St. Nazaire, Aug. 17, 1918. 500fr, Bleriot aircraft, 1st scheduled airmail delivery, Villacoublay-Vendome-Poitiers-Pauillac, Oct. 15, 1913. 1000fr, Henri Pequet and his aircraft, Feb. 18, 1911.

1987, Dec. 29   Litho.   *Perf. 13*
C179	AP45	200fr multi	2.25 .65
C180	AP45	300fr multi	3.25 1.00
C181	AP45	500fr multi	5.50 1.60

Perf. 12½x13
C182	AP46	1000fr multi	11.00 2.25
		Nos. C179-C182 (4)	22.00 5.50

Airmail history exposition, Allahabad.
For surcharges see Nos. 800S, 804D.

**Nos. C167-C170 Ovptd. in Red for
1988 Olympic Tennis Champions**

Overprint includes name of athlete and "Medaille d'or / Seoul" or "Medaille / d'argent / Seoul."

1988, Nov.   Litho.   *Perf. 13½*
C183	AP42	150fr "Miloslav Mecir / (Tchec.)"	1.25 .75
C184	AP42	250fr "Tim Mayotte / (U.S.A.)"	1.90 1.40
C185	AP42	500fr "Steffi Graf / (R.F.A.)"	5.00 2.75
C186	AP42	600fr "Gabriela Sabatini / (Argentine)"	6.00 3.75
		Nos. C183-C186 (4)	14.15 8.65

For surcharges see Nos. 800T, 815K, 816M, 816O.

Early Aviators and Aircraft — AP47

100fr, Alberto Santos-Dumont (1873-1932), & *Bagatelle*, 1st documented power flight in Europe, Oct. 23, 1906. 150fr, Wright Brothers & *Flyer A*. 200fr, Louis Bleriot (1872-1936) & *Bleriot XI*, 1st crossing of the English Channel in a heavier-than-air craft, July 25, 1909. 300fr, Henri Farman (1874-1958) & Voisin biplane, 1st fixed-route 1-kilometer circular flight, Jan. 13, 1908. 500fr, Gabriel (1880-1973) & Charles (1882-1912) Voisin, established 1st biplane factory (1908), & Voisin biplane. 800fr, Roland Garros (1888-1918), 1st trans-Mediterranean flight, Sept. 23, 1913.

1988, Dec. 7   Litho.   *Perf. 13*
C187	AP47	100fr pur	.90 .45
C188	AP47	150fr brt lil rose	1.60 .60
C189	AP47	200fr blk	2.00 .90
C190	AP47	300fr dark yel org	3.00 .90
C191	AP47	500fr dark blue	5.00 1.50
C192	AP47	800fr lt olive grn	7.50 3.00
		Nos. C187-C192 (6)	20.00 7.35

For surcharges see Nos. 800B, 800U, 804E, C209.

Souvenir Sheet

Space Achievements — AP48

Design: World Philatelic Programs stamp collecting emblem, Soviet satellite and Edmond Halley.

1988   Litho.   *Perf. 13½*
C193	AP48	750fr multi	8.00 1.50

**Nos. C108, C168, C151-C152, C128,
C145-C146 and C189 Surcharged**

1989   Litho.   *Perfs. as Before*
C202	AP27	5fr on 250fr #C108	.20 .20
C203	AP42	25fr on 250fr #C168	.20 .20
C204	AP38	50fr on 250fr #C151	.50 .20
C205	AP38	50fr on 250fr #C152	.50 .20
a.		Pair, #C204-C205 + label	1.25 1.25
C206	AP32	150fr on 200fr #C128	1.40 .60
C207	AP36	150fr on 200fr #C145	1.40 .60
C208	AP36	150fr on 200fr #C146	1.40 .60
a.		Pair, #C207-C208 + label	6.00 6.00
C209	AP47	150fr on 200fr #C189	1.40 .60
		Nos. C202-C209 (8)	7.00 3.20

World Cup Soccer, Championships,
Italy — AP50

Various soccer plays and map of Italy.

1990, June   Litho.   *Perf. 13*
C210	AP50	75fr multicolored	.60 .30
C211	AP50	150fr multicolored	1.40 .60
C212	AP50	500fr multicolored	4.25 1.90
C213	AP50	1000fr multicolored	8.75 4.00
		Nos. C210-C213 (4)	15.00 6.80

For surcharge see No. 800V.

Souvenir Sheet

Garry Kasparov, Anatoly Karpov,
Russian Chess Champions — AP51

Litho. & Embossed
1991, Aug. 5   *Perf. 13½*
C214	AP51	1500fr gold & multi	12.00 —

World Chess Championships.

1992
Summer
Olympics,
Barcelona
AP52

Litho. & Embossed
1992, July 28   *Perf. 13½*
C215	AP52	1500fr gold & multi	26.50 12.00

Sculpted Table —
AP52a

1994 (?)   Litho.   *Perf. 13¼x13½*
Background Color
C215A	AP52a	15fr blue	
C215B	AP52a	75fr green	
C215C	AP52a	100fr pink	
C215D	AP52a	225fr orange	

For surcharges see Nos. 826A-826E.

Sea Turtles
AP53

1995   Litho.   *Perf. 13½x13¼*
Frame Color
C216	AP53	10fr blue	
C217	AP53	25fr pink	
C218	AP53	30fr green	
C219	AP53	50fr lilac	

No. C215A
Surcharged in
Blue Violet

Perf. 13¼x13½
2001, June 16   Litho.
C220	AP52a	300fr on 15fr	—

AIR POST SEMI-POSTAL STAMP

Type of Air Post 1979

Design: IYC emblem, mother and son.

1979, July 31   Photo.   *Perf. 13½x13*
CB1	AP27	200fr + 30fr multi	3.50 3.50

International Year of the Child.
For surcharge see No. C121.

POSTAGE DUE STAMPS

Anjouan Mosque D1   Coelacanth D2

1950 Unwmk. Engr. Perf. 14x13

| J1 | D1 | 50c deep green | .80 | .80 |
| J2 | D1 | 1fr black brown | .80 | .80 |

1954

J3	D2	5fr dk brown & green	1.00	1.00
J4	D2	10fr gray & red brown	1.50	1.50
J5	D2	20fr indigo & blue	2.50	2.50
		Nos. J3-J5 (3)	5.00	5.00

Hibiscus D3

2fr, 15fr, 40fr, 50fr, vertical.

1977, Nov. 19 Litho. Perf. 13½

J6	D3	1fr shown	.35	.20
J7	D3	2fr Pineapple	.35	.20
J8	D3	5fr White butterfly	.35	.20
J9	D3	10fr Chameleon	.35	.20
J10	D3	15fr Blooming banana	.35	.20
J11	D3	20fr Orchids	.35	.20
J12	D3	30fr Allamanda cathartica	.50	.20
J13	D3	40fr Cashews	.95	.20
J14	D3	50fr Custard apple	1.10	.20
J15	D3	100fr Breadfruit	2.10	.95
J16	D3	200fr Vanilla	4.50	.95
J17	D3	500fr Ylang ylang	10.75	1.50
		Nos. J6-J17 (12)	22.00	5.00

OFFICIAL STAMPS

Comoro Flag — O1

Perf. 13x12½

1979-85 Litho. Unwmk.

O1	O1	5fr multi	.20	.20
O2	O1	10fr multi	.20	.20
O3	O1	20fr multi	.20	.20
O4	O1	30fr multi	.50	.20
O5	O1	40fr multi	.65	.25
O6	O1	60fr multi ('80)	.60	.25
O7	O1	75fr multi ('85)	.40	.25
O8	O1	100fr multi	1.25	.60
		Nos. O1-O8 (8)	4.00	2.15

See Nos. 526-530.

Pres. Said Mohamed Cheikh (1904-1970) — O2

1980-85

O9	O2	100fr multi	.65	.40
O10	O2	125fr multi ('85)	1.60	1.50
O11	O2	400fr multi	1.75	.90
		Nos. O9-O11 (3)	4.00	2.80

CONGO DEMOCRATIC REPUBLIC

ˌde-mə-ˈkra-tik ri-ˈpə-blik of ˈkänˌgō

LOCATION — Central Africa
GOVT. — Republic
AREA — 895,348 sq. mi. (estimated)
POP. — 22,480,000 (est. 1971)
CAPITAL — Kinshasa (Leopoldville)

Congo was an independent state, founded by Leopold II of Belgium, until 1908 when it was annexed to Belgium as a colony. Congo became an independent republic in 1960. The name was changed to Republic of Zaire, Oct. 28, 1971. In 1998 some issues again used the name Congo Democratic Republic. See Zaire in Vol. 6 for later issues.

100 Centimes = 1 Franc
100 Sengi = 1 Li-Kuta,
100 Ma-Kuta = 1 Zaire (1967)

> Catalogue values for all unused stamps in this country are for Never Hinged items.

Belgian Congo Flower Issue of 1952-53 Overprinted or Surcharged

Perf. 11½

1960, June 30 Photo. Unwmk.
Flowers in Natural Colors
Size: 21x25½mm
Granite Paper

323	A86	10c dp plum & ocher	.20	.20
324	A86	10c on 15c red & yel grn	.20	.20
325	A86	20c grn & gray	.20	.20
326	A86	40c grn & sal	.20	.20
327	A86	50c on 60c bl grn & pink	.20	.20
328	A86	50c on 75c dp plum & gray	.20	.20
329	A86	1fr car & yel	.30	.20
330	A86	1.50fr vio & ap grn	.30	.20
331	A86	2fr ol grn & buff	.30	.20
332	A86	3fr ol grn & pink	.45	.20
333	A86	4fr choc & lil	1.40	1.00
334	A86	5fr dp plum & lt bl	.55	.20
335	A86	6.50fr dk car & lil	.70	.20
336	A86	8fr grn & lt yel	.80	.30
337	A86	10fr dp plum & pale ol	1.40	.80
338	A86	20fr vio bl & dl sal	3.25	.80

Nos. 324, 327-328 exist without "CONGO" overprint but with surcharge, also without surcharge but with "CONGO." Inverted and double overprints exist. Values from $10 to $50 each.

Overprinted

Size: 22x32mm

339	A86	50fr dp plum & gray bl	18.00	6.00
340	A86	100fr grn & buff	42.50	10.00
		Nos. 323-340 (18)	71.15	20.80

Belgian Congo Animal Issue, Nos. 306-317, Overprinted or Surcharged in Red, Blue, Black or Brown

341	A92	10c bl & brn (R)	.20	.20
342	A92	20c red org & sl (Bl)	.20	.20
343	A92	40c brn & bl (Bk)	.20	.20
344	A93	50c brt ultra, red & sep (R)	.20	.20
345	A92	1fr brn, grn & blk (Br)	.20	.20
346	A92	1.50fr blk & org yel (R)	.20	.20
347	A92	2fr crim, blk & brn (Bl)	.45	.20
348	A93	3.50fr on 3fr blk, gray & lil rose (Bk)	.65	.20
349	A92	5fr brn, dk brn & brt grn (Br)	.85	.20
350	A93	6.50fr bl, brn & org yel (R)	1.00	.20
a.		Black overprint	1.75	.60
351	A92	8fr org brn, ol bis & lil (Br)	1.25	.40
352	A93	10fr multi (R)	1.60	.60
		Nos. 341-352 (12)	7.00	3.00

Inverted and double overprints exist. Values from $15 to $20 each.

Same Overprint on Belgian Congo No. 318

1960

| 353 | A94 | 50c gldn brn, ocher & red brn | 1.00 | 1.00 |

Same Overprint and Surcharge of New Value on Belgian Congo Nos. 321-322

Inscription in French

| 354 | A95 | 3.50fr on 3fr gray & red | 1.00 | .70 |

Inscription in Flemish

| 355 | A95 | 3.50fr on 3fr gray & red | 1.00 | .70 |
| | | Nos. 353-355 (3) | 3.00 | 2.40 |

Nos. 353-355 are known with inverted overprints. Value, each $10.

Map of Congo A93a

1960 Photo. Perf. 11½

356	A93a	20c brown	.20	.20
357	A93a	50c rose red	.20	.20
358	A93a	1fr green	.20	.20
359	A93a	1.50fr red brn	.20	.20
360	A93a	2fr rose car	.20	.20
361	A93a	3.50fr lilac	.20	.20
362	A93a	5fr brt bl	.20	.20
363	A93a	6.50fr gray	.25	.20
364	A93a	10fr orange	.40	.20
365	A93a	20fr ultra	.75	.25
		Nos. 356-365 (10)	2.80	2.05

Congo's Independence.
For overprints see Nos. 371-380.

Flag, People and Broken Chain — A94

1961, Jan. 4 Unwmk. Perf. 11½
Flag in Blue and Yellow

366	A94	2fr rose vio	.25	.20
367	A94	3.50fr vermilion	.25	.20
368	A94	6.50fr yel brn	.25	.20
369	A94	10fr brt grn	.30	.20
370	A94	20fr car rose	.45	.30
		Nos. 366-370 (5)	1.50	1.10

Signing of the Independence Agreement by Belgium, Jan. 4, 1959.

Nos. 356-365 Overprinted in Blue, Black or Red: "Conference Coquilhatville Avril Mai 1961"

1961

371	A93a	20c brn (Bl)	1.50	1.50
372	A93a	50c rose red (Bk)	1.50	1.50
373	A93a	1fr grn (R)	1.50	1.50
374	A93a	1.50fr red brn (Bl)	1.50	1.50
375	A93a	2fr rose car (Bk)	1.50	1.50
376	A93a	3.50fr lil (Bl)	1.50	1.50
377	A93a	5fr brt bl (R)	1.50	1.50
378	A93a	6.50fr gray (R)	1.50	1.50
379	A93a	10fr grn (Bk)	1.50	1.50
380	A93a	20fr ultra (R)	1.50	1.50
		Nos. 371-380 (10)	15.00	15.00

Coquilhatville Conf., Apr.-May, 1961.
Nos. 371-380 exist with inverted overprints.
Value $15 each.

Pres. Joseph Kasavubu — A95

Kasavubu and Map of Congo — A96

10fr-100fr, Kasavubu in uniform and map.

Perf. 11½

1961, June 30 Unwmk. Photo.
Portrait and Inscription in Dark Brown

381	A95	10c yellow	.20	.20
382	A95	20c dp rose	.20	.20
383	A95	40c bl grn	.20	.20
384	A95	50c salmon	.20	.20
385	A95	1fr lilac	.20	.20
386	A95	1.50fr lt brn	.20	.20
387	A95	2fr brt grn	.20	.20
388	A96	3.50fr rose pink	.20	.20
389	A96	5fr gray	5.75	.20
390	A96	6.50fr ultra	.80	.20
391	A96	8fr olive	.80	.20
392	A95	10fr lt vio	2.10	.80
393	A95	20fr orange	2.10	.20
394	A95	50fr lt bl	3.50	.35
395	A95	100fr apple green	5.75	.55
		Nos. 381-395 (15)	22.40	4.10

First anniversary of independence.

Nos. 381-387, 389 and 392 Overprinted: "REOUVERTURE du PARLEMENT JUILLET 1961"

1961

Portrait and Inscription in Dark Brown

396	A95	10c yellow	.20	.20
397	A95	20c dp rose	.20	.20
398	A95	40c bl grn	.20	.20
399	A95	50c salmon	.50	.35
400	A95	1fr lilac	.50	.35
401	A95	1.50fr lt brn	1.25	1.00
402	A95	2fr brt grn	1.25	1.00
403	A95	5fr gray	1.25	1.00
404	A95	10fr lt vio	1.25	1.00
		Nos. 396-404 (9)	6.60	5.30

Congolese parliament re-opening, 7/1961.
Nos. 396-404 exist with inverted overprints.
Value $9 each.

Dag Hammarskjold and Map of Africa with Congo — A97

Malaria Eradication Emblem and Mosquito — A98

1962, Jan. 20 Photo. Perf. 11½
Gray Background

405	A97	10c dk brn	.20	.20
406	A97	20c Prus bl	.20	.20
407	A97	30c brown	.20	.20
408	A97	40c dk bl	.20	.20
409	A97	50c brn red	.20	.20
410	A97	3fr ol grn	4.25	1.25
411	A97	6.50fr dk vio	1.25	.35
412	A97	8fr red brn	.20	.20
		Nos. 405-412 (8)	8.00	3.10

Souvenir Sheets
Imperf
413 A97 25fr blk brn 8.00 8.00
  a. Overprint in green 4.00 4.00

Dag Hammarskjold, Sec. Gen. of the UN, 1953-61.

No 413a is overprinted "30 Juin 1962" on stamp and "2eme Anniversaire de l'Independance" on sheet margin. Issued June 30, 1962.

For overprints see Nos. 417-424.

1962, June 15
Granite Paper
414 A98 1.50fr yel, blk & dk red .20 .20
415 A98 2fr yel grn, brn & bl grn .30 .20
416 A98 6.50fr ultra, blk & mar .40 .20
  Nos. 414-416 (3) .90 .60

WHO drive to eradicate malaria.

Nos. 405-412 Overprinted in Blue, Purple, Black or Carmine

1962, Oct. 15
Gray Background
417 A97 10c dk brn (Bl) .20 .20
418 A97 20c Prus bl (P) .20 .20
419 A97 30c brn (Bk) .20 .20
420 A97 40c dk bl (C) .20 .20
421 A97 50c brn red (Bl) 2.00 .75
422 A97 3fr ol grn (P) .20 .20
423 A97 6.50fr dk vio (Bk) .25 .20
424 A97 8fr red brn (C) .35 .20
  Nos. 417-424 (8) 3.60 2.15

Reorganization of Adoula administration. Inverted overprints exist. Value, $8.00 each.

Canceled to Order
Starting in 1963, values in the used column are for "canceled to order" stamps. Postally used copies sell for much more.

A99

1963, Jan. 28   Engr.   Perf. 10½x13
425 A99 2fr dull purple 1.25 .90
426 A99 4fr red .20 .20
427 A99 7fr dark blue .25 .20
428 A99 20fr slate green .50 .20
  Nos. 425-428 (4) 2.20 *1.50*

Congo's 1st participation at the UPU Cong., New Delhi, Mar. 1963.

An imperf sheet containing No. 428 in brown exists. Value $30.

For overprints see Nos. 468-471.

Shoebill — A100

Birds: 10c, Pelicans. 20c, Crested guinea fowl, horiz. 30c, Openbill. 40c, White-bellied storks, horiz. 3fr, Marabou. 3fr, Greater flamingos, horiz. 4fr, Congolese peacock. 5fr, Hartlaub ducks, horiz. 6fr, Secretary bird. 7fr, Black-casqued hornbill, horiz. 8fr, Sacred ibis and nest. 10fr, Crowned crane, horiz. 20fr, Saddle-bill stork, horiz.

1963   Unwmk.   Photo.   Perf. 11½
429 A100 10c pink, ultra & ocher .20 .20
430 A100 20c rose red, bl & blk .20 .20

---

431 A100 30c grn, ocher & blk .20 .20
432 A100 40c gray, org & blk .20 .20
433 A100 1fr brn, emer & gray .20 .20
434 A100 2fr gray, red & ind 3.25 .60
435 A100 3fr ol grn, blk & rose .20 .20
436 A100 4fr car rose, vio bl & grn .20 .20
437 A100 5fr lake, lt bl & blk .45 .20
438 A100 6fr pur, yel & blk 3.50 .60
439 A100 7fr bl grn, blk & ind .55 .20
440 A100 8fr yel, org & blk .65 .20
441 A100 10fr bl, blk & rose .65 .20
442 A100 20fr cit, blk & blk 1.20 .20
  Nos. 429-442 (14) 11.65 3.60

Nos. 436 and 438 exist in imperf sheets of one. Value, each $35.

Cinchona Ledgeriana — A101

Red Cross Nurse — A102

10c, 30c, 5fr, Strophanthus sarmentosus.

Perf. 12½x13½, 13½x12½
1963, May 25   Engr.   Unwmk.
Cross in Red
443 A101 10c vio & dl grn .20 .20
444 A101 20c magenta & bl .20 .20
445 A101 30c grn & org .20 .20
446 A101 40c bl & vio .20 .20
447 A101 5fr ol & rose claret .20 .20
448 A101 7fr org & blk .20 .20
449 A102 9fr gray olive & red .20 .20
450 A102 20fr purple & red 2.00 .75
  Nos. 443-450 (8) 3.40 2.15

International Red Cross centenary.

A souvenir sheet of three contains imperf. 5fr, 7fr, and 20fr stamps similar to Nos. 447, 448 and 450, but in changed colors. Size: 109x75mm. Value $30.

Men Joining Hands and Map of Congo A103

1963, June 29   Photo.   Perf. 11½
451 A103 4fr multi 1.25 .50
452 A103 5fr multi .20 .20
453 A103 9fr multi .20 .20
454 A103 12fr multi .35 .20
  Nos. 451-454 (4) 2.00 1.10

Issued to celebrate national reconciliation.

Bulldozer and Kabambare Sewer, Leopoldville — A104

Designs: 30c, 5fr, 12fr, Excavator and blueprint. 50c, 9fr, Building Ituri road.

1963, July 1   Engr.   Unwmk.
455 A104 20c multi .20 .20
456 A104 30c multi .20 .20
457 A104 50c multi .20 .20
458 A104 3fr multi 1.00 .40
459 A104 5fr multi .20 .20
460 A104 9fr multi .20 .20
461 A104 12fr multi .20 .20
  Nos. 455-461 (7) 2.20 1.60

Issued to publicize aid to Congo by the European Economic Community.

Leopoldville Airport N'Djili — A105

5fr, 7fr, 50fr, Tail assembly and airport.

1963, Nov. 30   Photo.   Perf. 11½
462 A105 2fr gray, yel & red brn .20 .20
463 A105 5fr mag, vio & yel .20 .20
464 A105 6fr bl, yel & dk brn 1.40 .50
465 A105 7fr multi .20 .20
466 A105 30fr lil, yel & ol .40 .25
467 A105 50fr multi .60 .30
  Nos. 462-467 (6) 3.00 1.65

Issued to publicize Air Congo.
For surcharge see No. 606.

Nos. 425-428 Overprinted with Silver Frame on Three Sides and Black Inscription: "15e anniversaire / 10 DECEMBRE 1948 / DROITS DE L'HOMME / 10 DECEMBRE 1963"
Engraved and Typographed
1963, Dec. 10   Perf. 10½x13
468 A99 2fr dull purple .20 .20
469 A99 4fr red .20 .20
470 A99 7fr dark blue .25 .20
471 A99 20fr slate green .30 .20
  Nos. 468-471 (4) .95 .80

Universal Declaration of Human Rights, 15th anniv.

Nos. 468-471 exist with side date panels transposed ("1963" at left, "1948" at right). Value, each $15.

Laboratory Technician and Atomic Emblem A106

1.50fr, 60fr, University. 8fr, 75fr, First African nuclear reactor. 25fr, 100fr, University and crest.

1964, Feb. 1   Photo.   Perf. 14x12½
472 A106 50c multi .20 .20
473 A106 1.50fr multi .20 .20
474 A106 8fr multi 2.50 2.25
475 A106 25fr multi .20 .20
476 A106 30fr multi .35 .20
477 A106 60fr multi .60 .35
478 A106 75fr multi .70 .60
479 A106 100fr multi 1.00 .80
  a. Souv. sheet of 3 6.50 6.50
  Nos. 472-479 (8) 5.75 4.80

Lovanium University, Leopoldville, 10th anniv.
No. 479a contains 3 imperf. multicolored stamps: 20fr, design as 50c; 30fr, as 8fr; 100fr.

Belgian Congo Issues of 1952-59 Overprinted "REPUBLIQUE DU CONGO" and Surcharged in Black on Overprinted Metallic Panels

1964   Perf. 11½
480 A93 1fr on 20c red org & sl (#307) .20 .20
481 A86 2fr on 1.50fr (#273) 10.00 3.25
482 A93 5fr on 6.50fr (#315) .80 .25
483 A86 8fr on 6.50fr (#278) 1.10 .35

Republic Issues of 1960-61 Surcharged in Black on Overprinted Metallic Rectangles or Ovals

484 A86 1fr on 6.50fr (#335) .20 .20
485 A93 1fr on 20c (#342) .20 .20
486 A86 2fr on 1.50fr (#330) .20 .20
487 A95 3fr on 20c (#382) .55 .25
488 A95 4fr on 40c (#383) .55 .25
489 A93 5fr on 6.50fr ("Congo" red) (#350) .80 .25
  a. "Congo" black .80 .25
490 A93a 6fr on 6.50fr (#363) .80 .25
491 A93a 7fr on 20c (#356) .80 .25
  Nos. 480-491 (12) 16.20 5.90

Pole Vault A107

7fr, 20fr, Javelin, vert. 8fr, 100fr, Hurdling.

Perf. 11½
1964, July 13   Unwmk.   Photo.
Granite Paper
492 A107 5fr gray, dk brn & car .20 .20
493 A107 7fr rose, vio & emer .95 .35
494 A107 8fr org, yel, red brn & vio bl .20 .20
495 A107 10fr bl, vio brn & mag .20 .20
496 A107 20fr gray grn, red brn & ver .25 .20
497 A107 100fr lil, dk brn & grn .95 .25
  a. Souv. sheet of 3 10.00 10.00
  Nos. 492-497 (6) 2.75 1.40

18th Olympic Games, Tokyo, Oct. 10-25. No. 497a contains 3 imperf. stamps (20fr orange & dark brown, pole vault; 30fr citron and dark brown, hurdling; 100fr dull green and dark brown, javelin). Sheet issued Sept. 10.

National Palace, Leopoldville — A108

1964, Sept. 15
Granite Paper
498 A108 50c lil rose & bl .20 .20
499 A108 1fr bl & lil rose .20 .20
500 A108 2fr brn red & vio .20 .20
501 A108 3fr emer & red .20 .20
502 A108 4fr org & vio bl .20 .20
503 A108 5fr gray vio & emer .20 .20
504 A108 6fr sep & org .20 .20
505 A108 7fr gray ol & red brn .20 .20
506 A108 8fr rose red & vio bl 2.00 .30
507 A108 9fr vio bl & rose red .20 .20
508 A108 10fr brn ol & grn .20 .20
509 A108 20fr bl & brn org .20 .20
510 A108 30fr dk car rose & grn .25 .20
511 A108 40fr ultra & dk car rose .35 .20
512 A108 50fr brn org & grn .40 .20
513 A108 100fr slate & ver .85 .20
  Nos. 498-513 (16) 6.05 3.30

For overprints and surcharges see Nos. 574-577, 593-598, 609-615, 670-671, 673-674, 676-677, 680, 684-687.

Pres. John F. Kennedy (1917-63) A109

1964, Dec. 8   Photo.   Perf. 13½
514 A109 5fr dk bl & blk .20 .20
515 A109 6fr rose claret & blk .20 .20
516 A109 9fr brn & blk .20 .20
517 A109 30fr pur & blk .55 .20
518 A109 40fr dl grn & blk 3.50 1.00
519 A109 60fr red brn & blk 1.20 .35
  Nos. 514-519 (6) 5.85 2.15

Souvenir Sheet
520 A109 150fr blk & mar 6.50 6.50

Rocket and Unisphere A110   Basketball A111

Engraved and Typographed
1965, Mar. 1   Unwmk.   Perf. 12
521 A110 50c lil & blk .20 .20
522 A110 1.50fr bl & lil .20 .20
523 A110 2fr red brn & brt grn .20 .20
524 A110 10fr brt grn & dk red 1.00 .55

484 CONGO DEMOCRATIC REPUBLIC

525	A110	18fr vio bl & brn	.20	.20
526	A110	27fr rose red & grn	.35	.20
527	A110	40fr gray & org	.45	.20
		Nos. 521-527 (7)	2.60	1.75

New York World's Fair, 1964-65.

1965, Apr. Photo. Perf. 13½

6fr, 40fr, Soccer, horiz. 15fr, 60fr, Volleyball.

528	A111	5fr blk, grnsh bl & ocher	.20	.20
529	A111	6fr blk, bl gray & crim	.20	.20
530	A111	15fr blk, org & yel grn	.20	.20
531	A111	24fr blk, rose lil & brt grn	.40	.20
532	A111	40fr blk, brt grn & ultra	2.00	.70
533	A111	60fr blk, bl & red lil	.70	.20
		Nos. 528-533 (6)	3.70	1.70

First African Games, Leopoldville, Mar. 31-Apr. 7, 1965.
For surcharges see Nos. 604-605.

Earth and Satellites A112

Designs: 9fr, 15fr, 20fr, 40fr, Satellites at left, globe at right.

Perf. 14x14½

1965, June 28 Photo. Unwmk.

534	A112	6fr blk, sal & vio	.20	.20
535	A112	9fr blk, lt grn & gray	.20	.20
536	A112	12fr org, gray & blk	.20	.20
537	A112	15fr grn, ultra & blk	.20	.20
538	A112	18fr, lt grn & gray	1.10	.30
539	A112	20fr blk, sal & vio	.20	.20
540	A112	30fr grn, ultra & blk	.25	.20
541	A112	40fr org, gray & blk	.30	.20
		Nos. 534-541 (8)	2.65	1.70

Cent. of the ITU.

Congolese Paratrooper and Parachutes A113

1965, July 5 Perf. 13x14

542	A113	5fr brt bl & brn	.20	.20
543	A113	6fr org & brn	.20	.20
544	A113	7fr br grn & brn	.40	.25
545	A113	9fr brt pink & brn	.20	.20
546	A113	18fr lem & brn	.20	.20
		Nos. 542-546 (5)	1.20	1.05

Fifth anniversary of independence.

Matadi Harbor and ICY Emblem — A114

ICY Emblem and: 8fr, 25fr, Katanga mines. 9fr, 60fr, Tshopo Dam, Stanleyville.

1965, Oct. 25 Photo. Perf. 13x14

547	A114	6fr ultra, blk & yel	.20	.20
548	A114	8fr org red, blk & bl	.20	.20
549	A114	9fr bl grn, blk & brn org	.20	.20
550	A114	12fr car rose, blk & gray	.75	.30
551	A114	25fr ol, blk & rose red	.20	.20
552	A114	60fr gray, blk & org	.55	.20
		Nos. 547-552 (6)	2.10	1.30

International Cooperation Year, 1965.
For overprints and surcharges see Nos. 559-560, 607-608.

Soldiers Giving First Aid — A115

The Army Serving the Country: 7fr, Bridge building. 9fr, Feeding child. 19fr, Maintenance of telegraph lines. 20fr, House building. 30fr, Soldier and flag. (19fr, 20fr, 30fr, vert.)

Perf. 12½x13, 13x12½

1965, Nov. 17

553	A115	5fr sal, brn & red	.20	.20
554	A115	7fr yel & grn	.20	.20
555	A115	9fr ol & brn	.20	.20
556	A115	19fr brt grn & brn	1.10	.60
557	A115	20fr lt bl & brn	.30	.20
558	A115	30fr multi	.50	.20
		Nos. 553-558 (6)	2.50	1.60

See Nos. 582-586. For surcharges see Nos. 602, 678-679, 683.

Nos. 551-552 Overprinted with UN Emblem and "6e Journée Météorologique Mondiale / 23.3.66." on Metallic Strip

1966, Mar. 23 Photo. Perf. 13x14

559	A114	25fr ol & blk	1.40	.55
560	A114	60fr gray & blk	1.40	.65

6th World Meteorological Day.

Woman's Head and Goat — A116

10fr, Sculptured heads. 12fr, Sitting figure and two heads, vert. 53fr, Figure with earrings and kneeling woman with bowl, vert.

Perf. 11½x13, 13x11½

1966, Apr. 23 Litho. Unwmk.

561	A116	10fr red, blk & gray	.20	.20
562	A116	12fr grn, blk & bl	.25	.20
563	A116	15fr dp bl, blk & lil	.30	.20
564	A116	53fr dp rose, blk & vio bl	1.50	1.10
		Nos. 561-564 (4)	2.25	1.70

Intl. Negro Arts Festival, Dakar, Senegal, Apr. 1-24.

Pres. Joseph Desiré Mobutu and Fishing Industry A117

Pres. Mobutu and: 4fr, Pyrethrum harvest. 6fr, Building industry. 8fr, Winnowing rice. 10fr, Cotton harvest. 12fr, Banana harvest. 15fr, Coffee harvest. 24fr, Pineapple harvest. No. 573a, Pres. Mobutu without cap, and men rolling up sleeves.

1966, May 1 Photo. Perf. 11½

565	A117	2fr dk brn & dk bl	.20	.20
566	A117	4fr dk brn & org	.20	.20
567	A117	6fr dk brn & ol	.75	.60
568	A117	8fr dk brn & brt grnsh bl	.20	.20
569	A117	10fr dk brn & brn red	.20	.20
570	A117	12fr dk brn & vio	.20	.20
571	A117	15fr dk brn & lt ol grn	.20	.20
572	A117	24fr dk brn & lil rose	.25	.20
		Nos. 565-572 (8)	2.20	2.00

Souvenir Sheet
Perf. 11x11½

573		Sheet of 4	2.00	2.00
a.		A117 15fr red, black & ultra	.45	.45

Lt. Gen. Joseph Desiré Mobutu, Pres. of Congo, and publicizing the "Back to Work" campaign.
For surcharges see Nos. 601, 603, 616, 619-624, 672, 675, 681-682.

Nos. 510-513 Overprinted

1966, June 13 Perf. 11½

574	A108	30fr dk car rose & grn	1.10	1.10
575	A108	40fr ultra & dk car rose	1.20	1.20
576	A108	50fr brn org & grn	1.40	1.40
577	A108	100fr slate & ver	1.40	1.40
		Nos. 574-577 (4)	5.10	5.10

Inauguration of WHO Headquarters, Geneva.

Soccer Player — A118

30fr, 2 soccer players. 50fr, 3 soccer players. 60fr, Jules Rimet Cup, soccer ball & globe.

1966, July 25 Photo. Perf. 14

578	A118	10fr ocher, vio & brt grn	.20	.20
579	A118	30fr brt rose lil, vio & ap grn	.45	.20
580	A118	50fr ap grn, Prus bl & tan	1.50	1.00
581	A118	60fr brt grn, dk brn & gold	1.50	.50
		Nos. 578-581 (4)	3.65	1.90

World Cup Soccer Championship, Wembley, England, July 11-30.
For overprints see Nos. 587-590.

Army Type of 1965

The Army Serving the Country: 2fr, Soldiers giving first aid. 6fr, Feeding child. 10fr, House building, vert. 18fr, Bridge building. 24fr, Soldier and flag, vert.

1966, Aug. 8 Perf. 12½x13, 13x12½

582	A115	2fr ver, ind & red	.20	.20
583	A115	6fr ultra red brn	.20	.20
584	A115	10fr yel grn & red brn	.75	.50
585	A115	18fr car rose & vio	.20	.20
586	A115	24fr multi	.25	.20
		Nos. 582-586 (5)	1.60	1.30

#578-581 Overprinted in Black ("a"), Carmine or Green ("b"): "FINALE / ANGLETERRE-ALLEMAGNE / 4-2"

1966, Nov. 14 Photo. Perf. 14

587	A118	10fr pair, B and C	.60	.60
588	A118	30fr pair, B and G	2.25	2.00
589	A118	50fr pair, B and C	3.50	2.50
590	A118	60fr pair, B and C	4.00	3.50
		Nos. 587-590 (4)	10.35	8.60

England's victory in the World Soccer Cup Championship. The two colors of the overprint alternate in the sheets.

Souvenir Sheets

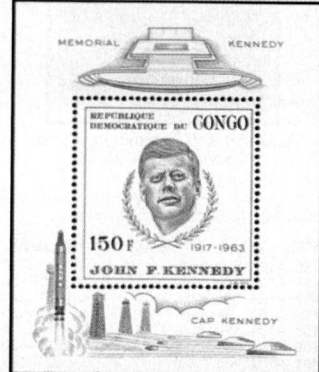

Pres. John F. Kennedy — A119

1966, Dec. 28 Engr. Perf. 13

591	A119	150fr brown	20.00	16.00
592	A119	150fr slate	20.00	16.00

Issued in memory of Pres. John F. Kennedy. No. 591 has slate green, No. 592 deep orange marginal design. Two imperf. sheets exist: 150fr brown with violet blue margin and 150fr slate with lilac margin. Size: 65x76mm. Values, $20 each.

Nos. 498-503 Surcharged in Black, Red or Maroon

1967, Sept. 11 Photo. Perf. 11½

593	A108	1k on 2fr	.20	.20
a.		Inverted overprint	5.00	
594	A108	3k on 5fr	.20	.20
595	A108	5k on 4fr	.35	.20
596	A108	6.60k on 1fr (R)	.50	.20
a.		Inverted overprint	5.00	
597	A108	9.60k on 50c	.70	.30
a.		Inverted overprint	5.00	
598	A108	9.80k on 3fr (M)	.75	.50
		Nos. 593-598 (6)	2.70	1.60

Souvenir Sheet

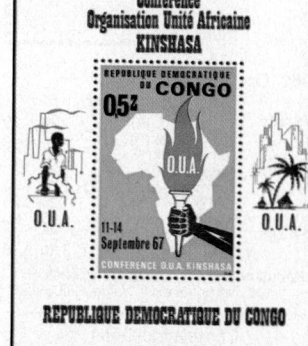

Map of Africa, Torch — A120

599	A120	50k grnsh bl, blk & red	2.50	2.50

4th meeting of the Org. for African Unity, Kinshasa (Leopoldville), Sept. 9-11.
No. 599 in other colors was not a postal issue.

Souvenir Sheet

Horn Blower and EXPO Emblem — A121

1967, Sept. 28 Engr. Perf. 11½

600	A121	50k dk brn	3.25	3.25

EXPO '67, International Exhibition, Montreal, Apr. 28-Oct. 27, 1967.

Nos. 565-566 and 582 Overprinted: "NOUVELLE CONSTITUTION 1967" and Surcharged with New Value on Metallic Panel in Magenta or Brown

Perf. 11½, 12½x13

1967, Oct. 9 Photo.

601	A117	4k on 2fr (M)	.25	.20
602	A115	5k on 2fr (B)	.45	.20
603	A117	21k on 4fr (M)	1.50	.90
		Nos. 601-603 (3)	2.20	1.30

Promulgation of the Constitution, June 4, 1967.

Nos. 528 and 530 Surcharged with
New Value and Overprinted: "1ers
Jeux Congolais / 25/6 au 2/7/1967 /
Kinshasa"

1967, Oct. 16   Photo.   Perf. 13½
604 A111   1k on 5fr multi   .35   .20
605 A111   9.60k on 15fr multi   .75   .65

First Congolese Games, Kinshasa, June 25-
July 2, 1967.

No. 465 Surcharged with New Value
and Overprinted: "1er VOL BAC /
ONE ELEVEN / 14/5/67"

1967, Oct. 16   Perf. 11½
606 A105   9.60k on 7fr multi   1.20   .25

1st flight of the BAC 111 in the service of Air
Congo, May 14, 1967.

Nos. 547 and 549 Surcharged in Red
or Black: "JOURNEE MONDIALE / DE
L'ENFANCE / 8-10-67"

1968, Feb. 10   Photo.   Perf. 13x14
607 A114   1k on 6fr multi (R)   .25   .20
608 A114   9k on 9fr multi (B)   .95   .70

Intl. Children's Day. The surcharge is on a
rectangle printed in metallic ink.

Nos. 498, 504 and 501 Surcharged in
Blue or Red: "Année Internationale /
du Tourisme 24-10-1967"

1968, Feb. 10   Perf. 11½
609 A108   5k on 50c lil rose & bl
            (Bl)   .45   .25
610 A108   10k on 6fr sepia & org
            (R)   .65   .55
611 A108   15k on 3fr emer & red
            (R)   1.00 1.00
        Nos. 609-611 (3)   2.10 1.80

International Tourist Year. The surcharge is
on a rectangle printed in metallic ink.

Nos. 500, 498 and 502 Surcharged in
Black, Violet Blue or Gold

1968, July   Photo.   Perf. 11½
612 A108   1k on 2fr   .30   .20
613 A108   2k on 50c (VBl)   .45   .25
614 A108   2k on 50c (G)   .45   .25
615 A108   9.60k on 4fr   2.00 1.10
        Nos. 612-615 (4)   3.20 1.80

The surcharge on No. 612 consists of a
black rectangle and new denomination in
upper right corner; the surcharge on No. 613
has a violet blue rectangle with denomination
in white on it; on No. 614 the rectangle
is gold and the denomination black; on No.
615 the rectangle is black and the denomination white.

No. 565 Surcharged in White on Black
Rectangle

1968, Oct.   Photo.   Perf. 11½
616 A117   10k on 2fr dk brn & dk bl .70 .20

Leopard
A122

1968, Nov. 5   Litho.   Perf. 10½
617 A122   2k brt grnsh bl & blk   .30   .20
618 A122   9.60k red & blk   1.20   .20

Mobutu Type of 1966 Surcharged

1968, Dec. 20   Photo.   Perf. 11½
619 A117   15s on 2fr sep & brt bl   .20   .20
620 A117   1k on 6fr sep & brn   .20   .20
621 A117   3k on 10fr sep & em-
            er   .20   .20
622 A117   5k on 12fr sep & org   .30   .20
623 A117   20k on 15fr sep & brt
            grn   1.00   .50
624 A117   50k on 24fr sep & brt
            lil   2.75 1.40
        Nos. 619-624 (6)   4.65 2.70

Human Rights
Flame — A123

1968, Dec. 30   Perf. 12½x13
625 A123   2k lt ultra & brt grn   .20   .20
626 A123   9.60k grn & dp car   .65   .30
627 A123   10k brt lil & brn   .65   .30
628 A123   40k org brn & pur   2.25 1.20
        Nos. 625-628 (4)   3.75 2.00

International Human Rights Year.

Type of 1968
Overprinted in Gold

1969, Jan. 27   Photo.   Perf. 12½x13
629 A123   2k ap grn & red brn   .20   .20
630 A123   9.60k rose & emer   .65   .30
631 A123   10k gray & ultra   .65   .30
632 A123   40k grnsh bl & pur   2.25 1.20
        Nos. 629-632 (4)   3.75 2.00

4th summit meeting of OCAM (Organisation
Communitee Afrique et Malgache), Kinshasa,
Jan. 27.

Kinshasa Fair Emblem and Cotton
Boll — A124

Fair Emblem and: 6k, Copper. 9.60k, Coffee. 9.80k, Diamond. 11.60k, Oil palm fruits.

1969, May 2   Photo.   Perf. 12½x13
633 A124   2k brt pur, gold &
            red lil   .25   .20
634 A124   6k grn, gold & bl
            grn   .95   .50
635 A124   9.60k brn, gold & lt
            brn   1.25   .40
636 A124   9.80k ultra & gold   1.40   .60
637 A124   11.60k hn brn, gold &
            brn   1.60   .90
        Nos. 633-637 (5)   5.45 2.60

Kinshasa Fair, Limete, June 30-July 21.

Fair Entrance, Emblem — A125

Fair Emblem and: 3k, Gecomin Mining Co.
Pavilion. 10k, Administration Building. 25k,
Pavilion of the Organization for African Unity.

1969, June 30   Photo.   Perf. 11½
            Granite Paper
638 A125   2k brt rose lil & gold   .20   .20
639 A125   3k blue & gold   .20   .20
640 A125   10k lt ol grn & gold   .80   .40
641 A125   25k copper red & gold 1.80 1.00
        Nos. 638-641 (4)   3.00 1.80

Kinshasa Fair, Limete, June 30-July 21.

Congo
Arms — A126

Pres.
Mobutu — A127

1969, July-Sept.   Litho.   Perf. 14
642 A126   10s org & blk   .20   .20
643 A126   15s ultra & blk   .20   .20
644 A126   30s brt grn & blk   .20   .20
645 A126   60s brt rose lil &
            blk   .20   .20
646 A126   90s dp bister & blk   .20   .20
            Perf. 13
647 A127   1k sky bl & multi   .20   .20
648 A127   2k org & multi   .20   .20
649 A127   3k multi   .30   .20
650 A127   5k brt rose &
            multi   .40   .20
651 A127   6k ultra & multi   .40   .25
652 A127   9.60k multi   .70   .40
653 A127   10k lt lil & multi   .90   .50
654 A127   20k yel & multi   1.75 1.00
655 A127   50k multi   4.75 2.50
656 A127   100k fawn & multi   9.50 6.00
        Nos. 642-656 (15)   20.10 12.45

Well Driller, by Oscar
Bonnevalle — A128

Paintings: 4k, Preparation of cocoa, by
Jean Van Noten. 8k, Dock workers, by Con-
stantin Meunier. 10k, Poultry shop, by Henri
Evenepoel. 15k, Steel industry, by Constantin
Meunier.

Perf. 13x14, 14x13 (8k)
1969, Dec. 15   Litho.
        Size: 41x41mm
657 A128   3k multi   .20   .20
658 A128   4k multi   .20   .20
        Size: 28x41mm
659 A128   8k multi   .45   .30
        Size: 41x41mm
660 A128   10k multi   .70   .40
661 A128   15k multi   1.40   .70
        Nos. 657-661 (5)   2.95 1.80

50th anniv. of the ILO.

Souvenir Sheet

Adoration of the Kings, by
Rubens — A129

1969, Dec.   Engr.   Perf. 13
662 A129   50k red lilac   4.50 4.50

Issued for Christmas 1969.

Pres.
Mobutu,
Map
and
Flag of
Congo
A130

1970, June 30   Litho.   Perf. 13½x13
663 A130   10s multi   .20   .20
664 A130   90s pur & multi   .20   .20
665 A130   1k brn & multi   .20   .20
666 A130   2k multi   .20   .20
667 A130   7k multi   .35   .20
668 A130   10k multi   .55   .25
669 A130   20k multi   1.10   .60
        Nos. 663-669 (7)   2.80 1.85

10th anniversary of independence.

Issues of 1964-1966 Surcharged

Perf. 11½, 12½x13, 13x12½
1970, Sept. 24   Photo.
670 A108   10s on 1fr (#499)   .25   .20
671 A108   20s on 2fr (#500)   .25   .20
672 A117   20s on 2fr (#565)   1.00   .50
673 A108   30s on 3fr (#501)   .25   .20
674 A117   40s on 4fr (#502)   .25   .20
675 A117   40s on 4fr (#566)   1.00   .50
676 A108   60s on 7fr (#505)   3.00 1.75
677 A108   90s on 9fr (#507)   3.00 1.75
678 A115   90s on 9fr (#555)   .60   .40
679 A115   1k on 7fr (#554)   .60   .40
680 A108   1k on 6fr (#504)   .50   .20
681 A117   1k on 12fr (#570)   2.75 1.75
682 A117   2k on 24fr (#572)   1.25   .50
683 A115   2k on 24fr (#586)   1.25   .50
684 A108   3k on 30fr (#510)   2.25 1.25
685 A108   4k on 40fr (#511)   .50   .20
686 A108   5k on 50fr (#512)   9.00 5.00
687 A108   10k on 100fr (#513)   2.25 1.25
        Nos. 670-687 (18)   29.95 16.75

Telecommunications Building,
Geneva — A131

Designs: 2k, 6.60k, UPU Headquarters,
Bern. 9.80k, 10k, 11k, UN Headquarters, NY.

1970, Oct. 24   Photo.   Perf. 11½
688 A131   1k pink & grn   .20   .20
689 A131   2k org & grn   .20   .20
690 A131   6.60k grnsh bl & rose
            car   .40   .25
691 A131   9.60k yel & vio bl   .50   .35
692 A131   9.80k lt ultra & brn .50   .35
693 A131   10k lt pur & brn   .50   .35
694 A131   11k rose & brn   .70   .45
        Nos. 688-694 (7)   3.00 2.15

ITU; new UPU Headquarters, Bern; 25th
anniv. of the UN.

Pres. Mobutu, Congolese Flag and
Arch — A132

1970, Nov. 24   Litho.   Perf. 13
695 A132   2k yel & multi   .20   .20
696 A132   10k bl & multi   .90   .50
697 A132   20k red & multi   2.10 1.50
        Nos. 695-697 (3)   3.20 2.20

Fifth anniversary of new government.

Apollo 11
in Flight
A133

Designs: 2k, Astronaut and spacecraft on moon. 7k, Pres. Mobutu decorating astronauts' wives. 10k, Pres. Mobutu with Neil A. Armstrong, Col. Edwin E. Aldrin, Jr. and Lt. Col. Michael Collins. 30k, Armstrong, Aldrin and Collins in space suits.

1970, Dec. 24   Perf. 13x13½

698	A133	1k bl & blk	.30	.20
699	A133	2k brt pur & blk	.50	.25
700	A133	7k dl org & blk	1.50	.85
701	A133	10k rose red & blk	1.75	1.25
702	A133	30k grn & blk	5.25	3.25
		Nos. 698-702 (5)	9.30	5.80

Visit of US Apollo 11 astronauts and their wives to Kinshasa.

Metopodontus Savagei — A134

Designs: Various insects of Congo.

1971, Jan. 25   Photo.   Perf. 11½

703	A134	10s dl rose & multi	.60	.25
704	A134	50s gray & multi	.60	.25
705	A134	90s multi	.60	.25
706	A134	1k citron & multi	.60	.25
707	A134	2k gray grn & multi	.60	.25
708	A134	3k lt vio & multi	1.25	.40
709	A134	5k bl & multi	4.25	1.50
710	A134	10k multi	6.00	2.10
711	A134	30k grn & multi	14.00	6.00
712	A134	40k ocher & multi	22.00	8.75
		Nos. 703-712 (10)	50.50	20.00

Colotis Protomedia — A135

Various butterflies and moths of Congo.

1971, Feb. 24

713	A135	10s lt ultra & multi	.65	.30
714	A135	20s choc & multi	.65	.30
715	A135	70s dp org & multi	.65	.30
716	A135	1k vio bl & multi	.65	.30
717	A135	3k multi	1.50	.50
718	A135	5k dk grn & multi	4.25	1.25
719	A135	10k multi	5.50	1.75
720	A135	15k emer & multi	10.00	3.00
721	A135	25k yel & multi	16.00	4.00
722	A135	40k multi	22.50	10.00
		Nos. 713-722 (10)	62.35	21.70

UN Emblem,
Racial
Unity — A136

1971, Mar. 21   Photo.   Perf. 11½

723	A136	1k lt grn & multi	.20	.20
724	A136	4k gray & multi	.20	.20
725	A136	5k lt lil & multi	.35	.25
726	A136	10k lt bl & multi	.75	.35
		Nos. 723-726 (4)	1.50	1.00

Intl. year against racial discrimination.

Hypericum
Bequaertii
A137

Flowers: 4k, Dissotis brazzae. 20k, Begonia wollastonii. 25k, Cassia alata.

1971, May 24   Litho.   Perf. 14

727	A137	1k multi	1.00	.25
728	A137	4k multi	1.75	.45
729	A137	20k multi	9.25	2.50
730	A137	25k multi	12.00	3.25
		Nos. 727-730 (4)	24.00	6.45

Obelisk at
N'sele, Pres.
Mobutu
A138

1971, May 20   Photo.   Perf. 11½

731	A138	4k gold & multi	.45	.20

4th anniversary of the People's Revolutionary Movement.

Radar
Station
A139

Designs: 1k, Waves. 6k, Map of Africa with telecommunications network.

1971, June 25   Photo.   Perf. 11½

732	A139	1k rose & multi	.20	.20
733	A139	3k yel & multi	.50	.35
734	A139	6k lt bl & multi	1.25	.95
		Nos. 732-734 (3)	1.95	1.50

3rd World Telecommunications Day, May 17 (1k); opening of satellite telecommunications ground station, Kinshasa, June 30 (3k); Pan-African telecommunication system (6k).

Grass
Monkeys
A140

Designs: 20s, Moustached monkeys, vert. 70s, De Brazza's monkeys. 1k, Yellow baboons. 3k, Pygmy chimpanzee, vert. 5k, Mangabeys, vert. 10k, Owlfaced monkeys. 15k, Diana monkeys. 25k, Black-and-white colobus, vert. 40k, L'Hoest's monkeys, vert.

1971, Aug.

735	A140	10s vio & multi	.75	.35
736	A140	20s lt bl & multi	.75	.35
737	A140	70s ocher & multi	1.10	.45
738	A140	1k gray & multi	1.10	.45
739	A140	3k rose & multi	1.75	.90
740	A140	5k brn & multi	4.00	2.40
741	A140	10k multi	8.25	4.50
742	A140	15k multi	13.00	6.25
743	A140	25k brt bl & multi	22.50	10.50
744	A140	40k red & multi	30.00	15.00
		Nos. 735-744 (10)	83.20	41.15

Hotel Inter-Continental,
Kinshasa — A141

1971, Oct. 2   Photo.   Perf. 13

745	A141	2k silver & multi	.25	.25
746	A141	12k gold & multi	.55	.25

Man Reading
A142

Designs: 2.50k, Open book and abacus. 7k, Five letters surrounding symbolic head.

1971, Oct. 24

747	A142	50s multi	.20	.20
748	A142	2.50k multi	.20	.20
749	A142	7k multi	1.25	1.00
		Nos. 747-749 (3)	1.65	1.40

Fight against illiteracy.

Succeeding issues are listed in Vol. 6 under Zaire. Beginning in 1998, Zaire reverted to using the Congo name, at least temporarily. Until the situation is resolved, the current stamps inscribed "Congo" will be listed under Zaire.

SEMI-POSTAL STAMPS

Women
Carrying
Food,
Wheat
Emblem,
and
Tractor
SP22

1963, Mar. 21   Photo.   Perf. 14x13

B48	SP22	5fr + 2fr multi	.25	.20
B49	SP22	9fr + 4fr multi	.40	.20
B50	SP22	12fr + 6fr multi	.45	.25
B51	SP22	20fr + 10fr multi	2.00	1.50
		Nos. B48-B51 (4)	3.10	2.15

FAO "Freedom from Hunger" campaign.
No. B51 exists in an imperf sheet of one, in light and dark violet. Value $30.

CONGO, PEOPLE'S REPUBLIC OF

'pē-pəls ri-'pə-blik of

ˈkäŋ͟ˌgō

(ex-French)

LOCATION — West Africa at equator
GOVT. — Republic
AREA — 132,046 sq. mi.
POP. — 2,716,814 (1999 est.)
CAPITAL — Brazzaville

The former French colony of Middle Congo became a member state of the French Community on November 28, 1958, and achieved independence on August 15, 1960. For some years before 1958, the colony was joined with three other French territories to form French Equatorial Africa. Issues of Middle Congo (1907-1933) are listed under that heading.

100 Centimes = 1 Franc

Catalogue values for all unused stamps in this country are for Never Hinged items.

Allegory of New Republic A7

1959   Unwmk.   Engr.   Perf. 13
89   A7   25fr brn, dp claret, org & ol   .60 .25

1st anniv. of the proclamation of the Republic.

Imperforates

Most stamps of the Republic of the Congo exist imperforate in issued and trial colors, and also in small presentation sheets in issued colors.

Common Design Types pictured following the introduction.

C.C.T.A. Issue
Common Design Type

1960   Unwmk.   Perf. 13
90   CD106 50fr dl grn & plum   .80 .80

President Fulbert Youlou — A8

Flag, Map and UN Emblem — A9

1960
91   A8   15fr grn, blk & car   .35 .35
92   A8   85fr indigo & car   2.00 .45

1961, Mar. 11   Perf. 13
Flag in Green, Yellow & Red
93   A9   5fr vio brn & dk bl   .25 .20
94   A9   20fr org & dk bl   .45 .25
95   A9   100fr grn & dk bl   2.00 .80
        Nos. 93-95 (3)   2.70 1.25

Congo's admission to United Nations.

Rainbow Runner A10

Fish: 50c, 3fr, Rainbow runner. 1fr, 2fr, Sloan's viperfish. 5fr, Hatchet fish. 10fr, A deep-sea fish.

1961, Nov. 28   **Engr.**
96   A10   50c brn, ol grn & sal   .25 .20
97   A10   1fr bl grn & sepia   .25 .20
98   A10   2fr ultra, sep & dk grn   .25 .20
99   A10   3fr dk bl, grn & salmon   .35 .20
100   A10   5fr red brn, grn & blk   .70 .25
101   A10   10fr blue & red brn   1.40 .30
        Nos. 96-101 (6)   3.20 1.35

Brazzaville Market — A11

1962, Mar. 23   Unwmk.   Perf. 13
102   A11   20fr blk, red & grn   .60 .20

Abidjan Games Issue
Common Design Type

20fr, Boxing. 50fr, Running, finish line.

1962, July 21   Photo.   Perf. 12½x12
103   CD109 20fr car, brt pink, brn & blk   .45 .25
104   CD109 50fr car, brt pink, brn & blk   .90 .30
        Nos. 103-104,C7 (3)   3.85 1.80

African-Malgache Union Issue
Common Design Type

1962, Sept. 8
105   CD110 30fr multicolored   1.00 .40

Waves Around Globe A11a

Design: 100fr, Orbit patterns around globe.

1963, Sept. 19   Perf. 12½
106   A11a   25fr org, grn & ultra   .50 .30
107   A11a   100fr lt red brn, bl & plum   1.60 .90

Issued to publicize space communications.

King Makoko's Collar — A12

Unwmk.
1963, Oct. 21   Engr.   Perf. 13
108   A12   10fr showm   .45 .25
109   A12   15fr Kebekebe mask   .60 .25

UNESCO Emblem, Scales and Tree A12a

1963, Dec. 10   Unwmk.   Perf. 13
110   A12a 25fr grn, dk bl & brn   .70 .30

15th anniv. of the Universal Declaration of Human Rights.

Barograph and WMO Emblem A12b

1964, Mar. 23   Engr.
111   A12b 50fr grn, red brn & ultra   1.00 .60

Fourth World Meteorological Day.

Mechanic with Machine — A13

1964, Apr. 8
112   A13   20fr grnsh bl, mag & dk brn   .60 .30

Training of technicians.

Corn and Tools A14

1964, Apr. 24   Unwmk.   Perf. 13
113   A14   80fr brn, grn & brn car   1.10 .60

Importance of manual labor.

Diaboua Ballet A15

Kébékébé Dance — A16

Carved Figure — A17

1964, May 8   Engr.
114   A15   30fr multicolored   1.25 .30
115   A16   60fr multicolored   2.25 .65

1964, May 22
116   A17   50fr brn red & sepia   1.50 .55

Classroom A18

1964, May 26
117   A18   25fr dk brn, red & blue   .60 .30

Issued to publicize education.

Type of Air Post Issue, 1963, Inscribed: "1er ANNIVERSAIRE DE LA REVOLUTION/FETE NATIONALE/15 AOUT 1964"

1964, Aug. 15   Photo.   Perf. 13x12
118   AP5   20fr lt bl, red, ocher, dk brn & grn   .50 .20

1st anniv. of the revolution and Natl. Feast Day, Aug. 15.

Fire Squid A19

15fr, Johnson's deep-sea angler (fish).

1964, Oct. 20   Engr.   Perf. 13
119   A19   2fr ver, lt grn & brn   .50 .20
120   A19   15fr vio, lt ol grn & dp cl   2.25 1.10

Cooperation Issue
Common Design Type

1964, Nov. 7   Unwmk.   Perf. 13
121   CD119 25fr car, brt grn & dk brn   .60 .35

Communications Emblems — A20

1965, Jan. 1   Litho.   Perf. 12½x13
122   A20   25fr ol, red brn & blk   .50 .25

Issued to commemorate the establishment of the national postal administration.

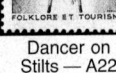

Sitatunga — A21

Dancer on Stilts — A22

Design: 20fr, Elephant, horiz.

1965, Mar. 15   Engr.   Perf. 13
123   A21   15fr redsh brn, dl grn & bl   .90 .40
124   A21   20fr blk, dp bl & sl grn   .90 .40
125   A22   85fr lil & multi   3.50 1.50
        Nos. 123-125 (3)   5.30 2.30

Pres. Alphonse Massamba-Debat A23

1965-66   Photo.   Perf. 12x12½
126   A23   20fr dk brn, grn & yel   .25 .20
127   A23   25fr brn, bl grn, emer & blk ('66)   .30 .20

128 A23 30fr brn, bl grn, org & blk
('66)   .45 .20
Nos. 126-128 (3)   1.00 .60

Soccer
Player
A24

Designs: 25fr, Games' emblem (map of
Africa and runners). 50fr, Field ball player.
85fr, Runner. 100fr, Bicyclist.

1965, July 17 Photo. Perf. 12½
Size: 28x28mm
129 A24 25fr blk, red, yel & grn   .50 .30
Size: 34x34mm
130 A24 40fr yel grn & multi   .70 .45
131 A24 50fr red & multi   .70 .45
132 A24 85fr blk & multi   1.25 .65
133 A24 100fr yel & multi   1.75 .75
  a. Min. sheet of 5, #129-133   7.50 7.50
Nos. 129-133 (5)   4.90 2.60

1st African Games, Brazzaville, July 18-25.

Arms of
Congo — A25

1965, Nov. 15 Litho. Perf. 12½x13
134 A25 20fr multicolored   .50 .20

Cooperative
Village
A26

30fr, Gymnastic drill team with streamers.

1966, Feb. 18   Perf. 12½x13
135 A26 25fr multicolored   .50 .25
136 A26 30fr multicolored   .50 .30

Sculptured
Mask — A27

Designs: 30fr, Weaver, painting. 85fr,
String instrument, painting, horiz.

Perf. 13x12½, 12½x13
1966, Apr. 9   Photo.
137 A27 30fr multicolored   .70 .30
138 A27 85fr multicolored   1.90 .70
139 A27 90fr multicolored   2.25 1.00
  Nos. 137-139 (3)   4.85 2.00

Intl. Negro Arts Festival, Dakar, Senegal,
4/1-24.

Men and
Clocks
A28

1966, Apr. 15   Perf. 12½x12
140 A28 70fr pale brn, ocher & dk
brn   1.00 .30
Introduction of the shorter work day (less
lunch time, earlier quitting time).

WHO Headquarters, Geneva — A29

1966, May 3 Photo. Perf. 12½x13
141 A29 50fr org yel, vio & bl   .80 .40
Inauguration of the WHO Headquarters,
Geneva.

Church of St.   Women's
Peter Claver   Basketball
A30   A31

1966, June 15 Photo. Perf. 13x12½
142 A30 70fr multicolored   1.00 .40

1966, July 15   Engr.   Perf. 13
Sport: 1fr, Women's volleyball, horiz. 3fr,
Women's field ball, horiz. 5fr, Athletes of various races. 10fr, Torch bearer. 15fr, Soccer
and gold medal of First African Games.
143 A31 1fr ultra, choc & ol   .20 .20
144 A31 2fr choc, grn & bl   .25 .20
145 A31 3fr dk grn, dk car &
choc   .25 .20
146 A31 5fr slate, emer & choc   .25 .20
147 A31 10fr dl bl, dk grn & vio   .45 .20
148 A31 15fr vio, car & choc   .50 .30
  Nos. 143-148 (6)   1.90 1.30

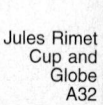

Jules Rimet
Cup and
Globe
A32

1966, July 15 Photo. Perf. 12½x13
149 A32 30fr brt red, gold, blk & bl   .90 .45
8th World Soccer Cup Championship, Wembley, England, July 11-30.

Savorgnan
de Brazza
School
A33

1966, Sept. 15 Photo. Perf. 12½x12
150 A33 30fr dk pur, grn, yel & blk   .60 .25

Pointe-Noire Railroad Station — A34

1966, Oct. 15   Engr.   Perf. 13
151 A34 60fr grn, red & brn   1.25 .60

Student with   Balumbu Mask
Microscope   A36
A35

1966, Nov. 28   Engr.   Perf. 13
152 A35 90fr brn, grn & ind   1.25 .70
20th anniv. of UNESCO.

1966, Dec. 12   Engr.   Perf. 13
Masks: 10fr, Kuyu. 15fr, Bakwélé. 20fr,
Batéké.
153 A36 5fr car rose & dk brn   .45 .20
154 A36 10fr Prus bl & brn   .50 .20
155 A36 15fr sep, dl org & dk bl   .60 .20
156 A36 20fr dp bl & multi   .80 .20
  Nos. 153-156 (4)   2.35 .80

Order of the
Revolution and
Map — A37

Learning
the
Alphabet
A38

Design: 45fr, Harvesting and loading sugar
cane, and sugar mill.

Perf. 12x12½, 12½x12
1967, Mar. 15   Photo.
157 A37 20fr org & multi   .50 .30
158 A38 25fr blk, ocher & dk car   .60 .35
159 A38 45fr blk, yel grn & lt bl   1.00 .30
  Nos. 157-159 (3)   2.10 .95

Issued to honor the members of the Order
of the Revolution (20fr); to publicize the literacy campaign (25fr); to publicize, sugar production (45fr).

Mahatma   Fruit
Gandhi — A39   Vendor — A40

1967, Apr. 21   Engr.   Perf. 13
160 A39 90fr bl & blk   1.75 .60
Issued in memory of Mohandas K. Gandhi
(1869-1948), Hindu nationalist leader.

1967, June   Photo.   Perf. 13x12½
Dolls: 5fr, "Elegant Lady." 25fr, Woman
pounding saka-saka. 30fr, Mother and child.
161 A40 5fr gold & multi   .25 .20
162 A40 10fr yel grn & multi   .45 .20
163 A40 15fr lt ultra & multi   .50 .20
164 A40 30fr multicolored   .60 .20
  Nos. 161-164 (4)   1.80 .80

ITY
Emblem,
Village and
Waterfall
A41

1967, July 5   Engr.   Perf. 13
165 A41 60fr rose cl, org & ol grn   .70 .40
Issued for International Tourist Year, 1967.

Symbols of   Arms of
Cooperation   Brazzaville
A42   A43

Europafrica Issue, 1967
1967, July 20 Photo. Perf. 12x12½
166 A42 50fr multicolored   .90 .30

1967, Aug. 15 Litho. Perf. 12½x13
167 A43 30fr yel & multi   .60 .35
Fourth anniversary of the revolution.

UN Emblem,   Boy and
Dove and   UNICEF
People — A44   Emblem — A45

1967, Oct. 24 Photo. Perf. 13x12½
168 A44 90fr bl, dk brn, red brn &
yel   1.60 .60
Issued for United Nations Day, Oct. 24.

1967, Dec. 11   Engr.   Perf. 13
169 A45 90fr mar, blk & ultra   1.60 .60
21st anniv. of UNICEF.

Albert
Luthuli,
Dove and
Globe
A46

1968, Jan. 29   Engr.   Perf. 13
170 A46 30fr brt grn & ol bis   .60 .35
Albert Luthuli (1899-1967) of South Africa,
winner of 1960 Nobel Peace Prize.

Arms of Pointe
Noire — A47

1968, Feb. 20 Litho. Perf. 12½x13
171 A47 10fr brt pink & multi   .50 .30

Motherhood
A48

Mayombe
Viaduct
A49

1968, May 25   Engr.   Perf. 13
172 A48 15fr dk car rose, sky bl & blk   .50 .30

Issued for Mother's Day.

1968, June 24
173 A49 45fr maroon, slate grn & bl   1.75 .45

A50

1968, July 29 Photo. Perf. 13x12½
174 A50 5fr Daimler, 1889   .45 .20
175 A50 20fr Berliet, 1897   .90 .30
176 A50 60fr Peugeot, 1898   1.75 .40
177 A50 80fr Renault, 1900   2.75 .70
178 A50 85fr Fiat, 1902   3.25 .90
Nos. 174-178,C67-C68 (7)   17.85 6.00

Tanker, Refinery and Map of Area
Served — A50a

1968, July 30   Perf. 12½
179 A50a 30fr multicolored   .80 .30

Issued to commemorate the opening of the Port Gentil (Gabon) Refinery, June 12, 1968.

UN Emblem and
Tree of Life — A51

1968, Nov. 28   Engr.   Perf. 13
180 A51 25fr dk grn, red & dp lil   .50 .30

20th anniv. of WHO.

Development Bank Issue
Common Design Type

1969, Sept. 10 Engr. Perf. 13
181 CD130 25fr car rose, grn & ocher   .35 .20
182 CD130 30fr bl, grn & ocher   .35 .20

Bicycle
A52

Bicycles & Motorcycles: 75fr, Hirondelle. 80fr, Folding bicycle. 85fr, Peugeot. 100fr, Excelsior Manxman. 150fr, Norton. 200fr,

Brough Superior "Old Bill." 300fr, Matchless and N.L.G.-J.A.P.S.

1969, Oct. 6   Engr.   Perf. 13
183 A52 50fr multicolored   1.25 .30
184 A52 75fr multicolored   1.50 .30
185 A52 80fr multicolored   1.75 .40
186 A52 85fr multicolored   2.00 .50
187 A52 100fr multicolored   2.75 .75
188 A52 150fr multicolored   3.75 .90
189 A52 200fr multicolored   5.00 1.50
190 A52 300fr multicolored   9.00 2.50
Nos. 183-190 (8)   27.00 7.15

Mayombe
Train and
Tourist Year
Emblem
A53

40fr, Train and Mbamba Tunnel, vert.

Perf. 13x12½, 12½x13
1969, Oct. 20   Photo.
191 A53 40fr multicolored   1.50 .40
192 A53 60fr multicolored   2.50 .65

Issued for African Tourist Year.

Loutete
Cement
Works
A54

Loutete Cement Works: 15fr, Mixing tower, vert. 25fr, Cable transport, vert. 30fr, General view of plant.

1969, Dec. 10   Engr.   Perf. 13
193 A54 10fr dk gray, rose cl & dk ol   .25 .20
194 A54 15fr Prus bl, red brn & pur   .50 .20
195 A54 25fr mar, brn & Prus bl   .60 .20
196 A54 30fr vio brn, ultra & blk   .70 .20
a.   Min. sheet of 4, #193-196   2.50 2.50
Nos. 193-196 (4)   2.05 .80

ASECNA Issue
Common Design Type

1969, Dec. 12
197 CD132 100fr dull brown   1.60 .40

Pineapple
Harvest
and ILO
Emblem
A55

30fr, Worker at lathe and ILO emblem.

1969, Dec. 20   Engr.   Perf. 13
198 A55 25fr bl, olive & brn   .35 .25
199 A55 30fr rose red, choc & slate   .50 .25

50th anniv. of the ILO.

SOTEXCO
Textile
Plant,
Kinsoundi
A56

20fr, Women in spinnery. 25fr, Hand-printing textiles. 30fr, Checking woven cloth.

1970, Jan. 20
200 A56 15fr grn, blk & lil   .45 .20
201 A56 20fr plum, car & sl grn   .45 .20
202 A56 25fr bl, slate & brn   .60 .20
203 A56 30fr gray, car rose & brn   .60 .25
Nos. 200-203 (4)   2.10 .85

Hotel
Cosmos,
Brazzaville
A57

1970, Jan. 30
204 A57 90fr slate grn, bl & red brn   1.25 .30

The status of the three sets for Kennedy, etc., Summer Olympics, and Baroque paintings is not certain.

Linzolo
Church — A58

Diosso
Gorge
A59

Design: 90fr, Foulakari waterfall.

1970   Engr.   Perf. 13
205 A58 25fr multicolored   .60 .20
206 A59 70fr multicolored   1.50 .30
207 A59 90fr multicolored   2.25 .40
Nos. 205-207 (3)   4.35 .90

Issue dates: 25fr, Feb. 10; others, Feb. 25.

Volvaria
Esculenta — A60

Mushrooms: 10fr, Termitomyces entolomoides. 15fr, Termitomyces microcarpus. 25fr, Termitomyces aurantiacus. 30fr, Termitomyces mammiformis. 50fr, Tremella fuciformis.

1970, Mar. 31 Photo. Perf. 13
208 A60 5fr multicolored   6.75 1.00
209 A60 10fr multicolored   9.00 1.40
210 A60 15fr multicolored   13.50 2.00
211 A60 25fr multicolored   22.50 4.00
212 A60 30fr multicolored   32.50 5.75
213 A60 50fr multicolored   70.00 10.00
Nos. 208-213 (6)   154.25 24.15

Laying
Coaxial
Cable
A61

Design: 30fr, Full view of rail car; 3 cable layers on railway roadbed.

1970, Apr. 30   Engr.   Perf. 13
214 A61 25fr dk brn & multi   1.00 .30
215 A61 30fr brn & multi   1.10 .60

Issued to publicize the laying of the coaxial cable linking Brazzaville and Pointe Noire.
For surcharges see Nos. 263-264.

UPU Headquarters Issue
Common Design Type

1970, May 20
216 CD133 30fr dk pur, gray & mag   .70 .25

Mother Feeding
Child — A62

Dag
Hammarskjold,
UN
Emblem — A63

Design: 90fr, Mother nursing infant.

1970, May 30   Photo.
217 A62 85fr vio bl & multi   .80 .30
218 A62 90fr lil & multi   .95 .40

Issued for Mother's Day.

1970, June 20   Engr.   Perf. 13

UN Emblem and: No. 220, Trygve Lie, horiz. No. 221, U Thant, horiz.

219 A63 100fr scar, dk red & dk pur   1.25 .75
220 A63 100fr dk red, ultra & ind   1.25 .75
221 A63 100fr grn, emer & dk red   1.25 .75
a.   Souv. sheet of 3, #219-221   5.00 5.00
Nos. 219-221 (3)   3.75 2.25

25th anniv. of the UN and to honor its Secretaries General.

Brillantaisia
Vogeliana
A64

Sternotomis
Variabilis — A65

Plants and Beetles: 2fr, Plectranthus decurrens. 3fr, Myrianthemum mirabile. 5fr, Connarus griffonianus. 15fr, Chelorrhina polyphemus. 20fr, Metopodontus savagei.

Perf. 12½x12, 12x12½
1970, June 30   Photo.
222 A64 1fr dk grn & multi   .45 .25
223 A64 2fr multicolored   .45 .25
224 A64 3fr indigo & multi   .50 .25
225 A64 5fr lemon & multi   1.00 .25
226 A65 10fr lilac & multi   2.25 .40
227 A65 15fr orange & multi   3.00 .40
228 A65 20fr multicolored   3.25 .60
Nos. 222-228 (7)   10.90 2.40

For surcharge see No. 288.

Stegosaurus — A66

Prehistoric Fauna: 20fr, Dinotherium, vert. 60fr, Brachiosaurus, vert. 80fr, Arsinoitherium.

1970, July 20
229 A66 15fr dl grn, ocher & red brn   .80 .30
230 A66 20fr lt bl & multi   2.75 .65
231 A66 60fr lt bl & multi   5.75 .95
232 A66 80fr lt bl & multi   7.50 1.75
Nos. 229-232 (4)   16.80 3.65

Mikado
141, 1932
A67

Locomotives: 60fr, Steam locomotive 130+032, 1947. 75fr, Alsthom BB 1100, 1962. 85fr, Diesel BB BB 302, 1969.

1970, Aug. 20   Engr.   Perf. 13

233	A67	40fr mag, bl grn & blk	2.75	.80
234	A67	60fr blk, bl & grn	3.00	.90
235	A67	75fr red, bl & blk	4.50	1.25
236	A67	85fr car, sl grn & ocher	7.00	1.75
		Nos. 233-236 (4)	17.25	4.70

Cogniauxia
Padolaena
A68

Green Night
Adder
A69

Tropical Flowers: 2fr, Celosia cristata. 5fr, Plumeria acutifolia. 10fr, Bauhinia variegata. 15fr, Poinsettia. 20fr, Thunbergia grandiflora.

1971, Feb. 10   Photo.   Perf. 12x12½

237	A68	1fr lil & multi	.25	.20
238	A68	2fr yel & multi	.25	.20
239	A68	5fr ultra & multi	.25	.20
240	A68	10fr yel & multi	1.10	.20
241	A68	15fr multicolored	1.60	.30
242	A68	20fr dk red & multi	2.75	.40
		Nos. 237-242 (6)	6.20	1.50

Perf. 12x12½, 12½x12

1971, June 26   Photo.

Reptiles: 10fr, African Egg-eating snake, horiz. 15fr, Flap-necked chameleon. 20fr, Nile crocodile, horiz. 25fr, Rock python, horiz. 30fr, Gaboon viper. 40fr, Brown house snake, horiz. 45fr, Jameson's mamba.

243	A69	5fr multicolored	.35	.20
244	A69	10fr multicolored	.35	.20
245	A69	15fr multicolored	1.25	.20
246	A69	20fr red & multi	2.10	.25
247	A69	25fr grn & multi	2.75	.35
248	A69	30fr multicolored	3.50	.75
249	A69	40fr bis & multi	4.00	.95
250	A69	45fr multicolored	5.25	1.00
		Nos. 243-250 (8)	19.55	3.90

Pseudimbrasia Deyrollei — A70

Caterpillars: 15fr, Bunaea alcinoe, vert. 20fr, Epiphora vacuna ploetzi. 25fr, Imbrasia eblis. 30fr, Imbrasia dione, vert. 40fr, Holocera angulata.

1971, July 3   Perf. 13

251	A70	10fr ver, blk & grn	1.00	.20
252	A70	15fr multicolored	1.50	.30
253	A70	20fr yel grn, blk & ocher	2.25	.40
254	A70	25fr multicolored	3.50	.60
255	A70	30fr red, blk & yel	5.00	.90
256	A70	40fr bl, blk & org	6.75	1.25
		Nos. 251-256 (6)	20.00	3.65

Boy Scout — A70a

Scouts, Lord Baden-Powell — A70b

Designs: c, Scout facing left. d, Scout facing forward. e, Lord Baden-Powell.

Embossed on Metallic Foil

1971, July 14   Die Cut Perf. 10½

256A	A70a	90fr Block of 4, #b.-e., silver	10.00	10.00
256F	A70b	1000fr gold	30.00	30.00

No. 256F is airmail.

Cymothoe
Sangaris
A71

Butterflies and Moths: 40fr, Papilio dardanus, vert. 75fr, Iolaus timon. 90fr, Papilio phorcas, vert. 100fr, Euchloron megaera.

1971, Oct. 15   Perf. 12½x12, 12x12½

257	A71	30fr yel & multi	1.50	.40
258	A71	40fr grn & multi	3.00	.65
259	A71	75fr multicolored	5.00	1.25
260	A71	90fr multicolored	6.75	1.90
261	A71	100fr ultra & multi	9.00	2.50
		Nos. 257-261 (5)	25.25	6.70

Black and White
Men Working
Together — A72

1971, Oct. 30   Perf. 13x12½

262	A72	50fr org & multi	.65	.35

Intl. Year Against Racial Discrimination.

Nos. 214-215 Surcharged

1971, Nov. 18   Engr.   Perf. 13

263	A61	30fr on 25fr multicolored	.50	.30
264	A61	40fr on 30fr multicolored	.75	.35

Inauguration of cable service between Brazzaville and Pointe Noire. Words of surcharge arranged differently on No. 264.

Map of
Congo — A73

1971, Dec. 31   Photo.   Perf. 12½x13

265	A73	30fr bl & multi	.35	.20
266	A73	40fr yel grn & multi	.45	.20
267	A73	100fr gray & multi	1.10	.40
		Nos. 265-267 (3)	1.90	.80

"Labor, Democracy, Peace."

Lion — A74

2fr, African elephants. 3fr, Leopard. 4fr, Hippopotamus. 5fr, Gorilla, vert. 20fr, Potto. 30fr, De Brazza's monkey. 40fr, Pygmy chimpanzee, vert.

1972, Jan. 31   Engr.   Perf. 13

268	A74	1fr grn & multi	.35	.20
269	A74	2fr red & multi	.50	.20
270	A74	3fr red brn & multi	.80	.20
271	A74	4fr vio & multi	1.00	.20
272	A74	5fr brn & multi	1.10	.25
273	A74	20fr org & multi	2.75	.35
274	A74	30fr ocher & multi	3.50	.45
275	A74	40fr Prus bl & multi	5.25	.75
		Nos. 268-275 (8)	15.25	2.60

WHO, 25th
Anniv. — A75

Perf. 12½x13, 13x12½

1973, June 30   Typo.

276	A75	40fr WHO Emblem	.60	.20
277	A75	50fr WHO emblem, horiz.	.70	.20

Kronenbourg Brewery — A76

Brewery Trademark and: 40fr, Laboratory. 75fr, Vats and controls. 85fr, Automatic control room. 100fr, Pressure room. 250fr, Bottling plant.

1973, July 15   Engr.   Perf. 13

278	A76	30fr red & multi	.50	.20
279	A76	40fr red & multi	.60	.20
280	A76	75fr red & multi	1.00	.30
281	A76	85fr red & multi	1.40	.40
282	A76	100fr red & multi	1.50	.55
283	A76	250fr red & multi	3.00	1.00
		Nos. 278-283 (6)	8.00	2.65

Kronenbourg Brewery, Brazzaville.

Golwe
Locomotive,
1935 — A77

Locomotives: 40fr, Diesel, 1935. 75fr, Diesel Whithcomb, 1946. 85fr, Diesel CC200.

1973, Aug. 1   Engr.   Perf. 13

284	A77	30fr indigo & multi	1.75	.50
285	A77	40fr vio bl & multi	2.75	.75
286	A77	75fr multicolored	4.00	1.25
287	A77	85fr multicolored	5.00	2.40
		Nos. 284-287 (4)	13.50	4.90

No. 225 Surcharged with New Value, 2 Bars, and Overprinted in Ultramarine: "SECHERESSE SOLIDARITE AFRICAINE"

1973, Aug. 16   Photo.   Perf. 12½x12

288	A64	100fr on 5fr multicolored	1.75	.60

African solidarity in drought emergency.

African Postal Union Issue
Common Design Type

1973, Sept. 12   Engr.   Perf. 13

289	CD137	100fr bl grn, vio & brn	1.50	.45

Bees,
Beehive,
Honeycomb
A78

1973, Dec. 10   Engr.   Perf. 13

290	A78	30fr sl grn, dk red & bl	1.10	.20
291	A78	40fr sl bl, sl grn & lt grn	1.50	.20

"Work and economy."

Family, UN
and FAO
Emblems
A79

40fr, Grain, emblems. 100fr, Grain, emblems, vert.

1973, Dec. 10

292	A79	30fr dk car & dk brn	.50	.20
293	A79	40fr dk grn, yel & ind	.60	.20
294	A79	100fr grn, brn & org	1.40	.40
		Nos. 292-294 (3)	2.50	.80

World Food Program, 10th anniversary.

Amilcar Cabral,
Cattle and
Child — A80

1974, July 15   Engr.   Perf. 13

295	A80	100fr multicolored	1.00	.60

First death anniversary of Amilcar Cabral (1924-1973), leader of anti-Portuguese guerrilla activity in Portuguese Guinea.

Félix Eboué, Cross of Lorraine A81

1974, Aug. 31   Litho.   Perf. 13
296 A81 30fr bl & multi   .60   .30
297 A81 40fr brt pink & multi 1.00   .60

Félix A. Eboué (1884-1944), Governor of Chad, first colonial governor to join Free French in WWII, 30th death anniversary.

Pineapples A82

1974, Nov. 12
298 A82 30fr shown   .60   .30
299 A82 30fr Bananas   .70   .30
300 A82 30fr Safous   .70   .30
301 A82 40fr Avocados   1.10 .30
302 A82 40fr Mangos   1.10 .30
303 A82 40fr Papaya   1.10 .30
304 A82 40fr Orange   1.10 .30
    Nos. 298-304 (7)   6.40 2.10

Charles de Gaulle and Conference Building — A83

1974, Nov. 25   Engr.   Perf. 13
305 A83 100fr multicolored   3.25   1.90

Brazzaville Conference, 25th anniversary.

George Stephenson and Various Locomotives — A84

1974, Dec. 15
306 A84 75fr slate green & olive   4.00   1.00

George Stephenson (1781-1848), English inventor and railroad founder.

UDEAC Issue

Presidents and Flags of Cameroun, CAR, Congo, Gabon and Meeting Center — A84a

1974, Dec. 8   Photo.   Perf. 13
307 A84a 40fr gold & multi   .60   .20

See note after Cameroun No. 595.
See No. C195.

Irish Setter A85

1974, Dec. 15   Photo.   Perf. 13x13½
308 A85 30fr shown   1.25   .30
309 A85 40fr Borzoi   1.50   .30
310 A85 75fr Pointer   3.25   .75
311 A85 100fr Great Dane 4.50   .80
    Nos. 308-311 (4)   10.50   2.15

1974, Dec. 15

Designs: Cats.

312 A85 30fr Havana chestnut 1.25   .30
313 A85 40fr Red Persian   1.50   .30
314 A85 75fr Blue British   3.25   .75
315 A85 100fr African serval 4.50   .80
    Nos. 312-315 (4)   10.50   2.15

Labor Party Flags and People A86

40fr, Hands holding flowers and tools.

1974, Dec. 31   Engr.   Perf. 13x12½
316 A86 30fr red & multi   .50   .20
317 A86 40fr red & multi   .60   .25

5th anniversary of Congolese Labor Party and of introduction of red flag.

Symbols of Development — A87

U Thant and UN Headquarters — A88

Paul G. Hoffman and UN Emblem A89

Perf. 13x12½, 12½x13
1975, Feb. 28   Litho.
318 A87 40fr multicolored   .60   .25
319 A88 50fr light blue & multi .60   .25
320 A89 50fr yellow & multi   .60   .25
    Nos. 318-320 (3)   1.80   .75

National economic development.

Map of China and Mao Tse-tung — A90

1975, Mar. 9   Engr.   Perf. 13
321 A90 75fr multicolored   3.25   1.40

25th anniv. of the PRC.

Woman Breaking Bonds, Women's Activities, Map of Congo A91

1975, June 20   Litho.   Perf. 12½
322 A91 40fr gold & multi   .60   .25

Revolutionary Union of Congolese Women, URFC, 10th anniversary.

CARA Soccer Team — A92

Design: 40fr, Team captain and manager receiving trophy, vert.

1975, July 15   Litho.   Perf. 12½
323 A92 30fr multicolored   .50   .25
324 A92 40fr multicolored   .60   .25

CARA team, winners of African Soccer Cup 1974.

Citroen, 1935 — A93

Designs: Early autombiles.

1975, July 17   Perf. 12
325 A93 30fr shown   .90   .40
326 A93 40fr Alfa Romeo, 1911 1.10   .40
327 A93 50fr Rolls Royce, 1926 1.40   .55
328 A93 75fr Duryea, 1893   2.75   .70
    Nos. 325-328 (4)   6.15   2.05

Tipoye Transport — A94

1975, Aug. 5
329 A94 30fr shown   .90   .40
330 A94 40fr Dugout canoe 1.00   .65

Traditional means of transportation.

Raising Red Flag — A95

1975, Aug. 15
331 A95 30fr shown   .50   .20
332 A95 40fr National Conference .60   .25

2nd anniv. of installation of popular power (30fr) and 3rd anniv. of Natl. Conf. (40fr).

Line Fishing — A96

Woman Pounding "Foufou" — A97

Traditional Fishing: 30fr, Trap fishing, horiz. 60fr, Spear fishing. 90fr, Net fishing, horiz.

1975, Aug. 31   Litho.   Perf. 12
333 A96 30fr multicolored   .70   .25
334 A96 40fr multicolored   .70   .30
335 A96 60fr multicolored   1.10   .40
336 A96 90fr multicolored   2.25   .90
    Nos. 333-336 (4)   4.75   1.85

1975, Sept. 5

Household Tasks: No. 338, Woman chopping wood. 40fr, Woman preparing manioc, horiz.

337 A97 30fr multicolored   .60   .20
338 A97 30fr multicolored   .60   .20
339 A97 40fr multicolored   .90   .25
    Nos. 337-339 (3)   2.10   .65

Musical Instruments A98

1975, Sept. 20   Perf. 12½
340 A98 30fr Esanga   .70   .20
341 A98 40fr Kalakwa   1.00   .25
342 A98 60fr Likembe   1.40   .30
343 A98 75fr Ngongui   1.75   .40
    Nos. 340-343 (4)   4.85   1.15

Dzeke (Congolese) Shell
Money — A99

Ancient Money: No. 346, like No. 344. Nos. 345, 347, Okengo, Congolese, iron bar. 40fr, Gallic coin, c. 60 B.C. 50fr, Roman denarius, 37 B.C. 60fr, Danubian coin, 2nd cent. B.C. 85fr, Greek stater, 4th cent. B.C.

1975-76		Engr.		Perf. 13	
344	A99	30fr red & multi		.60	.20
345	A99	30fr vio & multi		.60	.20
346	A99	35fr ol & multi		.90	.25
347	A99	35fr dk car rose & multi		.90	.25
348	A99	40fr Prus bl & brn		.90	.20
349	A99	50fr Prus bl & ol		1.00	.30
350	A99	60fr dk grn & brn		1.25	.35
351	A99	85fr mag & sl grn		2.10	.45
		Nos. 344-351 (8)		8.25	2.20

Nos. 346-347 inscribed "1976" and issued Mar. 1976; others issued Oct. 5, 1975.

Moschops — A100

Pre-historic Animals: 70fr, Tyrannosaurus. 95fr, Cryptocleidus. 100fr, Stegosaurus.

1975, Oct. 15		Litho.	Perf. 13	
352	A100	55fr multicolored	2.00	.30
353	A100	75fr multicolored	3.00	.35
354	A100	95fr multicolored	5.25	.75
355	A100	100fr multicolored	7.50	1.25
		Nos. 352-355 (4)	17.75	2.65

Albert Schweitzer
(1875-1965),
Medical
Missionary — A101

1975, Oct. 15			Engr.	
356	A101	75fr ol, brn & red	1.50	.40

Alexander
Fleming
A102

Designs: No. 358, André Marie Ampère. No. 359, Clement Ader.

1975, Nov. 15		Engr.	Perf. 13	
357	A102	60fr brn, grn & blk	1.00	.30
358	A102	85fr blk, red & grn	1.40	.40
359	A102	95fr red, blue & indigo	1.60	.40
		Nos. 357-359 (3)	4.00	1.10

Fleming (1881-1955), developer of penicillin; Ampère (1775-1836), physicist; Ader (1841-1925), aviation pioneer.

UN Emblem "ONU" and "30" — A103

1975, Dec. 20		Engr.	Perf. 13	
360	A103	95fr car, ultra & grn	1.25	.45

United Nations, 30th anniversary.

Women's Broken Chain — A104

Design: 60fr, Equality between man and woman, globe, IWY emblem.

1975, Dec. 20		Litho.	Perf. 12½	
361	A104	35fr mag, ocher & gray	.60	.20
362	A104	60fr ultra, brn & blk	.70	.30

International Women's Year, 1975.

Pres. Marien Ngouabi, Flag and
Workers — A105

Echo of the
P.C.T.
A106

1975, Dec. 31		Perf. 12½x12, 13x12½		
363	A105	30fr multicolored	.50	.20
364	A106	35fr multicolored	.50	.20

6th anniversary of the Congolese Labor Party (P.C.T.). See No. C215.

A.G. Bell
and 1876
Telephone
A107

1976, Apr. 25		Litho.	Perf. 12½x13	
365	A107	35fr yel, brn & org brn	.50	.20

Cent. of 1st telephone call by Alexander Graham Bell, Mar. 10, 1876. See No. C229.

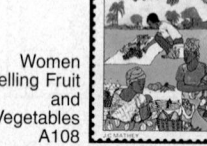

Women
Selling Fruit
and
Vegetables
A108

1976, Sept. 19		Litho.	Perf. 12½x13	
366	A108	35fr shown	.50	.20
367	A108	60fr Market scene	1.00	.30

Congolese
Coiffure — A109

Designs: Various women's hair styles.

1976, Oct. 10		Litho.	Perf. 13	
368	A109	35fr multicolored	.50	.20
369	A109	60fr multicolored	.90	.25
370	A109	95fr multicolored	1.40	.35
371	A109	100fr multicolored	1.60	.40
		Nos. 368-371 (4)	4.40	1.20

Pole Vault,
Map of
Central
Africa
A110

95fr, Long jump and map of Central Africa.

1976, Oct. 25			Perf. 12½	
372	A110	60fr yel & multi	.70	.25
373	A110	95fr yel & multi	1.25	.40
		Nos. 372-373,C230-C231 (4)	6.45	2.50

Gold medalists, 1st Central African Games, Yaoundé, July 27-30, 1975.

Antelope
A111

1976, Oct. 27		Litho.	Perf. 12½	
		Size: 36x36mm		
374	A111	5fr shown	.55	.20
375	A111	10fr Buffalos	.65	.20
376	A111	15fr Hippopotamus	1.00	.30
377	A111	20fr Wart hog	2.00	.35
378	A111	25fr Elephants	2.25	.40
		Nos. 374-378 (5)	6.45	1.45

1976, Dec. 8

Designs: Birds.

		Size: 26x36mm		
379	A111	5fr Saddle-bill storks	1.00	.25
		Size: 36x36mm		
380	A111	10fr Malachite kingfisher	1.25	.25
381	A111	20fr Crowned cranes	3.00	.60
		Nos. 379-381 (3)	5.25	1.10

Bicycling, Map of
Participants
A112

Heliotrope
A113

1976, Dec. 21		Photo.	Perf. 12½x13	
382	A112	35fr shown	.35	.20
383	A112	60fr Fieldball	.60	.25
384	A112	80fr Running	1.00	.35
385	A112	95fr Soccer	1.25	.40
		Nos. 382-385 (4)	3.20	1.20

First Central African Games, Libreville, Gabon, June-July 1976.

1976, Dec. 23		Photo.	Perf. 12½x13	

Flowers: 5fr, Water lilies. 15fr, Bird-of-paradise flower.

386	A113	5fr multicolored	.25	.20
387	A113	10fr multicolored	.35	.20
388	A113	15fr multicolored	.60	.20
		Nos. 386-388 (3)	1.20	.60

Torch and
Olive
Branches
A114

1976, Dec. 25		Litho.	Perf. 12½x13	
389	A114	35fr multicolored	.45	.20

National Pioneer Movement.

The Spirit of '76 — A115

125fr, Pulling down George III statue. 150fr, Battle of Princeton. 175fr, Generals of Revolutionary War. 200fr, Burgoyne's surrender at Saratoga. 500fr, Battle of Lexington.

1976, Dec. 29		Litho.	Perf. 14	
390	A115	100fr multicolored	1.00	.25
391	A115	125fr multicolored	1.10	.35
392	A115	150fr multicolored	1.60	.40
393	A115	175fr multicolored	2.00	.50
394	A115	200fr multicolored	2.25	.60
		Nos. 390-394 (5)	7.95	2.10

Souvenir Sheet

395	A115	500fr multicolored	5.75	1.50

American Bicentennial.

Dugout
Canoe
Race
A116

Design: 60fr, 2-man dugout canoes.

1977, Mar. 27		Litho.	Perf. 13x13½	
396	A116	35fr multicolored	.60	.20
397	A116	60fr multicolored	1.00	.35

Dugout canoe races on Congo River.

Lilan Goua
A117

Fresh-water Fish: 15fr, Liko ko. 25fr, Liyan ga. 35fr, Mbessi. 60fr, Mongandza.

1977, June 15 Litho. Perf. 12½
398	A117 10fr multicolored	.60	.20
399	A117 15fr multicolored	.70	.20
400	A117 25fr multicolored	.90	.20
401	A117 35fr multicolored	1.75	.30
402	A117 60fr multicolored	2.75	.45
	Nos. 398-402 (5)	6.70	1.35

Traditional Headdress — A118

1977, June 30 Litho. Perf. 12½
403	A118 35fr shown	.45	.30
404	A118 60fr Leopard cap	.90	.35

See Nos. C234-C235.

Bondjo Wrestling A119

40fr, 50fr, Bondjo wrestling, diff. 40fr, horiz.

1977, July 15
405	A119 25fr multicolored	.45	.20
406	A119 40fr multicolored	.50	.20
407	A119 50fr multicolored	.60	.30
	Nos. 405-407 (3)	1.55	.70

"Schwaben" LZ 10, 1911 — A120

Zeppelins: 60fr, "Viktoria Luise." LZ 11, 1913. 100fr, LZ 120. 200fr, LZ 127. 300fr, "Graf Zeppelin II" LZ 130.

1977, Aug. 5 Litho. Perf. 11
408	A120 40fr multicolored	.45	.20
409	A120 60fr multicolored	.70	.25
410	A120 100fr multicolored	1.10	.30
411	A120 200fr multicolored	2.25	.55
412	A120 300fr multicolored	3.50	.80
	Nos. 408-412 (5)	8.00	2.05

History of the Zeppelin. Exist imperf. See No. C236.

Coat of Arms and Rising Sun A121

1977, Aug. 15
413	A121 40fr multicolored	.45	.20

14th anniversary of the revolution.

Victor Hugo and The Hunchback of Notre Dame — A122

Designs (Hugo and): 60fr, Les Miserables. 100fr, Les Travailleurs de la Mer (octopus).

1977, Aug. 20 Engr. Perf. 13
414	A122 35fr multicolored	.50	.30
415	A122 60fr multicolored	.75	.30
416	A122 100fr multicolored	1.25	.45
	Nos. 414-416 (3)	2.50	1.05

Victor Hugo (1802-1885), French novelist.

Mao Tse-tung A123

Lithographed; Gold Embossed
1977, Sept. 9 Perf. 12x12½
417	A123 400fr red & gold	7.50	5.50

Chairman Mao Tse-tung (1893-1976), Chinese Communist leader, 1st death anniv.

Peter Paul Rubens A124

1977, Sept. 20 Gold Embossed
418	A124 600fr gold & lt bl	10.00	5.00

Peter Paul Rubens (1577-1640), painter.

Child Leading Blind Woman Across Street A125

1977, Oct. 22 Litho. Perf. 12½x13
419	A125 35fr multicolored	.60	.25

World Health Day: To see is life.

Paul Kamba and Records A126

1977, Oct. 29
420	A126 100fr multicolored	1.00	.45

Paul Kamba (1912-1950), musician.

Trajan Vuia and Flying Machine — A127

Designs: 75fr, Louis Bleriot and plane. 100fr, Roland Garros and plane. 200fr, Charles Lindbergh and Spirit of St. Louis. 300fr, Tupolev Tu-144. 500fr, Lindbergh and Spirit of St. Louis over ship in Atlantic.

1977, Nov. 18 Litho. Perf. 14
421	A127 60fr multicolored	.60	.20
422	A127 75fr multicolored	.90	.25
423	A127 100fr multicolored	1.10	.30
424	A127 200fr multicolored	2.25	.50
425	A127 300fr multicolored	3.25	.70
	Nos. 421-425 (5)	8.10	1.95

Souvenir Sheet
426	A127 500fr multicolored	5.75	1.25

History of aviation.

Elizabeth II and Prince Philip A128

Design: 300fr, Elizabeth II wearing Crown.

1977, Dec. 21
427	A128 250fr multicolored	2.25	.65
428	A128 300fr multicolored	2.75	.70

Reign of Queen Elizabeth II, 25th anniv. See #C239. For overprints see #468-469, C244.

King Baudouin A129

Design: No. 430, Charles de Gaulle.

1977, Dec. 21
429	A129 200fr multicolored	2.25	.65
430	A129 200fr multicolored	2.25	.65

King Baudouin of Belgium and Charles de Gaulle, president of France.

Ambete Sculpture A130

Congolese art: 85fr, Babembe sculpture.

1978, Feb. 18 Engr. Perf. 13
431	A130 35fr lt brn & multi	.60	.25
432	A130 85fr lt grn & multi	1.40	.45

St. Simon, by Rubens A131

Rubens Paintings: 140fr, Duke of Lerma. 200fr, Madonna and Saints. 300fr, Rubens and his Wife Helena Fourment. 500fr, Farm at Laeken.

1978, Mar. 7 Litho. Perf. 13½x14
433	A131 60fr gold & multi	.60	.20
434	A131 140fr gold & multi	1.50	.30
435	A131 200fr gold & multi	2.25	.45
436	A131 300fr gold & multi	3.25	.65
	Nos. 433-436 (4)	7.60	1.60

Souvenir Sheet
437	A131 500fr gold & multi	5.75	1.40

Peter Paul Rubens, 400th birth anniv.

Pres. Ngouabi and Microphones — A132

60fr, Ngouabi at his desk, horiz. 100fr, Portrait.

Perf. 12½x13, 13x12½
1978, Mar. 18 Litho.
438	A132 35fr multicolored	.45	.20
439	A132 60fr multicolored	.50	.25
440	A132 100fr multicolored	.90	.40
	Nos. 438-440 (3)	1.85	.85

Pres. Marien Ngouabi, 1st death anniv.

Ferenc Puskas and Argentina '78 Emblem — A133

Players and Emblem: 75fr, Giacinto Facchetti. 100fr, Bobby Moore. 200fr, Raymond Kopa. 300fr, Pele. 500fr, Franz Beckenbauer.

1978, Apr. 4 Perf. 14x13½
441	A133 60fr multicolored	.60	.20
442	A133 75fr multicolored	.70	.25
443	A133 100fr multicolored	1.10	.30
444	A133 200fr multicolored	2.25	.55
445	A133 300fr multicolored	3.25	.75
	Nos. 441-445 (5)	7.90	2.00

Souvenir Sheet
446	A133 500fr multicolored	6.25	1.25

11th World Cup Soccer Championship, Argentina, June 1-25.
For overprints see Nos. 481-486.

Pearl S. Buck and Chinese
Women — A134

Nobel Prize winners: 75fr, Fridtjof Nansen,
refugees and Nansen passport. 100fr, Henri
Bergson, book and flame. 200fr, Alexander
Fleming and Petri dish. 300fr, Gerhart
Hauptmann and book. 500fr, Henri Dunant
and Red Cross Station.

1978, Apr. 29
447	A134	60fr multicolored	.60	.25
448	A134	75fr multicolored	.70	.25
449	A134	100fr multicolored	1.10	.30
450	A134	200fr multicolored	2.00	.50
451	A134	300fr multicolored	2.75	.60
		Nos. 447-451 (5)	7.15	1.90

Souvenir Sheet
452	A134	500fr multicolored	5.75	1.40

African
Buffalos
A135

Endangered animals and Wildlife Fund
Emblem: 35fr, Okapi, vert. 85fr, Rhinoceros.
150fr, Chimpanzee, vert. 200fr, Hippopotamus. 300fr, Buffon's kob, vert.

1978   **Perf. 14½**
453	A135	35fr multicolored	.85	.30
454	A135	60fr multicolored	1.40	.40
455	A135	85fr multicolored	3.50	.60
456	A135	150fr multicolored	5.00	.80
457	A135	200fr multicolored	6.75	1.40
458	A135	300fr multicolored	12.50	2.00
		Nos. 453-458 (6)	30.00	5.50

Issue dates: 35fr, Aug. 11; others, July 11.

Emblem, Young
People, Gun and
Fist — A136

1978, July 28   **Perf. 12½**
459	A136	35fr multicolored	.50	.30

11th World Youth Festival, Havana, 7/28-8/5.

Pyramids and Camels — A137

Seven Wonders of the Ancient World: 50fr,
Hanging Gardens of Babylon. 60fr, Statue of
Zeus, Olympia. 95fr, Colossus of Rhodes.
125fr, Mausoleum of Halicarnassus. 150fr,
Temple of Artemis, Ephesus. 200fr, Light-
house, Alexandria. 300fr, Map of Eastern
Mediterranean showing locations. 50fr, 60fr,
95fr, 125fr, 200fr, vertical.

1978, Aug. 12   **Litho.**   **Perf. 14**
460	A137	35fr multicolored	.35	.20
461	A137	50fr multicolored	.45	.20
462	A137	60fr multicolored	.60	.20
463	A137	95fr multicolored	.80	.30

464	A137	125fr multicolored	1.00	.40
465	A137	150fr multicolored	1.25	.45
466	A137	200fr multicolored	1.75	.55
467	A137	300fr multicolored	2.25	.80
		Nos. 460-467 (8)	8.45	3.10

Nos. 427-428 Overprinted in Silver:
"ANNIVERSAIRE DU
COURONNEMENT 1953-1978"

1978, Sept.   **Litho.**   **Perf. 14**
468	A128	250fr multicolored	2.25	.90
469	A128	275fr multicolored	2.75	1.25

25th anniversary of coronation of Queen
Elizabeth II. See No. C244.

Kwame Nkrumah and Map of
Africa — A138

1978, Sept. 23   Litho.   Perf. 13x12½
470	A138	60fr multicolored	.60	.40

Nkrumah (1909-72), Pres. of Ghana.

Wild Boar Hunt — A139

Local hunting and fishing: 50fr, Fish smoking. 60fr, Hunter with spears and dog, vert.

1978   **Litho.**   **Perf. 12**
471	A139	35fr multicolored	2.00	.25
472	A139	50fr multicolored	.60	.25
473	A139	60fr multicolored	3.00	.25
		Nos. 471-473 (3)	5.60	.75

Issue dates: 35fr, 60fr, Oct. 5; 50fr, Oct. 10.

View of Kalchreut, by Dürer — A140

Paintings by Dürer: 150fr, Elspeth Tucher,
vert. 250fr, "The Great Piece of Turf," vert.
350fr, Self-portrait, vert.

1978, Nov. 23   Litho.   Perf. 14
474	A140	65fr multicolored	.60	.20
475	A140	150fr multicolored	1.40	.35
476	A140	250fr multicolored	2.25	.65
477	A140	350fr multicolored	3.50	.90
		Nos. 474-477 (4)	7.75	2.10

Albrecht Dürer (1471-1528), German painter.

Basketmaker
A141

Productive Labor: 90fr, Woodcarver. 140fr,
Women hoeing field.

1978, Nov. 18   Litho.   Perf. 12½
Size: 25x36mm
478	A141	85fr multicolored	.70	.40
479	A141	90fr multicolored	1.00	.50

Size: 27x48mm
Perf. 12
480	A141	140fr multicolored	1.50	.65
		Nos. 478-480 (3)	3.20	1.45

Nos. 441-446 Overprinted in Silver:
a. "1962 VAINQUEUR: BRESIL"
b. "1966 VAINQUEUR: / GRANDE
BRETAGNE"
c. "1970 VAINQUEUR: / BRESIL"
d. "1974 VAINQUEUR: /
ALLEMAGNE (RFA)"
e. "1978 VAINQUEUR: /
ARGENTINE"
f. "ARGENTINE-PAYS BAS 3-1/25
juin 1978"

1978, Nov.   **Perf. 14x13½**
481	A133 (a)	60fr multicolored	.60	.25
482	A133 (b)	75fr multicolored	.70	.35
483	A133 (c)	100fr multicolored	1.00	.45
484	A133 (d)	200fr multicolored	2.00	.65
485	A133 (e)	300fr multicolored	2.75	1.00
		Nos. 481-485 (5)	7.05	2.70

Souvenir Sheet
486	A133 (f)	500fr multicolored	5.75	2.40

Winners, World Soccer Cup Championships
1962-1978.

Heart and
Charts
A142

1978, Dec. 16   Engr.   Perf. 13
487	A142	100fr multicolored	1.00	.45

Fight against hypertension.

Party Emblem and Road — A143

1978, Dec. 31   Litho.   Perf. 12½x12
488	A143	60fr multicolored	.60	.25

Congolese Labor Party, 9th anniversary.

Capt. Cook, Polynesians and
House — A144

Capt. James Cook (1728-1779): 150fr,
Island scene. 250fr, Polynesian longboats.
350fr, Capt. Cook's ships off Hawaii.

1979, Jan. 16   **Perf. 14½**
489	A144	65fr multicolored	.60	.20
490	A144	150fr multicolored	1.40	.35
491	A144	250fr multicolored	2.25	.60
492	A144	350fr multicolored	3.50	1.00
		Nos. 489-492 (4)	7.75	2.15

Pres. Marien
Ngouabi — A145

1979, Mar. 18   Litho.   Perf. 12
493	A145	35fr multicolored	.35	.20
494	A145	60fr multicolored	.50	.25

Assassination of President Ngouabi, 2nd
anniv.

"1979," IYC
Emblem,
Child
A146

A146a

1979, Apr. 30   Litho.   Perf. 12½x13
495	A146	45fr multicolored	.45	.20
496	A146	75fr multicolored	.90	.35

Souvenir Sheet
Perf. 14½
496A	A146a	250fr multicolored	2.75	1.00

International Year of the Child.
Issued: 45fr, 75fr, Apr. 30; 250fr, Sept. 5.

Pottery Vases and Solanum — A147

Design: 150fr, Mail runner, Concorde, train,
UPU emblem, envelope.

1979, June 8   Litho.   Perf. 13
497	A147	60fr multicolored	1.25	.60

Engr.
498	A147	150fr multicolored	2.75	1.25

Philexafrique II, Libreville, Gabon, June 8-
17. Nos. 497, 498 each printed in sheets of 10
with 5 labels showing exhibition emblem.

Rowland Hill, Diesel Locomotive,
Germany No. 78 — A148

Designs (Rowland Hill and): 100fr, Old
steam locomotive and France No. B10. 200fr,
Diesel locomotive and US No. 245. 300fr,
Steam locomotive and England-Australia First
Aerialpost vignette, 1919. 500fr, Electric train,
Concorde and Middle Congo No. 75.

1979, June 30   **Perf. 14**
499	A148	65fr multicolored	.60	.20
500	A148	100fr multicolored	1.00	.25
501	A148	200fr multicolored	2.25	.50
502	A148	300fr multicolored	2.75	.75
		Nos. 499-502 (4)	6.60	1.70

Souvenir Sheet
503	A148	500fr multicolored	5.75	1.25

Sir Rowland Hill (1795-1879), originator of
penny postage.

Salvador Allende, Flags, Demonstrators — A149

1979, July 21   Litho.   Perf. 12½
504 A149 100fr multicolored   1.00 .45
Salvador Allende, president of Chile.

Old Man Telling Stories — A150

1979, July 28
505 A150 45fr multicolored   .60 .25
Story telling as education.

Handball Players A151

75fr, Players and ball. 250fr, Pres. Ngouabi, cup on map of Africa, player.

1979, July 31   Litho.   Perf. 12½
Size: 40x30mm, 30x40mm
506 A151 45fr multi   .50 .20
507 A151 75fr multi, vert.   .90 .25
Size: 22x40mm
Perf. 12x12½
508 A151 250fr multicolored   2.50 1.00
Marien Ngouabi Handball Cup.

Map and Flag of Congo — A152

1979, Aug. 15
509 A152 50fr multicolored   .45 .25
16th anniversary of revolution.

Souvenir Sheet

Virgin and Child, by Dürer — A153

1979, Aug. 13   Perf. 13½
510 A153 500fr red brn & lt grn   6.25 1.50
Albrecht Dürer (1471-1528), German engraver and painter.

Bach and Contemporary Instruments — A155

#512, Albert Einstein, astronauts on moon.

1979, Sept. 10   Perf. 13½
511 A155 200fr multicolored   2.25 .75
512 A155 200fr multicolored   2.25 .75

Yoro Fishing Port A156

1979, Sept. 26   Litho.   Perf. 12½
513 A156 45fr shown   .60 .20
514 A156 75fr Port at night   .90 .35

Mukukulu Dam — A157

1979, Oct. 5   Perf. 12½x12
515 A157 20fr multicolored   .25 .20
516 A157 45fr multicolored   .70 .25

Emblem, Control Tower, Jets A158

1979, Dec. 12   Litho.   Perf. 12½
517 A158 100fr multicolored   1.10 .50
ASECNA (Air Safety Board), 20th anniv.

Congolese Labor Party, 10th Anniversary A159

1979, Dec. 31
518 A159 45fr multicolored   .45 .20

A160

A161

1980, Mar. 30   Litho.   Perf. 12½
519 A160 45fr multicolored   .45 .20
520 A160 95fr multicolored   .90 .30
Post Office, 15th Anniversary.

1980, May 5
521 A161 100fr multicolored   2.00 .50
Visit of Pope John Paul II.

Rotary International, 75th Anniversary — A162

1980, May 10   Litho.   Perf. 12½
522 A162 150fr multicolored   1.50 .50

Pointe Noire Foundry A163

1980, June 18   Litho.   Perf. 12½
523 A163 30fr shown   .20 .20
524 A163 35fr Different view   .50 .20

Claude Chappe, Tower — A164

1980, June 21   Litho.   Perf. 12½
525 A164 200fr multicolored   2.25 1.00
Claude Chappe (1763-1805), French engineer.

Mossaka Harbor — A165

1980, June 23
532 A165 45fr shown   .50 .20
533 A165 90fr Different view   1.00 .25

Papilio Dardanus (Front and Back) — A167

Human Rights Emblem, People — A169

July 31st Hospital — A168

1980, July 12   Litho.   Perf. 12½
534 A167 5fr shown   .80 .30
535 A167 15fr Kalima aethiops   1.50 .30
536 A167 20fr Papilio demodocus   1.50 .40
537 A167 60fr Euphaedra   4.00 .75
538 A167 90fr Hypolimnas misippus 7.25 1.00
  Nos. 534-538 (5)   15.05 2.75

Souvenir Sheet
539 A167 300fr Charaxes smaragdalis 20.00 17.00

Nos. 534-536 also exist perf 12½x13. Values the same.

1980, July 31
540 A168 45fr multicolored   .60 .25

1980, Aug. 2
541 A169 350fr shown   2.75 1.00
542 A169 500fr Man breaking chain 4.50 1.50
Human Rights Convention, 32nd anniv.

Citizens and Congolese Arms A170

1980, Aug. 15   Perf. 12½
543 A170 75fr shown   .70 .30
544 A170 95fr Dove on flag, fists, vert.   .90 .30
545 A170 150fr Dove holding Congolese arms 1.40 .60
  Nos. 543-545 (3)   3.00 1.20
August 13-15th Revolution, 17th anniv.

Coffee and Cocoa Trees on Map of Congo — A171

Coffee and Cocoa Day: 95fr, Branches, map of Congo.

1980, Aug. 18   **Perf. 13½x13**
546 A171 45fr multicolored   .50 .20
547 A171 95fr multicolored   1.00 .40

Logging A172

1980, Aug. 28
548 A172 70fr shown   .80 .30
549 A172 75fr Wood transport   .80 .30

Pres. Neto of Angola, 1st Death Anniv. — A173

Lark — A174

1980, Sept. 11
550 A173 100fr multicolored   .90 .30

1980, Sept. 17

Designs: Birds.

551 A174 45fr multi, horiz.   .70 .30
552 A174 75fr multi, horiz.   1.00 .30
553 A174 90fr multi, horiz.   1.25 .35
554 A174 150fr multicolored   2.00 .50
555 A174 200fr multicolored   3.00 .90
556 A174 250fr multicolored   3.25 1.00
   a   Souv. sheet of 6, #551-556   4.50 4.50
     Nos. 551-556 (6)   11.20 3.35

World Tourism Conference, Manila, Sept. 27 — A175

1980, Sept. 27 Litho. Perf. 13½x13
557 A175 100fr multicolored   .90 .35

First Day of School Term — A176

1980, Oct. 2 Photo. Perf. 13
558 A176 50fr multicolored   .50 .20

First House in Brazzaville — A177

Brazzaville Centenary: 65fr, First native village. 75fr, Old Town Hall, 1912. 150fr, View from bank of Bacongo, 1912. 200fr, Meeting of explorer Savorgnan de Brazza and chief Makoko, 1880.

1980, Oct. 3 Litho. Perf. 12½
559 A177 45fr multicolored   .50 .20
560 A177 65fr multicolored   .70 .30
561 A177 75fr multicolored   1.00 .40
562 A177 150fr multicolored   1.75 .65
563 A177 200fr multicolored   2.25 1.00
     Nos. 559-563 (5)   6.20 2.55

Boys on Bank of Congo River — A178

1980, Oct. 30
564 A178 80fr shown   .70 .25
565 A178 150fr Djoue Bridge   1.60 .40

Revolutionary Stadium and Athletes — A179

1980, Nov. 20 Perf. 13x12½
566 A179 60fr multicolored   .70 .25

Rebuilt Railroad Bridge over Congo River A180

1980, Nov. 29 Perf. 13x13½
567 A180 75fr multicolored   .90 .30

Mangoes, Loudima Fruit Packing Station A181

1980, Dec. 2 Perf. 13
568 A181 10fr shown   .25 .20
569 A181 25fr Oranges   .50 .20
570 A181 40fr Citrons   .60 .20
571 A181 85fr Mandarins   1.10 .30
     Nos. 568-571 (4)   2.45 .90

African Postal Union, 5th Anniversary A182

1980, Dec. 24 Perf. 13½
572 A182 100fr multicolored   .90 .30

Moungouni Earth Satellite Station A183

1980, Dec. 30 Perf. 12½
573 A183 75fr multicolored   .60 .20

Hertzian Wave Communication, Brazzaville — A184

1980, Dec. 30 Perf. 12½x12
574 A184 150fr multicolored   1.25 .40

1980 African Handball Champion Team — A185

     Perf. 12½x13, 13x12½
1981, Jan. 26 Litho.
575 A185 100fr Receiving cup,
           vert.   1.10 .35
576 A185 150fr shown   1.30 .60

Pres. Denis Sassou-Nguesso — A186

1981, Feb. 5 Litho. Perf. 12½
577 A186 45fr multicolored   .45 .20
578 A186 75fr multicolored   .60 .20
579 A186 100fr multicolored   .90 .25
     Nos. 577-579 (3)   1.95 .65

Columbia Space Shuttle Orbiting Earth — A187

Space Conquest: 100fr, Luna 17, 1970. 200fr, 300fr, 500fr, Columbia space shuttle, 1981.

1981, May 4 Litho. Perf. 14x13½
580 A187 100fr multicolored   1.00 .25
581 A187 150fr multicolored   1.40 .40
582 A187 200fr multicolored   2.00 .55
583 A187 300fr multicolored   2.75 .80
     Nos. 580-583 (4)   7.15 2.00
     Souvenir Sheet
584 A187 500fr multicolored   5.00 1.40
    For overprint see No. 725.

Fight Against Apartheid — A188

Twin Palm Tree of Louingui — A189

1981, May 5 Litho. Perf. 12½
585 A188 100fr deep blue   .90 .25

1981, May 22 Perf. 12x12½
586 A189 75fr multicolored   1.00 .25

13th World Telecommunications Day — A190

1981, June 6 Perf. 12½
587 A190 120fr multicolored   1.25 .30

Rubber Extraction — A191

1981, June 27 Perf. 13
588 A191 50fr shown   .60 .20
589 A191 70fr Sap draining   .90 .30

Intl. Year of
the
Disabled
A192

1981, June 29   **Engr.**
590 A192 45fr multicolored   .45 .20
See No. B7.

Bird Trap — A194

Designs: Animal traps. 10fr vert.

1981, July
596 A194 5fr multicolored   1.10 .20
597 A194 10fr multicolored   1.10 .20
598 A194 15fr multicolored   1.10 .20
599 A194 20fr multicolored   1.10 .20
600 A194 30fr multicolored   1.60 .25
601 A194 35fr multicolored   2.25 .30
   Nos. 596-601 (6)   8.25 1.35

Mausoleum of King Maloango — A195

1981, July 4   **Litho.**   **Perf. 12½**
602 A195 75fr shown   .70 .20
603 A195 150fr Mausoleum, por-
       trait   1.25 .40

Prince
Charles
and
Lady
Diana,
Coach
A196

Royal wedding: Couple and coaches.

1981, Sept. 1   **Litho.**   **Perf. 14½**
604 A196 100fr multicolored   1.00 .25
605 A196 200fr multicolored   2.00 .55
606 A196 300fr multicolored   3.25 .80
   Nos. 604-606 (3)   6.25 1.60

Souvenir Sheet
607 A196 400fr multicolored   4.00 1.10

World Food
Day — A197

1981, Oct. 16   **Litho.**   **Perf. 13½x13**
608 A197 150fr multicolored   1.40 .55

12th World
UPU Day
A198

1981, Oct. 24   **Engr.**   **Perf. 13x12½**
609 A198 90fr multicolored   .90 .25

Royal
Guard
A199

1981, Oct. 31   **Litho.**   **Perf. 12½x13**
610 A199 45fr multicolored   .60 .20

Eradication of
Manioc
Beetle — A200

1981, Nov. 18   **Litho.**   **Perf. 12½**
611 A200 75fr multicolored   1.00 .25

Natl. Red
Cross — A201

1981, Nov. 18   **Perf. 13**
612 A201 10fr Bandaging patient   .20 .20
613 A201 35fr Treating child   .45 .20
614 A201 60fr Drawing well water .70 .25
   Nos. 612-614 (3)   1.35 .65

Giant
Baobab
("Tree of
Savorgnan
de Brazza")
A202

1981, Dec. 19   **Litho.**   **Perf. 13**
615 A202 45fr multicolored   .90 .20
616 A202 75fr multicolored   1.25 .30

Fetish
Figure — A203

Designs: Various carved figures.

1981, Dec. 19   **Perf. 13x12½**
617 A203 15fr multicolored   .20 .20
618 A203 25fr multicolored   .25 .20
619 A203 45fr multicolored   .45 .20

620 A203 50fr multicolored   .60 .20
621 A203 60fr multicolored   .70 .20
   Nos. 617-621 (5)   2.20 1.00

Nos. 617, 618 and 620 also exist perf
12½x13. Values the same.

Caves of
Bangou
A204

1981, Dec. 29   **Perf. 13x13½**
622 A204 20fr multicolored   .45 .20
623 A204 25fr multicolored   .45 .20

King Makoko and His Queen, Ivory
Sculptures by R. Engongodzo — A205

Perf. 13½x13, 13x13½
1982, Feb. 27   **Litho.**
624 A205 25fr Woman, vert.   .35 .20
625 A205 35fr Woman, diff.,
       vert.   .45 .20
626 A205 100fr shown   1.00 .30
   Nos. 624-626 (3)   1.80 .70

George Stephenson (1781-1848) and
Inter City 125, Gt. Britain — A206

Locomotives: 150fr, Sinkansen Bullet Train,
Japan. 200fr, Advanced Passenger Train, Gt.
Britain. 300fr, TGV-001, France.

1982, Mar. 2   **Litho.**   **Perf. 12½**
627 A206 100fr multicolored   1.00 .25
628 A206 150fr multicolored   1.60 .40
629 A206 200fr multicolored   2.25 .55
630 A206 300fr multicolored   3.25 .80
   Nos. 627-630 (4)   8.10 2.00

Scouting
Year
A207

1982, Apr. 13   **Litho.**   **Perf. 13**
631 A207 100fr Looking through
       binoculars   1.00 .25
632 A207 150fr Reading map   1.40 .40
633 A207 200fr Helping woman   2.00 .55
634 A207 300fr Crossing rope
       bridge   2.75 .80
   Nos. 631-634 (4)   7.15 2.00

Souvenir Sheet
635 A207 500fr Hiking, horiz.   5.00 1.75
   For overprint see No. 726.

Franklin
Roosevelt
A208

1982, June 12   **Litho.**   **Perf. 13**
636 A208 150fr shown   1.60 .40
637 A208 250fr Washington   2.75 .70
638 A208 350fr Goethe   3.25 .90
   Nos. 636-638 (3)   7.60 2.00

21st Birthday of Princess Diana,
July 1 — A209

1982, June 12   **Perf. 14**
639 A209 200fr Candles   2.00 .55
640 A209 300fr "21"   2.75 .80

Souvenir Sheet
641 A209 500fr Diana   5.00 1.40

5-Year
Plan, 1982-
1986
A210

Perf. 13x12½, 12½x13
1982, June 19
642 A210 60fr Road construc-
       tion   .70 .20
643 A210 100fr Communications,
       vert.   1.10 .30
644 A210 125fr Operating room
       equipment, vert. 1.40 .35
645 A210 150fr Hydroelectric
       power, vert.   1.60 .40
   Nos. 642-645 (4)   4.80 1.25

ITU Plenipotentiary Conference,
Nairobi — A211

1982, June 26   **Perf. 13**
646 A211 300fr multicolored   2.75 .90

Nos. 604-607 Overprinted in Blue:
"NAISSANCE ROYALE 1982"

1982, July 30   **Perf. 14½**
647 A196 100fr multicolored   .90 .30
648 A196 200fr multicolored   1.75 .60
649 A196 300fr multicolored   2.75 1.00
   Nos. 647-649 (3)   5.40 1.90

Souvenir Sheet
650 A196 400fr multicolored   3.50 2.50

Birth of Prince William of Wales, June 21.

Nutrition Campaign A212

1982, July 24　　Litho.　　Perf. 12½
651　A212　100fr multicolored　　　1.00　.25

WHO African Headquarters, Brazzaville — A213

1982, July 24　　Litho.　　Perf. 12½
652　A213　125fr multicolored　　　1.00　.45

TB Bacillus Centenary — A214

1982, Aug. 7　　　　　　Perf. 12½x12
653　A214　250fr Koch, bacillus　　3.00　1.10

Pres. Sassou-Nguesso and 1980 Simba Prize — A215

1982, Oct. 20　　Litho.　　Perf. 13
654　A215　100fr multicolored　　　.90　.30

Turtles — A216

Various turtles and tortoises.

1982, Dec. 1
655　A216　30fr multicolored　　　　.50　.20
656　A216　45fr multicolored　　　　.90　.25
657　A216　55fr multicolored　　　1.00　.30
　　　Nos. 655-657 (3)　　　　　2.40　.75

Boy Gathering Coconuts — A217

Nest in Tree Trunk — A218

1982, Dec. 11
658　A217　100fr multicolored　　　.90　.30

1982, Dec. 29　　　　　　Perf. 12½
659　A218　40fr shown　　　　　1.25　.20
660　A218　75fr Nests in palm tree　1.50　.20
661　A218　100fr Woven nest on
　　　　　　　　thorn branch　　1.60　.25
　　　Nos. 659-661 (3)　　　　　4.35　.65

Hertzian Wave Communication Network — A219

1982, Dec. 30　　　　　　Perf. 13x12½
662　A219　45fr multicolored　　　　.45　.20
663　A219　60fr multicolored　　　　.50　.20
664　A219　95fr multicolored　　　　.90　.30
　　　Nos. 662-664 (3)　　　　　1.85　.70

30th Anniv. of Customs Cooperation Council — A220

1983, Jan. 26　　Litho.　　Perf. 12½x13
665　A220　100fr Headquarters　　.90　.30

Mausoleum of Pres. Marien Ngouabi — A221

1983, Feb. 8　　　　　　Perf. 13
666　A221　60fr multicolored　　　　.50　.20
667　A221　80fr multicolored　　　　.80　.20

Ironsmiths — A222

1983　　　　　　　　　Perf. 12½
668　A222　45fr shown　　　　　　.50　.20
669　A222　150fr Weaver, vert.　　1.25　.50
　　Issue dates: 45fr, Mar. 5; 150fr, Feb. 24.

Carved Chess Pieces, by R. Engongonzo — A223

Various pieces.

1983, Feb. 26　　　　　　Perf. 13
670　A223　40fr multicolored　　　　.25　.20
671　A223　60fr multicolored　　　　.80　.20
672　A223　95fr multicolored　　　1.50　.50
　　　Nos. 670-672 (3)　　　　　2.55　.90

Easter 1983 A224

Raphael drawings. 200fr, 400fr vert.

1983, Apr. 20　　Litho.　　Perf. 13
673　A224　200fr Transfiguration
　　　　　　　　study　　　　2.00　.50
674　A224　300fr Deposition from
　　　　　　　　Cross　　　　3.00　.65
675　A224　400fr Christ in Glory　4.00　.85
　　　Nos. 673-675 (3)　　　　　9.00　2.00

Seashells A225

1983　　　　　Litho.　　Perf. 15x14
675A　A225　25fr multicolored　150.00　65.00
676　A225　35fr multicolored　　1.25　.30
677　A225　65fr multicolored　　1.60　.35

Dated 1982.

A226　　　　　　A227

Various traditional combs.

1983, May　　　　　　　Perf. 14
678　A226　30fr multicolored　　　　.35　.20
679　A226　70fr multicolored　　　　.90　.20
680　A226　85fr multicolored　　　1.00　.20
　　　Nos. 678-680 (3)　　　　　2.25　.60

Litho. & Engr.
1983, Aug. 10　　　　　Perf. 12½x13
681　A227　60fr multicolored　　　　.45　.20
682　A227　100fr multicolored　　　.90　.30
　　20th anniv. of revolution.

Centenary of the Arrival of Christian Missionaries — A228

Churches and Clergymen: 150fr, A. Carrie, Church of the Sacred Heart, Loango, vert. 250fr, Msgr. Augouard; St. Louis, Liranga; St. Joseph, Linzolo.

1983, Aug. 23　　　　　Perf. 12½
683　A228　150fr multicolored　　1.60　.40
684　A228　250fr multicolored　　2.75　.70

Local Flowers — A229

1984, Jan. 20　　Litho.　　Perf. 12½
685　A229　5fr Liana thunderaie,
　　　　　　　vert.　　　　　　.20　.20
686　A229　15fr Bougainvillea　　.35　.20
687　A229　20fr Anthurium, vert.　.50　.20
688　A229　45fr Allamanda　　　1.00　.20
689　A229　75fr Hibiscus, vert.　1.40　.30
　　　Nos. 685-689 (5)　　　　　3.45　1.10

35th Anniv. of World Peace Council A230

1984, Mar. 31　　Litho.　　Perf. 13x12½
690　A230　50fr multicolored　　　　.45　.20
691　A230　100fr multicolored　　　.90　.30

Anti-Nuclear Arms Campaign A231

1984, May 31　　Litho.　　Perf. 12x12½
692　A231　200fr Explosion, victims　1.75　.50

Agriculture Day A232

Perf. 13x13½, 13½x13

1984, June 30   **Litho.**

693	A232	10fr Rice	.20 .20
694	A232	15fr Pineapples	.20 .20
695	A232	60fr Manioc, vert.	.60 .25
696	A232	100fr Palm tree, map, vert.	1.10 .35
		Nos. 693-696 (4)	2.10 1.00

Congress Palace — A233

1984, July 27   **Perf. 13**

697	A233	60fr multicolored	.50 .20
698	A233	100fr multicolored	.90 .30

Chinese-Congolese cooperation.

CFCO-Congo Railways, 50th Anniv. — A234

1984, July 30   **Perf. 13½**

699	A234	10fr Loulombo Station	.25 .20
700	A234	25fr Les Bandas Chinese Labor Camp	.45 .20
701	A234	125fr "50"	2.00 .70
702	A234	200fr Admin. bldg.	4.50 1.00
		Nos. 699-702 (4)	7.20 2.10

Locomotives — A235

Ships on the Congo River — A236

1984, Aug. 24   **Perf. 12½**

703	A235	100fr CC 203	1.10 .35
704	A236	100fr Tugboat	1.10 .35
705	A235	150fr BB 103	1.60 .50
706	A236	150fr Pusher tugboat	1.60 .50
707	A235	300fr BB-BB 301	3.25 1.10
708	A235	300fr Dredger	3.25 1.10
709	A235	500fr BB 420 L'Eclair	5.25 1.75
710	A236	500fr Cargo ship	5.25 1.75
		Nos. 703-710 (8)	22.40 7.40

World Fisheries Year A237

1984, Oct. 16   **Perf. 13½**

711	A237	5fr Basket of fish	.25 .20
712	A237	20fr Net fishermen in boat	.45 .20
713	A237	25fr School of fish	.60 .20
714	A237	40fr Net fisherman	1.00 .25
715	A237	55fr Trawler	1.60 .30
		Nos. 711-715 (5)	3.90 1.15

Anti-polio Campaign A238

M'Bamou Palace Hotel, Brazzaville A239

1984, Oct. 30

716	A238	250fr Disabled men, hand	2.75 .90
717	A238	300fr Target, disabled women, horiz.	3.25 1.00

1984, Dec. 15   **Perf. 14½**

718	A239	60fr multicolored	.45 .20
719	A239	100fr multicolored	.90 .30

Fauna A240

1984, Dec.   **Perf. 15x14½**

720	A240	30fr Pangolin	3.50 .70
721	A240	70fr Bat	7.50 1.50
722	A240	85fr Civet cat	9.00 1.90
		Nos. 720-722 (3)	20.00 4.10

Congo River Logging A241

1984, Dec.   **Perf. 13½x13**

723	A241	60fr Log raft, crew hut	.60 .25
724	A241	100fr Tugboat pushing logs	1.25 .35

Souvenir Sheets
Nos. 584, 635 Ovptd. with Exhibition in Black or Green

1985, Mar. 8   **Perf. 14x13½, 13**

725	A187	500fr TSUKUBA EXPO '85	5.00 4.50
726	A207	500fr ITALIA '85 emblem, ROME (G)	5.00 4.50

See Nos. C336-C337.

Zonocerus Variegatus — A242

1985, Mar. 15   **Perf. 13**

727	A242	125fr multicolored	1.50 .35

Burial of a Teke Chief — A243

1985, Apr. 30   **Perf. 12½**

728	A243	225fr multicolored	2.25 .75

Edible Fruit A244

Perf. 13½, 13 (#732A), 13½x13¼ (#732B)

1985, June 15

729	A244	5fr Trichoscypha acuminata, vert.	.20 .20
730	A244	10fr Aframomum africanum	.20 .20
730A	A244	90fr like #730	
731	A244	125fr Gambeya lacuurtiana	1.40 .40
732	A244	150fr Landolphia jumelei	1.75 .55
732A	A244	205fr like #731	— —
732B	A244	300fr Like #732	— —

Sizes: #729, 22x36mm; #731, 732A, 36x22mm.
Nos. 730A, 732A, 732B inscribed "Congo" only.
For overprints, see Nos. 1170, 1183-1185.
Compare type A244 with type A352.

Lions Club Intl., 30th Anniv. — A245

1985, June 25   **Perf. 12½**

733	A245	250fr Flag, District 403B	2.25 .70

Russian Soldier, Kremlin, Fall of Berlin A246

1985, July 27   **Perf. 12**

734	A246	60fr multicolored	.50 .20

Defeat of Nazi Germany, end of World War II, 40th anniv.

Lady Olave Baden-Powell, Girl Guides Founder — A247

Anniversaries and events: 150fr, Girl Guides, 75th anniv. 250fr, Jacob Grimm, fabulist; Sleeping Beauty. 350fr, Johann Sebastian Bach, composer; European Music Year, St. Thomas Church organ, Leipzig. 450fr, Queen Mother, 85th birthday, vert. 500fr, Statue of Liberty, cent., vert.

1985, Aug. 26   **Perf. 13**

735	A247	150fr multicolored	1.60 .50
736	A247	250fr multicolored	2.25 .90
737	A247	350fr multicolored	2.75 1.25
738	A247	450fr multicolored	3.50 1.60
739	A247	500fr multicolored	5.00 2.00
		Nos. 735-739 (5)	15.10 6.25

PHILEXAFRICA '85, Lome, Togo, Nov. 16-24 — A248

1985, Oct. 10   **Perf. 13x12½**

740	A248	250fr shown	2.25 1.00
741	A248	250fr Airport, postal van	2.25 1.00
a.		Pair, #740-741 + label	5.25 5.25

Mushrooms — A249

1985, Dec. 14   **Litho.**   **Perf. 13**

742	A249	100fr Coprinus, vert.	1.25 .30
743	A249	150fr Cortinarius	2.00 .45
744	A249	200fr Armillariella mellea	2.75 .65
745	A249	300fr Dictyophora	3.50 1.00
746	A249	400fr Crucibulum vulgare	5.25 1.40
		Nos. 742-746 (5)	14.75 3.80

Arbor Day — A250

Children's Hoop Races — A251

1986, Mar. 6   **Perf. 13½**

747	A250	60fr Planting sapling	.45 .20
748	A250	200fr Map, lifecycle diagram	1.90 .90

1986, Apr. 30   **Perf. 12½**

749	A251	5fr Two boys	.20 .20
750	A251	10fr One boy	.20 .20
751	A251	60fr Three boys, horiz.	.50 .20
a.		Souvenir sheet of 3, #749-751	1.25 1.00
		Nos. 749-751 (3)	.90 .60

A252

A253

1986, June 5   Litho.   Perf. 13½
752 A252 60fr Garbage disposal   .50   .20
753 A252 125fr Dumping gar-
                bage   1.00   .40

Intl. Environment Day.

1986, July 15   Litho.   Perf. 13x12½

Traditional Modes of Transporting Goods:
5fr, Basket on head, child in sling carrier. 10fr,
Child in carrier on hip, large basket strapped to
forehead.   60fr, Man carrying load on
shoulder.

754 A253 5fr multicolored   .20   .20
755 A253 10fr multicolored   .60   .25
756 A253 60fr multicolored   .30   .20
       Nos. 754-756 (3)   1.10 .65

Mission of
the Sisters
of St.
Joseph of
Cluny,
Cent.
A254

1986, Aug. 19   Litho.   Perf. 12½x13
757 A254 230fr multicolored   2.40 1.25

A255

A256

1986, Aug. 30   Litho.   Perf. 13½
758 A255 40fr multicolored   .45   .20
759 A255 60fr multicolored   .55   .20
760 A255 100fr multicolored   1.00 .35
       Nos. 758-760 (3)   2.00 .75

UNESCO intl. communications development
program.

1986, Sept. 15   Litho.   Perf. 13½
761 A256 100fr multicolored   .90   .30

Intl. Peace Year.

World Food
Day
A257

1986, Oct. 16
762 A257 75fr Food staples   .80   .25
763 A257 120fr Mother feeding
                child   1.25   .40

UN Child
Survival
Campaign
A258

Mothers, children and pinwheels in various
designs.

1986, Oct. 27
764 A258 15fr multi, vert.   .20   .20
765 A258 30fr multi   .25   .20
766 A258 70fr multi, vert.   .70   .30
       Nos. 764-766 (3)   1.15   .70

A258a

A259

1986, Dec. 5   Litho.   Perf. 12x12½
766A A258a 100fr multicolored   1.50   .35

27th Soviet Communist Party congress.

1987, Feb. 10   Litho.   Perf. 13½
767 A259 30fr multicolored   .25   .20
768 A259 45fr multicolored   .45   .20
769 A259 75fr multicolored   .70   .25
770 A259 120fr multicolored   1.10   .35
       Nos. 767-770 (4)   2.50 1.00

Election of President Sassou-Nguesso,
head of the Organization of African States.

Traditional
Wedding
A260

1987, Feb. 18   Litho.   Perf. 12½x13
771 A260 5fr multicolored   .20   .20
772 A260 15fr multicolored   .25   .20
773 A260 20fr multicolored   .25   .20
       Nos. 771-773 (3)   .70   .60

The Blue Lake — A261

1987, July 16   Perf. 12½
774 A261 5fr multicolored   .20   .20
775 A261 15fr multicolored   .20   .20
776 A261 75fr multicolored   1.00   .30
777 A261 120fr multicolored   1.25   .40
       Nos. 774-777 (4)   2.65 1.10

Pres. Marien
Ngouabi
A262

Congress of
African
Scientists
A263

1987, July 16   Perf. 13
778 A262 75fr multicolored   .75   .30
779 A262 120fr multicolored   1.25   .40

Tenth death anniv.

1987, Sept. 10   Perf. 13x12½
780 A263 15fr multicolored   .20   .20
781 A263 90fr multicolored   .70   .30
782 A263 230fr multicolored   2.00   .80
       Nos. 780-782 (3)   2.90 1.30

4th African Games, Nairobi — A264

1987, Oct. 30   Perf. 12½
783 A264 75fr multicolored   .75   .40
784 A264 120fr multicolored   1.25   .60

Raoul Follereau (1903-1977),
Philanthropist — A265

1987, Oct. 20   Perf. 13½
785 A265 120fr multicolored   1.50   .60

Cure leprosy.

FAO, 40th Anniv. — A266

1987, Nov. 17   Perf. 12½
786 A266 300fr multicolored   2.75 1.10

Anti-
Apartheid
Campaign
A267

Nelson Mandela
A268

Perf. 13½x15, 14½x15
1987, Sept. 21   Litho.
787 A267 60fr multicolored   .60   .20
788 A268 240fr multicolored   2.25   .75

Natl. UNICEF
Vaccination
Campaign — A269

Africa
Fund — A270

Perf. 13½x14½, 14½x13½
1987, Sept. 28
789 A269 30fr Inoculating
                adults, horiz.   .25   .20
790 A269 45fr shown   .50   .20
791 A269 500fr Inoculating chil-
                dren, horiz.   5.25 2.00
       Nos. 789-791 (3)   6.00 2.40

No. 791 is airmail.

1987, Sept. 28   Perf. 13½x15
792 A270 25fr multicolored   .25   .20
793 A270 50fr multicolored   .40   .20
794 A270 70fr multicolored   .75   .25
       Nos. 792-794 (3)   1.40   .65

Self-sufficiency in Food Production by
the Year 2000 — A271

1987, Nov. 20   Litho.   Perf. 13½
795 A271 20fr multicolored   .25   .20
796 A271 55fr multicolored   .60   .20
797 A271 100fr multicolored   1.00   .35
       Nos. 795-797 (3)   1.85   .75

Simon Kimbangu (b. 1887), Founder
of the Church of Christ on
Earth — A272

1987, Nov. 28   Perf. 12½
798 A272 75fr Kimbangu,
                vert.   .70   .30
799 A272 120fr Kimbangu,
                parrot, vert.   1.10   .40
800 A272 240fr Kimbanguist
                Church,
                Nkamba   2.75 1.00
  a.   Souvenir sheet of 3, #798-
        800   5.75 5.00
       Nos. 798-800 (3)   4.55 1.70

October Revolution, Russia, 70th
Anniv. — A273

Lenin inspecting revolutionary troops, Red
Square, from an unspecified painting.

1988, Feb. 19   Litho.   Perf. 12½x12
801 A273 75fr multicolored   1.60   .60
802 A273 120fr multicolored   2.25 1.00

African Writers
Opposing
Apartheid — A274

Intl. Fund for
Agricultural
Development
(IFAD), 10th
Anniv. — A275

1988, Apr. 6   Litho.   Perf. 13½
803 A274 15fr multicolored   .20 .20
804 A274 60fr multicolored   .50 .25
805 A274 75fr multicolored   .80 .30
   Nos. 803-805 (3)   1.50 .75

For overprint see #1157.

1988, Apr. 30
806 A275 240fr multicolored   2.00 .85

Invention of the Telegraph by Samuel
Morse, 150th Anniv. (in 1987) — A276

1988, Apr. 28
807 A276 90fr Morse, vert.   .90 .30
808 A276 120fr shown   1.10 .40

A277

1988, Sept. 20   Litho.   Perf. 13½
809 A277 5fr Eucalyptus trees,
    Brazzaville   .30 .20
810 A277 10fr Stop cutting down
    trees   .30 .20

Fight against desertification.

1988, Aug. 12   Litho.   Perf. 13½
Campaigns: No. 812, Return to the Land
Campaign (farming). 120fr, Self-sufficiency in
food production.

A278

811 A278 75fr shown   .75 .30
812 A278 75fr multicolored   .75 .30
813 A278 120fr multicolored   .90 .40
   Nos. 811-813 (3)   2.40 1.00

Congo Revolution, 25th anniv.

Yoro
Fishing
Village
A279

1988, Sept. 1
814 A279 35fr shown   .45 .20
815 A279 40fr Liberty Place   .45 .20

Intl. Day for
the Fight
Against
AIDS
A280

1988, Dec. 1   Litho.   Perf. 13½
816 A280 60fr shown   .45 .20
817 A280 75fr Emblem   .70 .20
818 A280 180fr Modified UN em-
    blem, campaign
    emblem   1.75 .60
   Nos. 816-818 (3)   2.90 1.00

Natl. Committee for the Fight Against AIDS
and Evangelical Anglican Church of Congo
anti-AIDS campaign.

February 5
Movement,
10th Anniv.
A281

1989, Apr. 21   Litho.   Perf. 13½
819 A281 75fr Rally   .75 .30
820 A281 120fr Pres. Sassou-
    Nguesso, natl.
    achievements   .90 .40

UN
Declaration
of Human
Rights,
40th Anniv.
(in 1988)
A282

1989, May 19   Perf. 13
821 A282 120fr multicolored   .90 .40
822 A282 350fr multicolored   2.50 1.20

Marien
Nguabi,
Founder of
Congo
Labor Party
A282a

1989, July 31   Litho.   Perf. 12½x13
822A A282a 240fr red & yellow   2.00 .75

Red Cross
and Red
Crescent
Societies,
125th
Anniv.
A283

120fr, Dunant, emblem, Congo Red Cross.

1989, Sept. 19   Litho.   Perf. 13
823 A283 75fr shown   .90 .40
824 A283 120fr multicolored   1.00 .65

No. 824 is airmail.

Organization of
African Unity,
25th
Anniv. — A284

1989, Oct. 19   Litho.   Perf. 12½
825 A284 120fr multicolored   1.10 .40

African Development Bank, 25th
Anniv. — A285

1989, Dec. 22   Litho.   Perf. 12½x13
826 A285 75fr multicolored   .75 .35
827 A285 120fr multicolored   1.00 .40

WHO, 40th
Anniv. (in
1988)
A286

1989, Dec. 28   Litho.   Perf. 12½
828 A286 60fr shown   .75 .35
829 A286 75fr Blood donation,
    vert.   .90 .50

See Nos. 846-847 for overprints.

Congo Labor
Party (PCT), 20th
Anniv. — A287

1989, Dec. 22   Litho.   Perf. 13x12½
830 A287 75fr multicolored   .75 .35
831 A287 120fr multicolored   1.10 .40

Cacti
A288

Perf. 12½x13, 13x12½
1989, Nov. 22
832 A288 35fr Opuntia phaea-
    cantha discata   .35 .20
833 A288 40fr Opuntia ficus in-
    dica   .50 .20
834 A288 60fr Opuntia erinacea .90 .25
835 A288 75fr Opuntia rufida   1.25 .30
836 A288 120fr Opuntia leptocau-
    lis   1.75 .45
   Nos. 832-836 (5)   4.75 1.40

Souvenir Sheet
Perf. 12½
837 A288 220fr Opuntia com-
    presa   5.00 2.10

Nos. 832-833, 835 and 837 vert. No. 837
contains one 32x40mm stamp.

1992 Winter
Olympics,
Albertville
A289

1989, Dec. 22   Perf. 12½
838 A289 75fr Ice dancing   .60 .25
839 A289 80fr Nordic skiing   .60 .30
840 A289 100fr Speed skating   .90 .35
841 A289 120fr Luge   1.10 .45
842 A289 200fr Alpine skiing   1.75 .70
843 A289 240fr Ice hockey   2.25 .85
844 A289 400fr Ski jumping   3.25 1.40
   Nos. 838-844 (7)   10.45 4.30

Souvenir Sheet
Perf. 13
845 A289 500fr Bobsled   4.50 2.40

No. 845 contains one 32x40mm stamp.

Nos. 828-829 Ovptd. "NOTRE
PLANETE, NOTRE SANTE PENSER
GLOBALEMENT AGIR
LOCALEMENT" in 3 or 5 Lines
1989, Dec. 28   Perf. 12½
846 A286 60fr multicolored   .75 .45
847 A286 75fr multicolored   .90 .60

Health care for everyone.

Intl. Literacy
Year — A290

1990, June 26   Litho.   Perf. 13½
848 A290 75fr bl, blk & yel   .75 .35

Birds
A291

Designs: 25fr, Tourterelle des bois. 50fr,
Fauvette pitchou, vert. 70fr, Faucon crecerelle,
vert. 150fr, Perroquet gris, vert.

1990, July 10

849	A291	25fr multicolored	.35	.25
850	A291	50fr multicolored	.70	.30
851	A291	70fr multicolored	1.10	.55
852	A291	150fr multicolored	2.10	1.25
		Nos. 849-852 (4)	4.25	2.35

Dance
Masks — A292

Flowering
Plants — A293

1990, July 24   Perf. 13

853	A292	120fr Mondo	1.10	.40
854	A292	360fr Bapunu	3.50	1.25
855	A292	400fr Kwele	4.00	1.50
		Nos. 853-855 (3)	8.60	3.15

For overprints see #1172, 1173.

1990, Sept. 15   Litho.   Perf. 12½

856	A293	30fr Tournesol (sunflower)	.25	.20
857	A293	45fr Cassia alata, horiz.	.45	.20
858	A293	75fr Oeillette (opium poppy)	.70	.25
859	A293	90fr Acalypha sanderil	1.00	.35
		Nos. 856-859 (4)	2.40	1.00

1992 Summer Olympics,
Barcelona — A294

1990, June 28   Litho.   Perf. 13½

860	A294	100fr Street scene, vert.	.80	.30
861	A294	150fr shown	1.25	.35
862	A294	200fr Sailing, diff.	1.60	.40
863	A294	240fr Marketplace	2.00	.55
864	A294	350fr Harbor	3.00	.75
865	A294	500fr Monument, vert.	4.25	.90
		Nos. 860-865 (6)	12.90	3.25

Souvenir Sheet

866	A294	750fr Cathedral, vert.	5.00	3.50

Nos. 864-865 airmail. Nos. 860-865 exist in
miniature sheets of 1.

Royal
Necklaces
A295

1990, Aug. 18   Litho.   Perf. 13½

867	A295	75fr shown	.75	.35
868	A295	100fr Necklace, diff.	1.00	.60

Boy Scouts
Observing
Nature
A296

Scout: 35fr, Photographing butterfly,
Euphaedra eusimoides. 40fr, Picking mushrooms, Armillaria mellea. 75fr, Drawing butterfly, Palla decius. 80fr, Using magnifying glass,
Kallima ansorgei. 500fr, Using microscope,
Cortinarius speciocissimus. 600fr, Feeding
butterfly, Graphium illyris. 1500fr, Photographing butterfly, Berberia plistonax, horiz. 750fr,
Photographing mushrooms, Volvariella
bombycina.

1991, June 8   Litho.   Perf. 13½

869	A296	35fr multicolored	.20	.20
870	A296	40fr multicolored	.45	.20
871	A296	75fr multicolored	.60	.20
872	A296	80fr multicolored	.70	.20
873	A296	500fr multicolored	4.00	1.25
874	A296	600fr multicolored	4.00	1.25
a.		Min. sheet of 4, #869, 871-872, 874	7.50	3.75
		Nos. 869-874 (6)	9.95	3.30

Litho. & Embossed

874B	A296	1500fr gold & multi	14.00	—

Souvenir Sheet

875	A296	750fr multicolored	5.25	2.25

Nos. 869-874 exist in souvenir sheets of 1.
Nos. 873-875 are airmail.

Medicinal
Plants — A297

Designs: 15fr, Ocimum viride. 20fr,
Kalanchoe pinnata, vert. 30fr, Euphorbia hirta.
60fr, Catharanthus roseus, vert. 75fr, Bidens
pilosa, vert. 100fr, Brillantaisia patula, vert.
120fr, Cassia occidentalis, vert.

1991, Jan. 30   Litho.   Perf. 11½

876	A297	15fr multicolored	.20	.20
877	A297	20fr multicolored	.25	.20
878	A297	30fr multicolored	.25	.20
879	A297	60fr multicolored	.50	.25
880	A297	75fr multicolored	.70	.35
881	A297	100fr multicolored	1.00	.55
882	A297	120fr multicolored	1.10	.75
		Nos. 876-882 (7)	4.00	2.50

Mushrooms
A298

1991, Mar. 25   Litho.   Perf. 13

883	A298	30fr Amanita rubescens	.30	.20
883A	A298	45fr Catathelasma imperiale	.40	.20
883B	A298	75fr Amanita caesarea	.75	.25
883C	A298	90fr Boletus regius	.90	.25
883D	A298	120fr Pluteus cervinus	1.10	.40
883E	A298	150fr Boletus chrysenteron	1.50	.60
883F	A298	200fr Agaricus arvensis	2.10	.75
		Nos. 883-883F (7)	7.05	2.65

Souvenir Sheet   Perf. 12½

883G	A298	350fr Boletus versipellis, horiz.	5.00	2.00

No. 883G contains one 40x32mm stamp.

Trains
A298a

Designs: 75fr, TGV, France. 120fr, S350,
Italy. 200fr, DE24000, Turkey. 250fr, DE1024,
Germany.

1991, Apr. 10   Litho.   Perf. 12½x12¼

883I	A298a	75fr multi	.65	.30
883J	A298a	120fr multi	1.10	.45
883K	A298a	200fr multi	2.00	.75
883L	A298a	250fr multi	2.75	1.00

An additional stamp was issued in this set.
The editors would like to examine it.

African Tourism
Year — A299

1991, Apr. 15   Litho.   Perf. 13½

884	A299	75fr shown	.75	.35
885	A299	120fr Zebra, map	1.10	.60

Allegory of New
Republic — A300

1991, May 13   Litho.   Perf. 13

888	A300	15fr blue	.20	.20
889	A300	30fr brt grn	.25	.20
890	A300	60fr org yel	.30	.20
891	A300	75fr brt pink	.50	.30
892	A300	120fr dk brown	.90	.45
		Nos. 888-892 (5)	2.15	1.35

Trans-Siberian Railroad, Cent. — A301

1991, June 6   Litho.   Perf. 13

899	A301	120fr Map	1.50	.50
900	A301	240fr Map, train	2.75	1.20

Telecom 91 — A302

1991, June 29   Litho.   Perf. 13

901	A302	75fr multicolored	.75	.30
902	A302	120fr multi, vert.	1.10	.60

6th World Forum and Exposition on Telecommunications, Geneva, Switzerland.

Insects — A303

A304

1991, July 2   Perf. 12½

903	A303	75fr Peanut beetle	.90	.25
904	A303	120fr Centaur, horiz.	1.25	.45
905	A303	200fr Coffee beetle	2.00	.75
906	A303	300fr Goliath beetle	3.00	1.50
		Nos. 903-906 (4)	7.15	2.95

1991, July 16   Litho.   Perf. 12½

907	A304	75fr Water conservation	.75	.35

Amnesty
Intl., 30th
Anniv.
A305

Designs: 40fr, Candle, sun, vert. 75fr, "30,"
broken chains, vert.

1991, Aug. 13   Perf. 13½

908	A305	40fr multicolored	.35	.20
909	A305	75fr multicolored	.60	.20
910	A305	80fr multicolored	.70	.35
		Nos. 908-910 (3)	1.65	.80

Congo Postage Stamps, Cent. — A306

75fr, Similar to French Congo #1. 120fr,
Similar to French Congo #35. 240fr, Similar to
Congo Republic #89. 500fr, Similar to French
Congo #1, 35 and Congo Republic #89.

1991, Aug.   Litho. & Engr.   Perf. 13x13½

911	A306	75fr beige & dk grn	.80	.30
912	A306	120fr beige, dk grn & brn	1.10	.45
913	A306	240fr multicolored	2.25	1.10
914	A306	500fr multicolored	4.50	2.00
a.		Strip of 4, #911-914	10.00	9.00

Ducks
A307

1991, Aug. 8   Litho.   Perf. 12½

915	A307	75fr Anas acuta	1.00	.30
916	A307	120fr Somateria mollissima, vert.	1.25	.45
917	A307	200fr Anas clypeata, vert.	1.75	.75
918	A307	240fr Anas platyrhynchos	3.00	1.00
		Nos. 915-918 (4)	7.00	2.50

Automobiles and Space — A308

Designs: 35fr, Ferrari 512S by Pininfarina.
40fr, Vincenzo Lancia, Lancia Stratos by

Bertone. 75fr, Maybach Zeppelin type 12, Wilhelm Maybach. 80fr, Mars Observer, 1992. 500fr, Magellan probe surveying Venus. 600fr, Magnification of Sun, Ulysses probe. 750fr, Crew of Apollo 11.

1991, Aug. 23		Litho.	Perf. 13½	
919	A308	35fr multicolored	.30	.20
920	A308	40fr multicolored	.30	.20
921	A308	75fr multicolored	.60	.30
922	A308	80fr multicolored	.65	.30
923	A308	500fr multicolored	4.00	2.00
924	A308	600fr multicolored	4.75	2.40
		Nos. 919-924 (6)	10.60	5.40

Souvenir Sheet

925	A308	750fr multicolored	6.00	3.00

Nos. 923-925 are airmail. No. 925 contains one 60x42mm stamp.

Butterflies
A309

1991, Aug. 31			Perf. 11½	
926	A309	75fr Petit bleu	1.00	.30
927	A309	120fr Charaxe	1.25	.50
928	A309	240fr Papillon feuille, vert.	1.75	.80
929	A309	300fr Papillon de l'oranger, vert.	3.00	1.00
		Nos. 926-929 (4)	7.00	2.60

For overprints see Nos. 1156, 1165.

Celebrities and Organizations — A310

Designs: 100fr, Bo Jackson, baseball and football player. 150fr, Nick Faldo, golfer. 200fr, Rickey Henderson, Barry Bonds, baseball players. 240fr, Garry Kasparov, World Chess Champion. 300fr, Starving child, Lions and Rotary Clubs emblems. 350fr, Wolfgang Amadeus Mozart. 400fr, De Gaulle, Churchill. 500fr, Jean-Henri Dunant, founder of Red Cross. 750fr, De Gaulle, vert.

1991, Sept. 2			Perf. 13½	
930	A310	100fr multicolored	.85	.40
931	A310	150fr multicolored	1.25	.60
932	A310	200fr multicolored	1.60	.80
933	A310	240fr multicolored	1.90	.95
934	A310	300fr multicolored	2.40	1.25
935	A310	350fr multicolored	2.75	1.40
936	A310	400fr multicolored	3.25	1.60
937	A310	500fr multicolored	4.00	2.00
		Nos. 930-937 (8)	18.00	9.00

Souvenir Sheet

938	A310	750fr multicolored	6.00	3.00

Nos. 936-938 are airmail. No. 938 contains one 35x50mm stamp.
For overprint, see No. 1199.

Gen. Charles de Gaulle in Africa — A311

120fr, De Gaulle, Free French flag, vert. 240fr, De Gaulle, Appeal of Brazzaville, 1940.

1991, Sept. 2		Perf. 13½x13, 13x13½	
939	A311	75fr multicolored	.90	.40
940	A311	120fr multicolored	1.10	.60
941	A311	240fr multicolored	2.25	1.20
		Nos. 939-941 (3)	4.25	2.20

A312

Paintings — A313

1991, Oct. 12			Perf. 11½	
942	A312	75fr multicolored	.75	.35
943	A313	120fr multicolored	1.10	.45

Discovery of America, 500th Anniv. (in 1992) — A314

20fr, Portrait of Christopher Columbus by Sebastian Del Pombo. 35fr, Portrait of Columbus. 40fr, Portrait of Columbus facing right. 55fr, Santa Maria. 75fr, Nina. 150fr, Pinta. 200fr, Arms & signature of Columbus.

1991, May 30			Perf. 13	
944	A314	20fr multicolored	.35	.20
945	A314	35fr multicolored	.35	.20
946	A314	40fr multicolored	.45	.35
947	A314	55fr multicolored	.60	.35
948	A314	75fr multicolored	.85	.35
949	A314	150fr multicolored	1.60	.85
950	A314	200fr multicolored	2.10	1.00
		Nos. 944-950 (7)	6.30	3.30

Primates A315

1991, Dec. 13			Litho.	Perf. 13	
951	A315	30fr Cercopithecus diana	.35	.20
952	A315	45fr Pan troglodytes	.45	.20
953	A315	60fr Theropithecus gelada	.75	.20
954	A315	75fr Papio hamadryas	1.00	.35
955	A315	90fr Macaca nemestrina	1.25	.50
956	A315	120fr Gorilla gorilla	1.60	.50
957	A315	240fr Mandrillus sphinx	3.50	.75
		Nos. 951-957 (7)	8.90	2.70

Souvenir Sheet

958	A315	250fr Gorilla gorilla	4.00	1.40

Nos. 953-958 are vert.

Anniversaries and Events A316

Designs: 50fr, Launching of Sputnik II with dog, Laika, 1957. 75fr, Mahatma Gandhi and Martin Luther King, Jr. 1964. 120fr, Launching of Meteosat and ERS-1 over Europe and Africa. 240fr, Maybach Zeppelin automobile and Ferdinand von Zeppelin, 75th death anniversary. 300fr, Konrad Adenauer, 25th death

anniversary and opening of the Brandenburg Gate, 1989. 500fr, Pope John Paul II's visit to Africa. 600fr, Elvis Presley, American entertainer.

1992, Feb. 4			Litho.	Perf. 13½	
959	A316	50fr multicolored	.75	.25
960	A316	75fr multicolored	.75	.25
961	A316	120fr multicolored	1.25	.45
962	A316	240fr multicolored	2.75	.85
963	A316	300fr multicolored	2.50	.80
964	A316	500fr multicolored	5.25	1.40
a.		Souvenir sheet of 3, #960, 963-964	11.50	5.75
		Nos. 959-964 (6)	13.25	4.00

Souvenir Sheet

965	A316	600fr multicolored	6.00	2.40

Nos. 959-964 exist in souvenir sheets of 1. Nos. 962, 964-965 are airmail.

Explorers A317

Birds — A318

Genoa '92: 75fr, Juan de la Cosa, nautical chart. 95fr, Martin Alonso Pinzon, astrolabe. 120fr, Alonso de Ojeda, hour glass. 200fr, Vicente Yanez Pinzon, sun dial. 250fr, Bartholomew Columbus, quadrant.

1992, Oct. 21			Litho.	Perf. 13	
966	A317	75fr multicolored	1.00	.30
967	A317	95fr multicolored	1.10	.30
968	A317	120fr multicolored	1.75	.30
969	A317	200fr multicolored	2.25	.40
970	A317	250fr multicolored	2.75	.50
		Nos. 966-970 (5)	8.85	1.80

Souvenir Sheet

971	A317	400fr multi	14.00	14.00

1992, Oct. 21

Designs: 60fr, Sagittarius serpentarius. 75fr, Ephippiorhynchus senegalensis. 120fr, Bugeranus carunculatus. 200fr, Ardea melanocephala. 250fr, Phoenicopterus ruber roseus.

400fr, Balearica regulorum.

972	A318	60fr multicolored	.70	.20
973	A318	75fr multicolored	.80	.20
974	A318	120fr multicolored	1.10	.30
975	A318	200fr multicolored	2.00	.40
976	A318	250fr multicolored	2.75	.50
		Nos. 972-976 (5)	7.35	1.60

Souvenir Sheet

977	A318	400fr multi	4.00	1.00

For overprint, see No. 1191.

Wild Cats — A319

1992, Nov. 21			Litho.	Perf. 13	
978	A319	45fr Panthera leo	.50	.50
979	A319	60fr Panthera tigris	.60	.60
980	A319	75fr Lynx lynx	.70	.70
981	A319	95fr Caracal caracal	.80	.80
982	A319	250fr Leopardus pardalis	2.25	2.25
		Nos. 978-982 (5)	4.85	4.85

Souvenir Sheet

983	A319	400fr Acinonyx jubatus	4.50	1.75

No. 983 contains one 32x40mm stamp.

1992 Winter Olympics, Albertville — A320

1992 Summer Olympics, Barcelona A321

Gold medalists: 150fr, N. Mishkutyonok, A. Dmitriev, pairs figure skating, Unified team. 200fr, I. Appelt, H. Winkler, G. Haldacher, T. Schroll, 4-man bobsled, Austria. 500fr, Gunda Niemann, speed skating, Germany. 600fr, Bjorn Daehlie, cross-country skiing, Norway. 750fr, Alberto Tomba, giant slalom, Italy.

1992, Dec. 21			Litho.	Perf. 13½	
984	A320	150fr multicolored	1.25	1.25
985	A320	200fr multicolored	1.60	1.60
986	A320	500fr multicolored	4.00	4.00
987	A320	600fr multicolored	4.75	4.75
		Nos. 984-987 (4)	11.60	11.60

Souvenir Sheet

988	A320	750fr multicolored	6.00	6.00

Nos. 986-988 are airmail. No. 988 contains one 35x50mm stamp. Name on No. 987 spelled incorrectly.

1992, Dec. 21

Barcelona landmarks, Olympic event: 75fr, Steeple of La Sagrada Familia, baseball. 100fr, The Muse, Palace of Music, running. 150fr, Cupola interior, long jump. 200fr, St. Paul Hospital, pole vault. 400fr, Sculpture, by Miro, shot put. 500fr, Galley, Maritime Museum, table tennis. 750fr, La Sagrada Familia, tennis.

989	A321	75fr multicolored	.60	.30
990	A321	100fr multicolored	.80	.40
991	A321	150fr multicolored	1.25	.60
992	A321	200fr multicolored	1.60	.80
993	A321	400fr multicolored	3.25	3.25
994	A321	500fr multicolored	4.00	4.00
		Nos. 989-994 (6)	11.50	9.35

Souvenir Sheet

995	A321	750fr multicolored	6.00	6.00

Nos. 993-995 are airmail.

Christmas A321a

Paintings: 95fr, The Madonna of the Grand Duke, 120fr, Virgin and Child, by Francesco Mazzo. by Raphael. 200fr, The Madonna with a Book, by Botticelli. 250fr, The Madonna Carondelet, by Fra Bartolommeo. 400fr, Madonna and Child, by Raphael.

1992, Dec. 20   **Litho.**   *Perf. 12½*

995A	A321a	95fr	multicolored	1.25	.30
995B	A321a	120fr	multi	2.00	.65
995C	A321a	200fr	multicolored	2.75	.75
995D	A321a	250fr	multi	3.25	1.25

Nos. 995A-995D (4)   9.25   2.95

Souvenir Sheet

995E	A321a	400fr	multicolored	4.50	1.90

Nos. 995A-995E were not available until late 1993.

For overprint, see No. 1192.

Birds of Prey — A322

A323

1993, Jan. 15   **Litho.**   *Perf. 12½x13*

996	A322	45fr	Charognard	.50	.20
997	A322	75fr	Vulture	1.50	.30
998	A322	120fr	Eagle	2.00	.65

Nos. 996-998 (3)   4.00   1.15

1993, Dec. 21   **Litho.**   *Perf. 13½*

Traditional ceramics.

999	A323	45fr	Liloko	.60	.30
1000	A323	75fr	Mbeya	.95	.50
1001	A323	120fr	Jug with ladles, Mbeya	1.40	.85

Nos. 999-1001 (3)   2.95   1.65

1994 World Cup Soccer Championships, United States — A324

Design: 75fr, Player stretching to kick ball. 95fr, Goalie diving to stop ball. 120fr, Player stretching to kick ball. 200fr, Player kicking. 250fr, Goalie catching ball.

1993, Jan. 15   **Litho.**   *Perf. 12¾*

1002	A324	75fr	multi	1.20	.80
1003	A324	95fr	multi	1.25	1.10
1004	A324	120fr	multi	2.10	1.40
1005	A324	200fr	multi	3.00	2.10
1006	A324	250fr	multi	3.50	2.75

An additional stamps was issued in this set. The editors would like to examine any example.

Wild Animals A325

Designs: 60fr, Damaliscus lunatus. 75fr, Gazella granti. 95fr, Equus quagga. 120fr, Panthera pardus. 200fr, Syncerus caffer. 250fr, Hippopotamus ambibius. 350fr, Panthera leo.

1993, Feb. 20   **Litho.**   *Perf. 13*

1008	A325	60fr	Damaliscus lunatus	.75	.20
1009	A325	75fr	Gazella granti	1.25	.20

1010	A325	95fr	Equus quagga	1.40	.30
1011	A325	120fr	Panthera pardus	1.90	.30
1012	A325	200fr	Syncerus caffer	2.75	.40
1013	A325	250fr	Hippopotamus amphibius	3.50	.40
1014	A325	300fr	Necrosyrtes monachu	4.25	.40
1015	A325	350fr	Panthera leo	4.75	.75
a.			Sheet of 8, #1008-1015	20.00	20.00

No. 1008-1015 (8)   20.55   2.95

No. 1015a is a continuous design.

Wild Flowers — A326

Designs: 75fr, Hibiscus schizopetalus. 95fr, Pentas lanceolata. 120fr, Ricinus communis. 200fr, Delonix regia. 250fr, Stapelia gigantea.

1993, May 20   **Litho.**   *Perf. 12½*

1016	A326	75fr	multicolored	1.25	.30
1017	A326	95fr	multicolored	1.75	.40
1018	A326	120fr	multicolored	3.00	.50
1019	A326	200fr	multicolored	5.25	1.00
1020	A326	250fr	multicolored	6.50	1.60

Nos. 1016-1020 (5)   17.75   3.80

Deep Sea Submersibles A327

1993, June 25

1021	A327	75fr	Transport PC-1202	1.60	.75
1022	A327	95fr	J. Sea Link 1	2.00	1.00
1023	A327	120fr	Nemo	2.50	1.25
1024	A327	200fr	Robot	4.25	2.25
1025	A327	250fr	Alvin	5.50	2.75

Nos. 1021-1025 (5)   15.85   8.00

Souvenir Sheet

1026	A327	400fr	Star III	9.00	6.75

No. 1026 contains one 32x40mm stamp.

1996 Summer Olympic Games, Atlanta A329

Designs: 50fr, Equestrian. 75fr, Cycling. 120fr, Sailing. 240fr, shown. 300fr, Hurdles. 500fr, Women's basketball. 750fr, Running.

1993, Apr. 26   **Litho.**   *Perf. 13½*

1030-1035	A329	Set of 6		10.00	4.00
1035a		Sheet of 6, #1030-1035		10.00	5.00

Souvenir Sheet

1036	A329	750fr	multicolored	6.50	1.50

Nos. 1030-1036 exist imperf. Nos. 1030-1035 exist in souvenir sheets of 1.

Brasiliana '93 — A330

Birds: 75fr, Vidua whydah. 95fr, Vidua regia. 120fr, Steganura paradisea. 200fr, Vidua macroura. 250fr, Anthreptes platura. 400fr, Coliuspasser macrourus, horiz.

1993, July 15   **Litho.**   *Perf. 12x12½*

1037-1041	A330	Set of 5		13.00	13.00

Souvenir Sheet

1042	A330	400fr	multicolored	12.00	12.00

Prehistoric Animals — A331

1993, Aug. 20   **Litho.**   *Perf. 13*

1043	A331	75fr	Ichthyostega	1.75	1.25
1044	A331	95fr	Archaeopteryx	2.25	1.60
1045	A331	120fr	Brachiosaurus	3.00	2.10
1046	A331	200fr	Tyrannosaurus	4.75	3.50
1047	A331	250fr	Pteranodon, vert.	6.50	4.25

Nos. 1043-1047 (5)   18.25   12.70

Souvenir Sheet

1048	A331	400fr	Brontosaurus	13.00	6.50

No. 1048 contains one 32x40mm stamp.

Powered Flight, 90th Anniv. — A332

Designs: 75fr, Wilbur Wright, Model B airplane, vert. 95fr, Orville Wright and Model B biplane, vert. 120fr, First flight by Orville Wright. 200fr, Flight at Kitty Hawk. 250fr, Wright Brothers and airplane.

   Perf. 12¼x12½, 12½x12¼

1993, Dec. 17   **Litho.**

1049	A332	75fr	multi	.60	.60
1050	A332	95fr	multi	.75	.75
1051	A332	120fr	multi	.90	.90
1052	A332	200fr	multi	1.60	1.60
1053	A332	250fr	multi	2.10	2.10

Nos. 1049-1053 (5)   5.95   5.95

Evolution of the Elephant A333

1994, June 20   **Litho.**   *Perf. 12½*

1054	A333	25fr	Palaeomastodon	1.00	.50
1055	A333	45fr	Mammut	1.75	.90
1056	A333	50fr	Amebelodon	2.00	1.00
1057	A333	75fr	Platybelodon	3.00	1.50
1058	A333	120fr	Mammuthus	4.75	2.40

Nos. 1054-1058 (5)   12.50   6.30

Protection of Nature — A335

Designs: 50fr, Choeropsis liberiensis. 90fr, Hyemoschus aquaticus. 205fr, Taurotragus euryceros, vert. 300fr, Redunca redunca, vert.

1994, Aug. 27   **Litho.**   *Perf. 12½*

1063	A335	50fr	multicolored	.65	.30
1064	A335	90fr	multicolored	1.10	.30
1065	A335	205fr	multicolored	2.50	1.10
1066	A335	300fr	multicolored	3.25	1.60

Nos. 1063-1066 (4)   7.50   3.30

For overprint see #1167.

Seaplanes — A336

Designs: 30fr, Cant Z-505, Italy. 45fr, Martin Mariner PBM-3, US. No. 1069, E-59, Russia. No. 1070, Short Sunderland, Great Britain. No. 1071, Martin Mars XPB2M-1, US. 400fr, Boeing 314, US.

1994, Sept. 2   **Litho.**   *Perf. 12½*

1067	A336	30fr	multicolored	.40	.40
1068	A336	45fr	multicolored	.65	.65
1069	A336	90fr	multicolored	1.50	1.50
1070	A336	90fr	multicolored	1.50	1.50
1071	A336	90fr	multicolored	1.50	1.50

Nos. 1067-1071 (5)   5.55   5.55

Souvenir Sheet

1071A	A336	400fr	multicolored	5.00	2.50

No. 1071A contains one 40x32mm stamp.

Intl. Year of the Family — A337

1995, Jan. 28   **Litho.**   *Perf. 12½*

1072	A337	90fr	shown	1.10	.40
1073	A337	205fr	African map, child	2.25	1.00
1074	A337	300fr	Family, native huts	3.50	1.50

Nos. 1072-1074 (3)   6.85   2.90

For overprint see No. 1168.

Insects — A338

1994, July 24   **Litho.**   *Perf. 12½*

1075	A338	90fr	Tarantula	1.90	.40
1076	A338	205fr	Spider	4.50	1.10
1077	A338	240fr	Ladybug	5.00	1.25

Nos. 1075-1077 (3)   11.40   2.75

Souvenir Sheet

1078	A338	400fr	Bee	4.75	2.00

Costumes — A338a

1995   Litho.   Perf. 12¾x12½
1078A A338a 90fr M'Bochi   1.50   .75
1078B A338a 205fr Téké   2.00 1.00
1078C A338a 500fr Loango   5.00 1.75
    Nos. 1078A-1078C (3)   8.50 3.50

Rotary Intl., 90th Anniv. A339

Designs: 90fr, Polio victim. No. 1080, Playing ball with children. No. 1081, Children with food. 300fr, Delivering polio vaccine. 1500fr, Paul Harris, Rotary emblem.

1996, Feb. 6   Litho.   Perf. 14
1079 A339 90fr multicolored   .60   .25
1080 A339 205fr multicolored   1.25   .50
1081 A339 205fr multicolored   1.25   .50
1082 A339 300fr multicolored   1.60   .60
    Nos. 1079-1082 (4)   4.70 1.85

Souvenir Sheet
1083 A339 1500fr multicolored 7.50 3.25

For overprint, see Mo. 1201.

18th World Scout Jamboree, The Netherlands — A340

Designs: No. 1084, Handshake. No. 1085, Scout helping another with arm sling. 205fr, Saving life in water. 300fr, Lord Baden-Powell. 1000fr, Scout salute.

1996, Feb. 6   Litho.   Perf. 14
1084 A340 45fr multicolored   .45   .20
1085 A340 90fr multicolored   .45   .20
1086 A340 205fr multicolored 1.10   .40
1087 A340 300fr multicolored 1.75   .50
    Nos. 1084-1087 (4)   3.75 1.30

Souvenir Sheet
1088 A340 1000fr multicolored 4.25 2.10

1998 World Cup Soccer Tournament A340a

Various players. Denominations: 90fr, 150fr, 205fr, 300fr, 400fr, 500fr.

1996   Litho.   Perf. 12¾
1088A-1088F A340a Set of 6   7.25 7.25
Souvenir Sheet
Perf. 13¼x13
1088G A340a 1000fr Player's legs   4.50 4.50

No. 1088G contains one 40x31mm stamp.

Antique Automobiles — A341

90fr, 1936 Armstrong Siddeley Twelve. 150fr, 1935 Aston Martin Mark II. 205fr, 1938 Morris 8. 300fr, 1955-62 MG Series MGA. 400fr, 1932 SS1. 500fr, 1938 Alvis 25 SB.

1996, Apr. 30   Litho.   Perf. 12½x12
1089 A341 90fr multicolored   .45   .20
1090 A341 150fr multicolored   .75   .40
1091 A341 205fr multicolored 1.00   .50
1092 A341 300fr multicolored 1.50   .75
1093 A341 400fr multicolored 2.00 1.00
1094 A341 500fr multicolored 2.50 1.25
    Nos. 1089-1094 (6)   8.20 4.10

Domestic Cats — A342

90fr, Persian. 150fr, Siamese. 205fr, Norwegian forest. 300fr, Exotic shorthair. 400fr, Maine coon. 500fr, Red abyssinian. 1000fr, Turkish Angora.

1996, Mar. 10   Perf. 13x12½
1095 A342 90fr multicolored   .45   .20
1096 A342 150fr multicolored   .75   .40
1097 A342 205fr multicolored 1.00   .50
1098 A342 300fr multicolored 1.50   .75
1099 A342 400fr multicolored 2.00 1.00
1100 A342 500fr multicolored 2.50 1.25
    Nos. 1095-1100 (6)   8.20 4.10

Souvenir Sheet
1101 A342 1000fr multicolored 5.00 2.50

No. 1101 contains one 32x40mm stamp.

1996 Summer Olympic Games, Atlanta A343

1996   Perf. 13x12½, 12½x13
1102 A343 90fr Fencing, vert.   .50   .25
1103 A343 150fr Archery, vert.   .80   .40
1104 A343 205fr Basketball, vert.   1.10   .55
1105 A343 300fr Baseball, vert.   1.60   .80
1106 A343 400fr Volleyball   2.25 1.10
1107 A343 500fr 2-man kayak   2.50 1.25
    Nos. 1102-1107 (6)   8.75 4.35

Souvenir Sheet
1108 A343 1000fr Judo, vert.   5.25 2.50

No. 1108 contains one 32x40mm stamp.

Flowers — A344

Designs: 90fr, Nerium oleander. 150fr, Eucalyptus globulus. 205fr, Centaurea cyanus. 300fr, Coffea arabica. 400fr, Hibiscus sabdariffa. 500fr, Cassia angustifolia.

1996, May 10   Perf. 12½
1109 A344 90fr multicolored   .50   .25
1110 A344 150fr multicolored   .80   .40
1111 A344 205fr multicolored 1.10   .55

1112 A344 300fr multicolored 1.60   .80
1113 A344 400fr multicolored 2.25 1.10
1114 A344 500fr multicolored 2.50 1.25
    Nos. 1109-1114 (6)   8.75 4.35

Mother Carrying Baby — A345

1996   Litho.   Perf. 13
1115 A345 40fr blue   4.00 2.00
1116 A345 50fr violet brown   5.00 2.50
1117 A345 90fr orange   9.00 4.50
1118 A345 100fr green blue   10.00 5.00
1119 A345 115fr gray   11.00 5.50
1120 A345 205fr brown   20.00 10.00
    Nos. 1115-1120 (6) 59.00 29.50

It has been stated that this set was not issued.
See #1145-1150.

A346

1996, Aug. 31   Litho.   Perf. 13½
1121 A346 90fr orange & multi   .45   .30
1122 A346 205fr green & multi 1.00   .60

Investiture of Pres. Pascal Lissouba, 4th anniv.

Owls — A347

1996, Mar. 29   Perf. 14½
1123 A347 90fr Tyto alba   .70   .25
1124 A347 205fr Bubo poensis   1.40   .50
1125 A347 300fr Scotopelia peli   2.00   .90
1126 A347 500fr Asio capensis 3.25 1.50
    Nos. 1123-1126 (4)   7.35 3.15

Military Aircraft — A348

Designs: 90fr, Vought-Sikorsky Vindicator SB2U-1. 150fr, Grumman Wildcat F4F-3. 205fr, North American SNJ-2. 300fr, Brewster Bermuda. 400fr, Blackburn Skua 1. 500fr, Mitsubishi Type 98-1. 1000fr, P-40 Warhawk (Flying Tigers).

1996, June 24   Litho.   Perf. 12½x12
1127 A348 90fr multicolored   .45   .20
1128 A348 150fr multicolored   .75   .30
1129 A348 205fr multicolored 1.00   .50
1130 A348 300fr multicolored 1.50   .75
1131 A348 400fr multicolored 2.00 1.00
1132 A348 500fr multicolored 2.50 1.25
    Nos. 1127-1132 (6)   8.20 4.00

Souvenir Sheet
Perf. 13
1133 A348 1000fr multicolored 5.00 2.50

No. 1133 contains one 32x40mm stamp.

Aquatic Flowers — A348a

Design: 90fr, Cyrtosperma senegalense.

1996, July 3   Litho.   Perf. 14x14¼
1133A A348a 90fr multi   .50   .50

An additional stamp was issued in this set. The editors would like to examine it.

Crocodilians A348b

1996, July 16   Litho.   Perf. 14
1133C A348b 205fr Nile crocodile   —   —
1133D A348b 255fr Gavial   —   —
1133E A348b 300fr Caiman   —   —

Arctocebus Calabarensis A349

a, 90fr, With young. b, 205fr, Touching leaf. c, 300fr, Climbing to left. d, 255fr, Walking on branch.

1998, June 3   Litho.   Perf. 14
1134 A349 Strip of 4, #a.-d.   4.50 4.50

No. 1134 issued in sheets of 12 stamps. World Wildlife Fund.

Endangered Species — A350

#1135, Kabus defassa, vert. #1136, Caphalophus sylvicutor. 205fr, Potamochoerus porcus. 300fr, Tragelaplus spekei.

1996   Litho.   Perf. 14
1135 A350 90fr multi   .55   .25
1136 A350 90fr multi, vert. .55   .25
1137 A350 205fr multi, vert. 1.10   .45
1138 A350 300fr multi   1.60   .65
    Nos. 1135-1138 (4)   3.80 1.60

Diana, Princess of Wales (1961-97) A351

#1139-1141: Various portraits with white rose.
Diana, rose, famous people in sheet margin: 750fr, Henry Kissinger, vert. No. 1143, Mother Teresa, vert. No. 1144, Hillary Clinton, vert.

1998, Aug. 31   Litho.   Perf. 14
Sheets of 6
1139 A351 205fr #a.-f.   4.25 2.00
1140 A351 255fr #a.-f., vert. 5.25 2.75
1141 A351 300fr #a.-f., vert. 6.25 3.00

Souvenir Sheets

1142 A351 750fr multicolored   2.50 1.25
1143-1144 A351 1000fr each   3.50 1.75

Stamps of Type A345 inscribed only "Congo" ovptd.

1998   Litho.   Perf. 13
1145 A345   40fr blue
1146 A345   50fr violet brown
1147 A345   90fr orange
1148 A345   100fr green blue   — —
1149 A345   115fr gray
1150 A345   205fr brown

A352

Designs: 90fr, Aframomum africanum. 205fr, Gambeya lacuurtiana (37x24mm). 300fr, Landolphia jumeli.

Perf. 13½x13¼, 13 (#1152)
1998   Litho.
1151 A352   90fr multi
1152 A352   205fr multi   — —
1153 A352   300fr multi

No. 1153 has denomination in yellow.

No. 732A
Overprinted

No. 929
Overprinted

1998   Litho.   Perf. 13
1155 A244   205fr multi   — —
1156 A309   300fr multi   — —

An additional stamp was issued in this set. The editors would like to examine them.

Nos. 732B, 804, 854, 855, 929, 1066, 1074, 1118, 1133D Ovptd. Like

and

A355

Perfs. as before, Perf. 14 (#1164),
Perf. 13½x13¼ (#1170)
Methods as before, Litho. (#1164, 1170)
1998
1157 A274   60fr multi (#804)
1159 A345   100fr green blue
        (#1118)
1164 A348b   255fr multi (#1133D)
1165 A309   300fr multi (#929)
1167 A335   300fr multi (#1066)
    a.   Overprint reading horizontally
1168 A337   300fr multi (#1074)
1169 A355   300fr multi   — —
1170 A244   300fr multi (#732B)
    a.   Overprint reading horizontally
1172 A292   360fr multi (#854)
    a.   Inverted overprint
1173 A292   400fr multi (#855)   — —

Numbers have been reserved for additional overprinted stamps. Overprint reads horizontally on Nos. 1157, 1159, 1169, 1172 and 1173, vertically reading down on Nos. 1164, 1167, 1168 and 1170, and vertically reading up on No. 1165. No. 1170 has white denomination.

The editors would like to see examples of No. 1169 without the overprint.

1998 World Cup Soccer
Championships, France — A358

Designs: 90fr, Netherlands, 4th place. 205fr, Croatia, bronze medal. 300fr, Brazil, silver medal. 500fr, France, gold medal.

1998, Nov. 16   Litho.   Perf. 13x13¼
1175-1178 A358   Set of 4   — —

Masks — A359

Perf. 13¼x13½
1998, Nov. 20   Litho.
1179 A359   90fr Kwele wood
        mask
1180 A359   150fr Kwele wood
        mask
1181 A359   205fr Teke/Tsangui
        wood mask
1182 A359   205fr Kuyu wood
        mask

No. 732B Overprinted

Type I — Unserifed Upper and Lower
Case Letters, 7x3mm

Type II — Serifed Upper and Lower
Case Letters, 12x3mm

Type III — Upper Case Letters,
9x2mm

Methods and Perfs as Before
1999 ?
1183 A244   300fr multi (I)   — —
1184 A244   300fr multi (II)   — —
1185 A244   300fr multi (III)   — —

Nos. 934, 975, 995B, 1082, C342-C343 Overprinted Like No. 1157 and

A359a

Methods as Before, Litho. (#1204)
1999 ?   Perf. as Before, 12½ (#1204)
1187 AP120   200fr multi (#C342)   — —
1188 AP120   200fr multi (#C343)   — —
    a.   Horiz. pair, #1187-1188, +
        central label
1191 A318   200fr multi (#975)   — —
1192 A321a   200fr multi (#995B)   — —
1199 A310   300fr multi (#934)   — —
1201 A339   300fr multi (#1082)   — —
1204 A359a   300fr multi   — —

The editors would like to see examples of No. 1204 without the overprint. Overprint reads horizontally on No. 1204, horizontally and inverted on Nos. 1187-1188, vertically reading down on Nos. 1191 and 1199, and vertically reading up on Nos. 1192 and 1201.

PhilexFrance 99 — A360

Design: 205fr, Raffia cloth with tassels. 300fr, Woven raffia cloth.

1999, July 2   Litho.   Perf. 13x13¼
1211 A360   205fr multi
1212 A360   300fr multi   — —

First French
Postage
Stamp,
150th
Anniv.
A361

Litho. With Hologram
1999   Perf. 13x13¼
1213 A361   300fr multi   — —

Central African
Economic and
Monetary
Community
Week — A363

Designs: 90fr, Map and flags. 205fr, Map and circle of flags.

1999   Litho.   Perf. 14½
1227 A363   90fr multi   — —
1228 A363   205fr multi   — —

Additional stamps may exist in this set. The editors would like to examine any examples.

Third Pan-African
Music
Festival — A364

Designs: 120fr, Emblem. 270fr, Map of Africa with drummers.

2001, Aug. 4   Litho.   Perf. 13½x13
1229-1230 A364   Set of 2   1.60 1.60

Independence,
40th
Anniv. — A365

Designs: 90fr, Dove, vine, map, hands, people. 205fr, Tools, clasped and opened hands, map.

2001, Nov. 15   Litho.   Perf. 13¼x13
1231-1232 A365   Set of 2   — —

Birds — A366

Designs: 90fr, Egretta garzetta. 120fr, Ardea cenerea. 270fr, Ciconia nigra.

2001   Perf. 13¼
1233 A366   90fr multi
1234 A366   120fr multi   — —
1235 A366   270fr multi

Additional stamps may exist in this set. The editors would like to examine any examples.

Type of A345 Inscribed
"REPUBLIQUE DU CONGO"
Overprinted "LEGAL" Like No. 1145
2001 ?   Litho.   Perf. 13
1236 A345   90fr blue   — —

Fruit — A367

Designs: 40fr, Mbila esobe. 50fr, Ikami. 70fr, Tsia, vert. 80fr, Bamou. 120fr, Malombo. 270fr, Ntondolo, vert.

2002, June 25   Litho.   Perf. 13½
1237-1242 A367   Set of 6   — —

Birds — A368

Designs: 40fr, Calao (hornbill). 80fr, Cigogne blanche (white stork). 120fr, Grue cendrée (gray crane). 270fr, Marabout.

2002, July 23   *Perf. 13½x13*
1243-1246 A368   Set of 4   — —

Elephants A369

Designs; 120fr, Mammoth. 270fr, Elephant on savannah, horiz. 350fr, Elephant, horiz. 500fr, Forest elephant near lake.

    Perf. 13¼x13, 13x13¼
2003, June 20
1247-1250 A369   Set of 4   5.75 5.75

Flowers — A370

Designs: 120fr, Muflier (antirrhinum). 270fr, Pivoine (peony). 400fr, Petunia. 600fr, Mauve (mallow), horiz.

2003, July 6
1251-1254 A370   Set of 4   6.50 6.50

Moringa Olifera — A371

Highlighted portion: 30fr, Bark. 70fr, Root. 90fr, Leaves. 115fr, Seeds and open pod. 120fr, Flowers. 360fr, Pod.

2005, Feb. 3   **Litho.**   *Perf. 13¼x13*
1255-1260 A371   Set of 6   3.25 3.25
     Dated 2004.

Albert Einstein (1879-1955), Physicist — A373

2005, Aug. 17   **Litho.**   *Perf. 13¼x13*
1265 A373 400fr multi   4.25 4.25

A374

Brazzaville, 125th Anniv. — A375

2005, Oct. 3   *Perf. 13¼x13*
1266 A374 120fr multi   1.10 1.10
     Perf. 13½x13¼
1267 A375 360fr multi   3.25 3.25

Pope Benedict XVI A376

Pope Benedict XVI: 360fr, Waving. 500fr, Holding crucifix.

2005, Nov. 28   *Perf. 13¼x13½*
1268-1269 A376   Set of 2   3.75 3.75

Denis Sassou-Nguesso, President of African Union — A378

2006, Mar. 14   **Litho.**   *Perf. 13x13¼*
1274 A378 500fr multi   2.40 2.40

Léopold Sédar Senghor (1906-2001), First President of Senegal — A379

2006, May 15
1275 A379 360fr multi   1.75 1.75

SEMI-POSTAL STAMPS

Anti-Malaria Issue
Common Design Type
1962, Apr. 7   **Engr.**   *Perf. 12½x12*
B3 CD108 25fr + 5fr bister   .90 .90

Freedom from Hunger Issue
Common Design Type
1963, Mar. 21   **Unwmk.**   *Perf. 13*
B4 CD112 25fr + 5fr vio bl, bl grn
       & brn   .90 .90

Boy Suffering from Sleeping Sickness SP1

Fight Against Communicable Diseases; 40fr+5fr, Examination, treatment, vert.

1981, June 6   **Litho.**   *Perf. 13*
B5 SP1 40fr + 5fr multi   .60 .25
B6 SP1 65fr + 10fr multi   1.00 .30

    IYD Type of 1981
1981, June 29   *Perf. 12½*
B7 A192 75fr + 5fr multi   .90 .35

AIR POST STAMPS

Olympic Games Issue
French Equatorial Africa No. C37 Surcharged in Red Like Chad No. C1
1960   **Unwmk.**   **Engr.**   *Perf. 13*
C1 AP8 250fr on 500fr grnsh
      blk, blk & sl   7.50 7.50
   17th Olympic Games, Rome, 8/25-9/11.

Helicrysum Mechowiam — AP1

Flowers: 200fr, Cogniauxia podolaena. 500fr, Thesium tencio.

1961, Sept. 28   **Engr.**   *Perf. 13*
C2 AP1 100fr grn, lil & yel   3.25 1.25
C3 AP1 200fr bl grn, yel & brn   5.25 1.75
C4 AP1 500fr brn red, yel & sl
       grn   16.00 5.00
   Nos. C2-C4 (3)   24.50 8.00

Air Afrique Issue
Common Design Type
1961, Nov. 25   **Unwmk.**   *Perf. 13*
C5 CD107 50fr lil rose, sl grn &
       grn   1.25 .50

Loading Timber, Pointe-Noire Harbor — AP2

1962, June 8   **Photo.**   *Perf. 12½x12*
C6 AP2 50fr multicolored   1.50 .90
   Opening of the Intl. Fair and Exhib., Pointe-Noire, June 8-11.

Abidjan Games — AP3

Costus Spectabilis AP4

1962, July 21   *Perf. 12x12½*
C7 AP3 100fr Basketball   2.50 1.25

1963   **Unwmk.**   *Perf. 13*
   Design: 250fr, Mountain acanthus.
C8 AP4 100fr multicolored   4.00 1.75
C9 AP4 250fr multicolored   8.00 3.25

Brazzaville City Hall and Pres. Fulbert Youlou — AP4a

1963, Aug.   **Photo.**   *Perf. 13x12*
C10 AP4a 100fr multicolored   150.00 125.00

African Postal Union Issue
Common Design Type
1963, Sept. 8   *Perf. 12½*
C13 CD114 85fr pur, ocher & red   1.25 .75

Air Afrique Issue, 1963
Common Design Type
     Perf. 13x12
1963, Nov. 19   **Unwmk.**   **Photo.**
C14 CD115 50fr multicolored   .85 .50

Liberty Place, Brazzaville — AP5

1963, Nov. 28
C15 AP5 25fr multicolored   .55 .40
   See No. 118.

Europafrica Issue
Common Design Type
1963, Nov. 30   *Perf. 12x13*
C16 CD116 50fr gray, yel & dk brn   1.25 .90

Timber Industry — AP6

1964, May 12   **Engr.**   *Perf. 13*
C17 AP6 100fr grn, brn red & blk   2.10 .90

Chiefs of State Issue

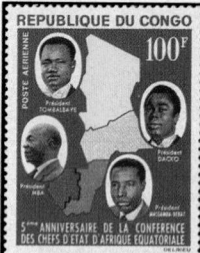

Map and Presidents of Chad, Congo, Gabon and CAR
AP6a

1964, June 23   Photo.   Perf. 12½
C18 AP6a 100fr multicolored   1.40 .80
See note after Central African Republic No. C19.

Europafrica Issue, 1964

Sunburst, Wheat, Cogwheel and Globe — AP7

1964, July 20   Perf. 12x13
C19 AP7 50fr yel, Prus bl & mar 1.00 .75
See note after Cameroun No. 402.

Hammer Thrower, Olympic Flame and Stadium — AP8

50fr, 100fr, vert.

1964, July 30   Engr.   Perf. 13
C20 AP8 25fr shown   .45   .25
C21 AP8 50fr Weight lifter   .80   .45
C22 AP8 100fr Volleyball   1.75 1.00
C23 AP8 200fr High jump   3.25 2.10
a.   Min. sheet of 4, #C20-C23 8.00 8.00
      Nos. C20-C23 (4)   6.25 3.80
18th Olympic Games, Tokyo, 10/10-25/64.

Communications Symbols — AP8a

1964, Nov. 2   Litho.   Perf. 12½x13
C24 AP8a 25fr dl rose & dk brn   .50 .30
See note after Chad No. C19.

Town Hall, Brazzaville — AP9

1965, Jan. 30   Photo.   Perf. 12½
C25 AP9 100fr multicolored   1.25 .60

Coupling Hooks — AP10

1965, Feb. 27   Photo.   Perf. 13x12
C26 AP10 50fr multicolored   1.00 .75
Economic Europe-Africa Association.

Breguet Dial Telegraph, ITU Emblem and Telstar — AP11

1965, May 17   Engr.   Perf. 13
C27 AP11 100fr dk bl, ocher & brn 2.25 .75
Cent. of the ITU.

Pope John XXIII (1881-1963), St. Peter's Cathedral — AP12

Perf. 12½x13
1965, June 26   Photo.   Unwmk.
C28 AP12 100fr gldn brn & multi 1.60 .75

Pres. John F. Kennedy — AP13

Log Rolling — AP14

Portraits: 25fr on 50fr, Patrice Lumumba, premier of Congo Republic (ex-Belgian). 50fr, Sir Winston Churchill. 80fr, Barthélémy Boganda, premier of Central African Republic.

1965, June   Perf. 12½
C29 AP13 25fr on 50fr dk
              brn & red   .50 .40
a.   Surcharge omitted   35.00 35.00
C30 AP13 50fr dk brn &
              yel grn   1.10 1.00
C31 AP13 80fr dk brn & bl   2.00 1.50
C32 AP13 100fr dk brn &
              org yel   2.75 2.25
a.   Min. sheet of 4, #C29-C32 6.25 6.25
      Nos. C29-C32 (4)   6.35 5.15
A second miniature sheet contains one each of Nos. C29a, C30-C32. Value, $50.
Issued: 25fr, 80fr, 6/25; 50fr, 100fr, #C32a, 6/26.

1965, Aug. 14   Engr.   Perf. 13
C33 AP14 50fr grn, brn & red brn .80 .50
Issued to publicize national unity.

World Map and Symbols of Agriculture and Industry — AP15

1965, Oct. 18   Engr.   Perf. 13
C34 AP15 50fr bl, blk, brn &
              org   1.10 .75
International Cooperation Year, 1965.

Abraham Lincoln — AP16

1965, Dec. 15   Photo.   Perf. 13
C35 AP16 90fr pink & multi   1.25 .60
Centenary of death of Abraham Lincoln.

Charles de Gaulle, Torch and Map of Africa — AP17

1966, Feb. 28   Engr.   Perf. 13
C36 AP17 500fr dk red, dk grn
              & dk red brn   35.00 26.00
22nd anniv. of the Brazzaville Conf.

D-1 Satellite over Brazzaville Space Tracking Station — AP18

Grain, Atom Symbol and Map of Africa and Europe — AP19

1966, May 15   Engr.   Perf. 13
C37 AP18 150fr blk, dl red & bl
              grn   2.25 1.25

1966, July 20   Photo.   Perf. 12x13
C38 AP19 50fr multicolored   .90 .50
See note after Gabon No. C46.

Pres. Massamba-Debat and President's Palace — AP20

3rd anniv. of the Revolution: 30fr, Robespierre and storming of the Bastille. 50fr, Lenin and storming of the Winter Palace.

1966, Aug. 15   Photo.   Perf. 12x12½
C39 AP20 25fr multicolored   .25 .20
C40 AP20 30fr multicolored   .35 .25
C41 AP20 50fr multicolored   1.60 .35
a.   Souv. sheet of 3, #C39-C41 2.25 2.25
      Nos. C39-C41 (3)   2.20 .80

Air Afrique Issue, 1966
Common Design Type

1966, Aug. 31   Photo.   Perf. 13
C42 CD123 30fr lilac, lemon & blk .60 .25

Dr. Albert Schweitzer — AP21

1966, Sept. 4   Photo.   Perf. 12½
C43 AP21 100fr red, blk, bl & li-
              lac   2.00 1.25
Issued to honor Dr. Albert Schweitzer (1875-1965), medical missionary.

AP22

AP23

1966, Dec. 26   Photo.   Perf. 13
C44 AP22 100fr Crab, micro-
              scope and pa-
              goda   1.50 1.00

9th Intl. Anticancer Cong., Tokyo. 10/23-29.

1967   Photo.   Perf. 13

Birds: 50fr, Social Weaver. 75fr, European
Bee-eater. 100fr, Lilac-breasted roller. 150fr,
Regal sunbird. 200fr, Crowned cranes. 250fr,
Secretary bird. 300fr, Knysna touraco.

C45 AP23 50fr multicolored   1.50   .60
C46 AP23 75fr multicolored   3.00   .90
C47 AP23 100fr multicolored   3.00   .90
C48 AP23 150fr multicolored   4.00   2.00
C49 AP23 200fr multicolored   7.00   2.40
C50 AP23 250fr multicolored   9.00   2.75
C51 AP23 300fr multicolored   12.50   4.50
      Nos. C45-C51 (7)   40.00 14.05

Issued: #C45-C47, 2/13; others, 6/20.

Shackled
Hands
AP24

1967, May 24   Photo.   Perf. 12½x13
C52 AP24 500fr multicolored   8.50   3.00
       Issued for African Liberation Day.

Sputnik 1, Explorer 6 and
Earth — AP25

Space Craft: 75fr, Ranger 6, Lunik 2 and
moon. 100fr, Mars 1, Mariner 4 and Mars.
200fr, Gemini, Vostok and earth.

1967, Aug. 1   Engr.   Perf. 13
C53 AP25 50fr multicolored   .65   .30
C54 AP25 75fr multicolored   1.10   .35
C55 AP25 100fr multicolored   1.60   .60
C56 AP25 200fr multicolored   2.75   1.50
      Nos. C53-C56 (4)   6.10   2.75
            Space explorations.

African Postal Union Issue, 1967
Common Design Type
1967, Sept. 9   Engr.   Perf. 13
C57 CD124 100fr ver, ol & emer   1.25   .60

Boy Scouts, Tents and Jamboree
Emblem — AP26

Design: 70c, Borah Peak, Idaho; tents,
Scout sign and Jamboree emblem.

1967, Sept. 29
C58 AP26 50fr multicolored   .90   .30
C59 AP26 70fr multicolored   1.25   .50

12th Boy Scout World Jamboree, Farragut
State Park, ID, Aug. 1-9.

Sikorsky S-43 and Map of
Africa — AP27

1967, Oct. 2   Photo.   Perf. 13
C60 AP27 30fr multicolored   .60   .30

30th anniv. of the 1st airmail connection by
Aeromaritime Lines from Casablanca to
Pointe-Noire.

Men of Four Races Dancing on
Globe — AP28

1968, Feb 8   Engr.   Perf. 13
C61 AP28 70fr dk brn, ultra & em-
              er   1.00   .45
        Friendship among peoples.

The Oath of the Horatii, by Jacques
Louis David — AP29

Paintings: 25fr, On the Barricades, by Delacroix. No. C63, Grandfather and Grandson, by
Ghirlandajo, vert. No. C64, The Demolition of
the Bastille, by Hubert Robert. 200fr, Negro
Woman Arranging Peonies, by Jean F. Bazille.

1968   Photo.   Perf. 12x12½, 12½x12
C62 AP29 25fr multicolored   1.75   .35
C63 AP29 30fr multicolored   .90   .30
C64 AP29 30fr multicolored   1.75   .50
C65 AP29 100fr multicolored   2.25   .90
C66 AP29 200fr multicolored   5.00   1.75
      Nos. C62-C66 (5)   11.65   3.80

Issue dates: Nos. C62, C64, Aug. 15. Nos.
C63, C65-C66, Mar. 20.
See Nos. C78-C81, C111-C115.

Early Automobile Type
1968, July 29   Photo.   Perf. 13x12½
C67 A50 150fr Ford, 1915   3.50   1.75
C68 A50 200fr Citroen, 1922   5.25   1.75

Europafrica Issue

Europafrica Issue

Square Knot — AP30

1968, July 20   Photo.   Perf. 13
C69 AP30 50fr multicolored   1.00   .50

5th anniv. of the economic agreement
between the European Economic Community
and the African and Malgache Union.

Martin Luther
King, Jr. — AP31

1968, Aug. 5   Perf. 12½
C70 AP31 50fr lt grn, Prus grn &
              blk   1.10   .40

1968, Sept. 30   Photo.   Perf. 13x12½
C71 AP32 50fr dp car, ap grn & blk .85   .40

Robert F.
Kennedy — AP32

Running — AP33

Olympic Rings and: 20fr, Soccer, vert. 60fr,
Boxing, vert. 85fr, High jump.

1968, Dec. 27   Engr.   Perf. 13
C72 AP33 5fr emer, brt bl &
              choc   .25   .20
C73 AP33 20fr dk bl, brn & dk
              grn   .45   .25
C74 AP33 60fr mar, brt grn &
              choc   .90   .60
C75 AP33 85fr blk, car rose &
              choc   1.75   .85
      Nos. C72-C75 (4)   3.35   1.90

19th Olympic Games, Mexico City, 10/12-27.

PHILEXAFRIQUE Issue

G. De
Gueidan,
by Nicolas
de
Largillière
AP34

1968, Dec. 30   Photo.   Perf. 12½
C76 AP34 100fr pink & multi   3.00   1.75

Issued to publicize PHILEXAFRIQUE, Philatelic Exhibition, in Abidjan, Feb. 14-23. Printed
with alternating pink label.
See Nos. C89-C93.

2nd PHILEXAFRIQUE Issue
Common Design Type
Design: 50fr, Middle Congo No. 72 and
Pointe-Noire harbor.

1969, Feb. 14   Engr.   Perf. 13
C77 CD128 50fr car rose, sl grn
              & bis brn   1.75   1.75

Painting Type of 1968.

Paintings: 25fr, Battle of Rivoli, by Carle
Vernet. 50fr, Battle of Marengo, by Jacques
Augustin Pajou. 75fr, Battle of Friedland, by
Horace Vernet. 100fr, Battle of Jena, by
Charles Thevenin.

1969, May 20   Photo.   Perf. 12x12½
C78 AP29 25fr vio bl & multi   1.25   .45
C79 AP29 50fr cop red & multi   1.75   .80
C80 AP29 75fr grn & multi   3.00   1.10
C81 AP29 100fr brn & multi   5.00   1.40
      Nos. C78-C81 (4)   11.00   3.75

Bicentenary of birth of Napoleon I.

Ernesto Ché
Guevara — AP35

1969, June 10   Photo.   Perf. 12½
C82 AP35 90fr brn, org & blk   1.00   .50

Issued in memory of Ernesto Ché Guevara
(1928-1967), Cuban revolutionist.

Doll, Train and Space Toy — AP36

1969, June 20   Engr.   Perf. 13
C83 AP36 100fr mag, org & gray   1.50   .75

International Toy Fair, Nuremberg, Germany.

Europafrica Issue, 1969

Ribbon Tied Around Bar — AP37

1969, Aug. 5   Photo.   Perf. 13x12
C84 AP37 50fr bl grn, lil & blk   .90   .35
See note after Chad No. C11.

Armstrong, Aldrin and Collins — AP38

Souvenir Sheet

Design: No. C85b, Blast-off from Moon.

Embossed on Gold Foil
1969, Sept. 15   Imperf.
C85 AP38 1000fr #a-b   35.00 35.00
See note after Algeria No. 427. No. C85 contains one each of Nos. C85a and C85b with simulated perforations.

Painter, Poto-Poto School — AP39

150fr, Sculpture lesson (man, infant and sculpture). 200fr, Potter working on vase.

1970, Feb. 20   Engr.   Perf. 13
C86 AP39 100fr multicolored   2.25   .60
C87 AP39 150fr multicolored   3.00   .95
C88 AP39 200fr multicolored   4.50 1.75
      Nos. C86-C88 (3)   9.75 3.30

Painting Type (Philexafrique)

Paintings: 150fr, Child with Cherries, by John Russell. 200fr, Erasmus, by Hans Holbein the Younger. 250fr, "Silence" (head), by Bernardino Luini. 300fr, Scene from the Massacre of Scio, by Delacroix. 500fr, The Capture of Constantinople by the Crusaders, by Delacroix.

1970   Photo.   Perf. 12½
C89 AP34 150fr lil & multi   4.50 1.50
C90 AP34 200fr multicolored   5.75 1.75
C91 AP34 250fr brn & multi   6.25 2.25
C92 AP34 300fr multicolored   8.00 3.25
C93 AP34 500fr brn & multi   13.50 4.50
      Nos. C89-C93 (5)   38.00 13.25

Aurichalcite — AP40

1970, Mar. 20
C94 AP40 100fr shown   5.25 1.75
C95 AP40 150fr Dioptase   8.00 2.50

Lenin — AP41

Karl Marx — AP42

1970, June 25   Photo.   Perf. 12½
C96 AP41 45fr shown   1.00   .35
C97 AP41 75fr Lenin, seated   1.75   .50
Centenary of the birth of Lenin (1870-1924), Russian communist leader.

1970, July 10   Engr.   Perf. 13
Design: No. C99, Friedrich Engels.
C98 AP42 50fr emer, dk brn & dk
             red   1.50   .35
C99 AP42 50fr ultra, dk brn & dk
             red   1.50   .35
Karl Marx (1818-1883) and Friedrich Engels (1820-1895), German socialist writers.

Otto Lilienthal's Glider, 1891 — AP43

Designs: 50fr, "Spirit of St. Louis," Lindbergh's first transatlantic solo flight, 1927. 70fr, Sputnik 1, first satellite in space. 90fr, First man on the moon, Apollo 11, 1969.

1970, Sept. 5   Engr.   Perf. 13
C100 AP43 45fr dp car, bl & ol
             bis   .90   .30
C101 AP43 50fr emer, sl grn &
             brn   .90   .35
C102 AP43 70fr brt bl, ol bis &
             dp car   1.25   .50
C103 AP43 90fr brn, bl & ol gray 1.75   .75
      Nos. C100-C103 (4)   4.80 1.90
Forerunners of space exploration.

Saint on Horseback AP44

Marilyn Monroe and NYC — AP45

Designs from Stained Glass Windows, Brazzaville Cathedral: 150fr, Saint with staff. 250fr, The Elevation of the Host, from rose window.

1970, Dec. 10   Photo.   Perf. 12½
C104 AP44 100fr multicolored   1.40   .50
C105 AP44 150fr multicolored   1.90   .85
C106 AP44 250fr multicolored   3.25 1.75
 a. Souv. sheet of 3, #C104-C106 6.75 6.75
      Nos. C104-C106 (3)   6.55 3.10
Christmas 1970.

1971, Mar. 16   Engr.   Perf. 13
Portraits: 150fr, Martine Carol and Paris. 200fr, Erich von Stroheim and Vienna. 250fr, Sergei Eisenstein and Moscow.
C107 AP45 100fr brt grn, red
             brn & ultra   7.00   .50
C108 AP45 150fr brn, brt lil &
             ultra   7.00   .75
C109 AP45 200fr choc & ultra   7.00 1.10
C110 AP45 250fr brt grn, brn
             vio & ultra   7.00 1.25
      Nos. C107-C110 (4)   28.00 3.60
History of motion pictures.

Painting Type of 1968

Paintings: 100fr, Christ Carrying Cross, by Paolo Veronese. 150fr, Christ on the Cross, Burgundian School, 1500, vert. 200fr, Descent from the Cross, by Rogier van der Weyden. 250fr, Christ Laid in the Tomb, Flemish School, 1500, vert. 500fr, Resurrection, by Hans Memling, vert.

1971, Apr. 26   Photo.   Perf. 13
C111 AP29 100fr green & multi   1.75   .75
C112 AP29 150fr green & multi   2.75   .90
C113 AP29 200fr green & multi   4.00 1.10
C114 AP29 250fr green & multi   4.50 1.60
C115 AP29 500fr green & multi   10.00 3.00
      Nos. C111-C115 (5)   23.00 7.35
Easter 1971.

Map of Africa and Telecommunications System — AP46

1971, June 18   Photo.   Perf. 12½
C116 AP46 70fr bl, gray & dk brn .80   .30
C117 AP46 85fr bl, lil rose & dk
             brn   1.25   .35
C118 AP46 90fr grn, yel & dk brn 1.60   .70
      Nos. C116-C118 (3)   3.65 1.35
Pan-African telecommunications system.

Globe and Waves — AP47

1971, June 19
C119 AP47 65fr lt bl & multi   .70   .30
3rd World Telecommunications Day.

Japanese Mask and Play — AP48

Olympic Torch and Rings — AP49

Design: 150fr, Japanese and African women, symbolic leaves.

1971, June 28   Engr.   Perf. 13
C120 AP48 75fr lil, blk & mag   1.00   .70
C121 AP48 150fr dk brn, brn red
             & red lil   1.60 1.10
PHILATOKYO '71 International Stamp Exhibition, Tokyo, Apr. 20-30.

13th World Boy Scout Jamboree, Japan, gold foil 1000fr airmail and silver foil souv. sheet of four 90fr, issued July 14. Nos. 71C01-71C02.

1971, July 20   Engr.   Perf. 13
350fr, Olympic rings and various sports.
C122 AP49 150fr multi   1.90   .95
C123 AP49 350fr multi, horiz.   4.50 2.50
Pre-Olympic Year, 1971.

Scout Emblem, Japanese Dragon and African Carved Canoe — AP50

Designs (Boy Scout Emblem and): 90fr, Japanese mask and African boy, vert. 100fr, Japanese woman and African drummer, vert. 250fr, Congolese mask.

1971, Aug. 25
C124 AP50 85fr multicolored   1.10   .30
C125 AP50 90fr multicolored   1.25   .35
C126 AP50 100fr multicolored   1.60   .45
C127 AP50 250fr multicolored   3.25   .90
      Nos. C124-C127 (4)   7.20 2.00
13th Boy Scout World Jamboree, Asagiri Plain, Japan, Aug. 2-10.

Olympic Rings and Running — AP51

Designs (Olympic Rings and): 85fr, Hurdles. 90fr, Weight lifting, boxing, discus, running, javelin. 100fr, Wrestling. 150fr, Boxing.

1971, Sept. 30
C128 AP51 75fr plum, bl & dk
             brn   .75   .35
C129 AP51 85fr scar, sl & dk
             brn   .85   .35
C130 AP51 90fr vio bl & dk brn   1.10   .60

C131 AP51 100fr brn & slate 1.40 .60
C132 AP51 150fr grn, red & dk
brn 2.40 1.00
Nos. C128-C132 (5) 6.50 2.90
75th anniv. of the 1st modern Olympic Games.

Congo No. C36 and de Gaulle — AP52

Pres. Marien Ngouabi's Tribute to de Gaulle — AP53

Design: No. C135, Charles de Gaulle.

1971, Nov. 9
C133 AP52 500fr slate grn &
multi 18.00 15.00

Lithographed; Gold Embossed
Perf. 12½
C134 AP53 1000fr gold, grn
& red 27.50 20.00
C135 AP53 1000fr gold, grn
& red 27.50 20.00
a. Pair, #C134-C135 55.00 55.00
Charles de Gaulle (1890-1970), president of France.

African Postal Union Issue, 1971
Common Design Type
Design: 100fr, Allegory of Congo Republic (woman) and UAMPT Building, Brazzaville.

1971, Nov. 13 Photo. Perf. 13x13½
C136 CD135 100fr bl & multi 1.40 .75

Flag of Congo Republic and "Revolution" — AP54

1971, Nov. 30
C137 AP54 100fr red & multi 1.75 .60
8th anniversary of revolution.

Workers and Flag — AP55

40fr, Flag of Congo Republic and sun.

1971, Dec. 31 Photo. Perf. 13x12½
C138 AP55 30fr multicolored .50 .25
C139 AP55 40fr red & multi 1.10 .40
2nd anniv. of founding of Congolese Labor Party (#C138), and adoption of red flag (#C139).

Book Year Emblem — AP56

1972, June 3 Litho. Perf. 12½
C140 AP56 50fr red, grn & yel .85 .40
International Book Year 1972.

Congolese Soccer Team — AP57

#C142, Captain of winning team and cup, vert.

1973, Feb. 22 Photo. Perf. 13
C141 AP57 100fr ultra, red & blk 1.50 .75
C142 AP57 100fr red, yel & blk 1.50 .75

Girl Holding Bird, Environment Emblem — AP58

1973, Mar. 5 Engr.
C143 AP58 85fr org, slate grn &
bl 1.75 .90
UN Conference on Human Environment, Stockholm, Sweden, June 5-16, 1972.

Miles Davis AP59

Designs: 140fr, Ella Fitzgerald. 160fr, Count Basie. 175fr, John Coltrane.

1973, Mar. 5 Photo. Perf. 13x13½
C144 AP59 125fr multicolored 4.00 .95
C145 AP59 140fr multicolored 4.00 1.00
C146 AP59 160fr multicolored 5.00 1.50
C147 AP59 175fr multicolored 5.00 1.50
Nos. C144-C147 (4) 18.00 4.95
Black American jazz musicians.

Olympic Rings, Hurdling — AP60

1973, Mar. 15 Engr. Perf. 13
C148 AP60 100fr shown 1.10 .60
C149 AP60 150fr Pole vault, vert. 1.75 .90
C150 AP60 250fr Wrestling 2.75 1.50
Nos. C148-C150 (3) 5.60 3.00
20th Olympic Games, Munich, 8/26-9/11/72.

Refinery and Storage Tanks, Djéno — AP61

Designs: 230fr, Off-shore drilling platform, vert. 240fr, Workers assembling drill, vert. 260fr, Off-shore drilling installation.

1973, Mar. 20
C151 AP61 180fr red, bl & indi-
go 3.25 1.50
C152 AP61 230fr red, bl & blk 4.00 1.50
C153 AP61 240fr red, ind & brn 4.50 1.60
C154 AP61 260fr red, bl & blk 7.25 2.25
Nos. C151-C154 (4) 19.00 6.85
Oil installations, Pointe-Noire.

Astronauts, Landing Module and Lunar Rover on Moon — AP62

1973, Mar. 31
C155 AP62 250fr multicolored 4.50 1.75
Apollo 17 US moon mission, 12/7-19/72.

ITU Emblem, Symbols of Communications AP63

1973, May 24 Engr. Perf. 13
C156 AP63 120fr multicolored 2.25 .90
5th International Telecommunications Day.

White Horse, by Delacroix — AP64

Designs: Paintings by Eugene Delacroix.

1973, June 30 Photo. Perf. 13
C157 AP64 150fr shown 2.25 1.50
C158 AP64 250fr Lion sleeping 5.00 2.40
C159 AP64 300fr Lion and tiger 5.25 2.50
Nos. C157-C159 (3) 12.50 6.40
See Nos. C169-C171.

Copernicus and Heliocentric System — AP65

1973, June 30 Engr.
C160 AP65 50fr multicolored 1.00 .45
500th anniversary of the birth of Nicolaus Copernicus (1473-1543), Polish astronomer.

Plane, Ship, Rocket, Village, Sun and Clouds — AP66

1973, July
C161 AP66 50fr red & multi 1.40 .60
Cent. of intl. meteorological cooperation.

Pres. Marien Ngouabi — AP67

1973, Aug. 12 Photo. Perf. 13
C162 AP67 30fr multicolored .35 .20
C163 AP67 40fr aqua & multi .45 .20
C164 AP67 75fr red & multi 1.00 .35
Nos. C162-C164 (3) 1.80 .75
10th anniversary of independence.

Stamps, Album, African Woman AP68

40fr, #C167, Stamps in shape of map of Congo, album, globe. #C168, Like 30fr.

1973, Aug. 12
C165 AP68 30fr pur & multi 1.90 .30
C166 AP68 40fr multicolored .25 .20
C167 AP68 100fr dk brn & multi 3.75 .80
C168 AP68 100fr ocher & multi .90 .40
Nos. C165-C168 (4) 6.80 1.70
Nos. C165, C168 for the 10th anniv. of the revolution, Nos. C166-C167 the Intl. Philatelic Exhib., Brazzaville.

Painting Type of 1973 Inscribed "EUROPAFRIQUE"
Designs: Details from "Earth and Paradise," by Jan Brueghel, the Elder.

1973, Oct. 10 Photo. Perf. 13
C169 AP64 100fr Spotted hyena 3.00 1.50
C170 AP64 100fr Leopard and
lion 3.00 1.50
C171 AP64 100fr Elephant and
creatures 3.00 1.50
Nos. C169-C171 (3) 9.00 4.50

US and Russian Spacecraft Docking — AP69

Design: 80fr, US and USSR spacecraft docked in space and emblems of 1975 joint space mission.

1973, Oct. 15 Engr. Perf. 13
C172 AP69 40fr bl, red & brn .50 .35
C173 AP69 80fr red, grn & bl 1.10 .50
Planned joint US and Soviet space missions.

For overprint see No. C251.

UPU Monument, Satellites, Big Dipper — AP70

1973, Nov. 20   Engr.   Perf. 13
C174 AP70 80fr vio bl & lt bl   1.00   .35
Universal Postal Union Day.

Astronauts Working in Space — AP71

40fr, Spacecraft & Skylab docking in space.

1973, Nov. 30
C175 AP71 30fr ultra, sl grn & choc   .60 .20
C176 AP71 40fr mag, org & sl grn   .60 .25
Skylab, first space laboratory.

Goalkeeper, Soccer — AP72

Design: 100fr, Soccer player kicking ball.

1973, Dec. 20
C177 AP72 40fr sl grn, sepia &
            brn   .60   .25
C178 AP72 100fr pur, red & slate
            grn   1.75   .75
World Soccer Cup, Munich, 1974.

John F. Kennedy (1917-1963) AP73

1973, Dec. 20   Photo.   Perf. 12½
C179 AP73 150fr ultra, gold & blk 1.75 .90

Runners — AP74

Flag over Map of Congo — AP75

1973, Dec. 20   Engr.   Perf. 13
C180 AP74 40fr sl grn, red &
            brn   .60   .25
C181 AP74 100fr red, sl grn, &
            brn   1.75   .75
2nd African Games, Lagos, Nigeria.

1973, Dec. 31   Photo.
C182 AP75 40fr dp grn & multi   .50 .25
4th anniversary of Congolese Labor Party and of the Congo Red Flag.

Soccer and Games Emblem — AP76

1974, June 20   Photo.   Perf. 13
C183 AP76 250fr multicolored   3.75 1.90
World Cup Soccer Championship, Munich, June 13-July 7.

Astronauts Yuri A. Gagarin and Alan B. Shepard — AP77

Designs: 30fr, Space, globe, Russian and American flags with names of astronauts who perished in space. 100fr, Alexei Leonov and Neil A. Armstrong in space and on moon.

1974, June 30   Engr.   Perf. 13
C184 AP77 30fr red, ultra & brn   .45   .20
C185 AP77 40fr red, bl & brn   .60   .25
C186 AP77 100fr car, grn & brn   1.40   .90
      Nos. C184-C186 (3)   2.45 1.35
For overprint see No. C254.

Soccer Game Superimposed on Ball — AP78

Link-up Emblem, Stages of Link-up — AP79

1974, July 31   Photo.   Perf. 13
C187 AP78 250fr multicolored   3.50 1.75
Germany's victory in World Cup Soccer Championship.

1974, Aug. 8   Engr.   Perf. 13
300fr, Spacecraft docking over globe.
C188 AP79 200fr pur, bl & red   2.25 1.10
C189 AP79 300fr multi, horiz.   3.50 1.50
Russo-American space cooperation.
For overprint see No. C255.

Symbols of Communications, UPU Emblem — AP80

1974, Aug. 10
C190 AP80 500fr blk & red   6.75 3.00
Centenary of Universal Postal Union.
For surcharge see No. C194.

Lenin and Pendulum Trace Pattern — AP81

1974, Sept. 16   Engr.   Perf. 13
C191 AP81 150fr multicolored   2.10 1.10
Lenin (1870-1924).

Churchill and Order of the Garter AP82

Marconi and Wireless Telegraph AP83

1974, Oct. 1   Litho.   Perf. 13
C192 AP82 200fr lt grn & multi   2.75 1.25
C193 AP83 200fr lt ultra & multi 2.75 1.25

No. C190 Surcharged in Violet Blue with New Value, 2 Bars and: "9 OCTOBER 1974"

1974, Oct. 9
C194 AP80 300fr on 500fr multi   3.50 1.75
Universal Postal Union Day.

UDEAC Issue

Presidents and Flags of Cameroun, CAR, Gabon and Congo — AP83a

1974, Dec. 8   Photo.   Perf. 13
C195 AP83a 100fr gold & multi   1.00 .50
See note after Cameroun No. 595.

Regatta at Argenteuil, by Monet — AP84

Impressionist Paintings: 40fr, Seated Dancer, by Degas. 50fr, Girl on Swing, by Renoir. 75fr, Girl with Straw Hat, by Renoir. All vertical.

1974, Dec. 15
C196 AP84 30fr gold & multi   1.50   .35
C197 AP84 40fr gold & multi   1.75   .35
C198 AP84 50fr gold & multi   2.75   .50
C199 AP84 75fr gold & multi   3.00   .80
      Nos. C196-C199 (4)   9.00 2.00

National Fair AP85

1974, Dec. 20
C200 AP85 30fr multicolored   .90   .35
National Fair, Aug. 24-Sept. 8.

Flags of Participating Nations, Map of Africa — AP86

1974, Dec. 20   Perf. 13
C201 AP86 40fr ultra & multi   .65   .35
Conference of Chiefs of State of Central and East Africa, Brazzaville, Aug. 31-Sept. 2.

"Five Weeks in a Balloon," by Jules Verne AP87

Design: 50fr, "Around the World in 80 Days," by Jules Verne.

1975, June 30   Litho.   Perf. 12½
C202 AP87 40fr multicolored   1.40   .50
C203 AP87 50fr multicolored   1.75 1.00
Jules Verne (1828-1905), French science fiction writer, 70th death anniversary.

Paris-Brussels Train, 1890 — AP88

Design: 75fr, Santa Fe, 1880.

1975, June 30
C204	AP88	50fr ocher & multi	2.00	.75
C205	AP88	75fr lt bl & multi	4.25	.90

Soyuz and Apollo-Soyuz
Emblem — AP89

Design: 100fr, Apollo and emblem.

1975, July 20   Litho.   Perf. 12½
C206	AP89	95fr org, blk & mag	1.25	.50
C207	AP89	100fr vio, bl & blk	1.40	.60

Apollo Soyuz space test project (Russo-American space cooperation), launching July 15; link-up, July 17.
For overprints see Nos. C252-C253.

Bicycling and Montreal Olympic
Emblem — AP90

Designs (Montreal Olympic Emblem and): 40fr, Boxing, vert. 50fr, Basketball, vert. 95fr, High jump. 100fr, Javelin. 150fr, Running.

Perf. 12½x13, 13x12½

1975, Oct. 30   Photo.
C208	AP90	40fr multicolored	.50	.25
C209	AP90	50fr red & multi	.60	.25
C210	AP90	85fr bl & multi	1.00	.35
C211	AP90	95fr org & multi	1.10	.45
C212	AP90	100fr multicolored	1.40	.50
C213	AP90	150fr multicolored	1.75	.80
		Nos. C208-C213 (6)	6.35	2.60

Pre-Olympic Year 1975.

Map of Africa,
Sports and
Flags — AP91

Workers and
Flag — AP92

1975, Dec. 20   Litho.   Perf. 12½
C214	AP91	30fr multicolored	.60	.35

1st African Games, Brazzaville, 10th anniv.

1975, Dec. 31   Litho.   Perf. 12½
C215	AP92	60fr multicolored	.60	.25

Congolese Labor Party (P.C.T.), 6th anniv.

Alphonse Fondere — AP93

Historic Ships: 5fr, like 30fr. 10fr, 40fr, Hamburg, 1839. 15fr, 50fr, Gomer, 1831. 20fr, 60fr, Great Eastern, 1858. 95fr, J.M. White II, 1878.

1976   Engr.   Perf. 13
C216	AP93	5fr multicolored	.25	.20
C217	AP93	10fr multicolored	.25	.20
C218	AP93	15fr multicolored	.25	.20
C219	AP93	20fr multicolored	.45	.20
C220	AP93	30fr multicolored	.60	.25
C221	AP93	40fr multicolored	.90	.35
C222	AP93	50fr multicolored	.90	.50
C223	AP93	60fr multicolored	1.40	.50
C224	AP93	95fr multicolored	2.00	.80
		Nos. C216-C224 (9)	7.00	3.20

Issued: #C216-C219, May; #C220-C224, Mar. 7.

Europafrica Issue 1976

Peasant Family, by Louis Le
Nain — AP94

Paintings: 80fr, Boy with Top, by Jean B. Chardin. 95fr, Venus and Aeneas, by Nicolas Poussin. 100fr, The Rape of the Sabine Women, by Jacques Louis David.

1976, Mar. 20   Litho.   Perf. 12½
C225	AP94	60fr gold & multi	1.25	.45
C226	AP94	80fr gold & multi	1.40	.70
C227	AP94	95fr gold & multi	1.90	.70
C228	AP94	100fr gold & multi	2.10	.85
		Nos. C225-C228 (4)	6.65	2.70

Nos. C225-C228 printed in sheets of 8 stamps and horizontal gutter with commemorative inscription.

Telephone Type of 1976
1976, Apr. 25   Litho.   Perf. 12½x13
C229	A107	60fr pink, mar & crim	.90	.30

Sports Type of 1976
Designs: 150fr, Runner and map of Central Africa. 200fr, Discus and map.

1976, Oct. 25   Perf. 12½
C230	A110	150fr multicolored	1.75	.75
C231	A110	200fr multicolored	2.75	1.10

Map of Africa, Flag
and OAU
Headquarters
AP95

1976, Dec. 16   Typo.   Perf. 13x14
C232	AP95	60fr multicolored	.70	.35

13th anniv. of the Organization for African Unity.

Europafrica Issue

Map of Europe and Africa — AP96

1977, June 28   Litho.   Perf. 13
C233	AP96	75fr multicolored	.90	.45

Headdress Type of 1977
1977, June 30   Perf. 12½
250fr, Two straw caps. 300fr, Beaded cap.
C234	A118	250fr multicolored	2.75	1.50
C235	A118	300fr multicolored	3.00	1.75

Zeppelin Type of 1977
Souvenir Sheet
Design: 500fr, LZ 127 over US Capitol.

1977, Aug. 5   Litho.   Perf. 11
C236	A120	500fr multicolored	6.75	2.00

No. C236 exists imperf.

Checkerboard
AP97

1977, Aug. 20   Engr.   Perf. 13
C237	AP97	60fr red & blk	.90	.35

Lomé Convention on General Agreement on Tariffs and Trade (GATT).

Newton, Intelsat Satellite and Classical
"Planets" — AP98

1977, Aug. 25
C238	AP98	140fr multicolored	2.00	.90

Isaac Newton (1642-1727), natural philosopher and mathematician.

Elizabeth II Type of 1977
Souvenir Sheet
Design: 500fr, Royal family on balcony.

1977, Dec. 21   Litho.   Perf. 14
C239	A128	500fr multicolored	5.75	1.75

For overprint see No. C244.

Mallard
AP99

Birds: 75fr, Purple heron, vert. 150fr, Reed warbler, vert. 240fr, Hoopoe, vert.

1978, May 22   Perf. 13x12½, 12½x13
C240	AP99	65fr multicolored	1.00	.50
C241	AP99	75fr multicolored	1.25	.50
C242	AP99	150fr multicolored	3.00	.90
C243	AP99	240fr multicolored	4.50	1.60
		Nos. C240-C243 (4)	9.75	3.50

Souvenir Sheet
No. C239 Overprinted in Silver:
"ANNIVERSAIRE DU /
COURONNEMENT / 1953-1978"

1978, Sept.   Litho.   Perf. 14
C244	A128	500fr multicolored	4.50	3.00

25th anniv. of coronation of Elizabeth II.

Philexafrique II-Essen Issue
Common Design Types
No. C245, Leopard and Congo No. C243.
No. C246, Eagle and Wurttemberg No. 1.

1978, Nov. 1   Litho.   Perf. 12½
C245	CD138	100fr multicolored	2.00	1.10
C246	CD139	100fr multicolored	2.00	1.10
a.		Pair, #C245-C246	5.25	5.25

Map of Africa,
Satellites
AP100

Map of Africa and
People — AP101

1978, Nov. 25   Engr.   Perf. 13
C247	AP100	100fr multicolored	1.25	.50

Pan-African Telecommunications Network, PANAFEL.

1979, Aug. 2   Litho.   Perf. 12½
C248	AP101	45fr multicolored	.50	.25
C249	AP101	75fr multicolored	.85	.40

5th Conference of Panafrican Youth Movement, Brazzaville, Aug. 2-7.

Abala
Peasant
Woman
AP102

1979, Aug. 20
C250	AP102	150fr multicolored	1.75	.90

Nos. C173, C206-C207, C186, C189
Overprinted "ALUNISSAGE APOLLO
XI / JUILLET 1969" and Emblem

Perf. 13, 12½

1979, Nov. 5   Engr., Litho.
C251	AP69	80fr multicolored	.90	.90
C252	AP89	95fr multicolored	1.00	1.00
C253	AP89	100fr multicolored	1.00	1.00
C254	AP77	100fr multicolored	1.00	1.00
C255	AP79	300fr multicolored	2.75	2.75
		Nos. C251-C255 (5)	6.65	6.65

Apollo 11 moon landing, 10th anniversary.

Runner, Olympic Rings — AP103

Pre-Olympic Year: 100fr, Boxing. 200fr, Fencing. 300fr, Soccer. 500fr, Moscow '80 emblem.

		1979	Litho.	Perf. 13½	
C256	AP103	65fr multi		.50	.20
C257	AP103	100fr multi		1.00	.25
C258	AP103	200fr multi, vert.		2.00	.50
C259	AP103	300fr multi		2.50	.75
C260	AP103	500fr multi, vert.		5.00	1.25
		Nos. C256-C260 (5)		11.00	2.95

Cross-Country Skiing — AP104

Lake Placid '80 Emblem and: 60fr, Slalom. 200fr, Ski jump, 350fr, Downhill skiing, horiz. 500fr, Woman skier.

1979, Dec   **Perf. 14½**
Size: 24x42mm, 42x24mm

C261	AP104	40fr multicolored	.45	.20
C262	AP104	60fr multicolored	.60	.20
C263	AP104	200fr multicolored	2.00	.45
C264	AP104	350fr multicolored	3.50	.90

Size: 31½x46½mm
Perf. 14

C265	AP104	500fr multicolored	5.00	1.40
		Nos. C261-C265 (5)	11.55	3.15

13th Winter Olympic Games, Lake Placid, NY, Feb. 12-24, 1980.

Overprinted with Names of Winners

1980, Apr. 28				
C266	AP104	40fr Zimiatov	.40	.20
C267	AP104	60fr Moser-Proell	.50	.25
C268	AP104	200fr Tomanen	1.90	.75
C269	AP104	350fr Stock	3.50	1.25
C270	AP104	500fr Stenmark-Wenzel	4.75	1.90
		Nos. C266-C270 (5)	11.05	4.35

Long Jump, Olympic Rings — AP105

1980, May 2		Litho.	Perf. 14½	
C271	AP105	75fr multi, vert.	.90	.20
C272	AP105	150fr multi	1.40	.30
C273	AP105	250fr multi, vert.	2.25	.50
C274	AP105	350fr multi, vert.	3.25	.70
		Nos. C271-C274 (4)	7.80	1.70

Souvenir Sheet

C275	AP105	500fr multicolored	5.00	1.60

22nd Summer Olympic Games, Moscow, July 19-Aug. 3.
For overprints see Nos. C292-C296.

Stadium, Mascot, Madrid Club Emblem — AP106

Stadium, Mascot and Club Emblem: 75fr, Zaragoza. 100fr, Madrid Athletic Club. 150fr, Valencia. 175fr, Spain. 250fr, Barcelona.

1980, June 23		Litho.	Perf. 14x13½	
C276	AP106	60fr multicolored	.60	.20
C277	AP106	75fr multicolored	.60	.20
C278	AP106	100fr multicolored	1.00	.25

C279	AP106	150fr multicolored	1.40	.35
C280	AP106	175fr multicolored	1.60	.50
		Nos. C276-C280 (5)	5.20	1.50

Souvenir Sheet

C281	AP106	250fr multicolored	2.25	.80

World Soccer Cup 1982.
For overprints see Nos. C298-C303.

Adoration of the Shepherds — AP107

Rembrandt Paintings: 100fr, The Burial. 200fr, Christ at Emmaus. 300fr, Annunciation, vert. 500fr, Crucifixion, vert.

1980, July 4			Perf. 12½	
C282	AP107	65fr multicolored	.60	.25
C283	AP107	100fr multicolored	.90	.35
C284	AP107	200fr multicolored	1.60	.55
C285	AP107	300fr multicolored	2.50	.75
C286	AP107	500fr multicolored	5.25	1.25
		Nos. C282-C286 (5)	10.85	3.15

Albert Camus (1913-1960), Writer — AP108

Design: 150fr, Jacques Offenbach (1819-1880), composer, vert.

1980, July 5		Engr.	Perf. 13	
C287	AP108	100fr multicolored	1.25	.50
C288	AP108	150fr multicolored	2.25	1.25

Raffia Dancing Skirts — AP109

Traditional Dancing Costumes: 300fr, Tam-tam dancers, vert. 350fr, Masks.

1980, Aug. 6		Litho.	Perf. 13½	
C289	AP109	250fr multicolored	2.75	.95
C290	AP109	300fr multicolored	3.25	1.50
C291	AP109	350fr multicolored	4.00	1.90
		Nos. C289-C291 (3)	10.00	4.35

Nos. C271-C275 Overprinted with Winner and Country

1980, Nov. 14		Litho.	Perf. 14½	
C292	AP105	75fr multicolored	.70	.30
C293	AP105	150fr multicolored	1.40	.60
C294	AP105	250fr multicolored	2.25	.90
C295	AP105	350fr multicolored	3.25	1.50
		Nos. C292-C295 (4)	7.60	3.30

Souvenir Sheet

C296	AP105	500fr multicolored	5.00	4.00

The Studio by Picasso — AP109a

1981, July 4			Perf. 12½	
C296A	AP109a	100fr shown	1.10	.50
C296B	AP109a	150fr Landscape	1.60	.75

C296C	AP109a	200fr Cannes Studio	2.10	1.00
C296D	AP109a	300fr Still Life	3.50	1.50
C296E	AP109a	500fr Still Life, diff.	6.00	2.50
		Nos. C296A-C296E (5)	14.30	6.25

1st Seminar on Petroleum, Gas and Energy Alternatives, Brazzaville AP109b

45fr, Emblem, oil platform, other energy sources. 150fr, Map, other energy sources. 200fr, Maps of Africa, Congo, oil worker.

1981		Litho.	Perf. 12½	
C296F	AP109b	45fr multi	20.00	13.00
C296G	AP109b	75fr multi	32.50	19.00
C296I	AP109b	150fr multi	65.00	40.00
C296J	AP109b	200fr multi	90.00	50.00

A number has been reserved for an additional stamp in this set. The editors would like to examine any examples.

1350th Anniv. of Mohamed's Death at Medina — AP110

1982, July 17		Litho.	Perf. 13	
C297	AP110	400fr Medina Mosque minaret	3.75	1.75

Nos. C276-C281 Overprinted with Finalists and/or Scores in Black on Silver

1982, Oct. 7		Litho.	Perf. 14x13½	
C298	AP106	60fr multicolored	.50	.25
C299	AP106	75fr multicolored	.60	.30
C300	AP106	100fr multicolored	.90	.45
C301	AP106	150fr multicolored	1.40	.60
C302	AP106	175fr multicolored	1.50	.60
		Nos. C298-C302 (5)	4.90	2.20

Souvenir Sheet

C303	AP106	250fr multicolored	2.25	1.90

30th Anniv. of Amelia Earhart's Transatlantic Flight — AP111

1982, Dec. 4		Engr.	Perf. 13	
C304	AP111	150fr multicolored	1.25	.75

Wind Surfing AP112

Various wind surfing scenes, 1984 Olympic Games, 100fr, 300fr, 400fr vert.

1983, June 4		Litho.	Perf. 13	
C305	AP112	100fr multicolored	.90	.25
C306	AP112	200fr multicolored	1.75	.50
C307	AP112	300fr multicolored	2.75	.70
C308	AP112	400fr multicolored	3.50	1.00
		Nos. C305-C308 (4)	8.90	2.45

Souvenir Sheet

C309	AP112	500fr multicolored	5.00	2.50

For overprint see No. C336.

Manned Flight Bicentenary AP113

Various balloons.

1983, June 7				
C310	AP113	100fr Montgolfiere, 1783	1.10	.20
C311	AP113	200fr Flesselles, 1784	2.10	.40
C312	AP113	300fr Auguste Piccard, 1931	3.00	.60
C313	AP113	400fr Don Piccard	4.50	.90
		Nos. C310-C313 (4)	10.70	2.10

Souvenir Sheet

C314	AP113	500fr Mail transport balloon, 1870	5.75	1.60

For overprint see No. C337.

Christmas 1983 AP114

Various Virgin and Child Paintings by Botticelli.

1984, Jan. 21		Litho.	Perf. 13	
C315	AP114	150fr multicolored	1.25	.50
C316	AP114	350fr multicolored	3.00	1.10
C317	AP114	500fr multicolored	4.50	1.50
		Nos. C315-C317 (3)	8.75	3.10

Vase of Flowers, by Manet (1832-83) AP115

Paintings: 200fr, Small Holy Family, by Raphael. 300fr, La Belle Jardiniere, by Raphael. 400fr, Virgin of Loretto, by Raphael. 500fr, Portrait of Richard Wagner (1813-83), by Giuseppe Tivoli.

1984, Feb. 24		Litho.	Perf. 13	
C318	AP115	100fr multicolored	.90	.30
C319	AP115	200fr multicolored	1.90	.70
C320	AP115	300fr multicolored	2.75	1.00
C321	AP115	400fr multicolored	3.75	1.40
C322	AP115	500fr multicolored	5.00	1.50
		Nos. C318-C322 (5)	14.30	4.90

1984 Summer Olympics — AP116

1984, Mar. 31   **Perf. 13**
C323	AP116	45fr Judo, vert.	.45	.20
C324	AP116	75fr Judo, diff.	.70	.25
C325	AP116	150fr Wrestling	1.40	.50
C326	AP116	175fr Fencing	1.60	.60
C327	AP116	350fr Fencing, diff.	3.25	1.10
		Nos. C323-C327 (5)	7.40	2.65

Souvenir Sheet
C328	AP116	500fr Boxing	5.00	2.50

1984 Summer Olympic Gold
Medalists — AP117

Sailing/yachting: 100fr, Stephan Van Den Berg, Netherlands, Windglider Class. 150fr, US, Soling Class. 200fr, Spain, 470 Class. 500fr, US, Flying Dutchman Class.

1984, Dec. 18   **Litho.**   **Perf. 13**
C329	AP117	100fr multi, vert.	1.00	.45
C330	AP117	150fr multi	1.40	.65
C331	AP117	200fr multi	2.00	.90
C332	AP117	500fr multi, vert.	4.50	2.25
		Nos. C329-C332 (4)	8.90	4.25

Virgin and Child, by Giovanni Bellini
(c. 1430-1516) — AP118

Religious paintings: 100fr, Holy Family, by Andrea del Sarto (1486-1530). 400fr, Virgin with Angels, by Cimabue (c. 1240-1302).

1985, Feb. 12   **Litho.**   **Perf. 13**
C333	AP118	100fr multi, vert.	1.00	.45
C334	AP118	200fr multi	2.00	.90
C335	AP118	400fr multi, vert.	3.75	1.75
		Nos. C333-C335 (3)	6.75	3.10

Christmas 1984.

Souvenir Sheets
Nos. C309, C314 Ovptd. with
Exhibition in Blue or Green

1985, Mar. 8   **Perf. 13**
C336	AP112	500fr OLYMPHILEX '85 / LAU-SANNE (B)	5.00	4.00
C337	AP113	500fr MOPHILA '85 / HAM-BURG (G)	5.00	4.00

Audubon Birth Bicentenary — AP119

Illustrations of North American bird species by Audubon. Nos. C338-C339 vert.

1985, Apr. 11   **Perf. 13½**
C338	AP119	100fr Passiformes fringillidae	1.00	.45
C339	AP119	150fr Eudocimus ruber	1.50	.65
C340	AP119	200fr Buteo jama-icensis	1.90	.90
C341	AP119	350fr Camptorhynchus labradorius	3.75	1.50
		Nos. C338-C341 (4)	8.15	3.50

PHILEXAFRICA '85, Lome — AP120

Youths in public service activities.

1985, May 20   **Perf. 13**
C342	AP120	200fr Community health care	2.25	1.50
C343	AP120	200fr Agriculture	2.25	1.50
a.		Pair, #C342-C343 + label	5.75	5.75

Admission to UN, 25th
Anniv. — AP121

1985, Aug. 13
C344	AP121	190fr multicolored	1.75	.75

UN, 40th
Anniv. — AP122

1985, Oct. 25   **Perf. 12½**
C345	AP122	180fr Rainbow, emblem	1.60	.65

Christmas — AP123

Paintings: 100fr, The Virgin and the Infant Jesus, by David. 200fr, Adoration of the Magi, by Hieronymus Bosch (1450-1516). 400fr, Virgin and Child, by Van Dyck.

1985, Dec. 20   **Litho.**   **Perf. 13**
C346	AP123	100fr multicolored	.90	.35
C347	AP123	200fr multicolored	1.90	.75
C348	AP123	400fr multicolored	3.50	1.75
		Nos. C346-C348 (3)	6.30	2.85

Nos. C346-C347 vert.

Halley's Comet — AP124

1986, Feb. 17
C349	AP124	125fr Halley, comet	1.00	.50
C350	AP124	150fr West's Comet, 1976	1.25	.60
C351	AP124	225fr Ikeya Seki's Comet, 1965	1.75	.90
C352	AP124	300fr Trajectory diagram	2.25	1.25
C353	AP124	350fr Comet, Vega probe	2.75	1.50
		Nos. C349-C353 (5)	9.00	4.75

Nos. C350-C351 vert.

Cosmos-Frantel Hotel — AP125

1986, May 1   **Perf. 13½**
C354	AP125	250fr multicolored	2.25	.90

1986 World Cup Soccer
Championships, Mexico — AP126

Various soccer plays.

1986, July 22   **Litho.**   **Perf. 13**
C355	AP126	150fr multicolored	1.25	.60
C356	AP126	250fr multicolored	2.00	1.00
C357	AP126	440fr multicolored	3.75	1.75
C358	AP126	600fr multicolored	6.50	2.50
		Nos. C355-C358 (4)	13.50	5.85

Air Africa, 25th
Anniv. — AP127

1986, Nov. 29   **Litho.**   **Perf. 13½**
C359	AP127	200fr multicolored	1.75	.75

1988 Winter Pre-Olympics,
Calgary — AP128

1986, Dec. 15   **Perf. 13**
C360	AP128	150fr Downhill skiing	1.25	.60
C361	AP128	250fr Bobsled	2.25	.95
C362	AP128	440fr Women's cross-country skiing	4.00	1.50
C363	AP128	600fr Ski jumping	5.75	2.40
		Nos. C360-C363 (4)	13.25	5.45

Nos. C361-C362 vert.

Christmas
AP129

Paintings by Rogier van der Weyden (c.1399-1464): 250fr, Virgin and Child. 440fr, The Nativity. 500fr, Virgin with Carnation.

1986, Dec. 23   **Perf. 13½**
C364	AP129	250fr multicolored	2.25	1.00
C365	AP129	440fr multicolored	4.50	1.75
C366	AP129	500fr multicolored	5.00	2.10
		Nos. C364-C366 (3)	11.75	4.85

Crocodiles, World Wildlife
Fund — AP130

1987, Jan. 22   **Perf. 13**
C367	AP130	75fr Osteolaemus tetraspis	2.50	1.00
C368	AP130	100fr Crocodylus cataphractus	3.00	1.10
C369	AP130	125fr Osteolaemus tetraspis, diff.	4.00	1.60
C370	AP130	150fr Crocodylus cataphractus, diff.	4.50	2.75
		Nos. C367-C370 (4)	14.00	6.45

1988 Summer Olympics,
Seoul — AP131

1987, July 11   **Litho.**   **Perf. 13**
C371	AP131	100fr Backstroke	.90	.35
C372	AP131	200fr Freestyle	1.75	.75
C373	AP131	300fr Breaststroke	2.75	1.10
C374	AP131	400fr Butterfly	3.50	1.40
		Nos. C371-C374 (4)	8.90	3.60

Souvenir Sheet
C375	AP131	750fr Start of event	6.75	3.50

Launch of Sputnik, First Artificial
Satellite, 30th Anniv. — AP132

1987, June 5   **Perf. 12½x12**
C376	AP132	60fr multicolored	.50	.25
C377	AP132	240fr multicolored	2.25	1.10

Butterflies — AP133

1987, Sept. 4   **Perf. 12½**
C378 AP133 75fr Precis
                   epicleli   1.00   .30
C379 AP133 120fr Deilephila
                   nerii   1.75   .45
C380 AP133 450fr Euryphene
                   senegalen-
                   sis   5.25 1.75
C381 AP133 550fr Precis al-
                   manta   7.00 2.40
     Nos. C378-C381 (4)   15.00 4.90

Coubertin, Eternal Flame and Greece
No. 125 — AP134

Cameo portrait, athletes and stamps: 120fr, Runners, France No. 198. 350fr, Congo Republic No. C22, hurdler. 600fr, High jump, Congo Republic No. C75.

1987, Nov. 4
C382 AP134 75fr shown   .80   .30
C383 AP134 120fr multicolored   1.10   .45
C384 AP134 350fr multicolored   3.50 1.25
C385 AP134 600fr multicolored   5.25 2.10
     Nos. C382-C385 (4)   10.65 4.10

Pierre de Coubertin (1863-1937), promulgator of the modern Olympics.

Arrival of Schweitzer in Lambarene,
75th Anniv. — AP135

1988, Apr. 17   Litho.   Perf. 12½
C386 AP135 240fr multicolored   2.75 1.25

Dr. Albert Schweitzer (1875-1965), Nobel Peace Prize winner of 1952, founded Lambarene Hospital, Gabon, in 1913.

1988 Summer Olympics,
Seoul — AP136

Pentathlon: 75fr, Swimming. 170fr, Cross-country running, vert. 200fr, Shooting. 600fr, Equestrian. 700fr, Fencing.

1988, June 10   Litho.   Perf. 13
C387 AP136 75fr multicolored   .70   .25
C388 AP136 170fr multicolored   1.60   .60
C389 AP136 200fr multicolored   1.75   .70
C390 AP136 600fr multicolored   5.00 2.00
     Nos. C387-C390 (4)   9.05 3.55

Souvenir Sheet

C391 AP136 750fr multicolored   6.75 3.75

Elimination Matches, 1990 World Cup
Soccer Championships — AP137

Various athletes and cities in Italy.

1989, June 15   Litho.   Perf. 13
C392 AP137 75fr Bari   .60   .30
C393 AP137 120fr Rome   1.00   .45
C394 AP137 500fr Florence   4.75 1.90
C395 AP137 550fr Naples   5.25 2.00
     Nos. C392-C395 (4)   11.60 4.65

PHILEXFRANCE '89 — AP138

Paintings: 300fr, Storming of the Bastille, July 14, 1789, from a gouache by J.P. Houel. 400fr, Eiffel Tower, by G. Seurat.

1989, June 22
C396 AP138 300fr multicolored   2.75 1.10
C397 AP138 400fr multicolored   3.75 1.50

French revolution, bicent. (300fr); Eiffel Tower, cent. (400fr).

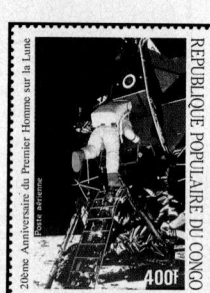

First Moon
Landing,
20th Anniv.
AP139

Man's first step on the Moon: No. C398, Astronaut on ladder. No. C399, Conducting experiments on the Moon's surface.

1989, June 22
C398 AP139 400fr multicolored   3.75 1.50
C399 AP139 400fr multicolored   3.75 1.50

World Cup Soccer Championships,
Italy — AP140

Various soccer plays and architecture.

1990, June 8   Litho.   Perf. 13
C400 AP140 120fr multicolored   1.00   .50
C401 AP140 240fr multicolored   2.10   .95
C402 AP140 500fr multicolored   4.25 2.00
C403 AP140 600fr multicolored   5.25 2.40
     Nos. C400-C403 (4)   12.60 5.85

Pan African
Postal Union,
10th Anniv.
AP141

1991, Jan. 10   Litho.   Perf. 13½
C404 AP141 60fr shown   .50   .25
C405 AP141 120fr Emblem   .95   .50

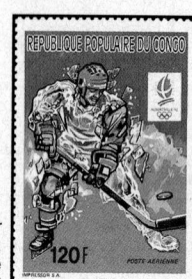

1992 Winter
Olympics,
Albertville
AP142

1991, June 8   Litho.   Perf. 13½
C406 AP142 120fr Ice hockey   1.40   .60
C407 AP142 300fr Speed
                   skating   3.00 1.50

Litho. & Embossed

C408 AP142 1500fr Slalom
                    skiing   15.00 15.00

Numbers have been reserved for souvenir sheets in this set.

1992
Summer
Olympics,
Barcelona
AP143

#C411, Equestrian. #C412, Long jump.

1992   Litho. & Embossed   Perf. 13½
C411 AP143 1500fr gold &
                    multi   16.00 16.00

Souvenir Sheet

C412 AP143 1500fr gold &
                    multi   21.00 21.00

Anniversaries
AP144

Designs: 90fr, Victor Schoelcher, missionary, death cent. 205fr, Martin Luther King, civil rights reformer, 25th death anniv. 300fr, Claude Chappe (1763-1805), bicent. of visual telegraph.

1993   Litho.   Perf. 14
C413 AP144 90fr multicolored   1.00 .50
C414 AP144 205fr multicolored   2.50 1.25
C415 AP144 300fr multicolored   3.50 1.75
     Nos. C413-C415 (3)   7.00 3.50

1994 Winter
Olympics,
Lillehammer
AP145

1993, Apr. 26   Litho.   Perf. 13
C416 AP145 400fr Ice dancing   3.50 1.40
C417 AP145 600fr Ice hockey   6.00 1.75

Souvenir Sheet

C418 AP145 750fr Downhill ski-
                   ing   7.00 4.00

Nos. C416-C417 exist in imperf. souvenir sheets of 1. Nos. C416-C418 exist imperf.

AIR POST SEMI-POSTAL STAMPS

Hathor
Pillar — SPAP1

Unwmk.

1964, Mar. 9   Engr.   Perf. 13
CB1 SPAP1 10fr + 5fr vio & chnt   .45   .30
CB2 SPAP1 25fr + 5fr org brn &
                   slate grn   .70   .60
CB3 SPAP1 50fr + 5fr slate grn &
                   brn red   1.90 1.60
    Nos. CB1-CB3 (3)   3.05 2.50

UNESCO world campaign to save historic monuments in Nubia.

POSTAGE DUE STAMPS

Messenger — D6

MH. 1521 Broussard Plane — D7

Early Transportation: 1fr, Litter. 2fr, Canoe. 5fr, Bicyclist. 10fr, Steam locomotive. 25fr, Seaplane.

Unwmk.

1961, Dec. 4   Engr.   Perf. 11
J34 D6 50c ultra, ol bis & red   .20   .20
  a.   Pair, #J34, J40   .25
J35 D6 1fr red brn, red & grn   .20   .20
  a.   Pair, #J35, J41   .30
J36 D6 2fr grn, ultra & brn   .20   .20
  a.   Pair, #J36, J42   .40
J37 D6 5fr pur & gray brn   .25   .25
  a.   Pair, #J37, J43   .50
J38 D6 10fr bl, grn & chocolate   .70   .70
  a.   Pair, #J38, J44   1.40 1.40
J39 D6 25fr bl, dk grn & dk brn   1.60 1.60
  a.   Pair, #J39, J45   3.25

Modern transportation: 1fr, Land Rover. 2fr, River boat transporting barge. 5fr, Trailer-truck. 10fr, Diesel locomotive. 25fr, Boeing 707 jet plane.

J40	D7	50c ultra, olive bis & red	.20	.20
J41	D7	1fr red & grn	.20	.20
J42	D7	2fr ultra, grn & brn	.20	.20
J43	D7	5fr pur & gray brn	.25	.25
J44	D7	10fr dk grn & chocolate	.70	.70
J45	D7	25fr bl, dk grn & sepia	1.60	1.60
		Nos. J34-J45 (12)	6.30	6.30

Pairs printed tête bêche, se-tenant at the base.

Flowers — D8

Flowers: 2fr, Phaeomeria magnifica. 5fr, Millettia laurentii. 10fr, Tuberose. 15fr, Pyrostegia venusta. 20fr, Hibiscus.

1971, Mar. 25 Photo. Perf. 12x12½

J46	D8	1fr multi	.35	.35
J47	D8	2fr multi	.45	.45
J48	D8	5fr pink & multi	.50	.50
J49	D8	10fr dk grn & multi	.60	.60
J50	D8	15fr multi	1.00	1.00
J51	D8	20fr multi	1.25	1.25
		Nos. J46-J51 (6)	4.15	4.15

Flowers and Fruit — D9

1986, June 5 Litho. Perf. 13

J52	D9	5fr Passiflora quadrangulares	.25	.25
J53	D9	10fr Cannaceae, vert.	.45	.45
J54	D9	15fr Ananas comosus, vert.	.55	.55
		Nos. J52-J54 (3)	1.25	1.25

OFFICIAL STAMPS

Coat of Arms — O1

Perf. 14x13

1968-70		**Unwmk.**		**Typo.**
O1	O1	1fr multi ('70)	.20	.20
O2	O1	2fr multi ('70)	.20	.20
O3	O1	5fr multi ('70)	.20	.20
O4	O1	10fr multi ('70)	.25	.20
O5	O1	25fr emer & multi	.45	.20
O6	O1	30fr red & multi	.60	.20
O7	O1	50fr multi ('70)	1.10	.50
O8	O1	85fr multi ('70)	2.25	.90
O9	O1	100frmulti ('70)	2.75	1.10
O10	O1	200frmulti ('70)	3.75	2.00
		Nos. O1-O10 (10)	11.75	5.70

COOK ISLANDS

ˈkuk ˈī-lənds

(Rarotonga)

LOCATION — South Pacific Ocean, northeast of New Zealand
GOVT. — Internal self-government, linked to New Zealand
AREA — 91 sq. mi.
POP. — 19,103 (1996)
CAPITAL — Avarua

Fifteen islands in Northern and Southern groups extend over 850,000 square miles of ocean.

Separate stamp issues used by Aitutaki (1903-32 and 1972 onward)

and Penrhyn Islands (1902-32 and 1973 onward). Niue is included geographically, but administered separately. It continues to issue separate stamps.

12 Pence = 1 Shilling
20 Shillings = 1 Pound
100 Cents = 1 Dollar (1967)

Catalogue values for unused stamps in this country are for Never Hinged items, beginning with Scott 127 in the regular postage section, Scott B1 in the semipostal section, Scott C1 in the air post section, Scott CB1 in the air post semi-postal section and Scott O16 in the official section.

Watermarks

Wmk. 61 — Single-lined N Z and Star Close Together

Wmk. 62 — Single-lined N Z and Star Wide Apart

Wmk. 253 — Multiple N Z and Star

A1

1892 Unwmk. Typo. Perf. 12½
Toned Paper

1	A1	1p black	32.50	30.00
2	A1	1 ½p violet	47.50	45.00
a.		Imperf, pair	19,000.	
3	A1	2 ½p blue	47.50	45.00
4	A1	10p carmine	160.00	150.00
		Nos. 1-4 (4)	287.50	270.00

White Paper

5	A1	1p black	32.50	30.00
a.		Vert. pair, imperf. between	11,000.	
6	A1	1 ½p violet	47.50	45.00
7	A1	2 ½p blue	47.50	45.00
8	A1	10p carmine	160.00	150.00
		Nos. 5-8 (4)	287.50	270.00

Queen Makea Takau — A2

Wrybill (Torea) — A3

1893-94 Wmk. 62 Perf. 12x11½

9	A2	1p brown	47.50	52.50
10	A2	1p blue ('94)	13.00	2.50
11	A2	1 ½p brt violet	11.00	8.50
12	A2	2 ½p rose	47.50	27.50
13	A2	5p olive gray	22.50	16.00
14	A2	10p green	82.50	57.50
		Nos. 9-14 (6)	224.00	164.50

Perf. 12½ examples of Nos. 10, 12 are from a part of the normal perf. 12x11½ sheets. They were caused by a partial deviation of the original perforating.

1898-1900 Perf. 11

15	A3	½p blue ('00)	6.50	9.00
a.		"d" omitted at upper right	1,750.	
16	A2	1p brown	22.50	21.00
17	A2	1p blue	6.00	5.50
18	A2	1 ½p violet	10.50	7.50
19	A3	2p chocolate	10.50	8.25
20	A2	2 ½p car rose	22.50	10.50
21	A2	5p olive gray	27.50	21.00
22	A3	6p red violet	22.50	29.00
23	A2	10p green	21.00	57.50
24	A3	1sh car rose	57.50	57.50
		Nos. 15-24 (10)	207.00	226.75

No. 17 Surcharged in Black

1899

25	A2	½p on 1p blue	40.00	50.00
a.		Double surcharge	1,200.	1,050.
b.		Inverted surcharge	1,000.	1,100.

No. 16 Overprinted in Black

1901

26	A2	1p brown	210.00	160.00
a.		Inverted overprint	2,400.	1,900.
c.		Double overprint	1,900.	1,900.

Some single stamps were overprinted by favor. Other varieties could exist. Forgeries exist.

Types of 1893-98

1902 Unwmk.

27	A3	½p green	5.25	5.00
a.		Vert. pair, imperf. horiz.	1,400.	
28	A2	1p rose	14.00	12.50
29	A2	2 ½p dull blue	15.00	25.00
		Nos. 27-29 (3)	34.25	42.50

1902 Wmk. 61 Perf. 11

30	A3	½p green	3.25	3.75
31	A2	1p rose	4.75	3.50
32	A2	1 ½p brt violet	4.75	10.00
33	A3	2p chocolate	6.50	12.00
a.		Figures of value omitted	2,750.	3,600.
b.		Perf. 11x14	2,250.	
34	A2	2 ½p dull blue	4.50	8.25
35	A2	5p olive gray	42.50	57.50
36	A3	6p purple	37.50	32.50
37	A2	10p blue green	55.00	120.00
38	A3	1sh car rose	55.00	82.50
a.		Perf. 11x14	2,700.	
		Nos. 30-38 (9)	213.75	330.00

1909-19 Perf. 14, 14x14½, 14½x14

39	A3	½p green, perf 14½x14 ('11)	7.00	9.50
a.		½p dp grn, wmk sideways, perf 14 ('15)	7.00	17.50
b.		As "a," wmk upright	9.00	16.50
40b	A2	1p red	6.50	7.25
41	A2	1 ½p purple ('15)	13.00	4.75
42	A3	2p dp brown ('19)	6.00	57.50
43	A2	10p dp green ('18)	22.50	110.00
44	A3	1sh car rose ('19)	32.50	110.00
		Nos. 39a,39-44 (7)	94.50	
		Nos. 39-44 (6)		299.00

Nos. 39-40 are on both ordinary and chalky paper; Nos. 41-44 on chalky paper.

New Zealand Stamps of 1909-19 Surcharged in Dark Blue or Red

1919 Typo. Perf. 14x13½, 14x14½

48	A43	½p yel green (R)	.45	1.25
a.		Pair, one without surcharge		
49	A42	1p carmine	1.25	3.50
50	A47	1 ½p brown org (R)	.60	.90
51	A43	2p yellow (R)	1.75	2.00
52	A43	3p chocolate	3.25	15.00

Engr.

53	A44	2 ½p dull blue (R)	2.25	2.75
54	A45	3p violet brown	2.75	2.25
55	A45	4p purple	2.00	5.00
56	A44	4 ½p dark green	2.00	9.50
57	A45	6p car rose	3.50	6.50
58	A44	7 ½p red brown	2.10	6.50

59	A45	9p ol green (R)	2.25	17.50
60	A45	1sh vermilion	3.25	21.00
		Nos. 48-60 (13)	27.40	93.65

The Polynesian surcharge restates the denomination of the basic stamp.

Landing of Capt. Cook A4

Avarua Waterfront A5

Capt. James Cook — A6

Palm — A7

Houses at Arorangi — A8

Avarua Harbor — A9

1920 Unwmk. Engr. Perf. 14

61	A4	½p green & black	4.75	25.00
62	A5	1p car & black	5.50	25.00
a.		Center inverted	600.00	
63	A6	1 ½p blue & black	10.00	10.00
64	A7	3p red brn & blk	2.50	6.50
65	A8	6p org & red brn	3.50	10.00
66	A9	1sh vio & black	6.00	20.00
		Nos. 61-66 (6)	32.25	96.50

The stamps overprinted or inscribed "Rarotonga" were used throughout the Cook Islands.
For surcharges see Nos. 78, 79.

New Zealand Postal-Fiscal Stamps of 1906-13 Overprinted in Red or Dark Blue

a

Perf. 14, 14½, 14x14½

1921		**Typo.**		**Wmk. 61**
67	PF1	2sh blue (R)	32.50	65.00
68	PF1	2sh6p brown	22.50	60.00
69	PF1	5sh green (R)	32.50	77.50
70	PF1	10sh claret	90.00	140.00
71	PF2	£1 rose	140.00	240.00
		Nos. 67-71 (5)	317.50	582.50

Types of 1920 Issue

1924-26 Engr. Perf. 14

72	A4	½p yel grn & black	5.25	10.00
73	A5	1p carmine & black	7.00	2.50

Issued: ½p, 5/13/26; 1p, 11/10/24.

New Zealand Stamps of 1926 Overprinted Type "a" in Red

1926-28 Typo. Perf. 14, 14½x14

74	A56	2sh blue ('27)	17.50	47.50
a.		2sh dark blue	12.00	47.50
75	A56	3sh violet ('28)	19.00	50.00

Rarotongan Chief (Te Po) — A10

Avarua Harbor — A11

1927, Oct. 15   Engr.   Perf. 14

76	A10	2½p dk bl & red brn	7.00	29.00
77	A11	4p dull vio & bl grn	10.00	20.00

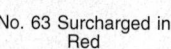
No. 63 Surcharged in Red

1931   Unwmk.

78	A6	2p on 1½p blue & blk	11.00	3.25

Same Surcharge on Type of 1920
Wmk. 61

79	A6	2p on 1½p blue & blk	5.50	13.00

No. 79 was not issued without surcharge.

New Zealand Postal-Fiscal Stamps of 1931-32 Overprinted Type "a" in Blue or Red

1931, Nov. 12   Typo.

80	PF5	2sh6p dp brn (Bl)	12.00	26.00
81	PF5	5sh green (R)	21.00	65.00
82	PF5	10sh dk car (Bl)	45.00	110.00
83	PF5	£1 pink (Bl) ('32)	105.00	190.00
		Nos. 80-83 (4)	183.00	391.00

See Nos. 103-108, 124A-126C.

Landing of Capt. Cook — A12

Capt. James Cook — A13

Double Canoe — A14

Islanders Unloading Ship — A15

View of Avarua Harbor — A16

R.M.S. Monowai — A17

King George V — A18

Unwmk.

1932, Mar. 16   Engr.   Perf. 13
Center in Black

84	A12	½p deep green	4.00	19.00
a.		Perf. 14	32.50	105.00
85	A13	1p brown lake	7.75	5.25
a.		Center inverted	8,500.	8,500.
b.		Perf. 14	17.50	28.00
86	A14	2p brown	3.50	6.50
b.		Perf. 14	10.00	24.00

87	A15	2½p dark ultra	18.00	65.00
b.		Perf. 14	18.00	65.00

Perf. 14

88	A16	4p ultra	12.00	65.00
a.		Perf. 13	25.00	75.00
b.		Perf. 14x13	35.00	130.00
89	A17	6p orange	5.00	17.50
a.		Perf. 13	30.00	57.50
90	A18	1sh deep violet	13.00	26.00
		Nos. 84-90 (7)	63.25	204.25

Nos. 84-90 were available for postage in Aitutaki, Penrhyn and Rarotonga and replaced the special issues for those islands.
Inverted centers of the 2p and 2½p are from printers waste.

1933-36   Wmk. 61   Perf. 14

91	A12	½p dp grn & blk	1.20	5.25
92	A13	1p dk car & black ('35)	1.50	2.40
93	A14	2p brn & blk ('36)	1.75	.60
94	A15	2½p dk ultra & blk	1.75	2.50
95	A16	4p blue & black	1.75	.60
96	A17	6p org & blk ('36)	2.00	2.50
97	A18	1sh dp vio & black ('36)	31.00	42.50
		Nos. 91-97 (7)	40.95	56.35

See Nos. 116-121.

Silver Jubilee Issue

Types of 1932 Overprinted in Black or Red

1935, May 7

98	A13	1p dk car & brn red	.40	2.00
99	A15	2½p dk ultra & bl (R)	1.00	3.50
100	A17	6p dull org & green	5.00	8.50
		Nos. 98-100 (3)	6.40	14.00
		Set, never hinged	12.50	

The vertical spacing of the overprint is wider on No. 100.

New Zealand Stamps of 1926 Overprinted in Black

b

1936, July 15   Typo.   Perf. 14

101	A56	2sh blue	15.00	50.00
102	A56	3sh violet	15.00	80.00

New Zealand Postal-Fiscal Stamps of 1931-35 Overprinted Type "b" in Black or Red

1932-36

103	PF5	2sh6p brown ('36)	21.00	80.00
104	PF5	5sh grn (R) ('36)	26.00	100.00
105	PF5	10sh dk car ('36)	55.00	200.00
106	PF5	£1 pink ('36)	85.00	210.00
107	PF5	£3 lt grn (R)	300.00	550.00
108	PF5	£5 dk blue (R)	210.00	375.00
		Nos. 103-108 (6)	697.00	1,515.

Issue dates: Mar. 1932, July 15, 1936.

New Zealand Stamps of 1937 Overprinted in Black

Perf. 14x13½

1937, June 1   Engr.   Wmk. 253

109	A78	1p rose carmine	.20	.20
110	A78	2½p dark blue	.25	.20
111	A78	6p vermilion	.35	.30
		Nos. 109-111 (3)	.80	.70
		Set, never hinged	2.40	

King George VI A19

Village and Palms A20

Coastal Scene with Canoe — A21

1938, May 2   Wmk. 61   Perf. 14

112	A19	1sh dp violet & blk	7.50	15.00
113	A20	2sh dk red brn & blk	15.00	19.00
114	A21	3sh yel green & blue	37.50	42.50
		Nos. 112-114 (3)	60.00	76.50
		Set, never hinged	87.50	

See Nos. 122-124.

Mt. Ikurangi behind Avarua — A22

Perf. 13½x14

1940, Sept. 2   Engr.   Wmk. 253

115	A22	3p on 1½p violet & blk	.70	.70

Issued only with surcharge. Stamps without surcharge are from the printer's archives.

Types of 1932-38

1944-46   Engr.   Perf. 14

116	A12	½p dk ol grn & blk ('45)	1.00	4.50
117	A13	1p dk car & blk ('45)	1.50	1.25
118	A14	2p brn & blk ('46)	.90	7.00
119	A15	2½p dk bl & blk ('45)	.60	2.00
120	A16	4p blue & black	2.50	15.00
121	A17	6p org & black	1.00	2.50
122	A19	1sh dp vio & blk	1.00	3.50
123	A20	2sh dk red brn & blk	27.50	50.00
124	A21	3sh yel green & blue ('45)	25.00	40.00
		Nos. 116-124 (9)	61.00	125.75
		Set, never hinged	100.00	

New Zealand Nos. AR76, AR78, AR85 and Type of 1931 Postal-Fiscal Stamps Overprinted Type "b" in Black or Red

1943-50   Wmk. 253   Typo.   Perf. 14

124A	PF5	2sh6p brn ('46)	11.50	22.50
125	PF5	5sh green (R)	7.75	22.50
126	PF5	10sh dp pink ('48)	35.00	90.00
126A	PF5	£1 pink ('47)	40.00	97.50
126B	PF5	£3 lt grn (R) ('46)	47.50	190.00
126C	PF5	£5 dk bl (R) ('50)	175.00	425.00
		Nos. 124A-126C (6)	316.75	847.50
		Set, never hinged	525.00	

For surcharges see Nos. 192-194.

> **Catalogue values for unused stamps in this section, from this point to the end of the section, are for Never Hinged items.**

Peace Issue
New Zealand Nos. 248, 250, 254 and 255 Overprinted in Black or Blue:

c

d

Perf. 13x13½, 13½x13

1946, June 1   Engr.

127	A94 (c)	1p emerald	.50	.20
128	A96 (d)	2p rose vio (Bl)	.50	.50
129	A100(c)	6p org red & red brn	.80	.70
130	A101(c)	8p brn lake & blk (Bl)	.80	.70
		Nos. 127-130 (4)	2.60	2.10

Ngatangiia Channel, Rarotonga A23

Capt. James Cook Statue and Map of Cook Islands — A24

Designs: 1p, Cook and map of Hervey Isls. 2p, Rev. John Williams, his ship Messenger of Peace, and map of Rarotonga. 3p, Aitutaki map and palms. 5p, Mail plane landing at Rarotonga airport. 6p, Tongareva (Penrhyn) scene. 8p, Islander's house, Rarotonga. 2sh, Thatched house, mat weaver. 3sh, Steamer Matua offshore.

Perf. 13½x13, 13x13½

1949, Aug. 1   Engr.   Wmk. 253

131	A23	½p brown & violet	.20	1.25
132	A23	1p green & orange	3.75	2.50
133	A23	2p carmine & brn	2.25	2.50
134	A23	3p ultra & green	2.00	2.50
135	A23	5p purple & grn	6.50	2.00
136	A23	6p car rose & blk	6.50	3.25
137	A23	8p orange & olive	.65	4.75
138	A24	1sh chocolate & bl	6.00	4.75
139	A24	2sh rose car & brn	4.50	16.00
140	A24	3sh bl grn & lt ultra	11.50	29.00
		Nos. 131-140 (10)	43.85	68.50

For surcharge see No. 147.

Coronation Issue
Type of New Zealand

1953, May 25   Photo.   Perf. 14x14½

145	A113	3p brown	1.10	1.10
146	A114	6p slate black	2.10	2.10

No. 135 Surcharged with New Value and Two Dots

1960, Apr. 1   Engr.   Perf. 13½x12

147	A23	1sh6p on 5p purple & grn	.50	.75

Tiare Maori — A25

Fishing God — A26

Queen Elizabeth II — A27

Island Scene A28

3sh, Administration building, Mangaia. 5sh, Ship in Rarotonga harbor. 3p, 5p, 6p, 1sh, horiz.

Perf. 13½x13, 13x13½
Litho.; Engr.; (1sh6p)
1963, June 4

148	A25	1p shown	.50	.65
149	A26	2p shown	.20	.65
150	A25	3p Frangipani	.70	.65
151	A25	5p Fairy tern	8.25	1.60
152	A25	6p Hibiscus	1.00	.70
153	A26	8p Bonito	4.50	2.00
154	A25	1sh Oranges	.40	.70
155	A27	1sh6p shown	2.75	2.75
156	A28	2sh gray & brown	1.00	1.10
157	A28	3sh emer & black	1.25	1.40
158	A28	5sh ultra & brown	11.00	5.25
		Nos. 148-158 (11)	31.55	17.45

For overprints and surcharges see #167-169, 179-181, 183-184, 186-190.

Solar Eclipse and Palm Tree — A29

1965, May 31   Litho.   Perf. 13x13½
159   A29 6p black, lt blue & yel   .40 .40

Observation of the solar eclipse on Manuae Island, May 30, 1965. Exists imperf.
For surcharge see No. 185.

Flag of New Zealand and Map of Cook Islands A30

Designs: 10p, London Missionary Society Church and graveyard. 1sh, Reading of Proclamation of Cession, Oct. 8, 1900, and Queen Elizabeth II. 1sh9p, Nikao School and flag of New Zealand.

Perf. 13½x13
1965, Sept. 16   Litho.   Wmk. 253

160	A30	4p blue & red	.20	.20
161	A30	10p multicolored	.20	.20
162	A30	1sh multicolored	.20	.20
163	A30	1sh9p multicolored	.50	.50
		Nos. 160-163 (4)	1.10	1.10

Establishment of internal self-government.
For surcharges see Nos. 182, 191.

Nos. 160-162 and 156-158
Overprinted in Red: "In Memoriam / Sir Winston Churchill / 1874-1965"

1966, Jan. 24   Litho.   Wmk. 253

164	A30	4p blue & red	.75	.30
165	A30	10p multicolored	2.25	.60
a.		Inverted overprint	275.00	
166	A30	1sh multicolored	2.25	.90
167	A28	2sh gray & brown	2.25	1.60
168	A28	3sh emer & black	2.25	1.60
169	A28	5sh ultra & brown	2.75	2.25
		Nos. 164-169 (6)	12.50	7.25

Statesman and WWII leader.

Adoration of the Wise Men, by Fra Angelico — A31

Paintings: 2p, Nativity, by Hans Memling, vert. 4p, Adoration of the Wise Men, by Velazquez. 10p, Adoration of the Wise Men, by Hieronymus Bosch. 1sh6p, Adoration of the Shepherds, by Jose Ribera, vert.

Perf. 13x14½, 14½x13
1966, Nov. 28   Photo.   Unwmk.

170	A31	1p multicolored	.20	.20
171	A31	2p multicolored	.20	.20
172	A31	4p multicolored	.20	.20
173	A31	10p multicolored	.55	.55
174	A31	1sh6p multicolored	.65	.65
		Nos. 170-174 (5)	1.80	1.80

Christmas. Issued in sheets of 6 with ornamental gold border.

Perf. 13x12, 12x13

170a	A31	1p	.45	.55
171a	A31	2p	14.00	11.50
172a	A31	4p	1.10	1.00
173a	A31	10p	2.40	4.50
174a	A31	1sh6p	30.00	6.75
		Nos. 170a-174a (5)	47.95	24.30

Tennis and Queen Elizabeth A32

Sport: 1p, Women's basketball and Games' emblem. 4p, Boxing and team emblem. 7p, Soccer and Queen Elizabeth II.

1967, Jan. 12   Perf. 13½

175	A32	½p brt olive & multi	.20	.20
176	A32	1p brt blue & multi	.20	.20
177	A32	4p purple & multi	.20	.20
178	A32	7p red & multi	.20	.20
		Nos. 175-178,C10-C11 (6)	1.25	1.25

Second South Pacific Games, Noumea, New Caledonia, Dec. 8-18, 1966.

Nos. 148-155, 157-161 Surcharged with New Value or Black or Red

Pair (#181b), with Type I on left (#181) and Type II on right (#181a)

1967

179	A25	1c on 1p	.40	1.75
180	A26	2c on 2p	.20	.20
181	A25	2½c on 3p (I)	.20	.20
a.		Type II	.20	.20
b.		Pair, #181 and #181a	.45	.45
182	A30	3c on 4p	.20	.20
183	A26	4c on 5p	6.00	.40
184	A25	5c on 6p	.20	.20
185	A29	5c on 6p	4.50	.70
186	A26	7c on 8p	.25	.20
187	A25	10c on 1sh	.20	.20
188	A27	15c on 1sh6p (R)	1.60	1.10
189	A28	30c on 3sh (R)	15.00	5.50
190	A28	50c on 5sh (R)	3.75	3.00
191	A30	$1 on 10p (R)	14.50	11.00
		Nos. 179-191 (13)	47.00	24.65

Issued: 2c, 2½c, 3c, 5c, 7c, 10c, 4/3; others 5/4.
No. 191 is surcharged "10/ $1.00" and 3 bars over old value.
Numerous varieties of surcharge include wrong-font "c," thin numerals, etc.

Nos. 126A, 126B and 126C
Surcharged in Red
Wmk. 253

1967, June 6   Typo.   Perf. 14

192	PF5	$2 on £1 pink	70.00	200.00
193	PF5	$6 on £3 lt green	140.00	225.00
194	PF5	$10 on £5 dk blue	250.00	375.00
		Nos. 192-194 (3)	460.00	800.00

Frequently found with stained gum.

Stamp of 1892, Village and Queen Victoria A33

Designs: 3c (4p), PO, Rarotonga, and Elizabeth II. 8c (10p), View of Avarua, Rarotonga, and 10p stamp of 1892. 18c (1sh9p), Map of Cook Islands, DC-3, S.S. Moana Roa and Capt. Cook.

Perf. 13½
1967, July 3   Photo.   Unwmk.

195	A33	1c (1p) multi	.20	.20
196	A33	3c (4p) multi	.20	.20
197	A33	8c (10p) multi	.35	.35
198	A33	18c (1sh9p) multi	1.50	.80
a.		Souvenir sheet of 4, #195-198	3.50	3.50
		Nos. 195-198 (4)	2.25	1.55

75th anniv. of the 1st Cook Islands stamps. Issued in sheets of 8 stamps and 1 label with inscription in yellow margin.

Hibiscus — A34

Elizabeth II — A35

Elizabeth II and Flowers — A36

Flowers: 1c, Rose of Sharon. 2c, 15c, Frangipani. 2½c, Butterfly pea. 3c, Suva queen and Queen Elizabeth II. 4c, Water lily. 5c, Bauhania. 6c, Yellow hibiscus. 8c, Alamanda and Queen Elizabeth II. 9c, Stephanotis. 10c, Flaymboyant poinciana. 20c, Thunbergia. 25c, Canna lily and Queen Elizabeth II. 30c, Poinsettia. 50c, Gardenia.

1967-69   Photo.   Perf. 14x13½

199	A34	½c gold & multi	.30	.20
200	A34	1c gold & multi	.30	.20
201	A34	2c gold & multi	.30	.20
202	A34	2½c gold & multi	.45	.20
203	A34	3c gold & multi	1.00	.20
204	A34	4c *Walter Lily*	1.40	1.75
205	A34	4c *Water Lily*	3.75	1.50
206	A34	5c gold & multi	.70	.20
207	A34	6c gold & multi	.75	.20
208	A34	8c gold & multi	.75	.20
209	A34	9c gold & multi	.75	.20
210	A34	10c gold & multi	.75	.20
211	A34	15c gold & multi	.75	.20
212	A34	20c gold & multi	8.50	.50
213	A34	25c gold & multi	1.50	.60
214	A34	30c gold & multi	1.25	.70
215	A34	50c gold & multi	1.90	1.00
216	A35	$1 gold & multi	4.00	2.25
217	A35	$2 gold & multi	9.00	3.50
218	A36	$4 multi ('68)	3.25	5.50
219	A36	$6 multi ('68)	3.75	7.50
219A	A36	$8 multi ('69)	11.00	11.00
220	A36	$10 multi ('68)	7.00	12.00
		Nos. 199-220 (23)	63.10	50.00

The $4 exists with "FOUR DOLLARS" in two widths: 32½mm and 33½mm.
Nos. 214-215 were surcharged "Plus 20c United Kingdom Special Mail Service" in 5 lines of capitals for use during the 1971 British mail strike. The strike ended Mar. 8, the day the 50c+20c, was released.
For surcharges see Nos. 290-291, 305-309, B1-B13, B17-B18, B20. For overprints see Nos. 277-283, 302-304, 315, 351-356, O1-O15.

Fluorescence
Since 1968 a number of stamps have been issued with a "fluorescent security underprinting" in a multiple coat of arms pattern. Some issues have this underprint, some do not.
Stamps issued both with and without the underprint are Nos. 199-203, 205-220, 283, 290-291.
From Nos. 292-296 onward, all stamps have this underprint unless otherwise noted.

Ia Orana Maria, by Gauguin A37

Gauguin Paintings: 3c, Riders on the Beach. 5c, Still Life with Flowers. 8c, Whispered Words. 15c, Maternity. 22c, Why Are You Angry?

1967, Oct. 23   Photo.   Perf. 13½

221	A37	1c gold & multi	.25	.25
222	A37	3c gold & multi	.25	.25
223	A37	5c gold & multi	.25	.25
224	A37	8c gold & multi	.25	.25
225	A37	15c gold & multi	.40	.40
226	A37	22c gold & multi	.60	.60
a.		Souvenir sheet of 6, #221-226	3.50	3.50
		Nos. 221-226 (6)	2.00	2.00

#221-226 are printed in sheets of 6 (3x2).

Holy Family by Rubens — A38

Paintings: 3c, Adoration of the Magi, by Albrecht Durer. 4c, The Lucca Madonna, by Jan Van Eyck. 8c, Adoration of the Shepherds, by Jacopo da Bassano. 15c, Nativity, by El Greco. 25c, Madonna and Child, by Antonio Allegri da Correggio.

1967, Dec. 4   Perf. 12x13

227	A38	1c gold & multi	.20	.20
228	A38	3c gold & multi	.20	.20
229	A38	4c gold & multi	.20	.20
230	A38	8c gold & multi	.20	.20
231	A38	15c gold & multi	.30	.30
232	A38	25c gold & multi	.35	.35
		Nos. 227-232 (6)	1.45	1.45

Christmas.

Capt. Cook and Matavai Bay, Tahiti, by Sydney Parkinson A39

1c, Ships off Huahine Island, Tahiti, by John & James Clevely. 2c, town & harbor of Kamchatka, by John Webber, & Queen Elizabeth II. 4c, "The Ice Islands" (Antarctica), by William Hodges.

1968, Sept. 12   Photo.   Perf. 13

233	A39	½c gold & multi	.20	.20
234	A39	1c gold & multi	.20	.20
235	A39	2c gold & multi	.20	.20
236	A39	4c gold & multi	.20	.20
		Nos. 233-236,C12-C15 (8)	6.45	6.45

Bicent. of Capt. Cook's 1st voyage of discovery. Printed in sheets of 10 stamps and 2 labels (3x4). Labels show portraits of Elizabeth II and Cook.

Gymnast
A40

1968, Oct. 21
237	A40	1c Sailing	.20	.20
238	A40	5c shown	.20	.20
239	A40	15c High jump	.20	.20
240	A40	20c Woman diver	.35	.20
241	A40	30c Bicyclist	.70	.20
242	A40	50c Woman hurdler	.55	.30
		Nos. 237-242 (6)	2.20	1.30

19th Olympic Games, Mexico City, Oct. 12-27. Printed in sheets of 10 stamps and 2 labels (3x4).

Virgin and Child, by Titian — A41

Paintings: 4c, Holy Family, by Raphael. 10c, Madonna of the Rosary, by Murillo. 20c, Adoration of the Magi, by Memling. 30c, Adoration of the Magi, by Ghirlandajo.

1968, Dec. 2   Photo.   Perf. 13
243	A41	1c gold & multi	.20	.20
244	A41	4c gold & multi	.20	.20
245	A41	10c gold & multi	.20	.20
246	A41	20c gold & multi	.30	.30
247	A41	30c gold & multi	.45	.45
a.		Souv. sheet, #243-247 + label	2.40	2.40
		Nos. 243-247 (5)	1.35	1.35

Issued in sheets of 6 (2x3).

Training on Ropeway A42

Designs: ½c, Boy Scouts cooking over campfire. 5c, Training with signal flags, and Queen Elizabeth II. 10c, Planting a tree. 20c, Erecting a hut. 30c, Lord Baden-Powell, lake and mountains (visit to Rarotonga in 1935).

1969, Feb. 6   Photo.   Perf. 13½
248	A42	½c multicolored	.20	.20
249	A42	1c multicolored	.20	.20
250	A42	5c multicolored	.20	.20
251	A42	10c multicolored	.25	.25
252	A42	20c multicolored	.30	.30
253	A42	30c multicolored	.55	.55
		Nos. 248-253 (6)	1.70	1.70

5th Natl. Boy Scout Jamboree, Christchurch, New Zealand, Jan. 2-12.
Issued in sheets of 10 stamps and 2 labels (4x3).

Soccer — A43

#254b, Pole vault. #255a, Weight lifting. #255b, Basketball, Elizabeth II. #256a, Long jump. #256b, Tennis. #257a, Running. #257b, Javelin, Elizabeth II. #258a, Boxing. #258b, Golf.

Perf. 13½x13
1969, July 7   Photo.   Unwmk.
254	A43	½c Pair, #a.-b.	.70	.70
255	A43	1c Pair, #a.-b.	.70	.70
256	A43	4c Pair, #a.-b.	1.50	1.50
257	A43	10c Pair, #a.-b.	2.10	2.10
258	A43	15c Pair, #a.-b.	3.50	3.50
c.		Souv. sheet, #254-258 + 2 labels	9.50	9.50
		Nos. 254-258 (5)	8.50	8.50

3rd South Pacifc Games, Port Moresby, Papua and New Guinea, Aug. 13-23.
Issued in sheets of 10.

Map of Cook Islands and Capt. Cook — A44

Map of Cook Islands and: 5c, Premier Albert Henry of New Zealand. 25c, Coat of arms of New Zealand. 30c, Queen Elizabeth II.

1969, Oct. 8   Photo.   Perf. 13
264	A44	5c red & multi	.50	.50
265	A44	10c lemon & multi	1.50	1.50
266	A44	25c green & multi	.75	.75
267	A44	30c blue & multi	.75	.75
		Nos. 264-267 (4)	3.50	3.50

South Pacific Conf., Noumea, Oct. 1969.

Madonna and Child, by Filippo Lippi A45

Paintings: 4c, Holy Family, by Baccio della Porta. 10c, Madonna and Child, by Anton Raphael Mengs. 20c, Madonna and Child, by Le Maitre de Flemalle. 30c, Madonna and Child by Correggio.

1969, Nov. 21   Photo.   Perf. 13½
268	A45	1c buff & multi	.20	.20
269	A45	4c buff & multi	.20	.20
270	A45	10c buff & multi	.20	.20
271	A45	20c buff & multi	.25	.25
272	A45	30c buff & multi	.25	.25
a.		Souv. sheet, #268-272 + label	2.00	2.00
		Nos. 268-272 (5)	1.10	1.10

Issued in sheets of 8 stamps, one label with portrait of Queen Elizabeth II.

Resurrection of Christ, by Raphael — A46

The Resurrection of Christ by: 8c, Dirk Bouts. 20c, Albert Altdorfer. 25c, Murillo.

1970, Mar. 12   Photo.   Perf. 13½
Size: 25½x56mm
273	A46	4c gold & multi	.20	.20
274	A46	8c gold & multi	.20	.20
275	A46	20c gold & multi	.20	.20
276	A46	25c gold & multi	.25	.25
a.		Souv. sheet, #273-276 + 2 labels	1.50	1.50
		Nos. 273-276 (4)	.85	.85

Easter 1970.
Printed in sheets of 8 stamps and a label (3x3) showing portrait of Queen Elizabeth II and name of painting and painter.
See Nos. 316-318.

Nos. 205, 208, 211-212, 214, 217 Overprinted: "KIA ORANA / APOLLO 13 /ASTRONAUTS / Te Atua to / Tatou Irinakianga"

1970, Apr.   Perf. 14x13½
277	A34	4c gold & multi	.30	.30
278	A34	8c gold & multi	.30	.30
279	A34	15c gold & multi	.30	.30
280	A34	20c gold & multi	.40	.40
281	A34	30c gold & multi	.55	.55
282	A35	$2 gold & multi	1.60	1.60

No. 218 Overprinted: "KIA ORANA / APOLLO 13 /ASTRONAUTS"

283	A36	$4 gold & multi	3.00	3.00
		Nos. 277-283 (7)	6.45	6.45

Splashdown of Apollo 13 west of Rarotonga, Apr. 17, 1970.
Issued: #277-282, 4/17; $4, 4/30.
Values for Nos. 283, 290-291 are for stamps with fluorescence. Stamps without fluorescence sell for more.

Queen Elizabeth II, Prince Philip, Princess Anne and Prince Charles — A47

Design: 30c, Wedgwood bust of Capt. Cook and "Endeavour." $1, Royal visit commemorative coin, obverse and reverse.

1970, June 12   Photo.   Perf. 13½
284	A47	5c gold & multi	.30	.30
285	A47	30c gold & multi	1.60	1.50
286	A47	$1 gold & multi	5.00	4.50
a.		Souv. sheet, #284-286 + label	11.50	11.50
		Nos. 284-286 (3)	6.90	6.30

Visit of the British royal family.

Nos. 284-286 Overprinted in Silver or Black: "Fifth Anniversary Self-Government August 1970"

1970, Aug. 27   Photo.   Perf. 13½
287	A47	5c gold & multi (S)	.50	.20
288	A47	30c gold & multi	1.50	1.00
289	A47	$1 gold & multi	2.50	1.40
		Nos. 287-289 (3)	4.50	2.60

5th anniv. of self-government. The overprint on No. 287 is arranged in one line around 3 sides of the design; the overprint on Nos. 288-289 is in 3 horizontal lines.

Nos. 219A-220 Surcharged

FOUR DOLLARS $4.00

1970, Nov. 11   Photo.   Perf. 14x13½
290	A36	$4 on $8 multi	4.25	4.25
291	A36	$4 on $10 multi	3.00	3.00

In each sheet of 15, 3 stamps have 2 surcharged bars instead of one. See second note after No. 283.

Nativity A48

Illuminations from 14th Century Robert de Lisle Psalter: 4c, Angel and shepherds. 10c, The Circumcision. 20c, The Adoration of the Kings. 30c, The Presentation at the Temple.

1970, Nov. 30   Photo.   Perf. 13½
292	A48	1c gold & multi	.20	.20
293	A48	4c gold & multi	.20	.20
294	A48	10c gold & multi	.30	.30
295	A48	20c gold & multi	.35	.35
296	A48	30c gold & multi	.45	.45
a.		Souv. sheet, #292-296 + label	1.50	1.50
		Nos. 292-296 (5)	1.50	1.50

Christmas.
Issued in sheets of 5 stamps and a label (3x2) showing portrait of Queen Elizabeth II and source of design.

Queen Elizabeth II and Prince Philip — A49

Designs: 4c, Royal family at Balmoral. 10c, Prince Philip sailing. 15c, Prince Philip as polo player. 25c, Prince Philip and royal yacht.

1971, Mar. 11   Litho.   Perf. 13½
297	A49	1c brt blue & multi	.20	.20
298	A49	4c brt blue & multi	.30	.30
299	A49	10c brt blue & multi	.75	.75
300	A49	15c brt blue & multi	1.10	1.10
301	A49	25c brt blue & multi	1.90	1.90
a.		Souv. sheet, #297-301 + 2 labels	5.75	5.75
		Nos. 297-301 (5)	4.25	4.25

Visit of Prince Philip, Duke of Edinburgh to Rarotonga, Feb. 27, 1971. Printed in sheets of 10 stamps and 2 labels showing Queen Elizabeth II commemorative coin and a portrait of Prince Philip.

Nos. 210, 213-214 Overprinted

1971, Sept. 8   Photo.   Perf. 14x13½
302	A34	10c gold & multi	.65	.65
303	A34	25c gold & multi	.65	.65
304	A34	30c gold & multi	.65	.65
		Nos. 302-304 (3)	1.95	1.95

4th South Pacific Games, Papeete, French Polynesia, Sept. 8-19.

Nos. 202, 205, 208-209 and 211 Surcharged with New Value and Three Bars

1971, Oct. 20
305	A34	10c on 2½c multi	.20	.20
306	A34	10c on 4c multi	.20	.20
307	A34	10c on 8c multi	.20	.20
308	A34	10c on 9c multi	.20	.20
309	A34	10c on 15c multi	.20	.20
		Nos. 305-309 (5)	1.00	1.00

Madonna and Child, by Bellini — A50

Christmas: Paintings of the Madonna and Child, by Giovanni Bellini.

1971, Nov. 30   Perf. 13½
310	A50	1c gold & multi	.20	.20
311	A50	4c gold & multi	.20	.20
312	A50	10c gold & multi	.30	.30
313	A50	20c gold & multi	.60	.60
314	A50	30c gold & multi	.90	.90
a.		Souv. sheet, #310-314 + label	2.75	2.75
		Nos. 310-314 (5)	2.20	2.20

See No. B14.

No. 216 Overprinted: "SOUTH PACIFIC / COMMISSION / FEB. 1947-1972"

1972, Feb. 17   Photo.   Perf. 14x13½
315 A35 $1 gold & multi   .90   .90
South Pacific Commission, 25th anniv.

Easter Type of 1970

Illuminations from 14th century Robert de Lisle Psalter: 5c, St. John. 10c, Christ crucified. 30c, Virgin Mary.

1972, Mar. 6   Photo.   Perf. 13½
Size: 21x68mm
316 A46 5c gold & multi   .20   .20
317 A46 10c gold & multi   .20   .20
318 A46 30c gold & multi   .50   .50
 a.   Souvenir sheet of 3, #316-318   1.50 1.50
      Nos. 316-318 (3)   .90   .90

Printed in sheets of 12.
For surcharges see Nos. B15-B16, B19.

Rocket over Moon — A51

#319a, Shown. #319b, Earth over moon. #320a, Landing module and astronaut. #320b, Astronaut collecting moon rocks. #321a, Earth and rocket over moon. #321b, Lunar rover and astronaut. #322a, Helicopter over raft in Pacific. #322b, Capsule and parachutes.

1972, Apr. 17
319 A51 5c Pair, #a.-b.   .20   .20
320 A51 10c Pair, #a.-b.   .60   .60
321 A51 25c Pair, #a.-b.   1.75 1.75
322 A51 30c Pair, #a.-b.   2.25 2.25
 c.   Souvenir sheet of 8   7.50 7.50
      Nos. 319-322 (4)   4.80 4.80

Apollo moon explorations.
No. 322c contains Nos. 319-322 arranged in 2 blocks of 4 divided by a map showing splashdown area of Apollo X, XII and XIII.
For surcharges see Nos. B21-B24.

High Jump, Olympic Rings — A52

Rest on Flight to Egypt, by Caravaggio — A53

1972, June 26
327 A52 10c shown   .30   .30
328 A52 25c Running   .65   .65
329 A52 30c Boxing   .65   .65
 a.   Souv. sheet, #327-329 + label 2.50 2.50
      Nos. 327-329 (3)   1.60 1.60

20th Olympic Games, Munich, Aug. 26-Sept. 10. Sheets of 8 stamps and label. See No. B29.

1972, Oct. 11   Photo.   Perf. 13½

Paintings: 5c, Virgin of the Swallows, by Guercino. 10c, Virgin with Green Cushion, by Andrea Solario. 20c, Virgin and Child, by

Lorenzo di Credi. 30c, Virgin and Child, by Giovanni Bellini.

330 A53 1c gold & multi   .30   .30
331 A53 5c gold & multi   .30   .30
332 A53 10c gold & multi   .40   .40
333 A53 20c gold & multi   .75   .75
334 A53 30c gold & multi   1.25 1.25
 a.   Souv. sheet, #330-334 + label 4.50 4.50
      Nos. 330-334 (5)   3.00 3.00

Christmas. See No. B30.

Princess Elizabeth and Prince Philip — A54

Designs: 5c, Wedding ceremony, Westminster Abbey. 15c, Bridal portrait. 30c, Official wedding picture of royal family.

1972, Nov. 20
Size: 29x40mm
335 A54 5c silver & multi   .40   .40
336 A54 10c silver & multi   .55   .55
Size: 40x40mm
337 A54 15c silver & multi   .70   .70
Size: 66x40mm
338 A54 30c silver & multi   .85   .85
      Nos. 335-338 (4)   2.50 2.50

25th anniversary of the marriage of Queen Elizabeth II and Prince Philip.
Nos. 335-337 printed in sheets of 8 stamps and one label; No. 338 in sheets of 6.

1c Coin with Queen Elizabeth II and Taro Leaf A55

Queen Elizabeth II Coins: 2c, Pineapples. 5c, Hibiscus. 10c, Oranges. 20c, Fairy terns. 50c, Bonito. $1, Tangaroa, Polynesian god of creation, vert.

1973, Mar. 15   Photo.   Perf. 13x13½
Size: 37x24mm
339 A55 1c dp car, blk & gold   .20   .20
340 A55 2c blue, blk & gold   .20   .20
341 A55 5c green, blk & gold   .20   .20
Size: 46x30mm
342 A55 10c vio, blue, blk & sil .25   .25
343 A55 20c dk green, blk & sil .40   .40
344 A55 50c dp car, black & sil .60   .60
Size: 32x54½mm
345 A55 $1 blue, blk & silver   .90   .90
      Nos. 339-345 (7)   2.75 2.75

Coinage commemorating silver wedding anniversary of Queen Elizabeth II.
Printed in sheets of 20 stamps and label showing Westminster Abbey.

"Noli me Tangere," by Titian — A56

Paintings: 10c, Descent from the Cross, by Rubens. 30c, The Lamentation of Christ, by Dürer.

1973, Apr. 9
346 A56 5c gold & multi   .20   .20
347 A56 10c gold & multi   .40   .40
348 A56 30c gold & multi   .50   .50
 a.   Souvenir sheet of 3, #346-348 1.40 1.40
      Nos. 346-348 (3)   1.10 1.10

Easter. Printed in sheets of 15 stamps and one label.

See Nos. 378-380, B31-B33, B39-B41.

Queen Elizabeth II in Coronation Regalia — A57

1973, June 1   Photo.   Perf. 14x13½
349 A57 10c gold & multi   1.25 1.25
Souvenir Sheet
Perf. 13½x14½
350 A57 50c gold & multi   3.50 3.50

20th anniv. of the coronation of Queen Elizabeth II. No. 349 printed in sheets of 5 stamps and one label.

Nos. 206, 208, 210, 212-214 Overprinted: "TENTH ANNIVERSARY / CESSATION OF / NUCLEAR TESTING / TREATY"

1973, July 25   Photo.   Perf. 14x13½
351 A34 5c gold & multi   .20   .20
352 A34 8c gold & multi   .20   .20
353 A34 10c gold & multi   .20   .20
354 A34 20c gold & multi   .20   .20
355 A34 25c gold & multi   .50   .50
356 A34 30c gold & multi   .50   .50
      Nos. 351-356 (6)   1.80 1.80

Nuclear Test Ban Treaty, 10th anniv. and as protest against French nuclear testing on Mururoa atoll.

Tipairua — A58

Historic South Pacific sailing vessels.

1973, Sept. 17   Photo.   Perf. 13½x13
357 A58 ½c shown   .30   .30
358 A58 1c Wa'a Kaulua   .30   .30
359 A58 1½c Tainui   .30   .30
360 A58 5c War canoe   .85   .85
361 A58 10c Pahi   1.00 1.00
362 A58 15c Amatasi   1.25 1.25
363 A58 25c Vaka   1.75 1.75
      Nos. 357-363 (7)   5.75 5.75

Annunciation A59

Princess Anne — A60

Designs from 15th Century Prayer Book: 5c, The Visitation. 10c, Adoration of the Shepherds. 20c, Adoration of the Kings. 30c, Slaughter of the Innocents.

1973, Oct. 30   Photo.   Perf. 13x13½
364 A59 1c multicolored   .20   .20
365 A59 5c multicolored   .20   .20
366 A59 10c multicolored   .20   .20
367 A59 20c multicolored   .40   .40
368 A59 30c multicolored   .65   .65
 a.   Souv. sheet, #364-368 + label 1.75 1.50
      Nos. 364-368 (5)   1.65 1.65

Christmas. See Nos. B34-B38.

1973, Nov. 14   Photo.   Perf. 14
369 A60 25c shown   .40   .40
370 A60 30c Mark Phillips   .60   .60
371 A60 50c Princess and Mark Phillips 1.00 1.00
 a.   Souv. sheet, #369-371 + label 2.50 2.50
      Nos. 369-371 (3)   2.00 2.00

Wedding of Princess Anne and Capt. Mark Phillips.

Running and Games Emblem A61

1c, Diving. 3c, Boxing. 10c, Weight lifting. 30c, Bicycling. 50c, Discobolus.

1974, Jan. 24   Photo.   Perf. 14
372 A61 1c multi, vert.   .20   .20
373 A61 3c multi, vert.   .20   .20
374 A61 5c multi   .20   .20
375 A61 10c multi   .25   .25
376 A61 30c multi   .75   .75
      Nos. 372-376 (5)   1.60 1.60

Souvenir Sheet
377 A61 50c multi, vert.   2.00 2.00

10th British Commonwealth Games, Christchurch, New Zealand, Jan. 24-Feb. 2. No. 377 contains one stamp 35x45mm.

Easter Type of 1973
Dated "1974"

Paintings: 5c, Jesus Carrying Cross, by Raphael. 10c, Jesus in the Arms of God, by El Greco. 30c, Descent from the Cross, by Caravaggio.

1974, Mar. 25   Perf. 13½x13
378 A56 5c gold & multi   .20   .20
379 A56 10c gold & multi   .25   .25
380 A56 30c gold & multi   .65   .65
 a.   Souvenir sheet of 3, #378-380 2.00 2.00
      Nos. 378-380 (3)   1.10 1.10

Easter. See Nos. B39-B41.

Phallicium Glaucum A62

Queen Elizabeth II — A63

Queen and Shells — A64

Cook Islands sea shells. The designs of the 2c, 5c, 10c, 30c include portrait of Queen Elizabeth II.

1974-75   Photo.   Perf. 13½
381 A62 ½c shown   .20   .20
382 A62 1c Vasum turbinellus   .20   .20

383	A62	1½c Corculum cardissa	.20 .20
384	A62	2c Terebellum terebellum	.20 .20
385	A62	3c Aulica vespertilio	.20 .20
386	A62	4c Strombus gibberulus	.20 .20
387	A62	5c Cymatium pileare	.20 .20
388	A62	6c Cyprae caputserpentis	.20 .20
389	A62	8c Bursa granularis	.20 .20
390	A62	10c Tenebra muscaria	.20 .20
391	A62	15c Mitra mitra	.40 .40
392	A62	20c Natica alapillonis roding	.60 .60
393	A62	25c Gloripallium pallium	.75 .75
394	A62	30c Conus miles	.90 .90
395	A62	50c Conus textile	1.50 1.25
396	A62	60c Oliva sericea roding	2.25 1.25
397	A63	$1 multicolored	3.50 2.25
398	A63	$2 multi ('75)	7.00 4.50

Perf. 14x13½

399	A64	$4 multi ('75)	10.50 6.50
400	A64	$6 multi ('75)	17.00 10.50
401	A64	$8 multi ('75)	21.00 13.00
402	A64	$10 multi ('75)	27.50 18.00
		Nos. 381-402 (22)	94.90 61.90

Issued: 50c, 60c, $1, 8/26; $2, 1/27; $4, 3/17; $6, 4/29; $8, 5/30; $10, 6/30; others, 5/17.

For surcharges & overprints see #488-498, 526-528, 991, O16-O26, O30-O31.

Soccer Player and Map of Oceania A65

50c, Munich stadium & map of Oceania. $1, Soccer player, Munich stadium & World Cup.

1974, July 5   Photo.   Perf. 13½
Size: 31x29mm

403	A65	25c multicolored	.45 .45
404	A65	50c multicolored	.90 .90

Size: 68x28½mm

405	A65	$1 multicolored	1.75 1.75
a.		Souvenir sheet of 3, #403-405	3.75 3.75
		Nos. 403-405 (3)	3.10 3.10

World Cup Soccer Championship, Munich, June 13-July 7. Nos. 403-405 printed in sheets of 8 and commemorative label.

$2.50 Capt. Cook Silver Coin — A66

Commemorative Silver Coins: $7.50, $7.50 coin with Queen Elizabeth II on obverse; Capt. Cook, map of Islands and "Resolution" on reverse. $2.50 coin shows "Resolution", "Adventure" and globe on reverse.

1974, July 22   Photo.   Perf. 14

406	A66	$2.50 sil, vio & blk	11.00 7.25
407	A66	$7.50 grn, sil & blk	29.00 22.50
a.		Souvenir sheet of 2, #406-407	55.00 37.50

Bicentenary of Capt. Cook's 2nd voyage of discovery. Nos. 406-407 printed in sheets of 5 and commemorative label.

Cook Islands Nos. 1, 49, 62, 66, 77 — A67

Stamps of Cook Islands: 25c, DC-3 over old Rarotonga landing strip, and No. 19. 30c, Rarotonga Post Office, UPU emblem and No. 65. 50c, UPU emblem and Nos. 1, 19, 49, 62, 65-66 and 77.

1974, Sept. 16 Photo.   Perf. 13½x14

408	A67	10c gold & multi	.20 .20
409	A67	25c gold & multi	.55 .55
410	A67	30c gold & multi	.65 .65
411	A67	50c gold & multi	1.25 1.25
a.		Souv. sheet, #408-411, perf. 13½	2.75 2.75
		Nos. 408-411 (4)	2.65 2.65

Cent. of UPU. Nos. 408-411 printed in sheets of 8 and commemorative label.

Virgin and Child, with St. John, by Raphael — A68

Paintings: 5c, Holy Family, by Andrea del Sarto. 10c, Nativity, by Correggio. 20c, Holy Family, by Rembrandt. 30c, Nativity, by Van der Weyden.

1974, Oct. 15   Photo.   Perf. 13½

412	A68	1c multicolored	.20 .20
413	A68	5c multicolored	.20 .20
414	A68	10c multicolored	.20 .20
415	A68	20c multicolored	.65 .65
416	A68	30c multicolored	.95 .95
a.		Souv. sheet, #412-416 + label	2.50 2.50
		Nos. 412-416 (5)	2.20 2.20

Christmas 1974. Nos. 412-416 printed in sheets of 15 and one label showing Queen Elizabeth II.
See Nos. B42-B46.

Churchill and Blenheim Palace A69

Sir Winston Churchill (1874-1965) and: 10c, Parliament. 25c, Chartwell. 30c, Buckingham Palace. 50c, St. Paul's Cathedral.

1974, Nov. 20   Photo.   Perf. 14

417	A69	5c violet & multi	.20 .20
418	A69	10c maroon & multi	.25 .25
419	A69	25c dk blue & multi	.65 .65
420	A69	30c brown & multi	.85 .85
421	A69	50c multicolored	1.60 1.60
a.		Souv. sheet, #417-421 + label	3.75 3.75
		Nos. 417-421 (5)	3.55 3.55

Nos. 417-421 printed in sheets of 5 stamps and one label showing $100 commemorative gold coin.

Vasco Nunez de Balboa — A70

5c, Ferdinand Magellan & route around South America. 10c, Juan Sebastian del Cano & ship. 25c, Andres de Urdaneta & ship. 25c, Miguel Lopez de Legaspi & ship.

1975, Feb. 3   Perf. 13½

422	A70	1c multicolored	.35 .20
423	A70	5c multicolored	.35 .20
424	A70	10c multicolored	1.25 .35
425	A70	25c multicolored	3.00 1.10
426	A70	30c multicolored	3.50 1.25
		Nos. 422-426 (5)	8.45 3.10

16th century explorers of the Pacific Ocean.

Apollo and Apollo-Soyuz Emblem — A71

Apollo-Soyuz Emblem &: #427b, Soyuz. #428a, Aleksei A. Leonov & Valery N. Kubasov. #428b, Donald K. Slayton, Vance D. Brand & Thomas P. Stafford. #429a, Cosmonaut inside Soyuz capsule. #429b, American astronauts inside Apollo capsule.

1975, July 15   Photo.   Perf. 13½

427	A71	25c Pair, #a.-b.	1.00 1.00
428	A71	30c Pair, #a.-b.	1.25 1.25
429	A71	50c Pair, #a.-b.	2.00 2.00
c.		Souvenir sheet of 6, #427-429	4.25 4.25
		Nos. 427-429 (3)	4.25 4.25

Apollo Soyuz space test project (Russo-American space cooperation), launching July 15; link-up, July 17. Printed sheets of 18 stamps and 2 labels showing flags.

$100 Gold Commemorative Coin — A72

1975, Aug. 8   Photo.   Perf. 13½x13

433	A72	$2 gold & dp violet	6.00 5.75

Bicentenary of the completion of Capt. Cook's second voyage of discovery.

Cook Islands' Flag, Map of Islands and New Zealand — A73

Prime Minister Sir Albert Henry — A74

Design: 25c, View of Rarotonga and flag.

1975, Aug. 8   Perf. 13½x13, 13x13½

434	A73	5c gold & multi	.60 .20
435	A74	10c gold & multi	.75 .20
436	A73	25c gold & multi	1.90 .55
		Nos. 434-436 (3)	3.25 .95

Tenth anniversary of self-government.

Virgin and Child, 15th Century, Flemish — A75

Paintings: 10c, Madonna in the Field, by Raphael. 15c, Holy Family, by Raphael. 20c, Adoration of the Shepherds, by J. B. Mayno. 35c, Annunciation, by Murillo.

1975, Dec. 1   Photo.   Perf. 13½

437	A75	6c gold & multi	.20 .20
438	A75	10c gold & multi	.20 .20
439	A75	15c gold & multi	.30 .30
440	A75	20c gold & multi	.40 .40
441	A75	35c gold & multi	.65 .65
a.		Souv. sheet of #437-441 + label	1.75 1.75
		Nos. 437-441 (5)	1.75 1.75

Christmas. See Nos. B47-B51.

Descent from the Cross, by Raphael A76

Paintings: 15c, Pieta, by Veronese. 35c, Pieta, by El Greco.

1976, Mar. 29   Photo.   Perf. 13½

442	A76	7c gold & multi	.20 .20
443	A76	15c gold & multi	.60 .60
444	A76	35c gold & multi	1.40 1.40
a.		Souvenir sheet of 3, #442-444	2.25 2.25
		Nos. 442-444 (3)	2.20 2.20

Easter. Nos. 442-444 printed in sheets of 20 with label showing Queen Elizabeth II.
See Nos. B52-B54.

Benjamin Franklin and "Resolution" — A77

Designs: $2, Capt. James Cook and "Resolution." $3, Cook, "Resolution" and Franklin.

1976, May 29   Photo.   Perf. 13½

445	A77	$1 gold & multi	5.50 3.00
446	A77	$2 gold & multi	11.50 6.25

Souvenir Sheet
Perf. 13

447	A77	$3 gold & multi	14.00 8.00

American Bicentennial. No. 447 contains one stamp 73x31mm. Nos. 445-446 printed in sheets of 5 and corner label with Franklin's request to assist Capt. Cook.
For overprint see No. O29.

Nos. 445-447 Overprinted "Royal Visit July 1976"

1976, July 6   Photo.   Perf. 13½

448	A77	$1 gold & multi	2.50 2.00
449	A77	$2 gold & multi	6.25 5.75

Souvenir Sheet
Perf. 13

450	A77	$3 gold & multi	13.00 9.00

Visit of Queen Elizabeth II and Prince Philip to the United States.

High Hurdles — A78

15c, Field hockey. 30c, Fencing. 35c, Soccer.

1976, July 22   Perf. 13½

451	A78	7c Pair, #a.-b.	.25 .25
452	A78	15c Pair, #a.-b.	.50 .50
453	A78	30c Pair, #a.-b.	1.25 1.25
454	A78	35c Pair, #a.-b.	1.50 1.50
c.		Souvenir sheet of 8, #451-454	4.50 4.50
		Nos. 451-454 (4)	3.50 3.50

21st Olympic Games, Montreal, Canada, 7/17-8/1. Printed in sheets of 10 stamps + 2 labels.

The
Visitation — A80

Designs: 10c, Virgin and Child. 15c, Adoration of the Shepherds. 20c, Adoration of the Kings. 35c, Holy Family. After painted Renaissance altar sculptures.

1976, Oct. 12   Photo.   Perf. 14x13½
459	A80	6c gold & multi	.20	.20
460	A80	10c gold & multi	.20	.20
461	A80	15c gold & multi	.25	.25
462	A80	20c gold & multi	.35	.35
463	A80	35c gold & multi	.60	.60
a.		Souv. sheet, #459-463 + label	1.75	1.75
		Nos. 459-463 (5)	1.60	1.60

Christmas. Nos. 459-463 printed in sheets of 20 with label showing Queen Elizabeth II. See Nos. B55-B59.

$5 Silver Coin, 1976 — A81

1976, Nov. 15   Photo.   Perf. 13½
464	A81	$1 multicolored	3.00	2.25

National Wildlife and Conservation Day. Issued in sheets of 5 stamps and commemorative label.
See Nos. 502, 536.

A82

#465a, Crown. #465b, Elizabeth II in Coronation Vestments. #466a, Westminster Abbey. #466b, Coach in procession. #467a, Queen and Prince Philip after coronation. 467b, Investiture of Sir Albert Henry, Premier of Cook Islands, 1974.

1977, Feb. 7   Photo.   Perf. 13½x13
465	A82	25c Pair, #a.-b.	1.00	.80
466	A82	50c Pair, #a.-b.	2.50	2.00
467	A82	$1 Pair, #a.-b.	5.00	4.00
c.		Souv. sheet, #465-467, perf. 13	8.75	7.50
		Nos. 465-467 (3)	8.50	6.80

Reign of Queen Elizabeth II, 25th anniv. Printed in sheets of 8.
For overprints see No. O27.

Crucifixion, by
Rubens — A83

Virgin and Child,
by
Memling — A84

Paintings by Rubens: 15c, Christ Between the Thieves. 35c, Descent from the Cross.

1977, Mar. 28   Photo.   Perf. 14x13½
471	A83	7c gold & multi	.50	.50
472	A83	15c gold & multi	.50	.50
473	A83	35c gold & multi	1.40	1.40
a.		Souv. sheet, #471-473, perf 13	2.50	2.50
		Nos. 471-473 (3)	2.40	2.40

Easter 1977, and 400th birth anniv. of Peter Paul Rubens (1577-1640), Flemish painter. Nos. 471-473 printed in sheets of 24 stamps and corner label with portrait of Queen Elizabeth II and description.
See Nos. B60-B62.

1977, Oct. 3   Photo.   Perf. 13½
Virgin and Child by: 10c, Hans Memling. 15c, Geertgen Tot Sin Jans. 20c, Carlo Crivelli. 35c, School of Henry Blex.
474	A84	6c gold & multi	.25	.25
475	A84	10c gold & multi	.25	.25
476	A84	15c gold & multi	.25	.25
477	A84	20c gold & multi	.45	.45
478	A84	35c gold & multi	.80	.80
a.		Souv. sheet, #474-478 + label	2.25	2.25
		Nos. 474-478 (5)	2.00	2.00

Christmas. Nos. 474-478 printed in sheets of 24 and label. See Nos. B63-B67.

$5-silver Coin, 1977 — A85

1977, Nov. 15   Photo.   Perf. 13½
479	A85	$1 silver & multi	3.50	1.60

National Wildlife Conservation Day. No. 479 issued in sheets of 5 and one label.

Capt. Cook, by Nathaniel Dance and
"Resolution" — A86

$1, "Capt. Cook Landing at Owyhee" and Capt. Cook. $2, Cook Islands $200 commemorative coin, 1978, and Cook Monument, Hawaii, 1825.

1978, Jan. 20   Litho.   Perf. 13½
480	A86	50c gold & multi	.90	.90
481	A86	$1 gold & multi	1.60	1.60
482	A86	$2 gold & multi	3.25	3.25
a.		Souvenir sheet of 3, #480-482	6.00	6.00
		Nos. 480-482 (3)	5.75	5.75

Bicentennial of Capt. Cook's arrival in Hawaii.
Nos. 480-482 issued in sheets of 5 with corner label showing ship off Hawaiian coast.
For overprints see Nos. 499-501a.

Pieta,
by
Rogier
van
der
Weyden
A87

Paintings, National Gallery, London: 35c, Burial of Jesus, by Michelangelo. 75c, Jesus at Emmaus, by Caravaggio.

1978, Mar. 20   Photo.   Perf. 13½x13
483	A87	15c gold & multi	.20	.20
484	A87	35c gold & multi	.50	.50
485	A87	75c gold & multi	1.10	1.10
a.		Souv. sheet, #483-485 + label	1.75	1.75
		Nos. 483-485 (3)	1.80	1.80

Easter. Nos. 483-485 printed in sheets of 5 and corner label showing National Gallery.
See Nos. B68-B70.

A88

A89

Souvenir Sheets

1978, June 6   Photo.   Perf. 13
486	Sheet of 4 + 2 labels	1.50	1.50
a.	A88 50c shown	.40	.40
b.	A88 50c Lion of England	.40	.40
c.	A88 50c Imperial State Crown	.40	.40
d.	A88 50c Tangaroa figure	.40	.40
487	Sheet of 4 + label	1.50	1.50
a.	A88 70c like 486a	.40	.40
b.	A88 70c Scepter with Cross	.40	.40
c.	A88 70c St. Edward's Crown	.40	.40
d.	A88 70c Rarotongan staff god	.40	.40
e.	Souv. sheet of 8, #486a-487d + label	3.00	3.00

Coronation of Queen Elizabeth II, 25th anniv.

Nos. 381, 383, 388-389, 393-396
Surcharged with New Value and Three
Bars in Silver, Black or Gold

1978, Nov. 10   Photo.   Perf. 13½
488	A62	5c on 1 ½c multi (S)	.25	.25
489	A62	7c on ½c multi	.35	.35
490	A62	10c on 6c multi (G)	.50	.50
491	A62	10c on 8c multi (G)	.50	.50
492	A62	15c on ½c multi	.80	.80
493	A62	15c on 25c multi (S)	.80	.80
494	A62	15c on 30c multi	.80	.80
495	A62	15c on 50c multi (S)	.80	.80
496	A62	15c on 60c multi (G)	.80	.80
497	A62	17c on ½c multi	.95	.95
498	A62	17c on 50c multi (S)	.95	.95
		Nos. 488-498 (11)	7.50	7.50

See Nos. 526-528.

Nos. 480-482a Overprinted in Black
on Silver Panel: "1728--250th
ANNIVERSARY OF COOK'S BIRTH--
1978"

1978, Nov. 13   Litho.   Perf. 13½
499	A86	50c gold & multi	1.00	1.00
500	A86	$1 gold & multi	2.00	2.00
501	A86	$2 gold & multi	4.00	4.00
a.		Souvenir sheet of 3, #499-501	18.00	18.00
		Nos. 499-501 (3)	7.00	7.00

250th anniv. of Capt. Cook's birth. Similar overprint in 4 lines was applied to labels. Label of No. 501a overprinted only with dates 1728, 1978.

Coin Type of 1976

$1, $5 Silver coin, 1978 (Polynesian warbler).

1978, Nov. 15   Photo.   Perf. 13½
502	A81	$1 multicolored	2.25	2.00

National Wildlife and Conservation Day. Sheets of 24 containing 4 panes of 6.

1978, Dec. 8   Photo.   Perf. 13
Virgin and Child by: 15c, Rogiervan der Weyden. 17c, Carlo Crivelli. 35c, Murillo.
503	A89	15c multicolored	.45	.45
504	A89	17c multicolored	.60	.60
505	A89	35c multicolored	.95	.95
a.		Souvenir sheet of 3, #503-505	2.10	2.10
		Nos. 503-505 (3)	2.00	2.00

Christmas. See Nos. B71-B73.

A90

A91

Descent from the Cross, by Gaspar de Crayer (Details): 10c, Pieta. 12c, St. John. 15c, Mary Magdalene. 20c, Cherubs.

1979, Apr. 5   Photo.   Perf. 13
506	A90	10c multicolored	.30	.30
507	A90	12c multicolored	.30	.30
508	A90	15c multicolored	.35	.35
509	A90	20c multicolored	.75	.75
		Nos. 506-509 (4)	1.70	1.70

Easter. See No. B74.

1979, July 23   Photo.   Perf. 14x13½
20c, Capt. Cook, by John Weber. 30c, Resolution, by Henry Roberts. 35c, Endeavour. 50c, Death of Capt. Cook, by George Carter.
510	A91	20c multicolored	.55	.55
511	A91	30c multicolored	.75	.75
512	A91	35c multicolored	.85	.85
513	A91	50c multicolored	1.10	1.10
a.		Souvenir sheet of 4	3.50	3.50
		Nos. 510-513 (4)	3.25	3.25

Capt. Cook (1728-1779), explorer. No. 513a contains 4 stamps similar to Nos. 510-513 with black frames.

Sir Rowland Hill, Originator of Penny
Postage — A92

#514a, Postrider. #514b, Stagecoach. #514c, Automobile. #514d, Streamlined train. #515a, Cap-Horniers, sailing ship. #515b, River steamer. #515c, Liner Deutschland. #515d, Liner United States. #516a, Balloon Neptune. #516b, Junkers F13. #516c, Graf Zeppelin. #516d, Concorde.

1979, Sept. 10   Perf. 14½
514	A92	30c Block of 4, #a.-d.	1.40	1.40
515	A92	35c Block of 4, #a.-d.	1.60	1.60
516	A92	50c Block of 4, #a.-d.	2.50	2.50
e.		Souv. sheet of 12, #514-516	6.00	6.00
		Nos. 514-516 (3)	5.50	5.50

Nos. 381, 383, 396 Surcharged in
Gold or Silver

1979, Sept. 12   Photo.   *Perf. 13½*
526 A62 6c on ½c multi .20 .20
527 A62 10c on 1½c multi (S) .30 .30
528 A62 15c on 60c multi .40 .40
Nos. 526-528 (3) .90 .90

Nos. 526-528 have 3 thick bars of equal
length over old value.

Girl and Baby,
IYC
Emblem — A93

IYC Emblem and: 50c, Boy playing tree
drum. 65c, Children dancing.

1979, Oct. 10   *Perf. 13*
529 A93 30c multicolored .40 .40
530 A93 50c multicolored .70 .70
531 A93 65c multicolored .90 .90
Nos. 529-531 (3) 2.00 2.00

See No. B75.

Apollo 11 Emblem
A94

Christmas Tree
Ornaments
A95

50c, Apollo 11 crew, lunar map. 60c, Astronaut walking on moon. 65c, Splashdown.

1979, Nov. 7   *Perf. 14*
532 A94 30c multicolored .40 .40
533 A94 50c multicolored .60 .60
534 A94 60c multicolored .75 .75
535 A94 65c multicolored .85 .85
a.   Souv. sheet, #532-535, perf. 13 3.50 3.50
Nos. 532-535 (4) 2.60 2.60

Apollo 11 moon landing, 10th anniv.

Coin Type of 1976

$1, $5 Silver coin, 1979 (Raratonga fruit
dove).

Perf. 13½x14½
1979, Nov. 15   Photo.
536 A81 $1 multicolored 2.00 2.00

National Wildlife and Conservation Day.

1979, Dec. 14   *Perf. 14*
Christmas (Flowers and): 10c, Star. 12c,
Bells and candle. 15c, Ancestral statue.
537 A95 6c multicolored .20 .20
538 A95 10c multicolored .20 .20
539 A95 12c multicolored .20 .20
540 A95 15c multicolored .20 .20
Nos. 537-540,B76-B79 (8) 1.80 1.80

A96

Bible illustrations by Gustave Doré, 1833-
1883: #541a, Flagellation. #541b, Jesus
Wearing Crown of Thorns. #542a, Jesus
Mocked. #542b, Jesus Falls. #543a, The Crucifixion. #543b, Descent from the Cross.

1980, Mar. 31   Photo.   *Perf. 13*
541 A96 20c Pair, #a.-b. .60 .60
542 A96 30c Pair, #a.-b. .90 .90
543 A96 35c Pair, #a.-b. 1.00 1.00
Nos. 541-543 (3) 2.50 2.50

Easter. See Nos. 553, B80-B83.

Doves
with Olive
Branch,
Rotary
Emblem
A97

1980, May 27   Photo.   *Perf. 14*
547 A97 30c shown .45 .45
548 A97 35c Flowers .50 .50
549 A97 50c Flags, globe .70 .70
Nos. 547-549 (3) 1.65 1.65

Rotary Intl., 75th anniv. See No. B87

Easter Type of 1980 and:

New Zealand No. 1 — A98

#550a, Postrider. #550b, Coach. #550c,
Automobile. #550d, Train.
New Zealand #2 and: #551a, Sailing ship.
#551b, River steamer. #551c, Transatlantic
liner (facing left). #551d, Transatlantic liner
(facing right).
New Zealand #3 and: #552a, 1870-71 mail
balloon. #552b, 1919 plane. #552c, Graf
Zeppelin. #552d, Concorde.

1980, Aug. 22   Photo.   *Perf. 14*
550 A98 30c Block of 4, #a.-d. 1.50 1.25
551 A98 35c Block of 4, #a.-d. 2.00 1.75
552 A98 50c Block of 4, #a.-d. 3.00 2.50
e.   Souvenir sheet of 12 7.50 6.50
Nos. 550-552 (3) 6.50 5.50

Souvenir Sheet
Perf. 13
553 A96 Sheet of 6, #541-543 5.00 3.50

ZEAPEX '80, New Zealand Intl. Stamp
Exhib., Auckland, Aug. 23-31. #552e contains
of #550-552 arranged horizontally (4x3). #553
has black on gold overprint: "ZEAPEX / '80 /
Auckland / +10c" in margin.

Queen Mother
Elizabeth, 80th
Birthday — A99

1980, Sept. 22   Photo.   *Perf. 13*
554 A99 50c multicolored 1.50 1.00

Souvenir Sheet
555 A99 $2 multicolored 2.75 2.75

No. 554 issued in sheets of 9 (3x3).

Johannes Kepler, Spacecraft — A100

Designs: Nos. 556a, 559a, Kepler, spacecraft (diff.). No. 559b, Kepler, lunar rover,
astronaut on moon. Nos. 557a-558b, Jules
Verne, various scenes from From Earth to
Moon, vert.

1980, Nov. 7   Photo.   *Perf. 13*
556 A100 12c Pair, #a-b .75 .75
557 A100 20c Pair, #a-b .75 .75
558 A100 30c Pair, #a-b 2.00 2.00
a.   Souvenir sheet #557-558 3.50 3.50
559 A100 50c Pair, #a-b 3.50 3.50
a.   Souv. sheet, #556, 559 4.50 4.50
Nos. 556-559 (4) 7.00 7.00

Death anniversaries of Johannes Kepler,
German astronomer and Jules Verne, French
science fiction writer.

Burning Bush
Coral — A101

Daisy Coral — A102

#564a, 570a, 576a, Siphonogorgia. #564b,
570b, 576b, Pavona practorta. #564c, 570c,
576c, Stylaster echinatus. #564d, 570d, 576d,
Stylaster echinatus. #565a, 571a, 577a, Millepora alcicornis. #565b, 571b, 577b, Junceella
gemmaea. #565c, 571c, 577c, Fungia
fungites. #565d, 571d, 577d, Heliofungia
actiniformis. #566a, 572a, 578a, Distichopora
violacea. #566b, 572b, 578b, Stylaster. #566c,
572c, 578c, Gonipora. #566d, 572d, 578d,
Caulastraea echinulata. #567a, 573a, 579a,
Ptilosarcus gurneyi. #567b, 573b, 579b,
Stylophora pistillata. #567c, 573c, 579c,
Melithaea squamata. #567d, 573d, 579d,
Porites andrewsi. #568a, 574a, 580a,
Lobophyllia bemprichii. #568b, 574b, 580b,
Palauastrea ramosa. #568c, 574c, 580c, Bellonella indica. #568d, 574d, 580d, Pectinia
alcicornis. #569a, 575a, 581a, Sarcophyton
digitatum. #569b, 575b, 581b, Melithaea albi-
tincta. #569c, 575c, 581c, Plerogyra sinuosa.
#569d, 575d, 581d, Dendrophyllia gracilis.

1980-82   *Perf. 13½x13*
Strips of 4
564 A101 1c #a.-d. .25 .25
565 A101 3c #a.-d. .30 .30
566 A101 4c #a.-d. .35 .35
567 A101 5c #a.-d. .45 .45
568 A101 6c #a.-d. .60 .60
569 A101 8c #a.-d. .70 .70
570 A101 10c #a.-d. .90 .90
571 A101 12c #a.-d. 1.10 1.10
572 A101 15c #a.-d. 1.40 1.40
573 A101 20c #a.-d. 1.60 1.60
574 A101 25c #a.-d. 2.25 2.25
575 A101 30c #a.-d. 2.50 2.50
576 A101 35c #a.-d. 3.00 3.00
577 A101 50c #a.-d. 4.00 4.00
578 A101 60c #a.-d. 5.25 5.25
579 A101 70c #a.-d. 5.75 5.75
580 A101 80c #a.-d. 6.25 6.25
581 A101 $1 #a.-d. 7.00 7.00

Perf. 14x13½
582 A102 $2 like #566c 5.50 5.50
583 A102 $3 like #565d 7.75 7.75
584 A102 $4 like #567b 10.00 10.00
585 A102 $6 like #564c 15.00 15.00
586 A102 $10 like #569b 22.50 22.50
Nos. 564-586 (23) 104.40 104.40

Issued: 1-8c, 11/21/80; 10-30c, 12/19/80;
35-60c, 3/16/81; 70c, 80c, 4/13/81; $1,
5/20/81; $2, $3, 11/27/81; $4, $6, 1/11/82;
$10, 3/5/82.
For surcharges see Nos. 710-714, 716, 738,
741, 811-815, 953-954, 956-957, 959, 961-
962, 964, 978-979, 984-986, B109-B111,
O50-O53. For overprints see Nos. 992, 1049.

Annunciation,
13th Century
Prayerbook
Illustration —
A102a

1980, Dec. 1   Photo.   *Perf. 14*
652 A102a 15c shown .20 .20
653 A102a 30c Visitation .40 .40
654 A102a 40c Nativity .50 .50
655 A102a 50c Epiphany .70 .70
a.   Souvenir sheet of 4, #652-655 2.00 2.00
Nos. 652-655 (4) 1.80 1.80

Christmas. See Nos. B88-B91.

Crucifixion, 12th Cent. Prayerbook
Illustration — A103

1981, Apr. 10   *Perf. 14*
656 A103 15c shown .20 .20
657 A103 25c Placing in Tomb .40 .40
658 A103 40c Marys at the Tomb .60 .60
Nos. 656-658 (3) 1.20 1.20

Easter. See Nos. B92-B95.

Prince Charles
and Lady
Diana — A104

1981, July 29   Photo.   *Perf. 14*
659 A104 $1 Charles 1.75 1.75
660 A104 $2 shown 3.50 3.50
a.   Souv. sheet of 2, #659-660 5.25 5.25

Royal Wedding. Issued in sheets of 4.
For overprints and surcharges see Nos.
679-680, 715, 835, 980-981, B97-B98.

Soccer Players — A105

Designs: Various soccer players.

1981, Oct 20   Photo.   *Perf. 14*
661 A105 20c Pair, #a.-b. 1.00 1.00
662 A105 30c Pair, #a.-b. 1.75 1.75
663 A105 35c Pair, #a.-b. 2.25 2.25
664 A105 50c Pair, #a.-b. 3.00 3.00
Nos. 661-664 (4) 8.00 8.00

ESPANA '82 World Cup Soccer Championships. See No. B96.

Virgin and Child,
by
Rubens — A107

Christmas: Rubens Paintings.

1981, Dec. 14   Photo.   Perf. 14x13½

669	A107	8c shown	.50	.50
670	A107	15c Coronation of St. Catherine	.50	.50
671	A107	40c Adoration of the Shepherds	1.50	1.50
672	A107	50c Adoration of the Kings	1.75	1.75
		Nos. 669-672 (4)	4.25	4.25

Souvenir Sheets

1982, Jan. 18

673	A107	75c +5c like #669	1.10	1.10
674	A107	75c +5c like #670	1.10	1.10
675	A107	75c +5c like #671	1.10	1.10
676	A107	75c +5c like #672	1.10	1.10

Surtax was for school children. See No. B99.

21st Birthday of Princess Diana
A108

#677a, 21st Birthday. #677b, 1 July 1982. #678a, Wedding portrait. #678b, 1 July 1982. #678d, $1.25, #678e, $2.50, both inscribed "21st Birthday / 1 July 1982."

1982, June 21   Photo.   Perf. 14

677	A108	$1.25 Pair, #a.-b.	4.50	4.50
678	A108	$2.50 Pair, #a.-b.	9.50	9.50
c.		Souv. sheet of 2, #d.-e.	9.50	9.50

Issued in sheets of 4.
See Nos. 681-682. For surcharges and overprints see Nos. 739-740, 833-834, 982.

Nos. 659-660a Overprinted: "ROYAL BIRTH 21 JUNE 1982" (a) or "PRINCE WILLIAM OF WALES" (b)

#680d, $1; #680e, $2, both inscribed "21 JUNE 1982 ROYAL BIRTH."

1982, July 12

679	A104	$1 Pair, #a.-b.	3.00	3.00
680	A104	$2 Pair, #a.-b.	5.50	5.50
c.		Souv. sheet of 2, #d.-e.	6.00	6.00

Issued in sheets of 4.
For surcharges see Nos. 987-988.

Design A108 Inscribed:
"Royal Birth" (a)
or "21 June 1982" (b)

#682d, $1.25; #682e, $2.50, both inscribed "Royal Birth / June 1982."

1982, Aug. 3

681	A108	$1.25 Pair, #a.-b.	3.75	3.75
682	A108	$2.50 Pair, #a.-b.	7.25	7.25
c.		Souv. sheet of 2, #d.-e.	7.50	7.50

Issued in sheets of 4.

Serenade, by Norman Rockwell (1894-1978)
A109

1982, Sept. 10   Photo.   Perf. 14

683	A109	5c shown	.20	.20
684	A109	10c The Hikers	.20	.20
685	A109	20c The Doctor and the Doll	.30	.30
686	A109	30c Home From Camp	.45	.45
		Nos. 683-686 (4)	1.15	1.15

Christmas
A110

Princess Diana Holding Prince William. Various Details from Virgin with Garlands, by Rubens.

1982, Nov. 30   Photo.   Perf. 14

687	A110	35c multicolored	1.50	1.10
688	A110	48c multicolored	2.00	1.50
689	A110	60c multicolored	2.25	1.75
690	A110	$1.70 multicolored	6.75	6.75
		Nos. 687-690 (4)	12.50	11.10

Souvenir Sheets
Perf. 13½

691		Sheet of 4	8.50	8.50
a.		A110 60c like 35c	2.00	2.00
b.		A110 60c like 48c	2.00	2.00
c.		A110 60c like #689	2.00	2.00
d.		A110 60c like $1.70	2.00	2.00
692	A110	75c + 5c like 35c	3.00	3.00
693	A110	75c + 5c like 48c	3.00	3.00
694	A110	75c + 5c like 60c	3.00	3.00
695	A110	75c + 5c like $1.70	3.00	3.00

No. 691 contains 4 stamps (27x32mm, showing only painting details) plus 2 labels showing Diana and William. Nos. 692-695 show Diana and William (27x39mm), multicolored margins show painting details. Surtax was for child welfare.

Commonwealth Day — A111

#696a, Tangaroa statue. #696b, Rarotonga oranges. #696c, Rarotonga Airport. #696d, Prime Minister Thomas Davis.

1983, Mar. 14   Photo.   Perf. 14

696	A111	60c Block of 4, #a.-d.	3.00	3.00

For overprints see No. O46.

Scouting Year — A112

1983, Apr. 5   Photo.   Perf. 13x13½

700	A112	12c Pair, #a.-b., shown	.75	.75
701	A112	36c Pair, #a.-b., Camping	2.25	2.25
702	A112	48c Pair, #a.-b., Rope swing	2.75	2.75
703	A112	60c Pair, #a.-b., Tree planting	3.50	3.50
		Nos. 700-703 (4)	9.25	9.25

Souvenir Sheet of 8

704		#a.-d.	8.00	8.00

#704 contains 2 each of #700-703 with 2c surtax.

Nos. 700-704 Overprinted: "XV WORLD JAMBOREE ALBERTA CANADA 1983"

1983, July 4   Photo.   Perf. 13x13½

705	A112	12c Pair, #a.-b.	.50	.50
706	A112	36c Pair, #a.-b.	2.25	2.25
707	A112	48c Pair, #a.-b.	2.75	2.75
708	A112	60c Pair, #a.-b.	3.50	3.50
		Nos. 705-708 (4)	9.00	9.00

Souvenir Sheet of 8

709	A112	#a.-d.	8.00	8.00

Nos. 569, 572, 574-575, 579, 587, 660 Surcharged in Black or Gold
Perf. 13½x13, 14x13½, 14

1983, Aug. 12   Photo.
Blocks of 4, #a.-d. (#710-714)

710	A101	18c on 8c #569	3.50	3.50
711	A101	36c on 15c #572	5.75	5.75
712	A101	36c on 30c #575	5.75	5.75
713	A101	48c on 25c #574	9.25	9.25
714	A101	72c on 70c #579	14.00	14.00
715	A104	96c on $2 #660 (G)	4.50	4.50
716	A102	$5.60 on $6 #587 (G)	29.00	29.00
		Nos. 710-716 (7)	71.75	71.75

A114

A115

1983, Sept. 9   Perf. 14

732		Pair	.85	.85
a.		A114 6c Gt. Britain	.40	.40
b.		A115 6c Cook Islds. Group Federal flag	.40	.40
733		Pair	1.10	1.10
a.		A114 12c Raratonga ensign	.55	.55
b.		A115 12c New Zealand	.55	.55
734		Pair	1.25	1.25
a.		A114 15c Cook Islds, 1973-79	.65	.65
b.		A115 15c Cook Islds, 1983	.65	.65
c.		Souvenir sheet of 6, #732-734	2.25	2.25
735		Pair	2.00	2.00
a.		A114 20c like #732a	.95	.95
b.		A115 20c like #732b	.95	.95
736		Pair	2.50	2.50
a.		A114 30c like #733a	1.25	1.25
b.		A115 30c like #733b	1.25	1.25
737		Pair	3.00	3.00
a.		A114 35c like #734a	1.50	1.50
b.		A115 35c like #734b	1.50	1.50
c.		Souvenir sheet of 6, #735-737	4.75	4.75
		Nos. 732-737 (6)	10.70	10.70

Nos. 732-737 have different background landscapes; Nos. 735-737 airmail with silver background. Nos. 734c, 737c perf. 13½.

Nos. 576, 586, 678 Surcharged in Black or Gold
Perf. 13½x13, 14x13½, 14

1983, Aug. 30   Photo.
Block of 4, #a.-d.

738	A101	36c on 35c #576	5.75	5.75

Pair, #a.-b. (#739)

739	A108	96c on $2.50 #678 (G)	9.25	9.25
740	A102	$5.60 on $10 #586 (G)	22.50	22.50
		Nos. 738-740 (3)	37.50	37.50

Satellite Earth Station — A116

Designs: Various satellites in orbit.

1983, Oct. 10   Litho.   Perf. 13½

744	A116	36c multicolored	1.00	1.00
745	A116	48c multicolored	1.50	1.50
746	A116	60c multicolored	1.75	1.75
747	A116	96c multicolored	2.75	2.75
		Nos. 744-747 (4)	7.00	7.00

Souvenir Sheet

748	A116	$2 multicolored	5.00	5.00

World Communications Year.

Christmas
A117

Manned Flight Bicent. — A118

Raphael Paintings: 12c, La Belle Jardiniere. 18c, Madonna and Child with Five Saints. 36c, Madonna and Child with Saint John. 48c, Madonna of the Fish. 60c, Madonna of the Baldacchino.

1983   Photo.   Perf. 14

749	A117	12c multicolored	1.10	1.10
750	A117	18c multicolored	1.10	1.10
751	A117	36c multicolored	2.00	2.00
752	A117	48c multicolored	2.50	2.50
753	A117	60c multicolored	3.75	3.75
		Nos. 749-753 (5)	10.45	10.45

Souvenir Sheets
Perf. 13½

754		Sheet of 5	4.00	4.00
a.		A117 12c + 3c like #749	.30	.30
b.		A117 18c + 3c like #750	.35	.35
c.		A117 36c + 3c like #751	.70	.70
d.		A117 48c + 3c like #752	.90	.90
e.		A117 60c + 3c like #753	1.10	1.10
755	A117	85c + 5c like #749	1.60	1.60
756	A117	85c + 5c like #750	1.60	1.60
757	A117	85c + 5c like #751	1.60	1.60
758	A117	85c + 5c like #752	1.60	1.60
759	A117	85c + 5c like #753	1.60	1.60

Nos. 749-753 issued in sheets of 5 + label. Surtax was for children's charities.
Issued: #749-754, Nov. 14; others, Dec. 9.

1984, Jan. 16   Photo.   Perf. 13

Various balloons.

760	A118	36c 1st manned flight, 1783	.85	.85
761	A118	48c Ascent of Adorne, Strasbourg, 1784	1.00	1.00
762	A118	60c balloon, 1785	1.10	1.10
763	A118	72c Man on horse, 1785	1.60	1.60
764	A118	96c Godard's aerial acrobatics, 1850	1.75	1.75
		Nos. 760-764 (5)	6.30	6.30

Souvenir Sheets

765	A118	$2.50 Blanchard & Jefferies, 1785	4.25	4.25
766		Sheet of 5	7.75	7.75
a.		A118 36c + 5c like 36c	.90	.90
b.		A118 48c + 5c like 48c	1.10	1.10
c.		A118 60c + 5c like 60c	1.50	1.50
d.		A118 72c + 5c like 72c	1.75	1.75
e.		A118 96c + 5c like 96c	2.25	2.25

#765 contains 1 stamp 30x48mm, perf. 13½.

Save the Whales Campaign
A119

1984, Feb. 10   Photo.   Perf. 13

767	A119	10c Cuvier's beaked whale	.40	.40
768	A119	18c Risso's dolphin	.60	.60
769	A119	20c True's beaked whale	.70	.70
770	A119	24c Long-finned pilot whale	.90	.90
771	A119	30c Narwhal	1.10	1.10
772	A119	36c Beluga whale	1.25	1.25
773	A119	42c Common dolphin	1.60	1.60

774	A119	48c Commerson's dolphin	1.75	1.75
775	A119	60c Bottle-nosed dolphin	2.25	2.25
776	A119	72c Sowerby's whale	2.75	2.75
777	A119	96c Common porpoise	3.25	3.25
778	A119	$2 Boutu	7.25	7.25
		Nos. 767-778 (12)	23.80	23.80

1984 Summer Olympics
A120

Posters of Various Summer Olympics. 72c, 96c, $1.20 airmail.

1984, Mar. 8   **Photo.**   **Perf. 13½**

779	A120	18c Athens, 1896	.35	.35
780	A120	24c Paris, 1900	.40	.40
781	A120	36c St. Louis, 1904	.65	.65
782	A120	48c London, 1948	.85	.85
783	A120	60c Tokyo, 1964	1.00	1.00
784	A120	72c Berlin, 1936	1.25	1.25
785	A120	96c Rome, 1960	1.75	1.75
786	A120	$1.20 Los Angeles, 1932	2.25	2.25
		Nos. 779-786 (8)	8.50	8.50

For overprints see Nos. 826-828.

Nos. 582-586 Surcharged and:

Coral — A121

1c, Siphonogorgia. 2c, Millepora alcicornis. 3c, Distichopora violacea. 5c, Ptilosarcus gurneyi. 10c, Lobophyllia bemprichii. 12c, Sarcophyton digitatum. 14c, Pavona praetorta. 18c, Junceela gemmacea. 20c, Stylaster. 24c, Stylophora pistillata. 30c, Palauastrea ramosa. 36c, Melithaea albitincta. 40c, Stylaster echinatus. 42c, Fungia fungites. 48c, Gonipora. 50c, Melithaea squamata. 52c, Bellonella indica. 55c, Plerogyra sinuosa. 60c, Tubastraea. 70c, Heliofungia actinformis. 85c, Caulastraea echinulata. 96c, Porites andrewsi. $1.10, Pectinia alcicornis. $1.20, Dendrophyllia gracilis.

1984   **Perf. 13½x13**

787	A121	1c multi	.20	.20
788	A121	2c multi	.20	.20
789	A121	3c multi	.20	.20
790	A121	5c multi	.20	.20
791	A121	10c multi	.20	.20
792	A121	12c multi	.20	.20
793	A121	14c multi	.30	.30
794	A121	18c multi	.40	.40
795	A121	20c multi	.40	.40
796	A121	24c multi	.50	.50
797	A121	30c multi	.60	.60
798	A121	36c multi	.75	.75
799	A121	40c multi	.80	.80
800	A121	42c multi	.90	.90
801	A121	48c multi	.95	.95
802	A121	50c multi	1.00	1.00
803	A121	52c multi	1.00	1.00
804	A121	55c multi	1.40	1.40
805	A121	60c multi	1.60	1.60
806	A121	70c multi	1.75	1.75
807	A121	85c multi	2.00	2.00
808	A121	96c multi	2.25	2.25
809	A121	$1.10 multi	3.00	3.00
810	A121	$1.20 multi	3.25	3.25

Perf. 14x13½

Size: 59½x38½mm

811	A102	$3.60 on $2 #582	8.00	8.00
812	A102	$4.20 on $3 #583	8.75	8.75
813	A102	$5 on $4 #584	10.50	10.50
814	A102	$7.20 on $6 #585	15.00	15.00
815	A102	$9.60 on $10 #586	17.50	17.50
		Nos. 787-815 (29)	83.80	83.80

Issued: #787-801, 3/23; #802-810, 5/15; #811-813, 6/28; #814, 7/20; #815, 8/10.
For surcharges & overprints see #948-952, 955, 958, 960, 963, 965-967, B105-B108, O32-O45.

Nos. 784-786 Overprinted With Winners

1984, Aug. 24   **Photo.**   **Perf. 13½**

826	A120	72c Team Dressage, Germany	1.00	1.00
827	A120	96c Daley Thompson, U.K.	1.50	1.50
828	A120	$1.20 Carl Lewis, USA	1.90	1.90
		Nos. 826-828 (3)	4.40	4.40

1984 Summer Olympics. Nos. 826-828 airmail.

AUSIPEX '84 — A123

1984, Sept. 20

829	A123	36c Captain Cook's cottage	1.60	1.60
830	A123	48c The Endeavour	2.10	2.10
831	A123	60c Cook's landing	2.50	2.50
832	A123	$2 Portrait, by John Webber	8.50	8.50
a.		Souv. sheet #829-832, 90c ea	12.50	12.50
b.		Sheet of 4, STAMPEX '86 emblem	10.50	10.50
		Nos. 829-832 (4)	14.70	14.70

No. 832b issued Aug. 4, 1986, for STAMPEX '86, Adelaide, Aug. 4-10; margin ovptd. with exhibition emblem, stamp picturing James Cook ovptd. with gold circle and black "Stampex 86 / Adelaide."

Nos. 677-678 Ovptd.:
"Commemorating -/15 Sept. 1984" or "Birth H.R.H./Prince Henry" and Surcharged in Gold.
No. 659 Ovptd. "Royal Birth/Prince Henry/15 Sept. 1984" and Surcharged in Silver.

1984, Oct. 15   **Photo.**   **Perf. 14**

833	A108	$1.25 Pair, #a.-b.	3.50	3.50
834	A108	$2.50 Pair, #a.-b.	7.75	7.75
835	A104	$3 on $1 No. 659	4.75	4.75
		Nos. 833-835 (3)	16.00	16.00

Nos. 833-835 printed in sheets of 4 stamps.

A124

Christmas (Paintings): 36c, Virgin on Throne with Child, by Giovanni Bellini (c. 1430-1516). 48c, Virgin and Child, 15th century, artistunknown. 60c, Virgin and Child with Saints, by Alvise Vivarini (c. 1446-1505). 96c, Virgin and Child with Angels, by Hans Memling (c. 1435-1494). $1.20, Adoration of the Magi, by Giovanni Tiepolo (1696-1770).

1984

838	A124	36c multicolored	.90	.90
839	A124	48c multicolored	1.25	1.25
840	A124	60c multicolored	1.60	1.60
841	A124	96c multicolored	2.50	2.50
842	A124	$1.20 multicolored	3.25	3.25
		Nos. 838-842 (5)	9.50	9.50

Souvenir Sheets
Perf. 13½

843		Sheet of 5	5.75	5.75
a.	A124	36c +5c like #838	.70	.70
b.	A124	48c +5c like #839	.85	.85
c.	A124	60c +5c like #840	1.00	1.00
d.	A124	96c +5c like #841	1.50	1.50
e.	A124	$1.20 +5c like #842	1.75	1.75
844	A124	95c + 5c like #838	1.75	1.75
845	A124	95c + 5c like #839	1.75	1.75
846	A124	95c + 5c like #840	1.75	1.75
847	A124	95c + 5c like #841	1.75	1.75
848	A124	95c + 5c like #842	1.75	1.75

Surtax of No. 843 for children's organizations, of Nos. 844-848 for youth education.
Issued: #838-843, 11/21; #844-848, 12/10.

1985, Apr. 23   **Perf. 13x13½**

Illustrations of North American bird species by artist, naturalist John J. Audubon.

849	A125	30c Downy woodpecker	1.50	1.50
850	A125	55c Black-throated blue warbler	2.75	2.75
851	A125	65c Yellow-throated warbler	3.00	3.00
852	A125	75c Chestnut-sided warbler	3.75	3.75
853	A125	95c Dickcissel	4.75	4.75
854	A125	$1.15 White-crowned sparrow	4.75	4.75
		Nos. 849-854 (6)	20.50	20.50

Souvenir Sheets

855	A125	$1.30 Red-cockaded woodpecker	3.00	3.00
856	A125	$2.80 Seaside sparrow	5.25	5.25
857	A125	$5.30 Zenaida dove	10.75	10.75

Audubon birth bicentenary.

Locomotives — A126

1985, May 14   **Litho.**   **Perf. 14x13½**

858	A126	20c Kingston Flyer, New Zealand	.20	.20
859	A126	55c Class 640, Italy	.50	.50
860	A126	65c Gotthard, Switzerland	.60	.60
861	A126	75c Union Pacific 6900, US	.70	.70
862	A126	95c Super Continental, Canada	.90	.90
863	A126	$1.15 TGV, France	1.00	1.00
864	A126	$2.20 Flying Scotsman, U.K.	2.00	2.00
865	A126	$3.40 Orient Express, Europe	3.00	3.00
		Nos. 858-865 (8)	8.90	8.90

Intl. Youth Year — A127

Paintings: 55c, Helena Fourment, by Rubens. 65c, Vigee-Lebrun and Daughter, by Elizabeth Vigee-Lebrun (1755-1842). 75c, on the Terrace, by Renoir. $1.30, Young Mother Sewing, by Mary Cassatt (1845-1926).

1985, June 6   **Photo.**   **Perf. 13x13½**

866	A127	55c multicolored	3.50	3.50
867	A127	65c multicolored	4.00	4.00
868	A127	75c multicolored	4.50	4.50
869	A127	$1.30 multicolored	7.50	7.50
		Nos. 866-869 (4)	19.50	19.50

Souvenir Sheet

870		Sheet of 4	11.00	11.00
a.	A127	55c + 10c like #866	1.75	1.75
b.	A127	65c + 10c like #867	2.10	2.10
c.	A127	75c + 10c like #868	2.40	2.40
d.	A127	$1.30 + 10c like #869	3.75	3.75

Surtax for youth organizations.

Queen Mother, 85th Birthday
A128

Portraits: 65c, Lady Elizabeth, 1908, by Mable Hankey. 75c, Duchess of York, 1923, by Savely Sorine. $1.15, Duchess of York, 1925, by Philip De Laslo. $2.80, $5.30, Queen Elizabeth, 1938, by Sir Gerald Kelly.

1985, June 28

871	A128	65c multi	.80	.80
872	A128	75c multi	.95	.95
873	A128	$1.15 multi	1.50	1.50
874	A128	$2.80 multi	3.25	3.25
874A		Sheet of 4 ('86)	6.50	6.50
b.-e.	A128	55c, like #871-874	1.50	1.50
		Nos. 871-874A (5)	13.00	13.00

Souvenir Sheet

875	A128	$5.30 multi	12.50	12.50

Nos. 871-874 printed in sheets of four.
#874A issued 8/4/86, for 86th birthday.
For surcharges see Nos. B114, B116, B122, B134, B140.

A129

Portraits of prime ministers.

1985, July 29

876	A129	30c Albert Henry, 1965-78	1.25	1.25
877	A129	50c Sir Thomas Davis, 1978-83	2.50	2.50
878	A129	65c Geoffrey Henry, 1983	3.00	3.00
		Nos. 876-878 (3)	6.75	6.75

Souvenir Sheet

879		Sheet of 3	11.50	11.50
a.	A129	55c like #876	3.50	3.50
b.	A129	55c like #877	3.50	3.50
c.	A129	55c like #878	3.50	3.50

Self-government, 20th anniv.

A130

1985, July 29   **Perf. 14**

880	A130	55c Golf	5.25	5.25
881	A130	65c Rugby	6.00	6.00
882	A130	75c Tennis	6.75	6.75
		Nos. 880-882 (3)	18.00	18.00

Souvenir Sheet

883		Sheet of 3	18.00	18.00
a.	A130	55c + 10c like #880	5.50	5.50
b.	A130	65c + 10c like #881	5.50	5.50
c.	A130	75c + 10c like #882	5.50	5.50

South Pacific Mini Games, Rarotonga, July 31-Aug. 10. Surtax for the benefit of the Mini Games.

A131

A132

Seahorse & conf. emblems: 55c, South Pacific Bureau for Economic Cooperation. 65c, South Pacific Forum. 75c, No. 887c, Pacific Islands Conf.

1985, July 29 **Perf. 14**
884 A131 55c blk, scar & gold 1.75 1.75
885 A131 65c blk, vio & gold 2.00 2.00
886 A131 75c blk, brt grn & gold 2.25 2.25
Nos. 884-886 (3) 6.00 6.00

Souvenir Sheet
887 50c Sheet of 3, #a.-c. 3.50 3.50
Pacific islands conf., Rarotonga, 7/30-8/10.

1985
Virgin and Child paintings by Botticelli.
888 A132 55c Madonna of the Magnificent 2.25 2.25
889 A132 65c Madonna with Pomegranate 2.75 2.75
890 A132 75c Madonna with Child & Six Angels 3.50 3.50
891 A132 95c Madonna & Child with St. John 4.50 4.50
Nos. 888-891 (4) 13.00 13.00

Souvenir Sheets
Perf. 13½
892 A132 $2.75 Sheet of 4 8.00 8.00
a. A132 50c like #888 1.75 1.75
b. A132 50c like #889 1.75 1.75
c. A132 50c like #890 1.75 1.75
d. A132 50c like #891 1.75 1.75

Imperf
893 A132 $1.20 like #888 2.50 2.50
894 A132 $1.45 like #889 2.75 2.75
895 A132 $2.20 like #890 4.50 4.50
896 A132 $2.75 like #891 5.25 5.25

Christmas. Issue dates: Nos. 888-892, Nov. 18; Nos. 893-896, Dec. 9.

Halley's Comet — A133

Elizabeth II, 60th Birthday — A134

Paintings: 55c, No. 902a, The Eve of the Deluge, by John Martin (1789-1854). 65c, No. 902b, Lot and His Daughters, by Lucas van Leyden (1494-1533). 75c, No. 902c, Auspicious Comet, 1587, anonymous. $1.25, No.

902d, Events Following Charles I, by Herman Saftleven (1609-1658). $2, No. 902e, Ossian Receiving Napoleonic Officers, by Anne Louis Girodet-Trioson (1764-1824). $4, Halley's Comet over the Thames, 1759, by Samuel Scott (1702-1772).

1986, Mar. 13 **Photo.** **Perf. 14**
897 A133 55c multicolored 1.40 1.40
898 A133 65c multicolored 1.75 1.75
899 A133 75c multicolored 2.10 2.10
900 A133 $1.25 multicolored 4.00 4.00
901 A133 $2 multicolored 5.75 5.75
Nos. 897-901 (5) 15.00 15.00

Souvenir Sheets
Perf. 13½
902 Sheet of 5 + label 8.00 8.00
a.-e. A133 70c, each single 1.50 1.50
903 A133 $4 multicolored 9.50 9.50
For surcharges see Nos. B113, B115, B117, B123, B129.

1986, Apr. 21 **Perf. 13x13½**
Various portraits.
904 A134 95c multi 1.75 1.75
905 A134 $1.25 multi 2.10 2.10
906 A134 $1.50 multi 2.40 2.40
Nos. 904-906 (3) 6.25 6.25

Souvenir Sheets
907 A134 $1.10 like #904 2.75 2.75
908 A134 $1.95 like #905 5.00 5.00
909 A134 $2.45 like #906 7.25 7.25
For surcharges see Nos. 972-974, B118, B124, B127, B136-B137, B139.

AMERIPEX '86 — A135

Designs: $1, US No. 1, The Resolution, Rarotonga. $1.50, Downtown Chicago. $2, No. 398, Benjamin Franklin, The Resolution.

1986, May 21 **Photo.** **Perf. 14**
910 A135 $1 multi 4.50 4.50
911 A135 $1.50 multi 6.50 6.50
912 A135 $2 multi 8.50 8.50
Nos. 910-912 (3) 19.50 19.50
For surcharges see Nos. B119, B128, B130.

Statue of Liberty, Cent. — A136

Wedding of Prince Andrew and Sarah Ferguson — A137

1986, July 4
913 A136 $1 Head 1.25 1.25
914 A136 $1.25 Torch 1.50 1.50
915 A136 $2.75 Liberty Is. 3.50 3.50
Nos. 913-915 (3) 6.25 6.25
For surcharges see Nos. B120, B125, B132.

1986, July 23
916 A137 $1 Sarah Ferguson 1.00 1.00
917 A137 $2 Prince Andrew 2.00 2.00

Size: 60x33½mm
Perf. 13½x13
918 A137 $3 Couple 3.00 3.00
Nos. 916-918 (3) 6.00 6.00
Nos. 916-918 each printed in sheets of 4.

For surch. see #975-977, B121, B131, B135.

Christmas A138

Paintings by Rubens: 55c, No. 922a, The Holy Family. $1.30, $6.40, No. 922b, Virgin with Garland. $2.75, No. 922c, Adoration of Magi.

1986, Nov. 17 **Litho.** **Perf. 13½**
919 A138 55c multi 1.75 1.75
920 A138 $1.30 multi 4.00 4.00
921 A138 $2.75 multi 8.25 8.25
Nos. 919-921 (3) 14.00 14.00

Souvenir Sheets
922 Sheet of 3 18.00 18.00
a.-c. A138 $2.40, any single 5.75 5.75
923 A138 $6.40 multi 19.00 19.00
No. 922 contains 3 stamps 38½x49mm.
For surcharges see Nos. B100-B104, B112, B126, B133, B138, B141.

Stamps of 1980-84 Surcharged in Black

1987, Feb. **Litho.** **Perfs. as before**
Blocks of 4, #a.-d.
(#953-954, 956-957, 959, 961-962, 964)
948 A121 5c on 1c #787 .20 .20
949 A121 5c on 2c #788 .20 .20
950 A121 5c on 3c #789 .20 .20
951 A121 5c on 12c #792 .20 .20
952 A121 5c on 14c #793 .20 .20
953 A101 10c on 15c #572 .55 .55
954 A101 10c on 25c #574 .55 .55
955 A101 18c on 24c #796 .20 .20
956 A101 18c on 12c #571 1.10 1.10
957 A101 18c on 20c #573 1.10 1.10
958 A101 55c on 52c #803 .90 .90
959 A101 55c on 35c #576 3.25 3.25
960 A101 65c on 42c #800 1.00 1.00
961 A101 65c on 50c #577 4.50 4.50
962 A101 65c on 60c #578 4.50 4.50
963 A121 75c on 48c #801 1.25 1.25
964 A101 75c on 70c #579 4.50 4.50
965 A121 95c on 96c #808 1.50 1.50
966 A121 95c on $1.10 #809 1.50 1.50
967 A121 95c on $1.20 #810 1.50 1.50

Stamps of 1981-86 Surcharged in Black (A102), Black and Gold (#969-970, A137) or Gold (#971, A134, A104, A108)
968 A123 $1.30 on 36c #829 1.90 1.90
969 A123 $1.30 on 48c #830 1.90 1.90
970 A123 $1.30 on 60c #831 1.90 1.90
971 A123 $1.30 on $2 #832 1.90 1.90
972 A134 $2.80 on 95c #904 4.25 4.25
973 A134 $2.80 on $1.25 #905 4.25 4.25
974 A134 $2.80 on $1.50 #906 4.25 4.25
975 A137 $2.80 on $1 #916 4.25 4.25
976 A137 $2.80 on $2 #917 4.25 4.25
977 A137 $2.80 on $3 #918 4.25 4.25
978 A102 $6.40 on $4 #584 9.25 9.25
979 A102 $7.20 on $6 #685 10.50 10.50
980 A104 $9.40 on $1 #659 14.50 14.50
981 A104 $9.40 on $2 #660 14.50 14.50

Pair, #a.-b.
982 A108 $9.40 on $2.50 #678 29.00 29.00
Nos. 948-982 (35) 139.75 139.75
Issued: 5c, #955, 958, 960, 963, 95c, $6.40, $7.20, 2/10; 10c, #956-957, 959, 961-962, 964, 2/11; $2.80, 2/12.
For surcharge see No. B111.

Stamps of 1980-82 Surcharged in Black (A102) or Gold (A104)
Perfs. as before
1987, June 17 **Photo.**
984 A102 $2.80 on $2 #582 3.25 3.25
985 A102 $5 on $3 #583 5.50 5.50
986 A102 $9.40 on $10 #586 10.00 10.00

Pairs, #a.-b.
987 A104 $9.40 on $1 #679 20.00 20.00
988 A104 $9.40 on $2 #680 20.00 20.00
Nos. 984-988 (5) 58.75 58.75

Souvenir Sheet
989 A104 $9.20 on #680c 19.00 19.00

Nos. 399 and 584 Ovptd. "ROYAL / WEDDING / FORTIETH / ANNIVERSARY" in Black on Gold Bar
1987, Nov. 20 **Photo.** **Perf. 14x13½**
991 A64 $4 on #399 5.00 5.00
992 A102 $4 on #584 5.00 5.00

Christmas — A139

The Holy Family, religious paintings by Rembrandt in European museums: $1.25, No. 996a, The Louvre, Paris. $1.50, No. 996b, $6, The Holy Family with Angels, The Hermitage, Leningrad. $1.95, No. 996c, The Alte Pinakothek, Munich.

1987, Dec. 7 **Photo.** **Perf. 13½**
993 A139 $1.25 multi 3.25 3.25
994 A139 $1.50 multi 4.50 4.50
995 A139 $1.95 multi 5.75 5.75
Nos. 993-995 (3) 13.50 13.50

Souvenir Sheets
996 Sheet of 3 12.00 12.00
a.-c. A139 $1.15 any single 3.75 3.75
Perf. 13x13½
997 A139 $6 multi 14.00 14.00
Size of Nos. 996a-996c: 49½x38½mm. No. 997 contains 1 stamp 39½x31½mm.

1988 Summer Olympics, Seoul A140

Designs: a, Cook Islands commemorative silver coin (obverse and reverse) issued on Aug. 20, 1987, for the '88 Summer Games. b, Seoul Olympic Park, torch and emblem. c, Steffi Graf, women's tennis champion, and '88 gold medal.

1988, Apr. 26 **Photo.** **Perf. 13½x14**
998 Strip of 3 17.00 17.00
a.-c. A140 $1.50 multicolored 5.75 5.75

Souvenir Sheet
Perf. 13½
999 A140 $10 multi 19.00 19.00
Participation of national athletes in the Olympics for the first time, introduction of tennis as an Olympic gold-medal event.
No. 999 contains one stamp 114x47mm combining the designs of Nos. 998a-998c.

Nos. 998-999 Ovptd. for Olympic Winners
a. "MILOSLAV MECIR CZECHO-SLOVAKIA GOLD MEDAL WINNER MEN'S TENNIS"
b. "TIM MAYOTTE UNITED STATES GABRIELA SABATINI ARGENTINA SILVER MEDAL WINNERS"
c. "GOLD MEDAL WINNER STEFFI GRAF WEST GERMANY"
d. "GOLD MEDAL WINNER SEOUL OLYMPIC GAMES STEFFI GRAF dash> WEST GERMANY"
1988, Oct. 12 **Photo.** **Perf. 13½x14**
1000 Strip of 3 15.00 15.00
a.-c. A140 $1.50 multicolored 5.00 5.00

Souvenir Sheet
Perf. 13½

1001 A140(d) $10 on No. 999 20.00 20.00

Margin of No. 1001 ovptd.: "STEFFI GRAF, WINNER OF AUSTRALIAN OPEN 24 JULY 1988, FRENCH OPEN / 4 JUNE 1988, WIMBLEDON 2 JULY 1988, U.S. OPEN 10 SEPTEMBER 1988. / FIRST GRAND SLAM WINNER IN 18 YEARS. GOLD MEDAL WINNER SEOUL / OLYMPICS 1 OCTOBER 1988."

Christmas A141

Paintings by Albrecht Durer: 70c, Virgin and Child. 85c, Virgin and Child, diff. 95c, Virgin and Child, diff. $1.25, Virgin and Child, diff. $6.40, The Nativity.

1988, Nov. 11   **Perf. 13½**
1002 A141 70c multi   3.25 3.25
1003 A141 85c multi   3.75 3.75
1004 A141 95c multi   4.25 4.25
1005 A141 $1.25 multi   5.75 5.75
  Nos. 1002-1005 (4)   17.00 17.00

Souvenir Sheet
1006 A141 $6.40 multi   11.00 11.00

No. 1006 contains one stamp 45x60mm.

Scene and Left Half of Mission Emblem A142

1st Moon Landing, 20th Anniv. — A144

#1007a, Launch vehicle in space. #1007b, Eagle landing on Moon. #1008a, Astronaut descending ladder. #1008, Astronaut on Moon. #1009a, Seismic experiment. #1009b, Solar wind experiment. #1010a, Liftoff from Moon. #1010b, Splashdown and recovery. The "b" stamps have the right half of the emblem.

1989, July 14 **Photo.**   **Perf. 13**
1007 A142 40c Pair, #a.-b.   3.25 3.25
1008 A142 55c Pair, #a.-b.   5.00 5.00
1009 A142 65c Pair, #a.-b.   6.00 6.00
1010 A142 75c Pair, #a.-b.   6.75 6.75
  Nos. 1007-1010 (4)   21.00 21.00

Souvenir Sheet
1011 A144 $4.20 Armstrong and Aldrin 11.00 11.00

Printed with continuous designs.

World Wildlife Fund A145

Endangered bird species.

1989, Oct. 4 Photo.   Perf. 13½x13
1016 A145 15c Pomarea dimidiata   1.50 1.50
1017 A145 20c Pomarea dimidiata (two)   2.25 2.25
1018 A145 65c Ptilinopus rarotongensis (two)   6.00 6.00
1019 A145 70c Ptilinopus rarotongensis   6.75 6.75
  Nos. 1016-1019 (4)   16.50 16.50

Souvenir Sheets
Without WWF Emblem
Perf. 13½

1020 A145 $1 like 15c   3.25 3.25
1021 A145 $1.25 like 20c   3.75 3.75
1022 A145 $1.50 like 65c   4.25 4.25
1023 A145 $1.75 like 70c   4.75 4.75

World Wildlife Fund. #1020-1023 are airmail and contain one 52x34mm stamp; decorative margins continue the designs.
For overprints see Nos. C24-C27.

Christmas — A146

Details of Adoration of the Magi, by Rubens: 70c, Witnesses. 85c, Madonna. 95c, Christ child. $1.50, Attendant. $6.40, Entire painting.

1989, Nov. 24 Photo.   Perf. 13½x13
1024 A146 70c multicolored   2.25 2.25
1025 A146 85c multicolored   2.50 2.50
1026 A146 95c multicolored   3.00 3.00
1027 A146 $1.50 multicolored   4.75 4.75
  Nos. 1024-1027 (4)   12.50 12.50

Souvenir Sheet
Perf. 13½
1028 A146 $6.40 multicolored   19.00 19.00

No. 1028 contains one 45x60mm stamp.

Religious History A147

70c, John Williams, LMS Mission Church. 85c, Bernardine Castanie, Roman Catholic Church. 95c, Osborne J.P. Widstoe, Church of Jesus Christ of Latter Day Saints. $1.60, J.E. Caldwell, Seventh Day Adventist Church.

1990, Feb. 19 Photo.   Perf. 13½x13
1029 A147 70c multicolored   1.25 1.25
1030 A147 85c multicolored   1.50 1.50
1031 A147 95c multicolored   1.75 1.75
1032 A147 $1.60 multicolored   3.00 3.00
  Nos. 1029-1032 (4)   7.50 7.50

Souvenir Sheet
Perf. 13½
1033   Sheet of 4   8.50 8.50
 a.   A147 90c like 70c   1.90 1.90
 b.   A147 90c like 85c   1.90 1.90
 c.   A147 90c like 95c   1.90 1.90
 d.   A147 90c like $1.60   1.90 1.90

No. 1033 contains 4 36x36mm stamps.

Penny Black, 150th Anniv. — A148

Paintings: 85c, No. 1038a, Woman Writing a Letter, by Gerard Terborch (1617-1681). $1.15, No. 1038b, Portrait of George Gisze, by Hans Holbein the Younger. $1.55, No. 1038c, Portrait of Mrs. John Douglas, by Thomas Gainsborough. $1.85, No. 1038d, Portrait of a Gentleman, by Albrecht Durer.

1990, May 2 Photo.   Perf. 13½
1034 A148 85c multicolored   1.75 1.75
1035 A148 $1.15 multicolored   2.50 2.50
1036 A148 $1.55 multicolored   3.25 3.25
1037 A148 $1.85 multicolored   4.00 4.00
  Nos. 1034-1037 (4)   11.50 11.50

Souvenir Sheet
1038   Sheet of 4   15.00 15.00
 a.-d.   A148 $1.05 any single   3.50 3.50

The margin of No. 1038 pictures the Stamp World '90 emblem and Great Britain #1-2.

1992 Olympics A149

Designs: a. Summer Games, Barcelona (runners). b. Eternal flame, commemorative coin obverse (Queen Elizabeth II) and reverse (athletes). c. Winter Games, Albertville (skier).

1990, June 15 Photo.   Perf. 14
1039   Strip of 3   19.00 19.00
 a.-c.   A149 $1.85 any single   6.00 6.00

Queen Mother, 90th Birthday A150

1990, July 20 Photo.   Perf. 13½
1040 A150 $1.85 multicolored   8.00 8.00

Souvenir Sheet
1041 A150 $6.40 multicolored   14.00 14.00

Christmas A151

Paintings: 70c, Adoration of the Magi by Memling. 85c, The Holy Family by Lotto. 95c, Madonna and Child with Saints John and Catherine by Titian. $1.50, The Holy Family by Titian. $6.40, Madonna and Child Enthroned, Surrounded by Saints by Vivarini.

1990, Nov. 29 Litho.   Perf. 14
1042 A151 70c multicolored   2.00 2.00
1043 A151 85c multicolored   2.75 2.75
1044 A151 95c multicolored   3.00 3.00
1045 A151 $1.50 multicolored   4.75 4.75
  Nos. 1042-1045 (4)   12.50 12.50

Souvenir Sheet
1046 A151 $6.40 multicolored   18.00 18.00

Souvenir Sheet

1992 Olympic Games — A152

Illustration reduced.

1991, Feb. 12   **Perf. 13½**
1047 A152 $6.40 multicolored   19.00 19.00

Discovery of America 500th Anniv. (in 1992) — A153

1991, Feb. 14 Photo.   Perf. 13½x13
1048 A153 $1 multicolored   4.25 4.25

No. 586 Ovptd. "65th BIRTHDAY" in Gold

1991, Apr. 22 Litho.   Perf. 14x13½
1049 A102 $10 multicolored   22.50 22.50

Christmas A154

Paintings: 70c, Adoration of the Child, by Delle Notti (Gerrit van Honthorst). 85c, Birth of the Virgin, by Murillo. $1.15, Adoration of the Shepherds, by Rembrandt. $1.50, Adoration of the Shepherds, by Le Nain. $6.40, Madonna and Child, by Fra Filippo Lippi, vert.

1991, Nov. 12 Litho.   Perf. 14
1050 A154 70c multicolored   2.00 2.00
1051 A154 85c multicolored   4.00 4.00
1052 A154 $1.15 multicolored   5.25 5.25
1053 A154 $1.50 multicolored   6.75 6.75
  Nos. 1050-1053 (4)   18.00 18.00

Souvenir Sheet
1054 A154 $6.40 multicolored   19.00 19.00

Marine Life — A155

A155a

5c, Red-breasted maori wrasse. 10c, Blue sea star. 15c, Black & gold angelfish. 20c, Spotted pebble crab. 25c, Black-tipped cod. 30c, Spanish dancer. 50c, Royal angelfish. 80c, Squirrel fish. 85c, Red pencil sea urchin. 90c, Red-spot rainbow fish. $1, Black-lined maori wrasse. $2, Longnose butterflyfish. $3, Red-spot rainbow fish. $5, Blue sea star. $7, Royal angelfish. $10, Spotted pebble crab. $15, Red pencil sea urchin.

1992-94   Litho.   Perf. 14½x13½
1058 A155 5c multi   .40 .40
1059 A155 10c multi   .40 .40
1062 A155 15c multi   .40 .40
1064 A155 20c multi   .50 .50
1065 A155 25c multi   .55 .55

1066	A155	30c multi	.65	.65
1071	A155	50c multi	1.10	1.10
1076	A155	80c multi	1.75	1.75
1077	A155	85c multi	1.75	1.75
1078	A155	90c multi	1.75	1.75
1080	A155	$1 multi	2.00	2.00
1081	A155	$2 multi	4.25	4.25
1082	A155a	$3 multi	6.50	6.50
1083	A155a	$5 multi	10.00	10.00
1085	A155a	$7 multi	14.50	14.50
1087	A155a	$10 multi	21.00	21.00
1089	A155a	$15 multi	32.50	32.50
	Nos. 1058-1089 (17)		100.00	100.00

Issued: 85c, 90c, $1, $2, 3/23/92; $3, $5, 10/25/93; $7, 12/6/93; $10, 1/31/94; $15, 9/9/94; others, 1/22/92.
See Nos. 1154-1176 for stamps with buff border. For overprints see Nos. O54-O68.
This is an expanding set. Numbers may change.

Endangered Wildlife — A156

#1095, Tiger. #1096, Asiatic elephant. #1097, Grizzly bear. #1098, Black rhinoceros. #1099, Chimpanzee. #1100, Asian bighorn. #1101, Heavisides dolphin. #1102, Eagle owl. #1103, Bee hummingbird. #1104, Feliscon-color cougar. #1105, European otter. #1106, Red kangaroo.

1992   Litho.   Perf. 14
1095-1106	$1.15 Set of 12	30.00	30.00

Issued: #1095, 4/6; #1096, 4/7; #1097, 4/8; #1098, 4/9; #1099, 4/10; #1100, 4/11; #1101, 7/13; #1102, 7/14; #1103, 7/15; #1104, 7/16; #1105, 7/17; #1106, 7/18.
See Nos. 1119-1124, 1134-1138.

Discovery of America, 500th Anniv. — A157

1992, May 22   Litho.   Perf. 14x14½
1107	A157	$6 multicolored	11.00	11.00

Souvenir Sheet
Perf. 15x14
1107A	A157	$10 Coming ashore	13.00	13.00

Issued: #1107, May 22. #1107A, Sept. 21. No. 1107A contains one 40x30mm stamp.

1992 Summer Olympics, Barcelona — A158

Designs: No. 1108a, $50 coin, soccer players. b, Flags of Spain, Cook Islands, Barcelona medal. c, $10 coin, basketball players. No. 1109a, Runners. b, $10, $50 coins. c, Cyclists. $6.40, Javelin.

1992, July 24   Litho.   Perf. 13
1108	A158	$1.75 Strip of 3, #a.-c.	12.00	12.00
1109	A158	$2.25 Strip of 3, #a.-c.	15.00	15.00

Souvenir Sheet
1110	A158	$6.40 multicolored	19.00	19.00

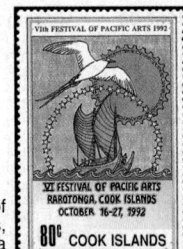

6th Festival of Pacific Arts, Rarotonga A159

80c, UNESCO poster. 85c, $1, $1.75, Different carvings of Rarotongan fertility god, Tangaroa.

1992, Oct. 16   Litho.   Perf. 15x14
1111	A159	80c multicolored	2.25	2.25
1112	A159	85c multicolored	2.50	2.50
1113	A159	$1 multicolored	3.00	3.00
1114	A159	$1.75 multicolored	4.75	4.75
	Nos. 1111-1114 (4)		12.50	12.50

For overprints see #1231-1234.

Ovptd. "ROYAL VISIT"
1992, Oct. 16
1115	A159	80c on #1111	3.00	3.00
1116	A159	85c on #1112	3.50	3.50
1117	A159	$1 on #1113	3.75	3.75
1118	A159	$1.75 on #1114	6.75	6.75
	Nos. 1115-1118 (4)		17.00	17.00

Endangered Wildlife Type of 1992
1992   Litho.   Perf. 14
1119	A156	$1.15 Jackass penguin	2.50	2.50
1120	A156	$1.15 Asian lion	2.50	2.50
1121	A156	$1.15 Peregrine falcon	2.50	2.50
1122	A156	$1.15 Persian fallow deer	2.50	2.50
1123	A156	$1.15 Key deer	2.50	2.50
1124	A156	$1.15 Alpine ibex	2.50	2.50
	Nos. 1119-1124 (6)		15.00	15.00

Issued: #1119, 11/2; #1120, 11/3; #1121, 11/4; #1122, 11/5; #1123, 11/6; #1124, 11/7.

Christmas A160

Paintings by El Parmigianino: 70c, Worship of Shepherds. 85c, $6.40, Virgin with Long Neck. $1.15, Virgin with Rose. $1.90, St. Margaret's Virgin.

1992, Nov. 20   Litho.   Perf. 13½
1125	A160	70c multicolored	1.50	1.50
1126	A160	85c multicolored	2.25	2.25
1127	A160	$1.15 multicolored	3.00	3.00
1128	A160	$1.90 multicolored	5.25	5.25
	Nos. 1125-1128 (4)		12.00	12.00

Souvenir Sheet
1129	A160	$6.40 multicolored	15.00	15.00

No. 1129 contains one 36x47mm stamp.

Queen Elizabeth II's Accession to the Throne, 40th Anniv. — A161

Various portraits of Queen Elizabeth II.

1992, Dec. 10   Litho.   Perf. 14
1130	A161	80c multicolored	2.25	2.25
1131	A161	$1.15 multicolored	3.00	3.00
1132	A161	$1.50 multicolored	4.25	4.25
1133	A161	$1.95 multicolored	5.50	5.50
	Nos. 1130-1133 (4)		15.00	15.00

Endangered Wildlife Type of 1992
1993   Litho.   Perf. 14
1134	A156	$1.15 English man-drill	3.00	3.00
1135	A156	$1.15 Gorilla	3.00	3.00
1136	A156	$1.15 Vanessa atlanta		
1137	A156	$1.15 Sichuan takin	3.00	3.00
1138	A156	$1.15 Ring tailed lemur	3.00	3.00
	Nos. 1134-1138 (5)		15.00	15.00

Issued: #1134, Feb. 1; #1135, Feb. 2; #1136, Feb. 3; #1137, Feb. 4; #1138, Feb. 5.

Coronation of Queen Elizabeth II, 40th Anniv. — A162

Designs: $1, Coronation ceremony. $2, Coronation portrait. $3, Queen, family on balcony, Buckingham Palace.

1993, June 2   Litho.   Perf. 14
1139	A162	$1 multicolored	2.50	2.50
1140	A162	$2 multicolored	5.25	5.25
1141	A162	$3 multicolored	8.25	8.25
	Nos. 1139-1141 (3)		16.00	16.00

Christmas A163

Paintings: 70c, Virgin with Child, by Filippo Lippi. 85c, Bargellini Madonna, by Lodovico Carracci. $1.15, Virgin of the Curtain, by Raphael. $2.50, Holy Family, by Il Bronzino. $4, Saint Zachary Virgin, by Il Parmigianino.

1993, Nov. 8   Litho.   Perf. 14
1142	A163	70c multicolored	1.25	1.25
1143	A163	85c multicolored	1.75	1.75
1144	A163	$1.15 multicolored	2.25	2.25
1145	A163	$2.50 multicolored	4.50	4.50

Size: 32x47mm
Perf. 13½
1146	A163	$4.00 multicolored	7.75	7.75
	Nos. 1142-1146 (5)		17.50	17.50

1994 Winter Olympics, Lillehammer — A164

Illustration reduced.

1994, Feb. 11   Litho.   Perf. 13½x14
1147	A164	$5 multicolored	11.00	11.00

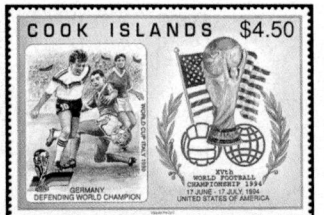

1994 World Cup Soccer Championships, US — A165

Illustration reduced.

1994, June 17   Litho.   Perf. 14
1148	A165	$4.50 multicolored	10.00	10.00

First Manned Moon Landing, 25th Anniv. — A166

Apollo 11 emblem and: No. 1149a, First step onto Moon, US flag. No. 1149b, Astronaut carrying experiment packs on Moon. No. 1150a, Astronaut, US flag. No. 1150b, Flag, reflection shown in astronaut's visor.

1994, July 20
1149	A166	$2.25 Pair, #a.-b. + label	11.50	11.50
1150	A166	$2.25 Pair, #a.-b. + label	11.50	11.50

Living Reef Type of 1992
1994   Litho.   Perf. 14½x13½
Size: 41x31mm
Buff & Multicolored
1154	A155	5c like #1058	.60	.60
1158	A155	15c like #1062	.60	.60
1160	A155	20c like #1064	.75	.75
1161	A155	25c like #1065	.85	.85
1162	A155	30c like #1066	.95	.95
1167	A155	50c like #1071	1.75	1.75
1172	A155	80c like #1076	2.75	2.75
1173	A155	85c like #1077	3.00	3.00
1174	A155	90c like #1078	3.25	3.25
1176	A155	$1 like #1080	3.50	3.50
	Nos. 1154-1176 (10)		18.00	18.00

Issued: 5c, 15c, 20c, 25c, 30c, 50c, 80c, 85c, 90c, $1, 10/24/94. This is an expanding set. Numbers may change.

Miniature Sheet

The Return of Tommy Tricker — A167

Scenes from film: a, Three people in canoe. b, Traditional dancers. c, Couple walking on beach. d, Aerial view of island. e, Girls performing hand gestures. f, Girls walking along sand bar.

1994, Nov. 23   Litho.   Perf. 14
1191	A167	85c Sheet of 6, #a.-f.	16.00	16.00

See No. 1213.

Christmas — A168

Paintings: No. 1192a, The Virgin and Child, by Morales. b, Adoration of Kings, by Gerard David. c, Adoration of Kings, by Vinc Foppa. d, The Madonna & Child with St. Joseph & Infant Baptist, by Baroccio.
No. 1193a, Madonna with Iris, in style of Durer. b, Adoration of Shepherds, by Le Nain. c, The Virgin and Child, by follower of Leonardo. d, The Mystic Nativity, by Botticelli.

1994, Nov. 30   Litho.   Perf. 14
1192	A168	85c Block of 4, #a.-d.	7.75	7.75
1193	A168	$1 Block of 4, #a.-d.	8.75	8.75

Robert Louis Stevenson (1850-94),
Writer — A169

Adventure scenes from books: a, "Treasure
Island." b, "David Balfour." c, "Dr. Jekyll and
Mr. Hyde." d, "Kidnapped."

1994, Dec. 12   **Perf. 14x15**
1194 A169 $1.50 Block of 4,
     #a.-d.   16.00 16.00

UN, 50th Anniv. — A170

$4.50, FAO, 50th anniv.

1995   **Litho.**   **Perf. 13x13½**
1195 A170 $4.75 multicolored   8.50 8.50
                                    Perf. 13½
1196 A170 $4.50 multicolored   8.00 8.00
     Each issued in sheets of 4.
     Issued: $4.75, 7/17; $4.50, 10/12.

Queen Mother, 95th Birthday — A172

1995, Aug. 31
1197 A172 $5 multicolored   15.00 15.00

End of World War II, 50th
Anniv. — A173

Designs: a, German surrender, Rheims. b,
Japanese surrender, Tokyo Bay.

1995, Sept. 4   **Perf. 13**
1198 A173 $3.50 Pair, #a.-b.   30.00 30.00
No. 1198 was issued in sheets of 4 stamps.

Year of the
Sea Turtle
A174

Designs: 85c, Green turtle in water. $1,
Hawksbill turtle in water. $1.75, Green turtle
nesting. $2.25, Hawksbill turtle hatchlings
leaving nest.

1995, Nov. 20   **Litho.**   **Perf. 14**
1199 A174 85c multicolored   2.50 2.50
1200 A174 $1 multicolored   3.50 3.50
1201 A174 $1.75 multicolored   5.25 5.25
1202 A174 $2.25 multicolored   7.25 7.25
     Nos. 1199-1202 (4)   18.50 18.50

1996
Summer
Olympics,
Atlanta
A175

1996, Jan. 12   **Litho.**   **Perf. 14**
1203 A175 85c Discus   1.75 1.75
1204 A175 $1 Torch bearer   2.25 2.25
1205 A175 $1.50 Sprinting   3.25 3.25
1206 A175 $1.85 Gymnastics   4.25 4.25
1207 A175 $2.10 Archery   5.00 5.00
1208 A175 $2.50 Javelin   5.50 5.50
     Nos. 1203-1208 (6)   22.00 22.00

Queen Elizabeth
II, 70th
Birthday — A176

Designs: $1.90, No. 1212a, In blue hat,
coat. $2.25, No. 1212b, Wearing tiara. $2.75,
No. 1212c, In robes of Order of the Garter.

1996, June 21   **Litho.**   **Perf. 14**
1209 A176 $1.90 multicolored   4.00 4.00
1210 A176 $2.25 multicolored   5.00 5.00
1211 A176 $2.75 multicolored   5.50 5.50
     Nos. 1209-1211 (3)   14.50 14.50
                    Sheet of 3
1212 A176 $2.50 #a.-c. + label 19.00 19.00
Nos. 1209-1211 were issued in sheets of 4.

"The Return of Tommy Tricker" Type of
1994
No. 1213a-1213f, like #1191a-1191f.

1997, Aug. 28   **Litho.**   **Perf. 14**
1213 A167 90c Sheet of 6,
     #a.-f.   12.00 12.00

Nos. 1213a-1213f Overprinted in Silver

a

b

1997, Sept. 12   **Litho.**   **Perf. 14**
1214 A167 90c Sheet 6, #a.-f.   9.00 9.00
  #1214a, 1214d-1214e are overprinted type
"a"; #1214b-1214c, 1214f type "b."

Butterflies
A177

5c, Lampides boeticus (female). 10c,
Vanessa atalanta. 15c, Lampides boeticus
(male). 20c, Papilio godeffroyi. 25c, Danaus
hamata. 30c, Xois sesara. 50c, Vagrans
egista. 70c, Parthenos sylvia. 80c, Hyblaea
sanguinea. 85c, Melanitis leda. 90c,
Ascalapha odorata. $1, Precis villida. $1.50,
Parthenos sylvia. $2, Lampides boeticus. $3,
Precis villida. $4, Melanitis leda. $5, Vagrans
egista. $7, Hyblaea sanguinea. $10, Vanessa
atalanta. $15, Papilio godeffroyi.

1997-98   **Litho.**   **Perf. 13**
1215 A177 5c multi   .20 .20
1216 A177 10c multi   .20 .20
1217 A177 15c multi   .20 .20
1218 A177 20c multi   .30 .30
1219 A177 25c multi   .35 .35
1220 A177 30c multi   .40 .40
1221 A177 50c multi   .65 .65
1222 A177 70c multi   .95 .95
1223 A177 80c multi   1.10 1.10
1224 A177 85c multi   1.10 1.10
1225 A177 90c multi   1.25 1.25
1226 A177 $1 multi   1.40 1.40
                    Perf. 13½
                    Size: 41x25mm
1226A A177 $1.50 multi   1.90 1.90
1226B A177 $2 multi   2.75 2.75
1226C A177 $3 multi   3.75 3.75
1226D A177 $4 multi   5.50 5.50
1226E A177 $5 multi   6.50 6.50
1226F A177 $7 multi   10.00 10.00
1226G A177 $10 multi   13.50 13.50
1226H A177 $15 multi   18.00 18.00
     Nos. 1215-1226H (20)   70.00 70.00
Issued: 5c, 10c, 15c, 20c, 25c, 30c, 50c,
70c, 10/22/97; 80c, 85c, 90c, $1, 11/12/97;
$1.50, $2, $3, 3/11/98; $4, $5, 6/19/98; $7,
$10, 9/18/98; $15, 11/13/98.
For surcharges, see Nos. 1259-1264.

Queen Elizabeth II and Prince Philip,
50th Wedding Anniv.
A178

1997, Nov. 20   **Perf. 14**
1227 A178 $2 multicolored   3.25 3.25
                    Souvenir Sheet
1228 A178 $5 like #1227,
          close-up   12.00 12.00
No. 1228 is a continuous design.

Diana, Princess of
Wales (1961-
97) — A179

1998, Mar. 18   **Litho.**   **Perf. 14**
1229 A179 $1.15 shown   1.75 1.75
                    Souvenir Sheet
1230 A179 $3.50 like #1229   5.25 5.25
No. 1229 was issued in sheets of 5 + label.
See No. B142.

**Nos. 1111-1114 Ovptd. "KIA ORANA
/ THIRD MILLENNIUM"**

1231ovpt

**Printing Methods and Perfs as
before**

1999, Dec. 31
1231 A159 80c on #1111   1.25 1.25
1232 A159 85c on #1112   1.25 1.25
1233 A159 $1 on #1113   1.50 1.50
1234 A159 $1.75 on #1114   2.50 2.50
     Nos. 1231-1234 (4)   6.50 6.50

Queen Mother, 100th Birthday — A180

No. 1235: a, As child. b, As young woman.
c, Wearing green hat. d, Wearing tiara.
Illustration reduced.

2000, Oct. 20   **Litho.**   **Perf. 14**
1235 A180 $4.50 Sheet of 4,
     #a-d   20.00 20.00
                    Souvenir Sheet
1236 A180 $6 Wearing blue
          hat   7.00 7.00

2000 Summer Olympics,
Sydney — A181

No. 1237: a, Ancient runner. b, Track and
field. c, Ancient archery. d, Archery.

2000, Nov. 14
1237 A181 $1.75 Sheet of 4,
     #a-d   11.00 11.00
                    Souvenir Sheet
1238 A181 $3.90 Torch bearer   4.50 4.50

Nos. 1095-1106 Surcharged in Gold

2001, Apr. 30   **Litho.**   **Perf. 14**
1239 A156 80c on $1.15
          #1101   1.00 1.00
1240 A156 80c on $1.15
          #1102   1.00 1.00
1241 A156 80c on $1.15
          #1103   1.00 1.00
1242 A156 80c on $1.15
          #1104   1.00 1.00
1243 A156 80c on $1.15
          #1105   1.00 1.00
1244 A156 80c on $1.15
          #1106   1.00 1.00
1245 A156 90c on $1.15
          #1095   1.25 1.25
1246 A156 90c on $1.15
          #1096   1.25 1.25
1247 A156 90c on $1.15
          #1097   1.25 1.25
1248 A156 90c on $1.15
          #1098   1.25 1.25
1249 A156 90c on $1.15
          #1099   1.25 1.25

1250 A156 90c on $1.15
#1100   1.25   1.25
Nos. 1239-1250 (12)   13.50 13.50

Nos. 1042-1045, 1050-1053
Surcharged or Overprinted in Black or
Gold

2002, Nov. 11   Litho.   **Perf. 14**
1251 A151 20c on 70c #1042   .20   .20
1252 A154 20c on 70c #1050   .20   .20
1253 A154 80c on $1.15
#1052 (G)   1.50   1.50
1254 A151 85c #1043   1.60   1.60
1255 A154 85c #1051   1.60   1.60
1256 A154 90c on $1.50
#1053   1.75   1.75
1257 A151 95c #1044   1.90   1.90
1258 A151 $1 on $1.50
#1045   2.25   2.25
Nos. 1251-1258 (8)   11.00 11.00

Nos. 1226A-1226F Surcharged

Methods and Perfs As Before
2003, June 30
1259 A177 20c on $1.50
#1226A   .30   .30
1260 A177 80c on $2 #1226B   1.00   1.00
1261 A177 85c on $3 #1226C   1.25   1.25
1262 A177 85c on $4 #1226D   1.25   1.25
1263 A177 90c on $5 #1226E   1.50   1.50
1264 A177 90c on $7 #1226F   1.50   1.50
Nos. 1259-1264 (6)   6.80   6.80

Obliterator on Nos. 1260-1264 is a Moai head.

United We
Stand — A182

2003, Sept. 30   Litho.   **Perf. 14**
1265 A182 90c multi   2.50   2.50

Printed in sheets of 4.

2004
Summer
Olympics,
Athens
A183

Designs: 40c, Poster for 1992 Barcelona Olympics. 60c, Pancration, horiz. $1, Cycling, horiz. $2, Gold medal, 1936 Berlin Olympics.

2004, Sept. 29   Litho.   **Perf. 14¼**
1266-1269 A183   Set of 4   6.50   6.50

Worldwide Fund for Nature
(WWF) — A184

Birds of Suwarrow National Park: 80c, Cook Islands reed warblers. 90c, Mangaia kingfishers. $1.15, Rarotonga starlings. $1.95, Atiu swiftlets.

2005, June 13   Litho.   **Perf. 14**
1270-1273 A184   Set of 4   8.00   8.00

Each stamp printed in sheets of 4.

Pope John Paul II
(1920-2005)
A185

2005, Nov. 11
1274 A185 $1.35 multi   2.40   2.40

Printed in sheets of 5 + label.

SEMI-POSTAL STAMPS

Catalogue values for unused stamps in this section are for Never Hinged items.

Nos. 203-204,
223, 210, 213,
215-216
Surcharged

Perf. 14x13½, 13½
1968, Feb. 12   Photo.
B1 A34 3c + 1c multi   .20   .20
B2 A34 4c + 1c multi   .20   .20
B3 A37 5c + 2c multi   .20   .20
B4 A34 10c + 2c multi   .25   .25
B5 A34 25c + 5c multi   .40   .40
B6 A34 50c + 5c multi   .90   .90
B7 A35 $1 + 10c multi   1.75   1.75
Nos. B1-B7 (7)   3.90   3.90

Surtax for the victims of hurricane of Dec. 15-18, 1967. The surcharge on No. B3 is printed on a silver rectangle. The surcharge on No. B7 is in smaller type with serifs, measuring 7½mm in depth.

Nos. 210, 213-
214 Surcharged in
Ultramarine

1971, Sept. 8   Photo.   **Perf. 14x13½**
B8 A34 10c + 1c multi   .25   .25
B9 A34 10c + 3c multi   .25   .25
B10 A34 25c + 1c multi   .65   .65
B11 A34 25c + 3c multi   .65   .65
B12 A34 30c + 1c multi   .75   .75
B13 A34 30c + 3c multi   .75   .75
Nos. B8-B13 (6)   3.30   3.30

4th South Pacific Games, Papeete, French Polynesia, Sept. 8-19.

Christmas Type of Regular Issue
Souvenir Sheet

50c+5c, Holy Family in a Garland of Flowers, by Jan Brueghel and Pieter van Avont.

1971, Nov. 30   Photo.   **Perf. 13½**
B14 A50 50c + 5c gold & multi   1.75   1.75

No. B14 contains one stamp 45x40mm.

Nos. 316-318, 211, 213 and 215
Surcharged in Red or Black

    a   b

1972, Mar. 30   Photo.   **Perf. 13½**
B15 A46(a) 5c + 2c multi (R)   .20   .20
B16 A46(a) 10c + 2c multi (R)   .20   .20
B17 A34(b) 15c + 5c multi   .35   .35
B18 A34(b) 25c + 5c multi   .65   .65
B19 A46(a) 30c + 5c multi (R)   .75   .75
B20 A34(b) 50c + 10c multi   1.40   1.40
Nos. B15-B20 (6)   3.55   3.55

Surtax for victims of hurricane of Mar. 22-26.

Nos. 319-322c with Surcharge Similar
to Type "a"

1972, May 24   Photo.   **Perf. 13½**
B21 A51 5c + 2c, pair, #a.-b.   .25   .25
B22 A51 10c + 2c, pair, #a.-b.   .45   .45
B23 A51 25c + 2c, pair, #a.-b.   1.00   1.00
B24 A51 30c + 2c, pair, #a.-b.   1.50   1.50
c. Souvenir sheet of 8   3.50   3.50
Nos. B21-B24 (4)   3.20   3.20

Surtax for victims of hurricane of Mar. 22-26. Stamps of No. B24c each surcharged 3c.

Olympic Type of Regular Issue
Souvenir Sheet

50c+5c, Pierre de Coubertin, Olympic rings.

1972, June 26
B29 A52 50c + 5c multi   3.25   3.25

Christmas Type of Regular Issue
Souvenir Sheet

Design: 50c+5c, Nativity, by Correggio.

1972, Oct. 11   Photo.   **Perf. 13½**
B30 A53 50c + 5c multi   2.25   2.00

No. B30 contains one stamp 30x40mm.

Easter Type of Regular Issue
Souvenir Sheets

1973, Apr. 30   Photo.   **Perf. 13½x14**
B31 A56 50c + 5c like #346   1.10   1.10
B32 A56 50c + 5c like #347   1.10   1.10
B33 A56 50c + 5c like #348   1.10   1.10
Nos. B31-B33 (3)   3.30   3.30

Surtax was for school children.

Christmas Type of Regular Issue
Souvenir Sheets

1973, Dec. 3   Photo.   **Perf. 13x13½**
B34 A59 50c + 5c like #364   .75   .75
B35 A59 50c + 5c like #365   .75   .75
B36 A59 50c + 5c like #366   .75   .75
B37 A59 50c + 5c like #367   .75   .75
B38 A59 50c + 5c like #368   .75   .75
Nos. B34-B38 (5)   3.75   3.75

Surtax was for school children.

Easter Type of 1973
Dated "1974"
Souvenir Sheets

1974, Apr. 22   **Perf. 13½x14**
B39 A56 50c + 5c like #378   1.00   1.00
B40 A56 50c + 5c like #379   1.00   1.00
B41 A56 50c + 5c like #380   1.00   1.00
Nos. B39-B41 (3)   3.00   3.00

Christmas Type of 1974
Souvenir Sheets

1974   Photo.   **Perf. 13½x13**
B42 A68 50c + 5c like #412   .75   .75
B43 A68 50c + 5c like #413   .75   .75
B44 A68 50c + 5c like #414   .75   .75
B45 A68 50c + 5c like #415   .75   .75
B46 A68 50c + 5c like #416   .75   .75
Nos. B42-B46 (5)   3.75   3.75

Christmas Type of 1975
Souvenir Sheets

1975, Dec. 1   **Perf. 13½**
B47 A75 75c + 5c like #437   1.10   1.10
B48 A75 75c + 5c like #438   1.10   1.10
B49 A75 75c + 5c like #439   1.10   1.10
B50 A75 75c + 5c like #440   1.10   1.10
B51 A75 75c + 5c like #441   1.10   1.10
Nos. B47-B51 (5)   5.50   5.50

Size of stamps: 23x40mm.

Easter Type of 1976
Souvenir Sheets

1976, May 3   Photo.   **Perf. 13½**
B52 A76 60c + 5c like #442   1.00   1.00
B53 A76 60c + 5c like #443   1.00   1.00
B54 A76 60c + 5c like #444   1.00   1.00
Nos. B52-B54 (3)   3.00   3.00

Size of stamps: 36x36mm.

Christmas Type of 1976
Souvenir Sheets

1976, Nov. 2   Photo.   **Perf. 14x13½**
B55 A80 75c + 5c like #459   1.25   1.25
B56 A80 75c + 5c like #460   1.25   1.25
B57 A80 75c + 5c like #461   1.25   1.25
B58 A80 75c + 5c like #462   1.25   1.25
B59 A80 75c + 5c like #463   1.25   1.25
Nos. B55-B59 (5)   6.25   6.25

Easter Type of 1977
Souvenir Sheets

1977, Apr. 18   Photo.   **Perf. 13½x14**
B60 A83 60c + 5c like #471   1.00   1.00
B61 A83 60c + 5c like #472   1.00   1.00
B62 A83 60c + 5c like #473   1.00   1.00
Nos. B60-B62 (3)   3.00   3.00

Size of stamps: 30x42mm.

Christmas Type of 1977
Souvenir Sheets

1977, Oct. 31   Photo.   **Perf. 14x13½**
B63 A84 75c + 5c like #474   1.10   1.10
B64 A84 75c + 5c like #475   1.10   1.10
B65 A84 75c + 5c like #476   1.10   1.10
B66 A84 75c + 5c like #477   1.10   1.10
B67 A84 75c + 5c like #478   1.10   1.10
Nos. B63-B67 (5)   5.50   5.50

Easter Type of 1978
Souvenir Sheets

1978, Apr. 10   Photo.   **Perf. 14x13½**
B68 A87 60c + 5c like #483   .85   .75
B69 A87 60c + 5c like #484   .85   .75
B70 A87 60c + 5c like #485   .85   .75
Nos. B68-B70 (3)   2.55   2.25

Christmas Type of 1978
Souvenir Sheets

1979, Jan. 12   Photo.   **Perf. 13**
B71 A89 75c + 5c like #503   .90   .90
B72 A89 75c + 5c like #504   .90   .90
B73 A89 75c + 5c like #505   .90   .90
Nos. B71-B73 (3)   2.70   2.70

Easter Type of 1979
Souvenir Sheet

1979, Apr. 5   Photo.   **Perf. 13**
B74   Sheet of 4   1.00   1.00
a. A90 10c + 2c like #506   .20   .20
b. A90 12c + 2c like #507   .20   .20
c. A90 15c + 2c like #508   .25   .25
d. A90 20c + 2c like #509   .35   .35

IYC Type of 1979
Souvenir Sheet

1979, Oct. 10
B75   Sheet of 3   2.25   2.25
a. A93 30c + 5c like #529   .45   .45
b. A93 50c + 5c like #530   .75   .75
c. A93 65c + 5c like #531   .90   .90

Christmas Type of 1979

1980, Jan. 15　　Photo.　　Perf. 14

B76	A95	6c + 2c like #537	.20	.20
B77	A95	10c + 2c like #538	.20	.20
B78	A95	12c + 2c like #539	.25	.25
B79	A95	15c + 2c like #540	.35	.35
		Nos. B76-B79 (4)	1.00	1.00

Easter Type of 1980

Souvenir Sheets

1980, Mar. 31　　Photo.　　Perf. 13

B80	A96	Sheet of 6, #a.-f.	2.25	2.25

#B80 contains #541-543, each stamp with 2c surcharge.

1980, Apr. 23

Souvenir Sheets

B81	A96	75c + 5c like #541a	1.00	1.00
B82	A96	75c + 5c like #541b	1.00	1.00
B83	A96	75c + 5c like #542a	1.00	1.00
B84	A96	75c + 5c like #542b	1.00	1.00
B85	A96	75c + 5c like #543a	1.00	1.00
B86	A96	75c + 5c like #543b	1.00	1.00
		Nos. B81-B86 (6)	6.00	6.00

Surtax was for school children.

Rotary Type of 1980

Souvenir Sheet

1980, May 27　　Photo.　　Perf. 14

B87		Sheet of 3	1.75	1.75
a.	A97	30c + 3c like #547	.45	.45
b.	A97	35c + 3c like #548	.55	.55
c.	A97	50c + 3c like #549	.75	.75

Christmas Type of 1980

Souvenir Sheets

1981, Jan. 9　　Photo.　　Imperf.

B88	A102a	75c + 5c like #652	1.00	1.00
B89	A102a	75c + 5c like #653	1.00	1.00
B90	A102a	75c + 5c like #654	1.00	1.00
B91	A102a	75c + 5c like #655	1.00	1.00
		Nos. B88-B91 (4)	4.00	4.00

Easter Type of 1981

Souvenir Sheets

1981, Apr. 10　　Photo.　　Perf. 13½

B92		Sheet of 3	1.50	1.50
a.	A103	15c + 2c like #656	.25	.25
b.	A103	25c + 2c like #657	.50	.50
c.	A103	40c + 2c like #658	.75	.75

1981, Apr. 28　　　　　Imperf.

B93	A103	75c + 5c like #656	1.50	1.50
B94	A103	75c + 5c like #657	1.50	1.50
B95	A103	75c + 5c like #658	1.50	1.50
		Nos. B93-B95 (3)	4.50	4.50

Surtax was for school children.

Espana '82 Soccer Type

Souvenir Sheet

1981　　Photo.　　Perf. 13½

B96	A105	Sheet of 8, #a.-h.	8.00	8.00

#B96 contains #661-664, each stamp with 3c surcharge.

Royal Wedding Type of 1981

Nos. 659-660a Surcharged in Black

1981, Nov. 10　　　　　Perf. 14

B97	A104	$1 + 5c multi	2.25	2.25
B98	A104	$2 + 5c multi	4.50	4.50
a.		Souvenir sheet of 2	7.50	7.50

Intl. Year of the Disabled. No. B98a contains Nos. B97-B98 each with 10c surtax, which was for benefit of the disabled; black overprint in margin.

Christmas Type of 1981

Souvenir Sheet

1981, Dec. 14　　Photo.　　Perf. 13½

B99		Sheet of 4	3.50	3.50
a.	A107	8c + 3c like #669	.25	.25
b.	A107	15c + 3c like #670	.40	.40
c.	A107	40c + 3c like #671	1.10	1.10
d.	A107	50c + 3c like #672	1.40	1.40

Surtax was for school children.

Nos. 919-923 Surcharged "FIRST PAPAL VISIT TO SOUTH PACIFIC / POPE JOHN PAUL II / *NOV 21-24 1986*" and Value in Silver

1986, Nov. 21　　Litho.　　Perf. 13½

B100	A138	55c + 10c multi	3.25	3.25
B101	A138	$1.30 + 10c multi	6.75	6.75
B102	A138	$2.75 + 10c multi	13.00	13.00
		Nos. B100-B102 (3)	23.00	23.00

Souvenir Sheets

B103		Sheet of 3	24.00	24.00
a.-c.		A138 $2.40 + 10c on Nos. 922a-922c, any single	8.00	8.00
B104	A138	$6.40 + 50c multi	24.00	24.00

No. B103 ovptd. in margin "VISIT TO SOUTH PACIFIC / OF POPE JOHN PAUL II" and "FIRST PAPAL VISIT / NOVEMBER 21-24 1986." No. B104 ovptd. around margin only, "'FIRST PAPAL VISIT TO SOUTH PACIFIC NOVEMBER 21-24 1986" and "PRE-CHRIST-MAS VISIT OF HIS HOLINESS POPE JOHN PAUL II."

For surcharge see No. B112.

Stamps of 1982 and 1987 Surcharged "HURRICANE RELIEF" in Sans-serif Capitals Plus New Value

Perfs. as before

1987, June 30　　　　　Photo.

Surcharged +25c

B105	A121	55c on #958	1.10	1.10
B106	A121	65c on #960	1.25	1.25
B107	A121	75c on #963	1.40	1.40
B108	A121	95c on #965	1.60	1.60

Surcharged +50c

B109	A101	$2.80 on #582	4.50	4.50
B110	A101	$5 on #583	7.75	7.75
B111	A102	$6.40 on #978	9.50	9.50
		Nos. B105-B111 (7)	27.10	27.10

Stamps of 1985-86 Surcharged "HURRICANE RELIEF / +50c" in Silver or Black

1987　　　　　Perfs. as before

Surcharged +50c

B112	A138	55c on #B100	1.40	1.40
B113	A133	55c on #897 (B)	1.40	1.40
B114	A128	65c on #871	1.50	1.50
B115	A133	65c on #898	1.50	1.50
B116	A128	75c on #872	1.60	1.60
B117	A133	75c on #899	1.60	1.60
B118	A134	95c on #908 (B)	1.90	1.90
B119	A135	$1 on #910	2.10	2.10
B120	A136	$1 on #913	2.10	2.10
B121	A137	$1 on #916	2.10	2.10
B122	A138	$1.15 on #873	2.25	2.25
B123	A133	$1.25 on #900	2.25	2.25
B124	A134	$1.25 on #905	2.25	2.25
B125	A136	$1.25 on #914 (B)	2.25	2.25
B126	A138	$1.30 on #920	2.50	2.50
B127	A134	$1.50 on #906 (B)	2.50	2.50
B128	A135	$1.50 on #911 (B)	2.50	2.50
B129	A135	$2 on #901 (B)	3.25	3.25
B130	A135	$2 on #912 (B)	3.25	3.25
B131	A137	$2 on #917	3.25	3.25
B132	A136	$2.75 on #915	4.50	4.50
B133	A138	$2.75 on #921	4.50	4.50
B134	A128	$2.80 on #874	4.50	4.50
B135	A137	$3 on #918	4.75	4.75
		Nos. B112-B135 (24)	61.70	61.70

Souvenir Sheets

B136	A134	$1.10 on #907 (B)	2.00	2.00
B137	A134	$1.95 on #908	3.00	3.00
B138		on #922,		
		#a.-c.	11.00	11.00
B139	A134	$2.45 on #909 (B)	3.75	3.75
B140	A128	$5.30 on #875	7.25	7.25
B141	A138	$6.40 on #804	8.50	8.50
		Nos. B136-B141 (6)	35.50	35.50

Issued: #B118, B121, B124, B127, B131, B135-B137, B139-B140, 7/31; others 6/30.

No. 1230 Surcharged "CHILDREN'S / CHARITIES" in Silver

Souvenir Sheet

1998, Nov. 20　　Litho.　　Perf. 14

B142	A179	$3.50 +$1 multi	5.75	5.75

AIR POST STAMPS

Stamps of 1936-63 Overprinted and Surcharged

Perf. 13x13½, 13½x13
Litho., Engr.

1966, Apr. 22　　　　　Wmk. 253

C1	A25	6p on #152	.25	.20
C2	A26	7p on 8p #153	.30	.25
C3	A25	10p on 3p #150	.40	.35
C4	A25	1sh on #154	.50	.45
C5	A27	1sh6p on #155	.75	.65
C6	A28	2sh3p on 3sh #157	1.25	1.00
C7	A28	5sh on #158	2.00	1.75
C8	A28	10sh on 2sh #156	4.00	4.00

Perf. 14

Typo.

C9	PF5	£1 on #106	15.00	14.00
a.		Airplane missing	30.00	42.50
		Nos. C1-C9 (9)	24.45	22.65

#C9a occurs on all stamps from the right vertical column of the sheet due to a lack of airplane symbols. The size and position of the airplane symbol varies in relation to "Airmail" on the other stamps. The surcharges are printed on silver ovals.

2nd So. Pacific Games' Type

Sport: 10p, Women runners and Games' emblem. 2sh3p, Runner and team emblem.

Perf. 13½

1967, Jan. 12　　Unwmk.　　Photo.

C10	A32	10p org & multi	.20	.20
C11	A32	2sh3p multi	.25	.25

Capt. Cook Type of Regular Issue

6c, The "Resolution" and "Discovery" Beating Through the Ice, by Webber. 10c, The Island of Otaheite, by Hodges, and Queen Elizabeth II. 15c, View of Karakakooa (Kealakekua), Hawaii, by Webber. 25c, The Landing at Middleburg, Tonga, by Hodges, & Captain Cook. (All horiz.)

1968, Sept. 12　　Photo.　　Perf. 13

C12	A39	6c gold & multi	.65	.65
C13	A39	10c gold & multi	1.00	1.00
C14	A39	15c gold & multi	1.25	1.25
C15	A39	25c gold & multi	2.75	2.75
		Nos. C12-C15 (4)	5.65	5.65

See note after No. 236.

Christmas Type of 1979

1979, Dec. 14　　Photo.　　Perf. 14

C16	A95	20c like #537	.25	.25
C17	A95	25c like #538	.35	.35
C18	A95	30c like #539	.40	.40
C19	A95	35c like #540	.50	.50
		Nos. C16-C19 (4)	1.50	1.50

Franklin D. Roosevelt — AP1

80c, Benjamin Franklin. $1.40, George Washington, by Gilbert Stuart.

1982, Sept. 30　　Photo.　　Perf. 14

C20	AP1	60c multicolored	.90	.90
C21	AP1	80c multicolored	1.10	1.10
C22	AP1	$1.40 multicolored	2.00	2.00
a.		Souvenir sheet of 3	5.25	5.25
		Nos. C20-C22 (3)	4.00	4.00

No. C22a contains Nos. C20-C22, perf. 13½ with portraits in square frames.

No. C22 Overprinted in Gold and Black

1983, Aug. 12　　Photo.　　Perf. 14

C23	AP1	96c on $1.40 multi	2.00	2.00

Endangered Bird Species Type

Souvenir Sheets

Nos. 1020-1023 Overprinted

1990, Dec. 5　　Litho.　　Perf. 13½

C24	A145	$1 Flycatcher	4.25	4.25
C25	A145	$1.25 Flycatchers	5.00	5.00
C26	A145	$1.50 Fruit dove	6.50	6.50
C27	A145	$1.75 Fruit doves	7.25	7.25
		Nos. C24-C27 (4)	23.00	23.00

Birdpex '90, 20th Intl. Ornithological Cong., New Zealand.

AIR POST SEMI-POSTAL STAMPS

Christmas Type of 1979

1980, Jan. 15　　Photo.　　Perf. 14

CB1	A95	20c + 4c like #C16	.40	.40
CB2	A95	25c + 4c like #C17	.45	.45
CB3	A95	30c + 4c like #C18	.50	.50
CB4	A95	35c + 4c like #C19	.65	.65
		Nos. CB1-CB4 (4)	2.00	2.00

OFFICIAL STAMPS

Flower Issue of 1967-69 Overprinted or Surcharged in Black on Silver

1975　　Photo.　　Unwmk.　　Perf. 14x13½

O1	A34	1c multi (#200)		.20
O2	A34	2c multi (#201)		.20
O3	A34	3c multi (#203)		.20
O4	A34	4c multi (#205)		.20
O5	A34	5c on 2 ½c multi (#202)		.20
O6	A34	8c multi (#208)		.25
O7	A34	10c on 6c multi (#207)		.30
O8	A34	18c on 20c multi (#212)		.40
O9	A34	25c on 9c multi (#209)		.60
O10	A34	30c on 15c multi (#211)		.70
O11	A34	50c multi (#215)		1.25
O12	A35	$1 multi (#216)		2.75
O13	A35	$2 multi (#217)		4.75
O14	A36	$4 multi (#218)		8.00
O15	A36	$6 multi (#219)		10.00
		Nos. O1-O15 (15)		30.00

No. O1-O15 were not sold to the public unused. Arrangement of surcharge varies on different denominations.

Silver panel on Nos. O14-O15 measures 26½x6mm and is rounded at both ends. Issue dates: 1c-$2, Mar. 17, $4-$6, May 19.

Nos. 381-382, 389, 393-396, 467, 446 Overprinted or Surcharged in Silver or Black

Photo., Litho.

1978, Oct. 19　　　　　Perf. 13½

O16	A62	1c multi (S)	.85	.20
O17	A62	2c on ½c multi	.85	.20
O18	A62	5c on ½c multi	.95	.20
O19	A62	10c on 8c multi (S)	1.10	.20
O20	A62	15c on 50c multi (S)	1.25	.20
O21	A62	18c on 60c multi (S)	1.25	.20
O22	A62	25c multicolored	1.60	.25
O23	A62	30c multi (S)	1.60	.30
O24	A62	35c on 60c multi (S)	1.60	.35
O25	A62	50c multi (S)	2.10	.50
O26	A62	60c multi (S)	2.40	.60
O27	A82	$1 Pair, #a.-b. (S)	10.00	2.00
O29	A77	$2 multicolored	7.25	2.00

O30	A64	$4 multi ('79)	13.50	4.00
O31	A64	$6 multi ('79)	13.50	6.50
		Nos. O16-O31 (15)	59.80	17.70

Diagonal overprints on No. O27. Overprint on No. O29: 19x4mm.

Nos. 790-791, 795, 797, 799, 805, 807, 809-810 Ovptd. or Surcharged "O.H.M.S." in Silver

1985, July 10   Photo.   Perf. 13½x13

O32	A121	5c multi	.55	.55
O33	A121	10c multi	.55	.55
O34	A121	20c multi	.65	.65
O35	A121	30c multi	.65	.65
O36	A121	40c multi	.65	.65
O37	A121	55c on 85c multi	.80	.80
O38	A121	60c multi	.80	.80
O39	A121	$1.10 multi	1.25	1.25
O40	A121	$2 on $1.20 multi	2.50	2.50
		Nos. O32-O40 (9)	8.40	8.40

Nos. 792-794, 802, 806, 696 and 583-586 Ovptd. or Surcharged "O.H.M.S." in Silver, Gold (75c) or Black and Silver ($5, $18)

1986-90   Photo.   Perfs. as Before

O41	A121	12c multi	5.00	5.00
O42	A121	14c multi	5.00	5.00
O43	A121	18c multi	5.00	5.00
O44	A121	50c multi	6.25	6.25
O45	A121	70c multi	6.75	6.75
O46	A111	75c on 60c, #a.-		
		d.	13.50	13.50
O50	A102	$5 on $3 multi	17.00	17.00
O51	A102	$9 on $4 multi	9.00	9.00
O52	A102	$14 on $6 multi	14.00	14.00
O53	A102	$18 on $10 multi	20.00	20.00
		Nos. O41-O53 (10)	101.50	101.50

Issued: $9, 5/30/89; $14, 7/12/89; $18, 6/4/90; others 5/5/86.

Nos. 1058-1059, 1062, 1064-1066, 1071, 1076-1078, 1080-1083, 1085 Ovptd. "O.H.M.S." in Silver

1995-98   Litho.   Perf. 14½x13½

O54	A155	5c multicolored	.50	.50
O55	A155	10c multicolored	.50	.50
O56	A155	15c multicolored	.65	.65
O57	A155	20c multicolored	.70	.70
O58	A155	25c multicolored	.75	.75
O59	A155	30c multicolored	.80	.80
O60	A155	50c multicolored	1.00	1.00
O61	A155	80c multicolored	1.60	1.60
O62	A155	85c multicolored	1.60	1.60
O63	A155	90c multicolored	1.60	1.60
O64	A155	$1 multicolored	1.90	1.90
O65	A155	$2 multicolored	3.00	3.00
O66	A155a	$3 multicolored	4.75	4.75
O67	A155a	$5 multicolored	5.75	5.75
O68	A155a	$7 multicolored	8.50	8.50
O69	A155a	$10 multicolored	10.50	10.50
		Nos. O54-O69 (16)	44.10	44.10

Overprint on Nos. O66-O69 has larger, sans serif letters.
Nos. O66-O69 were not sold unused to local customers.
Issued: 5c-90c, 2/24/95; $1-$2, 5/15/95; $3-$7, 7/17/98; $10, 11/12/98.

CORFU

kor-'fü

LOCATION — An island in the Ionian Sea opposite the Greek-Albanian border
GOVT. — A department of Greece
AREA — 245 sq. mi.
POP. — 114,620 (1938)
CAPITAL — Corfu

In 1922 Italy occupied Corfu (Kerkyra) during a controversy with Greece over the assassination of an Italian official in Epirus. Italy again occupied Corfu in 1941-43.

100 Centesimi = 1 Lira
100 Lepta = 1 Drachma

Watermark

Wmk. 140 — Crown

Wmk. 252 — Crowns

ISSUED UNDER ITALIAN OCCUPATION

Italian Stamps of 1901-23 Overprinted

1923, Sept. 20   Wmk. 140   Perf. 14

N1	A48	5c green	6.00	7.50
N2	A48	10c claret	6.00	7.50
N3	A48	15c slate	6.00	7.50
N4	A50	20c brown orange	6.00	7.50
N5	A49	30c orange brown	6.00	7.50
N6	A49	50c violet	6.00	7.50
N7	A49	60c blue	6.00	7.50
	a.	Vert. pair, one without overprint	1,000.	
N8	A46	1 l brown & green	6.00	7.50
		Nos. N1-N8 (8)	48.00	60.00
		Set, never hinged	120.00	

Italian Stamps of 1901-23 Surcharged

1923, Sept. 24

N9	A48	25 l on 10c claret	60.00	30.00
N10	A49	60 l on 25c blue	9.00	
N11	A49	70 l on 30c org brn	9.00	
N12	A49	1.20d on 50c violet	30.00	30.00
N13	A46	2.40d on 1 l brn & grn	30.00	30.00
N14	A46	4.75d on 2 l grn & org	13.50	
		Nos. N9-N14 (6)	151.50	90.00
		Set, never hinged	360.00	

Nos. N10, N11, N14 were not placed in use.

Issue for Corfu and Paxos

Nos. N15-N34, NC1-NC12, NJ1-NJ11 and NRA1-NRA3 have been extensively counterfeited, some with forged cancellations.

Stamps of Greece, 1937-38, Overprinted in Black

Perf. 12x13½, 12½x12, 13½x12

1941, June 5   Wmk. 252

N15	A69	5 l brn red & blue	6.00	3.00
	a.	Inverted overprint	60.00	35.00
	b.	Double overprint	85.00	85.00
N16	A70	10 l bl & brn red (On 397)	2.25	2.25
N17	A70	10 l bl & brn red (On 413)	1,300.	875.00
N18	A71	20 l black & grn	2.25	2.25
	a.	Inverted overprint	85.00	35.00
N19	A72	40 l green & blk	3.00	3.00
	a.	Inverted overprint	85.00	35.00
	b.	Double overprint	85.00	85.00
N20	A73	50 l brown & blk	2.25	2.25
	a.	Inverted overprint	60.00	32.50

N21	A74	80 l ind & yel brn	3.00	3.00
N22	A67	1d green	14.50	11.00
N23	A84	1.50d green	11.00	11.50
N24	A75	2d ultra	7.50	4.50
N25	A67	3d red brown	14.50	11.00
N26	A76	5d red	7.50	6.00
Ñ27	A77	6d olive brown	7.50	7.50
N28	A78	7d dark brown	11.00	7.50
N29	A67	8d deep blue	25.00	22.50
N30	A79	10d red brown	575.00	250.00
N31	A80	15d green	26.50	22.50
N32	A81	25d dark blue	22.50	22.50
N33	A84	30d org brn	100.00	90.00
N34	A67	100d carmine lake	325.00	225.00
		Nos. N15-N34 (20)	2,466.	1,582.
		Set, never hinged	4,250.	

AIR POST STAMPS

Greece Nos. C37 and C26-C35, Overprinted Like Nos. N15-N34

Perf. 12½x13, 13x12½, 13½x12½

1941, June 5   Unwmk.

NC1	D3	50 l dk brown	18.00	8.75
NC2	AP16	1d red	875.00	290.00
NC3	AP17	2d gray blue	21.00	8.75
NC4	AP18	5d violet	25.00	14.50
NC5	AP19	7d deep ultra	25.00	15.00
NC6	AP20	10d bister brn (On C26)	1,150.	500.00
NC7	AP20	10d brown org (On C35)	87.50	50.00
NC8	AP21	25d rose	130.00	55.00
NC9	AP22	30d dk grn	160.00	87.50
NC10	AP23	50d violet	130.00	65.00
	a.	Double overprint		425.00
NC11	AP24	100d brown	1,450.	725.00

On No. C36

Serrate Roulette 13½

NC12	D3	50 l vio brn	100.00	35.00
	a.	On No. C36a		
		Nos. NC1-NC12 (12)	4,171.	1,854.
		Set, never hinged	6,500.	

POSTAGE DUE STAMPS

Postage Due Stamps of Greece, 1913-35 Overprinted Like #N15-N34

1941, June 5   Unwmk.

Serrate Roulette 13½

NJ1	D3	10 l carmine	7.25	7.25
NJ2	D3	25 l ultra	11.00	7.25
NJ3	D3	80 l lilac brown	1,300.	350.00

Perf. 12½x13, 13½x12½

NJ4	D3	1d lt bl (On J80)	2,200.	800.00
NJ5	D3	2d light red	14.50	14.50
NJ6	D3	5d gray	29.00	29.00
NJ7	D3	10d gray green	25.00	25.00
NJ8	D3	15d red brown	29.00	25.00
NJ9	D3	25d light red	29.00	25.00
NJ10	D3	50d orange	29.00	25.00
NJ11	D3	100d slate green	750.00	450.00
		Nos. NJ1-NJ11 (11)	4,423.	1,758.

POSTAL TAX STAMPS

Greece Nos. RA61-RA63, Overprinted Like Nos. N15-N34

Wmk., Unwmk.

1941, June 5   Perf. 13½

NRA1	PT7	10 l brt rose, pale rose	3.00	5.75
NRA2	PT7	50 l gray grn, pale green	3.75	5.75
NRA3	PT7	1d dull blue, lt blue	32.50	26.00
		Nos. NRA1-NRA3 (3)	39.25	37.50
		Set, never hinged	80.00	

Stamps overprinted "CORFU" were replaced by Italian stamps overprinted "Isole Jonie." See Ionian Islands.

COSTA RICA

ˌkäs-tə-ˈrē-kə

LOCATION — Central America between Nicaragua and Panama
GOVT. — Republic
AREA — 19,730 sq. mi.
POP. — 3,674,490 (1999 est.)
CAPITAL — San Jose

8 Reales = 100 Centavos = 1 Peso
100 Centimos = 1 Colon (1900)

Catalogue values for unused stamps in this country are for Never Hinged items, beginning with Scott 238 in the regular postage section, Scott C117 in the air post section, Scott CE1 in the air post special delivery section, Scott E1 in the special delivery section, and Scott RA1 in the postal tax section.

Watermarks

Wmk. 215 — Small Star in Shield, Multiple

Wmk. 229 — Wavy Lines

Wmk. 334 — Rectangles

Values for unused stamps are for examples with original gum as defined in the catalogue introduction. Very fine examples of Nos. 1-22 will have perforations just clear of the design on one or more sides due to the placement of the stamps on the plates and to imperfect perforating methods.

Coat of Arms — A1

1863   Unwmk.   Engr.   Perf. 12

1	A1	½r blue	.40	1.10
	a.	½r light blue	.40	1.10
	b.	Pair, imperf. horiz.	1,500.	
2	A1	2r scarlet	1.75	2.25
3	A1	4r green	16.00	16.00
4	A1	1p orange	42.50	42.50
		Nos. 1-4 (4)	60.65	61.85

The ½r was printed from two plates. The second is in light blue with little or no sky over the mountains.
Imperforate examples of Nos. 1-2 are corner stamps from poorly perforated sheets.

Nos. 1-3 Surcharged in Red or Black:

a

b

c

d

e

1881-82
Red or Black Surcharge

7	A1(a)	1c on ½r ('82)	3.00	—
a.		On No. 1a	15.00	—
8	A1(b)	1c on ½r ('82)	18.00	—
9	A1(c)	2c on ½r, #1a	3.00	—
a.		On No. 1	8.00	—
12	A1(c)	5c on ½r	8.00	—
13	A1(d)	5c on ½r ('82)	55.00	—
14	A1(d)	10c on 2r (Bk) ('82)	70.00	—
15	A1(e)	20c on 4r ('82)	300.00	—

Overprints with different fonts and "OFICIAL" were never placed in use, and are said to have been surcharged to a dealer's order. The ½r surcharged "DOS CTS" is not a postage stamp. It probably is an essay.

Postally used examples of Nos. 7-15 are rare. Nos. 13-15 exist with a favor cancel having a hyphen between "San" and "Jose." Values same as unused. Fake cancellations exist.

Counterfeits exist of surcharges on Nos. 7-15.

Gen. Prospero
Fernández
A6

President
Bernardo Soto
Alfaro
A7

1883, Jan. 1

16	A6	1c green	3.00	1.50
17	A6	2c carmine	3.00	1.50
18	A6	5c blue violet	30.00	2.00
19	A6	10c orange	140.00	12.00
20	A6	40c blue	2.00	3.00
		Nos. 16-20 (5)	178.00	20.00

Unused examples of 40c usually lack gum.
For overprints see Nos. O1-O20, O24, Guanacaste 1-38, 44.

1887

21	A7	5c blue violet	7.00	.50
22	A7	10c orange	4.00	3.00

Unused examples of 5c usually lack gum.
For overprints see Nos. O22-O23, Guanacaste 42-43, 45.

A8

A9

1889
Black Overprint

23	A8	1c rose	5.00	3.00
24	A9	5c brown	7.00	3.00

Vertical and inverted overprints are fakes.

For overprints see Guanacaste Nos. 47-54.

President Soto Alfaro
A10   A11

A12

A13

A14   A15

A16

A17

A18

A19

1889   Perf. 14-16 & Compound

25	A10	1c brown	.35	.45
a.		Horiz. pair, imperf. vert	150.00	
b.		Imperf. pair	100.00	
c.		Horiz. or vert. pair, imperf. btwn.	150.00	
26	A11	2c dark green	.35	.45
a.		Imperf., pair	50.00	
b.		Vert. pair, imperf. horiz.	125.00	
c.		Horiz. pair, imperf. btwn.	125.00	
27	A12	5c orange	.45	.35
a.		Imperf., pair		250.00
b.		Horiz. pair, imperf. btwn.	150.00	
28	A13	10c red brown	.40	.35
a.		Vert. or horiz. pair, imperf. btwn.	150.00	
29	A14	20c yellow green	.30	.35
a.		Vert. pair, imperf. horiz.	200.00	
b.		Horizontal pair, imperf. btwn.	150.00	
30	A15	50c rose red	1.00	
		Telegram cancel		.75
31	A16	1p blue	1.25	
		Telegram cancel		.75
32	A17	2p dull violet	6.00	
a.		2p slate	6.00	
		Telegram cancel		4.00
33	A18	5p olive green	25.00	
		Telegram cancel		10.00
34	A19	10p black	100.00	
		Telegram cancel		60.00
		Nos. 25-34 (10)	135.10	

Nos. 30-34 normally were used on telegrams, and most examples were removed from the forms and sold by the government.
For overprints see Nos. O25-O30, Guanacaste 55-67.

A9

A8

Arms of Costa Rica
A20   A21

A22

A23

A24

A25

A26

A27

A28

A29

1892   Perf. 12-15 & Compound

35	A20	1c grnsh blue	.30	.40
36	A21	2c yellow	.30	.40
37	A22	5c red lilac	.30	.25
a.		5c violet	60.00	.30
38	A23	10c lt green	.75	.35
a.		Horiz. pair, imperf. btwn.	—	100.00
39	A24	20c scarlet	12.00	.20
a.		Horiz. pair, imperf. btwn.	—	100.00
40	A25	50c gray blue	4.00	4.25
41	A26	1p green, yel	1.00	1.00
42	A27	2p brown red, lilac	3.00	1.00
		2p rose red, pale lil	12.00	1.00
43	A28	5p dk blue, blue	2.00	1.00
44	A29	10p brown, pale buff	35.00	5.00
		10p brown, yellow	8.00	
		Nos. 35-44 (10)	58.65	13.85

Imperfs. of Nos. 35-44 are proofs.
For overprints see Nos. O31-O36.

Statue of Juan
Santamaría
A30

Juan Mora
Fernández
A31

View of Port
Limón — A32

Braulio Carillo
("Branlio" on
stamp) — A33

National
Theater — A34

José M.
Castro — A35

Birris
Bridge — A36

Juan Rafael
Mora — A37

Jesús
Jiménez — A38

Coat of
Arms — A39

1901, Jan.   Perf. 12-15½

45	A30	1c green & blk	3.25	.30
a.		Horiz. pair, imperf. btwn.	150.00	
46	A31	2c ver & blk	1.25	.30
47	A32	5c gray blue & blk	3.25	.30
a.		Vert. pair, imperf. btwn.		150.00
48	A33	10c ocher & blk	3.25	.35
49	A34	20c lake & blk	22.50	.25
a.		Vert. pair, imperf. btwn.	150.00	
50	A35	50c dull lil & dk bl	5.25	1.00
51	A36	1col ol bis & blk	110.00	3.50
52	A37	2col car rose & dk grn	16.00	3.00
53	A38	5col brown & blk	75.00	3.50
54	A39	10col yel grn & brn red	29.00	3.00
		Nos. 45-54 (10)	268.75	15.50

The 2c exists with center inverted.
Nos. 45-57 in other colors are private reprints made in 1948. They have little value.
For surcharge and overprints see Nos. 58, 78, O37-O44.

Remainders

In 1914 the government sold a large quantity of stamps at very much less than face value. The lot included most regular issues from 1901 to 1911 inclusive, postage due stamps of 1903 and Official stamps of 1901-03. These stamps were canceled with groups of five thin parallel bars. The higher valued used stamps, such as Nos. 64, 65-68a, sell for much less than the values quoted, which are for stamps with regular postal cancellations. A few sell for much higher prices.

José M.
Cañas — A40

Julián
Volio — A41

Eusebio Figueroa
Oreamuno — A42

1903   Perf. 13½, 14, 15

55	A40	4c red vio & blk	1.75	.70
56	A41	6c olive grn & blk	7.25	4.00
57	A42	25c gray lil & brn	16.00	.30
		Nos. 55-57 (3)	25.00	5.00

See note on private reprints following #54.
For overprints see Nos. 81, O45-O47.

No. 49 Surcharged in Black:

1905

58 A34 1c on 20c lake & blk .60 .60
a. Inverted surcharge 10.00 10.00
b. Diagonal surcharge .60 .60

Specimens surcharged in other colors are proofs.

Statue of Juan
Santamaria
A43

Juan Mora
Fernández
A44

José M.
Cañas
A45

Mauro
Fernández
A46

Braulio
Carrillo — A47

Julián
Volio — A48

Eusebio
Figueroa
Oreamuno
A49

José M.
Castro
A50

Jesús
Jiménez — A51

Juan Rafael
Mora — A52

Perf. 11x14, 14 (1c, 5c, 10c, 25c)

1907 **Unwmk.**

59 A43 1c red brn & ind 8.00 .40
a. Perf. 11x14 60.00 3.00
b. Imperf pair 15.00
60 A44 2c yel grn & blk 3.00 .30
a. Perf. 14 3.00 .30
b. Imperf pair 15.00
61 A45 4c car & indigo 12.00 2.50
a. Perf. 14 500.00 40.00
b. Imperf pair 15.00
62 A46 5c yel & dull bl 3.00 .30
a. Perf. 11x14 60.00 1.00
b. Imperf pair 15.00
63 A47 10c blue & blk 10.00 .50
a. Perf. 11x14 20.00 1.00
b. Imperf pair 30.00
64 A48 20c olive grn & blk 25.00 6.00
a. Perf. 14 25.00 6.00
  Remainder cancel 2.00
b. Imperf pair —
65 A49 25c gray lil & blk 3.00 3.00
  Remainder cancel 1.00
a. Perf. 11x14 100.00 50.00
b. Imperf pair —
66 A50 50c red lil & blue 55.00 25.00
  Remainder cancel 2.00
a. Perf. 14 100.00 50.00
b. Imperf pair —
67 A51 1col brown & blk 22.50 20.00
a. Perf. 14 22.50 20.00
  Remainder cancel 2.00
b. Imperf pair —

68 A52 2col claret & grn 160.00 100.00
a. Perf. 14 300.00 150.00
  Remainder cancel 3.00
b. Imperf pair 200.00
  Nos. 59-68 (10) 301.50 158.00

The remainder cancel value applies to both perforations.
The imperforate varieties of the above set are valued without gum. Ungummed stamps were probably placed on the market in London, while gummed stamps appear to have been sent to Costa Rica and accepted for postal use. There is a small premium for gummed stamps.
The 1c, 2c, 5c, 20c, 50c, 1 col and 2 col exist with center inverted.
Nos. 59-68 exist with papermaker's watermark.
No. 65b with brown vignette is a proof. Value, pair $40. The actual No. 65b (black vignette) is worth much more.
For overprints see Nos. 77, 79-80, 82-84, O48-O55, O60-O64.

Statue of Juan
Santamaria
A53

Juan Mora
Fernández
A54

José M.
Cañas
A55

Mauro
Fernández
A56

Braulio
Carrillo — A57

Julián
Volio — A58

Eusebio
Figueroa
Oreamuno
A59

Jesús Jiménez
A60

1910 **Perf. 12**

69 A53 1c brown .20 .20
70 A54 2c dp green .25 .20
71 A55 4c scarlet .35 .35
72 A56 5c orange 1.00 .20
73 A57 10c deep blue .25 .20
74 A58 20c olive grn .50 .35
75 A59 25c dp violet 17.00 1.50
76 A60 1col dk brown .50 .50
  Nos. 69-76 (8) 20.05 3.50

For overprints and surcharge see Nos. 111C-111J, B1, C2, O56-O59.

No. 60a Overprinted
in Red

1911 **Perf. 14**

77 A44 2c yel grn & blk 1.50 1.00
a. Inverted overprint 5.50 5.00
b. Double overprint, both inverted 45.00

Stamps of 1901-07
Overprinted in Red or
Black

78 A30 1c grn & blk (R) 2.00 1.00
a. Black overprint 32.50 18.00
b. Inverted overprint
79 A43 1c red brn & ind (Bk) 1.00 .40
a. Inverted overprint 4.50 3.50
b. Double overprint 5.50 5.00
80 A44 2c yel grn & blk (Bk) 1.00 .40
a. Inverted overprint 3.75 3.50
b. Dbl. ovpt., one as on No. 77 40.00 27.50
c. Double overprint, one inverted 15.00 15.00
d. Pair, one stamp No. 77 25.00 18.00
e. Perf. 11x14 30.00 10.00

No. 55 Overprinted in
Black

81 A40 4c red vio & blk 1.00 .65

Stamps of 1907
Overprinted in Blue,
Black or Rose

Perf. 14, 11x14 (#83, 84)

82 A46 5c yel & bl (Bl) 1.50 .20
a. "Habilitada" 3.25 2.50
b. "2911" 5.50 3.25
c. Roman "I" in "1911" 4.00 2.50
d. Double overprint 5.50 5.00
e. Inverted overprint 6.00 3.75
f. Black overprint — 2.00
g. Triple overprint 100.00
h. Vert. pair, imperf. horiz. 100.00
83 A47 10c blue & blk (Bk) 5.00 1.40
a. As #83, Roman "I" in "1911" 7.00 5.00
c. As #83, double overprint 20.00 11.50
d. Perf. 14 45.00 5.00
84 A47 10c blue & blk (R) 15.00 12.50
a. Roman "I" in "1911" 100.00 100.00
c. Perf. 14 100.00 100.00
  Nos. 77-84 (8) 28.00 17.55

Many counterfeits of overprint exist.

A61 A62

A63

Telegraph Stamps Surcharged in
Rose, Blue or Black

1911 **Perf. 12**

86 A61 1c on 10c bl (R) .30 .20
a. "Coereos" 7.75 5.50
b. Inverted surcharge
87 A61 1c on 10c bl (Bk) 200.00
a. "Coereos" 8.00 5.50
88 A61 1c on 25c vio (Bk) .30 .20
a. "Coereos" 8.00 5.50
b. Pair, one without surcharge 20.00
c. Double surcharge 9.00
e. Double surch., one inverted 12.50
89 A61 1c on 50c red brn (Bl) .50 .40
a. Inverted surcharge 5.50 5.00
b. Double surcharge 4.50
90 A61 1c on 1col brn (R) .50 .40
91 A61 1c on 5col red (Bl) .80 .55
92 A61 1c on 10col dk brn (R) 1.00 .70

Perf. 14

93 A62 2c on 5c brn org (Bk) 3.50 1.90
a. Inverted surcharge 9.00 3.75
b. "Correos" inverted 17.50
c. Double surcharge 9.00

Perf. 14x11

94 A62 2c on 10c bl (R) 100.00
a. Perf. 14 300.00
b. "Correos" inverted
c. As "b," perf. 14

95 A62 2c on 50c cl (Bk) .60 .50
a. Inverted surcharge 4.50 3.25
b. Double surcharge 12.50
c. Perf. 14 45.00 20.00
96 A62 2c on 1col brn (Bk) 1.00 .70
a. Inverted surcharge 12.50
b. Double surcharge 16.00
c. Perf. 14 2.00 .80
97 A62 2c on 2col car (Bk) .75 .60
a. Inverted surcharge 8.00 5.00
b. "Correos" inverted 10.00 5.50
c. Double surcharge
d. Perf. 14 25.00 15.00
98 A62 2c on 5col grn (Bk) .65 .65
a. Inverted surcharge 10.00 7.00
b. "Correos" inverted 16.00 4.25
c. Perf. 14 6.00 3.00
99 A62 2c on 10col mar (Bk) 1.00 .65
a. "Correos" inverted 400.00
b. Perf. 14 5.00 3.00

Perf. 12

100 A63 5c on 5c org (Bl) .40 .25
a. Double surcharge 25.00 15.00
b. Inverted surcharge 25.00 8.50
c. Pair, one without surcharge 16.00

Counterfeits exist of Nos. 87, 94 and all minor varieties. Genuine "Coereos" errors do not exist on No. 87. Used examples of No. 94 with target cancels are counterfeits.
Nos. 93-99 exist with papermaker's watermark.

Coffee Plantation — A64

1921, June 17 Litho. Perf. 11½

103 A64 5c bl & blk 3.00 3.00
a. Tête bêche pair 10.00 6.50
b. Imperf., pair 25.00
c. As "a," imperf. 125.00

Centenary of coffee raising in Costa Rica.

Liberty with Torch
of
Freedom — A65

1921 Typo. Perf. 11

104 A65 5c violet 1.00 .40
a. Imperf, pair 100.00

Cent. of Central American independence.
Beware of trimmed singles that look like No. 104a.
For overprint see No. 111.

Juan Mora and Julio Acosta — A66

1921, Sept. 15 Perf. 11½

105 A66 2c orange & blk 1.75 1.75
106 A66 3c green & blk 1.75 1.75
107 A66 6c scarlet & blk 3.00 3.00
108 A66 15c dk blue & blk 5.00 5.00
109 A66 30c orange brn & blk 6.50 6.50
  Nos. 105-109 (5) 18.00 18.00

Centenary of Central American independence. Issue requested by Costa Rican Philatelic Society. Authorized by decree calling for 2,000 of 30c and 5,000 each of other values. Many more were printed illegally including imperforates, color changes and inverted centers.
Each sheet of 20 (4x5) contains 5 tête-bêche pairs.

Simón Bolívar — A67

1921   Engr.   Perf. 12
110 A67 15c deep violet   .75   .20

For overprint No. 110a see set following No. 111. For surcharge see No. 148

No. 104 Overprinted

1922   Perf. 11
111 A65 5c violet   .75   .40
  a.   Inverted overprint   10.00
  b.   Double overprint   15.00

Fakes of Nos. 111a and 111b are common.

Stamps of 1910-1921 Overprinted in Blue, Red, Black or Gold

1922   Perf. 12
111C A53 1c brown (Bl)   .30   .20
111D A54 2c deep green (R)   .40   .20
111E A55 4c scarlet   .30   .20
111F A56 5c orange   2.00   .35
111G A57 10c deep blue (R)   .75   .35
111H A67 15c deep violet (G)   3.50   2.00
     Nos. 111C-111H (6)   7.25   3.30

Inverted overprints occur on all values. Counterfeits are very common for both normal and inverted overprints.

No. 72 Overprinted

1923
111J A56 5c orange   3.00   .75
  k.   "VD." for "UD."   75.00   75.00

Jesús Jiménez — A68

1923, June 18   Litho.   Perf. 11½
112 A68 2c brown   .40   .40
113 A68 4c green   .40   .40
114 A68 5c blue   .60   .40
115 A68 20c carmine   .85   .50
116 A68 1col violet   1.10   1.25
     Nos. 112-116 (5)   3.35   2.95

Pres. Jesús Jiménez (1823-98). Nos. 112-116, imperf, were not regularly issued. Value, set $5.
For overprints see Nos. O65-O69.

National Monument A70

Harvesting Coffee — A71

Banana Growing — A73

General Post Office A74

Columbus Soliciting Aid of Isabella A75

Christopher Columbus A76

Columbus at Cariari A77

Map of Costa Rica — A78

Manuel M. Gutiérrez — A79

1923-26   Engr.   Perf. 12
117 A70 1c violet   .25   .20
118 A71 2c yellow   .50   .20
119 A73 4c deep green   .75   .30
120 A74 5c light blue   1.50   .20
121 A74 5c yellow grn ('26)   .50   .20
122 A75 10c red brown   3.00   .20
123 A75 10c car rose ('26)   .50   .20
124 A76 12c carmine rose   10.00   3.00
125 A77 20c deep blue   10.00   .60
126 A78 40c orange   11.00   3.00
127 A79 1col olive green   2.00   .65
     Nos. 117-127 (11)   40.00   8.75

See #151-156. For surcharges & overprints see #136-140, 147, 189, 218, C2.

Rodrigo Arias Maldonado — A80

1924   Perf. 12½
128 A80 2c dark green   .20   .20
  a.   Perf. 14   .50   .25

See No. 162.

Map of Guanacaste A81

Mission at Nicoya A82

1924   Litho.   Perf. 12
129 A81 1c carmine rose   .30   .20
130 A81 2c violet   .30   .20
131 A81 5c green   .30   .20
132 A81 10c orange   2.25   .50
133 A82 15c light blue   1.00   .45
134 A82 20c gray black   2.00   1.00
135 A82 25c light brown   3.00   1.50
     Nos. 129-135 (7)   9.15   4.05

Centenary of annexation of Province of Guanacaste to Costa Rica.
Exist imperf. Value, set, $50.

Stamps of 1923 Surcharged:

a

b

1925
136 A74(a) 3c on 5c lt blue   .30   .20
137 A75(a) 6c on 10c red brn   .40   .25
138 A78(a) 30c on 40c orange   1.50   .40
139 A79(b) 45c on 1col ol grn   1.75   .50
  a.   Double surcharge   250.00
     Nos. 136-139 (4)   3.95   1.35

No. 124 Surcharged

1926
140 A76 10c on 12c car rose   1.50   .30

College of San Luis, Cartago A83

Chapui Asylum, San José — A84

Normal School, Heredia A85

Ruins of Ujarrás A86

1926   Unwmk.   Engr.   Perf. 12½
143 A83 3c ultra   .50   .20
144 A84 6c dark brown   .50   .20
145 A85 30c deep orange   2.00   .20
146 A86 45c black violet   4.00   1.00
     Nos. 143-146 (4)   7.00   1.65

For surcharges see Nos. 190-190D, 217.

No. 124 Surcharged in Black:

1928, Jan. 7   Perf. 12
147 A76 10c on 12c car rose   4.50   4.50

Issued in honor of Col. Charles A. Lindbergh during his Good Will Tour of Central America. The surcharge was privately reprinted using an original die. Reprints can be distinguished by distinct dots under the "10s." All errors and inverted surcharges are reprints.

No. 110 Surcharged

1928
148 A67 5(c) on 15c dp violet   .25   .25
  a.   Inverted surcharge   27.50

Type I — A88

Type II

Type III

Type IV

Type V

Surcharge Typo. (I-V) & Litho. (V)
1929   Perf. 12½
149 A88 5c on 2col car (I)   .50   .20
  a.-d.   Types II-V (typo.)   .60   .20
  e.   Type V (litho.)   3.00   3.00

Telegraph Stamp Surcharged for Postage as in 1929, Surcharge Lithographed

1929
150 A88 13c on 40c deep grn   .35   .25
  a.   Inverted surcharge   1.00   1.00

Excellent counterfeits exist of No. 150a.

Types of 1923-26 Issues Dated "1929"
Imprint of Waterlow & Sons

1930   Size: 26x21½mm   Perf. 12½
151 A70 1c dark violet   .35 .20
155 A74 5c green   .35 .20
156 A75 10c carmine rose   .35 .20
    Nos. 151-156 (3)   1.05 .60

Juan Rafael
Mora — A89

1931
157 A89 13c carmine rose   .60 .20
    For surcharge see No. 209.

Seal of Costa Rica Philatelic Society
("Octubre 12 de 1932") — A90

1932, Oct. 12   Perf. 12
158 A90 3c orange   .25 .20
159 A90 5c dark green   .40 .25
160 A90 10c carmine rose   .50 .25
161 A90 20c dark blue   .85 .30
    Nos. 158-161 (4)   2.00 1.00

Phil. Exhib., Oct. 12, 1932. See #179-183.

Maldonado Type of 1924

1934   Perf. 12½
162 A80 3c dark green   .20 .20

Red Cross
Nurse — A91

1935, May 31   Perf. 12
163 A91 10c rose carmine   7.50 .25

50th anniv. of the founding of the Costa
Rican Red Cross Society.

Air View of
Cartago
A92

Miraculous
Statuette and
View of
Cathedral
A93

Vision of
1635 — A94

1935, Aug.   Perf. 12½
164 A92 5c green   .20 .20
165 A93 10c carmine   .30 .20
166 A92 30c orange   .45 .20
167 A94 45c dark violet   1.10 .55
168 A93 50c blue black   1.75 1.00
    Nos. 164-168 (5)   3.80 2.15

Tercentenary of the Patron Saint, Our Lady
of the Angels, of Costa Rica.

Map of
Cocos
Island
A95

1936, Jan. 29   Perf. 14, 11½ (25c)
169 A95 4c ocher   .25 .20
170 A95 8c dark violet   .35 .20
171 A95 25c orange   .50 .20
172 A95 35c brown vio   .75 .20
173 A95 40c brown   1.00 .20
174 A95 50c yellow   1.10 .60
175 A95 2col yellow grn   11.00 10.00
176 A95 5col green   30.00 25.00
    Nos. 169-176 (8)   44.95 36.60

Exist imperf. Value, set, $50.
For surcharges see #196-200, C55-C56.

Map of
Cocos
Island and
Ships of
Columbus
A96

1936, Dec. 5   Perf. 12
177 A96 5c green   .20 .20
178 A96 10c carmine rose   .20 .20

For overprints see Nos. 247, O80-O81.

Seal of Costa Rica Philatelic Society
("Diciembre 1937") — A97

1937
179 A97 2c dark brown   .45 .20
180 A97 3c black   .45 .20
181 A97 5c green   .45 .20
182 A97 10c orange red   .45 .20
    Nos. 179-182 (4)   1.80 .80

Souvenir Sheet
Imperf
183   Sheet of 4   1.50 1.50
  a.   A97 2c dark brown   .20 .20
  b.   A97 3c black   .20 .20
  c.   A97 5c green   .20 .20
  d.   A97 10c orange red   .20 .20

Phil. Exhib., Dec. 1937.

Purple Guaria Orchid, National
Flower — A98

Tuna — A99

Native with
Donkey
Carrying
Bananas
A101

3c, Cacao pod. 10c, Coffee harvesting.

1937-38   Wmk. 229   Perf. 12½
184 A98 1c green & vio ('38)   .55 .20
185 A98 3c chocolate ('38)   .35 .20

Unwmk.   Perf. 12
186 A99 2c olive gray   .40 .20
187 A101 5c dark green   .55 .20
188 A101 10c carmine rose   .90 .20
    Nos. 184-188 (5)   2.75 1.00

National Exposition.

No. 125
Overprinted
in Black

1938   Unwmk.   Perf. 12
189 A77 20c deep blue   1.50 .20

No. 146 Surcharged in Red:

a

b

c

d

e

1940   Perf. 12½
190   A86(a) 15c on 45c blk vio   .60 .30
190A A86(b) 15c on 45c blk vio   .60 .30
190B A86(c) 15c on 45c blk vio   .60 .30
190C A86(d) 15c on 45c blk vio   .60 .30
190D A86(e) 15c on 45c blk vio   .60 .30
    Nos. 190-190D (5)   3.00 1.50

#190D exists with inverted surcharge.
Value, $5.

Allegory
A103

Overprinted "Dia Panamericano de la
Salud / 2 Diciembre 1940" and Arc

1940, Dec. 2   Engr.   Perf. 12
191 A103 5c green   .20 .20
192 A103 10c rose carmine   .25 .20
193 A103 20c deep blue   .25 .20
194 A103 40c brown   1.50 1.25
195 A103 55c orange yellow   2.50 2.25
    Nos. 191-195 (5)   5.00 4.15

Pan-American Health Day. See #C46-C54.
Exist without overprint.

Stamps of 1936 Surcharged in Black:

1941   Perf. 14, 11½
196 A95 15c on 25c orange   .50 .50
197 A95 15c on 35c brn vio   .50 .50
198 A95 15c on 40c brown   .50 .50
199 A95 15c on 2col yel grn   .50 .50
200 A95 15c on 5col green   1.00 1.00
    Nos. 196-200 (5)   3.00 3.00

Nos. 196-200 exist with surcharge inverted.
Value, set of 5, $20.

National
Stadium
A104

Engr.; Flags Typo. in Natl. Colors
1941, May 8   Perf. 12½
201 A104 5c green   .70 .20
  a.   Flags omitted   150.00
202 A104 10c orange   .55 .30
203 A104 15c car rose   .80 .40
204 A104 25c dk blue   .85 .55
205 A104 40c chestnut   3.25 1.40
206 A104 50c purple   4.25 2.00
207 A104 75c red orange   6.75 5.75
208 A104 1col dk carmine   13.00 10.50
    Nos. 201-208 (8)   30.15 21.10

Caribbean and Central American Soccer
Championship. See #C57-C66, C121-C123.

No. 157
Surcharged in
Black

1941   Perf. 12
209 A89 5c on 13c car rose   .20 .20

Cleto González
Viquez — A105

Design: 5c, José Rodriguez.

1941-45   Engr.   Perf. 12½
210   A105 3c dp orange   .25 .20
210A A105 3c dp plum ('43)   .25 .20
210B A105 3c carmine ('45)   .25 .20
211   A105 5c dp violet   .25 .20
211A A105 5c brown blk ('43)   .25 .20
    Nos. 210-211A (5)   1.25 1.00

See No. 256.

Old
University
of Costa
Rica
A106

New
National
University
A107

1941, Aug. 26   Perf. 12
212 A106 5c green   .35 .20
213 A107 10c yellow org   .40 .20
214 A106 15c lilac rose   .75 .20
215 A107 25c dull blue   1.00 .35
216 A106 50c fawn   7.50 2.25
    Nos. 212-216 (5)   10.00 3.20

National University, founded in 1940. See
Nos. C74-C80.

Nos. 144, 189 Surcharged in Black or
Red

1942   *Perf. 12½, 12*
217 A84 5c on 6c dk brn   .35 .20
218 A77 15c on 20c dp bl (R)   .65 .20

Nos. 217-218 exist with inverted surcharge.
Value, each $8.

Torch of Freedom,   Juan Mora
"Victory" and   Fernández
Flags of American   A109
Nations
   A108

1942, Sept. 25   *Perf. 12*
219 A108 5c rose   .30 .20
220 A108 5c yellow grn   .30 .20
221 A108 5c purple   .30 .20
222 A108 5c dp blue   .30 .20
223 A108 5c red orange   .30 .20
      Nos. 219-223 (5)   1.50 1.00

For overprints see Nos. 238-241.

1943-47   *Engr.*

Designs: 2c, Bruno Carranza. 3c, Tomas
Guardia. 5c, Manuel Aguilar. 15c, Francisco
Morazan. 25c, Jose M. Alfaro. 50c, Francisco
M. Oreamuno. 1col, Jose M. Castro. 2col,
Juan Rafael Mora.

224 A109 1c red lilac   .20 .20
225 A109 2c black   .20 .20
226 A109 3c deep blue   .20 .20
227 A109 5c brt blue grn   .20 .20
   a.   5c bright green ('47)   .20 .20
228 A109 15c scarlet   .20 .20
229 A109 25c brt ultra   1.00 .20
230 A109 50c dp violet   3.00 .45
231 A109 1col black brown   4.00 2.00
232 A109 2col deep orange   5.00 3.00
      Nos. 224-232 (9)   14.00 6.65

See Nos. 344-368, C81-C91A, C124-C127,
C154-C158, C179-C181, C768-C772, C790-
C794, C854-C858. For surcharges see Nos.
C154-C158, C182, C184-C185.

View of
San
Ramón
A118

1944, Jan. 19
233 A118 5c dark green   .20 .20
234 A118 10c orange   .20 .20
235 A118 15c rose pink   .25 .20
236 A118 40c gray black   1.00 .80
237 A118 50c deep blue   2.40 1.60
      Nos. 233-237 (5)   4.05 3.00

100th anniv. of the founding of the City of
San Ramón. See Nos. C94-C102.

Catalogue values for unused
stamps in this section, from this
point to the end of the section, are
for **Never Hinged** items.

Nos. 220-223
Overprinted in Red
or Black

1944, Sept. 18
238 A108 5c yel green   .30 .20
239 A108 5c purple (R)   .30 .20
240 A108 5c dp blue (R)   .30 .20
241 A108 5c red orange   .30 .20
      Nos. 238-241 (4)   1.20 .80

Amicable settlement of a boundary dispute
with Panama. This overprint also exists on No.
219.

Mauro Fernández
(1844-1905),
Statesman — A119

Unwmk.
1945, July 21   Engr.   *Perf. 14*
242 A119 20c deep green   .30 .20

For surcharge see No. 246.

Coffee Harvesting — A120

1945, Oct. 9   *Perf. 12*
243 A120 5c dk green & blk   .30 .20
244 A120 10c orange & blk   .30 .20
245 A120 20c car rose & blk   .40 .20
      Nos. 243-245 (3)   1.00 .60

No. 242 Surcharged in Red Brown

1946   Unwmk.   *Perf. 14*
246 A119 15c on 20c dp green   .25 .20

Exists with inverted surcharge. Value, $6.

No. O80 Overprinted in Red

1947, Mar. 19   *Perf. 12*
247 A96 5c green   .20 .20

Exist with inverted overprint. Value, $6.

Cervantes — A121   A122

Wmk. 215
1947, Nov. 10   Engr.   *Perf. 14*
249 A121 30c deep blue   .45 .30
250 A121 55c deep carmine   .55 .30

Miguel de Cervantes Saavedra, novelist,
playwright & poet, 400th birth anniv.

1947, Aug. 26   Unwmk.   *Perf. 12*
251 A122 5c brt green   .20 .20
252 A122 10c car rose   .20 .20
253 A122 15c ultra   .25 .20

---

254 A122 25c orange red   .35 .25
255 A122 50c lilac   .55 .30
   Nos. 251-255,C160-C167 (13)   6.95 5.75

Franklin D. Roosevelt. For surcharges see
Nos. C224-C226.

Small Portrait Type of 1941

Design: 3c, Bishop Bernardo A. Theil.

1948   *Perf. 12½*
256 A105 3c deep ultra   .20 .20

Old
University
of Costa
Rica
A123

1953, June 25   Litho.   *Perf. 12*
Black Surcharge
257 A123 5c on 10c green   .35 .25

Revenue Stamp
Surcharged in Red
or Blue — A124

1955-56   Unwmk.   Engr.   *Perf. 12*
258 A124 5c on 2c emerald   .25 .20
259 A124 15c on 2c emer (Bl)   .25 .20
260 A124 15c on 2c emer ('56)   .25 .20
   Nos. 258-260,C341-C344 (7)   1.85 1.60

For surcharges see #C341-C344, C431-
C433.

Justo A.   Anglo-Costa Rican
Facio   Bank
A125   A126

1960, Apr. 20   Photo.   *Perf. 13½*
261 A125 10c brown red   .40 .20

Centenary of the birth (in 1859) of Prof.
Justo A. Facio. Exists imperf. Value, $35.

Nos. RA12-RA15
Surcharged in Red

1963, Mar.
262 PT3 10c on 5c dk car   .20 .20
263 PT3 10c on 5c sepia   .20 .20
264 PT3 10c on 5c dull grn   .20 .20
265 PT3 10c on 5c blue   .20 .20
      Nos. 262-265 (4)   .80 .80

1963   Unwmk.   *Perf. 13½*
266 A126 10c gray   .35 .25

Centenary of the Anglo-Costa Rican Bank.

Arms of San
José — A127

Alberto M.
Brenes
Mora — A128

Coats of Arms: 35c, Cartago. 50c, Heredia.
55c, Alajuela. 65c, Guanacaste. 1col,
Puntarenas. 2col, Limon.

1969, Sept. 14   Litho.   *Perf. 14x13½*
267 A127 15c multicolored   .20 .20
268 A127 35c multicolored   .20 .20
269 A127 50c gray & multi   .25 .20
270 A127 55c buff & multi   .25 .20
271 A127 65c multicolored   .75 .25
272 A127 1col pink & multi   2.10 .25
273 A127 2col multicolored   3.75 .60
      Nos. 267-273 (7)   7.50 1.90

1976, Mar. 1   Litho.   *Perf. 10½*
274 A128 1col violet blue   .40 .20
      Nos. 274,C653-C657 (6)   6.65 3.55

Prof. Alberto Manuel Brenes Mora, botanist,
birth centenary.

Map of Costa
Rica, Reader
with
Book — A129

1978, July 17   Litho.   *Perf. 13½*
275 A129 50c multicolored   .25 .20

National five-year literacy plan.

A130   A131

1983, May 17   Litho.   *Perf. 13x13½*
276 A130 10c multicolored   .20 .20
277 A130 50c multicolored   .20 .20
278 A130 10col multicolored   .80 .25
      Nos. 276-278 (3)   1.20 .65

World Communications Year.

1983, May 30   Litho.   *Perf. 10½*
279 A131 20col black   1.40 1.40

1st World Cong. of Human Rights, 1982.

UPU Membership Centenary — A132

1983, June 30   Litho.   *Perf. 16*
280 A132 3col #17, monument   .75 .50
281 A132 10col #20, headquar-
                        ters   1.50 .50

French Alliance Centenary — A133

1983, July 21   Litho.   Perf. 11
282 A133 12col Scene in San Jose, by Christina Fournier   2.00 .50

Christmas 1983 — A134

Nativity tableau in continuous design. Illustration reduced.

1983, Dec. 5   Litho.   Perf. 13½
283   1.50col multi   .20 .20
284   1.50col multi   .20 .20
285   1.50col multi   .20 .20
a.   A134 Strip of 3, #283-285   1.00 1.00

Costa Rican Gardens Association.

Fishery Development Administration A135

1983, Dec. 19   Litho.   Perf. 13½
286 A135 8.50col multi   .65 .25

Local Birds — A136

1984, Jan. 9   Litho.   Perf. 13½
287 A136 10c Quetzal   .50 .20
288 A136 50c Cyanerpes cyaneus   .50 .20
289 A136 1col Turdus grayi   .50 .20
290 A136 1.50col Momotus momota   .50 .20
291 A136 3col Colibri thalassinus   1.40 .25
292 A136 10col Notiochelindon cyanoleuca   4.50 .30
Nos. 287-292 (6)   7.90 1.35

Dated 1983. 10c, 1.50col, 3col vert.

José Joaquin Mora, Hero of 1856 Independence Campaign — A137

Paintings, Juan Santamaria Museum, San José: 1.50col, Pancha Carrasco. 3 col, Death of Juan Santamaria, horiz. 8.50col, Juan Rafael Mora Porras.

1984, Apr. 10   Litho.   Perf. 10½
293 A137 50c multi   .20 .20
294 A137 1.50col multi   .20 .20
295 A137 3col multi   .25 .20
296 A137 8.50col multi   .75 .50
Nos. 293-296 (4)   1.40 1.10

For surcharge see No. 440.

Jesus Bonilla Chavarria, Composer A138

Musicians and Composers: 5col, Benjamin Gutierrez (b. 1937). 12col, Pilar Jimenez (1835-1922). 13col, Jose Daniel Zuniga Zeledon (1889-1981).

1984, May 30   Litho.   Perf. 13½
297 A138 3.50col black & lil   .30 .20
298 A138 5col black & pink   .40 .25
299 A138 12col black & grn   1.00 .75
300 A138 13col black & yel   1.10 .80
Nos. 297-300 (4)   2.80 2.00

Figurines, Jade Museum — A139

1984, June 27   Litho.   Perf. 13½
301 A139 4col Man (pendant)   .75 .20
302 A139 7col Seated man   1.50 .35
303 A139 10col Dish, horiz.   2.00 .45
Nos. 301-303 (3)   4.25 1.00

1984, July 27
304 A140 1col Basketball   .20 .20
305 A140 8col Swimming   .60 .20
306 A140 11col Bicycling   .80 .35
307 A140 14col Running   1.10 .60
308 A140 20col Boxing   1.60 1.00
309 A140 30col Soccer   2.50 1.25
Nos. 304-309 (6)   6.80 3.60

1984 Summer Olympics A140

Public Street Lighting Centenary A141

1984, Aug. 9   Litho.   Perf. 10½
310 A141 6col Street scene by Luis Chacon   .50 .30

10th Natl. Stamp Exhibition, Sept. 10-16 — A142

1984, Sept. 10   Litho.   Perf. 10½
311 A142 10col Natl. monument   .80 .45
312 A142 10col Juan Mora Fernandez monument   .80 .45
a.   Min. sheet, 2 each #311-312   15.00

Natl. Arms — A143

1984, Oct. 29   Engr.   Perf. 14x13½
313 A143 100col dk green   6.50 3.00
314 A143 100col yel org   6.50 3.00

Detail from Sistine Virgin by Raphael — A144

1984, Dec. 7   Litho.   Perf. 10½
315   3col multicolored   .25 .20
316   3col multicolored   .25 .20
a.   A144 Pair, #315-316   2.00 2.00

20th Intl. Bicycle Race, Costa Rica — A146

1984, Dec. 19   Litho.   Perf. 13½
317 A146 6col multi   .50 .30

Intl. Youth Year A147

1985, Jan. 31   Perf. 10½
322 A147 11col IYY emblem, #C476   1.40 .45

Scouting Movement, 75th anniv.

Labor Monument, San Jose — A148

Natl. values: 11col, Freedom of speech-wooden hand printing press. 13col, Neutrality-dove, natl. flag, outline map.

1985, Feb. 28
323 A148 6col shown   .75 .30
324 A148 11col bl, blk & yel   1.10 .45
325 A148 13col multi   1.25 .50
Size: 68x38mm
326 A148 30col Nos. 323-325   3.75 1.10
Nos. 323-326 (4)   6.85 2.35

Natl. Red Cross Cent., UN 40th Anniv. A149

1985, May 3   Perf. 10½
327 A149 3col No. 163, horiz.   2.00 .20
328 A149 5col No. C120   3.00 .25

Club Emblem A150

1st Club Pres., Ricardo Saprissa Ayma A151

Design: No. 330, Hands holding soccer ball.

1985, July 16   Perf. 10½
329 A150 3col multi   .25 .20
330 A150 3col multi   .25 .20
a.   Pair, #329-330   .50 .50
331 A151 6col multi   .50 .30
Nos. 329-331 (3)   1.00 .70

Saprissa Soccer Club, 50th Anniv.

Orchids — A152

1985, Dec. 3
332 A152 6col Brassia arcuigera   2.00 .80
333 A152 6col Encyclia peraltensis   2.00 .80
334 A152 6col Maxillaria especie   2.00 .80
a.   Strip of 3, #332-334   11.00 4.50
335 A152 13col Oncidium turialbae   2.00 1.40
336 A152 13col Trichopilia marginata   2.00 1.40
337 A152 13col Stanhopea ecornuta   2.00 1.40
a.   Strip of 3, #335-337   11.00 4.50
Nos. 332-337 (6)   12.00 6.60

11th Natl. Philatelic Exposition A153

1985, Dec. 3   Litho.   Perf. 13½
338 A153 20col No. C41   1.00 .45

Christmas 1985 — A153a

1985, Dec. 12   Litho.   Perf. 10½
338A A153a 3col multi   .25 .25

Compulsory Education, Cent. A154

Designs: 3col, Primary school, horiz. 30col, Mauro Fernandez Acuna, founder.

1986, Feb. 28   *Perf. 13½*
339 A154 3col pale yel & brn   .20 .20
340 A154 30col pale pink & brn   1.35 .60

Agriculture Students — A155

1986, Mar. 21   *Perf. 10½*
341 10col Students on farm   .40 .20
342 10col IDB emblem   .40 .20
343 10col Capo Bianco fisher-
        man   .40 .20
a.   A155 Strip of 3, #341-343   2.50 2.50
     Nos. 341-343 (3)   1.20 .60

Inter-American Development Bank Annual Governors' Assembly, San Jose.

Presidents Type of 1943

Designs: Nos. 344, 349, 354, 359, 364, Francisco J. Orlich Bolmarcich, 1962-66.
Nos. 345, 350, 355, 360, 365, Jose Joaquin Trejos Fernandez, 1966-70.
Nos. 346, 351, 356, 361, 366, Daniel Oduber Quiros, 1974-78.
Nos. 347, 352, 357, 362, 367, Rodrigo Carazo Oido, 1978-82.
Nos. 348, 353, 358, 363, 368, Luis Alberto Monge Alvarez, 1982-86.

1986, May 12   **Litho.**   *Perf. 10½*
344 A109 3col turq blue   .35 .20
345 A109 3col turq blue   .35 .20
346 A109 3col turq blue   .35 .20
347 A109 3col turq blue   .35 .20
348 A109 3col turq blue   .35 .20
a.   Strip of 5, #344-348   2.00 1.75
349 A109 6col yel brn   .50 .25
350 A109 6col yel brn   .50 .25
351 A109 6col yel brn   .50 .25
352 A109 6col yel brn   .50 .25
353 A109 6col yel brn   .50 .25
a.   Strip of 5, #349-353   4.00 3.50
354 A109 10col brn org   .60 .30
355 A109 10col brn org   .60 .30
356 A109 10col brn org   .60 .30
357 A109 10col brn org   .60 .30
358 A109 10col brn org   .60 .30
a.   Strip of 5, #354-358   5.25 5.00
359 A109 11col slate gray   .75 .40
360 A109 11col slate gray   .75 .40
361 A109 11col slate gray   .75 .40
362 A109 11col slate gray   .75 .40
363 A109 11col slate gray   .75 .40
a.   Strip of 5, #359-363   6.25 5.50
364 A109 13col olive   1.00 .45
365 A109 13col olive   1.00 .45
366 A109 13col olive   1.00 .45
367 A109 13col olive   1.00 .45
368 A109 13col olive   1.00 .45
a.   Strip of 5, #364-368   8.50 6.50
     Nos. 344-368 (25)   16.00 8.00
     Nos. 348a-368a (5)   25.00

1986 World Cup Soccer Championships, Mexico — A156

1986, May 30   **Litho.**   *Perf. 13½*
369 A156 1col Players   .20 .20
370 A156 1col Character trade-
        mark, vert.   .30 .20
371 A156 4col as No. 370   1.00 .20
372 A156 6col as No. 369   1.50 .20
373 A156 11col Players, diff.   3.25 .20
     Nos. 369-373 (5)   6.25 1.00

A second printing of No. 370 differs in paper and shade from the first printing, but the most obvious difference is in the absence of the initials "LIL" by the left foot of the soccer player. Unused copies are rare. Value for used, $3.

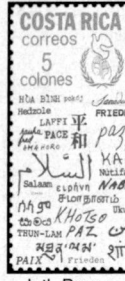

Intl. Peace Year — A157

Peace in many languages: a, "Hoa binh," etc. b, "Vrede," etc. c, "Pace," etc.

1986, July 31   **Litho.**   *Perf. 10½*
374   Strip of 3   4.00 .20
a.-c. A157 5col, any single   .50 .20

1986, Sept. 19   *Perf. 10½*
Designs: Various undescribed works of Pre-Columbian art.
375   Strip of 5   1.75 .30
a.-e. A158 6col any single   .25 .20
376   Strip of 5   3.25 .60
a.-e. A158 13col any single   .50 .20

Exist perf 13½, value $8 for the two strips of 5 unused

A159

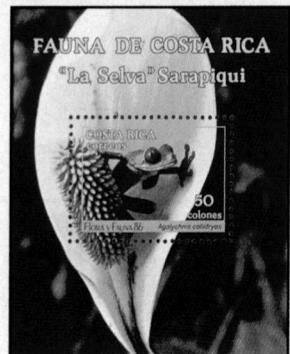

Fauna and Flora — A160

1986, Dec. 16   **Litho.**   *Perf. 13x13½*
377 A159 2col Centurio
        senex   .20 .20
378 A159 3col Glossophaga
        soricina   .45 .20
379 A159 4col Ectophylla al-
        ba   .60 .20
380 A159 5col Ectophylla al-
        ba, diff.   .85 .20
381 A159 6col Agalychnis
        callidryas   1.00 .20
382 A159 10col Dendrobates
        pumilio   1.40 .20
383 A159 11col Hyla ebraccata   1.60 .20
384 A159 20col Phyllobates
        lugubris   2.40 .20
     Nos. 377-384 (8)   8.50 1.60

Souvenir Sheet
Perf. 12½x12
385 A160 50col Agalychnis
        callidryas,
        diff.   70.00 47.50

Natl. Science and Technology Day — A161

Gold Museum, Central Bank of Costa Rica — A158

Mural (detail), by Francisco Amighetti, Clorito Picado Social Security Clinic.

1987, July 31   **Litho.**   *Perf. 10½*
386 A161 8col multi   6.00 .25

Natl. Museum, Cent. A162

Artifacts: No. 387a, Dowel-shaped figure of a man. No. 387b, Ape-like carved stone figurine. No. 387c, Polished stone ritual figure. No. 387d, Carved granite capital. No. 387e, Two-legged pot. No. 388a, Bowl. No. 388b, Sculpture. No. 388c, Water jar.

1987, Aug. 7
387   Strip of 5   2.25 .40
a.-e. A162 8col any single, vert.   .30 .20
388   Strip of 3   2.75 .45
a.-c. A162 15col any single   .60 .20
     Nos. 387-388 (2)   5.00 .85

Horse-drawn Wagon — A163

1987, Oct. 26
389 A163 20col shown   .75 .20
390 A163 20col Street in old San
        Jose   .75 .20
391 A163 20col Provincial coat of
        arms   .75 .20
     Nos. 389-391 (3)   2.25 .60

City of San Jose, 250th anniv. Rotary Club, 60th anniv.

Columbus Day A164

1987, Oct. 26   *Perf. 10½*
392 A164 30col Map, 16th cent.   2.00 .30

Day of the Race; 495th anniv. of Columbus's departure from Palos, Spain, on first journey to the New World.

Discovery of America, 500th Anniv. (in 1992) — A165   Pres. Oscar Arias, 1987 Nobel Peace Prize Winner — A166

Maps of Honduras, Nicaragua, Costa Rica and Panama, believed to be Asia by Columbus: No. 393, Costa Rica, 16th cent. No. 394, Map of "Asia" by Bartholomeu Columbus (1461-1514).

1987, Nov. 20   **Litho.**   *Perf. 13½*
393 A165 4col yel & dk red brn   .20 .20
394 A165 4col yel & dk red brn   .20 .20
a.   Pair, #393-394   1.50 .20

1987, Dec. 2   *Perf. 10½*
395 A166 10col multi   3.00 .20

Two Houses, a Watercolor by Fausto Pacheco (1899-1966) A167

1987, Dec. 22   **Litho.**   *Perf. 10½*
396 A167 1col multi   .40 .30

Intl. Year of Shelter for the Homeless.

17th General Conference for the Preservation of Natural Resources A168

1988, Feb. 1   **Litho.**   *Perf. 13½*
397 A168 5col Green turtle   .80 .25
398 A168 5col Emblem, golden
        toad   .80 .25
399 A168 5col Blue butterfly   .80 .25
a.   A168 Strip of 3, #397-399   2.50 2.50

Intl. Red Cross and Red Crescent Organizations, 125th Annivs. — A169

1988, Apr. 18   **Litho.**   *Perf. 10½*
400 A169 30col lt blue & dark red   1.00 .25

North and South Campaign A170

1988, June 6   **Photo.**   *Perf. 11½*
Granite Paper
401 A170 18col Adult education   .60 .20
402 A170 20col Cultural radio
        programs   .70 .20

Cultural cooperation with Liechtenstein. See Liechtenstein #886-887. For overprint see #C921.

A171   A172

1988, June 27   **Litho.**   *Perf. 10½*
403 A171 3col dk blue, dark red
        & yel   .30 .20

Anglo-Costa Rican Bank, 125th anniv.

1988, Sept. 16   **Litho.**   *Perf. 13½*
404 A172 25col Character trade-
        mark   .95 .20
405 A172 25col Games emblem   .95 .20
a.   Pair, #404-405   1.90 .55

1988 Summer Olympics, Seoul.

Girls' High School, Cent. A173

1988, Oct. 17   Litho.   Perf. 10½
406 A173 10col Student, court-
            yard   .50   .20

A174   A175

1988, Nov. 18
407 A174 10col gray, greenish bl
            & red brn   .35   .20

Educator Omar Dengo (1888-1928) and the
Teachers' College, Heredia.

1988, Nov. 28   Perf. 13½

Indian glass-bead and lion-tooth necklace.
408 A175 4col multi   .20   .20
Discovery of America, 500th anniv. (in 1992).

A176   A177

1988, Dec. 26   Litho.   Perf. 10½
409 A176 2col Observation tower .40   .20
Natl. Meteorological Institute, cent. For
surcharge see No. 439.

1989, Feb. 28

Designs: Indigenous flora.

410 A177   5col *Eschweilera cos-
              tarricensis*   .20   .20
411 A177 10col *Heliconia
              wagneriana*   .45   .20
412 A177 15col *Heliconia lopho-
              carpa*   .60   .20
413 A177 20col *Aechmea
              magdalenae*   .75   .20
414 A177 25col *Psammisia
              ramiflora*   .90   .20
415 A177 30col *Passiflora vitifolia* 1.10 .20
      Nos. 410-415 (6)   4.00 1.20

A178

A179

1989, July 1   Litho.   Perf. 10½
416 A178 30col Nation at Arms   .85   .20
French Revolution, bicent.

1989, Aug. 28   Litho.   Perf. 13½
417 A179 10col Sugar mill   .25   .20
Grecia County, 151st anniv.
For overprints see Nos. RA106-RA109.

America
Issue — A180

UPAE emblem and pre-Columbian stone
carvings: 50col, Three-footed bench for grinding corn. 100col, Sphere.

Litho. & Engr.
Perf. 12½x12
1989, Oct. 12   Wmk. 334
418 A180 50col multi   2.50 1.10
419 A180 100col multi   5.50 1.75
For overprint see No. C916.

A181   A182

Perf. 10½
1989, Oct. 23   Litho.   Unwmk.
420 A181 10col Orchid   2.00   .20
"100 Years of Democracy" summit of
Presidents.

Perf. 13½
1989, Nov. 27   Litho.   Unwmk.
421 A182 18col Map, H.F. Pittier,
            emblem   .45   .20
Natl. Geographic Institute, cent.
For surcharge see No. 452.

America
Issue — A183

Pre-Columbian gold frog figurine and facing
portraits of Ferdinand V and Isabella I on gold
coin struck by Spain from 1476 to 1516.

1989, Dec. 4   Perf. 10½
422 A183 4col multicolored   .20   .20
Discovery of America, 500th anniv. (in 1992).

Natl.
Theater,
Cent.
A184

Perf. 10½
1990, Feb. 27   Litho.   Unwmk.
423 A184 5col *Coffee Allegory* .20   .20

World Cup Soccer
Championships,
Italy — A185

1990, June 1   Litho.   Perf. 10½
424 A185 5col multicolored   .25   .20

Univ. of
Costa
Rica, 50th
Anniv.
A187

1990, Aug. 24   Litho.   Perf. 10½
426 A187 18col multicolored   .75   .20

Education,
Democracy,
Peace — A188

Litho. & Engr.
1990, Oct. 31   Perf. 12½
427 A188 100col shown   2.25 1.10
428 A188 200col Flag as map 4.50 1.75
429 A188 500col National arms 12.00 6.00
      Nos. 427-429 (3)   18.75 8.85
"Invisible" security printing is sometimes
visible.
For overprints see Nos. 448, C920.

Hospitals   America Issue
A190   A191

#431, St. Vincent de Paul Hospital, Heredia.
#432, Natl. Psychiatric hospital.

1990, Dec. 18   Engr.   Perf. 13x12½
431 A190 50col multicolored 1.10   .30
432 A190 100col multicolored 2.25   .55

1990, Dec. 21   Litho.   Perf. 10½
433 A191 18col Ara macao   .50   .20
434 A191 18col Ara ambigua   .50   .20
a.   Pair, #433-434   3.00 3.00
435 A191 24col Cassia grandis 1.00   .20
436 A191 24col Tabebuia
            ochracea   1.00   .20
a.   Pair, #435-436   3.00 3.00
      Nos. 433-436 (4)   3.00   .80

Costa Rica-Panama Border Treaty,
50th Anniv. — A192

Designs: a, Flags, national arms. b, Presidents. c, Map.

1991, May 24   Litho.   Perf. 10½
437 A192 10col Strip of 3, #a.-c. .70   .20

Discovery of
America, 500th
Anniv. (in
1992) — A193

1991, Oct. 11   Litho.   Perf. 13½
438 A193 4col multicolored   1.00   .20

Nos. 409, 296 Surcharged

1991, Oct. 21   Litho.   Perf. 10½
439 A176 1col on 2col #409   .20   .20
440 A137 3col on 8.50col #296 .20   .20

Former Presidents,
Supreme Court of
Justice — A194

Designs: a, Benito Serrano Jimenez. b, Luis
Davila Solera. c, Fernando Baudrit Solera. d,
Alejandro Alvarado Garcia.

Perf. 14½x13½
1992, Feb. 28   Litho.
441 A194 5col Strip of 4, #a.-d. 1.75   .45

DINADECO,
Natl.
Directorate of
Community
Development,
25th Anniv.
A195

1992, Apr. 28   Litho.   Perf. 10½
442 A195 15col multicolored   1.25   .35
Compare with No. C505.

A196   A197

1992, May 26   Litho.   Perf. 13½
443 A196 15col lake & black   1.25   .35
Dr. Solon Nunez Frutos, public health
pioneer.

1992, July 17   Litho.   Perf. 13

Solar Eclipse: a, Total eclipse. b, Post Office
Bldg. during eclipse. c, Partial eclipse.
444 A197 45col Strip of 3, #a.-c. 6.00 1.00

A198   A199

1992, Aug. 14   Litho.   Perf. 13½
445 A198 35col multicolored   1.10   .30

Interamerican Institute for Agricultural Cooperation, 50th anniv.

1992, Nov. 5   Litho.   Perf. 10½
446 A199   2col Waterfall   .25   .20
447 A199 15col Coastline   .25   .20

Cocos Island, 450th anniv. of discovery.

No. 427 Ovptd. "CENTENARIO / DE LIMON"
Litho. & Engr.
1992, Nov. 27   Perf. 12½
448 A188 100col black & blue   2.10 1.00

America Issue
A200

1992, Dec. 15   Litho.   Perf. 10½
449 A200 15col Anolis townsendi   2.50   .20
450 A200 35col Pinaroloxias in-
                  ornata   4.50   .30

Natl. Theater
A201

Detail from painting "Allegory of Fine Arts," by Roberto Fontana.

1993, Jan. 29   Litho.   Perf. 10½
451 A201 20col multicolored   .50   .20

No. 421 Surcharged

1993, Mar. 26   Litho.   Perf. 13½
452 A182   5col on 18col multi   .50   .20

50,000 stamps originally were overprinted with a tiny block and four thin bars over the value, but this was considered unacceptable. So these stamps plus 1,550,000 unoverprinted stamps were overprinted with the large black square and surcharge, as shown.

Protection of the Dolphin
A202

1993, May 17   Litho.   Perf. 10½
453 A202 10col Delphinus
                  delphis   .95   .20
454 A202 20col Stenella
                  coeruleoalbus   2.10   .35

Costa Rican Civil Service, 40th Anniv. — A203

1993, May 28   Litho.   Perf. 13½
455 A203   5col multicolored   .45   .20

Costa Rican Chamber of Industries, 50th Anniv. A204

1993, July 15   Perf. 10½
456 A204 45col multicolored   1.00   .60

School of Communication Sciences, University of Costa Rica, 25th Anniv. — A205

1993, Aug. 19   Litho.   Perf. 13½
457 A205 20col black, blue & red   .35   .20

Protection of the Tropical Rain Forest — A206

1993, Aug. 27   Perf. 10½
458 A206   2col Passiflora vitifolia .60   .20
459 A206 35col Gurania megis-
                  tantha   1.40   .40

Social Guarantees and Labor Code, 50th Anniv. A207

1993, Sept. 14   Litho.   Perf. 10½
460 A207 20col multicolored   .40   .20

A208   A209

1993, Oct. 25   Litho.   Perf. 13½
461 A208 45col multicolored   .90   .45

Intl. Assoc. of Professional Custom-House Agents, 15th Congress.

1993, Nov. 26   Perf. 10½
462 A209 20col multicolored   .55   .20

Miguel Angel Castro Carazo (1893-1960), educator and humanitarian.
For surcharge see No. 481.

A211   A212

1993, Dec. 23   Litho.   Perf. 10½
464 A211 20col multicolored   .55   .20

Law School of Costa Rica, 150th anniv.

1994, Mar. 8   Litho.   Perf. 13
465 A212 20col Natl. Theater   .55   .20

Marine Life — A213

5col, Cyphoma gibbosum. 10col, Ophioderma rubicundum. 15col, Myripristis jacobus. 20col, Holocanthus passer. 35col, Paranthias furcifer. 45col, Tubastraea coccinea. 50col, Acanthaster planci. 55col, Ocypode. 70col, Arothron meleagris. 100col, Thalassoma lucasanum.

Litho. & Embossed
1994, Apr. 29   Perf. 12½x12
466 A213   5col multicolored   .20   .20
467 A213 10col multicolored   .35   .20
468 A213 15col multicolored   .80   .20
469 A213 20col multicolored   1.25   .35
470 A213 35col multicolored   1.90   .55
471 A213 45col multicolored   2.50   .75
472 A213 50col multicolored   2.75   .85
473 A213 55col multicolored   3.25   .95
474 A213 70col multicolored   4.00 1.25
     Nos. 466-474 (9)   17.00 5.30

Souvenir Sheet
Perf. 13
475 A213 100col multicolored   5.00 4.50

America Issue
A214

Illustrations from 19th century Book of Figueroa: a, Man on horseback. b, Back of ox carrying bundles.

1994, Dec. 19   Litho.   Perf. 10½
476 A214 20col Pair, #a.-b. + la-
                  bel   1.75   .65

No. 476 is a continuous design.

Rotary Intl., 90th Anniv. — A215

1995, Mar.   Litho.   Perf. 13½
477 A215 20col multicolored   .75   .25

Antonio Jose de Sucre (1795-1830)   Guanacaste Institute, 50th Anniv.
A216   A217

Design: 30col, Jose Marti (1853-95).

1995, June   Litho.   Perf. 10½
478 A216 30col multicolored   .25   .20
479 A216 10col multicolored   .55   .25

1995, July 24   Perf. 13½
480 A217 50col grn, blk & bis   .85   .20

No. 462 Surcharged in Blue or Black

1995, Sept. 11   Litho.   Perf. 10½
481 A209   5col on 20col multi   .30   .20

UN, 50th Anniv. — A218

13th Natl. Philatelic Expo — A219

1995, Oct. 24   Litho.   Perf. 10½
482 A218   5col multicolored   .30   .20

1995, Dec. 1

Paintings by Lola Fernández: No. 483, Noviembre. No. 484, Enero.

483 A219 50col multicolored   .80   .40
484 A219 50col multicolored   .80   .40
  a.   Pair, Nos. 483-484   1.60   .80

America Issue
A220

30col, Jabiru mycteria. #486, View of coast. #487, River, trees. 50col, Atta cephalotes.

1995, Dec. 25 Litho.   Rouletted 13½
485 A220 30col multicolored   .60   .25
486 A220 40col multicolored   .85   .30
487 A220 40col multicolored   .85   .30
  a.   Pair, #486-487   2.00 1.25
488 A220 50col multicolored   1.75   .80
  a.   Souvenir sheet, #485-488 4.75 3.00
          Nos. 485-488 (4)   4.05 1.65

Seaport City of Limón
A221

Designs: a, Early picture of steam train. b, Photo of ship in port, 1922. c, Aerial view of seaport, 1995. d, Painting of fruit seller, by Diego Villalobos. e, Drawing of Calipso singers, by Jorge Esquivel.

1996, Jan. 31   Litho.   Perf. 10½
489 A221 30col Strip of 5, #a.-e.   2.50 1.25

Jerusalem, 3000th Anniv. — A222

1996, May 17   Litho.   Perf. 13½
490 A222 30col multicolored   .80 .25

1996 Summer Olympic Games, Atlanta
A223

Olympic swimmers, coaches from Costa Rica: a, F. Rivas, M.M. Paris. b, S. Poll, R. Yglesias. c, C. Poll, A. Cruz.

1996, July 18   Litho.   Perf. 10½
491 A223 5col Strip of 3, #a.-c.   1.00 .20

No. 491 is a continuous design.

A224   A225

First lady, presidents: a, Juana del Castillo. b, Juan Mora Fernández. c, J.M. Castro Madriz. d, Pacífica Fernández.

1996, Sept. 13   Litho.   Perf. 10½
492 A224 30col Block of 4, #a.-d.   3.00 1.00

Independence, 175th anniv. No. 492 was issued in sheets of 16 stamps.

1996, Oct. 4   Litho.   Perf. 13½
493 A225 15col multicolored   .40 .20

Aqueducts and sewage systems, 35th anniv. Exists imperf.

A226

America issue (Paintings): No. 494, Black from Lemon, by Manuel da la Cruz González. No. 495, Peasant Women, by Gonzalo Morales Alvarado, vert.

1996, Dec. 16   Perf. 10½
494 A226 45col multicolored   1.10 .40
495 A226 45col multicolored   1.10 .40

A227

Entrance of the Saints at San Ramón, parade of people: a, Building with palm trees on top. b, Church on hill. c, Tree, holy family.

1997, Aug. 14   Litho.   Perf. 13½
496 A227 30col Strip of 3, #a.-c.   2.00 1.25
Costa Rican traditions.

School of Fine Arts, Cent.
A228

1997, Sept. 24   Perf. 10½
497 A228 50col multicolored   1.40 .20

Radio Netherlands, 50th Anniv. — A229

1997, Sept. 26   Perf. 13½
498 A229 45col multicolored   1.00 .40
Exists imperf.

14th Natl. Philatelic Exhibition
A230

1997, Oct. 9   Perf. 10½
499 A230 30col Postmen   .65 .35
America Issue.

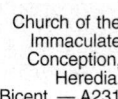

Church of the Immaculate Conception, Heredia, Bicent. — A231

1997, Nov. 10   Litho.   Perf. 10½
502 A231 50col multicolored   1.25 .70

Second Republic, 50th Anniv. — A232

Former Pres. José Figueres demolishing wall of Fort Bellavista: 10col, 45col, Complete photo. 30col, Detail of Figueres' head. 50col, Hammer head hitting wall.

Litho. & Engr.
1998, Mar. 30   Perf. 12½
503 A232 10col multicolored   .60 .20
504 A232 30col multicolored   .90 .20
505 A232 45col multicolored   1.40 .20
506 A232 50col multicolored   1.50 .25
  a.   Souvenir sheet of 2, #504, 506   2.00 2.00

Natl. University, 25th Anniv. — A233

1998, July 27   Litho.   Perf. 10½
507 A233 50col multicolored   1.50 .75

Butterflies
A234

10col, Caligo memnon. 15col, Morpho peleides. 20col, Papilio thoas. 30col, Siproeta stelenes. 35col, Ascia monuste. 40col, Parides iphidamas. 45col, Smyrna blonfildia. 50col, Callicore pitheas. 55col, Historis odius. 60col, Danaus plexippus.

1998, July
508 A234 10col multicolored   .40 .20
509 A234 15col multicolored   .45 .30
510 A234 20col multicolored   .70 .40
511 A234 30col multicolored   .95 .55
512 A234 35col multicolored   1.10 .60
513 A234 40col multicolored   1.40 .65
514 A234 45col multicolored   1.60 .70
515 A234 50col multicolored   1.75 .85
516 A234 55col multicolored   2.00 .95
517 A234 60col multicolored   2.25 1.10
  Nos. 508-517 (10)   12.60 6.30

1998 World Cup Soccer Championships, France — A235

1998, Feb. 27   Litho.   Perf. 10½
518 A235 50col multicolored   1.25 .80

A236   A237

1998, Nov. 30   Litho.   Perf. 13½
519 A236 50col brn, yel brn & lt yel   .75 .35
Carmen Lyra (1888-1949), author.

1998, Dec. 11   Litho.   Perf. 13½
520 A237 50col multicolored   1.25 .50
Gandhi (1869-1948).

Intl. Union for the Conservation of Nature, 50th Anniv.
A238

Turtles: a, 70col, Rhinociemmys pulcherrima. b, 60col, Trachemys scripta. c, 70col, Chelydra serpentina.

1998, Dec. 1
521 A238 Strip of 3, #a.-c.   6.00 6.00

Mushrooms
A239

a, Morchella esculenta. b, Boletus edulis.

1999, July 2   Litho.   Perf. 10½
522 A239 50col Pair, #a.-b.   2.25 2.25

SOS Children's Villages, 50th Anniv. — A240

1999, June   Litho.   Perf. 10½
523 A240 50col multicolored   1.25 .40

Costa Rican Institute of Electricity, 50th Anniv.
A241

1999, Sept. 21   Litho.   Perf. 13¼
524 A241 75col multi   .65 .35

A242   A243

1999, Oct. 7   Engr.   Perf. 13¾x14
525 A242 300col violet   2.25 2.00
Archbishop Víctor M. Sanabria (1899-1952). See No. 538.

1999, Oct. 29   Litho.   Perf. 13¼
526 A243 50col multi   .45 .25
Intl. Year of Older Persons.

Supreme Election Tribunal, 50th Anniv.
A244

1999, Nov. 5   Perf. 10½
527 A244 70col multi   .75 .25

UPU, 125th Anniv. A245

Carmen Granados (1915-99), Humorist A246

1999, Dec. 1   **Perf. 13¼**
528 A245 75col multi   .60 .25

1999, Dec. 1
529 A246 50col multi   .45 .20

America Issue, A New Millennium Without Arms — A247

1999, Dec. 1
530 A247 50col shown   .75 .20
531 A247 70col Face, hands, diff. 1.00 .50

PhilexFrance '99 — A248

1999, Dec. 1
532 A248 300col shown   3.00 1.00
533 A248 300col Flower, Eiffel Tower   3.00 1.00

Natl. Bank, 50th Anniv. — A249

No. 534 — Pre-Columbian artifacts: a, Jaguar. b, Scorpion. c, Bat. d, Crab. e, Beast with horns.
No. 535 — Obverse and reverse of coins: a, Gold, from 1825. b, Gold, from 1850. c, Silver one-eighth peso. d, Gold 20-peso. e, 1935 1-colon.

2000, Jan. 28   **Litho.**   **Perf. 13¼**
534   Vert. strip of 5   7.50 6.00
a.-e. A249 60col Any single   1.00 .50
535   Vert. strip of 5   15.00 10.00
a.-e. A249 90col Any single   2.00 1.00

2000 Summer Olympics, Sydney — A250

No. 536, 60col: a, Taekwando. b, Cycling. c, Swimming. d, Soccer.
No. 537, 70col: a, Running. b, Boxing. c, Men's rings. d, Tennis.
Illustration reduced.

2000, Aug. 31
Blocks of 4, #a-d
536-537 A250   Set of 2   7.00 7.00
There were two printings of Nos. 536-537. In the first printing, colors are paler, and the green Olympic ring is misregistered on Nos. 536a-536d. In the second, colors are more intense, and the green ring is properly registered. Values the same.

Famous Person Type of 1999
Pres. Rafael A. Calderón Guardia (1900-70).

2000   **Engr.**   **Perf. 12½**
538 A242 100col deep blue   1.00 .20
a.   Perf 13¾x14   3.00 .50

Paintings by Max Jiménez — A251

No. 539: a, Fishermen in Cojimar. b, Adamant.
Illustration reduced.

2000, Nov.   **Litho.**   **Perf. 10½**
539   Horiz. pair   2.50 2.50
a.-b. A251 50col Either single   1.00 .50

America Issue, Fight Against AIDS — A252

Designs: 60col, Stylized people. 90col, Stylized person.

2000, Dec.   **Perf. 13¼**
540-541 A252   Set of 2   1.40 1.25

Christmas — A253

2000, Dec.
542 A253 100col multi   1.00 .70

America Issue — UNESCO World Heritage A254

Birds form Cocos Island Natl. Park: 95col, Coccyzus ferrugineus. 115col, Pinaroloxias inornata.

2001, Apr. 5   **Litho.**   **Perf. 10½**
543-544 A254   Set of 2   3.50 2.50

Costa Rica — Netherlands Diplomatic Relations, 150th Anniv. — A255

2001, July
545 A255 65col multi   .60 .40

No. 429 Surcharged

2001   **Method and Perf. As Before**
546 A188 65col on 500col multi   .50 .50
547 A188 80col on 500col multi   .70 .70
548 A188 95col on 500col multi   .80 .80
Nos. 546-548 (3)   2.00 2.00
Issued: No. 846, 8/24. Nos. 547-548, 9/7.

Third Hispanic-Costa Rican Exposition — A256

Orchids: a, Guaria turrialba. b, Tricopilia.
Illustration reduced.

2001, Oct. 5   **Litho.**   **Perf. 13¼**
549 A256 65col Horiz. pair, #a-b 2.00 2.00

Campaign Against Child Labor — A257

2001, Nov. 15   **Perf. 13¼**
550 A257 100col multi   1.00 .65

Pres. Tomás Guardia (1832-82) and Locomotive — A258

2001, Nov. 21
551 A258 65col multi   1.00 .60
A second printing of No. 551 was issued in 2002. It features a lighter beige and has yellow gum. This printing of 500 sheets of 15 stamps was made to complete the contract. Value, unused $25.

Costa Rican Team for 2002 World Cup Soccer Championships, Japan and Korea — A259

Illustration reduced.

2002, Mar.   **Perf. 10½**
552 A259 65col multi   .60 .40

No. 428 Surcharged in Red

Litho. & Engr.
2002, Jan. 24   **Perf. 12½**
553 A188 65col on 200col multi   .60 .40

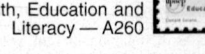

America Issue — Youth, Education and Literacy — A260

Designs: 65col, Children and globe. 100col, Blind person reading Braille.

Litho. & Embossed
2002, Mar.   **Perf. 10½**
554-555 A260   Set of 2   1.75 1.25

Taiwan Friendship Bridge A261

2002, Apr. 3   **Litho.**
556 A261 95col multi   1.00 .75

16th Rio Group Congress A262

2002, Apr. 10
557 A262 65col blue & green   .65 .40

Pan-American Health Organization, Cent. — A263

No. 558: a, People (red denomination at UR). b, Emblem. c, Mother and child (black denomination at LR). d, Child and man (red denomination at LR).
50col, Emblem.

2002, July 5
558 A263 10col Block of 4, #a-d   .50 .50
559 A263 50col multi   .50 .40

In Remembrance of Sept. 11, 2001 Terrorist Attacks — A264

Litho. & Embossed
2002, Sept. 11
560 A264 110col multi   1.10 1.10

Marine Life of Uvita Island A265

Designs: No. 561, 75col, Gorgona flabellum. No. 562, 75col, Ulva lactuca. No. 563, 75col, Cittarium pica. No. 564, 75col, Liriope tetraphyla.

Litho & Embossed
2002, Sept. 25
561-564 A265   Set of 4   4.50 4.50

Space Exploration — A266

No. 565: a, Dr. Franklin Chang-Diaz, astronaut, and space shuttle. b, Phanaeus changdiazi and satellite.
Illustration reduced.

Litho. & Embossed
2003, June 15 **Perf. 10½**
565 A266 115col Horiz. pair,
#a-b 1.40 1.40

Coco Island National Park — A267

No. 566: a, Denomination at UR. b, Denomination at UL.
Illustration reduced.

2003, Aug. 1
566 A267 75col Horiz. pair, #a-b .75 .75

America Issue - Fish — A268

No. 567: a, Archocentrus sajica. b, Astatheros diquis.
Illustration reduced.

2003
567 A268 110col Horiz. pair,
#a-b 5.00 1.50

Scenes from Cocorí, by Joaquín Gutiérrez — A269

No. 568: a, Boy, turtle, monkey and bird. b, Boy looking at reflection in water. c, Toucan in tree, boy and monkey on ground. d, Sailor, girl and boy. e, Boy, bird on branch. f, Jaguar, turtle armadillo, monkey, boy and father. g, Boy and monkey pushing turtle. h, Monkey with open arms, turtle, boy. i, Mother and boy. j, Mother, boy, rose bush. k, Boy, father playing musical instrument (80x150mm).

Litho. & Embossed
2003, Sept. 3 **Perf. 10½**
568 A269 Sheet of 11 3.00 3.00
a.-j. 25col Any single .20 .20
k. 225col multi 1.40 1.40

National Anthem, Cent. — A270

No. 569: a, Lyricist José Maria Zeledón (24x35mm). b, Flag, text of anthem (49x35mm).

2003, Sept. 10 **Litho.**
569 A270 75col Horiz. pair, #a-b .75 .75

Election of Pope John Paul II, 25th Anniv. — A271

2003, Oct. 16 Litho. Perf. 13¼x13½
570 A271 130col multi 1.50 1.50

Charles Lindbergh's Flight to Costa Rica, 75th Anniv. — A272

Litho. & Embossed
2003, Dec. 16 **Perf. 13½x13¼**
571 A272 110col multi .55 .55

Guayabo de Turrialba Archaeological Monument — A273

2003, Dec. 18
572 A273 110col multi .55 .55

America Issue A274

Flora: No. 573, 75col, Ceiba pentandra. No. 574, 75col, Tetranema floribundum. 90col, Ceiba pentandra, diff. 110col, Tetranema gamboanum.

2004, Mar. 23 Litho. Perf. 10½
573-576 A274 Set of 4 3.00 3.00

Volcanoes A275

Designs: 85col, Arenal. 120col, Irazú. 140col, Poás.

2004-05
577-579 A275 Set of 3 3.00 3.00
578a Perf. 13¼ ('05) .95 .95
579a Perf. 13¼ ('05) 1.10 1.10
Issued: Nos. 577-579, 6/24/04; 578a, 579a, 2005.
Nos. 578a and 579a have printer's inscription "LIL S.A."

2004 Summer Olympics, Athens A276

No. 580 — Various athletes in: a, Blue. b, Yellow orange. c, Green. d, Red.

2004, July 15
580 Horiz. strip of 4 2.25 2.25
a.-d. A276 120col Any single .55 .55

Dr. Miguel Angel Rodríguez, Organization of American States President
A277

2004, Sept. 15
581 A277 120col multi .55 .55

FIFA (Fédération Internationale de Football Association), Cent. — A278

No. 582: a, Emblem (34x34mm). b, Soccer player and field (39x34mm).
Illustration reduced.

2004, Feb. 15 **Litho.** **Perf. 10½**
582 A278 140col Horiz. pair, #a-b 1.25 1.25

Rotary International, Cent. — A279

No. 583: a, Emblem and frog. b, Centenary emblem. c, Emblem and butterfly.

2005, Feb. 23
583 Horiz. strip of 3 3.00 3.00
a.-c. A279 140col Any single 1.10 1.10

Souvenir Sheet

Popes — A280

No. 584: a, Pope John Paul II (1920-2005). b, Pope Benedict XVI.

2005, Aug. 22
584 A280 140col Sheet of 4, 2
each #a-b 2.40 2.40

An imperf. sheet lacking postal validity exists.

Intl. Year of Physics — A281

No. 585: a, Albert Einstein (1879-1955). b, Max Planck (1858-1947).

585 Horiz. pair 2.00 2.00
a.-b. A281 95col Either single 1.00 1.00

Flora and Fauna in National Parks — A282

No. 586: a, Passiflora vitifolia. b, Dryas iulia moderata. c, Potos flavus.

2005, Oct. 11 Litho. Perf. 10½
586 Strip of 3 1.10 1.10
a.-c. A282 85col Any single .35 .35

America Issue, Fight Against Poverty — A283

No. 587: a, Child at computer. b, Man sawing wood. c, Medical worker.

2005, Oct. 19
587 Strip of 3 1.50 1.50
a.-c. A283 120col Any single .50 .50

Intl. Year of Sports and Physical Education A284

2005, Dec. 6
588 A284 85col multi .35 .35

Cartago Sport Club, Cent. — A285

Illustration reduced.

2006, Mar. 20
589 A285 85col multi .35 .35

Miniature Sheet

National Campaign Against
Nicaraguan Pres. William Walker,
150th Anniv. — A286

No. 590: a, Juan Rafael Mora, National
Monument. b, Juan Santamaría Monument,
barracks. c, Map (50x40mm). d, Gen. José
María Cañas, Santa Rosa House. e, Luis
Molina, Joaquín Bernardo Calvo.

2006, Apr. 7
590 A286 85col Sheet of 5, #a-e 1.75 1.75

2006 World Cup Soccer
Championships, Germany — A287

2006, May 15
591 A287 120col multi   .50 .50

America Issue, Energy
Conservation — A288

2006, July 31 Litho.   Perf. 10½
592 A288 155col multi + label   .60 .60

Miniature Sheet

Birds and Marine Life of Cocos
Island — A289

No. 593: a, Sula sula. b, Mycteroperca olfax.
c, Zanclus cornutis. d, Eretmochely imbricaas.
e, Tursiops truncatus. f, Myripristis berndti. g,
Dendroica petechia aureola. h, Carcharhinus
limbatus. i, Anous stolidus. j, Acarus
rubroviolaceus.

2006, Aug. 25   Litho.   Perf. 10½
593 A289 180col Sheet of 10, #a-
           j   7.00 7.00

Pres. José Figueres Ferrer (1906-
90) — A290

2006, Sept. 25   Perf. 10½
594 A290 115col gray & multi +
         label   .45 .45
Souvenir Sheet
Imperf
595 A290 1000col tan & multi   4.00 4.00

Fruits
A291

No. 596: a, Hymenaea courbaril. b, Bixa
orellana. c, Garcinia intermedia.

2006, Oct. 12   Perf. 10½
596   Strip of 3   1.90 1.90
a.-c. A291 155col Any single   .60 .60

National Symbols — A292

No. 597: a, Flag. b, Coat of arms.
Illustration reduced.

2006, Nov. 27
597 A292 155col Pair, #a-b   1.25 1.25
Printed in sheets containing two pairs.

Pres. Francisco J. Orlich (1907-
69) — A293

2007, Mar. 7
598 A293 115col multi   .45 .45

Orchids — A294

No. 599: a, Guarianthe skinneri (pink flowers). b, Galeandra arundinis. c, Encyclia
ossenbachiana. d, Dracula inexperata. e,
Guarianthe skinneri (white flowers). f, Kefer-
steinia retanae. g, Coryanthes kaiseriana. h,
Psychopsis krameriana. i, Chondroscaphe
yamilethae. j, Cattleya dowiana.
   1000col, Brassia suavissima.

2007, Mar. 19   Litho.   Perf. 10½
599 A294 180col Sheet of 10,
         #a-j   7.00 7.00
Souvenir Sheet
Imperf
600 A294 1000col multi   4.00 4.00
   No. 599 contains ten 45x37mm stamps. No.
600 has simulated perforations.

Salesian
Order in
Costa Rica,
Cent. — A295

2007, Apr. 30   Perf. 10½
601 A295 110col multi   .45 .45

Miniature Sheet

Pre-Columbian Art — A296

No. 602: a, Frog-shaped gold pendant
(25x45mm). b, Bird-shaped jadeite pendant
(25x45mm). c, Stone metate, horiz.
(50x30mm). d, Ceramic censer with alligator

(25x45mm). e, Stone figure of warrior
(25x45mm).

2007, May 4
602 A296 155col Sheet of 5, #a-e 3.00 3.00

America Issue, Education For
All — A297

No. 603: a, 115col, Teacher and students. b,
155col, Family around fire.
Illustration reduced.

2007, June 8
603 A297 Horiz. pair, #a-b   1.10 1.10

Plasma Technology — A298

No. 604: a, Astronaut and spacecraft's robot
arm. b, Plasma containment vessel.
Illustration reduced.

2007, July 6
604 A298 240col Horiz. pair, #a-b 1.90 1.90

Guanacaste Musical
Instruments — A299

Designs: No. 605, 115col, Marimba. No.
606, 115col, Quijongo, vert. (30x50mm).

2007, July 25
605-606 A299 Set of 2   .90 .90
Nos. 605-606 were printed in sheets containing two of each stamp + label.

Virgin of the Angels Icon, 225th Anniv.
as Patron of Cartago — A300

No. 607 — Icon with denomination at: a, LR.
b, LL.
   1000col, Interior of Cartago Basilica, vert.
Illustration reduced.

2007, July 27
607 A300 115col Horiz. pair, #a-
              b   .90 .90
Souvenir Sheet
608 A300 1000col multi   4.00 4.00
   No. 608 contains one 75x115mm stamp.

POSTAL-FISCAL STAMPS

   From April 1884 through September
1889 revenue stamps were permitted
for postal use, when post offices
exhausted supplies of regular postage
stamps.
   Used values are for stamps with postal cancels.

PF1   PF2

1884   Engr.   Perf. 12
AR1 PF1   1c rose   .50 5.00
AR2 PF1   2c light blue   20.00 5.00
1888
AR3 PF2   5c brown   .50 3.00
AR4 PF2   10c blue   .25 3.00

SEMI-POSTAL STAMPS

No. 72 Surcharged in
Red

1922   Unwmk.   Perf. 12
B1 A56 5c + 5c orange   1.00   .40

Issued for the benefit of the Costa Rican
Red Cross Society. In 1928, owing to a temporary shortage of the ordinary 5c stamp, No.
B1 was placed on sale as a regular 5c stamp,
the surtax being disregarded.

Discus   Trophy — SP2
Thrower — SP1

Parthenon
SP3

1924   Litho.   Imperf.
B2 SP1   5c dark green   1.50   2.00
B3 SP2   10c carmine   1.50   2.00
B4 SP3   20c dark blue   20.00 20.00
  a. Tête bêche pair   60.00 60.00
        Perf. 12
B5 SP1   5c dark green   1.50   2.00
B6 SP2   10c carmine   1.50   2.00
B7 SP3   20c dark blue   3.00   3.50
  a. Tête bêche pair   14.00 16.00
        Nos. B2-B7 (6)   29.00 31.50

These stamps were sold at a premium of
10c each, to help defray the expenses of athletic games held at San José in Dec. 1924.

AIR POST STAMPS

Airplane
AP1

Perf. 12½
1926, June 4   Unwmk.   Engr.
C1 AP1   20c ultramarine   3.00   .50

No. 123 Overprinted

1930, Mar. 14   Perf. 12
C2 A75 10c carmine rose   2.00   .25

Inverted or double overprints are fakes.

AP3

1930-32   Perf. 12½
C3 AP3 5c on 10c dk brn ('32) .40 .25
C4 AP3 20c on 50c ultra   .50 .25
C5 AP3 40c on 50c ultra   .60 .25
        Nos. C3-C5 (3)   1.50 .75

The existence of genuine inverted or double
surcharges of Nos. C3-C5 is in doubt.

Telegraph Stamp
Overprinted

1930, Mar. 19
C6 AP3 1col orange   2.00   .50

No. O79 Surcharged
in Red

1930, Mar. 11
C7   O7 8c on 1col lilac & blk   .60   .50
C8   O7 20c on 1col lilac & blk .90   .50
C9   O7 40c on 1col lilac & blk 1.75 1.50
C10 O7 1col on 1col lilac & blk 2.75 1.50
        Nos. C7-C10 (4)   6.00 4.00

AP6   AP7

Red Surcharge on Revenue Stamps
1931-32   Perf. 12
C11 AP6 2col on 2col gray
              grn   35.00 35.00
C12 AP6 3col on 5col lil brn 35.00 35.00
C13 AP6 5col on 10col gray
              blk   35.00 35.00
        Nos. C11-C13 (3)   105.00 105.00

There were two printings of this issue, which
were practically identical in the colors of the
stamps and the surcharges.
  Nos. C11 and C13 have the date "1929" on
the stamp, No. C12 has "1930."

Black Overprint on Telegraph Stamp
1932, Mar. 8   Perf. 12½
C14 AP7 40c green   3.00   .30
  a. Inverted overprint   30.00

Unofficial "proofs," inverts and double overprints were made from a defaced plate.

Mail Plane
about to
Land
AP8

Allegory of
Flight
AP9

1934, Mar. 14   Perf. 12
C15 AP8 5c green   .20   .20
C16 AP8 10c carmine rose   .20   .20
C17 AP8 15c chocolate   .35   .20
C18 AP8 20c deep blue   .40   .20
C19 AP8 25c deep orange   .50   .20
C20 AP8 40c olive blk   1.75   .20
C21 AP8 50c gray blk   .85   .20
C22 AP8 60c orange yel   1.50   .20
C23 AP8 75c dull violet   2.75   .45
C24 AP9 1col deep rose   1.50   .20
C25 AP9 2col lt blue   6.00   .90
C26 AP9 5col black   5.00 4.75
C27 AP9 10col red brown   9.00 8.00
        Nos. C15-C27 (13) 30.00 15.90

Nos. C15-C27 with holes punched through
were for use of government officials.
  See Nos. C216-C219. For overprints see
Nos. C67-C73, C92-C93, C103-C116, CO1-
CO13.

Airplane over Poás Volcano — AP10

1937, Feb. 10
C28 AP10 1c black   .45   .35
C29 AP10 2c brown   .45   .35
C30 AP10 3c dk violet   .45   .35
        Nos. C28-C30 (3)   1.35 1.05

First Fair of Costa Rica.

Puntarenas — AP11

National
Bank
AP12

Perf. 12, 12½
1937, Dec. 15   Unwmk.
C31 AP11 2c black gray   .20   .20
C32 AP11 5c green   .20   .20
C33 AP11 20c deep blue   .30   .20
C34 AP11 1.40col olive brn 2.50 2.50
        Nos. C31-C34 (4)   3.20 3.10

1938, Jan. 11 Wmk. 229 Perf. 12½
C35 AP12 1c purple   .20   .20
C36 AP12 3c red orange   .20   .20
C37 AP12 10c carmine rose   .30   .20
C38 AP12 75c brown   2.50 2.00
        Nos. C35-C38 (4)   3.20 2.60

Nos. C31-C38 for the Natl. Products Exposition held at San José, Dec. 1937.

Airport Administration Building, La
Sabana — AP13

1940, May 2   Engr.   Unwmk.
C39 AP13 5c green   .20   .20
C40 AP13 10c rose pink   .20   .20
C41 AP13 25c lt blue   .20   .20
C42 AP13 35c red brown   .20   .20
C43 AP13 60c red org   .30   .30
C44 AP13 85c violet   1.40   .90
C45 AP13 2.35col turq grn 6.00 5.50
        Nos. C39-C45 (7)   8.50 7.50

Opening of the Intl. Airport at La Sabana.

Duran
Sanatorium
AP14

Overprinted "Dia Panamericano de la
Salud / 2 Diciembre 1940" and Bar
in Black

1940, Dec. 2   Perf. 12
C46 AP14 10c scarlet   .20   .20
C47 AP14 15c purple   .20   .20
C48 AP14 25c lt blue   .35   .35
C49 AP14 35c bister brn   .50   .50
C50 AP14 60c pck green   .75   .75
C51 AP14 75c olive   2.00 2.00
C52 AP14 1.35col red org   6.00 6.00
C53 AP14 5col sepia   45.00 40.00
C54 AP14 10col red lilac 125.00 100.00
        Nos. C46-C54 (9) 180.00 150.00

Pan-American Health Day. Exist without
overprint. Few examples of Nos. C53-C54
were sold for postal purposes, nearly all having been obtained by philatelic speculators.

No. 174 Surcharged in Black or Blue

1940, Dec. 17   Perf. 14
C55 A95 15c on 50c yel (Bk) 1.00 1.00
C56 A95 30c on 50c yel (Bl) 1.00 1.00

Pan-American Aviation Day, proclaimed by
President F. D. Roosevelt.
  The 15c surcharge exists normal and
inverted on No. 171. Value, inverted, $30.

International Soccer Game at National
Stadium — AP15

1941, May 8   Perf. 12
C57 AP15 15c red   .75   .20
C58 AP15 30c dp ultra   .85   .25
C59 AP15 40c red brn   .85   .35
C60 AP15 50c purple   1.25   .75
C61 AP15 60c brt green   1.50   .85
C62 AP15 75c yel org   2.50 1.40
C63 AP15 1col dull vio   4.25 4.25
C64 AP15 1.40col rose   8.75 8.75
C65 AP15 2col blue grn   20.00 17.50
C66 AP15 5col black   50.00 37.50
        Nos. C57-C66 (10) 90.70 71.80

Caribbean and Central American Soccer
Championship. See Nos. C121-C123. For
surcharges see Nos. C145-C147.

Air Post Stamps of 1934 Overprinted or Surcharged in Black with New Values and Bars

1941, June 2

C67	AP8	5c on 20c dp bl	.20	.20
C68	AP8	15c on 20c dp bl	.20	.20
C69	AP8	40c on 75c dl vio	.35	.20
C70	AP9	65c on 1col dp rose	.50	.50
C71	AP9	1.40col on 2col lt bl	3.25	3.00
C72	AP9	5col black	11.00	11.00
C73	AP9	10col red brn	14.50	12.50
		Nos. C67-C73 (7)	30.00	27.60

Issued in commemoration of the settlement of the Costa Rica-Panama border dispute.

Nos. C67-C73 are found with hyphen omitted in overprint.

Nos. C67-C69 exist with inverted overprint. Value, each, $35.

University Types of 1941

1941, Aug. 26   **Perf. 12**

C74	A107	15c salmon	.20	.20
C75	A106	30c lt blue	.30	.20
C76	A106	40c orange	.40	.30
C77	A106	60c turq green	.45	.40
C78	A107	1col violet	1.90	1.90
C79	A106	2col black	4.75	4.75
C80	A107	5col sepia	16.00	16.00
		Nos. C74-C80 (7)	24.00	23.75

Portrait Type of 1943-47

Designs: 40c, Manuel Aguilar. No. C83, Francisco Morazan. No. C83A, Jose R. De Gallegos. 50c, Jose M. Alfaro. 60c, Francisco M. Oreamuno. 65c, Jose M. Castro. 85c, Juan Rafael Mora. 1col, Jose M. Montealegre. 1.05col, Braulio Carrillo. 1.15col, Jesus Jimenez. 1.40col, Bruno Carranza. 2col, Tomas Guardia.

1943-45   **Engr.**

C81	A109	10c rose pink	.20	.20
C82	A109	40c blue	.20	.20
C82A	A109	40c car rose	.20	.20
C83	A109	45c magenta	.30	.20
C83A	A109	45c black	.20	.20
C84	A109	50c turq grn	1.50	.20
C84A	A109	50c red org	.30	.20
C85	A109	60c brt ultra	.40	.20
C85A	A109	60c brt green	.20	.20
C86	A109	65c scarlet	.75	.20
C86A	A109	65c brt ultra	.20	.20
C87	A109	85c dp org	.90	.30
C87A	A109	85c dull pur	1.10	.40
C88	A109	1col black	1.10	.40
C88A	A109	1col scarlet	.45	.20
C88B	A109	1.05col bis brn	.60	.40
C89	A109	1col red brn	1.50	1.40
C89A	A109	1.15col green	2.00	1.10
C90	A109	1.40col dp vio	2.25	1.90
C90A	A109	1.40col org yel	1.40	1.25
C91	A109	2col black	3.50	1.10
C91A	A109	2col olive grn	1.10	.35
		Nos. C81-C91A (22)	20.35	11.00

Issued: Nos. C82A, C83A, C84A, C85A, C86A, C87A, C88A, C88B, C89A, C90A, C91A, 1945.

See Nos. C124-C127, C179-C181. For surcharges see Nos. C154-C158, C182, C184-C185.

Nos. C26-C27 Overprinted in Red or Blue

1943, Sept. 16

C92	AP9	5col black (R)	4.25	3.00
C93	AP9	10col red brown (Bl)	5.00	3.25

Mercury and Plane
AP31

1944, Jan. 19

C94	AP31	10c red orange	.20	.20
C95	AP31	15c dk carmine	.20	.20
C96	AP31	40c brt ultra	.30	.20
C97	AP31	45c dp red lil	.35	.30
C98	AP31	60c turq green	.45	.40
C99	AP31	1col dk red brn	1.00	.80
C100	AP31	1.40col gray blk	7.50	5.00
C101	AP31	5col violet	20.00	15.00
C102	AP31	10col black	70.00	62.50
		Nos. C94-C102 (9)	100.00	84.60

City of San Ramón founding, 100th anniv.

Very few examples of the 5col or 10col stamps were used for postal purposes, nearly all having been obtained by philatelic speculators.

No. CO10 With Additional Overprint in Black

1944, Nov. 22

C103	AP9	1col deep rose	2.00	.35
a.		Blue overprint	100.00	100.00

Nos. CO1-CO13 Overprinted in Carmine or Black

1945, Jan. 12   Unwmk.   Perf. 12

C104	AP8	5c green	.60	.50
C105	AP8	10c car rose (Bk)	.60	.55
C106	AP8	15c chocolate	.60	.55
C107	AP8	20c deep blue	.50	.40
C108	AP8	25c dp org (Bk)	.60	.60
C109	AP8	40c olive blk	.35	.35
C110	AP8	50c gray blk	.60	.60
C111	AP8	60c org yel (Bk)	.90	.35
C112	AP8	75c dull violet	.75	.50
C113	AP9	1col dp rose (Bk)	.75	.35
C114	AP9	2col light blue	8.00	4.50
C115	AP9	5col black	8.00	5.50
C116	AP9	10col red brn (Bk)	11.00	8.25
		Nos. C104-C116 (13)	33.25	23.00

No. C104 exists inverted & overprinted in black. This is probably a trial color. Value, $50.

> **Catalogue values for unused stamps in this section, from this point to the end of the section, are for Never Hinged items.**

AP32

Telegraph Stamps Overprinted in Black or Carmine

1945, Feb. 28   Unwmk.   Perf. 12½

C117	AP32	40c green (C)	.25	.20
C118	AP32	50c ultra (C)	.30	.20
C119	AP32	1col orange (Bk)	1.00	.40
		Nos. C117-C119 (3)	1.55	.80

No. C117 exists with inverted overprint. Value, $10.

Florence Nightingale and Edith Cavell
AP33

1945   Engr.

C120	AP33	1col black & car	1.00	.50

Costa Rican Red Cross Soc., 60th anniv.
For surcharge see No. C183.

Soccer Type of 1941 Inscribed: "Febrero 1946"

1946, May 13   **Perf. 12**

C121	AP15	25c green	1.00	.60
C122	AP15	30c dull yellow	1.00	.60
C123	AP15	55c deep blue	1.40	.60
		Nos. C121-C123 (3)	3.40	1.80

Portrait Type of 1943-47

Designs: 25c, Aniceto Esquivel. 30c, Vicente Herrera. 55c, Prospero Fernandez. 75c, Bernardo Soto.

1946, May 12

C124	A109	25c blue	.20	.20
C125	A109	30c red brown	.25	.20
C126	A109	55c plum	.40	.30
C127	A109	75c blue green	.60	.40
		Nos. C124-C127 (4)	1.45	1.10

Hospital of St. John of God
AP38

1946, June 24   Unwmk.   Perf. 12½ Center in Black

C128	AP38	5c yellow grn	.20	.20
C129	AP38	10c dk brown	.20	.20
C130	AP38	15c carmine	.20	.20
C131	AP38	25c dk blue	.20	.20
C132	AP38	30c dp orange	.45	.25
C133	AP38	40c olive grn	.25	.20
C134	AP38	50c violet	.30	.25
C135	AP38	60c dk sl grn	.60	.55
C136	AP38	75c brown	.50	.40
a.		Horiz. pair, imperf. btwn.	100.00	
C137	AP38	1col blue	.60	.35
C138	AP38	2col brn org	1.00	.70
C139	AP38	3col dk vio brn	2.00	1.75
C140	AP38	5col carmine	2.50	2.25
		Nos. C128-C140 (13)	8.95	7.50

Nos. C128, C129, C132 and C135 exist imperf.

Rafael Iglesias — AP39

3col, Ascensión Esquivel. 5col, Cleto González Víquez. 10col, Ricardo Jiménez Oreamuno.

1947, Jan. 15   Wmk. 215   Perf. 14 Center in Black

C141	AP39	2col blue	1.50	1.00
C142	AP39	3col dp car	2.25	1.40
C143	AP39	5col dk green	3.75	1.90
C144	AP39	10col orange	6.50	4.50
		Nos. C141-C144 (4)	14.00	8.80

Nos. C141-C144 also exist in a souvenir sheet of 4. Value, $500. The sheet in sepia is a proof and worth less.

Nos. C121-C123 Surcharged in Black

1947, May 5   Unwmk.   Perf. 12

C145	AP15	15c on 25c green	.90	.75
C146	AP15	15c on 30c dull yel	.90	.75
C147	AP15	15c on 55c dp blue	.90	.75
		Nos. C145-C147 (3)	2.70	2.25

Nos. C145-C147 exist with inverted surcharge.

Columbus in Cariari
AP43

1947, May 19   Engr.   Perf. 12½ Center in Black

C148	AP43	25c green	.25	.20
C149	AP43	30c dp ultra	.25	.20
C150	AP43	40c red orange	.35	.20
C151	AP43	45c violet	.55	.30
C152	AP43	50c brt carmine	.60	.20
C153	AP43	65c brown org	1.50	.80
		Nos. C148-C153 (6)	3.50	1.90

For surcharges see Nos. C178, C220-C223.

Nos. C84A, C85A, C127, C88A, and C88B Surcharged with New Value in Black or Red

1947, June 3   **Perf. 12**

C154	A109	15c on 50c red org	.25	.20
C155	A109	15c on 60c brt grn (R)	.25	.20
C156	A109	15c on 75c bl grn (R)	.25	.20
C157	A109	15c on 1col scar	.30	.20
C158	A109	15c on 1.05col bis brn	.25	.20
		Nos. C154-C158 (5)	1.30	1.00

No. C155 is known with black surcharge. Value, $10. No. C156 with inverted surcharge. Value, $10.

Early Steam Locomotive — AP44

1947, Nov. 10   Perf. 12½

C159	AP44	35c bl grn & blk	2.25	.50

Electric railroad to the Pacific coast, 50th anniv.

Roosevelt Type of Regular Issue

1947, Aug. 26   **Perf. 12**

C160	A122	15c green	.20	.20
C161	A122	30c car rose	.20	.20
C162	A122	45c red brown	.20	.20
C163	A122	65c orange yel	.25	.20
C164	A122	75c blue	.30	.20
C165	A122	1col olive grn	.50	.35
C166	A122	2col black	1.25	1.00
C167	A122	5col scarlet	2.50	2.25
		Nos. C160-C167 (8)	5.40	4.60

For surcharges see Nos. C224-C226.

National Theater   Rafael Iglesias
AP46   AP47

1948, Jan. 26   Perf. 12½ Center in Black

C168	AP46	15c brt ultra	.20	.20
C169	AP46	20c red	.20	.20
C170	AP46	35c dk green	.30	.20
C171	AP46	45c purple	.40	.25
C172	AP46	50c carmine	.40	.25
C173	AP46	75c red violet	.90	.70
C174	AP46	1col olive	1.90	1.10
C175	AP46	2col red brn	3.00	1.50
C176	AP47	5col org yel	4.75	3.00
C177	AP47	10col brt blue	11.00	6.00
		Nos. C168-C177 (10)	23.05	13.40

50th anniversary of National Theater.

No. C150 Surcharged in Carmine ¢ 0.35

1948, Apr. 21
C178 AP43 35c on 40c   1.10 .45
Exists with surcharge inverted.

Portrait Type of 1943-47
5c, Salvador Lara. 15c, Carlos Duran.

1948		**Engr.**		**Perf. 12**	
C179	A109	5c sepia		.20	.20
C180	A109	10c olive brown		.20	.20
C181	A109	15c violet		.20	.20
Nos. C179-C181 (3)				.60	.60

Nos. C88B, C120, C89A and C90A Surcharged in Carmine or Black

Perf. 12½, 12

1949, Aug. 28			**Unwmk.**	
C182	A109	35c on 1.05col bis brn	.35	.20
C183	AP33	50c on 1col blk & car	.60	.45
a.		2nd & 3rd lines both read "125 Aniversario"	5.00	3.00
C184	A109	55c on 1.15col grn	.85	.70
C185	A109	55c on 1.40col org yel (Bk)	.90	.60
Nos. C182-C185 (4)			2.70	1.95

125th anniv. of the annexation of the province of Guanacaste.
Overprint differs on No. C183, with "Guanacaste" in capitals, and lower case "a" in "Anexión."
The variety "I" for "i" in "Anexion" is found on Nos. C182, C184 and C185.

Symbols of UPU AP48

1950, Jan. 11		**Photo.**	**Perf. 11½**	
C186	AP48	15c lilac rose	.20	.20
C187	AP48	25c chalky blue	.20	.20
C188	AP48	1col gray green	.40	.20
Nos. C186-C188 (3)			.80	.60

75th anniv. of the UPU.

Battle of El Tejar, Cartago AP49

Occupation of Limón — AP50   Bull (Cattle Raising) — AP51

25c, Lucha ranch. 35c, Trenches of San Isidro Battalion. 55c, 75c, Observation post. 80c, 1col, Dr. Carlos Luis Valverde.

Inscribed: "Guerra de Liberacion Nacional 1948"
Engraved; Center Photogravure

1950, July 20			**Perf. 12½**	
Center in Black				
C189	AP49	15c brt car	.20	.20
C190	AP50	20c dull green	.20	.20
C191	AP49	25c dull blue	.30	.20
C192	AP49	35c chestnut	.40	.20
C193	AP49	55c lilac	.70	.20
C194	AP49	75c red org	1.10	.30
C195	AP50	80c gray	1.10	.50
C196	AP50	1col org yel	1.50	.55
Nos. C189-C196 (8)			5.50	2.35

2nd anniv. of the War for Natl. Liberation.

Inscribed: "Feria Nacional Agricola Ganadera e Industrial Cartago 1950"
1950, July 27
1c, 10c, 2col, Bull. 2c, 30c, 3col, Tuna fishing. 3c, 65c, Pineapple. 5c, 50c, 5col, Bananas. 45c, 80c, 10col, Coffee picker.

Center in Black				
C197	AP51	1c brt green	.20	.20
C198	AP51	2c brt blue	.20	.20
C199	AP51	3c chocolate	.20	.20
C200	AP51	5c dp ultra	.20	.20
C201	AP51	10c green	.20	.20
C202	AP51	30c purple	.20	.20
C203	AP51	45c vermilion	.20	.20
C204	AP51	50c blue gray	.35	.20
C205	AP51	65c dk blue	.40	.20
C206	AP51	80c dp rose	.85	.60
C207	AP51	2col org yel	2.25	1.60
C208	AP51	3col blue	6.25	4.00
C209	AP51	5col carmine	7.25	6.00
C210	AP51	10col dp claret	7.25	6.00
Nos. C197-C210 (14)			26.00	20.00

National Agricultural, Livestock and Industrial Fair, Cartago, 1950.
For surcharge see No. RA1.

Queen Isabella I and Caravels of Columbus AP52

Unwmk.				
1952, Mar. 4		**Engr.**	**Perf. 13**	
C211	AP52	15c carmine	.25	.20
C212	AP52	20c orange	.45	.20
C213	AP52	25c ultra	.70	.20
C214	AP52	55c dp green	2.25	.25
C215	AP52	2col violet	4.75	.45
Nos. C211-C215 (5)			8.40	1.30

Birth of Queen Isabella I of Spain, 500th anniv.

Mail Plane Type of 1934

1952-53			**Perf. 12**	
C216	AP8	5c blue	.30	.20
C217	AP8	10c green	.30	.20
C218	AP8	15c car rose ('53)	.40	.20
C219	AP8	35c purple	1.00	.20
Nos. C216-C219 (4)			2.00	.80

Nos. C216-C217 were reprinted in 1953 in different shades. Values the same.

Nos. C149-C151, C153 Surcharged in Red: "HABILITADO PARA CINCO CENTIMOS 1953"

1953, Apr. 24			**Perf. 12½**	
Center in Black				
C220	AP43	5c on 30c dp ultra	1.00	.85
C221	AP43	5c on 40c red org	.20	.20
C222	AP43	5c on 45c vio	.20	.20
C223	AP43	5c on 65c brn org	.20	.20
Nos. C220-C223 (4)			1.60	1.45

Nos. C161-C163 Surcharged in Black

1953, Apr. 11			**Perf. 12**	
C224	A122	15c on 30c car rose	.25	.20
C225	A122	15c on 45c red brn	.25	.20
C226	A122	15c on 65c org yel	.25	.20
Nos. C224-C226 (3)			.75	.60

Refinery of Vegetable Oils and Fats — AP53

Industries: 10c, Pottery. 15c, Sugar. 20c, Soap. 25c, Lumber. 30c, Matches. 35c, Textiles. 40c, Leather. 45c, Tobacco. 50c, Preserving. 55c, Canning. 60c, General. 65c, Metals. 75c, Pharmaceuticals. 80c, Pharmaceuticals. 1col, Paper. 2col, Rubber. 3col, Airplane maintenance. 5col, Marble. 10col, Beer.

Engraved; Center Photogravure

1954-59		**Unwmk.**	**Perf. 13x12½**	
Center in Black				
C227	AP53	5c red	.20	.20
C228	AP53	10c dk blue	.20	.20
C229	AP53	15c green	.20	.20
C230	AP53	20c violet	.20	.20
C231	AP53	25c magenta	.20	.20
C232	AP53	30c purple	.50	.30
C233	AP53	35c red vio	.20	.20
C234	AP53	40c black	.50	.30
C235	AP53	45c dk green	.90	.30
C236	AP53	50c vio brown	.60	.20
C237	AP53	55c yellow	.45	.20
C238	AP53	60c brown	1.10	.55
C239	AP53	65c carmine	1.40	.80
C240	AP53	75c violet	2.10	.65
C240A	AP53	80c pur & gray	1.10	.65
a.		Imperf., pair	90.00	
C241	AP53	1col blue	.60	.30
C242	AP53	2col rose pink	1.90	1.00
C243	AP53	3col ol grn	2.75	1.50
C244	AP53	5col black	4.00	1.25
C245	AP53	10col yellow	12.00	8.00
Nos. C227-C245 (20)			31.10	17.20

Issued: 30c, 35c, 60c, 65c, 75c, 2col, 3col, Oct. 20; 80c, Oct. 2, 1959; others, Sept. 1.
See Nos. C252-C255. For surcharges and overprint, see Nos. C314-C315, C334-C336, RA2, RA11.

Globe, Rotary Emblem AP54   Map of Costa Rica AP55

25c, Hand protecting boy. 40c, 2col, Hospital. 45c, Globe & palm leaves. 60c, Lighthouse.

1956, Feb. 7		**Engr.**	**Perf. 12**	
C246	AP54	10c green	.20	.20
C247	AP54	25c dk blue	.20	.20
C248	AP54	40c dk brown	.35	.20
C249	AP54	45c brt red	.25	.20
C250	AP54	60c dk red vio	.30	.25
C251	AP54	2col yel org	1.25	.50
Nos. C246-C251 (6)			2.55	1.60

50th anniv. of Rotary Intl. (in 1955).

Industries Type of 1954
Designs as in 1954.

Engraved; Center Photogravure

1956, Feb. 17			**Perf. 12**	
Center in Black				
C252	AP53	5c ultra	.25	.20
C253	AP53	10c violet blue	.25	.20
C254	AP53	15c orange yel	.25	.20
C255	AP53	75c red orange	.45	.30
Nos. C252-C255 (4)			1.20	.90

1957, June 21 Engr. Perf. 13½x13
10c, Map of Guanacaste. 15c, Inn. 20c, House of Santa Rosa. 25c, Gen. Jose Manuel Quiros. 30c, Old Presidential Palace. 35c, Joaquin Bernardo Calvo. 40c, Luis Molina. 45c, Gen. Jose Joaquin Mora. 50c, Gen. Jose Maria Canas. 55c, Juan Santamaria monument. 60c, National monument. 65c, Antonio Vallerriestra. 70c, Ramon Castilla y Marquesado. 75c, San Carlos fortress. 80c, Francisco Maria Oreamuno. 1col, Pres. Juan Rafael Mora.

C256	AP55	5c lt blue	.20	.20
C257	AP55	10c green	.20	.20
C258	AP55	15c dp orange	.20	.20
C259	AP55	20c lt brown	.20	.20
C260	AP55	25c vio blue	.25	.20

C261	AP55	30c violet	.35	.20
C262	AP55	35c car rose	.35	.20
C263	AP55	40c slate	.35	.20
C264	AP55	45c rose red	.40	.20
C265	AP55	50c ultra	.45	.20
C266	AP55	55c ocher	.85	.20
C267	AP55	60c brt car	.65	.25
C268	AP55	65c carmine	.75	.25
C269	AP55	70c orange yel	.95	.30
C270	AP55	75c emerald	.85	.30
C271	AP55	80c dk brown	1.10	.35
C272	AP55	1col black	1.25	.35
Nos. C256-C272 (17)			9.40	4.00

Centenary of War of 1856-57.

Cleto Gonzalez Viquez — AP56

Highway and Gonzalez Viquez AP57

Designs: 10c, Ricardo Jimenez Oreamuno. 20c, Puntarenas wharf and Jimenez. 35c, Post and Telegraph Bldg. and Jimenez. 55c, Pipeline and Gonzalez Viquez. 80c, National Library and Gonzalez Viquez. 1col, Electric train and Jimenez. 2col, Gonzales and Jimenez.

1959, Nov. 23		**Engr.**	**Perf. 13½**	
C274	AP56	5c car & ultra	.20	.20
C275	AP56	10c red & gray	.20	.20
			Perf. 13½x13	
C276	AP57	15c dk bl grn & blk	.20	.20
C277	AP57	20c car & brn	.50	.20
C278	AP57	35c rose lil & bl	.50	.20
C279	AP57	55c olive & vio	.50	.20
C280	AP57	80c ultra	.60	.35
C281	AP57	1col orange & mar	.85	.50
C282	AP57	2col gray & mar	2.00	1.60
Nos. C274-C282 (9)			5.25	3.65

For surcharge and overprint see Nos. C337, C339.

Soccer AP58

Designs: Various soccer scenes.

		Perf. 13½		
1960, Mar. 7		**Unwmk.**	**Photo.**	
C283	AP58	10c black	.20	.20
C284	AP58	25c ultra	.20	.20
C285	AP58	35c red orange	.25	.25
C286	AP58	50c red brown	.30	.25
C287	AP58	85c Prus green	.75	.60
C288	AP58	5col dp claret	1.60	1.60
Nos. C283-C288 (6)			3.30	3.10

Souvenir Sheet
Imperf
C289 AP58 2col violet   4.50 4.50

3rd Pan-American Soccer Games, San José, Mar. 1960.
Nos. C283-C288 exist imperf.

WRY Uprooted Oak Emblem — AP59

1960, Apr. 7		**Unwmk.**	**Perf. 11½**	
Granite Paper				
C290	AP59	35c vio bl, blk & yel	.30	.25
C291	AP59	85c black & brt pink	.60	.50

Refugee Year, July 1, 1959-June 30, 1960.

Banner and "OEA" — AP60

35c, "OEA" in oval. 55c, Clasped hands. 2col, "OEA" & map of Americas. 5col, Flags forming bird. 10col, Map of Costa Rica, flags & "OEA."

1960, Aug. 15　　Litho.　　Perf. 10

C292	AP60	25c black & multi	.20	.20
a.		Multi, impression sideways	60.00	
C293	AP60	35c multicolored	.30	.30
a.		Pair, imperf. between	60.00	
C294	AP60	55c multicolored	.50	.40
C295	AP60	5col multicolored	3.00	2.75
C296	AP60	10col black & multi	5.00	4.00
		Nos. C292-C296 (5)	9.00	7.65

Souvenir Sheet
Imperf

C297	AP60	2col multicolored	2.75	2.75

Pan-American Conf., San Jose, Aug. 15.

St. Louisa de Marillac and Orphanage — AP61

St. Vincent de Paul — AP62

25c, St. Vincent & old seminary. 50c, St. Louisa & sickroom. 1col, St. Vincent & new seminary.

1960, Oct. 26　　Engr.　　Perf. 14x13½

C298	AP61	10c green	.20	.20
C299	AP61	25c carmine	.20	.20
C300	AP61	50c dk blue	.20	.20
C301	AP61	1col brown org	.40	.30
C302	AP62	5col brown	2.00	1.60
		Nos. C298-C302 (5)	3.00	2.50

St. Vincent (1581?-1660) and St. Louisa (1591-1660). Nos. C298-C302 exist imperf.

Runner
AP63

Sports: 2c, Woman swimmer. 3c, Bicyclist. 4c, Weight lifter. 5c, Woman tennis player. 10c, Boxers. 25c, Soccer player. 85c, Basketball player. 1col, Baseball batter. 5col, Romulus and Remus statue. 10col, Pistol marksman.

Perf. 13½x14

1960, Dec. 14　　Photo.　　Unwmk.
Designs in Black

C303	AP63	1c brt yellow	.20	.20
C304	AP63	2c lt ultra	.20	.20
C305	AP63	3c dp rose	.20	.20
C306	AP63	4c yellow	.20	.20
C307	AP63	5c brt yel grn	.20	.20

C308	AP63	10c pink	.20	.20
C309	AP63	25c lt bl grn	.20	.20
C310	AP63	85c lilac	1.10	.75
C311	AP63	1col gray	1.25	.95
C312	AP63	10col lt violet	10.00	7.25
		Nos. C303-C312 (10)	13.75	10.35

Souvenir Sheets
Perf. 14x13½

C313	AP63	5col multi	6.00	6.00

17th Olympic Games, Rome, 8/25-9/11. Nos. C303-C313 exist imperf.

No. C255 Surcharged and Overprinted in Blue or Ultramarine: "XV Campeonato Mundial de Beisbol de Aficionados"

Engraved and Photogravure
1961, Apr. 21　　Perf. 12
Center in Black

C314	AP53	25c on 75c red org (Bl)	.25	.20
C315	AP53	75c red orange (U)	.55	.20

15th Amateur Baseball Championships.

Alberto Brenes C. AP64

Miguel Obregon AP65

No. C317, Manuel Aguilar. No. C318, Agustin Gutierrez L. No. C319, Vicente Herrera.

1961, June 12　　Photo.　　Perf. 12

C316	AP64	10c deep claret	.25	.20
C317	AP64	10c blue	.25	.20
C318	AP64	25c bright violet	.25	.20
C319	AP64	25c gray	.25	.20
		Nos. C316-C319 (4)	1.00	.80

First Continental Congress of Lawyers, San José, June 11-15. Exist imperf. See Nos. C330-C333.

1961, July 19　　Litho.　　Perf. 13½

C320	AP65	10c Prussian green	.30	.20

Birth centenary of Prof. Miguel Obregon L. Exists imperf. Value $50.

UN Food and Agriculture Organization AP66

UN day (UN Organizations): 20c, WHO. 25c, ILO. 30, ITU. 35c, World Meteorological Organization. 45c, UNESCO. 85c, ICAO. 5col, "United Nations" holding the world. 10col, Int. Bank for Reconstruction and Development.

Perf. 11½

1961, Oct. 24　　Unwmk.　　Engr.

C321	AP66	10c lt green	.20	.20
C322	AP66	20c orange	.20	.20
C323	AP66	25c Prus grn	.20	.20
C324	AP66	30c dk blue	.20	.20
C325	AP66	35c carmine rose	.85	.20
C326	AP66	45c violet	.30	.20
C327	AP66	85c blue	.65	.50
C328	AP66	10col dk sl grn	4.75	4.00
		Nos. C321-C328 (8)	7.35	5.70

Souvenir Sheet
Imperf

C329	AP66	5col ultra	3.00	3.00

For overprint see No. C338.

Portrait Type of 1961

No. C330, Dr. José Maria Soto Alfaro. No. C331, Dr. Elias Rojas Roman. No. C332, Dr. Andres Saenz Llorente. No. C333, Dr. Juan José Ulloa Giralt.

1961　　Photo.　　Perf. 13½

C330	AP64	10c blue green	.25	.20
C331	AP64	10c violet	.25	.20
C332	AP64	25c dark gray	.25	.20
C333	AP64	25c deep claret	.25	.20
		Nos. C330-C333 (4)	1.00	.80

9th Congress of Physicians of Central America and Panama.

Nos. C229, C236 and C280 Surcharged in Black, Orange or Red
Engraved; Center Photogravure
1962　　Perf. 13x12½, 13½x13

C334	AP53	10c ("10") on 15c	.20	.20
C334A	AP53	10c ("c0.10") on 15c (R)	.20	.20
C335	AP53	25c on 15c	.20	.20
C336	AP53	35c on 50c (O)	.25	.20

Engr.

C337	AP57	85c on 80c (R)	.70	.55
		Nos. C334-C337 (5)	1.55	1.35

No. C336 exists with double surcharge. Value, $35.

Nos. C324 and C282 Overprinted in Red: "II CONVENCION FILATELICA CENTROAMERICANA SETIEMBRE 1962"

1962, Sept. 12　　Perf. 11½, 13½x13

C338	AP66	30c dark blue	.50	.40
C339	AP57	2col gray & mar	1.50	1.10

2nd Central American Phil. Convention.

Revenue Stamp Surcharged with New Values and "CORREO AEREO" in Red

1962　　Engr.　　Perf. 12

C341	A124	25c on 2c emer	.20	.20
C342	A124	35c on 2c emer	.20	.20
C343	A124	45c on 2c emer	.25	.20
C344	A124	85c on 2c emer	.45	.40
		Nos. C341-C344 (4)	1.10	1.00

Arms and Malaria Eradication Emblem AP67

1963, Feb. 14　　Photo.　　Perf. 11½

C345	AP67	25c brt rose	.20	.20
C346	AP67	35c brown org	.25	.20
C347	AP67	45c ultra	.30	.25
C348	AP67	85c blue grn	.60	.40
C349	AP67	1col dk base	1.00	.50
		Nos. C345-C349 (5)	2.35	1.55

WHO drive to eradicate malaria.

Central American Tapir — AP68

Designs: 5c, Paca. 25c, Jaguar. 30c, Ocelot. 35c, Whitetail deer. 40c, Manatee. 85c, White-throated capuchin monkey. 5col, White-lipped peccary.

Perf. 13½

1963, May　　Unwmk.　　Photo.

C354	AP68	5c yel ol & brn	.25	.20
C355	AP68	10c orange & sl	.25	.20
C356	AP68	25c blue & yel	.40	.20
C357	AP68	30c lt yel grn & brn	.60	.35
C358	AP68	35c bis & red brn	.90	.35
C359	AP68	40c emer & sl bl	1.10	.50
C360	AP68	85c green & blk	3.50	.50
C361	AP68	5col gray grn & choc	10.50	3.50
		Nos. C354-C361 (8)	17.50	5.80

Stamp of 1863 and Packet "Monarch" — AP69

Issue of 1863 and: 2col, Recaredo Bonilla Carrillo, Postmaster, 1862-63. 3col, Burros, overland mail transport, 1839. 10col, Burro railway car.

1963, June 26　　Litho.

C362	AP69	25c dl rose & chlky bl	.25	.20
C363	AP69	2col gray bl & org	1.60	1.10
C364	AP69	3col bister & emer	2.75	1.75
C365	AP69	10col dl grn & ocher	9.75	5.00
		Nos. C362-C365 (4)	14.35	8.05

Centenary of Costa Rica's stamps. No. C362 is inscribed "William Le Lacheur," the builder and captain of the "Monarch."

Souvenir Sheets

Stamps of 1863 and San José Postmark — AP70

Perf. 13½, Imperf.

1963, June 26　　Unwmk.

C366	AP70	5col bl, red, grn & org	4.25	4.25

Cent. of Costa Rica's stamps. In 1968 examples of No. C366 were overprinted "2-4 Agosto 1968" and "III Exposicion Filatelica Nacional / 'Costa Rica 68'". Value, each, $10.

Animal Type of 1963 Surcharged in Red

No. C367, Little anteater. No. C368, Gray fox. No. C369, Armadillo. No. C370, Great anteater.

1963, Sept. 14　　Photo.　　Perf. 13½

C367	AP68	10c on 1c brt grn & org brn	1.00	.25
C368	AP68	25c on 2c org yel & ol grn	1.00	.50
C369	AP68	35c on 3c bluish grn & brn	1.25	.20
C370	AP68	85c on 4c dp rose & dk brn	2.50	.50
		Nos. C367-C370 (4)	5.75	1.25

Examples of #C370 exist without surcharge.

Pres. Kennedy AP71

Ancestral Figure AP72

Portraits- Presidents: 25c, Francisco J. Orlich, Costa Rica. 30c, Julio A. Rivera, El Salvador. 35c, Miguel Ydigoras F., Guatemala. 85c, Dr. Ramon Villeda M., Honduras. 1col, Luis A. Somoza, Nicaragua. 3col, Roberto F. Chiari, Panama.

1963, Dec. 7   Unwmk.   *Perf. 14*
Portraits in Black Brown

C371	AP71	25c violet brn	.20 .20
C372	AP71	30c brt lil rose	.20 .20
C373	AP71	35c ocher	.20 .20
C374	AP71	85c gray blue	.30 .20
C375	AP71	1col orange brn	.35 .25
C376	AP71	3col lt ol grn	1.50 1.50
C377	AP71	5col gray	2.25 2.25
		Nos. C371-C377 (7)	5.00 4.80

Meeting of Central American Presidents with Pres. John F. Kennedy, San José, Mar. 18-20, 1963.

1963-64   Photo.   *Perf. 12*

Ancient Art: 5c, Dog, horiz. 10c, Ornamental stool, horiz. 25c, Male figure. 30c, Ceremonial dancer. 35c, Ceramic vase. 50c, Frog. 55c, Bell. 75c, Six-limbed figure. 85c, Seated man. 90c, Bird-shaped jug. 1col, Twin human beaker, horiz. 2col, Alligator, horiz. 3col, Twin-tailed lizard. 5col, Figure under arch. 10col, Polished stone figure.

C378	AP72	5c lt yel grn & Prus grn	.20 .20
C379	AP72	10c buff & dk grn	.20 .20
C380	AP72	25c rose & dk brn	.20 .20
C381	AP72	30c ocher & Prus grn ('64)	.25 .20
C382	AP72	35c sal & sl grn	.25 .20
C383	AP72	45c lt bl & dk brn	.25 .20
C384	AP72	50c dl bl & dk brn	.35 .20
C385	AP72	55c yel grn & dk brn	.50 .20
C386	AP72	75c ocher & dk red brn	.50 .20
C387	AP72	85c yel & red brn	1.25 1.25
C388	AP72	90c cit & red brn ('64)	1.60 1.60
C389	AP72	1col lt bl & dk brn ('64)	.95 .30
C390	AP72	2col buff & dk grn ('64)	1.50 .60
C391	AP72	3col yel grn & dk brn ('64)	5.00 .90
C392	AP72	5col cit & sep ('64)	5.00 5.00
C393	AP72	10col rose lil & sl grn	8.00 8.00
		Nos. C378-C393 (16)	26.00 19.45

For surcharges and overprint see Nos. C395, C397-C398, C400, C426-C428.

Flags of Central American States — AP73

Alfredo Gonzalez F. — AP74

1964   *Perf. 14*
C394   AP73   30c bl, gray, red & blk   1.00 .35

Central American Independence issue. For surcharge see No. C396.

Nos. C381, C394 and C387 Surcharged

1964, Oct.   *Perf. 12, 14*

C395	AP72	5c on 30c	.50 .25
C396	AP73	15c on 30c	.50 .25
C397	AP72	15c on 85c	.50 .25
		Nos. C395-C397 (3)	1.50 .75

No. C388 Surcharged: "C 0.15 / CONFERENCIA POSTAL / DE PARIS — 1864"

1964   *Perf. 12*
C398   AP72   15c on 90c cit & red brn   .25 .20

Paris Postal Conference.

1965, June   Photo.   *Perf. 12*
C399   AP74   35c dk blue green   3.00 .25

50th anniv. of the National Bank and honoring Alfredo Gonzalez F., 1st governor of the bank.

No. C390 Overprinted: "75 ANIVERSARIO / ASILO CHAPUI / 1890-1965"

1965, Aug. 14   Unwmk.   *Perf. 12*
C400   AP72   2col buff & dk grn   1.25 .60

75th anniv. of Chapui Asylum, San José.

Girl, FAO Emblem and Hands Holding Grain — AP75

Church of Nicoya — AP76

FAO Emblem and: 15c, Map of Costa Rica and silos, horiz. 50c, World population chart and children. 1col, Plane over map of Costa Rica, horiz.

1965   Litho.   *Perf. 14*

C401	AP75	15c lt brn & blk	.25 .20
C402	AP75	35c black & yel	.25 .20
C403	AP75	50c ultra & dk grn	.25 .20
C404	AP75	1col grn, blk & sil	.40 .25
		Nos. C401-C404 (4)	1.15 .85

FAO "Freedom from Hunger" campaign.

1965, Dec. 20   *Perf. 13½x14*

5c, Leonidas Briceno B. 15c, Scroll dated "25 de Julio de 1964." 35c, Map of Guanacaste and Nicoya peninsula. 50c, Dancing couple. 1col, Map showing local products.

C405	AP76	5c red brn & blk	.35 .20
C406	AP76	10c blue & gray	.35 .20
C407	AP76	15c bis & slate	.35 .20
C408	AP76	35c blue & slate	.35 .20
C409	AP76	50c gray & vio bl	.50 .20
C410	AP76	1col buff & slate	1.10 .35
		Nos. C405-C410 (6)	3.00 1.35

Acquisition of the Nicoya territory.

Runner and Olympic Rings AP77

Pres. Kennedy Speaking in San José Cathedral AP78

Olympic Rings and Emblem: 10c, Bicyclists. 40c, Judo. 65c, Basketball. 80c, Soccer. 1col, Hands holding torches, and Mt. Fuji.

1965, Dec. 23   *Perf. 13x13½*

C411	AP77	5c bister & multi	.20 .20
C412	AP77	10c lt lil & multi	.20 .20
C413	AP77	40c multicolored	.20 .20
C414	AP77	65c lemon & multi	.25 .20
C415	AP77	80c tan & multi	.35 .20
C416	AP77	1col multicolored	.45 .30
a.		Souvenir sheet of 2	3.00 3.00
		Nos. C411-C416 (6)	1.65 1.30

18th Olympic Games, Tokyo, Oct. 10-25, 1964. No. C416a contains two 1col stamps, one like No. C416, the other with gray background replacing yellow orange.

No. C416a was issued both perf and imperf. Same values.

Nos. C411-C416 exist imperf.

Perf. 13½x13, 13x13½
1965, Dec. 23   Litho.   Unwmk.

Designs: 45c, Friendship 7 capsule circling globe, and Kennedy, horiz. 85c, Kennedy and John, Jr. 1col, Curtis-Lee Mansion and flame from Kennedy grave, Arlington, Va.

C417	AP78	45c brt bl & lil	.25 .20
C418	AP78	55c org & brt bl	.30 .20
C419	AP78	85c gray, dk brn & red brn	.50 .30
C420	AP78	1col multicolored	.60 .40
a.		Souvenir sheet of 2	1.10 1.10
		Nos. C417-C420 (4)	1.65 1.10

President John F. Kennedy (1917-63). No. C420a contains two 1col stamps, one like No. C420, the other with green background replacing dark blue. Exists with light blue background instead of green; value $150.

No. C420a was issued both perf and imperf. Same values.

Nos. C417-C420 exist imperf.

For surcharges see Nos. C429-C430.

Firemen with Hoses — AP79

Designs: 5c, Fire engine "Knox," horiz. 10c, 1866 fire pump. 35c, Fireman's badge. 50c, Emblem and flags of Confederation of Central American Fire Brigades.

1966, Mar. 12   Litho.   *Perf. 11*

C421	AP79	5c black & red	.30 .20
C422	AP79	10c bister & red	.35 .20
C423	AP79	15c blk, red brn & red	.55 .20
C424	AP79	35c black & yel	.90 .25
C425	AP79	50c dk blue & red	1.90 .35
		Nos. C421-C425 (5)	4.00 1.20

Centenary of San José Fire Brigade.

Nos. C381, C383, C386 and C418-C419 Surcharged

a

b

1966   Photo.   *Perf. 12*

C426	AP72(a)	15c on 30c	.20 .20
C427	AP72(a)	15c on 45c	.20 .20
C428	AP72(a)	35c on 75c	.20 .20

     Litho.   *Perf. 13x13½*

C429	AP78(a)	35c on 55c	.20 .20
C430	AP78(b)	50c on 85c	.45 .30
		Nos. C426-C430 (5)	1.25 1.00

Revenue Stamps (Basic Type of A124) Surcharged

1966, Dec.   Engr.   *Perf. 12*

C431	A124	15c on 5c blue	.20 .20
C432	A124	35c on 10c claret	.25 .20
C433	A124	50c on 20c rose red	.35 .25
		Nos. C431-C433 (3)	.80 .65

Central Bank of Costa Rica — AP80

1967, Mar.   Litho.   *Perf. 11*

C434	AP80	5c brt green	.35 .20
C435	AP80	15c brown	.35 .20
C436	AP80	35c scarlet	.35 .20
		Nos. C434-C436 (3)	1.05 .60

Power Lines — AP81

Telecommunications Building, San Pedro — AP82

Electrification Program: 15c, Telephone Central. 25c, La Garita Dam. 35c, Rio Mache Reservoir. 50c, Cachi Dam.

1967, Apr. 24   Litho.   *Perf. 11*

C437	AP81	5c dark gray	.25 .20
C438	AP82	10c brt rose	.25 .20
C439	AP81	15c brown org	.25 .20
C440	AP82	25c brt ultra	.25 .20
C441	AP82	35c brt green	.25 .20
C442	AP82	50c red brown	.40 .30
		Nos. C437-C442 (6)	1.65 1.30

Chondrorhyncha Aromatica AP83

Institute Emblem AP84

Orchids: 10c, Miltonia endresii. 15c, Stanhopea cirrhata. 25c, Trichopilia suavis. 35c, Odontoglossum schlieperianum. 50c, Cattleya skinneri. 1col, Cattleya dowiana. 2col, Odontoglossum chiriquense.

1967, June 15   Engr.   *Perf. 13x13½*
Orchids in Natural Colors

C443	AP83	5c multicolored	.20 .20
C444	AP83	10c olive & multi	.35 .20
C445	AP83	15c multicolored	.35 .20
C446	AP83	25c multicolored	.80 .20
C447	AP83	35c dull vio & multi	.80 .20
C448	AP83	50c brown & multi	1.00 .20
C449	AP83	1col vio & multi	2.75 .75
C450	AP83	2col dk ol bis & multi	4.25 1.50
		Nos. C443-C450 (8)	10.50 3.45

Issued for the University Library.

1967, Oct. 6   Litho.   *Perf. 13x13½*
C451   AP84   50c vio bl, lt bl & bl   .25 .20

Inter-American Agriculture Institute, 25th anniv.

Church of Solitude — AP85

LACSA Emblem — AP86

Costa Rican Churches: 10c, Basilica of Santo Domingo, Heredia. 15c, Cathedral of Tilaran. 25c, Cathedral of Alajuela. 30c, Mercy Church. 35c, Basilica of Our Lady of Angels. 40c, Church of St. Raphael, Heredia. 45c, Ujarras ruins. 50c, Ruins of parish church, Cartago. 55c, Cathedral of San José. 65c, Parish church, Puntarenas. 75c, Church of Orosi. 80c, Cathedral of St. Isidro, the General. 85c, St. Ramon Church. 90c, Church of the Abandoned. 1col, Coronado Church. 2col, Church of St. Teresita. 3col, Parish Church, Heredia. 5col, Carmelite Church. 10col, Limon Cathedral.

1967, Dec. 15   Engr.   Perf. 12½

C452	AP85	5c green	.20	.20
C453	AP85	10c blue	.20	.20
C454	AP85	15c lilac	.20	.20
C455	AP85	25c dull yel	.20	.20
C456	AP85	30c orange brn	.20	.20
C457	AP85	35c lt blue	.25	.20
C458	AP85	40c dp orange	.25	.20
C459	AP85	45c dl bl grn	.25	.20
C460	AP85	50c olive	.35	.20
C461	AP85	55c brown	.35	.20
C462	AP85	65c car rose	.60	.25
C463	AP85	75c sepia	.65	.30
C464	AP85	80c yellow	1.25	.45
C465	AP85	85c violet blk	1.40	.45
C466	AP85	90c emerald	1.40	.65
C467	AP85	1col slate	1.10	.35
C468	AP85	2col brt green	5.00	1.75
C469	AP85	3col orange	7.25	3.00
C470	AP85	5col vio blue	7.25	3.00
C471	AP85	10col carmine	9.75	4.50
		Nos. C452-C471 (20)	38.10	16.70

Nos. C452 and C454 exist imperf; Nos. C455 and C470 exist imperf horiz.
See Nos. C561-C576.

Perf. 13x13½, 13½x13

1967, Dec. 12   Litho. & Engr.

45c, LACSA emblem, jet, horiz. 50c, Decorated wheel, anniversary emblem.

C472	AP86	40c ultra, grnsh bl & gold	.25	.20
C473	AP86	45c blk, pale grn, ultra & gold	.25	.20
C474	AP86	50c blue & multi	.25	.20
		Nos. C472-C474 (3)	.75	.60

20th anniv. (in 1966) of Lineas Aereas Costaricenses, LACSA, Costa Rican Airlines.

Scout Directing Traffic AP87

Runner AP88

Designs: 25c, Campfire under palm tree. 35c, Flag of Costa Rica, Scout flag and emblem. 50c, Encampment, horiz. 65c, Photograph of first Scout troop, horiz.

1968, Mar. 15   Perf. 13

C475	AP87	15c lt bl, blk & lt brn	.20	.20
C476	AP87	25c lt ultra, vio bl & org	.25	.20
C477	AP87	35c blue & multi	.35	.20
C478	AP87	50c multicolored	.60	.30
C479	AP87	65c sal, dk bl & brn	.75	.35
		Nos. C475-C479 (5)	2.15	1.25

Costa Rican Boy Scouts, 50th anniversary.

1968, Jan. 17   Litho.   Perf. 10x11

Sports: 40c, Women's running. 55c, Boxing. 65c, Bicycling. 75c, Weight lifting. 1col, High diving. 3col, Rifle shooting.

C481	AP88	30c multi	.20	.20
C482	AP88	40c multi	.20	.20
C483	AP88	55c multi	.25	.20
C484	AP88	65c lil & multi	.30	.20
C485	AP88	75c multi	.30	.20
C486	AP88	1col multi	.35	.25
C487	AP88	3col multi	1.50	.90
		Nos. C481-C487 (7)	3.10	2.15

19th Olympic Games, Mexico City, 10/12-27.

Philatelic Exhibition Emblem — AP89

1969, June 5   Litho.   Perf. 11x10

C488	AP89	35c multicolored	.20	.20
C489	AP89	40c pink & multi	.20	.20
C490	AP89	50c lt blue & multi	.25	.20
C491	AP89	2col multicolored	.90	.50
		Nos. C488-C491 (4)	1.55	1.10

4th Natl. Philatelic Exhib., San José, 6/5-8.

ILO Emblem AP90

1969, Oct. 29   Litho.   Perf. 10

C492	AP90	35c bl grn & blk	.25	.20
C493	AP90	50c scarlet & blk	.25	.20

50th anniv. of the ILO.

Soccer — AP91

Stylized Crab — AP92

Designs: 65c, Soccer ball, map of North and Central America. 85c, Soccer player. 1col, Two players in action.

1969, Nov. 23   Litho.   Perf. 11x10

C494	AP91	65c gray & multi	.30	.20
C495	AP91	75c multicolored	.30	.20
C496	AP91	85c multicolored	.35	.30
C497	AP91	1col pink & multi	.50	.35
		Nos. C494-C497 (4)	1.45	1.05

Issued to publicize the 4th Soccer Championships (CONCACAF), Nov. 23-Dec. 7.

1970, May 14   Litho.   Perf. 12½

C498	AP92	10c blk & lil rose	.25	.20
C499	AP92	15c blk & yel	.25	.20
C500	AP92	50c blk & brn org	.25	.20
C501	AP92	1.10col blk & emer	.50	.20
		Nos. C498-C501 (4)	1.25	.80

10th Inter-American Cancer Cong., 5/22-29.

Costa Rica No. 124, Magnifying Glass and Stamps — AP93

2col, Father, son with stamps, album.

1970, Sept. 14   Litho.   Perf. 11

C502	AP93	1col ultra, brn & car rose	.95	.20
C503	AP93	2col blk, pink & ultra	1.10	.50

The 5th National Philatelic Exhibition.

EXPO Emblem and Costa Rican Cart — AP94

EXPO Emblem and: 10c, Japanese floral arrangement, vert. 35c, Pavilion and Tower of the Sun. 40c, Japanese tea ceremony. 45c, Woman picking coffee, vert. 55c, Earth seen from moon, vert.

1970, Oct. 22   Litho.   Perf. 13x13½

C504	AP94	10c multicolored	.20	.20
C505	AP94	15c green & multi	.20	.20
C506	AP94	35c blue & multi	.35	.20
C507	AP94	40c gray & multi	.50	.20
C508	AP94	45c multicolored	.50	.20
C509	AP94	55c black & multi	.50	.20
		Nos. C504-C509 (6)	2.25	1.20

EXPO '70 International Exhibition, Osaka, Japan, Mar. 15-Sept. 13.

Escazu Valley, by Margarita Bertheau — AP95

Paintings: 25c, "Irazu," by Rafael A. Garcia, vert. 80c, Shore landscape, by Teodorico Quiros. 1col, "The Other Face," by Cesar Valverde. 2.50col, Mother and Child, by Luis Daell, vert.

1970, Nov. 4   Litho.   Perf. 12½

C510	AP95	25c multi	.75	.30
C511	AP95	45c multi	.75	.30
C512	AP95	80c multi	1.10	.55
C513	AP95	1col multi	1.10	.60
C514	AP95	2.50col multi	2.40	2.00
		Nos. C510-C514 (5)	6.10	3.75

Arms of Costa Rica, 1964 — AP96

National Theater AP97

Various Coats of Arms, dated: 10c, Nov. 27, 1906. 15c, Sept. 29, 1848. 25c, Apr. 21, 1840. 35c, Nov. 22, 1824. 50c, Nov. 2, 1824. 1col, Mar. 6, 1824. 2col, May 10, 1823.

1971, Feb. 10   Litho.   Perf. 14x13½

C515	AP96	5c buff & multi	.35	.20
C516	AP96	10c multi	.35	.20
C517	AP96	15c yel & multi	.45	.20
C518	AP96	25c pink & multi	.45	.20
C519	AP96	35c multi	.60	.20
C520	AP96	50c rose & multi	.70	.20
C521	AP96	1col beige & multi	.75	.40
C522	AP96	2col multi	1.50	.80
		Nos. C515-C522 (8)	5.15	2.40

1971, Apr. 14   Litho.   Perf. 11

C523	AP97	2col plum	.40	.30

Organization of American States meeting.

José Matias Delgado, Manuel José Arce AP98

Flag of Costa Rica — AP99

Independence Leaders: 10c, Miguel Larreinaga and Manuel Antonio de la Cerda, Nicaragua. 15c, José Cecilio del Valle, Dionisio de Herrera, Honduras. 35c, Pablo Alvarado and Florencio del Castillo, Costa Rica. 50c, Antonio Larrazabal and Pedro Molina, Guatemala. 2col, Costa Rica coat of arms.

1971, Sept. 14   Perf. 13

C524	AP98	5c multi	.20	.20
C525	AP98	10c multi	.20	.20
C526	AP98	15c gray, brn & blk	.20	.20
C527	AP98	35c multi	.20	.20
C528	AP98	50c multi	.20	.20
C529	AP99	1col multi	.20	.20
C530	AP99	2col multi	.40	.40
		Nos. C524-C530 (7)	1.60	1.60

Central American independence, sesqui.

Soccer Federation Emblem — AP100

Children of the World — AP101

1971, Dec. 6

C531	AP100	50c multi	.30	.20
C532	AP100	60c multi	.30	.20

50th anniv. of Soccer Federation of Costa Rica.

1972, Jan. 11   Perf. 12½

C533	AP101	50c multi	.25	.20
C534	AP101	1.10col red & multi	.40	.25

25th anniv. (in 1971) of UNICEF.

Tree of Guanacaste AP102

Designs: 40c, Hermitage, Liberia. 55c, Petroglyphs, Rincón Brujo. 60c, Painted head, sculpture from Curubandé, vert.

1972, Feb. 28   Perf. 11

C535	AP102	20c brn, ol & brt grn	.35	.20
C536	AP102	40c brn & ol	.35	.20
C537	AP102	55c blk & brn	.35	.20
C538	AP102	60c blk, buff & ver	.35	.20
		Nos. C535-C538 (4)	1.40	.80

Bicentenary of the founding of the city of Liberia, Guanacaste.

Farm and Family — AP103

Inter-American Exhibitions AP104

Designs: 45c, Cattle, dairy products and meat, horiz. 50c, Kneeling figure with plant. 10col, Farmer and map of Americas.

1972, June 30   Litho.   Perf. 12½
C539 AP103 20c multi .30 .20
C540 AP103 45c multi .30 .20
C541 AP103 50c dp yel, grn & blk .30 .20
C542 AP103 10col brn, org & blk 2.40 1.75
Nos. C539-C542 (4) 3.30 2.35

30th anniversary of the Inter-American Institute of Agricultural Sciences.

1972, Aug. 26   Litho.   Perf. 13
C543 AP104 50c orange & brn .20 .20
C544 AP104 2col blue & vio .40 .30

4th Interamerican Philatelic Exhibition, EXFILBRA, Rio de Janeiro, Aug. 26-Sept. 2.

First Book Printed in Costa Rica — AP105

Intl. Book Year: 50c, 5col, Natl. Library, horiz.

1972, Dec. 7   Litho.   Perf. 12½
C545 AP105 20c brt blue .35 .20
C546 AP105 50c gold & multi .35 .20
C547 AP105 75c multicolored .35 .20
C548 AP105 5col multicolored 1.75 .95
Nos. C545-C548 (4) 2.80 1.55

Road to Irazú Volcano AP106

1972-73   Perf. 11x11½, 11½x11
C549 AP106 5c like 20c .30 .20
C550 AP106 15c Coco-Culebra Bay .30 .20
C551 AP106 20c shown .30 .20
C552 AP106 25c like 15c .30 .20
C553 AP106 40c Manuel Antonio Beach .30 .20
C554 AP106 45c Tourist Office emblem .30 .20
C555 AP106 50c Lindora Lake .30 .20
C556 AP106 60c San Jose P.O., vert. .30 .20
C557 AP106 80c like 40c .35 .20
C558 AP106 90c like 45c .35 .20
C559 AP106 1col like 50c .35 .20
C560 AP106 2col like 60c .65 .45
Nos. C549-C560 (12) 4.10 2.65

Tourism year of the Americas.
Issued: 20c, 25c, 80c, 90c, 1col, 2col, 12/26; others, 3/21/73.
No. C555 exists with inverted center, used only. Value $3,500.

Church Type of 1967
Designs as before.

1973, July 16   Engr.   Perf. 12½
C561 AP85 5c slate grn .20 .20
C562 AP85 10c olive .20 .20
C563 AP85 15c orange .20 .20
C564 AP85 25c brown .20 .20
C565 AP85 30c rose claret .20 .20
C566 AP85 35c violet .20 .20
C567 AP85 40c brt green .20 .20
C568 AP85 45c dull yellow .20 .20
C569 AP85 50c rose magenta .20 .20
C570 AP85 55c blue .25 .20
C571 AP85 65c black .30 .20
C572 AP85 75c rose red .30 .20
C573 AP85 80c yellow grn .30 .20
C574 AP85 85c lilac .35 .25

C575 AP85 90c brt pink .35 .25
C576 AP85 1col dark blue .35 .25
Nos. C561-C576 (16) 4.00 3.35

Human Rights Flame — AP107

OAS Emblem — AP108

1973, Dec. 10   Photo.   Perf. 10½
C577 AP107 50c black & red .25 .20

25th anniversary of the Universal Declaration of Human Rights.

1973, Dec. 17   Litho.   Perf. 10½
C578 AP108 20c dk bl & dp car .25 .20

25th anniv. of the OAS.

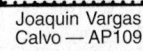

Joaquin Vargas Calvo — AP109   AP110

1974, Jan. 14
C579 AP109 20c shown .35 .20
C580 AP109 20c Alejandro Monestel .35 .20
C581 AP109 20c Julio Mata .35 .20
C582 AP109 60c Julio Fonseca .35 .20
C583 AP109 2col Rafael A. Chaves .80 .30
C584 AP109 5col Manuel M. Gutierrez 1.90 1.10
Nos. C579-C584 (6) 4.10 2.20

Costa Rican composers honored by the National Symphony Orchestra.

Revenue Stamps Overprinted "Habilitado para Correo Aereo"
1974, Apr. 5   Engr.   Perf. 12
C585 AP110 50c brown .20 .20
C586 AP110 1col violet .30 .20
C587 AP110 2col orange .70 .35
C588 AP110 5col olive 1.60 1.60
Nos. C585-C588 (4) 2.80 2.35

Telephone Building, San Pedro — AP111

EXFILMEX 74 Emblem AP112

Designs: 65c, Rio Macho Control, horiz. 85c, Turbines, Rio Macho Center. 1.25col,

Cachi Dam and reservoir, horiz. 2col, I.C.E. Headquarters.

1974, July 30   Litho.   Perf. 10½
C589 AP111 50c gold & multi .20 .20
C590 AP111 65c gold & multi .25 .20
C591 AP111 85c gold & multi .30 .20
C592 AP111 1.25col gold & multi .35 .20
C593 AP111 2col gold & multi .75 .30
Nos. C589-C593 (5) 1.85 1.10

25th anniversary of Costa Rican Electrical Institute (I.C.E.).

1974, Aug. 22   Perf. 13
C594 AP112 65c green .20 .20
C595 AP112 3col lilac rose .60 .40

5th Inter-American Philatelic Exhibition, EXFILMEX-74 UPU, Mexico City, Oct. 26-Nov. 3.

Map of Costa Rica, 4-S Emblem AP113

50c, Young harvesters and 4-S emblem.

1974, Oct. 7   Litho.   Perf. 12x11
C596 AP113 20c brt green .35 .20
C597 AP113 50c multicolored .35 .20

25th anniversary of 4-S Clubs of Costa Rica (similar to US 4-H Clubs).

Roberto Brenes Mesen — AP114

"Life Insurance" AP115

Designs: 85c, "Love and Death," manuscript. 5col, Hands of writer, horiz.

1974, Oct. 14   Litho.   Perf. 10½
C598 AP114 20c black & brn .20 .20
C599 AP114 85c black & red .25 .20
C600 AP114 5col black & red brn 1.50 .85
Nos. C598-C600 (3) 1.95 1.25

Mesen, educator & writer, birth centenary.

1974, Oct. 30   Perf. 14
Designs: 20c, Ricardo Jiménez Oreamuno and Tomás Soley Güell, horiz. 50c, Harvest Insurance (hand holding shovel), horiz. 85c, Maritime insurance (hand holding paper boat). 1.25col, INS emblem. 2col, Workers rehabilitation (arm with crutch). 2.50col, Workers' Compensation (hand holding wrench). 20col, Fire insurance (hands protecting house).

C601 AP115 20c multi .20 .20
C602 AP115 50c multi .20 .20
C603 AP115 65c multi .20 .20
C604 AP115 85c multi .20 .20
C605 AP115 1.25col multi .30 .20
C606 AP115 2col multi .55 .25
C607 AP115 2.50col multi .60 .40
C608 AP115 20col multi 3.75 3.75
Nos. C601-C608 (8) 6.00 5.40

Costa Rican Insurance Institute (Instituto Nacional de Seguros, INS), 50th anniversary. For surcharges see Nos. C721-C722.

WPY Emblem — AP116   Oscar J. Pinto F. — AP117

1974, Nov. 13   Litho.   Perf. 11x11½
C609 AP116 2col vio bl & red .45 .25
World Population Year.

1974, Dec. 2   Perf. 13
Designs: 50c, Alberto Montes de Oca D., champion sharpshooter. 1col, Eduardo Garnier, sports promoter. O. J. Pinto, introducer of soccer.

C610 AP117 20c gray & dk bl .20 .20
C611 AP117 50c gray & dk bl .20 .20
C612 AP117 1col gray & dk bl .45 .20
Nos. C610-C612 (3) .85 .60

First Central American Olympic Games, held in Guatemala, 1973.

Mormodes Buccinator AP118

Masdevallia Ephippium AP119

Designs: Orchids.

1975, Mar. 7   Litho.   Perf. 10½, 13½
C613 AP118 25c shown .60 .20
C614 AP118 25c Gongora claviodora .60 .20
C615 AP119 25c shown .60 .20
C616 AP119 25c Encyclia spondiadum .60 .20
a. Block of 4, #C613-C616 2.40 1.00
b. As "a," perf. 10½ 1.60
C617 AP118 65c Lycaste skinneri alba 1.50 .20
C618 AP118 65c Peristeria elata 1.50 .20
C619 AP119 65c Miltonia roezelii 1.50 .20
C620 AP119 65c Brassavola digbyana 1.50 .20
a. Block of 4, #C617-C620, perf. 13½ 6.00 2.00
b. As "a," perf. 10½ 16.00
C621 AP118 80c Epidendrum mirabile 2.00 .30
C622 AP118 80c Barkeria lindleyana 2.00 .30
C623 AP119 80c Cattleya skinneri 2.00 .30
C624 AP119 80c Sobralia macrantha 2.00 .30
a. Block of 4, #C621-C624 8.00 2.50
b. As "a," perf. 10½ 10.00
C625 AP118 1.40col Lycaste cruenta 2.50 .35
C626 AP118 1.40col Oncidium obryzatum 2.50 .35
C627 AP119 1.40col Gongora armeniaca 2.50 .35
C628 AP119 1.40col Sievekingia suavis 2.50 .35
a. Block of 4, #C625-C628 8.00 4.00
b. As "a," perf. 10½ 8.00
Perf. 13½
C629 AP118 1.75col Hexisea imbricata 1.50 .35
C630 AP118 2.15col Warcewiczella discolor 1.50 .50
C631 AP119 2.50col Oncidium kramerianum 2.50 1.00

C632 AP119 3.25col *Cattleya dowiana* 3.00 1.25
Nos. C613-C632 (20) 34.90 7.30

5th National Orchid Exhibition.
Nos. C613-C628 were printed in both perforations on two different papers: dull finish and shiny. Nos. C629-C632 were printed on shiny paper.
Most examples of Nos. C617-C620, perf 10½, were surcharged.
For overprints and surcharges see Nos. C715-C720, C723-C728.

Radio Club Emblem AP120

Members' Flags and Emblem — AP121

Design: 2col, Federation emblem.

1975, Apr. 16   Litho.   Perf. 13½
C633 AP120 1col blk & red lil .45 .20
C634 AP121 1.10col multi .55 .20
C635 AP120 2col black & bl .90 .25
Nos. C633-C635 (3) 1.90 .65

16th Central American Radio Amateurs' Convention, San José, May 2-4.

Nicoya Beach AP122

Designs: 75c, Driving cattle. 1col, Colonial Church, Nicoya. 3col, Savannah riders, vert.

1975, Aug. 1   Litho.   Perf. 13½
C636 AP122 25c gray & multi .20 .20
C637 AP122 75c gray & multi .25 .20
C638 AP122 1col gray & multi .30 .20
C639 AP122 3col gray & multi .90 .75
Nos. C636-C639 (4) 1.65 1.35

Sesqui. of annexation of Nicoya District.

Costa Rica #158 AP123

Designs (Type A90 of 1932): No. C641, #159. No. C642, #160. No. C643, #161.

1975, Aug. 14   Litho.   Perf. 12
C640 AP123 2.20col blk & org .40 .35
C641 AP123 2.20col blk & dk grn .40 .35
C642 AP123 2.20col blk & car rose .40 .35
C643 AP123 2.20col blk & dk bl .40 .35
a.   Block of 4, #C640-C643 3.50 3.50

6th Natl. Phil. Exhib., San José, Aug. 14-17.
For surcharges see Nos. C885-C892.

IWY Emblem AP124

1975, Oct. 9   Litho.   Perf. 10½
C644 AP124 40c vio bl & red .20 .20
C645 AP124 1.25col blk & ultra .35 .20

International Women's Year 1975.

UN Emblem AP125

UN, 30th Anniv.: 60c, UN General Assembly, horiz. 1.20col, UN Headquarters, NY.

1975, Oct. 24   Perf. 12
C646 AP125 10c bl & blk .20 .20
C647 AP125 60c multi .20 .20
C648 AP125 1.20col multi .40 .20
Nos. C646-C648 (3) .80 .60

The Visitation, by Jorge Gallardo AP126

"20-30" Club Emblem — AP127

Paintings by Jorge Gallardo: 1col, Nativity and Star. 5col, St. Joseph in his Workshop, Virgin and Child.

1975, Nov. 3   Perf. 10½
C649 AP126 50c multi .30 .20
C650 AP126 1col multi .45 .20
C651 AP126 5col multi 1.60 .70
Nos. C649-C651 (3) 2.35 1.10

Christmas 1975.

1976, Jan. 16   Litho.   Perf. 12
C652 AP127 1col multi .25 .20

"20-30" Club of Costa Rica, 20th anniv.

Quercus Brenessi Trel — AP128

"Literary Development" AP129

Plants: 30c, Maxillaria albertii schecht. 55c, Calathea brenesii standl. 2col, Brenesia costaricensis schlecht. 10col, Philodendron brenesii standl.

1976, Mar. 1   Perf. 10½
C653 AP128 5c multi .45 .20
C654 AP128 30c multi .45 .20
C655 AP128 55c multi .45 .20
C656 AP128 2col tan & multi .90 .35
C657 AP128 10col multi 4.00 2.40
Nos. C653-C657 (5) 6.25 3.35

Prof. Alberto Manuel Brenes Mora, botanist, birth centenary.

1976, Apr. 9   Litho.   Perf. 16
Designs: 1.10col, Man holding book, stylized. 5col, Costa Rican flag emanating from book, horiz.
C658 AP129 15c multi .20 .20
C659 AP129 1.10col multi .20 .20
C660 AP129 5col multi .90 .70
Nos. C658-C660 (3) 1.30 1.10

Publishing in Costa Rica.
Nos. C658-C660 exist imperf.

Postrider, 1839 — AP130

Costa Rica No. 13, Post Office AP131

Designs: 65c, Costa Rica No. 14 and Post Office. 85c, Costa Rica No. 15 and Post Office. 2col, UPU Monument, Bern, vert.

1976, May 24   Perf. 10½
C661 AP130 20c apple grn & blk .30 .20
C662 AP131 50c bister & multi .30 .20
C663 AP131 65c multi .30 .20
C664 AP131 85c multi .30 .20
C665 AP130 2col blk & lt bl .75 .40
Nos. C661-C665 (5) 1.95 1.40

Cent. of UPU (in 1974).
Nos. C662-C664 exist without the surcharges on reproductions of Nos. 13-15.

Telephones, 1876 and 1976 — AP132

Designs: 2col, Wall telephone. 5col, Alexander Graham Bell.

1976, June 28
C666 AP132 1.60col lt bl & blk .35 .20
C667 AP132 2col multicolored .45 .20
C668 AP132 5col yellow & blk 1.10 .90
Nos. C666-C668 (3) 1.90 1.30

Centenary of first telephone call by Alexander Graham Bell, Mar. 10, 1876.

Inverted Center Stamp of 1901 and Association Emblems — AP133

Design: 5col, 1901 stamp between Costa Rican Philatelic Society and Interamerican Philatelic Federation emblems.

1976, Nov. 11   Litho.   Perf. 10½
C669 AP133 50c multi .20 .20
C670 AP133 1col multi .20 .20
C671 AP133 2col multi .35 .20
Nos. C669-C671 (3) .75 .60

Souvenir Sheet
Perf. 12
C672 AP133 5col multi 2.40 2.40

7th Natl. Phil. Exhib. and 9th Plenary Assembly of the Interamerican Phil. Fed. (FIAF), San José, Nov. 1976.
No. C670 exists in colors of No. C671.
No. C671 exists on thin dull paper, with bright gum. Value, mint, $25.

No. C672 was issued both perf and imperf. Same values.

"Seeing Eye" and Map of Costa Rica AP134

Amadeo Quiros Blanco — AP135

1976, Nov. 22   Perf. 16
C673 AP134 35c black & blue .20 .20
C674 AP135 2col multicolored .50 .35

General Audit Office, 25th anniversary.

Nurse Attending Child — AP136

LACSA Circling Globe — AP137

1.10col, National Children's Hospital, horiz.

1976, Nov. 29
C675 AP136 90c multi .25 .20
C676 AP136 1.10col multi .35 .25

5th Panamerican Congress of Pediatric Surgery and 12th Congress of Pediatrics.

1976, Dec. 1   Perf. 10½
Designs: 1.20col, Route map. 3col, LACSA emblem and Costa Rican flag.
C677 AP137 1col multi .25 .20
C678 AP137 1.20col multi .35 .20
C679 AP137 3col multi 1.00 .60
Nos. C677-C679 (3) 1.60 1.00

Costa Rican Air Lines (LACSA), 30th anniversary.

Boston Tea Party AP138

US Bicent.: 5col, Declaration of Independence. 10col, Ringing Liberty Bell to announce Independence, vert.

1976, Dec. 24
C680 AP138 2.20col multi .35 .30
C681 AP138 5col multi .90 .70
C682 AP138 10col multi 1.75 1.40
Nos. C680-C682 (3) 3.00 2.40

Tree of Guanacaste AP139

Felipe J. Alvarado AP140

Designs (Rotary Emblem and): 60c, Dr. Paul Blanco Cervantes Hospital, horiz. 3col, Map of Costa Rica, horiz. 10col, Paul Harris.

1977, Mar. 31 Litho. Perf. 16
C683 AP139 40c multi .20 .20
C684 AP140 50c multi .20 .20
C685 AP139 60c multi .20 .20
C686 AP139 3col multi .90 .50
C687 AP140 10col multi 3.00 2.10
Nos. C683-C687 (5) 4.50 3.20
Rotary Club of San José, 50th anniversary.

Boruca Cloth
AP141

Design: 1.50col, Painted wood ornament.

1977, Feb. 22
C688 AP141 75c multi .20 .20
C689 AP141 1.50col multi .30 .20
Natl. Artisan & Small Industry Program.

Juana Pereira
AP142

Alonso de
Anguciana de
Gamboa
AP143

Designs: 1col, First Church of Our Lady of the Angels, horiz. 1.10col, Our Lady of the Angels (gold sculpture). 1.25col, Crown of Our Lady of the Angels.

1977, June 6 Litho. Perf. 10½
C690 AP142 50c multi .20 .20
C691 AP142 1col multi .20 .20
C692 AP142 1.10col multi .20 .20
C693 AP142 1.25col multi .40 .20
Nos. C690-C693 (4) 1.00 .80
50th anniv. of the coronation of Our Lady of the Angels, patron saint of Costa Rica.

1977, July 4 Litho. Perf. 10½
Designs: 75c, Church of Esparza. 1col, Statue of Our Lady of Candlemas. 2col, Statue of Diego de Artieda y Chirino.
C694 AP143 35c multi .20 .20
C695 AP143 75c multi .20 .20
C696 AP143 1col multi .30 .20
C697 AP143 2col multi .55 .30
Nos. C694-C697 (4) 1.25 .90
400th anniv. of the founding of Esparza. For surcharge see No. C883.

CARE Emblem and
Child — AP144

1col, CARE emblem and soybeans, horiz.

1977, Sept. 14 Litho. Perf. 16
C698 AP144 80c multi .25 .20
C699 AP144 1col multi .35 .20
20th anniversary of CARE (relief organization) in Costa Rica.

Institute's
Emblem — AP145

First Map of Americas, 1540 — AP146

1977, Oct. 21 Litho. Perf. 16
C700 AP145 50c blk & multi .45 .20
C701 AP146 1.40col blk & multi .90 .35
Hispanic Cultural Institute of Costa Rica, 25th anniversary.

Mercy Church,
by Ricardo
Ulloa B.
AP147

Health Ministry
Emblem
AP148

Paintings: 1col, Christ, by Floria Pinto de Herrero. 5col, St. Francis and the Birds, by Louisa Gonzalez Y Saenz.

1977, Nov. 9 Litho. Perf. 10½
C702 AP147 50c multi .35 .20
C703 AP147 1col multi .35 .20
C704 AP147 5col multi 1.60 .70
Nos. C702-C704 (3) 2.30 1.10

1977, Nov. 16 Perf. 16
C705 AP148 1.40col multi .35 .20
Creation of Ministry of Health.

Picnic — AP149

San
Martin — AP150

Designs: 50c, Weaver. 2col, Beach scene. 5col, Fruit and vegetable market. 10col, Swans on lake.

1978, Mar. 21 Litho. Perf. 10½
C706 AP149 50c blk & multi .20 .20
C707 AP149 1col blk & multi .20 .20
C708 AP149 2col blk & multi 1.00 .20
C709 AP149 5col blk & multi 1.90 .75
C710 AP149 10col blk & multi 1.90 1.90
Nos. C706-C710 (5) 5.20 3.25
Conf. of Latin American Tourist Organizations.

1978, Aug. 7 Litho. Perf. 10½
C711 AP150 5col multi 1.25 .65
Gen. José de San Martin (1778-1850), soldier and statesman, fought for South American independence.

Geographical
Institute
Emblem — AP151

University
Federation
Emblem — AP152

1978, Aug. 28 Litho. Perf. 12½
C712 AP151 5col multi 1.10 .60
Pan-American Geography and History Institute, 50th anniversary. Exists imperf.

1978, Sept. 18 Perf. 11
C713 AP152 80c ultra .25 .20
Central American University Federation, 30th anniversary.

Emblems — AP153

1978, Oct. 24 Perf. 16
C714 AP153 2col aqua, blk & gold .50 .35
6th Interamerican Philatelic Exhibition, Argentina 78, Buenos Aires, Oct. 1978.

Nos. C629-C631 Overprinted: "50 Aniversario del / primer vuelo de PAN AM / en Costa Rica / 1928-1978"
1978, Nov. 1 Litho. Perf. 13½
C715 AP118 1.75col multi .45 .30
C716 AP118 2.15col multi .60 .30
C717 AP119 2.50col multi .80 .40
Nos. C715-C717 (3) 1.85 1.00
1st Pan Am flight in Costa Rica, 50th anniv.

Nos. C629-C631 Overprinted: "50 Aniversario de la / visita de Lindbergh a / Costa Rica 1928-1978"
1978, Nov. 1
C718 AP118 1.75col multi 1.25 .30
C719 AP118 2.15col multi 1.40 .35
C720 AP119 2.50col multi 1.75 .45
Nos. C718-C720 (3) 4.40 1.10
50th anniversary of Lindbergh's visit.

Nos. C603 and C607 Surcharged with New Value, 4 Bars and: "Centenario del / Asilo Carlos / Maria Ulloa / 1878-1978"
1978, Nov. 8 Perf. 14
C721 AP115 50c on 65c multi .20 .20
C722 AP115 2col on 2.50col multi .50 .25
Asilo Carlos Maria Ulloa, birth centenary.

No. C617-C620, C630-C631 Surcharged with New Value and 4 Bars
Perf. 10½, 13½
1978, Nov. 13 Litho.
C723 AP118 50c on 65c .50 .50
C724 AP118 50c on 65c .50 .50
C725 AP119 50c on 65c .50 .50
C726 AP119 50c on 65c .50 .50
a. Block of 4, #C723-C726 2.00 2.00
C727 AP118 1.20col on 2.15col 1.25 .50
C728 AP119 2col on 2.50col 1.25 .50
Nos. C723-C728 (6) 4.50 3.00
Nos. C723-C726, perf. 13½, value $20, unused, $10, used, each. No. C726a, unused, $400.

Star over Map of
Costa
Rica — AP154

"Flying Men,"
Chorotega
AP155

1978, Nov. 13 Perf. 10½
C729 AP154 50c blue & blk .20 .20
C730 AP154 1col rose lil & blk .20 .20
C731 AP154 5col orange & blk 1.25 .60
a. Strip of 3, #C729-C731 1.75 1.75
Christmas 1978. Nos. C729-C731 printed in sheets of 100 and se-tenant in sheet of 15 (3x5). Value, se-tenant sheet, $20.

1978, Nov. 20 Perf. 11½
Designs: 1.20col, Oviedo giving his History of Indies to Duke of Calabria, horiz. 10col, Lord of Oviedo's coat of arms.
C732 AP155 85c multi .20 .20
C733 AP155 1.20col blk & lt bl .20 .20
C734 AP155 10col multi 1.90 1.90
Nos. C732-C734 (3) 2.30 2.30
500th birth anniv. of Gonzalo Fernandez de Oviedo, 1st chronicler of Spanish Indies.

Msgr. Domingo
Rivas
AP156

San José
Cathedral
AP157

1978, Dec. 6 Perf. 16, 13½ (20col)
C735 AP156 1col black & indigo .20 .20
C736 AP157 20col multicolored 3.50 3.25
Centenary of the Cathedral of San José.

View of Coco
Island
AP158

Designs: 2.10, 3, 5 col, various views of Coco Island. 10col, Installation of memorial plaque, people and flag. 5, 10col vert.

1979, Apr. 30 Litho. Perf. 10½
C737 AP158 90c multi .20 .20
C738 AP158 2.10col multi .90 .35
C739 AP158 3col multi 1.25 .45
C740 AP158 5col multi 1.90 1.75
C741 AP158 10col multi 3.75 3.75
a. Souv. sheet, #C737-C741 15.00 15.00
Nos. C737-C741 (5) 8.00 6.50
Visit of Pres. Rodrigo Carazo Odio to Coco Island, June 24, 1978, in the interest of national defense.
No. C741a exists imperf. Value $750.

Shrimp
AP159

Designs: 85c, Mahogany snapper. 1.80col, Corvina. 3col, Crayfish. 10col, Tuna.

1979, May 14 Litho. Perf. 13½
C742 AP159 60c multi .20 .20
C743 AP159 85c multi .20 .20
C744 AP159 1.80col multi .60 .20
C745 AP159 3col multi 1.00 .55
C746 AP159 10col multi 3.50 3.50
Nos. C742-C746 (5) 5.50 4.65
Marine life protection.

Hungry Nestlings, IYC Emblem AP160

Microwave Transmitters, Mt. Irazu AP161

1979, May 24   *Perf. 11*
C747 AP160 1col multi .75 .20
C748 AP160 2col multi 2.00 1.25
C749 AP160 20col multi 12.00 5.50
    Nos. C747-C749 (3) 14.75 6.95

International Year of the Child.

1979, June 28   **Litho.**   *Perf. 14*

Design: 1col, Arenal Dam, horiz.
C750 AP161 1col multi .20 .20
C751 AP161 5col multi 1.10 .60

Costa Rican Electricity Institute, 30th anniversary.

Costa Rica No. 1 and Rowland Hill AP162

Design: 10col, Penny Black and Hill.

1979, July 16   *Perf. 13*
C752 AP162 5col lil rose & bl
     gray 1.10 .50
C753 AP162 10col dl bl & blk 2.25 1.00

Sir Rowland Hill (1795-1879), originator of penny postage.

Poverty, by Juan Ramon Bonilla AP163

National Sculpture Contest: 60c, Hope, by Hernan Gonzalez. 2.10col, Cattle, by Victor M. Bermudez, horiz. 5col, Bust of Clorito Picado, by Juan Rafael Chacon. 20col, Mother and Child, by Francisco Zuniga.

1979, July 16   **Litho.**   *Perf. 12*
C754 AP163 60c multi .20 .20
C755 AP163 1col multi .20 .20
C756 AP163 2.10col multi .50 .25
C757 AP163 5col multi 1.40 1.10
C758 AP163 20col multi 4.50 2.25
    Nos. C754-C758 (5) 6.80 4.00

Danaus Plexippus — AP164

Butterflies: 1col, Phoebis philea. 1.80col, Rothschildia. 2.10col, Prepona omphale. 2.60col, Marpesia marcella. 4.05col, Morpho cypris.

1979, Aug. 31   **Litho.**   *Perf. 13½*
C759 AP164 60c multi 3.00 .40
C760 AP164 1col multi 5.00 .40
C761 AP164 1.80col multi 7.00 .65
C762 AP164 2.10col multi 10.00 1.25
C763 AP164 2.60col multi 10.00 2.50
C764 AP164 4.05col multi 18.00 3.50
    Nos. C759-C764 (6) 53.00 8.70

SOS Emblem, Houses AP165

Children's Drawings: 5col, 5.50col, Landscapes, diff.

1979, Sept. 18
C765 AP165 2.50col multi .50 .35
C766 AP165 5col multi 1.10 .70
C767 AP165 5.50col multi 1.50 1.10
    Nos. C765-C767 (3) 3.10 2.15

SOS Children's Villages, 30th anniversary.

President Type of 1943

Presidents of Costa Rica: 60c, Rafael Iglesias C. 85c, Ascension Esquivel Ibarra. 1col, Cleto Gonzalez Viquez. 2col, Ricardo Jimenez Oreamuno.

1979, Oct. 8   **Litho.**   *Perf. 13½*
C768 A109 10c dk blue .20 .20
C769 A109 60c dull purple .20 .20
C770 A109 85c red orange .25 .20
C771 A109 1col red orange .30 .20
C772 A109 2col brown .60 .30
  a. Strip of 5, #C768-C772 1.75 1.40
    Nos. C768-C772 (5) 1.55 1.10

Printed in sheets of 100 and se-tenant in sheets of 25 (5x5).
See Nos. C790-C794.

Holy Family, Creche AP167

Reforestation AP168

1979, Nov. 16   **Litho.**   *Perf. 12½*
C773 AP167 1col multi .25 .20
C774 AP167 1.60col multi .65 .25

Christmas 1979.

1980, Jan. 14   **Litho.**   *Perf. 11*
C775 AP168 1col multi .20 .20
C776 AP168 3.40col multi .65 .50

Anatomy Lesson, by Rembrandt AP169

1980, Feb. 7   **Litho.**   *Perf. 10½*
C777 AP169 10col multi 3.75 1.50

Legal medicine teaching in Costa Rica, 50th anniversary.

Rotary Intl., 75th Anniv. — AP170

Gulf of Nicoya, Satellite Photo — AP171

1980, Feb. 26   *Perf. 16*
C778 AP170 2.10col multi .35 .25
C779 AP170 5col multi 1.00 .60

1980, Mar. 10   **Litho.**   *Perf. 12½*
C780 AP171 2.10col Puerto Limon .35 .25
C781 AP171 5col shown 1.00 .60

14th Intl. Symposium on Remote Sensing of the Environment, San José, Apr. 23-30. Exist imperf.

Soccer, Moscow '80 Emblem — AP172

Poas Volcano AP173

1980, Apr. 16   **Litho.**   *Perf. 10½*
C782 AP172 1col shown *1.00* .20
C783 AP172 3col Bicycling *8.00* .75
C784 AP172 4.05col Baseball *8.00* 1.00
C785 AP172 20col Swim-
     ming *8.00* 6.00
    Nos. C782-C785 (4) 25.00 7.95

22nd Summer Olympic Games, Moscow, July 19-Aug. 3.

1980, May 14   **Litho.**   *Perf. 10½*
C786 AP173 1col shown .20 .20
C787 AP173 2.50col Cahuita Beach .40 .30

National Parks Service, 10th anniversary.

José Maria Zeledon Brenes, Score — AP174

Design: 10col, Manuel Maria Gutierrez.

1980, June 25   **Litho.**   *Perf. 12½*
C788 AP174 1col multi .25 .20
C789 AP174 10col multi 1.60 1.25

National anthem composed by Brenes (words) and Gutierrez (music). Nos. C788-C789 exist imperf.

President Type of 1943

1col, Alfredo Gonzalez F. 1.60col, Federico Tinoco G. 1.80col, Francisco Aguilar B. 2.10col, Julio Acosta G. 3col, Leon Cortes C.

1980, Aug. 14   **Litho.**   *Perf. 11*
C790 A109 1col dk red .20 .20
C791 A109 1.60col slate bl .25 .20
C792 A109 1.80col brown .30 .20
C793 A109 2.10col dull green .35 .25
C794 A109 3col dark purple .45 .35
    Nos. C790-C794 (5) 1.55 1.20

8th Natl. Phil. Exhib. — AP175

Fruits — AP176

1980, Sept. 11   *Perf. 13½*
C795 AP175 5col multi .80 .60
C796 AP175 20col multi 3.25 2.75

1980, Sept. 24   *Perf. 10½*
C797 AP176 10c shown .20 .20
C798 AP176 60c Cacao .20 .20
C799 AP176 1col Coffee .20 .20
C800 AP176 2.10col Bananas .30 .25
C801 AP176 3.40col Flowers .55 .40
C802 AP176 5col Sugar cane .80 .60
    Nos. C797-C802 (6) 2.25 1.45

Giant Tree, by Jorge Carvajal AP177

Virgin and Child, by Raphael AP178

Paintings: 2.10col, Secret Look, by Rolando Cubero. 2.45col, Consuelo, by Fernando Carballo. 3col, Volcano, by Lola Fernandez. 4.05col, attending Mass, by Francisco Amighetti.

1980, Oct. 22   **Litho.**   *Perf. 10½*
C803 AP177 1col multi .20 .20
C804 AP177 2.10col multi .40 .25
    Size: 28x30mm
C805 AP177 2.45col multi .55 .30
    Size: 22x36mm
C806 AP177 3col multi .75 .35
C807 AP177 4.05col multi 1.10 .45
    Nos. C803-C807 (5) 3.00 1.55

1980, Nov. 11   *Perf. 13½*

Christmas 1980: 10col, Virgin and Child and St. John, by Raphael.

C808 AP178 1col multi .40 .40
C809 AP178 10col multi 2.00 2.00

Juan Santamaria International Airport AP179

1980, Dec. 11   **Litho.**   *Perf. 10½*
  Sizes: 30x30mm, 31x25mm
  (1.30col), 25x32mm (2.60col)
C810 AP179 1col Caldera
     Harbor .25 .20
C811 AP179 1.30col shown .30 .20
C812 AP179 2.10col Rio Frio
     Railroad
     Bridge .45 .25
C813 AP179 2.60col Highway to
     Colon .55 .35
C814 AP179 5col Huetar post
     office 1.25 .60
    Nos. C810-C814 (5) 2.80 1.60

Paying your taxes means progress. For surcharge see No. C884.

Repertorio Americano Cover, J. Garcia Monge and Signature — AP180

1981, Jan. 2   **Litho.**   *Perf. 10½*
C815 AP180 1.60col multi .30 .20
C816 AP180 3col multi .60 .35

Birth centenary of J. Garcia Monge, founder of Repertorio Americano journal.

Arms of Aserri
(Site of Cornea
Bank)
AP181

Harpia Harpyja
AP182

1981, Jan. 28 Litho. Perf. 13½
C817 AP181 1col shown .20 .20
C818 AP181 1.80col Eye .30 .20
C819 AP181 5col Rojas .90 .60
Nos. C817-C819 (3) 1.40 1.00

Establishment of human cornea bank, founded by Abelardo Rojas.

1980, Dec. 23 Perf. 11
C820 AP182 2.10col shown 1.40 .35
C821 AP182 2.50col Ara macao 1.60 .55
C822 AP182 3col Felis con-
color 2.40 .65
C823 AP182 5.50col Ateles ge-
offrovi 4.75 1.10
Nos. C820-C823 (4) 10.15 2.65

Medical and
Surgical
Clinic
AP183

10c, Physiology class. 50c, Medical school, A. Chavarria (1st dean). 1.30col, Music school. 3.40col, Carlos Monge Alfaro Library. 4.05col, R.F. Brenes, rector (1952-61).

1981, Apr. 8 Litho. Perf. 10½
C824 AP183 5c multi .20 .20
C825 AP183 10c multi .20 .20
C826 AP183 50c multi .20 .20
C827 AP183 1.30col multi .40 .20
C828 AP183 3.40col multi .45 .20
C829 AP183 4.05col multi, vert. .55 .20
Nos. C824-C829 (6) 2.00 1.20

University of Costa Rica, 40th anniversary.

Mail Transport by Horse — AP184

1981, May 6 Litho. Perf. 10½
C830 AP184 1col shown .20 .20
C831 AP184 2.10col Train, 1857 .30 .25
C832 AP184 10col Mail carri-
ers, 1858 1.50 1.25
Nos. C830-C832 (3) 2.00 1.70

Heinrich von Stephan (1831-97), UPU founder.

13th World Telecommunications
Day — AP185

1981, May 18 Perf. 11
C833 AP185 5col multi .80 .60
C834 AP185 25col multi 4.00 4.00

Bishop
Bernardo Thiel
AP186

Juan Santamaria
AP187

1981, June 8 Litho. Perf. 10½
C835 Strip of 5, stained glass
windows .50 .40
a. AP186 1col Sts. Peter & Paul .20 .20
b. AP186 1col St. Vincent de Paul .20 .20
c. AP186 1col Death of St. Joseph .20 .20
d. AP186 1col Archangel Michael .20 .20
e. AP186 1col Holy Family .20 .20
C836 AP186 2col shown .20 .20

Consecration of Bernardo Augusto Thiel as Bishop of San Jose.

1981, June 26 Perf. 13½
C837 AP187 1col shown .20 .20
C838 AP187 2.45col Alajuela Ca-
thedral, horiz. .25 .20

Alajuela province.

Potters — AP188

1981, July 10 Litho. Perf. 10½
C839 AP188 15c shown .20 .20
C840 AP188 1.60col Bricklayers .20 .20
C841 AP188 1.80col Farmers .20 .20
C842 AP188 2.50col Fishermen .25 .20
C843 AP188 3col Nurse, pa-
tient .35 .20
C844 AP188 5col Children,
traffic po-
liceman .65 .25
Nos. C839-C844 (6) 1.85 1.25

Model of New
Natl. Archives
AP189

Natl. Archives Centenary: 1.40col, Leon Fernandez Bonilla, founder. vert. 2col, Arms. vert. 3col, St. Thomas University, former headquarters.

1981, Aug. 24 Litho. Perf. 13½
C845 AP189 1.40col multi .20 .20
C846 AP189 2col multi .20 .20
C847 AP189 3col multi .20 .20
C848 AP189 3.50col multi .25 .20
Nos. C845-C848 (4) .85 .80

Men
Reaching
for Sun,
Map
AP190

1981, Sept. 9 Litho. Perf. 11
C849 AP190 1col Man in
wheelchair,
stairs, vert. .30 .20
C850 AP190 2.60col Man reaching for
scale, vert. .70 .20
C851 AP190 10col shown 3.00 1.00
Nos. C849-C851 (3) 4.00 1.40

Intl. Year of the Disabled.

World Food
Day — AP191

1981, Oct. 16 Litho. Perf. 10½
C852 AP191 5col multi .40 .25
C853 AP191 10col multi .70 .50

President Type of 1943

1col, Rafael A. Calderon Guardia, 1940. 2col, Teodoro Picado Michalski, 1944. 3col, José Figueres Ferrer, 1953. 5col, Otilio Ulate Blanco, 1949. 10col, Mario Echandi Jimenez, 1958.

1981, Dec. 7 Litho. Perf. 13½
C854 A109 1col pink .20 .20
C855 A109 2col orange .20 .20
C856 A109 3col green .20 .20
C857 A109 5col dk bl .35 .25
C858 A109 10col blue .70 .55
Nos. C854-C858 (5) 1.65 1.40

Bar Assoc. of
Costa Rica
Centenary
(1981)
AP192

1982, Mar. 22 Litho. Perf. 13½
C859 AP192 1col Emblem,
horiz. .20 .20
C860 AP192 2col E. Figueroa,
1st pres. .20 .20
C861 AP192 20col Bar building,
horiz. 1.50 1.25
Nos. C859-C861 (3) 1.90 1.65

National
Progress
AP193

1982 Perf. 10½
C862 AP193 95c Housing .20 .20
C863 AP193 1.15col Agricultural
fair .20 .20
C864 AP193 1.45col Education .20 .20
C865 AP193 1.65col Drinkable
water .20 .20
C866 AP193 1.80col Rural medi-
cal care .20 .20
C867 AP193 2.10col Recreational
areas .20 .20
C868 AP193 2.35col Natl. Thea-
ter Square .20 .20
C869 AP193 2.60col Communica-
tions .20 .20
C870 AP193 3col Electric rail-
road .20 .20
C871 AP193 4.05col Irrigation .20 .20
Nos. C862-C871 (10) 2.00 2.00

Issue dates: 1.80col, 2.10col, 2.60col, 3col, 4.05col, May 5; others, June 16.

City of Alajuela
Bicentenary
AP194

Perez Zeledon
County, 50th
Anniv. (1981)
AP195

Designs: 5col, Central Park Fountain. 10col, Juan Santamaria Historical and Cultural Museum, horiz. 15col, Church of Christ of Esquipulas. 20col, Monsignor Esteban Lorenzo de Tristan, 25col, Father Juan Manuel Lopez del Corral.

1982, Aug. 9
C872 AP194 5col multi .30 .20
C873 AP194 10col multi .55 .25
C874 AP194 15col multi .80 .60
C875 AP194 20col multi 1.10 1.10
C876 AP194 25col multi 1.40 1.40
Nos. C872-C876 (5) 4.15 3.55

1982, Aug. 30
Designs: 10c, Saint's Stone. 50c, Monument to Mothers. 1col, Pedro Perz Zeledon. 1.25col, St. Isidore Labrador Church. 3.50col, Municipal Building, horiz. 4.25col, Arms.
C877 AP195 10c multi .20 .20
C878 AP195 50c multi .20 .20
C879 AP195 1col multi .20 .20
C880 AP195 1.25col multi .20 .20
C881 AP195 3.50col multi .20 .20
C882 AP195 4.25col multi .25 .20
Nos. C877-C882 (6) 1.25 1.20

Nos. 695 and C813 Surcharged
1982, Oct. 28 Litho. Perf. 10½
C883 AP143 3col on 75c multi .20 .20
C884 AP179 5col on 2.60col multi .30 .20

Nos. C640-C643 Surcharged and Overprinted: "IX EXPOSICION FILATELICA - 1982"
1982, Oct. 28 Perf. 12
C885 AP123 8.40col on #C640 .50 .40
C886 AP123 8.40col on #C641 .50 .40
C887 AP123 8.40col on #C642 .50 .40
C888 AP123 8.40col on #C643 .50 .40
C889 AP123 9.70col on #C640 .60 .50
C890 AP123 9.70col on #C641 .60 .50
C891 AP123 9.70col on #C642 .60 .50
C892 AP123 9.70col on #C643 .60 .50
Nos. C885-C892 (8) 4.40 3.60

9th Natl. Stamp Exhibition.

TB Bacillus
Centenary
AP196

Pan-American
Blood Donors'
Society, 7th
Cong. — AP197

1982, Nov. 19 Perf. 13½
C893 AP196 1.50col Koch .20 .20
C894 AP196 3col Koch, slide .20 .20
C895 AP196 3.30col Health Ministry .20 .20
Nos. C893-C895 (3) .60 .60

1982, Nov. 25 Perf. 11
C896 AP197 30col Natl. Blood
Assoc. em-
blem 1.75 1.75
C897 AP197 50col Cong. em-
blem 2.75 2.75

AP198

AP199

1982, Dec. 13 Litho. Perf. 10½
C898 AP198 8.40col Emblem,
horiz. .40 .20
C899 AP198 9.70col Emblem,
diff. .50 .25
C900 AP198 11.70col Hand-
shake,
horiz. .60 .25
C901 AP198 13.05col Emblem,
diff.,
horiz. .65 .40
Nos. C898-C901 (4) 2.15 1.00

Inter-Governmental Migration Committee, 30th anniv.

1983, Jan. 3   *Perf. 16*

4.80col, St. Francis of Assisi, by El Greco.
7.40col, Portrait, diff.

C902	AP199	4.80col multi	.25	.20
C903	AP199	7.40col multi	.35	.20

For surcharges see Nos. C908-C911.

Visit of Pope
John Paul II
AP200

Bolivar, by
Francisco
Zuniga
Chavarria
AP201

1983, Mar. 1   **Litho.**   *Perf. 10½*

C904	AP200	5col multi	2.75	.20
C905	AP200	10col multi	2.75	.50
C906	AP200	15col multi	6.00	.75
	Nos. C904-C906 (3)		11.50	1.45

1983, July 22   **Litho.**   *Perf. 16*

C907	AP201	10col multi	.55	.20

Nos. C902-C903 Surcharged

1983, Sept. 23   **Litho.**   *Perf. 16*

C908	AP199	10c on 4.80col	.20	.20
C909	AP199	50c on 4.80col	.20	.20
C910	AP199	1.50col on 7.40col	.20	.20
C911	AP199	3col on 7.40col	.20	.20
	Nos. C908-C911 (4)		.80	.80

LACSA Costa
Rica Airlines,
40th
Anniv. — AP202

Various childrens' drawings.

1986, Dec. 12   **Litho.**   *Perf. 13½*

C912	AP202	1col Adriana E. Hidalgo	.50	.20
C913	AP202	7col Osvaldo A.G. Vega	2.50	.30
C914	AP202	16col David V. Rodriguez	7.00	.75
	Nos. C912-C914 (3)		10.00	1.25

Nos. C912-C913 exist perf 11. Unused
examples are rare. Value used, $5 each.

Roman
Macaya
Lahmann,
Aviation
Pioneer
AP203

1988, Sept. 26   **Litho.**   *Perf. 10½*

C915	AP203	10col multi	.50	.20

No. 418
Ovptd.

1990, Nov. 5

C916	A180	50col multicolored	1.10	.30

Bagging Coffee
Beans — AP204

Perf. 10½

1990, Nov. 16   **Litho.**   **Unwmk.**

C917	AP204	50col multicolored	1.10	.30

AP205

AP206

1990, Dec. 6

C918	AP205	50col blue & black	1.10	.30

First postage stamps, 150th anniv.

1991, Mar. 25   **Litho.**   *Perf. 10½*

Banana Picker, 1897, by Alleardo Villa.

C919	AP206	30col multicolored	.65	.20

National Theater.

No. 428
Overprinted

Litho. & Engr.

1991, Sept. 13   *Perf. 12½*

C920	A188	200col	5.75 1.10

12th Natl. Philatelic Exposition.

No. 402
Overprinted

1991, Oct. 11   **Litho.**   *Perf. 11½*

Granite Paper

C921	A170	20col multicolored	4.75 1.00

Basketball, cent.

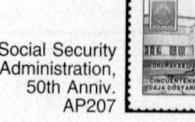

Social Security
Administration,
50th Anniv.
AP207

1991, Nov. 1   **Litho.**   *Perf. 13½*

C922	AP207	15col multicolored	2.50 .30

La Poesia by
Vespaciano
Bignami — AP208

1992, Jan. 24   **Litho.**   *Perf. 10½*

C923	AP208	35col multicolored	3.25	.65

National Theater.

Discovery of
America, 500th
Anniv.
AP209

Columbus' ships: a, Nina. b, Santa Maria. c,
Pinta.

1992, Oct. 8   **Litho.**   *Perf. 13½*

C924	AP209	45col Strip of 3, #a.-c.	4.00	.75

Intl. Arts
Festival — AP210

1993, Mar. 15   **Litho.**   *Perf. 13½*

C925	AP210	45col multicolored	1.25	.35

Telecommunications Institute, 30th
Anniv. — AP211

1993, Nov. 25   **Litho.**   *Perf. 13½*

C926	AP211	45col multicolored	.90	.45

Ministry of
the Interior,
150th
Anniv.
AP212

1994, Mar. 8   **Litho.**   *Perf. 10½*

C927	AP212	45col multicolored	.90	.45

Intl. Year of the
Family — AP213

1994, May 5   **Litho.**   *Perf. 10½*

C928	AP213	45col multicolored	1.00	1.00

LACSA, 50th
Anniv.
AP214

1996, Mar. 29   **Litho.**   *Perf. 10½*

C929	AP214	5col Douglas DC-3	.20	.20
C930	AP214	10col Curtiss C-46	.20	.20
C931	AP214	20col Beechcraft	.30	.20
C932	AP214	30col DC-6B	.45	.20
C933	AP214	35col BAC 1-11	.55	.25
C934	AP214	40col Convair CV 440	.65	.30
C935	AP214	45col Electra L-188	.70	.35
C936	AP214	50col Boeing 727-200	.80	.40
C937	AP214	55col Douglas DC-8	.90	.45
C938	AP214	60col Airbus A320	.95	.45
	Nos. C929-C938 (10)		5.70	3.00

No. C932
Surcharged

2001, Oct. 5   **Litho.**   *Perf. 10½*

C939	AP214	5col on 30col multi	.25	.20

10th Intl. Art
Festival — AP215

2006, Mar. 17   **Litho.**   *Perf. 10½*

C940	AP215	120col multi	.50	.50

AIR POST SPECIAL DELIVERY STAMPS

Catalogue values for unused
stamps in this section are for
Never Hinged items.

UPU Headquarters and Monument,
Bern — APSD1

Perf. 10x11

1970, May 20   **Litho.**   **Unwmk.**

CE1	APSD1	35c multi	.75	.25
CE2	APSD1	60c multi	.75	.25

Opening of the UPU Headquarters in Bern.
The red and black label attached to the 60c is
inscribed "EXPRES." Values are for stamps
with label attached.

Stamps with labels removed were used for
regular airmail.

AIR POST OFFICIAL STAMPS

Air Post Stamps of 1934 Overprinted
in Red

1934   **Unwmk.**   *Perf. 12*

CO1	AP8	5c green	.20	.20
CO2	AP8	10c car rose	.20	.20
CO3	AP8	15c chocolate	.35	.35
CO4	AP8	20c deep blue	.55	.55

CO5	AP8	25c deep org	.55	.55
CO6	AP8	40c olive blk	1.00	.60
CO7	AP8	50c gray blk	1.00	.60
CO8	AP8	60c org yel	1.25	.75
CO9	AP8	75c dull vio	1.25	.75
CO10	AP9	1col deep rose	5.00	1.10
CO11	AP9	2col light blue	8.00	3.50
CO12	AP9	5col black	9.00	6.50
CO13	AP9	10col red brown	8.00	8.00
		Nos. CO1-CO13 (13)	36.35	23.65

For overprints see Nos. C103-C116.

SPECIAL DELIVERY STAMPS

Catalogue values for unused stamps in this section are for Never Hinged items.

Winged Letter SD1

Unwmk.

1972, Mar. 20		**Litho.**	**Perf. 11**	
E1	SD1	75c brown & red	.30	.30
E2	SD1	1.50col blue & red	.50	.40
1973			**Perf. 11x12**	
E3	SD1	75c green & red	.30	.30
1973, Nov. 5		**Litho.**	**Perf. 12**	
E4	SD1	75c lilac & orange	1.50	.75

Exists perf 11x11½.

Concorde SD2

1976, May 17		**Litho.**	**Perf. 16**	
E5	SD2	1col vermilion & multi	.30	.30

SD3

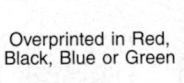

SD4

1979, June 15		**Litho.**	**Perf. 12½**	
E6	SD3	2col multi	.60	.40
1980, Dec. 18		**Litho.**	**Perf. 12½**	
E7	SD4	2col multi	.60	.40
1982, Dec. 20		**Litho.**	**Perf. 11**	
E8	SD4	4col multi	.60	.40

POSTAGE DUE STAMPS

D1 D2

1903	**Unwmk.**	**Engr.**	**Perf. 14**	
	Numerals in Black			
J1	D1	5c slate blue	6.00	.90
J2	D1	10c brown orange	6.00	.65
J3	D1	15c yellow green	3.00	1.75
J4	D1	20c carmine	4.00	1.60
J5	D1	25c slate gray	4.00	1.75
J6	D1	30c brown	5.00	2.50
J7	D1	40c olive bister	6.00	2.50
J8	D1	50c red violet	6.00	2.00
		Nos. J1-J8 (8)	40.00	13.65

1915		**Litho.**	**Perf. 12**	
J9	D2	2c orange	1.00	.50
J10	D2	4c dark blue	1.00	.50
J11	D2	8c gray green	1.00	.50
J12	D2	10c violet	1.00	.50
J13	D2	20c brown	1.00	.50
		Nos. J9-J13 (5)	5.00	2.50

OFFICIAL STAMPS

Values for unused stamps are for examples with original gum as defined in the catalogue introduction. Examples without gum have probably been used and are so regarded.

Very fine examples of Nos. O1-O24 will have perforations just clear of the design on one or more sides.

Nos. O1-O55 normally were not canceled when affixed to official mail. Occasionally they were canceled in a foreign country of destination. Used values are for favor-canceled specimens or for stamps without gum.

Regular Issues Overprinted

Overprinted in Red, Black, Blue or Green

1883-85		**Unwmk.**	**Perf. 12**	
O1	A6	1c green (R)	2.00	1.00
O2	A6	1c green (Bk)	4.00	1.00
O3	A6	2c carmine (Bk)	4.00	1.25
O4	A6	2c carmine (Bl)	2.00	1.40
O5	A6	5c blue vio (R)	7.00	2.75
O6	A6	10c orange (G)	10.00	3.50
O7	A6	40c blue (R)	10.00	3.50
		Nos. O1-O7 (7)	39.00	14.40

Overprinted

1886				
O8	A6	1c green (Bk)	3.00	1.00
O9	A6	2c carmine (Bk)	3.00	1.50
O10	A6	5c blue vio (R)	20.00	10.00
O11	A6	10c orange (Bk)	20.00	10.00
		Nos. O8-O11 (4)	46.00	22.50

Overprinted

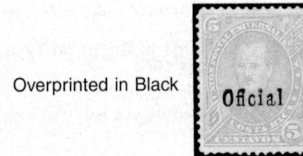

O12	A6	1c green (Bk)	3.00	.90
O13	A6	2c carmine (Bk)	3.00	1.25
O14	A6	5c blue vio (R)	20.00	10.00
O15	A6	10c orange (Bk)	20.00	10.00
		Nos. O12-O15 (4)	46.00	22.15

Nos. O8-O11 and O12-O15 exist se-tenant in vertical pairs.

Overprinted in Black

O16	A6	5c blue vio	50.00	30.00
O17	A6	10c orange	—	250.00

Overprinted

1887				
O18	A6	1c green	1.00	.50
O19	A6	2c carmine	1.00	.45
O21	A6	10c orange	32.50	20.00
c.		Double overprint	37.50	
O22	A7	5c blue vio	10.00	3.00
O23	A7	10c orange	.75	.45
c.		Double overprint	25.00	
O24	A6	40c blue	1.00	.45
		Nos. O18-O24 (6)	46.25	24.85

Overprinted "OFICAL"

O18a	A6	1c green	12.00	12.00
O19a	A6	2c carmine	12.00	
O22a	A7	5c blue violet	12.00	2.75
O23a	A7	10c orange	2.75	
O24a	A6	40c blue	15.00	15.00
		Nos. O18a-O24a (4)	51.00	

Dangerous counterfeits exist of Nos. O18a-O24a.

Without Period

O18b	A6	1c green	12.00	8.00
O19b	A6	2c carmine	12.00	8.00
O22b	A7	5c blue violet	12.00	8.00
O23b	A7	10c orange	12.00	8.00
		Nos. O18b-O23b (4)	48.00	32.00

Nos. O18b-O23b are from a separate plate without periods. No. O23 exists without period (position 32). These must be collected in pairs.

Issues of 1889-1901 Overprinted

1889			**Perf. 14, 15**	
O25	A10	1c brown	.20	.20
O26	A11	2c dk green	.20	.20
O27	A12	5c orange	.20	.20
O28	A13	10c red brown	.20	.20
O29	A14	20c yellow grn	.20	.20
O30	A15	50c rose red	1.00	1.00
		Nos. O25-O30 (6)	2.00	2.00

1892				
O31	A20	1c grnsh blue	.25	.25
O32	A21	2c yellow	.25	.25
O33	A22	5c violet	.25	.25
O34	A23	10c lt green	5.00	1.00
O35	A24	20c scarlet	.20	.20
O36	A25	50c gray blue	.50	.50
		Nos. O31-O36 (6)	6.45	2.45

1901-02				
O37	A30	1c green & blk	.35	.35
O38	A31	2c ver & blk	.35	.35
O39	A32	5c gray bl & blk	.35	.35
O40	A33	10c ocher & blk	.60	.60
O41	A34	20c lake & blk	.85	.85
O42	A35	50c lilac & dk bl	12.50	2.75
O43	A36	1col ol bis & blk	25.00	10.00
		Nos. O37-O43 (7)	40.00	15.25

No. 46 Overprinted in Green

1903				
O44	A31	2c ver & blk	2.25	2.25
b.		"PROVISIORO"	8.00	8.00
d.		Inverted overprint	8.00	8.00
f.		As "b," inverted	10.00	10.00

Counterfeit overprints exist.

Regular Issue of 1903 Overprinted Like Nos. O25-O43

1903		**Perf. 14, 12½x14**		
O45	A40	4c red vio & blk	1.10	1.10
O46	A41	6c ol grn & blk	1.25	1.25
O47	A42	25c gray lil & brn	8.00	4.50
		Nos. O45-O47 (3)	10.35	6.85

Counterfeit overprints exist.

Regular Issue of 1907 Overprinted

1908			**Perf. 14**	
O48	A43	1c red brn & ind	.20	.20
O49	A44	2c yel grn & blk	.20	.20
O50	A45	4c car & ind	.20	.20
O51	A46	5c yel & dull bl	.20	.20
O52	A47	10c blue & blk	2.00	.90
O53	A49	25c gray lil & blk	.30	.20
O54	A50	50c red lil & bl	.50	.30
O55	A51	1col brown & blk	1.00	.70
		Nos. O48-O55 (8)	4.60	2.90

Various varieties of the overprint exist. Imperfs exist of Nos. O48, O49 and O53. The Nos. O49 and O53 imperfs were found in 1970 (one sheet each) and are much scarcer than No. O48 imperf.

Regular Issue of 1910 Overprinted in Black

1917				
O56	A56	5c orange	.25	.25
a.		Inverted overprint	5.00	3.00
O57	A57	10c deep blue	.20	.20
a.		Inverted overprint	3.00	3.00

No. 74 Surcharged

1920	**Red Surcharge**		**Perf. 12**	
O58	A58	15c on 20c olive grn	.50	.50

Nos. 72, 61, 59, 65-67 Surcharged or Overprinted

A56 O60

A43

1921　Black Surcharge　Perf. 12

O59	A56	10c on 5c orange	.30	.25
a.		"10 CTS." inverted	16.00	

Perf. 14

O60	A45	4c car & indigo	.30	.30
a.		"1291" for "1921"	11.00	
O61	A43	6c on 1c red brn & ind	.40	.40
O62	A49	20c on 25c gray lil & blk	.50	.40

Overprinted like No. O60

O63	A50	50c red lil & bl	2.50	1.50
O64	A51	1col brown & blk	5.00	2.75
		Nos. O59-O64 (6)	9.00	5.60

Nos. O60 to O64 exist with date and new values inverted. These may be printer's waste but probably were deliberately made.

Regular Issue of 1923 Overprinted

1923　　　　　　Perf. 11½

O65	A68	2c brown	.20	.20
O66	A68	4c green	.20	.20
O67	A68	5c blue	.20	.20
O68	A68	20c carmine	.20	.20
O69	A68	1col violet	.30	.30
		Nos. O65-O69 (5)	1.10	1.10

Nos. O65 to O69 exist imperforate but were not regularly issued in that condition.

O7

1926　Unwmk.　Engr.　Perf. 12½

O70	O7	2c ultra & blk	.20	.20
O71	O7	3c mag & blk	.20	.20
O72	O7	4c lt bl & blk	.20	.20
O73	O7	5c grn & blk	.20	.20
O74	O7	6c ocher & blk	.20	.20
O75	O7	10c rose red & blk	.20	.20
O76	O7	20c ol grn & blk	.20	.20
O77	O7	30c red org & blk	.20	.20
O78	O7	45c brown & blk	.20	.20
O79	O7	1col lilac & blk	.20	.20
		Nos. O70-O79 (10)	2.00	2.00

See Nos. O82-O94. For surcharges see Nos. C7-C10.

Regular Issue of 1936 Overprinted in Black

1936　Unwmk.　Perf. 12

O80	A96	5c green	.20	.20
O81	A96	10c carmine rose	.20	.20

Type of 1926

1937　　　　　　Perf. 12½

O82	O7	2c vio & blk	.20	.20
O83	O7	3c bis brn & blk	.20	.20
O84	O7	4c rose car & blk	.20	.20
O85	O7	5c ol grn & blk	.20	
O86	O7	8c blk brn & blk	.20	
O87	O7	10c rose lake & blk	.20	
O88	O7	20c ind & blk	.20	.20
O89	O7	40c red org & blk	.20	.20
O90	O7	55c dk vio & blk	.30	
O91	O7	1col brn vio & blk	.25	.25
O92	O7	2col gray bl & blk	.20	.20
O93	O7	5col dl yel & blk	2.50	2.50
O94	O7	10col blue & blk	20.00	20.00
		Nos. O82-O94 (13)	25.15	

Nine stamps of this series exist with perforated star (2c, 3c, 4c, 20c, 40c, 1col, 2col, 5col, 10col). These were issued to officials for postal purposes. Unpunched stamps were sold to collectors but had no franking power. Values for unused are for unpunched.

POSTAL TAX STAMPS

> Catalogue values for unused stamps in this section are for Never Hinged items.

Most postal tax issues were to benefit the Children's Village and were obligatory on all mail during Dec.

No. C198 Surcharged in Red:
"Sello de Navidad Pro-Ciudad de Los Niños 5 5"

Engraved; Center Photogravure

1958　　Unwmk.　　Perf. 12½

RA1	AP51	5c on 2c brt bl & blk	.20	.20

Similar Surcharge in Green on Type of 1954

Design: Like No. C228, pottery.

RA2	AP53	5c on 10c dk bl & blk	.35	.20
a.		Inverted surcharge	7.50	

Father Edward J. Flanagan PT1　　Father Peralta PT2

Paintings: No. RA4, Boy by El Greco. No. RA5, Boy by Jose Ribera. No. RA6, Girl by Amadeo Modigliani.

Perf. 13½

1959, Nov. 25　Unwmk.　Photo.

RA3	PT1	5c green	.35	.20
RA4	PT1	5c dl gray vio	.35	.20
RA5	PT1	5c olive	.35	.20
RA6	PT1	5c lilac rose	.35	.20
		Nos. RA3-RA6 (4)	1.40	.80

Nos. RA3-RA6 exist imperf.

1960　　Litho.　　Perf. 14

Designs: No. RA8, Girl by Renoir. No. RA9, Boys with cups by Velazquez. No. RA10, Singing children, sculpture by F. Zuñiga.

RA7	PT2	5c chocolate	.40	.20
RA8	PT2	5c dp org	.40	.20
RA9	PT2	5c plum	.40	.20
RA10	PT2	5c grysh bl	.40	.20
		Nos. RA7-RA10 (4)	1.60	.80

Nos. RA7-RA10 exist imperf.

No. C229 Surcharged Like Nos. RA1-RA2

Engraved; Center Photogravure

1961　　　　　Perf. 13x12½

RA11	AP53	5c on 15c grn & blk	.40	.20

Nicolas, Son of Rubens — PT3　　Boys in Workshop — PT4

Designs: No. RA13, Madonna by Bellini. RA14, Angel playing stringed instrument by Melozzo. RA15, Msgr. Rubén Odio H.

1962　　Photo.　　Perf. 13½

RA12	PT3	5c dark carmine	.50	.20
RA13	PT3	5c sepia	.50	.20
RA14	PT3	5c dull green	.50	.20
RA15	PT3	5c blue	.50	.20
		Nos. RA12-RA15 (4)	2.00	.80

For surcharges see Nos. 262-265.

Type of 1962, Inscribed "1963"
Designs as before

1963　　Photo.　　Perf. 13½

RA16	PT3	5c sepia (RA12)	.45	.20
RA17	PT3	5c ultra (RA13)	.45	.20
RA18	PT3	5c dk car (RA14)	.45	.20
RA19	PT3	5c black (RA15)	.45	.20
		Nos. RA16-RA19 (4)	1.80	.80

1964　　Litho.　　Perf. 12½

Designs: No. RA21, Two playing boys. No. RA22, Teacher and children. No. RA23, Priest with boys.

RA20	PT4	5c bright green	.35	.20
RA21	PT4	5c rose lilac	.35	.20
RA22	PT4	5c blue	.35	.20
RA23	PT4	5c brown	.35	.20
		Nos. RA20-RA23 (4)	1.40	.80

Brother Casiano de Madrid PT5　　Christmas Ornaments PT6

Designs: No. RA25, National Children's Hospital. No. RA26, Poinsettia. No. RA27, Santa Claus with children (diamond).

1965, Dec. 10　Litho.　　Perf. 10

RA24	PT5	5c red brown	.25	.20
RA25	PT5	5c green	.25	.20
RA26	PT5	5c red	.25	.20
RA27	PT5	5c ultra	.25	.20
		Nos. RA24-RA27 (4)	1.00	.80

1966　　Litho.　　Perf. 11

RA28	PT6	5c shown	.25	.20
RA29	PT6	5c Angel	.25	.20
RA30	PT6	5c Church	.25	.20
RA31	PT6	5c Reindeer	.25	.20
		Nos. RA28-RA31 (4)	1.00	.80

General Post Office, San José — PT7

1967, Mar.　Litho.　　Perf. 11

RA32	PT7	10c blue	.25	.20

No. RA32 was issued as a postal tax stamp to be used by organizations normally allowed free postage. On Dec. 15, 1972, it was authorized for use as an ordinary postage stamp.

Madonna and Child — PT8　　Star of Bethlehem, Mother and Child — PT9

1967　　Litho.　　Perf. 11

RA33	PT8	5c olive green	.25	.20
RA34	PT8	5c dp lil rose	.25	.20
RA35	PT8	5c brt blue	.25	.20
RA36	PT8	5c grnsh blue	.25	.20
		Nos. RA33-RA36 (4)	1.00	.80

1968, Dec.　Litho.　　Perf. 12½

RA37	PT9	5c gray	.25	.20
RA38	PT9	5c rose red	.25	.20
RA39	PT9	5c dk rose brn	.25	.20
RA40	PT9	5c bister brn	.25	.20
		Nos. RA37-RA40 (4)	1.00	.80

Madonna and Child — PT10　　Christ Child, Star — PT11

1969, Dec.　Litho.　　Perf. 12½

RA41	PT10	5c dk blue	.25	.20
RA42	PT10	5c orange	.25	.20
RA43	PT10	5c brown red	.25	.20
RA44	PT10	5c blue green	.25	.20
		Nos. RA41-RA44 (4)	1.00	.80

1970, Dec.　Litho.　　Perf. 12½

RA45	PT11	5c brt purple	.25	.20
RA46	PT11	5c lilac rose	.25	.20
RA47	PT11	5c olive	.25	.20
RA48	PT11	5c ocher	.25	.20
		Nos. RA45-RA48 (4)	1.00	.80

Christ Child and "PAX" — PT12　　Madonna and Child — PT13

1971, Nov. 29

RA49	PT12	10c dk blue	.25	.20
RA50	PT12	10c orange	.25	.20
RA51	PT12	10c brown	.25	.20
RA52	PT12	10c blue green	.25	.20
		Nos. RA49-RA52 (4)	1.00	.80

1972, Nov. 30　　Perf. 11x11½

RA53	PT13	10c dk blue	.25	.20
RA54	PT13	10c brt red	.25	.20
RA55	PT13	10c lilac	.25	.20
RA56	PT13	10c green	.25	.20
		Nos. RA53-RA56 (4)	1.00	.80

Madonna and Child — PT14　　Boys Eating Cake, by Murillo — PT15

1973, Nov. 30　Litho.　　Perf. 12½

RA57	PT14	10c purple	.25	.20
RA58	PT14	10c car rose	.25	.20
RA59	PT14	10c gray	.25	.20
RA60	PT14	10c orange brn	.25	.20
		Nos. RA57-RA60 (4)	1.00	.80

1974, Nov. 25　　　Perf. 13

Paintings: No. RA62, Virgin and Child, with St. John, by Raphael. No. RA63, Maternity, by Juan R. Bonilla. No. RA64, Praying Child, by Reynolds.

RA61	PT15	10c brt pink	.25	.20
RA62	PT15	10c rose lilac	.25	.20
RA63	PT15	10c dk gray	.25	.20
RA64	PT15	10c violet bl	.25	.20
		Nos. RA61-RA64 (4)	1.00	.80

See No. RA110.

"Happy Dreams," by Sonia Romero PT16　　Virgin and Child, by Hans Memling PT17

Paintings: No. RA66, Virgin with Carnation, by Leonardo da Vinci. No. RA67, Children with Tortoise, by Francisco Amighetti. No. RA68, Boy with Pigeon, by Picasso.

1975, Nov. 25　Litho.　　Perf. 10½

RA65	PT16	10c gray	.25	.20
RA66	PT16	10c red lilac	.25	.20
RA67	PT16	10c orange brown	.25	.20
RA68	PT16	10c brt blue	.25	.20
		Nos. RA65-RA68 (4)	1.00	.80

1976, Nov. 24   Litho.   Perf. 10½
Paintings: No. RA70, Girl with Sombrero, by Auguste Renoir. No. RA71, Meditation (boy), by Floria Pinto de Herrero. No. RA72, Gaston de Mezerville (boy), by Lolita Zeller de Peralta.

RA69	PT17	10c rose lilac	.25	.20
RA70	PT17	10c rose carmine	.25	.20
RA71	PT17	10c gray	.25	.20
RA72	PT17	10c violet blue	.25	.20
	Nos. RA69-RA72 (4)		1.00	.80

Boy's Head, by
Amparo
Cruz — PT18

Boy with
Kite — PT19

Paintings: No. RA74, Girl's head, by Rubens. No. RA75, Girl and infant, by Cristina Fournier. No. RA76, Mariano Goya, by Goya.

1977, Nov.   Litho.   Perf. 10½

RA73	PT18	10c gray olive	.25	.20
RA74	PT18	10c rose red	.25	.20
RA75	PT18	10c brt ultra	.25	.20
RA76	PT18	10c brt rose lil	.25	.20
	Nos. RA73-RA76 (4)		1.00	.80

1978, Nov. 20   Litho.   Perf. 12½
Designs: Nos. RA78-RA79, Girl flying kite.

RA77	PT19	10c magenta	.25	.20
RA78	PT19	10c slate	.25	.20
RA79	PT19	10c lilac	.25	.20
RA80	PT19	10c violet blue	.25	.20
	Nos. RA77-RA80 (4)		1.00	.80

Boy Leaning on
Tree — PT20

Boy on
Swing — PT21

1979, Nov. 19   Litho.   Perf. 12½

RA81	PT20	10c blue	.25	.20
RA82	PT20	10c orange	.25	.20
RA83	PT20	10c magenta	.25	.20
RA84	PT20	10c green	.25	.20
	Nos. RA81-RA84 (4)		1.00	.80

1980, Nov. 18   Litho.   Perf. 12½

RA85	PT21	10c brt blue	.25	.20
RA86	PT21	10c brt yellow	.25	.20
RA87	PT21	10c crimson rose	.25	.20
RA88	PT21	10c brt green	.25	.20
	Nos. RA85-RA88 (4)		1.00	.80

Boy Riding Toy
Car
PT22

Youth
Running
Machine
PT23

1981, Nov. 19   Litho.   Perf. 11

RA89	PT22	10c blue	.25	.20
RA90	PT22	10c green	.25	.20
RA91	PT22	10c red	.25	.20
RA92	PT22	10c orange	.25	.20
	Nos. RA89-RA92 (4)		1.00	.80

1982, Nov. 19   Litho.   Perf. 10½

RA93	PT23	10c red	.25	.20
RA94	PT23	10c gray	.25	.20
RA95	PT23	10c purple	.25	.20
RA96	PT23	10c grnsh blue	.25	.20
	Nos. RA93-RA96 (4)		1.00	.80

Youths Working
on Wheelchair
PT24

Girl on Bicycle
PT25

1983, Nov. 24   Litho.   Perf. 16

RA97	PT24	10c red	.25	.20
RA98	PT24	10c orange	.25	.20
RA99	PT24	10c ultra	.25	.20
RA100	PT24	10c green	.25	.20
	Nos. RA97-RA100 (4)		1.00	.80

Christmas 1983.

1984, Nov. 20   Litho.   Perf. 10½

RA101	PT25	10c violet	.60	.20

Christmas 1984.

Taking a Child
in Out of the
Cold
PT26

Depressed
Child
PT27

1985, Dec. 1   Litho.   Perf. 13

RA102	PT26	10c dull brown	.60	.20

Christmas 1985.

1986, Dec. 1   Litho.   Perf. 10½

RA103	PT27	10c lemon	.60	.20

Christmas stamps, 25th anniv.; Christmas 1986.

Christmas
PT28

Teaching
Children
PT29

1987, Dec. 1   Litho.   Perf. 10½

RA104	PT28	10c dk ol bis & brt bl	.50	.20

No postal tax stamp was issued for 1988.

1989, Dec. 1   Litho.   Perf. 13½

RA105	PT29	1col blue, blk & brt apple grn	.40	.20

Christmas 1989.

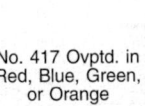
No. 417 Ovptd. in
Red, Blue, Green,
or Orange

1990, Nov. 16   Litho.   Perf. 13½

RA106	A179	10col multi (R)	.25	.20
RA107	A179	10col multi (Bl)	.25	.20
RA108	A179	10col multi (G)	.25	.20
RA109	A179	10col multi (O)	.25	.20
	Nos. RA106-RA109 (4)		1.00	.80

No. RA109 exists with a silver overprint.

Art Type of 1974
Design: 10col, Praying Child, by Reynolds.

1991, Nov. 18   Litho.   Perf. 10½

RA110	PT15	10col dark ultra	.70	.20

PT30

PT31

Boy in workshop.

1992, Dec. 1   Litho.   Perf. 10½

RA111	PT30	10col red	.30	.20

Christmas.

1993, Nov. 17

RA112	PT31	10col multicolored	.20	.20

Christmas.

PT32

PT33

1994, Nov. 23   Litho.   Perf. 10½

RA113	PT32	11col lilac & slate	.20	.20

Christmas.
No. RA113 exists imperf.

1995, Dec. 1   Perf. 13½
Painting of mother and child, by Claudio Carazo.

RA114	PT33	12col multicolored	.25	.20
a.		Miniature sheet, #RA114 + 5 labels	1.90	.90

No. RA114a contains 4 progressive proofs of No. RA114 + one label of text and sold for 112col.
Christmas.

PT34

PT35

1996, Dec. 1   Litho.   Perf. 10½

RA115	PT34	14col Sculpture	.50	.20

1997, Dec. 1
Bust of Antonio Obando Chan, by Olger Villegas Cruz.

RA116	PT35	15col multicolored	.40	.20

Christmas.

PT36

Designs: a, Flower. b, Flower up close, one in background. c, Berries on branch.

1998   Litho.   Perf. 13½

RA117	PT36	16col Strip of 3, #a.-c.	.70	.20

Christmas.

Children's
Village
PT37

1999, Dec. 1   Litho.   Perf. 13¼

RA118	PT37	17col multi	.45	.20

Child — PT38

Color: a, Green. b, Red. c, Blue. d, Brown.

2000, Dec. 1   Litho.   Perf. 10½

RA119		Horiz. strip of 4	1.00	.70
a.-d.	PT38	20col Any single	.20	.20

Child
Examining
Stamp — PT39

Panel color: a, Purple. b, Green. c, Red. d, Orange.

2001, Dec. 1   Litho.   Perf. 10½

RA120		Horiz. strip of 4	1.00	.70
a.-d.	PT39	21col Any single	.20	.20

Child — PT40

Panel color: a, Purple. b, Blue. c, Orange. d, Green.

2002   Litho.   Perf. 10½

RA121		Horiz strip of 4	1.00	.65
a.-d.	PT40	22col Any single	.20	.20

Child Pointing at
Star — PT41

No. RA122 — Background color: a, Purple. b, Green. c, Red. d, Yellow orange.

2003, Dec. 1   Litho.   Perf. 13½x13¼

RA122		Horiz. strip of 4	1.00	.55
a.-d.	PT41	23col Any single	.20	.20

Three
Magi — PT42

No. RA123 — Magi in: a, Lemon. b, Green. c, Purple. d, Red violet.

2004   Litho.   Perf. 13¼

RA123		Horiz. strip of 4	1.00	1.00
a.-d.	PT42	25col Any single	.20	.20

Children — PT43

No. RA124 — Denomination color: a, White. b, Buff. c, Dull orange. d, Red.

2005, Dec. 1   Litho.   Perf. 10½

RA124		Horiz. strip of 4	1.00 1.00
a.-d.		PT43 28col Any single	.20 .20

Surtax for Children's Village.

Child Reading PT44

No. RA125 — Frame color: a, Yellow bister. b, Dull brown. c, Olive green. d, Orange brown.

2006, Dec. 1   Litho.   Perf. 10½

RA125		Horiz. strip of 4	.50 .50
a.-d.		PT44 32col Any single	.20 .20

GUANACASTE

ˌgwä-nə-ˈkästä

(A province of Costa Rica)

LOCATION — Northwestern coast of Central America
AREA — 4,000 sq. mi. (approx.)
POP. — 69,531 (estimated)
CAPITAL — Liberia

Residents of Guanacaste were allowed to buy Costa Rican stamps, overprinted "Guanacaste," at a discount from face value because of the province's isolation and climate, which makes it difficult to keep mint stamps. Use was restricted to the province.

Counterfeits of most Guanacaste overprints are plentiful.

For 5c stamps between Nos. 5-43, unused examples without gum sell for slightly more than the used value.

Very fine examples of Nos. 1-54 will have perforations just clear of the design on one or more sides.

Dangerous counterfeits exist of Nos. 1-63.

On Issue of 1883
Overprinted Horizontally in Black

16mm

1885   Unwmk.   Perf. 12

1	A6	1c green	4.00 3.00
2	A6	2c carmine	4.00 3.00
a.		"Gnanacaste"	250.00
3	A6	10c orange	35.00 18.00
a.		"Gnanacaste"	500.00

Same Overprint in Red

4	A6	1c green	4.00 3.00
a.		"Gnanacaste"	200.00
b.		Overprinted in black & red	300.00
5	A6	5c blue violet	30.00 3.50
a.		"Gnanacaste"	350.00
6	A6	40c blue	25.00 18.00

Overprinted Horizontally in Black

17½mm

7	A6	1c green	10.00 7.00
8	A6	2c carmine	10.00 7.00
9	A6	5c blue violet	45.00 15.00
10	A6	10c orange	60.00 35.00
11	A6	40c blue	60.00 60.00

Same Overprint in Red

12	A6	5c blue violet	500.00 75.00
13	A6	40c blue	2,000.

Overprinted Horizontally in Black

18½mm — c

14	A6	2c carmine	10.00 7.00
15	A6	10c orange	100.00 75.00

Same Overprint in Red

16	A6	1c green	7.00 7.00
a.		Double ovpt., one in blk	250.00
17	A6	5c blue violet	45.00 15.00
18	A6	40c blue	75.00 75.00

Same Overprint, Vertically in Black

19	A6	1c green	5,000.
20	A6	2c carmine	4,250.
21	A6	5c blue violet	700.00 175.00
22	A6	10c orange	120.00 120.00

e   f   g   h   i

Overprinted Type e, Vertically

23	A6	1c green	2,000. 2,000.
24	A6	2c carmine	700.00 300.00
25	A6	5c blue violet	400.00 75.00
26	A6	10c orange	75.00 75.00

Overprinted Type f, Vertically

27	A6	1c green	2,000. 2,000.
28	A6	2c carmine	700.00 400.00
29	A6	5c blue violet	400.00 125.00
30	A6	10c orange	100.00 100.00

Overprinted Type g, Vertically

31	A6	1c green	2,500. 2,500.
32	A6	2c carmine	1,000. 1,000.
33	A6	5c blue violet	600.00 200.00
34	A6	10c orange	150.00 150.00

Overprinted Type h, Vertically

35	A6	1c green	2,000. 1,500.
36	A6	2c carmine	500.00 300.00
37	A6	5c blue violet	350.00 75.00
38	A6	10c orange	60.00 60.00

Overprinted Type i, Vertically

39	A6	1c green	—
39A	A6	2c carmine	275.00
40	A6	5c blue violet	20.00
41	A6	10c orange	200.00

On Issues of 1883-87

Overprinted Horizontally in Black

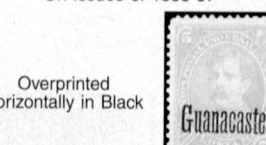

1888-89

42	A7	5c blue violet	15.00 3.00

Overprinted Horizontally in Black

43	A7	5c blue violet	15.00 3.00

Overprinted Horizontally in Black

44	A6	2c carmine	3.00
45	A7	10c orange	3.00

Inverted overprints are fakes.

On Issue of 1889
Overprinted Like Nos. 7-13, Horizontally

1889

47	A8	2c blue	20.00

Vertically

48	A8	2c blue (c)	250.00
49	A8	2c blue (e)	75.00
51	A8	2c blue (f)	75.00
52	A8	2c blue (g)	250.00
54	A8	2c blue (h)	75.00

Nos. 47-54 are overprinted "Correos." Copies without "Correos" are known postally used. Unused examples are valued the same as Nos. 47-54, unused. The 1c without "Correos" is known postally used. The 1c with "Correos" is counterfeit.

On Nos. 25-33

Overprinted Horizontally in Black

1889

55	A10	1c brown	5.00 3.00
56	A11	2c dark green	3.00 1.50
57	A12	5c orange	4.00 1.50
58	A13	10c red brown	4.00 1.50
59	A14	20c yellow green	1.00 1.50
60	A15	50c rose red	1.50 1.50
61	A16	1p blue	2.50 2.50
62	A17	2p violet	5.00 5.00
63	A18	5p olive green	35.00 30.00
		Nos. 55-63 (9)	61.00 48.00

Perf. 14 and 15

#61-63 with remainder cancels sell for about half the used values shown.

Overprinted "GUAGACASTE"

60a	A15	50c rose red	300.00 300.00
61a	A16	1p blue	300.00 300.00
62a	A17	2p violet	350.00 350.00
63a	A18	5p olive green	500.00 500.00

Values for #60a-63a used are for examples with remainder cancels.

Overprinted Horizontally in Black

64	A10	1c brown	2.00 1.50
a.		Vert. pair, imperf. between	
65	A11	2c dark green	2.00 1.50
66	A12	5c orange	2.00 1.50
67	A13	10c red brown	2.00 1.50
		Nos. 64-67 (4)	8.00 6.00

CRETE

ˈkrēt

LOCATION — An island in the Mediterranean Sea south of Greece
GOVT. — A department of Greece
AREA — 3,235 sq. mi.

POP. — 336,150 (1913)
CAPITAL — Canea

Formerly Crete was a province of Turkey. After an extended period of civil wars, France, Great Britain, Italy and Russia intervened and declaring Crete an autonomy, placed it under the administration of Prince George of Greece as High Commissioner. In October, 1908, the Cretan Assembly voted for union with Greece and in 1913 the union was formally effected.

40 Paras = 1 Piaster
4 Metallik = 1 Grosion (1899)
100 Lepta = 1 Drachma (1900)

Issued Under Joint Administration of France, Great Britain, Italy and Russia
British Sphere of Administration
District of Heraklion (Candia)

A1   A2

Handstamped

1898   Unwmk.   Imperf.

1	A1	20pa violet	450.00 250.00

1898   Litho.   Perf. 11½

2	A2	10pa blue	9.00 3.00
		Never hinged	17.50
a.		Horiz. pair, imperf. btwn.	
b.		Imperf., pair	275.00
3	A2	20pa green	15.50 3.00
		Never hinged	24.00
a.		Imperf., pair	275.00

1899

4	A2	10pa brown	9.50 3.00
		Never hinged	18.00
a.		Horiz. pair, imperf. btwn.	
b.		Imperf., pair	275.00
5	A2	20pa rose	21.00 3.00
		Never hinged	31.00
a.		Imperf., pair	275.00

Used values for Nos. 2-5 are for stamps canceled by the straight-line "Heraklion" town postmark. Stamps canceled with any other postmark used for postal duty are scarce and worth much more.

Counterfeits exist of Nos. 1-5.

Russian Sphere of Administration
District of Rethymnon

Coat of Arms
A3   A4

1899   Handstamped   Imperf.

10	A3	1m green	10.00 5.50
11	A3	2m black	10.00 5.50
12	A3	2m rose	300.00 275.00
13	A4	1m blue	80.00 50.00

Nos. 10-13 exist on both wove and laid papers. Counterfeits exist.

Poseidon's Trident — A5a
A5

1899   Litho.   Perf. 11½
With Control Mark Overprinted in Violet
Without Stars at Sides

14	A5	1m orange	80.	60.
15	A5	2m orange	80.	60.
16	A5	1gr orange	80.	70.
17	A5	1m green	80.	80.
18	A5	2m green	80.	60.
19	A5	1gr green	80.	70.
20	A5	1m yellow	80.	60.
21	A5	2m yellow	80.	60.
22	A5	1gr yellow	80.	60.
23	A5	1m rose	80.	75.
24	A5	2m rose	80.	60.
25	A5	1gr rose	80.	70.
26	A5	1m violet	80.	60.
27	A5	2m violet	80.	60.
28	A5	1gr violet	80.	75.
29	A5	1m blue	80.	60.
30	A5	2m blue	80.	60.
31	A5	1gr blue	80.	60.
32	A5	1m black	1,000.	975.
33	A5	2m black	1,000.	975.
34	A5	1gr black	1,000.	975.

With Stars at Sides

35	A5a	1m blue	25.00	15.00
36	A5a	2m blue	10.00	8.00
37	A5a	1gr blue	10.00	10.00
38	A5a	1m rose	50.00	40.00
39	A5a	2m rose	15.00	10.00
40	A5a	1gr rose	10.00	10.00
41	A5a	1m green	30.00	20.00
42	A5a	2m green	10.00	10.00
43	A5a	1gr green	10.00	10.00
44	A5a	1m violet	25.00	15.00
45	A5a	2m violet	10.00	5.25
46	A5a	1gr violet	10.00	5.00
		Nos. 35-46 (12)	215.00	158.25

Nearly all of Nos. 14 to 46 may be found without control mark, with double control marks and in various colors.
Counterfeits exist of Nos. 14-46.

Issued by the Cretan Government

Hermes — A6

Hera — A7

Prince George of Greece — A8

Talos — A9

Minos — A10   St. George and the Dragon — A11

1900, Mar. 1   Engr.   Perf. 14

50	A6	1 l violet brown	.30	.30
51	A7	5 l green	1.50	.30
52	A8	10 l red	1.75	.35
53	A7	20 l carmine rose	6.50	1.25
		Nos. 50-53 (4)	10.05	2.20

See #64-71. For overprints and surcharges see #54-63, 72-73, 85, 88, 93, 97-99, 108, 111.

Overprinted

Red Overprint

54	A8	25 l blue	3.00	.85
55	A6	50 l lilac	3.00	1.25
56	A9	1d gray violet	13.00	11.00
57	A10	2d brown	27.50	25.00
58	A11	5d green & blk	125.00	125.00
		Nos. 54-58 (5)	171.50	163.10

Black Overprint

59	A8	25 l blue	3.00	.85
60	A6	50 l lilac	3.00	1.75
61	A9	1d gray violet	12.50	4.50
a.		Inverted overprint	450.00	450.00
62	A10	2d brown	25.00	22.50
63	A11	5d green & blk	65.00	65.00
		Nos. 59-63 (5)	108.50	94.60

1901
Without Overprint

64	A6	1 l bister		.90
65	A7	20 l orange	4.75	.90
66	A8	25 l blue	11.00	.60
67	A6	50 l lilac	30.00	22.50
68	A6	50 l ultra	13.50	13.00
69	A9	1d gray violet	33.00	4.00
70	A10	2d brown	12.50	10.00
71	A11	5d green & blk	15.00	12.00
		Nos. 64-71 (8)		84.90
		Nos. 65-71 (7)	119.75	

No. 64 is a revenue stamp that was used for postage for a short time. Unused, it can only be considered as a revenue.
Types A6 to A8 in olive yellow, and types A9 to A11 in olive yellow and black are revenue stamps.
See note following No. 53.

Surcharges with the year "1922" on designs A6, A8, A9, A11, A13, A15-A23 and D1 are listed under Greece.

No. 66 Overprinted in Black

1901

72	A8	25 l blue	32.50	1.00
a.		First letter of ovpt. invtd.	325.00	250.00

No. 65 Surcharged in Black

1904, Dec.

73	A7	5 l on 20 l orange	4.50	1.00
a.		Without "5" at right	100.00	75.00

Mycenaean Seal — A12

Britomartis (Cortyna Coin) — A13

Prince George — A14

Kydon and Dog (Cydonia Coin) — A15

Triton (Itanos Coin) — A16

Ariadne (Knossos Coin) — A17

Zeus as Bull Abducting Europa (Cortyna Coin) A18

Palace of Minos Ruins, Knossos A19

Arkadi Monastery and Mt. Ida — A20

1905, Feb. 15

74	A12	2 l dull violet	1.90	.45
75	A13	5 l yellow grn	5.00	.45
76	A14	10 l red	5.00	.65
77	A15	20 l blue grn	5.50	1.00
78	A16	25 l ultra	6.50	1.10
79	A17	50 l yellow brn	7.50	4.75
80	A18	1d rose car & dp brn	62.50	60.00
81	A19	3d orange & blk	50.00	40.00
82	A20	5d ol grn & blk	25.00	20.00
		Nos. 74-82 (9)	168.90	128.40

For overprints see Nos.86-87, 89, 91-92, 94-95, 104, 106, 109-110, 112-113, 115-120.

The so-called revolutionary stamps of 1905 were issued for sale to collectors and, so far as can be ascertained, were of no postal value whatever.

A. T. A. Zaimis A21

Prince George Landing at Suda A22

1907, Aug. 28

83	A21	25 l blue & blk	37.50	1.25
84	A22	1d green & blk	13.00	11.00

Administration under a High Commissioner. For overprints see Nos. 90, 105, 107.

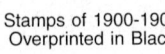

Stamps of 1900-1907 Overprinted in Black

1908, Sept. 21

85	A6	1 l violet brn	.60	.50
86	A12	2 l dull violet	.65	.50
87	A13	5 l yellow grn	.90	.50
88	A8	10 l red	1.75	.65
89	A15	20 l blue grn	4.50	.70
90	A21	25 l blue & blk	11.00	2.50
91	A17	50 l yellow brn	11.00	4.00

92	A18	1d rose car & dp brn	67.50	70.00
93	A10	2d brown	10.50	10.50
94	A19	3d orange & blk	40.00	37.50
95	A20	5d ol grn & blk	32.50	32.50
		Nos. 85-95 (11)	180.90	159.85

This overprint exists inverted and double, as well as with incorrect, reversed, misplaced and omitted letters. Similar errors are found on the Postage Due and Official stamps with this overprint.

Hermes by Praxiteles — A23

1908

96	A23	10 l brown red	3.25	.90
a.		Pair, one without overprint	25.00	
b.		Inverted overprint	25.00	
c.		Double overprint	35.00	

Nos. 96 and 114 were not regularly issued without overprint.
For overprints see Nos. 103, 114.

No. 53 Surcharged

1909

97	A7	5 l on 20 l car rose	125.00	130.00

Forgeries exist of No. 97.

On No. 65

98	A7	5 l on 20 l orange	1.75	1.25
a.		Inverted surcharge		

Overprinted on Nos. 64, J1

99	A6	1 l bister	1.75	1.75
100	D1	1 l red	1.75	1.75

No. J4 Surcharged

101	D1	2 l on 20 l red	1.75	1.75
b.		Inverted surcharge	75.00	
c.		Second letter of surcharge "D" instead of "P"	50.00	50.00

No. J4 Surcharged

102	D1	2 l on 20 l red	1.60	1.40

Overprinted in Black:

a   b

c

103	A23(a)	10 l brown red		4.75	1.25
a.		Inverted overprint		85.00	
104	A15(a)	20 l blue grn		6.25	1.25
105	A21(c)	25 l blue & blk		12.50	4.00
106	A17(a)	50 l yellow brn		10.00	5.25
107	A22(b)	1d green & blk		13.50	11.00
108	A10(a)	2d brown		13.50	12.50
109	A19(b)	3d org & blk		97.50	77.50
110	A20(b)	5d ol grn & blk		32.50	32.50
		Nos. 103-110 (8)		190.50	145.25

Stamps of 1900-08 Overprinted in Red or Black

1909-10

111	A6	1 l violet brown	.45	.25
112	A12	2 l dull violet	.45	.25
113	A13	5 l yellow green	.45	.25
114	A23	10 l brown red (Bk)	.85	.25
115	A15	20 l blue green	3.00	.70
116	A16	25 l ultra	3.50	.75
117	A17	50 l yellow brn	9.00	6.75
118	A18	1d rose car & dp brn (Bk)	70.00	70.00
119	A19	3d orange & blk	55.00	55.00
120	A20	5d ol grn & blk	45.00	40.00
		Nos. 111-120 (10)	187.70	174.20

POSTAGE DUE STAMPS

D1

1901   Unwmk.   Litho.   Perf. 14

J1	D1	1 l red	.30	.30
J2	D1	5 l red	.95	.60
J3	D1	10 l red	1.50	.60
J4	D1	20 l red	1.90	1.50
J5	D1	40 l red	14.00	14.00
J6	D1	50 l red	14.00	14.00
J7	D1	1d red	22.50	21.00
J8	D1	2d red	14.00	14.00
		Nos. J1-J8 (8)	69.15	66.00

For overprints and surcharges see Nos. 100-102, J9-J26.

Surcharged in Black

1901

J9	D1	1d on 1d red	12.00	12.00

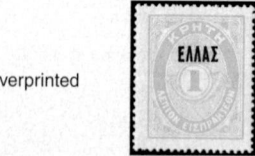

Overprinted

1908

J10	D1	1 l red	.60	.50
J11	D1	5 l red	1.10	.85
J12	D1	10 l red	1.25	.90
J13	D1	20 l red	3.00	2.25
J14	D1	40 l red	10.00	10.00
J15	D1	50 l red	10.00	10.00
J16	D1	1d red	125.00	125.00

J17	D1	1d on 1d red	10.00	10.00
J18	D1	2d red	18.50	17.50
		Nos. J10-J18 (9)	179.45	177.00

Nos. J10-J18 exist with inverted overprint. See note after No. 95.
Counterfeits of No. J16 exist.

Overprinted

1910

J19	D1	1 l red	.60	.30
J20	D1	5 l red	1.40	.25
J21	D1	10 l red	1.00	.50
J22	D1	20 l red	4.25	1.75
J23	D1	40 l red	10.00	9.00
J24	D1	50 l red	12.50	11.00
J25	D1	1d red	27.50	27.50
J26	D1	2d red	27.50	27.50
		Nos. J19-J26 (8)	84.75	77.80

OFFICIAL STAMPS

O1

O2

Unwmk.

1908, Jan. 14   Litho.   Perf. 14

O1	O1	10 l dull claret	20.00	2.50
O2	O2	30 l blue	42.50	2.50

Nos. O1-O2 exist imperf.

Overprinted

O3	O1	10 l dull claret	20.00	2.50
O4	O2	30 l blue	42.50	2.50

See note after No. 95.

Overprinted

1910

O5	O1	10 l dull claret	2.50	2.00
O6	O2	30 l blue	2.50	2.00

Nos. O5-O6 remained in use until 1922, nine years after union with Greece.

CROATIA

krō-ā-shē̠-ə

LOCATION — Southeastern Europe
GOVT. — Independent state
AREA — 44,453 sq. mi.
POP. — 7,000,000 (approx.)
CAPITAL — Zagreb

The Independent Croatian State of 1941-45 became part of the Yugoslav Federation in 1945.

Croatia declared its independence in 1991.

100 Paras = 1 Dinar
100 Banica = 1 Kuna

> **Catalogue values for unused stamps in this country are for Never Hinged items, beginning with Scott 1 in the regular postage section, Scott B1 in the semi-postal section, Scott C1 in the airmail section and Scott RA1 in the postal tax section.**

Watermark

Wmk. 278 — Network Connecting Circles

Yugoslavia Nos. 143 to 148B Overprinted in Black

Perf. 12½

1941, Apr. 12   Unwmk.   Typo.

1	A16	50p orange	2.00	2.75
a.		Inverted overprint	225.00	
2	A16	1d yellow grn	2.00	2.75
a.		Double overprint	110.00	
3	A16	1.50d red	2.25	1.50
a.		Double overprint	110.00	
4	A16	2d deep magenta	2.50	2.50
5	A16	3d dull red brn	4.00	5.00
a.		Double overprint	110.00	
6	A16	4d ultra	5.00	5.75
7	A16	5d dark blue	5.75	6.00
8	A16	5.50d dk violet brn	6.50	7.00
a.		Double overprint	110.00	
		Nos. 1-8 (8)	30.00	33.25

Counterfeit overprints exist of Nos. 1-8, especially the inverted and double overprint varieties.

Yugoslavia Nos. 142 to 154 Overprinted in Black

1941, Apr. 21

9	A16	25p black	.20	.40
a.		Inverted overprint	75.00	
b.		Double overprint	75.00	
10	A16	50p orange	.20	.40
a.		Inverted overprint	75.00	
11	A16	1d yellow grn	.20	.40
a.		Inverted overprint	—	
12	A16	1.50d red	.35	.40
a.		Double overprint	150.00	
13	A16	2d deep magenta	.35	.40
14	A16	3d dull red brn	.50	.75
15	A16	4d ultra	.75	1.10
16	A16	5d dark blue	1.00	1.10
a.		Double overprint	200.00	
17	A16	5.50d dk violet brn	1.25	1.40
a.		Inverted overprint	375.00	
b.		Double overprint	200.00	
18	A16	6d slate blue	1.50	1.90
19	A16	8d sepia	2.25	2.40
20	A16	12d brt violet	3.00	2.50
a.		Inverted overprint	375.00	
21	A16	16d dull violet	3.25	3.75
a.		Double overprint	200.00	
22	A16	20d blue	4.00	4.50
23	A16	30d bright pink	5.75	8.25
		Nos. 9-23 (15)	24.55	29.65

The overprint exists double, both inverted, on Nos. 16, 18 and 19.

Yugoslavia Nos. 147, 148 Surcharged in Black

1941, May 16

24	A16	1d on 3d dull red brn	.45	.45
a.		Inverted overprint	75.00	
b.		Double overprint	75.00	
25	A16	2d on 4d ultra	.45	.45
a.		Inverted overprint	75.00	
b.		Double overprint	75.00	

Postage Due Stamps of Yugoslavia, Nos. J28, J30 to J32, Overprinted in Black

1941, May 17

26	D4	50p violet	.45	.45
27	D4	2d deep blue	1.00	1.10
28	D4	5d orange	1.25	1.40
29	D4	10d chocolate	1.50	1.60
		Nos. 26-29 (4)	4.20	4.55

Counterfeit cancellations exist for Nos. 1-29 on cover.

Imperforates

Nearly all Croatian stamps, from No. 30 through 80, B3 through B76, J6 through J25, O1 through O24 and RA1 through RA7 exist imperforate, imperforate vertically, and imperforate horizontally. These are primarily from the special Ministerial Albums issued by the State Printing Office.

Ozalj Castle — A1

Designs: 50b, City of Jajce. 75b, Old Warasdin. 1k, Velebit Mountains. 1.50k, Zelanjak. 2k, Zagreb Cathedral. 3k, Osjek Cathedral. 4k, Drina River. No. 38, Konjica. No. 39, Zemun. 6k, Dubrovnik. 7k, Save River. 8k, Sarajevo. 10k, Plitvice. 12k, Klis Fortress, Split. 20k, Hvar. 30k, Syrmia. 50k, Senj. 100k, Banjaluka (without "F.I.").

Perf. 11¼.

1941-43   Unwmk.   Photo.

Ordinary Paper

30	A1	25b henna	.20	.20
31	A1	50b slate blue	.20	.20
32	A1	75b dk olive grn	.20	.20
33	A1	1k Prussian green	.20	.20
34	A1	1.50k deep green	.20	.20
35	A1	2k carmine lake	.20	.20
36	A1	3k brown red	.20	.20
37	A1	4k deep ultra	.20	.20
38	A1	5k black	2.25	1.25
39	A1	5k blue	.25	.20
40	A1	6k lt olive brn	.25	.20
41	A1	7k orange red	.30	.20
42	A1	8k chestnut	.50	.30
43	A1	10k dark plum	1.00	.45
44	A1	12k olive brown	1.40	.50
45	A1	20k golden brown	1.00	.40
46	A1	30k black brown	1.40	.50
47	A1	50k dk slate green	2.50	1.40
48	A1	100k violet	4.25	3.00
		Nos. 30-48 (19)	16.70	10.00

Nos. 30-48 exist with a variety of perforations, including 11¼x10¾ and 12.

Nos. 31, 35 and 43 exist on thin to pelure paper, as does No. 32, though the latter was not issued to the public. Shades of all values exist.

For overprints and surcharge see #49-51, 53.

Tête bêche Pairs

30a	A1	25b	1.75	2.75
31a	A1	50b	2.00	3.50
33a	A1	1k	2.50	4.00
34a	A1	1.50k	2.75	5.00
35a	A1	2k	3.00	6.00
37a	A1	4k	3.25	6.50
38a	A1	5k	7.00	7.50
40a	A1	6k	4.00	7.00
41a	A1	7k	4.50	7.25
42a	A1	8k	5.00	8.00

43a	A1	10k	5.50	9.50
45a	A1	20k	6.50	10.00
46a	A1	30k	7.25	11.00
47a	A1	50k	13.00	13.00
	Nos. 30a-47a (14)		68.00	101.00

Types of 1941 Overprinted in Brown or Green

1942, Apr. 9

49	A1	2k dark brown	.50	.40
50	A1	5k dark carmine	.65	.70
51	A1	10k dark blue green (G)	1.25	1.25
	Nos. 49-51 (3)		2.40	2.35

First anniversary of Croatian independence. The overprint exists double on No. 50.
Tête bêche pairs of Nos. 49-51 are from Ministerial Albums.

Banjaluka ("F.I." at upper right) — A20

1942, June 13

52	A20	100k violet	4.25	4.50

Banjaluka Philatelic Exhibition. Exists in se-tenant pair with No. 48. Value unused, $160.

No. 35 Surcharged in Red Brown with New Value and Bar

1942, June 23

53	A1	25b on 2k carmine lake	.60	.60
a.	Tête bêche pair		3.00	3.00

No. 53 exists with double surcharge. It is not scarce.

Trakoscan Castle — A21

Catherine Zrinski — A23

Design: 12.50k, Citadel of Veliki Tabor.

1943, Mar. 28
Pelure Paper

54	A21	3.50k brown carmine	.75	.65
55	A21	12.50k violet black	1.00	.95

Nos. 54 was reissued in 1944 on ordinary paper, perf 12. Value the same for both varieties. No. 55 also exists on ordinary paper. It is scarce.

1943, June 7 Engr. Perf. 12¼x12½

2k, Fran Krsto Frankopan. 3.50k, Peter Zrinski.

Various Frames

56	A23	1k dark blue	.40	.40
57	A23	2k dark olive green	.40	.40
58	A23	3.50k dark red	.50	.55
	Nos. 56-58 (3)		1.30	1.35

Many perforation varieties of this issue exist, including 12x12½, 12½x13, 12½, 13, 12½x14, 13x12½, and 14x12½.

Rugjer Boscovich — A26

Ante Pavelich — A27

1943, Dec. 13 Perf. 11

59	A26	3.50k copper red	.40	.35
60	A26	12.50k dk violet brn	.65	.50

Rugjer Boscovich (1711-1787). Mathematician and physicist.

1943-44 Litho. Perf. 12½, 14

61	A27	25b orange ver	.20	.20
62	A27	50b Prus blue	.20	.20
63	A27	75b olive green	.20	.20
64	A27	1k lt green	.20	.20
65	A27	1.50k dull gray vio	.20	.20
66	A27	2k rose lake	.20	.20
67	A27	3k rose brown	.20	.20
68	A27	3.50k bright blue	.20	.20
a.		3.50k dark blue, perf. 11½	3.25	3.00
69	A27	4k brt red violet	.20	.20
70	A27	5k ultra	.20	.20
71	A27	8k orange brn	.25	.25
72	A27	9k rose pink	.25	.25
73	A27	10k violet brn	.25	.20
74	A27	12k dk olive bis	.30	.25
75	A27	12.50k gray black	.30	.25
76	A27	18k dull brown	.35	.30
77	A27	32k dark brown	.60	.30
78	A27	50k grnsh blue	.90	.50
79	A27	70k orange	1.25	.90
80	A27	100k violet	1.75	1.50
	Nos. 61-80 (20)		8.20	6.60

Nos. 61 and 63 measure 20½x26mm. Nos. 62 and 64-80 measure 22x27½mm.
Nos. 61, 63, 67, 70, 71 and 72 are perf 12½. Nos. 62, 64-66, 68, 69, 73 and 75-80 are perf 14. No. 74 exists either perf 12½ or 14.
Issue dates: 2k, 1943; No. 68a, June 13, 1943, Pavelich's Saint's Day; others, 1944.

"Labor Day 1945" — A28

1945 Photo. Perf. 11½

81	A28	3.50k red brown	.75	1.60

> From 1951 to 1972 44 labels were circulated by a Croatian Government in Exile. These had no postal value.

GOVT. — Independent state
AREA — 21,823 sq. mi.
POP. — 4,676,865 (1999 est.)
CAPITAL — Zagreb

Croatia declared its independence from Yugoslavia in 1991.

100 Paras = 1 Dinar (1991)
100 Lipa = 1 Kuna (1994)

Nos. RA20, RA20a Surcharged in Black and Gold

1991, Nov. 21 Litho. Perf. 14

100	PT10	4d on 1.20d #RA20	.50	.50
a.		Perf. 11x10½	.60	.60

A35

A36

1991, Dec. 10 Perf. 12

101	A35	30d multicolored	1.60	.35

Declaration of independence, 10/8/91.

1991, Dec. 11 Perf. 12

Christmas: Creche figures of the Holy Family from Kosljun Monastery.

102	A36	4d multicolored	.60	.60

No. RA21 Surcharged in Black and Gold

1992, Jan. 3 Perf. 10½x11

103	PT11	20d on 1.70d #RA21	5.75	5.00

Croatian Arms — A37

1992, Jan. 15 Perf. 11x10½

104	A37	10d multicolored	.45	.45
a.		Perf. 14	.20	.20

See No. RA22.

1992 Winter Olympics, Albertville — A38

1992, Feb. 4 Perf. 11x10½

105	A38	30d multicolored	1.25	1.25

Croatian Cities and Landmarks — A39

A39a

Designs: 6d, Knin. 7d, Eltz Castle, Vukovar. 20d, Church, Ilok. 30d, Starcevic Street, Gospic. 45d, Rector's Palace, Dubrovnik. 50d, St. Jakov's Cathedral, Sibenik. 100d, Vinkovci. 200d, Pazin, vert. No. 115, Beli Monastery. 500d, Slavonski Brod. 1000d, Varazdin. 2000d, Karlovac. 5000d, Zadar, vert. 10,000d, Vis.

1992-94 Perf. 14

107	A39	6d multicolored	.20	.20
108	A39	7d multicolored	.20	.20
109	A39	20d multicolored	.25	
a.		Perf. 11x10½	1.00	
110	A39	30d multicolored	.60	.60
111	A39	45d multicolored	1.10	1.10
112	A39	50d multicolored	1.10	1.10
113	A39a	100d multicolored	.45	
114	A39a	200d multicolored	.35	
115	A39	300d multicolored	4.00	
117	A39a	500d multicolored	1.25	
118	A39a	1000d multicolored	1.90	
119	A39a	2000d multicolored	2.25	
120	A39a	5000d multicolored	2.50	
121	A39a	10,000d multicolored	4.50	
	Nos. 107-121 (14)		20.65	

Issued: 6d, 4/18; 7d, 4/8; #109, 2/28; #109a, 9/9; 30d, 5/21; 45d, 4/14; 50d, 4/28; 115, 6/26; 100d, 12/14; 500d, 2/9/93; 1000d, 3/16/93; 200d, 4/22/93; 2000d, 5/20/93; 5000d, 9/24/93; 10,000d, 2/22/94.
See Nos. 355-356, 437A, 456.

Statue of King Tomislav — A40

1992, May 5 Engr. Perf. 12½ Horiz. Coil Stamp

124	A40	10d dark green	.25	.20

Railroad Station, Zagreb, Cent. — A41

1992, June 30 Litho. Perf. 14

125	A41	30d multicolored	.50	.25

Matica, Society of Knowledge and Literacy, 150th Anniv. — A42

1992, July 8

126	A42	20d red, gold & black	.35	.25

Bishop Josip Juraj Strossmayer, Founder — A43

1992, July 9

127	A43	30d multicolored	.45	.45

Croatian Academy of Arts and Sciences, 125th anniv., in 1991.

1992 Summer
Olympics,
Barcelona
A44

Design: 105d, Abstract design.

1992, July 25
128 A44 40d shown   .50 .20
129 A44 105d multicolored   1.25 1.25

Flowers
A45

Designs: 30d, Edraianthus pumilio. 85d,
Degenia velebitica, vert.

1992, July 28
130 A45 30d multicolored   .40 .40
131 A45 85d multicolored   1.00 1.00

Wildlife — A46

40d, Monticola solitarius. 75d, Elaphe situla.

1992, July 31
132 A46 40d multicolored   .50 .50
133 A46 75d multicolored   .90 .90

Discovery of
America,
500th
Anniv. — A47

Europa: 30d, 60d, Sailing ship. 75d, 130d,
Indian in Chicago, by Ivan Mestrovic (1883-
1962).

1992, Sep. 4   Litho.   Perf. 14
134 A47 30d multicolored   .30 .20
135 A47 60d multicolored   .70 .60
136 A47 75d red & black   1.00 .90
137 A47 130d red, blk & gold 1.50 1.10
         Nos. 134-137 (4)   3.50 2.80

Issued: 30d, 75d, July 31; others, Sept. 4.

A48

A49

1992, Oct. 2
138 A48 40d multicolored   .35 .35
139 A48 130d multi, diff.   1.00 1.00

Declaration of Croatian Literary Language,
25th Anniv. (#133). Spelling reform by Dr. Ivan
Broz, cent. (#134).

1992, Oct. 16
140 A49 90d multicolored   .60 .40

City of Samobor, 750th Anniv.

Gift of the St.
Juraj Church
by Archbishop
Mucimir,
1100th
Anniv. — A50

1992, Oct. 30
141 A50 60d multicolored   .40 .30

Reign of King
Bela IV, 750th
Anniv. — A51

1992, Nov. 16   Litho.   Perf. 14
142 A51 180d multicolored   .95 .95

Christmas
A52

1992, Dec. 7
143 A52 80d multicolored   .40 .35

Blaz Lorkovic
(1839-1892),
Scientist — A53

Kolo Literature
Review, 150th
Anniv. — A54

1992, Dec. 21
144 A53 250d multicolored   .85 .85

1992, Dec. 22
145 A54 300d multicolored   1.10 1.10

Ivan Bunic-Vucic
(1592-1658)
A55

1992, Dec. 29
146 A55a 350d multicolored 1.25 1.25

— A55a

800th Anniversary of Krapina
1993, Jan. 15
146A A55a 300d multicolored   .80 .80

Nikola Tesla
(1856-1943),
Physicist
A56

1993, Jan. 30
147 A56 250d multicolored   .70 .70

Self-Portrait,
by Ferdo
Quiquerez
(1845-1893)
A57

1993, Feb. 10
148 A57 100d multicolored   .25 .25

Wildlife — A58

1993, Feb. 23   Litho.   Perf. 14
149 A58 500d Cervus elaphus   1.10 .90
150 A58 550d Haliaeetus albicilla 1.25 .95

Self-Portrait,
by Zlatko
Sulentic
(1893-1971)
A59

1993, Mar. 17
151 A59 350d multicolored   .65 .55

Lipik Health
and
Convalescent
Home,
Cent. — A60

1993, Apr. 22   Litho.   Perf. 14
152 A60 400d multicolored   .75 .75

Ivan Goran
Kovacic
(1913-1943),
Author — A61

1993, Apr. 24
153 A61 200d multicolored   .35 .35

59th PEN
Congress,
Dubrovnik
A62

1993, Apr. 24
154 A62 800d multicolored   1.40 1.40

Ivan
Kukuljevic
(1816-89),
Politician,
Historian,
Writer — A63

1993, May 2   Litho.   Perf. 14
155 A63 500d multicolored   .75 .75

Croatian Natl.
Theatre, Split,
Cent. — A64

Pag, 500th
Anniv. — A65

1993, May 6   Litho.   Perf. 14
156 A64 600d multicolored   .75 .75

1993, May 18
157 A65 800d multicolored   .90 .90

Croatian
Membership in
United Nations,
1st Anniv. — A66

1993, May 22
158 A66 500d multicolored   .60 .60

Europa
A67

Contemporary paintings by: 700d, Ivo Dulcic (1916-75). 1000d, Miljenko Stancic (1926-77). 1100d, Ljubo Ivancic (b. 1925).

1993, June 5
159	A67	700d multicolored	.90	.90
160	A67	1000d multicolored	1.25	1.25
161	A67	1100d multicolored	1.50	1.50
a.		Min. sheet, 2 each #159-161	8.00	8.00
		Nos. 159-161 (3)	3.65	3.65

Intl. Art Biennial, Venice — A68

Works of art by: 250d, Milivoj Bijelic. 600d, Ivo Dekovic. 1000d, Zeljko Kipke.

1993, June 10   Litho.   Perf. 14
162	A68	250d multicolored	.25	.25
a.		Souvenir sheet of 4	1.00	1.00
163	A68	600d multicolored	.75	.75
a.		Souvenir sheet of 4	3.00	3.00
164	A68	1000d multicolored	1.00	1.00
a.		Souvenir sheet of 4	4.00	4.00
		Nos. 162-164 (3)	2.00	

1993 Mediterranean Games — A69

1993, June 15   Litho.   Perf. 14
| 165 | A69 | 700d multicolored | .65 | .65 |

Adolf Waldinger (1843-1904), Painter — A70

1993, June 16
| 166 | A70 | 300d multicolored | .30 | .30 |

Famous Croatian Battles A71

1993, July 6   Litho.   Perf. 14
| 167 | A71 | 800d Krbavskom, 1493 | .65 | .65 |
| 168 | A71 | 1300d Sisak, 1593 | 1.10 | 1.10 |

Miroslav Krleza (1893-1981), Writer — A72

1993, July 7
| 169 | A72 | 400d multicolored | .35 | .35 |

Croatian Membership in UPU, 1st Anniv. — A73

1993, July 20   Litho.   Perf. 14
| 170 | A73 | 1800d multicolored | 1.40 | .80 |

Vlaho Paljetak (1893-1944), Composer A74

1993, Aug. 7
| 171 | A74 | 500d multicolored | .40 | .40 |

Stamp Day — A75

1993, Sept. 9   Litho.   Perf. 14
| 172 | A75 | 600d multicolored | .50 | .50 |

Map of Istria, 1620 — A76

1993, Sept. 20
| 173 | A76 | 2200d multicolored | 1.25 | 1.25 |

Incorporation of Istria, Rijeka and Zadar into Croatia, 50th anniv.

Tadija Smiciklas (1843-1914), Historian — A77

1993, Oct. 1
| 174 | A77 | 800d black, gold & red | .50 | .50 |

Archaelogical Museum, Split, Cent. — A78

1993, Oct. 27
| 175 | A78 | 1000d multicolored | .60 | .60 |

A79

A80

1993, Nov. 17   Litho.   Perf. 14
| 176 | A79 | 3000d multicolored | 1.50 | 1.50 |

Uprising of 13th Pioneer Battalion, Villefranche-de-Rouergue, France, 50th anniv.

1993, Nov. 18
900d, Josip Eugen Tomic (1843-1906), writer.
| 177 | A80 | 900d multicolored | .50 | .50 |

Publication of De Esscentiis, by Hermana Dalmatin, 850th Anniv. — A81

1993, Nov. 30
| 178 | A81 | 1000d multicolored | .60 | .50 |

Christmas A82

Paintings: 1000d, Christmas at the Front, by Miroslav Sutej. 4000d, Birth of Christ, 15th cent. fresco, Marienkirch of Dvigrad.

1993, Dec. 3
| 179 | A82 | 1000d multicolored | .50 | .40 |
| 180 | A82 | 4000d multicolored | 2.00 | 1.50 |

Organized Skiing in Croatia, Cent. — A83

1993, Dec. 15
| 181 | A83 | 1000d multicolored | .55 | .40 |

Croatian Natl. Guard, 125th Anniv. A84

1993, Dec. 22
| 182 | A84 | 1100d multicolored | .65 | .45 |

Printers of Senj, 500th Anniv. — A85

1994, Jan. 29
| 183 | A85 | 2200d multicolored | 1.10 | .75 |

1994 Winter Olympics, Lillehammer A86

1994, Feb. 12
| 184 | A86 | 4000d multicolored | 2.10 | 1.75 |

Dinosaurs from Western Istria — A87

a, 2400d, Iguanodons. b, 4000d, Map, skeleton.

1994, Mar. 7
| 185 | A87 | Pair, #a.-b. | 3.50 | 3.50 |

Nos. 185a-185b are a continuous design.

Zora Dalmatinska Magazine, 150th Anniv. — A88

1994, Mar. 15
| 186 | A88 | 800d multicolored | .45 | .30 |

Croatian University, Zagreb, 325th Anniv. — A89

Design: 2200d, University building, Emperor Leopold I's seal, vice-chancellor's chain.

1994, Apr. 19   Litho.   Perf. 14
| 187 | A89 | 2200d multicolored | 1.10 | .70 |

Protect the Environment A90

ILO, 75th
Anniv. — A91

1994, Apr. 22   **Litho.**   **Perf. 14**
188 A90 3800d Canis lupus   2.00 1.75

1994, May 2
189 A91 1000d multicolored   .60 .40

A92

Europa — A93

European inventions, discoveries: 3800d, Faust Vrancic (1551-1617), parachute. 4000d, Slavoljub Penkala (1871-1922), fountain pen.

1994, May 16
190 A92 3800d multicolored   1.40 1.25
191 A93 4000d multicolored   1.50 1.25

A94

1994, June 3
192 A94 2.40k Iris croatica   1.25 .60
193 A94   4k Colchicum visianii   2.00 1.25

1994, June 7
Drazen Petrovic (1964-93), basketball player.
194 A95 1k multicolored   .50 .45

A95

Tourism in Croatia, 150th Anniv. — A96

Designs: 80 l, Plitvice Lakes Natl. Park. 1k, Waterfalls, Krka River. 1.10k, Kornati Islands Natl. Park. 2.20k, Kopacki Trscak nature reserve. 2.40k Sailboats, Opatijska Riviera resort. 3.80k, Brijuni islands. 4k, Trakoscan castle, Zagorje.

1994, June 15   **Litho.**   **Perf. 14**
196 A96   80 l multicolored   .45 .20
197 A96   1k multicolored   .50 .25
198 A96 1.10k multicolored   .55 .30

199 A96 2.20k multicolored   1.10 .35
200 A96 2.40k multicolored   1.25 .50
201 A96 3.80k multicolored   1.90 .65
202 A96   4k multicolored   2.00 .90
   a.   Min. sheet of 7, #196-202 + 2 labels   8.00 5.75
   Nos. 196-202 (7)   7.75

Croatian Musicians A97

Designs: 1k, Kresimir Baranovic (1894-1975), composer, vert. 2.20k, Vatroslav Lisinski (1819-54), composer, vert. 2.40k, Pauline Liederbuch (b.1644), harpist.

1994, June 20
211 A97   1k multicolored   .50 .35
212 A97 2.20k multicolored   1.10 .75
213 A97 2.40k multicolored   1.25 .85
   Nos. 211-213 (3)   2.85

Croatian Fraternal Union, Cent. — A98

1994, Aug. 15   **Litho.**   **Perf. 14**
214 A98 2.20k multicolored   1.40 1.40

A99

A100

1994, Aug. 31
215 A99 80 l multicolored   .50 .50
Intl. Year of the Family.

1994, Sept. 10
216 A100 1k multicolored   .50 .50
Intl. Olympic Committee, cent.

Visit of Pope John Paul II — A101

1994, Sept. 10
217 A101 1k multicolored   .65 .55
No. 217 printed with se-tenant label.

Antoine de Saint-Exupery (1900-44), Aviator, Author A102

1994, Sept. 20
218 A102 3.80k multicolored   1.90 1.25

13th Intl. Congress on Early Christian Archeology A103

1994, Sept. 23
219 A103 4k multicolored   2.00 1.25
No. 219 printed with se-tenant label.

Modern Croatian Paintings A104

Designs: 2.40k, Still Life with Fruits and Basket, by Marino Tartaglia, 1926. 3.80k, In the Park, by Milan Steiner, c. 1918. 4k, Self-portrait, by Vilko Gecan, 1929.

1994, Oct. 12
220 A104 2.40k multicolored   1.25 .75
221 A104 3.80k multicolored   1.90 1.25
222 A104   4k multicolored   2.00 1.25
   Nos. 220-222 (3)   5.15

Ivan Belostenec (1594-1675), Writer & Lexicographer A105

1994, Nov. 9
223 A105 2.20k multicolored   1.10 .90

City of Zagreb, Zagreb Bishopric, 900th Anniv. — A106

Designs: No. 224a, 1k, Zagreb exchange building, designed by V. Kovacic, S. Penkala's airplane, Cibona office tower, designed by Hrzic, Pitesa and Serbetic. b, 1k, Maxi Cat, by Zlatko Grgic, Zagreb School of Animated Film. c, 1k, St. Mark's Church, Gradec; photo of gas lantern, by Toso Dabac. d, 4k, Late Gothic bishop's staff, Valvasor's view of Zagreb. 13.50k, Zagreb street scene, Penkala's airplane, vert.

1994, Nov. 16
224 A106 Strip of 4, #a.-d.   3.50 3.50
   Souvenir Sheet
225 A106 13.50k multicolored   6.75 6.75
No. 224 is a continuous design. No. 225 contains one 24x48mm stamp.

Christmas A107

Design: 1k, Epiphany, by unknown sculptor.

1994, Dec. 1   **Litho.**   **Perf. 14**
226 A107 1k multicolored   .60 .50

Virgin Mary's Sanctuary, Loreto, 700th Anniv. — A108

Design: 4k, The Moving of the Holy House, by Giovanni Battista Tiepolo.

1994, Dec. 10
227 A108 4k multicolored   2.00 1.50

Necktie in Croatia — A109

Tie designs: 1.10k, Businessman's, 1995. 3.80k, English Dandy, 1810. 4k, Croatian soldier, 1630.

1995, Jan. 19   **Litho.**   **Perf. 14**
228 A109 1.10k multicolored   .60 .40
229 A109 3.80k multicolored   1.75 1.25
230 A109   4k multicolored   1.90 1.50
   a.   Souvenir sheet of 3, #228-230   4.50 4.50
   Nos. 228-230 (3)   4.25

Croatian Monasteries — A110

1k, Jesuit Monastery, Zagreb, 350th anniv. 2.40k, Franciscan Monastery, Visovac, 550th anniv.

1995, Feb. 16
231 A110   1k multicolored   .45 .30
232 A110 2.40k multicolored   1.10 .85

Hunting Dogs — A111

Designs: 2.20k, Istrian short-haired. 2.40k, Posavinian. 3.80k, Istrian wire-haired.

1995, Mar. 9   **Litho.**   **Perf. 14**
233 A111 2.20k multicolored   1.00 .75
234 A111 2.40k multicolored   1.25 .80
235 A111 3.80k multicolored   1.75 1.40
   Nos. 233-235 (3)   4.00

Town of Split, 1700th Anniv. — A112

#236: a, 1k, Drawing of reconstruction of Diocletian's Palace. b, 2.20k, "Split Harbour," by Emanuel Vidovic, 1937. c, 4k, Modern view of town, bust of Marko Marulic by Ivan Mestrovic. 13.40k, Buildings, vert.

1995, Apr. 20 **Litho.** *Perf. 14*
236 A112 Strip of 3, #a.-c. 3.75 3.75
Souvenir Sheet
237 A112 13.40k multicolored 6.50 6.50
No. 237 contains one 24x48mm stamp.

World Team
Handball
Championships,
Iceland — A113

1995, May 4
238 A113 4k multicolored 1.75 1.10

Peace &
Freedom
A114

Europa: 2.40k, Clearing storm clouds. 4k,
Hands of angel, by Francisco Robba.

1995, May 9
239 A114 2.40k multicolored *1.25 1.00*
240 A114 4k multicolored *1.75 1.40*

Anti-Austria Demonstrations, 150th
Anniv. — A115

1995, May 15
241 A115 1.10k multicolored .75 .45
242 A115 3.80k multicolored 1.50 1.10
Croatian surrender to British forces at
Bleiburg, 50th anniv. (#242).

Independence
Day — A116

1995, May 30 **Litho.** *Perf. 14*
243 A116 1.10k multicolored .65 .35

Croatian Sculptures at Venice Biennial,
1995 — A117

2.20k, Installation (a part), by Martina
Kramer. 2.40k, Paracelsus Paraduchamps, by
Mirko Zrinscak, vert. 4k, Shadows, by Goran
Petercol.

1995, June 8 **Litho.** *Perf. 14*
244 A117 2.20k multicolored 1.00 .65
245 A117 2.40k multicolored 1.10 .75
246 A117 4k multicolored 1.90 1.75
Nos. 244-246 (3) 4.00

St. Anthony of Padua (1195-
1231) — A118

1995, June 13
247 A118 1k multicolored .45 .30

Marine
Life — A119

1995, June 29 **Litho.** *Perf. 14*
248 A119 2.40k Caretta caretta 1.25 .95
249 A119 4k Tursiops trun- 2.25 1.50
catus

Liberation of
the City of
Knin — A120

1995, Aug. 5 **Litho.** *Perf. 14*
250 A120 1.30k multicolored .60 .45

Krka River
Hydroelectric
Power Plant,
Cent. — A121

1995, Aug. 28
251 A121 3.60k multicolored 1.60 .90

Stamp
Day — A122

1995, Sept. 9 **Litho.** *Perf. 14*
252 A122 1.30k multicolored .60 .60

Franz von
Suppe (1819-
95),
Composer
A123

1995, Sept. 15
253 A123 6.50k multicolored 3.00 2.00
See Austria Nos. 1686-1687.

Liberation of
Petrinja from
Turkish Rule,
400th
Anniv. — A124

1995, Sept. 21
254 A124 2.20k multicolored 1.00 .80

Croatian
Music — A125

Composers, conductors: 1.20k, Ivo
Tijardovic (1895-1976). 1.40k, Lovro Von
Matacic (1899-1985). 6.50k, Jakov Gotovac
(1895-1982).

1995, Sept. 23
255 A125 1.20k multicolored .55 .50
256 A125 1.40k multicolored .65 .55
257 A125 6.50k multicolored 3.00 2.25
Nos. 255-257 (3) 4.20

Herman Bollé (1845-1926),
Architect — A126

2.40k, Izidor Krsnjavi (1845-1927), painter.
3.60k, Croatian National Theatre, cent.

1995, Oct. 14 **Litho.** *Perf. 14*
258 A126 1.80k multicolored .80 .50
259 A126 2.40k multicolored 1.00 .70
260 A126 3.60k multicolored 1.75 1.25
Nos. 258-260 (3) 3.55

Croatian
Towns — A127

1995, Oct. 20
261 A127 1k Bjelovar .45 .45
262 A127 1.30k Osijek, vert. .55 .55
263 A127 1.40k Cakovec, vert. .60 .60
264 A127 2.20k Rovinj 1.00 1.00
265 A127 2.40k Korcula 1.10 1.10
266 A127 3.60k Zupanja 1.50 1.50
Nos. 261-266 (6) 5.20
See No. 448.

UN, FAO, 50th
Anniv. — A128

No. 268, "5, 0" in form of cracker, FAO.

1995, Oct. 24
267 A128 3.60k multicolored 1.60 1.00
268 A128 3.60k multicolored 1.60 1.00
a. Pair, #267-268 3.25 3.25

Croatian
Scientists — A129

1k, Spiro Brusina (1845-1908). 2.20k,
Bogoslav Sulek (1816-95). 6.50k, Front of
European language dictionary, published by
Faust Vrancic (1551-1617).

1995, Oct. 30
269 A129 1k multicolored .50 .25
270 A129 2.20k multicolored .90 .65
271 A129 6.50k multicolored 2.75 2.00
Nos. 269-271 (3) 4.15

Institute for
Blind Children,
Cent. — A130

1995, Nov. 23 **Litho.** *Perf. 14*
272 A130 1.20k multicolored .60 .45

Christmas
A131

1995, Dec. 1
273 A131 1.30k multicolored .60 .45

Maroc
Polo's
Return from
China,
700th
Anniv.
A132

1995, Dec. 7
274 A132 3.60k multicolored 1.75 1.50

Liberated
Towns
A133

1995, Dec. 16
275 A133 20 l Hrvatska Kos- .20 .20
tajnica
276 A133 30 l Slunj .20 .20
277 A133 50 l Gracac .30 .30
278 A133 1.20k Drnis, vert. .60 .60
279 A133 6.50k Glina 2.75 2.75
280 A133 10k Obrovac, vert. 4.00 4.00
Nos. 275-280 (6) 8.05

Incunabula
A134

Designs: 1.40k, Lectionary of Bernardin of
Split. 3.60k, Spovid Opcena (General
Confession).

1995, Dec. 28
281 A134 1.40k multicolored .60 .35
282 A134 3.60k multicolored 1.50 1.10

Spirituality of
the Croats
A135

Political
Anniversaries
A136

Designs: No. 283, Mosaic of St. Marko
Krizevcanin (1589-1619), Catholic martyr. No.
284, Veneration of Miraculous Crucifix, St.
Guido's Church, Rijeka, 700th anniv. No. 285,
Ivan Merz (1896-1928), Catholic educator.

1996, Jan. 18　Litho.　Perf. 14
283	A135 1.30k multicolored	.60	.50
284	A135 1.30k multicolored	.60	.50
285	A135 1.30k multicolored	.60	.50
a.	Strip of 3, Nos. 283-285	2.00	2.00

1996, Feb. 28

1.20k, Rakovica Uprising by Eugen Kvaternik, 125th anniv., horiz. 1.40k, Ante Starcevic (1823-96). 2.20k, Constitution of Neutral Peasant Republic of Croatia, 75th anniv., Stjepan Radic (1871-1928). 3.60k, Labin Republic, 75th anniv.

286	A136 1.20k multicolored	.50	.45
287	A136 1.40k multicolored	.60	.55
288	A136 2.20k multicolored	.85	.75
289	A136 3.60k multicolored	1.40	1.25
	Nos. 286-289 (4)	3.35	

Institute for Pharmacognosy, University of Zagreb, Cent. — A137

1996, Mar. 23　Litho.　Perf. 14
290	A137 6.50k multicolored	2.75	2.00

Croatian Music — A138

a, Vinko Jelić (1596-1636), composer. b, First performance of opera "Love and Music." c, Josip Stolcer Slavenski (1896-1955), composer. d, "Lijepa Nasa," Croatian national anthem, 150th anniv.

1996, Mar. 28
291	A138 2.20k Strip of 4, #a.-d.	3.75	3.75

A139　　　　　A140

Famous Women Writers (Europa): 2.20k, Cvijeta Zuzoric (b. 1551 or 1552). 3.60k, Ivana Brlic Mazuranic (1874-1938).

1996, Apr. 11　Litho.　Perf. 14
292	A139 2.20k multicolored	1.25	1.00
293	A139 3.60k multicolored	1.50	1.25

1996, Apr. 30

The Zrinskis and The Frankopans: 1.30k, Nikola Subic Zrinski of Sziget (1508-56). 1.40k, Nikola Zrinski (1620-64). 2.20k, Petar Zrinski (1621-71). 2.40k, Katarina Zrinski (1625-73). 3.60k, Fran Krsto Frankopan (1643-71).

294	A140 1.30k multicolored	.45	.40
295	A140 1.40k multicolored	.50	.45
296	A140 2.20k multicolored	.80	.75
297	A140 2.40k multicolored	.90	.85
298	A140 3.60k multicolored	1.25	1.00
a.	Sheet of 5, #294-298	5.00	4.50
	Nos. 294-298 (5)	3.90	

Natl. Guard, 5th Anniv. A141　　Flowers A142

1996, May 28　Litho.　Perf. 14
299	A141 1.30k multicolored	.60	.45

1996, June 5

Designs: 2.40k, Campanula istriaca. 3.60k, Centaurea ragusina.

300	A142 2.40k multicolored	1.25	1.25
301	A142 3.60k multicolored	1.75	1.75

England '96, European Soccer Championship A143

1996, June 8
302	A143 2.20k red & black	.90	.80

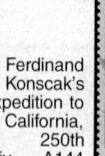

Father Ferdinand Konscak's Expedition to Lower California, 250th Anniv. — A144

1996, June 10
303	A144 2.40k multicolored	1.10	.90

1996 Summer Olympics, Atlanta A145

1996, July 4
304	A145 3.60k multicolored	1.75	1.25

A146　　　　　A147

1996, July 4
305	A146 1.40k multicolored	.65	.55

Josip Fon, founder of Croatian Sokol Gymnastics Society, 150th birth anniv.

1996, Sept. 9　Litho.　Perf. 14
306	A147 1.30k multicolored	.60	.35

Croatian postage stamps, 5th anniv.

1st Written Reference, Zumberak Region, 700th Anniv. — A148

1996, Sept. 14
307	A148 2.20k multicolored	1.00	1.00

A149　　　　　A150

1996, Sept. 19
308	A149 1.30k multicolored	.65	.45

First written record of fishing in Croatia, 1000th anniv.

1996, Sept. 19

Events of the early Middle Ages: 1.20k, Vekenega's Book of Gospels, 900th anniv. 1.40k, Visit by Saxon Benedictine abbot Gottschalk (805-870), to Duke Trpimir's court, 1150th anniv.

309	A150 1.20k multicolored	.55	.50
310	A150 1.40k multicolored	.65	.55

Scientists A151

Designs: a, Gjuro Pilar (1846-93), geologist. b, Frane Bulic (1846-1934), archeologist. c, Ante Sercer (1896-1968), otolaryngologist.

1996, Oct. 4　Litho.　Perf. 14
311	A151 2.40k Strip of 3, #a.-c.	3.00	3.00

Beginning of Higher Education in Croatia, 600th Anniv. — A152

Oldest preserved Croatian text written in Latin script, "Order and Law" of Dominican nuns, Zadar.

1996, Oct. 16　　　　Perf. 13½
312	A152 1.40k multicolored	.60	.45

Paintings — A153

Designs: 1.30k, Rain, by Menci Clement Crncic (1865-1930). 1.40k, The Peljesac-Korcula Channel, by Mato Celestin Medovic (1857-1919). 3.60k, Pink Dream, by Vlaho Bukovac (1855-1922).

1996, Nov. 7　Litho.　Perf. 14
313	A153 1.30k multicolored	.55	.55
314	A153 1.40k multicolored	.65	.65
315	A153 3.60k multicolored	1.60	1.60
	Nos. 313-315 (3)	2.80	

UNICEF, 50th Anniv. — A154

1996, Nov. 15
316	A154 3.60k multicolored	1.50	1.25

City of Osijek, 800th Anniv. A155　　Christmas A156

Views of city: No. 317, River bank, church, coat of arms. No. 318, Boats in water, view looking down covered walkway through building.

1996, Dec. 2　Litho.　Perf. 14
317	A155 2.20k multicolored	.85	.70
318	A155 2.20k multicolored	.85	.70
a.	Pair, #317-318	2.10	2.10

1996, Dec. 3
319	A156 1.30k multicolored	.55	.45

First Croatian Savings Bank, Zagreb, 150th Anniv. — A157

Design: 3.60k, Publishing of "The Bases of Corn Trade," by Josip Sipus, bicent.

1996, Dec. 14
320	A157 2.40k multicolored	.95	.75
321	A157 3.60k multicolored	1.50	1.00

Motion Pictures, Cent. — A158

Designs: a, Shooting of film, "Vatroslav Lisinski," Oktavijan Miletic, cameraman, director. b, Characters from animated series, "Professor Baltazar." c, Mirjana Bohanec, Relja Basic in "Who Sings Means No Harm."

1997, Jan. 16　Litho.　Perf. 14
322	A158 1.40k Strip of 3, #a.-c.	2.25	2.25

Great Europeans A159

Designs: 2.20k, Miguel de Cervantes (1547-1676), author. 3.60k, Johannes Gutenberg (1397-1468), printer, horiz.

1997, Feb. 7
323	A159 2.20k multicolored	.75	.65
324	A159 3.60k multicolored	1.25	1.10

Legends A160

Europa: 1.30k, Home Genies, from story, "Stribor's Forest." 3.60k, "Vili Joze," by Vladimir Nazor, vert.

1997, Mar. 6　Litho.　Perf. 14
325	A160 1.30k multicolored	.50	.50
326	A160 3.60k multicolored	1.25	1.25

Fauna of
Croatia — A161

1997, Apr. 22   Litho.   Perf. 14
327 A161 1.40k Pinna nobilis   .55   .55
328 A161 2.40k Radziella styx   .90   .90
329 A161 3.60k Tonna galea   1.50 1.50
   Nos. 327-329 (3)   2.95

Admission
of Croatia
to UN, 5th
Anniv.
A162

1997, May 22   Litho.   Perf. 14
330 A162 6.50k Pres. Franjo
   Tudjman   2.50 2.50

First
Croatian
Esperantist
Conference,
90th Anniv.
A163

Ludwig Lazarus Zamenhof, conf. logo.

1997, May 31
331 A163 1.20k multicolored   .45   .40

Congress of
Intl. Amateur
Rugby
Federation,
Dubrovnik
A164

1997, June 6
332 A164 2.20k multicolored   .85   .75

Siege of Vukovar, Serbo-Croatian War,
1991 — A165

Painting by Zlatko Kauzlaric Atac. Illustration reduced.

1997, June 8   Litho.   Perf. 14
333 A165 6.50k multicolored   2.50 2.50

Croatian
Kings — A166

1.30k, King Peter Svacic, 900th death anniv. 2.40k, King Stephen Drzislav, 1000th death anniv.

1997, July 3
334 A166 1.30k multicolored   .50   .50
335 A166 2.40k multicolored   1.00 1.00

16th
Century
Courier
from
Dubrovnik
A167

1997, Sept. 9   Litho.   Perf. 14
336 A167 2.30k multicolored   1.00   .90

Stamp Day.

Croatian Olympic
Medals — A168

Designs: 1k, Tennis, bronze, Barcelona, 1992. 1.20k, Basketball, silver, Barcelona 1992. 1.40k, Water polo, silver, Atlanta, 1996. 2.20k, Handball, gold, Atlanta, 1996.

1997, Sept. 10
337 A168   1k multicolored   .40   .40
338 A168 1.20k multicolored   .50   .50
   Size: 27x31mm
339 A168 1.40k multicolored   .60   .60
340 A168 2.20k multicolored   .90   .90
   Nos. 337-340 (4)   2.40

Defense of Sibenik — A169

Designs: No. 341, Fort, airplanes. No. 342, Turkish cavalry, fort.

1997, Sept. 18
341 A169 1.30k multicolored   .50   .50
342 A169 1.30k multicolored   .50   .50
   a.   Pair, #341-342   1.25 1.25

Serbo-Croatian War, 1991 (#341). War with the Turks, 350th anniv. (#342).

Anniversaries
A170

No. 343: a, Frane Petrić (1529-97), philosopher. b, Vicko Lovrin, 16th century painter. c, Frano Krsinić (1897-1982), sculptor. d, Dubravko Dujsin (1894-1947), actor.

1997, Oct. 17   Litho.   Perf. 14
343 A170 1.40k Strip of 4, #a.-d. 2.25 2.25

A171

A172

1997, Oct. 23
344 A171 2.20k multicolored   .85   .65
345 A172 3.60k multicolored   1.40   .90

Use of Croatian language in parliament, 150th anniv. (#344).
Croatian Grammar School, Zadar, cent. (#345).

Palaeontological
Finds in
Croatia — A173

Designs: 1.40k, Gomphotherium angustidens. 2.40k, Viviparus novskaensis.

1997, Nov. 6
346 A173 1.40k multicolored   .60   .60
347 A173 2.40k multicolored 1.10 1.10

Modern
Art
A174

Paintings: 1.30k, Painter in the Pond, by Nikola Masic (1852-1902). 2.20k, Angelus, by Emanuel Vidovic (1870-1953). 3.60k, Tree in the Snow, by Slava Raskaj (1877-1906).

1997, Nov. 14
348 A174 1.30k multicolored   .50   .40
349 A174 2.20k multicolored   .80   .50
350 A174 3.60k multicolored 1.40 1.00
   Nos. 348-350 (3)   2.70 1.90

Contemporary
Christmas
Painting, by Ivan
Antolcic — A175

"Birth of
Jesus," by
Isidor Krsnjavi
A176

1997, Nov. 28   Litho.   Perf. 13½
351 A175 1.30k multicolored   .50   .35
   Perf. 14
352 A176 3.60k multicolored 1.50 1.00

Croatian
Literature — A177

1997, Dec. 18   Perf. 14
353 A177   1k shown   .55   .40
354 A177 1.20k Book, words   .60   .40

Printing of the translation of "Electra," by Dominko Zlataric, 400th anniv. (No. 353). Publication of "The Best of Folk Speech and the Illyric or Croatian Language," by Filip Grabovac, 250th anniv. (No. 354).

Cities and Landmarks Type of 1992
1997   Litho.   Perf. 14
355 A39 5 l Ilok   .20   .20
356 A39 10 l Dubrovnik   .20   .20

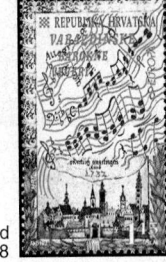

Events and
Festivals — A178

Europa: 1.45k, Varazdin Baroque Evenings, musical notes. 4k, Dubrovnik Summer Festival.

1998, Jan. 23   Perf. 13½
357 A178 1.45k multicolored   .50   .50
358 A178   4k multicolored 1.50 1.50

1998 Winter
Olympic Games,
Nagano — A179

1998, Feb. 7   Perf. 14
359 A179 2.45k multicolored   .80   .55

Croatian Events of 1848 — A180

a, 1.60k, Flag, battle near Moor. b, 4k, Portrait of Ban Josip Jelacic. c, 1.60k, Croatian Assembly.

1998, Mar. 25   Litho.   Perf. 14
360 A180 Strip of 3, #a.-c. 3.00 3.00
   No. 360b is 21x32mm.

Ante Topic
Mimara (1898-
1987), Art
Collector,
Painter
A181

1998, Apr. 7   Litho.   Perf. 14
361 A181 2.65k multicolored   .90   .70

572 CROATIA

A182 A183

Mushrooms: a, 1.30k, Amanita caesarea. b, 7.20k, Morchella conica. c, 1.30k, Lactarius deliciosus.

1998, Apr. 22
362 A182 Strip of 3, #a.-c. 3.75 3.75

1998, May 8
363 A183 1.50k multicolored .55 .45

Archbishop Alojzije Stepinac (1898-1960).

27th European Regional Conference of Interpol, Dubrovnik A184

1998, May 13
364 A184 2.45k multicolored .85 .65

Souvenir Sheet

Expo '98, Lisbon — A185

Illustration reduced.

1998, June 3 Litho. Perf. 14
365 A185 14.85k Fishing boat, Falkusa 5.25 5.25

1998 World Cup Soccer Championships, France — A186

1998, June 10
366 A186 4k multicolored 1.40 1.10

Writers A187

1.20k, Juraj Barakovic (1548-1628). 1.50k, Milan Begovic (1876-1948). 1.60k, Mate Balota (Mijo Mirkovic, 1898-1963). 2.45k, Antun Gustav Matos (1873-1914). 2.65k, Matija Antun Relkovic (1732-98). 4.00k, Antun Branko Simic (1898-1925).

1998, June 13 Litho. Perf. 14
367 A187 1.20k multicolored .45 .40
368 A187 1.50k multicolored .55 .50
369 A187 1.60k multicolored .60 .55
370 A187 2.45k multicolored .80 .75
371 A187 2.65k multicolored .90 .85
372 A187 4k multicolored 1.40 1.25
Nos. 367-372 (6) 4.70

19th Conference of the Countries of the Danube Region, Osijek — A188

1998, June 15
373 A188 1.80k multicolored .60 .45

Stjepan Betlheim (1898-1970), Psychiatrist A189

1998, July 22
374 A189 1.50k multicolored .65 .45

Souvenir Sheet

Croatian Soccer Team, Bronze Medalists at 1998 World Cup Soccer Championships, France — A190

Portions of team picture, denomination: a, red, LL. b, yellow, CR (player in yellow & blue shirt). c, yellow, CL. d, yellow, LR.

1998, July 24
375 A190 4k Sheet of 4, #a.-d. 6.00 6.00

Croatian Ships — A191

1.20k, Serilia Liburnica. 1.50k, Condura Croatica. 1.60k, Dubrovnik carrack. 1.80k, Bracera. 2.45k, Ship from the Neretva. 2.65k, Bark. 4k, Training ship, "Villa Velebita." 7.20k, Passenger ship, "Amorella." 20k, Missile gun boat, "Kralj Petar Kresimir IV."

1998, Aug. 27 Litho. Perf. 14
376 A191 1.20k multi .45 .45
376A A191 1.50k multi .55 .55
376B A191 1.60k multi .60 .60
376C A191 1.80k multi .65 .65
376D A191 2.45k multi .90 .90
376E A191 2.65k multi 1.00 1.00
376F A191 4k multi 1.40 1.40
376G A191 7.20k multi 2.40 2.40
376H A191 20k multi 6.75 6.75
i. Sheet of 9, #376-376H + 3 labels 16.75
Nos. 376-376H (9) 14.70 14.70

Stamp Day — A192

1998, Sept. 9
377 A192 1.50k multicolored .60 .45

Bishopric of Sibenik, 700th Anniv. — A193

1998, Sept. 29 Litho. Perf. 14
378 A193 4k multicolored 1.25 1.25

Pope John Paul II, Second Visit to Croatia A194

1998, Oct. 2
379 A194 1.50k multicolored .90 .90

History of Public Transportation A195

Designs: a, 1.50k, Horse tram. b, 1.50k, First automobile in Zagreb, 1901. c, 7.20k, Zagreb funicular. d, 1.50k, Karlovac-Rijeka Railway Line, 1873. e, 1.50k, New Highway, Zagreb-Rijeka.

1998, Oct. 23 Litho. Perf. 14
380 A195 Strip of 5, #a.-e. 5.25 5.25
No. 380c is 20x24mm.

Christmas — A196

Adoration of the Shepherds, by Juraj Julije Klovic (1498-1578).

1998, Nov. 21 Perf. 14x13
381 A196 1.50k multicolored .65 .60
See Vatican City No. 1088.

Father Luka Ibrisimovic (1620-98) A197

1998, Nov. 30 Litho. Perf. 14
382 A197 1.90k multicolored .70 .65

Universal Declaration of Human Rights, 50th Anniv. — A198

1998, Dec. 10
383 A198 5k multicolored 2.00 2.00

Modern Art A199

Paintings: 1.90k, Paromlin Road, by Josip Vanista. 2.20k, Cypresses, by Frano Simunovic, vert. 5k, Koma, by Dalibor Martinis, vert.

1998, Dec. 15
384 A199 1.90k multicolored .65 .65
385 A199 2.20k multicolored .75 .75
386 A199 5k multicolored 1.75 1.75
Nos. 384-386 (3) 3.15 3.15

Zagreb Intl. Trade Fair — A200

1999, Jan. 21 Litho. Perf. 14
387 A200 1.80k multicolored .65 .60

Cardinal Juraj Haulik (1788-1869), Archbishop of Zagreb — A201

Photo. & Engr.
1999, Jan. 28 Perf. 11½
388 A201 5k multicolored 1.75 1.75
See Slovakia 321.

National Parks — A202

Europa: 1.80k, Mljet Island. 5k, Lonja River Field.

1999, Mar. 12 Litho. Perf. 14
389 A202 1.80k multicolored 1.60 1.60
390 A202 5k multicolored 2.75 2.75

Vipera Ursinii — A203

World Wildlife Fund: a, One coiled in grass and rock. b, Two. c, Head. d, One coiled on rock.

1999, Apr. 27 Litho. Perf. 14
391 A203 2.20k Strip of 4, #a.-d. 3.75 3.75

Council of Europe, 50th Anniv. — A204

1999, May 5
392 A204 2.80k multicolored 1.10 1.10

19th Convention of the Foundation of European Carnival Cities, Dubrovnik — A205

1999, May 8
393 A205 2.30k multicolored .95 .90

Croatian Coins — A206

Designs: a, 2.30k, Obv., rev. of 1849 kreutzer. b, 5k, One kuna.

1999, May 30   Litho.   Perf. 14
394 A206 Pair, #a.-b.   2.75 2.75
Minting of Jelacic kreutzer, 150th anniv. (#394a). Croatian kuna, 5th anniv. (#394b).

Famous
Croats — A207

1.80k, Vladimir Nazor (1876-1949), poet. 2.30k, Ferdo Livadic (1799-1879), composer. 2.50k, Ivan Rendic (1849-1932), sculptor. 2.80k, Milan Lenuci (1849-1924), architect. 3.50k, Vjekoslav Klaic (1849-1929), historian, muscician. 4k, Emilij Laszowski (1868-1949), historian. 5k, Antun Kanizlic (1699-1777), poet, missionary.

1999, June 18
395 A207 1.80k multicolored   .60   .60
396 A207 2.30k multicolored   .85   .80
397 A207 2.50k multicolored   1.00   .95
398 A207 2.80k multicolored   1.10   1.10
399 A207 3.50k multicolored   1.25   1.25
400 A207   4k multicolored   1.40   1.40
401 A207   5k multicolored   1.75   1.75
    Nos. 395-401 (7)   7.95   7.85

Euphrasian Basilica, Porec — A208

1999, June 25
402 A208 4k multicolored   1.50 1.50

2nd World
Military
Games,
Zagreb
A209

1999, Aug. 7   Litho.   Perf. 14
403 A209 2.30k multicolored   .80   .70

Discovery of Early Krapina Man,
Cent. — A210

Designs: a, 1.80k, Bones, rendition of Krapina man. b, 4k, Ancient bones, paleontologist Dragutin Gorjanovic-Kramberger.

1999, Aug. 23
404 A210 Pair, #a.-b.   3.00 3.00

Stamp Day
and UPU,
125th
Anniv. — A211

1999, Sept. 9   Litho.   Perf. 14
405 A211 2.30k multicolored   .95   .90

Paulist Order
in Lepoglava,
600th
Anniv. — A212

a, Lace, Jesus Expelling the Money Changers from Temple, by Ivan Ranger, altar angel from St. Mary's Church, Lepoglava. b, St. Mary's Church facade, altar angel. c, St. Elizabeth, lace.

1999, Sept. 11   Litho.
406 A212 5k Strip of 3, #a.-c.   5.50 5.50

150th Anniv. of
"Jelacic March"
by Johann
Strauss the
Elder — A213

1999, Sept. 16   Litho.
407 A213 3.50k multicolored   1.25 1.25

World
Ozone
Layer
Protection
Day
A214

1999, Sept. 16   Litho.
408 A214 5k multicolored   1.90 1.75

Grammar
School
Anniversaries
A215

1999, Oct. 15   Litho.   Perf. 14
409 A215 2.30k Pazin, cent.   .80   .75
410 A215 3.50k Pozega, 300th
          anniv.   1.25 1.00

Andrija Hebrang
(1899-1949),
Politician — A216

1999, Oct. 21
411 A216 1.80k multicolored   .75   .70

Our Lady of
the Rose
Garden, by
Blaz Jurjev
Trogiranin
A217

1999, Oct. 28
412 A217 5k multicolored   1.90 1.75
Christmas, opening of exhibition of Croatian religious art and artifacts, Vatican City.

Christmas
A218

1999, Nov. 24   Litho.   Perf. 14
413 A218 2.30k multicolored   .80   .75

Modern
Art
A219

Designs: 2.30k, Winter Landscape, by Gabrijel Jurkic (1886-1974). 3.50k, Klek, by Oton Postruznik (1900-78). 5k, Stone Table, by Ignjat Job (1895-1936), vert.

1999, Dec. 15
414 A219 2.30k multicolored   1.00 1.00
415 A219 3.50k multicolored   1.25 1.25
416 A219   5k multicolored   1.75 1.75
    Nos. 414-416 (3)   4.00 4.00

Pres. Franjo
Tudjman (1922-
99) — A220

1999, Dec. 16   Vignette Color
417 A220 2.30k black   .80   .75
418 A220   5k blue   1.75 1.50

Millennium
A221

2000, Jan. 1   Litho.   Perf. 14
419 A221 2.30k multi   1.40 1.25

Valentine's
Day — A222

2000, Feb. 1
420 A222 2.30k multi   1.25 1.00

Split Grammar
School, 300th
Anniv. — A223

2000, Mar. 25   Litho.   Perf. 14
421 A223 2.80k multi   .90   .80

Croatian Writers'
Assoc., 100th
Anniv. — A224

2000, Apr. 22   Litho.   Perf. 14
422 A224 2.30k black & red   2.00 1.90

A225   A226

A227   A228

A229

2000, Apr. 22
423 A225 1.80k multi   .60   .55
424 A226 2.30k multi   .85   .80
425 A227 2.80k multi   1.00   .95
426 A228 3.50k multi   1.25 1.10
427 A229   5k multi   1.75 1.60
    Nos. 423-427 (5)   5.45 5.00

Lo Schiavone (Andrija Medulic, c. 1500-63), painter (1.80k); Matija Petar Katancic (1750-1825), writer (2.30k); Marija Ruzicka-Strozzi (1850-1937), actress (2.80k); Marko Marulic (1450-1524), writer (3.50k); Blaz Jurjev Trogiranin (c. 1390-1450), painter (5k).

Europa, 2000
Common Design Type and

A230

2000, May 9
428 A230 2.30k multi   1.10 1.00
429 CD17   5k multi   2.50 2.00

Independence
Day — A231

2000, May 30   Litho.   Perf. 14
430 A231 2.30k multi   .90   .85

Souvenir Sheet

Expo 2000, Hanover — A232

Illustration reduced.

2000, June 1
431 A232 14.40k multi   5.00 5.00

Flora — A233

No. 432: a, 3.50k, Micromeria croatica. b,
5k, Geranium dalmaticum.
Illustration reduced.

2000, June 5
432 A233 Pair, #a-b   4.00 4.00
  c. Booklet pane of 10 #432a   15.00
    Booklet, #432c   16.00
  d. Booklet pane of 10 #432b   20.00
    Booklet, #432d   21.00

Kastav
Statute, 600th
Anniv. — A234

2000, June 6
433 A234 1.80k multi   .65 .60

World
Mathematics
Year — A235

2000, June 15
434 A235 3.50k multi   1.40 1.25

Ivan Ranger
(1700-53),
Artist — A236

2000, June 19
435 A236 1.80k multi   .80 .70

Souvenir Sheet

Baska Stone Tablet, 900th
Anniv. — A237

Illustration reduced.

2000, June 24
436 A237 16.70k multi   6.25 6.25

Archdeacon
Toma of Split
(1200-68)
A238

2000, July 10
437 A238 3.50k multi   1.25 1.10

Type of 1992-94 Redrawn
2000, Aug. 1   Litho.   **Perf. 14**
437A A39a 3.50k Vis   1.40 .95

No. 437A has "HP" and post horn in LR
corner.

Stamp Day — A239

No. 438: a, 2.30k, Austria #5. b, 2.30k, Automatic mail sorting equipment.

2000, Sept. 9   Litho.   **Perf. 14**
438 A239 Pair, #a-b   2.00 2.00

First stamps used in Croatia, 150th anniv.
(#438a).

2000 Summer
Olympics,
Sydney
A240

2000, Sept. 15
439 A240 5k multicolored   2.50 2.50

Altarpiece,
Church of the
Blessed Virgin
Mary, Ostarije
A241

2000, Nov. 23
440 A241 2.30k multi   .90 .75
  a. Booklet pane of 10   9.00
    Booklet, #440a   9.50

Modern
Art
A242

Designs: 1.80k, Korcula, by Vladimir Varlaj.
2.30k, Brusnik, by Duro Tiljak. 5k, Boats, by
Ante Kastelacic.

2000, Dec. 1
441-443 A242 Set of 3   3.50 3.00

Start of New
Millennium
A243

2001, Jan. 1   Litho.   **Perf. 14**
444 A243 2.30k multi   1.40 1.25

Souvenir Sheet

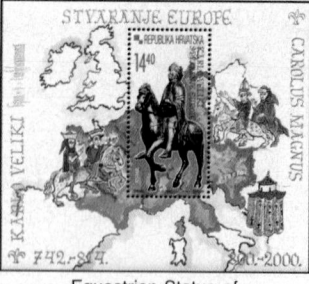

Equestrian Statue of
Charlemagne — A244

2001, Jan. 19
445 A244 14.40k multi   6.00 6.00

Crowning of Charlemagne as Emperor of
the Romans, 1200th anniv. (in 2000).

Dzore Drzic (1461-1501),
Writer — A245

2001, Mar. 15   Litho.   **Perf. 14**
446 A245 2.80k multi   1.10 .90

Comic Strip
"Black Rider,"
by Andrija
Maurovic
(1901-81)
A246

2001, Mar. 29
447 A246 5k multi   1.75 1.50

Makarska
A247

2001, Mar. 30
448 A247 2.30k multi   .90 .75
  a. Perf. 14 syncopated   .85 .85
    Issued: No. 448a, 6/2/06.

Janica
Kostelic,
Skier — A248

2001, Apr. 19   Litho.   **Perf. 14**
449 A248 2.80k multi   1.75 1.50

Kastel Stafilic
Olive Trees,
1500th
Anniv. — A249

2001, Apr. 20
450 A249 1.80k multi   .75 .65

Europa — A250

No. 451: a, 3.50k, Denomination at R. b, 5k,
Denomination at L.

2001, May 9
451 A250 Horiz. pair, #a-b   3.25 3.25

World No
Smoking
Day — A251

2001, May 31
452 A251 2.50k multi   1.00 .80

Butterflies
A252

Designs: 2.50k, Parnassius apollo. 2.80k,
Maculinea teleius. 5k, Coenonympha
oedippus.

2001, June 5
453-455 A252 Set of 3   4.00 4.00

Type of 1992 Redrawn
2001, June 21   Litho.   **Perf. 14**
456 A39 2.80k Eltz Castle,
    Vukovar   1.10 1.10
  a. Perf. 14 syncopated   1.00 1.00

No. 456 has "1991-2001" inscription, and
"HP" and post horn at LL.
Issued: No. 456a, 6/19/06.

Souvenir Sheet

Trsteno Arboretum — A253

2001, July 12   Litho.   **Perf. 14**
457 A253 14.40k multi   5.25 5.25

World
Esperanto
Congress,
Zagreb — A254

2001, July 21
458 A254 5k multi   1.80 1.75

Refugee
Organizations,
50th Annivs.
A255

Designs: 1.80k, UN High Commissioner for Refugees. 5k, Intl. Organization for Migration.

2001, July 28
459-460 A255   Set of 2   2.75 2.75

Victory of Goran Ivanisevic at Wimbledon A256

2001, Aug. 31
461 A256 2.50k multi   1.50 1.25
Printed in sheets of 9 + label.

Stamp Day — A257

2001, Sept. 9
462 A257 2.50k multi   .90   .80
Printed in sheets of 16 + 4 labels.

Native Dog Breeds A258

Designs: 1.80k, Croatian sheepdog. 5k, Dalmatian.

2001, Oct. 4
463-464 A258   Set of 2   2.50 2.50

Independence, 10th Anniv. — A259

2001, Oct. 8
465 A259 2.30k multi   .80   .75
Printed in sheets of 25 + 5 labels.

Year of Dialogue Among Civilizations — A260

2001, Oct. 9
466 A260 5k multi   1.50 1.40

Fortresses — A261

Designs: 1.80k, Klis, 16th cent. 2.50k, Ston, 14th-15th cents. 3.50k, Sisak, 16th cent.

2001, Oct. 26   **Litho.**   **Perf. 14**
467-469 A261   Set of 3   3.00 3.00

Adoration of the Magi Altarpeice, Church of the Visitation of Mary, Cucerje — A262

2001, Nov. 22   **Litho.**   **Perf. 14**
470 A262 2.30k multi   .90   .80

Modern Art Type of 2000

Designs: No. 471, 2.50k, Maternité du Port-Royal, by Leo Junek. No. 472, 2.50k, Amphitheater Ruins, by Vjekoslav Parac. 5k, Nude with a Baroque Figure, by Slavko Sohaj, vert.

2001, Dec. 1
471-473 A242   Set of 3   4.00 4.00

Croatian Nobel Laureates — A263

Laureates: 2.80k, Lavoslav (Leopold) Ruzicka, Chemistry, 1939. 3.50k, Vladimir Prelog, Chemistry, 1975. 5k, Ivo Andric, Literature, 1961.

2001, Dec. 5
474-476 A263   Set of 3   4.75 4.75

Famous Croats and Events — A264

Designs: 1.80k, Ivan Gucetic (1451-1502), writer. 2.30k, Dobrisa Cesaric (1902-80), writer. 2.50k, Publishing of Juraj Rattkay's *History of Croatian Rulers*, 350th anniv. 2.80k, Franjo Vranjanin Laurana (c. 1420-1502), sculptor. 3.50k, Beatification of Bishop Augustin Kazotic (c. 1260-1323), 300th anniv. 5k, Matko Laginja (1852-1930), politician and writer.

2002, Jan. 24   **Litho.**   **Perf. 14**
477-482 A264   Set of 6   7.00 7.00

2002 Winter Olympics, Salt Lake City — A265

2002, Feb. 8
483 A265 5k multi   2.00 2.00

Croatian Chamber of Economy, 150th Anniv. — A266

2002, Feb. 16
484 A266 2.50k multi   .90   .90

Souvenir Sheet

Trpimir's Deed of Gift, 1150th Anniv. — A267

2002, Mar. 4
485 A267 14.40k multi   5.75 5.75

Franjo Cardinal Kuharic (1919-2002) A268

2002, Mar. 25
486 A268 2.30k multi   .90   .90

Divan, by Vlaho Bukovac — A269

Litho. & Engr.
2002, Apr. 23   **Perf. 11¾**
487 A269 5k multi   2.00 2.00
See Czech Republic No. 3169.

Royal Borough of Krizevci, 750th Anniv. — A270

2002, Apr. 24   **Litho.**   **Perf. 14**
488 A270 1.80k multi   .70   .70

Varazdin Post Office, Cent. — A271

2002, Apr. 26
489 A271 2.30k multi   .85   .85

Europa — A272

Clown color: a, 3.50k, Orange. b, 5k, Blue. Illustration reduced.

2002, May 9   **Litho.**   **Perf. 14**
490 A272 Horiz. pair, #a-b   3.00 3.00

2002 World Cup Soccer Championships, Japan and Korea — A273

Stylized players facing: a, 3.50k, Left. b, 5k, Right.

2002, May 15
491 A273 Horiz. pair, #a-b   3.00 3.00

World Bowling Championships, Osijek — A274

2002, May 18
492 A274 3.50k multi   1.40 1.40

Oak Trees — A275

Designs: 1.80k, Quercus rober. 2.50k, Quercus petraea. 2.80k, Quercus ilex.

2002, June 5
493-495 A275   Set of 3   2.75 2.75
493a   Booklet pane of 10   5.00   —
              Complete booklet, #493a 5.25
494a   Booklet pane of 10 10.00   —
              Complete booklet, #494a 10.50
495a   Booklet pane of 10 12.50   —
              Complete booklet, #495a 13.00

15th World Animated Films Festival, Zagreb — A276

2002, June 18
496 A276 5k multi   1.90 1.90

Lace — A277

Lace from: 3.50k, Pag Island, Croatia. 5k, Liedekerke, Belgium.

2002, July 13   **Photo.**   **Perf. 11½**
497-498 A277   Set of 2   3.25 3.25
See Belgium Nos. 1927-1928.

Fortresses Type of 2001

Designs: No. 499, 2.50k, Nehaj, 16th cent. No. 500, 2.50k, Skocibuha, 16th cent. 5k, Veliki Tabor, 16th cent.

2002, Sept. 20   **Litho.**   **Perf. 14**
499-501 A261   Set of 3   3.75 3.75

Old Slavonic Academy, Krk, Cent. — A278

2002, Oct. 3   **Litho. & Embossed**
502 A278 4k red & black   1.75 1.75

Children's Help Line 48 26 051, 5th Anniv. — A279

2002, Oct. 15   **Litho.**
503 A279 2.30k multi   .90 .90

Christmas A280

2002, Nov. 21
504 A280 2.30k multi   .90 .90
   a.   Booklet pane of 10   9.00 —
     Complete booklet, #504a   9.25

Modern Art Type of 2002

Designs: No. 505, 2.50k, Flowers on the Window, by Antun Motika (1902-92), vert. No. 506, 2.50k, The Girl in the Boat, by Milivoj Uzelac (1897-1977), vert. 5k, On the Drava River, by Krsto Hegedusic (1901-75).

2002, Dec. 2   **Litho.**   **Perf. 14**
505-507 A242   Set of 3   4.00 4.00

Zagreb Bishopric, 150th Anniv. — A281

2002, Dec. 11
508 A281 2.80k multi   1.00 1.00
Printed in sheets of 19 + label.

Pavao Ritter Vitezovic (1652-1713), Writer — A282

2002, Dec. 13
509 A282 2.30k multi   .90 .90

Pacta Conventa, 900th Anniv. — A283

2002, Dec. 14
510 A283 3.50k multi   1.10 1.10

Fairies From Stories by Ivana Brlic Mazuranic — A284

No. 511: a, 2.30k, Kosjenka, fairy character from *Regoc*. b, 2.80k, Tintilinic, fairy character from *Suma Striborova*. Illustration reduced.

2003, Jan. 15
511 A284   Horiz. pair, #a-b   1.90 1.90

St. Valentine's Day — A285

Litho. With Foil Application
2003, Feb. 1
512 A285 2.30k multi   .90 .90

Astronomy and Meteorology A286

No. 513: a, 1.80k, Zagreb Astronomical Observatory, cent. b, 3.50k, Meteorological measurements in Zagreb, 150th anniv.; Meteorological station on Zavizan, 50th anniv.

2003, Feb. 17   **Litho.**
513 A286   Pair, #a-b   2.00 2.00

Souvenir Sheet

Croatia, 2003 World Handball Champions — A287

No. 514: a, Five team members, one wearing red shirt. b, Eight team members, one with arm extended. c, Six team members. d, Four team members, one wearing blue shirt.

2003, Feb. 20
514 A287 4k Sheet of 4, #a-d   6.00 6.00

Paulist High School, Lepoglava, 500th Anniv. — A288

2003, Mar. 1
515 A288 5k multi   1.90 1.90

Missal of Hrvoje Vukcic Hrvatinic, 600th Anniv. — A289

2003, Mar. 25
516 A289 5k multi   1.90 1.90

Land Mine Danger A290

2003, Apr. 8
517 A290 2.30k multi   .90 .90

Alpine Skiing World Cup Victories of Janica and Ivica Kostelic A291

No. 518: a, Janica. b, Ivica.

2003, Apr. 16
518 A291 3.50k Pair, #a-b   3.50 3.50
Printed in sheets containing 4 vertical pairs and 2 labels.

Christian Institutions in Rome Founded by Croatian Roman Brotherhood of St. Jerome, 550th Anniv. — A292

2003, Apr. 22
519 A292 2.80k multi   1.10 1.10

Famous Croatians A293

Designs: 1.80k, Antun Soljan (1932-93), writer. 2.30k, Hanibal Lucic (1485-1553), writer. 5k, Federiko Benkovic (1667-1753), painter.

2003, Apr. 22
520-522 A293   Set of 3   3.50 3.50

Poster for Performance of Marya Delvard, by Tomislav Krizman, 1907. — A294

Poster for Performance of "The Firebird," by Boris Bucan, 1983 — A295

2003, May 9   **Litho.**   **Perf. 14**
523 A294 3.50k multi   1.00 1.00
524 A295   5k multi   1.40 1.40
     Europa.

Fortresses Type of 2001

Designs; 1.80k, Kostajnica, 15th-18th cent. 2.80k, Slavonski Brod, 18th cent. 5k, Minceta Tower, 15th cent., vert.

2003, May 13
525-527 A261   Set of 3   3.50 3.50

Visit of Pope John Paul II — A296

2003, June 2
528 A296 2.30k multi   1.40 1.40

Rodents A297

Designs: 2.30k, Sciuris vulgaris. 2.80k, Glis glis. 3.50k, Castor fiber.

2003, June 5
529-531 A297   Set of 3   3.25 3.25
   531a   Booklet pane, 6 #529, 2 each #530-531   11.50
     Complete booklet, #531a   11.50

Souvenir Sheet

Robe of King Ladislaus, 11th Cent. — A298

2003, June 13
532 A298 10k multi   3.75 3.75

Stamp Day — A299

2003, Sept. 9   Litho.   Perf. 14
533 A299 2.30k multi   .90 .90

Souvenir Sheet

Primosten Vineyards — A300

Litho. with Foil Application
2003, Sept. 19
534 A300 10k multi   3.75 3.75

Ursuline Sisters in Croatia, 300th Anniv. — A301

2003, Oct. 20   Litho.
535 A301 2.50k multi   .90 .90

Christmas A302

2003, Nov. 20   Litho.   Perf. 14
536 A302 2.30k multi   .90 .90

Self-Adhesive
Serpentine Die Cut 5¼
537 A302 2.30k multi   1.00 1.00

Modern Art A304

Designs: 1.80k, Flower Girl II, by Slavko Kopac, vert. No. 539, 3.50k, Dry Stone Wall 5-71, by Oton Gliha. No. 540, 3.50k, Pont des Arts, by Josip Racic.

2003, Nov. 21   Perf. 14
538-540 A304   Set of 3   3.50 3.50

18th World Women's Handball Championships — A305

2003, Dec. 1
541 A305 5k multi   2.00 2.00

Musicians — A306

No. 542: a, Josip Hatze (1879-1959), composer. b, Zagreb Soloists, 50th anniv.

2004, Jan. 5   Litho.   Perf. 14
542 A306 5k Horiz. pair, #a-b   4.00 4.00

Hval's Manuscript, 600th Anniv. — A307

2004, Jan. 22
543 A307 2.30k multi   1.10 1.10

European Boxing Championships, Pula — A308

2004, Feb. 19   Litho.   Perf. 14
544 A308 2.80k multi   1.10 1.10

Worldwide Fund for Nature (WWF) — A309

Ardea purpurea: a, In grass. b, Standing with head extended. c, With young. d, In flight.

2004, Mar. 22
545   Strip or block of 4   7.25 7.25
  a.-d. A309 5k Any single   1.60 1.60

Famous Croats — A310

Designs: 2.30k, Ivan Lucic (1604-79), historian. No. 547, 3.50k, Antun Vrancic (1504-75), archbishop, writer. No. 548, 3.50k, St. Jerome, sculpture by Andrija Alesi (c. 1425-1504). 10k, Printing of Croatian grammar book, by Bartol Kasic (1575-1650), 400th anniv.

2004, Apr. 22
546-549 A310   Set of 4   7.25 7.25

Souvenir Sheet

Risnjak National Park — A311

2004, Apr. 22
550 A311 10k multi   3.75 3.75

Martyrdom of St. Domnio, 1700th Anniv. — A312

2004, May 7
551 A312 3.50k multi   1.40 1.40

Europa A313

Designs: No. 552, 3.50k, Summer vacation items. No. 553, 3.50k, Winter vacation items.

2004, May 9
552-553 A313   Set of 2   2.25 2.25

FIFA (Fédération Internationale de Football Association), Cent. A314

2004, May 21   Litho.   Perf. 14
554 A314 2.50k multi   .95 .95

Medicinal Herbs — A315

Designs: 2.30k, Rosa canina. 2.80k, Viola odorata. 3.50k, Mentha piperita.

2004, June 5
555-557 A315   Set of 3   3.50 3.50
  555a   Booklet pane of 10   9.00   —
             Complete booklet, #555a 9.25
  556a   Booklet pane of 10 11.00   —
             Complete booklet, #556a 11.50
  557a   Booklet pane of 10 15.00   —
             Complete booklet, #557a 15.50

Nos. 555-557 are impregnated with a floral scent.

Intl. Marionette Union Congress, Intl. Puppetry Art Festival, Rijeka A316

2004, June 6
558 A316 3.50k multi   1.25 1.25

European Soccer Championships, Portugal — A317

2004, June 12
559 A317 3.50k multi   1.40 1.40

Values are for stamps with surrounding selvage.

Restoration of Old Bridge, Mostar, Bosnia & Herzegovina A318

2004, July 23   Litho.   Perf. 14
560 A318 3.50k multi   1.40 1.40

2004 Summer Olympics, Athens — A319

2004, Aug. 13
561 A319 3.50k multi   1.25 1.25

Virovitica A320

2004, Aug. 16
562 A320 5k multi   2.00 2.00

Zagreb Post Office, Cent. A321

2004, Sept. 9
563 A321 2.30k multi   .90 .90

Printed in sheets of 16 + 4 labels.

Father Andrija Kacic Miosic (1704-60), Poet — A322

2004, Sept. 15
564 A322 2.80k multi   1.10 1.10

Fortresses Type of 2001

Designs: No. 565, 3.50k, Dubovac, 15th-19th cent. No. 566, 3.50k, Gripe, 17th cent. No. 567, 3.50k, Valpovo, 15th-18th cent.

2004, Sept. 29
565-567 A261 Set of 3   4.00 4.00

Modern Art Type of 2003

Designs: No. 568, 2.30k, Self-portrait, by Miroslav Kraljevic, vert. No. 569, 2.30k, Noon in Supetar, by Jerolim Mise, vert. No. 570, 2.30k, Stari Grad, by Juraj Plancic, vert.

2004, Nov. 15   Litho.   Perf. 14
568-570 A304 Set of 3   2.75 2.75

Christmas — A323

2004, Nov. 25
571 A323 2.30k multi   .90   .90

Antun and Stjepan Radic and Plowman — A324

2004, Dec. 22   Litho.   Perf. 14
572 A324 7.20k multi   2.75 2.75

Croatian People's Peasant Party, Cent.

Fairy Tale Characters — A325

No. 573: a, Mermaid Halugica. b, Dwarf Pedalj Muza Lakat Brade. Illustration reduced.

2005, Jan. 14
573 A325 5k Horiz. pair, #a-b   4.00 4.00

World Conference on the Information Society, Tunis — A326

2005, Feb. 10
574 A326 2.80k multi   1.10 1.10

Values are for stamps with surrounding selvage.

Souvenir Sheet

Bust of Livia Drusilla — A327

2005, Feb. 24
575 A327 10k multi   5.25 5.25

Souvenir Sheet

Expo 2005, Aichi, Japan — A328

2005, Mar. 25   Perf.
576 A328 10k multi   5.25 5.25

Pope John Paul II (1920-2005) — A329

2005, Apr. 8   Perf. 14
577 A329 2.30k multi   .95   .95

World Music Days, Zagreb — A330

Stjepan Sulek (1914-86), Composer — A331

2005, Apr. 15
578 A330 2.30k multi   .95   .95
579 A331 2.30k multi   .95   .95

Insects — A332

Designs: 1.80k, Coccinella septempunctata. 2.30k, Rosalia alpina. 3.50k, Lucanus cervus.

2005, Apr. 22
580-582 A332 Set of 3   3.25 3.25

Liberation of Western Slavonia, 10th Anniv. — A333

2005, May 1
583 A333 1.80k multi   .70   .70

Dr. Josip Buturac (1905-93), Historian — A334

2005, May 6
584 A334 2.80k multi   1.10 1.10

Europa — A335

No. 585: a, Loaf of bread. b, Glass of wine. Illustration reduced.

2005, May 9
585 A335 3.50k Horiz. pair, #a-b 2.75 2.75

Coast of Hvar Island — A336

No. 586: a, Rock at L, tree tops at bottom. b, Tree tops at LL. c, Rock at R. d, Canoe, rock at R. e, Small rock in center. f, Rocks at UL, trees. g, Rocks at R, trees. h, Tree tops at LL corner, rock at UR corner. i, Rocks at UL and LL corners. j, Rocks at LL.

2005, May 24   Litho.   Perf. 14
586 A336 Booklet pane of
           10   14.00   —
a.-e.   1.80k Any single   1.00 1.00
f.-j.   3.50k Any single   1.50 1.50
          Complete booklet, #586 15.00

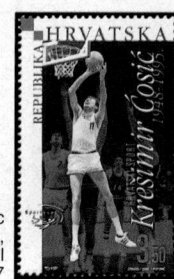

Kresimir Cosic (1948-95), Basketball Player — A337

2005, May 25
587 A337 3.50k multi   1.40 1.40

Printed in sheets of 9 + 1 label.

Krapanj Island Sponge and Coral Diving — A338

2005, June 2   Litho.
588 A338 3.50k multi   1.40 1.40

Portions of the design were applied by a thermographic process producing a shiny, raised effect.

Emperor Constantine's Bath, Varazdinske Toplice — A339

2005, June 20   Perf. 14
589 A339 1.80k multi   .75   .75

Intl. Fire Brigade Olympics, Varazdin — A340

2005, July 15
590 A340 2.30k multi   1.25 1.25

Printed in sheets of 8 + 2 labels.

European Philatelic Cooperation, 50th Anniv. (in 2006) — A341

Designs: 7.20k, Vignette of #134. 8k, Stylized gull.

2005, Sept. 8
591-592 A341 Set of 2   7.00 7.00
592a   Souvenir sheet, #591-592 19.50 19.50

Europa stamps, 50th anniv. (in 2006).

Telegraph — A342

2005, Sept. 9
593 A342 2.30k multi   .95   .95

First overhead telegraph lines in Croatia, 155th anniv., Stamp Day.

Fortresses Type of 2001

Designs: 1k, Ilok, 14th-15th cents. 2.30k, Motovun, 13th-15th cents., vert. 3.50k, St. Nicholas, 16th cent.

2005, Sept. 15
594-596 A261 Set of 3   2.75 2.75

Famous People — A343

Designs: 1k, Adam Baltazar Krcelic (1715-78), historian. No. 598, 2.30k, Dragutin Tadijanovic (b. 1905), poet. No. 599, 2.30k, Tin Ujevic (1891-1955), poet. 2.80k, Madonna and Child, by Juraj Culinovic (c.1433-1504).

2005, Nov. 4
597-600 A343 Set of 4   3.50 3.50

Clock Tower, Rijeka — A344

2005, Nov. 10   Litho.   Perf. 14
601 A344 3.50k multi   1.40 1.40
a.   Perf. 14 syncopated   1.40 1.40

Issued: No. 601a, 6/12/06.

Christmas
A345

2005, Nov. 22   *Perf. 14*
602 A345 2.30k multi   .95   .95

Booklet Stamp
Self-Adhesive
Serpentine Die Cut 5¼

603 A345 2.30k multi   .95   .95
  a.   Booklet pane of 10   9.50   9.50
     Complete booklet, #603a   9.50   9.50

Modern Art Type of 2003

Designs: 1.80k, Zadar, by Edo Murtic. 5k, Meander, by Julije Knifer. 10k, Drawing, by Miroslav Sutej, vert.

2005, Dec. 1   *Perf. 14*
604-606 A304   Set of 3   6.75   6.75

Davis Cup
and Members
of Croatian
Tennis
Team — A346

2005, Dec. 22   Litho.   *Perf. 14*
607 A346 5k multi   2.00   2.00
  Croatia, winners of 2005 Davis Cup. Printed in sheets of 9 + label.

Composers
A347

Designs: 1.80k, Boris Papandopulo (1906-91). 2.30k, Milo Cipra (1906-85). 2.80k, Ivan Brkanovic (1906-87).

2006, Jan. 17
608-610 A347   Set of 3   2.75   2.75

2006 Winter
Olympics,
Turin — A348

2006, Feb. 10
611 A348 3.50k multi   1.40   1.40

Rembrandt
(1606-69),
Painter
A349

2006, Mar. 7
612 A349 5k multi   2.00   2.00

Famous
Men — A350

Designs: No. 613, 1k, Andrija Ljudevit Adamic (1766-1828), merchant. No. 614, 1k, Josip Kozarac (1858-1906), writer. 5k, Vanja Radaus (1906-75), sculptor. 7.20k, Ljubo Karaman (1886-1971), art historian.

2006, Mar. 21   *Perf. 14 Syncopated*
613-616 A350   Set of 4   5.75   5.75

European Track and Field
Championships, Göteborg,
Sweden — A351

2006, Apr. 4
617 A351 2.30k multi   .95   .95

2006 World Cup
Soccer
Championships,
Germany
A352

2006, Apr. 4
618 A352 2.80k multi   1.10   1.10

Flag and Crowd — A353

No. 619 — Location and placement of denomination: a, At left, with denomination above crowd. b, At right, with top of numerals over red in flag. c, At left, with top of "8" and "0" above white in flag. d, At left, with serif of "1" above red in flag. e, At left, with entire denomination above red in flag. f, At right, with parts of "5" and "0" above red in flag. g, At right, with entire denomination above red in flag. h, At right, with entire denomination above white in flag. i, At left, with entire denomination above red in flag. j, At right, with denomination above crowd.

2006, Apr. 25
619   A353   Booklet pane of
        10   11.00   —
  a.-e.   1.80k Any single   .75   .75
  f.-j.   3.50k Any single   1.40   1.40
     Complete booklet, #619   11.50

Europa — A354

No. 620: a, Denomination at left. b, Denomination at right.

2006, May 9
620 A354 3.50k Horiz. pair, #a-b   *3.00 3.00*

Worldwide
Fund for
Nature
(WWF)
A355

No. 621 — Various views of Sterna albifrons with denomination in: a, Gray. b, Dull green. c, Yellow orange. d, Red.

2006, May 23
621   Strip of 4   8.50   8.50
  a.-d.   A355 5k Any single   2.00   2.00

Croatian Automobile Club,
Cent. — A356

Perf. 13¾x14 Syncopated
2006, June 4
622 A356 5k multi   2.00   2.00

Aquatic
Flowers
A357

Designs: 2.30k, Nymphaea alba. 2.80k, Nuphar lutea. 3.50k, Menyanthes trifoliata.

2006, June 5   *Perf. 14 Syncopated*
623-625 A357   Set of 3   3.50   3.50
  623a   Booklet pane of 10   9.50   9.50
     Complete booklet, #623a   9.50
  624a   Booklet pane of 10   11.00   11.00
     Complete booklet, #624a   11.00
  625a   Booklet pane of 10   14.00   14.00
     Complete booklet, #625a   14.00

Nikola Tesla (1856-1943),
Inventor — A358

Perf. 14x13½ Syncopated
2006, July 10   Litho.
626 A358 3.50k multi   1.40   1.40

Bjelovar,
250th Anniv.
A359

Perf. 14 Syncopated
2006, Aug. 22   Litho.
627 A359 2.80k multi   1.10   1.10

Stamp
Day — A360

2006, Sept. 9   **Litho. & Embossed**
628 A360 2.30k multi   .95   .95

Jewish Community
of Zagreb, 200th
Anniv. — A361

Perf. 14¼x13¾ Syncopated
2006, Sept. 15   Litho.
629 A361 5k multi   2.00   2.00

Fortresses Type of 2001

Designs: No. 630, 1k, St. Mary of Mercy Church, Vrboska, 16th cent. No. 631, 1k, Church of the Holy Spirit, Sudurad, 16th cent. 7.20k, Frankapan Citadel, Ogulin, 16th cent.

Perf. 13¾x14¼ Syncopated
2006, Sept. 21
630-632 A261   Set of 3   3.75   3.75

White Cane Safety Day — A362

Perf. 14 Syncopated
2006, Oct. 15   **Litho. & Embossed**
633 A362 1.80k black & red   .75   .75

Christmas
A363

Perf. 14¼ Syncopated
2006, Nov. 27   Litho.
634 A363 2.30k multi   .85   .85

Booklet Stamp
Self-Adhesive
Serpentine Die Cut 5¼

635 A363 2.30k multi   .85   .85
  a.   Booklet pane of 10   8.50
     Complete booklet, #635a   8.50

Modern Art Type of 2003

Designs: 1k, Still Life, by Vladimir Becic. 1.80k, Composition Tyma 3, by Ivan Picelj. 10k, Self-portrait as Hunter, by Nasta Rojc, vert.

2006, Dec. 1   *Perf. 14 Syncopated*
636-638 A304   Set of 3   4.75   4.75

Classical Gymnasium, Zagreb, 400th Anniv. — A364

Perf. 14 Syncopated
2007, Jan. 9 Litho.
639 A364 5k multi 1.75 1.75

Fairy Tale Characters — A365

No. 640: a, Monster Orko. b, Devil Macic. Illustration reduced.

2007, Jan. 18
640 A365 2.30k Horiz. pair, #a-b 1.60 1.60

National and University Library, Zagreb, 400th Anniv. A366

2007, Feb. 22
641 A366 5k multi 1.90 1.90

Crustaceans A367

Designs: 1.80k, Palinurus elephas. 2.30k, Nephrops norvegicus. 2.80k, Astacus astacus.

2007, Mar. 15
642	A367 1.80k multi		.65	.65
a.	Booklet pane of 10		6.50	—
	Complete booklet, #642a		6.50	
643	A367 2.30k multi		.85	.85
a.	Booklet pane of 10		8.50	—
	Complete booklet, #643a		8.50	
644	A367 2.80k multi		1.00	1.00
a.	Booklet pane of 10		10.00	—
	Complete booklet, #644a		10.00	
	Nos. 642-644 (3)		2.50	2.50

Native Breeds of Farm Animals A368

Designs: 2.80k, Istrian ox. 3.50k, Posavina horse. 5k, Dalmatian donkey.

2007, Mar. 20
645-647 A368 Set of 3 4.25 4.25

Europa — A369

No. 648: a, Scouting emblem and dove. b, Scout neckerchief.

2007, Apr. 16
648 A369 3.50k Horiz. pair, #a-b 2.60 2.60
Scouting, cent.

Scientists — A370

Designs: 5k, Andrija Mohorovicic (1857-1936), seismologist. 7.20k, Duro Baglivi (1668-1707), physician.

Perf. 14x13½ Syncopated
2007, Apr. 23
649-650 A370 Set of 2 4.50 4.50

Souvenir Sheet

World Championship Victory of Croatian Water Polo Team — A371

No. 651: a, Man with red shirt at right, denomination at UL. b, Man with red shirt at LR, denomination at UR. c, Man with red shirt at left, denomination at UR.

Litho. With Foil Application
2007, May 3 **Perf. 14¼ Syncopated**
651 A371 5k Sheet of 3, #a-c 5.75 5.75

World Table Tennis Championships, Zagreb — A372

Perf. 14 Syncopated
2007, May 21 **Litho. & Embossed**
652 A372 3.50k multi 1.40 1.40

Starting with No. 652 some stamps have an imprinted wing-shaped tagging design that looks like a watermark.

Diplomatic Relations Between Croatia and People's Republic of China, 15th Anniv. — A373

No. 653: a, "China" in Glagolithic letters. b, "Croatia" in Chinese characters. Illustration reduced.

2007, May 30 **Litho.** **Perf. 12**
653 A373 5k Horiz. pair, #a-b 3.75 3.75

Zagreb City Museum, Cent. — A374

2007, May 31 **Perf. 14 Syncopated**
654 A374 2.30k multi .85 .85

Souvenir Sheet

Red Lake — A375

2007, June 8
655 A375 10k multi 3.75 3.75

First Croatian Philatelic Exhibition, Cent. — A376

Perf. 14 Syncopated
2007, Sept. 9 **Litho. & Embossed**
656 A376 2.80k multi 1.10 1.10

Stamp Day.

Lighthouses — A377

Designs: No. 657, 5k, St. John on the Sea Lighthouse. No. 658, 5k, Porer Lighthouse. No. 659, 5k, Savudrija Lighthouse.

Perf. 13¾x14¼ Syncopated
2007, Sept. 14 **Litho.**
657-659 A377 Set of 3 5.75 5.75

Veprinac Statute, 500th Anniv. — A378

Perf. 14¼x13¾ Syncopated
2007, Oct. 2
660 A378 2.70k multi 1.10 1.10

City Views — A379

Designs: 1.80k, Omis. 2.30k, Koprivnica, horiz. 2.80k, Krk.

2007, Oct. 30 **Perf. 14 Syncopated**
661	A379 1.80k multi		.75	.75
662	A379 2.30k multi		.90	.90
663	A379 2.80k multi		1.10	1.10
	Nos. 661-663 (3)		2.75	2.75

Blanka Vlasic, 2007 World Women's High Jump Champion A380

2007, Nov. 8
664 A380 2.30k multi .95 .95

SEMI-POSTAL STAMPS

Catalogue values for unused stamps in this section are for Never Hinged items.

Types of Yugoslavia, 1941, Overprinted in Gold "NEZAVISNA / DRZAVA / HRVATSKA"

Perf. 11½
1941, May 10 **Unwmk.** **Engr.**
B1 SP80 1.50d + 1.50d bl blk 16.00 16.00
B2 SP81 4d + 3d choc 16.00 16.00

Panes of 16 stamps and 9 labels.
This overprint exists on Yugoslavia No. B124. Value $2,500.

Five thousand sets of Yugoslavia Nos. 142-154 were overprinted "NEZAVISNA DRZAVA HRVATSKA 10. IV. 1941" and small shield in red or blue, in 1941. Sold for double face value. Value, set, $550.

Costume of Sinj, Dalmatia — SP1 | Soldiers with Arms of the Axis States — SP4

Designs (Costumes): 2k+2k, Travnik, Bosnia. 4k+4k, Turopolje, Croatia.

1941, Oct. 12 **Photo.** **Perf. 10½x10**
B3	SP1	1.50k + 1.50k Prus bl & red	1.00	1.00
B4	SP1	2k + 2k ol brn & red	1.25	1.25
B5	SP1	4k + 4k brn lake & red	2.25	2.25
	Nos. B3-B5 (3)		4.50	4.50

The surtax aided the Croatian Red Cross. Panes of 20 stamps and 5 labels.

1941, Dec. 3 **Perf. 11**
B6 SP4 4k + 2k blue 3.00 3.75

The surtax was used for Croatian Volunteers in the East.
Issued in panes of 100 stamps.

Model Plane — SP5

Model
Plane — SP6

Designs: 3k+3k, Boy with model plane.
4k+4k, Model seaplane in flight.

1942, Mar. 25

B7	SP5	2k + 2k sepia	1.75	1.75
B8	SP6	2.50k + 2.50k dl grn	1.75	1.75
B9	SP5	3k + 3k brn car	1.75	1.75
B10	SP6	4k + 4k dp bl	1.75	1.75
		Nos. B7-B10 (4)	7.00	7.00

Nos. B7-B10 were issued both in panes of
25 and in panes of 24 plus label.

Values for used souvenir sheets
are for those with special philatelic
cancels. Faked postal cancellations
on souvenir sheets are common,
especially using cancellers stolen
after WWII. Genuine postal cancellations are the exception and sell for
much more. Expertization is
recommended.

Souvenir Sheets
Perf. 11

B11	Sheet of 2	47.50	45.00
a.	SP5 2k+8k brown carmine	12.00	12.00
b.	SP5 3k+12k deep blue	12.00	12.00

Imperf

B12	Sheet of 2	55.00	52.50
a.	SP5 2k+8k deep blue	14.00	14.00
b.	SP5 3k+12k brown carmine	14.00	14.00

The sheets measure 125x110mm.
Aviation Exposition of Zagreb. The surtax
aided society of Croatian Wings (Hrvatska
Krila).
Nos. B11-B12 exist with colors of stamps
and inscriptions transposed, with missing colors and with one stamp missing.

Boy Trumpeters
SP10

Triumphal
Arch — SP11

Mother and
Child — SP12

1942, July 5   **Perf. 11½**

B13	SP10	3k + 1k lake	1.50	1.50
B14	SP11	4k + 2k dk brn	1.50	1.50
B15	SP12	5k + 5k dp bl grn	1.50	1.50
		Nos. B13-B15 (3)	4.50	4.50

The surtax was for national welfare.
Issued in panes of 25.

Matthew Gubec
SP13

Ante Starcevich
SP14

SP15

1942, Nov. 22   **Perf. 14½**

B16	SP13	3k + 6k dark red	.80	.80
B17	SP14	4k + 7k sepia	.80	.80

Souvenir Sheets
Perf. 12, Imperf.

B18	SP15	5k + 20k dull blue	20.00	20.00

Heroes of Senj, May 9, 1937. Nos. B16-B17
were printed in panes of 16 + 9 labels, each
bearing a hero's name. The surtax aided the
Natl. Youth Soc.

Sestine Peasant
SP16

Croatian Labor
Corpsman
SP20

Designs: 3k+1k, Slavonian peasant. 4k+2k,
Bosnian peasant. 10k+5k, Dalmatian peasant.
13k+6k, Sestine peasant.

1942, Oct. 4   **Perf. 11½**

B20	SP16	1.50k + 50b org brn & red	1.50	1.50
B21	SP16	3k + 1k dl pur & red	1.50	1.50
B22	SP16	4k + 2k dp bl & red	2.25	2.25
B23	SP16	10k + 5k dk ol bis & red	3.25	3.25
B24	SP16	13k + 6k rose lake & red	6.00	6.00
		Nos. B20-B24 (5)	14.50	14.50

The surtax aided the Croatian Red Cross.
Issued in panes of 24 stamps plus label.

1943, Jan. 17   **Wmk. 278**   **Perf. 11**

Designs: 3k+3k, Corpsman with wheelbarrow. 7k+4k, Corpsman plowing.

B25	SP20	2k + 1k ol gray & sepia	4.00	4.25
B26	SP20	3k + 3k brn & sepia	4.00	4.25
B27	SP20	7k + 4k gray bl & sepia	4.00	4.25
		Nos. B25-B27 (3)	12.00	12.75

The surtax aided the State Labor Service
(Drzavna Radna Sluzba). Issued in panes of
9.

Arms of
Zagreb and
"Golden
Bull" — SP23

1943, Mar. 21   **Unwmk.**

B28	SP23	3.50k (+ 6.50k) ultra	4.00	4.25

700th anniversary of Zagreb's "Golden Bull,"
a Magna Carta of civic rights and privileges
granted to the city in 1242 by King Bela
because the Croats annihilated Tartar hordes
at Grobnik.
Issued in panes of 8 with marginal
inscriptions.

Ante
Pavelich — SP24

Sailor at Sea
of
Azov — SP26

1943, Apr. 10   **Perf. 13¾14**

B29	SP24	5k + 3k copper red	.60	.60
a.		Sheetlet of 16 #B29 + 9 la- bels	11.00	11.00
B30	SP24	7k + 5k dark green	.60	.60
a.		Sheetlet of 16 #B30 + 9 la- bels	11.00	11.00

Surtax aided the National Youth Society.
Nos. B29-B30 were issued in panes of 100
stamps. Nos. B29a and B30a were issued
Apr. 12 and are perf 14½.

Souvenir Sheets

1943, May 17   **Perf. 12, Imperf.**

B31	SP24	12k + 8k dp ultra	25.00	25.00

1943, July 1   **Perf. 11**

Designs: 2k+1k, Flier at Sevastopol and
Rzhev. 3.50k+1.50k, Infantrymen at Stalingrad. 9k+4.50k, Panzer Division at Don River.

B33	SP26	1k + 50b grn	.35	.25
B34	SP26	2k + 1k dk red	.35	.25
B35	SP26	3.50k + 1.50k dk bl	.35	.25
B36	SP26	9k + 4.50k chestnut	.35	.25
		Nos. B33-B36 (4)	1.40	1.00

Souvenir Sheets
Perf. 11, Imperf.

B37		Sheet of 4	7.00	7.00
a.	SP26	1k+50b dark blue	1.25	1.25
b.	SP26	2k+1k green	1.25	1.25
c.	SP26	3.50k+1.50k dk red brown	1.25	1.25
d.	SP26	9k+4.50k bluish black	1.25	1.25

Surtax aided the National Youth Society.
Issued to honor the Croatian Legion which
fought with the Germans in Russia. The surtax
aided the Legion.
Issued in panes of 100.

St. Mary's
Church
and
Cistercian
Cloister,
Zagreb, in
1650
SP31

1943, Sept. 12   **Engr.**   **Perf. 14½**

B39	SP31	18k + 9k dl gray vio	5.00	5.25

Souvenir Sheet
Perf. 12½

B40	SP31	18k + 9k blk brn	15.00	15.00

Croatian Phil. Soc. Exhibition at Zagreb.
No. B39 issued in pane of 40.

No. B39
Overprinted in
Red

HRVATSKO MORE
8. IX.
1943.

1943, Sept. 12

B41	SP31	18k + 9k dl gray vio	10.00	12.00

Return to Croatia of the Dalmatian and Croatian coasts.
The overprint exists inverted, double, and
double, one inverted.

Mother and
Children — SP33

Nurse and
Patient — SP34

1943, Oct. 3   **Litho.**   **Perf. 11**
Cross in Red

B42	SP33	1k + 50b bl grn	.75	.75
B43	SP33	2k + 1k bril car	.75	.75
B44	SP33	3.50k + 1.50k brt bl	.75	.75
B45	SP34	8k + 3k red brn	.90	.90
B46	SP34	9k + 4k yel grn	1.00	1.00
B47	SP33	10k + 5k dp vio	1.00	1.00
B48	SP34	12k + 6k brt ultra	1.00	1.00
B49	SP33	12.50k + 6k dk brn	1.50	1.50
B50	SP34	18k + 8k brn org	1.50	1.50
B51	SP34	32k + 12k dk gray	1.50	1.50
		Nos. B42-B51 (10)	10.65	10.65

The surtax aided the Croatian Red Cross.
Issued in panes of 100.

Post Horn and
Arms — SP35

Carrier Pigeon
and
Plane — SP36

Mercury — SP37

Winged
Wheel — SP38

1944, Feb. 3

B52	SP35	7k + 3.50k ol bis & red	.75	.75
B53	SP36	16k + 8k bl & dk bl	.75	.75
B54	SP37	24k + 12k red & rose red	.75	.75
B55	SP38	32k + 16k gray & red	.75	.75
		Nos. B52-B55 (4)	3.00	3.00

The surtax benefited communications and
railway employees. Panes of 9.

St.
Sebastian — SP39

War Invalids
SP40

Statue of Ancient
Croatian
King — SP41

Death of King
Peter Svacic,
1097 — SP42

1944, Feb. 15
B56	SP39	7k + 3.50k org red & rose car	.75	.75
B57	SP40	16k + 8k yel grn & dk grn	.75	.75
B58	SP41	24k + 12k yel brn & red	.75	.75
B59	SP42	32k + 16k bl & dk bl	.75	.75
		Nos. B56-B59 (4)	3.00	3.00

The surtax aided wounded war victims.
Issued in panes of eight stamps, with marginal inscriptions and a central label picturing St. Sebastian.

Black Legion in
Combat — SP43

Guarding the
Drina — SP44

Jure
Francetic — SP45

1944, May 22   Photo.   Imperf.
B60	SP43	3.50k + 1.50k brn red	.20	.20
B61	SP44	12.50k + 6.50k slate bl	.20	.20
B62	SP45	18k + 9k olive brn	.20	.20
		Nos. B60-B62 (3)	.60	.60

Third anniversary of Croatian independence. The surtax aided the National Youth Society. Panes of 20.

Perf. 14½
B63	SP45	12.50k + 287.50k int blk	11.00	11.00

Issued to commemorate Jure Francetic. Issued in pane of 30.

Labor Corpsmen
Marching
SP46

Corpsman
Digging
SP47

Designs: 18k+9k, Officer instructing corpsman. 32k+16k, Pavelich reviewing Labor Corps. Panes of 8 plus label.

Perf. 11½, 12½, 14½
1944, Aug. 20   Engr.
B65	SP46	3.50k + 1k dk red	.50	.50
B66	SP47	12.50k + 6k sepia	.50	.50
B67	SP47	18k + 9k dk bl	.50	.50
B68	SP47	32k + 16k gray grn	.50	.50
		Nos. B65-B68 (4)	2.00	2.00

Nos. B68 exists only perf 12½, while B65-B67 exist perf 11½, 12½ or 14½. Values are for copies perf 11½ or 12½. Values Nos. B65-B67 perf 14½, $5 each unused or used.

Souvenir Sheet
Perf. 12½
B69	SP47	32k + 16k dk brn, cr	4.00	4.50

The surtax aided the State Labor Service (Drzavna Radna Sluzba).

Palm
Leaf — SP51

1944, Nov. 12   Litho.   Perf. 11
B70	SP51	2k + 1k dl grn & red	.40	.40
B71	SP51	3.50k + 1.50k car lake & red	.40	.40
B72	SP51	12.50k + 6k ind & red	.40	.40
		Nos. B70-B72 (3)	1.20	1.20

The surtax aided the Croatian Red Cross. Panes of 16.

Men of Storm Division — SP52

70k+70k, Soldiers of Storm Division in action. 100k+100k, Storm Division emblem.

1944   Unwmk.   Litho.   Perf. 11
B73	SP52	50k + 50k brick red	120.00	125.00
B74	SP52	70k + 70k sepia	120.00	125.00
B75	SP52	100k + 100k chlky, pale & dp bl	120.00	125.00
		Nos. B73-B75 (3)	360.00	375.00

Nos. B73-B75 issued in panes of 20.

Souvenir Sheet
B76		Sheet of 3	1,450.	1,450.
a.		SP52 50k + 50k brick red	400.00	400.00
b.		SP52 70k + 70k sepia	400.00	400.00
c.		SP52 100k + 100k chalky, pale & deep blue	400.00	400.00

Nos. B76a to B76c are inscribed "O. A." in brick red at right below design. The sheet measures 216x132mm. The surtax aided the First Croatian Storm Division. Counterfeits are plentiful.

Postman
SP55

Telephone Line
Repairman
SP56

24k+12k, Switchboard operator. 50k+25k, 100k+50k, Postman delivering parcel.

1945   Photo.
B77	SP55	3.50k + 1.50k sl gray	.30	.30
B78	SP56	12.50k + 6k brn car	.30	.30
B79	SP56	24k + 12k dk grn	.30	.30
B80	SP56	50k + 25k brn vio	.30	.30
		Nos. B77-B80 (4)	1.20	1.20

Souvenir Sheet
B81	SP56	100k + 50k dp brn	9.00	9.00

The surtax on #B77-B81 aided employees of the P.T.T. Panes of 8.

Famous
Croatians
SP60

#B100, Ban Josip Jelacic (1801-59). #B101, Dr. Ante Starcevic (1823-96). 7d + 3d, Stjepan Radic (1871-1928).

1992   Litho.   Perf. 11x10½
B100	SP60	4d +2d multi	.45	.45
B101	SP60	4d +2d multi	.40	.35

Perf. 14
B102	SP60	7d +3d multi	.25	.25
		Nos. B100-B102 (3)	1.10	1.05

Issued: #B100, 2/1; #B101, 3/4; #B102, 4/2.
The surcharge on Nos. B100-B102 was initially an obligatory tax on all internal and overseas mail. From May 15, 1992, these stamps were valid for postage at their 6d or 10d face values.

AIR POST STAMPS

Catalogue values for unused stamps in this section are for Never Hinged items.

Airplane,
Zagreb
Cathedral and
Port of
Dubrovnik
AP1

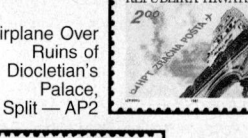

Airplane Over
Ruins of
Diocletian's
Palace,
Split — AP2

Coat of Arms,
Aiplane,
Zagreb
Cathedral and
Pula
Amphitheatre
AP3

Paper
Airplane Made
From Picture
of Osijek
Cathedral
AP4

1991-92   Litho.   Perf. 11x10½
C1	AP1	1d multicolored	.25	.20
a.		Perf. 14	.20	.20
C2	AP2	2d multicolored	.60	.25
a.		Perf. 14	.20	.20
C3	AP3	3d multicolored	.35	.20
C4	AP4	4d multicolored	.35	.20
		Nos. C1-C4 (4)		1.55

Issued: #C1, 9/9/91; #C1a, 6/24/92; #C2, 10/9/91; #C2a, 1992; #C3, 11/20/91; #C4, 2/14/92.

POSTAGE DUE STAMPS

Yugoslavia Nos. J28-
J32 Overprinted in
Black

1941, Apr. 26   Unwmk.   Perf. 12½
J1	D4	50p violet	.30	.50
a.		Double overprint	150.00	
b.		50p rose violet	5.00	10.00
c.		As "b," double overprint		200.00
J2	D4	1d deep magenta	.30	.50
a.		Inverted overprint	200.00	
J3	D4	2d deep blue	8.50	20.00
a.		Double overprint	300.00	
J4	D4	5d orange	.75	1.75
a.		Double overprint	300.00	
J5	D4	10d chocolate	4.50	11.00
		Nos. J1-J5 (5)	14.35	33.75
		Set, never hinged	32.50	

Counterfeit overprints exist, particularly of Nos. J3 and J5.

D1

D2

1941, Sept. 12   Litho.   Perf. 11
J6	D1	50b carmine lake	.20	.45
J7	D1	1k carmine lake	.20	.45
J8	D1	2k carmine lake	.25	.60
J9	D1	5k carmine lake	.40	.85
J10	D1	10k carmine lake	.75	1.25
		Nos. J6-J10 (5)	1.80	3.60
		Set, never hinged	3.50	

1943   Perf. 11½, 12x12½, 12½
Size: 24x24mm
J11	D2	50b lt blue & gray	.20	.25
J12	D2	1k lt blue & gray	.20	.25
J13	D2	2k lt blue & gray	.20	.25
J14	D2	4k lt blue & gray	.20	.40
J15	D2	5k lt blue & gray	.20	.40
J16	D2	6k lt blue & gray	.20	.45
J17	D2	10k blue & indigo	.20	1.10
J18	D2	15k blue & indigo	.20	1.10
J19	D2	20k blue & indigo	.65	1.60
		Nos. J11-J19 (9)	2.25	5.05
		Set, never hinged	4.50	

1942, July 30   Perf. 10½, 11½
Size: 25x24¼mm
J20	D2	50b lt blue & gray	.20	.40
J21	D2	1k lt blue & gray	.20	.40
J22	D2	2k lt blue & gray	.20	.50
J23	D2	5k lt blue & gray	.20	.50
J24	D2	10k lt blue & blue	.55	1.10
J25	D2	20k lt blue & blue	.85	1.10
		Nos. J20-J25 (6)	2.20	4.50
		Set, never hinged	5.25	

Nos. J21-J25 exist both perf 10½ and 11½. No. J20 exists only perf 11½.

OFFICIAL STAMPS

Croatian Coat of Arms
O1   O2

Perf. 10½, 11½

1942-43 Unwmk. Litho.
Ordinary Paper

O1	O1	25b rose lake	.20	.20
O2	O1	50b slate blk	.20	.20
O3	O1	75b gray grn	.20	.20
O4	O1	1k orange brn	.20	.20
O5	O1	2k turq blue	.20	.40
O6	O1	3k vermilion	.20	.20
O7	O1	4k brown vio	.20	.20
O8	O1	5k ultra	.20	.40
a.	Thin paper		4.50	2.00
O9	O1	6k brt violet	.20	.20
O10	O1	10k lt green	.20	.20
O11	O1	12k brown rose	.20	.30
O12	O1	20k dark blue	.20	.30
O13	O2	30k brn vio & gray	.25	.40
O14	O2	40k vio blk & gray	.30	.50
O15	O2	50k brn lake & gray	.35	.90
O16	O2	100k black & pink	.55	1.00
		Nos. O1-O16 (16)	3.85	5.80
		Set, never hinged	7.00	

Nos. O1-O16 exist perf 10½ and 11½. No. O8a exists only perf 11½.

1943-44 Thin Paper Perf. 11½

O17	O1	25b claret	.20	.20
O18	O1	50b gray	.20	.20
O19	O1	75b dull green	.20	.20
O20	O1	1k orange brn	.20	.20
O21	O1	2k slate blue	.20	.20
O22	O1	3.50k car rose	.20	.20
a.	Ordinary paper		3.00	3.00
O23	O1	6k brt red vio	.20	.20
O24	O1	12.50k deep orange	.20	.20
a.	Ordinary paper		2.00	2.00
		Set, never hinged	1.50	

POSTAL TAX STAMPS

Catalogue values for unused stamps in this section are for Never Hinged items.

Nurse and Soldier — PT1

Wounded Soldier — PT2

Unwmk.
1942, Oct. 4 Litho. Perf. 11
RA1 PT1 1k olive grn & red .85 .80

The tax aided the Croatian Red Cross. Issued in sheets of 24 plus label.

No. RA1 can be found with a red cross printed on the nurse's hat. The original design included this element, but it was removed for the final approved design. Early printings of No. RA1, probably trial printings, included the red cross.

1943, Oct. 3
RA2 PT2 2k blue & red .85 .85

The tax aided the Croatian Red Cross.

Ruins — PT3

Wounded Soldier — PT4

1944, Jan. 1 Photo. Perf. 12

RA3	PT3	1k dk slate green	.25	.25
RA4	PT4	2k carmine lake	.30	.30
RA5	PT4	5k black	.35	.35
RA6	PT4	10k deep blue	.55	.35
RA7	PT4	20k brown	1.00	.55
		Nos. RA3-RA7 (5)	2.45	1.80

Interior of Zagreb Cathedral PT10

1991, Apr. 1 Litho. Perf. 14
RA20 PT10 1.20d black & gold .60 .50
  a. Perf. 11x10½ .70 .60
  b. Perf. 11 15.00 12.00
  c. Imperf .90 .90

Worker's Fund. Required on mail during April 1991.
For surcharges see Nos. 100, 100a.

Shrine of the Virgin, 700th Anniv. PT11

1991, May 16 Perf. 10½x11
RA21 PT11 1.70d multicolored .65 .55
  a. Imperf .80 .70

Workers' Fund. Required on mail May 16-31.

Croatian Arms Type of 1992

1991, July 1 Perf. 11x10½
RA22 A37 2.20d multicolored .70 .60
  a. Imperf .95 .75

Required on mail during July.

Members of Parliament PT12

1991, Aug. 1 Perf. 11x10½
RA23 PT12 2.20d multicolored .70 .60
  a. Imperf .95 .80

Worker's Fund. Required on mail during Aug.

Red Cross and Tuberculosis PT13

1991, Sept 14 Perf. 11
RA24 PT13 2.20d blue & red .50 .45

Required on mail Sept. 14-21.

Re-erection of Ban Josip Jelacic Equestrian Statue, Zagreb PT14

1991, Nov. 1 Perf. 11x10½
RA25 PT14 2.20d multicolored .50 .45
  a. Imperf. .65 .50

Worker's Fund. Required on mail during Nov.

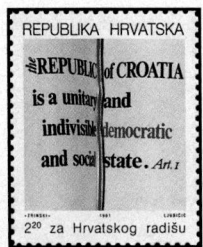

New Constitution PT15

1991, Dec. 2 Litho. Perf. 10¾x10½
Language of Inscription

RA26	PT15	2.20d English	2.25	2.00
RA27	PT15	2.20d Croatian	.80	.70
RA28	PT15	2.20d French	2.25	2.00
RA29	PT15	2.20d German	2.25	2.00
RA30	PT15	2.20d Russian	2.25	2.00
RA31	PT15	2.20d Spanish	2.25	2.00
a.	Vert. strip, #RA26-RA31		14.00	14.00

Nos RA26-RA31 were printed in sheet containing 15 of No. RA27, 2 each of the other stamps and five labels. Obligatory on mail Dec. 2-31.
Sheet exists imperf. Value $225.

"VUKOVAR" with Barbed Wire — PT16

1992, Jan. 1 Litho. Perf. 11x10½
RA32 PT16 2.20d black & brown .70 .55
  a. Imperf. 1.00 .90

Vukovar Refugee's Fund. Required on mail during Jan.

Red Cross PT17

Red Cross and Solidarity PT18

1992 Perf. 11
RA33 PT17 3d red & black .25 .20
RA34 PT18 3d red & black .25 .20

Issued: No. RA33, May 8. No. RA34, June 1. No. RA33 was required on mail May 8-15; No. RA34, June 1-7.

Madonna of Bistrica — PT19

Red Cross — PT20

1992, Aug. 1 Litho. Perf. 14
RA35 PT19 5d blue & gold .45 .40

Required on mail, Aug. 1-8.

1992, Sept. 21 Litho. Perf. 11
RA36 PT20 5d black & red .30 .25

Required on mail Sept. 14-21.

St. George Slaying Dragon PT21

1992, Nov. 4 Perf. 14
RA37 PT21 15d multicolored .30 .25

Cancer Research League. Required on mail Nov. 4-11.
See No. RA43.

Red Cross — PT22

1993, May 8 Litho. Rough Perf. 11
RA38 PT22 80d black & red .30 .25

Required on mail May 8-15.

Red Cross and Solidarity PT23

1993, June 1
RA39 PT23 100d black & red .30 .25

Required on mail June 1-7.

Cardinal Stepinac (1898-1960) PT24

1993, July 15 Litho. Perf. 14
RA40 PT24 150d multicolored .30 .25

Required on mail July 15-22.

Zrinski-Frankopan Foundation — PT25

Design: 200d, Gen. Peter Zrinski (1621-1671), Politician and Fran Krsto Frankopan, Count of Tersat (1643-1671), Poet.

1993, Aug. 12 Litho. Perf. 14
RA41 PT25 200d gray & blue .35 .25

Required on mail Aug. 12-19.

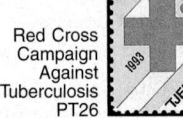

Red Cross Campaign Against Tuberculosis PT26

1993, Sept. 14 Litho. Perf. 11
RA42 PT26 300d gray, red & black .45 .40

Required on mail Sept. 14-21.

St. George Slaying Dragon Type of 1992

1993, Oct. 11   Litho.   Perf. 14
RA43 PT21 400d multicolored   .45   .40
Cancer Research League. Required on mail Oct. 11-31.

Save the Children of Croatia PT27

1993, Nov. 1   Perf. 13½x14
RA44 PT27 400d multicolored   .45   .40
Required on mail Nov. 1-30.

Croatian Red Cross — PT28

1994, May 5   Litho.   Perf. 11
RA45 PT28 500d multicolored   .30   .25
Required on mail May 8-15.

Red Cross Solidarity PT29

Ludberg Church PT30

1994, May 5   Litho.   Perf. 11
RA46 PT29 50 l multicolored   .45   .40
Required on mail June 1-7.

1994, July 15   Perf. 14
RA47 PT30 50 l multicolored   .30   .25
Required on mail July 15-22.

Save the Children of Croatia — PT31

St. George Slaying Dragon — PT32

1994, Aug. 16   Litho.   Perf. 14
RA48 PT31 50 l multicolored   .30   .25
Required on mail Aug. 16-29.

1994, Sept. 1
RA49 PT32 50 l multicolored   .30   .25
Cancer Research League. Required on mail Sept. 1-8.

PT33   PT34

1994, Sept. 14   Perf. 11
RA50 PT33 50 l blk, grn & red   .45   .40
Red Cross Campaign against Tuberculosis. Required on mail Sept. 14-21.

1994, Oct. 15   Litho.   Perf. 14
RA51 PT34 50 l multicolored   .30   .25
Town of Slavonski Brod, 750th anniv.

Homage to Olympia, by Ivan Lackovic PT35

Intl. Olympic Committee, Cent. — PT36

Designs: a, Tennis. b, Soccer. c, Basketball. d, Team handball. e, Canoeing, kayaking. f, Water polo. g, Track and field. h, Gymnastics.

1994, Nov. 2   Litho.   Perf. 14
RA52 PT35 50 l Pair, #a.-b.   1.40 1.25
Miniature Sheets of 8
RA53 PT36 50 l #a.-h.   6.25 6.25
RA54 PT36 50 l #a.-h.   6.25 6.25
Nos. RA52b, RA53a, RA53d-RA53e, RA53h, RA54b-RA54c, RA54f-RA54g have IOC centennial emblem. Others have emblem of Croatian Olympic Committee. Required on mail Nov. 2-15.

Natl. Olympic Committee PT37

Designs: a, Rowing. b, Pétanque. c, Monument to Drazen Petrovic, Olympic Park, Lausanne. d, Tennis. e, Basketball.

1995, Apr. 17   Litho.   Perf. 14
RA55 PT37 50 l Strip of 5, #a.-
          e.   1.75 1.75
Required on mail Apr. 17-30.

Red Cross Stamps
PT38   PT39

1995, May 8   Perf. 11
RA56 PT38 50 l multicolored   .30   .25
Required on mail May 8-15.

1995, June 1
RA57 PT39 50 l multicolored   .30   .25
Required on mail June 1-7.

Sts. Peter and Paul Cathedral, Osijek — PT40

1995, July 17   Perf. 14
RA58 PT40 65 l multicolored   .45   .40
Required on mail July 17-30.

Holy Mother of Freedom PT41

Design: No. RA59, Like No. RA60, but with black surcharge on white panel. #RA60, Croatian Pieta, by Ivan Lackovic. #RA61, Gedenkstatte Church Project.

1995, Aug. 14   Litho.   Perf. 14
RA59 PT41 65 l on 50 l multi   1.75 1.75
RA60 PT41 65 l multicolored   .40   .35
RA61 PT41 65 l multicolored   .40   .35
    Nos. RA59-RA61 (3)   2.55 2.45
No. RA59 not issued without surcharge. Examples without surcharge are printer's waste. Required on mail Aug. 14-27.

Red Cross and Tuberculosis PT42

Save the Croatian Children PT43

1995, Sept. 14   Litho.   Perf. 11
RA62 PT62 65 l multicolored   .45   .40
Required on mail Sept. 14-21.

1995, Oct. 16   Litho.   Perf. 14
RA63 PT43 65 l multicolored   .45   .40
Required on mail Oct. 16-29.

PT44

PT45

Performance scene: a, Woman seated at top of steps. b, Gathering of people. c, People, large statue in background.

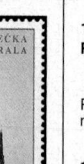

1995, Oct. 16
RA64 PT44 65 l Strip of 3, #a.-
          c.   1.40 1.40
Croatian Natl. Theater, Zagreb, cent. No. RA64 has continuous design. Required on mail 10/16-29.

1995, Nov. 6   Litho.   Perf. 14
RA65 PT45 65 l multicolored   .45   .35
Fight against drugs. Required on mail Nov. 20-30.

PT46

1995, Nov. 20   Litho.   Perf. 14x13¾
RA66 PT46 65 l multicolored   .45   .35
Croatian Anti-Cancer League. Required on mail Nov. 20-30.

PT47   PT48

1996, Feb. 15   Litho.   Perf. 14x13½
RA67 PT47 65 l multicolored   .45   .35
Croatian Anti-Cancer League. Required on mail Feb. 15-28.

1996, Mar. 18   Litho.   Perf. 14
RA68 PT48 65 l multicolored   .45   .35
Sanctuary of the Virgin Mary of Bistrica. Required on mail Mar. 18-31.

Croatian Olympic Committee PT49

1996, Apr. 17   Litho.   Perf. 14
RA69 PT49 65 l multi
No. RA69 exists imperf. and in booklets, which were not placed on sale. Required on mail Apr. 17-30.

PT50   PT51

1996, May 8   Litho.   Perf. 11
RA70 PT50 65 l multicolored   .45   .35
Red Cross. Required on mail May 8-15.

1996, June 6   Litho.   Perf. 11
RA71 PT51 65 l multicolored   .45   .35
Red Cross Solidarity Week. Required on mail June 1-7.

PT52

1996, June 14   Litho.   Perf. 14x13½
RA72 PT52 65 l multicolored   .45   .35
For Croatian children. Required on mail 6/14-27.

PT53

1996, July 3   Litho.   Perf. 14
RA73 PT53 65 l multicolored   .45   .35
Osijek, 800th anniv. Required on mail July 3-16.

PT54

1996, July 17   Litho.   Perf. 14
RA74 PT54 65 l multicolored   .45   .35
Renovation of Dakovaska Cathedral. Required on mail July 17-30.

PT55

1996, Aug. 1   Litho.   Perf. 14
RA75 PT55 65 l multicolored   .45   .35
Split, 1700th anniv. Required on mail Aug. 1-14.

PT56   PT57

1996, Aug. 16   Litho.   Perf. 14x13½
RA76 PT56 65 l multicolored   .45   .35
Aid to Vukovar. Required on mail 8/16-29.

1996, Sept. 1   Litho.   Perf. 14
RA77 PT57 65 l multicolored   .45   .35
Fight against drugs. Required on mail Sept. 1-12.

PT58

1996, Sept. 14   Litho.   Perf. 11
RA78 PT58 65 l multicolored   .45   .35
Red Cross Tuberculosis Week. Required on mail Sept. 14-21.

PT59

1996, Oct. 10   Litho.   Perf. 14
RA79 PT59 65 l multicolored   .45   .35
Isolation of insulin, 75th anniv. Required on mail Oct. 10-17.

PT60   PT61

1996, Nov. 11   Litho.   Perf. 14
RA80 PT60 65 l multicolored   .45   .35
Remete pilgrimage. Required on mail Nov. 11-24.

1997, Jan. 6   Litho.   Perf. 14
RA81 PT61 65 l multicolored   .45   .35
Antun Mihanovic (1796-1861), natl. anthem lyricist. Required on mail Jan. 6-26.

House of Dr. Ante Starcevic PT62

1997, Jan. 27   Litho.   Perf. 14
RA82 PT62 65 l multicolored   .45   .35
Required on mail Jan. 27-Feb. 14.

PT63   PT64

1997, Feb. 15   Litho.   Perf. 14
RA83 PT63 65 l multicolored   .45   .35
Croatian Anti-Cancer League. Required on mail Feb. 15-28.

1997, May 8   Litho.   Perf. 10½x11
RA84 PT64 65 l multicolored   .70   .50
a.   Perf 10½   .70   .50
b.   Perf 11   35.00
Red Cross. Required on mail May 8-15.

Numerous charity stamps were issued between 1997 and 2001, but their use on mail was not obligatory.

Red Cross Solidarity Week — PT65

2001, Dec. 8   Litho.   Perf. 14
RA85 PT65 1.15k red & black   .60   .50
Obligatory on mail Dec. 8-15.

Red Cross Week — PT66

2002, May 8
RA86 PT66 1.15k multi   .70   .60
Obligatory on mail May 8-15.

Red Cross Anti-Tuberculosis Week — PT67

2002, Sept. 14
RA87 PT67 1.15k multi   .60   .50
Obligatory on mail Sept. 14-21.

Red Cross Solidarity Week — PT68

2002, Dec. 8
RA88 PT68 1.15k multi   .60   .50
Obligatory on mail Dec. 8-15.

Red Cross Week — PT69

2003, May 8
RA89 PT69 1.15k multi   .65   .55
Obligatory on mail May 8-15.

Red Cross Anti-Tuberculosis Week — PT70

2003, Sept. 14
RA90 PT70 1.15k multi   .65   .55
Obligatory on mail Sept. 14-21.

Red Cross Solidarity Week — PT71

2003, Dec. 8
RA91 PT71 1.15k multi   .65   .55
Obligatory on mail Dec. 8-15.

Red Cross Week — PT72

2004, May 8
RA92 PT72 1.15k multi   .65   .55
Obligatory on mail May 8-15.

Red Cross Anti-Tuberculosis Week — PT73

2004, Sept. 14
RA93 PT73 1.15k multi   .65   .55
Obligatory on mail Sept. 14-21.

Red Cross Solidarity Week — PT74

2004, Dec. 8
RA94 PT74 1.15k multi   .65   .55
Obligatory on mail Dec. 8-15.

Red Cross Week — PT75

2005, May 8   Litho.   Perf. 14
RA95 PT75 1.15k multi   .40   .40
Obligatory on mail May 8-15.

Red Cross Anti-Tuberculosis Week — PT76

2005, Sept. 14
RA96 PT76 1.15k multi   .40   .40
Obligatory on mail Sept. 14-21.

Red Cross
Solidarity
Week — PT77

2005, Dec. 8
RA97 PT77 1.15k multi   .40   .40
   Obligatory on mail Dec. 8-15.

Red Cross
Week — PT78

2006, May 8   **Litho.**   **Perf. 14**
RA98 PT78 1.15k multi   .45   .45
   Obligatory on mail May 8-15.

Red Cross Anti-
Tuberculosis
Week — PT79

2006, Sept. 14
RA99 PT79 1.15k multi   .40   .40
   Obligatory on mail Sept. 14-21.

Red Cross Solidarity
Week — PT80

2006, Dec. 8
RA100 PT80 1.15k multi   .45   .45
   Obligatory on mail Dec. 8-15.

CUBA

'kyü-bə

LOCATION — The largest island of the West Indies; south of Florida
GOVT. — Former Spanish possession
AREA — 44,206 sq. mi.
POP. — 11,096,395 (1999 est.)
CAPITAL — Havana

Formerly a Spanish possession, Cuba made several unsuccessful attempts to gain her freedom, which finally led to the intervention of the US in 1898. In that year under the Treaty of Paris, Spain relinquished the island to the US in trust for its inhabitants.

In 1902 a republic was established and the Cuban Congress took over the government from the military authorities.

8 Reales Plata = 1 Peso
100 Centesimos = 1 Escudo or Peseta (1867)
1000 Milesimas =
100 Centavos = 1 Peso

Catalogue values for unused stamps in this country are for Never Hinged items, beginning with Scott 402 in the regular postage section, Scott B3 in the semi-postal section, Scott C38 in the airpost section, Scott CB1 in the airpost semi-postal section, Scott E13 in the special delivery section, and Scott RA1 in the postal tax section.

Pen cancellations are common on the earlier stamps of Cuba. Stamps so canceled sell for very much less than those with postmark cancellations.

Watermarks

Wmk. 104 — Loops

Loops from different rows may or may not be directly opposite each other.

Wmk. 105 — Crossed Lines

Wmk. 106 — Star

Wmk. 229 — Wavy Lines

Wmk. 320

Wmk. 321 — "R de C"

Wmk. 376 — "R de C"

Issued under Spanish Dominion

Used also in Puerto Rico: Nos. 1-3, 9-14, 17-21, 32-34, 35A-37, 39-41, 43-45, 47-49, 51-53, 55-57.
Used also in the Philippines: Nos. 2-3.
Identifiable cancellations of those countries will increase the value of the stamps.

Queen Isabella II — A1

Blue Paper

		1855	Typo.	Wmk. 104	Imperf.	
1	A1	½r p blue green		65.00	5.50
a.		½r p blackish green		75.00	10.00
2	A1	1r p gray green		55.00	3.75
3	A1	2r p carmine		350.00	12.00
4	A1	2r p orange red		825.00	17.50
		Nos. 1-4 (4)		1,295.	38.75

See Nos. 9-14. For surcharges see Nos. 5-8, 15.

Counterfeit surcharges are plentiful.

Nos. 3-4 Surcharged

1855-56

5	A1	¼r p on 2r p car	750.00	200.00
a.		Without fraction bar	1,600.	600.00
6	A1	¼r p on 2r p org red		550.00

Surcharged

7	A1	¼r p on 2r p car	650.00	190.00
a.		Without fraction bar		725.00
8	A1	¼r p on 2r p org red	1,000.	450.00
a.		Without fraction bar		1,150.

The "Y ¼" surcharge met the "Ynterior" rate for delivery within the city of Havana.

Rough Yellowish Paper

		1856		Wmk. 105
9	A1	½r p grnsh blue	6.50	.80
10	A1	1r p green	775.00	17.50
a.		1r p emerald	1,100.	20.00
11	A1	2r p orange red	375.00	15.00

White Smooth Paper

		1857		Unwmk.
12	A1	½r p blue	3.25	.65
13	A1	1r p gray green	3.00	.65
a.		1r p pale yellow green	2.75	.65
14	A1	2r p dull rose	17.50	3.00
		Nos. 12-14 (3)	23.75	4.30

Surcharged

1860

15	A1	¼r p on 2r p dl rose	225.00	80.00
a.		1 of ¼ inverted	325.00	140.00
b.		"1 ⅓" instead of 1 ¼		—

22 overprint varieties exist.

Queen Isabella II
A2   A3

		1862-64		Imperf.
16	A2	¼r p black	19.00	15.00
17	A3	¼r p blk, buff ('64)	19.00	14.00
18	A3	½r p green ('64)	4.75	.70
19	A3	½r p grn, pale rose ('64)	11.00	2.00
20	A3	1r p bl, sal ('64)	4.75	1.00
a.		Diagonal half used as ½r p on cover		125.00
21	A3	2r p ver, buff ('64)	25.00	6.00
a.		2r p red, buff	30.00	6.75
		Nos. 16-21 (6)	83.50	38.70

No. 17 Overprinted in Black

1866

22	A3	¼r p black, buff	75.00	80.00

Exists with handstamped "1866."

A5   A6

1866

23	A5	5c dull violet	40.00	26.00
24	A5	10c blue	2.50	1.00
25	A5	20c green	1.50	1.00
a.		Diag. half used as 10c on cover		150.00
26	A5	40c rose	9.50	8.00
		Nos. 23-26 (4)	53.50	36.00

For the Type A5 20c in dull lilac, see Spain No. 87.

Stamps Dated "1867"

		1867		Perf. 14
27	A5	5c dull violet	40.00	21.00
28	A5	10c blue	19.00	1.40
a.		Imperf., pair	110.00	6.50
b.		Diagonal half used as 5c on cover		140.00
29	A5	20c green	12.00	1.90
a.		Imperf., pair	110.00	70.00
b.		Diag. half used as 10c on cover		150.00
30	A5	40c rose	15.00	10.00
		Nos. 27-30 (4)	86.00	34.30

Stamps Dated "1868"

		1868		
31	A6	5c dull violet	18.00	8.25
32	A6	10c blue	3.75	1.75
a.		Diagonal half used as 5c on cover		140.00
33	A6	20c green	5.50	3.00
a.		Diag. half used as 10c on cover		140.00
34	A6	40c rose	14.00	8.00
a.		Diag. half used as 20c on cover		175.00
		Nos. 31-34 (4)	41.25	21.00

Nos. 31-34 Overprinted in Black

1868

35	A6	5c dull violet	62.50	29.00
35A	A6	10c blue	62.50	29.00
b.		Diag. half used as 5c on cover		275.00
36	A6	20c green	62.50	27.50
37	A6	40c rose	62.50	27.50
		Nos. 35-37 (4)	250.00	113.00

		1869	Stamps Dated "1869"	
38	A6	5c rose	37.50	12.00
39	A6	10c red brown	3.75	1.75
a.		Diag. half used as 5c on cover		125.00
40	A6	20c orange	6.50	2.25
41	A6	40c dull violet	30.00	9.50
		Nos. 38-41 (4)	77.75	25.50

Nos. 38-41 Ovptd. Like Nos. 35-37

42	A6	5c rose	150.00	42.50
43	A6	10c red brown	45.00	32.50
a.		Diag. half used as 5c on cover		—
44	A6	20c orange	37.50	32.50
a.		Diag. half used as 10c on cover		—
45	A6	40c dull violet	65.00	32.50
		Nos. 42-45 (4)	297.50	140.00

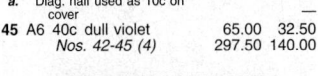

"Espana"
A8   A9

		1870		Perf. 14
46	A8	5c blue	175.00	60.00
47	A8	10c red brown	2.75	.85
a.		Diagonal half used as 5c on cover		150.00
48	A8	20c red brown	2.75	.85
a.		Diag. half used as 10c on cover		225.00
49	A8	40c rose	200.00	30.00

		1871		
50	A9	12c red lilac	20.00	10.00
a.		Imperf., pair	85.00	—
51	A9	25c ultra	2.25	.85
a.		Imperf., pair	40.00	—
b.		Diagonal half used as 12c on cover		140.00
52	A9	50c gray green	2.25	.85
a.		Imperf., pair	15.00	—
b.		Diagonal half used as 25c on cover		140.00
53	A9	1p pale brown	27.50	9.00
a.		Imperf., pair	125.00	—
		Nos. 50-53 (4)	52.00	20.70

King Amadeo — A10

		1873		Perf. 14
54	A10	12½c dark green	22.50	14.00
55	A10	25c gray	2.25	.85
a.		Diagonal half used as 12½c on cover		82.50
b.		25c lilac	6.00	1.10

c. As "b," half used as 12½c
on cover | | 110.00
56 A10 50c brown | 1.50 | .80
a. Imperf., pair | 55.00 | —
b. Half used as 25c on cover | | 90.00
57 A10 1p red brown | 300.00 | 40.00
a. Diagonal half used as 50c on cover | | 260.00

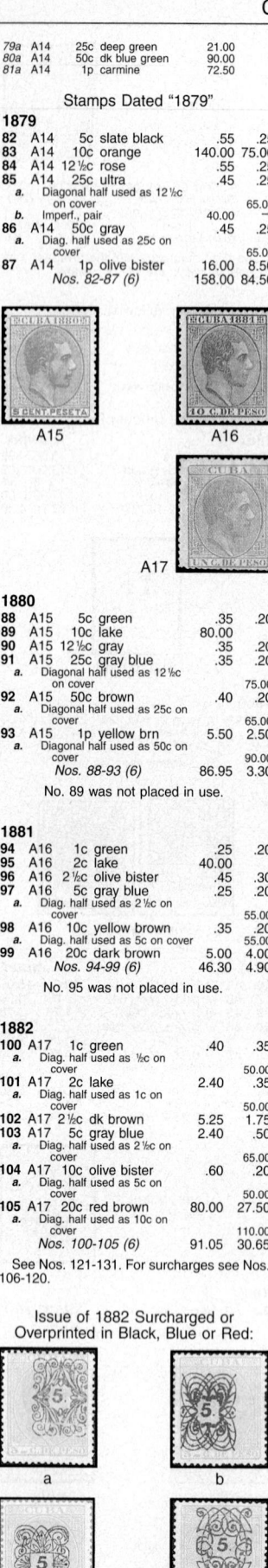

"España"
A11

Coat of Arms
A12

1874
58 A11 12½c brown | 18.00 | 8.25
a. Half used as 5c on cover | | 140.00
59 A11 25c ultra | .90 | .55
a. Diagonal half used as 12½c on cover | | 100.00
60 A11 50c dp violet | 1.60 | .80
a. Diagonal half used as 25c on cover | | 110.00
61 A11 50c gray | 1.60 | .80
a. Diagonal half used as 25c on cover | | 110.00
62 A11 1p carmine | 210.00 | 60.00
a. Imperf., pair | 600.00 | 210.00
Nos. 58-62 (5) | 232.10 | 70.40

1875
63 A12 12½c lt violet | .80 | .80
a. Imperf., pair | 75.00 |
64 A12 25c ultra | .40 | .30
a. Imperf., pair | 75.00 |
b. Diagonal half used as 12½c on cover | | 70.00
65 A12 50c blue green | .45 | .35
a. Imperf., pair | 75.00 |
b. Diag. half used as 25c on cover | | 65.00
66 A12 1p brown | 7.25 | 4.50
a. Diag. half used as 50c on cover | | 125.00
Nos. 63-66 (4) | 8.90 | 5.95

King Alfonso XII
A13   A14

1876
67 A13 12½c green | 1.75 | 1.50
a. 12½c emerald green | 2.00 | 2.00
68 A13 25c gray | .80 | .35
a. Diagonal half used as 12½c on cover | | 90.00
b. 25c pale violet | 1.50 | .30
d. 25c bluish gray | 2.25 | .35
69 A13 50c ultra | .80 | .40
a. Imperf., pair | 16.00 |
b. Diag. half used as 25c on cover | | 75.00
70 A13 1p black | 8.50 | 3.50
a. Imperf., pair | 40.00 |
b. Diag. half used as 50c on cover | | 125.00
Nos. 67-70 (4) | 11.85 | 5.75

1877
71 A14 10c lt green | 22.50 |
72 A14 12½c gray | 6.00 | 2.75
a. Imperf., pair | 35.00 |
b. Diagonal half used on cover | | 65.00
73 A14 25c dk green | .55 | .45
a. Imperf., pair | 35.00 |
b. Diagonal half used as 12½c on cover | | 65.00
74 A14 50c black | .55 | .45
a. Imperf., pair | 35.00 |
b. Half used as 25c on cover | | 75.00
75 A14 1p brown | 25.00 | 12.50
Nos. 71-75 (5) | 54.60

No. 71 was not placed in use.

Stamps Dated "1878"

1878
76 A14 5c blue | .55 | .45
77 A14 10c black | 62.50 |
78 A14 12½c brown bis | 3.25 | 1.75
a. 12½c gray bister | 4.00 | 1.50
c. Diagonal half used on cover | | 65.00
79 A14 25c yel green | .20 | .20
b. No. 79 or 79c, diagonal half used as 12½c on cover | | 60.00
c. 25c deep green | .20 | .20
80 A14 50c dk blue grn | .35 | .20
a. Diagonal half used as 25c on cover | | 60.00
81 A14 1p carmine | 10.00 | 4.50
b. 1p rose | 6.75 | 3.50
Nos. 76-81 (6) | 76.85 | 7.10

No. 77 was not placed in use.

Imperf., Pairs
76a A14 5c blue | 21.00
77a A14 10c black | 110.00
78b A14 12½c brown bister | 21.00

79a A14 25c deep green | 21.00
80a A14 50c dk blue green | 90.00
81a A14 1p carmine | 72.50

Stamps Dated "1879"

1879
82 A14 5c slate black | .55 | .25
83 A14 10c orange | 140.00 | 75.00
84 A14 12½c rose | .55 | .25
85 A14 25c ultra | .45 | .25
a. Diagonal half used as 12½c on cover | | 65.00
b. Imperf., pair | 40.00 |
86 A14 50c gray | .45 | .25
a. Diag. half used as 25c on cover | | 65.00
87 A14 1p olive bister | 16.00 | 8.50
Nos. 82-87 (6) | 158.00 | 84.50

A15   A16

A17

1880
88 A15 5c green | .35 | .20
89 A15 10c lake | 80.00 |
90 A15 12½c gray | .35 | .20
91 A15 25c gray blue | .35 | .20
a. Diagonal half used as 12½c on cover | | 75.00
92 A15 50c brown | .40 | .20
a. Diagonal half used as 25c on cover | | 65.00
93 A15 1p yellow brn | 5.50 | 2.50
a. Diagonal half used as 50c on cover | | 90.00
Nos. 88-93 (6) | 86.95 | 3.30

No. 89 was not placed in use.

1881
94 A16 1c green | .25 | .20
95 A16 2c lake | 40.00 |
96 A16 2½c olive bister | .45 | .30
97 A16 5c gray blue | .25 | .20
a. Diag. half used as 2½c on cover | | 55.00
98 A16 10c yellow brown | .35 | .20
a. Diagonal half used as 5c on cover | | 55.00
99 A16 20c dark brown | 5.00 | 4.00
Nos. 94-99 (6) | 46.30 | 4.90

No. 95 was not placed in use.

1882
100 A17 1c green | .40 | .35
a. Diag. half used as ½c on cover | | 50.00
101 A17 2c lake | 2.40 | .35
a. Diag. half used as 1c on cover | | 50.00
102 A17 2½c dk brown | 5.25 | 1.75
a. Diag. half used as 2½c on cover | | 65.00
103 A17 5c gray blue | 2.40 | .50
a. Diag. half used as 2½c on cover | | 65.00
104 A17 10c olive bister | .60 | .20
a. Diag. half used as 5c on cover | | 50.00
105 A17 20c red brown | 80.00 | 27.50
a. Diag. half used as 10c on cover | | 110.00
Nos. 100-105 (6) | 91.05 | 30.65

See Nos. 121-131. For surcharges see Nos. 106-120.

Issue of 1882 Surcharged or Overprinted in Black, Blue or Red:

a   b

c   d

---

e

1883
106 A17 5 on 5c (R) | 1.90 | 1.00
a. Triple surcharge
b. Double surcharge | 19.00 | 19.00
c. Inverted surcharge | 25.00 | 25.00
d. Without "5" in surcharge | 14.00 | 14.00
e. Dbl. surch., types "a" & "d"
107 A17 10 on 10c (Bl) | 1.90 | 1.10
a. Inverted surcharge
b. Double surcharge | 22.50 | 22.50
108 A17 20 on 20c | 25.00 | 21.00
a. "10" instead of "20" | 65.00 | 65.00
b. Double surcharge

Type "b"
109 A17 5 on 5c (R) | 1.90 | 1.00
a. Inverted surcharge | 22.50 | 22.50
b. Double surcharge | 19.00 | 19.00
110 A17 10 on 10c (Bl) | 5.50 | 2.25
a. Inverted surcharge | 27.50 | 27.50
111 A17 20 on 20c | 55.00 | 27.50
a. Double surcharge
b. Dbl. surch., types "b" & "c"

Type "c"
112 A17 5 on 5c (R) | 1.60 | 1.00
a. Inverted surcharge | 27.50 | 27.50
b. Dbl. surch., types "c" & "d"
113 A17 10 on 10c (Bl) | 5.50 | 2.50
a. Inverted surcharge | 32.50 | 32.50
b. Double surcharge | 32.50 | 32.50
114 A17 20 on 20c | 37.50 | 20.00
a. "10" instead of "20" | 82.50 | 65.00
b. Double surcharge | 82.50 | 82.50
c. Dbl. surch., types "a" & "c"

Type "d"
115 A17 5 on 5c (R) | 1.50 | .95
a. Inverted surcharge | 27.50 | 27.50
b. Double surcharge | 22.50 | 22.50
116 A17 10 on 10c (Bl) | 2.25 | 1.60
a. Inverted surcharge | 27.50 | 27.50
b. Double surcharge | 25.00 | 25.00
117 A17 20 on 20c | 55.00 | 22.50
a. Dbl. surch., types "a" & "d"

Type "e"
118 A17 5c gray blue (R) | 1.90 | 1.40
a. Double overprint | 30.00 | 30.00
119 A17 10c olive bis (Bl) | 4.50 | 4.50
a. Double overprint | 32.50 | 32.50
120 A17 20c red brown | 140.00 | 35.00
a. Double overprint | 110.00 | 110.00
Nos. 106-120 (15) | 340.95 | 143.30

Handstamped overprints and surcharges are counterfeits.
Numerous other varieties exist.

Type of 1882

Original

1st retouch

2d retouch

The differences between the stamps of 1882 and the various retouches are as follows:
Original state: The medallion is surrounded by a heavy line of color of nearly even thickness, touching the horizontal line below the word "Cuba" (or "Filipinas," "Puerto Rico," as the case may be); the opening in the hair above the temple is narrow and pointed.
1st retouch: The line around the medallion is thin, except at the upper right, and does not touch the horizontal line above it; the opening in the hair is slightly wider and a trifle rounded; the lock of hair above the forehead is shaped like a broad "V" and ends in a point; there is a faint white line below it, which is not found on the stamps in the original state. Owing to wear of the plate the shape of the lock of hair and the width of the white line below it vary.
2nd retouch: The opening in the hair forms a semi-circle; the lock above the forehead is

---

nearly straight, having only a slight wave, and the white line is much broader than before.

1883-86
121 A17 1c grn, 2nd retouch | 110.00 | 45.00
122 A17 2½c olive bister | .40 | .20
124 A17 2½c violet | .40 | .25
a. 2½c red lilac ('85) | .85 | .50
b. 2½c ultramarine | 95.00 | —
125 A17 5c gray bl, 1st retouch | 2.25 | .30
a. Diag. half used as 2½c on cover | | 45.00
126 A17 5c gray bl, 2nd retouch | 22.50 | 2.50
a. Diag. half used as 2½c on cover | | 50.00
127 A17 10c brn, 1st retouch | 2.75 | .45
a. Diagonal half used as 5c on cover | | 40.00
128 A17 20c olive bister | 13.00 | 2.75
Nos. 121-128 (7) | 151.30 | 51.50

1888
129 A17 2½c red brown | 1.60 | .90
130 A17 10c blue | 1.25 | .80
a. Diagonal half used as 5c on cover | | 175.00
131 A17 20c brnsh gray | 12.00 | 4.00
Nos. 129-131 (3) | 14.85 | 5.70

King Alfonso XIII
A18   A19

1890-97
132 A18 1c gray brown | 12.50 | 6.00
133 A18 1c ol gray ('91) | 7.50 | 3.25
134 A18 1c ultra ('94) | 3.25 | .90
135 A18 1c dk vio ('96) | .90 | .25
136 A18 2c slate blue | 7.00 | 4.00
137 A18 2c lilac brn ('91) | 1.50 | .45
138 A18 2c rose ('94) | 30.00 | 5.00
139 A18 2c claret ('96) | 7.75 | 4.00
140 A18 2½c emerald | 9.50 | 4.00
141 A18 2½c salmon ('91) | 45.00 | 9.00
142 A18 2½c lilac ('94) | 3.00 | .25
143 A18 2½c rose ('96) | .65 | .20
144 A18 5c olive gray | .75 | .60
145 A18 5c emerald ('91) | .90 | .40
146 A18 5c sl blue ('96) | .50 | .20
147 A18 10c brown violet | 2.75 | .75
148 A18 10c claret ('91) | 1.75 | .40
149 A18 10c emerald ('96) | 2.25 | .20
150 A18 20c dk violet | .85 | .55
151 A18 20c ultra ('91) | 8.25 | 7.25
152 A18 20c red brn ('94) | 24.00 | 9.50
153 A18 20c violet ('96) | 14.00 | 4.75
154 A18 40c orange brn ('97) | 29.00 | 11.00
155 A18 80c lilac brn ('97) | 52.50 | 17.00
Nos. 132-155 (24) | 265.95 | 84.10

Imperf., Pairs
134a A18 1c ultramarine | 80.00
138a A18 2c rose | 85.00
142a A18 2½c lilac | 80.00
145a A18 5c emerald | 85.00
148a A18 10c claret | 75.00
152a A18 20c red brown | 125.00

1898
156 A19 1m orange brn | .20 | .20
157 A19 2m orange brn | .20 | .20
158 A19 3m orange brn | .20 | .20
159 A19 4m orange brn | 4.25 | 1.40
160 A19 5m orange brn | .20 | .20
161 A19 1c black vio | .20 | .20
162 A19 2c dk blue grn | .20 | .20
163 A19 3c dk brown | .20 | .20
164 A19 4c orange | 12.50 | 3.50
165 A19 5c car rose | .85 | .20
166 A19 6c dk blue | .25 | .20
167 A19 8c gray brown | .90 | .35
168 A19 10c vermilion | .90 | .35
169 A19 15c slate green | 4.25 | .35
170 A19 20c maroon | .50 | .20
171 A19 40c dark lilac | 2.00 | .35
172 A19 60c black | 2.00 | .35
173 A19 80c red brown | 13.00 | 6.75
174 A19 1p yel green | 13.00 | 6.75
175 A19 2p slate blue | 25.00 | 6.75
Nos. 156-175 (20) | 80.80 | 28.90

Nos. 156-160 were issued for use on newspapers.
Nos. 156-175 exist imperf. Value, unused pairs, $1,500.
For surcharges see Nos. 176-189C, 196-200.

Issued under Administration of the United States
Puerto Principe Issue
Issues of Cuba of 1898 and 1896 Surcharged:

HABILITADO **1** cent. a

HABILITADO **1** cents. b

HABILITADO **2** cents. c

HABILITADO **2** cents. d

HABILITADO **3** cents. e

HABILITADO **3** cents. f

HABILITADO **5** cents. g

HABILITADO **5** cents. h

HABILITADO **5** cents. i

HABILITADO **5** cents. j

HABILITADO **3** cents. k

HABILITADO **3** cents. l

m

HABILITADO **10** cents.

Types a, c, d, e, f, g and h are 17½mm high, the others are 19½mm high.

Black Surcharge On Nos. 156, 157, 158 and 160
1898-99
#176-189 are Orange Brown

176	A19 (a)	1c on 1m	50.00	30.00
177	A19 (b)	1c on 1m	45.00	35.00
a.	Broken figure "I"		75.00	65.00
b.	Inverted surcharge			200.00
d.	As "a," inverted			250.00
178	A19 (c)	2c on 2m	24.00	18.00
a.	Inverted surcharge		250.00	50.00
179	A19 (d)	2c on 2m	40.00	35.00
a.	Inverted surcharge		350.00	100.00
179B	A19 (k)	3c on 1m	300.00	175.00
c.	Double surcharge		1,500.	500.00
179D	A19 (l)	3c on 1m	1,500.	750.00
e.	Double surcharge			
179F	A19 (e)	3c on 2m		1,500.

Value is for copy with minor faults.

179G	A19 (f)	3c on 2m	—	2,000.

Value is for copy with minor faults.

180	A19 (e)	3c on 3m	30.00	30.00
a.	Inverted surcharge			110.00
181	A19 (f)	3c on 3m	75.00	50.00
a.	Inverted surcharge			200.00
182	A19 (g)	3c on 3m	700.00	200.00
a.	Inverted surcharge			500.00
183	A19 (h)	5c on 1m	1,300.	500.00
a.	Inverted surcharge			700.00

184	A19 (g)	5c on 2m	750.00	250.00
185	A19 (h)	5c on 2m	1,500.	500.00
186	A19 (g)	5c on 3m	650.00	175.00
a.	Inverted surcharge		1,200.	700.00
187	A19 (h)	5c on 3m		400.00
a.	Inverted surcharge			1,000.
188	A19 (g)	5c on 5m	80.00	60.00
a.	Inverted surcharge		400.00	200.00
b.	Double surcharge		—	
189	A19 (h)	5c on 5m	350.00	250.00
a.	Inverted surcharge			400.00
b.	Double surcharge		—	

The 2nd printing of Nos. 188-189 has shiny ink. Values are for the 1st printing.

189C	A19 (i)	5c on 5m		7,500.

Black Surcharge on No. P25

190	N2 (g)	5c on ½m bl grn	250.00	75.00
a.	Inverted surcharge		500.00	150.00
b.	Pair, right stamp without surcharge			500.00

Value for No. 190b is for pair with unsurcharged copy at right. Exists with unsurcharged stamp at left.

191	N2 (h)	5c on ½m bl grn	300.00	90.00
a.	Inverted surcharge			200.00
192	N2 (i)	5c on ½m bl grn	550.00	200.00
a.	Dbl. surch., one diagonal			11,500.
193	N2 (j)	5c on ½m bl grn	800.00	300.00

Red Surcharge on No. 161

196	A19 (k)	3c on 1c blk vio	65.00	35.00
a.	Inverted surcharge			325.00
197	A19 (l)	3c on 1c blk vio	125.00	55.00
a.	Inverted surcharge			400.00
198	A19 (i)	5c on 1c blk vio	25.00	30.00
a.	Inverted surcharge			125.00
b.	Surcharge vert. up			3,500.
c.	Double surcharge		400.00	600.00
d.	Dbl. invtd. surch.			

No. 198b exists reading down.

199	A19 (j)	5c on 1c blk vio	55.00	55.00
a.	Inverted surcharge			250.00
b.	Vertical surcharge			2,000.
c.	Double surcharge		1,000.	600.00
200	A19 (m) 10c on 1c blk vio		20.00	50.00
a.	Broken figure "I"		40.00	100.00

Black Surcharge on Nos. P26-P30

201	N2 (k)	3c on 1m bl grn	350.	350.
a.	Inverted surcharge			450.
b.	"EENTS"		550.	450.
c.	As "b," inverted			850.
202	N2 (l)	3c on 1m bl grn	550.	400.
a.	Inverted surcharge			850.
203	N2 (k)	3c on 2m bl grn	850.	400.
a.	"EENTS"		1,250.	500.
b.	Inverted surcharge			850.
c.	As "a," inverted			950.
204	N2 (l)	3c on 2m bl grn	1,250.	600.
a.	Inverted surcharge			750.
205	N2 (k)	3c on 3m bl grn	900.	400.
a.	Inverted surcharge			500.
b.	"EENTS"		1,250.	450.
c.	As "b," inverted			700.
206	N2 (l)	3c on 3m bl grn	1,200.	550.
a.	Inverted surcharge			700.
211	N2 (i)	5c on 1m bl grn		1,800.
a.	"EENTS"		—	2,500.
212	N2 (j)	5c on 1m bl grn		2,250.
213	N2 (i)	5c on 2m bl grn		1,800.
a.	"EENTS"		—	1,900.
214	N2 (j)	5c on 2m bl grn		1,750.
215'	N2 (j)	5c on 3m bl grn		550.
a.	"EENTS"		—	1,000.
216	N2 (j)	5c on 3m bl grn		1,000.
217	N2 (i)	5c on 4m bl grn	2,500.	900.
a.	"EENTS"		3,000.	1,500.
b.	Inverted surcharge		—	2,000.
c.	As "a," inverted			2,000.
218	N2 (j)	5c on 4m bl grn		1,500.
a.	Inverted surcharge		—	2,000.
219	N2 (i)	5c on 8m bl grn	2,500.	1,250.
a.	Inverted surcharge		—	1,500.
b.	"EENTS"		—	1,800.
c.	As "b," inverted			2,500.
220	N2 (j)	5c on 8m bl grn		2,000.
a.	Inverted surcharge			2,500.

Beware of forgeries of the Puerto Principe issue. Obtaining expert opinions is recommended.

United States Nos. 279, 267, 267b, 279Bf, 279Bh, 268, 281, 282C and 283 Surcharged in Black

1899		**Wmk. 191**		**Perf. 12**
221	A87	1c on 1c yel grn	5.25	.40
222	A88	2c on 2c reddish car, type III	10.00	.75
b.	2c on 2c vermilion, type III		10.00	.75
222A	A88	2c on 2c reddish car, type IV	6.00	.40
c.	2c on 2c vermilion, type IV		6.00	.40
d.	As #222A, inverted surcharge		5,500.	5,000.
223	A88	2½c on 2c reddish car, type III	5.00	.80
b.	2½c on 2c vermilion, type III		5.00	.80
223A	A88	2½c on 2c reddish car, type IV	3.50	.50
c.	2½c on 2c vermilion		3.50	.50
224	A89	3c on 3c purple	14.00	1.75
a.	"CUB.A"		37.50	35.00
225	A91	5c on 5c blue	14.00	2.00
226	A94	10c on 10c brn, type I	25.00	6.50
b.	"CUBA" omitted		5,500.	4,000.
226A	A94	10c on 10c brn, type II	6,500.	
		Nos. 221-226 (8)	82.75	13.10

The 2½c was sold and used as a 2c stamp.
Excellent counterfeits of this and the preceding issue exist, especially inverted and double surcharges.

Issues of the Republic under U.S. Military Rule

Statue of Columbus A20

Royal Palms A21

"Cuba" — A22

Ocean Liner — A23

Cane Field — A24

		Wmk. US-C (191C)		
1899		**Engr.**		**Perf. 12**
227	A20	1c yel grn	3.75	.20
228	A21	2c carmine	3.75	.20
a.	2c scarlet		3.75	
b.	Booklet pane of 6 ('02)		3,750.	
229	A22	3c purple	3.75	.20
230	A23	5c blue	5.00	.20
231	A24	10c brown	12.00	.50
		Nos. 227-231 (5)	28.25	1.30

No. 228b was issued by the Republic. See Nos. 233-237. For surcharge see No. 232.

Issues of the Republic

No. 229 Surcharged in Carmine

1902, Sept. 30

232	A22	1c on 3c purple	1.50	.50
a.	Inverted surcharge		150.00	150.00
b.	Surcharge sideways (numeral horizontal)		200.00	200.00
c.	Double surcharge		200.00	200.00

Counterfeits of the errors are plentiful.

Re-engraved

The re-engraved stamps of 1905-07 may be distinguished from the issue of 1899 as follows:

ORIGINAL

RE-ENGRAVED

1c — The ends of the label inscribed "Centavo" are rounded instead of square.
2c — The foliate ornaments, inside the oval disks bearing the numerals of value, have been removed.
5c — Two lines forming a right angle have been added in the upper corners of the label bearing the word "Cuba."
10c — A small ball has been added to each of the square ends of the label bearing the word "Cuba."

1905		**Unwmk.**		**Perf. 12**
233	A20	1c green	1.60	.20
234	A21	2c rose	1.10	.20
a.	Booklet pane of 6		150.00	
236	A23	5c blue	37.50	1.00
237	A24	10c brown	3.00	.45
		Nos. 233-237 (4)	43.20	1.85

Maj. Gen. Antonio Maceo — A26

1907

238	A26	50c gray bl & blk	1.10	.75

Bartolomé Masó A27

Máximo Gómez A28

Julio Sanguily A29

Ignacio Agramonte A30

Calixto
García
A31

José M.
Rodriquez y
Rodriquez
(Mayia)
A32

Carlos Roloff — A33

1910, Feb. 1
239	A27	1c grn & vio	.85 .20
a.		Center inverted	260.00 260.00
240	A28	2c car & grn	1.60 .20
a.		Center inverted	575.00 575.00
241	A29	3c vio & bl	1.10 .20
242	A30	5c bl & grn	16.00 .80
243	A31	8c ol & vio	1.10 .30
244	A32	10c brn & bl	6.75 .65
a.		Center inverted	850.00
245	A26	50c vio & blk	1.60 .50
246	A33	1p slate & blk	7.75 4.00
		Nos. 239-246 (8)	36.75 6.85
		Set, never hinged	50.00

1911-13
247	A27	1c green	.55 .20
248	A28	2c car rose	.70 .20
a.		Booklet pane of 6 ('13)	82.50
250	A30	5c ultra	1.75 .20
251	A31	8c ol grn & blk	1.10 .60
252	A33	1p black	5.00 2.00
		Nos. 247-252 (5)	9.10 3.20
		Set, never hinged	16.00

Map of Cuba — A34

1914-15
253	A34	1c green	.90 .20
a.		Booklet pane of 6	100.00
254	A34	2c car rose	1.10 .20
a.		Booklet pane of 6	100.00
255	A34	2c red ('15)	1.75 .20
a.		Booklet pane of 6	100.00
256	A34	3c violet	5.50 .35
257	A34	5c blue	7.50 .20
258	A34	8c ol grn	6.00 .70
259	A34	10c brown	11.00 .35
260	A34	10c ol grn ('15)	13.00 .55
261	A34	50c orange	85.00 10.00
262	A34	1p gray	125.00 24.00
		Nos. 253-262 (10)	256.75 36.75
		Set, never hinged	450.00

Complete set of eight 1914 stamps, imperf.
pairs, value $1,500.

Nos. 253, 254, 256 and E5 exist with "1917
GOB./CONSTITUCIONAL/CAMAGUEY" overprint. These were not authorized.

Gertrudis
Gómez de
Avellaneda,
Cuban
Poetess
(1814-73)
A34a

1914
263	A34a	5c blue	14.00 5.00
		Never hinged	22.50

José Martí
A35

Máximo
Gómez
A36

José de la
Luz Caballero
A37

Ignacio
Agramonte
A39

Tomás
Estrada
Palma
A40

José A.
Saco — A41

Antonio
Maceo — A42

Carlos Manuel de
Céspedes — A43

1917-18   Unwmk.   Perf. 12
264	A35	1c bl grn	.75 .20
a.		Booklet pane of 6	40.00
b.		Booklet pane of 30	250.00
265	A36	2c rose	.75 .20
a.		Booklet pane of 6	50.00
b.		Booklet pane of 30	210.00
266	A36	2c lt red ('18)	.60 .20
a.		Booklet pane of 6	50.00
267	A37	3c violet	.75 .20
a.		Imperf. pair	275.00
b.		Booklet pane of 6	50.00
268	A38	5c dp bl	.75 .20
269	A39	8c red brn	3.50 .20
270	A40	10c yel brn	2.25 .20
271	A41	20c gray grn	14.00 1.60
272	A42	50c dl rose	14.00 .70
273	A43	1p black	14.50 .70
		Nos. 264-273 (10)	51.85 4.40
		Set, never hinged	75.00

1925-28   Wmk. 106   Perf. 12
274	A35	1c blue green	1.10 .20
a.		Booklet pane of 6	350.00
275	A36	2c brt rose	1.20 .20
a.		Booklet pane of 6	75.00
b.		Booklet pane of 30	350.00
276	A38	5c dp bl	2.50 .20
277	A39	8c red brn ('28)	5.75 .60
278	A40	10c yel brn ('27)	7.00 .70
279	A41	20c olive grn	11.00 1.10
		Nos. 274-279 (6)	28.55 3.00
		Set, never hinged	40.00

1926   Imperf.
280	A35	1c blue green	1.40 1.00
281	A36	2c brt rose	1.40 1.00
282	A38	5c deep blue	1.75 1.40
		Nos. 280-282 (3)	4.55 3.40
		Set, never hinged	5.00

See Nos. 304-310. For overprint and
surcharge see Nos. 317-318, 644.

Arms of
Republic
A44

1927, May 20   Unwmk.   Perf. 12
283	A44	25c violet	16.00 3.50
		Never hinged	24.00

25th anniversary of the Republic.
For surcharges see Nos. 355, C3.

Tomás
Estrada
Palma
A45

Designs: 2c, Gen. Gerardo Machado. 5c,
Morro Castle. 8c, Havana Railway Station.
10c, Presidential Palace. 13c, Tobacco Plantation. 20c, Treasury Building. 30c, Sugar Mill.
50c, Havana Cathedral. 1p, Galician Clubhouse, Havana.

1928, Jan. 2   Wmk. 106
284	A45	1c deep green	.45 .20
285	A45	2c brt rose	.50 .20
286	A45	5c deep blue	.75 .30
287	A45	8c lt red brn	3.00 .90
288	A45	10c bister brn	.75 .55
289	A45	13c orange	1.50 .55
290	A45	20c olive grn	1.75 .65
291	A45	30c dk violet	4.25 .55
292	A45	50c carmine rose	6.50 2.10
293	A45	1p gray black	13.00 5.00
		Nos. 284-293 (10)	32.45 11.00
		Set, never hinged	50.00

Sixth Pan-American Conference.

Capitol,
Havana
A55

1929, May 18
294	A55	1c green	.25 .25
295	A55	2c carmine rose	.30 .30
296	A55	5c blue	.45 .30
297	A55	10c bister brn	.75 .50
298	A55	20c violet	3.25 2.75
		Nos. 294-298 (5)	5.00 4.10
		Set, never hinged	9.00

Opening of the Capitol, Havana.

Hurdler — A56

1930, Mar. 15   Engr.
299	A56	1c green	.75 .35
300	A56	2c carmine	.75 .40
301	A56	5c deep blue	1.00 .40
302	A56	10c bister brn	2.00 .85
303	A56	20c violet	12.00 3.00
		Nos. 299-303 (5)	16.50 5.00
		Set, never hinged	24.00

2nd Central American Athletic Games.

Types of 1917 Portrait Issue
Flat Plate Printing

1930-45   Wmk. 106   Engr.   Perf. 10
304	A35	1c blue green	.75 .25
a.		Booklet pane of 6	50.00
b.		Booklet pane of 30	—
305	A36	2c brt rose	75.00 —
a.		Booklet pane of 6	1,200.
305B	A37	3c dk rose vio ('42)	4.00 .75
c.		Booklet pane of 6	42.50
306	A38	5c dk blue	2.75 .20
306A	A39	8c red brn ('45)	2.75 .25
307	A40	10c brown	2.75 .25
a.		10c yellow brown ('35)	3.50 .75
307B	A41	20c olive grn ('41)	4.75 .75
		Nos. 304-307B (7)	92.75 2.45

Nos. 305 and 305B were printed for booklet
panes and all copies have straight edges.
For surcharge see No. 644.

Rotary Press Printing
308	A35	1c blue grn	1.10 .20
309	A36	2c brt rose	1.10 .20
a.		Booklet pane of 50	
310	A37	3c violet	1.50 .20
a.		3c dull violet ('38)	1.10 .20
b.		3c rose violet ('41)	1.10 .20
c.		Booklet pane of 50	
		Nos. 308-310 (3)	3.70 .60

Flat plate stamps measure 18½x21½mm;
rotary press, 19x22mm.

The Mangos of
Baragua — A57

War
Memorial — A61

Battle of
Mal
Tiempo
A58

Battle of
Coliseo
A59

Maceo,
Gómez
and
Zayas
A60

Wmk. 229
1933, Apr. 23   Photo.   Perf. 12½
312	A57	3c dk brown	1.40 .30
313	A58	5c dk blue	1.25 .35
314	A59	10c emerald	2.25 .35
315	A60	13c red	2.75 .90
316	A61	20c black	5.50 2.10
		Nos. 312-316 (5)	13.15 4.00
		Set, never hinged	22.50

War of Independence and dedication of the
"Soldado Invasor" (the American Army that
came to the aid of the revolution against
Spain) monument.

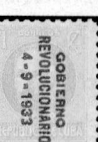

Types of 1917 Issues
with Carmine or Black
Overprint Reading Up
or Down

Rotary Press Printing
Wmk. 106
1933, Dec. 23   Engr.   Perf. 10
317	A35	1c blue green (C)	1.75 .20

**With Additional Surcharge of New
Value and Bars**
318	A37	2c on 3c vio (Bk)	1.75 .20

Establishment of a revolutionary junta.
Catalogue values for Nos. 317-318 unused
are for examples with overprint reading up.
Values for overprint reading down, $4.

Dr. Carlos J.
Finlay — A62

1934, Dec. 3   Engr.   Perf. 10
319	A62	2c dark carmine	1.00 .50
320	A62	5c dark blue	2.75 1.50
		Set, never hinged	6.00

Cent. of the birth of Dr. Carlos J. Finlay
(1833-1915), physician-biologist who found
that a mosquito transmitted yellow fever.

Pres. José Miguel Gómez — A63

Gómez Monument A64

1936, May **Perf. 10**
322 A63 1c green 1.50 .40
323 A64 2c carmine 2.25 .50
Set, never hinged 7.00

Unveiling of a monument to Gen. José Miguel Gómez, ex-president.

Matanzas Issue

Map of Cuba A65

2c, Map of Free Zone. 4c, S. S. "Rex" in Matanzas Bay. 5c, Ships in Matanzas Bay. 8c, Caves of Bellamar. 10c, Valley of Yumuri. 20c, Yumuri River. 50c, Ships Leaving Port.

Wmk. 229
1936, May 5 **Photo.** **Perf. 12½**
324 A65 1c blue green .40 .20
325 A65 2c red .60 .20
326 A65 4c claret 1.00 .20
327 A65 5c ultra 1.50 .20
328 A65 8c orange brn 2.50 .55
329 A65 10c emerald 2.75 .55
330 A65 20c brown 5.25 2.10
331 A65 50c slate 9.75 3.00
Nos. 324-331,C18-C21,CE1,E8 (14) 45.65 19.40
Set, never hinged 60.00

Issued both perf and imperf. Same values.

"Peace and Work" A73

Máximo Gómez Monument — A74

Torch — A75

"Independence" — A76

"Messenger of Peace" — A77

1936, Nov. 18 **Perf. 12½**
332 A73 1c emerald .50 .20
333 A74 2c crimson .60 .20
334 A75 4c maroon .70 .20
335 A76 5c ultra 2.75 .45
336 A77 8c dk green 4.00 1.00
Nos. 332-336,C22-C23,E9 (8) 17.80 6.65
Set, never hinged 35.00

Maj. Gen. Máximo Gómez, birth centenary. Issued both perf and imperf. Values for imperfs are approx. 400% higher.

Sugar Cane — A78

Primitive Sugar Mill — A79

Modern Sugar Mill — A80

Wmk. 106
1937, Oct. 2 **Engr.** **Perf. 10**
337 A78 1c yellow green 1.25 .40
338 A79 2c red .75 .25
339 A80 5c bright blue 1.75 .40
Nos. 337-339 (3) 3.75 1.05
Set, never hinged 6.00

Cuban sugar cane industry, 400th anniv.

Argentine Emblem — A81

Mountain Scene (Bolivia) — A82

Arms of Brazil — A83

Canadian Scene — A84

Camilo Henriquez (Chile) A85

Gen, Francisco de Paula Santander (Colombia) A86

Natl. Monument (Costa Rica) — A87

Autograph of José Marti (Cuba) — A88

Columbus Lighthouse (Dominican Rep.) — A89

Juan Montalvo (Ecuador) — A90

Abraham Lincoln (US) A91

Quetzal and Scroll (Guatemala) A92

Arms of Haiti A93

Francisco Morazán (Honduras) A94

Fleet of Columbus — A95

Wmk. 106
1937, Oct. 13 **Engr.** **Perf. 10**
340 A81 1c deep green .60 .60
341 A82 1c green .60 .60
342 A83 2c carmine .60 .60
343 A84 2c carmine .60 .60
344 A85 3c violet 1.60 1.60
345 A86 3c violet 1.60 1.60
346 A87 4c bister brown 1.90 1.90
347 A88 4c bister brown 3.50 3.50
348 A89 5c blue 1.75 1.75
349 A90 5c blue 1.75 1.75
350 A91 8c citron 12.50 12.50
351 A92 8c citron 3.00 3.00
352 A93 10c maroon 3.00 3.00
353 A94 10c maroon 3.00 3.00
354 A95 25c rose lilac 30.00 30.00
Nos. 340-354,C24-C29,E10-E11 (23) 125.50 125.50
Set, never hinged 160.00

Nos. 340-354 were sold by the Cuban PO for 3 days, Oct. 13-15, during which no other stamps were sold. They were postally valid for the full face value. Proceeds from their three-day sale above 30,000 pesos were paid by the Cuban POD to the Assoc. of American Writers and Artists. Remainders were overprinted "SVP" (Without Postal Value).

No. 283 Surcharged in Green

1937, Nov. 19 **Unwmk.** **Perf. 12**
355 A44 10c on 25c violet 12.50 3.50
Never hinged 19.00

Centenary of Cuban railroads.

Ciboney Indian and Cigar — A96

Cigar and Globe — A97

Tobacco Plant and Cigars — A98

1939, Aug. 28 **Wmk. 106** **Perf. 10**
356 A96 1c yellow green .35 .20
357 A97 2c red .50 .20
358 A98 5c brt ultra .90 .25
Nos. 356-358 (3) 1.75 .65
Set, never hinged 3.00

General Calixto García
A99   A100

1939, Nov. 6 **Perf. 10, Imperf.**
359 A99 2c dark red .75 .20
360 A100 5c deep blue 1.00 .30
Set, never hinged 3.00

Birth centenary of General Garcia. Values are for perf examples. Value of imperfs approx. 20% higher.

Gonzalo de Quesada — A101

1940, Apr. 30 **Engr.** **Perf. 10**
361 A101 2c rose red 1.25 .50
Never hinged 2.00

Pan American Union, 50th anniversary.

Rotary Club Emblem, Cuban Flag and Tobacco Plant — A102

Lions Emblem, Cuban Flag and Royal Palms — A103

1940, May 18   Wmk. 106   Perf. 10
362 A102 2c rose red   1.75 .75
    Never hinged   3.00

Rotary Intl. Convention held at Havana.

1940, July 23
363 A103 2c orange vermilion   1.75 .75
    Never hinged   3.00

Lions International Convention, Havana.

Dr. Nicolás J. Gutiérrez A104

1940, Oct. 28
364 A104 2c orange ver   1.00 .25
365 A104 5c blue   1.25 .25
  a. Sheet of four, imperf., unwmkd.   4.50 3.00
    Never hinged   6.50
  b. As "a," black overprint ('51)   5.00 4.00
    Never hinged   7.50
    Set, never hinged   3.00

100th anniv. of the publication of the 1st Cuban Medical Review, "El Repertorio Medico Habanero."

No. 365a contains 2 each of Nos. 364-365 imperf. and sold for 25c.

For overprint see No. C43A.

In 1951 No. 365a was overprinted in black: "50 Aniversario Descubrimiento Agente Transmisor de la Flebre Amarilla por el Dr. Carlos J. Finlay Honor a los Martires de la Ciencia 1901 1951." The overprint is illustrated over No. C43A, but does not include the plane and "Correo Aereo."

Major General Guillermo Moncada — A105

Moncada Riding into Battle A106

1941, June 25
366 A105 3c dk brown, *buff*   1.50 .30
367 A106 5c bright blue   1.50 .30
    Set, never hinged   4.50

Maj. Gen. Guillermo Moncada (1841-96).

Globe Showing Western Hemisphere A107

"Labor: Wealth of America" — A109

Maceo, Bolívar, Juárez, Lincoln and Arms of Cuba A108

Tree of Fraternity, Havana A110

Statue of Liberty — A111

Perf. 10, Imperf.
1942, Feb. 23   Wmk. 106
368 A107 1c emerald   .20 .20
369 A108 3c orange brown   .40 .20
370 A109 5c blue   .70 .20
371 A110 10c red violet   1.75 1.00
372 A111 13c red   1.25 .65
    Nos. 368-372 (5)   4.30 2.25
    Set, never hinged   7.00

Spirit of Democracy in the Americas. The imperforate varieties are without gum. Value, set mint $10, used $5.

Ignacio Agramonte Loynaz — A112

Rescue of Sanguily by Agramonte A113

1942, Apr. 10   Perf. 10
373 A112 3c bister brn   1.00 .50
374 A113 5c brt blue, *bluish*   2.00 1.00
    Set, never hinged   4.00

100th anniv. of the birth of Ignacio Agramonte Loynaz, patriot.

"Unmask the Fifth Columnists" — A114

"Be Careful, The Fifth Column is Spying on You" — A115

"Destroy it. The Fifth Column is like a Serpent" — A116

"Fulfill your Patriotic Duty by Destroying the Fifth Column" — A117

"Don't be Afraid of the Fifth Column. Attack it" — A118

1943, July 5
375 A114 1c dk blue grn   .35 .20
376 A115 3c red   .55 .20
377 A116 5c brt blue   .60 .20
378 A117 10c dull brown   2.00 .60
379 A118 13c dull rose vio   3.00 1.25
    Nos. 375-379 (5)   6.50 2.45
    Set, never hinged   10.00

General Eloy Alfaro and Flags of Cuba and Ecuador A119

1943, Sept. 20
380 A119 3c green   1.20 .25
    Never hinged   2.00

General Eloy Alfaro of Ecuador, 100th birth anniv.

Retirement Security A120

1943, Nov. 8   Wmk. 106   Perf. 10
381 A120 1c yellow green   .45 .20
382 A120 3c vermilion   .45 .20
383 A120 5c bright blue   .80 .25

1944, Mar. 18
384 A120 1c bright yel grn   1.00 .30
385 A120 3c salmon   1.00 .30
386 A120 5c light blue   2.00 .75
    Nos. 381-386 (6)   5.70 2.00
    Set, never hinged   10.00

Half the proceeds from the sale of Nos. 381-386 were used for the Communications Ministry Employees' Retirement Fund.

Portrait of Columbus — A121

Bartolomé de Las Casas — A122

First Statue of Columbus at Cárdenas — A123

Discovery of Tobacco A124

Columbus Sights Land A125

1944, May 19
387 A121 1c dk yellow grn   .30 .20
  a. Pair, imperf horiz.   75.00
388 A122 3c brown   .45 .20
389 A123 5c brt blue   .80 .20
390 A124 10c dark violet   2.50 .60
391 A125 13c dark red   3.00 1.40
    Nos. 387-391,C36-C37 (7)   9.85 3.40
    Set, never hinged   15.00

450th anniv. of the discovery of America.

Major General Carlos Roloff — A126

Americas Map and 1st Brazilian Postage Stamps — A127

1944, Aug. 21
392 A126 3c violet   1.25   .20
   Never hinged   2.00

Maj. Gen. Carlos Roloff, 100th birth anniv.

1944, Dec. 20   **Engr.**
393 A127 3c brown orange   2.00   .75
   Never hinged   3.00

Cent. of the 1st postage stamps of the Americas, issued by Brazil in 1843.

Seal of the Society — A128

Luis de las Casas and Luis Maria Penalyer A129

1945, Oct. 5   **Wmk. 106**   **Perf. 10**
394 A128 1c yellow green   .50 .20
395 A129 2c scarlet   1.25 .20
   Set, never hinged   2.75

Sesquicentenary of the founding of the Economic Society of Friends of the Country.

Aged Couple A130

1945, Dec. 27
396 A130 1c dk yellow grn   .20 .20
397 A130 2c scarlet   .40 .20
398 A130 5c cobalt blue   .90 .20

1946, Mar. 26
399 A130 1c brt yellow grn   .75 .20
400 A130 2c salmon pink   .45 .20
401 A130 5c light blue   .75 .25
   Nos. 396-401 (6)   3.45 1.25
   Set, never hinged   5.00

See note after No. 386.

> **Catalogue values for unused stamps in this section, from this point to the end of the section, are for Never Hinged items.**

Gabriel de la Concepcion Valdés Plácido A131

1946, Feb. 5
402 A131 2c scarlet   1.00 .30

Cent. of the death of the poet Gabriel de la Concepcion Valdés.

Manuel Marquez Sterling — A132

Globe and Cross — A133

1946, Apr. 30
403 A132 2c scarlet   2.25 .30

Founding of the Manuel Marquez Sterling Professional School of Journalism, 3th anniv.

1946, July 4   **Engr.**
404 A133 2c scarlet, *pink*   1.25 .20

80th anniv. of the Intl. Red Cross.

Cow and Milkmaid — A134

Franklin D. Roosevelt — A135

1947, Feb. 20   **Wmk. 106**   **Perf. 10**
405 A134 2c scarlet   2.00 .40

1947 National Livestock Exposition.

1947, Apr. 12
406 A135 2c vermilion   1.50 .20

2nd anniv. of the death of Franklin D. Roosevelt.

Antonio Oms Sarret and Aged Couple A136

1947, Oct. 20
407 A136 1c dp yellow grn   .50 .20
408 A136 2c scarlet   .50 .20
409 A136 5c lt blue   1.00 .40
   Nos. 407-409 (3)   2.00 .80

See note after No. 386.

Marta Abreu Arenabio de Estevez — A137

"Charity" — A138

Marta Abreu Monument, Santa Clara A139

"Patriotism" A140

1947, Nov. 29
410 A137 1c dp yellow grn   .50 .20
411 A138 2c scarlet   1.00 .20
412 A139 5c brt blue   2.00 .40
413 A140 10c dk violet   3.50 1.00
   Nos. 410-413 (4)   7.00 1.80

Birth cent. of Marta Abreu Arenabio de Estevez, philanthropist and humanitarian.

Armauer Hansen A141

1948, Apr. 9
414 A141 2c rose carmine   1.75 .40

International Leprosy Congress, Havana.

Mother and Child A142

1948, Oct. 15   **Engr.**
415 A142 1c yellow grn   .30 .20
416 A142 2c scarlet   .50 .20
417 A142 5c brt blue   1.20 .20
   Nos. 415-417 (3)   2.00 .60

See note after No. 386.

Death of José Martí — A143

Martí Rowing to Shore — A144

1948, Nov. 10   **Wmk. 106**   *Perf. 10*
418 A143 2c scarlet   .75 .20
419 A144 5c brt blue   2.25 .20

50th anniversary of the death of José Martí, patriot (in 1945).

Tobacco Picking — A145

Liberty Carrying Flag and Cigars — A146

Cigar and Arms of Cuba — A147

1948, Dec. 6   **Size: 22½x26mm**
420 A145 1c green   .35 .20
421 A146 2c rose car   .65 .20
422 A147 5c brt blue   1.25 .20
   Nos. 420-422 (3)   2.25 .60

Cuba's tobacco industry. See Nos. 445-447. For overprints and surcharge see Nos. 448-451, 512.

Equestrian Statue of Gen. Antonio Maceo — A148

Sword Salute to Maceo A149

Designs: 2c, Portrait of Maceo. 5c, Mausoleum, El Cacahual. 10c, East to West invasion. 20c, Battle of Peralejo. 50c, Declaration of Baragua. 1p, Death of Maceo at San Pedro.

1948, Dec. 15   **Wmk. 229**   **Perf. 12½**
423 A148 1c blue green   .40 .20
424 A148 2c red   .45 .20
425 A148 5c blue   .60 .20
426 A149 8c black & brown   .90 .30
427 A149 10c brown & bl grn   .90 .20
428 A149 20c blue & car   3.50 .90
429 A149 50c car & ultra   5.75 2.00
430 A149 1p black & violet   12.50 2.75
   Nos. 423-430 (8)   25.00 6.75

Birth cent. (in 1945) of Maceo.

Symbol of Pharmacy A150

Morro Lighthouse A151

1948, Dec. 28   **Perf. 10**
431 A150 2c rose carmine   1.25   .20

1st Pan-American Congress of Pharmacy, Havana, Dec. 1948.

1949, Jan. 17 Wmk. 229 Perf. 12½
432 A151 2c carmine   1.75   .20

Centenary (in 1944) of the erection of the Morro Lighthouse.

Jagua Castle, Cienfuegos A152

1949, Jan. 27 Wmk. 106 Perf. 10
433 A152 1c yellow green   .75   .20
434 A152 2c rose red   1.50   .20

200th anniv. of the construction of Jagua Castle and the cent. of the publication of the 1st newspaper in Cienfuegos.

Manuel Sanguily y Garritt — A153

Map of Isle of Pines — A154

1949, Mar. 31
435 A153 2c rose red   .75   .20
436 A153 5c blue   2.00   .20

Manuel Sanguily y Garritt (1848-1925), cabinet member, editor, author.

1949, Apr. 26
437 A154 5c blue   2.00   .35

20th anniv. of the recognition of Cuban ownership of the Isle of Pines.

Ismael Cespedes — A155

1949, Sept. 28
438 A155 1c yellow green   .60   .20
439 A155 2c scarlet   .60   .20
440 A155 5c brt blue   1.25   .20
   Nos. 438-440 (3)   2.45   .60

See note after No. 386.

Gen. Enrique Collazo — A156

Enrique José Varona — A157

1950, Feb. 28 Engr. Perf. 10
441 A156 2c scarlet   .75   .20
442 A156 5c brt blue   2.00   .20

Centenary (in 1948) of the birth of General Enrique Collazo.

1950, Feb. 28
443 A157 2c scarlet   .75   .20
444 A157 5c brt blue   2.00   .20

Centenary of the birth of Enrique José Varona, writer and patriot.

Tobacco Types of 1948
1950, June 20 Re-engraved
Size: 21x25mm
445 A145 1c green   1.10   .20
446 A146 2c rose red   1.10   .20
447 A147 5c blue   1.75   .20
   Nos. 445-447 (3)   3.95   .60

The re-engraved stamps show slight differences in many minor details.
For overprints and surcharge see #448-451, 512.

No. 446 Overprinted in Black

1950, Apr. 27
448 A146 2c rose red   1.75   .20

Natl. Bank of Cuba opening, Apr. 27, 1950.

Re-engraved Tobacco Types of 1950 Overprinted in Carmine

1950, May 18
449 A145 1c yellow green   .50   .20
450 A146 2c lilac rose   .75   .20
451 A147 5c light blue   1.50   .20
   Nos. 449-451 (3)   2.75   .60

75th anniv. (in 1949) of the UPU.
No. 451 exists with surcharge inverted.

Manuel Balanzategui, Antonio L. Pausa and Train Wreck A158

Fernando Figueredo — A159

1950, Sept. 21 Engr.
452 A158 1c yellow grn   .75   .20
453 A158 2c scarlet   .75   .20
454 A158 5c brt blue   2.00   .20
   Nos. 452-454 (3)   3.50   .60

1951, Mar. 17 Wmk. 106 Perf. 10
455 A159 1c green   1.50   .20
456 A159 2c scarlet   1.50   .20
457 A159 5c brt blue   2.00   .20
   Nos. 455-457 (3)   5.00   .60

Three-fourths of the proceeds from the sale of these stamps were used for the Communication Ministry Employees' Retirement Fund. See Nos. 474, C51-C56, E15. For surcharges see Nos. 474, C51-C56, E15.

Miguel Teurbe Tolón and Flag — A160

Narciso Lopez — A161

Emilia Teurbe Tolón Sewing Flag — A162

Cuban Flag — A163

Engraved and Lithographed
1951, July 3 Wmk. 229 Perf. 13
458 A160 1c Prus grn, ultra & red   .75   .30
459 A161 2c red & gray blk   1.00   .30
460 A162 5c ultra & red   2.10   .45
461 A163 10c rose vio, bl & red   3.25   .60
   Nos. 458-461,C41-C43,E13 (8)   24.85 5.40

Centenary of adoption of Cuba's flag.

Clara Louise Maass and Hospitals A164

Hospitals: Lutheran Memorial, Newark, N.J. and Las Animas, Havana.

Wmk. 106
1951, Aug. 24 Engr. Perf. 10
462 A164 2c scarlet   2.00   .20

75th anniv. of the birth of Clara Louise Maass, (1876-1901), American nurse and martyr in yellow fever fight.

Airmail Type and

José Raul Capablanca — A165

Capablanca Club, Havana A166

Wmk. 229
1951, Nov. 1 Photo. Perf. 13
463 A165 1c blue grn & org   3.50   .65
464 AP27 2c rose car & dk brn   4.50   1.25
465 A166 5c black & dp ultra   9.00   1.90
   Nos. 463-465,C44-C46,E14 (7)   67.00 13.60

Jose Raul Capablanca, World Chess titlist (1921). Value imperf., set of 7 pairs, $1,500.

Antonio Guiteras Holmes — A167

Guiteras Preparing Social Legislation A168

Fort of the Morrillo A169

Wmk. 106
1951, Oct. 22 Engr. Perf. 10
466 A167 1c yellow green   .30   .20
467 A168 2c rose carmine   .50   .20
468 A169 5c deep blue   .90   .20
   Nos. 466-468,C47-C49 (6)   13.85 3.35

16th anniv. of the Action of the Morrillo and to honor Antonio Guiteras Holmes, who was killed there.
Souvenir sheets containing stamps similar to Nos. 466-468, but in different colors, are listed as Nos. C49a-C49b.

Poinsettia A170

Maj. Gen. José Maceo A171

1951, Dec. 1 Engr. and Typo.
469 A170 1c green & car   3.50   .25
470 A170 2c rose car & grn   4.00   .40

See Nos. 498-499.

1952, Feb. 6 Engr.
471 A171 2c yellow brown   .75   .20
472 A171 5c indigo   1.50   .20

Birth centenary of Maceo.

Isabella I — A172

Receipt of Autonomy
A173

1952, Feb. 22
473 A172 2c bright red   1.25   .20

500th anniv. of the birth of Queen Isabella I of Spain.

Souvenir sheets containing 2c stamps of type A172 are listed as Nos. C50a-C50b.

Type of 1951 Surcharged in Green
1952, Mar. 18
474 A159 10c on 2c yel brn   2.00   .25

Wmk. 106
1952, May 27   Engr.   Perf. 12½

Designs: 2c, Tomas Estrada Palma and Luis Estevez Romero. 5c, Barnet, Finlay, Guiteras and Nuñez. 8c, Capitol. 20c, Map, Central Highway. 50c, Sugar Mill.

Centers in Black
475 A173 1c dk green   .25   .20
476 A173 2c dk carmine   .30   .20
477 A173 5c dk blue   .45   .20
478 A173 8c dk brown car   .70   .20
479 A173 20c dk olive grn   1.75   .40
480 A173 50c dp orange   3.50   .80
Nos. 475-480,C57-C60,E16 (11) 14.90 4.35

50th anniv. of the Republic of Cuba.

Hands Holding Coffee Beans
A174

Designs: 2c, Map and man picking coffee beans. 5c, Farmer with pan of beans.

1952, Aug. 22   Wmk. 229   Perf. 13½
481 A174 1c green   .50   .20
482 A174 2c rose red   1.25   .20
483 A174 5c dk vio bl & aqua 1.75 .20
    Nos. 481-483 (3)   3.50   .60

Bicentenary of coffee cultivation.

Col. Charles Hernandes y Sandrino
A175

Alonso Alvarez de la Campa
A176

1952, Oct. 7   Wmk. 106   Perf. 10
484 A175 1c yellow grn   .30   .20
485 A175 2c scarlet   .50   .20
486 A175 5c blue   .55   .20
487 A175 8c black   1.50   .30
488 A175 10c brown red   1.50   .30
489 A175 20c brown   6.00 2.50
Nos. 484-489,C63-C72,E17 (17) 44.65 16.30

See note after No. 457.

Frame Engraved; Center in Black
1952, Nov. 27

Portraits: 2c, Carlos A. Latorre. 3c, Anacleto Bermudez. 5c, Eladio G. Toledo. 8c, Angel Laborde. 10c, Jose M. Medina. 13c, Pascual Rodriguez. 20c, Carlos Verdugo.

490 A176 1c green   .40   .20
491 A176 2c carmine   .75   .20
492 A176 3c purple   .90   .20
493 A176 5c blue   .90   .20
494 A176 8c bister brn   2.00   .35
495 A176 10c orange brn   1.50   .25
496 A176 13c lilac rose   3.00   .40
497 A176 20c olive grn   4.50   .70
Nos. 490-497,C73-C74 (10) 20.70 4.10

Execution of 8 medical students, 81st anniv.

Christmas Type of 1951
Dated "1952-1953"
Frame Engr.; Center Typo.
1952, Dec. 1

Centers: Tree.
498 A170 1c yel grn & car 5.00 1.00
499 A170 3c vio & dk grn   5.00 1.00

Birthplace of José Martí — A177

Marti at St. Lazarus Quarry — A178

No. 501, Court martial. No. 502, Martiano house, Havana. No. 504, El Abra ranch, Isle of Pines. No. 505, Symbols, "Marti the Poet." No. 506, Marti and Bolivar statue, Caracas. No. 507, At desk in New York. No. 508, House where revolutionary party was formed. No. 509, 1st issue of "Patria."

1953   Engr.   Perf. 10
500 A177 1c dk grn & red brn   .50 .20
501 A177 1c dk grn & red brn   .50 .20
502 A177 3c purple & brn   .55 .20
503 A178 3c purple & brn   .55 .20
504 A177 5c dp bl & dk brn   1.00 .20
505 A178 5c ultra & brn   1.00 .20
506 A178 10c red brn & blk   2.00 .35
507 A178 10c brn & blk   2.00 .35
508 A178 13c dk ol grn & dk
              brn   3.25 .80
509 A177 13c dk ol grn & brn   3.25 1.00
Nos. 500-509,C79-C89 (21)   34.20 12.80

Centenary of birth of José Marti.

Rafael Montoro Valdez — A179

Francisco Carrera Justiz — A180

1953, Mar. 5
510 A179 3c dark violet   2.00   .20
Rafael Montoro Valdez, statesman, birth cent.

1953, Mar. 9
511 A180 3c rose red   2.50   .20
Francisco Carrera Justiz, educator, statesman.

No. 446 Surcharged with New Value
1953, June 16
512 A146 3c on 2c rose red 2.00   .20

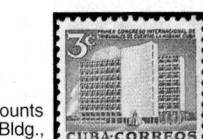

Board of Accounts Bldg., Havana — A181

1953, Nov. 3   Engr.
513 A181 3c blue   .40   .20
    Nos. 513,C90-C91 (3)   5.65 1.60

1st Intl. Cong. of Boards of Accounts, Havana, Nov. 2-9.

Miguel Coyula Llaguno — A182

Communications Assoc. Flag — A183

Designs: 3c, 8c, Enrique Calleja Hensell. 10c, Antonio Ginard Rojas.

1954   Dated 1953
514 A182 1c green   .30   .20
515 A182 3c rose red   .30   .20
516 A183 5c blue   1.40   .20
517 A182 8c brn car   2.25   .30
518 A182 10c brown   3.50   .50
Nos. 514-518,C92-C95,E19 (10) 25.05 7.65

Nos. 515 and 517 show the same portrait, but inscriptions are arranged differently. See note after No. 457.

Carlos J. Finlay
A184

Serafin Sanchez
A184a

Portraits: 1c, José Marti. 2c, Maximo Gomez. 3c, José de la Luz Caballero. 4c, Miguel Aldama. 5c, Calixto Garcia. 8c, Ignacio Agramont. 10c, Tomas Estrada Palma. 20c, José Antonio Saco. 50c, Antonio Maceo. 1p, Carlos Manuel de Cespedes.

1954-56   Wmk. 106   Perf. 10
519 A184   1c green   .45   .20
520 A184a 2c rose car   .45   .20
521 A184   3c violet   .45   .20
521A A184 4c red lil ('56) .50   .20
522 A184a 5c slate bl   .60   .20
523 A184a 8c car lake   .90   .20
524 A184 10c sepia   .90   .20
525 A184 13c org red   .75   .20
525A A184a 14c gray ('56)   1.25   .20
526 A184 20c olive   2.50   .20
527 A184a 50c org yel   3.50   .25
528 A184a 1p orange   7.00   .40
    Nos. 519-528 (12)   19.25 2.65

See Nos. 674-680. For surcharges see Nos. 636, 641-643.

Maj. Gen. José M. Rodriguez — A185

Design: 5c, Gen. Rodriguez on horseback.

1954, June 8   Engr.   Perf. 12½
Center in Dark Brown
529 A185 2c dark carmine   .75   .20
530 A185 5c deep blue   2.00   .20

Cent. of the birth of Maj. Gen. José Maria Rodriguez (in 1851).

Gen. Batísta Sanatorium — A186

1954, Sept. 21   Wmk. 106   Perf. 10
531 A186 3c deep blue   1.25   .20
See No. C107.

Santa Claus — A187

Maria Luisa Dolz — A188

1954, Dec. 15
532 A187 2c dk grn & car   5.00   .35
533 A187 4c car & dk grn   5.00   .35
Christmas 1954.

1954, Dec. 23
534 A188 4c deep blue   1.75   .20

Cent. of the birth of Maria Luisa Dolz, educator and defender of women's rights. See No. C108.

Cuban Flag and Scouts Saluting
A189

1954, Dec. 27   Perf. 12½
535 A189 4c dark green   2.25   .20

Issued to publicize the national patrol encampment of the Boy Scouts of Cuba.

Rotary Emblem and Paul P. Harris — A190

1955, Feb. 23   Engr.   Wmk. 106
536 A190 4c blue   1.50   .20

Rotary International, 50th anniversary. See No. C109.

Maj. Gen. Francisco Carrillo — A191

Portrait: 5c, Gen. Carrillo standing.

1955, Mar. 8   Perf. 10
537 A191 2c brt red & dk bl   .75   .20
538 A191 5c dk bl & dk brn   1.50   .20

Cent. of the birth of Maj. Gen. Francisco Carrillo (1851-1926).

Stamp of 1885 and Convent of San Francisco — A192

Designs (including 1855 stamp): 4c, Volanta carriage. 10c, Havana, 19th century. 14c, Captain general's residence.

1955, Apr.   Perf. 12½
539 A192 2c lil rose & dk
              grnsh bl   .95   .20
540 A192 4c ocher & dk grn 1.25   .20
541 A192 10c ultra & dk red 3.00   .85
542 A192 14c grn & dp org   7.00 1.00
Nos. 539-542,C110-C113 (8) 20.55 5.35

Cent. of Cuba's 1st postage stamps.

Maj. Gen.
Mario G.
Menocal
A193

Gen. Emilio
Nuñez
A194

Portraits: 10c, J. G. O. Gomez. 14c, A. Sanchez de Bustamente.

1955, June 22

543	A193	2c dark green	.65	.20
544	A194	4c lilac rose	.80	.20
545	A193	10c deep blue	1.50	.25
546	A194	14c gray violet	3.00	.35
Nos. 543-546,C114-C116,E20 (8)			18.95	5.05

See note after No. 457.

Turkey — A195

Gen. Emilio
Nuñez — A196

1955, Dec. 15 　　　　　　　Engr.

547	A195	2c slate grn & dk car	5.00	1.00
548	A195	4c rose lake & brt grn	5.00	.75

Christmas 1955.

1955, Dec. 27

549	A196	4c claret	1.10	.20
Nos. 549,C127-C128 (3)			6.35	1.10

Cent. of the birth of Gen. Emilio Nunez, Cuban revolutionary hero.

Francisco Cagigal
de la Vega (1695-
1777)
A197

Julian del Casal
A198

1956, Mar. 27 　　　　　　　*Perf. 12½*

552	A197	4c rose brn & slate bl	1.10	.20

Cuban post bicent. See No. C129.

1956, May 2

Portraits: 4c, Luisa Perez de Zambrana. 10c, Juan Clemente Zenea. 14c, José Joaquin Palma.

Portraits in Black

553	A198	2c green	.50	.20
554	A198	4c rose lilac	.50	.20
555	A198	10c blue	1.25	.20
556	A198	14c violet	2.50	.20
Nos. 553-556,C131-C133,E21 (8)			13.65	3.50

See note after No. 457.

Victor
Muñoz — A199

Masonic Temple,
Havana — A200

1956, May 13

557	A199	4c brown & green	1.00	.20

Victor Munoz (1873-1922), founder of Mother's Day in Cuba. See No. C134.

1956, June 5

558	A200	4c blue	1.50	.20

See No. C135.

Virgin of Charity,
El Cobre — A201

"The Cry of
Yara" — A202

1956, Sept. 8 　　　　　　　*Perf. 12½*

559	A201	4c brt blue & yel	1.25	.20

Issued in honor of Our Lady of Charity of Cobre, patroness of Cuba. See No. C149.

1956, Oct. 10

560	A202	4c dk grn & brn	1.40	.20

Cuba's independence from Spain.

Raimundo G.
Menocal
A203

The Three Wise
Men — A204

1956, Dec. 3　Wmk. 106 　*Perf. 12½*

561	A203	4c dark brown	1.25	.20

Cent. of the birth of Prof. Raimundo G. Menocal, physician.

1956, Dec. 1

562	A204	2c red & slate grn	4.50	1.00
563	A204	4c slate grn & red	4.50	1.00

Christmas 1956.

Martin Morua
Delgado — A205

Boy Scouts at
Campfire — A206

1957, Jan. 30

564	A205	4c dark green	1.00	.20

Delgado, patriot, birth cent.

1957, Feb. 22　Wmk. 106 　*Perf. 12½*

565	A206	4c slate grn & red	1.50	.20

Cent. of the birth of Lord Baden-Powell, founder of the Boy Scouts. See No. C152.

"The Blind,"
by M. Vega
A207

Paintings: 4c, "The Art Critics" by M. Melero. 10c, "Volanta in Storm" by A. Menocal. 14c, "The Convalescent" by L. Romañach.

1957, Mar.　　Engr.　　*Perf. 12½*
**Side and Lower Inscriptions
in Dark Brown**

566	A207	2c olive green	.40	.20
567	A207	4c orange red	.55	.20
568	A207	10c olive green	.90	.25
569	A207	14c ultra	1.25	.25
Nos. 566-569,C153-C155,E22 (8)			12.60	3.00

See note after No. 457.

Emblem of
Philatelic Club of
Cuba
A208

Juan F.
Steegers
A209

1957, Apr. 24

570	A208	4c ocher, blue & red	1.50	.25

Issued for Stamp Day, Apr. 24, and the National Philatelic Exhibition. See No. C156.

1957, Apr. 30

571	A209	4c blue	1.00	.25

Juan Francisco Steegers y Perera (1856-1921), dactyloscopy pioneer. See No. C157.

Victoria Bru
Sanchez
A210

Joaquin de
Aguero in
Battle of
Jucaral
A211

1957, June 3　Wmk. 106 　*Perf. 12½*

572	A210	4c indigo	1.25	.20

1957, July 4

573	A211	4c dark green	1.00	.20

Issued to honor Joaquin de Aguero, Cuban freedom fighter and patriot. See No. C162.

Boy, Dogs and
Cat — A212

Col. Rafael
Manduley del
Rio — A213

1957, July 17

574	A212	4c Prus green	2.00	.40

Mrs. Jeanette Ryder, founder of the Humane Society of Cuba. See Nos. C163-C163a.

1957, July 31

575	A213	4c Prus green	2.50	.50

Issued to honor Col. Manduley del Rio, patriot, on the cent. of his birth (in 1856).

Palace
of
Justice
A214

1957, Sept. 2　Engr.　*Perf. 12½*

576	A214	4c blue gray	1.25	.25

Opening of the new Palace of Justice in Havana. See No. C165.

Generals of the Liberation — A215

1957, Sept. 26

577	A215	4c dl grn & red brn	1.00	.20
578	A215	4c dl bl & red brn	1.00	.20
579	A215	4c rose & brown	1.00	.20
580	A215	4c org yel & brn	1.00	.20
581	A215	4c lt violet & brn	1.00	.20
Nos. 577-581 (5)			5.00	1.00

Generals of the army of liberation.

1st Publication
Printed in
Cuba — A216

Patio — A217

1957, Oct. 18　Wmk. 106　*Perf. 12½*

582	A216	4c slate blue	.70	.25
Nos. 582,C167-C168 (3)			3.45	.85

José Marti National Library.

1957, Nov. 19

583	A217	4c red brn & grn	.60	.25
Nos. 583,C173-C174 (3)			4.50	1.15

Cent. of the 1st Cuban Normal School.

Trinidad,
Founded
1514 — A218

Fortifications,
Havana,
1611 — A219

Views: 10c, Padre Pico street, Santiago de Cuba. 14c, Church of Our Lady, Camaguey.

1957, Dec. 17　Engr.　*Perf. 12½*

584	A218	2c brown & indigo	.30	.20
585	A219	4c slate grn & brn	.70	.20
586	A219	10c sepia & red	1.25	.20
587	A219	14c green & dk red	1.75	.20
Nos. 584-587,C175-C177,E23 (8)			12.00	3.15

See note after No. 457.

Nativity — A220

1957, Dec. 20
588 A220 2c multicolored 3.50 .75
589 A220 4c multicolored 3.50 .75

Christmas 1957.

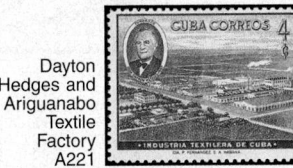

Dayton Hedges and Ariguanabo Textile Factory A221

1958, Jan. 30 Wmk. 106 Perf. 12½
590 A221 4c blue .50 .25

Issued to honor Dayton Hedges, founder of Cuba's textile industry. See No. C178.

Dr. Francisco Dominguez Roldan — A222 | José Ignacio Rivero y Alonso — A223

1958, Feb. 21
591 A222 4c green 1.25 .25

Roldan (1864-1942), who introduced radio-therapy and physiotherapy to Cuba.

1958, Apr. 1
592 A223 4c lt olive green 1.25 .50

José Ignacio Rivero y Alonso, editor of Diario de la Marina, 1919-44. See No. C179.

Map of Cuba and Mail Route, 1756 A224

1958, Apr. 24 Perf. 12½
593 A224 4c dk grn, aqua & buff 1.00 .25

Issued for Stamp Day, Apr. 24 and the National Philatelic Exhibition. See No. C180.

Maj. Gen. José Miguel Gomez A225 | Nicolas Ruiz Espadero A226

1958, June 6 Wmk. 106 Perf. 12½
594 A225 4c slate .75 .25

Maj. Gen. José Miguel Gomez, President of Cuba, 1909-13. See No. C181.

1958, June 27 Perf. 12½
Indigo Emblem

Musicians: 4c, Ignacio Cervantes. 10c, José White. 14c, Brindis de Salas.

595 A226 2c brown .50 .20
596 A226 4c dark gray .50 .20
597 A226 10c olive green .80 .20
598 A226 14c red 1.10 .20

Green Emblem

Physicians: 2c, Tomas Romay Chacon. 4c, Angel Arturo Aballi. 10c, Fernando Gonzalez del Valle. 14c, Vicente Antonio de Castro.

599 A226 2c brown .70 .20
600 A226 4c gray 1.10 .20
601 A226 10c dark carmine .80 .20
602 A226 14c dark blue 1.10 .20

Red Emblem

Lawyers: 2c, Jose Maria Garcia Montes. 4c, Jose A. Gonzalez Lanuza. 10c, Juan B. Hernandez Barreiro. 14c, Pedro Gonzalez Llorente.

603 A226 2c sepia .50 .20
604 A226 4c gray .80 .20
605 A226 10c olive grn 1.00 .20
606 A226 14c slate blue 1.10 .20
Nos. 595-606 (12) 10.00 2.45

For surcharges see Nos. 629-631.

Carlos de la Torre — A227

1958, Aug. 29 Engr. Wmk. 321
607 A227 4c violet blue .75 .25
Nos. 607,C182-C184 (4) 17.50 4.65

Dr. Carlos de la Torre y Huerta (1858-1950), naturalist. For surcharge see No. 632.

Poey's "Memorias" Title Page — A228 | Felipe Poey — A229

1958, Sept. 26 Wmk. 106
608 A228 2c black & lt violet .80 .25
609 A229 4c brown black .95 .25
Nos. 608-609,C185-C191,E26-E27 (11) 79.75 19.75

Felipe Poey (1799-1891), naturalist.

Theodore Roosevelt — A230 | Cattleyopsis Lindenii Orchid — A231

1958, Oct. 27 Perf. 12½
610 A230 4c gray green .70 .25

Theodore Roosevelt, birth cent. See No. C192.

Engraved and Photogravure
1958, Dec. 16 Wmk. 321 Perf. 12½

4c, Oncidium Guibertianum Orchid.

611 A231 2c multicolored 4.50 .75
612 A231 4c multicolored 4.50 .75

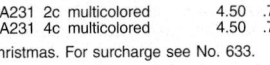

Christmas. For surcharge see No. 633.

Flag and Revolutionary A232 | Gen. Adolfo Flor Crombet (1848-95) A233

Engr. & Typo.
1959, Jan. 28 Wmk. 321
613 A232 2c car rose & gray .50 .25

Day of Liberation, Jan. 1, 1959.

1959, Mar. 18 Engr. Wmk. 106
614 A233 4c slate green .60 .25

For surcharge see No. 634.

Maria Teresa Garcia Montes A234 | Carlos Manuel de Cespedes A235

1959, Nov. 11 Perf. 12½
615 A234 4c brown .75 .25

Maria Teresa Garcia Montes (1880-1930), founder of the Musical Arts Society. See No. C198. For surcharge see No. 635.

1959, Oct. 10 Wmk. 106 Perf. 12½

Presidents: No. 617, Salvador Cisneros Betancourt. No. 618, Manuel de Jesus Calvar. No. 619, Bartolomé Maso. No. 620, Juan B. Spotorno. No. 621, Tomas Estrada Palma. No. 622, Francisco Javier de Céspedes. No. 623, Vicente Garcia.

616 A235 2c slate blue .55 .20
617 A235 2c green .55 .20
618 A235 2c deep violet .55 .20
619 A235 2c orange brown .55 .20
620 A235 4c dark carmine .70 .20
621 A235 4c deep brown .70 .20
622 A235 4c dark gray .70 .20
623 A235 4c dark violet .70 .20
Nos. 616-623 (8) 5.00 1.60

Issued to honor former Cuban presidents.

No. B3 Surcharged in Red:
"HABILITADO PARA / 2¢"

1960
624 SP2 2c on 2c + 1c car & ultra 1.00 .20
See No. C199.

Rebel Attack on Moncada Barracks A236

Designs: 2c, Rebels disembarking from "Granma." 10c, Battle of the Uvero. 12c, Map of Cuba and rebel ("The Invasion").

1960, Jan. 28 Wmk. 320
625 A236 1c gray ol, bl & ver .25 .20
626 A236 2c bl, gray ol & brn .25 .20
627 A236 10c bl, gray ol & red 1.00 .20
628 A236 12c brt bl, brn & grn 1.50 .20
Nos. 625-628,C200-C202 (7) 15.00 2.80

First anniversary of revolution.

Stamps of 1956-59 Surcharged with New Value in Carmine or Silver

1960, Feb. 3
629 A226 1c on 4c dk gray & ind .40 .20
630 A226 1c on 4c gray & grn .65 .25
631 A226 1c on 4c gray & red .40 .20

632 A227 1c on 4c violet bl .40 .20
633 A231 1c on 4c multi (S) 1.10 .50
634 A233 1c on 4c slate grn .35 .20
635 A234 1c on 4c brown .40 .20
636 A184a 2c on 14c gray .55 .20
Nos. 629-636,C203-C204 (10) 6.05 2.55

Tomas Estrada Palma Statue, Havana — A237

17th Olympic Games, Rome, Aug. 25-Sept. 11 — A238

Statues: 2c, Mambi Victorioso (Battle of San Juan Hill), Santiago de Cuba. 10c, Marta Abreo de Estevez. 12c, Ignacio Agramonte, Camaguey.

Wmk. 321
1960, Mar. 28 Engr. Perf. 12½
637 A237 1c brn & dk bl .20 .20
638 A237 2c green & red .30 .20
639 A237 10c choc & red .75 .20
640 A237 12c gray ol & vio .90 .20
Nos. 637-640,C206-C208 (7) 6.00 2.30

See note after No. 386.

Nos. 521A, 522 and 525 Surcharged "HABILITADO / PARA / 2¢" in Violet Blue, Red or Black

1960 Wmk. 106 Perf. 10
641 A184 2c on 4c red lil (VB) .75 .20
642 A184a 2c on 5c sl bl (R) 1.25 .20
643 A184 2c on 13c org red 1.25 .20

No. 307B Surcharged "HABILITADO / 10¢"
644 A41 10c on 20c ol grn .75 .20
Nos. 641-644 (4) 4.00 .80

Wmk. 321
1960, Sept. 22 Engr. Perf. 12½
645 A238 1c Sailboats .35 .20
646 A238 2c Marksman .50 .20
Nos. 645-646,C212-C213 (4) 3.10 1.00

For souvenir sheet see No. C213a.

Camilo Cienfuegos and View of Escolar A239

1960, Oct. 27 Litho. Unwmk.
647 A239 2c brn, bl, grn & red 1.25 .20

1st anniv. of the death of Camilo Cienfuegos, revolutionary hero.

Morning Glory A240

Tobacco and Christmas Hymn A241

1960 Litho. Perf. 12½
648 A240 1c red .75 .75
649 A241 1c Tobacco 1.00 1.00
650 A241 1c Mariposa 1.00 1.00

651	A241	1c Guaiacum	1.00	1.00
652	A241	1c Coffee	1.00	1.00
a.		Block of 4, #649-652	5.00	
653	A240	2c ultra	1.00	1.00
654	A241	2c Tobacco	3.00	3.00
655	A241	2c Mariposa	3.00	3.00
656	A241	2c Guaiacum	3.00	3.00
657	A241	2c Coffee	3.00	3.00
a.		Block of 4, #654-657	14.00	
658	A240	10c ocher	3.00	2.50
659	A241	10c Tobacco	10.00	6.00
660	A241	10c Mariposa	10.00	6.00
661	A241	10c Guaiacum	10.00	6.00
662	A241	10c Coffee	10.00	6.00
a.		Block of 4, #659-662	27.50	
		Nos. 648-662 (15)	60.75	44.25

Issued for Christmas 1960.
Nos. 648-662 were printed in three sheets of 25. Nine stamps of type A240 form a center cross, stamps of type A241 form a block of four in each corner with the musical bars joined in an oval around the floral designs.

"Public Capital for Economic Benefit" — A242

Designs: 2c, Chart and symbols of agriculture and industry. 6c, Cogwheels.

Perf. 11½

1961, Jan. 10		Unwmk.	Photo.	
663	A242	1c yel, blk & org	.40	.20
664	A242	2c bl, blk & red	1.00	.20
665	A242	6c yel, red org & blk	1.00	.25
		Nos. 663-665,C215-C218 (7)	8.80	2.55

Issued to publicize the conference of underdeveloped countries, Havana.

Jesus Menéndez and Sugar Cane — A243

1961, Jan. 22		Litho.	Perf. 12½	
666	A243	2c dk grn & brn	.50	.20

Jesus Menéndez, leader in sugar industry.

Same Overprinted in Red: "PRIMERO DE MAYO 1961 ESTAMOS VENCIENDO"

1961, May 2				
667	A243	2c dk grn & brn	1.50	.25

Issued for May Day, 1961.

Dove and UN Emblem — A244

1961, Apr. 12		Litho.	Perf. 12½	
668	A244	2c red brn & yel grn	.60	.20
669	A244	10c emer & rose lil	1.00	.20
a.		Souv. sheet, #668-669, imperf.	5.00	
		Nos. 668-669,C222-C223 (4)	3.45	.90

15th anniv. (in 1960) of the UN.

Maceo Stamp of 1907 and 1902
Simulated Cancel
A245

Stamp Day: 1c, Revolutionary 10c stamp of 1874, 1868 "cancel." 10c, #613, "cancel."

1961, Apr. 24			Unwmk.	
670	A245	1c dull rose & dk grn	.35	.20
671	A245	2c salmon & dk grn	.40	.20
672	A245	10c pale grn, car rose & blk	2.00	.25
		Nos. 670-672 (3)	2.75	.65

For overprint see No. 681.

Hand Releasing Dove — A246

1961, July 26			Perf. 12½	
673	A246	2c blk, red, yel & gray	1.50	.20

26th of July (1953) movement, Castro's revolt against Fulgencio Batista. Burelage on back consisting of wavy lines and diagonal rows of "CUBA CORREOS" in pale salmon.

Portrait Type of 1954

Designs: Same as before. On the 2c, "1833" is replaced by "?".

Wmk. 321 (Nos. 674, 676); Unwmkd.
Perf. 12½ (Nos. 674, 676); Rouletted

1961-69			Engr.	
674	A184	1c brown red	.50	.20
675	A184	1c lt blue ('69)	.30	.20
676	A184a	2c slate green	.50	.20
677	A184a	2c yel grn ('69)	.30	.20
678	A184	3c org ('64)	1.50	.20
679	A184	13c brn ('64)	1.50	.30
680	A184	20c lilac ('69)	.30	.20
		Nos. 674-680 (7)	4.90	1.50

Issued: #674, 676, 8/1; #678-679, 12/764; others, 9/69.
For No. 675, 677-680, see embargo note following No. 702.

No. 672
Ovptd. in Red

Perf. 12½

1961, Oct. 7		Litho.	Unwmk.	
681	A245	10c pale grn, car rose & blk	2.00	.45

1st Official Phil. Exhib., Havana, Oct. 7-17.

Education
Year — A247

Designs: One letter (per stamp) of "CUBA," book and various quotations by Jose Marti about the virtues of literacy.

1961, Nov. 22				
682	A247	1c pale grn, red & blk	.20	.20
683	A247	2c blue, red & blk	.20	.20
684	A247	10c vio, red & blk	.90	.25
685	A247	12c org, red & blk	1.75	.60
		Nos. 682-685 (4)	3.05	1.25

A248

Christmas
A249

1c, Snails. 2c, Birds, vert. 10c, Butterflies.

1961, Dec. 1				
686	A248	1c Polymita flammulata	.50	.20
687	A249	1c Polymita fulminata	.50	.20
688	A249	1c Polymita nigrofasciata	.50	.20
689	A249	1c Polymita fuscolimbata	.50	.20
690	A249	1c Polymita roseolimbata	.50	.20
a.		Block of 5 + label, Nos. 686-690	2.50	1.50
691	A248	2c Cuban grassquit	2.00	.50
692	A249	2c Cuban macaw	2.00	.50
693	A249	2c Cuban trogon	2.00	.50
694	A249	2c Bee hummingbird	2.00	.50
695	A249	2c Ivory-billed woodpecker	2.00	.50
a.		Block of 5 + label, Nos. 691-695	12.50	4.00
696	A248	10c Othreis toddi	3.00	1.00
697	A249	10c Uranidia boisduvalii	3.00	1.00
698	A249	10c Phoebis avellaneda	3.00	1.00
699	A249	10c Phaloe cubana	3.00	1.00
700	A249	10c Papilio gundlachianus	3.00	1.00
a.		Block of 5 + label, Nos. 696-700	15.00	7.50
		Nos. 686-700 (15)	27.50	8.50

Stamps of the same denomination printed se-tenant in sheets of 20 stamps plus 5 labels picturing bells and star. Stamps of Type A249 are arranged in blocks of 4; Type A248 stamps and labels form a cross in sheet.

See Nos. 760-774, 912-926, 1025-1039, 1179-1193, 1303-1317, 1464-1478, 1572-1586.

3rd Anniv. of
the Revolution
A250

1962, Jan. 3				
701	A250	1c multi	.85	.35
702	A250	2c multi	1.75	.45

See Nos. C226-C228.

Cuban goods have been embargoed by the United States since a Feb. 7, 1962 proclamation by President Kennedy, but according to the Office of Foreign Assets Control of the Treasury Department, used Cuban stamps can be imported and sold without limitation, and unused stamps may be imported for personal use, but not resold.

Natl.
Militia
A251

Silhouettes of militiamen and women and their peace-time occupations: 1c, Farmer. 2c, Welder. 3c, Seamstress.

1962, Feb. 26				
703	A251	1c blue grn & blk	.30	.20
704	A251	2c deep blue & blk	.60	.25
705	A251	10c brt org & blk	2.10	.55
		Nos. 703-705 (3)	3.00	1.00

Bay of Pigs
Invasion, 1st
Anniv. — A252

1962, Apr. 17				
706	A252	2c multi	.45	.20
707	A252	3c multi	.45	.20
708	A252	10c multi	3.00	.65
		Nos. 706-708 (3)	3.90	1.05

1st
West
Indies
Packet
A253

1962, Apr. 24				
709	A253	10c red & gray	2.25	.90

Stamp Day. See No. E32.

Intl. Labor
Day — A254

1962, May 1				
710	A254	2c ocher & blk	.35	.20
711	A254	3c ver & blk	.75	.25
712	A254	10c greenish blue & blk	2.50	.70
		Nos. 710-712 (3)	3.60	1.15

Natl. Sports Institute (INDER) Emblem
and Athletes — A255

1962, July 25			Wmk. 321	
713	A255	1c Judo	.35	.20
714	A255	1c Discus	.35	.20
715	A255	1c Gymnastics	.35	.20
716	A255	1c Wrestling	.35	.20
717	A255	1c Weight lifting	.35	.20
718	A255	2c Roller skating	.35	.20
719	A255	2c Equestrian	.35	.20
720	A255	2c Archery	.35	.20
721	A255	2c Bicycling	.35	.20
722	A255	2c Bowling	.35	.20
723	A255	3c Power boating	1.00	.20
724	A255	3c One-man kayak	1.00	.20
725	A255	3c Swimming	1.00	.20
726	A255	3c Sculling	1.00	.20
727	A255	3c Yachting	1.00	.20
728	A255	9c Soccer	.90	.35
729	A255	9c Volleyball	.90	.35
730	A255	9c Baseball	.90	.35
731	A255	9c Basketball	.90	.35
732	A255	9c Tennis	.90	.35
733	A255	10c Boxing	.90	.35
734	A255	10c Underwater fishing	.90	.35
735	A255	10c Model-plane flying	.90	.35
736	A255	10c Pistol shooting	.90	.35
737	A255	10c Water polo	.90	.35
738	A255	13c Paddleball	1.00	.50
739	A255	13c Fencing	1.00	.50
740	A255	13c Sports Palace	1.00	.50

741	A255	13c Chess	1.00	.50
742	A255	13c Jai alai	1.00	.50
		Nos. 713-742 (30)	22.50	9.00

Stamps of the same denomination printed se-tenant in sheets of 25. Various combinations possible.

9th Anniv. of the Revolution A256

Attack on Moncada Barracks: Abel Santamaria and: 2c, Barracks under siege. 3c, Children at Moncada School.

1962, July 26

743	A256	2c brn car & dark ultra	.65	.35
744	A256	3c dark ultra & brn car	1.10	.55

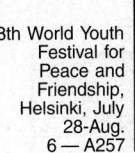

8th World Youth Festival for Peace and Friendship, Helsinki, July 28-Aug. 6 — A257

1962, July 28

745	A257	2c Dove, emblem	1.00	.25
746	A257	3c Hand grip, emblem	1.75	.55
a.		Min. sheet of 2, Nos. 745-746, imperf.	6.50	6.50

9th Central American and Caribbean Games, Kingston, Jamaica, Aug. 11-25 A258

1962, Aug. 27

747	A258	1c Boxing	.20	.20
748	A258	2c Tennis	.20	.20
749	A258	3c Baseball	.20	.20
750	A258	13c Fencing	2.40	.80
		Nos. 747-750 (4)	3.00	1.40

A259

First Natl. Congress of the Federation of Cuban Women — A260

1962, Oct. 1

751	A259	9c rose, blk & grn	1.10	.25
752	A260	13c blk, grn & lt blue	2.40	.65

Latin American University Games — A261

1962, Oct. 13 — **Wmk. 106**

753	A261	1c Running	.40	.20
754	A261	2c Baseball	.85	.20
755	A261	3c Basketball	1.25	.20
756	A261	13c World map	2.50	.55
		Nos. 753-756 (4)	5.00	1.15

World Health Organization Campaign to Eradicate Malaria — A262

Designs: 1c, Magnified specimen of the parasitic protozoa, microscope. 2c, Swamp and mosquito. 3c, Chemist's structural formulas for quinine, cinchona plant.

1962, Dec. 14

757	A262	1c multi	.50	.20
758	A262	2c multi	.50	.20
759	A262	3c multi	1.75	.20
		Nos. 757-759 (3)	2.75	.60

Christmas Type of 1961

2c, Reptiles. 3c, Insects, vert. 10c, Rodents.

1962, Dec. 21 — **Unwmk.**

760	A248	2c Epicrates angulifer	.65	.20
761	A249	2c Cricosaurus typica	.65	.20
762	A249	2c Anolis equestris	.65	.20
763	A249	2c Tropidophis wrighti	.65	.20
764	A249	2c Cyclura macleayi	.65	.20
a.		Block of 5 + label, Nos. 760-764	3.50	1.50
765	A248	3c Cubispa turquino	1.00	.60
766	A249	3c Chrysis superba	1.00	.60
767	A249	3c Essostruta roberto	1.00	.60
768	A249	3c Hortensia conciliata	1.00	.60
769	A249	3c Lachnopus argus	1.00	.60
a.		Block of 5 + label, Nos. 765-769	5.50	4.50
770	A248	10c Monophyllus cubanus	4.00	1.25
771	A249	10c Capromys pilorides	4.00	1.25
772	A249	10c Capromys prehensilis	4.00	1.25
773	A249	10c Solenodon cubensis	4.00	1.25
774	A249	10c Capromys pilorides (Blanca)	4.00	1.25
a.		Block of 5 + label, Nos. 770-774	21.00	9.00
		Nos. 760-774 (15)	28.25	10.25

Christmas 1962. See note after No. 700.

Around 1962 a 1ctv. label picturing Fidel Castro was used as a voluntary contribution stamp. It is not inscribed "Correos" and was not valid for postage.

Soviet Space Flights — A263

Spacecraft and cosmonauts: 1c, Vostok 1, Yuri A. Gagarin, Apr. 12, 1961. 2c, Vostok 2, Gherman S. Titov, Aug. 6-7, 1961. 3c, Vostok 3, Andrian G. Nikolaev, Aug. 11-15, 1962, and Vostok 4, Pavel R. Popovich, Aug. 12-15, 1962. 9c, Vostok 5, Valery F. Bykovsky, June 14-19, 1963. 13c, Vostok 6, Valentina V. Tereshkova, June 16-19, 1963.

1963-64 — **Wmk. 321**

775	A263	1c ultra, red & yel	.35	.20
776	A263	2c grn, yel & rose lake	.65	.25
777	A263	3c yel, vio & ver	.65	.25
778	A263	9c red, dark vio & yel	1.25	.45
779	A263	13c dark blue green, dull red brown & yel	3.25	.70
		Nos. 775-779 (5)	6.15	1.85

Issued: 1c, 2c, 3c, 2/26/63; others, 8/15/64.

Attack of the Presidential Palace, 6th Anniv. — A264

9c, Guerillas attacking palace. 13c, Four student leaders. 30c, Jose A. Echeverria, Menelad Mora.

1963, Mar. 13

780	A264	9c dark red & blk	1.10	.20
781	A264	13c chalky blue & sep	1.40	.20
782	A264	30c org & grn	3.50	1.00
		Nos. 780-782 (3)	6.00	1.40

4th Pan American Games, Sao Paulo, Brazil, Apr. 20-May 5 — A265

1963, Apr. 20

783	A265	1c Baseball	1.25	.35
784	A265	13c Boxing	3.25	.65

Stamp Day A266

3c, Mask mailbox, 19th cent. 10c, Mask mailbox at the Plaza de la Catedral, Havana.

1963, Apr. 25

785	A266	3c black & dark org	1.00	.20
786	A266	10c black & pur	2.50	.30

See Nos. 828-829, 956-957 and 1102-1103.

Labor Day — A267

1963, May 1

787	A267	3c shown	.50	.20
788	A267	13c Four workers	1.75	.30

Intl. Children's Week, June 1-7 — A268

1963, June 1

789	A268	3c blue blk & bister brn	.50	.20
790	A268	30c blue blk & red	2.75	.80

Ritual Effigy — A269

Broken Chains at Moncada A270

Taino Civilization artifacts: 3c, Wood-carved throne, horiz. 9c, Stone-carved figurine.

1963, June 29

791	A269	2c org & red brn	.75	.20
792	A269	3c ultra & red brn	.90	.25
793	A269	9c rose & gray	1.60	.45
		Nos. 791-793 (3)	3.25	.90

Montane Anthropology Museum, 60th anniv.

1963, July 26

2c, Attack on the Presidential Palace. 3c, The insurrection. 7c, Strike of April 9. 9c, Triumph of the revolution. 10c, Agricultural reform and nationalization of industry. 13c, Bay of Pigs victory.

794	A270	1c pink & blk	.20	.20
795	A270	2c lt blue & vio brn	.20	.20
796	A270	3c lt vio & brn	.20	.20
797	A270	7c apple green & rose	.20	.20
798	A270	9c olive bister & rose vio	.30	.20
799	A270	10c beige & sage grn	.85	.30
800	A270	13c pale org & slate blue	1.25	.50
		Nos. 794-800 (7)	3.20	1.80

Indigenous Fruit — A271

1963, Aug. 19

801	A271	1c Star apple	.20	.20
802	A271	2c Cherimoya	.20	.20
803	A271	3c Cashew nut	.35	.20
804	A271	10c Custard apple	2.00	.25
805	A271	13c Mangoes	2.50	.40
		Nos. 801-805 (5)	5.25	1.25

Geometric Shapes A272

View of a Town — A273

Designs: No. 806, Circle, triangle, square, vert. No. 807, Roof, window, vert. No. 808, View of a town. No. 809, View of a town in blue. No. 810, View of a town in olive bister and red. No. 811, Circle, triangle, vert. No. 812, House, roof and doorway, vert. No. 813, House, girders.

1963, Sept. 29 — **Unwmk.**

806	A272	3c multi	.50	.20
807	A272	3c multi	.50	.20
808	A273	3c multi	.50	.20
809	A273	3c multi	.50	.20
810	A273	13c multi	1.50	.50
811	A273	13c multi	1.50	.50
812	A272	13c multi	1.50	.50
813	A272	13c multi	1.50	.50
		Nos. 806-813 (8)	8.00	2.80

7th Intl. Congress of the Intl. Union of Architects.

Ernest Hemingway (1899-1961),
American Author — A274

Hemingway and: 3c, The Old Man and the
Sea. 9c, For Whom the Bell Tolls. 13c, Hemingway Museum (former residence), San Francisco de Paula, near Havana.

1963, Dec. 5   **Wmk. 321**

814	A274	3c brn & lt blue	.75	.20
815	A274	9c sage grn & pink	1.75	.20
816	A274	13c blk & yel grn	3.00	.60
		Nos. 814-816 (3)	5.50	1.00

Natl. Museum, 50th Anniv. — A275

Works of art: 2c, El Zapateo (Dance), by
Victor P. Landaluze. 3c, Abduction of the
Mulatto Women, by Carlos Enriquez, vert. 9c,
Greek Panathean amphora, vert. 13c, My
Beloved (bust of a young woman), by Jean
Antoine Houdon, vert.

1964, Mar. 19   **Unwmk.**

817	A275	2c multi	.20	.20
818	A275	3c multi	.80	.20
819	A275	9c multi	1.10	.30
820	A275	13c multi	2.40	.55
		Nos. 817-820 (4)	4.50	1.25

General Strike
on Apr. 9, 6th
Anniv. — A276

Rebel leaders: 2c, Bernardo Juan Borrell.
3c, Marcelo Salado. 10c, Oscar Lucero. 13c,
Sergio Gonzalez.

1964, Apr. 9

821	A276	2c blk, yel grn & dull		
		org	.40	.20
822	A276	3c blk, red & dull org	.70	.20
823	A276	10c blk, pur & beige	1.25	.25
824	A276	13c blk, brt blue &		
		beige	2.50	.40
		Nos. 821-824 (4)	4.85	1.05

Bay of Pigs
Invasion, 3rd
Anniv.
A277

Designs: 3c, Fish in net. 10c, Victory Monument. 13c, Fallen eagle, vert.

1964, Apr. 17

825	A277	3c multi	.30	.20
826	A277	10c multi	.70	.35
827	A277	13c multi	2.00	.70
		Nos. 825-827 (3)	3.00	1.25

Stamp Day Type of 1963

3c, Vicente Mora Pera, 1st postal director.
13c, Unissued provisional stamp, 1871.

1964, Apr. 24

828	A266	3c ocher & dull lil	.50	.20
829	A266	13c dull vio & lt olive		
		grn	2.50	.50

Labor
Day — A278

Diplomatic
Relations with
China — A279

1964, May 1

830	A278	3c Industry	.40	.20
831	A278	13c Agriculture	1.60	.20

1964, May 15

Designs: 1c, China Monument, Havana. 2c,
Cuban and Chinese farmers. 3c, Natl. flags.

832	A279	1c multi	.35	.20
833	A279	2c org brn, blk & apple		
		grn	.70	.20
834	A279	3c multi	1.40	.20
		Nos. 832-834 (3)	2.45	.60

15th UPU
Congress,
Vienna,
May-June
A280

1964, May 29

835	A280	13c Hemispheres on		
		world map	.85	.30
836	A280	30c Heinrich von Ste-		
		phan	1.90	.80
837	A280	50c UPU Monument,		
		Bern	4.00	1.40
		Nos. 835-837 (3)	6.75	2.50

Development
of Natl.
Industry
A281

1964, June 16

838	A281	1c Fish	.40	.20
839	A281	2c Cow	.60	.20
840	A281	13c Chickens	2.50	.60
		Nos. 838-840 (3)	3.50	1.00

Merchant Fleet — A282

1964, June 30

841	A282	1c Rio Jibacoa	.25	.20
842	A282	2c Camilo Cienfuegos	.40	.20
843	A282	3c Sierra Maestra	.60	.20
844	A282	9c Bahia de Siguanea	1.25	.20
845	A282	10c Oriente	3.50	.20
		Nos. 841-845 (5)	6.00	1.00

Unification of
Viet
Nam — A283

Designs: 2c, Vietnamese guerrilla, American soldier. 3c, Northerner and southerner
shaking hands over map of united Viet Nam.
10c, Ox-drawn plow, machinised harvester.
13c, Natl. flags and profiles of Cuban and
Vietnamese farmers.

1964, July 20

846	A283	2c multi	.30	.20
847	A283	3c multi	.45	.20
848	A283	10c multi	1.00	.25
849	A283	13c multi	2.75	.60
		Nos. 846-849 (4)	4.50	1.25

11th Anniv. of the
Revolution
A284

1964 Summer
Olympics, Tokyo,
Oct. 10-25
A285

Designs: 3c, Raul Gomez Garcia and poem.
13c, Cover of La Historia Me Absolvera, by
Fidel Castro.

1964, July 25

850	A284	3c red, tan & blk	.50	.20
851	A284	13c multi	3.00	.30

1964, Oct. 10   **Wmk. 376**   **Perf. 10**

852	A285	1c Gymnastics	.30	.20
853	A285	2c Rowing	.30	.20
854	A285	3c Boxing	.30	.20
855	A285	7c Running, horiz.	.70	.20
856	A285	10c Fencing, horiz.	1.50	.35
857	A285	13c Foil, cleats, oar,		
		boxing glove, sun,		
		horiz.	2.50	.60
		Nos. 852-857 (6)	5.60	1.75

Satellite
and Globe
A286

Satellite
and Partial
Globe
A287

No. C31
and
Partial
Globe
A288

Various satellites and rockets.

1964, Oct. 15

858	A286	1c shown	.20	.20
859	A287	1c shown	.20	.20
860	A287	1c Globe LL	.20	.20
861	A287	1c Globe UR	.20	.20
862	A287	1c Globe UL	.20	.20
a.		Block of 5 + label, Nos. 858-862	1.00	1.00
863	A286	2c Spacecraft and		
		globe	.55	.20
864	A287	2c Globe LR	.55	.20
865	A287	2c Globe LL	.55	.20
866	A287	2c Globe UR	.55	.20
867	A287	2c Globe UL	.55	.20
a.		Block of 5 + label, Nos. 863-867	3.00	1.50
868	A286	3c Satellite and		
		globe	.75	.35
869	A287	3c Globe LR	.75	.35
870	A287	3c Globe LL	.75	.35
871	A287	3c Globe UR	.75	.35

872	A287	3c Globe UL	.75	.35
a.		Block of 5 + label, Nos. 868-872	4.00	2.50
873	A286	9c Satellite and		
		globe, diff	1.75	.70
874	A287	9c Globe LR	1.75	.70
875	A287	9c Globe LL	1.75	.70
876	A287	9c Globe UR	1.75	.70
877	A287	9c Globe UL	1.75	.70
a.		Block of 5 + label, Nos. 873-877	11.00	5.00
878	A286	13c Satellite and		
		globe, diff.	2.25	1.75
879	A287	13c Globe LR	2.25	1.75
880	A287	13c Globe LL	2.25	1.75
881	A287	13c Globe UR	2.25	1.75
882	A287	13c Globe UL	2.25	1.75
a.		Block of 5 + label, Nos. 878-882	15.00	10.00
883	A288	50c blk & lt grn	4.00	2.50
a.		Souvenir sheet of one, Wmk. 321	15.00	12.50
		Nos. 858-883 (26)	31.50	18.50

Experimental Cuban postal rocket flight,
25th anniv. Stamps of the same denomination
printed se-tenant in sheets of 20 stamps and 5
inscribed labels. Stamps of Type A287
arranged in blocks of 4 with a complete globe
in center of block; Type A286 stamps and
labels form a cross in center of sheet.
Inscribed "1939-Cohete Postal Cubano-1964."
No. 883a contains one 46x28mm stamp.

Type of A288 Ovptd. in Silver

1964, Oct. 17   **Unwmk.**

884	A288	50c dark red brown &		
		lt grn	5.00	1.50

No. 884 not issued without overprint.

40th Death Anniv.
of Lenin — A289

Havana
Zoo — A290

Designs: 13c, Lenin Mausoleum, horiz. 30c,
Lenin, star, hammer and sickle.

1964, Nov. 7   **Wmk. 376**

885	A289	3c org & blk	.40	.20
886	A289	13c pur, pink & blk	1.10	.35
887	A289	30c blue & blk	2.25	.60
		Nos. 885-887 (3)	3.75	1.35

1964, Nov. 25

888	A290	1c Leopard, horiz.	.30	.20
889	A290	2c Elephant	.30	.20
890	A290	3c Fallow deer	.30	.20
891	A290	4c Kangaroo, horiz.	.30	.20
892	A290	5c Lions, horiz.	.40	.20
893	A290	6c Eland, horiz.	.50	.20
894	A290	7c Zebra, horiz.	.50	.20
895	A290	8c Hyena, horiz.	.75	.20
896	A290	9c Tiger, horiz.	.75	.20
897	A290	10c Guanaco, horiz.	.80	.20
898	A290	13c Chimpanzees,		
		horiz.	.90	.20
899	A290	20c Peccary, horiz.	1.10	.20
900	A290	30c Raccoon	1.60	.30
901	A290	40c Hippopotamus,		
		horiz.	2.25	.50
902	A290	50c Tapir, horiz.	3.00	.75
903	A290	60c Dromedary	4.50	1.00
904	A290	70c Bison, horiz.	4.75	1.00
905	A290	80c Black bear	5.00	2.00

906 A290 90c Water buffalo,
horiz. 5.50 2.00

Size: 47x32mm

907 A290 1p Deer in nature
park, horiz. 9.25 1.00
Nos. 888-907 (20) 43.25 10.95

Heroes of the 1895 War of
Independence — A291

1964, Dec. 7
908 A291 1c Jose Marti .20 .20
909 A291 2c Antonio Maceo .40 .20
910 A291 3c Maximo Gomez .75 .35
911 A291 13c Calixto Garcia 1.90 .70
Nos. 908-911 (4) 3.25 1.45

Christmas Type of 1961

2c, Coral. 3c, Jellyfish. 10c, Starfish, sea-
urchins.

1964, Dec. 18
912 A248 2c Dwarf cup coral .80 .20
913 A249 2c Eusmilia fastigiata .80 .20
914 A249 2c Acropora
palmata .80 .20
915 A249 2c Acropora
profilera .80 .20
916 A249 2c Diploria
labyrinthiformis .80 .20
a. Block of 5 + label, Nos. 912-
916 4.50 1.50
917 A248 3c Condyactis gigantea 1.25 .50
918 A249 3c Physalia physal-
is 1.25 .50
919 A249 3c Aurelia aurita 1.25 .50
920 A249 3c Linuche ungu-
iculata 1.25 .50
921 A249 3c Cassiopea
frondosa 1.25 .50
a. Block of 5 + label, Nos. 917-
921 7.50 3.00
922 A248 10c Neocrinus blakei 2.25 1.00
923 A249 10c Eucidaris
tribuloidas 2.25 1.00
924 A249 10c Tripneutes 2.25 1.00
925 A249 10c Ophiocoma
echinata 2.25 1.00
926 A249 10c Oreaster celicu-
latus 2.25 1.00
a. Block of 5 + label, Nos. 922-
926 12.50 7.00
Nos. 912-926 (15) 21.50 8.50

Christmas 1964. See note after No. 700.

Dr. Tomas Romay
(1764-1849),
Physician and
Scientist — A292

Romay Monument — A293

Designs: 2c, First vaccination against smallpox. 3c, Portrait and treatise on vaccination.

1964, Dec. 21
927 A292 1c blk & olive brn .50 .20
928 A292 2c blk & tan .50 .20
929 A293 3c olive & dark red
brown .60 .20
930 A293 10c bister & blk 2.40 .35
Nos. 927-930 (4) 4.00 .95

Second
Declaration of
Havana
A294

Map of Latin America and ripples or map of
Cuba and peasant breaking shackles under
text from the Declaration of Havana: No. 931a,
932a "Visperas de su muerte..." No. 931b,
932b, "Un continente, que juntos suponen
representos..." No. 931c, 932c, "Y no se
ocultaran ni el gobierna..." No. 931d, 932d,
"Millones de mulatos latinamericanos que
saben..." No. 931e, "A labran la tierra en
condiciones..."

1964, Dec. 23
931 Strip of 5 5.00 2.25
a.-e. A294 3c any single .75 .25
932 Strip of 5 15.00 8.50
a.-e. A294 13c any single 1.75 1.00
Nos. 931-932 printed in sheets of 25 (5x5).

Dioramas in New Cuban Postal
Museum — A295

1965, Jan. 4
Yellow & Black Border
933 A295 13c Maritime Post 3.25 .45
934 A295 30c Insurrection Post 2.50 .70

Souvenir Sheet
Imperf
935 Sheet of 2 8.50 7.50
a. A295 13c like #933, blue & blk
border 1.00 1.00
b. A295 30c like #934, blue & blk
border 3.00 3.00
Nos. 933-935 (3) 14.25 8.65

Stamps in No. 935 have simulated perforations; buff margin is inscribed "PRECIO 50c"
LR.

Fishing Fleet — A296

1965, May 1
936 A296 1c Schooner .20 .20
937 A296 2c Omicron .20 .20
938 A296 3c Victoria .30 .20
939 A296 9c Cardenas .45 .20
940 A296 10c Sigma 1.75 .30
941 A296 13c Lambda 2.75 .35
Nos. 936-941 (6) 5.65 1.45

Intl. Women's
Day — A297

1965, Mar. 8
942 A297 3c Lidia Doce 1.10 .25
943 A297 13c Clara Zetkin 1.60 .50

Technical Revolution — A298

Designs: 3c, Jose Antonio Echeverria University School. 13c, Stylized symbols of science and research, molecular structure and
satellite dish.

1965, Mar. 31
944 A298 3c tan, blk & dark red .50 .20
945 A298 13c multi 2.50 .70

Cosmonauts, Rocket — A299

30c, Cosmonauts Pavel I. Balyayev, Aleksei
A. Leonov taking first space walk.

1965, Apr. 2
946 A299 30c dark blue, blk &
brn 2.50 .55
947 A299 50c brt pink & blue blk 4.50 1.00
Flight of Voskhod 2, the first man to walk in
space, Mar. 17.

Abstract Wood
Carving by Eugenio
Rodriguez — A300

Abraham
Lincoln — A301

Paintings in the Natl. Museum, Havana: 3c,
Garden with Sunflowers, by Victor Manuel.
10c, Abstract, by Wilfredo Lam, horiz. 13c,
Children, by Enrique Ponce, horiz.

1965, Apr. 12
948 A300 2c multi .35 .20
Size: 35x46mm
949 A300 3c multi .55 .20
Size: 46x35mm
950 A300 10c multi 1.50 .45
Size: 43x37mm
951 A300 13c multi 2.50 .80
Nos. 948-951 (4) 4.90 1.65

1965, Apr. 15
Designs: 1c, Log cabin, birth site, horiz. 2c,
Memorial, Washington, DC, horiz. 3c, Monu-
ment, Washington, DC. 13c, Portrait, quote.

952 A301 1c yel bister, red brn
& gray .20 .20
953 A301 2c lt blue & dark blue .35 .20
954 A301 3c red org, blk & blue
blk 1.00 .35
955 A301 13c org, blk & blue blk 2.25 .60
Nos. 952-955 (4) 3.80 1.35

Stamp Day Type of 1963

Stamp Day 1965: 3c, 18th Cent. postmarks
and packet. 13c, No. C16 and airplanes over
capital.

1965, Apr. 24
956 A266 3c sep & dark org 3.00 .25
957 A266 13c brt blue, sal rose &
blk 2.75 .60

Intl. Quiet Sun
Year — A302

Intl. Telecommunications Union,
Cent. — A303

1965, May 10
958 A302 1c Sun, Earth's
magnetic pole,
horiz. .25 .20
959 A302 2c Sun Year emblem .25 .20
960 A302 3c Earth's magnetic
field, horiz. .55 .20
961 A302 6c Atmospheric
currents, horiz. .60 .20
962 A302 30c Solar rays on
planet surface 2.10 .55
963 A302 50c Effect on satellite orbits,
horiz. 2.75 1.40
a. Souv. sheet of one, imperf. 8.00 8.00
b. As "a," changed colors 14.00 14.00
Nos. 958-963 (6) 6.50 2.75

Stamps in Nos. 963a-963b have simulated
perforations.
Stamp in No. 963b is blue blk, Prus blue, org
yel & red. Issued Oct. 10 for the Philatelic
Space Exhibition, Havana, Oct. 10-17.

1965, May 17
964 A303 1c Station, horiz. .20 .20
965 A303 2c Satellite .20 .20
966 A303 3c Telstar, horiz. .30 .20
967 A303 10c Telstar, receiving
station 1.10 .25
968 A303 30c ITU emblem, horiz. 3.00 .80
Nos. 964-968 (5) 4.80 1.65

9th Communist World Youth and
Students Congress — A304

1965, June 10
969 A304 13c Flags of Cuba and
Algeria, emblem 1.50 .20
970 A304 30c Flags, guerrillas 2.50 .20

Matias Perez, Cuban Aeronautics
Pioneer — A305

1965, June 23
971 A305 3c pink & blk 1.75 .90
972 A305 13c dull vio & blk, diff. 2.75 .90

Flowers and
Maps of Their
Locations
A306

1965, July 20

973	A306	1c	Rosa canina, Europe	.20	.20
974	A306	2c	Chrysanthemum hortorum, Asia	.30	.20
975	A306	3c	Strelitzia reginae, Africa	.30	.30
976	A306	4c	Dahlia pinnata, No. America	.30	.20
977	A306	5c	Cattleya labiata, So. America	1.60	.20
978	A306	13c	Grevillea banksii, Oceania	3.25	.90
979	A306	30c	Brunfelsia nitida, Cuba	4.75	1.50
			Nos. 973-979 (7)	10.70	3.50

1st Natl. Games — A307

1965, July 25

980	A307	1c	Swimming	.20	.20
981	A307	2c	Basketball	.35	.20
982	A307	3c	Gymnastics	.70	.20
983	A307	30c	Hurdling	2.75	.20
			Nos. 980-983 (4)	4.00	.80

Revolution
Museum
Opening
A308

1965, July 26

984	A308	1c	Anti-tank guns	.20	.20
985	A308	2c	Tanks	.20	.20
986	A308	3c	Bazookas	.20	.20
987	A308	10c	Uniform, guerillas	.70	.20
988	A308	13c	Compass, yacht Granma	2.00	.20
			Nos. 984-988 (5)	3.30	1.00

A309

1965, Aug. 20

989	A309	1c	Finlay's signature	.20	.20
990	A309	2c	Anopheles mosquito	.20	.20
991	A309	3c	Portrait	.35	.20
992	A309	3c	Microscope	.45	.20
993	A309	9c	Dr. Claudio Delgado	.75	.20
994	A309	10c	Monument	1.90	.25
995	A309	13c	Discussing theory with doctors	3.00	.60
			Nos. 989-995 (7)	6.85	1.85

Carlos J. Finlay (1833-1915), discovered
transmission of yellow fever via aedes aegypti
(not anopheles) mosquito. Nos. 990-995 vert.

Butterflies
A310

1965, Sept. 22   **Unwmk.**

996	A310	2c	Dismorphia cubana	.30	.20
997	A310	2c	Anetia numidia briarea	.30	.20
998	A310	2c	Carathis gortynoides	.30	.20
999	A310	2c	Hymenitis cubana	.30	.20
1000	A310	2c	Eubaphe heros	.30	.20
a.			Strip of 5, Nos. 996-1000	2.25	1.50
1001	A310	3c	Lycorea ceres demeter	.40	.20
1002	A310	3c	Eubaphe disparitis	.40	.20
1003	A310	3c	Siderone nemesis	.40	.20
1004	A310	3c	Syntomidopsis variegata	.40	.20
1005	A310	3c	Ctenuchidia virgo	.40	.20
a.			Strip of 5, Nos. 1001-1005	2.75	1.75
1006	A310	13c	Prepona antimache crossina	2.00	.80
1007	A310	13c	Sylepta reginalis	2.00	.80
1008	A310	13c	Chlosyne perezi perezi	2.00	.80
1009	A310	13c	Anaea clytemnestra iphigenia	2.00	.80
1010	A310	13c	Anetia cubana	2.00	.80
a.			Strip of 5, Nos. 1006-1010	11.00	5.50
			Nos. 996-1010 (15)	13.50	6.00

Cuban
Mint,
50th
Anniv.
A311

Coins (obverse and reverse).

1965, Oct. 13

1011	A311	1c	20 centavos, 1962	.30	.20
1012	A311	2c	1 peso, 1934	.30	.20
1013	A311	3c	40 centavos, 1962	.30	.20
1014	A311	8c	1 peso, 1915	.80	.20
1015	A311	10c	Marti peso, 1953	1.90	.40
1016	A311	13c	20 pesos, 1915	2.75	.50
			Nos. 1011-1016 (6)	6.35	1.70

Tropical
Fruit — A312

1965, Nov. 15   **Perf. 12½**

1017	A312	1c	Oranges	.20	.20
1018	A312	2c	Custard apples	.20	.20
1019	A312	3c	Papayas	.20	.20
1020	A312	4c	Bananas	.35	.20
1021	A312	10c	Avocado	.60	.20
1022	A312	13c	Pineapple	.95	.70
1023	A312	20c	Guavas	2.50	.70
1024	A312	50c	Marmalade plums	5.50	1.25
			Nos. 1017-1024 (8)	10.50	3.65

Christmas Type of 1961

Birds.

1965, Dec. 1

1025	A248	3c	Icterus galbula	1.60	.30
1026	A249	3c	Passerina ciris	1.60	.30
1027	A249	3c	Setophaga ruticillar	1.60	.30
1028	A249	3c	Dendroica tusca	1.60	.30
1029	A249	3c	Pheucticus ludovicianus	1.60	.30
a.			Block of 5 + label, Nos. 1025-1029	9.00	1.75
1030	A248	5c	Pyranga olivacea	1.75	.40
1031	A249	5c	Dendroica dominica	1.75	.40
1032	A249	5c	Vermivora pinus	1.75	.40
1033	A249	5c	Protonotaria citrea	1.75	.40
1034	A249	5c	Wilsonia citrina	1.75	.40
a.			Block of 5 + label, Nos. 1030-1034	10.00	4.00
1035	A248	13c	Passerina cyanea	4.00	1.50

1036	A249	13c	Anas discors	4.00	1.50
1037	A249	13c	Aix sponsa	4.00	1.50
1038	A249	13c	Spatula clypeata	4.00	1.50
1039	A249	13c	Nycticorax hoactli	4.00	1.50
a.			Block of 5 + label, Nos. 1035-1039	21.00	10.00
			Nos. 1025-1039 (15)	36.75	11.00

Christmas 1965. See note after No. 700.

Intl. Athletic Competition, Havana, 7th
Anniv. — A313

1965, Dec. 11   Wmk. 376   Perf. 10

1040	A313	1c	Hurdling	.20	.20
1041	A313	2c	Discus	.20	.20
1042	A313	3c	Shot put	.55	.20
1043	A313	7c	Javelin	.55	.25
1044	A313	9c	High jump	.70	.35
1045	A313	10c	Hammer throw	1.40	.60
1046	A313	13c	Running	2.00	.90
			Nos. 1040-1046 (7)	5.60	2.70

Fish in the Natl. Aquarium — A314

1965, Dec. 5   Unwmk.   Perf. 12½

1047	A314	1c	Echeneis naucrates	.25	.20
1048	A314	2c	Katsuwonus pelamis	.25	.20
1049	A314	3c	Abudefduf saxatilis	.55	.20
1050	A314	4c	Istiophorus	.65	.20
1051	A314	5c	Epinephelus striatus	.65	.20
1052	A314	10c	Lutianus analis	.80	.25
1053	A314	13c	Ocyurus chrysurus	2.75	.60
1054	A314	30c	Holocentrus ascensionis	4.50	.95
			Nos. 1047-1054 (8)	10.40	2.80

Andre Voisin (d. 1964), French
Naturalist — A315

1965, Dec. 21   Wmk. 376

1055	A315	3c	shown	1.00	.25
1056	A315	13c	Portrait, flags, microscope, plant	2.50	.55

Transportation — A316

1965, Dec. 30

1057	A316	1c	Skoda bus, Czechoslovakia	.20	.20
1058	A316	2c	Ikarus bus, Hungary	.20	.20
1059	A316	3c	Leyland bus, G.B.	.20	.20

1060	A316	4c	TEM-4 locomotive, USSR	2.25	.70
1061	A316	7c	BB-69.000 locomotive, France	2.25	.70
1062	A316	10c	Remolcador tugboat, DDR	1.00	.80
1063	A316	13c	15 de Marzo freighter, Spain	1.75	.60
1064	A316	20c	Ilyushin 18 jet, USSR	2.50	1.00
			Nos. 1057-1064 (8)	10.35	3.95

A317

7th Anniv.
of the
Revolution
A318

1966, Jan. 2

1065	A317	1c	Guerrillas	.25	.20
1066	A317	2c	Commander and tank	.25	.20
1067	A317	3c	Sailor, patrol boat	.90	.20
1068	A318	10c	Jet aircraft	1.90	.45
1069	A318	13c	Rocket	2.25	.70
			Nos. 1065-1069 (5)	5.55	1.75

Conference of Asian, African and
South American Countries,
Havana — A319

1966, Jan. 3

1070	A319	2c	Emblem at R	.20	.20
1071	A319	3c	Emblem at L	.40	.20
1072	A319	13c	Emblem at center	2.10	.55
			Nos. 1070-1072 (3)	2.70	.95

Guardalabarca Beach — A320

1966, Feb. 10

1073	A320	1c	shown	.30	.20
1074	A320	2c	Gran Piedra mountain	.30	.20
1075	A320	3c	Guama Village	.90	.20
1076	A320	13c	Soroa waterfall, vert.	2.50	.60
			Nos. 1073-1076 (4)	4.00	1.20

11th Medical and 7th Natl. Dental
Congresses — A321

1966, Feb. 28   Wmk. 376

1077	A321	3c	multi	.25	.20
1078	A321	13c	multi, diff.	1.50	.55

Folk Art
A322

1966, Feb. 28 Unwmk.
1079 A322 1c Afro-cuban ritual
puppet .20 .20
1080 A322 2c Sombreros .20 .20
1081 A322 3c Ceramic vase .25 .20
1082 A322 7c Lanterns, lamp .25 .20
1083 A322 9c Table lamp .80 .20
1084 A322 10c Shark, wood
sculpture 1.25 .20
1085 A322 13c Snail-shell necklace, earrings 2.50 .30
Nos. 1079-1085 (7) 5.45 1.50

Nos. 1079-1083 vert.

Chelsea College, by Canaletto — A323

Ceramics and paintings in the National
Museum: 1c, Ming vase. 3c, Portrait of a Lady,
by Goya. 13c, Portrait of Fayum, encaustic
painting. Nos. 1086, 1088-1089 vert.

1966, Mar. 31 Wmk. 376
1086 A323 1c multi .20 .20
1087 A323 2c multi .85 .20
1088 A323 3c multi .75 .20
1089 A323 13c multi 3.00 .70
Nos. 1086-1089 (4) 4.80 1.30

First
Man in
Space,
5th
Anniv.
A324

Designs: 1c, Konstantin Eduardovich Tsi-
olkovsky (1857-1935), Soviet rocket and
space sciences pioneer. 2c, Cosmonauts in
training, vert. 3c, Yuri Gagarin, rocket, Earth.
7c, Cosmonauts Nikolaev and Popovich, vert.
9c, Tereshkova and Bykovsky. 10c, Komarov,
Feoktistov and Yegarov. 13c, Leonov taking
first space walk.

1966, Apr. 12
1090 A324 1c multi .20 .20
1091 A324 2c multi .20 .20
1092 A324 3c multi .35 .20
1093 A324 7c multi .60 .20
1094 A324 9c multi .85 .20
1095 A324 10c multi 1.10 .20
1096 A324 13c multi 2.25 .35
Nos. 1090-1096 (7) 5.55 1.55

Bay of
Pigs
Invasion,
5th
Anniv.
A325

1966, Apr. 17
1097 A325 2c Tank .20 .20
1098 A325 3c Burning ship,
plane crash .95 .20
1099 A325 9c Tank in ditch .40 .20
1100 A325 10c Soldier, gunners 1.75 .20
1101 A325 13c Operations map 3.00 .70
Nos. 1097-1101 (5) 6.30 1.50

Stamp Day Type of 1963

Designs: 3c, Cuban Postal Museum interior.
13c, No. 613 and stamp collector.

1966, Apr. 24
1102 A266 3c sage grn & sal
rose 1.25 .20
1103 A266 13c brn, sal rose &
blk 3.50 .80

Stamp Day 1966. 1st Anniv. of the Cuban
Postal Museum (No. 1102); 1st anniv. of the
Cuban Philatelic Federation (No. 1103).

Flowers and
Symbols of
Industry — A326

1966, May 1
1104 A326 2c Anvil .20 .20
1105 A326 3c Machete .30 .20
1106 A326 10c Hammer .70 .20
1107 A326 13c Hemisphere,
gearwheel 1.75 .90
Nos. 1104-1107 (4) 2.95 1.50

Labor Day.

Opening of the World Health
Organization Headquarters,
Geneva — A327

Views of WHO headquarters and emblem or
emblem on flag.

1966, May 3
1108 A327 2c blk & yel org .20 .20
1109 A327 3c blk, lt blue & yel
org .70 .20
1110 A327 13c blk, lt blue & yel
org 2.10 .50
Nos. 1108-1110 (3) 3.00 .90

10th Central American and Caribbean
Games, Puerto Rico, June 11-25
A328

1966, June 11
1111 A328 1c Running, vert. .20 .20
1112 A328 2c Rifle shooting .30 .20
1113 A328 3c Baseball, vert. .45 .20
1114 A328 7c Volleyball, vert. .45 .20
1115 A328 9c Soccer, vert. .80 .20
1116 A328 10c Boxing, vert. 1.00 .20
1117 A328 13c Basketball, vert. 3.50 .35
Nos. 1111-1117 (7) 7.10 1.55

Progress in
Education
A329

Designs: 1c, Makarenko School, Playa de
Tarara. 2c, Natl. Literacy Campaign Museum.
3c, Lantern, literacy campaign emblem for
1961. 10c, Frank Pais education team in the
mountains. 13c, Farmer, factory worker.

1966, June 15
1118 A329 1c grn & blk .20 .20
1119 A329 2c yel, olive bister &
blk .20 .20
1120 A329 3c brt blue, lt blue &
blk .30 .20

1121 A329 10c golden brn, brn &
blk .90 .20
1122 A329 13c multi 2.40 .30
Nos. 1118-1122 (5) 4.00 1.10

1st Graduating class of Makarenko School
(1c), 5th anniv. of the Natl. Literacy Campaign
(3c), 4th anniv. of agricultural and industrial
trade education (13c).

12th Congress of the Cuban Labor
Organization — A330

1966, Aug. 12
1123 A330 3c multi .75 .25

Sea
Shells — A331

1966, Aug. 25 Unwmk.
1124 A331 1c Liguus flammellus .30 .20
1125 A331 2c Cypraea zebra .40 .20
1126 A331 3c Strombus pugilis .60 .20
1127 A331 7c Aequipecten
muscosu .70 .20
1128 A331 9c Liguus fasciatus
crenatus .80 .20
1129 A331 10c Charonia variegata 1.50 .20
1130 A331 13c Liguus fasciatus
archeri 3.25 .40
Nos. 1124-1130 (7) 7.55 1.60

Breeding Messenger Pigeons — A332

1966, Sept. 18 Wmk. 376
1131 A332 1c shown .40 .20
1132 A332 2c Timer .40 .20
1133 A332 3c Coops .40 .20
1134 A332 7c Breeder tending
coops .80 .20
1135 A332 9c Pigeons in yard .80 .35
1136 A332 10c Two men, message 2.50 .50

Size: 47x32mm
1137 A332 13c Baracoa to Havana champion-
ship flight, July
26, 1959 3.75 .90
Nos. 1131-1137 (7) 9.05 2.55

Provincial and   17th World Chess
Natl. Coats of   Olympiad,
Arms, Map of   Havana — A334
Cuba — A333

1966, Oct. 10
1138 A333 1c Pinar del Rio .20 .20
1139 A333 2c Havana .30 .20
1140 A333 3c Matanzas .30 .20
1141 A333 4c Las Villas .40 .20
1142 A333 5c Camaguey .60 .20

1143 A333 9c Oriente 1.00 .45
Size: 30x48mm
1144 A333 13c National arms 2.25 .55
Nos. 1138-1144 (7) 5.05 2.00

1966, Oct. 18
1145 A334 1c Pawn .30 .20
1146 A334 2c Rook .30 .20
1147 A334 3c Knight .50 .20
1148 A334 9c Bishop 1.00 .20
1149 A334 10c Queen, games,
horiz. 2.40 .20
1150 A334 13c King and emblem, horiz. 3.25 .30
Nos. 1145-1150 (6) 7.75 1.30

Souvenir Sheet
Imperf
1151 A334 30c Capablanca
Vs. Lasker,
1914, horiz. 12.00 12.00
No. 1151 contains one 49½x31mm stamp.

Cuban-Soviet Diplomatic
Relations — A335

1966, Nov. 7
1152 A335 2c Lenin Hospital .20 .20
1153 A335 3c Oil tanker, world
map .35 .20
1154 A335 10c Workers,
gearwheels 1.10 .20
1155 A335 13c Agriculture 2.25 .25
Nos. 1152-1155 (4) 3.90 .85

2nd Song
Festival
A336

Cuban composers and their compositions.

1966, Nov. 18
1156 A336 1c Amadeo Roldan .20 .20
1157 A336 2c Eduardo Sanchez
de Fuentes .30 .20
1158 A336 3c Moises Simons .30 .20
1159 A336 7c Jorge Anck-
ermann .80 .20
1160 A336 9c Alejandro G.
Caturla .80 .25
1161 A336 10c Eliseo Grenet 3.00 .45
1162 A336 13c Ernesto Lecuona 4.00 .90
Nos. 1156-1162 (7) 9.40 2.40

Viet Nam
War — A337

Flag of Viet Nam and: 2c, US aircraft dis-
charging bombs, dead cattle. 3c, Gas mask
and victims. 13c, US bombs, women and
children.

1966, Nov. 23
1163 A337 2c multi .40 .20
1164 A337 3c multi .60 .20
1165 A337 13c multi 2.00 .60
Nos. 1163-1165 (3) 3.00 1.00

10th Anniv. of Successful Revolution
Campaigns — A338

Revolution leaders, scenes of the
insurrection.

1966, Nov. 30
1166 A338 1c Antonio Fernan-
            dez   .20   .20
1167 A338 2c Candido Gonza-
            lez   .20   .20
1168 A338 3c Jose Tey   .20   .20
1169 A338 7c Tony Aloma   .30   .20
1170 A338 9c Otto Paralleda   .60   .20
1171 A338 10c Juan Manuel
            Marquez   2.00   .50
1172 A338 13c Frank Pais   1.90   .80
      Nos. 1166-1172 (7)   5.40 2.30

Intl. Leisure Time and Recreation
Seminar — A339

1966, Dec. 2
1173 A339 3c shown   .20   .20
1174 A339 9c World map, stop-
            watch, eye   1.40   .20
1175 A339 13c Earth, clock, em-
            blem   1.75   .60
      Nos. 1173-1175 (3)   3.35 1.00

1st Natl. Telecommunications
Forum — A340

1966, Dec. 12
1176 A340 3c shown   .75   .20
1177 A340 10c Satellite in orbit   3.75   .20
1178 A340 13c Shell, satellite   5.50   .70
  a.   Souv. sheet of 3, #1176-
         1178, imperf.   15.00 15.00
      Nos. 1176-1178 (3)   10.00 1.10

No. 1178a sold for 30c.

Christmas Type of 1961
1966, Dec. 20   Unwmk.
1179 A248 1c Cypripedium
            eurylochus   .90   .20
1180 A249 1c Cattleya speci-
            osissima   .90   .20
1181 A249 1c Cattleya
            mendelii
            majestica   .90   .20
1182 A249 1c Cattleya tri-
            anae ame-
            siana   .90   .20
1183 A249 1c Cattleya labiata
            macfarlanei   .90   .20
  a.   Block of 5 + label, #1179-
         1183   5.00 1.00
1184 A248 3c Cypripedium
            morganiae
            burfordense   1.40   .20
1185 A249 3c Cattleya Count-
            ess of Derby   1.40   .20
1186 A249 3c Cypripedium
            hookerae
            volunteanum   1.40   .20
1187 A249 3c Cattleya war-
            scewiczii
            reginae
            burfordense   1.40   .20
1188 A249 3c Cypripedium
            stonei can-
            nartae   1.40   .20
  a.   Block of 5 + label, #1184-
         1188   8.00 1.00

1189 A248 13c Cattleya
            mendelii
            Duchess of
            Montrose   5.00   .50
1190 A249 13c Oncidium
            macranthum   5.00   .50
1191 A249 13c Cypripedium
            stonei
            platytoenium   5.00   .50
1192 A249 13c Cattleya dowi-
            ana aurea   5.00   .50
1193 A249 13c Laelia anceps   5.00   .50
  a.   Block of 5 + label, #1189-
         1193   27.50 2.75
      Nos. 1179-1193 (15)   36.50 4.50

Christmas 1966. See note after No. 700.

8th Anniv. of the Revolution — A341

1967, Jan. 2
1194 A341 3c Liberation, 1959   .30   .20
1195 A341 3c Agrarian Reform,
            1960   .30   .20
1196 A341 3c Education, 1961   .30   .20
1197 A341 3c Agriculture, 1965   .30   .20
  a.   Strip of 4, Nos. 1194-1197   1.25   .90
1198 A341 13c Rodin's Thinker,
            Planning, 1962   1.90   .45
1199 A341 13c Organization,
            1963   1.90   .45
1200 A341 13c Economy, 1964   1.90   .45
1201 A341 13c Solidarity, 1966   1.90   .45
  a.   Strip of 4, Nos. 1198-1201   7.75 4.25
      Nos. 1194-1201 (8)   8.80 2.60

Nos. 1198-1201 vert.

Spring, by Jorge Arche — A342

Paintings in the Natl. Museum: 1c, Coffee
Machine, by Angel Acosta Leon, vert. 2c,
Country People, by Eduardo Abela, vert. 13c,
Still-life, by Amelia Pelaez, vert. 30c, Land-
scape, by Gonzalo Escalante.

1967, Feb. 27
1202 A342 1c multi   .30   .20
1203 A342 2c multi   .50   .20
1204 A342 3c multi   .70   .20
1205 A342 13c multi   2.00   .30
1206 A342 30c multi   5.50   .60
      Nos. 1202-1206 (5)   9.00 1.50

Natl.
Events,
Mar. 13,
1957
A343

1967, Mar. 13   Wmk. 376
1207 A343 3c Attack on Presi-
            dential Palace   .20   .20

Size: 41x28mm

1208 A343 13c Landing of
            Corynthia   2.50   .70
1209 A343 30c Cienfuegos revolt   2.40   .80
      Nos. 1207-1209 (3)   5.10 1.70

Evolution of
Man — A344

Prehistoric men: 2c, Australopithecus. 3c,
Pithecanthropus erectus. 4c, Sinanthropus
pekinensis. 5c, Neanderthal man. 13c, Cro-
magnon man carving tusk. 20c, Cro-magnon
man painting petroglyph.

1967, Mar. 31   Unwmk.
1210 A344 1c multi   .30   .20
1211 A344 2c multi   .50   .20
1212 A344 3c multi   .50   .20
1213 A344 4c multi   .75   .20
1214 A344 5c multi   1.10   .20
1215 A344 13c multi   3.75   .30
1216 A344 20c multi   7.50   .45
      Nos. 1210-1216 (7)   14.40 1.75

Stamp
Day
A345

Carriages.

1967, Apr. 24
1217 A345 3c Victoria   .35   .20
1218 A345 9c Volante   2.00   .45
1219 A345 13c Quitrin   3.00   .80
      Nos. 1217-1219 (3)   5.35 1.45

EXPO '67, Montreal, Apr. 28-Oct.
27 — A346

1967, Apr. 28
1220 A346 1c Cuban pavilion   .40   .20
1221 A346 2c Space exploration   .40   .20
1222 A346 3c Petroglyph, hiero-
            glyph   .55   .20
1223 A346 13c Agriculture, com-
            puter technology   3.00   .20
1224 A346 20c Athletes   3.50   .20
      Nos. 1220-1224 (5)   7.85 1.00

Botanical
Gardens,
Sequicentennial
A347

Flowering plants.

1967, May 30
1225 A347 1c Eugenia malac-
            cencis   .20   .20
1226 A347 2c Jacaranda
            filicifolia   .20   .20
1227 A347 3c Coroupita gui-
            anensis   .45   .20
1228 A347 4c Spathodea
            campanulata   .45   .20
1229 A347 5c Cassia fistula   .90   .20
1230 A347 13c Plumieria alba   2.75   .35
1231 A347 20c Erythrina poep-
            pigiana   4.75   .40
      Nos. 1225-1231 (7)   9.70 1.75

Natl.
Ballet — A348

1967, June 15
1232 A348 1c Giselle   .35   .20
1233 A348 2c Swan Lake   .35   .20
1234 A348 3c Don Quixote   .50   .20
1235 A348 4c Calaucan   1.00   .20
1236 A348 13c Swan Lake   2.75   .70
1237 A348 20c Nutcracker   4.00 1.25
      Nos. 1232-1237 (6)   8.95 2.75

Intl. Ballet Festival, Havana.

5th Pan American
Games,
Winnipeg,
Canada, July 22-
Aug. 7 — A349

1st Conference
of Latin
American
Solidarity
Organization
(OLAS) — A350

1967, July 22
1238 A349 1c Baseball, horiz.   .20   .20
1239 A349 2c Swimming,
            horiz.   .35   .20
1240 A349 3c Basketball   .50   .20
1241 A349 4c Gymnastic rings   .85   .20
1242 A349 5c Water polo   1.00   .20
1243 A349 13c Weight lifting,
            horiz.   3.00   .45
1244 A349 20c Javelin   4.75   .80
      Nos. 1238-1244 (7)   10.65 2.25

1967, July 28   Wmk. 376

Portrait of representative, map of South
American homeland: No. 1245, Camilo Torres,
Colombia. No. 1246, Luis de la Puente Uceda,
Peru. No. 1247, Luis A. Turcios Lima, Guate-
mala. No. 1248, Fabricio Ojeda, Venezuela.

1245 A350 13c pale grn, blk &
            red   2.00   .50
1246 A350 13c lil, blk & red   2.00   .50
1247 A350 13c dark chalky blue,
            blk & red   2.00   .50
1248 A350 13c golden brn, blk &
            red   2.00   .50
      Nos. 1245-1248 (4)   8.00 2.00

Portrait of Sonny Rollins, by Alan
Davie — A351

Bathers, by
Gustave
Singier
A352

SALON DE MAYO HABANA 1967

Modern Art: No. 1250, Twelve Selenities, by Felix Labisse. No. 1251, Night of the Drinker, by Friedensreich Hundertwasser. No. 1252, Figure, by Mariano. No. 1253, All-Souls, by Wilfredo Lam. No. 1254, Darkness and Cracks, by Antonio Tapies. No. 1256, Torso of a Muse, by Jean Arp. No. 1257, Figure, by M.W. Svanberg. No. 1258, Oppenheimer's Information, by Erro. No. 1259, Where Cardinals Are Born, by Max Ernst. No. 1260, Havana Landscape, by Portocarrero. No. 1261, EG 12, by Victor Vasarely. No. 1262, Frisco, by Alexander Calder. No. 1263, The Man with the Pipe, by Picasso. No. 1264, Abstract Composition, by Sergei Poliakoff. No. 1265, Painting, by Bram van Velde. No. 1266, Sower of Fires, by R. Matta. No. 1267, The Art of Living, by Rene Magritte. No. 1268, Poem, by Joan Miro. No. 1269, Young Tigers, by Jean Messagier. No. 1270, Painting, by M. Vieira da Silva. No. 1271, Live Cobra, by Pierre Alechinsky. No. 1272, Stalingrad, by Asger Jorn. 30c, Warriors, by Edouard Pignon. 50c, Cloister, a mural at the exhibition representing the Salon de Mayo pictures.

1967, July 29 — Unwmk.

1249	A351	1c shown	.30	.20
1250	A351	1c multi	.30	.20
1251	A351	1c multi	.30	.20
1252	A351	1c multi	.30	.20
1253	A351	1c multi	.30	.20
a.		Strip of 5, Nos. 1249-1253	1.75	1.50
		Nos. 1249-1253 (5)	1.50	1.00

Sizes: 36½x54mm, 36½x53mm,
36½x45mm, 36½x41mm

1254	A352	2c shown	.60	.20
1255	A352	2c shown	.60	.20
1256	A352	2c multi	.60	.20
1257	A352	2c multi	.60	.20
1258	A352	2c multi	.60	.20
a.		Strip of 5, Nos. 1254-1258	3.50	2.50
		Nos. 1254-1258 (5)	3.00	1.00

Sizes: 36½x54mm, 36½x40mm,
36½x42mm, 36½x49mm

1259	A352	3c multi	1.50	.20
1260	A352	3c multi	1.50	.20
1261	A352	3c multi	1.50	.20
1262	A352	3c multi	1.50	.20
1263	A352	3c multi	1.50	.20
a.		Strip of 5, Nos. 1259-1263	7.50	3.50
		Nos. 1259-1263 (5)	7.50	1.00

Sizes: 35x15mm, 35x67mm,
35x46½mm, 35x55mm

1264	A352	4c multi	1.75	.80
1265	A352	4c multi	1.75	.80
1266	A352	4c multi	1.75	.80
1267	A352	4c multi	1.75	.80
1268	A352	4c multi	1.75	.80
a.		Strip of 5, Nos. 1264-1268	9.00	4.00
		Nos. 1264-1268 (5)	8.75	4.00

Sizes: 49x32mm, 49x35mm,
49x46mm

1269	A351	13c multi	4.50	2.75
1270	A351	13c multi	4.50	2.75
1271	A351	13c multi	4.50	2.75
1272	A351	13c multi	4.50	2.75
a.		Strip of 4, Nos. 1269-1272	19.00	11.00
		Nos. 1269-1272 (4)	18.00	11.00

Size: 54x32mm

1273	A351	30c multi	17.50	11.00

Souvenir Sheet
Imperf

1274	A351	50c multi	25.00	12.50

Salon de Mayo Art Exhibition, Havana. No. 1274 contains one 88x45mm stamp with simulated perforations. Issued Oct. 7.

World Underwater Fishing
Championships — A353

1967, Sept. 5

1275	A353	1c Green moray	.20	.20
1276	A353	2c Octopus	.20	.20
1277	A353	3c Great barracuda	.20	.20
1278	A353	4c Blue shark	.75	.20
1279	A353	5c Spotted jewfish	1.60	.20
1280	A353	13c Sting ray	3.25	.35
1281	A353	20c Green turtle	6.50	.45
		Nos. 1275-1281 (7)	12.70	1.80

Soviet Space
Program
A354

1967, Oct. 4 — Wmk. 376

1282	A354	1c Sputnik 1	.20	.20
1283	A354	2c Lunik 3	.20	.20
1284	A354	3c Venusik	.20	.20
1285	A354	4c Cosmos	.40	.20
1286	A354	5c Mars 1	.65	.20
1287	A354	9c Electron 1 & 2	.75	.20
1288	A354	10c Luna 9	1.10	.25
1289	A354	13c Luna 10	2.50	.30
a.		Souv. sheet of 8, #1282-1289, imperf.	15.00	15.00
		Nos. 1282-1289 (8)	6.00	1.75

Stamps in #1289a have simulated perfs.

50th Anniv.
of the
October
Revolution,
Russia
A355

Paintings: 1c, Storming the Winter Palace, by Sokolov, Skalia and Miasnikov. 2c, Lenin Addressing Congress, by W.A. Serov. 3c, Lenin, by H.D. Nalbandian. 4c, Lenin Explaining Electrification Map, by L.A. Schmatko. 5c, Dawn of the Five-Year Plan, by J.D. Romas. 13c, Kusnetzkroi Steel Furnace No. 1, by P. Kotov. 30c, Victory, by A. Krivonogov.

1967, Nov. 7 — Unwmk.

1290	A355	1c 64x36mm	.20	.20
1291	A355	2c 48x36mm	.20	.20
1292	A355	3c	.45	.20
1293	A355	4c 48x36mm	.45	.20
1294	A355	5c 50x36mm	3.75	.20
1295	A355	13c 36x50mm	3.00	.20
1296	A355	30c 50x36mm	4.00	.25
		Nos. 1290-1296 (7)	12.05	1.45

Castle of the Royal Forces,
Havana — A356

Historic architecture: 2c, Iznaga Tower, Trinidad, vert. 3c, Castle of Our Lady of the Angels, Cienfuegos. 4c, St. Francis de Paula Church, Havana. 13c, St. Francis Convent, Havana. 30c, Castle del Morro, Santiago de Cuba.

1967, Nov. 7 — Wmk. 376
Sizes: 26x47mm (1c), 41x29mm (3c, 4c), 38½x31mm (13c)

1297	A356	1c multi	.20	.20
1298	A356	2c multi	.20	.20
1299	A356	3c multi	.65	.20
1300	A356	4c multi	.65	.20
1301	A356	13c multi	3.25	.50
1302	A356	30c multi	5.00	1.00
		Nos. 1297-1302 (6)	9.95	2.30

Christmas Type of 1961
Birds.

1967, Dec. 20

1303	A248	1c Struthia camelus australis	1.75	.60
1304	A249	1c Chysolophus pictus	1.75	.60
1305	A249	1c Ciconia ciconia ciconia	1.75	.60
1306	A249	1c Balearica pavonina	1.75	.60
1307	A249	1c Dromiceius novaehollandiae	1.75	.60
a.		Block of 5 + label, Nos. 1303-1307	10.00	3.25
1308	A248	3c Anodorhynchus hyacinthus	2.40	1.00
1309	A249	3c Psittacus erithacus	2.40	1.00
1310	A249	3c Domicella garrula	2.40	1.00
1311	A249	3c Ramphastos sulfuratus	2.40	1.00
1312	A249	3c Kakatoe galerita galerita	2.40	1.00
a.		Block of 5 + label, Nos. 1308-1312	14.00	5.50
1313	A248	13c Phoenicopterus ruber	4.50	1.75
1314	A249	13c Pelecanus erythrorhynchos	4.50	1.75
1315	A249	13c Alopochen aegyptiacus	4.50	1.75
1316	A249	13c Dendronessa galericulata	4.50	1.75
1317	A249	13c Chenopsis atrata	4.50	1.75
a.		Block of 5 + label, Nos. 1313-1317	25.00	9.00
		Nos. 1303-1317 (15)	43.25	16.75

Christmas 1967. See note after No. 700.

Ernesto "Che" Guevara (1928-1967),
Revolution Leader — A356a

1968, Jan. 3

1318	A356a	13c blk, dark red & buff	2.50	.55

Cultural Congress, Havana — A357

Abstract designs: No. 1319, Independence fostering culture. No. 1320, Integral formation of man. No. 1321, Responsibility of intellectuals. No. 1322, Relationship between culture and the mass media. No. 1323, The arts versus science and technology.

1968, Jan. 4

1319	A357	3c multi, vert.	.20	.20
1320	A357	3c multi, vert.	.20	.20
1321	A357	13c multi, vert.	1.50	.20
1322	A357	13c multi, vert.	1.75	.20
1323	A357	30c multi	2.40	.25
		Nos. 1319-1323 (5)	6.05	1.05

Canaries and
Breeding
Cycles
A358

1968, Apr. 13

1324	A358	1c F.C.C. 4016	.20	.20
1325	A358	2c A.C.C. 774	.20	.20
1326	A358	3c A.C.C. 122	.40	.20
1327	A358	4c F.C.C. 4477	.40	.25
1328	A358	5c A.C.C. 117	.75	.20
1329	A358	13c A.N.R. 1175	4.00	.20
1330	A358	20c A.C.C. 777	5.50	.25
		Nos. 1324-1330 (7)	11.45	1.50

Stamp Day
A359

Paintings: 13c, The Village Postman, by J. Harris. 30c, The Philatelist, by G. Sciltian.

1968, Apr. 24 — Unwmk.

1331	A359	13c multi	2.00	.20
1332	A359	30c multi	3.00	.20

World Health Organization, 20th
Anniv. — A360

1968, May 10 — Wmk. 376

1333	A360	13c Nurse, mother, child	1.60	.20
1334	A360	30c Surgeons	2.10	.20
		Nos. 1333-1334 (2)	3.70	.40

Intl. Children's
Day — A361

1968, June 1

1335	A361	3c multi	1.25	.25

Seville Camaguey Flight, 35th
Anniv. — A362

1968, June 20

1336	A362	13c Plane Four Winds	2.25	.45
1337	A362	30c Capt. Barberan, Lt. Collar, pilots	2.75	.60

Natl. Food Production — A363

1968, June 29
1338	A363	1c Yellow tuna, can	.25	.20
1339	A363	2c Cow, dairy products	.25	.20
1340	A363	3c Rooster, eggs	.50	.20
1341	A363	13c Rum, sugar cane	3.00	.20
1342	A363	20c Crayfish, box	3.50	.30
		Nos. 1338-1342 (5)	7.50	1.10

Attack of Moncada Barracks, 15th Anniv. A364

1968, July 26
Size: 43x29mm (13c)
1343	A364	3c Siboney farmhouse	.20	.20
1344	A364	13c Assault route, Santiago de Cuba	1.75	.20
1345	A364	30c Students, school	3.00	.20
		Nos. 1343-1345 (3)	4.95	.60

Committee for the Defense of the Revolution, 8th Anniv. — A365

1968, Sept. 28
1346	A365	3c multi	2.00	.20

Guerilla Day A366

Che Guevara and: 1c, Rifleman and "En Cualquier Lugar..." 3c, Machine gunners and "Crear tres muchos Viet Nam." 9c, Silhouette of battalion and "Este Tipo De Lucha..." 10c, Guerillas cheering and "Hoy aquilatamos..." 13c, Map of Caribbean, So. America and "Hasta La Victoria Siempre."

1968, Oct. 8
1347	A366	1c gold, brt blue grn & blk	.20	.20
1348	A366	3c gold, org brn blk	.20	.20
1349	A366	9c multi	.60	.20
1350	A366	10c gold, lt olive grn & blk	1.40	.20
1351	A366	13c gold, red org & blk	2.50	.70
		Nos. 1347-1351 (5)	4.90	1.50

Cuban War of Independence, Cent. — A367

Independence fighters and scenes.

1968, Oct. 10   **Unwmk.**
1352	A367	1c C.M. de Cespedes, broken wheel	.20	.20
1353	A367	1c E. Betances, horsemen, flag	.20	.20
1354	A367	1c I. Agramonte, Clavellinas Monument	.20	.20
1355	A367	1c A. Maceo, Baragua Protest	.20	.20
1356	A367	1c J. Marti, horsemen	.20	.20
a.		Strip of 5, Nos. 1352-1356	1.00	1.00
1357	A367	3c M. Gomez, The Invasion	.25	.20
1358	A367	3c J.A. Mella, declaration	.25	.20
1359	A367	3c A. Guiteras, El Morrillo monument	.25	.20
1360	A367	3c A. Santamaria, attack on Moncada Barracks	.25	.20
1361	A367	3c F. Paiz memorial	.25	.20
a.		Strip of 5, Nos. 1357-1361	1.75	1.00
1362	A367	9c J. Echeverria, student protest	1.25	.20
1363	A367	13c C. Cienfuegos, insurrection	3.00	.70
1364	A367	30c Che Guevara, 1st Declaration of Havana	3.50	1.10
		Nos. 1352-1364 (13)	10.00	4.00

Souvenir Sheet

The Burning of Bayamo, by J.E. Hernandez Giro — A368

1968, Oct. 18   *Imperf.*
1365	A368	50c multi	9.00	4.00

Natl. Philatelic Exhibition, independence cent. Stamp in No. 1365 has simulated perforations.

19th Summer Olympics, Mexico City, Oct. 12-27 — A369

1968, Oct. 21   *Perf. 12½*
1366	A369	1c Parade of athletes	.20	.20
1367	A369	2c Women's basketball, vert.	.20	.20
1368	A369	3c Hammer throw, vert.	.20	.20
1369	A369	4c Boxing	.20	.20
1370	A369	5c Water polo	.45	.20
1371	A369	13c Pistol shooting	3.00	.25
		Nos. 1366-1371 (6)	4.25	1.25

Size: 32x50mm
1372	A369	30c Mexican flag, calendar stone	4.50	.40

Souvenir Sheet
Imperf
1373	A369	50c Running	15.00	4.00

Stamp in #173 has simulated perforations.

Civilian Activities of the Armed Forces A370

1968, Dec. 2   **Wmk. 376**   *Perf. 12½*
1374	A370	3c Crop dusting	.20	.20
1375	A370	9c Che Guevara's Brigade	.60	.20
1376	A370	10c Road building	1.00	.20
1377	A370	13c Plowing, harvesting	2.10	.70
		Nos. 1374-1377 (4)	3.90	1.30

San Alejandro School of Painting, Sesquicentennial — A371

Paintings: 1c, Manrique de Lara's Family, by Jean Baptiste Vermay, vert. 2c, Seascape, by Leopoldo Romanach. 3c, Wild Cane, by Antonio Rodriguez, vert. 4c, Self-portrait, by Miguel Melero, vert. 5c, The Lottery List, by Jose Joaquin Tejada. 13c, Portrait of Nina, by Armando B. Menocal, vert. 30c, Landscape, by Esteban B. Chartrand. 50c, Siesta, by Guillermo Collazo.

1968, Dec. 30   **Unwmk.**
Sizes: 38x48mm (1c, 3c), 39x50mm (4c, 13c), 53x36mm (30c)
1378	A371	1c multi	.20	.20
1379	A371	2c multi	.20	.20
1380	A371	3c multi	.30	.20
1381	A371	4c multi	.30	.20
1382	A371	5c multi	1.40	.20
1383	A371	13c multi	4.00	.25
1384	A371	30c multi	6.25	.40
		Nos. 1378-1384 (7)	12.65	1.65

Souvenir Sheet
Imperf
1385	A371	50c multi	9.00	3.50

No. 1385 contains one 52x41½mm stamp that has simulated perforations.

10th Anniv. of the Revolution A372

1969, Jan. 3   **Wmk. 376**   *Perf. 12½*
1386	A372	13c multi	2.00	.60

Villaclarenos Rebellion, Cent. — A373

1969, Feb. 6
1387	A373	3c Gutierrez and Sanchez	1.00	.25

Women's Day — A374

Design: Mariana Grajales, rose and statue.

1969, Mar. 8
1388	A374	3c multi	1.25	.20

Cuban Pioneers and Young Communists Unions — A375

1969, Apr. 4
1389	A375	3c Pioneers	.40	.20
1390	A375	13c Young Communists	2.25	.80

Guaimaro Assembly, Cent. — A376

1969, Apr. 10
1391	A376	3c dark brn	1.00	.20

The Postman, by Jean C. Cazin A377

Paintings: 30c, Portrait of a Young Man, by George Romney.

1969, Apr. 24   **Unwmk.**
1392	A377	13c multi	2.50	.20

Size: 35½x43½mm
1393	A377	30c multi	4.00	.20

Stamp Day.

Agrarian Reform, 10th Anniv. A378

1969, May 17   **Wmk. 376**
1394	A378	13c multi	2.25	.70

Marine Life A379

1969, May 20 — Unwmk.

1395	A379	1c Petrochirus bahamensis	.20	.20
1396	A379	2c Stenopus his- pidus	.40	.20
1397	A379	3c Panulirus argus	.40	.20
1398	A379	4c Callinectes sapidus	.50	.20
1399	A379	5c Gecarcinus ruricola	.50	.20
1400	A379	13c Macrobrachium carcinus	3.50	.45
1401	A379	30c Carpilius coralinus	5.25	.80
		Nos. 1395-1401 (7)	10.75	2.25

Intl. Labor Organization, 50th Anniv. — A380

1969, June 6 — Wmk. 376

1402	A380	3c shown	.45	.20
1403	A380	13c Blacksmith break- ing chains	2.25	.70

Paintings in the Natl. Museum — A381

Designs: 1c, Flowers, by Raul Milian, vert. 2c, Annunciation, by Antonia Eiriz. 3c, Factory, by Marcelo Pogolotti, vert. 4c, Territorial Waters, by Luis Martinez Pedro, vert. 5c, Miss Sarah Gale, by John Hoppner, vert. 13c, Two Women Wearing Mantilla, by Ignacio Zuloaga. 30c, Virgin and Child, by Francisco de Zurburan.

1969, June 15 — Unwmk.

1404	A381	1c 39x59mm	.20	.20
1405	A381	2c	.20	.20
1406	A381	3c 39½x49mm	1.10	.20
1407	A381	4c 39½x43mm	.30	.20
1408	A381	5c 39½x45½mm	.30	.20
1409	A381	13c 38x41½mm	2.10	.70
1410	A381	30c 39x45mm	3.25	.90
		Nos. 1404-1410 (7)	7.45	2.60

Broadcasting Institute — A382

1969, July 5 — Wmk. 376

1411	A382	3c shown	.40	.25
1412	A382	13c Hemispheres, tower	2.10	.80
1413	A382	1p Waves on graph	5.00	1.75
		Nos. 1411-1413 (3)	7.50	2.80

Fish A383

1969, July 20 — Unwmk.

1414	A383	1c Apogon macu- latus	.20	.20
1415	A383	2c Bodianus rufus	.20	.20
1416	A383	3c Microspathodon chrysurus	.40	.20
1417	A383	4c Gramma loreto	.40	.20
1418	A383	5c Chromis marginatus	.60	.20
1419	A383	13c Myripristis jaco- bus	3.75	.25
1420	A383	30c Nomeus gro- novii, vert.	5.25	.40
		Nos. 1414-1420 (7)	10.80	1.65

Natl. Film Industry, 10th Anniv. — A384

1969, Aug. 5 — Wmk. 376

1421	A384	1c Poster	.20	.20
1422	A384	3c Documentaries	.20	.20
1423	A384	13c Cartoons	3.00	.20
1424	A384	30c Entertainers	3.50	.20
		Nos. 1421-1424 (4)	6.90	.80

Napoleon in Milan, by Andrea Appiani — A385

Paintings in the Napoleon Museum, Havana: 2c, Hortensia de Beauharnais, by Francois Gerard. 3c, Napoleon as First Con- sul, by J.B. Regnault. 4c, Elisa Bonaparte, by Robert Lefevre. 5c, Napoleon Planning Coro- nation Ceremony, by J.G. Vibert, horiz. 13c, Napoleon as Cuirassier Corporal, by Jean Meissonier. 30c, Napoleon Bonaparte, by LeFevre.

1969, Aug. 20 — Unwmk.

1425	A385	1c	.20	.20
1426	A385	2c 41½x55mm	.25	.20
1427	A385	3c 45½x56mm	.25	.20
1428	A385	4c 43x62½mm	.45	.20
1429	A385	5c 63x47½mm	.70	.20
1430	A385	13c 43x62½mm	3.25	.40
1431	A385	30c 45x59½mm	4.25	.55
		Nos. 1425-1431 (7)	9.35	1.95

See Nos. 2448-2453.

Cuba's Victory at the 17th World Amateur Baseball Championships, Santo Domingo — A386

1969, Sept. 11

1432	A386	13c multi	2.75	.20

No. 1432 printed se-tenant with inscribed label listing finalists.

Alexander von Humboldt (1769-1859), German Naturalist — A387

1969, Sept. 14

1433	A387	3c Surinam eel	.20	.20
1434	A387	13c Night ape	2.50	.25
1435	A387	30c Condors	4.00	.25
		Nos. 1433-1435 (3)	6.70	.70

World Fencing Championships, Havana — A388

Designs: 1c, Ancient Egyptians in combat. 2c, Roman gladiators. 2c, Viking and Norman. 4c, Medieval tournament. 5c, French muske- teers. 13c, Japanese samurai. 30c, Mounted Cubans, War of Independence. 50c, Modern fencers.

1969, Oct. 2

1436	A388	1c multi	.20	.20
1437	A388	2c multi	.20	.20
1438	A388	3c multi	.20	.20
1439	A388	4c multi	.40	.20
1440	A388	5c multi	.65	.20
1441	A388	13c multi	3.00	.30
1442	A388	30c multi	4.75	.50
		Nos. 1436-1442 (7)	9.40	1.80

Souvenir Sheet
Imperf

1443	A388	50c multi	12.00	12.00

Stamp in No. 1443 has simulated perforations.

Natl. Revolutionary Militia, 10th Anniv. — A389

1969, Oct. 26 — Wmk. 376

1444	A389	3c multi	1.25	.20

Disappearance of Maj. Camilo Cienfuegos, 10th Anniv. — A390

1969, Oct. 28

1445	A390	13c multi	2.50	.20

Agriculture — A391

1969, Nov. 2 — Unwmk.

1446	A391	1c Strawberries, grapes	.25	.20
1447	A391	1c Onions, aspara- gus	.25	.20
1448	A391	1c Rice	.25	.20
1449	A391	1c Banana	.25	.20
a.		Strip of 4, #1446-1449	1.00	.80
1450	A391	3c Pineapple, vert.	.50	.50
1451	A391	3c Tobacco, vert.	.50	.50
1452	A391	3c Citrus fruits, vert.	.50	.50
1453	A391	3c Coffee, vert.	.50	.50
1454	A391	3c Rabbits, vert.	.50	.50
a.		Strip of 5, #1450-1454	2.75	2.50
1455	A391	10c Pigs, vert.	.50	.20
1456	A391	13c Sugar cane	2.75	.50
1457	A391	30c Bull	4.00	.65
		Nos. 1446-1457 (12)	10.75	4.65

Sporting Events — A392

1969, Nov. 15

1458	A392	1c 2nd Natl. Games	.25	.20
1459	A392	2c 11th Anniv. Games	.25	.20
1460	A392	3c Barrientos Com- memorative, vert.	.25	.20
1461	A392	10c 2nd Olympic Tri- als, vert.	.40	.20
1462	A392	13c 6th Socialist Bicy- cle Race, vert.	2.75	.20
1463	A392	30c 6th Capablanca Memorial Chess Championships, vert.	4.00	.30
		Nos. 1458-1463 (6)	7.90	1.30

Christmas Type of 1961

Flowering plants.

1969, Dec. 1

1464	A248	1c Plumbago capensis	.40	.20
1465	A249	1c Petrea volubilis	.40	.20
1466	A249	1c Clitoria ternatea	.40	.20
1467	A249	1c Duranta repens	.40	.20
1468	A249	1c Ruellia tuberosa	.40	.20
a.		Block of 5 + label, Nos. 1464- 1468	3.00	1.00
1469	A249	3c Turnera ulmifolia	1.00	.20
1470	A249	3c Thevetia peruvi- ana	1.00	.20
1471	A249	3c Hibiscus elatus	1.00	.20
1472	A249	3c Allamanda cathartica	1.00	.20
1473	A249	3c Cosmos sulphureus	1.00	.20
a.		Block of 5 + label, Nos. 1469- 1473	6.00	1.00
1474	A248	13c Delonix regia	2.25	.50
1475	A249	13c Nerium oleander	2.25	.50
1476	A249	13c Cordia sebestena	2.25	.50
1477	A249	13c Lochnera rosea	2.25	.50
1478	A249	13c Jatropha in- tegerrima	2.25	.50
a.		Block of 5 + label, Nos. 1474- 1478	11.00	2.50
		Nos. 1464-1478 (15)	18.25	4.50

Christmas 1969. See note after No. 700.

Zapata Swamp Fauna — A393

1969, Dec. 15

1479	A393	1c Trelanorhynus variabilis	.20	.20
1480	A393	2c Hyla insulsa	.20	.20
1481	A393	3c Atractosteus tristoechus	.20	.20
1482	A393	4c Capromys nana	.20	.20
1483	A393	5c Crocodylus rhombifer	.20	.20
1484	A393	13c Amazona leucocephala	4.50	.50
1485	A393	30c Agelaius phoeniceus as- similis	5.00	1.00
		Nos. 1479-1485 (7)	10.50	2.50

Nos. 1482, 1484-1485 vert.

Tourism
A394

1970, Jan. 25   **Wmk. 376**
1486	A394	1c Jibacoa Beach	.20	.20
1487	A394	3c Trinidad City	.20	.20
1488	A394	13c Santiago de Cuba	1.90	.80
1489	A394	30c Vinales Valley	2.75	1.00
		Nos. 1486-1489 (4)	5.05	2.20

Medicinal
Plants — A395

1970, Feb. 10   **Unwmk.**
1490	A395	1c Guarea guara	.20	.20
1491	A395	3c Ocimum sanctum	.20	.20
1492	A395	10c Canella winterana	.45	.20
1493	A395	13c Bidens pilosa	2.25	.60
1494	A395	30c Turnera ulmifolia	2.75	.75
1495	A395	50c Picramnia pentandra	4.00	.90
		Nos. 1490-1495 (6)	9.85	2.85

11th Central American and Caribbean
Games, Panama, Feb. 28-Mar.
14 — A396

1970, Feb. 28   **Wmk. 376**
1496	A396	1c Weight lifting	.20	.20
1497	A396	3c Boxing	.20	.20
1498	A396	10c Gymnastics	.20	.20
1499	A396	13c Running	2.40	.65
1500	A396	30c Fencing	3.50	.90
		Nos. 1496-1500 (5)	6.50	2.15

Souvenir Sheet
Imperf
1501	A396	50c Baseball	12.00	12.00

No. 1501 contains one 50x37mm stamp that
has simulated perforations.

EXPO '70, Osaka, Japan, Mar. 15-
Sept. 13 — A397

1970, Mar. 15
1502	A397	1c Enjoying life	.20	.20
1503	A397	2c Improving on nature, vert.	.40	.20
1504	A397	3c Better living standard	.40	.20
1505	A397	13c Intl. cooperation, vert.	2.75	.55
1506	A397	30c Cuban pavilion	4.00	.80
		Nos. 1502-1506 (5)	7.75	1.95

Speleological Soc., 30th
Anniv. — A398

Petroglyphs in Cuban caves: 1c, Ambrosio
Cave, Varadero Matanzas. 2c, Cave No. 1,
Punta del Este, Isle of Pines. 3c, Pichardo
Cave, Cubitas Camaguey Mountains. 4c,
Ambrosio Cave, diff. 5c, Cave No. 1, diff. 13c,
Garcia Ribiou Cave, Havana. 30c, Cave No. 2,
Punta del Este.

1970, Mar. 28   **Unwmk.**
Sizes: 29x45mm (1c, 3c, 4c, 13c)
1507	A398	1c multi	.20	.20
1508	A398	2c shown	.20	.20
1509	A398	3c multi	.20	.20
1510	A398	4c multi	.20	.20
1511	A398	5c multi	.20	.20
1512	A398	13c multi	2.25	.30
1513	A398	30c multi	4.75	.35
		Nos. 1507-1513 (7)	8.00	1.65

Aviation Pioneers — A399

1970, Apr. 10
1514	A399	3c Jose D. Blino	1.00	.20
1515	A399	13c Adolfo Teodore	3.50	.70

Lenin Birth Centenary — A400

Paintings and quotes: 1c, Lenin in Kazan, by
O. Vishniakov. 2c, Young Lenin, by V. Prager.
3c, Second Socialist Party Congress, by Y.
Vinagradov. 4c, First Manifesto, by F.
Golubkov. 5c, First Day of Soviet Power, by N.
Babasiuk. 13c, Lenin in Smolny, by M.
Sokolov. 30c, Autumn in Gorky, by A.
Varlamov. 50c, Lenin at Gorky, by N.
Bashkakov.

1970, Apr. 22
Sizes: 67½x46mm (1c, 4c, 5c)
1516	A400	1c multi	.20	.20
1517	A400	2c shown	.20	.20
1518	A400	3c multi	.20	.20
1519	A400	4c multi	.20	.20
1520	A400	5c multi	.20	.20
1521	A400	13c multi	2.75	.35
1522	A400	30c multi	3.25	.45
		Nos. 1516-1522 (7)	7.00	1.80

Souvenir Sheet
Imperf
1523	A400	50c multi	13.00	13.00

No. 1523 contains one 48x46mm stamp that
has simulated perforations.

Stamp
Day — A401

1970, Apr. 24
1524	A401	13c The Letter, by J. Arche	3.00	.25

Size: 30x44mm
1525	A401	30c Portrait of A Cadet, Anonymous	3.75	.30

Da Vinci's Anatomical Drawing, Earth,
Moon — A402

1970, May 17   **Wmk. 376**
1526	A402	30c multi	3.50	.20

World Telecommunications Day.

Ho Chi Minh (1890-1969), President of
North Viet Nam — A403

1970, May 19   **Unwmk.**
1527	A403	1c Vietnamese fisherman	.20	.20

Size: 32x44mm
1528	A403	3c Two women	.50	.20
1529	A403	3c Plowing field	.50	.20

Size: 33x45mm
1530	A403	3c Teacher, students in air-raid shelter	.50	.20
1531	A403	3c Nine women in paddy	.70	.20

Size: 34x41½mm
1532	A403	3c Camouflaged machine shop	.70	.20

Size: 34x39mm
1533	A403	13c shown	3.25	.70

Cuban
Cigar
Industry
A404

1970, July 5
1534	A404	3c Plantation, Eden cigar band	.20	.20
1535	A404	13c Factory, El Mambi band	2.25	.70
1536	A404	30c Packing cigars, Lopez Hermanos band	3.25	1.00
		Nos. 1534-1536 (3)	5.70	1.90

Projected Sugar Production: Over 10
Million Tons — A405

1970, July 26
1537	A405	1c Cane-crushing	.20	.20
1538	A405	2c Sowing and crop dusting	.20	.20

1539	A405	3c Cutting sugar cane	.25	.20
1540	A405	10c Transporting cane	5.00	.45
1541	A405	13c Modern cutting machine	1.50	.20
1542	A405	30c Intl. Brigade, cane cutters, vert.	2.25	.70
1543	A405	1p Sugar warehouse	4.00	2.00
		Nos. 1537-1543 (7)	13.40	4.00

Pedro Figueredo (d. 1870),
Composer — A406

Versions of the Natl. Anthem.

1970, Aug. 17
1544	A406	3c 1868 Version	.30	.20
1545	A406	20c 1898 Version	2.75	.60

Women's Federation, 10th
Anniv. — A407

1970, Aug. 23
1546	A407	3c multi	1.00	.50

Militia, by Servando C.
Moreno — A408

Paintings in the Natl. Museum: 2c,
Washerwomen, by Aristides Fernandez. 3c,
Puerta del Sol, Madrid, by L. Paret Y Alcazar.
4c, Fishermen's Wives, by Joaquin Sorolla.
5c, Portrait of a Woman, by Thomas de
Keyser. 13c, Mrs. Edward Foster, by Sir
Thomas Lawrence. 30c, Tropical Gypsy, by
Victor M. Garcia.

1970, Aug. 31
1547	A408	1c shown	.20	.20

Size: 45x41mm
1548	A408	2c multi	.20	.20
1549	A408	3c multi	.20	.20

Size: 40x41mm
1550	A408	4c multi	.20	.20

Size: 38x45½mm
1551	A408	5c multi	.20	.20
1552	A408	13c multi	2.50	.50
1553	A408	30c multi	4.00	.80
		Nos. 1551-1553 (3)	6.70	1.50

See #1640-1646, 1669-1675, 1773-1779.

Havana Declaration, 10th
Anniv. — A409

1970, Sept. 2
1554	A409	3c Jose Marti Square	.75	.20

Committee for the Defense of the Revolution, 10th Anniv. A410

1970, Sept. 28
1555 A410 3c multi   .40 .20

39th Sugar Technician's Assoc. (ATAC) Conference — A411

1970, Oct. 11
1556 A411 30c multi   3.25 .70

Wildlife — A412

1970, Oct. 20
1557	A412	1c Numida meleagris galeata	.65	.20
1558	A412	2c Dendrocygna arborea	.75	.20
1559	A412	3c Phasianus colchicus torquatus	.90	.20
1560	A412	4c Zenaida macroura macroura	1.00	.20
1561	A412	5c Colinus virginianus cubanensis	1.10	.25
1562	A412	13c Sus scrofa	1.90	1.00
1563	A412	30c Odocoileus virginianus	3.00	1.50
		Nos. 1557-1563 (7)	9.30	3.55

Black-magic Feast, by M. Puente — A413

Afro-Cuban folk paintings: 3c, Hat Dance, by V.P. Landaluze. 10c, Los Hoyos Conga Dance, by Domingo Ravenet. 13c, Climax of the Rumba, by Eduardo Abela.

1970, Nov. 5
Sizes: 36x48½mm (3c, 13c), 44½x44mm (10c)
1564	A413	1c shown	.20	.20
1565	A413	3c multi	.35	.20
1566	A413	10c multi	.90	.45
1567	A413	13c multi	2.50	.70
		Nos. 1564-1567 (4)	3.95	1.55

Road Safety Week A414

1970, Nov. 15
1568	A414	3c Zebra, road signs	1.10	.20
1569	A414	9c Prudence the Bear	1.60	.20

Intl. Education Year — A415

1970, Nov. 20
1570	A415	13c Abacus, "a"	2.50	.25
1571	A415	30c Cow, microscope	3.25	.70

Christmas Type of 1961

Birds.

1970, Dec. 1
1572	A248	1c Dives atroviolaceus	.80	.20
1573	A249	1c Glaucidium siju siju	.80	.20
1574	A249	1c Todus multicolor	.80	.20
1575	A249	1c Xiphidiopicus percussus percussus	.80	.20
1576	A249	1c Ferminia cerverai	.80	.20
a.		Block of 5 + label, Nos. 1572-1576	5.00	1.00
1577	A248	3c Teretistris fornsi	1.75	.35
1578	A249	3c Myadestes elisabeth elisabeth	1.75	.35
1579	A249	3c Polioptila lembeyei	1.75	.35
1580	A249	3c Vireo gundlachii gundlachii	1.75	.35
1581	A249	3c Teretistris fernandinae	1.75	.35
a.		Block of 5 + label, Nos. 1577-1581	10.00	2.00
1582	A248	13c Torreornis inexpectata inexpectata	2.50	.90
1583	A249	13c Chondrohierax wilsonii	2.50	.90
1584	A249	13c Accipiter gundlachi	2.50	.90
1585	A249	13c Starnoenas cyanocephala	2.50	.90
1586	A249	13c Aratinga euops	2.50	.90
a.		Block of 5 + label, Nos. 1582-1586	15.00	5.00
		Nos. 1572-1586 (15)	25.25	7.25

Christmas 1970. See note after No. 700.

Camilo Cienfuegos Military Academy — A416

1970, Dec. 2
1587 A416 3c multi   1.25 .25

7th Congress of the Intl. Organization of Journalists — A417

1971, Jan. 4
1588 A417 13c multi   2.25 .50

World Meteorology Day — A418

1971, Feb. 16
Size: 39½x35½mm (3c)
1589	A418	1c Class, weather chart, computer, vert.	.20	.20
1590	A418	3c Weather map	.20	.20
1591	A418	8c Equipment, vert.	1.00	.25
1592	A418	30c shown	4.75	1.25
		Nos. 1589-1592 (4)	6.15	1.90

6th Pan American Games, Cali, Colombia — A419

1971, Feb. 20
1593	A419	1c Emblem, vert.	.20	.20
1594	A419	2c Women's running, vert.	.20	.20
1595	A419	3c Rifle shooting	.20	.20
1596	A419	4c Gymnastics, vert.	.20	.20
1597	A419	5c Boxing, vert.	.20	.20
1598	A419	13c Water polo	2.40	.30
1599	A419	30c Baseball	3.00	.50
		Nos. 1593-1599 (7)	6.40	1.80

Porcelain and Mosaics in the Metropolitan Museum, Havana — A420

Designs: 1c, Parisian vase, 19th cent. 3c, Mexican bowl, 17th cent. 10c, Parisian vase, diff. 13c, Colosseum, Italian mosaic, 19th cent. 20c, Mexican bowl, 17th cent. 30c, St. Peter's Square, Italian mosaic, 19th cent.

1971, Mar. 11
Sizes: 34½x53mm (1c, 10c), 46x53mm (3c), 42x48mm (20c)
1600	A420	1c multi	.20	.20
1601	A420	3c multi	.20	.20
1602	A420	10c multi	.40	.20
1603	A420	13c shown	2.25	.40
1604	A420	20c multi	2.25	.40
1605	A420	30c multi	2.75	.50
		Nos. 1600-1605 (6)	8.05	1.70

See Nos. 1699-1705.

Natl. Child Centers, 10th Anniv. — A421

1971, Apr. 10
1606 A421 3c multi   .75 .20

Manned Space Flight 10th Anniv. — A422

Cosmonauts in training.

1971, Apr. 12
1607	A422	1c multi	.20	.20
1608	A422	2c multi, diff.	.20	.20
1609	A422	3c multi, diff.	.20	.20
1610	A422	4c multi, diff.	.20	.20
1611	A422	5c multi, diff.	.20	.20
1612	A422	13c multi, diff.	2.25	.30
1613	A422	30c multi, diff.	3.25	.60
		Nos. 1607-1613 (7)	6.50	1.90

Souvenir Sheet
Imperf
1614 A422 50c multi   10.00 10.00
Stamp in #1614 has simulated perf.

Bay of Pigs Invasion, 10th Anniv. A423

1971, Apr. 17
1615 A423 13c multi   1.75 .60

Stamp Day — A424

Packets: 13c, Jeune Richard attacking the Windsor Castle, 1807. 30c, Orinoco.

1971, Apr. 24
1616	A424	13c multi	2.40	.25
1617	A424	30c multi	3.50	.35

Cuban Intl. Broadcast Service, 10th Anniv. — A425

1971, May 1   **Wmk. 376**
1618	A425	3c multi	.40	.20
1619	A425	50c multi	4.50	.90

Orchids A426

1971, May 15
1620	A426	1c Cattleya skinnerii	.20	.20
1621	A426	2c Vanda hibrida	.20	.20
1622	A426	3c Cypripedium col-		
		lossum	.20	.20
1623	A426	4c Cypripedium		
		gloucophyllum	.20	.20
1624	A426	5c Vanda tricolor	.25	.20
1625	A426	13c Cypripedium		
		mowgh	2.40	.45
1626	A426	30c Cypripedium so-		
		lum	4.75	.85
		Nos. 1620-1626 (7)	8.20	2.30

See Nos. 1677-1683 and 1780-1786.

Enrique Loynaz del Castillo (b. 1861),
Composer — A427

1971, June 5 **Wmk. 376**
1627	A427	3c Portrait, Invasion Hymn	.90	.25

Bee Keeping — A428

1971, June 20 **Unwmk.**
1628	A428	1c Egg, larvae, pupa	.20	.20
1629	A428	3c Worker	.20	.20
1630	A428	9c Drone	.45	.20
1631	A428	13c Defense of hive	2.25	.25
1632	A428	30c Queen	3.50	.60
		Nos. 1628-1632 (5)	6.60	1.45

Children's Drawings — A429

1971, Aug. 30
Size: 45x39mm
1633	A429	1c Sailboat	.20	.20
1634	A429	3c The Little Train	.85	.20

**Sizes: 45½x35½mm (9c, 13c),
47x37½mm (10c)**
1635	A429	9c Sugar Cane Cutter	.20	.20
1636	A429	10c Return of the Fishermen	.40	.20
1637	A429	13c The Zoo	1.60	.25

Size: 47x42mm
1638	A429	20c House and Garden	2.50	.40

Size: 31½x50mm
1639	A429	30c Landscape	2.75	.65

Art Type of 1970

Paintings in the Natl. Museum: 1c, St. Catherine of Alexandria, by F. Zurburan. 2c, The Cart, by Federico Americo. 3c, St. Christopher and Child, by J. Bassano. 4c, Little Devil, by Rene Portocarrero. 5c, Portrait of a Woman, by Nicolas Maes. 13c, Phoenix, by Raul Martinez. 30c, Sir William Pitt, by Thomas Gainsborough.

1971, Sept. 20
1640	A408	1c 31x55mm	.20	.20
1641	A408	2c 48x37mm	.20	.20
1642	A408	3c 31x55mm	.20	.20
1643	A408	4c 37x48mm	.25	.20
1644	A408	5c 37x48mm	.40	.20
1645	A408	13c 39x48½mm	2.25	.45
1646	A408	30c 39x48½mm	3.25	.75
		Nos. 1640-1646 (7)	6.75	2.20

Sport Fishing — A431

1971, Oct. 30
1647	A431	1c Albula vulpes	.20	.20
1648	A431	2c Seriola species	.20	.20
1649	A431	3c Micropterus salmoides	.20	.20
1650	A431	4c Coryphaena hippurus	.25	.20
1651	A431	5c Megalops atlantica	.30	.20
1652	A431	13c Acanthocybium solandri	2.00	.40
1653	A431	30c Makaira ampla	3.25	.70
		Nos. 1647-1653 (7)	6.40	2.10

19th World Amateur Baseball
Championships — A432

1971, Nov. 22 **Wmk. 376**
1654	A432	3c shown	.25	.25
1655	A432	1p Globe as baseball	6.25	1.00

Execution
of Medical
Students,
Cent.
A433

Paintings: 3c, Dr. Fermin Valdez Dominguez, anonymous. 13c, Execution of the Medical Students, by M. Mesa. 30c, Capt. Federico Capdevila, anonymous.

1971, Nov. 27 **Unwmk.**
Size: 61½x46mm (13c)
1656	A433	3c multi	.35	.20
1657	A433	13c multi	1.90	.25
1658	A433	30c multi	3.00	.35
		Nos. 1656-1658 (3)	5.25	.80

Spindalis Zena Pretrei — A434

Birds: 1c, Falco sparverius sparverioides vigors. 2c, Glaucidium siju siju. 3c, Priotelus temnurus temnurus. 4c, Saurothera merlini merlini. 5c, Nesoceleus fernandinae. 30c, Mimocichla plumbea rubripes. 50c, Chlorostilbon ricordii ricordii and Archilochus colubris. Nos. 1659-1663 vert.

1971, Dec. 10
1659	A434	1c multi	.30	.20
1660	A434	2c multi	.30	.20
1661	A434	3c multi	.45	.20
1662	A434	4c multi	.50	.20
1663	A434	5c multi	.65	.20

1664	A434	13c shown	1.10	.20
1665	A434	30c multi	2.25	.40
		Nos. 1659-1665 (7)	5.55	1.60

Size: 55½x29mm
1666	A434	50c multi	4.25	.65

Death centenary of Ramon de la Sagra, naturalist.

Cuba's Victory at the World Amateur
Baseball Championships — A435

1971, Dec. 8 **Wmk. 376**
1667	A435	13c multi	2.00	.60

UNICEF,
25th Anniv.
A436

1971, Dec. 11
1668	A436	13c multi	2.50	.70

Art Type of 1970

Paintings in the Natl. Museum: 1c, Arrival of an Ambassador, by Vittore Carpaccio. 2c, Senora Malpica, by G. Collazo. 3c, La Chorrera Tower, by Esteban Chartrand. 4c, Creole Landscape, by Carlos Enriquez. 5c, Sir William Lemon, by George Romney. 13c, Landscape, by Henry Cleenewerk. 30c, Valencia Beach, by Joaquin Sorolla y Bastida.

1972, Jan. 25 **Unwmk.**
1669	A408	1c 50x33mm	.20	.20
1670	A408	2c 27½x52mm	.20	.20
1671	A408	3c 50x33mm	.20	.20
1672	A408	4c 35x43mm	.20	.20
1673	A408	5c 35x43mm	.20	.20
1674	A408	13c 43x33mm	2.00	.35
1675	A408	30c 43x33mm	3.50	.85
		Nos. 1669-1675 (7)	6.50	2.20

Academy of Sciences, 10th
Anniv. — A437

1972, Feb. 20 **Wmk. 376**
1676	A437	13c Capitol Type of 1929	2.00	.25

Orchid Type of 1971

1972, Feb. 25 **Unwmk.**
1677	A426	1c Brasso cattleya sindorossiana	.20	.20
1678	A426	2c Cypripedium doraeus	.20	.20
1679	A426	3c Cypripedium exul	.20	.20
1680	A426	4c Cypripedium rosy dawn	.20	.20
1681	A426	5c Cypripedium champolliom	.20	.20
1682	A426	13c Cypripedium bucolique	2.75	.65
1683	A426	30c Cypripedium sullanum	3.50	.80
		Nos. 1677-1683 (7)	7.25	2.45

Eduardo
Agramonte
(1849-1872),
Physicist
A438

1972, Mar. 8
1684	A438	3c Portrait by F. Martinez	.60	.20

World Health
Day — A439

1972, Apr. 7 **Wmk. 376**
1685	A439	13c multi	2.00	.20

Soviet Space Program — A440

1972, Apr. 12 **Unwmk.**
1686	A440	1c Sputnik 1	.20	.20
1687	A440	2c Vostok 1	.20	.20
1688	A440	3c Valentina Tereshkova	.20	.20
1689	A440	4c Alexei Leonov	.20	.20
1690	A440	5c Lunokhod 1, moon vehicle	.20	.20
1691	A440	13c Linking Soyuz capsules	2.10	.40
1692	A440	30c Victims of Soyuz 11 accident	2.50	.70
		Nos. 1686-1692 (7)	5.60	2.10

Stamp
Day — A441

Designs: 13c, Postmaster-Gen. Vicente Mora Pera, by Ramon Loy. 30c, Soldier's Letter, Cuba to Venezuela, 1897.

1972, Apr. 24
1693	A441	13c shown	1.75	.30

Size: 48x39mm
1694	A441	30c multi	2.75	.35

Labor
Day — A442

Jose Marti, Ho
Chi Minh — A443

3rd Conference Against War in Indo-
China, May 19 — A444

1972, May 1   **Wmk. 376**
1695 A442 3c multi   .90 .20

1972, May 19
1696 A443 3c shown   .40 .20
1697 A444 13c shown   1.60 .20
1698 A443 30c Roses, confer-
              ence emblem   2.00 .20
      Nos. 1696-1698 (3)   4.00 .60

Metropolitan Museum Type of 1971

Portraits: 1c, Salvador del Muro, by J. Del
Rio. 2c, Luis de las Casas, by Del Rio. 3c,
Cristopher Columbus, anonymous. 4c, Tomas
Gamba, by V. Escobar. 5c, Maria Galarraga,
by Escobar. 13c, Isabel II, by Federico
Madrazo. 30c, Carlos III, by Miguel Melero.

1972, May 25   **Unwmk.**
      Size: 34x43½mm
1699 A420 1c multi   .20 .20
1700 A420 2c multi   .20 .20
1701 A420 3c multi   .20 .20
1702 A420 4c multi   .40 .20
1703 A420 5c multi   .40 .20
      Size: 34x51½mm
1704 A420 13c multi   2.00 .40
1705 A420 30c multi   2.50 .70
      Nos. 1699-1705 (7)   5.90 2.10

Children's
Songs
Competition,
Natl. Library
A445

1972, June 5   **Wmk. 376**
1706 A445 3c multi   .80 .25

Thoroughbred Horses — A446

1972, June 30   **Unwmk.**
1707 A446 1c Tarpan   .20 .20
1708 A446 2c Kertag   .20 .20
1709 A446 3c Creole   .20 .20
1710 A446 4c Andalusian   .20 .20
1711 A446 5c Arabian   .20 .20
1712 A446 13c Quarter horse   3.00 .55
1713 A446 30c Pursang   3.50 .80
      Nos. 1707-1713 (7)   7.50 2.35

Frank Pais (d. 1957), Educator,
Revolutionary — A447

1972, July 26   **Wmk. 376**
1714 A447 13c blk & red   1.75 .50

1972 Summer Olympics, Munich, Aug.
26-Sept. 10 — A448

1972, Aug. 26   **Unwmk.**
1715 A448 1c Athlete, em-
              blems, vert.   .20 .20
1716 A448 2c "M," boxing   .20 .20
1717 A448 3c "U," weight lift-
              ing   .20 .20
1718 A448 4c "N," fencing   .20 .20
1719 A448 5c "I," rifle shoot-
              ing   .20 .20
1720 A448 13c "C," running   2.00 .35
1721 A448 30c "H," basketball 2.50 .65
      Nos. 1715-1721 (7)   5.50 2.00

      Souvenir Sheet
            Imperf
1722 A448 50c Gymnastics   6.00 1.90

Stamp in No. 1722 has simulated
perforations.

Intl. Hydrological Decade — A449

Landscapes: 1c, Tree Trunks, by Domingo
Ramos. 3c, Cyclone, by Tiburcio Lorenzo. 8c,
Vinales, by Ramos. 30c, Forest and Brook, by
Antonio R. Morey, vert.

1972, Sept. 20
1723 A449 1c multi   .20 .20
1724 A449 3c multi   .20 .20
1725 A449 8c multi   .80 .20
1726 A449 30c multi   2.50 .20
      Nos. 1723-1726 (4)   3.70 .80

Butterflies from the Gundlach
Collection — A450

1972, Sept. 25
1727 A450 1c Papilio thoas ovi-
              edo   .20 .20
1728 A450 2c Papilio devilliers .20 .20
1729 A450 3c Papilio polixenes
              polixenes   .20 .20
1730 A450 4c Papilio androgeus
              epidaurus   .20 .20
1731 A450 5c Papilio
              cayguanabus   .25 .20

1732 A450 13c Papilio an-
              draemon her-
              nandezi   2.75 .55
1733 A450 30c Papilio celadon 3.50 .70
      Nos. 1727-1733 (7)   7.30 2.25

A451

Miguel de Cervantes Saavedra (1547-
1616), Spanish Author — A452

Paintings by A. Fernandez: 3c, In La
Mancha, vert. 13c, Battle with Wine Skins.
30c, Don Quixote de La Mancha, vert. 50c,
Scene from Don Quixote, by Jose Moreno
Carbonero.

1972, Sept. 29
      Size: 34½x46mm (3c, 30c)
1734 A451 3c multi   .20 .20
1735 A451 13c shown   2.10 .30
1736 A451 30c multi   2.25 .35
      Nos. 1734-1736 (3)   4.55 .85

      Souvenir Sheet
      Perf. 12½ on 3 Sides
1737 A452 50c shown   5.00 1.25

Guerrilla Day, 5th Anniv. — A453

1972, Oct. 8
1738 A453 3c Ernesto "Che"
              Guevara   .20 .20
1739 A453 13c Tamara "Tania"
              Bunke   2.25 .50
1740 A453 30c Guido "Inti"
              Peredo   2.50 .60
      Nos. 1738-1740 (3)   4.95 1.30

Traditional
Musical
Instruments
A454

1972, Oct. 25
1741 A454 3c Abwe (rattles)   .20 .20
1742 A454 13c Bonko enchemiya
              (drum)   2.25 .30
1743 A454 30c Iya (drum)   2.50 .35
      Nos. 1741-1743 (3)   4.95 .85

MATEX '72, 3rd Natl. Philatelic
Exhibition, Matanzas — A455

1972, Nov. 18   **Wmk. 376**
1744 A455 13c No. 467   2.50 .35
1745 A455 30c No. C49   3.00 .40

Nos. 1744-1745 printed se-tenant with
insribed labels picturing Type A232, emblem
of the Cuban Philatelic Federation.

Historic
Ships
A456

1972, Nov. 30   **Unwmk.**
1746 A456 1c Viking long boat,
              6th-9th cent.   .20 .20
1747 A456 2c Caravel, 15th
              cent., vert.   .20 .20
1748 A456 3c Galleass, 16th
              cent.   .20 .20
1749 A456 4c Galleon, 17th
              cent., vert.   .30 .20
1750 A456 5c Clipper, 19th
              cent.   .35 .20
1751 A456 13c Steam packet,
              19th cent.   1.75 .75
      Nos. 1746-1751 (6)   3.00 1.75
      Size: 52½x29mm.
1752 A456 30c Atomic icebreaker
              Lenin   3.50 1.00

UNESCO Save Venice
Campaign — A457

1972, Dec. 8
1753 A457 3c Lion of St. Mark   .20 .20
1754 A457 13c Bridge of Sighs,
              vert.   1.75 .20
1755 A457 30c St. Mark's Cathe-
              dral   2.25 .35
      Nos. 1753-1755 (3)   4.20 .75

Cuba, World
Amateur
Baseball
Champion in
1972 — A458

Sport Events,
1972 — A459

1972, Dec. 15
1756 A458 3c Umpire   1.25 .30

1972, Dec. 22
1757 A459 1c shown   .20 .20
1758 A458 2c Pole vault   .20 .20
1759 A458 3c like No. 1756   .20 .20
1760 A458 4c Wrestling   .20 .20
1761 A458 5c Fencing   .20 .20
1762 A458 13c Boxing   1.75 .55
1763 A458 30c Marlin   2.50 .80
      Nos. 1757-1763 (7)   5.25 2.35

Barrientos Memorial Athletics Championships, 11th Amateur Baseball Championships,
Cerro Pelado Intl. Tournament, Central American and Caribbean Fencing Tournament,

Giraldo Cordova Tournament, Ernest Hemingway Natl. Fishing Contest.

No. 1759 inscribed "XI serie nacional de beisbol aficionado."

Medals Won by Cubans at the 1972 Summer Olympics, Munich A460

1c, Bronze, Women's 100-meter. 2c, Bronze, women's relay. 3c, Gold, 54kg boxing. 4c, Silver, 81kg boxing. 5c, Bronze, 51kg boxing. 13c, Gold, 87kg boxing. 30c, Gold, silver cup, heavyweight boxing. 50c, Bronze, basketball.

1973, Jan. 28

1764	A460	1c multi	.20	.20
1765	A460	2c multi	.20	.20
1766	A460	3c multi	.20	.20
1767	A460	4c multi	.20	.20
1768	A460	5c multi	.20	.20
1769	A460	13c multi	1.75	.60
1770	A460	30c multi	2.25	.90
		Nos. 1764-1770 (7)	5.00	2.50

Souvenir Sheet
Imperf

1771	A460	50c multi	6.00	1.25

Stamp in No. 1771 has simulated perforations.

A461

A462

Portrait by A.M. Esquivel.

1973, Feb. 10

1772	A461	13c multi	2.25	.30

Gertrudis Gomez de Avellaneda (1814-1873), poet.

Art Type of 1970

Paintings in the Natl. Museum: 1c, Bathers in the Lagoon, by C. Enriquez. 2c, Still-life, by W.C. Heda. 3c, Gallantry, by P. Landaluze. 4c, Return in the Late Afternoon, by C. Troyon. 5c, Elizabetta Mascagni, by F.X. Fabre. 13c, The Picador, by De Lucas Padilla, horiz. 30c, In the Garden, by Arburu Morell.

1973, Feb. 28
Sizes: 36x46mm, 46x36mm

1773	A408	1c multi	.20	.20
1774	A408	2c multi	.20	.20
1775	A408	3c multi	.20	.20
1776	A408	4c multi	.20	.20
1777	A408	5c multi	.20	.20
1778	A408	13c multi	1.60	.30
1779	A408	30c multi	2.25	.80
		Nos. 1773-1779 (7)	4.85	2.10

Orchid Type of 1971

1973, Mar. 26

1780	A426	1c Dendrobium hybrid	.20	.20
1781	A426	2c Cypripedium exul	.20	.20
1782	A426	3c Vanda miss. joaquin rose marie	.20	.20
1783	A426	4c Phalaenopsis schilleriana	.20	.20
1784	A426	5c Vanda gilbert tribulet	.40	.20
1785	A426	13c Dendrobium hybrid, diff.	3.00	.55

1786	A426	30c Arachnis catherine	3.50	.80
		Nos. 1780-1786 (7)	7.70	2.35

1973, Apr. 7   **Wmk. 376**

1787	A462	10c multi, *buff*	1.25	.25

World Health Day. World Health Organization, 25th anniv.

Anti-Polio Campaign — A463

1973, Apr. 9   **Unwmk.**

1788	A463	3c multi	.70	.20

Soviet Space Program — A464

1973, Apr. 12

1789	A464	1c Soyuz rocket launch, vert.	.20	.20
1790	A464	2c Luna 1, Moon	.20	.20
1791	A464	3c Luna 16 taking-off from Moon, vert.	.20	.20
1792	A464	4c Venus 7	.20	.20
1793	A464	5c Molnia 1, vert.	.20	.20
1794	A464	13c Mars 3	1.00	.55
1795	A464	30c Radar observation ship, Yuri Gagarin	3.00	.70
		Nos. 1789-1795 (7)	5.00	2.25

Stamp Day A465

Postmarks: 13c, Santiago de Cuba, 1760. 30c, Havana, 1760.

1973, Apr. 24

1796	A465	13c multi	1.90	.50
1797	A465	30c multi	2.10	.60
		See Nos. 1888-1891.		

Portrait by A. Espinosa A466

1973, May 11

1798	A466	13c multi	1.50	.25

Maj.-Gen. Ignacio Agramonte (1841-1873).

Copernicus Monument, Warsaw — A468

1973, May 25

1799	A467	3c shown	.20	.20
1800	A467	13c Copernicus, spacecraft	1.60	.20
1801	A467	30c Manuscript, Frombork Tower	3.00	.25
		Nos. 1799-1801 (3)	4.80	.65

Souvenir Sheet
Perf. 12½ on 3 Sides

1802	A468	50c shown	6.50	1.90

500th anniversary of the birth of Nicolaus Copernicus (1473-1543), Polish astronomer.

Improvement of School Education — A469

1973, June 12   **Wmk. 376**

1803	A469	13c multi	1.50	.20

Cattle — A470

1973, June 28   **Unwmk.**

1804	A470	1c Jersey	.20	.20
1805	A470	2c Charolaise	.20	.20
1806	A470	3c Creole	.20	.20
1807	A470	4c Swiss	.25	.20
1808	A470	5c Holstein	.25	.20
1809	A470	13c Santa Gertrudis	1.60	.40
1810	A470	30c Brahman	3.25	.75
		Nos. 1804-1810 (7)	5.95	2.15

A471

A472

1973, July 10   **Wmk. 376**

1811	A471	13c multi	1.50	.30

10th Communist Festival of Youths and Students, East Berlin.

1973, July 26   **Unwmk.**

1812	A472	3c Siboney Farm, Santiago de Cuba	.35	.20
1813	A472	13c Moncada Barracks	1.50	.20
1814	A472	30c Revolution Plaza, Havana	2.25	.20
		Nos. 1812-1814 (3)	4.10	.60

20th anniv. of the Revolution.

10th Anniv. of the Revolutionary Navy — A473

1973, Aug. 3   **Wmk. 376**

1815	A473	3c Midshipman, missile frigate	.60	.30

Interior, by Manuel Vicens A474

Paintings in the Natl. Museum: 1c, Amalia of Saxony, by J.K. Rossler. 3c, Margarita of Austria, by J. Pantoja de la Cruz. 4c, City Hall Official, anonymous. 5c, View of Santiago de Cuba, by Hernandez Giro. 13c, The Catalan, by J.J. Tejada. 30c, Alley in Guayo, by Tejada.

1973, Aug. 30   **Unwmk.**
Sizes: 26½x41mm (1c, 3c), 28½x39mm (4c, 13c, 30c)

1816	A474	1c multi	.20	.20
1817	A474	2c multi	.20	.20
1818	A474	3c multi	.25	.20
1819	A474	4c multi	.25	.20
1820	A474	5c multi	.25	.20
1821	A474	13c multi	1.90	.60
1822	A474	30c multi	2.50	.70
		Nos. 1816-1822 (7)	5.55	2.30

WMO Emblem, Paintings by J. Madrazo A475

1973, Sept. 4

1823	A475	8c Spring	.75	.20
1824	A475	8c Summer	.75	.20
1825	A475	8c Fall	.75	.20
1826	A475	8c Winter	.75	.20
		Nos. 1823-1826 (4)	3.00	.80

World Meteorogical Organization, cent. Nos. 1823-1826 printed se-tenant in strips of 4; frame reversed on 2nd and 4th stamp in strip.

A476

A477

27th World and 1st Pan American Weight Lifting Championships: Various weightlifting positions.

1973, Sept. 12
1827	A476	1c multi, diff.	.20	.20
1828	A476	2c shown	.20	.20
1829	A476	3c multi, diff.	.20	.20
1830	A476	4c multi, diff.	.20	.20
1831	A476	5c multi, diff.	.20	.20
1832	A476	13c multi, diff.	1.60	.45
1833	A476	30c multi, diff.	2.75	.90
		Nos. 1827-1833 (7)	5.35	2.35

1973, Sept. 28
Flowering plants.
1834	A477	1c Erythrina stan-dleyana	.20	.20
1835	A477	2c Lantana camara	.20	.20
1836	A477	3c Canavalia mariti-ma	.20	.20
1837	A477	4c Dichromena colorata	.20	.20
1838	A477	5c Borrichia arborescens	.20	.20
1839	A477	13c Anguria pedata	2.10	.65
1840	A477	30c Cordia sebestena	3.25	.90
		Nos. 1835-1840 (6)	6.15	2.35

8th World Trade Union Congress, Varna, Bulgaria — A478

1973, Oct. 5   **Wmk. 376**
1841	A478	13c multi	1.50	.35

Cuban Natl. Ballet, 25th Anniv. — A479

Sea Shells — A480

1973, Oct. 28   **Unwmk.**
1842	A479	13c gold & brt ultra	2.00	.40

1973, Oct. 29
1843	A480	1c Liguus fasciatus fasciatus	.20	.20
1844	A480	2c Liguus fasciatus guitarti	.20	.20
1845	A480	3c Liguus fasciatus whartoni	.20	.20
1846	A480	4c Liguus fasciatus angelae	.20	.20
1847	A480	5c Liguus fasciatus trinidadense	.20	.20
1848	A480	13c Liguus blainianus	2.75	.55
1849	A480	30c Liguus vittatus	3.75	.65
		Nos. 1843-1849 (7)	7.50	2.20

Maps of Cuba A481

1973, Oct. 29
1850	A481	1c Juan de la Cosa, 1502	.20	.20
1851	A481	3c Ortelius, 1572	.25	.20
1852	A481	13c Bellini, 1762	1.75	.20
1853	A481	40c 1973	2.10	.80
		Nos. 1850-1853 (4)	4.30	1.45

15th Anniversary of the Revolution — A482

1974, Jan. 2
1854	A482	1c No. 625	.20	.20
1855	A482	3c No. 626	.20	.20
1856	A482	13c No. C200	3.00	.30
1857	A482	40c No. C201	1.25	.50
		Nos. 1854-1857 (4)	4.65	1.25

Woman, by F. Ponce de Leon — A483

Amilcar Cabral — A484

Portraits in the Camaguey Museum: 3c, Mexican Girls, by J. Arche. 8c, Young Woman, by A. Menocal. 10c, Mulatto Woman Drinking from Coconut, by L. Romanach. 13c, Head of an Old Man, by J. Arburu.

1974, Jan. 10
1858	A483	1c multi	.20	.20
1859	A483	3c multi	.20	.20
1860	A483	8c multi	.35	.20
1861	A483	10c multi	1.10	.20
1862	A483	13c multi	1.60	.25
		Nos. 1858-1862 (5)	3.45	1.05

1974, Jan. 20
1863	A484	13c multi	1.40	.25
Amilcar Cabral, Guinea-Bissau freedom fighter, 1st death anniv.

Lenin, by I.V. Kosmin — A485

12th Central American and Caribbean Games, Santo Domingo — A486

1974, Jan. 21
1864	A485	30c multi	3.00	.30
50th death anniv. of Lenin.

1974, Feb. 8
1865	A486	1c Emblem	.25	.20
1866	A486	2c Javelin	.25	.20
1867	A486	3c Boxing	.25	.20
1868	A486	4c Baseball, horiz.	.25	.20
1869	A486	13c Basketball, horiz.	1.60	.20
1870	A486	30c Volleyball, horiz.	2.40	.70
		Nos. 1865-1870 (6)	5.00	1.70

Portrait by F. Martinez — A487

Portrait of a Man, by J.B. Vermay — A488

1974, Feb. 27
1871	A487	13c multi	1.40	.20
Carlos M. de Cespedes (d. 1874), patriot.

1974, Mar. 7
Paintings in the Natl. Museum: 2c, The Wet Nurse, by C.A. Van Loo. 3c, Cattle in River, by R. Morey. 4c, Village, by Morey. 13c, Faun and Bacchus, by Rubens. 30c, Young Woman Playing Cards, by R. Madrazo.
1872	A488	1c shown	.20	.20
1873	A488	2c multi	.20	.20
1874	A488	3c multi	.20	.20
1875	A488	4c multi	.20	.20
1876	A488	13c multi	1.40	.20
1877	A488	30c multi	2.50	.25
		Nos. 1872-1877 (6)	4.70	1.25

Council for Mutual Economic Assistance (COMECON), 25th Anniv. — A489

1974, Mar. 15
1878	A489	30c Comecon build-ing, Moscow	2.00	.70

Visit of Leonid I. Brezhnev to Cuba, Jan. 28-Feb. 3 — A490

1974, Mar. 28
1879	A490	13c Jose Marti, Lenin, flags	2.00	.25
1880	A490	30c Brezhnev, Fidel Castro	2.10	.25
		Nos. 1879-1880 (2)	4.10	.50

Science Fiction A491

Paintings by A. Sokolov.

1974, Apr. 12
1881	A491	1c Martian Crater	.25	.20
1882	A491	2c Fiery Labyrinth	.25	.20
1883	A491	3c Amber Wave	.25	.20
1884	A491	4c Flight Through Space	.25	.20
1885	A491	13c Planet in Nebula	2.00	.25
1886	A491	30c World of Two Suns	3.25	.60
		Nos. 1881-1886 (6)	6.25	1.65

Cosmonauts Day.

UPU, Cent. A492

1974, Apr. 15
1887	A492	30c Letter, 1874	2.50	.30

Stamp Day Type of 1973
Postmarks.

1974, Apr. 24
1888	A465	1c Havana	.25	.20
1889	A465	3c Matanzas	.40	.20
1890	A465	13c Trinidad	1.50	.20
1891	A465	20c Guana Vacoa	2.25	.35
		Nos. 1888-1891 (4)	4.40	.95

18th Sports Congress of Friendly Armies — A493

1974, May 5   **Wmk. 376**
1892	A493	3c multi	.80	.20

Felipe Poey (1799-1891), Naturalist — A494

Designs: 1c, 4c, Butterflies. 2c, 13c, Sea shells. 3c, 30c, 50c, Fish.

1974, May 26   *Perf. 12½x12*
1893	A494	1c Eumaeus atala atala	.20	.20
1894	A494	2c Pineria terebra	.20	.20
1895	A494	3c Chaetodon sedentarius	.20	.20
1896	A494	4c Eurema dina dina	.80	.20
1897	A494	13c Hemitrochus fuscolabiata	2.75	.35
1898	A494	30c Eupomacentrus partitus	3.50	.40
		Nos. 1893-1898 (6)	7.65	1.55

Souvenir Sheet
Imperf
1899 A494 50c Apogon binotatus 7.00 1.25

Stamp in #1899 has simulated perforations.

Havana Philharmonic Orchestra, 50th Anniv. — A495

1c, Antonio Mompo, cello. 3c, Cesar Perez Sentenat, piano. 5c, Pedro Mercado, trumpet. 10c, Pedro Sanjuan, Havana Philharmonic emblem. 13c, Roberto Ondina, flute.

1974, June 8   *Perf. 12½*
1900	A495	1c multi	.25	.20
1901	A495	3c multi	.25	.20
1902	A495	5c multi	.25	.20
1903	A495	10c multi	1.40	.20
1904	A495	13c multi	1.75	.25
		Nos. 1900-1904 (5)	3.90	1.10

Garden Flowers — A496

1974, June 12
1905	A496	1c Heliconia humilis	.20	.20
1906	A496	2c Anthurium andraeanum	.20	.20
1907	A496	3c Canna generalis	.20	.20
1908	A496	4c Alpinia purpurata	.25	.20
1909	A496	13c Gladiolus grandiflorus	1.75	.25
1910	A496	30c Amomum capitatum	4.50	.40
		Nos. 1905-1910 (6)	7.10	1.40

A497

A498

World Amateur Boxing Championships: Emblem and various boxers.

     Perf. 12x12½
1974, Aug. 24   Litho.   Unwmk.
1911	A497	1c multi	.20	.20
1912	A497	3c multi	.35	.20
1913	A497	13c multi	1.60	.20
		Nos. 1911-1913 (3)	2.15	.60

1974, Aug. 28   *Perf. 13*
Extinct birds.
1914	A498	1c Dodo	.20	.20
1915	A498	3c Ara de Cuba (parrot)	.20	.20
1916	A498	8c Passenger pigeon	.45	.20
1917	A498	10c Moa	1.40	.25
1918	A498	13c Great auk	1.75	.40
		Nos. 1914-1918 (5)	4.00	1.25

Pres. Salvador Allende of Chile (d. 1973) A499

1974, Sept. 11
1919 A499 13c multi   1.25 .45

Wildflowers A500

Model Aircraft — A501

1974, Sept. 14   *Perf. 13x12½*
1920	A500	1c Suriana maritima	.20	.20
1921	A500	3c Cassia ligustrina	.20	.20
1922	A500	8c Flaveria linearis	.30	.20
1923	A500	10c Stachytarpheta jamaicensis	2.10	.20
1924	A500	13c Bacopa monnieri	3.50	.40
		Nos. 1920-1924 (5)	6.30	1.20

1974, Sept. 22   *Perf. 12½*
1925	A501	1c shown	.20	.20
1926	A501	3c Sky diving	.20	.20
1927	A501	8c Glider	.45	.20
1928	A501	10c Crop dusting	1.25	.25
1929	A501	13c Commercial aviation	2.00	.25
		Nos. 1925-1929 (5)	4.10	1.10

Civil Aeronautic Institute, 10th anniv. Nos. 1927-1929 horiz.

History of Cuban Baseball — A502

1974, Oct. 3   *Perf. 13*
1930	A502	1c Indians playing ball	.20	.20
1931	A502	3c 1st Official game, 1874	.20	.20
1932	A502	8c Emilio Sabourin	.40	.20
1933	A502	10c Umpire, players, 1974	1.25	.20

1934	A502	13c Latin-American Stadium, Havana	2.10	.25
		Nos. 1930-1934 (5)	4.15	1.05
		Nos. 1930-1932 vert.		

Mambi 10c Stamp (Revolutionary Junta Issue), Cent. — A503

1974, Oct. 10
1935 A503 13c multi   1.50 .20

16th Conference of Customs Organizations of Socialist Countries — A504

1974, Oct. 15
1936 A504 30c Comecon Building, Moscow   2.00 .55

Disappearance of Major Camilo Cienfuegos, 15th Anniv. — A505

     Wmk. 376
1974, Oct. 28   Litho.   *Perf. 13*
1937 A505 3c multi   .75 .20

8th World Mining Conference — A506

1974, Nov. 3
1938 A506 13c multi   1.50 .25

Petroleum Institute, 15th Anniv. — A507

1974, Nov. 20
1939 A507 3c multi   .70 .20

Intersputnik Earth Station Opening — A508

1974, Nov. 30   Unwmk.
1940	A508	3c shown	.25	.20
1941	A508	13c Satellite, satellite dish	1.25	.20
1942	A508	1p Satellite, flags	3.25	1.10
		Nos. 1940-1942 (3)	4.75	1.50

Philatelic Federation, 10th Anniv. — A509

1974, Nov. 30   *Perf. 12½x13*
1943 A509 30c multi   2.40 .20

Souvenir Sheet

Mercury — A510

1974, Dec. 6   *Imperf.*
1944 A510 50c multi   6.00 .95

4th Natl. Phil. Exhib., Havana.

1st World Peace Congress, 25th Anniv. — A511

1974, Dec. 16   Wmk. 376   *Perf. 13*
1945 A511 30c *F. Joliot-Curie*, by Picasso   3.00 .25

Ruben Martinez Villena (b. 1899), Revolutionary — A512

1974, Dec. 20   Unwmk.
1946 A512 3c red org & yel   .75 .20

Souvenir Sheet

Cuban Victories, 1st Amateur Boxing Championships — A513

1975, Jan. 6   Litho.   Imperf.
1947 A513 50c Trophy   6.00   .95

The World, by Marcelo Pogolotti A514

Paintings in the Natl. Museum: 2c, *The Silk-Cotton Tree,* by Henry Cleenewerk. 3c, *Landscape,* by Guillermo Collazo. 5c, *Still-life,* by Francisco Peralta. 13c, *Maria Wilson,* by Federico Martinez, vert. 30c, *The Couple,* by Mariano Fortuny.

1975, Jan. 20   Perf. 13
1948 A514 1c multi   .20   .20
1949 A514 2c multi   .20   .20
1950 A514 3c multi   .20   .20
1951 A514 5c multi   .25   .20
1952 A514 13c multi   1.50   .20
1953 A514 30c multi   2.75   .40
   Nos. 1948-1953 (6)   5.10 1.40

Intl. Women's Year A515

1975, Feb. 6
1954 A515 13c multi   1.25   .25

Fishing Industry A516

Various fish and fishing vessels.

1975, Feb. 22
1955 A516 1c Long-finned tuna .20 .20
1956 A516 2c Tuna   .20 .20
1957 A516 3c Mediterranean
             grouper   .20 .20
1958 A516 8c Hake   .20 .20
1959 A516 13c Prawn   1.10 .35
1960 A516 30c Lobster   3.25 .35
   Nos. 1955-1960 (6)   5.15 1.50

Minerals — A517

1975, Mar. 15   Litho.   Perf. 13x12½
1961 A517 3c Nickel   .40   .20
1962 A517 13c Copper   1.60   .20
1963 A517 30c Chromium   2.75   .35
   Nos. 1961-1963 (3)   4.75   .75

Cosmonaut's Day — A518

1975, Apr. 12   Perf. 13x12½, 12½x13
1964 A518 1c Cosmodrome   .20   .20
1965 A518 2c Probe, vert.   .20   .20
1966 A518 3c Eclipse   .20   .20
1967 A518 5c Threshold to
             Space   .40   .20
1968 A518 13c Midday on Mars 1.50 .25
1969 A518 30c Cosmonaut's
             view of Earth   2.50 .45
   Nos. 1964-1969 (6)   5.00 1.50

The future of space.

Stamp Day A519

Various covers.

1975, Apr. 24   Perf. 13
1970 A519 3c multi   .20   .20
1971 A519 13c multi   1.40   .20
1972 A519 30c multi   2.10   .25
   Nos. 1970-1972 (3)   3.70   .65

Victory Over Fascism, 30th Anniv. — A520

Design: Raising red flag over Reichstag, Berlin.

1975, May 9   Perf. 13x12½
1973 A520 30c multi   2.00   .20

A521

Works in the Decorative Art Museum — A522

1c, Sevres porcelain vase, vert. 2c, Meissen porcelain statue *Shepherdess and Dancers,* vert. 3c, Chinese porcelain dish *Lady with Parasol.* 5c, Chinese screen detail *The Phoenix,* vert. 13c, *Allegory of Music,* by Francois Boucher (1703-70), vert. 30c, *Portrait of a Lady,* by L. Tocque, vert. 50c, *The Swing,* by Hubert Robert (1733-1808).

1975, May 10   Perf. 12½x13, 13x12½
1974 A521 1c multi   .20   .20
1975 A521 2c multi   .20   .20
1976 A521 3c shown   .25   .20
1977 A521 5c multi   .40   .20
1978 A521 13c multi   1.50   .20
1979 A521 30c multi   2.00   .40
   Nos. 1974-1979 (6)   4.55 1.40

Souvenir Sheet
Perf. 13x12½ on 3 Sides
1980 A522 50c shown   5.50   .95

No. 1980 contains one 25x39mm stamp.

Intl. Children's Day — A523

Wmk. 376
1975, May 31   Litho.   Perf. 13
1981 A523 3c multi   .50   .20

Indigenous Birds — A524

1975, June 18   Unwmk.
1982 A524 1c *Vireo gundlachi*   .20   .20
1983 A524 2c *Gymnoglaux
             lawrenci*   .20   .20
1984 A524 3c *Aratingo eoups*   .20   .20
1985 A524 5c *Staroenas cya-
             nocephala*   .35   .20
1986 A524 13c *Chondrohierax
             wilsoni*   1.50   .25
1987 A524 30c *Cyanolimnas
             cerverai*   2.25   .45
   Nos. 1982-1987 (6)   4.70 1.50

See #2121-2125, 2180-2182, C276-C276.

Scientific Investigation Center, 10th Anniv. — A525

1975, July 1   Perf. 12½
1988 A525 13c multi   1.40   .20

Irrigation and Drainage Commission, 25th Anniv. — A526

1975, Aug. 2   Perf. 13
1989 A526 13c multi   1.40   .20

Afforestation A527

1975, Aug. 20
1990 A527 1c *Cedrela mexicana*   .20   .20
1991 A527 3c *Swietenia
             mahagoni*   .40   .20
1992 A527 5c *Calophyllum
             brasiliense*   .40   .20
1993 A527 13c *Hibiscus tiliaceus* 1.10   .20
1994 A527 30c *Pinus caribaea*   1.75   .30
   Nos. 1990-1994 (5)   3.85 1.10

Cuban Women's Federation, 15th Anniv. — A528

1975, Aug. 23
1995 A528 3c multi   .50   .20

Intl. Conference on the Independence of Puerto Rico — A529

1975, Sept. 5   Litho.
1996 A529 13c multi   1.00   .20

A530

A531

7th Pan American Games, Mexico: Aztec calendar stone and various athletes.

1975, Sept. 20   *Perf. 12½x13*
1997	A530	1c Baseball	.25	.20
1998	A530	3c Boxing	.25	.20
1999	A530	5c Basketball	.25	.20
2000	A530	13c High jump	1.50	.25
2001	A530	30c Weight lifting	2.10	.25
		Nos. 1997-2001 (5)	4.35	1.10

Souvenir Sheet
Imperf
2002	A530	50c Stone, emblem	4.00	.95

1975, Sept. 28   *Perf. 12½x13*
2003	A531	3c multi	.50	.20

Revolutionary Defense Committees (CDR), 15th anniv.

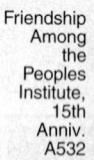

Friendship Among the Peoples Institute, 15th Anniv. A532

1975, Oct. 8   *Perf. 12½x13*
2004	A532	3c multi	.30	.20

Natl. Bank, 25th Anniv. A533

Designs: 1-peso coins and banknotes identified by serial numbers.

1975, Oct. 13   *Perf. 13x12½*
2005	A533	13c Coin, 1915	1.10	.20
2006	A533	13c C882736A, 1934	1.10	.20
2007	A533	13c A000387A, 1946	1.10	.20
2008	A533	13c 933906, 1964	1.10	.20
2009	A533	13c K000000, 1976	1.10	.20
a.		Strip of 5, Nos. 2005-2009	6.00	1.25
		Nos. 2005-2009 (5)	5.50	1.00

Locomotives — A534

1975, Oct. 28   **Unwmk.**   *Perf. 12½*
2010	A534	1c La Junta, 1837	.20	.20
2011	A534	3c Steam engine 2-8-0 No. 12	.30	.20
2012	A534	5c Diesel TEM 4 No. 51010	.30	.20
2013	A534	13c Diesel DVM 9 I-7 55	2.50	.20

2014	A534	30c Diesel M 62K No. 61601	3.00	.30
		Nos. 2010-2014 (5)	6.30	1.10

Railway history.

Development of the Textile Industry — A535

1975, Nov. 10   *Perf. 13x12½*
2015	A535	13c Bobbins, flag, loom operator	1.25	.20

Veterinary Medicine — A536

Parasites and host species.

1975, Nov. 25   **Litho.**   *Perf. 13*
2016	A536	1c Haemonchus, lamb	.25	.20
2017	A536	2c Ancylostoma caninum, dog	.25	.20
2018	A536	3c Dispharynx nasuta, rooster	.25	.20
2019	A536	5c Gasterophilus intestinalis, horse	.25	.20
2020	A536	13c Ascaris lumbricoides, pig	1.40	.20
2021	A536	30c Boophilus microplus, bull	2.50	.40
		Nos. 2016-2021 (6)	4.90	1.40

Manuel Ascunce Domenech Educational Detachment A537

1975, Nov. 27   **Litho.**
2022	A537	3c multi	.40	.20

Development of Agriculture and Animal Husbandry — A538

1975, Dec. 15   **Litho.**   *Perf. 13x12½*
2023	A538	13c Irrigation	1.25	.20

1st Communist Party Congress — A539

1975, Dec. 17   *Perf. 12½x13, 13x12½*
2024	A539	3c "1," revolutionaries, vert.	.20	.20
2025	A539	13c shown	1.10	.20
2026	A539	30c Party leaders	1.50	.30
		Nos. 2024-2026 (3)	2.80	.70

8th Latin-American Obstetrics and Gynecology Congress — A540

1976, Jan. 24   *Perf. 13*
2027	A540	3c multi	.60	.20

Paintings in Natl. Museums — A541

Designs: 1c, *Seated Woman*, by Victor Manuel, vert. 2c, *Garden*, by Santiago Rusinol. 3c, *Guadalquivir River*, by Manuel Barron y Carrillo. 5c, *Self-portrait*, by Jan Havicksz Steen, vert. 13c, *Portrait of a Woman*, by Louis Michel Van Loo, vert. 30c, *La Chula*, by Jose Arburu Morell, vert.

Perf. 13, 12½ (3c, 30c)

1976, Jan. 30
Sizes: 29x40mm (1c, 5c, 13c), 40x29mm (2c), 44x27mm (3c), 27x44mm (30c)
2028	A541	1c multi	.20	.20
2029	A541	2c multi	.20	.20
2030	A541	3c multi	.25	.20
2031	A541	5c multi	.25	.20
2032	A541	13c multi	1.40	.25
2033	A541	30c multi	2.25	.50
		Nos. 2028-2033 (6)	4.55	1.55

10th Cong. of Ministers from Socialist Communications Organizations, Feb. 12, Havana — A542

1976, Feb. 12   **Litho.**   *Perf. 13*
2034	A542	13c multi	1.40	.20

Hunting Dogs A543

1976, Feb. 20
2035	A543	1c American fox-hound	.25	.20
2036	A543	2c Labrador retriever	.25	.20
2037	A543	3c Borzoi	.25	.20
2038	A543	5c Irish setter	.25	.20
2039	A543	13c Pointer	1.40	.30
2040	A543	30c Cocker spaniel	2.50	.40
		Nos. 2035-2040 (6)	4.90	1.50

Socialist Constitution — A544

1976, Feb. 24   *Perf. 12½*
2041	A544	13c Natl. flag, arms, anthem	1.40	.20

Chess Champions — A545

Designs: 1c, Ruy Lopez Segura and chessboard. 2c, Francois Philidor and frontispiece of his book, *Analysis of the Game of Chess*. 3c, Wilhelm Steinitz and knight. 13c, Emanuel Lasker and king. 30c, Jose Raul Capablanca learning to play chess as a small boy.

1976, Mar. 15   *Perf. 13x12½*
2042	A545	1c multi	.20	.20
2043	A545	2c multi	.20	.20
2044	A545	3c multi	.25	.20
2045	A545	13c multi	1.75	.20
2046	A545	30c multi	1.90	.50
		Nos. 2042-2046 (5)	4.30	1.30

Havana Radio Intl. Broadcasts, 15th Anniv. — A546

1976, Mar. 26
2047	A546	50c multi	2.00	.70

World Health Day — A547

Child Care Centers, 15th Anniv. — A548

1976, Apr. 7
2048	A547	30c multi	1.50	.45

1976, Apr. 10   *Perf. 12½x13*
2049	A548	3c multi	.60	.20

1st Manned Space Flight, 15th Anniv. A549

1976, Apr. 12   *Perf. 13*
2050	A549	1c Gagarin, lift-off	.20	.20
2051	A549	2c V. Tesreshkova, rockets	.20	.20
2052	A549	3c A. Leonov's space walk, vert.	.25	.20
2053	A549	5c Spacecraft, vert.	.40	.20
2054	A549	13c Spacecraft, diff., vert.	1.10	.20
2055	A549	30c Space link-up	1.75	.35
		Nos. 2050-2055 (6)	3.90	1.35

Bay of Pigs Invasion, 15th
Anniv. — A550

1976, Apr. 17   Perf. 13x12½, 12½x13
2056 A550 3c shown   .25 .20
2057 A550 13c Bomber, pilot   .95 .20
2058 A550 30c Soldiers exulting,
              vert.   1.75 .45
     Nos. 2056-2058 (3)   2.95 .85

Natl. Militia, 17th anniv. (3c); Air Force, 15th
anniv. (13c); proclamation of the socialist
revolution, 15th anniv. (30c).

Nat. Assoc. of Small Farmers (ANAP),
15th Anniv. — A551

1976, May 17   Perf. 13x12½
2059 A551 3c multi   .60 .20

1976 Summer
Olympics,
Montreal — A552

1976, May 25   Perf. 12½x13
2060 A552 1c Volleyball   .20 .20
2061 A552 2c Basketball   .20 .20
2062 A552 3c Long jump   .20 .20
2063 A552 4c Boxing   .25 .20
2064 A552 5c Weight lifting   .25 .20
2065 A552 13c Judo   1.10 .20
2066 A552 30c Swimming   1.75 .45
     Nos. 2060-2066 (7)   3.95 1.65
     Souvenir Sheet
     Imperf
2067 A552 50c Character trade-
          mark (beaver)   4.00 1.25

See Nos. 2106, 2112.

Modern Secondary Schools — A553

1976, June 12   Litho.   Perf. 13
2068 A553 3c red, pale grn & blk   .60 .20

Indigenous Birds — A554

1976, June 15   Perf. 13x12½
2069 A554 1c Teretistris fornsi   .20 .20
2070 A554 2c Glaucidium siju   .20 .20
2071 A554 3c Nesoceleus fer-
            nandinae   .20 .25
2072 A554 5c Todus mutlicolor   .45 .25

2073 A554 13c Accipiter gun-
            dlachi   .90 .25
2074 A554 30c Priotelus
            temnurus   2.00 .80
     Nos. 2069-2074 (6)   3.95 1.95

EXPO
'76,
USSR
A555

1976, July 5   Perf. 12½x13, 13x12½
2075 A555 1c Anatomical scan-
            ning device   .20 .20
2076 A555 3c Child, doe   .20 .20
2077 A555 10c Cosmonauts   .50 .20
2078 A555 30c Tupolev super-
            sonic jet   2.50 .55
     Nos. 2075-2078 (4)   3.40 1.15

Public health and industrial safety (1c), environmental protection (3c), space exploration
(10c) and modern transportation (30c). Nos.
2075-2077 vert.

Death Cent. of
"El Inglesito"
A556

1976, Aug. 4   Perf. 13
2079 A556 13c Henry M. Reeve   .70 .20

Portrait of G.
Collazo, by
Jean
Dabour — A557

Paintings by Collazo: 2c, The Art Lovers,
horiz. 3c, The Patio. 5c, Coconut Tree. 13c,
New York Studio, horiz. 30c, R. Emelina
Collazo.

**Perf. 13, 12½x13 (5c, 30c), 13x12½
(13c)**

1976, Sept. 2
**Sizes: 33x44mm, 44x33mm (2c),
31x46mm (5c, 30c), 46x31mm (13c)**
2080 A557 1c multi   .20 .20
2081 A557 2c multi   .20 .20
2082 A557 3c multi   .20 .20
2083 A557 5c multi   .20 .20
2084 A557 13c multi   .65 .25
2085 A557 30c multi   2.10 .50
     Nos. 2080-2085 (6)   3.55 1.55

Camilo Cienfuegos Military Schools,
10th Anniv. — A558

1976, Sept. 23   Perf. 13
2086 A558 3c multi   .40 .20

Development of the Merchant
Marine — A559

Various cargo and passenger ships.

1976, Oct. 2   Perf. 12½
2087 A559 1c multi   .25 .20
2088 A559 2c multi   .25 .20
2089 A559 3c multi   .25 .20
2090 A559 5c multi   .35 .20
2091 A559 13c multi   1.00 .20
2092 A559 30c multi   2.00 .35
     Nos. 2087-2092 (6)   4.10 1.35

8th Intl. Health Film Festival of
Socialist Countries, Havana — A560

1976, Oct. 4   Perf. 13x12½
2093 A560 3c multi   .40 .20

5th Intl.
Ballet
Festival,
Havana
A561

Scenes from ballets. 2c, 5c, 13c, 30c vert.

1976, Nov. 6   Perf. 13
2094 A561 1c Apollo   .20 .20
2095 A561 2c The River and
            the Forest   .20 .20
2096 A561 3c Giselle   .20 .20
2097 A561 5c Oedipus Rex   .25 .20
2098 A561 13c Carmen   1.10 .20
2099 A561 30c Vital Song   2.10 .35
     Nos. 2094-2099 (6)   4.05 1.35

3rd
Military
Games
A562

1976, Nov. 25   Perf. 13
2100 A562 3c multi   .50 .20

Granma Landings, 20th Anniv. — A563

1976, Dec. 2   Perf. 13x12½
2101 A563 1c Landing craft   .20 .20
2102 A563 3c Landing force   .20 .20
2103 A563 13c Castro, soldiers   1.00 .20
2104 A563 30c Globe, rifles   1.60 .55
     Nos. 2101-2104 (4)   3.00 1.15

Souvenir Sheet

Cuban Landscape, by F.
Cadava — A564

1976, Dec. 8   Perf. 13x13½
2105 A564 50c multi   5.25 1.25

CIENFUEGOS '76, 5th natl. phil. exhib.

Summer Olympics Type of 1976 and

Victory of Cuban
Athletes at the
Montreal
Games — A565

1976, Dec. 10   Perf. 12½x13
2106 A565 1c Volleyball   .20 .20
2107 A565 2c Hurdles   .20 .20
2108 A565 3c Running (starting
            blocks)   .20 .20
2109 A565 8c Boxing   .25 .20
2110 A565 13c Running (finish
            line)   .85 .20
2111 A565 30c Judo   1.75 .45
     Nos. 2106-2111 (6)   3.45 1.45
     Souvenir Sheet
     Imperf
2112 A552 50c like No. 2063   5.00 .95

Paintings
in the
Natl.
Museum
A566

1c, Golden Cross Inn, by S. Scott. 3c, Portrait of a Man, by J.C. Versspronck, vert. 5c,
Venetian Landscape, by Francesco Guardi.
10c, Valley Corner, by H. Cleenewerck, vert.
13c, F. Xaviera Paula, anonymous, vert. 30c,
F. de Medici, by C. Allori, vert.

**Perf. 13, 12½x13 (3c, 10c, 30c); 12½
(13c)**

1977, Jan. 18
**Sizes: 40x29mm, 27x42mm (3c, 10c,
30c), 27x43½mm (13c)**
2113 A566 1c multi   .20 .20
2114 A566 3c multi   .20 .20
2115 A566 5c multi   .20 .20
2116 A566 10c multi   .55 .20
2117 A566 13c multi   .85 .20
2118 A566 30c multi   2.10 .40
     Nos. 2113-2118 (6)   4.10 1.40

Rural
Transport
A567

1977, Feb. 15   Perf. 13
2119 A567 3c multi   .80 .20

Constitution of Popular
Government — A568

1976, Dec. 1   **Perf. 13x12½**
2120 A568 13c multi   .70   .20

Bird Type of 1975

1977, Feb. 25   **Perf. 13**
2121 A524 1c *Xiphidiopicus*
                   percussus   .25   .20
2122 A524 4c *Tiaris canora*   .30   .20
2123 A524 10c *Dives atrovio-*
                   laceus   .60   .20
2124 A524 13c *Ferminia cerverai*   .85   .20
2125 A524 30c *Mellisuga*
                   helenae   1.75   .35
        Nos. 2121-2125 (5)   3.75   1.15

Lenin Park Aquarium, Havana — A569

1977, Mar. 15
2126 A569 1c *Chichlasoma*
                   meeki   .20   .20
2127 A569 3c *Barbus tetrazona*
                   tetrazona   .20   .20
2128 A569 5c *Cyprinus carpio*   .20   .20
2129 A569 10c *Betta splendens*   .30   .20
2130 A569 13c *Pterophyllum sca-*
                   lare, vert.   1.25   .25
2131 A569 30c *Hemigrammus*
                   caudovittatus   2.50   .50
        Nos. 2126-2131 (6)   4.65   1.55

Sputnik (1st Artificial Satellite), 20th
Anniv. — A570

1c, DDR No. 370, *Sputnik*. 3c, Hungary No.
1216, *Luna 16*. 5c, North Korean Intl. Geophysical Year 10-won stamp of 1958, *Cosmos*.
10c, Poland No. 822, *Sputnik 3*. 13c, Yugoslavia No. 870, Earth, Moon. 30c, Cuba No. 866,
Earth, Moon. 50c, Russia No. 2021, *Sputnik*.

1977, Apr. 12   **Perf. 13x12½**
2132 A570 1c multi   .25   .20
2133 A570 3c multi   .25   .20
2134 A570 5c multi   .25   .20
2135 A570 10c multi   .35   .20
2136 A570 13c multi   1.10   .20
2137 A570 30c multi   1.90   .35
        Nos. 2132-2137 (6)   4.10   1.35
               Souvenir Sheet
                    Imperf
2138 A570 50c multi   4.25   1.25
        No. 2138 has simulated perfs.

Antonio Maria Romeu (1876-1955),
Composer — A571

1977, May 10   **Litho.**   **Perf. 13**
2139 A571 3c multi   .35   .20
        See No. C251.

Flowering
Plants — A572

1977, May 31
2140 A572 1c *Hibiscus rosa*
                   sinensis   .20   .20
2141 A572 2c *Nerium oleander*   .20   .20
2142 A572 5c *Allamanda*
                   cathartica   .20   .20
2143 A572 10c *Pelargonium*
                   zonale   .40   .20
        Nos. 2140-2143 (4)   1.00   .80
Dr. Juan Tomas Roig (b. 1877), botanist.
See Nos. C252-C254.

Fire Prevention Week — A573

1977, June 20
2144 A573 1c shown   .20   .20
2145 A573 2c Horse-drawn fire
                   pump, diff.   .20   .20
2146 A573 6c Early motorized
                   vehicle   .25   .20
2147 A573 10c Modern truck   .50   .20
2148 A573 13c Turntable-ladder
                   truck   .90   .20
2149 A573 30c Crane vehicle   1.90   .40
        Nos. 2144-2149 (6)   3.95   1.40

Natl. Decorations
(Ribbons and
Medals of
Honor) — A574

1977, July 26   **Perf. 12x12½**
2150 A574 1c shown   .25   .20
2151 A574 3c multi, diff.   .25   .20
        See Nos. C255-C256.

Paintings by
Jorge
Arche — A575

Perf. 13x12½, 12½x13 (10c), 13 (5c)
1977, Aug. 25
      Sizes: 26x38mm, 29x40mm (5c),
             38x26mm (10c)
2152 A575 1c *Portrait of Mary*   .20   .20
2153 A575 3c *Jose Marti*   .20   .20
2154 A575 5c *Portrait of Aristi-*
                   des   .20   .20
2155 A575 10c *Bathers*   .50   .20
        Nos. 2152-2155 (4)   1.10   .80
Nos. 2152-2154 vert. See Nos. C257-C259.

4th Military
Spartakiad
(Summer
Sports) — A576

1977, Sept. 10   **Perf. 13**
2156 A576 1c Boxing   .20   .20
2157 A576 3c Volleyball   .20   .20
2158 A576 5c Parachuting   .20   .20
2159 A576 10c Running   .35   .20
        Nos. 2156-2159 (4)   .95   .80
        See Nos. C260-C261.

Intl.
Airmail
Service,
50th
Anniv.
A577

Designs: 1c, Biplane and No. C62. 2c,
Three-engine plane and Cuba-Key West 1st
flight cancel, Oct. 28, 1927. 5c, Flying boat
and intl. airmail service 1st flight cachet. 10c,
Jet aircraft and Havana-Madrid cachet, Apr.
26, 1948.

1977, Oct. 27   **Litho.**   **Perf. 12x12½**
2160 A577 1c multi   .20   .20
2161 A577 2c multi   .20   .20
2162 A577 5c multi   .20   .20
2163 A577 10c multi   .50   .20
        Nos. 2160-2163 (4)   1.10   .80
        See Nos. C263-C264.

October Revolution, Russia, 60th
Anniv. — A578

1977, Nov. 7   **Perf. 13x12½**
2164 A578 3c Cruiser *Aurora*   .20   .20
2165 A578 13c Lenin, Flags   .40   .20
2166 A578 30c Hammer, sickle,
                   symbols of agri-
                   culture, technol-
                   ogy   1.40   .25
        Nos. 2164-2166 (3)   2.00   .65

Felines, Havana
Zoo — A579

1977, Nov. 24   **Litho.**   **Perf. 13**
2167 A579 1c Cat   .20   .20
2168 A579 2c Black panther   .20   .20
2169 A579 8c Puma   .20   .20
2170 A579 10c Leopard   .85   .20
        Nos. 2167-2170 (4)   1.45   .80
        See Nos. C266-C267.

Martyrs of the Revolution, 20th Death
Annivs. — A580

1977, Dec. 2   **Perf. 12½x12**
2171 A580 3c Cienfuegos Upris-
                   ing   .20   .20
2172 A580 20c Siege on the
                   Presidential Pal-
                   ace   1.00   .20
        See No. C268.

Intl. Measurement System — A581

1977, Dec. 9
2173 A581 3c multi   .40   .20

Havana University, 250th
Anniv. — A582

1978, Jan. 5   **Perf. 13x12½**
2174 A582 3c multi   .25   .20
        See Nos. C270-C271.

Landscape with Figures, by J.
Pilliment — A583

Paintings in the Natl. Museum of Art: 1c,
Seated Woman, by R. Mandrazo, vert. 4c, *Girl*,
by J. Sorolla, vert. 10c, *The Cow*, by E. Abela.

Perf. 12x12½, 13 (4c, 6c, 10c)
1978, Feb. 20
      Sizes: 27x42mm, 29x40mm (4c),
             40x29mm (6c, 10c)
2175 A583 1c multi   .20   .20
2176 A583 4c multi   .20   .20
2177 A583 6c shown   .20   .20
2178 A583 10c multi   .60   .20
        Nos. 2175-2178 (4)   1.20   .80
        See Nos. C273-C274.

Frontier Troops,
15th
Anniv. — A584

1978, Mar. 5   **Perf. 13**
2179 A584 13c multi   1.50   .25

Bird Type of 1975
Perf. 13, 12½x12 (4c)
1978, Mar. 10   Size: 42x27mm

2180	A524	1c	Myadestes elisabeth	.35 .20
2181	A524	4c	Palioptila lembeyei	.40 .20
2182	A524	10c	Teretistris fernandinae	1.00 .25
		Nos. 2180-2182 (3)		1.75 .65

Name of bird inscribed below vignette. See Nos. C275-C276.

Cosmonaut's Day — A585

1978, Apr. 12   Perf. 13

2183	A585	1c	Intercosmos, vert.	.20 .20
2184	A585	2c	Luna 24	.20 .20
2185	A585	5c	Venus 9, vert.	.35 .20
2186	A585	10c	Cosmos	.35 .20
		Nos. 2183-2186 (4)		1.10 .80

See Nos. C278-C279.

9th World Trade Unions Congress, Prague — A586

1978, Apr. 16

2187	A586	30c	ver, deep brn & blk	1.00 .45

Cactus Flowers — A587

1978, May 15   Perf. 12½x13 (1c), 13

2188	A587	1c	Melocactus guitarti	.25 .20
2189	A587	4c	Leptocereus wrightii	.25 .20
2190	A587	6c	Opuntia militaris	.25 .20
2191	A587	10c	Cylindropuntia hystrix	.65 .25
		Nos. 2188-2191 (4)		1.40 .85

Natl. Botanical Gardens. See #C281-C282.

Lenin Park Aquarium, Havana — A588

1978, June 15   Perf. 13

2192	A588	1c	Barbus arulios	.20 .20
2193	A588	4c	Hiphessobrycon flammeus	.20 .20
2194	A588	6c	Poecilia reticulata	.20 .20
2195	A588	10c	Colis lalia	.45 .20
		Nos. 2192-2195 (4)		1.05 .80

See Nos. C286-C287.

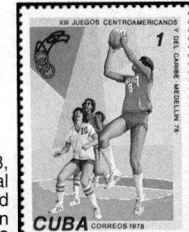

MEDELLIN '78, 13th Central American and Caribbean Games — A589

1978, July 1

2196	A589	1c	Basketball, vert.	.25 .20
2197	A589	3c	Boxing, vert.	.25 .20
2198	A589	5c	Weight lifting, vert.	.25 .20
2199	A589	10c	Fencing	.45 .20
		Nos. 2196-2199 (4)		1.20 .80

See Nos. C288-C289.

Attack on Moncada Barracks, 25th Anniv. — A590

1978, July 26

2200	A590	3c	multi	.25 .20

See Nos. C290-C291.

World Youth and Students Festival, Havana A591

Natl. flags and views of host cities.

1978, July 28

2201	A591	3c	Prague, 1947	.25 .20
2202	A591	3c	Budapest, 1949	.25 .20
2203	A591	3c	Berlin, 1951	.25 .20
2204	A591	3c	Bucharest, 1953	.25 .20
2205	A591	3c	Warsaw, 1955	.25 .20
a.		Strip of 5, Nos. 2201-2205		1.40 1.40
		Nos. 2201-2205 (5)		1.25 1.00

See Nos. C292-C297.

Young Workers' Army, 5th Anniv. — A592

1978, Aug. 3

2206	A592	3c	multi	.30 .20

Tuna Industry A593

1978, Aug. 30   Perf. 12½x12

2207	A593	1c	Tuna boat	.20 .20
2208	A593	2c	Processing ship	.20 .20
2209	A593	5c	Shrimp boat	.20 .20
2210	A593	10c	Inshore stern trawler	.35 .20
		Nos. 2207-2210 (4)		.95 .80

See Nos. C298-C299.

Paintings by Amelia Pelaez del Casal (1896-1968) — A594

Perf. 13x12½, 13 (3c, 6c), 12½x13
1978, Sept. 15

2211	A594	1c	The White Mantle	.20 .20
2212	A594	3c	Still-life with Flowers, vert.	.20 .20
2213	A594	6c	Women, vert.	.20 .20
2214	A594	10c	Fish, vert.	.45 .20
		Nos. 2211-2214 (4)		1.05 .80

See Nos. C301-C303.

African Fauna, Havana Zoo A595

1978, Oct. 20   Perf. 13

2215	A595	1c	Rhinoceros	.25 .20
2216	A595	4c	Okapi, vert.	.25 .20
2217	A595	6c	Mandrill	.25 .20
2218	A595	10c	Giraffe, vert.	.55 .20
		Nos. 2215-2218 (4)		1.30 .80

See Nos. C307-C308.

Natl. Ballet, 30th Anniv. — A596

1978, Oct. 28   Perf. 13x12½

2219	A596	3c	Grande Pas de Quatre	.25 .20

See Nos. C309-C310.

A597

A598

Flowers of the Pacific: Various species.

1978, Nov. 30   Litho.   Perf. 13

2220	A597	1c	multi	.20 .20
2221	A597	4c	multi	.20 .20
2222	A597	6c	multi	.25 .20
2223	A597	10c	multi	.50 .20
		Nos. 2220-2223 (4)		1.15 .80

See Nos. C311-C312.

1979, Jan. 1   Perf. 12½x13 (3c), 13

2224	A598	3c	Castro, soldier	.20 .20
2225	A598	13c	Industry	.50 .20
2226	A598	1p	Flag, globe, flame	3.25 .75
		Nos. 2224-2226 (3)		3.95 1.15

Triumph of the Revolution, 20th anniv.

Doves and Pigeons A599

1979, Jan. 30   Perf. 13

2227	A599	1c	Starnoenas cyanocephala	.35 .20
2228	A599	3c	Geotrygon chysia	.40 .20
2229	A599	7c	Geotrygon caniceps	.40 .20
2230	A599	8c	Geotrygon montana	.50 .20
2231	A599	13c	Columba leucocephala	.90 .20
2232	A599	30c	Columba inornata	1.90 .45
		Nos. 2227-2232 (6)		4.45 1.45

Paintings in the Natl. Museum of Art A600

Designs: 1c, Genre Scene, by David Teniers. 3c, Arrival of Spanish Troops, by J. Louis Meissonier. 6c, A Joyful Gathering, by Sir David Wilkie. 10c, A Robbery, by E. De Lucas Padilla. 13c, Tea Time, by R. Madrazo, vert. 30c, Peasants in Front of a Tavern, by Adriaen van Ostade.

1979, Feb. 20

2233	A600	1c	multi	.20 .20
2234	A600	3c	multi	.20 .20
2235	A600	6c	multi	.30 .20
2236	A600	10c	multi	.45 .20
2237	A600	13c	multi	.80 .20
2238	A600	30c	multi	1.75 .25
		Nos. 2233-2238 (6)		3.70 1.25

See Nos. 2262-2267, C317.

Marine Flora — A601

1979, Mar. 20

2239	A601	3c	Nymphaea capensis	.20 .20
2240	A601	10c	Nymphaea ampla	.40 .20
2241	A601	13c	Nymphaea coerulea	.65 .25
2242	A601	30c	Nymphaea rubra	1.50 .30
		Nos. 2239-2242 (4)		2.75 .95

All are incorrectly inscribed "Nymphaca."

A602

A603

1979, Mar. 24
2243 A602 3c multi

Cuban film industry, 20th anniv.

1979, Apr. 12
2244	A603	1c Rocket launch	.20	.20
2245	A603	4c Soyuz	.20	.20
2246	A603	6c Salyut	.35	.20
2247	A603	10c Link-up	.50	.20
2248	A603	13c Soyuz, Salyut	.85	.20
2249	A603	30c Parachute landing	1.90	.25
		Nos. 2244-2249 (6)	4.00	1.25

Cosmonaut's Day. See No. C315.

6th Summit Meeting of Non-Aligned Countries — A604

1979, Apr. 17
2250	A604	3c Understanding, cooperation	.25	.20
2251	A604	13c Fight colonialism	.50	.20
2252	A604	30c New world economic order	1.40	.40
		Nos. 2250-2252 (3)	2.15	.80

House of the Americas Museum, 20th Anniv. — A605

1979, Apr. 28   **Perf. 13x12½**
2253 A605 13c Cuna Indian tapestry   .40   .20

Agrarian Reform, 20th Anniv. — A606

1979, May 17   **Perf. 12½x12**
2254 A606 3c multi   .40   .20

Souvenir Sheet

The Party, by Jules Pascin — A607

1979, May 18   **Perf. 13**
2255 A607 50c multi   3.50   .90

PHILASERDICA '79 phil. exhib., Sofia.

Nocturnal Butterflies — A608

1979, May 25
2256	A608	1c Eulepidotis rectimargo	.20	.20
2257	A608	4c Othreis materna	.20	.20
2258	A608	6c Noropsis hieroglyphica	.40	.20
2259	A608	10c Heterochroma	.40	.20
2260	A608	13c Melanchroia regnatrix	.80	.20
2261	A608	30c Attera gemmata	2.00	.20
		Nos. 2256-2261 (6)	4.00	1.30

Art Type of 1979

Paintings by Victor Emmanuel Garcia (d. 1969): 1c, *Main Avenue, Paris.* 3c, *Portrait of Enmita.* 6c, *San Juan River, Matanzas.* 10c, *Woman Carrying Hay.* 13c, *Still-life with Vase.* 30c, *Street at Night.* Nos. 2262-2267 vert.

1979, June 15
2262	A600	1c multi	.20	.20
2263	A600	3c multi	.20	.20
2264	A600	6c multi	.20	.20
2265	A600	10c multi	.30	.20
2266	A600	13c multi	.45	.20
2267	A600	30c multi	1.60	.45
		Nos. 2262-2267 (6)	2.95	1.45

See No. C317.

World Peace Council, 30th Anniv. A609

1979, June 29   **Perf. 12½x13**
2268 A609 30c multi   1.00   .35

1980 Summer Olympics, Moscow — A610

1979, July 30   **Perf. 13x12½**
2269	A610	1c Wrestling	.20	.20
2270	A610	4c Boxing	.20	.20
2271	A610	6c Women's volleyball	.20	.20
2272	A610	10c Shooting	.25	.20
2273	A610	13c Weight lifting	.55	.20
2274	A610	30c High jump	1.50	.30
		Nos. 2269-2274 (6)	2.90	1.30

Roses — A611

A612

1979, Aug. 20   **Perf. 13**
2275	A611	1c Rosa eglanteria	.25	.20
2276	A611	2c Rosa centifolia anemonoides	.25	.20
2277	A611	3c Rosa indica vulgaris	.25	.20
2278	A611	5c Rosa eglanteria punicea	.25	.20
2279	A611	10c Rosa sulfurea	.25	.20
2280	A611	13c Rosa muscosa alba	.45	.20
2281	A611	20c Rosa gallica purpurea velutina	.90	.25
		Nos. 2275-2281 (7)	2.60	1.45

1979, Aug. 30
2282 A612 13c multi   .50   .20

Council for Mutual Economic Assistance, 30th anniv.

Cubana Airlines, 50th Anniv. A613

Various aircraft.

1979, Oct. 8
2283	A613	1c Ford trimotor	.20	.20
2284	A613	2c Sikorsky S-38	.20	.20
2285	A613	3c Douglas DC-3	.35	.20
2286	A613	4c Brittania	.35	.20
2287	A613	13c Ilyushin IL-14	.90	.20
2288	A613	40c Tupolev TU-104	2.50	.30
		Nos. 2283-2288 (6)	4.50	1.30

Disappearance of Camilo Cienfuegos, 20th Anniv. — A614

1979, Oct. 28
2289 A614 3c multi   .30   .20

Reinoso, Sugar Cane and Blossom A615

1979, Nov. 12
2290 A615 13c multi   .75   .20

Sugar Cane Research Institute, 15th anniv., and sesquicentennial of the birth of Alvaro Reinoso.

Zoo Animals A616

1979, Nov. 15
2291	A616	1c Chimpanzees	.20	.20
2292	A616	2c Leopards	.20	.20
2293	A616	3c Deer	.20	.20
2294	A616	4c Lion cubs	.20	.20
2295	A616	5c Bear cubs	.20	.20
2296	A616	13c Squirrels	.30	.20
2297	A616	30c Pandas	.70	.25
2298	A616	50c Tiger cubs	1.40	.35
		Nos. 2291-2298 (8)	3.40	1.80

Insects A617

1980, Jan. 25
2299	A617	1c Rhina oblita	.20	.20
2300	A617	5c Odontocera josemartii, vert.	.20	.20
2301	A617	6c Pinthocoelium columbinum	.20	.20
2302	A617	10c Calasoma splendida, vert.	.45	.20
2303	A617	13c Homophileurus cubanus, vert.	.90	.20
2304	A617	30c Heterops dimidiata, vert.	1.90	.70
		Nos. 2299-2304 (6)	3.85	1.70

1980 Summer Olympics, Moscow — A618

1980, Feb. 20   **Perf. 12½**
2305	A618	1c Weight lifting	.20	.20
2306	A618	2c Shooting	.20	.20
2307	A618	5c Javelin	.20	.20
2308	A618	6c Wrestling	.20	.20
2309	A618	8c Judo	.25	.20
2310	A618	10c Running	.25	.20
2311	A618	13c Boxing	.55	.20
2312	A618	30c Women's volleyball	1.40	.60
		Nos. 2305-2312 (8)	3.25	2.00

Souvenir Sheet
Imperf
2313 A618 50c Mischa character   3.00   1.60

No. 2313 contains one 32x40mm stamp.

Paintings in the Natl. Museum A619

Designs: 1c, *The Oak Trees,* by Henry Joseph Harpignies, vert. 4c, *Family Reunion,* by Willem van Mieris. 6c, *Domestic Fowl,* by Melchior De Hondecoeter, vert. 9c, *Innocence,* by William A. Bougereau, vert. 13c, *Venetial Scene II,* by Michele Marieschi. 30c, *Spanish Peasant Woman,* by Joaquin Dominguez Bequer, vert.

Perf. 12½, 13 (9c, 30c), 12½x13
(13c)

1980, Mar. 11
Sizes: 29x40mm, 40x29mm (4c),
28x42mm (9c, 30c), 38x26mm (13c)
2314	A619	1c multi	.20	.20
2315	A619	4c multi	.20	.20
2316	A619	6c multi	.20	.20
2317	A619	9c multi	.65	.20
2318	A619	13c multi	.85	.20
2319	A619	30c multi	1.90	.65
	Nos. 2314-2319 (6)		4.00	1.65

Souvenir Sheet

LONDON '80 — A620

1980, Apr. 1   *Perf. 13*
2320 A620 50c *Malvern Hall,* by
John Constable   3.50 1.60

Intercosmos Program — A621

1980, Apr. 12
2321	A621	1c Emblem, flags	.20	.20
2322	A621	4c Astrophysics	.20	.20
2323	A621	6c Satellite commu-		
		nications	.20	.20
2324	A621	10c Meteorology	.45	.20
2325	A621	13c Biology and		
		medicine	.60	.20
2326	A621	30c Surveying satel-		
		lite	1.90	.65
	Nos. 2321-2326 (6)		3.55	1.65

Cuban Postage Stamps, 125th
Anniv. — A622

1980, Apr. 24   *Perf. 12½*
2327 A622 30c Nos. 1, 7 and
613   1.25 .45

Orchids — A623

1980, May 20   *Perf. 13*
2328	A623	1c *Bletia purpurea*	.25	.20
2329	A623	4c *Oncidium leiboldii*	.25	.20
2330	A623	6c *Epidendrum*		
		cochleatum	.25	.20
2331	A623	10c *Cattleyopsis*		
		lindenii	.45	.20
2332	A623	13c *Encyclia fucata*	.80	.20
2333	A623	30c *Encyclia*		
		phoenicea	1.75	.60
	Nos. 2328-2333 (6)		3.75	1.60

Marine Mammals — A624

1980, June 20
2334	A624	1c *Tursiops trun-*		
		catus	.20	.20
2335	A624	3c *Megaptera*		
		novaeangliae,		
		vert.	.20	.20
2336	A624	13c *Ziphius cavirostris*	.60	.20
2337	A624	30c *Monachus tropi-*		
		calis	1.40	.40
	Nos. 2334-2337 (4)		2.40	1.00

Urban Reform
Campaign, 20th
Anniv. — A625

Nationalization of Foreign Industry,
20th Anniv. — A626

1980, July 26 *Perf. 13x12½, 12½x13*
2338	A625	3c multi	.20	.20
2339	A626	13c multi	.35	.20

Moncada Program.

Colonial
Copperware
A627

Perf. 12½, 12½x13 (13c)
1980, July 29
Sizes: 27x43½mm, 38x26mm (13c)
2340	A627	3c Wine pitcher,		
		19th cent.	.20	.20
2341	A627	13c Oil jar, 18th cent.	.70	.20
2342	A627	30c Lidded pitcher,		
		19th cent.	1.40	.20
	Nos. 2340-2342 (3)		2.30	.60

Cuban Women's
Federation, 20th
Anniv. — A628

1980, Aug. 23   *Perf. 13*
2343 A628 3c multi   .40 .20

Souvenir Sheet

ESPAMER '80, Madrid — A629

Design: *Clotilde Passing Through the Country Garden,* by Joaquin Sorolla y Bastida.

1980, Aug. 29
2344 A629 50c multi   3.50 1.60
Postage stamps of Spain, 130th anniv.

1st Havana
Declaration,
20th
Anniv. — A630

1980, Sept. 2
2345 A630 13c multi   .50 .20

Construction of Naval Vessels in
Cuba, 360th Anniv. — A631

Ships under construction: 1c, *Our Lady of
Atocha,* galleon, 1620. 3c, *El Rayo,* warship,
1749. 7c, *Santisima Trinidad,* 1769. 10c, *Santisima Trinidad,* diff., 1805, vert. 13c, Steamships *Congreso* and *Colon,* 1851. 30c, Cardenas and Chullima shipyards.

1980, Sept. 15
2346	A631	1c multi	.20	.20
2347	A631	3c multi	.20	.20
2348	A631	7c multi	.20	.20
2349	A631	10c multi	.40	.20
2350	A631	13c multi	.85	.20
2351	A631	30c multi	1.40	.60
	Nos. 2346-2351 (6)		3.25	1.60

A633

A634

1980, Sept. 26   *Perf. 13*
2354 A633 13c multi   .60 .20
Fidel Castro's 1st speech before the UN
General Assembly, 20th anniv.

1980, Sept. 28   *Perf. 13x12½*
2355 A634 3c multi   .30 .20
Revolutionary defense committees, 20th
anniv.

Souvenir Sheet

ESSEN '80, 49th Intl. Philatelic
Federation Congress — A635

Painting: *Portrait of a Lady,* by Ludger Tom
Ring The Younger.

1980, Oct. 2   **Litho.**   *Perf. 13*
2356 A635 50c multi   3.75 1.25

Early Locomotives — A636

1980, Oct. 15
2357	A636	1c Josefa	.25	.20
2358	A636	2c Chaparra Sugar		
		Co. No. 22	.25	.20
2359	A636	7c Steam storage lo-		
		comotive	.25	.20
2360	A636	10c 2-4-2 locomotive	.40	.20
2361	A636	13c 2-4-0 locomotive	.65	.20
2362	A636	30c Oil combustion		
		engine, 1909	1.60	.60
	Nos. 2357-2362 (6)		3.40	1.60

Lighthouses
A637

1980, Oct. 30
2363	A637	3c Roncali, San		
		Antonio	.20	.20
2364	A637	13c Jagua, Cienfue-		
		gos	.70	.20
2365	A637	30c Maisi Point,		
		Guantanamo	1.60	.20
	Nos. 2363-2365 (3)		2.50	.60

See Nos. 2440-2442, 2553-2555, 2614-2616.

622   CUBA

Victory of Cuban Athletes at the 1980
Summer Olympics, Moscow — A638

1980, Nov. 10   Litho.   Perf. 12½x12
2366 A638 13c Bronze medals   .50   .20
2367 A638 30c Silver medals   1.10   .25
2368 A638 50c Gold medals   2.25   .50
      Nos. 2366-2368 (3)   3.85   .95
Nos. 2366-2368 each printed se-tenant with
label containing statistical data.

Wildflowers
A639

1980, Nov. 20   Perf. 13
2369 A639 1c Pancratium aren-
              icolum   .20   .20
2370 A639 4c Urechites lutea   .20   .20
2371 A639 6c Solanum
              elaegnifolium   .25   .20
2372 A639 10c Hamelia patens   .45   .20
2373 A639 13c Morinda royoc   .70   .20
2374 A639 30c Centrosema
              virginianum   2.00   .30
      Nos. 2369-2374 (6)   3.80 1.30

Souvenir Sheet

7th Natl. Stamp Exhibition — A640

1980, Nov. 22
2375 A640 50c Mail train   3.00 1.25

2nd Communist
Party Congress
A641

1980, Dec. 17
2376 A641 3c shown   .20   .20
2377 A641 13c Industry, commu-
              nication   .40   .20
2378 A641 30c Athletics, elderly,
              education   1.10   .20
      Nos. 2376-2378 (3)   1.70   .60

Paintings
in the
Natl.
Museum
of Art
A642

Designs: 1c, Lady Mayo, by Anton Van
Dyck, vert. 6c, The Spinner, by Giovanni Bat-
tista Piazzeta, vert. 10c, Daniel Collyer, by
Francis Cotes, vert. 13c, Gardens, Palma de
Mallorca, by Santiago Rusinol Prats. 20c,
Landscape with Roadway and Houses, by
Frederick Waters Watts. 50c, Landscape with
Sheep, by Jean-Francois Millet.

1981, Jan. 20
2379 A642 1c multi   .20   .20
2380 A642 6c multi   .20   .20
2381 A642 10c multi   .50   .20
2382 A642 13c multi   .60   .20
2383 A642 20c multi   1.00   .30
2384 A642 50c multi   2.10   .60
      Nos. 2379-2384 (6)   4.60 1.70
      See Nos. 2510-2515.

Pelagic
Fish
A643

1981, Feb. 25
2385 A643 1c Isurus ox-
              yrhynchus   .25   .20
2386 A643 3c Lampris regius .25   .20
2387 A643 10c Istiophorus
              platypterus   .45   .20
2388 A643 13c Mola mola, vert. 1.75 .20
2389 A643 30c Coruphaena hip-
              purus   1.10   .30
2390 A643 50c Tetrapturus al-
              bidus   2.00   .70
      Nos. 2385-2390 (6)   5.80 1.80

1982 World Cup Soccer
Championships, Spain — A644

Globe and various soccer players.

1981, Mar. 20   Perf. 12½
2391 A644 1c multi   .20   .20
2392 A644 2c multi   .20   .20
2393 A644 3c multi   .20   .20
2394 A644 10c multi, vert.   .45   .20
2395 A644 13c multi, vert.   .45   .20
2396 A644 50c multi   1.75   .60
      Nos. 2391-2396 (6)   3.25 1.60

Souvenir Sheet
Perf. 13
2397 A644 1p Soccer ball, flag 4.75 1.60
No. 2397 contains one 40x32mm stamp.

Opening of the
1st
Kindergarten,
20th
Anniv. — A645

1981, Apr. 10   Perf. 13
2398 A645 3c multi   .40   .20

1st Man
in
Space,
20th
Anniv.
A646

Designs: 1c, Jules Verne, Russian scientist
Konstantin E. Tsiolkovski, and Sergei P.
Korolev, designer of the 1st Soviet spacecraft.
2c, Yuri Gagarin, 1st man in space. 3c,
Valentina Tereshkova, 1st woman in space,
and Vostok 6. 5c, Aleksei A. Leonov, 1st man
to walk in space. 13c, Konstantin Feoktistov,
Boris Yegorov and Vladimir Komarov,
Voskhod 1 crew, 1st 3-man orbital flight. 30c,
Valeri Ryumen and Leonid Popov, set a space
endurance record. 50c, Arnaldo Tamayo, 1st
Cuban cosmonaut, and Soviet cosmonaut Yuri
Romanenko on joint space flight, vert.

1981, Apr. 12   Perf. 12½
2399 A646 1c multi   .20   .20
2400 A646 2c multi   .20   .20
2401 A646 3c multi   .20   .20
2402 A646 5c multi   .20   .20
2403 A646 13c multi   .45   .20
2404 A646 30c multi   1.00   .35
2405 A646 50c multi   2.25   .60
      Nos. 2399-2405 (7)   4.50 1.95

A647

Designs: 3c, Rocket, aircraft. 13c, Hand
raising gun.

1981, Apr. 19   Litho.   Perf. 13
2406 A647 3c multi, vert.   .20   .20
2407 A647 13c multi, vert.   .40   .20
2408 A647 30c multi   .95   .60
      Nos. 2406-2408 (3)   1.55 1.00

Creation of armed forces (DAAFAR) (3c),
Bay of Pigs Invasion, 20th Anniv. (13c), Proclamation of the socialist revolution (30c).

Attack on Goicuria Barracks, 25th
Anniv. — A648

1981, Apr. 29
2409 A648 3c multi   .30   .20

Natl.
Assoc. of
Small
Farmers
(ANAP),
20th
Anniv.
A649

1981, May 17
2410 A649 3c multi   .50   .20

Souvenir Sheet

WIPA '81 — A650

1981, May 22   Litho.
2411 A650 50c Austria No. 643 2.50 .90

Fighting
Cocks
A651

1981, May 25   Perf. 12½x13, 13x12½
2412 A651 1c Canelo, vert.   .20   .20
2413 A651 3c Cenizo   .20   .20
2414 A651 7c Blanco, vert.   .25   .20
2415 A651 13c Pinto, vert.   .50   .20
2416 A651 30c Giro   1.25   .35
2417 A651 50c Jabao, vert. 2.25   .60
      Nos. 2412-2417 (6)   4.65 1.75

Ministry of the
Interior, 20th
Anniv. — A652

1981, June 6   Perf. 13
2418 A652 13c multi   .40   .20

Souvenir Sheet

Mother and Child, by Zlatka
Dabova — A653

1981, June 14
2419 A653 50c gold, sil & blk 2.25 .80
Bulgaria, 1300th anniv. BULGARIA '81 phil.
exhib.

Horse-drawn Carriages — A654

1981, June 25
2420 A654 1c Streetcar   .20   .20
2421 A654 4c Bus   .20   .20
2422 A654 9c Breake   .25   .20
2423 A654 13c Landau   .40   .20
2424 A654 30c Phaeton   1.40   .45
2425 A654 50c Funeral coach 2.50   .75
      Nos. 2420-2425 (6)   4.95 2.00

House in the
Country, by
Mario
Caridad — A655

1981, July 15   Perf. 12½
2426 A655 30c multi   1.25   .30
      Intl. Year of the Disabled.

Sandinistas, 25th Anniv. — A656

1981, July 23   **Perf. 13**
2427 A656 13c multi   .50   .20

State Institutions, 20th Annivs. — A657

1981, July 26   **Perf. 12½**
2428 A657 3c multi   .20   .20
2429 A657 13c multi, diff.   .45   .20
2430 A657 30c multi, diff.   1.25   .25
      Nos. 2428-2430 (3)   1.90   .65

Institute for Sports, Physical Education and Recreation (3c); Radio Havana (13c); and Ministry of Foreign Trade (MINCEX) (30c).

Carlos J. Finlay and Cent. of His Theory of Biological Vectors — A658

1981, Aug. 14   **Perf. 13**
2431 A658 13c multi   1.00   .20

Nonaligned Countries Movement, 20th Anniv. — A659

1981, Sept. 1
2432 A659 50c multi   1.50   .80

Horses — A660

Illustration reduced. Nos. 2433-2437 vert.

1981, Sept. 15   **Perf. 13**
Size: 29x40mm
2433 A660 1c multi   .20   .20
2434 A660 3c multi, diff.   .20   .20
2435 A660 8c multi, diff.   .20   .20
2436 A660 13c multi, diff.   .35   .20
2437 A660 30c multi, diff.   1.10   .45
      Nos. 2433-2437 (5)   2.05 1.25
Size: 68x27mm
Perf. 12½
2438 A660 50c Herd   1.75   .75

Souvenir Sheet

Idyll in a Tea House, by Kitagawa Utamaro — A661

1981, Oct. 9   **Perf. 13**
2439 A661 50c multi   2.75 1.25

PHILATOKYO '81.

Lighthouse Type of 1980

1981, Oct. 15   **Litho.**
2440 A637 3c North Rock   .20   .20
2441 A637 13c Lucrecia Point   .50   .20
2442 A637 40c East Guano   2.10   .30
      Nos. 2440-2442 (3)   2.80   .70

Jose Marti Natl. Library, 80th Anniv. — A662

Sugar mills, lithographs from *Los Ingenios,* by Eduardo Laplante (b. 1818): 3c, Flor de Cuba, 1838. 13c, El Progreso, 1845. 30c, Santa Teresa, 1847.

1981, Oct. 18   **Perf. 12½x12**
2443 A662 3c multi   .20   .20
2444 A662 13c multi   .35   .20
2445 A662 30c multi   1.25   .55
      Nos. 2443-2445 (3)   1.80   .95

Pablo Picasso (b. 1881) and No. 1263 A663

1981, Oct. 25   **Perf. 12½x13**
2446 A663 30c multi   1.25   .40

Souvenir Sheet

ESPAMER '81, Buenos Aires — A664

1981, Nov. 13   **Perf. 13**
2447 A664 1p Packet   4.00 1.60

Art Type of 1969

Paintings in the Napoleon Museum: 1c, *Napoleon in Coronation Costume,* anonymous. 3c, *Napoleon with Landscape in the Background,* by Jean Horace Vernet. 10c, *Bonaparte in Egypt,* by Edouard Detaille. 13c, *Napoleon on Horseback,* by Hippolyte Bellange. 30c, *Napoleon in Normandy,* by Bellange. 50c, *Death of Napoleon,* anonymous.

1981, Dec. 1   **Perf. 12½**
Sizes: 42x58mm, 58x42mm (3c, 13c, 30c, 50c)
2448 A385 1c multi   .20   .20
2449 A385 3c multi, horiz.   .20   .20
2450 A385 10c multi   .40   .20
2451 A385 13c multi, horiz.   .40   .20

2452 A385 30c multi, horiz.   1.25   .40
2453 A385 50c multi, horiz.   2.10   .70
      Nos. 2448-2453 (6)   4.55 1.90

Napoleon Museum, 20th anniv.

25th Annivs. A665

1981, Dec. 2   **Perf. 13**
2454 A665 3c Revolutionaries, vert. .20   .20
2455 A665 20c Marksman   .45   .20
2456 A665 1p Yacht *Granma*   5.25 1.40
      Nos. 2454-2456 (3)   5.90 1.80

November 30th insurrection (3c); creation of the revolutionary armed forces (20c); and disembarking of revolutionary forces (1p).

Fauna — A666

1981, Dec. 14 Litho.   Perf. 12½x12
2457 A666 1c Hummingbird   .20   .20
2458 A666 2c Parakeet   .20   .20
2459 A666 5c Hutia   .20   .20
2460 A666 20c Almiqui   .65   .20
2461 A666 35c Manatee   1.25   .25
2462 A666 40c Crocodile   1.00   .55
      Nos. 2457-2462 (6)   3.50 1.60

Fernando Ortiz, Folklorist, Birth Cent. A667

1981, Dec. 20   **Perf. 12½x13**
2463 A667 3c Portrait by Jorge Arche y Silva .20   .20
2464 A667 10c Hanging idol   .40   .20
2465 A667 30c Arara drum   1.50   .45
2466 A667 50c Chango statue   2.25   .70
      Nos. 2463-2466 (4)   4.35 1.55

Literacy Campaign, 20th Anniv. — A668

1981, Dec. 25   **Perf. 12½x12**
2467 5c Conrado Benitez   .30   .20
2468 5c Manuel Asunce   .30   .20
  a. A668 Pair, #2467-2468   .75   .25
      Nos. 2467-2468 (2)   .60   .40

A669

1982 World Cup Soccer Championships, Spain — A670

Various athletes.

1982, Jan. 15   **Perf. 13**
2469 A669 1c multi, vert.   .20   .20
2470 A669 2c multi, vert.   .20   .20
2471 A669 5c multi, vert.   .20   .20
2472 A669 10c multi, vert.   .30   .20
2473 A669 20c shown   .70   .20
2474 A669 40c multi   1.25   .50
2475 A669 50c multi, vert.   1.60   .70
      Nos. 2469-2475 (7)   4.45 2.20

Souvenir Sheet
2476 A670 1p shown   5.00 1.60

No. 2476 contains one 32x40mm stamp.

10th World Trade Unions Congress, Havana — A671

1982, Feb. 10   **Litho.**
2477 A671 30c Lazaro Pena, delegate 1.00   .25

Butterflies — A672

1982, Feb. 25   **Perf. 12½**
2478 A672 1c *Euptoieta hegesia*   .20   .20
2479 A672 4c *Metamorpha stelenes insularis* .20   .20
2480 A672 5c *Heliconius charithonius ramsdeni* .20   .20
2481 A672 20c *Phoebis avellaneda* 1.40   .25
2482 A672 30c *Hamadryas ferox diasia* 2.25   .40
2483 A672 50c *Marpesia eleuchea* 4.00   .70
      Nos. 2478-2483 (6)   8.25 1.95

Exports — A673

3c, Sugar (processing plant). 4c, Lobster (fishing boat). 6c, Canned fruits. 7c, Agricultural machinery. 8c, Nickel (passenger jet, industrial complex, car). 9c, Rum. 10c, Coffee. 30c, Fresh fruit. 50c, Tobacco. 1p, Cement. Nos. 2489-2493 vert.

1982, Feb. 26 Perf. 12x12½, 12½x12
2484	A673	3c lt grn	.20	.20
2485	A673	4c car rose	.20	.20
2486	A673	6c dull blue	.25	.20
2487	A673	7c brt org	.40	.20
2488	A673	8c brt vio	.40	.20
2489	A673	9c slate	.40	.20
2490	A673	10c dull red brn	.50	.20
2491	A673	30c bister	.75	.25
2492	A673	50c orange	2.10	.40
2493	A673	1p olive bister	4.00	1.25
		Nos. 2484-2493 (10)	9.20	3.30

Tulips A674

1982, Mar. 30 Perf. 12½x13
2494	A674	1c Greenland	.20	.20
2495	A674	3c Mariette	.25	.20
2496	A674	8c Ringo	.25	.20
2497	A674	20c La Tulipe Noire	.80	.20
2498	A674	30c Jewel of Spring	1.40	.40
2499	A674	50c Orange Parrot	1.90	.60
		Nos. 2494-2499 (6)	4.80	1.65

Communist Youth Organization, 20th Anniv. — A675

1982, Apr. 4 Perf. 13
2500	A675	5c multi	.30	.20

2nd UN Congress on the Peaceful Use of Outer Space — A676

1982, Apr. 12
2501	A676	1c Mars	.20	.20
2502	A676	3c Venera	.20	.20
2503	A676	6c Salyut-Soyuz link-up	.25	.20
2504	A676	20c Lunokhod moon vehicle	.50	.20
2505	A676	30c Venera with heat shield	1.40	.40
2506	A676	50c Cosmos	2.00	.60
		Nos. 2501-2506 (6)	4.55	1.70

Cover A677

1982, Apr. 24 Perf. 12½x12
2507	A677	20c Havana-Veracruz	.75	.25
2508	A677	30c Havana-Tampico	1.25	.25

Stamp Day. English post office, 1842-1877 (20c); and French post office, 1862-1877 (30c).

Broadcasting and Television Institute (ICRT), 20th Anniv. — A678

1982, May 24 Perf. 12x12½
2509	A678	30c multi	1.00	.25

Art Type of 1981 With Larger Type

Paintings in the Natl. Museum of Art: 1c, *Portrait of a Youth* (girl), by Jean B. Greuze, vert. 3c, *Procession in Brittany*, by Jules Breton. 9c, *Landscape*, by Jean Piliment. 20c, *Late Afternoon*, by William A. Bourgueran, vert. 30c, *Tiger*, by Ferdinand V.E. Delacroix. 40c, *The Chair*, by Wilfredo Lam, vert.

Perf. 13, 13x12½ (3c), 12x12½ (20c, 40c), 12½x12 (30c)
1982, May 31 Litho.
2510	A642	1c 29x40mm	.20	.20
2511	A642	3c 46x36mm	.20	.20
2512	A642	9c 40x29mm	.25	.20
2513	A642	20c 27x42mm	.65	.25
2514	A642	30c 42x27mm	1.25	.40
2515	A642	40c 27x42mm	2.00	.40
		Nos. 2510-2515 (6)	4.55	1.65

Souvenir Sheet

PHILEXFRANCE '82 — A679

1982, June 7 Perf. 13
2516	A679	1p Steamship *Louisiana* at St. Nazaire	5.00	1.60

DEPORFILEX '82 — A680

1982, June 10 Perf. 13x12½
2517	A680	20c Hurdler, No. 300	1.50	.25

Reptiles A681

1982, June 15 Perf. 13
2518	A681	1c Pseudemys decussata	.20	.20
2519	A681	2c Tropidophis pardalis	.20	.20
2520	A681	3c Crocodylus rhombifer	.25	.20
2521	A681	20c Cyclura nubila	.85	.25
2522	A681	30c Anolis allisonis	1.25	.30
2523	A681	50c Alsophis cantherigerus	2.40	.50
		Nos. 2518-2523 (6)	5.15	1.60

George Dimitrov (1882-1949), Bulgarian Prime Minister — A682

1982, June 18
2524	A682	30c multi	1.00	.25

Koch, Bacillus A683

1982, July 18
2525	A683	20c multi	1.25	.25

Discovery of the tubercle bacillus by Dr. Robert Koch, cent.

14th Central American and Caribbean Games — A684

1982, Aug. 1
2526	A684	1c Baseball	.20	.20
2527	A684	2c Boxing	.20	.20
2528	A684	10c Water polo	.35	.20
2529	A684	20c Javelin	.80	.30
2530	A684	35c Weight lifting	1.25	.45
2531	A684	50c Volleyball	2.00	.55
		Nos. 2526-2531 (6)	4.80	1.90

Hydraulic Development Plan, 20th Anniv. — A685

5c, Fruit, *Eichornia crassipes*, ship. 20c, Arid soil, *Nymphaea alba*, irrigation & reservoir systems.

1982, Aug. 9
2532	A685	5c multi	.35	.20
2533	A685	20c multi	.90	.25

Souvenir Sheet

DEPORFILEX '82, Intl. Stamp and Coin Exhibition — A686

1982, Aug. 10 Litho.
2534	A686	1p Cuco, character trademark	4.75	1.60

14th Central American and Caribbean Games.

Namibia Day — A687

1982, Aug. 26
2535	A687	50c multi	1.75	.75

1982 World Cup Soccer Championships, Spain — A688

Various athletes.

1982, Aug. 30
2536	A688	5c multi	.20	.20
2537	A688	20c multi	.75	.30
2538	A688	30c multi	1.10	.40
2539	A688	50c multi	1.90	.80
		Nos. 2536-2539 (4)	3.95	1.70

Also exist in miniature sheets of 16 + 9 labels containing 4 each Nos. 2536-2539 in blocks of 4.

Natl. Folklore Ensemble, 20th Anniv. — A689

Paintings by V.P. Landaluze.

1982, Sept. 10
2540	A689	20c Little Devil, vert.	.80	.25
2541	A689	30c Day of Kings	1.10	.45

Prehistoric Fauna — A690

1982, Sept. 15 Litho.
2542	A690	1c Ornimegalonyx oteroi, vert.	.50	.20
2543	A690	5c Crocodylus rhombifer	.20	.20
2544	A690	7c Aquila borrasi, vert.	2.10	.30
2545	A690	20c Geocapromys colombianus	.50	.20
2546	A690	35c Megalocnus rodens, vert.	.75	.35
2547	A690	50c Nesophontes micrus	1.10	.50
		Nos. 2542-2547 (6)	5.15	1.75

15th Death Anniv. of Che Guevara — A691

1982, Oct. 8   *Perf. 13x12½*
2548 A691 20c multi   1.00   .25

Discovery of America, 490th Anniv. — A692

1982, Oct. 12   *Perf. 13*
2549 A692 5c shown   1.10   .20
2550 A692 20c *Santa Maria*, vert.   1.25   .20
2551 A692 35c *Pinta*, vert.   1.90   .20
2552 A692 50c *Nina*, vert.   2.40   .30
    Nos. 2549-2552 (4)   6.65   .90

Lighthouse Type of 1980
1982, Oct. 25
2553 A637 5c Jutias Caye   .45   .20
2554 A637 20c Paredon Grande
           Caye   1.25   .20
2555 A637 30c Morro Santiago
           de Cuba   1.60   .45
    Nos. 2553-2555 (3)   3.30   .85

George Washington, 250th Birth Anniv. — A693

Designs: Quotations and anonymous oil paintings, 18th-19th cent.

1982, Oct. 29   *Perf. 12x12½*
2556 A693 5c multi   .25   .20
2557 A693 20c multi, diff.   .75   .20

Souvenir Sheet

8th Natl. Philatelic Exposition, Ciego de Avila — A694

1982, Nov. 13
2558 A694 1p Paddle steamer *Al-mendares*   5.00   1.60

   8th Congress of the Cuban Philatelic Federation, Nov. 13-22.

Lenin Natl. Park, 10th Anniv. A695

1982, Dec. 28
2559 A695 5c multi   .40   .20

Chess Champion Jose Raul Capablanca and King — A696

1982, Dec. 29
2560 A696 5c shown   .25   .20
2561 A696 20c Rook   1.10   .20
2562 A696 30c Knight   1.40   .30
2563 A696 50c Queen   2.25   .50
    a.   Bklt. pane of 4, Nos. 2560-
        2563   20.00   10.00
    Nos. 2560-2563 (4)   5.00   1.20

Exist in sheets of 4+2 labels picturing chessmen.

USSR, 60th Anniv. — A697

1982, Dec. 30   *Perf. 13x12½*
2564 A697 30c multi   1.25   .25

World Communications Year — A698

1983, Jan. 24   *Litho.*   *Perf. 13*
2565 A698 20c multi   .75   .25

No. 507 and Birthplace — A699

1983, Jan. 28   *Perf. 13x12½*
2566 A699 5c multi   .30   .20

   Jose Marti (b. 1853), writer, revolution leader.

1984 Summer Olympics, Los Angeles A700

1983, Jan. 31   *Perf. 13*
2567 A700 1c Javelin   .20   .20
2568 A700 5c Volleyball   .25   .20
2569 A700 6c Basketball   .25   .20
2570 A700 20c Weight lifting   .80   .20
2571 A700 30c Wrestling   1.10   .40
2572 A700 50c Boxing   1.75   .60
    a.   Block of 6, #2567-2572   4.50   2.00
    Nos. 2567-2572 (6)   4.35   1.80
Souvenir Sheet
Perf. 13½x13
2573 A700 1p Judo   5.00   2.50

No. 2573 contains one 32x40mm stamp.

Radio Rebelde, 25th Anniv. — A701

1983, Feb. 24   *Perf. 13*
2574 A701 20c multi   .70   .20

Karl Marx, Death Cent. A702

1983, Mar. 14
2575 A702 30c multi   1.00   .40

1st Manned Balloon Flight, Bicent. — A703

Various balloons.

1983, Mar. 30
2576 A703 1c multi   .20   .20
2577 A703 3c multi   .20   .20
2578 A703 5c multi   .20   .20
2579 A703 7c multi   .35   .20
2580 A703 30c multi   2.10   .60
2581 A703 50c multi   2.10   .60
    Nos. 2576-2581 (6)   5.15   2.00
Souvenir Sheet
2582 A703 1p Jose D. Blino   4.00   2.00

No. 2582 contains one 32x40mm stamp.

Cosmonauts' Day — A704

1983, Apr. 12   *Litho.*
2583 A704 1c *Vostok 1*   .20   .20
2584 A704 4c Satellite *Frances
           D1*   .20   .20
2585 A704 5c *Mars 2*   .20   .20
2586 A704 20c *Soyuz*   .75   .20
2587 A704 30c Meteorological
           satellite   1.10   .50
2588 A704 50c Intercosmos sat-
           ellite   1.75   .70
    Nos. 2583-2588 (6)   4.20   2.00

Stamp Day A705

1983, Apr. 24
2589 A705 20c Havana-Key West
           cover   .75   .30
2590 A705 30c Spain-Havana
           cover   1.25   .30

   1st Intl. airmail services.

Souvenir Sheet

TEMBAL '83, Basel — A706

1983, May 21   *Perf. 13½x13*
2591 A706 1p Weasel   5.00   2.50

Simon Bolivar, Liberator of South America A707

1983, July 24   *Perf. 12½x13*
2592 A707 5c Jose Rafael de
           las Heras   .20   .20
2593 A707 20c Bolivar   .60   .20

Attack of Moncada Barracks, 30th Anniv. — A708

Designs: 5c, Jose Marti, Moncada barracks. 20c, Abel Santamaria, Jose Luis Tasende and Boris Luis Santa Coloma, martyrs, vert. 30c, *History Will Absolve Me*, declaration of Fidel Castro, vert.

1983, July 26   *Perf. 13*
2594	A708	5c multi	.20	.20
2595	A708	20c multi	.70	.20
2596	A708	30c multi	.90	.50
	Nos. 2594-2596 (3)		1.80	.90

Souvenir Sheet

Alberto Santos-Dumont (1873-
1932) — A709

1983, July 29   *Perf. 13x13½*
2597	A709	1p Dumont's aircraft	5.00	2.50

BRASILIANA '83, Rio; 140th anniv. of 1st
stamp issued in the Americas.

9th Pan American Games,
Caracas — A710

1983, Aug. 14   *Perf. 13x12½*
2598	A710	1c Weight lifting	.20	.20
2599	A710	2c Volleyball	.20	.20
2600	A710	3c Baseball	.20	.20
2601	A710	20c High jump	.75	.20
2602	A710	30c Basketball	1.10	.50
2603	A710	50c Boxing	1.75	.70
	Nos. 2598-2603 (6)		4.20	2.00

Port, by Claude Joseph
Vernet — A711

1983, Sept. 5
2604	A711	30c multi	1.40	.35

French alliance, cent.

Pres. Salvador Allende of Chile
(d. 1973) — A712

1983, Sept. 12
2605	A712	20c multi	.70	.20

1st Congress of Farmers at Arms,
25th Anniv. — A713

1983, Sept. 21   *Perf. 12½x12*
2606	A713	5c multi	.25	.20

Raphael, 500th
Birth
Anniv. — A714

1983, Sept. 30   Litho.   *Perf. 13*
2607	A714	1c Girl with Veil	.20	.20
2608	A714	2c The Cardinal	.20	.20
2609	A714	5c Francesco M. Della Rovere	.20	.20
2610	A714	20c Portrait of a Youth	.75	.20
2611	A714	30c Magdalena Doni	1.10	.25
2612	A714	50c La Fornarina	1.75	.65
	Nos. 2607-2612 (6)		4.20	1.70

State
Quality
Seal
A715

1983, Oct. 14
2613	A715	5c multi	.25	.20

Lighthouse Type of 1980

1983, Oct. 20
2614	A637	5c Carapachibey	.20	.20
2615	A637	20c Cadiz Bay	.80	.30
2616	A637	30c Gobernadora Point	2.00	.50
	Nos. 2614-2616 (3)		3.00	1.00

Turtles
A716

1983, Nov. 15
2617	A716	1c Eretmochelys imbricata	.20	.20
2618	A716	2c Lepidochelys kempi	.20	.20
2619	A716	5c Chrysemys decussata	.25	.20
2620	A716	20c Caretta caretta	.80	.20
2621	A716	30c Chelonia mydas	1.40	.25
2622	A716	50c Dermochelys coriacea	2.75	.75
	Nos. 2617-2622 (6)		5.60	1.80

World Communications Year — A717

1983, Nov. 23
2623	A717	1c Bell's Gallow Frame, telephone	.20	.20
2624	A717	5c Telegram, airmail	.20	.20
2625	A717	10c Satellite, satellite dish	.45	.20
2626	A717	20c Television, radio	.75	.20
2627	A717	30c 24th Communications conf.	1.10	.40
	Nos. 2623-2627 (5)		2.70	1.20

Nos.
319
and
990
A718

1983, Dec. 3   *Perf. 13x12½*
2628	A718	20c multi	.70	.25

See note after No. 320.

Flowers, Birds   Flowers
A719   A720

1983, Dec. 20   *Perf. 13*
2629	A719	5c Opuntia dillenii	.40	.20
2630	A719	5c Euphorbia podocarpifolia	.40	.20
2631	A719	5c Dinema cubincola	.40	.20
2632	A719	5c Guaiacum officinale	.40	.20
2633	A719	5c Magnolia cubensis	.40	.20
a.	Strip of 5, Nos. 2629-2633		3.00	2.00
2634	A719	5c Jatropha angustifolia	.40	.20
2635	A719	5c Cochlospermum vitifolium	.40	.20
2636	A719	5c Tabebuia lepidota	.40	.20
2637	A719	5c Kalmiella ericoides	.40	.20
2638	A719	5c Jatropha integerrima	.40	.20
2639	A719	5c Melocactus actinacanthus	.40	.20
2640	A719	5c Cordia sebestana	.40	.20
2641	A719	5c Tabernae - montana apoda	.40	.20
2642	A719	5c Lantana camara	.40	.20
2643	A719	5c Cordia gerascanthus	.40	.20
a.	Block of 10, Nos. 2634-2643		5.00	4.00
2644	A719	5c Tiaris canora	.40	.20
2645	A719	5c Phaethon lepturus	.40	.20
2646	A719	5c Myadestes elisabeth	.40	.20
2647	A719	5c Saurothera merlini	.40	.20
2648	A719	5c Polioptila lembeyei	.40	.20
a.	Strip of 5, Nos. 2644-2648		3.00	2.00
2649	A719	5c Mellisuga helenae	.40	.20
2650	A719	5c Mimus polyglottos	.40	.20
2651	A719	5c Todus multicolor	.40	.20
2652	A719	5c Amazona leucocephala	.40	.20
2653	A719	5c Ferminia cerverai	.40	.20
2654	A719	5c Pelecanus occidentalis	.40	.20
2655	A719	5c Melanerpes superciliaris	.40	.20
2656	A719	5c Mimocichla plumbea	.40	.20
2657	A719	5c Aratinga euops	.40	.20

2658	A719	5c Sturnella magna	.40	.20
a.	Block of 10, Nos. 2649-2658		5.00	4.00
	Nos. 2629-2658 (30)		12.00	6.00

Souvenir Sheets
2658B	A719	100c Hedychium coronarium	5.00	4.50
2658C	A719	100c Priotelus temnurus	5.00	4.50

1983, Dec. 30   *Perf. 12½*
2659	A720	60c Tobacco	1.75	.55
2660	A720	70c Lily	2.25	.60
2661	A720	80c Mariposa	2.50	.70
2662	A720	90c Orchid	3.50	1.00
	Nos. 2659-2662 (4)		10.00	2.85

25th Anniv. of the Revolution — A721

1983, Dec. 31   Litho.   *Perf. 13*
2663	A721	5c shown	.20	.20
2664	A721	20c Flags, Santa Clara Rlwy. tracks	.80	.20

25th Anniv. of the Revolution — A722

1984, Jan. 8
2665		20c Guevara, Castro	.70	.25
2666		20c Star	.70	.25
2667		20c PCC emblem, workers	1.75	.80
a.	A722 Strip of 3, #2665-2667		3.25	1.50
	Nos. 2665-2667 (3)		3.15	1.30

Lenin,
60th
Death
Anniv.
A723

1984, Jan. 21   *Perf. 12½x12*
2668	A723	30p Spasski Tower, Russia Nos. 295, 265	1.25	.25

Cuban
Labor
Union,
45th
Anniv.
A724

1984, Jan. 28   *Perf. 13*
2669	A724	5c multi	.25	.20

Butterflies — A725

1984, Jan. 31   *Perf. 13x12½*
2670	A725	1c Ixias balice	.20	.20
2671	A725	2c Phoebis avellaneda	.20	.20
2672	A725	3c Anthocaris sara	.20	.20
2673	A725	5c Victorina	.20	.20

2674 A725 20c *Heliconius cydno cydnides* .70 .20
2675 A725 30c *Parides gundlachianus calzadillae* 1.25 .55
2676 A725 50c *Catagramma sorana* 2.10 .70
Nos. 2670-2676 (7) 4.85 2.25

Marine Mammals — A726

1984, Feb. 15 *Perf. 12x12½, 12½x12*
2677 A726 1c *Grampus griseus*, vert. .20 .20
2678 A726 2c *Delphinus delphis*, vert. .20 .20
2679 A726 5c *Physeter catodon* .20 .20
2680 A726 6c *Stenella plagiodon*, vert. .20 .20
2681 A726 10c *Pseudorca crassidens* .55 .20
2682 A726 30c *Tursiops truncatus*, vert. 1.25 .30
2683 A726 50c *Megaptera novaeangliae* 2.10 .55
Nos. 2677-2683 (7) 4.70 1.85

Augusto C. Sandino (1893-1934), Nicaraguan Revolutionary — A727

1984, Feb. 21 *Perf. 13*
2684 A727 20c multi .70 .25

Red Cross in Cuba, 75th Anniv. — A728

1984, Mar. 10
2685 A728 30c Flag, No. 404 1.25 .35

Cuban Film Industry, 25th Anniv. A729

1984, Mar. 24
2686 A729 20c multi .80 .20

Caribbean Flowers — A730

1984, Mar. 29
2687 A730 1c *Brownea grandiceps* .20 .20
2688 A730 2c *Couroupita guianensis* .20 .20

2689 A730 5c *Triplaris surinamensis* .20 .20
2690 A730 20c *Amherstia nobilis* .70 .25
2691 A730 30c *Plumieria alba* 1.00 .35
2692 A730 50c *Delonix regia* 1.75 .65
Nos. 2687-2692 (6) 4.05 1.85

Cosmonauts' Day — A731

1984, Apr. 12
2693 A731 2c *Electron 1*, 1964 .20 .20
2694 A731 3c *Electron 2*, 1964 .20 .20
2695 A731 5c *Intercosmos 1*, 1969 .20 .20
2696 A731 10c *Mars 5*, 1974 .40 .20
2697 A731 30c *Soyuz*, 1969 1.00 .35
2698 A731 50c USSR-Bulgaria space flight, 1979 1.90 .65
Nos. 2693-2698 (6) 3.90 1.80

Souvenir Sheet
Perf. 12½
2699 A731 1p *Luna 1*, 1959 4.00 1.60
No. 2699 contains one 32x40mm stamp.

Mothers' Day — A732

1984, Apr. 19 *Perf. 13*
2700 A732 20c Red roses .75 .20
2701 A732 20c Pink roses .75 .20

Stamp Day — A733

Designs: Mural, by R. Rodriguez Radillo (details).

1984, Apr. 24 *Perf. 13x12½*
2702 A733 20c Mexican runner .80 .20
2703 A733 30c Egyptian boatman 1.10 .35

See Nos. 2787-2788, 2860-2861, 3025-3026, 3122-3123, 3213-3214.

Souvenir Sheet

ESPANA '84, Madrid — A734

1984, Apr. 27 *Perf. 13x13½*
2704 A734 1p Clipper ship 4.75 1.60

Women's Basketball, 1984 Summer Olympics A735

1984, May 5 *Perf. 13*
2705 A735 20c multi 1.25 .35

Agrarian Reform Act, 25th Anniv. — A736

1984, May 17 *Perf. 13½x13*
2706 A736 5c multi .40 .20

Banco Popular de Ahorro, 1st Anniv. — A737

1984, May 18 *Perf. 13*
2707 A737 5c multi .40 .20

Early Locomotives — A738

1984, June 11 *Perf. 12½x12*
2708 A738 1c multi .20 .20
2709 A738 4c multi, diff. .20 .20
2710 A738 5c multi, diff. .20 .20
2711 A738 10c multi, diff. .25 .20
2712 A738 30c multi, diff. .75 .35
2713 A738 50c multi, diff. 1.25 .70
Nos. 2708-2713 (6) 2.85 1.85

Souvenir Sheet

19th UPU Congress, HAMBURG '84 — A739

1984, June 19 *Perf. 13x13½*
2714 A739 1p Nos. 73, 232 4.50 2.10

Intl. Olympic Committee, 90th Anniv. — A740

1984, June 23 *Perf. 13*
2715 A740 30c Coubertin, torchbearer 1.40 .35

Children's Day A741

1984, July 15 *Perf. 12½x13*
2716 A741 5c multi .25 .20

1984 Summer Olympics, Los Angeles A742

1984, July 28 *Perf. 13*
2717 A742 1c Wrestling .20 .20
2718 A742 3c Discus .20 .20
2719 A742 5c Volleyball .20 .20
2720 A742 20c Boxing .80 .25
2721 A742 30c Basketball 1.10 .35
2722 A742 50c Weight lifting 2.00 .65
Nos. 2717-2722 (6) 4.50 1.85

Souvenir Sheet
Perf. 12½
2723 A742 1p Baseball 4.50 1.60
No. 2723 contains one 32x40mm stamp.

Emilio Roig de Leuchsenring (1889-1964), Historian A743

1984, Aug. 8 *Perf. 13*
2724 A743 5c multi .25 .20

Friendship Games, Aug. 18-26, Havana — A744

1984, Aug. 18
2725 A744 3c Volleyball .20 .20
2726 A744 5c Women's volleyball .35 .20
2727 A744 8c Water polo .35 .20
2728 A744 30c Boxing 1.25 .35
Nos. 2725-2728 (4) 2.15 .95

Cattle
Breeding
A745

1984, Sept. 20
2729	A745	2c	Artificial pastures	.20	.20
2730	A745	3c	Cuban carib	.20	.20
2731	A745	5c	Charolaise, vert.	.20	.20
2732	A745	30c	Cuban cebu, vert.	1.25	.40
2733	A745	50c	White-udder	2.25	.75
		Nos. 2729-2733 (5)		4.10	1.75

Souvenir Sheet

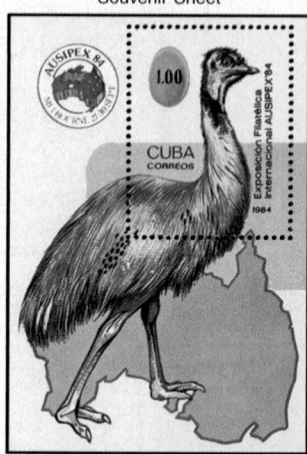

AUSIPEX '84, Sept. 21-30,
Melbourne — A746

1984, Sept. 21   *Perf. 12½*
2734	A746	1p Emu	4.75	2.50

Fauna — A747

1984, Oct. 10   *Perf. 13*
2735	A747	1c	Polymita	.20	.20
2736	A747	2c	Solenodon cubanus	.20	.20
2737	A747	3c	Alsophis canther-igerus	.20	.20
2738	A747	4c	Osteopilus septentrionalis	.20	.20
2739	A747	5c	Mellisuga helenae	.35	.20
2740	A747	10c	Capromys me-lanurus	.20	.20
2741	A747	30c	Todus multicolor	1.50	.45
2742	A747	50c	Parrots (cotorra)	2.25	.60
		Nos. 2735-2742 (8)		5.10	2.25

Souvenir Sheet

ESPAMER
'85,
Havana
A748

1984, Oct. 12
2743		Sheet of 4+2 labels	5.00	2.50
a.	A748	5c Ferdinand, Isabella	.20	.20
b.	A748	20c Departure from Palos	1.50	.70
c.	A748	30c Nina, Pinta, Santa Ma-ria	2.25	1.10
d.	A748	50c Landing in America	1.00	.50

Columbus Day.

Souvenir Sheet

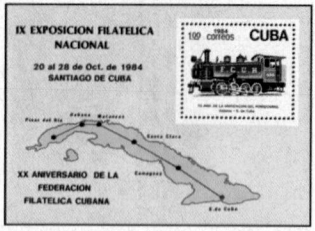

9th Natl. Phil. Exhibition, Oct. 20-28,
Santiago de Cuba — A749

1984, Oct. 20   *Perf. 12½*
2744	A749	1p multicolored	4.50	1.60

Natl. Revolutionary Militia, 25th
Anniv. — A750

1984, Oct. 26   *Perf. 12½x13*
2745	A750	5c multi	.30	.20

Disappearance of Camilo Cienfuegos,
25th Anniv. — A751

1984, Oct. 28   *Perf. 13x12½*
2746	A751	5c multi	.40	.20

UN Child
Survival
Campaign
A752

1984, Nov. 11   *Perf. 13*
2747	A752	5c Breast-feeding	.40	.20

Classic Automobiles — A753

1984, Nov. 25
2748	A753	1c	1909 Morgan	.20	.20
2749	A753	2c	1922 Austin	.20	.20
2750	A753	5c	1903 De Dion-Bouton	.20	.20
2751	A753	20c	1908 Ford Model T	.95	.20
2752	A753	30c	1885 Benz	1.50	.35
2753	A753	50c	1910 Benz	2.75	.70
		Nos. 2748-2753 (6)		5.80	1.85

Postal Museum, 20th Anniv. — A754

1985, Jan. 2   *Perf. 13x12½*
2754	A754	20c multi	.75	.25

Portrait of Celia Sanchez, by E.
Escobedo
A755

1985, Jan. 11   *Perf. 13*
2755	A755	5c multi	.40	.20

Celia Sanchez (1920-1980), party leader.

PORTO '85, Intl. Pigeon
Exhibition — A756

1985, Jan. 23
2756	A756	20c multi	1.25	.25

1986 World Cup Soccer
Championships, Mexico — A757

Athletes and Flags of previous host nations.

1985, Jan. 25
2757	A757	1c	Chile, 1962	.20	.20
2758	A757	2c	Great Britain, 1966	.20	.20
2759	A757	3c	Mexico, 1970	.20	.20
2760	A757	4c	Federal Republic of Germany, 1974	.25	.20
2761	A757	5c	Argentina, 1978	.25	.20
2762	A757	30c	Spain, 1982	1.40	.35
2763	A757	50c	Sweden, 1958	2.25	.60
		Nos. 2757-2763 (7)		4.75	1.95

Souvenir Sheet
Perf. 12½
2764	A757	1p Mexico, 1986	4.00	2.00

No. 2764 contains one 40x32mm stamp.

Bacanao Natl. Park — A758

Dinosaurs.

1985, Feb. 14   *Perf. 13x12½*
2765	A758	1c	Pteranodon	.30	.20
2766	A758	2c	Brontosaurus	.30	.20
2767	A758	4c	Iguanodontus	.30	.20
2768	A758	5c	Estegosaurus	.30	.20
2769	A758	8c	Monoclonius	.50	.20
2770	A758	30c	Corythosaurus	1.50	.35
2771	A758	50c	Tyrannosaurus	2.75	.55
		Nos. 2765-2771 (7)		5.95	1.90

13th Congress of the Postal Unions of
the Americas, Havana — A759

Design: Uruguay #196, congress emblem
and Brazil #287. Illustration reduced.

1985, Mar. 11   *Perf. 12½x12*
2772	A759	20c multi	.75	.25

ESPAMER
'85 — A760

Indian activities: 1c, Playing ball. 2c,
Medicine man preparing calumet and other ritual items. 5c, Net and spear fishing. 20c, Potter. 30c, Hunting. 50c, Hollowing-out canoe,
decorating paddle. 1p, Cooking.

1985, Mar. 19   *Perf. 12½x13*
2773	A760	1c	multi	.20	.20
2774	A760	2c	multi	.20	.20
2775	A760	5c	multi	.35	.20
2776	A760	20c	multi	.35	.20
2777	A760	30c	multi	.55	.20
2778	A760	50c	multi	2.50	.60
		Nos. 2773-2778 (6)		4.15	1.70

Souvenir Sheet
Perf. 12½
2779	A760	1p multi	5.00	1.60

No. 2779 contains one 32x40mm stamp.
An imperf. souvenir sheet exists containing
Nos. 2773-2779.

Cosmonauts' Day — A761

Designs: 2c, Spacecraft orbiting Moon. 3c,
Two spacecraft. 10c, Space walkers linked.
13c, Space walkers welding. 20c, *Vostok 2.*
50c, *Lunokhod 1* moon vehicle.

1985, Apr. 12   *Perf. 13x12½*
2780	A761	2c	multi	.20	.20
2781	A761	3c	multi	.20	.20
2782	A761	10c	multi	.45	.20
2783	A761	13c	multi	.65	.20
2784	A761	20c	multi	.75	.25
2785	A761	50c	multi	2.50	.70
		Nos. 2780-2785 (6)		4.75	1.75

12th Youth and Students Festival, Moscow A762

1985, Apr. 19   *Perf. 13*
2786 A762 30c Lenin Mausoleum   .50   .35

Stamp Day Type of 1984

Mural, by R. Rodriguez Radillo (1967), details: 20c, Roman charioteer (courier of *Cursus Publicus*). 35c, Medieval nobleman, monks (monastic messenger mail).

1985, Apr. 24   *Perf. 13x12½*
2787 A733 20c multi   .80   .20
2788 A733 35c multi   1.10   .30

Mothers' Day — A763

1985, May 2   *Perf. 13*
2789 A763 1c Peonies   .20   .20
2790 A763 4c Carnations   .20   .20
2791 A763 5c Dahlias   .20   .20
2792 A763 13c Roses   .45   .20
2793 A763 20c Roses, diff.   .75   .20
2794 A763 50c Tulips   2.00   .50
     Nos. 2789-2794 (6)   3.80 1.50

50th Death Anniv. of Antonio Guiteras and Carlos Aponte, Revolutionaries — A764

1985, May 9   *Perf. 12½x12*
2795 A764 5c multi   .25   .25

End of WWII, 40th Anniv. A765

1985, May 10
2796 A765 5c shown   .20   .20
2797 A765 20c Soviet memorial, Berlin-Treptow   .65   .25
2798 A765 30c Dove   1.10   .35
     Nos. 2796-2798 (3)   1.95   .80

Souvenir Sheet

ARGENTINA '85, Buenos Aires — A766

1985, June 5   *Perf. 13½x13*
2799 A766 1p *Vulture gryphus*   4.50 1.60

Motorcycle, Cent. — A767

1985, June 28   *Perf. 13*
2800 A767 2c 1885 Daimler   .20   .20
2801 A767 5c 1910 Kaiser Tricycle   .25   .20
2802 A767 10c 1925 Fanomobile   .55   .20
2803 A767 30c 1926 Mars A20   1.50   .30
2804 A767 50c 1936 Simson BSW   2.75   .70
     Nos. 2800-2804 (5)   5.25 1.60

Development of Health Care Since the Revolution — A768

1985, July 18   *Perf. 12½x12*
2805 A768 5c Hospitals   .25   .20

Federation of Cuban Women (FMC), 25th Anniv. — A769

1985, Aug. 23
2806 A769 5c multi   .25   .20
   No. 2806 printed se-tenant with label picturing federation emblem.

Universiade Games, Japan — A770

1985, Aug. 27   *Perf. 13*
2807 A770 50c multi   1.75   .35

1st Havana Declaration, 25th Anniv. — A771

1985, Sept. 2
2808 A771 5c Jose Marti statue, revolutionaries   .40   .20

Souvenir Sheet

ITALIA '85 — A772

1985, Sept. 25   *Perf. 12½*
2809 A772 1p Roman galley   5.00 1.60

Revolutionary Defense Committees (CDR), 25th Anniv. — A773

1985, Sept. 28   *Perf. 13*
2810 A773 5c multi   .25   .20

Aquarium Fish — A774

1985, Sept. 30   Litho.
2811 A774 1c *Centropyge argi*   .20   .20
2812 A774 3c *Holacanthus tricolor*   .20   .20
2813 A774 5c *Chaetodon capistratus*   .20   .20
2814 A774 10c *Chaetodon sedentarius*   .30   .20
2815 A774 20c *Chaetodon ocellatus*   .70   .20
2816 A774 50c *Holacanthus ciliaris*   1.75   .60
     Nos. 2811-2816 (6)   3.35 1.60

Communist Party Central Committee, 20th Anniv. — A775

1985, Oct. 1
2817 A775 5c multi   .40   .20

Souvenir Sheet

EXFILNA '85 — A776

1985, Oct. 18
2818 A776 1p Spain No. C45, Cuba No. 387   5.00 2.50

UN, 40th Anniv. — A777

1985, Oct. 24
2819 A777 20c multi   .90   .25

Sites on the UNESCO World Heritage List — A778

Designs: 2c, Plaza Vieja, 16th cent. 5c, Royal Army Castle, c. 1558. 20c, Havana Cathedral, c. 1748. 30c, Captains-General Palace (Havana City Museum), 1776. 50c, The Temple, 1827.

1985, Nov. 25
2820 A778 2c multi   .25   .20
2821 A778 5c multi   .25   .20
2822 A778 20c multi   .95   .25
2823 A778 30c multi   1.50   .45
2824 A778 50c multi   2.40   .60
     Nos. 2820-2824 (5)   5.35 1.70

1986 World Cup Soccer Championships, Mexico — A779

Various athletes.

1986, Jan. 20
2825 A779 1c multi   .20   .20
2826 A779 4c multi   .20   .20
2827 A779 5c multi   .20   .20
2828 A779 10c multi   .30   .20
2829 A779 30c multi   1.10   .25
2830 A779 50c multi   1.60   .40
     Nos. 2825-2830 (6)   3.60 1.45

Souvenir Sheet
Perf. 13½x13
2831 A779 1p multi   4.50 2.25
   No. 2831 contains one 32x40mm stamp.

3rd Communist Party Congress,
Havana — A780

1986, Feb. 4   **Perf. 13**
2832 A780 5c shown   .20 .20
2833 A780 20c Party and natl.
                flags, emblem   1.25 .25

Natl.
Sports
Institute
(INDER),
25th
Anniv.
A781

1986, Feb. 23
2834 A781 5c multi   .30 .20

A782   A783

1986, Feb. 23
2835 A782 5c multi   .30 .20

Ministry of Domestic Trade, 25th anniv.

1986, Feb. 25   **Perf. 12½x12**

Exotic flowers in the Botanical Gardens.

2836 A783 1c Tecomaria capen-
                sis   .20 .20
2837 A783 3c Michelia champa-
                ca   .20 .20
2838 A783 5c Thunbergia
                grandiflora   .20 .20
2839 A783 8c Dendrobium
                phalaenopsis   .20 .20
2840 A783 30c Allamanda vio-
                lacea   .75 .25
2841 A783 50c Rhodactus bleo   1.10 .40
           Nos. 2836-2841 (6)   2.65 1.45

Gundlach and Birds — A784

1986, Mar. 14 Litho. Perf. 13½x13
2842 A784 1c Agelaius assimilis   .20 .20
2843 A784 3c Dendroica pity-
                ophila   .20 .20
2844 A784 7c Myiarchus sagrae   .20 .20
2845 A784 9c Dendroica pete-
                chia gundlachi   .25 .20
2846 A784 30c Geotrygon
                caniceps   1.10 .30
2847 A784 50c Colaptes auratus
                chrysocaulosus   1.90 .45
           Nos. 2842-2847 (6)   3.85 1.55

Juan Cristobal Gundlach (d. 1896),
ornithologist.

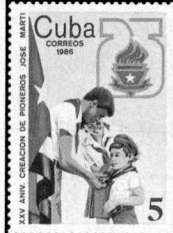

Pioneers Youth
Organization,
25th
Anniv. — A785

1986, Apr. 3   **Perf. 13**
2848 A785 5c Induction   .30 .20

150th Birth
Anniv. of
Maximo
Gomez — A786

1986, Apr. 4
2849 A786 20c multi   .90 .25

A787

1986, Apr. 10   **Perf. 12½**
2850 A787 5c multi   .40 .20

Kindergartens, 25th anniv.

1986, Apr. 12   **Perf. 13x13½**

1st Man in Space, 25th Anniv.: 1c, Vostok
and rocket designer Sergei Korolev. 2c, Yuri
Gagarin, Vostok 1. 5c, Valentina Tereshkova,
Vostok 6. 20c, Salyut-Soyuz space link. 30c,
Capsule landing. 50c, Soyuz rocket launch.
1p, Konstantin Tsiolkovski (1857-1935), rocket
scientist.

A788

2851 A788 1c multi   .20 .20
2852 A788 2c multi   .20 .20
2853 A788 5c multi   .20 .20
2854 A788 20c multi   .60 .20
2855 A788 30c multi   .80 .20
2856 A788 50c multi   1.75 .35
           Nos. 2851-2856 (6)   3.75 1.35

Souvenir Sheet
Perf. 12½
2857 A788 1p multi   4.50 1.60

No. 2857 contains one 32x40mm stamp.

Natl. Flag and
No. 2407
A789

1986, Apr. 19   **Perf. 13**
2858 A789 5c shown   .20 .20
2859 A789 20c Banners, natl.
                crest   1.10 .20

Bay of Pigs invasion, 25th anniv. (5c); Proclamation of Socialist Revolution, 25th anniv.
(20c).

Stamp Day Type of 1984
Mural, by R. Rodriguez Radillo (1967),
details.

1986, Apr. 24   **Perf. 13x12½**
2860 A733 20c Mail coach, 18th-
                19th cent.   .75 .20
2861 A733 30c Pony Express   1.00 .25

Radio Havana,
25th
Anniv. — A790

1986, May 1
2862 A790 5c multi   .40 .20

EXPO '86, Vancouver — A791

Locomotives: 1c, Stourbridge Lion, 1829,
US. 4c, Stephenson's Rocket, 1829, GB. 5c,
1st Russian locomotive, 1845. 8c, Seguin's
locomotive, 1830, France. 30c, 1st Canadian
locomotive, 1836. 50c, Urban locomotive, Belgian Grand Central Rlwy., 1872. 1p, US locomotive pulling Cuban sugar train, 1837.

1986, May 2 Litho. Perf. 12½x12
2863 A791 1c multi   .20 .20
2864 A791 4c multi   .20 .20
2865 A791 5c multi   .20 .20
2866 A791 8c multi   .20 .20
2867 A791 30c multi   .50 .20
2868 A791 50c multi   1.25 .25
           Nos. 2863-2868 (6)   2.55 1.25

Souvenir Sheet
Perf. 13x13½
2869 A791 1p multi   5.00 1.60

No. 2869 contains one 40x32mm stamp.

Assoc. of Small Farmers, (ANAP),
25th Anniv. — A792

1986, May 17   **Perf. 13**
2870 A792 5c multi   .40 .20

Intl.
Peace
Year
A793

1986, June 2
2871 A793 30c multi   1.00 .25

Ministry of the
Interior
(MININT), 25th
Anniv. — A794

1986, June 6
2872 A794 5c multi   .40 .20

Martin
Luther
King, Jr.
A795

1986, June 27   **Perf. 13½x13**
2873 A795 20c multi   1.00 .25

Bonifacio
Byrne (d.
1936),
Poet
A796

1986, July 5   **Perf. 13**
2874 A796 5c multi   .30 .20

Cuban Union of   Sandinista
Writers and Artists   Movement in
(UNEAC), 25th   Nicaragua
Anniv. — A797   (FSLN), 25th
                        Anniv. — A798

1986, July 10   **Perf. 13x12½**
2875 A797 5c multi   .30 .20

1986, July 23   **Perf. 13x12**

Augusto Cesar Sandino and Carlos
Fonseca.

2876 A798 20c multi   .75 .25

Ministry of Transportation, 25th
Anniv. — A799

1986, Aug. 1   **Perf. 13**
2877 A799 5c multi   .35 .20

7th University Games of Central America and the Caribbean A800

1986, Aug. 9
2878 A800 20c multi   1.00 .25

Souvenir Sheet

STOCKHOLMIA '86 — A801

Designs: a, 2c Mambi Revolutionary stamp of 1897. b, Sweden Type A7, cancellation.

1986, Aug. 28   **Perf. 12½**
2879 A801   Sheet of 2   4.50 1.60
   a.-b.   50c multi

Nonaligned Countries Movement, 25th Anniv. — A802

1986, Sept. 1   **Perf. 13½x13**
2880 A802 50c multi   2.00 .45

Orchids — A803

1986, Sept. 15   **Perf. 12½**
2881 A803 1c *Cattleya hardy-ana*   .20 .20
2882 A803 4c *Brassolaelio cat-tleya*   .20 .20
2883 A803 5c *Phalaenopsis marget moses*   .20 .20
2884 A803 10c *Laelio cattleya prism palette*   .25 .20
2885 A803 30c *Phalaenopsis vio-lacea*   1.00 1.00
2886 A803 50c *Disa uniflora*   1.60 .40
   Nos. 2881-2886 (6)   3.45 1.40

Latin American History — A804

Pre-Columbian artifacts: No. 2887, Mayan dwelling and votive jade sculpture. No. 2888, Inca vase and Tiahuanacu sun gate (Bolivia). No. 2889, Spain No. C47, discovery of America 500th anniv. emblem, scroll. No. 2890, Diaguitan duck-shaped pitcher and Pucara de Quitor ruins (Chile). No. 2891, San Agustin Archaeological Park megaliths and Quimbayan sculpture (Colombia). No. 2892, Moler grinding stone and Chorotega ceramic figurine. No. 2893, Tabaco idol and Indian

dwelling (Cuba). No. 2894, Spain No. C38. No. 2895, Taino dwelling and chair (Dominica). No. 2896, Tolita statue and Ingapirca Castle ruins. No. 2897, Maya vase and Tikal Temple (Guatemala). No. 2898, Copan ruins and Maya idol. No. 2899, Spain No. C37. No. 2900, Chichen Itza Temple and Zapotecan urn (Mexico). No. 2901, Punta de Zapote mega-liths and Ometepe ceramic figurine. No. 2902, Tonosi lidded ceramic bowl and Barriles mono-liths. No. 2903, Ruins at Machu-Picchu and Inca statue (Peru). No. 2904, Spain No. C49. No. 2905, Teepees and triangular sculpture (Puerto Rico). No. 2906, Fertility statue from Santa Ana and Santo Domingo Cave.

1986, Oct. 12   **Perf. 13**
2887 A804 1c multi   .20 .20
2888 A804 1c multi   .20 .20
2889 A804 1c multi   .20 .20
2890 A804 1c multi   .20 .20
2891 A804 1c multi   .20 .20
   a.   Strip of 5, Nos. 2887-2891   1.00 1.00
2892 A804 5c multi   .20 .20
2893 A804 5c multi   .20 .20
2894 A804 5c multi   .20 .20
2895 A804 5c multi   .20 .20
2896 A804 5c multi   .20 .20
   a.   Strip of 5, Nos. 2892-2896   1.00 1.00
2897 A804 10c multi   .30 .20
2898 A804 10c multi   .30 .20
2899 A804 10c multi   .30 .20
2900 A804 10c multi   .30 .20
2901 A804 10c multi   .30 .20
   a.   Strip of 5, Nos. 2897-2901   1.50 1.00
2902 A804 20c multi   .70 .30
2903 A804 20c multi   .70 .30
2904 A804 20c multi   .70 .30
2905 A804 20c multi   .70 .30
2906 A804 20c multi   .70 .30
   a.   Strip of 5, Nos. 2902-2906   3.50 1.50
   Nos. 2887-2906 (20)   7.00 4.50

Discovery of America, 500th anniv. (in 1992). See Nos. 2966-2985, 3065-3084, 3253-3272, 3463-3466.

Intl. Brigades, Spain, 50th Anniv. — A805

1986, Oct. 14   **Perf. 12½x12**
2907 A805 30c multi   .75 .35

Paintings in the Natl. Museum A806

Designs: 2c, *Two Children*, by Gutierrez de la Vega, vert. 4c, *Sed*, by Jean-Georges Vibert. 6c, *Virgin and Child*, by Niccolo Abbate, vert. 10c, *Bullfight*, by Eugenio de Lucas Velazquez. 30c, *The Five Senses*, anonymous. 50c, *Arrival at Thomops Castle*, by Jean Louis Ernest.

1986, Nov. 5   **Perf. 13**
2908 A806 2c multi   .25 .20
2909 A806 4c multi   .25 .20
2910 A806 6c multi   .25 .20
2911 A806 10c multi   .40 .20
2912 A806 30c multi   1.10 .20
2913 A806 50c multi   1.90 .25
   Nos. 2908-2913 (6)   4.15 1.25

Anniversaries — A807

1986, Dec. 2   **Litho.**   **Perf. 12½**
2914 A807 5c *Granma*   .45 .20

Size: 26x38mm

2915 A807 20c Soldier, rifle, flag   1.50 .20

Granma Landings, 30th anniv. (5c); Revolu-tionary Armed Forces, 30th anniv. (20c).

Scholarship Program, 25th Anniv. — A808

1986, Dec. 22   **Perf. 13**
2916 A808 5c Guevara, students   .30 .20

Natl. Literacy Campaign, 25th Anniv. — A809

1986, Dec. 25   **Perf. 13x12½**
2917 A809 5c Marti, man learn-ing to write   .30 .20

Siege of La Plata, 30th Anniv. A810

1987, Jan. 17   **Perf. 12½x12**
2918 A810 5c Map, revolutionar-ies   .30 .20

Paintings in the Natl. Museum A811

3c, *Gypsy*, by Joaquin Sorolla. 5c, *Sir Wal-ter Scott*, by Sir John W. Gordon. 10c, *Farm Meadows*, by Alfred de Breanski. 20c, *Still-life*, by Isaac van Duynen. 30c, *Landscape with Figures*, by Francesco Zuccarelli. 40c, *The Failure* (defeated bullfighter), by Ignacio Zuloaga.

1987, Feb. 5   **Perf. 13**
2919 A811 3c multi, vert.   .25 .20
2920 A811 5c multi, vert.   .25 .20
2921 A811 10c multi   .40 .20
2922 A811 20c multi   1.00 .20
2923 A811 30c multi   1.10 .20
2924 A811 40c multi, vert.   1.60 .25
   Nos. 2919-2924 (6)   4.60 1.25

Siege of the Presidential Palace, 30th Anniv. — A812

1987, Mar. 13   **Perf. 12½x12**
2925 A812 5c Palace, van, Echeverra   .30 .20

Lazarus Ludwig Zamenhof and Russia Type A77 — A813

1987, Mar. 16   **Perf. 13½x13**
2926 A813 30c multi   1.00 .25
   Esperanto, cent.

Souvenir Sheet

EXFILNA '87, 10th Natl. Stamp Exposition, Holguin — A814

1987, Mar. 28   **Perf. 13x13½**
2927 A814 1p Nos. 552, C129   4.50 2.25

25th Anniv. and 5th Cong. of the Youth Communist League (U.J.C.) — A815

1987, Apr. 4   **Perf. 13**
2928 A815 5c multi   .30 .20

Intercosmos, 20th Anniv. — A816

1987, Apr. 12   **Litho.**   **Perf. 12½x12**
2929 A816 3c *Intercosmos 1*   .20 .20
2930 A816 5c *Intercosmos 2*   .20 .20
2931 A816 10c *TD*   .30 .20
2932 A816 20c *Cosmos 93*   .75 .20
2933 A816 30c *Molniya*   1.00 .20
2934 A816 50c *Vostok 3*   1.60 .25
   Nos. 2929-2934 (6)   4.05 1.25

Souvenir Sheet
Perf. 13½x13

2935 A816 1p Rocket, *Vostok 3*   4.50 2.25

No. 2935 contains one 32x40mm stamp.

Stamp Day A817

Stamped covers and canceled stamps.

1987, Apr. 24   **Perf. 13**
2936 A817 30c Havana, 1890   1.25 .30
2937 A817 50c Santiago de Cu-ba, 1869   2.10 .60

Mothers' Day — A818

Various dahlias and roses.

1987, May 2
2938	A818	3c multi	.20	.20
2939	A818	5c multi	.20	.20
2940	A818	10c multi	.25	.20
2941	A818	13c multi	.30	.20
2942	A818	30c multi	.70	.20
2943	A818	50c multi	1.25	.30
	Nos. 2938-2943 (6)		2.90	1.30

Bone-lengthening Procedure (Femur in Frame) — A819

1987, May 4
2944	A819	5c multi	.30	.20

ORTOPEDIA '87, medical congress for orthopedists from Spanish and Portuguese-speaking countries, Havana.

Cuban Broadcasting and Television Institute, 25th Anniv. — A820

1987, May 24 Perf. 13
2945	A820	5c multi	.30	.20

Battle of Uvero, 30th Anniv. A821

1987, May 28 Perf. 13½x13
2946	A821	5c Views of monument, Sierra Maestra Mts.		.30	.20

CAPEX '87 — A822

Natl. flags, stamps and 19th cent. mail carriers pictured on cigarette cards: 3c, Messenger, llamas and Bolivia Type A9. 5c, Early p.o., automobile and France Type A17. 10c, Messengers riding elephants and Thailand Type A2. 20c, Messenger riding camel and stamp of Egypt, 1879. 30c, Mail troika and stamp of Russia. 50c, Post rider and stamp of Indo-China. 1p, Post rider and Mambi Revolutionary stamp.

1987, June 15 Perf. 12½x13
2947	A822	3c multi	.20	.20
2948	A822	5c multi	.20	.20
2949	A822	10c multi	.25	.20
2950	A822	20c multi	.50	.20
2951	A822	30c multi	.70	.20
2952	A822	50c multi	1.25	.30
	Nos. 2947-2952 (6)		3.10	1.30

Souvenir Sheet
Perf. 13½x13
2953	A822	1p multi	4.50	1.60

No. 2953 contains one 32x40mm stamp.

Dinosaur Exhibits, Bacanao Natl. Park A823

1987, June 25 Perf. 13
2954	A823	3c multi	.20	.20
2955	A823	5c multi	.20	.20
2956	A823	10c multi	.30	.20
2957	A823	20c multi	.65	.20
2958	A823	35c multi	1.10	.20
2959	A823	40c multi	1.25	.25
	Nos. 2954-2959 (6)		3.70	1.25

Frank Pais (d. 1957), Teacher and Student Leader — A824

1987, July 30 Perf. 12½x12
2960	A824	5c Pais, Rafael Maria Mendive University		.30	.20

10th Pan American Games, Indianapolis — A825

1987, Aug. 8
2961	A825	50c multi	1.75	.45

Printed se-tenant with inscribed label picturing the 1991 Havana Games character trademark.

Siege of Cienfuegos, 30th Anniv. — A826

1987, Sept. 5 Perf. 13
2962	A826	5c Memorial	.30	.20

Souvenir Sheet

HAFNIA '87, Denmark — A827

1987, Sept. 16 Perf. 13½x13
2963	A827	1p Danish mailman, 1887, Type A6		4.50	1.60

Souvenir Sheet

ESPAMER '87, La Coruna, Oct. 2-12 — A828

1987, Oct. 2
2964	A828	1p La Coruna Port, 1525		4.50	2.25

20th Heroic Guerrillas Day — A829

1987, Oct. 8 Perf. 12½x12
2965	A829	50c Coins, #1364	1.00	.55

Latin American History Type of 1986

Indians and birds: #2966, Tehuelche Indian of Argentina, *Habia rubica*. #2967, *Ramphastos cuvieri*, Tibirica Indian of Brazil. #2968, Spain #C31 & discovery of America 500th anniv. emblem. #2969, *Vulture gryphus*, Lautaro Indian of Chile. #2970, Calarca Indian of Colombia, *Opisthocomus hoazin*. #2971, *Priotelus temnurus*, Hatuey Indian of Cuba. #2972, *Columbigallina passerina*, Enriquillo Indian of the Dominican Republic. #2973, Spain #427. #2974, *Semnornis ramphastinus*, Ruminahui Indian of Ecuador. #2975, *Pharomachrus mocinno*, Tecum Uman Indian of Guatemala. #2976, Anacaona Indian of Haiti, *Aramas guarauna*. #2977, Lempira Indian of Honduras, *Diglossa baritula*. #2978, Spain #C42. #2979, *Onychorhinchus mexicanus*, Cuauhtemoc Indian of Mexico. #2980, *Setofaga picta*, Nicarao Indian of Nicaragua. #2981, *Rupicola peruviana*, Atahualpa Indian of Peru. #2982, Atlacatl Indian of El Salvador, *Bluteo jamaicensis*. #2983, Spain #432. #2984, Abayuba Indian of Uruguay, *Phytotoma rutila*. #2985, Guaycaypuro Indian of Venezuela, *Ara arauna*.

1987, Oct. 12 Perf. 13
2966	A804	1c multi	.20	.20
2967	A804	1c multi	.20	.20
2968	A804	1c multi	.20	.20
2969	A804	1c multi	.20	.20
2970	A804	1c multi	.20	.20
a.		Strip of 5, Nos. 2966-2970	1.00	1.00
2971	A804	5c multi	.20	.20
2972	A804	5c multi	.20	.20
2973	A804	5c multi	.20	.20
2974	A804	5c multi	.20	.20
2975	A804	5c multi	.20	.20
a.		Strip of 5, Nos. 2971-2975	1.00	1.00
2976	A804	10c multi	.40	.20
2977	A804	10c multi	.40	.20
2978	A804	10c multi	.40	.20
2979	A804	10c multi	.40	.20
2980	A804	10c multi	.40	.20
a.		Strip of 5, Nos. 2976-2980	2.00	1.00
2981	A804	20c multi	.50	.40
2982	A804	20c multi	.50	.40
2983	A804	20c multi	.50	.40
2984	A804	20c multi	.50	.40
2985	A804	20c multi	.50	.40
a.		Strip of 5, Nos. 2981-2985	2.50	2.00
	Nos. 2966-2985 (20)		6.50	5.00

Discovery of America, 500th anniv. (in 1992). *Vultur* is spelled incorrectly on No. 2969.

October Revolution, Russia, 70th Anniv. — A830

1987, Nov. 7 Perf. 12½x12
2986	A830	30c Soviet spacecraft, Russia No. 379		1.00	.25

Cuban Railway, 150th Anniv. — A831

Stamps on stamps.

1987, Nov. 19 Perf. 13x12½
2987	A831	3c No. 453	.20	.20
2988	A831	5c No. 1061	.20	.20
2989	A831	10c No. 2010	.20	.20
2990	A831	20c No. 2011	.40	.20
2991	A831	35c No. 2360	.85	.20
2992	A831	40c No. 2361	1.00	.20
	Nos. 2987-2992 (6)		2.85	1.25

Souvenir Sheet
Perf. 13x13½
2993	A831	1p No. 355	4.00	1.60

No. 2993 contains 40x32mm one stamp. An imperf. sheet containing Nos. 2987-2992 exists, inscribed to promote the 17th Pan American Railway Congress.

San Alejandro Art School, 170th Anniv. — A832

Paintings: 1c, *Landscape*, by Domingo Ramos. 2c, *Portrait of Rodriguez Morey*, by Eugenio Gonzalez Olivera. 3c, *Landscape with Malangas and Palm Trees*, by Valentin Sanz Carta. 5c, *Wagons*, by Eduardo Morales. 10c, *Portrait of Elena Herrera*, by Armando Menocal, vert. 30c, *Rape of Dejanira*, by Miguel Melero, vert. 50c, *The Card Player*, by Leopoldo Romanach.

1988, Jan. 12 Perf. 13x12½, 12½x13
2994	A832	1c multi	.20	.20
2995	A832	2c multi	.20	.20
2995A	A832	3c multi	.20	.20
2996	A832	5c multi	.20	.20
2997	A832	10c multi	.30	.20
2998	A832	30c multi	.85	.20
2999	A832	50c multi	1.50	.30
	Nos. 2994-2999 (7)		3.45	1.50

Poisonous Mushrooms A833

1988, Feb. 15 Perf. 13
3000	A833	1c *Boletus satanas*	.20	.20
3001	A833	2c *Amanita citrina*	.20	.20
3002	A833	3c *Tylopilus felleus*	.20	.20
3003	A833	5c *Paxillus involutus*	.20	.20

3004 A833 10c *Inocybe patouil-*
lardii .50 .20
3005 A833 30c *Amanita muscaria* 1.25 .20
3006 A833 50c *Hypholoma fas-*
ciculare 2.10 .40
Nos. 3000-3006 (7) 4.65 1.60

Radio Rebelde, 30th Anniv. — A834

1988, Feb. 24 *Perf. 12½x12*
3007 A834 5c multi .30 .20

Monuments
A835

1988 **Litho.** *Perf. 13*
3008 A835 5c Mario Munoz, Santiago de Cuba .45 .20
3009 A835 5c Frank Pais Memorial, eternal flame .45 .20

Battle fronts, 30th annivs. Issue dates: No.
3008, Mar. 5. No. 3009, Mar. 11.

Mothers'
Day — A836

1988, Mar. 30
3010 A836 1c Red roses .20 .20
3011 A836 2c Pale pink roses .20 .20
3012 A836 3c Daisies .20 .20
3013 A836 5c Dahlias .20 .20
3014 A836 13c White roses .30 .20
3015 A836 35c Carnations .90 .20
3016 A836 40c Pink roses 1.10 .20
Nos. 3010-3016 (7) 3.10 1.40

Cosmonauts' Day — A837

1988, Apr. 12
3017 A837 2c *Gorizont* .20 .20
3018 A837 3c *Mir-Kvant* space
link .20 .20
3019 A837 4c *Signo 3* .20 .20
3020 A837 5c Mars, space
probe .20 .20
3021 A837 10c *Phobos* .30 .20
3022 A837 30c *Vega* .85 .20
3023 A837 50c Spacecraft 1.50 .30
Nos. 3017-3023 (7) 3.45 1.50
Souvenir Sheet
Perf. 13½x13
3024 A837 1p Spacecraft, diff. 4.25 1.60
No. 3024 contains one 32x40mm stamp.

Stamp Day Type of 1984

Mural, by R. Rodriguez Radillo (1967)
details: 30c, Mail coach, telegraph operator.
50c, Passenger pigeon.

1988, Apr. 24 *Perf. 13x12½*
3025 A733 30c multi 1.10 .40
3026 A733 50c multi 1.90 .50

Institute for Research on Sugar Cane
and Byproducts (ICIDCA), 25th
Anniv. — A838

1988, May 23 *Perf. 12½x12*
3027 A838 5c multi .30 .20

Cubana Airlines Transatlantic
Flights — A839

1988, May 25
3028 A839 2c Madrid, 1948 .20 .20
3029 A839 4c Prague, 1961 .20 .20
3030 A839 5c Berlin, 1972 .20 .20
3031 A839 10c Luanda, 1975 .30 .20
3032 A839 30c Paris, 1983 1.00 .20
3033 A839 50c Moscow, 1987 1.60 .30
Nos. 3028-3033 (6) 3.50 1.30

Souvenir Sheet

FINLANDIA '88 — A840

1988, June 1 *Perf. 12½*
3034 A840 1p Steam packet
Furst Menschikoff 4.00 2.00

Postal Union of the Americas and
Spain (UPAE) Conference on Stamps
of the Americas, Havana — A841

Illustration reduced.

1988, June 20 *Perf. 12½x12*
3035 A841 20c multi .75 .35

Beetles
A842

1988, June 30 *Perf. 13*
3036 A842 1c *Megasoma*
elephas fabricus .20 .20
3037 A842 3c *Platycoelia flavos-*
cutellata ohaus,
vert. .20 .20
3038 A842 4c *Plusiotis argente-*
ola bates .20 .20
3039 A842 5c *Heterosternus*
oberthuri ohaus .20 .20
3040 A842 10c *Odontotaenius*
zodiacus truqui .30 .20
3041 A842 35c *Chrysophora*
chrysochlora la-
treille, vert. 1.00 .20

3042 A842 40c *Phanaeus lean-*
der waterhouse 1.25 .30
Nos. 3036-3042 (7) 3.35 1.50

Jose Raul Capablanca (1888-1942),
Chess Champion — A843

1988, July 15 *Perf. 12½x13, 13x12½*
3043 A843 30c Chessmen, vert. .60 .25
3044 A843 40c J. Corza,
Capablanca .90 .25
3045 A843 50c Lasker,
Capablanca .95 .30
3046 A843 1p Winning config-
uration, 1921,
vert. 2.40 .65
3047 A843 3p Portrait by E.
Valderrama,
vert. 7.25 1.75
3048 A843 5p Chessmen,
Capablanca 12.50 3.25
Nos. 3043-3048 (6) 24.60 6.45

Souvenir Sheets
3049 Sheet of 2 1.25 .65
a. A843 30c No. 464, vert. .45 .30
b. like No. 3043, size: 32x40mm .45 .30
3050 Sheet of 2 1.50 .75
a. A843 40c No. 465 .55 .35
b. like No. 3044, size: 40x32mm .55 .35
3051 Sheet of 2 2.00 1.00
a. A843 50c No. C44 .60 .45
b. like No. 3045, size: 40x32mm .60 .45
3052 Sheet of 2 4.00 2.00
a. A843 1p No. 464, vert. 1.25 .90
b. like No. 3046, size: 32x40mm 1.25 .90
3053 Sheet of 2 12.00 6.00
a. A843 3p No. C46, vert. 4.25 2.75
b. like No. 3047, size: 32x40mm 4.25 2.75
3054 Sheet of 2 20.00 10.00
a. A843 5p No. C45, vert. 6.50 4.75
b. like No. 3048, size: 32x40mm 6.50 4.75
Nos. 3049-3054 (6) 40.75 20.40

Attack
on
Moncada
Barracks,
35th
Anniv.
A844

1988, July 26 *Perf. 13*
3055 A844 5c blk, yel ocher &
red .30 .20

Souvenir Sheet

PRAGA '88 — A845

1988, Aug. 26 *Perf. 12½*
3056 A845 1p Czechoslovakia
#45 4.00 2.00

Czechoslovakian postage stamps, 70th
anniv.

Revolutionary Invasion Force, 30th
Anniv. — A846

1988, Aug. 31 *Perf. 12½x12*
3057 A846 5c multi .30 .20

World
Marxist
Review,
30th
Anniv.
A847

1988, Sept. 1 *Perf. 13*
3058 A847 30c multi 1.25 .35

Locomotives — A848

1988, Sept. 19 *Perf. 12½x13*
3059 A848 20c Stephenson's
Rocket, 1837 .40 .25
3060 A848 30c Miller, US,
1839 .80 .45
3061 A848 50c *La Junta* 1.75 .90
3062 A848 1p J.G. Brill trolley, US, 1922 3.00 1.25
3063 A848 2p TEM 4K,
USSR, c.
1960 6.00 3.00
3064 A848 5p CAP 9 electric,
c. 1988 13.00 8.00
Nos. 3059-3064 (6) 24.95 13.85

Latin American History Type of 1986

Natl. arms & patriots: #3065, San Martin,
Argentina. #3066, M.A. Padilla, Bolivia. #3067,
#390 & discovery of America 500th anniv.
emblem. #3068, Tiradentes, Brazil. #3069,
O'Higgins, Chile. #3070, A. Narino, Colombia.
#3071, Marti, Cuba. #3072, #391 & emblem.
#3073, Duarte, Dominican Republic. #3074,
Sucre, Ecuador. #3075, M.J. Arce, El Salva-
dor. #3076, Dessalines, Haiti. #3077, #C36 &
emblem. #3078, Hidalgo, Mexico. #3079, J.D.
Estrada, Nicaragua. #3080, Diaz, Paraguay.
#3081, F. Bolognesi, Peru. #3082, #C37 &
emblem. #3083, Artigas, Uruguay. #3084,
Bolivar, Venezuela.

1988, Oct. 12 *Perf. 13*
3065 A804 1c multi .20 .20
3066 A804 1c multi .20 .20
3067 A804 1c multi .20 .20
3068 A804 1c multi .20 .20
3069 A804 1c multi .20 .20
a. Strip of 5, Nos. 3065-3069 1.00 .50
3070 A804 5c multi .20 .20
3071 A804 5c multi .20 .20
3072 A804 5c multi .20 .20
3073 A804 5c multi .20 .20
3074 A804 5c multi .20 .20
a. Strip of 5, Nos. 3070-3074 1.00 .50
3075 A804 10c multi .25 .20
3076 A804 10c multi .25 .20
3077 A804 10c multi .25 .20
3078 A804 10c multi .25 .20
3079 A804 10c multi .25 .20
a. Strip of 5, Nos. 3075-3079 1.50 .75
3080 A804 20c multi .45 .20
3081 A804 20c multi .45 .20
3082 A804 20c multi .45 .20
3083 A804 20c multi .45 .20
3084 A804 20c multi .45 .20
a. Strip of 5, Nos. 3080-3084 2.50 1.25
b. Sheet of 20, Nos. 3065-
3084 7.50 7.50
Nos. 3065-3084 (20) 5.50 4.00

Discovery of America, 500th anniv. (in 1992).

Havana Museum, 20th Anniv. — A849

Design: Captain-General's Palace and
Maces of Municipal Havana.

1988, Oct. 16 **Litho.** *Perf. 12½x12*
3085 A849 5c multi + label .40 .20

Anniversaries — A850

1988, Oct. 28   **Perf. 13**
3086 A850 5c Swan Lake   .60   .20
3087 A850 5c Theater in 1838
      and 1988   .60   .20
   a.   Pair, Nos. 3086-3087.   1.25   .40

Natl. Ballet, 40th anniv. (No. 3086); Grand Theater of Havana, 150th anniv. (No. 3087).

Intl.
Literacy
Year
A851

1988, Dec. 5
3088 A851 5c multi   .30   .20

UN Declaration
of Human
Rights, 40th
Anniv. — A851a

1988, Dec. 10
3088A A851a 30c multi   1.25   .35

Battle of Santa Clara, 30th
Anniv. — A852

1988, Dec. 28   **Perf. 13x12½**
3089 A852 30c Monument, Che
      Guevara Plaza   1.25   .35

30th Anniv. of the Revolution — A853

1989, Jan. 1   **Perf. 13**
3090 A853 5c multi   .20   .20
3091 A853 20c multi   .65   .20
3092 A853 30c multi   .85   .20
3093 A853 50c multi   1.75   .45
    Nos. 3090-3093 (4)   3.45   1.05

Edible Mushrooms — A854

1989, Jan. 10
3094 A854 2c Pleurotus levis   .20   .20
3095 A854 3c Pleurotus
      floridanus   .20   .20
3096 A854 5c Amanita caesa-
      rea   .20   .20
3097 A854 10c Lentinus cubensis   .45   .20
3098 A854 40c Pleurotus os-
      treatus (brown)   1.60   .40
3099 A854 50c Pleurotus os-
      treatus (yellow)   1.75   .50
    Nos. 3094-3099 (6)   4.40   1.70

2c, 3c, 5c, 40c, 50c, vert.

Souvenir Sheet

INDIA '89 — A855

1989, Jan. 20
3100 A855 1p Indian River Post,
      1858   4.00   1.60

Central Organization of Cuban Trade
Unions (CTC), 50th Anniv. — A856

1989, Jan. 28   **Perf. 12½**
3101 A856 5c No. 2477, CTC
      emblem   .30   .20

Butterflies
A857

1989, Feb. 15
3102 A857 1c Metamorpho dido   .20   .20
3103 A857 3c Callithea saphhira   .20   .20
3104 A857 5c Papilio zagreus   .20   .20
3105 A857 10c Mynes sestia   .30   .20
3106 A857 30c Papilio dardanus   1.40   .30
3107 A857 50c Catagranma
      sorana   2.50   .55
    Nos. 3102-3107 (6)   4.80   1.65

1990 World Cup
Soccer
Championships,
Italy — A858

Various athletes.

1989, Mar. 15   **Perf. 13**
3108 A858 1c multi   .20   .20
3109 A858 3c multi, diff.   .20   .20
3110 A858 5c multi, diff.   .20   .20
3111 A858 10c multi, diff.   .25   .20
3112 A858 30c multi, diff.   1.00   .25
3113 A858 50c multi, diff.   1.75   .40
    Nos. 3108-3113 (6)   3.60   1.45

Souvenir Sheet
Perf. 12½
3114 A858 1p multi, diff., horiz.   4.00   1.60

No. 3114 contains one 40x32mm stamp.

Natl.
Revolutionary
Police (PNR),
30th
Anniv. — A859

1989, Mar. 23   **Perf. 13**
3115 A859 5c multi   .30   .20

Cosmonauts' Day — A860

Spacecraft and rocket mail covers: 1c, Zodiac and cover, Australia 1934. 3c, Lighthouse and cover, India, 1934. 5c, Cover, England, 1934. 10c, Icarus and cover, The Netherlands, 1935. 40c, La Douce France and cover, France, 1935. 50c, Rocket mail cover, Cuba, 1939.

1989, Apr. 12
3116 A860 1c multi   .20   .20
3117 A860 3c multi   .20   .20
3118 A860 5c multi   .20   .20
3119 A860 10c multi   .20   .20
3120 A860 40c multi   1.10   .35
3121 A860 50c multi   1.40   .50
    Nos. 3116-3121 (6)   3.30   1.65

Stamp Day Type of 1984

Details of mural by R. Rodriguez Radillo (1967): 30c, Mail coach, Satellite dish. 50c, Galleon, longboats, train, passenger pigeon, horses.

1989, Apr. 24   **Litho.**   **Perf. 13x12½**
3122 A733 30c multi   .25   .20
3123 A733 50c multi   2.00   .50

Casa de
Las
Americas,
30th Anniv.
A861

1989, Apr. 28   **Perf. 12½x13**
3124 A861 5c multi   .30   .20

BULGARIA '89 — A862

1989, May 1   **Perf. 12½**
3125 A862 1p Bulgaria No. 346   4.50   2.25

58th FIP Congress and 101st anniv. of Bulgarian Railways.

Cuban
Postal
Code
A863

1989, May 5   **Perf. 13**
3126 A863 5c multi   .30   .20

Mothers'
Day — A864

Perfume bottles and flowers.

1989, May 10
3127 A864 1c Habano, tobacco   .20   .20
3128 A864 3c Violeta, violets   .20   .20
3129 A864 5c Mariposa, mari-
      posa   .20   .20
3130 A864 13c Coral Negro,
      roses   .35   .20
3131 A864 30c Ala Alonso, jas-
      mine   1.00   .30
3132 A864 50c D'Man, lemon
      blossoms   1.75   .70
    Nos. 3127-3132 (6)   3.70   1.80

Agrarian Reform
Law, 30th
Anniv. — A865

1989, May 17   **Perf. 12x12½**
3133 A865 5c multi   .30   .20

Council for
Mutual
Economic
Assistance
(CAME),
40th Anniv.
A866

1989, June 1   **Litho.**   **Perf. 12½x13**
3134 A866 30c multi   1.25   .25

13th World Communist Youth and
Student Festival, Pyongyang — A867

1989, July 1   **Litho.**   **Perf. 12½**
3135 A867 30c multi   1.25   .25

Souvenir Sheet

Rouget de Lisle Singing La Marseillaise, by Pils — A868

1989, July 7   **Perf. 13**
3136 A868 1p multi   4.00 1.60

PHILEXFRANCE '89, French revolution bicent. and Cuban revolution 30th anniv.

BRASILIANA '89 — A869

Exotic birds. Illustration reduced.

1989, July 28   **Litho.**   **Perf. 12½**
3137 A869 1c *Ramphastos toco* .20 .20
3138 A869 3c *Agamia agami* .20 .20
3139 A869 5c *Eudocimus ruber* .25 .20
3140 A869 10c *Psophia leucoptera* .40 .20
3141 A869 35c *Harpia harpyja* 1.50 .35
3142 A869 50c *Cephatopterus ornatus* 2.00 .55
Nos. 3137-3142 (6) 4.55 1.70

Warships A870

1989, Sept. 29   **Litho.**   **Perf. 12½**
3143 A870 1c *El Fenix* .20 .20
3144 A870 3c *Triunfo* .20 .20
3145 A870 5c *El Rayo* .20 .20
3146 A870 10c *San Carlos* .30 .20
3147 A870 30c *San Jose* 1.25 .40
3148 A870 50c *San Genaro* 1.90 .70
Nos. 3143-3148 (6) 4.05 1.90

America Issue — A871

UPAE emblem and pre-Columbian art: 5p, Stone carving, Indians in dugout canoe. 20p, Petroglyph, Indian drawing on stone wall.

1989, Oct. 12   **Perf. 12½x12**
3149 A871 5c multi .20 .20
3150 A871 20c multi .80 .40

Latin American History — A872

Writers and orchids: No. 3151, Domingo Sarmiento (1811-1888), Argentine educator, and *Govenia utriculata.* No. 3152, Joaquim Maria Machado de Assis (1839-1908), Brazilian novelist, and *Laelia grandis.* No. 3153, Salvador No. 69 and discovery of America anniv. emblem. No. 3154, Jorge Isaacs (1837-1895), Colombian novelist, and *Cattleya trianae.* No. 3155, Alejo Carpentier, Cuban writer, and *Cochleanthes discolor.* No. 3156, Pablo Neruda (1904-1973), Chilean poet, and *Oxalis adenophylla.* No. 3157, Pedro Urena, Dominican writer, and *Epidendrum fragrans.* No. 3158, Salvador No. 86 and anniv. emblem. No. 3159, Juan Montalvo (1832-1889), Ecuadorian satirist, and *Miltonia vexillaria.* No. 3160, Miguel Asturias (1899-1974), Guatemalan writer awarded the 1966 Lenin Peace Prize and 1967 Nobel Prize for literature, and *Odontoglossum rossii.* No. 3161, Jose C. del Valle, Honduran writer, and *Laelia anceps.* No. 3162, Alfonso Reyes (1889-1959), Mexican poet, and *Laelia anceps alba.* No. 3163, Salvador No. 87 and anniv. emblem. No. 3164, Ruben Dario (1867-1917), Nicaraguan poet, and *Brassavola acaulis.* No. 3165, Belisario Porras (1856-1942), president of Panama, and *Pescatorea celina.* No. 3166, Ricardo Palma (1833-1919), Peruvian writer, and *Coryanthes leucocorys.* No. 3167, Eugenio Maria de Hostos (1839-1903), Puerto Rican writer, and *Guzmania berteroniana.* No. 3168, Salvador No. 88 and anniv. emblem. No. 3169, Jose E. Rodo (1872-1917), Uruguayan philosopher, essayist, and *Cypella heberti.* No. 3170, Romulo Gallegos, Venezuelan writer, and *Cattleya mossiae.*

1989, Oct. 27   **Litho.**   **Perf. 13**
3151 A872 1c multicolored .20 .20
3152 A872 1c multicolored .20 .20
3153 A872 1c multicolored .20 .20
3154 A872 1c multicolored .20 .20
3155 A872 1c multicolored .20 .20
   a. Strip of 5, Nos. 3151-3155 1.00 .50
3156 A872 5c multicolored .20 .20
3157 A872 5c multicolored .20 .20
3158 A872 5c multicolored .20 .20
3159 A872 5c multicolored .20 .20
3160 A872 5c multicolored .20 .20
   a. Strip of 5, Nos. 3156-3160 1.00 .50
3161 A872 10c multicolored .35 .20
3162 A872 10c multicolored .35 .20
3163 A872 10c multicolored .35 .20
3164 A872 10c multicolored .35 .20
3165 A872 10c multicolored .35 .20
   a. Strip of 5, Nos. 3161-3165 2.00 1.00
3166 A872 20c multicolored .55 .25
3167 A872 20c multicolored .55 .25
3168 A872 20c multicolored .55 .25
3169 A872 20c multicolored .55 .25
3170 A872 20c multicolored .55 .25
   a. Strip of 5, Nos. 3166-3170 3.00 1.50
   b. Sheet of 20, #3065-3084 8.00 8.00
Nos. 3151-3170 (20) 6.50 4.25

Discovery of America 500th anniv. (in 1992).

Disappearance of Camilo Cienfuegos, 30th Anniv. — A873

1989, Oct. 28
3171 A873 5c multicolored .30 .20

Founding of the City of Trinidad, 475th Anniv. A874

1989, Nov. 6   **Perf. 12½x13**
3172 A874 5c multicolored .30 .20

Paintings in the Natl. Museum — A875

Designs: 1p, *Familiar Scene,* by Antoine Faivre. 2p, *Flowers,* by Emile Jean Horace Vernet (1789-1863). 5p, *The Judgement of Paris,* by Charles Le Brun (1619-1690). 20p, *Outskirts of Nice,* by Eugene Louis Boudin (1824-1898). 30p, *Portrait of Sarah Bernhardt,* by G.J.V. Clairin. 50p, *Fishermen in Port,* by C.J. Vernet.

Perf. 12½, 12½x13 (30p)
1989, Nov. 20   **Litho.**
Size of 30p: 36x46mm
3173 A875 1c multicolored .20 .20
3174 A875 2c multicolored .20 .20
3175 A875 5c multicolored .20 .20
3176 A875 20c multicolored .85 .20
3177 A875 30c multicolored 1.10 .20
3178 A875 50c multicolored 2.25 .55
Nos. 3173-3178 (6) 4.80 1.55

11th Pan-American Games, Havana, 1991 — A876

1989, Dec. 15   **Litho.**   **Perf. 12½**
3179 A876 5c Cycling .25 .20
3180 A876 5c Fencing .25 .20
3181 A876 5c Water polo .25 .20
3182 A876 5c Shooting .25 .20
3183 A876 5c Archery .25 .20
3184 A876 20c Tennis, vert. .65 .20
3185 A876 30c Swimming, vert. 1.10 .20
3186 A876 35c Diving, vert. 1.40 .20
3187 A876 40c Field hockey 1.50 .20
3188 A876 50c Basketball, vert. 2.25 .40
Nos. 3179-3188 (10) 8.15 2.20

Jose Marti's *Golden Age,* Cent. — A877

1989, Dec. 20   **Perf. 13**
3189 A877 5c scar, light blue & blk .40 .20

Cuban Postal Museum, 25th Anniv. — A878

1990, Jan. 2   **Perf. 13x12½**
3190 A878 5c *Almendares* .20 .20
3191 A878 30c Mail train 1.00 .50

Speleological Soc., 50th Anniv. — A879

Illustration reduced.

1990, Jan. 15   **Perf. 12½**
3192 A879 30c multicolored 2.00 .35

1990 World Cup Soccer Championships, Italy — A880

Various Italian architecture and athletes: No. 3193a, Dribbling (in red and blue). No. 3193b, Heading (in red and green). No. 3193c, Kicking (in green). 10c, Goalie catching ball. 30c, Dribbling, diff. 50c, Kicking, diff. 1p, Goalie catching ball, diff.

1990, Jan. 30   **Litho.**   **Perf. 12½**
3193   Strip of 3 .20 .20
a.-c. A880 5c any single .20 .20
3194 A880 10c multicolored .25 .20
3195 A880 30c multicolored 1.25 .20
3196 A880 50c multicolored 2.10 .35
   a. Sheet of 6, #3193a-3193c, 3194-3196 + 3 labels 4.00 1.25
Nos. 3193-3196 (4) 3.80 .95

Souvenir Sheet
3197 A880 1p multicolored 3.50 1.75

No. 3193 has a continuous design picturing The Colosseum.

1992 Summer Olympics, Barcelona — A881

1990, Feb. 20   **Litho.**   **Perf. 12½**
3198 A881 1c Baseball .20 .20
3199 A881 4c Running .20 .20
3200 A881 5c Basketball .20 .20
3201 A881 10c Women's volleyball .45 .20
3202 A881 30c Wrestling 1.10 .20
3203 A881 50c Boxing 2.00 .40
Nos. 3198-3203 (6) 4.15 1.40

Souvenir Sheet
3204 A881 1p High jump 4.00 2.00

Nos. 3198-3201 and 3203 are vert. No. 3204 contains one 40x32mm stamp.

75th Universal Esperanto Congress — A882

1990, Mar. 7
3205 A882 30c Tower of Babel 1.25 .35

No. 3205 printed se-tenant with inscribed label publicizing the congress.

Souvenir Sheet

1992 Winter Olympics,
Albertville — A883

1990, Mar. 30   Litho.   Perf. 13
3206 A883 1p multicolored   4.50 1.25

Cosmonauts' Day — A884

Spacecraft and rocket mail covers: 1c, Austria, 1932. 2c, Germany, 1933. 3c, Netherlands, 1934. 10c, Belgium, 1935. 30c, Yugoslavia, 1935. 50c, United States, 1936.

1990, Apr. 12   Perf. 12½
3207 A884 1c multicolored   .20   .20
3208 A884 2c multicolored   .20   .20
3209 A884 3c multicolored   .20   .20
3210 A884 10c multicolored   .25   .20
3211 A884 30c multicolored   1.10 .20
3212 A884 50c multicolored   2.00 .50
  Nos. 3207-3212 (6)   3.95 1.50

Stamp Day Type of 1984

Details of mural by R. Rodriguez Radillo (1967): 30c, Train station. 50c, Jet aircraft in flight.

1990, Apr. 24   Perf. 13x12½
3213 A733 30c multicolored   2.10 .75
3214 A733 50c multicolored   1.10 .45

Labor
Day,
Cent.
A885

1990, Apr. 30   Perf. 13
3215 A885 5c multicolored   1.00 .20

Souvenir Sheet

Great Britain No. 1 on Cover — A886

1990, May 3
3216 A886 1p multicolored   4.00 2.00
Stamp World London '90, Penny Black 150th anniv.

Penny
Black,
150th
Anniv.
A887

Portraits of Sir Rowland Hill and stamps of Great Britain.

1990, May 6   Litho.   Perf. 12½x12
3217 A887 2c No. 1   .20   .20
3218 A887 3c No. 2   .20   .20
3219 A887 5c Type A5   .20   .20
3220 A887 10c No. 5   .25   .20

3221 A887 30c First day post-
              mark   1.25 .20
3222 A887 50c 5 #1 on Mulready
              envelope   2.25 .60
  Nos. 3217-3222 (6)   4.35 1.60

Celia Sanchez Manduley (1920-
1980) — A888

1990, May 9   Perf. 12½x13
3223 A888 5c multicolored   .50   .20

Ho Chi Minh
(1890-1969),
Vietnamese
Communist
Party
Leader — A889

1990, May 19   Perf. 12½
3224 A889 50c multicolored   1.25 .45

Oceanography Institute, 25th
Anniv. — A890

Designs: 5c, Specimen analysis and *Lachnolaimus maximus*. 30c, Research ship, fish, coral reef. 50c, Specimen collection and *Panulirus argus*.

1990, June 18   Litho.   Perf. 12½
3225 A890 5c multicolored   .20   .20
3226 A890 30c multicolored   1.00 .25
3227 A890 50c multicolored   1.60 .30
  Nos. 3225-3227 (3)   2.80 .75

5th Latin
American
Botanical
Conference
A891

1990, June 25   Litho.   Perf. 12½
3228 A891 3c Banara minu-
              tiflora   .20   .20
3229 A891 5c Oplonia nan-
              nophylla   .20   .20
3230 A891 10c Jacquinia brun-
              nescens   .35   .20
3231 A891 30c Rondeletia
              brachycarpa   1.10 .20
3232 A891 50c Rondeletia
              odorata   1.75 .60
  Nos. 3228-3232 (5)   3.60 1.40

Tourism
A892

1990, June 30
3233 A892 5c Wind surfing   .20   .20
3234 A892 10c Spear fishing   .35   .20
3235 A892 30c Deep sea fishing   1.00 .20
3236 A892 40c Hunting   1.60 .50
  Nos. 3233-3236 (4)   3.15 1.10
  Nos. 3233, 3236 vert.

Art
Treasures
A893

5c, "La Flauta Del Dios Pan." 20c, "Un Pastor." 50c, "Ganimedes." 1p, "Venus Anadiomena."

1990, July 20
3237 A893 5c multicolored   .20   .20
3238 A893 20c multicolored   .60   .25
3239 A893 50c multicolored   1.60 .40
3240 A893 1p multicolored   2.50 .75
  a. Sheet of 4, #3237-3240   5.00 5.00
  Nos. 3237-3240 (4)   4.90 1.60

Birds
A894

1990, Aug. 24   Litho.   Perf. 13
3241 A894 2c Podiceps cris-
              tatus   .20   .20
3242 A894 3c Gallirallus austral-
              is   .20   .20
3243 A894 5c Nestor notabilis   .20   .20
3244 A894 10c Xenicus longipes   .25   .20
3245 A894 30c Cracticus tor-
              quatus   .90   .35
3246 A894 50c "Prosthemadera"
              novaeseelandiae   1.50 .45
  Nos. 3241-3246 (6)   3.25 1.60

Souvenir Sheet
3247 A894 1p Kiwi   4.00 2.00
New Zealand '90. No. 3247 contains one 39x31mm stamp.

8th UN
Congress on
Crime
Prevention
A895

1990, Aug. 27   Litho.   Perf. 12½
3248 A895 50c blue, silver & red   1.75 .45

Discovery of America, 500th Anniv. (in
1992) — A896

1990, Oct. 12   Litho.   Perf. 12½
3249 A896 5c Ship, shore   .25   .20
3250 A896 20c Columbus, village   1.00 .35

Cuban Television, 40th Anniv. — A897

1990, Oct. 12   Litho.   Perf. 13
3251 A897 5c multicolored   .35   .20

Nationalization of Railroads, 30th
Anniv. — A898

1990, Oct. 13   Perf. 13x12½
3252 A898 50c multicolored   2.00 1.00

Latin American History Type of 1986

Latin American stamps or flags and costumes: No. 3253, Argentina. No. 3254, Bolivia. No. 3255, Argentina No. 91. No. 3256, Colombia. No. 3257, Costa Rica. No. 3258, Cuba. No. 3259, Chile. No. 3260, Dominican Republic No. 110. No. 3261, Ecuador. No. 3262, El Salvador. No. 3263, Guatemala. No. 3264, Mexico. No. 3265, Puerto Rico No. 133. No. 3266, Nicaragua. No. 3267, Panama. No. 3268, Paraguay. No. 3269, Peru. No. 3270, El Salvador No. 103. No. 3271, Puerto Rico. No. 3272, Venezuela.

1990, Oct. 27   Perf. 12½
3253 A804 1c multicolored   .20   .20
3254 A804 1c multicolored   .20   .20
3255 A804 1c multicolored   .20   .20
3256 A804 1c multicolored   .20   .20
3257 A804 1c multicolored   .20   .20
  a. Strip of 5, Nos. 3253-3257 1.00 .50
3258 A804 5c multicolored   .20   .20
3259 A804 5c multicolored   .20   .20
3260 A804 5c multicolored   .20   .20
3261 A804 5c multicolored   .20   .20
3262 A804 5c multicolored   .20   .20
  a. Strip of 5, Nos. 3258-3262 1.00 .50
3263 A804 10c multicolored   .30   .20
3264 A804 10c multicolored   .30   .20
3265 A804 10c multicolored   .30   .20
3266 A804 10c multicolored   .30   .20
3267 A804 10c multicolored   .30   .20
  a. Strip of 5, Nos. 3263-3267 1.50 .75
3268 A804 20c multicolored   .85   .20
3269 A804 20c multicolored   .85   .20
3270 A804 20c multicolored   .85   .20
3271 A804 20c multicolored   .85   .20
3272 A804 20c multicolored   .85   .20
  a. Strip of 5, Nos. 3268-3272 4.50 2.25
  b. Sheet of 20, #3253-3272   5.00 5.00
  Nos. 3253-3272 (20)   7.75 4.00

Discovery of America, 500th anniv. (in 1992).

11th Jai Alai
World
Championships
A899

1990, Nov. 14   Litho.   Perf. 12½
3273 A899 30c multicolored   1.25 .35
No. 3273 printed with se-tenant label.

11th Pan American Games,
Havana — A900

1990, Nov. 15	Litho.	Perf. 12½	
3274 A900	5c Judo	.20	.20
3275 A900	5c Sailing	.20	.20
3276 A900	5c Kayak	.20	.20
3277 A900	5c Rowing	.20	.20
3278 A900	5c Equestrian	.20	.20
3279 A900	10c Table tennis	.30	.20
3280 A900	20c Men's gymnas-tics, vert.	.60	.25
3281 A900	30c Baseball, vert.	.90	.25
3282 A900	35c Team handball, vert.	1.10	.35
3283 A900	50c Soccer, vert.	1.60	.70
Nos. 3274-3283 (10)		5.50	2.75

See Nos. 3311-3320.

A901

1990, Nov. 20	Litho.	Perf. 13	
3284 A901	5c Boxing	.20	.20
3285 A901	30c Baseball	1.10	.25
3286 A901	50c Volleyball	1.90	.30
Nos. 3284-3286 (3)		3.20	.75

16th Central American and Caribbean
Games, Mexico.

Butterflies
A902

1991, Jan. 25	Litho.	Perf. 12½	
3287 A902	2c Chioides marmorosa	.20	.20
3288 A902	3c Composia fidelis-sima	.20	.20
3289 A902	5c Danaus plexippus	.20	.20
3290 A902	10c Hypolimnas mis-ippus	.30	.20
3291 A902	30c Hypna iphigenia	.95	.25
3292 A902	50c Hemiargus am-mon	1.50	.50
Nos. 3287-3292 (6)		3.35	1.55

Jose Luis Guerra Aguiar (1914-1990),
Director of Postal Museum — A903

1991, Feb. 17	Litho.	Perf. 12½	
3293 A903	5c multicolored	.45	.20

A904

1991, Feb. 20			
3294 A904	1c Long jump	.20	.20
3295 A904	2c Javelin	.20	.20
3296 A904	3c Field hockey	.20	.20
3297 A904	5c Weight lifting	.20	.20
3298 A904	40c Cycling	1.25	.35
3299 A904	50c Gymnastics	1.75	.50
Nos. 3294-3299 (6)		3.80	1.65

Souvenir Sheet

3300 A904	1p Torchbearer	3.50	1.75

1992 Summer Olympics, Barcelona.

A905

1991, Apr. 12	Litho.	Perf. 13	

1st Man in Space, 30th anniv.: 5c, Yuri
Gagarin. No. 3302, Cosmonaut Y.
Romanenko. No. 3303, Cosmonaut A.
Tamayo. No. 3304, Mir space station. No.
3305, Mir space station, docked Soyuz, earth.
50c, Soviet space shuttle Buran.

3301 A905	5c multicolored	.20	.20
3302 A905	10c multicolored	.20	.20
3303 A905	10c multicolored	.20	.20
a.	Pair, #3302-3303	.40	
3304 A905	30c multicolored	1.00	.20
3305 A905	30c multicolored	1.00	.20
a.	Pair, #3304-3305	2.00	1.00
3306 A905	50c multicolored	1.60	.50
a.	Sheet of 6, #3301-3306	4.50	
Nos. 3301-3306 (6)		4.20	1.50

Proclamation of
the Socialist
Revolution, 30th
Anniv. — A906

Design: 50c, Ship, jet on fire.

1991, Apr. 19		Perf. 12½	
3307 A906	5c multicolored	.20	.20
3308 A906	50c multicolored	1.60	.80

Bay of Pigs invasion, 30th anniv., No. 3308.

Stamp Day
A907

Details from mural by R. Rodriguez Radillo:
30c, Rocket lift-off. 50c, Dish antenna, horiz.

1991, Apr. 24	Perf. 12½x13, 13x12½		
3309 A907	30c multicolored	1.00	.30
3310 A907	50c multicolored	1.75	.40

11th Pan American Games Type of
1990

1991, May 15	Litho.	Perf. 12½	
3311 A900	5c Volleyball	.20	.20
3312 A900	5c Rhythmic gym-nastics	.20	.20
3313 A900	5c Synchronized swimming	.20	.20
3314 A900	5c Weight lifting	.20	.20
3315 A900	5c Baseball	.20	.20
3316 A900	10c Bowling	.20	.20
3317 A900	20c Boxing	.55	.25
3318 A900	30c Running	.85	.25
3319 A900	35c Wrestling	1.10	.30
3320 A900	50c Karate	1.50	.50
Nos. 3311-3320 (10)		5.20	2.50

Nos. 3311-3315 & 3317 are vert.

Airships
A908

Designs: 5c, First ellipsoidal, 1784, J.B.M.
Meusnier. 10c, First with steam engine, 1852,
H. Giffard. 20c, First with gas engine, 1872, P.
Haenlein. 30c, First with gasoline engine,
1896, H. Wolfert. 50c, First rigid aluminum,
1897, D. Schwarz. 1p, LZ-129 Hindenburg,
1936, F. von Zeppelin.

1991, July 1	Litho.	Perf. 13	
3321 A908	5c multicolored	.20	.20
3322 A908	10c multicolored	.35	.20
3323 A908	20c multicolored	.70	.30
3324 A908	30c multicolored	.90	.50
3325 A908	50c multicolored	1.60	.95
3326 A908	1p multicolored	3.25	1.60
Nos. 3321-3326 (6)		7.00	3.75

Espamer '91, Buenos Aires, Argentina.

Simon
Bolivar
A909

1991, June 22	Litho.	Perf. 12½x13	
3327 A909	50c multicolored	2.00	.60

Amphictyonic Cong. of Panama, 165th anniv.

Birds
A910

Designs: 45c, Melanerpes superciliaris. 50c,
Myadestes elisabeth. 2p, Priotelus temnurus.
4p, Tiaris canora. 5p, Campephilus principalis.
10p, Amazona leucocephala, horiz. 16.45p,
Mellisuga helenae, horiz.

1991, July 15	Perf. 12½x13, 13x12½		
3328 A910	45c multicolored	1.25	.40
3329 A910	50c multicolored	1.50	.50
3330 A910	2p multicolored	5.25	2.00
3331 A910	4p multicolored	10.00	3.50
3332 A910	5p multicolored	12.50	4.25
3333 A910	10p multicolored	25.00	6.50
3334 A910	16.45p multicolored	40.00	13.00
Nos. 3328-3334 (7)		95.50	30.15

Tourism — A911

Designs: No. 3335, Varadero Beach, vert.
No. 3336, Cayo Largo, vert. No. 3337, Artiller-
ymen at fortress San Carlos de la Cabana.
No. 3338, Tres Reyes del Morro Castle.

1991, July 30			
3335 A911	20c multicolored	.60	.20
3336 A911	20c multicolored	.60	.20
3337 A911	30c multicolored	1.00	.30
3338 A911	30c multicolored	1.00	.30
Nos. 3335-3338 (4)		3.20	1.00

Panamfilex '91 — A912

11th Pan American Games venues: 5c, Pan
American Stadium. 20c, Swimming venue.
30c, Multisports center. 50c, Velodrome. 1p,
Havana City Coliseum and Sports Center.

1991, Aug. 4	Litho.	Perf. 12½	
3339 A912	5c multicolored	.20	.20
3340 A912	20c multicolored	.60	.30
3341 A912	30c multicolored	.80	.50
3342 A912	50c multicolored	1.50	.90
Nos. 3339-3342 (4)		3.10	1.90

Souvenir Sheet

3343 A912	1p multicolored	3.50	1.75

No. 3343 contains one 40x32mm stamp.

Paintings
A913

5c, Kataoka Dengoemon Takafusa, by Uta-
gawa Kuniyoshi. 10c, Evening Walk, by
Hosoda Eishi. 20c, Courtesans, by Torii
Kiyonaga. 30c, Conversation, by Utamaro.
50c, Bridge at Inari-bashi, by Hiroshige. 1p,
On the Terrace, by Kiyonaga.

1991, Sept. 9	Litho.	Perf. 12½x13	
3344 A913	5c multicolored	.20	.20
3345 A913	10c multicolored	.35	.20
3346 A913	20c multicolored	.70	.30
3347 A913	30c multicolored	.90	.40
3348 A913	50c multicolored	1.60	1.75
3349 A913	1p multicolored	3.25	1.75
Nos. 3344-3349 (6)		7.00	3.60

Phila Nippon '91, Tokyo.

638   CUBA

Souvenir Sheet

1992 Winter Olympics,
Albertville — A914

1991, Sept. 25   Litho.   Perf. 12½
3350 A914 1p multicolored   3.50 1.75

Cuban
Communist
Party, 4th
Congress
A915

1991, Oct. 10
3351 A915 5c shown   .20 .20
3352 A915 50c Congress symbol   1.75 .50

Discovery of America, 500th Anniv. (in
1992) — A916

Designs: 5c, Columbus, Vicente and Martin
Pinzon. 20c, Santa Maria, Nina and Pinta.

1991, Oct. 12
3353 A916 5c multicolored   .25 .20
3354 A916 20c multicolored   1.25 .25

Jose
Marti
A917

1991, Oct. 15   Perf. 13x12½
3355 A917 50c multicolored   2.00 .40

Publication of "Simple Verses," cent.

Latin
American
History
A918

Stamps or musicians and instruments: No.
3356, Julian Aguirre, Argentina, charango. No.
3357, Eduardo Caba, Bolivia, antara. No.
3358, Chile #2. No. 3359, Heitor Villalobos,
Brazil, resonator trumpet. No. 3360, Guillermo
Uribe-Holguin, Colombia, drum. No. 3361,

Miguel Failde, Cuba, claves. No. 3362,
Enrique Soro, Chile, drum. No. 3363, Chile
#57. No. 3364, Segundo L. Moreno, Ecuador,
xylophone. No. 3365, Ricardo Castillo, Guatemala, marimba. No. 3366, Carlos Chavez,
Mexico, guitar. No. 3367, Luis A. Delgadillo,
Nicaragua, maracas. No. 3368, Chile #69. No.
3369, Alfredo De Saint-Malo, Panama,
mejorana. No. 3370, Jose Asuncion Flores,
Paraguay, harp. No. 3371, Daniel Alomia,
Peru, flute. No. 3372, Juan Morell y Campos,
Puerto Rico, cuatro. No. 3373, Chile #72. No.
3374, Eduardo Farini, Uruguay, drums. No.
3375, Juan V. Lecuna, Venezuela, cuatro, diff.

1991, Oct. 27   Perf. 13
3356 A918 1c multicolored   .20 .20
3357 A918 1c multicolored   .20 .20
3358 A918 1c multicolored   .20 .20
3359 A918 1c multicolored   .20 .20
3360 A918 1c multicolored   .20 .20
  a.   Strip of 5, #3356-3360   1.00 .50
3361 A918 5c multicolored   .20 .20
3362 A918 5c multicolored   .20 .20
3363 A918 5c multicolored   .20 .20
3364 A918 5c multicolored   .20 .20
3365 A918 5c multicolored   .20 .20
  a.   Strip of 5, #3361-3365   1.00 .50
3366 A918 10c multicolored   .40 .20
3367 A918 10c multicolored   .40 .20
3368 A918 10c multicolored   .40 .20
3369 A918 10c multicolored   .40 .20
3370 A918 10c multicolored   .40 .20
  a.   Strip of 5, #3366-3370   2.00 1.00
3371 A918 20c multicolored   .80 .20
3372 A918 20c multicolored   .80 .20
3373 A918 20c multicolored   .80 .20
3374 A918 20c multicolored   .80 .20
3375 A918 20c multicolored   .80 .20
  a.   Strip of 5, #3371-3375   4.00 2.00
  b.   Sheet of 20, #3356-3375 8.00 —
      Nos. 3356-3375 (20)   8.00 4.00

Discovery of America, 500th anniv. in 1992
(Nos. 3358, 3363, 3368, 3373).

Jose Marti
Pioneers
Organization,
1st Congress
A919

1991, Oct. 29
3376 A919 5c multicolored   .35 .20

Toussaint L'Ouverture (1743-
1803) — A920

1991, Nov. 20   Perf. 12½x13
3377 A920 50c multicolored   2.00 .40

Haitian Revolution, Bicent.

Cuban Revolutionary Armed Forces,
35th Anniv. — A921

Design: 50c, Landing of the Granma expedition, 35th anniv., vert.

Perf. 12½x12, 12x12½
1991, Dec. 2   Litho.
3378 A921 5c multicolored   .25 .20
3379 A921 50c multicolored   1.75 .40

Gen. Ignacio Agramonte (1841-1873),
Revolutionary Hero — A922

1991, Dec. 23   Litho.   Perf. 12½x13
3380 A922 5c multicolored   .30 .20

Souvenir Sheet

1992 Winter Olympics,
Albertville — A923

1992, Jan. 15   Perf. 13
3381 A923 1p multicolored   3.50 1.75

1992 Summer Olympics,
Barcelona — A924

1992, Jan. 20   Litho.   Perf. 13x12½
3382 A924 3c Table tennis   .20 .20
3383 A924 5c Handball   .20 .20
3384 A924 10c Shooting   .30 .20
3385 A924 20c Long jump, vert.   .60 .20
3386 A924 35c Judo   1.25 .40
3387 A924 50c Fencing   1.60 .40
      Nos. 3382-3387 (6)   4.15 1.60

Souvenir Sheet
Perf. 12½
3388 A924 100c Rhythmic gym-
             nastics, vert.   3.50 1.75

No. 3388 contains one 32x40mm stamp.

Environmental
Protection
A925

1992, Feb. 10   Perf. 13
3389 A925 5c Terraced hillsides .25 .20
3390 A925 20c Save the whales   .60 .25
3391 A925 35c Ozone hole over
               Antarctica   1.25 .40
3392 A925 40c Nuclear disarma-
               ment   1.40 .40
      Nos. 3389-3392 (4)   3.50 1.25

Dogs
A926

1992, Mar. 10   Litho.   Perf. 13x12½
3393 A926 5c Boxer   .20 .20
3394 A926 10c Great dane   .20 .20
3395 A926 20c German shep-
               herd   .65 .20
3396 A926 30c Various breeds   1.10 .25
3397 A926 35c Doberman pin-
               scher   1.10 .30
3398 A926 40c Fox terrier   1.40 .40
3399 A926 50c Poodle   1.75 .50
      Nos. 3393-3399 (7)   6.40 2.05

Souvenir Sheet
Perf. 12½
3400 A926 1p Bichon frise, vert. 4.00 2.00

No. 3400 contains one 32x40mm stamp.
Nos. 3401-3404 will not be assigned.

Union of Young
Communists,
30th
Anniv. — A928

1992, Apr. 4   Litho.   Perf. 13
3405 A928 5c multicolored   .35 .20

Cuban Revolutionary Party,
Cent. — A929

1992, Apr. 10   Perf. 13x12½
3406 A929 5c multicolored   .25 .20
3407 A929 50c multicolored   1.75 .50

Discovery of America, 500th
Anniv. — A930

1992, Apr. 14   Perf. 12½
3408 A930 5c Landing at Bariay   .20 .20
3409 A930 20c Landing at San
               Salvador   .55 .25

Granada '92 Philatelic
Exhibition — A931

Views of the Alhambra, Granada: 5c, With
Sierra Nevada mountains beyond. 10c, Arches
at sunset. 20c, Interior architecture. 30c, Patio,
fountain of lions. 35c, Bedroom. 50c, View of
Albaicin.

1992, Apr. 17   *Perf. 13*

3410	A931	5c multicolored	.20	.20
3411	A931	10c multicolored	.25	.20
3412	A931	20c multicolored	.75	.20
3413	A931	30c multicolored	1.25	.25
3414	A931	35c multicolored	1.50	.40
3415	A931	50c multicolored	2.10	.50
		Nos. 3410-3415 (6)	6.05	1.75

La Bodeguita Del Medio Restaurant, 50th Anniv. — A932

1992, Apr. 26

3416	A932	50c multicolored	1.75	.50

Fish
A933

1992, May 15   Litho.   *Perf. 12½*

3417	A933	5c Holacanthus isabelita	.20	.20
3418	A933	10c Equetus lanceolatus	.20	.20
3419	A933	20c Acanthurus coeruleus	.65	.20
3420	A933	30c Abudefduf saxatilis	1.10	.25
3421	A933	50c Microspathodon chrysurus	1.90	.50
		Nos. 3417-3421 (5)	4.05	1.35

Orchids — A934

1992, June 20   Litho.   *Perf. 12½*

3422	A934	3c Cattleya hibrida	.20	.20
3423	A934	5c Phalaenopsis	.20	.20
3424	A934	10c Cattleyopsis lindenii	.20	.20
3425	A934	30c Bletia purpurea	1.00	.25
3426	A934	35c Oncidium luridum	1.10	.30
3427	A934	40c Vanda hibrida	1.40	.40
		Nos. 3422-3427 (6)	4.10	1.55

Soroa Orchid Garden, 40th anniv.

Mellisuga Helenae — A935

1992, July 7   *Perf. 13*

3428	A935	5c Sitting on nest	.50	.40
3429	A935	10c Wings extended	.70	.50
3430	A935	20c Sitting on branch	1.50	.60
3431	A935	30c In flight	2.50	1.25
		Nos. 3428-3431 (4)	5.20	2.75

World Wildlife Fund.

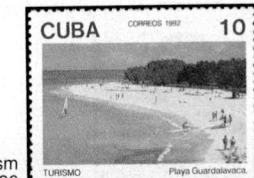

Tourism
A936

1992, July 15   Litho.   *Perf. 12½*

3432	A936	10c Guardalavaca Beach	.30	.20
3433	A936	20c Bucanero Hotel	.70	.20
3434	A936	30c Sailing ship, Havana	1.25	.40
3435	A936	50c Varadero Beach	1.75	.50
		Nos. 3432-3435 (4)	4.00	1.30

Souvenir Sheet

Expo '92, Seville — A937

1992, July 27   Litho.   *Perf. 13*

3436	A937	1.50p multicolored	4.00	2.00

1992 Summer Olympics, Barcelona
A938

Athlete, sport: 5c, Eligio (Kid Chocolate) Sardinas, boxing. 35c, Ramon Fonst, fencing. 40c, Sergio Martinez, cycling. 50c, Martin Dihigo, baseball.

1992, July 20   Litho.   *Perf. 12½x13*

3437	A938	5c multicolored	.20	.20
3438	A938	35c multicolored	1.10	.30
3439	A938	40c multicolored	1.25	.40
3440	A938	50c multicolored	1.75	.60
		Nos. 3437-3440 (4)	4.30	1.50

Olymphilex '92.

Discovery of America, 500th Anniv. — A939

5c, Alvarez Cabral. 10c, Alonso Pinzon. 20c, Alonso de Ojeda. 30c, Amerigo Vespucci. 35c, Prince Henry the Navigator. 40c, Bartolomeu Dias. 1p, Columbus' fleet.

1992, Sept. 18   Litho.   *Perf. 12½*

3441	A939	5c multicolored	.20	.20
3442	A939	10c multicolored	.30	.20
3443	A939	20c multicolored	.70	.20
3444	A939	30c multicolored	1.10	.30
3445	A939	35c multicolored	1.25	.30
3446	A939	40c multicolored	1.50	.40
		Nos. 3441-3446 (6)	5.05	1.60

Souvenir Sheet
Perf. 13

3447	A939	1p multi, vert.	3.00	1.50

Genoa '92. No. 3447 contains one 32x40mm stamp.

1992 Summer Olympics Medal Winners, Barcelona — A940

Medals and participants in events: No. 3448, Bronze, 4x100-meter relay, women's high jump, and women's 800-meter. No. 3449, Gold, high jump, women's discus. No. 3450, Silver, 4x400-meter relay, bronze, discus. No. 3451, Gold and silver, boxing. No. 3452, Gold, baseball. No. 3453, Gold, women's volleyball. No. 3454, Gold, silver, and bronze, judo. No. 3455, Gold and bronze, Greco-Roman and freestyle wrestling. No. 3456, Silver and bronze, fencing, silver, weight lifting.

1992, Sept. 24   Litho.   *Perf. 13*

3448	A940	5c multicolored	.20	.20
3449	A940	5c multicolored	.20	.20
3450	A940	5c multicolored	.20	.20
3451	A940	20c multicolored	.65	.20
3452	A940	20c multicolored	.65	.20
3453	A940	20c multicolored	.65	.20
3454	A940	50c multicolored	1.75	.50
3455	A940	50c multicolored	1.75	.50
3456	A940	50c multicolored	1.75	.50
		Nos. 3448-3456 (9)	7.80	2.70

6th World Track and Field Cup, Havana
A941

1992, Sept. 24   Litho.   *Perf. 13*

3457	A941	5c High jump	.20	.20
3458	A941	20c Javelin	.65	.20
3459	A941	30c Hammer throw	1.00	.25
3460	A941	40c Long jump, vert.	1.40	.40
3461	A941	50c Hurdles, vert.	1.75	.50
		Nos. 3457-3461 (5)	5.00	1.55

Souvenir Sheet

3462	A941	1p Women's relay	3.50	1.75

No. 3462 contains one 40x32mm stamp.

Latin American History Type of 1986

Discovery of America: No. 3463a, Columbus, Queen Isabella. b, Columbus at Rabida Monastery. c, Columbus, pointing up, outlining his plan. d, Columbus, with scroll, before Salamanca Council. e, Departure of Columbus' fleet from Palos.

No. 3464a, Three ships stopping at Canary Islands. b, Columbus speaking to crew. c, Land sighted, Oct. 12, 1492. d, Columbus landing in New World. e, Meeting natives.

No. 3465a, Grounding of Santa Maria at Hispanola. b, Arrival of Nina at Palos. c, Columbus welcomed in Barcelona. d, Columbus describes his voyage to Ferdinand and Isabella. e, Departure of fleet from Cadiz on second voyage.

No. 3466a, King and Queen welcome Columbus. b, Fleet on Columbus' third voyage. c, Columbus deported from Hispanola to Spain as prisoner. d, Columbus on ship, fourth voyage. e, Death of Columbus, May 20, 1506 in Valladolid.

1992, Oct. 3   *Perf. 13*

3463	A804	1c Strip of 5, #a.-e.	.65	.30
3464	A804	5c Strip of 5, #a.-e.	.65	.30
3465	A804	10c Strip of 5, #a.-e.	1.25	.75
3466	A804	20c Strip of 5, #a.-e.	4.00	1.50
		Nos. 3463-3466 (4)	6.55	2.85

Jose Maria Chacon y Calvo (1892-1969), Historian
A942

1992, Oct. 29   *Perf. 13*

3467	A942	30c multicolored	1.25	.40

Churches
A943

Designs: 5c, Basilica of Nuestra Senora de la Caridad del Cobre. 20c, Santa Maria del Rosario Church. 30c, Espiritu Santo Church. 50c, Santo Angel Custodio Church.

1992, Nov. 10   Litho.   *Perf. 12½*

3468	A943	5c multicolored	.20	.20
3469	A943	20c multicolored	.90	.20
3470	A943	30c multicolored	1.25	.25
3471	A943	50c multicolored	2.40	.30
		Nos. 3468-3471 (4)	4.75	.95

Development of the Diesel Engine — A944

1993, Jan. 20   Litho.   *Perf. 12½*

3472	A944	5c Truck	.20	.20
3473	A944	10c Automobile	.20	.20
3474	A944	30c Tugboat	.55	.40
3475	A944	40c Locomotive	2.50	1.25
3476	A944	50c Tractor	1.00	.65
		Nos. 3472-3476 (5)	4.45	2.70

Souvenir Sheet

3477	A944	1p Rudolf Diesel	3.50	1.75

No. 3477 contains one 40x32mm stamp. Rudolf Diesel, 80th anniv. of death (#3477).

Davis Cup Tennis Competition — A945

Various tennis players in action.

Perf. 12x12½, 12½x12

1993, Feb. 10   Litho.

3478	A945	5c multi, vert.	.20	.20
3479	A945	20c multi, vert.	.60	.20
3480	A945	30c multi, vert.	.90	.40
3481	A945	35c multicolored	1.00	.50
3482	A945	40c multicolored	1.25	.60
		Nos. 3478-3482 (5)	3.95	1.90

Souvenir Sheet
Perf. 12½

3483	A945	1p multicolored	2.50	1.25

No. 3483 contains one 40x32mm stamp.

Scientists
A946

Designs: 3c, Pierre-Paul-Emile Roux (1853-1933), bacteriologist. 5c, Carlos J. Finlay (1833-1915), suggested mosquito as carrier of yellow fever. 10c, Ivan Petrovich Pavlov (1849-1936), physiologist, investigated conditioned reflexes. 20c, Louis Pasteur, chemist, developer of pasteurization. 30c, Santiago Ramon y Cajal (1852-1934), histologist, isolated the neuron. 35c, Sigmund Freud, psychoanalyst. 40c, Wilhelm Conrad Roentgen, physicist, discoverer of x-ray. 50c, Joseph Lister, surgeon, introduced principle of antisepsis. 1p, Robert Koch, bacteriologist, developer of tuberculin, vert.

1993, Mar. 3	Litho.	Perf. 12½	
3484	A946	3c multicolored	.20	.20
3485	A946	5c multicolored	.20	.20
3486	A946	10c multicolored	.25	.20
3487	A946	20c multicolored	.55	.25
3488	A946	30c multicolored	.80	.40
3489	A946	35c multicolored	.90	.50
3490	A946	40c multicolored	1.10	.60
3491	A946	50c multicolored	1.25	.65
Nos. 3484-3491 (8)			5.25	3.00

Souvenir Sheet

| 3492 | A946 | 1p multicolored | 2.75 | 1.40 |

Bicycles — A947

Bicycles designed by: 3c, Leonardo da Vinci, 15th cent. 5c, Karl Von Drais de Sauerbrun, 1813. 10c, Ernest Michaux, 1856. 20c, James Starley, 1869. 30c, Harry Lawson, 1879. 35c, Guaso (Cuba), 1992.

1993, Apr. 14			Perf. 13	
3493	A947	3c multicolored	.20	.20
3494	A947	5c multicolored	.20	.20
3495	A947	10c multicolored	.45	.20
3496	A947	20c multicolored	.90	.25
3497	A947	30c multicolored	1.40	.40
3498	A947	35c multicolored	1.50	.50
Nos. 3493-3498 (6)			4.65	1.75

Cuban Natl. Museum, 80th Anniv. A948

Paintings by Joaquin Sorolla y Bastida (1863-1923): 3c, Child Eating Watermelon, 1920, vert. 5c, Valencian Fisherwomen, 1909. 10c, Regattas. 20c, Contadina, 1889. 40c, Summer, 1904. 50c, Boats on the Ocean, 1908.

1993, May 29	Litho.	Perf. 13x12½	
3499	A948	3c multicolored	.20	.20

Perf. 12½x13

3500	A948	5c multicolored	.30	.20
3501	A948	10c multicolored	.35	.20
3502	A948	20c multicolored	.65	.25
3503	A948	40c multicolored	1.25	.60
3504	A948	50c multicolored	1.75	.65
Nos. 3499-3504 (6)			4.50	2.10

Water Birds A949

Perf. 12½, 13x12½ (5, 30c)

1993, June 15				
3505	A949	3c Jacana spinosa	.20	.20
3506	A949	5c Ardea herodias, vert.	.20	.20
3507	A949	10c Himantopus mexicanus	.30	.20
3508	A949	20c Nycticorax nycticorax	.60	.25
3509	A949	30c Grus canadensis, vert.	.90	.40
3510	A949	50c Aramus guarauna	1.60	.90
Nos. 3505-3510 (6)			3.80	1.90

Brasiliana '93. Nos. 3506, 3510 are 27x44mm.

Anniversaries — A950

#3511, Jose Marti, Moncada Barracks. #3512, "History Will Absolve Me," declaration of Fidel Castro, Marti. #3513, Jose Marti, Rafael M. Mendive, vert. #3514, Carlos Manuel de Cespedes, gear wheels.

1993, July 26	Litho.	Perf. 13	
3511	A950	5c multicolored	.20	.20
3512	A950	5c multicolored	.20	.20
3513	A950	5c multicolored	.20	.20
3514	A950	5c multicolored	.20	.20
Nos. 3511-3514 (4)			.80	.80

Attack on Moncada Barracks, 40th anniv. (#3511). Declaration of Fidel Castro, 40th anniv. (#3512). Birth of Jose Marti, 140th anniv. (#3513). Declaration of the Ten Years' War, 125th anniv. (#3514).

Flowers from Cienfuegos Botanical Gardens A951

1993, Aug. 20				
3515	A951	3c Sedum allantoides	.20	.20
3516	A951	5c Heliconia caribaea	.20	.20
3517	A951	10c Anthurium andraeanum	.35	.20
3518	A951	20c Pseudobombax ellipticum	.70	.25
3519	A951	35c Ixora coccinea	1.10	.50
3520	A951	50c Callistemon specious	1.90	.65
Nos. 3515-3520 (6)			4.45	2.00

Bangkok '93, Intl. Philatelic Exhibition A952

Butterflies: 3c, Battus devillievs. 5c, Anteos maerula. 20c, Ascia monuste evonima. 30c, Junonia coenia. 35c, Anartia jatrophae guantanamo. 50c, Hypolimnas misippus.

1993, Sept. 10	Litho.	Perf. 13	
3521	A952	3c multicolored	.20	.20
3522	A952	5c multicolored	.25	.20
3523	A952	20c multicolored	.70	.25
3524	A952	30c multicolored	1.00	.40
3525	A952	35c multicolored	1.10	.40
3526	A952	50c multicolored	1.60	.65
Nos. 3521-3526 (6)			4.85	2.10

Endangered Species A953

1993, Oct. 12	Litho.	Perf. 13	
3527	A953	5c Phoenicopterus ruber	.25	.20
3528	A953	50c Ajaia ajaja	1.75	.65

Latin American Revolutionaries A954

Flags, map and: No. 3529, Simon Bolivar. No. 3530, Jose Marti. No. 3531, Benito Juarez, Mexican President. No. 3532, Ernesto "Che" Guevara.

1993, Oct. 27	Litho.	Perf. 13	
3529	A954	50c multicolored	1.40	.65
3530	A954	50c multicolored	1.40	.65
3531	A954	50c multicolored	1.40	.65
3532	A954	50c multicolored	1.40	.65
a.	Block of 4, #3529-3532	7.25	3.50
Nos. 3529-3532 (4)			5.60	2.60

17th Central American and Caribbean Games, Ponce, Puerto Rico — A955

1993, Nov. 10	Litho.	Perf. 12½	
3533	A955	5c Swimming	.20	.20
3534	A955	10c Pole vault	.20	.20
3535	A955	20c Boxing	.70	.25
3536	A955	35c Gymnastics, vert.	1.10	.40
3537	A955	50c Baseball, vert.	1.60	.60
Nos. 3533-3537 (5)			3.80	1.70

Souvenir Sheet

| 3538 | A955 | 1p Basketball | 3.75 | 1.75 |

No. 3538 contains one 40x32mm stamp.

Mariana Grajales (1808-93), Patriot — A956

1993, Nov. 27			Perf. 13	
3539	A956	5p multicolored	.30	.20

Peter I. Tchaikovsky (1840-93), Composer A957

1993, Nov. 30				
3540	A957	5c Portrait	.20	.20
3541	A957	20c Swan Lake Ballet	.65	.25
3542	A957	30c Statue	.90	.40
3543	A957	50c Museum, horiz.	1.25	.65
Nos. 3540-3543 (4)			3.00	1.50

A958

A959

1994, Jan. 1	Litho.	Perf. 13	
3544	A958	5c multicolored	.30	.20

35th anniv. of the Revolution.

1994, Jan. 1				
Various soccer players.				
3545	A959	5c multicolored	.20	.20
3546	A959	10c multicolored	.60	.25
3547	A959	30c multicolored	.85	.40
3548	A959	35c multicolored	.95	.40
3549	A959	40c multicolored	1.25	.50
3550	A959	50c multicolored	1.40	.65
Nos. 3545-3550 (6)			5.25	2.40

Souvenir Sheet

| 3551 | A959 | 1p multicolored | 3.00 | 1.50 |

1994 World Cup Soccer Championships, US. No. 3551 contains one 40x31mm stamp.

Cats A960

1994, Feb. 15	Litho.	Perf. 12½	
3552	A960	5c Blue Persian	.20	.20
3553	A960	10c Havana	.25	.20
3554	A960	20c Maine coon	.70	.25
3555	A960	30c Blue British shorthair	1.00	.40
3556	A960	35c Bicolor Persian	1.10	.40
3557	A960	50c Gold chinchilla	1.60	.65
Nos. 3552-3557 (6)			4.85	2.10

Souvenir Sheet
Perf. 13

| 3558 | A960 | 1p Abyssinian, vert. | 4.00 | 2.00 |

No. 3558 contains one 30x38mm stamp.

Medicinal Plants — A961

Designs: 5c, Salvia officinalis. 10c, Aloe barbadensis. 20c, Helianthus annuus. 30c, Matricaria chamomilla. 40c, Calendula officinalis. 50c, Tilia platyphyllos.

1994, Mar. 30	Litho.	Perf. 12½	
3559	A961	5c multicolored	.25	.20
3560	A961	10c multicolored	.25	.20
3561	A961	20c multicolored	.65	.25
3562	A961	30c multicolored	.90	.40
3563	A961	40c multicolored	1.25	.50
3564	A961	50c multicolored	1.50	.65
Nos. 3559-3564 (6)			4.80	2.20

Carriages — A962

Designs: 5c, Public coach, 1860. 10c, Coach of Ferdinand VII, Maria Louisa. 30c, Louis XV-style coach. 35c, Elizabeth II gala day's coach. 40c, Catalina II's summer coach. 50c, Volanta habanera.

1994, Apr. 20   **Perf. 12½x12**
3565	A962	5c multicolored	.20	.20
3566	A962	10c multicolored	.25	.20
3567	A962	30c multicolored	1.00	.40
3568	A962	35c multicolored	1.10	.40
3569	A962	40c multicolored	1.40	.50
3570	A962	50c multicolored	1.60	.65
		Nos. 3565-3570 (6)	5.55	2.35

No. 3570 is 68x37mm.

Aquaculture — A963

Designs: 5c, Crassostrea rhizophorae. 20c, Cardisoma guanhumi. 30c, Tilapia melanopleura. 35c, Hippospongia lachne. 40c, Panulirus argus. 50c, Cyprinus carpio.

1994, May 10   **Litho.**   **Perf. 12½**
3571	A963	5c multicolored	.35	.20
3572	A963	20c multicolored	.60	.25
3573	A963	30c multicolored	.85	.40
3574	A963	35c multicolored	1.00	.40
3575	A963	40c multicolored	1.25	.50
3576	A963	50c multicolored	1.50	.65
		Nos. 3571-3576 (6)	5.55	2.40

Intl. Olympic Committee, Cent. — A964

1994, June 23   **Litho.**   **Perf. 12½**
3577	A964	5c Flag, runners	.20	.20
3578	A964	30c Flag, world map	.85	.40
3579	A964	50c Flag, Olympic flame	1.50	.65
		Nos. 3577-3579 (3)	2.55	1.25

Scientists A965

Designs: 5c, Michael Faraday (1791-1867), physicist. 10c, Marie Curie (1867-1934), physical chemist. 20c, Pierre Curie (1859-1906), chemist. 30c, Albert Einstein (1879-1955), physicist, mathematician. 40c, Max Planck (1858-1947), theoretical physicist. 50c, Otto Hahn (1879-1968), physical chemist.

1994, July 20   **Litho.**   **Perf. 12½**
3580	A965	5c multicolored	.20	.20
3581	A965	10c multicolored	.25	.20
3582	A965	20c multicolored	.70	.20
3583	A965	30c multicolored	1.00	.40
3584	A965	40c multicolored	1.40	.50
3585	A965	50c multicolored	1.75	.65
		Nos. 3580-3585 (6)	5.30	2.20

Cactus Flowers A966

Designs: 5c, Opuntia dillenii. 10c, Opuntia millspaughii, vert. 30c, Leptocereus santamarinae. 35c, Pereskia marcanoi. 40c, Dendrocereus nudiflorus, vert. 50c, Pilocereus robinii.

1994, Aug. 15   **Litho.**   **Perf. 12½**
3586	A966	5c multicolored	.30	.20
3587	A966	10c multicolored	1.00	.40
3588	A966	30c multicolored	1.10	.40
3589	A966	35c multicolored	1.50	.50
3590	A966	40c multicolored	1.75	.65
3591	A966	50c multicolored		
		Nos. 3586-3591 (5)	5.65	2.15

Souvenir Sheet

2nd Spanish-Cuban Philatelic Exhibition, Havana — A967

Design: 1p, Cuban postal rocket, #C31.

1994, Sept. 18
3592	A967	1p multicolored	3.50	1.75

Experimental postal rocket flight, 55th anniv.

Dogs A968

1994, Sept. 20
3593	A968	5c Rough collie	.25	.20
3594	A968	20c American cocker spaniel	.70	.20
3595	A968	30c Dalmatian	.95	.25
3596	A968	40c Afghan hound	1.40	.40
3597	A968	50c English cocker spaniel	1.60	.65
		Nos. 3593-3597 (5)	4.90	1.70

Cayo Largo Island A969

Fauna: 15c, Carpilius corallinus. 65c, Cyclura nubila, vert. 75c, Pelecanus occidentalis. 4p, Chelonia mydas.

1994, Sept. 30   **Litho.**   **Perf. 12½**
3598	A969	15c multicolored	.40	.20
3599	A969	65c multicolored	2.25	.90
3600	A969	75c multicolored	2.50	1.00
3601	A969	1p multicolored	3.50	1.25
		Nos. 3598-3601 (4)	8.65	3.35

A970

A971

1994, Oct. 28
3602	A970	15c multicolored	.80	.20

Camilo Cienfuegos Gorriaran, revolutionary, 35th anniv. of disappearance.

1994, Oct. 30

Fauna of the Caribbean: 10c, Epinephelus flavolimbatus, horiz. No. 3604, Phoenicopterus ruber. No. 3605, Aetobatus narinari. No. 3606, Istiophorus platypterus, horiz. No. 3607, Tursiops truncatus, horiz. No. 3608, Pelecanus occidentalis.

3603	A971	10c multicolored	.40	.20
3604	A971	15c multicolored	.40	.20
3605	A971	15c multicolored	.40	.20
3606	A971	15c multicolored	.40	.20
3607	A971	65c multicolored	2.25	.90
3608	A971	65c multicolored	2.25	.90
		Nos. 3603-3608 (6)	6.10	2.60

ICAO, 50th Anniv. A972

1994, Nov. 9
3609	A972	65c multicolored	2.00	.90

Zoological Garden, Havana, 55th Anniv. — A973

1994, Nov. 14   **Litho.**   **Perf. 13**
3610	A973	15c Bronze monument	.20	.20
3611	A973	65c Ara chloroptera	1.10	.90
3612	A973	75c Carduelis carduelis	1.25	1.00
		Nos. 3610-3612 (3)	2.55	2.10

Cuban Philatelic Federation, 30th Anniv. — A974

1994, Nov. 20
3613	A974	15c multicolored	.50	.20

America Issue — A975

Postal transportation: 15c, 18th Cent. Spanish galleon, maritime postal service, vert. 65c,

19th Cent. postal rider, insurgent postal service.

1994, Dec. 12
3614	A975	15c multicolored	.25	.20
3615	A975	65c multicolored	1.75	.90

Postal Museum, 30th Anniv. — A976

1995, Jan. 2
3616	A976	15c multicolored	.50	.20

Lizards — A977

Designs: 15c, Anolis baracoae. 65c, Sphaerodactylus ramsdeni. 75c, Leiocephalus raviceps. 85c, Sphaerodactylus ruibali. 90c, Anolis ophiolepis. 1p, Sphaerodactylus armasi.

1994, Nov. 30   **Litho.**   **Perf. 12½**
3617	A977	15c multicolored	.30	.20
3618	A977	65c multicolored	1.60	.90
3619	A977	75c multicolored	1.75	1.00
3620	A977	85c multicolored	2.00	1.25
3621	A977	90c multicolored	2.25	1.25
3622	A977	1p multicolored	2.50	1.40
		Nos. 3617-3622 (6)	10.40	6.00

Cuban War of Independence, Cent. — A978

1995, Feb. 24   **Litho.**   **Perf. 12½**
3623	A978	15c Jose Marti, flag	.50	.20

Pan American Games, Mar del Plata, Argentina — A979

1995, Mar. 11   **Litho.**   **Perf. 13**
3624	A979	10c Boxing, vert.	.20	.20
3625	A979	15c Weight lifting, vert.	.25	.20
3626	A979	65c Volleyball, vert.	1.10	.80
3627	A979	75c Wrestling	1.25	1.00
3628	A979	85c Baseball	1.50	1.00
3629	A979	90c High jump	1.60	1.10
		Nos. 3624-3629 (6)	5.90	4.30

National Aquarium, 35th Anniv. — A980

Fish: 10c, Holacanthus cillaris. 15c, Hypoplectrus guttavarius. 65c, Anisotremus virginicus. 75c, Amblycirrhitus pinos. 85c, Pomaacanthus paru. 90c, Acanthurus coeruleus.

1995, Apr. 28   Litho.   Perf. 13

3630	A980	10c multicolored	.20	.20
3631	A980	15c multicolored	.25	.20
3632	A980	65c multicolored	1.00	.70
3633	A980	75c multicolored	1.10	.80
3634	A980	85c multicolored	1.90	1.10
3635	A980	90c multicolored	1.90	1.10
		Nos. 3630-3635 (6)	6.35	4.10

FAO, 50th Anniv. A981

1995, Apr. 7   Litho.   Perf. 13

3636	A981	75c multicolored	1.25	1.00

First Cuban Postage Stamp, 140th Anniv. — A982

65c, Ornamental letter drop, envelope.

1995, Apr. 24   Litho.   Perf. 12½

3637	A982	15c black & blue green	.30	.20
3638	A982	65c multicolored	1.40	.75

Jose Marti, Death Cent. A983

Designs: 15c, Marti killed in combat, signature, portrait. 65c, Landing of Marti, Cuban patriots on Playitas beach. 75c, Montecristi Manifesto signed in Domincan Republic, Marti. 85c, Meeting of Marti, Maceo, Gomez at La Mejorana Farm. 90c, Marti's mausoleum, Santiago, Cuba, vert.

1995, May 19   Perf. 12½x13, 13x12½

3639	A983	15c multicolored	.25	.20
3640	A983	65c multicolored	1.25	.80
3641	A983	75c multicolored	1.40	1.00
3642	A983	85c multicolored	1.75	1.00
3643	A983	90c multicolored	1.75	1.10
		Nos. 3639-3643 (5)	6.40	4.10

Antonio Maceo (1845-96), Revolutionary — A984

1995, June 14   Litho.   Perf. 12½

3644	A984	15c multicolored	.60	.20

Butterflies — A985

Designs: 10c, Dione vanillae. 15c, Eunica tatila. 65c, Melete salacia. 75c, Greta cubana. 85c, Eurema daira. 90c, Phoebis sennae.

1995, June 20   Perf. 12½x13

3645	A985	10c multicolored	.25	.20
3646	A985	15c multicolored	.25	.20
3647	A985	65c multicolored	1.25	.80
3648	A985	75c multicolored	1.40	1.00
3649	A985	85c multicolored	1.75	1.00
3650	A985	90c multicolored	1.75	1.10
		Nos. 3645-3650 (6)	6.65	4.30

World War II Combat Planes — A986

Designs: 10c, Supermarine "Spitfire," Great Britain. 15c, IL-2, Russia. 65c, Curtiss P-40, US. 75c, Messerschmitt Bf-109, Germany. 85c, Morane-Saunier 406, France.

1995, July 30   Litho.   Perf. 12½

3651	A986	10c multicolored	.30	.20
3652	A986	15c multicolored	.30	.20
3653	A986	65c multicolored	1.40	.80
3654	A986	75c multicolored	1.60	1.00
3655	A986	85c multicolored	1.90	1.00
		Nos. 3651-3655 (5)	5.50	3.20

A987

1995, Aug. 6   Litho.   Perf. 12½

3656	A987	15c multicolored	.50	.20

Ernesto Lecuona, composer, pianist, birth cent.

1995, Aug. 10

Color of Horse or Horses

3657	A988	10c golden brown, white	.40	.20
3658	A988	15c white, horiz.	.40	.20
3659	A988	65c dark brown, white	1.75	.80
3660	A988	75c red brown	2.10	1.00
3661	A988	85c tan	2.50	1.00
3662	A988	90c white	2.50	1.10
		Nos. 3657-3662 (6)	9.65	4.30

Singapore '95.

Souvenir Sheet

Beijing Intl. Stamp & Coin Expo '95 — A989

Illustration reduced.

1995, Aug. 28   Perf. 13

3663	A989	50c multicolored	1.25	.75

1996 Summer Olympics, Atlanta — A990

1995, Sept. 25   Litho.   Perf. 13

3664	A990	10c Wrestling	.20	.20
3665	A990	15c Weight lifting	.25	.20
3666	A990	65c Women's volleyball	1.10	.80
3667	A990	75c Women's athletics	1.25	1.00
3668	A990	85c Baseball	1.50	1.00
3669	A990	90c Women's judo	1.60	1.10
		Nos. 3664-3669 (6)	5.90	4.30

Souvenir Sheet

3670	A990	1p Boxing	3.00	1.50

No. 3670 contains one 30x36mm stamp.

Cuban Sugar Industry, 400th Anniv. A991

Paintings from "Los Ingenios," by Edouard Laplante, 1852: 15c, Steam train, sugar factory. 65c, Sugar factory, tower, bridge.

1995, Oct. 3

3671	A991	15c multicolored	1.25	.35
3672	A991	65c multicolored	.75	.70

UN, 50th Anniv. A992

1995, Oct. 24   Litho.   Perf. 13

3673	A992	65c multicolored	1.00	.80

Zoological Gardens, Havana — A993

Designs: 10c, Panthera leo, vert. 15c, Equus grevyi. 65c, Pongo pygmaeus, vert. 75c, Elephas maximus. 85c, Sciurus vulgaris. 90c, Procyon lotor.

1995, Oct. 30   Litho.   Perf. 13

3674	A993	10c multicolored	.25	.20
3675	A993	15c multicolored	.25	.20
3676	A993	65c multicolored	1.10	.80
3677	A993	75c multicolored	1.25	1.00
3678	A993	85c multicolored	1.50	1.00
3679	A993	90c multicolored	1.60	1.10
		Nos. 3674-3679 (6)	5.95	4.30

UNESCO, 50th Anniv. — A994

UNESCO World Culture and National Heritage sites: 65c, Santa Clara de Asis Convent. 75c, San Francisco de Asis Minor Basilica.

1995, Nov. 4

3680	A994	65c multicolored	1.10	.80
3681	A994	75c multicolored	1.25	1.00

Orchids — A995

Designs: 5c, Epidendrum porpax. 10c, Cyrtopodium punctatum. 15c, Polyrrhiza lindeni. 40c, Bletia patula. 45c, Galeandra beyrichii. 50c, Vanilla dilloniana. 65c, Macradenia lutescens. 75c, Oncidium luridum. 85c, Ionopsis utriculariodes.

1995, Nov. 10   Perf. 12½

3681A	A995	5c multicolored	.20	.20
3681B	A995	10c multicolored	.25	.20
3681C	A995	15c multicolored	.25	.20
3682	A995	40c multicolored	.80	.55
3683	A995	45c multicolored	.90	.55
3684	A995	50c multicolored	1.00	.65
3685	A995	65c multicolored	1.25	.80
3686	A995	75c multicolored	1.40	1.00
3687	A995	85c multicolored	1.75	1.00
		Nos. 3681A-3687 (9)	7.80	5.15

Issued: 40c-85c, 11/10/95; 5c-15c, 6/28/96.

Motion Pictures, Cent. — A996

1995, Dec. 7   Perf. 13

3688	A996	15c Lumiere Brothers	.30	.20
3689	A996	15c Marilyn Monroe	.30	.20
3690	A996	15c Marlene Dietrich	.30	.20
3691	A996	15c Vittorio DeSica	.30	.20
3692	A996	15c Charlie Chaplin	.30	.20
3693	A996	15c Greta Garbo	.30	.20
3694	A996	65c Humphrey Bogart	1.40	.80
3695	A996	75c Montaner	1.60	1.00
3696	A996	85c Cantinflas	1.90	1.00
		Nos. 3688-3696 (9)	6.70	4.30

Souvenir Sheet

4th Cuban-Spanish Philatelic Exhibition, Havana — A997

Illustration reduced.

1995, Dec. 11   Litho.   Perf. 13

3697	A997	1p multicolored	3.00	1.50

America Issue — A998

1995, Dec. 12

3698	A998	15c Centurus superciliaris	.35	.20
3699	A998	65c Todus multicolor	1.60	.80

Generals Who Died in 1895
War — A999

Designs: No. 3700, Alfonso Goulet Goulet, Francisco Adolfo Crombet Ballon. No. 3701, Jesus Calvar O, Jose Guillermo Moncada, Tomas Jordan. No. 3702, Francisco Borrero Lavadi, Francisco Inchaustegui Cabrera.

1995, Dec. 20   *Perf. 12½*
3700	A999	15c multicolored	.35	.20
3701	A999	15c multicolored	.35	.20
3702	A999	15c multicolored	.35	.20
a.		Strip of 3, #3700-3702	1.10	.90
		Nos. 3700-3702 (3)	1.05	.60

See Nos. 3758-3760.

Island of Coco Cay, Jardines del Rey A1000

Bird, scenic view: 10c, Sterna antillarum, aerial view of island. 15c, Eudocimus albus, people on beach. 45c, Spindalis zena, couple on steps of resort complex. 50c, Turdus plumbeus, resort. 65c, Mimus polyglottos, resort. 75c, Phoenicopterus ruber, couple in pool at resort.

1995, Dec. 23
3703	A1000	10c multicolored	.20	.20
3704	A1000	15c multicolored	.30	.20
3705	A1000	45c multicolored	1.00	.55
3706	A1000	50c multicolored	1.10	.60
3707	A1000	65c multicolored	1.40	.80
3708	A1000	75c multicolored	1.60	1.00
		Nos. 3703-3708 (6)	5.60	3.35

Patriots — A1001

Designs: 15c, Carlos M. de Céspedes (1819-74). 65c, José Marti (1853-95). 75c, Antonio Maceo (1845-96). 1.05p, Ignacio Agramonte (1841-73). 2.05p, Máximo Gómez (1836-1905). 3p, Calixto Garcia (1839-98).

1996, Jan. 10
3709	A1001	15c green	.25	.20
3710	A1001	65c blue	1.10	.80
3711	A1001	75c carmine	1.25	1.00
3712	A1001	1.05p lilac	1.90	1.40
3713	A1001	2.05p brown	3.75	2.50
3714	A1001	3p light brown	5.25	3.75
		Nos. 3709-3714 (6)	13.50	9.65

See Nos. 3755-3757.

Organization of Solidarity of the Peoples of Africa, Asia and Latin America (OSPAAAL), 30th Anniv. — A1002

1996, Jan. 14
3715	A1002	65c multicolored	1.50	.75

Scientists — A1003

10c, Leonardo da Vinci (1452-1519). 15c, Mikhail V. Lomonosov (1711-65), atmospheric scientist. 65c, James Watt (1736-1819), engineer, inventor. 75c, Guglielmo Marconi (1874-1937), physicist. 85c, Charles R. Darwin (1809-82), naturalist.

1996, Jan. 30   **Litho.**   *Perf. 12½*
3716	A1003	10c multicolored	.25	.20
3717	A1003	15c multicolored	.25	.20
3718	A1003	65c multicolored	1.25	.80
3719	A1003	75c multicolored	1.40	1.00
3720	A1003	85c multicolored	1.75	1.00
		Nos. 3716-3720 (5)	4.90	3.20

1996 Summer Olympics, Atlanta — A1004

1996, Feb. 15   **Litho.**   *Perf. 12½*
3721	A1004	10c Athletics, vert.	.30	.20
3722	A1004	15c Weight lifting, vert.	.30	.20
3723	A1004	65c Judo, vert.	1.40	.80
3724	A1004	75c Wrestling	1.60	1.00
3725	A1004	85c Boxing	1.90	1.00
		Nos. 3721-3725 (5)	5.50	3.20

Souvenir Sheet
3726	A1004	1p Baseball, vert.	3.00	1.50

No. 3726 contains one 40x32mm stamp.

Espamer '96, Aviation and Space, Philatelic Exhibition, Seville — A1005

1996, Mar. 4
3727	A1005	15c C-4 Autogiro	.25	.20
3728	A1005	65c CASA C-352	1.25	.80
3729	A1005	75c Alcotan C-201	1.60	1.00
3730	A1005	85c CASA C-212	1.75	1.00
		Nos. 3727-3730 (4)	4.85	3.00

Juan C. Gundlach (1810-1896), Ornithologist — A1006

Birds: 10c, Ceryle alcyon. 15c, Setophaga ruticilla. 65c, Geothlypis trichas. 75c, Passerina ciris. 85c, Bombycilla cedrorum. 1p, Vireo gundlachi.

1996, Mar. 15   *Perf. 12½*
3731	A1006	10c multicolored	.30	.20
3732	A1006	15c multicolored	.30	.20
3733	A1006	65c multicolored	1.40	.80
3734	A1006	75c multicolored	1.60	1.00
3735	A1006	85c multicolored	1.90	1.00
		Nos. 3731-3735 (5)	5.50	3.20

Souvenir Sheet
3736	A1006	1p multicolored	3.00	1.50

No. 3736 contains one 40x32mm stamp.

Souvenir Sheet

ESPAMER '96, Stamp Exhibition of America and Europe, Seville — A1007

Illustration reduced.

1996, Mar. 14   **Litho.**   *Perf. 12½*
3737	A1007	1p multicolored	3.00	1.50

First Man in Space, 35th Anniv. — A1008

Designs: 15c, Yuri A. Gagarin (1934-68). 65c, Spaceship, map showing orbital route.

1996, Apr. 12   **Litho.**   *Perf. 12½*
3738	A1008	15c multi	.25	.20
3739	A1008	65c multi, horiz.	1.10	.80

Bay of Pigs Invasion, 35th Anniv. — A1009

1996, Apr. 19
3740	A1009	15c shown	.35	.20
3741	A1009	65c Natl. flags	1.60	.80

Cuban Sailing Ships A1010

Designs: 10c, Bahama. 15c, Santísima Trinidad. 65c, Principe de Asturias. 75c, San Pedro de Alcántara. 85c, Santa Ana. 1p, San Genaro.

1996, May 8   **Litho.**   *Perf. 12½*
3742	A1010	10c multicolored	.20	.20
3743	A1010	15c multicolored	.30	.20
3744	A1010	65c multicolored	1.40	.80
3745	A1010	75c multicolored	1.60	1.00
3746	A1010	85c multicolored	1.75	1.00
		Nos. 3742-3746 (5)	5.25	3.20

Souvenir Sheet
3747	A1010	1p multicolored	2.00	1.00

CAPEX '96. No. 3747 contains one 40x32mm stamp.

Fauna of the Caribbean A1011

Designs: 10c, Todus multicolor. No. 3749, Eulampis jugularis. No. 3750, Aix sponsa. No.

3751, Chaetodon ocellatus. No. 3752, Papilio cresphontes. No. 3753, Hypoplectrus indigo.

1996, June 18   **Litho.**   *Perf. 12½*
3748	A1011	10c multicolored	.30	.20
3749	A1011	15c multicolored	.30	.20
3750	A1011	15c multicolored	.30	.20
3751	A1011	15c multicolored	.30	.20
3752	A1011	65c multicolored	1.40	.80
3753	A1011	65c multicolored	1.40	.80
		Nos. 3748-3753 (6)	4.00	2.40

Jose M. Maceo Grajales (1849-96), Revolutionary War Leader — A1012

1996, July 5
3754	A1012	15c multicolored	.50	.20

Patriot Type of 1996

Designs: 10c, Serafin Sánchez. 85c, Juan Gualberto Gomez. 90c, Quintin Bandera.

1996, July 10
3755	A1001	10c orange	.20	.20
3756	A1001	85c olive	1.75	1.00
3757	A1001	90c olive brown	2.00	1.10
		Nos. 3755-3757 (3)	3.95	2.30

Generals Who Died in 1895 War Type of 1995

#3758, Esteban Tamayo (1843-96), Angel Guerra (1842-96). #3759, Juan Fernández Ruz (1821-96), José Maria Aguirre (1843-96), Serafin Sánchez (1846-96). #3760, Juan Bruno Zayas (1867-96), Pedro Vargas Sotomayor (1868-96).

1996, July 30
3758	A999	15c multicolored	.35	.20
3759	A999	15c multicolored	.35	.20
3760	A999	15c multicolored	.35	.20
a.		Strip of 3, #3758-3760	1.70	.90
		Nos. 3758-3760 (3)	1.05	.60

Santiago de Cuba — A1013

Flower, scenic view: 15c, Jacaranda arborea, beach. 65c, Begonia bissei, Fort San Pedro de la Roca. 75c, Byrsonima crassifolia, palm trees, mountains, vert. 85c, Pereskia zinniiflora, church, vert.

Perf. 13x12½, 12½x13

1996, Sept. 27   **Litho.**
3761	A1013	15c multicolored	.30	.20
3762	A1013	65c multicolored	1.40	.80
3763	A1013	75c multicolored	1.60	1.00
3764	A1013	85c multicolored	1.75	1.00
		Nos. 3761-3764 (4)	5.05	3.00

Steam Locomotives — A1014

Designs: 10c, Baldwin 0-4-2, 1878. 15c, American 2-6-0, 1904. 65c, Baldwin 4-6-0, 1906. 75c, Rogers 2-4-4, 1914. 90c, Baldwin 2-8-0, 1920.

1996, Sept. 30   *Perf. 12½*
3765	A1014	10c multicolored	.25	.20
3766	A1014	10c multicolored	.25	.20
3767	A1014	65c multicolored	1.40	.80
3768	A1014	75c multicolored	1.60	.90
3769	A1014	90c multicolored	1.75	1.00
		Nos. 3765-3769 (5)	5.25	3.10

Traditional Costumes
A1015

America Issue: 15c, Free black couple, 19th cent. 65c, Guayabera couple, 20th cent.

1996, Oct. 12   Litho.   Perf. 12½
3770 A1015 15c multicolored   .35   .20
3771 A1015 65c multicolored   1.60   .80

UNICEF, 50th Anniv. — A1016

1996, Nov. 8   Litho.   Perf. 12½
3772 A1016 15c multicolored   .50   .20

World Chess Championship Won by José Raúl Capablanca, 75th Anniv. — A1017

Designs: 15c, Portrait, chess board. 65c, Portrait, seated at chess board. 75c, Rook with top shaped as world, portrait. 85c, Playing chess as a child. 90c, In championship match, 1921.

1996, Nov. 30   Litho.   Perf. 12½
3773 A1017 15c multicolored   .25   .20
3774 A1017 65c multicolored   1.25   .80
3775 A1017 75c multicolored   1.40   1.00
3776 A1017 85c multicolored   1.60   1.00
3777 A1017 90c multicolored   1.75   1.10
      Nos. 3773-3777 (5)   6.25   4.10

Revolutionary Armed Forces and Return of Castro from Mexico, 40th Anniv. — A1018

1996, Dec. 2
3778 A1018 15c Yacht Granma   .20   .20
3779 A1018 65c Armed forces   1.25   1.00

Maj. Gen. Antonio Maceo (1845-96) — A1019

Designs: 10c, Monument, Santiago, vert. No. 3781, Portrait, vert. No. 3782, Monument, Duaba. 65c, Detail of painting showing Maceo dying from combat wounds. 75c, Maceo, young man and monument, San Pedro.

1996, Dec. 7
3780 A1019 10c multicolored   .20   .20
3781 A1019 15c multicolored   .30   .20
3782 A1019 15c multicolored   .30   .20
3783 A1019 65c multicolored   1.50   1.10
3784 A1019 75c multicolored   1.75   1.40
      Nos. 3780-3784 (5)   4.05   3.10

Medals Won at 1996 Summer Olympic Games, Atlanta — A1020

Medal, sport: No. 3785a, Gold, judo. b, Bronze, wrestling.
No. 3786: a, Gold, weight lifting. b, Gold, wrestling. c, Silver, fencing. d, Silver, swimming.
No. 3787: a, Gold, women's volleyball. b, Gold, boxing. c, Silver, women's running. d, Gold, baseball.

1996, Dec. 10
3785 A1020 10c Pair, #a-b + 4
                  labels   .50   .25
3786 A1020 15c Block, #a-d + 2
                  labels   1.00   .50
3787 A1020 65c Block, #a-d + 2
                  labels   4.50   2.25
      Nos. 3785-3787 (3)   6.00   3.00

New Year 1996 (Year of the Rat) — A1021

1996, Dec. 28   Litho.   Perf. 12½
3788 A1021 15c multicolored   .50   .25

Espamer '98 — A1022

Locomotives: 15c, Minho Douro 0-6-0, Portugal. No. 3790, Vulcan Iron Works 0-4-0, Brazil. No. 3791, Baldwin 2-6-0, Dominican Republic. No. 3792, American Locomotive Co. 2-6-4, Panama. No. 3793, Baldwin 0-4-0, Puerto Rico. No. 3794, Slaughter, Gruning Co. 0-4-0, Spain. No. 3795, Yorkshire Engine Co. 4-4-0, Argentina. No. 3796, 2-6-0 Paraguay. No. 3797, H.K. Porter Co. 2-8-2, Chile. No. 3798, 2-6-0, Mexico.
1p, Baldwin 0-4-2 (1884), Cuba.

1996, Dec. 30
3789 A1022 15c multicolored   .20   .20
3790 A1022 65c multicolored   1.00   .65
3791 A1022 65c multicolored   1.00   .65
3792 A1022 65c multicolored   1.00   .65
3793 A1022 65c multicolored   1.00   .65
3794 A1022 65c multicolored   1.00   .65
3795 A1022 75c multicolored   1.25   .70
3796 A1022 75c multicolored   1.25   .70
3797 A1022 75c multicolored   1.25   .70
3798 A1022 75c multicolored   1.25   .70
      Nos. 3789-3798 (10)   10.20   6.25
            Souvenir Sheet
3799 A1022 1p multicolored   3.00   1.50
No. 3799 contains one 36x28mm.

Hong Kong '97, Intl. Philatelic Exhibition — A1023

Cats: 10c, Brown-point Siamese, vert. No. 3801, Japanese bobtail. No. 3802, Burmese, vert. No. 3803, Singapore. No. 3804, Korat.
1p, Blue-point Siamese.

1997, Jan. 15   Litho.   Perf. 12½
3800 A1023 10c multicolored   .20   .20
3801 A1023 15c multicolored   .25   .20
3802 A1023 15c multicolored   .25   .20
3803 A1023 65c multicolored   1.25   1.00
3804 A1023 75c multicolored   1.40   1.10
      Nos. 3800-3804 (5)   3.35   2.70
            Souvenir Sheet
3805 A1023 1p multicolored   3.00   1.50
No. 3805 contains one 40x31mm stamp.

Motion Pictures, Cent. A1024

Film scenes from: 15c, "El Romance del Palmar," directed by Ramón Peón. 65c, "Memorias del Subdesarrollo," directed by Tomás Gutiérrez Alea, vert.

1997, Jan. 24   Litho.   Perf. 13
3806 A1024 15c multicolored   .30   .20
3807 A1024 65c multicolored   1.60   1.00

Zoo Animals A1025

Designs: 10c, Camelus dromedarius. No. 3809, Ailuropada melanoleuca. No. 3810, Cerothoterium simun. 75c, Pongo pygmaeus. 90c, Bison bonasus.

1997, Feb. 20   Litho.   Perf. 12½
3808 A1025 10c multicolored   .20   .20
3809 A1025 15c multicolored   .25   .20
3810 A1025 15c multicolored   .25   .20
3811 A1025 65c multicolored   1.25   1.00
3812 A1025 90c multicolored   1.50   1.10
      Nos. 3808-3812 (5)   3.45   2.70

New Year 1997 (Year of the Ox) — A1026

1997, Feb. 22
3813 A1026 15c multicolored   .50   .25

Attack on the Presidential Palace, 40th Anniv. — A1027

1997, Mar. 13   Litho.   Perf. 12½
3814 A1027 15c Menelao Mora
                  Morales   .75   .20

1998 World Cup Soccer Championships, France — A1028

Action scenes: 10c, Three players. No. 3816, Player in green, player in blue & yellow. No. 3817, Player in yellow & black, player in green. 65c, Player in yellow & blue, player in blue and red. 75c, Player in red & blue, player in yellow & black.
1p, Player down.

1997, Mar. 25
3815 A1028 10c multicolored   .20   .20
3816 A1028 15c multicolored   .25   .20
3817 A1028 15c multicolored   .25   .20
3818 A1028 65c multicolored   1.25   1.00
3819 A1028 75c multicolored   1.50   1.10
      Nos. 3815-3819 (5)   3.45   2.70
            Souvenir Sheet
3820 A1028 1p multicolored   2.25   1.10
No. 3820 contains one 40x31mm stamp.

Young Communist League (UJC), 35th Anniv. — A1029

1997, Apr. 4
3821 A1029 15c multicolored   .75   .20

Paddle Steamer Caledonia — A1030

Stamp Day: 15c, Maritime Postal Service, 170th anniv. 65c, Air Postal Service, 70th anniv.

1997, Apr. 24   Litho.   Perf. 12½
3822 A1030 15c multicolored   .35   .20
3823 A1030 65c multicolored   1.40   .95

Death of Generals in War of 1895, 102nd Anniv. — A1031

#3824, Adolfo de Castillo, Enrique del Junco Cruz-Muñoz. #3825, Alberto Rodríguez Acosta, Mariano Sánchez Vaillant.

1997, May 18   Litho.   Perf. 12½
3824 A1031 15c multicolored   .30   .20
3825 A1031 15c multicolored   .30   .20
   a.   Pair, #3824-3825   .60   .40

Gen. Gregorio Luperon, Death Cent. — A1032

1997, May 20
3826 A1032 65c multicolored   1.35 1.00

Butterflies — A1033

Designs: 10c, Eurema nicippe. No. 3828, Eurema dina. No. 3829, Colobura dirce clementi. 65c, Vanesa atalanta. 85c, Kricogonia castalia.

1997, May 20
3827	A1033	10c multicolored	.20	.20
3828	A1033	10c multicolored	.25	.20
3829	A1033	15c multicolored	.25	.20
3830	A1033	65c multicolored	1.25	.90
3831	A1033	85c multicolored	1.40	1.00
	Nos. 3827-3831 (5)		3.35	2.50

Cuban Assoc. of the UN, 50th Anniv. A1034

1997, May 31
3832 A1034 65c multicolored   1.25 .95

Chinese In Cuba, 150th Anniv. — A1035

1997, May 29   *Perf. 13*
3833 A1035 15c multicolored   .50 .45

14th World Festival of Youth and Students A1036

Designs: 10c, Dove holding olive twig, rainbow. No. 3835, Children playing on playground equipment, vert. No. 3836, Monument with arms extended. 65c, Maj. Ernesto "Che" Guevara, revolutionary hero. 75c, Monument, diff.

1997, July 28   Litho.   *Perf. 12½*
3834	A1036	10c multicolored	.20	.20
3835	A1036	15c multicolored	.25	.20
3836	A1036	15c multicolored	.25	.20
3837	A1036	65c multicolored	1.40	.95
3838	A1036	75c multicolored	1.60	1.00
	Nos. 3834-3838 (5)		3.70	2.55

Frank País (1934-57), Revolutionary Hero — A1037

1997, July 30
3839 A1037 15c multicolored   .50 .20

Seven Wonders of the Ancient World A1038

Designs: 10c, Lighthouse of Alexandria. No. 3841, Pyramids of Egypt. No. 3842, Gardens of Semiramis at Babylon. No. 3843, Colossus at Rhodes. No. 3844, Mausoleum of Halicarnassus. No. 3845, Statue of Zeus at Olympia. 75c, Temple of Artemis at Ephesus.

1997, July 30
3840	A1038	10c multicolored	.20	.20
3841	A1038	15c multicolored	.25	.20
3842	A1038	15c multicolored	.25	.20
3843	A1038	15c multicolored	.25	.20
3844	A1038	65c multicolored	1.25	.95
3845	A1038	65c multicolored	1.25	.95
3846	A1038	75c multicolored	1.25	1.00
	Nos. 3840-3846 (7)		4.70	3.70

Independence of India, 50th Anniv. — A1039

1997, Aug. 15
3847 A1039 15c Mahatma Gandhi   .50 .20

Caribbean Birds — A1040

#3848, Sicalis flaveola. #3849, Eubucco bourcierii. #3850, Trogon curucui. #3851, Amazona leucocephala. #3852, Amazona ochrocephala. #3853, Hylocharis eliciae. #3854, Carduelis carduelis.

1997, Aug. 15
3848	A1040	15c multicolored	.30	.20
3849	A1040	15c multicolored	.30	.20
3850	A1040	15c multicolored	.30	.20
3851	A1040	15c multicolored	.30	.20
3852	A1040	65c multicolored	1.60	1.00
3853	A1040	65c multicolored	1.60	1.00
3854	A1040	75c multicolored	1.75	1.10
	Nos. 3848-3854 (7)		6.15	3.90

Famous Composers — A1041

10c, Liszt. #3856, Chopin. #3857, Bach. #3858, Beethoven. 65c, Ignacio Cervantes (1847-1905). 75c, Mozart.

1997, Sept. 15   Litho.   *Perf. 12½*
3855	A1041	10c multicolored	.25	.20
3856	A1041	15c multicolored	.25	.20
3857	A1041	15c multicolored	.25	.20
3858	A1041	15c multicolored	.25	.20
3859	A1041	65c multicolored	.90	.75
3860	A1041	75c multicolored	.95	.80
	Nos. 3855-3860 (6)		2.85	2.35

Tourism in Pinar del Rio — A1042

Bird, scene: 10c, Myadestes elisabeth, Viñales Valley. 15c, Corvus nasicus, Jutia Key. 65c, Dendroica pityophila, Soroa Falls. 75c, Tyrannus cubensis, San Juan River.

1997, Sept. 27   Litho.
3861	A1042	10c multi	.30	.20
3862	A1042	15c multi	.30	.20
3863	A1042	65c multi, vert.	1.10	.75
3864	A1042	75c multi, vert.	1.25	.80
	Nos. 3861-3864 (4)		2.95	1.95

Caribbean Flowers — A1043

Designs: No. 3865, Hibiscus elatus (majagua). No. 3866, Cordia sebestena (vomitel). No. 3867, Bidens pilosa (romerillo). No. 3868, Catharanthus roseus (vicaria). 65c, Reullia tuberosa (salta perico). 75c, Turnera ulmifolia (marilope).

1997, Sept. 30
3865	A1043	15c multicolored	.30	.20
3866	A1043	15c multicolored	.30	.20
3867	A1043	15c multicolored	.30	.20
3868	A1043	15c multicolored	.30	.20
3869	A1043	65c multicolored	1.10	.75
3870	A1043	75c multicolored	1.25	.80
	Nos. 3865-3870 (6)		3.55	2.35

Eastern University, 50th Anniv. — A1044

1997, Oct. 1   *Perf. 13*
3871 A1044 15c multicolored   .50 .20

Che Guevara (1928-67), 5th Cuban Communist Party Congress A1045

1997, Oct. 8
3872	A1045	15c Flags	.30	.20
3873	A1045	15c Text, Guevara	1.10	.75
3874	A1045	75c Portrait of Guevara	1.25	.75
	Nos. 3872-3874 (3)		2.65	1.70

America Issue — A1046

1997, Oct. 12   Litho.   *Perf. 13*
3875	A1046	15c 19th cent. postman	.20	.20
3876	A1046	65c 20th cent. postman	.75	.55

Hominids — A1047

Designs: 10c, Australopithecus. No. 3878, Pithecanthropus (Java man). No. 3879, Sinanthropus (Peking man). No. 3880, Neanderthal. 65c, Cro-magnon man. 75c, Oberkassel man.

1997, Oct. 30   *Perf. 12½*
3877	A1047	10c multicolored	.25	.20
3878	A1047	15c multicolored	.35	.20
3879	A1047	15c multicolored	.35	.20
3880	A1047	15c multicolored	.35	.20
3881	A1047	65c multicolored	1.25	.90
3882	A1047	75c multicolored	1.40	.90
	Nos. 3877-3882 (6)		3.95	2.60

October Revolution, 80th Anniv. — A1048

1997, Nov. 7   *Perf. 12½*
3884 A1048 75c multicolored   1.75 1.00

Cuban Railroad, 160th Anniv. — A1049

10c, John Bull, 1830, UK. No. 3886, Old Ironsides, Baldwin, 1832, US. No. 3887, Baldwin Pacific Type 4-6-2, 1910-13, US. 65c, TE.M4:1 diesel electric, 1970, USSR. 75c, TE.114-K, diesel electric, 1975, USSR.

1997, Nov. 19   Litho.   *Perf. 12½*
3885	A1049	10c multicolored	.20	.20
3886	A1049	15c multicolored	.25	.20
3887	A1049	15c multicolored	.25	.20
3888	A1049	65c multicolored	1.10	.90
3889	A1049	75c multicolored	1.25	.90
	Nos. 3885-3889 (5)		3.05	2.40

UN Conference on Commerce and
Employment, Havana, 50th
Anniv. — A1050

1997, Nov. 21
3890 A1050 65c multicolored   .75 .60

Victor
Manuel
Garcia,
Painter,
Birth Cent.
A1051

1997, Dec. 29   Litho.   Perf. 12½
3891 A1051 15c #1553, Garcia   .50 .25

Visit of
Pope
John
Paul II
A1052

Pope John Paul II, different coats of arms,
and: 65c, Havana Cathedral. 75c, Basilica of
Our Lady of Charity, Cobre, vert.
No. 3894, vert: a, Pope John Paul II greeting
Fidel Castro. b, Pope waving.

1998, Jan. 18   Litho.   Perf. 12½
3892 A1052 65c multicolored   2.75 1.00
3893 A1052 75c multicolored   3.25 1.00
                Souvenir Sheet of 2
3894 A1052 50c #a.-b.   4.50 2.25
   Nos. 3894a-3894b are 32x40mm.

Assassination of
Jesus
Menendez, 50th
Anniv. — A1053

1998, Jan. 22
3895 A1053 15c multicolored   .55 .20

1998 World Cup Soccer
Championships, France — A1054

Various soccer plays: 10c, 2 players. #3897,
Player in black & yellow. #3898, Player on
ground, 1 in striped shirt. #3899, 3 players, 2
in striped shirts. #3900, 3 players, 2 in blue
shirts.
   1p, Player with #11 on sleeve.

1998, Feb. 10   Litho.   Perf. 12½
3896 A1054 10c multi, vert.   .65 .20
3897 A1054 15c multi, vert.   .80 .20
3898 A1054 15c multi, vert.   .80 .20

3899 A1054 65c multi   3.00 1.00
3900 A1054 65c multi   3.00 1.00
   Nos. 3896-3900 (5)   8.25 2.60
                Souvenir Sheet
                   Perf. 13
3901 A1054 1p multicolored   4.50 2.25
   No. 3901 contains one 40x32mm stamp.

Capt. Isabel
Rubio Diaz,
Medical Aide
During
Revolution,
Death
Cent. — A1055

1998, Feb. 15   Perf. 13
3902 A1055 15c multicolored   .65 .25

Brig. Gen. Vidal
Ducasse Reeve
(1852-98)
A1056

1998, Feb. 19   Perf. 12½
3903 A1056 15c multicolored   .65 .25
   No. 3903 inscribed "Revee."

"Radio Rebelde," 40th Anniv. — A1057

1998, Feb. 23
3904 A1057 15c multicolored   .65 .25

Fire
Engines
A1058

Designs: 10c, 1901 Shand Mason & Co.,
London. No. 3905, 1905 Horse-drawn municipal fire wagon, Havana, 1905. No. 3906, 1921
American-La France Fire Engine Co. 65c,
1952 Chevrolet 6400, US. 75c, 1956 American-La France Foamite Co., US.

1998, Mar. 10
3905 A1058 10c multicolored   .25 .20
3906 A1058 15c multicolored   .30 .20
3907 A1058 15c multicolored   .30 .20
3908 A1058 65c multicolored   1.10 .90
3909 A1058 75c multicolored   1.25 .90
   Nos. 3905-3909 (5)   3.20 2.40

Protest of Baragua, 120th
Anniv. — A1059

1998, Mar. 15
3910 A1059 15c multicolored   .65 .25

Victory at Cuito
Cuanavale,
Angola, 10th
Anniv. — A1060

1998, Mar. 23   Litho.   Perf. 12½
3911 A1060 15c multicolored   .65 .25

New Year 1998
(Year of the
Tiger) — A1061

1998, Mar. 30
3912 A1061 15c multicolored   .65 .25

Dogs — A1062

1998, Apr. 15   Litho.   Perf. 12½
3913 A1062 10c Chihuahua   .20 .20
3914 A1062 15c Beagle   .25 .20
3915 A1062 15c Xoloitzcuintle   .25 .20
3916 A1062 65c German pointer   1.25 .90
3917 A1062 75c Chow chow   1.40 1.10
   Nos. 3913-3917 (5)   3.35 2.60

Evolution of the
Chimpanzee
A1063

Pan troglodytes and: 10c, Proconsul. No.
3919, Cranium. No. 3920, Right hand and foot.
65c, New-born chimpanzee. 75c, Map of
Africa showing chimpanzee's range.

1998, May 15   Litho.   Perf. 12½
3918 A1063 10c multicolored   .60 .20
3919 A1063 15c multicolored   .60 .20
3920 A1063 15c multicolored   .60 .20
3921 A1063 65c multicolored   3.00 1.25
3922 A1063 75c multicolored   3.25 1.25
   Nos. 3918-3922 (5)   8.05 3.10

Lisbon '98, World Stamp
Exhibition — A1064

Deep sea fish: No. 3923, Raja batis. No.
3924, Eurypharynx pelecanoides. 65c,
Caulophryne. 75c, Chauliodus sloani.

1998, May 22   Litho.   Perf. 12½
3923 A1064 15c multicolored   .70 .25
3924 A1064 15c multicolored   .70 .25
3925 A1064 65c multicolored   3.25 1.10
3926 A1064 75c multicolored   3.75 1.25
   Nos. 3923-3926 (4)   8.40 2.85

                Souvenir Sheet

Juvalux '98, World Stamp Exhibition
for Youth Philately and Postal History,
Luxembourg — A1065

Illustration reduced.

1998, May 20   Litho.   Perf. 12½
3927 A1065 1p Postman on bicy-
           cle   4.50 2.25

Federico Garcia Lorca (1898-1936),
Poet — A1066

1998, June 2
3928 A1066 75c multicolored   3.50 1.25

Intl. Year of the
Oceans
A1067

#3929, Canarreos flower coral, coral crab,
small fish. #3030, French angel fish, brain
coral, gorgonia.

1998, June 5
3929 A1067 65c multicolored   2.75 1.25
3930 A1067 65c multicolored   2.75 1.25
  a.   Pair, #3929-3930   6.00 3.00

Diana, Princess
of Wales (1961-
97)
A1068

Various portraits, color of clothes: No. 3931,
Pale yellow and pink. No. 3932, Black and
white. No. 3933, Multicolored print. No. 3934,
Red. No. 3935, Pink and black plaid. 65c,
White. 75c, Blue.

1998, June 30   Litho.   Perf. 13
3931 A1068 10c multicolored   .50 .20
3932 A1068 10c multicolored   .50 .20
3933 A1068 10c multicolored   .50 .20
3934 A1068 15c multicolored   .70 .25
3935 A1068 15c multicolored   .70 .25
3936 A1068 65c multicolored   3.25 1.10
3937 A1068 75c multicolored   3.75 1.25
   Nos. 3931-3937 (7)   9.90 3.45

Expo 2000, Hanover A1069

#3938, Mascot, "Twipsy." #3939, Mascot in London, 1851. #3940, Mascot in Brussels, 1958. #3941, German flag, map of Germany. 65c, Mascot in Paris, 1889. 75c, Mascot on top of world, fireworks.

1998, July 31   **Perf. 12½**
3938	A1069	15c multi, vert.	.70	.25
3939	A1069	15c multi	.70	.25
3940	A1069	15c multi	.70	.25
3941	A1069	15c multi	.70	.25
3942	A1069	65c multi, vert.	3.25	1.00
3943	A1069	75c multi	3.75	1.25
		Nos. 3938-3943 (6)	9.80	3.25

Maracaibo '98, 18th Central America and Caribbean Games — A1070

1998, Aug. 8
3944	A1070	15c multicolored	.65	.20

Attack on Moncada Barracks, 45th Anniv. — A1071

Designs: 15c, Siboney farmhouse, Abel Santamaría. 65c, Barracks, José Marti.

1998, July 26   **Litho.**   **Perf. 13**
3945	A1071	15c multicolored	.70	.25
3946	A1071	65c multicolored	3.25	1.00

Democratic Republic of Korea, 50th Anniv. — A1072

1998, Sept. 8   **Litho.**   **Perf. 13**
3947	A1072	75c Kim Il Sung (1912-94)	3.50	1.25

Japanese Immigration to Cuba, Cent. — A1073

1998, Sept. 9   **Litho.**   **Perf. 13**
3948	A1073	75c multicolored	3.50	1.25

Orchids A1074

10c, Coelogyne flaccida. #3950, Dendrobium fimbriatum. #3951, Arunding graminifolia. #3952, Bletia patula. #3953, Phaius tankervilliaea.

1998, Sept. 10
3949	A1074	10c multicolored	.50	.20
3950	A1074	15c multicolored	.70	.25
3951	A1074	15c multicolored	.70	.25
3952	A1074	65c multicolored	3.00	1.00
3953	A1074	65c multicolored	3.00	1.00
		Nos. 3949-3953 (5)	7.90	2.70

5th Congress of the Revolution Defense Committees A1075

1998, Sept. 25   **Litho.**   **Perf. 13**
3954	A1075	15c multicolored	.65	.20

World Tourism Day — A1076

Holguin Province, reptiles: 10c, Looking through gateway, city of Gibara, anolis equestris, vert. 15c, Mayabe Valley, anolis vermiculatus, vert. 65c, Guardalavaca Beach, anolis allisoni. 75c, Mayari pine forest, anolis mestrei.

1998, Sept. 27
3955	A1076	10c multicolored	.50	.20
3956	A1076	15c multicolored	.65	.25
3957	A1076	65c multicolored	3.00	1.00
3958	A1076	75c multicolored	3.50	1.25
		Nos. 3955-3958 (4)	7.65	2.70

Women Who Aided Cuban Revolutionary Movements A1077

America Issue: 65c, Bernarda Toro Pelegrin (1852-1911). 75c, Maria Magdalena Cabrales Issac (1842-1905).

1998, Oct. 12
3959	A1077	65c multicolored	3.00	1.00
3960	A1077	75c multicolored	3.50	1.25

World Wildlife Fund Protected Fauna — A1078

Cuban Natl. Ballet, 50th Anniv. — A1079

Arantinga Euops: 10c, Two on tree branch. 15c, One looking out of nest. 65c, One on tree branch. 75c, One up close.

1998, Oct. 21
3961	A1078	10c multicolored	.55	.30
3962	A1078	15c multicolored	.75	.50
3963	A1078	65c multicolored	3.00	1.25
3964	A1078	75c multicolored	3.50	1.50
		Nos. 3961-3964 (4)	7.80	3.55

1998, Oct. 28
3965	A1079	15c Swan Lake	.75	.25
3966	A1079	65c Giselle	3.25	1.00

Massacre of O'Farrill and Goicuria, 40th Anniv. — A1080

Rogelio Perea, Angel Ameijeiras, Pedro Gutiérrez.

1998, Nov. 8
3967	A1080	15c multicolored	.65	.20

Battle of Guisa, 40th Anniv. A1081

Design: Capt. Braulio Coroneaux, tank.

1998, Nov. 30   **Litho.**   **Perf. 12½**
3968	A1081	15c multicolored	.65	.20

A1082

A1083

1998, Dec. 10   **Litho.**   **Perf. 12½**
3969	A1082	65c multicolored	3.00	1.00

Universal Declaration of Human Rights, 50th anniv.

1998, Dec. 11   **Perf. 13**

Calixto Garcia Iñiguez (1839-98), revolutionary Major General.
3970	A1083	65c multicolored	2.75	1.00

Padre Félix Varela (1788-1853) — A1084

1998, Dec. 16
3971	A1084	75c multicolored	3.50	1.25

War for Independence, Cent. — A1085

War heroes, historical scene: No. 3972, Carlos Manuel de Céspedes. No. 3973, Ignacio Agramonte. No. 3974, Máximo Gómez. No. 3975, José Maceo. No. 3976, Salvador Cisneros. No. 3978, Calixto Garcia. No. 3979, Adolfo Flor. No. 3980, Serafin Sánchez. 65c, José Marti. 75c, Antonio Maceo.

1998, Dec. 25   **Litho.**   **Perf. 12½**
3972	A1085	15c multicolored	.25	.20
3973	A1085	15c multicolored	.25	.20
3974	A1085	15c multicolored	.25	.20
3975	A1085	15c multicolored	.25	.20
3976	A1085	15c multicolored	.25	.20
3977	A1085	15c multicolored	.25	.20
3978	A1085	15c multicolored	.25	.20
3979	A1085	15c multicolored	.25	.20
3980	A1085	65c multicolored	.90	.60
3981	A1085	75c multicolored	1.00	.70
a.		Sheet of 10, #3972-3981 + 3 labels	4.00	4.00
		Nos. 3972-3981 (10)	3.90	2.90

Battle for Palma Soriano, 40th Anniv. A1086

1998, Dec. 27   **Litho.**   **Perf. 13**
3982	A1086	15c multicolored	.65	.20

Cuban Revolution, 40th Anniv. — A1087

a, Boat, soldiers in water. b, Fidel Castro with soldier. c, Castro giving speech, pigeons.

1999, Jan. 1
3983 A1087 65c Strip of 3, #a.-c. 6.00 3.00

Natl. Revolutionary Police, 40th Anniv. — A1088

1999, Jan. 5
3984 A1088 15c multicolored   .55 .20

Cuban Workers' Trade Union Organization, 60th Anniv. — A1089

1999, Jan. 28 Litho. Perf. 12½
3985 A1089 15c multicolored   .55 .20

New Year 1999 (Year of the Rabbit) — A1090

1999, Feb. 5   Perf. 13
3986 A1090 75c multicolored 1.00 .70

Lenin (1870-1924) — A1091

1999, Feb. 21 Litho. Perf. 12½
3987 A1091 75c multicolored 3.00 1.00

Dinosaurs — A1092

1999, Mar. 10
3988 A1092 10c Ornithosuchus .40 .25
3989 A1092 15c Saltopus   .55 .25
3990 A1092 15c Bactrosaurus .55 .25
3991 A1092 65c Protosuchus 2.50 1.00
3992 A1092 75c Mussaurus 2.75 1.25
   Nos. 3988-3992 (5) 6.75 3.00

Cuban Musicians — A1093

1999, Mar. 22   Perf. 13
3993 A1093 5c Dámaso Pérez
        Prado   .20 .20
3994 A1093 15c Benny Moré .70 .25
3995 A1093 15c Chano Pozo .70 .25
3996 A1093 35c Miguelito
        Valdés 1.75 .50
3997 A1093 65c Bola de Nieve 3.25 1.00
3998 A1093 75c Rita Montaner 3.50 1.25
   Nos. 3993-3998 (6) 10.10 3.45

Simón Bolívar's Visit to Cuba, Bicent. A1094

1999, Mar. 25
3999 A1094 65c Portrait 2.50 1.00
4000 A1094 65c Monument 2.50 1.00
  a. Pair, #3999-4000 5.25 2.50

State Security Organization, 40th Anniv. — A1095

1999, Mar. 26 Litho. Perf. 12½
4001 A1095 65c multicolored 2.50 1.00

Souvenir Sheet

China '99 World Philatelic Exhibition — A1096

Illustration reduced.

1999, Apr. 10 Litho. Perf. 12½
4002 A1096 1p Giant panda 4.00 2.00

Stamp Day A1097

1999, Apr. 24
4003 A1097 15c Postal rocket .60 .20
4004 A1097 65c Post rider 2.50 .80

Test of Cuban Postal Rocket, 60th anniv. Insurgent Postal Service, 130th anniv.

Casa de las Américas, 40th Anniv. — A1098

1999, Apr. 24
4005 A1098 65c multicolored 3.00 .80

Souvenir Sheet

IBRA '99, World Philatelic Exhibition, Nuremberg — A1099

Illustration reduced.

1999, Apr. 27
4006 A1099 1p Train   4.00 2.00

Agrarian Reform Law, 40th Anniv. A1100

1999, May 17
4007 A1100 65c multicolored 1.25 .80

Felipe Poey, Scientist, Birth Bicent. A1101

Fish: 5c, Gramma loreto Poey. 15c, Liopropoma rubre Poey. #4010, Hypoplectrus gummigutta. #74011, Stegastes dorsopunicans. 1p, Portrait of Poey, hypoplectrus guttavarius.

1999, May 26 Litho. Perf. 12½
4008 A1101 5c multicolored .20 .20
4009 A1101 15c multicolored .55 .20
4010 A1101 65c multicolored 2.50 .80
4011 A1101 65c multicolored 2.50 .80
   Nos. 4008-4011 (4) 5.75 2.00

Souvenir Sheet
Perf. 13¼x13
4012 A1101 1p multicolored 4.00 2.00
No. 4012 contains one 32x40mm stamp.

Souvenir Sheet

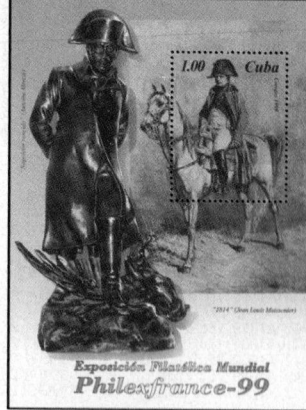

Philexfrance '99, World Philatelic Exhibition — A1102

Sculpture in sheet margin: "1814," by Jean Louis Meissonier (1815-1891). Illustration reduced.

1999, June 2   Perf. 13
4013 A1102 1p multicolored 4.00 2.00

1999 Pan-American Games, Winnipeg — A1103

1999, June 25 Litho. Perf. 13
4014 A1103 15c Baseball .50 .20
4015 A1103 65c Volleyball, vert 2.25 .80
4016 A1103 75c Boxing 2.50 .90
   Nos. 4014-4016 (3) 5.25 1.90

People's Republic of China, 50th Anniv. A1104

5c, Victory at Wioming, by Gao Hong. 15c, Nanchang Insurrection, by Cai Lang. 40c, Red Army Crossing a Swamp, by Gao Quan. 65c, Occupation of the Presidential Palace, by Cheng Yifei and Wei Jingshan. 75c, Proclamation of the People's Republic of China, by Dong Xiwen.

1999, Aug. 21 Litho. Perf. 12¾
4017 A1104 5c multicolored .20 .20
4018 A1104 15c multicolored .50 .20
4019 A1104 40c multicolored 1.50 .45
4020 A1104 65c multicolored 2.40 .70
4021 A1104 75c multicolored 2.75 .85
   Nos. 4017-4021 (5) 7.35 2.40

China 1999 World Philatelic Exhibition, Beijing — A1105

No. 4022, Morning Glories, by Qi Baishi. No. 4023, Three Galloping Horses, by Xu Beihong. No. 4024, Hunan Woman, by Fu Baoshi. No. 4025, Birthplace of Luxun, by Wu Guanzhong. No. 4026, Horse Riders, by Huangzhou. 40c, Pine Tree, by He Xiangning. 65c, Sleep, by Jin Shangyi. 75c, Poetic Scene in Xun Yang, by Chen Yifei.

1999, Aug. 22 Litho. Perf. 13
4022 A1105 5c multicolored .20 .20
4023 A1105 5c multicolored .20 .20
4024 A1105 15c multicolored .55 .20

4025 A1105 15c multicolored	.55	.20
4026 A1105 15c multicolored	.55	.20
4027 A1105 40c multicolored	1.60	.45
4028 A1105 65c multicolored	2.50	.70
4029 A1105 75c multicolored	2.75	.80
a. Sheet of 8, #4022-4029 + label	9.00	9.00
Nos. 4022-4029 (8)	8.90	2.95

UPU, 125th Anniv. A1106

1999, Sept. 16 Litho. Perf. 12¾
4030 A1106 75c multicolored 2.50 .80

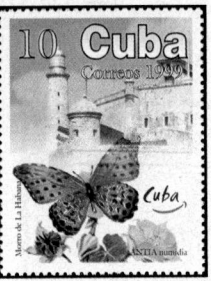

World Tourism Day A1107

Butterflies and Havana tourist sites: 10c, Antia numidia, Morro Castle. 15c, Papilio polyxenes, Havana Cathedral. 65c, Dryas julia, Convent of San Francisco. 75c, Eueides cleobaea, Capitol.

1999, Sept. 27 Perf. 12½x12¾
4031 A1107 10c multicolored .30 .20
4032 A1107 15c multicolored .50 .20
4033 A1107 65c multicolored 2.25 .70
4034 A1107 75c multicolored 2.50 .80
Nos. 4031-4034 (4) 5.55 1.90

Expo 2000, Hanover, Germany A1108

5c, World map, Expo 2000 emblem. #4036, "Twipsy" mascot, vert. #4037, "Twipsy" and 1876 Philadelphia Exposition. #4038, "Twipsy" and 1970 Osaka Exposition. 65c, "Twipsy" and 2000 Exposition. 75c, "Twipsy" and 1967 Montreal Exposition.

1999, Oct. 1 Perf. 12¾
4035 A1108 5c multicolored .20 .20
4036 A1108 15c multicolored .50 .20
4037 A1108 15c multicolored .50 .20
4038 A1108 15c multicolored .50 .20
4039 A1108 65c multicolored 2.40 .70
4040 A1108 75c multicolored 2.75 .80
Nos. 4035-4040 (6) 6.85 2.30

Cubana Airlines, 70th Anniv. — A1109

1999, Oct. 8 Perf. 12½x12¼
4041 A1109 15c Fokker .50 .20
4042 A1109 15c DC-10 .50 .20
4043 A1109 65c A-320 2.25 .70
4044 A1109 75c DC-3 2.50 .80
Nos. 4041-4044 (4) 5.75 1.90

America Issue, A New Millennium Without Arms — A1110

1999, Oct. 12 Perf. 12¾
4045 A1110 15c Pigeon, mushroom cloud .45 .20
4046 A1110 65c Dove, globe 2.25 .75

National Instiutions, 40th Anniv. — A1111

1999, Oct. 16 Perf. 12¾
4047 A1111 15c MINFAR .45 .20
4048 A1111 65c Natl. Revolutionary Militia 2.25 .75

Disappearance of Camilo Cienfuegos, 40th Anniv. — A1112

1999, Oct. 28 Litho. Perf. 12¾
4049 A1112 15c multicolored .50 .20

Souvenir Sheet

12th Congress of Cuban Philatelic Federation — A1113

Illustration reduced.

1999, Dec. 11 Perf. 13
4050 A1113 1p multicolored 4.00 2.00

Ernest Hemingway (1899-1961), Writer — A1114

1999, Dec. 15 Perf. 12½x12¼
4051 A1114 65c multicolored 2.50 .70

9th Summit of Ibero-American Heads of State and Government, Havana — A1115

Designs: 65c, Plaza Vieja. 75c, Plaza of St. Francis of Assisi. 1p, Plaza de Armas.

1999, Nov. 5 Litho. Perf. 12¾x12½
4052 A1115 65c multi 2.25 .70
4053 A1115 75c multi 2.50 .80

Souvenir Sheet
Perf. 13
4054 A1115 1p multi 4.50 2.25
No. 4054 contains one 40x31mm stamp.

Rubén Martínez Villena (1899-1934), Revolutionary — A1116

1999, Dec. 20 Perf. 12½x12¾
4055 A1116 15c multi .50 .20

Dr. Tomás Romay Chacón (1764-1849) A1117

1999, Dec. 21 Perf. 13
4056 A1117 65c multi 2.50 .70

New Year 2000 (Year of the Dragon) — A1118

2000, Jan. 10 Perf. 12½
4057 A1118 15c multi .50 .20

Folklore A1119

Paintings depicting Cuban folklore by Concepción Ferrant (1882-1968): 10c, Rumba Caliente. 15c, Cachumba. 65c, En Casa de un Babalao. 75c, Tata Cuñengue.

2000, Jan. 26 Perf. 12½x12¾
4058 A1119 10c multi .25 .20
4059 A1119 15c multi .35 .20
4060 A1119 65c multi 1.40 .80
4061 A1119 75c multi 1.60 .90
Nos. 4058-4061 (4) 3.60 2.10

Butterflies — A1120

10c, Helcyra superba. No. 4063, Pantaporia punctata. No. 4064, Neptis themis. 65c, Curetis acuta. 75c, Chrysozephyrus ataxus.

2000, Feb. 25 Perf. 12¾
4062 A1120 10c multi .30 .20
4063 A1120 15c multi .40 .20
4064 A1120 15c multi .40 .20
4065 A1120 65c multi 1.60 .80
4066 A1120 75c multi 1.90 .95
Nos. 4062-4066 (5) 4.60 2.35

Bangkok 2000 Stamp Exhibition.

Group of 77 South Summit, Havana — A1121

2000, Apr. 7 Litho. Perf. 13x12½
4067 A1121 75c multi 2.00 .90

Lenin, 130th Anniv. of Birth — A1122

2000, Apr. 22 Perf. 12¾
4068 A1122 75c multi 2.00 .90

Che Guevara in Congo, 35th Anniv. A1123

2000, Apr. 24
4069 A1123 65c multi 1.75 .80

Stamp Day — A1124

Designs: 65c, Cuba #2, building. 90c, Airplane, cover, Jaime Gonzáles, pilot of first experimental airmail flight in Cuba.

2000, Apr. 24
4070 A1124 65c multi   1.75 .80
4071 A1124 90c multi   2.25 1.10

Capt. San Luis (Elisio Reyes), Military Hero (1940-67) A1125

2000, Apr. 27
4072 A1125 65c multi   1.75 .80

The Stamp Show 2000, London A1126

Locomotives: 5c, 1882 Baldwin 0-6-0. 10c, 1895 Baldwin 2-8-0. 15c, 1912 Baldwin 2-8-0. 65c, 1919 Alco 2-8-0. 75c, 1925 Alco 2-8-2. 1p, 1920 Henschel 2-6-0.

2000, May 5   *Perf. 12¾*
4073 A1126 5c multi   .20 .20
4074 A1126 10c multi   .30 .20
4075 A1126 15c multi   .40 .20
4076 A1126 65c multi   1.60 .80
4077 A1126 75c multi   1.90 .90
   Nos. 4073-4077 (5)   4.40 2.30
Souvenir Sheet
Perf. 13
4078 A1126 1p multi   3.00 1.50
No. 4078 contains one 40x32mm stamp.

WIPA 2000 Philatelic Exhibition, Vienna — A1127

Airships of: 10c, Henri Giffart, 1852. 15c, Albert and Gaston Tissandier, 1883, vert. 50c, Charles Renard and Arthur Krebs, 1884. 65c, Pierre and Paul Lebaudy, 1903. 75c, August von Perseval, 1906. 1p, Ferdinand von Zeppelin.

Perf. 12½x12¼, 12¼x12½
2000, May 18
4079 A1127 10c multi   .35 .20
4080 A1127 15c multi   .50 .20
4081 A1127 50c multi   1.40 .60
4082 A1127 65c multi   1.90 .80
4083 A1127 75c multi   2.10 .90
   Nos. 4079-4083 (5)   6.25 2.70
Souvenir Sheet
Perf. 12½
4084 A1127 1p multi   3.00 1.50
No. 4084 contains one 40x32mm stamp.

Second World Meeting of Friendship and Solidarity With Cuba — A1128

2000, June 23   Litho.   *Perf. 12¾*
4085 A1128 65c multi   1.00 .75

José de la Luz y Caballero (1800-62), Educator — A1129

2000, July 11   *Perf. 12½x12¼*
4086 A1129 65c multi   1.00 .75

Amadeo Roldan (1900-39), Violinist — A1130

2000, July 12   *Perf. 12¾*
4087 A1130 65c multi   1.00 .75

La Edad de Oro, by José Marti — A1131

5c, Bebé y El Señor Don Pomposo. 10c, La Muñeca Negra. 15c, Nene Traviesa. 50c, Los Dos Ruiseñores. 65c, Frontispiece of La Edad de Oro. 75c, El Camarón Encantado.

2000, July 20
4088-4093 A1131   Set of 6   3.25 2.50
4093a   Sheet of 6, #4088-4093   3.25 3.25

Latin American Association for Integration — A1132

2000, Aug. 12
4094 A1132 65c multi   1.00 .75

Souvenir Sheet

Olymphilex 2000, Sydney — A1133

Illustration reduced.

2000, Aug. 17   *Perf. 13*
4095 A1133 1p multi   2.00 1.00

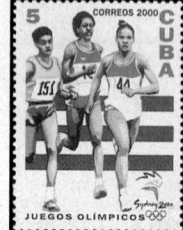

2000 Summer Olympics, Sydney A1134

Designs: 5c, Runners. 15c, Soccer. 65c, Baseball. 75c, Cycling.

2000, Aug. 20   *Perf. 12¾*
4096-4099 A1134   Set of 4   2.25 2.00

Dr. Pedro Kouri Esmeja (1900-64) A1135

2000, Aug. 21   Litho.
4100 A1135 65c multi   1.00 .75

Federation of Cuban Women, 40th Anniv. — A1136

2000, Aug. 23
4101 A1136 15c multi   .25 .20

España 2000 Intl. Philatelic Exhibition — A1137

Designs: 10c, 1851 Havana-Bilbao stampless cover, ship. No. 4103, 15c, Spain #1, Cibeles Fountain, Madrid. No. 4104, 15c, 1850 Zaragoza-Cadiz cover, Palacio de Cristal, Madrid. 65c, Spain #1-5, Palacio de Comunicaciones, Madrid. 75c, Cuba #1, Centro Gallego, Havana.

2000, Sept. 7   *Perf. 12¾x12½*
4102-4106 A1137   Set of 5   5.00 3.00
4106a   Sheet of 5, #4102-4106 + label   5.25 3.50

Souvenir Sheet
Perf. 12½
4107 A1137 100c Queen Isabella II, vert.   3.50 2.75
No. 4107 contains one 32x40mm stamp.

Beaches — A1138

#4108, Coconuts Bay, PRC. #4109, Varadero Beach, Cuba.

2000, Sept. 26   *Perf. 12½x12¼*
4108-4109 A1138 15c Set of 2   .45 .40
4109a   Pair, #4108-4109   .45 .40
See People's Republic of China No. 3052.

World Tourism Day — A1139

Marine life: 10c, Eretmochelys imbricata, vert. 15c, Epinephelus striatus, vert. 65c, Pomacanthus paru. 75c, Anisotremus surinamensis.

Perf. 12½x12¾, 12¾x12½
2000, Sept. 27
4110-4113 A1139   Set of 4   5.50 2.25

Committees of Defense of the Revolution, 40th Anniv. — A1140

2000, Sept. 28   *Perf. 12¾*
4114 A1140 15c multi   .50 .25

America Issue — AIDS Prevention A1141

Ribbon, heart-shaped map and: 15c, Family. 65c, Couple.

2000, Oct. 12
4115-4116 A1141   Set of 2   2.75 1.25

CUBA

651

Cuban Military in Angola, 25th Anniv. — A1142

2000, Nov. 7
4117 A1142 75c multi   1.40 1.10

Visit by Alexander von Humboldt, Bicent. — A1143

Humboldt and: 15c, House in Trinidad. 65c, House in Havana, Political Essay on the Island of Cuba.

2000, Dec. 19   Litho.   Perf. 12¾
4118-4119 A1143 Set of 2   2.50 1.25

20th Pan-American Railway Congress A1144

2000, Sept. 18   Litho.   Perf. 12¾
4120 A1144 65c multi   1.25 1.00

Millennium — A1145

Snails: a, Polymita versicolor. b, Polymita picta iolimbata. c, Polymita picta roseolimbata. d, Polymita picta picta. e, Polymita picta nigrolimbata.
Illustration reduced.

2000, Dec. 20
4121 A1145 65c Block of 5, #a-
          e, + label   10.00 5.00

New Year 2001 (Year of the Snake) — A1146

Illustration reduced.

2001, Jan. 10
4122 A1146 15c multi   1.00 .30

Hong Kong 2001 Stamp Exhibition — A1147

Birds: 5c, Aix galericulata. 10c, Chrysolophus pictus. 15c, Ardea cinerea. 65c, Gallus gallus. 75c, Streptotelia decaocto.

2001, Jan. 25   Perf. 12¾
4123-4127 A1147 Set of 5   3.00 2.50
Souvenir Sheet
Perf. 12½
4128 A1147 1p Grus grus   3.00 1.50
No. 4128 contains one 32x40mm stamp.

National Institute for Sport Physical Education and Recreation, 40th Anniv. — A1148

2001, Feb. 23   Perf. 12½x12¼
4129 A1148 65c multi   2.00 1.00

UN High Commissioner for Refugees, 50th Anniv. — A1149

2001, Mar. 15   Perf. 12¾x12½
4130 A1149 65c multi   2.00 .85

Antique Locomotives — A1150

Locomotives from, 10c, 1863. 15c, 1876. 40c, 1885. 65c, 1914. 75c, 1932.

2001, Mar. 20   Perf. 12½x12¼
4131-4135 A1150 Set of 5   5.75 3.00

105th Interparliamentary Union Congress, Havana — A1151

2001, Mar. 30   Perf. 12¾
4136 A1151 65c multi   2.00 .95

Bay of Pigs Invasion, 40th Anniv. — A1152

2001, Apr. 19   Perf. 12¾x12½
4137 A1152 65c multi   2.00 .95

Cats and Dogs A1153

Designs: 10c, Cats, emblem of Cat Aficionados Association. No. 4139, 15c, Dogs, Cats, emblem of Aniplant. No. 4140, 15c, Dogs, emblem of Cynological Federation of Cuba. 65c, Dogs, emblem of Sporting Dog Federation of Cuba. 75c, Dogs, cats.

2001, Apr. 25   Perf. 12½x12¾
4138-4142 A1153 Set of 5   5.50 2.50

Radio Havana, 40th Anniv. — A1154

2001, May 1   Perf. 12½x12¼
4143 A1154 65c multi   2.00 .95

Tourism Convention — A1155

2001, May 7   Perf. 12¾x12½
4144 A1155 65c multi   2.00 .95

Belgica 2001 Intl. Stamp Exhibition, Brussels A1156

Designs: 5c, St. Michel Cathedral. 10c, Sablon Church, horiz. 15c, Royal Residence, horiz. 65c, Sacred Heart Basilica, horiz. 75c, Atomium.
1p, Royal Palace.

2001, May 10   Perf. 12¾
4145-4149 A1156 Set of 5   5.50 2.50
Souvenir Sheet
Perf. 12½
4150 A1156 100c multi   3.00 1.50
No. 4150 contains one 32x40mm stamp.

Interior Ministry, 40th Anniv. A1157

2001, June 6   Perf. 12¾
4151 A1157 65c multi   1.25 .90

Phila Nippon '01, Japan A1158

Japanese trains: 5c, JR 500. 10c, JR 700. 15c, MAX 1. 65c, MAX 2. 75c, 300.

2001, June 20   Litho.   Perf. 12¾
4152-4156 A1158 Set of 5   5.50 2.25
Souvenir Sheet
Perf. 12½
4157 A1158 100c Zero   3.00 1.25
No. 4157 contains one 40x32mm stamp.

Republic of San Marino, 1700th Anniv. — A1159

2001, July 20   Litho.·Perf. 12½x12¼
4158 A1159 75c multi   2.25 1.00

Aquaculture — A1160

Designs: 5c, Tinca tinca. 10c, Rana temporaria. 15c, Cardisoma guanhumi. 65c, Mytius edulis. 75c, Tilapia mariae.
1p, Potamobius pallipes.

2001, Sept. 17   *Perf. 12¾*
4159-4163 A1160 Set of 5   5.00 2.25
Souvenir Sheet
Perf. 12½
4164 A1160 1p multi   3.00 1.50
No. 4164 contains one 40x32mm stamp.

Recovery of Raw Materials, 40th
Anniv. — A1161

2001, Sept. 21   *Perf. 12¾x12½*
4165 A1161 65c multi   2.00 .85

Tourism — A1162

Designs: 10c, Valle de Viñales. 15c, Trinidad. 65c, Sirena Beach, Cayo Largo del Sur. 75c, Morro Castle, Havana.

2001, Sept. 27
4166-4169 A1162 Set of 4   5.25 2.25

Year of Dialogue
Among
Civilizations
A1163

2001, Oct. 9   *Perf. 12¾*
4170 A1163 65c multi   2.00 .90

America
Issue —
UNESCO
World
Heritage
A1164

Flora and fauna from Desembarco del Granma Natl. Park: 15c, Tetramicra malpighiarum. 65c, Liggus vittatus.

2001, Oct. 12   *Perf. 12½x12¾*
4171-4172 A1164 Set of 2   2.25 1.10

José
Marti
National
Library,
Cent.
A1165

2001, Oct. 18   *Perf. 12¾*
4173 A1165 15c multi   .45 .20

Cuban Airliner
Explosion Near
Barbados, 25th
Anniv. — A1166

Various details of painting.

2001, Oct. 22
4174   Horiz. strip of 5   4.50 2.25
   a. A1166 5c shown   .20 .20
   b. A1166 10c multi   .30 .20
   c. A1166 15c multi   .40 .20
   d. A1166 50c multi   1.40 .70
   e. A1166 65c multi   1.90 .90

Eduardo R.
Chibas,
Communist
Leader, Cent. of
Birth — A1167

2001, Nov. 27   Litho.   *Perf. 13*
4175 A1167 65c multi   2.00 .90

Napoleonic Museum, 40th
Anniv. — A1168

Equestrian statues of Napoleon and map of battle of: No. 4176, 10c, Eylau. No. 4177, 10c, Marengo. 65c, Waterloo. 75c, Aboukir.

2001, Dec. 1   *Perf. 12¾x12½*
4176-4179 A1168 Set of 4   5.00 2.25

Pablo de la
Torriente Brau
(1901-36),
Poet — A1169

2001, Dec. 12   *Perf. 12¾*
4180 A1169 75c multi   2.25 1.00

Cuban
Federation
of Pigeon
Fanciers,
4th
Congress
A1170

Pigeons: No. 4181, 65c, Empedrado oscura 2021-61-ME. No. 4182, 65c, Empedrado claro 2241-55-ME. No. 4183, 65c, Mosaico 1561-66-HM. No. 4184, 65c, Mosaico, 3013-67-HM. No. 4185, 65c Bronceado, 338-59-HE.

2001, Dec. 14   *Perf. 12½*
4181-4185 A1170 Set of 5   9.75 4.25

Film Stars Who
Never Won
Academy
Awards
A1171

Designs: 5c, Tyrone Power. No. 4187, 10c, Ava Gardner. No. 4188, 10c, Steve McQueen. No. 4189, 15c, Rita Hayworth. No. 4190, 15c, Marilyn Monroe. No. 4191, 15c, James Dean. No. 4192, 65c, Rock Hudson. No. 4193, 65c, Natalie Wood. 75c, Richard Burton.

2001, Dec. 20
4186-4194 A1171 Set of 9   8.50 3.75
   a. Sheet of 9, #4186-4194   8.50 3.75

New Year 2002 (Year
of the
Horse) — A1172

2002, Jan. 21   Litho.   *Perf. 12½x12¾*
4195 A1172 15c multi   .45 .20

Cigar Production — A1173

Cigars and: 5c, Hat, Cuba No. 358, tobacco leaf. 10c, Clock, cigar cylinder. 15c, Map of Cuba, Simon Bolivar. 65c, Cuba Nos. 356, 357, map, cigar smoker. 75c, Flag, tobacco field, man.
1p, Fidel Castro, map, star.

2002, Feb. 15   *Perf. 12¾*
4196-4200 A1173 Set of 5   5.25 2.25
Souvenir Sheet
Perf. 1313¼
4201 A1173 1p multi   3.25 1.25
Fourth Havana Festival, Cohiba brand, 36th anniv. No. 4201 contains one 40x32mm stamp.

Second UPAEP Information
Workshop — A1174

Illustration reduced.

2002, Feb. 21   *Perf. 12½x12¼*
4202 A1174 65c multi   2.00 .90

Explorers
A1175

Explorers: 5c, Reading map. 15c, Tying knots. 50c, Starting campfire for cooking. 65c, Starting fire. 75c, Using orientation techniques.

2002, Mar. 20   *Perf. 12½*
4203-4207 A1175 Set of 5   6.50 2.75
   a. Sheet of 5, #4203-4207, + label   6.50 2.75

Union of Young Communists, 40th
Anniv. — A1176

2002, Apr. 4   *Perf. 12½x12¼*
4208 A1176 15c multi   .30 .20

ExpoVid 2002 Wine Event — A1177

Designs: 15c, Cigar smokers, wine bottles and glasses, map of wine producing areas. 65c, Wine glass and barrels. 75c, Wine glass and vineyard.

2002, June 5   *Perf. 12¾x12½*
4209-4211 A1177 Set of 3   4.50 2.00

2002 World Cup
Soccer
Championships,
Japan and
Korea — A1178

Player and flag from: No. 4212, 15c, South Korea. No. 4213, 15c, France. No. 4214, 15c, Germany. No. 4215, 15c, Brazil. No. 4216, 15c, Spain. 65c, Argentina. 75c, Italy. 85c, Japan.

2002, Apr. 21   Litho.   *Perf. 12½*
4212-4219 A1178 Set of 8   8.50 4.25
4219a   Sheet, #4212-4219   8.50 4.25

Souvenir Sheet

Hispano-Cubano Philatelic
Exposition — A1179

2002, Apr. 27   *Perf. 13*
4220 A1179 1p multi   3.00 1.50

Juan Tomas Roig, Botanist, 125th Anniv. of Birth A1180

Designs: 5c, Bust of Roig, experimental agronomic station, Santiago de las Vegas. 10c, Bust and house of Roig. 15c, Roig, laboratory glassware and Nicotiana tabacum. 50c, Building, Allophyllum roiggi, and sculpture of Roig. 65c, Roig, laboratory glassware and botanical dictionary.

2002, May 10	Perf. 12½x12¾		
4221-4225	A1180 Set of 5	4.25	2.00
4225a	Sheet, #4221-4225, + label	4.25	2.00

Medi Cuba Suiza — A1181

2002, June 18	Perf. 12¾x12½		
4226	A1181 75c multi	2.10	1.00

Mushrooms A1182

Designs: 5c, Amanita junquillea. 15c, Lepiota puellaris. 45c, Cortinarius cumatilis. 65c, Pholliota adiposa. 75c, Coprinus comatus.

2002, June 20	Perf. 12¾		
4227-4231	A1182 Set of 5	6.00	2.75
4231a	Sheet, #4227-4231, + label	6.00	2.75

Nicolás Guillén (1902-89), Poet — A1183

2002, July 10	Perf. 12¾x12½		
4232	A1183 65c multi	1.75	.90

Dockers, By Marcelo Pogolotti (1902-88) A1184

2002, July 12	Perf. 12¾		
4233	A1184 15c multi	.45	.20

Agostinho Neto (1922-79), Pres. of Angola — A1185

2002, Sept. 17	Perf. 12¾x12½		
4234	A1185 65c multi	1.75	.90

España 2002 Youth Philatelic Exposition, Salamanca — A1186

Birds: 5c, Calidris minutilla. 10c, Tringa melanoleucas. 15c, Charadius semipalmatus. 65c, Plurialis squatarola. 75c, Arenaria interpres. 1p, Porzana carolina.

2002, Sept. 20	Perf. 12½x12¼		
4235-4239	A1186 Set of 5	4.75	2.25
4239a	Sheet, #4235-4239, + label	5.00	2.25

Souvenir Sheet
Perf. 13

4240	A1186 1p multi	3.00	1.50

No. 4240 contains one 40x31mm stamp.

Third Intl. Meeting of War Correspondents — A1187

2002, Oct. 7	Perf. 12¾		
4241	A1187 65c multi	1.75	.90

Ernesto "Che" Guevara (1928-67), Revolutionary Leader — A1188

Various depictions of Guevara: 5c, 10c, 15c, 50c, 65c, 75c.

2002, Oct. 8	Litho.		
4242-4247	A1188 Set of 6	6.25	3.25
4247a	Sheet, #4242-4247	16.00	3.25

America Issue — Youth, Education and Literacy — A1189

Designs: 15c, Emblem of Literacy Army, man with book, teacher with student. 65c, Building, flag, children at computer.

2002, Oct. 12	Perf. 12½x12¼		
4248-4249	A1189 Set of 2	2.25	1.10

Old Automobiles — A1190

Designs: No. 4250, 5c, 1956 Pontiac Catalina. No. 4251, 5c, 1957 Mercury Monterrey. 15c, 1959 Cadillac Fleetwood. 65c, Hudson Hornet. 75c, 1957 Chevrolet Bel Air. 85c, 1957 Mercedes-Benz 190SL.

2002, Oct. 19	Perf. 12¾		
4250-4255	A1190 Set of 6	6.00	3.50
a.	Sheet, #4250-4255, + 6 labels	7.00	3.50

15th Intercontinental Baseball Cup — A1191

Baseball players: 5c, G. Mesa. 15c, A. Pacheco. 50c, O. Linares. 65c, O. Kindelan. 75c, L. Ulacia.

2002, Nov. 1			
4256-4260	A1191 Set of 5	5.00	3.00
4260a	Sheet of 5, #4256-4260 + 4 labels	5.50	3.50

20th Havana Intl. Fair — A1192

2002, Nov. 3			
4261	A1192 65c multi	1.75	.90

Railroads, 165th Anniv. — A1193

Designs: 5c, Rocket. 15c, Miller. 50c, Vulcan. 65c, Consolidation. 75c, Mikado.

2002, Nov. 12	Perf. 12½x12¼		
4262-4266	A1193 Set of 5	5.00	3.00
a.	Sheet, #4262-4266, + label	6.00	3.00

Camagüey Ballet, 35th Anniv. — A1194

Designs: 65c, Twelve dancers. 75c, Two dancers.

2002, Dec. 1	Perf. 12¾		
4267-4268	A1194 Set of 2	3.50	2.00

Pan-American Health Organization, Cent. — A1195

2002, Dec. 2			
4269	A1195 65c multi	1.50	.90

Paintings of Wilfredo Lam (1902-82) A1196

Designs: 15c, Emi Cosinca, 1950. 45c, Yo Soy, 1949. 65c, Retrado de H.H., 1941-42. 75c, Mujer Sentada, 1951.

2002, Dec. 8	Perf. 12¾		
4270-4273	A1196 Set of 4	5.00	3.00
a.	Sheet, #4270-4273, + 4 labels	7.00	3.00

Dulce M. Loynaz (1902-97), Writer A1197

	Perf. 12½x12¾		
2002, Dec. 19			Litho.
4274	A1197 65c multi	2.00	.90

Souvenir Sheet

Tursiops Truncatus — A1198

2002, Dec. 20	Perf. 12½		
4275	A1198 1p multi	3.00	1.50

Fifth National Philatelic Competition.

Prehistoric and Modern-Day Animals — A1199

Designs: 5c, Megaloceros, Cervus elaphus. 10c, Theropithecus, Papio anubis. 15c, Coelodonta, Diceros bicornis. 45c, Canis

654 CUBA

dirus, Canis lupus. 65c, Ursus spelaeus, Ursus arctos. 75c, Smilodon, Panthera leo. 1p, Mammuthus primigenius. Illustration reduced.

2002, Dec. 27   *Perf. 12½x12¼*
4276-4281 A1199   Set of 6   7.50 3.00
Souvenir Sheet
Perf. 13
4282 A1199 1p multi   3.50 1.50
No. 4282 contains one 40x32mm stamp.

New Year 2003 (Year of the Ram) A1200

Ram with background in: No. 4283, 15c, Green. No. 4284, 15c, Red.

2003, Jan. 6   *Perf. 12½*
4283-4284 A1200   Set of 2   1.00 .50

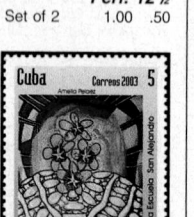

San Alejandro Academy for Arts, 185th Anniv. — A1201

Paintings by: 5c, Amelia Pelaez. 15c, René Portocarrero. 65c, Mario Carreña, horiz. 75c, Servando Cabrera.

2003, Jan. 12   *Perf. 12¾*
4285-4288 A1201   Set of 4   4.00 2.00

José Martí (1853-95), Patriot — A1202

Designs: 15c, Birthplace. No. 4290, 65c, Martí and text. No. 4291, 65c, Martí, sky and text, horiz. 75c, Portrait. 1p, Martí, horiz.

2003, Jan. 28   *Perf. 12¾*
4289-4292 A1202   Set of 4   7.75 2.75
Souvenir Sheet
Perf. 12½
4293 A1202 1p multi   3.50 1.50
No. 4293 contains one 40x32mm stamp.

Arrival of Europeans at Havana, 510th Anniv. — A1203

Various Cuban stamps and: No. 4294, 15c, Woman with Cigar boxes, map of Cuba (diamond-shaped). No. 4295, 15c, Men at table holding cigars and drinks (diamond-shaped). 50c, Tobacco farmer, field, hands rolling cigar.

65c, Building, Trinidad. 75c, Cigar, building, palm tree, people in room. 1p, Indian lighting cigar, vert.

2003, Feb. 6   *Perf. 12½*
4294-4298 A1203   Set of 5   7.75 2.75
Souvenir Sheet
4299 A1203 1p multi   3.50 1.50
No. 4299 contains one 32x40mm stamp.

Radio Rebelde, 45th Anniv. A1204

2003, Feb. 13   *Perf. 12¾*
4300 A1204 65c multi   2.25 .85

Félix Varela (1788-1853), Priest — A1205

2003, Feb. 25   *Perf. 12½*
4301 A1205 65c multi   2.25 .85

Military Units, 45th Anniv. — A1206

Designs: No. 4302, 15c, 2nd Frank Pais Front. No. 4303, 15c, 3rd Mario Muñoz Front.

2003   *Perf. 12¾*
4302-4303 A1206   Set of 2   1.10 .40
Issued: No. 4302, 3/5; No. 4303, 3/11.

16th World Sexology Congress A1207

2003, Mar. 11
4304 A1207 65c multi   2.25 .85

Transportation and Shipping — A1208

Designs: 5c, Container ship. 10c, Truck. 15c, Train. 65c, Airplane and delivery van. 75c, Airplane and delivery van, diff.

2003, Apr. 10   *Perf. 12½*
4305-4309 A1208   Set of 5   6.00 2.25

Flora & Fauna — A1209

Designs: 5c, Nymphaea ampla, Lepisosteus tristoechus. 10c, Magnolia grandiflora, Spindalis zena pretrei. 15c, Lillium candidum, Polymita picta. 65c, Strelitzia regiae, Solenodon cubanus. 75c, Hibiscus rosasinensis, Mellysuga helenae.

2003, May 15
4310-4314 A1209   Set of 5   6.25 2.25

Pan American Games, Santo Domingo, Dominican Republic A1210

Designs: 5c, Kayaking. 15c, Judo. 50c, Track. 65c, Volleyball.

2003, June 27   *Perf. 12½x12¾*
4315-4318 A1210   Set of 4   5.00 1.75

Attack on Moncada Barracks, 50th Anniv. — A1211

Designs: 15c, Men and barracks. 65c, Fidel Castro, text.

2003, July 26   *Perf. 12¾*
4319-4320 A1211   Set of 2   3.00 1.00

Railroads A1212

Designs: 5c, Three-wheeled handcar, 1930-35. 10c, Crane, 1920. 15c, B-B 120/120 E locomotive, 1925. 65c, DVM-9 Ganz Mavag locomotive, 1969. 75c, 2-6-0 locomotive, 1905.

2003, Aug. 7
4321-4325 A1212   Set of 5   7.00 2.25

UN Conference to Combat Desertification — A1213

Illustration reduced.

2003, Aug. 25   *Perf. 12½x12¼*
4326 A1213 65c multi   3.25 .85

Expo Bangkok A1214

Wildlife: 5c, Nyctea scandiaca. 10c, Fratercula arctica. 15c, Sula bassana. 65c, Ursus maritimus. 75c, Alopex lagopus. 1p, Pagolphilus groenlandicus.

2003, Aug. 28   *Perf. 12¾*
4327-4331 A1214   Set of 5   7.00 2.25
Souvenir Sheet
Perf. 12½
4332 A1214 1p multi   4.25 1.50
No. 4332 contains one 32x40mm stamp.

Butterflies and Flowers — A1215

Designs: 5c, Dione juno, Gardenia jasminoides. 15c, Apatura ilia, Chrysanthemus sinence. 65c, Inachis io, Hibiscus rosasinensis. 75c, Marpesia iole, Althaea rosea. 1p, Danaus plexippus, Zantedeschia aethiopica, vert.

2003, Sept. 11   *Litho.*   *Perf. 12½*
4333-4336 A1215   Set of 4   6.75 2.10
Souvenir Sheet
4337 A1215 1p multi   4.25 1.50
No. 4337 contains one 32x40mm stamp.

Ecotourism — A1216

Bird and location: 10c, Aratinga eops, Baracoa. 15c, Xiphiopicus percussus, Valle de los Ingenios. 65c, Tiaris canora, Sierra Maestra. 75c, Priotelus temnurus, Granma.

2003, Sept. 27   *Perf. 12¾x12½*
4338-4341 A1216   Set of 4   6.75 2.10

Worldwide Fund for Nature (WWF) — A1217

Crocodylus rhombifer: No. 4342, 15c, Eggs and hatchling. No. 4343, 15c, Adult at water's edge. 65c, Capturing prey. 75c, With open mouth.

2003, Sept. 30   *Litho.*   *Perf. 12¾*
4342-4345 A1217   Set of 4   6.00 2.25
4345a   Sheet, 4 each #4342-4345   24.00 15.00

America Issue — Flora and Fauna — A1218

Designs: 15c, Xiphidiopicus percussus. 65c, Encyclia phoenicea.

2003, Oct. 12
4346-4347 A1218 Set of 2 3.25 1.10

35th Baseball World Cup — A1219

Cuban players: 5c, Antonio Muñoz. 10c, Lourdes Gourriel. No. 4350, 15c, Jorge L. Valdes. No. 4351, 15c, Lazaro Vargas. 65c, Lazaro Valle. 75c, Javier Mendez.
1p, Players celebrating, vert.

2003, Oct. 17 **Perf. 12½x12¼**
4348-4353 A1219 Set of 6 7.75 2.40
Souvenir Sheet
Perf. 12½
4354 A1219 1p multi 4.25 1.50
No. 4354 contains one 32x40mm stamp.

Ballet — A1220

Designs: No. 4355, 65c, National Ballet of Cuba, 55th anniv. No. 4356, 65c, Alicia Alonso as Giselle, 60th anniv., vert.

Perf. 12¾x12½, 12½x12¾
2003, Oct. 28
4355-4356 A1220 Set of 2 5.00 1.75

Powered Flight, Cent. — A1221

Emblem and: 5c, Wright Brothers. 15c, Pitcairn PA-5. 65c, Stearman C-3MB. 75c, Douglas M-2.

2003, Dec. 17 **Perf. 12½x12¼**
4357-4360 A1221 Set of 4 6.00 2.10

Cuban Revolution, 45th Anniv. A1222

2004, Jan. 1 **Perf. 12¾**
4361 A1222 65c multi 1.25 .75

Expocuba, 15th Anniv. — A1223

Illustration reduced.

2004, Jan. 4 **Perf. 12½x12¼**
4362 A1223 65c multi 1.25 .75

2004 Summer Olympics, Athens — A1224

Sports: 10c, Baseball. 15c (#4363A), Track 65c, Boxing. 75c, Equestrian.
Illustration reduced.

2004, Jan. 6 **Litho.**
4363-4365 A1224 Set of 4 3.75 1.90

New Year 2004 (Year of the Monkey) A1225

Monkey with denomination in: No. 4366, 15c, Blue. No. 4367, 15c, Orange.

2004, Jan. 9 **Perf. 12¾**
4366-4367 A1225 Set of 2 1.00 .30

Julio A. Mella (1903-29), Communist Leader A1226

2004, Jan. 10
4368 A1226 65c multi 1.25 .75

José Martí (1853-95) — A1227

Designs: No. 4369, 5c, Martí in 1862, Colegio San Pablo, Prado No. 88. No. 4370, 5c, Martí's father, Mariano, Tapineria No. 16, Valencia. No. 4371, 5c, Martí's mother, Leonor Pérez, birthplace, Paula No. 41. No. 4372, 10c, Martí's high school, 1862, Martí, Fermín Valdés Domínguez, 1869. No. 4373, 10c, Martí in 1869, Havana Royal Jail. No. 4374, 15c, Martí in 1870, El Abra farm, Isle of Pines. No. 4375, 15c, Martí in 1870, Martí Forge. No. 4376, 15c, Martí and son, José Francisco, 1879, Guanabacoa Lyceum. 65c, Martí and son, 1879, Mercaderes Law Offices. 75c, Martí in 1895, La Jatía farm, Oriente.

2004, Jan. 28 **Perf. 12½x12¼**
4369-4378 A1227 Set of 10 4.50 2.50

Town of Santa María de Puerto del Principe, 490th Anniv. — A1228

2004, Feb. 2 **Perf. 12¾x12½**
4379 A1228 15c multi .50 .20

Trolleys A1229

Designs: 5c, Santiago. 10c, Havana. 15c, Camagüey. 65c, Matanzas. 75c, Camagüey, diff.
1p, Havana, diff.

2004, Feb. 20 **Perf. 12¾**
4380-4384 A1229 Set of 5 3.50 1.75
Souvenir Sheet
Perf. 12½
4385 A1229 1p multi 2.50 1.25
No. 4385 contains one 40x32mm stamp.

Souvenir Sheet

Cuba — Mexico Binational Philatelic Exhibition — A1230

2004, Feb. 25 **Perf. 12½**
4386 A1230 1p multi 2.50 1.25

EGREM Recording Co., 40th Anniv. — A1231

Recording artists: 10c, Cascarita, Julio Cuevas. 15c, Carlos Puebla. 65c, Benny Maré. 75c, Compay Segundo.

2004, Mar. 24 **Perf. 12¾**
4387-4390 A1231 Set of 4 3.50 1.75

España 2004 Intl. Philatelic Exhibition — A1232

Dogs: 5c, Spanish pointer. 10c, Spanish hound. 15c, Mallorquin bulldog. 65c, Catalan sheepdog. 75c, Pyrenean mastiff.
1p, Spanish mastiff.

2004, Mar. 24 **Perf. 12½x12¼**
4391-4395 A1232 Set of 5 3.50 1.75
Souvenir Sheet
Perf. 12½
4396 A1232 1p multi 2.50 1.25
No. 4396 contains one 40x32mm stamp.

National Police, 45th Anniv. — A1233

Illustration reduced.

2004, Mar. 26 **Perf. 12½x12¼**
4397 A1233 15c multi + label .30 .20

Souvenir Sheet

Second Cuban Sports Olympiad — A1234

2004, Apr. 18 **Perf. 12½**
4398 A1234 1p multi 2.50 1.25

Nature and Man Foundation, 10th Anniv. — A1235

2004, May 16 Litho. Perf. 12¼x12½
4399 A1235 65c multi 1.50 .75

FIFA (Fédération Internationale de Football Association), Cent. — A1236

FIFA emblem and various players: 10c, 15c, 65c, 75c.

2004, May 21 **Perf. 12¾**
4400-4403 A1236 Set of 4 3.50 1.75

Designs: 5c, Parakeets. 10c, Fish. 15c, Dogs. 65c, Cats. 75c, Finches. 1p, Horse, horiz.

Pets A1237

2004, June 25   **Perf. 12½x12¾**
4404-4408 A1237 Set of 5   3.50 1.75
Souvenir Sheet
Perf. 12½
4409 A1237 1p multi   2.50 1.25
No. 4409 contains one 40x32mm stamp.

Intl. Chess Federation, 80th Anniv. — A1238

Chess players: 15c, Maria Teresa Mora. 65c, José Raúl Capablanca, horiz. 75c, Ernesto "Che" Guevara.

2004, July 20   **Perf. 12¾**
4410-4412 A1238 Set of 3   3.50 1.75

Minerals — A1239

Designs: 5c, Corundum. 10c, Thenardite. 15c, Uraninite. 65c, Realgar. 75c, Fluorite. 1p, Copper.

2004, July 30   **Perf. 13**
4413-4417 A1239 Set of 5   3.50 1.75
Souvenir Sheet
Perf. 12½
4418 A1239 1p multi   2.50 1.25
No. 4418 contains one 40x32mm stamp.

Convention Hall, 25th Anniv. — A1240

2004, Sept. 3   **Perf. 12¾**
4419 A1240 65c multi   1.50 1.25

Cuban Aviation, 75th Anniv. — A1241

Designs: 15c, Lockheed Constellation. 65c, IL-62M. 75c, Airbus 330.

2004, Oct. 8   **Perf. 12½x12¼**
4420-4422 A1241 Set of 3   3.50 1.75

America Issue — A1242

Map of Cuba and: 15c, Bird over islands. 65c, Fish and marine life.

2004, Oct. 12
4423-4424 A1242 Set of 2   1.75 .90

Marine Mammals — A1243

Designs: 5c, Delphinus delphis. 10c, Lagenorhynchus obliquidens. 15c, Stenella attenuata. 65c, Grampus griseus. 75c, Tursiops truncatus. 1p, Orcinus orca.

2004, Oct. 20   **Perf. 12½x12¼**
4425-4429 A1243 Set of 5   3.50 1.75
Souvenir Sheet
Perf. 13
4430 A1243 1p multi   2.50 1.25
No. 4430 contains one 40x32mm stamp.

Disappearance of Camilo Cienfuegos, 45th Anniv. A1244

2004, Oct. 28   **Perf. 12¾**
4431 A1244 65c multi   1.50 .75

Railroad Stations, Cent. — A1245

Designs: 15c, Agramonte Station, 1906 ALCO No. 48 4-6-0. 65c, Aguacate Station, 1907 BLW No. 57 4-6-0. 75c, Guira de Melina Station, 1903 ALCO No. 7 4-4-0.

2004, Nov. 10   **Perf. 13**
4432-4434 A1245 Set of 3   3.50 1.75

Souvenir Sheet

13th Philatelic Congress, Havana — A1245a

2004, Nov. 20 **Litho.** **Perf. 12½**
4434A A1245a 1p multi   2.00 2.00

Founding of San Cristóbal de la Habana, 485th Anniv. A1246

Designs: 15c, Temple. 65c, Painting showing priest in red vestments at base of tree. 75c, Paintig showing group of men at base of tree.

Perf. 12½x12¾
2004, Nov. 30   **Litho.**
4435-4437 A1246 Set of 3   3.00 1.50

Latin American Parliament Foundation, 40th Anniv. — A1246a

2004, Nov. 30 **Litho.** **Perf. 12¾**
4437A A1246a 65c multi   1.40 .70

Ministry of Foreign Affairs, 45th Anniv. — A1247

2004, Dec. 23   **Perf. 12½x12¼**
4438 A1247 65c multi   1.40 .70

Alejo Carpentier (1904-80), Writer — A1248

2004, Dec. 26   **Perf. 12¾**
4439 A1248 65c multi   1.40 .70

First Baseball Game in Cuba, 130th Anniv. — A1249

Baseball players: 5c, Rey Vicente Anglada. 10c, Braudilio Vinent. 15c, Rogelio Garcia. 65c, Luis G. Casanova. 75c, Victor Mesa. 1p, Martin Dihigo, vert.

2004, Dec. 27   **Perf. 12½x12¼**
4440-4444 A1249 Set of 5   5.25 2.50
Souvenir Sheet
Perf. 12½
4445 A1249 1p multi   2.00 1.00
No. 4445 contains one 32x40mm stamp.

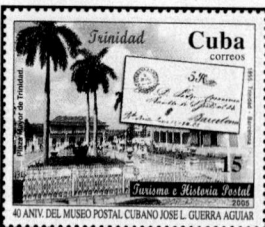

Jose L. Guerra Aguiar Cuban Postal Museum, 40th Anniv. — A1250

Designs:15c, Plaza Mayor, Trinidad and 1855 Trinidad to Barcelona cover. 65c, Charity Sanctuary, El Cobre and 1861 El Cobre to Santiago de Cuba cover. 85c, Matanzas Cathedral, Matanzas and 1848 Mantanzas to Havana cover.

2005, Jan. 2   **Perf. 12¾x12½**
4446-4448 A1250 Set of 3   3.50 1.75

New Year 2005 (Year of the Rooster) A1251

Designs: No. 4449, 15c, Rooster in air. No. 4450, 15c, Rooster on ground.

2005, Jan. 4   **Perf. 12¼x12½**
4449-4450 A1251 Set of 2   .60 .30

Ministry of Information Technology and Communications, 5th Anniv. — A1252

Illustration reduced.

2005, Jan. 12   **Perf. 12½x12¼**
4451 A1252 65c multi   1.40 .70

Dinosaurs — A1253

Designs: 5c, Carnotaurus. 10c, Oviraptor. 30c, Parasaurolophus. 65c, Sauropelta. 90c, Iguanodon.
1p, Velociraptor.

2005, Jan. 20   Litho.   Perf. 12½x12¼
4452-4456 A1253   Set of 5   4.00 2.00
Souvenir Sheet
Perf. 13
4457 A1253 1p multi   2.00 1.00
No. 4457 contains one 40x32mm stamp.

Miguel de Cervantes and Title Page of
Don Quixote — A1254

2005, Jan. 24   **Perf. 12¾x12½**
4458 A1254 65c multi   1.40 .70
Publication of *Don Quixote*, 400th anniv.

Bridges
A1255

Designs: 10c, Bacunayagua Bridge. 15c, La Concordia Bridge. 50c, El Triunfo Bridge. 65c, Yayabo Bridge. 75c, Canimar Bridge.
1p, Plaza Bridge.

2005, Feb. 5   **Perf. 13x12¾**
4459-4463 A1255   Set of 5   4.50 2.25
Souvenir Sheet
Perf. 13
4464 A1255 1p multi   2.00 1.00
No. 4464 contains one 40x32mm stamp.

Cuban Telecommunications Enterprise,
10th Anniv. — A1256

2005, Feb. 24   **Perf. 12½x12¾**
4465 A1256 90c multi   1.90 .95

Parrots — A1257

Designs: 5c, Amazona ochrocephala, Amazona leucocephala. 10c, Agapornis personata, Agapornis fischeri. 15c, Cacatua galerita, Cacatua leadbeateri. 65c, Psittacula krameri, Psittacula himalayana, vert. 1.05p, Aratinga guarouba, Aratinga euops.
1p, Ara macao, Ara araruana, Anodorhynchus hyacythus.

Perf. 12½x12¼, 12¼x12½
2005, Feb. 23   **Litho.**
4466-4470 A1257   Set of 5   4.00 2.00
Souvenir Sheet
Perf. 13
4471 A1257 1p multi   2.00 1.00
No. 4471 contain one 32x40mm stamp.

Cats
A1258

Various cats: 5c, 10c, 40c, 65c, 75c. 10c is vert.

2005, Mar. 15   **Perf. 12¾**
4472-4476 A1258   Set of 5   4.00 2.00
Perf. 13
4477 A1258 1p Two cats, vert.   2.00 1.00
No. 4477 contains one 32x40mm stamp.

Cuba — Canada Diplomatic Relations,
60th Anniv. — A1259

2005, Mar. 20   **Perf. 12¾x12½**
4478 A1259 65c multi   1.40 .70

Wildlife — A1260

2005, Mar. 21   **Perf. 12½x12¼**
4479 A1260 15c Manatee   .30 .20
4480 A1260 65c Parrot   1.40 .70
4481 A1260 75c Crocodile   1.50 .75
4482 A1260 90c Hummingbird   1.90 .95
    Nos. 4479-4482 (4)   5.10 2.60

World Water
Day — A1261

2005, Mar. 22   **Perf. 13**
4483 A1261 90c multi   1.90 .95

Boats — A1262

Designs: 10c, Fishing boat, fish. 20c, Schooner, fish. 30c, Bonito boat, bonito. 45c, Shrimp boat, shrimp. 90c, Lobster boat, lobster.
1p, Cargo ship, horiz.

2005, Apr. 15   **Perf. 12½**
4484-4488 A1262   Set of 5   4.00 2.00
Souvenir Sheet
4489 A1262 1p multi   2.00 1.00

First Cuban Postage Stamps, 150th
Anniv. — A1263

Designs: 15c, St. Francis of Assisi Convent, Cuba #1. 65c, Morro Lighthouse, Cuba #2. 75c, Colonial Post Office, Cuba #3.

2005, Apr. 24   **Perf. 12¾x12½**
4490-4492 A1263   Set of 3   3.25 1.60

Social Security For All — A1264

2005, May 5   **Litho.**
4493 A1264 65c multi   1.40 .70

Major General Máximo Gómez (1836-
1905) — A1265

2005, June 17   **Perf. 12½**
4494 A1265 1.05p multi   2.10 1.10

Souvenir Sheet

Santiago de Cuba, 490th
Anniv. — A1266

2005, July 4   **Perf. 13**
4495 A1266 1p multi   2.00 1.00

16th World Youth and Student Festival,
Venezuela — A1267

2005, July 29   **Perf. 12¾x12½**
4496 A1267 65c multi   1.40 .70

Dances
A1268

Parrot and: No. 4497, 65c, Samba dancers and Brazilian flag. No. 4498, 65c, Son dancers, Cuban flag.

2005, Aug. 15   **Perf. 12¾**
4497-4498 A1268   Set of 2   2.60 1.40
See Brazil Nos. 2967-2968.

Cuban — Soviet Space Flight, 25th
Anniv. — A1269

No. 4499: a, Cosmonaut Arnaldo Tamayo Mendez. b, Cosmonaut Yuri Romanenko. Illustration reduced.

2005, Sept. 18   **Perf. 12½**
4499 A1269 90c Horiz. pair, #a-b 3.75 1.90

Albert Einstein's
Visit to Cuba,
75th
Anniv. — A1270

Designs: 65c, Caricature of Einstein. 75c, Equation for energy, Einstein writing.

2005, Sept. 21
4500-4501 A1270   Set of 2   3.00 1.50

Locomotives — A1271

Designs: 5c, DSB B40, 1869. 10c, Great Northern, 1902. No. 4504, 15c, Minaret, 1929. No. 4505, 15c, C. F. White, 1885. 2.05p, Western Pacific FP7A 805D.
1p, 14th No. 4 Krauss & Co., 1884.

2005, May 10   Litho.   Perf. 12¾
4502-4506 A1271   Set of 5   5.00 2.50
Souvenir Sheet
Perf. 13
4507 A1271 1p multi   2.00 1.00
No. 4507 contains one 40x32mm stamp.

Zoo Animals
A1272

Designs: 10c, Loxodonta africana. 15c, Acunonyx jubatus, horiz. 50c, Synceros caffer, horiz. 65c, Giraffa camelopardalis. 75c, Panthera leo.
1p, Equus burchelli, horiz.

2005, July 21   Perf. 12¾
4508-4512 A1272   Set of 5   4.50 2.25
Souvenir Sheet
Perf. 13
4513 A1272 1p multi   2.00 1.00
No. 4513 contains one 40x32mm stamp.

Santiago de Cuba, 490th
Anniv. — A1273

2005, Sept. 22   Perf. 12¾x12½
4514 A1273 75c multi   1.50   .75

Revolutionary Defense Committees,
45th Anniv. — A1274

Illustration reduced.

2005, Sept. 28   Perf. 12½x12¼
4515 A1274 50c multi   1.00   .50

Diplomatic Relations Between Cuba
and People's Republic of China, 45th
Anniv. — A1275

No. 4516: a, Chinese General Secretary Hu Jintao and Cuban Pres. Fidel Castro. b, Great Wall of China and Morro Castle, Havana.
Illustration reduced.

2005, Sept. 28   Perf. 13x13¼
4516 A1275 15c Horiz. pair, #a-b   .60 .30

America Issue,
Fight Against
Poverty
A1276

Designs: 50c, Starving children, map of Africa. 75c, Woman and child, map of South America.

2005, Oct. 12   Perf. 12¾
4517-4518 A1276   Set of 2   2.50 1.25

Horses
A1277

Breeds: 10c, Gelderlander. 20c, Arabian. 30c, Quarterhorse. 65c, Wild horses. 75c, Lipizzaner.
100c, Holsteiner, vert.

2005, Oct. 21   Perf. 12¾
4519-4523 A1277   Set of 5   4.00 2.00
Souvenir Sheet
Perf. 12¾x12½
4524 A1277 100c multi   2.00 1.00
No. 4524 contains one 32x40mm stamp.

José Martí Type of 2004

Martí and: No. 4525, 5c, Central University, Madrid, 1871. No. 4526, 5c, Zaragoza University, 1871. No. 4527, 5c, F. Valdés Dominguez, Teatro Principal, Zaragoza, 1872. No. 4528, 10c, Victor Hugo House, Paris, 1872. No. 4529, 10c, Moneda No. 12, Mexico City, 1875. No. 4530, 15c, Normal School, Guatemala City, 1876. No. 4531, 15c, San Ildefonso No. 40, Mexico City, 1894. No. 4532, 15c, Plaza de Guardiola, Mexico City, 1894. 65c, Plaza Bolívar, Caracas, 1885. 75c, Santa María College, Caracas, 1893.
1p, Martínez Ibor Tobacco Factory, Tampa, 1892.

2005, Oct. 20   Perf. 12½x12¼
4525-4534 A1227   Set of 10   4.50 2.25
Souvenir Sheet
Perf. 13
4535 A1227 1p multi   2.00 1.00
No. 4535 contains one 40x32mm stamp.

World Summit on the Information
Society, Tunis — A1278

2005, Nov. 16   Perf. 12½x12¼
4536 A1278 75c multi   1.50   .75

Establishment of Local Delivery of Mail
in Havana, 150th Anniv. — A1279

Designs 15c, Cuba #7, cover to Havana. 65c, Cuba #16, Colonial Havana mailbox.

2005, Nov. 19   Perf. 12¾x12½
4537-4538 A1279   Set of 2   1.60   .80

Cuban
Men
Convicted
of
Terrorism
Imprisoned
In the
United
States
A1280

2005, Nov. 25   Perf. 12½x12¾
4539 A1280 65c multi   1.40   .70

Europa
Stamps,
50th Anniv.
(in 2006)
A1281

Designs: 1.30p, Spain #1126, Castilla de la Fuerza, Havana. 2.05p, Spain #1010, Santisima Church, Trinidad, Cuba. 2.55p, Spain #1526, Morro Castle, Santiago de Cuba. 3.90p, Spain #1263, San Cristóbal Cathedral, Havana.

2005, Nov. 30   Perf. 12½
4540-4543 A1281   Set of 4   20.00 10.00
4543a   Souvenir sheet, #4540-
                4543   20.00 10.00
Nos. 4540-4543, 4543a exist imperf.

Jewelry
A1282

Jewelry by: 5c, Antonio Barcala. 10c, Raúl Valladares. 45c, Carlos de la Torre. 65c, J. Carlo Rafart. 75c, Osvaldo Castilla.
1p, 19th cent. jewelry in Gold Museum.

2005, Dec. 1   Perf. 12¾
4544-4548 A1282   Set of 5   4.00 2.00
Souvenir Sheet
Perf. 12½
4549 A1282 1p multi   2.00 1.00
No. 4549 contains one 32x40mm stamp.

Friendship Among the Peoples
Institute, 45th Anniv. — A1283

2005, Dec. 14   Perf. 12¾x12½
4550 A1283 1.05p multi   2.10 1.10

Snails and
Mushrooms
A1284

Designs: 10c, Clathrus cancellatus. 20c, Polymita genus picta. 30c, Lepiota puellaris. 65c, Polymita genus muscarum. 75c, Clitocybe infundibuliformis.
1p, Polymita genus versicolor, horiz.

2005, Dec. 15   Perf. 12¾
4551-4555 A1284   Set of 5   4.00 2.00
Souvenir Sheet
Perf. 13
4556 A1284 1p multi   2.00 1.00
No. 4556 contains one 40x32mm stamp.

Hotel Inglaterra, 130th Anniv. — A1285

2005, Dec. 23   Perf. 12¾x12½
4557 A1285 65c multi   1.40   .70

New Year 2006
(Year of the
Dog) — A1286

Designs: No. 4558, 15c, Shih tzu. No. 4559, 15c, Pug.

2006, Jan. 4   Perf. 12¼x12½
4558-4559 A1286   Set of 2   .60   .30

Organization of
Solidarity of the
People of Asia,
Africa and
Latin America,
40th Anniv.
A1287

2006, Jan. 16   Perf. 12¾
4560 A1287 65c multi   1.40 .70

Establishment of Cuban Postal
Service, 250th Anniv. — A1288

Stampless cover and: 75c, Horse and rider.
2.05p, Ship.

2006, Mar. 1   Perf. 12½x12¼
4561-4562 A1288 Set of 2   5.75 2.75

OPEC Intl. Development Fund, 30th
Anniv. — A1289

2006, Mar. 23   Litho.
4563 A1289 75c multi   1.50 .75

Souvenir Sheet

Havana '06 Intl. Philatelic
Exhibition — A1290

2006, Mar. 25   Perf. 12½
4564 A1290 1p multi   2.00 1.00

Pope John Paul II (1920-
2005) — A1291

Designs: 65c, Pope, Mass in Santa Clara.
75c, Mass in Camagüey (44x27mm). 90c,
Mass in Santiago de Cuba (44x27mm). 1.05p,
Pope, Mass in Havana.
Illustration reduced.

2006, Apr. 2   Perf. 12½x12¼
4565-4568 A1291 Set of 4   6.75 3.50

Bay of Pigs
Invasion, 45th
Anniv. — A1292

2006, Apr. 17   Perf. 12¼x12½
4569 A1292 65c multi   1.40 .70

José Martí Type of 2004

Martí and: No. 4570, Madame Griffou's
Hotel, New York, 1890. No. 4571, Gonzalo de
Quesada, 116 West 64th Street, New York,
1893. No. 4572, Son, José Francisco, 324
Classon Ave., New York, 1885. No. 4573,
Masonic Temple, New York, 1888.
No. 4574: a, Cajobabo beach, Gomez mon-
ument. b, Martí monument, monument at Dos
Ríos.
Martí and: 75c, Hardman Hall, New York,
1891. 85c, Office, 120 Front Street, New York,
1891. 90c, María Mantilla, Bath Beach, Long
Island.
1p, Home of Teodoro Pérez, Cayo Hueso,
1893.

2006, May 19 Litho.   Perf. 12½x12¼
4570 A1227 5c multi   .20 .20
4571 A1227 5c multi   .20 .20
4572 A1227 10c multi   .20 .20
4573 A1227 10c multi   .20 .20
4574 A1227 15c Horiz. pair, #a-b .60 .60
4575 A1227 75c multi   1.50 1.50
4576 A1227 85c multi   1.75 1.75
4577 A1227 90c multi   1.75 1.75
   Nos. 4570-4577 (8)   6.40 6.40

Souvenir Sheet
Perf. 13
4578 A1227 1p multi   2.00 2.00
No. 4578 contains one 40x32mm stamp.

Prehistoric Animals — A1293

Designs: 5c, Dsungaripetrus, Yangchua-
nosaurus. 10c, Pterodactylus, Sprinosaurus.
30c, Pteranodon, Pachycephalosaurus. 35c,
Scaphognathus, Muttaburrasaurus. 65c,
Quetzalcoatlus, Stegosaurus. 1.05p, Sordes,
Saichania.
1p, Stenonychosaurus, vert.

2006, May 24   Perf. 12½x12¼
4579-4584 A1293 Set of 6   5.00 5.00
Souvenir Sheet
Perf. 12½
4585 A1293 1p multi   2.00 2.00
No. 4585 contains one 32x40mm stamp.

Ministry of the Interior, 45th
Anniv. — A1294

2006, June 6   Perf. 12½x12¼
4586 A1294 75c multi   1.50 1.50

Fowl — A1295

Designs: 5c, Chickens. No. 4588, 15c, Tur-
keys. No. 4589, 15c, Guinea fowl. 45c, Geese.
50c, Pheasants. 75c, Peafowl.
1p, Ducks.

2006, June 15   Perf. 12½x12¼
4587-4592 A1295 Set of 6   4.25 4.25
Souvenir Sheet
Perf. 13
4593 A1295 1p multi   2.00 2.00
No. 4593 contains one 40x32mm stamp.

Cerro Pelado
Declaration,
40th
Anniv. — A1296

Designs: 65c, Ship, man and crowd. 75c,
People in cargo hoist. 85c, Men assisting
woman down ship's stairs, flags of Cuba and
Puerto Rico.

2006, June 25   Perf. 12½x12¾
4594-4596 A1296 Set of 3   4.50 4.50

Genetic Engineering and
Biotechnology Center, 20th
Anniv. — A1297

2006, July 1   Perf. 12½x12¼
4597 A1297 65c multi   1.40 1.40

Comic Strips by Virgilio
Martinez — A1298

Designs: 15c, Pucho y Sus Perrerias. 65c,
Cucho.
Illustration reduced.

2006, July 16   Perf. 12¾x12¼
4598-4599 A1298 Set of 2   1.60 1.60

Airplanes — A1299

Designs: 10c, Granville GeeBee R2. No.
4601, 15c, Bücker Jungmann. No. 4602, 15c,
Comte AC-4 Gentleman. 50c, Mustang TF-51.
75c, Supermarine Spitfire. 85c, Lavochkin La-
9.
1p, Bücker Jungmeister.

2006, July 20   Perf. 12¾
4600-4605 A1299 Set of 6   5.00 5.00

Souvenir Sheet
Imperf
4606 A1299 1p multi   2.00 2.00
No. 4606 contains one 36x28mm stamp.

Dogs — A1300

Designs: 5c, Bulldog. 10c, American cocker
spaniel. 15c, Shar-pei. 20c, Airedale terrier.
35c, Pomeranian. 2.05p, Dalmatian.
1p, Whippet, vert.

2006, Aug. 18   Perf. 12½x12¼
4607-4612 A1300 Set of 6   6.00 6.00
Souvenir Sheet
Perf. 13
4613 A1300 1p multi   2.00 2.00

Recovery of Raw Materials, 45th
Anniv. — A1301

Designs: 15c, Ernesto "Che" Guevara. 65c,
Cuban and recovery program flags.

2006, Aug. 24   Perf. 12¾
4614-4615 A1301 Set of 2   1.60 1.60

14th Congress
of Non-Aligned
Countries,
Havana
A1302

2006, Sept. 10
4616 A1302 65c multi   1.40 1.40

Pedro Santacilia, Benito Juárez and
Mexico House, Havana — A1303

Illustration reduced.

2006, Sept. 15   Perf. 12½x12¼
4617 A1303 65c multi   1.40 1.40
Benito Juárez (1806-72), President of
Mexico.

Souvenir Sheet

7th Hispano-Cuban Philatelic
Exposition — A1304

No. 4618: a, Statue, arms of Cuba, denomination at LR. b, Statue, arms of Spain, denomination at LL.

2006, Sept. 20   *Imperf.*
4618 A1304 50c Sheet of 2, #a-b 2.00 2.00

España 06 World Philatelic Exposition,
Malaga, Spain — A1305

Designs: 5c, Rio Hanabanilla. 10c, Laguna
Bacanao. 15c, Sierra de la Gran Piedra. 20c,
Valle de los Ingenios. 50c, Laguna del Tesoro.
75c, Sierra Maestra.
1p, Valle de Viñales.

2006, Sept. 20   *Perf. 12¾*
4619-4624 A1305   Set of 6   3.50 3.50
Souvenir Sheet
Perf. 13
4625 A1305 1p multi   2.00 2.00
No. 4625 contains one 40x32mm stamp.

America Issue, Energy
Conservation — A1306

Equipment for harnessing energy source:
No. 4626, 65c, Petroleum. No. 4627, 65c,
Water. No. 4628, 65c, Solar. No. 4629, 65c,
Wind.

2006, Oct. 12   *Perf. 12¾*
4626-4629 A1306   Set of 4   5.25 5.25

Saiz Brothers
Association,
20th Anniv.
A1307

2006, Oct. 18
4630 A1307 75c multi   1.50 1.50

20th Intl. Ballet
Festival, Havana
A1308

Dancers: 75c, Alicia Alonso and Igor Yous-
kévitch. 85c, Alonso.

2006, Oct. 28   *Perf. 12¼x12½*
4631-4632 A1308   Set of 2   3.25 3.25

A1309

Belgica '06 Intl. Youth Philately
Exposition, Belgium — A1310

Trains: 5c, Rocket and Intercity Diesel-electric. 10c, Turbine locomotive, Diesel-electric
locomotive. 15c, Shinkasen and City of Los
Angeles. 65c, Steam locomotive, Diesel locomotive. 75c, TEE Diesel-electric, TGV electric.
85c, Brisbane electric monorail, Wuppertal
monorail.
No. 4639: a, Steam locomotive. b, Diesel
locomotive.

2006, Nov. 2   *Perf. 12¾*
4633-4638 A1309   Set of 6   5.25 5.25
Souvenir Sheet
Perf. 12½
4639 A1310 50c Sheet of 2, #a-b 2.00 2.00

TeleFood Emblem — A1311

2006, Nov. 11   *Perf. 12¾*
4640 A1311 75c multi   1.50 1.50

Animals Serving Man — A1312

Designs: 5c, Equus caballus, Greek horse-
drawn chariot. 15c, Camelus dromedarius, Ibn
Battuta on camel. 30c, Capra aegagrus,
Roman musician. 40c, Lama lama, Peruvian
pre-Columbian ceramic llama. 50c, Felis
catus, painting by Kuniyoshi Utagawa. 1.05p,
Elephas maximus, elephant with Indian
caparison.
1p, Canis familiaris, Grecian with dog.

2006, Oct. 1   **Litho.**   *Perf. 12½x12¼*
4641-4646 A1312   Set of 6   5.00 5.00
Souvenir Sheet
Perf. 12½
4647 A1312 1p multi   2.00 2.00
No. 4647 contains one 40x32mm stamp.

Fire Fighting and Rescue
Equipment — A1313

Designs: 5c, 1899 Horse-drawn ambulance,
Brazil, and megaphone. 10c, Fireman's hat,
and 1898 Merryweather fire truck, England.
20c, 1910 Laurin & Klement fire truck, Bohemia, and fire hydrant. 30c, 1939 American La
France ladder truck, US, and badge. 45c,
1925 Leyland Motors pumper motorcycle,
United Kingdom, and portable hose and tank.
90c, Brussels fire badge and 1930 Magirus
ladder truck, Germany.
1p, Fireman spraying water, vert.

2006, Nov. 13   *Perf. 12¾*
4648-4653 A1313   Set of 6   4.00 4.00
Souvenir Sheet
Perf. 12½
4654 A1313 1p multi   2.00 2.00
No. 4654 contains one 32x40mm stamp.

Santiago Rebellion, 50th
Anniv. — A1314

2006, Nov. 30   *Perf. 12½x12¼*
4655 A1314 65c multi   1.40 1.40

Governmental Reorganization, 30th
Anniv. — A1315

2006, Dec. 2
4656 A1315 75c multi   1.50 1.50

Granma Landings, 50th
Anniv. — A1316

Revolutionary Armed Forces, 50th
Anniv. — A1317

2006, Dec. 2   *Perf. 13*
4657 A1316 65c multi   1.40 1.40
4658 A1317 65c multi   1.40 1.40

Intl. Film and Television School, 20th
Anniv. — A1318

2006, Dec. 15   *Perf. 12¾*
4659 A1318 75c multi   1.50 1.50

Martí Forge Museum, 55th
Anniv. — A1319

Illustration reduced.

2006, Dec. 15   *Perf. 12½x12¼*
4660 A1319 90c multi   1.90 1.90

Literacy
Campaign,
45th Anniv.
A1320

2006, Dec. 19   *Perf. 12¾*
4661 A1320 65c multi   1.40 1.40

Major General Ignacio Agramonte y
Loinaz (1841-73) — A1321

2006, Dec. 23   *Perf. 12½x12¼*
4662 A1321 65c multi   1.40 1.40

Special Education, 45th
Anniv. — A1322

2007, Jan. 4   *Perf. 12¾*
4663 A1322 85c multi   1.75 1.75

Francesa
Pharmacy,
125th Anniv.
A1323

2007, Jan. 18   *Litho.*
4664 A1323 65c multi   1.40 1.40

Electric
Trains
A1324

Designs: 5c, First American electric locomotive, 1895. 10c, Locomotive, Netherlands. 15c, Interurban train, Australia. 65c, High-speed train, Italy. 85c, Helensburgh-Bridgeton train, Great Britain. 1.05p, Lyon-St. Etienne interurban train, France.
1p, High-speed train, Germany.

2007, Jan. 18   Perf. 12¾
4665-4670 A1324   Set of 6   5.75 5.75
Souvenir Sheet
Imperf
4671 A1324 1p multi   2.00 2.00
No. 4671 contains one 40x32mm stamp with simulated perforations.

12th Intl. Information Fair and
Convention — A1325

Illustration reduced.

2007, Feb. 12   Perf. 12½x12¼
4672 A1325 75c multi   1.50 1.50

Cats
A1326

Designs: 10c, Two cats. No. 4674, 15c, Kitten with paw raised. No. 4675, 15c, Cat. 50c, Cat and telephone. 75c, Cat with ball. 90c, Cat, diff.
1p, Cat, diff.

2007, Feb. 14   Perf. 12¾
4673-4678 A1326   Set of 6   .25 5.25
Souvenir Sheet
Imperf
4679 A1326 1p multi   2.00 2.00
No. 4679 contains one 40x32mm stamp with simulated perforations.

Fifth Congress of Cuban Pigeon
Fanciers Federation — A1327

2007, Feb. 24   Perf. 12¾
4680 A1327 75c multi   1.50 1.50

Souvenir Sheet

Patria Newspaper, 115th
Anniv. — A1328

Imperf. With Simulated Perforations
2007, Mar. 14
4681 A1328 1p multi   2.00 2.00

Animals in National Zoo — A1329

Designs: 5c, Ara ararauana. 10c, Tsetudo elephantopus. 15c, Balearica regulorum. 20c, Procyon lotor. 45c, Panthera pardus. 2.05p, Pongo pygmaeus.
1p, Giraffa camelopardalis, vert.

2007, Mar. 31   Perf. 12½x12¼
4682-4687 A1329   Set of 6   6.00 6.00
Souvenir Sheet
Imperf
4688 A1329 1p multi   2.00 2.00
No. 4688 contains one 32x40mm stamp with simulated perforations.

Raúl Roa García (1907-82), Foreign Minister A1330

2007, Apr. 18   Perf. 12¾
4689 A1330 65c multi   1.40 1.40

Union of Young Communists, 45th
Anniv. — A1331

2007, Apr. 4   Perf. 12½x12¼
4690 A1331 75c multi   1.50 1.50

José Martí Type of 2004
Martí and: No. 4691, 5c, Cuban High School, Tampa, 1892. No. 4692, 5c, Casa de los Pedrosa, Tampa, 1892. No. 4693, 10c, Hotel Duval, Cayo Hueso, 1891. No. 4694, 10c, Hotel Cherokee, Tampa, 1891. No. 4695, 15c, Cayo Hueso Committee, 1891 (68x28mm). No. 4696, 15c, F. Valdés Domínguez, Gato Brothers Cigar Factory, Cayo Hueso, 1894. 35c, Club San Carlos, Cayo Hueso, 1893. 40c, Hotel Myrtle Bank, Kingston, 1892. 50c, Gen. Francisco Gómez Toro, Friends of the Country Society Building, Santo Domingo, 1894. 65c, Máximo Gómez, Gómez's house, Montecristi.

2007, Apr. 10   Perf. 12½x12¼
4691-4700 A1227   Set of 10   5.00 5.00

World Food Program Children's Art
Exhibition, 10th Anniv. — A1332

2007, May 3   Litho.   Perf. 12¾
4701 A1332 65c multi   1.40 1.40

Folklore
Union — A1333

2007, May 7   Perf. 12¼x12½
4702 A1333 75c multi   1.50 1.50

Islands and Wildlife — A1334

Designs: 5c, Cayo Guillermo, pelican. No. 4704, 15c, Cayo Las Brujas, sea gull. No. 4705, 15c, Cayo Levisa, conches. 20c, Cayo Santa Maria, iguana. 50c, Cayo Ensenachos, plover. 85c, Cayo Largo, Carey turtle.
1p, Cayo Coco, flamingos.

2007, May 8   Perf. 12½x12¼
4703-4708 A1334   Set of 6   4.00 4.00
Souvenir Sheet
Imperf
4709 A1334 1p multi   2.00 2.00
No. 4709 contains one 40x32mm stamp.

Singers and
Songwriters
A1335

Designs: 5c, Benny Moré. 10c, Ignacio Piñeiro. 30c, Arsenio Rodríguez. 35c, Miguelito Cuní. 65c, Pio Leyva. 75c, Ibrahim Ferrer.
1p, Miguel Matamoros.

2007, May 10   Perf. 12¾
4710-4715 A1335   Set of 6   4.50 4.50
Souvenir Sheet
Imperf
4716 A1335 1p multi   2.00 2.00
No. 4716 contains one 32x40mm stamp with simulated perforations.

Souvenir Sheet

Martí Studies Youth Seminary, 35th
Anniv. — A1336

2007, May 19   Imperf.
4717 A1336 1p multi   2.00 2.00

Cuban Radio and Television Institute,
45th Anniv. — A1337

2007, May 24   Perf. 12½x12¼
4718 A1337 3p multi   6.00 6.00

Integral Development Group of the
Capital, 20th Anniv. — A1338

2007, May 25   Litho.
4719 A1338 65c multi   1.40 1.40

Cuban
Admission to
the United
Nations, 60th
Anniv.
A1339

2007, May 29   Perf. 12¾
4720 A1339 65c multi   1.40 1.40

2007 Pan American Games, Rio de
Janeiro — A1340

Designs: No. 4721, 15c, Fencing. No. 4722, 15c, Boxing. 20c, Wrestling. 45c, Running. 65c, Gymnastics. 75c, Cycling.
1p, Games emblem, vert.

2007, June 20   Perf. 12¾
4721-4726 A1340   Set of 6   4.75 4.75
Souvenir Sheet
Imperf
4727 A1340 1p multi   2.00 2.00
No. 4727 contains one 32x40mm stamp.

Third Technological Transfer and Intl.
Trade Workshop — A1341

2007, July 3　　　　　**Perf. 12½x12¼**
4728　A1341　65c multi　　　　1.40　1.40

Frank País (1934-57), Revolutionary
Hero — A1342

2007, July 30　　　　　**Perf. 12¾**
4729　A1342　65c multi　　　　1.40　1.40

Radio Cubana,
85th Anniv.
A1343

2007, Aug. 22　　　　　**Perf. 12¾**
4730　A1343　65c multi　　　　1.40　1.40

SEMI-POSTAL STAMPS

Common Design Types
pictured following the introduction.

Curie Issue
Common Design Type
Wmk. 106
1938, Nov. 23　　**Engr.**　　**Perf. 10**
B1　CD80　2c + 1c salmon　　　4.00　1.00
B2　CD80　5c + 1c deep ultra　　4.00　1.25
　　Set, never hinged　　　　　12.00

40th anniv. of the discovery of radium by
Pierre and Marie Curie. Surtax for the benefit
of the Intl. Union for the Control of Cancer.

**Catalogue values for unused
stamps in this section, from this
point to the end of the section, are
for Never Hinged items.**

"Agriculture"
Supporting
"Industry"
SP2

Engr., Center Typo.
1959, May 7　**Wmk. 321**　**Perf. 12½**
B3　SP2　2c + 1c car & ultra　　.50　.20

Agricultural reforms. See No. CB1. For
surcharges see Nos. 624, C199.

Nurse — SP3

Wmk. 229
1959, Sept. 22　**Photo.**　**Perf. 12½**
B4　SP3　2c + 1c crimson rose　.35　.25

Exists imperf, value about double.

AIR POST STAMPS

Seaplane
over Havana
Harbor
AP1

Wmk. 106
1927, Nov. 1　　**Engr.**　　**Perf. 12**
C1　AP1　5c dark blue　　　5.00　1.00
　　Never hinged　　　　　　8.00

For overprint see No. C30.

Type of 1927
Issue
Overprinted

1928, Feb. 8
C2　AP1　5c carmine rose　　4.00　1.60
　　Never hinged　　　　　　6.00

No. 283 Surcharged in Red

1930, Oct. 27　　　　　**Unwmk.**
C3　A44　10c on 25c violet　3.50　1.60
　　Never hinged　　　　　　4.75

Airplane and
Coast of
Cuba — AP3

For Foreign Postage

1931, Feb. 26　**Wmk. 106**　**Perf. 10**
C4　AP3　5c green　　　　.45　.20
C5　AP3　10c dk blue　　.45　.20
C6　AP3　15c rose　　　　.90　.30
C7　AP3　20c brown　　　.90　.20
C8　AP3　30c dk violet　1.25　.20
C9　AP3　40c dp orange　2.75　.35
C10　AP3　50c olive grn　3.25　.35
C11　AP3　1p black　　　5.25　.90
　　Nos. C4-C11 (8)　　15.20　2.70
　　Set, never hinged　　25.00

See No. C40. For surcharges see Nos. C16-
C17, C203, C225.

Airplane
AP4

For Domestic Postage

1931-46
C12　AP4　5c rose vio ('32)　　.35　.20
　　a.　5c brown violet ('36)　　.35　.20

C13　AP4　10c gray blk　　　.35　.20
C14　AP4　20c car rose　　2.50　.85
C14A　AP4　20c rose pink ('46)　1.10　.20
C15　AP4　50c dark blue　　4.25　.90
　　Nos. C12-C15 (5)　　8.55　2.35
　　Set, never hinged　　15.00

See #C130. For overprints see #C31, E29-
E30.

Type of 1931 Surcharged in Black

1935, Apr. 24　　　　　**Perf. 10**
C16　AP3　10c + 10c red　　11.00　7.50
　　Never hinged　　　　　18.00
　　a.　Double surcharge　　110.00

Imperf
C17　AP3　10c + 10c red　　25.00　25.00
　　Never hinged　　　　　35.00

Matanzas Issue

Air View
of
Matanzas
AP5

10c, Airship "Macon." 20c, Airplane "The
Four Winds." 50c, Air View of Fort San
Severino.

Wmk. 229
1936, May 5　**Photo.**　**Perf. 12½**
C18　AP5　5c violet　　　.75　.25
C19　AP5　10c yellow orange　.90　.40
C20　AP5　20c green　　3.25　1.75
C21　AP5　50c greenish slate　8.00　3.00
　　Nos. C18-C21 (4)　　12.90　5.40
　　Set, never hinged　　20.00

Exist imperf. Value 20% more.

"Lightning"
AP9

Allegory
of Flight
AP10

1936, Nov. 18
C22　AP9　5c violet　　　1.25　1.10
C23　AP10　10c orange brown　2.00　1.50
　　Set, never hinged　　4.25

Major Gen. Maximo Gomez, birth cent.

Flat Arch
(Panama) — AP11

Carlos Antonio
López
(Paraguay) — AP12

Inca Gate,
Cuzco
(Peru) — AP13

Atlacatl
(Salvador)
AP14

José Enrique
Rodó (Uruguay)
AP15

Simón Bolívar
(Venezuela)
AP16

Wmk. 106
1937, Oct. 13　**Engr.**　**Perf. 10**
C24　AP11　5c red　　　7.00　7.00
C25　AP12　5c red　　　7.00　7.00
C26　AP13　10c blue　　7.00　7.00
C27　AP14　10c blue　　7.00　7.00
C28　AP15　20c green　9.50　9.50
C29　AP16　20c green　9.50　9.50
　　Nos. C24-C29 (6)　47.00　47.00
　　Set, never hinged　60.00

See note after No. 354.

Type of 1927 Overprinted in Black

1938, May　　　　　**Wmk. 106**
C30　AP1　5c dark orange　5.00　1.50
　　Never hinged　　　　　7.50

1st airplane flight from Key West to Havana,
made by Domingo Rosillo, 1913.

Type of
1931-32
Overprinted

1939, Oct. 15
C31　AP4　10c emerald　40.00　3.00
　　Never hinged　　　　60.00

Issued in connection with an experimental
postal rocket flight held at Havana.

Sir Rowland Hill, Map of Cuba and
First Stamps of Britain, Spanish Cuba
and Republic of Cuba — AP17

1940, Nov. 28　**Engr.**　**Wmk. 106**
C32　AP17　10c brown　　4.50　2.00
　　Never hinged　　　　7.50

Souvenir Sheet

Unwmk.　　　　　**Imperf.**
C33　Sheet of 4　　　15.00　11.00
　　Never hinged　　　25.00
　　a.　AP17 10c light brown　2.75　1.25
　　Never hinged　　　3.50

Cent. of the 1st postage stamp.
Sheet sold for 60c.
No. C33 exists with each of the four stamps
overprinted in black: "Exposicion de la
ACNU/24 de Octubre de 1951/Dia de las
Naciones" and "Historia de la Aviacion" in
lower margin. Value, $60.
For overprints see Nos. C39, C211.

Poet José Heredia and Palms AP18

Heredia and Niagara Falls — AP19

1940, Dec. 30   **Wmk. 106**
C34 AP18 5c emerald   2.00 1.00
C35 AP19 10c greenish slate   3.00 1.50
    Set, never hinged   7.50

Death cent. of José Maria Heredia y Campuzano (1803-39), poet and patriot.

First Cuban Land Sighted by Columbus AP20

Columbus Lighthouse AP21

1944, May 19
C36 AP20 5c olive green   .90 .30
C37 AP21 10c slate black   1.90 .50

450th anniv. of the discovery of America.

> **Catalogue values for unused stamps in this section, from this point to the end of the section, are for Never Hinged items.**

Conference of La Mejorana (Meceo, Gomez and Marti) AP22

1948, May 21   **Wmk. 229**   **Perf. 12½**
C38 AP22 8c org yel & blk   3.00 .75

50th anniv. of the start of the War of 1895.

Souvenir Sheet
No. C33 Overprinted in Ultramarine

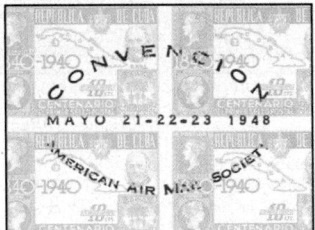

1948, May 21   **Unwmk.**   **Imperf.**
C39 AP17   Sheet of 4   15.00 9.50

The overprint is applied in the center of the four 10c stamps, so that a portion falls on each.
American Air Mail Soc. Convention, Havana, May 21 to 23, 1948. The sheets sold for 60c each.

Type of 1931
1948, June 15   **Wmk. 106**   **Perf. 10**
C40 AP3 8c orange brown   1.50 .30

Narciso Lopez Landing at Cárdenas AP23

Flag on Cuban Fort — AP24

Flag on Morro Castle, Havana — AP25

Engraved and Lithographed
1951, July 3   **Wmk. 229**   **Perf. 13**
C41 AP23 5c ol grn, ultra & red   2.25 .30
C42 AP24 8c red brn, bl & red   3.50 .30
C43 AP25 25c gray blk, bl & red   5.00 1.90
    Nos. C41-C43 (3)   10.75 2.50

Centenary of adoption of Cuba's flag.

Souvenir Sheet
No. 365a Overprinted in Green

Illustration reduced.

1951, Aug. 24   **Unwmk.**   **Imperf.**
C43A   Sheet of 4   12.00 9.00

50th anniv. of the discovery of the cause of yellow fever by Dr. Carlos J. Finlay, and to honor the martyrs of science.

Postage Type and

Resignation Play of Dr. Lasker AP26

Capablanca Making "The Exact Play" — AP27

Wmk. 229
1951, Nov. 1   **Photo.**   **Perf. 13**
C44 AP26 5c shown   5.00 .80
C45 AP27 8c shown   9.00 1.25
C46 A165 25c Capablanca   15.00 3.25
    Nos. C44-C46 (3)   29.00 5.30

30th anniv. of the winning of the World Chess title by José Raul Capablanca.

Morrillo Types of Regular Issue
Wmk. 106
1951, Nov. 22   **Engr.**   **Perf. 10**
C47 A167 5c violet   2.40 .50
C48 A168 8c deep green   3.25 .75
C49 A169 25c dark brown   6.50 1.50
  a.   Souv. sheet of 6, black brown, perf. 13   50.00 35.00

  b.   Souv. sheet of 6, green, imperf.   200.00 125.00
    Nos. C47-C49 (3)   12.15 2.75

Nos. C49a and C49b contain one each of the 1c, 2c and 5c of types A167-A169 and of the 5c, 8c and 25c airmail stamps of types A167-A169. Sheets are unwatermarked and measure 124x133mm.

Isabella Type of Regular Issue, 1952
1952, Feb. 22
C50 A172 25c purple   4.00 1.00
  a.   Souv. sheet of 2, perf. 11   17.50 17.50
  b.   Souv. sheet of 2, imperf.   20.00 20.00

Nos. C50a and C50b contain one each of a 2c of type A172 and a 25c air-mail stamp of type A172. In No. C50a, the 2c and marginal inscriptions are brown carmine; the 25c, dark blue. In No. C50b, the 2c and marginal inscriptions are dark blue; the 25c, brown carmine. Sheets measure 108x18mm.

Type of Regular Issue of 1951 Surcharged in Various Colors

1952, Mar. 18
Color: Yellow Brown
C51 A159 5c on 2c   .85 .25
C52 A159 8c on 2c (C)   1.75 .25
C53 A159 10c on 2c (Bl)   1.75 .25
C54 A159 25c on 2c (V)   2.75 1.00
C55 A159 50c on 2c (C)   8.50 1.50
C56 A159 1p on 2c (Bl)   19.00 6.00
    Nos. C51-C56 (6)   34.60 9.25

Country School AP32

Entrance, University of Havana — AP33

10c, Presidential Mansion. 25c, Banknote.

Wmk. 106
1952, May 27   **Engr.**   **Perf. 12½**
Centers Various Shades of Green
C57 AP32 5c dark purple   .45 .20
C58 AP33 8c dark red   .70 .20
C59 AP32 10c deep blue   1.40 .20
C60 AP32 25c dark violet brn   2.40 1.00
    Nos. C57-C60 (4)   4.95 1.60

Foundation of the Republic of Cuba, 50th anniv.

Plane and Map — AP34

Agustín Parlá — AP35

1952, July 22   **Engr.**   **Perf. 10**
C61 AP34 8c black   1.50 .55
  a.   Souv. sheet, 8c deep blue   15.00 10.00
  b.   Souv. sheet, 8c deep green   15.00 10.00
C62 AP35 25c ultra   4.00 1.60
  a.   Souv. sheet, 25c deep blue   15.00 10.00
  b.   Souv. sheet, 25c deep green   15.00 10.00

30th anniv. of the Key West-Mariel flight of Agustin Parla.
The four souvenir sheets are perf. 11.

Col. Charles Hernandes y Sandrino — AP36

1952, Oct. 7
C63 AP36 5c orange   .70 .20
C64 AP36 8c brt yel grn   .70 .20
C65 AP36 10c dk brown   .90 .20
C66 AP36 15c dk Prus grn   1.75 .50
C67 AP36 20c aqua   2.25 .65
C68 AP36 25c crimson   1.75 .65
C69 AP36 30c dk vio bl   4.50 1.60
C70 AP36 45c rose lilac   4.50 2.25
C71 AP36 50c indigo   2.75 1.60
C72 AP36 1p bister   10.00 3.25
    Nos. C63-C72 (10)   29.80 11.10

Three-fourths of the proceeds from the sale were used for the Communications Ministry Employees' Retirement Fund.

Entrance, University of Havana — AP37

F. V. Dominguez, M. Estebanez and F. Capdevila — AP38

Engr.; Center Typo.
1952, Nov. 27
C73 AP37 5c indigo & dk blue   1.75 .35
C74 AP38 25c org & dk grn   5.00 1.25

Execution of 8 medical students, 81st anniv.

AP39

Lockheed Constellation Airliners — AP40

1953, May 22   **Engr.**
C75 AP39 8c orange brn   1.25 .20
C76 AP39 15c scarlet   2.25 .70
Typographed and Engraved
C77 AP40 2p dp green & dk brn   27.50 10.00
C78 AP40 5p blue & dk brn   55.00 17.50
    Nos. C75-C78 (4)   86.00 28.40

See #C120-C121. For surcharge see #C224.

Page of Manifesto of Montecristi — AP42

House of Maximo Gomez AP43

#C79, Marti in Kingston, Jamaica. #C80, With Workers in Tampa, Florida. #C83, Marti addressing liberating army. #C84, Portrait. #C85, Dos Rios obelisk. #C86, Marti's first tomb. #C87, Present tomb. #C88, Monument in Havana. #C89, Martian forge.

1953			Engr.		Perf. 10
C79	AP42	5c dk car & blk		.30	.20
C80	AP42	5c dk car & blk		.30	.20
C81	AP43	8c dk green & blk		.50	.20
C82	AP42	8c dk green & blk		.50	.20
C83	AP42	10c dk blue & dk car		1.75	.75
C84	AP42	10c dk blue & dk car		1.75	.75
C85	AP42	15c violet & gray		1.00	.90
C86	AP42	15c violet & gray		1.00	.90
C87	AP42	25c brown & car		3.75	1.25
C88	AP42	25c brown & car		3.75	1.25
C89	AP43	50c yellow & bl		5.00	2.50
		Nos. C79-C89 (11)		19.60	9.10

Cent. of the birth of José Marti.

Board of Accounts Building — AP44

25c, Plane above Board of Accounts Bldg.

1953, Nov. 3

C90	AP44	8c rose carmine	1.75	.50
C91	AP44	25c dk gray grn	3.50	.90

1st Intl. Cong. of Boards of Account, Havana, Nov. 2-9, 1953.

Miguel Coyula Llaguno AP45 — Antonio Ginard Rojas AP46

Designs: 10c, Gregorio Hernandez Saez. 1p, Communications Association Flag.

1954

C92	AP45	5c dark blue	.50	.25
C93	AP46	8c red violet	.65	.25
C94	AP46	10c orange	1.40	.35
C95	AP45	1p black	9.50	4.50
		Nos. C92-C95 (4)	12.05	5.35

See note after No. C72.

Alvaro Reinoso — AP47

Plane and Harvesters Cutting Cane AP48

Designs in Lower Triangle: 5c, Four-engine Plane and Cane Field. 10c, Tractor pulling loaded wagons. 15c, Train of sugar cane. 20c, Modern train. 25c, Evaporators. 30, Sacks of sugar. 40c, Loading sugar on ship. 45c, Ox cart. 50c, Primitive sugar mill.

1954, Apr. 27				Engr.
C96	AP47	5c yellow green	.45	.20
C97	AP48	8c brown	1.25	.50
C98	AP48	10c dark green	1.25	.50
C99	AP48	15c henna brn	3.00	.50
C100	AP48	20c blue	1.25	.50
C101	AP48	25c scarlet	.95	.20

C102	AP48	30c lilac rose	2.50	.95
C103	AP48	40c deep blue	5.00	1.25
C104	AP48	45c violet	4.00	2.50
C105	AP48	50c brt blue	4.00	1.60
C106	AP47	1p dk gray blue	11.00	3.25
		Nos. C96-C106 (11)	34.65	11.65

For surcharges see Nos. C204.

Sanatorium Type of Regular Issue

1954, Sept. 21			Wmk. 106	Perf. 10
C107	A186	9c deep green	2.50	.50

Dolz Type of Regular Issue, 1954

1954, Dec. 23

C108	A188	12c carmine	2.00	.60

Rotary Type of Regular Issue, 1955

1955, Feb. 23

C109	A190	12c carmine	2.50	.50

Stamps of 1855 and 1905, Palace of Fine Arts AP52

Designs (including 2 stamps): 12c, Plaza de la Fraternidad. 24c, View of Havana. 30c, Plaza de la Republica.

1955, Apr. 24				Perf. 12½
C110	AP52	8c dk grnsh bl & grn	1.00	.35
C111	AP52	12c dk ol grn & red	1.10	.35
C112	AP52	24c dk red & ultra	2.00	.90
C113	AP52	30c dp org & brn	4.25	1.50
		Nos. C110-C113 (4)	8.35	3.10

Cent. of Cuba's 1st postage stamps.

Mariel Bay — AP53

Views: 12c, Varadero beach. 1p, Vinales valley.

1955, June 22			Wmk. 106	
C114	AP53	8c dk car & dk grn	.75	.25
C115	AP53	12c dk ocher & brt bl	1.75	.35
C116	AP53	1p dk grn & ocher	7.50	2.50
		Nos. C114-C116 (3)	10.00	3.10

See note after No. C72.

Map of Crocier's 1914 Flight — AP54

Design: 30c, Crocier in plane.

1955, July 4				Perf. 10
C117	AP54	12c red & dk grn	1.00	.25
C118	AP54	30c dk grn & mag	3.00	.60

35th anniv. of the death of Jaime Gonzalez Crocier, aviation pioneer.

Cuban Museum, Tampa, Fla. — AP55

1955, July 1 Engr. **Perf. 12½**

C119	AP55	12c red & dk brn	2.00	.50

Cent. of Tampa's incorporation as a town.

Lockheed Type of 1953

Typographed and Engraved

1955, Sept. 21			Wmk. 106	
C120	AP40	2p bl & ol grn	20.00	6.00
C121	AP40	5p dp rose & ol grn	42.50	15.00

Wright Brothers' Plane and Stamps AP56

Designs: 12c, Spirit of St. Louis. 24c, Graf Zeppelin. 30c, Constellation passenger plane. 50c, Convair jet fighter.

Engraved and Photogravure

1955, Nov. 12 Wmk. 106 Perf. 12½

Inscription and Plane in Black

C122	AP56	8c car & bl	1.00	.35
C123	AP56	12c yel grn & car	2.25	.70
C124	AP56	24c vio & car	6.75	2.50
C125	AP56	30c bl & red org	5.75	3.25
C126	AP56	50c ol grn & red org	7.75	4.00
a.		Souvenir sheet of 5	45.00	25.00
		Nos. C122-C126 (5)	23.50	10.80

International Centenary Philatelic Exhibition in Havana, Nov. 12-19, 1955.

No. C126a is printed on thick paper and measures 140x178mm. It contains one each of Nos. C122-C126 with the background of each stamp printed in a different color from the perforated stamps.

"Three Friends" and Gen. Emilio Nuñez AP57

Design: 12c, Landing on the Cuban Coast.

1955, Dec. 27 Engr. Unwmk.

C127	AP57	8c ultra & dk car	2.00	.40
C128	AP57	12c grn & dk red brn	3.25	.50

Gen. Emilio Nuñez, Cuban revolutionary hero, birth cent.

Post Type of Regular Issue, 1956

Bishop P. A. Morell de Santa Cruz (1694-1768).

1956, Mar. 27 Wmk. 106

C129	A197	12c dk brn & grn	1.75	.40

Plane Type of 1931-46

1956 Engr. Perf. 10

C130	AP4	50c greenish blue	3.00	1.00

Portrait Type of Regular Issue, 1956

1956, May 2 Perf. 12½

Portraits: 8c, Gen. Julio Sanguily. 12c, Gen. José Maria Aguirre. 30c, Col. Ernesto Ponts Sterling.

Portraits in Black

C131	A198	8c brown	.90	.20
C132	A198	12c dull yellow	1.25	.25
C133	A198	30c indigo	3.00	1.50
		Nos. C131-C133 (3)	5.15	1.95

See note after No. C72.

Mother and Child — AP60 — Masonic Temple Havana — AP61

1956, May 13 Wmk. 106 Perf. 12½

C134	AP60	12c ultra & red	2.50	.25

Issued in honor of Mother's Day 1956.

1956, June 5

C135	AP61	12c olive green	2.75	.40

Pigeon AP62

Gundlach Hawk — AP63

Birds: 8c, Wood duck. 19c, Herring gulls. 24c, White pelicans. 29c, Common merganser. 30c, Quail. 50c, Herons (great white, great blue and Wurdemann's). 1p, Northern caracara. 2p, Middle American jacana. 5p, Ivory-billed woodpecker.

1956

C136	AP62	8c blue	.50	.20
C137	AP62	12c gray blue	7.50	.20
C138	AP63	14c green	1.75	.25
C139	AP63	19c redsh brn	1.10	.55
C140	AP63	24c lilac rose	1.25	.55
C141	AP63	29c green	1.90	.55
C142	AP62	30c dk olive bis	2.25	.80
C143	AP63	50c slate blk	4.25	1.10
C144	AP63	1p dk car rose	6.50	2.25
C145	AP62	2p rose violet	13.00	4.25
C146	AP63	5p brt red	35.00	8.75
		Nos. C136-C146 (11)	75.00	19.45

See Nos. C205, C235-C237. For surcharges and overprints see #C147, C151, C197, C209-C210.

Type of 1956 Surcharged

Design: 24c, White pelicans.

1956, July 13

C147	AP63	8c on 24c deep org	2.50	.75

Opening of the new building of the Cuba Philatelic Club, Havana, July 14, 1956.

Hubert de Blanck — AP64 — Church of Our Lady of Charity — AP65

1956, July 6

C148	AP64	12c ultra	2.00	.30

Hubert de Blanck (1856-1932), composer.

1956, Sept. 8

C149	AP65	12c green & carmine	2.75	.40
a.		Souvenir sheet of 2, imperf.	14.00	8.00

Issued in honor of Our Lady of Charity of Cobre, patroness of Cuba.

No. C149a contains one each of Nos. 559 and C149. No. C149a exists with yellow of No. 559 omitted.

Benjamin
Franklin
AP66

1956, Oct. 5   Engr.   Perf. 12½
C150 AP66 12c red brown   2.00 .40

Type of 1956 Surcharged in Blue

Design: 2p, Middle American jacana.

1956, Oct. 26   Wmk. 106
C151 AP62 12c on 2p dark gray   2.00 .75

Issued in honor of the 12th Inter-American Press Association Conference, Havana.

Lord Baden-Powell
AP67

1957, Feb. 22
C152 AP67 12c slate   2.40 .50

Centenary of the birth of Lord Baden-Powell, founder of the Boy Scouts.

Hanabanilla
Waterfall
AP68

12c, Sierra de Cubitas. 30c, Puerto Boniato.

1957, Mar. 29
C153 AP68 8c blue & red   .75   .20
C154 AP68 12c green & red   2.25 .30
C155 AP68 30c ol grn & dk pur   3.00 .50
    Nos. C153-C155 (3)   6.00 1.00

See note after No. 457.

Philatelic Club,   Fingerprint
Havana   AP70
AP69

1957, Apr. 24   Wmk. 106   Perf. 12½
C156 AP69 12c yel, grn & brn   1.75 .30

Stamp Day, and the Natl. Phil. Exhib.

1957, Apr. 30
C157 AP70 12c claret brown   1.75 .30

Birth cent. (in 1856) of Juan Francisco Steegers y Perera, dactyloscopy pioneer.

Baseball
Player — AP71

1957, May 17   Wmk. 106   Perf. 12½
C158 AP71 8c shown   1.00 .35
C159 AP71 12c Ballerina   1.75 .40
C160 AP71 24c Girl diver   2.50 1.00
C161 AP71 30c Boxers   3.50 1.50
    Nos. C158-C161 (4)   8.75 3.25

Issued to honor young Cuban athletes.

Joaquin de   Jeanette Ryder
Aguero   AP73
AP72

1957, July 4
C162 AP72 12c indigo   1.50 .25

Issued to honor Joaquin de Aguero, Cuban freedom fighter and patriot.

1957, July 17
C163 AP73 12c dk red brn   2.50 .40
    a.   Pair, #574, C163   7.00 3.50

Mrs. Jeanette Ryder, founder of the Humane Society of Cuba.

José M. de   John Robert
Heredia y   Gregg — AP75
Girard — AP74

1957, Aug. 16   Engr.   Wmk. 106
C164 AP74 8c dk blue vio   1.50 .25

José Maria de Heredia y Girard (1842-1905), Cuban born French poet.

Justice Type of Regular Issue, 1957
1957, Sept. 2   Perf. 12½
C165 A214 12c green   2.00 .50

1957, Oct. 1
C166 AP75 12c dark green   2.00 .50

90th anniv. of the birth of John Robert Gregg, inventor of the Gregg shorthand system.

D. Figarola
Caneda — AP76

José Marti
National
Library
AP77

1957, Oct. 18   Wmk. 106   Perf. 12½
C167 AP76 8c ultra   .75   .25
C168 AP77 12c chocolate   2.00 .35

José Marti National Library.

Map of Cuba
and UN
Emblem
AP78

1957, Oct. 24
C169 AP78 8c dk green & brn   1.00 .25
C170 AP78 12c car rose & grn   1.50 .40
C171 AP78 30c ind & brt pink   3.50 1.00
    Nos. C169-C171 (3)   6.00 1.65

Issued for United Nations Day, 1957.

Map of Cuba
and Florida
AP79

1957, Oct. 28
C172 AP79 12c dk red brn & bl   1.75 .50

30th anniv. of airmail service from Key West to Havana.

Type of Regular Issue, 1957 and

Stairway and
Bell Tower
AP80

Design: 12c, Facade of Normal School.

1957, Nov. 19   Engr.   Perf. 12½
C173 A217 12c indigo & ocher   1.40 .30
C174 AP80 30c dk car & gray   2.50 .60

View Types of Regular Issue, 1957
Views: 8c, El Viso Fort, El Caney. 12c, Sancti Spiritus Church. 30c, Concordia Bridge, Matanzas.

1957, Dec. 17   Perf. 12½
C175 A218 8c dk gray & red   .75   .30
C176 A219 12c brown & gray   1.50 .30
C177 A218 30c red brn & bl gray 2.75 .75
    Nos. C175-C177 (3)   5.00 1.35

See note after No. C72.

Hedges Types of Regular Issue, 1958
8c, Dayton Hedges & Matanzas rayon factory.

1958, Jan. 30   Wmk. 106   Perf. 12½
C178 A221 8c green   2.00 .50

Diario de la
Marina
Building — AP81

1958, Apr. 1
C179 AP81 29c black   3.50 1.00

Jose Ignacio Rivero y Alonso, editor of the newspaper, Diario de la Marina.

Map
Showing
Sea
Mail
Route,
1765
AP82

1958, Apr. 24   Wmk. 106   Perf. 12½
C180 AP82 29c dk bl aqua & buff 4.75 1.25

Issued for Stamp Day, Apr. 24, and the National Philatelic Exhibition.

Gen. Gomez in   Snail (Polymita
Battle — AP83   Picta) — AP84

1958, June 6   Engr.
C181 AP83 12c slate green   2.00 .35

Issued in honor of Maj. Gen. José Miguel Gomez, President of Cuba, 1909-13.

1958, Aug. 29   Wmk. 321   Perf. 12½
12c, Megalocnus Rodens. 30c, Ammonite.

C182 AP84 8c gray, red & yel   3.25 .90
C183 AP84 12c brn, yel grn   5.50 1.50
C184 AP84 30c grn, pink   8.00 2.00
    Nos. C182-C184 (3)   16.75 4.40

Centenary of the birth of Dr. Carlos de la Torre, naturalist.

Papilio Caiguanabus
AP85

Cuban Sea
Bass — AP86

12c, Teria gundlachia. 14c, Teria ebriola. 19c, Nathalis felicia. 29c, Butter Hamlet. 30c, Tattler.

1958, Sept. 26   Wmk. 106   Perf. 12½
C185 AP85 8c multicolored   3.00 .50
C186 AP85 12c emer, blk & org   3.50 .50
C187 AP85 14c multicolored   5.25 .75
C188 AP85 19c bl, blk & yel   6.75 1.00
C189 AP86 24c multicolored   7.50 1.00
C190 AP86 29c blk, brn & ultra   11.00 1.25
C191 AP86 30c blk, yel grn &
              sep   16.00 1.75
    Nos. C185-C191 (7)   53.00 6.75

Felipe Poey (1799-1891), naturalist.

Battle of San
Juan Hill,
1898 — AP87

Wmk. 106
1958, Oct. 27   Engr.   Perf. 12½
C192 AP87 12c black brown   2.75 .30

Birth centenary of Theodore Roosevelt.

UNESCO
Building,
Paris — AP88

Design: 30c, "UNESCO" and map of Cuba.

1958, Nov. 7
C193 AP88 12c dk slate grn   1.50 .40
C194 AP88 30c dp ultra   3.00 1.25

UNESCO Headquarters in Paris opening, Nov. 3.

Postal Notice of 1765 — AP89

Musical Arts Building — AP90

Design: 30c, Administrative postal book of St. Cristobal, Havana, 1765.

1959, Apr. 24   Wmk. 321   Perf. 12½
C195 AP89 12c Prus blue & sep   1.50   .25
C196 AP89 30c sepia & Prus bl   2.50   1.00

Issued for Stamp Day, Apr. 24, and the National Philatelic Exhibition.

Type of 1956 Surcharged with New Value, Bar and "ASTA" Emblem in Dark Blue

1959, Oct. 17   Wmk. 321   Perf. 12½
C197 AP63 12c on 1p emerald   2.00   1.00

Issued to publicize the meeting of the American Soc. of Travel Agents, Oct. 17-23.

Wmk. 106

1959, Nov. 11   Engr.   Perf. 12½
C198 AP90 12c yellow green   3.00   .45

40th anniversary of the Musical Arts Society.

No. CB1 Surcharged in Red: "HABILITADO PARA / 12c"

Engr. & Typo.

1960   Wmk. 321   Perf. 12½
C199 SPAP1 12c on 12 + 3c car & grn   2.25   .75

Type of Regular Issue, 1960

8c, Battle of Santa Clara. 12c, Rebel forces entering Havana. 29c, Bank-note changing hands ("Clandestine activities in the cities").

Wmk. 320

1960, Jan. 28   Perf. 12½
C200 A236 8c bl, gray ol & sal   2.25   .25
C201 A236 12c gray ol & ocher   3.25   .25
C202 A236 29c gray & car   6.50   1.50
      Nos. C200-C202 (3)   12.00   2.00

Nos. C9 and C104 Surcharged "12c" in Red

1960, Feb. 3   Wmk. 106
C203 AP3   12c on 40c dp org   .90   .30
C204 AP48 12c on 45c vio   .90   .30

Pigeon Type of 1956

1960, Feb. 12   Wmk. 321
C205 AP62 12c brt blue grn   .50   .20

Statue Type of Regular Issue, 1960.

Statues: 8c, José Marti, Matanzas. 12c, Heroes of the Cacarajicara, Pinar del Rio. 30c, Cosme de la Torriente, Isle of Pines, horiz.

1960, Mar. 28   Perf. 12½
C206 A237 8c gray & car   .60   .25
C207 A237 12c blue & car   1.00   .25
C208 A237 30c violet & brn   2.25   1.00
      Nos. C206-C208 (3)   3.85   1.50

See note after No. 386.

Type of 1956 and No. C33 Overprinted in Dark Blue

1960, Apr. 24   Wmk. 321   Perf. 12½
C209 AP62 8c orange yel   .50   .20
C210 AP62 12c cerise   1.50   .20

Souvenir Sheet
C211 AP17   Sheet of 4   20.00 20.00

Stamp Day, 4/24/60, and Natl. Phil. Exhib. No. C211 has added marginal inscription in dark blue for cent. of the ¼r on 2r (No. 15).

Type of Olympic Games Issue, 1960

Wmk. 321
1960, Sept. 22   Engr.   Perf. 12½
C212 A238 8c Boxer   .75   .20
C213 A238 12c Runner   1.50   .40
      a.   Souvenir sheet of 4   4.00

17th Olympic Games, Rome, Aug. 25-Sept. 11. No. C213a contains one each imperf. of types of Nos. 645-646 and Nos. C212-C213 in dark blue.

No. C3 and Flight Symbols of 1930, 1960 — AP91

1960, Oct. 30   Litho.   Unwmk.
C214 AP91 8c multicolored   3.00   1.50

30th anniv. of national air mail service.

Sword of Sheaf of Wheat — AP92

12c, Two workers, horiz. 30c, Three maps, horiz. 50c, Hand inscribed "Peace" in 5 languages.

1961, Jan. 10   Photo.   Perf. 11½
Granite Paper
C215 AP92 8c multicolored   .60   .20
C216 AP92 12c multicolored   .90   .20
C217 AP92 30c black & red   2.50   .50
C218 AP92 50c blk, bl & red   3.00   1.00
      Nos. C215-C218 (4)   7.00   1.90

Conf. of Underdeveloped Countries, Havana.

José Marti and "Declaration of Havana" — AP93

Background in Spanish, English or French.

1961, Jan. 28   Litho.   Perf. 12½
C219 AP93 8c pale grn, blk & red   1.00   .60
C220 AP93 12c org yel, blk & pale vio   1.50   1.00
C221 AP93 30c pale bl, blk & pale brn   2.50   2.00
      a.   Souvenir sheet of 3   11.00 11.00
      Nos. C219-C221 (3)   5.00   3.60

Declaration of Havana, Sept. 1, 1960. Sheets of 25 are imprinted in margin "E" for Spanish, "I" for English or "F" for French. No. C221a contains one each of Nos. C219-C221, imperf. The 8c has background in Spanish, the 12c in English and the 30e in French.

UN Type of 1961

1961, Apr. 12   Unwmk.   Perf. 12½
C222 A244 8c dp car & yel   .60   .20
C223 A244 12c brt ultra & org   1.25   .30
      a.   Souv. sheet of 2, #C222-C223, imperf.   10.00

Nos. C76 and C7 Surcharged

HABILITADO PARA
8 cts.

1961, Oct. 1   Engr.   Perf. 10
C224 AP39 8c on 15c No. C76   1.00   .35
C225 AP3   8c on 20c No. C7   1.00   .35

Revolution Anniv. Type of 1962

Perf. 12½
1962, Jan. 3   Litho.   Unwmk.
C226 A250 8c multi   .85   .30
C227 A250 12c multi   1.90   .55
C228 A250 30c multi   2.50   .90
      Nos. C226-C228 (3)   5.25   1.75

1st Sugarcane Harvest in Socialist Cuba, 1st Anniv. — AP94

1962, Jan. 16
C229 AP94 8c salmon pink & dark brn   1.00   .20
C230 AP94 12c bluish lil & blk   2.50   .45

Cuban goods have been embargoed by the United States since a Feb. 7, 1962 proclamation by President Kennedy, but according to the Office of Foreign Assets Control of the Treasury Department, used Cuban stamps can be imported and sold without limitation, and unused stamps may be imported for personal use, but not resold.

Intl. Radio Service AP95

1962, Mar. 26   Wmk. 321
C231 AP95 8c multi   1.10   .25
C232 AP95 12c multi   2.25   .55
C233 AP95 30c multi   3.25   1.25
C234 AP95 1p multi   7.00   3.25
      Nos. C231-C234 (4)   13.60   5.30

Bird Type of 1956

1962, July 20   Engr.   Wmk. 321
C235 AP63 1p like #C144, royal blue   5.75   5.75
C236 AP62 2p like #C145, dark red   17.00 15.00
C237 AP63 5p like #C146, rose lake   37.50 32.50
      Nos. C235-C237 (3)   60.25 53.25

PRAGA '62 — AP96

1962, Aug. 18   Litho.
C238 AP96 31c Czechoslavakia No. 1080   3.50   1.50

Souvenir Sheet
Imperf
C239 AP96 31c like No. C238   13.00   9.00

No. C239 contains one 60x35½mm stamp.

Achievements of the Revolution — AP97

1966, July 26   Wmk. 376   Perf. 12½
C240 AP97 1c Agrarian reform   .20   .20
C241 AP97 2c Industrialization   .20   .20
C242 AP97 3c Urban reform   .50   .20
C243 AP97 7c Eradication of unemployment   .50   .20
C244 AP97 9c Education   .95   .20
C245 AP97 10c Public health   2.10   .20
C246 AP97 13c Excerpt from La Historia Me Absolvera, by Castro   2.75   .45
      Nos. C240-C246 (7)   7.20   1.65

Camaguey-Seville Flight, 35th Anniv. — AP98

1971, Jan. 12   Unwmk.
C247 AP98 13c Aircraft   2.75   .20
C248 AP98 30c Map, Lieut. Menendez Palaez   3.25   .40

Havana-Santiago de Chile Direct Air Service, 1st Anniv. — AP99

1972, June 26   Wmk. 376
C249 AP99 25c multi   3.00   .75

6th Congress of Latin American and Caribbean Exporters of Sugar, Havana — AP100

Perf. 12½x12
1977, Feb. 28   Unwmk.
C250 AP100 13c multi   .75   .20

Composer Type of 1977

1977, May 10   Perf. 13
C251 A571 13c Jorge Ankerman and score   1.00   .20

Flower Type of 1977

1977, May 31
C252 A572 13c Caesalpinia pulcherrima   .85   .20
C253 A572 30c Catharanthus roseus   1.75   .50

Souvenir Sheet
Perf. 13½x13
C254 A572 50c Juan Tomas Roig   4.00   .90

No. C254 contains one 32x40mm stamp.

Natl. Decorations Type of 1977

1977, July 26   Perf. 12x12½
C255 A574 13c multi, diff.   .80   .20
C256 A574 13c multi, diff.   1.50   .45

Art Type of 1977

Paintings by Jorge Arche: 13c, My Wife and I, vert. 30c, Domino Players. 50c, Self-portrait, vert.

1977, Aug. 25   Perf. 13x12½
Size: 26x38mm
C257 A575 13c multi   .65   .20
Size: 40x29mm
Perf. 13
C258 A575 30c multi   1.60   .40

Souvenir Sheet
Perf. 13½x13

C259 A575 50c multi   4.00 4.00

No. C259 contains one 32x40mm stamp.

Spartakiad Type of 1977
1977, Sept. 10   *Perf. 13*

C260 A576 13c Grenade-throwing   .60 .20

C261 A576 30c Rifle-shooting, horiz.   1.50 .40

10th Heroic Guerrilla's Day AP101

1977, Oct. 8   *Perf. 12½x13*

C262 AP101 13c Guerrilla fighters   1.00 .20

Airmail Service Type of 1977
1977, Oct. 27   *Perf. 12x12½*

C263 A577 13c Havana-Mexico cachet   .85 .20

C264 A577 30c Havana-Prague cachet   1.75 .35

Souvenir Sheet

Adoration of the Magi, by Rubens — AP102

1977, Nov. 18   *Perf. 13*

C265 AP102 50c multi   4.00 4.00

Ruben's 400th birth anniv.

Havana Zoo Type of 1977
1977, Nov. 24

C266 A579 13c Tiger   1.00 .20

C267 A579 30c Lion   1.40 .50

Revolution Martyrs Type of 1977
1977, Dec. 2   *Perf. 12½x12*

C268 A580 13c *Corynthia* landing   .75 .20

Pan American Health Organization (OPS), 75th Anniv. — AP103

1977, Dec. 2

C269 AP103 13c multi   .75 .20

Havana University Type of 1978
1978, Jan. 5   *Perf. 13x12½*

C270 A582 13c Crossed sabres, university   .75 .20

C271 A582 30c University, statue, crowd   1.10 .50

Portrait of Jose Marti (b. 1853), by A. Menocal AP104

1978, Jan. 28

C272 AP104 13c multi   .80 .20

Art Type of 1978
Paintings in the Nat. Museum of Art: 13c, *El Guadalquivir,* by M. Barron. 30c, *Portrait of H.E. Ridley,* by J.J. Masqueries, vert.

1978, Feb. 20   *Perf. 12½x12, 13*
Sizes: 42x27mm, 29x40mm

C273 A583 13c multi   1.00 .20

C274 A583 30c multi   1.10 .35

Bird Type of 1975
1978, Mar. 10   *Perf. 12½x12, 13*
Size: 42x27mm, 27x42mm

C275 A524 13c *Torreornis inexpectata,* horiz.   1.25 .50

C276 A524 30c *Ara tricolor*   1.75 1.10

Baragua Protest, Cent. — AP105

1978, Mar. 15   *Perf. 13x13½*

C277 AP105 13c *Antonio Maceo,* by A. Melero   .70 .20

Cosmonaut's Day Type of 1978
1978, Apr. 12   *Perf. 13*

C278 A585 13c *Venus 10*   .70 .20

Size: 36x46mm
Perf. 12½x13

C279 A585 30c *Lunokhod 2,* vert.   1.25 .50

SOCFILEX '78, Budapest — AP106

1978, May 7   *Perf. 13x12½*

C280 AP106 30c Parliament, Hungary No. 217   1.75 .55

Cactus Type of 1978
1978, May 15   *Perf. 13*

C281 A587 13c *Rhodocactus cubensis*   .90 .25

C282 A587 30c *Harrisia taetra*   1.50 .35

World Telecommunications Day — AP107

1978, May 17

C283 AP107 30c multi   1.25 .45

Organization of African Unity, 15th Anniv. — AP108

1978, May 25   *Perf. 13x12½*

C284 AP108 30c multi   1.00 .45

Souvenir Sheet

CAPEX '78, Toronto — AP109

1978, June 9   *Perf. 13x13½*

C285 AP109 50c *Niven, Wales,* by G.H. Russell   3.50 2.25

Aquarium Type of 1978
1978, June 15   *Perf. 13*

C286 A588 13c *Carassias auratus,* vert.   .80 .25

C287 A588 30c *Symphysodon aequifasciata axelrodi*   1.60 .50

MEDELLIN Games Type of 1978
1978, July 1

C288 A589 13c Volleyball   .60 .20

C289 A589 30c Running   1.25 .45

Attack on Moncada Type of 1978
1978, July 26

C290 A590 13c Soldiers bearing rifles   .45 .20

C291 A590 30c Stylized dove, banners   1.10 .35

Youth Festival Type of 1978
Natl. flags and views of host cities.

1978, July 28

C292 A591 13c Moscow, 1957   .70 .20

C293 A591 13c Vienna, 1959   .70 .20

C294 A591 13c Helsinki, 1962   .70 .20

C295 A591 13c Sofia, 1968   .70 .20

C296 A591 13c Berlin, 1973   .70 .20

     a.   Strip of 5, Nos. C292-C296   3.75 1.75

     Nos. C292-C296 (5)   3.50 1.00

Size: 46x36mm
Perf. 13x12½

C297 A591 30c Havana, 1978   1.50 .35

Tuna Industry Type of 1978
1978, Aug. 30   *Perf. 12½x12*

C298 A593 13c Stern trawler   .75 .20

C299 A593 30c Refrigerator ship   1.40 .60

Souvenir Sheet

PRAGA '78 — AP110

1978, Sept. 8   *Perf. 13*

C300 AP110 50c *Marina,* by A. Brandeis   3.75 .90

Art Type of 1978
Paintings by Amelia Pelaez del Casal (1896-1968).

1978, Sept. 15   *Perf. 12x12½, 13*

C301 A594 13c *Yellow Flowers,* vert.   .55 .20

C302 A594 30c *Still-life in Blue,* vert.   1.25 .45

Souvenir Sheet
Perf. 13½x13

C303 A594 50c *Portrait of Amelia,* by L. Romanach, vert. 4.00 .90

No. C303 contains one 32x40mm stamp.

Socialist Communication Organizations Congress (OSS), 20th Anniv. — AP111

1978, Sept. 25   *Perf. 13*

C304 AP111 30c multi   1.25 .25

Souvenir Sheet

EXFILNA '78, 6th Natl. Philatelic Exposition — AP112

1978, Oct. 10   *Imperf.*

C305 AP112 50c 1st Postal Card, issued in 1878 3.25 .90

No. C305 has simulated perfs.

Intl. Anti-Apartheid Year — AP113

1978, Oct. 16   *Perf. 12½*
C306 AP113 13c multi   .60 .20

Zoo Type of 1978

1978, Oct. 20   *Perf. 13*
C307 A595 13c *Acinonyx jubatos*   .80 .25
C308 A595 30c *Loxodonta africana*, vert.   1.75 .65

Natl. Ballet Type of 1978

1978, Oct. 28   *Perf. 12½x13*
C309 A596 13c *Giselle*, vert.   .85 .20
C310 A596 30c *Genesis*, vert.   1.60 .25

Pacific Flora Type of 1978

1978, Nov. 30   *Perf. 13*
C311 A597 13c multi, diff.   .80 .20
C312 A597 30c multi, diff.   1.60 .30

25th Death Anniv. of Julius and Ethel Rosenberg, American Communists Executed for Espionage — AP114

1978, Dec. 20
C313 AP114 13c multi   .60 .20

Julio A. Mella (d. 1929) AP115

1979, Jan. 10
C314 AP115 13c multi   .60 .20

Cosmonaut's Day Type of 1979
Souvenir Sheet

1979, Apr. 12   *Perf. 13½x13*
C315 A603 50c Orbital complex   3.75 .90
No. C315 contains one 32x40mm stamp.

Intl. Year of the Child — AP116

1979, June 1   *Perf. 13x12½*
C316 AP116 13c multi   1.00 .20

Art Type of 1979

1979, June 15   *Perf. 13½x13*
C317 A600 50c *Portrait of Victor Emmanuel Garcia*, by J. Arche, vert.   3.50 1.75
No. C317 contains one 32x40mm stamp.

CARIFESTA '79, Festival of Caribbean Peoples, Havana AP117

1979, July 16   *Perf. 12½x13*
C318 AP117 13c multi   .75 .20

10th World Universiade Games, Mexico City — AP118

1979, Sept. 1   *Perf. 13x12½*
C319 AP118 13c grn, pale grn & gold   .75 .20

6th Conference of Nonaligned Countries — AP119

1979, Sept. 3
C320 AP119 50c Convention Palace   1.75 .90

Sir Rowland Hill (d. 1879), Originator of Penny Postage — AP120

1979, Sept. 4   *Perf. 13½x13*
C321 AP120 30c Hill, casket   1.50 .25

SOCFILEX '79, Bucharest — AP121

Illustration reduced.

1979, Oct. 25   *Perf. 12½*
C322 AP121 30c Romania No. 683, flags   1.40 .40

Intl. Radio Consultative Committee (CCIR), 50th Anniv. — AP122

1979, Nov. 30   *Perf. 12½x12*
C323 AP122 30c Ground receiving station   1.25 .25

1st Soviet-Cuban Joint Space Flight — AP123

1980, Sept. 23   *Perf. 12½*
C324 AP123 13c multi   .50 .20
C325 AP123 30c multi   1.50 .35

Capt. Mariano Barberan, Lt. Joaquin Collar, and Their Airplane Cuatro Vientos. — AP124

1993, June 11   *Litho.*   *Perf. 13*
C326 AP124 30c multicolored   1.00 .45
1st Flight Seville-Camaguey, 60th anniv.

AIR POST SEMI-POSTAL STAMP

Catalogue values for unused stamps in this section are for Never Hinged items.

Farm Couple and Factory SPAP1

Engr. & Typo.
1959, May 7   **Wmk. 321**   *Perf. 12½*
CB1 SPAP1 12c + 3c car & grn   2.00 .50
Agricultural reforms. See No. C199.

AIR POST SPECIAL DELIVERY STAMP

Matanzas Issue

Matanzas Harbor APSD1

Wmk. 229
1936, May 5   **Photo.**   *Perf. 12½*
CE1 ASPD1 15c light blue   4.50 3.50
  Never hinged   7.00
Exists imperf. Value $5 unused, $2.50 used.

SPECIAL DELIVERY STAMPS

Issued under US Administration

US No. E5 Surcharged in Red

1899   **Wmk. 191**   *Perf. 12*
E1 SD3 10c on 10c blue   160.00 100.00
 a. No period after "CUBA"   575.00 400.00

Issues of the Republic under US Military Rule

Special Delivery Messenger SD2

Inscribed: "Immediata"
1899   **Wmk. U S-C (191C)**   **Engr.**
E2 SD2 10c orange   55.00 15.00

Issues of the Republic
Inscribed: "Inmediata"

1902   *Perf. 12*
E3 SD2 10c orange   3.00 1.00

J. B. Zayas SD3

1910   **Unwmk.**
E4 SD3 10c orange & blue   20.00 3.25
  Never hinged   30.00
 a. Center inverted   1,250.

Airplane and Morro Castle SD4

1914, Feb. 24   *Perf. 12*
E5 SD4 10c dark blue   15.00 1.25
Exists imperf. Value, pair $500.

1927   **Wmk. Star (106)**
E6 SD4 10c deep blue   12.00 .50
  Never hinged   18.00

1935   *Perf. 10*
E7 SD4 10c blue   12.00 .40
  Never hinged   15.00

Matanzas Issue

Mercury SD5

Wmk. Wavy Lines (229)
1936, May 5   **Photo.**   *Perf. 12½*
E8 SD5 10c deep claret   4.50 3.50
  Never hinged   7.00
Exists imperf. Value $6 unused, $2.50 used.

"Triumph of the Revolution" — SD6

1936, Nov. 18
E9 SD6 10c red orange 6.00 2.00
   Never hinged 8.00

Maj. Gen. Máximo Gómez (1836-1905).

Temple of
Quetzalcoatl
(Mexico)
SD7

Ruben Dario
(Nicaragua)
SD8

Wmk. 106
1937, Oct. 13 Engr. Perf. 10
E10 SD7 10c deep orange 6.25 6.25
E11 SD8 10c deep orange 6.25 6.25
   Set, never hinged 15.00

See note after No. 354.

Letter and Symbols of
Transportation — SD9

1945, Oct. 30
E12 SD9 10c olive brown 1.40 .25
   Never hinged 3.00

Catalogue values for unused
stamps in this section, from this
point to the end of the section, are
for Never Hinged items.

Governor's
Building,
Cárdenas
SD10

Engraved and Lithographed
1951, July 3 Wmk. 229 Perf. 13
E13 SD10 10c henna brn, ultra
   & red 7.00 1.25

Cent. of the adoption of Cuba's flag.

Chess Type of Regular Issue, 1951
1951, Nov. 1 Photo.
E14 A166 10c dk grn & rose
   brn 21.00 4.50

Type of Regular Issue
of 1951 Surcharged in
Red Violet

Wmk. 106
1952, Mar. 18 Engr. Perf. 10
E15 A159 10c on 2c yel brn 6.00 1.00

Arms and Bars
from National
Hymn — SD12

Roseate
Tern — SD13

1952, May 27 Perf. 12½
E16 SD12 10c dp org & bl 3.00 .75

Republic of Cuba founding, 50th anniv.

Type of Air Post Stamps of 1952
Inscribed: "Entrega Especial"
1952, Oct. 7 Perf. 10
E17 AP36 10c pale olive grn 4.50 1.50

Three-fourths of the proceeds from the sale
of No. E17 were used for the Communications
Ministry Employees' Retirement Fund.

1953, July 28
E18 SD13 10c blue 5.75 1.50

Gregorio
Hernandez
Saez
SD14

Felix Varela
SD15

1954, Feb. 23
E19 SD14 10c olive green 5.25 .90

1955, June 22 Perf. 12½
E20 SD15 10c brown car 3.00 .95

See note after No. E17.

Portrait Type of Regular Issue, 1956
Inscribed: "Entrega Especial"
Portrait: 10c, Jose Jacinto Milanes.

1956, May 2 Wmk. 106
E21 A198 10c dk car rose & blk 3.75 .75

See note after No. E17.

Painting Type of Regular Issue, 1957,
Inscribed: "Entrega Especial"
10c, "Yesterday" by E. Garcia Cabrera.

1957, Mar. 15 Engr. Perf. 12½
E22 A207 10c dk brn & turq bl 3.50 1.10

See note after No. E17.

View Type of Regular Issue, 1957,
Inscribed: "Entrega Especial."
10c, Independence square, Pino del Rio.

1957, Dec. 17
E23 A218 10c dk pur & brn 3.00 1.00

See note after No. E17.

View in
Havana
and
Messenger
SD16

1958, Jan. 10 Engr.
E24 SD16 10c blue 2.00 .75
E25 SD16 20c green 2.50 .75

See Nos. E28, E31.

Fish Type of Air Post Issue, 1958,
Inscribed "Entrega Especial."
Fish: 10c, Blackfish snapper. 20c,
Mosquitofish.

1958, Sept. 26 Wmk. 106 Perf. 12½
E26 AP86 10c blk, bl, pink &
         yel 6.00 2.50
E27 AP86 20c blk, ultra & pink 19.00 10.00

See note after No. C191.

Messenger Type of 1958
1960 Wmk. 321 Perf. 12½
E28 SD16 10c brt vio 3.50 .50

Plane Type of Air Post Issue, of 1931-
46, Surcharged in Black or Red:
"HABILITADO ENTREGA ESPECIAL
10¢"
1960 Wmk. 106 Perf. 10
E29 AP4 10c on 20c car rose 3.00 .50
E30 AP4 10c on 50c grnsh bl (R) 3.00 .50

Messenger Type of 1958
1961, June 28 Wmk. 321 Perf. 12½
E31 SD16 10c orange 3.50 .75

West Indies Packet Type of 1962
Perf. 12½
1962, Apr. 24 Litho. Unwmk.
E32 A253 10c buff, dull ultra &
        brn 5.00 1.75

POSTAGE DUE STAMPS

**Issued under Administration of the
United States**
Postage Due Stamps of the US Nos.
J38, J39, J41 and J42 Surcharged in
Black like Nos. 221-226A
1899 Wmk. 191 Perf. 12
J1 D2 1c on 1c dp claret 45.00 5.25
J2 D2 2c on 2c dp claret 45.00 5.25
  a. Inverted surcharge 4,000.
J3 D2 5c on 5c dp claret 45.00 5.25
J4 D2 10c on 10c dp claret 27.50 2.50
   Nos. J1-J4 (4) 162.50 18.25

Issues of the Republic

D1

1914 Unwmk. Engr. Perf. 12
J5 D1 1c carmine rose 6.50 1.00
J6 D1 2c carmine rose 8.00 1.00
J7 D1 5c carmine rose 12.00 2.00
   Nos. J5-J7 (3) 26.50 4.00

1927-28
J8 D1 1c rose red 3.50 .70
J9 D1 2c rose red 5.50 .70
J10 D1 5c rose red 6.50 1.00
   Nos. J8-J10 (3) 15.50 2.40

NEWSPAPER STAMPS

Issued under Spanish Dominion

N1 N2

1888 Unwmk. Typo. Perf. 14
P1 N1 ½m black .20 .25
P2 N1 1m black .20 .30
P3 N1 2m black .20 .30
P4 N1 3m black 1.50 1.00
P5 N1 4m black 1.90 2.00
P6 N1 8m black 7.25 8.50
   Nos. P1-P6 (6) 11.25 12.35

1890
P7 N2 ½m red brown .50 .65
P8 N2 1m red brown .50 .65
P9 N2 2m red brown .80 .95
P10 N2 3m red brown 1.00 1.10
P11 N2 4m red brown 7.50 5.50
P12 N2 8m red brown 7.50 5.50
   Nos. P7-P12 (6) 17.80 14.35

1892
P13 N2 ½m violet .20 .30
P14 N2 1m violet .20 .30
P15 N2 2m violet .20 .30
P16 N2 3m violet 1.00 .35
P17 N2 4m violet 3.75 1.90
P18 N2 8m violet 8.00 3.00
   Nos. P13-P18 (6) 13.35 6.15

1894
P19 N2 ½m rose .20 .30
  a. Imperf. pair 22.50
P20 N2 1m rose .45 .35
P21 N2 2m rose .50 .35
P22 N2 3m rose 1.90 1.40
P23 N2 4m rose 3.25 1.60
P24 N2 8m rose 5.50 4.00
   Nos. P19-P24 (6) 11.80 8.00

1896
P25 N2 ½m blue green .20 .30
P26 N2 1m blue green .20 .30
P27 N2 2m blue green .20 .30
P28 N2 3m blue green 2.50 1.50
P29 N2 4m blue green 5.25 7.00
P30 N2 8m blue green 9.50 10.00
   Nos. P25-P30 (6) 17.85 19.40

For surcharges see Nos. 190-193, 201-220.

POSTAL TAX STAMPS

Catalogue values for unused
stamps in this section are for
Never Hinged items.

Mother and
Child — PT1

Nurse with
Child — PT2

Wmk. Star. (106)
1938, Dec. 1 Engr. Perf. 10
RA1 PT1 1c bright green 1.25 .20

The tax benefited the National Council of
Tuberculosis fund for children's hospitals. Obligatory on all mail during December and January. This note applies also to Nos. RA2-RA4,
RA7-RA10, RA12-RA15, RA17-RA21.

1939, Dec. 1
RA2 PT2 1c orange vermilion .75 .20

"Health" Protecting
Children — PT3

1940, Dec. 1
RA3 PT3 1c deep blue .75 .20

Mother and
Child — PT4

Victory — PT5

1941, Dec. 1
RA4 PT4 1c olive bister .75 .20

1942-44
RA5 PT5 ½c orange .30 .20
RA6 PT5 ½c gray ('44) .45 .20

Issued: No. RA5, 7/1/42; No. RA6, 10/3/44.

Type of 1941 Overprinted "1942" in
Black

1942, Dec. 1
RA7 PT4 1c salmon .80 .25
  a. Inverted overprint 60.00 50.00

As
PT3 — PT6

As PT4 — PT7

1943, Dec. 1
RA8 PT6 1c brown .75 .20

1949, Dec. 9
RA9 PT7 1c blue .50 .20

Type of 1949 Inscribed: "1950"

1950, Dec. 1   **Engr.**
RA10 PT7 1c rose red .50 .20

Proposed Communications
Building
PT8   PT10

Woman Holding
Child
Aloft — PT9   Child — PT11

1951, June 5   Wmk. 106   Perf. 10
RA11 PT8 1c violet .75 .20

The tax was to help build a new Communications Building. This note applies also to Nos. RA16, RA34, RA43.

1951, Dec. 1
RA12 PT9 1c violet blue .45 .20
RA13 PT9 1c brown carmine .45 .20
RA14 PT9 1c olive bister .45 .20
RA15 PT9 1c deep green .45 .20
    Nos. RA12-RA15 (4) 1.80 .80

1952, Feb. 8
RA16 PT10 1c slate blue .30 .20
    See Nos. RA34, RA43.

1952, Dec. 1
RA17 PT11 1c rose carmine .75 .20
RA18 PT11 1c yellow green .75 .20
RA19 PT11 1c blue .75 .20
RA20 PT11 1c orange .75 .20
    Nos. RA17-RA20 (4) 3.00 .80

Hands
Reaching for
Lorraine
Cross
PT12

Child's Head,
Lorraine
Cross
PT13

1953, Dec. 1   **Perf. 9½**
RA21 PT12 1c rose carmine .50 .20

1954, Nov. 1   **Perf. 9½x10**
RA22 PT13 1c rose red .75 .20
RA23 PT13 1c violet .75 .20
RA24 PT13 1c bright blue .75 .20
RA25 PT13 1c emerald .75 .20
    Nos. RA22-RA25 (4) 3.00 .80

The tax benefited the Natl. Council of Tuberculosis fund for children's hospitals. Obligatory on all mail during Nov., Dec., Jan. & Feb. This note also applies to Nos. RA26-RA33, RA35-RA42.

Rose and
Watering Can
PT14

Child and
Protective
Hands
PT15

1955, Nov. 1
RA26 PT14 1c red orange .75 .20
RA27 PT14 1c red lilac .75 .20
RA28 PT14 1c bright blue .75 .20
RA29 PT14 1c orange yellow .75 .20
    Nos. RA26-RA29 (4) 3.00 .80

1956, Nov. 1
RA30 PT15 1c rose red .75 .20
RA31 PT15 1c yellow brown .75 .20
RA32 PT15 1c bright blue .75 .20
RA33 PT15 1c emerald .75 .20
    Nos. RA30-RA33 (4) 3.00 .80

Building Type of 1952

1957, Jan. 18   **Perf. 10**
RA34 PT10 1c rose red .30 .20

Mother and
Child by Silvia
Arrojo
Fernandez
PT16

National Council
of Tuberculosis
PT17

Wmk. 321
1957, Nov. 1   **Engr.**   **Perf. 10**
RA35 PT16 1c dull rose .70 .20
RA36 PT16 1c bright blue .70 .20
RA37 PT16 1c gray .70 .20
RA38 PT16 1c emerald .70 .20
    Nos. RA35-RA38 (4) 2.80 .80

1958
RA39 PT17 1c rose red .40 .20
RA40 PT17 1c red brown .40 .20
RA41 PT17 1c gray .40 .20
RA42 PT17 1c emerald .40 .20
    Nos. RA39-RA42 (4) 1.60 .80

Building Type of 1952

1958   **Wmk. 321**
RA43 PT10 1c rose red .30 .20

CYPRUS

'sī-prəs

LOCATION — An island in the Mediterranean Sea off the coast of Turkey
GOVT. — Republic
AREA — 3,572 sq. mi.
POP. — 754,064 (1999 est.)
CAPITAL — Nicosia

The British Crown Colony of Cyprus became a republic in 1960.
Turkey invaded Cyprus in 1974 resulting in the northern 40% of the island becoming the Turkish Republic of Northern Cyprus. No other country recognizes this division of the island.

See Turkey in Volume 6.
12 Pence = 1 Shilling
40 Paras = 1 Piaster
9 Piasters = 1 Shilling
20 Shillings = 1 Pound
1000 Milliemes = 1 Pound (1955)
100 Cents = 1 Cyprus Pound (1983)
100 Cents = 1 Euro (2008)

Catalogue values for unused stamps in this country are for Never Hinged items, beginning with Scott 156 in the regular postage section and Scott RA1 in the postal tax section.

Values for unused stamps are for examples with original gum as defined in the catalogue introduction. Very fine examples of Nos. 1, 2 and 7-10 will have perforations touching the design on at least one or more sides due to the narrow spacing of the stamps on the plates and to imperfect perforation methods. Stamps with perfs clear on all four sides are scarce and will command higher prices.

Watermark

Wmk. 344 — Map
of Cyprus and
KC/K Delta

Queen Victoria — A1

A2   A3

A4   A5

A6   A7

Various Watermarks as in Great Britain (#20, 23, 25, 27 & 29)

1880   **Typo.**   **Perf. 14**
1 A1 ½p rose (P 15) 125.00 110.00
    Plate 12 210.00 300.00
    Plate 19 5,750. 950.00
b.   Double overprint (P 15) 15,500.
2 A2 1p red (P 216) 19.00 45.00
    Plate 217 13.00 45.00
    Plate 174 1,400. 1,400.
    Plate 181 400.00 200.00
    Plate 184 14,500. 2,750.
    Plate 193 800.00
    Plate 196 700.00
    Plate 201 14.00 57.50
    Plate 205 65.00 57.50
    Plate 208 110.00 65.00
    Plate 215 13.00 57.50
    Plate 218 21.00 65.00
    Plate 220 550.00 475.00

b.   Double overprint (P 218) 5,400.
    Double overprint (P 208) 17,500.
c.   Pair, one without ovpt. (P 208) 22,000.
3 A3 2½p claret (P 14) 2.75 9.25
    Plate 15 4.00 27.50
4 A4 4p lt ol grn (P 16) 140.00 240.00
5 A5 6p ol gray (P 16) 575.00 750.00
6 A6 1sh green (P 13) 750.00 525.00

Black Surcharge
7 A7 30 paras on 1p red (P 216) 110.00 95.00
    Plate 201 140.00 100.00
    Plate 217 200.00 200.00
    Plate 220 175.00 190.00
b.   Dbl. surch., one invtd. (P 220) 1,500. 1,350.
    Dbl. surch., one invtd. (P 216) 4,250.

No. 2 Surcharged

18mm Long

1881
8 A2 ½p on 1p (205, 216) 80.00 100.00
    Plate 174 175.00 350.00
    Plate 181 175.00 200.00
    Plate 201 110.00 140.00
    Plate 205 80.00 100.00
    Plate 208 190.00 325.00
    Plate 215 750.00 800.00
    Plate 217 925.00 825.00
    Plate 218 525.00 640.00
    Plate 220 300.00 375.00

16mm Long

9 A2 ½p on 1p (P 201) 140.00 190.00
    Plate 216 400.00 450.00
    Plate 218 11,500.
a.   Double surcharge (P 201, 216) 3,200. 2,900.

13mm Long

10 A2 ½p on 1p red (P 215) 52.50 75.00
    Plate 205 290.00
    Plate 217 150.00 92.50
    Plate 218 80.00 110.00
c.   Double surcharge (P 215) 550.00 700.00
    Double surcharge (P 205) 800.00
e.   Triple surcharge (P 215) 800.00
    Triple surcharge (P 205) 4,000.
    Triple surcharge (P 217)
    Triple surcharge (P 218) 4,000.
h.   Quadruple surch. (P 205, 215) 5,000.
j.   "CYPRUS" double (P 218) 5,500.

A8

1881, July   **Typo.**   **Wmk. 1**
11 A8 ½pi emerald green 210.00 52.50
12 A8 1pi rose 425.00 37.50
13 A8 2pi ultramarine 525.00 37.50
14 A8 4pi olive green 1,050. 325.00
15 A8 6pi olive gray 1,750. 500.00

Postage and revenue stamps of Cyprus with "J.A.B." (the initials of Postmaster J.A. Bulmer) in manuscript, or with "POSTAL SURCHARGE" (with or without "J. A. B.") were not Postage Due stamps but were employed for accounting purposes between the chief PO at Larnaca and the sub-offices.
See Nos. 19-25, 28-37. For surcharges see Nos. 16-18, 26-27.

A9   A10

Black Surcharge

1882			Wmk. 1	
16	A9	½pi on ½pi grn	750.00	92.50
17	A10	30pa on 1pi rose	1,900.	140.00

1884			Wmk. 2	
18	A9	½pi on ½pi green	190.00	10.00
a.		Double surcharge		3,200.

See Nos. 26, 27.

1882-94   **Die B**

For description of Dies A and B see "Dies of British Colonial Stamps" in Table of Contents.

19	A8	½pi green	6.50	.85
20	A8	30pa violet	6.50	6.00
21	A8	1pi rose	14.50	2.40
22	A8	2pi blue	17.50	2.10
23	A8	4pi pale ol grn	27.50	29.00
24a	A8	6pi	210.00	675.00
25a	A8	12pi	160.00	400.00
		Nos. 19-25a (7)	442.50	1,115.

Die A

19a	A8	½pi	20.00	2.00
b.		½pi emerald	5,750.	475.00
20a	A8	30pa lilac	77.50	25.00
21a	A8	1pi	110.00	2.50
22a	A8	2pi	150.00	2.50
23a	A8	4pi	450.00	30.00
24	A8	6pi olive gray	60.00	21.00
25	A8	12pi brown org	225.00	45.00
		Nos. 19a-25 (7)	1,092.	128.00

A11

Type I — Figures "½" 8mm apart.
Type II — Figures "½" 6mm apart.
The space between the fraction bars varies from 5½ to 8½mm but is usually 6 or 8mm.

Black Surcharge Type I

1886			Wmk. 2	
26	A11	½pi on ½pi grn	400.00	15.00
a.		Type II	300.00	100.00
b.		Double surcharge, type II		

			Wmk. 1	
27	A11	½pi on ½pi grn	8,750.	500.00
a.		Type II	19,500.	

No. 27a probably is a proof.

1894-96			Wmk. 2	
28	A8	½pi grn & car rose	5.25	1.75
29	A8	30pa violet & green	3.00	2.00
30	A8	1pi rose & ultra	8.00	1.75
31	A8	2pi ultra & mar	8.25	1.75
32	A8	4pi ol green & vio	21.00	6.00
33	A8	6pi ol gray & grn	16.00	18.00
34	A8	9pi brown & rose	20.00	22.50
35	A8	12pi brn org & blk	22.50	70.00
36	A8	18pi slate & brown	60.00	60.00
37	A8	45pi dk vio & ultra	125.00	175.00
		Nos. 28-37 (10)	289.00	358.75

King Edward VII
A12

King George V
A13

1903			Typo.	
38	A12	½pi grn & car rose	5.00	1.40
39	A12	30pa violet & green	12.50	3.75
40	A12	1pi carmine rose & ultra	24.00	4.25
41	A12	2pi ultra & mar	70.00	12.50
42	A12	4pi ol green & vio	37.50	22.50
43	A12	6pi ol brown & grn	50.00	140.00
44	A12	9pi brn & car rose	125.00	225.00
45	A12	12pi org brn & blk	17.00	62.50
46	A12	18pi black & brown	100.00	175.00
47	A12	45pi dk vio & ultra	250.00	600.00
		Nos. 38-47 (10)	691.00	1,246.

1904-07			Wmk. 3	
48	A12	5pa bis & blk ('07)	1.25	.80
49	A12	10pa org & blk ('07)	4.00	.55
50	A12	½pi grn & car rose	5.75	.20
51	A12	30pa violet & green	18.00	1.75
52	A12	1pi car rose & ul- tra	7.25	1.10
53	A12	2pi ultra & maroon	9.00	2.00
54	A12	4pi ol grn & red vio	14.50	9.25
55	A12	6pi ol brn & green	20.00	17.00
56	A12	9pi brn & car rose	40.00	9.75
57	A12	12pi org brn & blk	32.50	45.00

58	A12	18pi black & brown	40.00	12.50
59	A12	45pi dk vio & ultra	95.00	175.00
		Nos. 48-59 (12)	287.25	274.90

1912				
61a	A13	10pa org yellow & green	2.75	1.60
62	A13	½pi grn & car rose	2.25	.25
63	A13	30pa violet & green	3.25	.80
64	A13	1pi car & ultra	5.00	2.25
65	A13	2pi ultra & ma- roon	8.50	2.50
66	A13	4pi ol grn & red vio	5.50	6.25
67	A13	6pi ol brn & green	4.50	11.00
68	A13	9pi brn & car rose	32.50	35.00
69	A13	12pi org brn & blk	20.00	47.50
70	A13	18pi black & brown	35.00	40.00
71	A13	45pi dl vio & ultra	100.00	160.00
		Nos. 61a-71 (11)	219.25	307.15

1921-23			Wmk. 4	
72	A13	10pa orange & grn	9.00	10.50
73	A13	10pa gray & yellow	16.00	9.50
74	A13	30pa violet & grn	3.25	.50
75	A13	30pa green	9.00	.50
76	A13	1pi rose & ultra	22.50	32.50
77	A13	1pi violet & car	4.00	5.00
78	A13	1½pi orange & blk	7.00	6.00
79	A13	2pi ultra & red vio	25.00	17.00
80	A13	2pi ultra & car	12.50	27.50
81	A13	2¾pi ultra & red vio	9.00	12.00
82	A13	4pi ol grn & red vio	16.00	22.50
83	A13	6pi ol brn & green	21.00	85.00
84	A13	9pi brn & carmine	32.50	90.00
85	A13	18pi black & brn	77.50	175.00
86	A13	45pi dl vio & ultra	225.00	325.00
		Nos. 72-86 (15)	489.25	818.50

			Wmk. 3	
87	A13	10sh grn & red, yel	425.00	875.00
88	A13	£1 vio & black, red	1,150.	2,100.

Years of issue: Nos. 73, 75, 77-78, 80-81, 87-88, 1923; others, 1921.

A14

1924-28			Chalky Paper	Wmk. 4	
89	A14	¼pi gray & brn org	1.10	.20
90	A14	½pi gray blk & blk	3.00	10.00
91	A14	½pi grn & dp grn ('25)	2.50	1.10
92	A14	¾pi grn & dp grn	2.50	1.10
93	A14	¾pi gray blk & blk ('25)	2.25	.20
94	A14	1pi brn vio & org brown	2.25	.80
95	A14	1½pi org & black	2.25	8.50
96	A14	1½pi carmine ('25)	2.90	.35
97	A14	2pi car & green	2.50	15.00
98	A14	2pi org & black ('25)	8.00	4.25
99	A14	2½pi ultra ('25)	3.50	.35
100	A14	2¾pi ultra & dull vio	3.75	3.50
101	A14	4pi ap grn & vio	3.75	3.75
102	A14	4½pi black & yel, emer	4.00	4.00
103	A14	6pi grn ol & grn	4.25	6.25
104	A14	9pi brn & dk vio	7.00	5.00
105	A14	12pi org brn & blk	10.50	62.50
106	A14	18pi blk & org	22.50	5.75
		Revenue cancel		1.00
107	A14	45pi gray vio & ultra	42.50	42.50
		Revenue cancel		1.50
108	A14	90pi grn & red, yel	100.00	200.00
		Revenue cancel		3.00

109	A14	£5 blk, yel ('28)	3,200.	7,000.
		Revenue cancel		175.00

			Wmk. 3	
110	A14	£1 vio & black, red	350.00	800.00
		Revenue cancel		10.00
		Nos. 89-108 (20)	231.00	375.10

Nos. 96 and 99 are on ordinary paper.

Silver Coin of Amathus — A15

Philosopher Zeno — A16

Map of Cyprus — A17

Discovery of Body of St. Barnabas — A18

Cloisters of Bella Paise Monastery — A19

Badge of the Colony — A20

Hospice of Umm Haram at Larnaca — A21

Statue of Richard Coeur de Lion, London — A22

St. Nicholas Cathedral, Famagusta — A23

King George V — A24

Perf. 12

1928, Feb. 1			Engr.	Wmk. 4	
114	A15	¾pi dark violet	3.50	1.25
115	A16	1pi Prus bl & blk	4.00	2.00
116	A17	1½pi red	6.00	2.50
117	A18	2½pi ultramarine	4.75	2.75
118	A19	4pi dp red brown	7.50	8.00
119	A20	6pi dark blue	10.00	27.50
120	A21	9pi violet brown	10.00	14.00
121	A22	18pi dk brn & blk	25.00	25.00
122	A23	45pi dp blue & vio	52.50	62.50

123	A24	£1 ol brn & deep blue	275.00	400.00
		Nos. 114-123 (10)	398.25	545.50

50th year of Cyprus as a British colony.

Ruins of Vouni Palace — A25

Columns at Salamis — A26

Peristerona Church — A27

Soli Theater — A28

Kyrenia Castle and Harbor — A29

Kolossi Castle — A30

St. Sophia Cathedral — A31

Bairakdar Mosque — A32

Queen's Window, St. Hilarion Castle — A33

Buyuk Khan, Nicosia — A34

Forest Scene — A35

1934, Dec. 1   Engr.   Perf. 12½
125	A25	¼pi yel brn & ultra	1.25	.65
		Never hinged	1.75	
a.		Vert. pair, imperf. between	26,500.	18,500.
126	A26	½pi green	1.90	1.25
		Never hinged	2.00	
a.		Vert. pair, imperf. between	12,750.	14,000.
127	A27	¾pi violet & blk	2.25	.25
		Never hinged	3.25	
a.		Vert. pair, imperf. between	29,000.	
128	A28	1pi brown & blk	1.60	1.10
		Never hinged	2.75	
a.		Vert. pair, imperf. between	15,000.	15,000.
b.		Horiz. pair, imperf. btwn.	11,750.	
129	A29	1½pi rose red	3.25	.70
		Never hinged	4.75	
130	A30	2½pi dark ultra	3.25	2.40
		Never hinged	5.00	
131	A31	4½pi dk car & blk	4.00	5.00
		Never hinged	11.00	
132	A32	6pi blue & black	11.50	16.00
		Never hinged	24.00	
133	A33	9pi dl vio & blk brown	10.50	6.50
		Never hinged	21.00	
134	A34	18pi ol grn & black	52.50	37.50
		Never hinged	110.00	
135	A35	45pi blk & emer	87.50	67.50
		Never hinged	175.00	
		Nos. 125-135 (11)	179.50	138.85

Common Design Types pictured following the introduction.

Silver Jubilee Issue
Common Design Type
1935, May 6   Perf. 11x12
136	CD301	¾pi gray blk & ultra	2.25	.50
137	CD301	1½pi car & dk bl	5.25	3.50
138	CD301	2½pi ultra & brn	4.75	2.00
139	CD301	9pi brn vio & ind	19.00	21.00
		Nos. 136-139 (4)	31.25	27.00
		Set, never hinged	50.00	

Coronation Issue
Common Design Type
1937, May 12   Perf. 11x11½
140	CD302	¾pi dark gray	.35	.20
141	CD302	1½pi dark carmine	.60	.85
142	CD302	2½pi deep ultra	1.25	1.40
		Nos. 140-142 (3)	2.20	2.45
		Set, never hinged	4.75	

Ruins of Vouni Palace — A36

Columns at Salamis — A37

Peristerona Church — A38

Soli Theater — A39

Kyrenia Castle and Harbor — A40

Kolossi Castle — A41

Map of Cyprus — A42

Bairakdar Mosque — A43

Citadel, Famagusta — A44

Buyuk Khan — A45

Forest Scene A46   King George VI A47

1938-44   Wmk. 4   Perf. 12½
143	A36	¼pi yel brn & ultra	.20	.20
144	A37	½pi green	.40	.20
145	A38	¾pi violet & blk	9.00	.65
146	A39	1pi orange	.50	.20
a.		Perf. 13½x12½ ('44)	350.00	30.00
		Never hinged	460.00	
147	A40	1½pi rose car	3.25	1.90
147A	A40	1½pi lt vio ('43)	.35	.35
147B	A38	2pi carmine & blk ('42)	.45	.20
c.		Perf. 12½x13½ ('44)	2.00	7.50
148	A41	2½pi ultramarine	13.00	4.25
148A	A41	3pi dp ultra ('42)	1.00	.20
149	A42	4½pi gray	.45	.20
150	A43	6pi blue & black	.80	1.25
151	A44	9pi dk vio & blk	1.25	.20
152	A45	18pi ol grn & blk	2.50	1.10
153	A46	45pi blk & emer	11.50	3.25

154	A47	90pi blk & brt vio	21.00	6.50
155	A47	£1 ind & dl red	45.00	30.00
		Nos. 143-155 (16)	110.65	50.65
		Set, never hinged	225.00	

See Nos. 164-166.

Catalogue values for unused stamps in this section, from this point to the end of the section, are for Never Hinged items.

Peace Issue
Common Design Type
1946, Oct. 21   Engr.   Perf. 13½x14
156	CD303	1½pi purple	.20	.20
157	CD303	3pi deep blue	.20	.20

Silver Wedding Issue
Common Design Types
1948, Dec. 20   Photo.   Perf. 14x14½
| 158 | CD304 | 1½pi purple | .70 | .20 |

Engr.; Name Typo.   Perf. 11½x11
| 159 | CD305 | £1 dark blue | 55.00 | 70.00 |

UPU Issue
Common Design Types
Perf. 13½, 11x11½
1949, Oct. 10   Engr.   Wmk. 4
160	CD306	1½pi violet	.45	.75
161	CD307	2pi deep carmine	1.75	1.75
162	CD308	3pi indigo	.80	1.70
163	CD309	9pi rose violet	2.00	2.00
		Nos. 160-163 (4)	5.00	5.60

Types of 1938-43
1951, July 2   Engr.   Perf. 12½
164	A37	½pi purple	3.00	.20
165	A40	1½pi deep green	4.00	.65
166	A41	4pi deep ultra	4.25	.30
		Nos. 164-166 (3)	11.25	1.15

Coronation Issue
Common Design Type
1953, June 2   Perf. 13½x13
| 167 | CD312 | 1½pi brt grn & black | 1.40 | .40 |

Carobs A48   Copper Pyrites Mine A49

St. Hilarion Castle A50

Queen Elizabeth II and Cyprian Coin Devices — A51

Designs: 3m, Grapes. 5m, Oranges. 15m, Troodos forest. 20m, Aphrodite beach. 25m, Coin of Paphos. 30m, Kyrenia. 35m, Harvest in Mesaoria. 40m, Famagusta harbor. 100m, Hala Sultan Tekke. 250m, Kanakaria church. £1, Queen Elizabeth II and devices of Byzantium, Lusignan, Ottoman Empire and Venice.

Perf. 11½
1955, Aug. 1   Engr.   Wmk. 4
168	A48	2m chocolate	.20	.50
169	A48	3m violet blue	.20	.20
170	A48	5m orange	1.00	.20
171	A49	10m gray grn & chocolate	1.25	.20
172	A49	15m indigo & olive	3.00	.50
173	A49	20m ultra & brown	1.00	.20
174	A49	25m aquamarine	2.50	.70
175	A49	30m carmine & blk	1.00	.20
176	A49	35m aqua & orange	.75	.50
177	A49	40m choc & dk grn	1.00	.75

Perf. 13½
178	A50	50m red brn & aqua	1.10	.25
179	A50	100m bl green & mag	12.50	.60
180	A50	250m vio brn & dk blue gray	10.50	7.50

Perf. 11x11½
181	A51	500m lilac rose & grnsh gray	27.50	10.00
182	A51	£1 grnsh gray & brn red	24.00	35.00
		Revenue cancel		1.00
		Nos. 168-182 (15)	88.50	57.35

Republic

Nos. 168-182 Overprinted in Dark Blue

1960, Aug. 16   Ovpt. 10x6½mm
183	A48	2m chocolate	.20	.20
184	A48	3m violet blue	.20	.20
185	A48	5m orange	.20	.20

Overprint 12½x11mm
186	A49	10m gray grn & choc	.25	.20
187	A49	15m indigo & ol	.45	.20
188	A49	20m ultra & brn	.50	.20
a.		Double overprint		8,500.
189	A49	25m aquamarine	.60	.35
190	A49	30m car & black	.75	.30
a.		Double overprint		13,500.
191	A49	35m aqua & org	1.00	.45
192	A49	40m choc & dk grn	1.10	.65

2-line overprint 2½mm apart
193	A50	50m red brown & aqua	1.25	.75
194	A50	100m bl grn & mag	3.00	2.00
195	A50	250m vio brn & dk blue gray	10.50	6.00

2-line overprint 22mm apart
196	A51	500m lil rose & grnsh gray	47.50	19.00
197	A51	£1 grnsh gray & brn red	87.50	47.50
		Nos. 183-197 (15)	155.00	78.20

The overprint, in Greek and Turkish, reads "Republic of Cyprus."

Map of Cyprus — A52

Wmk. 314
1960, Aug. 16   Engr.   Perf. 11½
198	A52	10m brown & green	.25	.20
199	A52	30m blue & brown	1.00	.70
200	A52	100m purple & black	2.75	2.25
		Nos. 198-200 (3)	4.00	3.15

Independence of Republic of Cyprus.

Europa Issue, 1961

Nineteen Doves Flying as One CD4

Perf. 14x13½
1962, Mar. 19   Litho.   Unwmk.
201	CD4	10m lilac	.30	.20
202	CD4	40m deep ultra	.90	.35
203	CD4	100m emerald	.90	.60
		Nos. 201-203 (3)	2.10	1.15

Admission of Cyprus to Council of Europe.

Malaria Eradication Emblem A54

1962, May 14   Perf. 14x13½
204	A54	10m gray green & blue	.25	.20
205	A54	30m red brown & black	.50	.50

WHO drive to eradicate malaria.

Iron Age Jug — A55

St. Barnabas Church, Salamis A56

Designs: 5m, Grapes. 10m, Head of Apollo. 15m, St. Sophia Church, Nicosia. 30m, Temple of Apollo. 35m, Head of Aphrodite. 40m, Skiing on Mt. Troodos. 50m, Ruins of Gymnasium, Salamis. 100m, Hala Sultan Tekke (sheep, Salt Lake Larnaca and tomb). 250m, Bella Paise Monastery. 500m, Cyprus mouflon. £1, St. Hilarion Castle.

Perf. 13½x14, 14x13½

1962, Sept. 17			**Wmk. 344**	
206	A55	3m dk brn & sal	.20	.30
207	A55	5m dull green & red lilac	.20	.20
208	A55	10m dk slate grn & yel green	.20	.20
209	A55	15m dk brn & rose vio	.40	.20
210	A56	25m salmon & brn	.45	.20
211	A56	30m lt bl & dk bl	.25	.20
212	A55	35m dk bl & pale grn	.45	.20
213	A56	40m vio bl & dk bl	1.50	1.75
214	A56	50m olive bis & dk grn	.60	.20
215	A55	100m brn & yel brn	4.25	.30
216	A56	250m tan & black	11.00	2.40
217	A55	500m brown & olive	21.00	9.00
218	A56	£1 gray & green	22.50	30.00
		Nos. 206-218 (13)	63.00	45.15

Wmk. 344 is found in two positions: normal or inverted on vertical stamps, and reading up or down on horizontal stamps.

For overprints see Nos. 232-236, 265-268.
For surcharge see No. 273.

Europa Issue, 1962
Common Design Type
Perf. 14x13½

1963, Jan. 28		**Wmk. 344**		
		Size: 36x20mm		
219	CD5	10m ultra & black	2.50	.20
220	CD5	40m red & black	10.00	1.40
221	CD5	150m green & black	37.50	2.75
		Nos. 219-221 (3)	50.00	4.35

Cypriot Farm Girl — A57

Cub Scout and Tents — A58

75m, Statue of Demeter, goddess of agriculture.

1963, Mar. 21		**Perf. 13½x14**		
222	A57	25m blk, ultra & ocher	.60	.45
223	A57	75m dk car, gray & blk	3.50	1.75

FAO "Freedom from Hunger" campaign.

1963, Aug. 21		**Wmk. 344**		

20m, Sea Scout. 150m, Boy Scout & mouflon.

224	A58	3m multicolored	.20	.20
225	A58	20m multicolored	.40	.25
226	A58	150m multicolored	2.00	2.50
a.		Souvenir sheet of 3	150.00	150.00
		Nos. 224-226 (3)	2.60	2.95

Boy Scout movement in Cyprus, 50th anniv. #226a contains 3 imperf. stamps similar to #224-226 with simulated perforations. Sold for 250m.

Red Cross Nurse — A59

Children's Home, Kyrenia A60

Perf. 13½x14, 14x13½

1963, Sept. 9		**Litho.**	**Wmk. 344**	
227	A59	10m multicolored	1.00	.70
228	A60	100m multicolored	4.00	4.00

Intl. Red Cross, cent.

Europa Issue, 1963

Stylized Links, Symbolizing Unity — CD6

1963, Nov. 4		**Perf. 14x13½**		
229	CD6	20m multicolored	4.75	.70
230	CD6	30m multicolored	5.25	.70
231	CD6	150m multicolored	35.00	3.75
		Nos. 229-231 (3)	45.00	5.15

Nos. 208, 211, 213-215 Overprinted in Ultramarine

1964, May 5		**Perf. 13½x14, 14x13½**		
232	A55	10m dk sl grn & yel grn	.20	.20
233	A55	30m lt blue & dk blue	.25	.20
234	A55	40m vio bl & dull bl	.35	.30
235	A55	50m ol bis & dk grn	.45	.35
236	A55	100m brn & yel brown	.75	.75
		Nos. 232-236 (5)	2.00	1.80

Decision by the UN and its Security Council to help restore the country to normality and to seek a solution of its problems.

Clay Mask and Soli Theater A62

Designs: 35m, Curium theater. 50m, Salamis theater. 100m, Performance of "Othello" in front of Othello Tower.

1964, June 15		**Perf. 13½x14**		
237	A62	15m multicolored	.40	.20
238	A62	35m multicolored	.40	.25
239	A62	50m multicolored	.40	.25
240	A62	100m multicolored	1.60	1.90
		Nos. 237-240 (4)	2.80	2.60

400th anniversary of Shakespeare's birth.

Boxers A63

14th century B.C. art: 10m, Runners, vert. 75m, Chariot.

1964, July 6		**Perf. 13½x14, 14x13½**		
241	A63	10m brn, bis & blk	.20	.20
242	A63	25m gray bl, bl & brn	.30	.25
243	A63	75m brick red, blk & brn	.75	.80
a.		Souvenir sheet of 3	10.00	13.50
		Nos. 241-243 (3)	1.25	1.25

18th Olympic Games, Tokyo, Oct. 10-25, 1964. No. 243a contains three imperf. stamps similar to Nos. 241-243 with gray marginal inscription. Sheet sold for 250m; the difference between face value and selling price went for the promotion of classical athletics in Cyprus.

Symbolic Daisy CD7

Satyr Drinking Wine, 5th Century B.C. Statuette A65

Modern Winery A66

Europa Issue, 1964
Perf. 13½x14

1964, Sept. 14		**Litho.**	**Wmk. 344**	
244	CD7	20m bis brn & red brn	2.50	.35
245	CD7	30m lt blue & dk blue	3.25	.35
246	CD7	30m grn & ol grn	30.00	2.75
		Nos. 244-246 (3)	35.75	3.45

CEPT, 5th anniv. The 22 petals of the flower symbolize the 22 members of the organization.

Perf. 14x13½, 13½x14

1964, Oct. 26			**Wmk. 344**	

Cypriot Wine Industry: 10m, Dionysus and Acme drinking wine, 3rd century mosaic. 50m, Commandaria wine, Knight Templar and Kolossi Castle.

247	A66	10m multicolored	.50	.20
248	A65	40m multicolored	.95	1.25
249	A65	50m multicolored	.95	.30
250	A66	100m multicolored	2.50	2.00
		Nos. 247-250 (4)	4.90	3.75

Pres. John F. Kennedy (1917-1963) — A67

1965, Feb. 15		**Litho.**	**Wmk. 344**	
251	A67	10m violet blue	.20	.20
252	A67	40m green	.50	.45
253	A67	100m rose claret	.65	.45
a.		Souvenir sheet of 3	4.75	6.75
		Nos. 251-253 (3)	1.35	1.10

No. 253a contains 3 imperf. stamps similar to Nos. 251-253 with simulated perforations. Sold for 250m, 100m going to charitable organizations in Cyprus.

Old Couple — A68

Mother and Children by A. Diamantis — A69

45m, Man with broken leg (accident insurance).

1965, Apr. 12		**Perf. 13½x14**		
254	A68	30m dull green & tan	.30	.20
255	A68	45m dk vio bl, bl & gray	.50	.30

Perf. 13½x12½

256	A69	75m buff & red brown	1.50	2.00
		Nos. 254-256 (3)	2.30	2.50

Introduction of Social Insurance Law.

ITU Emblem, Old and New Communication Equipment — A70

1965, May 17		**Litho.**	**Perf. 14x13½**	
257	A70	15m brn, yel & black	.75	.25
258	A70	60m grn, lt grn & black	8.50	3.25
259	A70	75m dk & lt bl & black	9.75	4.50
		Nos. 257-259 (3)	19.00	8.00

ITU, cent.

ICY Emblem A71

1965, May 17			**Wmk. 344**	
260	A71	50m multicolored	1.25	.20
261	A71	100m multicolored	2.00	.90

International Cooperation Year.

Europa Issue, 1965

Leaves and Fruit CD8

Perf. 14x13½

1965, Sept. 27		**Litho.**	**Wmk. 344**	
262	CD8	5m org, org brn & black	1.10	.25
263	CD8	45m lt grn, org brn & black	5.25	.80
264	CD8	150m gray, org brn & black	19.00	2.75
		Nos. 262-264 (3)	25.35	3.80

Nos. 206, 208, 211 and 216 Overprinted in Dark Blue

1966, Jan. 31		**Perf. 13½x14, 14x13½**		
265	A55	3m dk brn & salmon	.25	.30
266	A55	10m dk sl grn & yel green	.25	.20

267 A56 30m lt bl & dk blue   .25   .20
268 A56 250m tan & black   1.00 2.40
        Nos. 265-268 (4)   1.75 3.10

UN General Assembly's resolution to mediate the dispute between Greeks and Turks on Cyprus, Dec. 18, 1965.

St. Barnabas,
Ancient
Icon — A73

Chapel
over
Tomb of
St.
Barnabas
A74

Bishop Anthemios of Constantine
Dreaming of St. Barnabas, Discovering
Tomb, etc. — A75

Design: 15m, Discovery of body of St. Barnabas (scene as in type A18).

Perf. 13x14, 14x13
1966, Apr. 25   Litho.   Wmk. 344
269 A73 15m multicolored   .20   .20
270 A74 25m multicolored   .20   .20
271 A73 100m multicolored   .90 1.75

Size: 110x91mm
Imperf
272 A75 250m multicolored   6.50 12.00
        Nos. 269-272 (4)   7.80 14.15

1900th anniv. of the death of St. Barnabas.

No. 206 Surcharged with New Value
and Three Bars

Perf. 13½x14
1966, May 30   Litho.   Wmk. 344
273 A55 5m on 3m dk brn & sal   .40 .25

Gen. K. S.
Thimayya
A76

1966, June 6   Perf. 14x13½
274 A76 50m tan & black   .40 .25

In memory of Gen. Kodendera Subayya Thimayya (1906-1965), commander of the UN Peace-keeping Force on Cyprus.

Europa Issue, 1966

Symbolic
Sailboat — CD9

Perf. 13½x14
1966, Sept. 26   Litho.   Wmk. 344
275 CD9 20m multicolored   .50   .20
276 CD9 30m multicolored   .50   .25
277 CD9 150m multicolored   3.75 1.40
        Nos. 275-277 (3)   4.75 1.85

Stavrovouni
Monastery
A78

St. Nicholas
Cathedral,
Famagusta
A79

Ingot Bearer,
Bronze Age — A80

Designs: 5m, St. James' Church, Tricomo, vert. 10m, Zeno of Citium, marble bust, vert. 15m, Ship from 7th cent. BC vase, horiz. 20m, Silver coin, 4th cent. BC (head of Hercules with lion skin). 25m, Sleeping Eros (1st cent. marble statue; horiz.). 35m, Hawks on 11th cent. gold and enamel scepter from Curium. 40m, Marriage of David (7th cent. silver disc). 50m, Silver coin of Alexander the Great showing Hercules and Zeus, horiz. 100m, Bird catching fish on 7th cent. BC jug. 500m, The Rape of Ganymede (3rd cent. mosaic). £1, Aphrodite (1st cent. marble statue).

Perf. 12x12½, 12½x12
1966, Nov. 21   Litho.   Wmk. 344
278 A78 3m bl, dl yel, grn &
             black   .60   .20
279 A78 5m dk bl, ol & blk   .20   .20
280 A78 10m olive & black   .25   .20

Perf. 14x13½, 13½x14
281 A79 15m org brn, blk &
             red brn   .25   .20
282 A79 20m red brn & blk   1.75 1.40
283 A79 25m red brn, gray &
             black   .55   .20
284 A79 30m aqua, tan & blk   .75   .30
285 A79 35m dk car, yel &
             blk   .75   .45
286 A79 40m brt bl, gray &
             blk   1.00   .45
287 A79 50m org brn, gray &
             blk   1.50   .20
288 A79 100m gray, buff, blk &
             red   5.00   .20

Perf. 13x14
289 A80 250m dull yel, grn &
             blk   1.50   .50
290 A80 500m multicolored   3.50 1.00
291 A80 £1 gray, lt gray &
             black   3.00 7.00
        Nos. 278-291 (14)   20.60 12.50

Electric Power
Station,
Limassol — A81

Arghaka-Maghounda Dam — A82

Designs: 35m, Troodos Highway. 50m, Cyprus Hilton Hotel. 100m, Ships in Famagusta Harbor.

Perf. 14x13½, 13½x14
1967, Apr. 10   Litho.   Wmk. 344
292 A81 10m lt brn, dark brn &
             yellow   .20   .20
293 A82 15m lt bl, bl & grn   .25   .25
294 A82 35m dark gray, indigo
             & dark grn   .35   .35
295 A82 50m gray, olive & blue .35   .35
296 A82 100m gray, ind & bl   .35   .35
        Nos. 292-296 (5)   1.50 1.50

1st development program, 1962-66, completion.

Europa Issue, 1967
Common Design Type

1967, May 2   Perf. 13x14
Size: 21x37mm
297 CD10 20m yel grn & ol-
              ive   .50   .20
298 CD10 30m rose vio & pur   .50   .25
299 CD10 150m pale brn &
              brn   3.25 1.25
        Nos. 297-299 (3)   4.25 1.70

Javelin Thrower, Map of Eastern
Mediterranean and "Victory" — A83

Map of Eastern Mediterranean, Victory Statue and: 35m, Runner. 100m, High jumper. 250m, Amphora, map of Eastern Mediterranean and Victory statue.

Perf. 13½x13
1967, Sept. 4   Litho.   Wmk. 344
300 A83 15m multicolored   .20   .20
301 A83 35m multicolored   .35   .30
302 A83 100m multicolored   .75   .75

Size: 97x77mm
Imperf
303 A83 250m multicolored   3.50 6.50
        Nos. 300-303 (4)   4.80 7.75

Cyprus-Crete-Salonika Athletic Games.

Marble Forum at Salamis, Church of
St. Barnabas and Bellapais Abbey
A84

ITY Emblem and: 40m, Famagusta Beach. 50m, Plane and Nicosia International Airport. 100m, Youth Hostel and skiing on Mt. Troodos.

Perf. 13½x13
1967, Oct. 16   Litho.   Wmk. 344
304 A84 10m multicolored   .20   .20
305 A84 40m multicolored   .20 1.00
306 A84 50m multicolored   .30   .20
307 A84 100m multicolored   .50 1.00
        Nos. 304-307 (4)   1.20 2.40

Intl. Tourist Year, 1967.

St. Andrew, 6th
Century
Mosaic — A85

Crucifixion, 15th
Century — A86

The Three Kings,
15th Century
Fresco — A87

1967, Nov. 8   Perf. 13x13½
308 A85 25m multicolored   .20   .20
309 A86 50m multicolored   .20   .20
310 A87 75m multicolored   .20   .20
        Nos. 308-310 (3)   .60   .60

St. Andrew's Monastery, cent. (25m); Exhibition of Art of Cyprus, Paris, Nov. 7, 1967-Jan. 3, 1968 (50m); 20th anniv. of UNESCO (75m).

Human Rights
Flame and
Stars — A88

Designs: 90m, Human Rights flame and UN emblem. 250m, Scroll showing Article One of the Declaration of Human Rights.

Perf. 13½x14
1968, Mar. 18   Litho.   Wmk. 344
311 A88 50m multicolored   .20   .20
312 A88 90m multicolored   .40   .60

Size: 110x90mm
Imperf
313 A88 250m multicolored   1.40 4.50
        Nos. 311-313 (3)   2.00 5.30

Intl. Human Rights Year.

Europa Issue, 1968
Common Design Type

1968, Apr. 29   Perf. 14x13½
314 CD11 20m multicolored   .40   .25
315 CD11 30m dk car rose,
              gray brn & blk   .50   .25
316 CD11 150m multicolored   2.00 1.25
        Nos. 314-316 (3)   2.90 1.75

Boy
Holding
Milk,
UNICEF
Emblem
A89

Aesculapius and
WHO
Emblem — A90

Perf. 14x13½, 13½x14
1968, Sept. 2   Wmk. 344
317 A89 35m dk red, lt brn & blk .20 .20
318 A90 50m gray ol, blk & grn   .20 .20

21st anniv. of UNICEF (No. 317), 20th anniv. of the WHO (No. 318).

Discus
Thrower — A91

ILO
Emblem — A92

25m, Runners. 100m, Stadium, Mexico City.

Perf. 13½x14, 14x13½

1968, Oct. 24		**Litho.**	
319	A91	10m multicolored	.20	.20
320	A91	25m vio blue & multi	.20	.20
321	A91	100m blue & multi, horiz.	.30	1.00
		Nos. 319-321 (3)	.70	1.40

19th Olympic Games, Mexico City, 10/12-27.

Perf. 12x13½

1969, Mar. 3		**Wmk. 344**	
322	A92	50m bl, vio bl & org brn	.20	.20
323	A92	90m gray, blk & org brn	.25	.25

ILO, 50th anniv.

Ancient
Map of
Cyprus
A93

Design: 50m, Medieval map of Cyprus.

Perf. 13½x13

1969, Apr. 7		**Wmk. 344**	
324	A93	35m multicolored	.25	.25
325	A93	50m olive & multi	.25	.25

1st Intl. Congress of Cypriot Studies.

Europa Issue, 1969

"EUROPA"
and "CEPT"
CD12

1969, Apr. 28	**Litho.**	**Perf. 14x13½**	
326	CD12	20m bl, blk & gray	.55	.20
327	CD12	30m cop red, blk & ocher	.55	.20
328	CD12	150m grn, blk & yel	1.90	.85
		Nos. 326-328 (3)	3.00	1.25

CEPT, 10th anniv.

European
Roller — A95

Birds: 15m, Audouin's gull. 20m, Cyprus warbler. 30m, Eurasian jay, vert. 40m, Hoopoe, vert. 90m, Eleonora's falcon, vert.

Perf. 13½x13½12, 12x13½

1969, July 7		**Wmk. 344**	
329	A95	5m multicolored	.55	.20
330	A95	15m multicolored	.75	.20
331	A95	20m multicolored	.75	.20
332	A95	30m multicolored	.80	.25
333	A95	40m multicolored	.95	.30
334	A95	90m multicolored	2.10	4.50
		Nos. 329-334 (6)	5.90	5.65

Nativity,
Mural,
1192
A96

Christmas: 45m, Nativity, mural in Church of Ayios Nicolaos tis Steghis, 14th century. 250m, Virgin and Child between Archangels Michael and Gabriel, mosaic in Church of Panayia Angeloktistos, 6th-7th centuries. Design of 20m is a mural in Church of Panayia tou Arakos, Lagoudhera.

1969, Nov. 24	**Litho.**	**Perf. 13½x13**	
335	A96	20m multicolored	.20	.20
336	A96	45m multicolored	.30	.25

Size: 109x89mm

Imperf

337	A96	250m dk blue & multi	5.00	10.00
		Nos. 335-337 (3)	5.50	10.45

Mahatma
Gandhi
A97

1970, Jan. 26		**Perf. 14x13½**	
338	A97	25m multicolored	.25	.25
339	A97	75m multicolored	.25	.25

Birth cent. of Mohandas K. Gandhi (1869-1948), leader in India's struggle for independence.

Europa Issue, 1970

Interwoven
Threads
CD13

1970, May 4	**Litho.**	**Wmk. 344**	
340	CD13	20m brn, yel & org	.40	.25
341	CD13	30m brt bl, yel & org	.40	.25
342	CD13	150m brt rose lil, yel & orange	1.90	1.40
		Nos. 340-342 (3)	2.70	1.90

Landscape with
Flowers — A99

Designs: Various landscapes with flowers.

Perf. 13x14

1970, Aug. 3	**Litho.**	**Wmk. 344**	
343	A99	10m multicolored	.20	.20
344	A99	50m multicolored	.20	.20
345	A99	90m multicolored	.85	1.10
		Nos. 343-345 (3)	1.25	1.50

European Nature Conservation Year.

Education Year
Emblem — A100

Grapes and
Partridge
(Mosaic)
A101

UN
Emblem,
Dove,
Globe and
Wheat
A102

Perf. 13x14, 14x13

1970, Sept. 7	**Litho.**	**Wmk. 344**	
346	A100	5m tan, blk & brn	.20	.20
347	A101	15m multicolored	.20	.20
348	A102	75m multicolored	.20	.20
		Nos. 346-348 (3)	.60	.60

Intl. Education Year (No. 346); 50th General Assembly of the Intl. Vine and Wine Office (No. 347); 25th anniv. of the UN (No. 348).

Virgin and Child, Mural from Podhithou
Church, 16th Century — A103

Perf. 14x14½

1970, Nov. 23	**Photo.**	**Unwmk.**	
349	A103	Strip of three	.45	.45
a.		25m Left angel	.20	.20
b.		25m Virgin and Child	.20	.20
c.		25m Right angel	.20	.20
350	A103	75m multicolored	.35	.35

Christmas.
Design of No. 349 is same as No. 350, but divided by perforation into 3 stamps with 25m denomination each. Size of No. 349: 71x46mm; size of No. 350: 42x31mm.

Cotton
Napkin — A104

Festive
Costume — A105

Drinking
Cup, 7th
Cent. B.C.
A106

Mouflon from Mosaic Pavement, 3rd
Century — A107

Cypriot Art: 5m, St. George, bas-relief on pine board, 19th cent. 20m, kneeling donors, painting, Church of St. Mamas, 1465. 25m, Mosaic head, 5th cent. A.D. 30m, Athena mounting horse-drawn chariot, terracotta figurine, 5th cent. B.C. 40m, Shepherd playing pipe, 14th cent. fresco. 50m, Woman's head, limestone, 3rd cent. B.C. 75m, Angel, mosaic, 6th cent. 90m, Mycenaean silver bowl, 14th cent. B.C. 500m, Woman and tree, decoration from amphora, 7th-6th cent. B.C. £1, God statue (horned helmet), from Enkomi, 12th cent. B.C., vert.

**Perf. 12½x13½ (A104), 13x14 (A105),
14x13 (A106), 13½x13, 13x13½
(A107)**

1971, Feb. 22	**Litho.**	**Wmk. 344**	
351	A104	3m blk, red & brn	.40	.50
352	A104	5m citron, red brn & black	.20	.20
353	A105	10m multicolored	.20	.30
354	A106	15m bister brn, blk & slate	.25	.20
355	A105	20m slate, red brn & black	.45	.50
356	A105	25m multicolored	.35	.20
357	A106	30m multicolored	.35	.20
358	A105	40m gray & multi	1.25	1.10
359	A105	50m bl, bis & blk	1.00	.20
360	A105	75m cit & multi	2.25	1.25
361	A106	90m multicolored	2.50	2.50
362	A107	250m lt red brn, brn & black	1.90	.40
363	A107	500m tan & multi	1.00	.50
364	A107	£1 multicolored	1.90	.75
		Nos. 351-364 (14)	14.00	8.80

For surcharges & overprints see #403, 424-427, 444, RA1.

Europa Issue, 1971

"Fraternity, Co-operation, Common
Effort" — CD14

1971, May 3	**Litho.**	**Perf. 14x13½**	
		Size: 36½x23½mm	
365	CD14	20m lt bl, vio bl & blk	.30	.20
366	CD14	30m brt yel grn, grn & blk	.30	.20
367	CD14	150m yel, grn & blk	2.00	1.25
		Nos. 365-367 (3)	2.60	1.65

Archbishop
Kyprianos,
1821 — A109

Paintings: 30m, Young Greek Taking Oath, horiz. 100m, Bishop Germanòs of Patras Declaring Greek Independence.

Perf. 13x13½, 13½x13

1971, July 9		**Wmk. 344**	
368	A109	15m multicolored	.20	.20
369	A109	30m multicolored	.20	.20
370	A109	100m multicolored	.30	.30
		Nos. 368-370 (3)	.70	.70

150th anniversary of Greek independence.

Arch and
Castle
A110

Tourist Publicity: 25m, Decorated gourd and sun over shore, vert. 60m, Mountain road, vert. 100m, Village church.

Perf. 13½x13, 13x13½

1971, Sept. 20			
371	A110	15m vio bl & multi	.20	.20
372	A110	25m ocher & multi	.20	.20
373	A110	60m green & multi	.25	.25
374	A110	100m blue & multi	.25	.25
		Nos. 371-374 (4)	.90	.90

Virgin and Child — A111

Heart and Electrocardiogram — A112

1971, Nov. 22   **Perf. 13½x14**
375	A111	10m shown	.20 .20
376	A111	50m The Three Kings	.20 .20
377	A111	100m Shepherds	.30 .30
a.		Strip of 3, Nos. 375-377	.75 .75

Christmas.

1972, Apr. 11   **Perf. 13½x12½**
378	A112	15m bister & multi	.20 .20
379	A112	50m brown & multi	.30 .30

"Your heart is your health," World Health Day.

Europa Issue 1972

Sparkles, Symbolic of Communications CD15

1972, May 22   **Perf. 12½x13½**
380	CD15	20m brn, org & fawn	.60 .30
381	CD15	30m pur, org & lilac	.60 .55
382	CD15	150m dk ol, org & brt green	4.75 1.60
		Nos. 380-382 (3)	5.95 2.45

Archery, Olympic and Motion Emblems A114

1972, July 24   **Perf. 14x13½**
383	A114	10m shown	.25 .20
384	A114	40m Wrestling	.35 .25
385	A114	100m Soccer	.65 1.25
		Nos. 383-385 (3)	1.25 1.70

20th Olympic Games, Munich, 8/26-9/11.

Apollo, Silver Stater, Marion, 5th Century B.C. A115

Silver Staters of Cyprus: 30m, Eagle's head, Paphos, c. 460 B.C. 40m, Pallas Athena, Lapithos, 388-387 B.C. 100m, Sphinx (obverse) and lotus flower (reverse), Idalion, c. 460 B.C.

1972, Sept. 25   **Litho.**   **Wmk. 344**
Coins in Silver
386	A115	20m lt grnsh bl & blk	.20 .20
387	A115	30m pale bl & silver	.20 .20
388	A115	40m ol bister & black	.35 .30
389	A115	100m pale brn & blk	1.25 1.10
		Nos. 386-389 (4)	2.00 1.80

Bathing the Christ Child — A116

Christmas: 20m, The Three Kings. 100m, Nativity. 250m, The Nativity, 1466, mural in Church of the Holy Cross, Platanistasa. The designs of the 10m, 20m, 100m, show details from mural shown entirely on 250m.

1972, Nov. 20   **Litho.**   **Perf. 13½x14**
390	A116	10m multicolored	.30 .30
391	A116	20m multicolored	.30 .30
392	A116	100m multicolored	.40 .40

Size: 110x90mm
Imperf
393	A116	250m multicolored	2.75 2.75
		Nos. 390-393 (4)	3.75 3.75

Landscape, Troodos Mountains A117

100m, FIS Congress emblem and map of Cyprus.

Perf. 14x13½
1973, Mar. 13   **Wmk. 344**
394	A117	20m blue & multi	.20 .20
395	A117	100m blue & multi	.40 .40

29th Meeting of the Intl. Ski Fed. (FIS), Nicosia, June 1973.

Europa Issue 1973

Post Horn of Arrows CD16

1973, May 7   **Size: 37x21mm**
396	CD16	20m dl bl & multi	.40 .40
397	CD16	30m multicolored	.40 .35
398	CD16	150m multicolored	2.50 1.50
		Nos. 396-398 (3)	3.30 2.10

Archbishop's Palace, Nicosia — A119

Traditional Architecture: 30m, Konak, Nicosia, 18th century, vert. 50m, House, Gourri, 1850, vert. 100m, House, Rizokarpaso, 1772.

1973, July 23   **Perf. 14x13, 13x14**
399	A119	20m multicolored	.20 .20
400	A119	30m multicolored	.20 .20
401	A119	50m multicolored	.20 .20
402	A119	100m multicolored	.50 .50
		Nos. 399-402 (4)	1.10 1.10

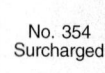

No. 354 Surcharged

1973, Sept. 24   **Perf. 14x13**
403	A106	20m on 15m multi	.40 .40

Cyprus Scout Emblem — A120

EEC Emblem A122

Cyprus Airways Emblem — A121

35m, FAO emblem. 100m, INTERPOL emblem.

1973, Sept. 24   **Perf. 13x14, 14x13**
404	A120	10m brn ol, ol & buff	.40 .35
405	A121	25m pur, bl & plum	.30 .30
406	A121	35m grn, gray grn & citron	.30 .30
407	A122	50m black & blue	.30 .30
408	A120	100m brown & fawn	.60 .60
		Nos. 404-408 (5)	1.90 1.85

60th anniv. of Cyprus Boy Scout Organ.; association of Cyprus with EEC; 10th anniv. of FAO; 25th anniv. of Cyprus Airways; 50th anniv. of Intl. Criminal Police Organization.

Archangel Gabriel — A123

Virgin and Child — A124

Christmas: 100m, Panaya tou Araka Church, horiz. Designs of 10m, 20m are from wall paintings in Arakas Church.

1973, Nov. 26   **Wmk. 344**
409	A123	10m multicolored	.20 .20
410	A124	20m multicolored	.20 .20
411	A124	100m multicolored	.60 .60
		Nos. 409-411 (3)	1.00 1.00

Grapes — A125

Rape of Europa — A126

1974, Mar. 18   **Litho.**   **Perf. 13x14**
412	A125	25m shown	.25 .20
413	A125	50m Grapefruit	.30 .20
414	A125	50m Oranges	.30 .20
415	A125	50m Lemons	.30 .20
a.		Strip of 3, #413-415	1.25 1.25
		Nos. 412-415 (4)	1.15 .90

Europa Issue 1974
1974, Apr. 29

Design shows a silver stater of Marion, second half of 5th century B.C.
416	A126	10m org brn & multi	.60 .30
417	A126	40m multicolored	.60 .60
418	A126	150m dk car & multi	2.75 1.40
		Nos. 416-418 (3)	3.95 2.30

Solon, 3rd Century Mosaic A127

Designs: 10m, Front page of "History of Cyprus," by Archimandrite Kyprianos, 1788, vert. 100m, St. Neophytos, mural, vert. 250m, Maps of Cyprus and Greek Islands, by Abraham Ortelius, 1584.

Perf. 13x14, 14x13
1974, July 22   **Litho.**   **Wmk. 344**
419	A127	10m multicolored	.20 .20
420	A127	25m multicolored	.20 .20
421	A127	100m multicolored	.85 .85

Size: 110x90mm
Imperf
422	A127	250m multicolored	3.00 3.25
		Nos. 419-422 (4)	4.25 4.50

2nd Intl. Congress of Cypriot Studies, Nicosia, Sept. 15-21. No. 422 has simulated perforations.

Nos. 353, 358-359, 362 Overprinted

Perf. 13x14, 13½x13
1974, Oct. 14   **Litho.**
424	A105	10m multicolored	.25 .25
425	A105	40m multicolored	.35 .35
426	A105	50m multicolored	.35 .35
427	A107	250m multicolored	.80 .80
		Nos. 424-427 (4)	1.75 1.75

UN Security Council Resolution No. 353 to end hostilities on Cyprus. Overprint is in 3 lines on No. 427.

Virgin and Child, 1466 A129

Adoration of the Kings, c. 1500 — A130

Christmas: 100m, Flight into Egypt, mural, Monastery Church of Ayios Meophytos, c. 1500. (50m is from same church). Mural on 10m is in Church of Stavros tou Ahiasmati.

Perf. 14x13, 13x14
1974, Dec. 2   **Wmk. 344**
429	A129	10m multicolored	.20 .20
430	A130	50m multicolored	.20 .20
431	A129	100m multicolored	.40 .40
		Nos. 429-431 (3)	.80 .80

CYPRUS

Disabled
Persons,
Emblem — A131

Council of
Europe
Flag — A132

1975, Feb. 17   Unwmk.   Perf. 14½
432	A131	30m ocher & ultra	.20	.20
433	A132	100m multicolored	.70	.60

8th European Meeting of the Intl. Society for the Rehabilitation of Disabled Persons (30m; design shows society's emblem); 25th anniv. of Council of Europe (100m).

First Mail
Coach in
Cyprus
A133

1975, Feb. 17
434	A133	20m multicolored	.20	.20
435	A133	50m ultra & multi	1.10	.40

Centenary (in 1974) of UPU.

The Distaff, by
Michael
Kashalos — A134

Europa (Paintings): 30m, Still Life, by Christoforos Savva. 150m, Virgin and Child of Liopetri, by Georghios P. Georghiou.

Perf. 13½x14½
1975, Apr. 28   Photo.
436	A134	20m multicolored	.30	.20
437	A134	30m multicolored	.35	.20
438	A134	150m multicolored	1.00	.60
a.		Strip of 3, #436-438	1.75	1.75

Red Cross Flag over
Cyprus — A135

Nurse and
Nurses
Emblem
A136

Steatite
Female
Figure, c.
3000
B.C. — A137

Perf. 12½x13½, 13½x12½
1975, Aug. 4   Litho.   Wmk. 344
439	A135	25m blue green & red	.25	.20
440	A136	30m dp blue & lt grn	.30	.25
441	A137	75m multicolored	.45	.40
		Nos. 439-441 (3)	1.00	.85

Cyprus Red Cross, 25th anniv.; Intl. Nurses' Day 1975; IWY.

Submarine
Cable — A138

International
Telephone
A139

Perf. 12½x13½, 13½x12½
1975, Oct. 13   Litho.
442	A138	50m multicolored	.35	.20
443	A139	100m purple & org	.60	.45

Telecommunications achievements.

No. 351 Surcharged

1976, Jan. 5   Perf. 12½x13½
444	A104	10m on 3m multi	.40	.40

Vessel in Shape
of Woman, 19th
Century — A140

Composite
Vessel, 2100-
2000
B.C. — A141

Europa: 100m, Byzantine goblet, 15th cent.

Perf. 13x14
1976, May 3   Litho.   Wmk. 344
445	A140	20m violet & multi	.35	.20
446	A141	60m gray & multi	.80	.70
447	A140	100m brown & multi	1.60	.95
		Nos. 445-447 (3)	2.75	1.85

Self-help
Housing
A142

Cyprus
Airways
Jet — A143

Designs: 25m, Women sewing in front of tents. 30m, Aforestation.

1976, May 3   Perf. 14x13
448	A142	10m multicolored	.20	.20
449	A142	25m multicolored	.20	.20
450	A142	30m multicolored	.20	.20
451	A143	60m multicolored	.40	.40
		Nos. 448-451 (4)	1.00	1.00

Re-activation of the economy.

Terracotta Statue,
7th-6th Centuries
B.C. — A144

Bronze
Plate with
Inscription,
Idalion, 5th
Century
B.C.
A145

Designs: 10m, Limestone head of bearded man, 5th cent. B.C. 20m, Gold necklace, Lamboussa, 6th cent. A.D. 25m, Terracotta warrior on horseback, 7th cent. B.C. 30m, Limestone figure, priest of Aphrodite, 5th cent. B.C. 50m, Mycenaean crater, 13th cent. B.C. 60m, Limestone sarcophagus, Amathus, 550-500 B.C. 100m, Gold bracelet, Lamboussa, 6th cent. A.D. 250m, Silver dish, Lamboussa, 6th cent. A.D. 500m, Bronze stand, 12th cent. B.C. £1, Marble statue of Artemis, Larnaca, 4th cent. B.C.

Perf. 12x13½
1976, June 7   Wmk. 344
Size: 22x33mm
452	A144	5m brn & multi	.20	.75
453	A144	10m gray & multi	.20	.65

Size: 24x37mm, 37x24mm
Perf. 13x14, 14x13
454	A144	20m red & multi	.20	.60
455	A144	25m lt brn & blk	.20	.20
456	A144	30m green & multi	.20	.20
457	A145	40m bis gray & blk	.20	.60
458	A145	50m brn & multi	.20	.20
459	A145	60m dk brn & multi	.25	.20
460	A145	100m crim & multi	.40	.60

Size: 28x40mm
Perf. 13x12½
461	A144	250m dk bl & multi	.90	1.50
462	A144	500m yel & multi	1.75	1.75
463	A144	£1 slate & multi	3.75	3.50
		Nos. 452-463 (12)	8.45	10.75

George
Washington
A146

1976, July 5   Perf. 13x13½
464	A146	100m multicolored	.70	.60

American Bicentennial.

Montreal Olympic
Games
Emblem — A147

Various
Sports
A148

100m, like 60m, with different sports.

1976, July 5   Unwmk.   Perf. 14
465	A147	20m yel, blk & dk car	.20	.20
466	A148	60m ultra & multi	.30	.30
467	A148	100m lilac & multi	.50	.50
		Nos. 465-467 (3)	1.00	1.00

21st Olympic Games, Montreal, Canada, July 17-Aug. 1.

Children in
Library — A149

Low-cost
Housing
Development
A150

Hands Shielding
Eye — A151

Perf. 13½x14, 13x13½
1976, Sept. 27   Litho.   Wmk. 344
468	A149	40m black & multi	.30	.30
469	A150	50m multicolored	.25	.20
470	A151	80m ultra & multi	.45	.35
		Nos. 468-470 (3)	1.00	.85

Books for Children (40m); Habitat, UN Conference on Human Settlements, Vancouver, Canada, May 31-June 11 (50m); World Health Day: Foresight prevents blindness (80m).

Archangel
Michael — A152

Christmas: 15m, Archangel Gabriel. 150m, Nativity. Icons in Ayios Neophytis Monastery, 16th century.

1976, Nov. 15   Unwmk.   Perf. 12½
471	A152	10m multicolored	.20	.20
472	A152	15m multicolored	.20	.20
473	A152	150m multicolored	.85	.75
		Nos. 471-473 (3)	1.25	1.15

Landscape, by A. Diamantis — A154

Europa (Paintings): 60m, Trees and Meadow, by T. Kanthos. 120m, Harbor, by V. Ioannides.

Perf. 13½x13
1977, May 2   Litho.   Unwmk.
475	A154	20m multicolored	.30	.20
476	A154	60m multicolored	.70	.40
477	A154	120m multicolored	1.25	.90
		Nos. 475-477 (3)	2.25	1.50

Cyprus No. 196 — A155

Perf. 13x13½

1977, June 13   Litho.   Wmk. 344
478 A155 120m multicolored   .55 .40
25th anniv. of reign of Queen Elizabeth II.

Silver Tetradrachm of Demetrios Poliorcetes — A156

Ancient Coins of Cyprus: 10m, Bronze coin of Emperor Trajan. 60m, Silver Tetradrachm of Ptolemy VIII. 100m, Gold octadrachm of Arsinoe II.

1977, June 13   Unwmk.   Perf. 14
479 A156 10m multicolored   .20 .20
480 A156 40m multicolored   .25 .20
481 A156 60m multicolored   .35 .30
482 A156 100m multicolored   .50 .50
  Nos. 479-482 (4)   1.30 1.20

Archbishop Makarios (1913-1977), Pres. of Cyprus — A157

20m, Archbishop in full vestments. 250m, Head.

Perf. 13x14

1977, Sept. 10   Litho.   Unwmk.
483 A157 20m multicolored   .20 .20
484 A157 60m multicolored   .25 .20
485 A157 250m multicolored   .95 .85
  Nos. 483-485 (3)   1.40 1.25

Handicrafts A158

Sputnik over Earth — A159

Designs: 40m, Map of Cyprus. 60m, Gold medals and sports emblems.

Perf. 13½x12

1977, Oct. 17   Wmk. 344
486 A158 20m multicolored   .20 .20
487 A158 40m multicolored   .20 .20
488 A158 60m multicolored   .25 .25
489 A159 80m multicolored   .35 .30
  Nos. 486-489 (4)   1.00 .95

Revitalization of handicrafts (20m); Man and the biosphere (40m); Gold medals won by secondary school students in France for long jump and 200 meter race (60m); 60th anniv. of Bolshevik Revolution (80m).

Nativity A160

Christmas (Children's Drawings): 10m, Three Kings following the star. 150m, Flight into Egypt.

Perf. 14x13½

1977, Nov. 21   Litho.   Unwmk.
490 A160 10m multicolored   .20 .20
491 A160 40m multicolored   .20 .20
492 A160 150m multicolored   .60 .55
  Nos. 490-492 (3)   1.00 .95

Demetrios Libertis (1866-1937) — A161

150m, Vasilis Michaelides (1849-1917).

1978, Mar. 6   Wmk. 344   Perf. 14x13
493 A161 40m bister & olive   .20 .20
494 A161 150m gray, ver & blk   .60 .55
Cypriot poets.

Chrysorrhogiatissa Monastery — A162

Europa: 75m, Kolossi Castle. 125m, Municipal Library, Paphos.

Perf. 14½x13

1978, Apr. 24   Litho.   Unwmk.
495 A162 25m multicolored   .30 .20
496 A162 75m multicolored   .80 .40
497 A162 125m multicolored   1.40 .70
  Nos. 495-497 (3)   2.50 1.30

Makarios as Archbishop 1950-1977 A163

"The Great Leader" — A164

Archbishop Makarios: 25m, Exiled, Seychelles, 1956-1957. 50m, President of Cyprus, 1960-1977. 75m, Soldier of Christ. 100m, Freedom fighter.

Perf. 14x14½

1978, Aug. 3   Litho.   Unwmk.
498 A163 15m multicolored   .20 .20
499 A163 25m multicolored   .20 .20
500 A163 50m multicolored   .25 .25
501 A163 75m multicolored   .35 .35
502 A163 100m multicolored   .50 .50
  a.   Strip of 5, #498-502   1.50 1.50

Size: 110x80mm
Imperf
503 A164 300m multicolored   3.50 2.50
  Nos. 498-503 (6)   5.00 4.00
Archbishop Makarios, President of Cyprus.

Blood Cells with Low Hemoglobin A165

Bust of Aristotle A166

Heads and Human Rights Emblem A167

Wilbur and Orville Wright, Flyer I A168

Perf. 13x14, 14x13

1978, Oct. 23   Unwmk.   Litho.
504 A165 15m multicolored   .20 .20
505 A166 35m multicolored   .20 .20
506 A167 75m black   .35 .35
507 A168 125m multicolored   .50 .50
  Nos. 504-507 (4)   1.25 1.25

Anemia prevention (15m); 2300th birth anniv. of Aristotle (35m); 30th anniv. of Universal Declaration of Human Rights (75m); 75th anniv. of first powered flight (125m).

Kiti Icon Stand — A169

Christmas: 35m, Athienou icon stand. 150m, Omodhos icon stand.

1978, Dec. 4   Perf. 14x14½
508 A169 15m multicolored   .20 .20
509 A169 35m multicolored   .20 .20
510 A169 150m multicolored   .75 .75
  Nos. 508-510 (3)   1.15 1.15

Venus Statue from Soli A170

125m, Birth of Venus, by Botticelli (detail).

1979, Mar. 12   Litho.   Perf. 14x13½
511 A170 75m multicolored   .35 .35
512 A170 125m multicolored   .55 .55

Mail Coach, Envelope and Truck A171

Europa: 75m, Old telephone, dish antenna and satellite. 125m, Steamship, jet and envelopes.

1979, Apr. 30   Litho.   Perf. 14x13½
513 A171 25m multicolored   .45 .25
514 A171 75m multicolored   .80 .40
515 A171 125m multicolored   2.50 1.00
  Nos. 513-515 (3)   3.75 1.65

Peacock Wrasse A172

Designs: 50m, Black partridge, vert. 75m, Cyprus cedar, vert. 125m, Mule.

Perf. 13½x12½, 12½x13½

1979, June 25   Litho.
516 A172 25m multicolored   .25 .20
517 A172 50m multicolored   .50 .40
518 A172 75m multicolored   .50 .35
519 A172 125m multicolored   .75 .55
  Nos. 516-519 (4)   2.00 1.50

Children Holding Globe, UNESCO Emblem — A173

Dove, Magnifying Glass, Album A174

Lord Kitchener, Map of Cyprus A175

Smiling Child, IYC Emblem A176

Soccer A177

Rotary Emblem — A178

1979, Oct. 1   Litho.   Perf. 12½
520 A173 15m multicolored   .20 .20
521 A174 25m multicolored   .20 .20
522 A175 50m multicolored   .25 .25
523 A176 75m multicolored   .30 .25
524 A177 100m multicolored   .50 .45
525 A178 125m multicolored   .55 .50
  Nos. 520-525 (6)   2.00 1.85

Intl. Bureau of Education, Geneva, 50th anniv.; Cyprus Philatelic Society, 20th anniv.; Horatio Herbert Kitchener's survey of Cyprus, cent.; IYC; European Soccer Assoc., 25th anniv.; Rotary Club of Cyprus, 75th anniv.

Jesus, Icon, 12th
Century — A179

Christmas (Icons): 35m, Nativity, 16th cent.
150m, Virgin and Child, 12th cent.

Perf. 13½x14, 13x14

1979, Nov. 5   Litho.

Sizes: 24x37mm; 27x40mm (35m)

526	A179	15m multicolored	.20	.20
527	A179	35m multicolored	.20	.20
528	A179	150m multicolored	.50	.40
	Nos. 526-528 (3)		.90	.80

Cyprus
No. 1,
Nicosia
Cancel
A180

Cyprus Stamp Centenary: 125m, #3,
Kyrenia cancel. 175m, #6, Larnaca cancel.
500m, #1-6.

1980, Mar. 17   Litho.   Perf. 14x13

529	A180	40m multicolored	.20	.20
530	A180	125m multicolored	.50	.50
531	A180	175m multicolored	.75	.75

Size: 105x85mm

Imperf

532	A180	500m multicolored	2.00	2.00
	Nos. 529-532 (4)		3.45	3.45

Holy Cross, St.
Barnabas Church,
Ayiasmati — A181

Europa: 125m, Zenon of Citium, Ny Car-
sberg Glyptothek, Copenhagen.

1980, Apr. 28   Perf. 12½

533	A181	40m multicolored	.25	.20
534	A181	125m multicolored	.45	.30

Sailing,
Moscow
'80
Emblem
A182

1980, June 23   Litho.   Perf. 14x13

535	A182	40m shown	.20	.20
536	A182	125m Swimming	.40	.40
537	A182	200m Gymnast	.70	.70
	Nos. 535-537 (3)		1.30	1.30

22nd Summer Olympic Games, Moscow,
July 19-Aug. 3.

Gold
Necklace — A183

Clay
Amphora — A184

Archaeological finds on Cyprus, 12th cent.
B.C. to 3rd cent. A.D. 15m, 40m, 150m, 500m,
horiz.

Perf. 13½x14, 14x13½

1980, Sept. 15   Litho.   Wmk. 344

538	A183	10m shown	.30	.30
539	A184	15m Bronze cow	.30	.30
540	A184	25m shown	.30	.30
541	A184	40m Lion, gold ring	.40	.40
542	A184	50m Bronze caul- dron	.40	.40
543	A184	75m Stele	1.25	1.25
544	A184	100m Clay jug	.90	.90
545	A184	125m Warrior, terra- cotta bust	.90	.90
546	A184	150m Lions attack- ing bull	1.50	1.50
547	A184	175m Faience and enamel vase	1.00	1.00
548	A184	200m Warrior god, bronze	1.00	1.00
549	A184	500m Stone bowl	1.00	1.00
550	A183	£1 Ivory plaque	1.25	1.25
551	A183	£2 Leda and the swan, mosaic	2.50	2.50
	Nos. 538-551 (14)		13.00	13.00

For surcharges see Nos. 584, 600-611.

Cyprus
Flag — A185

Archbishop
Makarios — A187

Treaty Signing Establishing Republic,
20th Anniversary — A186

1980, Oct. 1   Perf. 13½x14, 14x13

552	A185	40m multicolored	.20	.20
553	A186	125m multicolored	.45	.45
554	A187	175m multicolored	.65	.65
	Nos. 552-554 (3)		1.30	1.30

Dove and
Woman
A188

Perf. 14x13

1980, Nov. 29   Litho.   Wmk. 344

555	A188	40m shown	.20	.20
556	A188	125m Dove and man	.60	.60
a.	Pair, #555-556		.80	.80

Intl. Palestinian Solidarity Day.

Pulpit, Tripiotis
Church,
Nicosia — A189

Christmas: 100m, Iconostatis (Holy Door),
Panayia Church, Paralimni. 125m, Pulpit,
Ayios Lazaros Church, Larnaca.

1980, Nov. 29   Perf. 13½x14

557	A189	25m multicolored	.20	.20

Size: 24x37mm

558	A189	100m multicolored		.35	.35

Size: 21x37mm

559	A189	125m multicolored	.45	.45
	Nos. 557-559 (3)		1.00	1.00

Europa Issue 1981

Folk Dance — A190

1981, May 4   Photo.   Perf. 14

560	A190	40m shown	.35	.20
561	A190	175m Dance, diff.	.75	.50

Self-portrait, by
Leonardo Da
Vinci — A191

The Last Supper, by Da Vinci — A192

Perf. 13½x14, 12½x13½

1981, June 15   Wmk. 344   Litho.

562	A191	50m shown	.40	.30
563	A192	125m shown	.85	.70
564	A191	175m Lace pattern, Mi- lan Cathedral	1.25	1.00
	Nos. 562-564 (3)		2.50	2.00

Da Vinci's visit to Cyprus, 500th anniv.

Ophrys
Kotschyi — A193

Designs: Orchids.

1981, July 6   Perf. 13½x14

565	A193	25m shown	.35	.35
566	A193	50m Orchis puntulata	.65	.65
567	A193	75m Ophrys argolica elegantis	.95	.95
568	A193	150m Epipactis vera- trifolia	1.75	1.75
a.	Block of 4, #565-568		4.00	4.00

Prince
Charles
and Lady
Diana,
St. Paul's
Cathedral
A194

Perf. 14x13

1981, Sept. 28   Wmk. 344

569	A194	200m multicolored	1.00	1.00

Royal wedding.

Heinrich von Stephan (1831-1897),
UPU Founder — A195

World
Food Day
(Oct. 16)
A196

Intl. Year
of the
Disabled
A197

European Campaign for Urban
Renaissance — A198

1981, Sept. 28

570	A195	25m multicolored	.20	.20
571	A196	40m multicolored	.20	.20
572	A197	125m multicolored	.55	.55
573	A198	150m multicolored	.60	.60
	Nos. 570-573 (4)		1.55	1.55

Our Lady of
the Angels,
Transfiguration
Church,
Palekhori
A199

Christmas (Frescoes): 100m, Christ,
Madonna of Arakas Church, Lagoudera, vert.
125m, Baptism of Christ, Our Lady of Assinou
Church, Nikitari.

1981, Nov. 16   Perf. 12½

574	A199	25m multicolored	.25	.20
575	A199	100m multicolored	.65	.35
576	A199	125m multicolored	.80	.45
	Nos. 574-576 (3)		1.70	1.00

Bathing Aphrodite,
Sculpture, Soloi,
250 B.C. — A200

Design: 175m, Aphrodite Emerging from the
Water, by Titian, 16th cent.

Perf. 13½x14

1982, Apr. 12   Litho.   Wmk. 344

577	A200	125m multicolored	.80	.65
578	A200	175m multicolored	1.10	1.00

Europa Issue 1982

Liberation
by Emperor
Nicephorus
II Phocas,
965 A.D.
A201

Perf. 12½

1982, May 3   Photo.   Unwmk.

579	A201	40m shown	.50	.20
580	A201	175m Conversion of Sergius Paulus, 45 A.D.	.85	.75

Mosaic Chrismon A202

Cultural Heritage: 125m, King of Palaepaphos (High Priest of Aphrodite), sculpture, vert. 225m, Theseus Struggling with the Minotaur, mosaic.

1982, July 5   Litho.   Wmk. 344
581 A202 50m multicolored   .20 .20
582 A202 125m multicolored   .60 .60
583 A202 225m multicolored   1.10 1.10
     Nos. 581-583 (3)   1.90 1.90

No. 543 Surcharged

1982, Sept. 6   Litho.   Perf. 13½x14
584 A184 100m on 75m multi   .60 .60

Scouting Year A203

Christmas A204

Perf. 13½x12½, 12½x13½
1982, Nov. 8   Wmk. 344
585 A203 100m Emblem, horiz.   .50 .50
586 A203 125m Baden-Powell   .60 .60
587 A203 175m Camp site, horiz. .80 .80
     Nos. 585-587 (3)   1.90 1.90

Perf. 12½, 13½x14 (100m)
1982, Dec. 6

Designs: 25m, 250m, Christ Giving Holy Communion (bread, 25m: wine, 250m) to the Apostles, St. Neophytos Monastery Church, Paphos, horiz. 100m, Chalice, Church of St. Savvas, Nicosia.

588 A204 25m multicolored   .20 .20
589 A204 100m multicolored   .40 .40
590 A204 250m multicolored   1.00 1.00
     Nos. 588-590 (3)   1.60 1.60

A204a

1983, Mar. 14   Perf. 14x13½
591 A204a 50m Cyprus Forest
            Industries, Ltd.   .20 .20
592 A204a 125m Mosaic, 3rd
            cent.   .35 .35
593 A204a 150m Dancers   .45 .45
594 A204a 175m Royal Exhibition
            Building, Mel-
            bourne   .50 .50
     Nos. 591-594 (4)   1.50 1.50

Commonwealth Day.

Europa A205

50m, Cyprosyllabic script funerary stele, 6th cent. B.C. 200m, Copper ore, Enkomi ingot, 1400-1250 BC, bronze jug, 2nd cent.

1983, May 3   Photo.   Perf. 14½x14
595 A205 50m multicolored   .25 .20
596 A205 200m multicolored   .75 .50

Local Butterflies A206

Wmk. 344
1983, June 28   Litho.   Perf. 12½
597 A206 60m Pararge aegeria   .45 .45
598 A206 130m Aricia medon   .90 .90
599 A206 250m Glaucopsyche
            paphos   1.75 1.75
     Nos. 597-599 (3)   3.10 3.10

Nos. 538-549 Surcharged
Perf. 13½x14, 14x13½
1983, Oct. 3   Litho.   Wmk. 344
600 A183 1c on 10m multi   .20 .20
601 A184 2c on 15m multi   .20 .20
602 A184 3c on 25m multi   .20 .20
603 A184 4c on 40m multi   .20 .20
604 A184 5c on 50m multi   .25 .25
605 A184 6c on 75m multi   .25 .25
606 A184 10c on 100m multi   .45 .45
607 A184 13c on 125m multi   .65 .65
608 A184 15c on 150m multi   .75 .75
609 A184 20c on 200m multi   1.00 1.00
610 A184 25c on 175m multi   1.40 1.40
611 A184 50c on 500m multi   2.40 2.40
     Nos. 600-611 (12)   7.95 7.95

Electricity Authority of Cyprus, 30th Anniv. — A207

World Communications Year — A208

Intl. Maritime Org., 25th Anniv. — A209

Universal Declaration of Human Rights, 35th Anniv. — A210

Nicos Kazantzakis, 100th Birth Anniv. — A211

Archbishop Makarios III, 70th Birth Anniv. — A212

1983, Oct. 31   Litho.   Perf. 13½x14
612 A207 3c multicolored   .20 .20
613 A208 6c multicolored   .20 .20
614 A209 13c multicolored   .40 .40
615 A210 15c multicolored   .45 .45
616 A211 20c multicolored   .65 .65
617 A212 25c multicolored   .80 .80
     Nos. 612-617 (6)   2.70 2.70

Christmas — A213

Designs: 4c, Belfry, St. Lazaros Church, Larnaca. 13c, Belfry, St. Varvara Church, Kaimakli, Nicosia. 20c, Belfry, St. Ioannis Church, Larnaca.

1983, Dec. 12   Perf. 12½x14
618 A213 4c multicolored   .20 .20
619 A213 13c multicolored   .70 .70
620 A213 20c multicolored   1.00 1.00
     Nos. 618-620 (3)   1.90 1.90

Waterside Cafe at the Marina, Larnaca — A214

19th Century engravings. Size of 6c: 41x27mm; 75c, 110x85mm.

Perf. 14½x14 (6c), 14, Imperf. (75c)
1984, Mar. 6
621 A214 6c shown   .20 .20
622 A214 20c Bazaar, Larnaca   .65 .65
623 A214 30c East Gate, Nicosia .95 .95
624 A214 75c St. Lazarus
            Church Interior,
            Larnaca   2.50 2.50
     Nos. 621-624 (4)   4.30 4.30

Europa (1959-1984) — A215

1984, Apr. 30   Wmk. 344   Perf. 12½
625 A215 6c multicolored   .40 .20
626 A215 15c multicolored   .90 .75

1984 Summer Olympics A216

1984, June 18   Litho.   Perf. 14
627 A216 3c Running   .20 .20
628 A216 4c Olympic column   .20 .20
629 A216 13c Swimming   .60 .60
630 A216 20c Gymnastics   .90 .90
     Nos. 627-630 (4)   1.90 1.90

Turkish Invasion, 10th Anniv. A217

1984, July 20   Litho.   Perf. 14x13½
631 A217 15c Prisoners, barbed
            wire   .45 .45
632 A217 20c Map   .60 .60

Cyprus Philatelic Society, 25th Anniv. — A218

Cyprus Soccer Assoc., 50th Anniv. A219

George Papanicolaou (1883-1962), Cancer Researcher — A220

Medieval Map A221

1984, Oct. 15   Wmk. 344   Perf. 12½
633 A218 6c multicolored   .25 .25
634 A219 10c multicolored   .45 .45
635 A220 15c multicolored   .80 .80
636 A221 25c multicolored   1.50 1.50
     Nos. 633-636 (4)   3.00 3.00

Intl. Symposium of Cyprus Cartography and First Intl. Symposium on Medieval Paleography (25c).

Christmas — A222

1984, Nov. 26   Litho.   Perf. 12½
637 A222 4c St. Mark   .30 .30
638 A222 13c Gospel page (St.
            Mark)   1.00 1.00
639 A222 20c St. Luke   1.50 1.50
     Nos. 637-639 (3)   2.80 2.80

Landscapes — A223

Perf. 15x14, 14x15
1985, Mar. 18   Litho.
640 A223 1c Autumn at
            Platania   .20 .65
641 A223 2c Ayia Napa
            Monastery   .20 .65
642 A223 3c Phine Village   .20 .65
643 A223 4c Kykko Monas-
            tery   .20 .35
644 A223 5c Beach at
            Makronissos   .20 .20
645 A223 6c Village Street,
            Omodhos, vert.   .20 .20
646 A223 10c Sea view   .35 .35
647 A223 13c Water sports   .45 .45
648 A223 15c Beach at
            Protaras   .55 .55
649 A223 20c Forestry, vert. .65 .65
650 A223 25c Sunrise at
            Protaras, vert.   1.00 .85

651 A223 30c	Village houses, Pera Orinis	1.40 1.00
652 A223 50c	Apollo Hylates Sanctuary	2.75 1.25
653 A223 £1	Troodos Mountain, vert.	5.50 2.25
654 A223 £5	Personification of Autumn, Dionyssos House, vert.	19.00 17.00

Nos. 640-654 (15) 32.85 27.05

For surcharges see Nos. 684-685, 712.

Europa
A224

6c, Ceramic figures playing the double flute, lyre and tambourine, 7th-6th cent. B.C. 15c, Cypriot violin, lute, flute, the Fourth Women's Dance from the Cyprus Suite.

1985, May 6   **Litho.**   **Perf. 12½**
655 A224 6c multicolored .60 .40
656 A224 15c multicolored 1.40 1.10

Republic of Cyprus, 25th Anniv. — A225   UN 40th Anniv. — A229

Natl. Liberation Movement, 30th Anniv. — A226

Intl. Youth Year A227

Solon Michaelides (1905-1979), Conductor, European Music Year — A228

Perf. 14½ (#657), 14½x14, 15 (#661)
1985, Sept. 23   **Litho.**
657 A225 4c multicolored .30 .30
658 A226 6c multicolored .45 .45
659 A227 13c multicolored .95 .95
660 A228 15c multicolored 1.10 1.10
661 A229 20c multicolored 1.40 1.40
Nos. 657-661 (5) 4.20 4.20

Christmas — A230

Murals of the St. Ioannis Lampadistis Monastery, Kalopanyiotis: 4c, Virgin Mary's Visit to Elizabeth. 13c, The Nativity. 20c, The Candlemas, Church of Our Lady of Assinous, Nikitari.

1985, Nov. 18   **Litho.**   **Perf. 12½**
662 A230 4c multicolored .35 .35
663 A230 13c multicolored 1.00 1.00
664 A230 20c multicolored 1.65 1.65
Nos. 662-664 (3) 3.00 3.00

Hellenistic Platinum Spoon A231

Designs: 20c, Ionian helmet, foot of a sculpture. 25c, Union of Eros and Intellect personified, abstract. 30c, Statue profile.

1986, Feb. 17   **Perf. 15x14**
665 A231 15c multicolored .90 .90
666 A231 20c multicolored 1.25 1.25
667 A231 25c multicolored 1.60 1.60
668 A231 30c multicolored 2.00 2.00
   a. Souv. sheet of 4, #665-668 17.50 17.50
Nos. 665-668 (4) 5.75 5.75

Construction of the New Archaeological Museum, Nicosia. Department of Antiquities, 50th anniv. No. 668a sold for £1.

Europa Issue

Mouflon, Cedar Trees A232

1986, Apr. 28   **Litho.**   **Perf. 14x13**
669 A232 7c shown .40 .35
670 A232 17c Flamingos, Larnaca Salt Lake 1.50 1.25

Seashells A233

1986, July 1   **Perf. 14x13½**
671 A233 5c Chlamys pesfelis .45 .45
672 A233 7c Charonia variegata .55 .55
673 A233 18c Murex brandaris 1.40 1.40
674 A233 25c Cypraea spurca 1.90 1.90
Nos. 671-674 (4) 4.30 4.30

Overseas Cypriots Year A234

Halley's Comet A235

Anniversaries and events.

Perf. 13½x13
1986, Oct. 13   **Litho.**   **Wmk. 344**
675 A234 15c multicolored 1.25 1.25
676 A235 18c shown 1.75 1.75
677 A235 18c Comet tail, Edmond Halley 1.75 1.75
   a. Pair, #676-677 3.50 3.50
Nos. 675-677 (3) 4.75 4.75

No. 677a has continuous design.

Road Safety A236

1986, Nov. 10   **Perf. 14x13**
678 A236 5c Pedestrian crossing .75 .75
679 A236 7c Helmet, motorcycle controls 1.25 1.25
680 A236 18c Seatbelt, rearview mirror 3.00 3.00
Nos. 678-680 (3) 5.00 5.00

Intl. Peace Year, Christmas A237

Nativity frescoes (details): 5c, Church of Panayia tou Araka. 15c, Church of Panayia tou Moutoulla. 17c, Church of St. Nicholaos tis Steyis.

1986, Nov. 24   **Perf. 13½x14**
681 A237 5c multicolored .50 .50
682 A237 15c multicolored 1.50 1.50
683 A237 17c multicolored 1.90 1.90
Nos. 681-683 (3) 3.90 3.90

Nos. 645 and 647 Surcharged
Perf. 14x15, 15x14
1986, Oct. 13   **Litho.**   **Wmk. 344**
684 A223 7c on 6c multi 1.00 1.00
685 A223 18c on 13c multi 2.00 2.00

Miniature Sheet

Troodos Churches on UNESCO World Heritage List — A238

Churches and frescoes: a, Assinou, Nikitari. b, Moutoulla, Moutoullas. c, Podithou, Galata. d, Ayios Ioannis Lampadistis, Kalopanayiotis. e, Timios Stavros, Pelentri. f, Stavros Ayiasmati, Platanistasa. g, Archangelos Pedoula, Pedoulas. h, Ayios Nicolaos tis Steyis, Kakopetria. i, Araka, Lagoudera.

Perf. 12½
1987, Apr. 22   **Photo.**   **Unwmk.**
686 Sheet of 9 11.00 11.00
   a.-i. A238 15c any single 1.10 1.10

Europa Issue

Modern Architecture A239

Perf. 14x13½
1987, May 11   **Litho.**   **Wmk. 344**
687 A239 7c Central Bank of Cyprus .50 .40
688 A239 18c Cyprus Communications Authority 1.00 .90

Ships Named Kyrenia A240

1987, Oct. 3
689 A240 2c The Kyrenia, Kyrenia Castle .50 .30
690 A240 3c Kyrenia II, Perama Shipyard .70 .75
691 A240 5c Kyrenia II, Paphos .90 .50
692 A240 17c Kyrenia II, NY Harbor 1.90 1.50
Nos. 689-692 (4) 4.00 3.05

Blood Donation Coordinating Committee, 10th Anniv. — A241

European Campaign for Countryside — A242

TROODOS '87 — A243

Perf. 14x13½
1987, Nov. 2   **Litho.**   **Wmk. 344**
693 A241 7c multicolored .60 .55
694 A242 15c multicolored 1.40 1.25
695 A243 20c multicolored 2.00 1.75
Nos. 693-695 (3) 4.00 3.55

Christmas A244

1987, Nov. 30   **Perf. 14**
696 A244 5c Babe in a manger .40 .40
697 A244 15c Ornament 1.40 1.40
698 A244 17c Fruit bowl 1.75 1.75
Nos. 696-698 (3) 3.55 3.55

Cyprus Customs Union in Cooperation with the EEC — A245

Perf. 13x13½
1988, Jan. 11   **Wmk. 344**
699 A245 15c Natl. and EEC flags 1.25 1.25
700 A245 18c Maps 1.60 1.60

A246

Europa (Communication and transportation): No. 701, Electronic mail (Intelpost). No. 702, Cellular telephone system. No. 703, Cyprus Airways, technology vs. ecology (jet, 3 flamingos). No. 704, Cyprus Airways (jet, 4 flamingos).

1988, May 9   **Perf. 14x14½**
701	A246	7c multicolored	.55	.45
702	A246	7c multicolored	.55	.45
a.		Pair, #701-702	1.25	1.25
703	A246	18c multicolored	2.00	1.50
704	A246	18c multicolored	2.00	1.50
a.		Pair, #703-704	5.00	5.00
		Nos. 701-704 (4)	5.10	3.90

1988 Summer Olympics, Seoul — A247

Unwmk.
1988, June 27   **Photo.**   **Perf. 12**
Granite Paper
705	A247	5c Sailing	.45	.30
706	A247	7c Track	.50	.50
707	A247	10c Marksmanship	.55	.55
708	A247	20c Judo	1.25	1.25
		Nos. 705-708 (4)	2.75	2.60

Non-Aligned Foreign Minister's Conference — A248

Designs: 10c, Natl. coat of arms. 50c, Jawaharlal Nehru, Tito, Gamal Abdel Nasser and Makarios III (1913-77).

Perf. 14x13½
1988, Sept. 5   **Litho.**   **Wmk. 344**
709	A248	1c shown	.20	.20
710	A248	10c multicolored	.50	.50
711	A248	50c multicolored	2.75	2.75
		Nos. 709-711 (3)	3.45	3.45

No. 643 Surcharged

1988, Oct. 3   **Litho.**   **Perf. 15x14**
712	A223	15c on 4c multi	1.75	1.40

A249

A250

Christmas.

Perf. 13½x14
1988, Nov. 28   **Litho.**   **Wmk. 344**
713	A249	5c Candlemas	.45	.25
714	A249	15c Madonna and child	.95	.30
715	A249	17c Adoration of the Magi	1.40	1.40
		Nos. 713-715 (3)	2.80	1.95

1988, Dec. 10
716	A250	25c lt ultra & int blue	1.25	1.25

UN Declaration of Human Rights, 40th anniv.

3rd Games of Small European States, Nicosia A251

Perf. 13½
1989, Apr. 10   **Litho.**   **Unwmk.**
717	A251	1c Discus	.40	.30
718	A251	5c Javelin	.40	.30
719	A251	15c Wrestling	.90	.70
720	A251	18c Running	1.10	1.10

Size: 110x80mm
Imperf
721	A251	£1 Mythological woman, laurel, bird	8.00	8.00
		Nos. 717-721 (5)	10.80	10.40

Various Children's Games A252

Perf. 13x13½
1989, May 8   **Litho.**   **Unwmk.**
722	A252	7c multi (5 boys)	.85	.75
723	A252	7c multi (6 boys)	.85	.75
a.		Pair, #722-723	1.90	1.90
724	A252	18c multi (6 boys)	1.25	1.10
725	A252	18c multi (5 boys)	1.25	1.10
a.		Pair, #724-725	2.75	2.75
		Nos. 722-725 (4)	4.20	3.70

Europa.

French Revolution, Bicent. — A253

Perf. 11½
1989, July 7   **Litho.**   **Unwmk.**
Granite Paper
726	A253	18c multicolored	1.50	1.50

A254

A255

1989, Sept. 4   **Perf. 13½**
727	A254	15c multicolored	.70	.65
728	A255	30c multicolored	1.50	1.40

15c for Interparliamentary Union, cent. 30c for 9th Non-Aligned Summit Conf., Belgrade.

Apiculture A256

Annivs. & Events — A257

1989, Oct. 15   **Perf. 13½x14**
729	A256	3c Honeycomb	.55	.30
730	A256	10c Gathering nectar	1.00	.60
731	A256	15c Gathering nectar, diff.	1.25	.60
732	A256	18c Queen, worker bees	1.50	1.50
		Nos. 729-732 (4)	4.30	3.00

1989, Nov. 13

Designs: 3c, Armenian earthquake. 5c, Cyprus Philatelic Society. 7c, European Cancer Year. 17c, World Food Day.

733	A257	3c multicolored	.40	.40
734	A257	5c multicolored	.55	.30
735	A257	7c multicolored	.95	.95
736	A257	17c multicolored	1.40	1.40
		Nos. 733-736 (4)	3.30	3.05

A258

A259

Mosaics, 3rd-5th Cent. A260

Details: 1c, Winter, from *The Four Seasons*, House of Dionysos. 2c, Personification of Crete, from *Theseus Slaying the Minotaur*, Villa of Theseus. 3c, Centaur and Maenad, from *The Dionysiac Procession*, House of Aion, vert. 4c, *Poseidon and Amymone*, House of Dionysos. 5c, Leda, from *Leda and the Swan*, House of Aion. 7c, Apollon, from *Apollo and Marsyas*, House of Aion. 10c, Hermes and Dionysos, from *Hermes Presenting Dionysos to Tropheus*, House of Aion, vert. 15c, Cassiopeia, from *Cassiopeia and the Nereids*, House of Aion. 18c, Orpheus Playing

the Lyre, House of Orpheus. 20c, Nymphs preparing bath, from *Hermes Presenting Dionysos to Tropheus,* vert. 25c, Amazon holding double ax and reins, House of Orpheus, vert. 40c, Doris, one of 3 Nereids in *Cassiopeia and the Nereids.* 50c, Hercules and the lion, from *The First Labor of Hercules,* House of Orpheus. £1, *Apollon and Daphne,* House of Dionysos. £3, Cupid hunting, Villa of Theseus.

Perf. 13, 13x13½ (2c, 4c, 18c, 40c), 13½x13 (3c, 10c, 20c, 25c)
1989, Dec. 29
737	A258	1c multicolored	.40	1.25
738	A259	2c multicolored	.50	1.25
739	A259	3c multicolored	.65	1.50
740	A259	4c multicolored	.85	1.50
741	A258	5c multicolored	.85	.30
742	A258	7c multicolored	1.00	.35
743	A259	10c multicolored	1.25	.60
744	A258	15c multicolored	2.10	.65
745	A259	18c multicolored	2.10	.70
746	A259	20c multicolored	2.50	1.10
747	A259	25c multicolored	2.50	1.10
748	A259	40c multicolored	3.50	2.25

Perf. 13½x14
749	A260	50c multicolored	2.75	2.25
750	A260	£1 multicolored	5.50	4.50
751	A260	£3 multicolored	12.50	12.00
		Nos. 737-751 (15)	38.95	31.10

UNESCO World Literacy Year — A261

83rd Interparliamentary Conference, Nicosia — A262

Lions Europa Forum A263

Anniversaries & events.

1990, Apr. 3   **Perf. 14x13½**
752	A261	15c multicolored	.80	.80
753	A262	17c multicolored	.95	.95
754	A263	18c multicolored	1.25	1.25
		Nos. 752-754 (3)	3.00	3.00

Europa A264

Post Offices.

1990, May 10   **Litho.**   **Perf. 13x13½**
755	A264	7c Paphos	1.00	.45
756	A264	18c Limassol City Center	1.75	1.25

European Year of Tourism — A265

Designs: 5c, Hotel and Catering Institute, 25th anniv. 7c, Holy Church of St. Lazarus, 1100th anniv. 15c, Female silhouette, butterflies. 18c, Male silhouette, birds.

1990, July 9   **Perf. 14**
757	A265	5c multicolored	.65	.60
758	A265	7c multicolored	.85	.80
759	A265	15c multicolored	2.25	1.75
760	A265	18c multicolored	2.60	2.60
		Nos. 757-760 (4)	6.35	5.75

Republic of Cyprus, 30th Anniv. A266

1990, Sept. 29   **Photo.**   **Perf. 11½**
761	A266	15c Sun	.85	.60
762	A266	17c shown	1.10	.70
763	A266	18c Fish	1.40	.80
764	A266	40c Birds, flowers	3.00	3.00

Size: 90x90mm
Imperf
765	A266	£1 Stylized bird	6.50	6.50
		Nos. 761-765 (5)	12.85	11.60

Flowers — A267   Christmas — A268

1990, Nov. 5   **Litho.**   **Perf. 13½x13**
766	A267	2c Chionodoxa lochiae	.40	.70
767	A267	3c Pancrayium maritimum	.60	.70
768	A267	5c Paeonia mascula	.85	.60
769	A267	7c Cyclamen cyprium	1.10	.90
770	A267	15c Tulipa cypria	2.25	2.50
771	A267	18c Crocus cyprius	2.50	2.50
		Nos. 766-771 (6)	7.70	7.40

1990, Dec. 3   **Perf. 13½x14**
772	A268	5c Nativity	.90	.30
773	A268	15c Virgin and Child	1.90	.45
774	A268	17c Nativity, diff.	2.25	1.90
		Nos. 772-774 (3)	5.05	2.65

Mosaics From Kanakaria Church — A269

1991, Mar. 28   **Photo.**   **Perf. 12**
Granite Paper
775	A269	5c Archangel	.80	.20
776	A269	15c Christ Child	.85	.75
777	A269	17c St. James	1.75	1.75
778	A269	18c St. Matthew	2.00	2.00
		Nos. 775-778 (4)	5.40	4.70

Europa A270

1991, May 6   **Litho.**   **Perf. 13x13½**
779	A270	7c Spacecraft Ulysses	.75	.40
780	A270	18c Spacecraft Giotto	1.60	1.10

Oenanthe Cypriaca (Cyprus Wheatear) A271

1991, July 4   **Litho.**   **Perf. 13½**
781	A271	5c Juvenile bird	1.10	.50
782	A271	7c Autumn plumage	1.25	.50
783	A271	15c Male bird	1.50	.75
784	A271	30c Female bird	2.50	2.50
		Nos. 781-784 (4)	6.35	4.25

UN High Commissioner for Refugees, 40th Anniv. — A272

1991, Oct. 7   **Litho.**   **Perf. 14x13½**
785	A272	5c shown	.40	.25
786	A272	15c Legs	1.50	.75
787	A272	18c Faces	1.90	1.90
		Nos. 785-787 (3)	3.80	2.90

Christmas A273

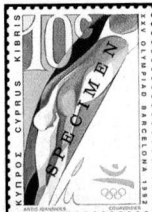

A274

1991, Nov. 25   **Litho.**   **Perf. 13½**
788	A273	5c Nativity scene	.40	.25
789	A273	15c St. Basil	.95	.85
790	A273	17c Baptism of Jesus	1.25	1.25
a.		Strip of 3, #788-790	3.00	3.00

Strips of 3 are from sheets of 9.

1992, Apr. 3   **Litho.**   **Perf. 12**
Granite Paper
791	A274	10c Swimming	.95	.50
792	A274	20c Long jump	1.50	1.00
793	A274	30c Running	2.10	2.10
794	A274	35c Discus	2.40	2.40
		Nos. 791-794 (4)	6.95	6.00

1992 Summer Olympics, Barcelona.

Expo '92, Seville A275

10th Youth Under 16 European Soccer Tournament — A276

Opening of University of Cyprus A277

1992, Apr. 20   **Litho.**   **Perf. 14**
795	A275	20c multicolored	2.00	.95
796	A276	25c multicolored	2.10	1.25
797	A277	30c multicolored	2.10	2.10
		Nos. 795-797 (3)	6.20	4.30

Discovery of America, 500th Anniv. A278

1992, May 29   **Litho.**   **Perf. 13x13½**
798	A278	10c Map	1.00	.90
799	A278	10c Embarkation at Palos	1.00	.90
a.		Pair, #798-799	2.25	2.25
800	A278	30c Three ships	1.50	1.25
801	A278	30c Columbus	1.50	1.25
a.		Pair, #800-801	3.25	3.25
		Nos. 798-801 (4)	5.00	4.30

Europa.

Reptiles A279

Designs: 7c, Chamaeleo chamaeleon. 10c, Lacerta laevis troodica. 15c, Mauremys caspica. 20c, Coluber cypriensis.

1992, Sept. 14   **Litho.**   **Perf. 14x13½**
802	A279	7c multicolored	1.10	.40
803	A279	10c multicolored	1.25	.65
804	A279	15c multicolored	1.75	1.10
805	A279	20c multicolored	2.00	2.00
		Nos. 802-805 (4)	6.10	4.15

Intl. Maritime and Shipping Conference — A280

Unwmk.
1992, Nov. 9   **Litho.**   **Perf. 14**
806	A280	50c multicolored	4.25	4.25

Christmas A281

Church wall paintings: 7c, , "Virgin Mary Greeting Elizabeth," Church of Timios Stavros, Pelendri. 15c, "The Virgin and Child," Church of Panayia tou Araka. 20c, "Holy Mother Odigitria," Church of Ayios Nicolaos tis Steyis.

1992, Nov. 9   **Perf. 13½x14**
807	A281	7c multicolored	.65	.35
808	A281	15c multicolored	1.10	.75
809	A281	20c multicolored	1.75	1.75
		Nos. 807-809 (3)	3.50	2.85

A282

A283

1993, Feb. 15   **Litho.**   **Perf. 14**
810	A282	10c multicolored	1.00	.80

Pancyprian Gymnasium, cent.

1993, Apr. 3   **Perf. 13½x14, 14x13½**
Europa: 10c, Bronze sculpture, Motherhood, by N. Dymiotis (1930-1990). 30c, Applique, Motherhood, by Savva (1924-1968), horiz.
811	A283	10c multicolored	.90	.65
812	A283	30c multicolored	1.60	1.25

13th European Cup for Women Athletes A284

Scouting in Cyprus, 80th Anniv. — A285

Water Skiing Moufflon Encouragement Cup — A286

Archbishop Makarios III, 80th Anniv. of Birth — A287

Perf. 13½x14, 14x13½
1993, May 24   **Litho.**
813	A284	7c multicolored	.60	.40
814	A285	10c multicolored	.80	.55
815	A286	20c multicolored	1.40	1.40
a.		Inscribed "MUFFLON"	25.00	
816	A287	25c multicolored	2.00	2.00
		Nos. 813-816 (4)	4.80	4.35

Fish — A288

1993, Sept. 6   **Litho.**   **Perf. 14x13½**
817	A288	7c Holocentrus ruber	.60	.30
818	A288	15c Scorpaena scrofa	.95	.60
819	A288	20c Serranus scriba	1.10	1.10
820	A288	30c Balistes capriscus	2.10	2.10
		Nos. 817-820 (4)	4.75	4.10

Maritime
Cyprus
A289

1993, Oct. 4   **Perf. 14**
821 A289 25c multicolored   2.50 2.50

12th Commonwealth Summit
Conference — A290

1993, Oct. 4   **Perf. 14x13½**
822 A290 35c red brown & tan   2.40 2.40
823 A290 40c olive brown & tan   3.00 3.00

Christmas
A291

7c, Carved wooden cross, Stavrovouni Monastery. 20c, Crucifixion, cross from Lefkara Church. 25c, Nativity, cross from Pedoulas Church.

1993, Nov. 22   **Litho.**   **Perf. 13½x14**
824 A291 7c multicolored   .40 .30
825 A291 20c multicolored   .95 .95

        Perf. 14x13½
826 A291 25c multi, horiz.   1.40 1.40
     Nos. 824-826 (3)   2.75 2.65

Copper
Industry
A292

Europa: 10c, Early smelting of copper. 30c, Map, boat, copper ingot.

1994, Mar. 1   **Litho.**   **Perf. 13x13½**
827 A292 10c multicolored   .45 .40
828 A292 30c multicolored   1.25 1.10

Persons with
Special
Needs — A293

Intl. Olympic
Committee,
Cent. — A294

World
Gymnasiade,
Nicosia — A295

Intl. Year of the
Family — A296

1994, May 9   **Litho.**   **Perf. 13**
829 A293 7c multicolored   .65 .35
830 A294 15c multicolored   1.10 .65
831 A295 20c multicolored   1.40 1.40
832 A296 25c multicolored   1.75 1.75
     Nos. 829-832 (4)   4.90 4.15

Turkish Invasion and Occupation of
Cyprus, 20th Anniv. — A297

1994, June 27   **Litho.**   **Perf. 14**
833 A297 10c Human rights   .90 .40
834 A297 50c Cultural heritage   3.50 3.50

Trees — A298

7c, Pinus nigra. 15c, Cedrus libani. 20c, Quercus alnifolia. 30c, Arbutus andrachne.

1994, Oct. 10   **Litho.**   **Perf. 13½**
835 A298 7c multicolored   .70 .40
836 A298 15c multicolored   1.10 .75
837 A298 20c multicolored   1.25 1.25
838 A298 30c multicolored   2.00 2.00
     Nos. 835-838 (4)   5.05 4.40

ICAO,
50th
Anniv.
A299

1994, Nov. 21   **Litho.**   **Perf. 14**
839 A299 30c multicolored   3.00 3.00

Christmas
A300

Designs: 7c, Virgin Mary (Vlahernitissa). 20c, Nativity. 25c, Archangel Michael.

1994, Nov. 21   **Perf. 13½**
840 A300 7c multicolored   .75 .40
841 A300 20c multicolored   1.75 1.10
842 A300 25c multicolored   2.00 2.00
     Nos. 840-842 (3)   4.50 3.50

Traditional
Costumes — A301

Costumes: 1c, Female, Phapos. 2c, Bridal, Karpess. 3c, Female, Phapos, diff. 5c, Female, Messaoria. 7c, Bridegroom's. 10c, Shepherd's, Messaoria. 15c, Festive female, Nicosia. 20c, Festive female, Karpass. 25c, Female, Mountain-Pitsillia. 30c, Festive female, Karpass, diff. 35c, Rural male. 40c, Plain festive male, Messaoria. 50c, Urban male. £1, Urban festive female, Sarka.

1994, Dec. 27   **Litho.**   **Perf. 13½x13**
843 A301 1c multicolored   .35 .35
844 A301 2c multicolored   .50 .50
845 A301 3c multicolored   .55 .55
846 A301 5c multicolored   .70 .70
847 A301 7c multicolored   .75 .75
848 A301 10c multicolored   1.00 1.00
849 A301 15c multicolored   1.75 1.75
850 A301 20c multicolored   1.75 1.75
851 A301 25c multicolored   2.00 2.00
852 A301 30c multicolored   2.00 2.00
853 A301 35c multicolored   2.00 2.00
854 A301 40c multicolored   2.25 2.25
855 A301 50c multicolored   3.50 3.50
856 A301 £1 multicolored   6.75 6.75
     Nos. 843-856 (14)   25.85 25.85

No. 856 exists inscribed "1998."

Third Intl.
Congress of
Cypriot
Studies — A302

Excavations: 20c, Hearth room, Ashlar building, Paliotaverna. 30c, Hall, Agios Demetrios area, Kalavasos. £1, Old Nicosia Archbishorpic building, 18th cent.

1995, Feb. 27   **Litho.**   **Perf. 14**
859 A302 20c multicolored   1.40 1.40
860 A302 30c multicolored   2.00 2.00

     Size: 107x71mm
       Imperf
861 A302 £1 multicolored   6.25 6.25
     Nos. 859-861 (3)   9.65 9.65

A303   A304

Liberation Monument, Nicosia: a, People walking left. b, Statue of Liberty, prisoners leaving prison. c, People walking right.

1995, Mar. 31   **Litho.**   **Perf. 13x14**
862   Strip of 3   4.75 4.75
  a.-c.   A303 20c any single   1.50 1.50
     No. 862 is a continuous design.
     Formation of EOKA (Natl. Organization of Cypriot Struggle), 40th anniv.

1995, May 8   **Litho.**   **Perf. 13½**
Europa: 10c, Concentration camp prisoners, dove, rainbow, map of Europe. 30c, Prisoner, dove.
863 A304 10c multicolored   1.00 .75
864 A304 30c multicolored   2.00 1.60
     Liberation of the concentration camps, 50th anniv.

Health
A305

7c, Proper nutrition, exercise. 10c, Fight against AIDS. 15c, Fight against illegal drugs. 20c, Stop smoking campaign.

1995, June 26   **Litho.**   **Perf. 13½**
865 A305 7c multi, vert.   .35 .30
866 A305 10c multi   .80 .80
867 A305 15c multi   .85 .85
868 A305 20c multi, vert.   1.25 1.25
     Nos. 865-868 (4)   3.25 3.20

European
Cultural
Month
A306

1995, Sept. 18   **Litho.**   **Perf. 13x13½**
869 A306 20c shown   .95 .95
870 A306 25c Map of Europe, building   1.25 1.25

     Souvenir Sheet

Eurofilex
'95
A307

Designs: a, Dove carrying letter, stars. b, Stars, exhibition emblem. Illustration reduced.

1995, Sept. 18   **Perf. 14**
871   Sheet of 2   9.50 9.50
  a.-b.   A307 50c any single   4.25 4.25

A limited number were surcharged £5 on each stamp and sold at "Europhilex '95" on Oct. 27 and 28, 1995.

UN, 50th
Anniv.
A308

Volleyball,
Cent. — A309

European
Conservation
Year — A310

World Clay Target Shooting
Championships — A311

CYPRUS

685

Perf. 13x13½, 13½x13

1995, Oct. 24   Litho.
872	A308	10c multicolored	.65	.65
873	A309	15c multicolored	1.00	.80
874	A310	20c multicolored	1.40	1.10
875	A311	25c multicolored	1.75	1.75
	Nos. 872-875 (4)		4.80	4.30

Christmas
A312

Various reliquaries, Kykko Monastery.

1995, Nov. 27   Litho.   **Perf. 13½x13**
876	A312	7c multicolored	.60	.45
877	A312	20c multicolored	1.40	1.10
878	A312	25c multicolored	1.75	1.75
	Nos. 876-878 (3)		3.75	3.30

A313

A314

A315

Anniversaries and
Events — A316

1996, Jan. 4   Litho.   **Perf. 13½x13**
879	A313	10c multicolored	.90	.70
880	A314	20c multicolored	1.60	1.10
881	A315	35c multicolored	2.40	2.40
882	A316	40c multicolored	2.50	2.50
	Nos. 879-882 (4)		7.40	6.70

Pancyprian Organization of Large Families, 25th anniv. (#879). Motion pictures, cent. (#880). UNICEF, 50th anniv. (#881). 13th Conf. of Commonwealth Speakers and Presiding Officers (#882).

Portraits of Women
A317   A318

1996, Apr. 8   Litho.   **Perf. 14**
883	A317	10c multicolored	*.75*	*.40*
884	A318	30c multicolored	*1.50*	*1.10*

Europa.

1996
Summer
Olympics,
Atlanta
A319

1996, June 10   Litho.   **Perf. 13**
885	A319	10c High jump	.90	.35
886	A319	20c Javelin	1.25	.70
887	A319	25c Wrestling	1.75	1.00
888	A319	30c Swimming	2.10	2.10
	Nos. 885-888 (4)		6.00	4.15

Mills of
Cyprus — A320

1996, Sept. 23   Litho.   **Perf. 13**
889	A320	10c Watermill	.95	.70
890	A320	15c Olivemill	1.40	1.00
891	A320	20c Windmill	1.50	1.40
892	A320	25c Handmill	2.25	2.25
	Nos. 889-892 (4)		6.10	5.35

Icons,
Religious
Landmarks
A321

Designs: No. 893, Icon of Our Lady of Iberia, Moscow. No. 894, Holy Monastery of Stavrovouni, Cyprus. No. 895, Icon of St. Nicholas, Cyprus. No. 896, Iveron Mother of God Resurrection Gate, Moscow.

1996, Nov. 13   Litho.   **Perf. 11½**
893	A321	30c multicolored	2.40	2.40
894	A321	30c multicolored	2.40	2.40
895	A321	30c multicolored	2.40	2.40
896	A321	30c multicolored	2.40	2.40
a.		Block of 4, #893-896	10.00	10.00

See Russia No. 6356.

Christmas
A322

Paintings from Church of the Virgin of Asinou: 7c, Detail from Nativity. 20c, Virgin Mary between Archangels Gabriel and Michael. 25c, Christ bestowing blessings, vert.

1996, Dec. 2   **Perf. 13x13½, 13½x13**
897	A322	7c multicolored	1.00	.50
898	A322	20c multicolored	2.25	1.25
899	A322	25c multicolored	2.75	2.75
	Nos. 897-899 (3)		6.00	4.50

Easter
A323

1997, Mar. 24   Litho.   **Perf. 13x13½**
900	A323	15c The Last Supper	1.25	.65
901	A323	25c The Crucifixion	1.75	1.75

A324

A325

1997, Mar. 24   **Perf. 13½x13**
902	A324	30c multicolored	4.00	3.75

European Men's Clubs Basketball Cup finals.

1997, May 5   Litho.   **Perf. 13½x13**

Europa (Stories and Legends): 30c, Man in red cape fighting Death, eagle above.
903	A325	15c shown	*.75*	*.45*
904	A325	30c multicolored	*1.25*	*1.00*

Insects
A326

10c, Oedipoda miniata. 15c, Acherontia atropos. 25c, Daphnis nerii. 35c, Ascalaphus macaronius.

1997, June 30   Litho.   **Perf. 13x13½**
905	A326	10c multicolored	.95	.55
906	A326	15c multicolored	1.40	.75
907	A326	25c multicolored	1.90	1.50
908	A326	35c multicolored	2.40	2.40
	Nos. 905-908 (4)		6.65	5.20

Archbishop
Makarios III
(1913-77),
1st Pres. of
Cyprus
Republic
A327

1997, Aug. 1   Litho.   **Perf. 13x13½**
909	A327	15c multicolored	1.50	1.50

Christmas
A328

Frescoes from Church of Ayios Ioannis Lambadestis: 10c, Nativity. 25c, Magi on way to Bethlehem. 30c, Flight into Egypt.

1997, Nov. 17   Litho.   **Perf. 13½x13**
910	A328	10c multicolored	.95	.65
911	A328	25c multicolored	2.40	1.40
912	A328	30c multicolored	2.75	2.75
	Nos. 910-912 (3)		6.10	4.80

Minerals
A329

1998, Mar. 9   Litho.   **Perf. 13½x13**
913	A329	10c Green jasper	.60	.40
914	A329	15c Iron pyrite	.90	.65
915	A329	20c Gypsum	1.40	1.40
916	A329	30c Chalcedony	1.75	1.75
	Nos. 913-916 (4)		4.65	4.20

1998 World Cup Soccer
Championships, France — A330

1998, May 4   Litho.   **Perf. 14**
917	A330	35c multicolored	3.00	1.75

Europa
A331

Festivals, holidays: 15c, "Katakklysmos" Larnaca. 30c, People watching proclamation of independence, 1960.

1998, May 4
918	A331	15c multicolored	*.80*	*.50*
919	A331	30c multicolored	*1.75*	*1.40*

Ovis
Gmelini
Ophion
A332

World Wildlife Fund: No. 920, Male, female, calf. No. 921, Group running. No. 922, Male up close. No. 923, Male with front legs up on rock, one grazing.

1998, June 22   Litho.   **Perf. 13x13½**
920	A332	25c multicolored	1.50	1.50
921	A332	25c multicolored	1.50	1.50
922	A332	25c multicolored	1.50	1.50
923	A332	25c multicolored	1.50	1.50
a.		Block of 4, #920-923	6.25	6.25

Issued in sheets of 16.

World
Stamp Day
A333

1998, Oct. 9   Litho.   **Perf. 14**
924	A333	30c multicolored	2.75	2.75
a.		Booklet pane of 8	24.00	
		Complete booklet, #924a	26.00	

A334

A335

1998, Oct. 9
925 A334 50c multicolored   2.25 2.25

Universal Declaration of Human Rights, 50th anniv.

1998, Nov. 16   Litho.   Perf. 14

Christmas (Scenes from paintings in the Church of the Virgin of Théosképasti, Kalopanayiotis): 10c, The Annunciation. 25c, The Nativity. 30c, Baptism of Christ.

926	A335	10c multicolored	.40 .40
927	A335	25c multicolored	1.10 1.10
928	A335	30c multicolored	3.25 3.25
a.		Souvenir sheet, #926-928	4.75 4.75
		Nos. 926-928 (3)	4.75 4.75

Mushrooms — A336

10c, Pleurotus eryngii. 15c, Lactarius deliciosus. 25c, Sparassis crispa. 30c, Morchella elata.

1999, Mar. 4   Litho.   Perf. 13½x13

929	A336	10c multicolored	.50 .50
930	A336	15c multicolored	1.00 .65
931	A336	25c multicolored	1.50 1.50
932	A336	30c multicolored	1.60 1.60
		Nos. 929-932 (4)	4.60 4.25

Natl. Parks and Nature Preserves A337

1999, May 6   Litho.   Perf. 14

933	A337	15c Tripylos Reserve	.80 .50
934	A337	30c Lara Reserve	1.40 1.00
a.		Booklet pane, 4 each #933-934	9.00
		Complete booklet, #934a	10.00

Europa.

Council of Europe, 50th Anniv. A338

1999, May 6
935 A338 30c multicolored   2.00 2.00

4000 Years of Hellenism — A339

a, Sanctuary of Apollo Hylates, Kourion. b, Mycenaean "Krater of the Warriors," Athens. c, Mycenaean amphoral krater, Cyprus Museum. d, Sanctuary of Apollo Epikourios, Delphi.

1999, June 28   Litho.   Perf. 13½x13
936 A339 25c Block of 4, #a.-d.   5.75 5.75

See Greece No. 1938.

UPU, 125th Anniv. A340

1999, Sept. 30   Litho.   Perf. 14

937	A340	15c shown	1.10 .80
938	A340	35c "125"	2.50 1.90

Souvenir Sheet

Maritime Cyprus Shipping Conference A341

Cyprus flag and: a, Container ship. b, Binoculars, chart, cap. c, Ship with yellow stripe on tower. d, Tanker.

1999, Sept. 30
939 A341 25c Sheet of 4, #a.-d.   5.00 5.00

Souvenir Sheet

Turkish Invasion of Cyprus, 25th Anniv. — A342

Illustration reduced.

1999, Nov. 11   Litho.   Imperf.
940 A342 30c multicolored   2.25 2.25

A343

A344

1999, Nov. 11   Perf. 14

941	A343	10c Angel	.65 .50
942	A343	25c Magi	1.25 1.10
943	A343	30c Madonna and child	1.40 1.40
		Nos. 941-943 (3)	3.30 3.00

Christmas.

Souvenir Sheet

2000, Mar. 30   Litho.   Perf. 13¼x13

Miss Universe 2000: a, 15c, Woman, stars. b, 35c, Armless nude statue of woman.

944 A344   Sheet of 2, #a.-b.   2.00 2.00

Jewelry — A345

Various pieces of jewelry. #945-952 vert.

2000, Mar. 30   Litho.   Perf. 14

945	A345	10c multi	.40 .40
946	A345	15c multi	.55 .55
947	A345	20c multi	.75 .75
948	A345	25c multi	.95 .95
949	A345	30c multi	1.10 1.10
950	A345	35c multi	1.25 1.25
951	A345	40c multi	1.50 1.50

952	A345	50c multi	2.00 2.00
953	A345	75c multi	2.75 2.75
954	A345	£1 multi	3.75 3.75
955	A345	£2 multi	7.50 7.50
956	A345	£3 multi	11.50 11.50
		Nos. 945-956 (12)	34.00 34.00

Cyprus Red Cross, 50th Anniv. A346

2000, May 9   Litho.   Perf. 13x13¼
957 A346 15c multi   2.00 2.00

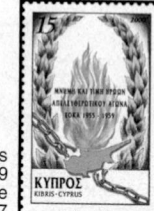
Memorial to Heroes of 1955-59 Independence Struggle — A347

2000, May 9   Perf. 13¼x13
958 A347 15c multi   1.75 1.75

Europa, 2000
Common Design Type

2000, May 9   Perf. 14
959 CD17 30c multi   1.40 1.00

World Meteorological Org., 50th Anniv. — A348

2000, May 9
960 A348 30c multi   2.00 2.00

European Convention of Human Rights, 50th Anniv. A349

2000, June 29   Litho.   Perf. 13¼x13
961 A349 30c multi   2.75 2.75

Churches Damaged Under Turkish Occupation A350

Designs: 10c, Monastery of Antifonitis, Kalograia, vert. 15c, Church of St. Themonianos, Lysi, vert. 25c, Church of Panagia Kanakaria, Lythragkomi. 30c, Avgasida Monastery Church, Milia.

Perf. 13¼x13, 13x13¼

2000, June 29

962	A350	10c multi	.80 .50
963	A350	15c multi	1.10 .70
964	A350	25c multi	1.50 1.40
965	A350	30c multi	1.75 1.75
		Nos. 962-965 (4)	5.15 4.35

2000 Summer Olympics, Sydney A351

Designs: 10c, Archery. 15c, Pommel horse. 25c, Diving. 35c, Trampoline.

2000, Sept. 14   Litho.   Perf. 13x13½
966-969 A351   Set of 4   5.25 5.25

Christmas — A352

Gospel covers: 10c, Annunciation. 25c, Nativity. 30c, Baptism of Jesus.

2000, Nov. 2   Perf. 13½x13
970-972 A352   Set of 3   4.25 4.25

Pavlos Liasides (1901-85), Poet — A353

2001, Mar. 12   Litho.   Perf. 13¼x13
973 A353 13c multi   1.00 .55

Commonwealth Day, 25th Anniv. — A354

2001, Mar. 12   Perf. 13x13¼
974 A354 30c multi   2.25 2.25

UN High Commissioner for Refugees, 50th Anniv. — A355

2001, Mar. 12
975 A355 30c multi   2.25 2.25

Europa A356

Designs: 20c, Bridge over Diarizos River. 30c, Akaki River.

2001, May 3

976-977	A356	Set of 2	2.25 1.40
977a		Booklet pane, 4 each #976-977	9.50
		Booklet, #977a	10.50

Crabs A357

Designs: 13c, Parthenope massena. 20c, Calappa granulata. 25c, Ocypode cursor. 30c, Pagurus bernhardus.

2001, June 7
978-981 A357 Set of 4   6.50 6.50

Loukis Akritas (1909-65), Writer A358

Christmas A359

2001, Oct. 25 Litho. Perf. 13½x13
982 A358 20c multi   1.50 .85

2001, Oct. 25

Holy Monastery of Macheras, 800th anniv.: 13c, Icon of Madonna. 25c, Monastery building. 30c, Crucifix.

983-985 A359 Set of 3   3.75 3.75

Cats — A360

No. 986, 20c: a, Red brown panel. b, Green panel.
No. 987, 25c: a, Dark brown panel. b, Orange brown panel.
Illustration reduced.

2002, Mar. 21 Litho. Perf. 13x13½
Horiz. Pairs, #a-b
986-987 A360 Set of 2   6.00 6.00

Europa — A361

Designs: 20c, Equestrian act. 30c, Tightrope walker.

2002, May 9 Perf. 13½x13
988-989 A361 Set of 2   2.25 1.40
a. Booklet pane, 4 each #988-989   9.50   —
    Booklet, #989a   10.50

Medicinal Plants A362

Designs: 13c, Myrtus communis. 20c, Lavandula stoechas. 25c, Capparis spinosa. 30c, Ocimum basilicum.

2002, June 13 Perf. 13x13½
990-993 A362 Set of 4   6.00 6.00

Mother Teresa (1910-97) — A363

2002, Sept. 12 Litho. Perf. 13½x13
994 A363 40c multi   3.25 3.25

Intl. Teachers' Day — A364

No. 995: a, 13c, Blackboard and teachers. b, 30c, Computer and teachers.
Illustration reduced.

2002, Sept. 12 Perf. 13x13½
995 A364 Horiz. pair, #a-b   2.75 2.75

Cyprus-Europhilex 02 Philatelic Exhibition — A365

No. 996: a, Seal, 490-470 B.C. (red brown background). b, Silver coin of Timoharis, 5th-4th cent B.C. (blue background) c, Silver coin of Stasioikos, 449 B.C. (yellow background).
No. 997: a, Clay oil lamp, 2nd cent. A.D. (olive green background). b, Clay statue of Europa on a bull, 7th-6th cent. B.C. (yellow background). c, Clay oil lamp, 1st cent. B.C. (lilac background).
No. 998: a, 15th cent. map of eastern Crete and western Cyprus, and statue of Aphrodite, 1st cent. B.C. b, Map of eastern Cyprus, and Abduction of Europe, by Francesco di Giorgio.

2002, Sept. 22
996   Horiz. strip of 3   4.25 4.25
a.-c. A365 20c Any single   1.40 1.40
997   Horiz. strip of 3   6.00 6.00
a.-c. A365 20c Any single   2.00 2.00
Souvenir Sheet
998   Sheet of 2, #a-b   8.75 8.75
a.-b. A365 50c Any single   3.50 3.50

Christmas A366

Wall painting in Church of Metamorphosis Sotiros, Palechori: 13c, Nativity, detail. 25c, Angels, detail. 30c, Entire painting (37x37mm).

Perf. 13x13½, 13¾ (30c)
2002, Nov. 21
999-1001 A366 Set of 3   4.25 4.25

Antique Automobiles A367

No. 1002: a, 20c, 1946 Triumph Roadster 1800. b, 25c, 1917 Ford Model T. c, 30c, 1932 Baby Ford.

2003, Mar. 20 Litho. Perf. 13x13½
1002 A367 Vert. strip of 3, #a-c 5.25 5.25

Europa — A368

2003, May 8 Perf. 13½x13
Color of Triangles
1003 A368 20c yellow   .85 .60
a.   Perf. 13½x13¾ on 3 sides 1.50 1.00
1004 A368 30c red   1.25 .90
a.   Perf. 13½x13¾ on 3 sides 2.50 1.50
b.   Booklet pane, 4 each
     #1003a-1004a   17.50   —
     Complete booklet, #1004b 20.00

European Ministers of Education, 7th Conference — A369

2003, June 12 Litho. Perf. 13½x13
1005 A369 30c multi   2.25 2.25

Worldwide Fund for Nature (WWF) — A370

Mediterranean horseshoe bat: a, In flight. b, Close-up. c, Hanging from rock. d, With open mouth.
Illustration reduced.

2003, June 12 Perf. 13x13½
1006 A370 25c Block of 4, #a-b 7.50 7.50

Birds of Prey — A371

No. 1007, 20c: a, Eleonora's falcon. b, Eleonora's falcons in flight.
No. 1008, 25c: a, Head of Imperial eagle. b, Imperial eagles in flight.
No. 1009, 30c: a, Owl on branch. b, Owl in flight, eggs.

2003, Sept. 25 Litho. Perf. 14
Horiz. pairs, #a-b
1007-1009 A371 Set of 3   8.00 8.00

Famous Men A372

Designs: No. 1010, 5c, Constantinos Spyridakis (1903-76), Education minister. No. 1011, 5c, Tefkros Anthias (1903-68), poet (23x31mm).

Perf. 13x13¼, 13¼x13
2003, Nov. 13
1010-1011 A372 Set of 2   1.00 1.00

Christmas A373

Details of Nativity icon from church in Kourdali: 13c, Angels. 30c, Three Magi on horses. 40c, Entire icon (37x60mm).

Perf. 13¾x13¼, 13¾x14 (40c)
2003, Nov. 13
1012-1014 A373 Set of 3   4.50 4.50

FIFA (Fédération Internationale de Football Association), Cent. — A374

Perf. 13¼x13¾
2004, Mar. 11 Litho.
1015 A374 30c multi   1.75 1.75

UEFA (European Soccer Union), 50th Anniv. — A375

2004, Mar. 11 Perf. 13¼x13
1016 A375 30c multi   1.75 1.75

Yiannos Kranidiotis (1947-99), Politician A376

2004, May 1 Perf. 13¼x13½
1017 A376 20c multi   1.00 1.00

Admission to European Union — A377

2004, May 1 Perf. 14¼x14
1018 A377 30c multi   1.75 1.75

Europa A378

Cliff and: 20c, Amphitheater, ship. 30c, Family at seashore, sculpture

2004, May 1 Perf. 13¾x13¼
1019 A378 20c multi   .80 .50
a.   Perf. 13¾ on 3 sides   1.00 .60
1020 A378 30c multi   1.25 .80
a.   Perf. 13¾ on 3 sides   1.50 1.00
b.   Booklet pane, 4 each #1019a,
     1020a   11.50
     Complete booklet, #1020b 13.00

2004 Summer Olympics,
Athens — A379

Designs: 13c, Equestrian. 20c, Runners.
30c, Swimmers. 40c, Athletes, man in robe.
Illustration reduced.

2004, June 10   Litho.   _Perf. 13¼x13_
1021-1024 A379   Set of 4   5.25 5.25

Mammals — A380

No. 1025, 20c — Tursiops truncatus: a, Blue
background. b, White background.
No. 1026, 30c — Vulpes vulpes indutus: a,
Green background. b, White background.
No. 1027, 40c, Lepus europaeus cyprium:
a, Orange brown background. b, White
background.
Illustration reduced.

2004, Sept. 9   Litho.   _Perf. 13¾x13½_
Horiz. Pairs, #a-b
1025-1027 A380   Set of 3   12.50 12.50

Georgios   Emilios
Philippou   Chourmouzios
Pierides (1904-   (1904-73),
99),   Writer — A382
Writer — A381

2004, Nov. 11   _Perf. 13¼x13_
1028 A381 5c multi   .40   .40
1029 A382 5c multi   .40   .40

Christmas
A383

Details from icon depicting the birth of
Christ, Monastery of Chrysoroyiatissa: 13c,
Angels. 30c, Magi on horseback. 40c, Annunciation, vert. (37x60mm).
£1, Adoration of the Shepherds.

Perf. 13¾x13¼, 13¾x14 (40c)
2004, Nov. 11
1030-1032 A383   Set of 3   6.00 6.00
Souvenir Sheet
Perf. 13¾ on 3 Sides
1033 A383 £1 multi   7.00 7.00
No. 1033 contains one 37x38mm stamp.

Carolina
Pelendritou,
Swimming Gold
Medalist at 2004
Paralympics
A384

2005, Mar. 3   Litho.   _Perf. 13¼x13¾_
1034 A384 20c multi   1.40 1.40

Rotary
International,
Cent. — A385

2005, Mar. 3
1035 A385 40c multi   2.25 2.25

Natl.
Organization of
Cypriot Struggle
(EOKA), 50th
Anniv. — A386

2005, Mar. 3
1036 A386 50c multi   2.75 2.75

Europa — A387

Table with food and: 20c, Purple grapes,
sailboat. 30c, Green grapes, steamship.

2005, May 5   _Perf. 13½x13_
White Frame All Around
1037 A387 20c multi   .90   .90
1038 A387 30c multi   1.40 1.40

Booklet Stamps
White Frame on 3 Sides
Perf. 13½ on 3 Sides
1039 A387 20c multi   1.25   .75
1040 A387 30c multi   1.75 1.25
  a.   Horiz. pair, #1039-1040   3.25 2.25
  b.   Booklet pane, 4 #1040a   13.50
       Complete booklet, #1040b 15.00
       Nos. 1037-1040 (4)   5.30 4.30

Dogs — A388

Designs: 13c, German shepherd. 20c, Hungarian vizsla. 30c, Labrador retriever. 40c,
Dalmatian.

2005, June 16   Litho.   _Perf. 13¼_
1041-1044 A388   Set of 4   5.50 5.50
  1044a   Booklet pane, #1041-1044   5.50
          Complete booklet, #1044a   5.50

Christmas
A389

Icons: 13c, Annunciation to the Shepherds.
30c, Adoration of the Magi. 40c, Madonna and
Child, vert. (38x60mm).

Perf. 13¼, 13¾x14 (40c)
2005, Nov. 10   Litho.
1045-1047 A389   Set of 3   4.25 4.25

Souvenir Sheet

Europa Stamps, 50th Anniv. — A390

No. 1048: a, Cyprus #246. b, Cyprus #202.
c, Cyprus #220. d, Cyprus #231.

2006, Feb. 23   Litho.   _Perf. 13¾_
1048 A390 30c Sheet of 4, #a-d   6.00 6.00

Postal
Museum,
25th Anniv.
A391

2006, Mar. 30   _Perf. 13¾x13¼_
1049 A391 25c multi   1.25 1.25

Rembrandt
(1606-69),
Painter
A392

2006, Mar. 30
1050 A392 40c multi   2.00 2.00

2006 World Cup
Soccer
Championships,
Germany
A393

2006, Mar. 30   _Perf. 13¼x13¾_
1051 A393 50c multi   2.50 2.50

Souvenir Sheet

Folk Dances — A394

No. 1052 — Folk dancers from: a, Cyprus.
b, India.

2006, Apr. 12   _Perf. 13x13½_
1052 A394 40c Sheet of 2, #a-b   4.00 4.00
See India No. 2151.

Europa — A395

2006, May 4   _Perf. 13½x13_
1053 A395 30c grn & multi   1.40 1.40
  a.   Perf. 13½x13¾ on 3 sides 1.40 1.40
1054 A395 40c red & multi   1.75 1.75
  a.   Perf. 13½x13¾ on 3 sides 1.75 1.75
  b.   Booklet pane, 4 each
       #1053a-1054a   13.00   —
       Complete booklet, #1054b 13.00

Organ Transplantation — A396

2006, June 15   Litho.   _Perf. 13¼_
1055 A396 13c multi   .65 .65

Fruit — A397

Designs: 20c, Elaeagnus angustifolia. 25c,
Mespilus germanica, horiz. 60c, Opuntia ficus
barbarica.

Perf. 13¼x13½, 13½x13¼
2006, June 15
1056-1058 A397   Set of 3   5.25 5.25

Fire Trucks
A398

Designs: 13c, Bedford water carrier. 20c,
Hino pump water tender. 50c, Bedford ladder
truck.

2006, Sept. 14   _Perf. 13¾x13¼_
1059-1061 A398   Set of 3   4.25 4.25

Nicos Nicolaides
(1884-1956),
Writer — A399

2006, Nov. 16   Litho.   _Perf. 13½x13_
1062 A399 5c multi   .25 .25

Christmas
A400

Items from Agiou Eleftheriou Church: 13c, Carved wood iconostasis. 30c, Cross. 40c, Bas-relief of cross, spear and sponge.

2006, Nov. 16   Perf. 13¼x13¾
1063-1065 A400   Set of 3   4.25 4.25

St. Xenon, the Postman — A401

Illustration reduced.

Litho. & Embossed
2007, Feb. 8   Imperf.
1066 A401 £1 multi   4.75 4.75

Echinoderms — A402

No. 1067: a, Antedon mediterranea. b, Centrostephanus longispinus. c, Astropecten jonstoni. d, Ophioderma longicadum.

2007, Feb. 8 Litho.   Perf. 13¾x13¼
1067   Horiz. strip of 4   4.75 4.75
a.-d. A402 25c Any single   1.10 1.10

Motorcycles
A403

Designs: 13c, 1972 Triumph Daytona. 20c, 1941 Matchless. 40c, 1940 BSA. 60c, 1939 Ariel Red Hunter.

2007, Mar. 15
1068-1071 A403   Set of 4   6.25 6.25

Treaty of Rome,
50th
Anniv. — A404

2007, May 3   Perf. 13¼x13¾
1072 A404 30c multi   1.40 1.40

Europa — A405

Scouting emblem in gold, knot in: 30c, Light blue. 40c, Buff.

Litho. & Embossed With Foil Application
2007, May 3
1073-1074 A405   Set of 2   3.25 3.25
1074a   Booklet pane, 4 each
            #1073-1074, perf. on 3
            sides   13.00   —
            Complete booklet, #1074a 13.00

Scouting, cent.

Social Insurance, 50th Anniv. — A406

No. 1075: a, Text in Greek. b, Text in English.
Illustration reduced.

2007, June 14 Litho.   Perf. 13x13¼
1075 A406 40c Horiz. pair, #a-b   3.75 3.75

Miniature Sheet

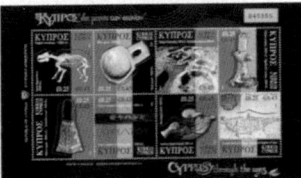

Cyprus Throughout the Ages — A407

No. 1076: a, Skeleton of pygmy hippopotamus, 10,000 B.C. b, Stone vessel, 7000 B.C. c, Choirokoitia Settlement, 7000 B.C. d, Female terracotta figurine, 3000 B.C. e, Terracotta vessel, 2000 B.C. f, Greek inscriptions on bronze skewer, 1000 B.C. g, Bird-shaped vessel, 800 B.C. h, Map of ancient kingdoms of Cyprus.

2007, Oct. 2   Perf. 13¾
1076 A407 25c Sheet of 8, #a-h   9.75 9.75

Neoclassical
Buildings
A408

Designs: 13c, Limassol District Administration Building. 15c, National Bank of Greece Building, Nicosia. 20c, Archaeological Research Unit Building, Nicosia. 30c, National Art Gallery, Nicosia. 40c, Paphos Municipal Library. 50c, A. G. Leventis Foundation Office Building, Nicosia. £1, Limassol Municipal Library. £3, Phaneromeni Gymnasium, Nicosia.

2007, Oct. 2   Perf. 13¾x13½
1077 A408 13c multi   .65   .65
1078 A408 15c multi   .75   .75
1079 A408 20c multi   1.00   1.00
1080 A408 30c multi   1.50   1.50
1081 A408 40c multi   2.00   2.00
1082 A408 50c multi   2.40   2.40
1083 A408 £1 multi   5.00   5.00
1084 A408 £3 multi   14.50 14.50
      Nos. 1077-1084 (8)   27.80 27.80

Christmas
A409

Murals from Chapel of St. Themonianus, Lysi: 13c, Virgin Mary. 30c, Archangel Gabriel. 40c, Christ Pantocrator (35x45mm).

Perf. 14x13¾, 13¾ (40c)
2007, Nov. 15
1085-1087 A409   Set of 3   4.25 4.25

POSTAL TAX STAMPS

> Catalogue values for unused stamps in this section are for Never Hinged items.

Unless otherwise stated, Cyprus postal tax stamps are for the Refugee Fund.

No. 352 Surcharged

Perf. 12x12½
1974, Dec. 2   Wmk. 344
RA1 A104 10m on 5m multi   .30   .30

Old Woman and
Child — PT1

Child and
Barbed
Wire — PT2

1974, Oct. 1   Perf. 12½x13½
RA2 PT1 10m gray & black   .30   .30

Perf. 13x12½
1977, Jan. 10 Litho.   Wmk. 344
RA3 PT2 10m black   .40   .40

Inscribed 1984

1984, June 18   Perf. 13x12½
RA4 PT2 1c black   .40   .40

There are two types of No. RA4.

Inscribed
1988 — PT3

1988-2006   Perf. 13x12½
Design Size 22x28mm
RA5 PT3 1c black & pale gray   .40   .40
Perf. 11½x12
RA6 PT3 1c Inscribed 1989   .40   .40
RA7 PT3 1c Inscribed 1990   .40   .40
Unwmk.
Perf. 13
RA8   PT3 1c Inscribed 1991   .40   .40
RA9   PT3 1c Inscribed 1992   .40   .40
RA10 PT3 1c Inscribed 1993   .40   .40
RA11 PT3 1c Inscribed 1994   .40   .40

Perf. 14½x13¾
Design Size 21x24.5mm
RA12 PT3 1c Inscribed 1995   .40   .40
RA13 PT3 1c Inscribed 1996   .40   .40
RA14 PT3 1c Inscribed 1997   .40   .40
RA15 PT3 1c Inscribed 1998   .40   .40
RA16 PT3 1c Inscribed 1999   .40   .40
RA17 PT3 1c Inscribed 2000   .40   .40
RA18 PT3 1c Inscribed 2001   .40   .40
Size: 22x27mm
Perf. 12¾
RA19 PT3 1c Inscribed 2002   .40   .40
RA20 PT3 1c Inscribed 2003   .40   .40
Perf. 12¾x13
RA21 PT3 1c Inscribed 2004   .40   .40
RA22 PT3 1c Inscribed 2005   .40   .40
RA23 PT3 1c Inscribed 2006   .40   .40
Perf. 13½x14
RA24 PT3 1c Inscribed 2007   .20   .20
      Nos. RA5-RA24 (20)   7.80   7.80

Issued: #RA5, 9/12/88; #RA6, 9/4/89; #RA7, 9/29/90; #RA8, 10/7/91; #RA9, 11/9/92; #RA10, 1993; #RA11, 11/21/94; #RA12, 10/24/95; #RA13, 6/10/96; #RA14, 6/30/97; #RA15, 1998; #RA16, 1999; #RA17, 2000; #RA18, 2001. #RA19, 2002. #RA19, 2003. #RA20, 2003. #RA21, 11/11/04. #RA22, 6/16/05. #RA23, 5/4/06. #RA24, 3/15/07.

CYRENAICA

,sir-ə-'nā-ə-kə

LOCATION — In northern Africa bordering on the Mediterranean Sea
GOVT. — Italian colony
AREA — 75,340 sq. mi.
POP. — 225,000 (approx. 1934)
CAPITAL — Bengasi (Benghazi)

Cyrenaica was an Italian Colony. In 1949 Great Britain granted the Amir of Cyrenaica autonomy in internal affairs. Cyrenaica was incorporated into the kingdom of Libya in 1951.

100 Centesimi = 1 Lira
1000 Milliemes = 1 Pound (1950)

> Catalogue values for unused stamps in this country are for Never Hinged items, beginning with Scott 65 in the regular postage section, Scott J1 in the postage due section.

> Used values in italics are for postally used stamps. CTO's sell for about the same as unused, hinged stamps.

Watermark

Wmk. 140 —
Crown

Propagation of the Faith Issue

Italy Nos. 143-146 Overprinted

1923, Oct. 24   Wmk. 140   Perf. 14

1	A68	20c ol grn & brn org	8.00	40.00
2	A68	30c claret & brn org	8.00	40.00
3	A68	50c vio & brn org	4.75	47.50
4	A68	1 l bl & brn org	4.75	60.00
		Nos. 1-4 (4)	25.50	187.50
		Set, never hinged	60.00	

Fascisti Issue

Italy Nos. 159-164 Overprinted in Red or Black

1923, Oct. 29   Unwmk.   Perf. 14

5	A69	10c dk grn (R)	8.00	14.50
6	A69	30c dk vio (R)	8.00	14.50
7	A69	50c brn car	8.00	16.00

Wmk. 140

8	A70	1 l blue	8.00	40.00
9	A70	2 l brown	8.00	47.50
10	A71	5 l blk & bl (R)	8.00	55.00
		Nos. 5-10 (6)	48.00	187.50
		Set, never hinged	125.00	

Manzoni Issue

Italy Nos. 165-170 Overprinted in Red

1924, Apr. 1   Perf. 14

11	A72	10c brn red & blk	13.00	40.00
12	A72	15c bl grn & blk	13.00	40.00
13	A72	30c blk & slate	13.00	40.00
14	A72	50c org brn & blk	13.00	40.00
15	A72	1 l bl & blk	80.00	275.00
a.		Double overprint	950.00	
		Never Hinged	1,400.	
16	A72	5 l vio & blk	525.00	2,100.
		Nos. 11-16 (6)	657.00	2,535.
		Set, never hinged	1,600.	

Vertical overprints on Nos. 11-14 are essays. On Nos. 15-16 the overprint is vertical at the left.
All examples of #15a are poorly centered.

Victor Emmanuel Issue

Italy Nos. 175-177 Overprinted

1925-26   Unwmk.   Perf. 11

17	A78	60c brn car	.80	8.00
18	A78	1 l dark blue	.80	8.00
19	A78	1.25 l dk bl ('26)	3.25	16.00
a.		Perf. 13½	240.00	600.00
		Never hinged	475.00	
		Nos. 17-19 (3)	4.85	32.00
		Set, never hinged	12.00	

Issue dates: Nov. 1925, July 1926.

Saint Francis of Assisi Issue

Italian Stamps of 1926 Overprinted

1926, Apr. 12   Wmk. 140   Perf. 14

20	A79	20c gray green	2.40	11.00
21	A80	40c dark violet	2.40	11.00
22	A81	60c red brown	2.40	20.00

Overprinted in Red

Unwmk.

23	A82	1.25 l dk bl, perf. 11	2.40	27.50
24	A83	5 l + 2.50 l ol grn	6.50	55.00
		Nos. 20-24 (5)	16.10	124.50
		Set, never hinged	36.00	

Volta Issue

Type of Italy 1927, Overprinted

1927, Oct. 10   Wmk. 140   Perf. 14

25	A84	20c violet	6.50	32.50
26	A84	50c dp org	8.00	20.00
27	A84	1.25 l brt bl	13.00	52.50
		Nos. 25-27 (3)	27.50	105.00
		Set, never hinged	65.00	

#25 exists with overprint omitted. See Italy.

Monte Cassino Issue

Types of 1929 Issue of Italy, Overprinted in Red or Blue

1929, Oct. 14

28	A96	20c dk grn (R)	4.75	17.50
29	A96	25c red org (Bl)	4.75	17.50
30	A98	50c + 10c crim (Bl)	4.75	20.00
31	A98	75c + 15c ol brn (R)	4.75	20.00
32	A96	1.25 l + 25c dk vio (R)	11.00	36.00
33	A98	5 l + 1 l saph (R)	11.00	40.00

Overprinted in Red

Unwmk.

34	A100	10 l + 2 l gray brn	11.00	55.00
		Nos. 28-34 (7)	52.00	206.00
		Set, never hinged	120.00	

Royal Wedding Issue

Type of Italian Stamps of 1930 Overprinted

1930, Mar. 17   Wmk. 140

35	A101	20c yel grn	1.60	4.75
36	A101	50c + 10c dp org	1.25	8.00
37	A101	1.25 l + 25c rose red	1.25	16.00
		Nos. 35-37 (3)	4.10	28.75
		Set, never hinged	10.00	

#35 exists with overprint omitted. See Italy.

Ferrucci Issue

Types of Italian Stamps of 1930, Overprinted in Red or Blue

1930, July 26

38	A102	20c violet (R)	4.75	4.75
39	A103	25c dk grn (R)	4.75	4.75
40	A103	50c black (R)	4.75	9.75
41	A103	1.25 l dp bl (R)	4.75	17.50
42	A104	5 l + 2 l dp car	9.75	32.50
		Nos. 38-42 (5)	28.75	69.25
		Set, never hinged	60.00	

Virgil Issue

Types of Italian Stamps of 1930 Overprinted in Red or Blue

1930, Dec. 4

43	A106	15c vio blk	1.25	8.00
44	A106	20c org brn (Bl)	1.25	3.25
45	A106	25c dk grn	1.25	3.25
46	A106	30c lt brn (Bl)	1.25	3.25
47	A106	50c dl vio	1.25	3.25
48	A106	75c rose red (Bl)	1.25	7.75
49	A106	1.25 l gray bl	1.25	8.00

Unwmk.

50	A106	5 l + 1.50 l dk vio	3.50	40.00
51	A106	10 l + 2.50 l ol brn (Bl)	3.50	60.00
		Nos. 43-51 (9)	15.75	136.75
		Set, never hinged	37.50	

Saint Anthony of Padua Issue

Types of Italian Stamps of 1931 Overprinted in Blue or Red

1931, May 7   Wmk. 140

52	A116	20c brown (Bl)	1.60	17.50
53	A116	25c green (R)	1.60	6.50
54	A118	30c gray brn (Bl)	1.60	6.50
55	A118	50c dl vio (Bl)	1.60	6.50
56	A120	1.25 l slate bl (R)	1.60	17.50

Overprinted like Nos. 23-24 in Red or Black

Unwmk.

57	A121	75c black (R)	1.60	32.50
58	A122	5 l + 2.50 l dk brn	6.50	67.50
		Nos. 52-58 (7)	16.10	154.50
		Set, never hinged	40.00	

Carabineer A1

1934, Oct. 16   Photo.   Wmk. 140

59	A1	5c dk ol grn & brn	4.00	20.00
60	A1	10c brn & blk	4.00	20.00
61	A1	20c scar & indigo	4.00	16.00
62	A1	50c pur & brn	4.00	16.00
63	A1	60c org brn & ind	4.00	24.00
64	A1	1.25 l dk bl & grn	4.00	40.00
		Nos. 59-64 (6)	24.00	136.00
		Set, never hinged	57.50	

2nd Colonial Art Exhibition held at Naples. See Nos. C24-C29.

> Catalogue values for unused stamps in this section, from this point to the end of the section, are for Never Hinged items.

Autonomous State

Senussi Warrior
A2   A3

Perf. 12½

1950, Jan. 16   Unwmk.   Engr.

65	A2	1m dark brown	.65	2.25
66	A2	2m rose car	.85	2.00
67	A2	3m orange	.85	2.00
68	A2	4m dark green	4.00	3.25
69	A2	5m gray	1.10	1.25
70	A2	8m red orange	1.25	1.50
71	A2	10m purple	1.25	1.50
72	A2	12m red	1.25	1.50
73	A2	20m deep blue	1.25	1.50
74	A3	50m choc & ultra	6.00	6.00
75	A3	100m bl blk & car rose	17.50	15.00
76	A3	200m vio & pur	20.00	40.00
77	A3	500m dk grn & org	95.00	110.00
		Nos. 65-77 (13)	150.95	187.75

SEMI-POSTAL STAMPS

Many issues of Italy and Italian Colonies include one or more semipostal denominations. To avoid splitting sets, these issues are generally listed as regular postage unless all values carry a surtax.

Holy Year Issue
Italian Semi-Postal Stamps of 1924 Overprinted in Black or Red

1925, June 1   Wmk. 140   Perf. 12

B1	SP4	20c + 10c dk grn & brn	3.25	20.00
B2	SP4	30c + 15c dk brn & brn	3.25	22.50
B3	SP4	50c + 25c vio & brn	3.25	20.00
B4	SP4	60c + 30c dp rose & brn	3.25	25.00
B5	SP8	1 l + 50c dp bl & vio (R)	3.25	32.50
B6	SP8	5 l + 2.50 l org brn & vio (R)	3.25	47.50
		Nos. B1-B6 (6)	19.50	167.50
		Set, never hinged	45.00	

Colonial Institute Issue

"Peace" Substituting Spade for Sword — SP1

1926, June 1   Typo.   Perf. 14

B7	SP1	5c + 5c brown	1.00	8.00
B8	SP1	10c + 5c olive grn	1.00	8.00
B9	SP1	20c + 5c blue grn	1.00	8.00
B10	SP1	40c + 5c brown red	1.00	8.00
B11	SP1	60c + 5c orange	1.00	8.00
B12	SP1	1 l + 5c blue	1.00	17.50
		Nos. B7-B12 (6)	6.00	57.50
		Set, never hinged	13.50	

Surtax for Italian Colonial Institute.

Types of Italian Semi-Postal Stamps of 1926 Overprinted like Nos. 17-19

1927, Apr. 21   Unwmk.   Perf. 11

B13	SP10	40c + 20c dk brn & blk	2.40	32.50
B14	SP10	60c + 30c brn red & ol brn	2.40	32.50
B15	SP10	1.25 l + 60c dp bl & blk	2.40	52.50
B16	SP10	5 l + 2.50 l dk grn & blk	4.00	72.50
		Nos. B13-B16 (4)	11.20	190.00
		Set, never hinged	28.00	

The surtax on these stamps was for the charitable work of the Voluntary Militia for Italian National Defense.

Allegory of Fascism and Victory — SP2

1928, Oct. 15   Wmk. 140   Perf. 14

B17	SP2	20c + 5c bl grn	2.40	12.00
B18	SP2	30c + 5c red	2.40	12.00
B19	SP2	50c + 10c purple	2.40	20.00
B20	SP2	1.25 l + 20c dk grn	3.25	24.00
		Nos. B17-B20 (4)	10.45	68.00
		Set, never hinged	25.00	

46th anniv. of the Societa Africana d'Italia. The surtax aided that society.

Types of Italian Semi-Postal Stamps of 1926 Overprinted in Red or Black like Nos. 52-56

1929, Mar. 4   Unwmk.   Perf. 11

B21	SP10	30c + 10c red & blk	4.00	20.00
B22	SP10	50c + 20c vio & blk	4.00	24.00
B23	SP10	1.25 l + 50c brn & bl	4.75	40.00
B24	SP10	5 l + 2 l ol grn & blk (Bk)	4.75	72.50
		Nos. B21-B24 (4)	17.50	156.50
		Set, never hinged	45.00	

Surtax for the charitable work of the Voluntary Militia for Italian Natl. Defense.

Types of Italian Semi-Postal Stamps of 1926 Overprinted in Black or Red like Nos. 52-56

1930, Oct. 20   Perf. 14

B25	SP10	30c + 10c dk grn & bl grn (Bk)	21.00	32.50
B26	SP10	50c + 10c dk grn & vio	21.00	42.50
B27	SP10	1.25 l + 30c ol brn & red brn	21.00	55.00
B28	SP10	5 l + 1.50 l ind & grn	62.50	160.00
		Nos. B25-B28 (4)	125.50	290.00
		Set, never hinged	300.00	

Surtax for the charitable work of the Voluntary Militia for Italian Natl. Defense.

Sower — SP3

1930, Nov. 27   Photo.   Wmk. 140

B29	SP3	50c + 20c ol brn	4.00	20.00
B30	SP3	1.25 l + 20c dp bl	4.00	20.00
B31	SP3	1.75 l + 20c green	4.00	22.50
B32	SP3	2.55 l + 50c purple	6.50	36.00
B33	SP3	5 l + 1 l dp car	7.00	52.50
		Nos. B29-B33 (5)	25.50	151.00
		Set, never hinged	55.00	

25th anniv. of the Italian Colonial Agricultural Institute. The surtax was for the aid of that institution.

AIR POST STAMPS

Air Post Stamps of Tripolitania, 1931, Overprinted in Blue like Nos. 38-42

1932, Jan. 7   Wmk. 140   Perf. 14

C1	AP1	50c rose car	1.60	.40
C2	AP1	60c dp org	4.75	12.00
C3	AP1	80c dl vio	4.75	20.00
		Nos. C1-C3 (3)	11.10	32.40
		Set, never hinged	28.00	

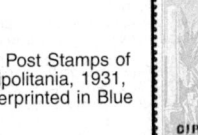

Air Post Stamps of Tripolitania, 1931, Overprinted in Blue

1932, May 12

C4	AP1	50c rose car	1.60	2.00
C5	AP1	80c dull violet	4.75	22.00
		Set, never hinged	16.00	

This overprint was also applied to the 60c, Tripolitania No. C9. The overprinted stamp was never used in Cyrenaica, but was sold at Rome in 1943 by the Postmaster General for the Italian Colonies. Value $5.

Arab on Camel — AP2

Airplane in Flight AP3

1932, Aug. 8   Photo.

C6	AP2	50c purple	8.00	.20
C7	AP2	75c brn rose	8.00	10.00
C8	AP2	80c deep blue	8.00	20.00
C9	AP3	1 l black	3.25	.20
C10	AP3	2 l green	3.25	10.00
C11	AP3	5 l deep car	6.50	20.00
		Nos. C6-C11 (6)	37.00	60.40
		Set, never hinged	82.50	

For surcharges and overprint see #C20-C23.

Graf Zeppelin Issue

Zeppelin and Clouds forming Pegasus AP4

Zeppelin and Ancient Galley AP5

Zeppelin and Giant Bowman AP6

1933, Apr. 15

C12	AP4	3 l dk brn	8.00	120.00
C13	AP5	5 l purple	8.00	120.00
C14	AP6	10 l dp grn	8.00	220.00
C15	AP5	12 l deep blue	8.00	240.00
C16	AP5	15 l carmine	8.00	240.00
C17	AP6	20 l black	8.00	325.00
		Nos. C12-C17 (6)	48.00	1,265.
		Set, never hinged	120.00	

North Atlantic Crossing Issue

Airplane Squadron and Constellations — AP7

1933, June 1

C18	AP7	19.75 l grn & dp bl	16.00	600.00
C19	AP7	44.75 l red & indigo	16.00	600.00
		Set, never hinged	80.00	

Type of 1932 Overprinted and Surcharged

1934, Jan. 20

C20	AP3	2 l on 5 l org brn	3.25	72.50
C21	AP3	3 l on 5 l yel grn	3.25	72.50
C22	AP3	5 l ocher	3.25	80.00
C23	AP3	10 l on 5 l rose	4.85	80.00
		Nos. C20-C23 (4)	14.60	305.00
		Set, never hinged	32.50	

For use on mail to be carried on a special flight from Rome to Buenos Aires.

Transport Plane AP8

Venus of Cyrene AP9

1934, Oct. 9

C24	AP8	25c sl bl & org red	4.00	20.00
C25	AP8	50c dk grn & ind	4.00	16.00
C26	AP8	75c dk brn & org red	4.00	16.00
a.		Imperf.	2,000.	
		Never hinged	2,000.	
C27	AP9	80c org brn & ol grn	4.00	20.00
C28	AP9	1 l scar & ol grn	4.00	24.00
C29	AP9	2 l dk bl & brn	4.00	40.00
		Nos. C24-C29 (6)	24.00	136.00
		Set, never hinged	56.00	

2nd Colonial Arts Exhib. held at Naples.

AIR POST SEMI-POSTAL STAMPS

King Victor Emmanuel III SPAP1

Wmk. 104

1934, Nov. 5   Photo.   Perf. 14

CB1	SPAP1	25c + 10c gray grn	6.50	14.50
CB2	SPAP1	50c + 10c brn	6.50	14.50
CB3	SPAP1	75c + 15c rose red	6.50	14.50
CB4	SPAP1	80c + 15c brn blk	6.50	14.50
CB5	SPAP1	1 l + 20c red brn	6.50	14.50
CB6	SPAP1	2 l + 20c brt bl	6.50	14.50
CB7	SPAP1	3 l + 25c pur	22.50	72.50
CB8	SPAP1	5 l + 25c org	22.50	72.50
CB9	SPAP1	10 l + 30c dp vio	22.50	72.50
CB10	SPAP1	25 l + 2 l dp grn	22.50	72.50
		Nos. CB1-CB10 (10)	129.00	377.00
		Set, never hinged	300.00	

65th birthday of King Victor Emmanuel III and the non-stop flight, Rome-Mogadiscio.

AIR POST SEMI-POSTAL OFFICIAL STAMP

Type of Air Post Semi-Postal Stamps, 1934, Overprinted Crown and "SERVIZIO DI STATO" in Black

1934, Nov. 5   Wmk. 140   Perf. 14

CBO1 SPAP1 25 l + 2 l cop
                       red   2,750.
       Never hinged   4,250.

POSTAGE DUE STAMPS

Catalogue values for unused stamps in this section are for Never Hinged items.

 D1

Perf. 12½

1950, July 1   Unwmk.   Engr.

J1	D1	2m dark brown	57.50	110.00
J2	D1	4m deep green	57.50	110.00
J3	D1	8m scarlet	57.50	110.00
J4	D1	10m vermilion	57.50	120.00
J5	D1	20m orange yel	57.50	120.00
J6	D1	40m deep blue	57.50	160.00
J7	D1	100m dark gray	57.50	225.00
		Nos. J1-J7 (7)	402.50	955.00

CZECHOSLOVAKIA

,che-kə-slō-'vä-kē-ə

LOCATION — Central Europe
GOVT. — Republic
AREA — 49,355 sq. mi.
POP. — 15,395,970 (1983 est.)
CAPITAL — Prague

The Czechoslovakian Republic consists of Bohemia, Moravia and Silesia, Slovakia and Ruthenia (Carpatho-Ukraine). In March 1939, a German protectorate was established over Bohemia and Moravia, as well as over Slovakia which had meanwhile declared its independence. Ruthenia was incorporated in the territory of Hungary. These territories were returned to the Czechoslovak Republic in 1945, except for Ruthenia, which was ceded to Russia. Czechoslovakia became a federal state on Jan. 2, 1969. On Jan. 1, 1993 Czechoslovakia separated into Slovakia and the Czech Republic. See Volume 5 for the stamps of Slovakia.

100 Haleru = 1 Koruna

Catalogue values for unused stamps in this country are for Never Hinged items, beginning with Scott 142 in the regular postage section, B144 in the semi-postal section, Scott C19 in the air post section, Scott EX1 in the personal delivery section, and Scott J58 in the postage due section, Scott O1 int he officials section, and Scott P14 in the newspaper section.

Watermarks

Wmk. 107 — Linden Leaves (Vertical)

Wmk. 135 — Crown in Oval or Circle, Sideways

Wmk. 136   Wmk. 136a

Wmk. 341 — Striped Ovals

Stamps of Austria overprinted "Ceskoslovenska Republika," lion and "Cesko Slovensky Stat," "Provisorni Ceskoslovenska Vlada" and Arms, and "Ceskoslovenska Statni Posta" and Arms were made privately. A few of them were passed through the post but all have been pronounced unofficial and unauthorized by the Postmaster General.

During the occupation of part of Northern Hungary by the Czechoslovak forces, stamps of Hungary were overprinted "Cesko Slovenska Posta," "Ceskoslovenska Statni Posta" and Arms, and "Slovenska Posta" and Arms. These stamps were never officially issued though copies have passed the post.

Hradcany at Prague — A1

1918-19   Unwmk.   Typo.   Imperf.

1	A1	3h red violet	.20	.20
2	A1	5h yellow green	.20	.20
3	A1	10h rose	.20	.20
4	A1	15h bluish green	.20	.20
5	A1	25h deep blue	.25	.20
6	A1	30h bister	.45	.20
7	A1	40h red orange	.45	.20
8	A1	100h brown	1.25	.20
9	A1	200h ultra	2.25	.20
10	A1	400h purple	3.50	.20

On the 3h-40h "Posta Ceskoslovenska" is in white on a colored background; on the higher values the words are in color on a white background.

The 25h in ultramarine was not valid for postage.

Nos. 1-6 exist as tete-beche gutter pairs.

See #368, 1554, 1600. For surcharges see #B130, C1, C4, J15, J19-J20, J22-J23, J30.

Perf. 11½, 13½

13	A1	5h yellow green	.80	.20
a.	Perf. 11½x10¾		2.50	.55
14	A1	10h rose	.40	.20
15	A1	20h bluish green	.40	.20
a.	Perf. 11½		.40	.20

16	A1	25h deep blue	.60	.20
a.	Perf. 11½		1.50	.65
20	A1	200h ultra	4.25	.20
		Nos. 1-10,13-16,20 (15)	15.40	3.00

All values of this issue exist with various private perforations and copies have been used on letters.

The 3, 30, 40, 100 and 400h formerly listed are now known to have been privately perforated.

For overprints see Eastern Silesia Nos. 2, 5, 7-8, 14, 16, 18, 30.

 A2

Type II — Sun behind cathedral. Colorless foliage in foreground.
Type III — Without sun. Shaded foliage in foreground.
Type IV — No foliage in foreground. Positions of buildings changed. Letters redrawn.

1919   Imperf.

23	A2	1h dark brown (II)	.20	.20
25	A2	5h blue green (IV)	.40	.20
27	A2	15h red (IV)	.85	.20
29	A2	25h dull violet (IV)	.65	.20
30	A2	50h dull violet (II)	.40	.20
31	A2	50h dark blue (IV)	.40	.20
32	A2	60h orange (III)	1.25	.20
33	A2	75h slate (IV)	.85	.20
34	A2	80h olive grn (III)	.95	.20
36	A2	120h gray black (IV)	2.50	.35
38	A2	300h dark green (III)	6.50	.65
39	A2	500h red brown (IV)	8.50	.50
40	A2	1000h violet (III)	19.00	1.20
a.	1000h bluish violet		42.50	1.75
		Nos. 23-40 (13)	42.45	4.50

For overprints see Eastern Silesia Nos. 1, 3-4, 6, 9-13, 15, 17, 20-21.

1919-20   Perf. 11½, 13¾, 13¾x11½

41	A2	1h dk brown (II)	.20	.20
42	A2	5h blue grn (IV), perf. 13½	.75	.20
a.	Perf. 11½		25.00	4.00
43	A2	10h yellow grn (IV)	.40	.20
a.	Imperf.		21.00	19.00
b.	Perf. 11¾		13.00	1.25
44	A2	15h red (IV)	.40	.20
a.	Perf. 11½x10¾		30.00	4.50
b.	Perf. 11½x13¾		85.00	22.50
c.	Perf. 13¾x10¾		125.00	26.00
45	A2	20h rose (IV)	.40	.20
a.	Imperf.		82.50	77.50
46	A2	25h dull vio (IV), perf. 11½	.65	.25
a.	Perf. 11½x10¾		5.00	1.10
b.	Perf. 13¾		175.00	40.00
47	A2	30h red violet (IV)	.35	.20
a.	Imperf.		190.00	190.00
b.	Perf. 13¾x13½		550.00	175.00
d.	30h deep violet		.70	.20
c.	As "c," perf. 13¾x13½		625.00	190.00
e.	As "c," imperf.		190.00	140.00
50	A2	60h orange (III)	.30	.20
a.	Imperf.		15.00	6.25
53	A2	120h gray black (IV)	3.75	.95
		Nos. 41-53 (9)	7.20	2.60

Nos. 43a, 45a, 47a and 47e were imperforate by accident and not issued in quantities as were Nos. 23 to 40.

Roulleted stamps of the preceding issues are said to have been made by a postmaster in a branch post office at Prague, or by private firms, but without authority from the Post Office Department.

The 50, 75, 80, 300, 500 and 1000h have been privately perforated.

Unlisted color varieties of types A1 and A2 were not officially released, and some are printer's waste.

For surcharges and overprints see Nos. B131, C2-C3, C5-C6, J16-J18, J21, J24-J29, J31, J42-J43, Eastern Silesia 22-29.

Pres. Thomas Garrigue Masaryk — A4

1920   Perf. 13½

61	A4	125h gray blue	1.50	.20
a.	125h ultramarine		30.00	19.00

62	A4	500h slate, grysh	4.75	2.50
63	A4	1000h blk brn, brnsh	8.00	5.00
		Nos. 61-63 (3)	14.25	7.70

#61-63 imperf were not regularly issued. Values, unused singles, #61, $15; #61a, $55; #62, $20; #63, $40.

For surcharge and overprints see Nos. B131, Eastern Silesia 31-32.

Carrier Pigeon with Letter — A5

Czechoslovakia Breaking Chains to Freedom — A6

Hussite Priest — A7   Agriculture and Science — A8

Two types of 40h:
Type I: 9 leaves by woman's hip.
Type II: 10 leaves by woman's hip.

1920   Perf. 14

65	A5	5h dark blue	.20	.20
a.	Perf. 13¾		325.00	150.00
66	A5	10h blue green	.20	.20
a.	Perf. 13¾		225.00	110.00
67	A5	15h red brown	.20	.20
68	A5	20h rose	.20	.20
69	A6	25h lilac brown	.20	.20
70	A6	30h red violet	.20	.20
71	A6	40h red brown	.60	.20
a.	Tête bêche pair		6.75	2.00
b.	Perf. 13½		1.50	.20
c.	Type II		.25	.20
72	A6	50h carmine	.50	.20
73	A6	60h dark blue	.50	.20
a.	Tête bêche pair		6.00	3.00
b.	Perf. 13½		2.00	.25

Photo.

74	A7	80h purple	.20	.20
75	A7	90h black brown	.30	.20

Typo.

76	A8	100h dark green	1.00	.20
77	A8	200h violet	1.50	.20
78	A8	300h vermilion	3.50	.20
a.	Perf. 13¾x13½		7.00	.35
79	A8	400h brown	6.00	.45
80	A8	500h deep green	7.00	.45
a.	Perf. 13¾x13½		100.00	5.50
81	A8	600h deep violet	9.00	.45
a.	Perf. 13¾x13½		275.00	7.00
		Nos. 65-81 (17)	31.30	4.15

No. 69 has background of horizontal lines. Imperfs. were not regularly issued.
Nos. 71 and 73 exist as tete-beche gutter pairs.

For surcharges and overprint see Nos. C7-C9, J44-J56.

1920-25   Perf. 14

Two types of 20h:
Type I: Base of 2 is long, interior of 0 is angular.
Type II: Base of 2 is short, interior of 0 is an oval.

Two types of 25h:
Type I: Top of 2 curves up.
Type II: Top of 2 curves down.

82	A5	5h violet	.20	.20
a.	Tête bêche pair		2.00	1.00
b.	Perf. 13½		1.00	.35
83	A5	10h olive bister	.20	.20
a.	Tête bêche pair		2.25	1.50
b.	Perf. 13½		.80	.20
84	A5	20h deep orange	1.00	.20
a.	Tête bêche pair		30.00	14.00
b.	Perf. 13½		6.00	.60
c.	Type II		.20	.20
85	A5	25h blue green	.20	.20
a.	Type II		.20	.20
86	A5	30h deep violet ('25)	3.00	.20
87	A6	50h yellow green	1.00	.20
a.	Tête bêche pair		60.00	27.50
b.	Perf. 13½		12.00	2.00
88	A6	100h dark brown	1.00	.20
a.	Perf. 13½		.20	.20
89	A6	150h rose	4.50	.50
a.	Perf. 13½		80.00	1.10

90	A6	185h orange	3.00 .20
91	A6	250h dark green	5.00 .25
		Nos. 82-91 (10)	19.10 2.35

Imperfs. were not regularly issued.
#82-84, 87 exist as tete-beche gutter pairs.

Type of 1920 Issue Redrawn

Type I — Rib of leaf below "O" of POSTA is straight and extends to tip. White triangle above book is entirely at left of twig. "P" has a stubby, abnormal appendage.
Type II — Rib is extremely bent; does not reach tip. Triangle extends at right of twig. "P" like Type I.
Type III — Rib of top left leaf is broken in two. Triangle like Type II. "P" has no appendage.

1923		Perf. 13¾, 13¾x13½	
92	A8	100h red, yellow, III, perf. 14x13½	1.00 .20
a.		Type I, perf. 13¾	1.25 .20
b.		Type I, perf. 13¾x13½	1.25 .20
c.		Type II, perf. 13¾x13½	1.50 .20
d.		Type II, perf. 13¾x13½	1.50 .20
e.		Type III, perf. 13¾	7.00 .20
93	A8	200h blue, yellow, II, perf. 14	5.00 .20
a.		Type II, perf. 13¾x13½	8.50 .25
b.		Type III, perf. 13¾	8.50 .25
c.		Type III, perf. 13¾x13½	52.50 .50
94	A8	300h violet, yellow, I, perf. 13¾	3.75 .20
a.		Type II, perf. 13¾	35.00 .25
b.		Type II, perf. 13¾x13½	50.00 .50
c.		Type III, perf. 13¾x13½	7.00 .20
d.		Type III, perf. 13¾	24.00 .35
		Nos. 92-94 (3)	9.75 .60

President Masaryk
A9   A10

Perf. 13¾x13½, 13¾

1925	Photo.	Wmk. 107	
		Size: 19½x23mm	
95	A9	40h brown orange	.75 .20
96	A9	50h olive green	1.50 .20
97	A9	60h red violet	1.75 .20
		Nos. 95-97 (3)	4.00 .60

Distinctive Marks of the Engravings.
I, II, III — Background of horizontal lines in top and bottom tablets. Inscriptions in Roman letters with serifs.
IV — Crossed horizontal and vertical lines in the tablets. Inscriptions in Antique letters without serifs.
I, II, IV — Shading of crossed diagonal lines on the shoulder at the right.
III — Shading of single lines only.
I — "T" of "Posta" over middle of "V" of "Ceskoslovenska." Three short horizontal lines in lower part of "A" of "Ceskoslovenska."
II — "T" over right arm of "V." One short line in "A."
III — "T" as in II. Blank space in lower part of "A."
IV — "T" over left arm of "V."

Engr.
I. First Engraving
Wmk. Horizontally (107)
Size: 19¾x22½mm

98	A10	1k carmine	.85 .20
99	A10	2k deep blue	2.00 .25
100	A10	3k brown	4.00 .65
101	A10	5k blue green	1.40 .20
		Nos. 98-101 (4)	8.25 1.55

Wmk. Vertically (107)
Size: 19¼x23mm

101A	A10	1k carmine	100.00 4.00
101B	A10	2k deep blue	100.00 12.50
101C	A10	3k brown	250.00 12.50
101D	A10	5k blue green	5.00 2.00
		Nos. 101A-101D (4)	455.00 31.00

II. Second Engraving
Wmk. Horizontally (107)
Size: 19x21½mm

102	A10	1k carmine	42.50 .50
103	A10	2k deep blue	3.50 .25
104	A10	3k brown	3.50 .50
		Nos. 102-104 (3)	49.50 1.25

III. Third Engraving
Size: 19-19½x21½-22mm
Perf. 10

105	A10	1k carmine rose	1.00 .20
a.		Perf. 14	12.50 .20

IV. Fourth Engraving
Size: 19x22mm

1926		Perf. 10	
106	A10	1k carmine rose	1.00 .20
		Perf. 14	
108	A10	3k brown	4.50 .20

There is a 2nd type of No. 106: with long mustache. Same values. See No. 130, design SP3.

Karlstein Castle — A11

1926, June 1		Engr.	Perf. 10
109	A11	1.20k red violet	.50 .30
110	A11	1.50k car rose	.30 .20
111	A11	2.50k dark blue	3.00 .30
		Nos. 109-111 (3)	3.80 .80

See Nos. 133, 135.

Karlstein   Pernstein
Castle — A12   Castle — A13

Orava Castle   Masaryk
A14   A15

Strahov
Monastery — A16

Hradcany at Prague A17

Great Tatra — A18

1926-27		Engr.	Wmk. 107
114	A13	30h gray green	1.25 .20
115	A14	40h red brown	.50 .20
116	A15	50h deep green	.50 .20
117	A15	60h red vio, lil	.85 .20
118	A16	1.20k red violet	4.00 1.50
		Perf. 13½	
119	A17	2k blue	.75 .20
a.		2k ultramarine	5.50 .75
120	A17	3k deep red	1.50 .20
121	A18	4k brn vio ('27)	3.50 .40
122	A18	5k dk grn ('27)	12.50 2.25
		Nos. 114-122 (9)	25.35 5.35

No. 116 exists in two types. The one with short, straight mustache at left sells for several times as much as that with longer wavy mustache.
See Nos. 137-140.

Coil Stamps
Perf. 10 Vertically

123	A12	20h brick red	.50 .40
a.		Vert. pair, imperf. horiz.	100.00
124	A13	30h gray green	.35 .20
a.		Vert. pair, imperf. horiz.	100.00
125	A15	50h deep green	.25 .20
		Nos. 123-125 (3)	1.10 .80

See No. 141.

1927-31		Unwmk.	Perf. 10
126	A13	30h gray green	.25 .20
127	A14	40h deep brown	.70 .20
128	A15	50h deep green	.20 .20
129	A15	60h red violet	.70 .20
130	A10	1k carmine rose	1.10 .20
131	A15	1k deep red	.75 .20
132	A16	1.20k red violet	.40 .20
133	A11	1.50k carmine ('29)	.55 .20
134	A13	2k dp grn ('29)	.50 .20
135	A11	2.50k dark blue	5.50 .30
136	A14	3k red brown ('31)	.60 .20
		Nos. 126-136 (11)	11.25 2.30

No. 130 exists in two types. The one with longer mustache at left sells for several times as much as that with the short mustache.

1927-28			Perf. 13½
137	A17	2k ultra	.85 .20
138	A17	3k deep red ('28)	1.90 .65
139	A18	4k brown violet ('28)	6.00 1.00
140	A18	5k dark green ('28)	6.25 .50
		Nos. 137-140 (4)	15.00 2.35

Coil Stamp

1927		Perf. 10 Vertically	
141	A12	20h brick red	.50 .20

> **Catalogue values for unused stamps in this section, from this point to the end of the section, are for Never Hinged items.**

Hradec Castle   Brno Cathedral
A19   A25

Masaryk — A27

10th anniv. of Czech. independence: 40h, Town Hall, Levoca. 50h, Telephone exchange, Prague. 60h, Town of Jasina. 1k, Hluboka Castle. 1.20k, Pilgrims' House, Velehrad. 2.50k, Great Tatra. 5k, Old City Square, Prague.

1928, Oct. 22			Perf. 13½
142	A19	30h black	.20 .20
143	A19	40h red brown	.20 .20
144	A19	50h dark green	.25 .20
145	A19	60h orange red	.25 .20
146	A19	1k carmine	.40 .40
147	A19	1.20k brown vio	.80 .80
148	A25	2k ultra	1.00 1.00
149	A19	2.50k dark blue	2.25 2.25
150	A27	3k dark brown	1.50 1.50
151	A25	5k deep violet	3.50 3.50
		Nos. 142-151 (10)	10.35 10.25

From one to three sheets each of Nos. 142-148, perf 12½, appeared on the market in the early 1950's.

Coat of Arms — A29

1929-37			Perf. 10
152	A29	5h dark ultra ('31)	.20 .20
153	A29	10h bister brn ('31)	.20 .20
154	A29	20h red	.20 .20
155	A29	25h green	.20 .20
156	A29	30h red violet	.20 .20
157	A29	40h dk brown ('37)	.50 .20
a.		40h red brown ('29)	2.00 .20
		Nos. 152-157 (6)	1.50 1.20

Coil Stamp
Perf. 10 Vertically

158	A29	20h red	.20 .20

For overprints see Bohemia and Moravia Nos. 1-5, Slovakia 2-6.

St. Wenceslas   Founding St.
A30   Vitus' Cathedral
                    A31

Design: 3k, 5k, St. Wenceslas martyred.

1929, May 14			Perf. 13½
159	A30	50h gray green	.40 .20
160	A30	60h slate violet	.60 .20
161	A31	2k dull blue	1.25 .40
162	A30	3k brown	1.50 .40
163	A30	5k brown violet	5.50 3.50
		Nos. 159-163 (5)	9.25 4.70

Millenary of the death of St. Wenceslas.

Statue of St. Wenceslas and National Museum, Prague — A33

1929			Perf. 10
164	A33	2.50k deep blue	.65 .20

Brno Cathedral   Tatra Mountain
A34   Scene
                   A35

Design: 5k, Old City Square, Prague.

1929, Oct. 15   **Perf. 13½**
165 A34 3k red brown   3.00 .20
166 A35 4k indigo   8.00 .50
167 A35 5k gray green   8.50 .45
   Nos. 165-167 (3)   19.50 1.15
   See No. 183.

A37

Type I

Type II

Two types of 50h:
I — A white space exists across the bottom of the vignette between the coat, shirt and tie and the "HALERU" frame panel.
II — An extra frame line has been added just above the "HALERU" panel which finishes off the coat and tie shading evenly.

1930, Jan. 2   **Perf. 10**
168 A37 50h myrtle green (II)   .20 .20
  a.   Type I   1.25 .20
169 A37 60h brown violet   1.00 .20
170 A37 1k brown red   .40 .20
   Nos. 168-170 (3)   1.60 .60
   See No. 234.

Coil Stamp
1931   **Perf. 10 Vertically**
171 A37 1k brown red   1.25 .65

President Masaryk — A38   St. Nicholas' Church, Prague — A39

1930, Mar. 1   **Perf. 13½**
175 A38 2k gray green   1.60 .40
176 A38 3k red brown   2.50 .40
177 A38 5k slate blue   6.50 1.50
178 A38 10k gray black   18.00 4.00
   Nos. 175-178 (4)   28.60 6.30

Eightieth birthday of President Masaryk.

1931, May 15
183 A39 10k black violet   12.50 2.50

Krivoklat Castle — A40   Krumlov Castle — A42

Design: 4k, Orlik Castle.

1932, Jan. 2   **Perf. 10**
184 A40 3.50k violet   2.50 1.25
185 A40 4k deep blue   3.25 .65
186 A42 5k gray green   5.00 .65
   Nos. 184-186 (3)   10.75 2.55

A43   A44

Miroslav Tyrs — A45

1932, Mar. 16
187 A43 50h yellow green   .55 .20
188 A43 1k brown carmine   1.40 .20
189 A44 2k dark blue   10.00 .50
190 A44 3k red brown   15.00 .50
   Nos. 187-190 (4)   26.95 1.40

1933, Feb. 1
191 A45 60h dull violet   .30 .20

Miroslav Tyrs (1832-84), founder of the Sokol movement; and the 9th Sokol Congress (#187-190).

First Christian Church at Nitra
A46   A47

1933, June 20
192 A46 50h yellow green   .40 .20
193 A47 1k carmine rose   8.00 .40

Prince Pribina who introduced Christianity into Slovakia and founded there the 1st Christian church in A.D. 833.
All gutter pairs are vertical.

Bedrich Smetana, Czech Composer and Pianist, 50th Death Anniv. — A48

1934, Mar. 26   **Engr.**   **Perf. 10**
194 A48 50h yellow green   .40 .20

Consecration of Legion Colors at Kiev, Sept. 21, 1914 — A49

Ensign Heyduk with Colors A51   Legionnaires A52

1k, Legion receiving battle flag at Bayonne.

1934, Aug. 15   **Perf. 10**
195 A49 50h green   .40 .20
196 A49 1k rose lake   .55 .20
197 A51 2k deep blue   3.00 .40
198 A52 3k red brown   5.00 .50
   Nos. 195-198 (4)   8.95 1.30

20th anniv. of the Czechoslovakian Legion which fought in WWI.

Antonin Dvorák, (1841-1904), Composer — A53

1934, Nov. 22
199 A53 50h green   .40 .20

Pastoral Scene — A54

1934, Dec. 17   **Perf. 10**
200 A54 1k claret   .65 .20
  a.   Souv. sheet of 15, perf. 13½   200.00 300.00
  b.   As "a," single stamp   10.00 12.50
201 A54 2k blue   1.75 .65
  a.   Souv. sheet of 15, perf. 13½   850.00 1,000.
  b.   As "a," single stamp   40.00 29.00

Centenary of the National Anthem.
Nos. 200-201 were each issued in sheets of 100 stamps and 12 blank labels.
Nos. 200a & 201a have thick paper, darker shades, no gum. Forgeries exist.

A55   President Masaryk — A56

1935, Mar. 1
202 A55 50h green, *buff*   .35 .20
203 A55 1k claret, *buff*   .40 .20
204 A56 2k gray blue, *buff*   2.00 .60
205 A56 3k brown, *buff*   3.25 .60
   Nos. 202-205 (4)   6.00 1.60

85th birthday of President Masaryk. See No. 235.
Nos. 204-205 were each issued in sheets of 100 stamps and 12 blank labels. Value with attached labels: mint $30; used $10.

Monument to Czech Heroes at Arras, France — A57

1935, May 4
206 A57 1k rose   .85 .20
207 A57 2k dull blue   3.00 .75

20th anniversary of the Battle of Arras.
Nos. 206-207 were each issued in sheets of 100 stamps and 12 blank labels. Value, set with attached labels: mint $22.50; used $10.

Gen. Milan Stefánik A58   Sts. Cyril and Methodius A59

1935, May 18
208 A58 50h green   .20 .20

1935, June 22
209 A59 50h green   .40 .20
210 A59 1k claret   .55 .20
211 A59 2k deep blue   2.00 .50
   Nos. 209-211 (3)   2.95 .90

Millenary of the arrival in Moravia of the Apostles Cyril and Methodius.

Masaryk — A60

Statue of Macha, Prague — A61

1935, Oct. 20   **Perf. 12½**
212 A60 1k rose lake   .20 .20

No. 212 exists imperforate. See No. 256. For overprints see Bohemia and Moravia Nos. 9-10, Slovakia 12.

1936, Apr. 30
213 A61 50h deep green   .20 .20
214 A61 1k rose lake   .50 .20

Karel Hynek Macha (1810-1836), Bohemian poet.
Nos. 213-214 were each issued in sheets of 100 stamps and 12 blank labels. Value, with attached labels: mint $2; used 80c.

Jan Amos Komensky (Comenius) — A61a

Pres. Eduard Benes A62   Gen. Milan Stefánik A63

1936
215 A61a 40h dark blue   .20 .20
216 A62 50h dull green   .20 .20
217 A63 60h dull violet   .20 .20
   Nos. 215-217 (3)   .60 .60

See #252, 255. For overprints see Bohemia and Moravia #6, 8, Slovakia 7, 9-11.

Castle Palanok near Mukacevo A64   Town of Banska Bystrica A65

Castle at Zvikov — A66   Ruins of Castle at Strecno — A67

Castle at Cesky Raj A68   Palace at Slavkov (Austerlitz) A69

Statue of King George of Podebrad A70

Town Square at Olomouc — A71

Castle Ruins at Bratislava A72

1936, Aug. 1

218	A64	1.20k rose lilac	.20	.20
219	A65	1.50k carmine	.20	.20
220	A66	2k dark blue green	.20	.20
221	A67	2.50k dark blue	.40	.20
222	A68	3k brown	.40	.20
223	A69	3.50k dark violet	1.60	.55
224	A70	4k dark violet	.65	.20
225	A71	5k green	.65	.20
226	A72	10k blue	1.10	.55
		Nos. 218-226 (9)	5.40	2.40

Nos. 224-226 were each issued in sheets of 100 stamps and 12 blank labels. Value, with attached labels: mint $7; used $2.75.

For overprints and surcharge see Nos. 237-238, 254A, Bohemia and Moravia 11-12, 14-19, Slovakia 13-14, 16-23.

President Benes — A73

Soldiers of the Czech Legion — A74

1937, Apr. 26   Unwmk.   Perf. 12½

227	A73	50h deep green	.20	.20

For overprints see Nos. 236, Slovakia 8.

1937, June 15

228	A74	50h deep green	.20	.20
229	A74	1k rose lake	.40	.20

20th anniv. of the Battle of Zborov. Nos. 228-229 were each issued in sheets of 100 stamps and 12 blank labels. Value, set with attached labels: mint $4; used $2.

Cathedral at Prague — A75

Jan Evangelista Purkyne — A76

1937, July 1

230	A75	2k green	1.00	.20
231	A75	2.50k blue	1.50	.80

Founding of the "Little Entente," 16th anniv. Nos. 230-231 were each issued in sheets with blank labels. Value, set with attached labels: mint $22.50; used $11.

1937, Sept. 2

232	A76	50h slate green	.25	.20
233	A76	1k dull rose	.30	.20

150th anniv. of the birth of Purkyne, Czech physiologist.

Masaryk Types of 1930-35

1937, Sept.   Perf. 12½

234	A37	50h black	.20	.20

With date "14.IX. 1937" in design

235	A56	2k black	.30	.20

Death of former President Thomas G. Masaryk on Sept. 14, 1937.

No. 235 was issued in sheets of 100 stamps and 12 inscribed labels. Value, with attached label: mint $1.20; used 60c.

International Labor Bureau Issue

Stamps of 1936-37 Overprinted in Violet or Black

1937, Oct. 6   Perf. 12½

236	A73	50h dp green (Bk)	.40	.25
237	A65	1.50k carmine (V)	.40	.25
238	A66	2k dp green (V)	.70	.50
		Nos. 236-238 (3)	1.50	1.00

Bratislava Philatelic Exhibition Issue
Souvenir Sheet

A77

1937, Oct. 24   Perf. 12½

239	A77	Sheet of 2	2.50	3.25
a.		50h dark blue	.80	1.20
b.		1k brown carmine	.80	1.20

The stamps show a view of Poprad Lake (50h) and the tomb of General Milan Stefanik (1k).

No. 239 overprinted with the Czechoslovak arms and "Czecho-Slovak Participation New York World's Fair 1939, Czecho-Slovak Pavilion" were privately produced to finance Czechoslovak participation in the exhibition. The overprint exists in black, green, red, blue, gold and silver.

No. 239 overprinted "Liberation de la Tchechoslovaquie, 28-X-1945" etc., was sold at a philatelic exhibition in Brussels, Belgium.

St. Barbara's Church, Kutna Hora — A79

Peregrine Falcon, Sokol Emblem — A80

1937, Dec. 4

240	A79	1.60k olive green	.20	.20

For overprints see Bohemia and Moravia Nos. 13, Slovakia 15.

1938, Jan. 21

241	A80	50h deep green	.20	.20
242	A80	1k rose lake	.25	.20

10th Intl. Sokol Games. Nos. 241-242 were each issued in sheets of 100 stamps and 12 inscribed labels. Value, with attached labels: mint $2; used $1.50. Imperf. copies of No. 242 are essays.

Legionnaires

A81   A82

Legionnaire — A83

1938

243	A81	50h deep green	.20	.20
244	A82	50h deep green	.20	.20
245	A83	50h deep green	.60	.60
		Nos. 243-245 (3)		

20th anniv. of the Battle of Bachmac, Vouziers and Doss Alto.
Nos. 243-245 were each issued in sheets of 100 stamps and 12 inscribed labels. Value, set with attached labels $3, mint or used.

Jindrich Fügner, Co-Founder of Sokol Movement — A84

1938, June 18   Perf. 12½

246	A84	50h deep green	.20	.20
247	A84	1k rose lake	.20	.20
248	A84	2k slate blue	.40	.20
		Nos. 246-248 (3)	.80	.60

10th Sokol Summer Games. Nos. 246-248 were each issued in sheets of 100 stamps and 12 inscribed labels. Value, set with attached labels: mint $2.50; used $2.

View of Pilsen — A85

Cathedral of Kosice — A86

1938, June 24

249	A85	50h deep green	.20	.20

Provincial Economic Council meeting, Pilsen. No. 249 was issued in sheets of 150 stamps and 10 labels depicting a flower within a cogwheel. Value, with attached label 40c, mint or used.

For overprint see Bohemia & Moravia #7.

1938, July 15   Perf. 12½

250	A86	50h deep green	.20	.20

Kosice Cultural Exhibition. No. 250 was issued in sheets of 150 stamps and 10 labels bunches of grapes. Value, with attached label 40c, mint or used.

Prague Philatelic Exhibition Issue
Souvenir Sheet

Vysehrad Castle — Hradcany — A87

1938, June 26   Perf. 12½

251	A87	Sheet of 2	5.00	5.00
a.		50h dark blue	1.50	1.50
b.		1k deep carmine	1.50	1.50

See No. 3036.

Stefánik Type of 1936

1938, Nov. 21

252	A63	50h deep green	.20	.20

Allegory of the Republic — A89

1938, Dec. 19   Unwmk.

253	A89	2k lt ultra	.30	.20
254	A89	3k pale brown	.50	.40

20th anniv. of Independence. Nos. 253-254 were each issued in sheets of 100 stamps and 12 blank labels. Value, set with attached labels $2.50, mint or used. See No. B153.

"Wir sind frei!"

Stamps of Czechoslovakia, 1918-37, overprinted with a swastika in black or red and "Wir sind frei!" were issued locally and unofficially in 1938 as Czech authorities were evacuating and German authorities arriving. They appeared in the towns of Asch, Karlsbad, Reichenberg-Maffersdorf, Rumburg, etc.

The overprint, sometimes including a surcharge or the town name (as in Karlsbad), exists on many values of postage, air post, semi-postal, postage due and newspaper stamps.

No. 226 Surcharged in Orange Red

1939, Jan. 18   Unwmk.   Perf. 12½

254A	A72	300h on 10k blue	1.25	1.60

Opening of the Slovakian Parliament.

View of Jasina — A89a

Perf. 12½
1939, Mar. 15   Engr.   Unwmk.

254B	A89a	3k ultra	25.00	90.00

Inauguration of the Carpatho-Ukraine Diet, Mar. 2, 1939.
Printed for use in the province of Carpatho-Ukraine but issued in Prague at the same time.
Used value is for red commemorative cancel.

Stefánik Type of 1936

1939   Engr.   Perf. 12½

255	A63	60h dark blue	45.00	37.50

Used exclusively in Slovakia.

Masaryk Type of 1935 with hyphen in Cesko-Slovensko

1939, Apr. 23

256	A60	1k rose lake	.20	.20

Linden Leaves and Buds — A90

1945   Photo.   Perf. 14

256A	A90	10h black	.20	.20
257	A90	30h yellow brown	.20	.20
258	A90	50h dark green	.20	.20
258A	A90	60h dark blue	.20	.20

Engr.
(Buds Open)
Perf. 12½

259	A90	60h blue	.20	.20
259A	A90	80h orange ver	.20	.20
260	A90	1.20k rose	.20	.20
261	A90	3k violet brown	.20	.20
262	A90	5k green	.20	.20
		Nos. 256A-262 (9)	1.80	1.80

Compare with Bohemia-Moravia type A1.

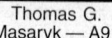

Thomas G. Masaryk — A91

Coat of Arms — A92

1945-46 Photo. Perf. 12
262A A91 5h dull violet ('46) .20 .20
262B A91 10h orange yel ('46) .20 .20
262C A91 20h dk brown ('46) .20 .20
263 A91 50h brt green .20 .20
264 A91 1k orange red .20 .20
265 A91 2k chalky blue .25 .25
Nos. 262A-265 (6) 1.25 1.25

1945 Imperf.
266 A92 50h olive gray .20 .20
267 A92 1k brt red vio .20 .20
268 A92 1.50k dk carmine .20 .20
269 A92 2k deep blue .20 .20
269A A92 2.40k henna brn .30 .20
270 A92 3k brown .20 .20
270A A92 4k dk slate grn .20 .20
271 A92 6k violet blue .25 .20
271A A92 10k sepia .40 .20
Nos. 266-271A (9) 2.15 1.80

Nos. 266, 268, 269, 270 and 271 exist in 2 printings. Stamps of the 1st printing have a coarse impression and are on thin, hard paper in sheets of 100; all values exist in the 2nd printing, with fine impressions on thick, soft wove paper in sheets of 200. Values are the same.

Staff Capt. Ridky (British Army) — A93

Dr. Miroslav Novak (French Army) — A94

Capt. Otakar Jaros (Russian Army) — A95

Staff Capt. Stanislav Zimprich (Foreign Legion) — A96

2nd Lt. Jiri Kral (French Air Force) A97

Josef Gabcik (Parachutist) A98

Staff Capt. Alois Vasatko (Royal Air Force) A99

Private Frantisek Adamek (British Colonial Service) A100

1945, Aug. 18 Engr. Perf. 11½x12½
272 A93 5h intense blue .20 .20
273 A94 10h dark brown .20 .20
274 A95 20h brick red .20 .20
275 A96 25h rose red .20 .20
276 A97 30h purple .20 .20
277 A98 40h sepia .20 .20
278 A99 50h dark olive .20 .20
279 A100 60h violet .20 .20
280 A93 1k carmine .20 .20

281 A94 1.50k lake .20 .20
282 A95 2k ultra .20 .20
283 A96 2.50k deep violet .20 .20
284 A97 3k sepia .20 .20
285 A98 4k rose lilac .20 .20
286 A99 5k myrtle green .20 .20
287 A100 10k brt ultra .65 .20
Nos. 272-287 (16) 3.65 3.20

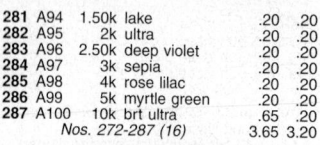

Flags of Russia, Great Britain, US and Czechoslovakia — A101

View of Banská Bystrica A102

Patriot Welcoming Russian Soldier, Turciansky A103

Ruins of Castle at Sklabina A104

Czech Patriot, Strecno A105

1945, Aug. 29 Photo. Perf. 10
288 A101 1.50k brt carmine .20 .20
289 A102 2k brt blue .20 .20
290 A103 4k dark brown .20 .20
291 A104 4.50k purple .25 .25
292 A105 5k deep green .50 .50
Nos. 288-292 (5) 1.35 1.35

National uprising against the Germans.
A card contains one each of Nos. 288-292 on thin cardboard, ungummed. Size: 148x210mm. Sold for 50k. Value, $35 unused, $125 used.

A106 A107

Stefánik — Benes — Masaryk — A108

1945-47 Engr. Perf. 12, 12½
293 A106 30h rose violet .20 .20
294 A107 60h blue .20 .20
294A A106 1k red org ('47) .20 .20
295 A108 1.20k car rose .20 .20
295A A108 1.20(k) rose lil ('46) .20 .20
296 A108 2.40(k) rose .20 .20
297 A107 3k red violet .20 .20
297A A108 4k dark blue ('46) .20 .20
298 A108 5k Prus green .20 .20
299 A107 7k gray .20 .20
300 A108 10k gray blue .35 .20
300A A106 20k sepia ('46) .75 .20
Nos. 293-300A (12) 3.10 2.40

Statue of Kozina and Chod Castle, Domazlice A109

Red Army Soldier A110

1945 Photo. Perf. 14
301 A108 50h brown .20 .20
302 A106 80h dark green .20 .20
303 A107 1.60(k) olive green .20 .20
304 A108 15k red violet .55 .20
Nos. 301-304 (4) 1.15 .80

1945, Nov. 28 Engr. Perf. 12½
305 A109 2.40k rose carmine .20 .20
306 A109 4k blue .25 .25

250th anniv. of the death of Jan Sladky Kozina, peasant leader.

1945, Mar. 26 Litho. Imperf.
307 A110 2k crimson rose .40 .40
308 A110 5k slate black 1.25 1.25
309 A110 6k ultramarine 1.25 1.25
Nos. 307-309 (3) 2.90 2.90

Souvenir Sheet
1945, July 16
Gray Burelage
310 Sheet of 3 4.00 4.00
a. A110 2k crimson rose .75 .75
b. A110 5k slate black .75 .75
c. A110 6k ultramarine .75 .75

Return of Pres. Benes, Apr., 1945.

Clasped Hands — A112

Karel Havlícek Borovsky — A113

1945 Rouletted 12½
311 A112 1.50k brown red 2.25 2.25
312 A112 9k red orange .50 .50
313 A112 13k orange brown .65 .65
314 A112 20k blue 1.75 1.75
Nos. 311-314 (4) 5.15 5.15

1946, July 5 Engr. Perf. 12½
315 A113 1.20k gray black .20 .20

Borovsky (1821-56), editor and writer.
Issued in sheets of 100 stamps and 12 inscribed labels. Value with attached label: $1.25.

Old Town Hall, Brno — A114

Hodonin Square — A115

Perf. 12½x12, 12x12½
1946, Aug. 3 Engr. Unwmk.
316 A114 2.40k deep rose .20 .20
317 A115 7.40k dull violet .30 .20

See No. B159.

President Eduard Benes — A116

1946, Oct. 28
318 A116 60h indigo .20 .20
319 A116 1.60k dull green .20 .20
320 A116 3k red lilac .20 .20
321 A116 8k sepia .25 .20
Nos. 318-321 (4) .85 .80

Flag, Symbols — A117

Saint Adalbert — A118

1947, Jan. 1 Perf. 12½
322 A117 1.20k Prus green .20 .20
323 A117 2.40k deep rose .20 .20
324 A117 4k deep blue .80 .20
Nos. 322-324 (3) 1.20 .65

Czechoslovakia's two-year reconstruction and rehabilitation program.
Nos. 322-324 each issued in sheets of 100 stamps and 12 inscribed labels. Value, set with attached labels, $3.

1947, Apr. 23
326 A118 1.60k gray .50 .30
327 A118 2.40k rose carmine .80 .65
328 A118 5k blue green 1.00 .40
Nos. 326-328 (3) 2.30 1.35

950th anniv. of the death of Saint Adalbert, Bishop of Prague.
Nos. 326-328 each issued in sheets of 100 stamps and 12 monogrammed labels. Value, set with attached labels, $40.

Grief — A119

Allegorical Figure — A120

1947, June 10 Engr.
329 A119 1.20k black .30 .25
330 A119 1.60k slate black .40 .40
331 A120 2.40k brown violet .50 .50
Nos. 329-331 (3) 1.20 1.15

Destruction of Lidice, 5th anniversary.
Nos. 329-331 each issued in sheets of 100 stamps and 12 inscribed labels. Value, set with attached labels, $10.

World Federation of Youth Symbol — A121

Thomas G. Masaryk — A122

1947, July 20
332 A121 1.20k violet brown .30 .20
333 A121 4k slate .35 .20

World Youth Festival held in Prague, July 20-Aug. 17.

1947, Sept. 14
334 A122 1.20k gray blk, *buff* .20 .20
335 A122 4k blue blk, *cream* .40 .20

Death of Masaryk, 10th anniv.
Nos. 334-335 each issued in sheets of 100 stamps and 12 inscribed labels. Value, set with attached labels, $7.50.

Msgr. Stefan Moyses
A123

1947, Oct. 19
336 A123 1.20k rose violet .20 .20
337 A123 4k deep blue .35 .20

150th anniversary of the birth of Stefan Moyses, first Slovakian chairman of the Slavic movement.
Each issued in sheets of 100 stamps and 12 labels with "MOYSES" and floral decoration. Value, set with attached labels, $9.50.

"Freedom from Social Oppression"
A124

1947, Oct. 26 Photo. Perf. 14
338 A124 2.40k brt carmine .20 .20
339 A124 4k brt ultra .35 .20

Russian revolution of Oct., 1917, 30th anniv.

Benes
A125

"Czechoslovakia" Greeting Sokol Marchers
A126

1948, Feb. 15 Photo.
Size: 17½x21½mm
340 A125 1.50k brown .20 .20
Size: 19x23mm
341 A125 2k deep plum .20 .20
342 A125 5k brt ultra .20 .20
Nos. 340-342 (3) .60 .60

1948, Mar. 7 Engr. Perf. 12½
343 A126 1.50k brown .20 .20
344 A126 3k rose carmine .20 .20
345 A126 5k blue .60 .20
Nos. 343-345 (3) 1.00 .60

The 11th Sokol Congress.
Nos. 343-345 each issued in sheets of 100 stamps and 12 labels depicting dates and bouquet. Values, set with attached labels: mint $2.50; used $1.50.

King Charles IV — A127

St. Wenceslas, King Charles IV — A128

1948, Apr. 7
346 A127 1.50k black brown .20 .20
347 A128 2k dark brown .20 .20
348 A128 3k brown red .20 .20
349 A128 5k dark blue .40 .20
Nos. 346-349 (4) 1.00 .80

600th anniv. of the foundation of Charles University, Prague.

Nos. 346-349 each issued in sheets of 100 stamps and 12 inscribed labels. Value, set with attached labels, $6.

Czech Peasants in Revolt
A129

Jindrich Vanicek
A130

Unwmk.
1948, May 14 Photo. Perf. 14
350 A129 1.50k dk olive brown .20 .20

Centenary of abolition of serfdom.

1948, June 10 Engr. Perf. 12½
Designs: 1.50k, 2k, Josef Scheiner.
351 A130 1k dark green .20 .20
352 A130 1.50k sepia .20 .20
353 A130 2k gray blue .20 .20
354 A130 3k claret .25 .20
Nos. 351-354 (4) .85 .80

11th Sokol Congress, Prague, 1948.
Nos. 351-354 each issued in sheets of 100 stamps and 12 labels depicting a sunflower. Values, set with attached labels: $3.75 mint; $3 used.

Frantisek Palacky & F. L. Rieger — A131

Miloslav Josef Hurban — A132

1948, June 20 Unwmk.
355 A131 1.50k gray .20 .20
356 A131 3k brown carmine .20 .20

Constituent Assembly at Kromeriz, cent.
Nos. 355-356 each issued in sheets of 100 stamps and 12 labels depicting a wreath. Value with attached labels, $1.50.

1948, Aug. 27 Perf. 12½
3k, Ludovit Stur. 5k, Michael M. Hodza.
357 A132 1.50k dark brown .20 .20
358 A132 3k carmine lake .20 .20
359 A132 5k indigo .25 .20
Nos. 357-359 (3) .65 .60

Cent. of 1848 insurrection against Hungary.
Nos. 357-359 each issued in sheets of 100 stamps and 12 labels depicting signatures. Values, set with attached labels: mint $3.50; used 1.50.

Eduard Benes
A133

Czechoslovak Family
A134

1948, Sept. 28
360 A133 8k black .20 .20

President Eduard Benes, 1884-1948.

1948, Oct. 28 Perf. 12½x12
361 A134 1.50k deep blue .20 .20
362 A134 3k rose carmine .20 .20

Czechoslovakia's Independence, 30th anniv.
Nos. 361-362 each issued in sheets of 100 stamps and 12 labels depicting dates, leaves. Value with attached labels, $1.50.

Pres. Klement Gottwald — A135

1948-49 Perf. 12½
Size: 18½x23½mm
363 A135 1.50k dk brown .20 .20
364 A135 3k car rose .40 .20
a. 3k rose brown 1.20 .20
365 A135 5k gray blue .25 .20
Size: 23½x29mm
366 A135 20k purple 1.10 .20
Nos. 363-366 (4) 1.95 .80

No. 366 was issued in sheets of 100 stamps and 12 monogrammed labels. Value, with attached label, $3.
See Nos. 373, 564, 600-604.

Souvenir Sheet
1948, Nov. 23 Unwmk. Imperf.
367 A135 30k rose brown 4.50 3.50

52nd birthday of Pres. Klement Gottwald (1896-1953).

Hradcany Castle Type of 1918 Souvenir Sheet
1948, Dec. 18
368 A1 10k dk blue violet 2.75 2.00

1st Czech postage stamp, 30th anniv.

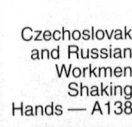
Czechoslovak and Russian Workmen Shaking Hands — A138

Lenin — A139

1948, Dec. 12 Perf. 12½
369 A138 3k rose carmine .20 .20

5th anniv. of the treaty of alliance between Czechoslovakia and Russia.
No. 369 issued in sheets of 100 stamps and 12 labels depicting Czech and Soviet flags. Value with attached label 60c.

1949, Jan. 21 Engr. Perf. 12½
370 A139 1.50k violet brown .30 .30
371 A139 5k deep blue .30 .30

25th anniversary of the death of Lenin.
Nos. 370-371 each issued in sheets of 100 stamps and 12 labels depicting torch. Value, set with attached labels: mint $1.75; used $1.50.

Gottwald Type of 1948 Inscribed: "UNOR 1948" and

Gottwald Addressing Meeting
A140

1949, Feb. 25 Photo. Perf. 14
372 A140 3k red brown .20 .20
Perf. 12½
Engr.
Size: 23½x29mm
373 A135 10k deep green .60 .25

1st anniv. of Gottwald's speech announcing the appointment of a new government. No. 372 exists in a souvenir sheet of 1. It was not sold to the public.
No. 373 issued in sheets of 100 stamps and 12 inscribed labels. Values with attached label: mint $3; used $2.

A141

A142

Writers: 50h, P. O. Hviezdoslav. 80h, V. Vancura. 1k, J. Sverma. 2k, Julius Fucik. 4k, Jiri Wolker. 8k, Alois Jirasek.

1949 Photo. Perf. 14
374 A141 50h violet brown .20 .20
375 A141 80h scarlet .20 .20
376 A141 1k dk olive green .20 .20
377 A141 2k brt blue .40 .20
Perf. 12½
Engr.
378 A141 4k violet brown .40 .20
379 A141 8k brown black .50 .20
Nos. 374-379 (6) 1.90 1.20

1949, May 20
3k, Stagecoach and Train. 5k, Postrider and post bus. 13k, Sailing ship and plane.
380 A142 3k brown carmine 1.25 1.25
381 A142 5k deep blue .80 .40
382 A142 13k deep green 1.25 .80
Nos. 380-382 (3) 3.30 2.45

75th anniv. of the UPU.

Reaping
A143

Communist Emblem and Workers
A144

Workman, Symbol of Industry — A145

Perf. 12½x12, 12x12½
1949, May 24 Unwmk.
383 A143 1.50k deep green .50 .45
384 A144 3k brown carmine .50 .45
385 A145 5k deep blue .50 .45
Nos. 383-385 (3) 1.50 1.35

No. 384 for the 9th meeting of the Communist Party of Czechoslovakia, 5/25/49.
Nos. 383-385 each issued in sheets of 100 stamps and 12 inscribed labels. Value, set with attached labels, $15.

Bedrich Smetana and Natl. Theater, Prague — A146

Aleksander Pushkin — A147

1949, June 4   *Perf. 12½x12*
386 A146 1.50k dull green   .20 .20
387 A146 5k deep blue   .55 .20
   Birth of Bedrich Smetana, composer, 125th anniv.

1949, June 6   *Perf. 12x12½*
388 A147 2k olive gray   .30 .25
Birth of Aleksander S. Pushkin, 150th anniv.

Frederic Chopin and Conservatory, Warsaw A148

1949, June 24   *Perf. 12½x12*
389 A148 3k dark red   .40 .20
390 A148 8k violet brown   .75 .50
   Cent. of the death of Frederic F. Chopin.

Globe and Ribbon — A149

Zvolen Castle — A150

1949, Aug. 20   *Perf. 12½x12*
391 A149 1.50k violet brown   .35 .20
392 A149 5k ultra   .75 .75
50th Prague Sample Fair, Sept. 11-18, 1949.

Starting in October, 1949, some commemorative sets included one "blocked" value, which could be obtained only by purchasing the complete set. These restricted values were printed in smaller quantities than other stamps in the set and were typically sold for more than face value.

1949, Aug. 28   *Perf. 12½*
393 A150 10k rose lake   .75 .20

Early Miners — A151

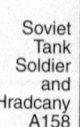

Miner of Today — A152

Design: 5k, Mining Machine.

1949, Sept. 11   *Perf. 12½*
394 A151 1.50k sepia   .80 .60
395 A152 3k carmine rose   6.50 2.50
396 A151 5k deep blue   5.00 1.75
   Nos. 394-396 (3)   12.30 4.85
   700th anniv. of the Czechoslovak mining industry; 150th anniv. of the miner's laws.

Construction Workers — A153   Joseph V. Stalin — A154

1949, Dec. 11   *Perf. 12½*
397 A153 1k shown   2.50 .75
398 A153 2k Machinist   1.50 .40
2nd Trade Union Congress, Prague, 1949.

1949, Dec. 21   **Unwmk.**
Design: 3k, Stalin facing left.

Cream Paper
399 A154 1.50k greenish gray   1.25 .60
400 A154 3k claret   4.75 2.00
   70th birthday of Joseph V. Stalin.

Skier — A155   Efficiency Badge — A156

1950, Feb. 15   *Perf. 12½, 13½*
401 A155 1.50k gray blue   3.00 1.50
402 A156 3k vio brn, *cr*   3.00 1.50
403 A155 5k ultramarine   2.25 1.25
   Nos. 401-403 (3)   8.25 4.25
   51st Ski Championship for the Tatra cup, Feb. 15-26, 1950.

Vladimir V. Mayakovsky, Poet, 20th Death Anniv. — A157

1950, Apr. 14   **Engr.**   *Perf. 12½*
404 A157 1.50k dark brown   2.50 1.25
405 A157 3k brown red   2.50 1.25
   See Nos. 414-417, 422-423, 432-433, 464-465, 477-478.

Soviet Tank Soldier and Hradcany A158

2k, Hero of Labor medal. 3k, Two workers (militiamen) and Town Hall, Prague. 5k, Text of government program and heraldic lion.

1950, May 5
406 A158 1.50k gray green   .40 .25
407 A158 2k dark brown   1.25 1.25
408 A158 3k brown red   .25 .20
409 A158 5k dark blue   .55 .25
   Nos. 406-409 (4)   2.45 1.95
5th anniv. of the Czechoslovak People's Democratic Republic.

Factory and Young Couple with Tools A159

Designs: 2k, Steam shovel. 3k, Farmer and farm scene. 5k, Three workers leaving factory.

1950, May 9   **Engr.**
410 A159 1.50k dark green   1.50 .75
411 A159 2k dark brown   1.50 .75
412 A159 3k rose red   1.00 .40
413 A159 5k deep blue   1.00 .40
   Nos. 410-413 (4)   5.00 2.30

Canceled to Order
   The government philatelic department started about 1950 to sell canceled sets of new issues. Values in the second ("used") column are for these canceled-to-order stamps. Postally used copies are worth more.

Portrait Type of 1950
Design: S. K. Neumann.

1950, June 5   **Unwmk.**   *Perf. 12½*
414 A157 1.50k deep blue   .20 .20
415 A157 3k violet brown   .95 .75
Stanislav Kostka Neumann (1875-1947), journalist and poet.

1950, June 21
Design: Bozena Nemcova.
416 A157 1.50k deep blue   1.25 .75
417 A157 7k dark brown   .30 .20
   Bozena Nemcova (1820-1862), writer.

Liberation of Colonies A160

Designs: 2k, Allegory, Fight for Peace. 3k, Group of Students. 5k, Marching Students with flags.

1950, Aug. 14
418 A160 1.50k dark green   .20 .20
419 A160 2k sepia   .85 .55
420 A160 3k rose carmine   .20 .20
421 A160 5k ultra   .40 .35
   Nos. 418-421 (4)   1.65 1.30
2nd International Students World Congress, Prague, Aug. 12-24, 1950.

Portrait Type of 1950
Design: Zdenek Fibich.

1950, Oct. 15
422 A157 3k rose brown   .90 .55
423 A157 8k gray green   .35 .20
Zdenek Fibich, musician, birth centenary.

Miner, Soldier and Farmer A161

Czech and Soviet Soldiers A162

1950, Oct. 6
424 A161 1.50k slate   .60 .60
425 A162 3k carmine rose   .30 .30
   Issued to publicize Czech Army Day.

Prague Castle, 16th Century A163

Prague, 1493 A164

3k, Prague, 1606. 5k, Prague, 1794.

1950, Oct. 21   *Perf. 14*
426 A163 1.50k black   4.50 3.00
427 A164 2k chocolate   4.50 3.00
428 A164 3k brown car   4.50 3.00
429 A164 5k gray   4.50 3.00
   a. Block of 4, #426-429   25.00 16.00
   See Nos. 434-435.

Communications Symbols — A165

1950, Oct. 25   *Perf. 12½*
430 A165 1.50k chocolate   .20 .20
431 A165 3k brown carmine   .85 .30
   1st anniv. of the foundation of the Intl. League of P.T.T. Employees.

Portrait Type of 1950
Design: J. Gregor Tajovsky.

1950, Oct. 26
432 A157 1.50k brown   1.00 .60
433 A157 5k deep blue   .65 .30
   10th anniversary of the death of J. Gregor Tajovsky (1874-1940), Slovakian writer.

Scenic Type of 1950
Design: Prague, 1950.

1950, Oct. 28
434 A164 1.50k indigo   .35 .20
   a. Souvenir sheet of 4, imperf.   40.00 20.00
435 A164 3k brown car   .65 .50

Czech and Soviet Steel Workers A166

1950, Nov. 4   **Unwmk.**
436 A166 1.50k chocolate   .40 .35
437 A166 5k deep blue   .90 .60
   Issued to publicize the 2nd meeting of the Union of Czechoslovak-Soviet Friendship.

Dove by Picasso A167

1951, Jan. 20   **Photo.**   *Perf. 14*
438 A167 2k deep blue   4.75 3.00
439 A167 3k brown   3.25 1.50
   1st Czechoslovak Congress of Fighters for Peace, held in Prague.

Julius
Fucik — A168

1951, Feb. 17   Engr.   Perf. 12½
440 A168 1.50k gray   .65   .30
441 A168 5k gray blue   1.50 1.50

Drop
Hammer — A169

Installing
Gear — A170

1951, Feb. 24
442 A169 1.50k gray blk   .20   .20
443 A170 3k violet brn   .20   .20
444 A169 4k gray blue   .60   .50
  Nos. 442-444 (3)   1.00   .90

Women
Machinists
A171

Apprentice Miners
A172

Designs: 3k, Woman tractor operator. 5k,
Women of different races.

1951, Mar. 8   Photo.   Perf. 14
445 A171 1.50k olive brown   .40   .30
446 A171 3k brown car   1.60 1.25
447 A171 5k blue   .80   .50
  Nos. 445-447 (3)   2.80 2.05

International Women's Day, Mar. 8.

1951, Apr. 12   Engr.   Perf. 12½
448 A172 1.50k gray   .55   .50
449 A172 3k red brown   .20   .20

Plowing
A173

Collective
Cattle
Breeding
A174

1951, Apr. 28   Photo.   Perf. 14
450 A173 1.50k brown   .65   .65
451 A174 2k dk green   1.50 1.50

Tatra Mountain Recreation
Center — A175

Mountain Recreation Centers: 2k, Beskydy
(Beskids). 3k, Krkonose (Carpathians).

1951, May 5   Engr.   Perf. 12½
452 A175 1.50k deep green   .20   .20
453 A175 2k dark brown   .75   .50
454 A175 3k rose brown   .30   .20
  Nos. 452-454 (3)   1.25   .90

Issued to publicize the summer opening of
trade union recreation centers.

Klement
Gottwald
and
Joseph
Stalin
A176

Factory
Militiaman
A177

Red Army Soldier
and Partisan
A178

Marx,
Engels,
Lenin and
Stalin
A179

1951   Unwmk.   Perf. 12½
455 A176 1.50k olive gray   .65   .25
456 A177 2k red brown   .25   .20
457 A178 3k rose brown   .25   .20
458 A176 5k deep blue   2.00 1.40
459 A179 8k gray   .60   .25
  Nos. 455-459 (5)   3.75 2.30

30th anniv. of the founding of the Czechoslovak Communist Party.

A180

A181

Design: 1k, 2k, Antonin Dvorák. 1.50k, 3k,
Bedrich Smetana.

1951, May 30
460 A180 1k redsh brown   .35   .20
461 A180 1.50k olive gray   1.50   .75
462 A180 2k dk redsh brn   1.50   .75
463 A180 3k rose brown   .35   .20
  Nos. 460-463 (4)   3.70 1.90

International Music Festival, Prague.

Portrait Type of 1950

1951, June 21

Portrait: Bohumir Smeral (facing right).

464 A157 1.50k dark gray   .45   .35
465 A157 3k rose brown   .40   .20

10th anniv. of the death of Bohumir Smeral,
political leader.

1951, June 21
466 A181 1k shown   .75   .35
467 A181 1.50k Discus   .75   .35
468 A181 3k Soccer   1.50   .35
469 A181 5k Skier   3.50 1.50
  Nos. 466-469 (4)   6.50 2.55

Issued to honor the 9th Congress of the
Czechoslovak Sokol Federation.

Scene
from "Fall
of Berlin"
A182

Scene
from "The
Great
Citizen"
A183

1951, July 14
470 A182 80h rose brown   .30   .20
471 A183 1.50k dark gray   .30   .20
472 A182 4k gray blue   1.25   .75
  Nos. 470-472 (3)   1.85 1.15

Intl. Film Festival, Karlovy Vary, July 14-29.

Alois
Jirásek — A184

"Fables
and Fate"
A185

Design: 4k, Scene from "Reign of Tabor."

1951, Aug. 23   Engr.   Perf. 12½
473 A184 1.50k gray   .55   .20
474 A184 5k dark blue   2.25 1.25

Photo.
Perf. 14
475 A185 3k dark red   .55   .20
476 A185 4k dark red   .55   .20
  Nos. 473-476 (4)   3.90 1.85

Cent. of the birth of Alois Jirásek, author.

Portrait Type of 1950

Design: Josef Hybes (1850-1921), co-
founder of Czech Communist Party.

1951, July 21   Engr.
477 A157 1.50k chocolate   .20   .20
478 A157 2k rose brown   .80   .65

"Ostrava
Region" — A186

Mining Iron
Ore — A187

1951, Sept. 9
479 A186 1.50k dk brown   .20   .20
480 A187 3k rose brown   .20   .20
481 A186 5k deep blue   1.25 1.00
  Nos. 479-481 (3)   1.65 1.40

Miner's Day, Sept. 9, 1951.

Soldiers on
Parade — A188

1k, Gunner and field gun. 1.50k, Klement
Gottwald. 3k, Tankman and tank. 5k, Aviators.

Photo. (80h, 5k), Engr.
1951, Oct. 6   Perf. 14 (80h, 5k), 12½
Inscribed: "Den CS Armady 1951"
482 A188 80h olive brown   .35   .30
483 A188 1k dk olive grn   .35   .30
484 A188 1.50k sepia   .35   .30
485 A188 3k claret   .75   .35
486 A188 5k blue   1.75   .75
  Nos. 482-486 (5)   3.55 2.00

Issued to publicize Army Day, Oct. 6, 1951.

Stalin and
Gottwald — A189

Lenin, Stalin and
Soldiers — A190

1951, Nov. 3   Engr.   Perf. 12½
487 A189 1.50k sepia   .20   .20
488 A190 3k red brown   .20   .20
489 A189 4k deep blue   1.10   .40
  Nos. 487-489 (3)   1.50   .80

Issued to publicize the month of Czechoslovak-Soviet friendship, 1951.

Peter Jilemnicky
A191

Ladislav
Zapotocky
A192

1951, Dec. 5   Unwmk.
491 A191 1.50k redsh brown   .25   .20
492 A191 2k dull blue   .80   .35

Peter Jilemnicky (1901-1949), writer.

1952, Jan. 12   Perf. 11½
493 A192 1.50k brown red   .20   .20
494 A192 4k gray   .75   .45

Centenary of the birth of Ladislav
Zapotocky, Bohemian socialist pioneer.

Jan Kollar — A193

Lenin and
Lenin
Hall — A194

1952, Jan. 30   Unwmk.   Perf. 11½
495 A193 3k dark carmine   .20   .20
496 A193 5k violet blue   1.25   .75

Jan Kollar (1793-1852), poet.

1952, Jan. 30   *Perf. 12½*
497 A194 1.50k rose carmine   .30   .20
498 A194 5k deep blue   1.25 .75
6th All-Russian Party Conf., 40th anniv.

Emil Holub and African — A195

Gottwald Metallurgical Plant — A196

1952, Feb. 21   *Perf. 11½*
499 A195 3k red brown   .50   .30
500 A195 5k gray   1.75 1.10
Death of Emil Holub, explorer, 50th anniv.

1952, Feb. 25   **Photo.**   *Perf. 14*
Designs: 2k, Foundry. 3k, Chemical plant.
501 A196 1.50k sepia   .25   .20
502 A196 2k red brown   1.50 .75
503 A196 3k scarlet   .25   .20
      Nos. 501-503 (3)   2.00 1.15

Student, Soldier and Worker — A197   Youths of Three Races — A198

1952, Mar. 21   **Unwmk.**   *Perf. 14*
504 A197 1.50k blue   .20   .20
505 A198 2k olive black   .25   .20
506 A197 3k lake   .85   .50
      Nos. 504-506 (3)   1.30 .90
International Youth Day, Mar. 25, 1952.

Similar to Type of 1951
Portrait: Otakar Sevcik.

1952, Mar. 22   **Engr.**   *Perf. 12½*
507 A184 2k choc, *cr*   .65   .45
508 A184 3k rose brn, *cr*   .20   .20
Otakar Sevcik, violinist, birth cent.

Jan A. Komensky A199   Industrial and Farm Women A200

1952, Mar. 28
509 A199 1.50k dk brown, *cr*   1.25 .60
510 A199 11k dk blue, *cr*   .25   .20
360th anniv. of the birth of Jan Amos Komensky (Comenius), teacher and philosopher.

1952, Mar. 8
511 A200 1.50k dp blue, *cr*   1.25 .50
International Women's Day Mar. 8, 1952.

Woman and Children A201   Antifascist A202

1952, Apr. 12
512 A201 2k chocolate, *cr*   2.00 1.25
513 A201 3k dp claret, *cr*   .20   .20
Intl. Conf. for the Protection of Children, Vienna, Apr. 12-16, 1952.

1952, Apr. 11   **Photo.**   *Perf. 14*
514 A202 1.50k red brown   .20   .20
515 A202 2k ultra   1.25 .75
Day of International Solidarity of Fighters against Fascism, Apr. 11, 1952.

Harvester A203

Design: 3k, Tractor and Seeders.

1952, Apr. 30
516 A203 1.50k deep blue   2.50 1.40
517 A203 2k brown   .30   .30
518 A203 3k brown red   .30   .30
      Nos. 516-518 (3)   3.10 2.00

Youths Carrying Flags — A204

1952, May 1
519 A204 3k brown red   .45   .25
520 A204 4k dk red brown   2.00 1.75
Issued to publicize Labor Day, May 1, 1952.

Crowd Cheering Soviet Soldiers — A205

1952, May 9
521 A205 1.50k dark red   .65   .50
522 A205 5k deep blue   2.50 2.00
Liberation of Czechoslovakia from German occupation, 7th anniversary.

Children A206

J. V. Myslbek — A207

Design: 3k, "Pioneer" teaching children.

1952, May 31   **Engr.**   *Perf. 12½*
523 A206 1.50k dk brn, *cr*   .20   .20
524 A206 2k Prus grn, *cr*   1.50 1.00
525 A206 3k rose brn, *cr*   .25   .20
      Nos. 523-525 (3)   1.95 1.40
International Children's Day May 31, 1952.

1952, June 2
Design: 8k, Allegory, "Music."
526 A207 1.50k red brown   .30   .20
527 A207 2k dark brown   1.50 1.25
528 A207 8k gray green   .25   .20
      Nos. 526-528 (3)   2.05 1.65
Joseph V. Myslbek (1848-1922), sculptor.

Beethoven — A208

House of Artists — A209

1952, June 7   **Unwmk.**   *Perf. 11½*
529 A208 1.50k sepia   .35   .25
530 A209 3k red brown   .40   .25
531 A208 5k indigo   1.25 .75
      Nos. 529-531 (3)   2.00 1.25
International Music Festival, Prague, 1952.

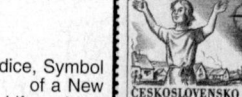

Lidice, Symbol of a New Life — A210

1952, June 10   *Perf. 12½*
532 A210 1.50k dk violet brn   .20   .20
533 A210 5k dark blue   1.25 .75
Destruction of Lidice, 10th anniversary.

Jan Hus — A211   Bethlehem Chapel — A212

1952, July 5
534 A211 1.50k brown   .20   .20
535 A212 3k red brown   .20   .20
536 A211 5k black   1.40 1.00
      Nos. 534-536 (3)   1.80 1.40
550th anniv. of the installation of Jan Hus as pastor of Bethlehem Chapel, Prague.

Doctor Examining Patient — A213

2k, Doctor, Nurse, Mother and child.

1952, July 31
537 A213 1.50k dark brown   1.50 1.00
538 A213 2k blue violet   .35   .20
539 A213 3k rose brown   .35   .20
      Nos. 537-539 (3)   2.20 1.40
Czechoslovakia's Unified Health Service.

Relay Race — A214

1952, Aug. 2   *Perf. 11½*
540 A214 1.50k shown   .85   .55
541 A214 2k Canoeing   2.50 1.00
542 A214 3k Cycling   .55   .50
543 A214 4k Hockey   *4.00* *2.90*
      Nos. 540-543 (4)   7.90 4.95
Issued to publicize Czechoslovakia's Unified Physical Education program.

F. L. Celakovski A215   Mikulas Ales A216

1952, Aug. 5   *Perf. 12½*
544 A215 1.50k dark brown   .20   .20
545 A215 2k dark green   1.60 1.25
Centenary of the death of Frantisek L. Celakovski, poet and writer.

Perf. 11x11½
1952, Aug. 30   **Engr.**   **Unwmk.**
546 A216 1.50k dk gray grn   .35   .25
547 A216 6k red brown   2.50 1.75
Birth centenary of Mikulas Ales, painter.

17th Century Mining Towers — A217

Jan Zizka — A218

Designs: 1.50k, Coal Excavator. 2k, Peter Bezruc mine. 3k, Automatic coaling crane.

1952, Sept. 14   *Perf. 12½*
548 A217 1k sepia   1.25 .80
549 A217 1.50k dark blue   .20   .20
550 A217 2k olive gray   .20   .20
551 A217 3k violet brown   .20   .20
      Nos. 548-551 (4)   1.85 1.40
Miners' Day, Sept. 14, 1952. No. 550 also for the 85th anniv. of the birth of Peter Bezruc (Vladimir Vasek), poet.

1952, Oct. 5   **Engr.**   *Perf. 11½*
Inscribed: ". . . . Armady 1952,"
Designs: 2k, Fraternization with Russians. 3k, Marching with flag.
552 A218 1.50k rose lake   .20   .20
553 A218 2k olive bister   .20   .20
554 A218 3k dk car rose   .20   .20
555 A218 4k gray   1.10 .85
      Nos. 552-555 (4)   1.70 1.45
Issued to publicize Army Day, Oct. 5, 1952.

Souvenir Sheet

Statues to Bulgarian Partisans and to Soviet Army — A219

1952, Oct. 18   Unwmk.   Perf. 12½
556 A219   Sheet of 2   110.00 25.00
  a. 2k deep carmine   35.00   7.50
  b. 3k ultramarine   35.00   7.50

National Philatelic Exhibition, Bratislava, Oct. 18-Nov. 2, 1952.

Danube River, Bratislava A220

1952, Oct. 18
557 A220 1.50k dark brown   .20 .20

National Philatelic Exhibition, Bratislava.

Conference with Lenin and Stalin — A221

Worker and Nurse Holding Dove and Olive Branch — A222

1952, Nov. 7
558 A221 2k brown black   1.00 .75
559 A221 3k carmine   .20 .20

35th anniv. of the Russian Revolution and to publicize Czechoslovak-Soviet friendship.

1952, Nov. 15   Photo.   Perf. 14
560 A222 2k brown   1.20 .65
561 A222 3k red   .20 .20

Issued to publicize the first State Congress of the Czechoslovak Red Cross.

Matej Louda, Hussite Leader, Painted by Mikulas Ales A223

3k, Dragon-killer Trutnov, painted by Ales.

1952, Nov. 18   Engr.   Perf. 11½
562 A223 2k red brown   .40 .20
563 A223 3k grnsh gray   .80 .25

Mikulas Ales, painter, birth cent.

Gottwald Type of 1948-49

1952, June 2   Unwmk.   Perf. 12½
Size: 19x24mm
564 A135 1k dark green   .60 .20

"Peace" Flags — A224   Dove by Picasso — A225

1952, Dec. 12   Photo.   Perf. 14
565 A224 3k red brown   .40 .20
566 A224 4k deep blue   1.50 1.00

Issued to publicize the Congress of Nations for Peace, Vienna, Dec. 12-19, 1952.

1953, Jan. 17
Design: 4k, Czech Family.
567 A225 1.50k dark brown   .20 .20
568 A225   4k slate blue   .75 .45

2nd Czechoslovak Peace Congress.

Smetana Museum — A226

Design: 4k, Jirásek Museum.

1953, Feb. 10   Engr.   Perf. 11½
569 A226 1.50k dk violet brn   .20 .20
570 A226   4k dark gray   1.50 .90

Prof. Zdenek Nejedly, 75th birth anniv.

Martin Kukucin — A227   Jaroslav Vrchlicky — A228

Designs: 2k, Karel Jaromir Erben. 3k, Vaclav Matej Kramerius. 5k, Josef Dobrovsky.

1953, Feb. 28
571 A227   1k gray   .20 .20
572 A228 1.50k olive   .20 .20
573 A228   2k rose lake   .20 .20
574 A228   3k lt brown   .75 .50
575 A228   5k slate blue   1.50 1.10
    Nos. 571-575 (5)   2.85 2.20

Issued to honor Czech writers and poets: 1k, 25th anniv. of death of Kukucin. 1.50k, birth cent. of Vrchlicky. 2k, cent. of completion of "Kytice" by Erben. 3k, birth bicent. of Kramerius. 5k, birth bicent. of Dobrovsky.

Militia — A229

Gottwald — A230

Design: 8k, Portraits of Stalin and Gottwald and Peoples Assembly.

Perf. 13½x14
1953, Feb. 25   Photo.   Unwmk.
576 A229 1.50k deep blue   .20 .20
577 A230   3k red   .20 .20
578 A229   8k dark brown   2.40 1.00
    Nos. 576-578 (3)   2.80 1.40

5th anniv. of the defeat of the attempt to reinstate capitalism.

Book and Torch — A231

Design: 3k, Bedrich Vaclavek.

1953, Mar. 5   Engr.   Perf. 11½
579 A231 1k sepia   1.50 .75
580 A231 3k orange brown   .20 .20

Bedrich Vaclavek (1897-1943), socialist writer.

Stalin Type of 1949
Inscribed "21 XII 1879-5 III 1953"

1953, Mar. 12
581 A154 1.50k black   .35 .25

Death of Joseph Stalin, Mar. 5, 1953.

Mother and Child — A232

Girl Revolutionist A233

1953, Mar. 8
582 A232 1.50k ultra   .20 .20
583 A233   2k brown red   1.25 .75

International Women's Day.

Klement Gottwald — A234

1953, Mar. 19
584 A234 1.50k black   .20 .20
585 A234   3k black   .20 .20

Souvenir Sheet
Imperf
586 A234   5k black   5.75 4.00

Death of Pres. Klement Gottwald, 3/14/53.

Josef Pecka, Ladislav Zapotocky and Josef Hybes — A236

1953, Apr. 7   Unwmk.   Perf. 11½
587 A236 2k lt violet brn   .20 .20

75th anniversary of the first congress of the Czech Social Democratic Party.

Cyclists — A237

1953, Apr. 29
588 A237 3k deep blue   .75 .35

6th International Peace Bicycle Race, Prague-Berlin-Warsaw.

Medal of "May 1, 1890" A238

Designs: 1.50k, Lenin and Stalin. 3k, May Day Parade. 8k, Marx and Engels.

Engraved and Photogravure
1953, Apr. 30   Perf. 11½x11, 14
589 A238   1k chocolate   1.50 .75
590 A238 1.50k dark gray   .20 .20
591 A238   3k carmine lake   .20 .20
592 A238   8k dk gray green   .35 .20
    Nos. 589-592 (4)   2.25 1.35

Issued to publicize Labor Day, May 1, 1953.

Sowing Grain — A239

1953, May 8   Photo.   Perf. 14
593 A239 1.50k shown   .35 .20
594 A239   7k Reaper   1.60 1.40

Socialization of the village.

Dam — A240

Welder — A241

Design: 3k, Iron works.

1953, May 8   Perf. 11½
595 A240 1.50k gray   1.25 .60
596 A241   2k blue gray   .20 .20
597 A240   3k red brown   .20 .20
    Nos. 595-597 (3)   1.65 1.00

Josef Slavik — A242   Leos Janacek — A243

1953, June 19   Photo.
598 A242 75h dp gray blue   .75 .20
599 A243 1.60k dark brown   1.00 .20

Issued on the occasion of the International Music Festival, Prague, 1953.

Gottwald Type of 1948-49
Perf. 12½ (15h, 1k), 11½ (20h, 3k)
1953
600	A135	15h yellow green	.35	.20
601	A135	20h dk violet brn	.50	.20
602	A135	1k purple	1.25	.20
603	A135	3k brown car	.20	.20
604	A135	3k gray	.80	.20
		Nos. 600-604 (5)	3.10	1.00

Nos. 600-604 vary slightly in size.

Pres. Antonin
Zapotocky — A244

1953, June 19   **Perf. 14**
605	A244	30h violet blue	.75	.20
606	A244	60h cerise	1.00	.20

Julius Fucik   Book and
A245   Carnation
         A246

1953, Sept. 8   **Engr.**   **Perf. 12½**
607	A245	40h dk violet brn	.30	.20
608	A246	60h pink	.50	.30

10th anniv. of the death of Julius Fucik, Communist leader executed by the Nazis.

Miner and
Flag — A247

Design: 60h, Oil field and workers.

1953, Sept. 10   **Perf. 11½**
609	A247	30h gray	.25	.20
610	A247	60h brown vio	1.25	.50

Miner's Day, Sept. 10, 1953.

Volleyball
Game — A248

Motorcyclist
A249

Design: 60h, Woman throwing javelin.

1953, Sept. 15
611	A248	30h brown red	5.25	1.50
612	A249	40h dk violet brn	3.25	1.00
613	A248	60h rose violet	2.75	1.00
		Nos. 611-613 (3)	11.25	3.50

Hussite Warrior   Pres. Antonin
A250   Zapotocky
       A251

Designs: 60h, Soldier presenting arms. 1k, Red army soldiers.

1953, Oct. 8
614	A250	30h brown	.30	.20
615	A250	60h rose lake	.65	.20
616	A250	1k brown red	1.50	1.25
		Nos. 614-616 (3)	2.45	1.65

Issued to publicize Army Day, Oct. 3, 1953.

1953   **Unwmk.**   **Perf. 11½, 12½**
617	A251	30h violet blue	.45	.20
618	A251	60h carmine rose	.80	.20

#617 is perf. 11½ & measures 19x23mm, #618 perf. 12½ & 18½x23½mm.
See No. 780.

Charles Bridge
and Prague
Castle — A252

Korean and Czech
Girls — A253

1953, Aug. 15   **Engr.**   **Perf. 11½**
619	A252	5k gray	3.00	.20

1953, Oct. 11   **Perf. 11x11½**
620	A253	30h dark brown	2.25	1.50

Czechoslovakia's friendship with Korea.

Flags, Hradcany Castle and
Kremlin — A254

Designs: 60h, Lomonosov University, Moscow. 1.20k, Lenin Ship Canal.

1953, Nov. 7
621	A254	30h dark gray	.80	.55
622	A254	60h dark brown	1.25	1.00
623	A254	1.20k ultra	4.00	2.00
		Nos. 621-623 (3)	6.05	3.55

Czechoslovak-Soviet friendship month.

Emmy Destinn,   National Theater,
Opera   Prague — A256
Singer — A255

Portrait: 2k, Eduard Vojan, actor.

1953, Nov. 18   **Perf. 14**
624	A255	30h blue black	1.25	.75
625	A256	60h brown	.40	.40
626	A255	2k sepia	3.25	1.25
		Nos. 624-626 (3)	4.90	2.40

Natl. Theater founding, 70th anniv.

Josef   Vaclav
Manes — A257   Hollar — A258

1953, Nov. 28   **Perf. 11x11½**
627	A257	60h brown carmine	.35	.20
628	A257	1.20k deep blue	1.50	.90

Issued to honor Josef Manes, painter.

1953, Dec. 5
Portrait: 1.20k, Head framed, facing right.
629	A258	30h brown black	.35	.20
630	A258	1.20k dark brown	1.50	.65

Vaclav Hollar, artist and etcher.

Leo N.
Tolstoi — A259

1953, Dec. 29   **Unwmk.**
631	A259	60h dark green	.35	.20
632	A259	1k chocolate	1.50	.65

Leo N. Tolstoi, 125th birth anniv.

Locomotive — A260

Design: 1k, Plane loading mail.

Engraved, Center Photogravure
1953, Dec. 29   **Perf. 11½x11**
633	A260	60h brn org & gray vio	1.50	.50
634	A260	1k org brn & brt bl	4.00	1.25

Lenin — A261

Lenin Museum, Prague — A262

1954, Jan. 21   **Engr.**   **Perf. 11½**
635	A261	30h dark brown	.45	.20
636	A262	1.40k chocolate	1.50	.90

30th anniversary of the death of Lenin.

Klement
Gottwald — A263

Design: 2.40k, Revolutionist with flag.

1954, Feb. 18   **Perf. 11x11½, 14x13½**
637	A263	60h dark brown	.30	.20
638	A263	2.40k rose lake	4.25	1.50

25th anniversary of the fifth congress of the Communist Party in Czechoslovakia.

Gottwald
Mausoleum,
Prague — A264

Gottwald
and
Stalin
A265

1.20k, Lenin & Stalin mausoleum, Moscow.

1954, Mar. 5   **Perf. 11½, 14x13½**
639	A264	30h olive brown	.35	.20
640	A265	60h deep ultra	.35	.20
641	A264	1.20k rose brown	2.25	1.00
		Nos. 639-641 (3)	2.95	1.40

1st anniv. of the deaths of Stalin and Gottwald.

Two
Runners — A266

Group of
Hikers — A267

Design: 1k, Woman swimmer.

1954, Apr. 24   **Perf. 11½**
642	A266	30h dark brown	2.25	1.00
643	A267	80h dark green	7.50	3.75
644	A266	1k dk violet blue	1.75	.75
		Nos. 642-644 (3)	11.50	5.50

Nurse — A268

Designs: 15h, Construction worker. 40h, Postwoman. 45h, Ironworker. 50h, Soldier. 75h, Lathe operator. 80h, Textile worker. 1k, Farm woman. 1.20k, Scientist and microscope. 1.60k, Miner. 2k, Physician and baby. 2.40k, Engineer. 3k, Chemist.

1954   **Perf. 12½x12, 11½x11**
645	A268	15h dark green	.30	.20
646	A268	20h lt violet	.35	.20
647	A268	40h dark brown	.45	.20
648	A268	45h dk gray blue	.35	.20
649	A268	50h dk gray green	.45	.20
650	A268	75h deep blue	.45	.20
651	A268	80h violet brown	.45	.20
652	A268	1k green	.75	.20
653	A268	1.20k dk violet blue	.45	.20
654	A268	1.60k brown blk	1.10	.20
655	A268	2k orange brown	1.60	.20

656 A268 2.40k violet blue 1.50 .20
657 A268 3k carmine 1.50 .20
Nos. 645-657 (13) 9.70 2.60

Antonin
Dvořák — A269

Prokop
Divis — A270

40h, Leos Janacek. 60h, Bedrich Smetana.

1954, May 22   *Perf. 11x11½*
658 A269 30h violet brown 2.00 .25
659 A269 40h brick red 2.50 .30
660 A269 60h dark blue 1.00 .20
Nos. 658-660 (3) 5.50 .75

"Year of Czech Music," 1954.

1954, June 15
661 A270 30h gray .30 .20
662 A270 75h violet brown 1.20 .50

200th anniv. of the invention of a lightning conductor by Prokop Divis.

Slovak
Insurrectionist
A271

Anton P.
Chekhov
A272

Design: 1.20k, Partisan woman.

1954, Aug. 28   *Perf. 11½*
663 A271 30h brown orange .20 .20
664 A271 1.20k dark blue .80 .75

Slovak national uprising, 10th anniv.

1954, Sept. 24
665 A272 30h dull gray grn .25 .20
666 A272 45h dull gray brn 1.00 .65

50th anniv. of the death of Chekhov, writer.

Soviet Representative Giving
Agricultural Instruction — A273

Designs: 60h, Soviet industrial instruction. 2k, Dancers (cultural collaboration).

1954, Nov. 6   *Perf. 11½x11*
667 A273 30h yellow brown .20 .20
668 A273 60h dark blue .20 .20
669 A273 2k vermilion 1.40 1.25
Nos. 667-669 (3) 1.80 1.65

Czechoslovak-Soviet friendship month.

Jan Neruda — A274

60h, Janko Jesensky. 1.60k, Jiri Wolker.

1954, Nov. 25   *Perf. 11x11½*
670 A274 30h dark blue .85 .20
671 A274 60h dull red 1.40 .10
672 A274 1.60k sepia .35 .20
Nos. 670-672 (3) 2.60 .90

Issued to honor Czechoslovak poets.

View of
Telc
A275

Views: 60h, Levoca. 3k, Ceske Budejovice.

1954, Dec. 10   **Engr. & Photo.**
673 A275 30h black & bis .35 .20
674 A275 60h brown & bis .35 .20
675 A275 3k black & bis 2.25 1.50
Nos. 673-675 (3) 2.95 1.90

Pres. Antonin
Zapotocky
A276

Attacking
Soldiers
A278

1954, Dec. 18   **Engr.**   *Perf. 11½*
676 A276 30h black brown .45 .20
677 A276 60h dark blue .45 .20

Souvenir Sheet
Imperf

678 A276 2k deep claret 15.00 7.50

70th birthday of Pres. Antonin Zapotocky. See Nos. 829-831.

1954, Oct. 3   *Perf. 11½*

Design: 2k, Soldier holding child.
679 A278 60h dark green .30 .20
680 A278 2k dark brown 1.20 1.00

Army Day, Oct. 6, 1954.

Woman Holding
Torch — A279

Comenius
University
Building
A280

Design: 45h, Ski jumper.

1955, Jan. 20   **Engr.**
681 A279 30h red 2.25 .50

Engraved and Photogravure
682 A279 45h black & blue 3.75 .50

First National Spartacist Games, 1955.

1955, Jan. 28   **Engr.**   *Perf. 11½*

Design: 75h, Jan A. Komensky medal.
683 A280 60h deep green .30 .20
684 A280 75h chocolate 1.20 .65

35th anniversary of the founding of Comenius University, Bratislava.

Czechoslovak
Automobile
A281

60h, Textile worker. 75h, Lathe operator.

1955, Mar. 15   **Unwmk.**
685 A281 45h dull green 1.50 .45
686 A281 60h dk violet blue .60 .20
687 A281 75h sepia .90 .20
Nos. 685-687 (3) 3.00 .85

Woman Decorating
Soviet
Soldier — A282

Stalin Memorial,
Prague — A283

Designs: 35h, Tankman with flowers. 60h, Children greeting soldier.

1955, May 5   **Engr.**   *Perf. 11½*
688 A282 30h blue .35 .20
689 A282 35h dark brown 1.50 .75
690 A282 60h cerise .35 .20

Photo.
691 A283 60h sepia .35 .20
Nos. 688-691 (4) 2.55 1.35

10th anniv. of Czechoslovakia's liberation.

Music and
Spring — A284

Foundry
Worker — A285

Design: 1k, Woman with lyre.

1955, May 12   **Engr. & Photo.**
692 A284 30h black & pale blue .35 .25
693 A284 1k black & pale rose 1.50 1.50

International Music Festival, Prague, 1955.

1955, May 12   **Engr.**

Design: 45h, Farm workers.
694 A285 30h violet .20 .20
695 A285 45h green 1.40 .75

Issued to publicize the third congress of the Trade Union Revolutionary Movement.

Woman
Athlete — A286

Jakub
Arbes — A287

60h, Dancing couple. 1.60k, Athlete.

1955, June 21
696 A286 20h violet blue 1.00 .50
697 A286 60h green .35 .20
698 A286 1.60k red .75 .30
Nos. 696-698 (3) 2.10 1.00

Issued to publicize the first National Spartacist Games, Prague, June-July, 1955.

1955

Portraits: 30h, Jan Stursa. 40h, Elena Marothy-Soltesova. 60h, Josef Vaclav Sladek. 75h, Alexander Stepanovic Popov. 1.40k, Jan Holly. 1.60k, Pavel Josef Safarik.

699 A287 20h brown .25 .20
700 A287 30h black .25 .20
701 A287 40h gray green .75 .20
702 A287 60h black .50 .20
703 A287 75h claret 1.75 .70
704 A287 1.40k black, *cr* .50 .20
705 A287 1.60k dark blue .50 .20
Nos. 699-705 (7) 4.50 1.90

Various anniversaries of prominent Slavs.

Girl and Boy of
Two
Races — A288

Costume of
Ocova,
Slovakia — A289

1955, July 20
706 A288 60h violet blue .75 .20

5th World Festival of Youth in Warsaw, July 31-Aug. 14.

1955, July 25

Regional Costumes: 75h, Detva man, Slovakia. 1.60k, Chodsko man, Bohemia. 2k, Hana woman, Moravia.

Frame and Outlines in Brown

707 A289 60h orange & rose 9.00 6.00
708 A289 75h orange & lilac 3.75 3.75
709 A289 1.60k blue & orange 11.00 6.75
710 A289 2k yellow & rose 11.00 6.75
Nos. 707-710 (4) 34.75 23.25

Carp
A290

Designs: 30h, Beetle. 35h, Gray Partridge. 1.40k, Butterfly. 1.50k, Hare.

1955, Aug. 8   **Engr. & Photo.**
711 A290 20h sepia & lt bl 2.25 .35
712 A290 30h sepia & pink 1.50 .30
713 A290 35h sepia & buff 1.50 .75
714 A290 1.40k sepia & cream 7.50 4.50
715 A290 1.50k sepia & lt grn 2.50 1.00
Nos. 711-715 (5) 15.25 6.90

Tabor
A291

45h, Prachatice. 60h, Jindrichuv Hradec.

1955, Aug. 26   **Engr.**
716 A291 30h violet brown .35 .20
717 A291 45h rose carmine 1.50 .75
718 A291 60h sage green .75 .20
Nos. 716-718 (3) 2.60 1.15

Issued to publicize the architectural beauty of the towns of Southern Bohemia.

Souvenir Sheet

Various Views of Prague — A292

1955, Sept. 10   **Engr.**   *Perf. 14x13½*
719 A292 Sheet of 5 24.00 27.50
   a.   30h gray black 4.50 5.25
   b.   45h gray black 4.50 5.25
   c.   60h rose lake 4.50 5.25
   d.   75h rose lake 4.50 5.25
   e.   1.60k gray black 4.50 5.25

International Philatelic Exhibition, Prague, Sept. 10-25, 1955. Size: 145x110mm. Exists imperf., value $40.

Motorcyclists
A293

Workers, Soldier
and Pioneer
A294

1955, Aug. 28
720 A293 60h violet brown   3.00 .75

30th International Motorcycle Races at
Gottwaldov, Sept. 13-18, 1955.

1955, Oct. 6   Unwmk.   Perf. 11½
Army Day: 60h, Tanks and planes.
721 A294 30h violet brown   .35 .20
722 A294 60h slate   1.75 1.25

Hans Christian
Andersen — A295

Portraits: 40h, Friedrich von Schiller. 60h,
Adam Mickiewicz. 75h, Walt Whitman.

1955, Oct. 27
723 A295 30h brown red   .35 .20
724 A295 40h dark blue   2.25 1.00
725 A295 60h deep claret   .35 .20
726 A295 75h greenish black   .75 .35
     Nos. 723-726 (4)   3.70 1.75

Issued in honor of these four poets and to
mark the 100th anniversary of the publication
of Walt Whitman's "Leaves of Grass."

Railroad
Bridge
A296

30h, Train crossing bridge. 60h, Train
approaching tunnel. 1.60k, Miners' housing
project.

Inscribed: "Stavba Socialismu"
1955, Dec. 15
727 A296 20h dull green   .40 .20
728 A296 30h violet brown   .80 .20
729 A296 60h slate   .80 .20
730 A296 1.60k carmine rose   .55 .20
     Nos. 727-730 (4)   2.55 .80

Issued to publicize socialist public works.

Hydroelectric
Plant — A297

Jewelry — A298

2nd Five Year Plan: 10h, Miner with drill.
25h, Building construction. 30h, Harvester.
60h, Metallurgical plant.

Inscribed: "Druhy Petilety Plan 1956-
1960."
1956, Feb. 20   Perf. 11½x11
731 A297 5h violet brown   .30 .20
732 A297 10h gray black   .30 .20
733 A297 25h dk car rose   .55 .20
734 A297 30h green   .35 .20
735 A297 60h violet blue   .55 .20
     Nos. 731-735 (5)   2.05 1.00

1956, Mar. 17   Perf. 11x11½
736 A298 30h shown   .55 .20
737 A298 45h Glassware   4.00 2.00
738 A298 60h Ceramics   .80 .20
739 A298 75h Textiles   .65 .30
     Nos. 736-739 (4)   6.00 2.70

Products of Czechoslovakian industries.

Karlovy Vary
(Karlsbad)
A299

"We Serve our
People"
A300

Various Spas: 45h, Marianske Lazne
(Marienbad). 75h, Piestany. 1.20k, Tatry
Vysne Ruzbachy (Tatra Mountains).

1956, Mar. 17
740 A299 30h olive green   1.50 .30
741 A299 45h brown   1.20 .30
742 A299 75h claret   6.00 4.00
743 A299 1.20k ultra   .80 .30
     Nos. 740-743 (4)   9.50 4.90

Issued to publicize Czechoslovakian spas.

1956, Apr. 9   Photo.   Perf. 11x11½
Designs: 60h, Russian War Memorial, Berlin. 1k, Tank crewman with standard.
744 A300 30h olive brown   .75 .20
745 A300 60h carmine rose   .75 .20
746 A300 1k ultra   4.75 3.00
     Nos. 744-746 (3)   6.25 3.40

Exhibition: "The Construction and Defense
of our Country," Prague, Apr., 1956.

Cyclists — A301

Girl Basketball
Players — A302

Athletes and Olympic Rings — A303

Engraved and Photogravure
1956, Apr. 25   Unwmk.   Perf. 11½
747 A301 30h green & lt blue   3.25 .30
748 A302 45h dk blue & car   1.25 .30
749 A303 75h brown & lemon   1.00 .65
     Nos. 747-749 (3)   5.50 1.25

9th Intl. Peace Cycling Race, Warsaw-Ber-
lin-Prague, May 1-15, 1956 (No. 747). 5th
European Womens' Basketball Championship
(No. 748). Summer Olympics, Melbourne,
Nov. 22-Dec. 8, 1956 (No. 749).

Mozart — A304

Home
Guard — A305

45h, Josef Myslivecek. 60h, Jiri Benda. 1k,
Bertramka House, Prague. 1.40k, Xaver
Dusek (1731-99) and wife Josepha. 1.60k,
Nostic Theater, Prague.

1956, May 12   Engr.
Design in Gray Black
750 A304 30h bister   1.50 .35
751 A304 45h gray green   13.50 9.00
752 A304 60h pale rose lilac   1.50 .35
753 A304 1k salmon   1.90 .35
754 A304 1.40k lt blue   4.50 .75
755 A304 1.60k lemon   3.00 .35
     Nos. 750-755 (6)   25.90 11.15

200th anniv. of the birth of Wolfgang
Amadeus Mozart and to publicize the International Music Festival in Prague.

1956, May 25
756 A305 60h violet blue   .75 .20

Issued to commemorate the first meeting of
the Home Guard, Prague, May 25-27, 1956.

Josef Kajetan
Tyl — A306

River
Patrol — A307

Portraits: 20h, Ludovit Stur. 30h, Frana
Sramek. 1.40k, Karel Havlicek Borovsky.

1956, June 23
757 A306 20h dull purple   .75 .20
758 A306 30h blue   .45 .20
759 A306 60h black   .45 .20
760 A306 1.40k claret   3.00 1.75
     Nos. 757-760 (4)   4.65 2.35

Issued to honor various Czechoslovakian
writers. See Nos. 781-784, 873-876.

1956, July 8   Perf. 11x11½
Design: 60h, Guard and dog.
761 A307 30h ultra   .85 .25
762 A307 60h green   .60 .20

Issued to honor men of Frontier Guard.

Type of 1956 and

Steeplechase — A308

1956, Sept. 8   Unwmk.   Perf. 11½
763 A308 60h indigo & bister   2.75 .70
764 A308 80h brown vio & vio   1.50 .30
765 A303 1.20k slate & orange   2.75 1.50
     Nos. 763-765 (3)   7.00 2.55

Steeplechase, Pardubice, 1956 (No. 763).
Marathon race, Kosice, 1956 (No. 764).
Olympic Games, Melbourne, Nov. 22-Dec. 8
(No. 765).

Woman Gathering
Grapes — A309

Fishermen — A310

35h, Women gathering hops. 95h, Logging.

1956, Sept. 20   Engr.
766 A309 30h brown lake   .35 .20
767 A309 35h gray green   .35 .20
768 A310 80h dark blue   .75 .20
769 A310 95h chocolate   2.25 1.00
     Nos. 766-769 (4)   3.70 1.60

Issued to publicize natural resources.

European Timetable
Conf., Prague, Nov.
9-13 — A311

A312

Locomotives: 10h, 1846. 30h, 1855. 40h,
1945. 45h, 1952. 60h, 1955. 1k, 1954.

1956, Nov. 9   Unwmk.   Perf. 11½
770 A311 10h brown   1.50 .30
771 A312 30h gray   3.00 .30
772 A312 40h green   4.50 .45
773 A312 45h brown car   13.50 6.75
774 A312 60h indigo   3.00 .30
775 A312 1k ultra   5.25 .45
     Nos. 770-775 (6)   30.75 8.55

Costume of
Moravia — A313

Regional Costumes (women): 1.20k, Blata,
Bohemia. 1.40k, Cicmany, Slovakia. 1.60k,
Novohradsko, Slovakia.

1956, Dec. 15   Perf. 13½
776 A313 30h brn, ultra & car   1.50 1.50
777 A313 1.20k brn, car & ultra   2.50 .35
778 A313 1.40k brn, ocher &
     ver   7.50 2.50
779 A313 1.60k brn, car & grn   3.00 .75
     Nos. 776-779 (4)   14.50 5.10

See Nos. 832-835.

Zapotocky Type of 1953
1956, Oct. 7   Unwmk.   Perf. 12½
780 A251 30h blue   .75 .20

Portrait Type of 1956
15h, Ivan Olbracht. 20h, Karel Toman. 30h,
F. X. Salda. 1.60k, Terezia Vansova.

1957, Jan. 18   Engr.   Perf. 11½

781	A306	15h dk red brn, cr	.30	.20
782	A306	20h dk green, cr	.30	.20
783	A306	30h dk brown, cr	.30	.20
784	A306	1.60k dk blue, cr	.60	.20
		Nos. 781-784 (4)	1.50	.80

Issued in honor of Czechoslovakian writers.

Kolin Cathedral — A315

Views: No. 786, Banska Stiavnica. No. 787, Uherske Hradiste. No. 788, Karlstein. No. 789, Charles Bridge, Prague. 1.25k, Moravska Trebova.

1957, Feb. 23

785	A315	30h dk blue gray	.30	.20
786	A315	30h rose violet	.45	.20
787	A315	60h deep rose	.45	.20
788	A315	60h gray green	.45	.20
789	A315	60h brown	.60	.20
790	A315	1.25k gray	2.50	1.50
		Nos. 785-790 (6)	4.75	2.50

Anniversaries of various towns and landmarks.

Komensky Mausoleum, Naarden A316

Jan A. Komensky A317

Old Prints: 40h, Komensky teaching. 1k, Sun, moon, stars and earth.

Perf. 11½x11, 14 (A317)

1957, Mar. 28   Engr.   Unwmk.

791	A316	30h pale brown	.45	.20
792	A316	40h dark green	.45	.20
793	A317	60h chocolate	3.00	.75
794	A316	1k carmine rose	.60	.20
		Nos. 791-794 (4)	4.50	1.35

300th anniv. of the publication of "Didactica Opera Omnia" by J. A. Komensky (Comenius). No. 793 issued in sheets of four.

1957, Mar. 22   Perf. 11½

795	A318	30h lt blue green	.75	.20

3rd Cong. of Agricultural Cooperatives.

Farm Woman — A318

Cyclists A319

Woman Archer A320

Boxers — A321

Rescue Team A322

1957, Apr. 30   Perf. 11½x11, 11x11½

796	A319	30h sepia & ultra	.60	.20
797	A319	60h dull grn & bis	2.25	1.25
798	A320	60h gray & emer	.45	.20
799	A321	60h sepia & org	.45	.20
800	A322	60h violet & choc	.75	.20
		Nos. 796-800 (5)	4.50	2.05

10th Intl. Peace Cycling Race, Prague-Berlin-Warsaw (#796-797). Intl. Archery Championships (#798). European Boxing Championships, Prague (#799). Mountain Climbing Rescue Service (#800).

Jan V. Stamic — A323

Musicians: No. 802, Ferdinand Laub. No. 803, Frantisek Ondricek. No. 804, Josef B. Foerster. No. 805, Vitezslav Novak. No. 806, Josef Suk.

1957, May 12   Perf. 11½

801	A323	60h purple	.35	.20
802	A323	60h black	.35	.20
803	A323	60h slate blue	.35	.20
804	A323	60h brown	.35	.20
805	A323	60h dull red brn	.90	.20
806	A323	60h blue green	.35	.20
		Nos. 801-806 (6)	2.65	1.20

Spring Music Festival, Prague.

Josef Bozek — A324

School of Engineering A325

60h, F. J. Gerstner. 1k, R. Skuhersky.

1957, May 25

807	A324	30h bluish black	.20	.20
808	A324	60h gray brown	.35	.20
809	A324	1k rose lake	.35	.20
810	A325	1.40k blue violet	.75	.20
		Nos. 807-810 (4)	1.65	.80

School of Engineering in Prague, 250th anniv.

Pioneer and Philatelic Symbols A326

Design: 60h, Girl and carrier pigeon.

Engraved and Photogravure

1957, June 8   Perf. 11½

811	A326	30h olive grn & org	.50	.20

Engr.   Perf. 13½

812	A326	60h brn & vio bl	1.50	1.00

Youth Philatelic Exhibition, Pardubice. No. 812 was printed in miniature sheets of 4. Value $12.

"Grief" A327

Motorcyclists A328

Design: 60h, Rose, symbol of new life.

1957, June 10

813	A327	30h black	.35	.20
814	A327	60h blk & rose red	1.25	.45

Destruction of Lidice, 15th anniversary.

1957, July 5   Perf. 11½

815	A328	60h dk gray & blue	1.50	.30

32nd International Motorcycle Race.

Karel Klic — A329

Josef Ressel — A330

1957, July 5

816	A329	30h gray black	.60	.20
817	A330	60h violet blue	.60	.20

Klic, inventor of photogravure, and Ressel, inventor of the ship screw.

Chamois — A331

Gentian A332

Designs: 30h, Brown bear. 60h, Edelweiss. 1.25k, Tatra Mountains.

1957, Aug. 28   Engr.   Perf. 11½

818	A331	20h emer & brnsh gray	1.00	.35
819	A331	30h lt blue & brn	1.00	.20
820	A332	40h gldn brn & vio bl	1.75	.35
821	A332	60h yellow & grn	1.00	.20

Size: 48x28½mm

822	A332	1.25k ol grn & bis	1.75	1.00
		Nos. 818-822 (5)	6.50	2.10

Tatra Mountains National Park.

"Marycka Magdonova" A333

Man Holding Banner of Trade Union Cong. A334

Engraved and Photogravure

1957, Sept. 15   Unwmk.   Perf. 11½

823	A333	60h black & dull red	.45	.20

90th birthday of Petr Bezruc, poet and author of "Marycka Magdonova."

1957, Sept. 28   Engr.

824	A334	75h rose red	.45	.20

4th Intl. Trade Union Cong., Leipzig, 10/4-15.

Television Transmitter and Antennas — A335

Design: 60h, Family watching television.

1957, Oct. 19   Engr.   Perf. 11½

825	A335	40h dk blue & car	.30	.20
826	A335	60h redsh brown & emer	.45	.20

Issued to publicize the television industry.

Worker, Globe and Lenin A336

60h, Worker, factory, hammer and sickle.

1957, Nov. 7   Perf. 12x11½

827	A336	30h claret	.20	.20
828	A336	60h gray blue	.25	.20

Russian Revolution, 40th anniversary.

Zapotocky Type of 1954 dated: 19 XII 1884-13 XI 1957

1957, Nov. 18   Unwmk.   Perf. 11½

829	A276	30h black	.20	.20
830	A276	60h black	.25	.20

Souvenir Sheet

Imperf

831	A276	2k black	4.00	2.00

Death of Pres. Antonin Zapotocky.

Costume Type of 1956

Regional Costumes: 45h, Pilsen woman, Bohemia. 75h, Slovacko man, Moravia. 1.25k, Hana woman, Moravia. 1.95k, Teshinsko woman, Silesia.

1957, Dec. 18   Engr.   Perf. 13½

832	A313	45h brn, bl & dk red	4.25	1.50
833	A313	75h dk brn, red & grn	3.00	.80
834	A313	1.25k dk brn, scar & ocher	5.25	1.50
835	A313	1.95k sepia, bl & ver	6.00	3.75
		Nos. 832-835 (4)	18.50	7.55

A337

A338

Designs: 30h, Radio telescope and observatory. 45h, Meteorological station in High Tatra. 75h, Sputnik 2 over Earth.

1957, Dec. 20   *Perf. 11½*
836	A337	30h violet brn & yel	1.75	.65
837	A338	45h sepia & lt bl	.45	.35
838	A337	75h claret & blue	2.50	1.00
		Nos. 836-838 (3)	4.70	2.00

IGY, 1957-58. No. 838 also for the launching of Sputnik 2, Nov. 3, 1957.

Girl Skater — A339

Litomysl Castle — A340

Designs: 40h, Canoeing. 60h, Volleyball. 80h, Parachutist. 1.60k, Soccer.

1958, Jan. 25   Engr.   Perf. 11½x12
839	A339	30h rose violet	1.25	.25
840	A339	40h blue	.25	.20
841	A339	60h redsh brown	.25	.20
842	A339	80h violet blue	1.50	.50
843	A339	1.60k brt green	.45	.20
		Nos. 839-843 (5)	3.70	1.35

Issued to publicize various sports championship events in 1958.

1958, Feb. 10   *Perf. 11½*

Design: 60h, Bethlehem Chapel.
844	A340	30h green	.30	.20
845	A340	60h redsh brown	.30	.20

80th anniversary of the birth of Zdenek Nejedly, restorer of Bethlehem Chapel.

Giant Excavator A341

Jewelry — A342

Peace Dove and: 60h, Soldiers, flame and banner, horiz. 1.60k, Harvester and rainbow, horiz.

1958, Feb. 25
846	A341	30h gray violet & yel	.20	.20
847	A341	60h gray brown & car	.30	.20
848	A341	1.60k green & dull yel	.50	.20
		Nos. 846-848 (3)	1.00	.60

10th anniv. of the "Victorious February."

Engraved and Photogravure
1958   Unwmk.   Perf. 11½

Designs: 45h, Dolls. 60h, Textiles. 75h, Kaplan turbine. 1.20k, Glass.
849	A342	30h rose car & blue	.40	.20
850	A342	45h rose red & pale lil	.40	.20
851	A342	60h violet & aqua	.60	.20
852	A342	75h ultra & salmon	1.50	.75
853	A342	1.20k blue grn & pink	.60	.20
		Nos. 849-853 (5)	3.50	1.55

Issued for the Universal and International Exposition at Brussels.

King George of Podebrad — A343

Design: 60h, View of Prague, 1628.

1958, May 19   **Engr.**
854	A343	30h carmine rose	.50	.20
855	A343	60h violet blue	.30	.20

Issued to publicize the National Archives Exhibition, Prague, May 15-Aug. 15.

"Towards the Stars" — A344

Women of Three Races — A345

Boy, Girl and Globes A346

1958, May 26
856	A344	30h carmine rose	.75	.35
857	A345	45h rose violet	.20	.20
858	A346	60h blue	.20	.20
		Nos. 856-858 (3)	1.15	.75

The Soc. for Dissemination of Political and Cultural Knowledge (#856). 4th Cong. of the Intl. Democratic Women's Fed. (#857). 1st World Trade Union Conf. of Working Youths, Prague, July 14-20 (#858).

Grain, Hammer and Sickle A347

Atomic Reactor A348

45h, Map of Czechoslovakia, hammer & sickle.

1958, May 26
859	A347	30h dull red	.25	.20
860	A347	45h green	.25	.20
861	A348	60h dark blue	.25	.20
		Nos. 859-861 (3)	.75	.60

11th Congress of the Czech Communist Party and the 15th anniv. of the Russo-Czechoslovakian Treaty.

Karlovy Vary A349

Various Spas: 40h, Podebrady. 60h, Marianske Lazne. 80h, Luhacovice. 1.20k, Strbske Pleso. 1.60k, Trencianske Teplice.

1958, June 25
862	A349	30h rose claret	.45	.20
863	A349	40h redsh brown	.45	.20
864	A349	60h gray green	.30	.20
865	A349	80h sepia	.45	.20
866	A349	1.20k violet blue	.60	.20
867	A349	1.60k lt violet	1.20	.75
		Nos. 862-867 (6)	3.45	1.75

Telephone Operator A350

Pres. Novotny A351

Design: 45h, Radio transmitter.

1958, June 20
868	A350	30h black & brn org	.30	.20
869	A350	45h black & lt grn	.45	.20

Conference of Postal Ministers of Communist Countries, Prague, June 30-July 9.

1958-59   *Perf. 12½*
870	A351	30h brt violet blue	.60	.20
b.		*Perf. 11½*	.60	.20
870A	A351	30h lt violet ('59)	4.00	1.75
871	A351	60h carmine rose	.50	.20

Perf. 11½
Redrawn
871A	A351	60h rose red	.50	.20
		Nos. 870-871A (4)	5.60	2.35

On No. 871 the top of the "6" turns down; on No. 871A it is open.

Czechoslovak Pavilion, Brussels — A352

1958, July 15   **Engr. & Photo.**
872	A352	1.95k lt blue & bis brn	.90	.20

Czechoslovakia Week at the Universal and International Exhibition at Brussels.

Portrait Type of 1956

30h, Julius Fucik. 45h, G. K. Zechenter 60h, Karel Capek. 1.40k, Svatopluk Cech.

1958, Aug. 20   Engr.   Perf. 11½
873	A306	30h rose red	.30	.20
874	A306	45h violet	1.50	.50
875	A306	60h dk blue gray	.50	.20
876	A306	1.40k gray	.50	.20
		Nos. 873-876 (4)	2.80	1.10

Death anniversaries of four famous Czechs.

The Artist and the Muse — A353

1958, Aug. 20   *Perf. 14*
877	A353	1.60k black	3.50	1.25

85th birthday of Max Svabinsky, artist and engraver.

No. 877 was printed in miniature sheets of 4. Value $24.

Children's Hospital, Brno — A354

Designs: 60h, New Town Hall, Brno. 1k, St. Thomas Church. 1.60k, View of Brno.

1958, Sept. 6   Unwmk.   Perf. 11½
Size: 40x23mm
878	A354	30h violet	.20	.20
879	A354	60h rose red	.20	.20
880	A354	1k brown	.45	.20

Perf. 14
Size: 50x28mm
881	A354	1.60k dk slate grn	1.90	1.75
		Nos. 878-881 (4)	2.75	2.35

Natl. Phil. Exhib., Brno, Sept. 9. No. 881 sold for 3.10k, including entrance ticket to exhibition. Issued in sheets of four.

Lepiota Procera — A355   Children on Beach — A356

Mushrooms: 40h, Boletus edulis. 60h, Krombholzia rufescens. 1.40k, Amanita muscaria L. 1.60k, Armillariella mellea.

1958, Oct. 6   *Perf. 14*
882	A355	30h dk brn, grn & buff	1.50	.75
883	A355	40h vio brn & brn org	2.25	.75
884	A355	60h black, red & buff	3.00	.75
885	A355	1.40k brown, scar & grn	3.75	2.00
886	A355	1.60k blk, red brn & ol	12.00	5.25
		Nos. 882-886 (5)	22.50	9.50

1958, Oct. 24   Unwmk.   Perf. 14

45h, Mother, child and bird. 60h, Skier.
887	A356	30h blue, yel & red	.30	.20
888	A356	45h ultra & carmine	1.25	.65
889	A356	60h brown, blue & yel	.30	.20
		Nos. 887-889 (3)	1.85	1.05

UNESCO Headquarters in Paris opening, Nov. 3.

Bozek's Steam Car of 1815 A357

Designs: 45h, "Präsident" car of 1897. 60h, "Skoda" sports car. 80h, "Tatra" sedan. 1k, "Autocar Skoda" bus. 1.25k, Trucks.

Engraved and Photogravure
1958, Dec. 1   **Perf. 11½x11**

890	A357	30h vio blk & buff	.75	.20
891	A357	45h ol & lt ol grn	.75	.30
892	A357	60h ol gray & sal	1.75	.30
893	A357	80h claret & bl grn	1.10	.30
894	A357	1k brn & lt yel grn	1.50	.30
895	A357	1.25k green & buff	2.25	.45
		Nos. 890-895 (6)	8.10	1.75

Issued to honor the automobile industry.

Stamp of 1918 and Allegory — A358

1958, Dec. 18   **Engr.**   **Perf. 11x11½**
896   A358   60h dark blue gray   1.00 .25

1st Czechoslovakian postage stamp, 40th anniv.

Ice Hockey A359

30h, Girl throwing javelin. 60h, Ice hockey. 1k, Hurdling. 1.60k, Rowing. 2k, High jump.

1959, Feb. 14   **Perf. 11½x11**

897	A359	20h dk brown & gray	.65	.20
898	A359	30h red brn & org brn	.45	.20
899	A359	60h dk bl & pale grn	.80	.20
900	A359	1k maroon & citron	.65	.20
901	A359	1.60k dull vio & lt bl	.95	.20
902	A359	2k red brn & lt bl	2.00	1.00
		Nos. 897-902 (6)	5.50	2.00

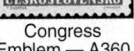

Congress Emblem — A360   "Equality of All Races" — A361

60h, Industrial & agricultural workers, emblem.

1959, Feb. 27   **Perf. 11½**
903   A360   30h maroon & lt blue   .45 .20
904   A360   60h dk blue & yellow   .45 .20

4th Agricultural Cooperative Cong. in Prague.

1959, Mar. 23

Designs: 1k, "Peace." 2k, Mother and Child: "Freedom for Colonial People."

905   A361   60h gray green   .30 .20
906   A361   1k gray   .45 .20
907   A361   2k dk gray blue   1.50 .50
    Nos. 905-907 (3)   2.25 .90

10th anniversary of the signing of the Universal Declaration of Human Rights.

Girl Holding Doll — A362   Frederic Joliot Curie — A363

40h, Pioneer studying map. 60h, Pioneer with radio. 80h, Girl pioneer planting tree.

1959, Mar. 28   **Engr. & Photo.**
908   A362   30h violet bl & yel   .35 .20
909   A362   40h indigo & ultra   .35 .20
910   A362   60h black & lilac   .35 .20
911   A362   80h brown & lt green   .75 .20
    Nos. 908-911 (4)   1.80 .80

10th anniv. of the Pioneer organization.

1959, Apr. 17   **Engr.**
912   A363   60h sepia   1.50 .25

Frederic Joliot Curie and the 10th anniversary of the World Peace Movement.

"Reaching for the Moon" — A364   Town Hall Pilsen — A365

1959, Apr. 17
913   A364   30h violet blue   .95 .25

2nd Cong. of the Czechoslovak Assoc. for the Propagation of Political and Cultural knowledge.

1959, May 2

Designs: 60h, Part of steam condenser turbine. 1k, St. Bartholomew's Church, Pilsen. 1.60k, Part of lathe.

914   A365   30h lt brown   .20 .20
915   A365   60h violet & lt grn   .25 .20
916   A365   1k violet blue   .30 .20
917   A365   1.60k black & yellow   1.25 .85
    Nos. 914-917 (4)   2.00 1.45

2nd Pilsen Stamp Exhib. in connection with the centenary of the Skoda (Lenin) armament works.

Factory and Emblem A366

Inscribed: "IV Vseodborovy sjezd, 1959"

1959, May 13
918   A366   30h shown   .35 .20
919   A366   60h Dam   .25 .20

4th Trade Union Congress.

Zvolen Castle A367

1959, June 13
920   A367   60h gray olive & yel   .60 .20

Regional Stamp Exhibition, Zvolen, 1959.

Frantisek Benda — A368   Aurel Stodola — A369

30h, Vaclav Kliment Klicpera. 60h, Karel V. Rais. 80h, Antonin Slavicek. 1k, Peter Bezruc.

1959, June 22   **Perf. 11½x11**

921	A368	15h violet blue	.25	.20
922	A368	30h orange brown	.25	.20
923	A369	40h dull green	.25	.20
924	A369	60h dull red brn	.35	.20
925	A369	80h dull violet	.65	.20
926	A368	1k dark brown	.65	.25
		Nos. 921-926 (6)	2.40	1.25

View of the Fair Grounds A370

Designs: 60h, Fair emblem and world map. 1.60k, Pavilion "Z."

Inscribed: "Mezinarodni Veletrh Brne 6.-20.IX. 1959"

Engraved and Photogravure
1959, July 20   **Unwmk.**   **Perf. 11½**
927   A370   30h lilac & yellow   .25 .20
928   A370   60h dull blue   .25 .20
929   A370   1.60k blue & bister   .75 .20
    Nos. 927-929 (3)   1.25 .60

International Fair at Brno, Sept. 6-20.

Revolutionist and Flag — A371

Slovakian Fighter — A372

1.60k, Linden leaves, sun and factory.

Perf. 11½
1959, Aug. 29   **Unwmk.**   **Engr.**
930   A371   30h black & rose   .20 .20
931   A372   60h carmine rose   .25 .20
932   A371   1.60k dk blue & yel   .45 .20
    Nos. 930-932 (3)   .90 .60

Natl. Slovakian revolution, 15th anniv. and Slovakian Soviet Republic, 40th anniv.

Alpine Marmots A373

1959, Sept. 25   **Engr. & Photo.**
933   A373   30h shown   1.40 .25
934   A373   40h Bison   1.00 .40
935   A373   60h Lynx, vert.   2.75 .25
936   A373   1k Wolf   2.75 .25
937   A373   1.60k Red deer   2.40 .55
    Nos. 933-937 (5)   10.30 1.70

Tatra National Park, 10th anniv.

Lunik 2 Hitting Moon and Russian Flag A374

1959, Sept. 23   **Perf. 11½**
938   A374   60h dk red & lt ultra   1.50 .25

Issued to commemorate the landing of the Soviet rocket on the moon, Sept. 13, 1959.

Stamp Printing Works, Peking A375

1959, Oct. 1
939   A375   30h pale green & red   .40 .20

10 years of Czechoslovakian-Chinese friendship.

Haydn — A376

Great Spotted Woodpecker A377

Design: 3k, Charles Darwin.

1959, Oct. 16   **Engr.**   **Perf. 11½**
940   A376   60h violet black   .50 .20
941   A376   3k dark red brown   1.50 .70

150th death anniv. of Franz Joseph Haydn, Austrian composer, and 150th birth anniv. of Charles Darwin, English naturalist.

1959, Nov. 16   **Perf. 14**

Birds: 30h, Blue tits. 40h, Nuthatch. 60th, Golden oriole. 80h, Goldfinch. 1k, Bullfinch. 1.20k, European kingfisher.

942	A377	20h multicolored	1.50	.60
943	A377	30h multicolored	1.50	.60
944	A377	40h multicolored	6.50	1.50
945	A377	60h multicolored	1.50	.60
946	A377	80h multicolored	2.50	.90
947	A377	1k multicolored	2.75	.90
948	A377	1.20k multicolored	5.00	1.25
		Nos. 942-948 (7)	21.25	6.35

Nos. 942-948 were each issued in miniature sheets of 10. Value, set $250.

Nikola Tesla A378

Designs: 30h, Alexander S. Popov. 35h, Edouard Branly. 60h, Guglielmo Marconi. 1k, Heinrich Hertz. 2k, Edwin Howard Armstrong and research tower, Alpine, N. J.

Engraved and Photogravure
1959, Dec. 7   **Perf. 11½**
949   A378   25h black & pink   .50 .20
950   A378   30h black & orange   .20 .20
951   A378   35h black & lt vio   .20 .20
952   A378   60h black & blue   .20 .20
953   A378   1k black & lt grn   .25 .20
954   A378   2k black & bister   1.50 .40
    Nos. 949-954 (6)   2.85 1.40

Issued to honor inventors in the fields of telegraphy and radio.

Gymnast — A379

2nd Winter Spartacist Games: 60h, Skier. 1.60k, Basketball players.

1960, Jan. 20 **Perf. 11½**
955	A379	30h salmon pink & brn	.95	.20
956	A379	60h lt blue & blk	.95	.20
957	A379	1.60k bister & brn	.85	.25
		Nos. 955-957 (3)	2.75	.65

1960, June 15 **Unwmk.**

Designs: 30h, Two girls in "Red Ball" drill. 60h, Gymnast with stick. 1k, Three girls with hoops.

958	A379	30h lt grn & rose claret	.65	.20
959	A379	60h pink & black	.50	.20
960	A379	1k ocher & vio bl	.85	.20
		Nos. 958-960 (3)	2.00	.60

2nd Summer Spartacist Games, Prague, June 23-July 3.

River Dredge Boat A380

Ships: 60h, River tug. 1k, Tourist steamer. 1.20k, Cargo ship "Lidice."

1960, Feb. 22 **Perf. 11½**
961	A380	30h slate grn & sal	2.75	.30
962	A380	60h maroon & pale bl	1.40	.30
963	A380	1k dk violet & yel	2.40	.30
964	A380	1.20k lilac & pale grn	3.50	.90
		Nos. 961-964 (4)	10.05	1.80

Ice Hockey Players — A381

Design: 1.80k, Figure skaters.

1960, Feb. 27
965	A381	60h sepia & lt blue	2.00	.40
966	A381	1.80k black & lt green	6.00	2.50

8th Olympic Winter Games, Squaw Valley, Calif., Feb. 18-29, 1960.

1960, June 15 **Unwmk.**

Designs: 1k, Running. 1.80k, Women's gymnastics. 2k, Rowing.

967	A381	1k black & orange	.85	.30
968	A381	1.80k black & sal pink	1.40	.40
969	A381	2k black & blue	2.25	.95
		Nos. 967-969 (3)	4.50	1.65

17th Olympic Games, Rome, 8/25-9/11.

Trencin Castle — A382

Castles: 10h, Bezdez. 20h, Kost. 30h, Pernstein. 40h, Kremnica. 50h, Krivoklát castle. 60h, Karlstein. 1k, Smolenice. 1.60k, Kokorin.

1960-63 **Engr.** **Perf. 11½**
970	A382	5h gray violet	.25	.20
971	A382	10h black	.25	.20
972	A382	20h brown org	.35	.20
973	A382	30h green	.25	.20
974	A382	40h brown	.35	.20

974A	A382	50h black ('63)	2.00	.20
975	A382	60h rose red	.40	.20
976	A382	1k lilac	.40	.20
977	A382	1.60k dark blue	.80	.20
		Nos. 970-977 (9)	5.05	1.80

1961, Oct. **Wmk. 341**
977A	A382	30h green	2.75	.40

Lenin — A383   Soldier Holding Child — A384

1960, Apr. 22 **Unwmk.**
978	A383	60h gray olive	1.25	.20

90th anniversary of the birth of Lenin.

1960, May 5 **Engr. & Photo.**

Designs: No. 980, Child eating pie. No. 981, Soldier helping concentration camp victim. No. 982, Welder and factory, horiz. No. 983, Tractor driver and farm, horiz.

979	A384	30h maroon & lt blue	.35	.20
980	A384	30h dull red	.35	.20
981	A384	30h green & dull blue	.40	.20
982	A384	60h dk blue & buff	.35	.20
983	A384	60h redsh brn & yel grn	.40	.20
		Nos. 979-983 (5)	1.85	1.00

15th anniversary of liberation.

Steelworker — A385

Design: 60h, Farm woman and child.

1960, May 24
984	A385	30h maroon & gray	.20	.20
985	A385	60h green & pale blue	.30	.20

1960 parliamentary elections.

Red Cross Nurse Holding Dove A386

Fire Fighters A387

1960, May 26 **Unwmk.**
986	A386	30h brown car & bl	.40	.20
987	A387	60h dk blue & pink	.60	.20

3rd Congress of the Czechoslovakian Red Cross (No. 986), and the 2nd Fire Fighters' Congress (No. 987).

Hand of Philatelist with Tongs and Two Stamps — A388

Design: 1k, Globe and 1937 Bratislava stamp (shown in miniature on 60h).

1960, July 11 **Perf. 11½**
988	A388	60h black & dull yel	.70	.20
989	A388	1k black & blue	.80	.20

Issued to publicize the National Stamp Exhibition, Bratislava, Sept. 24-Oct. 9. See Nos. C49-C50.

Stalin Mine, Ostrava-Hermanovice — A390

Viktorin Cornelius, Lawyer — A391

Designs: 20h, Power station, Hodonin. 30h, Gottwald iron works, Kuncice. 40h, Harvester. 60h, Oil refinery.

1960, July 25
992	A390	10h black & pale grn	.30	.20
993	A390	20h maroon & lt bl	.30	.20
994	A390	30h indigo & pink	.30	.20
995	A390	40h green & pale lilac	.30	.20
996	A390	60h dk blue & yel	.30	.20
		Nos. 992-996 (5)	1.50	1.00

Issued to publicize the new five-year plan.

1960, Aug. 23 **Engr.**

Portraits: 20h, Karel Matej Capek-Chod, writer. 30h, Hana Kvapilova, actress. 40h, Oskar Nedbal, composer. 60h, Otakar Ostrcil, composer.

997	A391	10h black	.25	.20
998	A391	20h red brown	.35	.20
999	A391	30h rose red	.50	.20
1000	A391	40h dull green	1.25	.60
1001	A391	60h gray violet	.35	.20
		Nos. 997-1001 (5)	2.70	1.40

See Nos. 1037-1041.

Skoda Sports Plane Flying Upside Down A392

1960, Aug. 28 **Engr. & Photo.**
1002	A392	60h violet blue & blue	1.50	.30

1st aerobatic world championships, Bratislava.

Constitution and "Czechoslovakia" — A393

1960, Sept. 18
1003	A393	30h violet bl & pink	.40	.20

Proclamation of the new socialist constitution.

Workers Reading Newspaper — A394

Man Holding Newspaper — A395

1960, Sept. 18
1004	A394	30h slate & ver	.25	.20
1005	A395	60h black & rose	.25	.20

Day of the Czechoslovak Press, Sept. 21, 1960, and 40th anniv. of the Rudé Právo paper.

Globes and Laurel A396

1960, Sept. 18 **Engr.**
1006	A396	30h dk blue & bister	.40	.20

World Federation of Trade Unions, 15th anniv.

Black-crowned Night Heron — A397   Doronicum Clusii (Thistle) — A398

Birds: 30h, Great crested grebe. 40h, Lapwing. 60h, Gray heron. 1k, Graylag goose, horiz. 1.60k, Mallard, horiz.

Engraved and Photogravure
1960, Oct. 24 **Unwmk.** **Perf. 11½**
Designs in Black
1007	A397	25h pale vio blue	.80	.20
1008	A397	30h pale citron	.70	.20
1009	A397	40h pale blue	.80	.30
1010	A397	60h pink	.55	.20
1011	A397	1k pale yellow	1.50	.20
1012	A397	1.60k lt violet	4.00	1.25
		Nos. 1007-1012 (6)	8.35	2.35

1960, Nov. 21 **Engr.** **Perf. 14**

Flowers: 30h, Cyclamen. 40h, Primrose. 60h, Hen-and-chickens. 1k, Gentian. 2k, Pasqueflower.

1013	A398	20h black, yel & grn	.85	.85
1014	A398	30h black, car rose & grn	.85	.85
1015	A398	40h black, yel & grn	.85	.85
1016	A398	60h black, pink & grn	.85	.85
1017	A398	1k black, bl, vio & grn	2.50	.85
1018	A398	2k black, lil, yel & grn	3.25	1.60
		Nos. 1013-1018 (6)	9.15	5.85

Alfons Mucha — A399

1960, Dec. 18 **Engr.** **Perf. 11½x12**
1019	A399	60h dk blue gray	2.50	.20

Day of the Czechoslovak Postage Stamp and birth cent. of Alfons Mucha, designer of the 1st Czechoslovakian stamp (Type A1).

Rolling-mill Control Bridge — A400

Athletes with Flags — A401

Designs: 30h, Turbo generator. 60h, Ditch-digging machine.

1961, Jan. 20   Unwmk.   Perf. 11½
1020	A400	20h blue	.30	.20
1021	A400	30h rose	.30	.20
1022	A400	60h brt green	.30	.20
		Nos. 1020-1022 (3)	.90	.60

Third Five-Year Plan.

Perf. 11x11½, 11½x11
1961, Feb. 20   Engr. & Photo.

Designs: No. 1024, Motorcycle race, horiz. 40h, Sculling, horiz. 60h, Ice skater. 1k, Rugby. 1.20k, Soccer. 1.60k, Long-distance runners.

1023	A401	30h rose red & bl	.20	.20
1024	A401	30h dk blue & car	.20	.20
1025	A401	40h dk gray & car	.35	.20
1026	A401	60h lilac & blue	.30	.20
1027	A401	1k ultra & yel	.30	.20
1028	A401	1.20k green & buff	.50	.20
1029	A401	1.60k sepia & salmon	2.00	1.00
		Nos. 1023-1029 (7)	3.85	2.20

Various sports events.

Exhibition Emblem A402

Rocket Launching A403

1961, Mar. 6   Engr.   Perf. 11½
1030	A402	2k dk blue & red	2.00	.20

"Praga 1962" International Stamp Exhibition, Prague, Sept. 1962.

1961, Mar. 6   Engr. & Photo.

30h, Sputnik III, horiz. 40h, As 20h, but inscribed "Start Kosmicke Rakety k Venusi — 12.II.1961". 60h, Sputnik I, horiz. 1.60k, Interplanetary station, horiz. 2k, Similar to type A404, without commemorative inscription.

1031	A403	20h violet & pink	.35	.20
1032	A403	30h dk green & buff	.65	.20
1033	A403	40h dk red & yel grn	.65	.30
1034	A403	60h violet & buff	.80	.20
1035	A403	1.60k dk bl & pale grn	.50	.25
1036	A403	2k mar & pale bl	1.90	1.10
		Nos. 1031-1036 (6)	4.85	2.25

Issued to publicize Soviet space research.

Portrait Type of 1960

No. 1037, Jindrich Mosna. No. 1038, Pavol Orszagh Hviezdoslav. No. 1039, Alois Mrstik. No. 1040, Joza Uprka. No. 1041, Josef Hora.

1961, Mar. 27   Perf. 11½
1037	A391	60h green	.25	.20
1038	A391	60h dark blue	.45	.20
a.		"ORSZACH" instead of "ORSZAGH"	400.00	100.00
1039	A391	60h dull claret	.60	.20
1040	A391	60h gray	.45	.20
1041	A391	60h sepia	.25	.20
		Nos. 1037-1041 (5)	2.00	1.00

Man Flying into Space A404

1961, Apr. 13
1042	A404	60h car & pale bl	.50	.20
1043	A404	3k ultra & yel	2.00	.60

1st man in space, Yuri A. Gagarin, Apr. 12, 1961. See No. 1036.

Flute Player — A405

Blast Furnace and Mine, Kladno — A406

1961, Apr. 24   Engr.
1044	A405	30h shown	.45	.20
1045	A405	30h Dancer	.45	.20
1046	A405	60h Lyre player	.60	.20
		Nos. 1044-1046 (3)	1.50	.60

Prague Conservatory of Music, 150th anniv.

1961, Apr. 24
1047	A406	3k dull red	.75	.20

Marching Workers — A407

Woman with Hammer and Sickle — A408

Klement Gottwald Museum A409

Designs: No. 1050, Lenin Museum. No. 1051, Crowd with flags. No. 1053, Man saluting Red Star.

1961, May 10
1048	A407	30h dull violet	.30	.20
1049	A409	30h dark blue	.30	.20
1050	A409	30h redsh brown	.30	.20
1051	A407	60h vermilion	.30	.20
1052	A408	60h dark green	.30	.20
1053	A408	60h carmine	.30	.20
		Nos. 1048-1053 (6)	1.80	1.20

Czech Communist Party, 40th anniversary.

Puppet — A410

Designs: Various Puppets.

Engraved and Photogravure
1961, June 20   Unwmk.   Perf. 11½
1054	A410	30h ver & yel	.20	.20
1055	A410	40h sepia & bluish grn	.20	.20
1056	A410	60h vio bl & sal	.20	.20
1057	A410	1k green & lt blue	.20	.20
1058	A410	1.60k mar & pale vio	1.10	.35
		Nos. 1054-1058 (5)	2.00	1.15

Woman, Map of Africa and Flag of Czechoslovakia — A411

1961, June 26
1059	A411	60h red & blue	.30	.20

Issued to publicize the friendship between the people of Africa and Czechoslovakia.

Map of Europe and Fair Emblem A412

Fair emblem and: 60h Horizontal boring machine, vert. 1k, Scientists' meeting and nuclear physics emblem.

1961, Aug. 14   Perf. 11½
1060	A412	30h dk bl & pale grn	.30	.20
1061	A412	60h green & pink	.30	.20
1062	A412	1k vio brn & lt bl	.60	.25
		Nos. 1060-1062 (3)	1.20	.65

International Trade Fair, Brno, Sept. 10-24.

Sugar Beet, Cup of Coffee and Bags of Sugar A413

Charles Bridge, St. Nicholas Church and Hradcany A414

1961, Sept. 18   Unwmk.   Perf. 11½
1063	A413	20h shown	.20	.20
1064	A413	30h Clover	.20	.20
1065	A413	40h Wheat	.20	.20
1066	A413	60h Hops	.20	.20
1067	A413	1.40k Corn	.35	.20
1068	A413	2k Potatoes	1.25	.55
		Nos. 1063-1068 (6)	2.40	1.55

1961, Sept. 25
1069	A414	60h violet bl & car	1.20	.20

26th session of the Governor's Council of the Red Cross Societies League, Prague.

Orlik Dam and Kaplan Turbine A415

Designs: 30h, View of Prague, flags and stamps. 40h, Hluboká Castle, river and fish. 60h, Karlovy Vary and cup. 1k, Pilsen and beer bottle. 1.20k, North Bohemia landscape and vase. 1.60k, Tatra mountains, boots, ice pick and rope. 2k, Ironworks, Ostrava Kuncice and pulley. 3k, Brno and ball bearing. 4k, Bratislava and grapes. 5k, Prague and flags.

1961   Unwmk.   Perf. 11½
Size: 41x23mm
1070	A415	20h gray & blue	1.25	.50
1071	A415	30h vio blue & red	.30	.20
1072	A415	40h dk blue & lt grn	1.25	.65
1073	A415	60h dk blue & yel	1.40	.65
1074	A415	1k mar & grn	1.00	.65
1075	A415	1.20k green & pink	1.40	.65
1076	A415	1.60k brn & vio bl	1.40	1.00
1077	A415	2k blk & ocher	1.60	1.00
1078	A415	3k ultra & yel	1.60	.50
1079	A415	4k purple & sal	2.40	1.10

Perf. 13½
Engr.
Size: 50x29mm
1080	A415	5k multicolored	27.00	17.50
		Nos. 1070-1080 (11)	40.60	24.40

"PRAGA 1962 World Exhib. of Postage Stamps," Aug. 18-Sept. 2, 1962. No. 1080 was printed in sheet of 4. Value $150.

Globe A416

Engraved and Photogravure
1961, Nov. 27   Perf. 11½
1081	A416	60h red & ultra	.50	.20

Issued to publicize the Fifth World Congress of Trade Unions, Moscow, Dec. 4-16.

Orange Tip Butterfly A417

Bicyclists A418

Designs (butterflies): 20h, Zerynthia hypsipyle Sch. 30h, Apollo. 40h, Swallowtail. 60h, Peacock. 80h, Mourning cloak (Camberwell beauty). 1k, Underwing (moth). 1.60k, Red admiral. 2k, Brimstone (sulphur).

1961, Nov. 27   Engr.
1082	A417	15h multicolored	.90	.30
1083	A417	20h multicolored	.90	.30
1084	A417	30h multicolored	.90	.30
1085	A417	40h multicolored	.90	.30
1086	A417	60h multicolored	.90	.30
1087	A417	80h multicolored	2.75	.90
1088	A417	1k multicolored	3.00	.90
1089	A417	1.60k multicolored	3.00	.90
1090	A417	2k multicolored	7.50	3.00
		Nos. 1082-1090 (9)	20.75	7.20

Printed in sheets of ten. Value, set $275.

Engraved and Photogravure
1962, Feb. 5   Unwmk.   Perf. 11½

Sports: 40h, Woman gymnast. 60h, Figure skaters. 1k, Woman bowler. 1.20k, Goalkeeper, soccer. 1.60k, Discus thrower.

1091	A418	30h black & vio bl	.20	.20
1092	A418	40h black & yel	.20	.20
1093	A418	60h slate & grnsh bl	.35	.20
1094	A418	1k black & pink	.35	.20
1095	A418	1.20k black & green	.35	.20
1096	A418	1.60k blk & dull grn	1.75	.80
		Nos. 1091-1096 (6)	3.20	1.80

Various 1962 sports events.
No. 1095 does not have the commemorative inscription.

Karel Kovarovic — A419

Frantisek Zaviska and Karel Petr A420

20h, Frantisek Skroup. 30h, Bozena Nemcova. 60h, View of Prague & staff of Aesculapius. 1.60k, Ladislav Celakovsky. 1.80k, Miloslav Valouch & Juraj Hronec.

1962, Feb. 26   **Engr.**

1097	A419	10h red brown	.20	.20
1098	A419	20h violet blue	.20	.20
1099	A419	30h brown	.20	.20
1100	A420	40h claret	.20	.20
1101	A419	60h black	.20	.20
1102	A419	1.60k slate green	.50	.20
1103	A420	1.80k dark blue	.60	.20
		Nos. 1097-1103 (7)	2.10	1.40

Various cultural personalities and events.

Miner and Flag A421

1962, Mar. 19   **Engr. & Photo.**
1104 A421 60h indigo & rose   .25 .20

30th anniv. of the miners' strike at Most.

"Man Conquering Space" — A422

Soviet Spaceship Vostok 2 — A423

40h, Launching of Soviet space rocket. 80h, Multi-stage automatic rocket. 1k, Automatic station on moon. 1.60k, Television satellite.

1962, Mar. 26

1105	A422	30h dk red & lt blue	.25	.20
1106	A422	40h dk blue & sal	.25	.20
1107	A423	60h dk blue & pink	.25	.20
1108	A423	80h rose vio & lt grn	.60	.20
1109	A422	1k indigo & citron	.35	.20
1110	A423	1.60k green & buff	1.75	.75
		Nos. 1105-1110 (6)	3.45	1.75

Issued to publicize space research.

Polar Bear — A424

Zoo Animals: 30h, Chimpanzee. 60h, Camel. 1k, African and Indian elephants, horiz. 1.40k, Leopard, horiz. 1.60k, Przewalski horse, horiz.

1962, Apr. 24   **Unwmk.**   **Perf. 11½**
Design and Inscriptions in Black

1111	A424	20h grnsh blue	.75	.20
1112	A424	30h violet	.75	.20
1113	A424	60h orange	.75	.20
1114	A424	1k green	.90	.20

1115	A424	1.40k carmine rose	.90	.20
1116	A424	1.60k lt brown	2.00	1.25
		Nos. 1111-1116 (6)	6.05	2.25

Child and Grieving Mother — A425   Klary's Fountain, Teplice — A426

60h, Flowers growing from ruins of Lezáky.

1962, June 9   **Engr. & Photo.**
1118 A425 30h black & red   .35 .20
1119 A425 60h black & dull bl   .65 .20

20th anniversary of the destruction of Lidice and Lezáky by the Nazis.

1962, June 9
1120 A426 60h dull grn & yel   .40 .20

1,200th anniversary of the discovery of the medicinal springs of Teplice.

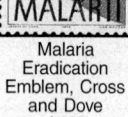

Malaria Eradication Emblem, Cross and Dove A427   Soccer Goalkeeper A428

3k, Dove and malaria eradication emblem.

1962, June 18
1121 A427 60h black & crimson   .20 .20
1122 A427 3k dk blue & yel   1.25 .60

WHO drive to eradicate malaria.

1962, June 20   **Unwmk.**   **Perf. 11½**
1123 A428 1.60k green & yellow   1.50 .20

Czechoslovakia's participation in the World Cup Soccer Championship, Chile, May 30-June 17. See No. 1095.

Soldier in Swimming Relay Race A429   "Agriculture" A430

Designs: 40h, Soldier hurdling. 60h, Soccer player. 1k, Soldier with rifle in relay race.

1962, July 20

1124	A429	30h green & lt ultra	.20	.20
1125	A429	40h dk purple & yel	.20	.20
1126	A429	60h brown & green	.20	.20
1127	A429	1k dk blue & sal pink	.35	.20
		Nos. 1124-1127 (4)	.95	.80

2nd Summer Spartacist Games of Friendly Armies, Prague, Sept., 1962.

1962   **Engr.**   **Perf. 13½**
Designs: 60h, Astronaut in capsule. 80h, Boy with flute, horiz. 1k, Workers of three races, horiz. 1.40k, Children dancing around

tree. 1.60k, Flying bird, horiz. 5k, View of Prague, horiz.

1128	A430	30h multicolored	1.50	.90
1129	A430	60h multicolored	.70	.55
a.		Miniature sheet of 8	20.00	20.00
1130	A430	80h multicolored	2.00	1.40
1131	A430	1k multicolored	2.00	1.40
1132	A430	1.40k multicolored	2.00	1.40
1133	A430	1.60k multicolored	3.50	3.50
		Nos. 1128-1133 (6)	11.70	9.15

Souvenir Sheet

1134	A430	5k multicolored	12.00	10.00
a.		Imperf.	45.00	35.00

"PRAGA 1962 World Exhib. of Postage Stamps," 8/18-9/2/62. No. 1133 also for FIP Day, Sept. 1. Printed in sheets of 10. Value: Nos. 1128-1133 $150; No. 1134 $80.

No. 1129a contains 4 each of Nos. 1128-1129 and 2 labels arranged in 2 rows of 2 se-tenant pairs of Nos. 1128-1129 with label between. Sold for 5k, only with ticket.

No. 1134 contains one 51x30mm stamp. Sold only with ticket.

Children in Day Nursery and Factory A431

Sailboat and Trade Union Rest Home, Zinkovy — A432

Engraved and Photogravure
1962, Oct. 29   **Unwmk.**   **Perf. 11½**
1135 A431 30h black & lt blue   .20 .20
1136 A432 60h brown & yellow   .20 .20

Cruiser "Aurora" A433

1962, Nov. 7
1137 A433 30h black & gray bl   .20 .20
1138 A433 60h black & pink   .20 .20

Russian October revolution, 45th anniv.

Cosmonaut and Worker — A434

Lenin — A435

1962, Nov. 7
1139 A434 30h dark red & blue   .20 .20
1140 A435 60h black & dp rose   .20 .20

40th anniversary of the USSR.

Symbolic Crane — A436

40h, Agricultural products, vert. 60h, Factories.

1962, Dec. 4
1141 A436 30h dk red & yel   .20 .20
1142 A436 40h gray blue & yel   .20 .20
1143 A436 60h black & dp rose   .30 .20
    Nos. 1141-1143 (3)   .70 .60

Communist Party of Czechoslovakia, 12th cong.

Ground Beetle — A437

Table Tennis — A438

Beetles: 30h, Cardinal beetle. 60h, Stag beetle, vert. 1k, Great water beetle. 1.60k, Alpine longicorn, vert. 2k, Ground beetle, vert.

1962, Dec. 15   **Engr.**   **Perf. 14**

1144	A437	20h multicolored	1.00	.40
1145	A437	30h multicolored	1.00	.40
1146	A437	60h multicolored	1.00	.40
1147	A437	1k multicolored	2.00	.60
1148	A437	1.60k multicolored	4.00	.60
1149	A437	2k multicolored	6.00	2.00
		Nos. 1144-1149 (6)	15.00	4.40

Nos. 1144-1149 were each printed in sheets of 10. Value, set $200.

Engraved and Photogravure
1963, Jan.   **Perf. 11½**

Sports: 60h, Bicyclist. 80h, Skier. 1k, Motorcyclist. 1.20k, Weight lifter. 1.60k, Hurdler.

1150	A438	30h black & dp grn	.20	.20
1151	A438	60h black & orange	.20	.20
1152	A438	80h black & ultra	.20	.20
1153	A438	1k black & violet	.40	.20
1154	A438	1.20k blk & pale brn	.40	.20
1155	A438	1.60k blk & car	.85	.20
		Nos. 1150-1155 (6)	2.25	1.20

Various 1963 sports events.

Industrial Plant, Laurel and Star — A439   Symbol of Child Welfare Home — A440

Industrial Plant and Symbol of Growth — A441

1963, Feb. 25   **Unwmk.**   **Perf. 11½**
1156 A439 30h carmine & lt bl   .20 .20
1157 A440 60h black & car   .20 .20
1158 A441 60h black & red   .20 .20
    Nos. 1156-1158 (3)   .60 .60

15th anniv. of the "Victorious February" and 5th Trade Union Cong.

Artists' Guild Emblem — A442   Juraj Jánosik — A443

Eduard Urx — A444

National Theater, Prague — A445

#1163, Woman reading to children. #1164, Juraj Pálkovic. 1.60k, Max Svabinsky.

Engr. & Photo.; Engr. (A444)
1963, Mar. 25   Unwmk.   Perf. 11½

1159	A442	20h black & Prus bl	.20	.20
1160	A443	30h car & lt bl	.20	.20
1161	A444	30h carmine	.20	.20
1162	A445	60h dl red brn & lt bl	.20	.20
1163	A444	60h green	.20	.20
1164	A444	60h black	.25	.20
1165	A444	1.60k brown	.50	.20
		Nos. 1159-1165 (7)	1.75	1.40

Various cultural personalities and events.

Boy and Girl with Flag A446

Television Transmitter A447

Engraved and Photogravure
1963, Apr. 18   Perf. 11½

1166	A446	30h slate & rose red	.35	.20

The 4th Congress of Czechoslovak Youth.

1963, Apr. 25

40h, Television camera, mast and set, horiz.

1167	A447	40h buff & slate	.40	.20
1168	A447	60h dk red & lt blue	.40	.20

Czechoslovak television, 10th anniversary.

Rocket to the Sun A448

50h, Rockets & Sputniks leaving Earth. 60h, Spacecraft to & from Moon. 1k, 3k, Interplanetary station & Mars 1. 1.60k, Atomic rocket & Jupiter. 2k, Rocket returning from Saturn.

1963, Apr. 25

1169	A448	30h red brn & buff	.20	.20
1170	A448	50h slate & bluish grn	.20	.20
1171	A448	60h dk green & yel	.25	.20
1172	A448	1k dk gray & sal	.45	.20
1173	A448	1.60k gray brn & lt grn	.75	.20
1174	A448	2k dk purple & yel	2.50	.75
		Nos. 1169-1174 (6)	4.35	1.75

Souvenir Sheet
Imperf

1175	A448	3k Prus grn & org red	12.00	6.00

No. 1175 issued for 1st Space Research Exhib., Prague, Apr. 1963.

Studio and Radio A449

1k, Globe inscribed "Peace" & aerial mast, vert.

1963, May 18   Unwmk.   Perf. 11½

1176	A449	30h choc & pale grn	.40	.20
1177	A449	1k bluish grn & lilac	.40	.20

40th anniversary of Czechoslovak radio.

Tupolev Tu-104B Turbojet A450

Design: 1.80k, Ilyushin Il-18 Moskva.

1963, May 25

1178	A450	80h violet & lt bl	1.00	.25
1179	A450	1.80k dk blue & lt grn	1.60	.25

40th anniversary of Czechoslovak airlines.

9th Cent. Ring, Map of Moravian Settlements A451

Woman Singing A452

1.60k, Falconer, 9th cent. silver disk.

1963, May 25

1180	A451	30h lt green & blk	.25	.20
1181	A451	1.60k dull yel & blk	.75	.20

1100th anniversary of Moravian empire.

1963, May 25   Engr.

1182	A452	30h bright red	.60	.20

60th anniversary of the founding of the Moravian Teachers' Singing Club.

Kromeriz Castle and Barley — A453

Centenary Emblem, Nurse and Playing Child — A454

Engraved and Photogravure
1963, June 20   Unwmk.   Perf. 11½

1183	A453	30h slate grn & yel	.40	.20

Natl. Agricultural Exhib. and 700th anniv. of Kromeriz.

1963, June 20

1184	A454	30h dk gray & car	.40	.20

Centenary of the International Red Cross.

Bee, Honeycomb and Emblem A455

Liberec Fair Emblem — A456

1963, June 20

1185	A455	1k brown & yellow	.75	.20

19th Intl. Beekeepers Cong., Apimondia, 1963.

1963, July 13

1186	A456	30h black & dp rose	.40	.20

Liberec Consumer Goods Fair.

Town Hall, Brno — A457

Cave, Moravian Karst — A458

Design: 60h, Town Hall tower, Brno.

1963, July 29

1187	A457	30h lt blue & maroon	.35	.20
1188	A457	60h pink & dk blue	.35	.20

International Trade Fair, Brno.

1963, July 29

#1190, Trout, Hornad Valley. 60h, Great Hawk Gorge. 80h, Macocha mountains.

1189	A458	30h brown & lt bl	.60	.20
1190	A458	30h dk bl & dull grn	.70	.20
1191	A458	60h green & blue	.60	.20
1192	A458	80h sepia & pink	.60	.20
		Nos. 1189-1192 (4)	2.50	.80

Blast Furnace A459

1963, Aug. 15   Unwmk.   Perf. 11½

1193	A459	60h blk & bluish grn	.40	.20

30th Intl. Cong. of Iron Founders, Prague.

White Mouse A460

1963, Aug. 15

1194	A460	1k black & carmine	.50	.20

2nd Intl. Pharmacological Cong., Prague.

Farm Machinery for Underfed Nations — A461

Wooden Toys — A462

1963, Aug. 15   Engr.

1195	A461	1.60k black	.50	.20

FAO "Freedom from Hunger" campaign.

1963, Sept. 2   Engr.   Perf. 13½

Folk Art (Inscribed "UNESCO"): 80h, Cock and flowers. 1k, Flowers in vase. 1.20k, Janosik, Slovak hero. 1.60k, Stag. 2k, Postilion.

1196	A462	60h red & vio bl	.75	.30
1197	A462	80h multi	.75	.30
1198	A462	1k multi	.75	.30
1199	A462	1.20k multi	.75	.30
1200	A462	1.60k multi	.75	.30
1201	A462	2k multi	3.25	1.75
		Nos. 1196-1201 (6)	7.00	3.25

Nos. 1196-1201 were printed in sheets of 10. Value, set $150.

Canoeing A463

Tree and Star — A464

Sports: 40h, Volleyball. 60h, Wrestling. 80h, Basketball. 1k, Boxing. 1.60k, Gymnastics.

Engraved and Photogravure
1963, Oct. 26   Perf. 11½

1202	A463	30h indigo & grn	.35	.20
1203	A463	40h red brn & lt bl	.35	.25
1204	A463	60h brn red & yel	.40	.20
1205	A463	80h dk pur & dp org	.50	.25
1206	A463	1k ultra & dp rose	.70	.35
1207	A463	1.60k vio bl & ultra	2.25	1.00
		Nos. 1202-1207 (6)	4.55	2.25

1964 Olympic Games, Tokyo.

1963, Dec. 11   Unwmk.   Perf. 11½

Design: 60h, Star, hammer and sickle.

1208	A464	30h bis brn & lt bl	.30	.20
1209	A464	60h carmine & gray	.30	.20

Russo-Czechoslovakian Treaty, 20th anniv.

Atom Diagrams
Surrounding
Head — A465

Chamois — A466

1963, Dec. 12   Engr.
1210 A465 60h dark purple   .40 .20

3rd Congress of the Association for the
Propagation of Scientific Knowledge.

1963, Dec. 14   Perf. 14
40h, Alpine ibex. 60h, Mouflon. 1.20k, Roe
deer. 1.60k, Fallow deer. 2k, Red deer.

1211 A466 30h multi   1.50   .35
1212 A466 40h multi   1.50   .35
1213 A466 60h brn, yel & grn 1.50   .35
1214 A466 1.20k multi   2.50 1.00
1215 A466 1.60k multi   3.00 1.25
1216 A466 2k multi   6.00 2.50
    Nos. 1211-1216 (6)   16.00 5.80

Figure
Skating — A467

Ice
Hockey — A468

80h, Skiing, horiz. 1k, Field ball player.

Engraved and Photogravure
1964, Jan. 20   Unwmk.   Perf. 11½
1217 A467 30h violet bl & yel   .30   .20
1218 A467 80h dk blue & org   .45   .20
1219 A467 1k brown & lilac   .75   .20
    Nos. 1217-1219 (3)   1.50   .60

Intl. University Games (30h, 80h) and the
World Field Ball Championships (1k).

1964, Jan. 20
1220 A468 1k shown   .85   .35
1221 A468 1.80k Toboggan   1.00   .60
1222 A468 2k Ski jump   2.50 2.25
    Nos. 1220-1222 (3)   4.35 3.20

9th Winter Olympic Games, Innsbruck, Jan.
29-Feb. 9, 1964.

Magura Rest
Home, High
Tatra — A469

Design: 80h, Slovak National Insurrection
Rest Home, Low Tatra.

1964, Feb. 19   Unwmk.   Perf. 11½
1223 A469 60h green & yellow   .30   .20
1224 A469 80h violet bl & pink .30   .20

Skiers
and Ski
Lift
A470

60h, Automobile camp, Telc. 1k, Fishing,
Spis Castle. 1.80k, Lake & boats, Cesky
Krumlov.

1964, Feb. 19   Engr. & Photo.
1225 A470 30h dk vio brn & bl   .40   .20
1226 A470 60h slate & car   .45   .20
1227 A470 1k brown & olive   .65   .20
1228 A470 1.80k slate grn & org 1.00 .35
    Nos. 1225-1228 (4)   2.50   .95

Moses, Day and Night by
Michelangelo — A471

Designs: 60h, "A Midsummer Night's
Dream," by Shakespeare. 1k, Man, telescope
and heaven, vert. 1.60k, King George of
Podebrad (1420-71).

1964, Mar. 20
1229 A471 40h black & yel grn   .35   .20
1230 A471 60h slate & car   .25   .20
1231 A471 1k black & lt blue   .90   .20
1232 A471 1.60k black & multi 1.00   .20
  a.   Souvenir sheet of 4 ('88) 9.00 6.00
    Nos. 1229-1232 (4)   2.50   .80

400th anniv. of the death of Michelangelo
(40h); 400th anniv. of the birth of Shakespeare
(60h); 400th anniv. of the birth of Galileo (1k);
500th anniv. of the pacifist efforts of King
George of Podebrad (1.60k).
No. 1232a for PRAGA '88.

Yuri A. Gagarin — A472

Astronauts: 60h, Gherman Titov. 80h, John
H. Glenn, Jr. 1k, Scott M. Carpenter, vert.
1.20k, Pavel R. Popovich and Andrian G. Niko-
layev. 1.40k, Walter M. Schirra, vert. 1.60k,
Gordon L. Cooper, vert. 2k, Valentina Tereshkova and Valeri Bykovski, vert.

1964, Apr. 27   Unwmk.   Perf. 11½
Yellow Paper
1233 A472 30h black & vio bl   .50   .25
1234 A472 60h dk grn & dk car   .25   .20
1235 A472 80h dk car & vio   .50   .20
1236 A472 1k ultra & rose vio   .25   .25
1237 A472 1.20k ver & ol gray   .50   .35
1238 A472 1.40k black & dl grn 1.25   .50
1239 A472 1.60k pale pur & Prus
                            grn   3.00 1.50
1240 A472 2k dk blue & red   1.00   .40
    Nos. 1233-1240 (8)   7.25 3.65

World's first 10 astronauts.

Creeping
Bellflower
A473

Film "Flower" and
Karlovy Vary
Colonnade
A474

Flowers: 80h, Musk thistle. 1k, Chicory.
1.20k, Yellow iris. 1.60k, Gentian. 2k, Corn
poppy.

1964, June 15   Engr.   Perf. 14
1241 A473 60h dk grn, lil &
                    org   1.25   .25
1242 A473 80h blk, grn & red
                    lil   1.25   .25
1243 A473 1k vio bl, grn &
                    pink   1.25   .45
1244 A473 1.20k black, yel &
                    grn   1.25   .30
1245 A473 1.60k violet & grn   3.00   .40
1246 A473 2k vio, red & grn   7.00 2.00
    Nos. 1241-1246 (6)   15.00 3.65

Nos. 1241-1246 were each issued in sheets
of 10. Value, set $225.

Engraved and Photogravure
1964, June 20   Unwmk.   Perf. 13½
1247 A474 60h black, blue & car 1.75 .30

14th Intl. Film Festival at Karlovy Vary, July
4-19.

Silesian Coat of
Arms — A475

Young Miner of
1764 — A476

1964, June 20   Perf. 11½
1248 A475 30h black & yel   .30   .20

150th anniv. of the Silesian Museum, Opava.

1964, June 20
1249 A476 60h sepia & lt grn   .30   .20

Mining School at Banska Stiavnica, bicent.

Skoda
Fire
Engine
A477

1964, June 20
1250 A477 60h car rose & lt bl 1.25 .20

Voluntary fire brigades in Bohemia, cent.

Gulls, Hradcany
Castle, Red
Cross — A478

Human
Heart — A479

1964, July 10
1251 A478 60h car & bluish gray .45   .20

4th Czechoslovak Red Cross Congress at
Prague.

1964, July 10
1252 A479 1.60k ultra & car   1.00   .20

4th European Cardiological Cong. at Prague.

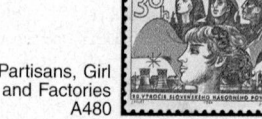

Partisans, Girl
and Factories
A480

Battle Scene,
1944 — A481

Design: 60h, Partisans and flame.

Engraved and Photogravure
1964, Aug. 17   Unwmk.   Perf. 11½
1253 A480 30h brown & red   .20   .20
1254 A480 60h dk blue & red   .20   .20
1255 A481 60h black & red   .20   .20
    Nos. 1253-1255 (3)   .60   .60

20th anniv. of the Slovak Natl. Uprising; No.
1255, 20th anniv. of the Battles of Dukla Pass.

Hradcany at
Prague — A482

Discus Thrower
and Pole
Vaulter — A483

Design: 5k, Charles Bridge and Hradcany.

1964, Aug. 30   Perf. 11½x12
1256 A482 60h black & red   .50   .20

Souvenir Sheet
            Engr.   Imperf.
1257 A482 5k deep claret   3.00 2.50

Millenium of the Hradcany, Prague.
No. 1257 stamp size: 30x50mm.

Engraved and Photogravure
1964, Sept. 2   Perf. 13½
Designs: 60h, Bicycling, horiz. 1k, Soccer.
1.20k, Rowing. 1.60k, Swimming, horiz. 2.80k,
Weight lifting, horiz.

1258 A483 60h multi   1.00   .30
1259 A483 80h multi   1.00   .30
1260 A483 1k multi   1.00   .30
1261 A483 1.20k multi   1.00   .30
1262 A483 1.60k multi   1.00   .30
1263 A483 2.80k multi   5.00 2.00
    Nos. 1258-1263 (6)   10.00 3.50

Issued to commemorate the 18th Olympic
Games, Tokyo, Oct. 10-25.
Nos. 1258-1263 were issued in sheets of
10. Value, set $200.

Miniature Sheet

Space Ship Voskhod I, Astronauts and
Globe — A484

1964, Nov. 12   Unwmk.   Perf. 11½
1264 A484 3k dk bl & dl lil, buff 6.00 4.00

Russian 3-man space flight of Vladimir M.
Komarov, Boris B. Yegorov and Konstantin
Feoktistov, Oct. 12-13.

Steam Engine
and Atomic
Power
Plant — A485

Diesel Engine "CKD Praha" — A486

1964, Nov. 16   **Engr.**
1265 A485 30h dull red brown .25 .20

Engraved and Photogravure
1266 A486 60h green & salmon .75 .20

Traditions and development of engineering; No. 1265 for 150th anniv. of the First Brno Engineering Works, No. 1266 for the engineering concern CKD Praha.

European Redstart — A487

Birds: 60h, Green woodpecker. 80h, Hawfinch. 1k, Black woodpecker. 1.20k, European robin. 1.60k, European roller.

1964, Nov. 16   **Litho.**   **Perf. 10½**
1267 A487 30h multicolored 1.00 .30
1268 A487 60h black & multi 1.00 .30
1269 A487 80h multicolored 1.25 .35
1270 A487 1k multicolored 1.75 .40
1271 A487 1.20k lt vio bl & blk 1.75 .40
1272 A487 1.60k yellow & blk 3.25 1.00
     Nos. 1267-1272 (6) 10.00 2.75

Dancer A488

"In the Sun" Preschool Children A489

Designs: 60h, "Over the Obstacles," teenagers. 1k, "Movement and Beauty," woman flag twirler. 1.60k, Runners at start.

Engraved and Photogravure
1965   **Unwmk.**   **Perf. 11½**
1273 A488 30h red & lt blue .20 .20
     Perf. 11½x12
1274 A489 30h vio bl & car .20 .20
1275 A489 60h brown & ultra .20 .20
1276 A489 1k black & yellow .25 .20
1277 A489 1.60k maroon & gray .60 .20
     Nos. 1273-1277 (5) 1.45 1.00

3rd Natl. Spartacist Games. Issue dates: No. 1273, Jan. 3; Nos. 1274-1277, May 24.

Mountain Rescue Service — A490

Arms and View, Beroun — A491

Designs: No. 1279, Woman gymnast. No. 1280, Bicyclists. No. 1281, Women hurdlers.

1965, Jan. 15   **Unwmk.**   **Perf. 11½**
1278 A490 60h violet & blue .25 .20
1279 A490 60h maroon & ocher .25 .20
1280 A490 60h black & carmine .25 .20
1281 A490 60h green & yellow .25 .20
     Nos. 1278-1281 (4) 1.00 .80

Mountain Rescue Service (#1278); 1st World Championship in Artistic Gymnastics, Prague, Dec. 1965 (#1279); World Championship in Indoor Bicycling, Prague, Oct. 1965 (#1280); "Universiada 1965," Brno (#1281).

1965, Feb. 15

Designs: No. 1283, Town Square, Domazlice. No. 1284, Old and new buildings, Frydek-Mystek. No. 1285, Arms and view, Lipnik. No. 1286, Fortified wall, City Hall and Arms, Policka. No. 1287, View and hops, Zatek. No. 1288, Small fortress and rose, Terezin.

1282 A491 30h vio bl & lt bl .30 .20
1283 A491 30h dull pur & yel .30 .20
1284 A491 30h slate & gray .30 .20
1285 A491 30h green & bis .30 .20
1286 A491 30h brown & tan .30 .20
1287 A491 30h dk blue & cit .30 .20
1288 A491 30h black & rose .30 .20
     Nos. 1282-1288 (7) 2.10 1.40

Nos. 1282-1287 for 700th anniv. of the founding of various Bohemian towns; No. 1288 the 20th anniv. of the liberation of the Theresienstadt (Terezin) concentration camp.

Sun's Corona A492

Space Research: 30h, Sun. 60h, Exploration of the Moon. 1k, Twin space craft, vert. 1.40k, Space station. 1.60k, Exploration of Mars, vert. 2k, USSR and US Meteorological collaboration.

1965, Mar. 15   **Perf. 12x11½, 11½x12**
1289 A492 20h rose & red lilac .25 .20
1290 A492 30h rose red & yel .25 .20
1291 A492 60h bluish blk & yel .25 .20
1292 A492 1k pur & pale bl .50 .20
1293 A492 1.40k black & salmon .50 .20
1294 A492 1.60k black & pink .50 .20
1295 A492 2k bluish blk & lt bl 1.50 1.00
     Nos. 1289-1295 (7) 3.75 2.20

Space research; Nos. 1289-1290 also for the Intl. Quiet Sun Year, 1964-65.

Frantisek Ventura, Equestrian; Amsterdam, 1928 — A493

Czechoslovakian Olympic Victories: 30h, Discus, Paris, 1900. 60h, Running, Helsinki, 1952. 1k, Weight lifting, Los Angeles, 1932. 1.40k, Gymnastics, Berlin, 1936. 1.60k, Double sculling, Rome, 1960. 2k, Women's gymnastics, Tokyo, 1964.

1965, Apr. 16   **Perf. 11½x12**
1296 A493 20h choc & gold .25 .20
1297 A493 30h indigo & emer .25 .20
1298 A493 60h ultra & gold .25 .20
1299 A493 1k red brn & gold .35 .25
1300 A493 1.40k dk sl grn & gold .75 .60
1301 A493 1.60k black & gold .80 .60
1302 A493 2k maroon & gold 1.10 .45
     Nos. 1296-1302 (7) 3.75 2.50

Astronauts Virgil Grissom and John Young — A494

Designs: No. 1304, Alexei Leonov floating in space. No. 1305, Launching pad at Cape Kennedy. No. 1306, Leonov leaving space ship.

1965, Apr. 17   **Perf. 11x11½**
1303 A494 60h slate bl & lil rose .45 .20
1304 A494 60h vio blk & blue .45 .20
1305 A494 3k slate bl & lil rose 1.75 1.00
   a.   Pair, #1303, 1305 3.75 2.00
1306 A494 3k vio blk & blue 1.75 1.00
   a.   Pair, #1304, 1306 3.75 2.00
     Nos. 1303-1306 (4) 4.40 2.40

Issued to honor American and Soviet astronauts. Printed in sheets of 25; one sheet contains 20 No. 1303 and 5 No. 1305, the other sheet contains 20 No. 1304 and 5 No. 1306.

Russian Soldier, View of Prague and Guerrilla Fighters A495

Designs: No. 1308, Blast furnace, workers and tank. 60h, Worker and factory. 1k, Worker and new constructions. 1.60k, Woman farmer, new farm buildings and machinery.

1965, May 5   **Engr.**   **Perf. 13½**
1307 A495 30h dk red, blk & ol .40 .20
1308 A495 30h multicolored .40 .20
1309 A495 60h vio bl, red & blk .40 .20
1310 A495 1k dp org, blk & brn .65 .20
1311 A495 1.60k yel, red & blk .70 .20
     Nos. 1307-1311 (5) 2.55 1.00

20th anniv. of liberation from the Nazis. Nos. 1307-1311 were each printed in sheets of 10. Value, set $85.

Slovakian Kopov Dog A496

Dogs: 40h, German shepherd. 60h, Czech hunting dog with pheasant. 1k, Poodle. 1.60k, Czech terrier. 2k, Afghan hound.

1965, June 10   **Perf. 12x11½**
1312 A496 30h black & red org .50 .20
1313 A496 40h black & yellow .50 .20
1314 A496 60h black & ver .80 .20
1315 A496 1k black & dk car rose 1.10 .30
1316 A496 1.60k black & orange 1.50 .35
1317 A496 2k black & orange 3.00 1.25
     Nos. 1312-1317 (6) 7.40 2.50

World Dog Show at Brno and the International Dog Breeders Congress, Prague.

UN Headquarters Building, NY — A497

Emblems: 60h, UN & inscription. 1.60k, ICY.

1965, June 24   **Perf. 12x11½**
1318 A497 60h dk red brn & yel .25 .20
1319 A497 1k ultra & lt blue .65 .25
1320 A497 1.60k gold & dk red .60 .35
     Nos. 1318-1320 (3) 1.50 .80

20th anniv. of the UN and the ICY, 1965.

Trade Union Emblem A498

1965, June 24   **Engr.**
1321 A498 60h dk red & ultra .40 .20

Intl. Trade Union Federation, 20th anniv.

Women and Globe — A499

1965, June 24   **Perf. 11½x12**
1322 A499 60h violet blue .40 .20

20th anniv. of the Intl. Women's Federation.

Children's House (Burgraves' Palace), Hradcany A500

Matthias Tower — A501

1965, June 25   **Perf. 11½**
1323 A500 30h slate green .30 .20
1324 A501 60h dark brown .30 .20

Issued to publicize the Hradcany, Prague.

Marx and Lenin — A502

1965, July 1   **Engr. & Photo.**
1325 A502 60h car rose & gold .30 .20

6th conf. of Postal Ministers of Communist Countries, Peking, June 21-July 15.

Joseph Navratil — A503

Jan Hus — A504

Gregor Johann Mendel A505

Costume Jewelry A506

Bohuslav Martinu A507

Seated Woman and University of Bratislava A508

ITU Emblem
and
Communication
Symbols
A509

Macromolecular
Symposium
Emblem
A510

Design: No. 1327, Ludovit Stur (diff. frame).

1965		Unwmk.	Perf. 11½	
1326	A503	30h black & fawn	.20	.20
1327	A503	30h black & dull grn	.20	.20
1328	A504	60h black & crimson	.20	.20
1329	A505	60h vio bl & red	.20	.20
1330	A506	60h purple & gold	.20	.20
1331	A507	60h black & orange	.20	.20
1332	A508	60h brn, yel	.20	.20
1333	A509	1k orange & blue	.35	.20
1334	A510	1k black & dp org	.35	.20
		Nos. 1326-1334 (9)	2.10	1.80

No. 1326, Navratil (1798-1865), painter; No. 1327, Stur (1815-56), Slovak author and historian; No. 1328, the 550th anniv. of the death of Hus, religious reformer;

No. 1329, cent. of publication of Mendel's laws of inheritance; No. 1330 publicizes the "Jablonec 1965" costume jewelry exhib.; No. 1331, Martinu (1890-1959), composer; No. 1332, 500th anniv. of the founding of the University of Bratislava as Academia Istropolitana; No. 1333, cent. of the ITU; No. 1334, Intl. Symposium on Macromolecular Chemistry, Prague, Sept. 1-8.

Issued: No. 1333, 7/10.

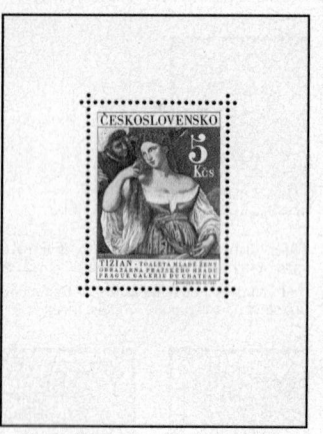

"Young Woman at her Toilette," by Titian — A512

Miniature Sheet

1965, Aug. 12
1336 A512 5k multicolored   6.00 4.00

Hradcany Art Gallery. #1336 contains one stamp.

Help for Flood
Victims — A513

Rescue
of Flood
Victims
A514

1965, Sept. 6   Engr.
1337 A513 30h violet blue   .20 .20

Engraved and Photogravure
1338 A514 2k dk ol grn & ol   .65 .45

Help for Danube flood victims in Slovakia.

Dotterel
A515

Mountain Birds: 60h, Wall creeper, vert. 1.20k, Lesser redpoll. 1.40k, Golden eagle, vert. 1.60k, Ring ouzel. 2k, Eurasian nutcracker, vert.

1965, Sept. 20		Litho.	Perf. 11	
1339	A515	30h multi	1.20	.20
1340	A515	60h multi	1.00	.20
1341	A515	1.20k multi	1.20	.20
1342	A515	1.40k multi	2.00	.40
1343	A515	1.60k multi	1.40	.50
1344	A515	2k multi	5.25	2.00
		Nos. 1339-1344 (6)	12.05	3.50

Levoca — A516

Medicinal
Plants — A517

Views of Towns: 10h, Jindrichuv Hradec. 20h, Nitra. 30h, Kosice. 40h, Hradec Králové. 50h, Telc. 60h, Ostrava. 1k, Olomouc. 1.20k, Ceske Budejovice. 1.60k, Cheb. 2k, Brno. 3k, Bratislava. 5k, Prague.

Engraved and Photogravure
1965-66   Perf. 11½x12
Size: 23x19mm

1345	A516	5h black & yel	.20	.20
1346	A516	10h ultra & ol bis	.65	.20
1347	A516	20h black & lt bl	.20	.20
1348	A516	30h vio bl & lt grn	.20	.20
1348A	A516	40h dk brn & lt bl ('66)	.20	.20
1348B	A516	50h black & ocher ('66)	.50	.20
1348C	A516	60h red & gray ('66)	1.00	.20
1348D	A516	1k pur & pale grn ('66)	.65	.20

Perf. 11½x11
Size: 30x23mm

1349	A516	1.20k slate & lt bl	.55	.20
1350	A516	1.60k indigo & yel	.80	.20
1351	A516	2k sl grn & pale yel	.75	.20
1352	A516	3k brn & yel	1.00	.20
1353	A516	5k black & pink	1.40	.20
		Nos. 1345-1353 (13)	8.10	2.60

1965, Dec. 3		Engr.	Perf. 14	
1354	A517	30h Coltsfoot	.40	.20
1355	A517	60h Meadow saffron	.40	.20
1356	A517	80h Corn poppy	1.25	.20
1357	A517	1k Foxglove	1.25	.40
1358	A517	1.20k Arnica	1.75	.75
1359	A517	1.60k Cornflower	1.75	.75
1360	A517	2k Dog rose	4.25	2.00
		Nos. 1354-1360 (7)	11.05	4.50

Nos. 1354-1360 were each printed in sheets of 10. Value, set $200.

Strip of "Stamps" — A518

Engraved and Photogravure
1965, Dec. 18   Perf. 11½
1361 A518 1k dark red & gold   3.00 2.25

Issued for Stamp Day, 1965.

Romain
Rolland
(1866-1944),
French Writer
A519

Symbolic
Musical
Instruments &
Names of
Composers
A520

Portraits: No. 1362, Stanislav Sucharda (1866-1916), sculptor. No. 1363, Ignac Josef Pesina (1766-1808), veterinarian. No. 1365, Donatello (1386-1466), Italian sculptor.

1966, Feb. 14		Engr.	Perf. 11½	
1362	A519	30h deep green	.20	.20
1363	A519	30h violet blue	.20	.20
1364	A519	60h rose lake	.20	.20
1365	A519	60h brown	.20	.20
		Nos. 1362-1365 (4)	.80	.80

1966, Jan. 15   Engr. & Photo.
1366 A520 30h black & gold   .50 .20

Czech Philharmonic Orchestra, 70th anniv.

Figure
Skating
Pair
A521

#1368, Man skater. #1369, Volleyball player, spiking, vert. 1k, Volleyball player, saving, vert. 1.60k, Woman skater. 2k, Figure skating pair.

1966, Feb. 17				
1367	A521	30h dk car rose	.20	.20
1368	A521	60h green	.20	.20
1369	A521	60h carmine & buff	.20	.20
1370	A521	1k vio & lt bl	.30	.20
1371	A521	1.60k brown & yellow	.40	.20
1372	A521	2k blue & grnsh bl	2.00	.40
		Nos. 1367-1372 (6)	3.30	1.40

#1367-1368, 1371-1372 for the European Figure Skating Championships, Bratislava; #1369-1370 for the World Volleyball Championships.

Souvenir Sheet

Girl Dancing — A522

1966, Mar. 21   Engr.   Imperf.
1373 A522 3k slate bl, red & bl   3.50 2.50

Cent. of the opera "The Bartered Bride" by Bedrich Smetana.

"Ajax"
1841
A523

Locomotives: 30h, "Karlstejn" 1865. 60h, Steam engine, 1946. 1k, Steam engine with tender, 1946. 1.60k, Electric locomotive, 1964. 2k, Diesel locomotive, 1964.

1966, Mar. 21   Perf. 11½x11
Buff Paper
1374	A523	20h sepia	1.25	.20
1375	A523	30h dull violet	1.60	.20
1376	A523	60h dull purple	1.10	.20
1377	A523	1k dark blue	1.25	.40
1378	A523	1.60k dk blue grn	2.25	.30
1379	A523	2k dark red	4.50	2.00
		Nos. 1374-1379 (6)	11.95	3.30

European
Perch
A524

30h, Brown trout, vert. 1k, Carp. 1.20k, Northern pike. 1.40k, Grayling. 1.60k, Eel.

Perf. 13x13½, 13½x13
1966, Apr. 22   Litho.   Unwmk.
1380	A524	30h multi	.70	.20
1381	A524	60h multi	.70	.20
1382	A524	1k multi	1.40	.20
1383	A524	1.20k multi	.70	.20
1384	A524	1.40k multi	1.00	.25
1385	A524	1.60k multi	2.75	1.10
		Nos. 1380-1385 (6)	7.25	2.15

Intl. Fishing Championships, Svit, Sept. 3-5.

WHO Headquarters, Geneva — A525

Engraved and Photogravure
1966, Apr. 25   Perf. 12x11½
1386 A525 1k dk blue & lt blue   .50 .20

Opening of the WHO Headquarters, Geneva.

Symbolic
Handshake and
UNESCO
Emblem
A526

1966, Apr. 25   Perf. 11½
1387 A526 60h bister & olive gray   .30 .20

20th anniv. of UNESCO.

Prague Castle Issue

Belvedere
Palace and St.
Vitus' Cathedral
A527

Crown of St. Wenceslas, 1346 — A528

Design: 60h, Madonna, altarpiece from St. George's Church.

1966, May 9   Engr.   Perf. 11½
1388 A527 30h dark blue   .40 .20

Engraved and Photogravure
1389 A527 60h blk & yel bis   .60 .20

Souvenir Sheet
Engr.
1390 A528 5k multi   6.50 3.25

See Nos. 1537-1539.

Tiger Swallowtail A529

Butterflies and Moths: 60h, Clouded sulphur. 80h, European purple emperor. 1k, Apollo. 1.20k, Burnet moth. 2k, Tiger moth.

1966, May 23   Engr.   Perf. 14
1391 A529 30h multi   .90 .25
1392 A529 60h multi   .90 .25
1393 A529 80h multi   1.25 .40
1394 A529 1k multi   1.90 .60
1395 A529 1.20k multi   1.90 .60
1396 A529 2k multi   5.50 2.00
Nos. 1391-1396 (6)   12.35 4.00

Nos. 1391-1396 were issued in sheets of 10. Value, set $250.

Flags of Russia and Czechoslovakia — A530

Designs: 60h, Rays surrounding hammer and sickle "sun." 1.60k, Girl's head and stars.

Engraved and Photogravure
1966, May 31   Perf. 11½
1397 A530 30h dk bl & crim   .20 .20
1398 A530 60h dk bl & red   .20 .20
1399 A530 1.60k red & dk bl   .30 .20
Nos. 1397-1399 (3)   .70 .60

13th Congress of the Communist Party of Czechoslovakia.

Dakota Chief — A531   Model of Molecule — A532

Designs: 20h, Indians, canoe and tepee, horiz. 30h, Tomahawk. 40h, Haida totem poles. 60h, Kachina, good spirit of the Hopis. 1k, Indian on horseback hunting buffalo, horiz. 1.20k, Calumet, Dakota peace pipe.

1966, June 20
Size: 23x40mm
1400 A531 20h vio bl & dp org   .25 .20
1401 A531 30h blk & dl org   .25 .20
1402 A531 40h blk & lt bl   .25 .20
1403 A531 60h grn & yel   .25 .20
1404 A531 1k pur & emer   .40 .20
1405 A531 1.20k vio bl & rose lil   .65 .30

Perf. 14
Engr.
Size: 23x37mm
1406 A531 1.40k multi   1.60 .90
Nos. 1400-1406 (7)   3.65 2.20

Cent. of the Náprstek Ethnographic Museum, Prague, and "The Indians of North America" exhibition.
No. 1406 was issued in sheets of 10. Value $60.

Engraved and Photogravure
1966, July 4   Unwmk.   Perf. 11½
1407 A532 60h blk & lt bl   .20 .20

Czechoslovak Chemical Society, cent.

"Guernica" by Pablo Picasso — A533

1966, July 5
Size: 75x30mm
1408 A533 60h blk & pale bl   2.50 1.25

30th anniversary of International Brigade in Spanish Civil War.
Sheets of 15 stamps and 5 labels inscribed "Picasso-Guernica 1937." Values: with tab attached, $3.75; sheet $75.

Pantheon, Bratislava A534   Atom Symbol and Sun A535

Designs: No. 1410, Devin Castle and Ludovit Stur. No. 1411, View of Nachod. No. 1412, State Science Library, Olomouc.

1966, July 25   Engr.
1409 A534 30h dl pur   .30 .20
1410 A534 60h dk bl   .35 .20
1411 A534 60h green   .35 .20
1412 A534 60h sepia   .30 .20
Nos. 1409-1412 (4)   1.30 .80

No. 1409, Russian War Memorial, Bratislava; No. 1410, the 9th cent. Devin Castle as symbol of Slovak nationalism; No. 1411, 700th anniv. of the founding of Nachod; No. 1412, the 400th anniv. of the State Science Library, Olomouc.

Engraved and Photogravure
1966, Aug. 29   Perf. 11½
1413 A535 60h blk & red   .40 .20

Issued to publicize Jachymov (Joachimsthal), where pitchblende was first discovered, "cradle of the atomic age."

Brno Fair Emblem — A536   Olympia Coin and Olympic Rings — A537

1966, Aug. 29
1414 A536 60h blk & red   .40 .20

8th International Trade Fair, Brno.

1966, Aug. 29
Design: 1k, Olympic flame, Czechoslovak flag and Olympic rings.
1415 A537 60h blk & gold   .30 .20
1416 A537 1k dk bl & red   1.00 .30

70th anniv. of the Olympic Committee.

Missile Carrier, Tank and Jet Plane A538

1966, Aug. 31
1417 A538 60h blk & apple grn   .40 .20

Issued to commemorate the maneuvers of the armies of the Warsaw Pact countries.

Mercury A539

30h, Moravian silver thaler, 1620, reverse & obverse, vert. 1.60k, Old & new buildings of Brno State Theater. 5k, Intl. Trade Fair Administration Tower & postmark, vert.

1966, Sept. 10
1418 A539 30h dk red & blk   .40 .20
1419 A539 60h org & blk   .40 .20
1420 A539 1.60k blk & brt grn   .75 .25
Nos. 1418-1420 (3)   1.55 .65

Souvenir Sheet
1421 A539 5k multi   3.50 3.50

Brno Philatelic Exhibition, Sept. 11-25. No. 1421 contains one 30x40mm stamp.

First Meeting in Orbit — A540

30h, Photograph of far side of Moon & Russian satellite. 60h, Photograph of Mars & Mariner 4. 80h, Soft landing on Moon. 1k, Satellite, laser beam & binary code. 1.20k, Telstar over Earth & receiving station.

1966, Sept. 26   Perf. 11½
1422 A540 20h vio & lt grn   .20 .20
1423 A540 30h blk & sal pink   .20 .20
1424 A540 60h slate & lilac   .25 .20
1425 A540 80h dk pur & lt bl   .25 .20
1426 A540 1k blk & vio   .30 .20
1427 A540 1.20k red & bl   1.60 .45
Nos. 1422-1427 (6)   2.80 1.45

Issued to publicize American and Russian achievements in space research.

Badger A541

Game Animals: 40h, Red deer, vert. 60h, Lynx. 80h, Hare. 1k, Red fox. 1.20k, Brown bear, vert. 2k, Wild boar.

1966, Nov. 28   Litho.   Perf. 13½
1428 A541 30h multi   .50 .20
1429 A541 40h multi   .50 .20
1430 A541 60h multi   .40 .20
1431 A541 80h multi   1.00 .25
a. 80h multi (europaeus)   6.00 3.50
1432 A541 1k multi   .75 .30
1433 A541 1.20k multi   1.00 .50
1434 A541 2k multi   2.50 1.25
Nos. 1428-1434 (7)   6.65 2.90

The sheet of 50 of the 80h contains 40 with misspelling "europaens" and 10 with "europaeus."

"Spring" by Vaclav Hollar, 1607-77 A542

Paintings: No. 1436, Portrait of Mrs. F. Wussin, by Jan Kupecky (1667-1740). No. 1437, Snow Owl by Karel Purkyne (1834-1868). No. 1438, Tulips by Vaclav Spála (1885-1964). No. 1439, Recruit by Ludovít Fulla (1902-1980).

1966, Dec. 8   Engr.   Perf. 14
1435 A542 1k black   3.75 3.50
1436 A542 1k multicolored   5.25 1.90
1437 A542 1k multicolored   2.40 1.90
1438 A542 1k multicolored   2.40 1.90
1439 A542 1k multicolored   19.00 16.00
Nos. 1435-1439 (5)   32.80 25.20

Printed in sheets of 4 stamps and 2 labels. The labels in sheet of No. 1435 are inscribed "Vaclav Hollar 1607-1677" in fancy frame. Other labels are blank. Value, set $150.
See No. 1484.

Symbolic Bird — A543

Engraved and Photogravure
1966, Dec. 17   Perf. 11½
1440 A543 1k dp blue & yel   1.00 .65

Issued for Stamp Day.

Youth — A544

1967, Jan. 16   Perf. 11½
1441 A544 30h ver & lt bl   .20 .20

5th Cong. of the Czechoslovak Youth Org.

Symbolic Flower and Machinery A545

1967, Jan. 16
1442 A545 30h carmine & yel .30 .20
6th Trade Union Congress, Prague.

Parents with Dead Child — A545a

1967, Jan. 16 Perf. 11½
1442A A545a 60h black & salmon .30 .20
"Peace and Freedom in Viet Nam."

View of Jihlava and Tourist Year Emblem A546

Views and Tourist Year Emblem: 40h, Spielberg Castle and churches, Brno. 1.20k, Danube, castle and churches, Bratislava. 1.60k, Vlatava River bridges, Hradcany and churches, Prague.

1967, Feb. 13 Engr. Perf. 11½
Size: 40x23mm
1443 A546 30h brown violet .20 .20
1444 A546 40h maroon .20 .20
Size: 75x30mm
1445 A546 1.20k violet blue .45 .20
1446 A546 1.60k black 1.50 .50
Nos. 1443-1446 (4) 2.35 1.10
International Tourist Year, 1967.

Black-tailed Godwit — A547

Birds: 40h, Shoveler, horiz. 60h, Purple heron. 80h, Penduline tit. 1k, Avocet. 1.40k, Black stork. 1.60k, Tufted duck, horiz.

1967, Feb. 20 Litho. Perf. 13½
1447 A547 30h multi .50 .30
1448 A547 40h multi .50 .30
1449 A547 60h multi .50 .30
1450 A547 80h multi .50 .30
1451 A547 1k multi .75 .30
1452 A547 1.40k multi 1.00 .60
1453 A547 1.60k multi 4.00 1.20
Nos. 1447-1453 (7) 7.75 3.30

Solar Research and Satellite — A548

Space Research: 40h, Space craft, rocket and construction of station. 60h, Man on moon and orientation system. 1k, Exploration of solar system and rocket. 1.20k, Lunar satellites and moon photograph. 1.60k, Planned lunar architecture and moon landing.

Engraved and Photogravure
1967, Mar. 24 Perf. 11½
1454 A548 30h yel & dk red .25 .20
1455 A548 40h vio bl & blk .35 .20
1456 A548 60h lilac & grn .35 .20
1457 A548 1k brt pink & sl .35 .20
1458 A548 1.20k lt violet & blk .50 .20
1459 A548 1.60k brn lake & blk 1.75 .60
Nos. 1454-1459 (6) 3.55 1.60

Gothic Painting, by Master Theodoric A549

Designs: 40h, "Burning of Master Hus," from Litomerice Hymnal. 60h, Modern glass sculpture. 80h, "The Shepherdess and the Chimney Sweep," Andersen fairy tale, painting by J. Trnka. 1k, Section of pressure vessel from atomic power station. 1.20k, Three ceramic figurines, by P. Rada. 3k, Montreal skyline and EXPO '67 emblem.

1967, Apr. 10 Engr. Perf. 14
Size: 37x23mm
1460 A549 30h multi .20 .20
1461 A549 40h multi .20 .20
1462 A549 60h multi .20 .20
1463 A549 80h multi .25 .20
1464 A549 1k multi 1.00 .25
1465 A549 1.20k multi 1.25 .60
Nos. 1460-1465 (6) 3.10 1.65

Souvenir Sheet
Perf. 11½
Size: 40x30mm
1466 A549 3k multi 3.00 2.50
EXPO '67, International Exhibition, Montreal, Apr. 28-Oct. 27, 1967.

Canoe Race A550

Women Playing Basketball — A551

#1468, Wheels, dove & emblems of Warsaw, Berlin, Prague. 1.60k, Canoe slalom.

Perf. 12x11½, 11½x12
1967, Apr. 17 Engr. & Photo.
1467 A550 60h black & brt bl .20 .20
1468 A550 60h black & salmon .20 .20
1469 A551 60h blk & grnsh bl .20 .20
1470 A551 1.60k black & brt vio 1.25 .50
Nos. 1467-1470 (4) 1.85 1.10

No. 1467, 5th Intl. Wild-Water Canoeing Championships; No. 1468, 20th Warsaw-Berlin-Prague Bicycle Race: No. 1469, Women's Basketball Championships; No. 1470, 10th Intl. Water Slalom Championships.

"Golden Street" — A552

Designs: 60h, Interior of Hall of King Wenceslas. 5k, St. Matthew, from illuminated manuscript, 11th century.

1967, May 9 Perf. 11½x11
1471 A552 30h rose claret .25 .20
1472 A552 60h bluish black .50 .20

Souvenir Sheet
Perf. 11½
1473 A552 5k multicolored 2.75 2.50
Issued to publicize the Castle of Prague.

Stylized Lyre with Flowers — A553 / Old-New Synagogue, Prague — A554

1967, May 10 Perf. 11½
1474 A553 60h dull pur & brt grn .30 .20
Prague Music Festival.

1967, May 22 Perf. 11½
30h, Detail from Torah curtain, 1593. 60h, Prague Printer's emblem, 1530. 1k, Mikulov jug, 1804. 1.40k, Memorial for Concentration Camp Victims 1939-45, Pincas Synagogue (menorah & tablet). 1.60k, Tombstone of David Gans, 1613.
1475 A554 30h dull red & lt bl .30 .20
1476 A554 60h blk & lt grn .20 .20
1477 A554 1k dk bl & rose lil .35 .20
1478 A554 1.20k dk brn & mar .65 .20
1479 A554 1.40k black & yellow .55 .20
1480 A554 1.60k green & yel 4.50 2.75
Nos. 1475-1480 (6) 6.55 3.75

Issued to show Jewish relics. The items shown on the 30h, 60h and 1k are from the State Jewish Museum, Prague.

"Lidice" A555 / Prague Architecture A556

1967, June 9 Unwmk. Perf. 11½
1481 A555 30h black & brt rose .30 .20
Destruction of Lidice by the Nazis, 25th anniv.

1967, June 10 Engr. & Photo.
1482 A556 1k black & gold .45 .20
Issued to publicize the 9th Congress of the International Union of Architects, Prague.

Peter Bezruc A557

1967, June 21
1483 A557 60h dull rose & blk .30 .20
Peter Bezruc, poet & writer, birth cent.

Painting Type of 1966
2k, Henri Rousseau (1844-1910), self-portrait.
Issued in shhets of 4. Value $12.50.

1967, June 22 Engr. Perf. 11½
1484 A542 2k multicolored 1.75 1.25
Praga 68, World Stamp Exhibition, Prague, June 22-July 7, 1968. Printed in sheets of 4 stamps (2x2), separated by horizontal gutter

with inscription and picture of Natl. Gallery, site of Praga 68.

View of Skalitz — A558

#1486, Mining tower & church steeple, Pribram. #1487, Hands holding book & view of Presov.

1967, Aug. 21 Engr. Perf. 11½
1485 A558 30h violet blue .20 .20
1486 A558 30h slate green .20 .20
1487 A558 30h claret .20 .20
Nos. 1485-1487 (3) .60 .60
Towns of Skalitz, Pribram, Presov, annivs.

Colonnade and Spring, Karlovy Vary and Communications Emblem — A559

1967, Aug. 21 Engr. & Photo.
1488 A559 30h violet bl & gold .30 .20
5th Sports & Cultural Festival of the Employees of the Ministry of Communications, Karlovy Vary.

Ondrejov Observatory and Galaxy — A560

1967, Aug. 22 Engr.
1489 A560 60h vio bl, rose lil & sil 1.50 .25
13th Cong. of the Intl. Astronomical Union.

Orchid — A561

Flowers from the Botanical Gardens: 30h, Cobaea scandens. 40h, Lycaste deppei. 60h, Glottiphyllum davisii. 1k, Anthurium. 1.20k, Rhodocactus. 1.40k, Moth orchid.

1967, Aug. 30 Litho. Perf. 12½
1490 A561 20h multicolored .35 .20
1491 A561 30h pink & multi .35 .20
1492 A561 40h multicolored .45 .20
1493 A561 60h lt blue & multi .45 .20
1494 A561 1k multicolored .65 .20
1495 A561 1.20k lt yellow & multi .75 .30
1496 A561 1.40k multicolored 2.00 .70
Nos. 1490-1496 (7) 5.00 2.00

Red Squirrel A562

Animals from the Tatra National Park: 60h, Wild cat. 1k, Ermine. 1.20k, Dormouse. 1.40k, Hedgehog. 1.60k, Pine marten.

Engraved and Photogravure
1967, Sept. 25 Perf. 11½
1497 A562 30h black, yel & org .25 .20
1498 A562 60h black & buff .25 .20
1499 A562 1k black & lt blue .30 .20
1500 A562 1.20k brn, pale grn & yel .20 .20

1501 A562 1.40k blk, pink & yel .60 .20
1502 A562 1.60k black, org & yel 2.50 1.00
Nos. 1497-1502 (6) 4.40 2.00

Rockets and
Weapons — A563

1967, Oct. 6   Engr.   Perf. 11½
1503 A563 30h slate green .30 .20

Day of the Czechoslovak People's Army.

Cruiser
"Aurora"
Firing at
Winter
Palace
A564

Designs: 60h, Hammer and sickle emblems
and Red Star, vert. 1k, Hands reaching for
hammer and sickle, vert.

1967, Nov. 7   Engr. & Photo.
1504 A564 30h black & dk car .20 .20
1505 A564 60h black & dk car .20 .20
1506 A564 1k black & dk car .20 .20
Nos. 1504-1506 (3) .60 .60

Russian October Revolution, 50th anniv.

The
Conjurer,
by
Frantisek
Tichy
A565

Paintings: 80h, Don Quixote, by Cyprian
Majernik. 1k, Promenade in the Park, by Nor-
bert Grund. 1.20k, Self-portrait, by Peter J.
Brandl. 1.60k, Saints from Jan of Jeren Epitaph, by Czech Master of 1395.

1967, Nov. 13   Engr.   Perf. 11½
1507 A565 60h multi .30 .20
1508 A565 80h multi .40 .25
1509 A565 1k multi .65 .40
1510 A565 1.20k multi .65 .40
1511 A565 1.60k multi 2.75 2.25
Nos. 1507-1511 (5) 4.75 3.50

Nos. 1507-1511 were issued in sheets of 4.
Value, set $27.50.
See Nos. 1589-1593, 1658-1662, 1711-
1715, 1779-1783, 1847-1851, 1908-1913,
2043-2047, 2090-2093, 2147-2151, 2265-
2269, 2335-2339, 2386-2390, 2437-2441,
2534-2538, 2586-2590, 2634-2638, 2810-
2813, 2843-2847, 2872-2874, 2908-2910,
2936-2938, 2973-2975, 2995, 3001-3002,
3028-3030, 3054-3055, 3075-3076, 3105-
3107.

Pres. Antonin
Novotny — A566

1967, Dec. 9   Engr.   Perf. 11½
1512 A566 2k blue gray 1.25 .20
1513 A566 3k brown 1.25 .20

Czechoslovakia Nos. 65, 71 and 81 of
1920 — A567

1967, Dec. 18
1514 A567 1k maroon & silver 1.25 .75

Issued for Stamp Day.

Symbolic Flag and
Dates — A568

1968, Jan. 15   Engr.   Perf. 11½
1515 A568 30h red, dk bl & ultra .60 .20

50th anniversary of Czechoslovakia.

Figure Skating and Olympic
Rings — A569

Olympic Rings and: 1k, Ski course. 1.60k,
Toboggan chute. 2k, Ice hockey.

1968, Jan. 29   Engr. & Photo.
1516 A569 60h blk, yel & ocher .25 .20
1517 A569 1k ol grn, lt bl &
lem .50 .20
1518 A569 1.60k blk, lil & bl grn .65 .20
1519 A569 2k blk, ap grn & lt
bl 1.10 .55
Nos. 1516-1519 (4) 2.50 1.15

10th Winter Olympic Games, Grenoble,
France, Feb. 6-18.

Factories and
Rising Sun — A570

Design: 60h, Workers and banner.

1968, Feb. 25   Perf. 11½x12
1520 A570 30h car & dk bl .20 .20
1521 A570 60h car & dk bl .20 .20

20th anniversary of February Revolution.

Map of Battle of
Sokolow
A571

Human Rights
Flame — A572

1968, Mar. 8   Perf. 11½
1522 A571 30h blk, brt bl & car .40 .20
Engr.
1523 A572 1k rose carmine 1.00 .35

25th anniv. of the Battle of Sokolow, Mar. 8,
1943, against the German Army, No. 1522;
Intl. Human Rights Year, No. 1523.

Janko Kral and
Liptovsky
Mikulas — A573

Karl
Marx — A574

Girl's
Head — A575

Arms and
Allegory — A576

Head — A577

1968, Mar. 25   Engr.
1524 A573 30h green .30 .20
1525 A574 30h claret .25 .20
Engraved and Photogravure
1526 A575 30h dk red & gold .25 .20
1527 A576 30h dk blue & dp org .25 .20
1528 A577 1k multicolored .50 .20
Nos. 1524-1528 (5) 1.55 1.00

The writer Janko Kral and the Slovak town
Liptovsky Mikulas (No. 1524); 150th anniv. of
the birth of Karl Marx (No. 1525); cent. of the
cornerstone laying of the Prague Natl. Theater
(No. 1526); 150th anniv. of the Prague Natl.
Museum (No. 1527); 20th anniv. of WHO (1k).

Symbolic
Radio
Waves
A578

No. 1530, Symbolic television screens.

1968, Apr. 29   Perf. 11½
1529 A578 30h blk, car & vio bl .20 .20
1530 A578 30h blk, car & vio bl .20 .20

45th anniv. of Czechoslovak broadcasting
(#1529), 15th anniv. of television (#1530).

Olympic Rings,
Mexican
Sculpture and
Diver — A579

Olympic Rings and: 40h, Runner and "The
Sanctification of Quetzalcoatl." 60h, Volleyball
and Mexican ornaments. 1k, Czechoslovak
and Mexican Olympic emblems and carved
altar. 1.60k, Soccer and ornaments. 2k, View
of Hradcany, weather vane and key.

1968, Apr. 30
1531 A579 30h black, bl & car .20 .20
1532 A579 40h multi .20 .20
1533 A579 60h multi .20 .20
1534 A579 1k multi .35 .20
1535 A579 1.60k multi .35 .20
1536 A579 2k black & multi 1.75 .40
Nos. 1531-1536 (6) 3.05 1.40

19th Olympic Games, Mexico City, 10/12-27.

Prague Castle Types of 1966

Designs: 30h, Tombstone of Bretislav I. 60h,
Romanesque door knocker, St. Wenceslas
Chapel. 5k, Head of St. Peter, mosaic from
Golden Gate of St. Vitus Cathedral.

1968, May 9   Perf. 11½
1537 A527 30h multicolored .40 .20
1538 A527 60h black, red & cit .40 .20
**Souvenir Sheet
Engr.**
1539 A528 5k multicolored 2.50 2.50

Pres. Ludvik
Svoboda — A580

1968-70   Engr.   Perf. 11½
1540 A580 30h ultramarine .20 .20
1540A A580 50h green ('70) .20 .20
1541 A580 60h maroon .20 .20
1541A A580 1k rose car ('70) .30 .20
Nos. 1540-1541A (4) .90 .80

Shades exist of No. 1541A.

"Business,"
Sculpture by
Otto Gutfreund
A581

Cabaret Performer, by Frantisek
Kupka — A582

Designs (The New Prague): 40h, Broadcasting Corporation Building. 60h, New Parliament. 1.40k, Tapestry by Jan Bauch "Prague
1787." 3k, Presidential standard.

**Engr. & Photo.; Engr. (2k)
1968, June 5**
1542 A581 30h black & multi .20 .20
1543 A581 40h black & multi .20 .20
1544 A581 60h dk brn & multi .20 .20
1545 A581 1.40k dk brn & multi .40 .20
1546 A582 2k indigo & multi .85 .70
1547 A581 3k black & multi .85 .30
Nos. 1542-1547 (6) 2.70 1.80

1968, June 21   Perf. 11½
Designs (The Old Prague): 30h, St.
George's Basilica. 60h, Renaissance fountain.
1k, Villa America-Dvorak Museum, 18th cent.
building. 1.60k, Emblem from the House of
Three Violins, 18th cent. 2k, Josefina, by
Josef Manes. 3k, Emblem of Prague, 1475.

1548 A581 30h green, gray &
yel .20 .20
1549 A581 60h dk vio, ap grn &
gold .20 .20

1550 A581   1k black, lt bl &
      pink   .30   .20
1551 A581   1.60k slate grn & mul-
      ti   .55   .20
1552 A582   2k brown & multi   1.25   .60
1553 A582   3k blk, yel, bl &
      pink   1.25   .60
     Nos. 1548-1553 (6)   3.75 2.00

Nos. 1542-1553 publicized the Praga 68 Philatelic Exhibition. Nos. 1542-1545, 1547-1551, 1553 issued in sheets of 15 + 15 labels with Praga 68 emblem and inscription.

Nos. 1546, 1552 issued in sheets of 4 (2x2) with one horizontal label between top and bottom rows showing Praga 68 emblem. Values for sheets of 4, each $8.

Souvenir Sheet

View of Prague and Emblems — A583

Engraved and Photogravure
1968, June 22   *Imperf.*
1554 A583   10k multicolored   3.00 2.50

Praga 68 and 50th anniv. of Czechoslovak postage stamps. Sold only together with a 5k admission ticket to the Praga 68 philatelic Exhibition. Value $20.

Madonna with the Rose Garlands, by Dürer — A584

1968, July 6   *Perf. 11½*
1555 A584   5k multicolored   3.00 1.75

FIP Day, July 6. Issued in sheets of 4 (2x2) with one horizontal label between, showing Praga 68 emblem.

Stagecoach on Rails — A585

Design: 1k, Steam and electric locomotives.

1968, Aug. 6
1556 A585   60h multicolored   .35   .20
1557 A585   1k multicolored   1.25   .45

No. 1556: 140th anniv. of the horse-drawn railroad Ceské Budejovice to Linz; No. 1557: cent. of the Ceské Budejovice to Plzen railroad.

6th Intl. Slavonic Cong. in Prague — A586

1968, Aug. 7   *Perf. 11½*
1558 A586   30h vio blue & car   .40   .20

Ardspach Rocks and Ammonite — A587

60h, Basalt formation & frog skeleton fossil. 80h, Rocks, basalt veins & polished agate. 1k, Pelecypoda (fossil shell) & Belanske Tatra mountains. 1.60k, Trilobite & Barrande rock formation.

1968, Aug. 8
1559 A587   30h black & citron   .20   .20
1560 A587   60h black & rose cl   .20   .20
1561 A587   80h black, lt vio &
      pink   .30   .20
1562 A587   1k black & lt blue   .40   .20
1563 A587   1.60k black & bister   1.40   .65
     Nos. 1559-1563 (5)   2.50 1.45

Issued to publicize the 23rd International Geological Congress, Prague, Aug. 8-Sept. 3.

Raising Slovak Flag A588

60h, Slovak partisans, and mountain.

1968, Sept. 9   Engr.   *Perf. 11½*
1564 A588   30h ultra   .20   .20
1565 A588   60h red   .20   .20

No. 1564 for the Slovak Natl. Council, No. 1565 the 120th anniv. of the Slovak national uprising.

Flowerpot, by Jiri Schlessinger (age 10) — A589

Drawings by Children in Terezin Concentration Camp: 30h, Jew and Guard, by Jiri Beutler (age 10). 60h, Butterflies, by Kitty Brunnerova (age 11).

Engraved and Photogravure
1968, Sept. 30   *Perf. 11½*
      Size: 30x23mm
1566 A589   30h blk, buff & rose lil   .25   .20
1567 A589   60h black & multi   .25   .20
      Perf. 12x11½
      Size: 41x23mm
1568 A589   1k black & multi   .80   .20
     Nos. 1566-1568 (3)   1.30   .60

30th anniversary of Munich Pact.

Arms of Regional Capitals A590

Arms of Prague — A591

1968, Oct. 21   *Perf. 11½*
1569 A590   60h Banská Bystrica   .20   .20
1570 A590   60h Bratislava   .20   .20
1571 A590   60h Brno   .20   .20
1572 A590   60h Ceské Budejovice   .20   .20
1573 A590   60h Hradec Králové   .20   .20
1574 A590   60h Kosice   .20   .20
1575 A590   60h Ostrava (horse)   .20   .20
1576 A590   60h Plzen   .20   .20
1577 A590   60h Ustí nad Labem   .20   .20
      Perf. 11½x16
1578 A591   1k shown   .75   .20
     Nos. 1569-1578 (10)   2.55 2.00

#1578 issued in sheets of 10. See #1652-1657, 1742-1747, 1886-1888, 2000-2001.

Flag and Linden Leaves A592

Bohemian Lion Breaking Chains (Type SP1 of 1919) — A593

Design: 60h, Map of Czechoslovakia, linden leaves, Hradcany in Prague and Castle in Bratislava.

1968, Oct. 28   *Perf. 12x11½*
1579 A592   30h dp blue & mag   .30   .20
1580 A592   60h blk, gold, red &
      ultra   .30   .20

Souvenir Sheet
      Engr.
      Perf. 11½x12
1581 A593   5k red   3.50 2.75

Founding of Czechoslovakia, 50th anniv.

Ernest Hemingway A594   Cinderlad A595

Caricatures: 30h, Karel Capek (1890-1938), writer. 40h, George Bernard Shaw. 60h, Maxim Gorki. 1k, Pablo Picasso. 1.20k, Taikan Yokoyama (1868-1958), painter. 1.40k, Charlie Chaplin.

Engraved and Photogravure
1968, Nov. 18   *Perf. 11½x12*
1582 A594   20h black, org & red   .20   .20
1583 A594   30h black & multi   .30   .20
1584 A594   40h blk, lic & car   .30   .20
1585 A594   60h black, sky bl &
      grn   .20   .20
1586 A594   1k black, brn & yel   .45   .20
1587 A594   1.20k black, dp car &
      vio   .45   .20
1588 A594   1.40k black, brn & dp
      org   1.75   .40
     Nos. 1582-1588 (7)   3.65 1.60

Cultural personalities of the 20th cent. and UNESCO. See Nos. 1628-1633.

Painting Type of 1967

Czechoslovakian Art: 60h, Cleopatra II, by Jan Zrzavy (1890-1977). 80h, Black Lake (man and horse), by Jan Preisler (1872-1918). 1.20k, Giovanni Francisci as a Volunteer, by Peter Michal Bohun (1822-1879). 1.60k, Princess Hyacinth, by Alfons Mucha (1860-1939). 3k, Madonna and Child, woodcarving, 1518, by Master Paul of Levoca.

1968, Nov. 29   Engr.   *Perf. 11½*
1589 A565   60h multi   .75   .35
1590 A565   80h multi   .75   .35
1591 A565   1.20k multi   .75   .35
1592 A565   1.60k multi   .75   .35
1593 A565   3k multi   2.50 2.50
     Nos. 1589-1593 (5)   5.50 3.90

Nos. 1589-1593 were issued in sheets of 4. Value, set $30.

1968, Dec. 18   **Engr. & Photo.**

Slovak Fairy Tales: 60h, The Proud Lady. 80h, The Ruling Knight. 1k, Good Day, Little Bench. 1.20k, The Spellbound Castle. 1.80k, The Miraculous Hunter. The designs are from illustrations by Ludovit Fulla for "Slovak Stories."

1594 A595   30h multi   .25   .20
1595 A595   60h multi   .25   .20
1596 A595   80h multi   .40   .20
1597 A595   1k multi   .55   .20
1598 A595   1.20k multi   .55   .20
1599 A595   1.80k multi   1.50   .65
     Nos. 1594-1599 (6)   3.50 1.65

Czechoslovakia Nos. 2 and 3 — A596

1968, Dec. 18
1600 A596   1k violet bl & gold   .75   .65

50th anniv. of Czechoslovakian postage stamps.

Crescent, Cross and Lion and Sun Emblems A597   ILO Emblem A598

60h, 12 crosses in circles forming large cross.

1969, Jan. 31   *Perf. 11½*
1601 A597   60h black, red & gold   .20   .20
1602 A597   1k black, ultra & red   .35   .20

No. 1601: 50th anniv. of the Czechoslovak Red Cross. No. 1602: 50th anniv. of the League of Red Cross Societies.

1969, Jan. 31
1603 A598   1k black & gray   .30   .20

50th anniv. of the ILO.

Cheb Pistol
A599

Historical Firearms: 40h, Italian pistol with Dutch decorations, c. 1600. 60h, Wheellock rifle from Matej Kubik workshop c. 1720. 1k, Flintlock pistol, Devieuxe workshop, Liege, c. 1760. 1.40k, Duelling pistols, from Lebeda workshop, Prague, c. 1835. 1.60k, Derringer pistols, US, c. 1865.

1969, Feb. 18

1604	A599	30h black & multi	.20	.20
1605	A599	40h black & multi	.20	.20
1606	A599	60h black & multi	.20	.20
1607	A599	1k black & multi	.25	.20
1608	A599	1.40k black & multi	.35	.20
1609	A599	1.60k black & multi	1.00	.50
	Nos. 1604-1609 (6)		2.20	1.50

Bratislava Castle, Muse and
Book — A600

#1611, Science symbols & emblem (Brno University). #1612, Harp, laurel & musicians' names. #1613, Theatrical scene. #1614, Arms of Slovakia, banner & blossoms. #1615, School, outstretched hands & woman with linden leaves.

1969, Mar. 24   Engr.   Perf. 11½

1610	A600	60h violet blue	.20	.20

Engraved and Photogravure

1611	A600	60h blk, gold & slate	.20	.20
1612	A600	60h gold, blue, blk & red	.20	.20
1613	A600	60h black & rose red	.20	.20
1614	A600	60h rose red, sil & bl	.20	.20
1615	A600	60h black & gold	.20	.20
	Nos. 1610-1615 (6)		1.20	1.20

50th anniv. of: Komensky University in Bratislava (#1610); Brno University (#1611); Brno Conservatory of Music (#1612); Slovak Natl. Theater (#1613); Slovak Soviet Republic (#1614); cent. of the Zniev Gymnasium (academic high school) (#1615).

Baldachin-top Car and Four-seat
Coupé of 1900-1905 — A601

Designs: 1.60k, Laurin & Klement Voiturette, 1907, and L & K touring car with American top, 1907. 1.80k, First Prague bus, 1907, and sectionalized Skoda bus, 1967.

1969, Mar. 25   Engr. & Photo.

1616	A601	30h blk, lil & lt grn	.55	.20
1617	A601	1.60k blk, org brn & lt bl	.70	.20
1618	A601	1.80k multi	1.25	.60
	Nos. 1616-1618 (3)		2.50	1.00

Peace, by Ladislav Guderna — A602

1969, Apr. 21   Perf. 11

1619	A602	1.60k multi	.50	.35

20th anniv. of the Peace Movement. Issued in sheets of 15 stamps and 5 tabs.

Horse and
Rider, by Vaclav
Hollar — A603

Old Engravings of Horses: 30h, Prancing Stallion, by Hendrik Goltzius, horiz. 80h, Groom Leading Horse, by Matthäus Merian, horiz. 1.80k, Horse and Soldier, by Albrecht Dürer. 2.40k, Groom and Horse, by Johann E. Ridinger.

1969, Apr. 24   Perf. 11x11½, 11½x11
Yellowish Paper

1620	A603	30h dark brown	.20	.20
1621	A603	80h violet brown	.20	.20
1622	A603	1.60k slate	.40	.20
1623	A603	1.80k sepia	.45	.20
1624	A603	2.40k multi	2.25	.60
	Nos. 1620-1624 (5)		3.50	1.40

M. R. Stefánik as Astronomy Professor
and French General — A604

1969, May 4   Engr.   Perf. 11½

1625	A604	60h rose claret	.40	.20

Gen. Milan R. Stefánik, 50th death anniv.

St. Wenceslas Pressing Wine, Mural
by the Master of Litomerice — A605

Design: No. 1627, Coronation banner of the Estates, 1723, with St. Wenceslas and coats of arms of Bohemia and Czech Crown lands.

1969, May 9   Engr.   Perf. 11½

1626	A605	3k multicolored	1.50	1.40
1627	A605	3k multicolored	1.50	1.40

Issued to publicize the art treasures of the Castle of Prague.
Issued in sheets of 4. Value, set $20.
See Nos. 1689-1690.

Caricature Type of 1968

Caricatures: 30h, Pavol Orszagh Hviezdoslav (1849-1921), Slovak writer. 40h, Gilbert K. Chesterton (1874-1936), English writer. 60h, Vladimir Mayakovski (1893-1930), Russian poet. 1k, Henri Matisse (1869-1954), French painter. 1.80k, Ales Hrdlicka (1869-1943), Czech-born American anthropologist. 2k, Franz Kafka (1883-1924), Austrian writer.

Engraved and Photogravure

1969, June 17   Perf. 11½x12

1628	A594	30h blk, red & bl	.20	.20
1629	A594	40h blk, bl & lt vio	.20	.20
1630	A594	60h blk, rose & yel	.20	.20
1631	A594	1k black & multi	.20	.20
1632	A594	1.80k blk, ultra & ocher	.20	.20
1633	A594	2k blk, yel & brt grn	1.50	.50
	Nos. 1628-1633 (6)		2.50	1.50

Issued to honor cultural personalities of the 20th century and UNESCO.

"Music," by
Alfons
Mucha — A606

Paintings by Mucha: 60h, "Painting." 1k, "Dance." 2.40k, "Ruby" and "Amethyst."

1969, July 14   Perf. 11½x11
Size: 30x49mm

1634	A606	30h black & multi	.80	.20
1635	A606	60h black & multi	.80	.20
1636	A606	1k black & multi	.90	.20

Size: 39x51mm

1637	A606	2.40k black & multi	2.00	1.25
	Nos. 1634-1637 (4)		4.50	1.85

Alfons Mucha (1860-1930), painter and stamp designer (Type A1).
No. 1637 was issued in sheets of 4. Value $18.

Pres.
Svoboda and
Partisans
A607

No. 1639, Slovak fighters and mourners.

1969, Aug. 29   Perf. 11

1638	A607	30h ol grn & red, yel	.20	.20
1639	A607	30h vio bl & red, yel	.20	.20

25th anniversary of the Slovak uprising and of the Battle of Dukla.

Tatra Mountain Stream and
Gentians — A608

Designs: 60h, Various views in Tatra Mountains. No. 1644, Mountain pass and gentians. No. 1645, Houses, Krivan Mountain and autumn crocuses.

1969, Sept. 8   Engr.   Perf. 11
Size: 71x33mm

1640	A608	60h gray	.25	.20
1641	A608	60h dark blue	.25	.20
1642	A608	60h dull gray vio	.25	.20

Perf. 11½
Size: 40x23mm

1643	A608	1.60k multi	.35	.20
1644	A608	1.60k multi	1.50	.50
1645	A608	1.60k multi	.40	.20
	Nos. 1640-1645 (6)		3.00	1.50

20th anniv. of the creation of the Tatra Mountains Natl. Park.
Nos. 1640-1642 are printed in sheets of 15 (3x5) with 5 labels showing mountain plants. Value, set with tabs $2.50.
Nos. 1643-1645 were issued in sheets of 10. Value, $55.

Bronze Belt
Ornaments
A609

Archaeological Treasures from Bohemia and Moravia: 30h, Gilt ornament with 6 masks. 1k, Jeweled earrings. 1.80k, Front and back of lead cross with Greek inscription. 2k, Gilt strap ornament with human figure.

Engraved and Photogravure

1969, Sept. 30   Perf. 11½x11

1646	A609	20h gold & multi	.20	.20
1647	A609	30h gold & multi	.20	.20
1648	A609	1k red & multi	.25	.20
1649	A609	1.80k dull org & multi	.50	.20
1650	A609	2k gold & multi	1.50	.40
	Nos. 1646-1650 (5)		2.65	1.20

"Mail
Circling
the
World"
A610

1969, Oct. 1   Engr.   Perf. 12

1651	A610	3.20k multi	.75	.50

16th UPU Cong., Tokyo, Oct. 1-Nov. 14. Issued in sheets of 4. Value $9.

Coat of Arms Type of 1968
Engraved and Photogravure

1969, Oct. 25   Perf. 11½

1652	A590	50h Bardejov	.25	.20
1653	A590	50h Hranice	.25	.20
1654	A590	50h Kezmarok	.25	.20
1655	A590	50h Krnov	.25	.20
1656	A590	50h Litomerice	.25	.20
1657	A590	50h Manetin	.25	.20
	Nos. 1652-1657 (6)		1.50	1.20

Painting Type of 1968

Designs: 60h, Requiem, 1944, by Frantisek Muzika. 1k, Resurrection, 1380, by the Master of the Trebon Altar. 1.60k, Crucifixion, 1950, by Vincent Hloznik. 1.80k, Girl with Doll, 1863, by Julius Bencur. 2.20k, St. Jerome, 1357-67, by Master Theodorik.

1969, Nov. 25   Perf. 11½

1658	A565	60h multi	1.00	.25
1659	A565	1k multi	1.00	.25
1660	A565	1.60k multi	1.10	.40
1661	A565	1.80k multi	1.40	.50
1662	A565	2.20k multi	3.00	2.00
	Nos. 1658-1662 (5)		7.50	3.40

Nos. 1658-1662 were each issued in sheets of 4. Value, set $40.

Symbolic Sheet of Stamps — A611

1969, Dec. 18   Perf. 11½x12

1663	A611	1k dk brn, ultra & gold	.30	.30

Issued for Stamp Day 1969.

Ski Jump — A612

Designs: 60h, Long distance skier. 1k, Ski jump and slope. 1.60k, Woman skier.

1970, Jan. 6   *Perf. 11½*

1664	A612	50h multi	.20	.20
1665	A612	60h multi	.20	.20
1666	A612	1k multi	.20	.20
1667	A612	1.60k multi	.60	.30
		Nos. 1664-1667 (4)	1.20	.90

Intl. Ski Championships "Tatra 1970."

Ludwig van Beethoven — A613

Portraits: No. 1669, Friedrich Engels (1820-95), German socialist. No. 1670, Maximilian Hell (1720-92), Slovakian Jesuit and astronomer. No. 1671, Lenin, Russian Communist leader. No. 1672, Josef Manes (1820-71), Czech painter. No. 1673, Comenius (1592-1670), theologian and educator.

1970, Feb. 17   **Engr.**   *Perf. 11x11½*

1668	A613	40h black	.20	.20
1669	A613	40h dull red	.20	.20
1670	A613	40h yellow brn	.20	.20
1671	A613	40h dull red	.20	.20
1672	A613	40h brown	.20	.20
1673	A613	40h black	.20	.20
		Nos. 1668-1673 (6)	1.20	1.20

Anniversaries of birth of Beethoven, Engels, Hell, Lenin and Manes, 300th anniv. of the death of Comenius, and to honor UNESCO.

Bells A614

80h, Machine tools & lathe. 1k, Folklore masks. 1.60k, Angel & Three Wise Men, 17th cent. icon from Koniec. 2k, View of Orlik Castle, 1787, by F. K. Wolf. 3k, "Passing through Koshu down to Mishima" from Hokusai's 36 Views of Fuji.

Engraved and Photogravure

1970, Mar. 13   *Perf. 11½x11*
Size: 40x23mm

1674	A614	50h multi	.20	.20
1675	A614	80h multi	.20	.20
1676	A614	1k multi	.25	.20

Size: 50x40mm
Perf. 11½

1677	A614	1.60k multi	.45	.30
1678	A614	2k multi	.60	.35
1679	A614	3k multi	1.60	1.00
		Nos. 1674-1679 (6)	3.30	2.25

EXPO '70 Intl. Exhib., Osaka, Japan, Mar. 15-Sept. 13, 1970.
Nos. 1674-1676 issued in sheets of 50, Nos. 1677-1679 in sheets of 4. Value, set of 3 sheets, $28.

Kosice Townhall, Laurel and Czechoslovak Arms — A615

1970, Apr. 5   *Perf. 11*
1680	A615	60h slate, ver & gold	.30	.20

Government's Kosice Program, 25th anniv.

"The Remarkable Horse" by Josef Lada — A616

Lenin — A617

Paintings by Josef Lada: 60h, Autumn, 1955, horiz. 1.80k, "The Water Sprite." 2.40k, Children in Winter, 1943, horiz.

1970, Apr. 21   *Perf. 11½*
1681	A616	60h black & multi	.25	.20
1682	A616	1k black & multi	.40	.20
1683	A616	1.80k black & multi	.70	.20
1684	A616	2.40k black & multi	1.40	.40
		Nos. 1681-1684 (4)	2.75	1.00

1970, Apr. 22

Design: 60h, Lenin without cap, facing left.
1685	A617	30h dk red & gold	.20	.20
1686	A617	60h black & gold	.20	.20

Lenin (1870-1924), Russian communist leader.

Fighters on the Barricades — A618

No. 1688, Lilac, Russian tank and castle.

1970, May 5   *Perf. 11x11½*
1687	A618	30h dull pur, gold & bl	.20	.20
1688	A618	30h dull grn, gold & red	.20	.20

No. 1687: 25th anniv. of the Prague uprising. No. 1688: 25th anniv. of the liberation of Czechoslovakia from the Germans.

Prague Castle Art Type of 1969

#1689, Bust of St. Vitus, 1486. #1690, Hermes and Athena, by Bartholomy Springer (1546-1611), mural from White Tower.

1970, May 7   **Engr.**   *Perf. 11½*
1689	A605	3k maroon & multi	1.75	1.50
1690	A605	3k lt blue & multi	1.75	1.50

Nos. 1689-1690 were issued in sheets of 4. Value, set of 2 sheets, $20.

Compass Rose, UN Headquarters and Famous Buildings of the World — A619

Engraved and Photogravure
1970, June 26   *Perf. 11*
1691	A619	1k black & multi	.40	.20

25th anniv. of the UN. Issued in sheets of 15 (3x5) and 5 labels showing UN emblem. Value of single with tab attached: unused 75c; used 40c.

Cannon from 30 Years' War and Baron Munchhausen — A620

Historical Cannons: 60h, Cannon from Hussite war and St. Barbara. 1.20k, Cannon from Prussian-Austrian war, and legendary cannoneer Javurek. 1.80k, Early 20th century cannon and spaceship "La Colombiad" (Jules Verne). 2.40k, World War I cannon and "Good Soldier Schweik."

1970, Aug. 31   *Perf. 11½*
1692	A620	30h black & multi	.20	.20
1693	A620	60h black & multi	.20	.20
1694	A620	1.20k black & multi	.20	.20
1695	A620	1.80k black & multi	.30	.20
1696	A620	2.40k black & multi	1.40	.65
		Nos. 1692-1696 (5)	2.30	1.45

"Rude Pravo" (Red Truth) A621

1970, Sept. 21   *Perf. 11½x11*
1697	A621	60h car, gold & blk	.20	.20

50th anniv. of the Rude Pravo newspaper.

"Great Sun" House Sign and Old Town Tower Bridge, Prague — A622

60h, "Blue Lion" & Town Hall Tower, Brno. 1k, Gothic corner stone & Town Hall Tower, Bratislava. 1.40k, Coat of Arms & Gothic Tower, Bratislava, & medallion. 1.60k, Moravian Eagle & Gothic Town Hall Tower, Brno. 1.80k, "Black Sun" & "Green Frog" house signs & New Town Hall, Prague.

1970, Sept. 23   *Perf. 11x11½*
1698	A622	40h black & multi	.20	.20
1699	A622	60h black & multi	.20	.20
1700	A622	1k black & multi	.20	.20
1701	A622	1.40k black & multi	1.10	.50
1702	A622	1.60k black & multi	.25	.20
1703	A622	1.80k black & multi	.80	.20
		Nos. 1698-1703 (6)	2.75	1.50

Germany-Uruguay Semifinal Soccer Match — A623

Designs: 20h, Sundisk Games' emblem and flags of participating nations. 60h, England-Czechoslovakia match and coats of arms. 1k, Romania-Czechoslovakia match and coats of arms. 1.20k, Brazil-Italy, final match and emblems. 1.80k, Brazil-Czechoslovakia match and emblems.

1970, Oct. 29   *Perf. 11½*
1704	A623	20h blk & multi	.20	.20
1705	A623	40h blk & multi	.20	.20
1706	A623	60h blk & multi	.20	.20
1707	A623	1k blk & multi	.30	.20
1708	A623	1.20k blk & multi	.35	.20
1709	A623	1.80k blk & multi	1.50	.30
		Nos. 1704-1709 (6)	2.75	1.30

9th World Soccer Championships for the Jules Rimet Cup, Mexico City, 5/30-6/21.

Congress Emblem — A624

1970, Nov. 9   **Engr. & Photo.**
1710	A624	30h blk, gold, ultra & red	.20	.20

Congress of the Czechoslovak Socialist Youth Federation.

Painting Type of 1967

Paintings: 1k, Seated Mother, by Mikulas Galanda. 1.20k, Bridesmaid, by Karel Svolinsky. 1.40k, Walk by Night, 1944, by Frantisek Hudecek. 1.80k, Banska Bystrica Market, by Dominik Skutecky. 2.40k, Adoration of the Kings, from the Vysehrad Codex, 1085.

1970, Nov. 27   **Engr.**   *Perf. 11½*
1711	A565	1k multi	.60	.25
1712	A565	1.20k multi	.75	.40
1713	A565	1.40k multi	.60	.30
1714	A565	1.80k multi	1.00	.40
1715	A565	2.40k multi	3.00	2.00
		Nos. 1711-1715 (5)	5.95	3.35

Nos. 1711-1715 were each issued in sheets of 4. Value, set $30.

Radar A625

Designs: 40h, Interkosmos 3, geophysical satellite. 60h, Molniya meteorological satellite. 1k, Astronaut and Vostok satellite. No. 1720, Interkosmos 4, space research satellite. No. 1720A, Space satellite (Sputnik) over city. 1.60k, Two-stage rocket on launching pad.

1970-71   **Engr. & Photo.**   *Perf. 11*
1716	A625	20h black & multi	.20	.20
1717	A625	40h black & multi	.20	.20
1718	A625	60h black & multi	.20	.20
1719	A625	1k black & multi	.20	.20
1720	A625	1.20k black & multi	.20	.20
1720A	A625	1.20k black & multi ('71)	.30	.20
1721	A625	1.60k black & multi	1.40	.35
		Nos. 1716-1721 (7)	2.70	1.55

"Interkosmos," the collaboration of communist countries in various phases of space research.
Issued: #1720A, 11/15/71; others, 11/30/70.

Face of Christ on Veronica's Veil — A626

Slovak Ikons, 16th-18th Centuries: 60h, Adam and Eve in the Garden, vert. 2k, St. George and the Dragon. 2.80k, St. Michael, vert.

1970, Dec. 17   **Engr.**   *Perf. 11½*
Cream Paper
1722	A626	60h multi	.80	.35
1723	A626	1k multi	1.10	.50
1724	A626	2k multi	1.40	.60
1725	A626	2.80k multi	2.00	1.25
		Nos. 1722-1725 (4)	5.30	2.70

Nos. 1722-1725 were each issued in sheets of 4. Value, set $30.

Carrier Pigeon Type of 1920 — A627

Engraved and Photogravure
1970, Dec. 18   *Perf. 11x11½*
1726 A627 1k red, blk & yel grn   .40 .30
Stamp Day.

Song of the Barricades, 1938, by Karel Stika — A628

Czech and Slovak Graphic Art: 50h, Fruit Grower's Barge, 1941, by Cyril Bouda. 60h, Moon (woman) Searching for Lilies of the Valley, 1913, by Jan Zrzavy. 1k, At the Edge of Town (working man and woman), 1931, by Koloman Sokol. 1.60k, Summer, 1641, by Vaclav Hollar. 2k, Gamekeeper and Shepherd of Orava Castle, 1847, by Peter M. Bohun.

Engr. & Photo.; Engr. (40h, 60h, 1k)
1971, Jan. 28   *Perf. 11½*
1727	A628	40h brown	.20	.20
1728	A628	50h black & multi	.20	.20
1729	A628	60h slate	.20	.20
1730	A628	1k black	.25	.20
1731	A628	1.60k black & buff	.25	.20
1732	A628	2k black & multi	1.25	.30
		Nos. 1727-1732 (6)	2.35	1.30

Saris Church   Bell Tower,
A629   Hronsek
             A630

Designs: 1k, Roofs and folk art, Horácko. 2.40k, House, Jicin. 3k, House and folk art, Melnik. 3.60k, Church of St. Bartholomew, Chrudim. 5k, Watch Tower, Nachod. 5.40k, Baroque house, Posumavi. 6k, Cottage, Orava. 9k, Cottage, Turnov. 10k, Old houses, Liptov. 14k, House and wayside bell stand. 20k, Houses, Cicmany.

Engraved and Photogravure
1971-72   *Perf. 11½x11, 11x11½*
1733	A630	1k multi	.20	.20
1734	A629	1.60k multi	1.25	.20
1735	A630	2k multi	1.90	.20
1736	A629	2.40k multi	1.10	.30
1736A	A630	3k multi ('72)	1.90	.20
1737	A629	3.60k multi	1.50	.20
1737A	A630	5k multi ('72)	1.90	.20
1738	A629	5.40k multi	.95	.20
1739	A630	6k multi	3.00	.20
1740	A629	9k multi	1.25	.20
1740A	A630	10k multi ('72)	2.75	.20
1741	A629	14k multi	3.00	.25
1741A	A629	20k multi ('72)	3.25	.30
		Nos. 1733-1741A (13)	23.95	2.85

Nos. 1736A, 1738, 1740 are horizontal. See No. 2870.

Coat of Arms Type of 1968
1971, Mar. 26   *Perf. 11½*
1742	A590	60h Zilina	.20	.20
1743	A590	60h Levoca	.20	.20
1744	A590	60h Ceska Trebova	.20	.20
1745	A590	60h Uhersky Brod	.20	.20
1746	A590	60h Trutnov	.20	.20
1747	A590	60h Karlovy Vary	.20	.20
		Nos. 1742-1747 (6)	1.20	1.20

"Fight of the Communards and Rise of the International" — A631

Design: No. 1749, World fight against racial discrimination, and "UNESCO."

1971, Mar. 18   *Perf. 11*
1748 A631 1k multicolored   .30 .20
1749 A631 1k multicolored   .30 .20

No. 1748 for cent. of the Paris Commune. No. 1749 for the Year against Racial Discrimination. Issued in sheets of 15 stamps and 5 labels. Value for single with attached tab, each 40c.

A632   A633

Edelweiss, mountaineering map & equipment.

1971, Apr. 27   *Perf. 11½x11*
1750 A632 30h multicolored   .25 .20
50th anniversary of Slovak Alpine Club.

1971, Apr. 27   *Perf. 11½*
1751 A633 30h Singer   .25 .20
50th anniversary of Slovak Teachers' Choir.

Abbess' Crosier, 16th Century A634

#1753, Allegory of Music, 16th cent. mural.

1971, May 9
1752 A634 3k gold & multi   1.75 1.25
1753 A634 3k blk, dk brn & buff   2.25 1.25

Nos. 1752-1753 were each issued in sheets of 4. Value, set $22.50.
See Nos. 1817-1818, 1884-1885, 1937-1938, 2040-2041, 2081-2082, 2114-2115, 2176-2177, 2238-2239, 2329-2330, 2384-2385, 2420-2421.

Lenin A635

40h, Hammer & sickle allegory. 60h, Raised fists. 1k, Star, hammer & sickle.

1971, May 14   *Perf. 11*
1754	A635	30h blk, red & gold	.20	.20
1755	A635	40h blk, ultra, red & gold	.20	.20
1756	A635	60h blk, ultra, red & gold	.20	.20
1757	A635	1k blk, ultra, red & gold	.30	.20
		Nos. 1754-1757 (4)	.90	.80

Czechoslovak Communist Party, 50th anniv.

Star, Hammer-Sickle Emblems — A636

60h, Hammer-sickle emblem, fist & people, vert.

Perf. 11½x11, 11x11½
1971, May 24   *Engr. & Photo.*
1758 A636 30h blk, red, gold & yel   .20 .20
1759 A636 60h blk, red, gold & bl   .20 .20

14th Congress of Communist Party of Czechoslovakia.

Ring-necked Pheasant — A637

Designs: 60h, Rainbow trout. 80h, Mouflon. 1k, Chamois. 2k, Stag. 2.60k, Wild boar.

1971, Aug. 17   *Perf. 11½x11*
1760	A637	20h orange & multi	.20	.20
1761	A637	60h lt blue & multi	.20	.20
1762	A637	80h yellow & multi	.20	.20
1763	A637	1k lt green & multi	.35	.20
1764	A637	2k lilac & multi	.50	.20
1765	A637	2.60k bister & multi	2.25	.65
		Nos. 1760-1765 (6)	3.70	1.65

World Hunting Exhib., Budapest, Aug. 27-30.

Diesel   Gymnasts and
Locomotive   Banners
A638   A639

1971, Sept. 2   *Perf. 11x11½*
1766 A638 30h lt bl, blk & red   .30 .20
Cent. of CKD, Prague Machine Foundry.

1971, Sept. 2   *Perf. 11½x11*
1767 A639 30h red brn, gold & ultra .20 .20
50th anniversary of Workers' Physical Exercise Federation.

Road Intersections and Bridge — A640

1971, Sept. 2   *Engr. & Photo.*
1768 A640 1k blk, gold, red & bl   .30 .20
14th World Highways and Bridges Congress. Sheets of 25 stamps and 25 labels printed se-tenant with continuous design. Value, single with attached tab, 40c.

Chinese Fairytale, by Eva Bednarova A641

Designs: 1k, Tiger and other animals, by Mirko Hanak. 1.60k, The Miraculous Bamboo Shoot, by Yasuo Segawa, horiz.

Perf. 11½x11, 11x11½
1971, Sept. 10
1769 A641 60h multi   .20 .20
1770 A641 1k multi   .30 .20
1771 A641 1.60k multi   .45 .20
    Nos. 1769-1771 (3)   .95 .60

Bratislava BIB 71 biennial exhibition of illustrations for children's books.

Apothecary Jars and Coltsfoot — A642

Intl. Pharmaceutical Cong.: 60h, Jars and dog rose. 1k, Scales and adonis vernalis. 1.20k, Mortars and valerian. 1.80k, Retorts and chicory. 2.40k, Mill, mortar and henbane.

1971, Sept. 20   *Perf. 11½x11*
    Yellow Paper
1772	A642	30h multi	.20	.20
1773	A642	60h multi	.20	.20
1774	A642	1k multi	.20	.20
1775	A642	1.20k multi	.20	.20
1776	A642	1.80k multi	.35	.20
1777	A642	2.40k multi	1.40	.45
		Nos. 1772-1777 (6)	2.55	1.45

Painting Type of 1967

Paintings: 1k, "Waiting" (woman's head), 1967, by Imro Weiner-Král. 1.20k, Resurrection, by Master of Vyssi Brod, 14th century. 1.40k, Woman with Pitcher, by Milos Bazovsky. 1.80k, Veruna Cudova (in folk costume), by Josef Mánes. 2.40k, Detail from "Feast of the Rose Garlands," by Albrecht Dürer.

1971, Nov. 27   *Perf. 11½*
1779	A565	1k multi	.35	.25
1780	A565	1.20k multi	.80	.40
1781	A565	1.40k multi	.65	.25
1782	A565	1.80k multi	1.20	.50
1783	A565	2.40k multi	2.00	.80
		Nos. 1779-1783 (5)	5.00	2.20

Nos. 1779-1783 were each issued in sheets of 4. Value, set $27.

Workers Revolt in Krompachy, by Julius Nemcik — A643

1971, Nov. 28   *Perf. 11x11½*
1784 A643 60h multi   .30 .20
History of the Czechoslovak Communist Party.

Wooden Dolls and Birds — A644

Folk Art and UNICEF Emblem: 80h, Jug handles, carved. 1k, Horseback rider. 1.60k,

Shepherd carrying lamb. 2k, Easter eggs and rattle. 3k, "Zbojnik," folk hero.

1971, Dec. 11　　　　　　**Perf. 11½**
1785	A644	60h multi	.30	.20
1786	A644	80h multi	.60	.20
1787	A644	1k multi	.30	.20
1788	A644	1.60k multi	.30	.20
1789	A644	2k multi	.30	.40
1790	A644	3k multi	1.75	.55
		Nos. 1785-1790 (6)	3.55	1.75

25th anniv. of UNICEF.
Nos. 1785-17903 were each issued in sheets of 10. Value, set $50.

Runners, Parthenon, Czechoslovak Olympic Emblem — A645

Designs: 40h, Women's high jump, Olympic emblem and plan for Prague Stadium. 1.60k, Cross-country skiers, Sapporo '72 emblem and ski jump in High Tatras. 2.60k, Discus thrower, Discobolus and St. Vitus Cathedral.

1971, Dec. 16　　　　**Engr. & Photo.**
1791	A645	30h multi	.20	.20
1792	A645	40h multi	.20	.20
1793	A645	1.60k multi	.25	.20
1794	A645	2.60k multi	1.25	.65
		Nos. 1791-1794 (4)	1.90	1.25

75th anniversary of Czechoslovak Olympic Committee (30h, 2.60k); 20th Summer Olympic Games, Munich, Aug. 26-Sept. 10, 1972 (40h); 11th Winter Olympic Games, Sapporo, Japan, Feb. 3-13, 1972 (1.60k).

Post Horns and Lion — A646

1971, Dec. 17　　　　**Perf. 11x11½**
1795	A646	1k blk, gold, car & bl	.30	.20

Stamp Day.

Figure Skating — A647

"Lezáky" — A648

Olympic Emblems and: 50h, Ski jump. 1k, Ice hockey. 1.60k, Sledding, women's.

1972, Jan. 13　　　　　　**Perf. 11½**
1796	A647	40h pur, org & red	.20	.20
1797	A647	50h dk bl, org & red	.20	.20
1798	A647	1k mag, org & red	.35	.20
1799	A647	1.60k bl grn, org & red	1.25	.30
		Nos. 1796-1799 (4)	2.00	.90

11th Winter Olympic Games, Sapporo, Japan, Feb. 3-13.

1972, Feb. 16

No. 1801, Boy's head behind barbed wire, horiz. No. 1802, Hand rising from ruins. No. 1803, Soldier and banner, horiz.
1800	A648	30h blk, dl org & red	.20	.20
1801	A648	30h blk & brn org	.20	.20
1802	A648	60h blk, yel & red	.20	.20
1803	A648	60h sl grn & multi	.20	.20
		Nos. 1800-1803 (4)	.80	.80

30th anniv. of: destruction of Lezáky (No. 1800) and Lidice (No. 1802); Terezin concentration camp (No. 1801); Czechoslovak Army unit in Russia (No. 1803).

Book Year Emblem A649

Steam and Diesel Locomotives A650

1972, Mar. 17　　　　**Perf. 11½x11**
1804	A649	1k blk & org brn	.30	.20

International Book Year 1972.

1972, Mar. 17　　　　**Perf. 11½x11**
1805	A650	30h multi	.75	.20

Centenary of the Kosice-Bohumin railroad.

"Pasture," by Vojtech Sedlacek A651

Designs: 50h, Dressage, by Frantisek Tichy. 60th, Otakara Kubina, by Vaclav Fiala. 1k, The Three Kings, by Ernest Zmetak. 1.60k, Woman Dressing, by Ludovit Fulla.

1972, Mar. 27　　　　**Perf. 11½x11**
1806	A651	40h multi	.20	.20
1807	A651	50h multi	.20	.20
1808	A651	60h multi	.20	.20
1809	A651	1k multi	.30	.20
1810	A651	1.60k multi	1.25	1.25
		Nos. 1806-1810 (5)	2.15	2.05

Czech and Slovak graphic art.
1.60k issued in sheets of 4. Value $12.
See #1859-1862, 1921-1924.

Ice Hockey A652

Design: 1k, Two players.

1972, Apr. 7　　　　　　**Perf. 11**
1811	A652	60h blk & multi	.20	.20
1812	A652	1k blk & multi	.40	.20

World and European Ice Hockey Championships, Prague.
For overprint see Nos. 1845-1846.

Bicycling, Olympic Rings and Emblem A653

1972, Apr. 7
1813	A653	50h shown	.20	.20
1814	A653	1.60k Diving	.40	.20
1815	A653	1.80k Canoeing	.55	.20
1816	A653	2k Gymnast	1.10	.40
		Nos. 1813-1816 (4)	2.25	1.00

20th Olympic Games, Munich, 8/26-9/11.

Prague Castle Art Type of 1971

Designs: No. 1817, Adam and Eve, column capital, St. Vitus Cathedral. No. 1818, Czech coat of arms (lion), c. 1500.

1972, May 9　　　　　　**Perf. 11½**
1817	A634	3k blk & multi	2.50	1.50
1818	A634	3k blk, red, sil & gold	1.25	.75

Nos. 1817-1818 were each issued in sheets of 4. Value, set $20.

Andrej Sladkovic (1820-1872), Poet — A654

#1820, Janko Kral (1822-1876), poet. #1821, Ludmilla Podjavorinska (1872-1951), writer. #1822, Antonin Hudecek (1872-1941), painter. #1823, Frantisek Bilek (1872-1941), sculptor. #1824, Jan Preisler (1872-1918), painter.

1972, June 14　　　　　　**Perf. 11**
1819	A654	40h pur, ol & bl	.20	.20
1820	A654	40h dk grn, bl & yel	.20	.20
1821	A654	40h blk & multi	.20	.20
1822	A654	40h brn, grn & bl	.20	.20
1823	A654	40h choc, grn & org	.20	.20
1824	A654	40h grn, sl & dp org	.20	.20
		Nos. 1819-1824 (6)	1.20	1.20

Men with Banners — A655

1972, June 14　　　　**Perf. 11x11½**
1825	A655	30h dk vio bl, red & yel	.20	.20

8th Trade Union Congress, Prague.

Art Forms of Wire A656

Ornamental Wirework: 60h, Plane and rosette. 80h, Four-headed dragon and ornament. 1k, Locomotive and loops. 2.60k, Tray and owl.

1972, Aug. 28　　　　**Perf. 11½x11**
1826	A656	20h sal & multi	.20	.20
1827	A656	60h multi	.20	.20
1828	A656	80h pink & multi	.30	.20
1829	A656	1k multi	.40	.20
1830	A656	2.60k rose & multi	1.40	.45
		Nos. 1826-1830 (5)	2.50	1.25

"Jiskra" A657

Engr. & Photo.
1972, Sept. 27　　　　**Perf. 11½x11**
Size: 40x22mm
Multicolored Design on Blue Paper
1831	A657	50h shown	.20	.20
1832	A657	60h "Mir"	.20	.20
1833	A657	80h "Republika"	.20	.20

Size: 48x29mm
Perf. 11x11½
1834	A657	1k "Kosice"	.30	.20
1835	A657	1.60k "Dukla"	.45	.20
1836	A657	2k "Kladno"	1.40	.55
		Nos. 1831-1836 (6)	2.75	1.55

Czechoslovak sea-going vessels.

Hussar, 18th Century Tile — A658

1972, Oct. 24　　　　**Perf. 11½x11**
1837	A658	30h shown	.20	.20
1838	A658	60h Janissary	.20	.20
1839	A658	80h St. Martin	.25	.20
1840	A658	1.60k St. George	.45	.20
1841	A658	1.80k Nobleman's guard	.70	.20
1842	A658	2.20k Slovakian horseman	1.40	.60
		Nos. 1837-1842 (6)	3.20	1.60

Horsemen from 18th-19th century tiles or enamel paintings on glass.

Worker, Flag Hoisted on Bayonet A659

Star, Hammer and Sickle A660

1972, Nov. 7　　　　**Perf. 11x11½**
1843	A659	30h gold & multi	.20	.20
1844	A660	60h rose car & gold	.20	.20

55th anniv. of the Russian October Revolution (30h); 50th anniv. of the Soviet Union (60h).

Nos. 1811-1812 Overprinted in Violet Blue or Black

1972　　　　　　　　　　**Perf. 11**
1845	A652	60h multi (VBl)	7.50	6.00
1846	A652	1k multi (Bk)	7.50	6.00

Czechoslovakia's victorious ice hockey team. The overprint on the 60h (shown) is in

Czech and reads CSSR/MISTREM/SVETA; the overprint on the 1k is in Slovak.

Painting Type of 1967

Designs: 1k, "Nosegay" (nudes and flowers), by Max Svabinsky. 1.20k, Struggle of St. Ladislas with Kuman nomad, anonymous, 14th century. 1.40k, Lady with Fur Hat, by Vaclav Hollar. 1.80k, Midsummer Night's Dream, 1962, by Josef Liesler. 2.40k, Pablo Picasso, self-portrait.

1972, Nov. 27   **Engr. & Photo.**
1847	A565	1k multi	.55	.35
1848	A565	1.20k multi	.70	.50
1849	A565	1.40k blk & cream	.85	.65
1850	A565	1.80k multi	1.10	1.00
1851	A565	2.40k multi	2.50	2.50
	Nos. 1847-1851 (5)		5.70	5.00

Nos. 1847-1851 were each issued in sheets of 4. Value, set $30.

Goldfinch
A661

Songbirds: 60h, Warbler feeding young cuckoo. 80h, Cuckoo. 1k, Black-billed magpie. 1.60k, Bullfinch. 3k, Song thrush.

1972, Dec. 15
Size: 30x48½mm
1852	A661	60h yel & multi	.20	.20
1853	A661	80h multi	.20	.20
1854	A661	1k lt bl & multi	.20	.20

Engr.
Size: 30x23mm
1855	A661	1.60k multi	1.40	.75
1856	A661	2k multi	1.40	.75
1857	A661	3k multi	1.40	.75
	Nos. 1852-1857 (6)		4.80	2.85

Post Horn and Allegory — A662

1972, Dec. 18   **Engr. & Photo.**
1858	A662	1k blk, red lil & gold	.30	.30

Stamp Day.

Art Type of 1972

Designs: 30h, Flowers in Window, by Jaroslav Grus. 60h, Quest for Happiness, by Josef Balaz. 1.60k, Balloon, by Kamil Lhotak. 1.80k, Woman with Viola, by Richard Wiesner.

1973, Jan. 25   **Perf. 11½x11**
1859	A651	30h multi	.20	.20
1860	A651	60h multi	.20	.20
1861	A651	1.60k multi	.35	.20
1862	A651	1.80k multi	1.40	.35
	Nos. 1859-1862 (4)		2.15	.95

Czech and Slovak graphic art.

Tennis Player — A663   Figure Skater — A664

Torch and Star — A665

1973, Feb. 22   **Perf. 11**
1863	A663	30h vio & multi	.20	.20
1864	A664	60h blk & multi	.20	.20
1865	A665	1k multi	.30	.20
	Nos. 1863-1865 (3)		.70	.60

80th anniversary of the tennis organization in Czechoslovakia (30h); World figure skating championships, Bratislava (60h); 3rd summer army Spartakiad of socialist countries (1k).

Star and Factories
A666

Workers' Militia, Emblem and Flag — A667

1973, Feb. 23
1866	A666	30h multi	.20	.20
1867	A667	60h multi	.20	.20

25th anniversary of the Communist revolution in Czechoslovakia and of the Militia.

Capt. Jan Nalepka, Major Antonin Sochor and Laurel
A668

Torch &: 40h, Evzen Rosicky, Mirko Nespor & ivy leaves. 60h, Vlado Clementis, Karol Smidke & linden leaves. 80h, Jan Osoha, Josef Molak & oak leaves. 1k, Marie Kuderikova, Jozka Jaburkova & rose. 1.60k, Vaclav Sinkule, Eduard Urx & palm leaf.

1973, Mar. 20   **Perf. 11½x11**
Yellow Paper
1868	A668	30h blk, ver & gold	.20	.20
1869	A668	40h blk, ver & grn	.20	.20
1870	A668	60h blk, ver & gold	.20	.20
1871	A668	80h blk, ver & gold	.20	.20
1872	A668	1k blk, ver & grn	.30	.20
1873	A668	1.60k blk, ver & sil	.60	.20
	Nos. 1868-1873 (6)		1.70	1.20

Fighters against and victims of Fascism and Nazism during German Occupation.

Virgil I. Grissom, Edward H. White, Roger B. Chaffee — A669

Designs: 20h, Soviet planetary station "Venera." 30h, "Intercosmos" station. 40h, Lunokhod on moon. 3.60k, Vladimir M. Komarov, Georgi T. Dobrovolsky, Vladislav N. Volkov, Victor I. Patsayev. 5k, Yuri A. Gagarin. Two types of 3.60k: type I, Cosmonaut on background of cross-hatched lines; type 2, Cosmonaut on background of parallel diagonal lines.

1973, Apr. 12   **Perf. 11½x11**
Size: 40x22mm
1874	A669	20h multi	.20	.20
1875	A669	30h multi	.20	.20
1876	A669	40h multi	.20	.20

Engr.
Perf. 11½
Size: 49x30mm
1877	A669	3k multi	.80	.50
1878	A669	3.60k multi, type 1	1.25	1.10
a.		Type 2	25.00	15.00
1879	A669	5k multi	3.00	2.00
	Nos. 1874-1879 (6)		5.65	4.20

In memory of American and Russian astronauts.

Nos. 1877-1879 were each issued in sheets of 4. Values: set (with No. 1878) $30; mset (with No. 1878a) $120.

Radio — A670

Telephone and Map of Czechoslovakia
A671

Television
A672

1973, May 1   **Perf. 11½x11**
1880	A670	30h blk & multi	.20	.20
1881	A671	30h lt bl, pink & blk	.20	.20
1882	A672	30h dp bl & multi	.20	.20
	Nos. 1880-1882 (3)		.60	.60

Czechoslovak anniversaries: 50 years of broadcasting (No. 1880); 20 years of telephone service to all communities (No. 1881); 20 years of television (No. 1882).

Coat of Arms and Linden Branch — A673

1973, May 9   **Perf. 11x11½**
1883	A673	60h red & multi	.20	.20

25th anniv. of the Constitution of May 9.

Prague Castle Art Type of 1971

No. 1884, Royal Legate, 14th century. No. 1885, Seal of King Charles IV, 1351.

1973, May 9   **Perf. 11½**
1884	A634	3k blue & multi	1.00	.75
1885	A634	3k gold, grn & dk brn	2.00	1.50

Nos. 1884-1885 were each issued in sheets of 4. Value, set $16.

Coat of Arms Type of 1968

1973, June 20
1886	A590	60h Mikulov	.20	.20
1887	A590	60h Zlutice	.35	.20
1888	A590	60h Smolenice	.35	.20
	Nos. 1886-1888 (3)		.90	.60

Coats of arms of Czechoslovakian cities.

Heraldic Colors of Olomouc and Moravia — A674

Anthurium — A675

1973, Aug. 23   **Engr. & Photo.**
1889	A674	30h multi	.25	.20

University of Olomouc, 400th anniv.

1973, Aug. 23   **Perf. 11½**

Sizes: 60h, 1k, 2k, 30x50mm; 1.60k, 1.80k, 3.60k, 23x39mm.
1890	A675	60h Tulips	.75	.35
1891	A675	1k Rose	.75	.35
1892	A675	1.60k shown	.40	.35
1893	A675	1.80k Iris	.40	.35
1894	A675	2k Chrysanthemum	1.90	1.00
1895	A675	3.60k Cymbidium	.75	.35
	Nos. 1890-1895 (6)		4.95	2.75

Flower Show, Olomouc, Aug. 18-Sept. 2. 60h, 1k, 2k issued in sheets of 4, others in sheets of 10. Value, set $100.

Hunting Dogs
A676

1973, Sept. 5
1896	A676	20h Irish setter	.40	.20
1897	A676	30h Czech terrier	.40	.20
1898	A676	40h Bavarian hunting dog	.55	.20
1899	A676	60h German pointer	.55	.20
1900	A676	1k Cocker spaniel	.85	.20
1901	A676	1.60k Dachshund	2.00	.50
	Nos. 1896-1901 (6)		4.75	1.50

Czechoslovak United Hunting Org., 50th anniv.

St. John, the Baptist, by Svabinsky
A677

Works by Max Svabinsky: 60h, "August Noon" (woman). 80h, "Marriage of True Minds" (artist and muse). 1k, "Paradise Sonata I" (Adam dreaming of Eve). 2.60k, Last Judgment, stained glass window, St. Vitus Cathedral.

1973, Sept. 17   **Litho. & Engr.**
1902	A677	20h blk & pale grn	.20	.20
1903	A677	60h black & buff	.20	.20

Engr.
1904	A677	80h black	.60	.20
1905	A677	1k slate green	.60	.25
1906	A677	2.60k multi	1.50	1.25
	Nos. 1902-1906 (5)		3.10	2.10

Centenary of the birth of Max Svabinsky (1873-1962), artist and stamp designer. 20h and 60h issued in sheets of 25; 80h and 1k setenant in sheets of 4 checkerwise (value $5); 2.60k in sheets of 4 (value $10).

Trade Union
Emblem
A678

1973, Oct. 15   Engr. & Photo.
1907 A678 1k red, bl & yel   .25 .20

8t (valueh Congress of the World Federation of Trade Unions, Varna, Bulgaria.

Painting Type of 1967

1k, Boy from Martinique, by Antonin Pelc. 1.20k, "Fortitude" (mountaineer), by Martin Benka. 1.80k, Rembrandt, self-portrait. 2k, Pierrot, by Bohumil Kubista. 2.40k, Ilona Kubinyiova, by Peter M. Bohun. 3.60k, Virgin and Child (Veveri Madonna), c. 1350.

1973, Nov. 27   Perf. 11½
1908 A565   1k multi, vio bl
                    inscriptions   2.50 1.25
a.   1k multi, black inscriptions   10.00 10.00
1909 A565   1.20k multi   2.50 1.25
1910 A565   1.80k multi   .80 .80
1911 A565   2k multi   .80 .80
1912 A565   2.40k multi   .80 .80
1913 A565   3.60k multi   .80 .80
          Nos. 1908-1913 (6)   8.20 5.70

Sheets of 4. Nos. 1910-1913 printed se-tenant with gold and black inscription on gutter. Value, set $35. No. 1908a in sheet of 4, value $45.
Central background bluish gray on No. 1908, light bluish green on No. 1908a.

Postilion — A679

1973, Dec. 18
1914 A679 1k gold & multi   .30 .20

Stamp Day 1974 and 55th anniversary of Czechoslovak postage stamps. Printed with 2 labels showing telephone and telegraph. Value of single with two labels, 60c.

Bedrich
Smetana — A681

Pablo Neruda,
Chilean
Flag — A682

"CSSR" — A680

Comecon
Building,
Moscow — A683

1974, Jan. 1
1915 A680 30h red, gold & ultra   .20 .20

5th anniversary of Federal Government in the Czechoslovak Socialist Republic.

1974, Jan. 4   Perf. 11x11½
1916 A681 60h shown   .20 .20
1917 A681 60h Josef Suk   .20 .20
1918 A682 60h shown   .20 .20
          Nos. 1916-1918 (3)   .60 .60

Smetana (1824-84), composer; Suk (1874-1935), composer, and Pablo Neruda (Neftali Ricardo Reyes, 1904-73), Chilean poet.

1974, Jan. 23
1919 A683 1k gold, red & vio bl   .25 .20

25th anniversary of the Council of Mutual Economic Assistance (COMECON).

Symbols of Postal Service — A684

1974, Feb. 20   Perf. 11½
1920 A684 3.60k multi   .95 .45

BRNO '74 National Stamp Exhibition, Brno, June 8-23.
No. 1920 was issue both in normal sheets of 25 stamps and in sheets containing 16 stamps se-tenant with 9 labels depicting Brno. Values: single stamp with attached tab $2.25; full sheet of 16 stamps and 9 labels $85.

Art Type of 1972

Designs: 60h, Tulips 1973, by Josef Broz. 1k, Structures 1961 (poppy and building), by Orest Dubay. 1.60k, Bird and flowers (Golden Sun-Glowing Day), by Adolf Zabransky. 1.80k, Artificial flowers, by Frantisek Gross.

1974, Feb. 21   Perf. 11½x11
1921 A651   60h multi   .20 .20
1922 A651   1k multi   .25 .20
1923 A651   1.60k multi   .35 .20
1924 A651   1.80k multi   .90 .30
          Nos. 1921-1924 (4)   1.70 .90

Czech and Slovak graphic art.

Oskar Benes and Vaclav
Prochazka — A685

40h, Milos Uher, Anton Sedlacek. 60h, Jan Hajecek, Marie Sedlackova. 80h, Jan Sverma, Albin Grznar. 1k, Jaroslav Neliba, Alois Hovorka. 1.60k, Ladislav Exnar, Ludovit Kukorelli.

1974, Mar. 21   Perf. 11½x11
1925 A685   30h indigo & multi   .20 .20
1926 A685   40h indigo & multi   .20 .20
1927 A685   60h indigo & multi   .20 .20
1928 A685   80h indigo & multi   .20 .20
1929 A685   1k indigo & multi   .25 .20
1930 A685   1.60k indigo & multi   .75 .25
          Nos. 1925-1930 (6)   1.80 1.25

Partisan commanders and fighters.

"Water,
the
Source
of
Energy"
A686

Symbolic Designs: 1k, Importance of water for agriculture. 1.20k, Study of the oceans. 1.60k, "Hydrological Decade." 2k, Struggle for unpolluted water.

1974, Apr. 25   Engr.   Perf. 11½
1931 A686   60h multi   .55 .20
1932 A686   1k multi   .55 .20
1933 A686   1.20k multi   1.00 .40
1934 A686   1.60k multi   1.00 .40
1935 A686   2k multi   2.00 1.50
          Nos. 1931-1935 (5)   5.10 2.70

Hydrological Decade (UNESCO), 1965-1974. Nos. 1931-1935 were each issued in sheets of 4. Value $30.

Allegory
Holding
"Molniya," and
Ground
Station — A687

Sousaphone
A688

1974, Apr. 30   Engr. & Photo.
1936 A687 30h vio bl & multi   .25 .20

"Intersputnik," first satellite communications ground station in Czechoslovakia.

Prague Castle Art Type of 1971

#1937, Golden Cock, 17th century locket. #1938, Glass monstrance, 1840.

1974, May 9   Engr.   Perf. 11½
1937 A634 3k gold & multi   1.50 1.25
1938 A634 3k blk & multi   2.00 1.50

Nos. 1937-1938 werre each issued in sheets of 4. Value, set $18.

Engraved and Photogravure
1974, May 12   Perf. 11x11½
1939 A688 20h shown   .20 .20
1940 A688 30h Bagpipe   .20 .20
1941 A688 40h Violin, by Martin
                    Benka   .20 .20
1942 A688 1k Pyramid piano   .20 .20
1943 A688 1.60k Tenor quinton,
                    1754   .80 .20
          Nos. 1939-1943 (5)   1.60 1.00

Prague and Bratislava Music Festivals. The 1.60k also commemorates 25th anniversary of Slovak Philharmonic Orchestra.

Child — A689

1974, June 1   Perf. 11½
1944 A689 60h multi   .20 .20

Children's Day. Design is from illustration for children's book by Adolf Zabransky.

Globe, People and Exhibition
Emblems — A690

Design: 6k, Rays and emblems symbolizing "Oneness and Mutuality."

1974, June 1
1945 A690 30h multi   .20 .20
1946 A690 6k multi   1.20 .75

BRNO 74 Natl. Stamp Exhib., Brno, June 8-23.
Nos. 2171-2172 were each issued both in sheet of 50 stamps and in sheets of 16 stamps and 14 labels. Values: stamps with attached labels, $1.75; sheet of 16 stamps and 14 labels $75.

Resistance
Fighter — A691

Actress Holding
Tragedy and
Comedy
Masks — A692

1974, Aug. 29   Perf. 11½
1947 A691 30h multi   .20 .20

Slovak National Uprising, 30th anniversary.

1974, Aug. 29
1948 A692 30h red, sil & blk   .20 .20

Bratislava Academy of Music and Drama, 25th anniversary.

Slovak Girl with
Flower — A693

1974, Aug. 29
1949 A693 30h multi   .20 .20

SLUK, Slovak folksong and dance ensemble, 25th anniversary.

Hero and
Leander
A694

Design: 2.40k, Hero watching Leander swim the Hellespont. No. 1952, Leander reaching shore. No. 1953, Hero mourning over Leander's body. No. 1954, Hermione, Leander's sister. No. 1955, Mourning Cupid. Designs are from 17th century English tapestries in Bratislava Council Palace.

1974-76
1950 A694   2k multi   1.25 1.10
1951 A694 2.40k multi   1.50 1.25
1952 A694   3k multi   1.00 .45
1953 A694   3k multi   1.75 1.75
1954 A694 3.60k multi   2.50 1.10
1955 A694 3.60k multi   .85 .60
          Nos. 1950-1955 (6)   8.85 6.25

Issued: #1950-1951, 9/25/74; #1952, 1954, 8/29/75; #1953, 1955, 5/9/76.
Nos. 1950-1951 were each issued in sheets of 6, with 2 blank labels. Nos. 1952-2955 were issued in sheets of 4. Value, set $50.

Soldier Standing Guard, Target, 1840 — A695

Painted Folk-art Targets: 60h, Landscape with Pierrot and flags, 1828. 1k, Diana crowning champion marksman, 1832. 1.60k, Still life with guitar, 1839. 2.40k, Salvo and stag in flight, 1834. 3k, Turk and giraffe, 1831.

1974, Sept. 26   *Perf. 11½*
Size: 30x50mm

1956	A695	30h black & multi	.20	.20
1957	A695	60h black & multi	.20	.20
1958	A695	1k black & multi	.25	.20

Engr.
Perf. 12
Size: 40x50mm

1959	A695	1.60k green & multi	.40	.35
1960	A695	2.40k sepia & multi	.70	.60
1961	A695	3k multi	2.25	2.25
		Nos. 1956-1961 (6)	4.00	3.80

Nos. 1959-1961 were each issued in sheets of 4. Value, set $25.

UPU Emblem and Postilion — A696

UPU Cent. (UPU Emblem and): 40h, Mail coach. 60h, Railroad mail coach, 1851. 80h, Early mail truck. 1k, Czechoslovak Airlines mail plane. 1.60k, Radar.

Engraved and Photogravure
1974, Oct. 9   *Perf. 11½*

1962	A696	30h multi	.20	.20
1963	A696	40h multi	.20	.20
1964	A696	60h multi	.20	.20
1965	A696	80h multi	.20	.20
1966	A696	1k multi	.30	.20
1967	A696	1.60k multi	1.00	.25
		Nos. 1962-1967 (6)	2.10	1.25

Sealed Letter — A697   Post Rider — A699

Stylized Bird — A698   Postal Code Symbol — A698a

20h, Post Horn, Old Town Bridge Tower. #1971, Carrier pigeon. #1979, Map of Czechoslovakia with postal code numbers.

1974, Oct. 31   *Perf. 11½x11*

1968	A699	20h multi	.20	.20
1969	A697	30h brn, bl & red	.20	.20
1970	A699	40h multi	.20	.20
1971	A697	60h bl, yel & red	.20	.20
		Nos. 1968-1971 (4)	.80	.80

Nos. 1968-1971 were reissued in 1979, printed on fluorescent paper. Value, set $15. See No. 2675.

Coil Stamps
1975   **Photo.**   *Perf. 14*

1976	A698	30h brt bl	.20	.20
1977	A698	60h carmine	.20	.20

1976   *Perf. 11½*

1978	A698a	30h emer	.20	.20
1979	A698a	60h scar	.20	.20

Nos. 1976-1979 have black control number on back of every fifth stamp.

Ludvik Kuba, Self-portrait, 1941 — A700

Paintings: 1.20k, Violinist Frantisek Ondricek, by Vaclav Brozik. 1.60k, Vase with Flowers, by Otakar Kubin. 1.80k, Woman with Pitcher, by Janko Alexy. 2.40k, Bacchanalia, c. 1635, by Karel Skreta.

1974, Nov. 27   **Engr.**   *Perf. 11½*

1980	A700	1k multi	.40	.25
1981	A700	1.20k multi	.65	.30
1982	A700	1.60k multi	.65	.45
1983	A700	1.80k multi	.80	.30
1984	A700	2.40k multi	2.00	1.40
		Nos. 1980-1984 (5)	4.50	2.70

Czech and Slovak art.
Nos. 1980-194 were each issued in sheets of 4. Value, set $25.
See Nos. 2209-2211, 2678-2682, 2721-2723, 2743, 2766-2768.

Post Horn — A701

Engraved and Photogravure
1974, Dec. 18   *Perf. 11x11½*

1985	A701	1k multicolored	.30	.20

Stamp Day.

Still-life with Hare, by Hollar — A702

Designs: 1k, The Lion and the Mouse, by Vaclav Hollar. 1.60k, Deer Hunt, by Philip Galle. 1.80k, Grand Hunt, by Jacques Callot.

1975, Feb. 26   *Perf. 11½x11*

1988	A702	60h blk & buff	.20	.20
1989	A702	1k blk & buff	.20	.20
1990	A702	1.60k blk & yel	.20	.20
1991	A702	1.80k blk & buff	1.00	.50
		Nos. 1988-1991 (4)	1.60	1.10

Hunting scenes from old engravings.

Guns Pointing at Family A703

Young Woman and Globe — A704

Designs: 1k, Women and building on fire. 1.20k, People and roses. All designs include names of destroyed villages.

1975, Feb. 26   *Perf. 11*

1992	A703	60h multi	.20	.20
1993	A703	1k multi	.20	.20
1994	A703	1.20k multi	.30	.20
		Nos. 1992-1994 (3)	.70	.60

Destruction of 14 villages by the Nazis, 30th anniversary.

1975, Mar. 7   *Perf. 11½x11*

1995	A704	30h red & multi	.20	.20

International Women's Year 1975.

Little Queens, Moravian Folk Custom A705

Folk Customs: 1k, Straw masks (animal heads and blackened faces), Slovak. 1.40k, The Tale of Maid Dorothea (executioner, girl, king and devil). 2k, Drowning of Morena, symbol of death and winter.

1975, Mar. 26   **Engr.**   *Perf. 11½*

1996	A705	60h blk & multi	.40	.20
1997	A705	1k blk & multi	.70	.40
1998	A705	1.40k blk & multi	.80	.55
1999	A705	2k blk & multi	1.00	.75
		Nos. 1996-1999 (4)	2.90	1.90

Nos. 1996-1999 were each issued in sheets of four. Value $15.

Coat of Arms Type of 1968
Engraved and Photogravure
1975, Apr. 17   *Perf. 11½*

2000	A590	60h Nymburk	.25	.20
2001	A590	60h Znojmo	.25	.20

Coats of arms of Czechoslovakian cities.

Czech May Uprising — A706

Liberation by Soviet Army — A707

Czechoslovak-Russian Friendship — A708

Engr. & Photo.; Engr. (A707)
1975, May 9

2002	A706	1k multi	.25	.20
2003	A707	1k multi	.25	.20
2004	A708	1k multi	.25	.20
		Nos. 2002-2004 (3)	.75	.60

30th anniv. of the May uprising of the Czech people and of liberation by the Soviet Army; 5th anniv. of the Czechoslovak-Soviet Treaty of Friendship, Cooperation and Mutual Aid.

Adolescents' Exercises — A709

Designs: 60th, Children's exercises. 1k, Men's and women's exercises.

Engraved and Photogravure
1975, June 15   *Perf. 12x11½*

2005	A709	30h lil & multi	.20	.20
2006	A709	60h multi	.20	.20
2007	A709	1k vio & multi	.25	.20
		Nos. 2005-2007 (3)	.65	.60

Spartakiad 1975, Prague, June 26-29. Nos. 2005-2007 each issued in sheets of 30 stamps and 40 labels, showing different Spartakiad emblems. Value, set with tabs, $1.

Datrioides Microlepis and Sea Horse — A710

Tropical Fish (Aquarium): 1k, Beta splendens regan and pterophyllum scalare. 1.20k, Carassius auratus. 1.60k, Amphiprion percula and chaetodon sp. 2k, Pomacanthodes semicirculatus, pomocanthus maculosus and paracanthus hepatus.

1975, June 27   *Perf. 11½*

2008	A710	60h multi	.20	.20
2009	A710	1k multi	.35	.20
2010	A710	1.20k multi	.40	.20
2011	A710	1.60k multi	.55	.20
2012	A710	2k multi	1.75	.50
		Nos. 2008-2012 (5)	3.25	1.30

Pelicans, by Nikita Charushin — A711

Book Illustrations: 30h, The Dreamer, by Lieselotte Schwarz. 40h, Hero on horseback, by Val Muntenau. 60h, Peacock, by Klaus Ensikat. 80h, Man on horseback, by Robert Dubravec.

1975, Sept. 5

2013	A711	20h multi	.20	.20
2014	A711	30h multi	.20	.20
2015	A711	40h multi	.25	.20
2016	A711	60h multi	.25	.20
2017	A711	80h multi	.50	.20
		Nos. 2013-2017 (5)	1.40	1.00

Bratislava BIB 75 biennial exhibition of illustrations for children's books.
Nos. 2013-2017 issued in sheets of 25 stamps and 15 labels with designs and inscriptions in various languages. Value, set with attached labels, $2.50.

Strakonice, 1951 — A712

Designs: Motorcycles.

1975, Sept. 29   **Perf. 11½**
2018 A712 20h shown   .20   .20
2019 A712 40h Jawa 250, 1945   .20   .20
2020 A712 60h Jawa 175, 1935   .20   .20
2021 A712 1k ITAR, 1921   .20   .20
2022 A712 1.20k ORION, 1903   .25   .20
2023 A712 1.80k Laurin & Kle-
                  ment, 1898   1.40   .40
      Nos. 2018-2023 (6)   2.45 1.40

Study of Shortwave Solar
Radiation — A713

Soyuz-Apollo Link-up in
Space — A714

60h, Study of aurora borealis & Oréol satellite. 1k, Study ofionosphere & cosmic radiation. 2k, Copernicus, radio map of the sun &
satellite.

1975, Sept. 30
2024 A713 30h multi   .20   .20
2025 A713 60h yel, rose red &
                  vio   .20   .20
2026 A713 1k bl, yel & vio   .20   .20
2027 A713 2k red, vio & yel   .35   .20
                  Engr.
2028 A714 5k vio & multi   2.00 1.50
      Nos. 2024-2028 (5)   2.95 2.30

International cooperation in space research.
   No. 2028 issued in sheets of 4. Value $15.
   The design of No. 2026 appears to be
inverted.

Slovnaft, Petrochemical Plant — A715

Designs: 60h, Atomic power station. 1k,
Construction of Prague subway. 1.20k, Construction of Friendship pipeline. 1.40k, Combine harvesters. 1.60k, Apartment house
construction.

Engraved and Photogravure
1975, Oct. 28
2029 A715 30h multi   .20   .20
2030 A715 60h multi   .20   .20
2031 A715 1k multi   .25   .20
2032 A715 1.20k multi   .25   .20
2033 A715 1.40k multi   .25   .20
2034 A715 1.60k multi   .75   .30
      Nos. 2029-2034 (6)   1.90 1.30

Socialist construction, 30th anniversary.
Nos. 2029-2034 printed se-tenant with labels.
Value, set with attached labels, $2.50.

Pres. Gustav
Husak — A716

1975, Oct. 28   **Engr.**
2035 A716 30h ultra   .20   .20
2036 A716 60h rose red   .20   .20

Prague Castle Art Type of 1971
3k, Gold earring, 9th cent. 3.60k, Arms of
Premysl Dynasty & Bohemia from lid of leather
case containing Bohemian crown, 14th cent.

1975, Oct. 29
2040 A634 3k blk, grn, pur &
                  gold   .75   .40
2041 A634 3.60k red & multi   1.50 1.25
   Nos. 2040-2041 each issued in sheets of 4.
Value, set $15.

Miniature Sheet

Ludvik Svoboda, Road Map, Buzuluk
to Prague, Carnations — A717

1975, Nov. 25
2042 A717 10k multi   9.00 7.00
   Pres. Ludvik Svoboda, 80th birthday.
   Exists imperf. Value, $40 unused, $25 used.

Art Type of 1967
Paintings: 1k, "May 1975" (Woman and
doves for 30th anniv. of peace), by Zdenek
Sklenar. 1.40k, Woman in national costume,
by Eugen Nevan. 1.80k, "Liberation of
Prague," by Alena Cermakova, horiz. 2.40k,
"Fire 1938" (woman raising fist), by Josef
Capek. 3.40k, Old Prague, 1828, by Vincenc
Morstadt.

1975, Nov. 27   Engr.   Perf. 11½
2043 A565 1k blk, buff & brn   .25   .20
2044 A565 1.40k multi   .50   .30
2045 A565 1.80k multi   .50   .30
2046 A565 2.40k multi   1.25   .75
2047 A565 3.40k multi   1.25 1.25
      Nos. 2043-2047 (5)   3.75 2.80

Nos. 2043-2047 were each issued in sheets
of 4. Value, set $22.50.

Carrier Pigeon — A718

Engraved and Photogravure
1975, Dec. 18   **Perf. 11½**
2048 A718 1k red & multi   .30 .20
   Stamp Day 1975.

Frantisek
Halas — A719

Wilhelm   Frantisek
Pieck — A720   Lexa — A721

Jindrich
Jindrich — A722

Ivan
Krasko — A723

1976, Feb. 25   **Perf. 11½**
2049 A719 60h multi   .20   .20
2050 A720 60h multi   .20   .20
2051 A721 60h multi   .20   .20
2052 A722 60h multi   .20   .20
2053 A723 60h multi   .20   .20
      Nos. 2049-2053 (5)   1.00 1.00

Halas (1901-49), poet; Pieck (1876-1960),
pres. of German Democratic Republic; Lexa
(1876-1960), professor of Egyptology; Jindrich
(1876-1967), composer and writer; Krasko
(1876-1958), Slovak poet. No. 2051 printed in
sheets of 10, others in sheets of 50. Value, No.
2051 sheet, $5.00.

Ski
Jump,
Olympic
Emblem
A724

Winter Olympic Games Emblem and: 1.40k,
Figure skating, women's. 1.60k, Ice hockey.

1976, Mar. 22   **Perf. 12x11½**
2054 A724 1k gold & multi   .20   .20
2055 A724 1.40k gold & multi   .20   .20
2056 A724 1.60k gold & multi   1.00   .30
      Nos. 2054-2056 (3)   1.40   .70
   12th Winter Olympic Games, Innsbruck,
Austria, Feb. 4-15.

Javelin and Olympic Rings — A725

1976, Mar. 22   **Perf. 11½**
2057 A725 2k shown   .25   .20
2058 A725 3k Relay race   .40   .20
2059 A725 3.60k Shot put   1.40   .90
      Nos. 2057-2059 (3)   2.05 1.30
   21st Olympic Games, Montreal, Canada,
July 17-Aug. 1.

Table
Tennis — A726

1976, Mar. 22   **Perf. 11x12**
2060 A726 1k multi   .30   .20
   European Table Tennis Championship,
Prague, Mar. 26-Apr. 4.

Symbolic of   Worker, Derrick,
Communist   Emblem — A728
Party — A727

1976, Apr. 12   **Perf. 11x12**
2061 A727 30h gold & multi   .20   .20
2062 A728 60h gold & multi   .20   .20
   15th Congress of the Communist Party of
Czechoslovakia.

Radio Prague
Orchestra
A729

Dancer, Violin,
Tragic
Mask — A730

Actors — A731

Folk Dancers
A732

Film
Festival — A733

1976, Apr. 26   **Perf. 11½**
2063 A729 20h gold & multi   .20   .20
2064 A730 20h pink & multi   .20   .20
2065 A731 20h lt bl & multi   .20   .20
2066 A732 30h blk & multi   .20   .20
2067 A733 30h vio bl, rose & grn   .20   .20
      Nos. 2063-2067 (5)   1.00 1.00

Czechoslovak Radio Symphony Orchestra,
Prague, 50th anniv. (No. 2063); Academy of
Music and Dramatic Art, Prague, 50th anniv.
(No. 2064); Nova Scena Theater Co., Brati-
slava, 30th anniv. (No. 2065); Intl. Folk Song
and Dance Festival, Straznice, 30th anniv.
(No. 2066); 20th Intl. Film Festival, Karlovy
Vary (No. 2067).

Hammer and Sickle
A734   A735

Design: 6k, Hammer and sickle, horiz.

1976, May 14
2068 A734 30h gold, red & dk bl   .20 .20
2069 A735 60h gold, red & dp
         car   .20 .20

Souvenir Sheet
2070 A735 6k red & multi   1.75 1.75
Czechoslovak Communist Party, 55th anniv.
#2070 contains a 50x30mm stamp.

Ships in Storm,
by Frans Huys
(1522-1562)
A736

Old Engravings of Ships: 60h, by Václav Hollar (1607-77). 1k, by Regnier Nooms Zeeman (1623-68). 2k, by Francois Chereau (1680-1729).

Engraved and Photogravure
1976, July 21   **Perf. 11x11½**
2071 A736 40h buff & blk   .20 .20
2072 A736 60h gray, buff & blk   .20 .20
2073 A736 1k lt grn, buff & blk   .20 .20
2074 A736 2k lt bl, buff & blk   1.10 .40
    Nos. 2071-2074 (4)   1.70 1.00

"UNESCO"
A737

1976, July 30   **Perf. 11½**
2075 A737 2k gray & multi   .40 .45
30th anniversary of UNESCO. Issued in sheets of 10. Value $8.

Souvenir Sheet

Hands
Holding
Infant,
Globe
and
Dove
A738

1976, July 30
2076   Sheet of 2   4.00 3.50
  a. A738 6k multi   2.50 2.00
European Security and Cooperation Conference, Helsinki, Finland, 2nd anniv.

Merino
Ram — A739

Couple
Smoking, WHO
Emblem and
Skull — A740

Designs: 40h, Bern-Hana milk cow. 1.60k, Kladruby stallion Generalissimus XXVII.

1976, Aug. 28   **Perf. 11½x12**
2077 A739 30h multi   .20 .20
2078 A739 40h multi   .20 .20
2079 A739 1.60k multi   .35 .20
    Nos. 2077-2079 (3)   .75 .60
Bountiful Earth Exhibition, Ceske Budejovice, Aug. 28-Sept. 12.

1976, Sept. 7   **Perf. 12x11½**
2080 A740 2k multi   .50 .30
Fight against smoking, WHO drive against drug addiction.
Printed in sheets of 10 (2x5) with WHO emblems and inscription in margin. Value $10.

Prague Castle Art Type of 1971
Designs: 3k, View of Prague Castle, by F. Hoogenberghe, 1572. 3.60k, Faun and Satyr, sculptured panel, 16th century.

1976, Oct. 22   **Engr.**   **Perf. 11½**
2081 A634 3k multi   2.00 1.75
2082 A634 3.60k multi   .75 .50
Nos. 2081-2082 were each issued in sheets of 4. Value $15.

Guernica 1937,
by Imro Weiner-
Kral
A741

1976, Oct. 22
2083 A741 5k multi   .75 .35
40th anniv. of the Intl. Brigade in Spain.

Zebras
A742

20h, Elephants. 30h, Cheetah. 40h, Giraffes. 60h, Rhinoceros. 3k, Bongos.

Engraved and Photogravure
1976, Nov. 3   **Perf. 11½x11, 11x11½**
2084 A742 10h multi   .20 .20
2085 A742 20h multi, vert.   .20 .20
2086 A742 30h multi   .25 .20
2087 A742 40h multi, vert.   .35 .20
2088 A742 60h multi   .35 .20
2089 A742 3k multi, vert.   1.75 .50
    Nos. 2084-2089 (6)   3.10 1.50
African animals in Dvur Kralove Zoo.

Art Type of 1967
Paintings of Flowers: 1k, by Peter Matejka. 1.40k, by Cyril Bouda. 2k, by Jan Breughel. 3.60k, J. Rudolf Bys.

1976, Nov. 27   **Engr.**   **Perf. 11½**
2090 A565 1k multi   .65 .40
2091 A565 1.40k multi   1.25 .75
2092 A565 2k multi   1.00 .75
2093 A565 3.60k multi   .75 .45
    Nos. 2090-2093 (4)   3.65 2.35
Nos. 2090-2093 were each issued in sheets of 4, with emblem and name of Praga 1978 on horizontal gutter. Value, set $25.

Postrider, 17th Century, and
Satellites — A743

1976, Dec. 18   **Engr. & Photo.**
2094 A743 1k multi   .25 .20
Stamp Day 1976.

Ice   Arms of
Hockey — A744   Vranov — A745

1977, Feb. 11   **Perf. 11½**
2095 A744 60h shown   .20 .20
2096 A744 1k Biathlon   .20 .20
2097 A744 1.60k Ski jump   .95 .25
2098 A744 2k Downhill skiing   .25 .20
    Nos. 2095-2098 (4)   1.60 .85
6th Winter Spartakiad of Socialist Countries' Armies.

1977, Feb. 20
Coats of Arms of Czechoslovak towns.
2099 A745 60h shown   .20 .20
2100 A745 60h Kralupy & Vltavou   .20 .20
2101 A745 60h Jicin   .20 .20
2102 A745 60h Valasske Mezirici   .20 .20
    Nos. 2099-2102 (4)   .80 .80
See Nos. 2297-2300.

Window, Michna
Palace — A746

Prague Renaissance Windows: 30h, Michna Palace. 40h, Thun Palace. 60h, Archbishop's Palace, Hradcany. 5k, St. Nicholas Church.

1977, Mar. 10
2103 A746 20h multi   .20 .20
2104 A746 30h multi   .20 .20
2105 A746 40h multi   .20 .20
2106 A746 60h multi   .20 .20
2107 A746 5k multi   1.50 .60
    Nos. 2103-2107 (5)   2.30 1.40
PRAGA 1978 International Philatelic Exhibition, Prague, Sept. 8-17, 1978.

Children,
Auxiliary
Police
A747

1977, Apr. 21   **Perf. 11½**
2108 A747 60h multi   .25 .20
Auxiliary Police, 25th anniversary.

Warsaw,
Polish Flag,
Bicyclists
A748

Congress
Emblem — A749

Designs: 60h, Berlin, DDR flag, bicyclists. 1k, Prague, Czechoslovakian flag, victorious bicyclist. 1.40k, Bicyclists on highways, modern views of Berlin, Prague and Warsaw.

1977, May 7
2109 A748 30h multi   .20 .20
2110 A748 60h multi   .20 .20
2111 A748 1k multi   .50 .20
2112 A748 1.40k multi   .35 .20
    Nos. 2109-2112 (4)   1.25 .80
30th International Bicycle Peace Race Warsaw-Prague-Berlin.

1977, May 25   **Perf. 11½**
2113 A749 30h car, red & gold   .20 .20
9th Trade Union Congress, Prague 1977.

Prague Castle Art Type of 1971
Designs: 3k, Onyx footed bowl, 1350. 3.60k, Bronze horse, 1619.

1977, June 7   **Engr.**
2114 A634 3k multi   .95 .90
2115 A634 3.60k multi   .90 .90
Nos. 2114-2115 were each issued in sheets of 4. Value, set $13.

French Postrider, 19th Century,
PRAGA '78 Emblem — A750

Postal Uniforms: 1k, Austrian, 1838. 2k, Austrian, late 18th century. 3.60k, Germany, early 18th century.

1977, June 8   **Engr. & Photo.**
2116 A750 60h multi   .20 .20
2117 A750 1k multi   .20 .20
2118 A750 2k multi   .30 .20
2119 A750 3.60k multi   1.20 .60
    Nos. 2116-2119 (4)   1.90 1.20
PRAGA 1978 International Philatelic Exhibition, Prague, Sept. 8-17, 1978.
Nos. 2116-2119 were each issued both in sheets of 50 and in sheets of 4 stamps with 4 inscribed labels and 2 blank labels. Value, set of sheets of 4, $16.

Coffeepots,   Mlada Boleslav
Porcelain   Costume — A752
Mark — A751

Czechoslovak Porcelain and Porcelain Marks: 30h, Urn. 40h, Vase. 60h, Cup and saucer, jugs. 1k, Candlestick and plate. 3k, Cup and saucer, coffeepot.

1977, June 15

2120	A751	20h multi	.20	.20
2121	A751	30h multi	.20	.20
2122	A751	40h multi	.20	.20
2123	A751	60h multi	.20	.20
2124	A751	1k multi	.20	.20
2125	A751	3k multi	1.10	.80
	Nos. 2120-2125 (6)		2.10	1.35

1977, Aug. 31   Engr.   Perf. 11½

PRAGA Emblem and Folk Costumes from: 1.60k, Vazek. 3.60k, Zavadka. 5k, Belkovice.

2126	A752	1k multi	1.00	.80
2127	A752	1.60k multi	1.00	.80
2128	A752	3.60k multi	1.00	.80
2129	A752	5k multi	1.00	.80
	Nos. 2126-2129 (4)		4.00	3.20

Issued in sheets of 10 and in sheets of 8 plus 2 labels showing PRAGA '78 emblem. Value, set: sheets of 10 $50; sheets of 8 $40.

Old Woman, Devil and Spinner, by Viera Bombova A753

Book Illustrations: 60h, Bear and tiger, by Genadij Pavlisin. 1k, Coach drawn by 4 horses (Hans Christian Andersen), by Ulf Lovgren. 2k, Bear and flamingos (Lewis Carroll), by Nicole Claveloux. 3k, King with keys, and toys, by Jiri Trnka.

1977, Sept. 9   Engr. & Photo.

2130	A753	40h multi	.20	.20
2131	A753	60h multi	.20	.20
2132	A753	1k multi	.20	.20
2133	A753	2k multi	.25	.20
2134	A753	3k multi	1.00	.35
	Nos. 2130-2134 (5)		1.85	1.15

Prize-winning designs, 6th biennial exhibition of illustrations for children's books, Bratislava.

Globe, Violin, Doves, View of Prague — A754

1977, Sept. 28   Perf. 11½

2135	A754	60h multi	.25	.20

Congress of International Music Council of UNESCO, Prague and Bratislava.

Souvenir Sheets

"For a Europe of Peace" A755

1.60k, "For a Europe of Cooperation." 2.40k, "For a Europe of Social Progress."

1977, Oct. 3

2136		Sheet of 2	.50	.50
a.	A755	60h multi	.20	.20
2137		Sheet of 2	1.00	1.00
a.	A755	1.60k multi	.25	.25
2138		Sheet of 2	2.00	1.75
a.	A755	2.40k multi	.50	.50

2nd European Security and Cooperation Conference, Belgrade. Nos. 2136-2138 each contain 2 stamps and 2 blue on buff inscriptions and ornaments.

S. P. Korolev, Sputnik I Emblem — A756

Sailors, Cruiser Aurora — A757

30h, Yuri A. Gagarin & Vostok I. 40h, Alexei Leonov. 1k, Neil A. Armstrong & footprint on moon. 1.60k, Construction of orbital space station.

1977, Oct. 4

2139	A756	20h multi	.20	.20
2140	A756	30h multi	.20	.20
2141	A756	40h multi	.20	.20
2142	A756	1k multi	.20	.20
2143	A756	1.60k multi	.60	.20
	Nos. 2139-2143 (5)		1.40	1.00

Space research, 20th anniv. of 1st earth satellite.

1977, Nov. 7

2144	A757	30h multi	.20	.20

60th anniv. of Russian October Revolution.

"Russia," Arms of USSR, Kremlin A758

"Science" A759

1977, Nov. 7

2145	A758	30h multi	.20	.20

55th anniversary of the USSR.

1977, Nov. 17

2146	A759	3k multi	.50	.20

Czechoslovak Academy of Science, 25th anniversary.

Art Type of 1967

Paintings: 2k, "Fear" (woman), by Jan Murdoch. 2.40k, Jan Francisci, portrait by Peter M. Bohun. 2.60k, Vaclav Hollar, self-portrait, 1647. 3k, Young Woman, 1528, by Lucas Cranach. 5k, Cleopatra, by Rubens.

1977, Nov. 27   Engr.   Perf. 11½

2147	A565	2k multi	.70	.40
2148	A565	2.40k multi	1.10	1.00
2149	A565	2.60k multi	1.10	1.00
2150	A565	3k multi	.70	.60
2151	A565	5k multi	1.40	1.40
	Nos. 2147-2151 (5)		5.00	4.40

Nos. 2147-2151 were each issued in sheets of 4. Value, set $28.

View of Bratislava, by Georg Hoefnagel — A760

Design: 3.60k, Arms of Bratislava, 1436.

1977, Dec. 6

2152	A760	3k multi	1.40	1.20
2153	A760	3.60k multi	.60	.40

Nos. 2152-21531 were issued in sheets of 4. Value, set $12.50.
See Nos. 2174-2175, 2270-2271, 2331-2332, 2364-2365, 2422-2423, 2478-2479, 2514-2515, 2570-2571, 2618-2619.

Stamp Pattern and Post Horn — A761

1977, Dec. 18   Engr. & Photo.

2154	A761	1k multi	.25	.20

Stamp Day.

Zdenek Nejedly — A762

Karl Marx — A763

1978, Feb. 10   Perf. 11½

2155	A762	30h multi	.20	.20
2156	A763	40h multi	.20	.20

Zdenek Nejedly (1878-1962), musicologist and historian; Karl Marx (1818-1883), political philosopher.

Civilians Greeting Guardsmen — A764

Intellectual, Farm Woman and Steel Worker, Flag — A765

1978, Feb. 25

2157	A764	1k gold & multi	.20	.20
2158	A765	1k gold & multi	.20	.20

30th anniv. of "Victorious February" (No. 2157), and Natl. Front (No. 2158). See note after 2190.

Yuri A. Gagarin, Vostok I — A766

10k Coin, 1964, and 25k Coin, 1965 — A767

Design: 30h, 3.60k, like No. 2140.

Engraved; Overprint Photogravure (Blue and carmine on 30h, green and lilac rose on 3.60k)

1978, Mar. 2   Perf. 11½x12

2159	A766	30h dk red	.20	.20
2160	A766	3.60k vio bl	2.25	2.00

Capt. V. Remek, 1st Czechoslovakian cosmonaut on Russian spaceship Soyuz 28, Mar. 2-9.

1978, Mar. 14   Engr. & Photo.

40h, Medal for Culture, 1972. 1.40k, Charles University medal, 1948. 3k, Ferdinand I medal, 1568. 5k, Gold florin, 1335.

2161	A767	20h sil & multi	.20	.20
2162	A767	40h sil & multi	.20	.20
2163	A767	1.40k gold & multi	1.00	.35
2164	A767	3k gold & multi	.35	.20
2165	A767	5k gold & multi	.35	.20
	Nos. 2161-2165 (5)		2.10	1.00

650th anniversary of Kremnica Mint.

Tire Tracks and Ball — A768

Congress Emblem — A769

1978, Mar. 15

2166	A768	60h multi	.25	.20

Road safety.

1978, Apr. 16   Perf. 11½

2167	A769	1k multi	.25	.20

9th World Trade Union Cong., Prague 1978.

Shot Put and Praha '78 Emblem A770

1k, Pole vault. 3.60k, Women runners.

1978, Apr. 26

2168	A770	40h multi	.20	.20
2169	A770	1k multi	.25	.20
2170	A770	3.60k multi	.60	.35
	Nos. 2168-2170 (3)		1.05	.75

5th European Athletic Championships, Prague 1978.

Ice Hockey — A771

Designs: 30h, Hockey. 2k, Ice hockey play.

1978, Apr. 26

2171	A771	30h multi	.30	.25
2172	A771	60h multi	.20	.20
2173	A771	2k multi	.40	.20
	Nos. 2171-2173 (3)		.90	.65

5th European Ice Hockey Championships and 70th anniversary of Bandy hockey.

Bratislava Type of 1977

Designs: 3k, Bratislava, 1955, by Orest Dubay. 3.60k, Fishpound Square, Bratislava, 1955, by Imro Weiner-Kral.

1978, May 9   Engr.   Perf. 11½

2174	A760	3k multi	.90	.75
2175	A760	3.60k multi	1.10	.75

Nos. 2174-2175 were each issued in sheets of 4. Value, set $12.

Prague Castle Art Type of 1971

3k, King Ottokar II, detail from tomb. 3.60k, Charles IV, detail from votive panel by Jan Ocka.

1978, May 9
2176	A634	3k multi	.75	.50
2177	A634	3.60k multi	3.25	2.00

Nos. 2176-2177 were each issued in sheets of 4. Value, set $20.

Ministry of Post, Prague
A772

Engraved and Photogravure
1978, May 29   *Perf. 12x11½*
2178	A772	60h multi	.25	.20

14th session of permanent COMECOM Commission (Ministers of Post and Telecommunications of Socialist Countries).

Palacky Bridge
A773

Prague Bridges and PRAGA '78 Emblem: 40h, Railroad bridge. 1k, Bridge of May 1. 2k, Manes Bridge. 3k, Svatopluk Cech Bridge. 5.40k, Charles Bridge.

1978, May 30
2179	A773	20h blk & multi	.20	.20
2180	A773	40h blk & multi	.20	.20
2181	A773	1k blk & multi	.20	.20
2182	A773	2k blk & multi	.20	.20
2183	A773	3k blk & multi	.45	.20
2184	A773	5.40k blk & multi	1.50	.75
	Nos. 2179-2184 (6)		2.75	1.75

PRAGA 1978 International Philatelic Exhibition, Prague, Sept. 8-17.

St. Peter and Apostles, Clock Tower, and Emblem
A774

Town Hall Clock, Prague, by Josef Manes, and PRAGA '78 Emblem: 1k, Astronomical clock. 2k, Prague's coat of arms. 3k, Grape harvest (September). 3.60k, Libra. 10k, Arms surrounded by zodiac signs and scenes symbolic of 12 months, horiz. 2k, 3k, 3.60k show details from design of 10k.

1978, June 20   *Perf. 11½x11*
2185	A774	40h multi	.20	.20
2186	A774	1k multi	.20	.20
2187	A774	2k multi	.25	.20
2188	A774	3k multi	1.50	.35
2189	A774	3.60k multi	.75	.25
	Nos. 2185-2189 (5)		2.90	1.20

Souvenir Sheet
Perf. 12x12
2190	A774	10k multi	10.00	7.50

PRAGA'78 Intl. Philatelic Exhibition, Prague, Sept. 8-17. No. 2190 contains one 50x40mm stamp. Sheet exists imperf. Value $30.

A non-valid souvenir sheet contains 4 imperf. copies of No. 2157. Sold only with PRAGA ticket.

Folk Dancers — A775

1978, July 7   *Perf. 11½x12*
2191	A775	30h multi	.20	.20

25th Folklore Festival, Vychodna.

Overpass and PRAGA Emblem — A776

1k, 2k, Modern office buildings, diff. 6k, Old & new Prague. 20k, Charles Bridge & Old Town, by Vincent Morstadt, 1828.

1978   *Perf. 12x11½*
2192	A776	60h blk & multi	.20	.20
2193	A776	1k blk & multi	.20	.20
2194	A776	2k blk & multi	.20	.20
2195	A776	6k blk & multi	1.50	.75
	Nos. 2192-2195 (4)		2.10	1.35

Souvenir Sheet
Engr.
2196	A776	20k multi	9.50	7.50

PRAGA 1978 Intl. Phil. Exhib., Prague, Sept. 8-17. No. 2196 also for 60th anniv. of Czechoslovak postage stamps. No. 2196 contains one 61x45mm stamp.
Issued: #2192-2195, 9/8; #2196, 9/10.

Souvenir Sheet

Apollo's Companion, by Titian — A777

#2197b, King Midas. Stamps show details from "Apollo Flaying Marsya" by Titian.

1978, Sept. 12   *Perf. 11½*
2197		Sheet of 2	10.00	8.00
a.	A777	10k multi	4.25	3.50
b.	A777	10k multi	4.25	3.50

Titian (1488-1576), Venetian painter. No. 2197 with dark blue marginal inscription "FIP" was sold only with entrance ticket to PRAGA Philatelic Exhibition. Value $25.

Exhibition Hall — A778

Engraved and Photogravure
1978, Sept. 13   *Perf. 11½x11*
2198	A778	30h multi	.20	.20

22nd International Engineering Fair, Brno.

Postal Newspaper Service — A779

TV Screen, Headquarters and Logo — A780

Newspaper, Microphone A781

1978, Sept. 21   *Perf. 11½*
2199	A779	30h multi	.20	.20
2200	A780	30h multi	.20	.20
2201	A781	30h multi	.20	.20
	Nos. 2199-2201 (3)		.60	.60

Postal News Service, 25th anniv.; Czechoslovakian television, 25th anniv.; Press, Broadcasting and Television Day.

Sulky Race A782

Pardubice Steeplechase: 10h, Falling horses and jockeys at fence. 30h, Race. 40h, Horses passing post. 1.60k, Hurdling. 4.40k, Winner.

1978, Oct. 6   *Perf. 12x11½*
2202	A782	10h multi	.20	.20
2203	A782	20h multi	.20	.20
2204	A782	30h multi	.20	.20
2205	A782	40h multi	.25	.20
2206	A782	1.60k multi	1.50	.65
2207	A782	4.40k multi	2.55	1.65
	Nos. 2202-2207 (6)			

Woman Holding Arms of Czechoslovakia A783

1978, Oct. 28   *Perf. 11½*
2208	A783	60h multi	.20	.20

60th anniversary of independence.

Art Type of 1974

2.40k, Flowers, by Jakub Bohdan (1660-1724). 3k, The Dream of Salas, by Ludovit Fulla, horiz. 3.60k, Apostle with Censer, Master of the Spissko Capitals (c. 1480-90).

1978, Nov. 27   **Engr.**
2209	A700	2.40k multi	.60	.45
2210	A700	3k multi	.70	.65
2211	A700	3.60k multi	2.50	2.00
	Nos. 2209-2211 (3)		3.80	3.10

Slovak National Gallery, 30th anniversary. Nos. 2209-2211 were each issued in sheets of 4. Value, set $22.50.

Musicians, by Jan Könyves — A784

Slovak Ceramics: 30h, Janosik on Horseback, by Jozef Franko. 40h, Woman in Folk

Costume by Michal Polasko. 1k, Three Girls Singing, by Ignac Bizmayer. 1.60k, Janosik Dancing, by Ferdis Kostka.

Engraved and Photogravure
1978, Dec. 5   *Perf. 11½x12*
2212	A784	20h multi	.20	.20
2213	A784	30h multi	.20	.20
2214	A784	40h multi	.20	.20
2215	A784	1k multi	.20	.20
2216	A784	1.60k multi	1.00	.30
	Nos. 2212-2216 (5)		1.80	1.10

Alfons Mucha and his Design for 1918 Issue — A785

1978, Dec. 18   *Perf. 11½*
2217	A785	1k multi	.25	.20

60th Stamp Day.

COMECON Building, Moscow — A786

1979, Jan. 1   *Perf. 11½*
2218	A786	1k multi	.25	.20

Council for Mutual Economic Aid (COMECON), 30th anniversary.

Woman's Head and Grain — A787

Woman, Workers, Child, Doves — A788

1979, Jan. 1
2219	A787	30h multi	.20	.20
2220	A788	60h multi	.20	.20

United Agricultural Production Assoc., 30th anniv. (30h); Czechoslovakian Federation, 10th anniv. (60h).

Soyuz 28, Rockets and Capsule — A789

60h, Astronauts Aleksei Gubarev and Vladimir Remek on launching pad, vert. 1.60k, Soviet astronauts J. Romanenko and G. Grecko, Salyut 6 and recovery ship. 2k, Salyut-Soyuz orbital complex, post office in space and Czechoslovakia No. 2153. 4k, Soyuz 28, crew after landing and trajectory map, vert. 10k, Gubarev and Remek, Intercosmos emblem, arms of Czechoslovakia and USSR.

1979, Mar. 2
2221	A789	30h multi	.20	.20
2222	A789	60h multi	.20	.20
2223	A789	1.60k multi	.20	.20

2224	A789	2k multi	1.25	.30
2225	A789	4k multi	.60	.25
		Nos. 2221-2225 (5)	2.45	1.15

Souvenir Sheet

2226	A789	10k multi	5.00	3.50

1st anniv. of joint Czechoslovak-Soviet space flight. Size of No. 2226: 76x93mm (stamp 39x55mm). No. 2226 has Cyrillic inscription, No. 2455a does not. No. 2226 exists imperf. Value, $22.50.

Alpine Bellflowers A790

Stylized Satellite, Dial, Tape A791

Mountain Flowers: 20h, Crocus. 30h, Pinks. 40h, Alpine hawkweed. 3k, Larkspur.

1979, Mar. 23   *Perf. 11½*

2227	A790	10h multi	.20	.20
2228	A790	20h multi	.20	.20
2229	A790	30h multi	.20	.20
2230	A790	40h multi	.20	.20

Perf. 14

2231	A790	3k multi	1.50	.75
		Nos. 2227-2231 (5)	2.30	1.55

Mountain Rescue Service, 25th anniversary. The 3k exists perf. 11½. Value, $40 unused, $20 used.
The 3k was issued in sheets of 10. Values: perf 14 (No. 2231), $25; perf 11½, $400.

1979, Apr. 2

2232	A791	10h multi	.20	.20

Telecommunications research, 30th anniv.

Artist and Model, Dove, Bratislava Castle — A792

Cog Wheels, Transformer and Student — A793

Musical Instruments, Bratislava Castle — A794

Pioneer Scarf, IYC Emblem — A795

Red Star, Man, Child and Doves — A796

1979, Apr. 2

2233	A792	20h multi	.20	.20
2234	A793	20h multi	.20	.20
2235	A794	30h multi	.20	.20

2236	A795	30h multi	.20	.20
2237	A796	60h multi	.20	.20
		Nos. 2233-2237 (5)	1.00	1.00

Fine Arts Academy, Bratislava, 30th anniv.; Slovak Technical University, 40th anniv.; Radio Symphony Orchestra, Bratislava, 30th anniv.; Young Pioneers, 30th anniv. and IYC; Peace Movement, 30th anniversary.

Prague Castle Art Type of 1971

3k, Burial crown of King Ottokar II. 3.60k, Portrait of Mrs. Reitmayer, by Karel Purkyne.

1979, May 9   *Perf. 11½*

2238	A634	3k multi	1.75	1.40
2239	A634	3.60k multi	.85	.50

Nos. 2238-2239 were each issued in sheets of 4. Value, set $15.

Arms of Vlachovo Brezi, 1538 — A797

Animals in Heraldry: 60h, Jesenik, 1509 (bear and eagle). 1.20k, Vysoke Myto, 1471 (St. George slaying dragon). 1.80k, Martin, 1854 (St. Martin giving coat to beggar). 2k, Zebrak, 1674 (mythological beast).

1979, May 25   *Perf. 11½x12*

2240	A797	30h multi	.20	.20
2241	A797	60h multi	.20	.20
2242	A797	1.20k multi	.20	.20
2243	A797	1.80k multi	1.00	.30
2244	A797	2k multi	.60	.20
		Nos. 2240-2244 (5)	2.20	1.10

Forest, Thriving and Destroyed A798

Designs: 1.80k, Water. 3.60k, City. 4k, Cattle. All designs show good and bad environment, separated by exclamation point; Man and Biosphere emblem.

1979, June 22   *Engr.*   *Perf. 11½*

2245	A798	60h multi	.20	.20
2246	A798	1.80k multi	.30	.25
2247	A798	3.60k multi	1.75	.75
2248	A798	4k multi	.75	.40
		Nos. 2245-2248 (4)	3.00	1.60

Man and Biosphere Program of UNESCO.

Blast Furnace — A799

Engraved and Photogravure
1979, Aug. 29   *Perf. 11x11½*

2249	A799	30h multi	.20	.20

Slovak National Uprising, 35th anniversary.

Frog and Goat A800

Book Illustrations (IYC Emblem and): 40h, Knight on horseback. 60h, Maidens. 1k, Boy with sled following rooster. 3k, King riding flying beast.

1979, Apr. 2   *Perf. 11½x11*

2250	A800	20h multi	.20	.20
2251	A800	40h multi	.20	.20
2252	A800	60h multi	.20	.20
2253	A800	1k multi	.20	.20
2254	A800	3k multi	1.50	.50
		Nos. 2250-2254 (5)	2.30	1.30

Prize-winning designs, 7th biennial exhibition of illustrations for children's books, Bratislava; International Year of the Child. Printed with labels showing story characters. Value, set with attached labels, $4.75.

"Bone Shaker" Bicycles, 1870 A801

Bicycles from: 20h, 1978. 40h, 1910. 60h, 1886. 3.60k, 1820.

1979, Sept. 14   *Perf. 12x11½*

2255	A801	20h multi	.20	.20
2256	A801	40h multi	.20	.20
2257	A801	60h multi	.20	.20
2258	A801	2k multi	.40	.20
2259	A801	3.60k multi	1.50	.50
		Nos. 2255-2259 (5)	2.50	1.30

Bracket Clock, 18th Century A802

Designs: 18th century clocks.

1979, Oct. 1   *Perf. 11½*

2260	A802	40h multi	.20	.20
2261	A802	60h multi	.20	.20
2262	A802	80h multi	.85	.20
2263	A802	1k multi	.25	.20
2264	A802	2k multi	.50	.20
		Nos. 2260-2264 (5)	2.00	1.00

Art Type of 1967

Paintings: 1.60k, Sunday by the River, by Alois Moravec. 2k, Self-portrait, by Gustav Mally. 3k, Self-portrait, by Ilia Yefimovic Repin. 3.60k, Horseback Rider, by Jan Bauch. 5k, Dancing Peasants, by Albrecht Dürer.

1979, Nov. 27   *Engr.*   *Perf. 12*

2265	A565	1.60k multi	.35	.30
2266	A565	2k multi	.50	.45
2267	A565	3k multi	.50	.45
2268	A565	3.60k multi	1.75	1.50
2269	A565	5k multi	1.40	1.10
		Nos. 2265-2269 (5)	4.50	3.80

Nos. 2265-2269 were each issued in sheets of 4. Value, set $25.

Bratislava Type of 1977

Designs: 3k, Bratislava Castle on the Danube, by L. Janscha, 1787. 3.60k, Bratislava Castle, stone engraving by Wolf, 1815.

1979, Dec. 5

2270	A760	3k multi	.70	.65
2271	A760	3.60k multi	1.80	1.50

Nos. 2270-2272 were each issued in sheets of 4. Value, set $15.

Stamp Day — A803

Engraved and Photogravure
1979, Dec. 18   *Perf. 11½x12*

2272	A803	1k multi	.25	.20

Electronic Circuits — A804

Designs: 50h, Satellite dish. 2k, Airplane. 3k, Computer punch tape.

1979-80   *Photo.*   *Perf. 11½x12*
Coil Stamps

2273	A804	50h red	.20	.20
2274	A804	1k brown	.25	.20
2275	A804	2k green ('80)	.30	.20
2276	A804	3k lake ('80)	.45	.25
		Nos. 2273-2276 (4)	1.20	.85

The 1k comes in two shades.

Runners and Dove A805

Engraved and Photogravure
1980, Jan. 29   *Perf. 12x11½*

2289	A805	50h multi	.20	.20

50th Intl. Peace Marathon, Kosice, Oct. 4.

Downhill Skiing — A806

1980, Jan. 29   *Perf. 11½x12*

2290	A806	1k shown	.25	.20
2291	A806	2k Speed skating	.80	.50
2292	A806	3k Four-man bobsled	.65	.30
		Nos. 2290-2292 (3)	1.70	.80

13th Winter Olympic Games, Lake Placid, NY, Feb. 12-24.

Basketball — A807

1980, Jan. 29   *Perf. 11½*

2293	A807	40h shown	.20	.20
2294	A807	1k Swimming	.30	.20
2295	A807	2k Hurdles	1.25	.30
2296	A807	3.60k Fencing	.95	.25
		Nos. 2293-2296 (4)	2.70	.95

22nd Olympic Games, Moscow, 7/19-8/3.

Arms Type of 1977

1980, Feb. 20   *Perf. 11½*

2297	A745	50h Bystrice Nad Pernstejnem	.20	.20
2298	A745	50h Kunstat	.20	.20
2299	A745	50h Rozmital Pod Tremsinem	.20	.20
2300	A745	50h Zlata Idka	.20	.20
		Nos. 2297-2300 (4)	.80	.80

Theatrical Mask — A808

Slovak National Theater, Actors — A809

1980, Mar. 1
2301 A808 50h multi .20 .20
2302 A809 1k multi .25 .20

50th Jiraskuv Hronov Theatrical Ensemble Review; Slovak National Theater, Bratislava, 60th anniversary.

Mouse in Space, Satellite — A810

Police Corps Banner, Emblem — A811

Intercosmos: 1k, Weather map, satellite. 1.60k, Intersputnik television transmission. 4k, Camera, satellite. 5k, Czech satellite station, 1978, horiz. 10k, Intercosmos emblem, horiz.

1980, Apr. 12 Perf. 11½x12, 12x11½
2303 A810 50h multi .20 .20
2304 A810 1k multi .30 .20
2305 A810 1.60k multi 1.75 .20
2306 A810 4k multi .75 .40
2307 A810 5k multi 1.00 .50
Nos. 2303-2307 (5) 4.00 1.50

Souvenir Sheet
2308 A810 10k multi 3.25 2.50

Intercosmos cooperative space program. No. 2308 exists imperf. Value, $30.

1980, Apr. 17 Perf. 11½
2309 A811 50h multi .20 .20

National Police Corps, 35th anniversary.

Lenin's 110th Birth Anniversary — A812

Design: #2311, Engels's 160th birth anniv.

1980, Apr. 22
2310 A812 1k tan & brn .25 .20
2311 A812 1k lt grn & brn .25 .20

Old and Modern Prague, Czech Flag, Bouquet A813

Boy Writing "Peace" A814

Pact Members' Flags, Dove — A815

Czech and Soviet Arms, Prague and Moscow Views A816

1980, May 6 Perf. 12x11½
2312 A813 50h multi .20 .20
2313 A814 1k multi .20 .20
2314 A815 1k multi .20 .20
2315 A816 1k multi .20 .20
Nos. 2312-2315 (4) .80 .80

Liberation by Soviet army, 35th anniv.; Soviet victory in WWII, 35th anniv.; Signing of Warsaw Pact (Bulgaria, Czechoslovakia, German Democratic Rep., Hungary, Poland, Romania, USSR), 25th anniv.; Czechoslovak-Soviet Treaty of Friendship, Cooperation and Mutual Aid, 10th anniv.

Souvenir Sheet

UN, 35th Anniv. A817

1980, June 3 Engr. Perf. 12
2316 Sheet of 2 3.50 2.75
a. A817 4k multicolored 1.50 1.25

Athletes Parading Banners in Strahov Stadium, Prague, Spartakiad Emblem — A818

Engraved and Photogravure
1980, June 3 Perf. 12x11½
2317 A818 50h shown .20 .20
2318 A818 1k Gymnast, vert. .20 .20

Spartakiad 1980, Prague, June 26-29.

Aechmea Fasciata — A819
A820

1980, Aug. 13 Perf. 12
2319 A819 50h Gerbera Jamesonii .35 .20
2320 A819 1k Aechmea fasciata 1.75 .60
2321 A819 2k Strelitzia reginae .50 .20
2322 A819 4k Paphiopedilum 1.90 .30
Nos. 2319-2322 (4) 4.50 1.30

Olomouc and Bratislava Flower Shows. Nos. 2319-2322 were each issued in sheets of 10. Value, set $70.

1980, Sept. 24 Perf. 11½x12

Designs: Folktale character embroideries.
2323 A820 50h Chad girl .20 .20
2324 A820 1k Punch and dog .20 .20
2325 A820 2k Dandy and Posy .75 .20

2326 A820 4k Lion and moon 1.30 .75
2327 A820 5k Wallachian dance .65 .20
Nos. 2323-2327 (5) 3.10 1.55

National Census A821

1980, Sept. 24 Perf. 12x11½
2328 A821 1k multi .25 .20

Prague Castle Type of 1971

Designs: 3k, Old Palace gateway. 4k, Armorial lion, 16th century.

1980, Oct. 28 Perf. 12
2329 A634 3k multi 1.25 1.10
2330 A634 4k multi 1.00 .65

Nos. 2329-2330 were each issued in sheets of 4. Value, set $18.

Bratislava Type of 1977

3k, View across the Danube, by J. Eder, 1810. 4k, The Old Royal Bridge, by J.A. Lantz, 1820.

1980, Oct. 28
2331 A760 3k multi 1.25 1.10
2332 A760 4k multi .75 .65

Nos. 2331-2332 were each issued in sheets of 4. Value, set $14.

10th Anniversary of Socialist Youth Federation — A822

1980, Nov. 9 Perf. 12x11½
2333 A822 50h multi .20 .20

No. 2137 Overprinted in Red: 3. / MEZINARODNI VELETRH ZNAMEK / ESSEN '80
1980, Nov. 18
2334 A755 1.60k multi 20.00 15.00

Czechoslovak Day/ ESSEN '80, 3rd International Stamp Exhibition, No. 2334 has overprinted red marginal inscription.

Art Type of 1967

Designs: 1k, Pavel Jozef Safarik, by Jozef B. Klemens. 2k, Peasant Revolt mosaic, Anna Podzemna. 3k, St. Lucia, 14th century statue. 4k, Waste Heaps, by Jan Zrzavy, horiz. 5k, Labor, sculpture by Jan Stursa.

1980, Nov. 27 Engr. Perf. 12
2335 A565 1k multi .95 1.10
2336 A565 2k multi 1.10 .95
2337 A565 3k multi .55 .50
2338 A565 4k multi .65 .55
2339 A565 5k multi .65 .55
Nos. 2335-2339 (5) 3.90 3.65

Nos. 2335-2339 were each issued in sheets of 4. Value, set $27.

Stamp Day — A823

Engraved and Photogravure
1980, Dec. 18 Perf. 11½x12
2340 A823 1k multi .25 .20

7th Five-year Plan, 1981-1985 A824

1981, Jan. 1 Perf. 11½
2341 A824 50h multi .20 .20

International Year of the Disabled A825

1981, Feb. 24
2342 A825 1k multi .25 .20

Landau, 1800 A826

1981, Feb. 25 Perf. 12x11½
2343 A826 50h shown .20 .20
2344 A826 1k Mail coach, 1830 .25 .20
2345 A826 3.60k Mail sled, 1840 1.25 .60
2346 A826 5k 4-horse mail coach, 1860 .85 .45
2347 A826 7k Open carriage, 1840 1.25 .85
a. Sheet of 4 13.00 10.00
Nos. 2343-2347 (5) 3.80 2.30

WIPA '81 Intl. Philatelic Exhibition, Vienna, Austria, May 22-31. #2347a issued May 10.

Wolfgang Amadeus Mozart — A827

Famous Men: #2348, Joesph Hlavka (1831-1908). #2349, Juraj Hronec (1881-1959). #2350, Jan Sverma (1901-44). #2351, Mikulas Schneider-Trnavsky (1881-1958). #2352, B. Bolzano (1781-1848). #2353, Dimitri Shostakovich, composer. #2354, George Bernard Shaw, playwright.

1981, Mar. 10 Perf. 11½
2348 A827 50h multi .20 .20
2349 A827 50h multi .20 .20
2350 A827 50h multi .20 .20
2351 A827 50h multi .20 .20
2352 A827 1k multi .75 .35
2353 A827 1k multi .25 .20
2354 A827 1k multi .25 .20
2355 A827 1k multi .25 .20
Nos. 2348-2355 (8) 2.30 1.75

Souvenir Sheet

Yuri Gagarin A828

1981, Apr. 5 Perf. 12
2356 Sheet of 2 3.75 3.00
a. A828 6k multicolored 1.75 1.10

20th anniv. of 1st manned space flight.

Workers and Banner A829

1981, Apr. 6 Perf. 12x11½
2357 A829 50h shown .20 .20
2358 A829 1k Hands holding banner .25 .20

2359 A829 4k Worker holding banner, vert. .35 .25
Nos. 2357-2359 (3) .80 .65
Czechoslovakian Communist Party, 60th anniv.

Congress Emblem, View of Prague — A830

1981, Apr. 6
2360 A830 50h shown .20 .20
2361 A830 1k Bratislava .25 .20
16th Communist Party Congress.

Agriculture Museum, 90th Anniv. A831 — Natl. Assembly Elections A832

1981, May 14 *Perf. 11½x12*
2362 A831 1k multi .25 .20

1981, June 1
2363 A832 50h multi .20 .20

Bratislava Type of 1977
Designs: 3k, Bratislava Castle, by G.B. Probst, 1760. 4k, Grassalkovic Palace, by C. Bschor, 1815.

1981, June 10 *Perf. 12*
2364 A760 3k multi 1.25 1.10
2365 A760 4k multi 1.00 .75
Nos. 2364-2365 were each issued in sheets of 4. Value, set $18.

Uran and Red October Hotels A833

Successes of Socialist Achievements Exhibition: 1k, Brno-Bratislava Highway, Jihlava. 2k, Nuclear power station, Jaslovske Bohunice.

1981, June 10 *Perf. 12x11½*
2366 A833 80h multi .20 .20
2367 A833 1k multi .20 .20
2368 A833 2k multi .20 .20
Nos. 2366-2368 (3) .60 .60

Border Defense Units, 30th Anniv. A834 — Civil Defense, 30th Anniv. A835

Army Cooperation, 30th Anniv. — A836

Rysy Youth Mountain Climbing Contest A837

Engraved and Photogravure
1981, July 11 *Perf. 11½*
2369 A834 40h multi .20 .20
2370 A835 50h multi .20 .20
2371 A836 1k multi .25 .20
2372 A837 3.60k multi .75 .30
Nos. 2369-2372 (4) 1.40 .90

30th Natl. Festival of Amateur Puppet Ensembles — A838

1981, July 2 *Perf. 11½*
2373 A838 2k Punch and Devil .50 .20

Souvenir Sheet

Guernica, by Pablo Picasso — A839

1981, July 2 Engr. *Perf. 11½x12*
2374 A839 10k multi 3.50 2.50
Picasso's birth centenary; 45th anniv. of Intl. Brigades in Spain.

Cat Holding Flower, by Etienne Delessert A840

8th Biennial Exhibition of Children's Book Illustrations (Designs by): 50h, Albin Brunovsky, vert. 1k, Adolf Born. 2k, Vive Tolli. 10k, Suekichi Akaba.

Engraved and Photogravure
1981, Sept. 5 *Perf. 11½*
2375 A840 50h multi .20 .20
2376 A840 1k multi .25 .20
2377 A840 2k multi .40 .20
2378 A840 4k multi .95 .40
2379 A840 10k multi 2.00 .75
Nos. 2375-2379 (5) 3.80 1.75

Prague Zoo, 50th Anniv. — A841

1981, Sept. 28 *Perf. 11½x12*
2380 A841 50h Gorillas .40 .20
2381 A841 1k Lions .75 .20
2382 A841 7k Przewalski's horses 2.10 .80
Nos. 2380-2382 (3) 3.25 1.20

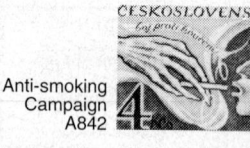

Anti-smoking Campaign A842

1981, Oct. 27 *Perf. 12*
2383 A842 4k multi 1.00 .60
No. 2383 was issued in sheets of 10, containing 8 stamps and 2 labels. Values: single with label attached, $1.50; sheet, $14.

Prague Castle Art Type of 1971
Designs: 3k, Carved dragon, Palais Lobkovitz, 16th cent. 4k, St. Vitus Cathedral, by J. Sember and G. Dobler, 19th cent.

1981, Oct. 28
2384 A634 3k multi .75 .45
2385 A634 4k multi 1.75 1.40
Nos. 2384-2385 were each issued in sheets of 4. Value, set $13.

Art Type of 1967
Designs: 1k, View of Prague, by Vaclav Hollar (1607-1677). 2k, Czechoslovak Academy medallion, engraved by Otakar Spaniel (1881-1955). 3k, Jihoceska Vysivka, by Zdenek Sklenar (b. 1910). 4k, Still Life, by A.M. Gerasimov (1881-1963). 5k, Standing Woman, by Pablo Picasso (1881-1973).

1981, Nov. 27 Engr. *Perf. 12*
2386 A565 1k multi 1.90 1.25
2387 A565 2k multi .50 .25
2388 A565 3k multi .65 .40
2389 A565 4k multi .75 .50
2390 A565 5k multi 1.25 1.00
Nos. 2386-2390 (5) 5.05 3.40
Nos. 2386-2390 were each issued in sheets of 4. Value, set $35.
Sheets of No. 2390 exist with center gutter inscribed with Philexfrance 82 and FIP emblems. Value, $22.

Stamp Day — A843

Engraved and Photogravure
1981, Dec. 18 *Perf. 11½x12*
2391 A843 1k Engraver Edward Karel .25 .20

Russian Workers' Party, Prague Congress, 70th Anniv. — A844

1982, Jan. 18 *Perf. 12*
2392 A844 2k Lenin .50 .20
a. Sheet of 4 5.00 4.00
No. 2392 issued in sheet of 8. Value $5.

1982 World Cup Soccer A845

Designs: Various soccer players.

1982, Jan. 29 *Perf. 12x11½*
2393 A845 1k multi .25 .20
2394 A845 3.60k multi .70 .30
2395 A845 4k multi 1.40 .50
Nos. 2393-2395 (3) 2.35 1.00

10th World Trade Union Congress, Havana — A846 — Arms of Hrob — A847

1982, Feb. 10 *Perf. 11½*
2396 A846 1k multi .25 .20

1982, Feb. 10 *Perf. 12x11½*
Arms of various cities.
2397 A847 50h shown .20 .20
2398 A847 50h Nove Mesto Nad Metuji .20 .20
2399 A847 50h Trencin .20 .20
2400 A847 50h Mlada Boleslav .20 .20
Nos. 2397-2400 (4) .80 .80
See Nos. 2499-2502, 2542-2544, 2595-2597, 2783-2786.

50th Anniv. of the Great Strike at Most — A848

1982, Mar. 23 *Perf. 11½*
2401 A848 1k multi .25 .20

60th Intl. Railway Union Congress — A849

1982, Mar. 23 *Perf. 12x11½*
2402 A849 6k Steam locomotive, 1922, electric, 1982 2.50 .75

10th Workers' Congress, Prague A850 — George Dimitrov A851

1982, Apr. 15
2403 A850 1k multi .25 .20

1982, May 1
2404 A851 50h multi .20 .20

A852 — 10th Lidice Intl. Children's Drawing Contest — A853

Engravings: 40h, The Muse Euterpe Playing a Flute, by Crispin de Passe (1565-1637). 50h, The Lute Player, by Jacob de Gheyn (1565-1629). 1k, Woman Flautist, by Adriaen Collaert (1560-1618). 2k, Musicians in a Hostel, by Rembrandt (1606-1669). 3k, Hurdygurdy Player, by Jacques Callot (1594-1635).

1982, May 18   **Perf. 11½x12**

2405	A852	40h multi	.20	.20
2406	A852	50h multi	.20	.20
2407	A852	1k multi	.20	.20
2408	A852	2k multi	.30	.20
2409	A852	3k multi	1.10	.60
	Nos. 2405-2409 (5)		2.00	1.40

1982, May 18

2410	A853	2k multi	1.25	1.00

Issued in sheets of 6. Value $10.

40th Anniv. of
Destruction of
Lidice and
Lezaky — A854

1982, June 4   **Perf. 11½**

2411	A854	1k Girl, rose	.45	.20
2412	A854	1k Hands, barbed wire	.45	.20

Souvenir Sheet

UN Disarmament Conference — A855

1982, June 4   **Perf. 12**

2413		Sheet of 2	12.00	8.00
a.	A855 6k Woman holding doves		5.00	3.50

Souvenir Sheet

2nd UN Conference on Peaceful Uses
of Outer Space, Vienna, Aug. 9-
21 — A856

1982, Aug. 9   **Engr. & Photo.**

2414		Sheet of 2	12.00	9.00
a.	A856 5k multi		5.00	3.50

Krivoklat
Castle
A857

1982, Aug. 31   **Perf. 12x11½**

2415	A857	50h shown	.25	.20
2416	A857	1k Statues (Krivoklat)	.25	.20
2417	A857	2k Nitra Castle	.30	.20
2418	A857	3k Pottery, lock (Nitra)	.40	.35
a.	Souv. sheet of 4, #2415-2418		1.60	1.25
	Nos. 2415-2418 (4)		1.20	.95

50th Anniv. of Zizkov
Hill Natl.
Monument — A858

1982, Sept. 16

2419	A858	1k multi	.25	.20

Prague Castle Art Type of 1971

Designs: 3k, St. George and the Dragon,
1373. 4k, Tomb of King Vratislav I, 10th cent.

1982, Sept. 28   **Perf. 12**

2420	A634	3k multi	1.40	1.00
2421	A634	4k multi	.75	.75

Nos. 2420-2421 were each issued in sheets
of 4. Value, set $13.

Bratislava Type of 1977

Designs: 3k, Paddle steamer, Parnik, 1818.
4k, View from Bridge, 19th cent.

1982, Sept. 29

2422	A760	3k multi	1.40	1.00
2423	A760	4k multi	1.10	1.00

Nos. 2422-2423 were each issued in sheets
of 4. Value, set $18.

European Danube
Commission — A859

1982, Sept. 29   **Perf. 11½x12**

2424	A859	3k Steamer, Bratislava Bridge	.75	.35
a.	Souvenir sheet of 4		5.00	4.00
2425	A859	3.60k Ferry, Budapest	.95	.50
a.	Souvenir sheet of 4		7.00	6.00

16th Communist Party
Congress — A860

1982, Oct. 28   **Perf. 12x11½**

2426	A860	20h Agriculture	.20	.20
2427	A860	1k Industry	.20	.20
2428	A860	3k Engineering	.35	.35
	Nos. 2426-2428 (3)		.75	.75

30th Anniv. of
Academy of
Sciences — A861

1982, Oct. 29   **Perf. 11½**

2429	A861	6k Emblem	.90	.35

65th Anniv. of October
Revolution — A862

Design: 1k, 60th anniv. of USSR.

1982, Nov. 7   **Perf. 12x11½**

2430	A862	50h multi	.20	.20
2431	A862	1k multi	.25	.20

Jaroslav Hasek,
Writer, Sculpture by
Josef
Malejovsky — A863

Sculptures: 2k, Jan Zrzavy, freedom fighter,
by Jan Simota. 4.40k, Leos Janacek, composer, by Milos Axman. 6k, Martin Kukucin,
freedom fighter, by Jan Kulich. 7k, Peaceful
Work, by Rudolf Pribis.

Engraved and Photogravure

1982, Nov. 26   **Perf. 11½x12**

2432	A863	1k multi	.20	.20
2433	A863	2k multi	.25	.20
2434	A863	4.40k multi	.85	.20
2435	A863	6k multi	1.20	.30
2436	A863	7k multi	1.50	.75
	Nos. 2432-2436 (5)		4.00	1.65

Nos. 2432-2436 were each issued in sheets
of 4. Value, set $30.

Art Type of 1967

1k, Revolution in Spain, by Josef Sima
(1891-1971). 2k, Woman Dressing, by Rudolf
Kremlicka (1886-1932). 3k, The Girl Bride, by
Dezider Milly (1906-1971). 4k, Performers, by
Jan Zelibsky (b. 1907). 5k, The Complaint of
the Birds, by Emil Filla (1882-1953).

1982, Nov. 27   **Perf. 12**

2437	A565	1k multi	.70	.40
2438	A565	2k multi	1.40	1.10
2439	A565	3k multi	.75	.75
2440	A565	4k multi	.75	.75
2441	A565	5k multi	1.40	1.10
	Nos. 2437-2441 (5)		5.00	4.10

Stamp Day — A864

1982, Dec. 8   **Perf. 11½**

2442	A864	1k Engraver Jaroslav Goldschmied (1890-1977)	.25	.20

A865   A866

1983, Jan. 10   **Engr.**   **Perf. 12x11½**

2443	A865	50h dark blue	.20	.20

Pres. Gustav Husak, 70th birthday. See No.
2686.

1983, Feb. 24   **Engr. & Photo.**

Designs: 50h, Jaroslav Hasek (1882-1923),
writer. 1k, Julius Fucik (1903-1943), antifascist
martyr. 2k, Martin Luther (1483-1546). 5k,
Johannes Brahms (1833-1897), composer.

2444	A866	50h multi	.20	.20
2445	A866	1k multi	.20	.20
2446	A866	2k multi	.25	.20
a.	Souvenir sheet of 4		20.00	10.00
2447	A866	5k multi	.85	.20
	Nos. 2444-2447 (4)		1.50	.80

Nordposta '83 Intl. Stamp Exhibition,
Hamburg.
No. 2446a issued Nov. 1.

Workers
Marching
A867

Family — A868

1983, Feb. 25   **Perf. 11½**

2448	A867	50h multi	.20	.20
2449	A868	1k multi	.25	.20

35th anniv. of "Victorious February" (50h),
and Natl. Front (1k).

World
Communications
Year — A869

Perf. 11½, 12x11½ (2k)

1983, Mar. 16

2450	A869	40h multi	.20	.20
2451	A869	1k multi	.20	.20
2452	A869	2k multi	.30	.20
2453	A869	3.60k multi	.60	.20
	Nos. 2450-2453 (4)		1.30	.80

Various wave patterns. 2k, 40x23mm; 3.60k,
49x19mm.

7th World Ski-
jumping
Championships
A870

1983, Mar. 16   **Perf. 11½**

2454	A870	1k multi	.25	.20

Souvenir Sheet

5th Anniv. of Czechoslovak-USSR
Intercosmos Cooperative Space
Program — A871

1983, Apr. 12   **Perf. 12**

2455		Sheet of 2	11.00	6.00
a.	A871 10k multi		4.75	2.50

See No. 2226.

Protected Species — A872

1983, Apr. 28   **Perf. 12x11½**

2456	A872	50h Butterfly, violets	.30	.20
2457	A872	1k Water lilies, frog	.65	.20
2458	A872	2k Pine cones, crossbill	.65	.30
2459	A872	3.60k Herons	.80	.35
2460	A872	5k Gentians, lynx	1.10	.45
2461	A872	7k Stag	2.50	1.00
	Nos. 2456-2461 (6)		6.00	2.50

A873   A874

Soviet Marshals.

1983, May 5   **Perf. 11½**

2462	A873	50h Ivan S. Konev	.20	.20
2463	A873	1k Andrei I. Sheremenko	.20	.20
2464	A873	2k Rodion J. Malinovsky	.25	.20
	Nos. 2462-2464 (3)		.65	.60

30th anniv. of Czechoslovak-Soviet defense
treaty.

1983, July 13 — **Perf. 12**
2465 A874 2k multi .40 .25
  a. Souvenir sheet of 4 6.00 5.00
World Peace and Life Congress, Prague.
No. 2465 issued in sheets of 8. Value $10.

Emperor Rudolf II by Adrian De Vries (1560-1626) A875

Art treasures of the Prague Castle: 5k, Kinetic relief, Timepiece, Rudolf Svoboda.

1983, Aug. 25 — **Perf. 11½**
2466 A875 4k multi .90 .60
2467 A875 5k multi .90 .60
Nos. 2466-2467 were each issued in sheets of 6. Value, set $15.
See Nos. 2518-2519, 2610-2611, 2654-2655, 2717-2718, 2744-2745, 2792-2793.

9th Biennial of Illustrations for Children and Youth — A876

Illustrators: 50h, Oleg K. Zotov, USSR. 1k, Zbigniew Rychlicki, Poland. 4k, Lisbeth Zwerger, Austria. 7k, Antonio Dominques, Angola.

1983, Sept. 9 — **Engr. & Photo.**
2468 A876 50h multi .20 .20
2469 A876 1k multi .20 .20
2470 A876 4k multi .35 .20
2471 A876 7k multi .75 .30
  a. Souv. sheet of 4, #2468-2471 5.00 3.00
Nos. 2468-2471 (4) 1.50 .90

World Communications Year — A877

Emblems and aircraft.

1983, Sept. 30 — **Perf. 11½**
2472 A877 50h red & black .20 .20
2473 A877 1k red & black, vert. .20 .20
2474 A877 4k red & black .75 .25
Nos. 2472-2474 (3) 1.15 .65
60th anniv. of the Czechoslovak Airlines.

16th Party Congress Achievements — A878

1983, Oct. 20 — **Perf. 12x11½**
2475 A878 50h Civil engineering construction .20 .20
2476 A878 1k Chemical industry .20 .20
2477 A878 3k Health services .40 .20
Nos. 2475-2477 (3) .80 .60

Bratislava Type of 1977
Designs: 3k, Two sculptures, Viktor Tilgner (1844-96). 4k, Mirbachov Palace, 1939, by Julius Schubert (1888-1947).

1983, Oct. 28 — **Perf. 12**
2478 A760 3k multi 1.25 1.00
2479 A760 4k multi 1.00 .80
Nos. 2478-2479 were each issued in sheets of 4 stamps. Value, set $16.

Natl. Theater, Prague, Centenary — A879

1983, Nov. 8 — **Engr.** — **Perf. 11½**
2480 A879 50h Natl. Theater building .20 .20
2481 A879 2k State Theater, Natl. Theater .30 .20

Messenger of Mourning, by Mikolas Ales — A880

Designs: 2k, Genius, theater curtain by Vojtech Hynais (1854-1925). 3k, Music, Lyric drawings by Frantisek Zenisek (1849-1916). 4k, Symbolic figure of Prague, by Vaclav Brozik (1851-1901). 5k, Hradcany Castle, by Julius Marak (1832-1899).

1983, Nov. 18 — **Engr.**
2482 A880 1k multi 1.20 .75
2483 A880 2k multi 1.50 1.10
2484 A880 3k multi .90 .45
2485 A880 4k multi 1.40 .45
2486 A880 5k multi 1.10 .60
Nos. 2482-2486 (5) 6.10 3.35
Nos. 2482-2486 were each issued in sheets of 4 stamps. Value, set $35.

Warrior with Sword and Shield, Engraving, 17th Cent. — A881

Engravings of Costumes: 50h, Bodyguard of Rudolf II, by Jacob de Gheyn (1565-1629). 1k, Lady with Lace Collar, by Jacques Callot (1592-1635). 4k, Lady, by Vaclav Hollar (1607-77). 5k, Man, by Antoine Watteau (1684-1721).

Engraved and Photogravure
1983, Dec. 2 — **Perf. 11½x12**
2487 A881 40h multi .20 .20
2488 A881 50h multi .20 .20
2489 A881 1k multi .20 .20
2490 A881 4k multi .75 .20
2491 A881 5k multi 1.25 .75
Nos. 2487-2491 (5) 2.60 1.55

Stamp Day — A882

1983, Dec. 18
2492 A882 1k Karl Seizinger (1889-1978), #114 .25 .20

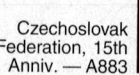

Czechoslovak Federation, 15th Anniv. — A883

1984, Jan. 1 — **Perf. 11½**
2493 A883 50h Bratislava, Prague Castles .20 .20

35th Anniv. of COMECON A884

1984, Jan. 23
2494 A884 1k Headquarters, Moscow .25 .20

1984 Winter Olympics A885

1984, Feb. 7 — **Perf. 12x11½**
2495 A885 2k Cross-country skiing .30 .20
2496 A885 3k Hockey .35 .20
  a. Souvenir sheet of 4 3.75 3.00
2497 A885 5k Biathlon 1.00 .35
Nos. 2495-2497 (3) 1.65 .75

Intl. Olympic Committee, 90th Anniv. — A886

1984, Feb. 7 — **Perf. 11½x12**
2498 A886 7k Rings, runners, torch 1.25 .35

City Arms Type of 1982
1984, Mar. 1 — **Perf. 12x11½**
2499 A847 50h Kutna Hora .20 .20
2500 A847 50h Turnov .20 .20
2501 A847 1k Martin .25 .20
2502 A847 1k Milevsko .25 .20
Nos. 2499-2502 (4) .90 .80

Intercosmos Space Program — A887

Various satellites. Nos. 2503-2507 se-tenant with labels showing flags.

1984, Apr. 12 — **Perf. 11½x12**
2503 A887 50h multi .20 .20
2504 A887 1k multi .20 .20
2505 A887 2k multi .35 .20
2506 A887 4k multi .75 .40
2507 A887 5k multi 1.40 .50
Nos. 2503-2507 (5) 2.90 1.50

Resistance Heroes — A888

Designs: 50h, Vendelin Opatrny (1908-44). 1k, Ladislav Novomesky (1904-44). 2k, Rudolf Jasiok (1919-44). 4k, Jan Nalepka (1912-43).

1984, May 9 — **Perf. 11x11½**
2508 A888 50h multi .20 .20
2509 A888 1k multi .20 .20
2510 A888 2k multi .30 .20
2511 A888 4k multi .50 .20
Nos. 2508-2511 (4) 1.20 .80

Music Year — A889

1984, May 11 — **Perf. 11½**
2512 A889 50h Instruments .20 .20
2513 A889 1k Organ pipes, vert. .30 .20

Bratislava Type of 1977
Designs: 3k, Vintners' Guild arms, 19th cent. 4k, View of Bratislava (painting commemorating shooting competition, 1827).

1984, June 1 — **Perf. 12**
2514 A760 3k multi 1.00 .75
2515 A760 4k multi 1.50 1.00
Nos. 2514-2515 were each issued in sheets of 4 stamps. Value, set $15.

Central Telecommunications Building, Bratislava — A890

1984, June 1 — **Perf. 11½**
2516 A890 2k multi .35 .20

A891   A893

1984, June 12 — **Perf. 12**
2517 A891 5k UPU emblem, dove, globe 2.50 2.00
1984 UPU Congress. Issued in sheet of 4 with and without Philatelic Salon text. Values, $40 with text, $12 without text.

Prague Castle Type of 1983
Designs: 3k, Crowing rooster, St. Vitus Cathedral, 19th cent. 4k, King David from the Roundnice, Book of Psalms illuminated manuscript, Bohemia, 15th cent.

1984, Aug. 9 — **Engr. & Photo.**
2518 A875 3k multi .65 .40
2519 A875 4k multi .90 .65
Nos. 2518-2519 were each issued in sheets of 4 stamps. Value, set $18.

1984, Aug. 28 — **Perf. 11½x12**
Playing cards.
2520 A893 50h Jack of Spades, 16th cent. .20 .20
2521 A893 1k Queen of spades, 17th cent. .20 .20
2522 A893 2k 9 of hearts, 18th cent. .25 .20
2523 A893 3k Jack of clubs, 18th cent. .35 .20
2524 A893 5k King of hearts, 19th cent. 1.00 .20
Nos. 2520-2524 (5) 2.00 1.00

Slovak Natl. Uprising, 40th Anniv. A894

1984, Aug. 29   **Perf. 12x11½**
2525 A894 50h Family, factories, flowers   .20 .20

Battle of Dukla Pass (Carpathians), 40th Anniv. — A895

1984, Sept. 8   **Perf. 11½x12**
2526 A895 2k Soldiers, flag   .40 .20

1984 Summer Olympics A896

1984, Sept. 9   **Perf. 12x11½**
2527 A896 1k Pole vault   .20 .20
2528 A896 2k Bicycling   .40 .20
2529 A896 3k Rowing   .60 .35
2530 A896 5k Weight lifting   1.00 .45
a.   Souv. sheet of 4, #2527-2530   3.00 2.00
       Nos. 2527-2530 (4)   2.20 1.20

16th Party Congress Goals and Projects — A897

1984, Oct. 28   **Perf. 12x11½**
2531 A897 1k Communications   .20 .20
2532 A897 2k Transportation   .25 .20
2533 A897 3k Transgas pipeline   .35 .25
a.   Souvenir sheet of 3   1.50 1.00
       Nos. 2531-2533 (3)   .80 .65

Art Type of 1967

1k, The Milevsky River, by Karel Stehlik (b. 1912). 2k, Under the Trees, by Viktor Barvitius (1834-1902). 3k, Landscape with Flowers, by Zolo Palugyay (1898-1935). 4k, King in Palace, Visehrad Codex miniature, 1085. 5k, View of Kokorin Castles, by Antonin Manes. #2534-2537 horiz.; issued in sheets of 4.

1984, Nov. 16   **Perf. 11½**
2534 A565 1k multi   2.50 .75
2535 A565 2k multi   2.50 .75
2536 A565 3k multi   1.80 .45
2537 A565 4k multi   2.50 .60
2538 A565 5k multi   2.50 .60
       Nos. 2534-2538 (5)   11.80 3.15
Nos. 2534-2538 were each issued in sheets of 4 stamps. Value, set $60.

Students' Intl., 45th Anniv. A898

Birth Cent., Antonin Zapotocky A899

1984, Nov. 17
2539 A898 1k Head, dove   .25 .20

Engr. & Photo.
1984, Dec. 18   **Perf. 11½**
2540 A899 50h multi   .25 .20

Stamp Day — A900

1984, Dec. 18   **Perf. 11½x12**
2541 A900 1k Engraver Bohumil Heinz (1894-1940)   .25 .20

City Arms Type of 1982

1985, Feb. 5   **Perf. 12x11½**
2542 A847 50h Kamyk nad Vltavou   .20 .20
2543 A847 50h Havirov   .20 .20
2544 A847 50h Trnava   .20 .20
       Nos. 2542-2544 (3)   .60 .60

University of Applied Arts, Prague, Centenary — A901

1985, Feb. 6   **Perf. 11½x12**
2545 A901 3k Art and Pleasure, sculpture   .40 .20

Trnava University, 350th Anniv. — A902

1985, Feb. 6   **Perf. 11½x12**
2546 A902 2k Town of Trnava   .40 .20

Military Museum Exposition — A903

1985, Feb. 7 Perf. 11½x12, 12x11½
2547 A903 50h Armor, crossbow, vert.   .20 .20
2548 A903 1k Medals, vert.   .20 .20
2549 A903 2k Biplane, spacecraft   .40 .20
       Nos. 2547-2549 (3)   .80 .60

Vladimir I. Lenin (1870-1924), 1st Chairman of Russia — A904

1985, Mar. 15 Engr.   Perf. 12
2550 A904 2k multi   .60 .30
       No. 2550 printed in sheets of 6 stamps. Value $5.

UN 40th Anniv., Peace Year 1986 A905

1985, Mar. 15
2551 A905 6k UN, Peace Year emblems   2.25 1.75
Issued in sheets of 4 stamps. Value $12.

A906   A907

Engraved and Photogravure
1985, Apr. 5   **Perf. 11½**
2552 A906 4k Natl. arms, twig, crowd   .60 .20
       Kosice govt. plan, Apr. 5, 1945.

1985, Apr. 5
2553 A907 50h Natl. arms, flag, soldiers   .20 .20
       Natl. Security Forces, 40th anniv.

Halley's Comet, INTERCOSMOS Project Vega — A908

Design: Emblem, space platform, interstellar map, intercept data.

1985, Apr. 12   **Perf. 12x11½**
2554   Sheet of 2   12.00 8.00
a.   A908 5k multicolored   3.50 2.25
       Project Vega, a joint effort of the USSR, France, German Democratic Republic, Austria, Poland, Bulgaria and CSSR, was for the geophysical study of Halley's Comet, Dec. 1984-Mar. 1986.

European Ice Hockey Championships, Prague, Apr. 17-May 3 — A909

1985, Apr. 13
2555 A909 1k Hockey players, emblem   .25 .20

No. 2555 Ovptd. "CSSR MISTREM SVETA" in Violet Blue
1985, May 31   **Perf. 12x11½**
2556 A909 1k multi   2.50 2.50

Natl. Chess Org., 80th Anniv. — A910

1985, Apr. 13   **Perf. 11½**
2557 A910 6k Emblem, game board, chessmen   .90 .50

Anniversaries — A911

1985, May 5   **Perf. 11½x12**
2558 A911 1k May Uprising, 1945   .20 .20
2559 A911 1k Soviet Army in CSSR, 1945   .20 .20
2560 A911 1k Warsaw Treaty, 1950   .20 .20
2561 A911 1k Czech-Soviet Treaty, 1970   .20 .20
       Nos. 2558-2561 (4)   .80 .80

Spartakiad '85, Strahov Stadium, Prague, June 27 — A912

Designs: 50h, Gymnasts warming up with rackets and balls. 1k, Rhythmic gymnastics floor exercise, Prague Castle.

1985, June 3 Perf. 11½, 11½x12
2562 A912 50h multi   .20 .20

Size: 53x22mm
2563 A912 1k multi   .20 .20

WWII Anti-Fascist Political Art — A913

Drawings and caricatures: 50h, Fire, and From the Concentration Camp, by Joseph Capek (1887-1945). 2k, The Conference on Disarmament in Geneva, 1927 and The Prophecy of Three Parrots, 1933, by Frantisek Bidlo (1895-1945). 4k, The Unknown Warrior to Order, 1936, and The Almost Peaceful Dove, 1937, by Antonin Pelc (1895-1967).

1985, June 4   **Perf. 12x11½**
2564 A913 50h multi   .20 .20
2565 A913 2k multi   .30 .20
2566 A913 4k multi   .60 .40
       Nos. 2564-2566 (3)   1.10 .80

Helsinki Conference on European Security and Cooperation, 10th Anniv. — A914

1985, July 1   Engr. & Photo.
2567 A914 7k multi   2.25 1.50
a.   Souvenir sheet of 4   12.00 8.00
       An imperf. souv. sheet similar to No. 2567a was issued June 1, 1988 for FINLANDIA '88 and PRAGA '88. Value $40.

12th World Youth Festival, Moscow A915

1985, July 2
2568 A915 1k Kremlin, youths   .20 .20

A916

A918

1985, Sept. 3   **Perf. 11½**
2569 A916 50h multi   .20 .20
       Federation of World Trade Unions, 40th anniv.

Bratislava Type of 1977

Designs: 3k, Castle and river, lace embroidery by Elena Holeczyova (1906-1983). 4k, Pottery cups and mugs, 1600-1500 B.C.

1985, Sept. 4   **Engr.**   **Perf. 12**
2570 A760 3k multi   1.40 .45
2571 A760 4k multi   2.10 .60

Nos. 2570-2571 were each issued in sheets of 4 stamps. Value, set $15.

Engraved and Photogravure
1985, Sept. 5   **Perf. 11½**

Children's book illustrations: 1k, Rocking Horse, by Kveta Pacovska, USSR. 2k, Fairies, by Gennadij Spirin, USSR. 3k, Butterfly and Girl, by Kaarina Kaila, Finland. 4k, Boy and Animals, by Erick Ingraham, US.

2572 A918 1k multi   .20 .20
2573 A918 2k multi   .30 .20
2574 A918 3k multi   .45 .25
2575 A918 4k multi   .60 .35
a.   Souv. sheet of 4, #2572-2575   4.00 3.00
    Nos. 2572-2575 (4)   1.55 1.00

10th biennial of illustrations.

5-Year Development Plan — A919

1985, Oct. 28   **Perf. 12x11½**
2576 A919 50h Construction machinery   .20 .20
2577 A919 1k Prague subway, map   .20 .20
2578 A919 2k Modern textile spinning   .20 .20
    Nos. 2576-2578 (3)   .60 .60

16th Communist Party Congress goals.

Prague Castle — A920   A921

Engr., Engr. & Photo. (3k)
1985, Oct. 28   **Perf. 12**
2579 A920 2k Presidential Palace Gate, 1768   .40 .40
2580 A920 3k St. Vitus' Cathedral   .50 .50

Nos. 2579-2580 were each issued in sheets of 6 stamps. Value, set $9.

Engraved and Photogravure
1985, Nov. 23   **Perf. 11½x12**

Glassware: 50h, Pitcher, Near East, 4th cent. 1k, Venetian pitcher, 16th cent. 2k, Bohemian goblet, c. 1720. 4k, Harrachov Bohemian vase, 18th cent. 6k, Jablonec Bohemian vase, c. 1900.

2581 A921 50h multi   .20 .20
2582 A921 1k multi   .20 .20
2583 A921 2k multi   .25 .20
2584 A921 4k multi   .40 .20
2585 A921 6k multi   .70 .35
    Nos. 2581-2585 (5)   1.75 1.15

Arts and Crafts Museum, Prague, cent.

Art Type of 1967

Designs: 1k, Young Woman in a Blue Gown, by Jozef Ginovsky (1800-1857). 2k, Lenin on the Charles Bridge, Prague, 1952, by Martin Sladky (b. 1920). 3k, Avenue of Poplars, 1935, by Vaclav Rabas (1885-1954). 4k, The Martyrom of St. Dorothea, 1516, by Hans Baldung Grien (c. 1484-1545). 5k, Portrait of Jasper Schade van Westrum, 1645, by Frans Hals (c. 1581-1666).

1985, Nov. 27   **Engr.**   **Perf. 12**
2586 A565 1k multi   1.60 .80
2587 A565 2k multi   1.10 .35
2588 A565 3k multi   1.50 .35

2589 A565 4k multi   .90 .50
2590 A565 5k multi   .90 .50
    Nos. 2586-2590 (5)   6.00 2.50

Nos. 2586-2590 were each issued in sheets of 4 stamps. Value, set $30.

Bohdan Roule (1921-1960), Engraver — A922

Engraved and Photogravure
1985, Dec. 18   **Perf. 11½x12**
2591 A922 1k multicolored   .25 .20

Stamp Day 1985.

Intl. Peace Year — A923

1986, Jan. 2
2592 A923 1k multi   .25 .20

Philharmonic Orchestra, 90th Anniv. — A924

EXPO '86, Vancouver A925

1986, Jan. 2   **Perf. 11½**
2593 A924 1k Victory Statue, Prague   .25 .20

1986, Jan. 23   **Perf. 11½**
Design: Z 50 LS monoplane, Cenyerth Prague-Kladno locomotive, Sahara Desert rock drawing, 5th-6th cent. B.C.
2594 A925 4k multicolored   .75 .20

City Arms Type of 1982
1986, Feb. 10   **Perf. 12x11½**
Size: 42x54mm
2595 A847 50h Myjava   .20 .20
2596 A847 50h Vodnany   .20 .20
2597 A847 50h Zamberk   .20 .20
    Nos. 2595-2597 (3)   .60 .60

17th Natl. Communist Party Congress, Prague, Mar. 24 — A926

1986, Mar. 20   **Perf. 11½**
2598 A926 50h shown   .20 .20
2599 A926 1k Industry   .20 .20

Natl. Communist Party, 65th Anniv. — A927

1986, Mar. 20   **Perf. 12x11½**
2600 A927 50h Star, man, woman   .20 .20
2601 A927 1k Hammer, sickle, laborers   .20 .20

Natl. Front Election Program A928

1986, Mar. 28
2602 A928 50h multi   .20 .20

Karlovy Vary Intl. Film Festival, 25th Anniv. — A929

1986, Apr. 3   **Perf. 11½**
2603 A929 1k multi   .25 .20

A930

A931

1986, Apr. 8   **Engr. & Photo.**
2604 A930 1k multi   .25 .20

Spring of Prague Music Festival.

1986, Apr. 25
2605 A931 50h multi   .40 .20

Prague-Moscow air service, 50th anniv.

Intl. Olympic Committee, 90th Anniv. — A932

1986, May 12   **Perf. 11½x12**
2606 A932 2k multi   .30 .20

1986 World Cup Soccer Championships, Mexico — A933

1986, May 15   **Perf. 12x11½**
2607 A933 4k multi   .60 .40

Women's World Volleyball Championships, Prague — A934

1986, May 19
2608 A934 1k multi   .25 .20

Souvenir Sheet

Intl. Philatelic Federation, FIP, 60th Anniv. — A935

1986, June 3   **Engr.**   **Perf. 12**
2609 A935 20k multi   6.00 5.00

Exists imperf and with perforations between stamps omitted. Values, $12 and $25, respectively.

Prague Castle Type of 1983

Designs: 2k, Jewelled funerary pendant, 9th cent. 3k, Allegory of Blossoms, sculpture by Jaroslav Horejc (1886-1983), St. Vitus' Cathedral.

1986, June 6   **Engr.**   **Perf. 12**
2610 A875 2k multi   .30 .30
2611 A875 3k multi   .70 .45

Nos. 2610-2611 were each issued in sheets of 6 stamps. Value, set $10.

UN Child Survival Campaign — A937

Toys.

Engraved and Photogravure
1986, Sept. 1   **Perf. 11½**
2612 A937 10h Rooster   .20 .20
2613 A937 20h Horse and rider   .20 .20
2614 A937 1k Doll   .25 .20
2615 A937 2k Doll, diff.   .50 .20
2616 A937 3k Tin omnibus, c. 1910   .65 .30
    Nos. 2612-2616 (5)   1.80 1.10

UNICEF, 40th anniv.

Registration, Cent. — A938

1986, Sept. 2   **Perf. 11½x12**
2617 A938 4k Label, mail coach   .45 .20

Bratislava Type of 1977
1986, Sept. 11   **Engr.**   **Perf. 12**
2618 A760 3k Sigismund Gate   1.00 .60
2619 A760 4k St. Margaret, bas-relief   1.00 .50

Nos. 2618-2619 were each issued in sheets of 4 stamps. Value, set $12.

Owls — A939

Engraved and Photogravure
1986, Sept. 18   **Perf. 11½**

2620	A939	50h Bubo bubo	.70	.20
2621	A939	2k Asio otus	.85	.30
2622	A939	3k Strix aluco	1.40	.30
2623	A939	4k Tyto alba	1.40	.40
2624	A939	5k Asio flammeus	2.00	6.00
		Nos. 2620-2624 (5)	6.35	7.20

Souvenir Sheet

Intl. Brigades in Spain — A940

Theater curtain: Woman Savaged by Horses, 1936, by Vladimir Sychra (1903-1963), Natl Gallery, Prague.

1986, Oct. 1   **Engr.**   **Perf. 12**

2625		Sheet of 2	4.50	3.50
	a.	A940 5k multi	2.00	1.25

Locomotives and Streetcars — A941

Engraved and Photogravure
1986, Oct. 6   **Perf. 12x11½**

2626	A941	50h KT-8	.20	.20
2627	A941	1k E458.1	.20	.20
2628	A941	3k T466.2	.75	.30
2629	A941	5k M152.0	.80	.20
		Nos. 2626-2629 (4)	1.95	.90

Paintings in the Prague and Bratislava Natl. Galleries — A942

Designs: 1k, The Circus Rider, 1980, by Jan Bauch (b. 1898). 2k, The Ventriloquist, 1954, by Frantisek Tichy (1896-1961). 3k, In the Circus, 1946, by Vincent Hloznik (b. 1919). 6k, Clown, 1985, by Karel Svolinsky (1896-1986).

1986, Oct. 13   **Engr.**   **Perf. 12**

2630	A942	1k multi	1.00	.50
2631	A942	2k multi	1.25	.65
2632	A942	3k multi	1.25	.65
2633	A942	6k multi	1.50	.75
		Nos. 2630-2633 (4)	5.00	2.55

Nos. 2630-2633 were each issued in sheets of 4 stamps. Value, set $30.

Art Type of 1967

1k, The Czech Lion, May 1918, by Vratislav H. Brunner (1886-1928). 2k, Boy with Mandolin, 1945, by Jozef Sturdik (b. 1920). 3k, Metra Building, 1984, by Frantisek Gross (1909-1985). 4k, Portrait of Maria Maximiliana at Sternberk, 1665, by Karel Skreta (1610-1674). 5k, Adam & Eve, 1538, by Lucas Cranach (1472-1553).

1986, Nov. 3   **Engr.**   **Perf. 12**

2634	A565	1k multi	3.00	2.25
2635	A565	2k multi	3.00	2.25
2636	A565	3k multi	3.00	2.25
2637	A565	4k multi	3.00	2.25
2638	A565	5k multi	3.00	2.25
		Nos. 2634-2638 (5)	15.00	11.25

Nos. 2634-2638 were each issued in sheets of 4 stamps. Value, set $100.

Stamp Day — A943

Design: V.H. Brunner (1886-1928), stamp designer, and No. 88.

Photo. & Engr.
1986, Dec. 18   **Perf. 11½x12**

2639	A943	1k multicolored	.25	.20

World Cyclocross Championships, Jan. 24-25, Central Bohemia — A944

1987, Jan. 22   **Perf. 11½**

2640	A944	6k multi	.80	.20

Czechoslovakian Bowling Union, 50th Anniv. — A945

1987, Jan. 22   **Perf. 11½**

2641	A945	2k multi	.35	.20

State Decorations — A946

Designs: 50h, Gold Stars of Socialist Labor and Czechoslovakia. 2k, Order of Klement Gottwald. 3k, Order of the Republic. 4k, Order of Victorious February. 5k, Order of Labor.

1987, Feb. 4   **Perf. 12x11½**

2642	A946	50h multi	.20	.20
2643	A946	2k multi	.25	.20
2644	A946	3k multi	.30	.20
2645	A946	4k multi	.45	.20
2646	A946	5k multi	.60	.40
		Nos. 2642-2646 (5)	1.80	1.20

Butterflies — A947

1987, Mar. 4

2647	A947	1k Limenitis populi	.70	.20
2648	A947	2k Smerinthus ocellatus	1.10	.25
2649	A947	3k Pericallia matronula	1.40	.40
2650	A947	4k Saturnia pyri	1.40	.40
		Nos. 2647-2650 (4)	4.60	1.25

Natl. Nuclear Power Industry A948

1987, Apr. 6

2651	A948	5k multi	.50	.20

11th Revolutionary Trade Union Movement Congress, Apr. 14-17, Prague — A949

1987, Apr. 7   **Perf. 11½**

2652	A949	1k multi	.20	.20

Souvenir Sheet

INTERCOSMOS, 20th Anniv. — A950

Cosmonauts Alexei Gubarev of the USSR & Vladimir Remek of Czechoslovakia, rocket & emblem.

1987, Apr. 12   **Engr.**   **Perf. 12**

2653		Sheet of 2	6.00	4.50
	a.	A950 10k multi	2.50	2.00
	b.	Souv. sheet of 4, litho. & engr., imperf.	8.00	8.00

No. 2653b issued Nov. 15, 1987.

Prague Castle Art Treasures Type of 1983

Designs: 2k, Three Saints, stained-glass window detail, c. 1870, St. Vitus Cathedral, by Frantisek Sequens (1830-1896). 3k, Coat of Arms, New Land Rolls Hall, 1605.

1987, May 9   **Perf. 11½**

2654	A875	2k multi	.40	.30
2655	A875	3k dk red, slate gray & yel org	.60	.45

Nos. 2634-2638 were each issued in sheets of 6 stamps. Value, set $9.

PRAGA '88 A951

Photo. & Engr.
1987, May 12   **Perf. 12x11½**

2656	A951	3k Telephone, 1894	.75	.20
2657	A951	3k Postal van, 1924	.75	.30
2658	A951	4k Locomotive tender, 1907	.75	.30
2659	A951	4k Tram, 1900	.75	.30
2660	A951	5k Steam roller, 1936	.75	.30
		Nos. 2656-2660 (5)	3.75	1.40

Printed in sheets of 8 + 2 labels picturing telephone or vehicles. Value $40.
Nos. 2657-2658 were also printed in sheets of 4 + label picturing vehicles. Value, $30 for both sheets.

Destruction of Lidice and Lezaky, 45th Anniv. — A952

Drawings: No. 2661, When the Fighting Ended, 1945, by Pavel Simon. No. 2662, The End of the game, 1945, by Ludmila Jirincova.

1987, June   **Perf. 11½**

2661	A952	1k blk, cerise & vio	.20	.20
2662	A952	1k blk, gold, pale lil & cerise	.20	.20

Union of Czechoslovakian Mathematicians and Physicists, 125th Anniv. — A953

Designs: No. 2663, Prague Town Hall mathematical clock, Theory of Functions diagram. No. 2664, J.M. Petzval (1807-1891), J. Strouhal (1850-1922) and V. Jarnik (1897-1970). No. 2665, Geographical measurement from A.M. Malletta's book, 1672, earth fold and Brownian motion diagrams.

1987, July 6   **Perf. 11½x12**

2663	A953	50h multi	.20	.20
2664	A953	50h multi	.20	.20
2665	A953	50h multi	.20	.20
		Nos. 2663-2665 (3)	.60	.60

A954

A955

Award-winning illustrations.

1987, Sept. 3   **Perf. 11½**

2666	A954	50h Asun Balzola, Spain	.20	.20
2667	A954	1k Frederic Clement, France	.20	.20
2668	A954	2k Elzbieta Gaudasinska, Poland	.40	.25
	a.	Souv. sheet of 2 + label	2.50	1.75
2669	A954	4k Marija Lucija Stupica, Yugoslavia	.80	.50
		Nos. 2666-2669 (4)	1.60	1.15

11th Biennial of Children's Book Illustration, Sept. 11-Oct. 30, Bratislava.

1987, Sept. 23

2670	A955	50h Eternal flame, flower	.20	.20

Theresienstadt Memorial for the victims from 23 European countries who died in the Small Fortress, Terezin, a Nazi concentration camp.

Socialist Communications Organization, 30th Anniv. — A956

1987, Sept. 23

2671	A956	4k Emblem, satellite, dish receiver	.40	.20

Jan Evangelista Purkyne (1787-1869), Physiologist A957

1987, Sept. 30

2672	A957	7k multicolored	.80	.20

Views of Bratislava — A958

Designs: 3k, Male and female figures supporting an oriel, Arkier Palace, c. 1552. 4k, View of Bratislava from Ware Conterfactur de Stadt Presburg, from an engraving by Hans Mayer, 1563.

1987, Oct. 1   **Engr.**   *Perf. 12*
2673 A958 3k multicolored   .50 .35
2674 A958 4k multicolored   .70 .45

Each printed in sheets of 4 with Bratislava Castle (from Mayer's engraving) between. Value, set $6.50.
See #2719-2720, 2763-2764, 2800-2801.

Type of 1974
Photo. & Engr.
1987, Nov. 1   *Perf. 12x11½*
2675 A699 1k Post rider   .20 .20

PRAGA '88, Aug. 26-Sept. 4, 1988. No. 2675 printed se-tenant with label picturing exhibition emblem. Value for single with attached label 40c.

October Revolution, Russia, 70th
Anniv. — A959

Establishment of the Union of Soviet
Socialist Republics, 65th
Anniv. — A960

1987, Nov. 6   *Perf. 12x11½*
2676 A959 50h multicolored   .20 .20
2677 A960 50h multicolored   .20 .20

Art Type of 1974

Paintings in national galleries: 1k, Enclosure of Dreams, by Kamil Lhotak (b. 1912). 2k, Tulips, by Ester Simerova-Martincekova (b. 1909). 3k, Triptych with Bohemian Landscape, by Josef Lada (1887-1957). 4k, Accordion Player, by Josef Capek (1887-1945). 5k, Self-portrait, by Jiri Trnka (1912-1969).

1987, Nov. 18   **Engr.**   *Perf. 12*
2678 A700 1k multi   2.40 .60
2679 A700 2k multi   3.50 1.20
2680 A700 3k multi   3.00 .85
2681 A700 4k multi   2.10 .60
2682 A700 5k multi   3.25 1.00
   Nos. 2678-2682 (5)   14.25 4.25

Czech and Slovak art.
Nos. 2678-2682 were each issued in sheets of 4. Value, set $75.

69th Stamp Day — A961

Portrait of Jacob Obrovsky (1882-1949), stamp designer, Bohemian Lion (Type SP1), sketch of a lion and PRAGA '88 emblem.

Photo. & Engr.
1987, Dec. 18   *Perf. 11½x12*
2683 A961 1k multicolored   .25 .20

No. 2683 printed in sheet of four with eight labels se-tenant with stamps, inscribed "100 Years of the National Philatelic Movement in Czechoslovakia" in Czech. The four labels between the "blocks of six" are blank. Value, sheet $3.

Czechoslovak Republic, 70th
Anniv. — A962

1988, Jan. 1
2684 A962 1k Woman, natl. arms, linden branch   .25 .20

Natl. Front, 40th
Anniv. — A963

1988, Feb. 25   *Perf. 11½*
2685 A963 50h multicolored   .25 .20

Husak Type of 1983
Photo. & Engr.
1988, Jan. 10   *Perf. 12x11½*
2686 A865 1k brt rose & dk carmine   .25 .20

Olympics — A965

1988, Feb. 1   *Perf. 11½x12*
2687 A965 50h Ski jumping, ice hockey   .20 .20
2688 A965 1k Basketball, soccer   .20 .20
2689 A965 6k Discus, weight lifting   .80 .40
   Nos. 2687-2689 (3)   1.20 .80

Exist in souv. sheets of 2, imperf. between and in souv. sheets of 2, imperf.

Victorious
February, 40th
Anniv. — A966

Statue of Klement Gottwald by Rudolf Svoboda.

1988, Feb. 25   *Perf. 11½*
2690 A966 50h multicolored   .20 .20

No. 2690 exists in a souvenir sheet of two No. 2690 and two postally invalid imperf impressions of No. 637. Value $9. Sheet exists imperf. Value $12.

Classic Automobiles — A967

1988, Mar. 1   *Perf. 12x11½*
2691 A967 50h 1914 Laurin & Klement   .20 .20
2692 A967 1k 1902 Tatra NW Type B   .20 .20
2693 A967 2k 1905 Tatra NW Type E   .30 .20
2694 A967 3k 1929 Tatra 12 Normandie   .60 .25
2695 A967 4k 1899 Meteor   .80 .40
   a. Bklt. pane, 2 3k, 3 4k + label   6.00 6.00
   Complete booklet, #2695a   7.00
   Nos. 2691-2695 (5)   2.10 1.25

Postal
Museum,
70th
Anniv.
A968

Praga '88 emblem and: 50h, Postman, Malostranske Namesti Square p.o., Prague, c. 1742, and Velka Javorina television transmitter, 1979. 1k, Telecommunications Center, Mlada Boleslav, 1986, and Carmelite Street p.o., Prague, c. 1792. 2k, Prague 1 (1873) and Bratislava 56 (1984) post offices. 4k, Communications Center, Prachatice (1982), postman and Maltetske Nameski Square p.o., Prague, c. 1622.

1988, Mar. 10
2696 A968 50h multi   .20 .20
2697 A968 1k multi   .20 .20
2698 A968 2k multi   .25 .20
2699 A968 4k multi   .45 .25
   a. Souv. sheet, 2 ea #2698-2699   2.25 1.50
   Nos. 2696-2699 (4)   1.10 .85

In No. 2699a the top pair of Nos. 2698-2699 is imperf. at top and sides.

A969

A970

1988, Mar. 29   *Perf. 11½*
2700 A969 50h multicolored   .20 .20

Matice Slovenska Cultural Assoc., 125th anniv.

1988, May 12   **Photo. & Engr.**
PRAGA '88. (Exhibition emblem and aspects of the Museum of Natl. Literature, Prague): 1k, Gate and distant view of museum. 2k, Celestial globe, illuminated manuscript, bookshelves and ornately decorated ceiling. 5k, Illuminated "B" and decorated binder of a medieval Bible. 7k, Celestial globe, illuminated manuscript, Zodiacal signs (Aries and Leo), view of museum.

2701 A970 1k multicolored   .25 .20
   a. Souvenir sheet of 4   1.25 1.00
2702 A970 2k multicolored   .50 .30
   a. Souvenir sheet of 4   3.50 3.00
2703 A970 5k multicolored   .75 .45
   a. Souvenir sheet of 4   5.50 4.50
2704 A970 7k multicolored   1.60 .75
   a. Souvenir sheet of 4   11.00 9.00
   b. Souv. sheet of 4, imperf., #2701-2704   4.00 3.50
   Nos. 2701-2704 (4)   3.10 1.70

PRAGA '88 — A971

Exhibition emblem and fountains, Prague.

1988, June 1   *Perf. 11½x12*
2705 A971 1k Waldstein Palace   .20 .20
2706 A971 2k Old town square   .25 .20
2707 A971 3k Charles University   .50 .25
2708 A971 4k Prague Castle   .70 .30
   a. Souv. sheet of 4, #2705-2708   3.00 2.00
   Nos. 2705-2708 (4)   1.65 .95

Souvenir Sheet

Soviet-US Summit Conference on
Arms Reduction, Moscow — A972

Design: The capital, Washington, and the Kremlin, Moscow.

1988, June 1   *Perf. 12x11½*
2709 A972 4k blue blk, dark red & gold   2.50 1.50

Exists imperf. Value $6.

PRAGA
'88
A973

Exhibition emblem and modern architecture, Prague: 50h, Trade Unions Central Recreation Center. 1k, Koospol foreign trade company. 2k, Motol Teaching Hospital. 4k, Culture Palace.

1988, July 1   *Perf. 12x11½*
2710 A973 50h multicolored   .20 .20
2711 A973 1k blk, lt blue & bister   .20 .20
2712 A973 2k multicolored   .20 .20
   a. Souv. sheet, 2 1k, 2 2k + 4 labels, imperf.   2.00 1.50
2713 A973 4k multicolored   .50 .35
   a. Souv. sheet, 2 50h, 2 4k + 4 labels, imperf.   2.00 1.50
   Nos. 2710-2713 (4)   1.10 .95

Souvenir Sheet

PRAGA '88 — A974

Design: Exhibition emblem and Alfons Mucha (1860-1939), designer of first Czech postage stamp.

1988, Aug. 18   **Engr.**   *Perf. 12*
2714 A974 Sheet of 2   4.50 2.50
   a. 5k multicolored   2.00 .85

Czech postage stamps, 70th anniv.

Souvenir Sheets

PRAGA
'88
A975

5k, *Turin, Monte Superga,* by Josef Navratil (1798-1865), Postal Museum, Prague.

Details of *Bacchus and Ariadne,* by Sebastiano Ricci (1659-1734), Natl. Gallery, Prague: No. 2716a, Ariadne. No. 2716b, Bacchus and creatures.

1988

2715	Sheet of 2	5.00	3.00
a.	A975 5k multi	2.00	1.20
2716	Sheet of 2	8.50	5.00
a.-b.	A975 10k any single	3.00	1.75

#2716 exists with emblem and inscription "DEN F.I.P. JOURNEE DE LA FEDERATION INTERNATIONALE DE PHILATELIE." Value $12.

Issue dates: 5k, Aug. 19; 10k, Aug. 26.

Prague Castle Type of 1983

2k, Pottery jug, 17th cent. 3k, *St. Catherine with Angel,* 1580, by Paolo Veronese.

1988, Sept. 28   Engr.   *Perf. 12*

2717	A875	2k shown	.50	.50
2718	A875	3k multi	1.25	.70

Nos. 2717-2718 were each issued in sheets of 6. Value, set $12.

Bratislava Views Type of 1987

3k, *Hlavne Square, circa 1840* an etching by R. Alt-Sandman, 1840. 4k, *Ferdinand House, circa 1850,* a pen-and-ink drawing by V. Reim.

1988, Oct. 19

2719	A958	3k multicolored	.50	.50
2720	A958	4k multicolored	1.25	1.25

Nos. 2719-2720 were each issued in sheets of 4. Value, set $9.

Art Type of 1974

Paintings in natl. galleries: 2k, *With Bundles,* 1931, by Martin Benka (1888-1971). 6k, *Blue Bird,* 1903, by Vojtech Preissig (1873-1944). 7k, *A Jaguar Attacking a Rider,* c. 1850, by Eugene Delacroix (1798-1863).

1988, Nov. 17   Engr.   *Perf. 12*

2721	A700	2k multicolored	2.75	1.40
2722	A700	6k multicolored	4.25	2.00
2723	A700	7k multicolored	4.25	2.00
	Nos. 2721-2723 (3)		11.25	5.40

Czech and Slovak art.

Nos. 2721-2723 were each issued in sheets of 4. Value, set $50.

Stamp Day — A978

Design: 1k, Jaroslav Benda (1882-1970), illustrator and stamp designer.

Photo. & Engr.
1988, Dec. 18   *Perf. 11½x12*

2724	A978	1k multicolored	.25	.20

Paris-Dakar Rally — A979

Trucks: 50h, Earth, Motokov Liaz. 1k, Liaz, globe. 2k, Earth, Motokov Tatra. No. 607. 4k, Map of racecourse, turban, Tatra.

1989, Jan. 2   *Perf. 12x11½*

2725	A979	50h multicolored	.20	.20
2726	A979	1k multicolored	.30	.20
2727	A979	2k multicolored	.45	.20
2728	A979	4k multicolored	.80	.30
	Nos. 2725-2728 (4)		1.75	.90

Czechoslovakian Federation, 20th Anniv. — A980

1989, Jan. 1

2729	A980	50h multicolored	.20	.20

Jan Botto
(1829-1881)
A981

Taras Grigorievich Shevchenko (1814-1861)
A982

Jean Cocteau
(1889-1963)
A983

Charlie Chaplin
(1889-1977)
A984

Jawaharlal Nehru
(1889-1964) and
"UNESCO" — A985

Famous men: No. 2732, Modest Petrovich Musorgsky (1839-1881).

Photo. & Engr.
1989, Mar. 9   *Perf. 12x11½*

2730	A981	50h brn blk & lt blue green	.20	.20
2731	A982	50h shown	.20	.20
2732	A982	50h multicolored	.20	.20
2733	A983	50h red brn, grnh blk & org brn	.20	.20
2734	A984	50h blk, int blue & dark red	.20	.20
2735	A985	50h brn blk & lt yel green	.20	.20
	Nos. 2730-2735 (6)		1.20	1.20

Shipping Industry
A986

1989, Mar. 27

2736	A986	50h *Republika*	.20	.20
2737	A986	1k *Pionyr,* flags	.20	.20
2738	A986	2k *Brno,* flags	.35	.20
2739	A986	3k *Trinec*	.60	.20
2740	A986	4k Flags, mast, *Orlik*	.80	.30
2741	A986	5k *Vltava,* communication hardware	1.00	.30
	Nos. 2736-2741 (6)		3.15	1.40

Pioneer Organization, 40th Anniv. — A987

Photo. & Engr.
1989, Apr. 20   *Perf. 11½*

2742	A987	50h multi	.20	.20

Art Type of 1974

Details of *Feast of Rose Garlands,* 1506, by Albrecht Durer, Natl. Gallery, Prague: a, Virgin and Child. b, Angel playing mandolin.

1989, Apr. 21   Engr.   *Perf. 12*
Miniature Sheet

2743	Sheet of 2	10.00	5.00
a.-b.	A700 10k any single	4.50	2.00

Prague Castle Art Type of 1983

2k, Bas-relief picturing Kaiser Karl IV, from Kralovske tomb by Alexander Colin (c. 1527-1612). 3k, Self-portrait, by V.V. Reiner (1689-1743).

1989, May 9   Photo. & Engr.

2744	A875	2k dark red, sepia & buff	.40	.30
2745	A875	3k multi	.60	.40

Nos. 2744-2745 were each issued in sheets of 6. Value, set $7.

Souvenir Sheet

PHILEXFRANCE '89, French Revolution Bicent. — A988

1989, July 14   Engr.   *Perf. 12*

2746	A988	5k brt blue, blk & dk red	2.00	1.50

Haliaeetus albicilla — A989

Photo. & Engr.
1989, July 17   *Perf. 12x11½*

2747	A989	1k multicolored	.50	.20

World Wildlife Fund — A990

Toads and newts.

1989, July 18   *Perf. 11½x12*

2748	A990	2k *Bombina bombina*	1.25	.30
2749	A990	3k *Bombina variegata*	1.50	.40
2750	A990	4k *Triturus alpestris*	1.75	.60
2751	A990	5k *Triturus montandoni*	2.00	.75
	Nos. 2748-2751 (4)		6.50	2.05

Slovak Folk Art Collective, 40th Anniv. — A991

1989, Aug. 29   *Perf. 12x11½*

2752	A991	50h multicolored	.20	.20

Slovak Uprising, 45th Anniv. — A992

Photo. & Engr.
1989, Aug. 29   *Perf. 11½x12*

2753	A992	1k multicolored	.20	.20

A993   A994

Award-winning illustrations.

1989, Sept. 4   *Perf. 11½*

2754	A993	50h Hannu Taina, Finland	.20	.20
2755	A993	1k Aleksander Aleksov, Bulgaria	.20	.20
2756	A993	2k Jurgen Spohn, West Berlin	.25	.20
2757	A993	4k Robert Brun, Czechoslovakia	.75	.20
a.	Souvenir sheet of 2	1.75	.75
	Nos. 2754-2757 (4)		1.40	.80

12th Biennial of Children's Book Illustration, Bratislava.

1989, Sept. 5   Engr.   *Perf. 11½x12*

Poisonous mushrooms.

2758	A994	50h *Nolanea verna*	.25	.20
2759	A994	1k *Amanita phalloides*	.30	.30
2760	A994	2k *Amanita virosa*	.45	.40
2761	A994	3k *Cortinarius orellanus*	.70	.55
2762	A994	5k *Galerina marginata*	.80	.55
	Nos. 2758-2762 (5)		2.50	2.00

Nos. 2758-2762 were each issued in sheets of 10. Value, set $40.

Bratislava Views Type of 1987

Views of Devin, a Slavic castle above the Danube, Bratislava.

1989, Oct. 16   Engr.   *Perf. 12*

2763	A958	3k Castle, flower	.65	.65
2764	A958	4k Castle, urn	.85	.85

Nos. 2763-2764 were each issued in sheets of 4. Value, set $7.

Jan Opletal (1915-39) — A996

Photo. & Engr.
1989, Nov. 17   *Perf. 12x11½*

2765	A996	1k multicolored	.20	.20

Intl. Student's Day. Funeral of Opletal, a Nazi victim, on Nov. 15, 1939, sparked student demonstrations that resulted in the closing of all universities in occupied Bohemia and Moravia.

Art Type of 1974

Paintings in Natl. Galleries: 2k, *Nirvana,* c. 1920, by Anton Jasusch (1882-1965). 4k, *Winter Evening in Town,* c. 1907, by Jakub

Schikaneder (1855-1924), horiz. 5k, *The Bakers*, 1926, by Pravoslav Kotik (1889-1970), horiz.

1989, Nov. 27   **Engr.**   *Perf. 12*
2766 A700 2k multicolored   .90 .55
2767 A700 4k multicolored   1.60 1.10
2768 A700 5k multicolored   1.50 1.10
   Nos. 2766-2768 (3)   4.00 2.75

Nos. 2766-2768 were each issued in sheets of 4. Value, set $17.

Stamp Day — A997

Design: Portrait of Cyril Bouda, stamp designer, art tools and falcon.

Photo. & Engr.
1989, Dec. 18   *Perf. 11½x12*
2769 A997 1k multicolored   .25 .20

A998

1990, Jan. 8   *Perf. 11½x12*
2770 A998 1k multicolored   .60 .20

UNESCO World Literacy Year. Printed setenant with inscribed label picturing UN and UNESCO emblems. Value, single with label attached 75c.

1990, Jan. 9   *Perf. 11½*
Famous men: No. 2771, Karel Capek, writer. No. 2772, Thomas G. Masaryk. 1k, Lenin. 2k, Emile Zola, French writer. 3k, Jaroslav Heyrovsky (1890-1987), chemical physicist. 10k, Bohuslav Martinu (1890-1959), composer.

A999

2771 A999 50h multicolored   .20 .20
2772 A999 50h multicolored   .20 .20
2773 A999 1k multicolored   .20 .20
2774 A999 2k multicolored   .30 .20
2775 A999 3k multicolored   .50 .30
2776 A999 10k multicolored   1.60 .90
   Nos. 2771-2776 (6)   3.00 2.00

#2771, 2775-2776 inscribed "UNESCO."

Pres. Vaclav   Handball Players
Havel   A1001
A1000

1990, Jan. 9   *Perf. 12x11½*
2777 A1000 50h red, brt vio & bl   .30 .20
   See Nos. 2879, 2948.

1990, Feb. 1   *Perf. 11½*
2778 A1001 50h multicolored   .20 .20

1990 Men's World Handball Championships, Czechoslovakia.

Flora — A1002   A1003

Photo. & Engr.
1990, Mar. 1   *Perf. 11½*
2779 A1002 50h *Antirrhinum majus*   .50 .20
2780 A1002 1k *Zinnia elegans*   .70 .20
2781 A1002 3k *Tigridia pavonia*   1.00 .25
   Perf. 12x12½
2782 A1002 5k *Lilium candidum*   1.30 .70
   Nos. 2779-2782 (4)   3.50 1.35

City Arms Type of 1982
Photo. & Engr.
1990, Mar. 28   *Perf. 12x11½*
2783 A847 50h Prostejov   .20 .20
2784 A847 50h Bytca   .20 .20
2785 A847 50h Sobeslav   .20 .20
2786 A847 50h Podebrady   .20 .20
   Nos. 2783-2786 (4)   .80 .80

1990, Apr. 16   *Perf. 11½x12*
2787 A1003 1k brn vio, rose & buff   .60 .20

Visit of Pope John Paul II.

World War II
Liberation
A1004

Photo. & Engr.
1990, May 5   *Perf. 11½*
2788 A1004 1k multicolored   .25 .20

Souvenir Sheet

150th Anniv. of the Postage
Stamp — A1005

1990, May 6   **Engr.**   *Perf. 12*
2789 A1005 7k multicolored   3.50 1.50
Stamp World London 90.

A1006

A1007

Photo. & Engr.
1990, May 8   *Perf. 11½*
2790 A1006 1k multicolored   .60 .20
World Cup Soccer Championships, Italy.

1990, June 1
2791 A1007 1k multicolored   .50 .20
Free elections.

Prague Castle Type of 1983
1990, June 6, 1990   **Engr.**
2792 A875 2k Gold and jeweled hand   .60 .30
2793 A875 3k Medallion   .90 .45

Art treasures of Prague Castle.

Nos. 2792-2793 were each issued in sheets of 6. Value, set $12.

Helsinki Conference, 15th
Anniv. — A1008

Photo. & Engr.
1990, June 21   *Perf. 12x11½*
2794 A1008 7k multicolored   1.10 .60

Dr.
Milada
Horakova
A1009

1990, June 25   *Perf. 12x11½*
2795 A1009 1k multicolored   .30 .20

Intercanis Dog Show, Brno — A1010

Designs: 50h, Poodles, 1k, Afghan hound, Irish wolfhound, greyhound. 4k, Czech terrier, bloodhound, Hannoverian hound. 7k, Cavalier King Charles Spaniel, cocker spaniel, American cocker spaniel.

1990, July 2
2796 A1010 50h multicolored   .55 .20
2797 A1010 1k multicolored   .85 .20
2798 A1010 4k multicolored   1.40 .40
2799 A1010 7k multicolored   2.00 .65
   Nos. 2796-2799 (4)   4.80 1.45

Bratislava Art Type of 1987
1990   **Engr.**   *Perf. 12*
2800 A958 3k Ancient Celtic coin   .80 .40
2801 A958 4k Gen. Milan Stefanik   .80 .50

Issue dates: 3k, Sept. 29. 4k, July 21. Nos. 2800-2801 were each issued in sheets of 4. Value, set $8.

Grand Pardubice Steeplechase,
Cent. — A1011

Photo. & Engr.
1990, Sept. 7   *Perf. 12x11½*
2802 A1011 50h multicolored   .20 .20
2803 A1011 4k multi, diff.   .70 .35

Protected Animals — A1012

Litho. & Engr.
1990, Oct. 1   *Perf. 12x11*
2804 A1012 50h Marmota marmota   .85 .20
2805 A1012 1k Felis silvestris   1.40 .20
2806 A1012 4k Castor fiber   1.60 .40
2807 A1012 5k Plecotus auritus   2.00 .65
   Nos. 2804-2807 (4)   5.85 1.45

Conf. of Civic Associations,
Helsinki — A1013

Litho. & Engr.
1990, Oct. 15   *Perf. 12x11½*
2808 A1013 3k blue, gold & yel   .50 .20

Christmas — A1014

Photo. & Engr.
1990, Nov. 15   *Perf. 11½x12*
2809 A1014 50h multicolored   .20 .20

Art Type of 1967
Works of art: 2k, Krucemburk by Jan Zrzavy (1890-1977), horiz. 3k, St. Agnes of Bohemia from the St. Wenceslas Monument, Prague by Josef V. Myslbek (1848-1922). 4k, The Slavs in their Homeland by Alfons Mucha (1860-1939). 5k, St. John the Baptist by Auguste Rodin (1840-1917).

1990, Nov. 27   **Engr.**   *Perf. 11½*
2810 A565 2k multicolored   1.25 .45
2811 A565 3k multicolored   1.50 1.50
2812 A565 4k multicolored   1.80 .50
2813 A565 5k multicolored   2.10 .50
   Nos. 2810-2813 (4)   6.65 2.95

Nos. 2810-2813 were each issued in sheets of 4. Value, set $30.

Karel Svolinsky (1896-1986), Vignette
from No. 1182 — A1016

1990, Dec. 18   **Photo. & Engr.**
2814 A1016 1k multicolored   .25 .20

Stamp Day.

A1017   A1018

1991, Jan. 10   *Perf. 11½*
2815 A1017 1k multicolored   .30 .20

European Judo Championships, Prague.

1991, Jan. 10
Design: A. B. Svojsik (1876-1938), Czech Scouting Founder.

2816 A1018 3k multicolored   1.00 .20

Scouting in Czechoslovakia, 80th Anniv.

Bethlehem Chapel, Prague, 600th Anniv. — A1019

1991, Feb. 4   **Perf. 12x11½**
2817 A1019 50h multicolored   .25 .20

Wolfgang Amadeus Mozart (1756-1791), Old Theatre — A1020

1991, Feb. 4
2818 A1020 1k multicolored   .20 .20

Steamship Bohemia, 150th Anniv. — A1021

1991, Feb. 4   **Perf. 11½x12**
2819 A1021 5k multicolored   1.00 .30

Famous Men A1022

Designs: No. 2820, Antonin Dvorak (1841-1904), composer. No. 2821, Andrej Kmet (1841-1908), botanist. No. 2822, Jaroslav Seifert (1901-1986), poet, Nobel laureate for Literature. No. 2823, Jan Masaryk (1886-1948), diplomat. No. 2824, Alois Senefelder (1771-1834), lithographer.

1991, Feb. 18   **Perf. 12x11½**
2820 A1022 1k multicolored   .20 .20
2821 A1022 1k multicolored   .30 .20
2822 A1022 1k multicolored   .40 .20
2823 A1022 1k multicolored   .50 .20
2824 A1022 1k multicolored   .60 .20
   Nos. 2820-2824 (5)   2.00 1.00

#2820-2824 printed with se-tenant labels. See No. 2831.

Europa — A1023   A1024

Photo. & Engr.
1991, May 6   **Perf. 11½x12**
2825 A1023 6k blk, bl & red   2.50 .75

Photo. & Engr.
1991, May 10   **Perf. 11½x12**
2826 A1024 1k multicolored   .25 .20
General Exhibition in Prague, cent.

Antarctic Treaty, 30th Anniv. A1025

1991, May 20   **Perf. 12x11½**
2827 A1025 8k multicolored   1.75 .60

Castles — A1026   Scenic Views — A1027

1991, June 3   **Perf. 11½**
2828 A1026 50h Blatna   .40 .20
2829 A1026 1k Bouzov   .50 .20
2830 A1026 3k Kezmarok   .60 .20
   Nos. 2828-2830 (3)   1.50 .60

Famous Men Type
Design: Jan Palach (1948-1969), Student.

Photo. & Engr.
1991, Aug. 9   **Perf. 12x11½**
2831 A1022 4k black   2.00 .30
Printed se-tenant with label.

Photo. & Engr.
1991, Aug. 28   **Perf. 11½**
2832 A1027 4k Krivan mountains   1.00 .60
2833 A1027 4k Rip mountain   1.00 .60

A1028   A1029

Illustrations by: 1k, Binette Schroeder, Germany. 2k, Stasys Eidrigevicius, Poland.

Photo. & Engr.
1991, Sept. 2   **Perf. 11½**
2834 A1028 1k multicolored   .40 .20
2835 A1028 2k multicolored   .40 .20
13th Biennial Exhibition of Children's Book Illustrators, Bratislava.

1991, Sept. 27   **Engr.**   **Perf. 11½**
Design: Father Andrej Hlinka (1864-1938), Slovak nationalist.
2836 A1029 10k blue black   1.60 .30

Art of Prague and Bratislava A1030

Designs: No. 2837, Holy Infant of Prague. No. 2838, Blue Church of Bratislava.

1991, Sept. 30
2837 A1030 3k multicolored   1.00 .75
2838 A1030 3k multicolored   1.00 .75
Nos. 2837-2838 were each issued in sheets of 8. Value, set $20.

Flowers A1031   Christmas A1033

Photo. & Engr.
1991, Nov. 3   **Perf. 12x11½**
2839 A1031 1k Gagea bohemica   .30 .20
2840 A1031 2k Aster alpinus   .60 .20
2841 A1031 5k Fritillaria meleagris   1.60 .25
2842 A1031 11k Daphne cneorum   2.50 .35
   Nos. 2839-2842 (4)   5.00 1.00

Art Type of 1967
Paintings: 2k, Everyday Homelife by Max Ernst. 3k, Lovers by Auguste Renoir. 4k, Head of Christ by El Greco. 5k, Coincidence by Ladislav Guderna. 7k, Two Maidens by Utamaro.

1991, Nov. 3   **Engr.**   **Perf. 11½**
2843 A565 2k multicolored   .80 .30
2844 A565 3k multicolored   1.00 .40
2845 A565 4k multicolored   1.50 .50
2846 A565 5k multicolored   1.50 .60
2847 A565 7k multicolored   2.00 1.00
   Nos. 2843-2847 (5)   6.80 2.80

Nos. 2843-2847 were each issued in sheets of 4. Value, set $30.

1991, Nov. 19
2848 A1033 50h multicolored   .30 .20

Stamp Day — A1034
Martin Benka (1888-1971), stamp engraver.

Photo. & Engr.
1991, Dec. 18   **Perf. 11½x12**
2849 A1034 2k multicolored   .45 .20

1992 Winter Olympics, Albertville — A1035

1992, Jan. 6   **Perf. 11½**
2850 A1035 1k Biathlon   .25 .20

Photo. & Engr.
1992, May 21   **Perf. 11½**
2851 A1035 2k Tennis   .30 .20
1992 Summer Olympics, Barcelona.

Jan Amos Komensky (Comenius), Educator — A1036

1992, Mar. 5   **Engr.**
2852 A1036 10k multicolored   4.50 3.00

World Ice Hockey Championships, Prague and Bratislava — A1037

1992, Mar. 31   **Photo. & Engr.**
2853 A1037 3k multicolored   .75 .20

Traffic Safety A1038

1992, Apr. 2
2854 A1038 2k multicolored   .50 .20

Expo '92, Seville — A1039

1992, Apr. 2
2855 A1039 4k multicolored   .75 .20

Discovery of America, 500th Anniv. — A1040

1992, May 5   **Engr.**
2856 A1040 22k multicolored   2.75 2.75
Europa. Printed in sheets of 8. Value $25.

Czechoslovak Military Actions in WWII — A1041

Designs: 1k, J. Kubis and J. Gabcik, assassins of Reinhard Heydrich, 1942. 2k, Pilots flying for France and Great Britain. 3k, Defense of Tobruk. 6k, Capture of Dunkirk, 1944-45.

1992, May 21 **Engr.** **Perf. 12x11½**
2857 A1041 1k multicolored .50 .20
2858 A1041 2k multicolored .60 .20
2859 A1041 3k multicolored .75 .25
2860 A1041 6k multicolored 1.60 .35
Nos. 2857-2860 (4) 3.45 1.00

A1042   A1043

Photo. & Engr.
1992, June 10 **Perf. 11½**
2861 A1042 2k multicolored .30 .20
Czechoslovakian Red Cross.

1992, June 30
2862 A1043 1k multicolored .30 .20
Junior European Table Tennis Championships, Topolcany.

Beetles
A1044

1992, July 15
2863 A1044 1k Polyphylla fullo .65 .20
2864 A1044 2k Ergates faber .90 .30
2865 A1044 3k Meloe violaceus 1.80 .45
2866 A1044 4k Dytiscus latissimus 1.80 .60
Nos. 2863-2866 (4) 5.15 1.55
The 1k exists with denomination omitted.

Troja
Castle
A1045

1992, Aug. 28 **Engr.** **Perf. 11½**
2867 A1045 6k shown 2.00 .75
2868 A1045 7k Statue of St. Martin, vert. 3.00 .80
2869 A1045 8k Lednice Castle 3.00 .95
Nos. 2867-2869 (3) 8.00 2.50
Nos. 2867-2869 were each issued in sheets
of 8. Value, set $75.

Chrudim Church Type of 1971
Photo. & Engr.
1992, Aug. 28 **Perf. 11½x11**
2870 A629 50h multicolored .75 .20

Postal
Bank — A1045a

Photo. & Engr.
1992, Aug. 28 **Perf. 11½x12**
2870A A1045a 20k multicolored 5.00 1.10

Antonius Bernolak, Georgius
Fandly — A1046

Photo. & Engr.
1992, Oct. 6 **Perf. 12x11½**
2871 A1046 5k multicolored 1.50 .50
Slovakian Educational Society, bicent.

Cesky
Krumlov — A1046a

Photo. & Engr.
1992, Oct. 19 **Perf. 11½x12**
2871A A1046a 3k brick red & brn .90 .20
See No. 2890.

Painting Type of 1967
6k Old Man on a Raft, by Koloman Sokol.
7k, Still Life of Grapes and Raisins, by
Georges Braque, horiz. 8k, Abandoned Cor-
set, by Toyen.

Perf. 11½x12, 12x11½
1992, Nov. 2 **Engr.**
2872 A565 6k multicolored 1.40 .55
2873 A565 7k multicolored 2.25 .65
2874 A565 8k multicolored 2.25 .75
Nos. 2872-2874 (3) 5.90 1.95
Nos. 2872-2874 were each issued in sheets
of 4. Value, set $30.

Christmas — A1047

Photo. & Engr.
1992, Nov. 9 **Perf. 12x11½**
2875 A1047 2k multicolored .60 .20

Jindra Schmidt (1897-1984), Graphic
Artist and Engraver — A1048

Photo. & Engr.
1992, Dec. 18 **Perf. 11½x12**
2876 A1048 2k multicolored .60 .20
Stamp Day.

On January 1, 1993, Czechoslovakia
split into Czech Republic and Slovakia.
Czech Republic listings continue here.
Slovakia can be found in Volume 5.

CZECH REPUBLIC
AREA — 30,449 sq. mi.
POP. — 10,280,513 (1999 est.)

Natl. Arms
A1049

Photo. & Engr.
1993, Jan. 20 **Perf. 11**
2877 A1049 3k multicolored .50 .20

1993 World
Figure Skating
Championships,
Prague
A1050

1993, Feb. 25 **Perf. 11½x11**
2878 A1050 2k multicolored .50 .20
Havel Type of 1990 Inscribed "Ceska
Republika"

Photo. & Engr.
1993, Mar. 2 **Perf. 12x11½**
2879 A1000 2k vio, vio brn &
blue .40 .20

St. John Nepomuk, Patron Saint of
Czechs, 600th Death Anniv. — A1051

1993, Mar. 11
2880 A1051 8k multicolored 1.00 .35
See Germany No. 1776; Slovakia No. 158.

Holy Hunger, by
Mikulas
Medek — A1052

1993, Mar. 11 **Perf. 11½**
2881 A1052 14k multicolored 4.00 2.00
Europa.

Sacred
Heart
Church,
Prague
A1053

1993, Mar. 30 **Engr.** **Perf. 11½**
2882 A1053 5k multicolored 1.10 .35

Brevnov Monastery, 1000th
Anniv. — A1054

Litho. & Engr.
1993, Apr. 12 **Perf. 12x11½**
2883 A1054 4k multicolored .65 .25

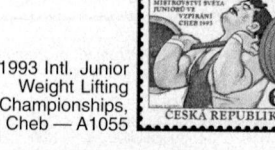

1993 Intl. Junior
Weight Lifting
Championships,
Cheb — A1055

Photo. & Engr.
1993, May 12 **Perf. 11½**
2884 A1055 6k multicolored 1.00 .35

Clock Tower and
Church,
Brno — A1056

1993, June 16 **Engr.** **Perf. 12x11½**
2885 A1056 8k multicolored 1.20 1.20
Brno, 750th anniv.

Arrival of St. Cyril and St. Methodius,
1130th Anniv. — A1057

1993, June 22 **Photo. & Engr.**
2886 A1057 8k multicolored 1.00 .50
See Slovakia No. 167.

Souvenir Sheet

State
Arms — A1058

1993, June 22 **Perf. 11½**
2887 A1058 8k Sheet of 2 3.00 3.00

Architecture Type of 1992 Inscribed
"Ceska Republika" and

A1059

Cities: 1k, Ceske Budejovice. 2k, Usti Nad
Labem. #2890, like #2871A. #2890A, Brno.
5k, Plzen. 6k, Slany. 7k, Ostrava. 8k,
Olomouc. 10k, Hradec Kralove. 20k, Prague.
50k, Opava.

Perf. 12x11½, 11½x12
1993-94 **Photo. & Engr.**
2888 A1059 1k dp cl & org .20 .20
2889 A1059 2k red vio & bl .25 .20
2890 A1046a 3k gray bl &
red .35 .20
Complete booklet, 5
#2890 6.00
2891 A1059 3k dk bl & red .35 .20
Complete booklet, 5
#2890A 5.00
2892 A1059 5k bluish green
& brn .60 .25
2893 A1059 6k grn & org
yel .75 .30
2894 A1059 7k blk brn &
grn .85 .30
2895 A1059 8k dp vio & yel .95 .30
2896 A1059 10k olive gray &
red 1.20 .40
2897 A1059 20k red & blue 2.50 .75
2898 A1059 50k brn & grn 6.00 1.75
Nos. 2888-2898 (11) 14.00 4.85
Issued: No. 2891, 3/30/94; 6k, 10/1/94; 7k,
11/23/94; others, 7/1/93.

World Rowing
Championships,
Racice
A1060

Photo. & Engr.
1993, Aug. 18   *Perf. 11½*
2901 A1060 3k multicolored   .50 .20

A1061   Trees — A1062

Famous men: 2k, August Sedlacek (1843-1926), historian. 3k, Eduard Cech (1893-1960), mathematician.

1993, Aug. 26   *Perf. 12x11½*
2902 A1061 2k multicolored   .25 .20
2903 A1061 3k multicolored   .35 .20

1993, Oct. 26   *Perf. 11½*
2904 A1062 5k Quercus robur   .75 .30
2905 A1062 7k Carpinus betulus   1.00 .40
2906 A1062 9k Pinus silvestris   1.50 .50
   Nos. 2904-2906 (3)   3.25 1.20

Christmas — A1063

A1064

Photo. & Engr.
1993, Nov. 8   *Perf. 11½*
2907 A1063 2k multicolored   .30 .20

Art Type of 1967 Inscribed "CESKA REPUBLIKA"

Paintings: 9k, Strahovska Madonna, by "Bohemian Master" in the year 1350. 11k, Composition, by Miro, horiz. 14k, Field of Green, by Van Gogh, horiz.

1993   *Engr.*   *Perf. 11½x12*
2908 A565 9k multicolored   2.25 2.25
         Perf. 12x11½
2909 A565 11k multicolored   2.25 2.25
2910 A565 14k multicolored   3.50 3.50
   Nos. 2908-2910 (3)   8.00 8.00

Issued: 11k, 14k, Nov. 8; 9k, Dec. 15.
Nos. 2908-2910 were each issued in sheets of 4. Value $35.

Photo. & Engr.
1994, Jan. 19   *Perf. 11½*
2911 A1064 2k multicolored   .30 .20

Intl. Year of the Family.

Jan Kubelik (1880-1940), Composer A1065

Photo. & Engr.
1994, Jan. 19   *Perf. 11½*
2912 A1065 3k multicolored   .40 .25

UNESCO — A1065a

Designs: 2k, Voltaire (1694-1778), philosopher. 6k, Georgius Agricola (1494-1555), mineralogist, humanist.

1994, Feb. 2   *Perf. 12x11½*
2913 A1065a 2k multicolored   .25 .20
2914 A1065a 6k multicolored   .80 .35

A1066   A1067

Photo. & Engr.
1994, Feb. 2   *Perf. 11½*
2915 A1066 5k multicolored   .65 .35

1994 Winter Olympics, Lillehammer.

Photo. & Engr.
1994, May 4   *Perf. 11½*
Europa (Marco Polo &): #2916, Stylized animals, Chinese woman. #2917, Stylized animals.

2916 A1067 14k multicolored   1.75 1.75
2917 A1067 14k multicolored   1.75 1.75
   a.   Pair, #2916-2917   3.50 3.50

A1068   A1070

Architectural Sights — A1069

1994, May 18
2918 A1068 5k Eduard Benes   .60 .20

1994, May 18
UNESCO: 8k, Houses at the square, Telc. 9k, Cubist house designed by Chochol, Prague.

2919 A1069 8k multicolored   1.00 .75
2920 A1069 9k multicolored   1.10 .75

Photo. & Engr.
1994, June 1   *Perf. 11½*
2921 A1070 2k Children's Day   .40 .20

Dinosaurs — A1071

     Perf. 11½x11, 11x11½
1994, June 1   *Litho.*
2922 A1071 2k Stegosaurus   .75 .20
2923 A1071 3k Apatosaurus   1.00 .25
2924 A1071 5k Tarbosaurus, vert. 1.25 .35
   Nos. 2922-2924 (3)   3.00 .80

A1072

A1073

Photo. & Engr.
1994, June 1   *Perf. 11½x11*
2925 A1072 8k multicolored   1.10 .50

1994 World Cup Soccer Championships, US.

1994, June 15   *Perf. 11x11½*
2926 A1073 2k multicolored   .30 .20

12th Pan-Sokol Rally, Prague.

Intl. Olympic Committee, Cent. — A1074

1994, June 15
2927 A1074 7k multicolored   .85 .50

UPU, 120th Anniv. A1075

1994, Aug. 3   *Engr.*   *Perf. 11½*
2928 A1075 11k multicolored   1.50 1.00

Songbirds — A1076

Designs: 3k, Saxicola torquata. 5k, Carpodacus erythrinus. 14k, Luscinia svecica.

Photo. & Engr.
1994, Aug. 24   *Perf. 11x11½*
2929 A1076 3k multicolored   .45 .25
2930 A1076 5k multicolored   .75 .30
2931 A1076 14k multicolored   1.80 .80
   Nos. 2929-2931 (3)   3.00 1.35

Historic Race Cars — A1077

Photo. & Engr.
1994, Oct. 5   *Perf. 11½*
2932 A1077 2k 1900 NW   .25 .20
2933 A1077 3k 1908 L&K   .55 .20
   Complete booklet, 5 #2933   3.50
2934 A1077 9k 1912 Praga   1.40 .50
   Nos. 2932-2934 (3)   2.20 .90

Christmas — A1078

Photo. & Engr.
1994, Nov. 9   *Perf. 11½*
2935 A1078 2k multicolored   .45 .20

Art Type of 1967 Inscribed "CESKA REPUBLIKA"

Engraving or paintings: 7k, Stary Posetilec A Zena, by Lucas Van Leyden. 10k, Moulin Rouge, by Henri de Toulouse-Lautrec. 14k, St. Vitus Madonna, St. Vitus Cathedral, Prague.

1994, Nov. 9   *Engr.*   *Perf. 12*
2936 A565 7k multicolored   .85 .85
2937 A565 10k multicolored   1.20 1.20
2938 A565 14k multicolored   1.75 1.75
   Nos. 2936-2938 (3)   3.80 3.80

Nos. 2936-2938 were each printed in sheets of 4. Value, set $14.

World Tourism Organization, 20th Anniv. A1079   Czech Stamp Production A1080

Photo. & Engr.
1995, Jan. 2   *Perf. 11x12*
2939 A1079 8k green blue & red .95 .50

1995, Jan. 20
2940 A1080 3k Design N1   .35 .25

Czech Republic & European Union Association Agreement A1081

1995, Jan. 20   *Litho.*   *Perf. 13½x12½*
2941 A1081 8k multicolored   .95 .65

Famous Men A1082

Designs: 2k, Johannes Marcus Marci (1595-1667). 5k, Ferdinand Peroutka (1895-1978). 7k, Premysl Pitter (1895-1976).

Photo. & Engr.
1995, Feb. 1   *Perf. 12x11*
2942 A1082 2k multicolored   .25 .20
2943 A1082 5k multicolored   .60 .25
2944 A1082 7k multicolored   .85 .35
   Nos. 2942-2944 (3)   1.70 .80

Theater Personalities — A1083

Designs: No. 2945, Jiri Voskovec (1905-81). No. 2946, Jan Werich (1905-80). No. 2947, Jaroslav Jezek (1906-42). 22k, Caricatures of Voskovec, Werich, and Jezek with piano.

1995 Photo. & Engr. Perf. 12x11

2945	A1083	3k multicolored	.50	.25
	Complete booklet, 3 #2945		2.00	
2946	A1083	3k multicolored	.50	.25
	Complete booklet, 3 #2946		2.00	
2947	A1083	3k multicolored	.50	.25
	Complete booklet, 3 #2947		2.00	
a.	Strip of 3, #2945-2947		1.75	1.50
	Complete booklet, 2 #2947a		4.00	
	Nos. 2945-2947 (3)		1.50	.75

Souvenir Sheet
Photo.
Perf. 12

2947B	A1083	22k yellow & black	2.50	2.50

Issued: 3k, 3/15; 22k, 9/20.

Havel Type of 1990 Inscribed "Ceska Republika"
Photo. & Engr.
1995, Mar. 22 Perf. 12x11½

2948	A1000	3.60k bl, vio & mag	.45	.20
	Complete booklet, 5 #2948		4.00	

Rural
Architecture
A1084

1995, Mar. 22 Perf. 11½

2949	A1084	40h shown	.20	.20
2950	A1084	60h Homes, diff.	.20	.20

European Nature
Conservation
Year — A1085

1995, Apr. 12

2951	A1085	3k Bombus terrestris	.35	.30
	Complete booklet, 5 #2951		4.00	
2952	A1085	5k Mantis religiosa	.60	.30
	Complete booklet, 5 #2952		4.50	
2953	A1085	6k Calopteryx splendens	.75	.30
	Complete booklet, 5 #2953		5.00	
	Nos. 2951-2953 (3)		1.70	.90

Peace &
Freedom
A1086

Photo. & Engr.
1995, May 3 Perf. 11½

2954	A1086	9k Rose, profiles	1.20	.35
2955	A1086	14k Butterfly, profiles	1.75	.75

Europa.

Natural
Beauties
in Czech
Republic
A1087

Designs: 8k, "Stone Organ" scenic mountain. 9k, Largest sandstone bridge in Europe.

Photo. & Engr.
1995, May 3 Perf. 11½

2956	A1087	8k multicolored	.95	.95
2957	A1087	9k multicolored	1.00	1.00

Nos. 2956-2957 were each issued in sheets of 8. Value, set $17.50.

Children's
Day — A1088

Photo. & Engr.
1995, June 1 Perf. 11½

2958	A1088	3.60k multicolored	.60	.25

First Train from Vienna to Prague,
150th Anniv.
A1089

3k, Chocen Tunnel. 9.60k, Entering Prague.

1995, June 21

2959	A1089	3k multicolored	.35	.25
	Complete booklet, 5 #2959		2.00	
2960	A1089	9.60k multicolored	1.15	.50

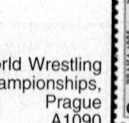

World Wrestling
Championships,
Prague
A1090

Photo. & Engr.
1995, Sept. 6 Perf. 11½

2961	A1090	3k multicolored	.35	.25

Cartoon Characters
A1091

Designs: 3k, Man playing violin, woman washing, by Vladimir Rencin. 3.60k, Angel, naked man, by Vladimir Jiranek. 5k, Circus trainer holding ring for champagne cork to pop through, by Jiri Sliva.

1995, Sept. 6

2962	A1091	3k multicolored	.35	.25
	Complete booklet, 5 #2962		2.00	
2963	A1091	3.60k multicolored	.45	.25
	Complete booklet, 5 #2963		2.50	
2964	A1091	5k multicolored	.60	.30
	Complete booklet, 5 #2964		3.50	
	Nos. 2962-2964 (3)		1.40	.80

A1092   A1093

1995, Sept. 20 Litho. Perf. 13½x13

2965	A1092	3k multicolored	.35	.20

SOS Children's Villages, 25th anniv.

Photo. & Engr.
1995-97 Perf. 12x11½

Designs: 2.40k, Gothic. 3k, Secession. 3.60k, Romance. 4k, Classic portal; 4.60k, Rococo. 9.60k, Renaissance Portal. 12.60k, Cubist. 14k, Baroque.

2966	A1093	2.40k red & green	.30	.20
2967	A1093	3k grn & bl	.35	.20
2967A	A1093	3.60k pur & grn	.45	.20
2968	A1093	4k blue & red	.50	.20
	Complete booklet, 5 #2967A		3.00	
2968A	A1093	4.60k multicolored	.55	.20
2969	A1093	9.60k blue & red	1.10	.45
2969A	A1093	12.60k red brn & bl	1.50	.45
2970	A1093	14k grn & pur	1.60	.60
	Nos. 2966-2970 (8)		6.35	2.50

Issued: 9.60k, 9/27; 2.40k, 14k, 10/11; 3k, 3.60k, 10/25; 4k, 6/12/96; 4.60k, 3/26/97; 12.60k, 6/25/97.

UN, 50th
Anniv.
A1094

1995, Oct. 11 Litho. Perf. 12x11½

2971	A1094	14k multicolored	1.60	.80

Wilhelm Röntgen (1845-1923),
Discovery of the X-Ray,
Cent. — A1095

1995, Oct. 11 Photo. & Engr.

2972	A1095	6k blk, buff & bl vio	.75	.35

Art Type of 1967 Inscribed "CESKA REPUBLIKA"

Designs: 6k, Parisiene, by Ludek Marold. 9k, Vase of Flowers, by J.K. Hirschely. 14k, Portrait of J. Malinsky, by Antonín Machek.

1995, Nov. 8 Perf. 12

2973	A565	6k multicolored	.75	.35
2974	A565	9k multicolored	1.00	.50
2975	A565	14k multicolored	1.60	.80
	Nos. 2973-2975 (3)		3.35	1.65

Nos. 2973-2975 were each printed in sheets of 4. Value, set $13.50.

Christmas — A1096

1995, Nov. 8 Perf. 11½

2976	A1096	3k multicolored	.40	.20
	Complete booklet, 3 #2976		1.50	

Czech Philharmonic Orchestra,
Cent. — A1097

Photo. & Engr.
1996, Jan. 2 Perf. 12x11½

2977	A1097	3.60k multicolored	.45	.25

Tradition of Czech
Stamp
Production — A1098

Photo. & Engr.
1996, Jan. 20 Perf. 11½x12

2978	A1098	3.60k Design A5 of 1920	.45	.25

Vera Mencikova (1906-44), Chess
Player — A1099

Photo. & Engr.
1996, Feb. 14 Perf. 12x11½

2979	A1099	6k multicolored	.75	.35

Easter — A1100

1996, Mar. 13 Perf. 11½x12

2980	A1100	3k multicolored	.35	.20
	Complete booklet, 5 #2980		1.75	

Josef Sudek
(1896-1976),
Photographer
A1101

Photo. & Engr.
1996, Mar. 13 Perf. 11

2981	A1101	9.60k multicolored	1.10	.55

Rulers from House of
Luxembourg — A1102

Designs: a, John of Luxembourg (1296-1346). b, Charles IV (1316-78). c, Wenceslas IV. (1361-1419). d, Sigismund (1368-1437).

1996, Mar. 27 Engr. Perf. 11½

2982	A1102	14k Sheet of 4, #a.-d. + label	6.75	6.75

Jiri Guth-
Jurkovsky,
Participant in
First Modern
Olympic
Games, Athens
A1103

Photo. & Engr.
1996, Mar. 27 Perf. 11½

2983	A1103	9.60k multicolored	1.10	.60

Modern Olympic Games, cent.

World Wildlife Fund — A1104

Ema Destinnova (1878-1930), Singer — A1105

Designs: a, 3.60k, Eliomys quercinus. b, 5k, Dryomys nitedula. c, 6k, Spermophilus citellus. d, 8k, Sicista betulina.

Photo. & Engr.
1996, Apr. 24 **Perf. 11½x12**
2984 A1104 Block of 4, #a.-d. 3.00 3.00
Issued in sheets of 8 stamps. Value $9.

1996, May 2 **Perf. 11½**
2985 A1105 8k multicolored .90 .40
Europa.
No. 2985 was issued in sheets of 10. Value $11.

A1106   A1107

Photo. & Engr.
1996, May 15 **Perf. 11x11½**
2986 A1106 12k multicolored 1.40 .65
Jean Gaspart Deburau (1796-1846), mime.

1996, May 29
2987 A1107 3k multicolored .35 .20
1996 Summmer Olympic Games, Atlanta.

Intl. Children's Day — A1108

Photo. & Engr.
1996, May 29 **Perf. 11½**
2988 A1108 3k multicolored .35 .20

Architectural Sites — A1109

UNESCO: 8k, St. Nepomuk Church, Zelena Hora. 9k, Loretta Tower, Prague.

1996, June 26 **Engr.** **Perf. 11½**
2989 A1109 8k multicolored .95 .95
2990 A1109 9k multicolored 1.00 1.00
Nos. 2989-2990 were each issued in sheets of 8. Value, set $16.
See Nos. 3056-3057.

UNICEF, 50th Anniv. A1110

Photo. & Engr.
1996, Sept. 11 **Perf. 12x11**
2991 A1110 3k multicolored .35 .20

Horses
A1111   A1112

Photo. & Engr.
1996, Sept. 25 **Perf. 11x11½**
2992 A1111 3k multicolored .50 .20
2993 A1112 3k multicolored .50 .20
a. Pair, #2992-2993 1.00 .75
Complete booklet, 3 #2992, 2 #2993 3.00
Complete booklet, 2 #2992, 3 #2993 3.00

Souvenir Sheet

Vaclav Havel, 60th Birthday — A1113

Illustration reduced.

1996, Oct. 5
2994 A1113 Sheet of 2 1.40 1.40
a. 6k red & blue .80 .50

Art Type of 1967 Inscribed "CESKA REPUBLICA"
The Baroque Chair, by Endre Nemes (1909-85).

1996, Oct. 5 **Engr.** **Perf. 11½**
2995 A565 20k multicolored 2.40 2.40
No. 2995 was issued in sheets of 4. Value $10.
See Slovakia No. 255; Sweden No. 2199.

Tycho Brahe (1546-1601), Astronomer — A1114

Photo. & Engr.
1996, Oct. 9 **Perf. 11½x11**
2996 A1114 5k multicolored .60 .30

Biplanes A1115

1996, Oct. 9
2997 A1115 7k Letov S1 (1920) .85 .40
2998 A1115 8k Aero A11 (1925) .95 .45
2999 A1115 10k Avia BH21 (1925) 1.20 .55
Nos. 2997-2999 (3) 3.00 1.40

Christmas A1116

Photo. & Engr.
1996, Nov. 13 **Perf. 11½**
3000 A1116 3k multicolored .45 .20
Complete booklet, 5 #3000 3.50

Art Type of 1967 Inscribed "CESKA REPUBLICA"
Designs: 9k, Garden of Eden, by Josef Váchal (1884-1969), horiz. 11k, Breakfast, by Georg Flegel (1566-1638).

1996, Nov. 13 **Engr.** **Perf. 11½**
3001 A565 9k multicolored 1.00 1.00
3002 A565 11k multicolored 1.25 1.25
Nos. 3001-3002 were each issued in sheets of 4. Value, set $10.

Czech Stamp Production — A1117

Photo. & Engr.
1997, Jan. 20 **Perf. 11½x12**
3003 A1117 3.60k #68, bl & red .40 .25

Easter — A1118   Flowers — A1119

Photo. & Engr.
1997, Mar. 12 **Perf. 11½**
3004 A1118 3k multicolored .65 .20
Complete booklet, 5 #3004 4.00

1997, Mar. 12 **Perf. 11x11½**
3.60k, Erythronium dens-canis. 4k, Calla palustris. 5k, Cypripedium calceolus. 8k, Iris pumila.
3005 A1119 3.60k multicolored .45 .20
Complete booklet, 5 #3005 2.50
3006 A1119 4k multicolored .45 .25
Complete booklet, 5 #3006 2.50
3007 A1119 5k multicolored .60 .30
Complete booklet, 5 #3007 3.50
3008 A1119 8k multicolored .95 .45
Complete booklet, 5 #3008 5.00
Nos. 3005-3008 (4) 2.45 1.20

A1120   A1121

Jewish Monuments in Prague: 8k, Altneuschul Synagogue. 10k, Tombstone of Rabbi Judah Loew MaHaRal.

1997, Apr. 30 **Perf. 11½**
3009 A1120 8k multicolored .90 .45
3010 A1120 10k multicolored 1.10 .55
a. Sheet, 4 each #3009-3010 8.00 4.00
See Israel Nos. 1302-1303.

1997, Mar. 26 **Litho.** **Perf. 13x13½**
Greetings stamp.
3011 A1121 4k Girl with cats .50 .25

A1122   A1123

1997, Apr. 23 **Engr.** **Perf. 11½**
3012 A1122 7k deep violet .85 .40
St. Adalbert (956-97). See Germany No. 1964, Hungary No. 3569, Poland No. 3337, Vatican City No. 1040.

Photo. & Engr.
1997, Apr. 30 **Perf. 11½x12**
Europa (Stories and Legends): No. 3013, Queen, knight with sword, lion, snakes. No. 3014, Man riding in chariot drawn by chickens, King looking through window.
3013 A1123 8k multicolored .95 .95
3014 A1123 8k multicolored .95 .95
Nos. 3013-3014 were each issued in sheets of 8. Value, set $16.

Souvenir Sheet

Collections of Rudolf II (1522-1612), Prague Exhibition A1124

Designs: a, 6k, Musical instruments, flowers, face of bearded man. b, 8k, Rudolf II wearing laurel wreath, holding rose, Muses. c, 10k, Rudolf II, skull, moth's wings, tree, flowers, fruit.

1997, May 14 **Engr.** **Perf. 12**
3015 A1124 Sheet of 3, #a.-c. 2.75 2.75

Intl. Children's Day — A1125

Photo. & Engr.
1997, May 28 **Perf. 11½**
3016 A1125 4.60k multicolored .55 .25

Frantisek Krizik (1847-1941), Electrical Engineer, Inventor of Arc Lamp — A1126

Photo. & Engr.

1997, June 25			Perf. 12x11½	
3017	A1126	6k multicolored	.70	.25

European Swimming & Diving Championships, Prague — A1127

Photo. & Engr.

1997, Aug. 27			Perf. 11½	
3018	A1127	11k multicolored	1.50	.40

"The Good Soldier Schweik," by Jaroslav Hasek, 110th Anniv. — A1128

4k, Mrs. Müller, Schweik in wheelchair. 4.60k, Lt. Lukás, Col. Kraus von Zillergut, dog. 6k, Schweik smoking pipe, winter scene.

Photo. & Engr.

1997, Sept. 10			Perf. 12x11½	
3019	A1128	4k multicolored	.50	.20
a.		Booklet pane of 8 + 4 labels	4.50	
		Complete booklet, #3019a	4.50	
3020	A1128	4.60k multicolored	.55	.20
a.		Booklet pane of 8 + 4 labels	5.00	
		Complete booklet, #3020a	5.00	
3021	A1128	6k multicolored	.70	.30
a.		Booklet pane of 8 + 4 labels	6.00	
		Complete booklet, #3021a	6.00	
		Nos. 3019-3021 (3)	1.75	.70

Praga 1998, Intl. Stamp Exhibition — A1129

#3022, Lesser Town, Prague Castle. #3023, Old Town, bridges over Vltava River.

Photo. & Engr.

1997, Sept. 24			Perf. 11½	
3022	A1129	15k multicolored	1.80	.70
3023	A1129	15k multicolored	1.80	.70
a.		Souvenir sheet, #3022-3023 + 2 labels	3.50	3.00

Historic Service Vehicles A1130

Designs: 4k, Postal bus, Prague. 4.60k, Sentinel truck, Skoda. 8k, Fire truck, Tatra.

Photo. & Engr.

1997, Oct. 8			Perf. 12x11½	
3024	A1130	4k multicolored	.45	.20
3025	A1130	4.60k multicolored	.55	.25
3026	A1130	8k multicolored	.95	.40
		Complete booklet, 5 #3026	5.00	
		Nos. 3024-3026 (3)	1.95	.85

A1131　　　　　A1132

Photo. & Engr.

1997, Nov. 12			Perf. 11½	
3027	A1131	4k multicolored	.50	.20
		Complete booklet, 5 #3027	2.75	

Christmas.

Art Type of 1967 Inscribed "CESKA REPUBLIKA"

7k, Landscape with Chateau in Chantilly, by Antonín Chittussi (1847-91). 12k, The Prophets Came Out of the Desert, by Frantisek Bílek (1872-1941). 1 6k, Parisian Antiquarians, by T. F. Simon (1877-1942).

1997, Nov. 12			Perf. 12	
3028	A565	7k multi, horiz.	.85	.85
3029	A565	12k multi	1.40	1.40
3030	A565	16k multi	1.90	1.90
		Nos. 3028-3030 (3)	4.15	4.15

Nos. 3028-3030 were each issued in sheets of 4. Value, set $17.

1998, Jan. 20	Litho.		Perf. 11½x12	
3031	A1132	7k multicolored	.85	.30

1998 Winter Olympic Games, Nagano.

Tradition of Czech Stamp Production — A1133

Photo. & Engr.

1998, Jan. 20			Perf. 12x11½	
3032	A1133	12.60k Type A8	1.50	.55
a.		Booklet pane of 8 + 4 labels	12.50	
		Complete booklet, #3032a	12.50	

Pres. Václav Havel A1134　　　Love A1135

1998, Jan. 22

3033	A1134	4.60k dark grn & red	.55	.20

See No. 3114.

1998, Feb. 4			Perf. 11½	
3034	A1135	4k multicolored	.45	.20
		Complete booklet, 5 #3034	2.50	

Skibob World Championship, Spindleruv Mlyn — A1136

1998, Feb. 25

3035	A1136	8k multicolored	.95	.35

Prague Philatelic Exhibition Type of 1938

Souvenir Sheet

1998, Feb. 25	Engr.		Perf. 12x11½	
3036	A87	Sheet of 2	7.00	4.00
a.		30k like #251a	3.50	1.50

Prague '98, Intl. Philatelic Exhibition.

Easter — A1137

Photo. & Engr.

1998, Mar. 25			Perf. 11x11½	
3037	A1137	4k multicolored	.45	.20

Ondrejov Observatory, Cent. — A1138

1998, Mar. 25			Perf. 12x11½	
3038	A1138	4.60k multicolored	.55	.20

Czech Ice Hockey Team, Gold Medalists at Nagano Winter Olympic Games — A1139

1998, Apr. 1	Litho.		Perf. 11½x12	
3039	A1139	23k Dominik Hasek	2.75	2.00

No. 3039 was issued in a sheet with two labels.

Charles University and New Town, Prague, 650th Anniv. — A1140

Designs: a, 15k, Hands forming arch, University seal. b, 22k, Charles IV (1316-78), Holy Roman Emperor, King of Bohemia. c, 23k, Groin vault, St. Vitus Cathedral, Prague.

1998, Apr. 1	Engr.		Perf. 12	
3040	A1140	Sheet of 3, #a.-c.	7.00	5.00

World Book and Copyright Day — A1141

1998, Apr. 23	Litho.		Perf. 12x11½	
3041	A1141	10k multicolored	1.20	.45

Nature Conservation A1142

			Perf. 13x13½	
1998, Apr. 23				
3042	A1142	4.60k Perdix perdix	.55	.20
3043	A1142	4.60k Lyrurus tetrix	.55	.20
a.		Pair, #3042-3043	1.10	.60
3044	A1142	8k Cervus elaphus	.95	.35

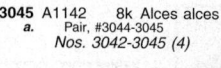

3045	A1142	8k Alces alces	.95	.35
a.		Pair, #3044-3045	1.90	1.10
		Nos. 3042-3045 (4)	3.00	1.10

Natl. Festivals and Holidays A1143

Europa: 11k, King's Ride. 15k, Wearing masks for Carnival.

Litho. & Engr.

1998, May 5			Perf. 11½	
3046	A1143	11k multicolored	1.25	.55
3047	A1143	15k multicolored	1.75	.75

Intl. Children's Day — A1144

Designs: 4k, Two satyr musicians. 4.60k, Character riding on fish.

Photo. & Engr.

1998, May 27			Perf. 11½	
3048	A1144	4k multicolored	.45	.20
a.		Booklet of 6 +4 labels	3.00	
		Complete booklet, #3048a	3.00	
3049	A1144	4.60k multicolored	.55	.20
a.		Booklet of 6 + 4 labels	3.50	
		Complete booklet, #3049a	3.50	

Famous Men — A1145

Designs: 4k, Frantisek Kmoch (1848-1912), bandleader, composer. 4.60k, Frantisek Palacky (1798-1876), historian, politician. 6k, Rafael Kubelík (1914-96), composer, conductor.

1998, May 27			Perf. 11½x12	
3050	A1145	4k multicolored	.45	.20
3051	A1145	4.60k multicolored	.55	.20
3052	A1145	6k multicolored	.70	.25
		Nos. 3050-3052 (3)	1.70	.65

Revolt of 1848, 150th Anniv. A1146

1998, May 27			Perf. 12x11½	
3053	A1146	15k multicolored	1.75	.50

Art Type of 1967 Inscribed "CESKA REPUBLIKA"

Praga 1998 Intl. Stamp Exhibition, works of art: 22k, Amorfa Dvoubarevna Fuga, by Frantisek Kupka (1871-1957), horiz. 23k, Escape, by Paul Gauguin (1848-1903), horiz.

1998, June 17	Engr.		Perf. 12	
3054	A565	22k multicolored	2.50	1.75
3055	A565	23k multicolored	2.75	1.75

Nos. 3054-3055 were each issued in sheets of 4. Value, set $22.

UNESCO World Heritage Sites Type of 1996

8k, St. Barbara Cathedral, Kutná Hora, horiz. 11k, The Chateau of Valtice, horiz.

1998, Oct. 7	Engr.		Perf. 11½x12	
3056	A1109	8k multicolored	.95	.40
3057	A1109	11k multicolored	1.25	.60

Nos. 3056-3057 were each issued in sheets of 8. Value, set $17.50.

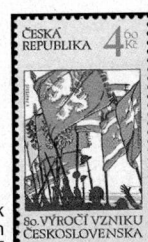

Czechoslovak Republic, 80th Anniv. — A1147

Designs based on World War I recruitment posters by Vojtech Preissig (1873-1944): 4.60k, Soldiers holding flags, guns. 5k, Three soldiers marching. 12.60k, Flags waving from city buildings.

Perf. 11½x11¾

1998, Oct. 28   **Litho. & Engr.**

3058	A1147	4.60k multicolored	.55	.25
3059	A1147	5k multicolored	.60	.25
3060	A1147	12.60k multicolored	1.50	.60
		Nos. 3058-3060 (3)	2.65	1.10

No. 3060 was issued in sheets of 6+2 labels. Value $25.

Christmas A1148

Designs: 4k, People following star. 6k, Angel blowing trumpet over town, vert.

Photo. & Engr.

1998, Nov. 18   **Perf. 11½**

3061	A1148	4k multicolored	.45	.20
		Complete booklet, 5 #3061	2.50	
3062	A1148	6k multicolored	.70	.25
		Complete booklet, 5 #3062	4.00	

Signs of the Zodiac — A1149

1998-2000   **Perf. 12x11½**

3063	A1149	1k Capricorn	.20	.20
3064	A1149	10k Aquarius	1.20	.25
3065	A1149	9k Libra	1.00	.25
3066	A1149	8k Cancer	.95	.25
3067	A1149	20k Sagittarius	2.25	.45

Photo. & Engr.
Perf. 11¾x11¼

3068	A1149	5k Taurus	.55	.25
		Booklet, 5 #3068	2.75	
3069	A1149	5.40k Scorpio	.60	.25
		Booklet, 5 #3069	3.00	
3070	A1149	2k Virgo	.25	.20
3071	A1149	40h Pisces	.20	.20
3072	A1149	12k Leo	1.40	.30
3073	A1149	17k Gemini	2.00	.65
3074	A1149	26k Aries	3.00	.95
		Nos. 3063-3074 (12)	13.60	4.20

Issued: 1k, 10k, 11/18; 9k, 5/5/99; 8k, 20k, 9/8/99; 5k, 5.40k, 12/8/99; 2k, 5/9/00. 40h, 1/20/01. 12k, 2/21/01. 17k, 9/1/02. 26k, 2/12/03.

Art Type of 1967 Inscribed "CESKA REPUBLIKA"

15k, Painting from the Greater Cycle, 1902, by Jan Preisler (1872-1918), horiz. 16k, Spinner, by Josef Navrátil (1798-1865).

1998, Dec. 9   **Perf. 12**

3075	A565	15k multicolored	1.75	1.00
3076	A565	16k multicolored	1.80	1.00

Nos. 3075-3076 were each issued in sheets of 4. Value, set $14.50.

A1150   A1151

Photo. & Engr.

1999, Jan. 20   **Perf. 11½x11¾**

3077	A1150	4.60k #164	.50	.20
a.		Booklet pane of 8 + 4 labels	4.00	
		Complete booklet, #3077a	4.00	

Tradition of Czech stamp production.

Photo. & Engr.

1999, Feb. 17   **Perf. 11½**

Domestic cats.

3078	A1151	4.60k shown	.55	.20
		Complete booklet, 5 #3078	2.75	
3079	A1151	5k Adult, kitten	.55	.25
		Complete booklet, 5 #3079	2.75	
3080	A1151	7k Two cats	.80	.30
		Complete booklet, 5 #3080	4.00	
		Nos. 3078-3080 (3)	1.90	.75

Easter — A1152   A1153

Photo. & Engr.

1999, Mar. 10   **Perf. 11¼x11½**

3081	A1152	3k multicolored	.35	.20

Perf. 12¾x13¼

1999, Mar. 10   **Litho.**

Protected birds: No. 3082, Merops apiaster. No. 3083, Upupa epops.
Protected butterflies: No. 3084, Catocala electa. No. 3085, Euphydryas maturna.

3082	A1153	4.60k multicolored	.55	.20
3083	A1153	4.60k multicolored	.55	.20
a.		Pair, #3082-3083	1.10	.60
		Complete booklet, 3 #3082, 2 #3083	2.75	
3084	A1153	5k multicolored	.55	.20
3085	A1153	5k multicolored	.55	.20
a.		Pair, #3084-3085	1.10	.60
		Complete booklet, 3 #3084, 2 #3085	2.75	

Nature conservation.

Czech Republic's Entry Into NATO — A1154

Photo. & Engr.

1999, Mar. 12   **Perf. 12x11½**

3086	A1154	4.60k multicolored	.55	.20

Council of Europe, 50th Anniv. A1155

Photo. & Engr.

1999, Apr. 14   **Perf. 11¾x11¼**

3087	A1155	7k multicolored	.80	.30

Natl. Olympic Committee, Cent. — A1156

Design: Josef Rössler-Orovsky (1869-1933), founder of Czech Olympic Committee.

1999, Apr. 14   **Perf. 11¼x11¾**

3088	A1156	9k multicolored	1.00	.35

Europa A1157

Natl. Parks: 11k, Sumava. 17k, Podyji.

1999, May 5   **Perf. 11¾x11¼**

3089	A1157	11k multicolored	1.25	.40
3090	A1157	17k multicolored	2.00	.65

Nos. 3089-3090 were each issued in sheets of 8. Value, set $27.

Ferda the Ant, Pytlik the Beetle and Ladybird A1158

Photo. & Engr.

1999, May 26   **Perf. 11½x11¼**

3091	A1158	4.60k multicolored	.55	.20

Bridges A1159

1999, May 26   **Engr.**   **Perf. 11¾**

3092	A1159	8k Stádlec, vert.	.90	.40
3093	A1159	11k Cernvír	1.25	.60

Nos. 3092-3094 were each issued in sheets of 8. Value, set $17.50.

Souvenir Sheet

Paleontologist Joachim Barrande (1799-1883) and Trilobite Fossils — A1160

a, 13k, Barrande, fossils. b, 31k, Delphon forbesi, Ophioceras simplex, Carolicrinus barrandei.

1999, June 23   **Engr.**   **Perf. 11¾**

3094	A1160	Sheet of 2, #a.-b. + 2 labels	5.00	4.00

Jihlava Mining Rights, 750th Anniv. A1161

Photo. & Engr.

1999, June 23   **Perf. 11¾x11¼**

3095	A1161	8k multicolored	.90	.35
a.		Bklt. pane of 8 + 4 labels	7.25	
		Complete booklet, #3095a	7.50	

UPU, 125th Anniv. — A1162

Litho. & Engr.

1999, June 23   **Perf. 11¾**

3096	A1162	9k multicolored	1.00	.40

Issued se-tenant with two labels.

Vincenc Preissnitz (1799-1851), Hydrotherapy Advocate A1163

Photo. & Engr.

1999, Sept. 8   **Perf. 11¼**

3097	A1163	4.60k multicolored	.50	.25

UNESCO.

Carved Beehives A1164   Cartoons by Miroslav Bartak A1165

Designs: 4.60k, Woman. 5k, St. Joseph and Infant Jesus. 7k, Chimney sweep.

Photo. & Engr.

1999, Sept. 29   **Perf. 11¼x11½**

3098	A1164	4.60k multi	.55	.25
		Complete booklet, 5 #3098	2.75	
3099	A1164	5k multi	.60	.25
		Complete booklet, 5 #3099	3.00	
3100	A1164	7k multi	.80	.30
		Complete booklet, 5 #3100	4.00	
		Nos. 3098-3100 (3)	1.95	.80

1999, Oct. 20

Designs: 4.60k, Doctor in clown mask, infant. 5k, Dog with pipe. 7k, Night seeping through window sill.

3101	A1165	4.60k multi	.55	.25
3102	A1165	5k multi	.60	.25
3103	A1165	7k multi	.80	.30
		Nos. 3101-3103 (3)	1.95	.80

Souvenir Sheet

Beuron Art School — A1166

Designs: a, 11k, Mater Dei, 1898. b, 13k, Pantocrator, 1911.

Litho. & Engr.
1999, Oct. 20   *Perf. 11¾*
3104 A1166 Sheet of 2, #a.-b.   2.75 2.00

Art Type of 1967 Inscribed "CESKA REPUBLIKA"

Designs: 13k, Red Orchid, by Jindrich Styrsky (1899-1942). 17k, Landscape with Marsh, by Julius Marák (1832-99). 26k, Monument, by Frantisek Hudecek (1909-90).

1999, Nov. 10   **Engr.**   *Perf. 11¾*
3105 A565 13k multi   1.50 1.00
3106 A565 17k multi   2.00 1.00
3107 A565 26k multi   3.00 2.00
   Nos. 3105-3107 (3)   6.50 4.50

Nos. 3105-3107 were each issued in sheets of 4. Value, set $26.

A1167   A1168

Photo. & Engr.
1999, Nov. 10   *Perf. 11¼x11½*
3108 A1167 3k multi   .35 .20
Christmas.

Photo. & Engr.
2000, Jan. 20   *Perf. 11¼x11¾*
3109 A1168 5.40k #B151   .60 .25
  a.   Bkt. pane of 8 + 4 labels   5.00
    Booklet, #3109a   5.00

Tradition of Czech stamp production.

Brno 2000 Philatelic
Exhibition — A1169

Designs: 5k, 1593 view of Brno. 50k, St. James's Church, vert.

2000, Jan. 20   *Perf. 11¾x11¼*
3110 A1169 5k multi   .60 .20

Souvenir Sheet
Perf. 11¼x11¾
3111 A1169 50k multi   5.75 4.00
No. 3110 printed in sheets of 35 stamps and 30 labels.

Kutna Hora Royal Mining Law, 700th Anniv. — A1170

2000, Mar. 1   *Perf. 11¼x11¾*
3112 A1170 5k multi   .60 .25
  a.   Booklet pane of 8 + 4 labels   5.00
    Booklet, #3112a   5.00

Souvenir Sheet

Pres. Thomas Garrigue Masaryk
(1850-1937) — A1171

Illustration reduced.

2000, Mar. 1   **Engr.**   *Perf. 11¾*
3113 A1171 17k multi   2.00 1.50

Pres. Havel Type of 1998
Photo. & Engr.
2000, Mar. 1   *Perf. 11¾x11¼*
3114 A1134 5.40k Prus bl & org brn   .60 .25

Easter — A1172

Photo. & Engr.
2000, Apr. 5   *Perf. 11¼x11½*
3115 A1172 5k multi   .60 .25

Souvenir Sheet

Prague, 2000 European City of
Culture — A1173

No. 3116: a, 9k, Statue of man. b, 11k, Statue of harpist. c, 17k, Statue of King Charles IV.
Illustration reduced.

Litho. & Engr.
2000, Apr. 5   *Perf. 11¾*
3116 A1173 #a-c + 3 labels   4.25 4.25

Souvenir Sheet

Trains — A1174

No. 3117: a, 8k, Train from 1900. b, 15k, Train from 2000.
Illustration reduced.

Litho. & Engr.
2000, May 5   *Perf. 11¾*
3117 A1174 Sheet of 2, #a-b, +3 labels   2.50 2.50

Czech Personalities
A1175

5k, Vítezslav Nezval (1900-58), writer. 8k, Gustav Mahler (1860-1911), composer.

Photo. & Engr.
2000, May 5   *Perf. 11¼x11¾*
3118-3119 A1175 Set of 2   1.50 .45

Europa, 2000
Common Design Type
2000, May 5   **Litho.**   *Perf. 12¾x13¼*
3120 CD17 9k multi   1.00 .40

Intl. Children's
Year — A1176

Photo. & Engr.
2000, May 31   *Perf. 11½x11¼*
3121 A1176 5.40k multi   .60 .20
  a.   Booklet pane of 8 + 2 labels   5.00
    Booklet, #3121a   5.00

1995 Proof of Fermat's Last Theorem
by Andrew Wiles
A1177

2000, May 31   *Perf. 11¾x11¼*
3122 A1177 7k multi   .80 .25
Intl. Mathematics Year.

Prague Landmarks — A1178

Designs: 9k, Charles Bridge tower. 11k, Nicholas's Church. 13k, Town Hall.

2000, June 28   **Engr.**   *Perf. 11¾*
3123-3125 A1178 Set of 3   3.75 1.10

Mushrooms — A1179

No. 3126, 5k: a, Geastrum pouzarii. b, Boletus satanoides.
No. 3127, 5.40k: a, Morchella pragensis. b, Verpa bohemica.

Photo. & Engr.
2000, June 28   *Perf. 11¼x11½*
Pairs, #a-b
3126-3127 A1179 Set of 2   2.40 .70
   Booklet, 3 #3126a, 2 #3126b   3.50
   Booklet, 3 #3127b, 2 #3127a   3.50

Meeting of Intl. Monetary Fund and
World Bank Group, Prague — A1180

2000, Aug. 30   *Perf. 11¾x11¼*
3128 A1180 7k multi   .60 .25

Ancient
Olympics
A1181

2000, Aug. 30
3129 A1181 9k multi   1.00 .35

2000 Summer Olympics,
Sydney — A1182

2000, Aug. 30
3130 A1182 13k multi   1.50 .45

Hunting — A1183

No. 3131: a, 5k, Falconry. b, 5k, Deer at feed trough.
No. 3132: a, 5.40k, Ducks and blind. b, 5.40k, Deer and blind.

Photo. & Engr.
2000, Oct. 4   *Perf. 11¼x11¾*
Horiz. Pairs, #a-b
3131-3132 A1183 Set of 2   2.40 .55
   Booklet, 3 #3131a, 2 #3131b   3.50
   Booklet, 3 #3132a, 2 #3132b   3.50

Art Type of 1967 Inscribed "CESKA REPUBLIKA"

Designs: 13k, St. Luke the Evangelist, by Master Theodoricus. 17k, Simeon With Infant Jesus, by Petr Jan Brandl. 26k, Brunette, by Alfons Mucha.

2000, Nov. 15 Engr. Perf. 11¾
3133-3135 A565 Set of 3 6.50 4.00

Nos. 3133-3135 were each issued in sheets of 4. Value, set $27.

Christmas — A1184

Photo. & Engr.
2000, Nov. 15 Perf. 11¼x11½
3136 A1184 5k multi .55 .20

End of Millennium A1185 — Advent of New Millennium A1186

2000, Nov. 22
3137 A1185 9k multi 1.00 .35

2001, Jan. 2
3138 A1186 9k multi 1.00 .35

Tradition of Czech Stamp Production A1187

2001, Jan. 20 Perf. 11¼x11¾
3139 A1187 5.40k #474 .60 .25
a. Booklet pane of 8 + 4 labels 5.00
Booklet, #3139a 5.00

Jan Amos Komensky (Comenius, 1592-1670), Theologian — A1188

Photo. & Engr.
2001, Mar. 14 Perf. 11¼x11½
3140 A1188 9k red & black 1.00 .35

Souvenir Sheet

Architecture — A1189

No. 3141: a, 13k, Church and decorations, Jakub. b, 17k, Arcade decorations, Bucovice Castle. c, 31k, Dance Hall, Prague.

2001, Mar. 28 Engr. Perf. 11¾x11½
3141 A1189 Sheet of 3, #a-c 7.00 4.00

Easter — A1190

Photo. & Engr.
2001, Mar. 28 Perf. 11¼x11½
3142 A1190 5.40k multi .60 .25

Souvenir Sheet

Allegory of Art, by Vaclav Vavrinec Reiner — A1191

Litho. & Engr.
2001, Apr. 18 Perf. 11¾
3143 A1191 50k multi 5.75 4.00

Europa A1192

Photo. & Engr.
2001, May 9 Perf. 11¾x11¼
3144 A1192 9k pur & lilac 1.00 .35

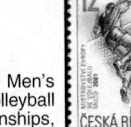
European Men's Volleyball Championships, Ostrova — A1193

Photo. & Engr.
2001, May 9 Perf. 11¼x11½
3145 A1193 12k multi 1.40 .40

Intl. Children's Day — A1194

Famous Men — A1195

Photo. & Engr.
2001, May 30 Perf. 11¼x11½
3146 A1194 5.40k multi .60 .25
a. Booklet pane of 8 + 2 labels 5.00
Booklet, #3146a 5.00

2001, May 30

Designs: 5.40k, Frantisek Skroup (1801-62), composer. 16k, Frantisek Halas (1901-49), writer.

3147-3148 A1195 Set of 2 2.50 .80

Congratulations A1196

2001, June 20
3149 A1196 5.40k multi .60 .25
Booklet, 5 #3149 3.00

Dogs — A1197

No. 3150: a, West Highland terrier. b, Beagle.
No. 3151: a, German shepherd. b, Golden retriever.

Photo. & Engr.
2001, June 20 Perf. 11½x11¼
3150 Pair 1.40 1.00
a.-b. A1197 5.40k Any single .65 .25
Booklet, 3 #3150a, 2 #3150b 3.25
Booklet, 3 #3150b, 2 #3150a 3.25
3151 Pair 1.40 1.00
a.-b. A1197 5.40k Any single .65 .25
Booklet, 3 #3151a, 2 #3151b 3.25

Zoo Animals A1198

No. 3152: a, Pongo pygmaeus. b, Panthera tigris altaica.
No. 3153: a, Ailurus fulgens. b, Fennecus zerda.

Photo. & Engr.
2001, Sept. 5 Perf. 11¾x11¼
3152 Pair 1.40 1.00
a.-b. A1198 5.40k Any single .65 .25
Booklet, 3 #3152b, 2 #3152a 3.25
3153 Pair 1.40 1.00
a.-b. A1198 5.40k Any single .65 .25
Booklet, 3 #3153b, 2 #3153a 3.25

UNESCO World Heritage Sites A1199

Designs: 12k, Kormeríz Castle and Gardens. 14k, Holasovice Historical Village Restoration.

2001, Oct. 9 Engr. Perf. 11½x11¾
3154-3155 A1199 Set of 2 3.00 1.25

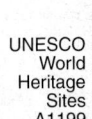
Year of Dialogue Among Civilizations A1200

Photo. & Engr.
2001, Oct. 9 Perf. 11¼x11½
3156 A1200 9k multi 1.00 .35

Mills A1201

Christmas A1202

Designs: 9k, Windmill. 14.40k, Water mill.

2001, Oct. 9
3157-3158 A1201 Set of 2 2.75 .80

Photo. & Engr.
2001, Nov. 14 Perf. 11¼x11½
3159 A1202 5.40k multi .60 .30

Art Type of 1967 Inscribed "CESKA REPUBLIKA"

Designs: 12k, The Annunciation of the Virgin Mary, by Michael J. Rentz. 17k, The Sans Souci Bar in Nimes, by Cyril Bouda. 26k, The Goose Keeper, by Vaclav Brozík.

2001, Nov. 14 Engr. Perf. 11¾
3160-3162 A565 Set of 3 6.25 4.00

Nos. 3160-3162 were each issued in sheets of 4. Value, set $25.

Tradition of Czech Stamp Production — A1203

Photo. & Engr.
2002, Jan. 20 Perf. 11¼x11¾
3163 A1203 5.40k Type A89 .60 .25
a. Booklet pane of 8 + 4 labels 5.00
Booklet, #3163a 5.00

2002 Winter Olympics, Salt Lake City — A1204

2002, Jan. 30 Perf. 11¼
3164 A1204 12k multi 1.40 .45

For overprint, see No. 3168.

2002 Winter Paralympics, Salt Lake City — A1205

2002, Jan. 30 Perf. 11¼x11½
3165 A1205 5.40k multi .60 .25

Composers Jaromír Vejvoda (1902-88), Josef Poncar (1902-86) and Karel Vacek (1902-82) — A1206

2002, Mar. 6 Perf. 11¾x11¼
3166 A1206 9k multi 1.00 .35

Easter — A1207

2002, Mar. 6 Perf. 11¼x11½
3167 A1207 5.40k multi .60 .25

No. 3164
Overprinted in
Blue

Photo. & Engr.
2002, Mar. 8 Perf. 11¼
3168 A1204 12k multi 1.40 .65

Divan, by Vlaho Bukovac (1855-1922) — A1208

Litho. & Engr.
2002, Apr. 23 Perf. 11¾
3169 A1208 17k multi 2.00 1.25

Printed in sheets of 4 + 2 labels. Value $9.
See Croatia No. 487.

Europa
A1209

Photo. & Engr.
2002, May 7 Perf. 11¾x11¼
3170 A1209 9k multi 1.00 .35

Souvenir Sheet

Czech Culture and France — A1210

No. 3171: a, 23k, Klávesy Piana-Jezero, by Frantisek Kupka. b, 31k, Man with Broken Nose, sculpture by Auguste Rodin.

Perf. 11¾x11½
2002, May 7 **Litho. & Engr.**
3171 A1210 Sheet of 2, #a-b 6.25 4.00

Intl. Children's
Day — A1211

Photo. & Engr.
2002, May 29 Perf. 11¼x11½
3172 A1211 5.40k multi .60 .25
a. Booklet pane of 8 + 2 labels 5.00
Complete booklet, #3172a 5.00

Margaritifera
Margaritifera
A1212

2002, June 6
3173 A1212 9k multi 1.00 .35

Jan Hus (1372-1415), Religious
Leader — A1213

2002, June 19
3174 A1213 9k multi + label 1.00 .35

Souvenir Sheet

Worldwide Fund for Nature
(WWF) — A1214

Butterflies: a, 5.40k, Maculinea nausithous. b, 5.40k, Maculinea alcon. c, 9k, Maculinea teleius. d, 9k, Maculinea arion.

Litho. & Engr.
2002, June 19 Perf. 11¾
3175 A1214 Sheet of 4, #a-d + 4 labels 3.25 2.50

Pansy — A1215

Photo. & Engr.
2002, Sept. 1 Perf. 11¾x11¼
3176 A1215 6.40k multi .75 .25

World Heritage Sites Type of 2001
Designs: 12k, Litomysl Castle. 14k, Holy Trinity Column, Olomouc, vert.

Perf. 11½x11¾, 11¾x11½
2002, Sept. 11 **Engr.**
3177-3178 A1199 Set of 2 2.75 2.00
Nos. 3177-3178 were each issued in sheets of 8. Value, set $25.

Emil Zátopek (1922-2000), Olympic Long
Distance
Runner — A1216

Photo. & Engr.
2002, Sept. 11 Perf. 11¼x11¾
3179 A1216 9k multi 1.00 .35

Pres. Havel Type of 1998
Photo. & Engr.
2002, Nov. 6 Perf. 11¾x11¼
3180 A1134 6.40k pur & blue .75 .25

St. Nicholas'
Day
A1217

Christmas
A1218

2002, Nov. 6 Perf. 11¼x11½
3181 A1217 6.40k multi .75 .25
a. Booklet pane of 8 + 2 labels 6.00 —
Complete booklet, #3181a 6.00

2002, Nov. 13
3182 A1218 6.40k multi .75 .25

NATO Summit,
Prague — A1219

2002, Nov. 14 Perf. 11¼x11¾
3183 A1219 9k multi 1.00 .30

Furniture — A1220

Designs: 6.40k, Armchair, 17th cent. 9k, Sewing table with hemispheric cover, 1820. 12k, Dressing table with mirror, 1860. 17k, Art deco amchair, 1923.

2003, Dec. 11
3184-3187 A1220 Set of 4 5.00 2.00

Art Type of 1967 Inscribed "CESKA REPUBLIKA"
Designs: 12k, The Abandoned, by Jaroslav Panuska, horiz. 20k, St. Wenceslas, by Mikoláš Ales. 26k, Portrait of a Young Man with a Lute, by Jan Petr Molitor.

2002, Dec. 11 **Engr.** Perf. 11¾
3188-3190 A565 Set of 3 6.50 3.50
Nos. 3188-3190 were each issued in sheets of 4. Value, set $27.

Souvenir Sheet

10. VÝROČÍ
ČESKÉ REPUBLIKY

Czech Republic, 10th Anniv. — A1221

Litho. & Engr.
2003, Jan. 1 Perf. 11¾
3191 A1221 25k multi 2.75 1.50

Tradition of Czech
Stamp
Production — A1222

Photo. & Engr.
2003, Jan. 20 Perf. 11¼x11¾
3192 A1222 6.40k Type A75 .75 .25
a. Booklet pane of 8 + 2 labels 6.00 —
Complete booklet, #3192a 6.00

Famous
Men — A1223

Designs: 6.40k, Jaroslav Vrchlicky (1853-1912), poet. 8k, Josef Thomayer (1853-1927), physician and writer.

2003, Feb. 12 Perf. 11½x11¼
3193-3194 A1223 Set of 2 1.60 .50

Easter — A1224

2003, Mar. 26 Perf. 11¼x11½
3195 A1224 6.40k multi .75 .25

Roses Above Prague — A1225

Perf. 12¾x13¼
2003, Mar. 26 **Litho.**
3196 A1225 6.40k multi + label .75 .35
Labels could be personalized.
Issued in sheets of 9 stamps and 12 labels. Value $9.

Lace
A1226

Designs: 6.40k, Netted lace. 9k, Bobbin lace.

Photo. & Engr.

2003, Mar. 26		Perf. 11¼	
3197	A1226 6.40k bl, dk bl & red	.75	.25
a.	Booklet pane of 6 + 4 labels	4.50	
	Complete booklet, #3197a	4.50	
3198	A1226 9k dk bl, bl & red	1.00	.35
a.	Booklet pane of 6 + 4 labels	6.00	
	Complete booklet, #3197a	6.00	

Europa — A1227

Litho. & Engr.

2003, May 7		Perf. 11¾	
3199	A1227 9k multi	1.00	.65

Geologic Attractions — A1228

Designs: 12k, Sandstone towers, Hrubá Skála Region. 14k, Punkva Caves, Moravian karst area.

2003, May 7	Engr.	Perf. 11½x11¾	
3200-3201	A1228	Set of 2	3.00 1.75

Nos. 3200-3201 were each issued in sheets of 8. Value, set $25.

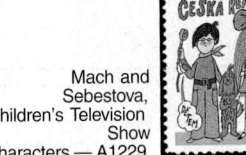

Mach and Sebestova, Children's Television Show Characters — A1229

Photo. & Engr.

2003, May 28		Perf. 11¼x11½	
3202	A1229 6.40k multi	.75	.35

First Electric Railway, Tábor — Bechyne, Cent. A1230

2003, May 28		Perf. 11¾x11¼	
3203	A1230 10k multi	1.10	.45

A1231

A1233

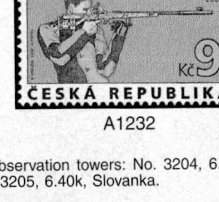

A1232

Observation towers: No. 3204, 6.40k, Klet. No. 3205, 6.40k, Slovanka.

2003, May 28		Perf. 11¼x11½	
3204-3205	A1231	Set of 2	1.50 .50

2003, June 25		Perf. 11¾x11¼	
3206	A1232 9k multi	1.00	.35

European Shooting Championships, Plzen and Brno.

2003, June 25		Perf. 11¼x11½	
3207	A1233 9k multi	1.00	.35

Josef Dobrovsky (1753-1829), linguist.

Pres. Vaclav Klaus — A1234

Photo. & Engr.

2003		Perf. 11¾x11¼	
3208	A1234 6.40k buff, red & vio bl	.75	.35
3209	A1234 6.50k Prus bl & pur	.75	.35

Issued: 6.40k, 7/30; 6.50k, 11/5.

Souvenir Sheet

Tropical Fish — A1235

No. 3210: a, 12k, Betta splendens (27x44mm). b, 14k, Pterophyllum scalare (27x44mm). c, 16k, Carassius auratus (54x44mm). d, 20k, Symphysodon aequifasciatus (54x44mm).

Litho. & Engr.

2003, Sept. 10		Perf. 11¾	
3210	A1235	Sheet of 4, #a-d	7.00 4.50

Oriental Carpets A1236

Designs: 9k, Turkish prayer carpet, 19th cent. 12k, Turkish carpet, 18th cent.

2003, Oct. 1	Engr.	Perf. 11¾	
3211-3212	A1236	Set of 2	2.40 1.50

Nos. 3211-3212 were each issued in sheets of 4. Value, set $10.

Tympanum, Porta Coeli Monastery, Predkláserí — A1237

Photo. & Engr.

2003, Oct. 15		Perf. 11¾x11¼	
3213	A1237 6.50k multi	.75	.45
a.	Booklet pane of 8 + 4 labels	6.00	
	Complete booklet, #3213a	6.00	

Birds of Prey — A1238

Designs: 6.50k, Milvus milvus. 8k, Falco peregrinus. 9k, Hieraaetus pennatus.

2003, Oct. 15		Perf. 11¼x11½	
3214	A1238 6.50k multi	.75	.25
	Booklet, 5 #3214	3.75	
3215	A1238 8k multi	.90	.30
	Booklet, 5 #3215	4.50	
3216	A1238 9k multi	1.00	.30
	Booklet, 5 #3216	5.00	
	Nos. 3214-3216 (3)	2.65	.85

Czech Fire Fighters, 140th Anniv. A1239

Fire engines: 6.50k, Wooden fire engine, 1822. 9k, Motorized fire engine, 1933. 12k, CAS 8/Avia Daewoo fire truck, 2002.

2003, Oct. 15		Perf. 11¾x11¼	
3217-3219	A1239	Set of 3	3.00 1.00

Flower Type of 2002

Designs: 50h, Cornflower (chrpa). 6.50k, Dahlia (jirina).

2003, Oct. 22			
3220	A1215 50h multi	.20	.20
3221	A1215 6.50k multi	.75	.25

Roses Over Prague Type of 2003 and

Prague Castle Lantern — A1240

2003, Oct. 22	Litho.	Perf. 12¾x13¼	
3222	A1225 6.50k multi + label	.75	.25
3223	A1240 9k multi + label	1.00	.30

Labels could be personalized. Nos. 3222-3223 were each issued in sheets of 9 stamps and 12 labels. Value, set $17.50.

Art Type of 1967 Inscribed "CESKA REPUBLIKA"

Designs: 17k, Poor Countryside, by Max Svabinsky, horiz. 20k, Autumn in Veltrusy, by Antonín Slavícek. 26k, Eleanora de Toledo, by Agnolo Bronzino.

2003, Nov. 5	Engr.	Perf. 11¾	
3224-3226	A565	Set of 3	7.25 3.50

Nos. 3224-3226 were each issued in sheets of 4. Value, set $30.

Christmas A1241

Photo. & Engr.

2003, Nov. 5		Perf. 11¼x11½	
3227	A1241 6.50k multi	.75	.35

Tradition of Czech Stamp Production A1242

Photo. & Engr.

2004, Jan. 20		Perf. 11¼x11¾	
3228	A1242 6.50k Vignette of #1703	.75	.35
a.	Booklet pane of 8 + 4 labels	6.00	
	Complete booklet, #3228a	6.00	

Church of the Assumption of the Virgin Mary, Brno — A1243

2004, Feb. 18	Engr.	Perf. 11¾	
3229	A1243 17k multi	2.00	1.00

Brno 2005 Philatelic Exhibition. No. 3229 was issued in sheets of 4. Value $8.

Industrial Building Historical Preservation A1244

Designs: 6.50k, Busek's Water Forging Hammer, Lniste. 17k, Iron Furnace, Stará Hut u Adamova.

Photo. & Engr.

2004, Feb. 18		Perf. 11½x11¼	
3230-3231	A1244	Set of 2	2.75 .90

Easter A1245

2004, Mar. 17			
3232	A1245 6.50k multi	.75	.25

Art Type of 1967 Inscribed "CESKA REPUBLIKA"

Design: Prometheus, by Antonín Procházka.

2004, Mar. 17	Engr.	Perf. 11¾	
3233	A565 26k multi	3.00	1.50

Brno 2005 Philatelic Exhibition. No. 3233 was issued in sheets of 4. Value $12.

World Ice Hockey
Championships,
Prague and
Ostrava — A1246

Photo. & Engr.
2004, Apr. 14 **Perf. 11¼x11¾**
3234 A1246 12k multi 1.40 .45

Admission to
European
Union
A1247

Photo. & Engr.
2004, May 1 **Perf. 11¼**
3235 A1247 9k multi 1.00 .35

Admission to the European
Union — A1248

2004, May 1 Litho. **Perf. 11¾x11¼**
3236 A1248 9k multi 1.00 .35
No. 3236 was issued in sheets of 10. Value
$8.

Europa
A1249

2004, May 5 **Perf. 11¼**
3237 A1249 9k multi 1.00 .35

Composers of
Czech
Operas — A1250

Designs: 6.50k, Dalibor, by Bedrich
Smetana (1824-84). 8k, Jakobín, by Antonín
Dvorák (1841-1904). 10k, Její Pastorkyna, by
Leos Janácek (1854-1928).

Photo. & Engr.
2004, May 5 **Perf. 11¼x11¾**
3238-3240 A1250 Set of 3 2.75 .95

For Children
A1251

Photo. & Engr.
2004, May 26 **Perf. 11½x11¼**
3241 A1251 6.50k multi .75 .25
a. Booklet pane of 8 + 2 labels 6.00 —
Complete booklet, #3241a 6.00

Statue of Radegast,
by Albín
Polásek — A1252

2004, May 26 **Perf. 11¼x11½**
3242 A1252 6.50k multi .75 .25
Brno 2005 Philatelic Exhibition.

Tourist Attractions — A1253

Designs: 12k, Holy Mountain, Príbram. 14k,
Holy Shrine, Bystrice pod Hostynem.

2004, May 26 Engr. **Perf. 11½x11¾**
3243-3244 A1253 Set of 2 3.00 1.50
Nos. 3243-3244 were each issued in sheets
of 8. Value, set $24.

A1254 A1255

Photo. & Engr.
2004, June 23 **Perf. 11¼x11¾**
3245 A1254 6.50k multi .75 .25
2004 Paralympics, Athens.

2004, June 23
3246 A1255 9k multi 1.00 .35
2004 Summer Olympics, Athens.

Petrarch (1304-74), Poet — A1256

2004, June 23 **Perf. 11¾x11¼**
3247 A1256 14k multi 1.60 .55

Famous
Trees — A1257

Designs: 6.50k, Singing lime tree, Telecí. 8k,
Jan Zizka oak tree, Podhradí.

Photo. & Engr.
2004, Sept. 8 **Perf. 11¼x11½**
3248 A1257 6.50k multi .75 .25
Complete booklet, 5 #3248 3.75
3249 A1257 8k multi .90 .30
Complete booklet, 5 #3249 4.50

Miniature Sheet

Parrots — A1258

No. 3250: a, 12k, Melopsittacus undulatus.
b, 14k, Agapornis personata. c, 16k, Psittacula
krameri. d, 20k, Ara chloroptera.

Litho. & Engr.
2004, Sept. 8 **Perf. 11¾**
3250 A1258 Sheet of 4, #a-d, + 7.00 4.00
4 labels

Compulsory School
Attendance, 230th
Anniv. — A1259

Photo. & Engr.
2004, Sept. 29 **Perf. 11¼x11½**
3251 A1259 6.50k multi .75 .25

Baby
Carriages — A1260

Carriages made about: 12k, 1880. 14k,
1890. 16k, 1900.

2004, Oct. 20
3252-3254 A1260 Set of 3 4.75 1.75

**Art Type of 1967 Inscribed "CESKA
REPUBLIKA"**

Designs: 20k, On the Outskirts of the Cesky
Ráj Region, by Alois Bubák, horiz. 22k, The
Long, the Broad and the Sharpsight, by Hanus
Schwaiger. 26k, The Spring, by Vojtéch
Hynais.

2004, Nov. 10 Engr. **Perf. 11¾**
3255-3257 A565 Set of 3 7.75 4.00
Nos. 3255-3257 were each issued in sheets
of 4. Value, set $32.

Christmas — A1261

Photo. & Engr.
2004, Nov. 10 **Perf. 11¼x11½**
3258 A1261 6.50k multi .75 .25

Tradition of Czech
Stamp Production
A1262

2005, Jan. 18 **Perf. 11¼x11¾**
3259 A1262 6.50k Design of
#975 .75 .30
a. Booklet pane of 8 + 4 labels 6.00
Complete booklet, #3259a 6.00

Peacock and Bugler Portal
Decoration — A1263

2005, Jan. 18 Litho. **Perf. 12¾x13¼**
3260 A1263 7.50k multi + label .85 .30
Labels could be personalized for an addi-
tional fee.
Issued in sheets of 9 stamps and 12 labels.
Value $8.

Souvenir Sheet

Moonscape, by Petr Ginz — A1264

Perf. 11¾x11½
2005, Jan. 18 Litho. & Engr.
3261 A1264 31k multi 3.50 2.00

Flower Type of 2002

Designs: 7.50k, Lily (lilie). 19k, Fuchsia
(fuchsie).

Photo. & Engr.
2005 **Perf. 11¾x11¼**
3262 A1215 7.50k multi .85 .30
3263 A1215 19k multi 2.10 .85
Issued: 7.50k, 1/20; 19k, 3/2.

Pres. Vaclav Klaus Type of 2003
2005, Feb. 9
3264 A1234 7.50k claret & red .85 .30

Granny, by Bozena Nemcová, 150th Anniv. of Publication A1265

2005, Feb. 9   *Perf. 11¼x11¾*
3265 A1265 7.50k multi   .85 .30

Easter — A1266

Photo. & Engr.
2005, Mar. 2   *Perf. 11¼x11½*
3266 A1266 7.50k multi   .85 .30

UNESCO World Heritage Sites Type of 2001

Designs: 14k, St. Prokop's Basilica, Trebíc, vert. 16k, Villa Tugendhat, Brno.

Perf. 11¾x11½, 11½x11¾
2005, Mar. 23   **Engr.**
3267-3268 A1199   Set of 2   3.50 1.90

Nos. 3267-32682 were each issued in sheets of 8. Value, set $28.

Famous Men — A1267

Designs: 7.50k, Bohuslav Brauner (1855-1935), chemist. 12k, Adalbert Stifter (1805-68), writer, painter. 19k, Mikulás Dacicky of Heslov (1555-1626), poet.

Photo. & Engr.
2005, Apr. 13   *Perf. 11¼x11¾*
3269-3271 A1267   Set of 3   4.50 1.60

Europa A1268

2005, May 4   **Litho.**   *Perf. 11¼*
3272 A1268 9k multi   1.00 .35

Battle of Austerlitz, Bicent. — A1269

Napoleon Before the Battle of Austerlitz, by Louis-François Lejeune — A1270

Photo. & Engr.
2005, May 4   *Perf. 11¾x11¼*
3273 A1269 19k multi   2.10 .85
Souvenir Sheet
Litho. & Engr.
Perf. 11¾
3274 A1270 30k multi   3.50 2.25

Brno 2005 Stamp Exhibition (#3274). See France No. 3115.

Kremílek and Vochomurka, by Václav Ctvrtek — A1271

Photo. & Engr.
2005, May 25   *Perf. 11¼x11½*
3275 A1271 7.50k multi   .85 .30
   a.   Booklet pane of 8 + 2 labels   7.00 —
     Complete booklet, #3275a   7.00

A1272   A1273

2005, May 25   *Perf. 11¼x11¾*
3276 A1272 12k multi   1.00 .50
Intl. Year of Physics.

2005, June 22
3277 A1273 9k multi   .75 .35
2005 European Baseball Championships.

Souvenir Sheet

Protected Flora and Fauna of the Krkonose Mountains — A1274

No. 3278: a, 12k, Viola lutea sudetica, Hedysarum hedysaroides (44x28mm). b, 14k, Cinclus cinclus, Leucojum vernum (44x28mm). c, 15k, Sorex alpinus, Salamandra salamandra, Primula minima (44x54mm). d, 22k, Mt. Snezka, Luscinia svecica svecica, Aeschna coerulea, Pneumonanthe asclepiadea (44x54mm).

Litho. & Engr.
2005, June 22   *Perf. 11¾*
3278 A1274   Sheet of 4, #a-d, + 4 labels   7.25 4.00

Church Bells — A1275

Bells from: 7.50k, Benesov, 1322, Havlíckuv Brod, 1335. 9k, Dobrs, 1561, 1596. 12k, Olomouc, 1827.

Photo. & Engr.
2005, Sept. 7   *Perf. 11½x11¾*
3279 A1275 7.50k multi   .85 .30
   Complete booklet, 5 #3279   4.25
3280 A1275 9k multi   1.00 .40
   Complete booklet, 5 #3280   5.00
3281 A1275 12k multi   1.40 .50
   Complete booklet, 5 #3281   7.00
   Nos. 3279-3281 (3)   3.25 1.20

Tractors A1276

Designs: 7.50k, 1923 John Deere 15/27. 9k, 1921 Lanz Bulldog HL-12, 1596. 18k, 1937 Skoda HT 40.

2005, Sept. 21   *Perf. 11½x11¼*
3282 A1276 7.50k multi   .85 .30
   Complete booklet, 5 #3282   4.25
3283 A1276 9k multi   1.00 .35
   Complete booklet, 5 #3283   5.00
3284 A1276 18k multi   2.00 .75
   Complete booklet, 5 #3284   10.00
   Nos. 3282-3284 (3)   3.85 1.40

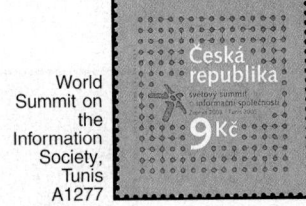

World Summit on the Information Society, Tunis A1277

2005, Sept. 21   *Perf. 11¼*
3285 A1277 9k org & violet   1.00 .35

Curling A1278

Photo. & Engr.
2005, Oct. 12   *Perf. 11¾x11¼*
3286 A1278 17k multi   2.00 .70

Art Type of 1967 Inscribed "CESKA REPUBLIKA"

Designs: 22k, Summer Landscape, by Adolf Kosárek. 25k, Deinotherium, by Zdeněk Burian. 26k, Osiky Near Velké Nemcice, by Alois Kalvoda.

2005, Nov. 9   **Engr.**   *Perf. 11¾*
3287-3289 A565   Set of 3   8.25 5.00

Nos. 3287-3289 were each issued in sheets of 4. Value, set $33.

A1279

Christmas A1280

Photo. & Engr.
2005, Nov. 9   *Perf. 11¼x11½*
3290 A1279 7.50k multi   .85 .30
Perf. 11½x11¼
3291 A1280 9k multi   1.00 .35

Tradition of Czech Stamp Production A1281

Photo. & Engr.
2006, Jan. 20   *Perf. 11¼x11¾*
3292 A1281 7.50k Portion of #C59   .85 .30
   a.   Booklet pane of 8 + 2 labels   7.00 —
     Complete booklet, #3292a   7.00

Flower Type of 2002

Designs: 11k, Marshmallow (ibisek). 24k, Daffodil (narcis).

2006   *Perf. 11¾x11¼*
3293 A1215 11k multi   1.25 .45
3294 A1215 24k multi   2.75 1.00

Issued: 11k, 2/1; 24k, 2/22.

Flowers — A1282

Flowers, Grapes, Glass of Wine — A1283

2006   **Litho.**   *Perf. 12¾x13¼*
3295 A1282 10k multi + label   1.10 .60
3296 A1283 12k multi + label   1.40 .75

Issued: 10k, 2/1; 12k, 2/22. Labels could be personalized for an additional fee.
Nos. 3295-3296 were issued in sheets of 9 stamps and 12 labels. Value, set $22.50.

Madonna of Zbraslav — A1284

2006, Feb. 8   Engr.   Perf. 11¾
3297 A1284 25k multi   2.75 1.50
Printed in sheets of 4. Value $11.

2006 Winter Paralympics,
Turin — A1285

Photo. & Engr.
2006, Feb. 8   Perf. 11¾x11¼
3298 A1285 7.50k multi   .85 .30

2006 Winter
Olympics,
Turin — A1286

2006   Perf. 11¼x11¾
3299 A1286 9k multi   1.00 .40
**With "K. NEUMANNOVA / ZLATA
MEDAILE" Overprinted in Red
Reading Up**
3300 A1286 9k multi   1.00 .40
Issued: No. 3299, 2/8; No. 3300, 3/15.

Famous
Men — A1287

Designs: 11k, Frantisek Josef Gerstner
(1756-1832), mathematician and educator.
12k, Jaroslav Jezek (1906-42), composer.
19k, Sigmund Freud (1856-1939),
psychoanalyst.

2006, Feb. 22   Perf. 11½x11¼
3301-3303 A1287 Set of 3   4.75 1.75

Easter — A1288

2006, Mar. 22   Perf. 11¼x11½
3304 A1288 7.50k multi   .85 .30

Osek Monastery — A1289

Kokorinsko Capstones — A1290

2006, Mar. 22 Engr. Perf. 11½x11¾
3305 A1289 12k multi   1.40 .65
3306 A1290 15k multi   1.75 .85
Nos. 3305-3306 were each issued in sheets
of 8. Value, set $25.

Love — A1291

Photo. & Engr.
2006, Apr. 26   Perf. 11¼x11½
3307 A1291 7.50k multi   .85 .35
Complete booklet, 5 #3307   4.25

Europa
A1292

Silhouette of person and: 10k, Horse. 20k,
Dog.

2006, May 3   Perf. 11¾x11¼
3308-3309 A1292 Set of 2   3.50 1.40

Rumcajs, Manka
and Cipísek, by V.
Ctvrtek — A1293

Photo. & Engr.
2006, May 31   Perf. 11¼x11½
3310 A1293 7.50k multi   .85 .35
a.   Booklet pane of 8 + 2 labels   7.00 —
     Complete booklet, #3310a   7.00

A1294

A1295

2006, June 14   Perf. 11¼x11¾
3311 A1294 19k multi   2.10 .85
Kamenice Pass, Czech Switzerland
National Park.

2006, June 14
Jewelry with garnets: 15k, Silver brooch
with pearl, 1904. 18k, Gold pendant, 1930.
3312-3313 A1295 Set of 2   3.75 1.50

Miniature Sheet

Bohemian Kings of Premyslid
Dynasty — A1296

No. 3314: a, 12k, Otakar I Premysl (c. 1155-
1230). b, 14k, Václav (Wenceslas) I (1205-53).
c, 15k, Otakar II Premysl (1230-78). d, 22k,
Václav (Wenceslas) II (1271-1305). e, 28k,
Václav (Wenceslas) III (1289-1306).

2006, June 14   Engr.   Perf. 11¾
3314 A1296   Sheet of 5, #a-e,
             + label   10.50 6.00

Souvenir Sheet

Mosaic of Prague Castle, by Giovanni
Castrucci — A1297

Litho. & Engr.
2006, Sept. 13   Perf. 11¾
3315 A1297 35k multi   3.25 1.60

Cacti — A1298

No. 3316: a, Gymnocalycium denudatum. b,
Obregonia denegrii.
No. 3317: a, Astrophytum asterias. b, Cintia
knizei.

Perf. 11¼x11¾
2006, Sept. 13   Litho.
3316 A1298 7.50k Pair, #a-b   1.40 .70
     Complete booklet, 2 #3316a, 3
     #3316b   3.50
3317 A1298 10k Pair, #a-b   1.90 .95
     Complete booklet, 2 #3317a, 3
     #3317b   4.75

Ecology
A1299

2006, Sept. 27   Perf. 11¾x11¼
3318 A1299 7.50k multi   .70 .35

Christmas — A1300

2006, Oct. 11   Perf. 12¾x13¼
3319 A1300 7.50k multi + label   .70 .35
Printed in sheets of 9 stamps + 12 labels.
Labels could be personalized.

Vrtbovská Garden,
Prague — A1301

Photo. & Engr.
2006, Oct. 11   Perf. 11½x11¾
3320 A1301 7.50k multi   .70 .35
a.   Booklet pane of 8 + 4 labels   5.75
     Complete booklet, #3320a   5.75
Praga 2008 Intl. Philatelic Exhibition, Prague.

Wooden Churches — A1302

Designs: 7.50k, Church of the Virgin Mary,
Broumov. 19k, Church of St. Andrew,
Hodslavice.

Photo. & Engr.
2006, Oct. 11   Perf. 11¾x11¼
3321-3322 A1302 Set of 2   2.40 1.25

**Art Type of 1967 Inscribed "CESKA
REPUBLIKA"**

Designs: 22k, Still Life with Fruit, by Jan
Davidsz de Heem. 25k, Montenegrin
Madonna, by Jaroslav Cermák. 28k, Pod
Suchym Skalím, by Frantisek Kaván, horiz.

2006, Nov. 8   Engr.   Perf. 11¾
3323-3325 A565 Set of 3   7.25 3.75

Christmas — A1303

Photo. & Engr.
2006, Nov. 8   *Perf. 11¾x11½*
3326 A1303 7.50k multi   .75 .35

Emblem of Praga
2008 Intl. Philatelic
Exhibition — A1304

2006, Dec. 1   **Litho.**
3327 A1304 7.50k multi   .75 .35

See No. 3341.

Czech Technical University, Prague,
300th Anniv. — A1305

Photo. & Engr.
2007, Jan. 10   *Perf. 11¾x11½*
3328 A1305 9k multi   .85 .40

Famous
Men — A1306

Designs: 7.50k, Frána Srámek (1877-1952),
writer. 19k, Karel Slavoj Amerling (1807-84),
educator.

2007, Jan. 10   *Perf. 11½x11¼*
3329-3330 A1306   Set of 2   2.50 1.25

Tradition of Czech
Stamp Production
A1307

2007, Jan. 20   *Perf. 11½x11¾*
3331 A1307 7.50k Type A242   .70 .35
   a.   Booklet pane of 8 + 4 labels   5.75
     Complete booklet, #3331a   5.75

Cancer Prevention
A1308

Photo. & Engr.
2007, Feb. 21   *Perf. 11¼x11½*
3332 A1308 7.50k multi   .70 .35

Snake — A1309

Perf. 11¼x11¾
2007, Feb. 21   **Litho.**
3333 A1309 12k multi   1.25 .60

Oriental
Art
A1310

Designs: 12k, Girl with a Puppet, by
Kunisawa Utagawa. 24k, Siva, Parvati and
Ganesa, 19th cent. Indian glass painting.

Litho. & Engr.
2007, Feb. 21   *Perf. 11¾*
3334-3335 A1310   Set of 2   3.50 1.75

Easter — A1311

Photo. & Engr.
2007, Mar. 14   *Perf. 11¼x11½*
3336 A1311 7.50k multi   .75 .35

Model of Mala Strana Area of Prague,
by Antonín Landweil — A1312

2007, Mar. 14   *Perf. 11¾x11¼*
3337 A1312 7.50k multi   .75 .35
Praga 2008 Intl. Philatelic Exhibition, Prague.

Stoclet House,
Brussels, Designed
by Josef
Hoffmann — A1313

Designs: 20k, Building interior. 35k, Building
exterior.

2007, Mar. 26   *Perf. 11¼x11¾*
3338-3339 A1313   Set of 2   5.25 2.60

See Belgium Nos. 2228-2229.

Flowers Type of 2006
Perf. 12¾x13¼
2007, Mar. 26   **Litho.**
3340 A1282 11k multi + label   1.10 .55
Label could be personalized for an additional fee.

Praga 2008 Emblem Type of 2006
2007, Apr. 4   *Perf. 11¾x11½*
3341 A1304 11k blue & multi   1.10 .55

Spas
A1314

Designs: 12k, Jurkovic House, Luhacovice.
15k, Gocár Pavillion, Lázne Bohdanec.

2007, Apr. 4   **Engr.**   *Perf. 11½x11¾*
3342-3343 A1314   Set of 2   2.60 1.40

Europa
A1315

Photo. & Engr.
2007, May 9   *Perf. 11¼*
3344 A1315 11k multi   1.10 .55
Scouting, cent.

Flowers Type of 2002
Designs: 1k, Cyclamen (bramborik). 23k,
Geranium (pelargonie).

Photo. & Engr.
2007   *Perf. 11¾x11¼*
3345 A1215   1k multi   .20 .20
3347 A1215   23k multi   2.25 1.10

Issued: 1k, 23k, 5/9.

Fast
Arrows,
Comic
Strip by
Jaroslav
Foglar
A1316

Photo. & Engr.
2007, May 30   *Perf. 11¾x11¼*
3348 A1316 7.50k multi   .75 .35
   a.   Booklet pane of 8 + 4 labels   6.00 —
     Complete booklet, #3348a   6.00

Historic
Stoves — A1317

Designs: 7.50k, Gothic era stove, Olomouc,
and tile. 12k, Renaissance era stove, Rícany u
Prahy and tile.

Photo. & Engr.
2007, June 20   *Perf. 11½x11¾*
3349 A1317 7.50k multi   .70 .35
     Complete booklet, 5 #3349   3.50
3350 A1317 12k multi   1.25 .60
     Complete booklet, 5 #3350   6.25

Souvenir Sheet

Vaclav Hollar (1607-77),
Engraver — A1318

Litho. & Engr.
2007, June 20   *Perf. 11¾*
3351 A1318 35k multi + 2 labels   3.50 1.75

Souvenir Sheet

Charles Bridge, Prague, 650th
Anniv. — A1319

2007, June 20
3352 A1319 45k multi   4.25 2.10
Praga 2008 World Philatelic Exhibition.

SEMI-POSTAL STAMPS

Nos. B1-B123 were sold at 1½ times
face value at the Philatelists' Window of
the Prague P.O. for charity benefit.
They were available for ordinary
postage.
Almost all stamps between Nos. B1-
B123 are known with misplaced or
inverted overprints and/or in pairs with
one stamp missing the overprint.
The overprints of Nos. B1-B123 have
been well forged.

Austrian Stamps of 1916-18
Overprinted in Black or Blue

a

1919			**Perf. 12½**	
B1	A37	3h brt violet	.20	.25
B2	A37	5h lt green	.20	.25
B3	A37	6h dp org (Bl)	.60	.80
B4	A37	6h dp org (Bk)	2,000.	2,000.
B5	A37	10h magenta	.80	1.00
B6	A37	12h lt blue	.80	.80
B7	A42	15h dull red	.20	.25
B8	A42	20h dark green	.20	.25
a.		20h green	55.00	40.00
B9	A42	25h blue	.35	.20
B10	A42	30h dull violet	.35	.25
B11	A39	40h olive grn	.40	.40
B12	A39	50h dk green	.40	.40
B13	A39	60h dp blue	.40	.40
B14	A39	80h orange brn	.40	.40
B15	A39	90h red violet	.80	.80
B16	A39	1k car, *yel* (Bl)	.60	.60
B17	A39	1k car, *yel* (Bk)	62.50	62.50
B18	A40	2k light blue	3.25	3.25
a.		2k dark blue	3,000.	2,000.
B19	A40	3k carmine rose	37.50	32.50
a.		3k claret	2,500.	900.00
B20	A40	4k yellow grn	20.00	15.00
a.		4k deep green	45.00	35.00
B21	A40	10k violet	300.00	160.00
a.		10k deep violet	375.00	275.00
b.		10k black violet	450.00	300.00

The used value of No. B18a is for copies
which have only a Czechoslovakian cancellation. Some of the copies of Austria No. 160
which were officially overprinted with type "a"
and sold by the post office, had previously
been used and lightly canceled with Austrian
cancellations. These canceled-before-over-
printing copies, which were postally valid, sell
for about one-fourth as much.

Granite Paper

B22	A40	2k light blue	4.00	2.90
B23	A40	3k carmine rose	10.00	8.25

The 4k and 10k on granite paper with this
overprint were not regularly issued.
Excellent counterfeits of Nos. B1-B23 exist.

Austrian Newspaper Stamps
Overprinted

b

Imperf
On Stamp of 1908

B26	N8	10h carmine	2,250.	2,000.

On Stamps of 1916

B27	N9	2h brown	.20	.20
B28	N9	4h green	.40	.40
B29	N9	6h deep blue	.40	.40
B30	N9	10h orange	5.00	5.00
B31	N9	30h claret	1.60	1.60
		Nos. B27-B31 (5)	7.60	7.60

Austrian Special Handling Stamps Overprinted in Blue or Black
Stamps of 1916 Overprinted

c

Perf. 12½

B32	SH1	2h claret, yel (Bl)	29.00	29.00
B33	SH1	5h dp grn, yel (Bk)	900.00	825.00

Stamps of 1917 Overprinted

d

B34	SH2	2h cl, yel (Bl)	.25	.35
a.		Vert. pair, imperf. btwn.	250.00	
B35	SH2	2h cl, yel (Bk)	60.00	35.00
B36	SH2	5h grn, yel (Bk)	.25	.25

Austrian Air Post Stamps, #C1-C3, Overprinted Type "c" Diagonally

B37	A40	1.50k on 2k lil	200.00	200.00
B38	A40	2.50k on 3k ocher	200.00	200.00
B39	A40	4k gray	1,000.	900.00

1919
Austrian Postage Due Stamps of 1908-13 Overprinted Type "b"

B40	D3	2h carmine	4,500.	2,750.
B41	D3	4h carmine	25.00	15.00
B42	D3	6h carmine	12.50	8.00
B43	D3	14h carmine	90.00	35.00
B44	D3	25h carmine	45.00	20.00
B45	D3	30h carmine	375.00	300.00
B46	D3	50h carmine	875.00	825.00

Austria Nos. J49-J56 Overprinted Type "b"

B47	D4	5h rose red	.20	.30
B48	D4	10h rose red	.20	.30
B49	D4	15h rose red	.20	.30
B50	D4	20h rose red	2.00	2.00
B51	D4	25h rose red	2.00	2.00
B52	D4	30h rose red	.65	.65
B53	D4	40h rose red	2.00	2.00
B54	D4	50h rose red	400.00	250.00

Austria Nos. J57-J59 Overprinted Type "a"

B55	D5	1k ultra	12.50	10.00
B56	D5	5k ultra	55.00	35.00
B57	D5	10k ultra	375.00	200.00

Austria Nos. J47-J48, J60-J63 Overprinted Type "c" Diagonally

B58	A22	1h gray	32.50	30.00
B59	A23	15h on 2h vio	125.00	110.00
B60	A38	10h on 24h blue	90.00	85.00
B61	A38	15h on 36h vio	1.00	1.00
B62	A38	20h on 54h org	90.00	85.00
B63	A38	50h on 42h choc	1.00	1.00

Hungarian Stamps Ovptd. Type "b"
1919   Wmk. 137   Perf. 15
On Stamps of 1913-16

B64	A4	1f slate	2,400.	1,600.
B65	A4	2f yellow	3.50	2.50
B66	A4	3f orange	45.00	25.00
B67	A4	6f olive green	4.50	4.50
B68	A4	50f lake, bl	1.25	1.00
B69	A4	60f grn, sal	50.00	20.00
B70	A4	70f red brn, grn	2,400.	1,600.

On Stamps of 1916

B71	A8	10f rose	300.00	175.00
B72	A8	15f violet	160.00	100.00

On Stamps of 1916-18

B73	A9	2f brown org	.20	.20
B74	A9	3f red lilac	.20	.20
B75	A9	5f green	.20	.20
B76	A9	6f grnsh blue	.60	.60
B77	A9	10f rose red	1.40	2.25
B78	A9	15f violet	.25	.25
B79	A9	20f gray brown	14.00	14.00
B80	A9	25f dull blue	1.00	.80

B81	A9	35f brown	10.00	10.00
B82	A9	40f olive green	3.25	2.50

Overprinted Type "d"

B83	A10	50f red vio & lil	1.25	1.60
B84	A10	75f brt bl & pale bl	1.25	1.60
B85	A10	80f yel grn & pale grn	1.25	1.60
B86	A10	1k red brn & cl	2.50	2.00
B87	A10	2k ol brn & bis	10.00	10.00
B88	A10	3k dk vio & ind	37.50	37.50
B89	A10	5k dk brn & lt brn	140.00	90.00
B90	A10	10k vio brn & vio	1,250.	800.00

Overprinted Type "b"
On Stamps of 1918

B91	A11	10f scarlet	.25	.25
B92	A11	20f dark brown	.30	.30
B93	A11	25f deep blue	1.40	1.25
B94	A12	40f olive grn	4.00	3.25
B95	A12	50f lilac	67.50	25.00

On Stamps of 1919

B96	A13	10f red	10.00	8.00
B97	A13	10f dk brn	6,750.	

Same Overprint On Hungarian Newspaper Stamp of 1914
Imperf

B98	N5	(2f) orange	.20	.30

Same Overprint On Hungarian Special Delivery Stamp
Perf. 15

B99	SD1	2f gray grn & red	.25	.35

Same Ovpt. On Hungarian Semi-Postal Stamps

B100	SP3	10f + 2f rose red	.80	.80
B101	SP4	15f + 2f violet	1.25	1.25
B102	SP5	40f + 2f brn car	7.00	3.50
		Nos. B98-B102 (5)	9.50	6.20

Hungarian Postage Due Stamps of 1903-18 Overprinted Type "b"
1919   Wmk. 135   Perf. 11½, 12

B103	D1	50f green & black	525.00	525.00

Wmk. Crown (136, 136a)
Perf. 11½x12, 15

B104	D1	1f green & black	1,200.	1,000.
B105	D1	2f green & black	1,000.	750.
B106	D1	12f green & black	4,250.	3,000.
B107	D1	50f green & black	275.	150.

Wmk. Double Cross (137)
Perf. 15
On Stamps of 1914

B110	D1	1f green & black	1,250.	600.
B111	D1	2f green & black	700.	550.
B112	D1	5f green & black	1,325.	900.
B113	D1	12f green & black	5,250.	4,000.
B114	D1	50f green & black	275.	150.

On Stamps of 1915-18

B115	D1	1f green & red	175.00	140.00
B116	D1	2f green & red	1.00	.80
B117	D1	5f green & red	12.50	10.00
B118	D1	6f green & red	1.50	1.50
B119	D1	10f green & red	.60	.60
a.		Pair, one without overprint		
B120	D1	12f green & red	2.00	2.00
B121	D1	15f green & red	7.50	5.00
B122	D1	20f green & red	1.00	1.00
B123	D1	30f green & red	80.00	70.00
		Nos. B115-B123 (9)	281.10	230.90

Excellent counterfeits of Nos. B1-B123 exist.

Bohemian Lion Breaking its Chains — SP1

Mother and Child — SP2

Perf. 11½, 13¾ and Compound
1919   Typo.   Unwmk.
Pinkish Paper

B124	SP1	15h gray green	.20	.20
B125	SP1	25h dark brown	.20	.25
a.		25h light brown	5.00	4.00
B126	SP1	50h dark blue	.20	.20

Photo.
Yellowish Paper

B127	SP2	75h slate	.20	.20
B128	SP2	100h brn vio	.20	.20
B129	SP2	120h vio, yel	.20	.20
		Nos. B124-B129 (6)	1.20	1.25

Nos. B124-B126 commemorate the 1st anniv. of Czechoslovak independence. Nos. B127-B129 were sold for the benefit of Legionnaires' orphans. Imperforates exist. See No. 1581.

Regular Issues of Czechoslovakia Surcharged in Red:

a

b

1920   Perf. 13¾

B130	A1(a)	40h + 20h bister	.50	.80
B131	A2(a)	60h + 20h green	.50	.80
B132	A4(b)	125h + 25h gray bl	2.00	2.25
		Nos. B130-B132 (3)	3.00	3.85

President Masaryk — SP3

Wmk. Linden Leaves (107)
1923   Engr.   Perf. 13¾x14¾

B133	SP3	50h gray green	.75	.50
B134	SP3	100h carmine	1.00	.80
B135	SP3	200h blue	3.00	2.75
B136	SP3	300h dark brown	3.25	4.00
		Nos. B133-B136 (4)	8.00	8.05

5th anniv. of the Republic.
The gum was applied through a screen and shows the monogram "CSP" (Ceskoslovenska Posta). These stamps were sold at double their face values, the excess being given to the Red Cross and other charitable organizations.

International Olympic Congress Issue

Semi-Postal Stamps of 1923 Overprinted in Blue or Red

1925

B137	SP3	50h gray green	10.00	8.50
B138	SP3	100h carmine	14.50	12.00
B139	SP3	200h blue, (R)	72.50	55.00
		Nos. B137-B139 (3)	97.00	75.50
		Set, never hinged	150.00	

These stamps were sold at double their face values, the excess being divided between a fund for post office clerks and the Olympic Games Committee.

Sokol Issue

Semi-Postal Stamps of 1923 Overprinted in Blue or Red

1926

B140	SP3	50h gray green	1.60	4.00
B141	SP3	100h carmine	3.25	4.00
B142	SP3	200h blue (R)	15.00	12.50
a.		Double overprint		
B143	SP3	300h dk brn (R)	20.00	20.00
		Nos. B140-B143 (4)	39.85	40.50
		Set, never hinged	100.00	

These stamps were sold at double their face values, the excess being given to the Congress of Sokols, June, 1926.

Catalogue values for unused stamps in this section, from this point to the end of the section, are for Never Hinged items.

Midwife Presenting Newborn Child to its Father; after a Painting by Josef Manes

SP4   SP5

1936   Unwmk.   Engr.   Perf. 12½

B144	SP4	50h + 50h green	.45	.20
B145	SP5	1k + 50h claret	.80	.65
B146	SP4	2k + 50h blue	2.25	1.60
		Nos. B144-B146 (3)	3.50	2.45

SP6

"Lullaby" by Stanislav Sucharda SP7

1937   Perf. 12½

B147	SP6	50h + 50h dull green	.50	.20
B148	SP6	1k + 50h rose lake	.80	.60
B149	SP7	2k + 1k dull blue	2.25	1.25
		Nos. B147-B149 (3)	3.55	2.05

President Masaryk and Little Girl in Native Costume — SP8

1938   Perf. 12½

B150	SP8	50h + 50h deep green	.65	.50
B151	SP8	1k + 50h rose lake	.85	.65

Souvenir Sheet
Imperf

B152	SP8	2k + 3k black	5.00	5.00

88th anniv. of the birth of Masaryk (1850-1937).
Nos. B150-B151 were each issued in sheets of 100 stamps and 12 blank labels. Value, set of singles with attached labels: mint $3.75; used $2.50.

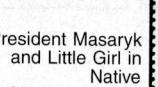

Allegory of the Republic Type
Souvenir Sheet

1938   *Perf. 12½*

B153 A89 2k (+ 8k) dark blue   4.00 4.00

The surtax was devoted to national relief for refugees.

"Republic" and Congress Emblem SP10

St. George Slaying the Dragon SP11

1945   **Engr.**

B154 SP10 1.50k + 1.50k car rose   .20 .20
B155 SP10 2.50k + 2.50k blue   .25 .20

Students' World Cong., Prague, 11/17/45.

1946

B156 SP11 2.40k + 2.60k car rose   .20 .20
B157 SP11 4k + 6k blue   .45 .20

Souvenir Sheet
Imperf

B158 SP11 4k + 6k blue   1.50 1.50

1st anniv. of Czechoslovakia's liberation. The surtax aided WW II orphans.
Nos. B156-B157 were each issued in sheets of 100 stamps and 12 inscribed labels. Value for set of singles with attached labels, mint or used $4.

Old Town Hall Type of 1946
Souvenir Sheet

1946, Aug. 3   *Imperf.*

B159 A114 2.40k rose brown   1.25 .80

Brno Natl. Stamp Exhib., Aug., 1946. The sheet was sold for 10k.

"You Went Away" — SP14

"You Remained Ours" — SP15

"You Came Back" — SP16

1946, Oct. 28   **Photo.**   *Perf. 14*

B160 SP14 1.60k + 1.40k red brn   .40 .40
B161 SP15 2.40k + 2.60k scarlet   .40 .40
B162 SP16 4k + 4k deep blue   .75 .75
      Nos. B160-B162 (3)   1.55 1.55

The surtax was for repatriated Slovaks.

Barefoot Boy — SP17

Woman and Child — SP18

2k+1k, Mother and child. 3k+1k, Little girl.

Perf. 12½

1948, Dec. 18   **Unwmk.**   **Engr.**

B163 SP17 1.50k + 1k rose lilac   .35 .20
B164 SP17 2k + 1k dp blue   .20 .20
B165 SP17 3k + 1k rose car   .35 .20
      Nos. B163-B165 (3)   .90 .60

The surtax was for child welfare.
Nos. B163-B165 were each issued in sheets of 100 stamps and 12 inscribed labels. Value for set of singles with attached labels: mint $3.50; used $1.75.

1949, Dec. 18   *Perf. 12½*

Design: 3k+1k, Man lifting child.

B166 SP18 1.50k + 50h gray   4.00 1.60
B167 SP18 3k + 1k claret   6.00 2.50

The surtax was for child welfare.

SP19

Dove Carrying Olive Branch — SP20

1949, Dec. 18

B168 SP19 1.50k + 50h claret   4.50 1.50
B169 SP20 3k + 1k rose red   4.50 1.50

The surtax was for the Red Cross.

AIR POST STAMPS

Nos. 9, 39-40, 20, and Types of 1919 Surcharged in Red, Blue or Green:

1920   **Unwmk.**   *Imperf.*

C1 A1 14k on 200h (R)   15.00 15.00
   a. Inverted surcharge   125.00
C2 A2 24k on 500h (Bl)   40.00 30.00
   a. Inverted surcharge   225.00
C3 A2 28k on 1000h (G)   30.00 30.00
   a. Inverted surcharge   150.00
   b. Double surcharge   200.00
      Nos. C1-C3 (3)   85.00 75.00

Perf. 13¾, 13¾x 13½ (#C6)

C4 A1 14k on 200h (R)   22.50 30.00
   a. Perf. 13¾x13½   95.00 95.00
C5 A2 24k on 500h (Bl)   45.00 70.00
   a. Perf. 13¾x13½   100.00 100.00
C6 A2 28k on 1000h (G)   20.00 27.50
   a. Inverted surcharge   400.00
   b. Perf. 13¾   475.00 700.00
   c. As "b," invtd. surcharge 350.00
      Nos. C4-C6 (3)   87.50 127.50
      Nos. C1-C6 (6)   172.50 202.50

Excellent counterfeits of the overprint are known.

Stamps of 1920 Surcharged in Black or Violet:

1922, June 15   *Perf. 13¾*

C7 A8 50h on 100h dl grn   1.50 1.50
   a. Inverted surcharge   150.00
   b. Double surcharge   160.00
C8 A8 100h on 200h vio   4.00 3.25
   a. Inverted surcharge   150.00

C9 A8 250h on 400h brn   6.00 7.50
      (V)
   a. Inverted surcharge   275.00
      Nos. C7-C9 (3)   11.50 12.25
      Set, never hinged   20.00

Fokker Monoplane AP3

Smolik S 19 AP4

Smolik S 19 — AP5

Fokker over Prague AP6

1930, Dec. 16   **Engr.**   *Perf. 13½*

C10 AP3 50h deep green   .20 .20
C11 AP3 1k deep red   .25 .25
C12 AP4 2k dark green   .60 .55
C13 AP4 3k red violet   1.25 1.00
C14 AP5 4k indigo   1.00 .80
C15 AP5 5k red brown   1.50 1.50
C16 AP6 10k vio blue   3.50 3.50
   a. 10k ultra   10.00 10.00
C17 AP6 20k gray violet 4.50 3.00
      Nos. C10-C17 (8)   12.80 10.80

Two types exist of the 50h, 1k and 2k, and three types of the 3k, differing chiefly in the size of the printed area. A "no hill at left" variety of the 3k exists.
Imperf. copies of Nos. C10-C17 are proofs.

Perf. 12

C10a AP3 50h deep green   2.75 4.75
C11a AP3 1k deep red   18.00 22.50
C12a AP4 2k dark green   15.00 22.50
C14a AP5 4k indigo   2.25 3.75
C17a AP6 20k gray violet   3.00 7.50

Perf. 12x13½, 13½x12

C11b AP3 1k deep red   4.00 7.50
C12b AP4 2k dark green   11.00 19.00

Perf. 13¾x12¼

C17b AP6 20k gray violet   1,100.

Perf. 12½

C15a AP5 5k red brown   2,000.

Type of 1930 with hyphen in Cesko-Slovensko

1939, Apr. 22   *Perf. 13½*

C18 AP3 30h rose lilac   .20 .20

> Catalogue values for unused stamps in this section, from this point to the end of the section, are for Never Hinged items.

Capt. Frantisek Novak — AP7

Plane over Bratislava Castle — AP8

Plane over Charles Bridge, Prague — AP9

1946-47   *Perf. 12½*

C19 AP7 1.50k rose red   .20 .20
C20 AP7 5.50k dk gray bl   .40 .20
C21 AP7 9k sepia ('47)   .75 .20
C22 AP8 10k dl grn   .75 .35
C23 AP7 16k violet   1.40 .60
C24 AP8 20k light blue   1.50 1.10
C25 AP7 24k dk bl, cr   .90 .65
C26 AP9 24k rose lake   1.50 1.00
C27 AP9 50k dk gray bl   3.00 2.60
      Nos. C19-C27 (9)   10.40 6.90

No. C25 was issued June 12, 1946, for use on the first Prague-New York flight.
Nos. C22, C24-C27 were each issued in sheets of 100 stamps and 12 labels depicting airplane over globe. Values for singles with attached labels (mint/used): C22, $2/$1.50; C24, $4/$3; C25, $7.50/$4; C26, $5.50/$4.50; C27, $9/$7.50.

Nos. C19-C24, C26-C27 Surcharged with New Value and Bars in Various Colors

1949, Sept. 1   *Perf. 12½*

C28 AP7 1k on 1.50k (Bl)   .20 .20
C29 AP7 3k on 5.50k (C)   .35 .20
C30 AP7 6k on 9k (Br)   .55 .20
C31 AP7 7.50k on 16k (C)   .75 .25
C32 AP8 8k on 10k (G)   .75 .75
C33 AP8 12.50k on 20k (Bl) 1.10 .55
C34 AP9 15k on 24k rose lake (Bl) 2.75 1.00
C35 AP9 30k on 50k (Bl)   2.00 .90
      Nos. C28-C35 (8)   8.45 4.05

Karlovy Vary (Karlsbad) — AP10

1951, Apr. 2   **Engr.**   *Perf. 13½*

C36 AP10 6k shown   3.00 1.50
C37 AP10 10k Piestany 3.00 1.50
C38 AP10 15k Marienbad 5.50 1.50
C39 AP10 20k Silac   8.50 4.00
      Nos. C36-C39 (4)   20.00 8.50

View of Cesky Krumlov — AP11

Views: 1.55k, Olomouc. 2.35k, Banska Bystrica. 2.75k, Bratislava. 10k, Prague.

1955   *Perf. 11½*
Cream Paper

C40 AP11 80h olive green   .80 .20
C41 AP11 1.55k violet brn 1.10 .35
C42 AP11 2.35k violet brn 1.50 .20
C43 AP11 2.75k rose brown 2.25 .35
C44 AP11 10k indigo   4.50 2.00
      Nos. C40-C44 (5)   10.15 3.10

Issue dates: 10k, Feb. 20. Others, Mar. 28.

Airline: Moscow-Prague-Paris — AP12

2.35k, Airline: Prague-Cairo-Beirut-Damascus.

Engraved and Photogravure

1957, Oct. 15   **Unwmk.**   *Perf. 11½*

C45 AP12 75h ultra & rose   .75 .20
C46 AP12 2.35k ultra & org yel .75 .20

Planes at First Czech Aviation School,
Pardubice — AP13

Design: 1.80k, Jan Kaspar and flight of first
Czech plane, 1909.

1959, Oct. 15
C47 AP13 1k gray & yel .20 .20
C48 AP13 1.80k blk & pale bl .75 .20

50th anniv. of Jan Kaspar's 1st flight Aug.
25, 1909, at Pardubice.

Mail Coach, Plane and Arms of
Bratislava — AP14

Design: 2.80k, Helicopter over Bratislava.

1960, Sept. 24 Unwmk. Perf. 11½
C49 AP14 1.60k dk bl & gray 1.50 .90
C50 AP14 2.80k grn & buff 2.00 1.10

Issued to publicize the National Stamp Exhibition, Bratislava, Sept. 24-Oct. 9.

AP15 AP16

Designs: 60h, Prague hails Gagarin. 1.80k,
Gagarin, rocket and dove.

1961, June 22
C51 AP15 60h gray & car .25 .20
C52 AP15 1.80k gray & blue .45 .20

No. C51 commemorates Maj. Gagarin's visit
to Prague, Apr. 28-29; No. C52 commemorates the first man in space, Yuri A. Gagarin,
Apr. 12, 1961.

1962, May 14 Engr. Perf. 14
"PRAGA" emblem and: 80h, Dove & Nest of
Eggs. 1.40k, Dove. 2.80k, Symbolic flower
with five petals. 4.20k, Five leaves.
C53 AP16 80h multicolored .75 .35
C54 AP16 1.40k blk, dk red & bl 1.90 1.50
C55 AP16 2.80k multicolored 1.90 1.50
C56 AP16 4.20k multicolored 2.25 1.50
Nos. C53-C56 (4) 6.80 4.85

PRAGA 1962 World Exhibition of Postage
Stamps, Aug. 18-Sept. 2, 1962.
Nos. C53-C56 were each issued in sheets
of 10. Value, set $110.

Vostok 5
and Lt.
Col.
Valeri
Bykovski
AP17

2.80k, Vostok VI & Lt. Valentina Tereshkova.

1963, June 26
C57 AP17 80h slate bl & pink .45 .20
C58 AP17 2.80k dl red brn & lt bl 1.80 .25

Space flights of Valeri Bykovski, June 14-19,
and Valentina Tereshkova, first woman astronaut, June 16-19, 1963.

PRAGA 1962
Emblem, View
of Prague and
Plane — AP18

Designs: 60h, Istanbul '63 (Hagia Sophia).
1k, Philatec Paris 1964 (Ile de la Cité). 1.40k,
WIPA 1965 (Belvedere Palace, Vienna). 1.60k,
SIPEX 1966 (Capitol, Washington). 2k,
Amphilex '67 (harbor and old town, Amster-
dam). 5k, PRAGA 1968 (View of Prague).

Engraved and Photogravure
1967, Oct. 30 Perf. 11½
Size: 30x50mm
C59 AP18 30h choc, yel & rose .20 .20
C60 AP18 60h grn, yel & lil .20 .20
C61 AP18 1k blk, brick red &
lt bl .35 .20
C62 AP18 1.40k vio, yel & dp org .40 .20
C63 AP18 1.60k ind, tan & lil .35 .20
C64 AP18 2k dk grn, org &
red .40 .25
Size: 40x50mm
C65 AP18 5k multi 2.25 1.25
Nos. C59-C65 (7) 4.15 2.50

PRAGA 1968 World Stamp Exhibition,
Prague, June 22-July 7, 1968. No. C59-C64
issued in sheets of 15 stamps and 15 bilingual
labels. Values, set of singles with attached
labels: mint $6.50; used $4.50. No. C65
issued in sheets of 4 stamps and one center
label. Value $15.

Glider L-13 — AP19

Airplanes: 60h, Sports plane L-40. 80h,
Aero taxi L-200. 1k, Crop-spraying plane Z-37.
1.60k, Aerobatics trainer Z-526. 2k, Jet trainer
L-29.

1967, Dec. 11
C66 AP19 30h multi .20 .20
C67 AP19 60h multi .20 .20
C68 AP19 80h multi .20 .20
C69 AP19 1k multi .25 .20
C70 AP19 1.60k multi .40 .20
C71 AP19 2k multi 1.25 .55
Nos. C66-C71 (6) 2.50 1.55

Charles Bridge,
Prague, and
Balloon — AP20

Designs: 1k, Belvedere, fountain and early
plane. 2k, Hradcany, Prague, and airship.

1968, Feb. 5 Unwmk. Perf. 11½
C72 AP20 60h multicolored .30 .30
C73 AP20 1k multicolored .45 .30
C74 AP20 2k multicolored .75 .30
Nos. C72-C74 (3) 1.50 .80

PRAGA 1968 World Stamp Exhibition,
Prague, June 22-July 7, 1968.

Astronaut,
Moon and
Manhattan
AP21

Design: 3k, Lunar landing module and J. F.
Kennedy Airport, New York.

1969, July 21
C75 AP21 60h blk, vio, yel & sil .20 .20
C76 AP21 3k blk, bl, ocher & sil 1.00 .50

Man's 1st landing on the moon, July 20,
1969, US astronauts Neil A. Armstrong and
Col. Edwin E. Aldrin, Jr., with Lieut. Col.
Michael Collins piloting Apollo 11.
Nos. C75-C76 printed with label inscribed
with names of astronauts and European date
of moon landing. Values for pair of singles with
attached labels: mint $2; used $1.

TU-104A
over
Bitov
Castle
AP22

Designs: 60h, IL-62 over Bezdez Castle.
1.40k, TU-13A over Orava Castle. 1.90k, IL-18
over Veveri Castle. 2.40k, IL-14 over Pernstejn
Castle. 3.60k, TU-154 over Trencin Castle.

1973, Oct. 24 Engr. Perf. 11½
C77 AP22 30h multi .20 .20
C78 AP22 60h multi .20 .20
C79 AP22 1.40k multi .25 .20
C80 AP22 1.90k multi .40 .20
C81 AP22 2.40k multi 1.50 .75
C82 AP22 3.60k multi .70 .20
Nos. C77-C82 (6) 3.25 1.75

50 years of Czechoslovakian aviation.
Nos. c77-c82 were each printed in sheets of
10. Values, set: mint $60; used $30.

Old Water Tower and Manes
Hall — AP23

Designs (Praga 1978 Emblem, Plane Sil-
houette and): 1.60k, Congress Hall. 2k, Pow-
der Tower. 2.40k, Charles Bridge and Old
Bridge Tower. 4k, Old Town Hall on Old Town
Square, vert. 6k, Prague Castle and St. Vitus'
Cathedral, vert.

Engraved and Photogravure
1976, June 23 Perf. 11½
C83 AP23 60h ind & multi .20 .20
C84 AP23 1.60k ind & multi .25 .20
C85 AP23 2k ind & multi .35 .20
C86 AP23 2.40k ind & multi .40 .20
C87 AP23 4k ind & multi .80 .30
C88 AP23 6k ind & multi 2.00 .80
Nos. C83-C88 (6) 4.00 1.90

PRAGA 1978 International Philatelic Exhibition, Prague, Sept. 8-17, 1978.

Zeppelin, 1909 and
1928 — AP24

PRAGA '78 Emblem and: 1k, Ader, 1890,
L'Eole & Dunn, 1914. 1.60k, Jeffries-
Blanchard balloon, 1785. 2k, Otto Lilienthal's
glider, 1896. 4.40k, Jan Kaspar's plane,
Pardubice, 1911.

1977, Sept. 15 Perf. 11½
C89 AP24 60h multi .20 .20
C90 AP24 1k multi .30 .20
C91 AP24 1.60k multi .35 .20
C92 AP24 2k multi .45 .20
C93 AP24 4.40k multi 2.25 1.50
Nos. C89-C93 (5) 3.55 1.30

History of aviation.
Nos. C89-C93 were each issued in sheets
of 30 stamps, 15 labels depicting the exhibition emblem, and 5 blank labels. Values for set
ofd singles with attached inscribed labels: mint
$5; used $2.50.

SPECIAL DELIVERY STAMPS

Doves — SD1

1919-20 Unwmk. Typo. Imperf.
E1 SD1 2h red vio, yel .20 .20
E2 SD1 5h yel grn, yel .20 .20
E3 SD1 10h red brn, yel ('20) .40 .40
Nos. E1-E3 (3) .80 .80

For overprints and surcharge see Nos. P11-
P13, Eastern Silesia E1-E2.

1921 White Paper
E1a SD1 2h red violet 8.00
E2a SD1 5h yellow green 5.25
E3a SD1 10h red brown 100.00
Nos. E1a-E3a (3) 113.25

It is doubted that Nos. E1a-E3a were regularly issued.

PERSONAL DELIVERY STAMPS

Catalogue values for unused
stamps in this section are for
Never Hinged items.

PD1

Design: No. EX2, "D" in each corner.

1937 Unwmk. Photo. Perf. 13½
EX1 PD1 50h blue .20 .25
EX2 PD1 50h carmine .20 .25

PD3

1946 Perf. 13½
EX3 PD3 2k deep blue .50 .75

POSTAGE DUE STAMPS

DOPLATIT 5 POSTA — D1

1918-20   Unwmk.   Typo.   Imperf.

J1	D1	5h deep bister	.20	.20
J2	D1	10h deep bister	.20	.20
J3	D1	15h deep bister	.20	.20
J4	D1	20h deep bister	.30	.20
J5	D1	25h deep bister	.45	.20
J6	D1	30h deep bister	.45	.20
J7	D1	40h deep bister	.60	.20
J8	D1	50h deep bister	.75	.20
J9	D1	100h blk brn	1.50	.20
J10	D1	250h orange	11.00	1.40
J11	D1	400h scarlet	15.00	1.40
J12	D1	500h gray grn	7.50	.20
J13	D1	1000h purple	7.50	.25
J14	D1	2000h dark blue	22.50	.60
		Nos. J1-J14 (14)	68.15	5.65

For surcharges and overprints see Nos. J32-J41, J57, Eastern Silesia J1-J11.

Nos. 1, 33-34, 10 Surcharged in Blue

100 DOPLATIT

1922

J15	A1	20h on 3h red vio	.30	.20
J16	A2	50h on 75h slate	1.50	.20
J17	A2	60h on 80h olive grn	.80	.20
J18	A2	100h on 80h olive grn	3.00	.20
J19	A1	200h on 400h purple	4.00	.20
		Nos. J15-J19 (5)	9.60	1.00

Same Surcharge on Nos. 1, 10, 30-31, 33-34, 36, 40 in Violet

1923-26

J20	A1	10h on 3h red vio	.20	.20
J21	A1	20h on 3h red vio	.30	.20
J22	A1	30h on 3h red vio	.20	.20
J23	A1	40h on 3h red vio	.20	.20
J24	A2	50h on 75h slate	1.25	.20
J25	A2	60h on 50h dk vio ('26)	4.00	1.25
J26	A2	60h on 50h dk bl ('26)	4.00	1.50
J27	A2	60h on 75h slate	.50	.20
J28	A2	100h on 80h ol grn	27.50	.20
J29	A2	100h on 120h gray blk	1.00	.20
J30	A1	100h on 400h pur ('26)	1.00	.20
J31	A2	100h on 1000h dp vio ('26)	1.60	.20
		Nos. J20-J31 (12)	41.75	4.75

Postage Due Stamp of 1918-20 Surcharged in Violet

DOPLATIT 50

1924

J32	D1	50h on 400h scar	.75	.20
J33	D1	60h on 400h scar	2.75	.50
J34	D1	100h on 400h scar	1.75	.20
		Nos. J32-J34 (3)	5.25	.90

Postage Due Stamps of 1918-20 Surcharged with New Values in Violet as in 1924

1925

J35	D1	10h on 5h bister	.20	.20
J36	D1	20h on 5h bister	.20	.20
J37	D1	30h on 15h bister	.20	.20
J38	D1	40h on 15h bister	.20	.20
J39	D1	50h on 250h org	.95	.20
J40	D1	60h on 250h org	1.25	.50
J41	D1	100h on 250h org	1.90	.20
		Nos. J35-J41 (7)	4.90	1.70

Stamps of 1918-19 Surcharged with New Values in Violet as in 1922

1926   Perf. 14, 11½

J42	A2	30h on 15h red	.50	.30
J43	A2	40h on 15h red	.50	.30

On #J44-J49

On #J50-J56

1926   Violet Surcharge   Perf. 14

J44	A8	30h on 100h dk grn	.20	.20
J45	A8	40h on 200h violet	.25	.20
J46	A8	40h on 300h ver	.95	.20
a.		Perf. 14x13½		60.00
J47	A8	50h on 500h dp grn	.50	.20
a.		Perf. 14x13½		2.75
J48	A8	60h on 400h brown	1.00	.20
J49	A8	100h on 600h dp vio	2.50	.35
a.		Perf. 14x13½	30.00	1.25
		Nos. J44-J49 (6)	5.40	1.40

1927   Violet Overprint

J50	A6	100h dark brown	.55	.20
a.		Perf. 13½	200.00	10.00

Surcharged with New Value in Violet

J51	A6	40h on 185h org	.20	.20
J52	A6	50h on 20h car	.20	.20
a.		50h on 50h carmine (error)		35,000.
J53	A6	50h on 150h rose	.20	.20
a.		Perf. 13½	12.50	2.00
J54	A6	60h on 25h brown	.25	.20
J55	A6	60h on 185h orange	.55	.20
J56	A6	100h on 25h brown	.55	.20
		Nos. J50-J56 (7)	2.50	1.40

No. J52a is known only used.

No. J12 Surcharged in Violet

DOPLATIT 200

1927   Imperf.

J57	D1	200h on 500h gray grn	6.00	2.50

> **Catalogue values for unused stamps in this section, from this point to the end of the section, are for Never Hinged items.**

10 HALÉRŮ DOPLATNÉ — D5

1928   Perf. 14x13½

J58	D5	5h dark red	.20	.20
J59	D5	10h dark red	.20	.20
J60	D5	20h dark red	.20	.20
J61	D5	30h dark red	.20	.20
J62	D5	40h dark red	.20	.20
J63	D5	50h dark red	.20	.20
J64	D5	100h dark red	.20	.20
J65	D5	1k ultra	.20	.20
J66	D5	2k ultra	.50	.20
J67	D5	5k ultra	.75	.20
J68	D5	10k ultra	1.90	.20
J69	D5	20k ultra	3.75	.30
		Nos. J58-J69 (12)	8.50	2.50

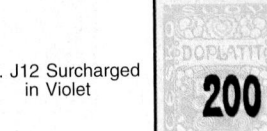

10h — D6

1946-48   Photo.   Perf. 14

J70	D6	10h dark blue	.20	.20
J71	D6	20h dark blue	.20	.20
J72	D6	50h dark blue	.35	.20
J73	D6	1k carmine rose	.35	.20
J74	D6	1.20k carmine rose	.35	.20
J75	D6	1.50k carmine rose ('48)	.35	.20
J76	D6	1.60k carmine rose	.35	.20
J77	D6	2k carmine rose ('48)	.35	.20
J78	D6	2.40k carmine rose	.35	.20
J79	D6	3k carmine rose	.70	.20
J80	D6	5k carmine rose	.70	.20
J81	D6	6k carmine rose ('48)	1.00	.20
		Nos. J70-J81 (12)	5.25	2.40

D7

D8

1954-55   Engr.   Perf. 12½, 11½

J82	D7	5h gray green ('55)	.20	.20
J83	D7	10h gray green ('55)	.20	.20
J84	D7	30h gray green	.20	.20
J85	D7	50h gray green ('55)	.20	.20
J86	D7	60h gray green ('55)	.20	.20
J87	D7	95h gray green	.35	.20
J88	D8	1k violet	.35	.20
J89	D8	1.20k violet ('55)	.35	.20
J90	D8	1.50k violet	.70	.20
J91	D8	1.60k violet ('55)	.45	.20
J92	D8	2k violet	.85	.20
J93	D8	3k violet	1.10	.20
J94	D8	5k violet ('55)	1.40	.25
		Nos. J82-J94 (13)	6.55	2.65

Perf. 11½ stamps are from a 1963 printing which lacks the 95h, 1.60k, and 2k.

Stylized Flower — D9

Designs: Various stylized flowers.

Engraved and Photogravure

1971-72   Perf. 11½

J95	D9	10h vio bl & pink	.20	.20
J96	D9	20h vio & lt bl	.20	.20
J97	D9	30h emer & lil rose	.20	.20
J98	D9	60h pur & emer	.20	.20
J99	D9	80h org & vio bl	.20	.20
J100	D9	1k dk red & emer	.25	.20
J101	D9	1.20k grn & org	.20	.20
J102	D9	2k blue & red	.40	.20
J103	D9	3k blk & yel	.50	.20
J104	D9	4k brn & ultra	.85	.20
J105	D9	5.40k red & lilac	1.00	.20
J106	D9	6k brick red & org	1.40	.20
		Nos. J95-J106 (12)	5.60	2.40

All except 5.40k issued in 1972.

OFFICIAL STAMPS

> **Catalogue values for unused stamps in this section are for Never Hinged items.**

50h — Coat of Arms — O1

1945   Unwmk.   Litho.   Perf. 10½x10

O1	O1	50h dp slate grn	.20	.20
O2	O1	1k dp bl vio	.20	.20
O3	O1	1.20k plum	.20	.20
O4	O1	1.50k crimson rose	.20	.20
O5	O1	2.50k bright ultra	.30	.20
O6	O1	5k dk vio brn	.30	.30
O7	O1	8k rose pink	.30	.30
		Nos. O1-O7 (7)	1.60	1.50

Redrawn

1947   Photo.   Perf. 14

O8	O1	60h red	.20	.20
O9	O1	80h dk olive grn	.20	.20
O10	O1	1k dk lilac gray	.20	.20
O11	O1	1.20k dp plum	.20	.20
O12	O1	2.40k dk car rose	.20	.20
O13	O1	4k brt ultra	.20	.20
O14	O1	5k dk vio brn	.20	.20
O15	O1	7.40k purple	.20	.20
		Nos. O8-O15 (8)	1.60	1.60

There are many minor changes in design, size of numerals, etc., of the redrawn stamps.

NEWSPAPER STAMPS

Windhover — N1

1918-20   Unwmk.   Typo.   Imperf.

P1	N1	2h gray green	.20	.20
P2	N1	5h green ('20)	.20	.20
a.		5h dark green	.40	.20
P3	N1	6h red	.30	.25
P4	N1	10h dull violet	.20	.20
P5	N1	20h blue	.20	.20
P6	N1	30h gray brown	.20	.20
P7	N1	50h orange ('20)	.30	.20
P8	N1	100h red brown ('20)	.40	.20
		Nos. P1-P8 (8)	2.00	1.65

Nos. P1-P8 exist privately perforated. For surcharges and overprints see Nos. P9-P10, P14-P16, Eastern Silesia P1-P5.

Stamps of 1918-20 Surcharged in Violet

5 ★ ★

1925-26

P9	N1	5h on 2h gray green	.50	.40
P10	N1	5h on 6h red ('26)	.25	.40

Special Delivery Stamps of 1918-20 Overprinted in Violet

NOVINY 5

1926

P11	SD1	5h apple grn, yel	.20	.20
a.		5h dull green, yellow	.50	.40
P12	SD1	10h red brn, yel	.20	.20

With Additional Surcharge of New Value

P13	SD1	5h on 2h red vio, yel	.35	.35
		Nos. P11-P13 (3)	.75	.75

> **Catalogue values for unused stamps in this section, from this point to the end of the section, are for Never Hinged items.**

Newspaper Stamps of 1918-20 Overprinted in Violet

O.T.

1934

P14	N1	10h dull violet	.20	.20
P15	N1	20h blue	.20	.20
P16	N1	30h gray brown	.20	.20
		Nos. P14-P16 (3)	.60	.60

Overprinted for use by commercial firms only.

5h — Carrier Pigeon — N2

1937   Imperf.

P17	N2	2h bister brown	.20	.20
P18	N2	5h dull blue	.20	.20
P19	N2	7h red orange	.20	.20
P20	N2	9h emerald	.20	.20
P21	N2	10h henna brown	.20	.20
P22	N2	12h ultra	.20	.20
P23	N2	20h dark green	.20	.20
P24	N2	50h dark brown	.20	.20
P25	N2	1k olive gray	.20	.20
		Nos. P17-P25 (9)	1.80	1.80

For overprint see Slovakia Nos. P1-P9.

Bratislava Philatelic Exhibition Issue
Souvenir Sheet

1937   *Imperf.*
P26 N2 10h henna brn, sheet of
25   4.00   4.00

Newspaper Delivery
Boy — N4

1945   **Unwmk.**   **Typo.**   *Imperf.*
P27	N4	5h dull blue	.20	.20
P28	N4	10h red	.20	.20
P29	N4	15h emerald	.20	.20
P30	N4	20h dark slate green	.20	.20
P31	N4	25h bright red vio	.20	.20
P32	N4	30h ocher	.20	.20
P33	N4	40h red orange	.20	.20
P34	N4	50h brown red	.20	.20
P35	N4	1k slate gray	.20	.20
P36	N4	5k deep vio blue	.20	.20
		Nos. P27-P36 (10)	2.00	2.00

CZECHOSLOVAK LEGION POST

The Czechoslovak Legion in Siberia
issued these stamps for use on its mail
and that of local residents. Forgeries
exist.

For more detailed listings of Czecho-
slovak Legion Post issues, see the
*Classic Specialized Catalogue of
Stamps and Covers.*

Russia No. 79 Overprinted

1918   **Typo.**   *Perf. 14x14½*
A1 A15 10k dark blue   1,750.—

No. A1 was sold for a few days in Chelya-
binsk. It was withdrawn because of a spelling
error ("CZESZKJA," instead of
"CZESZKAJA").

This overprint was also applied to Russia
Nos. 73-78, 80-81, 83-85, 119-121, 123 and
130-131. These were trial printings, never sold
to the public, although favor-cancelled covers
exist.

Urn and   Armored
Cathedral at   Railroad
Irkutsk — A1   Car — A2

Sentinel — A3   Lion of
              Bohemia

1919-20   **Litho.**   *Imperf.*
1	A1	25k carmine	10.50
a.		*Perf 11½ ('20)*	10.50
2	A2	50k yellow green	10.50
a.		*Perf 11½ ('20)*	10.50
3	A3	1r red brown	14.00
a.		*Perf 11½ ('20)*	14.00

Originals of Nos. 1-3 and 1a-3a have a
crackled yellow gum. Ungummed remainders,
which were given a white gum, exist imperforate and perforated 11½ and 13¼. Value per
set, $3.

Embossed
Perce en Arc in Blue
4 A4 (25k) blue & rose   2.00

Two types: 1 — 6 points on star-like mace
head at right of goblet; large saber handle;
measures 20x25¼mm. 2 — 5 points on mace
head; small saber handle; measures
19½x25mm.

No. 4 Overprinted

1920
5 A4 (25k) bl & rose   5.00
Both types of No. 4 received overprint.

No. 5 Surcharged with New Values in
Green

6	A4	2k bl & rose	26.00
7	A4	3k bl & rose	26.00
8	A4	5k bl & rose	26.00
9	A4	10k bl & rose	26.00
10	A4	15k bl & rose	26.00
11	A4	25k bl & rose	26.00
12	A4	35k bl & rose	26.00
13	A4	50k bl & rose	26.00
14	A4	1r bl & rose	26.00
		Nos. 6-14 (9)	234.00

BOHEMIA AND MORAVIA

Catalogue values for unused
stamps in this country are for
never hinged items, beginning
with Scott 20 in the regular postage section, Scott B1 in the semi-
postal section, Scott J1 in the
postage due section, Scott O1 in
the official section, and Scott P1 in
the newspaper section.

German Protectorate

Stamps of
Czechoslovakia, 1928-
39, Overprinted in
Black

Perf. 10, 12½, 12x12½
1939, July 15   **Unwmk.**
1	A29	5h dk ultra	.20	1.25
2	A29	10h brown	.20	1.25
3	A29	20h red	.20	1.25
4	A29	25h green	.20	1.25
5	A29	30h red vio	.20	1.25
6	A61a	40h dk bl	2.50	5.00
7	A85	50h dp grn	.20	1.25
8	A63	60h dl vio	2.50	5.00
9	A60	1k rose lake (212)	.75	1.75
10	A60	1k rose lake (256)	.30	1.25
11	A64	1.20k rose lilac	3.00	5.00
12	A65	1.50k carmine	2.50	5.75
13	A79	1.60k olive grn	2.50	5.75
a.		*"Mähnen"*	32.50	75.00
14	A66	2k dk bl grn	1.10	4.00
15	A67	2.50k dk bl	3.00	5.00
16	A68	3k brown	3.00	5.75
17	A70	4k dk vio	3.50	6.50

18	A71	5k green	3.50	10.00
19	A72	10k blue	4.75	15.00
		Nos. 1-19 (19)	34.10	83.25
		Set, never hinged	60.00	

Overprint size varies; #1-10 measure
17½x15½mm, #11-16 19x18mm, #17, 19
28x17½mm, #18 23½x23mm.

Catalogue values for unused
stamps in this section, from this
point to the end of the section, are
for never hinged items.

Linden Leaves and
Closed Buds — A1

1939-41   **Photo.**   *Perf. 14*
20	A1	5h dark blue	.20	.30
21	A1	10h blk brn	.20	.40
22	A1	20h crimson	.20	.30
23	A1	25h dk bl grn	.20	.30
24	A1	30h dp plum	.20	.30
24A	A1	30h golden brn ('41)	.20	.30
25	A1	40h orange ('40)	.20	.30
26	A1	50h slate grn ('40)	.20	.20
		Nos. 20-26 (8)	1.60	2.30

See Nos. 49-51.

Castle at   Karlstein
Zvikov — A2   Castle — A3

St. Barbara's   Cathedral at
Church, Kutna   Prague — A5
Hora — A4

Brno   Town Square,
Cathedral — A6   Olomouc — A7

1939   **Engr.**   *Perf. 12½*
27	A2	40h dark blue	.20	.30
28	A3	50h dk bl grn	.20	.30
29	A4	60h dl vio	.20	.30
30	A5	1k dp rose	.20	.30
31	A6	1.20k rose lilac	.40	.60
32	A6	1.50k rose car	.20	.30
33	A7	2k dk bl grn	.20	.50
34	A7	2.50k dark blue	.20	.30
		Nos. 27-34 (8)	1.80	2.90

No. 31 measures 23½x29½mm, No. 42
measures 18½x23mm.
See #52-53, 53B. For overprints see #60-
61.

Zlin — A8

Iron Works at
Moravská
Ostrava — A9

Prague — A10

1939-40
35	A8	3k dl rose vio	.20	.30
36	A9	4k slate ('40)	.20	.40
37	A10	5k green	.50	.80
38	A10	10k lt ultra	.40	1.00
39	A10	20k yel brn	1.25	2.00
		Nos. 35-39 (5)	2.55	4.50

Types of 1939 and

Neuhaus   Lainsitz Bridge near
A11   Bechyne
              A14

Pernstein   Samson Fountain,
Castle — A12   Budweis — A15

Pardubice
Castle — A13

Kromeriz   8K
A16

Wallenstein
Palace,
Prague — A17

1940   **Engr.**   *Perf. 12½*
40	A11	50h dk bl grn	.20	.20
41	A12	80h dp bl	.25	.40
42	A6	1.20k vio brn	.40	.25
43	A13	2k gray grn	.20	.20
44	A14	5k dk bl grn	.20	.20
45	A15	6k brn vio	.20	.50
46	A16	8k slate grn	.20	.30
47	A17	10k blue	.45	.30
48	A10	20k sepia	1.10	1.60
		Nos. 40-48 (9)	3.20	3.95

No. 42 measures 18½x23mm; No. 31,
23½x29½mm.

Types of 1939-40

1941
49	A1	60h violet	.20	.20
50	A1	80h red org	.20	.20
51	A1	1k brown	.20	.20
52	A5	1.20k rose red	.20	.20
53	A4	1.50k lil rose	.20	.25
53A	A13	2k light blue	.20	.20

53B	A6	2.50k ultra	.20	.20
53C	A12	3k olive	.20	.20
		Nos. 49-53C (8)	1.60	1.65

Nos. 49-51 show buds open. Nos. 52 and 53B measure 18¾x23½mm and have no inscriptions below design.
For overprints see Nos. 60-61.

Antonin
Dvorák — A18

1941, Aug. 25   Engr.   Perf. 12½

54	A18	60h dull lilac	.30	.50
55	A18	1.20k sepia	.30	.50

Antonin Dvorák (1841-1904), composer. Nos. 54-55 were issued in sheets of 50 stamps and 50 alternating inscribed labels. Value for set of singles with attached labels, unused or used, $1.50.

Farming
Scene — A19   Factories — A20

1941, Sept. 7   Photo.   Perf. 13½

56	A19	30h dk red brn	.20	.30
57	A19	60h dark green	.20	.30
58	A20	1.20k dk plum	.20	.30
59	A20	2.50k sapphire	.25	.65
		Nos. 56-59 (4)	.85	1.55

Issued to publicize the Prague Fair.

Nos. 52 and 53B
Overprinted in Blue
or Red

1942, Mar. 15   Perf. 12½

60	A5	1.20k rose red (Bl)	.60	.65
61	A6	2.50k ultra (R)	.65	1.00

3rd anniv. of the Protectorate of Bohemia and Moravia.

Adolf Hitler
A21   17th Century
Messenger
A22

1942   Photo.   Perf. 14
Size: 17½x21½mm

62	A21	10(h) gray blk	.20	.25
63	A21	30(h) bister brn	.20	.25
64	A21	40(h) slate blue	.20	.25
65	A21	50(h) slate grn	.20	.25
66	A21	60(h) purple	.20	.25
67	A21	80(h) org ver	.20	.25

Perf. 12½
Engr.
Size: 18x21mm

68	A21	1k dl brn	.20	.25
69	A21	1.20(k) carmine	.20	.30
70	A21	1.50(k) claret	.20	.30
71	A21	1.60(k) Prus grn	.20	.30
72	A21	2k light blue	.20	.30
73	A21	2.40(k) fawn	.20	.30

Size: 18½x24mm

74	A21	2.50(k) ultra	.20	.30
75	A21	3k olive grn	.20	.30
76	A21	4k brt red vio	.20	.30
77	A21	5k myrtle grn	.20	.30
78	A21	6k claret brn	.20	.40
79	A21	8k indigo	.20	.40

Size: 23½x29¾mm

80	A21	10k dk gray grn	.25	1.00
81	A21	20k gray vio	.40	1.00
82	A21	30k red	.75	2.00
83	A21	50k deep blue	1.50	3.00
		Nos. 62-83 (22)	6.50	12.25

1943, Jan. 10   Photo.   Perf. 13½

84	A22	60h dark rose violet	.40	.40

Stamp Day.

Scene from "Die
Meistersinger"
A23   Richard Wagner
A24

Scene from
"Siegfried" — A25

1943, May 22

85	A23	60h violet	.20	.20
86	A24	1.20k carmine rose	.20	.20
87	A25	2.50k deep ultra	.20	.20
		Nos. 85-87 (3)	.60	.60

Richard Wagner (1813-83).

St. Vitus'
Cathedral,
Prague — A26   Adolf
Hitler — A27

1944, Nov. 21   Engr.   Perf. 12½

88	A26	1.50k dull rose brn	.25	.25
89	A26	2.50k dull lilac blue	.25	.35

1944

90	A27	4.20k green	.50	.50

SEMI-POSTAL STAMPS

Catalogue values for unused stamps in this section are for never hinged items.

Nurse and
Wounded
Soldier — SP1

Perf. 13½

1940, June 29   Photo.   Unwmk.

B1	SP1	60h + 40h indigo	.90	1.10
B2	SP1	1.20k + 80h deep plum	.90	1.25

Surtax for German Red Cross. Nos. B1-B2 were issued in sheets of 50 stamps and 50 alternating inscribed labels. Value for set of singles with attached labels: unused $3; used $4.

Red Cross Nurse
and Patient — SP2

1941, Apr. 20

B3	SP2	60h + 40h indigo	.40	.60
B4	SP2	1.20k + 80h dp plum	.40	.65

Surtax for German Red Cross. Nos. B3-B4 were issued in sheets of 50 stamps and 50 alternating inscribed labels. Value for set of singles with attached labels: unused $1.80; used $2.75.

Old Theater,
Prague — SP3   Mozart — SP4

1941, Oct. 26

B5	SP3	30h + 30h brown	.20	.20
B6	SP3	60h + 60h Prus grn	.20	.20
B7	SP4	1.20k + 1.20k scar	.25	.25
B8	SP4	2.50k + 2.50k dk bl	.45	.55
		Nos. B5-B8 (4)	1.10	1.20

150th anniversary of Mozart's death. Labels alternate with stamps in sheets of Nos. B5-B8. The labels with Nos. B5-B6 show two bars of Mozart's opera "Don Giovanni." Those with Nos. B7-B8 show Mozart's piano. Value for set of singles with attached labels: unused $2; used $3.25.

Adolf
Hitler — SP5   Nurse and
Soldier — SP6

1942, Apr. 20   Engr.   Perf. 12½

B9	SP5	30h + 20h dl brn vio	.20	.20
B10	SP5	60h + 40h dl grn	.20	.20
B11	SP5	1.20k + 80h dp claret	.20	.25
B12	SP5	2.50k + 1.50k dl bl	.25	.40
		Nos. B9-B12 (4)	.85	1.05

Hitler's 53rd birthday. Nos. B9-B12 were issued in sheets of 100 stamps and 12 blank labels. Value for set of singles with attached labels: unused $3; used $2.25.

1942, Sept. 4   Perf. 13½

B13	SP6	60h + 40h deep blue	.25	.25
B14	SP6	1.20(k) + 80(h) dp plum	.25	.25

The surtax aided the German Red Cross.

Emperor
Charles IV
SP7   Peter Parler
SP8

John the Blind,
King of
Bohemia — SP9   Adolf
Hitler — SP10

1943, Jan. 29

B15	SP7	60h + 40h violet	.20	.20
B16	SP8	1.20k + 80h carmine	.20	.20
B17	SP9	2.50k + 1.50k vio bl	.20	.20
		Nos. B15-B17 (3)	.60	.60

The surtax was for the benefit of the German wartime winter relief.

1943, Apr. 20   Engr.   Perf. 12½

B18	SP10	60h + 1.40k dl vio	.25	.30
B19	SP10	1.20k + 3.80k carmine	.25	.30

Hitler's 54th birthday. Nos. B18-B19 were issued in sheets of 100 stamps and 12 blank labels. Value for set of singles with attached labels: unused $1.10; used 60c.

Deathmask of
Reinhard
Heydrich — SP11   Eagle and Red
Cross — SP12

1943, May 28   Photo.   Perf. 13½

B20	SP11	60h + 4.40k black	.65	1.60

No. B20 exists in a miniature sheet containing a single copy. It was given to high Nazi officials attending a ceremony one year after Heydrich's assassination.

1943, Sept. 16   Perf. 13

B21	SP12	1.20k + 8.80k blk & car	.50	.50

The surtax aided the German Red Cross.

Native Costumes
SP13   Nazi Emblem,
Arms of
Bohemia,
Moravia
SP14

1944, Mar. 15   Perf. 13½

B22	SP13	1.20(k) + 3.80(k) rose lake	.20	.20
B23	SP14	4.20(k) + 10.80(k) golden brn	.20	.20
B24	SP13	10k + 20k saph	.20	.30
		Nos. B22-B24 (3)	.60	.70

Fifth anniversary of protectorate.

Adolf
Hitler — SP15   Bedrich
Smetana — SP16

1944, Apr. 20

B25	SP15	60h + 1.40k olive blk	.25	.25
B26	SP15	1.20k + 3.80k slate grn	.25	.25

1944, May 12   Engr.   Perf. 12½

B27	SP16	60h + 1.40k dk gray grn	.25	.25
B28	SP16	1.20k + 3.80k brn car	.25	.25

Bedrich Smetana (1824-84), Czech composer and pianist.

PERSONAL DELIVERY STAMPS

PD1

1939-40   Unwmk. Photo.   Perf. 13½

EX1	PD1	50h indigo & blue ('40)	1.25	2.00
EX2	PD1	50h carmine & rose	1.60	2.50

POSTAGE DUE STAMPS

> Catalogue values for unused stamps in this section are for never hinged items.

D1

1939-40   Unwmk.   Typo.   Perf. 14

J1	D1	5h dark carmine	.25	.30
J2	D1	10h dark carmine	.25	.30
J3	D1	20h dark carmine	.25	.30
J4	D1	30h dark carmine	.25	.30
J5	D1	40h dark carmine	.25	.30
J6	D1	50h dark carmine	.25	.30
J7	D1	60h dark carmine	.25	.30
J8	D1	80h dark carmine	.25	.30
J9	D1	1k bright ultra	.25	.40
J10	D1	1.20k brt ultra ('40)	.30	.40
J11	D1	2k bright ultra	1.00	1.25
J12	D1	5k bright ultra	1.10	1.60
J13	D1	10k bright ultra	1.60	2.00
J14	D1	20k bright ultra	3.25	3.25
		Nos. J1-J14 (14)	9.50	11.30

OFFICIAL STAMPS

> Catalogue values for unused stamps in this section are for never hinged items.

Numeral   Eagle
O1   O2

Unwmk.

1941, Jan. 1   Typo.   Perf. 14

O1	O1	30h ocher	.25	.20
O2	O1	40h indigo	.25	.20
O3	O1	50h emerald	.25	.20
O4	O1	60h slate grn	.25	.20
O5	O1	80h org red	.80	.20
O6	O1	1k red brn	.40	.20
O7	O1	1.20k carmine	.40	.20
O8	O1	1.50k dp plum	.65	.20
O9	O1	2k brt bl	.65	.20
O10	O1	3k olive	.65	.20
O11	O1	4k red vio	.80	.50
O12	O1	5k org yel	2.00	1.00
		Nos. O1-O12 (12)	7.35	3.50

1943, Feb. 15

O13	O2	30(h) bister	.20	.30
O14	O2	40(h) indigo	.20	.30
O15	O2	50(h) yel grn	.20	.30
O16	O2	60(h) dp vio	.20	.30
O17	O2	80(h) org red	.20	.30
O18	O2	1k chocolate	.20	.30
O19	O2	1.20(k) carmine	.20	.30
O20	O2	1.50(k) brn red	.20	.30
O21	O2	2k lt bl	.20	.30
O22	O2	3k olive	.20	.30
O23	O2	4k red vio	.20	.30
O24	O2	5k dk grn	.20	.50
		Nos. O13-O24 (12)	2.40	3.80

NEWSPAPER STAMPS

> Catalogue values for unused stamps in this section are for never hinged items.

Carrier Pigeon — N1

1939   Unwmk.   Typo.   Imperf.

P1	N1	2h ocher	.20	.30
P2	N1	5h ultra	.20	.30
P3	N1	7h red orange	.20	.30
P4	N1	9h emerald	.20	.30
P5	N1	10h henna brown	.20	.30
P6	N1	12h dark ultra	.20	.30
P7	N1	20h dark green	.20	.30
P8	N1	50h red brown	.20	.40
P9	N1	1k greenish gray	.25	.80
		Nos. P1-P9 (9)	1.85	3.30

No. P5 Overprinted in Black

1940

P10	N1	10h henna brown	.40	.65

Overprinted for use by commercial firms.

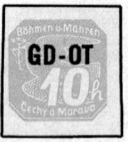

N2

1943, Feb. 15

P11	N2	2(h) ocher	.20	.20
P12	N2	5(h) light blue	.20	.20
P13	N2	7(h) red orange	.20	.20
P14	N2	9(h) emerald	.20	.20
P15	N2	10(h) henna brown	.20	.20
P16	N2	12(h) dark ultra	.20	.20
P17	N2	20(h) dark green	.20	.20
P18	N2	50(h) red brown	.20	.20
P19	N2	1k slate green	.20	.20
		Nos. P11-P19 (9)	1.80	1.80

DAHOMEY

də-'hō-mē

LOCATION — West coast of Africa
AREA — 43,483 sq. mi.
POP. — 3,030,000 (est. 1974)
CAPITAL — Porto-Novo

Formerly a native kingdom including Benin, Dahomey was annexed by France in 1894. It became part of the colonial administrative unit of French West Africa in 1895. Stamps of French West Africa superseded those of Dahomey in 1945. The Republic of Dahomey was proclaimed Dec. 4, 1958.

The republic changed its name to the People's Republic of Benin on Nov. 30, 1975. See Benin for stamps issued after that date.

100 Centimes = 1 Franc

> Catalog values for unused stamps in this country are for Never Hinged items, beginning with Scott 137 in the regular postage section, Scott B15 in the semipostal section, Scott C14 in the airpost section, Scott CQ1 in the airpost parcel post section, Scott J29 in the postage due section, and Scott Q1 int he parcel post section.

See French West Africa No. 71 for stamp inscribed "Dahomey" and "Afrique Occidentale Francaise."

Navigation and Commerce — A1

Perf. 14x13½

1899-1905   Typo.   Unwmk.
Name of Colony in Blue or Carmine

1	A1	1c black, lil bl ('01)	.95	.95
2	A1	2c brown, buff ('04)	1.60	1.00
3	A1	4c claret, lav ('04)	1.75	1.40
4	A1	5c yellow grn ('04)	4.25	2.40
5	A1	10c red ('01)	3.50	2.40
6	A1	15c gray ('01)	3.50	1.25
7	A1	20c red, grn ('04)	13.00	9.50
8	A1	25c black, rose ('99)	11.50	5.00
9	A1	25c blue ('01)	12.50	11.00
10	A1	30c brown, bis ('04)	17.00	8.75
11	A1	40c red, straw ('04)	18.00	11.00
12	A1	50c brn, az (name in red) ('01)	16.00	14.50
12A	A1	50c brn, az (name in bl) ('05)	25.00	16.00
13	A1	75c dp vio, org ('04)	65.00	42.50
14	A1	1fr brnz grn, straw ('04)	32.50	22.50
15	A1	2fr violet, rose ('04)	80.00	55.00
16	A1	5fr red lilac, lav ('04)	100.00	77.50
		Nos. 1-16 (17)	406.05	282.65

Perf. 13½x14 stamps are counterfeits.
For surcharges see Nos. 32-41.

Gen. Louis Faidherbe A2

Oil Palm — A3

Dr. Noel Eugène Ballay A4

1906-07   Perf. 13½x14
Name of Colony in Red or Blue

17	A2	1c slate	.95	.80
18	A2	2c chocolate	1.25	.85
19	A2	4c choc, gray bl	2.25	1.75
20	A2	5c green	6.50	1.75
21	A2	10c carmine (B)	16.00	2.75
22	A3	20c black, azure	10.00	8.95
23	A3	25c blue, pnksh	10.00	9.00
24	A3	30c choc, pnksh	11.50	9.00
25	A3	35c black, yellow	65.00	9.00
26	A3	45c choc, grnsh ('07)	14.50	11.00
27	A3	50c deep violet	14.50	11.00
28	A3	75c blue, orange	17.50	13.50
29	A4	1fr black, azure	21.00	16.00
30	A4	2fr blue, pink	85.00	85.00
31	A4	5fr car, straw (B)	75.00	75.00
		Nos. 17-31 (15)	350.95	254.35

#2-3, 6-7, 9-13 Surcharged in Black or Carmine

1912   Perf. 14x13½

32		5c on 2c brn, buff	1.25	1.25
33		5c on 4c claret, lav (C)	1.10	1.10
a.		Double surcharge	200.00	
34		5c on 15c gray (C)	1.25	1.25
35		5c on 20c red, grn	1.10	1.10
36		5c on 25c blue (C)	1.25	1.25
a.		Inverted surcharge	160.00	
37		5c on 30c brown, bis (C)	1.25	1.25
38		10c on 40c red, straw	1.25	1.25
a.		Inverted surcharge	250.00	
39		10c on 50c brn, az, name in bl (C)	1.60	1.60
40		10c on 50c brn, az, name in red	850.00	900.00
41		10c on 75c violet, org	4.25	4.25
a.		Double surcharge	4,500.	
		Nos. 32-39,41 (9)	14.30	14.30

Two spacings between the surcharged numerals are found on Nos. 32 to 41. For detailed listings, see the Scott Classic Specialized Catalogue of Stamps and Covers.

Man Climbing Oil Palm — A5

1913-39   Perf. 13½x14

42	A5	1c violet & blk	.20	.20
43	A5	2c choc & rose	.20	.20
44	A5	4c black & brn	.20	.20
45	A5	5c yel grn & bl grn	.80	.35
46	A5	5c vio brn & vio ('22)	.35	.35
47	A5	10c org red & rose	.80	.45
a.		Half used as 5c on wrapper or printed matter		
48	A5	10c yel grn & bl grn ('22)	.50	.50
49	A5	10c red & ol ('25)	.20	.20
50	A5	15c brn org & dk vio ('17)	.45	.35
51	A5	20c gray & choc	.35	.35
52	A5	20c bluish grn & grn ('26)	.20	.20
53	A5	20c mag & blk ('27)	.20	.20
54	A5	25c ultra & dp blue	1.40	.95
55	A5	25c vio brn & org ('22)	.70	.70
56	A5	30c choc & vio	2.00	1.60
57	A5	30c red org & rose ('22)	2.10	2.10
58	A5	30c yellow & vio ('25)	.20	.20
59	A5	30c dl grn & grn ('27)	.20	.20
60	A5	35c brown & blk	.60	.45
61	A5	35c bl grn & grn ('38)	.20	.20
62	A5	40c black & red org	.45	.45
63	A5	45c gray & ultra	.45	.45
64	A5	50c chocolate & brn	4.25	4.00
a.		Half used as 25c on cover		500.00
65	A5	50c ultra & bl ('22)	1.00	1.00
66	A5	50c brn red & bl ('26)	.85	.85
67	A5	55c gray grn & choc ('38)	.50	.35
68	A5	60c vio, pnksh ('25)	.20	.20
69	A5	65c yel brn & ol grn ('26)	.80	.80
70	A5	75c blue & violet	.80	.80
71	A5	80c henna brn & ultra ('38)	.20	.20
72	A5	85c dk bl & ver ('26)	1.00	1.00
73	A5	90c rose & brn red ('30)	.60	.50
74	A5	90c yel bis & red org ('39)	.75	.35
75	A5	1fr blue grn & blk	.80	.55
76	A5	1fr dk bl & ultra ('26)	1.00	1.00
77	A5	1fr yel brn & lt red ('28)	1.10	.80
78	A5	1fr dk red & red org ('38)	.75	.65
79	A5	1.10fr vio & bis ('28)	3.50	3.00
80	A5	1.25fr dp bl & dk brn ('33)	13.00	5.00
81	A5	1.50fr dk bl & lt bl ('30)	.95	.55
82	A5	1.75fr dk brn & dp buff ('33)	3.00	1.50
83	A5	1.75fr ind & ultra ('38)	1.00	.55
84	A5	2fr yel org & choc	.80	.80
85	A5	3fr red violet ('30)	2.00	.55
86	A5	5fr violet & dp bl	1.60	1.50
		Nos. 42-86 (45)	53.20	37.35

The 1c gray and yellow green and 5c dull red and black are Togo Nos. 193a, 196a.

Nos. 47a and 64a were authorized for use in Paouignan during the last part of November 1921. Other values exist as bisects but were not authorized.

For surcharges see #87-96, B1, B8-B11.

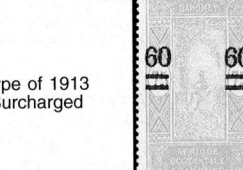

Type of 1913 Surcharged

1922-25

87	A5	60c on 75c vio, pnksh	.80	.80
a.		Double surcharge	140.00	
88	A5	65c on 15c brn org & dk vio ('25)	1.25	1.25
89	A5	85c on 15c brn org & dk vio ('25)	1.10	1.10
		Nos. 87-89 (3)	3.15	3.15

Stamps and Type of 1913-39 Surcharged with New Value and Bars

1924-27

90	A5	25c on 2fr org & choc	.80	.80
91	A5	90c on 75c cer & brn red ('27)	1.10	1.10
92	A5	1.25fr on 1fr dk bl & ultra (R) ('26)	.95	.95
93	A5	1.50fr on 1fr dk bl & grnsh bl ('27)	1.50	1.50
94	A5	3fr on 5fr olvn & dp org ('27)	7.25	7.25
95	A5	10fr on 5fr bl vio & red brn ('27)	5.75	5.75
96	A5	20fr on 5fr ver & dl grn ('27)	5.75	5.75
		Nos. 90-96 (7)	23.10	23.10

Common Design Types pictured following the introduction.

Colonial Exposition Issue
Common Design Types

1931   Engr.   Perf. 12½
Name of Country in Black

97	CD70	40c deep green	4.25	4.25
98	CD71	50c violet	4.25	4.25
99	CD72	90c red orange	4.25	4.25
100	CD73	1.50fr dull blue	4.25	4.25
		Nos. 97-100 (4)	17.00	17.00

Paris International Exposition Issue
Common Design Types

1937   Engr.   Perf. 13

101	CD74	20c deep violet	1.10	1.10
102	CD75	30c dark green	1.10	1.10
103	CD76	40c carmine rose	1.25	1.25
104	CD77	50c dark brown	1.25	1.25
105	CD78	90c red	1.25	1.25
106	CD79	1.50fr ultra	1.25	1.25
		Nos. 101-106 (6)	7.20	7.20

Souvenir Sheet
Imperf

107	CD77	3fr dp blue & blk	5.75	7.25

Caillié Issue
Common Design Type

1939, Apr. 5   Engr.   Perf. 12½x12

108	CD81	90c org brn & org	.90	.90
109	CD81	2fr brt violet	.90	.90
110	CD81	2.25fr ultra & dk blue	1.10	1.10
		Nos. 108-110 (3)	2.90	2.90

New York World's Fair Issue
Common Design Type

1939   Engr.

111	CD82	1.25fr carmine lake	.80	.80
112	CD82	2.25fr ultra	.80	.80

Man Poling a Canoe — A7

Pile House A8

Sailboat on Lake Nokoué — A9   Dahomey Warrior — A10

1941   Perf. 13

113	A7	2c scarlet	.20	.20
114	A7	3c deep blue	.20	.20
115	A7	5c brown violet	.45	.45
116	A7	10c green	.20	.20
117	A7	15c black	.20	.20
118	A8	20c violet brown	.20	.20
119	A8	30c dk violet	.20	.20
120	A8	40c scarlet	.50	.50
121	A8	50c slate green	.80	.80
122	A8	60c black	.20	.20
123	A8	70c brt red violet	.80	.80
124	A9	80c brown black	.80	.80
125	A9	1fr violet	.80	.80
126	A9	1.30fr brown violet	.95	.95
127	A9	1.40fr green	.80	.80
128	A9	1.50fr brt rose	.80	.80
129	A9	2fr brown orange	1.00	1.00
130	A10	2.50fr dark blue	1.00	1.00
131	A10	3fr scarlet	.80	.80
132	A10	5fr slate green	.80	.80
133	A10	10fr violet brown	1.50	1.50
134	A10	20fr black	1.75	1.75
		Nos. 113-134 (22)	14.95	14.95

Nos. 121, 122 without "RF," see Nos. 136A-136B.

Pile House and Marshal Pétain A11

1941   Perf. 12½x12

135	A11	1fr green	.55	—
136	A11	2.50fr blue	.55	—

For surcharges see Nos. B14A-B14B.

Type of 1941 without "RF"
1944 — **Perf. 13**
136A A8 50c slate green .75
136B A8 60c black .75

Nos. 136A-136B were issued by the Vichy government in France, but were not placed on sale in Dahomey.

> Catalogue values for unused stamps in this section, from this point to the end of the section, are for Never Hinged items.

Republic

Village Ganvié — A12

Unwmk.
1960, Mar. 1 Engr. **Perf. 12**
137 A12 25fr dk blue, brn & red .55 .20

For overprint see No. 152.

Imperforates
Most Dahomey stamps from 1960 onward exist imperforate in issued and trial colors, and also in small presentation sheets in issued colors.

C.C.T.A. Issue
Common Design Type
1960, May 16
138 CD106 5fr rose lilac & ultra .45 .20

Emblem of the Entente — A13

Prime Minister Hubert Maga — A14

Council of the Entente Issue
1960, May 29 Photo. **Perf. 13x13½**
139 A13 25fr multicolored .55 .30

1st anniv. of the Council of the Entente (Dahomey, Ivory Coast, Niger and Upper Volta).

1960, Aug. Engr. **Perf. 13**
140 A14 85fr deep claret & blk 1.60 .90

Issued on the occasion of Dahomey's proclamation of independence, Aug. 1, 1960. For surcharge see No. 149.

Weaver — A15

Doves, UN Building and Emblem — A16

2fr, 10fr, Wood sculptor. 3fr, 15fr, Fisherman and net, horiz. 4fr, 20fr, Potter, horiz.

1961, Feb. 17 Engr. **Perf. 13**
141 A15 1fr rose, org & red lilac .20 .20
142 A15 2fr bister brn & choc .20 .20
143 A15 3fr green & orange .20 .20
144 A15 4fr olive bis & claret .20 .20
145 A15 6fr rose, lt vio & ver .40 .20
146 A15 10fr blue & green .55 .40

147 A15 15fr red lilac & violet .75 .40
148 A15 20fr bluish vio & Prus bl .90 .55
Nos. 141-148 (8) 3.40 2.35

For surcharges see Nos. Q1-Q7.

No. 140 Surcharged with New Value, Bars and: "Président de la République"
1961, Aug. 1
149 A14 100fr on 85fr dp cl & blk 3.25 3.25

First anniversary of Independence.

1961, Sept. 20 Unwmk. **Perf. 13**
150 A16 5fr multicolored .35 .25
151 A16 60fr multicolored 1.10 .80

1st anniv. of Dahomey's admission to the UN. See #C16 and souvenir sheet #C16a.

No. 137 Overprinted: "JEUX SPORTIFS D'ABIDJAN 24 AU 31 DECEMBRE 1961"
1961, Dec. 24
152 A12 25fr dk blue, brn & red .55 .30

Abidjan Games, Dec 24-31.

Interior of Burned-out Fort Ouidah and Wrecked Car — A17

1962, July 31 Photo. **Perf. 12½**
153 A17 30fr multicolored .60 .45
154 A17 60fr multicolored 1.40 .60

Evacuation of Fort Ouidah by the Portuguese, and its occupation by Dahomey. 1st anniv.

African and Malgache Union Issue
Common Design Type
1962, Sept. 8 **Perf. 12½x12**
155 CD110 30fr red lil, bluish grn, red & gold .90 .90

Red Cross Nurses and Map — A18

1962, Oct. 5 Engr. **Perf. 13**
156 A18 5fr blue, choc & red .30 .20
157 A18 20fr blue, dk grn & red .60 .45
158 A18 25fr blue, brown & red .65 .45
159 A18 30fr blue, black & red .85 .70
Nos. 156-159 (4) 2.40 1.80

Ganvié Woman in Canoe — A19

Peuhl Herdsman and Cattle A20

Designs: 3fr, 65fr, Bariba chief of Nikki. 15fr, 50fr, Ouidah witch doctor, rock python. 20fr, 30fr, Nessoukoué women carrying vases on heads, Abomey. 25fr, 40fr, Dahomey girl. 60fr, Peuhl herdsman and cattle. 85fr, Ganvié woman in canoe.

1963, Feb. 18 Unwmk. **Perf. 13**
160 A19 2fr grnsh blue & vio .20 .20
161 A19 3fr blue & black .20 .20
162 A20 5fr brown, blk & grn .45 .20
163 A19 15fr brn, bl grn & red brn .45 .20
164 A19 20fr green, blk & car .35 .20
165 A20 25fr dk brn, bl & bl grn .45 .20

166 A19 30fr brn org, choc & mag .65 .40
167 A20 40fr choc, grn & brt bl .95 .40
168 A19 50fr blk, grn, brn & red brn 1.50 .55
169 A20 60fr choc, org red & ol 2.75 1.00
170 A19 65fr orange brn & choc 1.75 .65
171 A19 85fr brt blue & choc 2.75 1.00
Nos. 160-171 (12) 12.45 5.20

For surcharges see Nos. 211, 232, Benin 655A, 690F, 700, 722.

Boxers — A21

Designs: 1fr, 20fr, Soccer goalkeeper, horiz. 2fr, 5fr, Runners.

1963, Apr. 11 Engr.
172 A21 50c green & blue .20 .20
173 A21 1fr olive, blk & brn .20 .20
174 A21 2fr olive, blue & brn .20 .20
175 A21 5fr brown, crim & blk .20 .20
176 A21 15fr dk violet & brn .45 .20
177 A21 20fr multicolored .70 .55
Nos. 172-177 (6) 1.95 1.55

Friendship Games, Dakar, Apr. 11-21. For surcharge & overprint see Benin #697, 704.

President's Palace, Cotonou — A22

1963, Aug. 1 Photo. **Perf. 12½x12**
178 A22 25fr multicolored .45 .20

Third anniversary of independence.

Gen. Toussaint L'Ouverture — A23

UN Emblem, Flame, "15" — A24

1963, Nov. 18 Unwmk. **Perf. 12x13**
179 A23 25fr multicolored .40 .20
180 A23 30fr multicolored .70 .20
181 A23 100fr ultra, brn & red 1.40 .80
Nos. 179-181 (3) 2.50 1.20

Pierre Dominique Toussaint L'Ouverture (1743-1803), Haitian gen., statesman and descendant of the kings of Allada (Dahomey).

1963, Dec. 10 **Perf. 12**
182 A24 4fr multicolored .20 .20
183 A24 6fr multicolored .20 .20
184 A24 25fr multicolored .45 .20
Nos. 182-184 (3) .85 .60

15th anniversary of the Universal Declaration of Human Rights.

Somba Dance — A25

Regional Dances: 3fr, Nago dance, Pobe-Ketou, horiz. 10fr, Dance of the baton. 15fr, Nago dance, Ouidah, horiz. 25fr, Dance of the Sakpatassi. 30fr, Dance of the Nessouhouessi, horiz.

1964, Aug. 8 Engr. **Perf. 13**
185 A25 2fr red, emerald & blk .20 .20
186 A25 3fr dull red, blue & grn .20 .20
187 A25 10fr purple, blk & red .40 .20
188 A25 15fr magenta, blk & grn .40 .20
189 A25 25fr Prus blue, brn & org .80 .30
190 A25 30fr dk red, choc & org 1.00 .40
Nos. 185-190 (6) 3.00 1.50

Runner — A26

1964, Oct. 20 Photo. **Perf. 11**
191 A26 60fr shown 1.90 1.00
192 A26 85fr Bicyclist 3.00 1.40

18th Olympic Games, Tokyo, Oct. 10-25.

Cooperation Issue
Common Design Type
1964, Nov. 7 Engr. **Perf. 13**
193 CD119 25fr org, vio & dk brn .80 .35

UNICEF Emblem, Mother and Child — A27

IQSY Emblem and Apollo — A28

25fr, Mother holding child in her arms.

1964, Dec. 11 Unwmk. **Perf. 13**
194 A27 20fr yel grn, dk red & blk .40 .20
195 A27 25fr blue, dk red & blk .60 .45

18th anniv. of UNICEF.

1964, Dec. 22 Photo. **Perf. 13x12½**
100fr, IQSY emblem, Nimbus weather satellite.
196 A28 25fr green & lt yellow .55 .20
197 A28 100fr deep plum & yellow 1.60 .95

International Quiet Sun Year, 1964-65.

Abomey
Tapestry — A29

Designs (Abomey tapestries): 25fr, Warrior
and fight scenes. 50fr, Birds and warriors,
horiz. 85fr, Animals, ship and plants, horiz.

1965, Apr. 12   Photo.   Perf. 12½
198 A29 20fr multicolored   .75   .20
199 A29 25fr multicolored   .85   .40
200 A29 50fr multicolored   1.40   .80
201 A29 85fr multicolored   2.75 1.10
  a.   Min. sheet of 4, #198-201   7.50 7.50
     Nos. 198-201 (4)   5.75 2.50

Issued to publicize the local rug weaving
industry.

Baudot
Telegraph
Distributor
and Ader
Telephone
A30

1965, May 17   Engr.   Perf. 13
202 A30 100fr lilac, org & blk   2.10 1.60
       Cent. of the ITU.

Cotonou Harbor — A31

100fr, Cotonou Harbor, denomination at left.

1965, Aug. 1   Photo.   Perf. 12½
203 A31 25fr multicolored   .90   .20
204 A31 100fr multicolored   2.10 1.10
  a.   Pair, #203-204   3.75 2.10

The opening of Cotonou Harbor. No. 204a
has a continuous design.
For surcharges see Nos. 219-220.

Cybium
Tritor
A32

Fish: 25fr, Dentex filosus. 30fr, Atlantic sailfish. 50fr, Blackish tripletail.

1965, Sept. 20   Engr.   Perf. 13
205 A32 10fr black & brt blue   .55   .20
206 A32 25fr brt blue, org & blk   .80   .55
207 A32 30fr violet bl & grnsh bl 1.40   .80
208 A32 50fr black, gray bl & org 2.25 1.00
     Nos. 205-208 (4)   5.00 2.55

For surcharge see Benin No. 911.

Independence
Monument — A33

1965, Oct. 28   Photo.   Perf. 12x12½
209 A33 25fr gray, black & red   .40   .20
210 A33 30fr lt ultra, black & red .65   .20

October 28 Revolution, 2nd anniv.

No. 165 Surcharged

1965, Nov.   Engr.   Perf. 13
211 A20 1fr on 25fr   .30   .20

Porto Novo
Cathedral
A34

Designs: 50fr, Ouidah Pro-Cathedral, vert.
70fr, Cotonou Cathedral.

1966, Mar. 21   Engr.   Perf. 13
212 A34 30fr Prus bl, vio brn &
            grn   .55   .20
213 A34 50fr vio brn, Prus bl &
            brn   .70   .50
214 A34 70fr grn, Prus bl & vio
            brn   1.25   .75
     Nos. 212-214 (3)   2.50 1.45

Jewelry — A35

Designs: 30fr, Architecture. 50fr, Musician.
70fr, Crucifixion, sculpture.

1966, Apr. 4   Engr.   Perf. 13
215 A35 15fr dull red brn & blk   .45   .20
216 A35 30fr dk brn, ultra & brn
            red   .70   .45
217 A35 50fr brt blue & dk brn   1.10   .55
218 A35 70fr red brown & blk   2.25   .85
     Nos. 215-218 (4)   4.50 2.05

International Negro Arts Festival, Dakar,
Senegal, Apr. 1-24.

Nos. 203-204 Surcharged

1966, Apr. 24   Photo.   Perf. 12½
219 A31 15fr on 25fr multi   .55   .35
220 A31 15fr on 100fr multi   .55   .35
  a.   Pair, #219-220   1.50 1.10

Fifth anniversary of the Cooperation Agreement between France and Dahomey.

WHO Headquarters from the
East — A36

1966, May 3   Perf. 12½x13
       Size: 35x22½mm
221 A36 30fr multicolored   .55   .20

Inauguration of the WHO Headquarters,
Geneva. See No. C32.

Boy Scout
Signaling
A37

Designs: 10fr, Patrol standard with pennant,
vert. 30fr, Campfire and map of Dahomey,
vert. 50fr, Scouts building foot bridge.

1966, Oct. 17   Engr.   Perf. 13
222 A37 5fr dk brn, ocher & red   .20   .20
223 A37 10fr black, grn & rose cl .20   .20
224 A37 30fr org, red brn & pur   .55   .35
225 A37 50fr vio bl, grn & dk brn .95   .45
  a.   Min. sheet of 4, #222-225   2.75 2.75
     Nos. 222-225 (4)   1.90 1.20

Clappertonia   Lions Emblem,
Ficifolia — A38   Dancing
                      Children,
                      Bird — A39

Flowers: 3fr, Hewittia sublobata. 5fr, Butterfly pea. 10fr, Water lily. 15fr, Commelina forskalaei. 30fr, Eremomastax speciosa.

1967, Feb. 20   Photo.   Perf. 12x12½
226 A38 1fr multicolored   .20   .20
227 A38 3fr multicolored   .35   .20
228 A38 5fr multicolored   .55   .20
229 A38 10fr multicolored   .90   .35
230 A38 15fr multicolored   1.10   .55
231 A38 30fr multicolored   2.10   .90
     Nos. 226-231 (6)   5.20 2.40

For surcharges see Benin Nos. 707, 715.

Nos. 170-171 Surcharged with New
Value and Heavy Bar

1967, Mar. 1   Engr.   Perf. 13
232 A19 30fr on 65fr   .85   .60
  a.   Double surcharge   36.00
233 A19 30fr on 85fr   .85   .60
  a.   Double surcharge   60.00
  b.   Inverted surcharge   60.00

1967, Mar. 20
234 A39 100fr dl vio, dp bl & grn 1.50 1.10

50th anniversary of Lions International.

EXPO '67
"Man in the
City"
Pavilion
A40

Design: 70fr, "The New Africa" exhibit.

1967, June 12   Engr.   Perf. 13
235 A40 30fr green & choc   .70   .20
236 A40 70fr green & brn red   1.50   .65

EXPO '67, International Exhibition, Montreal, Apr. 28-Oct. 27, 1967. See No. C57 and
miniature sheet No. C57a.
For surcharges see Benin No. 897.

Europafrica Issue, 1967

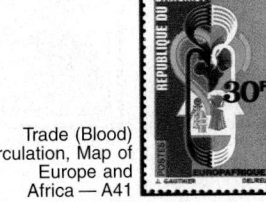

Trade (Blood)
Circulation, Map of
Europe and
Africa — A41

1967, July 20   Photo.   Perf. 12x12½
237 A41 30fr multicolored   .55   .20
238 A41 45fr multicolored   .80   .45

Scouts
Climbing
Mountain,
Jamboree
Emblem
A42

70fr, Jamboree emblem, Scouts launching
canoe.

1967, Aug. 7   Engr.   Perf. 13
239 A42 30fr brt bl, red brn & sl .50   .20
240 A42 70fr brt bl, sl grn & dk
            brn   1.25   .65

12th Boy Scout World Jamboree, Farragut
State Park, Idaho, Aug. 1-9. For souvenir
sheet see No. C59a.
For surcharges see Benin Nos. 902, 912.

Rhone
River and
Olympic
Emblems
A43

Designs (Olympic Emblems and): 45fr, View
of Grenoble, vert. 100fr, Rhone Bridge, Grenoble, and Pierre de Coubertin.

1967, Sept. 2   Engr.   Perf. 13
241 A43 30fr bis, dp bl & grn   .70   .40
242 A43 45fr ultra, grn & brn   .90   .55
243 A43 100fr choc, grn & brt bl 1.90 1.00
  a.   Min. sheet of 3, #241-243   4.00 4.00
     Nos. 241-243 (3)   3.50 1.95

10th Winter Olympic Games, Grenoble,
Feb. 6-18, 1968.
For surcharge see Benin No. 903.

Monetary Union Issue
Common Design Type

1967, Nov. 4   Engr.   Perf. 13
244 CD125 30fr grn, dk car & dk
              brn   .65   .65

Cape
Buffalo
A45

Animals from the Pendjari Reservation: 30fr,
Lion. 45fr, Buffon's kob. 70fr, African slender-
snouted crocodile. 100fr, Hippopotamus.

1968, Mar. 18   Photo.   Perf. 12½x13
245 A45 15fr multicolored   .50   .20
246 A45 30fr purple & multi   .75   .50
247 A45 45fr blue & multi   1.50   .60
248 A45 70fr multicolored   2.75   .75
249 A45 100fr multicolored   5.00 2.10
     Nos. 245-249 (5)   10.50 4.15

For surcharges see #310, Benin 655E, 725.

WHO
Emblem
A46

1968, Apr. 22   Engr.   Perf. 13
250 A46 30fr multicolored   .60   .20
251 A46 70fr multicolored   1.40   .70

20th anniv. of WHO.

Spotted
Hyena
A47

Animals: 5fr, Warthog. 30fr, Leopard. 60fr,
Spotted hyena. 75fr, Anubius baboon. 90fr,
Hartebeest.

1969, Feb. 10   Photo.   Perf. 12½x12
252 A47 5fr dark brown & multi   .20   .20
253 A47 30fr deep ultra & multi   .80   .50
254 A47 60fr dark green & multi 1.50   .70

255 A47 75fr dark blue & multi   3.50   .90
256 A47 90fr dark green & multi   4.50 2.10
       Nos. 252-256 (5)   10.50 4.40
   For surcharge, see Benin No. 708.

Heads,
Symbols of
Agriculture
and
Science,
and Globe
A48

1969, Mar. 10   Engr.   Perf. 13
257 A48 30fr orange & multi   .50   .20
258 A48 70fr maroon & multi   1.50   .70
   50th anniv. of the ILO.
   For surcharges see Benin Nos. 904, 913.

Arms of Dahomey — A49

1969, June 30   Litho.   Perf. 13½x13
259 A49 5fr yellow & multi   .35   .30
260 A49 30fr orange red & multi   1.25   .45
   See No. C101.

Development Bank Issue

Cornucopia and
Bank
Emblem — A50

1969, Sept. 10   Photo.   Perf. 13
261 A50 30fr black, grn & ocher   .75   .55
   African Development Bank, 5th anniv.
   For surcharge see Benin No. 905.

Europafrica Issue

Ambary
(Kenaf)
Industry,
Cotonou
A51

Design: 45fr, Cotton industry, Parakou.

1969, Sept. 22   Litho.   Perf. 14
262 A51 30fr multicolored   1.00   .50
263 A51 45fr multicolored   1.25   .75
   See Nos. C105-C105a.

Sakpata Dance and
Tourist Year
Emblem — A52

Dances and Tourist Year Emblem: 30fr,
Guelede dance. 45fr, Sato dance.

1969, Dec. 15   Litho.   Perf. 14
264 A52 10fr multicolored   .45   .30
265 A52 30fr multicolored   .90   .45
266 A52 45fr multicolored   1.25   .55
       Nos. 264-266 (3)   2.60 1.30
   See No. C108. For surcharges see Benin
Nos. 690J, 1054B.

UN
Emblem,
Garden and
Wall — A53

1970, Apr. 6   Engr.   Perf. 13
267 A53 30fr ultra, red org & slate   .70   .20
268 A53 40fr ultra, brn & sl grn   .90   .50
   25th anniversary of the United Nations.
   For surcharges see Nos. 294, Benin 647B.

ASECNA Issue
Common Design Type

1970, June 1   Engr.   Perf. 13
269 CD132 40fr red & purple   .90   .55
   For surcharge see Benin No. 906.

Mt. Fuji,
EXPO '70
Emblem,
Monorail
Train — A54

1970, June 15   Litho.   Perf. 13½x14
270 A54 5fr green, red & vio bl   .40   .20
   EXPO '70 International Exhibition, Osaka,
Japan, 3/15-9/13/70. See Nos. C124-C125.

Alkemy, King of
Ardres — A55

40fr, Sailing ships "La Justice" & "La Concorde," Ardres, 1670. 50fr, Matheo Lopes,
ambassador of the King of Ardres & his coat of
arms. 200fr, Louis XIV & fleur-de-lis.

1970, July 6   Engr.   Perf. 13
271 A55 40fr brt grn, ultra & brn   .65   .20
272 A55 50fr dk car, choc &
           emer   .90   .40
273 A55 70fr gray, lemon &
           choc   1.40   .65
274 A55 200fr Prus bl, dk car &
           choc   3.50 1.25
       Nos. 271-274 (4)   6.45 2.50
   300th anniv. of the mission from the King of
Ardres to the King of France, and of the audience with Louis XIV on Dec. 19, 1670.
   For surcharges see Benin Nos. 724, 914.

Star of the
Order of
Independence
A56

Bariba Warrior
A57

1970, Aug. 1   Photo.   Perf. 12
275 A56 30fr multicolored   .40   .20
276 A56 40fr multicolored   .60   .20
   10th anniversary of independence.
   For surcharge see Benin No. 720.

1970, Aug. 24   Perf. 12½x13
Designs: 2fr, 50fr, Two horsemen. 10fr, 70fr,
Horseman facing left.
277 A57 1fr yellow & multi   .20   .20
278 A57 2fr gray grn & multi   .30   .20
279 A57 10fr blue & multi   .20   .20
280 A57 40fr yellow grn & multi   1.40   .35
281 A57 50fr gold & multi   1.75   .50
282 A57 70fr lilac rose & multi   2.10   .80
       Nos. 277-282 (6)   6.10 2.25
   For surcharges see Benin Nos. 350-351,
613, 703.

Globe and
Heart
A58

Design: 40fr, Hands holding heart, vert.

1971, June 7   Engr.   Perf. 13
283 A58 40fr red, green & dk brn   .90   .35
284 A58 100fr green, red & blue   1.75   .90
   For surcharges see Benin Nos. 617, 647A,
712, 907.

   Intl. year against racial discrimination.

Ancestral Figures
and Lottery
Ticket — A59

King Behanzin's
Emblem (1889-
1894)
A60

1971, June 24   Litho.   Perf. 14
285 A59 35fr multicolored   .65   .20
286 A59 40fr multicolored   .80   .35
   4th anniv. of the National Lottery.
   For overprint see Benin #710.

Photo.; Litho. (25fr, 135fr)
1971-72   Perf. 12½
Emblems of the Kings of Abomey: 25fr,
Agoliagbo (1894-1900). 35fr, Ganyehoussou
(1620-45), bird and cup, horiz. 100fr, Guezo
(1818-58), bull, tree and birds. 135fr,
Ouegbadja (1645-85), horiz. 140fr, Glèle
(1858-89), lion and sword, horiz.
287 A60 25fr multicolored   .55   .20
288 A60 35fr green & multi   .90   .20
289 A60 40fr green & multi   1.25   .55
290 A60 100fr red & multi   2.25   .90
291 A60 135fr multicolored   3.25 1.40
292 A60 140fr brown & multi   3.75 1.90
       Nos. 287-292 (6)   11.95 5.15
   Issued: 25fr, 135fr, 7/17/72; others, 8/3/71.
   For surcharges, see Benin #614, 634B, 726,
791.

Kabuki Actor, Long-
distance
Skiing — A61

Brahms and
"Soir
d'été" — A62

1972, Feb.   Engr.   Perf. 13
293 A61 35fr dk car, brn & bl grn   1.60   .75
   11th Winter Olympic Games, Sapporo,
Japan, Feb. 3-13. See No. C153.

   No. 268 Surcharged

1972
294 A53 35fr on 40fr multi   .65   .35

1972, June 29   Engr.   Perf. 13
65fr, Brahms, woman at piano & music,
horiz.
295 A62 30fr red brn, blk & lilac   2.00   .80
296 A62 65fr red brn, blk & lilac   3.25 1.50
   75th anniversary of the death of Johannes
Brahms (1833-1897), German composer.
   For surcharge see Benin Nos. 654B, 718.

The Hare and The Tortoise, by La
Fontaine — A63

Fables: 35fr, The Fox and The Stork, vert.
40fr, The Cat, The Weasel and Rabbit.

1972, Aug. 28   Engr.   Perf. 13
297 A63 10fr multicolored   1.75   .75
298 A63 35fr dark red & multi   3.25 1.25
299 A63 40fr ultra & multi   4.25 1.75
       Nos. 297-299 (3)   9.25 3.75
   Jean de La Fontaine (1621-1695), French
fabulist.

West African Monetary Union Issue
Common Design Type

1972, Nov. 2   Engr.   Perf. 13
300 CD136 40fr choc, ocher & gray .65   .20

Dr. Hansen,
Microscope,
Bacilli — A65

Design: 85fr, Portrait of Dr. Hansen.

1973, May 14   Engr.   Perf. 13
301 A65 35fr ultra, vio brn & brn   .50   .35
302 A65 85fr yel grn, bis & ver   1.10   .75
   Centenary of the discovery by Dr. Armauer
G. Hansen of the Hansen bacillus, the cause
of leprosy.
   For surcharges see Benin Nos. 655G, 1084.

Arms of
Dahomey — A66

1973, June 25   Photo.   Perf. 13
303 A66 5fr ultra & multi   .20   .20
304 A66 35fr ocher & multi   .40   .20
305 A66 40fr red orange & multi   .60   .20
    Nos. 303-305 (3)   1.20   .60

For surcharge see Benin No. 690A.

INTERPOL
Emblem
and
Spiderweb
A67

Design: 50fr, INTERPOL emblem and communications symbols, vert.

1973, July   Engr.
306 A67 35fr ver, grn & brn   .60   .30
307 A67 50fr green, brn & red   1.00   .45

50th anniversary of International Criminal Police Organization (INTERPOL).
For surcharges see Benin Nos. 634A, 810.

Education
in Hygiene
and
Nutrition
A68

WHO, 25th Anniv.: 100fr, Prenatal examination and care, WHO emblem.

1973, Aug. 2   Photo.   Perf. 12½x13
308 A68 35fr multicolored   .50   .30
309 A68 100fr multicolored   1.50   .65

No. 248 Surcharged with New Value,
2 Bars, and Overprinted in Red:
"SECHERESSE SOLIDARITE
AFRICAINE"

1973, Aug. 16
310 A45 100fr on 70fr multi   2.10 1.00
African solidarity in drought emergency.

African Postal Union Issue
Common Design Type
1973, Sept. 12   Engr.   Perf. 13
311 CD137 100fr red, purple & blk 1.25   .55
For surcharge see Benin No. 690I.

Epinephelus Aeneus — A69

Fish: 15fr, Drepane africana. 35fr, Pragus ehrenbergi.

1973, Sept. 18
312 A69 5fr slate blue & indigo   1.00   .30
313 A69 15fr black & brt blue   1.50   .35
314 A69 35fr emerald, ocher &
        sep   3.50   .60
    Nos. 312-314 (3)   6.00 1.25

Chameleon
A70

40fr, Emblem over map of Dahomey, vert.

1973, Nov. 30   Photo.   Perf. 13
315 A70 35fr olive & multi   .55   .30
316 A70 40fr multicolored   1.25   .35
    1st anniv. of the Oct. 26 revolution.

The Chameleon in the Tree — A71

Designs: 5fr, The elephant, the hen and the dog, vert. 10fr, The sparrowhawk and the dog, vert. 25fr, The chameleon in the tree. 40fr, The eagle, the viper and the hen.

1974, Feb. 14   Photo.   Perf. 13
317 A71 5fr emerald & multi   .40   .20
318 A71 10fr slate blue & multi   .50   .20
319 A71 25fr slate blue & multi   .90   .30
320 A71 40fr light blue & multi   1.40   .45
    Nos. 317-320 (4)   3.20 1.15

Folktales of Dahomey.
For surcharges see Benin Nos. 709, 908.

German Shepherd — A72

1974, Apr. 25   Photo.   Perf. 13
321 A72 40fr shown   1.50   .35
322 A72 50fr Boxer   1.75   .35
323 A72 100fr Saluki   3.50   .80
    Nos. 321-323 (3)   6.75 1.50

Council Issue

Map and
Flags of
Members
A73

1974, May 29   Photo.   Perf. 13x12½
324 A73 40fr blue & multi   .80   .20

15th anniversary of the Council of Accord.

Locomotive 232, 1911 — A74

Designs: Locomotives.

1974, Sept. 2   Photo.   Perf. 13x12½
325 A74 35fr shown   .75   .30
326 A74 40fr Freight, 1877   1.50   .30
327 A74 100fr Crampton, 1849   2.25 1.00
328 A74 200fr Stephenson, 1846   4.50 1.60
    Nos. 325-328 (4)   9.00 3.20

For surcharges see Benin Nos. 654E, 690K, 727, 909.

Globe,
Money,
People in
Bank
A75

1974, Oct. 31   Engr.   Perf. 13
329 A75 35fr multicolored   .50   .35
World Savings Day.

Dompago Dance,
Hissi
Tribe — A76

Flags of
Dahomey and
Nigeria over
Africa — A77

Folk Dances: 25fr, Fetish Dance, Vaudou-Tchinan. 40fr, Bamboo Dance, Agbehoun. 100fr, Somba Dance, Sandoua, horiz.

1975, Aug. 4   Litho.   Perf. 12
330 A76 10fr yellow & multi   .50   .20
331 A76 25fr dk green & multi   1.00   .20
332 A76 40fr red & multi   1.25   .50
333 A76 100fr multicolored   2.25   .60
    Nos. 330-333 (4)   5.00 1.50

For surcharge and overprint see Benin Nos. 655D, 713.

1975, Aug. 11   Photo.   Perf. 12½x13
Design: 100fr, Arrows connecting maps of Dahomey and Nigeria, horiz.
334 A77 65fr multicolored   .75   .25
335 A77 100fr green & multi   1.00   .45

Year of intensified cooperation between Dahomey and Nigeria.
For surcharges & overprint see Benin Nos. 690H, 701, 899, 901.

Map, Pylons, Emblem — A78

Benin Electric
Community
Emblem and
Pylon — A79

1975, Aug. 18
336 A78 40fr multicolored   .75   .35
337 A79 150fr multicolored   2.00 1.00

Benin Electric Community and Ghana-Togo-Dahomey cooperation.
For surcharges see Benin #601, 900, 910.

Map of Dahomey,
Rising Sun — A80

Albert
Schweitzer,
Nurse,
Patient — A81

1975, Aug. 25   Photo.   Perf. 12½x13
338 A80 35fr multicolored   .50   .20

Cooperation Year for the creation of a new Dahoman society.
For overprint see Benin No. 690E.

1975, Sept. 22   Engr.   Perf. 13
339 A81 200fr olive, grn & red
        brn   5.00 1.50

Birth centenary of Albert Schweitzer (1875-1965), medical missionary and musician.
For surcharge see Benin No. 655F.

Woman Speaking
on Telephone,
IWY
Emblem — A82

150fr, IWY emblem and linked rings.

1975, Oct. 20   Engr.   Perf. 12½x13
340 A82 50fr Prus blue & lilac   .75   .35
341 A82 150fr emerald, brn & org   2.00   .80

International Women's Year 1975.
For surcharge see Benin No. 655C.

———

SEMI-POSTAL STAMPS

Regular Issue of
1913 Surcharged in
Red

1915   Unwmk.   Perf. 14x13½
B1 A5 10c + 5c orange red &
       rose   .90   .90

Curie Issue
Common Design Type
1938   Perf. 13
B2 CD80 1.75fr + 50c brt ultra   7.25 7.25

French Revolution Issue
Common Design Type
1939   Photo.
Name and Value Typo. in Black
B3 CD83 45c + 25c green   6.50 6.50
B4 CD83 70c + 30c brown   6.50 6.50
B5 CD83 90c + 35c red org   6.50 6.50
B6 CD83 1.25fr + 1fr rose
       pink   6.50 6.50
B7 CD83 2.25fr + 2fr blue   6.50 6.50
    Nos. B3-B7 (5)   32.50 32.50

Postage Stamps of
1913-38 Surcharged
in Black

1941   **Perf. 13½x14**
B8   A5   50c + 1fr brn red &
bl   1.50 1.50
B9   A5   80c + 2fr hn brn &
ultra   5.00 5.00
B10 A5   1.50fr + 2fr dk bl & lt bl 5.00 5.00
B11 A5   2fr + 3fr yel org &
choc   5.00 5.00
Nos. B8-B11 (4)   16.50 16.50

Common Design Type and

Radio
Operator — SP1

Senegalese
Artillerymen
SP2

1941   **Photo.**   **Perf. 13½**
B12 SP1   1fr + 1fr red   .95
B13 CD86 1.50fr + 3fr claret   .95
B14 SP2   2.50fr + 1fr blue   1.00
Nos. B12-B14 (3)   2.90

Surtax for the defense of the colonies.
Nos. B12-B14 were issued by the Vichy
government in France, but were not placed on
sale in Dahomey.

Nos. 135-136
Surcharged in Black or Red

1944   **Engr.**   **Perf. 12½x12**
B14A 50c + 1.50fr on 2.50fr deep
blue (R)   .55
B14B + 2.50fr on 1fr green   .55

Colonial Development Fund.
Nos. B14A-B14B were issued by the Vichy
government in France, but were not placed on
sale in Dahomey.

Catalogue values for unused
stamps in this section, from this
point to the end of the section, are
for Never Hinged items.

Republic
Anti-Malaria Issue
Common Design Type
1962, Apr. 7   Engr.   Perf. 12½x12
B15 CD108 25fr + 5fr orange brn .55 .55

Freedom from Hunger Issue
Common Design Type
1963, Mar. 21   Unwmk.   Perf. 13
B16 CD112 25fr + 5fr ol, brn red &
brn   .65 .65

AIR POST STAMPS

Common Design Type
1940   Unwmk.   Engr.   Perf. 12½
C1 CD85 1.90fr ultra   .20 .30
C2 CD85 2.90fr dk red   .40 .40
C3 CD85 4.50fr dk gray grn   .65 .65
C4 CD85 4.90fr yel bister   .85 .85
C5 CD85 6.90fr deep org   1.10 1.10
Nos. C1-C5 (5)   3.20 3.30

Common Design Types
1942
C6   CD88 50c car & bl   .20
C7   CD88 1fr brn & blk   .20
C8   CD88 2fr dk grn & red brn   .35
C9   CD88 3fr dk bl & scar   .80
C10 CD88 5fr vio & brn red   .80
Frame Engr., Center Typo.
C11 CD89 10fr ultra, ind & org   .80
C12 CD89 20fr rose car, mag &
blk   .80
C13 CD89 50fr yel grn, dl grn &
dp bl   1.50 3.25
a.   50fr yellow green, dull green &
pale blue   2.00 3.75
Nos. C6-C13 (8)   5.45

Nos. C6-C12 were issued by the Vichy government in France, but were not placed on
sale in Dahomey.

Catalogue values for unused
stamps in this section, from this
point to the end of the section, are
for Never Hinged items.

Republic

Somba House — AP4

Design: 500fr, Royal Court of Abomey.

Unwmk.
1960, Apr. 1   Engr.   Perf. 13
C14 AP4 100fr multi   3.25 .80
C15 AP4 500fr multi   13.50 4.00

For overprint see Benin No. C419.

Type of Regular Issue, 1961
1961, Sept. 20
C16 A16 200fr multi   3.00 2.25
a.   Souv. sheet of 3, #150-151, C16 6.00 6.00

Air Afrique Issue
Common Design Type
1962, Feb. 17   Perf. 13
C17 CD107 25fr ultra, blk & org brn .70 .30

Palace of the African and Malgache
Union, Cotonou — AP5

1963, July 27   Photo.   Perf. 13x12
C18 AP5 250fr multi   4.00 2.00

Assembly of chiefs of state of the African
and Malgache Union held at Cotonou in July.

African Postal Union Issue
Common Design Type
1963, Sept. 8   Unwmk.   Perf. 12½
C19 CD114 25fr brt bl, ocher & red .60 .25

See note after Cameroun No. C47.

Boeing 707 — AP6

Boeing 707: 200fr, On the ground. 300fr,
Over Cotonou airport. 500fr, In the air.

1963, Oct. 25   Engr.   Perf. 13
C20 AP6 100fr multi   2.00 .60
C21 AP6 200fr multi   3.00 2.00
C22 AP6 300fr multi   5.00 2.00
C23 AP6 500fr multi   10.00 2.50
Nos. C20-C23 (4)   20.00 7.10

For surcharges see Nos. CQ1-CQ5.

Priests Carrying Funerary Boat, Isis
Temple, Philae — AP7

1964, Mar. 9   Unwmk.   Perf. 13
C24 AP7 25fr vio bl & brn   1.50 .75

UNESCO world campaign to save historic
monuments in Nubia.

Weather Map and Symbols — AP8

1965, Mar. 23   Photo.   Perf. 12½
C25 AP8 50fr multi   .80 .55

Fifth World Meteorological Day.

ICY Emblem and Men of Various
Races — AP9

1965, June 26   Engr.   Perf. 13
C26 AP9 25fr dl pur, mar & grn   .40 .20
C27 AP9 85fr dp bl, mar & sl grn .90 .65

International Cooperation Year, 1965

Winston
Churchill — AP10

1965, June 15   Photo.   Perf. 12½
C28 AP10 100fr multi   2.10 1.75

Abraham Lincoln — AP11

1965, July 15   Perf. 13
C29 AP11 100fr multi   1.65 1.00

Centenary of death of Lincoln
For surcharge see No. C55.

John F. Kennedy and Arms of
Dahomey — AP12

1965, Nov. 22   Photo.   Perf. 12½
C30 AP12 100fr dp grn & blk   2.25 1.10

President John F. Kennedy (1917-63).
For surcharge see No. C56.

Dr. Albert Schweitzer and
Patients — AP13

1966, Jan. 17   Photo.   Perf. 12½
C31 AP13 100fr multi   2.50 1.25

Dr. Albert Schweitzer (1875-1965), medical
missionary, theologian and musician.
For surcharge see Benin No. C435.

WHO Type of Regular Issue
Design: WHO Headquarters from the West.

1966, May 3   Unwmk.   Perf. 13
Size: 47x28mm
C32 A36 100fr ultra, yel & blk 1.75 1.50

Pygmy
Goose — AP14

Broad-billed
Rollers — AP15

Birds: 100fr, Fiery-breasted bush-shrike.
250fr, Emerald cuckoos. 500fr, Emerald
starling.

1966-67   Perf. 12½
C33 AP14 50fr multi   2.00 .55
C34 AP14 100fr multi   3.00 .85
C35 AP15 200fr multi   10.00 2.25

C36 AP15 250fr multi 10.00 3.00
C37 AP14 500fr multi 15.00 6.00
    Nos. C33-C37 (5) 40.00 12.65

Issued: 50fr, 100fr, 500fr, 6/13/66; others, 1/20/67.

For surcharges see Nos. C107, Benin C353-C355, C357, C368, C426, C436, C448.

Industrial Symbols — AP16

1966, July 21   Photo.   *Perf. 12x13*
C38 AP16 100fr multi .... 1.60 .80

Agreement between European Economic Community & the African & Malagache Union, 3rd anniv.

Pope Paul VI and St. Peter's, Rome — AP17

Pope Paul VI and UN General Assembly AP18

70fr, Pope Paul VI and view of NYC.

1966, Aug. 22   Engr.   *Perf. 13*
C39 AP17 50fr multi .... .75 .45
C40 AP17 70fr multi .... .95 .55
C41 AP18 100fr multi 1.75 1.00
  a.   Min. sheet of 3, #C39-C41 ... 4.50 4.50
    Nos. C39-C41 (3) 3.45 2.00

Pope Paul's appeal for peace before the UN General Assembly, Oct. 4, 1965.

Air Afrique Issue, 1966
Common Design Type

1966, Aug. 31   Photo.   *Perf. 12½*
C42 CD123 30fr dk vio, blk & gray .... .75 .20

"Science" — AP20

Designs: 45fr, "Art" (carved female statue), vert. 100fr, "Education" (book and letters).

1966, Nov. 4   *Perf. 13*
C43 AP20 30fr mag, ultra & vio brn .... .45 .20
C44 AP20 45fr mar & grn .... .80 .55
C45 AP20 100fr blk, mar & brt bl 1.90 1.00
  a.   Min. sheet of 3, #C43-C45 .. 3.25 3.25
    Nos. C43-C45 (3) 3.15 1.75

20th anniversary of UNESCO.

Madonna by Alessio Baldovinetti AP21

Christmas: 50fr, Nativity after 15th century Beaune tapestry. 100fr, Adoration of the Shepherds, by José Ribera.

1966, Dec. 25   Photo.   *Perf. 12½x12*
C46 AP21 50fr multi 3.25 2.25
C47 AP21 100fr multi 4.50 3.25
C48 AP21 200fr multi 9.00 5.00
    Nos. C46-C48 (3) 16.75 10.50

See Nos. C95-C96, C109-C115. For surcharge see No. C60.

1967, Apr. 10   *Perf. 12½x12*

Paintings by Ingres: No. C49, Self-portrait, 1804. No. C50, Oedipus and the Sphinx.

C49 AP21 50fr multi 3.00 1.50
C50 AP21 100fr multi 3.00 1.50

Jean Auguste Dominique Ingres (1780-1867), French painter.

Three-master Suzanne — AP22

Windjammers: 45fr, Three-master Esmeralda, vert. 80fr, Schooner Marie Alice, vert. 100fr, Four-master Antonin.

1967, May 8   *Perf. 13*
C51 AP22 30fr multi .... 1.00 .50
C52 AP22 45fr multi .... 1.25 .75
C53 AP22 80fr multi 2.25 1.25
C54 AP22 100fr multi 3.00 1.50
    Nos. C51-C54 (4) 7.50 4.00

For overprint & surcharge see Benin Nos. C369, C420.

Nos. C29-C30 Surcharged

1967, May 29   Photo.   *Perf. 13, 12½*
C55 AP11 125fr on 100fr 2.00 1.25
C56 AP12 125fr on 100fr 2.00 1.25

50th anniv. of the birth of Pres. John F. Kennedy.

EXPO '67 "Man In Space" Pavilion — AP23

1967, June 12   Engr.   *Perf. 13*
C57 AP23 100fr dl red & Prus bl .... 2.25 .75
  a.   Min. sheet of 3, #235-236, C57 ... 4.00 4.00

EXPO '67, International Exhibition, Montreal, Apr. 28-Oct. 27, 1967.

Europafrica Issue, 1967

Konrad Adenauer, by Oscar Kokoschká AP24

1967, July 19   Photo.   *Perf. 12½x12*
C58 AP24 70fr multi .... 1.50 .75
  a.   Souv. sheet of 4 .... 7.00 7.00

Konrad Adenauer (1876-1967), chancellor of West Germany (1949-1963).

Jamboree Emblem, Ropes and World Map — AP25

1967, Aug. 7   *Perf. 13*
C59 AP25 100fr lil, sl grn & dp bl .... 1.90 .75
  a.   Souv. sheet of 3, #239-240, C59 ... 4.00 4.00

12th Boy Scout World Jamboree, Farragut State Park, Idaho, Aug. 1-9.

No. C48 Surcharged in Red

1967, Aug. 12   Photo.   *Perf. 12½x12*
C60 AP21 150fr on 200fr 3.00 2.25
  a.   "150F" omitted 300.00 300.00

Riccione, Italy Stamp Exhibition.

African Postal Union Issue, 1967
Common Design Type

1967, Sept. 9   Engr.   *Perf. 13*
C61 CD124 100fr red, brt lil & emer .... 1.25 .75

For surcharge see Benin No. C471.

Charles de Gaulle AP26

1967, Nov. 21   Photo.   *Perf. 12½x13*
C62 AP26 100fr multi 3.25 2.00
  a.   Souv. sheet of 4 .... 15.00 15.00

Pres. Charles de Gaulle of France on the occasion of Pres. Christophe Soglo's state visit to Paris, Nov. 1967.

Madonna, by Matthias Grunewald AP27

Paintings: 50fr, Holy Family by the Master of St. Sebastian, horiz. 100fr, Adoration of the Magi by Ulrich Apt the Elder. 200fr, Annunciation, by Matthias Grunewald.

1967, Dec. 11   Photo.   *Perf. 12½*
C63 AP27 30fr multi .... .55 .45
C64 AP27 50fr multi .... 1.10 .60
C65 AP27 100fr multi 2.00 1.25
C66 AP27 200fr multi 5.00 2.00
    Nos. C63-C66 (4) 8.65 4.30

Christmas 1967.

Venus de Milo and Mariner 5 — AP28

Gutenberg Monument, Strasbourg Cathedral AP29

#C68, Venus de Milo and Venus 4 Rocket.

1968, Feb. 17   Photo.   *Perf. 13*
C67 AP28 70fr grnsh bl & multi .... 1.50 .75
C68 AP28 70fr dp bl & multi .... 1.50 .75
  a.   Souv. sheet of 2, #C67-C68 .. 3.50 3.50

Explorations of the planet Venus, Oct. 18-19, 1967.
For surcharges see Nos. C103-C104.

1968, May 20   Litho.   *Perf. 14x13½*

Design: 100fr, Gutenberg Monument, Mainz, and Gutenberg press.

C69 AP29 45fr grn & org .... 1.00 .40
C70 AP29 100fr dk & lt bl 2.00 1.00
  a.   Souv. sheet of 2, #C69-C70 .. 3.75 3.75

500th anniv. of the death of Johann Gutenberg, inventor of printing from movable type.
For surcharge see Benin #C516.

Martin Luther King, Jr. — AP30

Designs: 30fr, "We must meet hate with creative love" in French, English and German. 100fr, Full-face portrait.

Perf. 12½, 13½x13

1968, June 17   **Photo.**

Size: 26x46mm

C71 AP30 30fr red brn, yel & blk   .55   .35

Size: 26x37mm

C72 AP30 55fr multi   .85   .45
C73 AP30 100fr multi   1.25   .90
   a.   Min. sheet of 3, #C71-C73   3.75   3.75
     Nos. C71-C73 (3)   2.65   1.70

Martin Luther King, Jr. (1929-68), American civil rights leader.
For surcharge, see Benin No. C517.

Robert Schuman — AP31

45fr, Alcide de Gasperi. 70fr, Konrad Adenauer.

1968, July 20   **Photo.**   **Perf. 13**
C74 AP31 30fr dp yel, blk & grn   .40   .40
C75 AP31 45fr org, dk brn & ol   .85   .50
C76 AP31 70fr multi   1.40   .50
     Nos. C74-C76 (3)   2.65   1.40

5th anniversary of the economic agreement between the European Economic Community and the African and Malgache Union.
For surcharge see Benin No. C462.

Battle of Montebello, by Henri Philippoteaux — AP32

Paintings: 45fr, 2nd Zouave Regiment at Magenta, by Riballier. 70fr, Battle of Magenta, by Louis Eugène Charpentier. 100fr, Battle of Solferino, by Charpentier.

1968, Aug. 12   **Perf. 12½x12**
C77 AP32 30fr multi   .90   .50
C78 AP32 45fr multi   1.25   .65
C79 AP32 70fr multi   2.50   1.25
C80 AP32 100fr multi   3.25   1.00
     Nos. C77-C80 (4)   7.90   3.40

Issued for the Red Cross.

Mail Truck in Village — AP33

Designs: 45fr, Mail truck stopping at rural post office. 55fr, Mail truck at river bank. 70fr, Mail truck and train.

1968, Oct. 7   **Photo.**   **Perf. 13x12½**
C81 AP33 30fr multi   .80   .50
C82 AP33 45fr multi   1.00   .55
C83 AP33 55fr multi   1.50   .55
C84 AP33 70fr multi   3.75   1.00
     Nos. C81-C84 (4)   7.05   2.60

For surcharges see Benin Nos. C352, C357A.

Aztec Stadium, Mexico City — AP34

45fr, Ball player, Mayan sculpture, vert. 70fr, Wrestler, sculpture from Uxpanapan, vert. 150fr, Olympic Stadium, Mexico City.

1968, Nov. 20   **Engr.**   **Perf. 13**
C85 AP34 30fr dp cl & sl grn   .60   .30
C86 AP34 45fr ultra & dk rose brn   1.10   .60
C87 AP34 70fr sl grn & dk brn   1.60   .65
C88 AP34 150fr dk car & dk brn   2.25   1.25
   a.   Min. sheet of 4, #C85-C88   5.50   5.50
     Nos. C85-C88 (4)   5.55   2.80

19th Olympic Games, Mexico City, Oct. 12-27. No. C88a is folded down the vertical gutter separating Nos. C85-C86 se-tenant at left and Nos. C87-C88 se-tenant at right.
For overprint and surcharges see Benin Nos. C457, C461, C513.

The Annunciation, by Foujita — AP35

Paintings by Foujita: 30fr, Nativity, horiz. 100fr, The Virgin and Child. 200fr, The Baptism of Christ.

Perf. 12x12½, 12½x12
1968, Nov. 25   **Photo.**
C89 AP35 30fr multi   .80   .55
C90 AP35 70fr multi   1.60   .80
C91 AP35 100fr multi   1.75   1.25
C92 AP35 200fr multi   4.00   2.75
     Nos. C89-C92 (4)   8.15   5.35

Christmas 1968.

PHILEXAFRIQUE Issue

Painting: Diderot, by Louis Michel Vanloo.

1968, Dec. 16   **Perf. 12½x12**
C93 AP35 100fr multi   3.50   3.50

PHILEXAFRIQUE, Philatelic Exhibition in Abidjan, Feb. 14-23. Printed with alternating label.
For surcharge, see Benin No. C522.

2nd PHILEXAFRIQUE Issue
Common Design Type

50fr, Dahomey #119 and aerial view of Cotonou.

1969, Feb. 14   **Engr.**   **Perf. 13**
C94 CD128 50fr bl, brn & pur   2.10   2.10

For surcharge see Benin No. C467.

Christmas Painting Type

Paintings: No. C95, Virgin of the Rocks, by Leonardo da Vinci. No. C96, Virgin with the Scales, by Cesare da Sesto.

1969, Mar. 17   **Photo.**   **Perf. 12½x12**
C95 AP21 100fr vio & multi   1.75   1.00
C96 AP21 100fr grn & multi   1.75   1.00

Leonardo da Vinci (1452-1519).

General Bonaparte, by Jacques Louis David AP36

Paintings: 60fr, Napoleon I in 1809, by Robert J. Lefevre. 75fr, Napoleon on the Battlefield of Eylau, by Antoine Jean Gros, horiz. 200fr, Gen. Bonaparte at Arcole, by Gros.

1969, Apr. 14   **Photo.**   **Perf. 12½x12**
C97 AP36 30fr multi   1.50   1.25
C98 AP36 60fr multi   2.75   1.75
C99 AP36 75fr multi   3.00   2.50
C100 AP36 200fr multi   7.25   5.50
     Nos. C97-C100 (4)   14.50   11.00

Bicentenary of the birth of Napoleon I.

Arms Type of Regular Issue, 1969
1969, June 30   **Litho.**   **Perf. 13½x13**
C101 A49 50fr multi   .55   .30

For overprint see Benin No. C417.

Apollo 8 Trip Around the Moon — AP37

Embossed on Gold Foil
1969, July   **Die-cut Perf. 10½**
C102 AP37 1000fr gold   20.00   20.00

US Apollo 8 mission, which put the 1st men into orbit around the moon, Dec. 21-27, 1968.

Nos. C67-C68 Surcharged

1969, Aug. 1   **Photo.**   **Perf. 13**
C103 AP28 125fr on 70fr, #C67   2.00   1.75
C104 AP28 125fr on 70fr, #C68   2.00   1.75

Man's 1st landing on the moon, July 20, 1969; US astronauts Neil A. Armstrong, Col. Edwin E. Aldrin, Jr., with Lieut. Col. Michael Collins piloting Apollo 11.

Europafrica Issue
Type of Regular Issue, 1969
Design: 100fr, Oil palm industry, Cotonou.

1969, Sept. 22   **Litho.**   **Perf. 14**
C105 A51 100fr multi   2.25   .35
   a.   Souv. sheet of 3, #262-263, C105   4.25   4.25

For surcharge see No. C523.

Dahomey Rotary Emblem — AP38

1969, Sept. 25   **Perf. 14x13½**
C106 AP38 50fr multi   1.00   .75

For surcharge see Benin No. C468.

No. C33 Surcharged

1969, Nov. 15   **Photo.**   **Perf. 12½**
C107 AP14 10fr on 50fr multi   .45   .20

Dance Type of Regular Issue

Design: Teke dance and Tourist Year emblem.

1969, Dec. 15   **Litho.**   **Perf. 14**
C108 A52 70fr multi   2.50   1.50

For surcharge see Benin No. C398.

Painting Type of 1966

Christmas: 30fr, Annunciation, by Vrancke van der Stockt. 45fr, Nativity, Swabian School, horiz. 110fr, Madonna and Child, by the Master of the Gold Brocade. 200fr, Adoration of the Kings, Antwerp School.

1969, Dec. 20   **Perf. 12½x12, 12x12½**
C109 AP21 30fr multi   .45   .40
C110 AP21 45fr red & multi   .80   .65
C111 AP21 110fr multi   2.00   1.25
C112 AP21 200fr multi   3.50   2.25
     Nos. C109-C112 (4)   6.75   4.55

For surcharges see Benin #C425, C463, C475, C532.

1969, Dec. 27   **Perf. 12½x12**

Paintings: No. C113, The Artist's Studio (detail), by Gustave Courbet. No. C114, Self-portrait with Hendrickje Stoffels, by Rembrandt. 150fr, Hendrickje Stoffels, by Rembrandt.

C113 AP21 100fr red & multi   2.25   1.25
C114 AP21 100fr grn & multi   2.25   1.25
C115 AP21 150fr multi   3.50   1.75
     Nos. C113-C115 (3)   8.00   4.25

For overprint and surcharge see Benin Nos. C458, C472.

Franklin D. Roosevelt AP39

Astronauts, Rocket, US Flag — AP40

1970, Feb.   **Photo.**   **Perf. 12½**
C116 AP39 100fr ultra, yel grn &
          blk   1.60 .60
25th anniversary of the death of Pres. Franklin Delano Roosevelt (1882-1945).

1970, Mar. 9   **Photo.**   **Perf. 12½**
Astronauts: 50fr, Riding rocket through space. 70fr, In landing module approaching moon. 110fr, Planting US flag on moon.
C117 AP40 30fr multi   .65 .25

Souvenir Sheet
C118   Sheet of 4   8.00 8.00
   a.   AP40 50fr violet blue & multi   .75 .75
   b.   AP40 70fr violet blue & multi   1.00 1.00
   c.   AP40 110fr violet blue & multi   1.25 1.25
See note after No. C104. No. C118 contains Nos. C117, C118a, C118b and C118c. For surcharge see No. C120.

Walt Whitman and Dahoman Huts — AP41

1970, Apr. 30   **Engr.**   **Perf. 13**
C119 AP41 100fr Prus bl, brn &
          emer   1.25 .60
Walt Whitman (1818-92), American poet.

No. C117 Surcharged in Silver with New Value, Heavy Bar and: "APOLLO XIII / SOLIDARITE / SPATIALE / INTERNATIONALE"

1970, May 15   **Photo.**   **Perf. 12½**
C120 AP40 40fr on 30fr multi   1.20 .75
The flight of Apollo 13. For surcharge see Benin No. C464.

Soccer Players and Globe — AP42

Designs: 50fr, Goalkeeper catching ball. 200fr, Players kicking ball.

1970, May 19
C121 AP42 40fr multi   .75 .40
C122 AP42 50fr multi   .95 .50
C123 AP42 200fr multi   3.50 1.25
    Nos. C121-C123 (3)   5.20 2.15
9th World Soccer Championships for the Jules Rimet Cup, Mexico City, May 30-June 21, 1970.
For surcharge see No. C126.

EXPO '70 Type of Regular Issue

EXPO '70 Emblems and: 70fr, Dahomey pavilion. 120fr, Mt. Fuji, temple and torii.

1970, June 15   **Litho.**   **Perf. 13½x14**
C124 A54 70fr yel, red & dk vio   1.25 .60
C125 A54 120fr yel, red & grn   2.25 1.00
For surcharges see Benin Nos. C470, C477.

No. C123 Surcharged with New Value and Overprinted: "Bresil-Italie / 4-1"

1970, July 13   **Photo.**   **Perf. 12½**
C126 AP42 100fr on 200fr multi   2.10 1.00
Brazil's victory in the 9th World Soccer Championships, Mexico City.
For surcharge see Benin No. C515.

Mercury, Map of Africa and Europe — AP43

Ludwig van Beethoven AP44

Europafrica Issue, 1970
1970, July 20   **Photo.**   **Perf. 12x13**
C127 AP43 40fr multi   .80 .40
C128 AP43 70fr multi   1.25 .60
For surcharges see Benin #C429, C488.

1970, Sept. 21   **Litho.**   **Perf. 14x13½**
C129 AP44 90fr brt bl & vio blk   1.40 .45
C130 AP44 110fr yel grn & dk brn   1.75 .65
Bicentenary of the birth of Ludwig van Beethoven (1770-1827), composer.
For surcharge see Benin No. C476.

Symbols of Learning — AP45

1970, Nov. 6   **Photo.**   **Perf. 12½**
C131 AP45 100fr multi   1.75 .75
Laying of the foundation stone for the University at Calavi.
For overprint see Benin No. C356.

Annunciation, Rhenish School, c.1340 — AP46

Paintings of Rhenish School, circa 1340: 70fr, Nativity. 110fr, Adoration of the Kings. 200fr, Presentation at the Temple.

1970, Nov. 9   **Perf. 12½x12**
C132 AP46 40fr gold & multi   .55 .40
C133 AP46 70fr gold & multi   1.00 .55
C134 AP46 110fr gold & multi   2.40 1.25
C135 AP46 200fr gold & multi   4.00 2.00
    Nos. C132-C135 (4)   7.95 4.20
Christmas 1970.
For surcharge see Benin No. C479.

Charles de Gaulle, Arc de Triomphe and Flag — AP47

Design: 500fr, de Gaulle as old man and Notre Dame Cathedral, Paris.

1971, Mar. 15   **Photo.**   **Perf. 12½**
C136 AP47 40fr multi   .80 .45
C137 AP47 500fr multi   6.50 3.25
Gen. Charles de Gaulle (1890-1970), President of France.
For surcharge see Benin No. C465.

L'Indifférent, by Watteau — AP48

Painting: No. C139, Woman playing stringed instrument, by Watteau.

1971, May 3   **Photo.**   **Perf. 13**
C138 AP48 100fr red brn & multi   3.25 1.75
C139 AP48 100fr red brn & multi   3.25 1.75
For overprints see Nos. C151-C152, Benin C357D, C456.

1971, May 29   **Photo.**   **Perf. 13**
Dürer Paintings: 100fr, Self-portrait, 1498. 200fr, Self-portrait, 1500.
C140 AP48 100fr bl grn & multi   2.25 1.25
C141 AP48 200fr dk grn & multi   4.50 2.25
Albrecht Dürer (1471-1528), German painter and engraver. See #C151-C152, C174-C175. For surcharge and overprint see Benin #C357B, C381.

Johannes Kepler and Diagram — AP49

200fr, Kepler, trajectories, satellite and rocket.

1971, July 12   **Engr.**   **Perf. 13**
C142 AP49 40fr brt rose lil, blk
           & vio bl   .90 .55
C143 AP49 200fr red, blk & dk bl   3.25 1.75
Kepler (1571-1630), German astronomer.
For overprint and surcharges see Benin Nos. C342, C348, C466, C480.

Europafrica Issue

Jet Plane, Maps of Europe and Africa — AP50

100fr, Ocean liner, maps of Europe and Africa.

1971, July 19   **Photo.**   **Perf. 12½x12**
C144 AP50 50fr blk, lt bl & org   1.00 .60
C145 AP50 100fr multi   1.60 1.00
For surcharges see Benin #C374, C404, C421.

African Postal Union Issue, 1971
Common Design Type

Design: 100fr, Dahomey coat of arms and UAMPT building, Brazzaville, Congo.

1971, Nov. 13   **Perf. 13x13½**
C146 CD135 100fr bl & multi   1.40 .60
For overprint see Benin No. C357E.

Flight into Egypt, by Van Dyck — AP51

Paintings: 40fr, Adoration of the Shepherds, by the Master of the Hausbuch, c. 1500, vert. 70fr, Adoration of the Kings, by Holbein the Elder, vert. 200fr, The Birth of Christ, by Dürer.

1971, Nov. 22   **Perf. 13**
C147 AP51 40fr gold & multi   .80 .45
C148 AP51 70fr gold & multi   1.25 .55
C149 AP51 100fr gold & multi   2.00 .80
C150 AP51 200fr gold & multi   4.75 1.75
    Nos. C147-C150 (4)   8.80 3.55
Christmas 1971
For overprint and surcharges see Benin Nos. C394, C394A, C397, C403, C405, C481, C503.

**Painting Type of 1971 Inscribed:
"25e ANNIVERSAIRE DE L'UNICEF"**

Paintings: 40fr, Prince Balthazar, by Velasquez. 100fr, Infanta Margarita Maria, by Velázquez.

1971, Dec. 11
C151 AP48 40fr gold & multi   1.00 .55
C152 AP48 100fr gold & multi   2.00 .85
25th anniv. of UNICEF.
For surcharges see Benin #C366, C418, C437.

Olympic Games Type

Design: 150fr, Sapporo '72 emblem, ski jump and stork flying.

1972, Feb.   **Engr.**   **Perf. 13**
C153 A61 150fr brn, dp rose lil &
          bl   3.00 1.25
11th Winter Olympic Games, Sapporo, Japan, Feb. 3-13.
For overprint and surcharge see Benin Nos. C347, C433.

Boy Scout and Scout Flag — AP52

Designs: 40fr, Scout playing marimba. 100fr, Scouts doing farm work.

1972, Mar. 19   **Photo.**   **Perf. 13**
Size: 26x35mm
C154 AP52 35fr multi   .50 .25
C155 AP52 40fr multi   .85 .40
Size: 26x46mm
C156 AP52 100fr yel & multi   1.75 .85
   a.   Souvenir sheet of 3, #C154-
       C156, perf. 12½   4.25 4.25
    Nos. C154-C156 (3)   3.10 1.50
World Boy Scout Seminar, Cotonou, Mar. 1972.
For overprint and surcharge see Benin Nos. C373, C414.

Workers Training Institute and
Friedrich Naumann — AP53

Design: 250fr, Workers Training Institute
and Pres. Theodor Heuss of Germany.

1972, Mar. 29   Photo.   Perf. 13x12
C157 AP53 100fr brt rose, blk &
　　　　　　vio　　　　　　1.25 .65
C158 AP53 250fr bl, blk & vio　2.75 1.25

Laying of foundation stone for National
Workers Training Institute.
For surcharges see Benin Nos. C380, C473,
Q25A.

Mosaic Floor, St. Mark's,
Venice — AP54

12th Century Mosaics from St. Mark's Basilica: 40fr, Roosters carrying fox on a pole.
65fr, Noah sending out dove.

1972, Apr. 10   Perf. 13
C159 AP54 35fr gold & multi　1.10 .75
C160 AP54 40fr gold & multi　1.25 .90
C161 AP54 65fr gold & multi　2.10 1.50
　　Nos. C159-C161 (3)　　4.45 3.15

UNESCO campaign to save Venice.
For surcharge see Benin No. 690G.

Neapolitan and Dahoman
Dancers — AP55

1972, May 3   Perf. 13½x13
C162 AP55 100fr multi　　1.50 .65

12th Philatelic Exhibition, Naples.
For surcharge see Benin No. C395.

Running,
German Eagle,
Olympic
Rings — AP56

85fr, High jump and Glyptothek, Munich.
150fr, Shot put and Propylaeum, Munich.

1972, June 12   Engr.   Perf. 13
C163 AP56 20fr ultra, grn & brn　.40 .25
C164 AP56 85fr brn, grn & ultra　.95 .60
C165 AP56 150fr grn, brn & ultra 2.00 1.00
　a.　Min. sheet of 3, #C163-C165　4.00 4.00
　　Nos. C163-C165 (3)　　3.35 1.85

20th Olympic Games, Munich, 8/26-9/10.
For overprints and surcharges see Nos.
C170-C172, Benin C343, C346, C370,
C404A.

Louis Blériot and his Plane — AP57

1972, June 26
C166 AP57 100fr vio, cl & brt bl　3.00 1.75

Birth centenary of Louis Blériot (1872-
1936), French aviation pioneer.
For surcharge see Benin No. C386.

Adam, by Lucas
Cranach — AP58

Design: 200fr, Eve, by Lucas Cranach.

1972, Oct. 24   Photo.
C167 AP58 150fr multi　　1.90 .65
C168 AP58 200fr multi　　3.25 1.25

Cranach (1472-1553), German painter.
For surcharge see Benin No. C402.

Pauline Borghese, by Canova — AP59

1972, Nov. 8
C169 AP59 250fr multi　　4.00 1.75

Antonio Canova (1757-1822), Italian sculptor.

Nos. C163-C165 Overprinted:
a. 5.000m-10.000m. / VIREN / 2
MEDAILLES D'OR
b. HAUTEUR DAMES / MEYFARTH /
MEDAILLE D'OR
c. POIDS / KOMAR / MEDAILLE
D'OR

1972, Nov. 13   Engr.   Perf. 13
C170 AP56(a) 20fr multi　　.45 .25
C171 AP56(b) 85fr multi　　1.25 .60
C172 AP56(c) 150fr multi　　2.25 1.25
　a.　Miniature sheet of 3　5.25 5.25
　　Nos. C170-C172 (3)　　3.95 2.10

Gold medal winners in 20th Olympic
Games: Lasse Viren, Finland, 5,000m. and
10,000m. races (20fr); Ulrike Meyfarth, Germany, women's high jump (85fr); Wladyslaw
Komar, Poland, shot put (150fr).

Louis
Pasteur — AP60

1972, Nov. 30
C173 AP60 100fr brt grn, lil & brn 2.25 1.00

Pasteur (1822-95), chemist and
bacteriologist.
For surcharge see Benin No. C344.

Painting Type of 1971

Paintings by Georges de La Tour (1593-
1652), French painter: 35fr, Vielle player.
150fr, The Newborn, horiz.

1972, Dec. 11   Photo.
C174 AP48 35fr multi　　.80 .40
C175 AP48 150fr multi　　2.25 1.25

For surcharges see Benin #C364, C490.

Annunciation, School of Agnolo
Gaddi — AP61

Paintings: 125fr, Nativity, by Simone dei
Crocifissi. 140fr, Adoration of the Shepherds,
by Giovanni di Pietro. 250fr, Adoration of the
Kings, by Giotto.

1972, Dec. 15
C176 AP61 35fr gold & multi　.55 .25
C177 AP61 125fr gold & multi　1.50 .65
C178 AP61 140fr gold & multi　2.00 1.00
C179 AP61 250fr gold & multi　3.25 1.50
　　Nos. C176-C179 (4)　　7.30 3.40

Christmas 1972. See Nos. C195-C198,
C234, C251, C253-C254. For overprint and
surcharges see Benin Nos. C384, C392,
C401, C444.

Statue of St. Teresa, Basilica of
Lisieux — AP62

100fr, St. Teresa, roses, and globe, vert.

1973, May 14   Photo.   Perf. 13
C180 AP62 40fr blk, gold & lt ul-
　　　　　　tra　　　　　　.75 .45
C181 AP62 100fr gold & multi　2.00 1.00

St. Teresa of Lisieux (Therese Martin, 1873-
97), Carmelite nun.
For surcharge see Benin No. C390.

Scouts, African Scout
Emblem — AP63

Designs (African Scout Emblem and): 20fr,
Lord Baden-Powell, vert. 40fr, Scouts building
bridge.

1973, July 2   Engr.   Perf. 13
C182 AP63 15fr bl, grn & choc　.45 .20
C183 AP63 20fr ol & Prus bl　　.75 .25
C184 AP63 40fr grn, Prus bl &
　　　　　　brn　　　　　　.90 .35
　a.　Souvenir sheet of 3　　3.00 3.00
　　Nos. C182-C184 (3)　　2.10 .80

24th Boy Scout World Conference, Nairobi,
Kenya, July 16-21. No. C184a contains 3
stamps similar to Nos. C182-C184 in changed
colors (15fr in ultramarine, slate green and
chocolate; 20fr in chocolate, ultramarine and
indigo; 40fr in slate green, indigo and
chocolate).
For surcharges see Nos. C217-C218, Benin
C365, C409.

Copernicus, Venera and Mariner
Satellites — AP64

125fr, Copernicus, sun, earth & moon, vert.

1973, Aug. 20   Engr.   Perf. 13
C185 AP64 65fr blk, dk brn &
　　　　　　org　　　　　　1.25 .55
C186 AP64 125fr bl, slate grn &
　　　　　　pur　　　　　　2.00 1.00
For surcharges see Benin Nos. C345, C375.

Head and City
Hall, Brussels
AP64a

1973, Sept. 17   Engr.   Perf. 13
C187 AP64a 100fr blk, Prus bl &
　　　　　　dk grn　　　　1.10 .60
African Weeks, Brussels, Sept. 15-30, 1973.
For surcharge see Benin No. C400.

WMO Emblem, World Weather
Map — AP65

1973, Sept. 25
C188 AP65 100fr ol grn & lt brn　1.25 .75
Cent. of intl. meteorological cooperation.
For surcharge and overprint see Nos. C199,
Benin C382.

Europafrica Issue

AP66

Design: 40fr, similar to 35fr.

1973, Oct. 1   Engr.   Perf. 13
C189 AP66 35fr multi　　.55 .35
C190 AP66 40fr bl, sepia & ultra　.70 .40

For overprint see Benin No. C411.

John F.
Kennedy — AP67

1973, Oct. 18

C191 AP67 200fr bl grn, vio & sl
        grn   2.75 2.75
  a.   Souvenir sheet   5.00 5.00

Pres. John F. Kennedy (1917-63). No. C191a contains one stamp in changed colors (bright blue, magenta & brown).
For surcharge see Benin No. C377.

Soccer — AP68

40fr, 2 soccer players. 100fr, 3 soccer players.

1973, Nov. 19 **Engr.** **Perf. 13**

C192 AP68 35fr multi   .55 .25
C193 AP68 40fr multi   .65 .25
C194 AP68 100fr multi   1.25 .65
  Nos. C192-C194 (3) 2.45 1.15

World Soccer Cup, Munich 1974.
For surcharges and overprint see Nos. C219-C220, Benin C396.

Painting Type of 1972

Christmas: 35fr, Annunciation, by Dirk Bouts. 100fr, Nativity, by Giotto. 150fr, Adoration of the Kings, by Botticelli. 200fr, Adoration of the Shepherds, by Jacopo Bassano, horiz.

1973, Dec. 20 **Photo.** **Perf. 13**

C195 AP61 35fr gold & multi .65 .40
C196 AP61 100fr gold & multi 1.25 .65
C197 AP61 150fr gold & multi 2.40 1.10
C198 AP61 200fr gold & multi 2.75 1.75
  Nos. C195-C198 (4) 7.05 3.90

For surcharges see Benin Nos. C378, C388, C410, C434., C442

No C188 Surcharged in Violet with New Value and: "OPERATION SKYLAB / 1973-1974"

1974, Feb. 4 **Engr.** **Perf. 13**

C199 AP65 200fr on 100fr multi 2.10 1.25

Skylab US space missions, 1973-74.

Skiers, Snowflake, Olympic Rings — AP69

1974, Feb. 25 **Engr.** **Perf. 13**

C200 AP69 100fr vio bl, brn & brt
        bl   1.75 1.10

50th anniversary of first Winter Olympic Games, Chamonix, France.

Marie Curie AP70

1974, June 7 **Engr.** **Perf. 13**

C201 AP70 50fr Lenin   1.40 .65
C202 AP70 125fr shown 1.75 .90
C203 AP70 150fr Churchill 2.00 1.40
  Nos. C201-C203 (3) 5.15 2.95

50th anniv. of the death of Lenin; 40th anniv. of the death of Marie Sklodowska Curie; cent. of the birth of Winston Churchill.
For surcharge see Benin No. C489.

Bishop, Persian, 18th Century — AP71

Frederic Chopin — AP72

200fr, Queen, Siamese chess piece, 19th cent.

1974, June 14 Photo. Perf. 12½x13

C204 AP71 50fr org & multi 2.50 1.00
C205 AP71 200fr brt grn & multi 6.00 2.50

21st Chess Olympiad, Nice, 6/6-30/74.
For surcharges and overprint see Benin Nos. C469, C482, Q11.

1974, June 24 **Engr.** **Perf. 13**

Design: No. C207, Ludwig van Beethoven.

C206 AP72 150fr blk & copper
        red   2.50 1.10
C207 AP72 150fr blk & copper
        red   2.50 1.10

Famous musicians: Frederic Chopin and Ludwig van Beethoven.
For surcharges see Benin #C376, C452, C459.

Astronaut on Moon, and Earth AP73

1974, July 10 **Engr.** **Perf. 13**

C208 AP73 150fr multi 2.75 1.50

5th anniversary of the first moon walk.
For surcharge and overprint see Benin Nos. C391, C460.

Litho. & Embossed 'Gold Foil' Stamps
These stamps generally are of a different design format than the rest of the issue. Since there is a commemorative inscription tying them to the issue a separate illustration is not being shown.

There is some question as to the status of 4 sets, Nos. C209-C216, C225-C232, C238-C249.

World Cup Soccer Championships, Munich — AP74

World Cup trophy and players and flags of: 35fr, West Germany, Chile, Australia, DDR. 40fr, Zaire, Scotland, Brazil, Yugoslavia. 100fr, Sweden, Bulgaria, Uruguay, Netherlands. 200fr, Italy, Haiti, Poland, Argentina. 300fr, Stadium. 500fr, Trophy and flags.

Perf. 14x13, 13x14

1974, July 16   **Litho.**

C209 AP74 35fr multicolored .30 .20
C210 AP74 40fr multicolored .40 .25
C211 AP74 100fr multicolored .80 .70
C212 AP74 200fr multicolored 1.50 1.25
C213 AP74 300fr multi, horiz. 2.00 1.50

Souvenir Sheet

C215 AP74 500fr multi, horiz. 4.00 4.00

It is uncertain if this issue was valid for postage or recognized by the Dahomey government.

Nos. C182-C183 Surcharged and Overprinted in Black or Red: "XIe JAMBOREE PANARABE DE BATROUN-LIBAN"

1974, July 19

C217 AP63 100fr on 15fr multi 1.25 .60
C218 AP63 140fr on 20fr multi (R) 1.75 .90

11th Pan-Arab Jamboree, Batrun, Lebanon, Aug. 1974. Overprint includes 2 bars over old denomination; 2-line overprint on No. C217, 3 lines on No. C218.

Nos. C193-C194 Overprinted and Surcharged with New Value and Two Bars: "R F A 2 / HOLLANDE 1"

1974, July 26 **Engr.** **Perf. 13**

C219 AP68 100fr on 40fr 1.10 .65
C220 AP68 150fr on 100fr 1.60 1.00

World Cup Soccer Championship, 1974, victory of German Federal Republic.

Earth and UPU Emblem — AP75

Designs (UPU Emblem and): 65fr, Concorde in flight. 125fr, French railroad car, c. 1860. 200fr, African drummer and Renault mail truck, pre-1939.

1974, Aug. 5 **Engr.** **Perf. 13**

C221 AP75 35fr rose cl & vio .55 .40
C222 AP75 65fr Prus grn & cl 1.10 .95
C223 AP75 125fr multi 2.50 1.50
C224 AP75 200fr multi 2.50 2.00
  Nos. C221-C224 (4) 6.65 4.85

Centenary of Universal Postal Union.
For surcharges, see Benin Nos. C422, C530, Q17B.

UPU, Cent. — AP76

Communications and transportation: 50fr, Rocket, Indian shooting arrow. 100fr, Airplane, dog sled, vert. 125fr, Rocket launch, balloon. 150fr, Rocket re-entry into Earth's atmosphere, drum. 200fr, Locomotive, Pony Express rider. 500fr, UPU headquarters. No. C230, Train, 1829. No. C232, Astronaut canceling envelope on moon.

1974 **Litho.** **Perf. 13x14, 14x13**

C225 AP76 50fr multicolored .50 .30
C226 AP76 100fr multicolored .75 .60
C227 AP76 125fr multicolored 1.00 .85
C228 AP76 150fr multicolored 1.75 1.00
C229 AP76 200fr multicolored 2.00 1.25

Litho. & Embossed
Perf. 13½

C230 AP76 1000fr gold & multi 12.00 12.00

Size: 48x60mm

Souvenir Sheets
Litho.
Perf. 13x14

C231 AP76 500fr multicolored 4.50 4.50

Litho. & Embossed
Perf. 13½

C232 AP76 1000fr gold & multi 6.50 6.50

Issued: #C230, C232, Oct. 9; others, Aug. 5. It is uncertain if this issue was valid for postage or recognized by the Dahomey government.

Painting Type of 1972 and

Lion of Belfort by Frederic A. Bartholdi — AP77

Painting: 250fr, Girl with Falcon, by Philippe de Champaigne.

1974, Aug. 20 **Engr.** **Perf. 13**

C233 AP77 100fr rose brn 2.50 1.00
C234 AP61 250fr multi   4.00 2.40

For surcharges see Benin Nos. C363, C445.

Prehistoric Animals — AP78

1974, Sept. 23   **Photo.**

C235 AP78 35fr Rhamphorhyn-
        chus   1.50 .80
C236 AP78 150fr Stegosaurus 5.00 2.25
C237 AP78 200fr Tyrannosaurus 7.00 2.75
  Nos. C235-C237 (3) 13.50 5.80

For surcharges see Benin #C349, C350.

Conquest of Space — AP79

Various spacecraft and: 50fr, Mercury. 100fr, Venus. 150fr, Mars. 200fr, Jupiter. 400fr, Sun.

1974, Oct. 31	Litho.		Perf. 13x14	
C238	AP79	50fr multicolored	.40	.30
C239	AP79	100fr multicolored	1.00	.50
C240	AP79	150fr multicolored	1.50	.90
C241	AP79	200fr multicolored	2.00	1.25
	Nos. C238-C241 (4)		4.90	2.95

Souvenir Sheet

C242	AP79	400fr multicolored	4.00	4.00

For surcharges, see Benin Nos. C407A, C424.

West Germany, World Cup Soccer Champions — AP80

Designs: 100fr, Team. 125fr, Paul Breitner. 150fr, Gerd Muller. 300fr, Presentation of trophy. 500fr, German team positioned on field.

1974, Nov.	Litho.		Perf. 13x14	
C243	AP80	100fr multicolored	.75	.50
C244	AP80	125fr multicolored	1.00	.75
C245	AP80	150fr multicolored	1.50	1.00
C246	AP80	300fr multicolored	3.25	2.00
	Nos. C243-C246 (4)		6.50	4.25

Souvenir Sheet

C248	AP80	500fr multicolored	4.50	4.50

Europafrica Issue

Globe, Cogwheel, Emblem — AP81

1974, Dec. 20	Typo.		Perf. 13	
C250	AP81	250fr red & multi	3.25	2.75

Printed tête bêche in sheets of 10.
For surcharges see Benin Nos. C430, C509.

Christmas Type of 1972 and

Nativity, by Martin Schongauer — AP82

Paintings: 35fr, Annunciation, by Schongauer. 100fr, Virgin in Rose Arbor, by Schongauer. 250fr, Virgin and Child, with St. John the Baptist, by Botticelli.

1974, Dec. 23	Photo.		Perf. 13	
C251	AP61	35fr gold & multi	.45	.30
C252	AP82	40fr gold & multi	.45	.40
C253	AP61	100fr gold & multi	1.25	.55
C254	AP61	250fr gold & multi	3.25	1.75
	Nos. C251-C254 (4)		5.40	3.00

For surcharges, see Benin Nos. C413, C431, C439, C446.

Apollo and Soyuz Spacecraft AP83

200fr, American and Russian flags, rocket take-off. 500fr, Apollo-Soyuz link-up.

1975, July 16	Litho.		Perf. 12½	
C255	AP83	35fr multi	.50	.30
C256	AP83	200fr vio bl, red & bl	2.40	1.25
C257	AP83	500fr vio bl, ind & red	5.00	3.00
	Nos. C255-C257 (3)		7.90	4.55

Apollo Soyuz space test project (Russo-American cooperation); launching July 15; link-up, July 17.
For surcharges see Benin #C406, C415-C416, C451.

Nos. C255-C256 Surcharged in Silver or Black: "RENCONTRE / APOLLO-SOYOUZ / 17 Juil. 1975"

1975, July 17	Litho.		Perf. 12½	
C258	AP83	100fr on 35fr (S)	1.25	.60
C259	AP83	300fr on 200fr	3.25	1.40

Apollo-Soyuz link-up in space, July 17, 1975.

ARPHILA Emblem, "Stamps" and Head of Ceres — AP84

1975, Aug. 22	Engr.		Perf. 13	
C260	AP84	100fr blk, bl & lilac	1.25	.75

ARPHILA 75, International Philatelic Exhibition, Paris, June 6-16.
For surcharges see Benin Nos. C383, C474.

Holy Family, by Michelangelo AP85

Infantry and Stars — AP86

Europafrica Issue

1975, Sept. 29	Litho.		Perf. 12	
C261	AP85	300fr gold & multi	3.50	1.50

For surcharge see Benin No. C447.

1975, Nov. 18	Engr.		Perf. 13	

American bicentennial (Stars and): 135fr, Drummers and fifer. 300fr, Artillery with cannon. 500fr, Cavalry.

C262	AP86	75fr grn car & pur	.85	.45
C263	AP86	135fr bl, mag & sep	1.50	.90
C264	AP86	300fr vio bl, ver & choc	2.75	1.75

C265	AP86	500fr ver, dk grn & brn	5.00	2.50
	Nos. C262-C265 (4)		10.10	5.60

For overprint and surcharges see Benin Nos. C247-C249, C385, C408, C412, C453, C478.

Diving and Olympic Rings AP87

Design: 250fr, Soccer and Olympic rings.

1975, Nov. 24				
C266	AP87	40fr vio, grnsh bl & ol brn	.55	.25
C267	AP87	250fr red, emer & brn	2.25	1.25

Pre-Olympic Year 1975.
For surcharge see Benin No. C341.

AIR POST SEMI-POSTAL STAMPS

Maternity Hospital, Dakar — SPAP1

Dispensary, Mopti — SPAP2

Nurse Weighing Baby — SPAP3

Perf. 13½x12½, 13 (#CB3)
Photo., Engr. (#CB3)

1942, June 22				
CB1	SPAP1	1.50fr + 3.50fr green	.55	3.50
CB2	SPAP2	2fr + 6fr brown	.55	3.50
CB3	SPAP3	3fr + 9fr car red	.55	3.50
	Nos. CB1-CB3 (3)		1.65	10.50

Native children's welfare fund.

Colonial Education Fund
Common Design Type
Perf. 12½x13½

1942, June 22			Engr.	
CB4	CD86a	1.20fr + 1.80fr blue & red	.55	3.50

AIR POST PARCEL POST STAMPS

Catalogue values for unused stamps in this section are for Never Hinged items.

Nos. C20-C23, C14 Surcharged in Black or Red

1967-69	Engr.		Perf. 13	
CQ1	AP6	200fr on 200fr	4.75	3.50
CQ2	AP6	300fr on 100fr	5.25	4.25
CQ3	AP6	500fr on 300fr	10.00	8.00
CQ4	AP6	1000fr on 500fr	21.00	16.00
CQ5	AP4	5000fr on 100fr		
	(R) ('69)		80.00	80.00
	Nos. CQ1-CQ5 (5)		121.00	111.75

On No. CQ5, "Colis Postaux" is at top, bar at right.

POSTAGE DUE STAMPS

Dahomey Natives — D1 | D2

1906	Unwmk.	Typo.	Perf. 14x13½	
J1	D1	5c grn, *grnsh*	1.75	1.75
J2	D1	10c red brn	3.00	3.00
J3	D1	15c dark blue	5.75	5.75
J4	D1	20c blk, *yellow*	4.25	4.25
J5	D1	30c red, *straw*	6.00	6.00
J6	D1	50c violet	17.50	17.50
J7	D1	60c blk, *buff*	10.00	10.00
J8	D1	1fr blk, *pinkish*	27.50	27.50
	Nos. J1-J8 (8)		75.75	75.75

1914				
J9	D2	5c green	.20	.20
J10	D2	10c rose	.35	.35
J11	D2	15c gray	.35	.35
J12	D2	20c brown	.80	.80
J13	D2	30c blue	.95	.95
J14	D2	50c black	1.10	1.10
J15	D2	60c orange	1.40	1.40
J16	D2	1fr violet	1.40	1.40
	Nos. J9-J16 (8)		6.55	6.55

Type of 1914 Issue Surcharged

1927				
J17	D2	2fr on 1fr lilac rose	4.00	4.00
J18	D2	3fr on 1fr org brn	4.00	4.00

Carved Mask — D3

1941	Engr.		Perf. 14x13	
J19	D3	5c black	.20	.20
J20	D3	10c lilac rose	.20	.20
J21	D3	15c dark blue	.20	.20
J22	D3	20c bright yel green	.20	.20
J23	D3	30c orange	.35	.35
J24	D3	50c violet brown	.55	.55
J25	D3	60c slate green	.95	.95
J26	D3	1fr rose red	1.10	1.10
J27	D3	2fr yellow	1.25	1.25
J28	D3	3fr dark purple	1.60	1.60
	Nos. J19-J28 (10)		6.60	6.60

Type D3 without "RF"

1944

J28A	D3	10c lilac rose	.20
J28B	D3	15c dark blue	.20
J28C	D3	20c bright yel green	.20
		Nos. J28A-J28C (3)	.60

Nos. J28A-J28C were issued by the Vichy government in France, but were not placed on sale in Dahomey.

> Catalogue values for unused stamps in this section, from this point to the end of the section, are for Never Hinged items.

Republic

Panther and Man — D4

Perf. 14x13½

1963, July 22   Typo.   Unwmk.

J29	D4	1fr green & rose	.20	.20
J30	D4	2fr brn & emerald	.20	.20
J31	D4	5fr org & vio bl	.20	.20
J32	D4	10fr magenta & blk	.50	.50
J33	D4	20fr vio bl & org	.75	.75
		Nos. J29-J33 (5)	1.85	1.85

Mail Boat — D5

No. J35, Heliograph. No. J36, Morse receiver. No. J37, Mailman on bicycle. No. J38, Early telephone. No. J39, Autorail. No. J40, Mail truck. No. J41, Radio tower. No. J42, DC-8F jet plane. No. J43, Early Bird communications satellite.

1967, Oct. 24   Engr.   Perf. 11

J34	D5	1fr brn, dl pur & bl	.20	.20
J35	D5	1fr dl pur, brn & bl	.20	.20
a.		Pair, #J34-J35	.25	
J36	D5	3fr dk brn, dk grn & org	.20	.20
J37	D5	3fr dk grn, dk brn & org	.20	.20
a.		Pair, #J36-J37	.25	
J38	D5	5fr ol bis, lil & bl	.35	.35
J39	D5	5fr lil, ol bis & bl	.35	.35
a.		Pair, #J38-J39	.75	
J40	D5	10fr brn org, vio & grn	.50	.50
J41	D5	10fr vio, brn org & grn	.50	.50
a.		Pair, #J40-J41	1.10	
J42	D5	30fr Prus bl, mar & vio	1.00	1.00
J43	D5	30fr vio, Prus bl & mar	1.00	1.00
a.		Pair, #J42-J43	2.25	
		Nos. J34-J43 (10)	4.50	4.50

Pairs printed tete beche, se-tenant at the base.

PARCEL POST STAMPS

> Catalogue values for unused stamps in this section are for Never Hinged items.

Nos. 141-146 and 148 Surcharged

1967, Jan.   Unwmk.   Engr.   Perf. 13

Q1	A15	5fr on 1fr multi	.25	.25
Q2	A15	10fr on 2fr multi	.35	.35
Q3	A15	20fr on 6fr multi	.60	.60
Q4	A15	25fr on 3fr multi	.70	.70
Q5	A15	30fr on 4fr multi	.80	.80

Q6	A15	50fr on 10fr multi	1.25	1.25
a.		"20" instead of "50"	100.00	
Q7	A15	100fr on 20fr multi	2.50	2.50
		Nos. Q1-Q7 (7)	6.45	6.45

The surcharge is arranged to fit the shape of the stamp.

No. Q6a occurred once on the sheet.

DALMATIA

dal-'mă-shē-ə

LOCATION — A promontory in the northwestern part of the Balkan Peninsula, together with several small islands in the Adriatic Sea.
GOVT. — Part of the former Austro-Hungarian crownland of the same name.
AREA — 113 sq. mi.
POP. — 18,719 (1921)
CAPITAL — Zara.

Stamps were issued during Italian occupation. This territory was subsequently annexed by Italy.

100 Centesimi = 1 Corona = 1 Lira

Used values are for postally used copies.

Issued under Italian Occupation

Italy No. 87 Surcharged

1919, May 1   Wmk. 140   Perf. 14

1	A46	1cor on 1 l brn & grn	3.25	6.50
a.		Pair, one without surcharge	800.00	300.00

Italian Stamps of 1906-08 Surcharged — a

1921-22

2	A48	5c on 5c green	1.60	2.40
3	A48	10c on 10c claret	1.60	2.40
a.		Pair, one without surcharge	575.00	
4	A49	25c on 25c blue ('22)	2.40	4.75
5	A49	50c on 50c vio ('22)	2.40	4.75
a.		Double surcharge	220.00	
b.		Pair, one without surcharge	800.00	

Italian Stamps of 1901-10 Surcharged — b

6	A46	1cor on 1 l brn & grn ('22)	4.00	16.00
7	A46	5cor on 5 l bl & rose ('22)	45.00	110.00
8	A51	10cor on 10 l gray grn & red ('22)	45.00	110.00
		Nos. 2-8 (7)	102.00	250.30

Surcharges similar to these but differing in style or arrangement of type were used in Austria under Italian occupation.

SPECIAL DELIVERY STAMPS

Italian Special Delivery Stamp No. E1 Surcharged type "a"

1921   Wmk. 140   Perf. 14

E1	SD1	25c on 25c rose red	3.25	12.00
a.		Double surcharge	325.00	475.00

Italian Special Delivery Stamp Surcharged **LIRE 1,20 DI CORONA**

1922

E2	SD2	1.20 l on 1.20 l	160.00
		Never hinged	400.00

No. E2 was not placed in use.

POSTAGE DUE STAMPS

Italian Postage Due Stamps and Type Surcharged types "a" or "b"

1922   Wmk. 140   Perf. 14

J1	D3 (a)	50c on 50c buff & mag	1.60	4.75
J2	D3 (b)	1cor on 1 l bl & red	4.00	16.00
J3	D3 (b)	2cor on 2 l bl & red	47.50	105.00
J4	D3 (b)	5cor on 5 l bl & red	47.50	105.00
		Nos. J1-J4 (4)	100.60	230.75

DANISH WEST INDIES

'dā-nish 'west 'in-dēs

LOCATION — A group of islands in the West Indies, lying east of Puerto Rico
GOVT. — A former Danish colony
AREA — 132 sq. mi.
POP. — 27,086 (1911)
CAPITAL — Charlotte Amalie

The US bought these islands in 1917 and they became the US Virgin Islands, using US stamps and currency.

100 Cents = 1 Dollar
100 Bit = 1 Franc (1905)

Watermarks

Wmk. 111 — Small Crown   Wmk. 112 — Crown

Wmk. 113 — Crown   Wmk. 114 — Multiple Crosses

Coat of Arms — A1

Yellowish Paper
Yellow Wavy-line Burelage, UL to LR

1856   Wmk. 111   Typo.   Imperf.

1	A1	3c dk car, brown gum	200.00	275.00
a.		3c dark carmine, yellow gum	220.00	275.00
b.		3c carmine, white gum	4,250.	

Reprint: 1981, carmine, back-printed across two stamps ("Reprint by Dansk Post og Telegrafmuseum 1978"), value, pair, $10.

White Paper
Yellow Wavy-line Burelage, UR to LL

1866

2	A1	3c rose	40.00	75.00

No. 2 reprints unwatermarked: 1930 carmine, value $100. 1942 rose carmine, back-printed across each row ("Nytryk 1942 G. A. Hagemann Danmark og Dansk Vestindiens Friemaerker Bind 2"), value $50.

1872   Perf. 12½

3	A1	3c rose	92.50	275.00

1873   Without Burelage

4	A1	4c dull blue	250.00	475.00
a.		Imperf., pair	750.00	—
b.		Horiz. pair, imperf. vert.	550.00	—

#4 reprints, unwatermarked, imperf.: 1930, ultramarine, value $100. 1942, blue back-printed like 1942 reprint of #2, value $60.

A2   Normal Frame

Inverted Frame

The arabesques in the corners have a main stem and a branch. When the frame is in normal position, in the upper left corner the branch leaves the main stem half way between two little leaflets. In the lower right corner the branch starts at the foot of the second leaflet. When the frame is inverted the corner designs are, of course, transposed.

White Wove Paper, Varying from Thin to Thick

1874-79		**Wmk. 112**	**Perf. 14x13½**	
5	A2	1c green & brn		
		red	20.00	30.00
a.	1c grn & rose lilac, thin paper		80.00	125.00
b.	1c grn & red violet, medium paper		45.00	65.00
c.	1c green & violet, thick paper		20.00	30.00
e.	Inverted frame		20.00	30.00
f.	As "a," inverted frame		475.00	
6	A2	3c blue & carmine	25.00	20.00
a.	3c lt bl & rose car, thin paper		65.00	50.00
b.	3c dp bl & dk car, medium paper		40.00	17.00
c.	3c greenish blue & lake, thick paper		32.50	17.00
d.	Imperf., pair		375.00	—
e.	Inverted frame		21.00	15.00
f.	As "a," inverted frame		350.00	
7	A2	4c brn & dull blue	16.00	19.00
b.	4c brown & ultramarine		190.00	225.00
c.	Diagonal half used as 2c on cover			140.00
d.	Inverted frame		825.00	1,400.
8	A2	5c green & gray ('76)	30.00	25.00
a.	5c yel grn & dk gray, thin paper		55.00	37.50
b.	Inverted frame		27.50	25.00
9	A2	7c lilac & orange	32.50	95.00
a.	7c lilac & yellow		90.00	100.00
b.	Inverted frame		60.00	150.00
10	A2	10c blue & brn ('76)	25.00	30.00
a.	10c dk bl & blk brn, thin paper		70.00	45.00
b.	"cent.s"		30.00	30.00
c.	Inverted frame		27.50	32.50
11	A2	12c red lilac & yel green ('77)	42.50	175.00
a.	12c lilac & deep green		150.00	200.00
12	A2	14c lilac & green	650.00	1,100.
a.	Inverted frame		2,500.	3,500.
13	A2	50c violet, thin paper ('79)	175.00	300.00
a.	50c gray violet, thick porous paper ('85)		225.00	350.00
		Nos. 5-13 (9)	1,016.	1,794.

The central element in the fan-shaped scrollwork at the outside of the lower left corner of Nos. 5a and 7b looks like an elongated diamond.
See Nos. 16-20. For surcharges see Nos. 14-15, 23-28, 40.

Nos. 9 and 13 Surcharged in Black

1887-95				
14	A2	1c on 7c lilac & org	100.00	200.00
a.	1c on 7c lilac & yellow		100.00	225.00
b.	Double surcharge		250.00	500.00
c.	Inverted frame		110.00	350.00
15	A2	10c on 50c violet ('95)	42.50	67.50

Type of 1873

1896-1901			**Perf. 13**	
16	A2	1c green & red vio ('98)	13.00	22.50
a.	Normal frame		290.00	450.00
17	A2	3c blue & lake ('98)	12.00	17.50
a.	Normal frame		250.00	425.00
18	A2	4c bister & dull blue ('01)	17.50	15.00
a.	Diagonal half used as 2c on cover			100.00
b.	Inverted frame		55.00	85.00
c.	As "b," diagonal half used as 2c on cover			350.00
19	A2	5c green & gray	35.00	35.00
a.	Normal frame		750.00	1,100.
20	A2	10c blue & brown ('01)	80.00	150.00
a.	Inverted frame		925.00	1,600.
b.	"cent.s"		160.00	300.00
		Nos. 16-20 (5)	157.50	240.00

Arms — A5

1900				
21	A5	1c light green	3.00	3.00
22	A5	5c light blue	17.50	25.00

See Nos. 29-30. For surcharges see Nos. 41-42.

Nos. 6, 17, 20 Surcharged:

c   d

Surcharge "c" in Black

1902			**Perf. 14x13½**	
23	A2	2c on 3c blue & car	575.00	725.00
a.	"2" in date with straight tail		650.00	800.00
b.	Normal frame		4,000.	
		Perf. 13		
24	A2	2c on 3c blue & lake	10.00	27.50
a.	"2" in date with straight tail		12.00	32.50
b.	Dated "1901"		600.00	650.00
c.	Normal frame		175.00	250.00
d.	Dark green surcharge		2,000.	
e.	As "d" & "a"		—	
f.	As "d" & "c"		—	
25	A2	8c on 10c blue & brn	25.00	42.50
a.	"2" with straight tail		30.00	45.00
b.	On No. 20b		32.50	45.00
c.	Inverted frame		250.00	425.00

Only one copy of No. 24f can exist.

Surcharge "d" in Black

27	A2	2c on 3c blue & lake	12.00	40.00
a.	Normal frame		240.00	425.00
28	A2	8c on 10c blue & brn	12.00	14.00
a.	On No. 20b		18.50	25.00
b.	Inverted frame		225.00	400.00
		Nos. 23-28 (5)	634.00	849.00

1903		**Wmk. 113**		
29	A5	2c carmine	8.00	22.50
30	A5	8c brown	27.50	30.00

King Christian IX — A8   St. Thomas Harbor — A9

1905		**Typo.**	**Perf. 13**	
31	A8	5b green	3.75	3.25
32	A8	10b red	3.75	3.25
33	A8	20b green & blue	8.75	8.25
34	A8	25b ultramarine	8.75	10.50
35	A8	40b red & gray	8.25	8.25
36	A8	50b yellow & gray	10.00	12.00

Frame Typo., Center Engr.
Wmk. Two Crowns (113)

			Perf. 12	
37	A9	1fr green & blue	17.50	45.00
38	A9	2fr org red & brown	30.00	60.00
39	A9	5fr yellow & brown	77.50	275.00
		Nos. 31-39 (9)	168.25	425.50

Favor cancels exist on #37-39. Value 25% less.

Nos. 18, 22, 30 Surcharged in Black

1905		**Wmk. 112**	**Perf. 13**	
40	A2	5b on 4c bis & dull blue	16.00	45.00
a.	Inverted frame		45.00	82.50
41	A5	5b on 5c light blue	14.00	37.50

			Wmk. 113	
42	A5	5b on 8c brown	14.00	37.50
		Nos. 40-42 (3)	44.00	120.00

Frederik VIII A10   Christian X A11

Frame Typo., Center Engr.

1907-08		**Wmk. 113**	**Perf. 13**	
43	A10	5b green	1.90	1.90
44	A10	10b red	1.90	1.90
45	A10	15b violet & brown	3.75	4.50
46	A10	20b green & blue	30.00	27.50
47	A10	25b blue & dk blue	1.90	2.50
48	A10	30b claret & slate	50.00	52.50
49	A10	40b ver & gray	5.75	9.50
50	A10	50b yellow & brown	5.75	14.00
		Nos. 43-50 (8)	100.95	114.30

1915		**Wmk. 114**	**Perf. 14x14½**	
51	A11	5b yellow green	4.00	4.25
52	A11	10b red	4.00	47.50
53	A11	15b lilac & red brown	4.00	47.50
54	A11	20b green & blue	4.00	47.50
55	A11	25b blue & dark blue	4.00	12.50
56	A11	30b claret & black	4.00	85.00
57	A11	40b orange & black	4.00	85.00
58	A11	50b yellow & brown	4.00	85.00
		Nos. 51-58 (8)	32.00	409.25

Forged and favor cancellations exist.

POSTAGE DUE STAMPS

POSTAGE DUE STAMPS

Royal Cipher, "Christian 9 Rex" D1

1902	**Unwmk.**	**Litho.**	**Perf. 11½**	
J1	D1	1c dark blue	4.50	17.50
J2	D1	4c dark blue	11.50	22.50
J3	D1	6c dark blue	19.00	60.00
J4	D1	10c dark blue	18.00	65.00
		Nos. J1-J4 (4)	53.00	165.00

There are five types of each value. On the 4c they may be distinguished by differences in the figures "4"; on the other values the differences are minute.
Used values of Nos. J1-J4 are for canceled stamps. Uncanceled examples without gum have probably been used. Value 60% of unused.
Counterfeits of Nos. J1-J4 exist.

D2

1905-13			**Perf. 13**	
J5	D2	5b red & gray	4.50	6.75
J6	D2	20b red & gray	7.50	14.00
J7	D2	30b red & gray	6.75	14.00
J8	D2	50b red & gray	6.00	35.00
a.	Perf. 14x14½ ('13)		37.50	140.00
b.	Perf. 11½		325.00	
		Nos. J5-J8 (4)	24.75	69.75

All values of this issue are known imperforate, but were not regularly issued.
Used values of Nos. J5-J8 are for canceled stamps. Uncanceled examples without gum have probably been used. Value 60% of unused.
Counterfeits of Nos. J5-J8 exist.
Danish West Indies stamps were replaced by those of the U.S. in 1917, after the U.S. bought the islands.

DANZIG

'dän t̠-sig

LOCATION — In northern Europe bordering on the Baltic Sea
AREA — 754 sq. mi.
POP. — 407,000 (approx. 1939)
CAPITAL — Danzig

Established as a "Free City and State" under the protection of the League of Nations in 1920, Danzig was seized by Germany in 1939. It became a Polish province in 1945.

100 Pfennig = 1 Gulden (1923)
100 Pfennig = 1 Mark

Watermarks

Wmk. 108 — Honeycomb   Wmk. 109 — Webbing

Wmk. 110 — Octagons

Wmk. 125 — Lozenges   Wmk. 237 — Swastikas

Used Values of 1920-23 are for favor-canceled stamps unless otherwise noted. Postally used copies bring much higher prices.

For additional varieties, see the *Scott Classic Catalogue.*

German Stamps of 1906-20 Overprinted in Black

		Perf. 14, 14½, 15x14½		
1920			**Wmk. 125**	
1	A16	5pf green	.25	.25
2	A16	10pf car rose	.25	.25
3	A22	15pf violet brown	.25	.25
4	A16	20pf blue violet	.25	1.10
5	A16	30pf org & blk, buff	.25	
6	A16	40pf car rose	.25	.25
7	A16	50pf pur & blk, buff	.50	.25
8	A17	1m red	.50	.60
9	A17	1.25m green	.50	.60
10	A17	1.50m yellow brn	.90	.85
11	A21	2m blue	3.00	4.75
a.	Double overprint		375.00	
	Never hinged		825.00	
12	A21	2.50m lilac rose	1.75	3.25
13	A19	3m black violet	7.00	10.00
14	A16	4m black & rose	4.75	6.00
15	A20	5m slate & car	1.75	2.00
a.	Center & "Danzig" invtd.		15,000.	
	Never hinged			
b.	Inverted overprint		20,000.	
		Nos. 1-15 (15)	22.15	30.65
	Set, never hinged		100.00	

The 5pf brown, 10pf orange and 40pf lake and black with this overprint were not regularly issued. Value for trio, $450.
Frame is inverted on No. 15a.

For surcharges see Nos. 19-23, C1-C3.
Issued: 40pf, 9/13; 1.50m, 3m 7/20; 4m, 12/21; others 6/14.

Nos. 5, 4 Surcharged in Various Sizes

1920

19	A16	5pf on 30pf (V)	.20	.25
20	A16	10pf on 20pf (R)	.20	.25
a.		Double surcharge	110.00	
		Never hinged	250.00	
21	A16	25pf on 30pf (G)	.20	.25
a.		Inverted surcharge	85.00	
		Never hinged	250.00	
22	A16	60pf on 30pf (Br)	.70	.85
a.		Double surcharge	85.00	290.00
		Never hinged	250.00	
23	A16	80pf on 30pf (V)	.70	.85

German Stamps Surcharged in Various Styles

Gray Burelage with Points Up

25	A16	1m on 30pf org & blk, buff (Bk)	.85	1.50
a.		Pair, one without surcharge		
26	A16	1¼m on 3pf brn (R)	1.00	1.50
27	A22	2m on 35pf red brn (Bl)	1.50	1.50
d.		Surcharge omitted	70.00	
		Never hinged	250.00	
28	A22	3m on 7½pf org (G)	1.00	1.50
29	A22	5m on 2pf gray (R)	1.00	2.00
30	A22	10m on 7½pf org (Bk)	3.00	7.00
		Nos. 19-30 (11)	10.35	17.45
		Set, never hinged	50.00	

Issued: #21, 8/10; #20, 8/17; #19, 22-23, 11/1.

Gray Burelage with Points Down

26a	A16	1¼m on 3pf brown	36.00	42.50
27a	A22	2m on 35pf red brn	300.00	325.00
28a	A22	3m on 7½pf org	11.00	13.50
29a	A22	5m on 2pf gray	11.50	30.00
30a	A22	10m on 7½pf org	5.75	11.00
		Nos. 26a-30a (5)	364.25	422.00
		Set, never hinged	1,440.	

Violet Burelage with Points Up

25b	A16	1m on 30pf org & blk, buff	57.50	37.50
26b	A16	1¼m on 3pf brown	4.50	6.50
27b	A22	2m on 35pf red brown	11.50	37.50
28b	A22	3m on 7½pf org	2.25	2.25
29b	A22	5m on 2pf gray	1.10	2.10
30b	A22	10m on 7½pf org	1.10	2.10
		Nos. 25b-30b (6)	77.95	87.95
		Set, never hinged	300.00	

Violet Burelage with Points Down

25c	A16	1m on 30pf org & blk, buff	1.10	2.50
26c	A16	1¼m on 3pf brown	5.50	11.00
27c	A22	2m on 35pf red brown	21.00	50.00
28c	A22	3m on 7½pf org	40.00	85.00
29c	A22	5m on 2pf gray	4.50	8.50
30c	A22	10m on 7½pf org	13.50	29.00
		Nos. 25c-30c (6)	85.60	186.00
		Set, never hinged	400.00	

Excellent counterfeits of the surcharges are known.

German Stamps of 1906-20 Overprinted in Blue

1920

31	A22	2pf gray	110.00	200.00
32	A22	2½pf gray	150.00	300.00
33	A16	3pf brown	11.00	17.00
a.		Double overprint	75.00	
		Never hinged	180.00	
34	A16	5pf green	.55	.60
a.		Double overprint	85.00	
		Never hinged	200.00	
35	A22	7½pf orange	40.00	57.50
36	A16	10pf carmine	3.75	7.00
37	A22	15pf dk violet	.55	.60
b.		Double overprint	85.00	
		Never hinged	200.00	
38	A16	20pf blue violet	.55	.60

Overprinted in Carmine or Blue

39	A16	25pf org & blk, yel	.55	.60
40	A16	30pf org & blk, buff	50.00	85.00
42	A16	40pf lake & blk	2.25	2.50
a.		Inverted overprint	200.00	
b.		Double overprint	—	
43	A16	50pf pur & blk, buff	175.00	300.00
44	A16	60pf mag (Bl)	1,250.	2,100.
45	A16	75pf green & blk	.55	.60
46	A16	80pf lake & blk, rose	2.40	4.25
47	A17	1m carmine	1,200.	2,100.
a.		Double overprint	4,000.	

Overprinted in Carmine

48	A21	2m gray blue	1,200.	2,100.

Counterfeit overprints of Nos. 31-48 exist. Nos. 44, 47 and 48 were issued in small quantities and usually affixed directly to the mail by the postal clerk.
For surcharge see No. 62.

Hanseatic Trading Ship
A8   A9

Serrate Roulette 13½

1921, Jan. 31		Typo.	Wmk. 108	
49	A8	5pf brown & violet	.20	.20
50	A8	10pf orange & dk vio	.20	.20
51	A8	25pf green & car rose	.50	.65
52	A8	40pf carmine rose	3.75	3.25
53	A8	80pf ultra	.50	.50
54	A9	1m car rose & blk	1.60	1.60
55	A9	2m dk blue & dk grn	5.00	4.75
56	A9	3m blk & grnsh bl	1.75	2.25
57	A9	5m indigo & rose red	1.75	2.25
58	A9	10m dk grn & brn org	2.50	4.50
		Nos. 49-58 (10)	17.75	20.15
		Set, never hinged	75.00	

Issued in honor of the Constitution.
Nos. 49 and 50 with center in red instead of violet and Nos. 49-51, 54-58 with center inverted are probably proofs. All values of this issue exist imperforate but are not known to have been regularly issued in that condition.

1921, Mar. 11			Perf. 14	
59	A8	25pf green & car rose	.50	.85
60	A8	40pf carmine rose	.50	.85
61	A8	80pf ultra	5.00	10.00
		Nos. 59-61 (3)	6.00	11.70
		Set, never hinged	30.00	

No. 45 Surcharged in Black

1921, May 6			Wmk. 125	
62	A16	60pf on 75pf	.55	.90
		Never hinged	3.25	
a.		Double surcharge	82.50	110.00
		Never hinged	200.00	

Arms — A11   Coat of Arms — A12

Wmk. 108 (Vert. or Horiz.)

1921-22			Perf. 14	
63	A11	5(pf) orange	.20	.20
64	A11	10(pf) dark brown	.20	.20
65	A11	15(pf) green	.20	.20
66	A11	20(pf) slate	.20	.20
67	A11	25(pf) dark green	.20	.20
68	A11	30(pf) blue & car	.25	.20
a.		Center inverted	50.00	
		Never hinged	160.00	
69	A11	40pf green & car	.20	.20
a.		Center inverted	50.00	
		Never hinged	140.00	
70	A11	50pf dk green & car	.20	.20
71	A11	60pf carmine	.45	.45
72	A11	80pf black & car	.35	.45

Paper With Faint Gray Network

73	A11	1m orange & car	.25	.40
a.		Center inverted	50.00	
		Never hinged	160.00	
74	A11	1.20m blue violet	1.25	1.25
75	A11	2m gray & car	3.25	4.00
76	A11	3m violet & car	9.00	10.00

Serrate Roulette 13½

77	A12	5m grn, red & blk	1.25	2.90
78	A12	9m rose, red & org	2.90	8.50
		('22)		
79	A12	10m ultra, red & blk	1.25	2.90
80	A12	20m red & black	1.25	2.90
		Nos. 63-80 (18)	22.85	35.35
		Set, never hinged	85.00	

In this and succeeding issues the mark values usually have the face of the paper covered with a gray network. This network is often very faint and occasionally is omitted.
Nos. 64-76 exist imperf. Value, each $16-$50 unused; $50-$150 never hinged.
See Nos. 81-93, 99-105. For surcharges and overprints see Nos. 96-98, O1-O33.

Type of 1921 and

A13

Coat of Arms — A13a

1922			Wmk. 108	Perf. 14	
81	A11	75(pf) deep violet		.20	.25
82	A11	80(pf) green		.20	.25
83	A11	1.25m violet & car		.20	.25
84	A11	1.50m slate gray		.20	.40
85	A11	2m car rose		.20	.25
86	A11	2.40m dk brn & car		.90	1.60
87	A11	3m car lake		.20	.40
88	A11	4m dark blue		.85	1.60
89	A11	5m deep green		.20	.35
90	A11	6m car lake		.20	.35
a.		6m car rose, wmk. 109 horiz.		1,800.	
		Never hinged		3,900.	
91	A11	8m light blue		.35	1.60
92	A11	10m orange		.20	.35
93	A11	20m orange brn		.20	.35
94	A13	50m gold & car		2.00	6.50
a.		50m gold & red		57.50	110.00
		Never hinged		210.00	
95	A13a	100m metallic grn & red		3.25	5.75
		Nos. 81-95 (15)		9.35	20.25
		Set, never hinged		35.00	

No. 95 has buff instead of gray network.
Nos. 81-83, 85-86, 88 exist imperf. Value, each $12.50.
Nos. 94-95 exist imperf. Value, each $50

Nos. 87, 88 and 91 Surcharged in Black or Carmine

1922

96	A11	6m on 3m car lake	.25	.55
a.		Double surcharge		
97	A11	8m on 4m dk blue	.25	.60
a.		Double surcharge	50.00	110.00
		Never hinged	125.00	
98	A11	20m on 8m lt bl (C)	.25	.60
		Nos. 96-98 (3)	.75	1.75
		Set, never hinged	2.50	

1922-23		Wmk. 109 (Horiz.)	Perf. 14	
99	A11	4m dark blue	.20	.40
100	A11	5m dark green	.20	.40
102	A11	10m orange	.20	.40
103	A11	20m orange brn	.20	.40

Paper Without Network

104	A11	40m pale blue	.20	.60
105	A11	80m red	.20	.60
		Nos. 99-105 (6)	1.20	2.80
		Set, never hinged	5.00	

Nos. 100, 102 and 103 also exist with watermark vertical. Values slightly higher.
Nos. 104-105 exist imperf. Values: each $12.50 unused; $32.50 never hinged.

A15   A15a

Coat of Arms A16

1923			Perf. 14	
		Paper With Gray Network		
106	A15	50m pale bl & red	.20	.40
107	A15a	100m dk grn & red	.20	.40
108	A15a	150m violet & red	.20	.40
109	A16	250m violet & red	.25	.40
110	A16	500m gray blk & red	.25	.40
111	A16	1000m brown & red	.25	.40
112	A16	5000m silver & red	1.25	6.00

Paper Without Network

113	A15	50m pale blue	.40	.60
114	A15a	100m deep green	.40	.60
115	A15	200m orange	.40	.60
		Nos. 106-115 (10)	3.80	10.20
		Set, never hinged	15.00	

#108-112 exist imperf. Value, each $50 unused, $125 never hinged.
Nos. 113-115 exist imperf. Value, each $35 unused, $92.50 never hinged.
See Nos. 123-125. For surcharges and overprints see Nos. 126, 137-140, 143, 156-167, O35-O38.

A17

1923			Perf. 14	
		Paper With Gray Network		
117	A17	250m violet & red	.20	.40
118	A17	300m blue grn & red	.20	.40
119	A17	500m gray & red	.20	.40
120	A17	1000m brown & red	.20	.40

121	A17	3000m violet & red	.20	.40
123	A16	10,000m orange & red	.40	.60
124	A16	20,000m pale bl & red	.40	1.00
125	A16	50,000m green & red	.40	1.00
		Set, never hinged	2.20	4.60
			10.00	

#117, 119-121 exist imperf. Value, each $12.50 unused, $32.50 never hinged; #123-125 also exist imperf. Values each, $25 unused, $85 never hinged.
See #127-135. For surcharges & overprints see #141-142, 144-155, O39-O41.

No. 124 Surcharged in Red

1923, Aug. 14

| 126 | A16 | 100,000m on 20,000m | .60 | 6.00 |
| | | Never hinged | 3.75 | |

No. 126 exists imperf. Value $40.00 unused, $100.00 never hinged.

1923   **Perf. 14**

Paper Without Network

127	A17	1000m brown	.20	.40
129	A17	5000m rose	.20	.40
131	A17	20,000m pale blue	.20	.40
132	A17	50,000m green	.20	.40

Paper With Gray Network

133	A17	100,000m deep blue	.20	.40
134	A17	250,000m violet	.20	.40
135	A17	500,000m slate	.20	.40
		Nos. 127-135 (7)	1.40	2.80
		Set, never hinged	4.00	

Nos. 127, 129, 131-135 exist imperf. Value each, $40 unused, $100 never hinged.

Abbreviations: th=(tausend) thousand mil=million

Nos. 115, 114, 132, and Type of 1923 Surcharged

1923   **Perf. 14**

Paper Without Network

137	A15	40th m on 200m	.85	2.00
a.		Double surcharge	85.00	
		Never hinged	160.00	
138	A15	100th m on 200m	.85	2.00
139	A15	250th m on 200m	6.25	13.00
140	A15a	400th m on 100m	.40	.40
141	A17	500th m on 50,000m	.40	.40
142	A17	1mil m on 10,000m org	3.75	12.50

The surcharges on Nos. 140-142 differ in details from those on Nos. 137-139.

Type of 1923 Surcharged

Paper With Gray Network

143	A16	10mil m on 1,000,000m org	.40	1.25
		Nos. 137-143 (7)	12.90	31.55
		Set, never hinged	50.00	

#142-143 exist imperf. Value: #142 unused $50; never hinged $125; #143 unused $25; never hinged $85.

Type of 1923 Surcharged

10,000m rose on paper without Network

144	A17	1mil m on 10,000m	.25	.40
145	A17	2mil m on 10,000m	.25	.40
146	A17	3mil m on 10,000m	.25	.40
147	A17	5mil m on 10,000m	.35	.40
b.		Double surcharge	85.00	
		Never hinged	160.00	

10,000m gray lilac on paper without Network

148	A17	10mil m on 10,000m	.40	.75
149	A17	20mil m on 10,000m	.40	.75
150	A17	25mil m on 10,000m	.20	.75
151	A17	40mil m on 10,000m	.20	.75
a.		Double surcharge	52.50	
		Never hinged	160.00	
152	A17	50mil m on 10,000m	.20	.75

Type of 1923 Surcharged in Red

10,000m gray lilac on paper without Network

153	A17	100mil m on 10,000m	.20	.75
154	A17	300mil m on 10,000m	.20	.75
155	A17	500mil m on 10,000m	.20	.75
		Nos. 144-155 (12)	3.10	7.60
		Set, never hinged	15.00	

#144-147 exist imperf. Value, each $25 unused, $100 never hinged. #148-155 exist imperf. Value, each $32.50 unused, $85 never hinged.

Types of 1923 Surcharged

1923, Oct. 31   **Wmk. 110**   **Perf. 14**

156	A15	5pf on 50m rose	.40	.40
157	A15	10pf on 50m rose	.40	.40
158	A15a	20pf on 100m rose	.40	.40
159	A15	25pf on 50m rose	3.25	9.00
160	A15	30pf on 50m rose	3.25	2.00
161	A15a	40pf on 100m rose	2.00	2.00
162	A15a	50pf on 100m rose	2.00	3.00
163	A15a	75pf on 100m rose	7.50	16.00

Type of 1923 Surcharged

1923, Nov. 5

164	A16	1g on 1mil m rose	4.00	6.25
165	A16	2g on 1mil m rose	11.50	17.50
166	A16	3g on 1mil m rose	20.00	60.00
167	A16	5g on 1mil m rose	25.00	65.00
		Nos. 156-167 (12)	79.70	181.95
		Set, never hinged	375.00	

Coat of Arms — A19

1924-37   **Wmk. 109**   **Perf. 14**

168	A19	3pf brn, yelsh ('36)	1.25	1.50
a.		3pf dp brn, white ('27)	1.60	1.75
		Never hinged	7.00	
170	A19	5pf org, yelsh ('36)	3.25	.55
a.		White paper	8.50	2.00
		Never hinged	40.00	
c.		Tête bêche pair	325.00	
		Never hinged	750.00	
d.		Syncopated perf., #170 ('37)	10.50	9.00
		Never hinged	29.00	
e.		Syncopated perf., #170a ('32)	21.00	10.50
		Never hinged	110.00	
171	A19	7pf yel grn ('33)	1.25	2.50
172	A19	8pf yel grn ('37)	1.60	1.00
173	A19	10pf grn, yelsh ('36)	5.50	.50
a.		White paper	8.50	2.00
		Never hinged	32.50	
c.		10pf blue grn, yellowish ('37)	5.00	1.10
		Never hinged	13.00	
d.		Tête bêche pair	325.00	

		Never hinged	750.00	
e.		Syncopated perf., #173 ('37)	18.00	10.50
		Never hinged	52.50	
f.		Syncopated perf., #173a (132)	26.00	13.00
		Never hinged	100.00	
g.		Syncopated perf., #173c ('37)	10.50	14.50
		Never hinged	32.50	
175	A19	15pf gray	3.75	.65
176	A19	15pf red, yelsh ('36)	2.10	1.10
a.		White paper ('25)	4.00	1.10
		Never hinged	20.00	
177	A19	20pf carmine & red	13.00	.65
178	A19	20pf gray ('35)	1.75	1.75
179	A19	25pf slate & red	21.00	3.75
180	A19	25pf carmine ('35)	16.50	1.60
181	A19	30pf green & red ('25)	12.50	.85
182	A19	30pf dk violet ('35)	1.60	4.25
183	A19	35pf ultra ('25)	2.90	1.50
184	A19	40pf dk blue & blue	10.00	1.00
185	A19	40pf yel brn & red ('35)	6.50	12.50
186	A19	40pf dk blue ('35)	1.60	3.75
a.		Imperf.	50.00	
		Never hinged	160.00	
187	A19	50pf blue & red	14.00	8.50
a.		Yellowish paper ('36)	25.00	11.50
		Never hinged	57.50	
188	A19	55pf plum & scar ('37)	5.00	14.00
189	A19	60pf dk grn & red ('35)	6.25	26.00
190	A19	70pf yel grn & red ('35)	2.10	5.75
191	A19	75pf violet & red, yellowish ('36)	7.50	29.00
a.		White paper	10.00	8.50
		Never hinged	32.50	
192	A19	80pf dk org brn & red ('35)	2.10	7.50
		Nos. 168-192 (23)	143.00	134.15
		Set, never hinged	500.00	

The 5pf and 10pf with syncopated perforations (Netherlands type C) are coils.
See Nos. 225-232. For overprints and surcharges see Nos. 200-209, 211-215, 241-252, B9-B11, O42-O52.

Oliva Castle and Cathedral A20

St. Mary's Church A23

Council Chamber on the Langenmarkt A24

2g, Mottlau River & Krantor. 3g, View of Zoppot.

1924-32   **Engr.**   **Wmk. 125**

193	A20	1g yel grn & blk	20.00	45.00
		Parcel post cancel		20.00
194	A20	1g org & gray blk ('25)	16.50	3.75
a.		1g red orange & blk ('32)	16.50	11.00
		Never hinged	65.00	
		Parcel post cancel		1.00
195	A20	2g red vio & blk	45.00	110.00
		Parcel post cancel		40.00
196	A20	2g rose & blk ('25)	3.75	6.50
		Parcel post cancel		1.75
197	A20	3g dk blue & blk	4.00	5.00
		Parcel post cancel		2.25
198	A23	5g brn red & blk	4.00	8.50
		Parcel post cancel		1.90
199	A24	10g dk brn & blk	20.00	100.00
		Parcel post cancel		18.00
		Nos. 193-199 (7)	113.25	278.75
		Set, never hinged	500.00	

See No. 233. For overprints and surcharges see Nos. 210, 253-254, C31-C35.

Stamps of 1924-25 Overprinted in Black, Violet or Red

		Never hinged	750.00	
e.		Syncopated perf., #173 ('37)	18.00	10.50
		Never hinged	52.50	

1930, Nov. 15   **Typo.**   **Wmk. 109**

200	A19	5pf orange	2.50	3.75
201	A19	10pf yellow grn (V)	3.50	4.50
202	A19	15pf red	6.00	10.50
203	A19	20pf carmine & red	3.75	5.75
204	A19	25pf slate & red	4.25	10.50
205	A19	30pf green & red	8.50	25.00
206	A19	35pf ultra (R)	40.00	100.00
207	A19	40pf dk bl & bl (R)	11.50	37.50
208	A19	50pf dp blue & red	40.00	85.00
209	A19	75pf violet & red	40.00	85.00

Wmk. Lozenges. (125)   **Engr.**

210	A20	1g orange & blk (R)	40.00	85.00
		Nos. 200-210 (11)	199.25	452.50
		Set, never hinged	575.00	

10th anniv. of the Free State. Counterfeits exist.

Nos. 171 and 183 Surcharged in Red Blue or Green:

Nos. 211-214   No. 215

1934-36

211	A19	6pf on 7pf (R)	.85	1.60
212	A19	8pf on 7pf (Bl) ('35)	2.00	2.25
213	A19	8pf on 7pf (R) ('36)	1.25	2.50
214	A19	8pf on 7pf (G) ('36)	.85	2.50
215	A19	30pf on 35pf (Bl)	12.00	25.00
		Nos. 211-215 (5)	16.95	33.85
		Set, never hinged	55.00	

Bathing Beach, Brösen A25

View of Brösen Beach A26

War Memorial at Brösen — A27

Skyline of Danzig — A28

1936, June 23   **Typo.**   **Wmk. 109**

216	A25	10pf deep green	.70	.70
217	A26	25pf rose red	1.00	2.40
218	A27	40pf bright blue	1.75	4.50
		Nos. 216-218 (3)	3.45	7.60
		Set, never hinged	11.50	

Village of Brösen, 125th anniversary. Exist imperf. Value each, $40 unused, $100 never hinged.

1937, Mar. 27

219	A28	10pf dark blue	.50	1.40
220	A28	15pf violet brown	1.60	2.00
		Set, never hinged	6.75	

Air Defense League.

Danzig Philatelic Exhibition Issue
Souvenir Sheet

St. Mary's Church — A29

1937, June 6 Wmk. 109 *Perf. 14*

221	A29	50pf dark opal green	3.25	*20.00*
		Never hinged	10.75	

Danzig Philatelic Exhib., June 6-8, 1937.

Arthur Schopenhauer
A30 A31

Design: 40pf, Full-face portrait, white hair.

Unwmk.
1938, Feb. 22 Photo. *Perf. 14*

222	A30	15pf dull blue	1.25	*1.60*
223	A31	25pf sepia	3.00	*7.50*
224	A31	40pf orange ver	1.25	*3.25*
		Nos. 222-224 (3)	5.50	*12.35*
		Set, never hinged	18.00	

150th anniv. of the birth of Schopenhauer.

Type of 1924-35

1938-39 Typo. Wmk. 237 *Perf. 14*

225	A19	3pf brown	.90	*6.50*
226	A19	5pf orange	.90	*2.10*
b.		Syncopated perf.	1.40	*7.50*
		Never hinged	5.25	
227	A19	8pf yellow grn	4.00	*23.00*
228	A19	10pf blue green	.90	*1.60*
b.		Syncopated perf.	3.00	*10.00*
		Never hinged	13.00	
229	A19	15pf scarlet	1.60	*8.50*
230	A19	25pf carmine	2.10	*12.50*
231	A19	40pf dark blue	2.10	*29.00*
232	A19	50pf brt bl & red ('39)	2.10	*100.00*

Engr.

233	A20	1g red org & blk	4.25	*85.00*
		Nos. 225-233 (9)	18.85	*268.20*
		Set, never hinged	62.50	

Sizes: #233, 32½x21¼mm; #194, 31x21mm.
Nos. 226b and 228b are coils with Netherlands type C perforation.

Knights in Tournament, 1500 — A33

French Leaving Danzig, 1814 — A35

Stamp Day: 10pf, Signing of Danzig-Sweden neutrality treaty, 1630. 25pf, Battle of Weichselmünde, 1577.

Unwmk.
1939, Jan. 7 Photo. *Perf. 14*

234	A33	5pf dark green	.40	*2.10*
235	A33	10pf copper brown	.85	*2.50*
236	A35	15pf slate black	.85	*3.00*
237	A35	25pf brown violet	1.25	*4.00*
		Nos. 234-237 (4)	3.35	*11.60*
		Set, never hinged	12.50	

Gregor Mendel — A37

15pf, Dr. Robert Koch. 25pf, Wilhelm Roentgen.

1939, Apr. 29 Photo. *Perf. 13x14*

238	A37	10pf copper brown	.40	*.85*
239	A37	15pf indigo	.40	*2.00*
240	A37	25pf dark olive green	.85	*2.50*
		Nos. 238-240 (3)	1.65	*5.35*
		Set, never hinged	5.50	

Issued in honor of the achievements of Mendel, Koch and Roentgen.

Issued under German Administration

Stamps of Danzig, 1925-39, Surcharged in Black:

a

b

c

1939 Wmk. 109 *Perf. 14*

241	A19(b)	4rpf on 35pf ultra	.75	*2.10*
242	A19(b)	12rpf on 7pf yel grn	1.25	*2.10*
243	A19(a)	20rpf gray	2.75	*8.00*

Wmk. 237

244	A19(a)	3rpf brown	.75	*2.25*
245	A19(a)	5rpf orange	.65	*2.75*
246	A19(a)	8rpf yellow grn	1.10	*4.00*
247	A19(a)	10rpf blue grn	2.25	*4.00*
248	A19(a)	15rpf scarlet	6.00	*11.50*
249	A19(a)	25rpf carmine	4.50	*10.75*
250	A19(a)	30rpf dk violet	2.00	*4.50*
251	A19(a)	40rpf dk blue	2.75	*5.75*
252	A19(a)	50rpf brt bl & red	4.00	*7.00*
253	A20(c)	1rm on 1g red org & blk	14.00	*57.50*

Wmk. 125

254	A20(c)	2rm on 2g rose & blk	17.50	*45.00*
		Nos. 241-254 (14)	60.25	*167.20*
		Set, never hinged	180.00	

#241-254 were valid throughout Germany.

SEMI-POSTAL STAMPS

St. George and Dragon — SP1

Wmk. 108
1921, Oct. 16 Typo. *Perf. 14*
Size: 19x22mm

B1	SP1	30pf + 30pf grn & org	.45	.85
B2	SP1	60pf + 60pf rose & org	1.25	1.25

Size: 25x30mm
Serrate Roulette 13½

B3	SP1	1.20m + 1.20m dk bl & org	1.90	1.25
		Nos. B1-B3 (3)	3.60	3.35
		Set, never hinged	11.50	

Nos. B1-B3 exist imperf. Values: each, $40 unused; $125 never hinged.

Aged Pensioner SP2

1923, Mar. Wmk. 109 *Perf. 14*
Paper With Gray Network

B4	SP2	50m + 20m lake	.20	*.60*
B5	SP2	100m + 30m red violet	.20	*.60*
		Set, never hinged	1.60	

Nos. B4-B5 exist imperf. Values: each, $20 unused; $110 never hinged.

Philatelic Exhibition Issue

Neptune Fountain — SP3

Various Frames.

1929, July 7 Engr. Unwmk.

B6	SP3	10pf yel grn & gray	2.00	1.60
B7	SP3	15pf car & gray	2.00	1.60
B8	SP3	25pf ultra & gray	8.50	*13.00*
a.		25pf violet blue & black	25.00	*60.00*
		Never hinged	90.00	
		Nos. B6-B8 (3)	12.50	16.20
		Set, never hinged	40.00	

These stamps were sold exclusively at the Danzig Philatelic Exhibition, June 7-14, 1929, at double their face values, the excess being for the aid of the exhibition.

Regular Issue of 1924-25 Surcharged in Black

1934, Jan. 15 Wmk. 109

B9	A19	5pf + 5pf orange	8.50	*20.00*
B10	A19	10pf + 5pf yel grn	20.00	*50.00*
B11	A19	15pf + 5pf carmine	12.50	*37.50*
		Nos. B9-B11 (3)	41.00	*107.50*
		Set, never hinged	210.00	

Surtax for winter welfare. Counterfeits exist.

Stock Tower — SP4

George Hall — SP6

City Gate, 16th Century SP5

1935, Dec. 16 Typo. *Perf. 14*

B12	SP4	5pf + 5pf orange	.50	*1.50*
B13	SP5	10pf + 5pf green	.85	*2.25*
B14	SP6	15pf + 10pf scarlet	2.00	*3.75*
		Nos. B12-B14 (3)	3.35	*7.50*
		Set, never hinged	11.00	

Surtax for winter welfare.

Milk Can Tower SP7

Frauentor SP8

Krantor — SP9

Langgarter Gate — SP10

High Gate SP11

1936, Nov. 25

B15	SP7	10pf + 5pf dk bl	1.25	*3.25*
a.		Imperf.	75.00	
		Never hinged	180.00	
B16	SP8	15pf + 5pf dull green	1.25	*5.00*
B17	SP9	25pf + 10pf red brown	2.10	*6.50*
B18	SP10	40pf + 20pf brn & red brn	3.00	*10.50*
B19	SP11	50pf + 20pf bl & dk bl	5.00	*16.50*
		Nos. B15-B19 (5)	12.60	*41.75*
		Set, never hinged	52.50	

Surtax for winter welfare.

SP12

SP13

1937, Oct. 30

B20	SP12	25pf + 25pf dk car	2.50	*5.25*
B21	SP13	40pf + 40pf blue & red	2.50	*5.25*
a.		Souv. sheet of 2, #B20-B21	60.00	*100.00*
		Never hinged	110.00	
		Set, never hinged	20.00	

Founding of Danzig community at Magdeburg.

Madonna SP14

Mercury SP15

Weather Vane,
Town Hall
SP16

Neptune
Fountain
SP17

St. George and
Dragon — SP18

1937, Dec. 13

B23	SP14	5pf + 5pf brt violet	2.50	6.25
B24	SP15	10pf + 10pf dk brn	2.50	6.25
B25	SP16	15pf + 5pf bl & yel brn	2.50	6.25
B26	SP17	25pf +10pf bl grn & grn	3.25	9.00
B27	SP18	40pf + 25pf brt car & bl	5.75	17.50
		Nos. B23-B27 (5)	16.50	45.25
		Set, never hinged	52.50	

Surtax for winter welfare. Designs are from
frieze of the Artushof.

"Peter von
Danzig" Yacht
Race — SP19

Ships: 10pf+5pf, Dredger Fu Shing.
15pf+10pf, S. S. Columbus. 25pf+10pf, S. S.
City of Danzig. 40pf+15pf, Peter von Danzig,
1472.

1938, Nov. 28   Photo.   Unwmk.

B28	SP19	5pf + 5pf dk blue	1.10	1.60
B29	SP19	10pf + 5pf gldn brown	1.40	3.00
B30	SP19	15pf + 10pf ol grn	1.60	3.00
B31	SP19	25pf + 10pf indigo	2.50	4.00
B32	SP19	40pf + 15pf vio brn	3.00	7.00
		Nos. B28-B32 (5)	9.60	18.60
		Set, never hinged	35.00	

Surtax for winter welfare.

AIR POST STAMPS

No. 6 Surcharged in Blue or Carmine

1920, Sept. 29   Wmk. 125   Perf. 14

C1	A16	40pf on 40pf	1.10	2.90
a.		Double surcharge	125.00	250.00
		Never hinged	325.00	
C2	A16	60pf on 40pf (C)	1.10	2.90
a.		Double surcharge	125.00	250.00
		Never hinged	325.00	
C3	A16	1m on 40pf	1.10	2.90
		Nos. C1-C3 (3)	3.30	8.70
		Set, never hinged	10.00	

Plane faces left on No. C2.

AP3

Plane over
Danzig
AP4

Wmk. Honeycomb (108)

1921-22   Typo.   Perf. 14

C4	AP3	40(pf) blue green	.25	.45
C5	AP3	60(pf) dk violet	.25	.45
C6	AP3	1m carmine	.25	.45
C7	AP3	2m orange brown	.25	.45

Serrate Roulette 13½

Size: 34½x23mm

C8	AP4	5m violet blue	1.25	2.25
C9	AP4	10m dp grn ('22)	2.00	4.50
		Nos. C4-C9 (6)	4.25	8.55
		Set, never hinged	18.00	

Nos. C4-C9 exist imperf. Value, each
$32.50 unused, $125 never hinged.

1923   Wmk. Webbing (109)   Perf. 14

C10	AP3	40(pf) blue green	.40	2.00
C11	AP3	60(pf) dk violet	.40	2.00
a.		Double impression		
C12	AP3	1m carmine	.40	2.00
C13	AP3	2m org brown	.40	2.00
C14	AP3	5m pale blue	.30	.55

Serrate Roulette 13½

Size: 34½x23mm

C15	AP4	5m violet blue	.40	.85
C16	AP4	10m deep green	.40	.85

Paper With Gray Network

C17	AP4	20m orange brown	.40	.85

Size: 40x23mm

C18	AP4	50m orange	.30	.55
C19	AP4	100m red	.30	.55
C20	AP4	250m dark brown	.30	.55
C21	AP4	500m carmine rose	.30	.55
		Nos. C10-C21 (12)	4.30	13.30
		Set, never hinged	17.00	

#C11, C12, C14-C21 exist imperf. Value,
#C11, C12, C15-C17, each $8.50 unused,
$32.50 never hinged. Value, #C14, C18-C21,
each $40 unused, $125 never hinged.

Issued: #C10, C13, C15-C16, 1/3/23. #C14,
C18, C20-C21, 4/27/23. #C17, 1/10/23. #C19,
2/5/23.

Nos. C18, C19 and C21 exist with wmk.
sideways, both perf and imperf. Value each,
$60 unused, $160 never hinged.

Post Horn and
Airplanes — AP5

1923, Oct. 18   Perf. 14

Paper Without Network

C22	AP5	250,000m scarlet	.25	1.10
C23	AP5	500,000m scarlet	.25	1.10
		Set, never hinged	2.10	

Exist imperf. Value, each: $50 unused; $125
never hinged.

Surcharged

C24	AP5	2mil m on 100,000m	.25	1.10
C25	AP5	5mil m on 50,000m	.25	1.10
b.		Cliché of 10,000m in sheet of 50,000m	32.50	125.00
		Never hinged	110.00	
		Set, never hinged	2.10	

Exist imperf. Value, each $125 unused;
$290 never hinged.

Nos. C24 and C25 were not regularly issued
without surcharge, although copies have been
passed through the post. Values: C24 unused
$8.50, never hinged $32.50; C25 unused $12,
never hinged $21.

AP6

Plane over
Danzig — AP7

1924

C26	AP6	10(pf) vermilion	22.50	3.75
C27	AP6	20(pf) carmine rose	2.00	1.50
C28	AP6	40(pf) olive brown	3.00	1.75
C29	AP6	1g deep green	3.00	1.75
C30	AP7	2½g violet brown	17.50	35.00
		Nos. C26-C30 (5)	48.00	43.75
		Set, never hinged	150.00	

Exist imperf. Value #C26, C30, $85 unused,
$200 never hinged; others, each $40 unused,
$110 never hinged.

Nos. 193, 195, 197-199 Surcharged in
Various Colors

1932   Wmk. 125

C31	A20	10pf on 1g (G)	8.50	23.00
C32	A20	15pf on 2g (V)	8.50	23.00
C33	A20	20pf on 3g (Bl)	8.50	23.00
C34	A23	25pf on 5g (R)	8.50	23.00
C35	A24	30pf on 10g (Br)	8.50	23.00
		Nos. C31-C35 (5)	42.50	115.00
		Set, never hinged	180.00	

Intl. Air Post Exhib. of 1932. The surcharges
were variously arranged to suit the shapes
and designs of the stamps. The stamps were
sold at double their surcharged values, the
excess being donated to the exhibition funds.
No. C31 exists with inverted surcharge and
with double surcharge. Value each, $85
unused, $210 never hinged.

Airplane
AP8   AP9

1935   Wmk. 109

C36	AP8	10pf scarlet	1.60	.85
C37	AP8	15pf yellow	1.60	1.25
C38	AP8	25pf dark green	1.60	1.60
C39	AP8	50pf gray blue	6.50	10.00
C40	AP9	1g magenta	3.25	13.00
		Nos. C36-C40 (5)	14.55	26.70
		Set, never hinged	57.50	

Nos. C36 and C40 exist imperf. Values: C36
unused $20, never hinged $62.50; C40
unused $29, never hinged $85.
See Nos. C42-C45.

Souvenir Sheet

St. Mary's Church — AP10

1937, June 6   Perf. 14

C41	AP10	50pf dark grayish blue	3.50	20.00
		Never hinged	10.50	

Danzig Phil. Exhib., June 6-8, 1937.

Type of 1935

1938-39   Wmk. 237

C42	AP8	10pf scarlet	1.25	3.25
C43	AP8	15pf yellow ('39)	2.25	13.00
C44	AP8	25pf dark green	1.60	5.75
C45	AP8	50pf gray blue ('39)	4.00	50.00
		Nos. C42-C45 (4)	9.10	72.00
		Set, never hinged	35.00	

POSTAGE DUE STAMPS

Danzig Coat of Arms
D1   D2

Wmk. Honeycomb (108)

1921-22   Typo.   Perf. 14

Paper Without Network

J1	D1	10(pf) deep violet	.25	.50
J2	D1	20(pf) deep violet	.25	.50
J3	D1	40(pf) deep violet	.25	.50
J4	D1	60(pf) deep violet	.25	.50
J5	D1	75(pf) dp violet ('22)	.25	.50
J6	D1	80(pf) deep violet	.25	.50
J7	D1	120(pf) deep violet	.25	.50
J8	D1	200(pf) dp violet ('22)	.85	1.10
J9	D1	240(pf) deep violet	.25	1.10
J10	D1	300(pf) dp violet ('22)	.85	1.10
J11	D1	400(pf) deep violet	.85	1.10
J12	D1	500(pf) deep violet	.85	1.10
J13	D1	800(pf) dp violet ('22)	.85	1.10
J14	D1	20m dp violet ('22)	.85	1.10
		Nos. J1-J14 (14)	7.10	11.20
		Set, never hinged	23.00	

Nos. J1-J14 exist imperf. Value, each $25
unused, $65 never hinged.

1923   Wmk. 109

J15	D1	100(pf) deep violet	.65	.85
J16	D1	200(pf) deep violet	2.50	4.00
J17	D1	300(pf) deep violet	.65	.85
J18	D1	400(pf) deep violet	.65	.85
J19	D1	500(pf) deep violet	.65	.85
J20	D1	800(pf) deep violet	1.40	4.00
J21	D1	10m deep violet	.65	1.10
J22	D1	20m deep violet	.65	.85
J23	D1	50m deep violet	.65	.85

Paper With Gray Network

J24	D1	100m deep violet	.65	1.10
J25	D1	500m deep violet	.65	1.10
		Nos. J15-J25 (11)	9.75	16.40
		Set, never hinged	24.00	

#J15, J17, J22-J25 exist imperf. Value each,
$12.50 unused, $40 never hinged.

Nos. J22-J23 and Type
of 1923 Surcharged

1923, Oct. 1

Paper without Network

J26	D1	5000m on 50m	.40	.85
J27	D1	10,000m on 20m	.40	.85
J28	D1	50,000m on 500m	.40	.85
J29	D1	100,000m on 20m	.85	1.25
		Nos. J26-J29 (4)	2.05	3.80
		Set, never hinged	8.25	

On No. J26 the numerals of the surcharge
are all of the larger size.
A 1000(m) on 100m deep violet was prepared but not issued. Value, $145, never
hinged $350.
Nos. J26-J28 exist imperf. Value each,
$16.50 unused, $40 never hinged.

1923-28   Wmk. 110

J30	D2	5(pf) blue & blk	.85	.85
J31	D2	10(pf) blue & blk	.40	.85
J32	D2	15(pf) blue & blk	1.25	1.25
J33	D2	20(pf) blue & blk	1.25	2.00
J34	D2	30(pf) blue & blk	8.50	2.00
J35	D2	40(pf) blue & blk	2.00	3.25
J36	D2	50(pf) blue & blk	2.00	2.50
J37	D2	60(pf) blue & blk	13.00	20.00
J38	D2	100(pf) blue & blk	16.50	10.50

Danzig (left column)

J39	D2	3g blue & car	7.50	45.00
a.		"Guldeu" instead of "Gulden"	325.00	1,050.
		Never hinged	1,050.	
		Nos. J30-J39 (10)	53.25	88.20
		Set, never hinged	170.00	

Used values of Nos. J30-J39 are for postally used copies.
See Nos. J43-J47.

Postage Due Stamps of 1923 Issue
Surcharged in Red

1932, Dec. 20

J40	D2	5pf on 40(pf)	2.50	7.50
J41	D2	10pf on 60(pf)	30.00	10.00
J42	D2	20pf on 100(pf)	2.50	7.50
		Nos. J40-J42 (3)	35.00	25.00
		Set, never hinged	110.00	

Type of 1923

1938-39   Wmk. 237   Perf. 14

J43	D2	10(pf) bl & blk ('39)	1.25	57.50
J44	D2	30(pf) blue & black	2.10	45.00
J45	D2	40(pf) bl & blk ('39)	6.25	85.00
J46	D2	60(pf) bl & blk ('39)	6.25	85.00
J47	D2	100(pf) blue & black	10.00	65.00
		Nos. J43-J47 (5)	25.85	337.50
		Set, never hinged	90.00	

OFFICIAL STAMPS

Regular Issues of 1921-22 Overprinted

a

1921-22   Wmk. 108   Perf. 14x14½

O1	A11	5(pf) orange	.25	.20
O2	A11	10(pf) dark brown	.25	.20
a.		Inverted overprint	50.00	
		Never hinged	140.00	
O3	A11	15(pf) green	.25	.20
O4	A11	20(pf) slate	.25	.20
O5	A11	25(pf) dark green	.25	.20
O6	A11	30(pf) blue & car	.60	.60
O7	A11	40(pf) green & car	.25	.20
O8	A11	50(pf) dk grn & car	.25	.20
O9	A11	60(pf) carmine	.25	.20
O10	A11	75(pf) dp vio ('22)	.20	.40
O11	A11	80(pf) black & car	.85	.85
O12	A11	80(pf) green ('22)	.20	2.50

Paper With Faint Gray Network

O14	A11	1m orange & car	.25	.20
O15	A11	1.20m blue violet	1.25	1.25
O16	A11	1.25m vio & car ('22)	.20	.40
O17	A11	1.50m sl gray ('22)	.20	.40
O18	A11	2m gray & car	14.00	11.50
a.		Inverted overprint	110.00	
		Never hinged	250.00	
O19	A11	2m car rose ('22)	.20	.40
O20	A11	2.40m dk brn & car ('22)	1.25	2.50
O21	A11	3m violet & car	8.50	11.50
O22	A11	3m car lake ('22)	.20	.40
O23	A11	4m dk blue ('22)	1.25	.85
O24	A11	5m dp grn ('22)	.20	.40
O25	A11	6m car lake ('22)	.20	.40
O26	A11	10m orange ('22)	.20	.40
O27	A11	20m org brn ('22)	.20	.40
		Nos. O1-O27 (26)	31.95	36.95
		Set, never hinged	160.00	

Double overprints exist on Nos. O1-O2, O5-O7, O10 and O12.

Same Overprint on No. 96

O28	A11	6m on 3m	.20	.75
		Never hinged	.65	
a.		Inverted overprint	29.00	
		Never hinged	85.00	

No. 77
Overprinted

1922   Serrate Roulette 13½

O29	A12	5m grn, red & blk	4.00	10.50
		Never hinged	18.00	

Nos. 99-103, 106-107 Overprinted
Type "a"

1923   Wmk. 109   Perf. 14

O30	A11	4m dark blue	.25	.40
O31	A11	5m dark green	.25	.40
O32	A11	10m orange	.25	.40
O33	A11	20m orange brn	.25	.40
O34	A15	50m pale bl & red	.25	.40
O35	A15a	100m dk grn & red	.25	.40

Nos. 113-115, 118-120 Overprinted
Type "a"

O36	A15	50m pale blue	.25	.50
a.		Inverted overprint	25.00	
		Never hinged	60.00	
O37	A15a	100m dark green	.20	.50
O38	A15	200m orange	.20	.50
a.		Inverted overprint	25.00	
		Never hinged	60.00	

Paper With Gray Network

O39	A17	300m bl grn & red	.25	.40
O40	A17	500m gray & red	.20	.50
O41	A17	1000m brown & red	.20	.50
		Nos. O30-O41 (12)	2.80	5.30
		Set, never hinged	11.00	

Regular Issue of 1924-25 Overprinted

1924-25   Perf. 14x14½

O42	A19	5pf orange	2.10	2.50
O43	A19	10pf yellow grn	2.10	2.50
O44	A19	15pf gray	2.10	2.50
O45	A19	15pf red ('25)	18.00	10.00
O46	A19	20pf car & red	2.10	1.60
O47	A19	25pf slate & red	18.00	26.00
O48	A19	30pf green & red	2.90	3.75
O49	A19	35pf ultra ('25)	40.00	50.00
O50	A19	40pf dk bl & dull bl	6.50	8.50
O51	A19	50pf dp blue & red	21.00	32.50
O52	A19	75pf violet & red	32.50	110.00
		Nos. O42-O52 (11)	147.30	249.85
		Set, never hinged	500.00	

Double overprints exist on Nos. O42-O44, O47, O50-O52.

DENMARK

'den-ˌmärk

LOCATION — Northern part of a peninsula which separates the North and Baltic Seas, and includes the surrounding islands
GOVT. — Kingdom
AREA — 16,631 sq. mi.
POP. — 5,294,860 (1/1/1999)
CAPITAL — Copenhagen

96 Skilling = 1 Rigsbank Daler
100 Ore = 1 Krone (1875)

Catalogue values for unused stamps in this country are for Never Hinged items, beginning with Scott 297 in the regular postage section, Scott B15 in the semipostal section, and Scott Q28 in the parcel post section.

Values for unused stamps are for examples with original gum as defined in the catalogue introduction. Very fine examples of Nos. 9-37 and O1-O9 will have perforations clear of the framelines but with the design noticeably off center. Well centered stamps are quite scarce and will command substantial premiums.

Watermarks

Wmk. 111 —
Small Crown

Wmk. 112 —
Crown

Wmk. 113 —
Crown

Wmk. 114 —
Multiple Crosses

A1

Royal Emblems — A2

1851   Typo.   Wmk. 111   Imperf.
With Yellow Brown Burelage

1	A1	2rs blue	2,750.	1,200.
a.		First printing	8,250.	2,250.

2	A2	4rs brown	500.00	40.00
a.		First printing	600.00	65.00
b.		4rs yellow brown	875.00	55.00

The first printing of Nos. 1 and 2 had the burelage printed from a copper plate, giving a clear impression with the lines in slight relief. The subsequent impressions had the burelage typographed, with the lines fainter and not rising above the surface of the paper.

Nos. 1-2 were reprinted in 1885 and 1901 on heavy yellowish paper, unwatermarked and imperforate, with a brown burelage. No. 1 was also reprinted without burelage, on both yellowish and white paper. Value for least costly reprint of No. 1, $50.

No. 2 was reprinted in 1951 in 10 shades with "Colour Specimen 1951" printed on the back. It was also reprinted in 1961 in 2 shades without burelage and with "Farve Nytryk 1961" printed on the back. Value for least costly reprint of No. 2, $8.50.

Dotting in
Spandrels
A3

Wavy Lines
in Spandrels
A4

1854-57

3	A3	2s blue ('55)	75.00	60.00
4	A3	4s brown	325.00	15.00
a.		4s yellow brown	350.00	15.00
5	A3	8s green ('57)	300.00	65.00
a.		8s yellow green	300.00	70.00
6	A3	16s gray lilac ('57)	525.00	175.00
		Nos. 3-6 (4)	1,225.	315.00

See No. 10. For denominations in cents see Danish West Indies Nos. 1-4.

1858-62

7	A4	4s yellow brown	65.00	9.00
a.		4s brown	67.50	9.50
b.		Wmk. 112 ('62)	62.50	10.00
8	A4	8s green	800.00	95.00

Nos. 2 to 8 inclusive are known with unofficial perforation 12 or 13, and Nos. 4, 5, 7 and 8 with unofficial roulette 9½.

Nos. 3, 6-8 were reprinted in 1885 on heavy yellowish paper, unwatermarked, imperforate and without burelage. Nos. 4-5 were reprinted in 1924 on white paper, unwatermarked, imperforate, gummed and without burelage. Value for No. 3, $15; Nos. 4-5, each $110; No. 6, $20; Nos. 7-8, each $15.

1863   Wmk. 112   Rouletted 11

9	A4	4s brown	100.00	15.00
a.		4s deep brown	100.00	15.00
10	A3	16s violet	1,400.	650.00

Royal Emblems — A5

1864-68   Perf. 13

11	A5	2s blue ('65)	65.00	35.00
12	A5	3s red vio ('65)	80.00	75.00
13	A5	4s red	40.00	8.00
14	A5	8s bister ('68)	275.00	95.00
15	A5	16s olive green	475.00	100.00
	Nos. 11-15 (5)		935.00	388.00

Nos. 11-15 were reprinted in 1886 on heavy yellowish paper, unwatermarked, imperforate and without gum. The reprints of all values except the 4s were printed in two vertical rows of six, inverted with respect to each other, so that horizontal pairs are always tête bêche. Value $12 each.

Nos. 13 and 15 were reprinted in 1942 with printing on the back across each horizontal row: "Nytryk 1942. G. A. Hagemann: Danmarks og Vestindiens Frimaerker, Bind 2." Value, $70 each.

Imperf

11a	A5	2s blue	95.00	95.00
12a	A5	3s red violet	140.00	
13a	A5	4s red	77.50	90.00
14a	A5	8s bister	375.00	
15a	A5	16s olive green	450.00	

1870   Perf. 12½

11b	A5	2s blue	275.00	350.00
12b	A5	3s red violet	475.00	650.00
14b	A5	8s bister	475.00	475.00
15b	A5	16s olive green	725.00	1,450.
	Nos. 11b-15b (4)		1,950.	2,925.

A6

NORMAL FRAME   INVERTED FRAME

The arabesques in the corners have a main stem and a branch. When the frame is in normal position, in the upper left corner the branch leaves the main stem half way between two little leaflets. In the lower right corner the branch starts at the foot of the second leaflet. When the frame is inverted the corner designs are, of course, transposed.

1870-71   Wmk. 112   Perf. 14x13½
Paper Varying from Thin to Thick

16	A6	2s gray & ultra ('71)	70.00	25.00
a.		2s gray & blue ('71)	70.00	25.00
17	A6	3s gray & brt lil ('71)	85.00	100.00
18	A6	4s gray & car	40.00	8.00
19	A6	8s gray & brn ('71)	200.00	75.00
20	A6	16s gray & grn ('71)	275.00	175.00

Perf. 12½

21	A6	2s gray & bl	2,000.	3,250.
22	A6	4s gray & car	150.00	125.00
24	A6	48s brn & lilac	450.00	275.00

Nos. 16-20, 24 were reprinted in 1886 on thin white paper, unwatermarked, imperforate and without gum. These were printed in

---

sheets of 10 in which 1 stamp has the normal frame (value $32.50 each) and 9 the inverted (value $11 each).

Imperf

16b	A6	2s	250.00
17a	A6	3s	240.00
18a	A6	4s	200.00
19a	A6	8s	250.00
20a	A6	16s	400.00
24a	A6	48s	425.00

Inverted Frame

16c	A6	2s	1,000.	775.00
17b	A6	3s	2,500.	2,000.
18b	A6	4s	775.00	87.50
19b	A6	8s	1,750.	900.00
20b	A6	16s	2,000.	1,750.
24b	A6	48s	2,750.	1,900.

1875-79   Perf. 14x13½

25	A6	3o gray blue & gray	18.00	15.00
a.		1st "A" of "DANMARK" missing	60.00	150.00
b.		Imperf.	750.00	
c.		Inverted frame	18.00	16.00
26	A6	4o slate & blue	25.00	.50
a.		4o gray & blue	25.00	1.10
b.		4o slate & ultra	90.00	17.00
c.		4o gray & ultra	75.00	16.00
d.		Imperf	75.00	
e.		Inverted frame	25.00	.50
27	A6	5o rose & blue ('79)	30.00	72.50
a.		Ball of lower curve of large "5" missing	125.00	300.00
b.		Inverted frame	1,000.	2,250.
28	A6	8o slate & car	22.50	.50
a.		8o gray & carmine	75.00	5.00
b.		Imperf	150.00	—
c.		Inverted frame	22.50	.50
29	A6	12o sl & dull lake	10.00	4.00
a.		12o gray & bright lilac	65.00	8.00
b.		12o gray & dull magenta	72.50	10.00
c.		Inverted frame	10.00	4.00
30	A6	16o slate & brn	40.00	3.50
a.		16o light gray & brown	70.00	5.00
b.		Inverted frame	32.50	4.25
31	A6	20o rose & gray	90.00	32.50
a.		20o carmine & gray	90.00	32.50
b.		Inverted frame	90.00	32.50
32	A6	25o gray & green	65.00	40.00
a.		Inverted frame	77.50	62.50
33	A6	50o brown & vio	70.00	30.00
a.		50o brown & blue violet	400.00	175.00
b.		Inverted frame	70.00	32.50
34	A6	100o gray & org ('77)	110.00	60.00
a.		Imperf	375.00	
b.		Inverted frame	150.00	60.00
	Nos. 25-34 (10)		480.50	258.50
	Set, never hinged		1,100.	

The stamps of this issue on thin semi-transparent paper are far scarcer than those on thicker paper.

See Nos. 41-42, 44, 46-47, 50-52. For surcharges see Nos. 55, 79-80, 136.

Arms — A7

Two types of numerals in corners:

⑤   ⑤

1882
Small Corner Numerals

35	A7	5o green	240.00	100.00
	Never hinged		500.00	
37	A7	20o blue	190.00	60.00
	Never hinged		550.00	

1884-88
Larger Corner Numerals

38	A7	5o green	15.00	3.00
a.		Imperf.	—	
39	A7	10o carmine ('85)	16.00	2.00
a.		Small numerals in corners ('88)	550.00	725.00
b.		Imperf., single	175.00	
c.		Pair, Nos. 39, 39a	600.00	875.00
40	A7	20o blue	30.00	5.00
a.		Pair, Nos. 37, 40	400.00	875.00
b.		Imperf.		
	Nos. 38-40 (3)		61.00	10.00
	Set, never hinged		175.00	

Stamps with large corner numerals have white line around crown and lower oval touches frame.

The plate for No. 39, was damaged and 3 clichés in the bottom row were replaced by clichés for post cards, which had small numerals in the corners.

Two clichés with small numerals were inserted in the plate of No. 40.

See Nos. 43, 45, 48-49, 53-54. For surcharge see No. 56.

1895-1901   Wmk. 112   Perf. 13

41	A6	3o blue & gray	7.50	5.00
42	A6	4o slate & bl ('96)	4.50	.40
43	A7	5o green	6.50	.65

44	A6	8o slate & car	4.50	.45
45	A7	10o rose car	12.00	.65
46	A6	12o sl & dull lake	5.00	4.00
47	A6	16o slate & brown	19.00	4.00
48	A7	20o blue	12.00	3.00
49	A7	24o brown ('01)	7.00	3.50
50	A6	25o gray & grn ('98)	62.50	15.00
51	A6	50o brown & vio ('97)	55.00	17.50
52	A6	100o slate & org	57.50	30.00
	Nos. 41-52 (12)		253.00	84.15
	Set, never hinged		525.00	

Inverted Frame

41b	A6	3o	10.00	5.75
42a	A6	4o	4.50	.45
44a	A6	8o	4.50	.50
46a	A6	12o	12.00	4.50
47a	A6	16o	22.50	4.50
50a	A6	25o	50.00	20.00
51a	A6	50o	85.00	25.00
52a	A6	100o	75.00	37.50
	Nos. 41b-52a (8)		263.50	98.20
	Set, never hinged		475.00	

1902-04   Wmk. 113

41c	A6	3o blue & gray	2.75	2.50
42b	A6	4o slate & blue	17.00	15.00
43a	A7	5o green	1.75	.25
44d	A6	8o slate & carmine	325.00	250.00
45a	A7	10o rose carmine	3.00	.25
48a	A7	20o blue	15.00	2.75
50b	A6	25o gray & green	7.25	4.50
51b	A6	50o brown & violet	27.50	17.00
52b	A6	100o slate & orange	25.00	15.00
	Nos. 41c-52b (9)		424.25	307.25
	Set, never hinged		750.00	

Inverted Frame

41d	A6	3o	75.00	40.00
42c	A6	4o	140.00	80.00
50c	A6	25o	175.00	47.50
51c	A6	50o	210.00	125.00
52c	A6	100o	175.00	125.00
	Nos. 41d-52c (5)		775.00	417.50
	Set, never hinged		1,750.	

1902   Wmk. 113

53	A7	1o orange	.70	.55
a.		Imperf.	—	
54	A7	15o lilac	10.50	.65
a.		Imperf, single	4,250.	

Nos. 44d, 44, 49 Surcharged:

a   b

1904-12   Wmk. 113

55	A6(a)	4o on 8o sl & car	3.00	4.00
a.		Wmk. 112 ('12)	17.00	55.00
		Never hinged	35.00	
b.		As "a," inverted frame		4,000.

Wmk. 112

56	A7(b)	15o on 24o brown	4.00	5.50
a.		Short "15" at right	27.50	75.00
		Never hinged	60.00	
	Set, never hinged		11.50	

A10

King Christian IX   A11   King Frederik VIII   A12

1905-17   Wmk. 113   Perf. 13

57	A10	1o orange ('06)	1.75	.60
58	A10	2o carmine	2.75	.35
a.		Perf. 14x14½ ('17)	3.00	16.00
59	A10	3o gray	6.00	.60
60	A10	4o dull blue	5.00	.60
a.		Perf. 14x14½ ('17)	7.50	30.00
61	A10	5o dp green ('12)	2.75	.30
62	A10	10o dp rose ('12)	3.75	.30
63	A10	15o lilac	14.00	1.40
64	A10	20o dk blue ('12)	25.00	.60
	Nos. 57-64 (8)		61.00	4.75
	Set, never hinged		175.00	

The three wavy lines in design A10 are symbolical of the three waters which separate the principal Danish islands. Compare with design A32.

See Nos. 85-96 and 1338-1342. For surcharges and overprints see Nos. 163, 181, J1, J38, Q1-Q2.

1904-05   Engr.

65	A11	10o scarlet	1.75	.30
66	A11	20o blue	14.00	1.90
67	A11	25o brown ('05)	19.00	2.75
68	A11	50o dull vio ('05)	55.00	90.00
69	A11	100o ocher ('05)	9.50	50.00
	Nos. 65-69 (5)		99.25	144.95
	Set, never hinged		275.00	

1905-06   Re-engraved

70	A11	5o green	2.75	.20
71	A11	10o scarlet ('06)	10.00	.30
	Set, never hinged		30.00	

The re-engraved stamps are much clearer than the originals, and the decoration on the king's left breast has been removed.

1907-12

72	A12	5o green	1.10	.30
a.		Imperf.		
73	A12	10o red	2.00	.30
a.		Imperf.		
74	A12	20o indigo	10.00	.30
a.		20o bright blue ('11)	12.00	1.40
75	A12	25o olive brn	21.00	1.10
76	A12	35o dp org ('12)	4.00	5.00
77	A12	50o claret	25.00	5.00
78	A12	100o bister brn	70.00	2.50
	Nos. 72-78 (7)		133.10	14.50
	Set, never hinged		500.00	

Nos. 47, 31 and O9 Surcharged:

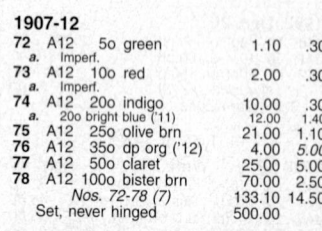

c   d

Dark Blue Surcharge

1912   Wmk. 112   Perf. 13

79	A6(c)	35o on 16o	12.00	50.00
a.		Inverted frame	175.00	400.00

Perf. 14x13½

80	A6(c)	35o on 20o	30.00	70.00
a.		Inverted frame	75.00	175.00

Black Surcharge

81	O1(d)	35o on 32o	30.00	90.00
	Nos. 79-81 (3)		72.00	210.00
	Set, never hinged		140.00	

General Post Office, Copenhagen — A15

1912   Engr.   Wmk. 113   Perf. 13

82	A15	5k dark red	350.00	150.00
		Never hinged	750.00	

See Nos. 135, 843.

Perf. 14x14½

1913-30   Typo.   Wmk. 114

85	A10	1o dp org ('14)	.30	.25
a.		Bklt. pane, 2 ea #85, 91 + 2 labels	20.00	
86	A10	2o car ('14)	1.50	.25
a.		Imperf.	110.00	225.00
b.		Booklet pane, 4 + 2 labels	27.50	
87	A10	3o gray ('13)	3.75	.25
88	A10	4o blue ('13)	5.00	.25
a.		Half used as 2o on cover		1,250.
89	A10	5o dk brown ('21)	.65	.25
a.		Imperf.	160.00	
b.		Booklet pane, 4 + 2 labels	14.00	
90	A10	5o lt green ('30)	1.25	.25
a.		Booklet pane, 4 + 2 labels	16.00	
b.		Booklet pane of 50		
91	A10	7o apple grn ('26)	4.00	6.00
a.		Booklet pane, 4 + 2 labels	20.00	
92	A10	7o dk violet ('30)	12.00	5.00
93	A10	8o gray ('21)	7.00	3.00
94	A10	10o green ('21)	.85	.25
a.		Imperf.	175.00	
b.		Booklet pane, 4 + 2 labels	37.50	
95	A10	10o bister brn ('30)	1.75	.25
a.		Booklet pane, 4 + 2 labels	16.00	
b.		Booklet pane of 50		
96	A10	12o violet ('26)	20.00	7.00
	Nos. 85-96 (12)		58.05	23.00
	Set, never hinged		160.00	

No. 88a was used with No. 97 in Faroe Islands, Jan. 3-23, 1919.

See surcharge and overprint note following #64.

King Christian X
A16   A17

1913-28	Typo.	Perf. 14x14½	
97	A16 5o green	1.10	.25
a.	Booklet pane of 4	11.00	
98	A16 7o orange ('18)	2.25	1.10
99	A16 8o dk gray ('20)	7.00	4.25
100	A16 10o red	1.50	.25
a.	Imperf.	200.00	
b.	Booklet pane of 4	11.00	
101	A16 12o gray grn ('18)	6.00	7.00
102	A16 15o violet	1.50	.25
103	A16 20o dp blue	8.00	.25
104	A16 20o brown ('21)	1.00	.25
105	A16 20o red ('26)	1.25	.25
106	A16 25o dk brown	8.50	.45
107	A16 25o brn & blk ('20)	57.50	5.00
108	A16 25o red ('22)	2.75	.70
109	A16 25o yel grn ('25)	3.00	.45
110	A16 27o ver & blk ('18)	25.00	60.00
111	A16 30o grn & blk ('18)	30.00	2.75
112	A16 30o orange ('21)	2.25	1.75
113	A16 30o dk blue ('25)	1.50	.45
114	A16 35o orange	16.00	4.50
115	A16 35o ver & blk ('19)	7.00	5.00
116	A16 40o vio & blk ('18)	10.00	3.50
117	A16 40o gray bl & blk ('20)	27.50	5.00
118	A16 40o dk blue ('22)	4.00	1.40
119	A16 40o orange ('25)	1.75	.90
120	A16 50o claret	30.00	4.50
121	A16 50o claret & blk ('19)	50.00	2.00
122	A16 50o lt gray ('22)	7.50	.30
a.	50o dark gray ('21)	50.00	6.00
	Never hinged	150.00	
123	A16 60o brn & bl ('19)	40.00	4.00
a.	60o brown & ultra ('19)	160.00	10.00
	Never hinged	500.00	
124	A16 60o grn bl ('21)	8.00	.80
125	A16 70o brn & grn ('20)	20.00	2.00
126	A16 80o bl grn ('15)	32.50	18.00
127	A16 90o brn & red ('20)	12.00	3.75
128	A16 1k brn & bl ('22)	35.00	2.00
129	A16 2k gray & cl ('25)	57.50	13.00
130	A16 5k vio & brn ('27)	5.25	5.00
131	A16 10k ver & yel grn ('28)	200.00	40.00
	Nos. 97-131 (35)	724.10	201.05
	Set, never hinged	2,500.	

#97 surcharged "2 ORE" is Faroe Islands #1.
Nos. 87 and 98, 89 and 94, 89 and 104, 90 and 95, 97 and 103, 100 and 102 exist se-tenant in coils for use in vending machines.
For surcharges and overprints see Nos. 161-162, 176-177, 182-184, J2-J8, M1-M2, Q3-Q10.

1913-20		Engr.	
132	A17 1k yellow brown	65.00	1.00
133	A17 2k gray	75.00	5.00
134	A17 5k purple ('20)	11.00	9.00
	Nos. 132-134 (3)	151.00	15.00
	Set, never hinged	525.00	

For overprint see No. Q11.

G.P.O. Type of 1912
Perf. 14x14½

1915	Wmk. 114	Engr.	
135	A15 5k dark red ('15)	350.00	150.00
	Never hinged	750.00	

Nos. 46 and O10 Surcharged in Black type "c" and:

e

1915	Wmk. 112	Typo.	Perf. 13
136	A6 (c) 80o on 12o	42.50	75.00
a.	Inverted frame	400.00	750.00
	Never hinged	600.00	
137	O1 (e) 80o on 8o	45.00	95.00
a.	"POSTERIM"	55.00	210.00
	Never hinged	70.00	
	Set, never hinged	140.00	

Newspaper Stamps Surcharged

1918	Wmk. 113	Perf. 13	
138	N1 27o on 1o olive	75.00	210.00
139	N1 27o on 5o blue	75.00	210.00
140	N1 27o on 7o car	75.00	210.00
141	N1 27o on 10o dp lil	75.00	210.00
142	N1 27o on 68o yel brn	5.00	30.00
143	N1 27o on 5k rose & yel grn	4.50	15.00
144	N1 27o on 10k bis & bl	5.00	25.00
	Nos. 138-144 (7)	314.50	910.00
	Set, never hinged	600.00	

On Issue of 1914-15
Wmk. Multiple Crosses (114)
Perf. 14x14½

145	N1 27o on 1o ol gray	2.75	11.00
146	N1 27o on 5o blue	6.25	22.50
147	N1 27o on 7o rose	2.75	8.00
148	N1 27o on 8o green	4.00	11.00
149	N1 27o on 10o dp lil	2.75	9.00
150	N1 27o on 20o green	4.00	10.50
151	N1 27o on 29o org yel	2.75	8.00
152	N1 27o on 38o orange	25.00	90.00
153	N1 27o on 41o yel brn	7.00	50.00
154	N1 27o on 1k bl grn & mar	2.75	8.00
	Nos. 145-154 (10)	60.00	228.00
	Set, never hinged	125.00	

Kronborg Castle — A20   Sonderborg Castle — A21

Roskilde Cathedral — A22

Perf. 14½x14, 14x14½

1920, Oct. 5		Typo.	
156	A20 10o red	2.75	.35
157	A21 20o slate	2.25	.35
158	A22 40o dark brown	10.00	4.50
	Nos. 156-158 (3)	15.00	5.20
	Set, never hinged	35.00	

Reunion of Northern Schleswig with Denmark.
See #159-160. For surcharges see #B1-B2.

1921			
159	A20 10o green	6.00	.45
160	A22 40o dark blue	50.00	9.00
	Set, never hinged	150.00	

Stamps of 1918 Surcharged in Blue

1921-22			
161	A16 8o on 7o org ('22)	1.60	5.00
162	A16 8o on 12o gray grn	1.75	8.00
	Set, never hinged	11.00	

No. 87 Surcharged

1921			
163	A10 8o on 3o gray	3.00	4.50
	Never hinged	5.50	

POSTFRIM. 27 ORE DANMARK

Christian X A23   Christian IV A24

A25   A26

1924, Dec. 1		Perf. 14x14½	
164	A23 10o green	6.50	6.00
165	A24 10o green	6.50	6.00
166	A25 10o green	6.50	6.00
167	A26 10o green	6.50	6.00
a.	Block of 4, #164-167	32.50	55.00
168	A23 15o violet	6.50	6.00
169	A24 15o violet	6.50	6.00
170	A25 15o violet	6.50	6.00
171	A26 15o violet	6.50	6.00
a.	Block of 4, #168-171	32.50	55.00
172	A23 20o dark brown	6.50	6.00
173	A24 20o dark brown	6.50	6.00
174	A25 20o dark brown	6.50	6.00
175	A26 20o dark brown	6.50	6.00
a.	Block of 4, #172-175	32.50	55.00
	Nos. 164-175 (12)	78.00	72.00
	Set, never hinged	150.00	
	#167a, 171a, 175a, never hinged	210.00	

300th anniv. of the Danish postal service.

Stamps of 1913-26 Surcharged in Blue or Black

No. 181

Nos. 182-184

1926-27 — Perf. 14x14½
181	A10	7o on 8o gray (Bl)	1.40	4.00
182	A16	7o on 27o ver & blk	4.25	10.00
183	A16	7o on 20o red ('27)	.65	.75
184	A16	12o on 15o violet	2.75	5.50

Surcharged on Official Stamps of 1914-23
185	O1 (e)	7o on 1o org	4.00	14.00
186	O1 (e)	7o on 3o gray	6.50	24.00
187	O1 (e)	7o on 4o blue	3.25	9.00
188	O1 (e)	7o on 5o grn	45.00	92.50
189	O1 (e)	7o on 10o grn	3.25	9.00
190	O1 (e)	7o on 15o vio	3.00	11.00
191	O1 (e)	7o on 20o ind	16.00	55.00
a.		Double surcharge	600.00	750.00
		Nos. 181-191 (11)	90.05	234.75
		Set, never hinged	140.00	

Caravel
A30

Christian X
A31

1927 — Typo. — Perf. 14x14½
192	A30	15o red	4.00	.30
193	A30	20o gray	7.00	1.50
194	A30	25o light blue	.70	.30
195	A30	30o ocher	.60	.30
196	A30	35o red brown	16.00	1.00
197	A30	40o yel green	15.00	.30
		Nos. 192-197 (6)	43.30	3.70
		Set, never hinged	140.00	

See #232-238J. For surcharges & overprints see #244-245, 269-272, Q12-Q14, Q19-Q25.

1930, Sept. 26
210	A31	5o apple grn	1.75	.25
a.		Booklet pane, 4 + 2 labels	18.00	
211	A31	7o violet	6.50	2.75
212	A31	8o dk gray	21.00	17.50
213	A31	10o yel brn	3.50	.25
a.		Booklet pane, 4 + 2 labels	29.00	
214	A31	15o red	7.25	.25
215	A31	20o lt gray	20.00	4.00
216	A31	25o lt blue	7.25	.75
217	A31	30o yel buff	7.25	1.75
218	A31	35o red brown	9.25	2.75
219	A31	40o dp green	8.00	1.00
		Nos. 210-219 (10)	91.75	31.25
		Set, never hinged	210.00	

60th birthday of King Christian X.

Wavy Lines and Numeral of Value — A32

Type A10 Redrawn
1933-40 — Unwmk. — Engr. — Perf. 13
220	A32	1o gray blk	.25	.25
221	A32	2o scarlet	.25	.25
222	A32	4o blue	.30	.25
223	A32	5o yel grn	1.00	.25
a.		5o gray green	27.50	40.00
b.		Tête bêche gutter pair	8.00	14.00
c.		Booklet pane of 4	11.00	
d.		Bklt. pane, 1 #223a, 3 #B6	37.50	
e.		As "b," without gutter, never hinged	17.50	
224	A32	5o rose lake ('38)	.25	.25
a.		Booklet pane of 4	.40	
b.		Booklet pane of 10	.90	
224C	A32	6o orange ('40)	.30	.25
225	A32	7o violet	2.00	.25
226	A32	7o yel grn ('38)	1.10	.25
226A	A32	7o lt brown ('40)	.25	.25
227	A32	8o gray	.60	.25
227A	A32	8o yellow grn ('40)	.25	.25
228	A32	10o yellow org	10.00	.25
a.		Tête bêche gutter pair	30.00	30.00
b.		Booklet pane of 4	110.00	
c.		As "a," without gutter, never hinged	45.00	
229	A32	10o lt brown ('37)	9.50	.25
a.		Booklet pane of 4	100.00	
b.		Booklet pane of 4, 1 #229, 3 #B7	30.00	

230	A32	10o violet ('38)	.60	.25
a.		Booklet pane of 4	2.75	
b.		Bklt. pane, 2 #230, 2 #B10	4.50	
		Nos. 220-230 (14)	26.65	3.50
		Set, never hinged	50.00	

Design A10 was typographed. They had a solid background with groups of small hearts below the heraldic lions in the upper corners and below "DA" and "RK" of "DANMARK." The numerals of value were enclosed in single-lined ovals.

Design A32 is line-engraved and has a background of crossed lines. The hearts have been removed and the numerals of value are now in double-lined ovals. Two types exist of some values.

The 1ö, No. 220, was issued on fluorescent paper in 1969.

No. 230 with wide margins is from booklet pane No. 230b.

Surcharges of 20, 50 & 60öre on #220, 224 & 224C are listed as Faroe Islands #2-3, 5-6.

See Nos. 318, 333, 382, 416, 437-437A, 493-498, 629, 631, 688-695, 793-795, 883-886, 1111, 1114. For overprints and surcharges see Nos. 257, 263, 267-268, 355-356, Q15-Q17, Q31, Q43.

Certain Tête Bêche pairs of 1938-55 issues which reached the market in 1971, and were not regularly issued, are not listed. This group comprises 24 different major-number vertical pairs of types A32, A47, A61 and SP3 (13 with gutters, 11 without), and pairs of some minor numbers and shades. They were removed from booklet pane sheets.

Type of 1927 Issue
Type I

Type I — Two columns of squares between sail and left frame line.

1933-34 — Engr. — Perf. 13
232	A30	20o gray	12.00	.25
233	A30	25o blue	70.00	25.00
234	A30	25o brown ('34)	25.00	.25
235	A30	30o orange yel	1.10	1.00
236	A30	30o blue ('34)	1.00	.25
237	A30	35o violet	.40	.25
238	A30	40o yellow org	5.00	.25
		Nos. 232-238 (7)	114.50	27.25
		Set, never hinged	275.00	

Type II

Type II — One column of squares between sail and left frame line.

1933-40
238A	A30	15o deep red	2.25	.25
k.		Booklet pane of 4	24.00	
l.		Bklt. pane, 1 #238A, 3 #B8	37.50	
238B	A30	15o yel grn ('40)	7.00	.25
238C	A30	20o gray blk ('39)	4.50	.25
238D	A30	20o red ('40)	.50	.25
238E	A30	25o dp brown ('39)	.50	.25
238F	A30	30o blue ('39)	1.75	.30
238G	A30	30o orange ('40)	.50	.25
238H	A30	35o violet ('40)	.60	.35
238I	A30	40o yel grn ('39)	10.00	.25
238J	A30	40o blue ('40)	1.00	.25
		Nos. 238A-238J (10)	28.60	2.65
		Set, never hinged	55.00	

Nos. 232-238J, engraved, have crosshatched background. Nos. 192-197, typographed, have solid background.

No. 238A surcharged 20 ore is listed as Faroe Islands No. 4.

See note on surcharges and overprints following No. 197.

King Christian X — A33

1934-41 — Perf. 13
239	A33	50o gray	.90	.25
240	A33	60o blue grn	1.75	.25
240A	A33	75o dk blue ('41)	.45	.25
241	A33	1k lt brown	3.00	.25
242	A33	2k dull red	5.75	.80
243	A33	5k violet	7.00	2.75
		Nos. 239-243 (6)	18.85	4.55
		Set, never hinged	60.00	

For overprints see Nos. Q26-Q27.

Nos. 233, 235 Surcharged in Black

1934, June 9
244	A30	4o on 25o blue	.40	.50
245	A30	10o on 30o org yel	1.90	2.75
		Set, never hinged	4.00	

"The Ugly Duckling"
A34

Andersen
A35

"The Little Mermaid" — A36

1935, Oct. 4 — Perf. 13
246	A34	5o lt green	2.50	.25
a.		Tête bêche gutter pair	9.00	9.50
b.		Booklet pane of 4	25.00	
c.		As "a," without gutter, never hinged	20.00	
247	A35	7o dull vio	2.00	2.50
248	A36	10o orange	4.50	.25
a.		Tête bêche gutter pair	12.00	20.00
b.		Booklet pane of 4	45.00	
c.		As "a," without gutter, never hinged	42.50	
249	A35	15o red	9.00	.25
a.		Tête bêche gutter pair	32.50	27.50
b.		Booklet pane of 4	95.00	
c.		As "a," without gutter, never hinged	80.00	
250	A35	20o gray	10.00	1.25
251	A35	30o dl bl	2.50	.35
		Nos. 246-251 (6)	30.50	4.85
		Set, never hinged	85.00	

Centenary of the publication of the earliest installment of Hans Christian Andersen's "Fairy Tales."

Nikolai Church
A37

Hans Tausen
A38

Ribe Cathedral — A39

1936 — Perf. 13
252	A37	5o green	1.10	.25
a.		Booklet pane of 4	21.00	
253	A37	7o violet	1.25	4.00
254	A38	10o lt brown	1.60	.25
a.		Booklet pane of 4	25.00	
255	A38	15o dull rose	2.40	.25
256	A39	30o blue	14.00	1.25
		Nos. 252-256 (5)	20.35	6.00
		Set, never hinged	55.00	

Church Reformation in Denmark, 400th anniv.

No. 229 Overprinted in Blue

1937, Sept. 17
257	A32	10o lt brown	1.40	1.50
		Never hinged	2.00	

Jubilee Exhib. held by the Copenhagen Phil. Club on their 50th anniv. The stamps were on sale at the Exhib. only, each holder of a ticket of admission (1k) being entitled to purchase 20 stamps at face value; of a season ticket (5k), 100 stamps.

Yacht and Summer Palace, Marselisborg
A40

Christian X in Streets of Copenhagen
A41

Equestrian Statue of Frederik V and Amalienborg Palace — A42

1937, May 15 — Perf. 13
258	A40	5o green	1.10	.25
a.		Booklet pane of 4	15.00	
259	A41	10o brown	1.10	.25
a.		Booklet pane of 4	15.00	
260	A42	15o scarlet	1.10	.25
a.		Booklet pane of 4	17.00	
261	A41	30o blue	15.00	2.10
		Nos. 258-261 (4)	18.30	2.85
		Set, never hinged	40.00	

25th anniv. of the accession to the throne of King Christian X.

Emancipation Column, Copenhagen — A43

1938, June 20 — Perf. 13
262	A43	15o scarlet	.50	.25
		Never hinged	1.25	

Abolition of serfdom in Denmark, 150th anniv.

No. 223 Overprinted in Red on Alternate Stamps

1938, Sept. 2
263	A32	5o yellow grn, pair	3.00	8.00
		Never hinged	5.00	

10th Danish Philatelic Exhibition.

Bertel Thorvaldsen
A44

Statue of Jason
A45

1938, Nov. 17 — Engr. — Perf. 13
264	A44	5o rose lake	.35	.25
265	A45	10o purple	.50	.25
266	A44	30o dark blue	1.40	.50
		Nos. 264-266 (3)	2.25	1.00
		Set, never hinged	4.50	

The return to Denmark in 1838 of Bertel Thorvaldsen, Danish sculptor.

Stamps of 1933-39 Surcharged with New Values in Black:

a

b

1940
267 A32 (a) 6o on 7o yel grn   .30 .25
268 A32 (a) 6o on 8o gray   .30 .25
269 A30 (b) 15o on 40o #238   .90 4.00
270 A30 (b) 15o on 40o #238I   .90 .80
271 A30 (c) 20o on 15o dp red   1.10 .25
272 A30 (b) 40o on 30o #238F   .90 .25
Nos. 267-272 (6)   4.40 5.80
Set, never hinged   6.00

Bering's Ship — A46

1941, Nov. 27   Engr.   Perf. 13
277 A46 10o dk violet   .30 .20
278 A46 20o red brown   .60 .25
279 A46 40o dk blue   .35 .30
Nos. 277-279 (3)   1.25 .75
Set, never hinged   2.10

Death of Vitus Bering, explorer, 200th anniv.

King Christian X — A47

1942-46   Unwmk.   Perf. 13
280 A47 10o violet   .25 .20
281 A47 15o yel grn   .35 .20
282 A47 20o red   .35 .20
283 A47 25o brown ('43)   .60 .30
284 A47 30o orange ('43)   .45 .20
285 A47 35o brt red vio ('44)   .40 .20
286 A47 40o blue ('43)   .45 .20
286A A47 45o ol brn ('46)   .35 .20
286B A47 50o gray ('45)   .45 .20
287 A47 60o bluish grn ('44)   .45 .20
287A A47 75o dk blue ('46)   .40 .20
Nos. 280-287A (11)   4.50 2.30
Set, never hinged   8.00

For overprints see Nos. Q28-Q30.

Round Tower — A48   Condor Plane — A49

1942, Nov. 27
288 A48 10o violet   .25 .20
Never hinged   .40

300th anniv. of the Round Tower, Copenhagen.
For surcharge see No. B14.

1943, Oct. 29
289 A49 20o red   .25 .20
Never hinged   .35

25th anniv. of the Danish Aviation Company (Det Danske Luftfartsselskab).

Ejby Church — A50

15ö, Oesterlars Church. 20ö, Hvidbjerg Church.

1944   Engr.   Perf. 13
290 A50 10o violet   .25 .20
291 A50 15o yellow grn   .30 .35
292 A50 20o red   .25 .20
Nos. 290-292 (3)   .80 .75
Set, never hinged   1.00

Ole Roemer A53   Christian X A54

1944, Sept. 25
293 A53 20o henna brown   .30 .20
Never hinged   .65

Birth of Ole Roemer, astronomer, 300th anniv.

1945, Sept. 26
294 A54 10o lilac   .20 .20
295 A54 20o red   .20 .20
296 A54 40o deep blue   .40 .25
Nos. 294-296 (3)   .80 .65
Set, never hinged   1.10

75th birthday of King Christian X.

> **Catalogue values for unused stamps in this section, from this point to the end of the section, are for Never Hinged items.**

Small State Seal — A55   Tycho Brahe — A56

1946-47   Unwmk.   Perf. 13
297 A55 1k brown   .85 .20
298 A55 2k red ('47)   .70 .20
299 A55 5k dull blue   1.25 .20
Nos. 297-299 (3)   2.80 .60

Nos. 297-299 issued on ordinary and fluorescent paper. Values for ordinary paper are much higher.
See Nos. 395-400, 441A-444D, 499-506, 643-650, 716-720A, 804-815, 909. For overprints see Nos. Q35, Q40, Q46-Q48.

1946, Dec. 14   Engr.
300 A56 20o dark red   .40 .20

Birth of Tycho Brahe, astronomer, 400th anniv.

First Danish Locomotive A57   Modern Steam Locomotive A58

Diesel Locomotive A59

1947, June 27
301 A57 15o steel blue   .40 .35
302 A58 20o red   .70 .30
303 A59 40o deep blue   3.00 .75
Nos. 301-303 (3)   4.10 1.40

Inauguration of the Danish State Railways, cent.

Jacobsen A60   Frederik IX A61

1947, Nov. 10   Perf. 13
304 A60 20o dark red   .30 .20

60th anniv. of the death of Jacob Christian Jacobsen, founder of the Glyptothek Art Museum, Copenhagen.

1948-50   Unwmk.   Perf. 13
Three types among 15ö, 20ö, 30ö:
I — Background of horizontal lines. No outline at left for cheek and ear. King's uniform textured in strong lines.
II — Background of vertical and horizontal lines. Contour of cheek and ear at left. Uniform same.
III — Background and facial contour lines as in II. Uniform lines double and thinner.

306 A61 15(o) green (II)   2.25 .20
a. Type III ('49)   1.60 .20
307 A61 20(o) dk red (I)   .85 .20
a. Type III ('49)   1.00 .20
308 A61 25(o) lt brown   1.25 .20
309 A61 30(o) org (II)   13.00 .20
a. Type III ('50)   16.00 .20
310 A61 40(o) dl blue ('49)   4.50 .50
311 A61 45(o) olive ('50)   1.75 .20
312 A61 50(o) gray ('49)   1.75 .20
313 A61 60(o) grnsh bl ('50)   2.50 .20
314 A61 75(o) lil rose ('50)   1.40 .20
Nos. 306-314 (9)   29.25 2.10

See Nos. 319-326, 334-341, 354, For surcharges see Nos. 357-358, 370, B20, B24-B25, Q32-Q34, Q36-Q39.

Legislative Assembly, 1849 — A62

Symbol of UPU — A63

1949, June 5
315 A62 20o red brown   .30 .20

Adoption of the Danish constitution, cent.

1949, Oct. 9
316 A63 40o dull blue   .65 .40

75th anniv. of the UPU.

Kalundborg Radio Station and Masts — A64

1950, Apr. 1   Engr.   Perf. 13
317 A64 20o brown red   .40 .20

Radio broadcasting in Denmark, 25th anniv.

Types of 1933-50

1950-51   Unwmk.   Perf. 13
318 A32 10o green   .30 .20
319 A61 15(o) lilac   .75 .20
b. 15(o) gray lilac   3.75 .25
320 A61 20(o) lt brown   .55 .20
321 A61 25(o) dark red   3.75 .20
322 A61 35(o) gray grn ('51)   .75 .20
323 A61 40(o) gray   .85 .20
324 A61 50(o) dark blue   3.00 .20
325 A61 55(o) brown ('51)   24.00 2.00
326 A61 70(o) deep green   2.75 .20
Nos. 318-326 (9)   36.70 3.60

Warship of 1701 — A65   Oersted — A66

1951, Feb. 26   Engr.   Perf. 13
327 A65 25o dark red   .50 .25
328 A65 50o deep blue   3.00 .75

250th anniv. of the foundation of the Naval Officers' College.

1951, Mar. 9   Unwmk.
329 A66 50o blue   1.40 .60

Cent. of the death of Hans Christian Oersted, physicist.

Post Chaise ("Ball Post") — A67   Marine Rescue — A68

1951, Apr. 1   Perf. 13
330 A67 15o purple   .60 .25
331 A67 25o henna brown   .60 .25

Cent. of Denmark's 1st postage stamp.

1952, Mar. 26
332 A68 25o red brown   .45 .30

Cent. of the foundation of the Danish Lifesaving Service.

Types of 1933-50

1952-53   Perf. 13
333 A32 12o lt yel grn   .30 .20
334 A61 25(o) lt blue   1.00 .20
335 A61 30(o) brown red   .55 .20
336 A61 50(o) aqua ('53)   .55 .20
337 A61 60(o) dp blue ('53)   .75 .20
338 A61 65(o) gray ('53)   .55 .20
339 A61 80(o) orange ('53)   .85 .20
340 A61 90(o) olive ('53)   3.00 .20
341 A61 95(o) red org ('53)   1.00 .25
Nos. 333-341 (9)   8.55 1.85

Jelling Runic Stone — A69

Designs: 15o, Vikings' camp, Trelleborg. 20o, Church of Kalundborg. 30o, Nyborg castle. 60o, Goose tower, Vordinborg.

1953-56   Perf. 13
342 A69 10o dp green   .20 .20
343 A69 15o lt rose vio   .20 .20
344 A69 20o brown   .20 .20
345 A69 30o red ('54)   .25 .20
346 A69 60o dp blue ('54)   .40 .20

Designs: 10o, Manor house, Spottrup. 15o, Hammershus castle ruins. 20o, Copenhagen stock exchange. 30o, Statue of Frederik V, Amalienborg. 60o, Soldier statue at Fredericia.

347 A69 10o green ('54)   .20 .20
348 A69 15o lilac ('55)   .20 .20
349 A69 20o brown ('55)   .20 .20
350 A69 30o red ('55)   .25 .20
351 A69 60o deep blue ('56)   .50 .20
Nos. 342-351 (10)   2.60 2.00

1000th anniv. of the Kingdom of Denmark. Each stamp represents a different century.

Telegraph
Equipment of 1854
A70

Frederik V
A71

1954, Feb. 2   *Perf. 13*
352 A70 30o red brown   .40 .25

Cent. of the telegraph in Denmark.

1954, Mar. 31
353 A71 30o dark red   .55 .30

200th anniv. of the founding of the Royal
Academy of Fine Arts.

Type of 1948-50
1955, Apr. 27
354 A61 25o lilac   .35 .20

Nos. 224C and 226A Surcharged with
New Value in Black. Nos. 307 and 321
Surcharged with New Value and 4
Bars

1955-56
355 A32   5o on 6o org   .25 .20
356 A32   5o on 7o lt brn   .25 .20
357 A61 30(o) on 20(o) dk
     red (I)   .30 .20
  a.   Type III   .35 .20
  b.   Double surcharge   1,050. 1,050.
  c.   Inverted surcharge   650.00
358 A61 30(o) on 25(o) dk
     red ('56)   .60 .20
  a.   Double surcharge   1,050.
     Nos. 355-358 (4)   1.40 .80

A72

A73

1955, Nov. 11   Unwmk.
359 A72 30o dark red   .30 .20

100th anniv. of the death of Sören Kierke-
gaard, philosopher and theologian.

1956, Sept. 12   Engr.
360 A73 30o Ellehammer's plane   .50 .20

50th anniv. of the 1st flight made by Jacob
Christian Hansen Ellehammer in a heavier-
than-air craft.

Northern Countries Issue

Whooper
Swans — A74

1956, Oct. 30   *Perf. 13*
361 A74 30o rose red   1.60 .60
362 A74 60o ultramarine   1.40 .65

Issued to emphasize the close bonds
among the northern countries: Denmark, Finland, Iceland, Norway and Sweden.

Prince's Palace
A75

Harvester
A76

Design: 60ö, Sun God's Chariot.

1957, May 15   Unwmk.
363 A75 30o dull red   .85 .20
364 A75 60o dark blue   .85 .45

150th anniv. of the National Museum.

1958, Sept. 4   Engr.   *Perf. 13*
365 A76 30o fawn   .30 .20

Centenary of the Royal Veterinary and Agricultural College.

Frederik IX
A77

Ballet Dancer
A78

1959, Mar. 11
366 A77 30o rose red   .40 .20
367 A77 35o rose lilac   .40 .35
368 A77 60o ultra   .40 .20
     Nos. 366-368 (3)   1.20 .75

King Frederik's 60th birthday.

1959, May 16
369 A78 35o rose lilac   .30 .20

Danish Ballet and Music Festival, May 17-
31. See Nos. 401, 422.

No. 319 Surcharged

1960, Apr. 7
370 A61 30o on 15o lilac   .30 .20

World Refugee Year, 7/1/59-6/30/60.

Seeder
and Farm
A79

30ö, Harvester combine. 60ö, Plow.

1960, Apr. 28   Engr.   *Perf. 13*
371 A79 12o green   .20 .20
372 A79 30o dull red   .30 .20
373 A79 60o dk blue   .50 .20
     Nos. 371-373 (3)   1.00 .60

King Frederik IX
and Queen
Ingrid — A80

1960, May 24   Unwmk.
374 A80 30o dull red   .45 .20
375 A80 60o blue   .45 .20

25th anniversary of the marriage of King
Frederik IX and Queen Ingrid.

Bascule
Light — A81

Finsen — A82

1960, June 8   Engr.
376 A81 30o dull red   .30 .20

400th anniv. of the Lighthouse Service.

1960, Aug. 1   *Perf. 13*
377 A82 30o dark red   .30 .20

Centenary of the birth of Dr. Niels R. Finsen, physician and scientist.

Nursing
Mother — A83

DC-8 Airliner — A84

1960, Aug. 16   Unwmk.
378 A83 60o ultra   .55 .20

10th meeting of the regional committee for
Europe of WHO, Copenhagen, Aug. 16-20.

Europa Issue, 1960
Common Design Type

1960, Sept. 19   *Perf. 13*
Size: 28x21mm
379 CD3 60o ultra   .55 .45

1961, Feb. 24
380 A84 60o ultra   .70 .50

10th anniv. of the Scandinavian Airlines
System, SAS.

Landscape
A85

Frederik IX
A86

1961, Apr. 21   *Perf. 13*
381 A85 30o copper brown   .30 .20

Denmark's Soc. of Nature Lovers, 50th
anniv.

Fluorescent Paper
as well as ordinary paper, was used
in printing many definitive and commemorative stamps, starting in 1962.
These include No. 220, 224; the 15, 20,
25, 30, 35 (Nos. 386 and 387), 50 and
60ö, 1.20k, 1.50k and 25k definitives of
following set, and Nos. 297-299, 318,
333, 380, 401-427, 429-435, 438-439,
493, 543, 548, B30.

Only fluorescent paper was used for
Nos. 436-437, 437A and 440 onward; in
semipostals from B31 onward.

1961-63   Engr.   *Perf. 13*
382 A32 15o green ('63)   .20 .20
383 A86 20o brown   .50 .20
384 A86 25o brown ('63)   .25 .20
385 A86 30o rose red   .65 .20
386 A86 35o olive grn   .65 .50
387 A86 35o rose red ('63)   .25 .20
388 A86 40o gray   1.00 .20
389 A86 50o aqua   .65 .20
390 A86 60o ultra   .85 .20
391 A86 70o green   1.60 .20
392 A86 80o red orange   1.60 .20
393 A86 90o olive bister   4.25 .20
394 A86 95o claret ('63)   1.00 .70
     Nos. 382-394 (13)   13.45 3.40

See Nos. 417-419, 438-441. For overprints
see Nos. Q41-Q42, Q44-Q45.

State Seal Type of 1946-47

1962-65
395 A55 1.10k lilac ('65)   4.25 1.40
396 A55 1.20k gray   3.75 .20
397 A55 1.25k orange   3.75 .20
398 A55 1.30k green ('65)   4.25 1.40
399 A55 1.50k red lilac   1.25 .20
400 A55 25k yellow grn   8.00 .30
     Nos. 395-400 (6)   25.25 3.70

Dancer Type of 1959 Inscribed "15-31 MAJ"

1962, Apr. 26
401 A78 60o ultra   .30 .20

Issued to publicize the Danish Ballet and
Music Festival, May 15-31.

Old Mill — A87

M.S.
Selandia — A88

1962, May 10   Unwmk.   *Perf. 13*
402 A87 10o red brown   .30 .20

Cent. of the abolition of mill monopolies.

1962, June 14   Engr.
403 A88 60o dark blue   1.60 1.40

M.S. Selandia, the 1st Diesel ship, 50th
anniv.

Violin
Scroll,
Leaves,
Lights and
Balloon
A89

1962, Aug. 31
404 A89 35o rose violet   .30 .20

150th anniv. of the birth of Georg Carsten-
sen, founder of Tivoli amusement park,
Copenhagen.

Cliffs on Moen
Island — A90

Germinating
Wheat — A91

1962, Nov. 22
405 A90 20o pale brown   .30 .20

Issued to publicize preservation of natural
treasures and landmarks.

1963, Mar. 21   Engr.
406 A91 35o fawn   .30 .20

FAO "Freedom from Hunger" campaign.

Railroad Wheel,
Tire Tracks,
Waves and
Swallow — A92

Sailing Vessel, Coach, Postilions and Globe — A93

1963, May 14   Unwmk.   Perf. 13
407 A92 15o green   .30 .20
Inauguration of the "Bird Flight Line" railroad link between Denmark and Germany.

1963, May 27
408 A93 60o dark blue   .45 .20
Cent. of the 1st Intl. Postal Conf., Paris, 1863.

Niels Bohr and Atom Diagram — A94

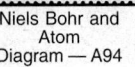
Early Public School Drawn on Slate — A95

1963, Nov. 21   Engr.
409 A94 35o red brown   .35 .20
410 A94 60o dark blue   .65 .20
50th anniv. of Prof. Niels Bohr's (1885-1962) atom theory.

1964, June 19   Unwmk.   Perf. 13
411 A95 35o red brown   .30 .20
150th anniversary of the royal decrees for the public school system.

Fish and Chart — A96

Danish Watermarks and Perforations A97

1964, Sept. 7   Engr.
412 A96 60o violet blue   .35 .20
Conference of the International Council for the Exploration of the Sea, Copenhagen.

1964, Oct. 10   Perf. 13
413 A97 35o pink   .30 .20
25th anniv. of Stamp Day and to publicize the Odense Stamp Exhibition, Oct. 10-11.

Landscape A98

Calculator, Ledger and Inkwell — A99

1964, Nov. 12   Engr.
414 A98 25o brown   .30 .20
Issued to publicize preservation of natural treasures and landmarks.

1965, Mar. 8   Unwmk.
415 A99 15o light olive green   .20 .20
First Business School in Denmark, cent.

Types of 1933 and 1961
1965, May 15   Engr.   Perf. 13
416 A32 25o apple green   .35 .20
417 A86 40o brown   .35 .20
418 A86 50o rose red   .40 .20
419 A86 80o ultra   .95 .20
Nos. 416-419 (4)   2.05 .80
For overprints see Nos. Q41-Q42.

ITU Emblem, Telegraph Key, Teletype Paper A100

Carl Nielsen (1865-1931), Composer A101

1965, May 17
420 A100 80o dark blue   .40 .20
Cent. of the ITU.

1965, June 9   Engr.
421 A101 50o brown red   .35 .20

Dancer Type of 1959 Inscribed "15-31 MAJ"
1965, Sept. 23
422 A78 50o rose red   .30 .20
Issued to publicize the Danish Ballet and Music Festival, May 15-31.

Bogo Windmill A102

Mylius Dalgas Surveying Wasteland A103

1965, Nov. 10   Engr.   Perf. 13
423 A102 40o brown   .30 .20
Issued to publicize the preservation of natural treasures and landmarks.

1966, Feb. 24
424 A103 25o olive green   .30 .20
Cent. of the Danish Heath Soc. (reclamation of wastelands), founded by Enrico Mylius Dalgas.

Christen Kold (1816-70), Educator — A104

1966, Mar. 29   Perf. 13
425 A104 50o dull red   .30 .20

Poorhouse, Copenhagen A105

Holte Allée, Bregentved A106

Dolmen (Grave) in Jutland — A107

1966   Unwmk.
426 A105 50o dull red   .25 .20
427 A106 80o dk blue   .55 .20
428 A107 1.50k dk slate grn   .80 .20
Nos. 426-428 (3)   1.60 .60
Publicizing preservation of national treasures and ancient monuments. Issued: 50o, May 12; 80o, June 16; 1.50k, Nov. 24.

George Jensen by Ejnar Nielsen A108

Music Bar and Instruments A109

1966, Aug. 31   Engr.   Perf. 13
429 A108 80o dark blue   .85 .30
George Jensen, silversmith, birth cent.

1967, Jan. 9
430 A109 50o dark red   .50 .20
Royal Danish Academy of Music, cent.

Cogwheels, and Broken Customs Duty Ribbon — A110

1967, Mar. 2
431 A110 80o dark blue   .80 .20
European Free Trade Association. Industrial tariffs were abolished Dec. 31, 1966, among EFTA members: Austria, Denmark, Finland, Great Britain, Norway, Portugal, Sweden and Switzerland.

Windmill and Medieval Fortress — A111

Designs: 40ö, Ship's rigging and baroque house front. 50ö, Old Town Hall. 80ö, New building construction.

1967   Engr.   Perf. 13
432 A111 25o green   .40 .20
433 A111 40o sepia   .35 .20
434 A111 50o red brown   .35 .20
435 A111 80o dk blue   .90 .30
Nos. 432-435 (4)   2.00 .90
The 800th anniversary of Copenhagen. Issued: #432-433, 4/6; #434-435, 5/11.

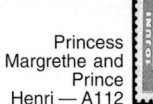
Princess Margrethe and Prince Henri — A112

1967, June 10
436 A112 50o red   .30 .20
Marriage of Crown Princess Margrethe and Prince Henri de Monpezat.

Types of 1933-1961
			Perf. 13	
1967-71		**Engr.**		
437	A32	30o dk green	.35	.25
437A	A32	40o orange ('71)	.35	.25
438	A86	50o brown	.60	.25
439	A86	60o rose red	.60	.25
440	A86	80o green	.60	.25
441	A86	90o ultra	.60	.25
441A	A55	1.20k Prus grn ('71)	1.75	.30
442	A55	2.20k orange	2.50	.25
443	A55	2.80k gray	2.50	.25
444	A55	2.90k rose vio	4.25	.25
444A	A55	3k dk sl grn ('69)	.95	.25
444B	A55	3.10k plum ('70)	7.75	.25

444C	A55	4k gray ('69)	1.40	.25
444D	A55	4.10k olive ('70)	7.75	.25
		Nos. 437-444D (14)	31.95	3.55

Issued: #437-441, 6/30/67; #442-443, 7/8/67; #444, 4/29/68; #444A, 444C, 8/28/69; #444B, 444D, 8/27/70; #437A, 441A, 6/24/71.
For overprints see Nos. Q44-Q45.

Sonne — A113

Cross-anchor and Porpoise — A114

1967, Sept. 21
445 A113 60o red   .30 .20
150th anniv. of the birth of Hans Christian Sonne, pioneer of the cooperative movement in Denmark.

1967, Nov. 9   Engr.   Perf. 13
446 A114 90o dk blue   .35 .25
Centenary of the Danish Seamen's Church in Foreign Ports.

Esbjerg Harbor — A115

Koldinghus A116

1968, Apr. 24
447 A115 30o dk yellow grn   .30 .20
Centenary of Esbjerg Harbor.

1968, June 13
448 A116 60o copper red   .35 .20
700th anniversary of Koldinghus Castle.

Shipbuilding Industry A117

Sower A118

Designs: 50o, Chemical industry. 60o, Electric power. 90o, Engineering.

1968, Oct. 24   Engr.   Perf. 13
449 A117 30o green   .25 .20
450 A117 50o brown   .25 .20
451 A117 60o red brown   .25 .20
452 A117 90o dark blue   .60 .30
Nos. 449-452 (4)   1.35 .90
Issued to publicize Danish industries.

1969, Jan. 29
453 A118 30o gray green   .30 .20
Royal Agricultural Soc. of Denmark, 200th anniv.

Five Ancient Ships A119

Frederik IX A120

Nordic Cooperation Issue
1969, Feb. 28   Engr.   Perf. 13
454 A119 60o brown red   .80 .20
455 A119 90o blue   1.25 .70

50th anniv. of the Nordic Soc. and cent. of postal cooperation among the northern countries: Denmark, Finland, Iceland, Norway and Sweden. The design is taken from a coin found at the site of Birka, an ancient Swedish town.

1969, Mar. 11
456 A120 50o sepia   .30 .20
457 A120 60o dull red   .30 .20

70th birthday of King Frederik IX.

Common Design Types pictured following the introduction.

Europa Issue, 1969
Common Design Type
1969, Apr. 28
Size: 28x20mm
458 CD12 90o chalky blue   .70 .55

Kronborg Castle — A121

Danish Flag — A122

1969, May 22   Engr.   Perf. 13
459 A121 50o brown   .30 .20

Association of Danes living abroad, 50th anniv.

1969, June 12
460 A122 60o bluish blk, red & gray .30 .20

750th anniversary of the fall of the Dannebrog (Danish flag) from heaven.

Nexo A123

Stensen A124

1969, Aug. 28
461 A123 80o deep green   .35 .20

Centenary of the birth of Martin Andersen Nexo (1869-1954), novelist.

1969, Sept. 25
462 A124 1k deep brown   .40 .20

300th anniv. of the publication of Niels Stensen's geological work "On Solid Bodies."

Abstract Design — A125

Symbolic Design — A126

1969, Nov. 10   Engr.   Perf. 13
463 A125 60o rose, red & ultra   .30 .20

1969, Nov. 20
464 A126 30o olive green   .30 .20

Valdemar Poulsen (1869-1942), electrical engineer and inventor.

Post Office Bank — A127

School Safety Patrol — A128

1970, Jan. 15   Engr.   Perf. 13
465 A127 60o dk red & org   .30 .20

50th anniv. of post office banking service.

1970, Feb. 19
466 A128 50o brown   .30 .20

Issued to publicize road safety.

Candle in Window A129   Deer A130

1970, May 4   Engr.   Perf. 13
467 A129 50o slate, dull bl & yel   .30 .20

25th anniv. of liberation from the Germans.

1970, May 28
468 A130 60o yel grn, red & brn   .30 .20

Tercentenary of Jaegersborg Deer Park.

Elephant Figurehead, 1741 A131

"The Homecoming" by Povl Christensen A132

1970, June 15   Perf. 11½
469 A131 30o multicolored   .30 .20

Royal Naval Museum, tercentenary.

1970, June 15   Perf. 13
470 A132 60o org, dl vio & ol grn   .30 .20

Union of North Schleswig and Denmark, 50th anniv.

Electromagnet A133

1970, Aug. 13   Engr.
471 A133 80o gray green   .35 .20

150th anniversary of Hans Christian Oersted's discovery of electromagnetism.

Bronze Age Ship A134

Ships: 50o, Viking shipbuilding, from Bayeux tapestry. 60o, Thuroe schooner with topgallant. 90o, Tanker.

1970, Sept. 24
472 A134 30o ocher & brown   .30 .20
473 A134 50o brn red & rose brn   .30 .20
474 A134 60o gray ol & red brn   .55 .20
475 A134 90o blue grn & ultra   .85 .60
Nos. 472-475 (4)   2.00 1.20

UN Emblem A135

1970, Oct. 22   Engr.   Perf. 13
476 A135 90o blue, grn & red   1.00 .75

25th anniversary of the United Nations.

Bertel Thorvaldsen A136

Mathide Fibiger A137

1970, Nov. 19
477 A136 2k slate blue   .70 .20

Bicentenary of the birth of Bertel Thorvaldsen (1768-1844), sculptor.

1971, Feb. 25
478 A137 80o olive green   .30 .20

Danish Women's Association centenary.

Refugees A138

Hans Egede A139

1971, Mar. 26   Engr.   Perf. 13
479 A138 50o brown   .25 .20
480 A138 60o brown red   .35 .20

Joint northern campaign for the benefit of refugees.

1971, May 27
481 A139 1k brown   .40 .20

250th anniversary of arrival of Hans Egede in Greenland and beginning of its colonization.

A140

A141

1971, Oct. 14
482 A140 30o Swimming   .25 .20
483 A140 50o Gymnastics   .40 .20
484 A140 60o Soccer   .55 .20
485 A140 90o Sailing   .80 .45
Nos. 482-485 (4)   2.00 1.05

1971, Nov. 11   Engr.   Perf. 13
486 A141 90o dark blue   .40 .20

Centenary of first lectures given by Georg Brandes (1842-1927), writer and literary critic.

A142

A143

1972, Jan. 27
487 A142 80o slate green   .40 .20

Centenary of Danish sugar production.

1972, Mar. 11   Engr.   Perf. 13
488 A143 60o red brown   .30 .20

Frederik IX (1899-1972).

Abstract Design A144

1972, Mar. 11
489 A144 1.20k brt rose lil, bl gray & brn   .60 .50

Danish Meteorological Institute, cent.

Nikolai F. S. Grundtvig A145

Locomotive, 1847, Ferry, Travelers A146

1972, May 4   Engr.   Perf. 13
490 A145 1k sepia   .50 .20

Nikolai Frederik Severin Grundtvig (1783-1872), theologian and poet.

1972, June 26
491 A146 70o rose red   .35 .20

125th anniversary of Danish State Railways.

Rebild Hills A147   "Tinker Turned Politician" A148

1972, June 26
492 A147 1k bl, sl grn & mar   .40 .20

Types of 1933-46
1972-78   Engr.   Perf. 13
493 A32 20o slate bl ('74)   .35 .20
494 A32 50o sepia ('74)   .35 .20
 a. Bklt. pane of 12 (4 #318, 4
  #493, 4 #494) ('85)   3.50
495 A32 60o apple grn ('76)   1.75 .55
496 A32 60o gray ('78)   .70 .60
497 A32 70o red   .90 .20
498 A32 70o apple grn ('77)   .35 .20
499 A55 2.50k orange   1.75 .20
500 A55 2.80k olive ('75)   1.25 .80
501 A55 3.50k lilac   2.00 .20
502 A55 4.5k olive   5.00 .20
503 A55 6k vio blk ('76)   1.75 .20
504 A55 7k red lilac ('78)   2.25 .20

505	A55	9k brown ol ('77)	3.25	.20
506	A55	10k lemon ('76)	3.00	.20
		Nos. 493-506 (14)	24.65	4.15

1972, Sept. 14
507 A148 70o dark red   .35 .20
250th anniv. of the comedies of Ludvig Holberg (1684-1754) on the Danish stage.

WHO Building, Copenhagen — A149

1972, Sept. 14
508 A149 2k bl, blk & lt red brn   .70 .35
Opening of WHO Building, Copenhagen.

Bridge Across Little Belt A150	Aeroskobing House c. 1740 A151

Highway engineering (Diagrams): 60o, Hanstholm Harbor. 70o, Lim Fjord Tunnel. 90o, Knudshoved Harbor.

1972, Oct. 19   **Engr.**   **Perf. 13**
509	A150	40o dk green	.20	.20
510	A150	60o dk brown	.30	.20
511	A150	70o dk red	.30	.20
512	A150	90o dk blue grn	.40	.20
		Nos. 509-512 (4)	1.20	.80

1972, Nov. 23
Danish Architecture: 60o, East Bornholm farmhouse, 17th century, horiz. 70o, House, Christianshavn, c. 1710. 1.20k, Hvide Sande Farmhouse, c. 1810, horiz.

Size: 20x28mm, 27x20mm
513	A151	40o red, brn & blk	.35	.25
514	A151	60o blk, vio bl & grn	.35	.25

Size: 18x37mm, 36x20mm
515	A151	70o red, dk red & blk	.45	.20
516	A151	1.20k dk brn, red & grn	.60	.55
		Nos. 513-516 (4)	1.75	1.25

Jensen A152	Guard Rails, Cogwheels A153

1973, Feb. 22   **Engr.**   **Perf. 13**
517 A152 90o green   .40 .20
Centenary of the birth of Johannes Vilhelm Jensen (1873-1950), lyric poet and novelist.

1973, Mar. 22
518 A153 50o sepia   .30 .20
Centenary of first Danish Factory Act for labor protection.

Abildgaard A154	Rhododendron A155

1973, Mar. 22
519 A154 1k dull blue   .60 .60
Bicentenary of Royal Veterinary College, Christianshaven, founded by Prof. P. C. Abildgaard.

1973, Apr. 26
Design: 70o, Dronningen of Denmark rose.
520	A155	60o brn, grn & vio	.50	.25
521	A155	70o dk red, rose & grn	.50	.25

Centenary of the founding of the Horticultural Society of Denmark.

Nordic Cooperation Issue 1973

Nordic House, Reykjavik A156

1973, June 26   **Engr.**   **Perf. 13**
522	A156	70o multicolored	.50	.20
523	A156	1k multicolored	1.50	1.00

A century of postal cooperation among Denmark, Finland, Iceland, Norway and Sweden, and in connection with the Nordic Postal Conference, Reykjavik.

Sextant, Stella Nova, Cassiopeia A157	St. Mark, from 11th Cent. Book of Dalby A158

1973, Oct. 18   **Engr.**   **Perf. 13**
524 A157 2k dark blue   .70 .20
400th anniversary of the publication of "De Nova Stella," by Tycho Brahe.

1973, Oct. 18   **Photo.**   **Perf. 14x14½**
525 A158 120o buff & multi   1.00 .65
300th anniversary of Royal Library.

Devil and Gossips, Fanefjord Church, 1480 — A159

Frescoes: No. 527, Queen Esther and King Ahasuerus, Tirsted Church, c.1400. No. 528, Miraculous Harvest, Jetsmark Church, c.1474. No. 529, Jesus carrying cross, and wearing crown of thorns, Biersted Church, c.1400. No. 530, Creation of Eve, Fanefjord Church, c.1480.

1973, Nov. 28   **Engr.**   **Perf. 13**
Cream Paper
526	A159	70o dk red, yel & grn	1.25	.30
527	A159	70o dk red, yel & grn	1.25	.30
528	A159	70o dk red, yel & grn	1.25	.30
529	A159	70o dk red, yel & grn	1.25	.30
530	A159	70o dk red, yel & grn	1.25	.30
a.		Bklt. pane, 2 each #526-530	35.00	
b.		Strip of 5, #526-530	6.25	

Blood Donors A160	Queen Margrethe A161

1974, Jan. 24
531 A160 90o purple & red   .50 .20
"Blood Saves Lives."

1974-81   **Engr.**   **Perf. 13**
532	A161	60o brown	.50	.30
533	A161	60o orange	.45	.20
534	A161	70o red	.45	.20
535	A161	70o dk brown	.45	.20
536	A161	80o green	.50	.20
537	A161	80o dp brn ('76)	.45	.20
538	A161	90o red lilac	.50	.20
539	A161	90o dull red	.45	.20
540	A161	90o slate grn ('76)	.50	.20
541	A161	100o dp ultra	.50	.20
542	A161	100o gray ('75)	.50	.20
543	A161	100o red ('76)	.50	.20
544	A161	100o brown ('77)	.50	.20
a.		Bklt. pane of 5 (#544, #494, 2 #493, #318)	1.75	
545	A161	110o orange ('78)	.55	.20
546	A161	120o slate	.65	.40
547	A161	120o red ('77)	.50	.20
548	A161	130o ultra ('75)	1.25	.95
549	A161	150o vio bl ('78)	.65	.65
550	A161	180o slate grn ('77)	.50	.30
551	A161	200o blue ('81)	.85	.85
		Nos. 532-551 (20)	11.20	6.25

See #630, 632-642. For overprint see #Q49.

Pantomime Theater — A162

Hverringe A163

1974, May 16
552 A162 100o indigo   .45 .20
Cent. of the Pantomime Theater, Tivoli.

1974, June 20   **Engr.**   **Perf. 13**
Views: 60o, Norre Lyndelse, Carl Nielsen's childhood home. 70o, Odense, Hans Chr. Andersen's childhood home. 90o, Hesselagergaard, vert. 120o, Hindsholm.
553	A163	50o brown & multi	.45	.20
554	A163	60o sl grn & multi	.40	.25
555	A163	70o red brn & multi	.40	.25
556	A163	90o dk green & mar	.55	.20
557	A163	120o red org & dk grn	.70	.45
		Nos. 553-557 (5)	2.50	1.35

Emblem, Runner with Map — A164	Iris — A165

1974, Aug. 22   **Engr.**   **Perf. 13**
558	A164	70o shown	.45	.30
559	A164	80o Compass	.45	.20

World Orienteering Championships 1974.

1974, Sept. 19
560	A165	90o shown	.45	.20
561	A165	120o Purple orchid	.65	.30

Copenhagen Botanical Garden centenary.

Mailman, 1624, and Postilion, 1780 — A166

Carrier Pigeon — A167

Design: 90o, Balloon and sailing ships.

1974, Oct. 9   **Engr.**   **Perf. 13**
562	A166	70o lemon & dk brn	.30	.35
563	A166	90o dull grn & sepia	.45	.20
564	A167	120o dark blue	.55	.30
		Nos. 562-564 (3)	1.25	.85

350th anniv. of Danish PO (70o, 90o) and cent. of UPU (120o).

Souvenir Sheet

Ferslew's Essays, 1849 and 1852 — A168

Engraved and Photogravure
1975, Feb. 27   **Perf. 13**
565	A168	Sheet of 4	7.25	8.50
a.		70o Coat of arms	1.75	2.00
b.		80o King Frederik VII	1.75	2.00
c.		90o King Frederik VII	1.75	2.00
d.		100o Mercury	1.75	2.00

HAFNIA 76 Intl. Stamp Exhib., Copenhagen, Aug. 20-29, 1976. Sold for 5k. See No. 585.

Early Radio Equipment A169	Flora Danica Plate A170

1975, Mar. 20   **Engr.**   **Perf. 13**
566 A169 90o dull red   .40 .20
Danish broadcasting, 50th anniversary.

1975, May 22
Danish China: 90o, Flora Danica tureen. 130o, Vase and tea caddy, blue fluted china.
567	A170	50o slate grn	.30	.20
568	A170	90o brown red	.60	.20
569	A170	130o violet bl	.90	.90
		Nos. 567-569 (3)	1.80	1.30

Church of Moravian Brethren, Christiansfeld A171

120o, Kongsgaard farmhouse, Lejre. 150o, Anna Queensstraede, Helsingor, vert.

1975, June 19

570	A171	70o sepia	.30	.25
571	A171	120o olive green	1.10	.30
572	A171	150o violet black	.50	.20
		Nos. 570-572 (3)	1.90	.75

European Architectural Heritage Year 1975.

Andersen
A172

Watchman's Square, Abenra
A173

Designs: 70o, Numbskull Jack, drawing by Vilh. Pedersen. 130o, The Marshking's Daughter, drawing by L. Frohlich.

1975, Aug. 28　　Engr.　　Perf. 13

573	A172	70o brown & blk	.60	.55
574	A172	90o brn red & dk brn	1.10	.30
575	A172	130o blue blk & sepia	1.40	1.40
		Nos. 573-575 (3)	3.10	2.25

Hans Christian Andersen (1805-75), writer.

1975, Sept. 25

Designs: 90o, Haderslev Cathedral, vert. 100o, Mögeltönder Polder. 120o, Mouth of Vidaaen at Höjer Floodgates.

576	A173	70o multicolored	.30	.25
577	A173	90o multicolored	.40	.20
578	A173	100o multicolored	.40	.20
579	A173	120o multicolored	.65	.35
		Nos. 576-579 (4)	1.75	1.05

European Kingfisher
A174

1975, Oct. 23　　Engr.　　Perf. 13

580	A174	50o shown	.45	.25
581	A174	70o Hedgehog	.45	.25
582	A174	90o Cats	.45	.20
583	A174	130o Avocets	.85	.75
584	A174	200o Otter	.70	.20
		Nos. 580-584 (5)	2.90	1.65

Protected animals, and for the centenary of the Danish Society for the Prevention of Cruelty to Animals (90ö).

HAFNIA Type of 1974
Souvenir Sheet

1975, Nov. 20　　Engr. & Photo.

585	A168	Sheet of 4	4.50	6.00
a.		50o buff & brown, No. 2	1.10	1.40
b.		70o buff, brown & blue, No. 1	1.10	1.40
c.		90o buff, blue & brown, No. 11	1.10	1.40
d.		130o olive, brown & buff, No. 19	1.10	1.40

HAFNIA 76 Intl. Stamp Exhib., Copenhagen, Aug. 20-29, 1976. Sold for 5k.

Copenhagen, Center — A175

View from Round Tower — A176

Copenhagen, Views: 100o, Central Station, interior. 130o, Harbor.

1976, Mar. 25　　Engr.　　Perf. 12½

586	A175	60o multicolored	.50	.20
587	A176	80o multicolored	.50	.20
588	A176	100o multicolored	.30	.20
589	A175	130o multicolored	1.50	1.50
		Nos. 586-589 (4)	2.80	2.10

Postilion, by Otto Bache
A177

Emil Chr. Hansen, Physiologist, in Laboratory
A178

1976, June 17　　Engr.　　Perf. 12½

590	A177	130o multicolored	1.25	1.25

Souvenir Sheet

591	A177	130o multicolored	9.25	10.50

HAFNIA 76 Intl. Stamp Exhib., Copenhagen, Aug. 20-29. No. 591 contains one stamp similar to No. 590 with design continuous into sheet margin. Sheet shows painting "A String of Horses Outside an Inn" of which No. 590 shows a detail. Sheet sold for 15k including exhibition ticket.

1976, Sept. 23　　Engr.　　Perf. 13

592	A178	100o orange red	.40	.20

Carlsberg Foundation (art and science), centenary.

Glass Blower Molding Glass — A179

Five Water Lilies — A180

Danish Glass Production: 80o, Finished glass removed from pipe. 130o, Glass cut off from foot. 150o, Glass blown up in mold.

1976, Nov. 18　　Engr.　　Perf. 13

593	A179	60o slate	.30	.25
594	A179	80o dk brown	.35	.25
595	A179	130o dk blue	1.00	.90
596	A179	150o red brown	.70	.25
		Nos. 593-596 (4)	2.35	1.65

Photogravure and Engraved
1977, Feb. 2　　　　Perf. 12½

597	A180	100o brt green & multi	.50	.30
598	A180	130o ultra & multi	1.50	1.40

Nordic countries cooperation for protection of the environment and 25th Session of Nordic Council, Helsinki, Feb. 19.

Road Accident — A181

Europa — A182

1977, Mar. 24　　Engr.　　Perf. 12½

599	A181	100o brown red	.40	.20

Road Safety Traffic Act, May 1, 1977.

1977, May 2　　Engr.　　Perf. 12½

600	A182	1k Allinge	.50	.45
601	A182	1.30k View, Ringsted	2.25	2.25

Kongeaen
A183

Hammers and Horseshoes
A184

Landscapes, Southern Jutland: 90o, Skallingen. 150o, Torskind. 200o, Jelling.

1977, June 30　　Engr.　　Perf. 12½

602	A183	60o multicolored	1.00	.90
603	A183	90o multicolored	.50	.30
604	A183	150o multicolored	.60	.35
605	A183	200o multicolored	.75	.25
		Nos. 602-605 (4)	2.85	1.80

See Nos. 616-619, 655-658, 666-669.

1977, Sept. 22　　Engr.　　Perf. 12½

Designs: 1k, Chisel, square and plane. 1.30k, Trowel, ceiling brush and folding ruler.

606	A184	80o dk brown	.30	.25
607	A184	1k red	.40	.20
608	A184	1.30k violet bl	.70	.30
		Nos. 606-608 (3)	1.40	.75

Danish crafts.

Globe Flower — A185

Handball — A186

Endangered Flora: 1.50k, Cnidium dubium.

1977, Nov. 17　　Engr.　　Perf. 12½

609	A185	1k multicolored	.50	.25
610	A185	1.50k multicolored	1.25	.65

1978, Jan. 19　　　　Perf. 12½

611	A186	1.20k red	.30	.20

Men's World Handball Championships.

Christian IV, Frederiksborg Castle
A187

Frederiksborg Museum
A188

1978, Mar. 16

612	A187	1.20k brown red	.40	.20
613	A188	1.80k black	.70	.30

Frederiksborg Museum, centenary.

Europa Issue

Jens Bang's House, Aalborg
A189

Frederiksborg Castle, Ground Plan and Elevation
A190

1978, May 11　　Engr.　　Perf. 12½

614	A189	1.20k red	.55	.45
615	A190	1.50k dk bl & vio bl	1.25	.70

Landscape Type of 1977

Landscapes, Central Jutland: 70o, Kongenshus Memorial Park. 120o, Post Office, Old Town in Aarhus. 150o, Lignite fields, Soby. 180o, Church wall, Stadil Church.

1978, June 15　　Engr.　　Perf. 12½

616	A183	70o multicolored	.30	.20
617	A183	120o multicolored	.55	.20
618	A183	150o multicolored	.70	.45
619	A183	180o multicolored	.85	.40
		Nos. 616-619 (4)	2.40	1.25

Boats in Harbor — A191

Edible Morel — A192

Danish fishing industry: 1k, Eel traps. 1.80k, Boats in berth. 2.50k, Drying nets.

1978, Sept. 7　　Engr.　　Perf. 12½

620	A191	70o olive gray	.45	.20
621	A191	1k redsh brown	.45	.20
622	A191	1.80k slate	.45	.20
623	A191	2.50k sepia	1.00	.35
		Nos. 620-623 (4)	2.35	.95

1978, Nov. 16　　Engr.　　Perf. 12½

Design: 1.20k, Satan's mushroom.

624	A192	1k sepia	.60	.40
625	A192	1.20k dull red	.90	.40

Telephones — A193

1979, Jan. 25　　Engr.　　Perf. 12½

626	A193	1.20k dull red	.45	.20

Centenary of Danish telephone.

University Seal
A194

Pentagram: University Faculties
A195

1979, Apr. 5　　Engr.　　Perf. 12½

627	A194	1.30k vermilion	.45	.20
628	A195	1.60k dk vio blue	.60	.55

University of Copenhagen, 500th anniv.

Types of 1933-1974

1979-82　　　Engr.　　Perf. 13

629	A32	80o green	.40	.20
630	A161	90o slate	2.00	1.75
631	A32	100o dp green ('81)	.50	.20
632	A161	110o brown	.65	.20
a.		Bklt. pane, #493-494, 632, 2 #318 ('79)	1.50	
633	A161	130o red	.55	.20
a.		Bklt. pane, 2 ea #494, 629, 632, 4 #633 ('79)	6.50	
634	A161	130o brown ('81)	.65	.40
635	A161	140o red org ('80)	1.40	1.40
636	A161	150o red org ('81)	.70	.65
637	A161	160o ultra	.95	.90
638	A161	160o red ('81)	.65	.20
a.		Bklt. pane, 2 ea #318, 634, 638, 8 #494)	12.00	
639	A161	180o ultra ('80)	1.25	1.10
640	A161	210o gray ('80)	1.40	1.40
641	A161	230o ol grn ('81)	1.25	.40
642	A161	250o blue grn ('81)	1.25	.70
643	A55	2.80k dull grn	.95	.20
644	A55	3.30k brn red ('81)	1.25	.55
645	A55	3.50k grnsh bl ('82)	2.00	2.00
646	A55	4.30k brn red ('80)	2.00	.50
647	A55	4.70k rose lil ('81)	2.50	2.50
648	A55	8k orange	2.40	.20
649	A55	12k red brn ('81)	4.00	.55

650 A55 14k dk red brn
('82)   4.50   .70
Nos. 629-650 (22)   33.20 18.40

A196

A197

Europa: 1.30k, Mail cart, 1785. 1.60k, Morse key and amplifier.

1979, May 10   *Perf. 12½*
651 A196 1.30k red   .85 .20
652 A196 1.60k dark blue   1.25 .70

1979, June 14   **Engr.**   *Perf. 13*
Viking Art: 1.10k, Gripping beast pendant. 2k, Key with gripping beast design.
653 A197 1.10k sepia   .50 .20
654 A197   2k grnsh gray   .90 .35

Landscape Type of 1977
Landscapes, Northern Jutland: 80o, Mols Bjerge. 90o, Orslev Kloster. 200o, Trans. 280o, Bovbjerg.

1979, Sept. 6   **Engr.**   *Perf. 12½*
655 A183 80o multicolored   .45 .45
656 A183 90o multicolored   1.10 .90
657 A183 200o multicolored   .90 .35
658 A183 280o multicolored   1.10 .80
Nos. 655-658 (4)   3.55 2.50

Adam Oehlenschläger (1799-1850), Poet and Dramatist A198

1979, Oct, 4   **Engr.**   *Perf. 13*
659 A198 1.30k dk carmine   .50 .25

Score, Violin, Dancing Couple — A199

Ballerina — A200

1979, Nov. 8   **Engr.**   *Perf. 13x12½*
660 A199 1.10k brown   .35 .20
661 A200 1.60k ultra   .65 .30

Jacob Gade (1879-63), composer; August Bournonville (1805-79), ballet master.

Royal Mail Guards' Office, Copenhagen, 1779 — A201

1980, Feb. 14   **Engr.**   *Perf. 13*
662 A201 1.30k brown red   .50 .25
National Postal Service, 200th anniversary.

Symbols of Occupation, Health and Education A202

1980, May 5   **Engr.**   *Perf. 13*
663 A202 1.60k dark blue   .65 .50
World Conference of the UN Decade for Women, Copenhagen, July 14-30.

Karen Blixen (1885-1962), Writer (Pen Name Isak Dinesen) — A203

Europa: 1.60k, August Krogh (1874-1949), physiologist.

1980, May 5
664 A203 1.30k red   .55 .20
665 A203 1.60k blue   1.10 .55

Landscape Type of 1977
Northern Jutland: 80o, Viking ship burial grounds, Lindholm Hoje. 110o, Lighthouse, Skagen, vert. 200o, Boreglum Monastery. 280o, Fishing boats, Vorupor Beach.

1980, June 19   **Engr.**   *Perf. 13*
666 A183 80o multicolored   .35 .35
667 A183 110o multicolored   .45 .45
668 A183 200o multicolored   .70 .30
669 A183 280o multicolored   1.50 1.50
Nos. 666-669 (4)   3.00 2.60

Nordic Cooperation Issue

Silver Tankard, by Borchardt Rollufse, 1641 — A204

1980, Sept. 9   **Engr.**   *Perf. 13*
670 A204 1.30k shown   .50 .35
671 A204 1.80k Bishop's bowl, Copenhagen fa-ience, 18th cent.   1.10 1.10

Frisian Sceat Facsimile, Obverse and Reverse, 9th Century A205

Coins: 1.40k Silver coin of Valdemar the Great and Absalom, 1157-1182, 1.80k, Gold 12-mark coin of Christian VII, 1781.

1980, Oct. 9   **Engr.**   *Perf. 13*
672 A205 1.30k red & redsh brn   .50 .45
673 A205 1.40k ol gray & sl grn   1.25 1.25
674 A205 1.80k dk bl & sl bl   1.10 1.10
Nos. 672-674 (3)   2.85 2.80

Tonder Lace Pattern, North Schleswig — A206

Designs: Tonder lace patterns.

1980, Nov. 13   **Engr.**   *Perf. 13*
675 A206 1.10k brown   .40 .45
676 A206 1.30k brown red   .50 .30
677 A206   2k olive gray   .70 .30
Nos. 675-677 (3)   1.60 1.05

Nyboder Development, Copenhagen, 350th Anniversary A207

Design: 1.30k, View of Nyboder, diff.

1981, Mar. 19
678 A207 1.30k dp org & ocher   .80 .80
679 A207 1.60k dp org & ocher   .55 .30

Tilting at a Barrel on Shrovetide A208

Design: 2k, Midsummer's Eve bonfire.

1981, May 4   **Engr.**   *Perf. 13*
680 A208 1.60k brown red   .50 .20
681 A208   2k dk blue   .90 .50

Soro Lake and Academy, Zealand — A209

Designs: Views of Zealand.

1981, June 18   **Engr.**   *Perf. 13*
682 A209 100o shown   .35 .35
683 A209 150o Poet N.F.S. Grundtvig's home, Udby   .60 .60
684 A209 160o Kaj Munk's home, Opager   .60 .30
685 A209 200o Gronsund   .80 .80
686 A209 230o Bornholm Isld.   .85 .80
Nos. 682-686 (5)   3.20 2.85

European Urban Renaissance Year — A210

1981, Sept. 10   **Engr.**   *Perf. 12½x13*
687 A210 1.60k dull red   .65 .25

Type of 1933

1981-85   **Engr.**   *Perf. 13*
688 A32   30o orange   .35 .35
   a. Bklt. pane 10 (2 #318, 2 #688, 6 #494)('84)   2.75
689 A32   40o purple   .35 .35
   a. Bklt. pane of 10 (4 #318, 2 #689, 4 #494) ('89)   2.25
690 A32   80o ol bis ('85)   .50 .50
691 A32 1000 blue ('83)   .70 .35
   b. Bklt. pane of 8 (2 #494, 4 #691, 2 #706) ('83)   8.50
692 A32 150o dk green ('82)   .50 .35
693 A32 200o green ('83)   .70 .70
694 A32 230o brt yel grn ('84)   .85 .35
695 A32 250o brt yel grn ('85)   1.10 .70
Nos. 688-695 (8)   5.05 3.65

Ellehammer's 18-horsepower Biplane, 1906 — A211

1981, Oct. 8   **Engr.**   *Perf. 13*
696 A211   1k shown   .45 .45
697 A211 1.30k R-1 Fokker CV reconnaissance plane, 1926   1.00 1.00
698 A211 1.60k Bellanca J-300, 1931   .55 .30
699 A211 2.30k DC-7C, 1957   .85 .70
Nos. 696-699 (4)   2.85 2.45

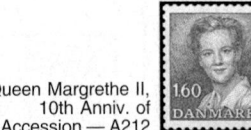
Queen Margrethe II, 10th Anniv. of Accession — A212

1982-85   **Engr.**   *Perf. 13*
700 A212 1.60k dull red   .60 .25
701 A212 1.60k dk ol grn   2.10 2.10
702 A212 1.80k sepia   .65 .45
703 A212   2k dull red   .90 .25
   b. Bklt. pane, 4 #494, 2 ea #493, 702, 703   12.00
704 A212 2.20k ol grn ('83)   .85 .35
705 A212 2.30k violet   .75 .25
706 A212 2.50k org red ('83)   2.75 2.75
707 A212 2.70k dk blue   .85 .65
708 A212 2.70k cop red ('84)   1.25 .25
   c. Booklet pane, 3 #688, 2 #494, 3 #708 ('84)   6.00

709 A212 2.80k cop red ('85)   1.00 .25
   b. Booklet pane, 3 #493, 2 #494, 3 #709 ('85)   4.50
710 A212   3k violet ('83)   1.00 .25
711 A212 3.30k bluish blk ('84)   1.50 .60
712 A212 3.50k blue ('83)   2.10 2.10
713 A212 3.50k dk vio ('85)   1.75 .95
714 A212 3.70k dp blue ('84)   1.25 .35
715 A212 3.80k dk blue ('85)   1.50 .25
See Nos. 796-803, 887, 889, 896, 899.

Arms Type of 1946
   Engr.   *Perf. 13*
716 A55 4.30k dk ol grn ('84)   4.00 4.00
717 A55 5.50k dk bl grn ('84)   2.40 2.40
718 A55 16k cop red ('83)   4.75 .65
719 A55 17k cop red ('84)   6.75 1.40
720 A55 18k brn vio ('85)   6.75 1.00
720A A55 50k dk red ('85)   13.50 2.00
Nos. 700-720A (22)   58.95 23.50

World Figure Skating Championships A213

1982, Feb. 25
721 A213 2k dark blue   .75 .30

A214

A215

1982, Feb. 25   **Engr.**   *Perf. 12½*
722 A214 1.60k Revenue schooner Argus   .60 .25
Customs Service centenary

1982, May 3   **Engr.**   *Perf. 12½*
723 A215   2k Abolition of ad-scription, 1788   1.00 .20
724 A215 2.70k Women's voting right, 1915   1.25 .60
Europa.

Butter Churn, Barn, Hjedding — A216

Records Office, 400th Anniv. — A217

1982, June 10   **Engr.**   *Perf. 13*
725 A216 1.80k brown   .75 .75
Cooperative dairy farming centenary.

1982, June 10
726 A217 2.70k green   1.10 .40

Steen Steensen Blicher (1782-1848), Poet, by J.V. Gertner — A218

1982, Aug. 26   **Engr.**   *Perf. 13*
727 A218 2k brown red   .75 .30

Robert Storm
Petersen
(1882-1949),
Cartoonist
A219

Printing in
Denmark, 500th
Anniv.
A220

Characters: 1.50k, Three little men and the number man. 2k, Peter and Ping the penguin, horiz.

1982, Sept. 23   Engr.   Perf. 12½
728 A219 1.50k dk bl & red   .70 .45
729 A219 2k red & ol grn   .90 .40

1982, Sept. 23
730 A220 1.80k Press, text, ink
                    balls   .75 .75

A221   A222

1982, Nov. 4
731 A221 2.70k Library seal   1.00 .50
500th anniv. of University Library.

1983, Jan. 27   Engr.   Perf. 13
732 A222 2k multicolored   .80 .30
World Communications Year.

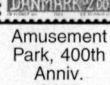

Amusement
Park, 400th
Anniv.
A223

Badminton
Championship
A224

1983, Feb. 24
733 A223 2k multicolored   .80 .30

1983, Feb. 24
734 A224 2.70k multicolored   1.10 .40

Nordic
Cooperation
Issue — A225

1983, Mar. 24
735 A225 2.50k Egeskov Castle   1.00 .40
736 A225 3.50k Troll Church,
                    North Jutland   1.40 .60

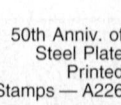

50th Anniv. of
Steel Plate
Printed
Stamps — A226

1983, Mar. 24   Engr.   Perf. 13
737 A226 2.50k car rose   1.00 .30

Europa
1983 — A227

Weights and
Measures
Ordinance,
300th
Anniv. — A228

2.50k, Kildekovshallen Recreation Center, Copenhagen. 3.50k, Salling Sound Bridge.

1983, May 5   Engr.   Perf. 13
738 A227 2.50k multicolored   1.00 .20
739 A227 3.50k multicolored   1.25 .45

1983, June 16
740 A228 2.50k red   1.00 .30

A229   A230

1983, Sept. 8   Engr.
741 A229 5k Codex titlepage   1.75 .60
Christian V Danish law, 300th anniv.

1983, Oct. 6   Engr.   Perf. 13
742 A230 1k Car crash, police   .40 .25
743 A230 2.50k Fire, ambulance
                    service   1.00 .35
744 A230 3.50k Sea rescue   1.40 .75
        Nos. 742-744 (3)   2.80 1.35
Life saving and salvage services.

Elderly in
Society — A231

1983, Oct. 6
745 A231 2k Stages of life   .80 .60
746 A231 2.50k Train passengers   1.00 .30

N.F.S.
Grundtvig
(1783-1872),
Poet — A232

Street Scene, by
C.W. Eckersberg
(1783-1853) — A233

1983, Nov. 3   Engr.
747 A232 2.50k brown red   1.00 .30
748 A233 2.50k brown red   1.00 .30

A234   A235

1984, Jan. 26   Litho. & Engr.
749 A234 2.70k Shovel, sapling   1.10 .30
Plant a tree campaign.

1984, Jan. 26   Engr.
750 A235 3.70k Game   1.50 .45
1984 Billiards World Championships, Copenhagen, May 10-13.

Hydrographic
Dept.
Bicentenary
A236

Pilotage Service,
300th
Anniv. — A237

1984, Mar. 22   Engr.   Perf. 13
751 A236 2.30k Compass   .90 .90
752 A237 2.70k Boat   1.10 .30

2nd European
Parliament
Elections
A238

Scouts Around
Campfire, Emblems
A239

Litho. & Engr.
1984, Apr. 12   Perf. 13
753 A238 2.70k org & dk bl   1.25 .30
754 A239 2.70k multi   1.10 .30

Europa (1959-
84)
A240

1984, May 3   Engr.   Perf. 12½
755 A240 2.70k red   1.10 .20
756 A240 3.70k blue   1.75 .80

Prince Henrik,
50th Birthday
A241

D Day, 40th
Anniv.
A242

1984, June 6   Engr.
757 A241 2.70k brown red   1.10 .30
758 A242 2.70k War Memorial,
                    Copenhagen   1.10 .30
See Greenland No. 160.

17th Cent.
Inn — A243

1984, June 6
759 A243 3k multicolored   1.25 1.00

Fishing
and
Shipping
A244

1984, Sept. 6   Engr.
760 A244 2.30k Research (Her-
                    ring)   .90 .90
761 A244 2.70k Sea transport   1.10 .60
762 A244 3.30k Deep-sea fishing   1.25 1.25
763 A244 3.70k Deep-sea, diff.   1.50 1.40
        Nos. 760-763 (4)   4.75 4.15

A245   A246

1984, Oct. 5   Litho. & Engr.
764 A245 1k Post bird   .35 .25

1984, Oct. 5
Holberg Meets with an Officer, by Wilhelm Marstrand (1810-73).
765 A246 2.70k multicolored   1.10 .30
Ludvig Holberg (1684-1754), writer.

Jewish
Community in
Copenhagen,
300th
Anniv. — A247

1984, Oct. 5
766 A247 3.70k Woman blessing
                    Sabbath can-
                    dles   1.50 1.00

Carnival in Rome, by Christoffer W.
Eckersberg (1783-1853) — A248

Paintings: 10k, Ymer and Odhumble (Nordic mythology figures), by Nicolai A. Abildgaard (1743-1809), vert.

Perf. 12½x13, 13x12½
1984, Nov. 22   Litho. & Engr.
767 A248 5k multicolored   2.75 2.75
768 A248 10k multicolored   5.25 5.25

German and
French Reform
Church, 300th
Anniv. — A249

1985, Jan. 24   Engr.   Perf. 13
769 A249 2.80k magenta   1.10 .25

Bonn-Copenhagen Declaration, 30th
Anniv. — A250

1985, Feb. 21   Litho.   Perf. 14
770 A250 2.80k Map, flags   1.40 .45

A251   A252

1985, Mar. 14   Perf. 13
771 A251 3.80k multicolored   1.50 .75
Intl. Youth Year.

Souvenir Sheet
Early postal ordinances.

1985, Mar. 14 — **Litho. & Engr.**
772 Sheet of 4 — 6.00 6.00
a. A252 1k Christian IV's Ordinance on Postmen, 1624 — 1.40 1.50
b. A252 2.50k Plague Mandate, 1711 — 1.40 1.50
c. A252 2.80k Ordinance on Prohibition of Mail by Means other than the Post, 1775 — 1.40 1.50
d. A252 3.80k Act on Postal Articles, 1831 — 1.40 1.50
HAFNIA '87 phil. exhib. Sold for 15k.

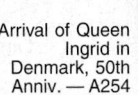

Europa 1985 — A253

1985, May 2
773 A253 2.80k Musical staff — 1.25 .35
774 A253 3.80k Musical staff, diff. — 1.50 .90

Arrival of Queen Ingrid in Denmark, 50th Anniv. — A254

1985, May 21
775 A254 2.80k Queen Mother, chrysanthemums — 1.10 .25
See Greenland No. 163.

Opening of the Faro Bridges — A255

1985, May 21 — **Litho.** — **Perf. 13**
776 A255 2.80k Faro-Falster Bridge — 1.10 .25

St. Cnut's Land Grant to Lund Cathedral, 900th Anniv. — A256

Seal of King Cnut and: 2.80k, Lund Cathedral. 3k, City of Helsingdorg, Sweden.

1985, May 21 — **Engr.**
777 A256 2.80k multi — 1.10 .45
778 A256 3k multi — 1.40 1.40
See Sweden Nos. 1538-1539.

UN Decade for Women A257

Sports A258

1985, June 27 — **Litho. & Engr.**
779 A257 3.80k Cyclist — 1.50 1.50

1985, June 27
780 A258 2.80k Women's floor exercise — 1.10 .30
781 A258 3.80k Canoe & kayak — 1.50 .80
782 A258 6k Cycling — 2.40 1.60
Nos. 780-782 (3) — 5.00 2.70

Kronborg Castle, Elsinore, 400th Anniv. — A259

UN 40th Anniv. — A260

1985, Sept. 5
783 A259 2.80k multi — 1.10 .25

1985, Sept. 5
784 A260 3.80k Dove, emblem — 1.50 .80

Niels Bohr (1885-1962), Physicist — A261

1985, Oct. 3 — **Perf. 13x12½**
785 A261 2.80k With wife Margrethe — 1.25 1.00
Winner of 1922 Nobel Prize in Physics for theory of atomic structure.

Hand Signing "D" — A262

Boat, by Helge Refn — A263

1985, Nov. 7 — **Engr.** — **Perf. 13**
786 A262 2.80k multicolored — 1.10 .25
Danish Assoc. for the Deaf, 50th anniv.

1985, Nov. 7 — **Litho.**
787 A263 2.80k multicolored — 1.25 .25

Abstract Iron Sculpture by Robert Jacobsen A264

Lithographed and Engraved
1985, Nov. 7 — **Perf. 13x12½**
788 A264 3.80k multicolored — 2.75 3.00

Painting by Bjorn Wiinblad A265

1986, Jan. 23 — **Litho.** — **Perf. 13x12½**
789 A265 2.80k multicolored — 1.25 1.25

Amnesty Intl., 25th Anniv. A266

Lithographed and Engraved
1986, Jan. 23 — **Perf. 13**
790 A266 2.80k multicolored — 1.10 .25

Miniature Sheet

HAFNIA '87 — A267

1986, Feb. 20
791 Sheet of 4 — 8.00 9.00
a. A267 100o Holstein carriage, c. 1840 — 1.75 2.00
b. A267 250o Iceboat, c. 1880 — 1.75 2.00
c. A267 280o 1st mail van, 1908 — 1.75 2.00
d. A267 380o Airmail service 1919 — 1.75 2.00
Sold for 15k.

Changing of the Guard — A268

1986, Mar. 20 — **Perf. 13**
792 A268 2.80k multicolored — 1.10 .25
Royal Danish Life Guards barracks and Rosenborg Drilling Ground, bicent.

Types of 1933-82

1986-90 — **Engr.** — **Perf. 13**
793 A32 5o brn org ('89) — .25 .25
794 A32 270o brt yel grn — 1.00 .80
b. Bklt. pane, 6 #318, 2 #691, 2 #794 — 4.75
795 A32 300o brt yel grn — 1.10 .35
796 A212 3k cop red — 1.10 .25
797 A212 3.20k deep vio — 1.25 .80
798 A212 3.20k carmine — 1.25 .25
c. Bklt. pane, 2 #693, 4 #798 — 7.00
799 A212 3.40k dk grn — 2.40 2.40
800 A212 3.80k dark vio — 1.60 1.60
801 A212 4.10k dark blue — 1.60 .40
802 A212 4.20k dk pur — 2.40 2.00
803 A212 4.40k dp bl — 1.60 .35
804 A55 4.60k gray — 3.25 3.25
805 A55 6.50k dp grn — 2.50 .80
806 A55 6.60k green — 2.50 2.75
807 A55 7.10k brn vio — 3.25 2.25
808 A55 7.30k green — 3.50 3.50
809 A55 7.70k dk brn vio — 3.00 1.40
810 A55 11k brown — 3.50 2.75
811 A55 20k dp ultra — 7.25 .70
812 A55 22k henna brn — 7.25 1.60
813 A55 23k dark olive grn — 8.00 1.10
814 A55 24k dark olive grn — 8.00 .80
815 A55 26k dark olive grn — 9.00 2.00
Nos. 793-815 (23) — 76.55 32.35

Issued: 6.50k, 20k, 1/9/86; 22k, 1/3/87; 270o, 3k, #797, 3.80k, 4.10k, 4.60k, 6.60k, 7.10k, 24k, 1/7/88; #794b, 1/28/88; 300o, #798, 3.40k, 4.20k, 4.40k, 7.30k, 7.70k, 11k, 26k, 1/26/89; 5o, 1989; 23k, 1/11/90.

No. 793 issued for use in lieu of currency of the same face value.

Soro Academy, 400th Anniv. — A269

1986, Apr. 28 — **Litho. & Engr.**
816 A269 2.80k multi — 1.10 .30

A270 — A271

1986, Apr. 28
817 A270 3.80k multi — 1.50 1.00
Intl. Peace Year.

1986, May 26 — **Litho.**
818 A271 2.80k multi — 1.50 .35
Crown Prince Frederik, 18th birthday.

Nordic Cooperation Issue 1986 — A272

Sister towns.

1986, May 27 — **Engr.**
819 A272 2.80k Aalborg Harbor — 1.00 .50
820 A272 3.80k Thisted Church and Town Hall — 1.50 .80

Hoje Tastrup Train Station Opening, May 31 — A273

1986, May 27 — **Litho.**
821 A273 2.80k multi — 1.10 .25

Mailbox, Telegraph Lines, Telephone A274

Natl. Bird Candidates A275

1986, June 19 — **Litho.** — **Perf. 13**
822 A274 2.80k multi — 1.10 .25
19th European Intl. PTT Congress, Copenhagen, Aug. 12-16.

1986, June 19 — **Litho. & Engr.**
Finalists: a, Corvus corax. b, Sturnus vulgaris. c, Cygnus olor (winner). d, Vanellus vanellus, e, Alauda arvensis.

823 Strip of 5 — 9.00 10.00
a.-e. A275 2.80k any single — 1.75 1.00

A276

HAFNIA
'87 — A277

1986, June 19
824 A276 2.80k multi   1.10 .25

Danish Rifle, Gymnastics and Sports Club, 125th anniv.

Souvenir Sheet
1986, Sept. 4
825   Sheet of 4   8.00 8.00
  a. A277 100o Mailcoach, c. 1841   1.60 1.60
  b. A277 250o Postmaster, c. 1840   1.60 1.60
  c. A277 280o Postman, c. 1851   1.60 1.60
  d. A277 380o Rural postman, c. 1893   1.90 1.90

Sold for 15k.

Europa
1986 — A278

Cupid — A279

1986, Sept. 4   **Engr.**
826 A278 2.80k Street sweeper   *1.25 .20*
827 A278 3.80k Garbage truck   *1.60 .70*

1986, Oct. 9   **Litho.**
828 A279 3.80k multi   1.50 .70

Premiere of The Whims of Cupid and the Ballet Master, by Vincenzo Galeotti, bicent.

Refugee — A280

A281

1986, Oct. 9   **Litho. & Engr.**
829 A280 2.80k multi   1.10 .25

Danish Refugee Council Relief Campaign.

1986, Oct. 9   **Litho.**   **Perf. 13**
Protestant Reformation in Denmark, 450th Anniv.: Sermon, altarpiece detail, 1561, Thorslunde Church, Copenhagen.
830 A281 6.50k multi   2.50 1.10

A282

Abstract by Lin Utzon — A283

1986, Nov. 6   **Litho. & Engr.**
831 A282 3.80k multi   1.75 1.75

Organization for Economic Cooperation and Development, 25th anniv.

1987, Jan. 22   **Litho.**   **Perf. 13**
832 A283 2.80k multi   1.10 .25

Art appreciation.

A284

A285

1987, Feb. 26   **Engr.**   **Perf. 13**
833 A284 2.80k lake & black   1.10 .25

Danish Consumer Council, 40th anniv.

1987, Apr. 9   **Litho.**   **Perf. 13**
Religious art (details) from Ribe Cathedral.
834 A285   3k Fresco   1.25 .85
835 A285 3.80k Stained-glass
         window   1.75 1.40
836 A285 6.50k Mosaic   2.75 2.75
    Nos. 834-836 (3)   5.75 5.00

Ribe Cathedral redecoration, 1982-1987, by Carl-Henning Pedersen.

A286

A287

Europa (Modern architecture): 2.80k, Central Library, Gentofte, 1985. 3.80k, Hoje Tastrup High School, 1985, horiz.

1987, May 4   **Engr.**   **Perf. 13**
837 A286 2.80k rose claret   *1.40 .35*
838 A286 3.80k bright ultra   *1.90 .90*

1987, May 4
839 A287 2.50k dk red & bl blk   1.40 1.00

Danish Academy of Technical Sciences (ATV), 50th anniv.

 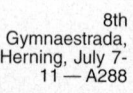
8th Gymnaestrada, Herning, July 7-11 — A288

1987, June 18   **Litho. & Engr.**
840 A288 2.80k multi   1.10 .25

A289

A290

1987, June 18
841 A289 3.80k multi   1.50 1.00

Danish Cooperative Bacon Factories, cent.

1987, Aug. 27   **Litho.**
842 A290 3.80k Single-sculler   1.50 .90

World Rowing Championships, Aug. 23-30.

HAFNIA '87, Bella Center, Copenhagen, Oct. 16-25 — A291

Litho. & Engr.
1987, Aug. 27   **Perf. 13x12½**
843   A291 280o Type A15,
        mail train c.
        1912   1.40 1.40
Souvenir Sheet
843A A291 280o like No. 843,
        green lawn
        and loco-
        motive   24.00 24.00

Purchase of No. 843A included admission to the exhibition. Sold for 45k.

Abstact by Ejler Bille — A292

1987, Sept. 24   **Litho.**   **Perf. 13**
844 A292 2.80k multi   1.10 .25

Rasmus Rask (1787-1832), Linguist — A293

1987, Oct. 15   **Engr.**   **Perf. 13x12½**
845 A293 2.80k dark henna
        brown   1.10 .25

A294

A295

Emblem: Miraculous Catch (Luke 5:4-7), New Testament.

1987, Oct. 15   **Perf. 13**
846 A294   3k carmine lake   1.25 .30

Clerical Assoc. for the Home Mission in Denmark, 125th anniv.

Photo. & Engr., Litho. (4.10k)
1988, Feb. 18   **Perf. 13**
Designs: 3k, Two lions from the gate of Rosenburg Castle around the monogram of Christian IV. 4.10k, Portrait of the monarch painted by P. Isaacsz, vert.
847 A295   3k blue gray & gold 1.25 .30
848 A295 4.10k multi   1.60 .75

Accession of Christian IV (1577-1648), King of Denmark and Norway (1588-1648), 400th anniv.

Ole Worm (1588-1654), Archaeologist, and Runic Artifacts — A296

1988, Feb. 18   **Engr.**
849 A296 7.10k chocolate   2.75 2.75

Odense, 1000th Anniv. — A297

A298

Design: St. Cnut's Church and statue of Hans Christian Andersen, Odense.

1988, Mar. 10   **Engr.**
850 A297 3k multi   1.25 .25

1988, Apr. 7   **Litho.**
851 A298 2.70k multi   1.10 .70

Danish Civil Defense and Emergency Planning Agency, 50th Anniv.

WHO, 40th Anniv. — A299

Abolition of *Stavnsbaand,* 200th Anniv. — A300

1988, Apr. 7   **Litho. & Engr.**
852 A299 4.10k multi   1.60 .85

1988, May 5   **Litho.**
Painting: King Christian VII riding past the Liberty Memorial, Copenhagen, by C.W. Eckersberg (1783-1853).
853 A300 3.20k multi   1.25 .80

Stavnsbaand (adscription) provided that all Danish farmers' sons from age 4 to 40 would be bound as villeins to the estates on which they were born, thus providing landowners with free labor.

A301

A302

Europa: Transport and communication.

1988, May 5
854 A301   3k Postwoman on
         bicycle   *1.00 .20*
855 A301 4.10k Mobile telephone *1.75 .70*

1988, June 16   **Litho.**
856 A302 4.10k multi   1.60 .75

1988 Individual Speedway World Motorcycle Championships, Denmark, Sept. 3.

Federation of Danish Industries, 150th Anniv. — A303

Painting (detail): *The Industrialists,* by P.S. Kroyer.

1988, June 16   **Perf. 13½x13**
857 A303 3k multi   1.25 .55

Danish Metalworkers' Union, Cent. — A304

1988, Aug. 18   **Litho.**   **Perf. 13**
858 A304 3k Glass mosaic by Niels Winkel   1.25 .35

Tonder Teachers' Training College, 200th Anniv. — A305

1988, Aug. 18   **Engr.**   **Perf. 13x12½**
859 A305 3k lake   1.25 .30

Homage to Leon Degand, Sculpture by Robert Jacobsen A306

1988, Sept. 22   **Perf. 11½x13**
860 A306 4.10k blk, lake & gray   2.50 *3.00*

Danish-French cultural exchange program, 10th anniv. See France No. 2130.

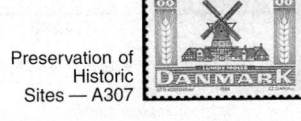

Preservation of Historic Sites — A307

1988, Oct. 13   **Engr.**   **Perf. 13x12½**
861 A307   3k Lumby Windmill, 1818   1.40 .30
862 A307 7.10k Vejstrup Water Mill, 1837   2.75 1.60

Paintings in the State Museum of Art, Copenhagen — A308

4.10k, *Bathing Boys,* 1902, by Peter Hansen (1868-1928). 10k, *The Hill at Overkaerby,* 1917, by Fritz Syberg (1862-1939).

Litho. & Engr.
1988, Nov. 3   **Perf. 13**
863 A308 4.10k multi   3.00 3.50
864 A308 10k multi   6.00 6.50

See #881-882, 951-952, 972-973, 1018-1019.

The Little Mermaid, Sculpture by Edvard Eriksen — A309

1989, Feb. 16   **Engr.**
865 A309 3.20k dark green   1.25 .30

Tourism industry, cent.

Danish Soccer Assoc., Cent. — A310   NATO Membership, 40th Anniv. — A311

1989, Mar. 16   **Litho.**
866 A310 3.20k multi   1.25 .30

1989, Mar. 16
867 A311 4.40k dk blue, gold & lt blue   1.75 1.00

Nordic Cooperation Issue — A312

Folk costumes.

1989, Apr. 20   **Litho. & Engr.**
868 A312 3.20k Woman from Valby   1.25 .40
869 A312 4.40k Pork butcher   1.75 1.00

European Parliament 3rd Elections A313

1989, May 11   **Litho.**
870 A313 3k blue & yellow   1.25 1.25

Europa 1989 — A314

Children's toys.

1989, May 11   **Litho. & Engr.**
871 A314 3.20k Lego blocks   *1.25* .20
872 A314 4.40k Wooden soldiers, by Kay Bojesen   *1.75* .55

Agricultural Museum, Cent. — A315

1989, June 15   **Engr.**   **Perf. 13**
873 A315 3.20k Tractor, 1889   1.25 .30

Interparliamentary Union, Cent. — A316

1989, June 15   **Litho. & Engr.**
874 A316 3.40k Folketing Chamber layout   2.40 2.40

Danish Fishery and Marine Research Institute, Cent. A317

1989, Aug. 24   **Litho. & Engr.**
875 A317 3.20k multi   1.10 .30

Bernhard Severin Ingemann (1789-1862), Poet and Novelist — A318

1989, Aug. 24   **Engr.**
876 A318 7.70k dark green   2.75 1.25

A319   A320

Danish Film Office, 50th Anniv.: 3k, Scene from the short feature film *They Reached the Ferry,* 1948. 3.20k, Bodil Ipsen (d. 1964), actress. 4.40k, Carl Th. Dreyer (1889-1968), screenwriter and director.

1989, Sept. 28   **Litho.**
877 A319   3k multi   1.10 1.10
878 A319 3.20k multi   1.10 .50
879 A319 4.40k multi   1.60 .85
   Nos. 877-879 (3)   3.80 2.45

1989, Nov. 10   **Litho. & Engr.**
880 A320 3.20k multi   1.25 .40

Stamp Day, 50th anniv.

Art Type of 1988

Paintings: 4.40k, *Part of the Northern Gate of the Citadel Bridge,* c. 1837, by Christen Kobke (1810-1848). 10k, *A Little Girl, Elise Kobke, With a Cup in Front of Her,* c. 1850, by Constantin Hansen (1804-1880).

1989, Nov. 10   **Perf. 12½x13**
881 A308 4.40k multi   2.40 2.75
882 A308 10k multi   5.75 6.25

Types of 1933-82 and:

A321   A321a
Queen Margrethe II

Perf. 12½, 13 (A321a)

1990-98   **Engr.**
883 A32   25o bluish black   .25   .25
  a.   Bklt. pane, 4 #691, 2 #883   1.90
884 A32   125o carmine lake   .50   .25
885 A32   325o lt yel grn   1.25 1.25
886 A32   350o yellow green   1.40   .75
887 A212 3.50k dark red   1.40   .25
  a.   Bklt. pane, 2 each #691, 885, 887   6.00
888 A321 3.50k henna brown   1.40   .25
  b.   Bklt. pane, 4 each #883, #884, #888 ('91)   8.50
889 A212 3.75k dark green   1.50 1.50
890 A321 3.75k green   1.75 1.60
891 A321 3.75k red   1.50   .25
  a.   Bklt. pane, 4 each #884, #891   8.50
  b.   Booklet pane, 2 each #691, 883, 891   4.50
   Complete booklet, #891b   4.50
892 A321a 3.75k red   1.50   .25
  a.   Booklet pane, 2 each #691, 883, 892   4.25
   Complete booklet, #892a   4.25

  b.   Booklet pane, 2 #883, 4 #494, 2 #892   4.25
   Complete booklet, #892b   4.25
893 A321   4k brown   1.60   .60
894 A321a   4k deep bl grn   1.60   .25
895 A321a 4.25k olive brown   1.75   .75
896 A212 4.50k brown violet   1.75 1.75
897 A321 4.50k violet   1.75 1.60
898 A321a 4.50k deep bl blk   1.75   .75
899 A212 4.75k dark blue   1.90   .30
900 A321 4.75k blue   1.90   .30
901 A321 4.75k violet   1.90 1.60
902 A321a 4.75k brown   1.90 1.50
903 A321a   5k violet   2.00   .25
904 A321   5k blue   2.00   .40
905 A321 5.25k black   2.10 1.50
906 A321a 5.25k deep blue   2.10   .25
907 A321 5.50k green   2.25 2.25
908 A321a 5.50k henna brown   2.25 2.10
909 A55   7.50k dark bl grn   3.00 2.50
   Nos. 883-909 (27)   45.95 25.25

Queen Margrethe II's 50th birthday (No. 888).

Issued: #888, 4/5; #890, 897, 900, 1990; #888a, 2/14/91; #886, 891, 891a, 901, 904, 6/10/92; 5.50k, 1/13/94; 4k, 5.25k, 6/27/96; #892, 892a, 1/14/97; #894, 902, 903, 906, 8/28/97; #895, 898, 908, 909, 3/26/98; others, 1/11/90.

See Nos. 1120, 1127, 1135.

A322   A323

Design: Silver coffee pot designed by Axel Johannes Kroyer, Copenhagen, 1726.

1990, Feb. 15   **Engr.**   **Perf. 13**
911 A322 3.50k dark blue & blk   1.40 .35

Museum of Decorative Art, cent.

1990, Feb. 15

Steam engine, 200th anniv.: Steam engine built by Andrew Mitchell, 1790.
912 A323 8.25k dull red brown   3.25 1.75

Nyholm, 300th Anniv. A324

1990, Apr. 5   **Engr.**
913 A324 4.75k black   1.90 1.00

Europa 1990 — A325

1990, Apr. 5   **Litho.**
914 A325 3.50k Royal Monogram, Haderslev P.O.   *1.75* .20
915 A325 4.75k Odense P.O.   *2.75* .70

A326   A327

Pieces from the Flora Danica Banquet Service produced for King Christian VII.

1990, May 3   **Litho.**
916 A326 3.50k Bell-shaped lid, dish   1.50 1.75
917 A326 3.50k Gravy boat, dish   1.50 1.75
918 A326 3.50k Ice pot, casserole, lid   1.50 1.75
919 A326 3.50k Serving dish   1.50 1.75
  a.   Strip of 4, #916-919   6.50

Flora Danica porcelain, 200th anniv.

1990, June 14

Endangered plant species.

920	A327	3.25k Marshmallow	1.25	1.25
921	A327	3.50k Red helleborine	2.25	.40
922	A327	3.75k Purple orchis	1.60	1.60
923	A327	4.75k Lady's slipper	2.00	.95
		Nos. 920-923 (4)	7.10	4.20

Village Churches, Jutland — A328

Perf. 13x12½, 12½x13

1990, Aug. 30   Engr.

924	A328	3.50k Gjellerup	1.40	.40
925	A328	4.75k Veng	1.90	.90
926	A328	8.25k Bredsten, vert.	3.25	2.10
		Nos. 924-926 (3)	6.55	3.40

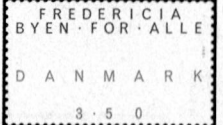

Fredericia, "The Town for Everybody" A329

Engr. & Embossed

1990, Oct. 5   Perf. 13

927	A329	3.50k black & red	1.40	.55

Tordenskiold (Peter Wessel, 1690-1720), Admiral — A330

1990, Oct. 5   Litho.   Perf. 13½x13

928	A330	3.50k multicolored	1.40	.55

Prevent Bicycle Thefts — A331

Design: 3.50k, Stop drunk driving.

1990, Nov. 8   Litho.   Perf. 13x12½

930	A331	3.25k shown	1.25	1.25
931	A331	3.50k Automobile, wine glass	1.40	.30

Locomotives — A332

1991, Mar. 14   Engr.   Perf. 13

932	A332	3.25k IC3 1990	1.25	1.25
933	A332	3.50k Class A 1882	1.40	.70
934	A332	3.75k Class MY 1954	1.50	1.50
935	A332	4.75k Class P 1907	1.90	1.00
		Nos. 932-935 (4)	6.05	4.45

Europa — A333   Jutland Law, 750th Anniv. — A334

Satellite photographs showing temperatures of Danish: 3.50k, Waters. 4.75k, Land.

1991, May 2   Litho.   Perf. 13

936	A333	3.50k multicolored	1.10	.25
937	A333	4.75k multicolored	1.60	.70

1991, May 2

938	A334	8.25k multicolored	3.00	3.00

Danish Islands — A335

1991, June 6

939	A335	3.50k Fano	1.40	.30
940	A335	4.75k Christianso	1.90	.70

Decorative Art — A336   Keep Denmark Clean — A337

Designs: 3.25k, Earthenware bowl and jars by Christian Poulsen. 3.50k, Chair by Hans Wegner, vert. 4.75k, Silver cutlery by Kay Bojesen, vert. 8k, Lamp by Poul Henningsen.

1991, Aug. 22   Litho.   Perf. 13

941	A336	3.25k multicolored	1.25	1.25
942	A336	3.50k multicolored	1.25	.40
943	A336	4.75k multicolored	1.90	1.00
944	A336	8.25k multicolored	3.25	3.25
		Nos. 941-944 (4)	7.65	5.90

1991, Sept. 19   Engr.   Perf. 13

Designs: 3.50k, Cleaning up after dog. 4.75k, Picking up litter.

945	A337	3.50k red	1.50	.30
946	A337	4.75k blue	2.00	1.00

Posters from Danish Museum of Decorative Arts — A338

Posters for: 3.50k, Nordic Advertising Congress, by Arne Ungermann (1902-1981). 4.50k, Poster Exhibition at Copenhagen Zoo (baboon), by Valdemar Andersen (1875-1928). 4.75k, Danish Air Lines, by Ib Andersen (1907-1969). 12k, The Sinner, by Sven Brasch (1886-1970).

1991, Sept. 19   Litho.

947	A338	3.50k multicolored	1.25	.40
948	A338	4.50k multicolored	2.25	2.25
949	A338	4.75k multicolored	1.75	1.75
950	A338	12k multicolored	4.25	2.50
		Nos. 947-950 (4)	9.50	6.90

Art Type of 1988

Designs: 4.75k, Lady at her Toilet by Harald Giersing (1881-1927), vert. 14k, Road through a Wood by Edvard Weie (1879-1943), vert.

Litho. & Engr.

1991, Nov. 7   Perf. 13x12½

951	A308	4.75k multicolored	1.90	1.90
952	A308	14k multicolored	5.50	5.50

A339   A340

Treasures of Natl. Museum: 3.50k, Earthenware bowl, Skarpsalling. 4.50k, Bronze dancer, Grevensvaenge. 4.75k, Bottom plate of silver cauldron, Gundestrup. 8.25k, Flint knife, Hindsgavl.

1992, Feb. 13   Engr.   Perf. 13

953	A339	3.50k dk vio & brown	1.40	.40
954	A339	4.50k dk bl & dk ol green	1.75	1.75
955	A339	4.75k brown & black	1.90	1.25
956	A339	8.25k dk ol grn & vio brown	3.25	3.25
		Nos. 953-956 (4)	8.30	6.65

1992, Mar. 12   Perf. 13½x13

957	A340	3.50k rose carmine	1.40	.50

Danish Society of Chemical, Civil, Electrical, and Mechanical Engineers, cent.

Souvenir Sheet

Queen Margaret I (1353-1412) — A341

Litho. & Engr.

1992, Mar. 12   Perf. 12½

958	A341	Sheet of 2	5.50	6.00
a.		3.50k Fresco	2.10	2.10
b.		4.75k Alabaster bust	2.75	2.75

Nordia '94, Scandinavian Philatelic Exhibition. No. 958 sold for 12k to benefit the exhibition.

Discovery of America, 500th Anniv. — A342

1992, May 7   Engr.   Perf. 12½

959	A342	3.50k Potato plant	1.60	.40
960	A342	4.75k Ear of corn	2.75	1.25

Europa.

Protect the Environment — A343

Litho. & Engr.

1992, June 10   Perf. 13

961	A343	3.75k Hare beside road	1.50	.30
962	A343	5k Fish, water pollution	2.00	.70
963	A343	8.75k Cut trees, vert.	3.50	2.00
		Nos. 961-963 (3)	7.00	3.00

Queen Margrethe II and Prince Henrik, 25th Wedding Anniv. — A344

1992, June 10   Litho.   Perf. 12½x13

964	A344	3.75k multicolored	1.50	.85

See Greenland No. 253.

A345   A346

1992, July 16   Perf. 13

965	A345	3.75k multicolored	1.50	.40

Denmark, European soccer champions.

1992, Aug. 27   Engr.   Perf. 13

966	A346	3.75k blue	1.50	.50

Danish Pavilion, Expo '92, Seville.

A347   A348

1992, Oct. 8   Litho. & Engr.   Perf. 13

967	A347	3.75k blue & org	1.50	.65

Single European market.

Litho. & Engr.

1992, Oct. 8   Perf. 12½

Cartoon characters: 3.50k, A Hug, by Ivar Gjorup. 3.75k, Love Letter, by Phillip Stein Jonsson. 4.75k, Domestic Triangle, by Nikoline Werdelin. 5k, Poet and His Little Wife, by Jorgen Mogensen.

968	A348	3.50k multicolored	1.40	1.00

Engr.

969	A348	3.75k red & purple	1.50	.30
970	A348	4.75k blk & red brn	1.90	1.90
971	A348	5k blue & red brn	2.00	.70
		Nos. 968-971 (4)	6.80	3.90

Art Type of 1988

5k, Landscape from Vejby, 1843, by John Thomas Lundbye. 10k, Motif from Halleby Brook, 1847, by Peter Christian Skovgaard.

Litho. & Engr.

1992, Nov. 12   Perf. 12½x13

972	A308	5k multicolored	2.00	2.00
973	A308	10k multicolored	4.00	4.00

A349   A350

1992, Nov. 12   **Perf. 13**
974 A349 3.75k Jacob's fight with angel   1.50 .30

Publication of new Danish bible.

Litho. & Engr.
1993, Feb. 4   **Perf. 13**

Archaeological Treasures. Anthropomorphic gold foil figures found in: 3.75k, Lundeborg, horiz. 5k, Bornholm.

975 A350 3.75k multicolored   1.50 .30
976 A350 5k multicolored   2.00 .70

A351   A352

Butterflies.

1993, Mar. 11   **Litho.**
977 A351 3.75k Small tortoise-shell   1.40 .40
978 A351 5k Large blue   2.10 .80
979 A351 8.75k Marsh fritillary   4.25 2.50
980 A351 12k Red admiral   4.75 3.25
   Nos. 977-980 (4)   12.50 6.95

1993, May 6   **Litho.**   **Perf. 12½**

Posters: 3.75k, Pierrot, by Thor Bogelund, 1947, horiz. 5k, Balloons, by Wilhelm Freddie, 1987.

981 A352 3.75k multicolored   1.50 .30
982 A352 5k multicolored   2.00 .80

Tivoli Gardens, 150th anniv.

A353

A354

Europa (Contemporary paintings by): 3.75k, Troels Worsel, horiz. 5k, Stig Brogger.

1993, May 6   **Perf. 13**
983 A353 3.75k multicolored   .80 .50
984 A353 5k multicolored   1.25 .60

1993, June 17   **Engr.**   **Perf. 13**
985 A354 5k dark blue green   2.00 .70

Danish-Russian relations, 500th anniv. See Russia No. 6154.

Training Ships
A355   A356
Perf. 13, 13½x13 (#987)
1993, June 17   **Litho. & Engr.**
986 A355 3.75k Danmark   1.50 .30
987 A356 4.75k Jens Krogh   1.90 1.90
988 A355 5k Georg Stage, horiz.   2.00 .85

Size: 39x28mm
Perf. 13x13½
989 A356 9.50k Marilyn Anne, horiz.   3.75 4.00
   Nos. 986-989 (4)   9.15 7.05

Child's Drawing   Letter Writing
of Viking   Campaign — A358
Ships — A357

1993, Aug. 19   **Litho.**   **Perf. 13**
990 A357 3.75k multicolored   1.50 .30
991 A358 5k lt & dk bl & blk   2.00 .70

Ethnic Jewelry — A359

1993, Sept. 16   **Litho.**   **Perf. 13**
992 A359 3.50k Falster   1.40 .70
993 A359 3.75k Amager   1.50 .30
994 A359 5k Laeso   2.00 .60
995 A359 8.75k Romo   3.50 2.00
   Nos. 992-995 (4)   8.40 3.60

Cubist Paintings A360

5k, Assemblage, by Vilhelm Lundstrom, 1929. 15k, Composition, by Franciska Clausen, 1929.

Litho. & Engr.
1993, Nov. 11   **Perf. 12½**
996 A360 5k multicolored   2.25 2.25
997 A360 15k multicolored   6.00 6.00
   See Nos. 1080-1081.

Conservation — A361

1994, Jan. 27   **Litho.**   **Perf. 13**
998 A361 3.75k Save water   1.50 .30
999 A361 5k CO2   2.00 .45

Castles A362

Castles: 3.50k, Marselisborg, Aarhus. 3.75k, Amalienborg, Copenhagen. 5k, Fredensborg, North Zealand. 8.75k, Graasten, South Jutland.

Litho. & Engr.
1994, Mar. 17   **Perf. 13x12½**
1000 A362 3.50k multicolored   1.40 .70
1001 A362 3.75k multicolored   1.50 .30
1002 A362 5k multicolored   2.00 .50
1003 A362 8.75k multicolored   3.50 3.50
   a.   Bklt. pane, #1000-1003   11.00 11.00

No. 1003a printed with 2 different labels. One shows a marching band, the other shows a ship.

Danmark Expedition, 1906-08 — A363

Europa: 3.75k, Expedition ship, Danmark, Alfred Wegener's weather balloon. 5k, Theodolite, Johan Peter Koch, cartographer.

1994, May 5   **Engr.**   **Perf. 13**
1004 A363 3.75k deep brn vio   .90 .20
1005 A363 5k dp slate grn   1.25 .50

Trams — A364

Designs: 3.75k, Copenhagen tram (Engelhardt). 4.75k, Aarhus car. 5k, Odense tram, vert. 12k, Horse-drawn tram.

Litho. & Engr.
1994, June 9   **Perf. 13**
1006 A364 3.75k multicolored   1.50 .30
1007 A364 4.75k multicolored   1.90 1.90
1008 A364 5k multicolored   2.00 .70
Size: 38x21mm
1009 A364 12k multicolored   4.75 4.25
   Nos. 1006-1009 (4)   10.15 7.15

Children's   ILO, 75th Anniv.
Stamp   A366
Competition
A365

1994, Aug. 25   **Litho.**   **Perf. 12½**
1010 A365 3.75k multicolored   1.50 .30

1994, Aug. 25   **Perf. 13**
1011 A366 5k multicolored   2.00 .40

A367

A368

Wild animals.

Litho. & Engr.
1994, Oct. 20   **Perf. 12½**
1012 A367 3.75k House sparrows   1.50 .35
1013 A367 4.75k Badger   1.90 1.50
1014 A367 5k Squirrel, vert.   2.00 .70
1015 A367 9.50k Black grouse   3.75 3.25
Size: 36x26mm
Perf. 13
1016 A367 12k Grass snake   4.75 4.00
   Nos. 1012-1016 (5)   13.90 9.80

1994, Nov. 10   **Litho.**   **Perf. 13**
1017 A368 3.75k multicolored   1.50 .30

Folk High Schools, 150th anniv.

Painting Type of 1988
Designs: 5k, Study of Italian Woman and Sleeping Child, by Wilhelm Marstrand. 15k,

Interior from Amaliegade with the Artist's Brothers, by Wilhelm Bendz.

Litho. & Engr.
1994, Nov. 10   **Perf. 12½x13**
1018 A308 5k multicolored   2.00 2.00
1019 A308 15k multicolored   6.00 6.00

Aarhus Cathedral School, 800th Anniv. — A369

Litho. & Engr.
1995, Jan. 26   **Perf. 13**
1020 A369 3.75k multicolored   1.50 .30

UN, 50th Anniv. — A370

Litho. & Engr.
1995, Jan. 26   **Perf. 13**
1021 A370 5k multicolored   2.00 .45
   Complete booklet, 10 #1021   30.00

Danish Islands A371

1995, Mar. 16   **Engr.**   **Perf. 13**
1022 A371 3.75k Avernako   1.50 .30
   Complete booklet, 10 #1022   15.00
1023 A371 4.75k Fejo   1.90 1.40
1024 A371 5k Fur   2.00 .75
1025 A371 9.50k Endelave   3.75 3.00
   a.   Booklet pane, #1022-1025 + 2 labels   10.00
   Complete booklet, 2 #1025a   21.00
   Nos. 1022-1025 (4)   9.15 5.45

No. 1025a printed with four different large labels. Labels with one pane are MF Faaborg II and MF Endelave. The other pane has MF Bukken-bruse and MF Fursund.

Liberation of Denmark, 50th Anniv. A372

Designs: 3.75k, Gen. Montgomery, Town Hall Square, vert. 5k, White busses returning from concentration camps. 8.75k, Airplane dropping supplies to resistance. 12k, Jews escape across the Sound to Sweden.

1995, May 4   **Litho.**   **Perf. 13**
1026 A372 3.75k multicolored   .90 .20
   Complete booklet, 10 #1026   11.00
1027 A372 5k multicolored   1.25 .60
1028 A372 8.75k multicolored   2.10 1.50
1029 A372 12k multicolored   3.00 2.75
   Nos. 1026-1029 (4)   7.25 5.05

Europa (Nos. 1026-1027).

A373   A374

1995, June 8   **Litho.**   **Perf. 13**
1030 A373 3.50k multicolored   1.40 .60

Danish Rhymed Chronicle, 500th anniv.

1995, June 8

3.75k, Roskilde Festival. 5k, Tonder Festival.

1031	A374	3.75k multi, horiz.	1.50	.30
	Complete booklet, 10 #1031		20.00	
1032	A374	5k multi	2.00	.50

No. 1031 is 28x21mm.

DANMARK 10.00   Paintings A375

Designs: 10k, "Sct. Hans Aften, 1955," by Jens Sondergaard. 15k, "Landskab-Gudhjem, 1939," by Niels Lergaard.

Litho. & Engr.

1995, Aug. 24   Perf. 13x12½

1033	A375	10k multicolored	4.00	4.00
1034	A375	15k multicolored	6.00	6.00

Tycho Brahe (1546-1601), Astronomer A376

3.75k, Uranienborg Observatory. 5.50k, Sextant.

Litho. & Engr.

1995, Oct. 27   Perf. 13

1035	A376	3.75k multicolored	1.50	.30
1036	A376	5.50k multicolored	2.10	1.75

See Sweden Nos. 2149-2150.

Toys A377

Designs: 3.75k, Tekno cars. 5k, Dolls, teddy bear. 8.75k, Model trains. 12k, Glud & Marstrand tin horse-drawn carriage & fire pumper.

1995, Nov. 9   Perf. 13x12½

1037	A377	3.75k multicolored	1.50	.30
	Complete booklet, 10 #1037		16.00	
1038	A377	5k multicolored	2.00	.75
1039	A377	8.75k multicolored	3.50	3.00
1040	A377	12k multicolored	4.75	4.75
	Nos. 1037-1040 (4)		11.75	8.80

A378   A379

Cartoonlike views of Copenhagen: 3.75k, Round Tower as music box. 5k, Christiansborg Castle. 8.75k, Marble Church as top of balloon. 12k, The Little Mermaid statue on stage.

1996, Jan. 25   Litho.   Perf. 13

1041	A378	3.75k multicolored	1.50	.30
	Complete booklet, 10 #1041		16.00	
1042	A378	5k multicolored	2.00	.70
1043	A378	8.75k multicolored	3.50	3.00
1044	A378	12k multicolored	4.75	4.25
	Nos. 1041-1044 (4)		11.75	8.25

Copenhagen, 1996 cultural capital of Europe.

1996, Mar. 21   Litho.   Perf. 13

1045	A379	3.75k Sports for disabled	1.50	.30
	Complete booklet, 10 #1045		16.00	
1046	A379	4.75k Swimming	1.90	1.50
1047	A379	5k Sailing	2.00	.50
1048	A379	9.50k Cycling	3.75	3.75
a.	Bklt. pane of 4, #1045-1048 + 2 labels		10.00	
	Complete booklet, 2 #1048a		20.00	

No. 1048a printed with two different large labels. One shows hands and soccer ball, second shows tennis racket and tennis balls.

Danish Federation for Sports for the Disabled (No. 1045). Modern Olympic Games, cent., Sports Confederation of Denmark, cent., 1996 Summer Olympics, Atlanta (Nos. 1046-1048).

A380   A381

1996, May 9   Litho.   Perf. 13

1049	A380	3.75k multicolored	1.50	.30

Danish Employers' Confederation, cent.

1996, May 9

Famous Danish Women (Europa): 3.75k, Karen Blixen (1885-1962), writer. 5k, Asta Nielsen (1881-1972), silent screen actress.

1050	A381	3.75k lt brn & dk brn	.90	.20
1051	A381	5k gray & dk blue	1.25	.40
	Complete booklet, 10 #1051		16.00	

A382   A383

Wooden Dinghies: 3.50k, Roskilde Fjord sail boat. 3.75k, Limfjorden skiff. 12.25k, Two-masted smack, South Funen Archipelago.

Perf. 13, 12½ (#1053)

1996, June 13   Engr.

1052	A382	3.50k multicolored	1.40	.85
1053	A382	3.75k multicolored	1.50	.30
	Complete booklet, 10 #1053		16.00	
1054	A382	12.25k multicolored	4.75	3.25
	Nos. 1052-1054 (3)		7.65	4.40

No. 1053 is 20x39mm.

Litho. & Engr.

1996, Sept. 12   Perf. 13x12½

Lighthouses.

1055	A383	3.75k Fornaes	1.50	.30
	Complete booklet, 10 #1055		16.00	
1056	A383	5k Blavandshuk	2.00	.40
a.	Bklt. pane, 8 #1055, 2 #1056		17.50	
	Complete booklet, #1056a		20.00	
1057	A383	5.25k Bovbjerg	2.10	1.50
1058	A383	8.75k Mon	3.50	2.25
	Nos. 1055-1058 (4)		9.10	4.45

Art Works of Thorvald Bindesboll (1846-1908) — A384

Litho. & Engr.

1996, Oct. 10   Perf. 13

1059	A384	3.75k Pitcher	1.50	.30
	Complete booklet, 10 #1059		16.00	

Litho.

1060	A384	4k Portfolio cover	1.60	1.10

DANMARK 10.00   Paintings A385

Designs: 10k, "At Lunch," by P.S. Kroyer, 1893. 15k, "The Girl with Sunflowers," by Michael Ancher, 1889.

Litho. & Engr.

1996, Nov. 7   Perf. 13x12½

1061	A385	10k multicolored	4.00	2.00
1062	A385	15k multicolored	5.75	3.00

A386   A387

Queen Margrethe II: 3.50k, With Prince Henrik. 3.75k, With Crown Prince Frederik. 4k, Delivering New Year speech. 5.25k, Waving to crowd.

1997, Jan. 14   Litho.   Perf. 13

1063	A386	3.50k multicolored	1.40	.50
1064	A386	3.75k multicolored	1.50	.30
	Complete booklet, 10 #1064		16.00	
1065	A386	4k multicolored	1.60	.50
1066	A386	5.25k multicolored	2.10	1.10
a.	Sheet of 4, #1063-1066 + 2 labels		7.00	7.00
	Nos. 1063-1066 (4)		6.60	2.40

Queen Margrethe II, 25th anniv. of coronation.

1997, Mar. 13   Engr.   Perf. 13

Open Air Museum, Copenhagen, Cent.: 3.50k, Kalstrup post mill. 3.75k, Ellested water mill. 5k, Fjellerup manor barn. 8.75k, Romo farm.

1067	A387	3.50k multicolored	1.40	.30
1068	A387	3.75k multicolored	1.50	.30
	Complete booklet, 10 #1068		16.00	
1069	A387	5k multicolored	2.00	1.25
	Complete booklet, 10 #1069		20.00	
1070	A387	8.75k multicolored	3.50	3.00
a.	Booklet pane, #1067-1070 + label		8.50	
	Complete booklet, 2 #1070a		17.00	
	Nos. 1067-1070 (4)		8.40	4.85

No. 1070a printed with two different large labels. One shows a view of Ellested water mill, the other shows a farm in Ejersted.

Great Belt Railway Link — A388

A389

1997, May 15   Litho.   Perf. 13

1071	A388	3.75k East Tunnel	1.50	.30
	Complete booklet, 10 #1071		15.00	
1072	A388	4.75k West Bridge	1.90	.85

1997, June 12   Litho.   Perf. 13

Kalmar Union, 600th Anniv.: No. 1073, Margrete I and Eric of Pomerania. No. 1074, The Three Graces symbolizing Denmark, Norway and Sweden.

1073	A389	4k multicolored	1.60	.60
1074	A389	4k multicolored	1.60	.60
a.	Pair, #1073-1074		3.50	1.40

No. 1074a is a continuous design.

Copenhagen-Roskilde Railway, 150th Anniv. — A390

Designs: 3.75k, Two modern trains under Carlsberg Bridge. 8.75k, Early steam train going under Carlsberg Bridge.

Litho. & Engr.

1997, June 12   Perf. 13

1075	A390	3.75k multicolored	1.50	.30
	Complete booklet, 10 #1075		15.00	
1076	A390	8.75k multicolored	3.50	1.50

End of Railway Mail Service A391

DANMARK 5.00

1997, June 12   Litho.

1077	A391	5k multicolored	2.00	.70

Stories and Legends A392

Europa: 3.75k, Large cat on top of treasure chest, from "The Tinder Box." 5.25k, Butterfly, pond, frog, from "Thumbelina."

1997, Aug. 28   Engr.   Perf. 13

1078	A392	3.75k multicolored	1.25	.20
1079	A392	5.25k multicolored	1.75	.90

Painting Type of 1993

Designs: 9.75k, "Dust Dancing in the Sun," by Vilhelm Hammershoi (1864-1916). 13k, "Woman Mountaineer," by J.F. Willumsen (1863-1958).

Litho. & Engr.

1997, Sept. 18   Perf. 13x12½

1080	A360	9.75k multicolored	3.75	1.60
1081	A360	13k multicolored	5.00	2.00

DANMARK 5.00   A393

Danish Design: 3.75k, Faaborg chair, vert. 4k, Margrethe bowl, vert. 5k, The Ant (chair). 12.25k, Georg Jensen silver bowl, vert.

1997, Nov. 6   Litho.   Perf. 13

1082	A393	3.75k multicolored	1.50	.30
	Complete booklet, 10 #1082		15.00	
1083	A393	4k multicolored	1.60	.70
1084	A393	5k multicolored	2.00	.45
1085	A393	12.25k multicolored	4.75	2.25
	Nos. 1082-1085 (4)		9.85	3.70

A394   A395

Danish Confederation of Trade Unions, Cent.: 3.50k, General Workers Union in Denmark (SiD). 3.75k, Danish Confederation of Trade Unions (LO). 4.75k, Danish Nurse's Organization. 5k, Union of Commercial and Clerical Employees in Denmark (HK).

1998, Jan. 22   **Litho.**   **Perf. 13**
1086	A394	3.50k multicolored	1.40	.75
1087	A394	3.75k multicolored	1.50	.30
	Complete booklet, 10 #1087		15.00	
1088	A394	4.75k multicolored	1.90	1.10
1089	A394	5k multicolored	2.00	.45
	Complete booklet, 10 #1089		20.00	
	Nos. 1086-1089 (4)		6.80	2.60

Litho. & Engr.

1998, Mar. 26   **Perf. 13**
1090	A395	3.75k multicolored	1.50	.65
	Complete booklet, 10 #1090		15.00	

City of Roskilde, 1000th anniv.

A396   A397

1998, Mar. 26   **Litho.**   **Perf. 13**
1091	A396	5k Ladybug	2.00	.30

Reduce poison.

1998, May 28   **Litho.**   **Perf. 13**

New Post & Tele Museum, Copenhagen: 3.75k, Postman, 1922. 4.50k, Morse code operator, c. 1910. 5.50k, Telephone operator, 1910. 8.75k, Modern postman.

1092	A397	3.75k multicolored	1.50	.30
	Complete booklet, 10 #1092		15.00	
a.	Booklet pane, 2 each #1087, 1089, 3 ea. 1090, 1092		20.00	
	Complete booklet, #1092a		20.00	
1093	A397	4.50k multicolored	1.75	.85
1094	A397	5.50k multicolored	2.10	1.00
1095	A397	8.75k multicolored	3.50	1.50
a.	Booklet pane, #1092-1095		9.00	
	Complete booklet, 2 #1095a		18.00	
	Nos. 1092-1095 (4)		8.85	3.65

No. 1095a is printed with two backgrounds. One shows part of King Christian IV's "Order Concerning Postmen," 1624. The other shows part of Copenhagen c. 1923. Complete booklets contain panes with each background.

Bridges over Great Belt A398

1998, May 28   **Engr.**   **Perf. 13**
1096	A398	5k West Bridge (shown)	2.00	.85
1097	A398	5k East Bridge (suspension)	2.00	.85
a.	Pair, #1096-1097 + label		4.25	2.00

Nordic Stamps — A399

Shipping: No. 1098, Signal flags, harbor master with binoculars. No. 1099, Radar

---

image of entrance to Copenhagen harbor, sextant.

1998, May 28   **Litho.**   **Perf. 13**
1098	A399	6.50k multicolored	2.50	1.10
1099	A399	6.50k multicolored	2.50	1.10
a.	Pair, #1098-1099		5.00	2.10
b.	Souvenir sheet, #1099a		5.00	2.10

National Festivals — A400

Europa: 3.75k, Horse at Danish agricultural show. 4.50k, Theater, tents at Arhus Festival Week, Arhus.

Litho. & Engr.

1998, Sept. 3   **Perf. 13**
1100	A400	3.75k multicolored	*1.25*	*.60*
	Complete booklet, 10 #1100		12.50	
1101	A400	4.50k multicolored	*1.50*	*.70*

Contemporary Art — A401

Paintings: 3.75k, Danish Autumn, by Per Kirkeby. 5k, Alpha, by Mogens Andersen, vert. 8.75k, Imagery, by Ejler Bille, vert. 19k, Celestial Horse, by Carl-Henning Pedersen.

Perf. 12½x13, 13x12½

1998, Oct. 15   **Litho. & Engr.**
1102	A401	3.75k multicolored	1.50	.30

Litho.
1103	A401	5k multicolored	2.00	.70
1104	A401	8.75k multicolored	3.50	.70
1105	A401	19k multicolored	7.50	1.75
	Nos. 1102-1105 (4)		14.50	3.45

See Nos. 1160-1161, 1190-1191.

A402

Fossil, name of Danish geologist: 3.75k, Ammonite, Ole Worm (1588-1654). 4.50k, Shark's teeth, Niels Stensen (1638-86). 5.50k, Sea Urchin, Soren Abildgaard (1718-91). 15k, Slit-shell snail, Erich Pontoppidan (1698-1764).

1998, Nov. 5   **Engr.**   **Perf. 13**
1106	A402	3.75k multicolored	1.50	.30
	Complete booklet, 10 #1106		15.00	
1107	A402	4.50k multicolored	1.75	.70
1108	A402	5.50k multicolored	2.10	.70
1109	A402	15k multicolored	5.75	1.75
a.	Souvenir sheet, #1106-1109		11.50	5.25

Wavy Lines and Queen Types of 1933, 1997 and:

Queen Margrethe II — A402a

1999-2000   **Engr.**   **Perf. 12¾**
1111	A32	150o purple	.60	.25
1112	A32	375o green	1.50	.70
1113	A32	400o green	1.25	.65
1114	A321a	4k red	1.60	.25
a.	Booklet pane, 4 #883, 2 #494, 2 #1114		4.00	
	Complete booklet, #1114a		4.00	

1115	A402a	4k red	1.60	.25
b.	Booklet pane, 4 #883, 2 #494, 2 #1115		2.50	
	Booklet, #1115b		2.50	
c.	Sheet of 8 + label		12.50	
1116	A32	425o green	1.60	.30
1117	A402a	4.25k blue	1.60	.30
1118	A402a	4.25k red	1.50	.70
b.	Booklet pane, 6 #883, 2 #1118		3.50	
c.	Sheet of 8 + central label		11.00	
1119	A402a	4.50k orange	1.75	.30
a.	Vert. strip of 10 + 10 etiquettes		17.50	
1120	A402a	4.50k red	1.75	.30
a.	Booklet pane, 2 #494, 2 #1120		4.00	
	Complete booklet, #1120a		4.00	
b.	Sheet of 8 + central label		13.50	
1121	A402a	4.75k sepia	1.90	.65
1122	A402a	5k dk green	2.00	.25
a.	Sheet of 8 + 8 etiquettes		11.00	
1123	A402a	5.25k ultra	2.10	.40
1124	A402a	5.50k violet	2.25	.40
a.	Sheet of 8 + label		14.00	
1125	A321a	5.75k blue	2.25	.60
1126	A402a	5.75k emerald	2.25	.60
1127	A402a	6k bister	2.40	.50
a.	Sheet of 10 + 10 etiquettes		22.50	
1128	A402a	6.25k green	2.50	1.10
1129	A402a	6.50k slate grn	2.50	.85
a.	Sheet of 8 + 8 etiquettes		20.00	20.00
b.	Sheet of 8 + central label		17.00	
1130	A321a	6.75k slate green	2.75	.60
1131	A402a	6.75k henna brn	2.75	1.00
1132	A402a	7k rose lilac	2.75	.50
1133	A402a	8.50k bright blue	3.25	1.50
1134	A55	10.50k dk bl gray	4.00	1.50
1135	A55	11.50k dk bl gray	4.50	1.90
1136	A55	12.50k gray	5.00	1.75
1137	A55	13k orange	5.00	1.90
1138	A55	15k blue	5.75	2.25
	Nos. 1111-1138 (28)		70.65	22.25

Issued: 375o, #1118, 1130, 1/13/99; #1125, 1/3/00; #1119, 1119a, 4.25k, 4.50k, 5k, 5.25k, 5.50k, #1126, 1131, 4/12/00; No. 1119b, 6k, 7k, 5/9/01; Nos. 1119c, 1121a, 1124a, 4/17/01; 150o, 4.75k, 6.50k, 10.50k, 1/2/02. 400o, No. 1120, 6.25k, 8.50k, 11.50k, 1/2/03. No. 1120b, 3/12. Nos. 1124b, 1129a, 3/12/03. Nos. 1128b, 1/2/03; No. 1122a, 4/2/02; 425o, No. 1120, 12.50k, 13k, 15k, 1/2/04. Nos. 1120b, 1127a, 1/2/04.

A403

1999, Jan. 13   **Litho.**   **Perf. 13**
1143	A403	4k Oersted Satellite	1.50	.55

Deciduous Trees A404

4k, Fagus sylvatica. 5k, Fraxinus excelsior, vert. 5.25k, Tilia cordata, vert. 9.25k, Quercus robur.

1999, Jan. 13   **Litho. & Engr.**
1144	A404	4k multicolored	1.60	.30
	Complete booklet, 10 #1144		16.00	
1145	A404	5k multicolored	2.00	.60
1146	A404	5.25k multicolored	2.10	.60
1147	A404	9.25k multicolored	3.50	1.25
	Nos. 1144-1147 (4)		9.20	2.75

50th Anniversaries — A405

Litho. & Engr.

1999, Feb. 24   **Perf. 13**
1148	A405	3.75k Home Guard	1.50	.30
1149	A405	4.25k NATO	1.60	.60

A406   A407

Harbingers of spring.

1999, Feb. 24   **Litho.**
1150	A406	4k Lapwing in flight	1.60	.30
	Complete booklet, 10 #1150		16.00	
1151	A406	5.25k Geese	2.10	.90
a.	Souvenir sheet, #1150-1151		5.50	1.75

Litho. & Engr.

1999, Apr. 28   **Perf. 13**

Nature Reserves.
1152	A407	4.50k Vejlerne	*1.50*	*.40*
1153	A407	5.50k Langli	*1.90*	*.60*

Europa.

Council of Europe, 50th Anniv. A408

1999, Apr. 28   **Engr.**
1154	A408	9.75k blue	3.75	1.25

Danish Constitution, 150th Anniv. — A409

1999, June 2   **Litho.**   **Perf. 13**
1155	A409	4k red & black	1.60	.30

Danish Revue, 150th Anniv. A410

Performers: 4k, Kjeld Petersen and Dirch Passer, comedians. 4.50k, Osvald Helmuth, singer. 5.25k, Preben Kaas and Jorgen Ryg, comedians, singers. 6.75k, Liva Weel, singer.

1999, June 2   **Engr.**   **Perf. 13**
1156	A410	4k deep red	1.60	.30
	Complete booklet, 10 #1156		16.00	
1157	A410	4.50k slate	1.75	.50
1158	A410	5.25k deep blue	2.10	.85
	Complete booklet, 10 #1158		21.00	
1159	A410	6.75k deep claret	2.75	1.10
a.	Bklt. pane, #1156-1159 + 2 labels		8.50	
	Complete booklet, 2 #1159a		17.00	
	Nos. 1156-1159 (4)		8.20	2.75

No. 1159a printed with two different pairs of labels. One version has showgirl label at left, the second version has showgirl label at right. Complete booklets contain one of each pane.

Contemporary Paintings Type

9.25k, Fire Farver, by Thomas Kluge. 16k, Dreng, by Lise Malinovsky.

1999, Aug. 25   **Litho.**   **Perf. 12¾**
1160	A401	9.25k multi, vert.	3.50	1.60
1161	A401	16k multi, vert.	6.25	2.50

Opening of New Extension of the Royal Library, "The Black Diamond" A411

1999, Aug. 25   Engr.   *Perf. 13¾*
1162 A411 8.75k black   3.00 1.25

Migratory Birds — A412

Litho. & Engr.
1999, Sept. 29   *Perf. 12¾*
1163 A412   4k Swallows   1.60 .30
   Complete booklet, 10 #1163   16.00
1164 A412 5.25k Gray-lag geese   2.10 .80
   a.   Souvenir sheet, #1163-1164   4.00 1.50
1165 A412 5.50k Common eider   2.25 .85
1166 A412 12.25k Arctic tern   4.75 2.10
   a.   Souvenir sheet, #1165-1166   7.50 3.00
   Nos. 1163-1166 (4)   10.70 4.05

Stamps from Nos. 1164a and 1166a lack white border found on Nos. 1163-1166.

New Year 2000 — A413

1999, Nov. 10   Litho.   *Perf. 13¼*
1167 A413 4k Hearts   1.60 .30
1168 A413 4k Wavy lines   1.60 .30
   a.   Bklt. pane, 5 ea #1167-1168   16.00
   Complete booklet, #1168a   16.00

The 20th Century — A414

4k, Prof. J.H. Deuntzer on front page of newspaper, 1901. 4.50k, Newspaper illustration, 1903. 5.25k, Asta Nielsen and Poul Reumert in the film "The Abyss," 1910. 5.75k, Advertising sticker showing woman on telephone, 1914.
See sheet of 16, #1184a.

2000, Jan. 12   Litho. & Engr.
1169 A414   4k buff & blk   1.60 .30
   Complete booklet, 10 #1169   16.00
1170 A414 4.50k multicolored   1.75 .50
1171 A414 5.25k multicolored   2.10 .85
   Complete booklet, 10 #1171   21.00
1172 A414 5.75k multicolored   2.25 .90
   Nos. 1169-1172 (4)   7.70 2.55

2000, May 9

4k, Allegory of women suffrage on front page of newspaper, 1915. 5k, Newspaper caricature of the Kanslergade Agreement, 1933. 5.50k, Film "Long and Short," 1927. 6.75k, Front page of Radio Weekly Review, 1925.

1173 A414   4k multi   1.60 .55
   Booklet, 10 #1173   16.00
1174 A414   5k multi   2.00 .65
1175 A414 5.50k multi   2.25 .75
1176 A414 6.75k multi   2.75 .85
   Nos. 1173-1176 (4)   8.60 2.80

2000, Aug. 23

4k, Liberation of Denmark on front page of newspaper, 1945. 5.75k, Newspaper caricature of new constitution, 1953. 6.75k, Poster for film "Café Paradise," 1950. 12.25k, Advertisement for Arena television, 1957.

1177 A414   4k multi   1.60 .55
   Booklet, 10 #1177   16.00

1178 A414 5.75k multi   2.25 .80
1179 A414 6.75k multi   2.75 .85
1180 A414 12.25k multi   4.75 1.60
   Nos. 1177-1180 (4)   11.35 3.80

2000, Nov. 8

4k, Entry of Denmark into European Community on front page of newspaper, 1972. 4.50k, Newspaper caricature of youth revolt, 1969. 5.25k, Poster for film "The Olsen Gang," 1968. 5.50k, Denmark Post website on Internet, 1999.

1181 A414   4k multi   1.60 .55
   Booklet, 10 #1181   16.00
1182 A414 4.50k multi   1.75 .60
1183 A414 5.25k multi   2.10 .70
   Booklet, 10 #1183   21.00
   a.   Booklet pane, #1171, 1175, 1179, 1183 + label   10.00
    Booklet, 2 #1183a   20.00
1184 A414 5.50k multi   2.25 .75
   a.   Sheet of 16, #1169-1184   35.00 13.00
   Nos. 1181-1184 (4)   7.70 2.60

No. 1183a comes with two different labels. Booklet contains one of each.

60th Birthday of Queen Margrethe II — A415

2000, Apr. 12   Litho.   *Perf. 12¾*
1185 A415   4k blk & car   1.60 .60
   Complete booklet, 10 #1185   16.00
1186 A415 5.25k blk & blue   2.10 .80
   a.   Souvenir sheet, #1185-1186   4.00 1.50

Oresund Bridge, Sweden-Denmark — A416

Illustration reduced.

Litho. & Engr.
2000, May 9   *Perf. 12¾*
1187 A416 4.50k shown   1.75 .60

Litho.
1188 A416 4.50k Map   1.75 .60
   a.   Pair, #1187-1188   3.50 1.25

See Sweden Nos. 2391-2393.

Europa, 2000
Common Design Type
2000, May 9   Litho.   *Perf. 13*
1189 CD17 9.75k multi   3.25 1.10

Contemporary Art Type of 1998
Designs: 4k, Pegasus, by Kurt Trampedach. 5.25k, Landscape, by Nina Sten-Knudsen.

2000, Sept. 27   *Perf. 12¾*
1190 A401   4k multi   1.60 .55
1191 A401 5.25k multi   2.10 .75

Royal Danish Air Force, 50th Anniv. A417

2000, Sept. 27   Engr.
1192 A417 9.75k black & red   3.75 1.25
   a.   Souvenir sheet of 1   3.75 1.25

Botanical Gardens, Copenhagen — A418

Litho. & Engr.
2001, Jan. 24   *Perf. 12¾*
1193 A418   4k Palm House   1.60 .60
   Booklet, 10 #1193   16.00

Size: 28x21mm
1194 A418   6k Lake   2.25 .85
1195 A418 12.25k Water lilies   4.75 1.75
   Nos. 1193-1195 (3)   8.60 3.20

"Use the Language" A419

2001, Mar. 28   Litho.   *Perf. 13*
1196 A419 4k "A," text   1.60 .55
   Booklet, 10 #1196   16.00
1197 A419 7k "Z," text   2.75 .90

Danish Postage Stamps, 150th Anniv. — A420

Portion of #2 and: 4k, Engraver Martinus Willam Ferslew. 5.50k, Printer Andreas Thiele. 6k, Head Copenhagen postmaster Frantz Christopher von Jessen. 10.25k, Postmaster General Magnus Otto Spohus Count Danneskjold-Samsoe.

Litho. & Engr.
2001, Apr. 1   *Perf. 13¼x13*
1198 A420   4k multi   1.60 .55
1199 A420 5.50k multi   2.25 .75
   Booklet, 10 #1199   22.50
1200 A420   6k multi   2.40 .80
1201 A420 10.25k multi   4.00 1.50
   a.   Booklet pane, #1198-1201 + label   10.50
    Booklet, 2 #1201a   21.00
   Nos. 1198-1201 (4)   10.25 3.60

No. 1201a printed with two different labels. One version has proof of stamp design, sketch of proposed design and Ferslew's letter to Danneskjold-Samsoe, and other shows two essays and letter from M. T. C. Bartholdy.

Europa — A421

Designs: 4.50k, Hands in water. 9.75k, Woman's head, water.

2001, May 9   Litho.   *Perf. 13¼x13*
1202 A421 4.50k multi   1.50 .50
   a.   Booklet pane of 5 + 5 etiquettes   7.50
    Booklet, 2 #1202a   15.00
1203 A421 9.75k multi   3.25 1.10

Contemporary Paintings Type of 1998
Designs: 18k, Missus, by Jorn Larsen, horiz. 22k, Postbillede, by Henning Damgaard-Sorensen.

Perf. 13x12½, 12½x13
2001, Aug. 22   Litho.
1204 A401 18k multi   7.00 2.50
1205 A401 22k multi   8.50 3.00

Youth Culture A422

Designs: 4k, Skateboarding. 5.50k, Kissing. 6k, Creating music. 10.25k, Tongue piercing.

2001, Aug. 22   *Perf. 13*
1206 A422   4k multi   1.60 .60
   Booklet, 10 #1206   16.00
1207 A422 5.50k multi   2.10 .80
   Booklet, 10 #1207   21.00
1208 A422   6k multi   2.40 .85
1209 A422 10.25k multi   4.00 1.50
   a.   Souvenir sheet, #1206-1209   10.50 3.50
   Nos. 1206-1209 (4)   10.10 3.75

Hafnia 01 Philatelic Exhibition, Copenhagen A423

Monarch and stamps: 4k, Queen Margrethe II, #757, 1000. 4.50k, King Frederik IX, #775, 1003. 5.50k, King Christian X, #1001, B10. 7k, King Christian IX, #1002, 66.

Litho. & Engr.
2001, Oct. 16   *Perf. 13x13¼*
1210 A423   4k multi   1.60 .60
1211 A423 4.50k multi   1.75 .65
1212 A423 5.50k multi   2.10 .80
1213 A423   7k multi   2.75 1.00
   a.   Souvenir sheet, #1210-1213   8.25 2.75
   b.   Strip, #1210-1213 + central label   8.25 2.75
   Nos. 1210-1213 (4)   8.20 3.05

Island Ferries A424

Designs: 3.75k, Bukken-Bruse. 4k, Ouro. 4.25k, Hjarno. 6k, Barsofaergen.

2001, Nov. 7   *Perf. 12¾*
1214 A424 3.75k multi   1.50 .55
1215 A424   4k multi   1.60 .60
   Booklet, 10 #1215   16.00
1216 A424 4.25k multi   1.60 .60
1217 A424   6k multi   2.40 .85
   Nos. 1214-1217 (4)   7.10 2.60

Comics and Cartoons — A425

Designs: 4k, Rasmus Klump, by Vilhelm Hansen. 5.50k, Valhalla, by Peter Madsen. 6.50k, Jungledyret Hugo, by Flemming Quist Moller. 10.50k, Cirkeline, by Hanne Hastrup.

2002, Jan. 16   Litho.   *Perf. 13¼x13*
1218 A425   4k multi   1.60 .55
   Booklet, 10 #1218   16.00
   a.   Sheet of 8 + label   15.00 4.00
1219 A425 5.50k multi   2.10 .75
   Booklet, 10 #1219   21.00
   a.   Sheet of 8 + label   21.00 5.50
1220 A425 6.50k multi   2.50 .85
1221 A425 10.50k multi   4.00 1.50
   a.   Souvenir sheet, #1218-1221   10.50 3.50
   Nos. 1218-1221 (4)   10.20 3.65

The Girls in the Airport, Sculpture by Hanne Varming — A426

Designs: 4k, Rear view. 5k, Front view.

Photo. & Engr.

2002, Mar. 13   **Perf. 12¾**
1222	A426	4k multi, *greenish*	1.60	.55
		Booklet, 10 #1222	16.00	
1223	A426	5k multi, *greenish*	2.00	.70

Europa — A427

Winning drawings in children's stamp design contest: 4k, Clown, by Luna Ostergard. 5k, Clown, by Camille Wagner Larsen.

2002, May 15   **Litho.**   **Perf. 13**
1224	A427	4k multi	1.40	.50
		Booklet, 10 #1224	14.00	
1225	A427	5k multi	1.75	.60
a.		Booklet pane of 5 + 5 etiquettes	8.75	—
		Booklet, 2 #1225a	17.50	

Landscapes
A428

2002, May 15   **Engr.**
1226	A428	4k Bornholm	1.60	.60
1227	A428	6k West Jutland	2.40	.85
1228	A428	6.50k Langeland	2.50	.90
1229	A428	12.50k Thy	5.00	1.75
		Nos. 1226-1229 (4)	11.50	4.10

Historic
Postal
Vehicles
A429

Designs: 4k, 1953 Nimbus motorcycle. 5.50k, 1962 Bedford van. 10k, 1984 Renault 4 van. 19k, 1998 Volvo FH12 tractor trailer.

Litho. & Engr.

2002, Aug. 21   **Perf. 13x13¼**
1230	A429	4k multi	1.60	.60
		Booklet, 10 #1230	16.00	
a.		Sheet of 8 + central label	14.00	—
1231	A429	5.50k multi	2.10	.80
		Booklet, 10 #1231	21.00	
1232	A429	10k multi	4.00	1.50
1233	A429	19k multi	7.50	2.75
a.		Booklet pane of 4, #1230-1233	16.00	
		Booklet, 2 #1233a	32.50	
		Nos. 1230-1233 (4)	15.20	5.65

No. 1233a is printed with two different labels. One shows a 1908 Berlíet van and the other a 2002 Peugeot Partner. Both are included in the booklet.

Opening of Copenhagen
Metro — A430

2002, Sept. 25   **Engr.**   **Perf. 12¾**
1234	A430	5.50k multi, *tan*	1.90	.75

Contemporary Paintngs Type of 1998

Designs: 5k, Children's Corner, by Jens Birkemose, vert. 6.50k, Maleren og Modellen, by Frans Kannik, vert.

2002, Sept. 25   **Perf. 13x12½**
1235	A401	5k red & blue	2.00	.80
1236	A401	6.50k multi	2.50	1.00

Intl. Council for the
Exploration of the
Sea, Cent. — A431

Atlantic cod and: 4k, Exploration ship Dana. 10.50k, Hirtshals lighthouse.

Litho. & Engr.

2002, Sept. 25   **Perf. 13¼x13**
1237	A431	4k multi	1.60	.65
1238	A431	10.50k multi	4.00	1.60
a.		Souvenir sheet, #1237-1238	5.75	2.25

See Faroe Islands No. 426, Greenland Nos. 401-402.

Danish
House
Architecture
A432

Designs: 4k, Dianas Have, Horsholm, by Vandkusten Design Studio, 1992. 4.25k, Blangstedgard, Odense, by Poul Ingemann, 1988. 5.50k, Dansk Folkeferie, Karrebaeksminde, by Stephan Kappel, 1979. 6.50k, Fredensborg Terraces, Fredensborg, by Jorn Utzon, 1963. 9k, Soholm, Klampenborg, by Arne Jacobsen, 1950.

Litho. & Engr.

2002, Nov. 8   **Perf. 12¾**
1239	A432	4k multi	1.60	.65
		Booklet, 10 #1239	16.00	
1240	A432	4.25k multi	1.60	.70
1241	A432	5.50k multi	2.10	.85
1242	A432	6.50k multi	2.50	1.00
1243	A432	9k multi	3.50	1.50
		Nos. 1239-1243 (5)	11.30	4.70

Youth Sports — A433

2003, Jan. 15   **Litho.**   **Perf. 12¾**
1244	A433	4.25k Soccer	1.50	.70
		Booklet, 10 #1244	16.00	
a.		Sheet of 8 + central label	13.00	—
1245	A433	5.50k Swimming	2.10	.90
		Booklet, 10 #1245	21.00	
1246	A433	8.50k Gymnastics	3.25	1.50
1247	A433	11.50k Handball	4.50	2.00
		Nos. 1244-1247 (4)	11.35	5.10

Danish Literary
Greenland
Expedition,
Cent. — A434

Designs: 4.25k, Expedition members Harald Moltke, Knud Rasmussen, Jorgen Bronlund, Ludvig Mylius-Erichsen and Gabriel Olsen. 7k, Campsite.

2003, Mar. 12   **Engr.**   **Perf. 12¾**
1248	A434	4.25k blue gray	1.60	.70

Size: 61x22mm
1249	A434	7k multi	2.75	1.25
a.		Souvenir sheet, #1248-1249 + label	4.50	1.90

See Greenland Nos. 407-408.

Europa
A435

Insects
A436

Poster art: 4.25k, Poster for Copenhagen International Theater Festival, by Ole Fick, 1985. 5.50k, Poster for Bertel Thorvaldsen Museum, by Ole Woldbye, 1970.

2003, May 14   **Litho.**   **Perf. 12¾**
1250	A435	4.25k multi	1.40	.70
		Booklet, 10 #1250	14.00	

Engr.
1251	A435	5.50k multi	1.75	.85
		Booklet, 10 #1251	17.50	
a.		Sheet of 8 + central label	14.00	—

2003, May 14   **Litho. & Engr.**

Designs: 4.25k, Ephemera danica. 6.50k, Dytiscus latissimus. 12k, Cordulegaster boltoni, vert.
1252	A436	4.25k multi	1.60	.80
a.		Sheet of 8 + central label	13.00	—
1253	A436	6.50k multi	2.50	1.25
a.		Sheet of 8 + central label	20.00	—

Size: 21x39mm
1254	A436	12k multi	4.75	2.40
a.		Souvenir sheet, #1252-1254	9.00	9.00
		Nos. 1252-1254 (3)	8.85	4.45

Contemporary Art Type of 1998

Designs: 5.50k, Baering, by Sys Hindsbo. 19k, Det Forjaettede Land, by Poul Anker Bech.

Litho. & Engr.

2003, Aug. 27   **Perf. 12½x13**
1255	A401	5.50k multi	2.10	1.00

Litho.
1256	A401	19k multi	7.50	3.50

Danish House Architecture Type of 2002

Designs: 4k, Bellahoj Apartment Complex, Copenhagen, by Tage Nielsen and Mogens Irming, 1944-58. 4.25k, Anchersvej, Klampenborg, by Mogens Lassen, 1935. 5.25k, Gerthasminde, Odense, by Anton Rosen, 1912-35. 9k, Solvang, Vallekilde College, by Andreas Bentsen and Martin Nyrop, 1889. 15k, Stenbrogard, Brorup, by Peter Holdensen, 1868.

Litho. & Engr.

2003, Aug. 27   **Perf. 12¾**
1257	A432	4k multi	1.60	.70
1258	A432	4.25k multi	1.60	.80
		Complete booklet, 10 #1258	16.00	
1259	A432	5.25k multi	2.10	.90
1260	A432	9k multi	3.50	1.60
1261	A432	15k multi	6.00	2.50
		Nos. 1257-1261 (5)	14.80	6.50

A437   A438

2003, Nov. 7   **Engr.**   **Perf. 12¾**
1262	A437	6.50k gray blue	2.50	1.25

Awarding of first Nobel Prize to a Dane (Niels Finsen for Physiology and Medicine), cent.

2003, Nov. 7   **Litho. & Engr.**

Artifacts from Royal Jelling World Heritage Site: 4.25k, Queen Thyra's stone. 5.50k, King Gorm's cup. 8.50k, King Harald's stone. 11.50k, Wall paintings, Jelling Church.
1263	A438	4.25k multi	1.60	.80
		Booklet, 10 #1263	16.00	
1264	A438	5.50k multi	2.10	1.10
		Booklet, 10 #1264	21.00	
1265	A438	8.50k multi	3.25	1.60
1266	A438	11.50k multi	4.50	2.25
		Nos. 1263-1266 (4)	11.45	5.75

A spiral-bound booklet, enclosed in a slipcase, with four booklet panes containing single stamps of Nos. 1263-1266, and a booklet pane containing a strip of Nos. 1263-1266, sold for 99k.

Danish House Architecture Type of 2002

Designs: 4.50k, Spurveskjul, Virum, by Nicolai Abildgaard, 1805. 6k, Liselund, Mon, by Andreas Kirkerup, 1792. 7k, Kampmann's Yard, Varde, by Hans Wolff Ollgaard, Hack Kampmann and Mikkel Stobberup, 1781. 12.50k, Harsdorff's House, Copenhagen, by Caspar Frederik Harsdorff, 1780. 15k, Nyso Manor, Praesto, by Jens Lauridsen.

Litho. & Engr.

2004, Jan.14   **Perf. 12¾**
1267	A432	4.50k multi	1.75	.85
		Booklet, 10 #1267	17.50	
1268	A432	6k multi	2.40	1.10
1269	A432	7k multi	2.75	1.40
1270	A432	12.50k multi	5.00	2.50
1271	A432	15k multi	6.00	2.75
		Nos. 1267-1271 (5)	17.90	8.60

Academy of Fine
Arts,
Copenhagen,
250th
Anniv. — A439

Litho. & Engr.

2004, Mar. 26   **Perf. 13¼x13**
1272	A439	5.50k multi	2.10	1.00
		Booklet, 10 #1272	21.00	

Norse
Gods — A440

Designs: 4.50k, Heimdal guarding Bifrost bridge. 6k, Gefion plowing Sjaelland out of Sweden.

2004, Mar. 26
1273	A440	4.50k multi	1.75	.85
a.		Sheet of 8 + central label	14.00	14.00
1274	A440	6k multi	2.40	1.10
a.		Souvenir sheet, #1273-1274	4.25	2.00
b.		Sheet of 8 + central label	19.00	19.00

Wedding of Crown Prince Frederik and
Mary Donaldson — A441

No. 1275: a, Couple facing right. b, Couple facing left.

Litho. & Photo.

2004, May 14   **Perf. 13x13¼**
1275	A441	Horiz. pair	3.50	1.75
		Booklet, 5 #1275	17.50	
a.-b.		4.50k Either single, denomination 8½ mm wide	1.75	.85
c.-d.		4.50k Either single, denomination 7½ mm wide	1.75	.85
e.		Souvenir sheet, #1275c-1275d + central label	3.50	1.75

Frederiksberg
Palace, 300th
Anniv. — A442

Designs: 4.25k, Doorway overlooking Sondermarken Park. 4.50k, Gatehouse archway, castle yard. 6.50k, Aerial view.

Litho. & Engr.

2004, May 14			*Perf. 13*
1276	A442	4.25k multi	1.60 .80
1277	A442	4.50k multi	1.75 .85

Size: 55x32mm

1278	A442	6.50k multi	2.50 1.25
a.	Souvenir sheet, #1276-1278		6.00 2.75
	Nos. 1276-1278 (3)		5.85 2.90

Prince Henrik, 70th Birthday — A443

2004, June 9	**Litho.**		*Perf. 12¾*
1279	A443	4.50k multi	1.75 .85

Europa
A444

2004, June 9			*Perf. 13*
1280	A444	6k Cyclists	2.00 1.00
1281	A444	9k Sailboats	3.00 1.50

Contemporary Paintings Type of 1998

Designs: 13k, Senses the Body Landscape, by Lars Ravn, vert. 21k, The Dog Bites, by Lars Norgard, vert.

Litho. & Engr.

2004, Aug. 25			*Perf. 13x12½*
1282	A401	13k multi	5.00 2.50

Litho.

1283	A401	21k multi	8.25 4.00

Viking Ship Museum, Roskilde A445

Designs: 4.50k, Skuldelev 1 on Roskilde Fjord. 5.50k, Reconstruction of Skuldelev 2. 6.50k, Cross-section of ship. 12.50k, Excavation of archaelogical site where ships were found.

Litho. & Engr.

2004, Aug. 25			*Perf. 13x13¼*
1284	A445	4.50k multi	1.75 .85
	Complete booklet, 10 #1284		17.50
1285	A445	5.50k multi	2.10 1.00
	Complete booklet, 10 #1285		21.00
1286	A445	6.50k multi	2.50 1.25
1287	A445	12.50k multi	5.00 2.40
	Nos. 1284-1287 (4)		11.35 5.50

A spiral-bound booklet, enclosed in a slipcase, with four booklet panes containing single stamps of Nos. 1284-1287 and a booklet pane containing a strip of Nos. 1284-1287, sold for 99k.

Birds of Prey A446

Designs: 4.50k, Falco tinnunculus. 5.50k, Accipiter nisus. 6k, Buteo buteo. 7k, Circus aeruginosus.

Litho. & Engr.

2004, Nov. 5			*Perf. 13*
1288	A446	4.50k multi	1.75 .90
	Complete booklet, 10 #1288		17.50
a.	Sheet of 8 + central label		14.00 14.00
1289	A446	5.50k multi	2.10 1.00
a.	Sheet of 8 + central label		17.00 17.00
1290	A446	6k multi	2.40 1.25
1291	A446	7k multi	2.75 1.40
	Nos. 1288-1291 (4)		9.00 4.55

Queen and Small State Seal Types of 1946-2000

2005-07		**Engr.**	*Perf. 12¾*
1295	A402a	4.75k red	1.90 .35
a.	Sheet of 8 + central label		15.00 —
1296	A402a	5.50k red	2.25 .50
1296A	A402a	6.50k blue	2.60 .50
1297	A402a	7.25k black violet	2.75 .60
1298	A402a	7.50k blue	3.00 .60
1299	A402a	7.75k vio blk	3.25 .60
1300	A402a	8k indigo	3.00 .65
1301	A402a	8.25k Prussian blue	3.25 .70
1302	A402a	8.75k Prus blue	3.50 .65
1304	A55	10k lemon	4.00 1.60
1305	A55	13.50k green	5.25 2.75
1309	A55	16.50k red brown	6.50 3.00
1310	A55	17k slate green	6.50 2.50
1311	A55	17.50k purple	6.75 3.50
1312	A55	20k blue	8.00 4.00
1313	A55	22k brown violet	8.50 4.25
	Nos. 1295-1313 (16)		71.00 26.75

Issued: 7.50k, 16.50k, 22k, 1/3. 4.75k, 8k, 11/11. 4.75k, 10k, 1/2/06. 7.25k, 8.25k, 11/10/06. 13.50k, 17.50k, 1/2/07. 20k, 11/8/07. 5.50k, 6.50k, 7.75k, 8.75k, 1/2/08. This is an expanding set. Numbers may change.

Danish House Architecture Type of 2002

Designs: 4.25k, Hjarup Manse, Vamdrup, c. 1665. 4.50k, Ejdersted Farm, Southwest Schleswig, 1653. 7.50k, Provstegade, Randers, c. 1650. 9.50k, Smith's Yard, Koge, c. 1550. 16.50k, Carmelite Monastery, Elsinore, c. 1500.

Litho. & Engr.

2005, Jan. 12			*Perf. 12¾*
1317	A432	4.25k multi	1.60 .85
1318	A432	4.50k multi	1.75 .90
	Complete booklet, 10 #1318		17.50
a.	Booklet pane, 4 #691, 8 #1318		16.00 —
	Complete booklet, #1318a		16.00
1319	A432	7.50k multi	3.00 1.50
1320	A432	9.50k multi	3.75 1.90
1321	A432	16.50k multi	6.50 3.25
	Nos. 1317-1321 (5)		16.60 8.40

Bonn-Copenhagen Declaration, 50th Anniv. — A447

2005, Mar. 2			**Litho.**
1322	A447	6.50k multi	2.50 1.40

See Germany No. 2330.

Hans Christian Andersen (1805-75), Author — A448

Paper Cutting by Andersen, Scissors — A449

Designs: 6.50k, Pen, inkwell, illustration of duckling, manuscript handwritten by Andersen. 7.50k, Andersen's drawing of Casino dell'Orlogio, Rome, and boots.

2005, Mar. 2			**Engr.**
1323	A448	4.50k black	1.75 .90
a.	Sheet of 8 + central label		14.00 14.00

Litho. & Engr.

1324	A449	5.50k multi	2.10 1.10
	Complete booklet, 10 #1324		21.00
a.	Sheet of 8 + central label		17.00 17.00
1325	A449	6.50k multi	2.50 1.40
1326	A449	7.50k multi	3.00 1.50
	Nos. 1323-1326 (4)		9.35 4.90

A spiral-bound booklet, enclosed in a slipcase, with four booklet panes containing single stamps of Nos. 1323-1326, and a booklet pane containing a strip of Nos. 1323-1326, sold fof 99k.

See Malta Nos. 1196-1199.

August Bournonville (1805-79), Choreographer A450

Bournonville and: 4.50k, Dancer. 5.50k, Dancers.

Litho. & Engr.

2005, May 4			*Perf. 13¼x13*
1327	A450	4.50k multi	1.75 .90
	Complete booklet, 10 #1327		17.50
a.	Sheet of 8 + central label		14.00 —
1328	A450	5.50k multi	2.10 1.00
a.	Sheet of 8 + central label		17.00 —
b.	Souvenir sheet, #1327-1328		4.00 2.00

Sailors in World War II — A451

Designs: 4.50k, Ship convoy. 7.50k, Unloading of ship's cargo.

2005, May 4	**Litho.**		*Perf. 13*
1329	A451	4.50k multi	1.75 .90
1330	A451	7.50k multi	3.00 1.50

Europa — A452

2005, May 4			*Perf. 12¾*
1331	A452	6.50k Hot dog	2.25 1.10
1332	A452	9.50k Fish	3.25 1.60

Contemporary Art Type of 1998

Designs: 5.50k, Telepathy, by Anna Fro Vodder, vert. 6.50k, Home Again, by Kaspar Bonnén, vert. 7.50k, Unrest, by John Korner, vert. 12.50k, Palace in the Morning, by Tal Rosenzweig.

2005, Aug. 24			**Litho.**
1333	A401	5.50k multi	2.10 1.00
1334	A401	6.50k multi	2.50 1.25
1335	A401	7.50k multi	3.00 1.40
1336	A401	12.50k multi	5.00 2.40
	Nos. 1333-1336 (4)		12.60 6.05

Perf. 13x12½, 12½x13

INDEX:2005 Intl. Design Exhibition, Copenhagen A453

2005, Aug. 24	**Engr.**		*Perf. 13¼*
1337	A453	4.50k black	1.75 .90
	Complete booklet, 10 #1337		17.50

Wavy Lines Type of 1905-17

2005-06		**Engr.**	*Perf. 12¾*
1338	A10	25o indigo	.25 .20
a.	Booklet pane, 2 each #1295, 1338 ('06)		3.50 —
	Complete booklet, #1338a		3.50
1339	A10	50o brown	.25 .20
1340	A10	100o bright blue	.40 .20
1341	A10	200o dark green	.75 .20
1342	A10	450o green	1.75 .30
	Nos. 1338-1342 (5)		3.40 1.10

Wavy Line stamps, cent.

Issued: Nos. 1338-1342, 10/28/05. #1328a, 1/2/06.

Seals A454

Designs: 4.50k, Phoca vitulina. 5.50k, Halichoerus grypus.

2005, Nov. 11	**Engr.**		*Perf. 13x13¼*
1343	A454	4.50k multi	1.75 .90
	Complete booklet, 10 #1343		17.50
1344	A454	5.50k indigo	2.10 .95
a.	Souvenir sheet, #1343-1344		3.75 3.75

Flowers — A455

Designs: 4.75k, Calanthus nivalis. 5.50k, Eranthis hyemalis. 7k, Crocus vernus hybrid. 8k, Anemone nemorosa.

2006, Jan. 11	**Engr.**		*Perf. 12¾*
1345	A455	4.75k multi	1.90 .90
	Complete booklet, 10 #1345		19.00
a.	Sheet of 8 + central label		15.00 —
1346	A455	5.50k multi	2.10 1.00
	Complete booklet, 10 #1346		21.00
a.	Sheet of 8 + central label		17.00 —
1347	A455	7k multi	2.75 1.25
1348	A455	8k multi	3.00 1.40
	Nos. 1345-1348 (4)		9.75 4.55

Creatures in Norse Mythology — A456

Designs: 4.75k, Elf king and elf girls. 7k, Incubi, werewolves, hel-horse, gnome and troll.

Litho. & Engr.

2006, Mar. 29			Perf. 13¼x13	
1349	A456	4.75k multi	1.90	.90
1350	A456	7k multi	2.75	1.25
a.	Souvenir sheet, #1349-1350		4.75	4.75

Rosenborg Castle, 400th Anniv. — A457

Designs: 4.75k, Castle exterior. 5.50k, Silver lion, thrones of king and queen. 13k, Royal coat of arms ceiling decoration.

2006, Mar. 29				
1351	A457	4.75k multi	1.90	.90
	Complete booklet, 10 #1351		19.00	
1352	A457	5.50k multi	2.10	1.00
1353	A457	13k multi	5.00	2.50
	Nos. 1351-1353 (3)		9.00	4.40

A spiral-bound booklet, enclosed in a slip-case, with four booklet panes containing single stamps of Nos. 1351-1353 and a booklet pane containing a strip of Nos. 1351-1353, sold for 99k.

New Carlsberg Glyptotek, Cent. — A458

Designs: 4.75k, Marble relief from Athenian graveyard. 5.50k, Conservatory dome. 8k, Dancer Looking at the Sole of Her Right Foot, sculpture by Edgar Degas.

2006, June 7				
1354	A458	4.75k multi	1.90	.90
	Complete booklet, 10 #1354		19.00	
1355	A458	5.50k multi	2.10	1.00
1356	A458	8k multi	3.00	1.40
a.	Souvenir sheet, #1354-1356		7.00	7.00
	Nos. 1354-1356 (3)		7.00	3.30

Race Cars A459

Designs: 4.75k, 1958 Alfa Dana Midget, Swebe Jap. 5.50k, 1965 Austin Mini Cooper S, 1965 Ford Cortina GT, 1965 Alfa Romeo 1600 GTA. 10k, 1963 Jaguar E Type, 1967 Volvo P 1800. 17k, 1965 Lotus Elan, Renault Alpine A 110.

2006, June 7			Perf. 13x13¼	
1357	A459	4.75k multi	1.90	.90
	Complete booklet, 10 #1357		19.00	
1358	A459	5.50k multi	2.10	1.00
	Complete booklet, 10 #1358		21.00	
1359	A459	10k multi	4.00	2.00
1360	A459	17k multi	6.50	3.25
	Nos. 1357-1360 (4)		14.50	7.15

Europa — A460

Winning designs in children's stamp design contest: 4.75k, Smiling children, by Rikke Veber Rasmussen. 7k, Two smiling children, by Anette Bertram Nielsen.

2006, Aug. 23		Litho.	Perf. 13¼x13	
1361	A460	4.75k multi	1.90	.90
	Booklet, 10 #1361		19.00	
1362	A460	7k blk & dull grn	2.75	1.25

Airplanes A461

Designs: 4.50k, J. C. H. Ellehammer's 1906 biplane. 4.75k, KZ II, 1946. 5.50k, KZ IV, 1944. 13k, KZ VII, 1947.

Litho. & Engr.

2006, Aug. 23			Perf. 12¾	
1363	A461	4.50k multi	1.75	.85
1364	A461	4.75k multi	1.90	.90
a.	Miniature sheet of 8 + central label		15.00	15.00
1365	A461	5.50k multi	2.10	1.00
a.	Miniature sheet of 8 + central label		17.00	17.00
1366	A461	13k multi	5.00	2.50
	Nos. 1363-1366 (4)		10.75	5.25

Paintings by COBRA Group Artists A462

Designs: 4.75k, Untitled, by Asger Jorn. 5.50k, Landscape of the Night, by Else Alfelt, vert. 7k, New Skin, by Pierre Alechinsky. 8k, The Olive Eater, by Egill Jacobsen, vert.

2006, Nov. 10		Perf. 13x13¼, 13¼x13	Litho.	
1367	A462	4.75k multi	1.90	.90
	Booklet, 10 #1367		19.00	
1368	A462	5.50k multi	2.10	1.00
1369	A462	7k multi	2.75	1.25
1370	A462	8k multi	3.00	1.40
	Nos. 1367-1370 (4)		9.75	4.55

See Belgium Nos. 2168-2169.

Danish Soldiers in United Nations Peace-keeping Forces, 50th Anniv. — A463

Litho. & Engr.

2007, Jan. 10			Perf. 13	
1371	A463	4.75k multi	1.90	.90

Intl. Polar Year A464

Designs: 7.25k, Wooden and walrus tusk carvings of Norse, Late Dorset and Thule cultures of Greenland. 13.50k, Research airplane used for measuring thickness of polar ice.

2007, Jan. 10			Perf. 13¼	
1372	A464	7.25k multi	2.75	1.40
1373	A464	13.50k multi	5.25	2.50
a.	Souvenir sheet, #1372-1373		8.00	8.00

Windmills — A465

Designs: 4.50k, Askov Mill, 1891. 4.75k, Gedser Mil, 1957. 6k, Bogo Mill, 1989. 8.25k, Middelgrunden, 2000.

2007, Jan. 10			Engr.	
1374	A465	4.50k brown	1.75	.90
1375	A465	4.75k red	1.90	.95
	Complete booklet, 10 #1375		19.00	
a.	Sheet of 8 + central label		15.00	15.00
1376	A465	6k green	2.40	1.25
	Complete booklet, 10 #1376		24.00	
a.	Sheet of 8 + central label		19.00	19.00
1377	A465	8.25k blue	3.25	1.60
	Nos. 1374-1377 (4)		9.30	4.70

Galathea 3 Scientific Expedition — A466

Satellite, ship and: 4.75k, Marine life. 7.25k, Globe showing route of expedition.

Litho. & Engr.

2007, Mar. 28			Perf. 12¾	
1378	A466	4.75k multi	1.75	.85
1379	A466	7.25k multi	2.60	1.40
a.	Souvenir sheet, #1378-1379		4.50	4.50

National Museum, Bicent. — A467

Designs: 4.75k, Ceremonial axes. 6k, Funen aquaemanale. 8.25k, Armillary sphere. 10.25k, Wooden mask, Borneo.

2007, Mar. 28			Perf. 13¼	
1380	A467	4.75k Prus bl & blk	1.75	.85
	Complete booklet, 10 #1380		17.50	
1381	A467	6k brn lake & blk	2.25	1.10
1382	A467	8.25k orange & blk	3.00	1.50
1383	A467	10.25k bl gray & blk	3.75	1.90
	Nos. 1380-1383 (4)		10.75	5.35

A spiral-bound booklet, enclosed in a slip-case, with four booklet panes containing single stamps of Nos. 1380-1383 and a booklet pane containing a strip of Nos. 1380-1383, sold for 109k.

Europa A468

Scouts: 4.75k, On hike. 7.25k, Around campfire.

2007, June 6			Perf. 13x13¼	
1384	A468	4.75k multi	1.75	.85
	Complete booklet, 10 #1384		17.50	
1385	A468	7.25k multi	2.60	1.40

Scouting, cent.

Modern Art A469

Designs: 4.75k, The Traveler, by Arne Haugen Sorensen. 8.25k, Trionfale, by Seppo Mattinen.

2007, June 6		Litho.	Perf. 13x12½	
1386	A469	4.75k multi	1.75	.85
a.	Miniature sheet of 8 + central label		14.00	14.00
1387	A469	8.25k multi	3.00	1.50

Mandatory Use of Metric System in Denmark, Cent. A470

Litho. & Engr.

2007, Aug. 22			Perf. 12¾	
1388	A470	4.75k black & red	1.75	.85

Nature of Denmark A471

Flora and fauna of Rabjerg Dune: 4.75k, Niobe fritillary butterfly (klitperlemorsommerfugl). 6k, Northern dune tiger beetle (sandspringer). 7.25k, Sand lizard (markfirben). 13.50k, Seaside pansy (klitstedmoderblomst).

2007, Aug. 22				
1389	A471	4.75k multi	1.75	.85
	Complete booklet, 10 #1389		17.50	
1390	A471	6k multi	2.25	1.10
	Complete booklet, 10 #1390		22.50	
1391	A471	7.25k multi	2.75	2.75
1392	A471	13.50k multi	5.00	2.50
a.	Souvenir sheet, #1389-1392		12.00	6.00
	Nos. 1389-1392 (4)		11.75	7.20

Famous Men — A472

Designs: 4.75k, Poul Henningsen (1894-1967), designer, and Artichoke lamp. 6k, Victor Borge (1909-2000), comedian, and piano keys. 7.25k, Arne Jacobsen (1902-71), architect, and Egg chair. 8.25k, Piet Hein (1905-96), inventor, and superellipse.

2007, Nov. 8		Engr.	Perf. 12¾	
1393	A472	4.75k multi	1.90	.95
	Complete booklet, 10 #1393		19.00	
1394	A472	6k blk & blue	2.40	1.25
1395	A472	7.25k multi	3.00	1.50
1396	A472	8.25k blk & purple	3.25	1.60
	Nos. 1393-1396 (4)		10.55	5.30

Danish National Theater A473

Designs: 5.50k, Old Stage. 6.50k, Playhouse. 7.75k, Copenhagen Opera House.

Litho. & Engr.

2008, Jan. 9			Perf. 13x13¼	
1397	A473	5.50k multi	2.25	1.10
	Complete booklet, 10 #1397		22.50	
a.	Sheet of 8 + central label		18.00	
1398	A473	6.50k multi	2.60	1.25
	Complete booklet, 10 #1398		26.00	
1399	A473	7.75k multi	3.25	1.60
	Nos. 1397-1399 (3)		8.10	3.95

SEMI-POSTAL STAMPS

Nos. 159, 157 Surcharged in Red

Wmk. Multiple Crosses (114)

1921, June 17			Perf. 14½x14	
B1	A20	10o + 5o green	14.00	50.00
B2	A21	20o + 10o slate	17.00	60.00
	Set, never hinged		85.00	

Crown and
Staff of
Aesculapius
SP1

Dybbøl Mill
SP2

1929, Aug. 1   **Engr.**

B3	SP1 10ø yellow green	3.75	5.00
a.	Booklet pane of 2	27.50	
B4	SP1 15ø brick red	5.75	8.75
a.	Booklet pane of 2	32.50	
B5	SP1 25ø deep blue	25.00	30.00
a.	Booklet pane of 2	135.00	
	Nos. B3-B5 (3)	34.50	43.75
	Set, never hinged	65.00	

These stamps were sold at a premium of 5 øre each for benefit of the Danish Cancer Committee.

1937, Jan. 20   **Unwmk.**   *Perf. 13*

B6	SP2 5ø + 5ø green	.55	1.00
B7	SP2 10ø + 5ø lt brown	2.40	4.00
B8	SP2 15ø + 5ø carmine	2.40	4.00
	Nos. B6-B8 (3)	5.35	9.00
	Set, never hinged	12.50	

The surtax was for a fund in memory of H. P. Hanssen, statesman.

Nos. 223a and B6, Nos. 229 and B7, Nos. 238A and B8 are found se-tenant in booklets. For booklet panes, see Nos. 223d, 229b and 238e.

Queen
Alexandrine
SP3

Princesses
Ingrid and
Margrethe
SP4

1939-40   *Perf. 13*

B9	SP3 5ø + 3ø rose lake & red ('40)	.20	.20
a.	Booklet pane of 4	2.00	2.00
B10	SP3 10ø + 5ø dk violet & red	.20	.20
B11	SP3 15ø + 5ø scarlet & red	.30	.50
	Nos. B9-B11 (3)	.70	.90
	Set, never hinged	1.40	

The surtax was for the Danish Red Cross.

Nos. 230 and B10 have been issued se-tenant in booklets. See No. 230b. In this pane No. 230 measures 23½x31mm from perf. to perf.

1941-43

B12	SP4 10ø + 5ø dk violet	.20	.25
a.	Booklet pane of 10	19.00	
B13	SP4 20ø + 5ø red ('43)	.20	.25
	Set, never hinged	.60	

Surtax for the Children's Charity Fund.

No. 288 Surcharged
in Red

1944, May 11

B14	A48 10ø + 5ø violet	.25	.25
a.	Booklet pane of 10	27.50	
	Never hinged	.30	

The surtax was for the Danish Red Cross.

Symbols of
Freedom
SP5

Explosions at
Rail Junction
SP6

Danish Flag
SP7

Princess Anne-
Marie
SP8

1947, May 4   **Engr.**   *Perf. 13*

B15	SP5 15ø + 5ø green	.35	.30
B16	SP6 20ø + 5ø dark red	.35	.30
B17	SP7 40ø + 5ø deep blue	.90	.75
	Nos. B15-B17 (3)	1.60	1.35

Issued in memory of the Danish struggle for liberty and the liberation of Denmark. The surtax was for the Liberty Fund.
For surcharges see Nos. B22-B23.

1950, Oct. 19   **Unwmk.**

B18	SP8 25ø + 5ø rose brown	.55	.50

The surtax was for the National Children's Welfare Association.

S. S.
Jutlandia — SP9

1951, Sept. 13   *Perf. 13*

B19	SP9 25ø + 5ø red	.65	.60

The surtax was for the Red Cross.

No. 335 Surcharged in
Black

1953, Feb. 13

B20	A61 30ø + 10ø brown red	1.50	1.25

The surtax was for flood relief in the Netherlands.

Stone
Memorial — SP10

1953, Mar. 26   *Perf. 13*

B21	SP10 30ø + 5ø dark red	1.40	1.25

The surtax was for cultural work of the Danish Border Union.

Nos. B15 and B16 Surcharged with
New Value and Ornamental Screen in
Black

1955, Feb. 17

B22	SP5 20ø + 5ø on No. B15	1.00	.85
B23	SP6 30ø + 5ø on No. B16	1.00	.85

The surtax was for the Liberty Fund.

No. 341 Surcharged

1957, Mar. 25

B24	A61 30ø + 5ø on 95ø red org	.65	.65

The surtax went to the Danish Red Cross for aid to Hungary.

#335 Surcharged: "Gronlandsfonden +
10"

1959, Feb. 23

B25	A61 30ø + 10ø brown red	.85	.85

The surtax was for the Greenland Fund.

Globe
Encircled by
Red Cross
Flags — SP11

Queen
Ingrid — SP12

1959, June 24   **Engr.**   *Perf. 13*

B26	SP11 30ø + 5ø rose red	.45	.40
B27	SP11 60ø + 5ø lt ultra & car	.80	.75

Centenary of the Intl. Red Cross idea. The surtax was for the Red Cross. Crosses photogravure on No. B27.

1960, Oct. 25   **Unwmk.**

B28	SP12 30ø + 10ø dark red	1.00	1.10

Queen Ingrid's 25th anniv. as a Girl Scout. The surtax was for the Scouts' fund for needy and sick children.

African Mother,
Child — SP13

Healthy and
Crippled
Hands — SP14

1962, May 24

B29	SP13 30ø + 10ø dark red	.75	1.00

Issued to aid underdeveloped countries.

1963, June 24   *Perf. 13*

B30	SP14 35ø + 10ø dark red	1.10	1.10

The surtax was for the benefit of the Cripples' Foundation.

Old Bridge at
Danish-German
Border — SP15

1964, May 28   **Engr.**

B31	SP15 35ø + 10ø henna brn	.85	.90

Surtax for the Danish Border Union.

Princesses
Margrethe,
Benedikte, Anne-
Marie — SP16

Happy
Child — SP17

1964, Aug. 24

B32	SP16 35ø + 10ø dull red	.75	.75
B33	SP16 60ø + 10ø dk bl & red	.95	.95

The surtax was for the Red Cross.

1965, Oct. 21   **Engr.**   *Perf. 13*

B34	SP17 50ø + 10ø brick red	.50	.50

The surtax was for the National Children's Welfare Association.

"Red Cross" in 32 Languages and Red
Cross, Red Lion and Sun, and Red
Crescent Emblems
SP18

1966, Jan. 20   **Engr.**   *Perf. 13*

B35	SP18 50ø + 10ø red	.50	.50

Engraved and Photogravure

B36	SP18 80ø + 10ø dk bl & red	1.00	1.00

The surtax was for the Red Cross.

"Refugees
66" — SP19

Symbolic
Rose — SP20

1966, Oct. 24   **Engr.**   *Perf. 13*

B37	SP19 40ø + 10ø sepia	.80	.80
B38	SP19 50ø + 10ø rose red	.80	.80
B39	SP19 80ø + 10ø blue	1.10	1.10
	Nos. B37-B39 (3)	2.70	2.70

The surtax was for aid to refugees.

1967, Oct. 12

B40	SP20 60ø + 10ø brown red	.50	.50

The surcharge was for the Salvation Army.

Two Greenland
Boys in Round
Tower — SP21

1968, Sept. 12   **Engr.**   *Perf. 13*

B41	SP21 60ø + 10ø dark red	.65	.65

The surtax was for child welfare work in Greenland.

Princess
Margrethe and
Prince Henrik
with Prince
Frederik — SP22

1969, Dec. 11

B42	SP22 50ø + 10ø brn & red	.65	.65
B43	SP22 60ø + 10ø brn red & red	.65	.65

The surtax was for the Danish Red Cross.

Child Seeking
Help — SP23

1970, Mar. 13
B44 SP23 60o + 10o brown red   .65 .65
Surtax for "Save the Children Fund."

Child — SP24

Marsh
Marigold — SP25

1971, Apr. 29   Engr.   Perf. 13
B45 SP24 60o + 10o copper red   .65 .65
Surtax was for the National Children's Wel-
fare Association.

1972, Aug. 17
B46 SP25 70o + 10o green & yel   .45 .45
Soc. and Home for the Disabled, cent.

Heimaey Town
and
Volcano — SP26

1973, Oct. 17   Engr.   Perf. 13
B47 SP26 70o + 20o vio blue & red .75 .75
The surtax was for the victims of the erup-
tion of Heimaey Volcano, Jan. 23, 1973.

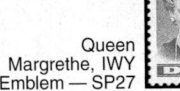

Queen
Margrethe, IWY
Emblem — SP27

1975, Mar. 20   Engr.   Perf. 13
B48 SP27 90o + 20o red & buff   .75 .75
International Women's Year 1975. Surtax
was for a foundation to benefit women primarily in Greenland and Faroe Islands.

Skuldelev I
SP28

Ships: 90o+20o, Thingvalla, emigrant
steamer. 100o+20o, Liner Frederick VIII, c.
1930. 130o+20o, Three-master Danmark.

1976, Jan. 22   Engr.   Perf. 13
B49 SP28 70 + 20o olive brown   .75 .85
B50 SP28 90 + 20o brick red   .75 .85
B51 SP28 100 + 20o olive green   .85 1.10
B52 SP28 130 + 20o violet blue   .85 1.10
      Nos. B49-B52 (4)   3.20 3.90
American Declaration of Independence,
200th anniv.

People and   Invalid in
Red Cross   Wheelchair
SP29   SP30

1976, Feb. 26   Engr.   Perf. 13
B53 SP29 100o + 20o red & black .65 .65
B54 SP29 130o + 20o bl, red & blk .80 .80
Centenary of Danish Red Cross.

1976, May 6   Engr.   Perf. 13
B55 SP30 100o + 20o ver & blk   .65 .65
The surtax was for the Foundation to Aid the
Disabled.

Mother and   Anti-Cancer
Child — SP31   Campaign — SP32

1977, Mar. 24   Engr.   Perf. 12½
B56 SP31 1k + 20o multicolored   .70 .70
Danish Society for the Mentally Handi-
capped, 25th anniv. Surtax was for the
Society.

1978, Oct. 12   Engr.   Perf. 13
B57 SP32 120o + 20o red   .65 .65
Danish Anti-Cancer Campaign, 50th anni-
versary. Surtax was for campaign.

Child and IYC
Emblem — SP33

1979, Jan. 25   Engr.   Perf. 12½
B58 SP33 1.20k + 20o red & brown .65 .65
International Year of the Child.

Foundation for
the Disabled,
25th Anniversary
SP34

1980, Apr. 10   Engr.   Perf. 13
B59 SP34 130o + 20o brown red   .65 .65

Children   Intl. Year of the
Playing Ball   Disabled
SP35   SP36

1981, Feb. 5   Engr.   Perf. 12½x13
B60 SP35 1.60k + 20o brown red   .65 .65
Surtax was for child welfare.

1981, Sept. 10   Engr.   Perf. 12½x13
B61 SP36 2k + 20o dark blue   .90 .90

Stem and Broken
Line — SP37

1982, May 3   Engr.   Perf. 13
B62 SP37 2k + 40o dull red   1.00 1.00
Surtax was for Danish Multiple Sclerosis
Society.

Nurse with Patient   1984 Olympic
SP38   Games
                     SP39

1983, Jan. 27   Engr.
B63 SP38 2k + 40o multicolored 1.25 1.25

1984, Feb. 23   Litho. & Engr.
B64 SP39 2.70k + 40o multi   1.40 1.40

Electrocardiogram Reading,
Heart — SP40

1984, Sept. 6   Engr.   Perf. 12½
B65 SP40 2.70k + 40o red   1.40 1.40
Surtax was for Heart Foundation.

SP41   SP42

1985, May 2   Litho.   Perf. 13
B66 SP41 2.80k + 50o multi   1.40 1.40
Liberation from German Occupation, 40th
Anniv. Surtax for benefit of World War II
veterans.

1985, Oct. 3   Litho. & Engr.
Design: Tapestry detail, by Caroline
Ebbeson (1852-1936), former patient, St.
Hans Hospital, Roskilade.
B67 SP42 2.80k + 40o multi   1.25 1.25
Natl. Soc. for the Welfare of the Mentally Ill,
25th Anniv. Surtax benefited the mentally ill.

Danish Arthritis
Assoc., 50th
Anniv. — SP43

1986, Mar. 20   Litho.   Perf. 13
B68 SP43 2.80k + 50o mul-
        ticolored   1.50 1.50
Surtax for the Arthritis Assoc.

Poul Reichhart (1913-
1985), as Papageno
in The Magic
Flute — SP44

1986, Feb. 6   Litho.   Perf. 13
B69 SP44 2.80k + 50o multi-
        ticolored   1.50 1.50
Surtax for the physically handicapped.

Danish Society
for the Blind,
75th
Anniv. — SP45

Litho. & Engr.   Perf. 13
B70 SP45 2.80k +50o blk, vio brn
        & dk red   1.50 1.50

Danish
Assoc. of
Epileptics,
25th Anniv.
SP46

1987, Sept. 24   Engr.   Perf. 13
B71 SP46 2.80k +50o dk red, brt
        ultra & dk grn   1.60 1.60

Folkekirkens
Nodhjaelp Relief
Organization — SP47

1988, Mar. 10   Engr.
B72 SP47 3k +50o multicolored   1.60 1.60
Surtax for the relief organization.

Natl. Council for
Unwed Mothers,
5th
Anniv. — SP48

1988, Sept. 22   Photo.
B73 SP48 3k +50o dk rose brn   1.60 1.60

SP49   SP50

1989, Feb. 16   Litho.
B74 SP49 3.20k +50o multi   2.00 2.00
Salvation Army.

1990, Aug. 30   Litho.   Perf. 13
B75 SP50 3.50k +50o Insulin
        crystal   2.25 2.25
Danish Diabetes Assoc., 50th anniv.

Children's
Telephone
SP51

1991, June 6   Engr.   Perf. 13
B76 SP51 3.50k +50o dark blue   1.75 1.75
Surtax benefits Borns Vilkar, children's wel-
fare organization.

Danish Dyslexia Assoc., 50th Anniv. SP52

Litho. & Engr.

1992, Aug. 27 | **Perf. 13**
B77 SP52 3.75k +50o multi   2.00 2.00

SP53   SP54

1993, Aug. 19 | **Litho.** | **Perf. 13**
B78 SP53 3.75k +50o multi   1.50 1.50
YMCA Social Work, 75th anniv.

Litho. & Engr.

1994, June 9 | **Perf. 13**
B79 SP54 3.75k +50o multi   1.50 1.50
Prince Henrik, 60th birthday. Surtax for Danish Red Cross.

Natl. Society of Polio and Accident Victims, 50th Anniv. SP55

1995, June 8 | **Litho.** | **Perf. 13**
B80 SP55 3.75k +50o red   1.50 1.50

SP56   SP57

1996, Oct. 10 | **Litho.** | **Perf. 13**
B81 SP56 3.75k +50o red & black   1.50 1.50
The AIDS Foundation.

1997, May 15 | **Litho.** | **Perf. 13**
B82 SP57 3.75k +50o multi   1.50 1.50
Asthma-Allergy Assoc.

Danish Cancer Society SP58

1998, Sept. 3 | **Litho.** | **Perf. 13**
B83 SP58 3.75k +50o multi   1.50 1.50

SP59

SP60

1999, Aug. 25 | **Litho.** | **Perf. 13**
B84 SP59 4k +50o blue & red   1.60 1.60
For the Alzheimer's Association.

2000, Sept. 27 | **Engr.** | **Perf. 13**
B85 SP60 4k +50o red & blue   1.60 1.60
For the Cerebral Palsy Association.

Amnesty International — SP61

2001, Jan. 24 | **Engr.** | **Perf. 12¾**
B86 SP61 4k +50o blk & red   1.60 1.60

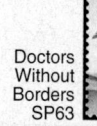
LEV National Association SP62

2002, Mar. 13 | **Engr.** | **Perf. 12¾**
B87 SP62 4k + 50o multi, *greenish*   1.60 1.60

Doctors Without Borders SP63

2003, Mar. 12 | **Litho.** | **Perf. 12¾**
B88 SP63 4.25k +50o multi   1.60 1.60
Booklet, 10 #B88   16.00

Children's Aid Day — SP64

2004, Jan. 14 | **Litho.** | **Perf. 12¾**
B89 SP64 4.50k +50o multi   1.75 1.75
Booklet, 10 #B89   17.50

SOS Children's Villages SP65

2005, Jan. 12 | **Litho.** | **Perf. 12¾**
B90 SP65 4.50k +50o multi   1.75 1.75
Complete booklet, 10 #B90   17.50

Surtax was originally intended for an SOS Children's Village in Burundi, but surtax went to the relief fund for Dec. 26, 2004 tsunami victims. A sticker noting this change was to be applied to the front covers of the booklets.

Danish Refugee Council, 50th Anniv. SP66

2006, Jan. 11 | **Engr.** | **Perf. 12¾**
B91 SP66 4.75k +50o blk & red, *tan*   1.90 1.90
Complete booklet, 10 #B91   19.00

Crown Prince Frederik, Crown Princess Mary, and Prince Christian SP67

2007, Jan. 10 | **Engr.** | **Perf. 13x13¼**
B92 SP67 4.75k +50o multi   1.90 1.90
Complete booklet, 10 #B92   19.00

Surtax for Crown Prince Frederik and Crown Princess Mary's Fund for Charitable and Humanitarian Purposes.

Danish Cancer Society, 80th Anniv. — SP68

2008, Jan. 9 | **Engr.** | **Perf. 12¾**
B93 SP68 5.50k +50o blk & red   2.40 2.40
Complete booklet, 10 #B93   24.00

AIR POST STAMPS

Airplane and Plowman AP1

Towers of Copenhagen AP2

Wmk. Multiple Crosses (114)

				1925-29	**Typo.**	**Perf. 12x12½**	
C1	AP1	10o yellow green	24.00	32.50
C2	AP1	15o violet ('26)	47.50	52.50
C3	AP1	25o scarlet	40.00	45.00
C4	AP1	50o lt gray ('29)	95.00	160.00
C5	AP1	1k choc ('29)	80.00	160.00
		Nos. C1-C5 (5)	286.50	450.00
		Set, never hinged	700.00	

Unwmk.

				1934, June 9	**Engr.**	**Perf. 13**	
C6	AP2	10o orange	.70	1.40
C7	AP2	15o red	2.50	5.00
C8	AP2	20o Prus blue	2.75	5.50
C9	AP2	50o olive black	2.75	5.50
C10	AP2	1k brown	11.00	21.00
		Nos. C6-C10 (5)	19.70	38.40
		Set, never hinged	42.50	

LATE FEE STAMPS

LF1

Coat of Arms — LF2

Perf. 14x14½

			1923	**Typo.**	**Wmk. 114**	
I1	LF1	10o green	12.00	4.50
		Never hinged	37.50	
a.		Double overprint	—	

No. I1 was, at first, not a postage stamp but represented a tax for the services of the post office clerks in filling out postal forms and writing addresses. In 1923 it was put into use as a Late Fee stamp.

1926-31

I2	LF2	10o green	8.50	1.10
I3	LF2	10o brown ('31)	8.25	.50
		Set, never hinged	45.00	

1934 | **Unwmk.** | **Engr.** | **Perf. 13**

I4	LF2	5o orange	.40	.25
I5	LF2	10o orange	.40	.25
		Set, never hinged	1.60	

POSTAGE DUE STAMPS

Regular Issues of 1913-20 Overprinted

Perf. 14x14½

				1921, May 1		**Wmk. 114**	
J1	A10	1o deep orange	1.40	2.10
J2	A16	5o green	4.25	3.25
J3	A16	7o orange	3.50	2.50
J4	A16	10o red	19.00	10.50
J5	A16	20o deep blue	11.00	6.25
J6	A16	25o brown & blk	27.50	3.50
J7	A16	50o claret & blk	9.00	4.25
		Nos. J1-J7 (7)	75.65	32.35
		Set, never hinged	190.00	

Same Overprint in Dark Blue On Military Stamp of 1917

1921, Nov. 23

J8	A16	10o red	12.00	8.50
		Never hinged	27.50	
a.		"S" inverted	140.00	200.00
		Never hinged	275.00	

Numeral of Value — D1

Typographed (Solid Panel)

				1921-30		**Perf. 14x14½**	
J9	D1	1o orange ('22)	.60	.50
J10	D1	4o blue ('25)	2.25	1.25
J11	D1	5o brown ('22)	2.25	.75
J12	D1	5o lt green ('30)	.85	.70
J13	D1	7o apple grn ('27)	13.00	13.00
J14	D1	7o dk violet ('30)	27.50	27.50
J15	D1	10o yellow grn ('22)	2.25	.50
J16	D1	10o lt brown ('30)	1.10	.40
J17	D1	20o grnsh blue ('21)	1.40	.60
a.		Double impression	2,500.	
J18	D1	20o gray ('30)	1.40	.95
J19	D1	25o scarlet ('23)	2.25	.80
J20	D1	25o violet ('26)	2.00	1.00
J21	D1	25o lt blue ('30)	5.00	2.75
J22	D1	1k dk blue ('21)	80.00	6.50
J23	D1	1k brn & dk bl ('25)	15.00	6.50
J24	D1	5k purple ('25)	20.00	9.00
		Nos. J9-J24 (16)	176.85	72.70
		Set, never hinged	400.00	

Engraved (Lined Panel)

				1934-55	**Unwmk.**	**Perf. 13**	
J25	D1	1o slate	.30	.25
J26	D1	2o carmine	.30	.25
J27	D1	5o yellow green	.30	.25
J28	D1	6o dk olive ('41)	.50	.25
J29	D1	8o magenta ('50)	2.00	2.25
J30	D1	10o orange	.30	.25
J31	D1	12o dp ultra ('55)	.40	.30
J32	D1	15o violet ('37)	.50	.25
J33	D1	20o gray	.45	.25
J34	D1	25o blue	.50	.25
J35	D1	30o green ('53)	.50	.25
J36	D1	40o claret ('49)	.60	.25
J37	D1	1k brown	.75	.25
		Nos. J25-J37 (13)	7.40	5.30
		Set, never hinged	12.00	

No. 96 Surcharged in Black

1934 | **Wmk. 114** | **Perf. 14x14½**

J38	A10	15o on 12o violet	5.00	3.50
		Never hinged	16.00	

MILITARY STAMPS

Nos. 97 and 100
Overprinted in Blue

1917		**Wmk. 114**	**Perf. 14x14½**	
M1	A16	5ø green	15.00	32.50
a.		"S" inverted	250.00	350.00
M2	A16	10ø red	16.00	26.00
a.		"S" inverted	200.00	275.00
		Set, never hinged	75.00	
		#M1a, M2a, never hinged	775.00	

The letters "S F" are the initials of "Soldater Frimaerke" (Soldier's Stamp).
For overprint see No. J8.

OFFICIAL STAMPS

Small State Seal — O1

		Wmk. Crown (112)		
1871		**Typo.**	**Perf. 14x13½**	
O1	O1	2s blue	150.00	100.00
a.		2s ultra	150.00	100.00
b.		Imperf	300.00	
O2	O1	4s carmine	50.00	10.00
a.		Imperf	250.00	
O3	O1	16s green	400.00	275.00
a.		Imperf	400.00	
		Perf. 12½		
O4	O1	4s carmine	5,000.	475.00
O5	O1	16s green	400.00	475.00
		#O1-O3, O5, never hinged 2,500.		

Nos. O4-O5 values are for examples with defective perfs.
Nos. O1-O3 were reprinted in 1886 upon white wove paper, unwatermarked and imperforate. Value $10 each.

1875			**Perf. 14x13½**	
O6	O1	3ø violet	11.00	30.00
O7	O1	4ø grnsh blue	11.00	3.00
O8	O1	8ø carmine	11.00	1.50
a.		Imperf		
O9	O1	32ø green	27.50	27.50
		Nos. O6-O9 (4)	60.50	62.00
		Set, never hinged	160.00	

For surcharge see No. 81.

1899-02			**Perf. 13**	
O9A	O1	3ø red lilac ('02)	3.75	5.00
c.		Imperf	275.00	
O9B	O1	4ø blue	2.75	2.50
O10	O1	8ø carmine	17.50	17.50
		Nos. O9A-O10 (3)	24.00	25.00
		Set, never hinged	77.50	

For surcharge see No. 137.

1902-06			**Wmk. 113**	
O11	O1	1ø orange	1.75	2.25
O12	O1	3ø red lilac ('06)	1.25	1.25
O13	O1	4ø blue ('03)	2.50	3.25
O14	O1	5ø green	1.75	.65
O15	O1	10ø carmine	2.50	2.50
		Nos. O11-O15 (5)	9.75	9.90
		Set, never hinged	25.00	

1914-23		**Wmk. 114**	**Perf. 14x14½**	
O16	O1	1ø orange	1.40	2.40
O17	O1	3ø gray ('18)	3.50	6.00
O18	O1	4ø blue ('16)	30.00	60.00
O19	O1	5ø green ('15)	2.10	1.75
O20	O1	5ø choc ('23)	5.00	20.00
O21	O1	10ø red ('17)	6.50	5.00
O22	O1	10ø green ('21)	3.00	5.00
O23	O1	15ø violet ('19)	14.00	35.00
O24	O1	20ø indigo ('20)	18.00	15.00
		Nos. O16-O24 (9)	83.50	150.15
		Set, never hinged	150.00	

Used value for No. O20 is for a CTO.
For surcharges see Nos. 185-191.
Official stamps were discontinued 4/1/24.

NEWSPAPER STAMPS

Numeral of Value — N1

1907		**Typo.**	**Wmk. 113**	**Perf. 13**
P1	N1	1ø olive	10.00	2.75
P2	N1	5ø blue	21.00	15.00
P3	N1	7ø carmine	9.00	1.25
P4	N1	10ø deep lilac	30.00	3.75
P5	N1	20ø green	19.00	1.40
P6	N1	38ø orange	30.00	1.50
P7	N1	68ø yellow brown	80.00	27.50
P8	N1	1k bl grn & claret	19.00	3.75
P9	N1	5k rose & yel grn	160.00	40.00
P10	N1	10k bister & blue	160.00	40.00
		Nos. P1-P10 (10)	538.00	136.90
		Set, never hinged	1,600.	

For surcharges see Nos. 138-144.

1914-15		**Wmk. 114**	**Perf. 14x14½**	
P11	N1	1ø olive gray	7.00	1.40
P12	N1	5ø blue	25.00	7.00
P13	N1	7ø rose	25.00	1.40
P14	N1	8ø green ('15)	20.00	1.40
P15	N1	10ø deep lilac	25.00	1.50
P16	N1	20ø green	250.00	2.75
a.		Imperf., pair	1,000.	
P17	N1	29ø orange yel ('15)	40.00	2.75
P18	N1	38ø orange	2,000.	160.00
		Never hinged	3,000.	
P19	N1	41ø yellow brn ('15)	45.00	2.00
P20	N1	1k blue grn & mar	77.50	2.50
		Nos. P11-P17, P19-P20 (9)	514.50	22.70
		Set, never hinged	2,400.	

For surcharges see Nos. 145-154.

PARCEL POST STAMPS

These stamps were for use on postal packets sent by the Esbjerg-Fano Ferry Service.

Regular Issues of 1913-30 Overprinted

1919-41		**Wmk. 114**	**Perf. 14x14½**	
Q1	A10	10ø green ('22)	9.00	15.00
Q2	A10	10ø bister brn ('30)	11.00	7.50
Q3	A16	10ø red	32.50	62.50
a.		"POSFFAERGE"	175.00	400.00
Q4	A16	15ø violet	13.50	32.50
a.		"POSFFAERGE"	175.00	400.00
Q5	A16	30ø orange ('22)	12.00	24.00
Q6	A16	30ø dk blue ('26)	3.50	3.50
Q7	A16	50ø cl & blk ('20)	250.00	325.00
Q8	A16	50ø lt gray ('22)	21.00	13.00
a.		50ø dark gray ('22)	150.00	300.00
Q9	A16	1k brn & bl ('24)	50.00	19.00
Q9A	A16	5k vio & brn ('41)	2.00	2.00
Q10	A16	10k ver & grn ('30)	70.00	100.00
		Engr.		
Q11	A17	1k yellow brn	100.00	160.00
a.		"POSFFAERGE"	1,500.	2,500.
		Nos. Q1-Q11 (12)	574.50	764.00
		Set, never hinged	1,200.	

1927-30				
Q12	A30	15ø red ('27)	20.00	16.00
Q13	A30	30ø ocher ('27)	17.00	17.00
Q14	A30	40ø yel grn ('30)	19.00	16.00
		Nos. Q12-Q14 (3)	56.00	49.00
		Set, never hinged	125.00	

Overprinted on Regular Issues of 1933-40

1936-42		**Unwmk.**	**Perf. 13**	
Q15	A32	5ø rose lake ('42)	.30	.30
Q16	A32	10ø yellow org	20.00	25.00
Q17	A32	10ø lt brown ('38)	1.40	1.90
Q18	A32	10ø purple ('39)	.30	.30
Q19	A30	15ø deep red	.75	1.50
Q20	A30	30ø blue, I	4.50	6.00
Q21	A30	30ø blue, II ('40)	10.00	17.50
Q22	A30	30ø org, II ('42)	.50	.75
Q23	A30	40ø yel grn, I	4.50	6.00

Q24	A30	40ø yel grn, II ('40)	10.00	17.50
Q25	A30	40ø blue, II ('42)	.75	1.50
Q26	A33	50ø gray	1.40	1.50
Q27	A33	1k lt brown	1.00	1.50
		Nos. Q15-Q27 (13)	55.40	81.25
		Set, never hinged	125.00	

> **Catalogue values for unused stamps in this section, from this point to the end of the section, are for Never Hinged items.**

Overprinted on Nos. 284, 286, 286B

1945				
Q28	A47	30ø orange	2.25	1.60
Q29	A47	40ø blue	1.60	1.10
Q30	A47	50ø gray	1.75	1.40
		Nos. Q28-Q30 (3)	5.60	4.10

Ovptd. on #318, 309, 310, 312, 297

1949-53				
Q31	A32	10ø green ('53)	.30	.30
Q32	A61	30ø orange	2.25	1.60
Q33	A61	40ø dull blue	2.75	1.60
Q34	A61	50ø gray ('50)	16.00	3.50
Q35	A55	1k brown ('50)	1.75	1.50
		Nos. Q31-Q35 (5)	23.05	8.50

Ovptd. on #335, 323, 336, 326, 397

1955-65				
Q36	A61	30ø brown red	1.50	1.50
Q37	A61	40ø gray	1.50	1.50
Q38	A61	50ø aqua	1.50	1.50
Q39	A61	70ø deep green	1.50	1.50
Q40	A55	1.25k orange ('65)	8.00	11.00
		Nos. Q36-Q40 (5)	14.00	17.00

Overprinted on Nos. 417 and 419

1967		**Engr.**	**Perf. 13**	
Q41	A86	40ø brown	.55	.55
Q42	A86	80ø ultra	.55	.55

Nos. 224, 438, 441, 297-299 Overprinted

1967-74		**Engr.**	**Perf. 13**	
Q43	A32	5ø rose lake	.35	.35
Q44	A86	50ø brown ('74)	.50	.50
Q45	A86	90ø ultra ('70)	1.10	1.10
Q46	A55	1k brown	2.50	2.50
Q47	A55	2k red ('72)	2.25	2.25
Q48	A55	5k dull bl ('72)	6.00	6.00
		Nos. Q43-Q48 (6)	12.70	12.70

Nos. Q44-Q45, Q47-Q48 are on fluorescent paper.

Overprinted on No. 541

1975, Feb. 27				
Q49	A161	100ø deep ultra	1.25	1.25

DIEGO-SUAREZ

dē-ˌā-gō ˈswär-əs

LOCATION — A town at the northern end of Madagascar
GOVT. — French colony
POP. — 12,237

From 1885 to 1896 Diego-Suarez, (Antsirane), a French naval base, was a separate colony and issued its own stamps. These were succeeded by stamps of Madagascar.

100 Centimes = 1 Franc

Values for unused stamps are for examples with original gum as defined in the catalogue introduction except for Nos. 6-10 and J1-J2 which are valued without gum.

Stamps of French Colonies Handstamp Surcharged in Violet

Ship Flying French Flag — A2   France — A5

1890	**Unwmk.**	**Perf. 14x13½**	
1	A9	15c on 1c blk, *bl*	275.00	92.50
2	A9	15c on 5c grn, *grnsh*	650.00	92.50
3	A9	15c on 10c blk, *lav*	300.00	92.50
4	A9	15c on 20c red, *grn*	650.00	80.00
5	A9	15c on 25c blk, *rose*	120.00	50.00

This surcharge is found inverted, double, etc. See the *Scott Classic Catalogue*. Counterfeits exist.

Symbolical of Union of France and Madagascar
A3   A4

1890	**Litho.**	**Imperf.**	
6	A2	1c black	1,150.	225.00
7	A3	5c black	1,100.	190.00
8	A4	15c black	200.00	90.00
9	A5	25c black	225.00	100.00

Counterfeits exist of Nos. 6-9.

A6

1891			
10	A6	5c black	325.00	100.00

Excellent counterfeits exist of No. 10.

Stamps of French Colonies Surcharged in Red or Black:

No. 11   No. 12

1892			**Perf. 14x13½**	
11	A9	5c on 10c blk, *lav* (R)	200.00	97.50
a.		Inverted surcharge	400.00	400.00
12	A9	5c on 20c red, *grn*	175.00	65.00
a.		Inverted surcharge	425.00	400.00

Stamps of French Colonies Overprinted in Black or Red

1892				
13	A9	1c blue (R)	27.50	17.50
14	A9	2c brown, *buff*	27.50	18.50
15	A9	4c claret, *lav*	47.50	40.00
16	A9	5c green, *grnsh*	110.00	80.00
17	A9	10c black, *lavender*	35.00	30.00
b.		Double overprint	210.00	150.00
18	A9	15c blue, *pale blue*	27.50	17.50
19	A9	20c red, *grn*	35.00	32.50
20	A9	25c black, *rose*	27.50	16.00
21	A9	30c brown, *bis* (R)	1,200.	925.00
22	A9	35c black, *yellow*	1,200.	925.00
23	A9	75c carmine, *rose*	65.00	45.00
a.		Double overprint	375.00	

24	A9	1fr brnz grn, *straw* (R)		75.00	52.50
a.		Double overprint		225.00	200.00

Inverted Overprint

13a	A9	1c		225.00	140.
14a	A9	2c		225.00	140.
15a	A9	4c			300.
16a	A9	5c		240.00	140.
17a	A9	10c		225.00	140.
20a	A9	25c		225.00	140.
21a	A9	30c			1,600.
22a	A9	35c			1,600.

Navigation and Commerce
A10   A11

1892   Typo.   Perf. 14x13½
Name of Colony in Blue or Carmine

25	A10	1c black, *blue*		2.00	2.00
26	A10	2c brown, *buff*		2.50	2.50
27	A10	4c claret, *lav*		3.00	3.00
28	A10	5c green, *grnsh*		6.00	6.00
29	A10	10c black, *lavender*		8.00	6.50
30	A10	15c bl, quadrille paper		14.00	9.75
31	A10	20c red, *green*		21.00	14.50
32	A10	25c black, *rose*		16.00	13.50
33	A10	30c brown, *bister*		21.00	14.50
34	A10	40c red, *straw*		26.00	16.00
35	A10	50c carmine, *rose*		45.00	32.50
36	A10	75c violet, *org*		47.50	40.00
37	A10	1fr brnz grn, *straw*		67.50	52.50
		Nos. 25-37 (13)		279.50	217.25

Perf. 13½x14 stamps are counterfeits.

1894   Perf. 14x13½

38	A11	1c black, *blue*		1.75	1.75
39	A11	2c brown, *buff*		2.60	2.25
40	A11	4c claret, *lav*		3.25	2.75
41	A11	5c green, *grnsh*		5.25	4.75
42	A11	10c black, *lavender*		7.25	6.00
43	A11	15c blue, quadrille paper		12.00	5.50
44	A11	20c red, *grn*		20.00	13.00
45	A11	25c black, *rose*		9.75	8.00
46	A11	30c brown, *bister*		12.00	5.50
47	A11	40c red, *straw*		12.00	5.50
48	A11	50c carmine, *rose*		18.50	12.00
49	A11	75c violet, *org*		10.50	8.00
50	A11	1fr brnz grn, *straw*		26.00	21.00
		Nos. 38-50 (13)		140.85	96.00

Bisected stamps of type A11 are mentioned in note after Madagascar No. 62.
For surcharges see Madagascar #56-57, 61-62.
Perf. 13½x14 stamps are counterfeits.

POSTAGE DUE STAMPS

D1   D2

1891   Unwmk.   Litho.   Imperf.

J1	D1	5c violet		210.00	77.50
J2	D2	50c black		225.00	92.50

Excellent counterfeits exist of Nos. J1-J2.

Postage Due Stamps of French Colonies Overprinted Like Nos. 13-24
1892

J3	D1	1c black		120.00	67.50
J4	D1	2c black		120.00	60.00
a.		Inverted overprint		450.00	375.00
J5	D1	3c black		120.00	60.00
J6	D1	4c black		120.00	60.00
J7	D1	5c black		120.00	67.50
J8	D1	10c black		32.50	27.50
a.		Inverted overprint		450.00	450.00
J9	D1	15c black		32.50	27.50
a.		Double overprint		575.00	500.00
J10	D1	20c black		190.00	125.00
a.		Double overprint		575.00	500.00
J11	D1	30c black		110.00	60.00
a.		Inverted overprint		450.00	275.00
J12	D1	60c black		1,100.	750.00
J13	D1	1fr brown		2,600.	1,500.

DJIBOUTI

jə-ˈbü-tē

LOCATION — East Africa
GOVT. — Republic
AREA — 8,958 sq. mi.
POP. — 447,439 (1999 est.)
CAPITAL — Djibouti

The French territory of Afars and Issas became the Republic of Djibouti June 27, 1977. For 1894-1902 issues with "Djibouti" or "DJ," see Somali Coast.

> Catalogue values for all unused stamps in this country are for Never Hinged items.

Afars and Issas Issues of 1972-1977 Overprinted and Surcharged with Bars and "REPUBLIQUE DE DJIBOUTI" in Black, Dark Green, Blue or Brown
Printing and Perforations as Before
1977

439	A63	1fr on 4fr (#358;B)		2.00	.25
440	A81	2fr on 5fr (#433;B)		2.00	.25
441	A75	5fr on 20fr (#421;B)		.25	.20
442	A70	8fr (#380;B)		.35	.25
443	A71	20fr (#387;DG)		3.50	.65
444	A81	30fr (#434;B)		3.75	.80
445	A71	40fr (#388;DG)		4.50	1.10
446	A71	45fr (#389;Bl)		5.00	1.25
447	A78	45fr (#428;B)		7.50	1.25
448	A72	50fr (#394;B)		8.00	1.60
449	A71	60fr (#391;Br)		7.00	1.60
450	A79	70fr (#430;B)		8.00	1.90
451	A81	70fr (#435;B)		5.50	2.25
452	A74	100fr(#418;B)		11.00	3.00
453	A72	150fr(#399;B)		11.50	3.50
454	A76	200fr(#422;B)		5.00	3.50
455	A80	200fr(#423;B)		5.75	4.00
456	A74	300fr(#419;B)		9.25	6.50
		Nos. 439-456,C106-C108 (21)		122.10	52.10

Map and Flag of Djibouti — A83

Water Pipe — A84

Design: 65fr, Map and flag of Djibouti, map of Africa, horiz.

1977, June 27   Litho.   Perf. 12½

457	A83	45fr multicolored		1.10	.40
458	A83	65fr multicolored		1.40	.60

Independence, June 27.

1977, July 4

459	A84	10fr Headrest, horiz.		.25	.20
460	A84	20fr shown		.50	.20
461	A84	25fr Pitcher		.70	.30
		Nos. 459-461 (3)		1.45	.70

Ostrich — A85

1977, Aug. 11   Litho.   Perf. 12½

462	A85	90fr shown		2.75	.80
463	A85	100fr Weaver		4.00	1.10

Snail
A86

Designs: 15fr, Fiddler crab. 50fr, Klipspringers. 70fr, Green turtle. 80fr, Priacanthus hamrur (fish). 150fr, Dolphinfish.

1977   Litho.   Perf. 12½

464	A86	15fr multicolored		.60	.20
465	A86	45fr multicolored		1.40	.40
466	A86	50fr multicolored		1.75	.50
467	A86	70fr multicolored		1.90	.60
468	A86	80fr multicolored		2.40	.75
469	A86	150fr multicolored		4.25	2.00
		Nos. 464-469 (6)		12.30	4.45

Issued: 45fr, 70fr, 80fr, 9/14; others, 12/5.

Pres. Hassan Gouled Aptidon and Djibouti Flag — A87

1978, Feb. 12   Litho.   Perf. 13

470	A87	65fr multicolored		1.00	.35

Charaxes Hansali — A88   Necklace — A89

Butterflies: 20fr, Colias electo. 25fr, Acraea chilo. 150fr, Junonia hierta.

1978, Mar. 13   Litho.   Perf. 12½x13

471	A88	5fr multicolored		.25	.20
472	A88	20fr multicolored		1.00	.25
473	A88	25fr multicolored		1.50	.50
474	A88	150fr multicolored		5.75	1.75
		Nos. 471-474 (4)		8.50	2.70

1978, May 29   Litho.   Perf. 12½x13

Design: 55fr, Necklace, diff.

475	A89	45fr pink & multi		1.00	.35
476	A89	55fr blue & multi		1.25	.40

Bougainvillea A90

Flowers: 35fr, Hibiscus schizopetalus. 250fr, Caesalpinia pulcherrima.

1978, July 10   Photo.   Perf. 12½x13

477	A90	15fr multicolored		.45	.20
478	A90	35fr multicolored		.90	.25
479	A90	250fr multicolored		5.25	.90
		Nos. 477-479 (3)		6.60	1.35

Charonia Nodifera — A91

Sea Shell: 80fr, Charonia variegata.

1978, Oct. 9   Litho.   Perf. 13

480	A91	10fr multicolored		1.10	.35
481	A91	80fr multicolored		3.75	.90

Chaetodon A92

30fr, Yellow surgeonfish. 40fr, Harlequinfish.

1978, Nov. 20   Litho.   Perf. 13x12½

482	A92	8fr multicolored		.75	.25
483	A92	30fr multicolored		1.40	.35
484	A92	40fr multicolored		2.75	.65
		Nos. 482-484 (3)		4.90	1.25

Alsthom BB 1201 at Dock — A93

55fr, Steam locomotive 231. 60fr, Steam locomotive 130 and map of route. 75fr, Diesel.

1979, Jan. 29   Litho.   Perf. 13

485	A93	40fr multicolored		1.25	.20
486	A93	55fr multicolored		1.40	.30
487	A93	60fr multicolored		1.75	.30
488	A93	75fr multicolored		2.25	.40
		Nos. 485-488 (4)		6.65	1.20

Djibouti-Addis Ababa railroad.

Children and IYC Emblem — A94

Design: 200fr, Mother, child, IYC emblem.

1979, Feb. 26   Litho.   Perf. 13

489	A94	20fr multicolored		.45	.20
490	A94	200fr multicolored		3.50	1.10

International Year of the Child.

Plane over Ardoukoba Volcano — A95

30fr, Helicopter over Ardoukoba Volcano.

1979, Mar. 19

491	A95	30fr multi, vert.		.90	.35
492	A95	90fr multi		2.50	.60

Rowland Hill, Postal Clerks, No.
C109 — A96

100fr, Somali Coast #22, Djibouti #457, letters, Rowland Hill. 150fr, Letters hoisted onto ship, smoke signals, Rowland Hill.

1979, Apr. 17   Litho.   Perf. 13x12½
493 A96 25fr multicolored   .35   .20
494 A96 100fr multicolored   1.75   .45
495 A96 150fr multicolored   2.75   .70
     Nos. 493-495 (3)   4.85 1.35
Sir Rowland Hill (1795-1879), originator of penny postage.

View of Djibouti, Bird and Local
Woman — A97

Design: 80fr, Map and flag of Djibouti, UPU emblem, Concorde, train and mail runner.

1979, June 8   Litho.   Perf. 13x12½
496 A97 55fr multicolored   2.10   .70
497 A97 80fr multicolored   2.75   .95
Philexafrique II, Libreville, Gabon, June 8-17. Nos. 496, 497 each printed in sheets of 10 with 5 labels showing exhibition emblem.

Solanacea
A98

Flowers: 2fr, Opuntia, vert. 15fr, Trichodesma. 45fr, Acacia etbaica. 50fr, Thunbergia alata, vert.

Perf. 13x13½, 13½x13
1979, June 18
498 A98 2fr multicolored   .20   .20
499 A98 8fr multicolored   .25   .20
500 A98 15fr multicolored   .50   .20
501 A98 45fr multicolored   1.00   .20
502 A98 50fr multicolored   1.25   .25
     Nos. 498-502 (5)   3.20 1.05

Running — A99

Olympic Emblem and: 70fr, Basketball, vert. 200fr, Soccer.

Perf. 12½x13, 13x12½
1979, Oct. 22   Litho.
503 A99 70fr multicolored   1.40   .25
504 A99 120fr multicolored   2.10   .50
505 A99 200fr multicolored   3.50   .75
     Nos. 503-505 (3)   7.00 1.50
          Pre-Olympic Year.

Cypraecassis Rufa — A100

Shells: 40fr, Lambis chiragra arthritica. 300fr, Harpa connaidalis.

1979, Dec. 22   Litho.   Perf. 13
506 A100 10fr multicolored   .20   .20
507 A100 40fr multicolored   .90   .20
508 A100 300fr multicolored   5.75 1.50
     Nos. 506-508 (3)   6.85 1.90

Rotary International, 75th
Anniversary — A101

1980, Feb. 19   Litho.   Perf. 13x12½
509 A101 90fr multicolored   1.75   .50

Lions Club of Djibouti — A102

1980, Feb. 19
510 A102 100fr multicolored   2.25   .75

Colotis
Danae — A103

1980, Mar. 17   Perf. 13x13½
511 A103 5fr shown   .70   .45
512 A103 55fr Danaus chrysip-
             pus   3.25 1.40

Chess Players, Knight — A104

Chess Federation Creation: 75fr, Chess Game, Florence, 1493.

1980, June 9   Litho.   Perf. 13
513 A104 20fr multicolored   .80   .20
514 A104 75fr multicolored   2.25   .30

Cribraria
A105

1980, Aug. 12   Litho.   Perf. 13
515 A105 15fr shown   .50   .20
516 A105 85fr Nautilius pompilius 2.00   .40

Alexander Fleming, Discoverer of
Penicillin — A106

Design: 130fr, Jules Verne, French science fiction writer; earth, moon and spacecraft.

1980, Sept. 1
517 A106 20fr multicolored   .80   .25
518 A106 130fr multicolored   2.25   .50

Capt. Cook and Endeavor — A107

Capt. James Cook Death Bicentenary: 90fr, Ships and Maps of voyages.

1980, Nov. 20   Litho.   Perf. 13
519 A107 55fr multicolored   1.00   .25
520 A107 90fr multicolored   1.75   .40
Souvenir sheets of 1 exist, perf. 12½x12.

Angel Fish
A108

1981, Apr. 13   Litho.   Perf. 12½
521 A108 25fr shown   .90   .20
522 A108 55fr Moorish idol   2.10   .35
523 A108 70fr Scad   2.25   .90
     Nos. 521-523 (3)   5.25 1.45

13th World Telecommunications
Day — A109

1981, May 17   Litho.   Perf. 13
524 A109 140fr multicolored   2.25   .60

Type 231 Steam Locomotive,
Germany, 1958 and Amtrak, US,
1980 — A110

Locomotives: 55fr, Stephenson and his Rocket, Djibouti Railways 230 engine. 65fr, Type TGV, France, Type 962, Japan.

1981, June 9   Litho.   Perf. 13
525 A110 40fr multicolored   1.25   .30
526 A110 55fr multicolored   1.75   .35
527 A110 65fr multicolored   2.25   .40
     Nos. 525-527 (3)   5.25 1.05

Radio Amateurs
Club — A111

1981, June 25
528 A111 250fr multicolored   4.50 1.00

Prince Charles and Lady
Diana — A112

1981, June 29
529 A112 180fr shown   3.50   .90
530 A112 200fr Couple, diff.   4.00 1.00
          Royal Wedding.

Lord Nelson and Victory — A113

1981, July 6   Litho.   Perf. 13x12½
531 A113 100fr multicolored   1.75   .45
532 A113 175fr multicolored   3.00   .90
     Lord Horatio Nelson (1758-1805).

Scout Tending Campfire — A114

1981, July 16   Litho.   Perf. 13
533 A114 60fr multicolored   2.75   .60
534 A114 105fr Scout giving sign 3.50   .70
28th World Scouting Conference, Dakar, Aug. (60fr); 4th Pan-African Scouting Conference, Abidjan, Aug. (105fr).

Pawn and Queen, Swedish Bone
Chess Pieces, 13th Cent. — A115

1981, Oct. 15   Litho.   Perf. 13
535 A115 50fr shown   1.50   .35
536 A115 130fr Pawn, knight,
             Chinese, 19th
             cent., vert.   2.50   .75
     For overprints see Nos. 542-543.

Sheraton Hotel Opening — A116

1981, Nov. 15   Litho.   Perf. 13x12½
537 A116 75fr multicolored   1.25 .35
For surcharge see No. 623.

Acacia
Mellifera
A117

1981, Dec. 21   Perf. 13
538 A117 10fr Clitoria ternatea,
              vert.   .35 .20
539 A117 30fr shown   .70 .20
540 A117 35fr Punica granatum   1.00 .20
541 A117 45fr Malvaceous plant,
              vert.   1.25 .30
   Nos. 538-541 (4)   3.30 .90
      See Nos. 558-560.

Nos. 535-536 Overprinted with
Winners' Names

1981, Dec.   Litho.   Perf. 13
542 A115 50fr multicolored   1.00 .35
543 A115 130fr multicolored   2.75 .75

World Chess Championship.

TB Bacillus
Centenary
A117a

1982, Mar. 24   Litho.   Perf. 13
544 A117a 305fr Koch, slide, mi-
             croscope   5.75 1.50

A117b

A118

1982, Apr. 8   Litho.   Perf. 13
545 A117b 125fr Ivory bishop   2.75 .65
546 A117b 175fr Queen, pawn,
              19th cent.   3.75 1.00
   1982 World Chess Championship.

1982, May 17
547 A118 150fr multicolored   2.25 .65
   14th World Telecommunications Day.
For surcharge see No. 647.

Bus and Jeep — A119

1982, July 27   Litho.   Perf. 13
548 A119 20fr shown   .45 .20
549 A119 25fr Dhow, ferry   .60 .20
550 A119 55fr Train, jet   1.25 .35
   Nos. 548-550 (3)   2.30 .75

Shells from
the Red
Sea
A120

1982, Nov. 20   Litho.   Perf. 12½
551 A120 10fr Cypraea ery-
              thraeensis   .30 .20
552 A120 15fr Conus sumatren-
              sis   .40 .30
553 A120 25fr Cypraea pulchra   .70 .35
554 A120 30fr Conus inscriptus   .90 .40
555 A120 70fr Casmaria
              ponderosa   2.00 .50
556 A120 150fr Cypraea exusta   4.00 1.50
   Nos. 551-556 (6)   8.30 3.25
      See Nos. 563-567.

Intl. Palestinian
Solidarity
Day — A121

1982, Nov. 29   Litho.   Perf. 13
557 A121 40fr multicolored   .60 .20

Local Flowers type of 1981
Various flowers. 5fr, 55fr, vert.

1983, Apr. 14   Litho.   Perf. 13
558 A117 5fr multicolored   .20 .20
559 A117 50fr multicolored   1.10 .40
560 A117 55fr multicolored   1.25 .40
   Nos. 558-560 (3)   2.55 1.00

World Communications Year — A123

1983, June 20   Litho.   Perf. 13
561 A123 500fr multicolored   7.50 2.00

Conference of Donors, Nov. 21-
23 — A124

1983, Nov. 21   Litho.   Perf. 13x12½
562 A124 75fr multicolored   1.25 .40

Shell Type of 1982

1983, Dec. 20   Litho.   Perf. 12½
563 A120 15fr Marginella obtusa   .45 .20
564 A120 30fr Conus jickelli   .90 .20
565 A120 55fr Cypraea macan-
              drewi   1.40 .40
566 A120 80fr Conus cuvieri   2.00 .50
567 A120 100fr Turbo petholatus   2.10 .65
   Nos. 563-567 (5)   6.85 1.95

Local
Butterflies
A125

1984, Jan. 24   Litho.   Perf. 13½x13
568 A125 5fr Colotis chryso-
              nome   .25 .20
569 A125 20fr Colias erate   .70 .25
570 A125 30fr Junonia orithyia   1.25 .35
571 A125 75fr Acraea
              doubledayi   3.75 1.00
572 A125 110fr Byblia ilithya   5.00 1.50
   Nos. 568-572 (5)   10.95 3.30

Landscapes and Animals — A126

1984, Apr. 29   Litho.   Perf. 13
573 A126 2fr Randa Klip-
             springer   .20 .20
574 A126 8fr Ali Sabieh, gazel-
             les   .20 .20
575 A126 10fr Lake Assal, oryx   .20 .20
576 A126 15fr Tadjoura, gazelle   .25 .20
577 A126 40fr Alaila Dada, jack-
             al, vert.   .60 .20
578 A126 45fr Lake Abbe, wart-
             hog   .60 .25
579 A126 55fr Obock, seagull   1.60 .60
580 A126 125fr Presidential Pal-
             ace, bird   3.25 1.10
   Nos. 573-580 (8)   6.90 2.95
For surcharges see #646, 657-658, 660.

Fire Prevention — A127

1984, Sept. 9   Litho.   Perf. 13
581 A127 25fr Fire truck   .80 .20
582 A127 95fr Hook & ladder   2.50 .45
583 A127 100fr Fire plane   2.75 .95
   Nos. 581-583 (3)   6.05 1.60

International
Olympic
Committee
Membership
A128

1984, July 22   Litho.   Perf. 13
584 A128 45fr Runners   .90 .35

Motor
Carriage,
1886
A128a

1984, Nov. 11   Litho.   Perf. 12½
585 A128a 35fr shown   .70 .30
586 A128a 65fr Cabriolet, 1896   1.40 .65
587 A128a 90fr Phoenix, 1900   2.00 .95
   Nos. 585-587 (3)   4.10 1.90
Gottlieb Daimler (1834-1900), pioneer automobile manufacturer.

Marie and Pierre
Curie — A129

1984, Dec. 3   Litho.   Perf. 12½
588 A129 150fr Pierre Curie   2.75 1.10
589 A129 150fr Marie Curie   2.75 1.10

A130

Audubon Bicentenary — A130a

Illustration A130a reduced.

1985, Jan. 27   Litho.   Perf. 13
590 A130 5fr Merops al-
             bicollis   .75 .35
591 A130 15fr Pterocles
             exustus   3.25 .85
592 A130 20fr Trachyphonus
             mar-
             garitatus
             somalicus   3.75 1.00

593 A130 25fr Coracias
garrulus 4.50 1.10
Nos. 590-593 (4) 12.25 3.30

Souvenir Sheet
Self-Adhesive
Perf. 12½
593A A130a 200fr Pandion
haliaetus,
vert. 26.00 26.00

No. 593A is airmail and printed on wood.

Intl. Youth
Year — A131

1985, Mar. 26   Litho.   Perf. 13
594 A131 10fr multicolored .20 .20
595 A131 30fr multicolored .50 .30
596 A131 40fr multicolored .70 .40
Nos. 594-596 (3) 1.40 .90

German Railways, 150th
Anniv. — A132

Designs: 55fr, Engine No. 29, Addis Ababa-
Djibouti Railways. 75fr, Adler, museum facsimile of the first German locomotive.

1985, Apr. 22   Litho.   Perf. 13
597 A132 55fr multicolored 2.00 .65
598 A132 75fr multicolored 3.00 .90

A133

A134

1985, May 23
599 A133 35fr Planting saplings .80 .35
600 A133 65fr Hygiene, family
health care 1.50 .65
Scouting.

1985, June 24   Litho.
80fr, Victor Hugo (1802-1885), Novelist.
100fr, Arthur Rimbaud (1854-1891), poet.
601 A134 80fr brt blue & slate 1.40 .80
602 A134 100fr multicolored 1.60 1.00

Sea Shells
A135

1985, July 15   Litho.   Perf. 12½
603 A135 10fr Cypraea nebrites .25 .20
604 A135 15fr Cypraea turdus .45 .20
605 A135 30fr Conus acuminatus 1.10 .25
606 A135 40fr Cypraea camelopardalis 1.25 .45
607 A135 55fr Conus terebra 2.10 .60
Nos. 603-607 (5) 5.15 1.70

1st World
Cup
Marathon
'85,
Hiroshima
A136

1985, Sept. 2   Perf. 12½x13
608 A136 75fr Winners 1.25 .75
609 A136 100fr Approaching finish 2.00 1.00

Halley's Comet — A137

Designs: 85fr, Bayeux Tapestry, Comet and
Halley. 90fr, Vega I, Giotto space probes, map
of planets, comet trajectory.

1986, Jan. 27   Litho.   Perf. 13
610 A137 85fr multicolored 1.25 .45
611 A137 90fr multicolored 1.60 .80

ISERST Solar Energy
Installation — A138

Designs: 50fr, Runners on beach. 150fr,
Windmill, headquarters, power control station.

1986, Mar. 20
612 A138 50fr multicolored .80 .40
613 A138 150fr multicolored 2.25 1.25

Ships from Columbus's Fleet,
1492 — A139

1986, Apr. 14
614 A139 60fr Santa Maria 1.40 .45
615 A139 90fr Nina, Pinta 2.25 .75

Fish, Red
Sea — A140

1986, June 16   Litho.   Perf. 13½x13
616 A140 20fr Elagatis bipinnu-
latus .65 .30
617 A140 25fr Valamugil seheli .75 .45
618 A140 55fr Lutjanus rivulatus 1.75 .70
Nos. 616-618 (3) 3.15 1.45

Public Buildings — A141

105fr, People's Palace. 115fr, Ministry of the
Interior, Posts & Telecommunications.

1986, July 21   Litho.   Perf. 13
619 A141 105fr multicolored 1.50 .90
620 A141 115fr multicolored 1.75 1.00

Sea-Me-We Building,
Keyboard — A142

1986, Sept. 8   Litho.   Perf. 13
621 A142 100fr multicolored 2.00 .70
Souvenir Sheet
Perf. 12½
622 A142 250fr multicolored 13.50 13.50

Southeast Asia, Middle East, Western
Europe Submarine Cable System
inauguration.

No. 537 Surcharged
"5e ANNIVERSAIRE."
1986, Nov. 15   Perf. 13x12½
623 A116 55fr on 75fr multi 1.00 .40

Pasteur Institute, Cent. — A143

1987, Feb. 19   Litho.   Perf. 13
624 A143 220fr multicolored 4.00 1.50
Natl. Vaccination Campaign.

Edible
Mushrooms
A144

1987, Apr. 16   Litho.   Perf. 13x12½
625 A144 35fr Macrolepiota imbricata 1.25 .65
626 A144 50fr Lentinus squar-
rosulus 2.00 .85
627 A144 95fr Terfezia boudieri 2.75 1.50
Nos. 625-627 (3) 6.00 3.00

Wildlife
A145

1987, May 14   Perf. 12½x13
628 A145 5fr Hare .25 .20
629 A145 30fr Dromedary 1.00 .30
630 A145 140fr Cheetah 4.50 1.00
Nos. 628-630 (3) 5.75 1.50

1988 Olympics, Seoul and
Calgary — A146

85fr, Pierre de Coubertin (1863-1937),
founder of the modern Olympics, & lighting of
the flame. 135fr, Ski jumping. 140fr, Running.

1987, July 16   Perf. 13
631 A146 85fr multicolored 1.50 .55
632 A146 135fr multicolored 2.50 .95
633 A146 140fr multicolored 2.75 1.00
Nos. 631-633 (3) 6.75 2.50

Traditional
Art — A147

UN Universal
Immunization by
1990 Campaign
A148

1988, Jan. 20   Litho.   Perf. 13
634 A147 30fr Nomad's comb .60 .30
635 A147 70fr Wash jug 1.25 .60

1988, Apr. 10   Perf. 12½
636 A148 125fr multicolored 2.25 1.00

16th Africa Cup Soccer
Championships, Morocco — A149

1988, Mar. 13   Perf. 13
637 A149 55fr Athletes, view of
Rabat 1.10 .50

1988 Winter
Olympics,
Calgary — A150

1988, May 7   Litho.   *Perf. 13*
638 A150 45fr Ski jump   .90 .40

Campaign
Against
Thirst
A151

1988, Sept. 10 Litho. *Perf. 12½x13*
639 A151 50fr multicolored   1.00 .40

Intl. Fund for Agricultural Development,
10th Anniv. — A152

1988, Nov. 14   *Perf. 13*
640 A152 135fr multicolored   2.25 1.00

Michel Lafoux Air Club, 40th
Anniv. — A153

1988, Dec. 6
641 A153 145fr 1948 Tiger Moth,
             1988 Tobago-10 2.75 1.00

Marine Life
A154

1989, Jan. 20   Litho.   *Perf. 12½*
642 A154 90fr Lobophyllia cos-
             tata   1.75 .25
643 A154 160fr Lambis truncata   3.25 1.10

Colotis
protomedia
A155

1989, Feb. 15
644 A155 70fr multicolored   2.50 1.25

Nos. 573 and 547 Surcharged
1989   *Perf. 13*
646 A126 70fr on 2fr No. 573   2.25 .50
647 A118 70fr on 150fr No. 547   2.25 .50
     Issued: 646, 12/20; 647, 12/29.

Folk
Dances — A157

Francolin of
Djibouti — A159

1989, Mar. 20
648 A157 30fr shown   .50 .25
649 A157 70fr multicolored, diff. 1.40 .50

1989, Apr. 10   Litho.   *Perf. 12½*
651 A159 35fr multicolored   1.40 .35

Rare Flora
A160

1989, June 12
652 A160 25fr Calotropis procera   .45 .20

A161

A162

1989, Aug. 10   Litho.   *Perf. 13*
653 A161 70fr multicolored   1.25 .50
     Interparliamentary Union, cent.

1989, Oct. 1
654 A162 145fr multicolored   2.75 1.10
     Intl. Literacy Year.

Petroglyph — A163

1989, Nov. 18   Litho.   *Perf. 13*
655 A163 5fr multicolored   .35 .20

Girl — A164

1989, Dec. 6
656 A164 55fr multicolored   1.00 .40

Nos. 574, 576-577 Surcharged
1989-1990   Litho.   *Perf. 13*
657 A126   30fr on 8fr multi   .50 .30
658 A126   50fr on 40fr multi   2.00 .55
660 A126 120fr on 15fr multi   2.00 .80
     Nos. 657-660 (3)   4.50 1.65
     Issue dates: 30fr, 12/20/89; 50fr, 7/3/90;
120fr, 3/17/90.

Water Conservation — A165

1990, May 5   Litho.   *Perf. 11½*
665 A165 120fr multicolored   1.75 .70

Traditional
Jewelry
A166

1990, Mar. 10
666 A166 70fr multicolored   1.25 .45

Commiphora — A167

1990, Feb. 20   *Perf. 12*
667 A167   30fr multicolored   .60 .35

Baskets — A168

1990, July 3
668 A168 30fr multicolored   .50 .20

A169   A170

1990, June 12   *Perf. 11½*
669 A169 100fr multicolored   1.50 .60
     World Cup Soccer Championships, Italy.

1990, Apr. 16   *Perf. 11½*
670 A170 55fr shown   1.00 .40
     20 kilometer race of Djibouti.

Vaccination
Campaign
A171

1990, Aug. 22   Litho.   *Perf. 11½*
Granite Paper
671 A171 300fr multicolored   4.50 1.75

Charles de   African Tourism
Gaulle — A172   Year — A173

1990, Sept. 16
Granite Paper
672 A172 200fr multicolored   3.50 1.25

1991, Jan. 23   Litho.   *Perf. 13*
673 A173 115fr multicolored   2.00 .80

Corals — A174

Aquatic Birds — A175

1991, Jan. 28   Perf. 12½
674 A174 40fr Acropora   .80   .40
675 A174 45fr Seriatopora hytrise 1.00   .40

1991, Feb. 12
676 A175 10fr Pelecanus rufes-
                          cens   .60   .20
677 A175 15fr Egretta gularis   1.40   .25
678 A175 20fr Ardea goliath,
                          horiz.   1.60   .30
679 A175 25fr Platalea
                          leucorodia, horiz. 1.75   .35
        Nos. 676-679 (4)   5.35 1.10

UNO Development Conference A176   Fossils A177

1990, Oct. 9   Litho.   Perf. 11½x12
Granite Paper
680 A176 45fr multicolored   .90   .40

1990, Nov. 1
Granite Paper
681 A177 90fr pur, org & blk   5.25 1.75

Papio Hamadryas — A178

1990, Dec. 6
Granite Paper
682 A178 50fr multicolored   .90   .30

Pandion Haliaetus A179

1991, Mar. 20   Litho.   Perf. 12x11½
683 A179 200fr multicolored   3.25 1.10

Traditional Game A180

1991, Apr. 4
684 A180 250fr multicolored   3.50 2.25
        See No. 696.

Djibouti-Ethiopia Railroad — A181

1991, May 25   Litho.   Perf. 11½
685 A181 85fr multicolored   1.25   .70

World Environment Day — A182

1991, June 10
686 A182 110fr multicolored   2.00   .50

Philexafrique — A183

1991, Jul. 16   Litho.   Perf. 11½
687 A183 120fr Islands   1.75 1.00

A184

1991, Sept. 25
688 A184 175fr Handball   2.25 1.60
        Pre-Olympic year.

1991, Oct. 16   Litho.   Perf. 11½x12
689 A185 105fr multicolored   2.10 1.10
        World Food Day.

A185

Underwater Cable Network — A186

1991, Nov. 28   Perf. 12x11½
690 A186 130fr multicolored   2.10   .80

Discovery of America, 500th Anniv. A187

1991, Dec. 19   Litho.   Perf. 11½
691 A187 145fr multicolored   2.25 1.40

Arthur Rimbaud (1854-1891) Poet and Merchant — A188

1991-92   Perf. 11½
692 A188 90fr   Young man, ship   2.00   .75
693 A188 150fr Old man, camels   2.25   .75
        Issued: 90fr, 2/5/92; 150fr, 12/23/91.

Djibouti-Ethiopia Railroad — A189

        Design: 250fr, Locomotive, map.

1992   Litho.   Perf. 12x11½
694 A189 70fr   multicolored   1.50   .60
Souvenir Sheet
Perf. 13x12½
695 A189 250fr multicolored   4.50 4.50
        Issue dates: 70fr, Feb. 2; 250fr, Jan. 30.

Traditional Game Type of 1991
1992, Feb. 10   Perf. 11½
696 A180 100fr Boys playing Go   1.50   .60

A190

1992, June 9   Litho.   Perf. 14
697 A190 80fr   multicolored   1.10   .70
        1992 Summer Olympics, Barcelona.

A191

1992   Litho.   Perf. 14x13½
        Traditional food preparation.
698   A191 30fr Pounding grain   .50   .30
698A A191 45fr Preparing mofo
699   A191 70fr Winnowing grain   1.10   .60
        Issued: Nos. 698, 699, 4/20; No. 698A, 12/6.
        An additional stamp was released in this
        set. The editors would like to examine it.

Discovery of America, 500th Anniv. A192

1992, May 16   Litho.   Perf. 11½
700 A192 125fr multicolored   2.10   .75

African Soccer Championships A193

Intl. Space Year — A194

1992, July 22   Perf. 14
701 A193 15fr multicolored   .25   .20

Perf. 14x13½, 13½x14
1992, Sept. 28
702 A194 120fr Rocket, satellite 1.75   .60
703 A194 135fr Astronaut, satel-
                          lite, horiz.   2.00   .70

Wildlife — 704

1992, Nov. 11   Perf. 14
704 A195 5fr   Dik-dik   .70   .20
705 A195 200fr Caretta caretta   3.25 1.25

Taeniura Lymma — A195a

Perf. 11½x11¾
1990, Mar. 24   Litho.
Panel Color
705A A195a 70fr   yellow
705B A195a 100fr green
705C A195a 120fr lilac   —   —

Nomad Girls in Traditional Costumes
A196

1993, Jan. 26   Litho.   *Perf. 13*
706 A196 70fr Girl beside hut   1.25   .35
707 A196 120fr shown   2.10   .60

White-eyed Seagull
A197

1993, Feb. 28   Litho.   *Perf. 12½*
708 A197 300fr multicolored   4.25 1.60

Amin Salman Mosque — A198

1993, Feb. 17   Litho.   *Perf. 13¾x14*
709 A198 500fr multicolored   52.50 4.25

Handcrafts — A199

Handicrafts Type of 1993
1993, Apr. 23   Litho.   *Perf. 13¾x14*
710 A199 100fr Neck rest   1.10 1.10

1993, Apr. 23   Litho.   *Perf. 13¾x14*
711 A199 125fr Sword   1.50 1.50

A number has been reserved for a 100fr stamp in this set. The editors would like to examine it.

Cercopithecus Aethiops — A200

1993, May 29   Litho.   *Perf. 14¼x13½*
712 A200 150fr multi   —   —

Organization of African Unity, 30th Anniv. — A201

Perf. 14¼x13½
1993, June 20   Litho.
713 A201 200fr multi   —   —

Water Carriers — A202

1993, July 6   Litho.   *Perf. 14x13¾*
714 A202 30fr Woman   .35   .35
715 A202 50fr Man   .60   .60

Conquest of Space — A203

1993, Sept. 30   Litho.   *Perf. 14x13¾*
716 A203 90fr multicolored   1.10 1.10

A204

A205

Traditional utensils.

1993, Sept. 30   Litho.   *Perf. 13½*
717 A204 15fr Weyso   .25   .20
718 A204 20fr Hangol   .45   .20
719 A204 25fr Saqaf   .50   .20
720 A204 30fr Subrar   .70   .25
        Nos. 717-720 (4)   1.90   .85

1993, Nov. 10   Litho.   *Perf. 14*
Traditional musical instruments.
721 A205 5fr Flute   .20   .20
722 A205 10fr Drum   .20   .20

Souvenir Sheet

Wedding of Japan's Crown Prince Naruhito and Masako Owada — A206

1994, Jan. 10   Litho.   *Perf. 13x12½*
Self-Adhesive
723 A206 500fr multicolored   13.50 13.50
    No. 723 printed on wood.

20 Kilometer Race of Djibouti A207   Promotion of Breastfeeding A208

1994   Litho.   *Perf. 11½*
724 A207 50fr multicolored   1.00   .40

1994
725 A208 40fr shown   1.25   .40
726 A208 45fr Mother, infant   1.40   .40

Hassan Gouled Aptidon Stadium A209

1994
727 A209 70fr multicolored   1.25   .55

Stenella Longirostris — A210

1994, May 1   Litho.   *Perf. 11¾x11½*
728 A210 120fr multicolored   1.25 1.25

World Housing Day — A211

1994, May 9   Litho.   *Perf. 11½x11¾*
729 A211 30fr multi   —   —

Eupodotis Senegalensis — A212

Perf. 11¾x11½
1994, June 16   Litho.
730 A212 10fr multicolored

1994 World Cup Soccer Tournament — A213

1994, Sept. 7
731 A213 200fr multicolored   160.00 1.60

Traditional Nomad Costume — A214

Design: 150fr, Dress of a village leader.

Perf. 11½x11¾
1994, Sept. 18   Litho.
732 A214 100fr multicolored   1.00 1.00
Perf. 11¾
733 A214 150fr multicolored   1.60 1.60

Canis Aureus A215

Perf. 11¾x11½
1994, Sept. 28   Litho.
734 A215 400fr multi   100.00 3.25

World Walking Day A216

1994, Oct. 19   Litho.   *Perf. 11¾x11½*
735 A216 75fr multicolored

A217

1994, Nov. 26   Litho.   *Perf. 11¾*
736 A217 55fr Book stand

A218

1994, Dec. 6   Litho.   *Perf. 11½x11¾*
737 A218 35fr Traditional dance

A219   A220

1995, Feb. 25   Litho.   Perf. 11¾
738 A219 70fr multicolored
    Volleyball, cent.

1995, Feb. 25
739 A220 120fr multicolored
    United Nations, 50th anniv.

Fight Against Thirst A221

Perf. 11¾x11½
1995, Mar. 29   Litho.
740 A221 100fr multicolored

Threskiornis Aethiopica — A222

1995, Apr. 5   Litho.   Perf. 11¾
742 A222 50fr multicolored
    A number has been reserved for a 30fr stamp in this set. The editors would like to examine it.

World Telecommunications Day — A223

Perf. 11¾x11½
1995, June 10   Litho.
743 A223 125fr multicolored   50.00   .90

Crocuta Crocuta A224

1995, June 12   Litho.   Perf. 11¾
744 A224 200fr multi   — —

People Meeting Under Tree A225

1995, July 3   Litho.   Perf. 11¾x11½
745 A225 150fr multi   50.00 1.10

A226   A227

1995, Aug. 9   Perf. 11¾
746 A226 45fr Nomads around
    fire   50.00   .30

1995, Sept. 27   Perf. 11½x11¾
747 A227 250fr multi   50.00 2.00
    FAO, 50th anniv.

Traditional Costume — A228

1995, Dec. 6   Litho.   Perf. 11¾
748 A228 90fr multicolored

African Development Bank, 30th Anniv. — A229

Perf. 11¾x11½
1995. Dec. 18   Litho.
749 A229 300fr multi   50.00 2.50

African Soccer Cup — A230

1996, Feb. 28   Litho.   Perf. 11¾
750 A230 70fr multicolored   160.00   .50

Leopard A232

1996, May 6   Litho.   Perf. 11¾
752 A232 70fr multi

Amber Necklace — A233

1996, June 13   Litho.   Perf. 11¾
753 A233 30fr multi   — —

1996 Summer Olympic Games, Atlanta — A234

Perf. 11½x11¾
1996, Sept. 21   Litho.
754 A234 105fr multicolored   100.00 1.00

Commicarpus Grandiflorus A236

1996, Oct. 6   Litho.   Perf. 11½x11¾
756 A236 350fr multi   50.00 2.75

Legend of the Lion and Three Bulls A238

1996, Nov. 28   Litho.   Perf. 11¾
758 A238 95fr multi   100.00   .80

Children's Day A239

1996, Dec. 17   Perf. 11¾x11½
759 A239 130fr multi   50.00 1.00

A240   A241

Legend of the Tortoise and the Fox: No. 760, Tortoise and fox at starting line. No. 761, Fox leaves tortoise behind. No. 762, Tortoise passes sleeping fox.

1997, Jan. 17   Perf. 11¾
760 A240 60fr multi
761 A240 60fr multi
762 A240 60fr multi
    a. Horiz. strip, #760-762   100.00

1997, Feb. 9   Litho.   Perf. 11¾
763 A241 80fr Mother, child   52.50
764 A241 90fr Hands around
    globe   52.50
    UNICEF, 50th anniv.

Dancers — A242

1997, May 14   Litho.   Perf. 11¾
765 A242 70fr multi   50.00

Fortune Teller A243

Designs: 200fr, Fortune teller and woman. 300fr, Fortune teller, camel.

1997, May 29   Litho.   Perf. 11¾
766 A243 200fr multi   — —
767 A243 300fr multi   — —

Woman's Day — A244

1997, May 30   Litho.   Perf. 11¾
768 A244 250fr multi   160.00

Traditional Objects — A245

Design: 30fr, Writing board, horiz. 400fr, Bowl and spoon.

1997, June 5   Litho.   Perf. 11¾
769 A245 30fr multi   — —
770 A245 400fr multi   — —

Telecommunications — A246

Designs: 30fr, Arta post office. 100fr, Map, building with antenna and satellite dishes. 120fr, Ships, map showing submarine cable route, horiz.

1997, June 27   Litho.   Perf. 11¾
771 A246 30fr multi   — —
772 A246 100fr multi   — —
773 A246 120fr multi   — —

Goats in
Tree
A247

1997, July 26   Litho.   Perf. 11¾
774 A247 120fr multi   — —

A248

A249

Portrait of Diana: a, 125fr. b, 130fr. c, 150fr.

1998, Mar. 25   Litho.   Perf. 13½
775 A248 Strip of 3, #a.-c.   5.75 5.75
Diana, Princess of Wales (1961-97).
No. 775 was isssued in sheets of 6 stamps.

1998   Litho.   Perf. 13½
776 A249 130fr multicolored   1.50 1.10
Mother Teresa (1910-97). No. 776 was
issued in sheets of 4.

Intl. Year
of the
Ocean
A250

a, Tangara chilensis. b, Agalychnis cal-
lidryas. c, Delphinus delphis, megaptera
novaeangliae. d, Cercopithecus aethiops (h).
e, Laticaudia colubrina (i), sphyrna mokarran.
f, Lactoria cornuta, delphinus delphis (g). g,
Delphinus delphis (k). h, Aspidontus taeniatus,
lo vulpinus. i, Sepioteuthis lessoniana. j, Prionace glauca (i), chaetodon ornatissimus. k,
Eupagurus bernherdus. l, Octopus vulgaris
(k).

1998, Apr. 20   Litho.   Perf. 13½
777 A250 75fr Sheet of 12,
         #a.-l.   14.00 14.00

Mahatma Gandhi
(1869-1948)
A251

1998, Apr. 20   Litho.   Perf. 11¾
778 A251 250fr multi   50.00 —

Traditional
Art — A252

1998, Apr. 25   Litho.   Perf. 11½x11¾
779 A252 30fr multicolored

Women's Rights and International
Peace — A253

1998, May 3   Perf. 11¾x11½
780 A253 70fr multicolored   50.00 —

World
Water Day
A254

1998, May 10   Litho.   Perf. 11¾
781 A254 45fr multi   50.00 —

1998 World Cup
Soccer
Championships,
France — A255

1998, June 10   Litho.   Perf. 11¾
782 A255 200fr multi   — —

Marine   Cats and
Life — A256   Bush — A257

Perf. 11½x11¾, 11¾x11½
1998, July 2   Litho.
783 A256 20fr Octopus   100.00 —
784 A256 25fr Shark, horiz.   100.00 —

1998, Aug. 30   Perf. 11½x11¾
785 A257 120fr multi   100.00 —

World Telecommunications
Day — A258

1996, Sept. 27   Litho.   Perf. 11¾
786 A258 150fr multi   — —

National
Bank — A259

1998, Sept. 30   Litho.   Perf. 11¾
787 A259 100fr multi   — —

Flags and IGAD
Emblem — A260

Perf. 11½x11¾
1998, Sept. 30   Litho.
788 A260 85fr multi   50.00 —

Traditional
Game
Goos
A261

1998, Oct. 1   Perf. 11¾x11½
789 A261 110fr multi   50.00 —

Fishing
Port
A262

1998
790 A262 100fr multi   50.00 —

Maskali
Island
A263

1998
791 A263 500fr multi   100.00 —

Fish
A264

1999   Litho.   Perf. 13¼x13½
792 A264 70fr multi   100.00 —

Antelope
— A264a

Perf. 13¼x13½
1999, Mar. 16   Litho.
792A A264a 120fr multi

Djibouti
Franc, 50th
Anniv.
A265

1999
793 A265 100fr multi   50.00

World Telecommunications
Day — A266

1999
794 A266 125fr multi   50.00 —

Worldwide Fund for Nature
(WWF) — A267

Phacochoerus africanus aeliani: a, Adult
and young. b, Adult standing. c, Head. d, Adult
walking.
     Illustration reduced.

2000, Apr. 13   Litho.   Perf. 14
795 A267 100fr Block of 4, #a-d   7.25 7.25

Wild Animals — A268

No. 796: a, Flamingo. b, Ostrich. c, Sifaka.
d, Yellow-billed stork. e, Scarlet macaw. f,
Dwarf puff adder. g, Toucan. h, Whooping
crane.

2000, Apr. 13
796 A268 100fr Sheet of 8, #a-h   9.00 9.00

Butterflies — A269

No. 797: a, Doxocopa cherubina. b, Heliconius charitonius. c, Cantonephele numili. d, Danaus gilippus. e, Morpho peleides. f, Heliconius doris.
No. 798, 250fr, Agraulis vanillae. No. 799, 250fr, Strymon melinus.

2000, Apr. 13
797 A269 100fr Sheet of 6, #a-f   9.00 9.00
Souvenir Sheets
798-799 A269 Set of 2   10.00 10.00
No. 797 contains six 28x42mm stamps.

Water Resources — A270

2000, Apr. 13
800 A270 500fr multi   7.25 7.25

Trains and Landmarks — A271

No. 801: a, 5fr, Class OJ 2-10-2, China. b, 25fr, Eurostar, France-England. c, 15fr, Glacier Express, Switzerland. d, 40fr, Unidentified train. e, 35fr, Class WP 4-6-2, India.
No. 802, 110fr: a, Nord Chapelon Pacific, France. b, Class 23 2-6-2, Germany. c, Class GS-4 4-8-4, US. d, Class A4 4-6-2, Great Britain. e, Pacific 4-6-2, South Africa. f, Class HP, India.
No. 803, 120fr: a, VT601, Germany. b, ICIII Bo-Bo EMU, Netherlands. c, TGV, France. d, ETR 450, Italy. e, AVE, Spain. f, Bullet Train, Japan.
No. 804, 250fr, GM War Bonnet, US. No. 805, 250fr, Class 8 Pacific, Great Britain.

2000, Apr. 28
801 A271 Horiz. strip of 5, #a-e   1.75 1.75
Sheets of 6, #a-f
802-803 A271 Set of 2   16.00 16.00
Souvenir Sheets
804-805 A271 Set of 2   7.00 7.00

Dancers A272

2000, Apr. 28
806 A272 75fr multi   1.10 1.10

Blacksmith — A273

2000, May 14
807 A273 100fr multi   1.50 1.50

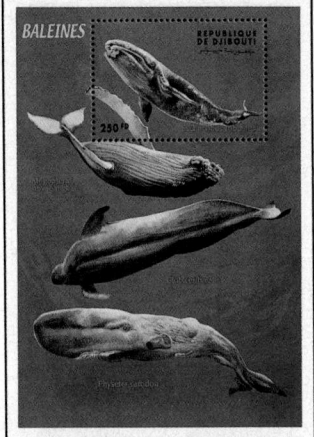

Marine Life — A274

No. 808, vert.: a, Dendrochirus biocellatus. b, Hippocampus. c, Amphiprion ocellaris, Amphiprion percula. d, Periclimenes imperator. e, Pomacnetridae. f, Octopus vulgaris.
No. 809, 50fr: a, Cephalopholis miniata. b, Ptereleotris hanae. c, Sphyraena genie. d, Tripterygion segmentatum. e, Odontaspididae. f, Cirrhitidae. g, Amphiprion. h, Capros aper. i, Balistidae. j, Trygonorhina fasciata. k, Cephalopholis. l, Corythoichthys ocellatus.
No. 810, 60fr: a, Lutjanus kasmira. b, Chaetodon fasciatus. c, Epinephelinae. d, Hypoplectrus gutavarius. e, Loligo opalescens. f, Diodontinae. g, Coelenterata. h, Sargocentron xantherythrum. i, Thalassoma lunare. j, Hemichromis bimaculatus. k, Dasyatis. l, Fromia monilis.
No. 811, 250fr, Eschrichtis robustus. No. 812, 250fr, Cheloniidae.

2000, May 14
808 A274 55fr Sheet of 6, #a-f   5.50 5.50
Sheets of 12, #a-l
809-810 A274 Set of 2   20.00 20.00
Souvenir Sheets
811-812 A274 Set of 2   8.00 8.00

Camels and Tender A275

2000, June 26
813 A275 35fr multi   .65 .65

Ships A276

Designs: 10fr, Thomas W. Lawson, 1902. 15fr, BT Global Challenge, 2000. 20fr, Reliance and Shamrock III, 1903. 25fr, Archibald Russell, 1905. 50fr, Greek merchantman, 8th cent. B.C.
No. 819, 130fr: a, Norman warship, 1066. b, Hanseatic cog, c. 1300. c, Santa Maria, 1492. d, Mary Rose, 1510. e, Golden Hind, 1577. f, Sovereign of the Seas, 1637.
No. 820:, 135fr: a, HMS Endeavour, 1768. b, USS Constitution, 1797. c, Chasse-Maree, 1800. d, Baltimore clipper, 1812. e, Lightning, 1853. f, Bluenose, 1921.
No. 821, 250fr, HM Yacht Britannia, 1893. No. 822, 250fr, Herzogin Cecilie, 1902.

2000, June 26
814-818 A276 Set of 5   2.00 2.00
Sheets of 6, #a-f
819-820 A276 Set of 2   25.00 25.00
Souvenir Sheets
821-822 A276 Set of 2   8.00 8.00

Millennium A277

2000, July 18
823 A277 125fr multi   2.00 2.00

Birds A278

2000, Aug. 23
824   Horiz. strip of 5   2.00 2.00
  a. A278 5fr Lanius excubitor   .20 .20
  b. A278 10fr Phoenicopterus minor   .20 .20
  c. A278 15fr Eupodatis senegalensis   .20 .20
  d. A278 40fr Noephron perchopterus   .45 .45
  e. A278 50fr Pterocles lichtensteinii   .55 .55

Space Exploration — A279

No. 825, 100fr, vert.: a, John Glenn and Mercury capsule, 1962. b, Soyuz capsule, Apollo-Soyuz mission, 1975. c, Hubble Telescope, 1990. d, Apollo capsule, Apollo-Soyuz mission. e, Glenn at speaker's stand, 1974. f, Space Shuttle Columbia, 1981.
No. 826, 100fr, vert.: a, Apollo 11 service module, 1969. b, Telstar, 1962. c, Ariane 4, 1988. d, Apollo 11 lunar module. e, Neil Armstrong, 1969. f, Splashdown of Apollo 11, 1969.
No. 827, 200fr, Astronaut on moon saluting. No. 828, 250fr, Astronauts conducting experiments on moon. No. 829, 250fr, Space Shuttle Challenger.

2000, Aug. 23   Sheets of 6, #a-f
825-826 A279 Set of 2   20.00 20.00
Souvenir Sheets
827-829 A279 Set of 3   12.00 12.00

2000 Summer Olympics, Sydney A280

Olympic flame, flag and: 80fr, Runner. 90fr, Tennis player.

2000   Perf. 14
830-831 A280 Set of 2   2.75 2.75

Items commemorating the death of Pope John Paul II were declared as "fraudulent" by Djibouti Post.

AIR POST STAMPS

Afars and Issas Nos. C104-C105, C103 Overprinted with Bars and "REPUBLIQUE DE DJIBOUTI" in Brown or Black

1977   Engr.   Perf. 13
C106 AP37 55fr multi (Br)   1.75 1.75
C107 AP37 75fr multi   7.00 3.00

Litho.   Perf. 12
C108 AP36 500fr multi   13.50 13.50
Nos. C106-C108 (3)   22.25 18.25

Map of Djibouti, Dove, UN Emblem — AP38

1977, Oct. 19   Photo.   Perf. 13
C109 AP38 300fr multi   5.50 3.50
Djibouti's admission to the United Nations.

Marcel Brochet MB 101, 1955 — AP39

Djibouti Aero Club: 85fr, Tiger Moth, 1960. 200fr, Rallye-Commodore, 1973.

1978, Feb. 27   Litho.   Perf. 13
C110 AP39 60fr multi   1.10 .35
C111 AP39 85fr multi   1.60 .60
C112 AP39 200fr multi   3.50 1.00
Nos. C110-C112 (3)   6.20 1.95

Old Man, by Rubens AP40

500fr, Hippopotamus Hunt, by Rubens.

1978, Apr. 24   Photo.   Perf. 13
C113 AP40 50fr multi   1.00 .35
C114 AP40 500fr multi, horiz.   10.00 3.25
Peter Paul Rubens (1577-1640).

Player Holding Soccer Cup — AP41

Design: 300fr, Soccer player, map of South America with Argentina, Cup and emblem.

1978, June 20   Litho.   Perf. 13
C115 AP41 100fr multi   1.75   .35
C116 AP41 300fr multi   5.25   1.00

11th World Cup Soccer Championship, Argentina, June 1-25.
For overprints see Nos. C117-C118.

Nos. C115-C116 Overprinted:
a. ARGENTINE/CHAMPION 1978
b. ARGENTINE/HOLLANDE/3-1

1978, Aug. 20   Litho.   Perf. 13
C117 AP41 (a) 100fr multi   1.75   .40
C118 AP41 (b) 300fr multi   5.25   1.25

Argentina's victory in 1978 Soccer Championship.

Tahitian Women, by Gauguin — AP42

Young Hare, by Dürer AP43

Perf. 13x12½, 12½x13
1978, Sept. 25   Litho.
C119 AP42 100fr multi   2.25   .40
C120 AP43 250fr multi   5.25   1.50

Paul Gauguin (1848-1903) and Albrecht Dürer (1471-1528), painters.

Common Design Types pictured following the introduction.

Philexafrique II-Essen Issue
Common Design Types

Designs: No. C121, Lynx and Djibouti No. 456. No. C122, Jay and Brunswick No. 3.

1978, Dec. 13   Litho.   Perf. 13x12½
C121 CD138 90fr multi   3.00   1.25
C122 CD139 90fr multi   3.00   1.25
a.   Pair, Nos. C121-C122 + label   6.25   6.25

UPU Emblem, Map of Djibouti, Dove — AP44

1978, Dec. 18   Engr.   Perf. 13
C123 AP44 200fr multi   3.00   1.10

Centenary of Congress of Paris.

Junkers JU-52 and Dewoitine D-338 — AP45

Powered Flight, 75th Anniversary: 250fr, Potez P63-11, 1941 and Supermarine Spitfire HF-VII, 1942. 500fr, Concorde, 1969 and Sikorsky S-40 "American Clipper," 1931.

1979, May 21   Litho.   Perf. 13x12½
C124 AP45 140fr multi   2.75   .60
C125 AP45 250fr multi   4.00   1.00
C126 AP45 500fr multi   8.50   1.75
    Nos. C124-C126 (3)   15.25   3.35

The Laundress, by Honoré Daumier AP46

1979, July 10   Litho.   Perf. 12½x13
C127 AP46 500fr multi   10.50   2.75

Olympic Emblem, Skis, Sleds — AP47

1980, Jan. 21   Litho.   Perf. 13
C128 AP47 150fr multi   2.75   .60

13th Winter Olympic Games, Lake Placid, N.Y., Feb. 12-24.
For surcharges see Nos. C133-C134.

Cathedral of the Archangel, Basketball, Moscow '80 Emblem — AP48

120fr, Lomonossov Univ., Moscow, soccer. 250fr, Cathedral of the Annunciation, running.

1980, Apr. 10   Litho.   Perf. 13
C129 AP48 60fr multi   1.00   .25
C130 AP48 120fr multi   2.00   .40
C131 AP48 250fr multi   4.00   1.00
    Nos. C129-C131 (3)   7.00   1.65

22nd Summer Olympic Games, Moscow, July 18-Aug. 3.

Air Djibouti, 1st Anniversary — AP49

1980, Mar. 29   Litho.   Perf. 13x12½
C132 AP49 400fr multi   7.50   2.00

No. C128 Surcharged in Black and Blue or Purple:
80fr.   A.M.   MOSER-PROEL / AUTRICHE / DESCENTE DAMES / MEDAILLE D'OR
200fr. HEIDEN / USA / 5 MEDAILLES D'OR / PATINAGE DE VITESSE

1980, Apr. 5   Litho.   Perf. 13
C133 AP47 80fr on 150fr   1.40   .40
C134 AP47 200fr on 150fr (P)   3.50   1.25

Apollo 11 Moon Landing, 10th Anniversary — AP50

Space Conquests: 300fr, Apollo-Soyuz space project, 5th anniversary.

1980, May 8
C135 AP50 200fr multi   3.50   .60
C136 AP50 300fr multi   5.25   1.00

Satellite Earth Station Inauguration — AP51

1980, July 3   Litho.   Perf. 13
C137 AP51 500fr multi   9.00   1.75

Graf Zeppelin — AP52

1980, Oct. 2   Litho.   Perf. 13
C138 AP52 100fr shown   2.25   .40
C139 AP52 150fr Ferdinand von Zeppelin, blimp   2.75   .60

Zeppelin flight, 80th anniversary.

Voyager Passing Saturn — AP53

1980, Dec. 21   Litho.   Perf. 13
C140 AP53 250fr multi   5.00   1.00

AP54

AP55

World Cup Soccer Preliminary Games: 200fr, Players, diff.

1981, Jan. 14
C141 AP54 80fr multi   1.40   .30
C142 AP54 200fr multi   3.50   .65

1981, Feb. 10   Litho.   Perf. 13
C143 AP55 100fr multi   2.50   .50

European-African Economic Convention.

5th Anniversary of Viking I Take-off to Mars — AP56

20th Anniversary of Various Space Flights: 75fr, Vostok I, Yuri Gagarin, vert. 150fr, Freedom 7, Alan B. Shepard, vert.

1981, Mar. 9   Litho.   Perf. 13
C144 AP56 75fr multi   1.40   .30
C145 AP56 120fr multi   2.00   .40
C146 AP56 150fr multi   2.75   .60
    Nos. C144-C146 (3)   6.15   1.30

Football Players, by Picasso (1881-1973) — AP57

Design: 400fr Man Wearing a Turban, by Rembrandt (1606-1669), vert.

Perf. 13x12½, 12½x13
1981, Aug. 3   Litho.
C147 AP57 300fr multi   6.25   1.40
C148 AP57 400fr multi   7.00   1.75

Columbia Space Shuttle — AP58

1981, Sept. 24   Litho.   Perf. 13
C149 AP58 90fr Shuttle, diff.,
vert.   1.75 .40
C150 AP58 120fr shown   2.25 .60

Nos. C149-C150 Overprinted in Brown
with Astronauts' Names and Dates

1981, Nov. 12   Perf. 13
C151 AP58 90fr multi   1.75 .50
C152 AP58 120fr multi   2.25 .75

1982 World Cup Soccer — AP59

Designs: Various soccer players.

1982, Jan. 20
C153 AP59 110fr multi   2.10 .60
C154 AP59 220fr multi   4.00 1.25

For overprints see Nos. C166-C167.

Space Anniversaries — AP60

Designs: 40fr, Luna 9 moon landing, 15th,
vert. 60fr, John Glenn's flight, 20th, vert.
180fr, Viking I Mars landing, 5th.

1982, Feb. 15
C155 AP60 40fr multi   .70 .20
C156 AP60 60fr multi   1.10 .30
C157 AP60 180fr multi   3.00 1.00
     Nos. C155-C157 (3)   4.80 1.50

21st
Birthday of
Princess
Diana of
Wales
AP61

1982, Apr. 29   Litho.   Perf. 12½x13
C158 AP61 120fr Portrait   2.00 .75
C159 AP61 180fr Portrait, diff. 3.00 1.00

For overprints see Nos. C168-C169.

No. 489, Boy Examining
Collection — AP62

1982, May 10   Perf. 13x12½
C160 AP62 80fr shown   1.40 .50
C161 AP62 140fr No. 495   2.75 .90
  a. Pair, Nos. C160-C161 + label 4.50 4.50

PHILEXFRANCE '82 Stamp Exhibition,
Paris, June 11-21.

1350th Anniv. of
Mohammed's
Death at
Medina — AP63

1982, June 8   Litho.   Perf. 13
C162 AP63 500fr Medina
Mosque   7.50 2.00

Scouting Year — AP64

1982, June 28
C163 AP64 95fr Baden-Powell   1.50 .50
C164 AP64 200fr Camp, scouts   3.50 1.25

2nd UN Conference on Peaceful Uses
of Outer Space, Vienna, Aug. 9-
21 — AP65

1982, Aug. 19
C165 AP65 350fr multi   3.00 1.40

Nos. C153-C154 Overprinted with
Winner's Name and Scores

1982, July 21   Litho.   Perf. 13
C166 AP59 110fr multi   2.00 .60
C167 AP59 220fr multi   4.00 1.10

Italy's victory in 1982 World Cup.

Nos. C158-C159 Overprinted in Blue
or Red with Date, Name and Title

1982, Aug. 9   Perf. 12½x13
C168 AP61 120fr multi   2.25 .75
C169 AP61 180fr multi (R)   3.25 1.00

Birth of Prince William of Wales, June 21.

Franklin D.
Roosevelt (1882-
1945)
AP66

1982, Oct. 7   Litho.   Perf. 13
C170 AP66 115fr shown   1.75 .50
C171 AP66 250fr George Wash-
ington   4.50 1.00

Manned Flight
Bicentenary
AP67

Pre-olympic
Year — AP68

1983, Jan. 20   Litho.
C172 AP67 35fr Montgolfiere,
1783   .65 .25
C173 AP67 45fr Giffard, Paris
Exposition,
1878   1.10 .30
C174 AP67 120fr Double Eagle
II, 1978   2.75 .80
     Nos. C172-C174 (3)   4.50 1.35

1983, Feb. 15
C175 AP68 75fr Volleyball   1.40 .50
C176 AP68 125fr Wind surfing   2.40 .80

50th Anniv. of Air France — AP69

1983, Mar. 20   Litho.   Perf. 13
C177 AP69 25fr Bloch 220   .40 .20
C178 AP69 100fr DC-4   1.75 .70
C179 AP69 175fr Boeing 747   3.25 1.10
     Nos. C177-C179 (3)   5.40 2.00

AP70

AP71

180fr, Martin Luther King, Jr. (1929-68), civil
rights leader. 250fr, Alfred Nobel (1833-96)

1983, May 18   Litho.   Perf. 13
C180 AP70 180fr multi   2.75 1.25
C181 AP70 250fr multi   3.75 2.00

1983, July 18   Litho.   Perf. 13
Service Clubs: 90fr, Rotary Club Intl., Sail-
ing Show, Toronto, June 5-9. 150fr, Lions
Club Intl., Honolulu Meeting, June 22-24, Dji-
bouti lighthouse.
C182 AP71 90fr multi   1.40 .60
C183 AP71 150fr multi   2.25 1.00
  a. Pair, Nos. C182-C183 + label 5.00 1.75

Vintage Motor Cars — AP72

1983, Sep. 20   Litho.   Perf. 13x12½
C184 AP72 60fr Renault, 1904   1.50 .40
C185 AP72 80fr Mercedes,
1910, vert.   2.00 .55
C186 AP72 110fr Lorraine-Die-
trich, 1912   2.50 .75
     Nos. C184-C186 (3)   6.00 1.70

Souvenir Sheet

Air France, 50th Anniv. — AP73

Illustration reduced.

**1983, Oct. 7   Litho.   Perf. 12½
Self-Adhesive**
C187 AP73 250fr multicolored 25.00 2.10

Printed on wood.

Vostok VI
AP74

1983, Oct. 20   Litho.   Perf. 12
C188 AP74 120fr shown   2.00 .80
C189 AP74 200fr Explorer I   3.50 1.10

1984 Winter Olympics — AP75

1984, Feb. 14   Litho.   Perf. 13
C190 AP75 70fr Speed skating   1.40 .50
C191 AP75 130fr Figure skating 2.25 1.00

For overprints see Nos. C196-C197.

Souvenir Sheet

Ship — AP76

1984, Feb. 14   Litho.   Perf. 12½
C192 AP76 250fr multi   11.00 1.75

Sea-Me-We (South-east Asia-Middle East-Western Europe) submarine cable construction agreement.

Motorized Hang Gliders — AP77

Various hang gliders.

1984, Mar. 12   Perf. 13x12½
C193 AP77 65fr multi   1.25 .50
C194 AP77 85fr multi   1.60 .60
C195 AP77 100fr multi   2.10 .75
    Nos. C193-C195 (3)   4.95 1.85

Nos. C190-C191 Overprinted with Winners' Names and Country

1984, Mar. 28   Perf. 13
C196 AP75 70fr multi   1.25 .50
C197 AP75 130fr multi   2.40 1.00

Portrait of Marguerite Matisse, 1910, by Henri Matisse AP78

Design: 200fr, Portrait of Mario Varvogli, by Amedeo Modigliani.

1984, Apr. 15   Litho.   Perf. 12½x13
C198 AP78 150fr multi   3.25 1.00
C199 AP78 200fr multi   4.00 1.40

1984 Summer Olympics — AP79

1984, May 24   Perf. 13
C200 AP79 50fr Running   1.00 .40
C201 AP79 60fr High jump   1.25 .40
C202 AP79 80fr Swimming   1.50 .60
    Nos. C200-C202 (3)   3.75 1.40

Battle Scene — AP80

1984, June 16   Litho.   Perf. 13x12½
C203 AP80 300fr multi   5.50 2.25

125th anniv. of Battle of Solferino and 120th anniv. of Red Cross.

Bleriot's Flight over English Channel, 75th Anniv. — AP81

1984, July 8
C204 AP81 40fr 14-Bis plans   .80 .30
C205 AP81 75fr Britten-Norman
                 Islander   1.40 .55
C206 AP81 90fr Air Djibouti jet   1.50 .65
    Nos. C204-C206 (3)   3.70 1.50

375th Anniv., Galileo's Telescope AP82

1984, Oct. 7   Litho.   Perf. 13
C207 AP82 120fr Telescopes,
                 spacecraft   2.25 .80
C208 AP82 180fr Galileo,
                 telescopes   3.25 1.10

1984 Soccer Events — AP83

1984, Oct. 20   Litho.   Perf. 13
C209 AP83 80fr Euro Cup   1.75 .60
C210 AP83 80fr Los Angeles
                 Olympics   1.75 .60
    a.   Pair, Nos. C209-C210 + label   4.25 1.25

Service Clubs — AP84

Telecommunications Technology — AP85

No. C213, Technician, researchist, operator. No. C214, Offshore oil rig, transmission tower, government building.

1985, July 2   Perf. 13x12½
C213 AP85 80fr multi   2.00 .55
C214 AP85 80fr multi   2.00 .55
    a.   Pair, Nos. C213-C214 + label   4.50 1.10

PHILEXAFRICA '85, Lome.

Telecommunications Development — AP86

1985, Oct. 2   Perf. 13
C215 AP86 50fr Intl. transmis-
                 sion center   .90 .35
C216 AP86 90fr Ariane rocket,
                 vert.   1.60 .65
C217 AP86 120fr ARABSAT sat-
                 ellite   2.00 .90
    Nos. C215-C217 (3)   4.50 1.90

Youths Windsurfing, Playing Tennis — AP87

No. C219, Tadjoura Highway construction.

1985, Nov. 13   Perf. 13x12½
C218 AP87 100fr multi   2.00 .70
C219 AP87 100fr multi   2.00 .70
    a.   Pair, Nos. C218-C219 + label   4.50 1.50

PHILEXAFRICA '85, Lome, Togo, 11/16-24.

1986 World Cup Soccer Championships, Mexico — AP88

1986, Feb. 24   Litho.   Perf. 13
C220 AP88 75fr shown   1.50 .50
C221 AP88 100fr Players, stadi-
                 um   2.00 .70

For overprints see Nos. C223-C224.

1985, Feb. 23   Litho.   Perf. 13
C211 AP84 50fr Lions, World Lep-
                 rosy Day   1.10 .40
C212 AP84 60fr Rotary, chess
                 board, pieces   1.25 .45

#C211-C212 exist in souvenir sheets of 1.

Statue of Liberty, Cent. — AP89

1986, May 21
C222 AP89 250fr multi   4.00 1.75

Nos. C220-C221 Ovptd. with Winners

1986, Sept. 15   Litho.   Perf. 13
C223   75fr "FRANCE -
                 BELGIQUE / 4-2"   1.10 .55
C224   100fr "3-2 ARGENTINE-
                 RFA"   1.50 .70

1986 World Chess Championships, May 1-19 — AP89a

Malayan animal chess pieces.

1986, Oct. 13   Litho.   Perf. 13
C225 AP89a 80fr Knight, bish-
                   ops   1.75 .60
C226 AP89a 120fr Rook, king,
                   pawn   2.75 .90

Yuri Gagarin, Sputnik Spacecraft — AP90

1986, Nov. 27   Litho.   Perf. 13
C227 AP90 150fr shown   3.00 1.10
C228 AP90 200fr Space rendez-
                 vous, 1966   3.25 1.25

First man in space, 25th anniv.; Gemini 8-Agena link-up, 20th anniv.

Historic Flights — AP91

1987, Jan. 22   Litho.   Perf. 13
C229 AP91 55fr Amiot 370   1.25 .40
C230 AP91 80fr Spirit of St.
                 Louis   1.75 .55
C231 AP91 120fr Voyager   2.50 .90
    Nos. C229-C231 (3)   5.50 1.85

First flight from Istria to Djibouti, 1942; Lindbergh's Transatlantic flight, 1927; nonstop world circumnavigation without refueling. For surcharge see No. C240.

Souvenir Sheet

Fight Against Leprosy — AP91a

Design: Raoul Follereau (b. 1903), care giver to lepers, Gerhard Hansen (1841-1912), discoverer of bacillus of leprosy. Illustration reduced.

1987, Mar. 23   Litho.   Perf. 13x12½
Self-Adhesive

C231A   AP91a 500fr multi   17.00 4.25

No. C231A printed on wood.

Pres. Aptidon, Natl. Crest and Flag AP92

1987, June 27   Litho.   Perf. 12½x13
C232   AP92 250fr multi   4.00 1.50

Natl. independence, 10th anniv.

Telstar, 25th Anniv. — AP93

1987, Oct. 1   Perf. 13
C233   AP93 190fr shown   3.00 1.25
C234   AP93 250fr Samuel Morse,
              telegraph key   3.75 1.50

Invention of the telegraph, 150th anniv. (250fr).

City of Djibouti, Cent. — AP94

100fr, Djibouti Creek & quay, 1887. 150fr, Aerial view of city, 1987. 250fr, Somali Coast #6, 20, postmarks of 1898 & 1903.

1987, Nov. 15   Litho.   Perf. 13x12½
C235   AP94 100fr blk & buff   2.00 1.10
C236   AP94 150fr multi   3.00 1.60
  a.   Pair, Nos. C235-C236 + label 6.00 2.75
Souvenir Sheet
237   AP94 250fr multi   5.50 2.75

No. C237 has decorative margin like design of 100fr.

Intl. Red Cross and Red Crescent Organizations, 125th Anniv. — AP95

1988, Feb. 17   Litho.   Perf. 13
C238   AP95 300fr multi   6.00 3.25

1988 Summer Olympics, Seoul — AP96

1988, June 15   Litho.   Perf. 13
C239   AP96 105fr multi   2.50 1.00

For overprint see No. C242.

No. C229 Surcharged in Black

1988, June 28
C240   AP91 70fr on 55fr multi   1.75   .70

Air race in memory of the Paris-Djibouti-St. Denis flight of French aviator Roland Garros (1888-1913).

World Post Day — AP97

1988, Oct. 9   Litho.   Perf. 13
C241   AP97 1000fr multi   15.00 10.00

No. C239 Ovptd. "AHMED SALAH / 1re MEDAILLE OLYMPIQUE"

1988, Dec. 15   Litho.   Perf. 13
C242   AP96 105fr multi   2.00 1.50

World Telecommunications Day — AP98

1989, May 17   Litho.   Perf. 12½
C243   AP98 150fr multi   2.75 1.50

PHILEXFRANCE '89, Declaration of Human Rights and Citizenship Bicent. — AP99

1989, July 14   Litho.   Perf. 12½x13
C244   AP99 120fr multi   2.25 1.25

Salt, Lake Assal — AP100

1989, Sept. 15   Litho.   Perf. 13
C245   AP100 300fr multicolored   4.50 3.00

POSTAGE DUE STAMP

Urn for Milking Camel — D1

1988, Jan. 20   Litho.   Perf. 13
J1   D1 60fr multi   .90   .65

DOMINICA

ˌdä-mə-ˈnē-kə

LOCATION — The largest island of the Windward group in the West Indies. Southeast of Puerto Rico.

GOVT. — Republic in British Commonwealth

AREA — 290 sq. mi.

POP. — 64,881 (1999 est.)

CAPITAL — Roseau

Formerly a Presidency of the Leeward Islands, Dominica became a separate colony under the governor of the Windward Islands on January 1, 1940. Dominica joined the West Indies federation April 22, 1958. In 1968, Dominica became an associate state of Britain; in 1978, an independent nation.

12 Pence = 1 Shilling
20 Shillings = 1 Pound
100 Cents = 1 Dollar (1949)

> Catalogue values for unused stamps in this country are for Never Hinged items, beginning with Scott 112.

Watermark

Wmk. 334 — Rectangles

Queen Victoria — A1

Perf. 12½

1874, May 4   **Typo.**   **Wmk. 1**

1	A1	1p violet	170.00	55.00
2	A1	6p green	625.00	115.00
3	A1	1sh deep lilac rose	375.00	80.00
		Nos. 1-3 (3)	1,170.	250.00

During 1875-87 some issues were manuscript dated with village names. These are considered postally used. Stamps with entire village names sell for much more, starting at $100.

1877-79   **Perf. 14**

4	A1	½p bister ('79)	16.00	60.00
5	A1	1p violet	8.25	2.50
a.		Diagonal or vertical half used as ½p on cover		2,100.
6	A1	2½p red brown ('79)	260.00	32.50
7	A1	4p blue ('79)	125.00	4.00
8	A1	6p green	170.00	22.50
9	A1	1sh dp lilac rose	140.00	57.50
		Nos. 4-9 (6)	719.25	179.00

For surcharges see Nos. 10-15.

No. 5 Bisected and Surcharged in Black or Red:

a   b   c

1882

10	A1(a)	½p on half of 1p	210.00	47.50
a.		Inverted surcharge	1,150.	900.00
b.		Surcharge tete beche pair	1,900.	1,750.
11	A1(b)	½p on half of 1p	72.50	27.50
a.		Surch. reading downward	72.50	27.50
b.		Double surcharge	900.00	

12	A1(c)	½p on half of 1p (R)	35.00	19.00
a.		Inverted surcharge	1,150.	550.00
b.		Double surcharge	1,850.	750.00
		Nos. 10-12 (3)	317.50	94.00

The existence of genuine examples of No. 10b has been questioned.

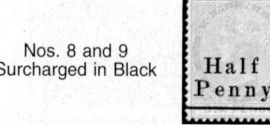

Nos. 8 and 9 Surcharged in Black

1886

13	A1	½p on 6p green	6.50	6.00
14	A1	1p on 6p green	24,000.	12,500.
15	A1	1p on 1sh	16.00	19.00
a.		Double surcharge	6,250.	3,500.

All examples of No. 14 may have small pin marks which may have been part of the surcharging process.

1883-88   **Wmk. 2**

16	A1	½p bister ('83)	3.75	11.50
17	A1	½p green ('86)	1.70	6.25
18	A1	1p violet ('86)	32.50	14.00
a.		Half used as ½p on cover		2,200.
19	A1	1p car rose ('87)	3.25	7.50
a.		1p rose	18.00	20.00
b.		Vert. half used as ½p on cover		2,100.
20	A1	2½p red brn ('84)	160.00	3.00
21	A1	2½p ultra ('88)	4.25	5.75
22	A1	4p gray ('86)	3.75	5.75
23	A1	6p orange ('88)	11.00	55.00
24	A1	1sh dp lil rose ('88)	180.00	325.00
		Nos. 16-24 (9)	400.20	433.75

Roseau, Capital of Dominica — A6

King Edward VII — A7

1903   **Wmk. 1**   **Perf. 14**

25	A6	½p gray green	5.25	3.25
26	A6	1p car & black	10.50	1.00
27	A6	2p brn & gray grn	3.25	5.75
28	A6	2½p ultra & blk	6.50	5.25
29	A6	3p black & vio	10.50	4.50
30	A6	6p org brn & blk	5.75	23.00
31	A6	1sh gray grn & red vio	35.00	52.50
32	A6	2sh red vio & blk	32.50	35.00
33	A6	2sh6p ocher & gray grn	23.00	92.50
34	A7	5sh brown & blk	125.00	175.00
		Nos. 25-34 (10)	257.25	397.75

Nos. 25 to 29 and 31 are on both ordinary and chalky paper. For detailed listings, see the *Scott Classic Specialized Catalogue of Stamps & Covers.*

1907-20   **Wmk. 3**

         Chalky Paper

35	A6	½p gray green	4.25	4.00
36	A6	1p car & black	2.50	.55
37	A6	2p brn & gray grn	6.75	20.00
38	A6	2½p ultra & black	5.50	27.50
39	A6	3p black & vio	5.00	17.00
40	A6	3p vio, *yel* ('09)	3.75	5.25
41	A6	6p org brn & blk ('08)	65.00	100.00
42	A6	6p vio & dl vio ('09)	12.50	19.00
43	A6	1sh gray grn & red vio	4.75	67.50
44	A6	1sh blk, *green* ('10)	3.75	3.50
45	A6	2sh red vio & blk ('08)	30.00	40.00
46	A6	2sh ultra & vio, *bl* ('19)	32.50	110.00
47	A6	2sh6p ocher & gray grn ('08)	27.50	75.00

48	A6	2sh6p red & blk, *bl* ('20)	32.50	125.00
49	A7	5sh brn & blk ('08)	75.00	75.00
		Nos. 35-49 (15)	311.25	689.30

Nos. 40, 42 and 44 are on both ordinary and chalky paper. For detailed listings, see the *Scott Classic Specialized Catalogue of Stamps & Covers.*

For type surcharged see No. 55.

1908-09   **Ordinary Paper**

50	A6	½p green	3.25	2.75
51	A6	1p scarlet	1.75	.55
a.		1p carmine	3.50	.35
52	A6	2p gray ('09)	4.00	14.00
53	A6	2½p ultramarine	9.50	7.00
a.		2½p bright blue ('18)	5.75	10.50
		Nos. 50-53 (4)	18.50	24.30

King George V — A8

1914   **Chalky Paper**   **Perf. 14**

54	A8	5sh grn & scar, *yel*	70.00	92.50

Type of 1903 Surcharged

1920

55	A6	1½p on 2½p orange	4.50	5.25

1921   **Wmk. 4**

         Ordinary Paper

56	A6	½p green	3.50	21.00
57	A6	1p rose red	2.75	5.50
58	A6	1½p orange	4.75	15.00
59	A6	2p gray	4.25	4.75
60	A6	2½p ultra	2.75	12.00
61	A6	6p vio & dl vio	3.50	50.00
62	A6	2sh ultra & vio, *bl*	45.00	125.00
63	A6	2sh6p red & blk, *bl*	45.00	140.00
		Nos. 56-63 (8)	111.50	373.25

No. 61 is on chalky paper.

Seal of Colony and George V — A9

1923-33   **Chalky Paper**   **Wmk. 4**

65	A9	½p green & blk	2.50	.85
66	A9	1p violet & blk	2.75	2.25
67	A9	1p scar & black	12.50	1.40
68	A9	1½p car & black	4.00	.90
69	A9	1½p dp brn & blk	12.50	.95
70	A9	2p gray & black	2.50	.65
71	A9	2½p org & black	2.00	12.00
72	A9	2½p ultra & black	5.50	2.75
73	A9	3p ultra & black	2.25	16.00
74	A9	3p red & blk, *yel*	2.25	1.40
75	A9	4p brown & blk	3.25	7.25
76	A9	6p red vio & blk	4.75	9.00
77	A9	1sh blk, *emerald*	3.00	3.75
78	A9	2sh ultra & blk, *bl*	14.00	27.50
79	A9	2sh6p red & blk, *bl*	25.00	27.50
80	A9	3sh vio & blk, *yel*	4.50	17.50
81	A9	4sh red & blk, *emer*	15.00	30.00
82	A9	5sh grn & blk, *yel*	30.00	62.50
		Nos. 65-82 (18)	148.25	224.15

Issue years: Nos. 80, 82, 1927; Nos. 72, 74, 1928; Nos. 67, 69, 1933; others, 1923.

1923   **Wmk. 3**

83	A9	3sh vio & blk, *yel*	5.75	80.00
84	A9	5sh grn & blk, *yel*	13.50	65.00
85	A9	£1 vio & blk, *red*	300.00	450.00
		Nos. 83-85 (3)	319.25	595.00

Common Design Types pictured following the introduction.

Silver Jubilee Issue
Common Design Type

Perf. 13½x14

1935, May 6   **Wmk. 4**   **Engr.**

90	CD301	1p car & blue	.30	.35
91	CD301	1½p gray blk & ultra	1.00	1.90
92	CD301	2½p blue & brn	3.75	4.50
93	CD301	1sh brt vio & ind	3.75	6.50
		Nos. 90-93 (4)	8.80	13.25
		Set, never hinged	17.00	

Coronation Issue
Common Design Type

1937, May 12   **Perf. 11x11½**

94	CD302	1p dark carmine	.20	.20
95	CD302	1½p brown	.20	.20
96	CD302	2½p deep ultra	.35	.60
		Nos. 94-96 (3)	.75	1.00
		Set, never hinged	1.50	

Fresh-Water Lake — A10

Layou River — A11

Picking Limes — A12

Boiling Lake — A13

1938-47   **Wmk. 4**   **Perf. 12½**

97	A10	½p grn & red brn	.20	.20
98	A11	1p car & gray	.20	.20
99	A12	1½p rose vio & grn	.20	1.10
100	A13	2p brn blk & dp rose	.55	1.50
101	A12	2½p ultra & rose vio	4.00	3.00
102	A11	3p red brn & ol	.20	.60
103	A12	3½p red vio & brt ultra	1.40	2.50
104	A10	6p vio & yel grn	.70	1.90
105	A10	7p org brn & grn	1.25	2.10
106	A13	1sh olive & vio	2.40	1.90
107	A11	2sh red vio & blk	5.50	12.00
108	A10	2sh6p scar ver & blk	12.00	7.75
109	A11	5sh dk brn & bl	6.75	12.00
110	A13	10sh dl org & blk	13.50	22.50
		Nos. 97-110 (14)	48.85	69.25
		Set, never hinged	60.00	

Issued: 3½p, 7p, 2sh, 10sh, 10/15/47; others, 8/15/38.

King George VI — A14

1940, Apr. 15   **Photo.**   **Perf. 14½x14**

111	A14	¼p brown violet	.40	.40

> Catalogue values for unused stamps in this section, from this point to the end of the section, are for Never Hinged items.

Peace Issue
Common Design Type

1946, Oct. 14   **Engr.**   **Perf. 13½x14**

112	CD303	1p carmine	.25	.25
113	CD303	3½p deep blue	.25	.25

Silver Wedding Issue
Common Design Types
1948, Dec. 1   Photo.   Perf. 14x14½
114 CD304   1p scarlet   .25   .25

Engraved; Name Typographed
Perf. 11½x11
115 CD305   10sh orange brn   16.00 32.50

UPU Issue
Common Design Types
Engr.: Name Typo. on 6c and 12c
1949, Oct. 10   Perf. 13½, 11x11½
116 CD306   5c blue   .20   .20
117 CD307   6c chocolate   1.40 1.40
118 CD308   12c rose violet   .70   .70
119 CD309   24c olive   .45   .45
Nos. 116-119 (4)   2.75 2.75

University Issue
Common Design Types
1951, Feb. 16   Engr.   Perf. 14x14½
120 CD310   3c purple & green   .70   .45
121 CD311   12c dp car & dk bl grn   .90   .70

George VI
A15

Drying Cocoa
A16

Picking
Oranges — A17

Designs: 2c and 60c, Carib Baskets. 3c and 48c, Lime Plantation. 4c, Picking Oranges. 5c, Bananas. 6c, Botanical Gardens. 8c, Drying Vanilla Beans. 12c and $1.20, Fresh Water Lake. 14c, Layou River. 24c, Boiling Lake.

Perf. 14½x14
1951, July 1   Photo.   Wmk. 4
122 A15   ½c brown   .20   .20

Perf. 13x13½
Engr.
123 A16   1c red org & blk   .20   .30
124 A16   2c dp grn & red brn   .20   .20
125 A16   3c red vio & bl grn   .20   .70
126 A16   4c dk brn & brn org   .45   .80
127 A16   5c rose red & blk   1.10   .30
128 A16   6c org brn & ol grn   1.10   .30
129 A16   8c dp bl & dp grn   .75   .70
130 A16   12c emer & gray   .60 1.90
131 A16   14c pur & blue   1.25 1.90
132 A16   24c rose car & red vio   1.00   .30
133 A16   48c red org & bl grn   3.50 8.25
134 A16   60c gray & car   3.50 7.00
135 A16 $1.20 gray & emer   5.50 7.00

Perf. 13½x13
136 A17 $2.40 gray & org   30.00 40.00
Nos. 122-136 (15)   49.55 69.85

Nos. 125, 127, 129 and 131 Overprinted in Black or Carmine

1951, Oct. 15   Perf. 13x13½
137 A16   3c red vio & bl green   .25   .25
138 A16   5c rose red & black   .50   .50
139 A16   8c dp blue & dp grn (C)   .65   .90
140 A16   14c purple & blue (C)   1.10 1.10
Nos. 137-140 (4)   2.50 2.50

Adoption of a new constitution for the Windward Islands, 1951.

Coronation Issue
Common Design Type
1953, June 2   Engr.   Perf. 13½x13
141 CD312   2c dk green & black   .40   .40

Types of 1951 with Portrait of Queen Elizabeth II
1954, Oct. 1   Photo.   Perf. 14½x14
142 A15   ½c brown   .20   .20

Perf. 13x13½
Engr.
143 A16   1c red org & blk   .20   .30
144 A16   2c dp grn & red brn   .90   .30
145 A16   3c red vio & bl grn   1.90   .70
146 A16   4c dk brn & brn org   .20   .30
147 A16   5c rose red & blk   1.90   .95
148 A16   6c org brn & ol   .55   .30
149 A16   8c dp bl & dp grn   1.25   .30
150 A16   12c emer & gray   .75   .30
151 A16   14c pur & bl   .30   .45
152 A16   24c rose car & red vio   .55   .70
153 A16   48c red org & bl grn   2.40 3.25
154 A16   60c gray & car   1.60 2.75
155 A16 $1.20 gray & emer   24.00 6.25

Perf. 13½x13
156 A17 $2.40 gray & org   24.00 14.00
Nos. 142-156 (15)   60.70 31.05

Mat
Making — A18

5c, Canoe making. 10c, Bananas.

1957, Oct. 15   Wmk. 4   Perf. 13x13½
157 A18   3c car rose & black   2.40 2.50
158 A18   5c brown & blue   7.50 1.10
159 A18   10c redsh brn & brt grn   4.00 2.25
160 A18   48c violet & brown   1.00 1.10
Nos. 157-160 (4)   14.90 6.95

West Indies Federation
Common Design Type
Perf. 11½x11
1958, Apr. 22   Wmk. 314
161 CD313   3c green   .50   .50
162 CD313   6c blue   .50   .50
163 CD313   12c car rose   1.00 1.00
Nos. 161-163 (3)   2.00 2.00

Sailing
Canoe — A19

Traditional
Costume — A20

Designs: 1c, Seashore, Rosalie. 2c, 5c, Queen Elizabeth II by Annigoni. 4c, Sulphur Springs. 6c, Road making. 8c, Dugout canoe. 10c, Frog (mountain chicken). 12c, Boats and Scotts Head. 15c, Bananas. 24c, Imperial parrot. 48c, View of Goodwill. 60c, Cacao tree. $1.20, Coat of Arms. $2.40, Trafalgar Falls. $4.80, Coconut palm.
Two types of 14c:
I — Mountain light violet. Girl's eyes look straight out.
II — Mountain blue. Eyes look sideways.

Perf. 14½x14, 14x14½
1963, May 16   Photo.   Wmk. 314
164 A19   1c blk, brn & grn   .20 1.10
165 A20   2c ultramarine   .20   .20
166 A19   3c lt ultra & blk   1.10 1.40
167 A19   4c sl, grn & brn   .20   .20
168 A20   5c magenta   .20   .20
169 A19   6c lt grn, vio & buff   .20   .20
170 A19   8c tan, blk & lt grn   .20   .20
171 A19   10c pink & brn   .20   .20
172 A19   12c bl, blk, grn & brn   .70   .20
173 A20   14c multi (II)   2.75 2.50
   a. Type I   .55   .75
174 A19   15c grn, yel & brn   1.10   .20
175 A20   24c multicolored   8.25   .20
176 A19   48c bl, blk & grn   .75   .55

---

177 A19   60c blk, grn, org & brn   1.10   .95
178 A19 $1.20 multicolored   7.00 1.40
179 A20 $2.40 grn, bl, brn & blk   3.25 3.25
180 A20 $4.80 bl, brn & grn   9.25 24.00
Nos. 164-180 (17)   36.65 36.95

For overprints see Nos. 211-232.

1966-67   Wmk. 314 Sideways
167a A19   4c ('67)   .20   .30
169a A19   6c   .25   .80
170a A19   8c   .65   .90
171a A19   10c ('67)   .70   .95
174a A19   15c ('67)   1.25 1.50
Nos. 167a-174a (5)   3.05 4.45

Freedom from Hunger Issue
Common Design Type
1963, June 4   Perf. 14x14½
181 CD314   15c lilac   .30   .30

Red Cross Centenary Issue
Common Design Type
Wmk. 314
1963, Sept. 2   Litho.   Perf. 13
182 CD315   5c black & red   .20   .20
183 CD315   15c ultra & red   .70   .90

Shakespeare Issue
Common Design Type
1964, Apr. 23   Photo.   Perf. 14x14½
184 CD316   15c lilac rose   .30   .30

ITU Issue
Common Design Type
1965, May 17   Litho.   Perf. 11x11½
185 CD317   2c emerald & blue   .20   .20
186 CD317   48c grnsh blue & slate   .60   .60

Intl. Cooperation Year Issue
Common Design Type
1965, Oct. 25   Perf. 14½
187 CD318   1c blue grn & claret   .20   .20
188 CD318   15c lt violet & grn   .40   .40

Churchill Memorial Issue
Common Design Type
1966, Jan. 24   Photo.   Perf. 14
Design in Black, Gold and Carmine Rose
189 CD319   1c bright blue   .20   .20
   a. Gold omitted   775.00
190 CD319   5c green   .20   .20
191 CD319   15c brown   .45   .45
192 CD319   24c violet   .65   .65
Nos. 189-192 (4)   1.50 1.50

Royal Visit Issue
Common Design Type
1966, Feb. 4   Litho.   Perf. 11x12
193 CD320   5c violet blue   .85   .20
194 CD320   15c dk car rose   2.40   .45

World Cup Soccer Issue
Common Design Type
1966, July 1   Litho.   Perf. 14
195 CD321   5c multicolored   .40   .20
196 CD321   24c multicolored   1.00   .60

WHO Headquarters Issue
Common Design Type
1966, Sept. 20   Litho.   Perf. 14
197 CD322   5c multicolored   .20   .20
198 CD322   24c multicolored   .60   .60

UNESCO Anniversary Issue
Common Design Type
1966, Dec. 1   Litho.   Perf. 14
199 CD323   5c "Education"   .35   .20
200 CD323   15c "Science"   .50   .20
201 CD323   24c "Culture"   .90   .20
Nos. 199-201 (3)   1.75   .60

Carib, Negro and Caucasian
Children — A21

10c, Columbus' ship Santa Maria & banderol. 15c, Hands with banderol. 24c, Belaire dancers.

1967, Nov. 3   Photo.   Wmk. 314
202 A21   5c multicolored   .20   .20
203 A21   10c multicolored   .30   .20
204 A21   15c multicolored   .20   .20
205 A21   24c multicolored   .90   .80
Nos. 202-205 (4)   .90   .80

Issued for National Day, Nov. 3.

John F. Kennedy and Human Rights
Flame — A22

Human Rights Flame and: 10c, Cecil E. A. Rawle (1891-1938), Dominican crusader for human rights. 12c, Pope John XXIII. 48c, Florence Nightingale. 60c, Dr. Albert Schweitzer.

Wmk. 314 Sideways
1968, Apr. 20   Litho.   Perf. 14
206 A22   1c multicolored   .20   .20
207 A22   10c multicolored   .20   .20
208 A22   12c multicolored   .45   .20
209 A22   48c multicolored   .30   .25
210 A22   60c multicolored   .30   .25
Nos. 206-210 (5)   1.45 1.10

International Human Rights Year.

Stamps and Types of 1963-67 Overprinted in Silver or Black: "ASSOCIATED / STATEHOOD"
Perf. 14½x14, 14x14½
1968, July 8   Photo.   Wmk. 314
211 A19   1c multi   .20   .20
212 A20   2c ultra   .20   .20
213 A19   3c lt ultra & blk   .20   .20
214 A19   4c multi   .20   .20
215 A20   5c magenta   .20   .20
216 A19   6c multi (B)   .20   .20
217 A19   8c multi (B)   .20   .20
218 A19   10c pink & brn   .55 1.40
219 A19   12c multi   .20   .20
   a. Watermark upright   .20   .20
220 A19   14c multi (II)   .20   .20
221 A19   15c multi   .20   .20
222 A20   24c multi   3.25   .20
223 A19   48c multi   .55 1.25
   a. Watermark upright   .50 1.25
224 A19   60c multi (B)   .90 2.10
225 A19 $1.20 multi (B)   1.00 2.40
226 A20 $2.40 multi   1.00 2.40
227 A20 $4.80 multi   1.25 3.00
Nos. 211-227 (17)   10.50 14.75

In this set, overprint was applied to 2c, 3c, 12c, 14c, 24c, 48c, 60c, $1.20, $2.40 and $4.80 with watermark upright. A reprinting of the 1c, 4c, 6c, 8c, 10c, 12c, No. 219, 15c and 48c, No. 223 on paper with watermark sideways was made. Same value.

Nos. 164-166, 173 and 178 Overprinted: "NATIONAL DAY / 3 NOVEMBER 1968"
Perf. 14½x14, 14x14½
1968, Nov. 3   Photo.   Wmk. 314
228 A19   1c blue, brn & grn   .20   .20
229 A20   2c ultra   .20   .20
230 A19   3c lt ultra & blk   .20   .20
231 A20   14c multi (I)   .20   .20
232 A19 $1.20 multicolored   .70   .70
Nos. 228-232 (5)   1.50 1.50

A23

#233a, 3 soccer players. #233b, Soccer player, goalie. #234a, Swimmers at start. #234b, Divers. #235a, Javelin thrower, hurdlers. #235b, Hurdlers. #236a, Basketball. #236b, 3 basketball players.

Perf. 11½
1968, Nov. 23   Unwmk.   Litho.
233 A23   1c Pair, #a-b   .20   .20
234 A23   5c Pair, #a-b   .20   .20
235 A23   48c Pair, #a-b   .60   .60
236 A23   60c Pair, #a-b   1.75 1.75
Nos. 233-236 (4)   2.75 2.75

19th Olympic Games, Mexico City, 10/12-27.

The Small Cowper Madonna, by Raphael A24

Perf. 12½x12

1968, Dec. 23   Photo.   Unwmk.
241 A24 5c multicolored   .30 .30

Christmas. No. 241 printed in sheets of 20. Sheets of 6 (3x2) exist containing two each of 12c, 24c, and $1.20 stamps, each picturing a different madonna painting. Value $6.

Venus and Adonis, by Rubens — A25

Paintings: 15c, The Death of Socrates, by Louis Jacques David. 24c, Christ at Emmaus, by Velazquez. 50c, Pilate Washing his Hands, by Rembrandt.

Perf. 14½x15

1969, Jan. 30   Litho.   Wmk. 314
242 A25 5c lilac & multi   .25 .25
243 A25 15c emerald & multi   .35 .35
244 A25 24c lt blue & multi   .35 .35
245 A25 50c crimson & multi   .55 .55
Nos. 242-245 (4)   1.50 1.50

20th anniv. (in 1968) of the WHO.

Citrus Fruit Picker — A26

1969, Mar. 10   Perf. 14½

#247, Woman and child. #248, Hotel. #249, Red-necked parrots. #250, Calypso band. #251, Women dancers. #252, Tropical fish and coelenterates. #253, Diver and turtle.

246 A26 10c multicolored   .20 .20
247 A26 10c multicolored   .20 .20
 a.   Pair, #246-247   .25
248 A26 12c multicolored   .20 .20
249 A26 12c multicolored   .20 .20
 a.   Pair, #248-249   .25
250 A26 24c multicolored   .35 .35
251 A26 24c multicolored   .35 .35
 a.   Pair, #250-251   .70
252 A26 48c multicolored   1.00 1.00
253 A26 48c multicolored   1.00 1.00
 a.   Pair, #252-253   2.00
Nos. 246-253 (8)   3.50 3.50

Tourist publicity.

Spinning, by Millet, Flags and ILO Emblem — A27

50th anniv. of the ILO (Etchings by Jean F. Millet, Flags and ILO Emblem): 30c, Threshing. 30c, Flax pulling.

1969, July   Unwmk.   Perf. 13½
254 A27 15c multicolored   .20 .20
255 A27 30c multicolored   .30 .30
256 A27 38c multicolored   .30 .30
Nos. 254-256 (3)   .80 .80

"Strength in Unity," Bananas and Cacao A28

"Strength in Unity" Emblem and: 8c, Map of Dominica and Hawker Siddeley 748. 12c, Map of Caribbean. 24c, Ships in harbor.

1969, July   Litho.
257 A28 5c orange & multi   .30 .30
258 A28 8c gray & multi   .30 .30
259 A28 12c lilac & multi   .30 .30
260 A28 24c lt blue & multi   .60 .60
Nos. 257-260 (4)   1.50 1.50

Caribbean Free Trade Area (CARIFTA).

Gandhi at Spinning Wheel and Big Ben, London A29

38c, Gandhi, Nehru and Fatehpur Sikri Mausoleum. $1.20, Gandhi & Taj Mahal.

1969, Oct.   Litho.   Perf. 14½
261 A29 6c multicolored   .45 .20
262 A29 38c multicolored   .75 .25
263 A29 $1.20 multicolored   .80 .80
Nos. 261-263 (3)   2.00 1.25

Mohandas K. Gandhi (1869-1948), leader in India's fight for independence. "Gandhi" is misspelled "Ghandi" on Nos. 261-263.

St. Joseph — A30

Stained Glass Windows, from 17th Century French Churches: 8c, St. John. 12c, St. Peter. 60c, St. Paul.

1969, Nov. 10   Litho.   Perf. 14
264 A30 6c black & multi   .20 .20
265 A30 8c black & multi   .20 .20
266 A30 12c black & multi   .20 .20
267 A30 60c black & multi   .40 .40
Nos. 264-267 (4)   1.00 1.00

National Day, Nov. 3. Issued in sheets of 16 (4x4) with control numbers and 4 tabs with a patriotic poem by W. O. M. Pond.

Queen Elizabeth II — A31

Purplethroated Carib (Hummingbird) — A32

2c, Poinsettia. 3c, Red-necked pigeon. 4c, Imperial parrot. 5c, Swallowtail butterfly. 6c, Brown Julia butterfly. 8c, Banana shipment. 10c, Portsmouth Harbor. 12c, Copra processing plant. 15c, Women with straw work. 25c, Timber plant. 30c, Mining pumice. 38c, Cricket, Grammar School. 50c, Roman Catholic Cathedral. 60c, Government headquarters. $1.20, Melville Hall Airport. $2.40, Coat of Arms. $4.80, Queen Elizabeth II.

Perf. 13½

1969, Nov. 26   Unwmk.   Photo.
268 A31 ½c silver & multi   .20 .20
269 A32 1c yellow & multi   .20 .20
270 A32 2c yellow & multi   .20 .20
271 A32 3c yellow & multi   .20 .20
272 A32 4c yellow & multi   .20 .20
273 A32 5c yellow & multi   .20 .20
274 A32 6c brown & multi   .20 .20
275 A32 8c brown & multi   .20 .20
276 A32 10c yellow & multi   .20 .20
277 A32 12c citron & multi   .20 .20
278 A32 15c blue & multi   .30 .30
279 A32 25c pink & multi   .65 .65
280 A32 30c olive & multi   .80 .75
281 A32 38c multicolored   1.00 1.10
282 A32 50c brown & multi   1.00 1.25

Wmk. Rectangles (334)
Perf. 14
Size: 38x26mm, 26x38mm
283 A32 60c yel & multi   1.60 1.40
284 A32 $1.20 yel & multi   3.25 3.25
285 A32 $2.40 gold & multi   7.25 7.00
286 A31 $4.80 gold & multi   14.00 13.50
Nos. 268-286 (19)   31.95 31.20

Madonna and Child, by Filippino Lippi — A33

Paintings: 10c, Holy Family with Lamb, by Raphael. 15c, Virgin and Child, by Perugino. $1.20, Madonna of the Rose Hedge, by Botticelli.

Perf. 14½

1969, Dec.   Unwmk.   Litho.
287 A33 6c lt blue & multi   .20 .20
288 A33 10c multicolored   .20 .20
289 A33 15c lilac & multi   .20 .20
290 A33 $1.20 lt grn & multi   .60 .60
 a.   Souvenir sheet of 2   1.50 1.50
Nos. 287-290 (4)   1.20 1.20

Christmas. No. 290a contains 2 imperf. stamps with simulated perforations similar to Nos. 289-290.

Neil A. Armstrong, First Man on the Moon — A34

Designs: 5c, American flag and astronauts on moon. 8c, Astronauts collecting moon rocks. 30c, Landing module, moon and earth. 50c, Memorial tablet left on moon. 60c, Astronauts Armstrong, Aldrin and Collins.

1970, Feb. 2   Litho.   Perf. 12½
291 A34 ½c lilac & multi   .20 .20
292 A34 5c lt blue & multi   .20 .20
293 A34 8c orange & multi   .20 .20
294 A34 30c blue & multi   .25 .25
295 A34 50c red brn & multi   .60 .60
296 A34 60c rose & multi   .80 .80
 a.   Souvenir sheet of 4   3.00 3.00
Nos. 291-296 (6)   2.25 2.25

See note after US No. C76. No. 296a contains 4 stamps similar to Nos. 293-296, but imperf. with simulated perforations.

Giant Green Turtle — A35

Designs: 24c, Flying fish. 38c, Anthurium lily. 60c, Imperial and red-necked parrots.

1970, Sept. 6   Litho.   Perf. 13½x13
297 A35 6c lt green & multi   .65 .65
298 A35 24c multicolored   .85 .85
299 A35 38c green & multi   1.00 1.00
300 A35 60c yellow & multi   4.00 4.00
 a.   Souvenir sheet of 4, #297-300   10.00 10.00
Nos. 297-300 (4)   6.50 6.50

Women in 18th Century Dress A36

Natl. Day: 8c, Carib mace & wife leader, 18th cent. $1, Map & flag of Dominica.

1970, Nov. 3   Litho.   Perf. 14
301 A36 5c yellow & multi   .20 .20
302 A36 8c green & multi   .20 .20
303 A36 $1 lt blue & multi   .60 .60
 a.   Souv. sheet of 3, #301-303 + 3 labels   1.75 2.00
Nos. 301-303 (3)   1.00 1.00

Marley's Ghost — A37

Designs (from A Christmas Carol, by Dickens): 15c, Fezziwig's Ball. 24c, Scrooge and his Nephew's Christmas Party. $1.20, The Ghost of Christmas Present.

1970, Nov. 23   Litho.   Perf. 14x14½
304 A37 2c blue & multi   .20 .20
305 A37 15c multicolored   .30 .30
306 A37 24c red & multi   .30 .30
307 A37 $1.20 multicolored   1.00 1.00
 a.   Souvenir sheet of 4, #304-307   3.25 3.25
Nos. 304-307 (4)   1.80 1.80

Christmas; Charles Dickens (1812-1870).

Hands and Red Cross A38

Designs: 8c, The Doctor, by Sir Luke Fildes. 15c, Dominica flag and Red Cross. 50c, The Sick Child, by Edvard Munch.

1970, Dec. 28   Perf. 14½x14
308 A38 8c multicolored   .20 .20
309 A38 10c multicolored   .20 .20
310 A38 15c multicolored   .20 .20
311 A38 50c multicolored   .75 .75
 a.   Souvenir sheet of 4, #308-311   2.25 2.50
Nos. 308-311 (4)   1.35 1.35

Centenary of the British Red Cross Society.

Marigot Primary School — A39

Education Year Emblem and: 8c, Goodwill Junior High School. 14c, University of the West Indies. $1, Trinity College, Cambridge, England.

1971, Mar. 1   **Litho.**   *Perf. 13½*
312	A39	5c multicolored	.20	.20
313	A39	8c multicolored	.20	.20
314	A39	14c multicolored	.20	.20
315	A39	$1 multicolored	.65	.65
a.		Souvenir sheet of 2, #314-315	1.00	1.00
		Nos. 312-315 (4)	1.25	1.25

International Education Year.

Waterfall and Bird-of-Paradise Flower — A40

Tourist Publicity: 10c, Boat building. 30c, Sailboat along North Coast. 50c, Speed boat and steamer.

1971, Mar. 22   *Perf. 13½x14*
316	A40	5c multicolored	.20	.20
317	A40	10c multicolored	.20	.20
318	A40	30c multicolored	.25	.25
319	A40	50c multicolored	.60	.60
a.		Souvenir sheet of 4, #316-319	1.25	1.25
		Nos. 316-319 (4)	1.25	1.25

UNICEF Emblem, Letter "D" A41

1971, June 14   **Litho.**   *Perf. 14*
320	A41	5c multicolored	.20	.20
321	A41	10c multicolored	.20	.20
322	A41	38c multicolored	.20	.20
323	A41	$1.20 multicolored	.50	.50
a.		Souvenir sheet of 2, #321, 323	1.00	1.00
		Nos. 320-323 (4)	1.10	1.10

25th anniv. of UNICEF.

Boy Scout, Jamboree Emblem, Torii, Camp and Mt. Fuji — A42

24c, British Scout, flag. 30c, Japanese Scout, flag. $1, Dominican Scout, flag.

1971, Oct. 18   **Unwmk.**   *Perf. 11*
324	A42	20c bister & multi	.25	.25
325	A42	24c green & multi	.30	.30
326	A42	30c red lilac & multi	.45	.45
327	A42	$1 blue & multi	1.75	1.75
a.		Souvenir sheet of 2, #326-327	2.75	2.75
		Nos. 324-327 (4)	2.75	2.75

13th Boy Scout World Jamboree, Asagiri Plain, Japan, Aug. 2-10.

Boats at Portsmouth — A43

15c, Carnival street scene. 20c, $1.20, Anthea Mondesire, Carifta Queen. 50c, Rock of Atkinson.

Perf. 13½x14, 14x13½

1971, Nov. 15   **Litho.**
328	A43	8c multi	.20	.20
329	A43	15c multi	.20	.20
330	A43	20c multi, vert.	.20	.20
331	A43	50c multi, vert.	.30	.30
		Nos. 328-331 (4)	.90	.90

Souvenir Sheet
Perf. 15
332	A43	$1.20 multi, vert.	1.00	1.00

National Day.

First Dominica Coin, 8 Reals, 1761 — A44

Early Dominica Coins: 30c, Eleven and 3-bit pieces, 1798. 35c, Two-real coin, 1770, vert. 50c, Three "mocos" and piece of 8, 1798.

1972, Feb. 7   **Litho.**   *Perf. 14*
333	A44	10c violet, silver & blk	.20	.20
334	A44	30c green, silver & blk	.20	.20
335	A44	35c ultra, silver & blk	.25	.25
336	A44	50c red, silver & blk	.35	.35
a.		Souvenir sheet of 2, #335-336	1.40	1.40
		Nos. 333-336 (4)	1.00	1.00

Margin of #336a inscribed "Christmas 1971."

Common Opossum, Environment Emblem — A45

Environment Emblem and: 35c, Agouti. 60c, Oncidium papillo (orchid). $1.20, Hibiscus.

1972, June 5
337	A45	½c yel grn & multi	.20	.20
338	A45	35c org brn & multi	.35	.35
339	A45	60c lt blue & multi	3.00	3.00
340	A45	$1.20 yellow & multi	2.50	2.50
a.		Souvenir sheet of 4, #337-340	8.25	8.25
		Nos. 337-340 (4)	6.05	6.05

UN Conf. on Human Environment, Stockholm, June 5-16.

100-meter Sprint, Olympic Rings — A46

Olympic Rings and: 35m, 400-meter hurdles. 58c, Hammer throw, vert. 72c, Broad jump, vert.

1972, Oct. 9   **Litho.**   *Perf. 14*
341	A46	30c dp org & multi	.20	.20
342	A46	35c blue & multi	.30	.30
343	A46	58c lilac rose & multi	.40	.40
344	A46	72c yel green & multi	.85	.85
a.		Souv. sheet, #343-344, perf. 15	1.50	1.50
		Nos. 341-344 (4)	1.75	1.75

20th Olympic Games, Munich, Aug. 26-Sept. 11.

General Post Office — A47

1972, Nov. 1   *Perf. 13½*
345	A47	10c shown	.20	.20
346	A47	20c Morne Diablotin Mountain	.20	.20
347	A47	30c Rodney's Rock	.20	.20
a.		Souv. sheet, #346-347, perf. 15	.75	.75
		Nos. 345-347 (3)	.60	.60

National Day.

Adoration of the Shepherds, by Caravaggio A48

Paintings: 14c, Madonna and Child, by Rubens. 30c, Madonna and Child, with St. Anne by Orazio Gentileschi. $1, Adoration of the Kings, by Jan Mostaert. (On 8c, painting is mistakenly attributed to Boccaccino, according to Fine Arts Philatelist.)

1972, Dec. 4.
348	A48	8c gold & multi	.20	.20
349	A48	14c gold & multi	.20	.20
350	A48	30c gold & multi	.20	.20
351	A48	$1 gold & multi	.65	.65
a.		Souvenir sheet of 2	1.50	1.50
		Nos. 348-351 (4)	1.25	1.25

Christmas. No. 351a contains one each of Nos. 350-351 with simulated perforations.

Silver Wedding Issue, 1972
Common Design Type

Design: Queen Elizabeth II, Prince Philip, bananas, sisseron parrot.

Perf. 14x14½

1972, Nov. 13   **Wmk. 314**
352	CD324	5c olive & multi	.20	.20
353	CD324	$1 multicolored	.60	.60

See note after Antigua No. 296.

Launching of Tiros Weather Satellite — A49

1c, Nimbus satellite. 2c, Radiosonde balloon & equipment. 30c, Radarscope. 35c, General circulation of atmosphere. 50c, Picture of hurricane transmitted by satellite. $1, Computer weather map. 30c, 35c, 50c, $1, horiz.

Perf. 14½

1973, July 16   **Unwmk.**   **Litho.**
354	A49	½c black & multi	.20	.20
355	A49	1c black & multi	.20	.20
356	A49	2c black & multi	.20	.20
357	A49	30c black & multi	.20	.20
358	A49	35c black & multi	.20	.20
359	A49	50c black & multi	.40	.40
360	A49	$1 black & multi	.80	.80
a.		Souvenir sheet of 2, #359-360	2.00	2.00
		Nos. 354-360 (7)	2.20	2.20

Intl. meteorological cooperation, cent.

Going to the Hospital A50

WHO Emblem and: 1c, Maternity and infant care. 2c, Inoculation against smallpox. 30c, Emergency service. 35c, Waiting patients. 50c, Examination. $1, Traveling physician.

1973, Aug. 20   **Unwmk.**   *Perf. 14½*
361	A50	½c lt blue & multi	.20	.20
362	A50	1c gray grn & multi	.20	.20
363	A50	2c yellow & multi	.20	.20
364	A50	30c lt vio & multi	.30	.30
365	A50	35c yel grn & multi	.40	.40
366	A50	50c multicolored	.50	.50
367	A50	$1 bister & multi	.95	.95
a.		Souvenir sheet of 2, #366-367, perf. 14x14½	2.25	2.25
		Nos. 361-367 (7)	2.75	2.75

WHO, 25th anniv. #367a exists perf. 14½.

Cyrique Crab — A51

1973, Oct.
368	A51	½c shown	.20	.20
369	A51	22c Blue land crab	.35	.35
370	A51	25c Breadfruit	.45	.45
371	A51	$1.20 Sunflower	2.00	2.00
a.		Souvenir sheet of 4, #368-371	5.00	5.00
		Nos. 368-371 (4)	3.00	3.00

Princess Anne and Mark Phillips — A52

1973, Nov. 14   *Perf. 13½*
372	A52	25c salmon & multi	.20	.20
373	A52	$2 blue & multi	.80	.80
a.		Souv. sheet of 2 (75c, $1.20)	1.75	1.75

Wedding of Princess Anne and Capt. Mark Phillips.
#372-373 were issued in sheets of 5 + label. No. 373a contains 2 stamps of type A52: 75c in colors of the 25c, and $1.20 in colors of the $2.

Nativity, by Brueghel A53

Paintings of the Nativity by: 1c, Botticelli. 2c, Dürer. 12c, Botticelli. 22c, Rubens. 35c, Dürer. $1, Giorgione (inscribed "Giorgeone").

1973   **Unwmk.**   *Perf. 14½x15*
374	A53	½c gray & multi	.20	.20
375	A53	1c gray & multi	.20	.20
376	A53	2c gray & multi	.20	.20
377	A53	12c gray & multi	.20	.20
378	A53	22c gray & multi	.20	.20
379	A53	35c gray & multi	.40	.40
380	A53	$1 gray & multi	1.10	1.10
a.		Souvenir sheet of 2	1.75	1.75
		Nos. 374-380 (7)	2.50	2.50

Christmas. No. 380a contains one each of Nos. 379-380 in changed colors.

Carib Basket Weaving — A54

Designs: 10c, Staircase of the Snake. 50c, Miss Caribbean Queen, Kathleen Telemacque, vert. 60c, Miss Carifta Queen, Esther Fadelle, vert. $1, La Jeune Etoille Dancers.

1973, Dec. 17   Perf. 13½x14, 14x13½

381	A54	5c buff & multi	.20	.20
382	A54	10c multicolored	.20	.20
383	A54	50c multicolored	.25	.25
384	A54	60c multicolored	.25	.25
385	A54	$1 multicolored	.35	.35
a.		Souv. sheet of 3, #381-382, 385	1.10	1.10
		Nos. 381-385 (5)	1.25	1.25

National Day.

U.W.I. Center, Dominica — A55

30c, Graduation. $1, University coat of arms.

1974, Jan. 21   Litho.   Perf. 13½x14

386	A55	12c dp orange & multi	.20	.20
387	A55	30c violet & multi	.20	.20
388	A55	$1 multicolored	.50	.50
a.		Souvenir sheet of 3, #386-388	.85	1.25
		Nos. 386-388 (3)	.90	.90

University of the West Indies, 25th anniv.

Dominica No. 1 and Map of Island A56

Designs: 1c, 50c, No. 8 and post horn. 2c, $1.20, No. 9 and coat of arms. 10c, Like ½c.

1974, May 4   Litho.   Perf. 14½

389	A56	½c brt pur & multi	.20	.20
390	A56	1c salmon & multi	.20	.20
391	A56	2c ultra & multi	.20	.20
392	A56	10c violet & multi	.20	.20
393	A56	50c yel grn & multi	.55	.55
394	A56	$1.20 rose & multi	1.40	1.40
a.		Souv. sheet, #392-394, perf. 15	2.10	2.10
		Nos. 389-394 (6)	2.75	2.75

Centenary of Dominican postage stamps.

Soccer Player and Cup, Brazilian Flag — A57

Soccer cup, various players and flags.

1974, July   Litho.   Perf. 14½

395	A57	½c shown	.20	.20
396	A57	1c Germany, Fed. Rep.	.20	.20
397	A57	2c Italy	.20	.20
398	A57	30c Scotland	.65	.65
399	A57	40c Sweden	.65	.65
400	A57	50c Netherlands	.85	.85
401	A57	$1 Yugoslavia	1.25	1.25
a.		Souvenir sheet of 2, #400-401, perf. 13½	1.60	1.60
		Nos. 395-401 (7)	4.00	4.00

World Cup Soccer Championship, Munich, June 13-July 7.

Indian Hole A58

40c, Teachers' Training College. $1, Petite Savane Co-operative Bay Oil Distillery.

1974, Nov. 1   Litho.   Perf. 13½x14

402	A58	10c multicolored	.20	.20
403	A58	40c multicolored	.35	.35
404	A58	$1 multicolored	.75	.75
a.		Souvenir sheet of 3, #402-404	1.00	1.00
		Nos. 402-404 (3)	1.30	1.30

Churchill at Race Track A59

Sir Winston Churchill (1874-1965): 1c, with Gen. Eisenhower. 2c, with Franklin D. Roosevelt. 20c, as First Lord of the Admiralty. 45c, painting outdoors. $2, giving "V" sign.

1974, Nov. 25   Litho.   Perf. 14½

405	A59	½c multicolored	.20	.20
406	A59	1c multicolored	.20	.20
407	A59	2c multicolored	.20	.20
408	A59	20c multicolored	.20	.20
409	A59	45c multicolored	.30	.30
410	A59	$2 multicolored	.75	.75
a.		Souvenir sheet of 2, #409-410, perf. 13½	1.75	1.75
		Nos. 405-410 (6)	1.85	1.85

Virgin and Child, by Oronzo Tiso — A60

Paintings (Virgin and Child): 1c, by Lorenzo Costa. 2c, by unknown Master. 10c, by G. F. Romanelli. 25c, Holy Family, by G. S. da Sermoneta. 45c, Adoration of the Shepherds, by Guido Reni. $1, Adoration of the Kings, by Cristoforo Caselli.

1974, Dec. 16   Litho.   Perf. 14

411	A60	½c multicolored	.20	.20
412	A60	1c multicolored	.20	.20
413	A60	2c multicolored	.20	.20
414	A60	10c multicolored	.35	.20
415	A60	25c multicolored	.50	.40
416	A60	45c multicolored	.65	.20
417	A60	$1 multicolored	.90	.50
a.		Souvenir sheet of 2, #416-417	2.00	2.00
		Nos. 411-417 (7)	3.00	1.90

Christmas.

Seamail, "Orinoco," 1851, and "Geesthaven," 1966 — A61

Cent. of UPU: $2, $2.40, Airmail, De Havilland 4, 1918, and Boeing 747, 1974.

1974, Dec. 4   Litho.   Perf. 13½

418	A61	10c multicolored	.20	.20
419	A61	$2 multicolored	1.75	1.75

Souvenir Sheet

419A		Sheet of 2	2.25	2.25
b.	A61	$1.20 multicolored	.75	.75
c.	A61	$2.40 multicolored	1.50	1.50

Oldwife A62

1975, June 2   Litho.   Perf. 14½

421	A62	½c shown	.20	.20
422	A62	1c Ocyurus chrysurus	.20	.20
423	A62	2c Blue marlin	.20	.20
424	A62	3c Swordfish	.20	.20
425	A62	20c Great barracuda	1.50	1.00
426	A62	$2 Grouper	5.25	2.75
a.		Souvenir sheet, perf. 13½	5.50	5.25
		Nos. 421-426 (6)	7.55	4.55

Myscelia Antholia A63

Designs: Butterflies.

1975, July 28   Litho.   Perf. 14½

427	A63	½c shown	.20	.20
428	A63	1c Lycorea ceres	.20	.20
429	A63	2c Siderone nemesis	.25	.25
430	A63	6c Battus polydamas	1.10	.95
431	A63	30c Anartia lytrea	3.00	1.00
432	A63	40c Morpho peleides	3.00	1.00
433	A63	$2 Dryas julia	4.25	6.75
a.		Souvenir sheet, perf. 13½	6.50	6.50
		Nos. 427-433 (7)	12.00	10.35

Royal Mail Ship Yare A64

Ships Tied in with Dominican History: 1c, Royal mail ship Thames. 2c, Canadian National S.S. Lady Nelson. 20c, C.N. S.S. Lady Rodney. 45c, Harrison Line M.V. Statesman. 50c, Geest Line M.V. Geestcape. $2, Geest Line M.V. Geeststar.

1975, Sept. 1   Perf. 14

434	A64	½c black & multi	.45	.35
435	A64	1c black & multi	.45	.35
436	A64	2c black & multi	.50	.40
437	A64	20c black & multi	1.90	.85
438	A64	45c black & multi	2.25	1.00
439	A64	50c black & multi	2.25	1.25
440	A64	$2 black & multi	4.25	4.75
a.		Souvenir sheet of 2, #439-440	6.75	4.25
		Nos. 434-440 (7)	12.05	8.95

IWY Emblem, Farm Women A65

$2, IWY emblem, dressmaker & saleswoman.

1975, Oct. 30   Litho.   Perf. 14

441	A65	10c pink & multi	.20	.20
442	A65	$2 yellow & multi	1.10	1.10

International Women's Year.

Public Library — A66

5c, Miss Caribbean Queen 1975. 30c, Citrus factory. $1, National Day Cup.

1975, Nov. 6

443	A66	5c multi, vert.	.30	.30
444	A66	10c multi	.30	.30
445	A66	30c multi	.30	.30
446	A66	$1 multi, vert.	.85	.85
a.		Souvenir sheet of 3	1.00	1.50
		Nos. 443-446 (4)	1.75	1.75

National Day. No. 446a contains 3 stamps similar to Nos. 444-446 with simulated perforations.

Virgin and Child, by Mantegna — A67

Christmas: Paintings of the Virgin and Child.

1975, Nov. 24

447	A67	½c shown	.20	.20
448	A67	1c Fra Filippo Lippi	.20	.20
449	A67	2c Bellini	.20	.20
450	A67	10c Botticelli	.20	.20
451	A67	25c Bellini	.25	.25
452	A67	45c Correggio	.30	.30
453	A67	$1 Durer	.65	.65
a.		Souvenir sheet of 2, #452-453	1.75	1.75
		Nos. 447-453 (7)	2.00	2.00

Hibiscus A68

Queen Elizabeth II — A69

Designs: 1c, African tulip. 2c, Castor oil tree. 3c, White cedar flower. 4c, Eggplant. 5c, Garfish. 6c, Okra. 8c, Zenaida doves. 10c, Screw pine. 20c, Mangoes. 25c, Crayfish. 30c, Manicou. 40c, Bay leaf groves. 50c, Tomatoes. $1, Lime factory. $2, Rum distillery. $5, Bay oil distillery.

1975, Dec. 8   Litho.   Perf. 14½

454	A68	½c ultra & multi	.20	.50
455	A68	1c lilac & multi	.25	.50
456	A68	2c orange & multi	.25	.50
457	A68	3c multicolored	.25	.50
458	A68	4c pink & multi	.25	.50
459	A68	5c multicolored	.30	.50
460	A68	6c gray & multi	.30	.65
461	A68	8c multicolored	4.00	.65
462	A68	10c violet & multi	.25	.20
463	A68	20c yellow & multi	.50	.20
464	A68	25c lemon & multi	.55	.20
465	A68	30c salmon & multi	1.50	.95
466	A68	40c multicolored	1.50	.95
467	A68	50c red & multi	.65	.55
468	A68	$1 citron & multi	.90	.65
469	A68	$2 multicolored	1.60	3.75
470	A68	$5 multicolored	2.00	5.50

Perf. 14

471	A69	$10 blue & multi	2.75	16.00
		Nos. 454-471 (18)	18.00	33.25

For overprints see Nos. 584-601, 640-643.

American Infantry — A70

Rowing — A71

Designs: 1c, English three-decker, 1782. 2c, George Washington. 45c, English sailors. 75c, English ensign with regimental flag. $2, Admiral Hood. All designs have old maps in background.

1976, Apr. 12   Litho.   Perf. 14½

472	A70	½c green & multi	.20	.20
473	A70	1c purple & multi	.20	.20
474	A70	2c orange & multi	.20	.20
475	A70	45c brown & multi	.90	.20
476	A70	75c ultra & multi	1.50	1.00
477	A70	$2 red & multi	1.75	3.00
a.		Souvenir sheet of 2	4.50	6.00
		Nos. 472-477 (6)	4.75	4.80

American Bicentennial. No. 477a contains 2 stamps similar to Nos. 476-477, perf. 13.

1976, May 24   Litho.   Perf. 14½

1c, Shot put. 2c, Swimming. 40c, Relay race. 45c, Gymnastics. 60c, Sailing. $2, Archery.

478	A71	½c ocher & multi	.20	.20
479	A71	1c ocher & multi	.20	.20
480	A71	2c ocher & multi	.20	.20
481	A71	40c ocher & multi	.20	.20
482	A71	45c ocher & multi	.20	.20
483	A71	60c ocher & multi	.30	.30
484	A71	$2 ocher & multi	.80	.80
a.		Souv. sheet of 3, #483-484, perf 13	2.00	2.00
		Nos. 478-484 (7)	2.10	2.10

21st Olympic Games, Montreal, Canada, July 17-Aug. 1.

Ringed Kingfisher A72

Birds: 1c, Mourning dove. 2c, Green heron. 15c, Broad-winged hawk. 30c, Blue-headed hummingbird. 45c, Banana-quit. $2, Imperial parrot. 15c, 30c, 45c, $2, vert.

1976, June 28

485	A72	½c multicolored	.25	.25
486	A72	1c multicolored	.25	.25
487	A72	2c multicolored	.25	.25
488	A72	15c multicolored	1.25	1.25
489	A72	30c multicolored	2.00	2.00
490	A72	45c multicolored	2.25	2.25
491	A72	$2 multicolored	5.00	5.00
a.		Souv. sheet of 3, #489-491, perf. 13	9.50	9.50
		Nos. 485-491 (7)	11.25	11.25

Map of West Indies, Bats, Wicket and Ball A72a

Prudential Cup — A72b

1976, July 26   Litho.   Perf. 14

492	A72a	15c lt blue & multi	.50	.50
493	A72b	25c lilac rose & black	1.00	1.00

World Cricket Cup, won by West Indies Team, 1975.

Viking Spacecraft — A73

Virgin and Child, by Giorgione — A74

1c, Titan launch center, horiz. 2c, Titan 3-D & Centaur D-IT. 3c, Orbiter & landing capsule. 45c, Capsule with closed parachute. 75c, Capsule with open parachute. $1, Landing capsule descending on Mars, horiz. $2, Viking on Mars, horiz.

1976, Sept. 20   Litho.   Perf. 15

494	A73	½c multicolored	.20	.20
495	A73	1c multicolored	.20	.20
496	A73	2c multicolored	.20	.20
497	A73	3c multicolored	.20	.20
498	A73	45c multicolored	.35	.35
499	A73	75c multicolored	.45	.45
500	A73	$1 multicolored	.55	.55
501	A73	$2 multicolored	.85	.85
a.		Souvenir sheet of 2, #500, 501, perf. 13½	2.00	2.00
		Nos. 494-501 (8)	3.00	3.00

Viking mission to Mars.

1976, Nov. 1   Litho.   Perf. 14

Virgin and Child by: 1c, Bellini. 2c, Mantegna. 6c, Mantegna. 25c, Memling. 45c, 50c, Correggio. $1, $3, Raphael.

502	A74	½c multicolored	.20	.20
503	A74	1c multicolored	.20	.20
504	A74	2c multicolored	.20	.20
505	A74	6c multicolored	.20	.20
506	A74	25c multicolored	.20	.20
507	A74	45c multicolored	.25	.25
508	A74	$3 multicolored	1.25	1.25
		Nos. 502-508 (7)	2.50	2.50

Souvenir Sheet

509		Sheet of 2	1.60	1.60
a.	A74	50c multicolored	.40	
b.	A74	$1 multicolored	.80	

Christmas.

Island Craft Co-operative — A75

National Day: 50c, Banana harvest, Castle Bruce Co-operative. $1, Banana shipping plant, Bourne Farmers' Co-operative.

1976, Nov. 22   Litho.   Perf. 13½x14

510	A75	10c multicolored	.20	.20
511	A75	50c multicolored	.25	.25
512	A75	$1 multicolored	.55	.55
a.		Souvenir sheet of 3, #510-512	1.25	1.25
		Nos. 510-512 (3)	1.00	1.00

Common Sundial — A76

Sea Shells: 1c, Flame helmet. 2c, Mouse cone. 20c, Caribbean vase. 40c, West Indian fighting conch. 50c, Short coral shell. $2, Long-spined star shell. $3, Apple murex.

1976, Dec. 20   Litho.   Perf. 14

513	A76	½c black & multi	.20	.20
514	A76	1c black & multi	.20	.20
515	A76	2c black & multi	.20	.20
516	A76	20c black & multi	.35	.20
517	A76	40c black & multi	.75	.55
518	A76	50c black & multi	.80	.65
519	A76	$3 black & multi	5.50	3.50
		Nos. 513-519 (7)	8.00	5.50

Souvenir Sheet

520	A76	$2 black & multi	3.00	3.00

Queen Enthroned — A77

Designs: 1c, Imperial crown. 45c, Elizabeth II and Princess Anne. $2, Coronation ring. $2.50, Ampulla and spoon. $5, Royal visit to Dominica.

1977, Feb. 7   Perf. 14

521	A77	½c multicolored	.20	.20
522	A77	1c multicolored	.20	.20
523	A77	45c multicolored	.25	.25
524	A77	$2 multicolored	1.10	1.10
525	A77	$2.50 multicolored	1.40	1.40
		Nos. 521-525 (5)	3.15	3.15

Souvenir Sheet

526	A77	$5 multicolored	2.50	2.50

25th anniv. of the reign of Elizabeth II.
Nos. 521-525 were printed in sheets of 40 (4x10), perf. 14, and sheets of 5 plus label, perf. 12, in changed colors.
For overprints see Nos. 549-554.

Joseph Haydn — A78

Designs: 1c, Fidelio, act I, scene IV. 2c, Dancer Maria Casentini. 15c, Beethoven working on Pastoral Symphony. 30c, "Wellington's Victory." 40c, Soprano Henriette Sontag. $2, Young Beethoven.

1977, Apr. 25   Litho.   Perf. 14

527	A78	½c multicolored	.20	.20
528	A78	1c multicolored	.20	.20
529	A78	2c multicolored	.20	.20
530	A78	15c multicolored	.45	.45
531	A78	30c multicolored	.45	.45
532	A78	40c multicolored	.45	.45
533	A78	$2 multicolored	2.75	2.75
a.		Souvenir sheet of 3, #531-533	3.75	3.75
		Nos. 527-533 (7)	4.70	4.70

Ludwig van Beethoven (1770-1827), composer.

Boy Scouts on Hike A79

Saluting Boy Scout and: 1c, First aid. 2c, Scouts setting up camp. 45c, Rock climbing. 50c, Kayaking. 75c, Map reading. $2, Campfire. $3, Sailing.

1977, Aug. 8   Litho.   Perf. 14

534	A79	½c multicolored	.20	.20
535	A79	1c multicolored	.20	.20
536	A79	2c multicolored	.20	.20
537	A79	45c multicolored	.50	.50
538	A79	50c multicolored	.60	.60
539	A79	$3 multicolored	2.50	2.50
		Nos. 534-539 (6)	4.20	4.20

Souvenir Sheet

540		Sheet of 2	2.50	2.50
a.	A79	75c multicolored	.75	
b.	A79	$2 multicolored	1.75	

6th Caribbean Jamboree, Kingston, Jamaica, Aug. 5-14.

Nativity A80

Christmas: 1c, Annunciation to the Shepherds. 2c, 45c, Presentation at the Temple (different). 6c, $2, $3, Flight into Egypt (different). 15c, Adoration of the Kings. 50c, Virgin and Child with Angels. ½c to 45c are illustrations from De Lisle Psalter, 14th century. 50c, $2, $3 are from other Psalters.

1977, Nov. 14   Litho.   Perf. 14

541	A80	½c multicolored	.20	.20
542	A80	1c multicolored	.20	.20
543	A80	2c multicolored	.20	.20
544	A80	6c multicolored	.20	.20
545	A80	15c multicolored	.20	.20
546	A80	45c multicolored	.40	.40
547	A80	$3 multicolored	1.10	1.10
		Nos. 541-547 (7)	2.50	2.50

Souvenir Sheet

548		Sheet of 2	1.75	1.75
a.	A80	50c multicolored	.25	
b.	A80	$2 multicolored	1.50	

Nos. 521-526 Overprinted "ROYAL VISIT / W.I. 1977"

1977, Nov. 24   Litho.   Perf. 12, 14

549	A77	½c multicolored	.20	.20
550	A77	1c multicolored	.20	.20
551	A77	45c multicolored	.20	.20
552	A77	$2 multicolored	.60	.60
553	A77	$2.50 multicolored	.65	.65
		Nos. 549-553 (5)	1.85	1.85

Souvenir Sheet
Perf. 14

554	A77	$5 multicolored	1.50	1.50

Caribbean visit of Queen Elizabeth II. #549-550 are perf. 12, others perf. 12 and 14.
Two types of No. 554: I. Overprinted only on stamp. II. Overprinted "W.I. 1977" on stamp and "Royal Visit W.I. 1977" on margin.

Masqueraders — A81

Designs: 1c, Sensay costume. 2c, Street musicians. 45c, Douiette band. 50c, Pappy Show wedding. $2, $2.50, Masquerade band.

1978, Jan. 9   Perf. 14

555	A81	½c multicolored	.20	.20
556	A81	1c multicolored	.20	.20
557	A81	2c multicolored	.20	.20
558	A81	45c multicolored	.30	.30
559	A81	50c multicolored	.35	.35
560	A81	$2 multicolored	1.40	1.40
		Nos. 555-560 (6)	2.65	2.65

Souvenir Sheet

561	A81	$2.50 multicolored	1.75	1.75

History of Carnival.

Lindbergh and Spirit of St. Louis A82

Designs: 10c, Spirit of St. Louis take-off, Long Island, May 20, 1927. 15c, Lindbergh and map of route New York to Paris. 20c, Lindbergh and plane in Paris. 40c, 1st Zeppelin, trial over Lake Constance. 50c, Spirit of St. Louis. 60c, Count Zeppelin and Zeppelin LZ-2, 1906. $2, Graf Zeppelin, 1928. $3, LZ-127, 1928.

1978, Mar. 13 Litho. *Perf. 14½*

562	A82	6c multicolored	.20	.20
563	A82	10c multicolored	.20	.20
564	A82	15c multicolored	.20	.20
565	A82	20c multicolored	.20	.20
566	A82	40c multicolored	.60	.60
567	A82	60c multicolored	.85	.85
568	A82	$3 multicolored	3.75	3.75
		Nos. 562-568 (7)	6.00	6.00

Souvenir Sheet

569		Sheet of 2	2.75	2.75
a.		A82 50c multicolored	.50	
b.		A82 $2 multicolored	2.00	

Charles A. Lindbergh's solo transatlantic flight from New York to Paris, 50th anniv., and flights of Graf Zeppelin.

Royal Family on Balcony — A83

Designs: 45c, Coronation. $2.50, Elizabeth II and Prince Philip. $5, Elizabeth II.

1978, June 2 Litho. *Perf. 14*

570	A83	45c multicolored	.20	.20
571	A83	$2 multicolored	.95	.95
572	A83	$2.50 multicolored	1.10	1.10
		Nos. 570-572 (3)	2.25	2.25

Souvenir Sheet

573	A83	$5 multicolored	2.00	2.00

Coronation of Queen Elizabeth II, 25th anniv. Nos. 570-572 were issued in sheets of 50, and in sheets of 3 stamps and label, in changed colors, perf. 12.

Wright Plane Coming out of Hangar A84

Designs: 40c, 1908 plane. 60c, Flyer I gliding. $2, Flyer I taking off. $3, Wilbur and Orville Wright and Flyer I.

1978, July 10 Litho. *Perf. 14½*

574	A84	30c multicolored	.20	.20
575	A84	40c multicolored	.30	.30
576	A84	60c multicolored	.40	.40
577	A84	$2 multicolored	1.60	1.60
		Nos. 574-577 (4)	2.50	2.50

Souvenir Sheet

578	A84	$3 multicolored	2.50	2.50

75th anniv. of first powered flight.

Two Apostles, by Rubens — A85

Rubens Paintings: 45c, Descent from the Cross. 50c, St. Ildefonso Receiving Chasuble. $2, Holy Family. $3, Assumption of the Virgin.

1978, Oct. 16 Litho. *Perf. 14*

579	A85	20c multicolored	.20	.20
580	A85	45c multicolored	.30	.30
581	A85	50c multicolored	.35	.35
582	A85	$3 multicolored	2.00	2.00
		Nos. 579-582 (4)	2.85	2.85

Souvenir Sheet

583	A85	$2 multicolored	1.50	1.50

Christmas.

Nos. 454-471 Overprinted: "INDEPENDENCE/ 3rd NOVEMBER 1978"

1978 Nov. 1 Litho. *Perf. 14½*

584	A68	½c ultra & multi	.20	.20
585	A68	1c lilac & multi	.20	.20
586	A68	2c orange & multi	.20	.20
587	A68	3c multicolored	.20	.20
588	A68	4c pink & multi	.20	.20
589	A68	5c multicolored	.20	.20
590	A68	6c gray & multi	.20	.20
591	A68	8c multicolored	.20	.20
592	A68	10c violet & multi	.20	.20
a.		Perf. 13½ ('79)	.20	.20
593	A68	20c yellow & multi	.20	.20
594	A68	25c lemon & multi	.20	.20
595	A68	30c salmon & multi	.30	.30
596	A68	40c multicolored	.40	.55
597	A68	50c red & multi	.55	.75
598	A68	$1 citron & multi	.95	1.40
599	A68	$2 multicolored	2.10	2.75
600	A68	$5 multicolored	4.25	5.50

Perf. 14

601	A69	$10 blue & multi	8.75	12.50
		Nos. 584-601 (18)	19.50	25.95

Map of Dominica with Parishes — A86

Rowland Hill — A87

25c, Sabinea carinalis, natl. flower, & map. 45c, New flag & map. 50c, Coat of arms & map. $2, Prime Minister Patrick John.

1978, Nov. 1 *Perf. 14*

602	A86	10c multicolored	.20	.20
603	A86	25c multicolored	.20	.20
604	A86	45c multicolored	.65	.65
605	A86	50c multicolored	.75	.75
606	A86	$2 multicolored	3.25	3.25
		Nos. 602-606 (5)	5.05	5.05

Souvenir Sheet

607	A86	$2.50 multicolored	*3.00*	*3.25*

Dominican independence.

1979, Mar. 19

45c, Great Britain #2. 50c, Dominica #1. $2, Maltese Cross handstamps. $5, Penny Black.

608	A87	25c multicolored	.20	.20
609	A87	45c multicolored	.20	.20
610	A87	50c multicolored	.25	.25
611	A87	$2 multicolored	.95	.95
		Nos. 608-611 (4)	1.60	1.60

Souvenir Sheet

612	A87	$5 multicolored	2.50	2.50

Sir Rowland Hill (1795-1879), originator of penny postage.

Nos. 608-611 printed in sheets of 5 plus label, perf. 12x12½, in changed colors.

For overprints see Nos. 663A-663D.

Boys and Dugout Canoe A88

IYC Emblem and: 40c, Children carrying bananas. 50c, Boys playing cricket. $3, Child feeding rabbits. $5, Boy showing catch of fish.

1979, Apr. 23 Litho. *Perf. 14*

613	A88	30c multicolored	.30	.30
614	A88	40c multicolored	.45	.45
615	A88	50c multicolored	.50	.50
616	A88	$3 multicolored	2.75	2.75
		Nos. 613-616 (4)	4.00	4.00

Souvenir Sheet

617	A88	$5 multicolored	3.25	3.25

Grouper A89

30c, Striped dolphin. 50c, White-tailed tropic birds. 60c, Brown pelicans. $1, Pilot whale. $2, Brown booby. $3, Elkhorn coral.

1979, May 21 Litho. *Perf. 14*

618	A89	10c multicolored	.20	.20
619	A89	30c multicolored	1.00	1.00
620	A89	50c multicolored	1.75	1.75
621	A89	60c multicolored	2.10	2.10
622	A89	$1 multicolored	3.50	3.50
623	A89	$2 multicolored	7.00	7.00
		Nos. 618-623 (6)	15.55	15.55

Souvenir Sheet

624	A89	$3 multicolored	3.50	3.50

Wildlife protection.

Capt. Cook, Bark Endeavour — A90

Capt. Cook and: 50c, Resolution, map of 2nd voyage. 60c, Discovery, map of 3rd voyage. $2, Cook's map of New Zealand, 1770. $5, Portrait.

1979, July 16 Litho. *Perf. 14*

625	A90	10c multicolored	.20	.20
626	A90	50c multicolored	1.00	1.00
627	A90	60c multicolored	1.25	1.25
628	A90	$2 multicolored	3.75	3.75
		Nos. 625-628 (4)	6.20	6.20

Souvenir Sheet

629	A90	$5 multicolored	3.00	3.00

200th death anniv. of Capt. James Cook (1728-1779).

Girl Guides Cooking A91

Girl Guides: 20c, Setting up emergency rain tent. 50c, Raising flag of independent Dominica. $2.50, Playing accordion and singing. $3, Leader and Guides of different ages.

1979, July 30

630	A91	10c multicolored	.20	.20
631	A91	20c multicolored	.20	.20
632	A91	50c multicolored	.40	.40
633	A91	$2.50 multicolored	2.00	2.00
		Nos. 630-633 (4)	2.80	2.80

Souvenir Sheet

634	A91	$3 multicolored	2.25	2.25

50th anniv. of Dominican Girl Guides.

Colvillea — A92

Flowering Trees: 40c, Lignum vitae. 60c, Dwarf poinciana. $2, Fern tree. $3, Perfume tree.

1979, Sept. 3 Litho. *Perf. 14*

635	A92	20c multicolored	.20	.20
636	A92	40c multicolored	.25	.25
637	A92	60c multicolored	.40	.40
638	A92	$2 multicolored	1.40	1.40
		Nos. 635-638 (4)	2.25	2.25

Souvenir Sheet

639	A92	$3 multicolored	2.40	2.40

Nos. 459, 466, 470-471 Overprinted: "HURRICANE / RELIEF"

Perf. 14½, 13½, 13½x14, 14

1979, Oct. 29 Litho.

640	A68	5c multicolored	.20	.20
641	A68	40c multicolored	.40	.40
642	A68	$5 multicolored	5.00	5.00
643	A68	$10 multicolored	10.00	10.00
		Nos. 640-643 (4)	15.60	15.60

Hurricane devastation, Aug. 29. Vertical overprint on No. 643, others horizontal.

Music Scenes A92a

1979, Nov. 2 Litho. *Perf. 11*

644	A92a	½c Mickey Mouse	.20	.20
645	A92a	1c Goofy playing guitar	.20	.20
646	A92a	2c Mickey Mouse and Goofy	.20	.20
647	A92a	3c Donald Duck	.20	.20
648	A92a	4c Minnie Mouse	.20	.20
649	A92a	5c Goofy playing accordion	.20	.20
650	A92a	10c Horace Horsecollar and Dale	.20	.20
651	A92a	$2 Huey, Dewey, Louie	3.00	3.00
652	A92a	$2.50 Donald and Huey	3.50	3.50
		Nos. 644-652 (9)	7.90	7.90

Souvenir Sheet

Perf. 13

653	A92a	$3 Mickey Mouse playing piano	4.50	4.50

Cathedral of the Assumption — A93

Cathedrals: 40c, St. Patrick's, New York. 45c, St. Paul's, London, vert. 60c, St. Peter's, Rome. $2, Cologne Cathedral. $3, Notre Dame, Paris, vert.

1979, Nov. 26 Litho. *Perf. 14*

654	A93	6c multicolored	.20	.20
655	A93	45c multicolored	.30	.30
656	A93	60c multicolored	.40	.40
657	A93	$3 multicolored	2.00	2.00
		Nos. 654-657 (4)	2.90	2.90

Souvenir Sheet

658		Sheet of 2	1.00	1.00
a.		A93 40c multicolored	.25	.25
b.		A93 $2 multicolored	.75	.75

Christmas.

Nurse and Patients, Rotary Emblem A94

1980, Mar. 31 Litho. Perf. 14
659	A94	10c shown	.20	.20
660	A94	20c Electrocardiogram machine	.20	.20
661	A94	40c Mental hospital	.30	.30
662	A94	$2.50 Paul Harris, founder	1.75	1.75
		Nos. 659-662 (4)	2.45	2.45

Souvenir Sheet
663	A94	$3 Map of Africa and Europe	2.25	2.25

Rotary International, 75th anniv. Nos. 659-662 each contain quadrant of Rotary emblem.

Nos. 608-611 Overprinted "LONDON 1980"

1980, May 6 Litho. Perf. 12
663A	A87	25c multicolored	.25	.25
663B	A87	45c multicolored	.45	.45
663C	A87	50c multicolored	.50	.50
663D	A87	$2 multicolored	2.00	2.00
		Nos. 663A-663D (4)	3.20	3.20

London 80 Intl. Stamp Exhib., May 6-14.

Shot Put, Moscow '80 Emblem A95

1980, May 27 Litho. Perf. 14
664	A95	30c shown	.20	.20
665	A95	40c Basketball	.30	.30
666	A95	60c Swimming	.40	.40
667	A95	$2 Gymnast	1.40	1.40
		Nos. 664-667 (4)	2.30	2.30

Souvenir Sheet
668	A95	$3 Running	2.00	2.00

22nd Summer Olympic Games, Moscow, July 19-Aug. 3.

Embarkation for Cythera, by Watteau — A96

Paintings: 20c, Supper at Emmaus, by Caravaggio. 25c, Charles I Hunting, by Van Dyck, vert. 30c, The Maids of Honor, by Velazquez, vert. 45c, Rape of the Sabine Women, by Poussin. $1, Embarkation for Cythera, by Watteau. $3, Holy Family, by Rembrandt. $5, Girl before a Mirror, by Picasso, vert.

Perf. 14x13½, 13½x14

1980, July 22 Litho.
669	A96	20c multicolored	.20	.20
670	A96	25c multicolored	.20	.20
671	A96	30c multicolored	.20	.20
672	A96	45c multicolored	.25	.25
673	A96	$1 multicolored	.65	.65
674	A96	$5 multicolored	2.40	2.40
		Nos. 669-674 (6)	3.90	3.90

Souvenir Sheet
675	A96	$3 multicolored	1.50	1.50

Queen Mother Elizabeth, 80th Birthday A97

1980, Aug. 4 Perf. 12, 14
676	A97	40c multicolored	.25	.25
677	A97	$2.50 multicolored	1.00	1.00

Souvenir Sheet
678	A97	$3 multicolored	1.25	1.75

Tinkerbell — A98

Designs: Scenes from Disney's Peter Pan.

1980, Oct. 1 Litho. Perf. 11
679	A98	½c multicolored	.20	.20
680	A98	1c multicolored	.20	.20
681	A98	2c multicolored	.20	.20
682	A98	3c multicolored	.20	.20
683	A98	4c multicolored	.20	.20
684	A98	5c multicolored	.20	.20
685	A98	10c multicolored	.20	.20
686	A98	$2 multicolored	3.25	1.60
687	A98	$2.50 multicolored	3.25	1.90
		Nos. 679-687 (9)	7.90	4.90

Souvenir Sheet
688	A98	$4 multicolored	6.00	6.00

Christmas.

Douglas Bay A99

1981, Feb. 12 Litho. Perf. 14
689	A99	20c shown	.20	.20
690	A99	30c Valley of Desolation	.20	.20
691	A99	40c Emerald Pool, vert.	.20	.20
692	A99	$3 Indian River, vert.	1.50	1.50
		Nos. 689-692 (4)	2.10	2.10

Souvenir Sheet
693	A99	$4 Trafalgar Falls	2.00	2.00

Pluto and Fifi — A100

$4, Pluto in Blue Note (1947 cartoon).

1981, Apr. 30 Litho. Perf. 13½x14
694	A100	$2 multicolored	2.00	2.00

Souvenir Sheet
695	A100	$4 multicolored	4.00	4.00

50th anniversary of Walt Disney's Pluto.

Forest Thrush A101

1981, Apr. 30 Perf. 14
696	A101	20c shown	.20	.20
697	A101	30c Stolid flycatcher	.40	.40
698	A101	40c Blue-hooded euphonia	.55	.55
699	A101	$5 Lesser antillean peewee	7.00	7.00
		Nos. 696-699 (4)	8.15	8.15

Souvenir Sheet
700	A101	$3 Sisserou parrot	4.50	4.50

Royal Wedding Issue
Common Design Type

1981, June 16 Litho. Perf. 14
701	CD331a	45c Couple	.25	.25
702	CD331a	60c Windsor Castle	.30	.30
703	CD331a	$4 Charles	2.00	2.00
		Nos. 701-703 (3)	2.55	2.55

Souvenir Sheet
704	CD331	$5 Helicopter	2.00	2.00

Booklet
705	CD331		8.25	
a.		Pane of 6 (3x25c, Lady Diana, 3x$2, Charles)	4.75	
b.		Pane of 1, $5, Couple	3.50	

No. 705 contains imperf., self-adhesive stamps.
Nos. 701-703 also printed in sheets of 5 plus label, perf. 12, in changed colors. Value, set of three sheets $10.

Elves Repairing Santa's Sleigh — A102

Christmas: Scenes from Walt Disney's Santa's Workshop.

1981, Nov. 2 Litho. Perf. 14
706	A102	½c multicolored	.20	.20
707	A102	1c multicolored	.20	.20
708	A102	2c multicolored	.20	.20
709	A102	3c multicolored	.20	.20
710	A102	4c multicolored	.20	.20
711	A102	5c multicolored	.20	.20
712	A102	10c multicolored	.20	.20
713	A102	45c multicolored	.60	.60
714	A102	$5 multicolored	7.50	7.50
		Nos. 706-714 (9)	9.50	9.50

Souvenir Sheet
715	A102	$4 multicolored	6.50	6.50

Ixora A103

1981, Dec. 1 Litho. Perf. 14
716	A103	1c shown	.20	.20
717	A103	2c Flamboyant	.20	.20
718	A103	4c Poinsettia	.20	.20
719	A103	5c Sabinea carinalis	.20	.20
720	A103	8c Annatto roucou	.20	.20
721	A103	10c Passion fruit	.20	.20
722	A103	15c Breadfruit	.20	.20
723	A103	20c Allamanda buttercup	.20	.20
724	A103	25c Cashew	.20	.20
725	A103	35c Soursop	.25	.25
726	A103	40c Bougainvillea	.30	.65
727	A103	45c Anthurium	.35	.70
728	A103	60c Cacao	.45	.95
729	A103	90c Pawpaw tree	.65	1.40
730	A103	$1 Coconut palm	.70	1.50
731	A103	$2 Coffee tree	1.40	2.75
732	A103	$5 Lobster claw	3.50	7.00
a.		Perf. 12½x12 ('85)	2.25	2.40
733	A103	$10 Banana fig	7.00	14.50
		Nos. 716-733 (18)	16.40	31.50

Nos. 721-722, 728, 732 exist dated "1985." For overprints see Nos. 852-853.

1984 Perf. 12
721a	A103	10c	.80	.80
730a	A103	$1	1.00	1.00
732a	A103	$5	3.50	3.50
733a	A103	$10	7.50	7.50

Dated "1984."

Intl. Year of the Disabled — A104   Bathers, by Picasso — A105

1981, Dec. 22 Litho. Perf. 14
734	A104	45c Ramp curb	.35	.35
735	A104	60c Bus steps	.50	.50
736	A104	75c Hand-operated car	.65	.65
737	A104	$4 Bus lift	3.00	3.00
		Nos. 734-737 (4)	4.50	4.50

Souvenir Sheet
738	A104	$5 Elevator buttons	6.00	6.00

1981, Dec. 30 Perf. 14½
739	A105	45c Olga in Armchair	.35	.35
740	A105	60c shown	.50	.50
741	A105	75c Woman in Spanish Costume	.65	.65
742	A105	$4 Dog and Cock	3.00	3.00
		Nos. 739-742 (4)	4.50	4.50

Souvenir Sheet
743	A105	$5 Sleeping Peasants	6.00	6.00

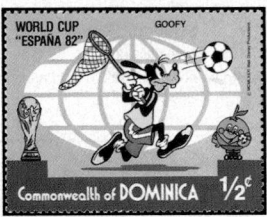

1982 World Cup Soccer — A106

Various Disney characters playing soccer.

1982, Jan. 29 Perf. 14
744	A106	½c multicolored	.20	.20
745	A106	1c multicolored	.20	.20
746	A106	2c multicolored	.20	.20
747	A106	3c multicolored	.20	.20
748	A106	4c multicolored	.20	.20
749	A106	5c multicolored	.20	.20
750	A106	10c multicolored	.20	.20
751	A106	60c multicolored	1.10	1.10
752	A106	$5 multicolored	8.50	8.50
		Nos. 744-752 (9)	11.00	11.00

Souvenir Sheet
753	A106	$4 multicolored	6.50	6.50

Golden Days, by Norman Rockwell A107

1982, Mar. 10 Litho. Perf. 14x13½
754	A107	10c shown	.20	.20
755	A107	25c The Morning News	.20	.20
756	A107	45c The Marbles Champ	.35	.35
757	A107	$1 Speeding Along	.75	.75
		Nos. 754-757 (4)	1.50	1.50

Intl. Decade for Women (1975-85) A108

Famous Women: 10c, Elma Napier (1890-1973), first woman elected to Legislative Council in British West Indies, 1940. 45c, Margaret Mead (1901-1978), anthropologist. $1, Mabel Caudiron (1909-1968), musician and folk historian. $3, Florence Nightingale, founder of modern nursing. $4, Eleanor Roosevelt.

1982, Apr. 15   **Litho.**   *Perf. 14*
758	A108	10c multicolored	.20	.20
759	A108	45c multicolored	.35	.35
760	A108	$1 multicolored	.75	.75
761	A108	$4 multicolored	3.25	3.25
		Nos. 758-761 (4)	4.55	4.55

Souvenir Sheet
762	A108	$3 multicolored	3.50	3.50

George Washington and Independence Hall, Philadelphia — A109

Washington or Roosevelt and: 60c, Capitol Building. 90c, The Surrender of Cornwallis, by John Trumbull. $2, Dam construction during New Deal (mural by William Gropper). $5, Washington, Roosevelt.

1982, May 1   **Perf. 14½**
763	A109	45c multicolored	.35	.35
764	A109	60c multicolored	.45	.45
765	A109	90c multicolored	.70	.70
766	A109	$2 multicolored	1.75	1.75
		Nos. 763-766 (4)	3.25	3.25

Souvenir Sheet
767	A109	$5 multicolored	3.50	3.50

George Washington's 250th birth anniv. and Franklin D. Roosevelt's birth cent.

Godman's Leaf Butterfly — A110

1982, June 1   **Litho.**   *Perf. 14*
768	A110	15c shown	.50	.50
769	A110	45c Zebra	2.25	2.25
770	A110	60c Mimic	2.50	2.50
771	A110	$3 Red rim	10.50	10.50
		Nos. 768-771 (4)	15.75	15.75

Souvenir Sheet
772	A110	$5 Southern dagger tail	8.00	8.00

Princess Diana Issue
Common Design Type

1982, July 1   **Litho.**   *Perf. 14½x14*
773	CD332	45c Buckingham Palace	.35	.35
774	CD332	$2 Engagement portrait	1.50	1.50
775	CD332	$4 Wedding	3.00	3.00
		Nos. 773-775 (3)	4.85	4.85

Souvenir Sheet
776	CD332	$5 Diana, diff.	4.25	4.25

Also issued in sheet of 5 plus label.
For overprints see Nos. 782-785.

Scouting Year A111

1982, July 1   **Litho.**   *Perf. 14*
777	A111	45c Cooking	.95	.95
778	A111	60c Meteorological study	1.50	1.50
779	A111	75c Sisserou parrot, cub scouts	1.75	1.75
780	A111	$3 Canoeing, Indian River	6.50	6.50
		Nos. 777-780 (4)	10.70	10.70

Souvenir Sheet
781	A111	$5 Flagbearer	4.50	4.50

Nos. 773-776 Overprinted: "ROYAL BABY / 21.6.82"

1982, Sept. 1   **Litho.**   *Perf. 14½x14*
782	CD332	45c multicolored	.35	.35
783	CD332	$2 multicolored	1.50	1.50
784	CD332	$4 multicolored	3.00	3.00
		Nos. 782-784 (3)	4.85	4.85

Souvenir Sheet
785	CD332	$5 multicolored	4.00	4.00

Birth of Prince William of Wales, June 21. Also issued in sheet of 5 plus label.

Christmas — A112

Holy Family Paintings by Raphael.

1982, Oct. 18   **Litho.**   *Perf. 14*
786	A112	25c multicolored	.20	.20
787	A112	30c multicolored	.20	.20
788	A112	90c multicolored	.60	.60
789	A112	$4 multicolored	2.75	2.75
		Nos. 786-789 (4)	3.75	3.75

Souvenir Sheet
790	A112	multicolored	4.25	4.25

Goosebeak Whale Eating Squid — A113

1983, Feb. 15   **Litho.**   *Perf. 14*
791	A113	45c shown	1.25	1.25
792	A113	60c Humpback whale	1.75	1.75
793	A113	75c Great right whale	2.25	2.25
794	A113	$3 Melonhead whale	9.25	9.25
		Nos. 791-794 (4)	14.50	14.50

Souvenir Sheet
795	A113	$5 Pygmy sperm whale	8.00	8.00

A113a

1983, Mar. 14
796	A113a	25c Banana industry	.20	.20
797	A113a	30c Road construction	.20	.20
798	A113a	90c Community nursing	.55	.55
799	A113a	$3 Basket weavers	1.75	1.75
		Nos. 796-799 (4)	2.70	2.70

Commonwealth Day.

World Communications Year — A114

1983, Apr. 18   **Litho.**   *Perf. 14*
800	A114	45c Hurricane pattern, map	.35	.35
801	A114	60c Air-to-ship communication	.45	.45

802	A114	90c Columbia shuttle, dish antenna	.70	.70
803	A114	$2 Walkie-talkie	1.50	1.50
		Nos. 800-803 (4)	3.00	3.00

Souvenir Sheet
804	A114	$5 Satellite	3.50	3.50

Manned Flight Bicentenary — A115

1983, July 19   **Litho.**   *Perf. 15*
805	A115	45c Mayo Composite	.50	.50
806	A115	60c Macchi M-39	.65	.65
807	A115	90c Fairey Swordfish	1.00	1.00
808	A115	$4 Zeppelin LZ-3	4.25	4.25
		Nos. 805-808 (4)	6.40	6.40

Souvenir Sheet
809	A115	$5 Double Eagle II, vert.	4.00	4.00

Duesenberg SJ, 1935 — A116

1983, Sept. 1   **Litho.**   *Perf. 14*
810	A116	10c shown	.20	.20
811	A116	45c Studebaker Avanti, 1962	.35	.35
812	A116	60c Cord 812, 1936	.45	.45
813	A116	75c MG-TC, 1945	.55	.55
814	A116	90c Camaro 350-SS, 1967	.70	.70
815	A116	$3 Porsche 356, 1948	2.25	2.25
		Nos. 810-815 (6)	4.50	4.50

Souvenir Sheet
816	A116	$5 Ferrari 312-T, 1975	4.00	4.00

Christmas — A117

Raphael Paintings.

1983, Oct. 4   **Litho.**   *Perf. 13½*
817	A117	45c multicolored	.35	.35
818	A117	60c multicolored	.50	.50
819	A117	90c multicolored	.75	.75
820	A117	$4 multicolored	3.25	3.25
		Nos. 817-820 (4)	4.85	4.85

Souvenir Sheet
821	A117	$5 multicolored	4.00	4.00

23rd Olympic Games, Los Angeles, July 28-Aug. 12 — A118

1984, Mar.   **Litho.**   *Perf. 14*
822	A118	30c Gymnastics	.25	.25
823	A118	45c Javelin	.35	.35
824	A118	60c Diving	.50	.50
825	A118	$4 Fencing	3.25	3.25
		Nos. 822-825 (4)	4.35	4.35

Souvenir Sheet
826	A118	$5 Equestrian	4.25	4.25

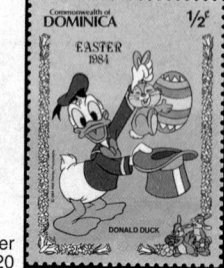

Local Birds A119

1984, May   **Litho.**
827	A119	5c Plumbeous warbler	3.25	3.25
828	A119	45c Imperial parrot	8.50	8.50
829	A119	60c Blue-headed hummingbird	12.50	12.50
830	A119	90c Red-necked parrot	18.00	18.00
		Nos. 827-830 (4)	42.25	42.25

Souvenir Sheet
831	A119	$5 Roseate flamingoes	13.00	13.00

Easter A120

Various Disney characters and Easter bunnies.

1984, Apr. 15   **Litho.**   *Perf. 11*
832	A120	½c multicolored	.20	.20
833	A120	1c multicolored	.20	.20
834	A120	2c multicolored	.20	.20
835	A120	3c multicolored	.20	.20
836	A120	4c multicolored	.20	.20
837	A120	5c multicolored	.20	.20
838	A120	10c multicolored	.20	.20
839	A120	$2 multicolored	4.00	4.00
840	A120	$4 multicolored	8.00	8.00
		Nos. 832-840 (9)	13.40	13.40

Souvenir Sheet
Perf. 14
841	A120	$5 multicolored	7.00	7.00

Ships A121

1984, June 14   **Litho.**   *Perf. 14*
842	A121	45c Atlantic Star	1.10	1.10
843	A121	60c Atlantic	1.40	1.40
844	A121	90c Carib fishing pirogue	2.50	2.50
845	A121	$4 Norway	10.50	10.50
		Nos. 842-845 (4)	15.50	15.50

Souvenir Sheet
846	A121	$5 Santa Maria	6.00	6.00

Local Plants — A122   Correggio & Degas — A122a

1984, Aug. 13
847	A122	45c Guzmania lingulata	.45	.45
848	A122	60c Pitcairnia angustifolia	.55	.55
849	A122	75c Tillandsia fasciculata	.75	.75

850 A122 $3 Aechmea smithi-
orum 3.25 3.25
Nos. 847-850 (4) 5.00 5.00

Souvenir Sheet

851 A122 $5 Tillandsia utriculata 4.00 4.00

Ausipex Intl. Stamp Exhibition.

Nos. 721, 732 Overprinted: "19th UPU / CONGRESS HAMBURG"

1984 Litho. Perf. 14
852 A103 10c multicolored .20 .20
853 A103 $5 multicolored 5.00 5.00

1984, Nov. Litho. Perf. 15

Correggio: 25c, Virgin and Child with Young St. John. 60c, Christ Bids Farewell to the Virgin Mary. 90c, Do Not Touch Me. $4, The Mystical Marriage of St. Catherine. No. 862, Adoration of the Magi.

Degas, horiz.: 30c, Before the Start. 45c, On the Racecourse. $1, Jockeys at the Flagpole. $3, Racehorses at Longchamp. No. 863, Self-portrait.

854 A122a 25c multicolored .20 .20
855 A122a 30c multicolored .20 .20
856 A122a 45c multicolored .40 .40
857 A122a 60c multicolored .55 .55
858 A122a 90c multicolored .75 .75
859 A122a $1 multicolored .90 .90
860 A122a $3 multicolored 2.50 2.50
861 A122a $4 multicolored 3.50 3.50
Nos. 854-861 (8) 9.00 9.00

Souvenir Sheets

862 A122a $5 multicolored 3.75 3.75
863 A122a $5 multicolored 3.75 3.75

A123

Cats A125

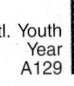

1984, Dec. Perf. 14
864 A123 30c Avro 748 .20 .20
865 A123 60c Twin Otter 1.40 1.40
866 A123 $1 Islander 2.40 2.40
867 A123 $3 Casa 7.00 7.00
Nos. 864-867 (4) 11.00 11.00

Souvenir Sheet

868 A123 $5 Boeing 747 7.50 7.50

Intl. Civil Aviation Org., 40th anniv.

1984, Nov. Litho.

Scenes from various Donald Duck movies.

869 A124 45c multicolored .95 .95
870 A124 60c multicolored 1.25 1.25
871 A124 90c multicolored 2.00 2.00
872 A124 $2 multicolored, perf. 12x12½ 4.00 4.00
873 A124 $4 multicolored 7.75 7.75
Nos. 869-873 (5) 15.95 15.95

Souvenir Sheet
Perf. 13½x14

874 A124 $5 multicolored 6.75 6.75

Christmas and 50th anniv. of Donald Duck.

1984, Nov. 12 Litho. Perf. 15
875 A125 10c Tabby .20 .20
876 A125 15c Calico shorthair .20 .20
877 A125 20c Siamese .20 .20
878 A125 25c Manx .20 .20
879 A125 45c Abyssinian .45 .45
880 A125 60c Tortoise shell longhair .55 .55
881 A125 $1 Rex .90 .90
882 A125 $2 Persian 2.10 2.10
883 A125 $3 Himalayan 3.25 3.25
884 A125 $5 Burmese 5.00 5.00
Nos. 875-884 (10) 13.05 13.05

Souvenir Sheet

885 A125 $5 Gray Burmese, Persian, American shorthair 6.25 6.25

Girl Guides, 75th Anniv. A126

1985, Feb. 18 Perf. 14
886 A126 35c Lady Baden-Powell .50 .50
887 A126 45c Inspecting Dominican troop .75 .75
888 A126 60c With Dominican troop leaders 1.00 1.00
889 A126 $3 Lord and Lady Baden-Powell, vert. 4.50 4.50
Nos. 886-889 (4) 6.75 6.75

Souvenir Sheet

890 A126 $5 Flag ceremony 6.75 6.75

John James Audubon A127

1985, Apr. 4
891 A127 45c King rails 1.00 1.00
892 A127 $1 Black & white warbler, vert. 2.10 2.10
893 A127 $2 Broad-winged hawks, vert. 4.00 4.00
894 A127 $3 Ring-necked ducks 6.25 6.25
Nos. 891-894 (4) 13.35 13.35

Souvenir Sheet

895 A127 $5 Reddish egrets, vert. 7.00 7.00

Nos. 891-894 exist vertically se-tenant with labels showing additional bird species. See Nos. 965-969.

Duke of Edinburgh Awards, 1984 — A128

1985, Apr. 30
896 A128 45c Woman at computer terminal .65 .65
897 A128 60c Medical staff, patient .85 .85
898 A128 90c Runners 1.25 1.25
899 A128 $4 Family jogging 5.25 5.25
Nos. 896-899 (4) 8.00 8.00

Souvenir Sheet

900 A128 $5 Duke of Edinburgh 5.50 5.50

Intl. Youth Year A129

1985, July 8 Litho. Perf. 14
901 A129 45c Cricket match 1.75 1.75
902 A129 60c Environmental study, parrot 2.25 2.25
903 A129 $1 Stamp collecting 3.25 3.25
904 A129 $3 Boating, leisure 11.50 11.50
Nos. 901-904 (4) 18.75 18.75

Souvenir Sheet

905 A129 $5 Youths join hands 4.75 4.75

Queen Mother, 85th Birthday — A130

Johann Sebastian Bach — A131

1985, July 15
906 A130 60c Visiting Sadlers Wells .55 .55
907 A130 $1 Fishing 1.25 1.25
908 A130 $3 At Clarence House, 1984 3.75 3.75
Nos. 906-908 (3) 5.55 5.55

Souvenir Sheet

909 A130 $5 Attending Windsor Castle Garter Ceremony 4.50 4.50

1985, Sept. 2

Portrait, signature, music from Explication and: 45c, Cornett 60c, Coiled trumpet. $1, Piccolo. $3, Violoncello piccolo.

910 A131 45c multicolored .85 .85
911 A131 60c multicolored 1.10 1.10
912 A131 $1 multicolored 1.75 1.75
913 A131 $3 multicolored 6.75 6.75
Nos. 910-913 (4) 10.45 10.45

Souvenir Sheet

914 A131 $5 Portrait 5.00 5.00

State Visit of Elizabeth II, Oct. 25 — A132

1985, Oct. 25 Perf. 14½
915 A132 60c Flags of UK, Dominica .55 .55
916 A132 $1 Elizabeth II, vert. .95 .95
917 A132 $4 HMS Britannia 4.50 4.50
Nos. 915-917 (3) 6.00 6.00

Souvenir Sheet

918 A132 $5 Map 4.50 4.50

Mark Twain — A133

Disney characters in Tom Sawyer.

1985, Nov. 11 Litho. Perf. 14
919 A133 20c multicolored .45 .45
920 A133 60c multicolored 1.10 1.10
921 A133 $1 multicolored 1.90 1.90
922 A133 $1.50 multicolored 3.50 3.50
923 A133 $2 multicolored 5.00 5.00
Nos. 919-923 (5) 11.95 11.95

Souvenir Sheet

924 A133 $5 multicolored 7.75 7.75

Christmas.

The Brothers Grimm — A134

Disney characters in Little Red Cap (Little Red Riding Hood).

1985, Nov. 11
925 A134 10c multicolored .45 .45
926 A134 45c multicolored .95 .95
927 A134 90c multicolored 1.75 1.75
928 A134 $1 multicolored 2.10 2.10
929 A134 $3 multicolored 6.25 6.25
Nos. 925-929 (5) 11.50 11.50

Souvenir Sheet

930 A134 $5 multicolored 9.25 9.25

Christmas.

UN, 40th Anniv. A135

Stamps of UN, famous men and events: 45c, No. 442 and Lord Baden-Powell. $2, No. 157 and Maimonides (1135-1204) Judaic scholar. $3, No. 278 and Sir Rowland Hill. $5, Apollo-Soyuz Mission, 10th anniv.

1985, Nov. 22 Perf. 14½
931 A135 45c multicolored .50 .50
932 A135 $2 multicolored 3.00 3.00
933 A135 $3 multicolored 4.50 4.50
Nos. 931-933 (3) 8.00 8.00

Souvenir Sheet

934 A135 $5 multicolored 4.50 4.50

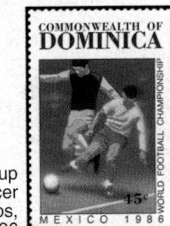

1986 World Cup Soccer Championships, Mexico — A136

Various soccer plays.

1986, Mar. 26 Perf. 14
935 A136 45c multicolored 1.00 1.00
936 A136 60c multicolored 1.40 1.40
937 A136 $1 multicolored 2.50 2.50
938 A136 $3 multicolored 7.50 7.50
Nos. 935-938 (4) 12.40 12.40

Souvenir Sheet

939 A136 $5 multicolored 10.00 10.00

For overprints see Nos. 974-978.

Statue of Liberty, Cent. A137

Statue and: 15c, New York police pursuing river pirates, c. 1890. 25c, Police patrol boat. 45c, Hoboken Ferry Terminal, c. 1890. $4, Holland Tunnel.

1986, Mar. 26
940 A137 15c multicolored .60 .60
941 A137 25c multicolored .60 .60
942 A137 45c multicolored .85 .85
943 A137 $4 multicolored 8.50 8.50
Nos. 940-943 (4) 10.55 10.55

Souvenir Sheet

944 A137 $5 Statue, vert. 6.50 6.50

Halley's Comet A138

5c, Jantal Mantar Observatory, Delhi, India, Nasir al Din al Tusi (1201-1274), astronomer. 10c, US Bell X-1 rocket plane breaking sound barrier. 45c, Astronomicum Caesareum, 1540, manuscript diagram of comet's trajectory, 1531. $4, Mark Twain, comet appeared at birth and death. $5, Comet.

1986, Apr. 17
945	A138	5c multicolored	.20	.20
946	A138	10c multicolored	.20	.20
947	A138	45c multicolored	.60	.60
948	A138	$4 multicolored	5.00	5.00
		Nos. 945-948 (4)	6.00	6.00

Souvenir Sheet
949	A138	$5 multicolored	4.50	4.50

For overprints see Nos. 984-988.

Queen Elizabeth II, 60th Birthday
Common Design Type

1986, Apr. 21   Litho.   Perf. 14
950	CD339	2c Wedding, 1947	.25	.25
951	CD339	$1 With Pope John Paul II, 1982	.75	.75
952	CD339	$4 Royal visit, 1971	3.00	3.00
		Nos. 950-952 (3)	4.00	4.00

Souvenir Sheet
953	CD339	$5 Age 10	4.25	4.25

AMERIPEX '86 — A139

Walt Disney characters involved in stamp collecting.

1986, May 22   Perf. 11
954	A139	25c Mickey Mouse and Pluto	.25	.25
955	A139	45c Donald Duck	.80	.80
956	A139	60c Chip-n-Dale	.95	.95
957	A139	$4 Donald, nephews	6.50	6.50
		Nos. 954-957 (4)	8.50	8.50

Souvenir Sheet
Perf. 14
958	A139	$5 Uncle Scrooge	7.25	7.25

British Monarchs — A140

1986, June 9   Perf. 14
959	A140	10c William I	.20	.20
960	A140	40c Richard II	.40	.40
961	A140	50c Henry VIII	.50	.50
962	A140	$1 Charles II	1.00	1.00
963	A140	$2 Queen Anne	2.10	2.10
964	A140	$4 Queen Victoria	4.50	4.50
		Nos. 959-964 (6)	8.70	8.70

Audubon Type of 1985
Perf. 12½x12, 12x12½
1986, June 18
965	A127	25c Black-throated diver	.45	.45
966	A127	60c Great blue heron	1.10	1.10
967	A127	90c Yellow-crowned night heron	1.75	1.75
968	A127	$4 Shoveler duck	8.00	8.00
		Nos. 965-968 (4)	11.30	11.30

Souvenir Sheet
Perf. 14
969	A127	$5 Goose	12.00	12.00
		Nos. 966-967 vert.		

Royal Wedding Issue, 1986
Common Design Type

1986, July 23   Perf. 14
970	CD340	45c Couple	.40	.40
971	CD340	60c Prince Andrew	.60	.60
972	CD340	$4 Prince, aircraft	3.00	3.00
		Nos. 970-972 (3)	4.00	4.00

Souvenir Sheet
973	CD340	$5 Couple, diff.	4.50	4.50

Nos. 935-939 Ovptd. "WINNERS / Argentina 3 / W. Germany 2" in Gold

1986, Sept. 15   Litho.   Perf. 14
974	A136	45c multicolored	.80	.80
975	A136	60c multicolored	1.25	1.25
976	A136	$1 multicolored	2.10	2.10
977	A136	$3 multicolored	6.75	6.75
		Nos. 974-977 (4)	10.90	10.90

Souvenir Sheet
978	A136	$5 multicolored	10.50	10.50

Paintings by Albrecht Durer — A141

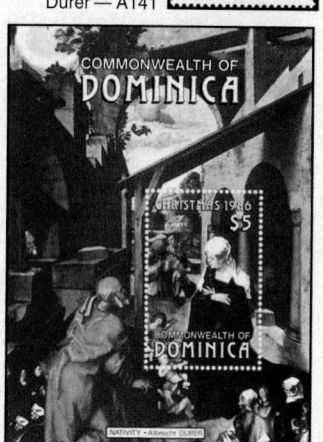

A142

1986, Dec. 2   Litho.   Perf. 14
979	A141	45c Virgin in Prayer	1.00	1.00
980	A141	60c Madonna and Child	1.25	1.25
981	A141	$1 Madonna and Child, diff.	2.25	2.25
982	A141	$3 Madonna and Child with St. Anne	6.50	6.50
		Nos. 979-982 (4)	11.00	11.00

Souvenir Sheet
983	A142	$5 Nativity	10.50	10.50

Nos. 945-949 Printed with Halley's Comet Logo in Black or Silver

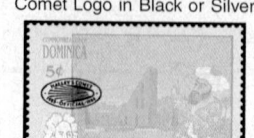

1986, Dec. 16
984	A138	5c multicolored	.20	.20
985	A138	10c multicolored	.20	.20
986	A138	45c multicolored	.60	.60
987	A138	$4 multicolored	4.75	4.75
		Nos. 984-987 (4)	5.75	5.75

Souvenir Sheet
988	A138	$5 multi (S)	5.25	5.25

Birds — A143

1987, Jan. 20   Litho.   Perf. 15
989	A143	1c Broad-winged hawk	.20	.20
990	A143	2c Ruddy quail dove	.20	.20
991	A143	5c Red-necked pigeon	.20	.20
992	A143	10c Green heron	.20	.20
993	A143	15c Common gallinule	.20	.20
994	A143	20c Ringed kingfisher	.20	.20
995	A143	25c Brown pelican	.20	.20
996	A143	35c White-tailed tropicbird	.30	.30
997	A143	45c Red-legged thrush	.40	.40
998	A143	60c Purple throated carib	.55	.55
999	A143	90c Magnificent frigatebird	.75	.75
1000	A143	$1 Trembler	.85	.85
1001	A143	$2 Black-capped petrel	1.75	1.75
1002	A143	$5 Barn owl	4.25	4.25
1003	A143	$10 Imperial parrot	8.75	8.75
		Nos. 989-1003 (15)	19.00	19.00

Inscribed "1989" and "Questa"
1989, Aug. 31   Litho.   Perf. 14
990a	A143	2c	.20	.20
991a	A143	5c	.20	.20
992a	A143	10c	.20	.20
993a	A143	15c	.20	.20
994a	A143	20c	.20	.20
995a	A143	25c	.30	.30
996a	A143	35c	.50	.50
997a	A143	45c	.60	.60
998a	A143	60c	.85	.85
1000a	A143	$1	1.40	1.40
1001a	A143	$2	2.75	2.75
1002a	A143	$5	6.75	6.75
1003a	A143	$10	14.00	14.00
		Nos. 990a-1003a (13)	28.15	28.15

Inscribed "1989" and "Questa"
1990   Litho.   Perf. 12
990b	A143	2c	.20	.20
991b	A143	5c	.20	.20
992b	A143	10c	.20	.20
993b	A143	15c	.20	.20
994b	A143	20c	.20	.20
995b	A143	25c	.30	.30
996b	A143	35c	.50	.50
997b	A143	45c	.60	.60
998b	A143	60c	.85	.85
1000b	A143	$1	1.40	1.40
1001b	A143	$2	2.75	2.75
1002b	A143	$5	6.75	6.75
1003b	A143	$10	14.00	14.00
		Nos. 990b-1003b (13)	28.15	28.15

Inscribed "1989" and "Questa"
1991   Litho.   Perf. 13x11½
990c	A143	2c	.20	.20
991c	A143	5c	.20	.20
992c	A143	10c	.20	.20
993c	A143	15c	.20	.20
994c	A143	20c	.20	.20
995c	A143	25c	.35	.35
996c	A143	35c	.55	.55
997c	A143	45c	.65	.65
998c	A143	60c	.95	.95
1000c	A143	$1	1.60	1.60
1001c	A143	$2	3.00	3.00
1002c	A143	$5	7.50	7.50
1003c	A143	$10	15.00	15.00
		Nos. 990c-1003c (13)	30.60	30.60

Paintings by Marc Chagall (1887-1985) A144

Designs: 25c, Artist and His Model. 35c, Midsummer Night's Dream. 45c, Joseph the Shepherd. 60c, the Cellist. 90c, Woman with Pigs. $1, the Blue Circus. $3, For Vava. $4, the Rider. No. 1012, Purim. No. 1013, Firebird design for the curtain of the Stravinsky Ballet production.

1987, Mar. 2   Perf. 14
1004	A144	25c multicolored	.25	.25
1005	A144	35c multicolored	.40	.40
1006	A144	45c multicolored	.45	.45
1007	A144	60c multicolored	.65	.65
1008	A144	90c multicolored	.90	.90
1009	A144	$1 multicolored	1.00	1.00
1010	A144	$3 multicolored	3.00	3.00
1011	A144	$4 multicolored	4.25	4.25

Size: 110x95mm
Imperf
1012	A144	$5 multicolored	4.00	4.00
1013	A144	$5 multicolored	4.00	4.00
		Nos. 1004-1013 (10)	18.90	18.90

A145   Conch Shells — A147

America's Cup — A146

1987, Feb. 5   Perf. 15
1014	A145	45c Reliance, 1903	.50	.45
1015	A145	60c Freedom, 1980	.60	.55
1016	A145	$1 Mischief, 1881	1.10	1.00
1017	A145	$3 Australia, 1977	3.25	2.00
		Nos. 1014-1017 (4)	5.45	4.00

Souvenir Sheet
1018	A146	$5 Courageous, Australia, 1977	5.00	5.00

1987, Apr. 13   Litho.

Designs: 35c, Morch Poulsen's triton. 45c, Swainson globe purple sea snail. 60c, Banded tulip. No. 1022, Lamarck deltoid rock shell. No. 1023, Junoia volute.

1019	A147	35c multicolored	.35	.35
1020	A147	45c multicolored	.50	.50
1021	A147	60c multicolored	.65	.65
1022	A147	$5 multicolored	4.25	4.25
		Nos. 1019-1022 (4)	5.75	5.75

Souvenir Sheet
1023	A147	$5 multicolored	5.25	5.25

CAPEX '87 A148

Mushrooms.

1987, June 15   Litho.   Perf. 14
1024	A148	45c Cantharellus cinnabarinus	.85	.85
1025	A148	60c Boletellus cubenis	1.25	1.25
1026	A148	$2 Eccilia cystiophorus	4.50	4.50
1027	A148	$3 Xerocomus guadelupae	6.75	6.75
		Nos. 1024-1027 (4)	13.35	13.35

Souvenir Sheet
1028	A148	$5 Gymnopilus chrysopellus	12.00	12.00

A149

Discovery of America, 500th Anniv. (in 1992) — A150

Explorations of Christopher Columbus: 10c, Discovery of Dominica. 15c, Ships greeted by Carib Indians. 45c, Claiming New World for Spain. 60c, Wrecking of the Santa Maria. 90c, Fleet setting sail. $1, Sighting land. $3, Trading with the Indians. No. 1036, First settlement. No. 1037, Arrival of Second Fleet at Dominica, Nov. 3, 1493. No. 1038, Map of exploration of the Leeward Islands.

1987, July 27   **Perf. 15**
1029	A149	10c multicolored	.25	.25
1030	A149	15c multicolored	.25	.25
1031	A149	45c multicolored	.50	.50
1032	A149	60c multicolored	.65	.65
1033	A149	90c multicolored	1.00	1.00
1034	A149	$1 multicolored	1.10	1.10
1035	A149	$3 multicolored	3.25	3.25
1036	A149	$5 multicolored	5.50	5.50
		Nos. 1029-1036 (8)	12.50	12.50

Souvenir Sheets
1037	A150	$5 multicolored	4.50	4.50
1038	A150	$5 multicolored	4.50	4.50

For overprints see Nos. 1083-1084.

Transportation — A151

10c, Warrior, 1st iron-clad warship. 15c, Maglev-MLU 001, fastest passenger train. 25c, Clipper Flying Cloud, fastest NYC-San Francisco voyage, 1852. 35c, 1st elevated railway, NYC. 45c, Tom Thumb, 1st US passenger train locomotive. 60c, Joshua Slocum, 1st solo circumnavigation of the world in a sloop. 90c, Se-Land Commerce, fastest Pacific crossing. $1, 1st cable car, San Francisco. $3, Orient Express. $4, The North River Steamboat of Clermont, invented by Robert Fulton, 1st successful commercial steamboat.

1987   **Litho.**   **Perf. 14**
1039	A151	10c multicolored	.20	.20
1040	A151	15c multicolored	.20	.20
1041	A151	25c multi, vert.	.45	.45
1042	A151	35c multi, vert.	.55	.55
1043	A151	45c multicolored	.70	.70
1044	A151	60c multi, vert.	1.00	1.00
1045	A151	90c multi, vert.	1.40	1.40
1046	A151	$1 multicolored	1.75	1.75
1047	A151	$3 multicolored	4.75	4.75
1048	A151	$4 multicolored	6.00	6.00
		Nos. 1039-1048 (10)	17.00	17.00

Issued: 10c, 15c, 45c, 60c, $4, 9/28; others 8/1.
For overprints see Nos. 1081-1082.

Christmas — A152

Paintings (details): 20c, Virgin and Child with St. Anne, by Durer. 25c, The Virgin and Child, by Murillo. $2, Madonna and Child, by Vincenzo Foppa (c. 1427-1516). $4, Madonna and Child, by Paolo Veronese (1528-1588). $5, Angel of the Annunciation, anonymous.

1987, Nov. 16
1049	A152	20c multicolored	.30	.30
1050	A152	25c multicolored	.30	.30
1051	A152	$2 multicolored	2.40	2.40
1052	A152	$4 multicolored	4.75	4.75
		Nos. 1049-1052 (4)	7.75	7.75

Souvenir Sheet
1053	A152	$5 multicolored	4.50	4.50

Mickey Mouse, 60th Anniv. A153

Disney theme parks and trains: 20c, People Mover, Disney World. 25c, Horse-drawn Trolley, Disneyland. 45c, Roger E. Broggie, Disney World. 60c, Big Thunder Mountain, Disneyland. 90c, Walter E. Disney, Disneyland. $1, Monorail, Disney World. $3, Casey Jr. from Dumbo. $4, Lilly Belle, Disney World. No. 1062, Rainbow Caverns Mine Train, Disneyland, horiz. No. 1063, Toy train from movie Out of Scale, horiz.

1987, Dec. 7   **Litho.**   **Perf. 14**
1054	A153	20c multicolored	.45	.45
1055	A153	25c multicolored	.45	.45
1056	A153	45c multicolored	.80	.80
1057	A153	60c multicolored	1.10	1.10
1058	A153	90c multicolored	1.40	1.40
1059	A153	$1 multicolored	1.75	1.75
1060	A153	$3 multicolored	5.00	5.00
1061	A153	$4 multicolored	6.75	6.75
		Nos. 1054-1061 (8)	17.70	17.70

Souvenir Sheets
1062	A153	$5 multicolored	4.75	4.75
1063	A153	$5 multicolored	4.75	4.75

40th Wedding Anniv. of Queen Elizabeth II and Prince Philip — A154

1988 Summer Olympics, Seoul — A155

1988, Feb. 15   **Litho.**   **Perf. 14**
1064	A154	45c Couple, wedding party, 1947	.55	.55
1065	A154	60c Elizabeth, Charles, c. 1952	.70	.70
1066	A154	$1 Royal Family, c. 1952	1.25	1.25
1067	A154	$3 Queen with tiara, c. 1960	3.25	3.25
		Nos. 1064-1067 (4)	5.75	5.75

Souvenir Sheet
1068	A154	$5 Elizabeth, 1947	4.00	4.00

1988, Mar. 15
1069	A155	45c Kayaking	.75	.75
1070	A155	60c Tae kwon-do	1.00	1.00
1071	A155	$1 Diving	1.75	1.75
1072	A155	$3 Parallel bars	4.50	4.50
		Nos. 1069-1072 (4)	8.00	8.00

Souvenir Sheet
1073	A155	$5 Soccer	4.00	4.00

For overprints see Nos. 1151-1155.

Reunion '88 Tourism Campaign A156

1988, Apr. 13   **Litho.**   **Perf. 15**
1074	A156	10c Carib Indian, vert.	.20	.20
1075	A156	25c Mountainous interior	.20	.20
1076	A156	35c Indian River, vert.	.25	.25
1077	A156	60c Belaire dancer, vert.	.40	.40
1078	A156	90c The Boiling Lake, vert.	.60	.60
1079	A156	$3 Coral reef	2.00	2.00
		Nos. 1074-1079 (6)	3.65	3.65

Souvenir Sheet
1080	A156	$5 Belaire dancer, diff., vert.	3.50	3.50

Independence, 10th anniv.

Nos. 1046-1047, 1037-1038 Ovptd. for Philatelic Exhibitions in Black

a

b

c

d

1988, June 1   **Litho.**   **Perf. 14**
1081	A151(a)	$1 multi	1.25	1.25
1082	A151(b)	$3 multi	4.50	4.50

Souvenir Sheets   **Perf. 15**
1083	A150(c)	$5 multi	4.75	4.75
1084	A150(d)	$5 multi	4.75	4.75

Miniature Sheet

Rain Forest Flora and Fauna — A157

Designs: a, White-tailed tropicbirds. b, Blue-throated euphonia. c, Smooth-billed ani. d, Scaly-breasted thrasher. e, Purple-throated carib. f, Southern daggertail and Clench's hairstreak. g, Trembler. h, Imperial parrot. i, Mangrove cuckoo. j, Hercules beetle. k, Orion. l, Red-necked parrot. m, Tillandsia. n, Polystacha luteola and bananaquit. o, False chameleon. p, Iguana. q, Hypolimnas. r, Green-throated carib. s, Heliconia. t, Agouti.

Intl. Fund for Agricultural Development (IFAD), 10th Anniv. — A158

1988, Sept. 5   **Litho.**   **Perf. 14**
1086	A158	45c Hen house	.65	.65
1087	A158	60c Pig farm	.80	.80
1088	A158	90c Cattle	1.25	1.25
1089	A158	$3 Black-belly sheep	4.25	4.25
		Nos. 1086-1089 (4)	6.95	6.95

Souvenir Sheet
1090	A158	$5 Mixed crops, vert.	4.50	4.50

Entertainers A159

1988, Sept. 8
1091	A159	10c Gary Cooper	.20	.20
1092	A159	35c Josephine Baker	.40	.40
1093	A159	45c Maurice Chevalier	.45	.45
1094	A159	60c James Cagney	.55	.55
1095	A159	$1 Clark Gable	.95	.95
1096	A159	$2 Louis Armstrong	2.00	2.00
1097	A159	$3 Liberace	2.75	2.75
1098	A159	$4 Spencer Tracy	3.75	3.75
		Nos. 1091-1098 (8)	11.05	11.05

Souvenir Sheets
1099	A159	$5 Elvis Presley	5.00	5.00
1100	A159	$5 Humphrey Bogart	5.00	5.00

Flowering Trees and Shrubs A160

1988, Sept. 29   **Litho.**   **Perf. 14**
1101	A160	15c Sapodilla	.20	.20
1102	A160	20c Tangerine	.20	.20
1103	A160	25c Avocado pear	.20	.20
1104	A160	45c Amherstia	.30	.30
1105	A160	90c Lipstick tree	.60	.60
1106	A160	$1 Cannonball tree	.65	.65
1107	A160	$3 Saman	2.10	2.10
1108	A160	$4 Pineapple	2.75	2.75
		Nos. 1101-1108 (8)	7.00	7.00

Souvenir Sheets
1109	A160	$5 Lignum vitae	4.25	4.25
1110	A160	$5 Sea grape	4.25	4.25

Paintings by Titian A161

Designs: 25c, Jacopo Strada, c. 1567. 35c, Titian's Daughter Lavinia, c. 1565. 45c, Andrea Navagero, c. 1515. 60c, Judith with Head of Holoferenes, c. 1570. $1, Emilia di Spilimbergo, c. 1560. $2, Martyrdom of St. Lawrence, c. 1548. $3, Salome With the Head of St. John the Baptist, 1560. $4, St. John the

1988, July 25   **Perf. 14½**
1085		Sheet of 20	17.50	17.50
	a.-t.	A157 45c any single	.75	.75

Baptist, c. 1540. No. 1119, Self-portrait, c. 1555. No. 1120, Sisyphus, 1549.

1988, Oct. 10   Litho.   Perf. 13½x14

1111	A161	25c multicolored	.20	.20
1112	A161	35c multicolored	.30	.30
1113	A161	45c multicolored	.45	.45
1114	A161	60c multicolored	.55	.55
1115	A161	$1 multicolored	1.50	1.50
1116	A161	$2 multicolored	1.75	1.75
1117	A161	$3 multicolored	2.75	2.75
1118	A161	$4 multicolored	3.50	3.50
		Nos. 1111-1118 (8)	11.00	11.00

Souvenir Sheets

1119	A161	$5 multicolored	4.00	4.00
1120	A161	$5 multicolored	4.00	4.00

A162   A163

1988, Oct. 31   Litho.   Perf. 14

1121	A162	20c Imperial parrot	.40	.40
1122	A162	45c No. 1, landscape	.60	.60
1123	A162	$2 No. 602, waterfall	2.50	2.50
1124	A162	$3 Carib wood	4.00	4.00
		Nos. 1121-1124 (4)	7.50	7.50

Souvenir Sheet

1125	A162	$5 Natl. band performing	4.50	4.50

Independence, 10th Anniv. Nos. 1122-1123 horiz.

1988, Nov. 22

1126	A163	20c With Jackie	.20	.20
1127	A163	25c Sailing Vicuna	.20	.20
1128	A163	$2 Walking in Hyannis Port	1.10	1.10
1129	A163	$4 Berlin Wall speech	2.75	2.75
		Nos. 1126-1129 (4)	4.25	4.25

Souvenir Sheet

1130	A163	$5 Portrait	4.25	4.25

John F. Kennedy. #1126-1128 horiz.

Miniature Sheet

Christmas, Mickey Mouse 60th Anniv. — A164

#1131: a, Huey, Dewey, Louie. b, Daisy Duck. c, Winnie-the-Pooh. d, Goofy. e, Donald Duck. f, Mickey Mouse. g, Minnie Mouse. h, Chip-n-Dale.
#1132, Mickey, Morty and Ferdy. #1133, Characters visiting shopping mall Santa.

1988, Dec. 1   Perf. 13½x14

1131	A164	Sheet of 8	7.75	7.75
a.-h.		60c any single	.95	.95

Souvenir Sheets

1132	A164	$6 multi	6.00	6.00
1133	A164	$6 multi, horiz.	6.00	6.00

UN Declaration of Human Rights, 40th Anniv. — A165

Designs: $3, Flag of Sweden and Raoul Wallenberg, who helped save 100,000 Jews in Budapest from deportation to Nazi concentration camps. $5, Human Rights Flame.

1988, Dec. 12   Perf. 14

1134	A165	$3 multicolored	3.50	3.50

Souvenir Sheet

1135	A165	$5 multi, vert.	4.75	4.75

Coastal Game Fish A166

1988, Dec. 22   Litho.   Perf. 14

1136	A166	10c Greater amberjack	.30	.30
1137	A166	15c Blue marlin	.30	.30
1138	A166	35c Cobia	.50	.50
1139	A166	45c Dolphin	.55	.55
1140	A166	60c Cero	.75	.75
1141	A166	90c Mahogany snapper	1.10	1.10
1142	A166	$3 Yellowfin tuna	3.75	3.75
1143	A166	$4 Rainbow parrotfish	5.25	5.25
		Nos. 1136-1143 (8)	12.50	12.50

Souvenir Sheets

1144	A166	$5 Manta ray	6.00	6.00
1145	A166	$5 Tarpon	6.00	6.00

Caribbean Insects and Reptiles A167

1988, Dec. 29

1146	A167	10c Leatherback turtle	.30	.30
1147	A167	25c Monarch butterfly	.70	.70
1148	A167	60c Green anole	1.75	1.75
1149	A167	$3 Praying mantis	9.25	9.25
		Nos. 1146-1149 (4)	12.00	12.00

Souvenir Sheet

1150	A167	$5 Hercules beetle	6.25	6.25

Nos. 1069-1072 Ovptd. for Olympic Winners
 a. "Men's c-1,500m O. Heukrodt DDR"
 b. "Women's Flyweight N.Y. Choo S. Korea"
 c. "Women's Platform Y. Xu China"
 d. "V. Artemov USSR"
 e. "USSR defeated Brazil 3-2 on penalty kicks after a 1-1 tie"

1989, Mar. 20   Litho.   Perf. 14

1151	A155(a)	45c multi	.40	.40
1152	A155(b)	60c multi	.50	.50
1153	A155(c)	$1 multi	.95	.95
1154	A155(d)	$3 multi	2.40	2.40
		Nos. 1151-1154 (4)	4.25	4.25

Souvenir Sheet

1155	A155(e)	$5 multi	4.50	4.50

Pre-Columbian Societies and Their Customs — A168

UPAE and discovery of America anniv. emblems and: 20c, Carib Indians canoeing. 35c, Bow hunting. $1, Canoe making. $3, Shield wrestling. $6, Dancing.

1989, May 8   Litho.   Perf. 14

1156	A168	20c multicolored	.30	.30
1157	A168	35c multicolored	.45	.45
1158	A168	$1 multicolored	1.25	1.25
1159	A168	$3 multicolored	3.50	3.50
		Nos. 1156-1159 (4)	5.50	5.50

Souvenir Sheet

1160	A168	$6 multicolored	5.50	5.50

Discovery of America 500th anniv. (in 1992).

Paintings by Yokoyama Taikan (1868-1958) A169

Designs: 10c, Lao-tzu. 20c, Red Maple Leaves (panels 1-2). 45c, King Wen Learns a Lesson from His Cook. 60c, Red Maple Leaves (panels 3-4). $1, Wild Flowers. $2, Red Maple Leaves (panels 5-6). $3, Red Maple Leaves (panels 7-8). $4, The Indian Ceremony of Floating Lamps on the River. No. 1169, Innocence. No. 1170, Red Maple Leaves (4 panels).

1989, Aug. 8   Litho.   Perf. 13½x14

1161	A169	10c multicolored	.20	.20
1162	A169	20c multicolored	.20	.20
1163	A169	45c multicolored	.40	.40
1164	A169	60c multicolored	.55	.55
1165	A169	$1 multicolored	.90	.90
1166	A169	$2 multicolored	1.60	1.60
1167	A169	$3 multicolored	2.40	2.40
1168	A169	$4 multicolored	3.25	3.25
		Nos. 1161-1168 (8)	9.50	9.50

Souvenir Sheets

1169	A169	$5 multicolored	4.25	4.25
1170	A169	$5 multicolored	4.25	4.25

Hirohito (1901-89) and enthronement of Akihito as emperor of Japan.

PHILEXFRANCE '89, July 7-17, Paris — A170

Designs: 10c, Map of Dominica with French place names, 1766. 35c, French coin, 1688. $1, French ship, 1720. $4, Introduction of coffee to Dominica by the French, 1772. $5, Text.

1989, July 17   Litho.   Perf. 14

1171	A170	10c multi, vert.	.20	.20
1172	A170	35c shown	.55	.55
1173	A170	$1 multicolored	1.25	1.25
1174	A170	$4 multicolored	4.50	4.50
		Nos. 1171-1174 (4)	6.50	6.50

Souvenir Sheet

1175	A170	$5 multicolored	6.25	6.25

Butterflies A171

Designs: 10c, Homerus swallowtail. 15c, Morpho peleides. 25c, Julia. 35c, Gundlach's swallowtail. 60c, Monarch. $1, Gulf fritillary. $3, Red-splashed sulphur. $5, Papilio andraemon. No. 1184, Heliconius doris, Adelpha cytherea, Calliona argenissa, Eurema proterpia. No. 1185, Adelpha iphicla, Dismorphia spio, Lucinia sida.

1989, Sept. 11   Litho.   Perf. 14

1176	A171	10c multicolored	.20	.20
1177	A171	15c multicolored	.20	.20
1178	A171	25c multicolored	.45	.45
1179	A171	35c multicolored	.65	.65
1180	A171	60c multicolored	1.10	1.10
1181	A171	$1 multicolored	1.75	1.75
1182	A171	$3 multicolored	4.50	4.50
1183	A171	$5 multicolored	8.00	8.00
		Nos. 1176-1183 (8)	16.85	16.85

Souvenir Sheets

1184	A171	$6 multicolored	7.00	7.00
1185	A171	$6 multicolored	7.00	7.00

Misspellings: No. 1181, "Frittillary"; No. 1182, "Sulper."

Orchids — A172

1989, Sept. 28

1186	A172	10c Oncidium pusillum	.20	.20
1187	A172	35c Epidendrum cochleata	.55	.55
1188	A172	45c Epidendrum ciliare	.60	.60
1189	A172	60c Cyrtopodium andersonii	.90	.90
1190	A172	$1 Habenaria pauciflora	1.50	1.50
1191	A172	$2 Maxillaria alba	3.00	3.00
1192	A172	$3 Selenipedium palmifolium	4.50	4.50
1193	A172	$4 Brassavola cucullata	6.00	6.00
		Nos. 1186-1193 (8)	17.25	17.25

Souvenir Sheets

1194	A172	$5 Oncidium lanceanum	7.00	7.00
1195	A172	$5 Comparettia falcata	7.00	7.00

1st Moon Landing, 20th Anniv. A173

1989, Oct. 31   Litho.   Perf. 14

1196	A173	10c Columbia in lunar orbit	.20	.20
1197	A173	60c Aldrin descending ladder	.85	.85
1198	A173	$2 Aldrin, Sea of Tranquillity	2.75	2.75
1199	A173	$3 Flag raising	4.00	4.00
		Nos. 1196-1199 (4)	7.80	7.80

Souvenir Sheet

1200	A173	$6 Liftoff	8.00	8.00

Souvenir Sheets

A174

1990 World Cup Soccer Championships, Italy — A175

Past championship match scenes, flags and soccer ball: a, Brazil vs. Italy, Mexico, 1970. b, England vs. West Germany, England, 1966. c, West Germany vs. Netherlands, West Germany, 1974. d, Italy vs. West Germany, Spain, 1982.

1989, Nov. 7   Perf. 14

1201	A174	Sheet of 4	9.50	9.50
a.-d.		$1 any single	2.25	2.25

Perf. 14

1202	A175	$6 shown	7.00	7.00

Souvenir Sheet

The Capitol, Washington, DC — A176

1989, Nov. 17   Litho.   Perf. 14
1203 A176 $4 multicolored   4.50 4.50
World Stamp Expo '89.

Miniature Sheets

American Presidency, 200th
Anniv. — A177

US presidents, historic events and monuments.

No. 1204: a, Washington, 1st inauguration. b, John Adams, presidential mansion, 1800. c, Jefferson, Graff House in Philadelphia, excerpt from the 1st draft of the Declaration of Independence. d, Madison, USS *Constitution* at the defeat of HMS *Guerriere*, 1812. e, Monroe, freed slaves settle Liberia, 1822. f, John Quincy Adams, opening of the Erie Canal, 1825.

No. 1205: a, Fillmore, Commodore Perry laying groundwork for US trade agreement with Japan. b, Pierce, Jefferson Davis and San Xavier del Bac mission, Tucson, AZ, Gadsden Purchase, 1853. c, Buchanan, Pony Express stamp, Buffalo Bill Cody as express rider. d, Lincoln, UPU emblem, Intl. Postal Congress, Paris, 1863. e, Andrew Johnson, polar bear, purchase of Alaska from Russia, 1867. f, Grant, 1st transcontinental railway link, Promontory Point, Utah, 1869.

No. 1206: a, Theodore Roosevelt, construction of the Panama Canal, 1904. b, Taft, Adm. Peary becomes 1st man to reach the North Pole, 1909. c, Wilson, US #C3, cancel commemorating 1st scheduled airmail service, 1918. d, Harding, airship USS *Shenandoah* at Lakehurst, NJ. e, Coolidge, Lindbergh's solo transatlantic flight, 1927. f, Mt. Rushmore, by Gutzon Borglum, 1927.

No. 1207: a, Lyndon B. Johnson, space exploration. b, Nixon visiting PRChina, 1971. c, Ford, tall ship in NY Harbor for Operation Sail, 1976, US bicentennial celebrations. d, Carter, Sadat of Egypt and Begin of Israel during the Camp David Accords, 1979. e, Reagan, European Space Agency emblem, flags and *Columbia* space shuttle. f, Bush, Grumman Avenger bomber he piloted during WWII.

1989, Nov. 17   Perf. 14
1204   Sheet of 6   6.00 6.00
 a.-f. A177 60c any single   .95   .95
1205   Sheet of 6   6.00 6.00
 a.-f. A177 60c any single   .95   .95
1206   Sheet of 6   6.00 6.00
 a.-f. A177 60c any single   .95   .95
1207   Sheet of 6   6.00 6.00
 a.-f. A177 60c any single   .95   .95

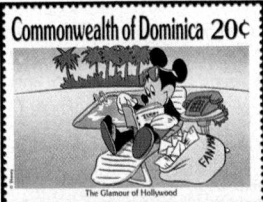

Mickey Mouse as a Hollywood
Star — A178

Walt Disney characters: 20c, Reading script. 35c, Television interview. 45c, Named a star in tabloid headline. 60c, Signing autographs. $1, In dressing room, holding fans at bay. $2, Riding in limousine. $3, With Minnie in the limelight. $4, Accepting award. No. 1216, Giving interview during celebrity tennis tournament. No. 1217, Footprint impression in cement outside theater.

1989, Nov. 30   Litho.   Perf. 14x13½
1208 A178 20c multicolored   .35   .35
1209 A178 35c multicolored   .50   .50
1210 A178 45c multicolored   .60   .60
1211 A178 60c multicolored   .80   .80
1212 A178 $1 multicolored   1.40 1.40
1213 A178 $2 multicolored   2.75 2.75
1214 A178 $3 multicolored   4.00 4.00
1215 A178 $4 multicolored   5.25 5.25
     Nos. 1208-1215 (8)   15.65 15.65

Souvenir Sheets
1216 A178 $5 multicolored   6.75 6.75
1217 A178 $5 multicolored   6.75 6.75

Christmas — A179

Religious paintings by Botticelli: 20c, *Madonna in Glory with Seraphim.* 25c, *The Annunciation.* 35c, *Madonna of the Pomegranate.* 45c, *Madonna of the Rose Garden.* 60c, *Madonna of the Book.* $1, *Madonna and Child Under a Baldachin with Three Angels.* $4, *Madonna and Child with Angels.* No. 1225, *Bardi Madonna.* No. 1226, *The Mystic Nativity.* No. 1227, *The Adoration of the Magi.*

1989, Dec. 4   Perf. 14
1218 A179 20c multicolored   .35   .35
1219 A179 25c multicolored   .35   .35
1220 A179 35c multicolored   .55   .55
1221 A179 45c multicolored   .65   .65
1222 A179 60c multicolored   .85   .85
1223 A179 $1 multicolored   1.25 1.25
1224 A179 $4 multicolored   5.00 5.00
1225 A179 $5 multicolored   6.00 6.00
     Nos. 1218-1225 (8)   15.00 15.00

Souvenir Sheets
1226 A179 $5 multicolored   6.00 6.00
1227 A179 $5 multicolored   6.00 6.00

Nehru — A180   Girl Guides — A181

1989, Dec. 27   Litho.   Perf. 14
1228 A180 60c shown   2.40 2.40

Souvenir Sheet
1229 A180 $5 Parliament
            House, New
            Delhi, horiz.   7.50 7.50

Jawaharlal Nehru (1889-1964), 1st prime minister of independent India.

1989, Dec. 29

Guide movement in Dominica, 60th anniv.: 60c, Lady Baden-Powell and Agatha Robinson, former Guide leader on Dominica. $5, Dorris Stockmann, chairman of the world committee of the World Assoc. of Girl Guides and Girl Scouts, and Judith Pestaina, chief commissioner of the Dominica Girl Guides Assoc., horiz.

1230 A181 60c multicolored   1.50 1.50

Souvenir Sheet
1231 A181 $5 multi, horiz.   6.50 6.50

Miniature Sheet

Marine Life A182

Designs: a, Cocoa damselfish. b, Stinging jellyfish. c, Dolphin. d, Queen angelfish. e, French angelfish. f, Blue striped grunt. g, Pork fish. h, Hammerhead shark. i, Spadefish. j, Great barracuda. k, Stingray. l, Black grunt. m, Two-spotted butterflyfish. n, Dog snapper. o, Southern puffer. p, Four-eyed butterflyfish. q, Lane snapper. r, Green moray.

1990   Litho.   Perf. 14
1232   Sheet of 18   11.00 11.00
 a.-r. A182 45c any single   .55   .55

Penny Black,
150th Anniv.
A183

Stamp World London '90: 50c, Post Office accelerator, 1830. 60c, $4, No. 1239, London skyline, St. Paul's Cathedral. 90c, Railway post car, 1838. $3, Center cycle, 1883. No. 1240, Mail truck, 1899.

1990, May 3   Litho.   Perf. 13½
1233 A183 45c green & black   .45   .45
1234 A183 50c blk & slate blue   .55   .55
1235 A183 60c dk blue & blk   .60   .60
1236 A183 90c black & green   .90   .90
1237 A183 $3 blk & dk bl vio   3.50 3.50
1238 A183 $4 dk bl vio & blk   4.50 4.50
     Nos. 1233-1238 (6)   10.50 10.50

Souvenir Sheet
1239 A183 $5 beige & black   5.00 5.00
1240 A183 $5 gray & red brn   5.00 5.00

A184   A185

Birds: 10c, Blue-headed hummingbird. 20c, Black-capped petrel. 45c, Red-necked parrot. 60c, Black swift. $1, Troupial. $2, Brown noddy. $4, Lesser Antillean pewee. $5. Little blue heron. No. 1249, House wren. No. 1250, Imperial parrot.

1990, July 16   Litho.   Perf. 14
1241 A184 10c multicolored   .45   .45
1242 A184 20c multicolored   .60   .60
1243 A184 45c multicolored   .90   .90
1244 A184 60c multicolored   1.10 1.10
1245 A184 $1 multicolored   2.00 2.00
1246 A184 $2 multicolored   3.00 3.00
1247 A184 $4 multicolored   4.75 4.75
1248 A184 $5 multicolored   5.25 5.25
     Nos. 1241-1248 (8)   18.05 18.05

Souvenir Sheets
1249 A184 $6 multicolored   7.75 7.75
1250 A184 $6 multicolored   7.75 7.75

1990, July 19

Shells: 10c, Reticulated cowrie-helmet. 20c, West Indian chank. 35c, West Indian fighting conch. 60c, True tulip. $1, Sunrise tellin. $2, Crown cone. $3, Common dove shell. $4, Atlantic fig shell. No. 1259, Giant tun. No. 1260, King helmet.

1251 A185 10c multicolored   .45   .45
1252 A185 20c multicolored   .60   .60
1253 A185 35c multicolored   .75   .75
1254 A185 60c multicolored   1.10 1.10
1255 A185 $1 multicolored   1.50 1.50
1256 A185 $2 multicolored   2.75 2.75
1257 A185 $3 multicolored   3.50 3.50
1258 A185 $4 multicolored   4.00 4.00
     Nos. 1251-1258 (8)   14.65 14.65

Souvenir Sheets
1259 A185 $5 multicolored   5.00 5.00
1260 A185 $5 multicolored   5.00 5.00

A186   A187

Queen Mother, 90th Birthday: various photos.

1990, Sept. 10
1261 A186 20c multicolored   .30   .30
1262 A186 45c multicolored   .50   .50
1263 A186 60c multicolored   .70   .70
1264 A186 $3 multicolored   3.00 3.00
     Nos. 1261-1264 (4)   4.50 4.50

Souvenir Sheet
1265 A186 $5 multicolored   4.00 4.00

1990, Nov. 5   Litho.   Perf. 14
1266 A187 45c Men's singles,
            tennis   .95   .95
1267 A187 60c Men's foil fenc-
            ing   1.40 1.40
1268 A187 $2 100m freestyle
            swimming   2.75 2.75
1269 A187 $3 Star class
            yachting   4.25 4.25
     Nos. 1266-1269 (4)   9.35 9.35

Souvenir Sheet
1270 A187 $5 Coxless pairs,
            rowing   8.00 8.00

1992 Summer Olympics, Barcelona.

Christmas A188

Walt Disney characters on carousel animals: 10c, Mickey, frog. 15c, Huey, Dewey & Louie, white elephant. 25c, Donald, polar bear. 45c, Goofy, goat. $1, Donald, giraffe. $2, Daisy, stork. $4, Goofy, lion. $5, Daisy, horse. No. 1279, Mickey, swan chariot, horiz. No. 1280, Mickey, Minnie & Goofy, griffin chariot.

1990, Dec. 13   Perf. 13½x14
1271 A188 10c multicolored   .20   .20
1272 A188 15c multicolored   .20   .20
1273 A188 25c multicolored   .35   .35
1274 A188 45c multicolored   .65   .65
1275 A188 $1 multicolored   1.25 1.25
1276 A188 $2 multicolored   2.40 2.40
1277 A188 $4 multicolored   4.75 4.75
1278 A188 $5 multicolored   6.00 6.00
     Nos. 1271-1278 (8)   15.80 15.80

Souvenir Sheets
Perf. 14x13½
1279 A188 $6 multicolored   8.00 8.00
1280 A188 $6 multicolored   8.00 8.00

World Cup Soccer Championships,
Italy — A189

Players and coaches from participating countries.

1990, Dec. 28   Litho.   Perf. 14
1281 A189 15c England   .40   .40
1282 A189 45c Brazil   .60   .60
1283 A189 60c West Germany   1.00 1.00
1284 A189 $4 Austria   5.75 5.75
     Nos. 1281-1284 (4)   7.75 7.75

Souvenir Sheets
1285 A189 $6 Ireland, vert.   5.75 5.75
1286 A189 $6 USSR, vert.   5.75 5.75

Cog Trains of Switzerland — A190

Designs: 10c, Glion-Roches de Naye, 1890. 35c, Electric cog rail car ascending Mt. Pilatus. 45c, Cog railway to Schynige Platte, view of Eiger, Monch and Jungfrau Mountains. 60c, Furka-Oberalp train on Bugnli Viaduct, vert. $1, 1910 Jungfraubahn Cog Railway, Jungfrau Mountain, 1910. $2, Testing Swiss rail cars built for Pike's Peak on Arth-Rigibahn, 1963. $4, Brienz-Rothorn Bahn, 1991. $5, Private 1870 Rigi-Scheideck Hotel post stamp, 1890 Arth-Rigi Railway Engine. No. 1295, Sherlock Holmes watching Bruniline train descending from Brunig Pass. No. 1296, Switzerland #738 and first passenger train to ascend Mt. Rigi, 1871.

				1991, Mar. 26	Litho.	Perf. 14
1287	A190	10c multicolored			.30	.30
1288	A190	35c multicolored			.40	.40
1289	A190	45c multicolored			.45	.45
1290	A190	60c multicolored			.60	.60
1291	A190	$1 multicolored			1.00	1.00
1292	A190	$2 multicolored			2.00	2.00
1293	A190	$4 multicolored			4.00	4.00
1294	A190	$5 multicolored			5.00	5.00
		Nos. 1287-1294 (8)			13.75	13.75

Souvenir Sheets
Perf. 13½

1295	A190	$6 multicolored	6.25	6.25
1296	A190	$6 multicolored	6.25	6.25

Nos. 1295-1296 each contain one 50x37mm stamp.

Voyages of Discovery A191

Explorer's ships: 10c, Gil Eannes, 1433-1434. 25c, Alfonso Gonclaves Baldaya, 1436. 45c, Bartolomeu Dias, 1487. 60c, Vasco da Gama, 1497-1499. $1, Vallarte the Dane. $2, Aloisio Cadamosto, 1456-1458. $4, Diogo Gomes, 1457. $5, Diogo Cao, 1482-1485.

			1991, Apr. 8	Litho.	Perf. 14
1297	A191	10c multicolored		.30	.30
1298	A191	25c multicolored		.45	.45
1299	A191	45c multicolored		.60	.60
1300	A191	60c multicolored		.75	.75
1301	A191	$1 multicolored		1.10	1.10
1302	A191	$2 multicolored		1.90	1.90
1303	A191	$4 multicolored		3.75	3.75
1304	A191	$5 multicolored		4.50	4.50
		Nos. 1297-1304 (8)		13.35	13.35

Souvenir Sheets

1305	A191	$6 Blue and yellow macaw	6.00	6.00
1306	A191	$6 Red and yellow macaw	6.00	6.00

Discovery of America, 500th anniv. (in 1992).

Japanese Costumes — A192

Walt Disney characters wearing Japanese costumes: 10c, Donald as soldier. 15c, Mickey as Kabuki actor. 25c, Mickey, Minnie in traditional wedding clothes. 45c, Daisy as Geisha girl, vert. $1, Mickey in sokutai dress of high government official, vert. $2, Goofy as mino farmer, vert. $4, Pete as shogun, vert. $5, Donald as warlord. No. 1315, Mickey, as Noh player, vert. No. 1316, Goofy as Kabubei-Jishi street performer, vert.

			1991, May 22	Litho.	Perf. 14
1307	A192	10c multicolored		.20	.20
1308	A192	15c multicolored		.20	.20
1309	A192	25c multicolored		.35	.35
1310	A192	45c multicolored		.65	.65
1311	A192	$1 multicolored		1.25	1.25
1312	A192	$2 multicolored		2.50	2.50
1313	A192	$4 multicolored		4.75	4.75
1314	A192	$5 multicolored		6.00	6.00
		Nos. 1307-1314 (8)		15.90	15.90

Souvenir Sheets

1315	A192	$6 multicolored	8.50	8.50
1316	A192	$6 multicolored	8.50	8.50

Phila Nippon '91.

Mushrooms A193

			1991, June 3	Litho.	Perf. 14
1318	A193	10c Horn of plenty		.20	.20
1319	A193	15c Shaggy mane		.30	.30
1320	A193	45c Yellow morel		.40	.40
1321	A193	60c Chanterelle		.60	.60
1322	A193	$1 Blewit		1.00	1.00
1323	A193	$2 Slippery jack		2.10	2.10
1324	A193	$4 Emetic russula		4.25	4.25
1325	A193	$5 Honey mushroom		5.00	5.00
		Nos. 1318-1325 (8)		13.85	13.85

Souvenir Sheets

1326	A193	$6 Beefsteak polypore	6.00	6.00
1327	A193	$6 Voluminous-latex milky	6.00	6.00

Royal Family Birthday, Anniversary
Common Design Type

			1991, June 17	Litho.	Perf. 14
1328	CD347	10c multicolored		.50	.50
1329	CD347	15c multicolored		.40	.40
1330	CD347	40c multicolored		.55	.55
1331	CD347	60c multicolored		1.10	1.10
1332	CD347	$1 multicolored		1.40	1.40
1333	CD347	$2 multicolored		3.75	3.75
1334	CD347	$4 multicolored		5.75	5.75
1335	CD347	$5 multicolored		9.75	9.75
		Nos. 1328-1335 (8)		23.20	23.20

Souvenir Sheets

1336	CD347	$5 Elizabeth, Philip	5.00	5.00
1337	CD347	$5 Charles, Diana, sons	6.50	6.50

10c, 60c, $2, $4, No. 1336, Queen Elizabeth II, 65th birthday. Others, Charles and Diana, 10th wedding anniversary.

Vincent Van Gogh (1853-1890), Painter — A194

Paintings: 10c, Thatched Cottages. 25c, The House of Pere Eloi. 45c, The Midday Siesta. 60c, Portrait of a Young Peasant, vert. $1, Still Life: Vase with Irises Against a Yellow Background, vert. $2, Still Life Vase with Irises. $4, Blossoming Almond Tree. $5, Irises. No. 1346, A Meadow in the Mountains: Le Mas De Saint-Paul. No. 1347, Doctor Gachet's Garden in Auvers, vert.

			1991, July 8	Litho.	Perf. 13½
1338	A194	10c multicolored		.30	.30
1339	A194	25c multicolored		.30	.30
1340	A194	45c multicolored		.55	.55
1341	A194	60c multicolored		.85	.85
1342	A194	$1 multicolored		1.25	1.25
1343	A194	$2 multicolored		2.75	2.75
1344	A194	$4 multicolored		5.00	5.00
1345	A194	$5 multicolored		6.00	6.00
		Nos. 1338-1345 (8)		17.00	17.00

Size: 101x75mm
Imperf

1346	A194	$6 multicolored	6.50	6.50
1347	A194	$6 multicolored	6.50	6.50

Intl. Literacy Year — A195

Scenes from Walt Disney's "The Little Mermaid": 10c, Ariel with Flounder and Sebastian. 25c, King Triton. 45c, Sebastian drums in "Kiss De Girl" concert. 60c, Flotsam and Jetsam taunt Ariel. $1, Scuttle, Flounder and Ariel. $2, Ariel and Flounder discover a book. $4, Prince Eric, dog Max, manservant Grimsby, and crew. $5, Ursula the sea witch. No. 1356, Ariel transformed into human being. No. 1357, Ariel and Prince Eric dancing in town, vert.

			1991, Aug. 6		Perf. 14
1348	A195	10c multicolored		.20	.20
1349	A195	25c multicolored		.35	.35
1350	A195	45c multicolored		.55	.55
1351	A195	60c multicolored		.80	.80
1352	A195	$1 multicolored		1.40	1.40
1353	A195	$2 multicolored		2.75	2.75
1354	A195	$4 multicolored		5.25	5.25
1355	A195	$5 multicolored		6.75	6.75
		Nos. 1348-1355 (8)		18.05	18.05

Souvenir Sheets

1356	A195	$6 multicolored	6.75	6.75
1357	A195	$6 multicolored	6.75	6.75

World Landmarks — A196

Designs: 10c, Empire State Building, US, vert. 25c, Kremlin, USSR. 45c, Buckingham Palace, United Kingdom. 60c, Eiffel Tower, France, vert. $1, Taj Mahal, India. $2, Sydney Opera House, Australia. $4, Colosseum, Italy. $5, Pyramids, Egypt. No. 1366, Galileo demonstrating laws of physics from Tower of Pisa, Italy. No. 1367, Great Wall of China and Emperor Shi Huang Ti.

			1991, Aug. 12	Litho.	Perf. 14
1358	A196	10c multicolored		.20	.20
1359	A196	25c multicolored		.35	.35
1360	A196	45c multicolored		.55	.55
1361	A196	60c multicolored		.80	.80
1362	A196	$1 multicolored		1.40	1.40
1363	A196	$2 multicolored		2.75	2.75
1364	A196	$4 multicolored		5.25	5.25
1365	A196	$5 multicolored		6.75	6.75
		Nos. 1358-1365 (8)		18.05	18.05

Souvenir Sheets

1366	A196	$6 multicolored	8.50	8.50
1367	A196	$6 multicolored	8.50	8.50

Japanese Attack on Pearl Harbor, 50th Anniv. A197

Designs: 10c, 6:00am, First wave of Japanese planes leave carrier Akagi. 15c, 6:40am, Destroyer Ward and PBY attack midget submarine. 45c, 7:00am, Second wave of Japanese planes leave carriers. 60c, 7:48am, Japanese Zeros attack on Kaneohe Air Station. $1, 8:30am, Destroyers Breeze, Medusa and Curtiss sink midget submarine. $2, 8:45am, Damaged battleship Nevada sorties. $4, 8:10am, Battleship Arizona explodes, killing 1,177 men. $5, 9:45am, Japanese attack ends. No. 1376, 8:00am, Japanese fighters and bombers attack Hickam Air Base. No. 1377, 7:55am, Pearl Harbor attack begins.

			1991, Sept. 2		
1368	A197	10c multicolored		.20	.20
1369	A197	15c multicolored		.30	.30
1370	A197	45c multicolored		.40	.40
1371	A197	60c multicolored		.60	.60
1372	A197	$1 multicolored		1.00	1.00
1373	A197	$2 multicolored		2.10	2.10
1374	A197	$4 multicolored		4.00	4.00
1375	A197	$5 multicolored		5.00	5.00
		Nos. 1368-1375 (8)		13.60	13.60

Souvenir Sheets

1376	A197	$6 multicolored	5.75	5.75
1377	A197	$6 multicolored	5.75	5.75

Butterflies — A198   A199

Perf. 13½x13, 13½x14 (2c, 10c, 15c, 25c, 45c, 90c, $1, $20)
1991-93

1378	A198	1c Little yellow	.25	.25
1379	A198	2c Gulf fritillary	.25	.25
1380	A198	5c Monarch	.25	.25
1381	A198	10c Red rim	.25	.25
1382	A198	15c Flambeau	.25	.25
1383	A198	20c Large orange sulphur	.25	.25
1384	A198	25c Caribbean buckeye	.25	.25
1385	A198	35c Polydamas swallowtail	.30	.30
1386	A198	45c Cassius blue	.40	.40
1386A	A198	55c Great southern white	.50	.50
1387	A198	60c Godman's leaf	.55	.55
1387A	A198	65c Hanno blue	.65	.65
1388	A198	90c Mimic	.90	.90
1389	A198	$1 Long-tailed skipper	1.00	1.00
1389A	A198	$1.20 Orion	1.25	1.25
1390	A198	$2 Cloudless sulphur	2.10	2.10
1391	A198	$5 Painted lady	5.00	5.00
1391A	A198	$10 Southern daggertail	11.50	11.50
1391B	A198	$20 White peacock	21.00	21.00
		Nos. 1379-1391B (18)	46.65	46.65

Issued: 55c, 65c, $1.20, 1/11/93; others, 10/14/91.

1991, Nov. 1

1392	A199	45c shown	2.00	2.00

Souvenir Sheet

1393	A199	$5 blk & bl, horiz.	6.25	6.25

Charles de Gaulle, birth cent.

Creole Week — A200   Credit Union, 40th Anniv. — A201

45c, Man in 18th cent. costume. 60c, Accordion player. $1, Dancers. $5, Stick fight c. 1785.

			1991, Nov. 1		Perf. 14
1394	A200	45c multicolored		.70	.70
1395	A200	60c multicolored		1.00	1.00
1396	A200	$1 multicolored		1.75	1.75
		Nos. 1394-1396 (3)		3.45	3.45

Souvenir Sheet

1397	A200	$5 multicolored	7.75	7.75

1991, Nov. 1

1398	A201	10c black	.65	.65
1399	A201	60c Emblem, founder, horiz.	1.60	1.60

Year of the Environment and
Shelter — A202

15c, Keep the beaches clean. 60c, No. 1402, Amazona imperalis. No. 1403, Lagoon outlet.

1991, Nov. 18
1400	A202	15c multicolored	1.10	1.10
1401	A202	60c multicolored	2.40	2.40

Souvenir Sheets
1402	A202	$5 multicolored	7.50	7.50
1403	A202	$5 multicolored	7.50	7.50

Christmas
A203

Paintings by Jan van Eyck: 10c, The Virgin Enthroned with Child (detail). 20c, The Madonna at the Fountain. 35c, The Virgin in a Church. 45c, The Madonna with Canon van der Paele. 60c, The Madonna with Canon van der Paele (detail). $1, The Madonna in an Interior. $3, The Annunciation. $5, The Annunciation, diff. No. 1412, The Madonna with Chancellor Rolin. No. 1413, Virgin and Child with Saints and Donor.

1991, Dec. 2   *Perf. 12*
1404	A203	10c multicolored	.20	.20
1405	A203	20c multicolored	.35	.35
1406	A203	35c multicolored	.45	.45
1407	A203	45c multicolored	.55	.55
1408	A203	60c multicolored	.80	.80
1409	A203	$1 multicolored	1.40	1.40
1410	A203	$3 multicolored	4.00	4.00
1411	A203	$5 multicolored	6.75	6.75
		Nos. 1404-1411 (8)	14.50	14.50

Souvenir Sheets
Perf. 14x14½
1412	A203	$6 multicolored	6.75	6.75
1413	A203	$6 multicolored	6.75	6.75

Queen Elizabeth II's Accession to the Throne, 40th Anniv.
Common Design Type

1992, Feb. 6   Litho.   *Perf. 14*
1414	CD348	10c multicolored	.20	.20
1415	CD348	15c multicolored	.20	.20
1416	CD348	$1 multicolored	.85	.85
1417	CD348	$5 multicolored	4.00	4.00
		Nos. 1414-1417 (4)	5.25	5.25

Souvenir Sheets
1418	CD348	$6 River scene	4.00	4.00
1419	CD348	$6 Seaside village	4.00	4.00

Botanical Gardens,
Cent. — A204

Designs: 10c, Cricket match. 15c, Scenic entrance. 45c, Traveller's tree. 60c, Bamboo house. $1, Old pavilion. $2, Ficus benjamina. $4, Cricket ground. $5, Thirty-five steps. No. 1428, Fountain. No. 1429, Cricket masters.

1992, Mar. 30   Litho.   *Perf. 14*
1420	A204	10c multicolored	.20	.20
1421	A204	15c multicolored	.20	.20
1422	A204	45c multicolored	.35	.35
1423	A204	60c multicolored	.55	.55
1424	A204	$1 multicolored	.95	.95
1425	A204	$2 multicolored	2.00	2.00
1426	A204	$4 multicolored	4.00	4.00
1427	A204	$5 multicolored	4.75	4.75
		Nos. 1420-1427 (8)	13.00	13.00

Souvenir Sheets
1428	A204	$6 multicolored	5.00	5.00
1429	A204	$6 multicolored	5.00	5.00

Spanish
Art — A205

Paintings or details from paintings by Velazquez: 10c, Pope Innocent X. 15c, 45c The Forge of Vulcan (different details). 60c, Queen Mariana of Austria. $1, Pablo de Valladolid. $2, Sebastian de Morra. $3, Felipe IV (detail). $4, Felipe IV. No. 1438, Surrender of Breda. No. 1439, The Drunkards.

1992, May 4   *Perf. 13*
1430	A205	10c multicolored	.20	.20
1431	A205	15c multicolored	.20	.20
1432	A205	45c multicolored	.45	.45
1433	A205	60c multicolored	.55	.55
1434	A205	$1 multicolored	.85	.85
1435	A205	$2 multicolored	1.75	1.75
1436	A205	$3 multicolored	2.75	2.75
1437	A205	$4 multicolored	3.75	3.75

Size: 120x95mm
Imperf
1438	A205	$6 multicolored	6.00	6.00
1439	A205	$6 multicolored	6.00	6.00
		Nos. 1430-1439 (10)	22.50	22.50

Granada '92.

Easter — A206

Paintings: 10c, The Supper at Emmaus, studio of Gerrit Van Honthorst. 15c, Christ before Caiaphas, by Van Honthorst, vert. 45c, The Taking of Christ, by Valentin de Boulogne. 60c, Pilate Washing his Hands, by Mattia Preti, vert. $1, The Last Supper (detail), by Master of the Reredos of The Chapel of the Church of S. Francisco D'Evora. $2, The Three Marys at the Tomb (detail), by Adolphe William Bouguereau, vert. $3, Denial of St. Peter, by Hendrik Terbrugghen, vert. $5, Doubting Thomas, by Bernardo Strozzi, vert. No. 1448, The Crucifixion (detail), by Mathias Grunewald, vert. No. 1449, The Resurrection (detail), by Caravaggio, vert.

1992   *Perf. 14*
1440	A206	10c multicolored	.20	.20
1441	A206	15c multicolored	.20	.20
1442	A206	45c multicolored	.35	.35
1443	A206	60c multicolored	.55	.55
1444	A206	$1 multicolored	.95	.95
1445	A206	$2 multicolored	2.00	2.00
1446	A206	$3 multicolored	2.75	2.75
1447	A206	$5 multicolored	4.75	4.75
		Nos. 1440-1447 (8)	11.75	11.75

Souvenir Sheets
1448	A206	$6 multicolored	5.75	5.75
1449	A206	$6 multicolored	5.75	5.75

Columbus and
New World Flora
and Fauna — A207

1992, May 18
1450	A207	10c Hercules beetle	.20	.20
1451	A207	25c Crapaud frog	.25	.25
1452	A207	75c Parrot	.70	.70
1453	A207	$2 Anole	2.10	2.10
1454	A207	$4 Royal gramma	4.25	4.25
1455	A207	$5 Hibiscus	5.25	5.25
		Nos. 1450-1455 (6)	12.75	12.75

Souvenir Sheets
1456	A207	$6 Giant katydid	6.00	6.00
1457	A207	$6 Columbus' fleet	6.00	6.00

Nos. 1456-1457 are horiz.

Hummingbirds — A208

10c, Purple throated carib. 15c, Rufous breasted hermit. 45c, Puerto Rican emerald. 60c, Antillean mango. $1, Green throated carib. $2, Blue headed. $4, Eastern streamertail. $5, Antillean crested. #1466, Green mango. #1467, Vervain hummingbird.

1992, May 28
1458	A208	10c multicolored	.20	.20
1459	A208	15c multicolored	.20	.20
1460	A208	45c multicolored	.40	.40
1461	A208	60c multicolored	.60	.60
1462	A208	$1 multicolored	1.00	1.00
1463	A208	$2 multicolored	2.10	2.10
1464	A208	$4 multicolored	4.25	4.25
1465	A208	$5 multicolored	5.25	5.25
		Nos. 1458-1465 (8)	14.00	14.00

Souvenir Sheets
1466	A208	$6 multicolored	7.75	7.75
1467	A208	$6 multicolored	7.75	7.75

Genoa '92.

Dinosaurs
A209

1992, June 23   Litho.   *Perf. 14*
1468	A209	10c Camptosaurus	.20	.20
1469	A209	15c Edmontosaurus	.20	.20
1470	A209	25c Corythosaurus	.30	.30
1471	A209	60c Stegosaurus	.60	.60
1472	A209	$1 Torosaurus	1.00	1.00
1473	A209	$3 Euoplocephalus	3.25	3.25
1474	A209	$4 Tyrannosaurus	4.00	4.00
1475	A209	$5 Parasaurolophus	5.50	5.50
		Nos. 1468-1475 (8)	15.05	15.05

Souvenir Sheets
1476	A209	$6 like #1472	6.00	6.00
1477	A209	$6 like #1470	6.00	6.00

Marine
Life
A210

No. 1478: a, Copper sweeper (b). b, Sea wasp (c). c, Nassau grouper. d, Glasseye snapper, margate. e, Green moray (f). f, Reef squid. g, Octopus. h, Porkfish (g, i). i, Reef squirrelfish (h). j, Coral crab, flower coral. k, Red coral shrimp, sea star, pillar coral (l, n). l, Cubbyu, brain coral (o). m, Basket starfish, thick finger coral. n, Belted cardinal fish, boulder coral (k, m). o, Fire worm, crenelated fire coral.
No. 1479: a, Trumpetfish, blue chromis. b, Queen triggerfish. c, Hawksbill turtle. d, Sergeant major, rock beauty. e, Sharksucker. f, Lemon shark. g, Spotted trunkfish, bluehead. h, Blue tang, yellowtail damselfish. i, Queen angelfish, banded butterflyfish. j, Spotted seahorse, flower coral. k, Stoplight parrotfish, pillar coral. l, Smallmouth grunt, brain coral. m, Flamingo tongue, thick finger coral. n, Arrow crab, boulder coral. o, Sharknose goby, crenelated fire coral.
No. 1480, Harlequin bass. No. 1481, Flamefish.

1992, July 20   Litho.   *Perf. 14*
1478	A210	65c Sheet of 15, #a.-o.	9.50	9.50
1479	A210	65c Sheet of 15, #a.-o.	9.50	9.50

Souvenir Sheets
1480	A210	$6 multicolored	7.75	7.75
1481	A210	$6 multicolored	7.75	7.75

A211

A212

1992, Aug. 10   Litho.   *Perf. 14*
1482	A211	10c Archery	.20	.20
1483	A211	15c Two-man canoeing	.20	.20
1484	A211	25c 110-meter hurdles	.35	.35
1485	A211	60c Men's high jump	.60	.60
1486	A211	$1 Greco-Roman wrestling	.90	.90
1487	A211	$2 Men's rings	1.75	1.75
1488	A211	$4 Men's parallel bars	3.75	3.75
1489	A211	$5 Equestrian	4.75	4.75
		Nos. 1482-1489 (8)	12.50	12.50

Souvenir Sheets
1490	A211	$6 Field hockey	6.25	6.25
1491	A211	$6 Women's platform diving	6.25	6.25

1992 Summer Olympics, Barcelona.

1992   Litho.   *Perf. 14½*
1492	A212	$1 Coming ashore	1.10	1.10
1493	A212	$2 Natives, ships	2.25	2.25

Discovery of America, 500th anniv. Organization of East Caribbean States.

Walt Disney's Goofy, 60th
Anniv. — A213

Scenes from Disney cartoon films: 10c, Two Weeks Vacation, 1952. 15c, Aquamania, 1961. 25c, Goofy Gymnastics, 1949. 45c, How to Ride a Horse, 1941. $1, Foul Hunting, 1947. $2, For Whom the Bulls Toil, 1953. $4, Tennis Racquet, 1949. $5, Double Dribble, 1946. No. 1502, Aquamania, 1961, vert. No. 1503, The Goofy Sports Story, 1956, vert.

1992, Nov. 11   Litho.   *Perf. 14x13½*
1494	A213	10c multicolored	.20	.20
1495	A213	15c multicolored	.20	.20
1496	A213	25c multicolored	.35	.35
1497	A213	45c multicolored	.65	.65
1498	A213	$1 multicolored	1.40	1.40
1499	A213	$2 multicolored	2.75	2.75
1500	A213	$4 multicolored	5.50	5.50
1501	A213	$5 multicolored	6.50	6.50
		Nos. 1494-1501 (8)	17.55	17.55

Souvenir Sheets
Perf. 13½x14
1502	A213	$6 multicolored	8.75	8.75
1503	A213	$6 multicolored	8.75	8.75

Model Trains
A214

15c, Brass Reno 4-4-0, HO scale, c. 1963. 25c, Union Pacific Golden Classic, G gauge, 1992. 55c, LMS 3rd class brake coach, OO scale, 1970s. 65c, Brass Wabash 2-6-0, HO scale, c. 1958. 75c, Pennsylvania RR T-1 duplex, O gauge, 1991. $1, Streamline engine 2-6-0, O gauge, post World War II. $3, Japanese Natl. Railways class C62, HO scale, c. 1960. $5, Tinplate friction-drive floor trains, 1960s. No. 1512, 1st "toy" train in Japan, 1854. No. 1513, Stephenson's Rocket, 1:26 scale, c. 1972, vert.

1992, Nov. 11   **Perf. 14**
1504 A214 15c multicolored .25 .25
1505 A214 25c multicolored .30 .30
1506 A214 55c multicolored .55 .55
1507 A214 65c multicolored .75 .75
1508 A214 75c multicolored .90 .90
1509 A214 $1 multicolored 1.25 1.25
1510 A214 $3 multicolored 3.50 3.50
1511 A214 $5 multicolored 5.75 5.75
Nos. 1504-1511 (8) 13.25 13.25

Souvenir Sheets
Perf. 13
1512 A214 $6 multicolored 6.00 6.00
1513 A214 $6 multicolored 6.00 6.00

No. 1512 contains one 52x40mm stamp, No. 1513 one 39x51mm stamp.

Hummel Figurines — A215

Angel: 20c, Playing violin. 25c, Playing horn. 55c, Playing mandolin. 65c, Seated, playing trumpet. 90c, On cloud with lantern. $1, Holding candle. $1.20, Flying. $6, On cloud with candle.

1992, Nov. 2   **Perf. 14**
1514 A215 20c multicolored .20 .20
1515 A215 25c multicolored .25 .25
1516 A215 55c multicolored .45 .45
1517 A215 65c multicolored .55 .55
  a. Sheet of 4, #1514-1517 2.25 2.25
1518 A215 90c multicolored .70 .70
1519 A215 $1 multicolored .85 .85
1520 A215 $1.20 multicolored 1.00 1.00
1521 A215 $6 multicolored 5.00 5.00
  a. Sheet of 4, #1518-1521 8.00 8.00
Nos. 1514-1521 (8) 9.00 9.00

Anniversaries and Events
A216   A217

Designs: 25c, Graf Zeppelin, 1929. No. 1523, Elderly man, plant. No. 1524, Elderly man on bicycle. No. 1525, Elderly man helping boy bait hook. No. 1526, Konrad Adenauer. No. 1527, Space shuttle. No. 1528, Wolfgang Amadeus Mozart. No. 1529, Snowy egret. No. 1530, Sir Thomas Lipton, Shamrock V, 1930. $2, Men pulling fishing net toward beach. $4, Helen Keller. No. 1533, Earth Resources Satellite. No. 1534, Map of Germany, 1949. No. 1535, Eland. $5, Count Ferdinand von Zeppelin. No. 1537, Cologne Cathedral, Germany. No. 1538, Scene from the Magic Flute. No. 1539, MIR Space Station. No. 1540, Engine of Graf Zeppelin. No. 1541, Rhinoceros hornbill.

1992   **Litho.**   **Perf. 14**
1522 A216 25c multicolored .25 .25
1523 A216 45c multicolored .35 .35
1524 A216 45c multicolored .35 .35
1525 A216 45c multicolored .35 .35
1526 A216 90c multicolored .95 .95
1527 A216 90c multicolored .65 .65
1528 A217 $1.20 multicolored 2.25 2.25
1529 A216 $1.20 multicolored 1.25 1.25
1530 A216 $1.20 multicolored 1.25 1.25
1531 A216 $2 multicolored 2.00 2.00
1532 A216 $3 multicolored 2.75 2.75
1533 A216 $4 multicolored 3.00 3.00
1534 A216 $4 multicolored 4.50 4.50
1535 A216 $4 multicolored 4.25 4.25
1536 A216 $5 multicolored 5.25 5.25
Nos. 1522-1536 (15) 29.40 29.40

Souvenir Sheets
1537 A216 $6 multicolored 7.00 7.00
1538 A217 $6 multicolored 7.50 7.50
1539 A216 $6 multicolored 7.00 7.00
1540 A216 $6 multicolored 7.00 7.00
1541 A216 $6 multicolored 6.50 6.50

Konrad Adenauer, 25th anniv. of death (#1526, 1534, 1537). Intl. Space Year (#1526, 1533, 1539). Mozart, 200th anniv. of death (in 1991) (#1528, 1538). Count Zeppelin, 75th anniv. of death (#1522, 1536, 1540). Intl. Day of the Elderly (#1523-1525). UN Earth Summit, Rio (#1529, 1535, 1541). America's Cup yacht race (#1530). WHO Intl. Conference on Nutrition, Rome (#1531). Lions Intl., 75th anniv. (#1532).
Issued: (#1528, 1539, Oct.; #1523-1527, 1533-1534, 1537-1538, Nov.; #1522, 1529, 1535-1536, 1540-1541, Dec.

Miniature Sheet

Louvre Museum, Bicent. — A218

Details or entire paintings by Titian: a-b, Madonna and Child with St. Catherine and a Rabbit (diff. details). c, A Woman at Her Toilet. d-e, The Supper at Emmaus (diff. details). f, The Pastoral Concert. g-h, An Allegory, Perhaps of Marriage (diff. details).
Painting by Hieronymus Bosch: $6, The Ship of Fools.

1993, Mar. 24   **Litho.**   **Perf. 12**
1542 A218 $1 Sheet of 8, #a.-
   h. + label 11.00 11.00

Souvenir Sheet
Perf. 14½
1543 A218 $6 multicolored 6.50 6.50

No. 1543 contains one 55x88mm stamp.

Elvis Presley, 15th Anniv. of Death (in 1992)
A219

a, Portrait. b, With guitar. c, Holding microphone.

1993, Feb.   **Perf. 14**
1544 A219 $1 Strip of 3, #a.-c. 3.75 3.75

Miniature Sheet

Birds of Dominica — A220

a, Plumbeous warbler. b, Black swift. c, Blue-hooded euphonia. d, Rufous-throated solitaire. e, Ringed kingfisher. f, Blue-headed hummingbird. g, Bananaquit. h, Trembler. i, Forest thrush. j, Purple-throated carib. k, Ruddy quail dove. l, Least bittern.
No. 1546, Imperial parrot. No. 1547, Red-necked parrot (Amazona arausiaca).

1993, Apr. 30
1545 A220 90c Sheet of 12,
   #a.-l. 18.00 18.00

Souvenir Sheet
1546 A220 $6 multicolored 6.50 6.50
1547 A220 $6 multicolored 6.50 6.50

Turtles
A221

25c, Leatherback laying eggs. 55c, Hawksbill. 65c, Atlantic Ridley. 90c, Green turtle laying eggs. $1, Green turtle at sea. $2, Hawksbill, diff. $4, Loggerhead. $5, Leatherback at sea. #1556, Green turtle hatchling. #1557, Head of hawksbill.

1993, May 26   **Litho.**   **Perf. 14**
1548 A221 25c multicolored .25 .25
1549 A221 55c multicolored .50 .50
1550 A221 65c multicolored .70 .70
1551 A221 90c multicolored .95 .95
1552 A221 $1 multicolored 1.10 1.10
1553 A221 $2 multicolored 2.10 2.10
1554 A221 $4 multicolored 4.00 4.00
1555 A221 $5 multicolored 5.25 5.25
Nos. 1548-1555 (8) 14.85 14.85

Souvenir Sheets
1556 A221 $6 multicolored 6.75 6.75
1557 A221 $6 multicolored 6.75 6.75

For overprints see Nos. 2103-2107.

Automobiles — A222

Designs: 90c, 1928 Model A Ford. $1.20, Mercedes-Benz winning Swiss Grand Prix, 1936. $4, Mercedes-Benz winning German Grand Prix, 1935. $5, 1915 Model T Ford. #1562: a, 1993 Mercedes-Benz coupe/roadster. b, 1893 Benz Viktoria. No. 1563, Ford GT-40.

1993, May   **Litho.**   **Perf. 14**
1558 A222 90c multicolored .80 .80
1559 A222 $1.20 multicolored 1.25 1.25
1560 A222 $4 multicolored 3.75 3.75
1561 A222 $5 multicolored 4.75 4.75
Nos. 1558-1561 (4) 10.55 10.55

Souvenir Sheets
1562 A222 $3 Sheet of 2,
   #a.-b. 5.50 5.50
1563 A222 $6 multicolored 5.50 5.50

No. 1563 contains one 57x42mm stamp. First Ford gasoline engine, cent. (#1558, 1561, 1563). Benz's first four-wheeled vehicle, cent. (#1559-1560, 1562).

Dominica Grammar School, Cent.
A223

Designs: 25c, School crest. 30c, V. A. A. Archer, first West Indian headmaster. 65c, Hubert A. Charles, first Dominican headmaster. 90c, Present school building.

1993, May
1564 A223 25c multicolored .25 .25
1565 A223 30c multicolored .35 .35
1566 A223 65c multicolored .70 .70
1567 A223 90c multicolored .95 .95
Nos. 1564-1567 (4) 2.25 2.25

Aviation Anniversaries — A224

Designs: 25c, New York ticker tape parade, 1928. 55c, BAC Lightning F2. 65c, Graf Zeppelin over Sphinx, pyramids, 1929. $1, Boeing 314 flying boat. $2, Astronaut stepping onto moon. $4, Viktoria Louise over Kiel harbor, 1912. $5, Supermarine Spitfire, vert. No. 1575, Royal Air Force Crest, vert. No. 1576, Hugo Eckener in airship cockpit, vert. No. 1577, Jean-Pierre Blanchard's hot air balloon, 1793, vert.

1993, May 28   **Litho.**   **Perf. 14**
1568 A224 25c multicolored .55 .55
1569 A224 55c multicolored .65 .65
1570 A224 65c multicolored 1.25 1.25
1571 A224 $1 multicolored 1.40 1.40
1572 A224 $2 multicolored 3.25 3.25
1573 A224 $4 multicolored 8.00 8.00
1574 A224 $5 multicolored 6.25 6.25
Nos. 1568-1574 (7) 21.35 21.35

Souvenir Sheets
1575 A224 $6 multicolored 7.00 7.00
1576 A224 $6 multicolored 7.00 7.00
1577 A224 $6 multicolored 6.50 6.50

Zeppelin Capt. Hugo Eckener, 125th anniv. of birth (#1568, 1570, 1573, 1576). Royal Air Force, 75th anniv. (#1569, 1574-1575).
Nos. 1575-1576 each contain one 42x57mm stamp.

Miniature Sheet

Coronation of Queen Elizabeth II, 40th Anniv.
A225

Designs: No. 1578a, 20c, Official coronation photograph. b, 25c, Ceremony. c, 65c, Gold State Coach. d, $5, Queen Elizabeth II, Queen Mother.
$6, Portrait, by Norman Hutchinson, 1969.

1993, June 2   **Litho.**   **Perf. 13½x14**
1578 A225 Sheet, 2 each
   #a.-d. 15.00 15.00

Souvenir Sheet
Perf. 14
1579 A225 $6 multicolored 7.50 7.50

No. 1579 contains one 28x42mm stamp. For overprints see Nos. 1688-1689.

Wedding of Japan's Crown Prince
Naruhito and Masako Owada
A226

Cameo photos of couple and: 90c, Crown
Prince holding flowers. $5, Princess wearing
full-length coat.
$6, Princess riding in limousine.

1993, June 14   Litho.   Perf. 14
1580 A226 90c multicolored   1.00 1.00
1581 A226 $5 multicolored   5.50 5.50
Souvenir Sheet
1582 A226 $6 multicolored   7.00 7.00

Inauguration of Pres. William J.
Clinton — A227

$5, Bill, Hillary Clinton. $6, Bill Clinton, vert.

1993, July 30   Litho.   Perf. 14
1583 A227 $5 multicolored   5.00 5.00
Souvenir Sheet
1584 A227 $6 multicolored   7.00 7.00

Willy Brandt (1913-92), German
Chancellor — A228

Brandt and: 65c, Pres. Eisenhower, 1959.
$5, N.K. Winston, 1964. $6, Portrait.

1993, July 30
1585 A228 65c black & brown   .75 .75
1586 A228 $5 black & brown   5.75 5.75
Souvenir Sheet
1587 A228 $6 black & brown   7.00 7.00

Picasso (1881-   Polska '93
1973)   A230
A229

Paintings: 25c, Bather with Beach Ball,
1929. 90c, Portrait of Leo Stein, 1906. $5, Por-
trait of Wilhelm Unde, 1910. $6, Man with a
Pipe, 1915.

1993, July 30
1588 A229 25c multicolored   .25 .25
1589 A229 90c multicolored   1.00 1.00
1590 A229 $5 multicolored   5.75 5.75
    Nos. 1588-1590 (3)   7.00 7.00
Souvenir Sheet
1591 A229 $6 multicolored   7.00 7.00

1993, July 30
Paintings: 90c, Self-portrait, by Marian
Szczyrbula, 1921. $3, Portrait of Bruno Jasien-
ski, by Tytus Czyzewski, 1921. $6, Miser, by
Tadeusz Makowski, 1973.

1592 A230 90c multicolored   1.25 1.25

1593 A230 $3 multicolored   4.25 4.25
Souvenir Sheet
1594 A230 $6 multicolored   7.00 7.00

A231   A232

90c, Monika Holzner, speedskating, 1984.
$4, US hockey players, Ray Leblanc, Tim
Sweeney, 1992. $6, Men's ski jump.

1993, July 30
1595 A231 90c multicolored   1.25 1.25
1596 A231 $4 multicolored   5.25 5.25
Souvenir Sheet
1597 A231 $6 multicolored   6.50 6.50
1994 Winter Olympics, Lillehammer, Norway.

1993, July 30
Designs: $1.20, Astronomer using quadrant.
$3, Observatory. $5, Copernicus.
1598 A232 $1.20 multicolored   2.00 2.00
1599 A232 $3 multicolored   4.50 4.50
Souvenir Sheet
1600 A232 $5 multicolored   7.00 7.00
    Copernicus (1473-1543).

Opening
of New
General
Post
Office
A233

New General Post Office and: 25c, Prince
Philip. 90c, Queen Elizabeth II.

1993, July 30
1601 A233 25c multicolored   .25 .25
1602 A233 90c multicolored   1.10 1.10

1994 World Cup
Soccer
Championships,
US — A234

1993, Sept. 8   Litho.   Perf. 14
1603 A234 25c Maradona,
            Buchwald   .30 .30
1604 A234 55c Gullit   .55 .55
1605 A234 65c Chavarria,
            Bliss   .70 .70
1606 A234 90c Maradona   1.00 1.00
1607 A234 90c Alvares   1.00 1.00
1608 A234 $1 Altobelli, Yong-
            hwang   1.25 1.25
1609 A234 $2 Referee,
            Stopyra   2.50 2.50
1610 A234 $5 Renquin,
            Yaremtchuk   5.75 5.75
    Nos. 1603-1610 (8)   13.05 13.05
Souvenir Sheets
1611 A234 $6 Brehme   5.75 5.75
1612 A234 $6 Fabbri   5.75 5.75

Taipei
'93 — A235

Chinese kites: No. 1617a, Chang E Rising
up to the Moon. b, Red Phoenix and Rising
Sun. c, Heavenly Judge. d, Monkey King. e,
Goddess of the Luo River. f, Heavenly Maiden
Scatters Flowers.

1993, Oct. 4   Litho.   Perf. 13½x14
1613 A235 25c Tiger Balm
            Gardens   .25 .25
1614 A235 65c Building,
            Kenting
            Park   .65 .65
1615 A235 90c Tzu-en Tower   1.00 1.00
1616 A235 $5 Villa, Lan
            Tao Island   5.00 5.00
    Nos. 1613-1616 (4)   6.90 6.90
Miniature Sheet
1617 A235 $1.65 Sheet of 6,
            #a.-f.   11.50 11.50
Souvenir Sheet
1618 A235 $6 Jade Girl,
            Liao Dynas-
            ty   6.00 6.00

With Bangkok '93 Emblem
Puppets: No. 1623a, Thai, Rama and Sita.
b, Burmese, Tha Khi Lek. c, Burmese, diff. d,
Thai, Demons, Wat Phra Kaew. e, Thai, Hun
Lek performing Khun Chang, Khun Phaen. f,
Thai, Hun Lek performing Ramakien.

1993
1619 A235 25c Tugu Monu-
            ment, Java   .25 .25
1620 A235 55c Candi
            Cangkuang,
            West Java   .65 .65
1621 A235 90c Pura Taman
            Ayun,
            Mengwi   1.00 1.00
1622 A235 $5 Stone mosa-
            ics, Ceto   5.00 5.00
    Nos. 1619-1622 (4)   6.90 6.90
Miniature Sheet
1623 A235 $1.65 Sheet of 6,
            #a.-f.   11.50 11.50
Souvenir Sheet
1624 A235 $6 Stone carv-
            ing, Thai-
            land   6.00 6.00

With Indopex '93 Emblem
Designs: 25c, Ornate Chedi, Wat Phra
Boromathat Chaiya. 55c, Preserved temple
ruins, Sukhothai Historical Park. 90c, Prasat
Hin Phimai, Thailand. $5, Main sanctuary,
Prasat Phanom Rung, Thailand.
Indonesian puppets — #1629: a, Arjuna &
Prabu Gilling Wesi. b, Loro Blonyo. c, Yogy-
anese puppets, Menak cycle. d, Wayang
gedog, Ng Setro. e, Wayang golek, Kencana
Wungu. f, Wayang gedog, Raden Damar
Wulan.
$6, Sculpture of Majapahit noble, Pura
Sada, Kapel.

1993, Oct. 4   Litho.   Perf. 13½x14
1625 A235 25c multicolored   .25 .25
1626 A235 55c multicolored   .65 .65
1627 A235 90c multicolored   1.00 1.00
1628 A235 $5 multicolored   5.00 5.00
    Nos. 1625-1628 (4)   6.90 6.90
Miniature Sheet
1629 A235 $1.65 Sheet of 6,
            #a.-f.   11.50 11.50
Souvenir Sheet
1630 A235 $6 multicolored   6.00 6.00

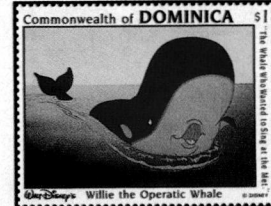

Willie the Operatic Whale — A236

Nos. 1631-1633, Characters and scenes
from Disney's animated film Willie the Operatic
Whale.

1993, Nov. 1   Litho.   Perf. 14x13½
1631 A236 $1 Sheet of 9, #a.-
            i.   14.00 14.00
Souvenir Sheets
1632 A236 $6 multicolored   5.50 5.50
Perf. 13½x14
1633 A236 $6 multi, vert.   5.50 5.50

Christmas
A237

25c, 55c, 65c, 90c (#1637), Details or entire
woodcut, The Adoration of the Magi, by Durer.
90c (#1638), $1, $3, $5, Details or entire
painting, The Foligni Madonna, by Raphael.
Souvenir Sheets: #1642, $6, The Adoration
of the Magi, by Durer. #1643, $6, The Foligni
Madonna, by Raphael.

1993, Nov. 8   Litho.   Perf. 13
1634-1643 A237 Set of 10   24.00 24.00

A238

Hong Kong
'94 — A239

Stamps, scene from Peak Tram: No. 1644,
Hong Kong #527, city buildings, trees. No.
1645, Trees, tram, #1292.
Chinese jade: No. 1646a, Horse. b, Cup
with handle. c, Vase with birthday peaches. d,
Vase. e, Fu dog and puppy. f, Drinking vessel.

1994, Feb. 18   Litho.   Perf. 14
1644 A238 65c multicolored   .60 .60
1645 A238 65c multicolored   .60 .60
    a.   Pair, #1644-1645   1.25 1.25
Miniature Sheet
1646 A239 65c Sheet of 6, #a.-f. 6.00 6.00

Nos. 1644-1645 issued in sheets of 5 pairs.
No. 1645a is a continuous design.
New Year 1994 (Year of the Dog) (#1646e).

Insects, Butterflies, & Birds — A240

Various Hercules beetles: 20c, 25c, 65c, Male. 90c, Female.
$1, Imperial parrot. $2, Southern dagger tail. $3, The mimic. $5, Purple-throated carib.
Each $6: No. 1655, Snout butterfly. No. 1656, Blue-headed hummingbird.

1994, Mar. 15   Litho.   Perf. 14
1647-1654 A240   Set of 8   16.50 16.50
1650a   Min. sheet, 3 each #1647-
1650   10.00 10.00
Souvenir Sheets
1655-1656 A240   Set of 2   15.00 15.00
World Wildlife Fund (#1647-1650).

Mushrooms   Orchids
A241   A242

Designs: 20c, Russula matoubenis. 25c, Leptonia caeruleocapita. 65c, Inocybe littoralis. 90c, Russula hygrophytica. $1, Pyrrhoglossum lilaceipes. $2, Hygrocybe konradii. $3, Inopilus magnificus. $5, Boletellus cubensis.
No. 1665, Gerronema citrinum. No. 1666, Lentinus strigosus.

1994, Apr. 18
1657 A241   20c multicolored   .20 .20
1658 A241   25c multicolored   .20 .20
1659 A241   65c multicolored   .55 .55
1660 A241   90c multicolored   .85 .85
1661 A241 $1 multicolored   .95 .95
1662 A241 $2 multicolored   2.00 2.00
1663 A241 $3 multicolored   2.75 2.75
1664 A241 $5 multicolored   4.50 4.50
    Nos. 1657-1664 (8)   12.00 12.00
Souvenir Sheets
1665 A241 $6 multicolored   6.00 6.00
1666 A241 $6 multicolored   6.00 6.00

1994, May 3
Designs: 20c, Laeliocattleya. 25c, Sophrolaeliocattleya. 65c, Odontocidium. 90c, Laeliocattleya, diff. $1, Cattleya. $2, Odontocidium, diff. $3, Epiphronitis. $4, Oncidium.
Each $6: #1675, Schombocattleya. #1676, Cattleya, diff.
1667-1674 A242   Set of 8   12.00 12.00
Souvenir Sheets
1675-1676 A242   Set of 2   12.50 12.50

New Year 1994
(Year of the
Dog) — A243

Designs: 20c, Dachshund. 25c, Beagle. 55c, Greyhound. 90c, Jack Russell terrier. $1, Pekingese. $2, White fox terrier. $4, English toy spaniel. $5, Irish setter.
#1686, Welsh corgi. #1687, Labrador retriever.

1994, May 17
1678 A243   20c multicolored   .20 .20
1679 A243   25c multicolored   .20 .20
1680 A243   55c multicolored   .45 .45
1681 A243   90c multicolored   .75 .75
1682 A243 $1 multicolored   .90 .90
1683 A243 $2 multicolored   1.75 1.75

1684 A243 $4 multicolored   3.50 3.50
1685 A243 $5 multicolored   4.25 4.25
    Nos. 1678-1685 (8)   12.00 12.00
Souvenir Sheets
1686 A243 $6 multicolored   6.00 6.00
1687 A243 $6 multicolored   6.00 6.00

Nos. 1578-1579 Ovptd. "ROYAL VISIT / FEBRUARY 19, 1994" in Black or Silver

1994, June 27   Litho.   Perf. 13½x14
1688 A225   Sheet, 2 ea #a-
d   17.00 17.00
Souvenir Sheet
1689 A225 $6 multicolored (S)   8.50 8.50
Overprint on No. 1689 appears in sheet margin.

Miniature Sheet

1994 World Cup Soccer
Championships, US — A244

No. 1690: a, Dos Armstrong, US. b, Dennis Bergkamp, Netherlands. c, Roberto Baggio, Italy. d, Rai, Brazil. e, Cafu, Brazil. f, Marco Van Basten, Netherlands.
Each $6: No. 1691, Roberto Mancini, Italy. No. 1692, Stanford Stadium, Palo Alto.

1994, July 5   Perf. 14
1690 A244 $1 Sheet of 6, #a.-
f.   6.75 6.75
Souvenir Sheets
1691-1692 A244   Set of 2   12.50 12.50

Butterflies
A245

1994, May 3   Litho.   Perf. 14
1693 A245   20c Florida white   .20 .20
1694 A245   25c Red rim   .20 .20
1695 A245   55c Barred
sulphur   .50 .50
1696 A245   65c Mimic   .60 .60
1697 A245 $1 Large orange
sulphur   1.00 1.00
1698 A245 $2 Southern
dagger tail   2.00 2.00
1698A A245 $3 Dominican
snout butter-
fly   2.75 2.75
1699 A245 $5 Caribbean
buckeye   4.75 4.75
    Nos. 1693-1699 (8)   12.00 12.00
Souvenir Sheets
1700 A245 $6 Clench's hair-
streak   6.00 6.00
1701 A245 $6 Painted lady   6.00 6.00

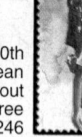

10th
Caribbean
Scout
Jamboree
A246

Designs: 20c, Backpacking. 25c, Cooking over campfire. 55c, Making camp. 65c, Camping. $1, Scout drum unit. $2, Planting trees. $4, Sailing. $5, Scout salute.
Each $6: No. 1710, Early Scout troop. No. 1711, Pres. C.A. Sorhaindo, vert.

1994, July 18   Litho.   Perf. 14
1702-1709 A246   Set of 8   13.00 13.00
Souvenir Sheets
1710-1711 A246   Set of 2   13.00 13.00
For overprints see Nos. 1762-1766.

D-Day,
50th
Anniv.
A247

Designs: 65c, US Waco glider brings reinforcements. $2, British Horsa gliders land more troops. $3, Glider troops take Pegasus Bridge.
$6, Hadrian glider.

1994, July 26
1712-1714 A247   Set of 3   6.00 6.00
Souvenir Sheet
1715 A247 $6 multicolored   5.50 5.50

A248

Intl. Olympic Committee,
Cent. — A249

Designs: 55c, Ulrike Meyfarth, Germany, high jump, 1984. $1.45, Dieter Baumann, Germany, 5000-meter run, 1992.
$6, Ji Hoon Chae, South Korea, 500-meter short track speed skating, 1994.

1994, July 26
1716 A248   55c multicolored   .60 .60
1717 A248 $1.45 multicolored   1.60 1.60
Souvenir Sheet
1718 A249 $6 multicolored   6.50 6.50

English
Touring
Cricket,
Cent.
A250

Designs: 55c, D.I. Goweer Leics, England, vert. 90c, E.C.L. Ambrose, Leeward Islands. $1, G.A. Gooch, England, vert. $3, First English team, 1895.

1994, July 26
1719-1721 A250   Set of 3   3.50 3.50
Souvenir Sheet
1722 A250 $3 multicolored   7.00 7.00

Miniature Sheet of 6

First
Manned
Moon
Landing,
25th
Anniv.
A251

#1723: a, Apollo 14 crew. b, Apollo 14 patch. c, Apollo 14 lunar module Antares at Fra Mauro Crater. d, Apollo 15 crew. e, Apollo 15 patch. f, Apollo 15 mission, Mount Hadley from rover.
$6, 25th anniv. emblem, lunar surface.

1994, July 26
1723 A251 $1 #a.-f.   5.75 5.75
Souvenir Sheet
1724 A251 $6 multicolored   6.50 6.50

A252

PHILAKOREA
'94 — A253

Designs: 65c, P'alsang-jon Hall, Korea. 90c, Popchu-sa Temple. $2, Uhwajong Pavillion, Korea.
Screen, Late Choson Dynasty showing flowers and: No. 1728a, c, e, Birds. b, g, Butterfly. d, Roosters. f, Duck. h, Pheasant. i, Cranes. j, Deer.
$4, Stylized "spirit post" guardian.

1994, July 26   Perf. 14, 13 (#1728)
1725-1727 A252   Set of 3   4.00 4.00
Miniature Sheet of 10
1728 A253   55c #a.-j.   7.50 7.50
Souvenir Sheet
1729 A252 $4 multicolored   3.50 3.50

Mickey
Mouse, 65th
Birthday
A254

Disney characters: 20c, Dippy dawg. 25c, Clarabelle Cow. 55c, Horace Horsecollar. 65c, Mortimer Mouse. $1, Joe Piper. $3, Mr. Casey. $4, Chief O'Hara. $5, Mickey and the Blot.
Each $6: No. 1738, Minnie, Tanglefoot. No. 1739, Pluto, Minnie, horiz.

Perf. 13½x14, 14x13½ (#1739)
1994, Oct. 3
1730-1737 A254   Set of 8   15.00 15.00
Souvenir Sheets
1738-1739 A254   Set of 2   15.00 15.00

A255   A256

Local Entertainers: 20c, Sonia Llyod, folk singer. 25c, Ophelia Marie, singer. 55c, Edney Francis, accordionist. 65c, Norman Letang, saxophonist. 90c, Edie Andre, steel drummer

1994, Dec. 1   Litho.   Perf. 14
1740-1744 A255   Set of 5   2.10 2.10

Miniature Sheet of 9
1994, Dec. 1

Marilyn Monroe (1926-62), Actress: #1745a-1745i, Various portraits. #1746, $6, Hands above head. #1747, $6, Holding hat.

1745 A256   90c #a.-i.   12.50 12.50
Souvenir Sheets
1746-1747 A256   Set of 2   12.00 12.00

Christmas
A257

Details or entire Spanish paintings: 20c, Madonna and child, by Luis de Morales. 25c, Madonna and Child with Yarn Winder, by Morales. 55c, Our Lady of the Rosary, by Zurbaran. 65c, Dream of the Patrician, by Bartolome Murillo. 90c, Madonna of Charity, by El Greco. $1, The Annunciation, by Zurbaran. $2, Mystical Marriage of St. Catherine, by Jusepe de Ribera. $3, The Holy Family with St. Bruno and Other Saints, by Ribera.
Each $6: No. 1756, Vision of the Virgin to St. Bernard, by Murillo. No. 1757, Adoration of the Shepherds, by Murillo.

1994, Dec. 2   *Perf. 13½x14*
1748-1755 A257   Set of 8   8.50   8.50
Souvenir Sheets
1756-1757 A257   Set of 2   12.00   12.00

Order of the Caribbean
Community — A258

First award recipients: 25c, Sir Shridath Ramphal, statesman, Guyana. 65c, William Gilbert Demas, economist, Trinidad & Tobago. 90c, Derek Walcott, writer, St. Lucia.

1994, Dec. 16   *Perf. 14*
1758-1760 A258   Set of 3   2.25   2.25

Jeffrey Edmund, 1994 World Cup Soccer Player A259

1994, Dec. 28
1761 A259 25c multicolored   .20   .20

Nos. 1705, 1708-1711 Ovptd.

18th World Scout Jamboree
Mondial, Holland, May 6, 1995.

1995, Mar. 21   **Litho.**   *Perf. 14*
1762-1764 A246   Set of 3   8.50   8.50
Souvenir Sheets
1765-1766 A246   Set of 2   12.50   12.50
Location of overprint varies.

New Year 1995 (Year of the Boar) — A260

Stylized boars: a, 25c, Facing right. b, 65c, Facing forward. c, $1, Facing left. d, $2, Two facing each other, horiz.

1995, Apr. 15   **Litho.**   *Perf. 14½*
1767 A260   Strip of 3, #a.-c.   1.75   1.75
   d.   Souv. sheet of 3, #1767a-1767c   1.75   1.75
Souvenir Sheet
1768 A260 $2 multicolored   1.60   1.60
No. 1767 was issued in sheets of 4 strips.

Birds
A261

Designs: 25c, Wood duck. 55c, Mallard. 65c, Blue-winged teal. $5, Blood eared parakeet.
No. 1773, vert.: a, Cattle egret. b, Snow goose (a, c). c, Peregrine falcon. d, Barn owl. e, Black-crowned night heron. f, Common grackle. g, Brown pelican. h, Great egret. i, Ruby-throated hummingbird. j, Laughing gull. k, Greater flamingo. l, Common moorhen.
No. 1774, Trumpeter swan, vert. No. 1775, White-eyed vireo.

1995, Apr. 15   **Litho.**   *Perf. 14*
1769-1772 A261   Set of 4   5.00   5.00
Miniature Sheet of 12
1773 A261   65c #a.-l.   16.00   16.00
Souvenir Sheets
1774 A261 $5 multicolored   5.00   5.00
1775 A261 $6 multicolored   6.00   6.00

Miniature Sheets of 6 or 8

End of World War II, 50th Anniv. A262

No. 1776: a, Mitsubishi A6M2 Zero. b, Aichi D3A1 Type 99 "Val." c, Nakajima 97-B5N "Kate." d, Zuikaku. e, Akagi. f, Ryuho.
No. 1777: a, German Panther tank, Ardennes. b, Allied fighter bomber. c, Patton's army crosses the Rhine. d, Rocket-powered ME 163. e, V-2 rocket on launcher. f, German U-boat surrenders in North Atlantic. g, Round the clock bombardment of Berlin. h, Soviet soldiers reach center of Berlin.
Each $6: No. 1778, Statue atop Dresden's town hall after Allied bombing. No. 1779, Japanese attack plane.

1995   **Litho.**   *Perf. 14*
1776 A262 $2 #a.-f. + label   10.50   10.50
1777 A262 $2 #a.-h. + label   15.00   15.00
Souvenir Sheets
1778-1779 A262   Set of 2   16.00   16.00
Issued: #1777-1778, 5/18; others, 7/21.

1996 Summer Olympics, Atlanta A263

Designs: 15c, Mark Breland, boxing. 20c, Lou Banach, Joseph Atiyeh, freestyle wrestling. 25c, Judo. 55c, Fencing. 65c, Matt Biondi, swimming. $1, Gushiken on rings, vert. $2, Cycling, vert. $5, Volleyball.
Each $6: No. 1788, Joe Cargis on Touch of Class, equestrian. No. 1789, Soccer, vert.

1995, July 21
1780-1787 A263   Set of 8   9.75   9.75
Souvenir Sheets
1788-1789 A263   Set of 2   12.00   12.00

UN, 50th Anniv. — A264

No. 1790: a, 65c, Signatures on UN charter, attendee. b, $1, Attendee. $2, Attendees. $6, Winston Churchill.

1995, Aug. 16   **Litho.**   *Perf. 14*
1790 A264   Strip of 3, #a.-c.   2.75   2.75
Souvenir Sheet
1791 A264 $6 multicolored   6.00   6.00
No. 1790 is a continuous design.

Souvenir Sheets

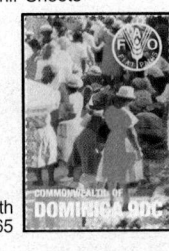

FAO, 50th Anniv. — A265

Street market scene: a, 90c, Woman in red dress. b, $1, Woman seated. c, $2, Vendors, women.
$6, Woman in field, woman holding water cans, vert.

1995, Aug. 16
1792 A265   Sheet of 3, #a.-c.   2.75   2.75
1793 A265 $6 multicolored   4.75   4.75
No. 1792 is a continuous design.

Queen Mother, 95th Birthday A266

No. 1794: a, Drawing. b, Wearing crown, green dress. c, Formal portrait. d, Blue dress. $6, Portrait as younger woman.

1995, Aug. 16   *Perf. 13½x14*
1794 A266 $1.65 Strip or block of 4, #a.-d.   5.50   5.50
Souvenir Sheet
1795 A266 $6 multicolored   6.50   6.50
No. 1794 was issued in sheets of 8 stamps.
Sheet margins of Nos. 1794-1795 exist with black frame and text "In Memoriam — 1900-2002" overprinted in sheet margins.

Rotary, 90th Anniv. A267

1995   *Perf. 14*
1796 A267 $1 Paul Harris, emblem   1.00   1.00
Souvenir Sheet
1797 A267 $6 Rotary emblems   5.25   5.25

Dinosaurs A268

20c, Monoclonius. 25c, Euoplocephalus. 55c, Coelophysis. 65c, Compsognathus.
No. 1802: a, Dimorphodon. b, Ramphorynchus. c, Giant alligator. d, Pentaceratops.
No. 1803: a, Ceratosaurus. b, Comptosaurus (a). c, Stegosaur. d, Camarasaurs. e, Baronyx. f, Dilophosaurus. g, Dromaeosaurids (f). h, Deinonychus. i, Dinicthys. j, Carcharodon (k). k, Nautiloid. l, Trilobite.
$5, Sauropelta. $6, Triceratops, vert.

1995, Sept. 8
1798-1801 A268   Set of 4   1.50   1.50

1802 A268   90c Strip of 4, #a.-
   b.   3.00   3.00
Miniature Sheet of 12
1803 A268 $1 #a.-l.   10.00   10.00
Souvenir Sheets
1804 A268 $5 multicolored   5.50   5.50
1805 A268 $6 multicolored   6.50   6.50
Singapore '95 (#1798-1801, #1803-1805).

Miniature Sheets of 6

Nobel Prize Fund Established, Cent. — A269

Recipients, each $2: No. 1806a, Oscar A. Sanchez, peace, 1987. b, Ernst B. Chain, medicine, 1945. c, Aage Bohr, physics, 1975. d, Jaroslav Seifert, literature, 1984. e, Joseph E. Murray, medicine, 1990. f, Jaroslav Heyrovsky, chemistry, 1959.
No. 1807, each $2: a, Adolf von Baeyer, chemistry, 1905. b, Edward Buchner, chemistry, 1907. c, Carl Bosch, chemistry, 1931. d, Otto Hahn, chemistry, 1944. e, Otto Paul Herman Diels, chemistry, 1950. f, Kurt Alder, chemistry, 1950.
No. 1808, Emil A. von Behring, medicine, 1901.

1995, Oct. 24   **Litho.**   *Perf. 14*
1806-1807 A269   Set of 2   19.00   19.00
Souvenir Sheet
1808 A269 $2 multicolored   1.90   1.90

Christmas A270

Details or entire paintings: 20c, Madonna and Child, by Pontormo. 25c, The Immaculate Conception, by Murillo. 55c, The Adoration of the Magi, by Filippino Lippi. 65c, Rest on the Flight into Egypt, by Van Dyck. 90c, Sacred Family, by Van Dyck. $5, The Annunciation, by Van Eyck.
No. 1815, The Virgin and the Infant, by Van Eyck. No. 1816, The Holy Family, by Ribera.

1995, Nov. 30   **Litho.**   *Perf. 13½x14*
1809-1814 A270   Set of 6   7.00   7.00
Souvenir Sheets
1815 A270 $5 multicolored   4.50   4.50
1816 A270 $6 multicolored   5.50   5.50

Miniature Sheets of 9

Sierra Club, Cent. A271

Designs: No. 1817, each $1: a, Florida panther with mouth open. b, Florida panther looking right. c, Manatee. d, Two manatees. e, Three sockeye salmon. f, Group of sockeye salmon. g, Two southern sea otters. h, Southern sea otter. i, Southern sea otter showing both front paws.
No. 1818, vert. each $1: a, Florida panther. b, Manatee. c, Sockeye salmon. d, Key deer facing left. e, Key deer. f, Key deer with antlers, up close. g, Wallaby with young in pouch. h, Wallaby. i, Wallaby with young.

1995, Dec. 10   *Perf. 14*
1817-1818 A271   Set of 2   15.00   15.00

Chinese Paintings, A City of Cathay A272

No. 1819, brown lettering, each 90c: a, Boats docked, people on shore. b, River, bridge. c, Two boats on river. d, River, pavilion along shore. e, Open sea, people in courtyard.

No. 1820, black lettering, each 90c: a, City scene. b, City scene, wall. c, Outside wall, river. d, Large boat on river. e, People crossing over bridge.

No. 1821, $2: a, Boat on river, city above. b, People walking across bridge.

No. 1822, $2: a, Lifting ramp to another boat, vert. b, Holding lines in water, tree, vert.

1995, Dec. 27   Litho.   Perf. 14½
Strips of 5
1819-1820 A272 Set of 2   9.00 9.00
Souvenir Sheets of 2
1821-1822 A272 Set of 2   7.00 7.00

Nos. 1819-1822 are each continuous designs.

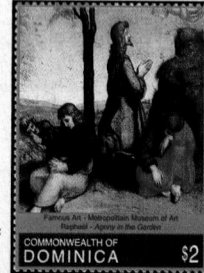

Classic Western Art — A273

Paintings by Raphael: No. 1823, Agony in the Garden. No. 1824, Pope Leo with Nephews. No. 1825, Bindo Altoviti.

$6, Triumphant entry of Constantine into Rome, by Rubens.

1995, Dec. 27   Perf. 14
1823-1825 A273 $2 Set of 3   6.00 6.00
Souvenir Sheet
1826 A273 $6 multicolored   6.00 6.00

New Year 1996 (Year of the Rat) — A274

Stylized rats, Chinese inscriptions: No. 1827a, 25c, purple & brown. b, 65c, orange & green. c, $1, red lilac & blue.

$2, Two rats, horiz.

1996, Jan. 16   Perf. 14½
1827 A274 Strip of 3, #a.-c.   1.90 1.90
Miniature Sheet
1828 A274 Sheet of 1 #1827   1.75 1.75
Souvenir Sheet
1829 A274 $2 multicolored   2.00 2.00

No. 1827 was issued in sheets of 12 stamps.

Miniature Sheet

Disney Lunar New Year — A275

Disney characters representing year of the: No. 1830a, Rat. b, Ox. c, Tiger. d, Hare. e, Dragon. f, Snake. g, Horse. h, Sheep. i, Monkey. j, Rooster. k, Dog. l, Pig.

$3, Rat character. $6, Pig, rat, ox characters on lunar calendar wheel.

1996, Jan. 16   Perf. 14x13½
1830 A275 55c Sheet of 12, #a.-l. 8.50 8.50
Souvenir Sheets
1831 A275 $3 multicolored   3.75 3.75
1832 A275 $6 multicolored   7.75 7.75

Methods of Transportation — A276

Designs: 65c, Donkey cart, 1965. 90c, 1910 Car. $2, 1950 Taxi. $3, 1955 Bus.

1996, Jan. 29   Litho.   Perf. 14
1833-1836 A276 Set of 4   7.50 7.50

Miniature Sheets

Locomotives — A277

No. 1837, each $2: a, "Dragon," Hawaii. b, "Regina," Italy. c, Calazo to Padua, Italy. d, "Mogul," Philippines. e, Nuremberg, Germany. f, "Stanislas," French Natl. Railway. g, "Black Five," Scotland. h, SNCF diesel electric, France. i, "Sir Nigel Gresley," England.

No. 1838, each $2: a, Hohi Line 9600 class, Japan. b, Peloponnese Express, Greece. c, Porter 2-4-0S, Hawaii. d, Norway-Swedish Jodemans Railway. e, 220 Diesel, Federal German Railway. f, 2-8-4T Indian Railways. g, East African Railways. h, Electrical trains, USSR. i, 0-8-0, Austria.

$5, "Duchess of Hamilton," England. $6, Diesel engine, China.

1996, Jan. 29
1837-1838 A277 Set of 2   30.00 30.00
Souvenir Sheets
1839 A277 $5 multicolored   5.50 5.50
1840 A277 $6 multicolored   6.25 6.25

No. 1837h has a face value of $1.

Giant Panda A278

Designs: a, With right leg up on rock. b, Front legs up on rock. c, Seated. d, Holding head down.

1996, May 15   Litho.   Perf. 13½x14
1841 A278 55c Block of 4, #a.-d. 3.75 3.75
Souvenir Sheet
Perf. 14x13½
1842 A278 $3 Panda, horiz.   3.25 3.25

CHINA '96, 9th Asian Intl. Philatelic Exhibition. No. 1841 was issued in sheets of 8 stamps.

See No. 1911.

Queen Elizabeth II, 70th Birthday A279

No. 1843: a, Portrait. b, Wearing regalia of Order of the Garter. c, Wearing bright blue dress, pearls.

$6, In uniform.

1996, May 16   Litho.   Perf. 13½x14
1843 A279 $2 Strip of 3, #a.-c. 5.00 5.00
Souvenir Sheet
1844 A279 $6 multicolored   5.00 5.00

No. 1843 was issued in sheets of 9 stamps.

Legendary Film Detectives A280

Designs: a, Humphrey Bogart as Sam Spade. b, Sean Connery as James Bond. c, Warren Beatty as Dick Tracy. d, Basil Rathbone as Sherlock Holmes. e, William Powell as the Thin Man. f, Sidney Toler as Charlie Chan, g, Peter Sellers as Inspector Clouseau. h, Robert Mitchum as Philip Marlowe. i, Peter Ustinov as Inspector Poirot.

$6, Margaret Rutherford as Miss Marple.

1996, July
1845 A280 $1 Sheet of 9, #a.-i. 9.75 9.75
Souvenir Sheet
1846 A280 $6 multicolored   6.50 6.50

1996 Summer Olympics, Atlanta A281

Designs: 20c, Olympic Stadium, Moscow, 1980. 25c, Hermine Joseph, vert. 55c, Women's field hockey, Zimbabwe, 1980. 90c, Jerome Romain, vert. $1, Polo, discontinued sport, vert. $2, Greg Louganis, diving.

1996   Perf. 14
1847-1852 A281 Set of 6   4.50 4.50

Local Entertainers A282

Designs: 25c, Irene Peltier, national dress of Dominica. 55c, Rupert Bartley, street band player. 65c, Rosemary Cools-Lartigue, pianist. 90c, Celestine "Orion" Theophile, belle queen, Grand Bay. $1, Cecil Bellot, former government band master.

1996, July 31   Litho.   Perf. 14
1853-1857 A282 Set of 5   3.00 3.00

Jerusalem, 3000th Anniv. — A283

Designs: a, 90c, Shrine of the Book, Israel Museum. b, $1, Church of All Nations. c, $2, The Great Synagogue.

$5, Hebrew University, Mount Scopus.

1996, July 31
1858 A283 Sheet of 3, #a.-c.   3.50 3.50
Souvenir Sheet
1859 A283 $5 multicolored   4.50 4.50

Radio, Cent. A284

Entertainers: 90c, Artie Shaw. $1, Benny Goodman. $2, Duke Ellington. $4, Harry James.

$6, Tommy Dorsey, Jimmy Dorsey, horiz.

1996, July 31
1860-1863 A284 Set of 4   6.50 6.50
Souvenir Sheet
1864 A284 $6 multicolored   5.75 5.75

UNICEF, 50th Anniv. A285

20c, Girl looking at globe. 55c, Boy with stethoscope, syringe. $5, Doctor examining child.

No. 1868, Girl, vert.

1996, July 31
1865-1867 A285 Set of 3   4.75 4.75
Souvenir Sheet
1868 A285 $5 multicolored   5.00 5.00

World Post Day — A286

Scenes of 18th cent. life in Dominica: 10c, Captain of ship taking letters by hand. 25c, Anthony Trollope vists Dominica to organize postal service. 55c, Steam vessel "Yare" carries mail around island. 65c, Post offices and agencies. 90c, Country postman carrying mail around mountain tracks. $1, West Indies Federation stamp, first airmail sent on German "goose" seaplane. $2, #602, General Post Office, old and new.

$5, Captain of ship.

1996, Oct. 1   Litho.   Perf. 14
1869-1875 A286 Set of 7   5.25 5.25
Souvenir Sheet
1876 A286 $5 multicolored   5.25 5.25

Fish — A287

Designs: 1c, Scrawled filefish. 2c, Lion fish. 5c, Porcupine fish. 10c, Powder blue surgeonfish. 15c, Red hind. 20c, Golden butterfly fish. 25c, Long-nosed butterfly fish. 35c, Pennant butterfly fish. 45c, Spotted drum. 55c, Blue-girdled angelfish. 60c, Scorpion fish. 65c, Harlequin sweetlips. 90c, Flame angelfish. $1, Queen trigger. $1.20, Stoplight parrot. $1.45, Black durgon. $2, Glasseye snapper. $5, Balloon fish. $10, Creole wrasse. $20, Seabass.

1996, Oct. 1   Litho.   Perf. 14

1877	A287	1c multicolored	.20	.20
1878	A287	2c multicolored	.20	.20
1879	A287	5c multicolored	.20	.20
1880	A287	10c multicolored	.20	.20
1881	A287	15c multicolored	.20	.20
1882	A287	20c multicolored	.20	.20
1883	A287	25c multicolored	.20	.20
1884	A287	35c multicolored	.35	.35
1885	A287	45c multicolored	.40	.40
1886	A287	55c multicolored	.50	.50
1887	A287	60c multicolored	.60	.60
1888	A287	65c multicolored	.65	.65
1889	A287	90c multicolored	.90	.90
1890	A287	$1 multicolored	.95	.95
1891	A287	$1.20 multicolored	1.25	1.25
1892	A287	$1.45 multicolored	1.40	1.40
1893	A287	$2 multicolored	1.90	1.90
1894	A287	$5 multicolored	4.75	4.75
1895	A287	$10 multicolored	9.75	9.75
1896	A287	$20 multicolored	19.00	19.00
	Nos. 1877-1896 (20)		43.80	43.80

See Nos. 2024-2039B for size 20x18mm stamps.

1996 Summer Olympic Games Type

Past Olympic medalists, vert, each 90c: No. 1897a, Ulrike Meyfarth, high jump. b, Pat McCormick, diving. c, Takeichi Nishi, equestrian. d, Peter Farkas, Greco-Roman wrestling. e, Carl Lewis, track & field. f, Agnes Keleti, gymnastics. g, Yasuhiro Yamashita, judo. h, John Kelly, single sculls. i, Naim Suleymanoglu, weight lifting.

No. 1898, vert, each 90c: a, Sammy Lee, diving. b, Bruce Jenner, decathlon. c, Olga Korbut, gymnastics. d, Steffi Graf, tennis. e, Florence Griffith-Joyner, track and field. f, Mark Spitz, swimming. g, Li Ning, gymnastics. h, Erika Salumae, cycling. i, Abebe Bikila, marathon.

#1899, $5, Joan Benoit, 1st women's marathon, vert.

#1900, $5, Milt Campbell, discus.

1996, June 7   Litho.   Perf. 14
Sheets of 9

1897-1898	A281	Set of 2	14.50	14.50

Souvenir Sheets

1899-1900	A281	Set of 2	8.50	8.50

A288   A289

Christmas (Details or entire paintings): 25c, Enthroned Madonna and Child, by Stefano Veneziano. 55c, Noli Me Tangere, by Beato Angelico. 65c, Madonna and Child, by Angelico. 90c, Madonna of Corneta Tarquinia, by Filippo Lippi. $2, Annunciation, by Angelico. $5, Madonna with Child, by Angelico, diff.

Each $6: No. 1907, Coronation of the Virgin, by Beato Angelico. No. 1908, Holy Family with St. Barbara, by Veronese, horiz.

1996, Nov. 25

1901-1906	A288	Set of 6	8.50	8.50

Souvenir Sheet

1907-1908	A288	Set of 2	11.50	11.50

1997   Litho.   Perf. 14

Paintings of "Herdboy and Buffalo," by Li Keran (1907-89): No. 1909: a, f, Herdboy Plays the Flute. b, g, Playing Cricket in the Autumn. c, h, Listen to the Summer Cicada. d, i, Grazing in the Spring.
$2, Return in Wind and Rain.

1909	A289	90c Strip of 4, #a.-d.	3.50	3.50

Souvenir Sheets

1909E	A289	55c Sheet of 4, #f.-i.	2.25	2.25

Perf. 15x14½

1910	A289	$2 multicolored	2.25	2.25

New Year 1997 (Year of the Ox).
No. 1909 was printed in sheets of 8 stamps.
No. 1910 contains one 34x52mm stamp.

Souvenir Sheet

Huangshan Mountain, China — A290

Illustration reduced.

1996, May 15   Litho.   Perf. 12

1911	A290	$2 multicolored	2.50	2.50

China '96. No. 1911 was not available until March 1997.

A291

Lee Lai-Shan, 1996 Olympic Gold Medalist in Wind Surfing — A291a

Illustration A291a reduced.

1997   Litho.   Perf. 15x14

1912	A291	$2 multicolored	1.90	1.90

Souvenir Sheet
Perf. 14

1913	A291	$5 multicolored	4.50	4.50

No. 1912 was issued in sheets of 3.
No. 1913 contains one 38x51mm stamp.

Litho. & Embossed
Perf. 9
Without Gum

1913A	A291a	$35 gold & multi, like #1913	

Butterflies
A292

No. 1914: a, Meticalla metis. b, Coeliades forestan. c, Papilio dardanus. d, Mylothris chloris. e, Poecilimitis thyshe. f, Myrina silenus.
g, Bematistes aganice. h, Euphaedra neophron. i, Precis hierta.

No. 1915, vert: a, Striped policeman. b, Mountain sandman. c, Brown-veined white. d, Bowker's widow. e, Foxy charaxes. f, Pirate. g, African clouded yellow. h, Garden inspector.

Each $6: No. 1916, Acraea natalica. No. 1917, Eurytela dryope.

1997, Apr. 1   Litho.   Perf. 14

1914	A292	55c Sheet of 9, #a.-i.	4.50	4.50
1915	A292	90c Sheet of 8, #a.-h.	6.50	6.50

Souvenir Sheets

1916-1917	A292	Set of 2	12.00	12.00

UNESCO, 50th Anniv. A293

55c, View from temple, China. 65c, Palace of Diocletian, Croatia. 90c, St. Mary's Cathedral, Hildesheim, Germany. $1, Monastery of Rossanou, Mount Athos, Greece. $2, Scandola Nature Reserve, France. $4, Church of San Antao, Portugal.

No. 1924: a, Ruins of Copan, Honduras. b, Cuzco Cathedral, Peru. c, Olinda, Brazil. d, Canaima Natl. Park, Venezuela. e, Galapagos Islands Natl. Park, Ecuador. f, Ruins of Church, Jesuit missions of Santisima, Paraguay. g, Fortress, San Lorenzo, Panama. h, Natl. Park, Fortress, Haiti.

Each $6: No. 1925, Chengde Lakes, China. No. 1926, Kyoto, Japan.

1997, Apr. 7   Perf. 13½x14

1918-1923	A293	Set of 6	10.00	10.00
1924	A293	$1 Sheet of 8, #a.-h. + label	9.00	9.00

Souvenir Sheets

1925-1926	A293	Set of 2	12.00	12.00

Disney Scenes "Sealed with a Kiss" A294

Cartoon film, year released: 25c, Mickey's Horse, Tanglefoot, 1933. 35c, Shanghaied, 1935. 55c, Pluto's Judgment Day, 1935. 65c, Race for Riches, 1935. 90c, Elmer Elephant, 1936. $1, Brave Little Tailor, 1938. $2, Donald's Crime, 1945. $4, In Dutch, 1946.

Each $6: No. 1935, Nifty Nineties, 1941. No. 1936, Mickey's Surprise Party, 1939.

1997, Apr. 15   Perf. 13½x14

1927-1934	A294	Set of 8	13.00	13.00

Souvenir Sheets

1935-1936	A294	Set of 2	10.00	10.00

Cats — A295   Dogs — A296

25c, Cream Burmese. $1, Snowshoe. $2, Sorrell Abyssinian. $5, Torbie Persian.

No. 1941: a, British bicolor shorthair (d, e). b, Maine coon kitten, Somali kitten (c). c, Maine coon kitten, diff. d, Lynx point Siamese
(e). e, Blue Burmese kitten, white Persian (odd-eyed) (f). f, Persian kitten.

No. 1942, Silver tabby.

1997, Apr. 24   Perf. 14

1937-1940	A295	Set of 4	7.50	7.50
1941	A295	$2 Sheet of 6, #a.-f.	11.50	11.50

Souvenir Sheet

1942	A295	$6 multicolored	6.00	6.00

1997, Apr. 24

Designs: 20c, Afghan hound. 55c, Cocker spaniel. 65c, Smooth fox terrier. 90c, West Highland white terrier.

No. 1947a, St. Bernard. b, Boy with grand basset. c, Rough collie. d, Golden retriever. e, Golden retriever, Tibetan spaniel, smooth fox terrier. f, Smooth fox terrier, diff.

$6, Shetland sheepdog.

1943-1946	A296	Set of 4	2.25	2.25
1947	A296	90c Sheet of 6, #a.-f.	5.75	5.75

Souvenir Sheet

1948	A296	$6 multicolored	6.00	6.00

Queen Elizabeth II and Prince Philip, 50th Wedding Anniv. A297

No. 1949: a, Queen Elizabeth II. b, Royal Arms. c, Prince, Queen walking among crowd. d, Queen, Prince in military attire. e, Buckingham Palace. f, Prince Philip.

$6, Portrait of Queen and Prince on balcony.

1997, May 29   Litho.   Perf. 14

1949	A297	$1 Sheet of 6, #a.-f.	6.50	6.50

Souvenir Sheet

1950	A297	$6 multicolored	6.00	6.00

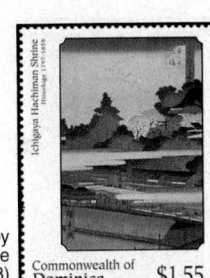

Paintings by Hiroshige (1797-1858) A298

#1951: a, Ichigaya Hachiman Shrine. b, Blossoms on the Tama River Embankment. c, Kumano Junisha Shrine, Tsunohazu ("Juniso"). d, Benkei Moat from Soto-Sakurada to Kojimachi. e, Kinokuni Hill & View of Akasaka Tameike. f, Naito Shinjuku, Yotsuya.

Each $6: No. 1952, Kasumigaseki. No. 1952A, Sanno Festival Procession at Kojimachi I-chome.

1997, May 29

1951	A298	$1.55 Sheet of 6, #a.-f.	10.00	10.00

Souvenir Sheets

1952-1952A	A298	Set of 2	14.00	14.00

Orchids
A299

Designs, vert: 20c, Oncidium altissimum. 25c, Oncidium papilio. 55c, Epidendrum fragrans. 65c, Oncidium lanceanum. 90c, Campylocentrum micranthum. $4, Pogonia rosea.

No. 1959: a, Brassavola cucculata. b, Epidendrum ibaguense. c, Ionopsis utricularioides. d, Rodriguezia lanceolata. e, Oncidium cebolleta. f, Epidendrum ciliare.

Each $5: No. 1960, Stanhopea grandiflora. No. 1961, Oncidium ampliatum.

1997, May 10   Litho.   Perf. 14

1953-1958	A299	Set of 6	8.00	8.00

1959 A299 $1 Sheet of 6, #a.-
　　　f.　　　　　　　　7.00　7.00

Souvenir Sheets
1960-1961 A299　Set of 2　　10.50　10.50

Paul P. Harris (1868-1947), Founder
of Rotary, Intl. — A300

Portrait of Harris and: $2, Rotary Village
Corps, irrigation project, Honduras. $6,
Emblems, world community service.

1997, May 29
1962 A300　$2 multicolored　　1.75　1.75

Souvenir Sheet
1963 A300　$6 multicolored　　7.00　7.00

Heinrich
von
Stephan
(1831-97)
A301

Portraits of Von Stephan and: No. 1964 a,
Kaiser Wilhelm II. b, UPU emblem. c, Postal
messenger, ancient Japan.
$6, Von Stephan, Russian dog team carry-
ing post, 1859.

1997, May 29
1964 A301　$2 Sheet of 3, #a.-c.　5.25　5.25

Souvenir Sheet
1965 A301　$6 multicolored　　5.25　5.25

PACIFIC 97.

Chernobyl
Disaster,
10th Anniv.
A302

Designs: No. 1966, Chabad's Children of
Chernobyl. No. 1967, UNESCO.

1997, May 29　　　Perf. 13½x14
1966 A302　$2 multicolored　　2.75　2.75
1967 A302　$2 multicolored　　2.75　2.75

Grimm's
Fairy Tales
A303

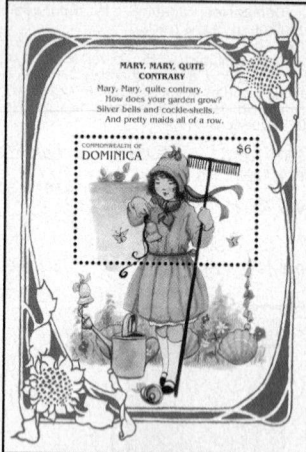

Mother Goose Rhymes — A304

The Goose Girl: No. 1968: a, Girl with
horse. b, Geese, pond, castle. c, Girl No.
1969, Girl, horiz.
No. 1970: Mary, Mary, Quite Contrary.

1997, May 29　　　Perf. 13½x14
1968 A303　$2 Sheet of 3, #a.-c.　7.00　7.00

Souvenir Sheets
　　　　　　Perf. 14x13½
1969 A303　$6 multicolored　　7.00　7.00

　　　　　　Perf. 14
1970 A304　$6 multicolored　　7.00　7.00

Return of Hong
Kong to
China — A305

Designs: $1, View of Hong Kong at night.
$1.45, View of Hong Kong in daytime. $2,
View of Hong Kong at night, diff.
Hong Kong skyline at dusk: No. 1974: a,
65c. b, 90c. c, $1. d, $3.

1997, July 1　　　　Perf. 14
1971-1973 A305　Set of 3　　4.25　4.25
1974 A305　Sheet of 4, #a.-d.　5.50　5.50

#1971-1973 were issued in sheets of 4.

1998 Winter
Olympics,
Nagano — A306

Medal winners: 20c, Yukio Kasaya, 1972 ski
jump. 25c, Jens Weissflog, 1994 ski jump. No.
1977, 55c, Anton Maier, 1968 men's speed
skating. No. 1978, 55c, Ljubov Egorova, 1994
women's cross-country skiing. 65c, 1994 Ice
hockey, Sweden. 90c, Bernhard Glass, 1980
men's luge. $4, Frank-Peter Roetsch, 1988
men's biathlon.
No. 1982: a, like #1975. b, like #1976. c, like
#1977. d, Christa Rothenburger, 1988
women's speed skating.
Each $5: No. 1983, Jacob Tullin Thams,
1924 ski jumping. No. 1984, Charles Jewtraw,
1924 men's speed skating.

1997, July 15
1975-1981 A306　Set of 7　　8.75　8.75
1982 A306　$1 Strip or block of
　　　4, #a.-d.　　　　5.00　5.00

Souvenir Sheets
1983-1984 A306　Set of 2　　8.50　8.50

No. 1982 issued in sheets of 8 stamps.

1998 World Cup Soccer
Championships, France — A307

Players, vert: 20c, Klinsmann, Germany.
55c, Bergkamp, Holland. 65c, Ravanelli, Italy.
90c, Kinkladze, Georgia. $2, Shearer,
England. $4, Dani, Portugal.
Stadiums: No. 1991, each 65c: a, Wembley,
England. b, Bernabeu, Spain. c, Maracana,
Brazil. d, Torino, Italy. e, Centenary, Uruguay.
f, Olympic, Germany. g, Rose Bowl, US. h,
Azteca, Mexico.
Team Captains: No. 1992, each 65c: a,
Meazza, Italy, 1934. b, Matthaus, Germany,
1990. c, Walter, W. Germany, 1954. d,
Maradona, Argentina, 1986. e, Beckenbauer,
Germany, 1974. f, Moore, England, 1966. g,
Dunga, Brazil, 1994. h, Zoff, Italy, 1982.
$5, Mario Kempes, Argentina, vert. $6, Ally
McCoist, Scotland, vert.

1997, July 21　　Litho.　　Perf. 14
1985-1990 A307　Set of 6　　9.00　9.00

Sheets of 8 + Label
1991-1992 A307　Set of 2　　10.00　10.00

Souvenir Sheets
1993 A307　$5 multicolored　　4.50　4.50
1994 A307　$6 multicolored　　5.50　5.50

Dominica
Credit
Union — A308

25c, Joffre Robinson, former Credit Union
president. 55c, Sister Alicia, founder credit
union movement in Dominica. 65c, Lorrel
Bruce, 1st Cooperative Credit Union president. 90c, Roseau Credit Union Building.
$5, Bruce, Robinson, Sister Alicia.

1997, Aug. 15　Litho.　Perf. 14x13½
1995-1998 A308　Set of 4　　2.40　2.40

Souvenir Sheet
　　　　　Perf. 14
1999 A308　$5 multicolored　　5.00　5.00

No. 1999 contains one 28x60mm stamp.

A309　　　　　　　A310

Medical Pioneers: 20c, Louis Pasteur, father
of bacteriology. 25c, Christiaan Barnard, performed first heart transplant. 55c, Sir Alexander Fleming, developer of penicillin. 65c,
Camillo Golgi, neurologist. 90c, Jonas Salk,
developer of polio vaccine. $1, Har Ghobind
Khorana, geneticist. $2, Elizabeth Blackwell,
first woman physician. $3, Sir Frank Macfar-
lane Burnet, immunologist.
$5, Fleming, diff. $6, Pasteur, diff.

1997, Sept. 1　　Litho.　　Perf. 14
2000-2007 A309　Set of 8　　9.00　9.00

Souvenir Sheets
2008 A309　$5 multicolored　　5.25　5.25
2009 A309　$6 multicolored　　6.25　6.25

1997, Oct. 20　　Litho.　　Perf. 14
Diana, Princess of Wales (1961-97): Various portraits.
2010 A310　$2 Sheet of 4, #a.-d.　8.00　8.00

Souvenir Sheet
2011 A310　$5 multicolored　　6.00　6.00

Christmas — A311

Entire paintings or details: 20c, Echo and
Narcissus, by Poussin. 55c, Angel Departing
from the Family of Tobias, by Rembrandt. 65c,
Seated Nymphs with Flute, by Francois
Boucher. 90c, Angel, by Rembrandt. $2, Dis-
pute of the Holy Sacrament, by Raphael. $4,
Garden of Love, by Rubens.
Each $6: No. 2018, Annunciation, by Botti-
celli. No. 2019, Christ on the Mount of Olives,
by El Greco.

1997, Nov. 10　　Litho.　　Perf. 14
2012-2017 A311　Set of 6　　8.00　8.00

Souvenir Sheets
2018-2019 A311　Set of 2　　12.00　12.00

The $4 is incorrectly inscribed Holy Trinity,
by Raphael. No. 2018 is incorrectly inscribed
Study of a Muse, by Raphael.

A312

A313

Paintings of tigers, by Ling-Nan School: No.
2020: a, 55c, Gao Qifeng. b, 65c, Zhao
Shao'ang. c, 90c, Gao Jianfu. d, $1.20, Gao
Jianfu, diff.
$3, Tiger running down mountain, by Gao
Jianfu.

1998, Jan. 5　　Litho.　　Perf. 14½
2020 A312　Sheet of 4, #a.-d.　3.25　3.25

Souvenir Sheet
　　　　Perf. 14x14½
2021 A312　$3 multicolored　　2.50　2.50

New Year 1998 (Year of the Tiger). No. 2021
contains one 44x36mm stamp.

Fish Type of 1996

1998			Perf. 13x13½	
			Size: 20x18mm	
2024	A287	5c	Porcupine fish	.20	.20
2025	A287	10c	Powder-blue surge-onfish	.20	.20
2026	A287	15c	Red hind	.20	.20
2027	A287	20c	Golden but-terflyfish	.20	.20
2028	A287	25c	Long-nosed butter-lyfish	.20	.20
2029	A287	35c	Pennant butterflyfish	.35	.35
2030	A287	45c	Spotted drum	.50	.50
2031	A287	55c	Blue-girdled angelfish	.55	.55

2032	A287	60c	Scorpion fish	.60	.60
2033	A287	65c	Harlequin sweetlips	.75	.75
2034	A287	90c	Flame angelfish	.90	.90
2035	A287	$1	Queen trigger	1.10	1.10
2036	A287	$1.20	Stoplight parrot	1.25	1.25
2037	A287	$1.45	Black durgon	1.40	1.40
2038	A287	$2	Glasseye snapper	2.10	2.10
2039	A287	$5	Balloon fish	5.25	5.25
2039A	A287	$10	Creole wrasse	11.00	11.00
2039B	A287	$20	Seabass	21.00	21.00
	Nos. 2024-2039B (18)			47.75	47.75

Numbers have been reserved for additional values in this set.

1998, Feb. 9   Litho.   *Perf. 14*

Famous 20th cent. athletes — #2040: a, Jesse Owens. b, Owens jumping in 1936 Summer Olympic Games, Berlin. c, Isaac Berger lifting weights. d, Berger. e, Boris Becker. f, Becker playing tennis. g, Arthur Ashe playing tennis, holding Wimbledon trophy. h, Ashe.
No. 2041, Franz Beckenbauer, soccer player, horiz.

Sheet of 8

2040	A313	$1 #a.-h.	8.50	8.50

Souvenir Sheet

2041	A313	$6 multi	7.00	7.00

Nos. 2040b-2040c, 2040f-2040g are each 53x38mm.

A314   A315

Japanese Cinema Stars — No. 2042: a, Akira Kurosawa. b, Kurosawa's 1950 film, "Rashomon." c, Toshiro Mifune in 1954 film, "Seven Samurai." d, Mifune. e, Yasujiro Ozu. f, Ozu's 1949 film, "Late Spring." g, Sessue Hayakawa in 1957 film, "Bridge on the River Kwai." h, Hayakawa.
No. 2043, Akira Kurosawa, director.

1998, Feb. 9   Litho.   *Perf. 14*

Sheet of 8

2042	A314	$1 #a.-h.	8.50	8.50

Souvenir Sheet

2043	A314	$6 multi	7.00	7.00

Nos. 2042b-2042c, 2042f-2042g are each 53x38mm.

1998, Mar. 2   Litho.   *Perf. 14*

Mushrooms: 10c, Omphalotus illudens. 15c, Inocybe fastigiata. 20c, Marasmius plicatulus. 50c, Mycena lilacifolia. 55c, Armillaria straminea. 90c, Tricholomopsis rutilans.
No. 2050, each $1: a, Lepiota naucina. b, Cortinarius violaceus. c, Boletus aereus. d, Tricholoma aurantium. e, Lepiota procera. f, Clitocybe geotropa. g, Lepiota acutesquamosa. h, Tricholoma saponaceum. i, Lycoperdon gemmatum.
No. 2051, each $1: a, Boletus ornatipes. b, Russula xerampelina. c, Cortinarius collinitus. d, Agaricus meleagris. e, Coprinus comatus. f, Amanita caesarea. g, Amanita brunnescens. h, Amanita muscaria. i, Morchella esculenta.
$6, Cortinarius violaceus.

2044-2049	A315	Set of 6	3.00	3.00

Sheets of 9

2050-2051	A315	Set of 2	21.00	21.00

Souvenir Sheet

2052	A315	$6 multicolored	6.00	6.00

Sailing Ships A316

Designs: 65c, Greek bireme. 90c, Egyptian felucca. $1, Viking longboat. $2, Chinese junk.
No. 2057: a, Two-masted topsail schooner. b, The Golden Hinde. c, Roman merchant ship. d, Gazela Primeriro. e, Moshulu. f, Bluenose.
Each $5: No. 2058, Pinta. No. 2059, Chesapeake Bay skipjack.

1998, Mar. 16   Litho.   *Perf. 14*

2053-2056	A316	Set of 4	5.00	5.00
2057	A316	55c Block of 6, #a.-f.	3.50	3.50

Souvenir Sheets

2058-2059	A316	Set of 2	11.00	11.00

No. 2053 incorrectly inscribed "Egyptian felucca."
No. 2057 was issued in sheets of 12 stamps.

Mickey & Minnie Mouse's 70th Anniv. — A317

25c, Steamboat Willie, 1928. 55c, The Brave Little Tailor, 1938. 65c, Nifty Nineties, 1941. 90c, Mickey Mouse Club, 1955. $1, Mickey, Minnie at the opening of Walt Disney World, 1971. $1.45, Mousercise Mickey & Minnie, 1980.
Each $5: No. 2061, Walt Disney, Mickey, Minnie. No. 2062, Surprise Party for Mickey & Minnie.

1998, June 16   Litho.   *Perf. 14x13½*

2060A	A317	25c black	.25	.25
2060B	A317	55c multicolored	.55	.55
2060C	A317	65c multicolored	.70	.70
2060D	A317	90c multicolored	.95	.95
2060E	A317	$1 multicolored	1.00	1.00
2060F	A317	$1.45 multicolored	1.50	1.50
	Nos. 2060A-2060F (6)		4.95	4.95

Souvenir Sheet of 7

2060G	#2060A-2060F, 2060h	13.00	13.00
h.	$5 Runaway brain, perf 13½ at left	4.00	4.00

Size: 130x104mm

Imperf

2061-2062	A317	Set of 2	11.00	11.00

Souvenir Sheet

Disney's The Lion King — A318

1998, June 16   Litho.   *Perf. 13½x14*

2063	A318	$5 multicolored	6.00	6.00

Sea Birds A319

25c, Erect crested penguin. 65c, Humboldt penguin. 90c, Red knot. $1, Audubon's shearwater.
No. 2068: a, Crested tern. b, Franklin's gull. c, Australian pelican. d, Fairy prion. e, Andean gull. f, Imperial shag. g, Red phalarope. h, Hooded grebe. i, Least auklet. j, Little grebe. k, Cape petrel. l, Horned grebe.
Each $5: No. 2069, Sula nebouxii. No. 2070, Fulmarus glacialis.

Designs: 65c, Greek bireme. 90c, Egyptian felucca. $1, Viking longboat. $2, Chinese junk.

1998, Aug. 4   *Perf. 14*

2064-2067	A319	Set of 4	3.00	3.00
2068	A319	90c Sheet of 12, #a.-l.	11.00	11.00

Souvenir Sheets

2069-2070	A319	Set of 2	12.00	12.00

Airplanes A320

20c, Jetstar II. 25c, AN 225. 55c, Dash-8. 65c, Beech-99. 90c, American Eagle. $2, HFB 320 Itansa Jet.
No. 2077, each $1: a, SR 71 "Blackbird." b, Stealth bomber. c, Northrop YF23. d, F-14 A "Tomcat." e, F-15 "Eagle S." f, MiG 29 "Fulcrum." g, Europa X5. h, Camion.
No. 2078, each $1: a, E400. b, CL-215 C-GKDN Amphibian. c, Piper jet. d, Beech Hawker. e, Lockheed YF22. f, Piper Seneca V. g, CL-215 Amphibian. h, Vantase.
Each $6: No. 2079, F-1 Fighter. No. 2080, Sea Hopper.

1998, Aug. 17

2071-2076	A320	Set of 6	5.50	5.50

Sheets of 8

2077-2078	A320	Set of 2	19.00	19.00

Souvenir Sheets

2079-2080	A320	Set of 2	13.00	13.00

Intl. Year of the Ocean A321

Marine life: 25c, Fridman fish. 55c, Hydrocoral. 65c, Feather star. 90c, Royal angelfish.
No. 2085, each $1: a, Monk seal. b, Galapagos penguin. c, Manta ray. d, Hawksbill turtle. e, Moorish idol. f, Nautilus. g, Giant clam. h, Tubeworms. i, Nudibranch.
No. 2086, each $1: a, Spotted dolphin. b, Atlantic sailfish. c, Sailfin flying fish. d, Fairy basslet. e, Atlantic spadefish. f, Leatherback turtle. g, Blue tang. h, Coral banded shrimp. i, Rock beauty.
No. 2087, Humpback whale. No. 2088, Leafy sea dragon.

1998, Sept. 7   Litho.   *Perf. 14*

2081-2084	A321	Set of 4	3.00	3.00

Sheets of 9

2085-2086	A321	Set of 2	18.00	18.00

Souvenir Sheets

2087	A321	$5 multicolored	5.25	5.25
2088	A321	$6 multicolored	6.25	6.25

Organization of American States, 50th Anniv. A322

1998, Sept. 1   Litho.   *Perf. 14*

2089	A322	$1 multicolored	1.50	1.50

Ferrari Sports Cars A323

55c, 365 GT 2+2. 90c, Boano/Ellena 250 GT. $1, 375 MM coupe. $5, 212.

1998, Sept. 1

2090-2092	A323	Set of 3	4.25	4.25

Souvenir Sheet

2093	A323	$5 multicolored	6.00	6.00

No. 2093 contains one 91x35mm stamp.

Gandhi — A324

1998, Sept. 1

2094	A324	90c shown	1.00	1.00

Souvenir Sheet

2095	A324	$6 Seated	6.00	6.00

No. 2094 was issued in sheets of 4.

Pablo Picasso A325

Paintings: 90c, The Painter and His Model, 1926. $1, The Crucifixion, 1930. $2, Nude with Raised Arms, 1908, vert.
$6, Cafe at Royan, 1940.

1998, Sept. 1   *Perf. 14½*

2096-2098	A325	Set of 3	5.00	5.00

Souvenir Sheet

2099	A325	$6 multicolored	6.50	6.50

Royal Air Force, 80th Anniv. A326

No. 2100: a, Nimrod MR2P. b, C-130 Hercules Mk3. c, Panavia Tornado GR1. d, C-130 Hercules landing.
$5, Biplane, hawk. $6, Hawker Hart, jet.

1998, Sept. 1   *Perf. 14*

2100	A326	$2 Sheet of 4, #a.-d.	8.00	8.00

Souvenir Sheets

2101	A326	$5 multicolored	5.25	5.25
2102	A326	$6 multicolored	6.25	6.25

No. 2100d incorrectly inscribed Panavia Tornado GR1.

Nos. 1548-1549, 1551-1552, 1554 Ovptd. "Save the Turtles"

1998, Sept. 14

2103-2107	A221	Set of 5	7.00	7.00

A327   A328

1998 World Scouting Jamboree, Chile: 65c, Scout sign. $1, Scout handshake. $2, World Scout flag.
$5, Lord Baden-Powell.

1998

2108-2110	A327	Set of 3	3.50	3.50

Souvenir Sheet

2111	A327	$5 multicolored	6.00	6.00

1998, Dec. 1   Litho.   Perf. 14

Birds: 25c, Northern cardinal. 55c, Eastern bluebird. 65c, Carolina wren. 90c, Blue jay. $1, Evening grosbeak. $2, Bohemian waxwing. $5, Northern parula. $6, Painted bunting.

| 2112-2117 | A328 | Set of 6 | 5.00 | 5.00 |

Souvenir Sheets

| 2118 | A328 | $5 multicolored | 5.25 | 5.25 |
| 2119 | A328 | $6 multicolored | 6.25 | 6.25 |

Christmas.

New Year 1999 (Year of the Rabbit) A329

Painting by Tsui Po (1050-1080).

1999, Jan. 4   Litho.   Perf. 14

| 2120 | A329 | $1.50 multicolored | 2.25 | 2.25 |

No. 2120 was issued in sheets of 4.

Orchids — A330

55c, Broughtonia sanguinea. 65c, Cattleyonia Keith Roth "Roma." 90c, Comparettia falcata. $2, Cochleanthes discolor.

No. 2125, each $1: a, Dracula erythiochaete. b, Lycasle aromatica. c, Masdevallia marguerile. d, Encyclia marfae. e, Laelia gouldiana. f, Huntleya meleagris. g, Galeandria baueri. h, Lycale deppei.

No. 2126, each $1: a, Anguloa clowesii. b, Lemboglossum cervantesii. c, Oncidium cebolleta. d, Millonia. e, Pescatorea lehmannll. f, Sophronitis coccinea. g, Pescatorea cerina. h, Encyclia vitellina.

Each $5: No. 2127, Lepanthes ovalis. No. 2128, Encyclia cochleata.

1999, Apr. 26   Litho.   Perf. 14

| 2121-2124 | A330 | Set of 4 | 4.50 | 4.50 |

Sheets of 8

| 2125-2126 | A330 | Set of 2 | 17.50 | 17.50 |

Souvenir Sheets

| 2127-2128 | A330 | Set of 2 | 11.00 | 11.00 |

Trains A331

No. 2129, each $1: a, Class 103.1 Co-Co, Germany. b, Class .24, "Trans Pennine," UK. c, GG1 2-Co-Co-2, US. d, LRC Bo-Bo, Canada. e, Class EW, New Zealand. f, Class SS1 "Shao-Shani," China. g, Gulf, Mobile Ohio, US. h, Class 9100 2-Do-2, France.

No. 2130, each $1: a, County Donegal Petrol Rail Car No. 10, Ireland. b, RDC Single Rail Car, US. c, WDM Class Co-Co, India. d, Bi-Polar No. E-2, US. e, Class X Co-Co, Australia. f, Beijing Bo-Bo, China. g, Class E428 2-Bo-Bo-2, Italy. h, Class 581 Twelve-Car Train, Japan.

$5, X-2000 Tilting Express Train, Sweden, vert. $6, Class 87 Bo-Bo, Great Britain, vert.

1999, May 10   Litho.   Perf. 14

Sheets of 8

| 2129-2130 | A331 | Set of 2 | 15.00 | 15.00 |

Souvenir Sheets

| 2131 | A331 | $5 multicolored | 4.50 | 4.50 |
| 2132 | A331 | $6 multicolored | 5.50 | 5.50 |

Australia '99, World Stamp Expo.

Prehistoric Animals — A332

25c, Tyrannosaurus, vert. 65c, Hypacrosaurus. 90c, Sauropelta. $2, Zalambdalestes.

No. 2137, each $1: a, Barosaurus. b, Rhamphorhynchus. c, Apatosaurus. d, Archaeopteryx. e, Diplodocus. f, Ceratosaurus. g, Stegosaurus. h, Elaphrosaurus. i, Vulcanodon.

No. 2138, each $1: a, Psittacosaurus. b, Pteranodon. c, Ichthyornis. d, Spinosaurus. e, Parasaurolophus. f, Ornithomimus. g, Anatosaurus. h, Triceratops. i, Baronyx.

$5, Yangchuanosaurus. $6, Brachiosaurus.

1999, June 1   Litho.   Perf. 14

| 2133-2136 | A332 | Set of 4 | 3.50 | 3.50 |

Sheets of 9

| 2137-2138 | A332 | Set of 2 | 18.00 | 18.00 |

Souvenir Sheets

| 2139 | A332 | $5 multicolored | 5.25 | 5.25 |
| 2140 | A332 | $6 multicolored | 6.25 | 6.25 |

Wedding of Prince Edward and Sophie Rhys-Jones A333

No. 2141: a, Sophie. b, Sophie, Edward. c, Edward.
$6, like No. 2141b.

1999, June 19   Litho.   Perf. 13½

| 2141 | A333 | $3 Sheet of 3, #a.-c. | 7.75 | 7.75 |

Souvenir Sheet

| 2142 | A333 | $6 multicolored | 5.50 | 5.50 |

IBRA '99, World Philatelic Exhibition, Nuremberg — A334

Exhibition emblem, sailing ship Eendraght and: 65c, Cameroun #58, #56. 90c, Cameroun #11, #9.
Emblem, early German train and: $1, Cameroun #19. $2, Cameroun #6.
$6, Cover with Cameroun #19.
Illustration reduced.

1999, June 22   Perf. 14

| 2143-2146 | A334 | Set of 4 | 4.50 | 4.50 |

Souvenir Sheet

| 2147 | A334 | $6 multicolored | 7.00 | 7.00 |

Souvenir Sheets

PhilexFrance '99 — A335

Trains: $5, L'Aigle, 1855. $6, Mainline diesel locomotive, 1963.
Illustration reduced.

1999, June 22   Perf. 13¾

| 2148 | A335 | $5 multicolored | 5.00 | 5.00 |
| 2149 | A335 | $6 multicolored | 6.00 | 6.00 |

Apollo 11 Moon Landing, 30th Anniv. A336

No. 2150: a, Command Module separation b, Service Module separation. c, 3rd Stage Booster separation. d, Landing, Command Modules go to the moon. e, Apollo Ground Tracker. f, Goldstone Radio Telescope.
$6, Apollo 11 after splashdown.

1999, June 22   Perf. 14

| 2150 | A336 | $1.45 Sheet of 6, #a.-f. | 9.00 | 9.00 |

Souvenir Sheet

| 2151 | A336 | $6 multicolored | 6.00 | 6.00 |

Paintings by Hokusai (1760-1849) A337

Details or entire paintings — No. 2152:, each $2 a, Pilgrims at Kirifuri Waterfall. b, Kakura-Sato (rats looking at book, pulling on rope). c, Travelers on the Bridge by Ono Waterfall. d, Fast Cargo Boat Battling the Waves. e, Kakura-Sato (rats working with bales). f, Buufinfinh and Weeping cherry.

No. 2153, each $2: a, Cuckoo and Azalea. b, Soldiers (spear in left hand). c, Lover in the snow. d, Ghost of Koheiji. e, Soldiers (spear in right hand). f, Chinese Poet in Snow.

$5, Empress Jitó. $6, One Hundred Poems by One Hundred Poets.

Perf. 13½x13¾

1999, June 22   Litho.

Sheets of 6

| 2152-2153 | A337 | Set of 2 | 19.00 | 19.00 |

Souvenir Sheets

| 2154 | A337 | $5 multicolored | 4.50 | 4.50 |
| 2155 | A337 | $6 multicolored | 5.50 | 5.50 |

Johann Wolfgang von Goethe (1749-1832), Poet — A338

No. 2156: a, Faust perceives an astrological sign. b, Portrait of Goethe and Friedrich von Schiller (1759-1805). c, Faust tempted by Mephistopheles.
$6, Profile portrait of Goethe.

1999, June 22   Perf. 14

| 2156 | A338 | $2 Sheet of 3, #a.-c. | 5.00 | 5.00 |

Souvenir Sheet

| 2157 | A338 | $6 multicolored | 5.00 | 5.00 |

Rights of the Child — A339

No. 2158: a, Woman, child. b, Child in blue sweater. c, Two children.
$6, Dove, horiz.

1999, June 22   Litho.   Perf. 14

| 2158 | A339 | $3 Sheet of 3, #a.-c. | 7.50 | 7.50 |

Souvenir Sheet

| 2159 | A339 | $6 multicolored | 5.00 | 5.00 |

Queen Mother (b. 1900) — A340

A340a

Gold Frames

No. 2160: a, In 1939. b, In Australia, 1958. c, At Badminton, 1982.
d, Hatless, in 1982.

$6, In 1953.

1999, Aug. 4   Perf. 14

| 2160 | A340 | $2 Sheet of 4, #a.-d. + label | 7.50 | 7.50 |

Souvenir Sheet

Perf. 13¾

| 2161 | A340 | $6 multicolored | 5.00 | 5.00 |

No. 2161 contains one 38x51mm stamp.
Compare with Nos. 2345-2346. Backdrop of photo is more pink on No. 2161 than on No. 2346. No. 2161 has embossed arms in margin, while No. 2346 does not.

Litho. & Embossed
Die Cut Perf. 8¾
Without Gum

| 2161A | A340a | $20 gold & multi | 20.00 | 20.00 |

Flora & Fauna A341

Designs: 25c, Heliconia lobster claw. 65c, Broad winged hawk. $1, Anthurium. $1.55, Blue-headed hummingbird. $2, Bananaquit. $4 Agouti.

No. 2168: a, White-throated sparrow. b, Blue-winged teal. c, Raccoon. d, Alfalf butterfly. e, Bridge. f, Whitetail deer. g, Gray squirrel. h, Banded purple butterfly. i, Snowdrop. j, Bullfrog. k, Mushrooms. l, Large-blotched ensatina.

$5, Eastern chipmunk. $6, Black-footed ferret.

1999

| 2162-2167 | A341 | Set of 6 | 9.00 | 9.00 |

Sheet of 12

| 2168 | A341 | 90c #a.-l. | 10.00 | 10.00 |

Souvenir Sheets

| 2169 | A341 | $5 multicolored | 5.00 | 5.00 |
| 2170 | A341 | $6 multicolored | 6.00 | 6.00 |

A342   A343

Dominica Festival Commission: 25c, Domfesta. 55c, $5, Dominica's 21st anniv. as a republic. 65c, Carnival development committee. 90c, World Creole Music Festival.

1999   **Perf. 12½**
2171-2174 A342 Set of 4   2.00 2.00
Souvenir Sheet
Perf. 13¼
2175 A342 $5 multicolored   4.50 4.50
No. 2175 contains one 38x51mm stamp.

1999, Aug. 4   **Perf. 14**
Intl. Year of the Elderly: 25c, Family. 65c, Four people. 90c, Four people, one in chair.
2176 A343 Sheet of 3, #a.-c.   1.40 1.40

A345

A346

Christmas: 25c, Yellow-crowned parrot. 55c, Red bishop. 65c, Troupial. 90c, Puerto Rican woodpecker. $2, Mangrove cuckoo. $3, American robin.
$6, Mary with Child Beside the Wall, by Albrecht Dürer.

1999, Dec. 7   Litho.   Perf. 14
2178-2183 A345 Set of 6   6.75 6.75
Souvenir Sheet
2184 A345 $6 multi   5.25 5.25
Inscription on No. 2181 is misspelled.

Perf. 12¾x12½
1999, Dec. 31   Litho.
Millennium (Highlights of the early 13th Cent.) — #2185: a, Leonardo Fibonacci publishes "Liber Abaci," 1202. b, St. Francis of Assisi. c, Mongols conquer China. d, Children's Crusade begins, 1212. e, Magna Carta signed, 1215. f, Founding of Salamanca University, 1218. g, Snorri Sturluson writes "Prose Edda". h, Chinese painter Ma Yuan dies, 1225. i, Genghis Khan dies, 1227. j, Zen Buddhism in Japan. k, Sixth Crusade. l, Lubeck-Hamburg League. m, Inquisitions begin, 1231. n, Cordoba conquered by Castilians, 1236. o, Democracy in San Marino. p, Maimonides (60x40mm). q, Notre Dame Cathedral, Paris.
Highlights of the 1940s — No. 2186: a, Japan bombs Pearl Harbor. b, Churchill becomes Prime Minister of Great Britain. c, Regular television broadcasting begins in the US. d, Anne Frank hid in Amsterdam. e, D-Day Invasion. f, Yalta Conference. g, Establishment of the UN. h, Germany surrenders, concentration camps exposed. i, Russians hoist flag over gutted Reichstag building. j, Eniac computer. k, Independence for India. l, Bell Laboratories produce 1st transistor. m, Gandhi assassinated. n, Israel achieves statehood. o, Blockade of West Berlin, Berlin Airlift. p, Atomic bomb tested in New Mexico (60x40mm). q, Establishment of People's Republic of China.

Sheets of 17
2185 A346 55c #a.-q. + label   8.50 8.50
2186 A346 55c #a.-q. + label   8.50 8.50
See Nos. 2249-2252.

New Year 2000 (Year of the Dragon) A347

2000, Feb. 5   Perf. 13¾
2187 A347 $1.50 shown   1.50 1.50
Souvenir Sheet
2188 A347 $4 Dragon, horiz.   3.75 3.75
No. 2187 printed in sheets of 4.

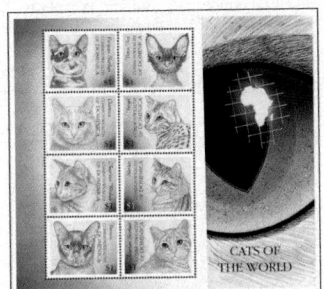

Cats — A348

No. 2189, each $1: a, European Shorthair. b, Devon Rex. c, Chartreux. d, Bengal. e, American Wirehair. f, Siberian. g, Burmese. h, American Shorthair.
No. 2190, each $1: a, Asian Longhair. b, Burmilla. c, Snowshoe. d, Pekeface Persian. e, Himalayan Persian. f, Japanese Bobtail. g, Seychelles Longhair. h, Exotic Shorthair.
Each $6: No. 2191, Awake cat. No. 2192, Sleeping cat.

2000, Feb. 21   Perf. 14¼
Sheets of 8, #a.-h.
2189-2190 A348 Set of 2   16.00 16.00
Souvenir Sheets
2191-2192 A348 Set of 2   12.00 12.00

Puppies — A349

No. 2193: a, Jack Russell Terrier. b, Shar Peis. c, Basset Hound. d, Boxers. e, Wirehaired Terrier. f, Golden Retrievers.
No. 2194, Beagle.

2000, Feb. 21   Perf. 14½x14¼
2193 A349 $1 Sheet of 6, #a.-f.   6.00 6.00
Souvenir Sheet
2194 A349 $6 multi   6.00 6.00

Flowers A350

Various flowers making up a photomosaic of Princess Diana.

2000, Apr. 3   Perf. 13¾
2195 A350 $1 Sheet of 8, #a.-h.   7.50 7.50
See No. 2225.

Butterflies A351

No. 2196, each $1.50: a, Giant swallowtail. b, Tiger pierid. c, Orange theope. d, White peacock. e, Blue tharops. f, Mosaic.
No. 2197, each $1.50: a, Banded king shoemaker. b, Figure-of-eight. c, Grecian shoemaker. d, Blue night. e, Monarch. f, Common morpho.
No. 2198, each $1.50: a, Orange-barred sulphur. b, Clorinde. c, Small flambeau. d, Small lace-wing. e, Polydamas swallowtail. f, Atala.
Each $6: No. 2199, Polydamas swallowtail, vert. No. 2200, Sloane's urania, vert. No. 2201, Blue-green reflector, vert.

2000, Apr. 10   Perf. 14
Sheets of 6, #a.-f.
2196-2198 A351 Set of 3   26.00 26.00
Souvenir Sheets
2199-2201 A351 Set of 3   17.50 17.50

Flowers — A352

Designs: 65c, Passion flower. 90c, Spray orchid. $1, Peach angel's trumpet. $4, Allamanda.
No. 2206, each $1.65: a, Bird of paradise. b, Lobster claw heliconia. c, Candle bush. d, Flor de San Miguel. e, Hibiscus. f, Oleander.
No. 2207, each $1.65: a, Anthurium. b, Fire ginger. c, Shrimp plant. d, Sky vine thunbergia. e, Ceriman. f, Morning glory.
Each $6: No. 2208, Bird of paradise, diff. No. 2109, Hibiscus, diff.

2000, Apr. 25   Litho.   Perf. 14
2202-2205 A352 Set of 4   6.00 6.00
Sheets of 6, #a-f
Perf. 13¾
2206-2207 A352 Set of 2   19.00 19.00
Souvenir Sheets
Perf. 13½x 13¾
2208-2209 A352 Set of 2   12.00 12.00
Size of stamps: Nos. 2106-2107, 32x48mm; Nos. 2108-2109, 38x51mm.

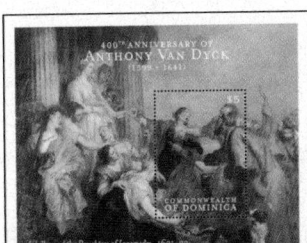

Paintings of Anthony Van Dyck — A353

No. 2210, each $1.65: a, Lady Jane Goodwin. b, Philip Herbert, 4th Earl of Pembroke. c, Philip, Lord Wharton. d, Sir Thomas Hammer. e, Olivia Porter, Wife of Enymion Porter. f, Sir Thomas Chaloner.
No. 2211, horiz. each $1.65: a, Ladies in Waiting. b, Thomas Wentworth, Earl of Strafford, with Sir Philip Mainwaring. c, Dorothy Rivers Savage, Viscountess Andover and Her Sister Lady Elizabeth Thimbleby. d, Mountjoy Blount, Earl of Newport, and Lord George Goring with a Page. e, Thomas Killigrew and

an Unidentified Man. f, Elizabeth Villiers, Lady Dalkeith, and Cecilia Killigrew.
No. 2212, horiz. each $1.65: a, The Ages of Man. b, Portrait of a Girl as Erminia Accompanied by Cupid. c, Cupid and Psyche. d, Vertumnus and Pomona. e, The Continence of Scipio. f, Diana and Endymion Surprised by a Satyr.
No. 2213, $5, Achilles and the Daughters of Lycomedes. No. 2214, $5, Amaryllis and Mirtillo. No. 2215, $6, Thomas Howard, 2nd Earl of Arundel, with Alathea, Countess of Arundel. Illustration reduced.

2000, May 29   Perf. 13¾
Sheets of 6, #a-f
2210-2212 A353 Set of 3   27.00 27.00
Souvenir Sheets
2213-2214 A353 Set of 2   9.00 9.00
2215 A353 $6 multi   5.50 5.50

First Zeppelin Flight, Cent. — A354

No. 2216: a, Count Ferdinand von Zeppelin (1838-1917). b, First takeoff of LZ-1. c, LZ-10 over field. d, LZ-6 and Deutschland in hangar. e, Arrival of Z-4 at Luneville. f, Victoria Luise.
No. 2217, LZ-1, diff.
Illustration reduced.

2000, June 21   Litho.   Perf. 14
2216 A354 $1.65 Sheet of 6, #a-f   9.00 9.00
Souvenir Sheet
2217 A354 $6 multi   5.50 5.50

Berlin Film Festival, 50th Anniv. — A355

No. 2218: a, Director Satyajit Ray. b, Mahangar. c, Fanfan La Tulipe. d, Le Salaire de la Peur. e, Les Cousins. f, Hon Dansade en Sommar.
No. 2219, Buffalo Bill and the Indians.
Illustration reduced.

2000, June 21
2218 A355 $1.65 Sheet of 6, #a-f   9.00 9.00
Souvenir Sheet
2219 A355 $6 multi   5.50 5.50

100th Test Match at Lord's Ground — A356

2000, June 21
2220 A356 $4 Norbert Philip   3.50 3.50
Souvenir Sheet
2221 A356 $6 Lord's Ground   5.50 5.50

Souvenir Sheets

2000 Summer Olympics,
Sydney — A357

a, Jesse Owens. b, Pole vault. c, Lenin Stadium Moscow, Soviet Union flag. d, Ancient Greek discus thrower.
Illustration reduced.

2000, June 21
2222 A357 $2 Sheet of 4, #a-d   8.00 8.00

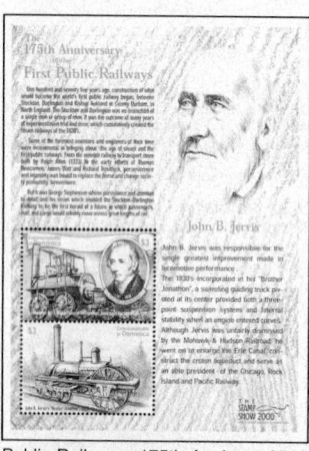

Public Railways, 175th Anniv. — A358

No. 2223: a, Locomotion No. 1, George Stephenson. b, Brother Jonathon.
Illustration reduced.

2000, June 21
2223 A358 $3 Sheet of 2, #a-b   6.25 6.25
The Stamp Show 2000, London.

Johann Sebastian Bach — A359

Illustration reduced.

2000, June 21
2224 A359 $6 multi   5.50 5.50

Flower Type of 2000
Various pictures of religious sites making up a photomosaic of Pope John Paul II.

2000, June 21   Litho.   Perf. 13¾
2225 A350 $1 Sheet of 8, #a-h   8.00 8.00

Apollo-Soyuz Mission, 25th
Anniv. — A360

No. 2226, vert.: a, Saturn IB launch vehicle. b, Apollo 18. c, Donald K. Slayton.
$6, Apollo and Soyuz docking.
Illustration reduced.

2000, June 21   Perf. 14
2226 A360 $3 Sheet of 3, #a-c   9.50 9.50
Souvenir Sheet
2227 A360 $6 multi   6.00 6.00

Souvenir Sheet

Albert Einstein (1879-1955) — A361

2000, June 21   Perf. 14¼
2228 A361 $6 multi   5.50 5.50

Prince William, 18th Birthday — A362

No. 2229: a, In ski gear. b, In jacket and red sweater. c, In suit and tie. d, In plaid shirt.
$6, With Prince Harry.
Illustration reduced.

2000, June 22   Perf. 14
2229 A362 $1.65 Sheet of 4,
     #a-d   6.25 6.25
Souvenir Sheet
     Perf. 13¾
2230 A362 $6 multi   5.50 5.50
No. 2229 contains four 28x42mm stamps.

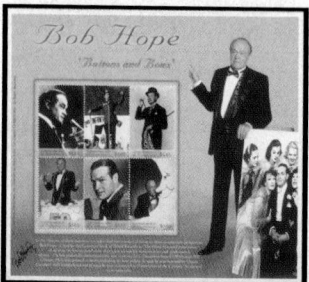

Bob Hope — A363

No. 2231: a, Microphone at right. b, Entertaining troops. c, Wearing bowler. d, Standing in cake. e, Microphone at left. f, With moon.
Illustration reduced.

2000, Aug. 7   Perf. 14
2231 A363 $1.65 Sheet of 6,
     #a-f   10.00 10.00

Monty Python and the Holy Grail, 25th
Anniv. — A364

No. 2232: a, Close-up of Eric Idle. b, Terry Jones, Graham Chapman and John Cleese as three-headed giant, horiz. c, Knights facing castle wall. d, Chapman as King Arthur, with helmeted knight. e, Beheaded knight. f, Armless and legless Black Knight and King Arthur.

2000, Aug. 7   Perf. 13¾
2232 A364 90c Sheet of 6, #a-f   5.25 5.25

Souvenir Sheet

Popes — A365

No. 2233: a, Clement X, 1670-76. b, Innocent X, 1644-55. c, Nicholas V, 1447-55. d, Martin V, 1417-31. e, Julius III, 1550-55. f, Innocent XII, 1691-1700.
$6, Clement XIV, 1769-74.
Illustration reduced.

2000, Sept. 5
2233 A365 $1.65 Sheet of 6,
     #a-f   10.00 10.00
Souvenir Sheet
2234 A365 $6 multi   5.50 5.50

Monarchs — A366

No. 2235: a, Edward IV of England, 1461-83. b, Peter the Great of Russia, 1682-1725. c, Henry VI of England, 1422-61. d, Henry III of England, 1216-72. e, Richard III of England, 1483-85. f, Edward I of England, 1272-1307.
$6, Henry VIII of England, 1509-47.
Illustration reduced.

2000, Sept. 5
2235 A366 $1.65 Sheet of 6,
     #a-f   10.00 10.00
Souvenir Sheet
2236 A366 $6 multi   5.50 5.50

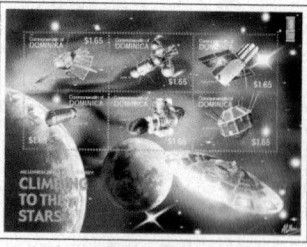

World Stamp Expo 2000,
Anaheim — A367

Spacecraft — No. 2237, $1.65: a, Explorer 14. b, Luna 16. c, Copernicus. d, Explorer 16. e, Luna 10. f, Arybhattan.
No. 2238, $1.65: a, Essa 8. b, Echo 1. c, Topex Poseidon. d, Diademe. e, Early Bird. f, Molnya.
#2239, $6, Hipparcos. #2240, $6, Eole.
Illustration reduced.

2000, June 21   Litho.   Perf. 14¼x14
Sheets of 6, #a-f
2237-2238 A367   Set of 2   20.00 20.00
Souvenir Sheets
2239-2240 A367   Set of 2   11.00 11.00

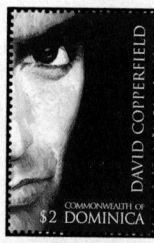 David Copperfield,
Magician — A368

2000, Aug. 8   Perf. 14
2241 A368 $2 multi   1.75 1.75
Printed in sheets of 4.

Souvenir Sheet

Female Recording Groups of the
1960s — A369

No. 2242 — The Crystals, yellow spotlight covering: a, UR, LL and LR corners. b, UL and LL corners. c, UR and LR corners. d, UL, LL and LR corners.
Illustration reduced.

2000, Aug. 8
2242 A369 90c Sheet of 4, #a-d   3.50 3.50

Christmas — A370

Angel: 25c, No. 2247a, Looking right, purple and yellow green background. 65c, No. 2247b, At left, looking left, purple background. 90c, No. 2247c, At right, purple and orange background. $5, No. 2247d, At center, blue and purple background.

2000, Dec. 4
2243-2246 A370   Set of 4   6.25 6.25
Sheet of 4
2247 A370 $1.90 #a-d   7.00 7.00
Souvenir Sheet
2248 A370 $6 Angel   5.50 5.50

Millennium Type of 1999

Chinese Art — No. 2249, 55c: a, Eight Prize Steeds, by Giuseppe Castiglione. b, Oleanders, by Wu Hsi Tsai. c, Mynah and Autumn Flowers, by Chang Hsiung. d, Hen and Chicks Beneath Chrysanthemums, by Chu Ch'ao. e, Long Living Pine and Crane, by Xugu. f, Flowers and Fruits, by Chu Lien. g, Lotus and Willow, by Pu Hua. h, Kuan-Yin, by Ch'ien Hui-An. i, Human Figures, by Jen hsun. j, Han-Shan and Shih-Te, by Ren Yi. k, Landscape and Human Figure, by Jen Yu. l, Poetic Thoughts While Walking With a Staff, by Wangchen. m, Peony, by Chen Heng-Ko. n, Plum and Orchids, by Wu Chang-Shih. o, Monkey, by Kao Chi-Feng. p, Grapes and Locust, by Ch'i Pai-Shih and Galloping Horse, by Xu Beihong (60x40mm). q, The Beauty, by Lin Fengmian.

History of Change — No. 2250, 55c: a, Star charts. b, Precision tools. c, Science of the stars. d, Investigation into healing a human being. e, Sharing of medical information. f, Church. g, Water alarm clock. h, Weighted clock. i, Spring-loaded miniature clock. j, New technology of glass blowing. k, First screws. l, Wood lathe. m, New systems for assembly blocks for ships. n, Interchangeable parts for rifles. o, Study of movement. p, Efficiency and the Industrial Revolution (60x40mm). q, Concept of efficiency.

Highlights of the 1960s — No. 2251, 55c: a, First birth control pill developed. b, Yuri Gagarin becomes first man in space. c, The first hit for the Beatles in Britain. d, Assassination of John F. Kennedy. e, Dr. Martin Luther King's "I Have a Dream" speech. f, Betty Friedan writes "The Feminine Mystique." g, Kenya gains independence. h, U.S. Surgeon General warns about smoking-related health hazards. i, U.S. Congress passes Civil Rights Act. j, U.S. increases military presence in South Viet Nam. k, Ernesto "Che" Guevara. l, First heart transplant. m, Israel wins Six-day War. n, Ho Chi Minh dies. o, First man on the Moon. p, Communists build wall to divide East and West Berlin (60x40mm). q, Woodstock rock concert.

Highlights of the late 14th Century — No. 2252: a, Minnesingers. b, Acampitzin, King of the Aztecs. c, Black Death eases. d, Giotto's campanile built. e, First French franc. f, Ming Dynasty in China. g, Tamerlane begins conquest of Asia. h, Triumph of Death painted by Francesco Traini. i, Robin Hood. j, Geoffrey Chaucer writes "The Canterbury Tales." k, Succession dispute in Japan. l, Jewish exodus from France. m, Temple of the Golden Pavilion built . n, Strasbourg Cathedral built. o, Alhambra Palace (60x40mm). p, Ife bronzes in Nigeria.

2000, Dec. 31   **Perf. 12¾x12½**
Sheets of 17, #a-q

2249-2251 A346 Set of 3   26.00 26.00
2252 A347 65c Sheet of 17,
        #a-h, j-p, 2 #i   10.00 10.00

Hummingbirds — A371

No. 2253, $1.25: a, Green-throated carib. b, Bee, on branch. c, Bee, in flight. d, Bahama woodstar. e, Antillean mango. f, Blue-headed.
No. 2254, $1.65: a, Eastern streamertail. b, Purple-throated carib. c, Vervain. d, Bahama woodstar. e, Puerto Rican emerald. f, Antillean crested.
No. 2255, $5, Feeders. No. 2256, $6, Hispaniolan.
Illustration reduced.

2000, Dec. 18   **Litho.**   **Perf. 14**
Sheets of 6, #a-f

2253-2254 A371 Set of 2   17.00 17.00
Souvenir Sheets

2255-2256 A371 Set of 2   11.00 11.00
Misspellings abound on Nos. 2253-2254.

New Year 2001 (Year of the Snake) A372

2001, Jan. 2   **Perf. 12x12¼**
2257 A372 $1.20 multi   1.00 1.00
Printed in sheets of 4.

Fauna A373

Designs: 15c, Puerto Rican crested toad. 20c, Axolotl. $1.90, Panamanian golden frog. $2.20, Manatee.
No. 2262, $1.45: a, St. Vincent parrot. b, Indigo macaw. c, Cock of the rock. d, Cuban solenodon. e, Cuban hutia. f, Chinchilla.
No. 2263, $1.45: a, South American flamingo. b, Golden conure. c, Ocelot. d, Giant armadillo. e, Margay. f, Maned wolf.
No. 2264, $6, Anteater. No. 2265, $6, Hawksbill turtle.

2000, Dec. 18   **Litho.**   **Perf. 14**
2258-2261 A373 Set of 4   5.00 5.00
Sheets of 6, #a-f

2262-2263 A373 Set of 2   17.00 17.00
Souvenir Sheets

2264-2265 A373 Set of 2   12.00 12.00

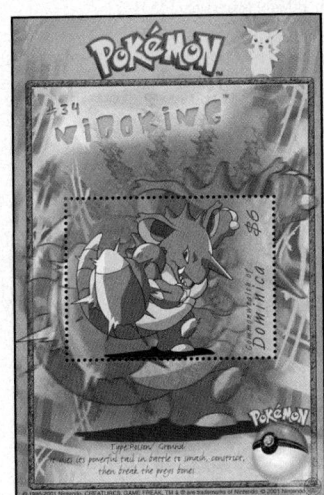

Pokémon — A374

No. 2266, horiz.: a, Butterfree. b, Bulbasaur. c, Caterpie. d, Charmander. e, Squirtle. f, Pidgeotto.

2001, Feb.   **Perf. 13¾**
2266 A374 $1.65 Sheet of 6, #a-f   9.00 9.00
Souvenir Sheet

2267 A374 $6 Nidoking   5.50 5.50

A375

Marine Life A376

Designs: No. 2268, 15c, Banded sea snake. 25c, Soldier fish. 55c, Banner fish. No. 2271, 90c, Crown of thorns starfish.
No. 2272, 15c, Fish. 65c, Ray. No. 2274, 90c, Octopus. $3, Fish, diff.
No. 2276, $1.65: a, White-tip reef shark, lionfish, sergeant major. b, Blue-striped snappers. c, Great hammerhead shark, stovepipe sponge, pink vase sponge. d, Hawaiian monk seal, blue tube coral. e, Seahorse, common clownfish, red feather star coral. f, Bat starfish, brown octopus.
No. 2277, $1.65: a, Red sponge, shoal of Anthias. b, Orange-striped triggerfish. c, Coral grouper, soft tree coral. d, Peacock fan worms, gorgonian sea fan. e, Sweetlips, sea fan. f, Giant clam, golden cup coral.
No. 2278: a, Shark. b, Starfish. c, Seahorse. d, Fish. e, Crab. f, Eel.
No. 2279, $5, Royal angelfish. No. 2280, $5, Pink anemone fish. No. 2281, Turtle.

2001, Feb. 27   **Perf. 14**
2268-2271 A375 Set of 4   2.00 2.00
2272-2275 A376 Set of 4   5.00 5.00
Sheets of 6, #a-f

2276-2277 A375 Set of 2   19.00 19.00
2278 A376 $2 Sheet of 6, #a-f 11.00 11.00
Souvenir Sheets

2279-2280 A375 Set of 2   10.00 10.00
2281 A376 $5 multi   5.00 5.00

Phila Nippon '01, Japan — A377

Art: 25c, Gathering of Chinese Women, by Tsuji Kako. 55c, Village by Bamboo Grove, by Takeuchi Seiho. 65c, Mountain Village in Spring, by Suzuki Hyakunen. 90c, Gentleman Amusing Himself, by Domoto Insho. $1, Calmness of Spring Light, by Seiho. $2, Su's Embankment on a Spring Morning, by Tomioka Tessai.
No. 2288, $1.65: a, Thatched Cottages in the Willows, by Kako. b, Joy in the Garden, by Kako. c, Azalea and butterfly, by Kikuchi Hobun. d, Pine Grove, by Kako. e, Woodcutters Talking in Autumn Valley, by Kubota Beisen.
No. 2289, $1.65: a, Waterfowl in Snow, by Kako. b, Heron and Willow, by Kako. c, Crow and Cherry Blossoms, by Hobun. d, Chrysanthemum Immortal, by Yamamoto Shunkyo. e, Cranes of Immortality, by Kako.
No. 2290, $6, Kamo Riverbank in the Misty Rain, by Kako. No. 2291, $6, Diamond Gate, by Kako. No. 2292, $6, Woman, by Suzuki Harunobu.

2001, May 15   **Litho.**   **Perf. 14**
2282-2287 A377 Set of 6   5.25 5.25
Sheets of 5, #a-e

2288-2289 A377 Set of 2   15.00 15.00
Souvenir Sheets
Perf. 13¾

2290-2292 A377 Set of 3   16.00 16.00
Nos. 2290-2292 each contain one 38x51mm stamp.

Queen Victoria (1819-1901) — A378

No. 2293: a, Prince Albert in uniform. b, Victoria with silver crown. c, Victoria with gold crown. d, Albert in suit.
$6, Victoria as old woman.

2001, May 15   **Perf. 14**
2293 A378 $2 Sheet of 4, #a-d   7.25 7.25
Souvenir Sheet
Perf. 13¾

2294 A378 $6 multi   5.50 5.50
No. 2294 contains one 38x51mm stamp.

Queen Elizabeth II, 75th Birthday — A379

No. 2295: a, With crown. b, With white dress. c, Formal portrait by Pietro Annigoni. d, With orange coat. e, With child. f, With green dress.
$6, In uniform.

2001, May 15   **Perf. 14**
2295 A379 $1.20 Sheet of 6, #a-f 6.25 6.25
Souvenir Sheet

2296 A379 $6 multi   5.50 5.50

Toulouse-Lautrec Paintings — A380

No. 2297: a, Two Women Waltzing. b, The Medical Inspection. c, The Two Girlfriends. d, Woman Pulling Up Her Stocking.

2001, May 15		**Litho.**		**Perf. 13¾**		
2297	A380	$2 Sheet of 4, #a-d			7.25	7.25
		Souvenir Sheet				
2298	A380	$6 Self-portrait			5.50	5.50

Giuseppe Verdi (1813-1901), Opera Composer — A381

No. 2299: a, Verdi. b, Lady Macbeth. c, Orchestra. d, Score.

2001, May 15				**Perf. 14**		
2299	A381	$2 Sheet of 4, #a-d			7.25	7.25
		Souvenir Sheet				
2300	A381	$6 Verdi, score			5.50	5.50

Mushrooms A382

Designs: 15c, Cantharellus cibarius. 25c, Hygrocybe pratensis. 55c, Leccinum aurantiacum. $3, Mycena haematopus.
No. 2305, 90c, horiz.: a, Caesar's amanita. b, Agaricus augustus. c, Clitocybe nuda. d, Hygrocybe plavescens. e, Stropharia kaufmanii. f, Hygrophorus speciosus.
No. 2306, $2: a, Marasmiellus candidus. b, Calostoma cinnabarina. c, Cantharellus infundibuliformis. d, Hygrocybe punicea. e, Basket stinkhorn. f, Agrocybe praecox.
No. 2307, $5, Fly agaric, horiz. No. 2308, $5, Gymnopilus spectabilis, horiz.

2001, June 18						
2301-2304	A382	Set of 4			4.50	4.50
		Sheets of 6, #a-f				
2305-2306	A382	Set of 2			18.00	18.00
		Souvenir Sheets				
2307-2308	A382	Set of 2			10.00	10.00

Mao Zedong (1893-1976) — A383

No. 2309 — Picture from: a, 1945. b, 1926. c, 1949.
$3, 1930.

2001, May 15		**Litho.**		**Perf. 14**		
2309	A383	$2 Sheet of 3, #a-c			5.25	5.25
		Souvenir Sheet				
2310	A383	$3 multi			2.75	2.75

Monet Paintings — A384

No. 2311, horiz.: a, The Basin of Argenteuil. b, The Bridge at Argenteuil. c, The Railway Bridge, Argenteuil. d, The Seine Bridge at Argenteuil.
$6, Woman with a Parasol — Madame Monet and Her Son.

2001, May 15				**Perf. 13¾**		
2311	A384	$2 Sheet of 4, #a-d			7.25	7.25
		Souvenir Sheet				
2312	A384	$6 multi			5.25	5.25

Fauna — A385

No. 2313: a, St. Vincent parrot. b, Painted bunting. c, Jamaican giant anole. d, White-fronted capuchin. e, Strand racerunner. f, Agouti.
No. 2314: a, Cook's tree boa. b, Tamandua. c, Common iguana. d, Solenodon.
No. 2315, $5, Purple gallinule. No. 2316, $5, Rufous-tailed jacamar. No. 2317, $5, Ruby-throated hummingbird, horiz. No. 2318, $5, Bottlenose dolphins, horiz.

2001, Sept. 3				**Perf. 14**		
2313	A385	$1.45 Sheet of 6, #a-f			8.75	8.75
2314	A385	$2 Sheet of 4, #a-d			8.25	8.25
		Souvenir Sheets				
2315-2318	A385	Set of 4			19.00	19.00

Birds — A386

Designs: 5c, Yellow warbler. 10c, Palmchat. 15c, Snowy cotinga. 20c, Blue-gray gnatcatcher. 25c, Belted kingfisher. 55c, Red-legged thrush. 65c, Bananaquit. 90c, Yellow-bellied sapsucker. $1, White-tailed tropicbird. $1.45, Ruby-throated hummingbird. $1.90, Painted bunting. $2, Great frigatebird. $5, Brown trembler. $10, Red-footed booby. $20, Sooty tern.

2001, Sept. 3		**Litho.**		**Perf. 14¾x14**		
2319	A386	5c multi			.20	.20
2320	A386	10c multi			.20	.20
2321	A386	15c multi			.20	.20
2322	A386	20c multi			.20	.20
2323	A386	25c multi			.20	.20
2324	A386	55c multi			.50	.50
2325	A386	65c multi			.55	.55
2326	A386	90c multi			.85	.85
2327	A386	$1 multi			1.00	1.00
2328	A386	$1.45 multi			1.40	1.40
2329	A386	$1.90 multi			1.75	1.75
2330	A386	$2 multi			2.00	2.00
2331	A386	$5 multi			5.00	5.00
2332	A386	$10 multi			10.00	10.00
2333	A386	$20 multi			19.00	19.00
Nos. 2319-2333 (15)					43.05	43.05

No. 2323 exists dated "2005."
See No. 2513.

Photomosaic of Queen Elizabeth II — A387

2001, Nov. 15				**Perf. 14**		
2334	A387	$1 multi			1.00	1.00

Issued in sheets of 8.

Christmas — A388

Paintings by Giovanni Bellini: 25c, Madonna and Child. 65c, Madonna and Child, diff. 90c, Baptism of Christ. $1.20, Madonna and Child, diff. $4, Madonna and Child, diff.
$6, Madonna and Child with Sts. Catherine and Mary Magdalene.

2001, Dec. 3						
2335-2339	A388	Set of 5			6.75	6.75
		Souvenir Sheet				
2340	A388	$6 multi			5.50	5.50

2002 World Cup Soccer Championships, Japan and Korea — A389

No. 2341, $2: a, US team, 1950. b, Poster, 1954. c, Poster, 1958. d, Zozimo, 1962. e, Gordon Banks, 1966. f, Pelé, 1970.
No. 2342, $2: a, Daniel Passarella, 1978. b, Paolo Rossi, 1982. c, Diego Maradona, 1986. d, Poster, 1990. e, Seo Jungulon, 1994. f, Jürgen Klinsmann, 1998.
No. 2343, $5, Face on World Cup, 1930. No. 2344, $5, Face and globe on Jules Rimet Trophy, 2002.

2001, Dec. 13				**Perf. 13¾x14¼**		
		Sheets of 6, #a-f				
2341-2342	A389	Set of 2			21.00	21.00
		Souvenir Sheets				
		Perf. 14¼				
2343-2344	A389	Set of 2			10.00	10.00

Queen Mother Type of 1999 Redrawn

No. 2345: a, In 1939. b, In Australia, 1958. c, At Badminton, 1982. d, Hatless, in 1982.
$6, In 1953.

2001, Dec.				**Perf. 14**		
		Yellow Orange Frames				
2345	A340	$2 Sheet of 4, #a-d, + label			7.00	7.00

		Souvenir Sheet				
		Perf. 13¾				
2346	A340	$6 multi			5.25	5.25

Queen Mother's 101st birthday. No. 2346 contains one 38x51mm stamp with a bluer backdrop than that found on No. 2161. Sheet margins of Nos. 2345-2346 lack embossing and gold arms and frames found on Nos. 2160-2161.

Souvenir Sheets

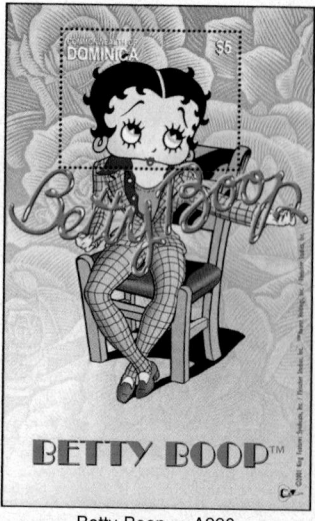

Betty Boop — A390

Betty Boop: No. 2347, $5, In chair, pink rose background. No. 2348, $5, Wearing blue blouse, in jungle. No. 2349, $5, With heart and stars, cat with film reel. No. 2350, $5, Wearing nurse's cap.

2001, Oct. 1		**Litho.**		**Perf. 13¾**		
2347-2350	A390	Set of 4			18.00	18.00

The Three Stooges — A391

No. 2351: a, Man, Larry, Moe with sledgehammer, Joe Besser. b, Larry, woman, Joe Besser, Moe. c, Joe Besser, Larry and Moe on hands and knees. d, Larry grabbing throat of woman holding Joe Besser and Moe. e, Joe Besser drinking from baby bottle, pony, Moe and Larry. f, Military policeman, Joe Besser, Larry, woman. g, Larry. h, Joe Besser. i, Moe.
No. 2352, $5, Moe and Larry, "On the air" sign. No. 2353, $5, Larry and pony.

2001, Oct. 1		**Litho.**		**Perf. 13¾**		
2351	A391	$1 Sheet of 9, #a-i			8.00	8.00
		Souvenir Sheets				
2352-2353	A391	Set of 2			9.00	9.00

Souvenir Sheet

New Year 2002 (Year of the Horse) — A392

No. 2354: a, Man with pole, horse. b, Horses grazing. c, Man currying horse. d, Horses with heads up.

2001, Dec. 17   **Perf. 14**
2354 A392 $1.65 Sheet of 4, #a-d   6.00 6.00

Reign of Queen Elizabeth II, 50th Anniv. — A393

No. 2355: a, Wearing blue coat. b, With Prince Philip. c, Wearing tiara. d, Wearing flowered hat.
$6, With Prince Philip, diff.

2002, Feb. 6   **Perf. 14¼**
2355 A393 $2 Sheet of 4, #a-d   7.00 7.00
Souvenir Sheet
2356 A393 $6 multi   5.00 5.00

United We Stand — A394

2002, Feb.   **Perf. 13½x13¼**
2357 A394 $2 multi   1.50 1.50
Printed in sheets of 4.

Shirley Temple in "Just Around the Corner" — A395

No. 2358, horiz.: a, Temple, woman with dogs. b, Temple, man and woman. c, Temple and man. d, Boy eating turkey leg, Temple carving turkey. e, Temple with old man. f, Temple with group of boys.

No. 2359: a, Boy, Temple with purse. b, Man and Temple using fingers as guns. c, Temple and man. d, Temple cutting boy's hair.
$6, Temple with black man on toadstool.

2002, Apr. 8   **Perf. 12¼**
2358 A395 $1.90 Sheet of 6, #a-f   10.00 10.00
2359 A395 $2 Sheet of 4, #a-d   7.25 7.25
Souvenir Sheet
2360 A395 $6 multi   5.25 5.25

Japanese Art — A396

No. 2361, $1.20: a, The Courtesan Tsukioka of the Teahouse Hyogo-Ya, by Eisui Ichirakutei. b, Woman and Servant in the Snow, by Choki Eishosai. c, The Courtesan Shiratsuyu of the Teahouse Wakana-Ya, by Eisho Chokosai. d, Ohisa of the Takashima-Ya, by Toyokuni Utagawa. e, Woman and a Cat, by Kunimasa Utagawa. f, One of "Genre Scenes of Beauties," by Eisen Keisai.
No. 2362, $1.65: a, Women Inside and Outside a Mosquito Net, by Harushige Suzuki. b, Komachi at Shimizu, by Harushige Suzuki. c, Women Viewing Plum Blossoms, by Harunobu Suzuki. d, Women Cooling Themselves at Shijogawara in Kyoto, by Toyohiro Utagawa. e, Woman Reading a Letter, by Utamaro Kitagawa. f, Women Dressed for the Kashima Dance at the Niwaka Festival, by Utamaro Kitagawa.
No. 2363, $1.90: a, Actor Kiyotaro Iwai, by Kunimasa Utagawa. b, Actors Hiriji Otani III and Ryuzo Arashi, by Sharaku Toshusai. c, Actor Komazo Ichikawa II, by Shunko Katsukawa. d, Actors Yaozo Ichikawa and Hangoro Sakata III, by Sharaku Toshusai. e, Actor Torazo Tanimura, by Sharaku Toshusai. f, Actor Kiyotaro Iwai as Oishi, by Toyokuni Utagawa.
No. 2464, $5, Actor Riko Nakamura, by Shunsho Katsukawa. No. 2365, $5, Actors Hanshiro Iwai IV and Sojuro Sawamura III, by Kiyonaga Torii, horiz. No. 2366, $6, Ofuji, Daughter of the Motoyanagi-Ya, by Harunobu Suzuki.

2002, June 17   **Perf. 14¼**
Sheets of 6, #a-f
2361-2363 A396 Set of 3   24.00 24.00
Souvenir Sheets
2364-2366 A396 Set of 3   12.00 12.00
Souvenir Sheet

Intl. Year of Mountains — A397

No. 2367: a, Mt. Everest. b, Mt. Kilimanjaro. c, Mt. McKinley.

2002, July 15   **Perf. 14**
2367 A397 $2 Sheet of 3, #a-c   5.00 5.00

2002 Winter Olympics, Salt Lake City A398

Designs: No. 2368, $2, Skiing. No. 2369, $2, Bobsled.

2002, July 15   **Perf. 13½**
2368-2369 A398 Set of 2   3.50 3.50
   a. Souvenir sheet, #2368-2369   3.50 3.50

First Solo Trans-Atlantic Flight, 75th Anniv. — A399

No. 2370: a, Charles Lindbergh and Spirit of St. Louis. b, Charles and Anne Morrow Lindbergh.
$6, Charles Lindbergh and Spirit of St. Louis, diff.

2002, July 15   **Perf. 14**
2370 A399 $3 Sheet of 2, #a-b   5.00 5.00
Souvenir Sheet
2371 A399 $6 multi   5.00 5.00

Popeye in New York — A400

No. 2372, $1: a, Olive Oyl. b, Brutus. c, Sweet Pea. d, Wimpy. e, Jeep. f, Popeye.
No. 2373, $1.90: a, Popeye and Olive Oyl, giraffe at Bronx Zoo. b, Popeye and Olive Oyl, Statue of Liberty. c, Popeye, Olive Oyl, Empire State Building. d, Popeye skating at Rockefeller Center. e, Popeye at Yankee Stadium. f, Popeye helping firefighters.
No. 2374, $6, Popeye, Atlas Statue, Rockefeller Center. No. 2375, $6, Popeye, Olive Oyl and Radio City Music Hall Rockettes, horiz.

2002, July 22
Sheets of 6, #a-f
2372-2373 A400 Set of 2   15.00 15.00
Souvenir Sheets
2374-2375 A400 Set of 2   10.50 10.50

20th World Scout Jamboree, Thailand — A401

No. 2376: a, Lord Robert Baden-Powell (facing forward). b, Lady Olave Baden-Powell. c, Maceo Johnson.
$6, Lord Baden-Powell (profile).

2002, July 15   **Litho.**   **Perf. 14¼x14**
2376 A401 $3 Sheet of 3, #a-c   8.00 8.00
Souvenir Sheet
2377 A401 $6 multi   5.25 5.25

Birds, Insects, Moths and Whales — A402

No. 2378, $1.50, vert. — Birds: a, Brown trembler. b, Snowy ctinga. c, Bananaquit. d, Painted bunting. e, Belted kingfisher. f, Ruby-throated hummingbird.
No. 2379, $1.50, vert. — Insects: a, Field cricket. b, Migratory grasshopper. c, Honey bee. d, Hercules beetle. e, Black ant. f, Cicada.
No. 2380, $1.50, vert. — Moths: a, Carolina sphinx. b, White-lined sphinx. c, Orizaba silkmoth. d, Hieroglyphic moth. e, Hickory tussock moth. f, Diva moth.
No. 2381, $1.50, vert. — Whales: a, Sei. b, Killer. c, Blue. d, White. e, Pygmy. f, Sperm.
No. 2382, $6, Yellow-bellied sapsucker. No. 2383, $6, Bumble bee. No. 2384, $6, Ornate moth. No. 2385, $6, Gray whale.

2002, July 29   **Perf. 14**
Sheets of 6, #a-f
2378-2381 A402 Set of 4   32.50 32.50
Souvenir Sheets
2382-2385 A402 Set of 4   20.00 20.00

A403

A404

Amphilex 2002 Intl. Stamp Exhibition,
Amsterdam — A405

No. 2386 — Dutch Nobel Prize winners: a,
Willem Einthoven, Medicine, 1924. b, Nobel
Economics medal. c, Peter J. W. Debye,
Chemistry, 1936. d, Frits Zernike, Physics,
1953. e, Jan Tinbergen, Economics, 1969. f,
Simon van der Meer, Physics, 1984.
No. 2387 — Dutch lighthouses: a, Marken.
b, Harlingen. c, Den Oever. d, De Ven. e, Urk.
f, Oosterleek.
No. 2388 — Traditional women's costumes:
a, South Holland woman with small white head
covering (facing forward). b, Zeeland woman
with large white head covering (facing backwards). c, Limburg woman with black scarf.

2002, Aug. 30   Perf. 13½x13¼
2386 A403 $1.50 Sheet of 6,
          #a-f   8.00   8.00
2387 A404 $1.50 Sheet of 6,
          #a-f   8.00   8.00
            Perf. 13½
2388 A405 $3 Sheet of 3,
          #a-c   8.00   8.00

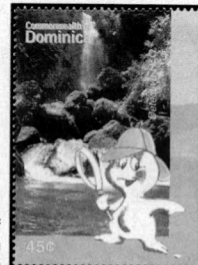

Intl. Year of
Ecotourism
A406

Island scenes and cartoon characters: 45c,
Detective H2O. 50c, Factman. 55c, B.B. 60c,
Stanley the Starfish. 90c, Toxi. $1.20, Adopt.
$6, Litterbit.

2002, Oct. 16   Perf. 14¼
2389-2394 A406 Set of 6   3.25   3.25
            Souvenir Sheet
2395 A406 $6 multi   5.00   5.00

Elvis Presley
(1935-77)
A407

2002, Oct. 28   Perf. 13¾
2396 A407 $1.50 multi   1.10   1.10
    Printed in sheets of 6 stamps with slightly
differing frames.

Amerigo Vespucci (1454-1512),
Explorer — A408

No. 2397: a, Compass rose. b, Vespucci
with map. c, Map scroll.
$5, Two men.

2002, Nov. 28   Perf. 13¾
2397 A409 $3 Sheet of 3, #a-c   8.00   8.00
            Souvenir Sheet
            Perf. 14
2398 A409 $5 multi   4.50   4.50
    No. 2397 contains three 50x38mm stamps.

Pres. John F. Kennedy (1917-
63) — A409

No. 2399, $1.90: a, Wearing military uni-
form. b, With red denomination at UL. c, With
blue denomination at UR. d, Wearing tan suit.
No. 2400, $1.90 (denominations at UL in
blue): a, Wearing red tie. b, Wearing blue tie
(profile). c, Wearing black tie. d, With hand on
chin.

2002, Dec. 16   Perf. 14
        Sheets of 4, #a-d
2399-2400 A409 Set of 2   13.50 13.50

Pres. Ronald Reagan — A410

No. 2401, $1.90: a, Wearing cowboy hat. b,
Wearing blue green sweater. c, Wearing red
sweater. d, Wearing blue sweater.
No. 2402, $1.90, horiz.: a, Wearing blue
shirt, and with wife, Nancy. b, Nancy and US
flag. c, Ronald. d, Wearing pink shirt, and with
wife.

2002, Dec. 16   Litho.   Perf. 14
        Sheets of 4, #a-d
2401-2402 A410 Set of 2   13.50 13.50

Princess Diana (1961-97) — A411

2002, Dec. 16
2403 A411 $1.90 Sheet of 4,
          #a-d   7.00   7.00
            Souvenir Sheet
2404 A411 $5 multi   4.50   4.50

Elizabeth "Ma
Pampo" Israel,
128th
Birthday — A412

2003, Jan. 27   Perf. 13½x13¼
2405 A412 90c multi   .70   .70

New Year 2003
(Year of the
Ram) — A413

2003, Feb. 10   Perf. 13¾
2406 A413 $1.65 multi   1.25   1.25
    Printed in sheets of 4.

        Souvenir Sheets

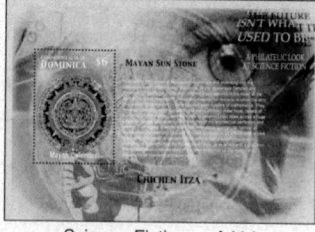

Science Fiction — A414

Designs: No. 2407, $6, Mayan calendar. No.
2408, $6, Atlas. No. 2409, $6, Confucius. No.
2410, $6, Nazca Lines. No. 2411, $6, Pres.
Franklin D. Roosevelt and Pres. John F. Kennedy. No. 2412, $6, Zoroaster.

2003, Feb. 10   Perf. 13¼
2407-2412 A414 Set of 6   27.50 27.50

A415

Coronation of Queen Elizabeth II, 50th
Anniv. — A416

No. 2413: a, Wearing white dress, no crown.
b, Wearing black robe. c, Wearing crown.
$6, Wearing crown, diff. $20, Wearing red
robe.

2003   Litho.   Perf. 14
2413 A415 $3 Sheet of 3,
          #a-c   6.75   6.75
            Souvenir Sheet
2414 A415 $6 multi   4.50   4.50
            Miniature Sheet
        Litho. & Embossed
Perf. 13¼x13
2415 A416 $20 gold & multi   15.00 15.00
    Issued: Nos. 2413-2414, 5/13; No. 2415,
2/24.

Prince William, 21st Birthday — A417

No. 2416: a, Wearing dark blue shirt. b,
Wearing blue suit, holding flowers. c, In polo
uniform.
$6, Wearing black suit.

2003, June 21   Litho.   Perf. 14
2416 A417 $3 Sheet of 3, #a-c   6.75 6.75
Souvenir Sheet
2417 A417 $6 multi   4.50 4.50

Intl. Year of Fresh Water — A418

No. 2418: a, Trafalgar Falls. b, YS Falls. c,
Dunn's River.
$6, Annandale Falls.

2003, June 21   Perf. 13½
2418 A418 $3 Sheet of 3, #a-c   6.75 6.75
Souvenir Sheet
2419 A418 $6 multi   4.50 4.50

Teddy Bears, Cent. — A419

No. 2420 — Bear with: a, Purple shirt. b,
Pink shirt and party favor. c, Green shirt and
party favor. d, Black hat. e, Purple hat. f, Pink
shirt and birthday cake.
No. 2421 — Bear with: a, Reindeer sweater,
text at top. b, Santa Claus costume, text at top.
c, Santa Claus costume, text at bottom. d,
Reindeer sweater, text at bottom.

2003, June 21   Perf. 13½
2420 A419 $1.65 Sheet of 6,
            #a-f   7.50 7.50
2421 A419 $2 Sheet of 4,
            #a-d   6.00 6.00
No. 2421 contains four 37x51mm stamps.

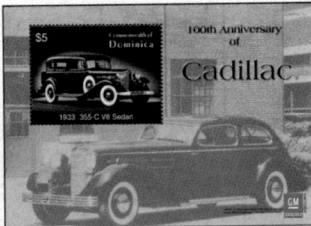

General Motors Automobiles — A420

No. 2422, $2 — Cadillacs: a, 1903 Model A
Runabout. b, 1912 Model 30. c, 1918 Type 57
Victoria Coupe. d, 1927 Lasalle Convertible
Coupe.
No. 2423, $2 — Corvettes: a, 1953. b, 1956.
c, 1957. d, 1962.
No. 2424, $5, 1933 Cadillac 355-C V8
sedan. No. 2425, $5, 1959 Corvette.

2003, June 21   Perf. 13¼
Sheets of 4, #a-d
2422-2423 A420 Set of 2   12.00 12.00
Souvenir Sheets
2424-2425 A420 Set of 2   7.50 7.50

Tour de France Bicycle Race,
Cent. — A421

No. 2426 — Champions: a, Firmin Lambot,
1919. b, Phillippe Thys, 1920. c, Léon Scieur,
1921. d, Lambot, 1922.
$5, François Faber.

2003, June 21
2426 A421 $2 Sheet of 4, #a-d   6.00 6.00
Souvenir Sheet
2427 A421 $5 multi   3.75 3.75

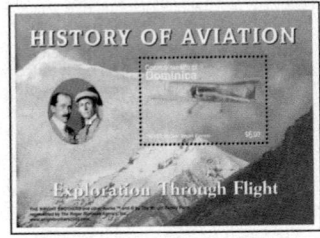

History of Aviation — A422

No. 2428: a, Sputnik, first orbiting satellite,
1957. b, Yuri Gagarin, first man in space,
1961. c, Neil Armstrong, first man on the
Moon, 1969. d, Skylab 1, 1973.
$6, Flight over Mt. Everest, 1933.

2003, June 21   Perf. 14
2428 A422 $2 Sheet of 4, #a-d   6.50 6.50
Souvenir Sheet
2429 A422 $6 multi   5.00 5.00

Lewis &
Clark
Expedition
A423

Designs: 20c, Dealing with the Chinook Indians. 50c, Compass used in expedition. 55c,
Rocky Mountains. 65c, Medals presented to
the Indians, vert. 90c, First encounter with
grizzly bear. $1, Befriending Shoshone Indi-
ans. $2, Lewis after the expedition, vert. $4,
Lewis & Clark, vert.
No. 2438, $5, Meriwether Lewis, vert. No.
2439, $5, William Clark, vert.

2003, June 21
2430-2437 A423 Set of 8   7.50 7.50
Souvenir Sheets
2438-2439 A423 Set of 2   7.50 7.50

2002 World Cup Soccer
Championships, Japan and
Korea — A424

No. 2440, $1.45: a, Danny Mills. b, Paul
Scholes. c, Darius Vassell. d, Michael Owen.
e, Emile Heskey. f, Rio Ferdinand.
No. 2441, $1.45: a, Bobby Moore. b, Roger
Hunt. c, Gordon Banks. d, Bobby Charlton. e,
Alan Ball. f, Geoff Hurst.
No. 2442, $3: a, Ashley Cole. b, David
Seaman.
No. 2443, $3: a, Sven-Goran Eriksson. b,
Nikki Butt.
No. 2444, $3: a, Robbie Fowler. b, Sol
Campbell.
No. 2445, $3: a, Charlton, Ball and Hunt. b,
Nobby Stiles.
No. 2446, $3: a, Franz Beckenbauer. b, Oli-
ver Kahn.

2003, June 21   Perf. 13¼
Sheets of 6, #a-f
2440-2441 A424 Set of 2   13.00 13.00
Souvenir Sheets of 2, #a-b
2442-2446 A424 Set of 5   22.50 22.50

CARICOM, 30th Anniv. — A425

2003, July 25   Perf. 13½
2447 A425 $1 multi   .75 .75

Christmas
A426

Painting details: 50c, Madonna and Child
with the Young St. John, by Correggio. 90c,
Madonna in Glory with the Christ Child and
Sts. Frances and Alvise with the Donor, by
Titian. $1.45, Madonna and Child with Angels
Playing Musical Instruments, by Correggio.
$3, Madonna of the Cherries, by Titian.
$6, Holy Family with John the Baptist, by
Andrea del Sarto.

2003, Nov. 17   Litho.   Perf. 14¼
2448-2451 A426 Set of 4   4.50 4.50
Souvenir Sheet
2452 A426 $6 multi   4.50 4.50

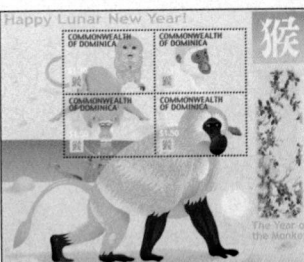

New Year 2004 (Year of the
Monkey) — A427

No. 2453: a, Orange monkey, hindquarters
of brown monkey. b, Monkey with brown face.
c, Brown monkey drinking water. d, Monkey
with blue face.

2004, Jan. 5   Litho.   Perf. 14
2453 A427 $1.50 Sheet of 4,
            #a.-d.   4.50 4.50

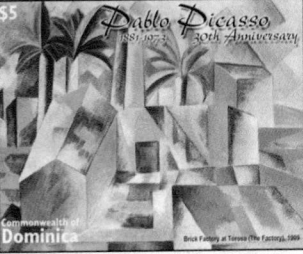

Paintings of Pablo Picasso — A428

No. 2454, vert.: a, Portrait of Manuel Pal-
larés. b, Woman with Vase of Flowers. c,
Woman with a Fan (Fernande). d, Portrait of
Clovis Sagot.
$5, Brick Factory at Torosa (The Factory).

2004, Mar. 8   Perf. 14¼
2454 A428 $1 Sheet of 4, #a.-d.   3.00 3.00
Imperf
2455 A428 $5 multi   3.75 3.75
No. 2454 contains four 38x50mm stamps.

Paintings of Paul Gauguin — A429

No. 2456: a, Village Tahitien avec la Femme
en Marche. b, La Barriere. c, Bonjour, Monsieur Gauguin. d, Vegetation Tropicale.
$5, Petites Bretonnes Devant la Mer.
Illustration reduced.

2004, Mar. 8   Perf. 14¼
2456 A429 $2 Sheet of 4, #a.-d.   6.00 6.00
Imperf
2457 A429 $5 multi   3.75 3.75
No. 2456 contains four 38x50mm stamps.

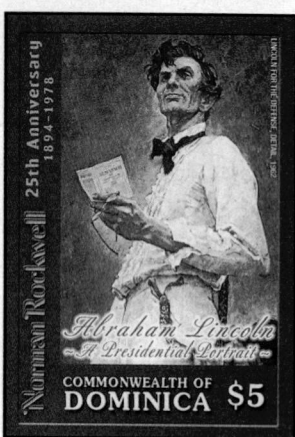

Paintings of Presidents by Norman Rockwell — A430

No. 2458: a, Dwight D. Eisenhower. b, John F. Kennedy. c, Lyndon B. Johnson. d, Richard M. Nixon.
$5, Abraham Lincoln.

2004, Mar. 8		Perf. 14¼		
2458	A430	$2 Sheet of 4, #a.-d.	6.00	6.00
		Imperf		
2459	A430	$5 multi	3.75	3.75

No. 2458 contains four 38x50mm stamps.

Paintings of James McNeill Whistler — A431

Designs: 50c, Symphony in White No. 3. $1, The Artist's Studio, vert. $1.65, The Thames in Ice, vert. No. 2463, $2, Arrangement in Black: Portrait of F. R. Leyland, vert.
No. 2464, $2, vert.: a, Arrangement in Brown & Black: Portrait of Miss Rosa Corder. b, Harmony in Red: Lamplight. c, Symphony in Flesh Color & Pink: Portrait of Mrs. Frances Leyland. d, Arrangement in Yellow & Gray: Effie Deans.
$5, Harmony in Gray and Green: Miss Cicely Alexander, vert.

2004, Mar. 8		Perf. 14¼		
2460-2463	A431	Set of 4	4.00	4.00
		Perf. 13½		
2464	A431	$2 Sheet of 4, #a-d	6.00	6.00
		Imperf		
		Size: 71x103mm		
2465	A431	$5 multi	3.75	3.75

No. 2464 contains four 35x70mm stamps.

Fish
A432

Designs: 20c, Banded butterflyfish. 25c, Queen angelfish. 55c, Porkfish. No. 2469, $5, Redband parrotfish.
No. 2470: a, Beaugregory. b, Porkfish, diff. c, Bicolor cherubfish. d, Rock beauty. e, Blackfin snapper. f, Blue tang.
No. 2471, $5, Indigo hamlet.

2004, Mar. 8		Perf. 14¼x14¾		
2466-2469	A432	Set of 4	4.50	4.50
		Perf. 14		
2470	A432	$2 Sheet of 6, #a-f	9.00	9.00
		Souvenir Sheet		
2471	A432	$5 multi	3.75	3.75

Nos. 2470-2471 each contain 42x28mm stamps.

Shells
A433

Designs: 20c, Siratus perelegans. 90c, Polystira albida. $1.45, Cypraea cervus. $2, Strombus gallus.
No. 2476: a, Strombus pugilis. b, Cittarium pica. c, Distorsio clathrata. d, Melongena morio. e, Prunum labiata. f, Chione paphia.
$5, Strombus alatus, vert.

2004, Mar. 8		Perf. 14¼x14¾		
2472-2475	A433	Set of 4	3.50	3.50
		Perf. 14		
2476	A433	$1.90 Sheet of 6, #a-f	8.50	8.50
		Souvenir Sheet		
2477	A433	$5 multi	3.75	3.75

No. 2476 contain six 42x28mm stamps; No. 2477 contains one 28x42mm stamp.

Orchids — A434

Designs: 25c, Epidendrum pseudepidendrum. 55c, Aspasia epidendroides. $1.50, Cochleanthes discolor. $4, Brassavola nodosa.
No. 2482: a, Laelia anceps. b, Caularthron bicornutum. c, Cattleya velutina. d, Cattleya warneri. e, Oncidium splendidum. f, Psychlis atropurpurea.
$5, Maxillaria cuculata, vert.

2004, Mar. 8		Perf. 14¼x14¾		
2478-2481	A434	Set of 4	4.75	4.75
		Perf. 14		
2482	A434	$1.90 Sheet of 6, #a-f	8.50	8.50
		Souvenir Sheet		
2483	A434	$5 multi	3.75	3.75

No. 2482 contains six 42x28mm stamps; No. 2483 contains one 28x42mm stamp.

Butterflies — A435

Designs: 50c, Small flambeau. 90c, Tiger pierid. $1, White peacock. No. 2469, $2, Cramer's mesene.
No. 2488, $2: a, Figure-of-eight. b, Orange theope. c, Clorinde. d, Grecian shoemaker. e, Orange-barred sulphur. f, Common morpho.
$5, Giant swallowtail, vert.

2004, Mar. 8		Perf. 14¼x14¾		
2484-2487	A435	Set of 4	3.25	3.25
		Perf. 14		
2488	A435	$2 Sheet of 6, #a-f	9.00	9.00
		Souvenir Sheets		
2489	A435	$5 multi	3.75	3.75

No. 2488 contains six 42x28mm stamps; No. 2489 contains one 28x42mm stamp.

Olympic Gold Medalists A436

Designs: 20c, Elizabeth Robinson, Amsterdam, 1928. 25c, Károly Takács, London, 1948. 55c, Bob Beamon, Mexico City, 1968. 65c, Mildred Didrikson, Los Angeles, 1932. $1, Ville Ritola, Paris, 1924. $1.65, Alfred Hajós (Guttman), Athens, 1896. $2, Paavo Nurmi, Antwerp, 1920. $4, Nedo Nadi, Antwerp, 1920.

2004, Apr. 12		Perf. 13¼		
2490-2497	A436	Set of 8	7.75	7.75

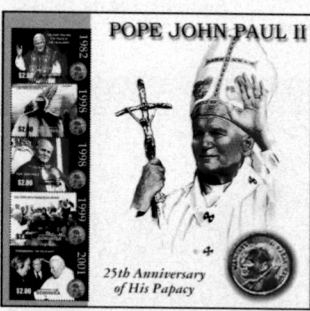

Election of Pope John Paul II, 25th Anniv. (in 2003) — A437

No. 2498: a, Praying for peace in Falkland Islands, 1982. b, In Croatia, 1998. c, Seated, 1998. d, With Franciscan monks, 1999. e, Remembering the Holocaust, 2001.

2004, June 21		Litho.	Perf. 14	
2498	A437	$2 Sheet of 5, #a-e	7.50	7.50

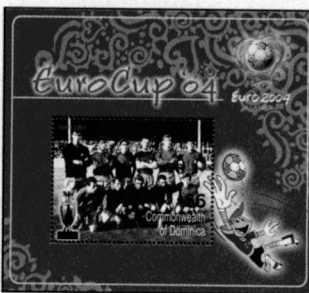

European Soccer Championships, Portugal — A438

No. 2499, vert.: a, Jose Luis Villalonga. b, Lev Yashin. c, Marcelino Martinez. d, Santiago Bernabeu Stadium.
$6, 1964 Spain team.

2004, June 21		Perf. 14		
2499	A438	$2 Sheet of 4, #a-d	6.00	6.00
		Souvenir Sheet		
		Perf. 14¼		
2500	A438	$6 multi	4.50	4.50

No. 2499 contains four 28x42mm stamps.

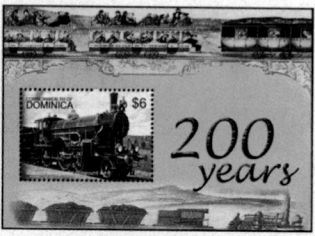

Trains — A439

No. 2501, $1: a, Engine #22, V7 T4-4-0, V7T4-6-0. b, Don J12. c, Baldwin 2-D-D. d,

Southern Engine #20. e, 143-890 2DB class electric locomotive. f, Engine #1.
No. 2502, $1: a, Canadian Pacific freight train. b, Queensland Rail IM U railroad. c, Green and white Shinkansen locomotive. d, Amtrak locomotive. e, Shinkansen locomotive in station. f, YPDMU rail cars.
No. 2503, $1: a, Santa Fe Railroad locomotive. b, Via Rail train, Canada. c, Two Conrail road switchers. d, Strasburg Railroad #90. e, Deltic diesel-electric engine. f, Brighton Belle.
No. 2504, $6: a, Golsdorf two cylinder compound locomotive 4-4-0. No. 2505, $6, Southern Pacific 4449 4-8-4. No. 2506, $6, White, yellow and blue Shinkansen.

2004, July 12		Perf. 13¼x13½		
		Sheets of 6, #a-f		
2501-2503	A439	Set of 3	13.50	13.50
		Souvenir Sheets		
2504-2506	A439	Set of 3	13.50	13.50

D-Day, 60th Anniv. A440

Designs: $1, Eddie Hannath. $4, Pres. Franklin D. Roosevelt.
No. 2509: a, Rangers make their way towards the cliffs of Pointe du Hoc. b, Rangers begin scaling the cliffs of Pointe du Hoc. c, British troops advance on Sword Beach. d, An AVRE Petard heads inland off Sword Beach.
$6, British troops landing on Sword Beach.

2004, July 22		Perf. 14		
		Stamp + Label (#2507-2508)		
2507-2508	A440	Set of 2	3.75	3.75
2509	A440	$2 Sheet of 4, #a-d	6.00	6.00
		Souvenir Sheet		
2510	A440	$6 multi	4.50	4.50

George Herman "Babe" Ruth (1895-1948), Baseball Player — A441

No. 2511: a, Swinging bat. b, Swinging bat, looking up. c, Holding three bats. d, Hand on knee.

2004, Aug. 18		Perf. 13½x13¼		
2511	A441	$2 Sheet of 4, #a-d	6.00	6.00

Marilyn Monroe (1926-62),
Actress — A442

No. 2512: a, Wearing earrings and necklace. b, Wearing earrings. c, Wearing no earrings or necklace. d, Wearing necklace.

2004, Aug. 18
2512 A442 $2 Sheet of 4, #a-d   6.00 6.00

Bird Type of 2001
2004, Sept. 3   **Perf. 14¾x14**
2513 A386 50c Baltimore oriole   .40 .40
Exists dated "2005."

Queen
Juliana of the
Netherlands
(1909-2004)
A443

2004, Sept. 21   **Perf. 13¼**
2514 A443 $2 multi   1.50 1.50
Printed in sheets of 6.

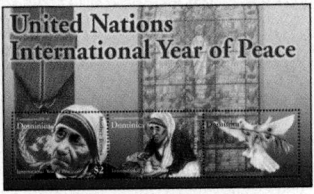

Intl. Year of Peace — A444

No. 2515: a, Mother Teresa, UN emblem. b,
Mother Teresa feeding poor. c, Dove.

2004, Sept. 21   **Perf. 14**
2515 A444 $2 Sheet of 3, #a-c   4.50 4.50

Souvenir Sheet

Deng Xiaoping (1904-97) and Mao
Zedong (1893-1976), Chinese
Leaders — A445

2004, Sept. 21   **Perf. 14**
2516 A445 $6 multi   4.50 4.50

National Soccer Team — A446

2004, Nov. 8   **Litho.**   **Perf. 12**
2517 A446 90c multi   .70 .70

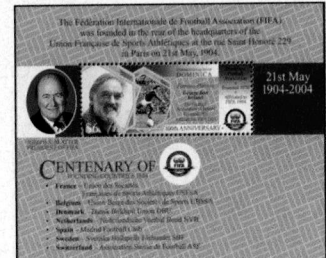

FIFA (Fédération Internationale de
Football Association), Cent. — A447

No. 2518: a, Ferenc Puskas. b, Rivaldo. c,
Carsten Jancker. d, Johan Cruyff.
$6, George Best.

2004, Nov. 8   **Perf. 12¾x12½**
2518 A447 $2 Sheet of 4, #a-d   6.00 6.00
Souvenir Sheet
2519 A447 $6 multi   4.50 4.50

Worldwide Fund for Nature
(WWF) — A448

No. 2520: a, Green-throated Carib (denomination in blue). b, Purple-throated Carib
(denomination in white). c, Green-throated
Carib (denomination in white). d, Purple-
throated Carib (denomination in red).
Illustration reduced.

2005, Jan. 10   **Perf. 14**
2520 A448 $2 Block of 4, #a-d   6.00 6.00
   e.   Miniature sheet, 2 each   12.00 12.00
        #2520a-2520d

Prehistoric Animals — A449

No. 2521, $2: a, Tyrannosaurus rex. b,
Velociraptor.   c,   Stegosaurus.   d,
Psittacosaurus.
   No. 2522, $2: a, Mammuthus columbi. b,
Spinosaurus. c, Ankylosaurus. d, Mammuthus
primigenius.
   No. 2523, $2: a, Pterodactylus. b, Ptera-
nodon. c, Sordes. d, Caudiptheryx zoui.
   $3, Compsognathus. $5, Archaeopteryx. $6,
Mammuthus primigenius, diff.

2005, Jan. 10   **Perf. 12¾**
Sheets of 4, #a-d
2521-2523 A449   Set of 3   18.00 18.00
Souvenir Sheets
2524-2526 A449   Set of 3   10.50 10.50

Birds
A450

Designs: 25c, Brown booby. 90c, Brown pelican. $1, Red-billed tropicbird. $4, Northern
gannet.
   No. 2531: a, Great egret. b, Black-necked
grebe. c, Turkey vulture. d, Snail kite.
$6, Red knot.

2005, Jan. 10   **Perf. 14**
2527-2530 A450   Set of 4   4.75 4.75
2531 A450 $2 Sheet of 4, #a-d   6.00 6.00
Souvenir Sheet
2532 A450 $6 multi   4.50 4.50

Mushrooms — A451

No. 2533: a, Cortinarius mucosus. b, Cortinarius splendens. c, Cortinarius rufo-
olivaceus. d, Inocybe erubescens.
$6, Split fibercap.

2005, Jan. 10
2533 A451 $2 Sheet of 4, #a-d   6.00 6.00
Souvenir Sheet
2534 A451 $6 multi   4.50 4.50

Miniature Sheet

Flowers — A452

No. 2535: a, Sweetshrub. b, Pink turtle-
heads. c, Flowering quince. d, Water lily.
$6, Glory of the snow, vert.

2005, Jan. 10   **Litho.**   **Perf. 14**
2535 A452 $2 Sheet of 4, #a-d   6.00 6.00
Souvenir Sheet
2535E A452 $6 multi   4.50 4.50

New Year 2005
(Year of the
Rooster) — A453

2005, Jan. 24   **Perf. 12¾x12½**
2536 A453 $1 shown   .75 .75
Souvenir Sheet
Perf. 12
2537 A453 $4 Roosters   3.00 3.00
No. 2537 contains one 56x36mm stamp.

A454

Elvis Presley (1935-77) — A455

Elvis Presley (1935-77) — A455a

No. 2538: a, Green background under country name and near shirt collar. b, Guitar. c,
Large red violet areas at side of head. d, Dark
green background under country name, blue
background near shirt collar. e, Purple background near shirt collar. f, Small red violet
areas at side of head.
   No. 2539: a, Country name in white, blue
background at UR. b, Country name in white,
pink background at UR. c, Country name in
white, orange background at UR. d, Country
name in blue, green background at UR. e,
Presley and guitar. f, Country name in blue,
yellow background at UR. g, Country name in
blue, blue background at UR.
   No. 2539H illustration reduced.

2005, Apr. 5   **Perf. 13½**
2538 A454 $1 Sheet of 9, #a-
         c, 2 each #d-f   6.75 6.75
2539 A455 $1 Sheet of 9, #a,
         c, e-g, 2 each
         #b, d   6.75 6.75
Litho. & Embossed
Variable Serpentine Die Cut
Without Gum
2539H A455a$20 gold & multi   15.00 15.00
   No. 2539H was not available in the marketplace until 2006.

Miniature Sheet

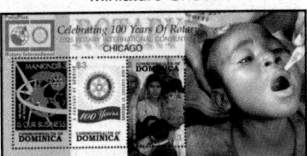

Rotary International, Cent. — A456

No. 2540: a, Globe and Rotary emblem. b,
Rotary emblem. c, Women and children.

2005, Sept. 7   **Perf. 12½x12¾**
2540 A456 $3 Sheet of 3, #a-c   6.75 6.75

Battle of Trafalgar, Bicent. — A457

Designs: 55c, Admiral Horatio Nelson explaining plan of attack before battle. 65c, Orient explodes during the Battle of the Nile, vert. $1, Nelson and his men board San Nicolas during the Battle of Cape St. Vincent, vert. $2, Ships Agamemnon and Ca Ira in battle. $6, HMS Victory.

2005, Sept. 7   **Perf. 13¼**
2541-2544 A457   Set of 4   3.25 3.25
     Souvenir Sheet
     Perf. 12
2545 A457 $6 multi   4.50 4.50

Hans Christian Andersen (1805-75), Author — A458

No. 2546: a, The Swineherd. b, The Nightingale. c, The Fir Tree. $6, The Ugly Duckling.

2005, Sept. 7   **Perf. 12¾**
2546 A458 $2 Sheet of 3, #a-c   4.50 4.50
     Souvenir Sheet
     Perf. 12
2547 A458 $6 multi   4.50 4.50
No. 2546 contains three 42x28mm stamps.

Friedrich von Schiller (1759-1805), Writer — A459

No. 2548, vert. — Schiller and German Democratic Republic stamps: a, #241. b, #242. c, #243. $6, Statue of Schiller.

2005, Sept. 7   **Perf. 12¾**
2548 A459 $3 Sheet of 3, #a-c   6.75 6.75
     Souvenir Sheet
2549 A459 $6 multi   4.50 4.50

Jules Verne (1828-1905), Writer — A460

No. 2550: a, Men, dog and rooster in space. b, Astronauts. c, Men looking at undersea creature. d, Submarine. $6, Portrait of Verne.

2005, Sept. 7
2550 A460 $2 Sheet of 4, #a-d   6.00 6.00
     Souvenir Sheet
2551 A460 $6 multi   4.50 4.50

World Cup Soccer Championships, 75th Anniv. — A461

No. 2552: a, 1934 Italy team. b, Scene from 1934 Italy victory over Czechoslovakia. c, Flaminio Stadium. d, Angelos Schiavo. $6, Italian team celebrating.

2005, Sept. 7   **Perf. 12**
2552 A461 $2 Sheet of 4, #a-d   6.00 6.00
     Souvenir Sheet
2553 A461 $6 multi   4.50 4.50

Christmas — A462

Painting details: 25c, Madonna and Child with Two Angels, by Sandro Botticelli. 50c, Madonna and Child with Angels, by Botticelli. 65c, Madonna and Child, by Pietro Lorenzetti. 90c, Madonna del Roseto, by Botticelli. $1.20, Adoration of the Magi, by Lorenzetti. $3, Madonna in Glory with the Seraphim, by Botticelli. $5, Madonna of Frari, by Titian, horiz.

2005, Nov. 15   **Perf. 12¾**
2554-2559 A462   Set of 6   5.00 5.00
     Souvenir Sheet
2560 A462 $5 multi   3.75 3.75

Pope John Paul II (1920-2005) and Princess Diana (1961-97) — A463

2005   **Perf. 13½x13¼**
2561 A463 $3 multi   2.25 2.25

Pope Benedict XVI — A464

2005   **Litho.**   **Perf. 13½x13¼**
2562 A464 $2 multi   1.50 1.50
    Printed in sheets of 4.

     Souvenir Sheet

New Year 2006 (Year of the Dog) — A465

No. 2563 — Dog figurines with background colors of: a, Pale green and green. b, Orange and pink. c, Rose pink and yellow.

2006, Jan. 3   **Perf. 13¼x13½**
2563 A465 $1 Sheet of 3, #a-c   2.25 2.25

     Miniature Sheets

National Basketball Association Players and Team Emblems — A466

No. 2564, 90c: a, Orlando Magic emblem. b, Hedo Turkoglu.
No. 2565, 90c: a, Denver Nuggets emblem. b, Kenyon Martin.
No. 2566, 90c: a, Miami Heat emblem. b, Antoine Walker.
No. 2567, 90c: a, Golden State Warriors emblem. b, Jason Richardson.
No. 2568, 90c: a, Phoenix Suns emblem. b, Amaré Stoudemire.
No. 2569, 90c: a, Los Angeles Clippers emblem. b, Elton Brand.

2006, Feb. 14   **Perf. 14**
Sheets of 12, 2 each #a, 10 each #b
2564-2569 A466   Set of 6   50.00 50.00

Léopold Sédar Senghor (1906-2001), First President of Senegal — A467

2006, Mar. 20   **Perf. 13¼**
2570 A467 $2 multi   1.50 1.50

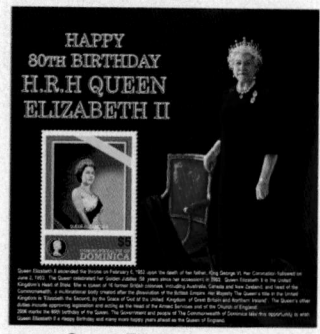

2006 Winter Olympics, Turin — A468

Designs: 75c, Yugoslavia #1670. 90c, 1984 Sarajevo Winter Olympics poster, vert. $2, Japan #2607g, vert. $3, 1998 Nagano Winter Olympics poster, vert.

2006, Mar. 29
2571-2574 A468   Set of 4   5.00 5.00
    Each stamp printed in sheets of 4.

Queen Elizabeth II, 80th Birthday — A469

No. 2575: a, As infant, with mother. b, As young child. c, As baby, wearing bonnet. d, As young girl, wearing jacket. $5, Wearing tiara and sash.

2006, Mar. 29
2575 A469 $2 Sheet of 4, #a-d   6.00 6.00
     Souvenir Sheet
2576 A469 $5 multi   3.75 3.75

Marilyn Monroe (1926-62), Actress — A470

2006, Apr. 7
2577 A470 $3 multi   2.25 2.25
    Printed in sheets of 4.

No. 2631, $5, Flamboyant. No. 2632, $5, Oncidium altissimum.

2007, Apr. 11   Litho.   Perf. 12¾
2625-2628 A485 Set of 4   4.75 4.75
2629 A485 Sheet of 4, #a-d   4.50 4.50
2630 A485 $2 Sheet of 4, #a-d   6.00 6.00
Souvenir Sheets
2631-2632 A485 Set of 2   7.50 7.50

Princess Diana (1961-97) — A486

No. 2633: a, Holding flowers, wearing purple hat. b, Without hat. c, Not holding flowers, wearing purple hat. d, Close-up of #2633a, lines on face. e, Close-up of #2633b, lines on face. f, Close-up of #2633c, lines on face. $5, Wearing purple sweater.

2007, June 11   Perf. 13½
2633 A486 $1 Sheet of 6, #a-f   4.50 4.50
Souvenir Sheet
2634 A486 $5 multi   3.75 3.75

No. 2633 contains six 28x42mm stamps.

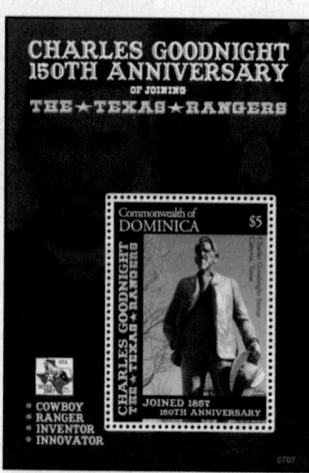

Texas Rangers — A487

No. 2635, horiz.: a, Two Rangers on horses. b, Seven Rangers in front of building with pillars. c, Ten rangers showing rifles. d, Rangers on horses. e, Rangers around still. f, Three Rangers at Justice of the Peace office. g, Rangers and tents. h, Rangers and locomotive. i, Five Rangers on horses near house. $5, Statue of Charles Goodnight.

2007, June 15   Perf. 13½
2635 A487 $1 Sheet of 9, #a-i   6.75 6.75
Souvenir Sheet
2636 A487 $5 multi   3.75 3.75

American Topical Association National Topical Stamp Show, Irving, TX.

Miniature Sheet

New Year 2007 (Year of the Pig) — A488

No. 2637 — Text in: a, Red. b, Green. c, Blue green. d, Purple.

2007, July 2
2637 A488 $2 Sheet of 4, #a-d   6.00 6.00

WAR TAX STAMPS

No. 50 Surcharged in Red

1916   Wmk. 3   Perf. 14
MR1 A6 ½p on ½p green   .80   .80

No. 50 Overprinted in Black

1918
MR2 A6 ½p green   3.25 6.75

Nos. 50, 40 in Black or Red

1918
MR3 A6 ½p green   .20   .55
MR4 A6 3p violet, yel (R)   1.60 4.50

Type of 1908-09 Surcharged in Red

1919
MR5 A6 1½p on 2½p orange   .20   .60

DOMINICAN REPUBLIC

də-'mi-ni-kən ri-'pə-blik

LOCATION — Comprises about two-thirds of the island of Hispaniola in the West Indies
GOVT. — Republic
AREA — 18,700 sq. mi.
POP. — 8,129,734 (1999 est.)
CAPITAL — Santo Domingo

8 Reales = 1 Peso
100 Centavos = 1 Peso (1880)
100 Centimos = 1 Franco (1883)
100 Centavos = 1 Peso (1885)

Catalogue values for unused stamps in this country are for Never Hinged items, beginning with Scott 437 in the regular postage section, Scott B1 in the semi-postal section, Scott C75 in the airpost section, Scott CB1 in the airpost semi-postal section, Scott E7 in the special delivery section, Scott G13 in the insured letter section, Scott J14 in the postage due section, Scott O26 in the officials section, and Scott RA20 in the postal tax section.

Watermarks

Wmk. 115   Wmk. 116
Diamonds   Crosses and
                Circles

Coat of Arms
A1   A2

1865   Unwmk.   Typo.   Imperf.
Wove Paper
1 A1 ½r black, rose   600.00 600.00
2 A1 1r black, dp green   975.00 950.00
        Twelve varieties of each.
Laid Paper
3 A2 ½r black, pale
        green   550.00 475.00
4 A2 1r black, straw   1,700. 1,100.
   Twelve varieties of the ½r, ten of the 1r.

A3   A4

1866   Laid Paper   Unwmk.
5 A3 ½r black, straw   200.00 150.00
6 A3 1r black, pale green   2,500. 2,000.
7 A4 1r black, pale green   175.00 125.00
   Nos. 5-8 have 21 varieties (sheets of 21).

Wmk. 115
8 A3 1r black, pale green   13,000. 13,000.
a. "CORREOS" and "Un Real"
    doubled   21,000.

The unique example of No. 8a is centered in the grade of fine, has a shallow thin spot and pinhole.

1866-67   Wove Paper   Unwmk.
9 A3 ½r black, rose
        ('67)   47.50 47.50
10 A3 1r blk, pale green   85.00 75.00
a. Inscription dbl., top &
    bottom   400.00 400.00
11 A3 1r black, blue
        ('67)   50.00 30.00
a. 1r black, light blue ('67) 50.00 30.00
b. No space btwn. "Un" and
    "real"   600.00 500.00
c. Without inscription at top
    & bottom   1,500. 1,000.
d. Inscription invtd., top &
    bottom   —
   Nos. 9-11 (3)   182.50 152.50

1867-71
Pelure Paper
13 A3 ½r black, rose   150.00 75.00
15 A3 1r black, lav ('68)   250.00 210.00
a. Without inscription at top
    and bottom   525.00
b. Dbl. inscriptions, one
    invtd.   425.00
16 A3 ½r black, grnsh
        gray ('68)   260.00 225.00
17 A3 ½r black, yellow
        ('68)   12,000.
18 A3 ½r black, ol ('69)   3,000. 5,500.
22 A3 1r black, blue   4,000.
23 A3 1r black, lavender   225.00 200.00
24 A4 1r black, rose
        ('68)   225.00 225.00
25 A4 1r black, mag
        ('69)   225.00 225.00
26 A4 1r black, sal ('71) 2,250. 1,300.

Value for No. 17 is for an example with very fine centering and small faults. Value for No. 22 is for a faulty example with very fine centering and appearance.

A5   A6

1870-73
Ordinary Paper
27 A3 ½r black, magenta   2,500. 4,750.
28 A3 ½r blue, rose (blk
        inscription)
        ('71)   50.00 42.50
a. Blue inscription   500.00 500.00
b. Without inscription at top
    and bottom
29 A3 ½r black, yel ('73)   30.00 21.00
a. Without inscription at top
    and bottom   700.00 700.00
30 A4 1r black, vio ('73)   30.00 21.00
a. Without inscription at top
    and bottom   700.00 700.00
31 A4 1r black, dk grn   60.00 50.00

Nos. 9-31 have 21 varieties (sheets of 21). Nos. 29 and 30 are known pin-perforated, unofficially.
Bisects are known of several of the early 1r stamps.

1879   Perf. 12½x13
32 A5 ½r violet   2.50 1.50
a. Imperf., pair   9.00 9.00
b. Horiz. pair, imperf. vert. 17.00
33 A5 ½r violet, bluish   2.50 1.50
a. Imperf., pair   9.00 7.50
34 A5 1r carmine   3.50 1.50
a. Imperf., pair   11.50 9.00
b. Perf. 13   11.50 7.50
c. Perf. 13x12½   11.50 7.50
35 A5 1r carmine, sal   2.50 1.50
a. Imperf., pair   8.25 8.25
   Nos. 32-35 (4)   11.00 6.00

In 1891 15 stamps of 1879-83 were surcharged "U P U," new values and crossed diagonal lines.

1880   Typo.   Rouletted in Color
36 A6 1c green   1.25   .90
b. Laid paper   50.00 50.00
37 A6 2c red   1.00   .75
a. Pelure paper   40.00 40.00
b. Laid paper   40.00 40.00
38 A6 5c blue   1.25   .60
39 A6 10c rose   3.25   .90
40 A6 20c brown   2.00   .75
41 A6 25c violet   2.25 1.10
42 A6 50c orange   2.50 1.50
43 A6 75c ultra   5.00 2.50
a. Laid paper   40.00 40.00
44 A6 1p gold   6.50 4.00
a. Laid paper   50.00 50.00
b. Double impression   42.50 42.50
   Nos. 36-44 (9)   25.00 13.00

1881
Network Covering Stamp
45 A6 1c green   .90   .45
46 A6 2c red   .90   .45
47 A6 5c blue   1.25   .45
48 A6 10c rose   1.50   .60
49 A6 20c brown   1.50   .80
50 A6 25c violet   1.75   .90
51 A6 50c orange   2.00 1.25
52 A6 75c ultra   6.00 4.00
53 A6 1p gold   8.00 6.50
   Nos. 45-53 (9)   23.80 15.40

Preceding Issues (Type A6) Surch. with Value in New Currency:

a   b

c   d

Column 1 (left)

1

1

Franco.
e

franco
f

**1
franco,
25
céntimos.**
g

5

francos.
i

5

francos h

1883

Without Network

54	(a)	5c on 1c green		1.40	1.50
b.		Inverted surcharge		21.00	21.00
c.		Surcharged "25 céntimos"		50.00	50.00
d.		Surcharged "10 céntimos"		27.50	27.50
55	(b)	5c on 1c green		25.00	9.00
b.		Double surcharge		100.00	
c.		Inverted surcharge		65.00	65.00
56	(c)	5c on 1c green		17.00	9.50
b.		Surcharged "10 céntimos"		35.00	35.00
c.		Surcharged "25 céntimos"		37.50	37.50
57	(a)	10c on 2c red		5.00	3.00
a.		Inverted surcharge		27.50	27.50
d.		Surcharged "5 céntimos"		52.50	52.50
e.		Surcharged "25 céntimos"		75.00	75.00
58	(b)	10c on 2c red		4.50	3.50
a.		"Céntimso"			
b.		Inverted surcharge		37.50	37.50
c.		Surcharged "25 céntimos"		60.00	60.00
d.		"10" omitted		60.00	
59	(a)	25c on 5c blue		6.50	4.00
a.		Surcharged "5 céntimos"		52.50	
b.		Surcharged "10 céntimos"		52.50	52.50
c.		Surcharged "50 céntimos"		75.00	75.00
d.		Inverted surcharge		50.00	50.00
60	(c)	25c on 5c blue		7.50	3.50
a.		Inverted surcharge		45.00	37.50
b.		Surcharged "10 céntimos"		45.00	37.50
e.		"25" omitted		75.00	
f.		Surcharged on back			75.00
61	(a)	50c on 10c rose		25.00	11.50
a.		Inverted surcharge		50.00	45.00
62	(c)	50c on 10c rose		35.00	17.50
a.		Inverted surcharge		52.50	52.50
63	(d)	1fr on 20c brown		15.00	9.75
64	(e)	1fr on 20c brown		17.50	9.75
a.		Comma after "Franco,"		27.50	27.50
65	(f)	1fr on 20c brown		25.00	17.50
a.		Inverted surcharge			15.00
66	(g)	1fr25c on 25c violet		21.00	15.00
a.		Inverted surcharge		65.00	65.00
67	(g)	2fr50c on 50c orange		15.00	10.50
a.		Inverted surcharge		35.00	12.00
68	(g)	3fr75c on 75c ultra		27.50	25.00
b.		Inverted surcharge		60.00	60.00
c.		Laid paper		75.00	75.00
70	(i)	5fr on 1p gold		550.00	500.00
a.		"s" of "francos" inverted		700.00	700.00

With Network

71	(a)	5c on 1c green		3.00	2.50
b.		Inverted surcharge		22.50	22.50
c.		Double surcharge		22.50	22.50
d.		Surcharged "25 céntimos"		42.50	42.50
e.		"5" omitted		75.00	
72	(b)	5c on 1c green		21.00	9.00
b.		Inverted surcharge		60.00	60.00
73	(c)	5c on 1c green		27.50	11.50
b.		Surcharged "10 céntimos"		50.00	42.50
c.		Surcharged "25 céntimos"		60.00	
74	(a)	10c on 2c red		3.75	2.25
a.		Surcharged "5 céntimos"		52.50	45.00
b.		Surcharged "25 céntimos"		67.50	67.50
c.		"10" omitted		57.50	
75	(c)	10c on 2c red		3.00	2.00
a.		Inverted surcharge		30.00	17.00
76	(a)	25c on 5c blue		7.50	3.50
a.		Surcharged "10 céntimos"		75.00	
b.		Surcharged "5 céntimos"		60.00	
b.		Surcharged "50 céntimos"		67.50	
77	(c)	25c on 5c blue		60.00	30.00
a.		Inverted surcharge			
b.		Surcharged on back			
78	(a)	50c on 10c rose		25.00	7.50
a.		Inverted surcharge		50.00	30.00
b.		Surcharged "25 céntimos"		60.00	
79	(c)	50c on 10c rose		30.00	9.50
a.		Inverted surcharge		60.00	
80	(d)	1fr on 20c brown		12.00	9.75
81	(e)	1fr on 20c brown		14.50	12.50
a.		Comma after "Franco,"		35.00	35.00
b.		Inverted surcharge		75.00	
82	(f)	1fr on 20c brown		25.00	20.00
83	(g)	1fr25c on 25c violet		45.00	30.00
a.		Inverted surcharge		75.00	
84	(g)	2fr50c on 50c orange		19.00	12.50
a.		Inverted surcharge		35.00	27.50

85	(g)	3fr75c on 75c ultra		45.00	42.50
86	(h)	5fr on 1p gold		140.00	140.00
a.		Inverted surcharge			
87	(i)	5fr on 1p gold		190.00	190.00

Many minor varieties exist in Nos. 54-87: accent on "i" of "centimos"; "5" with straight top; "1" with straight serif.

A7

A7a

1885-91			Engr.	**Perf. 12**	
88	A7	1c green		.90	.45
89	A7	2c vermilion		.90	.45
90	A7	5c blue		1.25	.45
91	A7a	10c orange		2.00	.60
92	A7a	20c dark brown		2.00	.75
93	A7a	50c violet ('91)		7.00	6.00
94	A7	1p carmine ('91)		18.00	12.00
95	A7	2p red brown ('91)		22.50	14.00
		Nos. 88-95 (8)		54.55	34.70

Nos. 93, 94, 95 were issued without gum.
Imperf. varieties are proofs.
For surcharges see Nos. 166-168.

Coat of Arms — A8

1895				**Perf. 12½x14**	
96	A8	1c green		1.10	.45
97	A8	2c orange red		1.10	.45
98	A8	5c blue		1.10	.45
99	A8	10c orange		2.25	1.40
		Nos. 96-99 (4)		5.55	2.75

Nos. 96-99 exist imperforate but were not issued.

1897				**Perf. 14**	
96a	A8	1c green		1.40	.50
97a	A8	2c orange red		8.00	.75
98a	A8	5c blue		1.40	.75
99a	A8	10c orange		2.75	1.50
		Nos. 96a-99a (4)		13.55	3.50

Voyage of Diego Méndez from Jamaica — A9

Enriquillo's Revolt — A10

Sarcophagus of Columbus A11

"Española" Guarding Remains of Columbus A12

Toscanelli Replying to Columbus A13

Bartolomé de las Casas Defending Indians — A14

Columbus at Salamanca A15

Columbus' Mausoleum A16

1899, Feb. 27			Litho.	**Perf. 11½**	
100	A9	1c brown violet		5.00	4.00
102	A10	2c rose red		1.75	.70
103	A11	5c blue		2.00	.70
104	A12	10c orange		4.25	1.25
a.		Tête bêche pair		42.50	42.50
105	A13	20c brown		6.50	5.00
106	A14	50c yellow green		8.00	6.00
a.		Tête bêche pair		57.50	57.50
107	A15	1p black, *gray bl*		20.00	15.00
108	A16	2p bister brown		37.50	37.50

1900, Jan.					
109	A11	¼c black		.70	1.25
110	A15	½c black		.70	1.25
110A	A9	1c gray green		.70	.50
		Nos. 100-110A (11)		87.10	73.15

Nos. 100-110A were issued to raise funds for a Columbus mausoleum.

Imperf., Pairs

100a	A9	1c brown violet		15.00	
102a	A10	2c rose red		5.00	
103a	A11	5c blue		5.75	
104b	A12	10c orange		8.75	
105a	A13	20c brown		15.00	
106b	A14	50c yellow green		17.50	
c.		As "b," tête bêche pair		125.00	
107a	A15	1p black, *gray blue*		42.50	
108a	A16	2p bister brown		70.00	
109a	A11	¼c black		2.10	2.50
110b	A15	½c black		2.10	2.50
110c	A9	1c gray green		3.50	

Map of Hispaniola A17

A18

1900, Oct. 21			Unwmk.	**Perf. 14**	
111	A17	¼c dark blue		.65	.40
112	A17	½c rose		.65	.40
113	A17	1c olive green		.65	.40
114	A17	2c deep green		.65	.40
115	A17	5c red brown		.65	.40
a.		Vertical pair, imperf. between		17.50	

				Perf. 12	
116	A17	10c orange		.65	.40
117	A17	20c lilac		2.75	2.10
a.		20c rose (error)		5.75	5.75
118	A17	50c black		2.50	2.25
119	A17	1p brown		2.75	2.25
		Nos. 111-119 (9)		11.90	9.00

Several varieties in design are known in this issue. They were deliberately made. Counterfeits of Nos. 111-119 abound.

1901-06			Typo.	**Perf. 14**	
120	A18	½c carmine & vio		.65	.35
121	A18	½c blk & org ('05)		1.50	.85
122	A18	½c grn & blk ('06)		.80	.30
123	A18	1c ol grn & vio		.65	.20
124	A18	1c blk & ultra			
		('05)		1.50	.70
125	A18	1c car & blk ('06)		1.00	.45
126	A18	2c dp grn & vio		.70	.20
127	A18	2c blk & vio ('05)		2.00	.60
128	A18	2c org brn & blk			
		('06)		1.00	.20
129	A18	5c org brn & vio		.75	.25
130	A18	5c black & cl			
		('05)		2.25	1.00
131	A18	5c blue & blk			
		('06)		1.25	.30
132	A18	10c orange & vio		1.25	.35
133	A18	10c blk & grn ('05)		3.75	2.00

134	A18	10c red vio & blk			
		('06)		1.25	.35
135	A18	20c brn vio & vio		2.25	.70
136	A18	20c blk & ol ('05)		11.50	7.50
137	A18	20c ol grn & blk			
		('06)		6.50	2.50
138	A18	50c gray blk & vio		7.00	5.00
139	A18	50c blk & red brn			
		('05)		40.00	30.00
140	A18	50c brn & blk			
		('06)		7.50	7.00
141	A18	1p brn & vio		16.00	9.50
142	A18	1p blk & gray			
		('05)		175.00	200.00
143	A18	1p violet & blk			
		('06)		17.50	12.00
		Nos. 120-143 (24)		303.55	282.30

Issued: 11/15/01; 5/11/05; 8/17/06.
See Nos. 172-176. For surcharges see Nos. 151-156.

Francisco Sánchez — A19

Juan Pablo Duarte — A20

Ramón Mella — A21

Ft. Santo Domingo — A22

1902, Feb. 25			Engr.	**Perf. 12**	
144	A19	1c dk green & blk		.25	.25
145	A20	2c scarlet & blk		.25	.25
146	A20	5c blue & blk		.25	.25
147	A19	10c orange & blk		.25	.25
148	A21	12c purple & blk		.25	.25
149	A21	20c rose & blk		.35	.35
150	A22	50c brown & blk		.50	.50
		Nos. 144-150 (7)		2.10	2.10

Center Inverted

144a	A19	1c		5.00	3.50
145a	A20	2c		5.00	3.50
146a	A20	5c		5.00	3.50
148a	A21	12c		5.00	3.50
149a	A21	20c		5.00	3.50
150a	A22	50c		5.00	3.50
		Nos. 144a-150a (6)		30.00	21.00

400th anniversary of Santo Domingo. Imperforate varieties of Nos. 144-150 were never sold to the public.

Nos. 138, 141 Surcharged in Black

1904, Aug.					
151	A18	2c on 50c		7.00	6.00
152	A18	2c on 1p		10.50	7.00
b.		"2" omitted		50.00	50.00
153	A18	5c on 50c		3.75	2.10
154	A18	5c on 1p		4.00	3.50
155	A18	10c on 50c		7.00	6.50
156	A18	10c on 1p		7.00	6.50
		Nos. 151-156 (6)		39.25	31.60

Inverted Surcharge

151a	A18	2c on 50c		14.00	14.00
152a	A18	2c on 1p		14.00	14.00
c.		As "a," "2" omitted		80.00	80.00
153a	A18	5c on 50c		5.00	3.50
154a	A18	5c on 1p		7.00	6.50
155a	A18	10c on 50c		14.00	14.00
156a	A18	10c on 1p		10.00	10.00
		Nos. 151a-156a (6)		64.00	62.00

Official Stamps
of 1902
Overprinted

Red Overprint

1904, Aug. 16
157	O1	5c dk blue & blk	5.00	2.75
a.		Inverted overprint	6.50	5.50

Black Overprint
158	O1	2c scarlet & blk	12.50	4.00
a.		Inverted overprint	15.00	5.00
159	O1	5c dk blue & blk	3,500.	3,500.
160	O1	10c yellow grn & blk	9.25	9.00
a.		Inverted overprint	12.50	12.50

Surcharged

161	O1	1c on 20c yellow & blk	4.00	2.75
a.		Inverted surcharge	6.50	5.00

Nos. J1-J2
Surcharged or
Overprinted

Surcharged "CENTAVOS"

1904-05

Black Surcharge
162	D1	1c on 2c olive gray	250.00	200.00
a.		"entavos"		—
b.		"Dominican"	350.00	300.00
c.		"Centavo"	350.00	300.00

Carmine Surcharge or Overprint
163	D1	1c on 2c olive gray	2.25	1.00
a.		Inverted surcharge	3.50	2.50
b.		"Domihicana"	15.00	15.00
c.		As "b," inverted	40.00	40.00
d.		"Dominican"	10.50	10.50
e.		"Centavos" omitted	30.00	30.00
f.		"entavos"	30.00	30.00
163F	D1	1c on 4c olive gray	35.00	7.00
164	D1	2c olive gray	.80	.50
a.		"Domihicana"	11.00	11.00
b.		Inverted overprint	1.90	1.90
c.		As "a," inverted	25.00	25.00
d.		"Dominican"	5.75	5.75
e.		"Centavo" omitted	12.50	10.00
f.		"entavos"	12.50	12.50
g.		As "f," inverted	40.00	40.00
h.		As "d," inverted	40.00	40.00

Surcharged "CENTAVO"
165	D1	1c on 4c olive gray	.80	.65
a.		Inverted surcharge	10.00	10.00
c.		Inverted surcharge	1.75	1.75
d.		"1" omitted	3.50	3.50
e.		As "a," inverted	32.50	32.50
f.		As "d," inverted	40.00	40.00
g.		Double surcharge	30.00	30.00

No. 92 Surcharged in
Red

1905, Apr. 4
166	A7a	2c on 20c dk brown	7.00	5.00
a.		Inverted surcharge	15.00	15.00
167	A7a	5c on 20c dk brown	4.00	1.75
a.		Inverted surcharge	16.00	16.00
b.		Double surcharge	25.00	25.00
168	A7a	10c on 20c dk brown	7.00	5.00
		Nos. 166-168 (3)	18.00	11.75

Nos. 166-168 exist with inverted "A" for "V" in "CENTAVOS" in surcharge.

Nos. J2, J4, J3 Surcharged:

1906, Jan. 16   *Perf. 14*

Red Surcharge
169	D1	1c on 4c olive gray	.85	.50
a.		Inverted surcharge	10.50	10.50
b.		Double surcharge	25.00	

1906, May 1

Black Surcharge
170	D1	1c on 10c olive gray	1.00	.40
a.		Inverted surcharge	10.50	10.50
b.		Double surcharge	14.00	14.00
c.		"OMINICANA"	20.00	20.00
d.		As "c," inverted	150.00	
171	D1	2c on 5c olive gray	1.00	.40
a.		Inverted surcharge	10.50	10.50
b.		Double surcharge	35.00	

The varieties small "C" or small "A" in "REPUBLICA" are found on Nos. 169-171.

Arms Type of 1901-06

1907-10   *Wmk. 116*
172	A18	½c grn & blk ('08)	.75	.20
173	A18	1c carmine & blk	.75	.20
174	A18	2c orange brn & blk	.75	.20
175	A18	5c blue & blk	.75	.20
176	A18	10c red vio & blk ('10)	8.00	1.00
		Nos. 172-176 (5)	11.00	1.85

No. O6
Overprinted in
Red

1911, July 11   *Perf. 13½x14, 13½x13*
177	O2	2c scarlet & black	1.25	.50
a.		"HABILITADO"	8.75	6.00
b.		Inverted overprint	21.00	
c.		Double overprint	21.00	

A23   Juan Pablo
Duarte — A24

1911-13   *Perf. 14*

Center in Black
178	A23	½c orange ('13)	.25	.20
179	A23	1c green	.25	.20
180	A23	2c carmine	.25	.20
181	A23	5c gray blue ('13)	.25	.20
182	A23	10c red violet	1.25	.45
183	A23	20c olive green	8.00	7.00
184	A23	50c yellow brn ('12)	3.25	3.25
185	A23	1p violet ('12)	5.50	3.50
		Nos. 178-185 (8)	19.50	15.00

See Nos. 230-232.

1914, Apr. 13   *Perf. 13x14*

Background Red, White and Blue
186	A24	½c orange & blk	.55	.30
187	A24	1c green & blk	.55	.30
188	A24	2c rose & blk	.55	.30
189	A24	5c slate & blk	.55	.40
190	A24	10c magenta & blk	1.25	.70
191	A24	20c olive grn & blk	2.25	1.90
192	A24	50c brown & blk	3.00	2.75
193	A24	1p dull lilac & blk	5.00	4.00
		Nos. 186-193 (8)	13.70	10.65

Cent. of the birth of Juan Pablo Duarte (1813-1876), patriot and revolutionary.

Official Stamps of 1909-12 Surcharged
in Violet or Overprinted in Red:

a

b

1915, Feb.   *Perf. 13½x13, 13½x14*
194	O2 (a)	½c on 20c orange & blk	.50	.35
a.		Inverted surcharge	6.00	6.00
b.		Double surcharge	8.75	8.75
c.		"Habilitado" omitted	5.25	5.25
195	O2 (b)	1c blue grn & blk	.80	.25
a.		Inverted overprint	6.00	6.00
b.		Double overprint	7.00	
c.		Overprinted "1915" only	12.50	
196	O2 (b)	2c scarlet & blk	.80	.25
a.		Inverted overprint	5.25	5.25
b.		Double overprint	7.75	7.75
c.		Overprinted "1915" only	8.75	
d.		"1915" double		
197	O2 (b)	5c dk blue & blk	1.00	.25
a.		Inverted overprint	7.00	7.00
b.		Double overprint	8.75	8.75
c.		Double ovpt., one invtd.	27.50	
d.		Overprinted "1915" only	8.50	
198	O2 (b)	10c yel grn & blk	2.75	2.40
a.		Inverted overprint	15.00	
199	O2 (b)	20c orange & blk	9.00	6.50
a.		"Habilitado" omitted		
		Nos. 194-199 (6)	14.85	10.00

Nos. 194 and 196-198 are known with both perforations. Nos. 195 and 199 are only perf. 13½x13.

The variety "L" for "I" in "Habilitado" occurs once in each sheet in all denominations.

A25

Type of 1911-13 Redrawn
Overprinted "1915" in Red

TWO CENTAVOS:
Type I — "DOS" in small letters.
Type II — "DOS" in larger letters with white dot at each end of the word.

1915   *Unwmk.*   *Litho.*   *Perf. 11½*
200	A25	½c violet & blk	.75	.20
a.		Imperf., pair	5.75	
201	A25	1c yel brn & blk	.75	.20
a.		Imperf., pair	6.50	
b.		Vert. pair, imperf. horiz.	10.50	
c.		Horiz. pair, imperf. vert.	10.50	
202	A25	2c ol grn & blk (I)	3.75	.25
a.		Imperf., pair	10.00	
203	A25	2c ol grn & blk (II)	6.00	.00
a.		Center omitted	87.50	
b.		Frame omitted	87.50	
c.		Imperf., pair	15.00	
d.		Horiz. pair, imperf. vert.	15.00	
204	A25	5c magenta & blk	3.25	.25
a.		Pair, one without overprint	65.00	
b.		Imperf., pair	6.50	
205	A25	10c gray blue & blk	3.75	.50
a.		Imperf., pair	7.75	
b.		Horiz. pair, imperf. vert.	35.00	
206	A25	20c rose red & blk	6.50	1.40
a.		Imperf., pair	12.50	
207	A25	50c green & blk	8.50	4.00
a.		Imperf., pair	25.00	
208	A25	1p orange & blk	17.50	7.00
a.		Imperf., pair	52.50	
		Nos. 200-208 (9)	50.75	14.00

Type of 1915 Overprinted "1916" in Red

1916
209	A25	½c violet & blk	1.25	.20
a.		Imperf., pair	21.00	
210	A25	1c green & blk	2.00	.20
a.		Imperf., pair	21.00	

Type of 1915 Overprinted "1917" in Red

1917-19
213	A25	½c red lilac & blk	2.25	.30
a.		Horiz. pair, imperf. btwn.	47.50	47.50
214	A25	1c yellow grn & blk	1.50	.20
a.		Vert. pair, imperf. btwn.	50.00	
215	A25	2c olive grn & blk	1.40	.20
a.		Imperf., pair	50.00	
216	A25	5c magenta & blk	16.00	.70
		Nos. 213-216 (4)	21.15	1.40

Type of 1915 Overprinted "1919" in Red

1919
219	A25	2c olive grn & blk	10.00	.20

Type of 1915 Overprinted "1920" in Red

1920-27
220	A25	½c lilac rose & blk	.50	.25
a.		Horiz. pair, imperf. btwn.	25.00	25.00
b.		Inverted overprint		
c.		Double overprint		
d.		Double overprint, one invtd.		
221	A25	1c yellow grn & blk	.75	.20
a.		Overprint omitted	70.00	
b.		Horiz. pair, imperf. btwn.	40.00	
222	A25	2c olive grn & blk	.75	.20
a.		Vertical pair, imperf. between	27.50	
223	A25	5c dp rose & blk	9.00	.50
224	A25	10c blue & black	5.00	.20

225	A25	20c rose red & blk	7.00	.50
226	A25	50c green & blk ('27)	52.50	17.50
		Nos. 220-226 (7)	75.50	19.40

Type of 1915 Overprinted "1921" in Red

1921
227	A25	1c yellow grn & blk	3.00	.30
a.		Horiz. pair, imperf. btwn.	45.00	45.00
b.		Imperf., pair	45.00	45.00
228	A25	2c olive grn & blk	5.00	.30
a.		Vert. pair, imperf. btwn.	45.00	

Redrawn Design of 1915 without
Overprint

1922
230	A25	1c green	2.25	.20
231	A25	2c carmine (II)	2.50	.20
232	A25	5c blue	4.00	.25
		Nos. 230-232 (3)	8.75	.65

Nos. 230-232 exist imperf.

A26   A27

Second Redrawing

TEN CENTAVOS:
Type I — Numerals 2mm high. "DIEZ" in thick letters with large white dot at each end.
Type II — Numerals 3mm high. "DIEZ" in thin letters with white dot with colored center at each end.

1924-27
233	A26	1c green	.90	.20
a.		Vert. pair, imperf. btwn.	35.00	35.00
234	A26	2c red	.70	.20
235	A26	5c blue	1.10	.20
236	A26	10c pale bl & blk (I) ('26)	12.00	3.00
236A	A26	10c pale bl & blk (II)	22.50	1.10
236B	A26	50c gray grn & blk ('26)	45.00	27.50
237	A26	1p orange & blk ('27)	16.00	10.50
		Nos. 233-237 (7)	98.20	42.70

In the second redrawing the shield has a flat top and the design differs in many details from the stamps of 1911-13 and 1915-22.

1927
238	A27	½c lilac rose & blk	.30	.20

Exhibition
Pavilion — A28

1927   *Unwmk.*   *Perf. 12*
239	A28	2c carmine	.80	.50
240	A28	5c ultra	1.75	.50

Natl. and West Indian Exhib. at Santiago de los Caballeros.

Ruins of
Columbus'
Fortress
A29

1928
241	A29	½c lilac rose	.60	.35
242	A29	1c deep green	.50	.20
a.		Horiz. pair, imperf. btwn.	25.00	
243	A29	2c red	.50	.20
244	A29	5c dark blue	1.50	.35
245	A29	10c light blue	1.75	.30
246	A29	20c rose	3.00	.40
247	A29	50c yellow green	10.50	6.50
248	A29	1p orange yellow	27.50	20.00
		Nos. 241-248 (8)	45.85	28.30

Reprints exist of 1c, 2c and 10c.
Issued: 1c, 2c, 10c, Oct. 1; others, Dec.

Horacio Vasquez — A30

Convent of San Ignacio de Loyola — A31

1929, May-June
249	A30	½c dull rose	.50	.30
250	A30	1c gray green	.50	.20
251	A30	2c red	.60	.20
252	A30	5c dark ultra	1.25	.35
253	A30	10c pale blue	1.75	.50
		Nos. 249-253 (5)	4.60	1.55

Signing of the "Frontier" treaty with Haiti. Issue dates: 2c, May; others, June.

Imperf., Pairs
249a	A30	½c	12.50
250a	A30	1c	12.50
251a	A30	2c	12.50
252a	A30	5c	14.00

1930, May 1   **Perf. 11½**
254	A31	½c red brown	.65	.45
a.		Imperf., pair	55.00	55.00
255	A31	1c deep green	.50	.20
256	A31	2c vermilion	.50	.20
a.		Imperf., pair	60.00	
257	A31	5c deep blue	1.25	.35
258	A31	10c light blue	3.00	1.00
		Nos. 254-258 (5)	5.90	2.20

Cathedral of Santo Domingo, First Church in America A32

1931   **Perf. 12**
260	A32	1c deep green	.65	.20
a.		Imperf., pair	50.00	
261	A32	2c scarlet	.45	.20
a.		Imperf., pair	50.00	
262	A32	3c violet	.65	.20
263	A32	7c dark blue	2.00	.25
264	A32	8c bister	2.75	.85
265	A32	10c light blue	4.50	1.00
a.		Imperf., pair	35.00	
		Nos. 260-265 (6)	11.00	2.70

Issued: 3c-7c, Aug. 1; others, July 11. For overprint see No. RAC8.

A33

Overprinted or Surcharged in Black
1932, Dec. 20
Cross in Red   **Perf. 12**
265B	A33	1c yellow green	.50	.45
265C	A33	3c on 2c violet	.70	.55
265D	A33	5c blue	4.00	4.25
265E	A33	7c on 10c turq bl	5.50	5.75
		Nos. 265B-265E (4)	10.70	11.00

Proceeds of sale given to Red Cross. Valid Dec. 20 to Jan. 5, 1933.
Inverted and pairs, one without surcharge or overprint, exist on Nos. 265B-265D, as well as missing letters.

Fernando Arturo de Merino (1833-1906) as President — A35

Cathedral of Santo Domingo A36

Designs: ½c, 5c, 8c, Tomb of Merino. 1c, 3c, 10c, as Archbishop.

1933, Feb. 27   Engr.   Perf. 14
266	A35	½c lt violet	.45	.35
267	A35	1c yellow green	.60	.25
268	A35	2c lt red	1.00	.75
269	A35	3c deep violet	.75	.30
270	A35	5c dark blue	.80	.35
271	A35	7c ultra	1.40	.50
272	A35	8c dark green	1.75	.75
273	A35	10c orange yel	1.50	.50
274	A35	20c carmine rose	3.00	1.25
275	A36	50c lemon	11.25	6.00
276	A36	1p dark brown	24.75	14.00
		Nos. 266-276 (11)	47.25	25.00

For surcharges see Nos. G1-G7.

Tower of Homage, Ozama Fortress — A37

1932   Litho.   Perf. 12
278	A37	1c green	1.25	.20
279	A37	3c violet	.80	.20

Issue dates: 1c, July 2; 3c, June 22.

"CORREOS" added at left
1933, May 28
283	A37	1c dark green	.40	.20

President Rafael L. Trujillo
A38   A39

1933, Aug. 16   Engr.   Perf. 14
286	A38	1c yellow grn & blk	.75	.35
287	A39	3c dp violet & blk	.90	.35
288	A38	7c ultra & blk	2.00	.75
		Nos. 286-288 (3)	3.65	1.45

42nd birthday of President Rafael Leonidas Trujillo Molina.

San Rafael Bridge — A40

1934   Litho.   Perf. 12
289	A40	½c dull violet	.70	.35
290	A40	1c dark green	.90	.20
291	A40	3c violet	1.40	.20
		Nos. 289-291 (3)	3.00	.75

Opening of San Rafael Bridge.
Issue dates: ½c, 3c, Mar. 3; 1c, Feb. 17.

Trujillo Bridge A41

1934
292	A41	½c red brown	.50	.25
293	A41	1c green	.75	.20
294	A41	3c purple	1.10	.20
		Nos. 292-294 (3)	2.35	.65

Opening of the General Trujillo Bridge near Ciudad Trujillo.
Issue dates: 1c, Aug. 24. Others, Sept. 7.

Ramfis Bridge A42

1935, Apr. 6
295	A42	1c green	.45	.20
296	A42	3c yellow brown	.50	.20
297	A42	5c brown violet	1.60	1.00
298	A42	10c rose	3.25	1.40
		Nos. 295-298 (4)	5.80	2.80

Issued in commemoration of the opening of the Ramfis Bridge over the Higuamo River.

President Trujillo — A43

A44

A45

1935   Perf. 11
299	A43	3c yellow & brown	.25	.20
300	A44	5c org red, bl, red & bis	.35	.20
301	A45	7c ultra, bl, red & brn	.50	.20
302	A44	10c red vio, bl, red & bis	.75	.20
		Nos. 299-302 (4)	1.85	.80

Ratification of a treaty setting the frontier between Dominican Republic and Haiti.
Issued: 3c, 10/29; 5c, 10c, 11/25; 7c, 11/8.

National Palace A46

1935, Apr. 1   Perf. 11½
303	A46	25c yellow orange	2.75	.30

Obligatory for all mail addressed to the president and cabinet ministers.

Post Office, Santiago A47

1936
304	A47	½c bright violet	.30	.35
305	A47	1c green	.30	.20

Issue dates: ½c, Jan. 14; 1c, Jan. 4.

George Washington Ave., Ciudad Trujillo — A48

1936, Feb. 22
306	A48	½c brn & vio brn	.40	.45
a.		Imperf., pair	52.50	
307	A48	2c carmine & brn	.40	.30
308	A48	3c yellow org & red brn	.65	.20
309	A48	7c ultra, blue & brn	1.25	1.25
a.		Imperf., pair	52.50	
		Nos. 306-309 (4)	2.70	2.20

Dedication of George Washington Avenue, Ciudad Trujillo.

José Nuñez de Cáceres — A49

Felix M. del Monte — A55

Proposed National Library — A56

1c, Gen. Gregorio Luperon. 2c, Emiliano Tejera. 3c, Pres. Trujillo. 5c, Jose Reyes. 7c, Gen. Antonio Duverge. 25c, Francisco J. Peynado. 30c, Salome Urena. 50c, Gen. Jose M. Cabral. 1p, Manuel de Jesus Galvan. 2p, Gaston F. Deligne.

1936 Unwmk. Engr. Perf. 13½, 14
310	A49	½c dull violet	.30	.20
311	A49	1c dark green	.25	.20
312	A49	2c carmine	.30	.20
313	A49	3c violet	.30	.20
314	A49	5c deep ultra	.55	.30
315	A49	7c slate blue	1.00	.55
316	A55	10c orange	1.00	.30
317	A56	20c olive green	3.75	2.75
318	A55	25c gray violet	6.00	8.00
319	A55	30c scarlet	7.50	10.00
320	A55	50c black brown	8.00	5.50
321	A55	1p black	27.50	32.50
322	A55	2p yellow brown	65.00	80.00
		Nos. 310-322 (13)	121.45	140.70

The funds derived from the sale of these stamps were returned to the National Treasury Fund for the erection of a building for the National Library and Archives.
Issued: 3c, 7c, Mar. 18; others, May 22.

President Trujillo and Obelisk — A62

1937, Jan. 11   Litho.   Perf. 11½
323	A62	1c green	.20	.20
324	A62	3c violet	.40	.20
325	A62	7c blue & turq blue	1.00	1.00
		Nos. 323-325 (3)	1.60	1.40

1st anniv. of naming Ciudad Trujillo.

Discus Thrower and Flag — A63

1937, Aug. 14
Flag in Red and Blue
326	A63	1c dark green	8.00	.75
327	A63	3c violet	10.50	.75
328	A63	7c dark blue	19.00	3.75
		Nos. 326-328 (3)	37.50	5.25

1st Natl. Olympic Games, Aug. 16, 1937.

Symbolical of Peace, Labor and
Progress — A64

1937, Sept. 18   *Perf. 12*
329 A64 3c purple   .35 .20

"8th Year of the Benefactor."

Monument to
Father Francisco
Xavier Billini (1837-
90) — A65

1937, Dec. 29
330 A65 ½c deep orange   .20 .20
331 A65 5c purple   .45 .20

Globe and
Torch of
Liberty — A66

1938, Feb. 22   *Perf. 11½*
332 A66 1c green   .40 .20
333 A66 3c purple   .50 .20
334 A66 10c orange   1.00 .20
   Nos. 332-334 (3)   1.90 .60

150th anniv. of the Constitution of the US.

Pledge of Trinitarians, City Gate and
National Flag — A67

1938, July 16   *Perf. 12*
335 A67 1c green, red & dk bl   .40 .20
336 A67 3c purple, red & bl   .45 .20
337 A67 10c orange, red & bl   .90 .40
   Nos. 335-337 (3)   1.75 .80

Trinitarians and patriots, Francisco Del
Rosario Sanchez, Ramon Matias Mella and
Juan Pablo Duarte, who helped free their
country from foreign domination.

Seal of the
University of Santo
Domingo — A68

1938, Oct. 28
338 A68 ½c orange   .30 .25
339 A68 1c dp green & lt green   .30 .20
340 A68 3c purple & pale vio   .40 .20
341 A68 7c dp blue & lt blue   .75 .35
   Nos. 338-341 (4)   1.75 1.00

Founding of the University of Santo Domingo, on Oct. 28, 1538.

Trylon and Perisphere, Flag and
Proposed Columbus
Lighthouse — A69

1939, Apr. 30   Litho.   Perf. 12
Flag in Blue and Red
342 A69 ½c red org & org   .35 .20
343 A69 1c green & lt green   .40 .20
344 A69 3c purple & pale vio   .40 .20
345 A69 10c orange & yellow   1.25 .65
   Nos. 342-345,C33 (5)   3.80 1.85

New York World's Fair.

A70   A71

1939, Sept.   *Typo.*
346 A70 ½c black & pale gray   .30 .20
347 A70 1c black & yel grn   .40 .20
348 A70 3c black & yel brn   .40 .20
349 A70 7c black & dp ultra   1.00 .90
350 A70 10c black & brt red vio   1.50 .40
   Nos. 346-350 (5)   3.60 1.90

José Trujillo Valdez (1863-1935), father of
President Trujillo Molina.

1940, Apr. 14   Litho.   Perf. 11½
Map of the Americas and flags of 21 American republics.

Flags in National Colors
351 A71 1c deep green   .35 .20
352 A71 2c carmine   .45 .20
353 A71 3c red violet   .60 .20
354 A71 10c orange   1.25 .20
355 A71 1p chestnut   15.00 9.50
   Nos. 351-355 (5)   17.65 10.30

Pan American Union, 50th anniv.

Sir Rowland
Hill — A72

1940, May 6   *Perf. 12*
356 A72 3c brt red vio & rose lil   3.00 .40
357 A72 7c dk blue & lt blue   6.00 1.40

Centenary of first postage stamp.

Julia
Molina
Trujillo
A73

1940, May 26
358 A73 1c grn, lt grn & dk grn   .35 .20
359 A73 2c brt red, buff & dp
       rose   .35 .25
360 A73 3c org, dl org & brn org   .50 .20
361 A73 7c bl, pale bl & dk bl   1.00 .35
   Nos. 358-361 (4)   2.20 1.00

Issued in commemoration of Mother's Day.

Map of
Caribbean
A74

1940, June 6   *Perf. 11½*
362 A74 3c brt car & pale rose   .40 .20
363 A74 7c dk blue & lt blue   .75 .20
364 A74 1p yel grn & pale grn   7.50 6.50
   Nos. 362-364 (3)   8.65 6.90

2nd Inter-American Caribbean Conf. held at
Ciudad Trujillo, May 31 to June 6.

Marion Military
Hospital — A75

1940, Dec. 24
365 A75 ½c chestnut & fawn   .25 .20

Fortress,
Ciudad
Trujillo
A76

Statue of
Columbus, Ciudad
Trujillo — A77

1941
366 A76 1c dk green & lt green   .20 .20
367 A77 2c brt red & rose   .20 .20
368 A77 10c orange brn & buff   .55 .25
   Nos. 366-368 (3)   .95 .65

Issue dates: 1c, Mar. 27; others, Apr. 7.

Sánchez, Duarte, Mella and
Trujillo — A78

1941, May 16
369 A78 3c brt red lil & red
       vio   .25 .20
370 A78 4c brt red, crim &
       pale rose   .40 .20
371 A78 13c dk blue & lt blue   .60 .35
372 A78 15c orange brn & buff   2.00 1.50
373 A78 17c lt bl, bl & pale bl   2.00 1.50
374 A78 1p org, yel brn &
       pale org   7.75 7.00
375 A78 2p lt gray & pale
       gray   17.00 7.25
   Nos. 369-375 (7)   30.00 18.00

Trujillo-Hull Treaty signed Sept. 24, 1940
and effective Apr. 1, 1941.

Bastion of
February
27 — A79

1941, Oct. 20
376 A79 5c brt blue & lt blue   .50 .20

School, Torch of Knowledge, Pres.
Trujillo — A80

1941
377 A80 ½c chestnut & fawn   .20 .20
378 A80 1c dk green & lt green   .25 .20

Education campaign.
Issue dates: ½c, Dec. 12, 1c, Dec. 2.

Reserve
Bank of
Dominican
Republic
A81

1942   *Unwmk.*
379 A81 5c lt brown & buff   .40 .20
380 A81 17c dp blue & lt blue   .70 .45

Founding of the Reserve Bank, 10/24/41.

Representation of
Transportation
A82   Virgin of
Altagracia
A83

1942, Aug. 15
381 A82 3c dk brn, grn yel & lt
       bl   3.00 .50
382 A82 15c pur, grn, yel & lt bl   8.25 3.50

Day of Posts and Telegraph, 8th anniv.

1942, Aug. 15
383 A83 ½c gray & pale gray   .75 .20
384 A83 1c dp grn & lt grn   1.50 .20
385 A83 3c brt red lil & lil   9.50 .20
386 A83 5c dk vio brn & vio
       brn   2.00 .20
387 A83 10c rose pink & pink   6.75 .20
388 A83 15c dp blue & lt blue   7.50 .30
   Nos. 383-388 (6)   28.00 1.35

20th anniv. of the coronation of Our Lady of
Altagracia.

Bananas — A84

Cows — A85

1942-43
389 A84 3c dk brn & grn ('43)   .50 .20
390 A84 4c vermilion & blk ('43)   .50 .30
391 A85 5c dp blue & cop brn   .50 .20
392 A85 15c dk pur & blue grn   .75 .40
   Nos. 389-392 (4)   2.25 1.10

Issue date: 5c, 15c, Aug. 18.

Emblems of
Dominican
and
Trujillista
Parties
A86

1943, Jan. 15
393	A86	3c orange	.40 .20
394	A86	4c dark red	.50 .20
395	A86	13c brt red lilac	1.10 .20
396	A86	1p lt blue	5.00 1.60
		Nos. 393-396 (4)	7.00 2.20

Re-election of President Rafael Trujillo Molina, May 16, 1942.

Model Market, Ciudad Trujillo A87

1944
397	A87	2c dk brown & buff	.20 .20

Bastion of Feb. 27 and National Flag — A88

1944, Feb. 27   Unwmk.
Flag in Dark Blue and Carmine
398	A88	½c ocher	.20 .20
399	A88	1c yellow green	.20 .20
400	A88	2c scarlet	.20 .20
401	A88	3c brt red vio	.20 .20
402	A88	5c yellow orange	.20 .20
403	A88	7c brt blue	.25 .25
404	A88	10c orange brown	.40 .30
405	A88	20c olive green	.65 .60
406	A88	50c lt blue	1.90 1.75
		Nos. 398-406,C46-C48 (12)	7.00 5.80

Souvenir Sheet
Imperf
407	A88	Sheet of 12	110.00 110.00
a.-l.		Single stamp	3.00 3.00

Centenary of Independence.
No. 407 contains 1 each of Nos. 398-406 and C46-C48 with simulated perforations. Size: 141x205mm.

Battlefield and Nurse with Child A90

1944, Aug. 1
408	A90	1c dk bl grn, buff & car	.20 .20
a.		Vertical pair, imperf. btwn.	15.00
b.		Horiz. pair, imperf. vert.	15.00
409	A90	2c dk brn, buff & car	.30 .20
410	A90	3c brt bl, buff & car	.30 .20
411	A90	10c rose car, buff & car	.60 .20
		Nos. 408-411 (4)	1.40 .80

80th anniv. of the Intl. Red Cross.

Municipal Building, San Cristóbal A91

Emblem of Communications A92

Unwmk.
1945, Jan. 10   Litho.   *Perf. 12*
412	A91	½c blue & lt blue	.20 .20
413	A91	1c dk green & green	.20 .20
414	A91	2c red org & org	.20 .20
415	A91	3c dk brown & brown	.20 .20
416	A91	10c ultra & gray blue	.60 .20
		Nos. 412-416 (5)	1.40 1.00

Centenary of the constitution.

1945, Sept. 1
Center in Dark Blue and Carmine
417	A92	3c orange	.20 .20
418	A92	20c yellow green	.75 .20
419	A92	50c light blue	1.50 .55
		Nos. 417-419,C53-C56 (7)	4.35 1.80

Palace of Justice, Ciudad Trujillo A93

1946   *Perf. 11½*
420	A93	3c dk red brown & buff	.20 .20

Map of Hispaniola — A94

1946, Aug. 4   *Perf. 12*
421	A94	10c multicolored	.45 .20
		Nos. 421,C62-C63 (3)	1.40 .60

450th anniv. of the founding of Santo Domingo.

Waterfall of Jimenoa — A95

1946-47
Center Multicolored
422	A95	1c yellow grn ('47)	.20 .20
423	A95	2c carmine ('47)	.20 .20
424	A95	3c deep blue	.20 .20
425	A95	13c red violet ('47)	.40 .30
426	A95	20c chocolate ('47)	.75 .30
427	A95	50c orange ('47)	1.50 1.10
		Nos. 422-427,C64-C67 (10)	6.55 4.70

Nos. 422-423, 425-427 issued Mar. 18.
For surcharge see No. 540.

Executive Palace A96

1948, Feb. 27
428	A96	1c yellow green	.20 .20
429	A96	3c deep blue	.20 .20
		Nos. 428-429,C68-C69 (4)	3.80 2.65

Church of San Francisco Ruins — A97

1949, Apr. 13   *Perf. 11½*
430	A97	1c dk grn & pale grn	.20 .20
431	A97	3c dp bl & pale bl	.20 .20
		Nos. 430-431,C70-C73 (6)	2.25 1.50

Gen. Pedro Santana — A98

Pigeon and Globe — A99

1949, Aug. 10
432	A98	3c deep blue & blue	.20 .20

Battle of Las Carreras, cent. See #C74.

1950, Mar. 23
Center and Inscriptions in Brown
433	A99	1c green & pale green	.20 .20
434	A99	2c yel grn & yel	.20 .20
435	A99	5c blue & pale blue	.20 .20
436	A99	7c dk vio bl & pale bl	.40 .20
		Nos. 433-436 (4)	1.00 .80

75th anniv. of the UPU.

Catalogue values for unused stamps in this section, from this point to the end of the section, are for Never Hinged items.

Hotel Jimani A100

Hotels: 1c, 2c, Hamaca. 5c, Montana. 15c, San Cristobal. 20c, Maguana.

1950-52
437	A100	½c org brn & buff	.20 .20
438	A100	1c dp grn & grn ('51)	.20 .20
439	A100	2c red org & sal ('52)	.20 .20
440	A100	5c blue & lt blue	.30 .20
441	A100	15c dp orange & yel	.55 .20
442	A100	20c lilac & rose lilac	1.00 .20
443	A100	1p chocolate & yel	4.00 1.60
		Nos. 437-443,C75-C76 (9)	9.95 5.00

Issue dates: 1c, Dec. 1, 1951; 2c, Jan. 11, 1952; others, Sept. 8, 1950.
The ½c, 15c and 20c exist imperf.

Ruins of Church and Hospital of San Nicolas de Bari A101

School of Medicine — A102

Queen Isabella I — A103

1950, Oct. 2
444	A101	2c dk green & rose brn	.20 .20
445	A102	5c vio blue & org brn	.40 .20
		Nos. 444-445,C77 (3)	1.20 .60

13th Pan-American Health Conference. Nos. 444-445 and C77 exist imperf.

1951, Oct. 12
446	A103	5c dk blue & red brn	.50 .20

500th anniversary of the birth of Queen Isabella I of Spain. Exists imperf.

Dr. Salvador B. Gautier Hospital A104

1952, Aug.
447	A104	1c dark green	.20 .20
448	A104	2c red	.20 .20
449	A104	5c violet blue	.40 .20
		Nos. 447-449,C78-C79 (5)	3.90 2.95

Columbus Lighthouse and Flags of 21 Republics A105

1953, Jan. 6   Engr.   *Perf. 13*
450	A105	2c dark green	.25 .20
451	A105	5c deep blue	.35 .20
452	A105	10c deep carmine	.60 .25
		Nos. 450-452,C80-C86 (10)	5.35 3.65

Treasury Building, Ciudad Trujillo A106

Sugar Industry, "Central Rio Haina" A107

1953   Litho.   *Perf. 11½*
453	A106	½c brown	.20 .20
454	A106	2c dark blue	.20 .20
455	A107	5c blue & vio brn	.20 .20
456	A106	15c orange	.75 .25
		Nos. 453-456 (4)	1.35 .85

For surcharge see No. 539.

José Marti — A108

Monument to the Peace of Trujillo — A109

1954   *Perf. 12½*
457	A108	10c dp blue & dk brown	.45 .20

Centenary of the birth of Jose Marti (1853-1895), Cuban patriot.

1954, May 25
458	A109	2c green	.20 .20
459	A109	7c blue	.25 .20
460	A109	20c orange	.75 .20
		Nos. 458-460 (3)	1.20 .60
		See No. 493.	

Rotary
Emblem
A110

1955, Feb. 23   *Perf. 12*
461 A110 7c deep blue   .60 .20

50th anniv., Rotary Intl. See No. C90.

Gen. Rafael L.
Trujillo — A111

4c, Trujillo in civilian clothes. 7c, Trujillo statue. 10c, Symbols of culture & prosperity.

1955, May 16   Engr.   Perf. 13½x13
462 A111 2c red   .30 .20
463 A111 4c lt olive green   .30 .20
464 A111 7c indigo   .35 .20
465 A111 10c brown   .85 .20
    Nos. 462-465,C91-C93 (7)   4.50 1.80

25th anniversary of the Trujillo era.

General Rafael L.
Trujillo — A112

Angelita
Trujillo — A113

1955, Dec. 20   Unwmk.   Perf. 13
466 A112 7c deep claret   .35 .20
467 A112 10c dark blue   .50 .20
    Nos. 466-467,C94 (3)   1.20 .60

1955, Dec. 20   Litho.   Perf. 12½
468 A113 10c blue & ultra   .45 .20

Nos. 466-468 were issued to publicize the International Fair of Peace and Brotherhood in Ciudad Trujillo, Dec. 1955.

Airport
A114

Cedar — A115

1956, Apr. 6   Perf. 12½
469 A114 1c brown   .20 .20
470 A114 2c red orange   .20 .20
    Nos. 469-470,C95 (3)   .80 .60

3rd Caribbean conf. of the ICAO.

1956, Dec. 8   Perf. 11½x12
471 A115 5c car rose & grn   1.10 .20
472 A115 6c red vio & grn   1.40 .20
    Nos. 471-472,C96 (3)   4.10 .60

Reforestation program.

Fair Emblem
A116

Fanny Blankers-
Koen,
Netherlands
A117

1957, Jan. 10   Perf. 12½
473 A116 7c blue, lt brn & ver   .35 .20

2nd International Livestock Show, Ciudad Trujillo, Jan. 10-20, 1957. Exists imperf.

Engraved & Lithographed
1957, Jan. 24   Perf. 11½, Imperf.

Olympic Winners and Flags: 2c, Jesse Owens, US. 3c, Kee Chung Sohn, Japan. 5c, Lord Burghley, England. 7c, Bob Mathias, US.

Flags in National Colors
474 A117 1c brn, lt bl, vio & mar   .20 .20
475 A117 2c dk brn, lt bl & vio   .20 .20
476 A117 3c red lilac & red   .20 .20
477 A117 5c red org & vio   .20 .20
478 A117 7c green & violet   .20 .20
    Nos. 474-478,C97-C99 (8)   1.75 1.75

16th Olympic Games, Melbourne, Nov. 22-Dec. 8, 1956.
Miniature sheets of 5 exist, perf. and imperf., containing Nos. 474-478. Value, 2 sheets, perf. and imperf., $15.
For surcharges see Nos. B1-B5, B26-B30, CB1-CB3, CB16-CB18.

Lars Hall, Sweden, Pentathlon — A118

Olympic Winners and Flags: 2c, Betty Cuthbert, Australia, 100 & 200 meter dash. 3c, Egil Danielsen, Norway, javelin. 5c, Alain Mimoun, France, marathon. 7c, Norman Read, New Zealand, 50 km. walk.

Perf. 13½, Imperf.
1957, July 18   Photo.   Unwmk.
Flags in National Colors
479 A118 1c brn & brt bl   .20 .20
480 A118 2c org ver & dk bl .20 .20
481 A118 3c dark blue   .20 .20
482 A118 5c ol & dk bl   .20 .20
483 A118 7c rose brn & dk bl .20 .20
    Nos. 479-483,C100-C102 (8) 1.75 1.75

1956 Olympic winners.
Miniature sheets of 8 exist, perf. and imperf., containing Nos. 479-483 and C100-C102. The center label in these sheets is printed in two forms: Olympic gold medal or Olympic flag. Sheets measure 140x140mm. Value, 4 sheets, perf. and imperf., medal and flag, $18.
A third set of similar miniature sheets (perf. and imperf.) with center label showing an incorrect version of the Dominican Republic flag (colors transposed) was printed. These sheets are said to have been briefly sold on the first day, then withdrawn as the misprint was discovered. Value, 2 sheets, perf. & imperf., $150.
For surcharges see Nos. B6-B10, CB4-CB6.

Gerald Ouellette, Canada, Small Bore
Rifle, Prone — A119

Ron Delaney, Ireland, 1,500 Meter
Run — A120

Olympic Winners and Flags: 3c, Tenley Albright, US, figure skating. 5c, Joaquin Capilla, Mexico, platform diving. 7c, Ercole Baldini, Italy, individual road race (cycling).

Engraved and Lithographed
1957, Nov. 12   Perf. 13½, Imperf.
Flags in National Colors
484 A119 1c red brown   .20 .20
485 A120 2c gray brown   .20 .20
486 A119 3c violet   .20 .20
487 A120 5c red orange   .20 .20
488 A119 7c Prus green   .20 .20
    Nos. 484-488,C103-C105 (8) 1.75 1.75

1956 Olympic winners.
Miniature sheets of 5 exist, perf. and imperf., containing Nos. 484-488. Value, 2 sheets, perf. and imperf., $5.50.
For surcharges see Nos. B11-B20, CB7-CB12.

Mahogany
Flower — A121

Cervantes,
Globe,
Book — A122

1957-58   Litho.   Perf. 12½
489 A121 2c green & maroon   .20 .20
Perf. 12
490 A121 4c lilac & rose ('58) .20 .20
491 A121 7c ultra & gray grn   .20 .20
492 A121 25c brown & org ('58) 1.00 .35
    Nos. 489-492 (4)   1.75 .95

Sizes: No. 489, 25x29¼mm; Nos. 490-492, 24x28¾mm. In 1959, the 2c was reissued in size 24¼x28½mm with slightly different tones of green and maroon.
Issued: 2c, 10/24; 7c, 11/6; 4c, 25c, 4/7/58.
For surcharges see Nos. 537-538.

Type of 1954, Redrawn
Perf. 12x11½
1957, June 12   Unwmk.
493 A109 7c bright blue   .55 .20

On No. 493 the cent symbol is smaller, the shading of the sky and steps stronger and the letters in "Correos" shorter and bolder.

1958, Apr. 23   Litho.   Perf. 12½
494 A122 4c yellow green   .20 .20
495 A122 7c red lilac   .20 .20
496 A122 10c lt olive brown .35 .20
    Nos. 494-496 (3)   .75 .60

4th Book Fair, Apr. 23-28. Exist imperf.

Gen. Rafael L.
Trujillo — A123

1958, Aug. 16   Perf. 12
497 A123 2c red lilac & yel   .25 .20
498 A123 4c green & yel   .25 .20
499 A123 7c brown & yel   .25 .20
a. Souv. sheet of 3, #497-499, imperf.   1.00 .80
    Nos. 497-499 (3)   .75 .60

25th anniv. of Gen. Trujillo's designation as "Benefactor of his country."

S. S.
Rhadames
A124

1958, Oct. 27   Perf. 12½
500 A124 7c bright blue   1.00 .30

Day of the Dominican Merchant Marine. Exists imperf.

Shozo Sasahara, Japan,
Featherweight Wrestling — A125

Olympic Winners and Flags: 1c, Gillian Sheen, England, fencing, vert. 2c, Milton Campbell, US, decathlon, vert. 5c, Madeleine Berthod, Switzerland, downhill skiing. 7c, Murray Rose, Australia, 400 & 1,500 meter freestyle.

Perf. 13½, Imperf.
1958, Oct. 30   Photo.
Flags in National Colors
501 A125 1c rose, ind & ultra   .20 .20
502 A125 2c brown & blue   .20 .20
503 A125 3c gray, vio, blk & buff .20 .20
504 A125 5c rose, dk bl, brn &
             red   .20 .20
505 A125 7c lt brn, dk bl & red   .20 .20
    Nos. 501-505,C106-C108 (8)   1.75 1.75

1956 Olympic winners.
Miniature sheets of 5 exist, perf. and imperf. containing Nos. 501-505. Value, 2 sheets, perf. and imperf., $5.
For surcharges see Nos. B21-B25, CB13-CB15.

Globe and
Symbolic
Fire — A126

1958, Nov. 3   Litho.   Perf. 11½
506 A126 7c blue & dp carmine   .30 .20

UNESCO Headquarters in Paris opening, Nov. 3.

Dominican
Republic
Pavilion,
Brussels
Fair — A127

1958, Dec. 9   Unwmk.   Perf. 12½
507 A127 7c blue green   .25 .20
    Nos. 507,C109-C110 (3)   1.20 .80

Universal & Intl. Exposition at Brussels.

Gen. Trujillo Placing Wreath on Altar of the Nation — A128

1959, July 10 **Perf. 12**
508 A128 9c brn, grn, red & gold .25 .20
a. Souv. sheet of 1, imperf. 1.00 .75

29th anniversary of the Trujillo regime.

Lt. Leonidas Rhadames Trujillo, Team Captain — A129

Jamaican Polo Team A130

Design: 10c, Lt. Trujillo on polo pony.

1959, May 15
509 A129 2c violet .20 .20
510 A130 7c yellow brown .35 .25
511 A130 10c green .45 .25
Nos. 509-511,C111 (4) 1.35 1.00

Jamaica-Dominican Republic polo match at Ciudad Trujillo.

Symbolical of Census A131

1959, Aug. 15 **Litho.** **Perf. 12½**
Flag in Ultramarine and Red
512 A131 1c blue & black .20 .20
513 A131 9c green & black .25 .20
514 A131 13c orange & black .50 .25
Nos. 512-514 (3) .95 .65

Issued to publicize the 1960 census.

Trujillo Stadium — A132

1959, Aug. 27
515 A132 9c green & gray .40 .25

Issued to publicize the 3rd Pan American Games, Chicago, Aug. 27-Sept. 7.

Charles V A133

Rhadames Bridge — A134

1959, Oct. 12 **Unwmk.** **Perf. 12**
516 A133 5c bright pink .25 .20
517 A133 9c violet blue .40 .20

400th anniv. of the death of Charles V (1500-1558), Holy Roman Emperor.

1959-60 **Litho.** **Perf. 12**
1c and No. 520, Different view of bridge.
518 A134 1c green & gray ('60) .30 .20
519 A134 2c ultra & gray .30 .20
520 A134 2c red & gray ('60) .30 .20
521 A134 5c brn & dull red brn .30 .20
Nos. 518-521 (4) 1.20 .80

Issued: No. 519, 10/22; 5c, 11/30; 1c, No. 520, 2/6.
For surcharge see No. 536.

Sosua Refugee Settlement and WRY Emblem — A135

1960, Apr. 7 **Perf. 12½**
Center in Gray
522 A135 5c red brn & yel grn .20 .20
523 A135 9c carmine & lt blue .20 .20
524 A135 13c orange & green .50 .20
Nos. 522-524,C113-C114 (5) 2.30 1.20

World Refugee Year, 7/1/59-6/30/60.
For surcharges see Nos. B31-B33.

Sholam Takhti, Iran, Lightweight Wrestling — A136

Olympic Winners: 2c, Masaru Furukawa, Japan, 200 meter breast stroke. 3c, Mildred McDaniel, US, high jump. 5c, Terence Spinks, England, featherweight boxing. 7c, Carlo Pavesi, Italy, fencing.

Perf. 13½, Imperf.
1960, Sept. 14 **Photo.**
Flags in National Colors
525 A136 1c red, yel grn & blk .20 .20
526 A136 2c org, grnsh bl & brn .20 .20
527 A136 3c henna brn & bl .20 .20
528 A136 5c brown & ultra .20 .20
529 A136 7c grn, bl & rose brn .20 .20
Nos. 525-529,C115-C117 (8) 1.70 1.70

17th Olympic Games, Rome, 8/25-9/11.
Miniature sheets of 5 exist, perf. and imperf., containing Nos. 525-529, $5. Value, 2 sheets, perf. & imperf., $5.
For surcharges see Nos. B34-B38, CB21-CB23.

Post Office, Ciudad Trujillo A137

1960, Aug. 26 **Litho.** **Perf. 11½x12**
530 A137 2c ultra & gray .25 .20
Exists imperf.

Cattle A138

1960, Aug. 30
531 A138 9c carmine & gray .25 .20

Issued to publicize the Agricultural and Industrial Fair, San Juan de la Maguana.

Nos. 518, 490-491, 453, 427 Surcharged in Red, Black or Blue

1960-61 **Perf. 12**
536 A134 2c on 1c grn & gray (R) .20 .20
537 A121 9c on 4c lilac & rose .50 .20
a. Inverted surcharge 21.00
538 A121 9c on 7c ultra & gray grn (R) .20 .20
539 A106 36c on ½c brown 1.40 1.25
a. Inverted surcharge 18.00
540 A95 1p on 50c multi (Bl) 3.25 2.40
Nos. 536-540 (5) 5.85 4.25

Issue dates: No. 536, Dec. 30, 1960; No. 537, Dec. 20, 1960; others, Feb. 4, 1961.

Trujillo Memorial A139

Coffee, Cacao A140

1961 **Unwmk.** **Perf. 11½**
548 A139 1c brown .20 .20
549 A139 2c green .20 .20
550 A139 4c rose lilac .35 .30
551 A139 5c light blue .35 .20
552 A139 9c red orange .35 .20
Nos. 548-552 (5) 1.45 1.10

Gen. Rafael L. Trujillo (1891-1961).
Issued: 2c, 8/7; 4c, 10/24; others 8/30.

1961, Dec. 30 **Litho.** **Perf. 12½**
553 A140 1c blue green .20 .20
554 A140 2c orange brown .20 .20
555 A140 4c violet .20 .20
556 A140 5c blue .20 .20
557 A140 9c gray .20 .20
Nos. 553-557,C118-C119 (7) 1.90 1.75

Nos. 553-557 exist imperf.

Dagger Pointing at Mosquito — A141

1962, Apr. 29 **Photo.** **Perf. 12**
558 A141 10c brt pink & red lilac .30 .20
559 A141 20c pale brn & brn .45 .25
560 A141 25c pale grn & yel grn .60 .30
Nos. 558-560,B39-B40,C120-C121,CB24-CB25 (9) 4.10 2.80

WHO drive to eradicate malaria.

Broken Fetters and Laurel A142

"Justice," Map of Dominican Republic — A143

Farm, Factory and Flag — A144

Design: 20c, Flag, torch and inscription.

1962, May 30 **Litho.** **Perf. 12½**
561 A142 1c grn, yel, ultra & red .20 .20
562 A143 9c bister ultra & red .30 .20
563 A142 20c lt blue, ultra & red .60 .25
a. Souvenir sheet of 3, #561-563 1.25 1.25
564 A143 1p lilac, ultra & red 3.00 1.40
Nos. 561-564,C122-C123 (6) 5.50 3.05

1st anniv. of end of Trujillo era. Nos. 561-564 exist imperf.

1962, May 22
565 A144 1c ultra, red & green .20 .20
566 A144 2c ultra & red .20 .20
567 A144 3c ultra, red & brown .20 .20
568 A144 5c ultra, red & blue .20 .20
569 A144 15c ultra, red & orange .30 .30
Nos. 565-569 (5) 1.10 1.10

Map and Laurel A145

1962, June 14 **Litho.**
570 A145 1c black .30 .20

Honoring the martyrs of June 1959 revolution.

Western Hemisphere and Carrier Pigeon — A146

Archbishop Adolfo Alejandro Nouel — A147

1962, Oct. 23 **Unwmk.** **Perf. 12½**
571 A146 2c rose red .20 .20
572 A146 9c orange .20 .20
573 A146 14c blue green .35 .20
Nos. 571-573,C124-C125 (5) 1.40 1.20

50th anniv. of the founding of the Postal Union of the Americas and Spain, UPAE.

1962, Dec. 18
574	A147	2c bl grn & dull bl	.20	.20
575	A147	9c orange & red brn	.25	.20
576	A147	13c maroon & vio brn	.30	.20
		Nos. 574-576,C126-C127 (5)	1.60	1.30

Cent. of the birth of Archbishop Adolfo Alejandro Nouel, President of Dominican Republic in 1911.

Globe, Banner and Emblems A148

1963, Apr. 15   Unwmk.   Perf. 11½
Banner in Dark Blue & Red
577	A148	2c green	.20	.20
578	A148	5c brt rose lilac	.20	.20
579	A148	9c orange	.35	.20
		Nos. 577-579,B41-B43 (6)	1.45	1.30

FAO "Freedom from Hunger" campaign.

Juan Pablo Duarte — A149

1963, July 7   Litho.   Perf. 12x11½
580	A149	2c shown	.25	.20
581	A149	7c Francisco Sanchez	.25	.20
582	A149	9c Ramon Mella	.25	.20
		Nos. 580-582 (3)	.75	.60

120th anniv. of separation from Haiti. See #C128.

Ulises F. Espaillat, Benigno F. de Rojas and Pedro F. Bono — A150

Designs: 4c, Generals Santiago Rodriguez, Jose Cabrera and Benito Moncion. 5c, Capotillo monument. 9c, Generals Gaspar Polanco, Gregorio Luperon and Jose A. Salcedo.

1963, Aug. 16   Unwmk.   Perf. 11½
583	A150	2c green	.20	.20
584	A150	4c red orange	.20	.20
585	A150	5c brown	.20	.20
586	A150	9c bright blue	.20	.20
a.	Souvenir sheet of 4		1.00	1.00
		Nos. 583-586 (4)	.80	.80

Cent. of the Restoration. No. 586a contains 4 imperf. stamps similar to Nos. 583-586.

Patient and Nurse — A151

Scales, Globe, UNESCO Emblem A152

1963, Oct. 25   Unwmk.   Perf. 12½
587	A151	3c gray & carmine	.20	.20
588	A151	6c emerald & red	.20	.20
		Nos. 587-C588,C129 (3)	.70	.65

Centenary of International Red Cross. Nos. 587-588 exist imperf. See No. C129.

1963, Dec. 10   Litho.
589	A152	6c pink & deep pink	.20	.20
590	A152	50c lt green & green	.65	.65
		Nos. 589-590,C130-C131 (4)	1.35	1.25

Universal Declaration of Human Rights, 15th anniv. Nos. 589-590 exist imperf.

Ramses II Battling the Hittites (from Abu Simbel) — A153

Design: 6c, Two heads of Ramses II.

1964, Mar. 8   Unwmk.   Perf. 12½
591	A153	3c pale pink & ver	.25	.20
592	A153	6c pale blue & ultra	.25	.20
593	A153	9c pale rose & red brn	.25	.20
		Nos. 591-593,C132-C133 (5)	1.25	1.00

UNESCO world campaign to save historic monuments in Nubia.
For surcharges see Nos. B44-B46.

Maximo Gomez — A154   Palm Chat — A155

1964, Apr. 30   Litho.
| 594 | A154 | 2c lt blue & blue | .25 | .20 |
| 595 | A154 | 6c dull pink & dull claret | .25 | .20 |

Bicent. of the founding of the town of Bani.

1964, June 8   Unwmk.   Perf. 12½

Design: 6c, Hispaniolan parrot.

Size: 27x37½mm
596	A155	3c ultra, brn & yel	1.90	.20
597	A155	6c gray & multi	2.40	.20
		Nos. 596-597,C134 (3)	8.55	.60

See Nos. 602-604.

Rocket Leaving Earth A156

Designs: 1c, Launching of rocket, vert. 3c, Space capsule orbiting earth. 6c, As 2c.

1964, July 28   Litho.
598	A156	1c sky blue	.20	.20
599	A156	2c emerald	.20	.20
600	A156	3c blue	.20	.20
601	A156	6c sky blue	.35	.20
		Nos. 598-601,C135-C136 (6)	1.50	1.25

Conquest of space.

Bird Type of 1964

Designs: 1c, Narrow-billed tody. 2c, Hispaniolan emerald hummingbird. 6c, Hispaniolan trogon.

1964, Nov. 7   Perf. 11½
Size: 26x37mm
Birds in Natural Colors
602	A155	1c bright pink	1.90	.20
603	A155	2c dark brown	1.90	.20
604	A155	6c blue	3.00	.20
		Nos. 602-604 (3)	6.80	.60

Universal Postal Union and United Nations Emblems A157

1964, Dec. 5   Litho.   Perf. 12½
605	A157	1c red	.20	.20
606	A157	4c green	.20	.20
607	A157	5c orange	.20	.20
		Nos. 605-607,C138 (4)	.85	.80

15th UPU Cong., Vienna, May-June 1964.

International Cooperation Year Emblem A158

1965, Feb. 16   Unwmk.   Perf. 12½
608	A158	2c lt blue & ultra	.25	.20
609	A158	3c emerald & dk grn	.25	.20
610	A158	6c salmon pink & red	.250	.20
		Nos. 608-610,C139 (4)	3.30	.85

UN Intl. Cooperation Year.

Virgin of Altagracia A159

1965, Mar. 18   Unwmk.   Perf. 12½
611	A159	2c grn, emer & dp rose	.20	.20
612	A159	6c multicolored	.30	.25
		Nos. 611-612,C140 (3)	.80	.70

4th Mariological Cong. and 11th Intl. Marian Cong. #612 exists imperf.

Flags of 21 American Nations — A160

Design: 2c, Hands holding lily.

1965, Apr. 14   Litho.   Perf. 11½
| 613 | A160 | 2c brown, yel & multi | .20 | .20 |
| 614 | A160 | 6c red lilac & multi | .30 | .20 |

Organization of American States.

Stamp of 1865 (No. 1) — A161

1965, Dec. 28   Litho.   Perf. 12½
615	A161	1c pink, buff & blk	.25	.20
616	A161	2c blue, buff & blk	.25	.20
617	A161	6c emerald, buff & blk	.25	.20
a.	Souvenir sheet of 2		1.00	1.00
		Nos. 615-617,C142-C143 (5)	1.25	1.00

Cent. of 1st Dominican postage stamps. No. 617a shows replicas of Nos. 1-2. Sold for 50c.

WHO Headquarters, Geneva — A162

1966, May 21   Litho.   Perf. 12½
| 618 | A162 | 6c blue | .20 | .20 |
| 619 | A162 | 10c red lilac | .30 | .20 |

New WHO Headquarters, Geneva.

Man Holding Map of Republic — A163

1966, May 23
| 620 | A163 | 2c black & brt green | .20 | .20 |
| 621 | A163 | 6c black & dp orange | .35 | .20 |

General elections, June 1, 1966.

Ascia Monuste — A164   Natl. Altar — A165

1966   Litho.   Perf. 12½
Various Butterflies in Natural Colors
Size: 31x21mm
622	A164	1c blue & vio bl	.50	.20
623	A164	2c lt grn & brt grn	.40	.20
624	A164	3c lt gray & gray	.40	.20
625	A164	6c pink & magenta	.65	.30
626	A164	8c buff & brown	.40	.40
		Nos. 622-626,C146-C148 (8)	19.45	3.55

Issued: 1c, 9/7; 3c, 9/11; others, 11/8.
For surcharges see Nos. B47-B51, CB28-CB30.

1967, Jan. 18   Litho.   Perf. 11½
627	A165	1c bright blue	.20	.20
628	A165	2c carmine rose	.20	.20
629	A165	3c emerald	.20	.20
630	A165	4c gray	.20	.20
631	A165	5c orange yellow	.20	.20
632	A165	6c orange	.20	.20
		Nos. 627-632,C149-C151 (9)	1.90	1.85

Map of Republic and Emblem A166

1967, Mar. 30   Litho.   Perf. 12½
633	A166	2c yellow, blue & blk	.20	.20
634	A166	6c orange, blue & blk	.20	.20
635	A166	10c emerald, blue & blk	.60	.45
		Nos. 633-635 (3)	1.00	.85

Development Year, 1967.

Rook and Knight A167

1967, June 23   Litho.   Perf. 12½
636 A167 25c multicolored   2.25 .40

5th Central American Chess Championships, Santo Domingo. See Nos. C152-C152a.

Alliance for Progress A168

Institute Emblem A169

1967, Sept. 16   Litho.   Perf. 12½
637 A168 1c bright green   .20 .20
     Nos. 637,C153-C154 (3)   .85 .70

6th anniv. of the Alliance for Progress.

1967, Oct. 7
638 A169 3c bright green   .25 .20
639 A169 6c salmon pink   .25 .20
     Nos. 638-639,C155 (3)   .95 .65

25th anniversary of the Inter-American Agriculture Institute.

Globe and Satellite A170

1968, June 15   Typo.   Perf. 12
640 A170 6c black & multi   .25 .20
     Nos. 640,C156-C157 (3)   .85 .70

World Meteorological Day, Mar. 23.

Boxers A171

1968, June 29
641 A171 6c rose red & dp claret   .25 .20
     Nos. 641,C158-C159 (3)   .80 .60

Fight between Carlos Ortiz, Puerto Rico, and Teo Cruz, Dominican Republic, for the World Lightweight Boxing Championship.

Lions Emblem — A172

1968, Aug. 9   Litho.   Perf. 11½
642 A172 6c brown & multi   .25 .20

Lions Intl., 50th anniv. (in 1967). See No. C160.

Wrestling and Olympic Emblem A173

1968, Nov. 12   Litho.   Perf. 11½
643 A173 1c shown   .20 .20
644 A173 6c Running   .25 .20
645 A173 25c Boxing   .75 .40
     Nos. 643-645,C161-C162 (5)   2.20 1.65

19th Olympic Games, Mexico City, 10/12-27.

Map of Americas and House — A174

1969, Jan. 25   Litho.   Perf. 12½
646 A174 6c brt bl, lt bl & grn   .20 .20

7th Inter-American Conference for Savings and Loans, Santo Domingo, Jan. 25-31. See No. C163.

Stool in Human Form A175

1969, Jan. 31   Litho.   Perf. 12½
Taino Art: 2c, Wood carved mother figure, vert. 3c, Face carved on 3-cornered stone. 4c, Stone hatchet, vert. 5c, Clay pot.
647 A175 1c yellow, org & blk   .30 .20
648 A175 2c lt grn, grn & blk   .30 .20
649 A175 3c citron, ol & brt grn   .30 .20
650 A175 4c lt lil, lil & brt grn   .30 .20
651 A175 5c yellow, org & brn   .30 .20
     Nos. 647-651,C164-C166 (8)   2.25 1.70

Taino art flourished in the West Indies at the time of Columbus.

Community Day Emblem — A176

COTAL Emblem — A177

Headquarters Building and COTAL Emblem — A178

1969, Mar. 25   Litho.   Perf. 12½
652 A176 6c dull green & gold   .25 .20

Community Development Day, Mar. 22.

1969, May 25   Litho.   Perf. 12½
Design: 2c, Boy and COTAL emblem.
653 A177 1c lt & dk blue & red   .25 .20
654 A177 2c emerald & dk grn   .25 .20
655 A178 6c vermilion & pink   .25 .20
     Nos. 653-655,C167 (4)   1.00 .80

12th Congress of the Confederation of Latin American Tourist Organizations (COTAL), Santo Domingo, May 25-29.

ILO Emblem — A179

Sliding into Base — A180

1969, June 27   Litho.   Perf. 12½
656 A179 6c lt grnsh bl, grnsh bl & blk   .25 .20

50th anniv. of the ILO. See No. C168.

1969, Aug. 15   Litho.   Perf. 12½
Designs: 1c, Catching a fly ball. 2c, View of Cibao Stadium, horiz.

Size: 21x31mm (1c, 3c); 43x30mm (2c)
657 A180 1c green & gray   .30 .20
658 A180 2c green & lt green   .30 .20
659 A180 3c purple & red brown   .30 .20
     Nos. 657-659,C169-C171 (6)   6.20 4.20

17th World Amateur Baseball Championships, Santo Domingo.

Las Damas Dam A181

Tavera Dam — A182

Designs: 2c, Las Damas hydroelectric station, vert. 6c, Arroyo Hondo substation.

1969   Litho.   Perf. 12
660 A181 2c green & multi   .30 .20
661 A181 3c dk blue & multi   .30 .20
662 A181 6c brt rose lilac   .30 .20
663 A182 6c multicolored   .50 .20
     Nos. 660-663,C172-C173 (6)   2.15 1.20

National electrification plan.
Issued: Nos. 660-662, Sept. 15; No. 663, Oct. 15.

Juan Pablo Duarte — A183

Map of Republic, People, Census Emblem A184

1970, Jan. 26   Litho.   Perf. 12
664 A183 1c emerald & dk grn   .25 .20
665 A183 2c sal pink & dp car   .25 .20
666 A183 3c brt pink & plum   .25 .20
667 A183 6c blue & violet blue   .25 .20
     Nos. 664-667,C174 (5)   1.45 1.05

Issued for Duarte Day in memory of Juan Pablo Duarte (1813-1876), liberator.

1970, Feb. 6   Perf. 11
Design: 6c, Census emblem and inscription.
668 A184 5c emerald & blk   .25 .20
669 A184 6c ultra & blue   .25 .20
     Nos. 668-669,C175 (3)   .95 .65

Census of 1970.

Abelardo Rodriguez Urdaneta — A185

"One of Many" A186

1970, Feb. 20   Litho.   Perf. 12½
670 A185 3c ultramarine   .25 .20
671 A186 6c green & yel grn   .25 .20
     Nos. 670-671,C176 (3)   .80 .60

Issued to honor Abelardo Rodriguez Urdaneta, sculptor.

Masonic Symbols — A187

1970, Mar. 2
672 A187 6c green   .25 .20

8th Inter-American Masonic Conference, Santo Domingo, Mar. 1-7. See No. C177.

Communications Satellite — A188

1970, May 25   Litho.   Perf. 12½
673 A188 20c olive & gray   .50 .30
World Telecommunications Day. See #C178.

UPU Headquarters, Bern — A189

1970, June 5   Perf. 11
674 A189 6c gray & brown   .25 .20
Inauguration of the new UPU headquarters in Bern. See No. C179.

Education Year Emblem — A190

Pedro Alejandrino Pina — A191

1970, June 26   Litho.   Perf. 12½
675 A190 4c rose lilac   .25 .20
Issued for International Education Year, 1970. See No. C180.

1970, Aug. 24   Litho.   Perf. 12½
676 A191 6c lt red brn & blk   .25 .20
Pedro Alejandrino Pina (1820-70), author.

Children Reading A192

1970, Oct. 12   Litho.   Perf. 12½
677 A192 5c dull green   .25 .20
    Nos. 677,C181-C182 (3)   .80 .60
1st World Exhibition of Books and Culture Festival, Santo Domingo, Oct. 11-Dec. 11.

Virgin of Altagracia — A193

Rodriguez Objio — A194

1971, Jan. 20   Litho.   Perf. 12½
678 A193 3c multicolored   .25 .20
Inauguration of the Basilica of Our Lady of Altagracia. See No. C184.

1971, June 18   Litho.   Perf. 11
679 A194 6c light blue   .25 .20
Manuel Rodriguez Objio (1838-1871), poet.

Boxing and Canoeing — A195

1971, Sept. 10
680 A195 2c shown   .25 .20
681 A195 5c Basketball   .25 .20
    Nos. 680-681,C186 (3)   .75 .60
2nd National Games.

Goat and Fruit A196

Designs: 2c, Cow and goose. 3c, Cacao and horse. 6c, Bananas, coffee and pig.

1971, Sept. 29   Perf. 12½
682 A196 1c brown & multi   .25 .20
683 A196 2c plum & multi   .25 .20
684 A196 3c green & multi   .25 .20
685 A196 6c blue & multi   .25 .20
    Nos. 682-685,C187 (5)   1.50 1.10
6th Natl. agriculture and livestock census.

José Nuñez de Cáceres — A197

Shepherds and Star — A198

1971, Dec. 1   Perf. 11
686 A197 6c lt bl, lil & dk bl   .25 .20
Sesquicentennial of first national independence. See No. C188.

1971, Dec. 10   Perf. 12½
687 A198 6c blue, brown & yel   .25 .20
Christmas 1971. See No. C189.

UNICEF Emblem, Child on Beach — A199

1971, Dec. 14   Litho.   Perf. 11
688 A199 6c gray blue & multi   .25 .20
UNICEF, 25th anniv. See No. C190.

Book Year Emblem A200

Taino Mask — A201

1972, Jan. 25   Perf. 12½
689 A200 1c green, ultra & red   .25 .20
690 A200 2c brown, ultra & red   .25 .20
    Nos. 689-690,C191 (3)   .80 .65
Intl. Book Year 1972.

1972, May 10   Litho.   Perf. 11
4c, Ladle and amulet. 6c, Human figure.
691 A201 2c pink & multi   .40 .20
692 A201 4c black, bl & ocher   .40 .20
693 A201 6c gray & multi   .40 .20
    Nos. 691-693,C194-C196 (6)   3.70 1.45
Taino art. See note after No. 651.

Globe A202

1972, May 17   Perf. 12½
694 A202 6c blue & multi   .25 .20
4th World Telecommunications Day. See No. C197.

"1972," Stamps and Map of Dominican Republic A203

1972, June 3
695 A203 2c green & multi   .25 .20
First National Philatelic Exhibition, Santo Domingo, June 3-17. See No. C198.

Basketball — A204

1972, Aug. 25   Litho.   Perf. 12½
696 A204 2c blue & multi   .25 .20
20th Olympic Games, Munich, Aug. 26-Sept. 11. See No. C199.

Club Emblem A205

1972, Sept. 29   Litho.   Perf. 10½
697 A205 1c lt green & multi   .25 .20
50th anniversary of the Club Activo 20-30 International. See No. C200.

Emilio A. Morel A206

1972, Oct. 20   Perf. 12½
698 A206 6c brt pink & multi   .25 .20
Emilio A. Morel (1884-1958), poet and journalist. See No. C201.

Central Bank Building A207

1972, Oct. 23
699 A207 1c shown   .25 .20
700 A207 5c 1-peso note   .25 .20
    Nos. 699-700,C202 (3)   1.15 .85
25th anniv. of Central Bank.

Holy Family — A208

Poinsettia A209

1972, Nov. 21
701 A208 2c rose lil, pur & gold .25 .20
702 A209 6c red & multi .25 .20
Nos. 701-702,C203 (3) .95 .60
Christmas 1972.

Mail Box
and
Student
A210

1972, Dec. 15
703 A210 2c rose red .20 .20
704 A210 6c blue .20 .20
705 A210 10c emerald .35 .20
Nos. 703-705 (3) .75 .60
Publicity for correspondence schools.

Tavera
Dam
A211

1973, Feb. 26   Litho.   Perf. 12½
706 A211 10c multicolored .30 .20
Inauguration of the Tavera Dam.

Various Sports — A212

Designs: a, UL. b, UR. c, LL. d, LR.

1973, Mar. 30   Perf. 13½x13
707 A212 Block of 4 .40 .50
a.-d. 2c, any single .20 .20
708 A212 Block of 4 3.75 3.75
a.-d. 25c, any single .75 .75
Nos. 707-708,C204-C205 (4) 8.15 8.25
12th Central American and Caribbean
Games, Santo Domingo, Summer 1974.

Christ
Carrying
the Cross
A213

6c, Belfry of Church of Our Lady of Carmen.

1973, Apr. 18   Litho.   Perf. 10½
709 A213 2c multicolored .25 .20
710 A213 6c multicolored, vert. .25 .20
Nos. 709-710,C206 (3) .90 .60
Holy Week, 1973.

WMO Emblem,
Weather
Satellite,
"Weather"
A214

Mask,
Cibao — A215

1973, Aug. 10 Litho.   Perf. 13½x13
711 A214 6c magenta & multi .25 .20
Centenary of international meteorological
cooperation. See No. C208.

1973, Oct. 12   Litho.   Perf. 10½
712 A215 1c Maguey drum, horiz .25 .20
713 A215 2c Carved amber, horiz .25 .20
714 A215 4c shown .25 .20
715 A215 6c Pottery .25 .20
Nos. 712-715,C210-C211 (6) 1.50 1.20
Opening of Museum of Mankind in Santo
Domingo.

Nativity
A216

Christmas: 6c, Stained glass window, vert.

Perf. 13½x13, 13x13½
1973, Nov. 26
716 A216 2c black, bl & yel .25 .20
717 A216 6c rose & multi .25 .20
Nos. 716-717,C212 (3) .75 .60
No. 717 exists imperf.

Dominican
Scout
Emblem
A217

Design: 5c, Scouts and flag.

1973, Dec. 7   Litho.   Perf. 12
    Size: 35x35mm
718 A217 1c ultra & multi .25 .20
    Size: 26x36mm
719 A217 5c black & multi .25 .20
Nos. 718-719,C213 (3) 1.15 .95
Dominican Republic Boy Scouts, 50th anniv.

Sports
Palace,
Basketball
Players
A218

Design: 6c, Bicyclist and race track.

1974, Feb. 25   Litho.   Perf. 13½
720 A218 2c red brown & multi .25 .20
721 A218 6c yellow & multi .25 .20
Nos. 720-721,C214-C215 (4) 1.10 .80
12th Central American and Caribbean
Games, Santo Domingo, 1974.

Bell Tower,
Cathedral of
Santo
Domingo — A219

Mater
Dolorosa — A220

1974, June 27   Litho.   Perf. 13½
722 A219 2c multicolored .25 .20
723 A220 6c multicolored .30 .20
Nos. 722-723,C216 (3) .85 .60
Holy Week 1974.

Francisco del Rosario Sanchez
Bridge — A221

1974, July 12   Perf. 12
724 A221 6c multicolored .35 .20
See No. C217.

Map, Emblem and Patient — A222

Design: 5c, Map of Dominican Republic,
diabetics' emblem and pancreas.

1974, Aug. 22   Litho.   Perf. 13
725 A222 4c blue & multi .25 .20
726 A222 5c yellow grn & multi .25 .20
Nos. 725-726,C218-C219 (4) 2.00 1.40
Fight against diabetes.

Train and
UPU
Emblem
A223

Design: 6c, Mail coach and UPU emblem.

1974, Oct. 9   Litho.   Perf. 13½
727 A223 2c blue & multi .60 .60
728 A223 6c brown & multi .25 .20
Nos. 727-728,C220-C221 (4) 2.85 1.55
Cent. of UPU.

Golfers — A224

Design: 2c, Championship emblem and
badge of Dominican Golf Association, horiz.

1974, Oct. 24 Perf. 13x13½, 13½x13
729 A224 2c yellow & blk .25 .20
730 A224 6c blue & multi .35 .20
Nos. 729-730,C222-C223 (4) 1.75 1.00
World Amateur Golf Championships.

Christmas
Decorations
A225

Virgin and
Child — A226

1974, Dec. 3   Litho.   Perf. 12
731 A225 2c multicolored .25 .20
732 A226 6c multicolored .25 .20
Nos. 731-732,C224 (3) .80 .60
Christmas 1974.

Tomatoes, FAO Emblem — A227

1974, Dec. 5
733 A227 2c shown .70 .20
734 A227 3c Avocados .70 .20
735 A227 5c Coconuts .70 .20
Nos. 733-735,C225 (4) 3.20 .80
World Food Program, 10th anniv.

Fernando A.
Defillo
A228

Tower, Our
Lady of the
Rosary Convent
A229

1975, Feb. 14   Litho.   Perf. 13½x13
736 A228 1c dull brown .25 .20
737 A228 6c dull green .25 .20
Dr. Defillo (1874-1949), physician.

1975, Mar. 26   Litho.   Perf. 13½

Design: 2c, Jesus saying "I am the Resurrection and the Life."

738	A229	2c brown & multi	.25	.20
739	A229	6c multicolored	.25	.20
		Nos. 738-739,C226 (3)	.80	.60

Holy Week 1975.

Hands (Steel Beams) with Symbols of Agriculture, Industry — A230

1975, May 19   Litho.   Perf. 10½x10

740	A230	6c dull blue & multi	.25	.20

16th Assembly of the Governors of the International Development Bank, Santo Domingo, May 1975. See No. C228.

Satellite Tracking Station — A231

1975, June 21   Litho.   Perf. 13½

741	A231	5c multicolored	.25	.20

Opening of first earth satellite tracking station in Dominican Republic. See No. C229.

Apollo A232

1975, July 24
Size: 35x25mm

742	A232	1c shown	.25	.20
743	A232	4c Soyuz	.25	.20
		Nos. 742-743,C230 (3)	5.75	3.65

Apollo Soyuz space test project (Russo-American cooperation), launching July 15; link-up, July 17.

Father Rafael C. Castellanos A233

1975, Aug. 6   Litho.   Perf. 12

744	A233	6c brown & buff	.25	.20

Castellanos (1875-1934), 1st Apostolic Administrator in Dominican Republic.

Women and Men Around IWY Emblem — A234

1975, Aug. 6   Perf. 13

745	A234	3c orange & multi	.25	.20

International Women's Year 1975.

Guacanagarix A235

Basketball A236

Indian Chiefs: 2c, Guarionex. 3c, Caonabo. 4c, Bohechio. 5c, Cayacoa. 6c, Anacona (woman). 9c, Hatuey.

1975, Sept. 27   Litho.   Perf. 12

746	A235	1c yellow & multi	.25	.20
747	A235	2c salmon & multi	.25	.20
748	A235	3c violet bl & multi	.25	.20
749	A235	4c green & multi	.25	.20
750	A235	5c blue & multi	.25	.20
751	A235	6c violet & multi	.25	.20
752	A235	9c rose & multi	.30	.25
		Nos. 746-752,C231-C233 (10)	2.65	2.20

1975, Oct. 24   Litho.   Perf. 12

Design: 6c, Baseball and Games' emblem.

753	A236	2c pink & multi	.30	.20
754	A236	6c orange & multi	.30	.20
		Nos. 753-754,C234-C235 (4)	1.20	.85

7th Pan-American Games, Mexico City, Oct. 13-26.

Carolers — A237

6c, Dominican nativity with farmers & shepherds.

1975, Dec. 12   Litho.   Perf. 13x13½

755	A237	2c yellow & multi	.25	.20
756	A237	6c blue & multi	.25	.20
		Nos. 755-756,C236 (3)	.75	.60

Christmas 1975.

Abudefdul Marginatus — A238

1976, Jan. 23   Litho.   Perf. 13

757	A238	10c shown	.45	.25
758	A238	10c Doncella	.45	.25
759	A238	10c Carajuelo	.45	.25
760	A238	10c Reina de los Angeles	.45	.25
761	A238	10c Pargo Colorado	.45	.25
a.		Strip of 5, #757-761	5.75	5.75

Ascension, by J. Priego — A239

"Separacion Dominicana" and Adm. Cambiaso A240

2c, Mary Magdalene, by Enrique Godoy.

1976, Apr. 14   Litho.   Perf. 13½

762	A239	2c blue & multi	.25	.20
763	A239	6c yellow & multi	.25	.20
		Nos. 762-763,C238 (3)	.80	.65

Holy Week 1976.

1976, Apr. 15   Perf. 13½x13

764	A240	20c multicolored	.85	.45

Naval Battle off Tortuga, Apr. 15, 1844.

Maps of US and Dominican Republic — A241

Design: 9c, Maps within cogwheels.

1976, May 29   Litho.   Perf. 13½

765	A241	6c violet bl & multi	.25	.20
766	A241	9c violet bl & multi	.25	.20
		Nos. 765-766,C239-C240 (4)	1.95	1.70

American Bicentennial.

Flags of Dominican Republic and Spain A242

1976, May 31

767	A242	6c multicolored	.35	.20

Visit of King Juan Carlos I and Queen Sofia of Spain. See No. C241.

Various Telephones A243

1976, July 15   Perf. 12x12½

768	A243	6c multicolored	.25	.20

Cent. of 1st telephone call by Alexander Graham Bell, Mar. 10, 1876. See No. C242.

Vision of Duarte, by Luis Desangles — A244

Juan Pablo Duarte, by Rhadames Mejia — A245

1976, July 20   Litho.   Perf. 13x13½

769	A244	2c multicolored	.25	.20

Perf. 13½

770	A245	6c multicolored	.25	.20
		Nos. 769-770,C243-C244 (4)	1.90	1.35

Juan Pablo Duarte, liberation hero, death centenary.

Fire Hydrant — A246

Design: 6c, Firemen's emblem.

1976, Sept. 13   Litho.   Perf. 12

771	A246	4c multicolored	.25	.20
772	A246	6c multicolored	.25	.20
		Nos. 771-772,C245 (3)	.90	.60

Honoring firemen. Nos. 771-772 inscribed "Corrreos."

Radio and Atom Symbols A247

1976, Oct. 8   Litho.   Perf. 13½

773	A247	6c red & black	.25	.20

Dominican Radio Club, 50th anniv. See #C246.

Spain, Central and South America, Galleon A248

1976, Oct. 22   Litho.   Perf. 13½

774	A248	6c multicolored	.25	.20

Spanish heritage. See No. C247.

Boxing and Montreal Emblem A249

Design: 3c, Weight lifting.

1976, Oct. 22   Perf. 12

775	A249	2c blue & multi	.25	.20
776	A249	3c multicolored	.25	.20
		Nos. 775-776,C248-C249 (4)	1.65	1.10

21st Olympic Games, Montreal, Canada, July 17-Aug. 1.

Virgin and Child — A250

Three Kings — A251

1976, Dec. 8   Litho.   Perf. 13½
777 A250 2c multicolored   .25 .20
778 A251 6c multicolored   .25 .20
    Nos. 777-778,C250 (3)   .80 .65
        Christmas 1976.

Cable Car and Beach Scenes A252

1977, Jan. 7
779 A252 6c multicolored   .25 .20
    Nos. 779,C251-C253 (4)   1.25 .90
        Tourist publicity.

Championship Emblem — A253

1977, Mar. 4   Litho.   Perf. 13½
780 A253 3c rose & multi   .25 .20
781 A253 5c yellow & multi   .25 .20
    Nos. 780-781,C254-C255 (4)   1.65 1.10

10th Central American and Caribbean Children's and Young People's Swimming Championships, Santo Domingo.

Christ Carrying Cross — A254

Design: 6c, Head with crown of thorns.

1977, Apr. 18   Litho.   Perf. 13½x13
782 A254 2c multicolored   .25 .20
783 A254 6c black & rose   .25 .20
    Nos. 782-783,C256 (3)   .80 .60
        Holy Week 1977.

Doves, Lions Emblem A255

1977, May 6   Perf. 13½x13
784 A255 2c lt blue & multi   .25 .20
785 A255 6c salmon & multi   .25 .20
    Nos. 784-785,C257 (3)   .75 .60

12th annual Dominican Republic Lions Convention.

Battle Scene A256

1977, June 15   Litho.   Perf. 13x13½
786 A256 20c multicolored   .70 .35
        Dominican Navy.

Water Lily — A257

National Botanical Garden: 4c, "Flor de Mayo" (orchid). 6c, Sebesten.

1977, Aug. 19   Litho.   Perf. 12
787 A257 2c multicolored   .35 .20
788 A257 4c multicolored   .35 .20
789 A257 6c multicolored   .35 .20
    Nos. 787-789,C259-C260 (5)   2.45 1.60

Chart and Computers — A258

1977, Nov. 30   Litho.   Perf. 13
790 A258 6c multicolored   .25 .20

7th Interamerican Statistics Conf. See No. C261.

Solenodon Paradoxus — A259

Design: 20c, Iguana and Congress emblem.

1977, Dec. 29   Litho.   Perf. 13
791 A259 6c multicolored   1.75 .20
792 A259 20c multicolored   3.25 .30
    Nos. 791-792,C262-C263 (4)   10.50 1.30

8th Pan-American Veterinary and Zoo-technical Congress.

Main Gate, Casa del Cordon, 1503 — A260

Crown of Thorns, Tools at the Cross — A261

1978, Jan. 19   Perf. 13x13½
        Size: 26x36mm
793 A260 6c multicolored   .25 .20
        Spanish heritage. See No. C264.

1978, Mar. 21   Litho.   Perf. 12
6c, Head of Jesus with crown of thorns.

        Size: 22x33mm
794 A261 2c multicolored   .20 .20
795 A261 6c slate   .35 .20
    Nos. 794-795,C265-C266 (4)   1.20 .90
        Holy Week 1978.

Cardinal Octavio A. Beras Rojas — A262

Pres. Manuel de Troncoso — A263

1978, May 5   Litho.   Perf. 13
796 A262 6c multicolored   .25 .20

First Cardinal from Dominican Republic, consecrated May 24, 1976. See No. C268.

1978, June 12   Litho.   Perf. 13½
797 A263 2c black, rose & brn   .20 .20
798 A263 6c black, gray & brn   .35 .25

Manuel de Jesus Troncoso de la Concha (1878-1955), pres. of Dominican Republic, 1940-42.

Father Juan N. Zegri y Moreno — A264

1978, July 11   Litho.   Perf. 13x13½
799 A264 6c multicolored   .25 .20

Congregation of the Merciful Sisters of Charity, centenary. See No. C273.

Boxing and Games' Emblem A265

1978, July 21   Perf. 12
800 A265 2c shown   .25 .20
801 A265 6c Weight lifting   .30 .20
    Nos. 800-801,C274-C275 (4)   1.40 .90

13th Central American & Caribbean Games, Medellin, Colombia.

Sun over Landscape A266

Ships of Columbus, Map of Dominican Republic — A267

Design: 6c, Sun over beach and boat.

1978, Sept. 12   Litho.   Perf. 12
802 A266 2c multicolored   .30 .20
803 A266 6c multicolored   .30 .20
    Nos. 802-803,C280-C281 (4)   1.25 .80
        Tourist publicity.

1978, Oct. 12   Litho.   Perf. 13½
804 A267 2c multicolored   .25 .20

Spanish heritage. See No. C282.

Dove, Lamp, Poinsettia A268

Design: 6c, Dominican family and star, vert.

1978, Dec. 5   Litho.   Perf. 12
805 A268 2c multicolored   .30 .20
806 A268 6c multicolored   .40 .20
    Nos. 805-806,C284 (3)   1.00 .65
        Christmas 1978.

Starving Child, IYC Emblem — A269

1979, Feb. 26   Litho.   Perf. 12
807 A269 2c orange & black   .25 .20
    Nos. 807,C287-C289 (4)   1.85 1.35
        Intl. Year of the Child.

Crucifixion A270

1979, Apr. 9   Litho.   Perf. 13½
Design: 3c, Jesus carrying cross, horiz.

808 A270 2c multicolored   .25 .20
809 A270 3c multicolored   .35 .20
    Nos. 808-809,C290 (3)   1.85 1.30
        Holy Week.

Stigmaphyllon Periplocifolium — A271

1979, May 17   Litho.   Perf. 12
810 A271 50c multicolored   1.00 .50
    Nos. 810,C293-C295 (4)   2.25 1.50

Dr. Rafael M. Moscoso National Botanical Garden.

Heart,
Diseased
Blood
Vessel
A272

Design: 1p, Cardiology Institute and heart.

1979, June 2   Litho.   Perf. 13½
811 A272 3c multicolored   .20   .20
812 A272 1p multicolored   1.75   .75
    Nos. 811-812,C296 (3)   2.55 1.35
    Dominican Cardiology Institute.

Baseball,
Games'
Emblem
A273

3c, Bicycling and Games' emblem, vert.

1979, June 20
813 A273 2c multicolored   .25   .20
814 A273 3c multicolored   .25   .20
    Nos. 813-814,C297 (3)   .80   .65
    8th Pan American Games, Puerto Rico,
June 30-July 15.

Soccer — A274

Thomas A.
Edison — A275

Design: 25c, Swimming, horiz.

1979, Aug. 9   Litho.   Perf. 12
815 A274 2c multicolored   .25   .20
816 A274 25c multicolored   .35   .25
    Nos. 815-816,C298 (3)   .90   .70
    Third National Games.

1979, Aug. 27   Perf. 13½
817 A275 25c multicolored   .60   .45
    Cent. of invention of electric light. See No.
C300.

Hand
Holding
Electric
Plug
A276

Design: 6c, Filling automobile gas tank.

1979, Aug. 30
818 A276 2c multicolored   .25   .20
819 A276 6c multicolored   .30   .25
    Energy conservation.

Parrot
A277

Birds: 6c, Temnotrogon roseigaster.

1979, Sept. 12   Litho.   Perf. 12
820 A277 2c multicolored   1.50   .20
821 A277 6c multicolored   1.50   .20
    Nos. 820-821,C301-C303 (5)   14.40 1.80

A278

A279

Lions Emblem, Map of Dominican Republic.

1979, Nov. 13   Litho.   Perf. 12
822 A278 20c multicolored   .45   .35
    Lions International Club of Dominican
Republic, 10th anniversary. See No. C304.

1979, Dec. 18   Litho.   Perf. 12
823 A279 2c Holy Family   .25   .20
    Christmas 1979. See No. C305.

A280

A281

Design: Jesus Carrying Cross.

1980, Mar. 27   Litho.   Perf. 12
824 A280 3c multicolored   .25   .20
    Nos. 824,C306-C307 (3)   .75   .65
    Holy Week.

1980, May 15   Litho.   Perf. 13½
825 A281 1c shown   .40   .20
826 A281 2c Coffee   .40   .20
827 A281 3c Plantain   .40   .20
828 A281 4c Sugar cane   .40   .20
829 A281 5c Corn   .40   .20
    Nos. 825-829 (5)   2.00 1.00
    Cacao Harvest (Agriculture Year)

Cotuf Gold
Mine,
Pueblo
Viejo, Flag
of
Dominican
Republic
A282

1980, July 8   Litho.   Perf. 13½
830 A282 6c multicolored   .25   .20
    Nos. 830,C310-C311 (3)   1.55 1.10
    Nationalization of gold mining.

Blind Man's
Buff
A283

1980, July 21   Perf. 12
831 A283 3c shown   .25   .20
832 A283 4c Marbles   .25   .20
833 A283 5c Drawing in sand   .30   .25
834 A283 6c Hopscotch   .30   .25
    Nos. 831-834 (4)   1.10   .90

Iguana
A284

1980, Aug. 30   Litho.   Perf. 12
835 A284 20c multicolored   2.00   .45
    Nos. 835,C314-C317 (5)   11.85 2.55

Dance,
by
Jaime
Colson
A285

Perf. 13x13½, 13½x13
1980, Sept. 23   Litho.
836 A285 3c shown   .25   .20
837 A285 50c Woman, by Gilber-
            to Hernandez
            Ortega, vert.   .90   .60
    Nos. 836-837,C318-C319 (4)   1.95 1.40

Three
Kings — A286

Salcedo Province
Cent. — A287

1980, Dec. 5   Litho.   Perf. 13½
838 A286 3c shown   .25   .20
839 A286 6c Carolers   .25   .20
    Nos. 838-839,C327 (3)   .80   .65
    Christmas 1980.

1981, Jan. 14   Litho.   Perf. 13½
840 A287 6c multicolored   .25   .20
    See No. C328.

Juan Pablo
Duarte, Liberation
Hero, 105th
Anniv. of
Death — A288

1981, Feb. 6   Litho.   Perf. 12
841 A288 2c sepia & deep bister   .30   .20

Gymnast — A289

Mother
Mazzarello
A290

1981, Mar. 31   Litho.   Perf. 13½
842 A289 1c shown   .30   .20
843 A289 2c Running   .30   .20
844 A289 6c Pole vault   .30   .20
845 A289 6c Boxing   .30   .20
    Nos. 842-845,C331 (5)   1.75 1.15
    5th National Games.

1981, Apr. 14   Perf. 12
846 A290 6c multicolored   .30   .20
    Mother Maria Mazzarello (1837-1881),
founder of Daughters of Mary.

A291

A292

1981, May 18   Litho.   Perf. 13½
847 A291 6c gray vio & lt gray   .25   .20
    Pedro Henriquez Urena, Historian (1884-
1946)

1981, June 30   Litho.   Perf. 12
848 A292 2c multicolored   .20   .20
849 A292 6c River, forest   .30   .20
    Forest conservation.

Family in
House,
Census
Emblem
A293

1981, Aug. 14   Litho.   Perf. 12
850 A293 3c shown   .20 .20
851 A293 6c Farmer   .30 .20
1981 natl. population and housing census.

A294

A295

1981, Dec. 23   Litho.   Perf. 13½
852 A294 2c Bells   .25 .20
853 A294 3c Poinsettia   .25 .20
    Nos. 852-853,C353 (3)   1.00 .70
Christmas.

1982, Jan. 29   Litho.   Perf. 13½
854 A295 2c Juan Pablo Duarte .25 .20

National
Elections
A296

Designs: Voters casting votes. 3c, 6c vert.

1982, Mar. 30   Litho.   Perf. 13½
855 A296 2c multicolored   .20 .20
856 A296 3c multicolored   .20 .20
857 A296 6c multicolored   .30 .25
    Nos. 855-857 (3)   .70 .65

A297

A298

Energy Conservation: Various forms of energy.

1982, May 10   Litho.   Perf. 12
858 A297 1c multicolored   .25 .20
859 A297 2c multicolored   .25 .20
860 A297 3c multicolored   .25 .20
861 A297 4c multicolored   .35 .25
862 A297 5c multicolored   .35 .25
863 A297 6c multicolored   .35 .25
    Nos. 858-863 (6)   1.80 1.35

1982, Aug. 2   Perf. 12x12½
864 A298 6c multicolored   .25 .20
Emilio Prud'Homme (1856-1932), composer.

Pres. Antonio
Guzman
Fernandez (1911-
1982)
A299

1982, Aug. 4   Perf. 13x13½
865 A299 6c multicolored   .25 .20

14th
Central
American
and
Caribbean
Games
A300

1982, Aug. 13   Perf. 12, Imperf.
866 A300 3c Baseball   .50 .20
See Nos. C368-C370.

San Pedro de Macoris Province
Centenary — A301

1982, Aug. 26   Perf. 13
867 A301 1c Wagon   .30 .20
868 A301 2c Stained-glass window .30 .20
869 A301 5c Views   .40 .25
    Nos. 867-869,C375 (4)   1.40 .95
Size of 2c, 25x35mm.

St. Teresa of
Jesus of Avila
(1515-1582)
A302

1982, Nov. 17   Litho.   Perf. 13½
870 A302 6c multicolored   .45 .20

Christmas
1982 — A303

Environmental
Protection
A304

Various Christmas balls.

1982, Dec. 8
871 A303 6c multicolored   .25 .20
See No. C380.

1982, Dec. 15   Perf. 12
872 A304 2c Bird   .20 .20
873 A304 3c Water   .20 .20
874 A304 6c Forest   .20 .20
875 A304 20c Fish   .50 .35
    Nos. 872-875 (4)   1.10 .95

Natl.
Literacy
Campaign
A305

1983, Mar. 9   Litho.   Perf. 13½
876 A305 2c Vowels on blackboard .20 .20
877 A305 3c Writing, reading   .20 .20
878 A305 6c Children, pencil   .35 .20
    Nos. 876-878 (3)   .75 .60

A306

A307

5c, similar arms, incorporating stylized centenary monument.

1983, Apr. 4   Perf. 12
879 A306 1c multicolored   .25 .20
880 A306 5c multicolored   .30 .20
Mao City centenary.

1983, Apr. 25   Litho.   Perf. 12
Dominican Historians: 2c, Antonio del
Monte y Tejada (1780-1861). 3c, Manuel
Ubaldo Gomez (1857-1941). 5c, Emiliano
Tejera (1841-1923). 6c, Bernardo Pichardo
(1877-1924). 7c, Americo Lugo (1870-1952).
10c, José Gabriel Garcia (1834-1910). 7c, 10c
airmail.

881 A307 2c multicolored   .25 .20
882 A307 3c multicolored   .25 .20
883 A307 5c multicolored   .25 .20
884 A307 6c multicolored   .25 .20
885 A307 7c multicolored   .25 .25
886 A307 10c multicolored   .30 .30
    Nos. 881-886 (6)   1.55 1.35

National
Anthem,
100th
Anniv.
A308

Emilio Prud'Homme, & Jose Reyes, composer.

1983, Sept. 13   Litho.   Perf. 13½
887 A308 6c copper red & blk   .30 .20

Free Masons,
125th
Anniv. — A309

Church of Our
Lady of Regla,
300th
Anniv. — A310

1983, Oct. 24   Litho.   Perf. 12
888 A309 4c Emblem   .25 .20

1983, Nov. 5   Perf. 13½
889 A310 3c Church   .25 .20
890 A310 6c Statue   .30 .20

450th Anniv. of
Monte Cristi
Province — A311

6th Natl.
Games — A312

1983, Nov. 25   Perf. 12
891 A311 1c Tower   .25 .20
892 A311 2c Arms   .25 .20
893 A311 5c Cuban independence
               site, horiz.   .30 .20
894 A311 7c Workers, horiz.   .30 .20
    Nos. 891-894 (4)   1.10 .80

1983, Dec. 9
895 A312 6c Bicycling, boxing,
               baseball   .25 .20
896 A312 10c Gymnast, weight lift-
               ing, swimming   .30 .20
10c airmail.

Restoration of
the Republic,
120th Anniv.
A313

1983, Dec. 30   Litho.   Perf. 13½
897 A313 1c Capotillo Heroes
               Monument   .30 .20

140th Anniv. of Independence — A314

Designs: 6c, Matia Ramon Mella (Patriot),
flag. 25c, Mella's Blunderbuss rifle, Gate of
Deliverance (independence declaration site).

1984, Feb. 24   Litho.   Perf. 13½
898 A314 6c multicolored   .20 .20
899 A314 25c multicolored   .60 .35

Heriberto Pieter (1884-1972), Physician, First Negro Graduate — A315

1984, Mar. 16
900 A315 3c multicolored   .25 .20

Battle of Barranquita, 67th Anniv. — A316

1983, Dec. 30   Perf. 12
901 A316 5c multicolored   .30 .20

Battle of Santiago, 140th Anniv. A317

1984, Mar. 29   Perf. 13½
902 A317 7c multicolored   .35 .25

Coast Guard Ship DC-1, 1934 A318

1984, Apr. 13   Litho.
903 A318 10c multicolored   .40 .20
Navy Day and 140th anniv. of Battle of Tortuguero.

Birth Centenary of Pedro Henriquez Urena — A319

1984, June 29   Litho.   Perf. 12
904 A319 7c Salome Urena   .20 .20
905 A319 10c Text   .25 .25
906 A319 22c Urena   .30 .25
    Nos. 904-906 (3)   .75 .70

Monument to Heroes of June 1959 A320

1984, June 20   Perf. 13½
907 A320 6c silver & blue   .40 .25
The feat of Constanza Maimon and Estero Hondo, 25th anniv.

1984 Summer Olympics A321

1984, Aug. 1
908 A321 1p Hurdles   1.60 1.60
909 A321 1p Weightlifting   1.60 1.60
910 A321 1p Boxing   1.60 1.60
911 A321 1p Baseball   1.60 1.60
  a. Block of 4, #908-911   12.00 12.00
    Nos. 908-911 (4)   6.40 6.40

Protection of Fauna — A322

1984, Oct. 3   Litho.   Perf. 12
912 A322 10c Owl   2.25 .20
913 A322 15c Flamingo   3.00 .30
914 A322 25c Wild Pig   3.75 .35
915 A322 35c Solenodon   5.25 .55
    Nos. 912-915 (4)   14.25 1.45

500th Anniv. of Discovery of America A323

1984, Oct. 10   Litho.   Perf. 13½x13
916 A323 10c Landing on Hispaniola   .20 .20
917 A323 35c Destruction of Ft. Navidad .50 .30
918 A323 65c First Mass in America   .85 .60
919 A323 1p Battle of Santo Cerro   1.25 .80
    Nos. 916-919 (4)   2.80 1.90

Visit of Pope John Paul II — A324

1984, Oct. 11   Litho.   Perf. 13x13½
920   Block of 4   7.50 7.50
  a. A324 75c shown   1.50 1.50
  b. A324 75c Pope, map of Caribbean   1.50 1.50
  c. A324 75c Pope, globe   1.50 1.50
  d. A324 75c Bishop's crozier   1.50 1.50

150th Anniv. of Birth of Maximo Gomez (1986) A325

1984, Dec. 6   Litho.   Perf. 13½
921 A325 10c Gomez on horseback   .25 .20
922 A325 20c Maximo Gomez   .25 .20

Christmas 1984 A326

Perf. 13½x13, 13x13½
1984, Dec. 14   Litho.
923 A326 5c multicolored   .25 .20
924 A326 10c multicolored, vert. .25 .25

Sacrifice of the Child, by Eligio Pichardo A327

Paintings and sculpture: 10c, The Pumpkin Sellers, by Gaspar Mario Cruz; 25c, The Market, by Celeste Woss y Gil; 50c, Horses in the Rain, by Dario Suro.

1984, Dec. 19   Litho.   Perf. 13½
925 A327 5c multi   .45 .20
926 A327 10c multi, vert.   .45 .20
927 A327 25c multi   .50 .25
928 A327 50c multi   1.10 .35
    Nos. 925-928 (4)   2.50 1.00

Day of Our Lady of Altagracia A328

1985, Jan. 21
929 A328 5c Old church at Higuey, 1572   .25 .20
930 A328 10c Our Lady of Altagracia 1514, vert.   .25 .20
931 A328 25c Basilica of the Protector, Higuey 1971, vert.   .50 .30
    Nos. 929-931 (3)   1.00 .70

Independence, 141st Anniv. — A329

Painting: The Fathers of Our Country (Duarte, Sanchez and Mella).

1985, Mar. 8   Perf. 12½
932 A329 5c multicolored   .25 .20
933 A329 10c multicolored   .30 .20
934 A329 25c multicolored   .50 .25
    Nos. 932-934 (3)   1.05 .65

Battle of Azua, 141st Anniv. A330

1985, Apr. 8   Litho.   Perf. 13½
935 A330 10c Gen. Antonio Duverge, Statue   .35 .20

A331

A332

1985, Apr. 15   Litho.
936 A331 25c Santo Domingo Lighthouse, 1853   .50 .25
Battle of Tortuguero, 141st anniv.

1985, Apr. 15   Litho.   Perf. 12
937 A332 35c multicolored   .85 .30
American Airforces Cooperation System, 25th anniv.

A333

A334

1985, May 24   Litho.   Perf. 13½
938 A333 10c Don Carlos M. Rojas, 1st gov.   .40 .30
Espaillat Province cent.

1985, July 5   Litho.   Perf. 12
939 A334 5c Table tennis   .25 .20
940 A334 10c Walking race   .30 .30
MOCA '85, 7th Natl. Games.

Intl. Youth Year A335

1985, July 29   Perf. 13½
941 A335 5c Youth   .30 .20
942 A335 25c The Haitises   .85 .30
943 A335 35c Mt. Duarte summit   .90 .30
944 A335 2p Mt. Duarte   5.75 2.25
    Nos. 941-944 (4)   7.80 3.05

Interamerican Development Bank, 25th Anniv. — A336

10c, Haina Harbor. 25c, Map of development sites. 1p, Tavera-Bao-Lopez Hydroelectric Complex.

1985, Aug. 23
945 A336 10c multicolored   .25 .20
946 A336 25c multicolored   .50 .35
947 A336 1p multicolored   2.25 1.50
    Nos. 945-947 (3)   3.00 2.05

Intl. Decade for Women — A337

15th Central American and Caribbean Games, Santiago — A338

Design: Evangelina Rodriguez (1879-1947), first Dominican woman doctor.

1985, Sept. 26
948 A337 10c multicolored .30 .20

1985, Oct. 9 *Perf. 12*
949 A338 5c multicolored .40 .25
950 A338 25c multicolored 1.10 .35

4th Adm. Christopher Columbus Regatta, Casa de Espana A339

Designs: 50c, Founding of Santo Domingo, 1496. 65c, Chapel of Our Lady of the Rosary, 1496, Santo Domingo. 1p, Columbus, American Indian and old Spanish coat of arms.

1985, Oct. 10 *Perf. 13½*
951 A339 35c multicolored 1.10 .60
952 A339 50c multicolored 1.40 .90
953 A339 65c multicolored 1.90 1.10
954 A339 1p multicolored 3.50 1.90
    Nos. 951-954 (4) 7.90 4.50

Discovery of America, 500th anniv. (in 1992).

Cacique Enriquillo — A340

Archbishop Fernando Arturo de Merino — A341

Designs: 5c, Enriquillo in the Bahuroco Mountains, mural detail.

1985, Oct. 31
955 A340 5c multicolored .20 .20
956 A340 10c multicolored .45 .25

Enriquillo (d. 1536), leader of revolution against Spain. Size of No. 955: 47x33mm.

1985, Dec. 3 *Perf. 12*
957 A341 25c multicolored .50 .35

Cent. of holy orders granted to Merino (1833-1906), pres. of the republic 1880-82.

Mirabal Sisters, Political Martyrs 1960 A342

1985, Dec. 18 *Perf. 13½*
958 A342 10c multicolored .30 .20

Christmas A343

1985, Dec. 18
959 A343 10c multicolored .30 .20
960 A343 25c multicolored .70 .35

Day of Independence, Feb. 27 — A344

Design: Mausoleum of founding fathers Duarte, Sanchez and Mella.

1986, Feb. 26 *Litho.* *Perf. 13½*
961 A344 5c multicolored .25 .20
962 A344 10c multicolored .25 .25

Holy Week A345

Colonial churches.

1986, Apr. 10
963 A345 5c San Miguel .40 .25
964 A345 5c San Andres .40 .25
965 A345 10c Santa Barbara .40 .25
966 A345 10c San Lazaro .40 .25
967 A345 10c San Carlos .40 .25
    Nos. 963-967 (5) 2.00 1.25

Navy Day A346

Design: Juan Bautista Cambiaso, Juan Bautista Maggiolo and Juan Alejandro Acosta, 1884 independence battle heroes.

1986, Apr. 15
968 A346 10c multicolored .30 .20

Natl. Elections — A347

Natl. Postal Institute Inauguration A348

1986, Apr. 29
969 A347 5c Voters, map .25 .20
970 A347 10c Ballot box .30 .25

1986, June 10
971 A348 10c gold, blue & red .30 .20
972 A348 25c silver, blue & red .70 .30
973 A348 50c black, blue & red 1.40 .50
    Nos. 971-973 (3) 2.40 1.00

Central America and Caribbean Games, Santiago — A349

1986, July 17 *Litho.* *Perf. 13½*
974 A349 10c Weight lifting .30 .20
975 A349 25c Gymnastics .60 .30
976 A349 35c Diving .90 .35
977 A349 50c Equestrian 1.10 .55
    Nos. 974-977 (4) 2.90 1.40

Historians A350

Designs: 5c, Ercilia Pepin (b. 1886), vert. 10c, Ramon Emilio Jimenez (b. 1886) and Victor Garrido (1886-1972).

1986, Aug. 1 *Litho.* *Perf. 13½*
978 A350 5c silver & dull brn .25 .20
979 A350 10c silver & dull brn .25 .20

A351

A352

Discovery of America, 500th Anniv. (in 1992) — A353

Designs: 25c, Yachts racing, 5th Adm. Christopher Columbus Regatta, Casa de Espana. 50c, Columbus founding La Isabela

City. 65c, Exploration of the hidalgos. 1p, Columbus returning to the Court of Ferdinand and Isabella. 1.50p, Emblems.

1986, Oct. 10 *Litho.* *Perf. 13½*
980 A351 25c multicolored .55 .30
981 A352 50c multicolored 1.25 .45
982 A352 65c multicolored 1.50 .75
983 A352 1p multicolored 2.25 1.00
Textured Paper
Size: 86x58mm
Imperf
984 A353 1.50p multicolored 5.00 5.00
    Nos. 980-984 (5) 10.55 7.50

1986 World Cup Soccer Championships, Mexico — A354

Medicinal Plants — A355

Various soccer plays.

1986, Oct. 21 *Perf. 13½*
985 A354 50c multicolored 1.10 .50
986 A354 75c multicolored 2.25 .85

1986, Dec. 5
987 A355 5c Zea mays .20 .20
988 A355 10c Bixa orellana .20 .20
989 A355 25c Momordica
        charantia .50 .20
990 A355 50c Annona muricata 1.00 .40
    Nos. 987-990 (4) 1.90 1.00

Second Caribbean Pharmacopeia Seminar.

Christmas A356

1986, Dec. 19
991 A356 5c Urban scene .40 .25
992 A356 25c Rural scene 1.00 .30

A357

A358

1986, Dec. 31   Litho.   Perf. 13½
993   A357   10c shown   .30   .20
994   A357   25c Portrait, c. 1900   .60   .30
    Maximo Gomez (1836-1905), revolutionary,
statesman.

1987, Mar. 30   Litho.   Perf. 13½
995   A358   50c brt blue, blk & red   1.10   .55
    16th Pan American Ophthalmological Conf.,
Apr. 5-10.

A359

A360

Stained-glass window, San Juan Bosco
church, Santo Domingo: Ascension of Christ
to Heaven.

1987, May 28
996   A359   35c multicolored   1.10   .40

1987, Aug. 21

Edible plants.

997   A360   5c Sorghum bicolor   .20   .20
998   A360   25c Martanta
                    arundinacea   .40   .25
999   A360   65c Calathaea allouia   1.50   .75
1000   A360   1p Voandzeia subter-
                    ranea   2.25   1.10
    Nos. 997-1000 (4)   4.35   2.30

Activo 20-
30 Intl.,
25th Anniv.
A361

1987, Aug. 26
1001   A361   35c multicolored   1.00   .35

Adm.
Christopher
Columbus
Regatta
A362

A363

Columbus Memorial, Santo
Domingo — A364

1987, Oct. 14
1002   A362   50c shown   1.25   .45
1003   A363   75c shown   1.75   .65
1004   A363   1p Building Ft.
                    Santiago   2.40   .90
1005   A363   1.50p Columbus im-
                    prisoned by
                    Bombadilla   3.75   1.40

Size: 82x70mm

Imperf

1006   A364   2.50p shown   8.00   5.00
    Nos. 1002-1006 (5)   17.15   8.40
Discovery of America, 500th anniv. in 1992.

A365

A366

1987, Sept. 28
1007   A365   40c multicolored   .85   .40
    Junior Olympics, La Vega, 50th anniv.

1987, Nov. 10   Litho.   Perf. 13½
    Historians and authors: 10c, Jose Antonio
Hungria. 25c, Joaquin Sergio Inchaustegui.
1008   A366   10c buff & brown   .25   .20
1009   A366   25c pale grn & grn   .60   .25

SAN CRISTOBAL '87, 8th Natl.
Games — A367

1987, Nov. 19
1010   A367   5c Baseball   .50   .20
1011   A367   10c Boxing   .25   .20
1012   A367   50c Judo   1.10   .55
    Nos. 1010-1012 (3)   1.85   .95

Christmas
1987
A368

1987, Dec. 9   Litho.   Perf. 13½
1013   A368   10c Roasting pig   .40   .20
1014   A368   50c Arriving at airport   1.10   .45

Fr. Xavier Billini
(b. 1837) — A369

1987, Dec. 18   Litho.   Perf. 13½
1015   A369   10c Statue   .25   .20
1016   A369   25c Portrait   .55   .30
1017   A369   75c Ana Hernandez
                    de Billini, his
                    mother   1.60   .90
    Nos. 1015-1017 (3)   2.40   1.40

Frank Feliz,
Sr., and
Aircraft
A370

1987, Dec. 22
1018   A370   25c shown   .45   .25

Size: 86x106mm

Imperf

1019   A370   2p No. C30, map   6.50   6.00
    Pan-American goodwill flight to South Amer-
ican countries by the planes Colon, Pinta,
Nina and Santa Maria, 50th anniv.

Flora
A371

1988, Feb. 3   Litho.   Perf. 13½
1020   A371   50c Bromelia pinguin   1.40   .55
1021   A371   50c Tillandsia fascicu-
                    lata   1.40   .55
1022   A371   50c Tillandsia hotte-
                    ana, vert.   1.40   .55
1023   A371   50c Tillandsia com-
                    pacta, vert.   1.40   .55
    Nos. 1020-1023 (4)   5.60   2.20

St. John Bosco
(1815-1888)
A372

1988, Feb. 23   Litho.   Perf. 13½
1024   A372   10c shown   .25   .20
1025   A372   70c Stained-glass win-
                    dow   1.10   .75

Dominican Rehabilitation Assoc., 25th
Anniv. — A373

1988, Mar. 1
1026   A373   20c multicolored   .45   .25

A374

A375

1988, Apr. 6   Litho.   Perf. 13½
1027   A374   20c dk red brn & lt fawn   .45   .25
    Dr. Manuel Emilio Perdomo (b.1886).

1988, Apr. 29   Litho.   Perf. 13½
1028   A375   20c multicolored   .45   .25
    Dominican College of Engineers, Architects
and Surveyors (CODIA), 25th Anniv.

Independence
Day,
Mexico — A376

    Flags and: No. 1029, Fr. Miguel Hidalgo y
Costilla (1753-1811), Mexican revolutionary.
No. 1030, Juan Pablo Duarte (1813-1876),
father of Dominican independence.

1988, Sept. 12   Litho.   Perf. 13½
1029   A376   50c multicolored   1.10   .50
1030   A376   50c multicolored   1.10   .50

1988
Summer
Olympics,
Seoul
A377

1988, Sept. 21   Litho.   Perf. 13½
1031   A377   50c Running, vert.   .95   .20
1032   A377   70c Table tennis,
                    vert.   1.50   .35
1033   A377   1p Judo, vert.   2.40   .40
1034   A377   1.50p Mural by Tete
                    Marella   3.50   .75
    Nos. 1031-1034 (4)   8.35   1.70

A378

Discovery of America, 500th Anniv. (in 1992) — A379

Designs: 50c, 7th Adm. Christopher Columbus Regatta, Casa de Espana, 1988. 70c, La Concepcion Fortress, La Vega Real, 1494. 1.50p, Ft. Bonao. 2p, Nicolas de Ovando (c. 1451-1511), governor of Spanish possessions in America from 1502 to 1509. 3p, Mausoleum of Christopher Columbus, Santo Domingo Cathedral.

1988, Oct. 14   **Perf. 13½**
1035 A378 50c multicolored   .95 .50
1036 A378 70c multicolored   1.60 .75
1037 A378 1.50p multicolored   3.25 1.50
1038 A378 2p multicolored   4.75 1.90
   Size: 78x109mm
   Imperf
1039 A379 3p multicolored   5.00 5.00
   Nos. 1035-1039 (5)   15.55 9.65
Discovery of America, 500th anniv. (in 1992). No. 1038 inscribed "1501-1509."

Duverge Parish, Cent. — A380

1988, July 13   **Litho.**   **Perf. 13½**
1040 A380 50c multicolored   1.25 .40

A381

Trinitarians, 150th Anniv. — A382

1988, Nov. 11
1041 A381 10c shown   .40 .20
1042 A382 1p Trinitarian Plaza   1.90 .40
1043 A382 5p Independence Plaza   11.50 3.00
   Nos. 1041-1043 (3)   13.80 3.60
   See footnote after No. 337.

Pharmacology and Biochemistry A383

The Holy Family, 1504, by Miguel Angel — A384

1988, Nov. 28   **Litho.**   **Perf. 13½**
1044 A383 1p multicolored   1.50 1.25
13th Pan American and 16th Central American Congresses.

1988, Dec. 12
1045 A384 10c shown   .25 .20
1046 A384 20c Stained-glass window   .45 .30
   Christmas.

Municipal Technical Advisory Organization (LIGA), 50th Anniv. — A385

Ana Teresa Paradas (1890-1960), 1st Female Lawyer of the Republic, 1913 — A386

1988, Dec. 23
1047 A385 20c multicolored   .45 .30

1988, Dec. 26
1048 A386 20c deep claret   .45 .30

French Revolution Bicent. A387

1989, Mar. 10   **Litho.**   **Perf. 13½**
1049 A387 3p red & violet blue   2.25 2.25

Battle of Tortuga, Apr. 15, 1844 A388

1989, Apr. 14   **Litho.**   **Perf. 13½**
1050 A388 40c multicolored   .70 .45

Natl. Anti-drug Campaign A389

1989, May 15
1051 A389 10c multicolored   .30 .20
1052 A389 20c multicolored   .35 .20
1053 A389 50c multicolored   .60 .20
1054 A389 70c multicolored   .85 .30
1055 A389 1p multicolored   1.25 .30
1056 A389 1.50p multicolored   1.75 .40
1057 A389 2p multicolored   2.40 .60
1058 A389 5p multicolored   6.00 1.25
1059 A389 10p multicolored   11.50 3.00
   Nos. 1051-1059 (9)   25.00 6.45

Mother's Day A390

1989, May 30   **Litho.**   **Perf. 13½**
1060 A390 20c multicolored   .25 .20

Eugenio Maria de Hostos (b. 1839) — A391

Gen. Gregorio Luperon (b. 1839) — A392

1989, Aug. 22   **Litho.**   **Perf. 13½**
1061 A391 20c multicolored   .35 .20

1989, Aug. 28
1062 A392 20c multicolored   .35 .20

Little League Baseball, 50th Anniv. A393

1989, Sept. 29
1063 A393 1p multicolored   1.50 .75

Diabetes '89, 7th Latin American Congress A394

1989, Oct. 9   **Litho.**   **Perf. 13½**
1064 A394 1p multicolored   1.50 .60

America Issue A395

UPAE emblem, pre-Columbian artifacts and customs: 20c, Cohoba silver statue and ritual dance. 1p, Taina mortar, pestle and family preparing cazabe.

1989, Oct. 12
1065 A395 20c multicolored   .40 .20
1066 A395 1p multicolored   2.25 1.25

8th Adm. Christopher Columbus Regatta, Casa de Espana — A396

European Colonization of the Americas — A397

Designs: 70c, Fr. Pedro de Cordoba converting the Indians to Catholicism. 1p, Christopher Columbus trading with the Indians. 3p, Sermon of Pedro de Cordoba.

1989, Oct. 13
1067 A396 50c shown   .45 .25
1068 A397 70c shown   .60 .40
1069 A397 1p multicolored   .80 .55
1070 A397 3p multicolored   2.75 1.60
   Nos. 1067-1070 (4)   4.60 2.80
Discovery of America, 500th anniv. (in 1992).

Natl. Afforestation A398

1989, Oct. 30   **Litho.**   **Perf. 13½**
1071 A398 10c shown   .20 .20
1072 A398 20c Tree   .25 .20
1073 A398 50c Forest   .70 .45
1074 A398 1p Sapling, mature trees   1.60 .90
   Nos. 1071-1074 (4)   2.75 1.75

9th Natl. Games, La Vega — A399

Holy Week
(Easter) — A400

1990, Mar. 20   Litho.   Perf. 13½
1075 A399 10c Cycling   .20   .20
1076 A399 20c Running   .30   .25
1077 A399 50c Basketball   .85   .60
        Nos. 1075-1077 (3)   1.35 1.05

1990, Apr. 5
1078 A400 20c shown   .30   .25
1079 A400 50c Jesus carrying
                  cross   .85   .60

Labor Day,
Cent.
A401

1990, Apr. 30   Litho.   Perf. 13½
1080 A401 1p multicolored   1.50   .65

Urban
Renewal
A402

1990, May 10
1081 A402 10c shown   .20   .20
1082 A402 20c Highway under-
                  pass   .20   .20
1083 A402 50c Library   .70   .25
1084 A402 1p City street   1.60   .65
        Nos. 1081-1084 (4)   2.70 1.30

No. 1084 inscribed $100 instead of $1.00.

Penny Black,
150th
Anniv. — A403

1990, May 29
1085 A403 1p multicolored   1.50 1.10

Size: 62x80mm
Imperf
1086 A403 3p Sir Rowland Hill,
                  Penny Black   4.50 4.50

Organization of American States,
Cent. — A404

1990, Oct. 5   Litho.   Perf. 13½
1087 A404 2p Flags   3.50 2.25

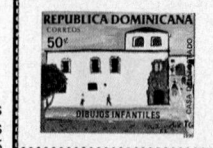

Children's
Drawings
A405

1990, Aug. 7
1088 A405 50c House of Tostado   .85   .55
1089 A405 50c Ruins of St. Nico-
                  las of Bari   .85   .55

Discovery
of America,
500th
Anniv. (in
1992)
A406

Designs: 1p, Fight at the Gulf of Arrows. 2p, Columbus talking with Guacanagari Indians. 5p, Columbus and Caonabo Indian prisoner.

1990, Oct. 12
1090 A406 1p multicolored   1.75 1.10
1091 A406 2p multicolored   3.50 2.25
1092 A406 5p multicolored   8.75 5.75
        Nos. 1090-1092 (3)   14.00 9.10

9th Adm.
Christopher
Columbus
Regatta — A407

1990, Oct. 12
1093 A407 50c multicolored   .75   .55

America
Issue
A408

UPAE emblem and: 50c, Men in canoe. 3p, Man on hammock.

1990, Nov. 7   Litho.   Perf. 13½
1094 A408 50c multicolored   .85   .60
1095 A408 3p multicolored   5.00 3.75

A409

A410

Discovery of Hispaniola: 50c, 1st official mass in Americas. 1p, Arms of 1st religious order in Americas. 3p, Map of island, horiz. 4p, Christopher Columbus, 1st viceroy and governor in Americas.

1991, July 17   Litho.   Perf. 13½
1096 A409 50c multicolored   .75   .40
1097 A409 1p multicolored   1.50   .85
1098 A409 3p multicolored   3.00 1.50
1099 A409 4p multicolored   7.50 4.25
        Nos. 1096-1099 (4)   12.75 7.00

1991
1100 A410 30c Boxing   .40   .20
1101 A410 50c Cycling   1.25   .50
1102 A410 1p Bowling   2.50 1.00
        Nos. 1100-1102 (3)   4.15 1.70

11th Pan American Games, Havana.

Dr. Tomas Eudoro
Perez Rancier,
Birth
Cent. — A411

1991, July 3
1103 A411 2p yellow & black   4.25 1.50

10th Columbus
Regatta, Casa de
Espana — A412

Discovery
of America,
500th
Anniv. (in
1992)
A413

Designs: 50c, Encounter of three cultures. 3p, Columbus and Dr. Alvarez Chanca caring for sick. 4p, Rebellion of Enriquillo.

1991, Oct. 15   Litho.   Perf. 13½
1104 A412 30c multicolored   .60   .20
1105 A413 50c multicolored   .75   .30
1106 A413 3p multicolored   4.50 1.75
1107 A413 4p multicolored   6.00 2.50
        Nos. 1104-1107 (4)   11.85 4.75

        See No. 1116.

A414

A415

1991, Nov. 18
1108 A414 3p black & red   4.25 1.75

        Cornea Bank.

1991   Litho.   Perf. 13½
1109 A415 1p Santa Maria   1.00   .50
1110 A415 3p Christopher Co-
                  lumbus   3.00 2.10

        America issue.

33rd Meeting of Inter-American
Development Bank Governors, Santo
Domingo — A416

1992   Litho.   Perf. 13½
1111 A416 1p multicolored   1.50   .75

A417

A418

1992   Litho.   Perf. 13½
1112 A417 3p multicolored   4.50 1.75

Espanola '92 Philatelic Exposition.

1992   Litho.   Perf. 13½

Valentin Salinero, Order of the Apostles founder.

1113 A418 1p blue & brown   1.50   .75

        Order of the Apostles, cent.

Ruins of
Monastery
of San
Francisco
A419

Designs: 3p, Ruins of San Nicolas hospital, first in the Americas.

1992, July 28
1114 A419 50c multicolored   .60   .35
1115 A419 3p multicolored   4.75 2.50

        Type of 1991 and

A420

Designs: 50c, Racing yacht. 1p, Native women, Columbus. 2p, Natives offering Columbus tobacco. 3p, Native woman, Columbus, corn.

1992, Oct. 6   Litho.   Perf. 13½
1116 A412 50c multicolored   .70   .35
1117 A420 1p multicolored   1.60   .75
1118 A420 2p multicolored   3.25 1.50
1119 A420 3p multicolored   4.25 1.75
        Nos. 1116-1119 (4)   9.80 4.35

11th Columbus Regatta (No. 1116), Discovery of America, 500th anniv. (Nos. 1117-1119).

23rd Convention of the Alliance of Panamerican Round Tables, Santo Domingo — A421

1992, Oct. 14
1120 A421 1p multicolored 1.50 .60

Visit by Pope John Paul II A422

Cathedrals: 50c, Vega. 3p, Santo Domingo.

1992, Oct. 1 Photo.
1121 A422 50c multicolored 1.40 .60
1122 A422 3p multicolored 4.00 1.75

Columbus Lighthouse A423

1992, Oct. 12 Litho.
1123 A423 30c multicolored .85 .35
1124 A423 1p multicolored 1.75 .60

Size: 70x133mm
Imperf
1125 A423 3p Lighthouse at night 5.00 5.00

America Issue A424

Designs: 50c, First royal residence in America, Santo Domingo. 3p, First viceregal residence in America, Royal Palace, Colon.

1992, Nov. 13 Litho. **Perf. 13½**
1126 A424 50c multicolored .50 .35
1127 A424 3p multicolored 2.75 1.75

A425

Natl. Census — A426

1992, Dec. 2 Litho. **Perf. 13½**
1128 A425 30c Torch bearer .40 .20
1129 A425 1p Emblems 1.25 .50
1130 A425 4p Judo 6.50 2.50
Nos. 1128-1130 (3) 8.15 3.20

1992 Natl. Sports Games, San Juan. Secretary of Sports, Education, Exercise and Recreation (No. 1129).

1992-93 Litho. **Perf. 13½**
1131 A426 50c black, buff & blue .70 .25
1132 A426 1p blk, brn & blue 1.40 .50
1133 A426 3p blk, gray & bl 4.75 1.75
1134 A426 4p blk, yel grn & bl 6.00 2.00
Nos. 1131-1134 (4) 12.85 4.50

Issued: 50c, 1p, 5/12/92; 3p, 4p, 9/9/93.

A427

A428

1993, May 30
1135 A427 30c multicolored .45 .20
1136 A427 50c multicolored .75 .30
1137 A427 1p multicolored 1.60 .60
Nos. 1135-1137 (3) 2.80 1.10

Ema Balaguer, humanitarian.

1993, Oct. 7 Litho. **Perf. 13½**
1138 A428 30c shown .90 .45
1139 A428 1p Emblem, flags 2.75 1.00

Rotary Club of Santo Domingo, 50th anniv.

17th Central American & Caribbean Games, Ponce A429

1993, Dec. 21 Litho. **Perf. 13½**
1140 A429 50c Tennis .60 .20
1141 A429 4p Swimming 6.25 1.50

Natl. Education Plan — A430

Spanish America — A431

1993, Dec. 8
1142 A430 1.50p multicolored 2.25 .75

1993, Dec. 28
1143 A431 50c First university lecturn .70 .25
1144 A431 3p First city coat of arms 4.75 1.25

America Issue A432

1993, Dec. 30
1145 A432 1p Aratinga chloroptera 1.25 .50
1146 A432 3p Cyclura cornuta 4.75 2.00

Opening of New Natl. Post Office A433

1993, Nov. 12
Color of Inscription
1147 A433 1p olive .75 .50
1148 A433 3p red 2.25 1.40
1149 A433 4p blue 3.00 1.75
1150 A433 5p green 3.75 2.00
1151 A433 10p black 7.50 4.00

Size: 105x96mm
Imperf
1152 A433 5p black 8.75 8.75
Nos. 1147-1152 (6) 26.00 18.40

First Mass in America, 500th Anniv. — A434

1994, Feb. 3 Litho. **Perf. 13½**
1153 A434 2p multicolored 3.00 1.00

5th Natl. Philatelic Exhibition A435

1994, Feb. 25
1154 A435 3p multicolored 4.50 1.40

Natl. Independence, 150th Anniv. — A436

No. 1155: a, Men with document, left side of table. b, Document on right side of table, men. c, Flag. d, Couple at window. e, Child holding material, mother making flag.
No. 1156: a, Men looking upward, shooting muskets. b, Men with guns, swords looking backwards. c, Natl. coat of arms. d, Men with guns, swords, one pointing upward. e, Men with weapons, one with flag.
10p, Three men, angel carrying musket, flag.

1994, Feb. 26
Strips of 5
1155 A436 2p #a.-e. 8.25 4.00
1156 A436 3p #a.-e. 12.50 6.00

Size: 161x104mm
Imperf
1157 A436 10p multicolored 11.50 11.50
Nos. 1155-1157 (3) 32.25 21.50

Nos. 1155a-1155b, 1155d-1155e, 1156a-1156b, 1156d-1156e have a continuous design.

Solenodon Paradoxus A437

Designs: a, Crawling on rock. b, Walking in leaves. c, Looking up. d, With food in mouth.

1994, Mar. 15 Litho. **Perf. 13½**
1158 A437 1p Block of 4, #a.-d. 8.00 2.50
World Wildlife Fund.

Battle of March 19, 150th Anniv. A438

No. 1160, Soldiers advancing uphill toward fort.

1994
1159 A438 2p multicolored 3.00 1.00
1160 A438 2p multicolored 3.00 1.00
Issued: No. 1159, Mar. 18; No. 1160, Mar. 29.

Virgin of Amparo — A439

Natl. Elections, May 16 — A440

1994, Apr. 15 Litho. **Perf. 13½**
1161 A439 3p multicolored 4.50 1.40
Battle of Puerto Tortuguero, 150th anniv.

1994, Apr. 4
1162 A440 2p multicolored 3.00 1.00

1994 World Cup Soccer Championships, US — A441

1994, June 24 Litho. **Perf. 13½**
1163 A441 4p multicolored 4.75 1.50
1164 A441 6p multicolored 6.75 2.00

Ema Balaguer City of Children A442

1994, July 20   Litho.   Perf. 13½
1165 A442 1p magenta & brown   2.75   .40

Stamp Day A443

1994, Oct. 18   Litho.   Perf. 13½
1166 A443 5p Type A3   7.25   2.00

America Issue — A444

1994, Oct. 28
1167 A444 2p Pony Express   2.75   1.00
1168 A444 6p Sailing ship   9.00   3.00

Province of La Vega, 500th Anniv. A445

3p, Ruins of San Francisco Monastery.

1994, Nov. 24   Litho.   Perf. 13½
1169 A445 3p multicolored   6.75   1.40

First Church the New World, 500th Anniv. — A446

a, "La Isabela," cradle of evangelization. b, "Temple of the Americas," first mission.

1994, Dec. 5   Perf. 11½
1170 A446 3p Pair, #a.-b.   9.00   2.50

A447

A448

1994, Nov. 6   Perf. 13½
1171 A447 3p multicolored   4.50   1.40

Constitution, 150th anniv.

1994, Nov. 18

Christmas: 2p, Holy family's flight into Egypt. 3p, Modern family of three standing at river's edge.

1172 A448 2p multicolored   3.25   1.00
1173 A448 3p multicolored   4.25   1.40

Intl. Year of the Family.

Firsts in America — A449

1994, Dec. 21   Litho.   Perf. 13½
1174 A449 2p Circulating coins   3.00   .75
1175 A449 5p Sermon for Justice   7.00   2.00

Snakes A450

No. 1176, Hypsirhynchus ferox. No. 1177, Antillophis parvifrons. No. 1178, Uromacer catesbyi. No. 1179, Epicrates striatus.

1994, Dec. 26
1176 A450 2p multicolored   3.00   .75
1177 A450 2p multicolored   3.00   .75
   a.   Pair, #1176-1177   6.00   5.50
1178 A450 2p multicolored   3.00   .75
1179 A450 2p multicolored   3.00   .75
   a.   Pair, #1178-1179   6.00   5.50

Nos. 1177a, 1179a are continuous designs.

Pan American Games, Mar Del Plata, Argentina A451

1995, Apr. 20   Perf. 13½
1180 A451 4p Tae kwon do   4.50   1.50
1181 A451 13p Tennis   13.50   4.50

FAO, 50th Anniv. — A452

1995, Apr. 21   Litho.   Perf. 11½
1182 A452 4p multicolored   4.50   1.50

A453

A454

Designs: 2p, Jose Marti, Maximo Gomez. 3p, Marti. 4p, Marti seated at desk, Gomez.

1995, May 19   Litho.   Perf. 13½
1183 A453 2p multicolored   1.40   .20
1184 A453 3p multicolored   1.90   .30
1185 A453 4p multicolored   2.75   .40
   Nos. 1183-1185 (3)   6.05   .90

Jose Marti (1853-95), Montecristi Manifesto, cent.

1995, May 22
1186 A454 3p multicolored   2.75   .45

Basketball, cent.

Medicinal Plants — A455

1995, May 26
1187 A455 2p Pimenta ozua   1.60   .20
1188 A455 2p Melocactus communis   1.60   .20
1189 A455 3p Smilax   2.10   .30
1190 A455 3p Zamia   2.10   .30
   Nos. 1187-1190 (4)   7.40   1.00

Tourism A456

4p, San Souci Port. 5p, Barahona Airport. 6p, G. Luperon Airport. 13p, Airport of the Americas.

1995, June 21
1191 A456   4p multicolored   2.50   .40
1192 A456   5p multicolored   3.25   .60
1193 A456   6p multicolored   4.00   .70
1194 A456 13p multicolored   8.25   1.50
   Nos. 1191-1194 (4)   18.00   3.20

Santiago de Los Caballeros, 500th Anniv. A457

1995, July 29   Litho.   Perf. 13½
1195 A457 3p Jacagua ruins   4.50   .70

Whales A458

Designs: No. 1196, Physeter macrocephalus. No. 1197, Balaenoptera borealis. No. 1198, Ziphius cavirostris. No. 1199, Megaptera novaeangliae.

1995, Aug. 14
1196 A458 3p multicolored   2.25   .40
1197 A458 3p multicolored   2.25   .40
1198 A458 3p multicolored   2.25   .40
1199 A458 3p multicolored   2.25   .40
   Nos. 1196-1199 (4)   9.00   1.60

Stamp Day A459

1995, Oct. 18   Litho.   Perf. 13½
1200 A459 4p No. 37   3.00   .40

Popular Singers — A460

1995, Oct. 8
1201 A460 2p Rafael Colon   1.50   .20
1202 A460 3p Casandra Damiron   2.00   .30

Cathedral of Santiago, Cent. A461

1995, Dec. 28   Litho.   Perf. 13½
1203 A461 3p multicolored   2.25   .30

4th World Conference of Women, Beijing — A462

1995, Nov. 23
1204 A462 2p multicolored   5.25   .20

Volleyball, Cent. — A463

Norceca '95 — A464

Singers — A465

1995, Oct. 19 *Imperf.*
1205 A463 5p multicolored 3.75 .60
Perf. 13½
1206 A464 6p multicolored 4.25 .70

1995, Dec. 27 *Perf. 13½*
1207 A465 2p Antonio Mesa 1.60 .20
1208 A465 2p Julieta Otero 1.60 .20
1209 A465 2p Susano Polanco 1.60 .20
Nos. 1207-1209 (3) 4.80 .60

Columbus Lighthouse A466

1995, Dec. 5
1210 A466 10p dk bl, bl & gray 8.50 1.25
See Nos. 1241, 1265, 1299, 1337, 1371.

A467

UN, 50th Anniv. A468

1995, Oct. 24
1211 A467 2p multicolored 1.50 .20
Perf. 11½
1212 A468 6p multicolored 4.50 .70

Environmental Protection — A469

America issue: 2p, Flamingos, sea gull. 6p, Manglar.

1995, Dec. 19 *Litho.* *Perf. 13½*
1213 A469 2p multicolored 1.40 .25
1214 A469 6p multicolored 4.50 .75

Dominican Republic Air Force, 50th Anniv. A470

Aircraft: a, O2U-35D Corsair. b, PT-17 Stearman. c, AT-6 Texan. d, PBY-5A Catalina. e, TF-10 Beaufighter. f, FB-6 Mosquito. g, P-38 Lightning. h, P-51D Mustang. i, B-17G Flying Fortress. j, P-47D Thunderbolt. k, FB-5 Vampire. l, C-46 Commander. m, B-26 Invader. n, C-47 Skytrain. o, T-28D Trojan. p, T-33A Silverstar. q, Cessna T-41D. r, T-34 Mentor. s, Cessna O-2A. t, A-37B Dragonfly.

1995, Dec. 30
1215 A470 2p Sheet of 20, #a-t 11.00 5.50
See No. 1228.

UNICEF, 50th Anniv. — A471

1996, Feb. 23
1216 A471 2p shown 1.25 .25
1217 A471 4p Mirror image of #1216 2.25 .50

Intl. Sailing Competition A472

1996, Mar. 8
1218 A472 5p multicolored 3.00 .70

Eduardo Brito, Singer, 50th Death Anniv. — A473

1996, Jan. 15
1219 A473 1p shown .45 .20
1220 A473 2p With maracas .95 .25
1221 A473 3p Portrait 1.50 .40
Nos. 1219-1221 (3) 2.90 .85
No. 1220 is 54x35mm.

Natl. Journalist Day — A474

Design: Arturo J. Pellerano Alfau, Dr. Freddy Gaton Arce, Rafael Herrera Cabral.

1996, Apr. 17 *Litho.* *Perf. 13½*
1222 A474 5p multicolored 3.50 .70

ESPAMER '96, Seville — A475

1996, June 7 *Litho.* *Perf. 13½*
1223 A475 15p multicolored 9.00 1.50

1996 Summer Olympic Games, Atlanta — A476

1996, July 5
1224 A476 5p Judo 3.75 .70
1225 A476 15p Torch 9.75 1.75

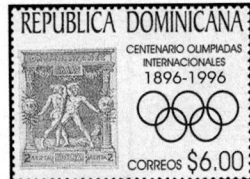

Modern Olympic Games, Cent. — A477

1996, July 5
1226 A477 6p Greece No. 118 3.50 .70
1227 A477 15p No. 328 8.50 1.50

Dominican Republic Air Force, 50th Anniv. Type of 1995

Helicoptors: a, Sikorsky S-55. b, Alouette II. c, Alouette III. d, OH-6A Cayuse. e, Bell 205 A-1. f, Dauphin II SA.365C.

1996, July 31 *Litho.* *Perf. 13½*
1228 A470 3p Sheet of 6, #a.-f. 5.75 2.50

World Day Against Illegal Drugs — A478

1996, Sept. 23 *Litho.* *Perf. 13½*
1229 A478 15p multicolored 8.50 1.50

Mail Delivery A479

No. 1230, World delivery, putting mail in letter box, mailman receiving mail on motorcycle. No. 1231, Woman giving mail to man on horseback, vert. No. 1232, Child holding letter beside mailbox.

1996, July 17 *Litho.* *Perf. 13½*
1230 A479 3p multicolored 2.00 .45
1231 A479 3p multicolored 2.00 .45
1232 A479 3p multicolored 2.00 .45
Nos. 1230-1232 (3) 6.00 1.35

America Issue — A480

1996, Oct. 15 *Litho.* *Perf. 13½*
1233 A480 2p Men's costume 1.25 .25
1234 A480 6p Women's costume 3.50 .75

Stamp Day A481

1996, Oct. 18
1235 A481 5p No. 142 3.00 .70

26th Intl. Sunfish Championships — A482

6p, Sun, natl. flag, sailboat, vert. 10p, Man sailing boat.

1996, Oct. 16
1236 A482 6p multicolored 3.50 .90
1237 A482 10p multicolored 5.75 1.40

A483

A484

1996, Nov. 25 **Litho.** **Perf. 13½**
1238 A483 5p green & multi 3.00 .65
1239 A483 10p pink & multi 5.75 1.25

Intl. Day to End Violence Against Women.

1996, Nov. 11

Birds: a, Buteo ridgwayi. b, Aratinga chloroptera. c, Amazona ventralis. d, Hyetornis rufigularis. e, Saurothera longirostris. f, Siphonorhis brewsteri. g, Chlorostilbon swainsonii. h, Todus angustirostris. i, Todus subulatus. j, Temnotrogon roseigaster. k, Nesoctites micromegas. l, Melanerpes striatus. m, Turdus swalesi. n, Carduelis dominicensis. o, Dulus dominicus. p, Microligea palustris. q, Vireo nanus. r, Xenoligea montanta. s, Turdus swalesi dodae. t, Calyptophilus frugivorus tertius. u, Corvus leucognaphalus. v, Calyptophilus frugivorus neibae.

1240 A484 2p Sheet of 22, #a-
v 35.00 27.50

Lighthouse Type of 1995
1996, Dec. 27 **Litho.** **Perf. 13½**
1241 A466 10p grn, sil & gray 6.50 1.40

Turtles
A485

a, Dermochelys coriacea. b, Caretta caretta. c, Chelonia mydas. d, Eretmochelys imbricata.

1996, Dec. 30
1242 A485 5p Block of 4, #a.-d. 11.00 9.00

Natl. Youth
Day — A486

National
Anthem — A487

1997, Jan. 31
1243 A486 3p multicolored 1.75 .45

1997, Feb. 26

Designs: 2p, Lyrics, by Emilio Prudhome. 3p, Music, by Jose Reyes.

1244 A487 2p multicolored 1.25 .25
1245 A487 3p multicolored 1.75 .40

Salomé Urena
(1850-97),
Poet — A488

Comet Hale-Bopp
A489

1997, Mar. 6 **Perf. 13½**
1246 A488 3p multicolored 1.75 .40

1997, Apr. 1
1247 A489 5p multicolored 4.25 .65
Size: 72x47mm
Imperf
1248 A489 10p multicolored 11.00 11.00

A490

11th Natl.
Sports
Games,
Mao
'97 — A491

2p, Mascot running with torch. 3p, Mascot in batting stance, vert. 5p, Runner breaking finish line.

1997, Apr. 3
1249 A490 2p multicolored 1.75 .25
1250 A491 3p multicolored 2.75 .40
1251 A491 5p multicolored 4.25 .65
Nos. 1249-1251 (3) 8.75 1.30

A492

A493

Design: 10p, 5p, Heinrich von Stephan (1831-97), founder of UPU.

1997, Apr. 8 **Litho.** **Perf. 13½**
1252 A492 10p multicolored 5.75 1.25

Souvenir Sheet
Imperf
1253 A492 5p like #1252 3.00 .65

No. 1253 has simulated perforations.

1997, Apr. 29 **Perf. 13½**
1254 A493 10p multicolored 8.75 1.25

25th Intl. Congress of CLAHT (Caracas and Latin American Group of Hemostasis and Thrombosis).

Gregorio Luperón
(1839-1897),
Politician — A494

House of Spain,
80th
Anniv. — A495

1997, May 21
1255 A494 3p multicolored 1.75 .40

1997, July 4
1256 A495 5p multicolored 3.00 .65

First Peso
Coin, Cent.
A496

1997, Aug. 6 **Litho.** **Perf. 13½**
1257 A496 2p multicolored 1.50 .20

A497

Coronation of
the Image of
Our Lady of
Alta Gracia,
75th
Anniv. — A498

1997, Aug. 12
1258 A497 3p multicolored 1.75 .20
1259 A498 5p multicolored 3.00 .35

America
Issue
A499

Life of a postman: 2p, Dog grabbing pants leg of postman on motorcycle. 6p, Dog tearing pants leg of postman with letter.

1997, Oct. 9 **Litho.** **Perf. 13½**
1260 A499 2p multicolored 1.25 .30
Size: 35½x35½mm
1261 A499 6p multicolored 3.25 .70

Mother
Teresa
(1910-97)
A500

1997, Oct. 17
1262 A500 5p multicolored 3.00 .65

Stamp
Day — A501

1997, Oct. 18
1263 A501 5p Nos. 108, 322 2.50 .55

Central Bank of the Dominican
Republic, 50th Anniv. — A502

1997, Oct. 30 **Perf. 11½**
1264 A502 10p multicolored 5.00 1.10

Lighthouse Type of 1995
1997, Dec. 15 **Litho.** **Perf. 13½**
1265 A466 10p bright rose & gray 6.50 1.75

Bats
A503

a, Erophylius bombifrons. b, Brachyphylla nana. c, Molossus molossus. d, Lasiurus borealis.

1997, Nov. 11
1266 A503 5p Block of 4, #a.-d. 8.50 8.50

Dominican
Air Force,
50th Anniv.
A504

Insignias: a, Air Force, red, white, and blue target. b, Northern Air Command, "shark plane." c, Air Command, eagle's wings over target. d, Rescue Force, eagle. e, Maintenance Command. f, Combat Force, dragon, target.

1997, Dec. 19
1267 A504 3p Sheet of 6, #a.-
f.   11.00 11.00

Construction of the National Palace,
50th Anniv. — A505

1997, Dec. 30   Litho.   Perf. 13½
1268 A505 10p multicolored   5.75 1.50

First Regional
Symposium on
Pre-Columbian
Culture and
Caribbean
Contemporary
Art — A506

1998, Jan. 28
1269 A506 6p multicolored   3.50 .85

A507

A508

1998, Apr. 2   Litho.   Perf. 13½
1270 A507 10p multicolored   5.75 .65
American Chamber of Commerce of the
Dominican Republic, 75th anniv.

1998, Apr. 26
Book Fair: 3p, Natl. Book Fair, 25th anniv.
5p, Intl. Book Fair, Santo Domingo '98.
1271 A508 3p black, blue & red   1.75 .20
Size: 35x33mm
1272 A508 5p black, blue & red   3.00 .35

Organization of American States, 50th
Anniv. — A509

1998, Apr. 30
1273 A509 5p blue & multi   3.00 .35
1274 A509 5p pink & multi   3.00 .35

Establishment of the State of Israel,
50th Anniv. — A510

1998, Apr. 30
1275 A510 10p multicolored   8.00 .90

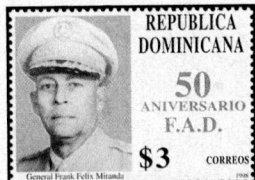

Dominican Air Force, 50th
Anniv. — A511

a, Gen. Frank Felix Miranda, portrait at left.
b, Early aircraft. c, Col. Ernesto Tejeda, portrait at right. d, As "c," portrait at left. e, As "a,"
portrait at right.

1998, June 26
Sheet of 6
1276 A511 3p #a, c-e, 2 b   10.00 10.00

City of
Santo
Domingo,
500th
Anniv.
A512

2p, Sun clock. 3p, St. Lazaro Church & Hos-
pital. 4p, First Cathedral in America. 5p, Royal
Palace. 6p, Tower of Honor. 10p, St. Nicolas of
Bari Church & Hospital.

1998, Aug. 6   Litho.   Perf. 13½
1277 A512 2p multi, vert.   1.10 .20
1278 A512 3p multi   1.75 .20
1279 A512 4p multi   2.25 .25
1280 A512 5p multi   3.00 .35
1281 A512 6p multi   3.50 .40
1282 A512 10p multi, vert.   5.75 .60
Nos. 1277-1282 (6)   17.35 2.00

National Theater, 25th Anniv. — A513

1998, Aug. 14   Perf. 13x13½
1283 A513 10p multicolored   5.75 .65

Latin
Union, 44th
Anniv.
A514

1998, Aug. 26   Perf. 13½
1284 A514 10p multicolored   5.75 .65

ICCO (Intl. Cocoa Organization of
America & Europe), 25th
Anniv. — A515

1998, Sept. 3
1285 A515 10p multicolored   7.00 .80

Nino Ferrua
(1909-79),
Stamp Designer
A516

1998, Oct. 18   Litho.   Perf. 13½x13
1286 A516 5p multicolored   3.00 .35
Stamp Day.

Pontificate
of John
Paul II,
20th Anniv.
A517

1998, Oct. 22   Perf. 13½
1287 A517 5p shown   3.25 .40
1288 A517 10p Portrait, diff.   6.75 .75

Medicinal
Plants — A518

a, Pimenta racemosa. b, Pimenta haitiensis.
c, Cymbopogon citratus. d, Citrus aurantium.

1998, Nov. 2
1289 A518 3p Block of 4, #a.-d. 6.50 .75

Famous
Women
A519

America Issue: 2p, Juana Saltitopa standing
with cannon. 6p, Anacaona, Indian maiden,
group of Indians.

1998, Nov. 5
1290 A519 2p multicolored   1.75 .30
1291 A519 6p multicolored   4.25 .50

A520

A521

1998, Nov. 20
1292 A520 5p multicolored   4.00 .90
Intl. Year of the Ocean.

1998, Nov. 23
1293 A521 5p multicolored   1.75 .40
Expofila '98, Santo Domingo. Santo Domingo, 500th anniv.

National Military
Heroes — A522

Designs: a, Fernando Valerio. b, Benito
Moncion. c, Jose Maria Cabral. d, Antonio
Duverge. e, Gregorio Luperon. f, Jose A.
Salcedo. g, Fco. A. Salcedo. h, Gaspar
Polanco. i, Santiago Rodriguez. j, Juan Bta.
Cambiaso. k, Jose J. Puello. l, Jose Ma.
Imbert. m, Juan A. Acosta. n, Marcos Adon. o,
Matias R. Mella. p, Francisco R. Sanchez. q,
Juan Pablo Duarte. r, Olegario Tenares. s,
Pedro Santana. t, Juan Sanchez Ramirez.

1998, Nov. 29
1294 A522 3p Sheet of 20,
#a.-t.   19.00 17.50

1st Natl. Paper Money, 150th
Anniv. — A523

1998, Nov. 30   Perf. 11½
1295 A523 10p multicolored   3.25 .65

Christmas
A524

1998, Dec. 7   Perf. 13½
1296 A524 2p Roasting hog   .75 .20
1297 A524 5p Magi   2.25 .45

Universal
Declaration
of Human
Rights,
50th Anniv.
A525

1998, Dec. 10
1298 A525 10p multicolored   3.25 .65

Columbus Lighthouse Type of 1995
1998, Dec. 11
1299 A466 10p orange & black   5.00 1.00

Shells
A526

Designs: a, Lyria vegai. b, Strombus gigas. c, Cittarium pica. d, Nerita peloronta.

1998, Dec. 16
1300 A526 5p Block of 4, #a.-d.   10.00 1.90

Gaspar Hernández (1798-1858), Priest — A527

1998, Dec. 18
1301 A527 3p multicolored   1.00 .20

Dominican Society of Endocrinology and Nutrition, 25th Anniv. — A528

1999, Feb. 24   **Litho.**   **Perf. 13¼**
1302 A528 10p multicolored   3.25 .65

Office of Comptroller General — A529

1999, May 4   **Litho.**   **Perf. 13¼**
1303 A529 2p multicolored   .65 .20

Export Industries A530

    Perf. 13½x13¼, 13¼x13½
1999, Apr. 30   **Litho.**
1304 A530 6p Tobacco   2.00 .40
1305 A530 10p Textiles, vert.   3.25 .65

Pan American Games, Winnipeg - A530a

1999, July 29 Litho.   Perf. 13¼x13½
1306 A530a 5p Baseball   1.75 .40
1307 A530a 6p Weight lifting   2.25 .45

Native Plants — A531

Designs: a, Pseudophoenix ekmanii. b, Murtigia calabura. c, Pouteria dominguensis. d, Rubus dominguensis focke.

1999, July 13
1308 A531 5p Block of 4, #a.-d.   6.50 6.50

Presidents of the Dominican Republic A532

Designs: a, Tomas Bobadilla y Briones. b, Pedro Santana. c, Manuel Jimenez. d, Buenaventura Baez. e, Manuel de Regla Mota. f, José Desiderio Valverde. g, José A. Salcedo. h, Gaspar Polanco.

1999, Aug. 31   **Perf. 13½x13¼**
1309 A532 3p Sheet of 8, #a.-h.   6.00 6.00
        + label

A533

Sovereign Military Order of Malta A534

     Perf. 13¼x13½
1999, Sept. 20   **Litho.**
1310 A533 2p multicolored   .75 .20
        Perf. 13½
1311 A534 10p multicolored   3.50 .65

Paintings by José Vela Zanetti (1913-99) — A535

Various paintings.

    Perf. 13½x13¼, 13¼x 13½
1999, Sept. 8
1312 A535 2p multi, vert.   .40 .20
1313 A535 3p multi, vert.   .65 .20
1314 A535 5p multi   1.00 .30
1315 A535 6p multi, vert.   1.25 .40
1316 A535 10p multi, vert.   2.00 .60
    Nos. 1312-1316 (5)   5.30 1.70

Insects A536

Designs: a, Strataegus quadrifoveatus. b, Anetia jaegeri. c, Polyancistroydes tettigonidae. d, Aploppus phasmidae.

1999, Sept. 10   **Perf. 13½x13¼**
1317 A536 5p Block of 4, #a.-d.   6.50 6.50

SOS Children's Villages, 50th Anniv. — A537

Intl. Year of the Elderly — A538

1999, Sept. 29   **Perf. 13¼x13½**
1318 A537 10p multicolored   2.00 .80

1999, Oct. 1
1319 A538 2p Man   .30 .20
1320 A538 5p Woman   .80 .40

A539

A540

1999, Oct. 5
1321 A539 5p multicolored   .75 .35
    World Education Day.

1999, Oct. 18
Designs: 2p, Skull and crossbones, land mines, shattered gun. 6p, Mushroom cloud.

1322 A540 2p multicolored   .65 .40
1323 A540 6p multicolored   1.90 1.00
    America Issue, a new millennium without arms.

Stamp Day — A541

1999, Oct. 22
1324 A541 5p Luis F. Thomen   .75 .35

Account of Gen. Juan Pablo Duarte A542

1999, July 16   **Perf. 13½**
1325 A542 3p multicolored   .90 .20

A543

Contemporary Writers — A544

    Perf. 13¼x13½, 13½x13¼
1999, June 23
1326 A543 2p multicolored   .25 .20
1327 A544 10p multicolored   1.75 .85

Dermatological Society, 50th Anniv. — A545

1999, Sept. 15 Litho.   Perf. 13¼
1328 A545 3p multi   .60 .20

Millennium — A546

3p, Earth, trees. 5p, Scientific achievements.

     Perf. 13¼x13½
1999, Nov. 10   **Litho.**
1329 A546 3p multi   1.25 .75
1330 A546 5p multi   2.25 1.10

2nd Summit of African, Caribbean and Pacific Heads of State — A547

Emblem and: 5p, Map of Caribbean area, whale. 6p, Map of Pacific area, Easter Island statues. 10p, Map of Africa, lion.

1999, Nov. 23
1331	A547	5p multi	1.10	.60
1332	A547	6p multi	1.50	.65
1333	A547	10p multi	2.40	1.10
		Nos. 1331-1333 (3)	5.00	2.35

UPU, 125th Anniv. A548

6p, Globe, envelope, computer, electronic circuits. 10p, Envelope, electronic circuits.

1999, Nov. 29
1334	A548	6p multi	1.50	.70

Size: 50x75mm
Imperf
1335	A548	10p multi	3.00	1.40

Union of Latin American Universities, 50th Anniv. — A549

1999, Dec. 3   **Perf. 13½x13¼**
1336	A549	6p multi	1.10	.50

Lighthouse Type of 1995
1999, Dec. 14   **Perf. 13¼x13½**
1337	A466	10p brown & silver	2.50	1.10

Classical Musicians A550

No. 1338, José de Jésus Ravelo (1876-1951), clarinet. No. 1339, Juan Francisco Garcia (1892-1974), cornet. No. 1340, Manuel Simo (1916-88), saxophone.

1999, Dec. 17
1338	A550	5p multi	.75	.40
1339	A550	5p multi	.75	.40
1340	A550	5p multi	.75	.40
		Nos. 1338-1340 (3)	2.25	1.20

Municipal Notes, Cent. — A551

Notes and background colors — No. 1341: a, Santo Domingo, San Pedro de Macorís, deep purple. b, Puerto Plata, Moca, purple.

No. 1342, vert.: a, Santiago, Cotui, blue green. b, San Francisco de Macorís, La Vega, golden brown. c, San Cristobal, Samana, peacock blue.
No. 1343: a, As No. 1342a, green background. b, As No. 1342b, brown background. c, As No. 1342c, Prussian blue background.

1999, Dec. 30   **Perf. 13¼**
1341	A551	2p Pair, #a.-b.	.75	.40
1342	A551	2p Strip of 3, #a.-c.	1.00	.45

Souvenir Sheet
Imperf
1343	A551	2p Sheet of 5, Nos. 1341a-1341b, 1343a-1343c	3.50	1.75

Chamber of Spanish Commerce and Industry, 75th Anniv. — A552

1999, Dec. 30   **Perf. 13¼x13½**
1344	A552	10p multi	1.75	.85

Fight Against Drugs A553

2000, Feb. 17   Litho.   Perf. 13½
1345	A553	5p multi	1.00	.45

Hogar Crea Dominicana Inc., 25th anniv.

Duarte Institute — A554

2000, Feb. 25   **Perf. 13¼**
1346	A554	2p multi	.40	.20

Prevention of Child Abuse — A555

2000, Mar. 31
1347	A555	2p multi	.60	.20

National Police A556

2000, Apr. 6   **Perf. 13½**
1348	A556	2p shown	.50	.20

Size: 37x28mm
Perf. 13½x13¼
1349	A556	5p Crest	1.25	.60

Dominican Institute of Industrial Technology, 25th Anniv. A557

2000, Apr. 11   **Perf. 13½**
1350	A557	2p multi	.60	.20

Independencia Province, 50th Anniv. — A558

2000, Apr. 15
1351	A558	3p multi	.60	.20

A559

12th Natl. Games, La Romana A560

2000, Apr. 27   **Perf. 13½x13¼**
1352	A559	2p Baseball	.40	.20
1353	A559	3p Boxing	.70	.20

Perf. 13½
1354	A560	5p Emblem	1.10	.50
		Nos. 1352-1354 (3)	2.20	.90

Paintings A561

Designs: 5p, The Violinist, by Darío Suro. 10p, Self-portrait, by Théodore Chassériau.

2000, May 5   **Perf. 13¼**
1355	A561	5p multi	.95	.45
1356	A561	10p multi	1.75	.95

Presidential Elections A562

2000, May 12
1357	A562	2p multi	.50	.20

Classical Musicians A563

#1358, Julio Alberto Hernandez Camejo (1900-99), pianist. #1359, Ramon Diaz (1901-76), bassoonist. #1360, Enrique de Marchena Dujarric (1908-88), pianist.

2000, May 31   **Perf. 13½**
1358	A563	5p multi	.70	.30
1359	A563	5p multi	.70	.30
1360	A563	5p multi	.70	.30
		Nos. 1358-1360 (3)	2.10	.90

Expo 2000, Hanover A564

2000, June 1
1361	A564	5p shown	.75	.35
1362	A564	10p Emblem, diff.	1.40	.70

Art by Jaime Colson — A565

Designs: 2p, Woman on horseback. 3p, Abstract. 5p, Musicians and dancers, horiz. 6p, Nudes. 10p, Colson.

2000   Litho.   Perf. 13¼
1363-1367	A565	Set of 5	6.00	3.00

Holy Year 2000 A566

Churches: 2p, Santo Cristo de los Milagros de Bayaguana Sanctuary. 5p, Santa Maria la Menor Cathedral, first in the Americas, vert. 10p, Nuestra Señora de la Altagracia Basilica, vert.

2000   Perf. 13½x13¼, 13¼x13½
1368-1370	A566	Set of 3	3.00	1.50

Lighthouse Type of 1995
2000   Perf. 13¼x13½
1371	A466	10p buff, brn & sil	3.25	1.75

Dominican Republic — Republic of China Diplomatic Relations A566a

Flags of Dominican Republic and Republic of China and: 5p, Illustration of dragon. 10p, Carved dragon.

Serpentine Die Cut 11¼
2000, Dec. 15　　　　**Litho.**
Self-Adhesive
1371A-1371B　A566a　Set of 2　3.25　1.60

America Issue — Campaign Against AIDS — A566b

Designs: 2p, Child. 6p, AIDS patient (38x38mm).

2000, Dec. 21　　　**Self-Adhesive**
1371C-1371D　A566b　Set of 2　3.00　1.50

UN High Commissioner for Refugees, 50th Anniv. — A566c

2000, Dec. 29　　　**Self-Adhesive**
1371E　A566c　10p multi　　　2.00　1.00

Environmental Protection — A567

Designs: 2p, Lizard on leaf, vert. $3, House. $5, River rapids, vert.

Serpentine Die Cut 11¼
2000　　　　　　　**Litho.**
Self-Adhesive
1372-1374　A567　Set of 3　　2.00　1.00

Lighthouse Type of 1995
2001　　**Litho.**　**Perf. 13¼x13½**
1375　A466　15p lt bl, dk bl & sil　3.50　1.75

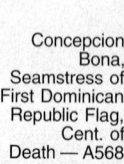

Concepcion Bona, Seamstress of First Dominican Republic Flag, Cent. of Death — A568

2001　　　　**Perf. 13½x13¼**
1376　A568　10p multi　　　1.75　.85

Stamp Day — A569

2001
1377　A569　5p multi　　　1.00　.50

Year of Dialogue Among Civilizations A570

2001　　　　**Perf. 13¼x13½**
1378　A570　12p multi　　　3.00　1.50

America Issue — UNESCO World Heritage A571

Designs: 4p, San Felipe Fort. 15p, Ruins of San Nicolas de Bari Hospital (27x37mm).

2001　**Perf. 13½, 13¼x13½ (15p)**
1379-1380　A571　Set of 2　5.00　2.50

Lighthouse Type of 1995
2002, Oct. 17 Litho. Perf. 13½x13¾
1382　A466　15p yel & multi　3.50　1.75

Mushrooms — A572

No. 1383: a, Pycnoporus sanguineus. b, Morchella elata. c, Mycena epipterygia. d, Coriolopsis polyzona.

Perf. 13¼x13½
2001, Sept. 13　　　　**Litho.**
1383　A572　6p Block of 4, #a-d　6.00　3.00

National Botanical Gardens, 25th Anniv. — A573

No. 1384: a, Isidorea pungens. b, Pereskia quisqueyana. c, Goetzea ekmanii. d, Cubanola domingensis.

Perf. 13¼x13½
2001, Sept. 20　　　　**Litho.**
1384　A573　4p Block of 4, #a-d　　—　—

Presidents of the Dominican Republic — A574

No. 1385: a, Gen. José María Cabral. b, Gen. Gregório Luperón. c, Gen. Ignacio María González. d, Ulises Espaillat. e, Pedro A. Pimentel. f, Federico de Jesús García. g, Frenando Arturo de Mariño. h, Gen. Ulises Heureaux.

2001, Sept. 27 Litho. Perf. 13¼
1385　A574　6p Sheet of 8, #a-h,
　　　　　+ label　　12.00　6.00

Blessed Josemaría Escrivá de Balaguer (1902-75), Founder of Opus Dei — A575

2002, Aug. 29　　　　**Perf. 13½x13¼**
1386　A575　10p multi　　　3.50　1.75

Loyola Polytechnic Institute, 50th Anniv. — A576

2002, Oct. 24　　　**Perf. 13¼x13½**
1387　A576　6p multi　　　　1.75　.85

12th Iberoamerican Heads of State Summit — A577

Designs: 12p, Flags below map. 15p, Flags above map.

Perf. 13¾x13½
2002, Nov. 14　　　　**Litho.**
1388-1389　A577　Set of 2　6.00　3.00

America Issue — Youth Education and Literacy — A578

Designs: 4p, Teacher helping child write. 15p, Child writing on blackboard.

2002, Dec. 20　　　**Perf. 13¼x13½**
1390-1391　A578　Set of 2　5.00　2.50

Coccothrinax Spissa — A579

Perf. 13¼x13½
2002, Dec. 20　　　　**Litho.**
1392　A579　10p multi　　　2.75　1.40

2003 Pan American Games, Santo Domingo — A580

Color of "2003" in design: 4p, Light green blue. 6p, Blue. 12p, Red.

2003, Feb. 25
1393-1395　A580　Set of 3　　4.00　2.00

Medicinal Plants — A581

No. 1396: a, Hymenaea courbaril. b, Spondias mombin. c, Genipa americana. d, Guazuma ulmifonia.

2003, June 17
1396 A581 5p Block of 4, #a-d   4.00 2.00

Dr. José Francisco Peña Gomez (1937-98), Politician A582

Litho. & Engr.
2003, Dec. 17   **Perf. 11½**
1397 A582 10p multi   2.50 1.25

José Marti (1853-95), Cuban Patriot — A583

2003, Nov. 5   Litho.   Perf. 13x13¼
1398 A583 15p multi   2.50 1.25

Pan American Health Organization, Cent. (in 2002) — A583a

2003   Litho.   Perf. 13½x13¼
1398A A583a 20p multi   3.75 1.90

America Issue — Flora and Fauna — A584

Designs: 5p, Aristelliger lar. 15p, Cornpernicia berteroana, vert.

Perf. 13½x13¼, 13¼x13½
2004, Jan. 19
1399-1400 A584   Set of 2   4.25 2.10
Nos. 1399-1400 are dated "2003."

Election of Pope John Paul II, 25th Anniv. — A585

Pope John Paul II: 10p, With hand touching face. 15p, Blessing crowd, horiz. 25p, Vignettes of 10p and 15p stamps.

Perf. 13¼x13½, 13½x13¼
2005, Nov. 26
1401-1402 A585   Set of 2   5.50 2.75
Size: 57x85mm
Imperf
1403 A585 25p multi   5.50 2.75

National Council for Children A586

2004, Mar. 10   Perf. 13½x13¼
1404 A586 7p multi   1.25 .60

Exfilna National Philatelic Exhibition A587

2004, Dec. 8   Litho.   Perf. 13½x13¼
1405 A587 7p multi   2.25 1.10

America Issue — Fight Against Poverty A588

Design: 10p, Shack. 20p, Poor man.

2004, Dec. 23
1406-1407 A588   Set of 2   6.75 3.50

Dominican Republic - Canada Diplomatic Relations, 50th Anniv. A589

2004, Dec. 31
1408 A589 20p multi   4.50 2.25

Interexpo '05 Intl. Philatelic Exhibition A590

Designs: 7p, Dove and stamp. 20p, Map highlighting Dominican Republic, vert.

Perf. 13½x13¼, 13¼x13½
2005   Litho.
1409-1410 A590   Set of 2   6.50 3.25
Dominican Republic Philatelic Society, 50th anniv.
Issued: 20p, 10/16; 7p, 10/17.

America Issue — Environmental Protection A591

Prevention of: 10p, Water pollution. 20p, Air pollution.

2005   Perf. 13¼x13½
1411-1412 A591   Set of 2   5.50 2.75

Monte Plata Maternity Clinic A592

Perf. 13½x13¼
2005, Nov. 14   Litho.
1413 A592 15p multi   2.75 1.40

Proclamation of Sister City Status of Santo Domingo and La Guardia, Spain — A593

2005, Nov. 11
1414 A593 10p multi   1.90 .95

Stamp Day A594

2005   Litho.   Perf. 13½x13¼
1415 A594 10p multi   1.90 .95

Palace of Fine Arts, 50th Anniv. A595

2006, Oct. 10   Litho.   Perf. 13¾x13¼
1416 A595 7p multi   1.40 .70

Dominican History Academy, 75th Anniv. — A596

2006, Oct. 30   Perf. 13¼
1417 A596 10p multi   1.60 .80

16th Intl. Boxing Congress, Santo Domingo — A597

2006, Nov. 2   Perf. 13¼x13½
1418 A597 20p multi   3.25 1.60

Pope John Paul II (1920-2005) A598

Pope and: 10p, Crucifix. 20p, Dove, horiz.

2006, Nov. 4   Perf. 13½
1419-1420 A598   Set of 2   4.75 2.40

Blessing of Natl. Sacred Heart of Jesus Sanctuary, 50th Anniv. — A599

2006, Nov. 24   Perf. 13½x13¼
1421 A599 10p multi   1.60 .80

Ninth Latin American Botanical Congress A600

2006   Perf. 13¼x13½
1422 A600 20p multi   3.25 1.60

America Issue, Energy Conservation — A601

Designs: 10p, Light bulb in hands. 20p, Transmission lines and tower.

2006   **Perf. 13x13¼**
1423-1424 A601   Set of 2   4.75 2.40

Pres. Joaquin Balaguer (1906-2002)
A602

Balaguer: 7p, Wearing bow tie. 10p, Holding book.

2006   **Perf. 13¼x13½**
1425-1426 A602   Set of 2   3.00 1.50

Office of the First Lady
A603

Emblem and: 10p, Tree. 25p, Computer and keyboard.

2007, Mar. 1   **Perf. 13½x13¼**
1427-1428 A603   Set of 2   5.50 2.75

Selection of Nicolás de Jesus Cardinal López Rodríguez as Archbishop of Santo Domingo, 25th Anniv. — A604

López Rodríguez: 10p, Standing next to chair. 15p, With Pope John Paul II. 25p, Holding crucifix.

2007, May 25   **Perf. 13¼x13½**
1429-1431 A604   Set of 3   8.00 4.00

2007 Pan American Games, Rio de Janeiro — A605

Designs: 15p, High jump. 20p, Weight lifting.

2007, July 6   **Litho.**
1432-1433 A605   Set of 2   5.50 2.75

SEMI-POSTAL STAMPS

Catalogue values for unused stamps in this section are for Never Hinged items.

Nos. 474-478
Surcharged in Red

Engraved and Lithographed
1957, Feb. 8   Unwmk.   Perf. 11½
Flags in National Colors

B1	A117	1c + 2c brn, lt bl, vio & mar	.20	.20
B2	A117	2c + 2c dk brn, lt bl & vio	.20	.20
B3	A117	3c + 2c red lilac & red	.20	.20
B4	A117	5c + 2c red orange & vio	.20	.20
B5	A117	7c + 2c green & violet	.30	.30
	Nos. B1-B5,CB1-CB3 (8)		2.20	2.20

The surtax was to aid Hungarian refugees. A similar 25c surcharge was applied to the miniature sheets described in the footnote following No. 478. Value, 2 sheets, perf. and imperf., $32.50

Nos. 479-483 Surcharged in Red Orange

1957, Sept. 9   Photo.   Perf. 13½
Flags in National Colors

B6	A118	1c + 2c brown & brt bl	.20	.20
B7	A118	2c + 2c org ver & dk bl	.30	.30
B8	A118	3c + 2c dark blue	.35	.35
B9	A118	5c + 2c olive & dk bl	.45	.45
B10	A118	7c + 2c rose brn & dk bl	.50	.50
	Nos. B6-B10,CB4-CB6 (8)		3.55	3.50

Cent. of the birth of Lord Baden Powell and the 50th anniv. of the Scout Movement. The surtax was for the Dominican Republic Boy Scouts.
A similar 5c surcharge was applied to the miniature sheets described in the footnote following No. 483. Value 4 sheets, perf. and imperf., medal and flag, $60.

Types of Olympic Regular Issue, 1957, Surcharged in Carmine

a

b

1958, May 26   Engr. & Litho.
Flags in National Colors
Pink Paper

B11	A119(a)	1c + 2c red brown	.20	.20
B12	A119(b)	1c + 2c red brown	.20	.20
B13	A120(a)	2c + 2c gray brown	.25	.25
B14	A120(b)	2c + 2c gray brown	.25	.25
B15	A119(a)	3c + 2c violet	.25	.25
B16	A119(b)	3c + 2c violet	.25	.25
B17	A120(a)	5c + 2c red orange	.35	.35
B18	A120(b)	5c + 2c red orange	.35	.35
B19	A119(a)	7c + 2c Prus green	.40	.40
B20	A119(b)	7c + 2c Prus green	.40	.40
	Nos. B11-B20,CB7-CB12 (16)		5.00	5.00

Surtax for the UN Relief and Works Agency for Palestine Refugees.
A similar 5c surcharge, plus marginal United Nations emblem and "UNRWA", was applied to the miniature sheets described in the footnote following No. 488. Value, 4 sheets, perf. and imperf., $20.

Nos. 501-505
Surcharged

Perf. 13½
1959, Apr. 13   Photo.   Unwmk.
Flags in National Colors

B21	A125	1c + 2c rose, indigo & ultra	.30	.30
B22	A125	1c + 2c brown & blue	.35	.35
B23	A125	3c + 2c gray, vio, blk & buff	.40	.40
B24	A125	5c + 2c rose, dk bl, brn & red	.50	.50
B25	A125	7c + 2c lt brn, dk bl & red	.55	.55
	Nos. B21-B25,CB13-CB15 (8)		4.30	4.30

International Geophysical Year, 1957-58.
A similar 5c surcharge was applied to the miniature sheets described in the footnote following No. 505. Value, 2 sheets, perf. and imperf., $40.

Type of 1957
Surcharged in Red

Engraved and Lithographed
1959, Sept. 10   Unwmk.   Imperf.
Flags in National Colors

B26	A117	1c + 2c brn, lt bl, vio & mar	.30	.30
B27	A117	2c + 2c dk brn, lt bl & vio	.30	.30
B28	A117	3c + 2c red lilac & red	.35	.35
B29	A117	5c + 2c red org & vio	.35	.35
B30	A117	7c + 2c green & violet	.45	.45
	Nos. B26-B30,CB16-CB18 (8)		3.25	3.25

3rd Pan American Games, Chicago, Aug. 27-Sept. 7, 1959.

Nos. 522-524 Surcharged in Red

1960, Apr. 7   Litho.   Perf. 12½
Center in Gray

B31	A135	5c + 5c red brn & yel grn	.30	.30
B32	A135	9c + 5c car & lt bl	.30	.30
B33	A135	13c + 5c org & grn	.65	.65
	Nos. B31-B33,CB19-CB20 (5)		2.00	2.00

World Refugee Year, July 1, 1959-June 30, 1960. The surtax was for aid to refugees.
Souvenir sheets exist perf. and imperf., containing one each of Nos. B31-B33 and CB19-CB20. Value, 2 sheets, perf. and imperf., $12.50

Nos. 525-529 Surcharged: "XV ANIVERSARIO DE LA UNESCO +2c"

1962, Jan. 8   Photo.   Perf. 13½
Flags in National Colors

B34	A136	1c + 2c red, yel grn & blk	.25	.25
B35	A136	2c + 2c org, grnsh bl & brn	.25	.25
B36	A136	3c + 2c henna brn & bl	.25	.25

B37	A136	5c + 2c brown & ultra	.25	.25
B38	A136	7c + 2c grn, bl & rose brn	.25	.25
	Nos. B34-B38,CB21-CB23 (8)		2.10	2.10

15th anniv. (in 1961) of UNESCO.
A similar 5c surcharge was applied to the miniature sheets described in the footnote following No. 529. Value, 2 sheets, perf. and imperf., $16.

Anti-Malaria Type of 1962
1962, Apr. 29   Litho.   Perf. 12

B39	A141	10c + 2c brt pink & red lil	.30	.30
B40	A141	20c + 2c pale brn & brn	.45	.45

Freedom from Hunger Type of 1963
1963, Apr. 15   Unwmk.   Perf. 11½
Banner in Dark Blue & Red

B41	A148	2c + 1c green	.20	.20
B42	A148	5c + 2c brt rose lil	.25	.25
B43	A148	9c + 2c orange	.25	.25
	Nos. B41-B43 (3)		.70	.70

A souvenir sheet contains three imperf. stamps similar to Nos. B41-B43. Value, $1.50.

Nos. 591-593 Surcharged

1964, Mar. 8   Perf. 12½

B44	A153	3c + 2c pale pink & ver	.20	.20
B45	A153	6c + 2c pale bl & ultra	.20	.20
B46	A153	9c + 2c pale rose & red brn	.25	.25
	Nos. B44-B46,CB26-CB27 (5)		1.15	1.05

UNESCO world campaign to save historic monuments in Nubia.

Nos. 622-626
Surcharged

1966, Dec. 9   Litho.   Perf. 12½
Size: 31x21mm

B47	A164	1c + 2c multi	.85	.25
B48	A164	2c + 2c multi	.65	.20
B49	A164	3c + 2c multi	.65	.20
B50	A164	6c + 4c multi	.85	.45
B51	A164	8c + 4c multi	1.25	.55
	Nos. B47-B51,CB28-CB30 (8)		11.85	7.10

Surtax for victims of Hurricane Inez.

AIR POST STAMPS

Map of Hispaniola — AP1

Perf. 11½
1928, May 31   Litho.   Unwmk.
C1   AP1   10c deep ultra   4.50 2.00

1930
C2	AP1	10c ocher	3.00	2.00
a.	Vert. pair, imperf. btwn.		600.00	
C3	AP1	15c scarlet	6.00	3.00
C4	AP1	20c dull green	2.75	.50
C5	AP1	30c violet	6.00	3.25
	Nos. C2-C5 (4)		17.75	8.75

Nos. C2-C5 have only "CENTAVOS" in lower panel. Issued: 10c, 20c, 1/24; 15c, 30c, 2/14.

1930
C6	AP1	10c light blue	1.50	.60
C7	AP1	15c blue green	3.00	.90
C8	AP1	20c yellow brown	3.25	.45
a.		Horiz. pair, imperf. vert.	450.00	450.00
C9	AP1	30c chocolate	5.50	1.50
		Nos. C6-C9 (4)	13.25	3.45

Issue dates: 10c, 15c, 20c, Sept.; 30c, Oct.

Batwing Sundial Erected in 1753 — AP2

1931-33   *Perf. 12*
C10	AP2	10c carmine	3.25	.50
C11	AP2	10c light blue	1.40	.50
C12	AP2	10c dark green	5.50	2.50
C13	AP2	15c rose lilac	2.50	.50
C14	AP2	20c dark blue	5.50	2.10
a.		Numerals reading up at left and down at right	5.00	2.50
b.		Imperf., pair	250.00	
C15	AP2	30c green	2.25	.25
C16	AP2	50c red brown	5.50	.50
C17	AP2	1p deep orange	7.50	2.50
		Nos. C10-C17 (8)	33.40	9.35

Issued: No. C11, 7/2/32; No. C12, 5/28/33; others 8/16.

Airplane and Ozama Fortress AP3

1933, Nov. 20
C18	AP3	10c dark blue	3.00	.50

Airplane and Trujillo Bridge AP4

1934, Sept. 20
C19	AP4	10c dark blue	3.00	.50

Symbolic of Flight AP5

1935, Apr. 29
C20	AP5	10c lt blue & dk blue	1.40	.40

AP6

1936, Feb. 11   *Perf. 11½*
C21	AP6	10c dk bl & turq bl	2.25	.40

Allegory of Flight AP7

1936, Oct. 17
C22	AP7	10c dk bl, bl & turq bl	2.00	.30

Macoris Airport AP8

1937, Oct. 22
C23	AP8	10c green	.90	.20

Fleet of Columbus AP9

Air Fleet AP10

Proposed Columbus Lighthouse — AP11

1937, Nov. 9   *Perf. 12*
C24	AP9	10c rose red	1.50	1.25
C25	AP10	15c purple	1.25	.85
C26	AP11	20c dk bl & lt bl	1.25	.90
C27	AP10	25c red violet	1.75	1.00
C28	AP11	30c yellow green	1.50	1.00
C29	AP10	50c brown	3.25	1.25
C30	AP11	75c dk olive grn	9.00	9.00
C31	AP9	1p orange	5.50	1.75
		Nos. C24-C31 (8)	25.00	17.00

Goodwill flight to all American countries by the planes "Colon," "Pinta," "Nina" and "Santa Maria."

No. C30 was reproduced imperf. on No. 1019.

Pan American Clipper AP12

1938, July 30
C32	AP12	10c green	1.00	.20

Trylon and Perisphere, Plane and Proposed Columbus Lighthouse — AP13

1939, Apr. 30
C33	AP13	10c green & lt green	1.40	.60

New York World's Fair.

Airplane AP14

1939, Oct. 18
C34	AP14	10c green & dp green	1.40	.20
a.		Pair, imperf. btwn.	450.00	

Proposed Columbus Lighthouse, Plane and Caravels — AP15

Christopher Columbus and Proposed Lighthouse — AP16

Proposed Lighthouse — AP17

Christopher Columbus — AP18

Caravel — AP19

1940, Oct. 12
C35	AP15	10c sapphire & lt bl	.85	.45
C36	AP16	15c org brn & brn	1.10	.75
C37	AP17	20c rose red & red	1.10	.75
C38	AP18	25c brt red lil & red vio	1.10	.35
C39	AP19	50c green & lt green	2.25	1.25
		Nos. C35-C39 (5)	6.40	3.55

Discovery of America by Columbus and proposed Columbus memorial lighthouse in Dominican Republic.

Posts and Telegraph Building, San Cristobal AP20

1941, Feb. 21
C40	AP20	10c brt red lil & pale lil rose	.40	.20

Globe, Wing and Letter AP21

1942, Feb. 13
C41	AP21	10c dark violet brn	.50	.25
C42	AP21	75c deep orange	2.75	1.75

Plane AP22

1943, Sept. 1
C43	AP22	10c brt red lilac	.30	.20
C44	AP22	20c dp blue & blue	.35	.20
C45	AP22	25c yellow olive	5.00	2.40
		Nos. C43-C45 (3)	5.65	2.80

Plane, Flag, Coat of Arms and Torch of Liberty — AP23

1944, Feb. 27   *Perf. 11½*
Flag in Gray, Dark Blue, Carmine
C46	AP23	10c multicolored	.35	.20
C47	AP23	20c multicolored	.45	.20
C48	AP23	1p multicolored	2.00	1.50
		Nos. C46-C48 (3)	2.80	1.90

Centenary of Independence. See No. 407 for souvenir sheet listing.

Communications Building, Ciudad Trujillo — AP24

1944, Nov. 12   Litho.   *Perf. 12*
C49	AP24	9c yel grn & blue	.20	.20
C50	AP24	13c dull brn & rose car	.25	.20
C51	AP24	25c org & dull red	.35	.20
b.		Vert. pair, imperf. btwn.	45.00	
C52	AP24	30c black & ultra	.75	.65
		Nos. C49-C52 (4)	1.55	1.25

Twenty booklets of 100 (25 panes of 4) of the 25c were issued. All booklets are still intact.

Communications Type

1945, Sept. 1
Center in Dark Blue and Carmine
C53	A92	7c deep yellow green	.30	.25
C54	A92	12c red orange	.35	.20
C55	A92	13c deep blue	.45	.20
C56	A92	25c orange brown	.80	.20
		Nos. C53-C56 (4)	1.90	.85

AP26

Flags and National Anthem AP27

Unwmk.
1946, Feb. 27   Litho.   *Perf. 12*
Center in Dark Blue, Deep Carmine and Black
C57	AP26	10c carmine	.40	.30
C58	AP26	15c blue	.90	.75
C59	AP26	20c chocolate	1.10	.75
C60	AP26	35c orange	1.25	.85
C61	AP27	1p grn, yel grn & cit	12.00	8.75
		Nos. C57-C61 (5)	15.65	11.40

Nos. C57-C61 exist imperf.

Map Type of Regular Issue
1946, Aug. 4
C62	A94	10c multicolored	.35	.20
C63	A94	13c multicolored	.60	.20

Waterfall Type of Regular Issue

1947, Mar. 18   **Litho.**

Center Multicolored

C64	A95	18c light blue	.45 .35
C65	A95	23c carmine	.70 .55
C66	A95	50c red violet	.90 .50
C67	A95	75c chocolate	1.25 1.00
		Nos. C64-C67 (4)	3.30 2.40

Palace Type of Regular Issue

1948, Feb. 27

C68	A96	37c orange brown	.90 .75
C69	A96	1p orange yellow	2.50 1.50

Ruins Type of Regular Issue

1949   **Unwmk.**   **Perf. 11½**

C70	A97	7c ol grn & pale ol grn	.25 .20
C71	A97	10c orange brn & buff	.25 .20
C72	A97	15c brt rose & pale pink	.55 .25
C73	A97	20c green & pale green	.80 .45
		Nos. C70-C73 (4)	1.85 1.10

Issue dates: 10c, Apr. 4; others, Apr. 13.

Las Carreras
Monument — AP32

1949, Aug. 10

C74	AP32	10c red & pink	.25 .20

Cent. of the Battle of Las Carreras.

> Catalogue values for unused stamps in this section, from this point to the end of the section, are for Never Hinged items.

Hotel Type of Regular Issue

Hotels: 12c, Montana. 37c, San Cristobal.

1950, Sept. 8

C75	A100	12c dk blue & blue	.50 .20
C76	A100	37c carmine & pink	3.00 2.00

Map, Plane and
Caduceus
AP34

1950, Oct. 2

C77	AP34	12c orange brn & yel	.60 .20

13th Pan-American Health Conf. Exists imperf.

Hospital Type of Regular Issue

1952, Aug.

C78	A104	23c deep blue	.85 .85
C79	A104	29c carmine	2.25 1.50

Columbus
Lighthouse and
Plane
AP36

Ano Mariano
Initials in
Monogram
AP37

1953, Jan. 6   **Engr.**   **Perf. 13**

C80	AP36	12c ocher	.30 .20
C81	AP36	14c dark blue	.20 .20
C82	AP36	20c black brown	.60 .45
C83	AP36	23c deep plum	.35 .30
C84	AP36	25c dark blue	.70 .55
C85	AP36	29c deep green	.60 .50

C86	AP36	1p red brown	1.40 .80
a.		Miniature sheet of 10	15.00 15.00
		Nos. C80-C86 (7)	4.15 3.00

No. C86a is lithographed and contains Nos. 450-452 and C80-C86, in slightly different shades. Sheet measures 190x130mm and is imperf. with simulated perforations.

A miniature sheet similar to No. C86a, but measuring 200x163mm and in folder, exists. Value $100.

1954, Aug. 5   **Litho.**   **Perf. 11½**

C87	AP37	8c claret	.20 .20
C88	AP37	11c blue	.20 .20
C89	AP37	33c brown orange	.80 .50
		Nos. C87-C89 (3)	1.20 .90

Marian Year. Nos. C87-C89 exist imperf.

Rotary Type of Regular Issue

1955, Feb. 23   **Perf. 12**

C90	A110	11c rose red	.35 .20

Flags — AP39

Portraits of General Hector B. Trujillo: 25c, In civilian clothes. 33c, In uniform.

1955, May 16   **Engr.**   **Perf. 13½x13**

C91	AP39	11c blue, yel & car	.55 .20
C92	AP39	25c rose violet	.90 .30
C93	AP39	33c orange brown	1.25 .50
		Nos. C91-C93 (3)	2.70 1.00

The center of No. C91 is litho. 25th anniv. of the inauguration of the Trujillo era.

Fair Type of Regular Issue

1955, Dec. 20   **Unwmk.**   **Perf. 13**

C94	A112	11c vermilion	.35 .20

ICAO Type of Regular Issue

1956, Apr. 6   **Litho.**   **Perf. 12½**

C95	A114	11c ultra	.40 .20

Tree Type of Regular Issue

Design: 13c, Mahogany tree.

1956, Dec. 8   **Litho.**   **Perf. 11½x12**

C96	A115	13c orange & green	1.60 .20

Type of Regular Issue, 1957

Olympic Winners and Flags: 11c, Paavo Nurmi, Finland. 16c, Ugo Frigerio, Italy. 17c, Mildred Didrikson ("Didrickson" on stamp), US.

Engraved and Lithographed
Perf. 11½, Imperf.

1957, Jan. 24   **Unwmk.**

Flags in National Colors

C97	A117	11c ultra & red org	.25 .25
C98	A117	16c carmine & lt grn	.25 .25
C99	A117	17c black, vio & red	.25 .25
		Nos. C97-C99 (3)	.75 .75

16th Olympic Games, Melbourne, Nov. 22-Dec. 8, 1956.

Souvenir sheets of 3 exist, perf. and imperf., containing Nos. C97-C99. Value, 2 sheets, perf. & imperf., $15.

For surcharges see Nos. CB1-CB3, CB16-CB18.

Type of Regular Issue

Olympic Winners and Flags: 11c, Robert Morrow, US, 100 & 200 meter dash. 16c, Chris Brasher, England, steeplechase. 17c, A. Ferreira Da Silva, Brazil, hop, step and jump.

Perf. 13½, Imperf.

1957, July 18   **Photo.**

Flags in National Colors

C100	A118	11c yellow grn & dk bl	.25 .25
C101	A118	16c lilac & dk blue	.25 .25
C102	A118	17c brown & blue grn	.25 .25
		Nos. C100-C102 (3)	.75 .75

1956 Olympic winners.

See note on miniature sheets following No. 483.

For surcharges see Nos. CB4-CB6.

Types of Regular Issue

Olympic Winners and Flags: 11c, Hans Winkler, Germany, individual jumping. 16c, Alfred

---

Oerter, US, discus throw. 17c, Shirley Strickland, Australia, 800 meter hurdles.

Engraved and Lithographed
Perf. 13½, Imperf.

1957, Nov. 12   **Unwmk.**

Flags in National Colors

C103	A119	11c ultra	.25 .25
C104	A120	16c rose carmine	.25 .25
C105	A119	17c claret	.25 .25
		Nos. C103-C105 (3)	.75 .75

1956 Olympic winners.

Miniature sheets of 3 exist, perf. and imperf., containing Nos. C103-C105. Value, 2 sheets, perf. and imperf., $5.50.

For surcharges see Nos. CB7-CB12.

Type of Regular Issue

Olympic Winners and Flags: 11c, Charles Jenkins, 400 & 800 meter run, and Thomas Courtney, 1,600 meter relay, US. 16c, Field hockey team, India. 17c, Yachting team, Sweden.

Perf. 13½, Imperf.

1958, Oct. 30   **Unwmk.**   **Photo.**

Flags in National Colors

C106	A125	11c blue, olive & brn	.25 .25
C107	A125	16c lt grn, org & dk bl	.25 .25
C108	A125	17c ver, blue & yel	.25 .25
		Nos. C106-C108 (3)	.75 .75

1956 Olympic winners.

Miniature sheets of 3 exist, perf. and imperf., containing Nos. C106-C108. Value, 2 sheets, perf. and imperf., $3.

For surcharges see Nos. CB13-CB15.

Fair Type of Regular Issue

1958, Dec. 9   **Litho.**   **Perf. 12½**

C109	A127	9c gray	.25 .20
C110	A127	25c lt violet	.70 .40
a.		Souv. sheet of 3, #C109-C110, 507, imperf.	1.75 1.75

Polo Type of Regular Issue

1959, May 15   **Perf. 12**

C111	A130	11c Dominican polo team	.35 .30

"San Cristobal" Plane — AP42

Perf. 11½

1960, Feb. 25   **Unwmk.**   **Litho.**

C112	AP42	13c org, bl, grn & gray	.30 .20

Dominican Civil Aviation.

Children
and WRY
Emblem
AP43

1960, Apr. 7   **Perf. 12½**

C113	AP43	10c plum, gray & grn	.60 .30
C114	AP43	13c gray & green	.80 .30

World Refugee Year, 7/1/59-6/30/60.
For surcharges see Nos. CB19-CB20.

Olympic Type of Regular Issue

Olympic Winners: 11c, Pat McCormick, US, diving. 16c, Mithat Bayrack, Turkey, welterweight wrestling. 17c, Ursula Happe, Germany, 200 meter breast stroke.

Perf. 13½, Imperf.

1960, Sept. 14   **Photo.**

Flags in National Colors

C115	A136	11c blue, gray & brn	.20 .20
C116	A136	16c red, brown & ol	.25 .25
C117	A136	17c black, blue & ocher	.25 .25
		Nos. C115-C117 (3)	.70 .70

17th Olympic Games, Rome, 8/25-9/11.

Miniature sheets of 3 exist, perf. and imperf., containing Nos. C115-C117. Value, 2 sheets, perf. and imperf., $3.75.

For surcharges see Nos. CB21-CB23.

Coffee-Cacao Type of Regular Issue

1961, Dec. 30   **Litho.**   **Perf. 12½**

C118	A140	13c orange ver	.25 .25
C119	A140	33c brt yellow	.50 .50

Nos. C118-C119 exist imperf.

Anti-Malaria Type of Regular Issue

1962, Apr. 29   **Unwmk.**   **Perf. 12**

C120	A141	13c pink & red	.40 .20
C121	A141	33c org & dp org	.70 .45

See Nos. CB24-CB25.

Type of Regular Issue

Designs: 13c, Broken fetters and laurel. 50c, Flag, torch and inscription.

1962, May 30   **Perf. 12½**

C122	A142	13c brn, yel, ol, ultra & red	.30 .20
C123	A142	50c rose lilac, ultra & red	1.10 .75

No. C122 exists imperf.

UPAE Type of Regular Issue

1962, Oct. 23   **Perf. 12½**

C124	A146	13c bright blue	.25 .20
C125	A146	22c dull red brown	.40 .40

Nos. C124-C125 exist imperf.

Nouel Type of Regular Issue

Design: Frame altered with rosary and cross surrounding portrait.

1962, Dec. 18

C126	A147	13c blue & pale blue	.35 .20
C127	A147	25c vio & pale vio	.50 .50
a.		Souv. sheet, #C126-C127, imperf	1.00 1.00

Nos. C126-C127 exist imperf.

Sanchez,
Duarte,
Mella
AP44

1963, July 7   **Litho.**   **Perf. 11½x12**

C128	AP44	15c orange	.30 .25

120th anniv. of separation from Haiti.

World Map
AP45

1963, Oct. 25   **Unwmk.**   **Perf. 12½**

C129	AP45	10c gray & carmine	.30 .25

Cent. of Intl. Red Cross. Exists imperf.

Human Rights Type

1963, Dec. 10   **Litho.**

C130	A152	7c fawn & red brn	.25 .20
C131	A152	10c lt blue & blue	.25 .20

Nos. C130-C131 exist imperf.

Ramses II Battling
the Hittites (from
Abu
Simbel) — AP46

1964, Mar. 8   **Perf. 12½**

C132	AP46	10c brt violet	.25 .25
C133	AP46	13c yellow	.25 .20

UNESCO world campaign to save historic monuments in Nubia.

Nos. C132-C133 exist imperf.
For surcharges see Nos. CB26-CB27.

Striated Woodpecker — AP47

1964, June 8   **Litho.**
C134 AP47 10c multicolored   4.25 .20

Type of Space Issue

Designs: 7c, Rocket leaving earth. 10c, Space capsule orbiting earth.

1964, July 28   **Unwmk.**   **Perf. 12½**
C135 A156 7c brt green   .25 .20
C136 A156 10c violet blue   .30 .25
   a.   Souvenir sheet   3.00 3.00

No. C136a contains 7c and 10c stamps similar to Nos. C135-C136 with simulated perforations.

Pres. John F.
Kennedy — AP48

1964, Nov. 22   **Perf. 11½**
C137 AP48 10c buff & dk brown   .45 .25

President John F. Kennedy (1917-63). Sheets of 10 (5x2) and sheets of 50.

UPU Type of Regular Issue
1964, Dec. 5   **Litho.**   **Perf. 12½**
C138 A157 7c blue   .25 .20

ICY Type of Regular Issue
1965, Feb. 16   **Unwmk.**   **Perf. 12½**
C139 A158 10c lilac & violet   .30 .25

Basilica of Our Lady of
Altagracia — AP49

1965, Mar. 18   **Unwmk.**   **Perf. 12½**
C140 AP49 10c multicolored   .30 .25

Fourth Mariological Congress and the Eleventh International Marian Congress.

Abraham
Lincoln — AP50

1965, Apr. 15   **Litho.**   **Perf. 12½**
C141 AP50 17c bright blue   .45 .35

Cent. of the death of Abraham Lincoln.

Stamp Centenary Type of 1965

Design: Stamp of 1865, (No. 2).

1965, Dec. 28   **Litho.**   **Perf. 12½**
C142 A161 7c violet, lt grn & blk   .25 .20
C143 A161 10c yellow, lt grn & blk   .25 .20

ITU Emblem, Old and New
Communication Equipment — AP51

1966, Apr. 6   **Litho.**   **Perf. 12½**
C144 AP51 28c pink & carmine   .65 .65
C145 AP51 45c brt grn & grn   1.00 1.00

Cent. (in 1965) of the ITU.

Butterfly Type of Regular Issue
1966, Nov. 8   **Litho.**   **Perf. 12½**
Various Butterflies in Natural Colors
Size: 35x24mm
C146 A164 10c lt violet & violet   5.25 .25
C147 A164 50c org & dp org   5.50 .90
C148 A164 75c pink & rose red   5.75 1.10
   Nos. C146-C148 (3)   16.50 2.25

For surcharges see Nos. CB28-CB30.

Altar Type of Regular Issue
1967, Jan. 18   **Litho.**   **Perf. 11½**
C149 A165 7c olive green   .20 .20
C150 A165 10c lilac   .20 .20
C151 A165 20c yellow brown   .30 .25
   Nos. C149-C151 (3)   .70 .65

Chess Type of Regular Issue

Design: 10c, Pawn and Bishop.

1967, June 23   **Litho.**   **Perf. 12½**
C152 A167 10c ol, lt ol & blk   1.10 .25
   a.   Souvenir sheet   3.00 .60

No. C152a contains 2 imperf. stamps similar to Nos. 636 and C152.

Alliance for Progress Type
1967, Sept. 16   **Litho.**   **Perf. 12½**
C153 A168 8c gray   .30 .25
C154 A168 10c blue   .35 .25

Cornucopia and   Latin American
Emblem — AP52   Flags — AP53

1967, Oct. 7
C155 AP52 12c multicolored   .45 .25

25th anniversary of the Inter-American Agriculture Institute.

Satellite Type of Regular Issue
1968, June 15   **Typo.**   **Perf. 12**
C156 A170 10c dp blue & multi   .25 .20
C157 A170 15c purple & multi   .35 .30

Boxing Type of Regular Issue

Designs: Two views of boxing match.

1968, June 29
C158 A171 7c orange yel & grn   .25 .20
C159 A171 10c gray & blue   .30 .20

See note after No. 641.

Lions Type of Regular Issue
1968, Aug. 9   **Litho.**   **Perf. 11½**
C160 A172 10c ultra & multi   .25 .20

Olympic Type of Regular Issue

Designs (Olympic Emblem and): 10c, Weight lifting. 33c, Pistol shooting.

1968, Nov. 12   **Litho.**   **Perf. 11½**
C161 A173 10c buff & multi   .25 .25
C162 A173 33c pink & multi   .75 .60

1969, Jan. 25   **Litho.**   **Perf. 12½**
C163 AP53 10c pink & multi   .25 .20

7th Inter-American Savings and Loan Conference, Santo Domingo, Jan. 25-31.

Taino Art Type of Regular Issue

7c, Various vomiting spoons with human heads, vert. 10c, Female torso forming drinking vessel. 20c, Vase with human head, vert.

1969, Jan. 31   **Litho.**   **Perf. 12½**
C164 A175 7c lt bl, bl & lem   .20 .20
C165 A175 10c pink, ver & brn   .25 .20
C166 A175 20c yellow, org & brn   .30 .30
   Nos. C164-C166 (3)   .75 .70

COTAL Type of Regular Issue

10c, Airport of the Americas and COTAL emblem.

1969, May 25   **Litho.**   **Perf. 12½**
C167 A178 10c brown & pale fawn   .25 .20

ILO Type of Regular Issue
1969, June 27   **Litho.**   **Perf. 12½**
C168 A179 10c rose, red & black   .25 .20

Baseball Type of Regular Issue

Designs: 7c, Bleachers, Tetelo Vargas Stadium, horiz. 10c, Batter, catcher and umpire. 1p, Quisqueya Stadium, horiz.

1969, Aug. 15   **Litho.**   **Perf. 12½**
Size: 43x30mm (7c, 1p); 21x31mm (10c)
C169 A180 7c magenta & org   .50 .30
C170 A180 10c mar & rose red   .55 .30
C171 A180 1p violet blue & brn   4.25 3.00
   Nos. C169-C171 (3)   5.30 3.60

Electrification Types of Regular Issue

Design: No. C172, Rio Haina steam plant. No. C173, Valdesa Dam.

1969   **Litho.**   **Perf. 12**
C172 A181 10c orange ver   .35 .20
C173 A182 10c multicolored   .40 .20

Issued: #C172, Sept. 15; #C173, Oct. 15.

Duarte Type of Regular Issue
1970, Jan. 26   **Litho.**   **Perf. 12**
C174 A183 10c brown & dk brown   .45 .20

Census Type of Regular Issue

Design: 10c, Buildings and census emblem.

1970, Feb. 6   **Perf. 11**
C175 A184 10c lt blue & multi   .45 .25

Sculpture Type of Regular Issue

Design: 10c, The Prisoner, by Abelardo Rodriguez Urdaneta, vert.

1970, Feb. 20   **Litho.**   **Perf. 12½**
C176 A186 10c bluish gray   .30 .20

Masonic Type of Regular Issue
1970, Mar. 2
C177 A187 10c brown   .25 .20

Satellite Type of Regular Issue
1970, May 25   **Litho.**   **Perf. 12½**
C178 A188 7c blue & gray   .25 .20

UPU Type of Regular Issue
1970, June 5   **Perf. 11**
C179 A189 10c yellow & brown   .25 .20

Education Year Type of Regular Issue
1970, June 26   **Litho.**   **Perf. 12½**
C180 A190 15c bright pink   .45 .25

Dancers
AP54

Album, Globe and
Emblem — AP55

Design: 10c, UN emblem and wheel.

1970, Oct. 12   **Litho.**   **Perf. 12½**
C181 AP54 7c blue & multi   .25 .20
C182 AP54 10c pink & multi   .30 .20

1st World Exhib. of Books and Culture Festival, Santo Domingo, Oct. 11-Dec. 11.

1970, Oct. 26   **Litho.**   **Perf. 11**
C183 AP55 10c multicolored   .30 .25

EXFILCA 70, 2nd Interamerican Philatelic Exhibition, Caracas, Venezuela, 11/27-12/6.

Basilica of Our Lady of
Altagracia — AP56

1971, Jan. 20   **Litho.**   **Perf. 12½**
C184 AP56 17c multicolored   .65 .35

Inauguration of the Basilica of Our Lady of Altagracia.

Map of
Dominican
Republic,
CARE
Package
AP57

1971, May 28   **Litho.**   **Perf. 12½**
C185 AP57 10c blue & green   .25 .20

25th anniversary of CARE, a US-Canadian Cooperative for American Relief Everywhere.

Sports Type of Regular Issue
1971, Sept. 10   **Perf. 11**
C186 A195 7c Volleyball   .25 .20

Animal Type of Regular Issue

Design: 25c, Cock and grain.

1971, Sept. 29   **Perf. 12½**
C187 A196 25c black & multi   .50 .30

Independence Type

10c, Dominican-Colombian flag of 1821.

1971, Dec. 1   **Perf. 11**
C188 A197 10c vio bl, yel & red   .50 .30

Christmas Type of Regular Issue
1971, Dec. 10   **Perf. 12½**
C189 A198 10c Bell, 1493   .25 .20

UNICEF Type of Regular Issue

Design: UNICEF emblem & child on beach.

1971, Dec. 14   **Perf. 11**
C190 A199 15c multicolored   .45 .30

Book Year Type of Regular Issue
1972, Jan. 25   **Litho.**   **Perf. 12½**
C191 A200 12c lilac, dk bl & red   .30 .25

Magnifying Glass
over Peru on Map
of
Americas — AP58

"Your Heart is your Health" — AP59

1972, Mar. 7   Litho.   Perf. 12
C192 AP58 10c blue & multi   .30 .25
EXFILIMA '71, 3rd Inter-American Philatelic Exposition, Lima, Peru, Nov. 6-14, 1971.

1972, Apr. 27   Litho.   Perf. 11
C193 AP59 7c red & multi   .25 .20
World Health Day.

Taino Art Type of 1972

Taino Art: 8c, Ritual vessel showing human figures. 10c, Trumpet (shell). 25c, Carved vomiting spoons. All horiz.

1972, May 10   Litho.   Perf. 11
C194 A201   8c multicolored   .40 .20
C195 A201 10c lt blue & multi   .60 .20
C196 A201 25c multicolored   1.50 .45
    Nos. C194-C196 (3)   2.50 .85

Telecommunications Type of Regular Issue

1972, May 17   Perf. 12½
C197 A202 21c yellow & multi   .60 .30

Exhibition Type of Regular Issue
1972, June 3
C198 A203 33c orange & multi   .60 .40

Olympic Type of Regular Issue
1972, Aug. 25   Litho.   Perf. 12½
C199 A204 33c Running   .75 .50

Club Type of Regular Issue
1972, Sept. 29   Litho.   Perf. 10½
C200 A205 20c blue & multi   .40 .25

Morel Type of Regular Issue
1972, Oct. 20   Litho.   Perf. 12½
C201 A206 10c multicolored   .25 .20

Bank Type of Regular Issue
25c, 1947 silver coin, entrance to the Mint.
1972, Oct. 23
C202 A207 25c ocher & multi   .65 .45

"La Navidad" Fortress, 1492 AP60

1972, Nov. 21   Litho.   Perf. 12½
C203 AP60 10c multicolored   .45 .20
Christmas 1972.

Sports Type of Regular Issue
Various sports; a, UL. b, UR. c, LL. d, LR.
1973, Mar. 30   Litho.   Perf. 13½x13
C204 A212   Block of 4   1.50 1.50
a.-d.   8c, any single   .25 .25
C205 A212   Block of 4   2.50 2.50
a.-d. 10c, any single   .50 .30

Easter Type 1973
10c, Belfry of Church of Our Lady of Help.
1973, Apr. 18   Litho.   Perf. 10½
C206 A213 10c multicolored   .40 .20

North and South America on Globe — AP61

1973, May 29   Litho.   Perf. 12
C207 AP61 7c multicolored   .25 .20
Pan-American Health Organization, 70th anniversary (in 1972).

WMO Type of Regular Issue
1973, Aug. 10   Litho.   Perf. 13½x13
C208 A214 7c green & multi   .25 .20

INTERPOL Emblem Police Scientist AP62

1973, Sept. 28   Litho.   Perf. 10½
C209 AP62 10c vio bl, bl & emer   .35 .20
50th anniversary of International Criminal Police Organization.

Handicraft Type of Regular Issue
1973, Oct. 12
C210 A215   7c Sailing ship, mosaic .20 .20
C211 A215 10c Maracas rattles,
                horiz.   .30 .20

Christmas Type of Regular Issue
Design: 10c, Angels adoring Christ Child.
1973, Nov. 26   Litho.   Perf. 13½x13
C212 A216 10c multicolored   .25 .20

Scout Type of Regular Issue
21c, Scouts cooking, Lord Baden-Powell.
1973, Dec. 7   Litho.   Perf. 12
C213 A217 21c red & multi   .65 .55

Sport Type of Regular Issue
10c, Olympic swimming pool and diver. 25c, Olympic Stadium, soccer and discus.
1974, Feb. 25   Litho.   Perf. 13½
C214 A218 10c blue & multi   .20 .20
C215 A218 25c multicolored   .40 .20

The Last Supper AP63

1974, June 27   Litho.   Perf. 13½
C216 AP63 10c multicolored   .30 .20
Holy Week 1974.

Bridge Type
Design: 10c, Higuamo Bridge.
1974, July 12   Perf. 12
C217 A221 10c multicolored   .40 .20

Diabetes Type
Map of Dominican Republic, Diabetics' Emblem and: 7c, Kidney. 33c, Eye & heart.
1974, Aug. 22   Litho.   Perf. 13
C218 A222   7c yellow & multi   .25 .25
C219 A222 33c lt blue & multi   1.25 .75

UPU Type
1974, Oct. 9   Perf. 13½
C220 A223   7c Ships   .50 .25
C221 A223 33c Jet   1.50 .50
a.   Souvenir sheet of 4   4.50 4.50
No. C221a contains Nos. 727-728, C220-C221 forming continuous design.

Golfers and Championship Emblem — AP64

20c, Golfer and Golf Association emblem.
1974, Oct. 24   Litho.   Perf. 13x13½
C222 AP64 10c green & multi   .40 .20
C223 AP64 20c green & multi   .75 .40
World Amateur Golf Championships.

Hand Holding Dove AP65

1974, Dec. 3   Litho.   Perf. 12
C224 AP65 10c multicolored   .30 .20
Christmas 1974.

FAO Type
10c, Bee, beehive and barrel of honey.
1974, Dec. 5
C225 A227 10c multicolored   1.10 .20

Chrismon, Lamb, Candle and Palm — AP66   Spain No. 1, España 75 Emblem — AP67

1975, Mar. 26   Litho.   Perf. 13½
C226 AP66 10c gold & multi   .30 .20
Holy Week 1975.

1975, Apr. 10
C227 AP67 12c red, yel & blk   .40 .25
Espana 75, International Philatelic Exhibition, Madrid, Apr. 4-13.

Development Bank Type
1975, May 19   Litho.   Perf. 10½x10
C228 A230 10c rose car & multi   .30 .20

Three Satellites and Globe AP68

1975, June 21   Litho.   Perf. 13½
C229 AP68 15c multicolored   .45 .35
Opening of first earth satellite tracking station in Dominican Republic.

Apollo Type
Design: 2p, Apollo-Soyuz link-up over earth.
1975, July 24   Perf. 13
Size: 42x28mm
C230 A232 2p multicolored   5.25 3.25

Indian Chief Type
7c, Mayobanex. 8c, Cotubanama & Juan de Esquivel. 10c, Enriquillo & Mencia.

1975, Sept. 27   Litho.   Perf. 12
C231 A235   7c lt green & multi   .25 .25
C232 A235   8c orange & multi   .30 .25
C233 A235 10c gray & multi   .30 .25
    Nos. C231-C233 (3)   .85 .75

Volleyball AP69

10c, Weight lifting and Games' emblem.
1975, Oct. 24   Litho.   Perf. 12
C234 AP69   7c blue & multi   .25 .20
C235 AP69 10c multicolored   .35 .25
7th Pan-American Games, Mexico City, Oct. 13-26.

Christmas Type
Design: 10c, Dove and peace message.
1975, Dec. 12   Litho.   Perf. 13x13½
C236 A237 10c yellow & multi   .25 .20

Valdesia Dam — AP70

1976, Jan. 26   Litho.   Perf. 13
C237 AP70 10c multicolored   .35 .20

Holy Week Type 1976
Design: 10c, Crucifixion, by Eliezer Castillo.
1976, Apr. 14   Litho.   Perf. 13½
C238 A239 10c multicolored   .30 .25

Bicentennial Type and

George Washington, Independence Hall — AP71

Design: 10c, Hands holding maps of US and Dominican Republic.
1976, May 29   Litho.   Perf. 13½
C239 A241 10c vio bl, grn & blk   .35 .20
C240 AP71 75c black & orange   1.10 1.10
American Bicentennial; No. C240 also for Interphil 76 International Philatelic Exhibition, Philadelphia, Pa., May 29-June 6.

King Juan Carlos I and Queen Sofia — AP72

1976, May 31
C241 AP72 21c multicolored   .60 .60
Visit of King Juan Carlos I and Queen Sofia of Spain.

Telephone Type

Design: 10c, Alexander Graham Bell and telephones, 1876 and 1976.

1976, July 15
C242 A243 10c multicolored .30 .20

Duarte Types

10c, Scroll with Duarte letter and Dominican flag. 33c, Duarte return from Exile, by E. Godoy.

1976, July 20   Litho.   Perf. 13½
C243 A245 10c blue & multi .30 .20
Perf. 13x13½
C244 A244 33c brown & multi 1.10 .75

Fire Engine AP73

1976, Sept. 13   Litho.   Perf. 12
C245 AP73 10c multicolored .40 .20
Honoring firemen.

Radio Club Type

1976, Oct. 8   Litho.   Perf. 13½
C246 A247 10c blue & black .30 .20

Various People — AP74

1976, Oct. 22   Litho.   Perf. 13½
C247 AP74 21c multicolored .35 .35
Spanish heritage.

Olympic Games Type

1976, Oct. 22   Perf. 12
C248 A249 10c Running .30 .20
C249 A249 25c Basketball .85 .50

Christmas Type

Design: 10c, Angel with bells.

1976, Dec. 8   Litho.   Perf. 13½
C250 A251 10c multicolored .30 .25

Tourist Activities AP75

Tourist publicity: 12c, Angling and hotel. 25c, Horseback riding and waterfall, vert.

1977, Jan. 7
Size: 36x36mm
C251 AP75 10c multicolored .25 .20
Size: 34x25½mm, 25½x34mm
C252 AP75 12c multicolored .25 .20
C253 AP75 25c multicolored .50 .30
Nos. C251-C253 (3) 1.00 .70

Championship Type

1977, Mar. 4   Litho.   Perf. 13½
C254 A253 10c yel grn & multi .30 .20
C255 A253 25c lt brown & multi .85 .50

Holy Week Type 1977

Design: 10c, Belfry and open book.

1977, Apr. 18   Litho.   Perf. 13½x13
C256 A254 10c multicolored .30 .20

Lions Type

1977, May 6   Perf. 13½x13
C257 A255 7c lt green & multi .25 .20

Caravel under Sail — AP76

Melon Cactus — AP77

1977, July 16   Litho.   Perf. 13
C258 AP76 10c multicolored .45 .30
Miss Universe Contest, held in Dominican Republic.

1977, Aug. 19   Litho.   Perf. 12
Design: 33c, Coccothrinax (tree).
C259 AP77 7c multicolored .30 .25
C260 AP77 33c multicolored 1.10 .75
National Botanical Garden.

Chart and Factories — AP78

1977, Nov. 30   Litho.   Perf. 13x13½
C261 AP78 28c multicolored .50 .50
7th Interamerican Statistics Conference.

Animal Type

Congress Emblem and: 10c, "Dorado," red Roman stud bull. 25c, Flamingo, vert.

1977, Dec. 29   Litho.   Perf. 13
C262 A259 10c multicolored 2.00 .30
C263 A259 25c multicolored 3.50 .50

Spanish Heritage Type

21c, Window, Casa del Tostado, 16th cent.

1978, Jan. 19   Perf. 13x13½
Size: 28x41mm
C264 A260 21c multicolored .45 .35

Holy Week Type, 1978

7c, Facade, Santo Domingo Cathedral. 10c, Facade of Dominican Convent.

1978, Mar. 21   Litho.   Perf. 12
Size: 27x36mm
C265 A261 7c multicolored .25 .25
C266 A261 10c multicolored .40 .25

Schooner Duarte AP79

1978, Apr. 15   Litho.   Perf. 13½
C267 AP79 7c multicolored .35 .20
Dominican naval forces training ship.

Cardinal Type

1978, May 5   Litho.   Perf. 13
C268 A262 10c multicolored .30 .20

Antenna AP80

1978, May 17   Litho.   Perf. 13½
C269 AP80 25c silver & multi .55 .35
10th World Telecommunications Day.

No. C1 and Map AP81

1978, June 6
C270 AP81 10c multicolored .30 .20
1st Dominican Rep. airmail stamp, 50th anniv.

Globe, Soccer Ball, Emblem — AP82

Crown, Cross and Rosary Emblem — AP83

33c, Soccer field, Argentina '78 emblem, globe.

1978, June 29
C271 AP82 12c multicolored .40 .30
C272 AP82 33c multicolored .85 .85
11th World Cup Soccer Championship, Argentina, June 1-25.

1978, July 11   Perf. 13x13½
C273 AP83 21c multicolored .65 .65
Congregation of the Merciful Sisters of Charity, centenary.

Sports Type

1978, July 21   Litho.   Perf. 13½
C274 A265 7c Baseball, vert. .40 .25
C275 A265 10c Basketball, vert. .45 .25

Wright Brothers and Glider, 1902 AP84

Designs: 7c, Diagrams of Flyer I and jet, vert. 13c, Diagram of air flow over wing. 45c, Flyer I over world map.

1978, Aug. 8   Perf. 12
C276 AP84 7c multicolored .25 .20
C277 AP84 10c multicolored .35 .20
C278 AP84 13c multicolored .55 .25
C279 AP84 45c multicolored 1.50 .95
Nos. C276-C279 (4) 2.65 1.60
75th anniversary of first powered flight.

Tourist Type

Designs: 7c, Sun and musical instruments. 10c, Sun and plane over Santo Domingo.

1978, Sept. 12   Litho.   Perf. 12
C280 A266 7c multicolored .30 .20
C281 A266 10c multicolored .35 .20

People and Globe AP85

1978, Oct. 12   Litho.   Perf. 13½
C282 AP85 21c multicolored .45 .45
Spanish heritage.

Dominican Republic and UN Flags AP86

1978, Oct. 23   Perf. 12
C283 AP86 33c multicolored .60 .60
33rd anniversary of the United Nations.

  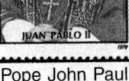
Statue of the Virgin — AP87   Pope John Paul II — AP88

1978, Dec. 5   Litho.   Perf. 12
C284 AP87 10c multicolored .30 .25
Christmas 1978.

1979, Jan. 25   Litho.   Perf. 13½
C285 AP88 10c multicolored 3.00 3.00
Visit of Pope John Paul II to the Dominican Republic, Jan. 25-26.

Map of Beata Island AP89

1979, Jan. 25   Perf. 12
C286 AP89 10c multicolored .50 .30
1st expedition of radio amateurs to Beata Is.

Year of the Child Type, 1979

Designs (ICY Emblem and): 7c, Children reading book. 10c, Symbolic head and protective hands. 33c, Hands and jars.

1979, Feb. 26
C287 A269 7c multicolored .20 .20
C288 A269 10c multicolored .30 .20
C289 A269 33c multicolored 1.10 .75
Nos. C287-C289 (3) 1.60 1.15

Pope John Paul II Giving Benediction AP90

Adm. Juan Bautista Cambiaso AP91

1979, Apr. 9　　Litho.　　Perf. 13½
C290　AP90　10c multicolored　　1.25　.90
Holy Week.

1979, Apr. 14　　Perf. 12
C291　AP91　10c multicolored　　.30　.20
135th anniv. of the Battle of Tortuguero.

Map of Dominican Rep., Album, Magnifier AP92

1979, Apr. 18
C292　AP92　33c multicolored　　.60　.60
EXFILNA, 3rd National Philatelic Exhibition, Apr. 18-22.

Flower Type
Designs: 7c, Passionflower. 10c, Isidorea pungens. 13c, Calotropis procera.

1979, May 17　　Litho.　　Perf. 12
C293　A271　7c multicolored　　.30　.30
C294　A271　10c multicolored　　.40　.25
C295　A271　13c multicolored　　.55　.45
　Nos. C293-C295 (3)　　1.25　1.00

Cardiology Type, 1979
10c, Figure of man showing blood circulation.

1979, June 2　　Litho.　　Perf. 13½
C296　A272　10c multicolored, vert.　.60　.40

Sports Type
7c, Runner and Games' emblem, vert.

1979, June 20
C297　A273　7c multicolored　　.30　.25

Soccer Type
1979, Aug. 9　　Litho.　　Perf. 12
C298　A273　10c Tennis, vert.　　.30　.25

Rowland Hill, Dominican Republic No. 1 — AP93

1979, Aug. 21　　Perf. 13½
C299　AP93　2p multicolored　　3.00　2.50
Sir Rowland Hill (1795-1879), originator of penny postage.

Electric Light Type
Design: 10c, "100" and light bulb, horiz.

1979, Aug. 27　　Perf. 13½
C300　A275　10c multicolored　　.30　.25

Bird Type
Birds: 7c, Phaenicophilus palmarum. 10c, Calyptophilus frugivorus tertius. 45c, Icterus dominicensis.

1979, Sept. 12　　Litho.　　Perf. 12
C301　A277　7c multicolored　　1.90　.25
C302　A277　10c multicolored　　2.75　.25
C303　A277　45c multicolored　　6.75　.90
　Nos. C301-C303 (3)　　11.40　1.40

Lions Type
10c, Melvin Jones, organization founder.

1979, Nov. 13　　Litho.　　Perf. 12
C304　A278　10c multicolored　　.50　.30

Christmas Type
Christmas: 10c, Three Kings riding camels.

1979, Dec. 18　　Litho.　　Perf. 12
C305　A279　10c multicolored　　.25　.25

Holy Week Type
1980, Mar. 27　　Litho.　　Perf. 12
C306　A280　7c Crucifixion　　.20　.20
C307　A280　10c Resurrection　　.30　.25

Navy Day — AP94

1980, Apr. 15　　Litho.　　Perf. 13½
C308　AP94　21c multicolored　　.45　.40

Dominican Philatelic Society, 25th Anniversary AP95

1980, Apr. 18
C309　AP95　10c multicolored　　.30　.25

Gold Type
1980, July 8　　Litho.　　Perf. 13½
C310　A282　10c Drag line mining　.45　.35
C311　A282　33c Mine　　.85　.55

Tourism Secretariat Emblem — AP96

1980, Aug. 26　　Litho.　　Perf. 13½
C312　AP96　10c shown　　.30　.25
C313　AP96　33c Conf. emblem　　1.10　.75
World Tourism Conf., Manila, Sept. 27.

Iguana Type
1980, Aug. 30　　Perf. 12
C314　A284　7c American croco-
　　　　　dile　　1.60　.30
C315　A284　10c Cuban rat　　1.75　.35
C316　A284　25c Manatee　　2.75　.60
C317　A284　45c Turtle　　3.75　.85
　Nos. C314-C317 (4)　　9.85　2.10

Painting Type
1980, Sept. 23　　Litho.　　Perf. 13½x13
C318　A285　10c Abstract, by Paul
　　　　　Guidicelli, vert.　　.30　.25
C319　A285　17c Farmer, by Yoryi
　　　　　Morel, vert.　　.50　.35

Visit of Radio Amateurs to Catalina Island AP97

1980, Oct. 3
C320　AP97　7c multicolored　　.50　.50

Rotary International, 75th Anniversary — AP98

1980, Oct. 23　　Litho.　　Perf. 12
C321　AP98　10c Globe, emblem,
　　　　　vert.　　.40　.30
C322　AP98　33c shown　　.75　.75

Carrier Pigeons, UPU Emblem AP99

1980, Oct. 31　　Perf. 13½
C323　AP99　33c shown　　.30　.25
C324　AP99　45c Pigeons, diff.　.45　.30
C325　AP99　50c Pigeon, stamp　.90　.45
　Nos. C323-C325 (3)　　1.65　1.00

Souvenir Sheet
Imperf
C326　AP99　1.10p UPU emblem　1.50　1.50
　UPU cent. No. C326 contains one 48½x31mm stamp.

Christmas Type
1980, Dec. 5　　Litho.　　Perf. 13½
C327　A286　10c Holy Family　　.30　.25
Christmas 1980.

Salcedo Type
Design: Map and arms of Salcedo.

1981, Jan. 14　　Litho.　　Perf. 13½
C328　A287　10c multicolored　　.25　.25

AP100

AP101

Industrial Symbols, Seminar Emblem.

1981, Feb. 18　　Litho.　　Perf. 13½
C329　AP100　10c shown　　.30　.25
C330　AP100　33c Seminar emblem　.55　.25
CODIA Chemical Engineering Seminar.

National Games Type
1981, Mar. 31　　Litho.　　Perf. 13½
C331　A289　10c Baseball　　.55　.35

1981, Apr. 15
Design: Admiral Juan Alejandro Acosta.
C332　AP101　10c multicolored　　.25　.20
Battle of Tortuguero anniversary.

13th World Telecommunications Day — AP102

1981, May 16　　Litho.　　Perf. 12
C333　AP102　10c multicolored　　.25　.20

Heinrich von Stephan AP103

Worker in Wheelchair AP104

1981, July 15　　Litho.　　Perf. 13½
C334　AP103　33c tan & lt red brn　.75　.75
Birth sesquicentennial of UPU founder.

1981, July 24
C335　AP104　7c Stylized people　.30　.30
C336　AP104　33c shown　　.75　.75
Intl. Year of the Disabled.

EXPURIDOM '81 Intl. Stamp Show, Santo Domingo, July 31-Aug. 2 — AP105

1981, July 31
C337　AP105　7c multicolored　　.50　.35

Bullet Holes in Target, Competition Emblem AP106

1981, Aug. 12
C338　AP106　10c shown　　.20　.20
C339　AP106　15c Riflemen　　.30　.25
C340　AP106　25c Pistol shooting　.50　.40
　Nos. C338-C340 (3)　　1.00　.85
2nd World Sharpshooting Championship.

Exports — AP107

World Food
Day — AP108

1981, Oct. 16   Litho.   Perf. 12
C341 AP107 7c Jewelry   .35   .25
C342 AP107 10c Handicrafts   .45   .25
C343 AP107 11c Fruit   .35   .30
C344 AP107 17c Vegetables   .60   .40
    Nos. C341-C344 (4)   1.75 1.20

1981, Oct. 16   Litho.   Perf. 13½
C345 AP108 10c Fruits   .45   .25
C346 AP108 50c Vegetables   1.10 1.00

5th Natl.
Games
AP109

1981, Dec. 5   Litho.   Perf. 13½
C347 AP109 10c Javelin, vert.   .30   .25
C348 AP109 50c Cycling   1.50 1.50

Orchids
AP110

1981, Dec. 14
C349 AP110 7c Encyclia
              cochleata   .55   .20
C350 AP110 10c Broughtonia
              domingensis   .75   .25
C351 AP110 25c Encyclia trun-
              cata   1.10   .55
C352 AP110 75c Elleanthus
              capitatus   2.50 1.50
    Nos. C349-C352 (4)   4.90 2.50

Christmas Type
1981, Dec. 23
C353 A294 10c Dove, sun   .50   .30

Battle of
Tortuguero
Anniv.
AP111

1982, Apr. 15   Litho.   Perf. 13½
C354 AP111 10c Naval Academy,
              cadets   .30   .25

1982 World Cup
Soccer — AP112

American Air
Forces
Cooperation
System — AP113

Designs: Various soccer players.
1982, Apr. 19
C355 AP112 10c multicolored   .40   .30
C356 AP112 21c multicolored   .40   .25
C357 AP112 33c multicolored   .75   .75
    Nos. C355-C357 (3)   1.55 1.30

1982, Apr. 12   Perf. 12
C358 AP113 10c multicolored   .30   .25

Scouting
Year
AP114

1982, Apr. 30   Litho.   Perf. 13½
C359 AP114 10c Baden-Powell,
              vert.   .25   .20
C360 AP114 15c Globe   .35   .25
C361 AP114 25c Baden-Powell,
              scout, vert.   .50   .30
    Nos. C359-C361 (3)   1.10   .75

Dancers — AP115

Espamer '82
Emblem — AP116

1982, June 1   Litho.   Perf. 13½
C362 AP115 7c Emblem   .20   .20
C363 AP115 10c Cathedral, Ca-
              sa del Tos-
              tado, Santo
              Domingo   .25   .20
C364 AP115 33c shown   .85   .85
    Nos. C362-C364 (3)   1.30 1.25

Tourist Org. of the Americas, 25th Congress
(COTAL '82), Santo Domingo.

1982, July 5
    Espamer '82 Intl. Stamp Exhibition, San
Juan, Oct. 12-17: Symbolic stamps.
C365 AP116 7c multi   .20   .20
C366 AP116 13c multi, horiz.   .30   .25
C367 AP116 50c multi, horiz.   1.40 1.10
    Nos. C365-C367 (3)   1.90 1.55

Sports Type
1982, Aug. 13   Perf. 12, Imperf.
C368 A300 10c Basketball   .30   .20
C369 A300 13c Boxing   .50   .25
C370 A300 25c Gymnast   .65   .30
    Nos. C368-C370 (3)   1.45   .75

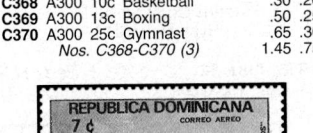

Harbor, by Alejandro Bonilla — AP117

Paintings: 10c, Portrait of a Woman, by Leopoldo Navarro. 45c, Amelia Francasci, by Luis
Desangles. 2p, Portrait, by Abelardo Rodriguez Urdaneta. 10c, 45c, 2p vert.

1982, Aug. 20   Perf. 13, Imperf.
C371 AP117 7c multicolored   .25   .20
C372 AP117 10c multicolored   .30   .25
C373 AP117 45c multicolored   1.50 1.00
C374 AP117 2p multicolored   6.75 4.00
    Nos. C371-C374 (4)   8.80 5.45

San Pedro de Macoris Type
1982, Aug. 26
    Size: 42x29mm
C375 A301 7c Lake   .40   .30

35th
Anniv.
of
Central
Bank
AP118

1982, Oct. 22   Litho.   Perf. 13½x13
C376 AP118 10c multicolored   .50   .35

490th
Anniv. of
Discovery
of America
AP119

1982, Oct. 7   Litho.   Perf. 13½
C377 AP119 7c Map   1.00   .80
C378 AP119 10c Santa Maria,
              vert.   1.25   .90
C379 AP119 21c Columbus, vert.   1.50   .90
    Nos. C377-C379 (3)   3.75 2.60

Christmas Type
1982, Dec. 8
C380 A303 10c multicolored   .50   .35

French Alliance
Centenary
AP120

1983, Mar. 31   Litho.   Perf. 13½
C381 AP120 33c multicolored   .50   .45

Battle of
Tortuguero
Anniv.
AP121

1983, Apr. 15   Litho.   Perf. 13½
C382 AP121 15c Frigate Mella-451 .60   .25

World
Communications
Year — AP122

1983, May 6   Litho.   Perf. 13½
C383 AP122 10c dk blue & blue   .30   .25

AP123

AP124

1983, July 5   Litho.   Perf. 13½
C384 AP123 9c multicolored   .50   .35

Simon Bolivar (1783-1830).

1983, Aug. 22   Litho.   Perf. 12
C385 AP124 7c Gymnast, bas-
              ketball   .35   .20
C386 AP124 10c Highjump, box-
              ing   .45   .20
C387 AP124 15c Baseball,
              weight lifting,
              bicycling   .55   .25
    Nos. C385-C387 (3)   1.35   .65

9th Pan American Games, Caracas, Aug.
13-28.

491st
Anniv. of
Discovery
of America
AP125

1983, Oct. 11   Litho.   Perf. 13½
C388 AP125 10c Columbus'
              ships, map   1.10   .35
C389 AP125 21c Santa Maria
              (trophy)   1.60   .55
C390 AP125 33c Yacht
              Sotavento,
              vert.   1.75   .60
    Nos. C388-C390 (3)   4.45 1.50
    Size: 103x103mm
    Imperf
C391 AP125 50c Ship models   15.00 15.00

10th Anniv. of Latin American Civil
Aviation Commission — AP126

1983, Dec. 7
C392 AP126 10c dark blue   .50   .35

Funeral Procession, by Juan Bautista
Gomez — AP127

Designs: 15c, Meeting of Maximo Gomez
and Jose Marti in Guayubin, by Enrique Garcia Godoy. 21c, St. Francis, by Angel
Perdomo, vert. 33c, Portrait of a Girl, by Adri-
ana Billini, vert.

1983, Dec. 26   Perf. 13½
C393 AP127 10c multicolored   .35   .20
C394 AP127 15c multicolored   .35   .20
C395 AP127 21c multicolored   .45   .25
C396 AP127 33c multicolored   .70   .25
    Nos. C393-C396 (4)   1.85   .90

Christmas
1983 — AP128

1983, Dec. 13　Litho.　Perf. 13½
C397　AP128　10c Bells, orna-
　　　　　　ments　　　　　　　　.30　.20

AIR POST SEMI-POSTAL STAMPS

> Catalogue values for unused
> stamps in this section are for
> Never Hinged items.

**Nos. C97-C99 Surcharged in Red like
Nos. B1-B5**

Engraved and Lithographed
1957, Feb. 8　Unwmk.　Perf. 11½
Flags in National Colors
CB1　A117　11c + 2c ultra & red
　　　　　　org　　　　　　　　.30　.30
CB2　A117　16c + 2c car & lt grn　.40　.40
CB3　A117　17c + 2c blk, vio & red　.40　.40
　　　Nos. CB1-CB3 (3)　　　1.10　1.10

The surtax was to aid Hungarian refugees.
A similar 25c surcharge was applied to the
souvenir sheets described in the footnote following No. C99. Value, 2 sheets, perf. and
imperf., $17.50.

**Nos. C100-C102 Surcharged in Red
Orange like Nos. B6-B10**

1957, Sept. 9　Photo.　Perf. 13½
Flags in National Colors
CB4　A118　11c + 2c yel grn & dk
　　　　　　bl　　　　　　　　.50　.45
CB5　A118　16c + 2c lilac & dk bl　.60　.60
CB6　A118　17c + 2c brn & bl grn　.65　.65
　　　Nos. CB4-CB6 (3)　　　1.75　1.70

See note after No. B10.
A similar 5c surcharge was applied to the
miniature sheets described in the footnote following No. 483. Value, 4 sheets, perf. &
imperf., medal and flag, $40.

**Types of Olympic Air Post Stamps,
1957, Surcharged in Carmine like Nos.
B11-B20**

1958, May 26　　Engr. & Litho.
Flags in National Colors
Pink Paper
CB7　A119(a)　11c + 2c ultra　.30　.30
CB8　A119(b)　11c + 2c ultra　.30　.30
CB9　A120(a)　16c + 2c rose car　.35　.35
CB10　A120(b)　16c + 2c rose car　.35　.35
CB11　A119(a)　17c + 2c claret　.40　.40
CB12　A119(b)　17c + 2c claret　.40　.40
　　　Nos. CB7-CB12 (6)　　2.10　2.10

A similar 5c surcharge, plus marginal UN
emblem and "UNRWA," was applied to the
miniature sheets described in the footnote following No. C105. Value, 4 sheets, perf. and
imperf., $20.

**Nos. C106-C108 Surcharged like Nos.
B21-B25**

1959, Apr. 13　Photo.　Perf. 13½
Flags in National Colors
CB13　A125　11c + 2c blue, ol &
　　　　　　brn　　　　　　　.50　.50
CB14　A125　16c + 2c lt grn, org &
　　　　　　dk bl　　　　　.70　.70
CB15　A125　17c + 2c ver bl & yel　1.00　1.00
　　　Nos. CB13-CB15 (3)　　2.20　2.20

A similar 5c surcharge was applied to the
miniature sheets described in the footnote following No. C108. Value, 2 sheets, perf. and
imperf., $25.

**Type of Regular Issue 1957
Surcharged in Red like Nos. B26-B30**
Engraved and Lithographed
1959, Sept. 10　　　　Imperf.
Flags in National Colors
CB16　A117　11c + 2c ultra & red
　　　　　　org　　　　　　　.45　.45
CB17　A117　16c + 2c carmine & lt
　　　　　　grn　　　　　　　.50　.50

CB18　A117　17c + 2c black, vio &
　　　　　　red　　　　　　　.55　.55
　　　Nos. CB16-CB18 (3)　　1.50　1.50

**Nos. C113-C114 Surcharged in Red
like Nos. B31-B33**
1960, Apr. 7　Litho.　Perf. 12½
CB19　AP43　10c + 5c plum, gray &
　　　　　　grn　　　　　　　.30　.30
CB20　AP43　13c + 5c gray & green　.45　.45

World Refugee Year.
For souvenir sheets see note after No. B33.

**Nos. C115-C117 Surcharged: "XV
ANIVERSARIO DE LA UNESCO + 2c"**
**　　　　　　Perf. 13½**
1962, Jan. 8　Unwmk.　Photo.
Flags in National Colors
CB21　A136　11c + 2c blue, gray &
　　　　　　brn　　　　　　.25　.25
CB22　A136　16c + 2c red, brn & ol　.30　.30
CB23　A136　17c + 2c blk, bl & ocher　.30　.30
　　　Nos. CB21-CB23 (3)　　.85　.85

See note after No. B38.
A similar 5c surcharge was applied to the
miniature sheets described in the footnote following No. C117. Value, 2 sheets, perf. and
imperf., $7.50.

Anti-Malaria Type of 1962
1962, Apr. 29　Litho.　Perf. 12
CB24　A141　13c + 2c pink & red　.30　.25
CB25　A141　33c + 2c org & dp org　.60　.40

Souvenir sheets exist, perf. and imperf. con-
taining one each of Nos. B39-B40, CB24-
CB25 and a 25c+2c pale grn and yel grn.
Value, 2 sheets, perf. and imperf., $7.50.

**Nos. C132-C133 Surcharged like Nos.
B44-B46**
1964, Mar. 8
CB26　AP46　10c + 2c brt violet　.25　.20
CB27　AP46　13c + 2c yellow　.25　.20

**Nos. C146-C148 Surcharged like Nos.
B47-B51**
1966, Dec. 9　Litho.　Perf. 12½
Size: 35x24mm
CB28　A164　10c + 5c multi　1.60　.60
CB29　A164　50c + 10c multi　2.50　2.10
CB30　A164　75c + 10c multi　3.50　2.75
　　　Nos. CB28-CB30 (3)　7.60　5.45

AIR POST OFFICIAL STAMPS

**Nos. O13-O14
Overprinted in Blue**

　　　　　　Unwmk.
1930, Dec. 3　Typo.　Perf. 12
CO1　O3　10c light blue　11.50　12.00
　　a.　Pair, one without ovpt.　900.00
CO2　O3　20c orange　11.50　12.00

SPECIAL DELIVERY STAMPS

Biplane
SD1

**　　　　　　Perf. 11½**
1920, Apr.　Unwmk.　Litho.
E1　SD1　10c deep ultra　5.50　1.25
　　a.　Imperf., pair

Special Delivery Messenger — SD2

1925
E2　SD2　10c dark blue　16.00　4.50

SD3

1927
E3　SD3　10c red brown　5.00　1.25
　　a.　"E EXPRESO" at top　55.00　55.00

Type of 1927
1941　　　　　　Redrawn
E4　SD3　10c yellow green　2.75　3.00
E5　SD3　10c dark blue green　2.40　.60
The redrawn design differs slightly from SD3.
Issue dates: No. E4, Mar. 27; No. E5, Aug.
7.

Emblem of Communications — SD4

1945, Sept. 1　　　　Perf. 12
E6　SD4　10c rose car, car & dk
　　　　　　bl　　　　　　.90　.20

> Catalogue values for unused
> stamps in this section, from this
> point to the end of the section, are
> for Never Hinged items.

SD5

1950　　　Litho.　　Unwmk.
E7　SD5　10c multicolored　.50　.20
　　　　　Exists imperf.

Modern Communications
System — SD6

1956, Aug. 18　　　Perf. 11½
E8　SD6　25c green　1.00　.30

Carrier
Pigeon
SD7

1967　　　Litho.　　Perf. 11½
E9　SD7　25c light blue　.55　.25

Carrier Pigeon,
Globe — SD8

Messenger,
Plane — SD9

1978, Aug. 2　Litho.　Perf. 13½
E10　SD8　25c multicolored　.75　.30
1979, Nov. 30　　　Perf. 13½
E11　SD9　25c multicolored　.45　.25

Motorcycling — SD10

1989, May　Litho.　Perf. 13½
E12　SD10　1p multicolored　2.50　1.10

Postman
SD11

1999　　Litho.　Perf. 13½x13¼
E13　SD11　8p multicolored　2.75　2.75

INSURED LETTER STAMPS

Merino Issue of
1933 Surcharged
in Red or Black

1935, Feb. 1　Unwmk.　Perf. 14
G1　A35　8c on 7c ultra　.60　.20
　　a.　Inverted surcharge　18.00
G2　A35　15c on 10c org yel　.65　.20
　　a.　Inverted surcharge　18.00
G3　A35　30c on 8c dk green　1.75　.90
G4　A35　45c on 20c car rose
　　　　　(Bk)　　　　　3.00　1.00
G5　A36　70c on 50c lemon　6.00　1.25
　　　Nos. G1-G5 (5)　　12.00　3.55

Merino Issue of
1933 Surcharged
in Red

1940
G6　A35　8c on ½c lt vio　2.00　2.00
G7　A35　8c on 7c ultra　3.25　3.25

Coat of
Arms — IL1

1940-45   Litho.   Perf. 11½
Arms in Black

G8	IL1	8c brown red	.60	.25
a.		8c dk red, no shading on inner frame	1.00	1.00
G9	IL1	15c dp orange ('45)	1.25	.20
G10	IL1	30c dk green ('41)	1.50	.20
a.		30c yellow green	1.50	
G11	IL1	45c ultra ('44)	1.50	.30
G12	IL1	70c olive brn ('44)	1.75	.30
		Nos. G8-G12 (5)	6.60	1.25

See Nos. G13-G16, G24-G27.

> **Catalogue values for unused stamps in this section, from this point to the end of the section, are for Never Hinged items.**

Redrawn Type of 1940-45

1952-53
Arms in Black

G13	IL1	8c car lake ('53)	2.40	.50
G14	IL1	15c red orange ('53)	1.75	.75
G15	IL1	70c dp brown car	5.25	1.50
		Nos. G13-G15 (3)	9.40	2.75

Larger and bolder numerals on 8c and 15c. Smaller and bolder "70." There are many other minor differences in the design.

Type of 1940-45

1954
Arms in Black, 15x16mm

G16	IL1	10c carmine	.75	.25

Coat of
Arms — IL2

1955-69 Unwmk. Litho. Perf. 11½
Arms in Black, 13½x11½mm

G17	IL2	10c carmine rose	.35	.20
G18	IL2	15c red orange ('56)	3.75	1.50
G19	IL2	20c red orange ('58)	.90	.30
a.		20c orange ('69)	.90	.30
b.		20c orange, retouched ('69)	3.50	1.25
G20	IL2	30c dark green ('55)	1.40	.30
G21	IL2	40c dark green ('58)	1.50	.90
a.		40c lt yellow grn ('62)	1.50	.45
G22	IL2	45c ultra ('56)	4.00	3.75
G23	IL2	70c dp brn car ('56)	5.00	2.00
		Nos. G17-G23 (7)	16.90	8.95

On No. G19b the horizontal shading lines of shield are omitted.
See Nos. G28-G37.

Type of 1940-45
Second Redrawing

1963   **Perf. 12½**
Arms in Black, 17x16mm

G24	IL1	10c red orange	1.25	.30
G25	IL1	20c orange	1.50	.50

Third Redrawing

1966   **Litho.   Perf. 12½**
Arms in Black, 14x14mm

G26	IL1	10c violet	.40	.20
G27	IL1	40c orange	1.50	1.00

Type of 1955-62

1968   **Litho.   Perf. 11½**
Arms in Black, 13½x11½mm

G28	IL2	20c red	2.00	.75
G29	IL2	60c yellow	1.50	1.50

1973-76   **Litho.   Perf. 12½**
Arms in Black, 11x11mm

G30	IL2	10c car rose ('76)	.50	.35
G31	IL2	20c yellow	1.40	.90
G32	IL2	20c orange ('76)	1.75	.50
G33	IL2	40c yel grn	1.60	1.00
a.		40c green ('76)	3.00	3.00
G34	IL2	70c blue	1.75	1.90
		Nos. G30-G34 (5)	4.65	

1973   **Perf. 11½**
Arms in Black, 13½x11½mm

G35	IL2	10c dark violet	.90	.30

1978, Aug. 9   **Perf. 10½**
Arms in Black, 11x11mm

G36	IL2	10c rose magenta	.35	.20
G37	IL2	40c bright green	1.50	1.50

IL3

1982-83   **Litho.   Perf. 10½**
Arms in Black

G38	IL3	10c deep magenta	.20	.20
G39	IL3	20c deep orange	.35	.30
G40	IL3	40c bluish green	.75	.50
		Nos. G38-G40 (3)	1.30	1.00

IL4

1986   **Litho.   Perf. 10½**
Arms in Black

G41	IL4	20c brt rose lilac	.30	.25
G42	IL4	60c orange	1.00	.70
G43	IL4	1p light blue	1.60	1.10
G44	IL4	1.25p pink	2.10	1.40
G45	IL4	1.50p vermilion	2.50	1.50
G46	IL4	3p light green	5.00	3.25
G47	IL4	3.50p olive bister	6.00	3.75
G48	IL4	4p yellow	6.75	4.50
G49	IL4	4.50p lt blue grn	7.50	5.00
G50	IL4	5p brown olive	8.25	5.50
G51	IL4	6p gray	9.75	6.75
G52	IL4	6.50p lt ultra	11.00	7.50
		Nos. G41-G52 (12)	61.75	41.20

Issue dates: Nos. G42-G43, G45, July 16. Nos. G46-G52, Sept. 2. Nos. G41, G44, Nov. 6.

Coat of
Arms — IL5

1989-90   **Litho.   Perf. 13½**
Arms in Black

G53	IL5	20c brt lilac rose	.25	.20
G54	IL5	60c orange ('90)	.75	.45
G55	IL5	1p sky blue	1.25	.75
G56	IL5	1.25p lt salmon pink	1.50	.90
G57	IL5	1.50p dark red	1.90	1.10
		Nos. G53-G57 (5)	5.65	3.40

"RD$" in lower left square on Nos. G55-G57.

IL6

1994, Oct.   Litho.   Perf. 13½
Arms in Black

G58	IL6	50c lilac rose	.20	.20
G59	IL6	1p sky blue	.25	.25
G60	IL6	1.50p red	.30	.30
G61	IL6	2p pink	.50	.50
G62	IL6	3p violet blue	.60	.60
G63	IL6	5p yellow	.90	.90
G64	IL6	6p apple green	1.25	1.25
G65	IL6	8p green	1.40	1.40
G66	IL6	10p silver gray	1.90	1.90
		Nos. G58-G66 (9)	7.30	7.30

POSTAGE DUE STAMPS

D1

1901   Unwmk.   Typo.   Perf. 14

J1	D1	2c olive gray	.70	.20
J2	D1	4c olive gray	.90	.20
J3	D1	5c olive gray	1.50	.30
J4	D1	10c olive gray	2.75	.75
		Nos. J1-J4 (4)	5.85	1.45

For surcharges and overprint see Nos. 162-165, 169-171.

1909   **Wmk. 116**

J5	D1	2c olive gray	1.50	.50
J6	D1	4c olive gray	1.50	.50
J7	D1	6c olive gray	2.00	.75
J8	D1	10c olive gray	4.00	2.50
		Nos. J5-J8 (4)	9.00	4.25

1913

J9	D1	2c olive green	.45	.20
J10	D1	4c olive green	.50	.20
J11	D1	6c olive green	.80	.35
J12	D1	10c olive green	.90	.40
		Nos. J9-J12 (4)	2.65	1.15

1922   Unwmk.   Litho.   Perf. 11½

J13	D1	1c olive green	.55	.55

> **Catalogue values for unused stamps in this section, from this point to the end of the section, are for Never Hinged items.**

D2

D3

1942

J14	D2	1c dk red & pale pink	.25	.20
J15	D2	2c dk bl & pale bl	.25	.20
J16	D2	4c dk grn & pale grn	.25	.25
J17	D2	6c green & buff	.35	.25
J18	D2	8c yel org & pale yel	.35	.30
J19	D2	10c mag & pale pink	.45	.40
		Nos. J14-J19 (6)	1.90	1.60

1955
Size: 20½x25mm

J20	D2	2c dark blue	1.40	1.00

1959   Litho.   Perf. 11½
Size: 21x25½mm

J21	D3	1c dark car rose	1.25	1.25
J22	D3	2c dark blue	1.25	1.25
J23	D3	4c green	3.00	3.00
		Nos. J21-J23 (3)	5.50	5.50

OFFICIAL STAMPS

Bastion of
February 27
O1

Unwmk.
1902, Feb. 25   Litho.   Perf. 12

O1	O1	2c scarlet & blk	.50	.30
O2	O1	5c dk blue & blk	.65	.25
O3	O1	10c yel grn & blk	.75	.45
O4	O1	20c yellow & blk	1.00	.40
a.		Imperf., pair	10.00	
		Nos. O1-O4 (4)	2.90	1.40

For overprints and surcharge see Nos. 157-161.

Bastion of Feb. 27
O2

Columbus
Lighthouse
O3

Perf. 13½x13, 13½x14
1909-12   Wmk. 116   Typo.

O5	O2	1c blue grn & blk	.30	.20
O6	O2	2c scarlet & blk	.35	.20
O7	O2	5c dk blue & blk	.75	.30
O8	O2	10c yel grn & blk ('12)	1.10	.70
O9	O2	20c orange & blk ('12)	2.00	1.60
		Nos. O5-O9 (5)	4.50	3.00

The 2c, 5c are found in both perforations; 1c, 20c perf. 13½x13; 10c perf. 13½x14.
For overprints and surcharge see Nos. 177, 194-199.

1928   Unwmk.   Perf. 12

O10	O3	1c green	.20	.20
O11	O3	2c red	.20	.20
O12	O3	5c ultramarine	.25	.25
O13	O3	10c light blue	.30	.30
O14	O3	20c orange	.45	.45
		Nos. O10-O14 (5)	1.40	1.40

For overprints see Nos. CO1-CO2.

Proposed
Columbus
Lighthouse
O4

1937   Litho.   Perf. 11½

O15	O4	3c dark purple	.85	.20
O16	O4	7c indigo & blue	.90	.30
O17	O4	10c orange yellow	1.00	.45
		Nos. O15-O17 (3)	2.75	.95

Proposed
Columbus
Lighthouse
O5

1939-41

O18	O5	1c dp grn & lt grn	.35	.20
O19	O5	2c crim & pale pink	.35	.20
O20	O5	3c purple & lt vio	.35	.20
O21	O5	5c dk bl & lt bl ('40)	.60	.30
O21A	O5	5c lt blue ('41)	1.50	1.00
O22	O5	7c brt bl & lt bl ('41)	1.10	.20
O23	O5	10c yel org & pale org ('41)	1.10	.35
O24	O5	20c brn org & buff ('41)	3.00	.50
O25	O5	50c brt red lil & pale lil ('41)	3.50	1.50
		Nos. O18-O25 (9)	11.85	4.45

> **Catalogue values for unused stamps in this section, from this point to the end of the section, are for Never Hinged items.**

Type of 1939

1950   Redrawn

O26	O5	50c dp car & rose	6.25	1.25

The numerals "50" measure 3mm, and are close to left and right frames; numerals measure 4mm on No. O25. There are other minor differences.

Denominations in "Centavos Oro"

1950

O27	O5	5c light blue	.55	.20
O28	O5	10c yel & pale yel	.65	.30
O29	O5	20c dl org brn & buff	.70	.50
		Nos. O27-O29 (3)	1.90	1.00

Letters of top inscription are 1½mm high.

Type of 1939-41
Second Redrawing
Denominations in "Centavos Oro"

1956	Unwmk.		Perf. 11½
O30	O5	7c blue & lt blue	.50 .50
O31	O5	20c yellow brn & buff	1.25 1.25
O32	O5	50c red lil & brt pink	3.25 3.25
		Nos. O30-O32 (3)	5.00 5.00

The letters of top inscription are 2mm high, the trees at base of monument have been redrawn, etc. On No. O32 the numerals are similar to No. O26.

POSTAL TAX STAMPS

Santo Domingo after Hurricane PT1

Hurricane's Effect on Capital PT2

1930, Dec.	Unwmk.	Litho.	Perf. 12
RA1	PT1	1c green & rose	.20 .20
RA2	PT1	2c red rose	.20 .20
RA3	PT2	5c ultra & rose	.30 .30
RA4	PT2	10c yellow & rose	.35 .30

Imperf

RA5	PT1	1c green & rose	.40 .30
RA6	PT1	2c red rose	.50 .30
RA7	PT2	5c ultra & rose	.60 .50
RA8	PT2	10c yellow & rose	.90 .75
		Nos. RA1-RA8 (8)	3.45 2.75

For surcharges see Nos. RAC1-RAC7.

Tête bêche Pairs

RA1a	PT1	1c green & rose	1.75 1.75
RA2a	PT1	2c red rose	1.75 1.50
RA3a	PT1	5c ultra & rose	1.75 2.10
RA4a	PT1	10c yellow & rose	2.10 2.10
RA5a	PT1	1c green & rose	1.75 1.75
RA6a	PT1	2c red & rose	1.75 1.75
RA7a	PT1	5c ultra & rose	2.10 2.10
RA8a	PT1	10c yellow & rose	2.10 2.10
		Nos. RA1a-RA8a (8)	15.05 15.15

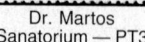

Dr. Martos Sanatorium — PT3

Nurse and Child — PT4

1944, Apr. 1	Litho.	Perf. 11½
RA9	PT3	1c dp bl, sl bl & red	.30 .25

1947, Apr. 1		Unwmk.
RA10	PT4	1c dp bl, pale bl & car	.45 .25

Sanatorium of the Holy Help — PT5

1949, Apr. 1
RA11 PT5 1c dp bl, pale bl & car   .35 .25

Youth Holding Banner PT6

"Suffer Little Children to Come Unto Me" PT7

1950, Apr. 1   **Perf. 11½**
RA12 PT6 1c dp bl, pale bl & car   .25 .25

1950, Dec. 1   **Perf. 12**
Size: 22½x32mm
RA13 PT7 1c lt bl & pale bl   .60 .25
    b.   Perf. 12½ ('52)   3.00 .25

Vertical line centering side borders merges into dots toward the bottom. See Nos. RA13A, RA17, RA19, RA26, RA32, RA35.
The tax was for child welfare.

1951, Dec. 1   **Redrawn**
RA13A PT7 1c lt blue & pale blue   3.00 .25

In the redrawn stamp, the standing child, a blonde in No. RA13, is changed to a brunette; more foliage has been added above child's head and to branches showing in upper right corner. Vertical dashes in side borders.

Tuberculosis Sanatorium, Santiago — PT8

1952, Apr. 1   **Litho.**   **Perf. 11½**
RA14 PT8 1c lt blue & car   .25 .25

Sword, Serpent and Crab — PT9

1953, Feb. 1   **Unwmk.**   **Perf. 12.**
RA15 PT9 1c carmine   .35 .25

The tax was for the Dominican League Against Cancer. See Nos. RA18, RA21, RA43, RA46, RA51, RA56, RA61, RA67, RA72, RA76, RA82, RA88, RA93, RA96.

Tuberculosis Dispensary for Children — PT10

1953, Apr. 1   **Litho.**   **Perf. 12½**
RA16 PT10 1c dp bl, pale bl & red   .25 .25
    See No. RA22.

Jesus Type of 1950
Second Redrawing
1953, Dec. 1   **Perf. 11½**
Size: 22x31mm
RA17 PT7 1c blue   .35 .20

Solid shading in sky reduced to a few scattered dots. Girl's left arm indicated. Rough white dots in side borders.

Cancer Type of 1952
1954, Oct. 1   **Redrawn**   **Perf. 12½**
RA18 PT9 1c rose carmine   .25 .20
    a.   1c red orange ('58)   .30 .20
    b.   1c carmine ('70)   1.25 .20

Upper right serif of numeral "1" eliminated; diagonal line added through "C" and period removed; sword extended, placing top on a

---

line with top of "1." Dots of background screen arranged diagonally. Many other differences.
The tax was for the Dominican League Against Cancer. No. RA18a exists imperf.
On No. RA18b background screen eliminates white outline of crab.

Jesus Type of 1950
1954, Dec. 1   **Third Redrawing**
Size: 23x32¾mm
RA19 PT7 1c bright blue   .25 .20
    a.   1c pale blue ('59)   .20 .20

Center completely screened. Tiny white horizontal rectangles in side borders.

> Catalogue values for unused stamps in this section, from this point to the end of the section, are for Never Hinged items.

Lorraine Cross as Bell Clapper — PT11

1955, Apr. 1   **Litho.**   **Perf. 11½x12**
RA20 PT11 1c black, yel & red   .30 .25

Cancer Type of 1952
Second Redrawing
1956, Oct. 1   **Perf. 12½**
RA21 PT9 1c carmine   .35 .20
    a.   1c red orange ('64)   1.00 .50

Similar to No. RA18, but dots of background screen arranged in vertical and horizontal rows. Outlines of central device, lettering and frame clearly delineated. "C" of cent-sign smaller. Upper claw in solid color.

TB Dispensary Type of 1953
Redrawn
1954, Apr. 1
RA22 PT10 1c blue & red   .70 .25
    a.   Red (cross) omitted   55.00

No. RA22 has third color omitted; clouds added; bolder letters and numerals.

Angelita Trujillo PT12   Lorraine Cross PT13

1955, Dec. 1   **Unwmk.**   **Perf. 12½**
RA23 PT12 1c violet   .60 .25
    The tax was for child welfare.

1956, Apr. 1   **Litho.**   **Perf. 11½**
RA24 PT13 1c blk, grn, lem & red   .30 .25

The tax was for the Anti-Tuberculosis League. Inscribed: B.C.G. (Bacillus Calmette-Guerin).

PT14   PT15

1957, Apr. 1
RA25 PT14 1c red, blk, yel, grn & bl .30 .25

Jesus Type of 1950
Fourth Redrawing
1956, Dec. 1   **Unwmk.**   **Perf. 12**
Size: 21¾x31¼mm
RA26 PT7 1c blue   .30 .20

Thin white lines around numeral boxes. Girl's bouquet touches Jesus' sleeve. Tiny white squares or rectangles in side borders. Foliage at either side of "Era de Trujillo" panel.

1958, Apr. 1   **Litho.**   **Perf. 12½**
RA27 PT15 1c brown car & red   .25 .20

Inscribed "1959"
1959, Apr. 1
RA28 PT15 1c brown car & red   .25 .20

PT16

PT17

1960, Apr. 1   **Litho.**   **Perf. 12**
RA29 PT16 1c bl, pale yel & red   .30 .25

1961, Apr. 1   **Unwmk.**   **Perf. 11½**
RA30 PT17 1c blue & red   .25 .20

Nos. RA29-RA30: tax was for the Anti-Tuberculosis League.
See No. RA33.

Maria de los Angeles M. de Trujillo and Housing Project PT18

1961, Aug. 1   **Litho.**   **Perf. 12**
RA31 PT18 1c carmine rose   .30 .25

The tax was for aid to the needy.
Nos. RA31-RA33 exist imperf.

Jesus Type of 1950
Fifth Redrawing
1961, Dec. 1   **Unwmk.**   **Perf. 12½**
RA32 PT7 1c blue   .30 .25

No. RA32 is similar to No. RA19, but "Era de Trujillo" has been replaced by a solid color panel.

Type of 1961 Dated "1962"
1962, Apr. 2   **Perf. 12½**
RA33 PT17 1c blue & red   .60 .25

Tax for the Anti-Tuberculosis League.

Man's Chest PT19   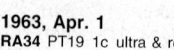 Hibiscus PT20

1963, Apr. 1   **Perf. 12x11½**
RA34 PT19 1c ultra & red   .30 .25

Jesus Type of 1950
Sixth Redrawing

1963, Dec. 1   *Perf. 11½*
Size: 21¾x32mm

RA35 PT7 1c blue   .30 .25
  a.   1c deep blue ('64)   .30 .25

No. RA35 is similar to No. RA26, but "Era de Trujillo" panel has been omitted.

1966, Apr. 1   Litho.   *Perf. 11½*
RA36 PT20 1c emerald & car   .25 .20

Tax for the Anti-Tuberculosis League.

Domingoa
Nodosa — PT21

Civil Defense
Emblem — PT22

1967, Apr. 1   Litho.   *Perf. 12½*
RA37 PT21 1c lilac & red   .75 .25

Tax for the Anti-Tuberculosis League.

1967, July 1   Litho.   *Rouletted 13*
RA38 PT22 1c multicolored   .25 .20

Tax for the Civil Defense Organization.

Boy, School and
Yule Bells — PT23

Hand Holding
Invalid — PT24

1967, Dec. 1   Litho.   *Perf. 12½*
RA39 PT23 1c rose red & pink   .35 .25

1968   *Perf. 11*
RA40 PT23 1c vermilion   .30 .20

No. RA40 has screened background; No. RA39, smooth background.
The tax was for child welfare.
See Nos. RA49A, RA52, RA57, RA62, RA68, RA73, RA77, RA81.

1968, Mar. 19   Litho.   *Perf. 12½*
RA41 PT24 1c green & yellow   .25 .20
  a.   1c olive green & deep yellow,
     perf. 11½x12 ('69)   .25 .20

The tax was for the rehabilitation of the handicapped. See Nos. RA47, RA50, RA54.

Dogbane
PT25

Schoolyard,
Torch
PT26

1968, Apr. 25   Litho.   *Perf. 12½*
RA42 PT25 1c emerald, yel & red   .25 .20

The tax was for the Anti-Tuberculosis League. See Nos. RA45, RA49.

Redrawn Cancer Type of 1955
1968, Oct. 1   Litho.   *Perf. 12*
RA43 PT9 1c emerald   .25 .20

The tax was for the Dominican League against Cancer.

1969, Feb. 1   Litho.   *Perf. 12½*
RA44 PT26 1c light blue   .30 .25

Issued for Education Year 1969.

Flower Type of 1968
Design: No. RA45, Violets.

1969, Apr. 25   Litho.   *Perf. 12½*
RA45 PT25 1c emerald, lil & red   .45 .25

Tax for the Anti-Tuberculosis League.

Redrawn Cancer Type of 1955
1969, Oct. 1   Litho.   *Perf. 11*
RA46 PT9 1c brt rose lilac   .25 .20

Tax for Dominican League against Cancer.

Invalid Type of 1968
1970, Mar. 2   *Perf. 12½*
RA47 PT24 1c blue   .25 .20

The tax was for the rehabilitation of the handicapped.

Book, Sun and
Education Year
Emblem
PT27

Communications
Emblem
PT28

1970, Feb. 6   *Perf. 11*
RA48 PT27 1c bright pink   .25 .20

International Education Year.

Flower Type of 1968
Design: 1c, Eleanthus capitatus; cross in upper left corner, denomination in lower right.

1970, Apr. 30   *Perf. 11*
RA49 PT25 1c emerald, red & yel   .75 .25

Tax for Anti-Tuberculosis League.

Boy Type of 1967
1970, Dec. 1   *Perf. 12½*
RA49A PT23 1c orange   .30 .25

1971, Jan. 2   Litho.   *Perf. 11*
Size: 17½x20½mm
RA49B PT28 1c vio bl & red (white
     frame)   .30 .25

Tax was for Postal and Telegraph Communications School.
See Nos. RA53, RA58, RA63, RA69, RA78, RA91.

Invalid Type of 1968
1971, Mar. 1   Litho.   *Perf. 11*
RA50 PT24 1c brt rose lilac   .30 .25

Tax for rehabilitation of the handicapped.

Cancer Type of 1952
Third Redrawing

1971, Oct. 1   *Perf. 11½*
RA51 PT9 1c dp yellow green   .30 .25

Background of No. RA51 appears white and design stands out. No. RA43 has greenish background and design appears faint. Numeral "1" on No. RA51 is 3½mm high, on No. RA43 it is 3mm.

Boy Type of 1967
1971, Dec. 1   Litho.   *Perf. 11*
RA52 PT23 1c green   .30 .25

Communications Type of 1971
1972, Jan. 3   Litho.   *Perf. 12½*
Size: 19x22mm
RA53 PT28 1c dk bl & red (bl
     frame)   .25 .20

Tax was for the Postal and Telegraph Communications School.

Invalid Type of 1968
1972, Mar. 1   Litho.   *Perf. 11½*
RA54 PT24 1c brown   .60 .25

Orchid — PT29

1972, Apr. 2   *Perf. 11*
RA55 PT29 1c lt grn, red & yel   1.10 .30

Tax was for the Anti-Tuberculosis League.

Redrawn Cancer Type of 1954-58
1972, Oct. 2   *Perf. 12½*
RA56 PT9 1c orange   .25 .20

Tax for Dominican League against Cancer.

Boy Type of 1967
1972, Dec. 1   *Perf. 12*
RA57 PT23 1c violet   .25 .20

Tax was for child welfare.

Communications Type of 1971
1973, Jan. 2   *Perf. 10½*
Size: 19x22mm
RA58 PT28 1c dk bl & red (red
     frame)   .25 .20

Tax was for Postal and Telegraph Communications School.

Invalid
PT30

Hibiscus
PT31

1973, Mar. 1   Litho.   *Perf. 12½*
Size: 21x25mm
RA59 PT30 1c olive   .25 .20

Tax was for the Dominican Rehabilitation Association. See Nos. RA66, RA70, RA74, RA79, RA86.

1973, Apr. 17   Litho.   *Perf. 10½*
RA60 PT31 1c multicolored   .75 .25

Tax was for Anti-Tuberculosis League. Exists imperf.

Cancer Type of 1952 Redrawn and "1973" Added
1973, Oct. 1   *Perf. 13½*
RA61 PT9 1c olive green   .30 .25

Tax was for Dominican League Against Cancer.

Boy Type of 1967
1973, Dec. 1   Litho.   *Perf. 13x13½*
RA62 PT23 1c blue   .60 .25

Communications Type of 1971
1973, Nov. 3   *Perf. 10½*
Size: 19x22mm
RA63 PT28 1c bl & red (lt grn
     frame)   .25 .20

Tax was for Postal and Telegraph Communications School. Exists imperf.

Invalid Type of 1973
1974, Mar. 1   Litho.   *Perf. 10½*
Size: 22x27½mm
RA66 PT30 1c light ultra   .30 .25

See note after No. RA59.

Cancer Type of 1952 Redrawn and "1974" Added
1974, Oct. 1   *Perf. 12*
RA67 PT9 1c orange   .30 .25

Tax for Dominican League Against Cancer.

Boy Type of 1967
1974, Dec. 2   Litho.   *Perf. 11½*
RA68 PT23 1c dk brown & buff   .25 .20

Communications Type of 1971
1974, Nov. 13   *Perf. 10½*
RA69 PT28 1c blue & red (yel
     frame)   .25 .20

Invalid Type of 1973 Dated "1975"
1975, Mar. 1   *Perf. 13½x13*
Size: 21x32mm
RA70 PT30 1c olive brown   .30 .25

See note after No. RA59.

Catteeyopsis
Rosea
PT32

Oncidium
Colochilum
PT33

1975, Apr. 1   *Perf. 12*
RA71 PT32 1c blue & multi   1.10 .75

Tax was for Anti-Tuberculosis League.

Cancer Type of 1952 Redrawn and "1975" Added
1975, Oct. 1   Litho.   *Perf. 12*
RA72 PT9 1c violet blue   .30 .25

Tax was for Dominican League Against Cancer. Exists imperf.

Boy Type of 1967
1975, Dec. 1   Litho.   *Perf. 12*
RA73 PT23 1c red orange   .25 .20

Tax was for child welfare.

Invalid Type of 1973 Dated "1976"
1976, Mar. 1   Litho.   *Perf. 12*
Size: 21x31mm
RA74 PT30 1c ultra   .30 .25

See note after No. RA59.

1976, Apr. 6   *Perf. 13x13½*
RA75 PT33 1c green & multi   .60 .25

Tax was for Anti-Tuberculosis League. See Nos. RA80, RA84.

Cancer Type of 1952 Redrawn and "1976" Added
1976, Oct. 1   Litho.   *Perf. 13½*
RA76 PT9 1c green   .30 .25

Tax was for Dominican League Against Cancer.

Boy Type of 1967
1976, Dec. 1   Litho.   *Perf. 13½*
RA77 PT23 1c purple   .30 .25

Tax was for child welfare.

Communications Type of 1971
1977, Jan. 7   Litho.   *Perf. 10½*
Size: 19x22mm
RA78 PT28 1c blue & red (lil frame) .25 .20

Tax was for Postal and Telegraph Communications School.

Invalid Type of 1973 Dated "1977"
1977, Mar. 11   *Perf. 12*
Size: 21x31mm
RA79 PT30 1c ultra   .30 .25

See note after No. RA59.

Orchid Type of 1976 Dated "1977"
Orchid: Oncidium variegatum.

1977, Apr. 22   Litho.   *Perf. 13½*
RA80 PT33 1c multicolored   .75 .25

Tax was for Anti-Tuberculosis League.

DOMINICAN REPUBLIC

Boy Type of 1967

1977, Dec. 27　Litho.　Perf. 12
RA81 PT23 1c emerald　　.25 .20

Tax was for child welfare.

Cancer Type of 1952 Redrawn and "1977" Added

1978, Oct. 2　Litho.　Perf. 13½
RA82 PT9 1c lilac rose　　.30 .25

Tax for Dominican League Against Cancer.

Mother, Child, Holly — PT34

University Seal — PT35

1978, Dec. 1　Litho.　Perf. 13½
RA83 PT34 1c green　　.25 .20

Tax was for child welfare.
See Nos. RA89, RA92, RA97.

Orchid Type of 1973 Dated "1978"

Flower: Yellow alder.

1979, Apr.　Litho.　Perf. 13½
RA84 PT33 1c lt blue & multi　　.75 .25

Tax was for Anti-Tuberculosis League.

1979, Feb. 10　Litho.　Perf. 13½
RA85 PT35 2c ultra & gray　　.25 .20

450th anniv. of University of Santo Domingo.

Invalid Type of 1973 Dated "1978"

1979, Mar. 1　Litho.　Perf. 12
RA86 PT30 1c emerald　　.25 .20

See note after No. RA59.

Invalid PT36

Turnera Ulmifolia (Marilope) PT37

1980, Mar. 28　Litho.　Perf. 13½
RA87 PT36 1c olive & citron　　.60 .25

Cancer Type of 1952 Redrawn and "1980" Added

1980, Oct. 1
RA88 PT9 1c violet & dk pur　　.25 .20

Mother and Child Type of 1978

1980, Dec. 1　Litho.　Perf. 13½
RA89 PT34 1c bright blue　　.25 .20

1981, Apr. 27　Litho.　Perf. 12
RA90 PT37 1c multicolored　　.25 .20

Tax was for Anti-Tuberculosis League.
See Nos. RA98-RA99.

Communications Type of 1971

1981, Feb.　Litho.　Perf. 10½
RA91 PT28 1c blue & red (lt bl frame)　　.60 .25

Mother and Child Type of 1978

1982, Dec. 1　Litho.　Perf. 12x12½
RA92 PT34 1c lt bluish green　　.25 .20

Inscribed 1981.

Cancer Type of 1952 Redrawn and "1981" Added

1982　Litho.　Perf. 13½
RA93 PT9 1c blue & dp blue　　.60 .25

PT38

Disabled — PT39

1983, Apr. 29　Litho.　Perf. 12
RA94 PT38 1c multicolored　　.25 .20

Tax was for Red Cross.

1984　Litho.　Perf. 13½
RA95 PT39 1c sky blue　　.25 .20

Cancer Type of 1952 Redrawn and "1983" Added

1983, Oct. 1　Litho.　Perf. 13½
RA96 PT9 1c lt bluish grn & dk grn　　.25 .20

Mother and Child Type of 1978

1983, Dec. 1　Litho.　Perf. 12
RA97 PT34 1c light green　　.25 .20

Inscribed 1983.

Flower Type of 1981 Dated "1983" or "1984"

1983-85　Litho.　Perf. 12x12½
RA98 PT37 1c 1983　　.25 .20
RA99 PT37 1c 1984　　.25 .20

Issued: #RA98, 4/19/83; #RA99, 4/1/85.

POSTAL TAX AIR POST STAMPS

Postal Tax Stamps Surcharged in Red or Gold

1930, Dec. 3　Unwmk.　Perf. 12
RAC1 PT2 5c + 5c blk & rose (R)　　25.00 25.00
　a.　Tête bêche pair　　125.00
　b.　"Habilitado Para" missing　　52.50
RAC2 PT2 10c + 10c blk & rose (R)　　25.00 25.00
　a.　Tête bêche pair　　125.00
　b.　"Habilitado Para" missing　　52.50
　c.　Gold surcharge　　95.00 95.00
　d.　As "c," tête bêche pair　　450.00
　e.　As "c" and "b"　　95.00

Nos. RAC1-RAC2 were on sale one day.

RAC4 PT2 5c + 5c ultra & rose (R)　　6.00 6.00
　a.　Tête bêche pair　　45.00
　b.　Inverted surcharge　　42.50
　c.　Tête bêche pair, inverted surcharge　　600.00
　d.　Pair, one without surcharge　　190.00
　e.　"Habilitado Para" missing　　15.00
RAC5 PT2 10c + 10c yel & rose (G)　　4.50 4.50
　a.　Tête bêche pair　　42.50
　b.　"Habilitado Para" missing　　18.00

Imperf

RAC6 PT2 5c + 5c ultra & rose (R)　　6.00 6.00
　a.　Tête bêche pair　　52.50
　b.　"Habilitado Para" missing　　18.00
RAC7 PT2 10c + 10c yel & rose (G)　　6.00 6.00
　a.　Tête bêche pair　　52.50
　b.　"Habilitado Para" missing　　18.00
Nos. RAC1-RAC7 (6)　　72.50 72.50

It was obligatory to use Nos. RA1-RA8 and RAC1-RAC7 on all postal matter, in amounts equal to the ordinary postage.
This surtax was for the aid of sufferers from the hurricane of Sept. 3, 1930.

No. 261 Overprinted in Green

1933, Oct. 11
RAC8 A32 2c scarlet　　.35 .30
　a.　Double overprint　　9.00
　b.　Pair, one without overprint　　375.00

By official decree, this stamp, in addition to the regular postage, had to be used on every letter, etc., sent by the internal air post service.

DUBAI

ₔdü-'bī

LOCATION — Oman Peninsula, Arabia, on Persian Gulf
GOVT. — Sheikdom under British protection
AREA — 1,500 sq. mi.
POP. — 60,000
CAPITAL — Dubai

Dubai is one of six Persian Gulf sheikdoms to join the United Arab Emirates which proclaimed its independence Dec. 2, 1971. See United Arab Emirates.

100 Naye Paise = 1 Rupee
100 Dirhams = 1 Riyal (1966)

Imperforate
Many issues were accompanied by smaller quantities of imperforate stamps.

Catalogue values for all unused stamps in this country are for Never Hinged items.

Hermit Crab — A1

Sheik Rashid bin Said al Maktum — A2

2np, 20np, Cuttlefish. 3np, 25np, Snail. 4np, 30np, Crab. 5np, 35np, Sea urchin. 10np, 50np, Sea shell. 1r, Fortress wall. 2r, View of Dubai. 3r, Fortress wall. 5r, View of Dubai.

1963, June 15　Litho.			**Unwmk.**	
1	A1	1np dl bl & car rose	.30	.20
2	A1	2np lt bl & bis brn	.35	.20
3	A1	3np green & sepia	.35	.20
4	A1	4np pink & orange	.35	.20
5	A1	5np violet & blk	.35	.20
6	A1	10np brn org & blk	.35	.20
7	A1	15np gray ol & dp car	.70	.35
8	A1	20np rose red & org brn	.75	.40
9	A1	25np ap grn & red brn	.90	.40
10	A1	30np gray & red	1.00	.40
11	A1	35np dl lil & dl vio	1.00	.40
12	A1	50np org & sepia	1.60	.75
13	A1	1r brt bl & red org	3.50	1.25
14	A1	2r dull yel & brn	7.25	3.00
15	A1	3r rose car & blk	13.00	4.50
16	A1	5r grn & dl red brn	22.00	8.50

Perf. 12
17 A2 10r rose lake, grnsh bl & blk　　50.00 17.50
　Nos. 1-17 (17)　　103.75 38.60

Nos. 13-17 exist perf 10½. Values are much higher.

Dhows A3

Designs: 2np, First-aid tent. 3np, Camel caravan. 4np, Butterfly.

1963, Sept. 1　Unwmk.　Perf. 12
18 A3 1np ultra, yel & red　　.70 .35
19 A3 2np brn, yel & red　　.70 .35
20 A3 3np red brn, org & red　　.70 .35
21 A3 4np brn, brt grn & red　　.70 .35
　Nos. 18-21,C9-C12 (8)　　9.90 4.10

Intl. Red Cross, cent. Exist perf. 10½. Values, each $1.75.
Four imperf. souvenir sheets exist in the denominations and designs of Nos. C9-C12, with "Air-Mail" omitted and colors changed. Size: 119x99mm. Value $50.
For overprints see Nos. C52-C54.

A4

A5

Anopheles Mosquito: 2np, Mosquito and entwined snakes. 3np, Mosquitoes over swamp.

1963, Dec. 20　Unwmk.　Perf. 12
22 A4 1np emer & red brn　　.25 .20
23 A4 1np red & dark brn　　.25 .20
24 A4 1np blue & carmine　　.25 .20
25 A4 2np brn & orange　　.25 .20
26 A4 2np carmine & blue　　.25 .20
27 A4 3np org brn & blue　　.25 .20
　Nos. 22-27,C13-C15 (9)　　3.50 2.00

WHO drive to eradicate malaria.

1964　　Unwmk.

Designs: 1np, Scouts forming pyramid. 2np, Bugler. 3np, Cub Scouts. 4np, Scouts and bugler. 5np, Scouts presenting flag.

28 A5 1np dk brn & ocher　　.20 .20
29 A5 2np car rose & sep　　.20 .20
30 A5 3np blue & red org　　.20 .20
31 A5 4np carmine & blue　　.20 .20
32 A5 5np ind & bluish grn　　.35 .20
　Nos. 28-32,C20-C24 (10)　　6.30 2.90

11th Boy Scout Jamboree, Marathon, Greece, Aug., 1963.
For overprints see Nos. C47-C51.

Unisphere, New York Skyline and Dubai Harbor — A6

2np, 4np, 10np, Views of NYC and Dubai.

1964, Apr. 22   Litho.   Perf. 12
33	A6	1np dk bl & rose red	.20	.20
34	A6	2np dl red, lil rose & bl	.20	.20
35	A6	3np brown & green	.20	.20
36	A6	4np emer, brt grn & red	.20	.20
37	A6	5np ol, sl grn & lil	.20	.20
38	A6	10np brn org, red org & blk	.80	.50

Nos. 33-38,C36-C38 (9)   6.45   3.80

New York World's Fair, 1964-65.

Gymnast — A8

Designs: 2np, 5np, 20np, 40np, Various exercises on bar. 3np, 30np, Various exercises on vaulting horse. 4np, 10np, 1r, Various exercises on rings.

1964   Photo.   Perf. 14
43	A8	1np org brn & yel grn	.20	.20
44	A8	2np dk brn & grnsh bl	.20	.20
45	A8	3np ultra & org brn	.20	.20
46	A8	4np dk pur & yel	.25	.20
47	A8	5np ocher & dk bl	.25	.20
48	A8	10np brt bl & ocher	.30	.20
49	A8	20np ol & lil rose	.50	.20
50	A8	30np dk bl & yel	1.00	.25
51	A8	40np Prus grn & dl org	1.75	.50
52	A8	1r rose vio & grnsh bl	4.25	1.25

Nos. 43-52 (10)   8.90   3.40

18th Olympic Games, Tokyo, Oct. 10-25, 1964. An imperf. miniature sheet contains a 67x67mm stamp similar to No. 52. Value $11.

Palace — A9

Sheik Rashid bin Said — A10

Designs: 20np, 25np, View of new Dubai. 35np, 40np, Bridge and dhow. 60np, 1r, Bridge. 1.25r, Minaret. 1.50r, 3r, Old Dubai.

1966, May 30   Photo.   Perf. 14x14½
Size: 23x18mm
53	A9	5np brown & indigo	.20	.20
54	A9	10np black & orange	.20	.20
55	A9	15np ultra & brown	.35	.25

Perf. 13
Size: 27½x20½mm
56	A9	20np blue & red brn	.45	.30
57	A9	25np org ver & ultra	.45	.40
58	A9	35np violet & emer	.70	.50
59	A9	40np grnsh bl & bl	1.10	.50

Perf. 14½
Size: 31½x24mm
60	A9	60np yel grn & org ver	1.60	1.00
61	A9	1r ultra & blue	2.50	1.50
62	A9	1.25r brn org & blk	3.00	2.00
63	A9	1.50r rose lil & yel grn	5.25	2.10
64	A9	3r dk ol bis & vio	9.75	4.00

Engr.
Perf. 14
65	A10	5r rose carmine	18.00	7.50
66	A10	10r dark blue	36.00	16.00

Nos. 53-66 (14)   79.55   36.45

Nos. 53-62, 64-66 Overprinted with New Currency Names and Bars
1967
67	A9	5d on 5np	.25	.20
68	A9	10d on 10np	.25	.20
69	A9	15d on 15np	.45	.20
70	A9	20d on 20np	.90	.25
71	A9	25d on 25np	1.00	.25
72	A9	35d on 35np	1.10	.25
73	A9	40d on 40np	1.50	.30
74	A9	60d on 60np	2.50	.40
75	A9	1r on 1r	3.50	.65
76	A9	1.25r on 1.25r	6.75	1.25
77	A9	3r on 3r	11.50	3.50
78	A10	5r on 5r	21.00	7.00
79	A10	10r on 10r	34.00	13.50

Nos. 67-79 (13)   84.70   27.95

Sheik and Falcon — A11

Dhow — A12

Litho. & Engr.
1967, Aug. 21   Perf. 13½
80	A11	5d dp car & org	1.00	.30
81	A11	10d sepia & green	1.00	.20
82	A11	20d dp cl & bl gray	1.25	.30
83	A11	35d slate & car	1.75	.30
84	A11	60d vio bl & emer	3.25	.50
85	A11	1r green & lilac	4.75	.50
86	A12	1.25r lt bl & claret	4.75	.65
87	A12	3r dull vio & claret	8.25	1.75
88	A12	5r brt grn & vio	18.00	3.75
89	A12	10r lil rose & grn	26.00	6.75

Nos. 80-89 (10)   70.00   15.00

S. S. Bamora, 1914 — A13

35d, De Havilland 66 plane, 1930. 60d, S. S. Sirdhana, 1947. 1r, Armstrong Whitworth 15 "Atlanta," 1938. 1.25r, S. S. Chandpara, 1949. 3r, BOAC Sunderland amphibian plane, 1943. No. 96, Freighter Bombala, 1961, and BOAC Super VC10, 1967.

1969, Feb. 12   Litho.   Perf. 14x13½
90	A13	25d lt grn, bl & blk	.25	.20
91	A13	35d multicolored	.25	.20
92	A13	60d multicolored	.80	.20
93	A13	1r lil, blk & dl yel	1.00	.20
94	A13	1.25r gray, blk & dp org	1.25	.20
95	A13	3r pink, blk & bl grn	2.10	.35

Nos. 90-95 (6)   5.65   1.35

Miniature Sheet
Imperf
96	A13	1.25r pink, blk & bl grn	7.50	7.50

60 years of postal service.

Mother and Children, by Rubens A14

Arab Mother's Day: 60d, Madonna and Child, by Murillo. 1r, Mother and Child, by Francesco Mazzuoli. 3r, Madonna and Child, by Correggio.

Porkfish — A15

1969, May 26   Litho.   Perf. 11
101	A15	60d shown	1.75	.35
102	A15	60d Spotted grouper	1.75	.35
103	A15	60d Moonfish	1.75	.35
104	A15	60d Sweetlips	1.75	.35
105	A15	60d Blue angel	1.75	.35
106	A15	60d Texas skate	1.75	.35
107	A15	60d Striped butterlyfish	1.75	.35
108	A15	60d Imperial angelfish	1.75	.35
a.		Block of 8, #101-108	25.00	

Nos. 101-108 (8)   14.00   2.80

Nos. 101-108 printed in same sheet of 16 (4x4).

Explorers and Map of Arabia — A16

1969, July 21   Litho.   Perf. 13½x13
109	A16	35d brown & green	.95	.20
110	A16	60d vio & sepia	1.40	.20
111	A16	1r green & dl bl	4.25	.20
112	A16	1.25r gray & rose car	5.25	.20

Nos. 109-112 (4)   11.85   .80

European explorers of Arabia: Sir Richard Francis Burton (1821-1890), Charles Montagu Doughty (1843-1926), Johann Ludwig Burckhardt (1784-1817) and Wilfred Patrick Thesiger (1910-).

Construction of World's First Underwater Oil Storage Tank — A17

Designs: 20d, Launching of oil storage tank. 35d, Oil storage tank in place on ocean ground. 60d, Sheik Rashid bin Said, offshore drilling platform and monument commemorating first oil export. 1r, Offshore production platform and helicopter port.

1969, Oct. 13   Litho.   Perf. 11
113	A17	5d blue & multi	.25	.20
114	A17	20d blue & multi	.85	.20
115	A17	35d blue & multi	1.60	.20
116	A17	60d blue & multi	2.50	.20
117	A17	1r blue & multi	3.50	.20

Nos. 113-117 (5)   8.70   1.00

Astronauts Collecting Moon Rocks — A18

Designs: 1r, Astronaut at foot of ladder. 1.25r, Astronauts planting American flag.

1969, Mar. 21   Litho.   Perf. 13½
97	A14	60d silver & multi	.75	.20
98	A14	1r silver & multi	1.50	.20
99	A14	1.25r silver & multi	1.75	.20
100	A14	3r silver & multi	3.50	.45

Nos. 97-100 (4)   7.50   1.05

1969, Dec. 15   Litho.   Perf. 14½
118		Strip of 3	4.50	.30
a.	A18	60d multicolored	.45	.20
b.	A18	1r multicolored	.90	.20
c.	A18	1.25r multicolored (airmail)	1.90	.20

The 1.25r is inscribed "AIRMAIL."
Sizes: 60d and 1r, 28½x41mm; 1.25r, 60½x41mm.
See note after US No. C76.

Ocean Weather Ship Launching Radio Sonde, and Hastings Plane — A19

WMO Emblem and: 1r, Kew-type radio sonde, weather balloon and radar antenna. 1.25r, Tiros satellite and weather sounding rocket. 3r, Ariel satellite and rocket launching.

1970, Mar. 23   Litho.   Perf. 11
121	A19	60d dl grn, brn & blk	.45	.20
122	A19	1r brown & multi	.85	.20
123	A19	1.25r dk blue & multi	.95	.20
124	A19	3r multicolored	2.25	.30

Nos. 121-124 (4)   4.50   .90

10th World Meteorological Day.

UPU Headquarters and Monument, Bern — A20

60d, UPU monument, Bern, telecommunications satellite and London PO tower.

1970, May 20   Litho.   Perf. 13½x14
125	A20	5d lt green & multi	.65	.20
126	A20	60d dp blue & multi	1.60	.20

UPU Headquarters opening, May 20.

Charles Dickens, London Skyline — A21

60d, Dickens' portrait, vert. 1.25r, Dickens & "Old Curiosity Shop." 3r, Bound volumes.

1970, July 23   Litho.   Perf. 13½
127	A21	60d olive & multi	.70	.20
128	A21	1r multicolored	.85	.20
129	A21	1.25r buff & multi	1.00	.20
130	A21	3r multicolored	3.25	.50

Nos. 127-130 (4)   5.80   1.10

Dickens (1812-70), English novelist.

The Graham Children, by William Hogarth — A22

Paintings: 60d, Caroline Murat and her Children, by François Pascal Gerard, vert. 1r, Napoleon with the Children on the Terrace in St. Cloud, by Louis Ducis.

1970, Oct. 1   **Litho.**   **Perf. 13½**
131 A22 35d multicolored .75 .20
132 A22 60d multicolored 1.25 .20
133 A22 1r multicolored 2.00 .20
   Nos. 131-133 (3) 4.00 .60

Issued for Children's Day.

National Bank of Dubai A24

Sheik Rashid bin Said — A23

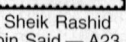

Television Station — A25

Designs: 10d, Boat building. 20d, Al Maktum Bascule Bridge. 35d, Great Mosque, Dubai, vert. 1r, Dubai International Airport, horiz. 1.25r, Port Rashid harbor project, horiz. 3r, Rashid Hospital, horiz. 5r, Dubai Trade School, horiz.

Perf. 14x14½, 14½x14

1970-71   **Litho.**
134 A23 5d multi ('71) .30 .20
135 A24 10d multi ('71) .30 .20
136 A24 20d multi ('71) .50 .20
137 A24 35d multi ('71) .65 .20
138 A24 60d multicolored 1.00 .20

Perf. 14
139 A25 1r multicolored 1.50 .20
140 A25 1.25r multicolored 1.50 .20
141 A25 3r multicolored 4.50 .25
142 A25 5r multicolored 7.25 .40
143 A25 10r multi ('71) 17.50 .85
   Nos. 134-143 (10) 35.00 2.90

Dubai Airport A26

Designs: 1.25r, Airport entrance.

1971, May 15 **Litho.** **Perf. 13½x14**
144 A26 1r multicolored 3.25 .20
145 A26 1.25r multicolored 4.00 .20

Opening of Dubai International Airport.

Map With Tracking Stations, Satellites A27

1971, June 21 **Litho.** **Perf. 14½**
146 A27 60d multicolored .60 .30

Outer Space Telecommunications Cong., Paris, Mar. 29-Apr. 2. See Nos. C55-C56.

Fan, Scout Emblem, Map of Japan — A28

Designs: 1r, Boy Scouts in kayaks. 1.25r, Mountaineering. 3r, Campfire, horiz.

Perf. 14x13½, 13½x14
1971, Aug. 30   **Litho.**
147 A28 60d multicolored .50 .20
148 A28 1r multicolored 1.00 .20
149 A28 1.25r multicolored 1.25 .20
150 A28 3r multicolored 2.75 .30
   Nos. 147-150 (4) 5.50 .90

13th Boy Scout World Jamboree, Asagiri Plain, Japan, Aug. 2-10.

Albrecht Dürer, Self-portrait A29

1971, Oct. 18   **Perf. 14x13½**
151 A29 60d gold & multi .80 .20

See Nos. C57-C59.

Boy in Meadow A30

5r, Boys playing and UNICEF emblem.

1971, Dec. 11   **Perf. 13½**
152 A30 60d multi .45 .20
153 A30 5r multi, horiz. 3.50 .50

25th anniv. of UNICEF. See No. C60.

Ludwig van Beethoven A31

Portrait: 10d, Leonardo da Vinci.

1972, Feb. 7
154 A31 10d lt tan & multi .30 .20
155 A31 35d lt tan & multi .45 .20

See Nos. C61-C62.

Olympic Emblems, Gymnast on Rings — A32

1972, July 31   **Litho.**   **Perf. 13½**
156 A32 35d shown .55 .20
157 A32 40d Fencing .65 .20
158 A32 65d Hockey .80 .20
   Nos. 156-158,C65-C67 (6) 7.50 1.20

20th Olympic Games, Munich, 8/26-9/11.

Stamps of Dubai were replaced in 1972 by those of United Arab Emirates.

AIR POST STAMPS

Type of Regular Issue and

Peregrine Falcon — AP1   Wheat — AP2

Design: A1, Falcon over bridge.

Perf. 12x11½, 11½x12

1963, June 15   **Unwmk.**
C1 A1 20np dk red brn & lt blue 2.00 .25
C2 AP1 25np ol & blk brn 2.10 .30
C3 A1 30np red org & blk 2.50 .35
C4 AP1 40np grayish brn & dk violet 2.75 .40
C5 A1 50np emer & rose cl 3.50 .55
C6 AP1 60np brn org & blk 4.00 .55
C7 A1 75np vio & dp grn 6.00 .60
C8 AP1 1r org & red brn 7.25 .75
   Nos. C1-C8 (8) 30.10 3.75

Red Cross Type

Designs: 20np, Dhows. 30np, First-aid tent. 40np, Camel caravan. 50np, Butterfly.

1963, Sept. 1   **Unwmk.**   **Perf. 12**
C9 A3 20np brown, yel & red 1.25 .50
C10 A3 30np dk bl, buff & red 1.25 .50
C11 A3 40np black, yel & red 1.60 .60
C12 A3 50np vio, lt bl & red 3.00 1.10
   Nos. C9-C12 (4) 7.10 2.70

Malaria Type

Designs: 30np, Anopheles mosquito. 40np, Mosquito and coiled arrows. 70np, Mosquitoes over swamp.

1963, Dec. 20   **Unwmk.**   **Perf. 12**
C13 A4 30np purple & emer .50 .20
C14 A4 40np red & dull grn .60 .25
C15 A4 70np slate & citron .90 .35
   Nos. C13-C15 (3) 2.00 .80

Three imperf. souv. sheets exist containing 4 stamps each in changed colors similar to #C13-C15. Value $30.

1963, Dec. 30   **Litho.**
40np, Wheat and palm tree. 70np, Hands holding wheat. 1r, Woman carrying basket.
C16 AP2 30np vio bl & ocher .55 .30
C17 AP2 40np red & olive .80 .45
C18 AP2 70np green & orange 1.25 .65
C19 AP2 1r org brn & Prus bl 1.90 1.00
   Nos. C16-C19 (4) 4.50 2.40

Boy Scout Type

Designs: 20np, Human pyramid. 30np, Bugler. 40np, Cub Scouts. 70np, Scouts and bugler. 1r, Scouts presenting flag.

1964, Jan. 20
C20 A5 20np green & dk brn .30 .20
C21 A5 30np lilac & ocher .65 .25
C22 A5 40np vio bl & yel grn .80 .30
C23 A5 70np dk grn & gray 1.40 .45
C24 A5 1r vio bl & red org 2.00 .70
   Nos. C20-C24 (5) 5.15 1.90

Five imperf. souv. sheets exist containing 4 stamps each in changed colors similar to #C20-C24. Value $60.
For overprints see Nos. C47-C51.

John F. Kennedy and US Seal AP3

1964, Jan. 15   **Litho.**
C25 AP3 75np grn & blk, lt grn .90 .55
C26 AP3 1r ocher & blk, tan 1.25 .60
C27 AP3 1.25r mag & blk, gray 1.60 .85
   Nos. C25-C27 (3) 3.75 2.00

Pres. John F. Kennedy (1917-1963). A souvenir sheet contains one imperf. 1.25r in buff and black with simulated perforations. Value $6.
For overprints see Nos. C52-C54.

Spacecraft — AP4

Designs: 1np, 5np, Ascending rocket, vert. 2np, 1r, Mercury capsule, vert. 4np, 2r, Twin spacecraft.

1964, Jan. 25   **Unwmk.**   **Perf. 12**
C28 AP4 1np emerald & org .20 .20
C29 AP4 2np multicolored .20 .20
C30 AP4 3np multicolored .25 .20
C31 AP4 4np multicolored .25 .20
C32 AP4 5np blue & orange .25 .20
C33 AP4 1r vio bl, dp car & buff .90 .70
C34 AP4 1.50r vio bl, dp car & buff 1.60 1.25
C35 AP4 2r blue, yel & red 2.00 1.50
   Nos. C28-C35 (8) 5.65 4.45

Issued to honor the astronauts. An imperf. souvenir sheet contains one stamp similar to No. C35. Value $7.

New York World's Fair Type

Statue of Liberty and ships in Dubai harbor.

1964, Apr. 22   **Litho.**
C36 A6 75np gray bl, ultra & blk .90 .40
C37 A6 2r gray grn, dk brn & bis 1.50 .80
C38 A6 3r dl grn, gray ol & dp org 2.25 1.10
   Nos. C36-C38 (3) 4.65 2.30

An imperf. souvenir sheet contains 2 stamps in Statue of Liberty design: 2r dark brown and rose carmine, and 3r ultramarine and gold. Value $10.

Scales and Flame AP5

1964, Apr. 30   **Litho.**   **Perf. 12**
C39 AP5 35np bl, brn & scar .60 .30
C40 AP5 50np lt bl, dk grn & scar .75 .35
C41 AP5 1r grnsh bl, blk & scar 1.40 .60
C42 AP5 3r lt ultra, ultra, & scar 4.00 2.00
   Nos. C39-C42 (4) 6.75 3.25

15th anniv. of the Universal Declaration of Human Rights. An imperf. souvenir sheet contains one 3r light green, ultramarine and scarlet stamp. Value $7.50.

Nos. C20-C24 Overprinted in Red and Black (Shield in Red)

1964, June 20
C47 A5 20np green & dk brn .90 .40
C48 A5 30np lilac & ocher 1.10 .50
C49 A5 40np vio bl & yel grn 1.75 .75
C50 A5 70np dk grn & gray 3.00 1.25
C51 A5 1r vio bl & red org 4.25 1.75
   Nos. C47-C51 (5) 11.00 4.65

9th Winter Olympic Games, Innsbruck, Austria, Jan. 29-Feb. 9, 1964.

A similar but unauthorized overprint, with shield in black, exists on Nos. 28-32, C20-C24, and the five souvenir sheets mentioned below No. C24. The Dubai G.P.O. calls this black-shield overprint "bogus."

Nos. C25-C27 Overprinted in Brown or Green

1964, Sept. 15
C52	AP3	75np (Br)	2.00	2.00
C53	AP3	1r (G)	2.40	2.40
C54	AP3	1.25r (G)	3.00	3.00
		Nos. C52-C54 (3)	7.40	7.40

Pres. John F. Kennedy 48th birth anniv. The same overprint in black was applied to the souv. sheet noted after No. C27.

Communications Type

Designs: 1r, Intelsat 4, tracking station on globe and rocket. 5r, Eiffel Tower, Syncom 3 and Goonhilly radar station.

1971, June 21 Litho. Perf. 14½
C55	A27	1r brown & multi	.60	.20
C56	A27	5r multicolored	3.00	.45

Portrait Type

1r, Newton. 1.25r, Avicenna. 3r, Voltaire.

1971, Oct. 18 Litho. Perf. 14x13½
C57	A29	1r gold & multi	1.10	.20
C58	A29	1.25r gold & multi	1.40	.20
C59	A29	3r gold & multi	4.00	.50
		Nos. C57-C59 (3)	6.50	.90

UNICEF Type

1r, Mother, children, UNICEF emblem.

1971, Dec. 11 Perf. 13½
C60	A30	1r gold & multi	1.00	.20

Portrait Type

75d, Khalil Gibran. 5r, Charles de Gaulle.

1972, Feb. 7 Litho. Perf. 13½
C61	A31	75d lt tan & multi	.75	.20
C62	A31	5r lt tan & multi	5.25	.35

Infant Health Care AP6

Design: 75d, Nurse supervising children at meal, and WHO emblem, vert.

1972, Apr. 7 Litho. Perf. 14x13½
C63	AP6	75d multicolored	1.60	.20
C64	AP6	1.25r multicolored	2.40	.25

World Health Day.

Olympic Type

1972, July 31 Litho. Perf. 13½
C65	A32	75d Water polo	1.50	.20
C66	A32	1r Steeplechase	1.75	.20
C67	A32	1.25r Running	2.25	.20
		Nos. C65-C67 (3)	5.50	.60

POSTAGE DUE STAMPS

Type of Regular Issue

Designs: 1np, 4np, 15np, Clam. 2np, 5np, 25np, Mussel. 3np, 10np, 35np, Oyster.

Perf. 12x11½
1963, June 15 Litho. Unwmk.
J1	A1	1np gray grn & ver	.75	.35
J2	A1	2np lemon & brt bl	.90	.45
J3	A1	3np dl rose & green	1.40	.75
J4	A1	4np light grn & mag	1.75	.90
J5	A1	5np vermilion & blk	2.25	1.00
J6	A1	10np citron & violet	2.75	1.40
J7	A1	15np brt ultra & ver	3.75	1.60
J8	A1	25np buff & olive grn	4.25	1.75
J9	A1	35np turq bl & dp org	5.00	2.00
		Nos. J1-J9 (9)	22.80	10.20

Sheik Rashid bin Said — D1

1972, May 22 Litho. Perf. 14x14½
J10	D1	5d blk & gray grn	1.25	.50
J11	D1	10d vio bl, blk & bis	1.75	.75
J12	D1	20d sl grn, blk & brick red	3.75	1.00
J13	D1	30d grnsh gray, blk & lil	5.00	2.00
J14	D1	50d lilac, brn & bis	9.00	4.00
		Nos. J10-J14 (5)	20.75	8.25

EAST AFRICA AND UGANDA PROTECTORATES

ˈēst ˈa-fri-kə and ü-ˈgan-də

prə-ˈtek-t̩ə-ˌrəts

LOCATION — Central East Africa, bordering on the Indian Ocean
GOVT. — British Protectorate
AREA — 350,000 sq. mi. (approx.)
POP. — 6,503,507 (approx.)
CAPITAL — Mombasa

This territory, formerly administered by the British East Africa Colony, was divided between Kenya Colony and the Uganda Protectorate. See Kenya, Uganda and Tanzania.

16 Annas = 1 Rupee
100 Cents = 1 Rupee (1907)

Altered high value stamps of East Africa and Uganda are plentiful. Expertization by competent authorities is recommended.

A1

A2

King Edward VII
1903 Typo. Wmk. 2 Perf. 14
1	A1	½a gray green	5.00	16.00
2	A1	1a car & black	2.25	1.50
3	A1	2a vio & dull vio	10.50	3.00
4	A1	2½a ultramarine	14.50	60.00
5	A1	3a gray grn & brn	22.50	67.50
6	A1	4a blk & gray grn	13.50	27.50
7	A1	5a org brn & blk	22.50	60.00
8	A1	8a pale blue & blk	26.00	50.00

Wmk. 1
9	A2	1r gray green	20.00	67.50
10	A2	2r vio & dull vio	87.50	100.00
11	A2	3r blk & gray grn	120.00	225.00
12	A2	4r lt green & blk	125.00	225.00
13	A2	5r car & black	140.00	225.00
14	A2	10r ultra & black	275.00	450.00
15	A2	20r ol gray & blk	675.00	1,600.
16	A2	50r org brn & blk	1,900.	3,750.
		Nos. 1-14 (14)	884.25	1,578.

Nos. 9 and 14 are on both ordinary and chalky paper. Values are for examples on ordinary paper. Values are for the least expensive varieties. See "Scott Classic Specialized Catalogue of Stamps & Covers" for detailed listings.

1904-07 Wmk. 3 Chalky Paper
17	A1	½a gray green	10.50	3.75
18a	A1	1a car & black	4.50	1.00
19	A1	2a vio & dull vio	3.50	3.25
20	A1	2½a blue	10.00	37.50
a.		2½a blue & ultramarine	9.50	21.00
21	A1	3a gray grn & brn	4.75	35.00
22	A1	4a blk & gray grn	9.25	22.50

23	A1	5a org brn & blk	8.00	18.50
24a	A1	8a pale blue & blk	8.75	10.50
25	A2	1r gray green	34.00	75.00
26	A2	2r vio & dl vio	47.50	67.50
27	A2	3r blk & gray	67.50	125.00
28	A2	4r lt green & blk	100.00	180.00
29	A2	5r car & black	115.00	150.00
29A	A2	10r ultra & black	225.00	300.00
30	A2	20r ol gray & blk	675.00	1,250.
30A	A2	50r org brn & blk	2,100.	3,750.
		Nos. 17-29 (13)	423.25	729.50

Nos. 17-19, 21-24 are on both ordinary and chalky paper. No. 20 is on ordinary paper. Values are for the least expensive varieties. See "Scott Classic Specialized Catalogue of Stamps & Covers" for detailed listings.

1907-08
31	A1	1c brown ('08)	3.00	.20
32	A1	3c gray green	17.50	.80
33	A1	6c carmine, ptd from two plates ('07)	3.25	.20
34	A1	10c citron & violet	11.00	10.00
35	A1	12c red vio & dl vio	12.00	3.50
36	A1	15c ultramarine	30.00	11.00
37	A1	25c blk & blue green	11.00	8.50
38	A1	50c org brn & green	14.50	14.50
39	A1	75c pale bl & gray blk ('08)	5.50	40.00
		Nos. 31-39 (9)	107.75	88.70

Nos. 31-33, 36 are on ordinary paper.
There are two dies of the 6c differing very slightly in many details.

A3

King George V — A4

1912-18 Ordinary Paper Wmk. 3
40	A3	1c black	.40	2.10
41	A3	3c green	2.50	.75
a.		Booklet pane of 6	1.50	.70
42	A3	6c carmine	2.50	.65
a.		Booklet pane of 6		
43	A3	10c yel orange	2.50	.65
44	A3	12c gray	3.25	.65
45	A3	15c ultramarine	3.25	1.00

Chalky Paper
46	A3	25c scar & blk, yel	.65	1.60
47	A3	50c violet & black	1.90	1.60
48	A3	75c blk & red, green	1.90	21.00
a.		75c black, emerald	13.50	65.00
b.		75c blk, bl grn, olive back	7.25	9.25
c.		75c blk, emer, olive back	50.00	175.00
49	A3	1r black, green	2.25	5.25
a.		1r black, emerald	6.00	60.00
50	A4	2r blk & red, bl	24.50	45.00
51	A4	3r gray grn & vio	24.50	110.00
52	A4	4r grn & red, yel	55.00	125.00
53	A4	5r dl vio & ul-tra	60.00	175.00
54	A4	10r grn & red, grn	175.00	275.00
55	A4	20r vio & blk, red	425.00	425.00
56	A4	20r bl & violet, blue ('18)	500.00	550.00
57	A4	50r gray grn & rose red	725.00	975.00
58	A4	100r blk & vio, red	6,000.	3,000.
59	A4	500r red & grn, grn	22,000.	
		Nos. 40-54 (15)	359.10	765.30

1914 Surface-colored Paper
60	A3	25c scarlet & blk, yel	.65	5.50
61	A3	75c black, green	1.25	19.50

Stamps of types A3 and A4 with watermark 4 are listed under Kenya, Uganda and Tanzania.

The 1r through 50r with revenue cancellations sell for minimal prices. The 100r and 500r were available for postage but were nearly always used fiscally.

For surcharge see No. 62.

No. 42 Surcharged

1919
62	A3	4c on 6c carmine	1.50	.20
a.		Double surcharge	150.00	240.00
b.		Without squares over old value	50.00	85.00
c.		Pair, one without surcharge	2,000.	2,250.
d.		Inverted surcharge	350.00	475.00

For later issues see Kenya, Uganda and Tanzania.
For stamps of East Africa and Uganda overprinted "G. E. A." see German East Africa.

EASTERN RUMELIA

ˈē-stərn rü-ˈmēl-yə

(South Bulgaria)

LOCATION — In southern Bulgaria
GOVT. — An autonomous unit of the Turkish Empire.
CAPITAL — Philippopolis (Plovdiv)

In 1885 the province of Eastern Rumelia revolted against Turkish rule and united with Bulgaria, adopting the new name of South Bulgaria. This union was assured by the Treaty of Bucharest in 1886, following the war between Serbia and Bulgaria.

40 Paras = 1 Piaster

Counterfeits of all overprints are plentiful.

No. 1

A2

A3

Stamps of Turkey, 1876-84, Overprinted in Blue
1880 Unwmk. Perf. 13½
1	A5	½pi on 20pa yel grn	47.50	40.00
3	A2	10pa blk & rose	55.00	
4	A2	20pa vio & grn	60.00	47.50
6	A2	2pi blk & buff	80.00	72.50
7	A2	5pi red & bl	300.00	350.00
8	A3	10pa blk & red lil	40.00	

Nos. 3 and 8 were not placed in use. Inverted and double overprints of all values exist.

Same, with Extra Overprint "R. O."
9	A3	10pa blk & red lil	67.50	67.50

Crescent and Turkish Inscriptions of Value — A4

1881 Typo. Perf. 13½
10	A4	5pa blk & olive	8.00	1.00
11	A4	10pa blk & green	14.00	1.00
12	A4	20pa blk & rose	1.25	.80
13	A4	1pi blk & blue	4.00	3.25
14	A4	5pi rose & blue	40.00	60.00

Tête bêche pairs, imperforates and all perf. 11½ copies of Nos. 10-14 were not placed in use, and were found only in the remainder stock. This is true also of a 10pa cliché in the 20pa plate, and of a cliché of Turkey No. 63 in the 1pi plate. See the *Scott Classic Catalogue*.

1884			Perf. 11½	
15	A4	5pa lil & pale lil	.40	.40
16	A4	10pa grn & pale grn	.20	.40
17	A4	20pa car & pale rose	.40	
18	A4	1pi bl & pale bl	.80	
19	A4	5pi brn & pale brn	275.00	

Nos. 17-19 were not placed in use. Nos. 15-19 imperf. are from remainders. See the *Scott Classic Catalogue* for perf 13½ listings.

For overprints see Turkey Nos. 542-545.

South Bulgaria

Counterfeits of all overprints are plentiful.

Nos. 10-14 Overprinted in Two Types:

a   b

Type a — Four toes on each foot.
Type b — Three toes on each foot.

1885		Unwmk.	Perf. 13½	
		Blue Overprint		
20	A4 (a)	5pa blk & olive	240.00	275.00
21	A4 (a)	10pa blk & grn	600.00	600.00
22	A4 (a)	20pa blk & rose	240.00	
23	A4 (a)	1pi blk & blue	40.00	80.00
24	A4 (b)	5pi rose & bl	400.00	—

See the *Scott Classic Catalogue* for #22-23, type b, #24, type a, and #22, perf 11½, types a and b.

		Black Overprint		
24B	A4 (a)	20pa blk & rose	275.00	—
25	A4 (a)	1pi blk & bl	12.50	27.50
26	A4 (b)	5pi rose & bl	475.00	—

See the *Scott Classic Catalogue* for #25 type b.

Same Overprint on Nos. 15-17
Perf. 11½, 13½ (#30)

		Blue Overprint		
27	A4 (b)	5pa lil & pale lil	16.00	40.00
28	A4 (b)	10pa grn & pale grn	29.00	55.00
29	A4 (b)	20pa car & pale rose	200.00	240.00

		Black Overprint		
30	A4 (b)	5pa lil & pale lil	27.50	47.50
31	A4 (a)	10pa grn & pale grn	40.00	80.00
32	A4 (b)	20pa car & pale rose	40.00	47.50

See the *Scott Classic Catalogue* for detailed listings of #27-32.

Nos. 10-17 Handstamped in Black in Two Types:

a   b

Type a — First letter at top circular.
Type b — First letter at top oval.

1885			Perf. 13½	
33	A4 (b)	5pa blk & olive, type "b"	300.00	250.00
34	A4 (b)	10pa blk & grn, type "b"	225.00	250.00
35	A4 (b)	20pa blk & rose, type "b"	67.50	80.00
36	A4 (a)	1pi blk & bl, type "a"	60.00	80.00
37	A4 (a)	5pi rose & blue, type "a"	2,500.	—

See the *Scott Classic Catalogue* for #33-35 type a and #36 type b.

		Perf. 13½		
38	A4 (a)	5pa lil & pale lil	16.00	20.00

		Perf. 11½		
39	A4 (a)	10pa grn & pale grn	20.00	25.00
40	A4 (a)	20pa car & pale rose	20.00	36.00

See the *Scott Classic Catalogue* for #38-40, type b, and #38, perf 11½, types a and b.

Nos. 20-40 exist with inverted and double handstamps. Overprints in unlisted colors are proofs.

The stamps of South Bulgaria were superseded in 1886 by those of Bulgaria.

EASTERN SILESIA

ˈē-stərn sī-ˈlē-zhē-ə

LOCATION — In central Europe
GOVT. — Austrian crownland
AREA — 1,987 sq. mi.
POP. — 680,422 (estimated 1920)
CAPITAL — Troppau

After World War I, this territory was occupied by Czechoslovakia and eventually was divided between Poland and Czechoslovakia, the dividing line running through Teschen.

100 Heller = 1 Krone
100 Fennigi = 1 Marka

Plebiscite Issues

Stamps of Czechoslovakia 1918-20, Overprinted in Black, Blue, Violet or Red

1920		Unwmk.		Imperf.
1	A2	1h dark brown	.20	.30
2	A1	3h red violet	.20	.20
3	A2	5h blue green	23.50	22.50
4	A2	15h red	11.50	11.00
5	A2	20h blue green	.20	.20
6	A2	25h dull violet	.75	.75
7	A1	30h bister (R)	.20	.20
8	A1	40h red orange	.30	.30
9	A2	50h dull violet	.60	.45
10	A2	50h dark blue	2.60	1.50
11	A2	60h orange (Bl)	.75	.75
12	A2	75h slate (R)	.50	.75
13	A2	80h olive grn (R)	.50	.75
14	A1	100h brown	1.10	1.10
15	A2	120h gray blk (R)	1.60	2.25
16	A1	200h ultra (R)	1.60	2.00
17	A2	300h green (R)	6.25	7.50
18	A1	400h purple (R)	2.60	3.00
20	A2	500h red brn (Bl)	5.25	6.00
a.		Black overprint	6.25	9.00
21	A2	1000h violet (Bl)	13.00	13.50
a.		Black overprint	62.50	39.00
		Nos. 1-21 (20)	73.20	75.00

		Perf. 11½, 13¾		
22	A2	1h dark brown	.20	.20
23	A2	5h blue green	.30	.25
24	A2	10h yellow green	.30	.25
a.		Imperf.	260.00	210.00
25	A2	15h red	.50	.20
26	A2	20h rose	.50	.35
a.		Imperf.	300.00	250.00
27	A2	25h dull violet	.50	.35
28	A2	30h red violet (Bl)	.35	.35
29	A2	60h orange (Bl)	.50	.50
30	A1	200h ultra (R)	3.00	3.00
		Nos. 22-30 (9)	6.15	5.45

The letters "S. O." are the initials of "Silésie Orientale."
Forged cancellations are found on #1-30.

Overprinted in Carmine or Violet

31	A4	500h sl, *grysh* (C)	40.00	
32	A4	1000h blk brn, *brnsh*	40.00	

Excellent counterfeits of this overprint exist.

Stamps of Poland, 1919, Overprinted

1920			Perf. 11½	
41	A10	5f green	.20	.20
42	A10	10f red brown	.20	.20
43	A10	15f light red	.20	.20
44	A11	25f olive green	.20	.20
45	A11	50f blue green	.20	.20

Overprinted

46	A12	1k deep green	.20	.20
47	A12	1.50k brown	.20	.20
48	A12	2k dark blue	.20	.20
49	A13	2.50k dull violet	.30	.20
50	A14	5k slate blue	.30	.20
		Nos. 41-50 (10)	2.20	2.00

SPECIAL DELIVERY STAMPS

Czechoslovakia Special Delivery Stamps Overprinted in Blue

1920		Unwmk.		Imperf.
E1	SD1	2h red violet, *yel*	.20	.20
a.		Black overprint	4.75	.80
E2	SD1	5h yellow green, *yel*	.20	.20
a.		Black overprint	8.00	5.00

Nos. E1-E2a exist on white paper.

POSTAGE DUE STAMPS

Czechoslovakia Postage Due Stamps Overprinted In Blue or Red

1920		Unwmk.		Imperf.
J1	D1	5h deep bis (Bl)	.25	.20
a.		Black overprint	72.50	62.50
J2	D1	10h deep bister	.25	.20
J3	D1	15h deep bister	.25	.20
J4	D1	20h deep bister	.25	.20
J5	D1	25h deep bister	.25	.20
J6	D1	30h deep bister	.25	.20
J7	D1	40h deep bister	.50	.25
J8	D1	50h deep bister	2.60	3.00
J9	D1	100h blk brn (R)	2.60	3.00
J10	D1	500h gray grn (R)	5.75	4.50
J11	D1	1000h purple (R)	8.50	11.50
		Nos. J1-J11 (11)	21.45	23.45

Forged cancellations exist.

NEWSPAPER STAMPS

Czechoslovakia Newspaper Stamps Overprinted in Black like Nos. 1-30

1920		Unwmk.		Imperf.
P1	N1	2h gray green	.30	.30
P2	N1	6h red	.20	.20
P3	N1	10h dull violet	.40	.20
P4	N1	20h blue	.65	.25
P5	N1	30h gray brown	.65	.25
		Nos. P1-P5 (5)	2.20	1.20

ECUADOR

'e-kwə-,dor

LOCATION — Northwest coast of South America, bordering on the Pacific Ocean
GOVT. — Republic
AREA — 116,270 (?) sq. mi.
POP. — 12,562,496 (1999 est.)
CAPITAL — Quito

The Republic of Ecuador was so constituted on May 11, 1830, after the Civil War which separated the original members of the Republic of Colombia, founded by Simon Bolivar by uniting the Presidency of Quito with the Viceroyalty of New Grenada and the Captaincy of Venezuela. The Presidency of Quito became the Republic of Ecuador.

8 Reales = 1 Peso
100 Centavos = 1 Sucre (1881)
100 Cents = 1 Dollar (2000)

Catalogue values for unused stamps in this country are for Never Hinged items, beginning with Scott 453 in the regular postage section, Scott C147 in the airpost section, Scott CO19 in the airpost officials section, Scott O201 in the officials section, Scott RA60 in the postal tax section, and all entries in the Galapagos section.

Watermarks

Wmk. 117 — Liberty Cap

Wmk. 127 Quatrefoils

Wmk. 233 — "Harrison & Sons, London" in Script Letters

Wmk. 340 — Alternating Interlaced Wavy Lines

Wmk. 367 — Liberty Cap, Emblem, Inscription

Wmk. 395 — Emblem, Inscription

Coat of Arms
A1   A2

1865-72   Unwmk.   Typo.   Imperf.
Quadrille Paper
| 1 | A1 | 1r yellow ('72) | 60.00 | 55.00 |

Wove Paper
2	A1	½r ultra	40.00	15.00
a.	½r gray blue ('67)		40.00	15.00
b.	Batonne paper ('70)		50.00	25.00
c.	Blue paper ('72)		250.00	100.00
3	A1	1r buff	25.00	18.00
a.	1r orange buff		30.00	20.00
4	A1	1r yellow	25.00	18.00
a.	1r olive yellow ('66)		32.50	22.50
b.	Laid paper		175.00	110.00
c.	Half used as ½r on cover			900.00
d.	Batonne paper		40.00	30.00
5	A1	1r green	300.00	50.00
a.	Half used as ½r on cover			900.00
6	A2	4r red ('66)	500.00	200.00
a.	4r red brown ('66)		700.00	200.00
b.	Arms in circle		500.00	250.00
c.	Printed on both sides		550.00	
d.	Half used as 2r on cover			1,600.
	Nos. 1-6 (6)		950.00	353.00

Letter paper embossed with arms of Ecuador was used in printing a number of sheets of Nos. 2, 4-6.
Papermakers' watermarks are known on No. 2 ("Bath" and crown) and No. 4 ("Rolland Freres").
On the 4r the oval holding the coat of arms is usually 13½-14mm wide, but on about one-fifth of the stamps in the sheet it is 15-15½mm wide, almost a circle.
The 2r, 8r and 12r, type A1, are bogus.
Proofs of the ½r, type A1, are known in black and green.
An essay of type A2 shows the condor's head facing right.

1871-72
Blue-surface Paper
| 7 | A1 | ½r ultra | 50.00 | 25.00 |
| 8 | A1 | 1r yellow | 300.00 | 100.00 |

Unofficial reprints of types A1-A2 differ in color, have a different sheet makeup and lack gum. Type A1 reprints usually have a double frameline at left. All stamps on blue paper with horiz. blue lines are reprints.

A3

A4

1872   White Paper   Litho.   Perf. 11
9	A3	½r blue	30.00	5.00
10	A4	1r yellow	40.00	7.00
11	A3	1p rose	5.00	25.00
	Nos. 9-11 (3)	75.00	37.00

The 1r surcharged 4c is fraudulent.

A5   A6

A7   A8

A9   A10

1881, Nov. 1   Engr.   Perf. 12
12	A5	1c yellow brn	.40	.20
13	A6	2c lake	.40	.20
14	A7	5c blue	10.00	.40
15	A8	10c orange	.40	.20
16	A9	20c gray violet	.40	.20
17	A10	50c blue green	2.00	2.00
	Nos. 12-17 (6)	13.60	3.20

The 1c surcharged 3c, and 20c surcharged 5c are fraudulent.
For overprints see Nos. O1-O6.

DIEZ
CENTAVOS

No. 17 Surcharged in Black

1883, Apr.
| 18 | A10 | 10c on 50c blue grn | 50.00 | 30.00 |
| a. | Double surcharge | | |

Dangerous forgeries exist.

A12   A13

A14   A15

1887
19	A12	1c blue green	.50	.40
20	A13	2c vermilion	1.00	.40
21	A14	5c blue	3.00	.50
22	A15	80c olive green	6.00	15.00
	Nos. 19-22 (4)	10.50	16.30

For overprints see Nos. O7-O10.

President Juan Flores — A16

1892
23	A16	1c orange	.30	1.00
24	A16	2c dk brown	.30	1.00
25	A16	5c vermilion	.30	1.00
26	A16	10c green	.30	1.00
27	A16	20c red brown	.30	1.00
28	A16	50c maroon	.30	2.00
29	A16	1s blue	.30	4.00
30	A16	5s purple	1.00	8.00
	Nos. 23-30 (8)	3.10	19.00

The issues of 1892, 1894, 1895 and 1896 were printed by the Hamilton Bank Note Co., New York, to the order of N. F. Seebeck, who held a contract for stamps with the government of Ecuador.
No. 30 in green is said to be an essay or color trial.
For surcharges and overprints see Nos. 31-37, O11-O17.

Nos. 29 and 30 Surcharged in Black

1893
Surcharge Measures 25½x2½mm
31	A16	5c on 1s blue	6.00	6.00
32	A16	5c on 5s purple	10.00	9.00
a.	Double surcharge		

Surcharge Measures 24x2¼mm
33	A16	5c on 1s blue	3.00	3.00
a.	Double surcharge, one inverted		
34	A16	5c on 5s purple	12.00	10.00
a.	Double surcharge, one invtd.		

Nos. 28-30 Surcharged in Black

35	A16	5c on 50c maroon	2.00	2.00
a.	Inverted surcharge		5.00
36	A16	5c on 1s blue	2.50	2.00
37	A16	5c on 5s purple	10.00	10.00
	Nos. 31-37 (7)	45.50	42.00

Pres. Juan Flores
A19

Pres. Vicente Rocafuerte
A20

| 38 | A19 | 5c on 5s lake | 4.00 | 4.00 |

It is stated that No. 38 was used exclusively as a postage stamp and not for telegrams.

1894   Dated 1894   Perf. 12
Various Frames
39	A20	1c blue	.40	.40
40	A20	2c yellow brn	.40	.40
41	A20	5c green	.40	.40
b.	Perf. 14		6.00	2.00
42	A20	10c vermilion	.70	.60
43	A20	20c black	1.10	.70
44	A20	50c orange	6.00	2.00
45	A20	1s carmine	9.50	4.00
46	A20	5s dark blue	12.00	6.00
	Nos. 39-46 (8)	30.50	14.50

1895
Same, Dated "1895"
47	A20	1c blue	.90	.70
48	A20	2c yellow brn	.90	.70
49	A20	5c green	.70	.50
50	A20	10c vermilion	.70	.40
51	A20	20c black	1.00	1.00
52	A20	50c orange	3.50	2.25
53	A20	1s carmine	21.00	8.00
54	A20	5s dark blue	8.50	4.00
	Nos. 47-54 (8)	37.20	17.55

Reprints of the 2c, 10c, 50c, 1s and 5s of the 1894-95 issues are generally on thick paper. Original issues are on thin to medium thick paper. To distinguish reprints from originals, a comparison of paper thickness, paper color, gum, printing clarity and direction of paper weave is necessary. Value 20 cents each.
For overprints see #77-112, O20-O33, O50-O91.

A21

A22

A23

A24

A25

A26

A27

A28

1896   **Wmk. 117**

55	A21	1c dk green	.70	.60
56	A22	2c red	.70	.40
57	A23	5c blue	.70	.40
58	A24	10c bister brn	.60	.90
59	A25	20c orange	1.40	2.00
60	A26	50c dark blue	5.00	3.00
61	A27	1s yellow brn	4.00	4.00
62	A28	5s violet	14.00	5.50
		Nos. 55-62 (8)	27.10	16.80

Unwmk.

62A	A21	1c dk green	1.00	.40
62B	A22	2c red	1.10	.40
62C	A23	5c blue	1.10	.70
62D	A24	10c bister brn	.70	1.40
62E	A25	20c orange	6.00	5.50
62F	A26	50c dark blue	2.00	2.75
62G	A27	1s yellow brn	6.00	8.00
62H	A28	5s violet	15.00	6.00
		Nos. 62A-62H (8)	32.90	25.15

Reprints of Nos. 55-62H are on very thick paper, with paper weave direction vertical. Value 20 cents each.

For surcharges and overprints see Nos. 74, 76, 113-114, O34-O49.

Vicente Roca, Diego Noboa and José Olmedo — A28a

General Juan Francisco Elizalde — A28b

Perf. 11½

1896, Oct. 9   **Unwmk.**   **Litho.**

63	A28a	1c rose	.35	.40
64	A28b	2c blue	.35	.45
65	A28a	5c green	.50	.50
66	A28b	10c ocher	.50	.50
67	A28a	20c red	.70	2.00
68	A28b	50c violet	1.10	3.25
69	A28a	1s orange	2.00	5.50
		Nos. 63-69 (7)	5.50	12.60

Success of the Liberal Party in 1845 & 1895.
For overprints see Nos. 115-125.

A29

Black Surcharge

1896, Nov.   **Perf. 12**

70	A29	1c on 1c ver, "1893-1894"	1.00	.60
	a.	Inverted surcharge	2.50	2.00
	b.	Double surcharge	8.00	7.00
71	A29	2c on 2c bl, "1893-1894"	2.00	1.75
	a.	Inverted surcharge	4.00	3.50
72	A29	5c on 10c org, "1887-1888"	2.00	.60
	a.	Inverted surcharge	4.00	1.00
	b.	Double surcharge	7.00	4.00
	c.	Surcharged "2cts"	1.00	.80
	d.	"1893-1894"	6.00	5.00
73	A29	10c on 4c brn, "1887-1888"	2.00	1.10
	a.	Inverted surcharge	4.00	1.75
	b.	Double surcharge	6.00	3.50
	c.	Double surcharge, one inverted		
	d.	Surcharged "1 cto"	2.00	2.75
	e.	"1891-1892"	17.00	13.50
		Nos. 70-73 (4)	7.00	4.05

Similar surcharges of type A29 include: Dated "1887-1888" — 1c on 1c blue green, 1c on 2c red, 1c on 4c brown, 1c on 10c yellow; 2c on 2c red, 2c on 10c yellow; 10c on 1c green.
Dated "1891-1892" — 1c on 1c blue green, 1c on 4c brown.
Dated "1893-1894" — 2c on 10c yellow; 10c on 1c vermilion, 10c on 10s black.
For overprints see Nos. O18-O19.

Nos. 59-60 Surcharged in Black or Red

1896, Oct.   **Wmk. 117**

74	A25	5c on 20c orange	40.00	40.00
76	A26	10c on 50c dk bl (R)	50.00	50.00
	a.	Double surcharge		

The surcharge is diag., horiz. or vert.

Overprinted

On Issue of 1894

1897   **Unwmk.**

77	A20	1c blue	2.25	2.25
78	A20	2c yellow brn	1.90	1.30
79	A20	5c green	.90	.90
80	A20	10c vermilion	2.75	2.25
81	A20	20c black	3.00	2.75
82	A20	50c orange	6.50	3.25
83	A20	1s carmine	19.00	6.50
84	A20	5s dark blue	110.00	90.00
		Nos. 77-84 (8)	146.30	109.20

On Issue of 1895

85	A20	1c blue	6.00	5.50
86	A20	2c yellow brn	2.25	2.25
87	A20	5c green	1.90	1.60
88	A20	10c vermilion	7.00	6.00
89	A20	20c black	1.90	1.75
90	A20	50c orange	32.50	13.00
91	A20	1s carmine	14.50	7.50
92	A20	5s dark blue	14.50	14.50
		Nos. 85-92 (8)	80.55	52.10

Overprinted

On Issue of 1894

1897

93	A20	1c blue	1.40	.90
94	A20	2c yellow brn	1.20	.75
95	A20	5c green	.60	.50
96	A20	10c vermilion	3.50	1.75
97	A20	20c black	3.75	2.50

98	A20	50c orange	7.00	2.75
99	A20	1s carmine	13.00	8.50
100	A20	5s dark blue	115.00	85.00
		Nos. 93-100 (8)	145.45	102.65

On Issue of 1895

101	A20	1c blue	3.25	1.60
102	A20	2c yellow brn	1.60	1.60
103	A20	5c green	1.75	1.00
104	A20	10c vermilion	5.50	4.50
105	A20	20c black	5.00	1.20
106	A20	50c orange	1.75	1.75
107	A20	1s carmine	8.00	7.00
108	A20	5s dark blue	9.50	9.50
		Nos. 101-108 (8)	36.35	28.15

Overprints on Nos. 77-108 are to be found reading upward from left to right and downward from left to right, as well as inverted.

Overprinted   **1897 y 1898**

On Issue of 1894

1897

109	A20	10c vermilion	—	—

On Issue of 1895

110	A20	2c yellow brn	—	—
111	A20	1s carmine	—	—
112	A20	5s dark blue	—	—
		Nos. 109-112 (0)	.00	.00

Nos. 56, 59 Overprinted like Nos. 93-108

1897, June   **Wmk. 117**

113	A22	2c red	—	—
114	A25	20c orange	—	—

Many forged overprints on Nos. 77-114 exist, made on original stamps and reprints.

Stamps or Types of 1896 Overprinted like Nos. 93-108

1897   **Unwmk.**   **Perf. 11½**

115	A28a	1c rose	3.75	3.75
116	A28b	2c blue	3.00	3.00
117	A28b	10c ocher	3.00	3.00
118	A28a	1s yellow	15.00	15.00
		Nos. 115-118 (4)	24.75	24.75

No. 63 Overprinted like Nos. 77-92

1897

119	A28a	1c rose	.60	.50

Nos. 63-66 Overprinted in Black

1897

122	A28a	1c rose	4.50	4.00
123	A28b	2c blue	4.50	4.00
124	A28a	5c green	4.50	4.00
125	A28b	10c ocher	4.50	4.00
	a.	Double overprint	10.50	9.50
		Nos. 122-125 (4)	18.00	16.00

The 20c, 50c and 1s with this overprint in black and all values of the issue overprinted in blue are reprints.

Overprint Inverted

122a	A28a	1c	6.00	5.50
123a	A28b	2c	6.00	5.50
124a	A28a	5c	6.00	5.50
125b	A28b	10c	6.00	5.50

Coat of Arms — A33

1897, June 23   **Engr.**   **Perf. 14-16**

127	A33	1c dk yellow grn	.30	.20
128	A33	2c orange red	.30	.20
129	A33	5c lake	.30	.20
130	A33	10c dk brown	.30	.20
131	A33	20c yellow	.45	.40
132	A33	50c dull blue	.45	.65
133	A33	1s gray	.85	.80
134	A33	5s dark lilac	1.50	1.10
		Nos. 127-134 (8)	4.45	3.75

No. 135

No. 136

1899, May

135	A33	1c on 2c orange red	3.00	1.50
136	A33	5c on 10c brown	2.50	1.00
	a.	Double surcharge		

Luis Vargas Torres
A36

Abdón Calderón
A37

Juan Montalvo
A38

José Mejia
A39

Santa Cruz y Espejo — A40

Pedro Carbo — A41

José Joaquin Olmedo
A42

Pedro Moncayo
A43

1899   **Perf. 12½-16**

137	A36	1c gray blue & blk	.40	.20
	a.	Horiz. pair, imperf. vert.		
138	A37	2c brown lil & blk	.40	.20
139	A38	5c lake & blk	.70	.20
140	A39	10c violet & blk	.70	.20
141	A40	20c green & blk	.70	.20
142	A41	50c lil rose & blk	1.75	.55
143	A42	1s ocher & blk	8.00	1.75
144	A43	5s lilac & blk	14.50	5.50
		Nos. 137-144 (8)	27.15	8.30

1901

145	A36	1c scarlet & blk	.45	.20
146	A37	2c green & blk	.45	.20
147	A38	5c gray lil & blk	.45	.20
148	A39	10c dp blue & blk	.50	.25
149	A40	20c gray & blk	.50	.25
150	A41	50c lt blue & blk	1.60	.65
151	A42	1s brown & blk	6.00	1.75
152	A43	5s gray blk & blk	9.00	4.00
		Nos. 145-152 (8)	18.95	7.50

In July, 1902, following the theft of a quantity of stamps during a fire at Guayaquil, the Government authorized the governors of the provinces to handstamp their stocks. Many varieties of these handstamps exist.
Other control marks were used in 1907.
For overprints see Nos. O103-O106, O167.

A44

Surcharged on Revenue Stamp
Dated 1901-1902

		1903-06		**Perf. 14, 15**
153	A44	1c on 5c gray lil		
		('06)	.75	.40
154	A44	1c on 20c gray		
		('06)	10.00	4.50
155	A44	1c on 25c yellow	1.50	.40
a.		Double surcharge		
156	A44	1c on 1s bl ('06)	77.50	50.00
157	A44	3c on 5c gray lil		
		('06)	10.00	4.00
158	A44	3c on 20c gray		
		('06)	25.00	15.00
159	A44	3c on 25c yel		
		('06)	24.00	15.00
159A	A44	3c on 1s blue		
		('06)	3.75	2.25
		Nos. 153-159A (8)	152.50	91.55

Counterfeits are plentiful.
See #191-197.

Capt. Abdón Calderón
A45   A46

		1904, July 31		**Perf. 12**
160	A45	1c red & blk	.40	.30
161	A45	2c blue & blk	.50	.35
162	A46	5c yellow & blk	1.50	1.00
163	A45	10c red & blk	6.00	1.00
164	A45	20c blue & blk	10.00	2.50
165	A46	50c yellow & blk	65.00	35.00
		Nos. 160-165 (6)	83.40	40.15

Centenary of the birth of Calderón.

Presidents

Vicente   Diego
Roca — A47   Noboa — A48

Francisco   José M.
Robles — A49   Urvina — A50

García   Jerónimo
Moreno — A51   Carrión — A52

Javier   Antonio
Espinoza   Borrero
A53   A54

		1907, July		**Perf. 14, 15**
166	A47	1c red & blk	1.00	.20
167	A48	2c pale blue & blk	2.00	.20
168	A49	3c orange & blk	3.00	.20
169	A50	5c lilac rose & blk	3.75	.20
170	A51	10c dp blue & blk	7.50	.20
171	A52	20c yellow grn & blk	10.00	.35

172	A53	50c violet & blk	22.50	.70
173	A54	1s green & blk	30.00	2.00
		Nos. 166-173 (8)	79.75	4.05

The stamps of the 1907 issue frequently have control marks similar to those found on the 1899 and 1901 issues. These marks were applied to distinguish the stamps issued in the various provinces and to serve as a check on local officials.

Locomotive — A55

García Moreno — A56

Gen. Eloy Alfaro — A57

Abelardo Moncayo — A58

Archer Harman — A59

James Sivewright — A60

Mt. Chimborazo
A61

		1908, June 25		
174	A55	1c red brown	.75	1.50
175	A56	2c blue & blk	1.00	1.60
176	A57	5c claret & blk	1.90	3.75
177	A58	10c ocher & blk	1.40	2.10
178	A59	20c green & blk	1.40	2.75
179	A60	50c gray & blk	1.40	2.75
180	A61	1s black	2.75	5.50
		Nos. 174-180 (7)	10.60	19.95

Opening of the Guayaquil-Quito Railway.

José Mejía   Principal
Vallejo — A62   Exposition
    Building — A70

Designs: 2c, Francisco J. E. Santa Cruz y Espejo. 3c, Francisco Ascásubi. 5c, Juan Salinas. 10c, Juan Pio de Montúfar. 20c, Carlos de Montúfar. 50c, Juan de Dios Morales. 1s, Manuel R. de Quiroga.

		1909, Aug. 10		**Perf. 12**
181	A62	1c green	.25	.45
182	A62	2c blue	.25	.45
183	A62	3c orange	.25	.50
184	A62	5c claret	.25	.50
185	A62	10c yellow brn	.30	.50
186	A62	20c gray	.30	.70
187	A62	50c vermilion	.30	.70
188	A62	1s olive grn	.35	.95
189	A70	5s violet	.75	1.90
		Nos. 181-189 (9)	3.00	6.65

National Exposition of 1909.

Surcharged

		1909		
190	A68	5c on 50c vermilion	.80	.50

Revenue Stamps Surcharged as in 1903

		1910		**Perf. 14, 15**
		Stamps Dated 1905-1906		
191	A44	1c on 5c green	2.25	1.75
192	A44	5c on 20c blue	9.50	2.00
193	A44	5c on 25c violet	18.00	3.50
		Stamps Dated 1907-1908		
194	A44	1c on 5c green	.40	.40
195	A44	5c on 20c blue	14.00	9.50
196	A44	5c on 25c violet	1.20	.40
		Stamp Dated 1909-1910		
197	A44	5c on 20c blue	80.00	60.00
		Nos. 191-197 (7)	125.35	77.55

Presidents

Roca — A71   Noboa — A72

Robles — A73   Urvina — A74

Moreno — A75   Borrero — A76

		1911-28		**Perf. 12**
198	A71	1c scarlet & blk	.80	.20
199	A71	1c orange ('16)	.80	.20
200	A71	1c lt blue ('25)	.40	.20
201	A72	2c blue & blk	1.10	.20
202	A72	2c green ('16)	1.10	.20
203	A72	2c dk violet ('25)	1.10	.20
204	A73	3c orange & blk ('13)	2.25	.30
205	A73	3c black ('15)	1.50	.20
206	A74	5c scarlet & blk	1.90	.20
207	A74	5c violet ('15)	1.90	.20
208	A74	5c rose ('25)	.70	.20
209	A74	5c dk brown ('28)	.70	.20
210	A75	10c dp blue & blk	2.25	.20
211	A75	10c dp blue ('15)	2.25	.20
212	A75	10c yellow grn ('25)	.70	.20
213	A75	10c black ('28)	1.60	.20
214	A76	1s green & blk	12.00	1.10
215	A76	1s orange & blk ('27)	8.00	.20
		Nos. 198-215 (18)	41.05	4.60

For overprints see Nos. 260-262, 264-265, O107-O122, O124-O134, O156-O157, O160-O162, O164-O166, O168-O173, O175-O178, O183-O184, O189, RA1.

A77

		1912		**Perf. 14, 15**
216	A77	1c on 1s green	1.00	1.00
217	A77	2c on 2s carmine	2.50	1.00
218	A77	2c on 5s dull blue	1.50	1.50
219	A77	2c on 10s yellow	5.00	5.00
a.		Inverted surcharge	16.00	12.00
		Nos. 216-219 (4)	10.00	9.00

No. 216 exists with narrow "V" and small "U" in "UN" and Nos. 217, 218 and 219 with "D" with serifs or small "O" in "DOS."

Enrique   Jerónimo
Váldez — A78   Carrión — A79

Javier
Espinoza — A80

		1915-17		**Perf. 12**
220	A78	4c red & blk	.40	.20
221	A79	20c green & blk ('17)	3.50	.20
222	A80	50c dp violet & blk	6.00	.45
		Nos. 220-222 (3)	9.90	.85

For overprints see #O123, O135, O163, O174.

Olmedo — A86   Monument to
    "Fathers of the
    Country" — A95

Laurel Wreath and
Star — A104

Designs: 2c, Rafael Ximena. 3c, Roca. 4c, Luis F. Vivero. 5c, Luis Febres Cordero. 6c, Francisco Lavayen. 7c, Jorge Antonio de Elizalde. 8c, Baltazar Garcia. 9c, Jose de Antepara. 15c, Luis Urdaneta. 20c, Jose M. Villamil. 30c, Miguel Letamendi. 40c, Gregorio Escobedo. 50c, Gen. Antonio Jose de Sucre. 60c, Juan Illingworth. 70c, Roca. 80c, Rocafuerte. 1s, Simon Bolivar.

		1920		
223	A86	1c yellow grn	.30	.20
224	A86	2c carmine	.30	.20
225	A86	3c yellow brn	.30	.20
226	A86	4c myrtle green	.45	.20
227	A86	5c pale blue	.45	.20
228	A86	6c red orange	.80	.30
229	A86	7c brown	2.25	.75
230	A86	8c apple green	1.10	.35
231	A86	9c lake	4.25	1.25
232	A95	10c lt blue	1.50	.20
233	A86	15c dk gray	2.25	.35
234	A86	20c dk violet	2.25	.20
235	A86	30c brt violet	4.25	1.00
236	A86	40c dk brown	7.50	1.75
237	A86	50c dk green	5.25	.35
238	A86	60c dk blue	9.50	1.90
239	A86	70c gray	16.00	4.25
240	A86	80c orange yel	16.50	4.25

241 A104 90c green 17.00 4.25
242 A86 1s pale blue 24.00 7.00
　　　Nos. 223-242 (20) 116.20 29.15

Cent. of the independence of Guayaquil.
For overprints and surcharges see Nos.
263, 274-292, O136-O155, O179-O182,
O185-O188.

Postal Tax Stamp
of 1924
Overprinted

1925
259 PT6 20c bister brown 4.00 1.50

Stamps of 1915-25
Overprinted in Black
or Red Upright (1c,
3c, 5c) or Inverted
(2c, 4c, 10c)

1926
260 A71 1c lt blue 11.00 9.50
261 A72 2c dk violet 11.00 9.50
262 A73 3c black (R) 11.00 9.50
263 A86 4c myrtle green 11.00 9.50
264 A74 5c rose 16.00 9.50
265 A75 10c yellow grn 16.00 9.50
　　　Nos. 260-265 (6) 76.00 57.00

Quito-Esmeraldas railway opening.
Upright overprints on 2c, 4c, 10c and
inverted overprints on 1c, 3c, 5c sell for more.

Postal Tax
Stamps of 1920-
24 Overprinted

1927
266 PT6 1c olive green .50 .20
　a. "POSTAI" 1.40 .85
　b. Double overprint 2.00 .85
　c. Inverted overprint 2.00 .85
267 PT6 2c deep green .50 .20
　a. "POSTAI" 1.40 .85
　b. Double overprint 2.00 .85
268 PT6 20c bister brown 1.00 .20
　a. "POSTAI" 8.50 5.00
　　　Nos. 266-268 (3) 2.00 .60

Quito Post
Office — A109

1927, June
269 A109 5c orange .50 .20
270 A109 10c dark green .70 .20
271 A109 20c violet .80 .20
　　　Nos. 269-271 (3) 2.00 .60

Opening of new Quito P.O.
For overprint see No. O190.

Postal Tax Stamp of
1924 Overprinted in
Dark Blue

POSTAL

1928
273 PT6 20c bister brown .50 .20
　a. Double overprint, one inverted 2.00 .70

See No. 339 for 10c with same overprint.

Nos. 235, 239-240 Overprinted in
Red Brown and
Surcharged in Dark Blue

1928, July 8
274 A86 10c on 30c violet 15.00 15.00
275 A86 50c on 70c gray 18.00 18.00
276 A86 1s on 80c org yel 21.00 21.00
　　　Nos. 274-276 (3) 54.00 54.00

Quito-Cayambe railway opening.

Stamps of 1920
Surcharged

1928, Oct. 9
277 A86 1c on 1c yel grn 15.00 15.00
278 A86 1c on 2c car .30 .30
279 A86 2c on 3c yel brn 2.25 2.25
　a. Dbl. surch., one reading up 30.00 30.00
280 A86 2c on 4c myr grn 1.50 1.50
281 A86 2c on 5c lt blue .60 .45
　a. Dbl. surch., one reading up 30.00 30.00
282 A86 2c on 7c brown 75.00 75.00
283 A86 5c on 6c red org .40 .30
　a. "5 ctvos." omitted 37.50 37.50
284 A86 10c on 7c brown 1.25 1.25
285 A86 20c on 8c apple grn .35 .30
　a. Double surcharge
286 A95 40c on 10c blue 4.25 4.25
287 A86 40c on 15c dk gray 1.25 1.25
288 A86 50c on 20c dk vio 13.25 13.25
289 A86 1s on 40c dk brown 4.50 4.50
290 A86 5s on 50c dk green 5.25 5.25
291 A86 10s on 50c dk blue 19.50 19.50

With Additional
Surcharge in Red

292 A86 10c on 2c on 7c
　　brn .50 .50
　a. Red surcharge double 30.00 30.00
　　　Nos. 277-292 (16) 145.15 144.85

National Assembly of 1928.
Counterfeit overprints exist of #277-291.

A111　　　　　　A112

Surcharged in Various Colors

1928, Oct. 31　　　　*Perf. 14*
293 A111 5c on 20c gray lil
　　(Bk) 3.00 1.75
294 A111 10c on 20c gray lil
　　(R) 3.00 1.75
295 A111 20c on 1s grn (O) 3.00 1.75
296 A111 50c on 1s grn (Bl) 3.75 1.40
297 A111 1s on 1s grn (V) 4.75 1.75
298 A111 5s on 2s red (G) 15.00 9.00
299 A111 10s on 2s red (Br) 18.00 12.00
　a. Black surcharge 15.00 10.00
　　　Nos. 293-299 (7) 50.50 29.40

Quito-Otavalo railway opening.
See Nos. 586-587.

Postal Tax Stamp
of 1924
Overprinted in
Red

1929　　　　　　*Perf. 12*
302 PT6 2c deep green .50 .20

There are two types of overprint on No. 302
differing slightly.

1929

Red Overprint
303 A112 1c dark blue .50 .20
　a. Overprint reading down .75 .50
　　　See Nos. 586-587.

Plowing — A113

Cultivating
Cacao — A114

Cacao
Pod — A115

Loading Sugar
Cane — A119

Growing
Tobacco — A116

Exportation of
Fruits — A117

Landscape — A118

Scene in
Quito
A120

Scene in
Quito
A121

Olmedo — A122

Monument to Simón Bolívar — A125

Designs: 2s, Sucre. 5s, Bolivar.

1930, Aug. 1　　　　*Perf. 12½*
304 A113 1c yellow & car .30 .20
305 A114 2c yellow & grn .30 .20
306 A115 5c dp grn & vio brn .35 .20
307 A116 6c yellow & red .40 .20
308 A117 10c orange & ol grn .40 .20
309 A118 16c red & yel grn .50 .25
310 A119 20c ultra & yel .80 .20
311 A120 40c orange & sepia 1.10 .20
312 A121 50c orange & sepia 1.10 .40
313 A122 1s dp green & blk 4.25 .45
314 A122 2s dk blue & blk 6.50 2.00
315 A122 5s dk violet & blk 11.50 3.00
316 A125 10s car rose & blk 40.00 6.00
　　　Nos. 304-316 (13) 67.50 13.50

Centenary of founding of republic.
For surcharges and overprints see Nos.
319-320, 331-338, RA25, RA33, RA43.

A126　　　　　　A127

Red Overprint
1933　　　　　　*Perf. 15*
317 A126 10c olive brown 1.15 .20

Blue Overprint
318 A127 10c olive brown .70 .20
　a. Inverted overprint 5.00 5.00

For overprint see No. 339.

Nos. 307, 309 Surcharged in Black

1933　　　　　　*Perf. 12½*
319 A116 5c on 6c yellow & red 1.00 .20
320 A118 10c on 16c red & yel
　　grn 2.00 .20
　a. Inverted overprint 4.00 4.00

Landscape　　　Mt. Chimborazo
A128　　　　　　A129

1934-45　　　　*Perf. 12*
321 A128 5c violet 1.40 .45
322 A128 5c blue 1.40 .45
323 A128 5c dark brown 1.40 .45

323A	A128	5c slate blk ('45)	1.40	.45
324	A128	10c rose	1.40	.45
325	A128	10c dark green	1.40	.45
326	A128	10c brown	1.40	.45
327	A128	10c orange	1.40	.45
328	A128	10c olive green	1.40	.45
329	A128	10c gray blk ('35)	1.40	.45
329A	A128	10c red lilac ('44)	1.40	.45

Perf. 14

330	A129	1s carmine rose	1.60	.50
	Nos. 321-330 (12)		17.00	5.45

Stamps of 1930 Surcharged or Ovptd. in various colors similar to:

INAUGURACION MONUMENTO A BOLIVAR
5 ctvs.
QUITO, 24 DE JULIO DE 1935

1935   **Perf. 12½**

331	A116	5c on 6c (Bl)	.90	.35
332	A116	10c on 6c (G)	1.25	.35
333	A119	20c (R)	1.75	.35
334	A120	40c (G)	2.50	.35
335	A121	50c (G)	3.00	.40
336	A122	1s on 5s (Gold)	7.00	1.00
337	A122	2s on 5s (Gold)	9.50	1.60
338	A125	5s on 10s (Bl)	12.00	4.25
	Nos. 331-338,C35-C38 (12)		87.90	28.65

Unveiling of a monument to Bolivar at Quito, July 24, 1935.

The 5-stamp Sociedad Colombista Panamericana series of 1935 and 5 airmail stamps of a similar design are not recognized by this Catalogue as having been issued primarily for postal purposes. Value for 10-value set, unused $3.25, used $6.50.

Telegraph Stamp Overprinted Diagonally in Red like No. 273

1935   **Perf. 14½**

339	A126	10c olive brown	.75	.25

Map of Galápagos Islands A130

Galapagos Land Iguana A131

Galápagos Tortoise — A132

Charles R. Darwin — A133

Columbus A134

Island Scene A135

1936   **Perf. 14**

340	A130	2c black	1.00	.25
341	A131	5c olive grn	1.25	.25
342	A132	10c brown	2.25	.30
343	A133	20c dk violet	2.50	.40

344	A134	1s dk carmine	4.00	.75
345	A135	2s dark blue	6.00	1.25
	Nos. 340-345 (6)		17.00	3.20

Cent. of the visit of Charles Darwin to the Galápagos Islands, Sept. 17, 1835.
For overprints see Nos. O191-O195.

Tobacco Stamp Overprinted in Black

POSTAL

1936   **Rouletted 7**

346	PT7	1c rose red	.50	.25
	a.	Horiz. pair, imperf. vert.		
	b.	Double surcharge		

No. 346 is similar to type PT7 but does not include "CASA CORREOS."

Louis Godin, Charles M. de la Condamine and Pierre Bouguer A136

Portraits: 5c, 20c, Antonio Ulloa, La Condamine and Jorge Juan.

1936   **Engr.**   **Perf. 12½**

347	A136	2c deep blue	.50	.30
348	A136	5c dark green	.50	.30
349	A136	10c deep orange	.50	.30
350	A136	20c violet	.80	.30
351	A136	50c dark red	1.25	.30
	Nos. 347-351,C39-C42 (9)		6.60	2.45

Bicentenary of Geodesical Mission to Quito.

Independence Monument — A137

1936   **Perf. 13½x14**

352	A137	2c green	2.00	1.10
353	A137	5c dark violet	2.00	1.10
354	A137	10c carmine rose	2.00	1.10
355	A137	20c black	2.00	1.10
356	A137	50c blue	2.75	1.75
357	A137	1s dark red	3.75	3.25
	Nos. 352-357,C43-C50 (14)		45.50	37.40

1st Intl. Philatelic Exhibition at Quito.

Coat of Arms — A138

Overprint in Black or Red

1937   **Perf. 12½**

359	A138	5c olive green	2.00	.30
360	A138	10c dark blue (R)	2.00	.25

For overprint see No. 562.

Andean Landscape A139

Atahualpa, the Last Inca A140

Hat Weavers — A141

Coast Landscape A142

Gold Washing A143

1937, Aug. 19   **Perf. 11½**

361	A139	2c green	.50	.25
362	A140	5c deep rose	.50	.25
363	A141	10c blue	.50	.25
364	A142	20c deep rose	1.50	.30
365	A143	1s olive green	2.00	.35
	Nos. 361-365 (5)		5.00	1.40

For overprints see Nos. O196-O200.

"Liberty" Carrying Flag of Ecuador — A144

Engraved and Lithographed
1938, Feb. 22   **Perf. 12**
Center Multicolored

366	A144	2c blue	.25	.20
367	A144	5c violet	.30	.20
368	A144	10c black	.40	.20
369	A144	20c brown	.55	.20
370	A144	50c black	.85	.20
371	A144	1s olive blk	1.25	.30
372	A144	2s dk brn	2.50	.40
	Nos. 366-372,C57-C63 (14)		20.60	3.80

US Constitution, 150th anniversary.
For overprints and surcharges see Nos. 413-415, 444-446, RA46, RA52.

A145   A146

A147   A148

Designs: 10c, Winged figure holding globe. 50c, Cactus, winged wheel. 1s, "Communications." 2s, "Construction."

        Perf. 13, 13x13½
1938, Oct. 30   **Engr.**

373	A145	10c bright ultra	.40	.20
374	A146	50c deep red violet	.40	.20
375	A147	1s copper red	.70	.20
376	A148	2s dark green	1.10	.20
	Nos. 373-376 (4)		2.60	.80

Progress of Ecuador Exhibition.
For overprints see Nos. C105-C113.

Parade of Athletes — A149

Runner — A150

Basketball — A151

Wrestlers A152

Diver A153

1939, Mar.   **Perf. 12**

377	A149	5c carmine rose	2.75	.45
378	A150	10c deep blue	3.25	.55
379	A151	50c gray olive	5.25	.75
380	A152	1s dull violet	7.50	.75
381	A153	2s dull olive green	11.00	.95
	Nos. 377-381,C65-C69 (10)		71.25	5.60

First Bolivarian Games (1938), Bogota.

Dolores Mission A154

Trylon and Perisphere A155

1939, June 16   **Perf. 12½x13**

382	A154	2c blue green	.50	.25
383	A154	5c rose red	.50	.25
384	A154	10c ultra	.50	.25
385	A154	50c yellow brown	1.20	.25
386	A154	1s black	1.90	.25
387	A154	2s purple	1.25	.40
	Nos. 382-387,C73-C79 (13)		11.25	3.05

Golden Gate International Exposition.
For surcharges see Nos. 429, 436.

1939, June 30

388	A155	2c lt olive green	.70	.35
389	A155	5c red orange	.70	.35
390	A155	10c ultra	.70	.35
391	A155	50c slate gray	1.00	.35
392	A155	1s rose carmine	1.75	.35
393	A155	2s black brown	2.00	.40
	Nos. 388-393,C80-C86 (13)		15.10	3.55

New York World's Fair.
For surcharge see No. 437.

Flags of the 21 American Republics — A156

1940   **Perf. 12**

394	A156	5c dp rose & blk	1.00	.30
395	A156	10c dk blue & blk	.40	.20
396	A156	50c Prus green & blk	.60	.20
397	A156	1s dp violet & blk	1.00	.30
	Nos. 394-397,C87-C90 (8)		7.85	2.45

Pan American Union, 50th anniversary.

Francisco J. E. Santa
Cruz y
Espejo — A157

1941, Dec. 15
398	A157	30c blue	1.25	.20
399	A157	1s red orange	2.50	.35
		Nos. 398-399,C91-C92 (4)	20.00	1.20

Exposition of Journalism held under the auspices of the Natl. Newspaper Men's Union.

Francisco de
Orellana
A158

Gonzalo Pizarro
A159

View of
Guayaquil
A160

View of
Quito — A161

1942, Jan. 30
400	A158	10c sepia	.90	.35
401	A159	40c deep rose	2.50	.35
402	A160	1s violet	3.50	.35
403	A161	2s dark blue	4.50	.45
		Nos. 400-403,C93-C96 (8)	23.45	2.75

400th anniv. of the discovery and exploration of the Amazon River by Orellana.

Remigio
Crespo Toral
A162

Alfredo
Baquerizo
Moreno
A163

1942 *Perf. 13½*
404	A162	10c green	.60	.20
405	A162	50c brown	1.00	.20
		Nos. 404-405,C97 (3)	2.85	.85

1942
| 406 | A163 | 10c green | .25 | .25 |

Mt.
Chimborazo
A164

1942-47 *Perf. 12*
407	A164	30c red brown	.60	.25
407A	A164	30c lt blue ('43)	.60	.25
407B	A164	30c red orange ('44)	.60	.25
407C	A164	30c green ('47)	.60	.25
		Nos. 407-407C (4)	2.40	1.00

View of
Guayaquil
A165

1942-44
| 408 | A165 | 20c red | .45 | .20 |
| 408A | A165 | 20c deep blue ('44) | .45 | .20 |

Gen. Eloy
Alfaro — A166

Devil's
Nose — A167

President Alfaro (1842-1912): 30c, Military College. 1s, Montecristi, Alfaro's birthplace.

1942
409	A166	10c dk rose & blk	.60	.20
410	A167	20c ol blk & red brn	.60	.20
411	A167	30c ol gray & grn	.75	.20
412	A167	1s slate & salmon	1.80	.25
		Nos. 409-412,C98-C101 (8)	20.15	3.70

Nos. 370-372 Overprinted in Red Brown

1943, Apr. 15 *Perf. 11½*
413	A144	50c multicolored	.60	.60
414	A144	1s multicolored	1.10	1.10
415	A144	2s multicolored	2.40	2.40
		Nos. 413-415,C102-C104 (6)	14.10	9.70

Visit of US Vice-Pres. Henry A. Wallace.

"30 Centavos" — A170

Black Surcharge

1943 *Perf. 12½*
| 416 | A170 | 30c on 50c red brn | 1.00 | .25 |
| a. | | Without bars | 1.00 | .25 |

Map Showing US and
Ecuador — A171

1943, Oct. 9 *Perf. 12*
417	A171	10c dull violet	.70	.50
418	A171	20c red brown	.70	.50
419	A171	30c orange	.70	.50
420	A171	50c olive green	.80	.60

421	A171	1s deep violet	.90	.65
422	A171	10s olive bister	7.50	5.25
		Nos. 417-422,C114-C118 (11)	29.80	15.10

Good will tour of Pres. Arroyo del Rio in 1942.

1944, Feb. 7
423	A171	10c yellow green	.60	.45
424	A171	20c rose pink	.60	.45
425	A171	30c dark gray brown	.60	.45
426	A171	50c deep red lilac	.60	.45
427	A171	1s olive gray	.90	.65
428	A171	10s red orange	9.50	6.00
		Nos. 423-428,C119-C123 (11)	23.60	13.40

For surcharges see Nos. B1-B6.

No. 385 Surcharged
in Black

1944 **Unwmk.** *Perf. 12½x13*
| 429 | A154 | 30c on 50c yel brn | 2.00 | .20 |

Archbishop Federico
González Suárez,
Birth Cent. — A172

1944 *Perf. 12*
430	A172	10c deep blue	.40	.20
431	A172	20c green	.40	.20
432	A172	30c dk violet brn	.50	.20
433	A172	1s dull violet	.90	.25
		Nos. 430-433,C124-C127 (8)	15.50	3.75

Air Post Stamps
Nos. C76 and C83
Surcharged in Black

1944 *Perf. 12½x13*
| 434 | AP15 | 30c on 50c rose vio | .40 | .20 |
| 435 | AP16 | 30c on 50c sl grn | .40 | .20 |

Nos. 382 and 388
Surcharged in Black

1944-45
436	A154	5c on 2c bl grn	.50	.20
a.		Double surcharge	4.00	
437	A155	5c on 2c lt ol grn ('45)	.50	.20

Government
Palace,
Quito — A173

1944 **Engr.** *Perf. 11*
| 438 | A173 | 10c dark green | .50 | .20 |
| 439 | A173 | 30c blue | .50 | .20 |

For surcharges see Nos. 452, RAC1-RAC2.

Symbol of
the Red
Cross
A174

1945, Apr. 25 *Perf. 12*
Cross in Rose
440	A174	30c bister brown	1.75	.35
441	A174	1s red brown	2.40	.45
442	A174	5s turq green	4.25	1.10
443	A174	10s scarlet	11.50	3.00
		Nos. 440-443,C131-C134 (8)	55.90	11.30

International Red Cross, 80th anniversary.

Nos. 370 to 372 Overprinted in Dark Blue and Gold

1945, Oct. 2 *Perf. 11½*
Center Multicolored
444	A144	50c multicolored	.80	.70
a.		Double overprint		
445	A144	1s olive black	1.40	1.40
446	A144	2s dark brown	2.75	2.50
		Nos. 444-446,C139-C141 (6)	9.95	8.25

Visit of Pres. Juan Antonio Rios of Chile.

General Antonio
José de Sucre,
150th Birth
Anniv. — A175

1945, Nov. 14 **Engr.** *Perf. 12*
447	A175	10c olive	.50	.25
448	A175	20c red brown	.50	.20
449	A175	40c olive gray	.50	.20
450	A175	1s dark green	1.00	.25
451	A175	2s sepia	2.00	.75
		Nos. 447-451,C142-C146 (10)	12.00	5.20

No. 438 Surcharged in Blue

1945 *Perf. 11*
| 452 | A173 | 20c on 10c dark green | .50 | .20 |
| a. | | Fancy bar omitted | | |

Catalogue values for unused stamps in this section, from this point to the end of the section, are for Never Hinged items.

Map of Pan-
American Highway
and Arms of
Loja — A176

1946, Apr. 22 **Engr.** *Perf. 12*
453	A176	20c red brown	.75	.50
454	A176	30c bright green	.75	.50
455	A176	1s bright ultra	.75	.50
456	A176	5s deep red lilac	2.25	1.50
457	A176	10s scarlet	6.00	4.75
		Nos. 453-457,C147-C151 (10)	21.60	12.05

Torch of
Democracy — A177

Popular
Suffrage
A178

Flag of
Ecuador — A179

Pres. José M.
Velasco
Ibarra — A180

1946, Aug. 9   Unwmk.   Perf. 12½
458	A177	5c dark blue	.25	.20
459	A178	10c Prus green	.25	.20
460	A179	20c carmine	.30	.20
461	A180	30c chocolate	.55	.20
		Nos. 458-461,C152-C155 (8)	3.75	1.85

Revolution of May 28, 1944, 2nd anniv.

"30 Ctvs." — A181

Black Surcharge
1946
462	A181	30c on 50c red brown	1.00	.20

For overprint see No. 484.

Nos. CO13-CO14 With Additional
Overprint in Black

1946   Perf. 11½
463	AP7	10c chestnut	1.00	.20
464	AP7	20c olive black	1.00	.20

Instructor and
Student — A182

1946, Sept. 16   Perf. 12½
465	A182	10c deep blue	.60	.60
466	A182	20c chocolate	.60	.60
467	A182	30c dark green	.60	.60
468	A182	50c bluish blk	1.20	1.20
469	A182	1s dark red	1.50	1.40
470	A182	10s dark violet	9.00	2.40
		Nos. 465-470,C156-C160 (11)	29.95	11.95

Campaign for adult education.

Mariana de
Jesus Paredes y
Flores — A183

Urn — A184

1946, Nov. 28
471	A183	10c black brown	.60	.60
472	A183	20c green	.60	.60
473	A183	30c purple	.60	.60
474	A184	1s rose brown	.80	.60
		Nos. 471-474,C161-C164 (8)	8.00	6.10

300th anniv. of the death of the Blessed
Mariana de Jesus Paredes y Flores.

Pres. Vicente
Rocafuerte
A185

Jesuits' Church
Quito
A186

45c, 50c, 80c, F.J.E. de Santa Cruz y
Espejo.

1947, Nov. 27   Perf. 12
475	A185	5c redsh brown	.30	.20
476	A185	10c sepia	.30	.20
477	A185	15c gray black	.30	.20
478	A186	20c redsh brown	.30	.20
479	A186	30c red violet	.35	.20
480	A186	40c brt ultra	.45	.20
481	A185	45c dk slate grn	.50	.20
482	A185	50c olive black	.50	.20
483	A185	80c orange red	.80	.20
		Nos. 475-483,C165-C171 (16)	7.80	3.20

For overprints and surcharges see Nos.
489, 496, 525-527.

Type of 1946, Overprinted "POSTAL"
in Black but Without Additional
Surcharge

1948   Engr.
484	A181	10c orange	.75	.25

Andrés Bello
A188

Flagship of
Columbus
A189

1948, Apr. 21   Perf. 13
485	A188	20c lt blue	.50	.25
486	A188	30c rose carmine	.50	.25
487	A188	40c blue green	.50	.25
488	A188	1s black brown	.70	.25
		Nos. 485-488,C172-C174 (7)	3.90	1.65

83rd anniversary of the death of Andrés
Bello (1781-1865), educator.

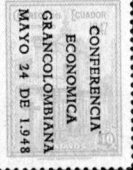

No. 480
Overprinted in
Black

1948, May 24   Perf. 12
489	A186	40c bright ultra	1.00	.30

See No. C175.

1948   Perf. 14
490	A189	10c dark blue green	.60	.60
491	A189	20c brown	.60	.60
492	A189	30c dark purple	1.50	.60
493	A189	50c deep claret	1.75	.60
494	A189	1s ultra	3.75	1.50
495	A189	5s carmine	6.75	1.60
		Nos. 490-495,C176-C180 (11)	34.80	17.00

Issued to publicize the proposed Columbus
Memorial Lighthouse near Ciudad Trujillo,
Dominican Republic.

No. 483 Overprinted
in Blue

1948   Perf. 12
"MANANA" Reading Down
496	A185	80c orange red	.50	.25

Issued to publicize the National Fair of
Today and Tomorrow, 1948. See No. C181.

Telegrafo I in
Flight — A190

Book and
Pen — A191

1948   Engr.   Perf. 12½
497	A190	30c red orange	.75	.25
498	A190	40c rose lilac	.75	.25
499	A190	60c violet blue	.75	.25
500	A190	1s brown red	.75	.25
501	A190	3s brown	2.40	.35
502	A190	5s gray black	2.75	.35
		Nos. 497-502,C182-C187 (12)	16.40	3.45

25th anniversary (in 1945) of the first postal
flight in Ecuador.

1948, Oct. 12   Unwmk.   Perf. 14
503	A191	10c deep claret	.60	.20
504	A191	20c brown	.60	.20
505	A191	30c dark green	.75	.20
506	A191	50c red	.75	.20
507	A191	1s purple	1.00	.30
508	A191	10s dull blue	10.00	1.00
		Nos. 503-508,C188-C192 (11)	34.70	9.75

Campaign for adult education.

A192

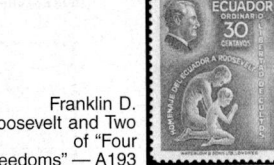

Franklin D.
Roosevelt and Two
of "Four
Freedoms" — A193

1948, Oct. 24   Perf. 12½
509	A192	10c rose brn & gray	.45	.40
510	A192	20c brn ol & bl	.45	.40
511	A193	30c ol bis & car rose	.45	.40
512	A193	40c red vio & sep	.60	.40
513	A193	1s org brn & car	.65	.50
		Nos. 509-513,C193-C197 (10)	7.15	3.35

Maldonado and
Map — A194

Riobamba
Aqueduct
A195

Maldonado on
Bank of
Riobamba
A196

Pedro V.
Maldonado
A197

1948, Nov. 17   Engr.   Unwmk.
514	A194	5c gray blk & ver	.60	.20
515	A195	10c car & gray blk	.70	.20
516	A196	30c bis brn & ultra	.80	.20
517	A195	40c sage grn & vio	1.10	.20
518	A194	50c grn & car	1.40	.30
519	A197	1s brn & slate bl	1.75	.35
		Nos. 514-519,C198-C201 (10)	10.95	2.25

Bicentenary of the death of Pedro Vicente
Maldonado, geographer.
For overprints and surcharges see Nos.
537-540.

A198

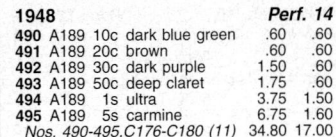

Miguel de
Cervantes
Saavedra
A199

1949, May 2   Perf. 12½x12
520	A198	30c dk car rose & dp ultra	1.00	.25
521	A199	60c bis & brn vio	1.50	.40
522	A198	1s grn & rose car	1.60	.25
523	A199	2s gray blk & red brn	3.50	.40
524	A198	5s choc & aqua	6.25	1.10
		Nos. 520-524,C202-C206 (10)	29.85	5.90

400th anniv. of the birth of Miguel de
Cervantes Saavedra, novelist, playwright and
poet.

No. 480
Surcharged in
Carmine

1949, June 15   Perf. 12
525	A186	10c on 40c brt ultra	.50	.20
526	A186	20c on 40c brt ultra	.70	.20
	a.	Double surcharge		
527	A186	30c on 40c brt ultra	.70	.20
		Nos. 525-527,C207-C209 (6)	3.30	1.20

2nd Natl. Eucharistic Cong., Quito, 6/49.
No. 526 exists se-tenant with No. 527.

Monument on Equator — A200

1949, June   Engr.   Perf. 12½x12
528 A200 10c deep plum   .50   .20

For overprint see No. 536.

No. 542 Surcharged in Black and Carmine

1949   Perf. 12x12½
529 A203 10c on 50c green   .50   .25
530 A203 20c on 50c green   .50   .25
531 A203 30c on 50c green   .60   .25
     Nos. 529-531,C210-C213 (7)   7.00 2.75

Universal Postal Union, 75th anniversary.

Consular Service Stamps Surcharged in Black

Arms of Ecuador — R1

1949   Perf. 12
532 R1 20c on 25c red brown   .75   .20
533 R1 30c on 50c gray   .75   .20

For other overprints and surcharges on type R1 see Nos. 544-549, 566-570, C245, C249-C252, RA60-RA62, RA72.

Nos. RA49A and RA55 Overprinted in Black

a

1950   Unwmk.   Perf. 12
534 PT18 5c green   .50   .20
535 PT21 5c blue   .50   .20

Overprint 15mm on No. 534.

Nos. 528 and 517 to 519 Overprinted or Surcharged in Black or Carmine

1950, Feb. 10   Perf. 12½x12
536 A200 10c dp plum   .75   .75

Perf. 12½
537 A195 20c on 40c sage grn
             & vio   1.40 1.40
538 A195 30c on 40c sage grn
             & vio   1.50 1.50
539 A194 50c grn & car   2.25 2.25
540 A197 1s brn & slate bl
             (C)   3.00 3.00

No. C220 Overprinted Type "a" in Carmine

Perf. 11

Overprint 15mm long
541 A173 10s violet   7.50 3.75
     Nos. 536-541,C216-C220 (11)   36.15 24.65

Nos. 536-541 publicize adult education.

San Pablo Lake — A203

Perf. 12x12½
1950, May   Engr.   Unwmk.
542 A203 50c green   .75   .20

For surcharges see Nos. 529-531.

Consular Service Stamp Surcharged "CORREOS" and New Value Vertically in Black

1950   Perf. 12
544 R1 30c on 50c gray   .75   .25

Consular Service Stamps Overprinted or Surcharged in Black

b   c

d   e

f   g

1951   Unwmk.   Perf. 12
545 R1 (b) 5c on 10c car rose   .75   .25
546 R1 (c) 10c car rose   .75   .25
547 R1 (d) 10c car rose   .75   .25
548 R1 (e) 20c on 25c red brn   .75   .25
549 R1 (e) 30c on 50c gray   .75   .25
550 R2 (f) 40c on 25c blue   .75   .25
551 R2 (g) 50c on 25c blue   .75   .25
     Nos. 545-551 (7)   5.25 1.75

See #552-554, C233-C234, C246-C248, RA67.

Consular Service Stamps Surcharged in Black

1951
552 R2 20c on 25c blue   .75   .20
553 R2 30c on 25c blue   .75   .20

Adult education. See Nos. C225-C226.

Consular Service Stamp Surcharged in Black

1951
554 R2 $0.30 on 50c car rose   .75   .25

Reliquary of St. Mariana and Vatican — A204

Perf. 12½x12
1952, Feb.   Engr.   Unwmk.
555 A204 10c emer & red brn   .90   .70
556 A204 20c dp bl & pur   .90   .70
557 A204 30c car & bl grn   .90   .70
     Nos. 555-557,C227-C230 (7)   7.90 3.70

Issued to publicize the canonization of Mariana de Jesus Paredes y Flores.

Presidents Galo Plaza and Harry Truman — A205

2s, Pres. Plaza addressing US Congress.

1952, Mar. 26   Perf. 12
558 A205 1s rose car & gray blk   .70   .60
559 A205 2s dl bl & sepia   1.75 .90
     Nos. 558-559,C231-C232 (4)   5.45 4.20

1951 visit of Pres. Galo Plaza y Lasso to the US.

R3

Fiscal Stamps Surcharged or Overprinted Type "c" Horizontally in Carmine or Black

1952   Unwmk.   Engr.   Perf. 12
560 R3 20c on 30c dp bl (C)   .75   .25
561 R3 30c deep blue   .75   .20

Diagonal Overprint
562 A138 50c purple   .75   .20
     Nos. 560-562 (3)   2.25 .65

For overprints and surcharge see Nos. RA68-RA69, RA71.

Pres. José M. Urvina, Slave and "Liberty" — A206

Hyphen-hole Perf. 7x6½
1952   Litho.
563 A206 20c red & green   .60   .40
564 A206 30c red & vio bl   .75   .40
565 A206 50c blue & car   1.20   .40
     Nos. 563-565,C236-C239 (7)   26.55 5.00

Centenary of abolition of slavery in Ecuador. Counterfeits exist.

Consular Service Stamps Surcharged in Black — f

1952-53   Unwmk.   Perf. 12
566 R1 10c on 20s blue ('53)   .75   .20
567 R1 20c on 10s gray ('53)   .75   .20
568 R1 20c on 20s blue   .75   .20
569 R1 30c on 10s gray ('53)   .75   .20
570 R1 30c on 20s blue   .75   .20
     Nos. 566-570 (5)   3.75 1.00

Similar surcharges of 60c and 90c on the 20s blue are said to be bogus.

Teacher and Students — A207

New Citizens Voting — A208

Designs: 10c, Instructor with student. 30c, Teaching the alphabet.

1953, Apr. 13   Engr.
571 A207 5c lt bl   .30   .20
572 A207 10c dk car rose   .45   .20
573 A208 20c brt brn org   .50   .20
574 A208 30c dp red lil   .75   .20
     Nos. 571-574,C240-C241 (6)   6.00 1.20

1952 adult education campaign.

A209   Cuicocha Lagoon — A210

Black Surcharge
1953
575 A209 40c on 50c purple   1.00   .25

1953   Engr.   Perf. 13x12½

Designs: 10c, Equatorial Line monument. 20c, Quininde countryside. 30c, Tomebamba river. 40c, La Chilintosa rock. 50c, Iliniza Mountains.

Frames in Black

576	A210	5c brt bl	.50	.50
577	A210	10c brt grn	.50	.50
578	A210	20c purple	.50	.50
579	A210	30c brown	.50	.50
580	A210	40c orange	.50	.50
581	A210	50c dp car	.90	.50
	Nos. 576-581 (6)		3.40	3.00

A211

A212

Carlos Maria Cardinal de la Torre and arches.

1954, Jan.   Photo.   Perf. 8½

582	A211	30c blk & ver	.60	.60
583	A211	50c blk & rose lil	.60	.60
	Nos. 582-583,C253-C255 (5)		4.45	3.00

1st anniv. of the elevation of Archbishop de la Torre to Cardinal.

1954, Apr. 22

584	A212	30c blk & gray	1.20	1.20
585	A212	50c blk brn & yel	1.20	1.20
	Nos. 584-585,C256-C260 (7)		8.40	5.40

Queen Isabella I (1451-1504) of Spain, 500th birth anniv.

Type of 1929; "POSTAL" Overprint Larger, No Letterspacing

1954-55   Unwmk.   Perf. 12

586	A112	5c ol grn ('55)	.75	.20
587	A112	10c orange	.75	.20

The normal overprint on Nos. 586-587 reads up. It also exists reading down.

Indian Messenger A213

Products of Ecuador A214

1954, Aug. 2   Litho.   Perf. 11

588	A213	30c dk brn	1.00	.20

Day of the Postal Employee. See No. C263.

1954, Sept. 24   Photo.

589	A214	10c orange	.40	.20
590	A214	20c vermilion	.40	.20
591	A214	30c rose pink	.40	.20
592	A214	40c dk gray grn	.60	.20
593	A214	50c yel brn	.80	.20
	Nos. 589-593 (5)		2.60	1.00

José Abel Castillo — A215

Babahoyo River Los Rios — A216

Perf. 11½x11

1955, Oct. 19   Engr.   Unwmk.

594	A215	30c olive bister	.60	.20
595	A215	50c dk gray	.60	.20
	Nos. 594-595,C282-C286 (7)		15.40	2.25

30th anniv. of the 1st flight of the "Telegrafo I" and to honor Castillo, aviation pioneer.

1955-56   Photo.   Perf. 13

Designs: 5c, Palms, Esmeraldas. 10c, Fishermen, Manabi. 30c, Guayaquil, Guayas. 50c, Pital River, El Oro. 70c, Cactus, Galapagos

Isls. 80c, Orchids, Napo-Pastaza. 1s, Aguacate Mission, Zamora-Chinchipe. 2s, Jibaro Indian, Morona-Santiago.

596	A216	5c yel grn ('56)	1.50	.30
597	A216	10c blue ('56)	1.50	.30
598	A216	20c brown	1.50	.30
599	A216	30c dk gray	1.50	.30
600	A216	50c bl grn	1.50	.30
601	A216	70c ol ('56)	1.50	.30
602	A216	80c dp vio ('56)	3.75	.30
603	A216	1s org ('56)	2.00	.30
604	A216	2s rose red ('56)	3.75	.30
	Nos. 596-604 (9)		18.50	2.70

See #620-630, 670, C288-C297, C310-C311.

Brother Juan Adam Schwarz, S. J. — A217

1956, Aug. 27   Engr.   Perf. 13½

605	A217	5c yel grn	.40	.20
606	A217	10c org red	.40	.20
607	A217	20c lt vio	.40	.20
608	A217	30c dk grn	.40	.20
609	A217	40c blue	.40	.20
610	A217	50c dp ultra	.40	.20
611	A217	70c orange	.40	.20
	Nos. 605-611,C302-C305 (11)		5.20	2.20

Bicentennial of printing in Ecuador and honoring Brother Juan Adam Schwarz, S.J.

Andres Hurtado de Mendoza — A218

Gil Ramirez Davalos A219

Designs: 20c, Brother Vincent Solano.

1957, Apr. 7   Unwmk.   Perf. 12

612	A218	5c dk bl, *pink*	.30	.20
613	A219	10c grn, *grnsh*	.30	.20
614	A218	20c choc, *buff*	.30	.20
a.	Souvenir sheet of 4, imperf.		.60	.60
	Nos. 612-614,C312-C314 (6)		1.65	1.20

4th cent. of the founding of Cuenca. #614a contains 2 5c gray & 2 20c brown red stamps in designs similar to #612, 614. It was printed on white ungummed paper.

Francisco Marcos, Gen. Pedro Alcantara Herran and Santos Michelena A220

1957, Sept. 5   Engr.   Perf. 14½x14

615	A220	40c yellow	.40	.20
616	A220	50c ultra	.40	.20
617	A220	2s dk red	1.00	.20
	Nos. 615-617 (3)		1.80	.60

7th Postal Congress of the Americas and Spain (in 1955).

Souvenir Sheets

Various Railroad Scenes — A221

1957   Litho.   Perf. 10½x11

618	A221	20c Sheet of 5	7.50	4.25
619	A221	30c Sheet of 5	7.50	4.25

Issued to commemorate the opening of the Quito-Ibarra-San Lorenzo railroad. Nos. 618-619 contain 2 orange yellow, 1 ultramarine and 2 carmine stamps, each in a different design.

Scenic Type of 1955-56.

Designs as before, except: 40c, as 70c. 90c, as 80c. No. 629, San Pablo, Imbabura.

1957-58   Photo.   Perf. 13

620	A216	5c light blue	1.75	.20
621	A216	10c brown	1.75	.20
622	A216	20c crimson rose	1.75	.20
623	A216	20c yel green	1.75	.20
624	A216	30c rose red	2.50	.20
625	A216	40c chalky blue	1.75	.20
626	A216	50c lt vio	2.50	.20
627	A216	90c brt ultra	1.75	.20
628	A216	1s dark brown	1.75	.20
629	A216	1s gray blk ('58)	1.75	.20
630	A216	2s brown	2.75	.20
	Nos. 620-630 (11)		21.75	2.20

Blue and Yellow Macaw — A222

Birds: 20c, Red-breasted toucan. 30c, Condor. 40c, Black-tailed and sword-tailed hummingbirds.

Perf. 13½x13

1958, Jan. 7   Litho.   Unwmk.

Birds in Natural Colors

634	A222	10c red brn	.85	.20
635	A222	20c dk gray	.85	.20
636	A222	30c brt yel grn	2.25	.20
637	A222	40c red org	2.25	.20
	Nos. 634-637 (4)		6.20	.80

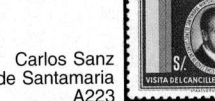
Carlos Sanz de Santamaria A223

Richard M. Nixon and Flags — A224

#640, Dr. Ramon Villeda Morales, flags. 2.20s, José Carlos de Macedo Soares, horizontal flags.

1958   Perf. 12

Flags in Red, Blue, Yellow & Green

638	A223	1.80s dl vio	.50	.20
639	A224	2s dk grn	.50	.20
640	A224	2s dk brn	.50	.20
641	A223	2.20s blk brn	.50	.20
	Nos. 638-641 (4)		2.00	.80

Visits: Colombia's Foreign Minister Dr. Carlos Sanz de Santamaria; US Vice Pres. Nixon, May 9-10; Pres. Ramon Villeda Morales of

Honduras; Brazil's Foreign Minister José Carlos de Macedo Soares. See Nos. C419-C421. For overprints and surcharges see Nos. 775-775C, C419-C421, C460.

Locomotive of 1908 A225

Garcia Moreno, Jose Caamano, L. Plaza and Eloy Alfaro — A226

Design: 50c, Diesel locomotive.

Perf. 13½x14, 14

1958, Aug. 9   Photo.   Unwmk.

642	A225	30c brn blk	.20	.20
643	A225	50c dk car	.30	.20
644	A226	5s dk brn	1.10	.70
	Nos. 642-644 (3)		1.60	1.10

Guayaquil-Quito railroad, 50th anniv.

Cardinal — A227

Birds: 30c, Andean cock-of-the-rock. 50c, Glossy cowbird. 60c, Red-fronted Amazon.

1958   Litho.   Perf. 13½x13

Birds in Natural Colors

645	A227	20c bluish grn, blk & red	1.00	.20
646	A227	30c buff, blk & brt bl	1.10	.20
647	A227	50c org, blk & grn	1.40	.35
648	A227	60c pale rose, blk & bluish grn	2.75	.35
	Nos. 645-648 (4)		6.25	1.10

UNESCO Building and Eiffel Tower, Paris — A228

1958, Nov. 3   Engr.   Perf. 12½

649	A228	80c brown	.45	.20

UNESCO Headquarters in Paris opening, Nov. 3.

Globe and Satellites — A229

Virgin of
Quito — A230

1958, Dec. 20   Photo.   Perf. 14x13½
650   A229 1.80s dark blue   1.00 .45

International Geophysical Year, 1957-58.
For overprints see Nos. 718, C422.

1959, Sept. 8   Unwmk.   Perf. 13
651   A230   5c ol grn   .25 .20
652   A230 10c yel brn   .25 .20
653   A230 20c purple   .25 .20
654   A230 30c ultra   .25 .20
655   A230 80c dk car rose   .25 .20
     Nos. 651-655 (5)   1.25 1.00

See No. C290. For surcharges and overprint
see Nos. 695-699.

Uprooted Oak
Emblem — A231

1960, Apr. 7   Litho.   Perf. 14x13
656   A231 80c rose car & grn   .25 .20

World Refugee Year, 71/59-630/60.
For overprints see Nos. 709, 719, O205.

Great Anteater
and
Arms — A232

Animals: 40c, Tapir and map. 80c, Specta-
cled bear and arms. 1s, Puma and map.

1960, May 14   Photo.   Perf. 13
657   A232 20c org, grn & blk   .45 .20
658   A232 40c yel grn, bl grn &
                   brn   .65 .20
659   A232 80c bl, blk & red brn   1.10 .20
660   A232   1s Prus bl, plum &
                   ocher   1.90 .45
     Nos. 657-660 (4)   4.10 1.05

Founding of the city of Baeza, 4th cent.
See Nos. 676-679.

Hotel Quito
A233

#662, Dormitory, Catholic University. #663,
Dormitory, Central University. #664, Airport,
Quito. #665, Overpass on Highway to Quito.
#666, Security Bank. #667, Ministry of For-
eign Affairs. #668, Government Palace. #669,
Legislative Palace.

Perf. 11x11½
1960, Aug. 8   Engr.   Unwmk.
661   A233   1s dk pur & redsh brn   .40 .20
662   A233   1s dk bl & brn   .40 .20
663   A233   1s blk & red   .40 .20
664   A233   1s dk bl & ultra   .40 .20
665   A233   1s dk pur & dk car
                   rose   .40 .20
666   A233   1s blk & ol bis   .40 .20
667   A233   1s dk pur & turq   .40 .20
668   A233   1s dk bl & grn   .40 .20
669   A233   1s dk pur & grn   .40 .20
     Nos. 661-669 (9)   3.60 1.80

11th Inter-American Conference, Quito.
For surcharges see Nos. 700-708.

Type of Regular Issue, 1955-56
Souvenir Sheet

Design: Orchids, Napo-Pastaza.

1960   Photo.   Perf. 13
Yellow Paper
670   Sheet of 2   2.75 2.75
 a. A216 80c deep violet   .85 .40
 b. A216 90c deep green   .85 .40

25th anniv. of Asociacion Filatelica Ecuatori-
ana. Marginal inscription in silver. Exists with
silver inscription omitted.

"Freedom of
Expression" — A234

Manabi
Bridge
A235

10c, "Freedom to vote." 20c, "Freedom to
work." 30c, Coins, "Monetary stability."

1960, Aug. 29   Litho.   Perf. 13
671   A234   5c dk bl   .75 .20
672   A234 10c lt vio   .75 .20
673   A234 20c orange   .75 .20
674   A234 30c bluish grn   .75 .20
675   A235 40c brn & bluish grn   .75 .20
     Nos. 671-675 (5)   3.75 1.00

Achievements of President Camilo Ponce
Enriquez. See Nos. C370-C374.

Animal Type of 1960.

Animals: 10c, Collared peccary. 20c, Kinka-
jou. 80c, Jaguar. 1s, Mountain coati.

Unwmk.
1961, July 13   Photo.   Perf. 13
676   A232 10c grn, rose red & blk   .50 .20
677   A232 20c vio, grnsh bl & brn   .90 .20
678   A232 80c red org, dl yel &
                   blk   1.60 .40
679   A232   1s brn, brt grn & org   2.50 .50
     Nos. 676-679 (4)   5.50 1.30

Founding of the city of Tena, 400th anniv.

Graphium
Pausianus
A236

Butterflies: 30c, Papilio torquatus leptalea.
50c, Graphium molops molops. 80c, Battus
lycidas.

1961, July 13   Litho.   Perf. 13½
680   A236 20c pink & multi   .45 .20
681   A236 30c lt ultra & multi   .90 .20
682   A236 50c org & multi   .90 .20
683   A236 80c bl grn & multi   1.75 .20
     Nos. 680-683 (4)   4.00 .80

See Nos. 711-713.

Galapagos Islands Nos. L1-L3
Overprinted in Black or Red

1961, Oct. 31   Photo.   Perf. 12
684   A1   20c dk brn   .25 .20
685   A2   50c violet   .25 .20
686   A1   1s dk ol grn (R)   .55 .30
     Nos. 684-686,C389-C391 (6)   2.75 1.75

Establishment of maritime biological sta-
tions on Galapagos Islands by UNESCO.
Overprint arranged differently on 20c, 1s.
See Nos. C389-C391.

Daniel
Enrique
Proano
School
A237

Designs: 60c, Loja-Zamora highway, vert.
80c, Aguirre Abad College, Guayaquil. 1s,
Army quarters, Quito.

Perf. 11x11½, 11½x11
1962, Jan. 10   Engr.   Unwmk.
687   A237 50c dl bl & blk   .45 .20
688   A237 60c ol grn & blk   .45 .20
689   A237 80c org red & blk   .45 .20
690   A237   1s rose lake & blk   .45 .20
     Nos. 687-690 (4)   1.80 .80

Pres.   Protection for The
Arosemena,   Family — A239
Flags of
Ecuador,
US — A238

Designs (Arosemena and): 10c, Flags of
Ecuador. 20c, Flags of Ecuador and Panama.

1963, July 1   Litho.   Perf. 14
691   A238 10c buff & multi   .40 .20
692   A238 20c multi   .50 .20
693   A238 60c multi   .50 .20
     Nos. 691-693,C409-C411 (6)   3.40 1.35

Issued to commemorate Pres. Carlos J.
Arosemena's friendship trip, July 1962.

Imperfs exist. Value $9.

1963, July 9   Unwmk.   Perf. 14
694   A239 10c ultra, red, gray & blk .50 .20

Social Insurance, 25th anniv. See #C413.

No. 655 Overprinted or Surcharged in
Black or Blue

1963   Photo.   Perf. 13
695   A230 10c on 80c dk car rose   .50 .20
696   A230 20c on 80c dk car rose   .50 .20
697   A230 50c on 80c dk car rose   .50 .20
698   A230 60c on 80c dk car rose
                   (Bl)   .50 .20
699   A230 80c dk car rose   .50 .20
     Nos. 695-699 (5)   2.50 1.00

Nos. 661-669 Surcharged

1964, Apr. 20   Engr.   Perf. 11x11½
700   A233 10c on 1s dk pur &
                   redsh brn   .75 .20
701   A233 10c on 1s dk pur &
                   turq   .75 .20
702   A233 20c on 1s dk bl & brn   .75 .20
703   A233 20c on 1s blk & red   .75 .20
704   A233 30c on 1s dk pur & dk
                   car rose   .75 .20
705   A233 40c on 1s blk & ol bis   .75 .20
706   A233 80c on 1s blk & red   .75 .20
707   A233 80c on 1s dk bl & ultra   .75 .20
708   A233 80c on 1s blk & vio   .75 .20
     Nos. 700-708 (9)   6.75 1.80

No. 656 Overprinted in Black or Light
Ultramarine

1964   Litho.   Perf. 14x13
709   A231 80c rose car & grn   5.25 1.25

Butterfly Type of 1961

Butterflies: Same as on Nos. 680, 682-683.

1964, June   Litho.   Perf. 13½
711   A236 20c brt grn & multi   .75 .20
712   A236 50c sal pink & multi   1.10 .20
713   A236 80c lt red brn & multi   1.75 .20
     Nos. 711-713 (3)   3.60 .60

Alliance for
Progress
Emblem,
Agriculture
and
Industry
A240

Designs: 50c, Emblem, gear wheels, mountain and seashore. 80c, Emblem, banana
worker, fish, factory and ship.

1964, Aug. 26   Unwmk.   Perf. 12
715   A240 40c bis brn & vio   .20 .20
716   A240 50c red org & blk   .25 .20
717   A240 80c bl & dk brn   .35 .20
     Nos. 715-717 (3)   .80 .60

Issued to publicize the Alliance for Progress
which aims to stimulate economic growth and
raise living standards in Latin America.

No. 650 Overprinted in Red

1964   Photo.   Perf. 14x13½
718   A229 1.80s dark blue   2.75 2.25

No. 656 Overprinted

Illustration reduced.

1964, July   Litho.   Perf. 14x13
719   A231 80c block of 4   3.50 3.50

Organization of American States.

World Map and Banana Tree — A241

1964, Oct. 26   Perf. 12½x12
720 A241 50c dk brn, gray & gray
    ol   .25 .20
721 A241 80c blk, org & gray ol   .25 .20

Issued to publicize the Banana Conference, Oct.-Nov. 1964. See Nos. C427-C428a.

King Philip II of Spain and Map of Upper Amazon River A242

Designs (Map and): 20c, Juan de Salinas de Loyola. 30c, Hernando de Santillan.

1964, Dec. 6   Litho.   Perf. 13½
722 A242 10c rose, blk & buff   .25 .25
723 A242 20c bl grn, blk & buff .25 .25
724 A242 30c bl, blk & buff   .25 .25
    Nos. 722-724 (3)   .75 .75

4th centenary of the establishment of the Royal High Court in Quito.

Pole Vaulting A243

1964, Dec. 16   Perf. 14x13½
725 A243 80c vio bl, yel grn & brn .25 .20

18th Olympic Games, Tokyo, Oct. 10-25. See Nos. C432-C434.

Peter Fleming and Two-toed Sloth — A244

Designs: 20c, James Elliot and armadillo. 30c, T. Edward McCully, Jr., and squirrel. 40c, Roger Youderian and deer. 60c, Nathaniel (Nate) Saint and plane over Napo River.

1965   Unwmk.   Perf. 13½
726 A244 20c emerald & multi   .90 .30
727 A244 30c yellow & multi   .90 .30
728 A244 40c lilac & multi   .90 .30
729 A244 60c multi   .90 .30
730 A244 80c multi   .90 .30
    Nos. 726-730 (5)   4.50 1.50

Issued in memory of five American Protestant missionaries, killed by the Auca Indians, 1/8/56.
Issue dates: 80c, May 11; others, July 8.

Juan B. Vázquez and Benigno Malo College — A245

1965, June 6   Litho.   Perf. 14
731 A245 20c blk, yel & vio bl   .20 .20
732 A245 60c blk, red, yel & vio bl .20 .20
733 A245 80c blk, emer, yel & vio
    bl   .20 .20
    Nos. 731-733 (3)   .60 .60

Centenary (in 1964) of the founding of Benigno Malo National College.

National Anthem, Juan Leon Mera and Antonio Neumane A246

1965, Aug. 10   Litho.   Perf. 13½
734 A246 50c pink & blk   .20 .20
735 A246 80c lt grn & blk .35 .20
736 A246 5s bis & blk   .75 .45
737 A246 10s lt ultra & blk 1.40 1.00
    Nos. 734-737 (4)   2.70 1.85

Cent. of the national anthem. The name of the poet Juan Leon Mera is misspelled on the stamps.
For surcharges see Nos. 766C, 766H.

Torch and Athletes (Shot Put, Discus, Javelin and Hammer Throw) — A247

50c, 1s, Runners. 60c, 1.50s, Soccer.

1965, Nov. 20   Perf. 12x12½
738 A247 40c org, gold & blk   .20 .20
739 A247 50c org ver, gold &
    blk   .20 .20
740 A247 60c bl, gold & blk   .20 .20
741 A247 80c brt yel grn, gold
    & blk   .30 .20
742 A247 1s lt vio, gold & blk .30 .20
743 A247 1.50s brt pink, gold &
    blk   .60 .45
    Nos. 738-743,C435-C440 (12) 5.00 3.10

Issued to publicize the 5th Bolivarian Games, held at Guayaquil and Quito.
For surcharges see #766B, 766D, C449.

Stamps of 1865 A248

1965, Dec. 30   Litho.   Perf. 13½
Stamps of 1865 in Yellow, Ultramarine & Green
744 A248 80c rose red   .20 .20
745 A248 1.30s rose lilac .40 .20
746 A248 2s chocolate   .55 .20
747 A248 4s black   .85 .20
  a.   Souv. sheet of, #744-747, imperf. 3.00 3.00
    Nos. 744-747 (4)   2.00 .80

Cent. of Ecuadorian postage stamps.

The postal validity of some of the following sets has been questioned.

ITU Centenary — A248a

1966, Jan. 27   Litho.   Perf. 12x12½
748 A248a 10c Telstar   .20 .20
748A A248a 10c Syncom   .20 .20
748B A248a 80c Relay   .20 .20
748C A248a 1.50s Luna 3 .40 .35
748D A248a 3s Echo II   2.25 1.40
  f.   Souv. sheet of 3, #748,
       748B, 748D, perf.
       14x12½   18.00

748E A248a 4s E. Branly,
            Marconi,
            Bell, E.
            Belin   2.50 2.00
  g.   Souv. sheet of 3, #748A,
       748C, 748E, perf.
       14x12½   18.00
    Nos. 748-748E (6)   5.75 4.35

1.50s, 3s, 4s are airmail.
Nos. 748Df, 748Eg are printed on surface colored paper. Exist imperf. Value, each $18.

Space Exploration — A248b

10c, Edward White's space walk, June 8, 1965. 1s, Gemini 5, Aug. 21, 1965. 1.30s, Solar system. 2s, Charles Conrad, L. Gordon Cooper, Gemini 5, Aug. 21-29, 1965. 2.50s, Gemini 5. 3.50s, Alexei L. Leonov's space walk, Mar. 18, 1965.

1966, Jan. 27   Perf. 12x12½
749 A248b 10c multi   .20 .20
749A A248b 1s multi   .45 .20
749B A248b 1.30s multi .45 .20
749C A248b 2s multi   1.40 .65
749D A248b 2.50s multi 1.40 .65
749E A248b 3.50s multi 3.00 2.50
  f.   Souv. sheet of 3, #749,
       749B, 749E, perf.
       14x12½   15.00 10.00
    Nos. 749-749E (6) 6.90 4.40

1.30s, 2s, 2.50s, 3.50s are airmail.
No. 749Ef is printed on surface colored paper. Exists imperf. Value $15.

Dante's Dream by Rossetti — A248c

Designs: 80c, Dante and Beatrix by Holliday. 2s, Galileo Galilei, 400th birth cent., vert. 3s, Dante, 700th birth cent., vert.

1966, June   Perf. 13½x14, 14x13½
750 A248c 10c multicolored   .20 .20
750A A248c 80c multicolored   .20 .20
750B A248c 2s multicolored   2.50 1.75
750C A248c 3s multicolored   2.75 2.75
  d.   Souv. sheet of 3, #750,
       750A, 750C, perf.
       12x12½   18.00 18.00
    Nos. 750-750C (4)   5.65 4.90

Nos. 750A-750B are airmail. No. 750Cd exists imperf. Value $18.

Pavonine Quetzal — A249

Birds: 50c, Blue-crowned motmot. 60c, Paradise tanager. 80c, Wire-tailed manakin.

1966, June 17   Litho.   Perf. 13½
Birds in Natural Colors
751 A249 40c dl rose & blk   1.25 .20
751A A249 50c sal & blk   1.25 .20
751B A249 60c lt ocher & blk 1.25 .20
751C A249 80c lt bl & blk   1.25 .20
    Nos. 751-751C,C441-C448 (12) 26.80 5.10

For surcharges see Nos. 766E-766F, C450, C455-C457.

Pope Paul VI — A249a

Pope Paul VI and: 1.30s, Nativity. 3.50s, Virgin of Merced.

1966, June 24   Perf. 12½x12
752 A249a 10c multicolored   .30 .20
752A A249a 1.30s multicolored .80 .60
752B A249a 3.50s multicolored 2.50 2.50
  c.   Souv. sheet of 3, #752,
       perf. 14x13½, 752A-
       752B, perf. 12½x12   18.00 18.00
    Nos. 752-752B (3)   3.60 3.30

Nos. 752A-752B are airmail.
No. 752Bc is printed on surface colored paper. Exists imperf. Value $18.

Sir Winston Churchill, (1874-1965) — A249b

Famous Men: 10c, Dag Hammarskjold, vert. 1.50s, Albert Schweitzer, vert. 2.50s, John F. Kennedy, vert. 4s, Churchill, Kennedy.

Perf. 14x13½, 13½x14
1966, June 24
753 A249b 10c vio bl, brn
          & blk   .20 .20
753A A249b 1s ver, bl &
          blk   .35 .20
753B A249b 1.50s brn, lil rose
          & blk   .90 .45
753C A249b 2.50s ver, bl &
          blk   2.25 1.25
753D A249b 4s bl, blk &
          brn   2.75 2.00
  e.   Souv. sheet of 3, #753,
       753B, 753D   32.50 32.50
    Nos. 753-753D (5)   6.45 4.10

Nos. 753C-753D are airmail.
No. 753De is printed on surface colored paper. 10c stamp is perf. 14x13½. 1.50s is perf. 14x13½x14x12, 4s is perf. 12x12½x13x12½. Exists imperf. Value $32.50.

History of Summer Olympics — A249c

1966, June 27   Perf. 12x12½
754 A249c 10c Long jump   .20 .20
754A A249c 10c Wrestling   .20 .20
754B A249c 80c Discus,
          javelin   .55 .20
754C A249c 1.30s Chariot rac-
          ing   1.25 .45
754D A249c 3s High jump   2.10 1.00
  f.   Souv. sheet of 3, #754,
       754B, 754D   13.50 8.50
754E A249c 3.50s Discus   3.50 1.25
  g.   Souv. sheet of 3, #754A,
       754C, 754E   13.50 9.50
    Nos. 754-754E (6)   7.80 3.30

Nos. 754C-754D are airmail.

Nos. 754Df, 754Eg are printed on surface colored paper.
Nos. 754Df and 754Eg exist imperf. Value $13.50.

1968 Winter Olympics,
Grenoble — A249d

1966, June 27			Perf. 14	
755	A249d	10c Speedskating	.20	.20
755A	A249d	1s Ice hockey	.45	.20
755B	A249d	1.50s Ski jumping	.70	.35
755C	A249d	2s Cross country skiing	1.40	.55
755D	A249d	2.50s Downhill skiing	1.75	1.75
755E	A249d	4s Figure skating	2.25	2.25
f.		Souv. sheet of 3, #755, 755B, 755E, perf. 14x13½	9.00	7.25
		Nos. 755-755E (6)	6.75	5.30

Nos. 755B-755E are airmail.
No. 755Ef is printed on surface colored paper. Exists imperf. Value same as perf.

French-American Cooperation in
Space — A249e

Designs: 1.50s, French satellite D-1, Mt. Gros observatory, vert. 4s, John F. Kennedy, satellites.

1966		Perf. 13½x14, 14x13½		
756	A249e	10c multicolored	.50	.30
756A	A249e	1.50s multicolored	2.00	1.40
756B	A249e	4s multicolored	4.25	2.75
c.		Sheet of 3, #756-756B	18.00	14.00
		Nos. 756-756B (3)	6.75	4.45

Nos. 756A-756B are airmail.
No. 756Bc exists imperf. Value same as perf.

Moon
Exploration
A249f

1966			Perf. 14	
758	A249f	10c Surveyor	.20	.20
758A	A249f	80c Luna 10	.20	.20
758B	A249f	1s Luna 9	.20	.20
758C	A249f	2s Astronaut flight trainer	.80	.55
758D	A249f	2.50s Ranger 7	1.10	.85
758E	A249f	3s Lunar Orbiter 1	1.50	1.50
f.		Sheet of 3, #758, 758A, 758E	13.50	13.50
		Nos. 758-758E (6)	4.00	3.50

Nos. 758C-758E are airmail. Stamps in No. 758f have colored pattern in border.
No. 758f exists imperf. Value same as perf.

1968 Summer Olympics, Mexico
City — A249g

Paintings by Mexican artists: 10c, Wanderer by Diego Rivera. 1s, Workers by Jose Orozco. 1.30s, Pres. Juarez by Orozco. 2s, Mother and Child by David Siqueiros. 2.50s, Two Women by Rivera. 3.50s, New Democracy by Siqueiros.

1967, Mar. 13			Perf. 14	
759	A249g	10c multicolored	.20	.20
759A	A249g	1s multicolored	.65	.20
759B	A249g	1.30s multicolored	.90	.40
759C	A249g	2s multicolored	1.10	.65
759D	A249g	2.50s multicolored	1.40	1.40
759E	A249g	3.50s multicolored	2.50	2.25
f.		Sheet of 3, #759, 759B, 759E	18.00	
		Nos. 759-759E (6)	6.75	5.10

Nos. 759B-759E are airmail.
No. 759f is printed on surface colored paper that differs slightly from Nos. 759-759E. Exists imperf. Value same as perf.

1968 Summer Olympics, Mexico
City — A249h

1967, Mar. 13				
760	A249h	10c Soccer	.20	.20
760A	A249h	10c Hurdles	.20	.20
760B	A249h	80c Track	.20	.20
760C	A249h	1.50s Fencing	.90	.40
760D	A249h	3s High jump	1.75	1.25
f.		Souv. sheet of 3, #760A, 760B, 760D	18.00	11.00
760E	A249h	4s Swimming	3.50	1.75
g.		Souv. sheet of 3, #760, 760C, 760E	13.50	8.50
		Nos. 760-760E (6)	6.75	4.00

Nos. 760C-760E are airmail.
Nos. 760f-760g are printed on surface colored paper. Exist imperf. Value same as perf.

4th Natl.
Eucharistic
Congress
A249i

Paintings: 10c, Madonna and Child by unknown artist. 60c, Holy Family by Rodriguez. 80c, Madonna and Child by Samaniego. 1s, Good Shepherd by Samaniego. 1.50s, Assumption of the Virgin by Vargas. 2s, Man in Prayer by Santiago.
10s, Chalice, eucharist, church, wheat.

1967, May 10				
761	A249i	10c multicolored	.20	.20
761A	A249i	60c multicolored	.75	.35
761B	A249i	80c multicolored	.95	.35
761C	A249i	1s multicolored	1.10	.60
761D	A249i	1.50s multicolored	1.75	.85
761E	A249i	2s multicolored	2.75	.85
		Nos. 761-761E (6)	7.50	3.20
Souvenir Sheet				
761F	A249i	10s multi	7.50	7.50

Nos. 761D-761E are airmail. Frames and inscriptions vary greatly.
No. 761F exists imperf. with an orange margin color. Value, same.

Madonna
and Child
Enthroned
by Guido
Reni
A249j

Paintings of the Madonna and Child by: 40c, van Hemesen. 50c, Memling. 1.30s, Durer. 2.50s, Raphael. 3s, Murillo.

1967, May 25			Perf. 14x13½	
762	A249j	10c multicolored	.20	.20
762A	A249j	40c multicolored	.20	.20
762B	A249j	50c multicolored	.20	.20
762C	A249j	1.30s multicolored	.80	.40
762D	A249j	2.50s multicolored	2.10	1.10
762E	A249j	3s multicolored	3.25	1.40
		Nos. 762-762E (6)	6.75	3.50

Nos. 762C-762E are airmail.

Portrait of a
Young
Woman by
Rogier van
der
Weyden
A249k

Designs: 1s, Helene Fourment by Rubens. 1.50s, Venetian Woman by Durer. 2s, Lady Sheffield by Gainsborough. 2.50s, Suzon by Manet. 4s, Lady with a Unicorn by Raphael.

1967, Sept. 9			Perf. 14x13½	
763	A249k	10c multicolored	.20	.20
763A	A249k	1s multicolored	.65	.40
763B	A249k	1.50s multicolored	1.40	.50
763C	A249k	2s multicolored	1.75	.70
763D	A249k	2.50s multicolored	2.75	.90
763E	A249k	4s multicolored	3.25	1.40
f.		Sheet of 3, #763, 763B, 763E, perf. 14	13.50	9.50
		Nos. 763-763E (6)	10.00	4.10

Nos. 763B-763E are airmail.
Stamps in No. 763f have colored pattern in border. Exists imperf. Value same as perf.

John F.
Kennedy,
50th Birth
Anniv.
A249l

JFK and: No. 764A, Dag Hammarskjold. 80c, Pope Paul VI. 1.30s, Konrad Adenauer. 3s, Charles de Gaulle. 3.50s, Winston Churchill.

1967, Sept. 11		Perf. 14x13½, 13½x14		
764	A249l	10c lil, brn & bl	.20	.20
764A	A249l	10c yel, brn & sky bl	.20	.20
764B	A249l	80c yel, brn & sal	.20	.20
764C	A249l	1.30s yel, brn & pink	2.40	.90
764D	A249l	3s yel, brn & yel grn	3.25	1.60
764E	A249l	3.50s yel, brn & bl	4.75	2.25
		Nos. 764-764E (6)	11.00	5.35
Souvenir Sheets				
764F		Sheet of 3	18.00	10.00
h.		like #764, 35x27mm		
i.		like #764B, 35x27mm		
j.		like #764D, 35x27mm		
764G		Sheet of 3	18.00	10.00
k.		like #764A, 35x27mm		
l.		like #764C, 35x27mm		
m.		like #764E, 35x27mm		

Nos. 764C-764E are airmail. Nos. 764A-764E horiz. Stamps in Nos. 764F-764G have colored pattern in border.
Nos. 764F and 764G exist imperf. Values same as perf.

Christmas — A249m

Designs: No. 765A, Children's procession. 40c, Candlelight procession. 50c, Children singing. 60c, Processional. 2.50s, Christmas celebration.

1967, Dec. 29			Perf. 13x14	
765	A249m	10c multi	.45	.20
765A	A249m	10c multi	.45	.20
765B	A249m	40c multi	.45	.20
765C	A249m	50c multi	.45	.20
765D	A249m	60c multi	.45	.20
765E	A249m	2.50s multi	13.00	10.50
		Nos. 765-765E (6)	15.25	11.50

No. 765E is airmail. See Nos. 768-768F.

Various Surcharges on Issues of 1956-66

1967-68				
766	AP72	30c on 1.10s (C337)	.40	.20
766A	AP66	40c on 1.70s (C292)	.40	.20
766B	A247	40c on 3.50s (C438)	.40	.20
766C	A246	50c on 5s (736) ('68)	.40	.20
766D	A247	80c on 1.50s (743)	.45	.20
766E	A249	80c on 2.50s (C445)	.45	.20
766F	A249	1s on 4s (C447)	.55	.20
766G	AP66	1.30s on 1.90s (C293)	.65	.55
766H	A246	2s on 10s (737) ('68)	.90	.20
		Nos. 766-766H,C449-C450 (11)	5.50	2.70

The surcharge on Nos. 766B-766C, 766E and 766G-766H includes "Resello." The obliteration of old denomination and arrangement of surcharges differ on each stamp.

Bust of
Peñaherrera,
Central University,
Quito — A250

50c, Law books. 80c, Open book, laurel, horiz.

		Perf. 12x12½, 12½x12		
1967, Dec. 29			Litho.	
767	A250	50c brt grn & blk	.20	.20
767A	A250	60c rose & blk	.20	.20
767B	A250	80c rose lil & blk	.20	.20
		Nos. 767-767B,C451-C452 (5)	1.10	1.00

Cent. (in 1964) of the birth of Dr. Victor Manuel Peñaherrera (1864-1932), author of the civil and criminal codes of Ecuador.

Christmas Type of 1967

Native Christian Art: 10c, Mourning of the Death of Christ, by Manuel Chili. 80c, Ascension of the Holy Virgin, vert. 1s, The Holy Virgin. 1.30s, Coronation of the Holy Virgin, by Bernardo Rodriguez, vert. 1.50s, Madonna and Child with the Heavenly Host, vert. 2s, Madonna and Child, by Manuel Samaniego, vert. 3s, Immaculate Conception, by Bernardo de Legranda, vert. 3.50s, Passion of Christ, by

Chili, vert. 4s, The Holy Virgin of Quito, by de Legranda, vert.

1968 Jan. 19   Perf. 13½x14, 14x13½
768   A249m   10c multi   .30   .30
768A A249m   80c multi   .30   .30
768B A249m   1s multi   .30   .30
768C A249m   1.30s multi   .30   .30
768D A249m   1.50s multi   .65   .35
768E A249m   2s multi   .85   .85
      Nos. 768-768E (6)   2.70 2.40
Souvenir Sheet
Perf. 14
768F   Sheet of 3   18.00 11.00
  g. A249m 3s multicolored
  h. A249m 3.50s multicolored
  i. A249m 4s multicolored

Nos. 768C-768F are airmail. No. 768F exists imperf. Value same.

Tourism Year — A250a

20c, Woman from Otavalo. 30c, Colorado Indian. 40c, Petroglyph of a cat. 50c, Petroglyph of a mythological predator. 60c, Woman in a bazaar. 80c, 1s, 1.30s, Petroglyphs, diff. 1.50s, Colonial street, Quito. 2s, Amulet.

1968, Apr. 1   Perf. 13½x14
769   A250a 20c multicolored   .20 .20
769A A250a 30c multicolored   .20 .20
769B A250a 40c multicolored   .20 .20
769C A250a 50c multicolored   .20 .20
769D A250a 60c multicolored   .20 .20
769E A250a 80c multicolored   .20 .20
769F A250a 1s multicolored   .30 .20
769G A250a 1.30s multicolored .20 .20
769H A250a 1.50s multicolored .30 .20
769I A250a 2s multicolored   .35 .20
      Nos. 769-769I (10)   2.35 2.00

Ninth Congress of the Confederation of Latin American Tourist Organizations (COTAL). Nos. 769G-769I are airmail.

Otto Arosemena Gomez — A251

Lions Emblem — A252

Design: 1s, Page from the Constitution.

1968, May 9   Litho.   Perf. 13½x14
770   A251 80c lil & multi   .20 .20
770A A251 1s multi   .20 .20
      Nos. 770-770A,C453-C454 (4) .90 .80

First anniversary of the administration of Pres. Otto Arosemena Gomez.

1968, May 24   Litho.   Perf. 13½x14
771   A252 80c multi   .20 .20
771A A252 1.30s multi   .25 .20
771B A252 2s pink & multi   .30 .20
  c. Souvenir sheet of 1   5.25 5.25
      Nos. 771-771B (3)   .75 .60

50th anniv. (in 1967) of Lions Intl. No. 771c contains one 5s 39x49mm stamp. Exists imperf. Value same as perf.

Pope Paul VI, Visit to Latin America — A252a

39th Intl. Eucharistic Congress, Bogota, Colombia A252b

60c, Pope Paul VI, vert. 1s, Madonna by Botticelli. 1.30s, Pope Paul VI with flags of South American nations. 2s, Madonna and Child by Durer.

1969   Perf. 13½x14, 14x13½
772   A252a 40c multicolored .20 .20
772A A252a 60c multicolored .70 .20
772B A252b 1s multicolored   2.25 .70
772C A252a 1.30s multicolored 1.60 .75
  e. Souv. sheet of 3, #772, 772A,
      772C, imperf.   4.50 2.75
772D A252b 2s multicolored   2.25 1.00
  f. Souv. sheet of 2, #772B,
      772D, imperf.   4.50 2.75
      Nos. 772-772D (5)   7.00 2.85

Nos. 772C-772D are airmail. Nos. 772-772f overprinted in silver with the national coat of arms.

Madonna with the Angel by Rogier van der Weyden A252c

Paintings by various artists showing the life of the Virgin Mary.

1969   Perf. 14x13½, 13½x14
773   A252c 40c shown   .25 .25
773A A252c 60c Van der
             Weyden, diff.   .25 .25
773B A252c 1s Raphael   .35 .25
773C A252c 1.30s Veronese   1.25 .65
  e. Souv. sheet of 2, #773B-
      773C, imperf.   6.75 3.25
773D A252c 2s Van der
             Weyden, horiz.   2.40 1.10
  f. Souv. sheet of 3, #773-773A,
      773D, imperf.   6.75 3.25
      Nos. 773-773D (5)   4.50 2.50

Nos. 773-773Df overprinted in silver with the national coat of arms. Nos. 773C-773D are airmail.

Nos. C331 and C326 Surcharged in Violet and Dark Blue

a

b

1969, Jan. 10   Perf. 11½, 14x13½
774   AP79 (a) 40c on 1.30s (V)   .50 .25
774A AP76 (b) 50c on 1.30s
             (DBl)   .50 .25

Type of 1958 Surcharged and Overprinted in Plum and Black

1969, Mar.   Litho.   Perf. 12
Flags in Red, Blue and Yellow
775   A223 50c on 2s sepia   .20 .20
775A A223 80c on 2s sepia   .20 .20
775B A223 1s on 2s sepia   .20 .20
775C A223 2s sepia   .20 .20
      Nos. 775-775C,C455-C457 (7) 2.30 1.55

Nos. 775-775C were not issued without overprint. The obliteration of old denomination on No. 775A is a small square around a star. Overprint is plum, except for the black small coat of arms on right flag.

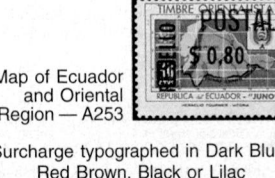

Map of Ecuador and Oriental Region — A253

Surcharge typographed in Dark Blue, Red Brown, Black or Lilac
1969   Litho.   Perf. 14
776   A253 20c on 30c (DBl)   .50 .30
776A A253 40c on 30c (RBr)   .50 .30
777   A253 50c on 30c (DBl)   .50 .30
778   A253 60c on 30c (DBl)   .50 .30
778A A253 60c on 30c (Bk)   .65 .65
778B A253 80c on 30c (DBl)   — 25.00
779   A253 80c on 30c (Bk)   .50 .30
780   A253 1s on 30c (L)   .50 .30
780A A253 1s on 30c (DBl)   2.00 1.25
781   A253 1.30s on 30c (Bk) .90 .40
782   A253 1.50s on 30c (Bk) .90 .40
783   A253 2s on 30c (DBl)   1.00 .40
784   A253 3s on 30c (DBl)   1.25 .45
784A A253 4s on 30c (DBl)   3.25 3.25
785   A253 4s on 30c (Bk)   1.25 .40
786   A253 5s on 30c (Bk)   1.60 .55
      Nos. 776-786 (16)   15.80 34.55

Not issued without surcharge.

M. L. King, John and Robert Kennedy — A254

Thecla Coronata — A255

1969-70   Typo.   Perf. 12½
787   A254 4s blk, bl, grn & buff   .45 .20

Perf. 13½
788   A254 4s blk, lt bl & grn ('70) .45 .20

In memory of John F. Kennedy, Robert F. Kennedy and Martin Luther King, Jr.

1970   Litho.   Perf. 12½
Butterflies: 20c, Papilio zabreus. 30c, Heliconius chestertoni. 40c, Papilio pausanias. 50c, Pereute leucodrosime. 60c, Metamorpha dido. 80c, Morpho cypris. 1s, Catagramma astarte.

789   A255 10c buff & multi   1.75 .40
790   A255 20c lt grn & multi   1.75 .40
791   A255 30c pink & multi   1.75 .40
792   A255 40c lt bl & multi   1.75 .20
793   A255 50c gold & multi   1.75 .20
794   A255 60c salmon & multi   1.75 .20
795   A255 80c silver & multi   1.75 .20
796   A255 1s lt grn & multi   1.75 .20

Same, White Background
Perf. 13½
797   A255 10c multi   1.75 .40
798   A255 20c multi   1.75 .40
799   A255 30c multi   1.75 .40
800   A255 40c multi   1.75 .20
801   A255 50c multi   1.75 .20
802   A255 60c multi   1.75 .20
803   A255 80c multi   1.75 .20
804   A255 1s multi   1.75 .20
      Nos. 789-804,C461-C464 (20) 35.00 5.20

Surcharged Revenue Stamps
A256   A257

1970, June 16   Litho.   Perf. 14
Red Surcharge
805   A256 1s on 1s light blue   .20 .20
806   A256 1.30s on 1s light blue .30 .30
807   A256 1.50s on 1s light blue .30 .30
808   A256 2s on 1s light blue   .35 .20
809   A256 5s on 1s light blue   .75 .35
810   A256 10s on 1s light blue   1.50 .60
      Nos. 805-810 (6)   3.30 1.85

1970   Typo.   Perf. 12
Black Surcharge
811   A257 60c on 1s violet   .20 .20
812   A257 80c on 1s violet   .20 .20
813   A257 1s on 1s violet   .20 .20
814   A257 1.10s on 1s violet .20 .20
815   A257 1.30s on 1s violet .20 .20
816   A257 1.50s on 1s violet .35 .20
817   A257 2s on 1s violet   .35 .20
818   A257 2.20s on 1s violet .40 .20
819   A257 3s on 1s violet   .55 .20
      Nos. 811-819 (9)   2.65 1.80

1970
820   A257 1.10s on 2s green   .20 .20
821   A257 1.30s on 2s green   .20 .20
822   A257 1.50s on 2s green   .35 .20
823   A257 2s on 2s green   .35 .20
824   A257 3.40s on 2s green   .55 .20
825   A257 5s on 2s green   .80 .20
826   A257 10s on 2s green   1.25 .20
827   A257 20s on 2s green   2.40 .80
828   A257 50s on 2s green   5.00 2.50
      Nos. 820-828 (9)   11.10 4.70

1970
829   A257 3s on 5s blue   .55 .20
830   A257 5s on 5s blue   .65 .35
831   A257 10s on 40s orange 1.25 .65
      Nos. 829-831 (3)   2.45 1.20

Arms of Zamora Chinchipe — A258   Flags of Ecuador and Chile — A259

Design: 1s, Arms and flag of Esmeraldas.

1971   Litho.   Perf. 10½
832   A258 50c pale yel & multi .25 .25
833   A258 1s sal & multi   .25 .25
      Nos. 832-833,C465-C469 (7) 3.70 1.95

1971, Sept.   Perf. 12½
840   A259 1.30s blk & multi   .20 .20
      Nos. 840,C481-C482 (3)   .70 .60

Visit of Pres. Salvador Allende of Chile, Aug. 24.

Ismael Pérez
Pazmiño — A260

1971, Sept. 16　　**Perf. 12x11½**
841 A260 1s grn & multi　　.25　.20
　　Nos. 841,C485-C486 (3)　.90　.60

"El Universo," newspaper founded by Ismael Pérez Pazmiño, 50th anniv.

CARE
Package — A261

Flags of Ecuador
and
Argentina — A262

1971-72　　**Perf. 12½**
842 A261 30c lilac ('72)　　.20　.20
843 A261 40c emerald ('72)　.20　.20
844 A261 50c blue　　　　.20　.20
845 A261 60c carmine　　　.20　.20
846 A261 80c lt brn ('72)　　.20　.20
　　Nos. 842-846 (5)　　1.00　1.00

25th anniversary of CARE, a US-Canadian Cooperative for American Relief Everywhere.

1972　　　　**Perf. 11½**
847 A262 1s blk & multi　　.20　.20
　　Nos. 847,C491-C492 (3)　.90　.70

Visit of Lt. Gen. Alejandro Agustin Lanusse, president of Argentina, Jan. 25.

Jesus Giving
Keys to St.
Peter, by Miguel
de Santiago
A263

Ecuadorian Paintings: 1.10s, Virgin of Mercy, Quito School. 2s, Virgin Mary, by Manuel Samaniego.

1972, Apr. 24 Litho.　**Perf. 14x13½**
848 A263　50c black & multi　.25　.25
849 A263 1.10s black & multi　.35　.35
850 A263　2s black & multi　.60　.60
　　a.　Souvenir sheet of 3　2.00　2.00
　　Nos. 848-850,C494-C495 (5)　2.80　2.15

No. 850a contains 3 imperf. stamps similar to Nos. 848-850.

1972, May 4

Ecuadorian Statues: 50c, Our Lady of Sorrow, by Caspicara. 1.10s, Nativity, Quito School. 2s, Virgin of Quito, anonymous.

851 A263　50c blk & multi　.20　.20
852 A263 1.10s blk & multi　.35　.35
853 A263　2s blk & multi　.55　.55
　　a.　Souv. sheet of 3　3.25　2.75
　　Nos. 851-853,C496-C497 (5)　2.70　2.05

Letters of "Ecuador" 3mm high on Nos. 851-853, 7mm high on Nos. 848-850. No. 853a contains 3 imperf. stamps similar to Nos. 851-853.

A264

A265

Designs: 30c, Gen. Juan Ignacio Pareja. 40c, Juan José Flores. 50c, Leon de Febres Cordero. 60c, Ignacio Torres. 70c, Francisco de Paula Santander. 1s, José M. Cordova.

1972, May 24　　**Perf. 12½**
854 A264 30c blue & multi　.20　.20
855 A264 40c blue & multi　.20　.20
856 A264 50c blue & multi　.20　.20
857 A264 60c blue & multi　.20　.20
858 A264 70c blue & multi　.20　.20
859 A264　1s blue & multi　.20　.20
　　Nos. 854-859,C498-C503 (12)　5.10　3.50

Sesquicentennial of the Battle of Pichincha and the liberation of Quito.

1972, July　**Photo.**　**Perf. 13**

Designs: 2s, Woman Wearing Poncho. 3s, Striped poncho. 5s, Embroidered poncho. 10s, Metal vase.

860 A265　2s multicolored　.25　.25
861 A265　3s multicolored　.55　.35
862 A265　5s multicolored　.65　.60
863 A265 10s dp blue & multi　1.50　1.10
　　a.　Souvenir sheet of 4　4.50　4.50
　　Nos. 860-863,C504-C507 (8)　6.15　4.20

Handicraft of Ecuador. No. 863a contains 4 imperf. stamps similar to Nos. 860-863.

Sucre Statue,
Santo
Domingo — A266

Radar
Station — A267

1.80s, San Agustin Convent. 2.30s, Plaza de la Independencia. 2.50s, Bolivar statue, La Alameda. 4.75s, Chapel door.

1972, Dec. 6　**Litho.**　**Perf. 11½**
864 A266 1.20s yel & multi　.25　.25
865 A266 1.80s yel & multi　.25　.25
866 A266 2.30s yel & multi　.25　.25
867 A266 2.50s yel & multi　.40　.25
868 A266 4.75s yel & multi　.55　.30
　　Nos. 864-868,C518-C524 (12)　5.80　3.50

Sesquicentennial of the Battle of Pichincha.

1973, Apr. 5　　**Wmk. 367**
869 A267　1s multicolored　.25　.20

Inauguration of earth telecommunications station, Oct. 19, 1972.

Blue-footed
Boobies
A268

Wmk. 367, Unwmkd. (#872)
1973　**Litho.**　**Perf. 11½x12**
870 A268 30c shown　　.40　.20
871 A268 40c Blue-faced booby　.40　.20
872 A268 50c Oyster-catcher　.40　.20
873 A268 60c California sea lions　.85　.25
874 A268 70c Galapagos giant
　　　　　tortoise　　1.00　.25
875 A268　1s California sea lion　1.40　.25
　　Nos. 870-875,C527-C528 (8)　8.65　1.75

Elevation of Galapagos Islands to a province of Ecuador.

Issue dates: 50c, Oct. 3; others Aug. 16.

Black-chinned Mountain
Tanager — A269

Birds of Ecuador: 2s, Moriche oriole. 3s, Toucan barbet, vert. 5s, Masked crimson tanager, vert. 10s, Blue-necked tanager, vert.

Perf. 11x11½, 11½x11
1973, Dec. 6　**Litho.**　**Unwmk.**
876 A269　1s brick red & multi　.60　.20
877 A269　2s lt blue & multi　1.00　.20
878 A269　3s lt green & multi　1.00　.20
879 A269　5s pale lilac & multi　2.10　.60
880 A269 10s pale yel grn & multi　4.25　1.25
　　Nos. 876-880 (5)　8.95　2.45

Two souvenir sheets exist: one contains 2 imperf. stamps similar to Nos. 876-877 with yellow margin and black inscription; the other 3 stamps similar to Nos. 878-880; gray margin and black inscription including "Aereo." Both sheets dated "1972." Size: 143x84mm.

Marco T. Varea,
Botanist — A270

Portraits: 60c, Pio Jaramillo Alvarado, writer. 70c, Prof. Luciano Andrade M. No. 883, Marco T. Varea, botanist. No. 884, Dr. Juan Modesto Carbo Noboa, medical researcher. No. 885, Alfredo J. Valenzuela. No. 886, Capt. Edmundo Chiriboga G. 1.20s, Francisco Campos R., scientist. 1.80s, Luis Vernaza Lazarte, philanthropist.

1974　**Unwmk.**　**Perf. 12x11½**
881 A270　60c crimson rose　.20　.20
882 A270　70c lilac　　　.20　.20
883 A270　1s ultra　　　.20　.20
884 A270　1s orange　　.20　.20
885 A270　1s emerald　　.20　.20
886 A270　1s brown　　.20　.20
887 A270 1.20s apple green　.30　.20
888 A270 1.80s lt blue　　.40　.25
　　Nos. 881-889 (8)　1.90　1.65

Arcade
A271

Designs: 30c, Monastery, entrance. 40c, Church. 50c, View of Church through gate, vert. 60c, Chapel, vert. 70c, Church and cemetery, vert.

Perf. 11½x12, 12x11½
1975, Feb. 4　　　　**Litho.**
896 A271 20c yellow & multi　.25　.20
897 A271 30c yellow & multi　.25　.20
898 A271 40c yellow & multi　.25　.20
899 A271 50c yellow & multi　.25　.20
900 A271 60c yellow & multi　.25　.20
901 A271 70c yellow & multi　.25　.20
　　Nos. 896-901 (6)　1.50　1.20

Colonial Monastery, Tilipulo, Cotopaxi Province.

Angel Polibio
Chaves, Founder
of Bolivar
Province — A272

Portrait: No. 903, Emilio Estrada Ycaza (1916-1961), archeologist.

1975　　**Litho.**　**Perf. 12x11½**
902 A272 80c violet bl & lt bl　.20　.20
903 A272 80c vermilion & pink　.20　.20

Issue dates: #902, Feb. 21; #903, Mar. 25.

R. Rodriguez
Palacios and A.
Duran
Quintero — A273

"Woman of
Action" — A274

1975, Apr. 1 Litho.　**Perf. 12x11½**
910 A273　1s multicolored　.20　.20
　　Nos. 910,C547-C548 (3)　.70　.60

Meeting of the Ministers for Public Works of Ecuador and Colombia, July 27, 1973.

1975, June

Design: No. 912, "Woman of Peace."

911 A274　1s yellow & multi　.20　.20
912 A274　1s blue & multi　.20　.20

International Women's Year 1975.

Planes,
Soldier and
Ship — A275

1975, July 9　　**Perf. 11½x12**
913 A275　2s multicolored　.30　.25

3 years of Natl. Revolutionary Government.

Hurdling — A276

Designs: Modern sports drawn Inca style.

1975, Sept. 11　**Litho.**　**Perf. 11½**
914 A276 20c shown　　.45　.35
915 A276 20c Chess　　.45　.35
916 A276 30c Basketball　.45　.35
917 A276 30c Boxing　　.45　.35
918 A276 40c Bicycling　.45　.35
919 A276 40c Steeplechase　.45　.35
920 A276 50c Soccer　　.45　.35
921 A276 50c Fencing　.45　.35
922 A276 60c Golf　　　.45　.35
923 A276 60c Vaulting　.45　.35
924 A276 70c Judo (standing)　.45　.35
925 A276 70c Wrestling　.45　.35
926 A276 80c Swimming　.45　.35
927 A276 80c Weight lifting　.45　.35
928 A276　1s Table Tennis　.45　.35
929 A276　1s Paddle ball　.45　.35
　　Nos. 914-929,C554-C558 (21)　10.00　6.85

3rd Ecuadorian Games.

"Genciana" 0,30 Genciana A277

Designs: Ecuadorian plants.

Perf. 12x11½, 11½x12

1975, Nov. 18 Litho.
930 A277 20c Orchid, vert .25 .25
931 A277 30c shown .25 .25
932 A277 40c Bromeliaceae
cactacceae, vert .30 .25
933 A277 50c Orchid .30 .25
934 A277 60c Orchid .35 .25
935 A277 80c Flowering cactus .35 .25
936 A277 1s Orchid .60 .25
Nos. 930-936,C559-C563 (12) 5.75 3.60

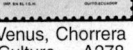

Venus, Chorrera Culture — A278   Female Mask, Tolita Culture — A279

Designs: 30c, Venus, Valdivia Culture. 40c, Seated man, Chorrera Culture. 50c, Man with poncho, Panzaleo Culture (late). 60c, Mythical head, Cashaloma Culture. 80c, Musician, Tolita Culture. No. 943, Chief Priest, Mantefia Culture. No. 945, Ornament, Tolita Culture. No. 946, Angry mask, Tolita Culture.

1976, Feb. 12 Perf. 11½
937 A278 20c multicolored .30 .20
938 A278 30c multicolored .30 .20
939 A278 40c multicolored .30 .20
940 A278 50c multicolored .30 .20
941 A278 60c multicolored .30 .20
942 A278 80c multicolored .30 .20
943 A278 1s multicolored .30 .20
944 A279 1s multicolored .30 .20
945 A279 1s multicolored .30 .20
946 A279 1s multicolored .30 .20
Nos. 937-946,C568-C572 (15) 5.45 3.30

Archaeological artifacts.

Strawberries A280   Carlos Amable Ortiz (1859-1937) A281

1976, Mar. 30
947 A280 1s blue & multi .35 .20
Nos. 947,C573-C574 (3) 1.35 .60

25th Flower and Fruit Festival, Ambato.

1976, Mar. 15 Litho. Perf. 11½

No. 949, Sixto Maria Duran (1875-1947). No. 950, Segundo Cueva Celi (1901-1969). No. 951, Cristobal Ojeda Davila (1910-1952). No. 952, Luis Alberto Valencia (1918-1970).

948 A281 1s ver & multi .25 .20
949 A281 1s orange & multi .25 .20
950 A281 1s lt green & multi .25 .20
951 A281 1s blue & multi .25 .20
952 A281 1s lt brn & multi .25 .20
Nos. 948-952 (5) 1.25 1.00

Ecuadorian composers and musicians.

Institute Emblem A282

1977, Aug. 15 Litho. Perf. 11½x12
953 A282 2s multicolored .25 .20

11th General Assembly of Pan-American Institute of Geography and History, Quito, Aug. 15-30. See Nos. C597-C597a.

Hands Holding Rotary Emblem A283

José Peralta — A284

1977, Aug. 31 Litho. Perf. 12
954 A283 1s multicolored .20 .20
955 A283 2s multicolored .30 .20

Souvenir Sheets
Imperf

956 A283 5s multicolored 1.10 1.10
957 A283 10s multicolored 1.40 1.40

Rotary Club of Guayaquil, 50th anniv.

1977 Litho. Perf. 11½

Design: 2.40s, Peralta statue.

958 A284 1.80s multi .20 .20
959 A284 2.40s multi .25 .20
Nos. 958-959,C609 (3) .80 .65

José Peralta (1855-1937), writer.

Blue-faced Booby A285

Galapagos Birds: 1.80s, Red-footed booby. 2.40s, Blue-footed boobies. 3.40s, Gull. 4.40s, Galapagos hawk. 5.40s, Map of Galapagos Islands and boobies, vert.

Perf. 11½x12, 12x11½
1977, Nov. 29 Litho.
960 A285 1.20s multi .45 .20
961 A285 1.80s multi .60 .20
962 A285 2.40s multi 1.10 .20
963 A285 3.40s multi 1.60 .20
964 A285 4.40s multi 2.25 .35
965 A285 5.40s multi 3.00 .35
Nos. 960-965 (6) 9.00 1.50

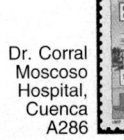

Dr. Corral Moscoso Hospital, Cuenca A286

1978, Apr. 12 Litho. Perf. 11½x12
966 A286 3s multicolored .25 .20
Nos. 966,C613-C614 (3) 1.75 1.00

Inauguration (in 1977) of Dr. Vicente Corral Moscoso Regional Hospital, Cuenca.

Surveyor Plane over Ecuador — A287   Latin-American Lions Emblem — A288

1978, Apr. 12 Litho. Perf. 11½
967 A287 6s multicolored .55 .30
Nos. 967,C619-C620 (3) 2.85 2.20

Military Geographical Institute, 50th anniv.

1978
968 A288 3s multi .70 .25
969 A288 4.20s multi 1.00 .25
Nos. 968-969,C621-C623 (5) 4.75 2.55

7th meeting of Latin American Lions, Jan. 25-29.

70th Anniversary Emblem — A289

1978, Sept. Litho. Perf. 11½
970 A289 4.20s gray & multi .45 .30

70th anniversary of Filanbanco (Philanthropic Bank). See No. C626.

Goalmouth and Net — A290

Designs: 1.80s, "Gauchito" and Games emblem, vert. 4.40s, "Gauchito," vert.

1978, Nov. 1 Litho. Perf. 12
971 A290 1.20s multi .20 .20
972 A290 1.80s multi .20 .20
973 A290 4.40s multi .55 .20
Nos. 971-973,C627-C629 (6) 3.15 1.85

11th World Cup Soccer Championship, Argentina, June 1-25.

Symbols for Male and Female — A291

1979, Feb. 15 Litho. Perf. 12x11½
974 A291 3.40s multi .45 .30

Inter-American Women's Commission, 50th anniversary.

Emblem A292

1979, June 21 Litho. Perf. 11½x12
975 A292 4.40s multi .40 .30
976 A292 5.40s multi .50 .30

Ecuadorian Mortgage Bank, 16th anniv.

Street Scene, Quito — A293

Perf. 12x11½
1979, Aug. 3 Litho. Unwmk.
977 A293 3.40s multi .35 .20
Nos. 977,C651-C653 (4) 5.50 2.65

Natl. heritage: Quito & Galapagos Islands.

Jose Joaquin de Olmedo (1780-1847), Physician — A294   Chief Enriquillo, Dominican Republic — A295

1980, Apr. 29 Litho. Perf. 12x11½
978 A294 3s multi .25 .25
979 A294 5s multi .45 .40
Nos. 978-979,C662 (3) 1.70 1.30

First Pres. of Free State of Guayaquil, 1820.

Wmk. 367, Unwmkd. (#981-983)
1980, May 12

Indo-American Tribal Chiefs: 3.40s, Guaycaypuro, Venezuela. No. 982, Abayuba, Uruguay. No. 983, Atlacatl, Salvador.

980 A295 3s multi .45 .20
981 A295 3.40s multi .75 .35
982 A295 5s multi 1.75 .55
983 A295 5s multi 1.75 .55
Nos. 980-983,C663-C678 (20) 40.95 9.90

King Juan Carlos and Queen Sofia, Visit to Ecuador A296

Perf. 11½x12
1980, May 18 Unwmk.
984 A296 3.40s multi .45 .30

See No. C679.

Cofan Indian, Napo Province — A297

1980, June 10 Litho. Perf. 12x11½
985 A297 3s shown .45 .20
986 A297 3.40s Zuleta woman, Imbabura .45 .20
987 A297 5s Chota woman, Imbabura .65 .20
Nos. 985-987,C681-C684 (7) 7.25 4.90

Basilica, Our Lady of Mercy Church, Quito A298

1980, July 7　Litho.　Perf. 11½
988 A298 3.40s shown .45 .20
989 A298 3.40s Balcony .45 .20
989A A298 3.40s Dome and cupolas .45 .20
Sizes: 91x116mm, 116x91mm
Imperf
990 A298 5s multi 1.60 1.60
990A A298 5s multi, horiz. 1.60 1.60
990B A298 5s multi 1.60 1.60
Nos. 988-990B,C685-C691 (13) 14.25 9.40

Virgin of Mercy, patron saint of Ecuadorian armed forces. No. 990 contains designs of Nos. C686, C685, 989. No. 990A contains designs of Nos. C688, C691, C690. No. 990B contains designs of Nos. C689, C687, 989A, 988.

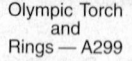

Olympic Torch and Rings — A299

Coronation of Virgin of Cisne, 50th Anniv. — A300

Perf. 12x11½
1980, July 19　　　Wmk. 395>
991 A299 5s multi .70 .20
992 A299 7.60s multi 1.25 .30
Nos. 991-992,C695-C696 (4) 3.65 1.70
Souvenir Sheet
Imperf
993 A299 30s multi 6.75 6.75

22nd Summer Olympic Games, Moscow, July 19-Aug. 3.
No. 993 contains vignettes in designs of Nos. 991 and C695.

1980　　Litho.　　Perf. 11½
994 A300 1.20s shown .30 .30
995 A300 3.40s Different statue .40 .30

J.J. Olmeda, Father de Velasco, Flags of Ecuador and Riobamba, Constitution A301

1980, Sept. 20　Litho.　Perf. 11½
996 A301 3.40s multi .30 .30
997 A301 5s multi .70 .45
Nos. 996-997,C700-C701 (4) 2.70 1.60
Souvenir Sheet
Imperf
998 A301 30s multi 3.25 3.25

Constitutional Assembly of Riobamba sesquicentennial. #998 contains vignettes in designs of #996-997.

Young Indian Girl — A302

Perf. 12x11½
1980, Oct. 9　Litho.　Wmk. 395
999 A302 1.20s multi .20 .20
1000 A302 3.40s multi .20 .20
Nos. 999-1000,C703-C704 (4) 3.00 1.55
Democratic government, 1st anniversary.

OPEC Emblem A303

1980, Nov. 8　　　Perf. 11½x12
1001 A303 3.40s multi .45 .20
20th anniversary of OPEC. See No. C706.

Decorative Hedges, Capitol Gardens, Carchi A304

1980, Nov. 21　　　　Perf. 13
1002 A304 3s multi .50 .25
Nos. 1002,C707-C708 (3) 3.75 1.90
Carchi province centennial.

Cattleya Maxima A305

Designs: Orchids.

1980, Nov. 22　　　　Perf. 11½x12
1003 A305 1.20s *shown* .55 .20
1004 A305 3s *Comparattia speciosa* .95 .40
1005 A305 3.40s *Cattleya iricolor* 1.25 .45
Nos. 1003-1005,C709-C712 (7) 22.50 6.35
Souvenir Sheet
Imperf
1006 A305 20s multi 5.75 4.25
No. 1006 contains vignettes in designs of Nos. 1003-1005.

Pope John Paul II and Children — A306

1980, Dec. 27　　　　Perf. 12
1007 A306 3.40s multi .60 .30
Nos. 1007,C715-C716 (3) 2.80 1.40
Christmas and visit of Pope John Paul II.

Carlos and Jorge Mantilla Ortega, Editors of El Comercio — A307

El Comercio Newspaper, 75th Anniv.: 3.40s, Editors Cesar & Carlos Mantilla Jacome.

1981, Jan. 6
1008 A307 2s multi .25 .25
1009 A307 3.40s multi .45 .25

Soldier on Map of Ecuador A308

1981, Mar. 10　Litho.　Perf. 13
1010 A308 3.40s multi .25 .25
1011 A308 3.40s Pres. Roldos .25 .25
National defense.

Theodore E. Gildred and Ecuador I A309

1981, Mar. 31　Litho.　Perf. 13
1012 A309 2s lt bl & blk .25 .25
Ecuador-US flight, 50th anniv.

A310　　　　　A311

1981, Apr. 10
1013 A310 2s multi .30 .20
Octavio Cordero Palacios (1870-1930), humanist.

1981　　Litho.　　Perf. 13
1014 A311 2s multi .30 .30
Nos. 1014,C721-C722 (3) 2.70 1.55
Radio station HCJB, 50th anniv.

Virgin of Dolorosa A312

1981, Apr. 30　Litho.　Perf. 12
1015 A312 2s shown .20 .20
1016 A312 2s San Gabriel College Church .20 .20
Miracle of the painting of the Virgin of Dolorosa at San Gabriel College, 75th anniv.

Dr. Rafael Mendoza Aviles Bridge Inauguration A313

1981, July 25　　　　Perf. 13
1017 A313 2s multi .30 .20

Pablo Picasso (1881-1973), Painter — A313a

1981, Oct. 26　Litho.　Imperf
1017A A313a 20s multi 2.75 2.75
Nos. 1017A,C728-C731 (5) 7.35 6.30
No. 1017A contains design of No. C728, additional portrait.

World Food Day — A314

1981, Dec. 31　Litho.　Perf. 13½x13
1018 A314 5s multi .45 .20
See No. C732

Transnave Shipping Co. 10th Anniv. — A315

Intl. Year of the Disabled — A316

1982, Jan. 21　Litho.　Perf. 13
1019 A315 3.50s Freighter Isla Salango .45 .20

1982, Feb. 25
1020 A316 3.40s Man in wheelchair .40 .20
Nos. 1020,C733-C734 (3) 2.00 1.05

Arch — A317

Juan Montalvo Birth Sesqui. — A318

1982, May　Litho.　Perf. 13
1021 A317 2s shown .25 .25
1022 A317 3s Houses .45 .25

Miniature Sheet
Perf. 12½ on 2 Sides
1023 Sheet of 4, 18th cent. map of Quito 5.00 4.50
a.-d. A317 6s multi 1.10 .50
QUITEX '82, 4th Natl. Stamp Exhib., Quito, Apr. 16-22. #1023 contains 4 48x31mm stamps.

1982　　　　　　Perf. 13
1024 A318 2s Portrait .25 .25
1025 A318 3s Mausoleum .25 .25
Nos. 1024-1025,C735 (3) 1.50 1.05

American Air
Forces
Cooperation
System — A319

4th World
Swimming
Champ.,
Guayaquil
A320

1982
1026 A319 5s Emblem .45 .35

1982, July 30
1027 A320 1.80s Stadium .20 .20
1028 A320 3.40s Water polo .35 .20
  Nos. 1027-1028,C736-C737 (4) 2.50 1.25

A321   A322

1982, Dec. Litho. Perf. 13
1029 A321 5.40s shown .25 .25
1030 A321 6s Statue .35 .25

Juan L. Mera (1832-?), Writer, by Victor Mideros.

1983, Mar. 28 Litho. Perf. 13
1031 A322 2s multi .35 .25

St. Teresa of Jesus of Avila (1515-82).

Sea Lions   Flamingoes
A323   A324

1983, June 17 Litho. Perf. 13
1032 A323 3s multi .90 .20
1033 A324 5s multi 1.60 .20

Ecuadorian rule over Galapagos Islds., sesqui. (3s); Charles Darwin (1809-1882).

Pres. Rocafuerte   Simon Bolivar
A325   A326

Perf. 13x13½
1983, Aug. 26 Litho. Wmk. 395
1034 A325 5s Statue .30 .20
1035 A325 20s Portrait .85 .35
1036 A326 20s Portrait .85 .35
  Nos. 1034-1036 (3) 2.00 .90

Vicente Rocafuerte Bejarano, president, 1833-39 (Nos. 1034-1035).

A327   A328

1983, Sept. 3
1037 A327 5s River .40 .20
1038 A327 10s Dam .70 .55

Size: 110x89mm
Imperf
1039 A327 20s Dam, river 2.75 2.75
  Nos. 1037-1039 (3) 3.85 3.50

Paute hydroelectric plant opening. No. 1039 is airmail.

Wmk. 395
1983, Oct. 11 Litho. Perf. 13
1040 A328 2s multi .35 .25

World Communication Year.

A329   A330

1983, Sept. Litho. Perf. 13
1041 A329 3s multi .35 .25

Cent. of Bolivar and El Oro Provinces (1984).

1984, Mar. Litho. Perf. 13
1042 A330 15s Engraving .45 .30

Atahualpa (1497-1529), last Incan ruler.

A331

Christmas
1983 — A331a

Creche figures.

Perf. 13½x13, 13x13½
1984, July 7 Litho.
1043 A331 5s Jesus & the teachers .25 .20
1044 A331 5s Three kings .25 .20
1045 A331 5s Holy Family .25 .20
1046 A331a 6s Priest .25 .20
  Nos. 1043-1046 (4) 1.00 .80

Foreign
Policy of
Pres.
Hurtado
A332

State visits.

1984, July 10 Perf. 13½x13
1047 A332 8s Brazil .40 .20
1048 A332 9s PRC .45 .20
1049 A332 24s UN 1.25 .90
1050 A332 28s US 1.60 .95

1051 A332 29s Venezuela 1.60 1.10
1052 A332 37s Latin American Economic Conf., Quito 2.00 1.40
  Nos. 1047-1052 (6) 7.30 4.75

Miguel Diaz
Cueva
(1884-1942),
Lawyer
A333

1984, Aug. 8 Litho. Perf. 13½x13
1053 A333 10s multicolored .70 .35

1984 Winter   Manned Flight
Olympics   Bicentenary
A334   A335

Perf. 13x13½, 12x11½ (6s)
1984, Aug. 15
1054 A334 2s Emblem .20 .20
1055 A334 4s Ice skating .20 .20
1056 A334 6s Skating, diff. .20 .20
1057 A334 10s Skiing .80 .20
  Nos. 1054-1057 (4) 1.40 .80

Size: 90x100mm
1057A A334 20s Figure skating 35.00 15.00

1984, Aug. 15 Perf. 13x13½
1058 A335 3s Montgolfier .20 .20
1059 A335 6s Charlier's balloon, Paris, 1789 .35 .20

Souvenir Sheet
1060 A335 20s Graf Zeppelin, Montgolfier 1.75 1.10

No. 1060 is airmail and contains one imperf. stamp (50x37mm).

SAN MATEO
'83,
Esmeraldas
A336

1984 Litho. Perf. 13
1061 A336 8s La Marimba folk dance 1.75 .25

Size: 89x110mm
Imperf
1061A A336 15s La Marimba, diff. 1.10 1.10

No. 1061A is airmail.

Jose Maria de
Jesus Yerovi (b.
1824), 4th
Archbishop of
Quito — A337

1984
1062 A337 5s multi .35 .25

Canonization
of Brother
Miguel
A338

1984 Litho. Perf. 13
1063 A338 9s Academy of Languages .50 .20
1064 A338 24s Vatican City, vert. 1.00 .70

Imperf
Size: 110x90mm
1065 A338 28s Home of Brother Miguel 3.25 2.10
  Nos. 1063-1065 (3) 4.75 3.00

No. 1065, airmail, has black control number.

State Visit of Pope   Beatification of
John   Mercedes de
Paul II — A339   Jesus
                       Molina — A340

1985, Jan. 23 Litho. Perf. 13x13½
1066 A339 1.60s Papal arms 1.50 .20
1067 A339 5s Blessing crowd 1.50 .20
1068 A339 9s World map, itinerary 1.50 .20
1069 A339 28s Pope waving 3.75 .45
1070 A339 29s Portrait 4.00 .55

Size: 90x109mm
Imperf
1071 A339 30s Pope holding crosier 10.00 10.00
  Nos. 1066-1071 (6) 22.25 11.60

1985, Jan. 23

Paintings, sculpture.

1072 A340 1.60s Portrait .30 .20
1073 A340 5s Czestochowa Madonna .30 .20
1074 A340 9s Alborada Madonna .75 .20

Size: 90x110mm
Imperf
1075 A340 20s Mercedes de Jesus, children 5.00 5.00
  Nos. 1072-1075 (4) 6.35 5.60

Visit of Pope John Paul II, birth bimillennium of the Virgin Mary.

Samuel Valarezo
Delgado,
Naturalist,
Politician — A341

1985, Feb.
1076 A341 2s Bird .20 .20
1077 A341 3s Swordfish, tuna .20 .20
1078 A341 6s Portrait .30 .20
  Nos. 1076-1078 (3) .70 .60

ESPANA '84,
Madrid
A342

1985, Apr. 25 Perf. 13½x13
1079 A342 6s Emblem .20 .20
1080 A342 10s Spanish royal family .70 .20

Size: 110x90mm
Imperf
1081 A342 15s Retiro Park, exhibition site 1.50 1.50

Dr. Pio Jaramillo Alvarado (1884-1968), Historian
A343

1985, May 17
1082 A343 6s multi   .25 .20

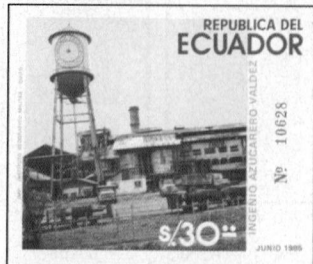

Ingenio Valdez Sugar Refinery — A344

Designs: 50s, Sugar cane, emblem. 100s, Rafael Valdez Cervantes, founder.

1985, June   Litho.   Perf. 13
1082A A344 50s multi   1.25 .65
1082B A344 100s multi   2.75 1.40
   Size: 110x90mm
   Imperf
1083 A344 30s multi   2.00 2.00
   Nos. 1082A-1083 (3)   6.00 4.05

Chamber of Commerce, 10th Anniv. A345

50s, Natl. and American Statues of Liberty.

1985, Aug. 15   Perf. 13½x13
1084 A345 24s multicolored   .80 .45
1085 A345 28s multicolored   1.00 .65
   Size: 110x90mm
   Imperf
1086 A345 50s multicolored   2.75 2.75
   Nos. 1084-1086 (3)   4.55 3.85

Natl. Philatelic Assoc., AFE, 50th Anniv. — A346

1985, Aug. 25   Perf. 12
1087 A346 25s AFE emblem   .60 .40
1088 A346 30s No. 357, horiz.   1.00 .65

Guayaquil Fire Dept., 150th Anniv. A347

1985, Oct. 10   Perf. 13½x13
1089 A347 6s Steam fire pump, 1882   .20 .20
1090 A347 10s Fire Wagon, 1899   .50 .20
1091 A347 20s Anniv. emblem, natl. flag   .90 .70
   Nos. 1089-1091 (3)   1.60 1.10

Natl. Infant Survival Campaign A348   1st Natl. Phil. Cong., Quito, Nov. 25-28 A349

1985, Oct.   Perf. 13x13½
1092 A348 10s Boy, girl, tree   .45 .30

1985, Nov.   Perf. 13x13½, 13½x13
20th cent. illustrations, natl. cultural collection: 5s, Supreme Court, Quito, by J. M. Roura. 10s, Riobamba Cathedral, by O. Munaz. 15s, House of 100 Windows, by J. M. Roura, horiz. 20s, Rural cottage near Cuenca, by J. M. Roura.
No. 1097: a, Stampless cover, 1779, Riobamba. b, Hand press, 1864, Quito. c, Postrider, 1880, Cuenca. d, Monoplane, 1st airmail flight, 1919, Guayaquil.
1093 A349 5s multi   .20 .20
1094 A349 10s multi   .50 .20
1095 A349 15s multi   .65 .50
1096 A349 20s multi   .90 .65
   Nos. 1093-1096 (4)   2.25 1.55
   Souvenir Sheet
1097   Sheet of 4   1.00 1.00
 a.-d.   A349 5s, any single   .20 .20
AFE, 50th anniv. #1097 contains 53x42mm stamps, perf. 13x12½ on 2 sides.

10th Bolivarian Games, Cuenca A350

1985, Nov.   Perf. 13½x13
1098 A350 10s Boxing   .50 .20
1099 A350 25s Women's gymnastics   .65 .35
1100 A350 30s Discus   .85 .40
   Nos. 1098-1100 (3)   2.00 .95

BAE Calderon, Navy Cent. — A351

Military anniv.: #1102, Fighter plane, Air Force 65th anniv. #1103, Army & paratroops emblems, Special Forces 30th anniv.

1985, Dec.   Perf. 13x13½
1101 A351 10s multi   .45 .20
1102 A351 10s multi   .45 .20
1103 A351 10s multi   .45 .20
   Nos. 1101-1103 (3)   1.35 .60

UN, 40th Anniv. A352

1985, Oct.   Litho.   Perf. 13
1104 A352 10s UN flag   .45 .20
1105 A352 20s Natl. flag   .45 .20
   Size: 110x90mm
   Imperf
1106 A352 50s UN Building   1.25 1.25
   Nos. 1104-1106 (3)   2.15 1.65

Christmas A353   Indigenous Flowers A354

1985, Nov.
1107 A353 5s Child riding donkey   .20 .20
1108 A353 10s Baked goods   .45 .20
1109 A353 15s Riding donkey, diff.   .60 .45
   Size: 90x110mm
   Imperf
1110 A353 30s like 5s   1.50 1.50
   Nos. 1107-1110 (4)   2.75 2.35

1986, Feb.
1111 A354 24s Embotrium grandiforum   1.00 .45
1112 A354 28s Topobea sp.   1.75 .45
1113 A354 29s Befaria resinosa mutis   2.25 .50
   Size: 110x90mm
   Imperf
1114 A354 15s multi   7.25 5.00
   Nos. 1111-1114 (4)   12.25 6.40
No. 1114 contains designs of Nos. 1111, 1113, 1112; black control number.

Discovery of the Galapagos Islds., 450th Anniv. A355

Map of the Islands — A356

1986, Feb. 12
1115 A355 10s Land iguana   .45 .20
1116 A355 20s Sea lion   .90 .45
1117 A355 30s Frigate birds   1.40 .70
1118 A355 40s Penguins   1.75 1.00
1119 A355 50s Sea turtle   2.25 1.10
1120 A355 100s Charles Darwin   4.50 2.50
1121 A355 200s Bishop Tomas de Berlenga, discoverer   8.75 4.50
   Perf. 12½ on 2 Sides
1122 A356   Sheet of 4   11.00 11.00
 a.-d.   50s, any single   1.50 1.50
   Nos. 1115-1122 (8)   31.00 21.45
No. 1122 contains 53x42mm stamps.

Inter-American Development Bank, 25th Anniv. — A357

5s, Antonio Ortiz Mena, pres. 1971-88. 10s, Felipe Herrera, pres. 1960-71. 50s, Emblem.

1986, Mar. 6
1123 A357 5s multi   .40 .20
1124 A357 10s multi   .60 .20
1125 A357 50s multi   1.00 .80
   Nos. 1123-1125 (3)   2.00 1.20

Guayaquil Tennis Club, 75th Anniv. A358

1986, Mar. 7
1126 A358 10s Emblem   .45 .20
1127 A358 10s Francisco Segura Cano, vert.   .45 .20
1128 A358 10s Andres Gomez Santos, vert.   .45 .20
   Nos. 1126-1128 (3)   1.35 .60

1986 World Cup Soccer Championships, Mexico — A359

1986, May 5
1129 A359 5s Shot   .20 .20
1130 A359 10s Block   .80 .20
An imperf. stamp exists picturing flags, player and emblem. Value $8.50.

Meeting of Presidents Cordero and Betancourt of Colombia, Feb. 1985 A360

1986   Litho.   Perf. 13½x13
1131 A360 20s Presidents   .45 .20
1132 A360 20s Embracing   .45 .20

Exports A361

35s, #1137c, Shrimp. 40s, #1137b, Tuna. 45s, #1137a, Sardines. #1137d, MICIP emblem.

1986, Apr. 12
1133 A361 35s ultra & ver   1.00 .55
1134 A361 40s red & yel grn   1.00 .55
1135 A361 45s car & dk yel   1.15 .75
   Perf. 12½ on 2 Sides
1137   Sheet of 4   2.25 2.25
 a.-d.   A361 10s, any single   .40 .40
   Nos. 1133-1137 (4)   5.40 4.10
No. 1137 contains 4 53x42mm stamps.

A362

La Condamine's First Geodesic Mission, 250th Anniv. — A363

#1141a, Triangulation map for determining equatorial meridian, 1736. #1141b, Partial map of the Maranon & Amazon Rivers, by Samuel Fritz, 1743-1744. #1141c, Base of measurement, Yaruqui plains. #1141d, Caraburo & Dyambaru Pyramids near Quito. #1141 has a continuous design.

1986, July 10 Litho. **Perf. 13½x13**
1138 A362 10s La Condamine .35 .20
1139 A362 15s Maldonado .45 .20
1140 A362 20s Middle of the World, Quito .55 .20
Nos. 1138-1140 (3) 1.35 .60

Souvenir Sheet
Perf. 12½ on 2 Sides
1141 A363 Sheet of 4 2.75 2.75
a.-d. 10s any single .40 .40

Chambers of Commerce A364

1986 Litho. **Perf. 13½x13**
1142 A364 10s Pichincha .25 .20
1143 A364 10s Cuenca .25 .20
1144 A364 10s Guayaquil .25 .20
Nos. 1142-1144 (3) .75 .60

Civil Service and Communications Ministry, 57th Anniv. — A365

Organization emblems.

1986, Dec. Litho. **Perf. 13x13½**
1145 A365 5s State railway .20 .20
1146 A365 10s Post office .20 .20
1147 A365 15s Communications .55 .20
1148 A365 20s Ministry of Public Works .65 .40
Nos. 1145-1148 (4) 1.60 1.00

A366   A367

1987, Feb. 16 Litho. **Perf. 13x13½**
1149 A366 5s multi .35 .25
Chamber of Agriculture of the 1st Zone, 50th anniv.

Litho. & Typo.
1988, Jan. 6 **Perf. 13**

Col. Luis Vargas Torres (d. 1887): 50s, Portrait. #1151, Combat unit, c. 1885. #1152a, Torres & his mother, Delfina. #1152b, Letter to Delfina written by Torres during imprisonment, 1882. #1152c, Arms of Ecuador & combat unit.

1150 A367 50s yel grn, blk & gold 1.00 .80

1151 A367 100s ver, gold & ultra 2.25 1.40
Size: 95x140mm
Perf. 12 on One or Two Sides
1152 Block of 3 6.75 6.75
a.-c. A367 100s any single 1.50 1.50
Nos. 1150-1152 (3) 10.00 8.95
Sizes: #1152a, 1152c, 95x28mm; #1152b, 95x83mm.

Founding of Guayaquil, 450th Anniv. A368

15s, Street in Las Penas. 30s, Rafael Mendoza Aviles Bridge. 40s, Francisco de Orellana (c. 1490-1546), Spanish explorer, founder, & reenactment of landing, 1538.

1988, Feb. 19 Litho. **Perf. 13**
1153 A368 15s multi, vert. .20 .20
1154 A368 30s multi .45 .20
1155 A368 40s multi .60 .20
Nos. 1153-1155 (3) 1.25 .60

Social Security Foundation (IESS), 60th Anniv. A369

1988, Mar. 11
1156 A369 50s shown .75 .40
1157 A369 100s multi, diff. 1.50 1.00

Dr. Pedro Moncayo y Esparza (1807-1888), Author, Politician A370

1988, Apr. 28 Litho. **Perf. 14x13½**
1158 A370 10s Yaguarcocha Lake .20 .20
1159 A370 15s shown .20 .20
1160 A370 20s Residence .20 .20
Size: 89x110mm
Imperf
1161 A370 100s Full-length portrait 1.10 1.10
Nos. 1158-1161 (4) 1.70 1.70

A371

Avianca Airlines, 60th Anniv. — A372

1988, May 12 Litho. **Perf. 14x13½**
1162 A371 10s Junkers F-13 .20 .20
1163 A371 20s Dornier Wal seaplane .20 .20
1164 A371 30s Ford 5AT trimotor .35 .20
1165 A371 40s Boeing 247-D .45 .20
1166 A371 50s Boeing 720-059B .55 .35
1167 A371 100s Douglas DC-3 1.25 .55
1168 A371 200s Boeing 727-200 2.25 1.25
1169 A371 300s Sikorsky S-38 4.00 1.75
Perf. 13½x14
1170 A372 500s shown 6.25 3.00
Nos. 1162-1170 (9) 15.50 7.70

San Gabriel College, 125th Anniv. A373

1988, July 25 Litho. **Perf. 14x13½**
1171 A373 15s Contemporary facility .20 .20
1172 A373 35s College entrance, 19th cent. .50 .30

A374

Military Geographical Institute, 60th Anniv. A375

1988, July 25 **Perf. 12½ on 2 Sides**
Size of No. 1173: 110x90mm
1173 A374 Block of 4 1.75 1.75
a.-d. 5s any single .30 .30
Perf. 13½
1174 A375 25s Planetarium .45 .20
1175 A375 50s Zeiss projector .80 .20
1176 A375 60s Anniv. emblem 1.00 .35
1177 A375 500s Creation, mural by E. Kingman 6.25 3.25
Nos. 1173-1177 (5) 10.25 5.75

In 1996 Nos. 1174, 1183, 1265 were surcharged 800s, 2600s 400s respectively. Only a few sets were sold to the public. The balance were sold by postal employees at greatly inflated prices.

Salesian Brothers in Ecuador, Cent. A376

Designs: 10s, St. John Bosco (1815-88), vert. 50s, 1st Salesian Cong. in Ecuador. 100s, Bosco, Salesian Brothers monument and Andes Mountains.

1988, July 29 Litho. **Perf. 13½**
1178 A376 10s multi .25 .25
1179 A376 50s multi .75 .40
Size: 89x110mm
Imperf
1180 A376 100s multi 2.25 1.60
Nos. 1178-1180 (3) 3.25 2.25

Francisco Coello, Founder — A377

Social Services Council, Guayaquil, Cent. — A378

Flag: a, Emblem (upper left portion). b, Emblem (upper right portion). c, Emblem (lower left portion) and "100 ANOS." d, Emblem (lower right portion) and "DE TRADICION DE FE, AMPARO Y ESPERANZA."

1988, Nov. 24 Litho. **Perf. 13½x14**
1181 A377 15s shown .20 .20
1182 A377 20s Eduardo Arosemena, 1st Director .20 .20
1183 A377 45s Emblem .45 .20
Size: 110x90mm
Perf. 12½ on 2 Sides
1184 A378 Block of 4 1.25 1.25
a.-d. 10s any single .20 .20
Nos. 1181-1184 (4) 2.10 1.85
For surcharge see note following No. 1177.

A379

Azuay Bank, 75th Anniv. — A380

Perf. 14x13½, 13½x14
1989, Mar. 1 Litho.
1185 A379 20s multi .20 .20
1186 A379 40s multi, vert. .30 .20
Size: 90x110mm
Imperf
1187 A380 500s shown 9.00 2.40
Nos. 1185-1187 (3) 9.50 2.80

1988 Summer Olympics, Seoul — A381

Character trademark demonstrating sports.

1989, Mar. 20 **Perf. 13½x14**
1188 A381 10s Running .20 .20
1189 A381 20s Boxing .20 .20
1190 A381 30s Cycling .40 .20
1191 A381 40s Shooting .40 .20
1192 A381 100s Diving .90 .60
1193 A381 200s Weight lifting 1.75 1.25
1194 A381 300s Tae kwon do 2.75 1.75

Size: 90x110mm

Imperf

1195   A381   200s Emblems   2.75   2.75
Nos. 1188-1195 (8)   9.35   7.15

RUMINAHUI
'88 — A382

Designs: 50s, *Bird,* by Joaquin Tinta, vert. 70s, Matriz Church, Sangolqui. 300s, Monument to Ruminahui in Sangolqui, Pichincha.

Perf. 14x13½, 13½x14

1989, May 2   Litho.   Wmk. 395

1196   A382   50s multi   .80   .20
1197   A382   70s multi   1.00   .20

Size: 90x111mm

Imperf

1198   A382   300s multi   5.75   1.10
Nos. 1196-1198 (3)   7.55   1.50

Cantonization, 50th anniv.

Benjamin
Carrion
Mora,
Educator
A383

Perf. 13½x14, 14x13½

1989, May 10   Litho.

1199   A383   50s Portrait, vert.   .45   .20
1200   A383   70s Loja land-
       scape   .55   .20
1201   A383   1000s University   8.00   3.50

Size: 110x90mm

Imperf

1202   A383   200s Portrait, diff.   1.50   1.50
Nos. 1199-1202 (4)   10.50   5.40

2nd Intl. Art
Biennial
A384

Prize-winning art: 40s, *The Gilded Frame,* by Myrna Baez. 70s, *Paraguay III,* by Carlos Colorabino, vert. 100s, Ordinance establishing the art exhibition. 180s, *Modulation 892,* by Julio Le Parc, vert.

Perf. 14x13½, 13½x14, Imperf. (100s)

1989, June 2   Litho.
Size of No. 1205: 110x90mm

1203   A384   40s multi   .45   .20
1204   A384   70s multi   .90   .20
1205   A384   100s multi   1.75   .75
1206   A384   180s multi   1.50   .95
Nos. 1203-1206 (4)   4.60   2.10

Guayaquil
Chamber of
Commerce,
Cent.
A385

Perf. 13½x14, 14x13½, Imperf. (No. 1208)

1989, June 20   Litho.
Size of No. 1208: 110x91mm

1207   A385   50s Founder Ignacio
       Molestina, vert.   .75   .35
1208   A385   200s Flags   3.25   2.00
1209   A385   300s Headquarters   2.25   2.25
1210   A385   500s Flags, diff.   1.50   1.50
Nos. 1207-1210 (4)   7.75   6.10

French
Revolution,
Bicent.
A386

20s, French natl. colors, anniv. emblem. 50s, Cathedral fresco. 100s, Rooster. 200s, Symbols of the revolution. 600s, Story board showing events of the revolution.

1989, July 11   Perf. 13½x14, 14x13½

1211   A386   20s multi, vert.   .20   .20
1212   A386   50s multi   .45   .20
1213   A386   100s multi, vert.   .70   .45

Size: 90x110mm

Imperf

1214   A386   200s multi, vert.   1.50   1.50
1215   A386   600s multi, vert.   6.00   6.00
Nos. 1211-1215 (5)   8.85   8.35

A387

Ministry of Public
Works and
Communications
A388

#1216a, MOP emblem, 2-lane roadway. #1216b, State railway emblem, train. #1216c, Postal service emblem, airmail cover. #1216d, Telecommunications (IETEL) emblem, wall telephone. #1217, MOP, IETEL, postal service & state railway emblems. 100s, IETEL emblem. 200s, MOP emblem.

1989, July 7   Perf. 12½ on 2 Sides

1216   A387   Block of 4   2.00   2.00
a.-d.   50s any single   .40   .40

Perf. 13½x14

1217   A388   50s shown   .35   .20
1218   A388   100s multi   .65   .40
1219   A388   200s multi   1.50   .85
Nos. 1216-1219 (4)   4.50   3.45

MOP, 60th anniv.; national communications, 105th anniv. (No. 1216d, 100s).

Natl. Red Cross, Intl. Red Cross and
Red Crescent Societies, 125th Anniv.
A389

1989, Sept. 14   Litho.   Perf. 13½

1220   A389   10s Medical volun-
       teer, vert.   .20   .20
1221   A389   30s shown   .20   .20
1222   A389   200s Two volunteers   1.40   .85
Nos. 1220-1222 (3)   1.80   1.25

Juan
Montalvo
(1832-1889),
Writer
A390

1989, Nov. 11   Litho.   Perf. 14x13½

1223   A390   50s Mausoleum,
       Ambato   .35   .20
1224   A390   100s Portrait (detail)   .90   .55
1225   A390   200s Monument,
       Ambato   1.60   1.25

Size: 90x110mm

Imperf

1226   A390   200s Portrait   1.25   1.25
Nos. 1223-1226 (4)   4.10   3.25

America
Issue
A391

UPAE emblem and pre-Columbian pottery.

1990, Mar. 6   Litho.   Perf. 13½

1227   A391   200s La Tolita incen-
       sory, vert.   1.60   1.10
1228   A391   300s Warrior (plate)   2.50   1.60

Dated 1989.

Dr. Luis
Carlos
Jaramillo
Leon,
Founder
A392

#1233a, Dr. Leon. #1230, 1233b, Federico Malo Andrade, honorary president. 130s, #1233c, Roberto Crespo Toral, 1st president. 200s, Alfonso Jaramillo Leon, founder.

1990, Jan. 17   Litho.   Perf. 13½

1229   A392   100s shown   .80   .55
1230   A392   100s multicolored   .80   .55
1231   A392   130s multicolored   1.10   .70
1232   A392   200s multicolored   1.60   1.10

Size: 91x38mm

Perf. 12½ Horiz. on 1 or 2 sides

1233   Block of 3   2.75   2.75
a.-c.   A392 100s any single   .50   .50
Nos. 1229-1233 (5)   7.05   5.65

Chamber of Commerce, 70th anniversary.

World Cup
Soccer,
Italy — A393

1990, July 12   Litho.   Perf. 13½

1234   A393   100s shown   .55   .20
1235   A393   200s Soccer player   1.10   .55
1236   A393   300s Map of Italy, tro-
       phy   1.75   .80

Imperf

Size: 110x90mm

1237   A393   200s Player, flags   1.50   1.50

Size: 60x90mm

1238   A393   300s World Cup Tro-
       phy   2.25   2.25
Nos. 1234-1238 (5)   7.15   5.30

Nos. 1235-1236, 1238 vert.

A394   A396

A395

1990, June 12   Perf. 13½

1239   A394   100s multi   .60   .20
1240   A394   200s Church tower,
       book   1.00   .60

College of St. Mariana, cent.

1990, Sept. 7   Litho.   Perf. 13½

Tourism: No. 100s, No. 1244c, Iguana. 200s, No. 1244b, La Compania Church, Quito. 300s, No. 1244a, Old man from Vilcabamba. No. 1244d, Locomotive.

1241   A395   100s multi   .70   .20
1242   A395   200s multi, vert.   1.40   .45
1243   A395   300s multi   1.90   .65

Size: 111x90mm

Perf. 12½ on 2 sides

1244   Block of 4   6.75   3.25
a.-d.   A395 100s any single   .35   .20
Nos. 1241-1244 (4)   10.75   4.55

1990, Sept. 1   Perf. 13½

National Census: 100s, No. 1248a, People and house. 200s, No. 1248b, Map. 300s, No. 1248c, Census breakdown, pencil.

1245   A396   100s multicolored   .45   .20
1246   A396   200s multicolored,
       horiz.   1.00   .45
1247   A396   300s multicolored   1.40   .65

Size: 109x88mm

Perf. 12½ on 2 sides

1248   Block of 3   1.50   1.50
a.-c.   A396 100s any single   .30   .30
Nos. 1245-1248 (4)   4.35   2.80

A397   A398

1990, Nov. 2   Litho.   Perf. 14

1249   A397   200s Flags   .95   .35
1250   A397   300s shown   1.40   .50

Organization of Petroleum Exporting Countries (OPEC), 30th anniv.

1990, Oct. 31   Perf. 13½x14

1251   A398   200s Emblem   .95   .35
1252   A398   300s Wooden parrots   1.40   .50

Size: 92x110mm

Imperf

1253   A398   200s Wooden parrots,
       diff.   1.60   1.60
Nos. 1251-1253 (3)   3.95   2.45

Artisans' Organization, 25th anniv.

Flowers — A399

Wmk. 395
1990, Nov. 12   Litho.   Perf. 13½
1254 A399 100s Sobralia   .90   .20
1255 A399 100s Blakea, vert.   .90   .20
1256 A399 100s Cattleya, vert.   .90   .20
1257 A399 100s Loasa, vert.   .90   .20
   Nos. 1254-1257 (4)   3.60   .80

Discovery of America, 500th Anniv. (in 1992) A400

1990, Dec. 31   Litho.   Perf. 13½
1258 A400 100s Ancient dwelling   .55   .20
1259 A400 200s Mangrove
              swamp   1.25   .35

Natl. Union of Journalists, 50th Anniv. A401

1991, Feb. 28
1260 A401 200s shown   .95   .65
1261 A401 300s Eugenio Espejo,
              writer   1.60   .70
1262 A401 400s Union emblem   1.75   .95
   Nos. 1260-1262 (3)   4.30 2.30

Radio Quito, 50th Anniv. A402

Designs: 200s, Man with microphone, vert. 500s, Family listening to radio.

1991, Apr. 10
1263 A402 200s multicolored   .75   .35
1264 A402 500s multicolored   1.60   .85

Dr. Pablo A. Suarez, Birth Cent. — A403

1991, Sept. 16   Wmk. 395
1265 A403 70s multicolored   .35   .25
   Dated 1990.
   For surcharge see note following No. 1177.

America Issue A404

UPAEP emblem and: 200s, Columbus' ships. 500s, Columbus, landing in America.

1991, Oct. 18   Litho.   Perf. 13½x13
1266 A404 200s multicolored   1.00   .65
1267 A404 500s multicolored   1.90 1.25

A405   A406

Designs: Cultural artifacts.

Wmk. 395
1991, Nov. 14   Litho.   Perf. 13½
1268 A405 100s Cat censer   .50   .20
1269 A405 200s Statue of old
              man's head   1.00   .35
1270 A405 300s Zoomorphic
              statue   1.75   .60
   Nos. 1268-1270 (3)   3.25 1.15

   Dated 1990. See No. 1291.

1991   Perf. 13
Design: 500s, Woman in profile.
1271 A406 300s shown   1.00   .55
1272 A406 500s multicolored   1.90 1.00

Day of Non-violence Toward Women.

Jacinto Jijon y Caamano, Archaeologist, Birth Cent. — A407

1991, Dec. 11   Perf. 13½
1273 A407 200s Portrait, vert.   .70   .35
1274 A407 300s shown   1.10   .55

Pres. Rodrigo Borja, Ecuador and Pres. Jaime Paz Zamora, Bolivia — A408

1991, Dec. 10   Perf. 14x13½
1275 A408 500s multicolored   1.75   .90

Pres. Rodrigo Borja's Visit to the UN — A409

Wmk. 395
1992, Jan. 24   Litho.   Perf. 14
1276 A409 100s multicolored   .40   .20
1277 A409 1000s Flags, world
              map   3.00 1.60

Battle of Jambeli, 50th Anniv. — A410

#1278, Gunboat Calderon and Capt. Raphael Moran Valverde. #1279, Dispatch boat Atahualpa and Ens. Victor Naranjo Fiallo. #1280, Valverde, Fiallo and ships.

1992, Apr. 7
1278 A410 300s multicolored   .55   .40
1279 A410 500s multicolored   1.25   .90
   Size: 110x90mm
   Imperf
1280 A410 500s multicolored   2.75 2.40
   Nos. 1278-1280 (3)   4.55 3.70

Galapagos Islands Wildlife — A411

Designs: No. 1281, Giant tortoise. No. 1282, Galapagos penguin, vert. No. 1283, Zalophus californianus, vert. No. 1284, Swallow-tailed gull. No. 1285, Fregata minor. No. 1286, Land iguana.

1992, Apr. 10   Litho.   Perf. 13½
1281 A411 100s multicolored   .55   .35
1282 A411 100s multicolored   .55   .35
1283 A411 100s multicolored   .55   .35
1284 A411 100s multicolored   .55   .35
1285 A411 100s multicolored   .55   .35
1286 A411 100s multicolored   .55   .35
   Nos. 1281-1286 (6)   3.30 2.10

Vicente Rocafuerte National College, 150th Anniv. (in 1991) A412

Perf. 14x13½
1992, Apr. 29   Litho.   Wmk. 395
1287 A412 200s shown   .70   .35
1288 A412 400s Vicente Rocafu-
              erte   1.10   .60

Eloy Alfaro (1842-1912), President — A413

Designs: 300s, Portrait, vert.

Perf. 13½x14, 14x13½
1992, Aug. 26   Litho.   Wmk. 395
1289 A413 300s multicolored   .90   .70
1290 A413 700s multicolored   1.60 1.00

   Cultural Artifacts Type of 1991

1992, Sept. 6   Litho.   Perf. 13½
1291 A405 400s Ceremonial
              mask   1.40   .75
   Dated 1990.

Discovery of America, 500th Anniv. A414

Wmk. 395
1992, Oct. 15   Litho.   Perf. 13½
1292 A414 200s Sailing ship   .75   .50
1293 A414 400s Columbus, map,
              vert.   1.40   .85

Andres F. Cordova (b. 1892) A415

1992, Nov. 17   Litho.   Perf. 13½
1294 A415 300s multicolored   .90   .55

Beatification of Narcisa of Jesus — A416

1992, Nov. 30   Perf. 13½
1295 A416 100s multicolored   .35   .20

A417   A418

Christmas: 300s, Infant Jesus of Saqueo, 18th cent. 600s, Stable scene, Infant Jesus asleep on hay.

1992, Dec. 14   Perf. 13½
1296 A417 300s multicolored   .95   .60
1297 A417 600s multicolored   1.75 1.00

1992, Dec. 29
1298 A418 200s multicolored   .70   .45
   Father Juan de Velasco, Death Bicent.

Frogs — A419   A420

Perf. 13½x14
1993, Jan. 28   Litho.   Wmk. 395
1299 A419 300s Agalychnis
              spurelli   .50   .35
1300 A419 300s Atelopus
              bomolochos   .50   .35
1301 A419 600s Gastrotheca
              plumbea   1.40   .90
1302 A419 600s Hyla picturata 1.40   .90
1303 A419 900s Dendrobates sp. 2.10 1.40
1304 A419 900s Sphaenorhyncus
              lacteus   2.10 1.40
   Nos. 1299-1304 (6)   8.00 5.30

1993, Feb. 16   Litho.   Perf. 13x13½
1305 A420 300s blue   .80   .20
   J. Roberto Paez, (1893-1983), co-founder of social security.

A421   A422

1993, Mar. 16   Perf. 13½x14
1306 A421 500s No. 168   1.25   .45
   Francisco Robles (1811-93).

Perf. 13½x14
1993, Mar. 25   Litho.   Wmk. 395
1307 A422 300s Natl. police   .70   .50

Pres. Jose Maria Velasco Ibarra (1893-1979)
A423

Perf. 14x13½
1993, Mar. 31   Litho.   Wmk. 395
1308 A423 500s multicolored   1.25   .45

Insects — A424

Wmk. 395
1993, May 27   Litho.   Perf. 13½
1309 A424 150s Fulgora laternaria   .55   .20
1310 A424 200s Semiotus ligneus   .65   .20
1311 A424 300s Taeniotes pulverulenta   1.10   .35
1312 A424 400s Danaus plexippus   1.25   .40
1313 A424 600s Erotylus onagga   2.10   .65
1314 A424 700s Xylocopa darwini   2.25   .75
    Nos. 1309-1314 (6)   7.90 2.55

A425

Wmk. 395
1993, May 31   Litho.   Perf. 13½
1315 A425 1000s multicolored   2.25 1.25

Pedro Fermin Cevallos Villacreces (1812-93), historian and founder of Academy of Language.

First Latin-American Children's Peace Assembly, Quito — A426

1993, June 7
1316 A426 300s multicolored   .70   .45

Juan Benigno Vela Hervas (1843-97), Jurist
A427

Perf. 13x13½
1993, July 8   Litho.   Wmk. 395
1317 A427 2000s multicolored   4.50 2.40

Guillermo Bustamante, Birth Cent.
A428

1993, Sept. 23   Perf. 13½
1318 A428 1500s multicolored   4.00 1.75

University of Ecuador School of Medicine, 300th Anniv.
A429

Perf. 14x13½
1993, Sept. 7   Litho.   Wmk. 395
1319 A429 300s multicolored   .70   .45

Maldonado-La Condamine Amazon Expedition, 250th Anniv. — A430

Designs: 150s, Cinchona cordifolia. 200s, Pedro V. Maldonado, 1500s, Charles La Condamine (1701-74), explorer.

1993, Aug. 20
1320 A430 150s multicolored   .35   .20
1321 A430 200s multicolored   .45   .20
1322 A430 1500s multicolored   3.00 1.75
    Nos. 1320-1322 (3)   3.80 2.15

A431   A432

Wmk. 395
1993, Nov. 27   Litho.   Perf. 13
1323 A431 500s multicolored   1.00   .55
Dr. Carlos A. Arroyo del Rio, birth cent.

1993, Oct. 15   Perf. 13½x13, 13x13½
Endangered species: 400s, Dinomys branickii, horiz. 800s, Ara severa.
1324 A432 400s multicolored   1.25   .60
1325 A432 800s multicolored   2.25 1.10
    America issue.

Christmas
A433

600s, Holy Family, 18th cent. Tagua miniatures. 900s, Mother and child, vert.

Wmk. 395
1993, Dec. 1   Litho.   Perf. 13
1326 A433 600s multicolored   1.25   .80
1327 A433 900s multicolored   2.00 1.25

A434   A435

1994, Jan. 18   Litho.   Perf. 13
1328 A434 300s grn, blk & org   .30   .30
    Intl. Year of the Family.

1994, Jan. 25
1329 A435 500s multicolored   1.60   .90
Dr. Julio Tobar Donoso, birth cent.

Orchids — A436

Wmk. 395
1994, Feb. 7   Litho.   Perf. 13½
1330 A436 150s Dracula hirtzii   .35   .20
1331 A436 150s Sobralia dichotoma   .35   .20
1332 A436 300s Encyclia pulcherrima   .70   .30
1333 A436 300s Lepanthes delhierroi   .70   .30
1334 A436 600s Masdevallia rosea   1.40   .55
1335 A436 600s Telipogon andicola   1.40   .55
    Nos. 1330-1335 (6)   4.90 2.10
First Convention on the Conservation of Andean Orchids.

A437   A438

1994, Apr. 12   Perf. 13
1336 A437 200s multicolored   .45   .20
Federico Gonzalez Suarez (1844-1917).

1994, Jan. 11
1337 A438 400s multicolored   1.00   .55
    Scouting in Ecuador.

Dr. Miguel Egas Cabezas (1823-94)
A439

Wmk. 395
1994, Mar. 10   Litho.   Perf. 13
1338 A439 100s multicolored   .30   .20

A440   A441

1994, July 12
1339 A440 200s multicolored   .70   .45
Fr. Aurelio Espinosa, birth cent.

Wmk. 395
1994, June 10   Litho.   Perf. 13
#1341, 1343d, Mascot. 900s, Player.
#1343: a, Emblem. b, "COPA MUNDIAL FUTBOL '94," emblem. c, "COPA MUNDIAL, USA 94."
1340 A441 300s shown   .90   .55
1341 A441 600s Mascot   1.75   .90
1342 A441 900s Soccer player   2.75 1.40

Perf. 12 on 2 Sides
1343 A441 600s Block of 4, #a.-d.   7.00 6.00
    Nos. 1340-1343 (4)   12.40 8.85
1994 World Cup Soccer Championships, US. No. 1343 contains two 50x25mm stamps, two 50x51mm stamps.

Ecuador in Antarctica
A442

1994, July 19   Perf. 13
1344 A442 600s Outpost   2.00   .70
1345 A442 900s Ship, B/1 Orion   3.25 1.10

ILO, 75th Anniv.
A443

1994   Litho.   Wmk. 395   Perf. 13
1346 A443 100s multicolored   .30   .20

Ecuadorian Culture Center, 50th Anniv.
A444

1994
1347 A444 700s Benjamin Carrion, vert.   2.10 1.40
1348 A444 900s Cultural center   3.25 1.60

Natl. Lottery, Cent.
A445

1994
1349 A445 1000s multicolored   3.60 1.75

Junior World Cycling Championships, Quito — A446

Wmk. 395
1994, June 22   Litho.   Perf. 13
1350 A446 300s shown   .50   .35
1351 A446 400s Stylized cyclist, vert.   .75   .40

Postal Transportation   Christmas
A447   A448

America Issue: No. 1352, Van, airplane, ship, horiz. No. 1353, Airplane, mail bag.

1994
1352 A447 600s multicolored .70 .35
1353 A447 600s multicolored .90 .45

1994

#1354, Simulated stamp showing globe circled by envelope, horiz. #1355, Nativity.
1354 A448 600s multicolored 1.00 .75
1355 A448 900s multicolored 1.00 .75

Juan Leon Mera, Death Cent.
A449   A450

Wmk. 395
1994, Dec. 21   Litho.   Perf. 13
1356 A449 600s Mera's home .85 .65
1357 A450 900s multicolored 2.00 1.25

Gen. Antonio Jose de Sucre (1795-1830) — A451

Perf. 14x13½
1995, Mar. 14   Litho.   Wmk. 395
1358 A451 1500s shown 2.50 1.50
1359 A451 2000s Portrait at right 3.75 2.00

Size: 80x105
Imperf
1360 A451 3000s In military uniform 4.00 4.00
Nos. 1358-1360 (3) 10.25 7.50

Beatification of Josemaria Escriva, 3rd Anniv. — A452

1995, May 17   Perf. 13x13½
1361 A452 900s multicolored 1.10 .80

Gen. Eloy Alfaro (1842-1912), Alfarista Revolution, Cent. A453

1995, June 5   Perf. 13½x13
1362 A453 800s multicolored 1.10 .80

A454

Conflict Between Ecuador & Peru — A455

Designs: 200s, Soldier writing to children. 400s, Hand holding flag of Ecuador. 800s, Soldier in wilderness.

1995, July   Perf. 13½, 13 (#1364)
1363 A454 200s multicolored .35 .20
1364 A455 400s multicolored .75 .35
1365 A454 800s multicolored 1.25 .65
Nos. 1363-1365 (3) 2.35 1.20

CARE, 50th Anniv. — A456

1995, July 14   Perf. 13½
1366 A456 400s Girl, vert. .50 .30
1367 A456 800s shown 1.50 1.00

CAF (Andes Development Corporation), 25th Anniv. — A457

1995, Aug. 22   Perf. 13
1368 A457 1000s multicolored 2.10 .85

A458   A459

1995, Sept. 2   Litho.   Perf. 13
1369 A458 500s Virgin of Cisne .60 .45

1995, Sept. 28
1370 A459 400s multicolored .70 .45
Natl. Institute of Children and Families (INNFA), 35th anniv.

UN, 50th Anniv. A460

Wmk. 395
1995, Oct. 6   Litho.   Perf. 13
1371 A460 1000s bl, blk & bis 1.75 .90

Intl. Decade for Natural Disaster Reduction A461

Civil defense emblem and: No. 1372, House surrounded by flood waters. No. 1373, Family

leaving site of erupting volcano. No. 1374, People under table during earthquake. No. 1375, Couple planting seedlings on hillside. No. 1376, Man reading instruction booklet for natural disaster preparation.

1995, Oct. 11
1372 A461 1000s multicolored 1.60 .85
1373 A461 1000s multicolored 1.60 .85
1374 A461 1000s multicolored 1.60 .85
1375 A461 1000s multicolored 1.60 .85
1376 A461 1000s multicolored 1.60 .85
Nos. 1372-1376 (5) 8.00 4.25

FAO, 50th Anniv. A462

1995, Oct. 16
1377 A462 1300s multicolored 2.25 1.25

Women's Culture Club, 50th Anniv. A463

1995, Oct. 20
1378 A463 1500s multicolored 2.00 1.50

29th Assembly of Inter-America Philatelic Federation, Quito — A464

1995, Nov. 11
1379 A464 1000s blue & red 1.25 .85

A465   A466

Christmas: 2000s, Santa, sleigh, reindeer on top of world. 2600s, Man on decorated horse, children.

Wmk. 395
1995, Dec.   Litho.   Perf. 13
1380 A465 2000s multicolored 4.00 2.40
1381 A465 2600s multicolored 4.50 2.40

1995, Dec.

Indigenous Birds: #1382, Aglaiocercus kingi.
#1383: a, Coeligena torquata. b, Phaethornis superciliosus. c, Ocreatus underwoodii. d, Oreotrochilus chimborazo. e, Aglaiocercus coelestis.
1382 A466 1000s multicolored 1.75 .85
1383 A466 1000s Strip of 5, #a.-e. 9.25 6.25

Ecuadoran Air Force, 75th Anniv. A467

1995, Dec.
1384 A467 1000s multicolored 1.75 .95

Year of Folk Music — A468

2000s, Julio Jaramillo (1935-78), musician, composer. 3000s, Jaramillo, wall.

1996, Jan. 16   Litho.   Perf. 13
1385 A468 2000s multicolored 3.50 1.75

Imperf
1386 A468 3000s multicolored 4.50 4.00

Advancement of Ecuador, 4 Year Program — A469

Designs show symbols for: 1500s, Mail delivery. 2000s, Customs crossing. 2600s, Telecommunications. 3000p, Ports.

Wmk. 395
1996, July 23   Litho.   Perf. 13
1387 A469 1000s multicolored 1.60 .70
1388 A469 1500s multicolored 2.40 1.10
1389 A469 2000s multicolored 3.00 1.50
1390 A469 2600s multicolored 4.00 1.75
a. Pair, #1388, #1390 5.25 5.25
b. Pair, #1389, #1390 6.00 6.00
1391 A369 3000s multicolored 5.00 2.75
a. Pair, #1387, #1391 5.50 5.50
b. Pair, #1389, #1391 6.75 6.75
Nos. 1387-1391 (5) 16.00 7.80

Nos. 1387-1391 were issued in strips of 2 each.

Esmeraldas '96, 8th National Games A470

Mascot depicting two sports on each stamp: No. 1392, Tennis, boxing. No. 1393, Basketball, soccccer. 600s, Racketball, swimming. 800s, Weight lifting, karate. 1000s, Volleyball, gymnastics. 1200s, Athletics, judo. No. 1398, Chess, wrestling.
No. 1399, Mascot holding flag, emblem, surrounded by flags.

1996, July 30
1392 A470 400s multicolored .50 .20
1393 A470 400s multicolored .50 .20
1394 A470 600s multicolored .80 .40
a. Pair, #1392, #1394 1.25 1.25
1395 A470 800s multicolored 1.10 .55
a. Pair, #1394-1395 1.75 1.75
1396 A470 1000s multicolored 1.50 .65
a. Pair, #1393, #1396 1.90 1.90
b. Pair, #1395-1396 2.40 2.40
1397 A470 1200s multicolored 1.60 .85
1398 A470 2000s multicolored 3.00 1.25
Nos. 1392-1398 (7) 9.00 4.10

Size: 120x100mm
1399 A470 2000s multicolored 3.00 3.00

Nos. 1392-1396 were printed in strips of 2 each.

Civil Aviation, 50th Anniv. A471

1996, Aug. 8
1400 A471 2000s multicolored 2.50 1.10

1996
Summer
Olympic
Games,
Atlanta
A472

Atlanta Games emblem and: 1000s, Mascot carrying torch. No. 1402, Emblem of Olympic Committee of Ecuador. 3000s, Jefferson Perez, vert.

No. 1404, Perez, gold medalist, 20-kilometer walk, walking.

1996
1401 A472 1000s multicolored 1.25 .55
1402 A472 2000s multicolored 3.00 1.75
  a. Pair, #1401-1402 3.50 3.50
1403 A472 3000s multicolored 4.25 2.25
  Nos. 1401-1403 (3) 8.50 4.55

Size: 100x120mm
Imperf
1404 A472 2000s multicolored 3.00 3.00

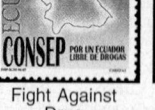

Fight Against Drug Abuse — A473

Dr. Eduardo Salazar Gomez, Birth Cent. — A474

1996 Litho. Wmk. 395 Perf. 13
1408 A473 2000s multicolored 3.75 2.00

1996
1409 A474 1000s multicolored 2.00 1.00

Catholic University, Quito, 50th Anniv. A475

Junior League Organization A476

Designs: 400s, Outside view of building, horiz. 800s, Entrance.

1996
1410 A475 400s multicolored .80 .45
1411 A475 800s multicolored 1.60 .85

1996
1412 A476 2000s Children's faces, horiz. 4.00 2.50
1413 A476 2600s shown 5.00 3.00

Catholic University, Quito, 50th Anniv. A477

1996, Nov.
1414 A477 2000s multicolored 3.75 2.00

The Universe Daily Newspaper, 75th Anniv. — A478

1996, Dec.
1415 A478 2000s multicolored 3.75 2.00

Private Technical University, Loja — A479

1996, Dec. 9
1416 A479 4700s multicolored 9.00 4.50

UNICEF, 50th Anniv. A480

1996, Dec. 11
1417 A480 2000s multicolored 3.75 2.00

Christmas A481

Children's paintings: 600s, Merry Chrismas All Over the World. 800s, World of Peace and Love. 2000s, Christmas.

1996, Dec. 19
1418 A481 600s multicolored 1.25 .75
1419 A481 800s multicolored 1.50 .90

Size: 51x31mm
Perf. 13½
1420 A481 2000s multicolored 3.50 1.90
  Nos. 1418-1420 (3) 6.25 3.55

Preserving the Ecological System A482

America '95: 1000s, Voltur grypus. 1500s, Harpia harpyja, vert.

1996, Dec. 30 Perf. 13
1421 A482 1000s multicolored 2.00 1.25
1422 A482 1500s multicolored 3.00 1.75

Typical Children's Costumes — A483

America '96: No. 1423, "Bordando" girl, Zuleta. No. 1424, Girl from Otavalo.

1996, Dec. 30
1423 A483 2600s multicolored 4.50 1.50
1424 A483 2600s multicolored 4.50 4.00
  a. Pair, #1423-1424 11.00 11.00

Mejia Natl. Institute, Cent. A484

Design: Jose Mejia Lequerica, building.

1997, Jan. 10
1425 A484 1000s multicolored 2.00 1.00

Army Polytechnical School, 75th Anniv. A485

Wmk. 395
1997, June 16 Typo. Perf. 13
1426 A485 400s multicolored .90 .50

Natl. Experimental College, Ambato, 50th Anniv. A486

1997, June 20
1427 A486 600s multicolored 1.10 .70

Vicente Rocafuerte (1783-1847), First Constitutional President of Ecuador — A487

1997, July 1
1428 A487 400s multicolored .90 .50

49th Intl. Congress of the Americanists A488

1997, July 3
1429 A488 2000s multicolored 3.75 1.90

Butterflies A489

Designs: 400s, Actinote equatoria. 600s, Dismorphia amphione. 800s, Marpesia corinna. 2000s, Marpesia berania. 2600s, Morpho helenor.

1997, July 21
1430 A489 400s multicolored .70 .30
1431 A489 600s multicolored .95 .35
1432 A489 800s multicolored 1.60 .65
1433 A489 2000s multicolored 3.75 1.60
1434 A489 2600s multicolored 5.50 2.00
  Nos. 1430-1434 (5) 12.50 4.90

Air Club of Ecuador, 66th Anniv. A490

1997, July 23
1435 A490 2600s multicolored 5.25 2.10

Orchids — A491

400s, Epidendrum secundum. 600s, Epidendrum. 800s, Oncidium cultratrum. 2000s, Oncidium sp mariposa. 2600s, Pleurothalis corrulensis.

1997, Aug. 14 Litho. Perf. 13
1436 A491 400s multicolored .70 .30
1437 A491 600s multicolored .95 .40
1438 A491 800s multicolored 1.60 .65
1439 A491 2000s multicolored 3.75 1.60
1440 A491 2600s multicolored 5.50 2.00
  Nos. 1436-1440 (5) 12.50 4.95

Rocks and Minerals — A492

1997, Oct. 6 Litho. Perf. 13
1441 A492 400s Quartz .70 .30
1442 A492 600s Chalcopyrite .95 .40
1443 A492 800s Gold 1.60 .65
1444 A492 2000s Petrified wood 3.75 1.60
1445 A492 2600s Pyrite 5.50 2.00
  Nos. 1441-1445 (5) 12.50 4.95

A493 A494

Christmas (Children's designs): 400s, Santa as postman delivering letters over world. 2600s, Star on Christmas tree reaching for letters, airplane under tree. 3000s, Child dreaming of angels carrying letters.

1997, Dec. 22 Litho. Perf. 13
1446 A493 400s multicolored .70 .30
1447 A493 2600s multicolored 5.25 2.00
1448 A493 3000s multicolored 6.50 2.50
  Nos. 1446-1448 (3) 12.45 4.80

1997, Dec. 29
1449 A494 800s Life of a Postman 1.40 .70
1450 A494 2000s On bicycle 4.00 1.60
  America issue.

A495 A496

Matilde Hidalgo de Procel (1889-1974), physician, social reformer.

1998, Mar. 6 Litho. Perf. 13
1451 A495 2000s multicolored 3.50 2.50
  Intl. Women's Day.

Wmk. 395
1998, Apr. 22 Litho. Perf. 13
1452 A496 2000s multicolored 6.25 4.00
  Dr. Misael Acosta Solis, botanist.

Organization of American States (OAS), 50th Anniv. A497

1998, Apr. 30
1453 A497 2600s multicolored   4.50 3.25

1998 World Cup Soccer Championships, France — A498

Designs: 2600s, Trophy, mascot, vert. 3000s, Two players, trophy.

1998, May
1454 A498 2000s multicolored   3.50 2.25
1455 A498 2600s multicolored   4.50 2.75
1456 A498 3000s multicolored   5.50 3.25
    Nos. 1454-1456 (3)   13.50 8.25

Flowers — A499   Galapagos Flora — A500

600s, Gypsophila paniculata. 800s, Banana flowers. 2000s, Roses. 2600s, Asters.

1998, June
1457 A499 600s multicolored   1.25 .60
1458 A499 800s multicolored   1.50 .90
1459 A499 2000s multicolored   3.50 2.25
1460 A499 2600s multicolored   4.50 2.75
    Nos. 1457-1460 (4)   10.75 6.50

1998, July
Designs: 600s, Jasminocereus thouarsii. 1000s, Cordia lutea lamarck. 2600s, Momordica charantia.

1461 A500 600s multicolored   1.00 .60
1462 A500 1000s multicolored   1.75 1.00
1463 A500 2600s multicolored   4.50 2.75
    Nos. 1461-1463 (3)   7.25 4.35

Tourism A501

600s, St. Augustine Church, Quito. 800s, Monument to the Heroes of the Independence, Guayaquil. 2000s, Equator Monument, Quito. 2600s, Mojanda Lake.

1998, July
1464 A501 600s multi, vert.   1.25 .60
1465 A501 800s multi, vert.   1.50 .90
1466 A501 2000s multi   3.50 2.25
1467 A501 2600s multi   4.50 2.75
    Nos. 1464-1467 (4)   10.75 6.50

Emiliano Ortega Espinosa (1898-1974), Educator A502

Perf. 13¼x13, 13x13¼
1998   **Litho.**   **Wmk. 395**
1468 A502 400s shown   .75 .50
1469 A502 4700s Portrait, vert.   10.00 8.25

A503   A504

Carlos Cueva Tamariz (1898-1991), educator.

Perf. 13x13¼
1998, Nov.   **Litho.**   **Wmk. 395**
1470 A503 2600s multicolored   4.50 3.50

Wmk. 395
1998, Nov. 20   **Litho.**   **Perf. 13**
1471 A504 600s multicolored   1.10 .90
Radio Club of Guayaquil, 75th anniv.

6th South American Games — A505

Designs: 400s, Mascot. 1000s, Games poster, tennis rackets, hurdles, sailing, hammer throw, bowling, boxing. 2600s, Mascot, parallel bars, wrestling, judo, fencing, running, swimming, shooting, cycling.

1998
1472 A505 400s multicolored   1.00 .50
1473 A505 1000s multicolored   1.75 1.00
1474 A505 2600s multicolored   4.50 2.75
    Nos. 1472-1474 (3)   7.25 4.25

Paintings by Eduardo Kingman (1913-85) A506

Designs: 600s, Ecuadoran Woman, vert. 800s, World Without Answers.

1998, Dec. 10
1475 A506 600s multicolored   1.00 .60
1476 A506 800s multicolored   1.50 .90

Manuela Sáenz (1797-1856), Mistress of Simon Bolívar — A507

1999, Jan. 19
1477 A507 1000s multicolored   1.50 .95
America issue. Exists imperf.

Christmas A508

Children's drawings: 1000s, Santa posting letters on tree. 2600s, People holding up giant letter, vert. 3000s, Santas parachuting with letters, nativity scene, tree, vert.

1998, Dec. 22
1478 A508 1000s multicolored   1.50 .95
1479 A508 2600s multicolored   4.00 2.50
1480 A508 3000s multicolored   4.50 2.75
    Nos. 1478-1480 (3)   10.00 6.20

Los Tayos Caves A509

1999, Feb. 25   **Litho.**   **Perf. 13**
1481 A509 1000s Man in cave, vert.   1.40 .90
1482 A509 2600s shown   4.00 2.50

Napal, the Age of Wrath, by Oswaldo Guayasamin (1919-99) — A510

Wmk. 395
1999, May 12   **Litho.**   **Perf. 13**
1483 A510 2000s multicolored   3.25 1.10
Iberoamerica art exhibition.

Universal Day of Human Rights A511

1999, May 28
1484 A511 4000s multicolored   6.25 4.00

Eloy Alfaro Superior Military College, Cent. A512

5200s, Cannon, monument, flags, buildings. 9400s, Honor Guard, modern building.

1999, June 4
1485 A512 5200s multicolored   8.00 5.00
1486 A512 9400s multicolored   13.50 8.50

Puyo, 100th Anniv. — A513

Designs: a, Bromeliad. b, Ara chloroptera.

1999, June 2
1487 A513 4000s Pair, #a.-b.   11.50 8.00

Dr. Rafael Barahona Andrade (1827-98) A514

Perf. 13¼x13
1999, June 17   **Litho.**   **Wmk. 395**
1488 A514 5200s multi   8.00 4.50

Generals — A515

Designs: 2000s, Manuel Antonio de Luzarraga y Echezurria (1776-1859). 4000s, Tomas Carlos Wright (1799-1868).

1999, Aug. 11   **Perf. 13x13¼**
1489-1490 A515 Set of 2   9.50 6.00

Galapagos Islands Flora and Fauna A516

No. 1491, vert.: a, Phoenicopterus ruber. b, Buteo galapagoensis. c, Amblyrhynchus cristatus. d, Conolophus subcristatus. e, Opuntia galapageia. f, Pyrocephalus rubinus. g, Sula nebouxii. h, Sula dactylatra. i, Scalesia villosa. j, G. elephantopus abingdoni.

No. 1492: a, Brachycereus nesioticus. b, Dendroica petechia. c, Nannopterum harrisi. d, Tursiops truncatus. e, Pentaceraster cumingi. f, G. elephantopus porteri. g, Microlophus albemarlensis. h, Arctocephalus galapagoensis. i, Spheniscus mendiculus. j, Geospiza scandens.

Perf. 13x13¼, 13¼x13
1999, Sept. 3   **Litho.**   **Wmk. 395**
1491 Strip of 10   70.00 37.50
    a.-j. A516 7000s Any single   3.50 1.25
1492 Strip of 10   140.00 90.00
    a.-j. A516 15,000s Any single   7.00 4.50

Intl. Year of Older Persons A517

Designs: No. 1493, 1000s, Hands of child and old person. No. 1494, 1000s, Emblem.

Perf. 13¼x13
1999, Sept. 22   **Litho.**   **Wmk. 395**
1493-1494 A517 Set of 2   2.75 1.75

SOS Children's Villages, 50th Anniv. — A518

a, 2000s, Two children. b, 2000s, One child. Illustration reduced.

1999, Sept. 30
1495 A518 Pair, #a-b   4.00 2.50

America Issue, A World Without Arms — A519

No. 1496: a, World map. b, Tree, bird, Earth. Illustration reduced.

Perf. 13¼x13
1999, Dec. 11   **Litho.**   **Wmk. 395**
1496 A519 4000s Pair, #a-b   *9.00 5.50*

UPU, 125th Anniv. A520

Design: 8000s, UPU emblem. 1000s, Ecuadorian Postal Service mascot, vert. 4000s, Dove with letter, vert.

Perf. 13¼x12¾

1999, Dec. 11   Litho.   Wmk. 395
1497 A520 1000s multi   .75   .45
1498 A520 4000s multi   3.00   1.75
1499 A520 8000s multi   6.25   4.00
Nos. 1497-1499 (3)   10.00   6.20

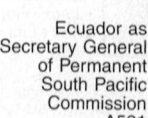

Ecuador as Secretary General of Permanent South Pacific Commission A521

Perf. 13x13¼
1999, Dec. 21   Litho.   Wmk. 395
1500 A521 7000s multi   6.75   4.50

Machala Tourism A522

Designs: No. 1501, Banana flower and city. No. 1502, vert.: a, Monument to banana plantation workers. b, City Hall.

1999, Dec. 28   Perf. 13¼x13, 13x13¼
1501 A522 3000s multi   2.75   1.60
1502 A522 3000s Pair, #a-b   5.75   3.25

EMELEC Soccer Team — A523

#1503: a, Jorge Bolanos. b, Carlos Raffo. No. 1504, EMELEC team photo, 1957. No. 1505, Player, vert.

Perf. 13x13¼, 13¼x13
2000, Jan. 7   Litho.
1503 A523 1000s Pair, #a-b   2.25   2.25
1504 A523 2000s multi   2.25   1.40
1505 A523 2000s multi   2.25   1.40

Guayas Philanthropic Society, 150th Anniv. A524

Designs: 1000s, Building. 2000s, Founder Juan Maria Martinez Coello. 4000s, Emblem.

Perf. 13¼x13
2000, Jan. 19   Litho.   Wmk. 395
1506-1508 A524   Set of 3   1.75   1.00

Dual Nationality Day — A525

2000, Jan. 24   Perf. 13x13¼
1509 A525 7000s multi   1.75   1.10

Cuenca, World Heritage Site — A526

No. 1510: a, Buildings. b, Puente Roto and Tomebamba River. c, Church bell gable, Concepcion Monastery. d, Cathedral and city skyline. e, San José Church.

2000, Mar. 24   Perf. 13¼x13
1510   Horiz. strip of 5   4.50   4.50
a.-e. A526 4000s Any single   .65   .35

Nicolas Lapentti, Tennis Player — A527

2000, Mar. 26   Perf. 13¼x13
1511 A527 8000s multi   2.00   1.25

Birds — A528

No. 1512: a, Diglossa cyanea. b, Oreotrochilus chimborazo. c, Trogon personatus. d, Colibri coruscans. e, Atlapetes rufinucha.

2000, Apr. 7
1512   Horiz. strip of 5   9.00   9.00
a.-e. A528 8000s Any single   1.40   .95

Relocation of Riobamba, Bicent. A529

Designs: No. 1513, Mt. Chimborazo. No. 1514: a, Riobamba Cathedral. b, Statue of Pedro Vicente Maldonado.

2000, Apr. 13   Perf. 13¼x13, 13x13¼
1513 A529 8000s multi   1.75   1.00
1514 A529 8000s Pair, #a-b   3.50   3.50

Gen. Eloy Alfaro, Founder of Natl. Music Conservatory A530

2000, Apr. 19   Perf. 13x13¼
1515 A530 10,000s multi   2.75   1.60
Natl. Music Conservatory, cent.

Climbing of Mt. Everest by Ivan Vallejo Ricaurte A531

2000, May 23   Perf. 13¼x13
1516 A531 8000s multi   2.75   1.50

100 Cents=1 Dollar

Dolores Sucre Fiscal College, 50th Anniv. — A532

Perf. 13x13¼
2000   Litho.   Wmk. 395
1517 A532 32c multi   2.10   1.00

Training Ship Guayas — A533

2000, July 5   Perf. 13¼x13
1518 A533 68c multi   1.40   .70

Imperf
Size: 90x110mm
1519 A533 $1 multi   4.50   2.50

Battle of Jambeli, 59th Anniv., Navy Day — A534

2000   Perf. 13¼x13
1520 A534 16c multi   1.10   .20

Guayaquil Civic Renovation A535

2000, July   Perf. 13¼x13
1521 A535 84c multi   5.40   2.50

Megaptera Novaeangliae — A536

2000, Aug. 3   Perf. 13¼x13
1522 A536 84c multi   5.25   2.50

Imperf
Size: 90x110mm
1523 A536 $1 Two whales   7.25   3.50

American and Caribbean Dog Show, Quito A537

2000, Aug.   Perf. 13¼x13
1524 A537 68c multi   4.00   2.00

Guayaquil Tennis Club, 90th Anniv. A538

2000, Aug.   Wmk. 395
1525 A538 84c multi   5.00   2.50

Alberto Spencer, Soccer Player — A539

2000   Perf. 13x13¼
1526 A539 68c multi   4.00   2.00

Imperf
Size: 69x99mm
1527 A539 $1 Spencer, crowd   6.25   3.00

2000 Summer Olympics, Sydney — A540

Ecuadoran team emblem, Games emblem and: 32c Mascots. 68c, Runner Jefferson Perez Marchista. 84c, Weight lifter Boris Burov, Olympic flag, horiz.

2000, Sept.   Perf. 13x13¼, 13¼x13
1528-1530 A540   Set of 3   10.75   5.50

Salinas Yacht Club, 60th Anniv. A541

Designs: No. 1531a, Lighthouse, vert. Nos. 1531b, 1533, Sailboat, vert. 68c, Sailboats, fisherman, waterskier, scuba diver.

2000, Oct.   Perf. 13¼x13
1531 A541 32c Horiz. pair, #a-b   3.75   2.00
Perf. 13¼x13
1532 A541 68c multi   4.25   2.10

Imperf
Size: 69x100mm
1533 A541 $1 multi   6.25   3.00

Inter-American Development Bank, 40th Anniv. — A542

Designs: No. 1534a, 68c, No. 1536a, 25c, Salsipuedes Bridge, Felipe Herrera. No. 1534b, 68c, No. 1536b, 25c, Daule-Peripa Dam, Antonio Ortiz Mena. No. 1535a, 84c,

No. 1536c, 25c, Enrique Iglesias, Ucubamba Water Treatment Plant. No. 1535b, 84c, No. 1536d, 25c, Bank emblem, History Museum, Quito.
Illustration reduced.

2000, Oct. 27   *Perf. 13¼x13*
Horiz. Pairs, #a-b
1534-1535 A542   Set of 2   18.00 9.00
Rouletted 14 on 2 sides
1536 A542 25c Sheet of 4, #a-d   6.25 3.00
   Size of Nos. 1536a-1536b, 75x48mm; Nos. 1536c-1536d, 75x42mm.

National Union of Journalists
A543

2000, Nov. 1   *Perf. 13¼x13*
1537 A543 16c multi   1.00 .20

Civil Registry, Cent. — A544

   No. 1538: a, People, flag, computer. b, Fingerprint, family.

2000, Oct. 27   *Perf. 13x13¼*
1538 A544 68c Horiz. pair, #a-b   8.00 3.00

Mama Negra Festival, Latacunga — A545

   No. 1539: a, Mama Negra with doll. b, Man in Moor King costume.

2000, Nov.   *Perf. 13x13¼*
1539 A545 32c Horiz. pair, #a-b   3.75 2.00
Imperf
Size: 100x68mm
1540 A545 $1 Mama Negra, doll, diff.   5.75 2.10

Ministry of Labor, 75th Anniv. — A546

2000, Nov. 15   *Perf. 13x13¼*
1541 A546 68c multi   3.75 1.40

Intl. Fruits and Flowers Festival, Ambato, 50th Anniv. A547

   No. 1542, horiz.: a, Tungurahua Volcano. b, Aerial view of Ambato.
   No. 1544, horiz.: a, Flower. b, Fruit.

2000, Nov.   *Perf. 13¾*
1542 A547 32c Vert. pair, #a-b   3.75 2.00
1543 A547 84c shown   5.25 2.50
1544 A547 84c Vert. pair, #a-b   10.50 5.25
   Nos. 1542-1544 (3)   19.50 9.75
Imperf
Size: 68x100mm
1545 A547 $1 Ambato   5.75 2.75

Christmas — A548

   Children's art by — No. 1546, 68c: a, Giannina Rhor Isaias. b, Josue Remache Romero.
   No. 1547, 84c: a, Maria Cedeño Bazurtto. b, Juan Alban Salazar.
   $1, Walther Carvache.
   Illustration reduced.

2000, Dec. 15   *Perf. 13¼x13*
Horiz. Pairs, #a-b
1546-1547 A548   Set of 2   18.00 9.00
Imperf
Size: 100x69mm
1548 A548 $1 multi   5.75 2.75

Expoflores Flower Producer and Exporter Association
A549

2000   *Perf. 13x13¼*
1549 A549 68c multi   4.00 2.00

Man's Chapel, Guayasamin
A550

2000   *Perf. 13¼x13*
1550 A550 16c multi   1.10 .20

Spanish Chamber of Commerce in Ecuador, 80th Anniv. — A551

2000, Dec.   *Perf. 13¼x13*
1551 A551 16c multi   1.10 .20

Intl. Volunteers Year — A552

2000   **Wmk. 395**
1552 A552 16c multi   1.10 .20

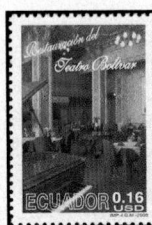

Restoration of Bolivar Theater, Quito — A553

   Designs: 16c, Piano, banquet room. 32c, Stage, orchestra, horiz.

2000, Dec.   *Perf. 13x13¼, 13¼x13*
1553-1554 A553   Set of 2   3.25 1.50

Spondylus Princeps
A554

2000, Dec. 16   *Perf. 13¾*
1555 A554 84c multi   5.00 2.50
Imperf
Size: 69x99mm
1556 A554 $1 multi   5.75 2.75

America Issue, Fight Against AIDS — A555

   No. 1557: a, Strands. b, Earth.

2000   *Perf. 13x13¼*
1557 A555 84c Horiz. pair, #a-b   11.00 5.25

Guayas Province Red Cross, 90th Anniv. A556

2000   *Perf. 13¼x13*
1558 A556 16c multi   1.10 .55

Guayas Sports Federation, 78th Anniv. — A557

2000, Dec.   *Perf. 13x13¼*
1559 A557 16c multi   1.10 .55

Landscapes A557a

   Designs: No. 1559A, 16c, Andean region. No. 1559B, 16c, Pacific coast. 32c, Tourism emblem. 68c, Amazonia. 84c, Galápagos Islands.

     Perf. 13¼x12¾
2001, Jan. 24   **Litho.**   **Wmk. 395**
1559A A557a 16c multi   1.25 .60
1559B A557a 16c multi   1.25 .60
1559C A557a 32c multi   2.50 1.10
1559D A557a 68c multi   4.75 2.40
1559E A557a 68c multi   4.75 2.40
   Nos. 1559A-1559E (5)   14.50 7.10

Guayas Soccer Team, 50th Anniv.
A558

2001, Mar. 8   *Perf. 13¼x13*
1560 A558 68c multi   4.00 1.90

Census — A558a   Census — A558b

     Perf. 12¾x13¼
2001, Mar. 12   **Litho.**   **Wmk. 395**
1560A A558a 68c multi   4.00 4.00
1560B A558b 68c multi   4.00 4.00
   c.   Horiz. pair, #1560A-1560B   8.00 8.00

Dr. Raúl Clemente Huerta
A559

2001, Apr. 4   *Perf. 13¼x13*
1561 A559 68c multi   4.50 2.25

Dr. Antonio J. Quevedo, Birth Cent.
A560

2001, Apr. 5   **Litho.**
1562 A560 84c multi   5.50 2.50

Military Geographic Institute A560a

No. 1562A: b, Soldier, building. c, Computer, printing press.

Perf. 13¼x12¾
2001, Apr. 11   Litho.   Wmk. 395
1562A A560a 68c Vert. pair, #b-c 9.00 4.50

Automobile Club of Ecuador, 50th Anniv. A561

2001, May 15   Wmk. 395
1563 A561 84c multi 5.50 2.50

San Francisco de Peleusí Church, Azogues — A561a

Perf. 12¾x13¼
2001, May   Litho.   Wmk. 395
1563A A561a 84c multi 5.50 2.50

Women's Training Institute — A562

2001, Apr. 10   Perf. 13x13¼
1564 A562 84c multi 5.50 2.50

Intl. Women's Day A563

No. 1565: a, Woman, child, corn. b, Woman, emblem.

2001, Apr. 2   Perf. 13¼x13
1565 A563 84c Vert. pair, #a-b 11.00 5.25

Secular Education at Manuela Cañizares University, Cent. A564

2001, Mar. 29   Wmk. 395
1566 A564 84c multi 5.50 2.50

Ecuador Merchant Marines, Cent. — A565

2001, Jan. 2001   Perf. 13x13¼
1567 A565 16c multi 1.10 .55

Ambato Technical University, 32nd Anniv. A566

No. 1568: a, Building. b, Painting.

2001   Perf. 13¼x13
1568 A566 32c Vert. pair, #a-b 4.50 2.25

Galapagos Islands Scenes — A567

No. 1569: a, Española Island (shown). b, San Cristobal Island. c, Bartolome Island. d, Española Island, diff. e, Bartolome and Santiago Islands.
$1, Bird on rock, Española Island.

2001, Feb. 17   Perf. 13¾
1569   Horiz. strip of 5 5.00 2.25
a.-e.   A567 16c Any single .35 .20

Imperf
Size: 100x70mm
1570 A567 $1 multi 6.75 3.25

Alexander von Humboldt (1769-1859), Naturalist — A568

Perf. 13x13¼
2001, June 14   Litho.   Wmk. 395
1571 A568 84c multi 5.00 2.40

Ecuadorian Atomic Energy Commission A568a

2001, Aug. 3   Litho.   Perf. 12¾x13¼
1571A A568a 70c multi 4.50 2.25

Lebanese Union, 80th Anniv. — A569

No. 1572: a, Building and emblem. b, Emblem.
Illustration reduced.

2001, Aug. 30   Perf. 13¼x13
1572 A569 16c Horiz. pair, #a-b 2.40 1.25

Manta Port Authority — A570

No. 1573: a, Emblem. b, Ships in port.
Illustration reduced.

2001, Sept. 28
1573 A570 68c Horiz. pair, #a-b 8.00 4.00

Esmereldas Province Tourism — A571

No. 1574: a, Beach. b, Musicians and dancers on beach.
Illustration reduced.

2001
1574 A571 86c Horiz. pair, #a-b 10.00 5.00

Latin American Writers — A572

No. 1575: a, Claudia Lars (1899-1974), Salvadoran poet. b, Federico Proaño (1848-94), Ecuadoran journalist.

2001, Aug. 28   Perf. 13x13¼
1575 A572 86c Horiz. pair, #a-b 12.00 5.75

Andean Condor Preservation — A573

No. 1576: a, Condor and chick. b, Condor heads, FRAPZOO emblem.
$1, Condor in flight, FRAPZOO emblem.

2001, July 23   Perf. 13x13¼
1576 A573 86c Horiz. pair, #a-b 10.00 5.00

Imperf
Size: 68x99mm
1577 A573 $1 multi 6.25 3.00

Ecuador — Peru Peace Accords A574

No. 1578: a, Map of Ecuador and Peru. b, Soldier. c, Flags of military obeservers. d, Amazon River. e, Men in field.

2001, May 22   Perf. 13¼x13
1578   Horiz. strip of 5 22.50 11.00
a.-e.   A574 68c Any single 4.00 2.00

Archidona Canton — A575

No. 1579: a, Phragmipedium orchid. b, Saimiri sciureus. c, B. macrophylla. d, Church. e, Kichwa Indian family.

2001, Apr. 28   Perf. 13x13¼
1579   Vert. strip of 5 27.50 13.50
a.-e.   A575 84c Any single 5.00 2.40

Ecotourism in Baños A576

No. 1580: a, Orchid. b, Basilica, Baños. c, Tungurahua Volcano. d, Pailon del Diablo Waterfall. e, Statue of Virgin of Rosario de Agua Santa.
$1, Pailon del Diablo Waterfall, orchid.

2001   Perf. 13¼x13
1580   Horiz. strip of 5 24.00 12.00
a.-e.   A576 86c Any single 4.50 2.25

Imperf
Size: 68x99mm
1581 A576 $1 multi 6.25 3.00

Guayas Educational Journalists Association, 30th Anniv. A577

Perf. 13¼x13
2001, Oct. 15   Litho.   Wmk. 395
1582 A577 16c multi 1.10 .60

Foundation for Development of Cattle Ranching, 15th Anniv. — A578

2001, Aug. 15   Perf. 13x13¼
1583 A578 16c multi 1.10 .60

City Gates, Loja — A579

2001   *Perf. 13¼x13*
1584 A579 32c multi   2.10 .95

Quito Municipal District Directorate of Security A580

2001, Nov. 26
1585 A580 68c multi   4.00 2.00

Salvador Bustamante Celi (1876-1935), Musician A581

2001
1586 A581 68c multi   4.50 2.25

Marcel Laniado de Wind (1927-98), First Pres. of Natl. Modernization Council — A582

2001, Aug. 6   *Perf. 13x13¼*
1587 A582 70c multi   4.50 2.25

Bernardino Cardinal Echeverria (1912-2000) A583

2001, Nov. 14
1588 A583 84c multi   5.50 2.50

José Joaquin Olmedo (1780-1847), Statesman and Poet — A584

2001, Nov. 8
1589 A584 84c multi   5.50 2.50

El Angel Ecological Reserve — A585

No. 1590: a, Paja de Paramo. b, Frailejón. Illustration reduced.

2001   *Perf. 13¼x13*
1590 A585 16c Horiz. pair, #a-b   2.20 1.00

Yahuarcocha Race Track — A586

No. 1591: a, Race track and lake. b, Lake. Illustration reduced.

2001, Nov. 30
1591 A586 68c Horiz. pair, #a-b   8.00 4.00

World Food Day — A587

No. 1592: a, Wheat ears. b, Food baskets. Illustration reduced.

2001, Nov. 5
1592 A587 84c Horiz. pair, #a-b   11.00 5.50

Art of Voroshilov Bazante A588

No. 1593: a, Spatial composition. b, Abstract, artists name at LR. c, Urban landscape. d, Abstract, diff., "Abstracto" at UL, denomination at LL. e, Abstract, denomination at LR.

2001, Nov.
1593   Horiz. strip of 5   27.50 12.50
   a.-e. A588 84c Any single   5.00 2.50

Wilson Popenoe Private Foundation A589

2001, Nov. 19 Litho.   *Perf. 13¼x13*
1594 A589 16c multi   1.10 .55

FAO Food Program A590

2001, Aug. 15
1595 A590 84c multi   5.50 2.50

Rotary District 4400, 75th Anniv. — A591

2001, Nov. 30   *Perf. 13x13¼*
1596 A591 84c multi   5.50 2.50

Pres. Camilo Ponce Enriquez (1912-76) A592

Pedro Vicente Maldonado (1702-48), Geographer A593

2001
1597 A592 84c multi   5.50 2.50

2001, Dec. 12
1598 A593 84c multi   5.50 2.50

Otonga Foundation — A595

No. 1599: a, Frog on branch. b, Mustela frenata.

2001, Oct. 31
1599 A595 16c Horiz. pair, #a-b   2.20 1.10

Tourism in Zaruma — A596

No. 1600: a, Virgen del Carmen. b, Orchid. Illustration reduced.

2001, Dec. 12   *Perf. 13¼x13*
1600 A596 68c Horiz. pair, #a-b   8.00 4.00

Radio HCJB, 70th Anniv. — A597

No. 1601: a, Microphone. b, Announcer. Illustration reduced.

2001, Dec. 21
1601 A597 68c Horiz. pair, #a-b   8.00 4.00

Tennis A598

No. 1602: a, Davis Cup. b, K. Lapentti, G. Lapentti, L.A. Morejón, A. Intriago and R. Viver. c, Francisco Guzman and Miguel Olvera. d, Pancho Segura. e, Andres Gomez.

2001, Nov. 1
1602   Horiz. strip of 5   21.00 10.50
   a.-e. A598 68c Any single   4.00 2.00

Church Paintings of Wilfrido Martínez — A599

No. 1603: a, San Francisco (artist's name is vert.). b, Guapulo. c, San Francisco (artist's name is horiz.). d, La Compania. e, El Rosario.

2002, Apr. 9   *Perf. 13¾*
1603   Horiz. strip of 5   24.00 12.00
   a.-e. A599 90c Any single   4.50 2.25

First Judicial Summit of the Americas, Quito A600

     Perf. 13¼x13
2002, Jan. 8 Litho.   *Wmk. 395*
1604 A600 68c multi   4.00 2.00

Union Club, Guayaquil — A601

2002, Apr. 25   *Perf. 13x13¼*
1605 A601 90c multi   5.50 2.75

South American Soccer Confederation A602

Designs: 25c, Confederation Pres. Nicolás Leoz. 40c, Confederation emblem, soccer players. 70c, Emblem of Emelec team.

2002, Jan. 29
1606-1608 A602 Set of 3   8.00 4.00

World Conservation Union — A603

Designs: 70c, Fish, man's head. 85c, Leopard, man, horiz.
$1, Bird, animals, women and children, horiz.

2002, Feb. 21   *Perf. 13x13¼, 13¼x13*
1609-1610 A603 Set of 2   9.00 4.50
     Imperf
     Size: 100x70mm
1611 A603 $1 multi   6.25 3.00

UN High Commissioner for Refugees — A604

Designs: 70c, Emblem. 85c, Child. $1, Refugees carrying belongings, horiz.

2002, Feb. 28   *Perf. 13x13¼*
1612-1613 A604 Set of 2   9.00 4.50
     Imperf
     Size: 100x70mm
1614 A604 $1 multi   6.25 3.00

Ecuadorian Educational Credit and Scholarship Institute — A605

No. 1615: a, Student using microscope. b, Emblem.

2002, Apr. 30 *Perf. 13x13¼*
1615 A605 25c Horiz. pair, #a-b 2.50 1.25

Cuenca Soccer Team — A606

No. 1616: a, Team photo. b, Emblem, player dribbling.
Illustration reduced.

2002, Apr. 19 *Perf. 13¼x13*
1616 A606 25c Horiz. pair, #a-b 2.50 1.25

Imbabura Province History — A607

No. 1617: a, Building. b, Statue.

2002, Mar. 27 *Perf. 13x13¼*
1617 A607 40c Horiz. pair, #a-b 5.00 2.40

Crucita — A608

No. 1618: a, Parachutist with sun on horizon. b, Prachutist above beach.
Illustration reduced.

2002, Mar. 28 *Perf. 13¼x13*
1618 A608 40c Horiz. pair, #a-b 5.00 2.40

Mountains A609

No. 1619: a, Mt. Altar (trees in foreground). b, Mt. Chimborazo. c, Mt. Carihuayrazo. d, Mt. Altar (lake in foreground). e, Mt. Cubillin.

2002, Apr. 19
1619 Horiz. strip of 5 24.00 12.00
a.-e. A609 90c Any single 4.50 2.25

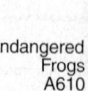
Endangered Frogs A610

No. 1620: a, Atelopus bomolochos. b, Atelopus longirostris. c, Atelopus pachydermus. d, Atelopus arthuri. e, Atelopus sp.
$1, Atelopus ignescens.

2002, Mar. 25
1620 Horiz. strip of 5 24.00 12.00
a.-e. A610 $1.05 Any single 4.50 2.10
Imperf
Size: 100x70mm
1621 A610 $1 multi 6.25 3.00

National Anti-narcotics Police — A611

No. 1622: a, Policeman and dog. b, Emblem.

Perf. 13x13¼
2002, Apr. 23 Litho. Wmk. 395
1622 A611 40c Horiz. pair, #a-b 5.00 2.50

2002 World Cup Soccer Championships, Japan and Korea — A612

Designs: 90c, Ecuadorian Soccer Federation emblem, vert. $1.05, $2, Emblem, team photo, players in action.

2002, Apr. 28 *Perf. 13x13¼, 13¼x13*
1623-1624 A612 Set of 2 7.25 3.50
Imperf
Size: 100x70mm
1625 A612 $2 multi 7.25 3.50

Dr. Servio Aguirre Villamagua, Forest Conservationist — A613

No. 1626: a, Aguirre. b, Plant.
Illustration reduced.

2002, May 22 *Perf. 13¼x13*
1626 A613 40c Horiz. pair, #a-b 3.00 1.50

Food and Agriculture Organization in Ecuador, 50th Anniv. A614

2002, May 30
1627 A614 $1.05 multi 4.00 2.00

Galapagos Islands Fauna A615

No. 1628: a, Grapsus grapsus. b, Conolophus subcristatus.
No. 1629, vert.: a, Sula sula websteri. b, Phoenicoptrus ruber.
No. 1630, Amblyrhynchus cristatus.
No. 1631, vert.: a, Pair of Zalophus californianus wollebacki. b, One Zalophus californianus wollebacki.
No. 1632, Sula nebouxxi excisa, vert.
No. 1633, vert.: a, Sula dactylatra granti. b, Emblem of Iberoamerican Summit on Tourism and Environment.
$2, Bird, tourists, tourist ship.

2002, May 31 Perf. 13¼x13, 13x13¼
1628 A615 25c Horiz. pair, #a-b 2.00 1.00
1629 A615 40c Horiz. pair, #a-b 3.00 1.50
1630 A615 90c multi 3.75 1.75
1631 A615 90c Horiz. pair, #a-b 7.50 3.75
1632 A615 $1.05 multi 4.25 2.10
1633 A615 $1.05 Horiz. pair, #a-b 8.50 4.00
Nos. 1628-1633 (6) 29.00 14.10
Imperf
Size: 100x68mm
1634 A615 $2 multi 7.50 3.75

Ministry of Foreign Relations — A616

2002, June 5 *Perf. 13x13¼*
1635 A616 90c multi 3.50 1.60

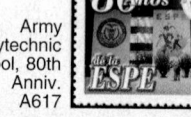

Army Polytechnic School, 80th Anniv. A617

2002, June 13 *Perf. 13¼x13*
1636 A617 25c multi 1.25 .60

Military Engineers, Cent. A618

Designs: No. 1637, 40c, Castle of Engineering. No. 1638, 40c, Castle of Engineering, Military engineers in action, vert. $2, Castle of Engineering, engineers in action, emblems of military groups.

Perf. 13¼x13, 13x13¼
2002, June 19 Set of 2
1637-1638 A618 3.20 1.60
Imperf
Size: 100x68mm
1639 A618 $2 multi 7.25 3.50

Dr. Alfredo Pérez Guerrero (1901-66), Academic — A619

2002, July 4 *Perf. 13x13¼*
1640 A619 25c multi 1.25 .60

20th Anniv. of Ecuador's Second Place Finish In World Taekwondo Championships — A620

2002, July 18 *Perf. 13¼x13*
1641 A620 40c multi 1.60 .80

Orellana Province — A621

No. 1642: a, Three native men. b, Man in tree.
Illustration reduced.

2002, July 30 Wmk. 395
1642 A621 25c Horiz. pair, #a-b 2.50 1.25

CARE in Ecuador, 40th Anniv. — A622

No. 1643: a, Two children. b, Boy.

2002, July 30 *Perf. 13¼x13*
1643 A622 90c Horiz. pair, #a-b 7.25 3.50

Macará Region A623

2002, Aug. 10 *Perf. 13¼x13*
1644 A623 40c multi 1.60 .80

Intl. Organization for Migration, 50th Anniv. — A624

Quito Philharmonic Society, 50th Anniv. — A625

2002, Aug. 18 *Perf. 13x13¼*
1645 A624 $1.05 multi 4.00 2.00

2002, Aug. 29
1646 A625 25c multi 1.25 .60

Comptroller General, 75th Anniv. — A625a

Perf. 13¼x13¼
2002, Sept. 26 Litho. Wmk. 395
1646A A625a 40c multi 1.60 .80

Second World Meeting of Mountain People — A626

No. 1647 — Emblem of World Meeting and: a, Mountain. b, Group of people. c, Houses in valley. d, Town. e, Other emblems.

ECUADOR

935

2002, Sept. 18
1647 Horiz. strip of 5   18.00 9.00
a.-e. A626 90c Any single   3.50 1.60

Pujili
Dancer — A627

Perf. 13x13¼
2002, Oct. 14 Litho. Wmk. 395
1648 A627 $1.05 multi   4.00 2.00

Paintings of Milton Estrella
Gavidia — A628

No. 1649 — Various paintings with background colors of: a, Blue violet. b, Brown violet. c, Olive green. d, Blue. e, Gray lilac.

Wmk. 395
2002, May 17 Litho. Perf. 13¾
1649 Horiz. strip of 5   18.00 9.00
a.-e. A628 90c Any single   3.50 1.60

Paintings of
Leonardo
Hidalgo
A629

No. 1650: a, La Dolorosa. b, El Hombre Cargando su Fruto. c, Frida Kahlo. d, El Hombre Fuerte del Mar. e, Jesus.

Wmk. 395
2002, Oct. 3 Litho. Perf. 13¾
1650 Horiz. strip of 5   18.00 9.00
a.-e. A629 90c Any single   3.50 1.60

Pan-American Health Organization,
Cent. — A630

2002, Dec. 2 Perf. 13¼x12¾
1651 A630 $1.05 multi   4.00 2.00

Lo Nuestro Art Exhibition — A631

No. 1652: a, Wall with six works of art. b, Walls with 16 works of art.
Illustration reduced.

2002, Dec. 15
1652 A631 25c Horiz. pair, #a-b   2.00 1.00

Catholic
University,
40th Anniv.
A632

2002, Dec. 18
1653 A632 40c multi   1.60 .80

America Issue — UNESCO World
Heritage Sites — A633

No. 1654: a, Cupola of San Blas Church, Cuenca. b, Society of Jesus Church, Quito.

2002, Dec. 18 Perf. 12¾x13¼
1654 A633 25c Horiz. pair, #a-b   2.50 1.25
Dated 2001.

America Issue — Youth, Education
and Literacy — A634

No. 1655: a, Students and blackboard. b, Toddler and books.
Illustration reduced.

2002, Dec. 18 Perf. 13¼x12¾
1655 A634 25c Horiz. pair, #a-b   2.50 1.25

Second Meeting of South American
Presidents, Guayaquil — A635

No. 1656: a, Meeting emblem. b, Emblem, presidents and flags.
Illustration reduced.

2003, Jan. 13
1656 A635 $1.05 Horiz. pair, #a-b   7.25 3.50

Papal Benediction
for Ecuadorian
Emigrants — A636

2003, Jan. 24 Perf. 12¾x13¼
1657 A636 $1.05 multi   3.60 1.75
Size: 68x100mm
Imperf
1658 A636 $2 multi   7.25 3.50

World
Vison — A637

2003, Feb. 6 Perf. 12¾x13¼
1659 A637 40c multi   1.40 .70

Intl. Women's
Day — A638

2003, Mar. 8 Wmk. 395
1660 A638 $1.05 multi   3.60 1.75

Agustin Cueva
Vallejo (1820-73),
Physician — A639

2003, Mar. 13 Litho.
1661 A639 40c multi   1.40 .70

Blasco Moscoso
Cuesta, Founder of
Pichincha Sports
Writers
Association — A640

2003, Mar. 14
1662 A640 25c multi   .90 .45

Cuenca
Artisan
Products
A641

No. 1663: a, Azuay University domes. b, Tinware. c, Jewelry. d, Fireworks. e, Saddles.
No. 1664: a, Engraving. b, Metallurgy. c, Baskets. d, Embroidery. e, Ceramics.
$2, Assorted products.

2003, Mar. 27 Perf. 13¼x12¾
1663 Horiz. strip of 5   4.50 2.10
a.-e. A641 25c Any single   .80 .40
1664 Horiz. strip of 5   18.00 8.75
a.-e. A641 $1.05 Any single   3.25 1.50
Size: 100x68mm
Imperf
1665 A641 $2 multi   7.25 3.50

Flora and
Fauna
A642

No. 1666: a, Curculionidae. b, Lycidae. c, Acridoidea. d, Arachnidae. e, Liliacea.

2003, Apr. 4 Perf. 13¼x12¾
1666 Horiz. strip of 5   18.00 8.75
a.-e. A642 $1.05 Any single   3.50 1.60

Military
Geographic
Institute, 75th
Anniv.
A643

Designs: No. 1667, 40c, No. 1669, $2, Painting by Eduardo Kingman. No. 1668, 40c, Institute emblem, vert.

Perf. 13¼x12¾, 12¾x13¼
2003, Apr. 11
1667-1668 A643 Set of 2   2.90 1.40

Size: 100x68mm
Imperf
1669 A643 $2 multi   7.25 3.50

Galápagos Marine
Reserve — A644

Designs: 40c, Stylized butterfly.
No. 1671, $1.05, horiz.: a, Sphyrna lewini. b, Chelonia mydas agassisi.
No. 1672, $1.05, horiz.: a, Xanthichthys mento. b, Zanclus cornutus.
$2, Tubastrea coccinea, horiz.

Perf. 12¾x13¼, 13¼x12¾
2003, May 9
1670 A644 40c multi   1.40 .70
Horiz. Pairs, #a-b
1671-1672 A644 Set of 2   14.50 7.25
Size: 100x68mm
Imperf
1673 A644 $2 multi   7.25 3.50

Intl. Tourism
Trade Fair of
Ecuador
A645

No. 1674: a, Monkey in tree. b, Birds. c, Embroidery. d, Mountain. e, Hat seller on beach.

2003, May 14 Perf. 13¼x12¾
1674 Vert. strip of 5   4.50 2.25
a.-e. A645 25c Any single   .80 .40

Artifacts of Pre-Columbian
Cultures — A646

No. 1675, 25c: a, Gold bell with monkey. b, Amphora.
No. 1676, 25c: a, Sculpture of a man. b, Three-footed pot.

Perf. 13x13¼
2003, May 16 Litho. Wmk. 395
Horiz. pairs, #a-b
1675-1676 A646 Set of 2   3.50 1.75

Central Bank
of Ecuador
A647

No. 1677, vert.: a, Tolita Culture mask. b, Guayaquil Historic Park.
$1.05, Pumapungo Museum.

Perf. 13x13¼, 13¼x13
2003, June 5 Litho.
1677 A647 25c Horiz. pair, #a-b   1.00 .50
1678 A647 $1.05 multi   2.10 1.10

Philately and Guayaquil A648

No. 1679, horiz.: a, British consular cover to Veracruz with British stamp and cancel. b, Stampless cover.
No. 1680, horiz.: a, SCADTA first flight cover. b, French consular cover to Lima with French stamps and cancels.
$1.05, Philatelic magazines.
$2, Guayaquil Philatelic Club emblem, Ecuadoran stamps, horiz.

2003, July 22   **Perf. 13¾**
1679	A648	40c Vert. pair, #a-b	2.75	1.40
1680	A648	40c Vert. pair, #a-b	2.75	1.40
1681	A648	$1.05 multi	3.50	1.75
		Nos. 1679-1681 (3)	9.00	4.55

Size: 100x69mm
Imperf
1682	A648	$2 multi	4.00	2.00

Guayaquil Urban Renewal A649

No. 1683: a, Punta Cerro Santa Ana. b, Plaza Colón. c, Malecón Gardens. d, Crystal Palace. e, Plaza de San Francisco.

2003, July 26   **Perf. 13¼x13**
1683		Horiz. strip of 5	15.00	7.25
a.-e.	A649	90c Any single	2.75	1.40

World Bird Festival A650

Designs: No. 1684, $1.05, Geranoaetus melanoleucus. No. 1685, $1.05, Harpia harpyja, vert.

2003, Sept. 2   **Perf. 13¼x13, 13x13¼**
1684-1685	A650	Set of 2	7.25	3.50

Zamora-Chinchipe Province, 50th Anniv. — A651

No. 1686: a, Shown. b, Eira barbara. c, Boa constrictor. d, Tapirus terrestris. e, Psophia crepitans.

2003, Nov. 7   **Perf. 13¼x13**
1686		Vert. strip of 5	4.50	2.25
a.-e.	A651	25c Any single	.80	.40

America Issue — Flora and Fauna — A652

No. 1687: a, Semnornis ramphastinus. b, Bomarea glaucescens.

Perf. 13x13¼
2003, Nov. 1   **Litho.**   **Wmk. 395**
1687	A652	$1.05 Horiz. pair, #a-b	6.25	3.00

Selection of Quito as World Heritage Site, 25th Anniv. A653

Churches: 40c, El Sagrario. No. 1689a, La Compañia de Jesus. No. 1689b, Santa Barbara. $1.05, San Francisco, vert.

2003, Nov. 1   **Perf. 13¼x13, 13x13¼**
1688	A653	40c multi	1.00	.50
1689	A653	90c Horiz. pair, #a-b	5.00	2.50
1690	A653	$1.05 multi	3.00	1.40
		Nos. 1688-1690 (3)	9.00	4.40

Christmas A654

Children's art by: No. 1691a, Stephanie Pacheco. No. 1691b, Sebastián Tejada. 40c, María Claudia Iturralde, vert. 90c, Luis Antonio Ortega. $1.05, Angel Andrés Castro, vert.

2003, Nov. 1
1691	A654	25c Horiz. pair, #a-b	1.50	.70
1692	A654	40c multi	1.25	.55
1693	A654	90c multi	2.75	1.25
1694	A654	$1.05 multi	3.00	1.50
		Nos. 1691-1694 (4)	8.50	4.00

Treasures of Guayaquil Municipal Museum A655

No. 1695: a, Santiago de Guayaquil Act of Independence. b, Punaes ceremonial stone. c, Proclamation of Mariano Donoso. d, Tzantzas. e, Manteño-Huancavilca totem.

2003, Dec. 1   **Perf. 13¼x13**
1695		Horiz. strip of 5	5.75	2.75
a.-e.	A655	40c Any single	1.10	.55

Selection of Galapagos Islands as World Heritage Site, 25th Anniv. — A656

No. 1696: a, Zalophus californianus wollebacki. b, Fregata minor palmerstoni. c, Sula nebouxxi excisa. d, Isla Bartolomé. e, Two Sula nebouxxi excisa shaped as "25."

2003, Nov. 26   **Perf. 13¼x13**
1696		Horiz. strip of 5	5.75	2.75
a.-e.	A656	40c Any single	1.10	.55

Army Aviation Instruction, 50th Anniv. — A657

No. 1697, 40c: a, Mountain, airplanes, emblem. b, Airplane in flight, men on ground.
No. 1698, 40c, horiz.: a, Helicopter and soldiers. b, Airplanes, mountain, people.

2004, Jan. 21   **Perf. 13x13¼, 13¼x13**
Horiz. pairs, #a-b
1697-1698	A657	Set of 2	4.50	2.25

Military Geographical Institute's Role in National Development — A658

2004, Apr. 14   **Perf. 13¼x13**
1699	A658	$1.05 multi	3.00	1.50

Commander Rafael Morán Valverde, Military Hero — A659

2004, Apr. 5   **Perf. 13x13¼**
1700	A659	$1.05 multi	3.00	1.50

Intl. Philately Day — A660

No. 1701: a, Ecuador #2, Greece #1. b, Cover with six stamps.
$2, Various stamps, tongs, magnifying glass, stamp catalogues.
Illustration reduced.

2004, May 6   **Perf. 13¼x13**
1701	A660	75c Horiz. pair, #a-b	5.00	2.50

Imperf
Size: 100x68mm
1702	A660	$2 multi	6.25	3.00

Ecuadorian Volleyball Federation A661

Perf. 13x13¼
2004, May 27   **Litho.**   **Wmk. 395**
1703	A661	75c multi	2.50	1.10

2004 Miss Universe Pageant A662

2004, May 29   **Perf. 13¾**
1704	A662	75c multi	2.50	1.25

Sculpture by Mario Tapia A663

No. 1705: a, Adolescencia. b, Beato Chaminade. c, Delfin de Galapagos. d, Pelicano. e, Homenaje a Carlo Vidano.
$2, Similar to No. 1705b.

2004, June 1   **Perf. 13¼x13**
1705		Horiz. strip of 5	13.50	6.75
a.-e.	A663	90c Any single	1.80	.90

Imperf
Size: 100x69mm
1706	A663	$2 multi	7.25	3.75

Pedro Vicente Maldonado (1704-48), Cartographer A664

2004, June 25   **Perf. 13x13¼**
1707	A664	90c multi	2.50	1.25

Dr. Agustín Cueva Tamariz (1903-79) — A665

2004, June 30   **Litho.**
1708	A665	90c multi	2.50	1.25

34th General Assembly of the Organization of American States — A666

2004, July 4   **Wmk. 395**
1709	A666	75c multi	2.50	1.25

Dr. Angel Felicísmo Rojas (b. 1909), Writer — A667

2004, July 11
1710	A667	50c multi	1.60	.80

Ecuadoran and Spanish Postal Money Orders A668

2004, Aug. 3   **Perf. 13¼x13**
1711	A668	$1.05 multi	3.00	1.50

2004 Summer Olympics, Athens — A669

No. 1712 — 2004 Summer Olympics emblem, Ecuadoran Olympic Committee emblem and: a, 2004 Olympics mascots. b, Alexandra Escobar Guerrero.

2004, Aug. 3   *Perf. 13x13¼*
1712 A669 $1.05 Horiz. pair,
#a-b   6.25   3.25

Ecuador Orchid Association, 30th Anniv. — A670

Designs: 25c, Cattleya maxima. $1.05, Epidendrum bracteolatum.

2004, Sept. 30
1713-1714 A670   Set of 2   3.75   1.90

Guayaquil Symphony Orchestra — A671

Perf. 13x13¼
2004, Nov. 19   **Litho.**   **Wmk. 395**
1715 A671 90c multi   2.50   1.25

Christmas — A672

Children's art: 40c, Christmas stocking with envelopes. $1.05, Santa Claus giving letter to Christmas tree, horiz.

2004, Dec. 12   *Perf. 13x13¼, 13¼x13*
1716-1717 A672   Set of 2   4.00   2.00

America Issue - Environmental Protection — A673

Designs: 40d, Buddha and trees. $1.05, Mother Earth.

2004, Dec. 23   *Perf. 13x13¼*
1718-1719 A673   Set of 2   4.00   2.00

Galapagos Islands Fauna A674

Designs: 40c, Chelonoidis abingdonii. 90c, Amblyrhynchus cristatus, vert. $2.15, Sula granti. $3, Fregata magnificens. $2, Creagrus furcatus, vert.

2005, Feb. 18   *Perf. 13¼x13, 13x13¼*
1720-1723 A674   Set of 4   13.00   6.50
Imperf
Size: 68x98mm
1724 A674 $2 multi   4.00   2.00

El Mercurio Newspaper, 80th Anniv. A675

Designs: $1.25, Masthead. $2, Dr. Nicanor Merchan Bermeo, newspaper co-founder. $2.25, Miguel Merchan Ochoa.

2005, Mar. 4   *Perf. 13¼x13, 13x13¼*
1725-1727 A675   Set of 3   11.00   5.50

Tourism A676

2005, Mar. 22   *Perf. 13¼x13*
1728 A676 $3.75 multi   7.50   3.75

Ecuadorian Chess Federation, 25th Anniv. — A677

2005, Apr. 1   *Perf. 13x13¼*
1729 A677 $1.25 multi   2.50   1.25

Ecuadorian Olympic Academy, 25th Anniv. — A678

Perf. 13x13¼
2005, June 20   **Litho.**   **Wmk. 395**
1730 A678 $1.25 shown   2.50   1.25
Imperf
Size: 69x100mm
1731 A678 $2 Emblems   4.00   2.00

Rotary International, Cent. — A679

Rotary emblem and: 40c, Man on Mt. Chimborazo. 90c, People on Mt. Cotopaxi. $2, Man on Mt. Shisha Pangma, Nepal.

2005, June 29   *Perf. 13¼x13*
1732-1734 A679   Set of 3   6.75   3.25

Guayaquil Conference, 183rd Anniv. — A680

No. 1735 — Guayaquil Philatelic Club emblem and: a, José de San Martín, Argentina #1. b, Simón Bolívar, Venezuela #1. $2, Bolívar, San Martín, monument. Illustration reduced.

2005, July 22   *Perf. 13¼x13*
1735 A680 90c Horiz. pair, #a-b   3.75   1.90
Imperf
Size:98x68mm
1736 A680 $2 multi   4.00   2.00

Intl. Year of Books and Reading — A681

Perf. 13x13¼
2005, July 22   **Litho.**   **Wmk. 395**
1737 A681 25c multi   .50   .25

Dr. Juan Isaac Lovato Vargas (1904-2001), Judge — A682

Perf. 13¼x13
2005, July 28   **Litho.**   **Wmk. 395**
1738 A682 $1.25 multi   2.50   1.25

Mountain and Eastern Cattleman's Association — A683

No. 1739 — Emblem and: a, Mountains. b, Head of cow.

2005, Aug. 4   *Perf. 13x13¼*
1739 A683 40c Horiz. pair, #a-b   1.60   .80

University Sports League of Quito, 75th Anniv. A684

No. 1740: a, University Sports League Stadium. b, 1969 University Sports League soccer team. c, Emblem. d, Children playing at school. e, Statue of emblem, League Country Club.
$2, Soccer shirt, vert.

2005, Aug. 4   *Perf. 13¼x13*
1740   Horiz. strip of 5   4.00   2.00
a.-e. A684 40c Any single   .80   .40
Imperf
Size: 68x98mm
1741 A684 $2 multi   4.00   2.00

15th Bolivarian Games, Armenia and Pereira A685

2005, Aug. 8   *Perf. 13¼x13*
1742 A685 25c multi   .50   .25

1938 South American Swimming Champions, Trophy and Swimming Federation Emblem A686

2005, Aug. 8   **Litho.**
1743 A686 25c multi   .50   .25

First Ecuadoran victory in international sports competition.

Virgin of Cisne — A687

2005, Sept. 6   *Perf. 13¾*
1744 A687 $1.25 multi   2.50   1.25

History of the Ecuadoran Army A688

No. 1745: a, Troops in Esmeraldas, 1916. b, Military school cadets, 1928. c, Cayambe Battalion. d, Arms and Grandsons of Gen. Eloy Alfaro. e, Imbabura Battalion.
$2, Battle for emancipation of Guayaquil.

2005, Sept. 15   *Perf. 13¼x13*
1745   Horiz. strip of 5   4.00   2.00
a.-e. A688 40c Any single   .80   .40
Imperf
Size: 98x67mm
1746 A688 $2 multi   4.00   2.00

Carchi Province Arms — A689

No. 1747: a, Tulcán Canton. b, Bolívar Canton.
No. 1748: a, Carchi Province. b, Huaca Canton. c, Mira Canton. d, Espejo Canton. e, Montúfar Canton.

2005, Sept. 26   *Perf. 13x13¼*
1747   Horiz. pair   1.60   .80
a.-b. A689 40c Either single   .80   .40
1748   Horiz. strip of 5   4.00   2.00
a.-e. A689 40c Any single   .80   .40

Tourism — A690

No. 1749: a, Cerro Santa Ana, Guayaquil. b, Esmereldas. c, Misahualli. d, Tsunki Shuar, Pastaza.
No. 1750: a, Cisne Church, Loja. b, Ingapirca Ruins. c, Seal, Galapagos Islands. d, Sea turtle, Galapagos Islands.
Illustration reduced.

Perf. 13¼x13
2005, Sept. 26   Litho.   Wmk. 395
1749 A690 30c Block of 4, #a-d   2.40 1.25
1750 A690 40c Block of 4, #a-d   3.25 1.60

St. Mariana de Jesús Paredes y Flores A691

2005, Oct. 19
1751 A691 25c multi   .50   .25

Popes Reigning in 2005 — A692

No. 1752: a, $1.25, Pope John Paul II (1920-2005). b, $2, Pope Benedict XVI.
Illustration reduced.

2005, Oct. 19
1752 A692 Horiz. pair, #a-b   6.50 3.25

Cenepa War With Peru, 10th Anniv. — A693

No. 1753: a, Mirage F1-JA airplanes. b, Cessna A-37B airplanes. c, Kfir-C2 airplanes. d, Lt. Col. Carlos Uscategui and airplane.
Illustration reduced.

2005, Oct. 26
1753 A693 $1.25 Block of 4, #a-d   10.00 5.00

First Guayaquil to Cauca Airmail Flight, 85th Anniv. — A694

No. 1754: a, 25c, Tail of Telegrafo I airplane, flight manager José Abel Castillo. b, $1, Front of Telegrafo I airplane, pilot Elia Liut.

Illustration reduced.
2005, Nov. 12
1754 A694   Horiz. pair, #a-b   2.50 1.25

Ecuadorian Armed Forces in United Nations Peacekeeping Forces — A695

No. 1755: a, Female soldier. b, Two soldiers wearing helmets. c, Soldiers with flags. d, United Nations and Ecuadorian flags, beret of Peacekeeping forces.
Illustration reduced.

2005, Nov. 25   *Perf. 13x13¼*
1755 A695 75c Block of 4, #a-d   6.00 3.00

Christmas — A696

No. 1756 — Children's drawings by: a, Pamela Alejandra Castillo Rocha. b, Kira Cedeño. c, Silvia Moran Burgos. d, Carol Garcia.

2005, Nov. 25
1756 A696 $1.25 Block of 4, #a-d   10.00 5.00

18th Cent. Watercolors of Ecuadorians A697

No. 1757: a, Water bearer. b, Indian governor's wife. c, Dancer. d, Cuenca Indian. e, Municipal council piper. f, Indian carrying skyrockets. g, Woman (Mina gigante). h, Majordomo. i, Society woman (Chola pinganilla). j, Street sweeper.

2005, Nov. 30   *Perf. 13¾*
1757   Block of 10   5.00 2.50
a.-j. A697 25c Any single   .50   .25

Publication of Don Quixote, 400th Anniv. — A698

No. 1758 — Drawings of Don Quixote and: a, Windmills. b, Tree.

2005, Dec. 7   *Perf. 13x13¼*
1758 A698 $2 Horiz. pair, #a-b   8.00 4.00

Colonial Religious Art — A699

Colonial Religious Art — A700

No. 1759: a, St. Joseph and Baby Jesus. b, Resurrected Christ. c, Virgin of Quito. d, St. Augustine.
No. 1760: $2, The Divine Shepherd.

2005, Dec. 9
1759 A699 40c Block of 4, #a-d   3.25 1.60
Souvenir Sheet
Imperf
1760 A700 $2 multi   4.00 2.00

El Comercio Newspaper, Cent. (in 2006) A701

"100" and: No. 1761, Statue at LL, newspaper masthead. No. 1762a, Statue at LR. No. 1762b, Statue in "0." No. 1763, Statue in seal. No. 1764, Statue at LL, newspaper masthead, simulated perforations.

Perf. 13¼x13
2006, Jan. 2   Litho.   Wmk. 395
1761 A701 40c multi   .80   .40
1762 A701 40c Horiz. pair, #a-b 1.60   .80
Size: 55x35mm
Perf. 13¾
1763 A701 50c multi   1.00   .50
  Nos. 1761-1763 (3)   3.40   1.70
Size: 100x69mm
Imperf
1764 A701 $2 multi   4.00 2.00
Dated 2006.

Quito Tourism A702

2006, Jan. 11   *Perf. 13¼x13*
1765 A702 25c multi   .50   .25
Dated 2005.

35th Latin American and Caribbean Lions' Club Forum, Quito — A703

Color of oceans: 90c, White. $2, Orange.

2006, Jan. 19   *Perf. 13x13¼*
1766 A703 90c multi   1.90   .90
Size: 68x99mm
Imperf
1767 A703 $2 multi   4.00 2.00

Biodiversity of Puyo A704

Designs: $1, Cromacris sp. $1.20, Desmodus rotundus.

2006, Mar. 22   *Perf. 13¼x13*
1768-1769 A704   Set of 2   4.50 2.25

America Issue, Fight Against Poverty A705

Various Pre-Columbian Guayasamin figurines: 40c, 80c, $1, $1.20.

2006, Feb. 12
1770-1773 A705   Set of 4   7.00 3.50

Benito Juarez (1806-72), President of Mexico — A706

2006, Mar. 21   *Perf. 13x13¼*
1774 A706 $1.20 multi   2.40 1.25

Manteña Raft A707

2006, Mar. 23   *Perf. 13¼x13*
1775 A707 $1 multi   2.00 1.00

Straw Hat Makers A708

Designs: No. 1776, 40c, Hat maker. No. 1777, 40c, Hat maker wearing hat, vert.

2006, Apr. 8   Perf. 13¼x13, 13x13¼
1776-1777 A708 Set of 2   1.60 .80

Federation of University Students — A709

2006, Apr. 21   Perf. 13x13¼
1778 A709 30c multi   .60 .30

Miracle of Colegio San Gabriel, Cent. — A710

2006, Apr. 21   Wmk. 395
1779 A710 80c multi   1.60 .80

Ibarra, 400th Anniv. A711

2006, Apr. 28   Perf. 13¼x13
1780 A711 20c shown   .40 .20
Size: 68x100mm
Imperf
1781 A711 $2.50 Painting, diff.   5.00 2.50

Baltazara Calderon — A712

2005, May 16   Perf. 13x13¼
1782 A712 $1 multi   2.00 1.00

18th Cent. Military Uniforms A713

No. 1783: a, Compañia Fija de Quito. b, Dragones de Quito. c, Infanteria de Quito. d, Dragones de Guayaquil (gray horse). e, Dragones de Guayaquil (brown horse).

2006, May 18   Perf. 13¾
1783   Horiz. strip of 5   2.00 1.00
a.-e. A713 20c Any single   .40 .20

Mushrooms and Fauna of Podocarpus Park A714

Designs: 20c, Basidiomicetes. 25c, Tremarctus ornatus. 90c, Harpya harpyja, vert.

Perf. 13¼x13, 13x13¼
2006, May 22   Litho.   Wmk. 395
1784-1786 A714 Set of 3   2.75 1.40

Wolfgang Amadeus Mozart (1756-91), Composer A715

2006, May 31   Perf. 13¼x13
1787 A715 20c multi   .40 .20

UNICEF, 60th Anniv. A716

Designs: 75c, Child, butterfly, and sun. $1, Children and books.

Perf. 13¼x13
2006, June 1   Litho.   Wmk. 395
1788-1789 A716 Set of 2   3.50 1.75

Eloy Alfaro Military School A717

2006, June 5
1790 A717 80c multi   1.60 .80

Banco Pichincha, Cent. A718

Designs: No. 1791, 1906 1-sucre banknote. No. 1792 — First bank building: a, Denomination at left. b, Denomination at right.

2006, June 8
1791 A718 40c shown   .80 .40
1792 A718 40c Horiz. pair, #a-b   1.60 .80

2006 World Cup Soccer Championships, Germany — A719

FIFA emblem and: 40c, World Cup. 80c, 2006 World Cup emblem. $1, Mascot. $1.20, World Cup and flags of competing countries.

Perf. 13¼x13
2006, June 9   Litho.   Wmk. 395
1793-1796 A719 Set of 4   7.00 3.50

Designs: No. 1797C, Like #1796. No. 1797D, Similar to #1796, but with scores of Ecuador team's first round victories.

2006   Litho.   Wmk. 395   Imperf.
Size: 60x40mm
1797C A719 $2 multi   4.00 2.00
1797D A719 $2 multi   4.00 2.00

A720

Plaza de Mayo Mothers of Argentina — A721

Illustration A721 reduced.

Perf. 13¼x13
2006, June 19   Litho.   Wmk. 395
1798 A720 80c multi   1.60 .80
Imperf
1799 A721 $2.50 multi   5.00 2.50

Machala Canton, 182nd Anniv. A722

2006, June 20   Perf. 13¼x13
1800 A722 30c multi   .60 .30

Machala Canton, 182nd Anniv. — A723

Flags of 2006 World Cup Soccer Championship participants, FIFA emblem and: No. 1801, Flag of Ecuador. No. 1802, Soccer shoes and ball.

2006   Litho.   Wmk. 395   Imperf.
1801 A723 $2 multi   4.00 2.00
1802 A723 $2 multi   4.00 2.00

2006 World Cup Soccer Championships, Germany.

Garibaldi Italian Assistance Society — A724

2006, July 7   Perf. 13x13¼
1803 A724 90c multi   1.90 .95

Souvenir Sheet

Municipal Railroads — A726

Wmk. 395
2006, July 20   Litho.   Imperf.
1806 A726 $2 multi   4.00 2.00

Simón Bolívar Experimental College — A727

2006, July 25   Litho.   Perf. 13x13¼
1807 A727 20c multi   .40 .20
Imperf
1808 A728 $10 multi   20.00 10.00

Bolívar A728

Spondylus Shell Carvings in National Institute of Cultural Heritage A729

Designs: 25c, Necklace. No. 1810, vert.: a, Figurine of trader. b, Figurine of fishermen in boat.

2006, July 26   Perf. 13¼x13, 13x13¼
1809 A729 25c multi   .50 .25
1810 A729 $1 Horiz. pair, #a-b   4.00 4.00

Indian Postal Runner and Ecuador Post Emblem — A730

Background colors: 25c, White. 30c, Dark blue. 40c, Black. 60c, Beige. 80c, Olive green

2006, Aug. 5   *Perf. 13x13¼*
1811-1815 A730   Set of 5   4.75 2.75

Ecuadorian Olympic Committee A731

2006, Aug. 15   Litho.
1816 A731 30c multi   .60 .30

Writers — A732

Designs: $1, Jorge Icaza (1906-78). $1.20, Pablo Palacio (1906-47).

2006, Sept. 18   Wmk. 395
1817-1818 A732   Set of 2   4.50 2.25

Ecuadorian Food — A733

No. 1819: a, Bandera Manabi. b, Viche de Manabi.
Illustration reduced.

2006, Sept. 23   *Perf. 13¼x13*
1819 A733 $1 Horiz. pair, #a-b   4.00 2.00

Orchids — A734

No. 1820: a, Caucaea olivaceum. b, Cyrtochilum macranthum. c, Miltoniopsis vexillaria. d, Odontoglossum harryanum. e, Cyrtochilum pastasae. f, Cyrtochilum loxense. g, Cyrtochilum eduardii. h, Odontoglossum epidendroides. i, Cyrtochilum retusum. j, Cyrtochilum geniculatum.
$2, Cyrtochilum macranthum, diff.

2006, Sept. 29   *Perf. 13x13¼*
1820   Block of 10   6.00 3.00
  a.-j.   A734 30c Any single   .60 .30

Imperf
Size: 66x95mm
1821 A734 $2 multi   4.00 2.00

America Issue, Energy Conservation — A735

Background color: $1, Brown. $1.20, Blue.

2006, Oct. 4   *Perf. 13¼x13*
1822-1823 A735   Set of 2   4.50 2.25

Natural Fiber Art, by Giti Neuman — A736

Designs: No. 1824, En la Ventana.
No. 1825: a, Forma en Movimiento. b, Caminantes.
No. 1826, horiz.: a, Caminando. b, Cabezas Huecas.

2006, Oct. 4   *Perf. 13x13¼, 13¼x13*
1824 A736 30c multi   .60 .30
1825 A736 30c Vert. pair, #a-b   1.25 .60
1826 A736 30c Horiz. pair, #a-b   1.25 .60
    Nos. 1824-1826 (3)   3.10 1.50

Tourism in Otovalo A737

Designs: 25c, El Lechero tree. 30c, El Jordan Church. 75c, Young girl, vert. $1, Costume for El Coraza Festival, vert.

2006, Oct. 18   *Perf. 13¼x13, 13x13¼*
1827-1830 A737   Set of 4   4.75 2.40

Eruption of Tungurahua Volcano — A738

No. 1831: a, Ash cloud above volcano. b, Lava flowing down volcano.

2006, Oct. 20   *Perf. 13x13¼*
1831 A738 $1 Horiz. pair, #a-b   4.00 2.00

Urban Renewal of Guayaquil A739

No. 1832: a, Municipal Palace, denomination at left. b, Municipal Palace, denomination at right. c, Vulcan forge. d, José Joaquín de Olmedo Airport. e, Bus station.

2006, Oct. 24   *Perf. 13¼x13*
1832   Horiz. strip of 5   10.00 5.00
  a.-e.   A739 $1 Any single   2.00 1.00

Radio Station HCJB, 75th Anniv. A740

2006, Oct. 26   Wmk. 395
1833 A740 $1 multi   2.00 1.00

Millennium Development Objectives of the United Nations — A741

2006, Oct. 27   *Perf. 13¾*
1834 A741 $2 multi   4.00 2.00

Pres. Galo Plaza Lasso (1906-87) — A742

Designs: 40c, Photograph. 80c, Tree.

2006, Oct. 27   *Perf. 13x13¼*
1835-1836 A742   Set of 2   2.40 1.25

German Shepherd Breeding Association A743

2006, Oct. 28   Litho.   *Perf. 13¼x13*
1837 A743 $1 multi   2.00 1.00

Military Parachuting, 50th Anniv. A744

Designs: 20c, Soldiers. 40c, Soldiers and airplane. 60c, Soldier and troop emblem. 80c, Paratrooper in air.

      Perf. 13¼x13, 13x13¼
2006, Oct. 31   Litho.   Wmk. 395
1838-1841 A744   Set of 4   4.00 2.00

Galapagos Islands Fauna — A745

No. 1842, horiz.: a, Sea turtle. b, Sea gull. c, Marine iguana. d, Blue-footed boobies. e, Sea lion.
80c, Flamingo. $1, Crab. $1.20, Fish.

2006, Nov. 1
1842 A745   30c Horiz. strip of
              5, #a-e   3.00 1.50
1843 A745   80c multi   1.60 .80
1844 A745 $1 multi   2.00 1.00
1845 A745 $1.20 multi   2.40 1.25
    Nos. 1842-1845 (4)   9.00 4.55

Christmas — A746

2006, Nov. 28   *Perf. 13x13¼*
1846 A746 80c multi   1.60 .80

Monsignor Juan I. Larrea Holguín (1927-2006) — A747

No. 1847: a, In bishop's robes. b, In judicial robes.

2006, Dec. 8   *Perf. 13¾*
1847 A747 40c Horiz. pair, #a-b   1.60 .80

Freemasonry A748

Designs: 25c, Masonic altar, beehive. 40c, Compass and square.

2006, Dec. 11   *Perf. 13x13¼*
1848-1849 A748   Set of 2   1.40 .70

Quito Zoo Animals — A749

No. 1850: a, Parrot. b, Frog.
No. 1851: a, Harpy eagle. b, Jaguar.
$2, Parrot on branch.

2006, Dec. 11   *Perf. 13x13¼*
1850 A749 60c Horiz. pair, #a-b   2.40 1.25
1851 A749 80c Horiz. pair, #a-b   3.25 1.60
Imperf
Size: 40x65mm
1852 A749 $2 multi   4.00 2.00

Erotic and Fertility Figurines — A750

Designs: 10c, Nursing mother. 20c, Copulating couple. $1.20, Pregnant woman. $2, Man with erect penis.

2006, Dec. 12   *Perf. 13x13¼*
1853-1856 A750   Set of 4   7.00 3.50

Admiral Juan Illingworth Naval Museum — A751

Emblem of Ecuador Navy and Illingworth: 20c, On rope ladder, 1880. 25c, As Marine Guard, 1854.

2006, Dec. 15   Litho.
1857-1858 A751   Set of 2   .90 .45

Colors of Ecuador Flag — A752

2006, Dec. 15   Wmk. 395
1859 A752 $10 multi   20.00 10.00

Postmen and Bicycles A753

Color of photograph: 20c, Gray brown. 40c, Gray blue. 80c, Red.

2006, Dec. 17   Perf. 13¼x13
1860-1862 A753   Set of 3   3.00 1.50

Pets A754

Designs: 25c, Puppy. 40c, Dog, vert. 50c, Cat with brown and blue eyes, vert. 80c, Dog running. $1, Cat with blue eyes, vert.

2006, Dec. 17   Perf. 13¼x13, 13x13¼
1863-1867 A754   Set of 5   6.00 3.00

Cuenca Biennale A755

Art by: 5c, Alexander Apóstol. 15c, Ricardo González Elias, vert.

2006, Dec. 20
1868-1869 A755   Set of 2   .40 .20

Independence Monument, 50th Anniv. — A756

No. 1870: a, Head of statue. b, Entire statue.

Illustration reduced.

2006, Dec. 21   Perf. 13¾
1870 A756 20c Horiz. pair, #a-b   .80 .40

Quito Fair — A757

Designs: No. 1871, Matador Manolo Caena. No. 1872 — Matadors: a, Sebastián Castella. b, El Juli.
No. 1873, horiz. — Quito Bull Ring: a, At right. b, At left.
$3, Sculpture of Jesus, horiz.

Perf. 13x13¼, 13¼x13
2006, Dec. 27   Litho.
1871 A757 50c multi   1.00 .50
1872 A757 50c Horiz. pair, #a-b   2.00 1.00
1873 A757 50c Horiz. pair, #a-b   2.00 1.00
  Nos. 1871-1873 (3)   5.00 2.50

Litho. With Foil Application
Imperf
Size: 65x40mm
1874 A757 $3 multi   6.00 3.00

Pirates A758

No. 1875, vert.: a, Jolly Roger flag, ship, sea lions. b, Sea lions, ships. c, Ships, Jolly roger flag. d, Armed pirate on ship. e, Ship, Jolly Roger flag.
No. 1876: a, Map of Galapagos Islands, Jolly Roger flag, Sir Francis Drake. b, Ship, map, skull.
$1, Ship, map, skull, William Dampier.

Perf. 13x13¼, 13¼x13
2006, Dec. 27   Litho.
1875 A758 30c Horiz. strip of 5, #a-e   3.00 1.50
1876 A758 40c Horiz. pair, #a-b   1.60 .80
1877 A758 $1 multi   2.00 1.00
  Nos. 1875-1877 (3)   6.60 3.30

SEK International University, Quito A759

Perf. 13¼x13
2006, Dec. 29   Wmk. 395
1878 A759 10c multi   .20 .20

SEMI-POSTAL STAMPS

Nos. 423-428 Surcharged in Carmine or Blue:

1944, May 9   Unwmk.   Perf. 12
B1 A171 10c + 10c yel grn (C)   .60 .30
B2 A171 20c + 20c rose pink   .60 .30
B3 A171 30c + 20c dk gray brn   .60 .30
B4 A171 50c + 20c dp red lil   1.20 .60
B5 A171 1s + 50c ol gray (C)   2.00 1.00
B6 A171 10s + 2s red orange   7.00 3.50
  Nos. B1-B6 (6)   12.00 6.00

The surtax aided Mendez Hospital.

AIR POST STAMPS

In 1928-30, the internal airmail service of Ecuador was handled by the Sociedad Colombo-Alemana de Transportes Aereos ("SCADTA") under government sanction. During this period SCADTA issued stamps which were the only legal franking for airmail service except that handled under contract with Pan American-Grace Airways. SCADTA issues are Nos. C1-C6, C16-C25, CF1-CF2.

Colombia Air Post Stamps of 1923 Surcharged in Carmine

"Provisional" at 45 degree Angle
Perf. 14x14½
1928, Aug. 28   Wmk. 116
C1 AP6 50c on 10c green   110.00 70.00
C2 AP6 75c on 15c car   210.00 160.00
C3 AP6 1s on 20c gray   70.00 42.50
C4 AP6 1½s on 30c blue   45.00 35.00
C5 AP6 3s on 60c brown   85.00 52.50
  Nos. C1-C5 (5)   520.00 360.00

"Provisional" at 41 degree Angle
1929, Mar. 20
C1a AP6 50c on 10c green   125.00 110.00
C2a AP6 75c on 15c carmine   225.00 175.00
C3a AP6 1s on 20c gray   225.00 175.00
  Nos. C1a-C3a (3)   575.00 460.00

Same with "Cts." Between Surcharged Numerals
C6 AP6 50c on 10c green   700.00 1,700.

A 75c on 15c carmine with "Cts." between the surcharged numerals exists. There is no evidence that it was regularly issued or used. For overprints see Nos. CF1-CF1a.

Plane over River Guayas — AP1

Unwmk.
1929, May 5   Engr.   Perf. 12
C8 AP1 2c black   .40 .20
C9 AP1 5c carmine rose   .40 .20
C10 AP1 10c deep brown   .40 .20
C11 AP1 20c dark violet   .90 .20
C12 AP1 50c deep green   1.60 .45
C13 AP1 1s dark blue   6.00 2.75
C14 AP1 5s orange yellow   25.00 11.00
C15 AP1 10s orange red   135.00 57.50
  Nos. C8-C15 (8)   169.70 72.50

Establishment of commercial air service in Ecuador. The stamps were available for all forms of postal service and were largely used for franking ordinary letters.
Nos. C13-C15 show numerals in color on white background. Counterfeits of No. C15 exist.
See #C26-C31. For overprints and surcharge see #C32-C38, C287, CO1-CO12.

Jesuit Church La Compania AP2

Mount Chimborazo AP3

Wmk. 127
1929, Apr. 1   Litho.   Perf. 14
C16 AP2 50c red brown   4.50 2.25
C17 AP2 75c green   4.50 2.25
C18 AP2 1s rose   7.00 2.25
C19 AP2 1½s gray blue   7.00 2.25
C20 AP2 2s violet   11.50 4.50
C21 AP2 3s brown   11.50 4.50
C22 AP3 5s lt blue   40.00 14.00
C23 AP3 10s lt red   85.00 30.00
C24 AP3 15s violet   140.00 60.00
C25 AP3 25s olive green   190.00 70.00
  Nos. C16-C25 (10)   501.00 192.00

For overprint see No. CF2.

Plane Type of 1929
1930-44   Unwmk.   Engr.   Perf. 12
C26 AP1 1s carmine lake   6.50 .55
C27 AP1 1s green ('44)   1.00 .20
C28 AP1 5s olive green   10.00 3.75
C29 AP1 5s purple ('44)   2.00 .20
C30 AP1 10s black   30.00 5.50
C31 AP1 10s brt ultra ('44)   4.50 .30
  Nos. C26-C31 (6)   54.00 10.50

Nos. C26-C31 show numerals in color on white background.
For surcharge see No. C287.

Type of 1929 Overprinted in Various Colors

AP4

1930, June 4
C32 AP4 1s car lake (Bk)   22.50 22.50
  a. Double ovpt. (R Br + Bk)   75.00
C33 AP4 5s olive grn (R)   22.50 22.50
C34 AP4 10s black (R Br)   22.50 22.50
  Nos. C32-C34 (3)   67.50 67.50

Flight of Capt. Benjamin Mendez from Bogota to Quito, bearing a crown of flowers for the tomb of Grand Marshal Sucre.

Air Post Official Stamps of 1929-30 Overprinted in Various Colors or Surcharged Similarly in Upper & Lower Case

1935, July 24
C35 AP1 50c deep green (Bl)   12.50 5.00
C36 AP1 50c olive brn (R)   12.50 5.00
C37 AP1 1s on 5s ol grn (Bk)   12.50 5.00
  a. Double surcharge   95.00
C38 AP1 2s on 10s black (R)   12.50 5.00
  Nos. C35-C38 (4)   50.00 20.00

Unveiling of a monument to Bolívar at Quito, July 24th, 1935.

Geodesical Mission Issue

Nos. 349-351 Overprinted in Blue or Black and Type of Regular issue

1936, July 3   Perf. 12½
C39 A136 10c deep orange (Bl)   .60 .20
C40 A136 20c violet (Bk)   .60 .20
C41 A136 50c dark red (Bl)   .60 .20
C42 A136 70c black   1.25 .35
  Nos. C39-C42 (4)   3.05 .95

For surcharge see No. RA42.

Philatelic Exhibition Issue
Type of Regular Issue Overprinted "AEREA"

1936, Oct. 20   Perf. 13½x14
C43 A137 2c rose   4.50 4.50
C44 A137 5c brown orange   4.50 4.50
C45 A137 10c brown   4.50 4.50
C46 A137 20c ultra   4.50 4.50

C47	A137	50c red violet	4.50	4.50
C48	A137	1s green	4.50	4.50

Nos. C43-C48 (6) 27.00 27.00

Condor and Plane — AP6

Perf. 13½

C49	AP6	70c orange brown	2.00	.50
C50	AP6	1s dull violet	2.00	.50

Nos. C43-C50 were issued for the 1st Intl. Phil. Exhib. at Quito.

Condor over "El Altar" — AP7

1937-46　　　　**Perf. 11½, 12**

C51	AP7	10c chestnut	5.00	.20
C52	AP7	20c olive black	6.50	.20
C53	AP7	40c rose car ('46)	6.50	.20
C54	AP7	70c black brown	9.00	.20
C55	AP7	1s gray black	14.00	.20
C56	AP7	2s dark violet	24.00	.20

Nos. C51-C56 (6) 65.00 1.65

Issue dates: 40c, Oct. 7; others, Aug. 19.
For overprints see #463-464, CO13-CO17.

Portrait of Washington, American Eagle and Flags — AP8

Engraved & Litho.
1938, Feb. 9　　　　**Perf. 12**
Center Multicolored

C57	AP8	2c brown	.40	.20
C58	AP8	5c black	.40	.20
C59	AP8	10c brown	.40	.20
C60	AP8	20c dark blue	.80	.20
C61	AP8	50c violet	1.75	.20
C62	AP8	1s black	3.25	.20
C63	AP8	2s violet	7.50	.90

Nos. C57-C63 (7) 14.50 2.10

150th anniv. of the US Constitution.
In 1947, Nos. C61-C63 were overprinted in dark blue: "Primero la Patria!" and plane. These revolutionary propaganda stamps were later renounced by decree. Value $20.
For overprints see #C102-C104, C139-C141.

No. RA35 Surcharged in Red

1938, Nov. 16　　　　**Perf. 13½**

C64	PT12	65c on 3c ultra	.40	.20

A national airmail concession was given to the Sociedad Ecuatoriano de Transportes Aereos (SEDTA) in July, 1938. No. RA35 was surcharged for SEDTA postal requirements. SEDTA operated through 1940.

Army Horseman — AP9　　　Woman Runner — AP10

Tennis — AP11　　　Boxing — AP12

Olympic Fire — AP13

1939, Mar.　Engr.　Perf. 12

C65	AP9	5c lt green	1.50	.20
C66	AP10	10c salmon	2.00	.20
C67	AP11	50c redsh brown	10.50	.20
C68	AP12	1s black brown	12.50	.45
C69	AP13	2s rose carmine	15.00	1.10

Nos. C65-C69 (5) 41.50 2.15

First Bolivarian Games (1938).

Plane over Chimborazo AP14

1939, May 1　　　**Perf. 13x12½**

C70	AP14	1s yellow brown	.40	.20
C71	AP14	2s rose violet	.70	.20
C72	AP14	5s black	1.90	.20

Nos. C70-C72 (3) 3.00 .60

Golden Gate Bridge and Mountain Peak — AP15　　Empire State Building and Mountain Peak — AP16

1939　　　**Perf. 12½x13**

C73	AP15	2c black	.40	.20
C74	AP15	5c rose red	.40	.20
C75	AP15	10c indigo	.40	.20
C76	AP15	50c rose violet	.40	.20
C77	AP15	1s chocolate	.80	.20
C78	AP15	2s yellow brown	1.00	.20
C79	AP15	5s emerald	2.00	.20

Nos. C73-C79 (7) 5.40 1.40

Golden Gate International Exposition.
For surcharge & overprint see #434, CO18.

1939

C80	AP16	2c brown orange	.60	.20
C81	AP16	5c dark carmine	.60	.20
C82	AP16	10c indigo	.60	.20
C83	AP16	50c slate green	.60	.20
C84	AP16	1s deep orange	1.20	.20
C85	AP16	2s dk red violet	1.40	.20
C86	AP16	5s dark gray	3.25	.20

Nos. C80-C86 (7) 8.25 1.40

New York World's Fair.
For surcharge see No. 435.

Map of the Americas and Airplane — AP17

1940, July 9

C87	AP17	10c red org & blue	.40	.20
C88	AP17	70c sepia & blue	.40	.20
C89	AP17	1s copper brn & blue	.80	.20
C90	AP17	10s black & blue	3.25	.85

Nos. C87-C90 (4) 4.85 1.45

Pan American Union, 50th anniversary.

Journalism Type
1941, Dec. 15

C91	A157	3s rose carmine	5.25	.20
C92	A157	10s yellow orange	11.00	.45

See note after No. 399.

Old Map of South America Showing Amazon River — AP19　　Panoramic View of Amazon River — AP20

Designs: 70c, Gonzalo de Pineda. 5s, Painting of the expedition.

1942, Jan. 30

C93	AP19	40c black & buff	1.90	.20
C94	AP19	70c olive	2.90	.20
C95	AP20	2s dark green	3.25	.20
C96	AP19	5s rose	4.00	.65

Nos. C93-C96 (4) 12.05 1.25

See note after No. 403.

Remigio Crespo Toral Type
1942, Sept. 1　　　**Perf. 13½**

C97	A162	10c dull violet	1.25	.45

Alfaro Types

70c, Gen. Eloy Alfaro. 1s, Devils's Nose. 3s, Military College. 5s, Montecristi, Alfaro's birthplace.

1943, Feb. 16　　　**Perf. 12**

C98	A166	70c dk rose & blk	1.90	.20
C99	A167	1s ol blk & red brn	3.25	.65
C100	A167	3s ol gray & grn	4.50	.90
C101	A167	5s slate & salmon	6.75	1.10

Nos. C98-C101 (4) 16.40 2.85

Nos. C61-C63 Overprinted in Red Brown

1943, Apr. 15　　　**Perf. 11½**
Center Multicolored

C102	AP8	50c violet	2.75	1.50
C103	AP8	1s black	3.25	1.60
C104	AP8	2s violet	4.00	2.50

Nos. C102-C104 (3) 10.00 5.60

Visit of US Vice-Pres. Henry A. Wallace.

Nos. 374-376 Overprinted "AEREO LOOR A BOLIVIA JUNIO 11-1943" (like Nos. C111-C113)

1943, June 11　　　**Perf. 13**

C105	A146	50c dp red violet	.40	.20
C106	A147	1s copper red	.60	.20
C107	A148	2s dark green	.70	.20

Nos. C105-C107 (3) 1.70 .60

Visit of Pres. Eurique Penaranda of Bolivia.
Vertical overprints on Nos. C105-C106.

Nos. 374-376 Overprinted "AEREO LOOR A PARAGUAY JULIO 5-1943" (like Nos. C111-C113)

1943, July 5

C108	A146	50c dp red violet	.40	.20
a.		Double overprint	75.00	
C109	A147	1s copper red	1.00	.50
C110	A148	2s dark green	1.40	.70

Nos. C108-C110 (3) 2.80 1.40

Visit of Pres. Higinio Morinigo of Paraguay.
Vertical overprints on Nos. C108-C109.

Nos. 374-376 Overprinted in Black

1943, July 23

C111	A146	50c dp red violet	.40	.20
C112	A147	1s copper red	.60	.20
C113	A148	2s dark green	.70	.20

Nos. C111-C113 (3) 1.70 .60

Issued to commemorate the visit of President Isaias Medina Angarita of Venezuela. Vertical overprint on Nos. C111-C112.
See Nos. C105-C110.

President Arroyo del Rio Addressing US Congress — AP26

1943, Oct. 9　　　**Perf. 12**

C114	AP26	50c dark brown	.90	.50
C115	AP26	70c brt rose	1.20	.50
C116	AP26	3s dark blue	1.40	.65
C117	AP26	5s dark green	3.00	1.20
C118	AP26	10s olive black	12.00	4.25

Nos. C114-C118 (5) 18.50 7.10

Good will tour of Pres. Arroyo del Rio in 1942.
For surcharges see Nos. CB1-CB5.

1944, Feb. 7

C119	AP26	50c dp red lilac	.90	.65
C120	AP26	70c red brown	1.75	.65
C121	AP26	3s turq green	1.75	.65
C122	AP26	5s brt ultra	2.90	1.40
C123	AP26	10s scarlet	3.50	1.60

Nos. C119-C123 (5) 10.80 4.95
Nos. C114-C123 (10) 29.30 12.05

Church of San Francisco, Quito — AP27

1944, Feb. 13

C124	AP27	70c turq green	1.90	.45
C125	AP27	1s olive	1.90	.45
C126	AP27	3s red orange	4.25	.90
C127	AP27	5s carmine rose	5.25	1.10

Nos. C124-C127 (4) 13.30 2.90

See note after No. 433.

Palace Type
1944　　　**Engr.**　　　**Perf. 11**

C128	A173	3s orange	1.00	.20
C129	A173	5s dark brown	1.75	.20
C130	A173	10s dark red	4.00	.20

Nos. C128-C130 (3) 6.75 .60

See No. C221. For overprints and surcharges see Nos. 541, C136-C138, C210-C213, C218-C220, C223-C224, C277-C279.

Red Cross Type
1945, Apr. 25　Unwmk.　Perf. 12
Cross in Rose

C131	A174	2s deep blue	4.00	.70
C132	A174	3s green	4.50	.85
C133	A174	5s dark violet	6.50	1.10
C134	A174	10s carmine rose	21.00	3.75

Nos. C131-C134 (4) 36.00 6.40

No. RA55 Surcharged in Black

1945, June 8

C135	PT21	40c on 5c blue	1.00	.20
a.		Double surcharge	10.00	

Counterfeits exist.

Nos. C128-C130 Overprinted in Green

1945, Sept. 6   *Perf. 11*
C136 A173 3s orange   1.00 .50
   a.   Inverted overprint   50.00
   b.   Double overprint   50.00
C137 A173 5s dark brown   1.25 .65
C138 A173 10s dark red   3.25 1.25
   Nos. C136-C138 (3)   5.50 2.40

Nos. C61-C63 Overprinted in Dark Blue and Gold like Nos. 444-446

1945, Oct. 2   *Perf. 12*
Center Multicolored
C139 AP8 50c violet   1.25 .25
C140 AP8 1s black   1.50 1.50
C141 AP8 2s violet   2.25 1.90
   Nos. C139-C141 (3)   5.00 3.65

Visit of Pres. Juan Antonio Rios of Chile.

Monument to Liberty — AP30

1945, Nov. 14   *Engr.*
C142 AP30 30c blue   .40 .20
C143 AP30 40c rose carmine   .40 .20
C144 AP30 1s dull violet   1.20 .45
C145 AP30 3s gray black   2.25 1.10
C146 AP30 5s purple brown   3.25 1.60
   Nos. C142-C146 (5)   7.50 3.55

Gen. Antonio Jose de Sucre, 150th birth anni.

> **Catalogue values for unused stamps in this section, from this point to the end of the section, are for Never Hinged items.**

Highway Type
1946, Apr. 22   *Unwmk.*
C147 A176 1s carmine rose   1.20 .40
C148 A176 2s violet   1.40 .70
C149 A176 3s turq green   2.00 1.00
C150 A176 5s red orange   2.75 1.20
C151 A176 10s dark blue   3.75 1.00
   Nos. C147-C151 (5)   11.10 4.30

Revolution Types
1946, Aug. 9   *Perf. 12½*
C152 A177 40c deep claret   .25 .20
C153 A178 1s sepia   .25 .20
C154 A179 2s indigo   .70 .20
C155 A180 3s olive green   1.20 .45
   Nos. C152-C155 (4)   2.40 1.05

National Union of Periodicals, Initials and Quill Pen — AP36

1946, Sept. 16
C156 AP36 50c dull purple   1.00 .60
C157 AP36 70c dark green   1.20 .60
C158 AP36 3s red   2.25 1.00
C159 AP36 5s indigo   3.00 1.20
C160 AP36 10s chocolate   9.00 1.75
   Nos. C156-C160 (5)   16.45 5.15

Campaign for adult education.

The Blessed Mariana Teaching Children — AP37

"Lily of Quito" — AP38

1946, Nov. 28   *Unwmk.*
C161 AP37 40c chocolate   .40 .40
C162 AP37 60c deep blue   .70 .70
C163 AP38 3s orange yellow   1.30 1.10
C164 AP38 5s green   3.00 1.50
   Nos. C161-C164 (4)   5.40 3.70

300th anniv. of the death of the Blessed Mariana de Jesus Paredes y Flores.

Rocafuerte Type
60c-1.10s, Jual de Velasco. 1.30s-2s, Riobamba Irrigation Canal.

1947, Nov. 27   *Perf. 12*
C165 A185 60c dark green   .40 .20
C166 A185 70c purple   .40 .20
C167 A185 1s black brown   .40 .20
C168 A185 1.10s car rose   .40 .20
C169 A185 1.30s deep blue   .40 .20
C170 A185 1.90s olive bister   1.00 .20
C171 A185 2s olive green   1.00 .20
   Nos. C165-C171 (7)   4.00 1.40

For overprints & surcharges see #C175, C181, C207-C209, C215, C216-C217, C222, C235.

Bello Type
1948, Apr. 21   *Perf. 13*
C172 A188 60c magenta   .40 .20
C173 A188 1.30s dk blue grn   .70 .20
C174 A188 1.90s dk rose car   .60 .25
   Nos. C172-C174 (3)   1.70 .65

No. C166 Overprinted in Black

1948, May 24   *Perf. 12*
C175 A185 70c purple   1.00 .35

Columbus — AP42

1948, May 26   *Perf. 14*
C176 AP42 50c olive green   .80 .80
C177 AP42 70c rose carmine   .80 .80
C178 AP42 3s ultra   2.75 2.40
C179 AP42 5s brown   3.50 3.50
C180 AP42 10s deep violet   12.00 4.00
   Nos. C176-C180 (5)   19.85 11.50

See note after No. 495.

No. C169 Overprinted in Carmine like No. 496 (MANANA reads up)

1948, Aug. 26   *Unwmk.*   *Perf. 12*
C181 A185 1.30s deep blue   .80 .25

National Fair of Today and Tomorrow, 1948.

Elia Liut and Telegrafo I AP43

Teacher and Pupils AP44

1948, Sept. 10   *Perf. 12½*
C182 AP43 60c rose red   1.00 .20
C183 AP43 1s green   1.00 .25
C184 AP43 1.30s deep claret   1.00 .25
C185 AP43 1.90s deep violet   1.00 .25
C186 AP43 2s dark brown   1.50 .30
C187 AP43 5s blue   2.75 .50
   Nos. C182-C187 (6)   8.25 1.75

25th anniv. (in 1945) of the 1st postal flight in Ecuador.

1948, Oct. 12   *Perf. 14*
C188 AP44 50c violet   1.75 .60
C189 AP44 70c deep blue   1.75 .60
C190 AP44 3s dark green   3.50 1.60
C191 AP44 5s red   5.00 2.10
C192 AP44 10s brown   9.00 2.75
   Nos. C188-C192 (5)   21.00 7.65

Campaign for adult education.

AP45

Franklin D. Roosevelt and Two of "Four Freedoms" — AP46

1948, Oct. 24   *Perf. 12½*
C193 AP45 60c emer & org brn   .40 .25
C194 AP45 1s car rose & slate   .40 .25
C195 AP46 1.50s grn & red brn   .40 .25
C196 AP46 2s red & black   1.10 .25
C197 AP46 5s ultra & blk   2.25 .25
   Nos. C193-C197 (5)   4.55 1.25

Maldonado Types
1948, Nov. 17
C198 A196 60c dp org & rose car   .80 .20
C199 A197 90c red & gray blk   .80 .20
C200 A196 1.30s pur & dp org   1.50 .20
C201 A197 2s dp bl & dull grn   1.50 .20
   Nos. C198-C201 (4)   4.60 .80

See note after No. 519.

Juan Montalvo and Cervantes AP47

Don Quixote — AP48

1949, May 2   *Engr.*   *Perf. 12½x12*
C202 AP47 1.30s ol brn & ultra   5.00 2.50
C203 AP48 1.90s grn & rose car   1.20 .30
C204 AP47 3s vio & org brn   1.80 .30
C205 AP48 5s red & gray blk   3.00 .20
C206 AP47 10s red lil & aqua   5.00 .20
   Nos. C202-C206 (5)   16.00 3.50

400th anniv. of the birth of Miguel de Cervantes Saavedra, novelist, playwright and poet, and the 60th anniv. of the death of Juan Montalvo (1832-89), Ecuadorean writer. For surcharges see Nos. C225-C226.

No. C168 Surcharged in Blue

1949, June 15   *Perf. 12*
C207 A185 50c on 1.10s car rose   .40 .20
C208 A185 60c on 1.10s car rose   .40 .20
C209 A185 90c on 1.10s car rose   .60 .20
   Nos. C207-C209 (3)   1.40 .60

2nd Eucharistic Cong., Quito, June 1949.

No. C128 Surcharged in Black

1949, Oct. 11   *Perf. 11*
C210 A173 60c on 3s orange   .90 .60
   a.   Double surcharge   30.00
C211 A173 90c on 3s orange   .90 .20
C212 A173 1s on 3s orange   1.10 .60
C213 A173 2s on 3s orange   2.50 .60
   Nos. C210-C213 (4)   5.40 2.00

"SUCRE(S)" in capitals on Nos. C212-C213. 75th anniv. of the UPU.

AP49

Black Surcharge

1950   *Unwmk.*   *Perf. 12*
C214 AP49 60c on 50c gray   .75 .20
   a.   Double surcharge   15.00

No. C170 Surcharged with New Value in Black
C215 A185 90c on 1.90s ol bis   .75 .20

Nos. C168, C128-C129 and Type of 1944 Surcharged or Overprinted in Black or Carmine

1950, Feb. 10   *Perf. 12*
C216 A185 50c on 1.10s   1.75 1.75
C217 A185 70c on 1.10s   2.25 1.75

    Perf. 11
C218 A173 3s orange   3.25 3.00
C219 A173 5s dark brown (C)   5.00 2.50
C220 A173 10s violet (C)   7.50 3.00
   Nos. C216-C220 (5)   19.75 12.00

Issued to publicize adult education. For overprint see No. 541.

Govt. Palace Type of 1944
1950, May 15   *Engr.*   *Perf. 11*
C221 A173 10s violet   2.25 .20

For surcharges see Nos. C277-C279.

No. C169 Surcharged with New Value in Black

1950   *Perf. 12*
C222 A185 90c on 1.30s dp blue   .40 .20

See No. C235.

Nos. C128-C129 Overprinted in Black

1951, July 28   Unwmk.   Perf. 11
C223 A173 3s orange   1.90   .95
C224 A173 5s dark brown   3.75 1.75

   20,000th crossing of the equator by Pan American-Grace Airways planes.

Nos. C202-C203 Surcharged in Black

CAMPAÑA
ALFABETIZACIÓN
1,00 Sucre 1,00

1951   Unwmk.   Perf. 12½x12
C225 AP47 60c on 1.30s   .50   .20
C226 AP48 1s on 1.90s   .50   .20
  a.   Inverted surcharge   20.00

   Issued to publicize adult education.

St. Mariana de
Jesus — AP50

1952, Feb. 15   Engr.
C227 AP50 60c plum & aqua   1.10   .40
C228 AP50 90c dk grn & lt ultra   1.30   .40
C229 AP50 1s car & dk grn   1.40   .40
C230 AP50 2s indigo & rose lil   1.40   .40
   Nos. C227-C230 (4)   5.20 1.60

   Canonization of Mariana de Jesus Paredes y Flores.

Plaza Visit to US Issue

3s, as No. 558. 5s, as No. 559.

1952, Mar. 26   Perf. 12
C231 A205 3s lilac & bl grn   1.00   .70
C232 A205 5s red brn & ol gray   2.00 2.00
  a.   Souv. sheet of 2, #C231-C232   4.50   9.00

Consular Service Stamps Surcharged
"AEREO" and New Value in Black

1952   Unwmk.   Perf. 12
C233 R2 60c on 1s green   .50   .20
C234 R2 1s on 1s green   .50   .20

   Type R2 illustrated above No. 545.

**No. C169 Surcharged with New
Value in Carmine**
C235 A185 90c on 1.30s dp bl   .50   .20
   Nos. C233-C235 (3)   1.50   .60

   See No. C222.

Pres. José M.
Urvina and
Allegory of
Freedom
AP52

Torch of
Knowledge
AP53

Hyphen-hole Perf. 7x6½
1952, Nov. 18   Litho.
C236 AP52 60c rose red & blue   6.00 1.20
C237 AP52 90c lilac & red   6.00 1.40
C238 AP52 1s orange & green   6.00   .40
C239 AP52 2s red brn & blue   6.00   .80
   Nos. C236-C239 (4)   24.00 3.80

   Centenary of abolition of slavery in Ecuador. Counterfeits exist.

Unwmk.
1953, Apr. 13   Engr.   Perf. 12
   Design: 2s, Aged couple studying alphabet.
C240 AP53 1s dark blue   1.75   .20
C241 AP53 2s red orange   2.25   .20

   1952 adult education campaign.

Globe
Showing Part
of Western
Hemisphere
AP54

1953, June 5   Perf. 12½x12
C242 AP54 60c orange yellow   .40   .20
C243 AP54 90c dark blue   .70   .35
C244 AP54 3s carmine   1.10   .45
   Nos. C242-C244 (3)   2.20 1.00

   Issued to publicize the crossing of the equator by the Pan-American highway.

Consular Service Stamps Surcharged
in Black

   a   b

1953-54   Perf. 12
C245 R1 (a) 60c on 2s brown   .35   .20
C246 R2 (a) 60c on 5s sep ('54)   .35   .20
C247 R2 (a) 70c on 5s sep ('54)   .35   .20
C248 R2 (a) 90c on 50c car rose
            ('54)   .35   .20
C249 R1 (b) 1s on 2s brown   .35   .20
C250 R1 (a) 1s on 2s brn ('54)   .35   .20
C251 R1 (a) 2s on 2s brn ('54)   .65   .20
C252 R1 (a) 3s on 5s vio ('54)   .90   .20
   Nos. C245-C252 (8)   3.65 1.60

   Surcharge is horizontal on Nos. C245, C247 and C248.

Carlos Maria
Cardinal de la
Torre — AP55

Queen Isabella
I — AP56

1954, Jan. 13   Photo.   Perf. 8½
Center in Black
C253 AP55 60c rose lilac   .75   .60
C254 AP55 90c green   1.00   .60
C255 AP55 3s orange   1.50   .60
   Nos. C253-C255 (3)   3.25 1.80

   1st anniv. of the elevation of Archbishop de la Torre to Cardinal.

1954, Apr. 22
C256 AP56 60c dk grn & grn   .60   .60
C257 AP56 90c lil rose   .60   .60
C258 AP56 1s blk & pale lil   .60   .60
C259 AP56 2s blk brn & pale bl   1.20   .60
C260 AP56 5s blk brn & buff   3.00   .60
   Nos. C256-C260 (5)   6.00 3.00

   See note with No. 585.

Post Office,
Guayaquil
AP57

1954, May 19   Engr.   Perf. 12½x12
Black Surcharge
C261 AP57 80c on 20c red   .30   .20
C262 AP57 1s on 20c red   .30   .20

   25th anniversary of Pan American-Grace Airways' operation in Ecuador.

Plane, Gateway
and
Wheel — AP58

Unwmk.
1954, Aug. 2   Litho.   Perf. 11
C263 AP58 80c blue   .35   .20

   Day of the Postal Employee.

San Pablo
Lagoon
AP59

1954, Sept. 24   Photo.
C264 AP59 60c orange   .30   .20
C265 AP59 70c rose pink   .30   .20
C266 AP59 90c dp grn   .30   .20
C267 AP59 1s dk gray grn   .30   .20
C268 AP59 2s blue   .40   .20
C269 AP59 3s yel brn   .65   .20
   Nos. C264-C269 (6)   2.25 1.20

Glorification
of Abdon
Calderon
Garaicoa
AP60

Capt.
Calderon — AP61

1954, Oct. 1
C270 AP60 80c rose pink   .55   .20
C271 AP61 90c blue   .55   .20

   150th anniversary of the birth of Capt. Abdon Calderon Garaicoa.

El Cebollar
College
AP62

Brother Miguel
Instructing
Boys — AP63

   Designs: 90c, Francisco Febres Cordero (Brother Miguel). 2.50s, Tomb of Brother Miguel. 3s, Monument to Brother Miguel.

1954, Dec. 3   Unwmk.   Perf. 11
C272 AP62 70c dk grn   .25   .20
C273 AP63 80c dk brn   .25   .20
C274 AP63 90c dk gray bl   .25   .20
C275 AP63 2.50s indigo   .45   .20
C276 AP62 3s lil rose   .65   .35
   Nos. C272-C276 (5)   1.85 1.15

   Centenary of the birth of Francisco Febres Cordero (Brother Miguel).

No. C221 Surcharged in Various
Colors

1955, May 25
C277 A173 1s on 10s vio (Bk)   .30   .20
C278 A173 1.70s on 10s vio (C)   .50   .20
C279 A173 4.20s on 10s vio (Br)   .80   .35
   Nos. C277-C279 (3)   1.60   .75

   Denomination in larger type on No. C279. National Exhibition of Daily Periodicals.

"La
Rotonda,"
Guayaquil,
and Rotary
Emblem
AP64

   Design: 90c, Eugenio Espejo hospital, Quito, and Rotary emblem.

1955, July 9   Engr.   Perf. 12½
C280 AP64 80c dark brown   .25   .25
C281 AP64 90c dark grown   .35   .35

   50th anniv. of the founding of Rotary Intl.

José Abel
Castillo
AP65

   2s, 5s, José Abel Castillo, Map of Ecuador.

1955, Oct. 19   Perf. 11x11½
C282 AP65 60c chocolate   1.60   .20
C283 AP65 90c light olive green   1.60   .20
C284 AP65 1s lilac   2.50   .20
C285 AP65 2s vermilion   2.75   .70
C286 AP65 5s ultra   5.75   .55
   Nos. C282-C286 (5)   14.20 1.85

   See note after No. 595.

No. C29 Surcharged in Black

1955, Oct. 24   *Perf. 12*
C287 AP1 1s on 5s purple   1.00 .20

A similar surcharge on No. C29, set in two lines with letters 5mm high and no X's or black-out line of squares, was privately applied.

San Pablo, Imbabura — AP66

50s, Rumichaca Caves. 1.30s, Virgin of Quito. 1.50s, Cotopaxi Volcano. 1.70s, Tungurahua Volcano, Tungurahua. 1.90s, Guanacos. 2.40s, Mat market. 2.50s, Ruins at Incapirca. 4.20s, El Carmen, Cuenca, Azuay. 4.80s, Santo Domingo Church.

1956, Jan. 2   Photo.   Perf. 13
C288 AP66 50c slate blue   2.75 .20
C289 AP66 1s ultra   2.75 .20
C290 AP66 1.30s crimson   4.25 .20
C291 AP66 1.50s dp grn   2.75 .20
C292 AP66 1.70s yel brn   1.75 .20
C293 AP66 1.90s olive   3.50 .20
C294 AP66 2.40s red org   3.75 .20
C295 AP66 2.50s violet   3.75 .20
C296 AP66 4.20s black   4.75 .20
C297 AP66 4.80s yel org   7.50 .30
      Nos. C288-C297 (10)   37.50 2.10

See Nos. C310-C311. For surcharges see Nos. 766A, 766G.

Honorato Vazquez — AP67   Title Page of First Book — AP68

1956, May 28   Engr.
Various Portraits
C298 AP67 1s yellow green   .50 .20
C299 AP67 1.50s red   .50 .20
C300 AP67 1.70s bright blue   .50 .20
C301 AP67 1.90s slate blue   .50 .20
      Nos. C298-C301 (4)   2.00 .80

Birth centenary (in 1955) of Honorato Vazquez, statesman.

1956, Aug. 27   Unwmk.   Perf. 13½
C302 AP68 1s black   .60 .20
C303 AP68 1.70s slate bl   .60 .20
C304 AP68 2s blk brn   .60 .20
C305 AP68 3s redsh brn   .60 .20
      Nos. C302-C305 (4)   2.40 .80

Bicentenary of printing in Ecuador.

Hands Reaching for UN Emblem AP69

1956, Oct. 24   Perf. 14
C307 AP69 1.70s red org   1.00 .20

10th anniv. of the UN (in 1955). See Nos. C319. For overprint see No. C426.

Coat of Arms and Basketball Player — AP70

Designs: 1.70s, Map of South America with flags and girl basketball players.

1956, Dec. 28 Photo.   Perf. 14½x14
C308 AP70 1s red lilac   .50 .20
C309 AP70 1.70s deep green   .75 .20

6th South American Women's Basketball Championship, Aug. 1956.

Scenic Type of 1956
1957, Jan. 2   Perf. 13
C310 AP66 50c bl grn   1.75 .20
C311 AP66 1s orange   1.75 .20

Type of Regular Issue, 1957
Designs: 50c, Map of Cuenca, 16th century. 80c, Cathedral of Cuenca. 1s, Modern City Hall.

Unwmk.
1957, Apr. 7   Photo.   Perf. 12
C312 A219 50c brn, *cr*   .20 .20
   a.   Souvenir sheet of 4   1.00 1.00
C313 A219 80c red, *bluish*   .25 .20
C314 A219 1s pur, *yel*   .30 .20
   a.   Souvenir sheet of 3   2.00 2.00
      Nos. C312-C314 (3)   .75 .60

No. C312a contains 4 imperf. 50c stamps similar to No. 613, but inscribed "AEREO" and printed in green. The sheet is printed on white ungummed paper.
No. C314a contains 3 imperf. stamps in designs similar to Nos. C312-C314, but with colors changed to orange (50c), brown (80c), violet (1s). The sheet is printed on white ungummed paper.

Gabriela Mistral — AP71   Arms of Espejo, Carchi — AP72

Unwmk.
1957, Sept. 18   Litho.   Perf. 14
C315 AP71 2s lt bl, blk & red   .40 .20

Issued to honor Gabriela Mistral (1889-1957), Chilean poet and educator. See Nos. C406-C407.

1957, Nov. 16   Perf. 14½x13½
Arms of Cantons: 2s, Montufar. 4.20s, Tulcan.

Coat of Arms Multicolored
C316 AP72 1s carmine   .40 .20
C317 AP72 2s black   .40 .20
C318 AP72 4.20s ultra   .75 .20
      Nos. C316-C318 (3)   1.55 .60

Province of Carchi.
See Nos. C334-C337, C355-C364, C392-C395. For surcharge see No. 766.

Redrawn UN Type of 1956
1957, Dec. 10   Engr.   Perf. 14
C319 AP69 2s greenish blue   .40 .25

Honoring the UN. Dates, as on No. C307, are omitted; inscribed: "Homenaje a las Naciones Unidas."

Mater Dolorosa, San Gabriel College — AP73   Rafael Maria Arizaga — AP74

#C321, 1s, Door of San Gabriel College, Quito.

1958, Apr. 27   Engr.   Perf. 14
C320 AP73 30c rose cl, *dp rose*   .25 .20
C321 AP73 30c rose cl, *dp rose*   .25 .20
   a.   Pair, #C320-C321   .60 .60
C322 AP73 1s dk bl, *lt bl*   .25 .20
C323 AP73 1.70s dk bl, *lt bl*   .25 .20
   a.   Pair, #C322-C323   .60 .60

Miracle of San Gabriel College, Quito, 50th anniv.

1958, July 21   Litho.
C324 AP74 1s multi   .30 .20

Rafael Maria Arizaga (1858-1933), writer. See Nos. C343, C350, C412.

Daule River Bridge AP75

1958, July 25   Engr.   Perf. 13½x14
C325 AP75 1.30s green   .35 .20

Issued to commemorate the opening of the River Daule bridge in Guayas province. See Nos. C367-C369.

Basketball Player — AP76

Symbolical of the Eucharist — AP77

1958, Sept. 1   Photo. Perf. 14x13½
C326 AP76 1.30s dk grn & lt brn   .35 .30

South American basketball championships. For surcharge see No. 774A.

1958, Sept. 25   Litho.   Unwmk.
Design: 60c, Cathedral of Guayaquil.
C327 AP77 10c vio & buff   .35 .20
C328 AP77 60c org & vio brn   .35 .20
C329 AP77 1s brn & lt bl   .35 .20
      Nos. C327-C329 (3)   1.05 .60

Souvenir Sheet

Symbolical of the Eucharist — AP78

Perf. 13½x14
C330 AP78 Sheet of 4   1.75 1.50
   a.-d.   40c dark blue, any single .20 .20

3rd National Eucharistic Congress.

Stamps of 1865 and 1920 — AP79

Designs: 2s, Stamps of 1920 and 1948. 4.20s, Municipal museum and library.

1958, Oct. 8   Photo.   Perf. 11½
Granite Paper
C331 AP79 1.30s grn & brn red   .20 .20
C332 AP79 2s bl & vio   .50 .30
C333 AP79 4.20s dk brn   .60 .40
      Nos. C331-C333 (3)   1.30 .90

National Philatelic Exposition (EXFIGUA), Guayaquil, Oct. 4-14.
For surcharge see No. 774.

Coat of Arms Type of 1957
Province of Imbabura
Arms of Cantons: 50c, Cotacachi. 60c, Antonio Ante. 80c, Otalvo. 1.10s, Ibarra.

1958, Nov. 9 Litho. Perf. 14½x13½
Coats of Arms Multicolored
C334 AP72 50c blk & red   .35 .20
C335 AP72 60c blk, bl & red   .35 .20
C336 AP72 80c blk & yel   .35 .20
C337 AP72 1.10s blk & red   .35 .20
      Nos. C334-C337 (4)   1.40 .80

Charles V — AP80   Paul Rivet — AP81

Engr. & Photo.
1958, Dec. 12   Perf. 14x13½
C338 AP80 2s brn red & dk brn   .30 .20
C339 AP80 4.20s dk gray & red brn   .40 .30

400th anniv. of the death of Charles V, Holy Roman Emperor.

1958, Dec. 29   Photo.   Perf. 11½
Granite Paper
C340 AP81 1s brown   .30 .20

Issued in honor of Paul Rivet (1876-1958), French anthropologist.

1959, May 6
Portrait: 2s, Alexander von Humboldt.
C341 AP81 2s slate   .25 .20

Cent. of the death of Alexander von Humboldt, German naturalist and geographer.

Front Page of "El Telegrafo" — AP82

1959, Feb.   Litho.   Perf. 13½
C342 AP82 1.30s bl grn & blk   .25 .20

75th anniv. of Ecuador's oldest newspaper.

Portrait Type of 1958
José Luis Tamayo (1858-1947), lawyer.

1959, June 26   Unwmk.   Perf. 14
Portrait Multicolored
C343 AP74 1.30s lt grn, bl & sal   .30 .20

El Sagrario &
House of
Manuela
Canizares
AP83

Condor — AP84

Designs: 80c, Hall at San Agustin. 1s, First
words of the constitutional act. 2s, Entrance to
Cuartel Real. 4.20s, Allegory of Liberty.

Unwmk.

1959, Aug. 28	**Photo.**	**Perf. 14**	
C344	AP83	20c ultra & lt brn	.25	.20
C345	AP83	80c brt bl & dp org	.25	.20
C346	AP83	1s dk red & dk ol	.25	.20
C347	AP84	1.30s brt bl & org	.25	.20
C348	AP84	2s ultra & org brn	.25	.20
C349	AP84	4.20s scar & brt bl	.40	.30
	Nos. C344-C349 (6)		1.65	1.30

Sesquicentennial of the revolution.

Portrait Type of 1958

1s, Alfredo Baquerizo Moreno (1859-1951),
statesman.

1959, Sept. 26	**Litho.**	**Perf. 14**
C350	AP74	1s gray, red & salmon	.30	.20

Pope
Pius XII — AP85

1959, Oct. 9	**Unwmk.**	**Perf. 14½**
C351	AP85	1.30s multi	.35	.20

Issued in memory of Pope Plus XII.

Flags of Argentina, Bolivia, Brazil,
Guatemala, Haiti, Mexico and
Peru — AP86

Flags of: 80c, Chile, Costa Rica, Cuba,
Dominican Republic, Panama, Paraguay,
United States. 1.30s, Colombia, Ecuador,
Honduras, Nicaragua, Salvador, Uruguay,
Venezuela.

1959, Oct. 12		**Perf. 13½.**
C352	AP86	50c multi	.20	.20
C353	AP86	80c yel, red & bl	.20	.20
C354	AP86	1.30s multi	.35	.20
	Nos. C352-C354 (3)		.75	.60

Organization of American States.
For overprints see #C423-C425, CO19-
CO21.

Arms of the Cantons Type of 1957
Province of Pichincha

10c, Rumiñahui. 40c, Pedro Moncayo. 1s,
Mejia. 1.30s, Cayambe. 4.20s, Quito.

			Perf. 14½x13½	
1959-60		**Unwmk.**	**Litho.**	
Coat of Arms Multicolored				
C355	AP72	10c blk & dk red ('60)	.35	.20
C356	AP72	40c blk & yel	.35	.20
C357	AP72	1s blk & brn ('60)	.35	.20
C358	AP72	1.30s blk & grn ('60)	.35	.20
C359	AP72	4.20s blk & org	.35	.20
	Nos. C355-C359 (5)		1.75	1.00

Province of Cotopaxi

40c, Pangua. 60c, Pujili. 70c, Saquisili. 1s,
Salcedo. 1.30s, Latacunga.

1960			
Coat of Arms Multicolored			
C360	AP72	40c blk & car	.25	.20
C361	AP72	60c blk & bl	.25	.20
C362	AP72	70c blk & turq	.25	.20
C363	AP72	1s blk & red org	.25	.20
C364	AP72	1.30s blk & org	.30	.20
	Nos. C360-C364 (5)		1.30	1.00

Flags of American Nations — AP87

1960, Feb. 23		**Perf. 13x12½**
C365	AP87	1.30s multi	.20	.20
C366	AP87	2s multi	.20	.20

11th Inter-American Conference, Feb. 1960.

Bridge Type of 1958.

Bridges: No. C367, Juntas. No. C368, Sara-
cay. 2s, Railroad bridge, Ambato.

1960		**Litho.**	**Perf. 13½**
C367	AP75	1.30s chocolate	.25	.20

		Photo.	**Perf. 12½**
C368	AP75	1.30s emerald	.25	.20
C369	AP75	2s brown	.35	.20
	Nos. C367-C369 (3)		.85	.60

Building of three new bridges.

Bahia-Chone Road — AP88

Pres.
Camilo
Ponce
Enriquez
AP89

Designs: 4.20s, Public Works Building,
Cuenca. 5s, El Coca airport. 10s, New Harbor, Guayaquil.

1960, Aug.		**Litho.**	**Perf. 14**
C370	AP88	1.30s blk & dl yel	.20	.20
C371	AP88	4.20s rose car & lt grn	.30	.30
C372	AP88	5s dk brn & yel	.45	.35
C373	AP88	10s dk bl & bl	1.00	.35
		Perf. 11x11½	
C374	AP89	2s org brn & blk	1.40	.25
	Nos. C370-C374 (5)		3.35	1.45

Nos. C370-C374 publicize the achievements of Pres. Camilo Ponce Enriquez (1956-
1960).
Issued: #C370-C373, 8/24; #C374, 8/31.

Red Cross
Building, Quito
and Henri
Dunant
AP90

1960, Oct. 5		**Unwmk.**	**Perf. 13x14**
C375	AP90	2s rose vio & car	.45	.20

Centenary (in 1959) of Red Cross idea.

For overprint see No. C408.

El Belen
Church,
Quito — AP91

1961, Jan. 14		**Perf. 12½**
C376	AP91	3s multi	.40	.20

Ecuador's participation in the 1960 Barcelona Philatelic Congress.

Map of
Ecuador
and
Amazon
River
System
AP92

1961, Feb. 27		**Litho.**	**Perf. 10½**
C377	AP92	80c salmpn, claret & grn	.25	.20
C378	AP92	1.30s gray, slate & grn	.35	.20
C379	AP92	2s beige, red & grn	.50	.20
	Nos. C377-C379 (3)		1.10	.60

Amazon Week, and the 132nd anniversary
of the Battle of Tarqui against Peru.

Juan
Montalvo,
Juan Leon
Mera, Juan
Benigno
Vela — AP93

1961, Apr. 13		**Unwmk.**	**Perf. 13**
C380	AP93	1.30s salmon & blk	.35	.20

Centenary of Tungurahua province.

Hugo Ortiz
G. — AP94

1961, May 25		**Perf. 14x14½**
Design: No. C382, Ortiz monument.		
C381	AP94	1.30s grnsh bl, blk & yel	.25	.20
C382	AP94	1.30s grnsh bl, pur, ol & brn	.25	.20

Lt. Hugo Ortiz G., killed in battle 8/2/41.

Condor
and
Airplane
Stamp
of 1936
AP95

1.30s, Map of South America and stamp of
1865. 2s, Bolivar monument stamp of 1930.

	Perf. 10½		
1961, May 25		**Litho.**	**Unwmk.**
Size: 41x28mm			
C383	AP95	80c org & vio	.20	.20
Size: 41x34mm			
C384	AP95	1.30s bl, yel, ol & car	.30	.25
Size: 40½x37mm			
C385	AP95	2s car rose & blk	.45	.25
	Nos. C383-C385 (3)		.95	.70

Third National Philatelic Exhibition, Quito,
May 25-June 3, 1961.

Arms of Los
Rios and
Egret — AP96

1961, May 27		**Perf. 14½x13½**
Coat of Arms Multicolored		
C386	AP96	2s bl & blk	.35	.30

Centenary (in 1960) of Los Rios province.

Gabriel Garcia
Moreno — AP97

Remigio Crespo
Toral — AP98

1961, Sept. 24		**Unwmk.**	**Perf. 12**
C387	AP97	1s bl, brn & buff	.30	.20

Centenary of the restoration of national
integrity.

1961, Nov. 3		**Unwmk.**	**Perf. 14**
C388	AP98	50c multi	.30	.20

Centenary of the birth of Remigio Crespo
Toral, poet laureate of Ecuador.

Galapagos Islands Nos. LC1-LC3
Overprinted in Black or Red:
"Estacion de Biologia Maritima de
Galapagos" and "UNESCO 1961"
(Similar to #684-686)

1961, Oct. 31		**Photo.**	**Perf. 12**
C389	A1	1s dp bl	.35	.20
a.	"de Galapagos" on top line		2.00	2.00
C390	A1	1.80s rose vio	.60	.30
a.	UNESCO emblem omitted		1.25	1.25
C391	A1	4.20s blk (R)	.75	.55
	Nos. C389-C391 (3)		1.70	1.05

Establishment of maritime biological stations on Galapagos Islands by UNESCO.

Arms of the Cantons Type of 1957
Province of Tungurahua

50c, Pillaro. 1s, Pelileo. 1.30s, Baños. 2s,
Ambato.

		Perf. 14½x13½	
1962, Mar. 30	**Litho.**	**Unwmk.**	
Coats of Arms Multicolored			
C392	AP72	50c black	.20	.20
C393	AP72	1s black	.20	.20
C394	AP72	1.30s black	.25	.20
C395	AP72	2s black	.45	.20
	Nos. C392-C395 (4)		1.10	.80

Pres. Arosemena and Prince Philip,
Arms of Ecuador and Great Britain
and Equator Monument
AP99

	Perf. 14x13½	
1962, Feb. 17		**Wmk. 340**
C396	AP99	1.30s bl, sepia, red & yel	.20	.20
C397	AP99	2s multi	.35	.20

Visit of Prince Philip, Duke of Edinburgh, to
Ecuador, Feb. 17-20, 1962.

Mountain Farming — AP100

Perf. 12½
1963, Mar. 21   Unwmk.   Litho.
C398 AP100 30c emer, yel & blk   .20 .20
C399 AP100 3s dl red, grn & org   .50 .20
C400 AP100 4.20s blk, blk & yel   .70 .45
   Nos. C398-C400 (3)   1.40 .85

FAO "Freedom from Hunger" campaign. Exist imperf. Value $32.50.

Mosquito and Malaria Eradication Emblem AP101

1963, Apr. 17   Unwmk.   Perf. 12½
C401 AP101 50c multi   .20 .20
C402 AP101 80c multi   .20 .20
C403 AP101 2s multi   .30 .20
   Nos. C401-C403 (3)   .70 .60

WHO drive to eradicate malaria.

Stagecoach and Jet Plane AP102

1963, May 7   Litho.
C404 AP102 2s org & car rose   .30 .20
C405 AP102 4.20s claret & ultra   .50 .35

1st Intl. Postal Conference, Paris, 1863.

Type of 1957 Inscribed "Islas Galapagos," Surcharged with New Value and Overprinted "Ecuador" in Black or Red

1963, June 19   Unwmk.   Perf. 14
C406 AP71 5s on 2s gray, dk bl & red   .80 .60
C407 AP71 10s on 2s gray, dk bl & red (R)   1.40 1.40

The basic 2s exists without surcharge and overprint. No. C407 exists with "ECUADOR" omitted, and with both "ECUADOR" and "10 SUCRES" double.

No. C375 Overprinted: "1863-1963/Centenario/de la Fundación/ de la Cruz Roja/Internacional"

1963, June 21   Photo.   Perf. 13x14
C408 AP90 2s rose vio & car   .30 .20

Intl. Red Cross, centenary.

Type of Regular Issue, 1963
Arosemena and: 70c, Flags of Ecuador. 2s, Flags of Ecuador, Panama. 4s, Flags of Ecuador, US.

1963, July 1   Litho.   Perf. 14
C409 A238 70c pale bl & multi   .25 .20
C410 A238 2s pink & multi   .50 .20
C411 A238 4s lt bl & multi   1.25 .35
   Nos. C409-C411 (3)   2.00 .75

Imperfs exist. Value $15.

Portrait Type of 1958
Portrait: 2s, Dr. Mariano Cueva (1812-82).

Unwmk.
1963, July 4   Litho.   Perf. 14
C412 AP74 2s lt grn & multi   .35 .20

Social Insurance Symbol — AP103

Mother and Child — AP104

1963, July 9   Litho.
C413 AP103 10s brn, bl, gray & ocher   .90 .70

25th anniversary of Social Insurance. Exists imperf. Value $9.

1963, July 28   Perf. 12½
C414 AP104 1.30s org, dk bl & blk   .20 .20
C415 AP104 5s gray, red & brn   .45 .45

7th Pan-American and South American Pediatrics Congresses, Quito.

Simon Bolivar Airport, Guayaquil AP105

1963, July 25   Perf. 14
C416 AP105 60c gray   .20 .20
C417 AP105 70c dl grn   .20 .20
C418 AP105 5s brn vio   .50 .35
   Nos. C416-C418 (3)   .90 .75

Opening of Simon Bolivar Airport, Guayaquil, July 15, 1962. Exist imperf. Value $4.50.

Nos. 638, 640-641 Overprinted "AEREO"

1964   Perf. 12
Flags in National Colors
C419 A223 1.80s dl vio   .50 .35
C420 A224 2s dk brn   .50 .35
C421 A223 2.20s blk brn   .50 .35
   Nos. C419-C421 (3)   1.50 1.05

On 1.80s and 2.20s, "AEREO" is vertical, reading down.

No. 650 Overprinted in Gold: "FARO DE COLON / AEREO"

1964   Photo.   Perf. 14x13½
C422 A229 1.80s dk bl   2.50 1.50

Nos. C352-C354 Overprinted

Illustration reduced.

1964   Litho.   Perf. 13½
C423 AP86 50c bl & multi   .65 .45
C424 AP86 80c yel & multi   .65 .45
C425 AP86 1.30s pale grn & multi   .65 .45
   Nos. C423-C425 (3)   1.95 1.35

No. C307 Overprinted: "DECLARACION / DERECHOS HUMANOS / 1964 / XV-ANIV"

Unwmk.
1964, Sept. 29   Engr.   Perf. 14
C426 AP69 1.70s red org   .35 .20

15th anniversary (in 1963) of the Universal Declaration of Human Rights.

Banana Type
1964, Oct. 26   Litho.   Perf. 12½x12
C427 A241 4.20s blk, bis & gray ol   .30 .20
C428 A241 10s blk, scar & gray ol   .50 .40
  a.   Souv. sheet of 4   2.10 2.10

No. C428a contains imperf. stamps similar to Nos. 720-721 and C427-C428.

John F. Kennedy, Flag-draped Coffin and John Jr. — AP106

1964, Nov. 22   Litho.   Perf. 14
C429 AP106 4.20s multi   .85 .65
C430 AP106 5s multi   1.10 .80
C431 AP106 10s multi   2.00 1.10
  a.   Souv. sheet of 3   7.00 7.00
   Nos. C429-C431 (3)   3.95 2.55

President John F. Kennedy (1917-63). No. C431a contains stamps similar to Nos. C429-C431, imperf.

Olympic Type
1.30s, Gymnast, vert. 1.80s, Hurdler. 2s, Basketball.

Perf. 13½x14, 14x13½
1964, Dec. 16   Unwmk.
C432 A243 1.30s vio bl, ver & brn   .25 .20
C433 A243 1.80s vio bl & multi   .25 .20
C434 A243 2s red & multi   .25 .20
  a.   Souv. sheet of 4   2.90 2.90
   Nos. C432-C434 (3)   .75 .60

No. C434a contains stamps similar to Nos. 725 and C432-C434, imperf.

Sports Type
Torch and Athletes: 2s, 3s, Diver, gymnast, wrestlers and weight lifter. 2.50s, 4s, Bicyclists. 3.50s, 5s, Jumpers.

1965, Nov. 20   Litho.   Perf. 12x12½
C435 A247 2s bl, gold & blk   .50 .20
C436 A247 2.50s org, gold & blk   .50 .20
C437 A247 3s brt pink, gold & blk   .50 .20
C438 A247 3.50s lt vio, gold & bl   .55 .55
C439 A247 4s brt yel grn, gold & blk   .55 .20
C440 A247 5s red org, gold & blk   .60 .30
  a.   Souv. sheet of 12   8.00 8.00
   Nos. C435-C440 (6)   3.20 1.65

No. C440a contains 12 imperf. stamps similar to Nos. 738-743 and C435-C440. For surcharges see Nos. 766B, C449.

Bird Type
Birds: 1s, Yellow grosbeak. 1.30s, Black-headed parrot. 1.50s, Scarlet tanager. 2s, Sapphire quail-dove. 2.50s, Violet-tailed sylph. 3s, Lemon-throated barbet. 4s, Yellow-tailed oriole. 10s, Collared puffbird.

1966, June 17   Litho.   Perf. 13½
Birds in Natural Colors
C441 A249 1s lt red brn & blk   1.10 .20
C442 A249 1.30s pink & blk   1.10 .20
C443 A249 1.50s pale grn & blk   1.10 .20
C444 A249 2s sal & blk   2.25 .40
C445 A249 2.50s lt yel grn & blk   2.25 .40
C446 A249 3s sal & blk   3.25 .45
C447 A249 4s gray & blk   4.25 .70
C448 A249 10s beige & blk   6.50 1.75
   Nos. C441-C448 (8)   21.80 4.30

For surcharges see Nos. 766E-766F, C450, C455-C457.

Nos. C436 and C443 Surcharged

1967
C449 A247 80c on 2.50s multi   .45 .20
C450 A249 80c on 1.50s multi   .45 .20

Old denomination on No. C449 is obliterated with heavy bar; the surcharge on No. C450 includes "Resello" and an ornament over old denomination.

Peñaherrera Monument, Quito — AP107

Design: 2s, Peñaherrera statue.

1967, Dec. 29   Litho.   Perf. 12x12½
C451 AP107 1.30s blk & org   .25 .20
C452 AP107 2s blk & lt ultra   .25 .20

See note after No. 763.

Arosemena Type
1.30s, Inauguration. 2s, Pres. Arosemena speaking in Punta del Este.

1968, May 9   Litho.   Perf. 13½x14
C453 A251 1.30s multi   .25 .20
C454 A251 2s multi   .25 .20

No. C448 Surcharged in Plum, Dark Blue or Green

1969, Jan. 9   Litho.   Perf. 13½
Bird in Natural Colors
C455 A249 80c on 10s beige (P)   .50 .25
C456 A249 1s on 10s beige (DBl)   .50 .25
C457 A249 2s on 10s beige (G)   .50 .25
   Nos. C455-C457 (3)   1.50 .75

"Operation Friendship" AP108

1969-70   Typo.   Perf. 13½
C458 AP108 2s yel, blk, red & lt bl   .25 .20
  a.   Perf. 12½
C459 AP108 2s bl, blk, car & yel ('70)   .25 .20

Friendship campaign. Medallion background on Nos. C458 and C458a is blue; on No. C459, yellow. No. C459 exists imperf. Value $5.

No. 639 Surcharged in Gold "S/. 5 AEREO" and Bar

1969, Nov. 25   Litho.   Perf. 12
C460 A224 5s on 2s multi   1.60 .50

Butterfly Type
Butterflies: 1.30s, Morpho peleides. 1.50s, Anartia amathea.

1970   Litho.   Perf. 12½
C461 A255 1.30s multi   1.75 .20
C462 A255 1.50s pink & multi   1.75 .20

Same, White Background
1970   Perf. 13½
C463 A255 1.30s multi   1.75 .20
C464 A255 1.50s multi   1.75 .20

Arms Type
Provincial Arms and Flags: 1.30s, El Oro. 2s, Loja. 3s, Manabi. 5s, Pichincha. 10s, Guayas.

1971   Litho.   Perf. 10½
C465 A258 1.30s pink & multi   .30 .20
C466 A258 2s multi   .35 .20
C467 A258 3s multi   .55 .30
C468 A258 5s multi   .75 .35
C469 A258 10s multi   1.25 .40
   Nos. C465-C469 (5)   3.20 1.45

Presentation of the Virgin — AP109

Pres. Allende and Chilean Flag AP110

Art of Quito: 1.50s, Blessed Anne at Prayer. 2s, St. Theresa de Jesus. 2.50s, Altar of Carmen, horiz. 3s, Descent from the Cross. 4s, Christ of St. Mariana de Jesus. 5s, Shrine of St. Anthony. 10s, Cross of San Diego.

1971   Perf. 11½
Inscriptions in Black

C473	AP109	1.30s multi	.20	.20
C474	AP109	1.50s multi	.25	.20
C475	AP109	2s multi	.30	.20
C476	AP109	2.50s multi	.40	.20
C477	AP109	3s multi	.55	.20
C478	AP109	4s multi	.65	.20
C479	AP109	5s multi	.65	.35
C480	AP109	10s multi	1.50	.65
	Nos. C473-C480 (8)		4.50	2.20

1971, Aug. 24   Perf. 12½

2.10s, Pres. José M. Velasco Ibarra of Ecuador, Pres. Salvador Allende of Chile, national flags.

C481	AP110	2s multi	.25	.20
C482	AP110	2.10s multi	.25	.20

Visit of Pres. Salvador Allende of Chile, Aug. 24.

Globe and Emblem AP111

1971

C483	AP111	5s black	1.00	.35
C484	AP111	5.50s dl pur & blk	1.00	.35

Opening of Postal Museum, Aug. 24, 1971. Exist imperf. Value $7.50.

Pazmiño Type

1971, Sept. 16   Perf. 12x11½

C485	A260	1.50s grn & multi	.25	.20
C486	A260	2.50s grn & multi	.40	.20

AP112

AP113

Designs: 5s, Map of Americas. 10s, Converging roads and map. 20s, Map of Americas and Equator. 50s, Mountain road and monument on Equator.

1971   Perf. 11½

C487	AP112	5s org & multi	.85	.45
C488	AP112	10s org & blk	1.25	1.00
C489	AP112	20s blk, bl & brt rose	2.40	1.60
C490	AP112	50s bl, blk & gray	3.50	2.50
	Nos. C487-C490 (4)		8.00	5.55

11th Pan-American Road Congress. Issued: 5s, 10s, 50s, 11/15; 20s, 11/22. No. C488 exists imperf. Value $8.

1972

Design: 3s, Arms of Ecuador and Argentina. 5s, Presidents José M. Velasco Ibarra and Alejandro Agustin Lanusse.

C491	AP113	3s blk & multi	.25	.20
C492	AP113	5s blk & multi	.45	.30

Visit of Lt. Gen. Alejandro Agustin Lanusse, president of Argentina, Jan. 25.

Flame, Scales, Map of Americas AP114

1972, Apr. 24   Litho.   Perf. 12½

C493	AP114	1.30s bl & red	.30	.20

17th Conference of the Interamerican Federation of Lawyers, Quito, Apr. 24.

Religious Paintings Type of Regular Issue

Ecuadorian Paintings: 3s, Virgin of the Flowers, by Miguel de Santiago. 10s, Virgin of the Rosary, by Quito School.

1972, Apr. 24   Perf. 14x13½

C494	A263	3s blk & multi	.35	.35
C495	A263	10s blk & multi	1.25	.60
a.	Souv. sheet of 2, #C494-C495		1.50	1.50

1972, May 4

Ecuadorian Statues: 3s, St. Dominic, Quito School. 10s, St. Rosa of Lima, by Bernardo de Legarda.

C496	A263	3s blk & multi	.35	.35
C497	A263	10s blk & multi	1.25	.60
a.	Souv. sheet of 2, #C496-C497		2.50	2.10

Letters of "Ecuador" 3mm high on #C496-C497, 7mm high on #C494-C495.

Portrait Type

Designs (Generals, from Paintings): 1.30s, José Maria Saenz. 3s, Tomás Wright. 4s, Antonio Farfan. 5s, Antonio José de Sucre. 10s, Simon Bolivar. 20s, Arms of Ecuador.

1972, May 24

C498	A264	1.30s bl & multi	.20	.20
C499	A264	3s bl & multi	.25	.20
C500	A264	4s bl & multi	.30	.20
C501	A264	5s bl & multi	.50	.30
C502	A264	10s bl & multi	.90	.50
C503	A264	20s bl & multi	1.75	.90
	Nos. C498-C503 (6)		3.90	2.30

Artisan Type

Handicraft of Ecuador: 2s, Woman wearing flowered poncho. 3s, Striped poncho. 5s, Poncho with roses. 10s, Gold sunburst sculpture.

1972, July   Photo.   Perf. 13

C504	A265	2s multi	.30	.25
C505	A265	3s multi	.55	.30
C506	A265	5s multi	.85	.40
C507	A265	10s org red & multi	1.50	.95
a.	Souv. sheet of 4, #C504-C507		3.50	3.50
	Nos. C504-C507 (4)		3.20	1.90

Epidendrum Orchid — AP115

1972   Photo.   Perf. 12½

C508	AP115	4s shown	1.40	1.25
C509	AP115	6s Canna	1.75	1.50
C510	AP115	10s Jimson weed	3.25	3.00
a.	Souv. sheet of 3, #C508-C510		10.00	8.25
	Nos. C508-C510 (3)		6.40	5.75

Exists imperf.

Oil Drilling Towers — AP116

Coat of Arms — AP117

1972, Oct. 17   Litho.   Perf. 11½

C511	AP116	1.30s bl & multi	.25	.20

Ecuadorian oil industry.

1972, Nov. 18   Litho.   Perf. 11½
Arms Multicolored

C512	AP117	2s black	.25	.20
C513	AP117	3s black	.25	.20
C514	AP117	4s black	.30	.20
C515	AP117	4.50s black	.30	.20
C516	AP117	6.30s black	.65	.30
C517	AP117	6.90s black	.65	.30
	Nos. C512-C517 (6)		2.40	1.40

Pichincha Type

Designs: 2.40s, Corridor, San Agustin. 4.50s, La Merced Convent. 5.50s, Column base. 6.30s, Chapter Hall, San Agustin. 6.90s, Interior, San Agustin. 7.40s, Crucifixion, Cantuña Chapel. 7.90s, Decorated ceiling, San Agustin.

1972, Dec. 6   Wmk. 367

C518	A266	2.40s yel & multi	.30	.20
C519	A266	4.50s yel & multi	.45	.20
C520	A266	5.50s yel & multi	.55	.20
C521	A266	6.30s yel & multi	.60	.40
C522	A266	6.90s yel & multi	.65	.40
C523	A266	7.40s yel & multi	.75	.40
C524	A266	7.90s yel & multi	.80	.40
	Nos. C518-C524 (7)		4.10	2.20

UN Emblem — AP118

OAS Emblem — AP119

1973, Mar. 23   Unwmk.

C525	AP118	1.30s lt bl & blk	.25	.20

25th anniversary of the Economic Committee for Latin America (CEPAL).

1973, Apr. 14   Wmk. 367

C526	AP119	1.50s multi	.30	.20
a.	Unwatermarked		.30	.20

Day of the Americas and "Philately for Peace."

Bird Type

1973   Unwmk.   Perf. 11½x11

C527	A268	1.30s Blue-footed booby	2.10	.20
C528	A268	3s Brown pelican	2.10	.20

Presidents Lara and Caldera AP120

1973, June 15   Wmk. 367

C529	AP120	3s multi	.35	.20

Visit of Venezuela Pres. Rafael Caldera, Feb. 5-7.

Silver Coin, 1934 — AP121

Globe, OPEC Emblem, Oil Derrick — AP122

Ecuadorian Coins: 10s, Silver coin, obverse. 50s, Gold coin, 1928.

Unwmk.

1973, Dec. 14   Photo.   Perf. 14

C530	AP121	5s multi	.50	.35
C531	AP121	10s multi	.85	.55
C532	AP121	50s multi	4.00	2.25
a.	Souvenir sheet of 3		6.00	6.00
	Nos. C530-C532 (3)		5.35	3.15

No. C532a contains one each of Nos. C530-C532; Dated "1972." Exists imperf. Value, same.

A gold marginal overprint was applied in 1974 to No. C532a (perf. and imperf.): "X Campeonato Mundial de Football / Munich - 1974." Value, each $60.

A carmine overprint was applied in 1974 to No. C532a (perf. and imperf.): "Seminario de Telecommunicaciones Rurales, / Septiembre-1974 / Quito-Ecuador" and ITU emblem. Value, each $8.50.

1974, June 15   Litho.   Perf. 11½

C533	AP122	2s multi	.30	.20

Meeting of Organization of Oil Exporting Countries, Quito, June 15-24.

Ecuadorian Flag, UPU Emblem — AP123

1974, July 15   Litho.   Perf. 11½

C534	AP123	1.30s multi	.25	.20

Centenary of Universal Postal Union. Two 25s souvenir sheets exist. These were sold on a restricted basis. Value, each $40.

Teodoro Wolf AP124

Capt. Edmundo Chiriboga AP125

1974   Litho.   Perf. 12x11½

C535	AP124	1.30s blk & ultra	.20	.20
C536	AP125	1.50s gray	.25	.20

Teodoro Wolf, geographer; Edmundo Chiriboga, national hero. Issued: #C535, Nov. 29; #C536, Dec. 4.

Congress Emblem AP126

1974, Dec. 8   Litho.   Perf. 11½x12

C537	AP126	5s bl & multi	.35	.20

8th Inter-American Postmasters' Cong., Quito.

Map of Americas and Coat of Arms
AP127

Manuel J. Calle, Journalist
AP128

1975, Feb. 1   **Perf. 12x11½**
C538 AP127 3s bl & multi   .35 .20
EXFIGUA Stamp Exhibition and 5th General Assembly of Federation Inter-Americana de Filatelia, Guayaquil, Nov. 1973.

1975   **Perf. 12x11½**
#C540, Leopoldo Benites V., president of UN General Assembly, 1973-74; #C541, Adofo H. Simmonds G. (1892-1969), journalists; #C542, Juan de Dios Martinez Mera, President of Ecuador, birth centenary.

C539 AP128 5s lilac rose   .45 .20
C540 AP128 5s gray   .45 .20
C541 AP128 5s violet   .45 .30
C542 AP128 5s blk & rose red   .45 .20
     Nos. C539-C542 (4)   1.80 .90

Pres. Guillermo Rodriguez Lara — AP129

1975   **Unwmk.**   **Perf. 12**
C546 AP129 5s vermilion & blk   .50 .30
State visit of Pres. Guillermo Rodriguez Lara to Algeria, Romania and Venezuela.

Meeting Type of 1975
1.50s, Rafael Rodriguez Palacio & Argelino Duran Quintero meeting at border in Ruichacha. 2s, Signing border agreement.

1975, Apr. 1   **Litho.**   **Perf. 12x11½**
C547 A273 1.50s multi   .25 .20
C548 A273 2s multi   .25 .20

Sacred Heart (Painting) AP130

Quito Cathedral AP131

Design: 2s, Monstrance.

1975, Apr. 28   **Litho.**   **Perf. 12x11½**
C549 AP130 1.30s yel & multi   .20 .20
C550 AP130 2s bl & multi   .20 .20
C551 AP131 3s multi   .30 .20
     Nos. C549-C551 (3)   .70 .60
3rd Bolivarian Eucharistic Congress, Quito, June 9-16, 1974.

J. Delgado Panchana with Trophy — AP132

J. Delgado Panchana Swimming AP133

Perf. 12x11½, 11½x12
1975, June 12   **Unwmk.**
C552 AP132 1.30s bl & multi   .20 .20
C553 AP133 3s blk & multi   .30 .20
Jorge Delgado Panchana, South American swimming champion, 1971 and 1974.

Sports Type of 1975
1975, Sept. 11   **Litho.**   **Perf. 11½**
C554 A276 1.30s Tennis   .45 .25
C555 A276 2s Target shooting   .45 .25
C556 A276 2.80s Volleyball   .55 .25
C557 A276 3s Raft with sails   .55 .25
C558 A276 5s Mask   .80 .25
     Nos. C554-C558 (5)   2.80 1.25

Flower Type of 1975
1975, Nov. 18   **Litho.**   **Perf. 11½x12**
C559 A277 1.30s Pitcairnia
     pungens   .25 .25
C560 A277 2s Scarlet sage   .40 .25
C561 A277 3s Amaryllis   .60 .35
C562 A277 4s Opuntia
     quitense   .85 .40
C563 A277 5s Amaryllis   1.25 .60
     Nos. C559-C563 (5)   3.35 1.85

Tail Assemblies and Emblem — AP134

Planes over Map of Ecuador — AP135

1975, Dec. 17   **Litho.**   **Perf. 11½**
C564 AP134 1.30s bl & multi   .30 .20
C565 AP135 3s multi   .35 .20
TAME, Military Transport Airline, 13th anniv.

Benalcázar Statue — AP136

1976, Feb. 6   **Litho.**   **Perf. 11½**
C566 AP136 2s multi   .25 .20
C567 AP136 3s multi   .25 .20
Sebastián de Benalcázar (1495-1550), Spanish conquistador, founder of Quito.

Archaeology Type of 1975
1.30s, Seated man, Carchi Culture. 2s, Funerary urn, Tuncahuan Culture. 3s, Priest, Bahia de Caraquez Culture. 4s, Snail's shell, Cuasmal Culture. 5s, Bowl supported by figurines, Guangala Culture.

1976, Feb. 12   **Litho.**   **Perf. 11½**
C568 A278 1.30s multi   .20 .20
C569 A278 2s multi   .30 .20
C570 A278 3s multi   .45 .30
C571 A278 4s multi   .65 .30
C572 A278 5s multi   .85 .30
     Nos. C568-C572 (5)   2.45 1.30

Fruit Type of 1976
1976, Mar. 30
C573 A280 2s Apples   .40 .20
C574 A280 5s Rose   .60 .20

Lufthansa Jet — AP137

1976, June 25   **Litho.**   **Perf. 12**
C575 AP137 10s bl & multi   1.50 .35
Lufthansa, 50th anniversary.
An imperf. 20s miniature sheet exists, similar to No. C575 enlarged, with overprinted black bar covering line below "Lufthansa." Size: 90x115mm.

Projected PO, Quito — AP138

Fruit Peddler — AP139

1976, Aug. 10   **Litho.**   **Perf. 12**
C576 AP138 5s blk & multi   .30 .20
Design for new General Post Office, Quito.

1976, July 25
#C578, Longshoreman. #C579, Cerros del Carmen & Santa Ana, hills of Guayaquil, horiz. #C580, Sebastián de Belalcázar. #C581, Francisco de Orellana. #C582, Chief Guayas & his wife Quila.

C577 AP139 1.30s red & multi   .20 .20
C578 AP139 1.30s red & multi   .20 .20
C579 AP139 1.30s red & multi   .20 .20
C580 AP139 2s red & multi   .20 .20
C581 AP139 2s red & multi   .20 .20
C582 AP139 2s red & multi   .20 .20
     Nos. C577-C582 (6)   1.20 1.20
Founding of Guayaquil, 441st anniversary.

Emblem and Laurel AP140

1976, Aug. 9
C583 AP140 1.30s yel & multi   .25 .20
Bolivarian Soc. of Ecuador, 50th anniv.

Western Hemisphere and Equator Monument AP141

Congress Emblem AP142

1976, Sept. 6
C584 AP141 2s multi   .25 .20
Souvenir Sheet
Imperf
C585 AP141 5s multi   2.75 2.75
3rd Conf. of Pan-American Transport Ministers, Quito, Sept. 6-11. No. C585 contains design similar to No. C584 with black denomination and red control number in margin.

1976, Sept. 27   **Litho.**   **Perf. 11½**
C586 AP142 1.30s bl & multi   .30 .20
C587 AP142 3s bl & multi   .40 .30
Souvenir Sheet
Imperf
C588 AP142 10s bl & multi   1.50 1.00
10th Inter-American Congress of the Construction Industry, Quito, Sept. 27-30.

George Washington AP143

American Bicentennial: 5s, Naval battle, Sept. 23, 1779, in which the Bonhomme Richard, commanded by John Paul Jones, defeated and captured the Serapis, British man-of-war, off Yorkshire coast, horiz.

1976, Oct. 18   **Litho.**   **Perf. 12**
C589 AP143 3s blk & multi   .60 .30
C590 AP143 5s red brn & yel   .90 .45

Dr. Hideyo Noguchi — AP144

Luis Cordero — AP145

1976   **Litho.**   **Perf. 11½**
C591 AP144 3s yel & multi   .35 .20
Dr. Hideyo Noguchi (1876-1928), bacteriologist (at Rockefeller Institute). A 10s imperf. miniature sheet exists in same design without "Aereo." Size: 95x114mm.

1976, Dec.   **Litho.**   **Perf. 11½**
C592 AP145 2s multi   .25 .20
Luis Cordero (1833-1912), president of Ecuador.

Mariuxi Febres Cordero — AP146

1976, Dec.   **Perf. 11½**
C593 AP146 3s multi   .25 .20
Mariuxi Febres Cordero, South American swimming champion.

Flags and Monument AP147

1976, Nov. 9   **Perf. 12**
C594 AP147 3s multi   .25 .20

Miniature Sheet
Imperf

C595 AP147 5s multi　　　　1.60 .50

2nd Meeting of the Agriculture Ministers of the Andean Countries, Quito, Nov. 8-10.

Sister Catalina — AP148　　Congress Hall, Quito — AP149

1977, June 17　Litho.　*Perf. 12x11½*
C596 AP148 1.30s blk & pale salm-
　　　　　on　　　　　　　　.30 .20

Sister Catalina de Jesus Herrera (1717-1795), writer.

1977, Aug. 15　Litho.　*Perf. 12x11½*
C597 AP149 5s multi　　　　.45 .20
　a.　10s souvenir sheet　　1.50 1.50

11th General Assembly of Pan-American Institute of Geography and History, Quito, Aug. 15-30. No. C597a contains the designs of types A282 and AP149 without denominations and with simulated perforations.

Pres. Alfonso López Michelsen, Flag of Colombia — AP150

Designs: 5s, Pres. López M. of Colombia, Pres. Alfredo Povedo B. of Ecuador and aide. 7s, as 5s, vert. 9s, 10s, Presidents with aides.

1977　　　　　　　*Perf. 12*
C598 AP150 2.60s multi　　.45 .20
C599 AP150 5s multi　　　.65 .25
C600 AP150 7s multi　　　.70 .35
C601 AP150 9s multi　　　1.10 .55

Imperf
C602 AP150 10s multi　　　.85 .70
　　Nos. C598-C602 (5)　　3.75 2.05

Meeting of the Presidents of Ecuador and Colombia and Declaration of Putumayo, Feb. 25, 1977. Nos. C598-C602 are overprinted in multiple fluorescent, colorless rows: INSTITUTO GEOGRAFICO MILITAR GOBIERNO DEL ECUADOR.

Ceramic Figure, Tolita Culture AP151

9s, Divine Shepherdess, sculpture by Bernardo de Legarda. 11s, The Fruit Seller, sculpture by Legarda. 20s, Sun God, pre-Columbian gold mask.

1977, Aug. 24　　　　*Perf. 12*
C603 AP151 7s gold & multi　1.25 .40
C604 AP151 9s gold & multi　1.60 .45
C605 AP151 11s gold & multi　2.10 1.00
　　Nos. C603-C605 (3)　　4.95 1.85

Souvenir Sheet
Gold Embossed
Imperf

C606 AP151 20s vio, bl, blk &
　　　　　gold　　　　8.00 4.25

Central Bank of Ecuador, 50th anniversary. Nos. C603-C605 overprinted like Nos. C598-C602.

Lungs — AP152　　Brother Miguel, St. Peter's, Rome — AP153

1977, Oct. 5　Litho.　*Perf. 12x11½*
C607 AP152 2.60s multi　　.30 .25

3rd Cong. of the Bolivarian Pneumonic Soc. and cent. of the founding of the medical faculty of the University of Guayaquil.

1977
C608 AP153 2.60s multi　　.25 .20

Beatification of Brother Miguel.

Peralta Type

2.60s, Titles of works by Peralta & his bookmark.

1977　　　　　　　*Perf. 11½*
C609 A284 2.60s multi　　.35 .25

Broadcast Tower — AP154　　Remigio Romero y Cordero — AP155

1977, Dec. 2　Litho.　*Perf. 12x11½*
C610 AP154 5s multi　　　.35 .35

9th World Telecommunications Day.

1978, Mar. 2　Litho.　*Perf. 12½x11½*
C611 AP155 3s multi　　　.30 .20
C612 AP155 10.60s multi　　.45 .25

Imperf
C612A AP155 10s multi　　1.10 1.10
　　Nos. C611-C612A (3)　　1.85 1.55

Remigio Romero y Cordero (1895-1967), poet. No. C612A contains a vignette similar to Nos. C611-C612.

Dr. Vicente Corral Moscoso AP156　　Faces AP157

5s, Hospital emblem with Caduceus.

1978, Apr. 12　Litho.　*Imperf.*
C613 AP156 5s multi　　　.55 .30

　　　　　　Perf. 12x11½
C614 AP156 7.60s multi　　.95 .50

Inauguration (in 1977) of Dr. Vicente Corral Moscoso Regional Hospital, Cuenca.

1978, Mar. 17

Designs: 9s, Emblems and flags of Ecuador. 10s, 11s, Hands reaching for light.

C615 AP157 7s multicolored　.60 .20
C616 AP157 9s multicolored　.85 .20
C617 AP157 11s multicolored　1.00 .20

Imperf
C618 AP157 10s multicolored　1.00 1.00
　　Nos. C615-C618 (4)　　3.45 1.60

Ecuadorian Social Security Institute, 50th anniv.

Geographical Institute Type

7.60s, Plane over map of Ecuador with mountains.

1978, Apr. 12　Litho.　*Perf. 11½*
C619 A287 7.60s multi　　.90 .50

Imperf
C620 A287 10s multi　　　1.40 1.40

No. C620 contains 2 vignettes with simulated perforations in designs of Nos. 967 and C619.

Lions Type

1978　　　　　　　*Perf. 11½*
C621 A288 5s multi　　　.65 .25
C622 A288 6.20s multi　　1.00 .40

Imperf
C623 A288 10s multi　　　1.40 1.40
　　Nos. C621-C623 (3)　　3.05 2.05

No. C623 contains a vignette similar to Nos. C621-C622.

San Martin — AP158

1978, Apr. 13　Litho.　*Perf. 12*
C624 AP158 10.60s multi　　1.40 .50

Imperf
C625 AP158 10s multi　　　1.40 1.40

Gen. José de San Martin (1778-1850), soldier and statesman. No. C625 contains a vignette similar to No. C624.

Bank Type

Design: 5s, Bank emblem.

1978, Sept.　Litho.　*Perf. 11½*
C626 A289 5s gray & multi　.30 .20

Soccer Type

Designs: 2.60s, "Gauchito" and Games' emblem. 5s, "Gauchito." 7s, Soccer ball. 9s, Games' emblem, vert. 10s, Games' emblem.

1978, Nov. 1　　　　*Perf. 12*
C627 A290 2.60s multi　　.30 .20
C628 A290 7s multi　　　.80 .40
C629 A290 9s multi　　　1.10 .65

Imperf
C630 A290 5s blk & bl　　5.25 5.25
C631 A290 10s blk & bl　　5.25 5.25
　　Nos. C627-C631 (5)　　12.70 11.75

Bernardo O'Higgins AP159　　Old Men of Vilcabamba AP160

1978, Nov. 11　Litho.　*Perf. 12x11½*
C632 AP159 10.60s multi　　.70 .30

Imperf
C633 AP159 10s multi　　1.25 .75

Gen. Bernardo O'Higgins (1778-1842), Chilean soldier and statesman. No. C633 contains a vignette similar to No. C632.

1978, Nov. 11　　　*Perf. 12x11½*
C634 AP160 5s multi　　　.40 .25

Vilcabamba, valley of longevity.

Humphrey AP161　　Virgin and Child AP162

1978, Nov. 27　Litho.　*Perf. 12x11½*
C635 AP61 5s multi　　　.40 .25

Hubert H. Humphrey (1911-1978), Vice President of the US.

1978

Children's Drawings: 4.60s, Holy Family. 6.20s, Candle and children.

C636 AP162 2.20s multi　　.20 .20
C637 AP162 4.60s multi　　.45 .25
C638 AP162 6.20s multi　　.75 .25
　　Nos. C636-C638 (3)　　1.40 .80

Christmas 1978.

Village, by Anibal Villacis AP163

Ecuadorian Painters: No. C640, Mountain Village, by Gilberto Almeida. No. C641, Bay, by Roura Oxandaberro. No. C642, Abstract, by Luis Molinari. No. C643, Statue, by Oswaldo Viteri. No. C644, Tools, by Enrique Tabara.

1978, Dec. 9　　　　*Perf. 12*
C639 AP163 5s multi　　　.50 .25
C640 AP163 5s multi　　　.50 .25
C641 AP163 5s multi　　　.50 .25
C642 AP163 5s multi　　　.50 .25
C643 AP163 5s multi　　　.50 .25
C644 AP163 5s multi　　　.50 .25
　　Nos. C639-C644 (6)　　3.00 1.50

House and Monument AP164

Design: 3.40s, Monument, vert.

1979, Feb. 27　Litho.　*Perf. 12*
C645 AP164 2.40s multi　　.30 .20
C646 AP164 3.40s multi　　.30 .20

Imperf
C647 AP164 10s multi　　　1.00 1.00
　　Nos. C645-C647 (3)　　1.60 1.40

Sesquicentennial of Battle of Portete and Tarqui. #C647 contains vignettes similar to #C645-C646.

Fish and Ship — AP165

Flags of Ecuador and U.S. — AP166

7s, Map of Ecuador & Galapagos showing territorial waters. 9s, Map of South America with west-coast territorial waters.

Perf. 12x11½, 11½x12

1979, July 23	Litho.	Wmk. 367	
C648	AP165	5s multi	.75	.25
C649	AP165	7s multi, horiz.	1.00	.35
C650	AP165	9s multi	1.40	.50
		Nos. C648-C650 (3)	3.15	1.10

Declaration of 200-mile territorial limit, 25th anniversary.

1979, Aug. 3   Perf. 12x11½

Designs: 10.60s, Bells in Quito clock tower, horiz. 13.60s, Aerial view of Galapagos coast.

C651	A293	10.60s multi	1.25	.60
C652	A293	13.60s multi	1.40	.75

Size: 115x91mm
Imperf
Unwmk.

C653	A293	10s multi	2.50	1.10
		Nos. C651-C653 (3)	5.15	2.45

National heritage: Quito and Galapagos Islands. No. C653 contains vignettes similar to Nos. 977, C651-C652.

1979, Aug.   Wmk. 367   Perf. 11½x12

C654	AP166	7.60s multi	.40	.40
C655	AP166	10.60s multi	.60	.60

Size: 115x91mm
Imperf
Unwmk.

C656	AP166	10s multi	1.00	.65
		Nos. C654-C656 (3)	2.00	1.65

5th anniv. of Ecuador-US Chamber of Commerce. No. C656 contains vignettes similar to Nos. C654-C655.

Smiling Girl, IYC Emblem — AP167

Perf. 12x11½

1979, Sept. 7   Litho.   Wmk. 367

C657	AP167	10s multi	.70	.40

International Year of the Child.

Citizens and Flag of Ecuador AP168

Design: 10.60s, Pres. Jaime Roldas Aguilera, flag of Ecuador, vert.

Perf. 11½

1979, Sept. 27   Litho.   Unwmk.

C658	AP168	7.60s multi	.85	.35

Wmk. 367

C659	AP168	10.60s multi	1.00	.30

Restoration of democracy to Ecuador.

Ecuador Coat of Arms, Olympic Rings and Eagle — AP169

Perf. 12x11½

1979, Nov. 23   Unwmk.

C660	AP169	28s multi	2.00	1.25

5th National Games, Cuenca.

CIESPAL Building, Quito AP170

Perf. 11½x12½

1979, Dec. 26   Wmk. 367

C661	AP170	10.60s multi	.70	.40

Opening of Ecuadorian Institute of Engineers building.

Olmedo Type
Perf. 12x11½

1980, Apr. 29   Litho.   Unwmk.

C662	A294	10s multi	1.00	.65

Tribal Chief Type

Indo-American Tribal Chiefs: #C663, Cuauhtemoc, Mexico. #C664, Lempira, Honduras. #C665, Nicaragua. #C666, Lambaré, Paraguay. #C667, Urraca, Panama. #C668, Anacaona, Haiti. #C669, Caupolican, Chile. #C670, Tacun-Uman, Guatemala. #C671, Calarca, Colombia. #C672, Garabito, Costa Rica. #C673, Hatuey, Cuba. #C674, Cmarao, Brazil. #C675, Tehuelche, Argentina. #C676, Tupaj Katri, Bolivia. 17.80s, Sequoyah, US. 22.80s, Ruminahui, Ecuador.

Wmk. 367 (#C663, C667), Unwmkd.
1980, May 12

C663	A295	7.60s multi	1.75	.35
C664	A295	7.60s multi	1.75	.35
C665	A295	7.60s multi	1.75	.35
C666	A295	10s multi	1.90	.40
C667	A295	10s multi	1.90	.40
C668	A295	10.60s multi	1.90	.40
C669	A295	10.60s multi	1.90	.40
C670	A295	10.60s multi	1.90	.40
C671	A295	12.80s multi	2.50	.55
C672	A295	12.80s multi	2.50	.55
C673	A295	12.80s multi	2.50	.55
C674	A295	13.60s multi	2.50	.55
C675	A295	13.60s multi	2.50	.55
C676	A295	13.60s multi	2.50	.55
C677	A295	17.80s multi	3.00	.65
C678	A295	22.80s multi	3.50	1.25
		Nos. C663-C678 (16)	36.25	8.25

Royal Visit Type
Perf. 11½x12

1980, May 18   Unwmk.

C679	A296	10.60s multi	.65	.40

Pichincha Provincial Development Council Building — AP171

1980, June 1   Perf. 12x11½

C680	AP171	10.60s multi	1.10	.50

Progress in Pichincha Province.

Indian Type

1980, June 10   Litho.   Perf. 12x11½

C681	A297	7.60s	Salasaca boy, Tungurahua	1.10	.85
C682	A297	10s	Amula woman, Chimborazo	1.25	.95
C683	A297	10.60s	Canar woman, Canar	1.60	1.10
C684	A297	13.60s	Colorado Indian, Pichincha	1.75	1.40
			Nos. C681-C684 (4)	5.70	4.30

Virgin of Mercy Type

1980, July 7   Litho.   Perf. 11½

C685	A298	7.60s	Cupola, cloisters	.90	.50
C686	A298	7.60s	Gold screen	.90	.50
C687	A298	7.60s	Quito from basilica tower	.90	.50
C688	A298	10.60s	Retable	1.10	.50
C689	A298	10.60s	Pulpit	1.10	.50
C690	A298	13.60s	Cupola	1.60	.75
C691	A298	13.60s	Statue of Virgin	1.60	.75
			Nos. C685-C691 (7)	8.10	4.00

UPU Monument AP172

Marshal Sucre, by Marco Sales AP173

Design: 17.80s, Mail box, 1880.

1980, July 7   Perf. 12

C692	AP172	10.60s multi	1.25	.65
C693	AP172	17.80s multi	2.25	1.00

Souvenir Sheet

C694	AP172	25s multi	3.00	2.50

UPU membership cent. No. C694 contains designs of C692 and C693, horiz., perf. 11½.

Olympic Type.

Design: 10.60s, 13.60s, Moscow '80 emblem, Olympic rings.

Perf. 12x11½

1980, July 19   Wmk. 395

C695	A299	10.60s multi	.70	.50
C696	A299	13.60s multi	1.00	.70

Souvenir Sheet

C697	A299	30s multi	6.75	6.75

No. C697 contains vignettes in designs of Nos. 991 and C695.

1980

C698	AP173	10.60s multi	.70	.50

Marshal Antonio Jose de Sucre, death sesquicentennial.

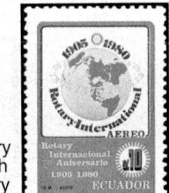
Rotary International, 75th Anniversary AP174

1980, Aug. 4   Perf. 11½

C699	AP174	10s multi	1.10	.50

Riobamba Type

Design: 7.60s, 10.60s, Monstrance, Riobamba Cathedral, vert.

1980, Sept. 20   Litho.   Perf. 11½

C700	A301	7.60s multi	.70	.40
C701	A301	10.60s multi	1.00	.45

Souvenir Sheet
Imperf

C702	A301	30s multi	1.90	1.90

No. C702 contains vignettes in designs of Nos. 996-997.

Democracy Type

7.60s, 10.60s, Pres. Aguilera and voter.

Perf. 12x11½

1980, Oct. 9   Litho.   Wmk. 395

C703	A302	7.60s multi	1.00	.55
C704	A302	10.60s multi	1.25	.60

Souvenir Sheet
Imperf

C705	A302	15s multi	1.10	1.10

No. C705 contains vignettes in designs of Nos. 999 and C703.

OPEC Type

20th Anniversary of OPEC: 7.60s, Men holding OPEC emblem, vert.

1980, Nov. 8   Perf. 11½x12

C706	A303	7.60s multi	.55	.45

Carchi Province Type

10.60s, Governor's Palace, vert. 17.80s, Victory Museum, Central Square, vert.

1980, Nov. 21   Perf. 13

C707	A304	10.60c multi	1.25	.65
C708	A304	17.80s multi	2.00	1.00

Orchid Type
Perf. 12x11½, 11½x12

1980, Nov. 22

C709	A305	7.60s	Anguloa uniflora	2.75	.70
C710	A305	10.60s	Scuticaria salesiana	3.50	.45
C711	A305	50s	Helcia sanguinolenta, vert.	5.75	1.40
C712	A305	100s	Anguloa virginalis	7.75	2.75
			Nos. C709-C712 (4)	19.75	5.30

Souvenir Sheets
Imperf

C713	A305	20s multi	4.50	3.25
C714	A305	20s multi	4.50	3.25

Nos. C713-C714 contain vignettes in designs of Nos. C709, C711 and C710, C712 respectively.

Christmas Type

7.60s, Pope blessing crowd. 10.60s, Portrait.

1980, Dec. 27   Perf. 12

C715	A306	7.60s multi, vert.	.95	.50
C716	A306	10.60s multi, vert.	1.25	.60

Isidro Cueva — AP175

Simon Bolivar, by Marco Salas — AP176

1980, Nov. 20   Perf. 13

C717	AP175	18.20s multi	2.25	1.10

Dr. Isidro Ayora Cueva, former president, birth centenary.

1980, Dec. 17   Perf. 11½

C718	AP176	13.60s multi	1.75	.90

Simon Bolivar death sesquicentennial.

Turtle, Galapagos Islands AP177

100s, Oldest Ecuadorian mail box, 1793.

1981, Feb. 12   Litho.   Perf. 13

C719	AP177	50s multi	6.50	4.25
C720	AP177	100s multi, vert.	8.00	5.50

HCJB Type

1981   Litho.   Perf. 13

C721	A311	7.60s Emblem, horiz.	1.00	.55
C722	A311	10.60s Emblem, diff.	1.40	.70

Soccer
Players — AP178

1981, July 8

C723	AP178	7.60s Emblem	1.00	.60
C724	AP178	10.60s shown	1.25	.60
C725	AP178	13.60s World Cup	1.60	.90
		Nos. C723-C725 (3)	3.85	2.10

Souvenir Sheets

C726	AP178	20s multi	3.25	3.25
C727	AP178	20s multi	3.25	3.25

1982 World Cup Soccer Championship.
Nos. C726-C727 contain vignettes in designs
of Nos. C723 and C724 respectively.

Picasso Type

1981, Oct. 26		**Litho.**	**Perf. 13**	
C728	A313a	7.60s Still-life	.70	.35
C729	A313a	10.60s First Communion, vert.	.85	.45
C730	A313a	13.60s Las Meninas, vert.	.95	.65

Size: 110x90mm
Imperf

C731	A313a	20s multi	2.10	2.10
		Nos. C728-C731 (4)	4.60	3.55

No. C731 contains designs of Nos. C730, C729.

World Food Day Type

1981, Dec. 31		**Litho.**	**Perf. 13x13½**	
C732	A314	10.60s Farming, vert.	1.00	.50

IYD Type

1982, Feb. 25		**Litho.**	**Perf. 13**	
C733	A316	7.60s Emblem	.70	.40
C734	A316	10.60s Man with crutch	.90	.45

Montalvo Type

1982		**Litho.**	**Perf. 13**	
C735	A318	5s Home, horiz.	1.00	.55

Swimming Type

1982, July 30				
C736	A320	10.20s Emblem, vert.	.85	.40
C737	A320	14.20s Diving, vert.	1.10	.45

Pres. Jaime Roldos, (1940-81), Mrs.
Martha Roldos, Independence
Monument, Quito — AP179

1983, May 25		**Litho.**	**Perf. 12**	
C738	AP179	13.60s multi	.55	.40

Souvenir Sheet
Imperf

C739	AP179	20s multi	.85	.85

AIR POST SEMI-POSTAL STAMPS

Nos. C119-C123 Surcharged in Blue
or Red:

1944, May 9   Unwmk.   Perf. 12

CB1	AP26	50c + 50c	6.50	3.25
CB2	AP26	70c + 30c	6.50	3.25
CB3	AP26	3s + 50c (R)	6.50	3.25
CB4	AP26	5s + 1s (R)	6.50	3.25
CB5	AP26	10s + 2s	6.50	3.25
		Nos. CB1-CB5 (5)	32.50	16.25

The surtax aided Mendez Hospital.

AIR POST REGISTRATION STAMPS

Issued by Sociedad Colombo-Alemana de Transportes Aereos (SCADTA)

Nos. C3 and C3a Overprinted "R" in
Carmine

1928-29	**Wmk. 116**		**Perf. 14x14½**	
CF1	AP6	1s on 20c (#C3)	140.00	110.00
a.		1s on 20c (#C3a) ('29)	175.00	140.00

No. C18 Overprinted "R" in Black

1929, Apr. 1	**Wmk. 127**		**Perf. 14**	
CF2	AP2	1s rose	75.00	60.00

AIR POST OFFICIAL STAMPS

Nos. C8-C15
Overprinted in
Red or Black

1929, May		**Unwmk.**	**Perf. 12**	
CO1	AP1	2c black (R)	1.00	.50
CO2	AP1	5c carmine rose	1.00	.50
CO3	AP1	10c deep brown	1.00	.50
CO4	AP1	20c dark violet	1.00	.50
CO5	AP1	50c deep green	4.00	2.00
CO6	AP1	1s dark blue	4.00	2.00
a.		Inverted overprint	240.00	
CO7	AP1	5s orange yellow	18.00	7.75
CO8	AP1	10s orange red	210.00	75.00
		Nos. CO1-CO8 (8)	240.00	88.75

Establishment of commercial air service in
Ecuador.
Counterfeits of No. CO8 exist.
See Nos. CO9-CO12. For overprints and
surcharges see Nos. C35-C38.

1930, Jan. 9				
CO9	AP1	50c olive brown	3.50	1.75
CO10	AP1	1s carmine lake	4.50	2.25
CO11	AP1	5s olive green	11.00	5.50
CO12	AP1	10s black	21.00	10.50
		Nos. CO9-CO12 (4)	40.00	20.00

For surcharges & overprint see #C36-C38.

Air Post Stamps
of 1937
Overprinted in
Black

1937, Aug. 19				
CO13	AP7	10c chestnut	.50	.20
CO14	AP7	20c olive black	.50	.20
CO15	AP7	70c black brown	.60	.25
CO16	AP7	1s gray black	.70	.25
CO17	AP7	2s dark violet	.70	.35
		Nos. CO13-CO17 (5)	3.00	1.25

For overprints see Nos. 463-464.

No. C79 Overprinted in Black

1940, Aug. 1			**Perf. 12½x13**	
CO18	AP15	5s emerald	1.75	.65

> **Catalogue values for unused stamps in this section, from this point to the end of the section, are for Never Hinged items.**

Nos. C352-C354 Overprinted: "1961
oficial"

1964			**Perf. 13½**	
CO19	AP86	50c multi	1.75	.85
CO20	AP86	80c multi	1.75	.85
CO21	AP86	1.30s multi	1.75	.85
		Nos. CO19-CO21 (3)	5.25	2.55

SPECIAL DELIVERY STAMPS

SD1

1928		**Unwmk.**	**Perf. 12**	
E1	SD1	2c on 2c blue	8.00	9.00
E2	SD1	5c on 2c blue	7.00	9.00
E3	SD1	10c on 2c blue	7.00	6.00
a.		"10 CTVOS" inverted	21.00	25.00
E4	SD1	20c on 2c blue	10.00	9.00
E5	SD1	50c on 2c blue	12.00	9.00
		Nos. E1-E5 (5)	44.00	42.00

No. RA49A
Surcharged in Red

1945				
E6	PT18	20c on 5c green	3.00	2.00

LATE FEE STAMP

No. RA49A
Surcharged in Black

1945		**Unwmk.**	**Perf. 12**	
I1	PT18	10c on 5c green	1.00	1.00

POSTAGE DUE STAMPS

Numeral — D1   Coat of Arms — D2

1896	**Engr.**	**Wmk. 117**	**Perf. 12**	
J1	D1	1c blue green	6.00	6.50
J2	D1	2c blue green	6.00	6.50
J3	D1	5c blue green	6.00	6.50
J4	D1	10c blue green	6.00	6.50
J5	D1	20c blue green	6.00	8.50

J6	D1	50c blue green	6.00	13.00
J7	D1	100c blue green	6.00	17.00
		Nos. J1-J7 (7)	42.00	64.50

Reprints are on very thick paper with distinct
watermark and vertical paper-weave direction.
Value 20c each.

Unwmk.

J8	D1	1c blue green	5.00	6.00
J9	D1	2c blue green	5.00	6.00
J10	D1	5c blue green	5.00	6.00
J11	D1	10c blue green	5.00	6.00
J12	D1	20c blue green	5.00	7.50
J13	D1	50c blue green	5.00	10.50
J14	D1	100c blue green	5.00	15.00
		Nos. J8-J14 (7)	35.00	57.00

1929				
J15	D2	5c deep blue	.40	.40
J16	D2	10c orange yellow	.40	.40
J17	D2	20c red	.60	.60
		Nos. J15-J17 (3)	1.40	1.40

Numeral — D3

		Perf. 13½		
1958, Nov.		**Unwmk.**	**Litho.**	
J18	D3	10c bright lilac	.50	.40
J19	D3	50c emerald	.50	.40
J20	D3	1s maroon	.60	.40
J21	D3	2s red	.70	.40
		Nos. J18-J21 (4)	2.30	1.60

OFFICIAL STAMPS

Regular Issues of
1881 and 1887
Handstamped in Black

1886		**Unwmk.**	**Perf. 12**	
O1	A5	1c yellow brown	2.50	2.50
O2	A6	2c lake	3.00	3.00
O3	A7	5c blue	6.75	8.75
O4	A8	10c orange	5.25	3.25
O5	A9	20c gray violet	5.25	5.25
O6	A10	50c blue green	15.00	11.50
		Nos. O1-O6 (6)	37.75	34.25

1887				
O7	A12	1c green	3.25	2.50
O8	A13	2c vermilion	3.25	3.25
O9	A14	5c blue	5.25	2.50
O10	A15	80c olive green	17.50	10.00
		Nos. O7-O10 (4)	29.25	18.25

Nos. O1-O10 are known with red handstamp but these are believed to be
speculative.
The overprint on the 1886-87 issues is
handstamped and is found in various
positions.

Flores — O1   Arms — O1a

1892				
		Carmine Overprint		
O11	O1	1c ultramarine	.20	.40
O12	O1	2c ultramarine	.20	.40
O13	O1	5c ultramarine	.20	.40
O14	O1	10c ultramarine	.20	.60
O15	O1	20c ultramarine	.20	.60
O16	O1	50c ultramarine	.20	.90
O17	O1	1s ultramarine	.35	1.00
		Nos. O11-O17 (7)	1.55	4.30

1894			
O18	O1a	1c slate green (R)	15.00
O19	O1a	2c lake (Bk)	20.00

Nos. O18 and O19 were not placed in use.

Rocafuerte
O20 ovpt

Dated 1894

1894

Carmine Overprint

O20	O2	1c gray black	.40	.70
O21	O2	2c gray black	.40	.40
O22	O2	5c gray black	.40	.40
O23	O2	10c gray black	.50	.70
O24	O2	20c gray black	.70	.70
O25	O2	50c gray black	2.50	2.50
O26	O2	1s gray black	4.00	4.00
		Nos. O20-O26 (7)	8.90	9.40

Dated 1895

1895

Carmine Overprint

O27	O2	1c gray black	3.50	3.50
O28	O2	2c gray black	5.00	5.00
O29	O2	5c gray black	1.00	5.00
O30	O2	10c gray black	5.00	5.00
O31	O2	20c gray black	7.50	7.00
O32	O2	50c gray black	50.00	50.00
O33	O2	1s gray black	2.50	2.50
		Nos. O27-O33 (7)	74.50	74.00

Reprints of 1894-95 issues are on very thick
paper with paper weave found both horizontal
and vertical for all denominations. Values:
Nos. O20-O26, 35c each; O27-O33, 20c each.
Generally they are blacker than originals.
For overprints see Nos. O50-O91.

Types of 1896
Overprinted in
Carmine

1896   Wmk. 117

O34	A21	1c olive bister	1.00	1.00
O35	A22	2c olive bister	1.00	1.00
O36	A23	5c olive bister	1.00	1.00
O37	A24	10c olive bister	1.00	1.00
O38	A25	20c olive bister	1.00	1.00
O39	A26	50c olive bister	1.00	1.00
O40	A27	1s olive bister	3.00	3.00
O41	A28	5s olive bister	6.00	6.00
		Nos. O34-O41 (8)	15.00	15.00

Reprints of Nos. O34-O41 are on thick
paper with vertical paper weave direction.
Value 20 cents each.

Unwmk.

O42	A21	1c olive bister	3.00	3.00
O43	A22	2c olive bister	3.00	3.00
O44	A23	5c olive bister	3.00	3.00
O45	A24	10c olive bister	3.00	3.00
O46	A25	20c olive bister	3.00	3.00
O47	A26	50c olive bister	3.00	3.00
O48	A27	1s olive bister	7.50	7.50
O49	A28	5s olive bister	10.50	10.50
		Nos. O42-O49 (8)	36.00	36.00

Reprints of Nos. O42-O49 all have overprint
in black. Value 20 cents each.

#O20-O26 Overprinted

1897-98

O50	O2	1c gray black	8.00	8.00
O51	O2	2c gray black	10.00	10.00
O52	O2	5c gray black	90.00	90.00
O53	O2	10c gray black	8.50	8.50
O54	O2	20c gray black	4.00	2.50
O55	O2	50c gray black	20.00	20.00
O56	O2	1s gray black	32.50	32.50
		Nos. O50-O56 (7)	173.00	171.50

#O20-O26
Overprinted

O57	O2	1c gray black	2.50	2.50
O58	O2	2c gray black	6.00	2.00
O59	O2	5c gray black	70.00	70.00
O60	O2	10c gray black	90.00	90.00
O61	O2	20c gray black	2.50	2.50

O62	O2	50c gray black	9.50	7.50
O63	O2	1s gray black	120.00	120.00
		Nos. O57-O63 (7)	300.50	294.50

#O20-O26   1897 y 1898
Overprinted

O64	O2	1c gray black	17.00	17.00
O65	O2	2c gray black	17.00	17.00
O66	O2	5c gray black	17.00	17.00
O67	O2	10c gray black	17.00	17.00
O68	O2	20c gray black	17.00	17.00
O69	O2	50c gray black	17.00	17.00
O70	O2	1s gray black	17.00	17.00
		Nos. O64-O70 (7)	119.00	119.00

#O27-O33 Overprinted in Black like Nos. O50-O56

O71	O2	1c gray black	4.00	4.00
O72	O2	2c gray black	3.00	3.00
O73	O2	5c gray black	4.00	4.00
O74	O2	10c gray black	4.00	4.00
O75	O2	20c gray black	8.00	8.00
O76	O2	50c gray black	275.00	275.00
O77	O2	1s gray black	80.00	80.00
		Nos. O71-O77 (7)	378.00	378.00

#O27-O33 Overprinted like #O57-O63

O78	O2	1c gray black	1.75	1.75
O79	O2	2c gray black	1.40	1.40
O80	O2	5c gray black	3.50	3.50
O81	O2	10c gray black	1.40	1.40
O82	O2	20c gray black	1.40	.90
O83	O2	50c gray black	2.75	1.10
O84	O2	1s gray black	12.00	12.00

#O27-O33 Overprinted like #O64-O70

O85	O2	1c gray black	80.00	80.00
O86	O2	2c gray black	2.25	2.25
O87	O2	5c gray black	1.40	1.40
O88	O2	10c gray black	70.00	70.00
O89	O2	20c gray black	120.00	120.00
O90	O2	50c gray black	26.00	26.00
O91	O2	1s gray black	160.00	160.00
		Nos. O85-O91 (7)	459.65	459.65

Many forged overprints of Nos. O50-O91
exist, made on the original stamps and
reprints.

O3

Black Surcharge

1898-99   Perf. 15, 16

O92	O3	5c on 50c lilac	.50	.50
a.		Inverted surcharge	4.00	4.00
O93	O3	10c on 20s org	1.00	1.00
a.		Double surcharge	5.50	3.00
O94	O3	10c on 50c lilac	140.00	140.00
O95	O3	20c on 50c lilac	3.75	3.75
O96	O3	20c on 50s green	3.75	3.75
		Nos. O92-O96 (5)	149.00	149.00

Green Surcharge

O97	O3	5c on 50c lilac	2.00	2.00
a.		Double surcharge	5.00	
b.		Double surcharge, blk and grn	12.00	
c.		As "b," blk surch. invtd.	5.00	

Red Surcharge

1899

O98	O3	5c on 50c lilac	2.25	2.25
a.		Double surcharge	5.00	
b.		Dbl. surch., blk and red	6.00	
O99	O3	20c on 50s green	3.75	3.75
a.		Inverted surcharge	10.00	
b.		Dbl. surch., red and blk	16.00	

Similar Surcharge in Black
Value in Words in Two Lines

O100	O3	1c on 5c blue	650.00

Red Surcharge

O101	O3	2c on 5c blue	1,150.
O102	O3	4c on 20c blue	800.00

Types of Regular Issue of 1899
Overprinted in Black

1899   Perf. 14, 15

O103	A37	2c orange & blk	.70	1.60
O104	A39	10c orange & blk	.70	1.60
O105	A40	20c orange & blk	.50	2.50
O106	A41	50c orange & blk	.50	3.25
		Nos. O103-O106 (4)	2.40	8.95

For overprint see No. O167.

The above overprint was applied to
remainders of the postage stamps of
1904 with the idea of increasing their
salability. They were never regularly in
use as official stamps.

Regular Issue of
1911-13 Overprinted
in Black

1913   Perf. 12

O107	A71	1c scarlet & blk	3.50	3.50
O108	A72	2c blue & blk	3.50	3.50
O109	A73	3c orange & blk	2.25	2.25
O110	A74	5c scarlet & blk	4.50	4.50
O111	A75	10c blue & blk	4.50	4.50
		Nos. O107-O111 (5)	18.25	18.25

Regular Issue of
1911-13 Overprinted

Overprint 22x3½mm

1916-17

O112	A72	2c blue & blk	25.00	18.00
O113	A74	5c scarlet & blk	25.00	18.00
O114	A75	10c blue & blk	15.00	12.00
		Nos. O112-O114 (3)	65.00	48.00

Overprint 25x4mm

O115	A71	1c scarlet & blk	1.10	1.10
O116	A72	2c blue & blk	1.60	1.60
a.		Inverted overprint	5.00	5.00
O117	A73	3c orange & blk	1.00	1.00
O118	A74	5c scarlet & blk	1.60	1.60
O119	A75	10c blue & blk	1.60	1.60
		Nos. O115-O119 (5)	6.90	6.90

Same Overprint
On Regular Issue of 1915-17

O120	A71	1c orange	1.40	1.40
O121	A72	2c green	1.40	1.40
O122	A73	3c black	2.25	2.25
O123	A78	4c red & blk	2.25	2.25
a.		Inverted overprint	15.00	
O124	A74	5c violet	1.40	1.40
O125	A75	10c blue	2.75	2.75
O126	A79	20c green & blk	15.00	15.00
		Nos. O120-O126 (7)	26.45	26.45

Regular Issues of
1911-17 Overprinted
in Black or Red

O127	A71	1c orange	.90	.90
O128	A72	2c green	.70	.70
O129	A73	3c black (Bk)	.90	.90
O130	A73	3c black (R)	.90	.70
a.		Inverted overprint		
O131	A78	4c red & blk	.90	.90
O132	A74	5c violet	1.75	.70
O133	A75	10c blue & blk	4.50	1.75
O134	A75	10c blue	.90	.90
O135	A79	20c green & blk	4.50	1.75
		Nos. O127-O135 (9)	15.95	9.20

Regular Issue of
1920 Overprinted

1920

O136	A86	1c green	1.25	1.25
a.		Inverted overprint	17.00	
O137	A86	2c carmine	1.00	1.00
O138	A86	3c yellow brn	1.25	1.25
O139	A86	4c dark green	2.00	2.00
a.		Inverted overprint	17.00	
O140	A86	5c blue	2.00	2.00
O141	A86	6c orange	1.25	1.25
O142	A86	7c brown	2.00	2.00
O143	A86	8c yellow green	2.50	2.50
O144	A86	9c red	3.25	3.25
O145	A95	10c blue	2.00	2.00
O146	A86	15c gray	11.00	11.00
O147	A86	20c deep violet	14.50	14.50
O148	A86	30c violet	17.00	17.00
O149	A86	40c dark brown	21.00	21.00
O150	A86	50c dark green	14.50	14.50
O151	A86	60c dark blue	17.00	17.00
O152	A86	70c gray	17.00	17.00
O153	A86	80c yellow	21.00	21.00
O154	A104	90c green	21.00	21.00
O155	A86	1s blue	45.00	45.00
		Nos. O136-O155 (20)	217.50	217.50

Cent. of the independence of Guayaquil.

Stamps of 1911
Overprinted

1922

O156	A71	1c scarlet & blk	9.00	9.00
O157	A72	2c blue & blk	4.50	4.50

Revenue Stamps of 1919-1920
Overprinted like Nos. O156 and O157

1924

O158	PT3	1c dark blue	2.00	2.00
O159	PT3	2c green	12.50	12.50

Regular Issues of
1911-17 Overprinted

1924

O160	A71	1c orange	7.00	7.00
a.		Inverted overprint	15.00	

Overprinted in Black
or Red

O161	A72	2c green	.60	.60
O162	A73	3c black (R)	.80	.80
O163	A78	4c red & blk	1.25	1.25
O164	A74	5c violet	1.25	1.25
O165	A75	10c deep blue	1.25	1.25
O166	A76	1s green & blk	7.00	7.00
		Nos. O160-O166 (7)	19.15	19.15

No. O106 with
Additional Overprint

1924   Perf. 14, 15

O167	A41	50c orange & blk	2.25	2.25

#O160-O167 exist with inverted overprint.

No. 199 Overprinted

1924   *Perf. 12*
O168 A71 1c orange   5.50 5.50

Regular Issues of
1911-25 Overprinted

1925
O169 A71 1c scarlet & blk   10.00 4.25
  a.   Inverted overprint   15.00
O170 A71 1c orange   .60 .60
  a.   Inverted overprint   4.00
O171 A72 2c green   .60 .60
  a.   Inverted overprint   4.00
O172 A73 3c black (Bk)   .60 .60
O173 A73 3c black (R)   1.10 1.10
O174 A78 4c red & blk   .60 .60
O175 A74 5c violet   .80 .80
O176 A74 5c rose   .80 .80
O177 A75 10c deep blue   .60 .60
      Nos. O169-O177 (9)   15.70 9.95

Regular Issues of 1916-25 Overprinted
Vertically Up or Down

1927, Oct.
O178 A71 1c orange   2.00 2.00
O179 A86 2c carmine   2.00 2.00
O180 A86 3c yellow brown   2.00 2.00
O181 A86 4c myrtle green   2.00 2.00
O182 A86 5c pale blue   2.00 2.00
O183 A75 10c yellow green   2.00 2.00
      Nos. O178-O183 (6)   12.00 12.00

Regular Issues of
1920-27 Overprinted

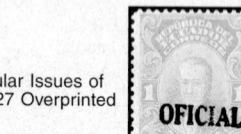

1928
O184 A71 1c lt blue   1.25 1.25
O185 A86 2c carmine   1.25 1.25
O186 A86 3c yellow brown   1.25 1.25
  a.   Inverted overprint   5.00
O187 A86 4c myrtle green   1.25 1.25
O188 A86 5c lt blue   1.25 1.25
O189 A75 10c yellow green   1.25 1.25
O190 A109 20c violet   11.00 2.50
  a.   Overprint reading up   3.50 2.25
      Nos. O184-O190 (7)   18.50 10.00

The overprint is placed vertically reading
down on No. O190.

Regular Issue of 1936
Overprinted in Black

1936   *Perf. 14*
O191 A131 5c olive green   1.50 .50
O192 A132 10c brown   1.50 .50
O193 A133 20c dark violet   1.90 .70
O194 A134 1s dark carmine   2.25 1.10
O195 A135 2s dark green   2.50 1.75
      Nos. O191-O195 (5)   9.65 4.55

Regular Postage
Stamps of 1937
Overprinted in Black

1937   *Perf. 11½*
O196 A139 2c green   .40 .40
O197 A140 5c deep rose   .40 .40
O198 A141 10c blue   .40 .40
O199 A142 20c deep rose   .40 .40
O200 A143 1s olive green   .40 .40
      Nos. O196-O200 (5)   2.00 2.00

> Catalogue values for unused
> stamps in this section, from this
> point to the end of the section, are
> for Never Hinged items.

Tobacco Stamp, Overprinted in Black
CORRESPONDENCIA OFICIAL

1946   **Unwmk.**   *Rouletted*
O201 PT7 1c rose red   1.75 1.75

Communications Building, Quito — O4

1947   **Unwmk.**   **Litho.**   *Perf. 11*
O202 O4 30c brown   .60 .40
O203 O4 30c greenish blue   .60 .40
  a.   Imperf., pair
O204 O4 30c purple   .60 .40
      Nos. O202-O204 (3)   1.80 1.20

Nos. O202 to O204 overprinted "Primero la
Patria!" and plane in dark blue are said to be
essays.

No. 719 with Additional Diagonal
Overprint

Illustration reduced.

1964   *Perf. 14x13*
O205 A231 80c block of 4   6.00 6.00
The "OEA" overprint covers four stamps, the
"oficial" overprint is applied to every stamp.

A set of 20 imperforate items in the
above Roosevelt design, some overprinted with the initials of various government ministries, was released in
1949. Later that year a set of 8 miniature sheets, bearing the same design

plus a marginal inscription, "Pre-
sidencia (or Vicepresidencia) de la
Republica," and a frame-line were
released. In the editors' opinion, information justifying the listing of these
issues has not been received.

POSTAL TAX STAMPS

Roca — PT1

1920   **Unwmk.**   *Perf. 12*
RA1 PT1 1c orange   .60 .30

PT2   PT3

RA2 PT2 1c red & blue   1.10 .20
  a.   "de" inverted   10.50 5.25
  b.   Double overprint   10.00 .60
  c.   Inverted overprint   10.00 .60
RA3 PT3 1c deep blue   1.25 .20
  a.   Inverted overprint   6.00 1.00
  b.   Double overprint   6.00 1.00

For overprints see Nos. O158-O159.

PT4   PT5

Red or Black Surcharge or Overprint
Stamp Dated 1911-1912
RA4 PT4 20c deep blue   — 30.00
Stamp Dated 1913-1914
RA5 PT4 20c deep blue (R)   2.25 .35
Stamp Dated 1917-1918
RA6 PT4 20c olive green (R)   6.50 .55
  a.   Dated 1919-20   25.00
RA7 PT5 1c on 2c green   .90 .20
Stamp Dated 1911-1912
RA8 PT5 1c on 5c green   .90 .20
  a.   Double surcharge
Stamp Dated 1913-1914
RA9 PT5 1c on 5c green   8.00 .55
  a.   Double surcharge   12.00 4.00

On Nos. RA7, RA8 and RA9 the surcharge
is found reading upward or downward.
For surcharges see Nos. RA15-RA16.

Post Office — PT6

1920-24   **Engr.**
RA10 PT6 1c olive green   .40 .20
RA11 PT6 2c deep green   .40 .20
RA12 PT6 20c bister brn ('24)   1.75 .20
RA13 PT6 2s violet   11.50 3.25
RA14 PT6 5s blue   20.00 5.75
      Nos. RA10-RA14 (5)   34.05 9.60

For overprints and surcharge see Nos. 259,
266-268, 273, 302, RA17.

Revenue Stamps of 1917-18
Surcharged Vertically in Red reading
up or down

1921-22
RA15 PT5 20c on 1c dk blue   55.00 6.50
RA16 PT5 20c on 2c green   55.00 6.50

No. RA12
Surcharged in
Green

1924
RA17 PT6 2c on 20c bis brn   .60 .20
  a.   Inverted surcharge   12.00 5.00
  b.   Double surcharge   4.00 2.00

PT7

1924   *Rouletted 7*
RA18 PT7 1c rose red   .90 .20
  a.   Inverted overprint   3.50

Similar Design, Eagle at left
Perf. 12
RA19 PT7 2c blue   .90 .20
  a.   Inverted overprint   3.50

For overprints & surcharges see #346,
O201, RA32, RA34, RA37, RA44-RA45,
RA47.

PT8

Inscribed "Timbre Fiscal"
1924
RA20 PT8 1c yellow   4.50 .85
RA21 PT8 2c dark blue   1.40 .35
Inscribed "Region Oriental"
RA22 PT8 1c yellow   .70 .30
RA23 PT8 2c dark blue   1.40 .35
      Nos. RA20-RA23 (4)   8.00 1.85

Overprint on No. RA22 reads down or up.

Revenue Stamp
Overprinted in Blue

1934
RA24   2c green   .40 .20
  a.   Blue overprint inverted   3.50 1.75
  b.   Blue ovpt. dbl., one invtd.   4.00 1.25

No. 310 Overprinted in Red
Perf. 12½
RA25 A119 20c ultra & yel   .50 .20

Telegraph Stamp
Overprinted in Red,
like No. RA24, and
Surcharged diagonally
in Black

1934   **Perf. 14**
RA26   2c on 10c olive brn   .70 .20
   a.   Double surcharge   5.50

Overprint Blue, Surcharge Red
RA27   2c on 10c olive brn   .70 .20

PT9   PT10

   Symbols of
Post and
Telegraph
Service
PT11

1934-36   **Perf. 12**
RA28   PT9 2c green   .60 .20
   a.   Both overprints in red ('36)   .60 .20

Postal Tax stamp of 1920-24, overprinted in
red "POSTAL" has been again overprinted
"CASA de Correos y Teleg. de Guayaquil" in
black.

1934   **Perf. 14½x14**
Photo.   **Wmk. 233**
RA29   PT10 2c yellow green   .40 .20

For the rebuilding of the GPO at Guayaquil.
For surcharge see No. RA31.

1935
RA30   PT11 20c claret   .50 .20

For the rebuilding of the GPO at Guayaquil.

No. RA29 Surcharged
in Red and Overprinted
in Black

1935
RA31   PT10 3c on 2c yel grn   .40 .20
   a.   Double surcharge

Social and Rural Workers' Insurance Fund.

Tobacco Stamp Surcharged in Black

Seguro Social **3**
del Campesino *ctvs.*

1936   **Unwmk.**   **Rouletted 7**
RA32   PT7 3c on 1c rose red   .60 .20
   a.   Lines of words reversed   2.00 .20
   b.   Horiz. pair, imperf. vert.

Issued for the Social and Rural Workers'
Insurance Fund.

No. 310
Overprinted in
Black

1936   **Perf. 12½**
RA33   A119 20c ultra & yel   .60 .20
   a.   Double overprint

Tobacco Stamp Surcharged in Black

SEGURO SOCIAL **3**
DEL CAMPESINO *ctvs.*

1936   **Rouletted 7**
RA34   PT7 3c on 1c rose red   .60 .20
Social and Rural Workers' Insurance Fund.

Worker — PT12

1936   **Engr.**   **Perf. 13½**
RA35   PT12 3c ultra   .40 .20

Social and Rural Workers' Insurance Fund.
For surcharges see Nos. C64, RA36, RA53-
RA54.

Surcharged in Black   **5**
Centavos
Dect. Junio
13 de 1936

1936
RA36   PT13 5c on 3c ultra   .60 .20

This combines the 2c for the rebuilding of
the post office with the 3c for the Social and
Rural Workers' Insurance Fund.

National Defense Issue
Tobacco Stamp, Surcharged in Black

TIMBRE PATRIOTICO
DIEZ CENTAVOS

1936   **Rouletted 7**
RA37   PT7 10c on 1c rose   .90 .20
   a.   Double surcharge

   Symbolical of
Defense — PT14

1937-42   **Perf. 12½**
RA38   PT14 10c deep blue   .90 .20

A 1s violet and 2s green exist in type PT14.
For surcharge see No. RA40.

PT15

Overprinted or Surcharged in Black
Perf. 13½, 11½
1937   **Engr. & Typo.**
RA39   PT15   5c lt brn & red   2.00   .25
   d.   Inverted overprint   20.00

1942   **Perf. 12, 11½**
RA39A   PT15 20c on 5c rose
          pink & red   75.00 20.00
RA39B   PT15 20c on 1s yel
          brn & red   75.00 20.00
RA39C   PT15 20c on 2s grn &
          red   75.00 20.00
  Nos. RA39A-RA39C (3)   225.00 60.00

A 50c dark blue and red exists.

No. RA38 Surcharged
in Red

1937   **Engr.**   **Perf. 12½**
RA40   PT14 5c on 10c dp blue   1.10 .20

Map of
Ecuador — PT16

1938   **Perf. 14x13½**
RA41   PT16 5c carmine rose   .70 .20
Social and Rural Workers' Insurance Fund.

No. C42 Surcharged in Red

1938   **Perf. 12½**
RA42   AP5 20c on 70c black   1.10 .20

No. 307
Surcharged in
Red

1938
RA43   A116 5c on 6c yel & red   .40 .20

This stamp was obligatory on all mail from
Nov. 23rd to 30th, 1938. The tax was for the
Intl. Union for the Control of Cancer.

Tobacco Stamp, Surcharged in Black

POSTAL ADICIONAL
CINCO CENTAVOS

1939   **Rouletted**
RA44   PT7 5c on 1c rose   .70 .20
   a.   Double surcharge
   b.   Triple surcharge

Tobacco Stamp, Surcharged in Blue

CASAS DE CORREOS
Y TELEGRAFOS
CINCO CENTAVOS

1940
RA45   PT7 5c on 1c rose red   1.00 .20
   a.   Double surcharge   3.50 3.50

No. 370 Surcharged in Carmine

1940   **Perf. 11½**
RA46   A144 20c on 50c blk & multi   .50 .20
   a.   Double surcharge, one inverted

Tobacco Stamp, Surcharged in Black
TIMBRE PATRIOTICO
VEINTE CENTAVOS

1940   **Rouletted**
RA47   PT7 20c on 1c rose red   6.00 .50

Farmer Plowing   Communication
PT17   Symbols
             PT18

1940   **Perf. 13x13½**
RA48   PT17 5c carmine rose   .70 .20

1940-43   **Perf. 12**
RA49   PT18 5c copper brown   .70 .20
RA49A   PT18 5c green ('43)   .70 .20

For overprint & surcharges see #534, E6, I1.

Pursuit Planes   Warrior
PT19   Shielding
           Women
           PT20

1941   **Perf. 11½x13**
RA50   PT19 20c ultra   1.10 .20

The tax was used for national defense.

1942-46   **Engr.**   **Perf. 12**
RA51   PT20 20c dark blue   1.10 .20
RA51A   PT20 40c black brown
         ('46)   1.10 .20

The tax was used for national defense.
A 20c carmine, 20c brown and 30c gray
exist lithographed in type PT20.

No. 370 Surcharged in Carmine

1942   **Perf. 11½**
RA52   A144 20c on 50c multi   1.10 .20
   a.   Double surcharge   10.00

No. RA35 Surcharged in
Red

1943   **Perf. 13½**
RA53   PT12 5c on 3c ultra   .60 .20

ADICIONAL
CINCO
CENTAVOS

No. RA53 with
Additional Surcharge
in Black

1943
RA54 PT12 5c on 5c on 3c ultra　1.10　.20

Peons — PT21

Coat of
Arms — PT22

1943　　　　　**Perf. 12**
RA55 PT21 5c blue　　　.90　.20

The tax was for farm workers.
For overprint & surcharge see #535, C135.

Revenue Stamp (as No. RA64)
Overprinted or Surcharged in Black

No. RA56

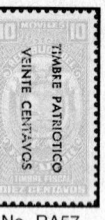

No. RA57

1943　　　　　**Perf. 12½**
RA56　20c red orange　　75.00 1.50

1943　　　　　**Perf. 12**
RA57　20c on 10c orange　　2.25　.25
　a.　Double surcharge

1943　　　　　**Perf. 12½**
RA58 PT22 20c orange red　　.70　.20

The tax was for national defense.

No. RA58 Surcharged
in Black

1944
RA59 PT22 30c on 20c org red　　.70　.20
　a.　Double surcharge

Catalogue values for unused
stamps in this section, from this
point to the end of the section, are
for Never Hinged items.

Consular Service
Stamps Surcharged in
Black

1951　　Unwmk.　　**Perf. 12**
RA60 R1 20c on 1s red　　　.60　.20
RA61 R1 20c on 2s brown　　.60　.20
RA62 R1 20c on 5s violet　　.60　.20
　Nos. RA60-RA62 (3)　　1.80　.60

Teacher and Pupils
in Schoolyard — PT23

PT24

1952　　Engr.　　**Perf. 13**
RA63 PT23 20c blue green　　.60　.20

Revenue Stamp Overprinted
"PATRIOTICO / SANITARIO"

1952　　　　　**Perf. 12**
RA64 PT24 40(c) olive green　　1.10　.20

For overprints & surcharges see #RA56-
RA57

Woman
Holding
Flag — PT25

PT26

1953　　　　　**Perf. 12½**
RA65 PT25 40c ultra　　1.25　.20

Telegraph Stamp Surcharged
"ESCOLAR 20 Centavos" in Black

1954　　Unwmk.　　**Perf. 13**
RA66 PT26 20c on 30c red brn　　1.00　.20

PT26a

PT26b

PT26c

Revenue Stamps Surcharged or
Overprinted Horizontally in Black
"PRO TURISMO 1954"

1954　　Unwmk.　　**Perf. 12**
RA67 PT26a 10c on 25c blue　　1.25　.20
RA68 PT26b 10c on 50c org red　1.25　.20
RA69 PT26c 10c carmine　　1.25　.20
　Nos. RA67-RA69 (3)　　3.75　.60

PT27

Telegraph Stamp Surcharged "Pro-
Turismo 1954 10 ctvs. 10"

1954　　　　　**Perf. 13**
RA70 PT27 10c on 30c red brn　　2.25　.20

Revenue Stamp
Overprinted in
Black

1954　　　　　**Perf. 12**
RA71 R3 20c olive black　　1.75　.20

Consular Service
Stamp Surcharged in
Black

1954
RA72 R1 20c on 10s gray　　1.75　.20

Young
Student at
Desk
PT28

Globe, Ship,
Plane
PT29

Imprint: "Heraclio Fournier.-Vitoria"

1954　　Photo.　　**Perf. 11**
RA73 PT28 20c rose pink　　1.10　.20
　See No. RA76.

1954　　Engr.　　**Perf. 12**
RA74 PT29 10c dp magenta　　1.60　.20

Soldier Kissing
Flag — PT30

1955　　Photo.　　**Perf. 11**
RA75 PT30 40c blue　　2.25　.20
　See No. RA77.

Types of 1954-55 Redrawn.
Imprint: "Thomas de la Rue & Co.
Ltd."

1957　　Unwmk.　　**Perf. 13**
RA76 PT28 20c rose pink　　1.10　.20
　　　　　　Perf. 14x14½
RA77 PT30 40c blue　　2.25　.20

No. RA77 is inscribed "Republica del
Ecuador."

The above stamp is believed to have
been used only for fiscal purposes.

AIR POST POSTAL TAX STAMPS

No. 438
Surcharged in
Black or
Carmine

1945　　Unwmk.　　**Perf. 11**
RAC1 A173 20c on 10c dk grn　　.75　.20
　a.　Pair, one without surcharge　90.00
RAC2 A173 20c on 10c dk grn
　　　　　(C)　　　.75　.20

Obligatory on letters and parcel post carried
on planes in the domestic service.

Liberty,
Mercury
and
Planes
PTAP1

1946　　Engr.　　**Perf. 12**
RAC3 PTAP1 20c orange brown　　.75　.20

GALAPAGOS ISLANDS

Issued for use in the Galapagos
Islands (Columbus Archipelago), a
province of Ecuador, but were commonly used throughout the country.

Catalogue values for unused
stamps in this section are for
Never Hinged items.

Sea
Lions — A1

Map — A2

Design: 1s, Marine iguana.

**　　　　Unwmk.**
1957, July 15　Photo.　　**Perf. 12**
L1　A1 20c dark brown　　1.25　.25
L2　A2 50c violet　　　.80　.25
L3　A1 1s dull olive green　　4.25　.65
　Nos. L1-L3 (3)　　6.30　1.15
　Nos. L1-L3,LC1-LC3 (6)　16.00　3.10

125th anniv. of Ecuador's possession of the
Galapagos Islands, and publicizing the
islands.
　See Nos. LC1-LC3. For overprints see Nos.
684-686, C389-C391.

collecting accessories

2.5" Crystal View Magnifier

Form and function come together with this attractive, high quality 4x magnifier. Dome-shaped magnifier "draws light like a magnet," illuminating the intricate details of stamps or coins. Magre availfits in handsome solid oak ring and slides easily across any flat surface.

ITEM	DESCRIPTION	RETAIL
MG25	Crystal View Magnifier	$39.99

Lighted 4x and 10X Magnifier

An inexpensive tool for anyone who needs illuminated magnification. Spring-loaded lens hidden within the body of the magnifer

ITEM	DESCRIPTION	RETAIL
MG4XL	Red 4x	$13.99
MG10XL	Black 10x	$17.99

5X-20X Folding Pocket Magnifier

This folding pocket magnifier contains three separate glass lenses housed in a durable plastic swing-away case. Seven different powers of magnification from 5x to 20x can be created when the lenses are used in combination. Depending on magnification, the focal distance is between .5" and 2".

ITEM	DESCRIPTION	RETAIL
MG520	5X-20X Magnifier	$29.99

Scott/Linn's Multi Gauge

"The best peforation gauge in the world just got better!" The gauge used by the Scott Editorial staff to perf stamps for the Catalogue has been improved. Not only is the Scott/Linn's gauge graduated in tenths, each division is marked by thin lines to assist collectors in gauging stamp to the tenth. The Scott/Linn's Multi-Gauge is a perforation gauge, cancellation gauge, zero-center ruler and millimeter ruler in one easy-to-use instrument. It's greate for measuring multiples and stamps on cover.

ITEM	DESCRIPTION	RETAIL
LIN01	Multi-Gauge	$6.95

Rotary Mount Cutter

German engineered mount cutter delivers precise and accurate cuts. The metal base features cm-measurements across the top and down both sides. The rotary cutter has an exchangeable, self-sharpening blade that rotates within a plastic casing, safely insuring perfectly straight and rectangular cuts.

ITEM	DESCRIPTION	RETAIL
980RMC	Mount Cutter	$74.00

These accessories and others are available from your favorite stamp dealer or direct from:

SCOTT AMOS ADVANTAGE

1-800-572-6885
P.O. Box 828, Sidney OH 45365-0828
www.amosadvantage.com

EGYPT

ʾē-jəpt

LOCATION — Northern Africa, bordering on the Mediterranean and the Red Sea
GOVT. — Republic
AREA — 386,900 sq. mi.
POP. — 61,404,000 (1997 est.)
CAPITAL — Cairo

Modern Egypt was a part of Turkey until 1914 when a British protectorate was declared over the country and the Khedive was deposed in favor of Hussein Kamil under the title of sultan. In 1922 the protectorate ended and the reigning sultan was declared king of the new monarchy. Egypt became a republic on June 18, 1953. Egypt merged with Syria in 1958 to form the United Arab Republic. Syria left this union in 1961. In 1971 Egypt took the name of Arab Republic of Egypt.

40 Paras = 1 Piaster

1000 Milliemes = 100 Piasters = 1 Pound (1888)

1000 Milliemes = 1 Pound (1953)

1000 Milliemes = 100 Piasters = 1 Pound (1982)

> Catalogue values for unused stamps in this country are for Never Hinged items, beginning with Scott 241 in the regular postage section, Scott B1 in the semipostal section, Scott C38 in the airpost section, Scott CB1 in the airpost semi-postal section, Scott E5 in the special delivery section, Scott J40 in the postage due section, Scott M16 in the military stamps section, Scott O60 in the officials section, Scott N1 in the occupation section, Scott NC1 in the occupation airpost section, Scott NE1 in the occupation special delivery section, and Scott NJ1 in the occupation postage due section.

Watermarks

Wmk. 118 — Pyramid and Star

Wmk. 119 — Crescent and Star

Wmk. 120 — Triple Crescent and Star

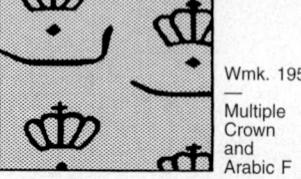

Wmk. 195 — Multiple Crown and Arabic F

"F" in watermark stands for Fuad.

Wmk. 315 — Multiple Eagle

Wmk. 318 — Multiple Eagle and "Misr"

Wmk. 328 — U A R

Wmk. 342 — Coat of Arms, Multiple

Values for unused stamps are for examples with original gum as defined in the catalogue introduction. Very fine examples of Nos. 1-15 will have perforations that are clear of the framelines but with the design noticeably off center. Well centered stamps are extremely scarce and will command substantial premiums.

Turkish Suzerainty

A1

A2

A3

A4

A5

A6

A7

Surcharged in Black
Wmk. 118
1866, Jan. 1　Litho.　Perf. 12½

1	A1	5pa greenish gray	47.50	30.00
a.		Imperf., pair	225.00	
b.		Pair, imperf. between	350.00	
c.		Perf. 12½x13	57.50	55.00
d.		Perf. 13	300.00	350.00
2	A2	10pa brown	65.00	32.50
a.		Imperf., pair	190.00	
b.		Pair, imperf. between	400.00	
c.		Perf. 13	200.00	210.00
d.		Perf. 12½x15	300.00	325.00
e.		Perf. 12½x13	92.50	55.00
3	A3	20pa blue	82.50	35.00
a.		Imperf., pair	275.00	
b.		Pair, imperf. between	450.00	
c.		Perf. 12½x13	110.00	95.00
d.		Perf. 13	475.00	325.00
4	A4	2pi yellow	110.00	47.50
a.		Imperf.	125.00	125.00
b.		Imperf. vert. or horiz., pair	400.00	400.00
c.		Perf. 12½x15	150.00	
d.		Diagonal half used as 1pi on cover		2,600.
e.		Perf. 12½x13, 13x12½	140.00	55.00
5	A5	5pi rose	300.00	250.00
a.		Imperf.	400.00	375.00
b.		Imperf. vert. or horiz., pair	1,200.	
c.		Inscription of 10pi, imperf.	950.00	850.00
e.		Perf. 12½x13, 13x12½	350.00	275.00
f.		As "d," perf. 12½x15	1,000.	550.00
6	A6	10pi slate bl	350.00	325.00
a.		Imperf.	450.00	450.00
b.		Pair, imperf. between	2,250.	
c.		Perf. 12½x13, 13x12½	550.00	550.00
d.		Perf. 13	1,850.	

Unwmk.
Typo.

7	A7	1pi rose lilac	67.50	5.50
a.		Imperf.	110.00	
b.		Horiz. pair, imperf. vert.	500.00	
c.		Perf. 12½x13, 13x12½	100.00	25.00
d.		Perf. 13	350.00	210.00
		Nos. 1-7 (7)	1,022.	725.50

Single imperforates of types A1-A10 are sometimes simulated by trimming wide-margined examples of perforated stamps.

No. 4d must be dated between July 16 and July 31, 1867.

Proofs of Nos. 1-7 are on smooth white paper, unwatermarked and imperforate. Proofs of No. 7 are on thinner paper than No. 7a.

Sphinx and Pyramid — A8

Perf. 15x12½
1867-69　Litho.　Wmk. 119

8	A8	5pa orange	25.00	11.00
a.		Imperf.	250.00	
b.		Horiz. pair, imperf between	175.00	
c.		Vert. pair, imperf between	—	
9	A8	10pa lilac ('69)	62.50	11.00
a.		10pa violet	82.50	14.00
b.		Half used as 5pa on newspaper piece		850.00
11	A8	20pa yel grn ('69)	110.00	11.00
a.		20pa blue green	125.00	17.00
13	A8	1pi rose red	11.00	1.10
a.		Imperf., pair	150.00	
b.		Pair, imperf. between	300.00	
d.		Rouletted	70.00	
e.		1pi lake red	130.00	32.50
14	A8	2pi blue	150.00	17.00
a.		Imperf.	250.00	
b.		Horiz. pair, imperf. vert.	500.00	
d.		Perf. 12½	250.00	
15	A8	5pi brown	350.00	200.00
		Nos. 8-15 (6)	708.50	251.10

There are 4 types of each value, so placed that any block of 4 contains all types.

A9

A10

Clear Impressions
Thick Opaque Paper
Typographed by the Government at Boulac
Perf. 12½x13½ Clean-cut
1872　Wmk. 119

19	A9	5pa brown	9.25	5.00
20	A9	10pa lilac	9.00	3.75
21	A9	20pa blue	50.00	4.00

22	A9	1pi rose red	57.50	2.25
h.		Half used as 20pa on cover		700.00
23	A9	2pi dull yellow	97.50	15.00
j.		Half used as 1p on cover		1,200.
24	A9	2½pi dull violet	82.50	11.00
25	A9	5pi green	325.00	35.00
i.		Tête bêche pair		
		Nos. 19-25 (7)	630.75	76.00

Perf. 13½ Clean-cut

19a	A9	5pa brown	27.50	9.25
20a	A9	10pa dull lilac	9.00	4.25
21a	A9	20pa blue	90.00	20.00
22a	A9	1pi rose red	82.50	8.00
23a	A9	2pi dull yellow	55.00	8.00
24a	A9	2½pi dull violet	1,200.	225.00
25a	A9	5pi green	375.00	75.00

Litho.

21m	A9	20pa blue, perf. 12½x13½	150.00	50.00
21n	A9	20pa blue, perf. 13½	225.00	80.00
21p	A9	20pa blue, imperf.	250.00	
22m	A9	1pi rose red, perf. 12½x13½	550.00	20.00
22n	A9	1pi rose red, perf. 13½	875.00	50.00

Typographed
Blurred Impressions
Thinner Paper
Perf. 12½ Rough
1874-75　Wmk. 119

26	A10	5pa brown ('75)	7.25	3.50
e.		Imperf.	200.00	200.00
f.		Vert. pair, imperf. horiz.	1,000.	
g.		Tête bêche pair	40.00	40.00
20b	A9	10pa gray lilac	10.00	3.50
g.		Tête bêche pair	225.00	225.00
21b	A9	20pa gray blue	90.00	4.00
k.		Half used as 10pa on cover		
22b	A9	1pi vermilion	7.50	1.75
f.		Imperf.	—	150.00
g.		Tête bêche pair	150.00	125.00
23b	A9	2pi yellow	75.00	5.75
i.		Tête bêche pair	600.00	600.00
24b	A9	2½pi deep violet	9.25	3.50
e.		Imperf.	—	
f.		Tête bêche pair	600.00	600.00
25b	A9	5pi yellow green	60.00	22.50
e.		Imperf.	400.00	

No. 26f normally occurs tête-bêche.

Perf. 13½x12½ Rough

26c	A10	5pa brown	7.50	4.50
i.		Tête bêche pair	62.50	62.50
20c	A9	10pa gray lilac	12.00	3.25
h.		Tête bêche pair	225.00	225.00
21c	A9	20pa gray blue	8.50	3.75
h.		Pair, imperf. between	350.00	
22c	A9	1pi vermilion	55.00	3.25
i.		Tête bêche pair	500.00	500.00
23c	A9	2pi yellow	10.00	6.00
g.		Tête bêche pair	500.00	500.00
k.		Half used as 1pi on cover		2,800.

Perf. 12½x13½ Rough

23d	A9	2pi yellow ('75)	62.50	10.00
h.		Tête bêche pair	1,250.	
24d	A9	2½pi dp violet ('75)	45.00	12.50
i.		Tête bêche pair	1,150.	1,000.
25d	A9	5pi yel green ('75)	350.00	225.00

Nos. 24b, 24d
Surcharged in Black

1879, Jan. 1　Perf. 12½ Rough

27	A9	5pa on 2½pi dull vio	8.75	8.75
a.		Imperf.	400.00	400.00
b.		Tête bêche pair	7,500.	
c.		Inverted surcharge	125.00	75.00
d.		Perf. 12½x13½ rough	11.00	11.00
e.		As "d," tête bêche pair	7,500.	
f.		As "d," inverted surcharge	140.00	95.00
28	A9	10pa on 2½pi dull vio	11.00	11.00
a.		Imperf.	400.00	400.00
b.		Tête bêche pair	2,500.	
c.		Inverted surcharge	125.00	82.50
d.		Perf. 12½x13½ rough	17.00	17.00
e.		As "d," tête bêche pair	3,000.	
f.		As "d," inverted surcharge	150.00	125.00

A11

A12

A13

A14

A15

A16

1879-93 **Typo.** **Perf. 14x13½**

29	A11	5pa brown	1.50	.60
30	A12	10pa violet	45.00	5.00
31	A12	10pa lil rose ('81)	65.00	6.25
32	A12	10pa gray ('82)	13.25	1.60
33	A12	10pa green ('84)	.80	.65
34	A13	20pa ultra	62.50	2.25
35	A13	20pa rose ('84)	17.00	1.25
36	A14	1pi rose	25.00	.30
37	A14	1pi ultra ('84)	3.50	.20
38	A15	2pi orange yel	32.50	1.50
39	A15	2pi orange brn	25.00	1.50
40	A16	5pi green	70.00	8.75
41	A16	5pi gray ('84)	22.00	.50
		Nos. 29-41 (13)	383.05	30.35

Nos. 29-31, 35-41 imperf. are proofs.
Nos. 37, 39, 41, exist on both ordinary and chalky paper. See *Scott Classic Specialized Catalogue of Stamps & Covers* for detailed listings.
For overprints see Nos. 42, O6-O7.

A17

1884, Feb. 1

42	A17	20pa on 5pi green	13.00	2.25
a.		Inverted surcharge	70.00	62.50

A18

A19

A20

A21

A22

A23

1888-1906

43a	A18	1m brown	.65	.20
44a	A19	2m green	.90	.20
45	A20	3m maroon ('92)	7.00	1.25
46a	A20	3m orange ('93)	2.75	.20
47	A21	4m brown red ('06)	1.60	.20
48	A22	5m carmine rose	2.00	.20
49	A23	10p purple ('89)	35.00	1.00
		Nos. 43a-49 (7)	49.90	3.25

Nos. 43-44, 47-48 imperf. are proofs.
Nos. 43-44, 46, 48-49 exist on both ordinary and chalky paper, No. 47 only on chalk-surfaced paper. See *Scott Classic Specialized Catalogue of Stamps & Covers* for detailed listings.
For overprints, see O2-O5, O8-O10, O14-O15.

Boats on Nile
A24

Cleopatra
A25

Ras-el-Tin
Palace
A26

Giza
Pyramids
A27

Sphinx
A28

Colossi of
Thebes
A29

Pylon of Karnak
and Temple of
Khonsu — A30

Citadel at
Cairo — A31

Rock Temple of
Abu
Simbel — A32

Aswan
Dam — A33

Perf. 13½x14

1914, Jan. 8 **Wmk. 119**
Chalk-surfaced Paper

50	A24	1m olive brown	.60	.80
51	A25	2m dp green	1.10	.20
52	A26	3m orange	1.40	.50
53	A27	4m red	2.00	.75
54	A28	5m lake	1.60	.20
a.		Booklet pane of 6	225.00	
55	A29	10m dk blue	4.00	.40

Perf. 14

56	A30	20m olive grn	6.75	.70
57	A31	50m red violet	13.50	1.10
58	A32	100m black	30.00	1.40
59	A33	200m plum	37.50	3.75
		Nos. 50-59 (10)	98.45	9.80

All values of this issue exist imperforate on both watermarked and unwatermarked paper but are not known to have been issued in that condition.
See Nos. 61-69, 72-74. For overprints and surcharge see Nos. 60, 78-91, O11-O13, O16-O27, O30.

British Protectorate

No. 52 Surcharged

1915, Oct. 15

60	A26	2m on 3m orange	1.75	1.75
a.		Inverted surcharge	225.00	225.00

Scenic Types of 1914 and

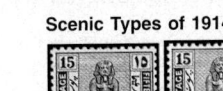

Statue of Ramses II
A34   A35

1921-22 **Wmk. 120** **Perf. 13½x14**
Chalk-surfaced Paper

61	A24	1m olive brown	.60	.80
62	A25	2m dp green	2.50	1.75
63	A25	2m red ('22)	2.00	.60
64	A26	3m orange	1.50	.70
65	A27	4m green ('22)	3.75	4.00
66	A28	5m lake	2.25	.20
67	A28	5m pink	2.50	.20
68	A29	10m dp blue	2.75	.20
69	A29	10m lake ('22)	2.25	.50
70	A34	15m indigo ('22)	3.00	.20
71	A35	15m indigo ('22)	16.00	2.50

Perf. 14

72	A30	20m olive green	10.00	.40
73	A31	50m maroon	12.00	1.00
74	A32	100m black	55.00	6.75
		Nos. 61-74 (14)	116.10	19.30

For overprints see Nos. O28-O29.

Independent Kingdom

Stamps of 1921-22
Overprinted

1922, Oct. 10

78	A24	1m olive brown	.95	.70
a.		Inverted overprint	350.00	450.00
b.		Double overprint	200.00	—
79	A25	2m red	.70	.40
a.		Double overprint	200.00	—
80	A26	3m orange	1.50	.95
81	A27	4m green	.90	.60
b.		Inverted overprint	225.00	—
82	A28	5m pink	2.10	.20
83	A29	10m lake	2.10	.20
84	A34	15m indigo	4.75	.90
85	A35	15m indigo	3.75	.90

Perf. 14

86	A30	20m olive green	5.00	.60
a.		Inverted overprint	200.00	—
b.		Double overprint	300.00	—
87	A31	50m maroon	8.00	.60
a.		Inverted overprint	400.00	500.00
88	A32	100m black	20.00	1.25
a.		Inverted overprint	500.00	160.00
b.		Double overprint	400.00	150.00
		Nos. 78-88 (11)	49.75	7.30

Same Overprint on Nos. 58-59
Wmk. Crescent and Star (119)

90	A32	100m black	80.00	50.00
91	A33	200m plum	27.50	1.50

Proclamation of the Egyptian monarchy.
The overprint signifies "The Egyptian Kingdom, March 15, 1922." It exists in four types, one lithographed and three typographed on Nos. 78-87, but lithographed only on Nos. 88-91.

King Fuad
A36   A37

1923-24 **Photo.** **Perf. 13½**
Size 18x22½mm

92	A36	1m orange	.20	.20
93	A36	2m black	.50	.20
94	A36	3m brown	.75	.40
a.		Imperf., pair	200.00	
95	A36	4m yellow grn	.65	.50
96	A36	5m orange brn	.20	.20
a.		Imperf., pair	50.00	
97	A36	10m rose	1.10	.20
98	A36	15m ultra	2.75	.20

Perf. 14
Size: 22x28mm

99	A36	20m dk green	5.50	.20
100	A36	50m myrtle grn	8.25	.20
101	A36	100m red violet	21.00	.55
102	A36	200m violet ('24)	37.50	1.75
a.		Imperf., pair	300.00	
103	A37	£1 ultra & dk vio ('24)	175.00	25.00
a.		Imperf., pair	1,600.	
		Nos. 92-103 (12)	253.40	29.60

For overprints & surcharge see No. 167, O31-O38.

Thoth Carving
Name of King
Fuad — A38

1925, Apr. **Litho.** **Perf. 11**

105	A38	5m brown	7.50	4.75
106	A38	10m rose	11.00	8.00
107	A38	15m ultra	13.50	9.50
		Nos. 105-107 (3)	32.00	22.25

International Geographical Congress, Cairo.
Nos. 106-107 exist with both white and yellowish gum.

Oxen
Plowing
A39

1926 **Wmk. 195** **Perf. 13x13½**

108	A39	5m lt brown	2.25	1.00
109	A39	10m brt rose	2.00	.90
110	A39	15m dp blue	2.25	.90
111	A39	50m Prus green	12.00	3.00
112	A39	100m brown vio	17.50	5.00
113	A39	200m brt violet	25.00	15.00
		Nos. 108-113 (6)	61.00	25.80

12th Agricultural and Industrial Exhibition at Gezira.
For surcharges see Nos. 115-117.

King Fuad — A40

Perf. 14x14½
1926, Apr. 2 **Photo.** **Wmk. 120**

114	A40	50p brn vio & red vio	125.00	22.50

58th birthday of King Fuad.
For overprint and surcharge see Nos. 124, 166.

Nos. 111-113 Surcharged

Perf. 13x13½
1926, Aug. 24 **Wmk. 195**

115	A39	5m on 50m Prus grn	2.00	2.00
116	A39	10m on 100m brn vio	2.00	2.00
117	A39	15m on 200m brt vio	2.00	2.00
a.		Double surcharge	300.00	
		Nos. 115-117 (3)	6.00	6.00

Ship of Hatshepsut — A41

1926, Dec. 9   Litho.   Perf. 13x13½
118	A41	5m brown & blk	2.25	1.40
119	A41	10m dp red & blk	3.25	1.50
120	A41	15m dp blue & blk	3.25	1.50
		Nos. 118-120 (3)	8.75	4.40

International Navigation Congress, Cairo.
For overprints see Nos. 121-123.

Nos. 118-120, 114 Overprinted

1926, Dec. 21
121	A41 (a)	5m	225.00	150.00
122	A41 (a)	10m	225.00	150.00
123	A41 (a)	15m	225.00	150.00

Perf. 14x14½
Wmk. 120
124	A40 (b)	50p	1,400.	875.00

Inauguration of Port Fuad opposite Port Said.
Nos. 121-123 have a block over "Le Caire" at lower left.
Forgeries of Nos. 121-124 exist.

Branch of Cotton
A42

Perf. 13x13½
1927, Jan. 25   Wmk. 195
125	A42	5m dk brown & sl grn	1.25	.80
126	A42	10m dp red & slate grn	2.00	1.50
127	A42	15m dp blue & slate grn	2.00	1.50
		Nos. 125-127 (3)	5.25	3.80

International Cotton Congress, Cairo.

A43

King Fuad — A44

A45

A46

Perf. 13x13½
1927-37   Wmk. 195   Photo.
128	A43	1m orange	.35	.20
129	A43	2m black	.35	.20
130	A43	3m olive brn	.35	.20
131	A43	3m dp green ('30)	.65	.20
132	A43	4m yellow grn	.85	.40
133	A43	4m brown ('30)	1.00	.40
134	A43	4m dp green ('34)	.85	.40
135	A43	5m dk red brn ('29)	.95	.40
b.		5m chestnut	.95	.20
136	A43	10m dk red ('29)	1.25	.20
a.		10m orange red	1.25	.20
137	A43	10m purple ('34)	2.75	.20
138	A43	13m car rose ('32)	1.50	.40
139	A43	15m ultra	2.50	.20
140	A43	15m dk violet ('34)	5.25	.20
141	A43	20m ultra ('34)	9.25	.30

Early printings of Nos. 128, 129, 130, 132, 135, 136 and 139 were from plates with screen of vertical dots in the vignette; later printings show screen of diagonal dots.

Perf. 13½x14
142	A44	20m olive grn	3.25	.40
143	A44	20m ultra ('32)	4.00	.20
144	A44	40m olive brn ('32)	3.25	.20
145	A44	50m Prus green	3.50	.20
a.		50m greenish blue	5.50	
146	A44	100m brown vio	6.00	.20
a.		100m claret	9.00	.20
147	A44	200m deep violet	6.00	.50

Printings of Nos. 142, 145 and 146, made in 1929 and later, were from new plates with stronger impressions and darker colors.

Lithographed; Center Photogravure
Perf. 13x13½
148	A45	500m choc & Prus bl ('32)	125.00	11.50
a.		Entirely photogravure	125.00	25.00
149	A46	£1 dk grn & org brn ('37)	140.00	7.00
a.		Entirely photogravure	140.00	8.25
		Nos. 128-149 (22)	318.85	24.10

Statue of Amenhotep,
Son of Hapu — A47

1927, Dec. 29 Photo.   Perf. 13½x13
150	A47	5m orange brown	1.25	.45
151	A47	10m copper red	1.50	.50
152	A47	15m deep blue	2.75	.55
		Nos. 150-152 (3)	5.50	1.50

Statistical Congress, Cairo.

Imhotep — A48

Mohammed Ali Pasha — A49

1928, Dec. 15
153	A48	5m orange brown	1.10	.50
154	A49	10m copper red	1.25	.50

Intl. Congress of Medicine at Cairo and the cent. of the Faculty of Medicine at Cairo.

Prince Farouk — A50

1929, Feb. 11   Litho.
155	A50	5m choc & gray	1.60	1.10
156	A50	10m dull red & gray	1.90	1.25
157	A50	15m ultra & gray	1.90	1.25
158	A50	20m Prus blue & gray	1.90	1.25
		Nos. 155-158 (4)	7.30	4.85

Ninth birthday of Prince Farouk.
Nos. 155-158 with black or brown centers are trial color proofs. They were sent to the UPU, but were never placed on sale to the public, although some are known used.

Tomb Fresco at El-Bersheh — A51

1931, Feb. 15   Perf. 13x13½
163	A51	5m brown	.90	.55
164	A51	10m copper red	1.60	1.25
165	A51	15m dark blue	2.25	1.50
		Nos. 163-165 (3)	4.75	3.30

14th Agricultural & Industrial Exhib., Cairo.

Nos. 114 and 103 Surcharged with
Bars and

1932   Wmk. 120   Perf. 14x14½
166	A40	50m on 50p	18.00	2.75

Perf. 14
167	A37	100m on £1	240.00	190.00

Locomotive of 1852 — A52

Perf. 13x13½
1933, Jan. 19   Litho.   Wmk. 195
168	A52	5m shown	13.00	5.25
169	A52	13m 1859	19.00	9.00
170	A52	15m 1862	19.00	9.00
171	A52	20m 1932	19.00	9.00
		Nos. 168-171 (4)	70.00	32.25

International Railroad Congress, Heliopolis.

Commercial Passenger
Airplane — A56

Dornier
Do-X
A57

Graf
Zeppelin
A58

1933, Dec. 20   Photo.
172	A56	5m brown	6.00	2.10
173	A56	10m brt violet	14.00	8.50
174	A57	13m brown car	17.00	11.00
175	A57	15m violet	17.00	10.50
176	A58	20m blue	22.50	19.00
		Nos. 172-176 (5)	76.50	51.10

International Aviation Congress, Cairo.

A59

Khedive Ismail
Pasha — A60

1934, Feb. 1   Perf. 13½
177	A59	1m dp orange	.50	1.00
178	A59	2m black	.55	1.00
179	A59	3m brown	.60	1.25
180	A59	4m blue green	.90	.40
181	A59	5m red brown	.95	.20
182	A59	10m violet	2.00	.20
183	A59	13m copper red	3.00	1.25
184	A59	15m dull violet	3.00	1.10
185	A59	20m ultra	2.00	.30
186	A59	50m Prus blue	7.00	.60
187	A59	100m olive grn	16.50	1.00
188	A59	200m dp violet	55.00	5.50

Perf. 13½x13
189	A60	50p brown	175.00	75.00
190	A60	£1 Prus blue	285.00	125.00
		Nos. 177-190 (14)	552.00	213.80

10th Congress of UPU, Cairo.

King Fuad — A61

1936-37   Perf. 13½
191	A61	1m dull orange	.50	.80
192	A61	2m black	1.60	.20
193	A61	4m dk green	1.75	.20
194	A61	5m chestnut	1.25	.20
195	A61	10m purple ('37)	2.25	.20
196	A61	15m brown violet	2.50	.20
197	A61	20m sapphire	3.00	.20
		Nos. 191-197 (7)	12.85	2.30

Entrance to
Agricultural
Building — A62

Agricultural Building — A63

Design: 15m, 20m, Industrial Building.

1936, Feb. 15   Perf. 13½x13
198	A62	5m brown	1.00	.85

Perf. 13x13½
199	A63	10m violet	1.25	.95
200	A63	13m copper red	1.50	2.00
201	A63	15m dark violet	1.10	1.00
202	A63	20m blue	2.25	2.00
		Nos. 198-202 (5)	7.10	6.80

15th Agricultural & Industrial Exhib., Cairo.

Signing of Treaty — A65

1936, Dec. 22   *Perf. 11*

203	A65	5m brown	.65	.55
204	A65	15m dk violet	.75	.70
205	A65	20m sapphire	2.00	.90
		Nos. 203-205 (3)	3.40	2.15

Signing of Anglo-Egyptian Treaty, 8/26/36.

King Farouk — A66

Medal for Montreux Conf. — A67

1937-44   *Wmk. 195*   *Perf. 13x13½*

206	A66	1m brown org	.30	.20
207	A66	2m vermilion	.30	.20
208	A66	3m brown	.30	.20
209	A66	4m green	.30	.20
210	A66	5m red brown	.50	.20
211	A66	6m lt yel grn ('40)	.60	.20
212	A66	10m purple	.30	.20
213	A66	13m rose car	.60	.35
214	A66	15m dk vio brn	.50	.20
215	A66	20m blue	.75	.35
216	A66	20m lil gray ('44)	.75	.20
		Nos. 206-216 (11)	5.20	2.50

For overprints see Nos. 301, 303, 345, 348, 360E, N3, N6, N8, N22, N25, N27.

1937, Oct. 15   *Perf. 13½x13*

217	A67	5m red brown	.80	.55
218	A67	15m dk violet	1.25	1.10
219	A67	20m sapphire	1.25	1.25
		Nos. 217-219 (3)	3.30	2.90

Intl. Treaty signed at Montreux, Switzerland, under which foreign privileges in Egypt were to end in 1949.

Eye of Ré — A68

1937, Dec. 8   *Perf. 13x13½*

220	A68	5m brown	.60	.70
221	A68	15m dk violet	.90	.70
222	A68	20m sapphire	1.10	.80
		Nos. 220-222 (3)	2.60	2.20

15th Ophthalmological Congress, Cairo, December, 1937.

King Farouk, Queen Farida — A69

1938, Jan. 20   *Perf. 11*

223	A69	5m red brown	7.00	4.25

Royal wedding of King Farouk and Farida Zulficar.

Inscribed: "11 Fevrier 1938"

1938, Feb. 11

224	A69	£1 green & sepia	175.00	110.00

King Farouk's 18th birthday.

Cotton Picker — A70

1938, Jan. 26   *Perf. 13½x13*

225	A70	5m red brown	.50	.50
226	A70	15m dk violet	2.00	.85
227	A70	20m sapphire	1.50	.75
		Nos. 225-227 (3)	4.00	2.10

18th International Cotton Congress at Cairo.

Pyramids of Giza and Colossus of Thebes A71

1938, Feb. 1   *Perf. 13x13½*

228	A71	5m red brown	1.00	.65
229	A71	15m dk violet	1.50	.80
230	A71	20m sapphire	1.75	.80
		Nos. 228-230 (3)	4.25	2.25

Intl. Telecommunication Conf., Cairo.

Branch of Hydnocarpus — A72

1938, Mar. 21   *Perf. 13x13½*

231	A72	5m red brown	1.00	.50
232	A72	15m dk violet	1.60	.60
233	A72	20m sapphire	1.60	.60
		Nos. 231-233 (3)	4.20	1.70

International Leprosy Congress, Cairo.

King Farouk and Pyramids — A73

King Farouk
A74   A75

Backgrounds: 40m, Hussan Mosque. 50m, Cairo Citadel. 100m, Aswan Dam. 200m, Cairo University.

1939-46   *Photo.*   *Perf. 14x13½*

234	A73	30m gray	.75	.20
a.		30m slate gray	.75	.20
234B	A73	30m ol grn ('46)	.80	.20
235	A73	40m dk brown	.85	.20
236	A73	50m Prus green	1.00	.20
237	A73	100m brown vio	1.40	.20
238	A73	200m dk violet	4.25	.20

Perf. 13½x13

239	A74	50p green & sep	9.75	3.00
240	A75	£1 dp bl & dk brn	21.00	5.75
		Nos. 234-240 (8)	39.80	9.95

For £1 with A77 portrait, see No. 269D. See Nos. 267-269D. For overprints see Nos. 310-

314, 316, 355-358, 360, 363-364, N13-N19, N32-N38.

> Catalogue values for unused stamps in this section, from this point to the end of the section, are for Never Hinged items.

King Fuad A76   King Farouk A77

1944, Apr. 28   *Perf. 13½x13*

241	A76	10m dk violet	.50	.20

8th anniv. of the death of King Fuad.

1944-50   *Wmk. 195*   *Perf. 13x13½*

242	A77	1m yellow brn ('45)	.45	.20
243	A77	2m red org ('45)	.45	.20
244	A77	3m sepia ('46)	.50	.40
245	A77	4m dp green ('45)	.45	.20
246	A77	5m red brown ('46)	.45	.20
247	A77	10m dp violet	.45	.20
247A	A77	13m rose red ('50)	12.00	4.25
248	A77	15m dk violet ('45)	.45	.20
249	A77	17m olive grn	.50	.20
250	A77	20m dk gray ('45)	.75	.20
251	A77	22m dp blue ('45)	.75	.20
		Nos. 242-251 (11)	17.20	6.45

For overprints see Nos. 299-300, 302, 304-309, 343-344, 346-347, 349-354, 360B, 361-362, N1-N2, N4-N5, N7, N9-N12, N20-N21, N23-N24, N26, N28-N31.

King Farouk — A78   Khedive Ismail Pasha — A79

1945, Feb. 10   *Perf. 13½x13*

252	A78	10m deep violet	.40	.20

25th birthday of King Farouk.

1945, Mar. 2   *Photo.*

253	A79	10m dark olive	.35	.20

50th anniv. of death of Khedive Ismail Pasha.

Flags of Arab Nations — A80

1945, July 29

254	A80	10m violet	.35	.20
255	A80	22m dp yellow grn	.50	.20

League of Arab Nations Conference, Cairo, Mar. 22, 1945.

Flags of Egypt and Saudi Arabia A81

1946, Jan. 10   *Perf. 13x13½*   *Wmk. 195*

256	A81	10m dp yellow grn	.35	.20

Visit of King Ibn Saud, Jan. 1946.

Citadel, Cairo A82

1946, Aug. 9

257	A82	10m yel brn & dp yel grn	.40	.20

Withdrawal of British troops from Cairo Citadel, Aug. 9, 1946.

King Farouk and Inchas Palace, Cairo A83

2m, Prince Abdullah, Yemen. 3m, Pres. Bechara el-Khoury, Lebanon. 4m, King Abdul Aziz ibn Saud, Saudi Arabia. 5m, King Faisal II, Iraq. 10m, Amir Abdullah ibn Hussein, Jordan. 15m, Pres. Shukri el Kouatly, Syria.

1946, Nov. 9

258	A83	1m dp yellow grn	.60	.20
259	A83	2m sepia	.60	.20
260	A83	3m deep blue	.60	.20
261	A83	4m brown orange	.60	.20
262	A83	5m brown red	.60	.20
263	A83	10m dark gray	.75	.20
264	A83	15m deep violet	.75	.20
		Nos. 258-264 (7)	4.50	1.40

Arab League Cong. at Cairo, May 28, 1946.

Parliament Building, Cairo — A84

1947, Apr. 7   *Photo.*

265	A84	10m green	.35	.20

36th conf. of the Interparliamentary Union, Apr. 1947.

Raising Egyptian Flag over Kasr-el-Nil Barracks — A85   King Farouk — A85a

1947, May 6   *Perf. 13½x13*

266	A85	10m dp plum & yel grn	.40	.20

Withdrawal of British troops from the Nile Delta.

Farouk Types 1939 Redrawn

1947-51   *Wmk. 195*   *Perf. 14x13½*

267	A73	30m olive green	.50	.20
268	A73	40m dk brown	.60	.20
269	A73	50m Prus grn ('48)	.90	.20
269A	A73	100m dk brn vio ('49)	5.75	.75
269B	A73	200m dk violet ('49)	11.00	1.25

Perf. 13½x13
269C	A85a	50p green & sep ('51)	25.00	8.50
269D	A75	£1 dp bl & dk brn ('50)	36.00	3.75
		Nos. 267-269D (7)	79.75	14.85

The king faces slightly to the left and clouds have been added in the sky on Nos. 267-269B. Backgrounds as in 1939-46 issue. Portrait on £1 as on type A77.

For overprints see Nos. 315, 359.

Field and Branch of Cotton — A86

Map and Infantry Column — A87

Perf. 13½x13
1948, Apr. 1   **Wmk. 195**
| 270 | A86 | 10m olive green | .40 | .20 |

Intl. Cotton Cong. held at Cairo in Apr. 1948.

1948, June 15   **Perf. 11½x11**
| 271 | A87 | 10m green | .40 | .20 |

Arrival of Egyptian troops at Gaza, 5/15/48.

Ibrahim Pasha (1789-1848) — A88

1948, Nov. 10   **Perf. 13x13½**
| 272 | A88 | 10m brn red & dp grn | .40 | .20 |

Statue, "The Nile" A89

Protection of Industry and Agriculture — A90

Perf. 13x13½
1949, Mar. 1   **Photo.**   **Wmk. 195**
273	A89	1m dk green	.40	.20
274	A89	10m purple	1.00	.20
275	A89	17m crimson	1.00	.20
276	A89	22m deep blue	1.00	.40

Perf. 11½x11
| 277 | A90 | 30m dk brown | 1.50 | .50 |
| | | Nos. 273-277 (5) | 4.90 | 1.50 |

Souvenir Sheets
Photo. & Litho.
Imperf
278		Sheet of 4	3.25	3.25
a.	A89	1m red brown	.60	.60
b.	A89	10m dark brown	.60	.60

c.	A89	17m brown orange	.60	.60
d.	A89	22m dark Prussian green	.60	.60
279		Sheet of 2	3.25	3.25
a.	A90	10m violet gray	1.50	1.50
b.	A90	30m red orange	1.50	1.50

16th Agricultural & Industrial Expo., Cairo.

Mohammed Ali and Map — A93

Globe — A94

Perf. 11½x11
1949, Aug. 2   **Wmk. 195**
| 280 | A93 | 10m orange brn & grn | .60 | .20 |

Centenary of death of Mohammed Ali.

1949, Oct. 9   **Perf. 13x13½**
281	A94	10m rose brown	.85	.60
282	A94	22m violet	1.75	.85
283	A94	30m dull blue	2.40	1.10
		Nos. 281-283 (3)	5.00	2.55

75th anniv. of the UPU.

Scales of Justice A95

1949, Oct. 14   **Perf. 13x13½**
| 284 | A95 | 10m deep olive green | .40 | .20 |

End of the Mixed Judiciary System, 10/14/49.

Desert Scene A96

1950, Dec. 27
| 285 | A96 | 10m violet & red brn | .45 | .20 |

Opening of the Fuad I Institute of the Desert.

Fuad I University A97

1950, Dec. 27
| 286 | A97 | 22m dp green & claret | .60 | .25 |

Founding of Fuad I University, 25th anniv.

Globe and Khedive Ismail Pasha A98

1950, Dec. 27
| 287 | A98 | 30m claret & dp grn | .55 | .25 |

75th anniv. of Royal Geographic Society of Egypt.

Picking Cotton — A99

1951, Feb. 24
| 290 | A99 | 10m olive green | .35 | .20 |

International Cotton Congress, 1951.

King Farouk and Queen Narriman — A100

1951, May 6   **Photo.**   **Perf. 11x11½**
| 291 | A100 | 10m green & red brn | 2.75 | 2.75 |
| a. | | Souvenir sheet | 12.00 | 16.00 |

Marriage of King Farouk and Narriman Sadek, May 6, 1951.

Stadium Entrance A101

Arms of Alexandria and Olympic Emblem — A102

King Farouk A103

1951, Oct. 5   **Perf. 13x13½, 13½x13**
292	A101	10m brown	.75	.60
293	A102	22m dp green	.95	.95
294	A103	30m blue & dp grn	.95	.95
a.		Souvenir sheet of 3, #292-294	12.00	16.00
		Nos. 292-294 (3)	2.65	2.50

Issued to publicize the first Mediterranean Games, Alexandria, Oct. 5-20, 1951.

Winged Figure and Map — A105

Designs: 22m, King Farouk and Map. 30m, King Farouk and Flag.

Dated "16 Oct. 1951"
1952, Feb. 11   **Perf. 13½x13**
296	A105	10m dp green	.55	.25
297	A105	22m plum & dp grn	.85	.45
298	A105	30m green & brown	1.10	.55
a.		Souvenir sheet of 3, #296-298	9.00	9.00
		Nos. 296-298 (3)	2.50	1.25

Abrogation of the Anglo-Egyptian treaty.

Stamps of 1937-51 Overprinted in Various Colors

Perf. 13x13½
1952, Jan. 17   **Wmk. 195**
299	A77	1m yellow brown	.35	.20
300	A77	2m red org (Bl)	.35	.20
301	A66	3m brown (Bl)	.35	.50
302	A77	4m dp green (RV)	.35	.20
303	A66	6m lt yel grn (RV)	.90	.70
304	A77	10m dp vio (C)	.35	.25
305	A77	13m rose red (Bl)	1.75	.75
306	A77	15m dk violet (C)	2.00	.75
307	A77	17m olive grn (C)	1.90	.30
308	A77	20m dk gray (RV)	1.40	.30
309	A77	22m dp blue (C)	2.50	1.50

No. 244, the 3m sepia, exists with this overprint but was not regularly issued or used.

Same Overprint, 24½mm Wide, on Nos. 267 to 269B

Perf. 14x13½
310	A73	30m olive grn (DkBl)	1.25	.20
a.		Black overprint	1.50	
311	A73	40m dk brown (G)	.90	.20
312	A73	50m Prus grn (C)	1.25	.25
313	A73	100m dk brn vio (C)	2.75	.40
314	A73	200m dk violet (C)	13.00	1.25

Same Overprint, 19mm Wide, on Nos. 269C-269D

Perf. 13½x13
315	A85a	50p grn & sep (C)	25.00	4.75
316	A75	£1 dp bl & dk brn (Bl)	40.00	5.25
		Nos. 299-316 (18)	96.35	17.95

The overprint translates: King of Egypt and the Sudan, Oct. 16, 1951.

Overprints in colors other than as listed are color trials.

Egyptian Flag — A106

Perf. 13½x13
1952, May 6   **Photo.**   **Wmk. 195**
| 317 | A106 | 10m org yel, dp bl & dp grn | .40 | .20 |
| a. | | Souvenir sheet of 1 | 5.25 | 5.25 |

Issued to commemorate the birth of Crown Prince Ahmed Fuad, Jan. 16, 1952.

"Dawn of New Era" A107

Symbolical of Egypt Freed — A108

Designs: 10m, "Egypt" with raised sword. 22m, Citizens marching with flag.

Perf. 13x13½, 13½x13

1952, Nov. 23
Dated: "23 Juillet 1952"

318	A107	4m dp green & org	.35	.25
319	A107	10m dp grn & cop brn	.35	.50
320	A108	17m brn org & dp grn	.75	.60
321	A108	22m choc & dp grn	1.00	.45
		Nos. 318-321 (4)	2.45	1.80

Change of government, July 23, 1952.

Republic

Farmer A109

Soldier A110

Mosque of Sultan Hassan — A111

Queen Nefertiti — A112

1953-56   *Perf. 13x13½*

322	A109	1m red brown	.35	.20
323	A109	2m dk lilac	.35	.20
324	A109	3m brt blue	.35	.40
325	A109	4m dk green	.35	.20
326	A110	10m dk brown ("Defence")	.40	.40
327	A110	10m dk brown ("Defense")	.55	.20
328	A110	15m gray	.35	.20
329	A110	17m dk grnsh blue	.45	.20
330	A110	20m purple	.35	.20

Perf. 13½

331	A111	30m dull green	.35	.20
332	A111	32m brt blue	.70	.20
333	A111	35m violet ('55)	.90	.20
334	A111	37m gldn brn ('56)	1.75	.60
335	A111	40m red brown	.70	.20
336	A111	50m violet brn	1.20	.20
337	A112	100m henna brn	1.50	.20
338	A112	200m dk grnsh blue	3.75	.50
339	A112	500m purple	11.00	1.00
340	A112	£1 dk grn, blk & red	22.00	3.25
		Nos. 322-340 (19)	47.35	8.75

Nos. 327-330 are inscribed "Defense." See No. 490. For overprints and surcharges see Nos. 460, 500, N44-N56, N72.

Stamps of 1939-51 Overprinted in Black with Three Bars to Obliterate Portrait

1953   *Perf. 13x13½, 13½x13*

343	A77	1m yellow brn	.35	.20
344	A77	2m red orange	.35	.20
345	A66	3m brown	.50	.50
346	A77	3m sepia	.35	.20
347	A77	4m dp green	.35	.20
348	A66	6m lt yellow grn	.35	.20
349	A77	10m dp violet	.35	.20
350	A77	13m rose red	.50	.20
351	A77	15m dk violet	.35	.20

352	A77	17m olive grn	.35	.20
353	A77	20m dk gray	.50	.20
354	A77	22m deep blue	.55	.20
355	A73	30m ol grn (#267)	.60	.20
356	A73	50m Prus grn (#269)	1.00	.25
357	A73	100m dk brn vio (#269A)	1.50	.40
358	A73	200m dk violet (#269B)	4.50	1.00
359	A85a	50p grn & sepia	15.00	5.00
360	A75	£1 dk bl & dk brn (#269D)	30.00	4.75
		Nos. 343-360 (18)	57.45	14.30

No. 206 with this overprint is a forgery.

Same Overprint on Nos. 300, 303-305, 311 and 314

360B	A77	2m red orange	.40	.20
360E	A66	6m lt yel grn	50.00	
361	A77	10m dp violet	4.00	4.00
362	A77	13m rose red	1.25	.75
363	A73	40m dk brown	6.00	.75
364	A73	200m dk violet	4.00	.90
		Nos. 360B,361-364 (5)	15.65	6.60

Practically all values of Nos. 343-364 exist with double overprint. Other values of the 1952 overprinted issue are known with counterfeit bars.

Symbols of Electronic Progress A113

1953, Nov. 23   **Photo.**   *Perf. 13x13½*
365   A113   10m brt blue   .50   .20

Electronics Exposition, Cairo, Nov. 23.

Crowd Acclaiming the Republic A114

Farmer A115

Design: 30m, Crowd, flag and eagle.

Perf. 13½x13

1954, June 18   **Wmk. 195**
366	A114	10m brown	.55	.25
367	A114	30m deep blue	.90	.60

Proclamation of the republic, 1st anniv.

1954-55   *Perf. 13x13½*
368	A115	1m red brown	.35	.20
369	A115	2m dark lilac	.35	.20
370	A115	3m brt blue	.35	.20
371	A115	4m dk green ('55)	.70	.45
372	A115	5m dp car ('55)	.35	.20
		Nos. 368-372 (5)	2.10	1.25

For overprints see Nos. N39-N43.

Egyptian Flag, Map — A116

Globe — A117

Design: 35m, Bugler, soldier and map.

1954, Nov. 4   *Perf. 13½x13*
373	A116	10m rose vio & grn	.45	.25
374	A116	35m ver, blk & bl grn	.65	.55

Agreement of Oct. 19, 1954, with Great Britain for the evacuation of the Suez Canal zone by British troops.

Arab Postal Union Issue

1955, Jan. 1
375	A117	5m yellow brn	.45	.20
376	A117	10m green	.45	.20
377	A117	37m violet	.90	.80
		Nos. 375-377 (3)	1.80	1.20

Founding of the Arab Postal Union, 7/1/54. For overprints see Nos. 381-383.

Paul P. Harris and Rotary Emblem — A118

35m, Globe, wings and Rotary emblem.

Perf. 13½x13

1955, Feb. 23   **Wmk. 195**
378	A118	10m claret	.95	.30
379	A118	35m blue	1.25	.40

50th anniv. of the founding of Rotary Intl.

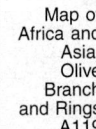

Nos. 375-377 Overprinted

1955, Nov. 1
381	A117	5m yellow brown	.70	.60
382	A117	10m green	.85	.35
383	A117	37m violet	1.00	.80
		Nos. 381-383 (3)	2.55	1.75

Arab Postal Union Congress held at Cairo, Mar. 15, 1955.

Map of Africa and Asia, Olive Branch and Rings A119

Globe, Torch, Dove and Olive Branch — A120

1956, July 29   *Perf. 13x13½, 13½x13*
384	A119	10m chestnut & green	.40	.25
385	A120	35m org yel & dull pur	.80	.70

Afro-Asian Festival, Cairo, July, 1956.

Map of Suez Canal and Ship — A121

Queen Nefertiti — A122

Perf. 11½x11

1956, Sept. 26   **Wmk. 195**
386   A121   10m blue & buff   .55   .55

Nationalization of the Suez Canal, July 26, 1956. See No. 393.

1956, Oct. 15   *Perf. 13½x13*
387   A122   10m dark green   .90   .90

Intl. Museum Week (UNESCO), Oct. 8-14.

Egyptians Defending Port Said — A123

1956, Dec. 20   **Litho.**   *Perf. 11x11½*
388   A123   10m brown violet   1.00   .60

Honoring the defenders of Port Said.

No. 388 Overprinted in Carmine Rose

1957, Jan. 14
389   A123   10m brown violet   .60   .60

Evacuation of Port Said by British and French troops, Dec. 22, 1956.

Old and New Trains A124

1957, Jan. 30   **Photo.**   *Perf. 13x13½*
390   A124   10m red violet & gray   1.00   .90

100th anniv. of the Egyptian Railway System (in 1956).

Mother and Children A125

1957, Mar. 21
391   A125   10m crimson   .50   .35

Mother's Day, 1957.

Battle Scene A126

Perf. 13x13½
1957, Mar. 28 **Wmk. 195**
392 A126 10m bright blue .40 .30

Victory over the British at Rosetta, 150th anniv.

Type of 1956; New Inscriptions in English

1957, Apr. 15 **Perf. 11½x11**
393 A121 100m blue & yel grn 1.25 1.00

Reopening of the Suez Canal.
No. 393 is inscribed: "Nationalisation of Suez Canal Co. Guarantees Freedom of Navigation" and "Reopening 1957."

Map of Gaza Strip — A127

Perf. 13½x13
1957, May 4 **Photo.** **Wmk. 195**
394 A127 10m Prus blue .95 .70

"Gaza Part of Arab Nation."
For overprint see No. N57.

Al Azhar University A128

1957, Apr. 27 **Perf. 13x13½**
New Arabic Date in Red
395 A128 10m brt violet .40 .40
396 A128 15m violet brown .55 .35
397 A128 20m dark gray .95 .70
 Nos. 395-397 (3) 1.90 1.45

Millenary of Al Azhar University, Cairo.

Shepheard's Hotel, Cairo — A129

Gate, Palace and Eagle — A130

Perf. 13½x13
1957, July 20 **Wmk. 195**
398 A129 10m brt violet .40 .20

Reopening of Shepheard's Hotel, Cairo.

Perf. 11½x11
1957, July 22 **Wmk. 315**
399 A130 10m yellow & brown .40 .20

First meeting of New National Assembly.

Amasis I in Battle of Avaris, 1580 B.C. A131

Designs: No. 401, Sultan Saladin, Hitteen, 1187 A. D. No. 402, Louis IX of France in chains, Mansourah, 1250, vert. No. 403, Map of Middle East, Ein Galout, 1260. No. 404, Port Said, 1956.

Inscribed:
"Egypt Tomb of Aggressors 1957"
1957, July 26 **Perf. 13x13½, 13½x13**
400 A131 10m carmine rose 1.00 1.00
401 A131 10m dk olive grn 1.00 1.00
402 A131 10m brown violet 1.00 1.00
403 A131 10m grnsh blue 1.00 1.00
404 A131 10m yellow brown 1.00 1.00
 Nos. 400-404 (5) 5.00 5.00

No. 400 exists with Wmk. 195.

Ahmed Arabi Speaking to the Khedive A132

Perf. 13x13½
1957, Sept. 16 **Wmk. 315**
405 A132 10m deep violet .40 .20

75th anniversary of Arabi Revolution.

Hafez Ibrahim — A133

Portrait: No. 407, Ahmed Shawky.

1957, Oct. 14 **Perf. 13½x13**
406 A133 10m dull red brn .30 .20
407 A133 10m olive green .30 .20
 a. Pair, #406-407 .70 .70

25th anniv. of the deaths of Hafez Ibrahim and Ahmed Shawky, poets.

MiG and Ilyushin Planes A134

Design: No. 409, Viscount plane.

1957, Dec. 19 **Perf. 13x13½**
408 A134 10m ultra .50 .20
409 A134 10m green .50 .20
 a. Pair, #408-409 1.20 1.20

25th anniv. of the Egyptian Air Force and of Misrair, the Egyptian airline.

Pyramids, Dove and Globe A135

1957, Dec. 26 **Photo.** **Wmk. 315**
410 A135 5m brown orange .40 .25
411 A135 10m green .40 .20
412 A135 15m brt violet .40 .20
 Nos. 410-412 (3) 1.20 .65

Afro-Asian Peoples Conf., Cairo, 12/26-1/2.

Farmer's Wife A136

Ramses II A137

"Industry" — A138

1957-58 **Wmk. 315** **Perf. 13½**
413 A136 1m blue green ('58) .30 .20
414 A137 10m violet .30 .20

1958 **Wmk. 318**
415 A136 1m lt blue green .30 .20
416 A138 5m brown .35 .20
417 A137 10m violet .45 .20
 Nos. 413-417 (5) 1.70 1.00

See Nos. 438-444, 474-488, 535. For overprints see Nos. N58-N63, N66-N68, N75, N77-N78.

Cyclists — A139

Mustafa Kamel — A140

Perf. 13½x13
1958, Jan. 12 **Wmk. 315**
418 A139 10m lt red brown .50 .30

5th Intl. Bicycle Race, Egypt, Jan. 12-26.

1958, Feb. 10 **Photo.** **Wmk. 318**
419 A140 10m blue gray .50 .20

50th anniversary of the death of Mustafa Kamel, orator and politician.

United Arab Republic

Linked Maps of Egypt and Syria — A141

Cotton — A142

Perf. 11½x11
1958, Mar. 22 **Wmk. 318**
436 A141 10m yellow & green .50 .20

Birth of United Arab Republic. See No. C90.
See also Syria-UAR Nos. 1 and C1.

1958, Apr. 5 **Perf. 13½x13**
437 A142 10m Prussian blue .40 .20

Intl. Fair for Egyptian Cotton, Apr., 1958.

Types of 1957-58 Inscribed "U.A.R. EGYPT" and

Princess Nofret — A143

Designs: 1m, Farmer's wife. 2m, Ibn-Tulun's Mosque. 4m, 14th century glass lamp (design lacks "1963" of A217). 5m, "Industry" (factories and cogwheel). 10m, Ramses II. 35m, "Commerce" (eagle, ship and cargo).

1958 **Perf. 13½x14**
438 A136 1m crimson .20 .20
439 A138 2m blue .20 .20
440 A143 3m dk red brown .20 .20
441 A217 4m green .20 .20
442 A138 5m brown .20 .20
443 A137 10m violet .55 .30
444 A138 35m lt ultra 2.00 .40
 Nos. 438-444 (7) 3.55 1.70

See Nos. 474-488, 532-533, N62-N68, N75-N78.

Qasim Amin — A144

Doves, Broken Chain and Globe — A145

1958, Apr. 23 **Perf. 13½x13**
445 A144 10m deep blue .40 .20

50th anniversary of the death of Qasim Amin, author of "Emancipation of Women."

1958, June 18
446 A145 10m violet .40 .20

5th anniv. of the republic and to publicize the struggle of peoples and individuals for freedom.
For overprint see No. N69.

Cement Industry — A146

UAR Flag — A147

Industries: No. 448, Textile. No. 449, Iron & steel. No. 450, Petroleum (Oil). No. 451, Electricity and fertilizers.

Perf. 13½x13
1958, July 23 **Photo.** **Wmk. 318**
447 A146 10m red brown .35 .20
448 A146 10m blue green .35 .20
449 A146 10m bright red .35 .20
450 A146 10m olive green .35 .20
451 A146 10m dark blue .35 .20
 a. Strip of 5, #447-451 2.10 2.10

Souvenir Sheet
Imperf

452 A147 50m grn, dp car & blk   15.00 13.00

Revolution of July 23, 1952, 6th anniv.

Sayed Darwich
A148

Hand Holding Torch, Broken Chain and Flag
A149

1958, Sept. 15   *Perf. 13½x13*
453 A148 10m violet brown   .40 .20

35th anniv. of the death of Sayed Darwich, Arab composer.

1958, Oct. 14 Photo. Wmk. 318
454 A149 10m carmine rose   .40 .20

Establishment of the Republic of Iraq. See Syria-UAR No. 13.

Maps and Cogwheels — A150

1958, Dec. 8   *Perf. 13x13½*
455 A150 10m blue   .40 .20

Issued to publicize the Economic Conference of Afro-Asian Countries, Cairo, Dec. 8.

Overprinted in Red in English and Arabic in 3 Lines: "Industrial and Agricultural Production Fair"

1958, Dec. 9
456 A150 10m lt red brown   .40 .20

Issued to publicize the Industrial and Agricultural Production Fair, Cairo, Dec. 9.

Dr. Mahmoud Azmy and UN Emblem
A151

1958, Dec. 10
457 A151 10m dull violet   .35 .20
458 A151 35m green   .75 .40

10th anniv. of the signing of the Universal Declaration of Human Rights. For overprints see Nos. N70-N71.

University Building, Sphinx, "Education" and God Thoth — A152

1958, Dec. 21 Photo. Wmk. 318
459 A152 10m grnsh black   .40 .20

50th anniversary of Cairo University.

No. 337 Surcharged

1959, Jan. 20 Wmk. 195 Perf. 13½
460 A112 55m on 100m henna brn   3.00 .75

For overprint see No. N72.

Emblem
A153

1959, Feb. 2   *Perf. 13x13½*
461 A153 10m lt olive green   .40 .20

Afro-Asian Youth Conf., Cairo, Feb. 2.

See Syria UAR issues for stamps of designs A141, A149, A154, A156, A157, A162, A170, A172, A173, A179 with denominations in piasters (p).

Arms of UAR — A154

Perf. 13½x13
1959, Feb. 22 Photo. Wmk. 318
462 A154 10m green, blk & red   .40 .20

First anniversary, United Arab Republic. See Syria UAR No. 17.

Nile Hilton Hotel
A155

1959, Feb. 22   *Perf. 13x13½*
463 A155 10m dark gray   .40 .20

Opening of the Nile Hilton Hotel, Cairo.

Globe, Radio and Telegraph
A156

1959, Mar. 1
464 A156 10m violet   .40 .20

Arab Union of Telecommunications. See Syria-UAR Nos. C20-C21.

United Arab States Issue

Flags of UAR and Yemen
A157

1959, Mar. 8
465 A157 10m sl grn, car & blk   .40 .20

First anniversary of United Arab States. See Syria-UAR No. 16.

Oil Derrick and Pipe Line — A158

Perf. 13½x13
1959, Apr. 16 Litho. Wmk. 318
466 A158 10m lt bl & dk bl   .45 .20

First Arab Petroleum Congress, Cairo.

Railroad
A159

Designs: No. 468, Bus on highway. No. 469, River barge. No. 470, Ocean liner. No. 471, Telecommunications on map. No. 472, Stamp printing building, Heliopolis. No. 472A, Ship, train, plane and motorcycle mail carrier.

1959, July 23 Photo. Perf. 13x13½
Frame in Gray

467 A159 10m maroon   .85 .30
468 A159 10m green   .85 .30
469 A159 10m violet   .85 .30
470 A159 10m dark blue   .85 .30
471 A159 10m dull purple   .85 .30
472 A159 10m scarlet   .85 .30
   Nos. 467-472 (6)   5.10 1.80

Souvenir Sheet
Imperf

472A A159 50m green & red   12.00 12.00

No. 472A for the 7th anniv. of the Egyptian revolution of 1952 and was sold only with 5 sets of Nos. 467-472.

Globe, Swallows and Map — A160

1959, Aug. 8   *Perf. 13½x13*
473 A160 10m maroon   .40 .20

Convention of the Assoc. of Arab Emigrants in the US.

Types of 1953-58 without "Egypt" and

St. Simon's Gate, Bosra, Syria — A161

Designs: 1m, Farmer's wife. 2m, Ibn-Tulun's Mosque. 3m, Princess Nofret. 4m, 14th century glass lamp (design lacks "1963" of A217). 5m, "Industry" (factories and cogwheel). 10m, Ramses II. 15m, Omayyad Mosque, Damascus. 20m, Lotus vase, Tutankhamen treasure. 35m, Eagle, ship and cargo. 40m, Scribe statue. 45m, Saladin's citadel, Aleppo. 55m, Eagle, cotton and wheat. 60m, Dam and factory. 100m, Eagle, hand, cotton and grain. 200m, Palmyra ruins, Syria. 500m, Queen Nefertiti, inscribed "UAR" (no ovpt.).

Perf. 13½x14, 14x13½
1959-60   Wmk. 328   Photo.
474 A136 1m vermilion   .20 .20
475 A138 2m dp blue ('60)   .20 .20
476 A143 3m maroon   .20 .20
477 A217 4m green ('60)   .20 .20
478 A138 5m black ('60)   .20 .20
479 A137 10m dk ol grn   .30 .20
480 A138 15m deep claret   .30 .20
481 A138 20m crimson ('60)   .30 .20
482 A161 30m brown vio   .35 .20

---

483 A138 35m lt vio bl ('60)   .50 .20
484 A143 40m sepia   .55 .20
485 A161 45m lil gray ('60)   .90 .20
486 A138 55m brt blue grn   1.00 .20
487 A138 60m dp purple ('60)   1.25 .20
488 A138 100m org & sl grn ('60)   2.25 .30
489 A161 200m lt blue & mar ('60)   4.00 .50
490 A112 500m dk gray & red ('60)   12.00 1.25
   Nos. 474-490 (17)   24.70 4.85

See Nos. 532-535.

Shield and Cogwheel — A162

Perf. 13½x13
1959, Oct. 20 Photo. Wmk. 328
491 A162 10m brt car rose   .40 .20

Issued for Army Day, 1959. See Syria-UAR No. 32.

Cairo Museum
A163

1959, Nov. 18   *Perf. 13x13½*
492 A163 10m olive gray   .40 .20

Centenary of Cairo museum.

Abu Simbel Temple of Ramses II — A164

1959, Dec. 22   *Perf. 11x11½*
493 A164 10m lt red brn, pnksh   .50 .25

Issued as propaganda to save historic monuments in Nubia threatened by the construction of Aswan High Dam.

Postrider, 12th Century A165

1960, Jan. 2   *Perf. 13x13½*
494 A165 10m dark blue   .40 .20

Issued for Post Day, Jan. 2.

Hydroelectric Power Station, Aswan Dam — A166

1960, Jan. 9
495 A166 10m violet blk   .40 .20

Inauguration of the Aswan Dam hydroelectric power station, Jan. 9.

A167

10m, Arabic and English Description of Aswan High Dam. 35m, Architect's Drawing of Aswan High Dam.

1960, Jan. 9   *Perf. 11x11½*
496   10m claret   .45 .30
497   35m claret   .95 .30
  a.   A167 Pair, #496-497   1.50 1.50

Start of work on the Aswan High Dam.

Symbols of
Agriculture and   Arms and
Industry — A169   Flag — A170

1960, Jan. 16   *Perf. 13½x13*
498 A169 10m gray grn & sl grn   .35 .20
Industrial and Agricultural Fair, Cairo.

1960, Feb. 22   Photo.   Wmk. 328
499 A170 10m green, blk & red   .35 .20
2nd anniversary of the proclamation of the United Arab Republic.
See Syria-UAR No. 38.

No. 340 Overprinted "UAR" in English and Arabic in Red

Perf. 13½ Wmk. 195
1960
500 A112 £1 dk grn, blk & red 19.00 5.00

"Art" — A171

Perf. 13½x13
1960, Mar. 1   Wmk. 328
501 A171 10m brown   .40 .20
Issued to publicize the 3rd Biennial Exhibition of Fine Arts in Alexandria.

Arab
League
Center,
Cairo
A172

1960, Mar. 22   Photo.   Perf. 13x13½
502 A172 10m dull grn & blk   .35 .20
Opening of Arab League Center and Arab Postal Museum, Cairo.
See Syria-UAR No. 40.

Refugees
Pointing to
Map of
Palestine
A173

1960, Apr. 7
503 A173 10m orange ver   .40 .20
504 A173 35m Prus blue   .60 .20
World Refugee Year, 7/1/59-6/30/60.
See Nos. N73-N74. See also Syria-UAR Nos. 43-44.

Weight Lifter — A174

Stadium, Cairo — A175

Sports: No. 506, Basketball. No. 507, Soccer. No. 508, Fencing. No. 509, Rowing. 30m, Steeplechase, horiz. 35m, Swimming, horiz.

Perf. 13½x13
1960, July 23   Photo.   Wmk. 328
505 A174   5m gray   .45 .20
506 A174   5m brown   .45 .20
507 A174   5m dp claret   .45 .20
508 A174 10m brt carmine   .45 .20
509 A174 10m gray green   .45 .20
  a.   Vert. or horiz. strip, #505-509   2.50
510 A174 30m purple   .60 .20
511 A174 35m dark blue   .70 .20
  Nos. 505-511 (7)   3.55 1.40

Souvenir Sheet
Imperf
512 A175 100m car & brown   3.00 3.00
Nos. 505-511 for the 17th Olympic Games, Rome, Aug. 25-Sept. 11.

Dove and UN
Emblem — A176

35m, Lights surrounding UN emblem, horiz.

Perf. 13½x13
1960, Oct. 24   Wmk. 328
513 A176 10m purple   .25 .20
514 A176 35m brt rose   .35 .20
15th anniversary of United Nations.

Abu Simbel Temple of Queen
Nefertari — A177

Perf. 11x11½
1960, Nov. 14   Photo.   Wmk. 328
515 A177 10m ocher, *buff*   .55 .20
Issued as propaganda to save historic monuments in Nubia and in connection with the UNESCO meeting, Paris, Nov. 14.

Model
Post
Office
A178

1961, Jan. 2   *Perf. 13x13½*
516 A178 10m brt car rose   .35 .20
Issued for Post Day, Jan. 2.

Eagle, Fasces
and Victory   Wheat and
Wreath — A179   Globe
                     Surrounded by
                     Flags — A180

1961, Feb. 22   *Perf. 13½x13*
517 A179 10m dull violet   .35 .20
3rd anniversary of United Arab Republic.
See Syria-UAR No. 50.

1961, Mar. 21   Wmk. 328
518 A180 10m vermilion   .35 .20
Intl. Agricultural Exhib., Cairo, 3/21-4/20.

Patrice   Reading Braille
Lumumba and   and WHO
Map   Emblem
A181   A182

1961, Mar. 30   *Perf. 13½x13*
519 A181 10m black   .35 .20
Africa Day, Apr. 15 and 3rd Conf. of Independent African States, Cairo, Mar. 25-31.

1961, Apr. 6   Photo.
520 A182 10m red brown   .35 .20
WHO Day. See Nos. B21, N80.

Tower of   Arab Woman
Cairo — A183   and Son,
                     Palestine
                     Map — A184

1961, Apr. 11   *Perf. 13½x13*
521 A183 10m grnsh blue   .35 .20
Opening of the 600-foot Tower of Cairo, on island of Gizireh. See No. C95.

1961, May 15   Wmk. 328
522 A184 10m brt green   .40 .20
Issued for Palestine Day.
See No. N79.

Symbols
of Industry
and
Electricity
A185

Chart and Workers — A186

#524, New buildings and family. #525, Ship, train, bus and radio. #526, Dam, cotton and field. #527, Hand holding candle and family.

1961, July 23   Photo.   Perf. 13x13½
523 A185 10m dp carmine   .45 .20
524 A185 10m brt blue   .45 .20
525 A185 10m dk vio brown   .45 .20
526 A185 35m dk green   .55 .20
527 A185 35m brt purple   .55 .20
  Nos. 523-527 (5)   2.45 1.00

Souvenir Sheet
Imperf
528 A186 100m red brown   3.00 2.25
9th anniv. of the revolution.

Map of Suez Canal
and Ships — A187

Perf. 11½x11
1961, July 26   Unwmk.
529 A187 10m olive   .40 .20
Suez Canal Co. nationalization, 5th anniv.

Various Enterprises of Misr
Bank — A188

Perf. 13x13½
1961, Aug. 22   Wmk. 328
530 A188 10m red brn, pnksh   .35 .20
The 41st anniversary of Misr Bank.

Flag, Ship's Wheel
and
Battleship — A189

1961, Aug. 29 Photo. Perf. 13½x13
531 A189 10m deep blue   .40 .20
Issued for Navy Day.

**Type A136 Redrawn, Type A138,
Type A217 and:**

Eagle of Saladin
over Cairo — A190

Designs: 1m, Farmer's wife. 4m, 14th cent.
glass lamp. 35m, "Commerce."

1961, Aug. 31 Unwmk.   Perf. 11½
532 A136 1m blue   .25 .20
533 A217 4m olive   .25 .20
534 A190 10m purple   .25 .20
535 A138 35m slate blue   .30 .20
    Nos. 532-535 (4)   1.05 .80

Smaller of two Arabic inscriptions in new
positions: 1m, at right above Egyptian
numeral; 4m, upward to spot beside waist of
lamp; 35m, upper left corner below "UAR." On
4m, "UAR" is 2mm deep instead of 1mm.
"Egypt" omitted as in 1959-60.

UN Emblem, Book,
Cogwheel,
Corn — A191

Perf. 13½x13
1961, Oct. 24   Wmk. 328
Design: 35m, Globe and cogwheel, horiz.
536 A191 10m black & ocher   .25 .20
537 A191 35m blue grn & brn   .45 .20
UN Technical Assistance Program and 16th
anniv. of the UN.
See Nos. N81-N82.

Trajan's Kiosk, Philae — A192

1961, Nov. 4 Unwmk.   Perf. 11½
Size: 60x27mm
538 A192 10m dp vio blue   .75 .30
15th anniv. of UNESCO, and to publicize
UNESCO's help in safeguarding the monuments of Nubia.

Palette,   Atom and
Brushes, Map   Educational
of   Symbols
Mediterranean   A194
A193

1961, Dec. 14 Wmk. 328 Perf. 13½
539 A193 10m dk red brown   .35 .20
Issued to publicize the 4th Biennial Exhibition of Fine Arts in Alexandria.

1961, Dec. 18
540 A194 10m dull purple   .35 .20
Issued to publicize Education Day.
See No. N83.

Arms of
UAR
A195

1961, Dec. 23 Unwmk.   Perf. 11½
541 A195 10m brt pink, brt grn &
         blk   .35 .20
Victory Day. See No. N84.

Sphinx at
Giza — A196

1961, Dec. 27   Perf. 11x11½
542 A196 10m black   .45 .30
Issued to publicize the "Sound and Light"
Project, the installation of floodlights and
sound equipment at the site of the Pyramids
and Sphinx.

Post
Office
Printing
Plant,
Nasser
City
A197

1962, Jan. 2 Photo. Perf. 11½x11
543 A197 10m dk brown   .35 .20
Issued for Post Day, Jan. 2.

Map of Africa, King
Mohammed V of
Morocco and
Flags — A198

1962, Jan. 4   Perf. 11x11½
544 A198 10m indigo   .35 .20
African Charter, Casablanca, 1st anniv.

Girl Scout
Saluting
and
Emblem
A199

Perf. 13x13½
1962, Feb. 22   Wmk. 328
545 A199 10m bright blue   1.00 .30
Egyptian Girl Scouts' 25th anniversary.

Arab Refugees,   Mother and
Flag and   Child — A201
Map — A200

1962, Mar. 7   Perf. 13½x13
546 A200 10m dark slate green   .35 .20
5th anniv. of the liberation of the Gaza Strip.
See No. N85.

1962, Mar. 21   Photo.
547 A201 10m dk violet brn   1.00 .20
Issued for Arab Mother's Day, Mar. 21.

Map of Africa and
Post Horn — A202

1962, Apr. 23   Wmk. 328
548 A202 10m crimson & ocher   .30 .20
549 A202 50m dp blue & ocher   .60 .20
Establishment of African Postal Union.

Cadets on
Parade
and
Academy
Emblem
A203

1962, June 18   Perf. 13x13½
550 A203 10m green   .35 .20
Egyptian Military Academy, 150th anniv.

Malaria   Theodor
Eradication   Bilharz — A205
Emblem — A204

1962, June 20   Perf. 13½x13
551 A204 10m dk brown & red   .25 .20
552 A204 35m dk green & blue   .30 .20
WHO drive to eradicate malaria.
See Nos. N87-N88.

1962, June 24   Perf. 11x11½
553 A205 10m brown orange   .35 .20
Dr. Theodor Bilharz (1825-1862), German
physician who first described bilharziasis, an
endemic disease in Egypt.

Patrice   Hand on
Lumumba and   Charter — A207
Map of
Africa — A206

1962, July 1 Photo. Wmk. 342
554 A206 10m rose & red   .35 .20
Issued in memory of Patrice Lumumba
(1925-61), Premier of Congo.

1962, July 10   Perf. 11x11½
555 A207 10m brt blue & dk brn .35 .20
Proclamation of the National Charter.

"Birth of the
Revolution"
A208

Symbolic Designs: #557, Proclamation
(Scroll and book). #558, Agricultural Reform
(Farm and crescent). #559, Bandung Conference (Dove, globe and olive branch). #560,
Birth of UAR (Eagle and flag). #561, Industrialization (cogwheel, factory, ship and bus).
#562, Aswan High Dam. #563, Social Revolu-
tion (Modern buildings and emblem). 100m,
Arms of UAR, emblems of Afro-Asian and African countries and UN.

1962, July 23   Perf. 11½
556 A208 10m brn, dk red brn
         & pink   .20 .20
557 A208 10m dk blue & sepia   .20 .20
558 A208 10m sepia & brt bl   .20 .20
559 A208 10m olive & dk ultra   .20 .20
560 A208 10m grn, blk & red   .20 .20
561 A208 10m brn org & indigo   .20 .20
562 A208 10m brn org & vio blk .20 .20
563 A208 10m orange & blk   .20 .20
    Nos. 556-563 (8)   1.60 1.60
Souvenir Sheets
Perf. 11½
564 A208 100m grn, pink, red &
         blk   2.50 2.25
10th anniv. of the revolution.
No. 564 exists imperf. Same value.

Mahmoud Moukhtar, Museum and Sculpture A209

1962, July 24 *Perf. 11½x11*
565 A209 10m lt vio bl & olive .35 .20

Opening of the Moukhtar Museum, Island of Gezireh. The sculpture is "La Vestale de Secrets" by Moukhtar.

Flag of Algeria and Map of Africa Showing Algeria — A210

1962, Aug. 15 *Perf. 11x11½*
566 A210 10m multicolored .35 .20

Algeria's independence, July 1, 1962.

Rocket, Arms of UAR and Atom Symbol — A211

1962, Sept. 1 Photo. Wmk. 342
567 A211 10m brt grn, red & blk .40 .20

Launching of UAR rockets.

Rifle and Target — A212

Map of Africa, Table Tennis Paddle, Net and Ball — A213

1962, Sept. 18 *Perf. 11½*
568 A212 5m green, blk & red .45 .25
569 A213 5m green, blk & red .45 .25
a. Pair, #568-569 1.00 1.00
570 A212 10m bister, bl & dk grn .55 .40
571 A213 10m bister, bl & dk grn .55 .40
a. Pair, #570-571 1.25 1.25
572 A212 35m dp ultra, red & blk 1.25 .85
573 A213 35m dp ultra, red & blk 1.25 .85
a. Pair, #572-573 2.75 2.75
Nos. 568-573 (6) 4.50 3.00

38th World Shooting Championships and the 1st African Table Tennis Tournament. Types A212 and A213 are printed se-tenant at the base.

Dag Hammarskjold and UN Emblem — A214

1962, Oct. 24 Photo. Wmk. 342
Perf. 11½x11
Portrait in Slate Blue
574 A214 5m deep lilac .40 .20
575 A214 10m olive .50 .20
576 A214 35m deep ultra .65 .20
Nos. 574-576 (3) 1.55 .60

Dag Hammarskjold, Secretary General of the UN, 1953-61, and 17th anniv. of the UN. See Nos. N89-N91.

Queen Nefertari Crowned by Isis and Hathor — A215

1962, Oct. 31 *Perf. 11½*
577 A215 10m blue & ocher .80 .40

Issued to publicize the UNESCO campaign to safeguard the monuments of Nubia.

Jet Trainer, Hawker Hart Biplane and College Emblem A216

1962, Nov. 2 *Perf. 11½x11*
578 A216 10m bl, dk bl & crim .35 .20

25th anniversary of Air Force College.

14th Century Glass Lamp and "1963" — A217

Yemen Flag and Hand with Torch — A218

1963, Feb. 20 *Perf. 11x11½*
579 A217 4m dk brn, grn & car .35 .20

Issued for use on greeting cards.
See Nos. 441, 477, 533, N76, N92. For overprint see No. N65.

1963, Mar. 14 Photo. Wmk. 342
580 A218 10m olive & brt car .35 .20

Establishment of Yemen Arab Republic.

Tennis Player, Pyramids and Globe A219

Perf. 11½x11
1963, Mar. 20 **Unwmk.**
581 A219 10m gray, blk & brn .50 .20

Intl. Lawn Tennis Championships, Cairo.

Cow, UN and FAO Emblems A220

Designs: 10m, Corn, wheat and emblems, vert. 35m, Wheat, corn and emblems.

Perf. 11½x11, 11x11½
1963, Mar. 21 **Wmk. 342**
582 A220 5m violet & dp org .40 .25
583 A220 10m ultra & yel .45 .25
584 A220 35m blue, yel & blk .55 .40
Nos. 582-584 (3) 1.40 .90

FAO "Freedom from Hunger" campaign. See Nos. N93-N95.

Centenary Emblem — A221

Design: 35m, Globe and emblem.

1963, May 8 Unwmk. Perf. 11x11½
585 A221 10m lt blue, red & mar .30 .20
586 A221 35m lt blue & red .60 .20

Centenary of the Red Cross. See Nos. N96-N97.

Arab Socialist Union Emblem A222

50m, Tools, torch & symbol of National Charter.

Wmk. 342
1963, July 23 Photo. Perf. 11½
587 A222 10m slate & rose pink .35 .20
Souvenir Sheets
Perf. 11½
588 A222 50m vio bl & org yel 1.90 1.60

11th anniv. of the revolution and to publicize the Arab Socialist Union.
No. 588 exists imperf. Same value.

Television Station, Cairo, and Screen A223

1963, Aug. 1 *Perf. 11½x11*
589 A223 10m dk blue & yel .35 .20

2nd Intl. Television Festival, Alexandria, 9/1-10.

Queen Nefertari A224

Swimmer and Map of Suez Canal A225

Designs: 10m, Great Hypostyle Hall, Abu Simbel. 35m, Ramses in moonlight.

Wmk. 342
1963, Oct. 1 Photo. Perf. 11
Size: 25x42mm (5m, 35m); 28x61mm (10m)
590 A224 5m brt vio blue & yel .40 .25
591 A224 10m gray, blk & red .60 .30
org .60 .30
592 A224 35m org yel & blk 1.00 .45
Nos. 590-592 (3) 2.00 .90

UNESCO world campaign to save historic monuments in Nubia. See Nos. N98-N100.

1963, Oct. 15
593 A225 10m blue & sal rose .35 .20

Intl. Suez Canal Swimming Championship.

Ministry of Agriculture — A226

Perf. 11½x11
1963, Nov. 20 **Wmk. 342**
594 A226 10m multicolored .35 .20

50th anniv. of the Ministry of Agriculture.

Modern Building and Map of Africa and Asia A227

1963, Dec. 7
595 A227 10m multicolored .35 .20

Afro-Asian Housing Congress, Dec. 7-12.

Scales, Globe, UN Emblem A228

1963, Dec. 10
596 A228 5m dk green & yel .30 .20
597 A228 10m blue, gray & blk .35 .20
598 A228 35m rose red, pink & red .40 .30
Nos. 596-598 (3) 1.05 .70

15th anniv. of the Universal Declaration of Human Rights. See Nos. N101-N103.

Sculpture, Arms of Alexandria and Palette with Flags — A229

1963, Dec. 12 *Perf. 11x11½*
599 A229 10m pale bl, dk bl & brn .35 .20

Issued to publicize the 5th Biennial Exhibition of Fine Arts in Alexandria.

Lion and Nile Hilton Hotel — A230

Vase, 13th Century — A231

Pharaoh
Userkaf
(5th
Dynasty)
A232

100M

Designs: 1m, Vase, 14th century. 2m, Ivory headrest. 3m, Pharaonic calcite boat. 4m, Minaret and gate. 5m, Nile and Aswan High Dam. 10m, Eagle of Saladin over pyramids. 15m, Window, Ibn Tulun's mosque. No. 608, Mitwalli Gate, Cairo. 35m, Nefertari. 40m, Tower Hotel. 55m, Sultan Hassan's Mosque. 60m, Courtyard, Al Azhar University. 200m, Head of Ramses II. 500m, Funerary mask of Tutankhamen.

1964-67   Unwmk.   Photo.   Perf. 11
**Size: Nos. 608, 612, 19x24mm;
   others, 24x29mm**

600	A231	1m citron & ultra	.20	.20
601	A230	2m magenta & bis	.20	.20
602	A230	3m sal, org & bl	.20	.20
603	A235	4m och, blk & ultra	.35	.20
604	A230	5m brn & brt blue	.20	.20
a.		5m brown & dark blue	.50	.20
605	A231	10m green, dk brn & lt brn	.30	.20
606	A230	15m ultra & yel	.30	.20
607	A230	20m brn org & blk	.70	.20
608	A231	20m lt olive grn ('67)	1.50	.20
609	A231	30m yellow & brown	.70	.20
610	A231	35m sal, och & ultra	.60	.20
611	A231	40m ultra & yellow	1.50	.40
612	A231	55m brt red lil ('67)	2.00	.20
613	A231	60m grnsh bl & yel brn	.80	.30

Wmk. 342

614	A232	100m dk vio brn & sl	4.00	.85
615	A232	200m bluish blk & yel brn	7.00	1.00
616	A232	500m ultra & dp org	15.00	3.00
		Nos. 600-616 (17)	35.55	7.95

Nos. 603 & N107 lack the vertically arranged dates which appear at lower right on No. 619.
See Nos. N104-N116.

HSN Commission
Emblem — A233

Perf. 11x11½
1964, Jan. 10   Wmk. 342
617 A233 10m dull bl, dk bl & yel   .35 .20

1st conf. of the Commission of Health, Sanitation and Nutrition.

Arab League Emblem — A234

1964, Jan. 13   Perf. 11
618 A234 10m brt green & blk   .35 .20

1st meeting of the Heads of State of the Arab League, Cairo, January.
See No. N117.

Minaret at
Night — A235

1964   Unwmk.   Perf. 11
619 A235 4m emerald, blk & red   .35 .20

Issued for use on greeting cards.
See Nos. 603, N107, N118.

Old and
New
Dwellings
and Map
of Nubia
A236

Perf. 11½x11
1964, Feb. 27   Photo.   Wmk. 342
620 A236 10m dull vio & yel   .35 .20

Resettlement of Nubian population.

Map of
Africa and
Asia and
Train
A237

1964, Mar. 21
621 A237 10m dull bl, dk bl & yel .90 .50

Asian Railway Conference, Cairo, Mar. 21.

Ikhnaton and
Nefertiti with
Children — A238

1964, Mar. 21   Perf. 11x11½
622 A238 10m dk brown & ultra   .50 .30

Issued for Arab Mother's Day, Mar. 21.

APU   WHO
Emblem — A239   Emblem — A240

1964, Apr. 1   Photo.   Wmk. 342
623 A239 10m org brn & bl, sal   .35 .20

Permanent Office of the APU, 10th anniv.
See No. N119.

1964, Apr. 7
624 A240 10m dk blue & red   .35 .20

World Health Day (Anti-Tuberculosis).
See No. N120.

Statue of Liberty, World's Fair Pavilion
and Pyramids
A241

1964, Apr. 22   Perf. 11½x11
625 A241 10m brt green & ol, grysh .35 .20

New York World's Fair, 1964-65.

Nile and
Aswan High
Dam
A242

1964, May 15   Unwmk.   Perf. 11½
626 A242 10m black & blue   .35 .20

The diversion of the Nile.

"Land Reclamation" — A243

Design: No. 628, "Electricity," Aswan High Dam hydroelectric station.

1964, July 23   Perf. 11½
627 A243 10m yellow & emer   .35 .20
628 A243 10m green & blk   .35 .20

Land reclamation and hydroelectric power due to the Aswan High Dam.
An imperf. souvenir sheet, issued July 23, contains two 50m black and blue stamps showing Aswan High Dam before and after diversion of the Nile. Value $2.

Map of Africa and 34 Flags — A244

1964, July 17   Photo.
629 A244 10m brn, brt bl & blk   .35 .20

Assembly of Heads of State and Government of the Organization for African Unity at Cairo in July.

Jamboree Emblem — A245

Design: No. 631, Emblem of Air Scouts.

1964, Aug. 28   Unwmk.   Perf. 11½
630 A245 10m red, grn & blk   .40 .25
631 A245 10m green & red   .40 .25
 a.   Pair, #630-631   1.00 1.00

The 6th Pan Arab Jamboree, Alexandria.

Flag of
Algeria
A246

1964, Sept. 5   Perf. 11½x11
Flags in Original Colors

632	A246	10m Algeria	.55	.30
633	A246	10m Iraq	.55	.30
634	A246	10m Jordan	.55	.30
635	A246	10m Kuwait	.55	.30
636	A246	10m Lebanon	.55	.30
637	A246	10m Libya	.55	.30
638	A246	10m Morocco	.55	.30
639	A246	10m Saudi Arabia	.55	.30
640	A246	10m Sudan	.55	.30
641	A246	10m Syria	.55	.30
642	A246	10m Tunisia	.55	.30
643	A246	10m UAR	.55	.30
644	A246	10m Yemen	.55	.30
		Nos. 632-644 (13)	7.15	3.90

2nd meeting of the Heads of State of the Arab League, Alexandria, Sept. 1964.

World Map, Dove, Olive Branches and
Pyramids — A247

1964, Oct. 5   Perf. 11½
645 A247 10m slate blue & yel   .35 .20

Conference of Heads of State of Non-Aligned Countries, Cairo, Oct. 1964.

Pharaonic
Athletes
A248

Designs from ancient decorations: 10m, Four athletes, vert. 35m, Wrestlers, vert. 50m, Pharaoh in chariot hunting.

Perf. 11½x11, 11x11½
1964, Oct. 10   Photo.   Unwmk.
Sizes: 39x22mm, 22x39mm

646	A248	5m lt green & org	.25	.20
647	A248	10m slate bl & lt brn	.35	.20
648	A248	35m dull vio & lt brn	.65	.50

Size: 58x24mm

649	A248	50m ultra & brn org	1.25	.75
		Nos. 646-649 (4)	2.50	1.65

18th Olympic Games Tokyo, Oct. 10-25.

Emblem, Map of   Map of Africa,
Africa and Asia   Communication
A249   Symbols
                      A250

1964, Oct. 10   Perf. 11x11½
650 A249 10m violet & yellow   .35 .20

First Afro-Asian Medical Congress.

1964, Oct. 24
651 A250 10m green & blk   .35 .20

Pan-African and Malagasy Posts and Telecommunications Cong., Cairo, Oct. 24-Nov. 6.

Horus and Facade of Nefertari Temple, Abu Simbel A251

Ramses II — A252

Designs: 35m, A god holding rope of life, Abu Simbel. 50m, Isis of Kalabsha, horiz.

1964, Oct. 24   Perf. 11½, 11x11½
652 A251 5m grnsh bl & yel
            brn   .45 .30
653 A252 10m sepia & brt yel   .75 .30
654 A251 35m brown org & in-
            digo   1.50 .90
    Nos. 652-654 (3)   2.70 1.50

Souvenir Sheet
Imperf
655 A252 50m olive & vio blk   13.50 13.50

"Save the Monuments of Nubia" campaign. No. 655 contains one horiz. stamp.

Emblems of Cooperation, Rural Handicraft and Women's Work — A253

1964, Dec. 8   Photo.   Unwmk.
656 A253 10m yellow & dk blue   .35 .20
25th anniv. of the Ministry of Social Affairs.

UN, UNESCO Emblems, Pyramids A254

Minaret, Mardani Mosque A255

1964, Dec. 24   Perf. 11x11½
657 A254 10m ultra & yellow   .35 .20
Issued for UNESCO Day.

1965, Jan. 20   Photo.   Perf. 11
658 A255 4m blue & dk brown   .35 .20
Issued for use on greeting cards. See No. N121.

Police Emblem over City A256

Oil Derrick and Emblem A257

Perf. 11x11½
1965, Jan. 25   Wmk. 342
659 A256 10m black & yellow   .55 .20
Issued for Police Day.

1965, Mar. 16   Photo.
660 A257 10m dk brown & yellow   .45 .20
5th Arab Petroleum Congress and the 2nd Arab Petroleum Exhibition.

Flags and Emblem of the Arab League — A258

Red Crescent and WHO Emblem — A259

Design: 20m, Arab League emblem, horiz.

1965, Mar. 22   Wmk. 342
661 A258 10m green, red & blk   .50 .30
662 A258 20m ultra & brown   .85 .40
20th anniversary of the Arab League. See Nos. N122-N123.

1965, Apr. 7   Photo.
663 A259 10m blue & crimson   .35 .20
World Health Day (Smallpox: Constant Alert). See No. N124.

Dagger in Map of Palestine — A260

1965, Apr. 9   Perf. 11x11½
664 A260 10m black & red   1.00 .20
Deir Yassin massacre, Apr. 9, 1948. See No. N125.

ITU Emblem, Old and New Communication Equipment — A261

1965, May 17   Perf. 11½x11
665 A261 5m violet blk & yel   .30 .25
666 A261 10m red & yellow   .35 .20
667 A261 35m dk blue, ultra &
            yel   1.10 .80
    Nos. 665-667 (3)   1.75 1.30
Cent. of the ITU. See Nos. N126-N128.

Library Aflame and Lamp A262

1965, June 7   Photo.   Wmk. 342
668 A262 10m black, grn & red   .40 .20
Burning of the Library of Algiers, 6/7/62.

Sheik Mohammed Abdo (1850-1905), Mufti of Egypt — A263

1965, July 11   Perf. 11x11½
669 A263 10m Prus blue & bis brn   .35 .20

Pouring Ladle (Heavy Industry) A264

President Gamal Abdel Nasser and Emblems of Arab League, African Unity Organization, Afro-Asian Countries and UN — A265

#670, Search for off-shore oil. #672, Housing, construction in Nasser City (diamond shaped).

1965, July 23   Perf. 11½
670 A264 10m indigo & lt blue   .60 .35
671 A264 10m brown & yellow   .60 .35
672 A264 10m yel brn & blk   .60 .35
673 A265 100m lt green & blk   4.25 3.25
    Nos. 670-673 (4)   6.05 4.30

13th anniversary of the revolution.
The 100m was printed in sheets of six, consisting of two singles and two vertical pairs. Margins and gutters contain multiple UAR coat of arms in light green. Size: 240x330mm.

4th Pan Arab Games Emblem A266

Map and Emblems of Previous Games — A267

#675, Swimmers Zeitun & Abd el Gelil, arms of Alexandria. 35m, Race horse "Saadoon."

Perf. 11½x11; 11½ (#676)
1965, Sept. 2   Photo.   Wmk. 342
674 A266 5m blue & red   .30 .20
675 A266 10m dp blue & dk brn   .45 .40
676 A267 10m org brn & dp bl   .50 .40
677 A266 35m green & brown   1.00 .75
    Nos. 674-677 (4)   2.25 1.75

4th Pan Arab Games, Cairo, Sept. 2-11. No. 675 for the long-distance swimming competition at Alexandria, a part of the Games.

Map of Arab Countries, Emblem of Arab League and Broken Chain A268

1965, Sept. 13   Photo.   Perf. 11½
678 A268 10m brown & yellow   .35 .20
3rd Arab Summit Conf., Casablanca, 9/13.

Land Forces Emblem and Sun — A269

Perf. 11x11½
1965, Oct. 20   Wmk. 342
679 A269 10m bister brn & blk   .40 .20
Issued for Land Forces Day.

Map of Africa, Torch and Olive Branches — A270

1965, Oct. 21   Perf. 11½
680 A270 10m dull pur & car rose   .35 .20
Assembly of Heads of State of the Organization for African Unity.

Ramses II, Abu Simbel, and ICY Emblem A271

Pillars, Philae, and UN Emblem — A272

Designs: 35m, Two Ramses II statues, Abu Simbel and UNESCO emblem. 50m, Cartouche of Ramses II and ICY emblem, horiz.

Wmk. 342
1965, Oct. 24   Photo.   Perf. 11½
681 A271 5m yellow & slate grn   .75   .35
682 A272 10m blue & black   1.25   .40
683 A271 35m dk violet & yel   2.75   1.25
Nos. 681-683 (3)   4.75   2.00

Souvenir Sheet
Imperf
684 A272 50m brt ultra & dk brn   3.75   3.00

Intl. cooperation in saving the Nubian monuments. No. 684 also for the 20th anniv. of the UN. No. 684 contains one 42x25mm stamp.

Al-Maqrizi, Buildings and Books A273

Perf. 11½x11
1965, Nov. 20   Photo.   Wmk. 342
685 A273 10m olive & dk slate grn   .35   .20
Ahmed Al-Maqrizi (1365-1442), historian.

Flag of UAR, Arms of Alexandria and Art Symbols — A274

1965, Dec. 16   Perf. 11x11½
686 A274 10m multicolored   .35   .20
6th Biennial Exhibition of Fine Arts in Alexandria, Dec. 16, 1965-Mar. 31, 1966.

Parchment Letter, Carrier Pigeon and Postrider A275

1966, Jan. 2   Wmk. 342   Perf. 11½
687 A275 10m multicolored   .45   .20
Nos. 687,CB1-CB2 (3)   5.95   4.45
Post Day, Jan. 2.

Lamp and Arch — A276

Exhibition Poster — A277

1966, Jan. 10   Unwmk.   Perf. 11
688 A276 4m violet & dp org   .30   .20
Issued for use on greeting cards.

Perf. 11x11½
1966, Jan. 27   Wmk. 342
689 A277 10m lt blue & blk   .35   .20
Industrial Exhibition, Jan. 29-Feb.

Arab League Emblem — A278

Printed Page and Torch — A279

1966, Mar. 22   Photo.   Wmk. 342
690 A278 10m brt yellow & pur   .35   .20
Arab Publicity Week, Mar. 22-28.

1966, Mar. 25   Perf. 11x11½
691 A279 10m dp orange & sl blue   .35   .20
Centenary of the national press.

Traffic Signal at Night — A280

Hands Holding Torch, Flags of UAR & Iraq — A281

1966, May 4   Photo.   Wmk. 342
692 A280 10m green & red   .55   .20
Issued for Traffic Day.

1966, May 26   Perf. 11x11½
693 A281 10m dp claret, rose red & brt grn   .35   .20
Friendship between UAR and Iraq.

Workers and UN Emblem A282

Perf. 11½x11
1966, June 1   Photo.   Wmk. 342
694 A282 5m blue grn & blk   .30   .25
695 A282 10m brt rose lil & grn   .35   .25
696 A282 35m orange & black   .90   .70
Nos. 694-696 (3)   1.55   1.20
50th session of the ILO.

Mobilization Dept. Emblem, People and City — A283

1966, June 30   Perf. 11x11½
697 A283 10m dull pur & brn   .35   .20
Population sample, May 31-June 16.

"Salah el Din," Crane and Cogwheel A284

Present-day Basket Dance and Pharaonic Dance — A285

#699, Transfer of first stones of Abu Simbel. #700, Development of Sinai (map of Red Sea area and Sinai Peninsula). #701, El Maadi Hospital and nurse with patient.

Wmk. 342
1966, July 23   Photo.   Perf. 11½
698 A284 10m orange & multi   .45   .30
699 A284 10m brt green & multi   .45   .30
700 A284 10m yellow & multi   .45   .30
701 A284 10m lt blue & multi   .45   .30
Nos. 698-701 (4)   1.80   1.20

Souvenir Sheet
Imperf
702 A285 100m multicolored   5.00   3.75
14th anniv. of the revolution.

Suez Canal Headquarters, Ships and Map of Canal — A286

1966, July 26   Perf. 11½
703 A286 10m blue & crimson   1.00   .40
Suez Canal nationalization, 10th anniv.

Cotton, Farmers with Plow and Tractor A287

Perf. 11½x11
1966, Sept. 9   Photo.   Wmk. 342
704 A287 5m shown   .30   .25
705 A287 10m Rice   .30   .25
706 A287 35m Onions   .80   .50
Nos. 704-706 (3)   1.40   1.00
Issued for Farmer's Day.

WHO Headquarters, Geneva — A288

Designs: 10m, UN refugee emblem. 35m, UNICEF emblem.

Perf. 11½x11
1966, Oct. 24   Wmk. 342
707 A288 5m olive & brt pur   .40   .25
708 A288 10m orange & brt pur   .40   .25
709 A288 35m lt blue & brt pur   .70   .45
Nos. 707-709 (3)   1.50   .95
21st anniversary of the United Nations. See Nos. N129-N131.

World Map and Festival Emblem A289

1966, Nov. 8   Photo.
710 A289 10m brt purple & yellow   .35   .20
5th Intl. Television Festival, Nov. 1-10.

Arms of UAR, Rocket and Pylon A290

1966, Dec. 23   Wmk. 342   Perf. 11½
711 A290 10m brt grn & car rose   .40   .20
Issued for Victory Day.
See No. N132.

Jackal A291

35m, Alabaster head from Tutankhamen treasure.

1967, Jan. 2   Photo.
712 A291 10m slate, yel & brn   1.10   .30
713 A291 35m bl, dk vio & ocher   2.25   .55
Issued for Post Day, Jan. 2.

Carnations A292

Workers Planting Tree A293

1967, Jan. 10   Unwmk.   Perf. 11
714 A292 4m citron & purple   .35   .20
Issued for use on greeting cards.

Perf. 11x11½
1967, Mar. 15   Wmk. 342
715 A293 10m brt green & blk vio   .35   .20
Issued to publicize the Tree Festival.

Gamal el-Dine el-Afaghani and Arab League Emblem — A294

1967, Mar. 22   Photo.   Wmk. 342
716 A294 10m dp green & dk brn   .35 .20
Arab Publicity Week, Mar. 22-28.
See No. N133.

Census Emblem, Man, Woman and Factory A295

1967, Apr. 23   Perf. 11½x11
717 A295 10m black & dp org   .35 .20
First industrial census.

Brickmaking Fresco, Tomb of Rekhmire, Thebes, 1504-1450 B.C. — A296

1967, May 1   Photo.   Wmk. 342
718 A296 10m olive & orange   .35 .20
Issued for Labor Day, 1967.
See No. N134.

Ramses II and Queen Nefertari — A297

Design: 35m, Shooting geese, frieze from tomb of Atet at Meidum, c. 2724 B. C.

Perf. 11½x11
1967, June 7   Photo.   Wmk. 342
719 A297 10m multicolored   .75 .40
720 A297 35m dk green & org   3.00 1.00
  Nos. 719-720,C113-C115 (5)   10.75 4.65
Issued for International Tourist Year, 1967.

President Nasser, Crowd and Map of Palestine A298

1967, June 22   Perf. 11½
721 A298 10m dp org, yel & ol   2.00 .75
Issued to publicize Arab solidarity for "the defense of Palestine."

Souvenir Sheet

National Products — A299

1967, July 23   Wmk. 342   Imperf.
722 A299 100m multicolored   3.25 2.50
15th anniv. of the revolution.

Salama Higazi — A300

Perf. 11x11½
1967, Oct. 14   Photo.   Wmk. 342
723 A300 20m brown & dk blue   .80 .20
50th anniversary of the death of Salama Higazi, pioneer of Egyptian lyric stage.

Stag on Ceramic Disk A301

Design: 55m, Apse showing Christ in Glory, Madonna and Saints, Coptic Museum, and UNESCO Emblem.

1967, Oct. 24   Perf. 11½
724 A301 20m dull rose & dk bl   .65 .35
725 A301 55m dk slate grn & yel   1.30 .60
  Nos. 724-725,C117 (3)   3.20 1.80
22nd anniv. of the UN.

Savings Bank and Postal Authority Emblems A302

1967, Oct. 31   Perf. 11½x11
726 A302 20m sal pink & dk blue   .40 .20
International Savings Day.

Rose — A303

Unwmk.
1967, Dec. 15   Photo.   Perf. 11
727 A303 5m green & rose lilac   .35 .20
Issued for use on greeting cards.

Pharaonic Dress — A304

Aswan High Dam and Power Lines — A305

Designs: Various pharaonic dresses from temple decorations.

Perf. 11x11½
1968, Jan. 2   Wmk. 342
728 A304 20m brown, grn & buff   .90 .30
729 A304 55m lt grn, yel & sepia   1.60 .60
730 A304 80m dk brn, bl & brt
      rose   2.25 .90
  Nos. 728-730 (3)   4.75 1.80
Issued for Post Day, Jan. 2.
See Nos. 752-755.

1968, Jan. 9
731 A305 20m yel, bl & dk brn   .35 .20
1st electricity generated by the Aswan Hydroelectric Station.

Alabaster Vessel, Tutankhamen Treasure A306

Girl, Moon and Paint Brushes A308

Capital of Coptic Limestone Pillar A307

Perf. 11x11½, 11½
1968, Jan. 20   Photo.   Wmk. 342
732 A306 20m dk ultra, yel & brn   .60 .25
733 A307 80m lt grn, dk pur & ol
      grn   1.00 .75
2nd International Festival of Museums.

1968, Feb. 15   Perf. 11x11½
734 A308 20m brt blue & black   .35 .20
7th Biennial Exhibition of Fine Arts, Alexandria, Feb. 15.

Cattle and Veterinarian — A309

Perf. 11½x11
1968, May 4   Photo.   Wmk. 342
735 A309 20m brown, yel & grn   .55 .20
8th Arab Veterinary Congress, Cairo.

Human Rights Flame — A310

Perf. 11x11½
1968, July 1   Photo.   Wmk. 342
736 A310 20m citron, crim & grn   .40 .25
737 A310 60m sky blue, crim & grn   .65 .50
International Human Rights Year, 1968.

Open Book with Symbols of Science, Victory Election Result A311

Workers, Cogwheel with Coat of Arms and Open Book — A312

1968, July 23   Perf. 11½
738 A311 20m rose red & sl grn   .35 .20
Souvenir Sheet
Imperf
739 A312 100m lt grn, org & pur   3.00 2.25
16th anniversary of the revolution.

Imhotep and WHO Emblem A313

No. 741, Avicenna and WHO emblem.

Perf. 11½x11½
1968, Sept. 1   Photo.   Wmk. 342
740 A313 20m blue, yel & brn   .80 .30
741 A313 20m yellow, bl & brn   .80 .30
  a.   Pair, #740-741   2.00 1.75
20th anniv. of the WHO. Nos. 740-741 printed in checkerboard sheets of 50 (5x10).

Table Tennis — A314

Perf. 11x11½
1968, Sept. 20   Photo.   Wmk. 342
742 A314 20m lt green & dk brn   1.00 .35
First Mediterranean Table Tennis Tournament, Alexandria, Sept. 20-27.

Factories and Fair Emblem
A315

1968, Oct. 20   Wmk. 342   Perf. 11½
743 A315 20m bl gray, red & sl bl   .35 .20
Cairo International Industrial Fair.

Temples of Philae — A316

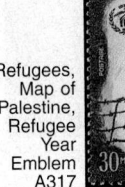

Refugees, Map of Palestine, Refugee Year Emblem A317

55m, Temple at Philae & UNESCO emblem.

1968, Oct. 24   Photo.
744 A316 20m multicolored   .60 .25
745 A317 30m multicolored   .85 .60
746 A317 55m lt blue, yel & blk   1.40 .90
   Nos. 744-746 (3)   2.85 1.75
Issued for United Nations Day, Oct. 24.

Egyptian Boy Scout Emblem — A318

1968, Nov. 1
747 A318 10m dull org & vio bl   .60 .30
50th anniversary of Egyptian Boy Scouts.

Pharaonic Sports A319

Design: 30m, Pharaonic sports, diff.

1968, Nov. 1
748 A319 20m pale ol, pale sal & blk   .55 .25
749 A319 30m pale blue, buff & pur   1.00 .55
19th Olympic Games, Mexico City, 10/12-27.

Aly Moubarak A320

Lotus A321

1968, Nov. 9   Perf. 11½
750 A320 20m green, brn & bister   .35 .20
Aly Moubarak (1823-93), founder of the modern educational system in Egypt.

1968, Dec. 11   Photo.   Wmk. 342
751 A321 5m brt blue, grn & yel   .35 .20
Issued for use on greeting cards.

Son of Ramses III — A322

Hefni Nassef — A323

Pharaonic Dress: No. 753, Ramses III. No. 754, Girl carrying basket on her head. 55m, Queen of the New Empire in transparent dress.

1969, Jan. 2   Photo.   Perf. 11½
752 A322 5m blue & multi   .45 .20
753 A322 20m blue & multi   .75 .30
754 A322 20m blue & multi   .90 .35
755 A322 55m blue & multi   2.25 .65
   Nos. 752-755 (4)   4.35 1.50
Issued for Post Day, Jan. 2.

Perf. 11x11½
1969, Mar. 2   Photo.   Wmk. 342
Portrait: No. 757, Mohammed Farid.
756 A323 20m purple & brown   .50 .20
757 A323 20m emerald & brown   .50 .20
a. Pair, #756-757   1.10 1.00

50th anniv. of the death of Hefni Nassef (1860-1919) writer and government worker, and Mohammed Farid (1867-1919), lawyer and Speaker of the Nationalist Party.

Teacher and Children A324

ILO Emblem and Factory Chimneys A325

1969, Mar. 2   Perf. 11x11½
758 A324 20m multicolored   .35 .20
Arab Teacher's Day.

1969, Apr. 11   Photo.   Wmk. 342
759 A325 20m brown, ultra & car   .35 .20
50th anniv. of the ILO.

Flag of Algeria, Africa Day and Tourist Year Emblems A326

Perf. 11½x11
1969, May 25   Litho.   Wmk. 342
760 A326 10m Algeria   .75 .35
761 A326 10m Botswana   .75 .35
762 A326 10m Burundi   .75 .35
763 A326 10m Cameroun   .75 .35
764 A326 10m Cent. Afr. Rep.   .75 .35
765 A326 10m Chad   .75 .35
766 A326 10m Congo, ex-Belgian   .75 .35
767 A326 10m Congo, ex-French   .75 .35
768 A326 10m Dahomey   .75 .35
769 A326 10m Equatorial Guinea   .75 .35
770 A326 10m Ethiopia   .75 .35
771 A326 10m Gabon   .75 .35
772 A326 10m Gambia   .75 .35
773 A326 10m Ghana   .75 .35
774 A326 10m Guinea   .75 .35
775 A326 10m Ivory Coast   .75 .35
776 A326 10m Kenya   .75 .35
777 A326 10m Lesotho   .75 .35
778 A326 10m Liberia   .75 .35
779 A326 10m Libya   .75 .35
780 A326 10m Malagasy   .75 .35
781 A326 10m Malawi   .75 .35
782 A326 10m Mali   .75 .35
783 A326 10m Mauritania   .75 .35
784 A326 10m Mauritius   .75 .35
785 A326 10m Morocco   .75 .35
786 A326 10m Niger   .75 .35
787 A326 10m Nigeria   .75 .35
788 A326 10m Rwanda   .75 .35
789 A326 10m Senegal   .75 .35
790 A326 10m Sierra Leone   .75 .35
791 A326 10m Somalia   .75 .35
792 A326 10m Sudan   .75 .35
793 A326 10m Swaziland   .75 .35
794 A326 10m Tanzania   .75 .35
795 A326 10m Togo   .75 .35
796 A326 10m Tunisia   .75 .35
797 A326 10m Uganda   .75 .35
798 A326 10m UAR   .75 .35
799 A326 10m Upper Volta   .75 .35
800 A326 10m Zambia   .75 .35
   Nos. 760-800 (41)   30.75 14.35

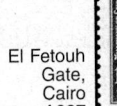

El Fetouh Gate, Cairo A327

Sculptures from the Egyptian Museum, Cairo — A328

Millenary of Cairo — A329

#802, Al Azhar University. #803, The Citadel. #805, Sculptures, Coptic Museum. #806, Glass plate and vase, Fatimid dynasty, Islamic Museum. #807a, Islamic coin. #807b, Fatimist era jewelry. #807c, Copper vase. #807d, Coins and plaque.

Perf. 11½x11
1969, July 23   Photo.   Wmk. 342
801 A327 10m dk brown & multi   .50 .20
802 A327 10m green & multi   .50 .20
803 A327 10m blue & multi   .50 .20

Perf. 11½
804 A328 20m yellow grn & multi   .75 .30
805 A328 20m dp ultra & multi   .75 .30
806 A328 20m brown & multi   .75 .30
   Nos. 801-806 (6)   3.75 1.50

Souvenir Sheet
807 A329 Sheet of 4   8.50 7.50
a. 20m dark blue & multi   1.75 1.50
b. 20m lilac & multi   1.75 1.50
c. 20m yellow & multi   1.75 1.50
d. 20m dark green & multi   1.75 1.50
Millenium of the founding of Cairo.

African Development Bank Emblem — A330

Perf. 11x11½
1969, Sept. 10   Photo.   Wmk. 342
808 A330 20m emerald, yel & vio   .35 .20
African Development Bank, 5th anniv.

Pharaonic Boat and UN Emblem A331

Temple of Philae Inundated and UNESCO Emblem A332

Design: 5m, King and Queen from Abu Simbel Temple and UNESCO Emblem (size: 21x38mm).

Perf. 11x11½, 11½x11
1969, Oct. 24   Photo.   Wmk. 342
809 A332 5m brown & multi   .80 .25
810 A331 20m yellow & ultra   .40 .25

Perf. 11½
811 A332 55m yellow & multi   1.25 .65
   Nos. 809-811 (3)   2.45 1.15
Issued for United Nations Day.

Ships of 1869 and 1967 and Maps of Africa and Suez Canal — A333

1969, Nov. 15   Perf. 11½x11
812 A333 20m lt blue & multi   1.10 .40
Centenary of the Suez Canal.

Cairo Opera House and Performance of Aida — A334

1969, Nov. 15
813 A334 20m multicolored   .75 .35
Centenary of the Cairo Opera House.

Crowd with Egyptian and
Revolutionary Flags — A335

1969, Nov. 15   *Perf. 11½x11*
814 A335 20m brt grn, dull lil & red   .85   .35
Revolution of 1919.

Ancient
Arithmetic
and
Computer
Cards
A336

Perf. 11½x11
1969, Dec. 17   Photo.   Wmk. 342
815 A336 20m multicolored   .40 .20
Intl. Congress for Scientific Accounting,
Cairo, Dec. 17-19.

Poinsettia
A337

Sakkara Step
Pyramid
A338

El Fetouh Gate,
Cairo — A339

Fountain, Sultan
Hassan
Mosque,
Cairo — A340

King Khafre
(Ruled c.
2850 B.C.)
A341

1969, Dec. 24   Unwmk.   *Perf. 11*
816 A337 5m yellow, grn & car   .30 .20
Issued for use on greeting cards.

Wmk. 342 (20m, £1), Unwmkd.
Photo.; Engr. (20m, 55m)
1969-70   *Perf. 11*
Designs: 5m, Al Azhar Mosque. 10m, Luxor
Temple. 50m, Qaitbay Fort, Alexandria.

817 A338 1m multi ('70)   .30   .40
818 A338 5m multi ('70)   .50   .20
819 A338 10m multi ('70)   .50   .20
820 A339 20m dark brown   2.25   .35
821 A338 50m multi ('70)   2.25   .50
822 A340 55m slate green   3.50   .30

Perf. 11½
Photo. & Engr.
823 A341 £1 org & sl grn
     ('70)   45.00 10.00
Nos. 817-823 (7)   54.30 11.95
See Nos. 889-891, 893-897, 899, 901-902,
904.

Veiled Women, by Mahmoud
Said — A342

Perf. 11x11½
1970, Jan. 2   Photo.   Wmk. 342
824 A342 100m blue & multi   3.00 2.40
Post Day. Sheet of 8 with 2 panes of 4.

Parliament, Scales, Globe and
Laurel — A343

1970, Feb. 2   *Perf. 11½x11*
825 A343 20m blue, vio bl & ocher   .55 .20
Intl. Conf. of Parliamentarians on the Middle
East Crisis, Cairo, Feb. 2-5.

Map of
Arab
League
Countries,
Flag and
Emblem
A344

Perf. 11½x11
1970, Mar. 22   Photo.   Wmk. 342
826 A344 30m brn org, grn & dk
     pur   .45 .20
Arab League, 25th anniv. See No. B42.

Mena House and Sheraton
Hotel — A345

1970, Mar. 23
827 A345 20m olive, org & bl   .55 .20
Centenary of Mena House and the inauguration of the Cairo Sheraton Hotel.

Manufacture of Medicine — A346

1970, Apr. 20
828 A346 20m brown, yel & bl   .90 .25
Production of medicines in Egypt, 30th anniv.

Mermaid — A347

1970, Apr. 20   *Perf. 11x11½*
829 A347 20m orange, blk & ultra   .35 .20
8th Biennial Exhibition of Fine Arts, Alexandria, March 12.

Misr Bank and
Talaat
Harb — A348

ITU
Emblem — A349

1970, May 7   Photo.   Wmk. 342
830 A348 20m multicolored   .35 .20
50th anniversary of Misr Bank.

1970, May 17   *Perf. 11x11½*
831 A349 20m dk brn, yel & dull bl   .45 .20
World Telecommunications Day.

UPU Headquarters, Bern — A350

1970, May 20   *Perf. 11½x11*
832 A350 20m multicolored   .40 .20
Inauguration of the UPU Headquarters in
Bern. See No. C128.

Basketball Player
and Map of
Africa — A351

UPU, UN
and
U.P.A.F.
Emblems
A352

No. 834, Soccer player, map of Africa & cup,
horiz.

Perf. 11x11½, 11½x11
1970, May 25   Photo.   Wmk. 342
833 A351 20m lt blue, yel & brn   .65 .30
834 A351 20m yellow & multi   .55 .25
835 A352 20m ocher, grn & blk   .45 .20
Nos. 833-835 (3)   1.65 .75
Africa Day. No. 833 also for the 5th African
basketball championship for men; No. 834 the
annual African Soccer championship; No. 835
publicizes the African Postal Union seminar.

Fist and Freed
Bird — A353

1970, July 23   Photo.   *Perf. 11*
836 A353 20m lt green, org &
    blk   .50 .20
Souvenir Sheet
Imperf
837 A353 100m lt blue, dp org &
    blk   3.25 2.40
18th anniv. of the revolution.

Al Aqsa Mosque on Fire — A354

1970, Aug. 21   Wmk. 342   *Perf. 11*
838 A354 20m multicolored   .85 .25
839 A354 60m brt blue & multi   1.90 1.25
1st anniv. of the burning of Al Aqsa Mosque,
Jerusalem.

Standardization Emblems — A355

1970, Oct. 14   Wmk. 342   *Perf. 11*
840 A355 20m yellow, ultra & grn   .55 .20
World Standards Day and 25th anniv. of the
Intl. Standardization Organization, ISO.

UN Emblem, Scales and Dove — A356

Temple at
Philae
A357

Child,
Education
Year and
UN
Emblems
A358

Designs: 10m, UN emblem. No. 845, 2nd
Temple at Philae (denomination at left).

Perf. 11 (5m), 11½ (others)
1970, Oct. 24   Photo.   Wmk. 342
841 A356 5m lt bl, rose lil & sl   .20 .20
842 A357 10m yel, brn & lt bl   .25 .20
843 A358 20m slate & multi   .45 .20
844 A357 55m brn, bl & ocher   1.00 .40

845 A357 55m brn, bl & ocher 1.00 .60
  a. Strip of 3, #842, 844-845 2.50 2.00
    Nos. 841-845, B43 (6) 3.65 2.40

25th anniv. of the UN. #843 also for Intl. Education Year; Nos. 842, 844-845, the work of UNESCO in saving the Temples of Philae. No. 845a printed in sheets of 35 (15 No. 842, 10 each Nos. 844-845). Nos. 844-845 show continuous picture of the Temples at Philae.

Gamal Abdel Nasser — A359

1970, Nov. 6 Wmk. 342 Perf. 11
846 A359 5m sky blue & blk .20 .20
847 A359 20m gray green & blk .50 .50
  Nos. 846-847, C129-C130 (4) 3.20 1.50

Gamal Abdel Nasser (1918-70), Pres. of Egypt.

Medical Association Building — A360

#849, Old & new National Library. #850, Egyptian Credo (Nasser quotation). #851, Engineering Society, old & new buildings. #852, Government Printing Offices, old & new buildings.

1970, Dec. 20 Photo. Perf. 11
848 A360 20m yel, grn & brn .55 .30
849 A360 20m green & multi .55 .30
850 A360 20m lt blue & multi .55 .30
851 A360 20m blue, yel & brn .55 .30
852 A360 20m blue, yel & brn .55 .30
  a. Strip of 5, #848-852 3.25 3.25

50th anniv. of Egyptian Medical Assoc. (No. 848); cent. of Natl. Library (No. 849); Egyptian Engineering Assoc. (No. 851); sesqui. of Government Printing Offices (No. 852).

Map and Flags of UAR, Libya, Sudan A361

1970, Dec. 27 Perf. 11½
853 A361 20m lt grn, car & blk .55 .20

Signing of the Charter of Tripoli affirming the unity of UAR, Libya & the Sudan, 12/27/70.

Qalawun Minaret — A362

Designs (Minarets): 10m, As Saleh. 20m, Isna. 55m, Al Hakim.

1971, Jan. 2 Wmk. 342 Perf. 11
854 A362 5m green & multi .40 .20
855 A362 10m green & multi 1.00 .40
856 A362 20m green & multi 2.00 .80
857 A362 55m green & multi 3.50 1.60
  a. Strip of 4, #854-857 + label 8.75 5.75
    Post Day, 1971.
See Nos. 905-908, 932-935.

Gamal Abdel Nasser A363

Photogravure and Engraved
1971 Wmk. 342 Perf. 11½
858 A363 200m brn vio & dk bl 5.00 .90
859 A363 500m blue & black 12.00 3.00

Souvenir Sheet
Design: Portrait facing right.

Imperf
860 Sheet of 2 11.50 9.50
  a. A363 100m light green & black 3.50 2.50
  b. A363 200m blue & black 5.50 4.00

No. 860 commemorates inauguration of the Aswan High Dam, which is shown in margin. Issued: No. 860, 1/15; Nos. 858-859, 2/1. See No. 903.

Cotton and Globe A364

1971, Mar. 6 Photo. Perf. 11½x11
861 A364 20m lt green, blue & brn .40 .20
  Egyptian cotton.

Arab Countries, and Arab Postal Union Emblem A365

1971, Mar. 6 Wmk. 342
862 A365 20m lt bl, org & sl grn .40 .20
9th Arab Postal Cong., Cairo, 3/6-25. See No. C131.

Cairo Fair Emblem — A366

1971, Mar. 6 Perf. 11x11½
863 A366 20m plum, blk & org .50 .20
Cairo International Fair, March 2-23.

Nesy Ra, Apers Papyrus and WHO Emblem A367

Perf. 11½x11
1971, Apr. 30 Photo. Wmk. 342
864 A367 20m yellow bis & pur .70 .20
World Health Organization Day.

Gamal Abdel Nasser — A368

1971, May 1 Perf. 11
865 A368 20m purple & bl gray 1.00 .35
866 A368 55m blue & purple 3.25 1.10

Map of Africa, Telecommunications Symbols — A369

1971, May 17 Perf. 11½x11
867 A369 20m blue & multi .60 .20
Pan-African telecommunications system.

Wheelwright A370   Hand Holding Wheat and Laurel A371

Candle Lighting Africa — A372

Perf. 11x11½
1971, July 23 Photo. Wmk. 342
868 A370 20m yellow & multi .45 .25
869 A371 20m tan, grn & ocher .45 .25

Souvenir Sheet
Imperf
870 A372 100m blue & multi 4.75 4.75

19th anniv. of the July Revolution. No. 870 contains one stamp with simulated perforations in gold.

Arab Postal Union Emblem A373

1971, Aug. 3 Perf. 11½
871 A373 20m black, yel & grn .35 .20
25th anniv. of the Conf. of Sofar, Lebanon, establishing the APU. See No. C135.

Arab Republic of Egypt

Three Links A374

Perf. 11½x11
1971, Sept. 28 Photo. Wmk. 342
872 A374 20m gray, org brn & blk .50 .25
Confederation of Arab Republics (Egypt, Syria and Libya). See No. C136.

Gamal Abdel Nasser A375   Blood Donation A376

1971, Sept. 28 Perf. 11x11½
873 A375 5m slate grn & vio brn .40 .20
874 A375 20m violet brn & ultra .60 .20
875 A375 30m ultra & brown 1.10 .40
876 A375 55m brown & emerald 1.90 .50
  Nos. 873-876 (4) 4.00 1.30

Death of Pres. Gamal Abdel Nasser, 1st anniv.

1971, Oct. 24
877 A376 20m green & carmine .70 .20
"Blood Saves Lives."

Princess Nursing Child, UNICEF Emblem A377   Submerged Pillar, Philae, UNESCO Emblem A379

Equality Year Emblem A378

Perf. 11x11½, 11½x11
1971, Oct. 24 Photo. Wmk. 342
878 A377 5m buff, blk & org brn .30 .20
879 A378 20m red brn, grn, yel & blk .55 .20
880 A379 55m black, lt bl, yel & brn 1.25 .20
  Nos. 878-880, C137 (4) 3.70 1.00

UN Day. No. 878 honors UN Intl. Children's Fund; No. 879 for Intl. Year Against Racial Discrimination; No. 880 honors UNESCO.

Postal Traffic Center, Alexandria A380

1971, Oct. 31 Perf. 11½x11
881 A380 20m blue & bister .70 .20
Opening of Postal Traffic Center in Alexandria.

Sunflower
A381

Abdalla El
Nadim
A382

1971, Nov. 13   **Perf. 11**
882 A381 5m lt blue & multi   .35 .20
For use on greeting cards.

1971, Nov. 14   **Perf. 11x11½**
883 A382 20m green & brown   .50 .20
Abdalla El Nadim (1845-1896), journalist, publisher, connected with Orabi Revolution.

Section of Earth's Crust, Map of Africa on Globe
A383

1971, Nov. 27   **Perf. 11½x11**
884 A383 20m ultra, yel & brn   .85 .20
75th anniv. of Egyptian Geological Survey and Intl. Conference, Nov. 27-Dec. 1.

Postal Union Emblem, Letter and Dove
A384

55m, African Postal Union emblem and letter.

1971, Dec. 2
885 A384   5m multicolored   .45 .20
886 A384   20m olive, blk & org   .90 .20
887 A384   55m red, blk & blue   2.00 .90
     Nos. 885-887,C138 (4)   4.75 1.70
10th anniversary of African Postal Union.

Money and Safe Deposit Box
A385

1971, Dec. 23   **Perf. 11½**
888 A385 20m rose, brn & grn   .70 .20
70th anniversary of Postal Savings Bank.

Types of 1969-70, 1971
Inscribed "A. R. Egypt" and

Ramses II — A385a

Designs as before and: No. 894, King Citi I. No. 897, View of Alexandria. No. 898, Queen Nefertari. No. 900, Sphinx and Middle Pyramid. 100m, Cairo Mosque. 200m, Head of Pharaoh Userkaf.

Wmk. 342 (892A, 901-904)
1972-76   **Photo.**   **Unwmk.**   **Perf. 11**
889 A338   1m multi   .25 .25
890 A338   1m dk brn ('73)   .25 .25
891 A338   5m multi   .30 .20
892 A385a   5m olive ('73)   .35 .20

892A A385a   5m bister ('76)   .40 .20
893 A338   10m multi   .50 .25
894 A338   10m lt brn ('73)   .45 .25
895 A339   20m olive   .90 .25
896 A339   20m purple ('73)   1.00 .25
897 A338   50m multi   2.00 .30
898 A385a   50m dull bl ('73)   2.25 .30
899 A340   55m red lilac   3.25 .75
900 A340   55m green ('74)   1.75 .50
901 A339   100m lt blue, dp org & blk   2.50 .50

Perf. 11½
Photo. & Engr.
902 A341   200m yel grn & brn   6.00 1.25
903 A363   500m bl & choc   16.00 3.25
904 A341   £1 orange & sl grn   35.00 8.00
    Nos. 889-904 (17)   73.15 16.95

Minaret Type of 1971
5m, West Minaret, Nasser Mosque. 20m, East Minaret, Nasser Mosque. 30m, Minaret, Al Gawli Mosque. 55m, Minaret, Ibn Tulun Mosque.

Wmk. 342
1972, Jan. 2   **Photo.**   **Perf. 11**
905 A362   5m dk green & multi   .40 .20
906 A362   10m dk green & multi   1.10 .20
907 A362   30m dk green & multi   2.50 .50
908 A362   55m dk green & multi   3.50 1.40
   a.   Strip of 4, #905-908 + label   8.00 2.50
Post Day, 1972.

Police Emblem and Activities — A386

1972, Jan. 25   **Perf. 11½**
909 A386 20m dull blue, brn & yel 1.75 .35
Police Day 1972.

UNESCO, UN and Book Year Emblems — A387

1972, Jan. 25   **Perf. 11x11½**
910 A387 20m lt yel grn, vio bl & yel   .70 .20
International Book Year 1972.

Alexandria Biennale
A388

1972, Feb. 15   **Wmk. 342**   **Perf. 11½**
911 A388 20m black, brt rose & yel .70 .20
9th Biennial Exhibition of Fine Arts, Alexandria, Mar., 1972.

Fair Emblem
A389

Abdel Moniem
Riad
A390

1972, Mar. 5   **Perf. 11x11½**
912 A389 20m blue, org & yel grn   .70 .20
International Cairo Fair.

1972, Mar. 21   **Photo.**   **Wmk. 342**
913 A390 20m blue & brown   1.00 .20
In memory of Brig. Gen. Abdel Moniem Riad (1919-1969), military hero.

Bird Feeding Young
A391

1972, Mar. 21   **Perf. 11½**
914 A391 20m yellow & multi   .50 .20
Mother's Day.

Tutankhamen — A392

Design: 55m, Back of chair with king's name and symbols of eternity.

1972, May 22   **Unwmk.**
915 A392 20m gray, blk & ocher   1.75 .50
916 A392 55m purple & yellow   4.75 1.00
   Nos. 915-916,C142-C143 (4)   23.50 10.00
Discovery of the tomb of Tutankhamen by Howard Carter & Lord Carnarvon, 50th anniv. See No. C144.

Queen Nefertiti
A393

Wmk. 342
1972, May 22   **Photo.**   **Perf. 11½**
917 A393 20m red, blk & gold   .70 .20
Soc. of the Friends of Art, 50th anniv.

Map of Africa — A394

1972, May 25   **Perf. 11x11½**
918 A394 20m purple, bl & brn   .40 .20
Africa Day.

Atom Symbol, "Faith and Science"
A395

Design: No. 920, Egyptian coat of arms.

1972, July 23   **Perf. 11½**
919 A395 20m blue, claret & blk   .75 .20
920 A395 20m ol grn, gold & blk   .75 .20
20th anniversary of the revolution.

Boxing, Olympic and Motion Emblems — A396

Designs (Olympic and Motion Emblems and): 10m, Wrestling. 20m, Basketball.

1972, Aug. 17   **Perf. 11½x11**
921 A396   5m blue & multi   .30 .20
922 A396   10m yellow & multi   .45 .20
923 A396   20m ver & multi   .50 .30
   Nos. 921-923,C149-C152 (7)   6.00 3.15
20th Olympic Games, Munich, 8/26-9/11.

Flag of Confederation of Arab Republics — A397

1972, Sept. 1   **Wmk. 342**   **Perf. 11½**
924 A397 20m carmine, bis & blk   .60 .20
Confederation of Arab Republics, 1st anniv.

Red Crescent, TB and UN Emblems — A398

Heart and WHO Emblem
A399

Refugees, UNRWA Emblem, Map of Palestine — A400

Design: 55m, Inundated Temple of Philae, UNESCO emblem.

Perf. 11x11½ (#925), 11½ (#926, 928), 11 (#927)

1972, Oct. 24   **Photo.**
925 A398 10m brn org, red & bl   .40 .25
926 A399 20m green, yel & blk   .70 .30
927 A400 30m lt bl, pur & lt brn   1.90 .65
928 A399 55m brn, gold & bluish
     gray   2.25 .75
   Nos. 925-927 (3)   3.00 1.20

UN Day. No. 925 is for the 14th Regional Tuberculosis Conf., Cairo, 1972; No. 926 World Health Month; No. 927 publicizes aid to refugees and No. 928 the UN campaign to save the Temples at Philae.

Morning Glory — A401

1972, Oct. 24   ***Perf. 11***
929 A401 10m yel, lilac & grn   .50 .20

For use on greeting cards.

"Seeing Eye"
A402

1972, Nov. 30   ***Perf. 11½***
930 A402 20m multicolored   .70 .20

Social Work Day.

Sculling Race, View of Luxor — A403

1972, Dec. 17   **Wmk. 342**   ***Perf. 11***
931 A403 20m blue & brown   1.10 .30

3rd Nile Intl. Rowing Festival, Dec. 1972.

Minaret Type of 1971

10m, Al Maridani, 1338. 20m, Bashtak, 1337. 30m, Qusun, 1330. 55m, Al Gashankir, 1306.

1973, Jan. 2
   Frame in Bright Yellow Green
932 A362 10m multicolored   .70 .20
933 A362 20m multicolored   1.20 .30
934 A362 30m multicolored   2.50 .55
935 A362 55m multicolored   3.50 1.25
   a.   Strip of 4, #932-935 + Label   9.50 6.50

Post Day, 1973.

Cairo Fair Emblem
A404

Perf. 11½x11
1973, Mar. 21   **Photo.**   **Wmk. 342**
936 A404 20m gray & multi   .50 .20

International Cairo Fair.

Family — A405

1973, Mar. 21   ***Perf. 11x11½***
937 A405 20m multicolored   .60 .20

Family planning.

Sania Girls' School and Hoda Sharawi
A406

Perf. 11½x11
1973, July 15   **Photo.**   **Wmk. 342**
938 A406 20m ultra & green   .60 .20

Centenary of education for girls and 50th anniversary of the Egyptian Women's Union, founded by Hoda Sharawi.

Rifaa el Tahtawi — A407

1973, July 15   ***Perf. 11x11½***
939 A407 20m brt green, ol & brn   .60 .20

Centenary of the death of Rifaa el Tahtawi, champion of democracy and principal of language school.

Omar Makram
A408

Abdel Rahman al Gabarti, Historian
A409

"Reconstruction and Battle" — A410

No. 941, Mohamed Korayem, martyr.

1973, July 23
940 A408 20m yel grn, bl & brn   .45 .25
941 A408 20m lt grn, bl & brn   .45 .25
942 A409 20m ocher & brown   .45 .25
   Nos. 940-942 (3)   1.35 .75
     Souvenir Sheet
     Imperf
943 A410 110m gold, bl & blk   3.25 3.00

Revolution establishing the republic, 21st anniv.

Grain, Cow, FAO Emblem
A411

Perf. 11½x11
1973, Oct. 24   **Wmk. 342**
944 A411 10m brn, dk bl & yel grn   .50 .20

10th anniv. of the World Food Org.

Inundated Temples at Philae
A412

1973, Oct. 24   ***Perf. 11½***
945 A412 55m blue, pur & org   3.00 1.00

UNESCO campaign to save the temples at Philae.

Bank Building
A413

1973, Oct. 24
946 A413 20m brn org, grn & blk   .50 .20

75th anniv. of the National Bank of Egypt.

Rose — A414

1973, Oct. 24   ***Perf. 11***
947 A414 10m blue & multi   .40 .20

For use on greeting cards.

Human Rights Flame
A415

Taha Hussein
A416

Perf. 11x11½
1973, Dec. 8   **Photo.**   **Wmk. 342**
948 A415 20m yel grn, dk bl & car   .45 .20

25th anniversary of the Universal Declaration of Human Rights.

1973, Dec. 10
949 A416 20m dk blue, brn & emer   .35 .20

Dr. Taha Hussein (1893-1973), "Father of Education" in Egypt, writer, philosopher.

Pres. Sadat, Flag and Battle of Oct. 6 — A417

1973, Dec. 23   ***Perf. 11x11½***
950 A417 20m yellow, blk & red   1.25 1.00

October War against Israel (crossing of Suez Canal by Egyptian forces, Oct. 6, 1973). See No. 959.

WPY Emblem and Chart — A418   Cairo Fair Emblem — A419

1974, Mar. 21   **Wmk. 342**   ***Perf. 11***
951 A418 55m org, grn & dk bl   .85 .30

World Population Year.

1974, Mar. 21   **Photo.**
952 A419 20m blue & multi   .40 .20

Cairo International Fair.

Nurse and Medal of Angels of Ramadan 10 — A420

1974, May 15   ***Perf. 11½***
953 A420 55m multicolored   1.40 .35

Nurses' and World Hospital Day.

Workers, Relief Carving from Queen Tee's Tomb, Sakhara — A421

1974, May 15   *Perf. 11*
954 A421 20m yellow, blue & brn   .60 .20
Workers' Day.

Pres. Sadat, Troops Crossing Suez Canal — A422

"Reconstruction," Map of Suez Canal and New Building — A423

Sheet of Aluminum A424

Design: 110m, Pres. Sadat's "October Working Paper," symbols of science and development.

1974, July 23   **Photo.**   *Perf. 11x11½*
955 A422 20m multicolored   .70 .35
956 A423 20m blue, gold & blk   .70 .35
     Perf. 11½
957 A424 20m plum & silver   .70 .35
   Nos. 955-957 (3)   2.10 1.05
     Souvenir Sheet
     Imperf
958 A424 110m green & multi   3.50 3.00

22nd anniv. of the revolution establishing the republic and for the end of the October War. No. 958 contains one 52x59mm stamp.

Pres. Sadat and Flag — A425

1974, Oct. 6   **Wmk. 342**
Perf. 11x11½
959 A425 20m yellow, blk & red   1.25 .60
1st anniv. of Battle. See No. 950.

Palette and Brushes A426

1974, Oct. 6   *Perf. 11½*
960 A426 30m purple, yel & blk   .70 .20
6th Exhibition of Plastic Art.

Teachers and Pupils — A427

1974, Oct. 6   *Perf. 11x11½*
961 A427 20m multicolored   .55 .20
Teachers' Day.

     Souvenir Sheet

UPU Monument, Bern — A428

1974, Oct. 6   *Imperf.*
962 A428 110m gold & multi   5.00 4.25
Cent. of the UPU.

Emblems, Cogwheel and Calipers — A429

Refugee Camp under Attack and UN Refugee Organization Emblem — A430

Child and UNICEF Emblem A431

Temple of Philae — A432

1974, Oct. 24   *Perf. 11½, 11x11½*
963 A429 10m black, bl & yel   .40 .20
964 A430 20m dp org, bl & blk   .75 .20
965 A431 30m green, bl & brn   1.00 .40
966 A432 55m black, bl & yel   2.40 .85
   Nos. 963-966 (4)   4.55 1.65

UN Day. World Standards Day (10m); Palestinian refugee repatriation (20m); Family Planning (30m); Campaign to save Temple of Philae (55m).

Calla Lily — A433

1974, Nov. 7   *Perf. 11*
967 A433 10m ultra & multi   .40 .20
For use on greeting cards.

10m-coins, Smokestacks and Grain — A434

1974, Nov. 7   *Perf. 11½x11*
968 A434 20m yel grn, dk bl & sil   .40 .20
International Savings Day.

Organization Emblem and Medical Services — A435

1974, Nov. 7   *Perf. 11½*
969 A435 30m vio, red & gold   .65 .20
Health Insurance Organization, 10th anniv.

Mustafa Lutfy El Manfalouty A436

Abbas Mahmoud El Akkad A437

     Perf. 11x11½
1974, Dec. 8   **Photo.**   **Wmk. 342**
970 A436 20m blue blk & brn   .40 .25
971 A437 20m brown & bl blk   .40 .25
  a.   Pair, #970-971   1.00 .80

Arab writers; El Manfalouty (1876-1924) and El Akkad (1889-1964).

Goddess Maat Facing God Thoth — A438

Fish-shaped Vase — A439

Pharaonic Golden Vase — A440

Sign of Life, Mirror — A441

     Wmk. 342
1975, Jan. 2   **Photo.**   *Perf. 11½*
972 A438 20m silver & multi   .75 .25
973 A439 30m multicolored   1.00 .25
974 A440 55m multicolored   1.40 .65
975 A441 110m blue & multi   2.25 1.25
   Nos. 972-975 (4)   5.40 2.40

Post Day 1975. Egyptian art works from 12th-5th centuries B.C.

Om
Kolthoum — A442

Perf. 11½
1975, Mar. 3   Photo.   Unwmk.
976 A442 20m brown   .70 .20
In memory of Om Kolthoum, singer.

Crescent, Globe, Al
Aqsa and
Kaaba — A443

Cairo Fair
Emblem — A444

1975, Mar. 25
977 A443 20m multicolored   .70 .20
Mohammed's Birthday.

Perf. 11x11½
1975, Mar. 25   Wmk. 342
978 A444 20m multicolored   .40 .20
International Cairo Fair.

Kasr El
Ainy
Hospital
WHO
Emblem
A445

Perf. 11½x11
1975, May 7   Photo.   Wmk. 342
979 A445 20m dk brown & blue   .60 .20
World Health Organization Day.

Children
Reading
Book — A446

Children and
Line
Graph — A447

1975, May 7   Perf. 11x11½
980 A446 20m multicolored   .70 .20
981 A447 20m multicolored   .70 .20
Science Day.

Suez Canal, Globe, Ships, Pres.
Sadat — A448

1975, June 5   Perf. 11½
982 A448 20m blue, brn & blk   1.00 .30
    Nos. 982,C166-C167 (3)   5.00 2.00
Reopening of the Suez Canal, June 5.

Belmabgoknis
Flowers — A449

1975, July 30   Photo.   Wmk. 342
983 A449 10m green & blue   .40 .20
For use on greeting cards.

Sphinx and Pyramids
Illuminated — A450

Rural Electrification — A451

Map of Egypt with Tourist
Sites — A452

Illustration A452 is reduced.

1975, July 23
984 A450 20m black, org & grn   .55 .25
985 A451 20m dk blue & brown   .55 .25
        Perf. 11
986 A452 110m multicolored   5.50 4.75
    Nos. 984-986 (3)   6.60 5.25
23rd anniversary of the revolution establishing the republic. No. 986 printed in sheets of 6 (2x3). Size: 71x80mm.

Volleyball — A453

1975, Aug. 2   Photo.   Perf. 11x11½
987 A453 20m shown   .70 .25
988 A453 20m Running   .70 .25
989 A453 20m Torch and flag
                 bearers   .70 .25

990 A453 20m Basketball   .70 .25
991 A453 20m Soccer   .70 .25
  a. Strip of 5, #987-991   4.00 3.50
6th Arab School Tournament.

Egyptian
Flag and
Tanks
A454

1975   Photo.   Unwmk.   Perf. 11½
992 A454 20m multicolored   1.00 .30
**Two-line Arabic Inscription
in Bottom Panel, "M" over "20"**
992A A454 20m multicolored   1.00 .30
No. 992 for 2nd anniv. of October War against Israel, "The Spark;" No. 992A, the Intl. Symposium on October War against Israel 1973, Cairo University, Oct. 27-31.
    Issue dates: No. 992, Oct. 6; No. 992A, Oct. 24.

Arrows Pointing
to Fluke, and
Emblems
A455

Submerged Wall
and Sculpture,
UNESCO Emblem
A456

Perf. 11x11½
1975, Oct. 24   Wmk. 342
993 A455 20m multicolored   .65 .30
994 A456 55m multicolored   1.90 .50
UN Day. 20m for Intl. Conf. on Schistosomiasis (Bilharziasis); 55m for UNESCO help in saving temples at Philae. See Nos. C169-C170.

Pharaonic Gate,
University
Emblem — A457

Al
Biruni — A458

1975, Nov. 15   Photo.   Wmk. 342
995 A457 20m multicolored   .35 .20
Ain Shams University, 25th anniversary.

1975, Dec. 23   Photo.   Perf. 11x11½
Arab Philosophers: No. 997, Al Farabi and lute. No. 998, Al Kanady, book and compass.
996 A458 20m blue, brn & grn   1.10 .30
997 A458 20m blue, brn & grn   1.10 .30
998 A458 20m blue, brn & grn   1.10 .30
    Nos. 996-998 (3)   3.30 .90

Ibex
(Prow) — A459

Post Day (from Tutankhamen's Tomb): 30m, Lioness. 55m, Cow's head (Goddess Hawthor). 110m, Hippopotamus' head (God Horus).

1976, Jan. 2   Unwmk.   Perf. 11½
999 A459 20m multicolored   3.25 1.25
        Wmk. 342
1000 A459 30m brown, gold
                 & ultra   5.25 1.50
1001 A459 55m multicolored   9.50 3.25
1002 A459 110m multicolored   13.00 8.00
    Nos. 999-1002 (4)   31.00 14.00

Lake, Aswan Dam, Industry and
Agriculture — A460

Perf. 11½x11
1976, Jan. 27   Photo.   Wmk. 342
1003 A460 20m multicolored   .60 .20
Filling of lake formed by Aswan High Dam.

Fair
Emblem — A461

Commemorative
Medal — A462

1976, Mar. 15   Perf. 11x11½
1004 A461 20m orange & purple   .35 .20
9th International Cairo Fair, Mar. 8-27.

1976, Mar. 15   Wmk. 342
1005 A462 20m olive, yel & blk   .35 .20
11th Biennial Exhibition of Fine Arts, Alexandria.

Hands
Shielding
Invalid
A463

1976, Apr. 7   Photo.   Perf. 11½
1006 A463 20m dk grn, lt grn & yel   .40 .20
Founding of Faithfulness and Hope Society.

Eye and WHO Emblem A464

1976, Apr. 7
1007 A464 20m dk brn, yel & grn .60 .20
World Health Day: "Foresight prevents blindness."

Pres. Sadat, Legal Department Emblem — A465

Perf. 11½x11
1976, May 15 Photo. Wmk. 342
1008 A465 20m olive & multi .60 .20
Centenary of State Legal Department.

Scales of Justice — A466

1976, May 15 Perf. 11x11½
1009 A466 20m carmine, blk & grn .60 .20
5th anniversary of Rectification Movement.

Al-Ahram Front Page, First Issue A467

Perf. 11½x11
1976, June 25 Photo. Wmk. 342
1010 A467 20m bister & multi .45 .20
Centenary of Al-Ahram newspaper.

World Map, Pres. Sadat and Emblems — A468

1976, July 23 Perf. 11x11½
1011 A468 20m bl, blk & yel .55 .30
Size: 240x216mm
Imperf
1012 A468 110m bl, brn & yel 5.50 4.75
24th anniv. of the revolution. No. 1012 design is similar to No. 1011.

Scarborough Lily — A469

1976, Sept. 10 Photo. Perf. 11
1013 A469 10m multicolored .35 .20
For use on greeting cards.

Reconstruction of Sinai by Irrigation — A470

Abu Redice Oil Wells and Refinery — A471

Unknown Soldier, Memorial Pyramid for October War — A472

1976, Oct. 6 Perf. 11x11½
1014 A470 20m multicolored .65 .35
1015 A471 20m multicolored .65 .35
Size: 65x77mm
1016 A472 110m grn, bl & blk 6.00 5.00
October War against Israel, 3rd anniv.

Papyrus with Children's Animal Story — A473

Al Aqsa Mosque, Palestinian Refugees — A474

55m, Isis, from Philae Temple, UNESCO emblem, vert. 110m, UNESCO emblem & "30."

Perf. 11½, 11½x11
1976, Oct. 24 Photo. Wmk. 342
1017 A473 20m dk bl, bis & brn .45 .20
1018 A473 30m brn, grn & blk .65 .30
1019 A473 55m dk blue & bister 1.10 .45
1020 A474 110m lt grn, vio bl & red 1.75 1.25
Nos. 1017-1020 (4) 3.95 2.20
30th anniversary of UNESCO.

Census Chart A475

1976, Nov. 22 Photo. Perf. 11½x11
1021 A475 20m multicolored .40 .20
10th General Population and Housing Census.

A476   A477

Design: Nile and commemorative medal.

1976, Nov. 22 Perf. 11x11½
1022 A476 20m green & brown .45 .20
Geographical Soc. of Egypt, cent. (in 1975).

1977, Jan. 2 Photo. Perf. 11x11½
Post Day: 20m, Ikhnaton. 30m, Ikhnaton's daughter. 55m, Nefertiti, Ikhnaton's wife. 110m, Ikhnaton, front view.
1023 A477 20m multicolored .30 .20
1024 A477 30m multicolored .30 .20
1025 A477 55m multicolored .65 .25
1026 A477 110m multicolored 2.75 .60
Nos. 1023-1026 (4) 4.00 1.25

Policeman, Emblem and Emergency Car — A478

1977, Feb. 25 Photo. Perf. 11½x11
1027 A478 20m multicolored .85 .20
Police Day.

Map of Africa, Arab League Emblem — A479

1977, Mar 7 Perf. 11x11½
1028 A479 55m multicolored .70 .20
First Afro-Arab Summit Conference, Cairo.

Fair Emblem, Pharaonic Ship A480

1977, Mar. 7 Perf. 11½x11
1029 A480 20m green, blk & red .45 .20
10th International Cairo Fair.

King Faisal — A481   Healthy and Crippled Children — A482

1977, Mar. 22 Photo. Perf. 11x11½
1030 A481 20m indigo & brown .35 .20
King Faisal Ben Abdel-Aziz Al Saud of Saudi Arabia (1906-1975).

1977, Apr. 12 Wmk. 342
1031 A482 20m multicolored .50 .20
National campaign to fight poliomyelitis.

APU Emblem, Members' Flags A483

1977, Apr. 12 Perf. 11½
1032 A483 20m blue & multi .25 .20
1033 A483 30m gray & multi .25 .20
25th anniv. of Arab Postal Union (APU).

Children's Village A484

Perf. 11½x11
1977, May 7 Photo. Wmk. 342
1034 A484 20m multicolored .25 .20
1035 A484 55m multicolored .75 .40
Inauguration of Children's Village, Cairo.

Loom, Spindle and Factory A485

1977, May 7
1036 A485 20m multicolored .35 .20
Egyptian Spinning and Weaving Company, El Mehalla el Kobra, 50th anniv.

Satellite, Globe, ITU Emblem — A486

1977, May 17   *Perf. 11x11½*
1037 A486 110m dk blue & multi   1.25 .50
World Telecommunications Day.

Flag and "25" A487

Egyptian Flag and Eagle — A488

Perf. 11½x11½
1977, July 23   Photo.   Wmk. 342
1038 A487 20m silver, car & blk   .30 .20

Perf. 11x11½
1039 A488 110m multicolored   1.50 1.00
25th anniversary of July 23rd Revolution. No. 1039 printed in sheets of six. Size: 75x83mm.

Saad Zaghloul A489

Archbishop Capucci, Map of Palestine A490

Perf. 11x11½
1977, Aug. 23   Photo.   Wmk. 342
1040 A489 20m dk green & dk brn   .20 .20
Saad Zaghloul, leader of 1919 Revolution, 50th death anniversary.

1977, Sept. 1
1041 A490 45m emerald & blue   .75 .25
Palestinian Archbishop Hilarion Capucci, jailed by Israel in 1974.

Bird-of-Paradise Flower — A491

1977, Sept. 3
1042 A491 10m multicolored   .20 .20
For use on greeting cards.

Proclamation Greening the Land — A492

Perf. 11x11½
1977, Sept. 25   Photo.   Wmk. 342
1043 A492 20m multicolored   .20 .20
Agrarian Reform Law, 25th anniversary.

Soldier, Tanks, Medal of Oct. 6 A493

Anwar Sadat — A494

1977, Oct. 6   *Perf. 11½x11*
1044 A493 20m multicolored   .30 .20
Unwmk.
Perf. 11
1045 A494 140m dk brn, gold & red   4.75 4.75
October War against Israel, 4th anniv. No. 1045 printed in sheets of 16.

Refugees Looking at Al Aqsa Mosque A495

Goddess Taueret and Spirit of Flight (Horus) A496

Mural Relief, Temple of Philae — A497

Wmk. 342
1977, Oct. 24   Photo.   *Perf. 11*
1046 A495 45m green, red & blk   .40 .20
1047 A496 55m dp blue & yellow   .60 .25
1048 A497 140m ol bis & dk brn   1.50 .80
    Nos. 1046-1048 (3)   2.50 1.25
United Nations Day.

Electric Trains, First Egyptian Locomotive — A498

1977, Oct. 22
1049 A498 20m multicolored   1.00 .20
125th anniversary of Egyptian railroads.

Film and Eye A499

1977, Nov. 16   *Perf. 11½x11*
1050 A499 20m gray, blk & gold   .35 .20
50th anniversary of Egyptian cinema.

Natural Gas Well and Refinery — A500

1977, Nov. 17   Photo.
1051 A500 20m multicolored   .40 .20
National Oil Festival, celebrating the acquisition of Sinai oil wells.

Pres. Sadat and Dome of the Rock A501

Perf. 11½x11
1977, Dec. 31   Photo.   Wmk. 342
1052 A501 20m green, brn & blk   .60 .20
1053 A501 140m green, blk & brn   2.25 .80
Pres. Sadat's peace mission to Israel.

Ramses II — A502

Post Day: 45m, Queen Nefertari, bas-relief.

1978, Jan. 2   *Perf. 11½*
1054 A502 20m green, blk & gold   .60 .20
1055 A502 45m orange, blk & ol   1.25 .70
Post Day 1978.

Water Wheels, Fayum — A503

Flying Duck, from Floor in Ikhnaton's Palace A504

5m, Birdhouse. 10m, Statue of Horus. 20m, 30m, Al Rifa'i Mosque, Cairo. 50m, Monastery, Wadi al-Natrun. 55m, Ruins of Edfu Temple. 70m, 80m, Bridge of Oct. 6. 85m, Medum pyramid. 100m, Facade, El Morsi Mosque, Alexandria. 200m, Column, Alexandria, Sphinx. 500m, Arabian stallion.

Wmk. 342, Unwmkd. (30m, 70m, 80m)

1978-85   *Perf. 11½*
1056	A503	1m slate blue	.20	.20
a.		Unwmkd. ('79)	.20	.20
b.		1m gray ('83)	.20	.20
c.		1m gray, unwmkd. ('83)	.20	.20
1057	A503	5m bister brn	.20	.20
a.		5m dull brn, unwmkd. (79)	.20	.20
1058	A503	10m brt green	.20	.20
a.		Unwmkd. ('79)	.20	.20
1059	A503	20m dk brown	.20	.20
b.		Unwmkd. ('79)	.20	.20
1059A	A503	30m sepia	.20	.20
a.		Unwmkd. ('79)	.20	.20
1060	A503	50m Prus blue	.25	.20
a.		Unwmkd. ('79)	.25	.20
b.		Unwmkd., brt blue ('87)	.25	.20
1061	A503	55m olive	.25	.20
1062	A503	70m olive ('79)	.30	.20
1062A	A503	80m olive ('82)	.35	.20
1063	A503	85m dp purple	.40	.20
a.		Unwmkd. ('85)	.40	.20
1064	A503	100m brown	.45	.20
a.		Unwmkd. ('85)	.65	.25
1065	A503	200m bl & indigo	2.00	.60
1066	A504	500m multicolored	5.00	1.50
1067	A504	£1 multicolored	7.50	2.00
		Nos. 1056-1067 (14)	17.50	6.30

Issued: 500m, £1, 2/27/78; 70m, 8/22/79; others, 7/23/78.

Fair Emblem and Wheat A505

1978, Mar. 15   *Perf. 11½*
1072 A505 20m multicolored   .20 .20
11th Cairo International Fair, Mar. 11-25.

Emblem, Kasr El Ainy School A506

1978, Mar. 18   *Perf. 11½x11*
1073 A506 20m lt blue, blk & gold   .20 .20
Kasr El Ainy School of Medicine, 150th anniv.

A507

#1074, Soldiers and Emblem. #1075, Youssef El Sebai.

1978, Mar. 30   **Perf. 11x11½**
1074   20m multicolored   .30 .20
1075   20m bister brown   .30 .20
   a.   A507 Pair, #1074-1075   .60 .20

Youssef El Sebai, newspaper editor, assassinated on Cyprus and in memory of the commandos killed in raid on Cyprus.

Biennale Medal, Statue for Entrance to Port Said A509

1978, Apr. 1   **Perf. 11½**
1076 A509 20m blue, grn & blk   .25 .25

12th Biennial Exhibition of Fine Arts, Alexandria.

Child with Smallpox, UN Emblem A510

1978, Apr. 7   **Photo.**   **Perf. 11½**
1077 A510 20m multicolored   .20 .20

Eradication of smallpox.

Heart & Arrow, UN Emblem — A511   Anwar Sadat — A512

1978, Apr. 7   **Wmk. 342**
1078 A511 20m multicolored   .20 .20

Fight against hypertension.

1978, May 15   **Photo.**   **Perf. 11½x11**
1079 A512 20m green, brn & gold   .35 .20

7th anniversary of Rectification Movement.

Social Security Emblem — A513

1978, May 16   **Perf. 11**
1080 A513 20m lt green & dk brn   .20 .20

General Organization of Insurance and Pensions (Social Security), 25th anniversary.

New Cities on Map of Egypt — A514

Map of Egypt and Sudan, Wheat — A515

            Wmk. 342
1978, July 23   **Photo.**   **Perf. 11½**
1081 A514 20m multicolored   .50 .20
1082 A515 45m multicolored   1.00 .20

26th anniversary of July 23rd revolution.

Symbols of Egyptian Ministries — A516

1978, Aug. 28   **Photo.**   **Perf. 11½x11**
1083 A516 20m multicolored   .35 .20

Centenary of Egyptian Ministerial System.

Pres. Sadat and "Spirit of Egypt" Showing Way — A517

1978, Oct. 6   **Photo.**   **Perf. 11x11½**
1084 A517 20m multicolored   .50 .20

October War against Israel, 5th anniv.

Human Rights Emblem — A518

Dove and Human Rights Emblem — A520

Kobet al Sakra Mosque, Refugee Camp A519

UN Day: 55m, Temple at Biga and UNESCO emblem, horiz.

Perf. 11, 11½ (45m)
1978, Oct. 24   **Photo.**   **Wmk. 342**
1085 A518 20m multicolored   .30 .20
1086 A519 45m multicolored   .85 .20
1087 A518 55m multicolored   .40 .20
1088 A518 140m multicolored   2.10 .30
    Nos. 1085-1088 (4)   3.65 .90

Pilgrims, Mt. Arafat and Holy Kaaba — A521

1978, Nov. 7   **Photo.**   **Perf. 11**
1089 A521 45m multicolored   .80 .20

Pilgrimage to Mecca.

Tahtib Horse Dance — A522

1978, Nov. 7
1090 A522 10m multicolored   .45 .20
1091 A522 20m multicolored   .45 .20

UN Emblem, Globe and Grain A523

1978, Nov. 11   **Photo.**   **Perf. 11½**
1092 A523 20m green, dk bl & yel   .30 .20

Technical Cooperation Among Developing Countries Conf., Buenos Aires, Sept. 1978.

Pipes, Map and Emblem of Sumed Pipeline A524

1978, Nov. 11
1093 A524 20m brown, bl & yel   .45 .20

Inauguration of Sumed pipeline from Suez to Alexandria, 1st anniversary.

Mastheads A525   Abu el Walid A526

1978, Dec. 24   **Perf. 11x11½**
1094 A525 20m brown & black   .45 .20

El Wakea el Masriya newspaper, 150th anniv.

1978, Dec. 24
1095 A526 45m brt green & indigo   .55 .20

800th death anniv. of Abu el Walid ibn Rashid.

Helwan Observatory and Sky — A527

1978, Dec. 30   **Wmk. 342**
1096 A527 20m multicolored   .60 .20

Helwan Observatory, 75th anniversary.

Second Daughter of Ramses II A528

Ramses Statues, Abu Simbel, and Cartouches — A529

1979, Jan. 2   Photo.   Perf. 11
1097 A528 20m brown & yellow   .50 .25
    Perf. 11½x11
1098 A529 140m multicolored   1.75 .35
    Post Day 1979.

Book, Reader and Globe A530

    Perf. 11½x11
1979, Feb. 1   Photo.   Wmk. 342
1099 A530 20m yellow grn & brown .35 .20
    Cairo 11th International Book Fair.

Wheat, Globe, Fair Emblem — A531

    Perf. 11x11½
1979, Mar. 17   Photo.   Unwmk.
1100 A531 20m blue, org & blk   .35 .20
    12th Cairo International Fair, Mar.-Apr.

Skull, Poppy, Agency Emblem — A532

1979, Mar. 20   Perf. 11
1101 A532 70m multicolored   1.25 .35
    Anti-Narcotics General Administration, 50th anniv.

Isis Holding Horus — A533

1979, Mar. 21
1102 A533 140m multicolored   2.10 .50
    Mother's Day.

World Map and Book — A534

    Perf. 11x11½
1979, Mar. 22   Wmk. 342
1103 A534 45m yellow, bl & brn   .45 .25
    Cultural achievements of the Arabs.

Pres. Sadat's Signature, Peace Doves A535

    Wmk. 342
1979, Mar. 31   Photo.   Perf. 11½
1104 A535 70m brt green & red   1.00 .25
1105 A535 140m yellow grn & red   2.00 .60
    Signing of Peace Treaty between Egypt and Israel, Mar. 26.

1979, May 26   Photo.   Perf. 11½
1106 A535 20m yellow & dk brn   .40 .20
    Return of Al Arish to Egypt.

Honeycomb with Food Symbols A536

1979, May 15
1107 A536 20m multicolored   .30 .20
    8th anniversary of movement to establish food security.

Coins, 1959, 1979 A537

    Perf. 11½x11
1979, June 1   Wmk. 342   Photo.
1108 A537 20m yellow & gray   .35 .20
    25th anniversary of the Egyptian Mint.

Egypt No. 1104 under Magnifying Glass — A538

1979, June 1   Perf. 11
1109 A538 20m green, blk & brn   .40 .20
    Philatelic Society of Egypt, 50th anniversary.

Book, Atom Symbol, Rising Sun — A539

"23 July," "Revolution" and "Peace" — A540

    Perf. 11½x11
1979, July 23   Wmk. 342
1110 A539 20m multicolored   .35 .20
    Miniature Sheet
    Imperf
1111 A540 140m multicolored   3.00 1.50
    27th anniversary of July 23rd revolution.

Musicians — A541

1979, Aug. 22   Perf. 11½
1112 A541 10m multicolored   .20 .20
    For use on greeting cards.

Dove over Map of Suez Canal A542

    Wmk. 342
1979, Oct. 6   Perf. 11½
1113 A542 20m blue & brown   .40 .20
    October War against Israel, 6th anniv.

Prehistoric Mammal Skeleton, Map of Africa — A543

    Perf. 11½x11
1979, Oct. 9   Photo.   Wmk. 342
1114 A543 20m multicolored   1.25 .25
    Egyptian Geological Museum, 75th anniv.

T Square on Drawing Board — A544

1979, Oct. 11   Perf. 11
1115 A544 20m multicolored   .50 .20
    Engineers Day.

Human Rights Emblem Over Globe — A545

Boy Balancing IYC Emblem — A546

    Perf. 11½
1979, Oct. 24   Photo.   Unwmk.
1116 A545 45m multicolored   .50 .25
1117 A546 140m multicolored   1.25 .50
    UN Day and Intl. Year of the Child.

International Savings Day — A547

1979, Oct. 31
1118 A547 70m multicolored   .75 .30

A548   A549

Design: Shooting championship emblem.

1979, Nov. 16
1119 A548 20m multicolored   .40 .20
    20th International Military Shooting Championship, Cairo.

1979, Nov. 29   Perf. 11x11½
1120 A549 45m multicolored   .75 .25
    International Palestinian Solidarity Day.

Dove Holding Grain, Rotary Emblem, Globe A550

1979, Dec. 3   Photo.   Perf. 11½
1121 A550 140m multicolored   1.25 .60
    Rotary Intl., 75th anniv,; Cairo Rotary Club, 50th anniv.

Arms Factories, 25th
Anniversary — A551

Perf. 11½x11
1979, Dec. 23   Photo.   Wmk. 342
1122 A551 20m lt olive grn & brn   .35 .20

Aly El Garem
(1881-1949)
A552

Pharaonic Capital
A553

Poets: No. 1124, Mahmoud Samy El
Baroudy (1839-1904).

1979, Dec. 25   Perf. 11x11½
1123 A552 20m dk brn & yel brn   .40 .20
1124 A552 20m brown & dk brown   .40 .20
  a.   Pair, #1123-1124   .80 .80

1980, Jan. 2   Unwmk.   Perf. 11½
Post Day: Various Pharaonic capitals.
1125 A553   20m multicolored   .35 .25
1126 A553   45m multicolored   .50 .35
1127 A553   70m multicolored   .70 .20
1128 A553   140m multicolored   2.00 .40
  a.   Strip of 4, #1125-1128   4.75 2.40

Golden Goddess
of Writing, Fair
Emblem — A554

Exhibition
Catalogue and
Medal — A555

1980, Feb. 2   Photo.   Perf. 11½
1129 A554 20m multicolored   .60 .20
12th Cairo Intl. Book Fair, Jan. 24-Feb. 4.

1980, Feb. 2
1130 A555 20m multicolored   .45 .20
13th Biennial Exhibition of Fine Arts,
Alexandria.

13th Cairo
International
Fair — A556

1980, Mar. 8   Photo.   Perf. 11x11½
1131 A556 20m multicolored   .45 .20

Kiosk of Trajan — A557

a, Kiosk of Tratan. b, Temple of Korasy,
entry at right. c, Temple of Ksalabsha, carvings on frame. d, Temple of Philae, 5
columns..

1980, Mar. 10   Perf. 11½
1132   Strip of 4 + label   5.00 5.00
  a.-d. A557 70m, any single   1.00 .60
UNESCO campaign to save Nubian monuments, 20th anniversary. Shown on stamps
are Temples of Philae, Kalabsha, Korasy.

Physicians'
Day — A558

1980, Mar. 18   Perf. 11x11½
1133 A558 20m multicolored   .45 .20

Rectification Movement, 9th
Anniversary — A559

Perf. 11½x11
1980, May 15   Photo.   Wmk. 342
1134 A559 20m multicolored   .45 .20

Re-opening of Suez Canal, 5th
Anniversary — A560

1980, June 5   Perf. 11½
1135 A560 140m multicolored   1.40 .50

Prevention
of Cruelty
to Animals
Week
A561

1980, June 5
1136 A561 20m lt yel grn & gray   .70 .20

Industry
Day
A562

Perf. 11½x11
1980, July 12   Photo.   Wmk. 342
1137 A562 20m multicolored   .35 .20

Leaf with
Text
A563

Family Protection Emblem — A564

1980, July 23   Perf. 11½
1138 A563   20m multicolored   .45 .20
Souvenir Sheet
Imperf
1139 A564 140m multicolored   2.75 .55
July 23rd Revolution, 28th anniv.; Social
Security Year.

Erksous Seller and
Nakrazan
Player — A565

Perf. 11½
1980, Aug. 8   Unwmk.   Photo.
1140 A565 10m multicolored   .30 .20
For use on greeting cards.

October War Against Israel, 7th
Anniv. — A566

1980, Oct. 6   Litho.
1141 A566 20m multicolored   .75 .20

Islamic and
Coptic
Columns
A567

International Telecommunications
Union Emblem — A568

Wmk. 342
1980, Oct. 24   Photo.   Perf. 11½
1142 A567 70m multicolored   .70 .55
1143 A568 140m multicolored   1.40 .85
UN Day. Campaign to save Egyptian monuments (70m), Intl. Telecommunications Day
(140m).

Hegira
(Pilgrimage
Year)
A569

1980, Nov. 9   Litho.   Perf. 11x11½
1144 A569 45m multicolored   .60 .25

Opening
of Suez
Canal
Third
Branch
A570

Perf. 11½x11
1980, Dec. 16   Photo.   Wmk. 342
1145 A570 70m multicolored   .80 .30

Mustafa Sadek El-
Rafai (1880-1927),
Writer — A571

No. 1147, Ali Mustafa Mousharafa (1898-
1950), mathematician (with glasses). No.
1148, Ali Ibrahim (1880-1947), surgeon.

1980, Dec. 23   *Perf. 11x11½*
1146 A571 20m green & brown   .45 .25
1147 A571 20m green & brown   .45 .25
1148 A571 20m green & brown   .45 .25
   a.   Strip of 3, #1146-1148   1.90 .75
See Nos. 1178-1179.

Ladybug Scarab Emblem — A572   von Stephan, UPU — A573

Perf. 11½
1981, Jan. 2   Photo.   Unwmk.
1149 A572 70m shown   .90 .25
1150 A572 70m Scarab, reverse   .90 .25
Post Day.

Perf. 11x11½
1981, Jan. 7   Wmk. 342
1151 A573 140m grnsh bl & dk brn   1.75 .70
Heinrich von Stephan (1831-97), founder of UPU.

13th Cairo International Book Fair — A574

1981, Feb. 1   *Perf. 11½x11*
1152 A574 20m multicolored   .40 .20

14th Cairo International Fair, Mar. 14-28 — A575

Perf. 11x11½
1981, Mar. 14   Photo.   Wmk. 342
1153 A575 20m multicolored   .40 .20

Rural Electrification Authority, 10th Anniversary — A576

1981, Mar. 18
1154 A576 20m multicolored   .45 .20

Veterans' Day — A577   Intl. Dentistry Conf., Cairo — A578

1981, Mar. 26
1155 A577 20m multicolored   .50 .20

Perf. 11x11½
1981, Apr. 14   Photo.   Wmk. 342
1156 A578 20m red & olive   .50 .20

Trade Union Emblem — A579   Nurses' Day — A580

Perf. 11x11½
1981, May 1   Photo.   Wmk. 342
1157 A579 20m brt blue & dk brn   .40 .20
International Confederation of Arab Trade Unions, 25th anniv.

1981, May 12
1158 A580 20m multicolored   .40 .20

Irrigation Equipment (Electrification Movement) — A581

1981, May 15   *Perf. 11½*
1159 A581 20m multicolored   .40 .20

Air Force Day — A582

Perf. 11x11½
1981, June 30   Photo.   Wmk. 342
1160 A582 20m multicolored   .50 .20

Flag Surrounding Map of Suez Canal — A583

Wmk. 342
1981, July 23   Photo.   *Perf. 11½*
1161 A583 20m multicolored   .45 .20
1162 A583 20m Emblems   .45 .20
July 23rd Revolution, 29th anniv.; Social Defense Year.

1981 Feasts — A584

Wmk. 342
1981, July 29   Photo.   *Perf. 11*
1163 A584 10m multicolored   .40 .20

A585   A586

1981, Aug. 10   *Perf. 11x11½*
1164 A585 140m Kemal Ataturk   2.00 .80

Perf. 11x11½
1981, Sept. 9   Photo.   Wmk. 342
1165 A586 20m Arabi Pasha, Leader of Egyptian Force   .40 .20
Orabi Revolution centenary.

A587   A588

1981, Sept. 14
1166 A587 45m Athlete, Pyramids, Sphinx   .80 .20
World Muscular Athletics Championships, Cairo.

Perf. 11x11½
1981, Sept. 26   Photo.   Wmk. 342
1167 A588 45m multicolored   .60 .20
Ministry of Industry and Mineral Resources, 25th anniv.

20th Intl. Occupational Health Congress, Cairo — A589

1981, Sept. 28   *Perf. 11½x11*
1168 A589 20m multicolored   .50 .20

October War Against Israel, 8th Anniv. A590

1981, Oct. 6
1169 A590 20m multicolored   .70 .20

World Food Day A591

13th World Telecommunications Day — A592

Intl. Year of the Disabled — A593

Fight Against Apartheid A594

Perf. 11½x11, 11x11½
1981, Oct. 24   Photo.   Wmk. 342
1170 A591 10m multicolored   .30 .20
1171 A592 20m multicolored   .30 .20
1172 A593 45m multicolored   .50 .25
1173 A594 230m multicolored   3.00 1.10
   Nos. 1170-1173 (4)   4.10 1.75
United Nations Day.

Pres. Anwar Sadat (1917-81) — A595

Perf. 11x11½
1981, Nov. 14   Unwmk.
1174 A595 30m multicolored   1.40 .65
1175 A595 230m multicolored   3.50 2.50

Establishment of Shura Family Council — A596

Perf. 11½x11
1981, Dec. 12   Photo.   Wmk. 342
1176 A596 45m purple & yellow   .50 .20

Agricultural Credit and Development Bank, 50th Anniv. — A597

1981, Dec. 15   *Perf. 11x11½*
1177 A597 20m multicolored   .40 .20

Famous Men Type of 1980

30m, Ali el-Ghayati (1885-1956), journalist. 60m, Omar Ebn sl-Fared (1181-1234), Sufi poet.

Perf. 11x11½
1981, Dec. 21   Photo.   Wmk. 342
1178 A571 30m green & brown   .40 .20
1179 A571 60m green & brown   .60 .20
   a.   Pair, #1178-1179   1.00 .50

20th Anniv. of African Postal Union A598

1981, Dec. 21   *Perf. 11½x11*
1180 A598 60m multicolored   .90 .30

14th Cairo Intl. Book Fair — A599

Arab Trade Union of Egypt, 25th Anniv. — A600

1982, Jan. 28
1181 A599 3p brown & yellow   .60 .20

1982, Jan. 30
1182 A600 3p multicolored   .40 .20

Khartoum Branch of Cairo University, 25th Anniv. A601

Perf. 11½x11
1982, Mar. 4   Wmk. 342
1183 A601 6p blue & green   .80 .35

15th Cairo Intl. Fair — A602

1982, Mar. 13   *Perf. 11x11½*
1184 A602 3p multicolored   .40 .20

50th Anniv. of Al-Ghardaka Marine Biological Station — A603

Fish of the Red Sea.

1982, Apr. 24   Litho.   *Perf. 11½x11*
1185 10m Lined butterfly fish   .65 .45
1186 30m Blue-banded sea perch   .95 .50
1187 60m Batfish   1.10 .75
1188 230m Blue-spotted boxfish   3.00 1.40
  a.   A603 Block of 4, #1185-1188   6.00 2.00

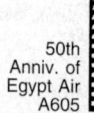

Liberation of the Sinai — A604

1982, Apr. 25   Photo.   *Perf. 11x11½*
1189 A604 3p multicolored   .60 .20

50th Anniv. of Egypt Air A605

1982, May 7   Photo.   *Perf. 11½x11*
1190 A605 23p multicolored   2.50 1.40

Minaret — A606

Al Azhar Mosque — A607

a, shown. b, Two terraces. c, Three terraces. d, Two turrets at top.

Perf. 11x11½
1982, June 28   Photo.   Wmk. 342
1191   Strip of 4 + label   3.50 3.50
  a.-d.   A606 6p any single, multi   .55 .30

Souvenir Sheet
Unwmk.   *Imperf.*
1192 A607 23p multicolored   6.00 3.00
Al Azhar Mosque millennium. No. 1192 airmail.

Dove — A608

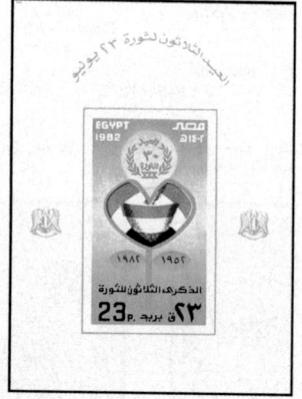

Flower in Natl. Colors — A609

Perf. 11x11½
1982, July 23   Photo.   Wmk. 342
1193 A608 3p multicolored   .40 .20

Souvenir Sheet
Imperf
1194 A609 23p multicolored   4.25 2.10
30th anniv. of July 23rd Revolution.

World Tourism Day A610

Design: Sphinx, pyramid of Cheops, St. Catherine's Tower.

Perf. 11½x11
1982, Sept. 27   Photo.   Wmk. 342
1195 A610 23p multicolored   2.75 1.40

October War Against Israel, 9th Anniv. A611

1982, Oct. 6
1196 A611 3p Memorial, map   .60 .20

Biennale of Alexandria Art Exhibition — A612

1982, Oct. 17   *Perf. 11x11½*
1197 A612 3p multicolored   .45 .20

10th Anniv. of UN Conference on Human Environment — A613

2nd UN Conference on Peaceful Uses of Outer Space, Vienna, Aug. 9-21 — A614

Scouting Year A615

TB Bacillus Centenary A616

Perf. 11½x11, 11½ (A615)
1982, Oct. 24
1198 A613 3p multicolored   .40 .20
1199 A614 6p multicolored   .70 .20
1200 A615 6p multicolored   .70 .20
1201 A616 8p multicolored   .80 .20
  Nos. 1198-1201 (4)   2.60 .80

United Nations Day.

50th Anniv. of Air Force A617

1982, Nov. 2   *Perf. 11½x11*
1202 A617 3p Jet, plane   .60 .20

Ahmed Chawki (1868-1932) and Hafez Ibrahim (1871-1932), Poets — A618

Perf. 11½x11
1982, Nov. 25   Photo.   Wmk. 342
1203 A618 6p multicolored   .60 .20

Natl. Research Center, 25th Anniv. — A619

1982, Dec. 12   Photo.   *Perf. 11x11½*
1204 A619 3p red & blue   .65 .20

50th Anniv. of Arab Language Society A620

1982, Dec. 25   *Perf. 11½x11*
1205 A620 6p multicolored   .65 .20

Year of the
Aged — A621

1982, Dec. 25   Perf. 11x11½
1206 A621 23p multicolored   2.50 1.40

Post Day
A622

1983, Jan. 2   Perf. 11½
1207 A622 3p multicolored   .50 .20

15th Cairo Intl. Book
Fair — A623

Perf. 11x11½
1983, Jan. 25   Photo.   Wmk. 342
1208 A623 3p blue & red   .50 .20

Police Day
A624

1983, Jan. 25   Perf. 11½x11
1209 A624 3p multicolored   .60 .20

16th Cairo Intl.   5th UN African
Fair — A625   Map Conf.,
   Cairo — A626

Perf. 11x11½
1983, Mar. 2   Photo.   Wmk. 342
1210 A625 3p multicolored   .50 .20

1983, Mar. 2
1211 A626 3p lt green & blue   .60 .20

African Ministers of Transport,
Communications and Planning, 3rd
Conference — A627

1983, Mar. 8   Perf. 11½x11
1212 A627 23p green & blue   1.75 1.00

A628   A629

1983, Mar. 20   Perf. 11x11½
1213 A628 3p Heading   .50 .20
1214 A628 3p Kick   .50 .20
  a. Pair, #1213-1214   1.25 1.25
Victory in African Soccer Cup.

Perf. 11x11½
1983, Apr. 2   Photo.   Wmk. 342
1215 A629 3p olive & red   .70 .20
World Health Day and Natl. Blood Donation
Campaign.

Org. of
African
Trade
Union
Unity
A630

Perf. 11½x11
1983, Apr. 21   Photo.   Wmk. 342
1216 A630 3p multicolored   .50 .20

1st Anniv. of   75th Anniv. of
Sinai Liberation   Entomology
A631   Society
   A632

1983, Apr. 25   Perf. 11x11½
1217 A631 3p multicolored   .75 .20

1983, May 23
1218 A632 3p Emblem (Holy Scarab)   .75 .20

Flowers — A633

1983, June 11   Photo.   Perf. 11½x11
1219 A633 20m green & org red   .40 .20

5th African Handball Championship,
Cairo — A634

Perf. 11½x11
1983, July 22   Photo.   Wmk. 342
1220 A634 6p brown & dk grn   .60 .20

31st Anniv. of   Simon Bolivar
Revolution   (1783-1830)
A635   A636

1983, July 23   Perf. 11½
1221 A635 3p multicolored   .40 .20

1983, Aug.   Perf. 11x11½
1222 A636 23p brown & dull grn   1.25 .80

Centenary
of Arrival
of Natl.
Hero
Orabi in
Ceylon
A637

Perf. 11½x11
1983, Aug. 25   Photo.   Wmk. 342
1223 A637 3p Map, Orabi, El-Zahra
School   .40 .20

Islamic
Vase,
Museum
Building
A638

1983, Sept. 14   Photo.   Perf. 11½x11
1224 A638 3p yel brn & dk brn   .70 .20
Reopening of Islamic Museum.

October War   2nd Pharaonic
Against Israel,   Race — A640
10th
Anniv. — A639

1983, Oct. 6   Perf. 11½
1225 A639 3p multicolored   .70 .20

1983, Oct. 17   Perf. 11½
1226 A640 23p multicolored   2.00 1.25

United Nations
Day — A641

1983, Oct. 24   Photo.   Perf. 11
1227 A641 3p IMO, ships, horiz.   .40 .20
1228 A641 6p ITU, UPU   .40 .20
1229 A641 6p FAO, UN, grain   .40 .20
1230 A641 23p UN, ocean   2.00 .60
  Nos. 1227-1230 (4)   3.20 1.20

4th World Karate Championship,
Cairo — A642

1983, Nov.   Photo.   Perf. 13
1231 A642 3p multicolored   .60 .20

Intl. Palestinian Cooperation
Day — A643

1983, Nov. 29   Photo.   Perf. 13x13½
1232 A643 6p Dome of the Rock   1.00 .20

75th Anniv.
of Faculty
of Fine
Arts, Cairo
A644

1983, Nov. 30   Perf. 13
1233 A644 3p multicolored   .40 .20

75th Anniv. of Cairo
University — A645

1983, Nov. 30   Perf. 11x11½
1234 A645 3p multicolored   .40 .20

Intl.
Egyptian
Society of
Mother
and Child
Care
A646

1983, Nov. 30   Perf. 11½x11
1235 A646 3p multicolored   .40 .20

Org. of African   World Heritage
Unity, 20th   Convention, 10th
Anniv. — A647   Anniv. — A648

Perf. 11x11½
1983, Dec. 20   Photo.   Wmk. 342
1236 A647 3p multicolored   .40 .20

1983, Dec. 24
1237		Strip of 3	2.50	2.50
a.	A648	3p Wood carving, Islamic	.75	.40
b.	A648	3p Coptic tapestry	.75	.40
c.	A648	3p Ramses II Thebes	.75	.40

Post Day
A649

Restored Forts: 6p, Quatbay. 23p, Mosque, Salah El-Din.

1984, Jan. 2   *Perf. 13*
1238	A649	6p multicolored	.50	.20
1239	A649	23p multicolored	2.00	1.25

Misr Insurance Co., 50 Anniv. A650

1984, Jan. 14   *Perf. 11½x11*
1240	A650	3p multicolored	.35	.20

16th Cairo Intl. Book Fair — A651

Perf. 13½x13
1984, Jan. 26   Photo.   Wmk. 342
1241	A651	3p multicolored	.40	.20

17th Cairo Intl. Fair A652

Perf. 11½x11
1984, Mar. 10   Photo.   Wmk. 342
1242	A652	3p multicolored	.45	.20

25th Anniv. of Asyut University A653

75th Anniv. of Cooperative Unions A654

1984, Mar. 10   *Perf. 11x11½*
1243	A653	3p multicolored	.40	.20

1984, Mar. 17
1244	A654	3p multicolored	.40	.20

World Theater Day — A655

Mahmoud Mokhtar (1891-1934), Sculptor — A656

Perf. 11x11½, 11½x11
1984, Mar. 27   Photo.   Unwmk.
1245	A655	3p Masks	.45	.20
1246	A656	3p Pride of the Nile	.45	.20

World Health Day and Fight Against Polio — A657

Perf. 11½x11
1984, Apr. 7   Photo.   Wmk. 342
1247	A657	3p Polio vaccine	.60	.20

2nd Anniv. of Sinai Liberation — A658

1984, Apr. 25
1248	A658	3p Doves, map	.50	.20

Africa Day A659

Perf. 12½x13½
1984, May 25   Photo.   Wmk. 342
1249	A659	3p Map, UN emblem	.40	.20

Satellite, Waves — A660

Flower — A661

1984, May 31   *Perf. 11x11½*
1250	A660	3p multicolored	.50	.20

Radio broadcasting in Egypt, 50th anniv.

1984, June 1
1251	A661	2p red & green	.35	.20

Intl. Cairo Arab Arts Biennale — A662

1984, June 1   *Perf. 13½x12½*
1252	A662	3p multicolored	.50	.20

July Revolution, 32nd Anniv. — A663

Wmk. 342
1984, July 23   Photo.   Perf. 11
1253	A663	3p Atomic energy, agri-culture	.50	.20

A664   A665

1984 Summer Olympics: a, Boxing. b, Basketball. c, Volleyball. d, Soccer.

1984, July 28
1254		Strip of 4 + label	4.50	4.50
a.-d.	A664	3p any single	.40	.40

Size: 130x80mm
Imperf
1255	A664	30p like No. 1254	4.25	4.25

Wmk. 342
1984, Aug. 13   Photo.   Perf. 11
1256	A665	3p bl & multi	.45	.20
1257	A665	23p grn & multi	1.90	.90

2nd Genl. Conference of Egyptians Abroad, Aug. 11-15, Cairo.

Youth Hostels, 30th Anniv. — A666

Egypt Tour Co., 50th Anniv. — A667

Perf. 11x11½
1984, Sept. 22   Photo.   Wmk. 342
1258	A666	3p Youths, emblem	.40	.20

1984, Sept. 27
1259	A667	3p Emblem, sphinx	.50	.20

October War Against Israel, 11th Anniv. — A668

Egypt-Sudan Unity — A669

1984, Oct. 6
1260	A668	3p Map, eagle	.40	.20

1984, Oct. 12
1261	A669	3p Map of Nile, arms	.50	.20

UN Day — A670

Tanks, Emblem — A671

Perf. 13½x12½
1984, Oct. 24   Photo.   Wmk. 342
1262	A670	3p UNICEF Emblem, child	.40	.20

UN campaign for infant survival.

1984, Nov. 10
1263	A671	3p multicolored	.50	.20

Military Equipment Exhibition, Cairo, Nov. 10-14.

Tolon Mosque, Egypt A672

1984, Dec. 23   Photo.   Perf. 11½x11
1264	A672	3p multicolored	.60	.20

Ahmed Ebn Tolon (A.D. 835-884), Gov. of Egypt, founder of Kataea City.

A673   A674

1984, Dec. 23   *Perf. 11x11½*
1265	A673	3p multicolored	.40	.20

Kamel el-Kilany (1897-1959), author.

Perf. 11x11½
1984, Dec. 26   Photo.   Wmk. 342

Globe and congress emblem.
1266	A674	3p lt blue, ver & blk	.60	.20

29th Intl. Congress on the History of Medicine, Dec. 27, 1984-Jan. 1, 1985, Cairo.

Academy of the Arts, 25th Anniv. A675

1984, Dec. 31 *Perf. 13*
1267 A675 3p Emblem in spotlights .60 .20

Pharaoh Receiving Message, Natl. Postal Museum, Cairo A676

1985, Jan. 2 *Perf. 11½x11*
1268 A676 3p brown, lt bl & ver .60 .20

Postal Museum, 50th anniv.

Intl. Union of Architects, 15th Conference, Jan. 14-Feb. 15 — A677

1985, Jan. 20
1269 A677 3p multicolored .60 .20

Seated Pharaonic Scribe — A678

Wheat, Cogwheels, Fair Emblem — A679

1985, Jan. 22 *Perf. 11x11½*
1270 A678 3p brt org & dk blue grn .60 .20

17th Intl. Book Fair, Jan. 22-Feb. 3, Cairo.

1985, Mar. 9 *Perf. 13½x13*
1271 A679 3p multicolored .60 .20

18th Intl. Fair, Mar. 9-22, Cairo.

Return of Sinai to Egypt, 3rd Anniv. — A680

1985, Apr. 25 **Wmk. 342** **Litho.**
1272 A680 5p multicolored .60 .20

Ancient Artifacts — A681

A681a

Designs: 1p, God Mout, limestone sculpture, 360-340 B.C. 2p, No. 1281, Five wading birds, bas-relief. 3p, No. 1276, Seated statue, Ramses II, Temple of Luxor. No. 1276A, Vase. 8p, 15p, Slave bearing votive fruit offering, mural. 10p, Double-handled flask. 11p, Sculpted head of woman. No. 1282, Pitcher. 30p, 50p, Decanter. 35p, Temple of Karnak carved capitals. £1, Mosque.

1985-90 Photo. Unwmk. Perf. 11½
1273	A681	1p brown olive	.40	.20
1274	A681	2p brt grnsh bl	.40	.20
1275	A681	3p yellow brown	.40	.20
1276	A681	5p dk violet	.40	.20
1276A	A681	5p lemon	.40	.20
1277	A681	8p pale ol grn, sep & brn	.50	.20
1278	A681	10p dk vio & bl	.60	.20
1279	A681	11p dk violet	.60	.30
1280	A681	15p pale yel, sep & brn	.60	.30
1281	A681	20p yellow green	.60	.30
1282	A681	20p dk grn & yel	.60	.30
1283	A681	30p ol bis & buff	.70	.50
1284	A681	35p sep & pale yel	1.00	.60
1285	A681	50p purple & buff	1.40	.80
1285A	A681a	£1 brown & buff	3.75	3.75
1286	A681a	£2 sepia & yel	6.00	6.00
	Nos. 1273-1286 (16)	18.35	14.25

Issued: 1p, 2p, 3p, No. 1276, 8p, 11p, 15p, 5/1/85; 35p, 7/7/85; No. 1281, 4/1/86; 10p, 10/1/89; £2, 12/1/89; No. 1282, 2/1/90; 30p, 50p, 2/5/90; £1, 2/8/90; No. 1276A, 12/15/90. Nos. 1276A, 1278 are 18x23mm.
No. 1278 exists dated "1990."
See Nos. 1467, 1470, 1472.

Helwan University School of Music, 50th Anniv. A682

1985, May 15
1287 A682 5p multicolored .50 .20

El-Moulid Bride, Folk Doll — A683

1985
1288 A683 2p orange & multi .40 .20
1289 A683 5p red & multi .40 .20

Festivals 1985. Issued: 2p, 6/11; 5p, 8/10.

A684 A685

Winning teams: a, b, Cairo Sports Stadium. c, El-Mokawiloon Club, white uniform, 1983. d, Natl. Club, red uniform, 1984. e, El-Zamalek Club, orange uniform, 1984.

1985, June 17 *Perf. 13½x13*
1290 Strip of 5 5.00 5.00
a.-e. A684 5p any single 1.00 1.00

1985 Africa Cup Soccer Championships. Cairo Sports Stadium, 25th anniv. Nos. 1290a-1290b have continuous design.

1985, July 23 *Perf. 11½x11*
1291 A685 5p blue, brn & yel .65 .20

Egyptian Television, 25th anniv. Egyptian Revolution, 33rd anniv.

Suez Canal Reopening, 10th Anniv. — A686

Perf. 13x13½
1985, July 23 Litho. Wmk. 342
1292 A686 5p multicolored .65 .20

Egyptian Revolution, 33rd anniv.

Ahmed Hamdi Memorial Underwater Tunnel — A687

1985, July 23 *Perf. 13½x13*
1293 A687 5p blue, vio & org .50 .20

Egyptian Revolution, 33rd anniv.

Souvenir Sheet

Aswan High Dam, 25th Anniv. — A688

Wmk. 342
1985, July 23 Photo. Imperf.
1294 A688 30p multicolored 3.50 2.75

Heart, Map, Olive Laurel, Conference Emblem — A689

1985, Aug. 10 Litho. Perf. 13½x13
1295 A689 15p multicolored 1.25 .85

Egyptian Emigrants, 3rd general conference, Aug. 10-14, Cairo.

Natl. Tourism Ministry, 50th Anniv. — A690

1985, Sept. 10 *Perf. 13x13½*
1296 A690 5p multicolored .45 .20

October War Against Israel, 12th Anniv. — A691

1985, Oct. 6
1297 A691 5p multicolored .45 .20

Air Scouts Assoc., 30th Anniv. — A692

1985, Oct. 15 Photo. Perf. 11½
1298 A692 5p Emblem .55 .20

A693

UN, 40th Anniv. — A694

1985, Oct. 24
1299 A693 5p UN emblem, weather map .45 .20

UN Day, Meteorology Day.

1985, Oct. 24
1300 A694 15p multicolored 1.25 .85

Intl. Youth Year — A695

A696

1985, Oct. 24
1301 A695 5p multicolored .45 .20

1985, Oct. 24
1302 A696 15p blue & int blue 1.25 .85

Intl. Communications Development Program.

A697   A698

Emblem, hieroglyphics of Hassi Raa, 1st known dentist.

1985, Oct. 29   *Perf. 11x11½*
1303 A697 5p beige & pale bl vio .75 .25
2nd Intl. Dentistry Conference.

1985, Nov. 18   Photo.   Perf. 11½
1304 A698 5p Emblem, squash player .45 .20
1985 World Squash Championships, Nov. 18-Dec. 4.

A699   A700

1985, Nov. 2   Litho.   Perf. 13½x13
1305 A699 5p multicolored .45 .20
4th Intl. Conference on the Biography and Sunna of Mohammed.

1985, Dec. 1   Photo.   Perf. 11x11½
1306 A700 5p multicolored .45 .20
1st Conference on the Development of Vocational Training.

Natl. Olympic Committee, 75th Anniv. — A701   18th Intl. Book Fair, Cairo — A702

1985, Dec. 28   Photo.   Perf. 13x13½
1307 A701 5p multicolored .50 .20

1986, Jan. 21   Perf. 11x11½
1308 A702 5p Pharaonic scribe .45 .20

CODATU III — A703

1986, Jan. 26   Perf. 11½
1309 A703 5p lt ol grn, ver & grnsh bl .40 .20
3rd Intl. Conference on Urban Transportation in Developing Countries, Cairo.

Central Bank, 25th Anniv. — A704

1986, Jan. 30   Perf. 13x13½
1310 A704 5p multicolored .40 .20

Cairo Postal Traffic Center Inauguration — A705

1986, Jan. 30   Perf. 11½x11
1311 A705 5p blue & dk brown .40 .20

Pharaonic Mural, Btah Hotteb's Tomb at Saqqara A706

1986, Feb. 27   Photo.   Perf. 11½x11
1312 A706 5p yel, gldn brn & brn .60 .25
Faculty of Commerce, Cairo Univ., 75th anniv.

Cairo Intl. Fair, Mar. 8-21 — A707

1986, Mar. 8   Litho.   Perf. 13½x13
1313 A707 5p multicolored .40 .20

Queen Nefertiti, Sinai — A708

Perf. 13x13½
1986, Apr. 25   Litho.   Wmk. 342
1314 A708 5p multicolored .50 .20
Return of the Sinai to Egypt, 4th anniv.

Ministry of Health, 50th Anniv. — A709

1986, Apr. 10   Perf. 13½x13
1315 A709 5p multicolored .45 .20

1986 Census — A710

1986, May 26   Photo.   Perf. 11½
1316 A710 15p brn, grnsh bl & yel bis 1.00 1.00

Egypt, Winner of African Soccer Cup — A711   Festivals, Roses — A712

1986, May 31   Perf. 13½x13
1317 A711 5p English inscription below cup .50 .50
1318 A711 5p Arabic .50 .50
  a. Pair, #1317-1318 1.00 1.00

1986, June 2   Perf. 11½
1319 A712 5p multicolored .40 .20

World Environment Day — A713

1986, June 5   Perf. 13½x13
1320 A713 15p Emblem, smokestacks 1.10 1.10

July 23rd Revolution, 34th Anniv. A714

1986, July 23   Litho.   Perf. 13
1321 A714 5p gray grn, scar & yel bis .40 .20

6th African Roads Conference, Cairo, Sept. 22-26 — A715

Perf. 13½x13
1986, Sept. 21   Litho.   Wmk. 342
1322 A715 15p multicolored 1.00 1.00

October War Against Israel, 13th Anniv. A716

1986, Oct. 6   Litho.   Perf. 13
1323 A716 5p multicolored .70 .25

Engineers' Syndicate, 40th Anniv. A717

1986, Oct. 11   Photo.   Perf. 11½
1324 A717 5p lt blue, brn & pale grn .40 .20

Workers' Cultural Education Assoc., 25th Anniv. — A718

1986, Oct. 11   *Perf. 11x11½*
1325 A718 5p orange & rose vio   .40 .20

Intl. Peace Year — A719

1986, Oct. 24
1326 A719 5p blue, grn & pale sal   .35 .20

First Oil Well in Egypt, Cent. — A720

1986, Nov. 7   Photo.   *Perf. 11½*
1327 A720 5p dull grn, blk & pale yel   .60 .25

UN Child Survival Campaign A721

1986, Nov. 20   Litho.   *Perf. 13*
1328 A721 5p multicolored   .60 .25

Ahmed Amin, Philosopher A722

National Theater, 50th Anniv. — A723

1986, Dec. 20   *Perf. 11½*
1329 A722 5p pale grn, pale yel & brn   .40 .20

1986, Dec. 20   *Perf. 13½x13*
1330 A723 5p multicolored   .45 .20

Post Day A724

Step Pyramid, Saqqara, King Zoser.

       Perf. 13x13½
1987, Jan. 2   Litho.   Wmk. 342
1331 A724 5p multicolored   .60 .25

19th Intl. Book Fair, Cairo A725

1987, Jan. 25   Litho.   *Perf. 13*
1332 A725 5p multicolored   .40 .20

5th World Conference on Islamic Education A726

       Wmk. 342
1987, Mar. 8   Litho.   *Perf. 13*
1333 A726 5p multicolored   .45 .20

20th Intl. Fair, Cairo — A727

1987, Mar. 21   Photo.   *Perf. 11½*
1334 A727 5p Good workers medal   .40 .20

Veteran's Day A728

1987, Mar. 26
1335 A728 5p multicolored   .40 .20

Intl. Gardens Inauguration, Nasser City — A729

1987, Mar. 30   Litho.   *Perf. 13*
1336 A729 15p multicolored   1.00 1.00

World Health Day A730

1987, Apr. 7   Photo.   *Perf. 11½*
1337 A730 5p Mother feeding child   .45 .20
       Litho.
       Perf. 13
1338 A730 5p Oral rehydration therapy   .45 .20

A731

Natl. Team Victory at 1986 Intl. Soccer Championships — A732

Trophies: No. 1339a, Al Ahly Cup. No. 1339b, National Cup. No. 1339c, Al Zamalek Cup. No. 1340, Natl. flag, Cairo Stadium and trophies pictured on No. 1339.

1987, Apr. 19   Litho.   *Perf. 13½x13*
1339   Strip of 3   1.50 1.50
  a.-c.   A731 5p any single   .50 .50
       Size: 115x85mm
       Imperf
1340 A732 30p multicolored   3.50 3.50

A733

A734

Salah El Din Citadel, Pharoah's Is., Sinai.

1987, Apr. 25
1341 A733 5p sky blue & lt brown   .50 .20
Return of the Sinai to Egypt, 5th anniv.

1987, May 21   Photo.   *Perf. 11½*
Festivals.
1342 A734 5p Dahlia   .40 .20

Cultural Heritage Exhibition — A735

1987, June 17   Litho.   *Perf. 13x13½*
1343 A735 15p multicolored   1.00 1.00

Tourism Year — A736

a, Column and Sphinx, Alexandria. b, St. Catherine's Monastery, Mt. Sinai. c, Colossi of Thebes. d, Temple of Theban Triad, Luxor.

1987, June 18
1344   Block of 4   4.00 4.00
  a.-d.   A736 15p any single   1.00 1.00
       See No. C187.

National Day A737

1987, June 26   *Perf. 13*
1345 A737 5p multicolored   .40 .20

Industry-Agriculture Exhibition — A738

1987, July 23   Photo.   *Perf. 11½*
1346 A738 5p grn, dull org & blk   .40 .20

Intl. Year of Shelter for the Homeless A739

1987, Sept. 2   Litho.   *Perf. 13*
1347 A739 5p multicolored   .40 .20
World Architects' Day.

Aida, Performed at Al Ahram Pyramid, Giza A740

Radamis and troops returning from Ethiopia.

1987, Sept. 21
1348 A740 15p multicolored 1.25 1.25
Size: 70x70mm
Imperf
1349 A740 30p multicolored 5.00 5.00

Greater Cairo Subway Inauguration — A741

1987, Sept. 27 *Perf. 13x13½*
1350 A741 5p multicolored .85 .25

Industry Day A742

1987, Oct. 1 *Perf. 13*
1351 A742 5p multicolored .40 .20

Battle of Hettin, 700th Anniv. — A743

1987, Oct. 6 Photo. *Perf. 11x11½*
1352 A743 5p multicolored .50 .20

UPU Emblem A744

Perf. 11½
1987, Oct. 24 Unwmk. Photo.
1353 A744 5p multicolored .45 .20
UN Executive Council, 40th anniv.; UPU Consultative Council, 30th anniv.

16th Art Biennial of Alexandria A745

1987, Nov. 7 Litho. *Perf. 13½x13*
1354 A745 5p multicolored .45 .20

Second Intl. Defense Equipment Exhibition, Cairo, Nov. 9-13 — A746

Perf. 13x13½
1987, Nov. 9 Litho. Unwmk.
1355 A746 5p multicolored .45 .20

2nd Pan-Arab Congress on Anaesthesia and Intensive Care — A747

Unwmk.
1987, Dec. 1 Litho. *Perf. 13*
1356 A747 5p multicolored .50 .20

Intl. Orthopedic and Traumatology Conference A748

1987, Dec. 1 *Perf. 13½x13*
1357 A748 5p gray, red brn & bl .50 .20

Selim Hassan (1887-1961), Egyptologist, and Hieroglyphs A749

Abdel Hamid Badawi (1887-1965), Jurist, and Scales of Justice — A750

Perf. 13½x13
1987, Dec. 30 Litho. Unwmk.
1358 A749 5p multicolored .45 .20
1359 A750 5p multicolored .45 .20

Stamp Day 1988 — A751

Pyramids of the Pharaohs and: a, Cheops. b, Chefren. c, Mycerinus. No. 1360 has a continuous design.

1988, Jan. 2
1360 A751 Strip of 3 4.00 4.00
a.-c. 15p, any single 1.25 1.25

Afro-Asian Peoples Solidarity Organization, 30th Anniv. — A752

1988, Jan. 10 *Perf. 13x13½*
1361 A752 15p multicolored 1.00 1.00

20th Intl. Book Fair, Cairo — A753

1988, Jan. 26 *Perf. 13½x13*
1362 A753 5p multicolored .40 .20

Martrans (Natl. Shipping Line), 25th Anniv. A754

Unwmk.
1988, Mar. 3 Litho. *Perf. 13*
1363 A754 5p multicolored .60 .25

Cairo Intl. Fair A755

1988, Mar. 12 Photo. *Perf. 11½x11*
1364 A755 5p multicolored .40 .20

World Health Day 1988: Diabetes A756

1988 Festivals A757

Perf. 11x11½
1988, Apr. 7 Photo. Unwmk.
1365 A756 5p multicolored .45 .20
1988, Apr. 17 *Perf. 11½*
1366 A757 5p grn, brn org & brn .45 .20

African Postal Union, 25th Anniv. — A758

1988, Apr. 23 Litho. *Perf. 13x13½*
1367 A758 15p brt blue 1.00 1.00

Oppose Racial Discrimination — A759

1988, May 25 Photo. *Perf. 11½*
1368 A759 5p multicolored .40 .20

Taw Fek-Hakem (1902-1987), Playwright, Novelist — A760

1988, Aug. 5 Photo. *Perf. 11½*
1369 A760 5p brt grn bl & org brn .60 .25
See Nos. 1383-1384, 1479-1480, 1486, 1500-1502, 1543-1546.

Faculty of Art Education, 50th Anniv. A761

Perf. 11½
1370 A761 5p multicolored   .50 .20

A762

1988 Summer Olympics, Seoul — A763

1988, Sept. 17   Litho.   *Perf. 13*
1371 A762 15p multicolored   1.25 1.25
Size: 96x91mm
Imperf.
1372 A763 30p multicolored   5.00 5.00
No. 1371 is airmail.

October War Against Israel, 15th Anniv. — A764

Perf. 13x13½
1988, Oct. 6   Litho.   Unwmk.
1373 A764 5p multicolored   .50 .20

A765

Opening of the Opera House — A766

1988, Oct. 10   *Perf. 11½*
1374 A765 5p multicolored   .50 .20
Size: 112x75mm
Imperf
1375 A766 50p multicolored   3.50 3.50

Intl. Red Cross and Red Crescent Organizations, 125th Annivs. — A767

Perf. 11½
1988, Oct. 24   Photo.   Unwmk.
1376 A767 5p green, blk & red   .40 .20

WHO, 40th Anniv. — A768

1988, Oct. 24   *Perf. 11x11½*
1377 A768 20p multicolored   1.10 1.10

Naguib Mahfouz, 1988 Nobel Prize Winner for Literature — A769

1988, Nov. 7   Litho.   *Perf. 13x13½*
1378 A769 5p multicolored   .60 .25
See No. C190.

Arab Scouting Organization, 75th Anniv. — A770

1988, Nov. 10
1379 A770 25p multicolored   1.10 1.10

Return of Taba to Egypt — A771

1988, Nov. 15
1380 A771 5p multicolored   .40 .20

Intl. Conference on Orthopedic Surgery, Cairo, Nov. 15-18 — A772

1988, Nov. 15 Photo.   *Perf. 11½x11*
1381 A772 5p buff, brt yel grn & brn   .40 .20

A773

1988, Dec. 3   *Perf. 11½*
1382 A773 5p multicolored   .40 .20
Ministry of Agriculture, 75th anniv.

A774

Perf. 13½x13
1988, Dec. 29   Litho.   Unwmk.
Famous Men: No. 1383, Mohamed Hussein Hekal (1888-1956), author, politician. No. 1384, Ahmed Lotfi El Sayed (1872-1963), educator, politician.
1383 A774 5p green & red brn   .40 .20
1384 A774 5p green & red brn   .40 .20
  a.   Pair, #1383-1384   .80 .40

A775

A776

Statues: 5p, Statue of K. Abr, a priest, 5th cent. No. 1386, Queen Nefert, 4th Dynasty. No. 1387, King Ra Hoteb, 4th Dynasty.

1989, Jan. 2
1385 A775 5p multicolored   .40 .20
1386 A775 25p multicolored   1.40 1.40
1387 A775 25p multicolored   1.40 1.40
  a.   Pair, #1386-1387   3.25 3.25
  Nos. 1385-1387 (3)   3.20 3.00
Stamp Day.

1989, Jan. 10
1388 A776 5p dull green   .50 .20
Jawaharlal Nehru (1889-1964), 1st Prime Minister of independent India.

Nile Hilton Hotel, 30th Anniv. — A777

1989, Feb. 22   Litho.   *Perf. 13x13½*
1389 A777 5p multicolored   .50 .20

Return of Taba to Egypt A778

Unwmk.
1989, Mar. 15   Litho.   *Perf. 13*
1390 A778 5p multicolored   .40 .20

2nd Stage of Cairo Subway A779

1989, Apr. 12   Litho.   *Perf. 13*
1391 A779 5p multicolored   .50 .20

Festivals — A780

1989, May 4   Photo.   *Perf. 11½*
1392 A780 5p multicolored   .40 .20

1st Arab Olympic Day A781

1989, May 24
1393 A781 5p tan, blk & dull grn   .50 .20

Interparliamentary Union, Cent. — A782

Pyramids and the Parliament Building, Cairo.

1989, June 29   Litho.   *Perf. 13x13½*
1394 A782 25p shown   1.25 1.25
Size: 87x76mm
Imperf
1395 A782 25p multi, diff.   2.75 2.75

French Revolution, Bicent. — A783

1989, July 14   Photo.   Perf. 11½
1396 A783 25p multicolored   1.25 1.25

African
Development
Bank, 25th
Anniv. — A784

Perf. 11½
1989, Oct. 1   Photo.   Unwmk.
1397 A784 10p multicolored   .40 .20

A785

October War Against
Israel, 16th
Anniv. — A786

1989, Oct. 6   Perf. 13
1398   Strip of 3   1.50 1.50
  a. A785 10p shown   .50 .50
  b. A786 10p shown   .50 .50
  c. A785 10p Battle scene   .50 .50

See No. 1424.

Aga Khan Award
for Architecture
A788

Perf. 11½
1989, Oct. 15   Photo.   Unwmk.
1400 A788 35p multicolored   1.00 1.00

Natl. Health
Insurance
Plan, 25th
Anniv.
A789

1989, Oct. 24
1401 A789 10p blk, gray & ver   .45 .20

World Post
Day — A790

1989, Oct. 24   Perf. 11x11½
1402 A790 35p blue, blk & brt yel   .90 .90

Statues of Memnon, Thebes — A791

Perf. 11½
1989, Nov. 12   Photo.   Unwmk.
1403 A791 10p lt vio, blk & brt
             yel grn   .40 .20
Intl. Cong. & Convention Assoc. (ICCA)
annual convention, Nov. 11-18, Cairo.

Cairo University
School of
Agriculture,
Cent. — A792

1989, Nov. 15
1404 A792 10p pale grn, blk &
             brt yel   .35 .20

Cairo Intl. Conference Center — A793

1989, Nov. 20   Perf. 11½x11
1405 A793 5p multicolored   .35 .20

Road Safety Soc., 20th Anniv. — A794

1989, Nov. 20   Perf. 11½
1406 A794 10p multicolored   .40 .20

Alexandria
University, 50th
Anniv. — A795

1989, Nov. 30   Perf. 11x11½
1407 A795 10p pale blue & tan   .35 .20

Portrait of
Pasha,
Monument
in Opera
Square,
Cairo
A796

Perf. 11½x11
1989, Dec. 31   Photo.   Unwmk.
1408 A796 10p multicolored   .45 .20
Ibrahim Pasha (d. 1838), army commander
from 1825 to 1828.

Famous Men
A797   A798

1989, Dec. 31   Perf. 11x11½
1409 A797 10p grn & dk ol grn   .40 .20
1410 A798 10p golden brown   .40 .20
Abd El-Rahman El-Rafei (b. 1889), historian
(No. 1409); Abdel Kader El Mazni (b. 1889),
man of letters (No. 1410).
See Nos. 1431-1432.

Statue of Priest
Ranofr — A799

Relief Sculpture
of Betah
Hoteb — A800

1990, Jan. 2   Perf. 13½x13
1411 A799 30p multicolored   .90 .90
1412 A800 30p multicolored   .90 .90
  a. Pair, #1411-1412   2.00 2.00
Stamp Day.

Arab Cooperation Council, 1st
Anniv. — A801

Perf. 13x13½
1990, Feb. 16   Photo.   Unwmk.
1413 A801 10p multicolored   .40 .20
1414 A801 35p multicolored   1.00 1.00

Emblem,   Road Safety
Conference Center   Emblems
A802   A803

Perf. 13½x13
1990, Mar. 10   Litho.   Unwmk.
1415 A802 10p brt yel grn, red &
             blk   .50 .20
Size: 80x59mm
Imperf
1416 A802 30p multicolored   1.25 1.25
African Parliamentary Union 13th general
conference, Mar. 10-15.

1990, Mar. 19   Photo.   Perf. 11x11½
1417 A803 10p multicolored   .60 .25
Intl. Conference on Road Safety & Accidents in Developing Countries, Mar. 19-22.

Festivals
1990 — A804

1990, Apr. 24   Perf. 11½
1418 A804 10p multicolored   .40 .20

Sinai
Liberation,
8th Anniv.
A805

1990, Apr. 25
1419 A805 10p blue, blk & yel
             grn   .50 .20

World Cup
Soccer
Championships,
Italy — A806

1990, May 26   Litho.   Perf. 13½x13
1420 A806 10p multicolored   .40 .20
Souvenir Sheet
Imperf
1421 A806 50p Flags, trophy   1.75 1.75

World Basketball Championships,
Argentina — A807

1990, Aug. 8   *Perf. 13x13½*
1422 A807 10p multicolored   .50   .20

Natl. Population
Council, 5th
Anniv. — A808

1990, Sept. 15   *Perf. 13½x13*
1423 A808 10p brown & yel grn   .50   .20

October War Against Israel Type

1990, Oct. 6   **Litho.**   *Perf. 13x13½*
1424   Strip of 3   1.75   1.75
   a. A785 10p Bunker, tank   .55   .55
   b. A786 10p like #1398b   .55   .55
   c. A785 10p Troops with flag, flame
      thrower   .55   .55

Egyptian Postal Service, 125th
Anniv. — A809

1990, Oct. 9
1425 A809 10p lt blue, blk & red   .50   .20

Dar El
Eloum
Faculty,
Cent.
A810

1990, Oct. 13   **Litho.**   *Perf. 13*
1426 A810 10p multicolored   .40   .20

UN Development Program, 40th
Anniv. — A811

ITU, 125th
Anniv. — A812

1990, Oct. 24   *Perf. 11½*
1427 A811 30p yel, bl grn & yel
      grn   .75   .75
     Perf. 13
1428 A812 30p multicolored   .75   .75
     UN Day.

Ras Mohammed Natl. Park — A813

Various tropical fish and coral reefs.

1990, Dec. 22   **Litho.**   *Perf. 13*
1429 A813 Block of 4   3.50   3.50
   a.-b.   10p any single   .75   .75
   c.-d.   20p any single   1.00   1.00

Day of the
Disabled — A814

1990, Dec. 15   **Photo.**   *Perf. 11*
1430 A814 10p multicolored   .60   .25

Mohamed
Fahmy Abdel
Meguid Bey,
Medical
Reformer
A815

Nabaweya
Moussa (1890-
1951), Educator
A816

        Perf. 11x11½
1990, Dec. 30   **Unwmk.**
1431 A815 10p Prus bl, brn & org   .40   .20
1432 A816 10p grn, org brn & blk   .40   .20

Stamp
Day — A817

1991, Jan. 1   **Litho.**   *Perf. 13½x13*
1433 A817   5p No. 1   .40   .20
1434 A817 10p No. 2   .40   .20
1435 A817 20p No. 3   .60   .60
   a.   Strip of 3, #1433-1435   1.40   1.40
     See Nos. 1443-1446, 1459-1460.

Veterinary Surgeon Syndicate, 50th
Anniv. — A818

1991, Feb. 28   **Photo.**   *Perf. 11½*
1436 A818 10p multicolored   .40   .20

Syndicate of Journalists, 50th
Anniv. — A819

1991, Apr.   **Photo.**   *Perf. 11½*
1437 A819 10p multicolored   .40   .20

Festivals — A820

1991, Apr. 13
1438 A820 10p multicolored   .40   .20

Giza Zoo, Cent. — A821

1991, June 15   **Litho.**   **Imperf.**
       Size: 80x63mm
1439 A821 50p multicolored   3.00   3.00

Mahmoud Mokhtar (1891-1934),
Sculptor — A822

Mohamed Nagi
(1888-1956),
Painter — A823

    Perf. 13x13½, 13½x13
1991, June 11   **Litho.**
1440 A822 10p multicolored   .40   .20
1441 A823 10p multicolored   .40   .20

Faculty of Engineering — A824

1991, June 30   *Perf. 13x13½*
1442 A824 10p multicolored   .40   .20

      Stamp Day Type

   Designs: No. 1443, No. 5. No. 1444, No. 4.
No. 1445, No. 7. No. 1446, Sphinx, pyramid,
No. 6.

1991, July 23   *Perf. 13*
1443 A817 10p orange & blk   .40   .20
1444 A817 10p yellow & blk   .40   .20
1445 A817 10p lilac & blk   .40   .20
   a.   Strip of 3, #1443-1445   1.25   1.25
     Size: 80x60mm
       Imperf
1446 A817 50p multicolored   1.75   1.75
   Nos. 1443-1446 (4)   2.95   2.35

Mohamed
Abdel el
Wahab,
Musician
A825

1991, Aug. 28   *Perf. 13*
1447 A825 10p multicolored   .40   .20

5th Africa Games, Cairo — A826

   No. 1448, Karate, judo. No. 1449, Table tennis, field hockey, tennis. No. 1450, Running,
gymnastics, swimming. No. 1451, Soccer,
basketball, shooting. No. 1452, Boxing, wrestling, weightlifting. No. 1453, Handball, cycling,
volleyball. No. 1454, Games mascot, vert. No.
1455, Mascot, emblem, torch.

     Perf. 13x13½
1991, Sept.   **Litho.**   **Unwmk.**
1448 A826 10p multicolored   .45   .20
1449 A826 10p multicolored   .45   .20
   a.   Pair, #1448-1449   .90   .90
1450 A826 10p multicolored   .45   .20
1451 A826 10p multicolored   .45   .20
   a.   Pair, #1450-1451   .90   .90
1452 A826 10p multicolored   .45   .20
1453 A826 10p multicolored   .45   .20
   a.   Pair, #1452-1453   .90   .90
     Perf. 13½x13
1454 A826 10p multicolored   .45   .20
     Size: 80x60mm
       Imperf
1455 A826 50p multicolored   1.75   1.75
   Nos. 1448-1455 (8)   4.90   3.15

Intl.
Statistics
Institute,
48th
Session
A827

1991, Sept. 9
1456 A827 10p multicolored   .40   .20

Opening of Dar Al Eftaa Religious Center — A828

1991, Oct. 1   Litho.   Perf. 13
1457 A828 10p multicolored   .40   .20

October War Against Israel, 18th Anniv. — A829

1991, Oct. 6   Perf. 13x13½
1458 A829 10p multicolored   .50   .20

Stamp Day Type

Designs: 10p, No. 6. £1, Stamp exhibition emblem, hieroglyphics, pyramids, sphinx.

1991, Oct. 7   Perf. 13
1459 A817 10p blue & black   .50   .20

Size: 90x60mm
Imperf
1460 A817 £1 multicolored   5.00 5.00

Natl. Philatelic Exhibition, Cairo, 10/7-12 (No. 1460). No. 1460 sold with £1 at exhibition.

Ancient Artifacts Type of 1985
Perf. 11½x11
1990-92   Unwmk.   Photo.
Size: 18x23mm
1467 A681 10p like #1278   .60   .25
1470 A681 30p like #1283   1.00 1.00
1472 A681 50p like #1285   1.75 1.75
   Nos. 1467-1472 (3)   3.35 3.00

Issued: 10p, 1/20/90; 30p, 9/1/91; 50p, 7/11/92.

United Nations Day — A830

No. 1477, Brick hands housing people. No. 1478, Woman learning to write, fingerprint, vert.

Perf. 13x13½, 13½x13
1991, Oct. 24   Litho.
1476 A830 10p shown   .40   .20
1477 A830 10p multicolored   .40   .20
1478 A830 10p multicolored   .40   .20
   Nos. 1476-1478 (3)   1.20   .60

Famous Men Type of 1988
Inscribed "1991"

Designs: No. 1479, Dr. Zaki Mubarak (1891-1952), writer and poet. No. 1480, Abd El Kader Hamza (1879-1941), journalist.

1991, Dec. 23   Photo.   Perf. 13½x13
1479 A760 10p olive brown   .40   .20
1480 A760 10p gray   .40   .20

A831

Post Day — A832

1992, Jan. 2   Litho.   Perf. 13
1481 A831 10p shown   .40   .25
1482 A831 45p Bird mosaic   1.00 1.00
Perf. 14
1483 A832 70p shown   1.75 1.75
   Nos. 1481-1483 (3)   3.15 3.00

Nos. 1482-1483 are airmail.

Police Day — A833

1992, Jan. 25   Perf. 14
1484 A833 10p multicolored   .40   .20

25th Cairo Intl. Fair A834

1992, Feb. 15   Litho.   Perf. 14
1485 A834 10p multicolored   .40   .20

Famous Men Type of 1988
Inscribed "1992"

10p, Sayed Darwish (1882-1923), musician.

1992, Mar. 17   Photo.   Perf. 14x13½
1486 A760 10p dull org & olive   .40   .20

Festivals — A835

1992, Mar. 18   Perf. 11½
1487 A835 10p Egyptian hoopoe   .40   .20

World Health Day A836

1992, Apr. 20   Litho.   Perf. 13
1488 A836 10p multicolored   .50   .20

Aswan Dam, 90th Anniv. A837

1992, July   Litho.   Perf. 13
1489 A837 10p No. 487   .50   .20

20th Arab Scout Jamboree — A838

1992, July 10   Perf. 13x13½
1490 A838 10p multicolored   .50   .20

A839

A840

1992, July 20   Perf. 13½x13
1491 A839 10p multicolored   .40   .20
Size: 80x60mm
Imperf
1492 A839 70p Summer Games' emblem   1.75 1.75
   1992 Summer Olympics, Barcelona.

1992, Sept. 14   Litho.   Perf. 13½x13
1493 A840 10p multicolored   .40   .20
   El Helal Magazine, cent.

Alexandria World Festival — A841

1992, Sept. 27   Perf. 13x13½
1494 A841 70p multicolored   1.60 1.60

Congress of Federation of World and American Travel Companies, Cairo — A842

1992, Sept. 20
1495 A842 70p multicolored   1.50 1.50

World Post Day A843

1992, Oct. 9   Litho.   Perf. 13
1496 A843 10p dk bl, lt bl & blk   .40   .20

Children's Day — A844

1992, Oct. 24   Litho.   Perf. 13½x13
1497 A844 10p multicolored   .50   .20

Intl. Conference on Food, Agriculture and World Health A845

1992, Oct. 24   Perf. 13
1498 A845 70p multicolored   1.50 1.50

A846

A847

1992, Nov. 21   *Perf. 13½x13*
1499 A846 10p multicolored   .50 .20
20th Arab Scout Conference, Cairo.

Famous Men Type of 1988
Inscribed "1992"

No. 1500, Talaat Harb, economist. No. 1501, Mohamed Taymour, writer. No. 1502, Dr. Ahmed Zaki Abu Shadi (with glasses), physician & poet.

1992, Dec. 23 Photo.   *Perf. 13½x13*
1500 A760 10p blue & brown   .40 .20
1501 A760 10p citron & blue gray   .40 .20
1502 A760 10p citron & blue gray   .40 .20
  a.   Pair, #1501-1502   .80 .80
  Nos. 1500-1502 (3)   1.20 .60

1993, Jan. 2 Litho.   *Perf. 13½x13*
Pharaohs: 10p, Sesostris I. 45p, Amenemhet III. 70p, Hur I.
1503 A847 10p brown & yellow   .45 .20
1504 A847 45p brown & yellow   .65 .65
1505 A847 70p brown & yellow   1.00 1.00
  a.   Strip of 3, #1503-1505   2.10 2.10

Post Day.

Intl. Book Fair, Cairo — A848

1993, Jan. 26 Litho.   *Perf. 13½x13*
1506 A848 15p multicolored   .40 .20

A849

A849a

A849b

A849c

A849d   A849e

A849f   A849g

A849h

Artifacts: A849, Bust. A849a, Sphinx. A849b, Bust of princess. A849c, Ramses II. A849d, Queen Ti. A849e, Horemheb. A849f, As A849b. A849g, Amenhotep III. £1, Head of a woman. £2, Woman wearing headdress. £5, Pharaonic capital.

Photo., Litho. (#1511)
1993-99 Unwmk.   *Perf. 11½x11,*
1507 A849 5p multi   .30 .20
1508 A849a 15p brn & bis   .30 .20
1509 A849a 15p brn & bis   .30 .20
1510 A849b 25p brn & org brn   .30 .25
1511 A849c 55p blk & bl   .65 .65

Size: 21x25mm
Perf. 11¼
1512 A849 5p dp cl & brick red   .30 .20
1513 A849d 5p brown   .30 .20
  a.   Wmk. 342   .30 .20
1514 A849a 15p brn & bis   .30 .20
1515 A849e 20p blk & gray   .30 .20
  a.   Wmk. 342   .30 .20
1516 A849f 25p brn & org brn   .35 .30
1517 A849f 25p black brown   .30 .20
1518 A849c 55p blk & lt bl   .60 .60
1519 A849g 75p blk & brn   .80 .80

Perf. 11½
1520 A849h £1 slate & blk   2.25 2.25
1521 A849h £2 brn & grn   5.00 5.00
1521A A849h £5 brn & gold   10.00 10.00
  Nos. 1507-1521A (16)   22.35 21.45

Warning: Avoid using watermark fluid on Nos. 1513-1513a and 1515-1515a. Images will be adversely affected.
Body of Sphinx on Nos. 1509, 1514 stops above value, and extends through value on No. 1508.
Issued: Nos. 1507-1508, 2/1; No. 1509, 3/10; £1, £2, 4/1; No. 1511, 7/1/93; £5, 8/1/93; Nos. 1512, 1514, 1518, 10/30/94; No. 1516, 6/25/94; 20p, 2/1/97; 75p, 3/25/97; No. 1517, 1998; Nos. 1513a, 1515a, 1999.
See Nos. C204-C206.

Architects' Association, 75th Anniv. — A850

1993, Feb. 28 Litho.   *Perf. 13x13½*
1522 A850 15p multicolored   .40 .20

New Building for Ministry of Foreign Affairs A851

1993, Mar. 15   *Perf. 13*
1523 A851 15p multicolored   .40 .20
1524 A851 80p multicolored   1.10 1.10
Diplomacy Day (No. 1523). No. 1524 is airmail.

Feasts — A852

1993, Mar. 20 Litho.   *Perf. 13x13½*
1525 A852 15p Opuntia   .40 .20

Newspaper, Le Progres Egyptien, Cent. — A853

1993, Apr. 15 Litho.   *Perf. 13x13½*
1526 A853 15p multicolored   .40 .20

A854   A855

1993, May 15 Litho.   *Perf. 13½x13*
1527 A854 15p multicolored   .50 .20
World Telecommunications Day.

1993, June 15 Litho.   *Perf. 13½x13*
1528 A855 15p multicolored   .40 .20
UN Conference on Human Rights, Vienna.

Organization of African Unity — A856

1993, June 26   *Perf. 13*
1529 A856 15p yel grn & multi   .40 .20
1530 A856 80p red violet & multi   1.10 1.10
No. 1530 is airmail.

World PTT Conference, Cairo — A857

1993, Sept. 4 Litho.   *Perf. 13*
1531 A857 15p multicolored   .40 .20

Salah El-Din El Ayubi (1137-1193), Dome of the Rock — A858

1993, Sept. 4
1532 A858 55p multicolored   1.10 1.10

A859

A860

1993, Oct. 6
1533 A859 15p multicolored   .50 .20
October War Against Israel, 20th Anniv.

1993, Oct. 12   *Perf. 13½x13*
1534 A860 15p cream & multi   .40 .20
1535 A860 55p silver & multi   1.10 1.10
1536 A860 80p gold & multi   1.50 1.50

Imperf
Size: 90x70mm
1537 A860 80p multicolored   3.00 3.00
  Nos. 1534-1537 (4)   6.00 5.80
Pres. Mohamed Hosni Mubarak, Third Term.

Reduction of Natural Disasters A861

1993, Oct. 24 Litho.   *Perf. 13*
1538 A861 80p multicolored   1.10 1.10

Electricity in Egypt, Cent. — A862

1993, Oct. 24   *Perf. 13½x13*
1539 A862 15p multicolored   .40 .20

Intl. Conference on Big Dams,
Cairo — A863

1993, Nov. 19   Litho.   Perf. 13
1540 A863 15p multicolored   .40   .20

35th Military Intl. Soccer
Championship — A864

1993, Dec. 1   Litho.   Perf. 13x13½
1541 A864 15p orange & multi   .40   .20
1542 A864 15p Trophy, emblem   .40   .20
9th Men's Junior World Handball Championship (No. 1542).

Famous Men Type of 1988
Inscribed "1993"

No. 1543, A. Al. Bishry. No. 1544, M.F. Abu
Hadeed. No. 1545, M.B. Al. Tunisy. No. 1546,
Ali Moubarak.

1993, Dec. 25   Perf. 13½x13
1543 A760 15p blue   .40   .20
1544 A760 15p blue black   .40   .20
1545 A760 15p light violet   .40   .20
1546 A760 15p green   .40   .20
      Nos. 1543-1546 (4)   1.60   .80

Post Day — A865

1994, Jan. 2
1547 A865 15p Amenhotep III   .40   .20
1548 A865 55p Queen Hatshep-
           sut   1.00 1.00
1549 A865 80p Thutmose III   1.10 1.10
      Nos. 1547-1549 (3)   2.50 2.30

Congress of Egyptian Sedimentary
Geology Society — A866

1994, Jan. 4   Litho.   Perf. 13x13½
1550 A866 15p multicolored   .40   .20

Birds
A867

1994, Mar. 3   Litho.   Perf. 13
1551 A867 Block of 4, #a.-d.   1.60 1.60
  a.   15p Egyptian swallow   .40   .40
  b.   15p Fire crest   .40   .40
  c.   15p Rose-ringed parrot   .40   .40
  d.   15p Goldfinch   .40   .40
      Festivals 1994.

A868

A869

1994, Mar. 25   Perf. 13½x13
1552 A868 15p multicolored   .40   .20
      Arab Scouting, 40th anniv.

1994, Apr. 9   Litho.   Perf. 13½x13
1553 A869 15p multicolored   .40   .20
      27th Cairo Intl. Fair.

A870

A871

1994, Apr. 15   Litho.   Perf. 13
1554 A870 15p green & brown   .40   .20
      1994 African Telecommunications Exhibi-
tion, Cairo.

1994, Apr. 30   Litho.   Perf. 13
1555 A871 15p grn, blk & blue   .40   .20
      Natl. Afforestation Campaign.

5th Arab Energy
Conference,
Cairo. — A872

Litho.
Perf. 13
1994, July 5
1556 A872 15p multicolored   .40   .20

Signing of Washington Accord for
Palestinian Self-Rule in Gaza and
Jericho — A873

1994, May 4   Litho.   Perf. 13
1557 A873 15p multicolored   .60   .25

18th Biennial Art Exhibition,
Alexandria — A874

1994, May 21
1558 A874 15p yel, blk & gray   .40   .20

Organization of
African
Unity — A875

1994, May 25
1559 A875 15p multicolored   .40   .20

Natl. Reading Festival — A876

1994, June 15
1560 A876 15p multicolored   .40   .20

ILO, 75th
Anniv. — A877

1994, June 28   Litho.   Perf. 13½x13
1561 A877 15p multicolored   .60   .25

Intl. Conference on Population and
Development, Cairo — A878

15p, Conference, UN emblems. 80p, Drawings, hieroglyphics, conference emblem.

1994, Sept. 5   Litho.   Perf. 13
1562 A878 15p multi   .40   .20
1563 A878 80p multi, vert.   1.10 1.10
      No. 1563 is airmail.

World Junior Squash
Championships — A879

1994, Sept. 14   Litho.   Perf. 13
1564 A879 15p multicolored   .40   .20

World
Post
Day
A880

1994, Oct. 9   Litho.   Perf. 13
1565 A880 15p multicolored   .50   .20

Intl. Red Cross &
Red Crescent
Societies, 75th
Anniv. — A881

1994, Oct. 24
1566 A881 80p multicolored   1.50 1.50

Akhbar El-Yom Newpaper, 50th Anniv. — A882

1994, Nov. 11
1567 A882 15p multicolored .40 .20

African Field Hockey Club Championships — A883

1994, Nov. 14 Litho. Perf. 13
1568 A883 15p multicolored .40 .20

A884

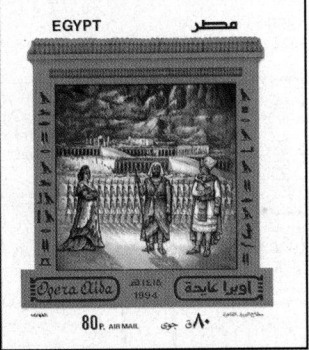

Opera Aida, by Verdi — A885

1994, Nov. 26
1569 A884 15p multicolored .40 .20
Imperf
Size: 58x69mm
1570 A885 80p multicolored 2.50 2.50
No. 1570 is airmail.

Intl. Olympic Committee, Cent. — A886

Egyptian Youth Hostels Assoc., 40th Anniv. — A887

1994, Dec. 10 Perf. 13
1571 A886 15p multicolored .40 .20

1994, Dec. 24
1572 A887 15p multicolored .40 .20

Intl. Speed Ball Federation, 10th Anniv. — A888

1994, Dec. 25
1573 A888 15p multicolored .40 .20

African Development Bank, 30th Anniv. — A889

1994, Dec. 26
1574 A889 15p multicolored .40 .20

Opening of Suez Canal, 125th Anniv. — A890

Design: 80p, Map, inaugural ceremony.

1994, Dec. 27
1575 A890 15p multicolored .40 .20
1576 A890 80p multicolored 1.25 1.25
No. 1576 is airmail.

Famous Men — A891

Post Day — A892

1994, Dec. 29
1577 A891 15p Hassan Fathy, engineer .40 .20
1578 A891 15p Mahmoud Taimour, writer .40 .20

1995, Jan. 2 Litho. Perf. 13½x13
15p, Statue of Akhenaton. 55p, Golden mask of King Tutankhamen. 80p, Statue of Nefertiti.
1579 A892 15p multicolored .40 .20
1580 A892 55p multicolored 1.00 1.00
1581 A892 80p multicolored 1.25 1.25
Nos. 1579-1581 (3) 2.65 2.45

World Tourism Organization, 20th Anniv. — A893

1995, Jan. 2 Perf. 13x13½
1582 A893 15p multicolored .40 .20

Festivals — A894

1995, Feb. 25 Litho. Perf. 13x13½
1583 A894 15p multicolored .40 .20

Egyptian Women's Day — A895

1995, Mar. 16 Litho. Perf. 13½x13
1584 A895 15p multicolored .40 .20

Arab League, 50th Anniv. — A896

1995, Mar. 22 Perf. 13½x13
1585 A896 15p blue & multi .40 .20
1586 A896 55p green & multi .75 .75

Sheraton Hotel, Cairo, 25th Anniv. — A897

1995, Mar. 28 Perf. 13x13½
1587 A897 15p multicolored .40 .20

Misr Bank, 75th Anniv. — A898

1995, May 7 Litho. Perf. 13½x13
1588 A898 15p multicolored .60 .25

World Telecommunications Day — A899

1995, May 31 Perf. 13x13½
1589 A899 80p multicolored 1.00 1.00

Wilhelm Roentgen (1845-1923), Discovery of the X-Ray, Cent. — A900

1995, May Litho. Perf. 13½x13
1590 A900 15p multicolored .60 .25

Membership in World Heritage Committee, 20th Anniv. (in 1994) — A901

Artifacts from the Shaft of Luxor: No. 1591, Goddess Hathor. No. 1592, God Atoum. 80p, God Amon and Horemheb.

1995, July 23 Litho. Perf. 13½x13
1591 15p multicolored .40 .20
1592 15p multicolored .40 .20
a. A901 Pair, #1591-1592 .80 .80
1593 A901 80p multicolored 1.10 1.10
Nos. 1591-1593 (3) 1.90 1.50
No. 1592a is a continuous design. No. 1593 is airmail.

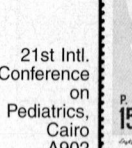

21st Intl. Conference on Pediatrics, Cairo
A902

1995, Sept. 10　Litho.　Perf. 13
1594 A902 15p multicolored　　　.60　.25

Intl. Ozone Day — A903

1995, Sept. 16　Litho.　Perf. 13x12½
1595 A903 15p green & multi　　　.40　.20
1596 A903 55p brown & multi　　　.85　.85
1597 A903 80p blue & multi　　　1.10　1.10
　　Nos. 1595-1597 (3)　　2.35　2.15
　　See Nos. 1622-1623.

World Tourism Day
A904

1995, Sept. 25　　　Perf. 12½x13
1598 A904 15p multicolored　　　.40　.20

Government Printing House, 175th Anniv. — A905

1995, Sept. 27
1599 A905 15p multicolored　　　.40　.20

Sun Verticality on Abu Simbel Temple
A906

1995, Oct. 22　Litho.　Perf. 12½x13
1600 A906 15p multicolored　　　.75　.30

Opening of New Esna Dam — A907

1995, Nov. 25　　　Perf. 12½
1601 A907 15p multicolored　　　.75　.30

Egyptian Engineers Assoc., 75th Anniv.
A908

1995, Dec. 20　　　Perf. 13
1602 A908 15p multicolored　　　.40　.20

A909　　　　　　A910

Famous artists.

1995, Dec. 9　Litho.　Perf. 13x12½
1603 A909 15p A. Hafez　　　.40　.20
1604 A909 15p Y. Wahby　　　.40　.20
1605 A909 15p N. El. Rihany　　　.40　.20
　　Nos. 1603-1605 (3)　　1.20　.60

1995, Dec. 23　Litho.　Perf. 13x12½
1606 A910 15p multicolored　　　.40　.20

Motion Pictures, cent.

Post Day
A911

Ancient paintings: 55p, Man facing right. 80p, Man facing left. 100p, Playing flute, dancers.

1996, Jan. 2　Litho.　Perf. 13½x13
1607　　55p multicolored　　　.60　.60
1608　　80p multicolored　　　.90　.90
　a.　A911 Pair, Nos. 1607-1608　1.50　1.50
　　　　Imperf
　　　Size: 88x72mm
1609 A911 100p multicolored　　1.25　1.25
　　Nos. 1607-1608 are airmail.

Feasts — A912

1996, Feb. 15　　　Perf. 12½
1610 A912 15p blue flowers　　　.30　.20
1611 A912 15p red flowers　　　.30　.20
　a.　Pair, No. 1610-1611　　　.60　.60

A913　　　　　　A914

1996, Mar. 13　Litho.　Perf. 13x12½
1612 A913 15p pink & multi　　　.40　.20
1613 A913 80p brown & multi　　　.90　.90
　　Summit of Peace Makers, Sharm al-Sheikh. No. 1613 is airmail.

1996, Mar. 16
1614 A914 15p multicolored　　　.40　.20
　　29th Intl. Fair, Cairo.

Egyptian Geological Survey, Cent.
A915

1996, Mar. 18　　　Perf. 12½x13
1615 A915 15p multicolored　　　.40　.20

A916　　　　　　A917

1996, Apr. 11　Litho.　Perf. 13x12½
1616 A916 15p blue & multi　　　.40　.20
1617 A916 80p pink & multi　　　.90　.90
　　Signing of African Nuclear Weapon-Free Zone Treaty.

1996, Apr. 20　Litho.　Perf. 13x12½
1618 A917 15p multicolored　　　.40　.20
　　Egyptian Society of Accountants and Auditors, 50th anniv.

A918　　　　　　A919

1996, May 4
1619 A918 15p multicolored　　　.40　.20
　　General census.

1996, July 15　Litho.　Perf. 13x12½
　　1996 Summer Olympics, Atlanta: 15p, Atlanta 1996 emblem. £1, Emblem surrounded by sports pictograms.
1620 A919 15p lilac & multi　　　.40　.20
　　　Size: 63x103mm
　　　Imperf
1621 A919 £1 black & multi　　1.60　1.60
　　No. 1621 is airmail.

Intl. Ozone Day Type of 1995
1996, Sept. 16　Litho.　Perf. 13x12½
1622 A903 15p pink & multi　　　.40　.20
1623 A903 80p gray & multi　　　1.10　1.10
　　No. 1623 is airmail.

A920　　　　　　A921

1996, Sept. 19
1624 A920 80p multicolored　　1.00　1.00
　　2nd Alexandriate World Festival.

1996, Sept. 21
1625 A921 15p grn, blk & bl　　　.50　.20
　　Scientific Research and Technology Academy, 25th anniv.

Opening of 2nd Line of Greater Cairo Subway System
A922

1996, Oct. 7　　　Perf. 12½x13
1626 A922 15p multicolored　　　.50　.20

Rowing Festival
A923

1996
1627 A923 15p multicolored　　　.40　.20

Courts of the State Council, 50th Anniv.
A924

1996, Nov. 2　Litho.　Perf. 12½x13
1628 A924 15p blue & claret　　　.40　.20

A925　　　　　　A926

1996, Nov. 4　　　Perf. 13x12½
1629 A925 15p yel, blk & blue　　　.40　.20
　　Intl. Federation Training Development Organization World Conf.

1996, Nov. 12　Litho.　Perf. 13x12½
　　Cairo Economic Summit (MENA): £1, Graph, earth, gear, olive branch, wheat.
1630 A926 15p shown　　　.75　.30
　　　Size: 65x45mm
　　　Imperf
1631 A926 £1 multicolored　　1.75　1.75
　　No. 1631 is airmail.

A927

A928

1996, Nov. 13 ***Perf. 13x12½***

1632 A927 15p multicolored .40 .20

1996 World Food Summit, Rome.

1996, Nov. 16

National Day of El-Gharbia Governorate: Al Sayd Ahmed El-Badawy mosque, Tanta.

1633 A928 15p multicolored .40 .20

A929

A930

Famous artists.

1996, Dec. 28 **Litho.** ***Perf. 13x12½***

1634 A929 20p Ali El-Kassar .45 .20
1635 A929 20p George Abyad .45 .20
1636 A929 20p Mohamed Kareem .45 .20
1637 A929 20p Fatma Roshdi .45 .20
Nos. 1634-1637 (4) 1.80 .80

See Nos. 1666-1669.

1997, Jan. 2

1638 A930 20p multicolored .45 .20

Size: 61x80mm

Imperf

1639 A930 £1 multicolored 2.00 2.00

Discovery of Tutankhamen's tomb, 75th anniv.

No. 1639 is airmail.

Police Day A931

1997, Jan. 25 **Litho.** ***Perf. 13x13½***

1640 A931 20p multicolored .40 .20

Feasts — A932

1997, Feb. 1 ***Perf. 13***

1641 A932 20p pink flowers .40 .20
1642 A932 20p white fowers .40 .20
a. Pair, #1641-1642 .80 .80

World Civil Defense Day A933

1997, Mar. 10 **Litho.** ***Perf. 13x13½***

1643 A933 20p multicolored .40 .20

30th Cairo Intl. Fair — A934

1997, Mar. 19 ***Perf. 13½x13***

1644 A934 20p multicolored .40 .20

Mahmoud Said, Photographer, Artist, Birth Cent. — A935

The City, By Mahmoud Said — A936

Illustration reduced (A936).

1997, Apr. 12 **Litho.** ***Perf. 12½***

1645 A935 20p multicolored .40 .20

Size: 80x60mm

Imperf

1646 A936 £1 multicolored 1.25 1.25

No. 1646 is airmail.

Institute of African Research and Studies, 50th Anniv. — A937

1997, May 27 **Litho.** ***Perf. 13***

1647 A937 75p multicolored .65 .65

New Headquarters of State Information Service — A938

1997, Aug. 16 **Litho.** ***Perf. 12½***

1648 A938 20p multicolored .40 .20

A939

A940

£1, Mascot, soccer ball, playing field, emblems.

1997, Sept. 4 ***Perf. 13x12½***

1649 A939 20p multicolored .40 .20
1650 AP81 75p multicolored .65 .65

Size: 75x55mm

Imperf

1651 A939 £1 multicolored 1.75 1.75

Nos. 1650-1651 are airmail. Under 17 FIFA World Soccer Championships, Egypt.

1997, Sept. 16 ***Perf. 13***

1652 A940 20p lt bl grn & multi .40 .20
1653 A940 £1 pink & multi 1.25 1.25

Montreal Protocol on Substances that Deplete the Ozone Layer, 10th anniv. No. 1653 is airmail.

Completion of Second Stage of Metro Line No. 2 — A941

1997, Sept. 27 ***Perf. 12½x13***

1654 A941 20p multicolored .40 .20

Premiere in Egypt of Opera Aida, by Verdi, 125th Anniv. A942

1997, Oct. 12 ***Perf. 13***

1655 A942 20p multicolored .50 .20

Size: 80x75mm

Imperf

1656 A942 £1 like #1655 1.75 1.75

No. 1656 is airmail.

Queen Nefertari — A943

1997, Oct. 25 **Litho.** ***Perf. 13***

1657 A943 £1 multicolored 1.25 1.25

A944

A945

1997, Nov. 17 **Litho.** ***Perf. 13***

1658 A944 20p multicolored .40 .20

Intl. Congress of Orthopedics, Cairo.

1997, Nov. 22 ***Perf. 13x12½***

Designs: 20p, Goddess Selket. £1, Scarab, baboon pendant.

1659 A945 20p black & gold .40 .20

Size: 73x62mm

Imperf

1660 A945 £1 multicolored 1.25 1.25

No. 1660 is airmail. Discovery of King Tutanhkamen's tomb, 75th anniv.

Inauguration of Nubia Monument Museum — A946

1997, Nov. 23 ***Perf. 13***

1661 A946 20p multicolored .60 .25

Arab Land Bank, 50th Anniv. — A947

1997, Dec. 10 ***Perf. 12½***

1662 A947 20p multicolored .60 .25

5th Pan Arab Congress on Anesthesia and Intensive Care — A948

1997, Dec. 9 **Litho.** ***Perf. 13***

1663 A948 20p multicolored .60 .25

El Salaam Canal — A949

1997, Dec. 28

1664 A949 20p multicolored .60 .25

Liberation of Sinai, 15th anniv.

A950   A951

Famous Artists Type of 1996 and A950

1997, Dec. 23   Litho.   Perf. 13x12½

1665	A950	20p blue	.40	.20
1666	A929	20p Zaky Tolaimat	.40	.20
1667	A929	20p Ismael Yassen	.40	.20
1668	A929	20p Zaky Roustom	.40	.20
1669	A929	20p Soliman Naguib	.40	.20
a.		Strip of 5, #1665-1669	2.00	2.00

1998, Jan. 2   Perf. 13

Stamp Day: 20p, King Tutankhamen's guard. 75p, King Ramses III. £1, Cover of King Tutankhamen's coffin.

1670	A951	20p multicolored	.50	.20
1671	A951	75p multicolored	1.10	1.10

Size: 26x43mm

1672	A951	£1 multicolored	2.25	2.25

Nos. 1671-1672 are airmail.

Feasts — A952

1998, Jan. 20

1673		20p multicolored	.40	.20
1674		20p multicolored	.40	.20
a.		A952 Pair, #1673-1674	.80	.80

Intl. Cairo Fair — A954

Natl. Bank of Egypt, Cent. — A955

1998, Mar. 11   Litho.   Perf. 13

1675	A954	20p multicolored	.50	.20

1998, Mar. 12

1676	A955	20p multicolored	.50	.20

Tutankhamen   Thutmose IV
A956   A957

1998   Litho.   Perf. 13½x12½

1677	A956	£2 multicolored	1.75	1.75
1678	A957	£5 purple & black	4.25	4.25

Issued: £2, 4/23; £5, 3/23.

A958

A959

1998, Apr. 14   Perf. 13

1679	A958	20p green & multi	.40	.20
1680	A958	75p blue & multi	1.10	1.10

Size: 70x52mm

Imperf

1681	A958	£1 Natl. flags, map, trophy	2.25	2.25

Egypt, winners of 21st African Cup of Nations soccer competition.
Nos. 1680-1681 are airmail.

1998, May 30   Litho.   Perf. 13

1682	A959	20p Egyptian Satellite "Nile Sat"	.50	.20

World Environment Day — A960

1998, June 5

1683	A960	20p shown	.60	.25

Size: 43x62mm

Imperf

1684	A960	£1 Fauna, emblems	2.00	2.00

No. 1684 is airmail.

A961

A962

1998, June 14

1685	A961	20p blue & black	.40	.20
1686	A961	£1 yellow, green & black	1.10	1.10

Dr. Ahmed Zewail, winner of Franklin Institute award.
No. 1686 is airmail.

1998, July 15

Imam Sheikh Mohamed Metwalli Al-Shaarawi.

1687	A962	20p buff & multi	.40	.20
1688	A962	£1 green & multi	1.10	1.10

No. 1688 is airmail.

A963

A964

1998, Sept. 12   Litho.   Perf. 13

1689	A963	20p multicolored	.50	.20

Day of the Nile Flood.

1998, Sept. 30   Litho.   Perf. 13

1690	A964	20p multicolored	.50	.20

Chemistry Administration, cent.

October War Against Israel, 25th Anniv. — A965

1998, Oct. 6   Litho.   Perf. 13

1691	A965	20p multicolored	.60	.25

Size: 50x70mm

Imperf

1692	A965	£2 like No. 1691	4.00	4.00

No. 1692 is airmail.

Egyptian Survey Authority, Cent. — A966

1998, Oct. 15   Perf. 13

1693	A966	20p multicolored	.50	.20

Cairo University, 90th Anniv. — A967

1998, Dec. 7   Litho.   Perf. 13

1694	A967	20p multicolored	.50	.20

A968

A970

1998, Dec. 17   Litho.   Perf. 13

1695	A968	20p multicolored	.40	.20

Egyptian trade unions, cent.

1999, Jan. 2   Litho.   Perf. 13

Post Day (19th Dynasty): 20p, Queen Nefertari, Goddess Isis. 125p, God Osiris, Goddess Isis.

1696	A970	20p multicolored	.50	.20

Size: 41x61mm

Imperf

1697	A970	125p multicolored	2.00	2.00

No. 1697 is airmail.

Feasts — A971

1999, Jan. 5   **Perf. 13**
1698	20p multicolored	.40	.20
1699	20p multicolored	.40	.20
a.	A971 Pair, #1698-1699	.80	.80

Intl. Women's Day — A973

1999, Mar. 7   **Litho.**   **Perf. 13**
1700	A973 20p multicolored	.50	.20

Cairo Intl.
Fair — A974

1999, Mar. 9
1701	A974 20p multicolored	.50	.20

Opening of Metro Line Beneath Nile
River — A975

1999, Apr.   **Litho.**   **Perf. 13**
1702	A975 20p multicolored	.60	.25

UPU, 125th
Anniv. — A976

1999, Apr. 21
1703	A976 20p shown	.40	.20
1704	A976 £1 multi	1.00	1.00
1705	A977 125p shown	1.10	1.10

Size: 50x70mm
Imperf
1706	A977 125p multi	2.25	2.25
	Nos. 1703-1706 (4)	4.75	4.55

Nos. 1704-1706 are airmail.

A978

A980

1999, May 8   **Perf. 13**
1707	A978 20p green & multi	.40	.20
1708	A978 125p buff, red & multi	1.25	1.25

Geneva Conventions, 50th anniv. No. 1708
is airmail.

1999, May 20   **Litho.**   **Perf. 13x12¾**
1710	A980 20p green & multi	.40	.20
1711	A980 £1 buff & multi	1.10	1.10

African Development Bank, 35th Meeting,
Cairo. No. 1711 is airmail.

16th Men's Handball World
Championship — A981

20p, Stylized player with ball, pyramids. 1£,
Mascot with ball, Sphinx, pyramids, globe.
125p, Mascot with ball, goalie, pyramids.

1999, June 1   **Perf. 13**
1712	A981 20p multicolored	.40	.20
1713	A981 £1 multicolored	1.00	1.00
1714	A981 125p multicolored	1.10	1.10
	Nos. 1712-1714 (3)	2.50	2.30

Nos. 1713-1714 are airmail.

Goddess
Selket — A982

1999, June 23   **Litho.**   **Perf. 13**
1715	A982 25p multicolored	.60	.25

See Nos. 1750, 1754.

SOS Children's Village, 50th
Anniv. — A983

1999, June 23   **Perf. 12¾x13¼**
1716	A983 20p grn, blk & blue	.40	.20
1717	A983 125p buff, blk & bl	1.10	1.10

No. 1717 is airmail.

A984

A985

No. 1718, Sameera Moussa (1917-52),
Physicist. No. 1719, Aisha Abdul Rahman
(1913-98), writer. No. 1720, Ahmed
Eldemerdash Touny (1907-97), member of
Intl. Olympic Committee.

1999   **Litho.**   **Perf. 13x12¾**
1718	A984 20p multicolored	.45	.20
1719	A984 20p multicolored	.45	.20
1720	A984 20p multicolored	.45	.20
	Nos. 1718-1720 (3)	1.35	.60

Issued: Nos. 1718-1719, 7/23; No. 1720,
8/13.

See Nos. 1730-1733.

1999, Oct. 5   **Litho.**   **Perf. 13x12¾**
1721	A985 20p org & multi	.40	.20
1722	A985 £1 silver & multi	1.00	1.00
1723	A985 125p gold & multi	1.10	1.10

Imperf
1724	A985 125p multicolored	2.25	2.25
	Nos. 1721-1724 (4)	4.75	4.55

Pres. Hosni Mubarak, 4th term.
Nos. 1722-1724 are airmail.

A986

A987

1999, Nov. 15   **Litho.**   **Perf. 13¼x13**
Background Color
1725	A986 20p green	.40	.20
1726	A986 £1 red vio	1.00	1.00
1727	A986 125p purple	1.10	1.10
	Nos. 1725-1727 (3)	2.50	2.30

Intl. Year of the Elderly. Nos. 1726-1727 are
airmail.

1999, Nov. 20
1728	A987 20p multi	.50	.20

Children's Day.

Famous People Type of 1999

No. 1730, Farid El Attrash (1913-76), singer,
movie star. No. 1731, Laila Mourad (1918-95),
singer, movie star. No. 1732, Anwar Wagdi
(1911-55), actor, director. No. 1733, Asia
Dagher (1901-86), actor, producer.

1999, Dec. 30   Litho.   Perf. 13x12¾
1730	A984 20p lt bl & blk	.40	.20
1731	A984 20p lt bl & blk	.40	.20
1732	A984 20p lt bl & blk	.40	.20
1733	A984 20p lt bl & blk	.40	.20
	Nos. 1730-1733 (4)	1.60	.80

Millennium
A989

20p, "1999" & "2000." 125p, Countdown of
years. £2, Holy Family, Virgin Tree.

2000, Jan. 1   **Perf. 13x12¾**
1734	A989 20p multi	.40	.20
1735	A989 125p multi	1.10	1.10

Size: 70x50mm
Imperf
1736	A989 £2 multi, horiz.	4.00	4.00
	Nos. 1734-1736 (3)	5.50	5.30

Nos. 1735-1736 are airmail.

A990

Post Day — A991

2000, Jan. 2   **Perf. 13¼x12¾**
1737	A990 20p multi	.50	.20
1738	A991 20p multi	.50	.20
a.	Pair, #1737-1738	1.00	1.00

Size: 70x50mm
Imperf
1739	A991 125p Chariot, horiz.	2.00	2.00
	Nos. 1737-1739 (3)	3.00	2.40

Ain Shams University, 50th
Anniv. — A992

2000, Jan. 3   **Perf. 13¼x13**
1740	A992 20p multi	.50	.20

Feasts
A993 A994

2000, Jan. 5 **Perf. 13x13¼**
1741 A993 20p multi .35 .20
1742 A994 20p multi .35 .20
  a. Pair, #1741-1742 .70 .70

A995

2000, Jan. 20 **Perf. 13¼x13**
1743 A995 20p multi .50 .20
Islamic Development Bank, 25th anniv.

2000, Feb. 28 **Perf. 13¼x12¾**
1744 A996 125p multi 1.10 1.10
Common Market for Eastern and Southern Africa Economic Conference.

Death of Om Kolthoum, 25th Anniv. — A997

Europe-Africa Summit, Cairo — A999

8th Intl. Congress of Egyptologists — A998

2000, Mar. 11 **Perf. 13¼x13**
1745 A997 20p multi .50 .20

2000, Mar. 28 **Perf. 13x13¼**
1746 A998 20p multi .50 .20

2000, Apr. 3 **Perf. 13¼x13**
1747 A999 125p multi 1.25 1.25

Group of 15 Developing Nations, 10th Summit, Cairo — A1000

Perf. 12¾x13¼
2000, June 19 **Litho.**
1748 A1000 125p multi 1.25 1.25

Goddess Selket Type of 1999 and

Scene from 20th Dynasty Nofret, Wife of Rahotep
A1003 A1004

King Seostris Princess Merit
A1005 Aton
  A1006

50p 20th Dynasty — A1007

Pyramid at Snefru Wife of Sheikh-
A1008 el-Balad
  A1009

King King
Psusennes I Tutankhamen
A1010 A1011

Obelisk of Temple of
Ramses II Karnak
A1011a A1012

Perf. 12¾x13¼, 11¼ (1752-1755, 1757), 11x11½ (1758-1760), 13¼x12¾ (1756, 1761, 1763)
Photo., Litho. (1751, 1761, 1763)
2000-2002
1750 A982 10p multi .40 .20
1750A A982 10p multi, Type II 3.00 3.00
1751 A1003 10p multi .40 .20
1752 A1004 20p multi .40 .20
1753 A1005 25p multi .40 .20
1754 A982 30p multi .50 .20
1755 A1006 30p multi .40 .20
1756 A1007 50p multi .40 .20
1757 A1008 £1 multi .60 .60
1758 A1009 110p multi .65 .65
1759 A1010 125p multi .75 .75
1760 A1011 150p multi .85 .85
1761 A1011a 225p multi 1.50 1.50
1763 A1012 £5 multi 4.25 4.25
  Nos. 1750-1763 (14) 14.50 13.00

Issued: 20p, 6/25; No. 1750, 3/25/01; No. 1750A, 2001 (?); 30p, 6/11/01. Nos. 1751, 1755, 225p, 5/25/02; 110p, 6/4/02; 125p, 6/20/02; 150p, 6/15/02; £5, 6/1/02. 30p, 50p, #1, 6/30/02.

Type I (No. 1750), has "Goddess" in smaller type than "Silakht." Type II (No. 1750A), has "Goddess" and "Silakht" in type the same height.

Intl. Day Against Drug Abuse — A1013

Perf. 12¾x13¼
2000, June 26 **Litho.**
1764 A1013 20p multi .50 .20
See No. 1796.

Natl. Insurance Company, Cent. — A1014

Perf. 13¼x12¾
2000, Aug. 20 **Litho.**
1765 A1014 20p shown .50 .20

Imperf
Size: 96x75mm
1766 A1014 125p Emblem, building, horiz. 2.25 2.25

2000 Summer Olympics, Sydney
A1015

Background colors: 20p, Light blue. 125p, Pink.

2000, Sept. 9 **Perf. 13¼x12¾**
1767-1768 A1015 Set of 2 1.40 1.40
No. 1768 is airmail.

Productive Cooperative Union, 25th Anniv. — A1016

2000, Sept. 15 **Perf. 12¾x13¼**
1769 A1016 20p multi .50 .20

Opening of Fourth Stage of Second Cairo Subway Line — A1017

2000, Oct. 7
1770 A1017 20p multi .50 .20

World Post Day — A1018

2000, Oct. 9
1771 A1018 125p multi 1.10 1.10

Solidarity with Palestinians — A1019

Palestinian Authority flag and: 20p, Dome of the Rock, Jerusalem, vert. No. 1773, 125p, shown. No. 1774, 125p, Dome of the Rock, father and boy, vert.

Perf. 13¼x12¾, 12¾x13¼
2000, Nov. 29
1772-1774 A1019 Set of 3 2.75 2.75
No. 1774 is airmail.

Opening of El-Ferdan Railway
Bridge — A1020

2000, Dec. 2   *Perf. 12¾x13¼*
1775 A1020 20p multi   .50 .20

Disabled
Person's
Day — A1021

2000, Dec. 9   *Perf. 13¼x12¾*
1776 A1021 20p multi   .50 .20

Opening of Al-Azhar Professorial
Building — A1022

2000, Dec. 10   *Perf. 12¾x13¼*
1777 A1022 20p multi   .50 .20

Famous
Egyptians
A1023

No. 1778: a, Karem Mahmoud, artist (yellow
background). b, Mahmoud El-Miligi, artist
(green background). c, Mohamed Fawzi, musician (pink background). d, Hussein Riyad, artist (lilac background). e, Abdel Wares Asser,
artist (light blue background).

2000, Dec. 24   *Perf. 13¼x12¾*
1778   Horiz. strip of 5   2.00 2.00
a.-e. A1023 20p Any single   .40 .20

Feasts — A1024

a, Red and yellow flowers. b, Purple flowers.

Perf. 12¾x13¼
2000, Dec. 23   **Litho.**
1779 A1024 20p Pair, #a-b   .80 .80

Jerusalem, City of Peace — A1025

Illustration reduced.

2001, Jan. 1   *Imperf.*
1780 A1025 £2 multi   2.75 2.75

Post Day — A1026

Ancient Egyptian art: 20p, 8 standing
figures. No. 1782, 125p, 3 large standing
figures.

2001, Jan. 2   *Perf. 12¾x13¼*
1781-1782 A1026   Set of 2   1.40 1.40
Imperf
Size: 80x60mm
1783 A1026 125p Chariot   2.25 2.25
No. 1782 is airmail.

Arab Labor
Organization,
36th
Anniv. — A1027

Perf. 13¼x12¾
2001, Feb. 10   **Litho.**
1784 A1027 20p multi   .50 .20

Postal Savings
Bank,
Cent. — A1028

2001, Mar. 1
1785 A1028 20p multi   .50 .20

Natl. Council for Women, 1st
Anniv. — A1029

Background colors: 30p, Pink. 125p, Blue.

2001, Mar. 16   *Perf. 12¾x13¼*
1786-1787 A1029   Set of 2   2.00 1.60
No. 1787 is airmail.

Cairo Intl.
Fair — A1030

2001, Mar. 21   *Perf. 13¼x12¾*
1788 A1030 30p multi   .50 .20

Helwan University, 25th
Anniv. — A1031

2001, May 4   *Perf. 12¾x13¼*
1789 A1031 30p multi   .50 .20

Inauguration of Alexandria
Library — A1032

2001, May 20
1790 A1032 125p multi   1.10 1.10

African
Conference on
the Future of
Children
A1033

Background color: 30p, Blue. 125p, Red.

2001, May 28   *Perf. 13¼x12¾*
1791-1792 A1033   Set of 2   2.00 1.60
No. 1792 is airmail.

World
Environment
Day — A1034

2001, June 5   **Litho.**   *Perf. 13¼x12¾*
1793 A1034 125p multi   1.25 1.25

World Military
Soccer
Championships
A1035

Designs: 30p, Emblem. 125p, Emblem and
map.

Perf. 13¼x12¾
2001, June 21   **Litho.**
1794-1795 A1035   Set of 2   2.00 1.60

**Intl. Day Against Drug Abuse Type
of 2000**
2001, June 26   *Perf. 12¾x13¼*
1796 A1013 30p multi   .50 .20

Egypt's Victory in World Military
Soccer Championships — A1036

Illustration reduced.

2001, July 6   **Litho.**   *Imperf.*
1797 A1036 125p multi   2.25 2.25

Egyptian Railways, 150th
Anniv. — A1037

2001, July 12   *Perf. 12¾x13¼*
1798 A1037 30p multi   .60 .25

Poets — A1038

No. 1799: a, Aziz Abaza Pasha (1898-73),
blue background. b, Ahmed Rami (1892-
1981), pink background.

2001, July 28   *Perf. 13¼x12¾*
1799 A1038 30p Horiz. pair, #a-b   .70 .70

Intl. Volunteers
Year — A1039

2001, Aug. 18
1800 A1039 125p multi   1.10 1.10

Ismailia Folklore
Festival — A1040

2001, Aug. 20
1801 A1040 30p multi   .60 .25

Satellite Telecommunications Ground
Stations, 25th Anniv. — A1041

2001, Sept. 8   **Perf. 12¾x13¼**
1802 A1041 30p multi   .60 .25

Year of Dialogue
Among
Civilizations
A1042

Designs: No. 1803, 125p, Emblem. No.
1804, 125p, UN emblem, globe, symbols of
various civilizations, horiz.

Perf. 13¼x12¾, 12¾x13¼
2001, Oct. 9
1803-1804 A1042   Set of 2   3.00 2.50

Opening of Suez Canal
Bridge — A1043

No. 1805: a, 30p, Bridge, ship. b, 125p,
Bridge, road.
No. 1806, Bridge, ship and flags of Egypt
and Japan.
Illustration reduced.

2001, Oct. 10   **Perf. 12¾x13¼**
1805 A1043   Horiz. pair, #a-b   1.50 1.50
Imperf
Size: 81x60mm
1806 A1043 125p multi   2.25 2.25

Ancient Gold Masks — A1044

Designs: No. 1807, 30p, Mask of San Xing
Dui, China, green background. No. 1808, 30p,
Funerary mask of King Tutankhamun, brown
background.

2001, Oct. 12   **Perf. 12¾x13¼**
1807-1808 A1044 Set of 2   .75 .75
See People's Republic of China 3141-3142.

Opening of Azhar
Tunnels,
Cairo — A1045

2001, Oct. 28   **Perf. 13¼x12¾**
1809 A1045 30p multi   .60 .25

El-Menoufia
University, 25th
Anniv. — A1046

2001, Nov. 25
1810 A1046 30p multi   .60 .25

Feasts — A1047

No.1811: a, Black and white bird on branch.
b, Sea gulls. c, Parrot. d, Blue bird on branch.

2001, Dec. 5
1811 A1047 30p Block of 4, #a-d   2.00 1.10

Musicians — A1048

No. 1812: a, Zakaria Ahmed (1896-1961)
with scarf around neck (4). b, Riyadh El-
Sonbati (1908-81) with glasses with rectangular lenses (3). c, Mahmoud El-Sherif (1912-90)
(2). d, Mohamed El-Kasabgi (1898-1966) with
glasses with round lenses (1). Stamp numbers, shown in parentheses, are found at the
bottom center in Arabian script. Illustration
reduced.

2001, Dec.
1812 A1048 30p Horiz. strip of 4   2.00 1.10

Painting From Tomb of Anhur
Khawi — A1049

Painting from Tomb of
Irinefer — A1050

Illustration A1050 reduced.

2002, Jan. 2   Litho.   Perf. 12¾x13¼
1813 A1049 30p multi   .60 .25
Imperf
Size: 79x60mm
1814 A1050 125p multi   2.25 2.25
Stamp Day.

Intl. Nephrology
Congress
A1051

2002, Jan. 16   Litho.   Perf. 13¼x12¾
1815 A1051 30p multi   .60 .25

Police
Day,
50th
Anniv.
A1052

2002, Jan. 25   **Perf. 12¾x13¼**
1816 A1052 30p multi   .60 .25
Imperf
Size: 79x50mm
1817 A1052 30p multi   1.75 1.75

Return of Sinai to
Egypt, 20th
Anniv. — A1053

2002, Apr. 25   **Perf. 13¼x12¾**
1818 A1053 30p multi   .60 .25

Cairo Bank, 50th
Anniv. — A1054

2002, May 15
1819 A1054 30p multi   .60 .25

Weight Lifters — A1055

No. 1820: a, Ibrahim Shams, 1948 (weights
over head). b, Khidre el Touney, 1936 (weights
at knees).

2002, June 1
1820 A1055 30p Horiz. pair, #a-b   .60 .25

Al Akhbar Newspaper, 50th
Anniv. — A1056

2002, June 15   **Perf. 12¾x13¼**
1821 A1056 30p multi   .60 .25

Nos. 318-321 and Egyptian
Arms — A1057

Illustration reduced.

2002, July 23   Litho.   Imperf.
1822 A1057 125p multi   1.60 1.60
July 23rd Revolution, 50th anniv.

Aswan Dam, Cent. — A1058

No. 1823: a, Dam. b, Dam and buildings.
Illustration reduced.

2002, Aug. 15   **Perf. 12¾x13¼**
1823 A1058 30p horiz. pair, #a-b   .60 .60

Intl. Day for
Preservation of
the Ozone
Layer — A1059

2002, Sept. 16 *Perf. 13¼x12¾*
1824 A1059 125p multi 1.25 1.25

18th Intl.
Conference on
Road Safety,
Cairo — A1060

2002, Sept. 22
1825 A1060 30p multi .60 .25

17th Congress of Intl. Federation of
Otorhinolaryngological Societies,
Cairo — A1061

2002, Sept. 28
1826 A1061 30p multi .60 .25

World Post
Day — A1062

2002, Oct. 9
1827 A1062 125p multi 1.10 1.10

Opening of Alexandria
Library — A1063

Ancient Alexandria Library — A1064

Designs: 30p, Library exterior. 125p, Pillar,
sun on horizon, vert.

Perf. 12¾x13¼, 13¼x12¾
2002, Oct. 16
1828-1829 A1063 Set of 2 1.50 1.50
Size: 60x80mm
Imperf
1830 A1064 125p multi 1.60 1.60

Hassan Faek,
Actor — A1065

Aziza Amir,
Actress — A1066

Farid Shawki,
Actor — A1067

Mary Mounib,
Actress — A1068

2002, Nov. 23 *Perf. 13¼x12¾*
1831 Horiz. strip of 4 1.60 1.60
 a. A1065 30p tan & black .40 .20
 b. A1066 30p tan & black .40 .20
 c. A1067 30p tan & black .40 .20
 d. A1068 30p tan & black .40 .20

A1069

A1070

A1071

Birds — A1072

2002, Dec. 3 *Perf. 13¼x12¾*
1832 Block of 4 1.60 1.60
 a. A1069 30p multi .40 .20
 b. A1070 30p multi .40 .20
 c. A1071 30p multi .40 .20
 d. A1072 30p multi .40 .20

Egyptian Museum, Cent. — A1073

2002, Dec. 11 *Perf. 12¾x13¼*
1833 A1073 30p shown .60 .25
Size: 80x60mm
Imperf
1834 A1073 125p Entrance, statue of Cheops 1.75 1.75

Opening of Aswan Suspension
Bridge — A1074

No. 1835: a, Bridge and support cables. b,
Bridge towers.
Illustration reduced.

2002, Dec. 17 *Perf. 12¾x13¼*
1835 A1074 30p Horiz. pair, #a-b .75 .75

Suez Canal
University, 25th
Anniv. — A1075

2002, Dec. 29 *Perf. 13¼x12¾*
1836 A1075 30p multi .50 .20

Toshka Land Reclamation
Project — A1076

2002, Dec. 31 *Perf. 12¾x13¼*
1837 A1076 30p multi .50 .20

A1077

A1078

Post Day — A1079

2003, Jan. 2
1838 A1077 30p multi .40 .20
1839 A1078 30p multi .40 .20
1840 A1079 125p multi 1.10 1.10
 Nos. 1838-1840 (3) 1.90 1.50

Cairo Intl.
Communications
and Information
Technology
Fair — A1080

2003, Jan. 12 Litho. *Perf. 13¼x12¾*
1841 A1080 30p multi .60 .25

Intl. Nile Children's Song
Festival — A1081

Background color: 30p, Brown. 125p,
Green.

2003, Jan. 28 *Perf. 12¾x13¼*
1842-1843 A1081 Set of 2 1.25 1.25

Intl. Table Tennis
Championships — A1082

Background color: 30p, Blue. 125p, Orange.

2003, Feb. 3
1844-1845 A1082 Set of 2 1.25 1.25

Tenth Intl. Building and Construction Conference A1083

Background color: 30p, Orange. 125p, Blue.

2003, Apr. 1 *Perf. 13¼x12¾*
1846-1847 A1083 Set of 2 1.10 1.10

Arab Lawyer's Union, 60th Anniv. — A1084

Background color: 30p, Blue. 125p, Lilac.

2003, Apr. 25 *Perf. 12¾x13¼*
1848-1849 A1084 Set of 2 1.10 1.10

Inauguration of First Phase of Smart Village Project — A1085

Denomination color: 30p, White. 125p, Yellow. £1, White.

2003, July 1 *Perf. 12¾x13¼*
1850-1851 A1085 Set of 2 1.10 1.10
Size: 79x59mm
Imperf
1852 A1085 £1 multi 2.00 2.00

Writers — A1086

No. 1853: a, Ihsan Abdul Qudous (1919-90) (wearing checked tie). b, Youssef Idris (1927-91) (wearing solid tie).

2003, July 28 *Perf. 13¼x12¾*
1853 A1086 30p Horiz. pair, #a-b .75 .75

African Men's Basketball Championships A1087

Background color: 30p, Black. 125p, Blue.

2003, Aug. 12
1854-1855 A1087 Set of 2 1.10 1.10

Natl. Institute of Astronomical and Geophysical Research, Cent. — A1088

2003, Sept. 7 *Perf. 12¾x13¼*
1856 A1088 30p multi .75 .30

World Tourism Day — A1089

Denomination color: 30p, White. 125p, Red.

Perf. 12¾x13¼
2003, Sept. 27 Litho.
1857-1858 A1089 Set of 2 1.10 1.10

Egypt's Bid for Hosting 2010 World Cup Soccer Championships — A1090

Designs: 30p, Emblem, vert. 125p, Emblem, funerary mask of King Tutankhamen.

Perf. 13¼x12¾, 12¾x13¼
2003, Sept. 27
1859-1860 A1090 Set of 2 1.10 1.10

October War Against Israel, 30th Anniv. — A1091

2003, Oct. 6 *Perf. 13¼x12¾*
1861 A1091 30p multi .75 .30

World Post Day — A1092

2003, Oct. 9
1862 A1092 125p multi .80 .80

National Bar Association, 91st Anniv. — A1093

2003, Oct. 30
1863 A1093 30p multi .50 .20

Festivals — A1094

No. 1864: a, Pink orchids. b, White rose. c, Red rose. d, Sunflower.

2003, Nov. 23 *Perf. 14*
1864 A1094 30p Block of 4, #a-d 1.25 1.25

Film Directors — A1095

No. 1865: a, Salah Abou Seif (balding man with open collar). b, Kamal Selim (round eyeglasses) c, Henri Barakat (square eyeglasses). d, Hassan El Emam. Illustration reduced.

2003, Dec. 1 *Perf. 13¼x12¾*
1865 A1095 30p Horiz. strip of 4, #a-d 1.25 1.25

El Gomhoreya Newspaper, 50th Anniv. — A1096

2003, Dec. 7
1866 A1096 30p multi .50 .20

Cairo Bourse, Cent. — A1097

2003, Dec. 7 *Perf. 12¾x13¼*
1867 A1097 30p multi .50 .20

Mrs. Suzanne Mubarak, Emblems of Fifth E-9 Ministerial Review Meeting and UNESCO — A1098

Background color: 30p, Blue. 125p, Orange. £2, Blue.

Perf. 12¾x13¼
2003, Dec. 18 Litho.
1868-1869 A1098 Set of 2 1.10 1.10
Imperf
Size: 79x60mm
1870 A1098 £2 multi 2.25 2.25

Delta International Bank, 25th Anniv. — A1099

Background color: 30p, Green. 125p, Blue. £2, Green and blue, horiz.

2004, Jan. 1 *Perf. 12¾x13¼*
1871-1872 A1099 Set of 2 1.00 1.00
Imperf
Size: 80x60mm
1873 A1099 £2 multi 2.25 2.25

Post Day A1100

Denominations: 30p, 125p.

2004, Jan. 2 *Perf. 12¾x13¼*
1874-1875 A1100 Set of 2 1.00 1.00

Eighth Intl. Telecommunications Conference — A1101

2004, Jan. 17
1876 A1101 30p multi .70 .30

Treasures of Egypt A1102

No. 1877: a, Sinai. b, Pyramids at dusk. c, Egyptian Bedouin. d, Red Sea corals. e, Suez Canal, Ferdinand-Marie de Lesseps, Khedive Ismail. f, Ramadan lanterns. g, Nile felucca. h, White Western Desert. i, Maydum Pyramid.
No. 1878: a, St. Catherine Monastery, Sinai. b, Icon of Sts. Paul and Anthony. c, Mosque of Muhammad Ali. d, Lamp, Old Cairo. e, Emblem of Sultan Qaytbay. f, Minaret, Cairo. g, Mosque of al-Azhar. h, Coptic priest and icon, Cairo. i, Ben Ezra Synagogue.
No. 1879: a, Ankh. b, Rosetta Stone. c, Sarcophagus of Ahmes Meritamun. d, Stela of Amenmhat. e, Sphinx. f, Udjat. g, Canopic jars

EGYPT

of Tutankhamun. h, Cartouche of Tutankhamun. i, Egyptian scribe.
No. 1880: a, Sphinx, diff. b, Queen Nefertiti. c, Tutankhamun.

2004, Jan. 22 Litho. *Perf. 13x13¼*

1877	Booklet pane of 9	2.25	—
a.-i.	A1102 30p Any single	.40	.20
1878	Booklet pane of 9	11.00	—
a.-i.	A1102 125p Any single	1.25	1.25

Litho. & Embossed, Litho. & Embossed With Foil Application (£10)

1879	Booklet pane of 9	17.50	—
a.-i.	A1102 £2 Any single	1.90	1.90

Perf. 13¼

1880	Booklet pane of 3	19.00	—
a.-b.	A1102 £5 Either single, 38x51mm	4.50	4.50
c.	A1102 £10 gold & multi, 38x51mm	9.00	9.00
	Complete booklet, #1877-1880	50.00	

Complete booklet sold for £80.

Morkos Hanna — A1103

Ahmed Lotfi — A1104

Mahmoud Abu el Nasr — A1105

Abd el Aziz Fahmy — A1106

Ibrahim el Helbawi — A1107

Makram Ebeid — A1108

Mohammad Naguib el Gharabli — A1109

Mohammad Bassiouni A1110

Mohammad Hafez Ramadan A1111

Mohammad Abu Shadi — A1112

Mahmoud Fahmi Goundia — A1113

Kamel Youssof Saleh — A1114

Abd el Hamid Abd el Hakk — A1115

Mohammad Ali Allouba — A1116

Kamel Sedki Beck — A1117

Bar Association Emblem — A1118

Abd el Rahman el Rafei — A1119

Abd el Fattah el Shalkany A1120

Mohammad Sabri Abu Alam — A1121

Omar Omar — A1122

Sameh Ashour — A1123

Ahmed el Khawaga A1124

Abd el Aziz el Shorgabi A1125

Mostafa el
Baradei — A1126

2004, Feb.   Litho.   Perf. 13¼x12¾
1881   Block of 25   10.00 10.00
  a. A1103 30p bright blue & black   .40   .20
  b. A1104 30p bright blue & black   .40   .20
  c. A1105 30p bright blue & black   .40   .20
  d. A1106 30p bright blue & black   .40   .20
  e. A1107 30p bright blue & black   .40   .20
  f. A1108 30p pink & black   .40   .20
  g. A1109 30p pink & black   .40   .20
  h. A1110 30p pink & black   .40   .20
  i. A1111 30p pink & black   .40   .20
  j. A1112 30p pink & black   .40   .20
  k. A1113 30p orange & black   .40   .20
  l. A1114 30p orange & black   .40   .20
  m. A1115 30p orange & black   .40   .20
  n. A1116 30p orange & black   .40   .20
  o. A1117 30p orange & black   .40   .20
  p. A1118 30p green & multi   .40   .20
  q. A1119 30p green & black   .40   .20
  r. A1120 30p green & black   .40   .20
  s. A1121 30p green & black   .40   .20
  t. A1122 30p green & black   .40   .20
  u. A1118 30p dark blue & multi   .40   .20
  v. A1123 30p dark blue & black   .40   .20
  w. A1124 30p dark blue & black   .40   .20
  x. A1125 30p dark blue & black   .40   .20
  y. A1126 30p dark blue & black   .40   .20

National Bar Association, 92nd anniv.

IBM Corporation
in Egypt, 50th
Anniv. — A1127

2004, Feb. 24
1882 A1127 30p multi   .50   .20

Cairo Rotary
Club, 75th
Anniv. — A1128

2004, Mar. 11
1883 A1128 30p multi   .50   .20

Egyptian Victory
in Regional
Computer
Programming
and Information
Technology
Competition
A1129

2004, Mar. 15
1884 A1129 30p multi   .60   .25

National
Women's
Day — A1130

Background colors: 30p, Blue. 125p, Red
orange.

2004, Mar. 16   **Litho.**
1885-1886 A1130 Set of 2   1.00 1.00

Anti-Narcotics General Administration,
75th Anniv. — A1131

2004, Mar. 20   **Perf. 12¾x13¼**
1887 A1131 30p multi   .75   .30
Imperf
Size: 80x60mm
1888 A1131 125p multi   2.00 2.00

Orphan's
Day — A1132

2004, Apr. 2   **Perf. 13¼x12¾**
1889 A1132 30p multi   .60   .25
Compare with Types A1169 and A1199.

Telecom Africa Fair and Conference,
Cairo — A1133

2004, May 4   **Perf. 12¾x13¼**
1890 A1133 30p multi   .60   .25

Egyptian
Philatelic Society,
75th
Anniv. — A1134

Designs: 30p, Emblem. 125p, Emblem,
stamp, magnifying glass, tongs.

2004, May 20   **Perf. 13¼x12¾**
1891 A1134 30p multi   .60   .25

Imperf
Size: 80x60mm
1892 A1134 125p multi   2.00 2.00

State Information Service, 50th
Anniv. — A1135

2004, May 30   **Perf. 12¾x13¼**
1893 A1135 30p multi   .50   .20

Tenth Radio and
Television
Festival,
Cairo — A1136

Designs: 30p, Festival emblem, green background. £1, Festival emblem, brown background. 125p, Sphinx, festival emblem, film,
horiz. £2, Like 125p, horiz.

Perf. 13¼x12¾, 12¾x13¼
2004, June 1
1894-1896 A1136   Set of 3   1.75 1.75
Imperf
Size: 80x60mm
1897 A1136 £2 multi   2.25 2.25

Pres. Hosni Mubarak, "Education for
All" Arab Regional Conference
Emblem — A1137

Stylized Children,
Emblems
A1138

Perf. 12¾x13¼, 13¼x12¾
2004, June 1
1898 A1137 30p yel & multi   .35   .20
1899 A1137 125p red org & multi   .60   .60
1900 A1138 125p multi   .60   .60
  Nos. 1898-1900 (3)   1.55 1.40
Imperf
Size: 80x60mm
1901 A1137   £2 blue & multi   2.25 2.25

Construction and
Housing Bank,
25th
Anniv. — A1139

2004, June 24   **Perf. 13¼x12¾**
1902 A1139 30p multi   .60   .25

2004 Summer
Olympics,
Athens — A1140

Background color: 30p, Gray. 150p, Orange
yellow.

Perf. 13¼x12¾
2004, Aug. 13   **Litho.**
1903-1904 A1140 Set of 2   1.40 1.40

Scouting in Egypt, 90th
Anniv. — A1141

2004, Aug. 15   **Perf. 12¾x13¼**
1905 A1141 30p multi   .70   .30

14th Intl. Folklore
Festival,
Ismailia — A1142

2004, Aug. 24   **Perf. 13¼x12¾**
1906 A1142 30p multi   .60   .25

Administrative
Attorneys, 50th
Anniv. — A1143

2004, Sept. 16   **Perf. 13¼x12¾**
1907 A1143 30p multi   .60   .25
Imperf
Size: 60x80mm
1908 A1143 £1 multi   3.00 3.00

Egyptian National Archives, 50th
Anniv. — A1144

2004, Sept. 20   *Perf. 12¾x13¼*
1909 A1144 30p multi   .60 .25

Light and Hope Society, 50th
Anniv. — A1145

2004, Sept. 26
1910 A1145 30p multi   .60 .25

General Arab
Journalists
Union, 10th
Conference
A1146

2004, Oct. 2   *Perf. 13¼x12¾*
1911 A1146 125p multi   .80 .80

Telecom Egypt, 150th Anniv. A1146a

2004, Oct. 3 Litho.   *Perf. 12¾x13¼*
1911A A1146a 30p multi   9.00 9.00

No. 1911A was withdrawn from sale after a
few days as anniversary emblem was
incorrect.

Military Production Day, 50th
Anniv. — A1147

2004, Oct. 6   *Perf. 12¾x13¼*
1912 A1147 30p multi   .70 .30

World Post Day — A1148

2004, Oct. 9
1913 A1148 150p multi   1.00 1.00

Egyptian Youth
Hostels
Association, 50th
Anniv. — A1149

2004, Oct. 20   *Perf. 13¼x12¾*
1914 A1149 30p multi   .60 .25

Rose — A1150

Songbird
A1151

    Perf. 12¾x13¼
2004, Nov. 10   *Litho.*
1915 A1150 30p multi   .50 .20
    Perf. 13¼x12¾
1916 A1151 30p multi   .50 .20

24th Arab Scouting
Congress — A1152

2004, Nov. 27   *Perf. 12¾x13¼*
1917 A1152 30p multi   .65 .25

Arab Scouting Organization, 50th
Anniv. — A1153

2004, Dec. 4
1918 A1153 30p multi   .65 .25

Islamic Art
Museum
Foundation,
Cent. — A1154

2004, Dec. 15   *Perf. 13¼x12¾*
1919 A1154 30p multi   .65 .25

FIFA (Fédération Internationale de
Football Association), Cent. — A1155

2004, Dec. 15   *Perf. 12¾x13¼*
1920 A1155 150p multi   1.00 1.00

Fekri Abaza
(1896-1979),
Journalist
A1156

Abd El Rahman
El Sharqawi
(1920-87),
Journalist
A1157

2004, Dec. 28   *Perf. 13¼x12¾*
1921 A1156 30p multi   .40 .20
1922 A1157 30p multi   .40 .20

Telecom Egypt, 150th Anniv. — A1158

Color of central panel: 30p, White. 125p,
Gray.

2004, Dec. 30   *Perf. 12¾x13¼*
1923-1924 A1158 Set of 2   1.10 1.10

First Sale of Natural Gas to
Jordan — A1159

2005, Jan. 1
1925 A1159 30p multi   .70 .30

Post
Day — A1160

2005, Jan. 2   *Perf. 13¼x12¾*
1926 A1160 30p multi   .60 .25

Opening of Om El Massrean — El
Moneib Subway Line, Cairo — A1161

2005, Jan. 16   *Perf. 12¾x13¼*
1927 A1161 30p multi   .60 .25
    Imperf
    Size: 80x59mm
1928 A1161 150p multi   1.75 1.75

Police
Day — A1162

Pres. Hosni Mubarak and flag stripes
aligned: 30p, Vertically. £1, Horizontally.

2005, Jan. 25   *Perf. 13¼x12¾*
1929 A1162 30p multi   .50 .20
    Imperf
    Size: 80x59mm
1930 A1162 £1 multi   1.50 1.50

El Mohandes
Insurance
Company, 25th
Anniv. — A1163

2005, Jan. 26   *Perf. 13¼x12¾*
1931 A1163 30p multi   .60 .25

9th Intl. Telecommunications and
Information Conference,
Cairo — A1164

2005, Feb. 1
1932 A1164 30p multi .60 .25

7th University
Youth
Week — A1165

2005, Feb. 5
1933 A1165 30p multi .60 .25

Rotary
International,
Cent. — A1166

2005, Feb. 23 Litho.
1934 A1166 30p multi .70 .30

38th Intl. Fair,
Cairo — A1167

2005, Mar. 15
1935 A1167 30p multi .40 .20

Arab League,
60th
Anniv. — A1168

2005, Mar. 22
1936 A1168 30p multi .50 .20

Orphan's
Day — A1169

2005, Apr. 2
1937 A1169 30p multi .50 .20

Heliopolis Foundation, Cent. — A1170

2005, May 5 Perf. 12¾x13¼
1938 A1170 30p multi .60 .25

National Center
of Social and
Criminological
Research, 50th
Anniv. — A1171

2005, May 22 Litho. Perf. 13¼x12¾
1939 A1171 30p multi .60 .25

Egyptian-European Association
Agreement, 1st Anniv. — A1172

2005, June 1
1940 A1172 150p multi .80 .80

World Environment Day — A1173

2005, June 5 Perf. 12¾x13¼
1941 A1173 30p multi .75 .30

World Summit on
the Information
Society,
Tunis — A1174

2005, July 31 Litho. Perf. 13¼x12¾
1942 A1174 150p multi 1.25 1.25

Ministry of Youth,
50th
Anniv. — A1175

Background colors: 30p, Green. 125p, Olive
green.

2005, Aug. 13
1943-1944 A1175 Set of 2 1.00 1.00

Presidential
Elections
A1176

2005, Sept. 7
1945 A1176 30p multi .60 .25

13th World
Psychiatry
Congress,
Cairo — A1177

Designs: 30p, Emblem. 150p, Emblem and
funerary mask of King Tutankhamen, horiz.

2005, Sept. 10 Perf. 13¼x12¾
1946 A1177 30p multi .60 .25
Imperf
Size: 80x60mm
1947 A1177 150p multi 1.75 1.75

World Literacy Day — A1178

2005, Sept. 24 Perf. 12¾x13¼
1948 A1178 30p multi .50 .20

Re-election of
Pres. Hosni
Mubarak
A1179

2005, Sept. 27 Perf. 13¼x12¾
1949 A1179 30p multi .50 .20

Mohamed El-
Baradei, Director
General of Intl.
Atomic Energy
Agency — A1180

Background colors: 30p, Blue green. 150p,
Rose lilac.

2005, Oct. 8
1950-1951 A1180 Set of 2 1.50 1.50
Awarding of 2005 Nobel Peace Prize to El-
Baradei and IAEA.

World Post
Day — A1181

Denominations: 30p, 150p.

2005, Oct. 9
1952-1953 A1181 Set of 2 1.25 1.25

Intl. Year of
Sports and
Physical
Education
A1182

2005, Oct. 24
1954 A1182 150p multi 1.00 1.00

United Nations, 60th Anniv. — A1183

2005, Oct. 24 Perf. 12¾x13¼
1955 A1183 150p multi 1.00 1.00

Festivals
A1184

2005, Nov. 1   **Perf. 13¼x12¾**
1956 A1184 30p multi   .65   .25

Alexandria
Biennale, 50th
Anniv. — A1185

2005, Dec. 1
1957 A1185 30p multi   .60   .25

K-8 Training Airplane — A1186

Denominations: 30p, 150p.

      Perf. 12¾x13¼
2005, Dec. 26   **Litho.**
1958-1959 A1186   Set of 2   1.00 1.00

Saved Mekawi,
Musician
A1187

Mohamed El
Mogi (1923-95),
Musician
A1188

Kamal El Taweel,
Composer
A1189

Ali Ismael (1921-
75), Composer
A1190

Mohamed
Roshdi, Folk
Singer — A1191

2005, Dec. 31   **Perf. 13¼x12¾**
1960   Horiz. strip of 5   1.25 1.25
   a.   A1187 30p green & multi   .25   .20
   b.   A1188 30p blue & multi   .25   .20
   c.   A1189 30p lilac & black   .25   .20
   d.   A1190 30p org & black   .25   .20
   e.   A1191 30p brt org & black   .25   .20

Post
Day — A1192

2006, Jan. 2
1961 A1192 30p multi   .40   .20

25th Africa Cup
of Nations
Soccer
Tournament
A1193

2006, Jan. 20
1962 A1193 30p multi   .40   .20

Arab University Youth Week — A1194

2006, Feb. 4
1963 A1194 30p multi   **Perf. 12¾x13¼**
                         .40   .20

Intl. Telecommunications, Information
and Networking Exhibition,
Cairo — A1195

2006, Feb. 5   **Perf. 13¼x12¾**
1964 A1195 30p multi   .40   .20

Pres. Hosni Mubarak Holding African
Cup of Nations — A1196

2006, Feb. 10   **Perf. 12¾x13¼**
1965 A1196   30p multi   .40   .20
      Size: 80x60mm
        Imperf
1966 A1196 150p multi   1.10 1.10

Information and
Decision Support
Center, 20th
Anniv. — A1197

2006, Mar. 27   **Perf. 13¼x12¾**
1967 A1197 30p multi   .40   .20

Total Solar Eclipse of March 29,
2006 — A1198

2006, Mar. 29   **Perf. 12¾x13¼**
1968 A1198 30p multi   .40   .20
      Size: 82x60mm
        Imperf
1969 A1198 150p multi   1.10 1.10

Orphan's
Day — A1199

2006, Apr. 2   **Perf. 13¼x12¾**
1970 A1199 30p multi   .40   .20
Compare with types A1132 and A1169.

Gamal Hemdan
(1928-93),
Geographical
Historian
A1200

2006, Apr. 16
1971 A1200 30p lilac & black   .40   .20

Abd El-Rahman
ibn Khaldun
(1332-1406),
Historian
A1201

2006, May 27
1972 A1201 30p multi   .40   .20

World Environment Day — A1202

Designs: 30p, Stone pillar in White Desert.
150p, Trees in desert.

2006, June 5   **Perf. 12¾x13¼**
1973-1974 A1202   Set of 2   1.25 1.25

Diplomatic Relations Between Egypt
and People's Republic of China, 50th
Anniv. — A1203

No. 1975: a, Abu Simbel Temple, Egypt. b,
South Gate Pavilion, China.
Illustration reduced.

2006, July 13   **Litho.**   **Perf. 12**
1975 A1203 £1.50 Horiz. pair,
             #a-b, + cen-
             tral label   1.40 1.40
   c.   Souvenir sheet, #1975   1.10 1.10

Military Academy Headquarters,
Heliopolis, 50th Anniv. — A1204

2006, July 19　　　　**Perf. 12¾x13¼**
1976 A1204 30p multi　　　　　　.40　.20

Nationalization of
the Suez Canal,
50th
Anniv. — A1205

2006, July 26　　　　**Perf. 13¼x12¾**
1977 A1205 30p multi　　　　　　.40　.20

World Post
Day — A1206

Denominations: 30p, 150p.

2006, Oct. 9
1978-1979 A1206　Set of 2　　　1.25 1.25

China - Africa Summit — A1206a

No. 1979A: b, Chinese mask. c, African
mask.

2006, Nov. 5　Litho.　Perf. 12
1979A　Horiz. pair with central
　　　　label　　　　　　　1.10 1.10
　b.-c. A1206a £1.50 Either single　.55　.55

National Housing
Census — A1207

2006, Nov. 21　Litho.　Perf. 13¼x13
1980 A1207 30p multi　　　　　　.20　.20

Al-Ahram Newspaper — A1208

No. 1981: a, Newspaper headquarters. b,
Newspaper emblem.
150p, Headquarters and emblem.
Illustration reduced.

2006, Nov. 26　　　　**Perf. 13x13¼**
1981 A1208　30p Horiz. pair, #a-
　　　　b, + central
　　　　label　　　　　　　　.20　.20

Imperf
Size: 80x60mm
1982 A1208 150p multi　　　　　.55　.55

Natl. Council for Childhood and
Motherhood — A1209

2006, Dec. 27　　　　**Perf. 13x13¼**
1983 A1209 150p multi　　　　　.55　.55

Feasts — A1210

2006, Dec. 30
1984 A1210 30p multi　　　　　　.20　.20

Post Day — A1211

2007, Jan. 2
1985 A1211 30p multi　　　　　　.20　.20

Ali El Kassar
(1888-1957),
Artist — A1212

2007, Jan. 15　　　　**Perf. 13¼x13**
1986 A1212 30p multi　　　　　　.20　.20

Automobile and Touring Club of
Egypt — A1213

2007, Jan. 14　Litho.　Perf. 12¾x13¼
1987 A1213　30p multi　　　　　.20　.20

Imperf
Size: 80x60mm
1988 A1213 150p multi　　　　　.55　.55

Police Day — A1214

2007, Jan. 25　　　　**Perf. 12¾x13¼**
1989 A1214 30p multi　　　　　　.20　.20

Imperf
Size: 80x60mm
1990 A1214 150p multi　　　　　.55　.55

Rededication of National
Library — A1215

2007, Feb. 25　　　　**Perf. 12¾x13¼**
1991 A1215 30p multi　　　　　　.20　.20

Arabic Language
Academy, 75th
Anniv. — A1216

2007, Mar. 17　　　　**Perf. 13¼x12¾**
1992 A1216 30p multi　　　　　　.20　.20

World Health Day — A1217

2007, Apr. 7　Litho.　Perf. 12¾x13¼
1993 A1217 30p multi　　　　　　.20　.20

Egyptian Trade
Union
Federation, 50th
Anniv. — A1218

2007, May 1　　　　**Perf. 13¼x12¾**
1994 A1218 30p multi　　　　　　.20　.20

Egypt Air, 75th Anniv. — A1219

Anniversary emblem and: 30p, Biplane.
150p, Biplane and jet.

2007, May 7　　　　**Perf. 12¾x13¼**
1995-1996 A1219　Set of 2　　　.65　.65

Return of Sinai to Egypt, 25th
Anniv. — A1220

No. 1997: a, Monastery of St. Catherine. b,
Salah el Din Castle. c, Sharm el-Sheikh. d,
Oasis of Nabq.
Illustration reduced.

2007, Apr. 25　Litho.　Perf. 12¾x13¼
1997 A1220 30p Block of 4, #a-d　.45　.45

Mevlana Jalal ad-
Din ar-Rumi
(1207-73),
Islamic
Philosopher
A1221

2007, May 8　　　　**Perf. 13¼x12¾**
1998 A1221 150p multi　　　　　.55　.55

World
Environment
Day — A1222

Designs: 30p, Sinai baton blue butterfly.
150p, Melting ice, horiz.

Perf. 13¼x12¾, 12¾x13¼
2007, June 5
1999-2000 A1222　Set of 2　　　.65　.65

Scouting, Cent. — A1223

2007, June 6　　　　**Perf. 12¾x13¼**
2001 A1223 150p multi　　　　　.55　.55

EuroMed Postal Conference, Marseille, France — A1224

2007, July 9
2002 A1224 150p multi   .55   .55

Diplomatic Relations Between Egypt and Nepal, 50th Anniv. — A1225

2007, July 16
2003 A1225 150p multi   .55   .55

Egyptian Air Force, 75th Anniv. — A1226

2007, Oct. 14   Litho.   Perf. 13x13¼
2004 A1226 30p multi   .20   .20

SEMI-POSTAL STAMPS

Catalogue values for unused stamps in this section are for Never Hinged items.

Princess Ferial — SP1

Perf. 13½x14
1940, May 17   Photo.   Wmk. 195
B1 SP1 5m + 5m copper brown 2.00 .65

No. B1 Overprinted in Green

1943, Nov. 17
B2 SP1 5m + 5m   8.00   4.25
a. Arabic date "1493"   200.00 200.00

The surtax on Nos. B1 and B2 was for the children's fund.

First Postage Stamp of Egypt SP2

Khedive Ismail Pasha SP3

No. B5, King Fuad. No. B6, King Farouk.

Perf. 13x13½
1946, Feb. 28   Wmk. 195
B3 SP2 1m + 1m gray   .30   .25
B4 SP3 10m + 10m violet   .40   .25
B5 SP3 17m + 17m brown   .40   .25
B6 SP3 22m + 22m yel grn   .40   .25
a. Souv. sheet, #B3-B6, perf. 8½ 35.00 35.00
b. As "a," imperf.   35.00 35.00
    Nos. B3-B6 (4)   1.50   1.00

80th anniv. of Egypt's 1st postage stamp.
Nos. B6a, B6b measure 129x171mm.

Goddess Hathor, King Men-kau-Re (Mycerinus) and Jackalheaded Goddess — SP7

Ramesseum, Thebes — SP8

Queen Nefertiti SP9

Funerary Mask of King Tutankhamen SP10

Perf. 13½x13
1947, Mar. 9   Wmk. 195
B9   SP7 5m + 5m slate   2.00   .50
B10 SP8 15m + 15m dp blue 2.00   .70
B11 SP9 30m + 30m henna brn 2.00 1.00
B12 SP10 50m + 50m brown   3.00 1.10
     Nos. B9-B12 (4)   9.00 3.30

Intl. Exposition of Contemporary Art, Cairo.

Boy Scout Emblem — SP11

Scout Emblems: 20m+10m, Sea Scouts. 35m+15m, Air Explorers.

1956, July 25   Photo.   Perf. 13½x13
B13 SP11 10m + 10m green   1.00   .40
B14 SP11 20m + 10m ultra   1.50   .60
B15 SP11 35m + 15m blue   2.00   .70
     Nos. B13-B15 (3)   4.50 1.70

2nd Arab Scout Jamboree, Alexandria-Aboukir, 1956.
Souvenir sheets, perf. and imperf., contain one each of Nos. B13-B15. Size: 118x158mm. Value $750 each.

Ambulance — SP12

1957, May 13   Perf. 13x13½
B16 SP12 10m + 5m rose red .40   .20

50th anniv. of the Public Aid Society.

United Arab Republic

Eye and Map of Africa, Europe and Asia SP13

Postal Emblem SP14

Perf. 13½x13
1958, Mar. 1   Photo.   Wmk. 318
B17 SP13 10m + 5m orange 1.00   .40

1st Afro-Asian Cong. of Ophthalmology, Cairo.
The surtax was for centers to aid the blind.

1959, Jan. 2
B18 SP14 10m + 5m bl grn, red & blk   .40   .20

Post Day. The surtax went to the social fund for postal employees.
See Syria UAR issues No. B1 for similar stamp with denominations in piasters (p).

Children and UN Emblem SP15

Arab League Building, Cairo, and Emblem SP16

1959, Oct. 24   Wmk. 328
B19 SP15 10m + 5m brown lake   .30   .20
B20 SP15 35m + 10m dk blue   .50   .20

Issued for International Children's Day and to honor UNICEF.

Braille Type of Regular Issue, 1961
1961, Apr. 6   Perf. 13½x13
B21 A182 35m + 15m yel & brn   .75   .25

1962, Mar. 22   Photo.   Wmk. 328
B22 SP16 10m + 5m gray   .40   .20

Arab Publicity Week, Mar. 22-28.
See No. N86.

Postal Emblem — SP17

Stamp of 1866 — SP18

1963, Jan. 2   Wmk. 342   Perf. 11½
B23 SP17 20m +10m brt grn, red & blk   .80   .60
B24 SP18 40m +20m blk & brn org   1.50   .90
B25 SP18 40m +20m brn org & blk   1.50   .90
a.   Pair, #B24-B25   3.50 3.00
     Nos. B23-B25 (3)   3.80 2.40

Post Day, Jan. 2 and 1966 exhibition of the FIP.

Arms of UAR and Pyramids SP19

1964, Jan. 2   Wmk. 342   Perf. 11
B26 SP19 10m + 5m org yel & grn   1.40   .80
B27 SP19 80m + 40m grnsh bl & blk   2.75 1.25
B28 SP19 115m + 55m org brn & blk   3.25 1.75
     Nos. B26-B28 (3)   7.40 3.80

Issued for Post Day. Jan. 2.

Type of 1963 and

SP20

Postal Emblem — SP20a

No. B30, Emblem of Postal Secondary School. 80m+40m, Postal emblem, gearwheel, laurel wreath.

Perf. 11½
1965, Jan. 2   Unwmk.   Photo.
B29 SP20 10m + 5m lt grn & car   .60   .40
B30 SP20 10m + 5m ultra, car & blk   .60   .40
a.   Pair, #B29-B30   1.50 1.25
B31 SP20a 80m + 40m rose, brt grn & blk   2.50 1.50
     Nos. B29-B31 (3)   3.70 2.30

Issued for Post Day, Jan. 2. No. B31 also publicizes the Stamp Centenary Exhibition.

Souvenir Sheet

Stamps of Egypt, 1866 — SP21

1966, Jan. 2   Wmk. 342   Imperf.
B32 SP21 140m + 60m blk, sl bl
& rose   3.75 3.25

Post Day, 1966, and cent. of the 1st Egyptian postage stamps.

Pharaonic
"Mediator" — SP22

Design: 115m+40m, Pharaonic guard.

1967, Jan. 2   Wmk. 342   Perf. 11½
B33 SP22 80m + 20m multi   3.00 2.00
B34 SP22 115m + 40m multi   4.75 3.00

Issued for Post Day, Jan. 2.

Grand Canal, Doges' Palace, Venice,
and Santa Maria del Fiore,
Florence — SP23

115m+30m, Piazetta and Campanile, Venice, and Palazzo Vecchio, Florence.

Perf. 11½x11
1967, Dec. 9   Photo.   Wmk. 342
B35 SP23 80m + 20m grn, yel
& brn   1.50 1.00
B36 SP23 115m + 30m ol, yel &
sl bl   2.25 1.75

The surtax was to help save the cultural monuments of Venice and Florence, damaged in the 1966 floods.

Boy and   Emblem and
Girl — SP24   Flags of Arab
                 League — SP25

Design: No. B38, Five children and arch.

1968, Dec. 11   Photo.   Perf. 11
B37 SP24 20m + 10m car, bl & lt
brn   .75 .50
B38 SP24 20m + 10m vio bl, sep &
lt grn   .75 .50

Children's Day & 22nd anniv. of UNICEF.

1969, Mar. 22   Perf. 11x11½
B39 SP25 20m + 10m multi   .45 .25

Arab Publicity Week, Mar. 22-28.

Refugee
Family
SP26

1969, Oct. 24   Photo.   Perf. 11½
B40 SP26 30m + 10m multi   .70 .40

Issued for United Nations Day.

Men of
Three
Races,
Human
Rights
Emblem
SP27

1970, Mar. 21   Perf. 11½x11
B41 SP27 20m + 10m multi   .95 .70

Issued to publicize the International Day for the Elimination of Racial Discrimination.

Arab League Type
1970, Mar. 22   Wmk. 342
B42 A344 20m + 10m bl, grn & brn .70 .55

Map of
Palestine
and
Refugees
SP28

Perf. 11½x11
1970, Oct. 24   Photo.   Wmk. 342
B43 SP28 20m + 10m multi   .75 .60

25th anniv. of the UN and to draw attention to the plight of the Palestinian refugees.

Arab Republic of Egypt

Blind Girl, WHO and
Society
Emblems — SP29

1973, Oct. 24   Photo.   Perf. 11x11½
B44 SP29 20m + 10m blue & gold .65 .50

25th anniv. of WHO and for the Light and Hope Soc., which educates and helps blind girls.

Map of Africa,   Social Work Day
OAU Emblem   Emblem
SP30   SP31

Perf. 11x11½
1973, Dec. 8   Photo.   Wmk. 342
B45 SP30 55m + 20m multi   1.75 1.00

Organization for African Unity, 10th anniv.

1973, Dec. 8
B46 SP31 20m + 10m multi   .75 .65

Social Work Day.

Jihan al Sadat Consoling Wounded
Man — SP32

1974, Mar. 21   Wmk. 342   Perf. 11
B47 SP32 20m + 10m multi   .90 .70

Faithfulness and Hope Society.

Afghan
Solidarity
SP33

Wmk. 342
1981, July 15   Photo.   Perf. 11½
B48 SP33 20m + 10m multi   1.25 1.25

Size: 30x25mm

1981   Photo.   Perf. 11½
B49 SP33 20m + 10m multi   4.00 3.50

Map of Sudan,
Dunes, Dead
Tree — SP34

1986, Mar. 25   Photo.   Perf. 13x13½
B50 SP34 15p + 5p multi   1.60 1.00

Fight against drought and desertification of the Sudan. Surtax for drought relief.

Organization of African Unity, 25th
Anniv. — SP35

1988, May 25   Litho.   Perf. 13
B51 SP35 15p +10p multi   .90 .90

AIR POST STAMPS

Mail Plane
in Flight
AP1

Perf. 13x13½
1926, Mar. 10   Wmk. 195   Photo.
C1 AP1 27m deep violet   17.00 15.00

1929, July 17
C2 AP1 27m orange brown   4.50 2.25

Zeppelin Issue
No. C2 Surcharged in Blue or Violet

1931, Apr. 6
C3 AP1 50m on 27m (Bl)   52.50 52.50
  a. "1951" instead of "1931" 57.50 57.50
C4 AP1 100m on 27m (V)   52.50 62.50

Airplane
over Giza
Pyramids
AP2

1933-38   Litho.   Perf. 13x13½
C5 AP2 1m orange & blk   .40 .25
C6 AP2 2m gray & blk   .80 .55
C7 AP2 2m org red & blk
         ('38)   2.00 .75
C8 AP2 3m ol brn & blk   .60 .25
C9 AP2 4m green & blk   .90 .45
C10 AP2 5m dp brown & blk   .40 .20
C11 AP2 6m dk green & blk   1.50 .65
C12 AP2 7m dk blue & blk   1.00 .55
C13 AP2 8m violet & blk   .60 .20
C14 AP2 9m dp red & blk   2.50 .25
C15 AP2 10m violet & brn   .75 .25
C16 AP2 20m dk green & brn   .60 .20
C17 AP2 30m dull blue & brn   .75 .20
C18 AP2 40m dp red & brn   15.00 .60
C19 AP2 50m orange & brn   12.00 .25
C20 AP2 60m gray & brn   3.75 .55
C21 AP2 70m dk blue & bl
         grn   3.50 .50
C22 AP2 80m ol brn & bl grn   3.50 .50
C23 AP2 90m org & bl grn   4.00 .50
C24 AP2 100m vio & bl grn   7.00 .50
C25 AP2 200m dp red & bl grn   10.00 1.00
     Nos. C5-C25 (21)   71.55 9.60

See Nos. C34-C37. For overprint see No. C38.

Type of 1933

			Photo.	
1941-43				
C34	AP2	5m copper brn ('43)	.25	.25
C35	AP2	10m violet	.50	.25
C36	AP2	25m dk vio brn ('43)	.50	.25
C37	AP2	30m green	.65	.25
	Nos. C34-C37 (4)		1.90	1.00

> Catalogue values for unused stamps in this section, from this point to the end of the section, are for Never Hinged items.

No. C37 Overprinted in Black

1946, Oct. 1
C38	AP2	30m green	.50	.35
a.	Double overprint		400.00	—
b.	Inverted overprint		400.00	—

Middle East Intl. Air Navigation Congress, Cairo, Oct. 1946.

King Farouk, Delta Dam and DC-3 Plane AP3

Perf. 13x13½

			Photo.	Wmk. 195
1947, Feb. 19				
C39	AP3	2m red orange	.25	.55
C40	AP3	3m dk brown	.25	.60
C41	AP3	5m red brown	.25	.20
C42	AP3	7m dp yellow org	.45	.20
C43	AP3	8m green	.45	.70
C44	AP3	10m violet	.40	.20
C45	AP3	20m brt blue	.50	.20
C46	AP3	30m brown violet	.60	.20
C47	AP3	40m carmine rose	1.50	.60
C48	AP3	50m Prus green	1.75	.70
C49	AP3	100m olive green	3.25	.75
C50	AP3	200m dark gray	7.00	2.75
	Nos. C39-C50 (12)		16.65	7.65

For overprints see Nos. C51-C64, C67-C89, NC1-NC30.

Nos. C49 and C50 Surcharged in Black

1948, Aug. 23
C51	AP3	13m on 100m	.50	.40
C52	AP3	22m on 200m	.60	.75
a.	Date omitted			

Inaugural flights of "Services Aeriens Internationaux d'Egypte" from Cairo to Athens and Rome, Aug. 23, 1948.

Nos. C39 to C50 Overprinted in Various Colors

Overprint 27mm Wide

1952, Jan.		**Wmk. 195**	**Perf. 13x13½**	
C53	AP3	2m red orange (Bl)	.35	.20
C54	AP3	3m dark brown		
		(RV)	.80	.80
C55	AP3	5m red brown	.35	.35
C56	AP3	7m dp yel org (Bl)	.70	.40
C57	AP3	8m green (RV)	1.00	.80
C58	AP3	10m violet (G)	.80	.80
C59	AP3	20m brt blue (RV)	3.25	1.00
C60	AP3	30m brown vio (G)	1.00	.40
C61	AP3	40m carmine rose	4.00	3.00
C62	AP3	50m Prus green		
		(RV)	1.50	1.25
C63	AP3	100m olive green	5.00	2.00
C64	AP3	200m dark gray (RV)	10.00	4.00
	Nos. C53-C64 (12)		28.75	15.00

See notes after No. 316.

Delta Dam and Douglas DC-3 AP4

1953   Photo.
C65	AP4	5m red brown	.50	.50
C66	AP4	15m olive green	1.00	1.00

For overprints see Nos. NC31-NC32.

Nos. C39-C49 Overprinted in Black with Three Bars to Obliterate Portrait

1953
C67	AP3	2m red orange	1.50	1.50
C68	AP3	3m dk brown	1.20	1.20
C69	AP3	5m red brown	.80	.80
C70	AP3	7m dp yellow org	.50	.50
C71	AP3	8m green	1.20	1.20
C72	AP3	10m violet	35.00	
C73	AP3	20m brt blue	1.50	.30
C74	AP3	30m brown violet	1.75	.90
C75	AP3	40m carmine rose	1.75	1.00
C76	AP3	50m Prus green	3.25	1.75
C77	AP3	100m olive green	4.25	2.75
C77A	AP3	200m gray	60.00	

Nos. C72 and C77A are in question. They are not known postally used.

Nos. C53-C64 Overprinted in Black with Three Bars to Obliterate Portrait

1953
C78	AP3	2m red orange	.50	.35
C79	AP3	3m dark brown	.90	.80
C80	AP3	5m red brown	.30	.25
C82	AP3	8m green	.60	1.50
C83	AP3	10m violet	.50	1.25
C85	AP3	30m brown violet	1.25	1.25
C87	AP3	50m Prus green	3.00	2.00
C88	AP3	100m olive green	4.75	2.75
C89	AP3	200m dark gray	8.00	8.00
	Nos. C78-C89 (9)		19.80	18.15

Practically all values of Nos. C67-C89 exist with double overprint. The 7m, 20m and 40m with this overprint are forgeries.

United Arab Republic
Type of Regular Issue
Perf. 11½x11

1958, Mar. 22		**Photo.**	**Wmk. 318**	
C90	A141	15m ultra & red brn	.40	.25

Pyramids at Giza AP5

Al Azhar University AP6

Designs: 15m, Colossi of Memnon, Thebes. 90m, St. Catherine Monastery, Mt. Sinai.

1959-60		**Wmk. 328**	**Perf. 13x13½**	
C91	AP5	5m bright red	.25	.20
C92	AP5	15m dk dull violet	.35	.30
C93	AP6	60m dk green	.75	.50
C94	AP5	90m brown car ('60)	1.50	1.00
	Nos. C91-C94 (4)		2.85	2.00

Nos. C91-C93 exist imperf. See Nos. C101, C105, NC33.

Tower of Cairo Type, Redrawn
1961, May 1		**Perf. 13½x13**		
C95	A183	50m bright blue	.90	.45

Top inscription has been replaced by two airplanes.

Weather Vane, Anemometer and UN World Meteorological Organization Emblem — AP7

Perf. 11½x11
1962, Mar. 23		**Photo.**	**Unwmk.**	
C96	AP7	60m yellow & dp blue	1.50	.90

2nd World Meteorological Day, Mar. 23.

Patrice Lumumba and Map of Africa — AP8

Perf. 13½x13
1962, July 1		**Wmk. 328**		
C97	AP8	35m multicolored	.65	.35

Patrice Lumumba (1925-61), Premier of Congo.

Maritime Station, Alexandria — AP9

Designs: 30m, International Airport, Cairo. 40m, Railroad Station, Luxor.

1963, Mar. 18		**Perf. 13x13½**		
C98	AP9	20m dark brown	.60	.20
C99	AP9	30m carmine rose	.85	.35
C100	AP9	40m black	1.50	.90
	Nos. C98-C100 (3)		2.95	1.45

Type of 1959-60 and

Temple of Queen Nefertari, Abu Simbel AP10

Arch and Tower of Cairo — AP11

Designs: 80m, Al Azhar University seen through arch. 140m, Ramses II, Abu Simbel.

1963-65		**Photo.**	**Perf. 11½x11, 11x11½**	**Wmk. 342**
C101	AP6	80m vio blk & brt		
		bl	3.00	1.50
C102	AP10	115m brown & yel	2.25	1.25
C103	AP10	140m pale vio, blk & org red	2.25	1.25

Unwmk.
C104	AP11	50m yel brn & brt bl	1.75	1.00
C105	AP6	80m vio bl & lt bl	2.75	1.50
	Nos. C101-C105 (5)		12.00	6.50

Issued: 50m, 11/2/64; No. C105, 2/13/65; others, 10/24/63.
See Nos. NC34-NC36.

Weather Vane, Anemometer and WMO Emblem — AP12

Perf. 11½x11
1965, Mar. 23		**Wmk. 342**		
C106	AP12	80m dk blue & rose lil	2.50	1.25

Fifth World Meteorological Day.
See No. NC37.

Game Board from Tomb of Tutankhamen — AP13

1965, July 1		**Photo.**	**Unwmk.**	
C107	AP13	10m yellow & dk blue	1.25	.40

See No. NC38.

Temples at Abu Simbel — AP14

1966, Apr. 28		**Wmk. 342**	**Perf. 11½**	
C108	AP14	20m multicolored	.80	.40
C109	AP14	80m multicolored	1.75	1.10

Issued to commemorate the transfer of the temples of Abu Simbel to a hilltop, 1963-66.

Scout Camp and Jamboree Emblem AP15

1966, Aug. 10		**Perf. 11½x11**		
C110	AP15	20m olive & rose	1.40	.45

7th Pan-Arab Boy Scout Jamboree, Good Daim, Libya, Aug. 12.

St. Catherine Monastery, Mt. Sinai — AP16

1966, Nov. 30		**Photo.**	**Wmk. 342**	
C111	AP16	80m multicolored	2.10	1.25

St. Catherine Monastery, Sinai, 1400th anniv.

Cairo Airport AP17

1967, Apr. 26   *Perf. 11½x11*
C112 AP17 20m sky bl, sl grn & lt
     brn   .85 .35

Hotel El
Alamein
and Map of
Nile Delta
AP18

Intl. Tourist Year: 80m, The Virgin's Tree,
Virgin Mary and Child. 115m, Fishing in the
Red Sea.

1967, June 7   **Wmk. 342**   *Perf. 11½*
C113 AP18 20m dull pur, sl
     grn & dl
     org   .75 .25
C114 AP18 80m blue & multi   2.25 1.00
C115 AP18 115m brown, org &
     bl   4.00 2.00
    Nos. C113-C115 (3)   7.00 3.25

Oil
Derricks,
Map of
Egypt
AP19

1967, July 23   **Photo.**
C116 AP19 50m org & bluish blk 1.10 .75
   15th anniversary of the revolution.

Type of Regular Issue, 1967

Design: 80m, Back of Tutankhamen's throne
and UNESCO emblem.

1967, Oct. 24   **Wmk. 342**   *Perf. 11½*
C117 A301 80m blue & yellow   1.25 .85

Koran — AP20

1968, Mar. 25   **Wmk. 342**   *Perf. 11½*
C118 AP20 30m lilac, bl & yel   .75 .60
C119 AP20 80m lilac, bl & yel   1.50 .80
   a.   Pair, #C118-C119 + label   3.00 2.50

1400th anniv. of the Koran. Nos. C118-
C119 are printed in miniature sheets of 4 containing 2 each of Nos. C118-C119.

St. Mark and St. Mark's
Cathedral — AP21

1968, June 25   **Wmk. 342**   *Perf. 11½*
C120 AP21 80m brt grn, dk brn &
     dp car   1.50 .70

Martyrdom of St. Mark, 1900th anniv. and
the consecration of St. Mark's Cathedral,
Cairo.

Map of United Arab Airlines and
Boeing 707
AP22

Design: No. C122, Ilyushin 18 and routes of
United Arab Airlines.

1968-69   **Photo.**   *Perf. 11½x11*
C121 AP22 55m blue, ocher &
     car   1.25 .65
C122 AP22 55m bl, yel & vio blk
     ('69)   1.10 .65

1st flights of a Boeing 707 and an Ilyushin
18 for United Arab Airlines.

Mahatma
Gandhi, Arms of
India and UAR
AP23

Imam El
Boukhary
AP24

1969, Sept. 10   *Perf. 11x11½*
C123 AP23 80m lt blue, ocher &
     brn   3.25 1.50
Mohandas K. Gandhi (1869-1948), leader in
India's fight for independence.

1969, Dec. 27   **Photo.**   **Wmk. 342**
C124 AP24 30m lt olive & dk brown .70 .20
1100th anniv. of the death of the Imam El
Boukhary (824-870), philosopher and writer.

Azzahir
Beybars
Mosque
AP25

1969, Dec. 27   **Engr.**   *Perf. 11½x11*
C125 AP25 30m red lilac   .50 .20
700th anniv. of the founding of the Azzahir
Beybars Mosque, Cairo.

Lenin (1870-
1924) — AP26

Perf. 11x11½
1970, Apr. 22   **Photo.**   **Wmk. 342**
C126 AP26 80m lt green & brown 1.75 1.00

Phantom
Fighters
and
Destroyed
Factory
AP27

1970, May 1   *Perf. 11½x11*
C127 AP27 80m yel, grn & dk vio
     brn   1.50 .90
Issued to commemorate the destruction of
the Abu-Zaabal factory by Israeli planes.

UPU Type of Regular Issue
1970, May 20   **Photo.**   **Wmk. 342**
C128 A350 80m multicolored   1.20 .85

Nasser and Burial Mosque — AP28

1970, Nov. 6   **Wmk. 342**   *Perf. 11*
C129 AP28 30m olive & blk   .75 .30
C130 AP28 80m brown & blk   1.75 .80
Gamal Abdel Nasser (1918-70), Pres. of
Egypt.

Postal Congress Type
Perf. 11½x11
1971, Mar. 6   **Photo.**   **Wmk. 342**
C131 A365 30m lt ol, org & sl grn   .80 .40

Nasser,
El Rifaei
and
Sultan
Hussein
Mosques
AP29

Designs: 85m, Nasser and Ramses Square,
Cairo. 110m, Nasser, Sphinx and pyramids.

Perf. 11½x11
1971, July 1   **Photo.**   **Wmk. 342**
C132 AP29 30m multicolored   2.50 .75
C133 AP29 85m multicolored   4.00 1.00
C134 AP29 110m multicolored   5.50 1.50
   Nos. C132-C134 (3)   12.00 3.25

APU Type of Regular Issue
1971, Aug. 3   **Wmk. 342**   *Perf. 11½*
C135 A373 30m brown, yel & bl   .85 .40

Arab Republic of Egypt
Confederation Type
Perf. 11½x11
1971, Sept. 28   **Photo.**   **Wmk. 342**
C136 A374 30m gray, sl grn & dk
     pur   .80 .40

Al Aqsa
Mosque
and
Woman
AP30

Wmk. 342
1971, Oct. 24   **Photo.**   *Perf. 11½*
C137 AP30 30m bl, yel, brn & grn 1.60 .40
25th anniv. of the UN (in 1970) and return of
Palestinian refugees.

Postal Union Type
30m, African Postal Union emblem & letter.

1971, Dec. 2   *Perf. 11½x11*
C138 A384 30m green, blk & bl   1.40 .40

Aida,
Triumphal
March
AP31

1971, Dec. 23   **Wmk. 342**   *Perf. 11½*
C139 AP31 110m dk brn, yel & sl
     grn   5.50 2.75
Centenary of the first performance of the
opera Aida, by Giuseppe Verdi.

Globe, Glider,
Rocket Club
Emblem
AP32

St. Catherine's
Monastery on Fire
AP33

1972, Feb. 11   *Perf. 11x11½*
C140 AP32 30m blue, ocher & yel 1.25 .40
International Aerospace Education Confer-
ence, Cairo, Jan. 11-13.

Perf. 11½x11
1972, Feb. 15   **Unwmk.**
C141 AP33 110m dp car, org &
     blk   4.25 3.00
The burning of St. Catherine's Monastery in
Sinai Desert, Nov. 30, 1971.

Tutankhamen in
Garden — AP34

Tutankhamen, from 2nd
Sarcophagus — AP35

Design: No. C143, Ankhesenamun.

1972, May 22   **Photo.**   *Perf. 11½*
C142 AP34 110m brn org, bl &
     grn   8.50 4.00
C143 AP34 110m brn org, bl &
     grn   8.50 4.00
   a.   Pair, #C142-C143   24.00 20.00

Souvenir Sheet
Imperf
C144 AP35 200m gold & multi 30.00 27.50
50th anniv. of the discovery of the tomb of
Tutankhamen. No. C143a has continuous
design.

Souvenir Sheet

Flag of Confederation of Arab Republics — AP36

1972, July 23   Photo.   Imperf.
C145 AP36 110m gold, dp car & blk 4.25 4.00

20th anniversary of the revolution.

Temples at Abu Simbel AP37

Designs: 30m, Al Azhar Mosque and St. George's Church. 110m, Pyramids at Giza.

1972   Wmk. 342   Perf. 11½x11
C146 AP37 30m blue, brn & buff 2.00 .35
C147 AP37 85m bl, brn & ocher 3.00 1.25
C148 AP37 110m multicolored 4.75 1.25
    Nos. C146-C148 (3) 9.75 2.85

Issued: Nos. C146, C148, 11/22; No. C147, 8/1.

Olympic Type of Regular Issue

Olympic and Motion Emblems and: No. C149, Handball. No. C150, Weight lifting. 50m, Swimming. 55m, Gymnastics. All vertical.

1972, Aug. 17   Perf. 11x11½
C149 A396 30m multicolored .75 .35
C150 A396 30m yellow & multi .75 .35
C151 A396 50m blue & multi 1.50 .80
C152 A396 55m multicolored 1.75 .90
    Nos. C149-C152 (4) 4.75 2.40

Champollion, Rosetta Stone, Hieroglyphics — AP38

1972, Oct. 16
C153 AP38 110m gold, grn & blk 7.50 2.50

Sesquicentennial of the deciphering of Egyptian hieroglyphics by Jean-François Champollion.

World Map, Telephone, Radar, ITU Emblem — AP39

1973, Mar. 21   Photo.   Perf. 11
C154 AP39 30m lt bl, dk bl & blk .90 .25

5th World Telecommunications Day.

Karnak Temple, Luxor — AP40

Hand Dripping Blood and Falling Plane — AP41

1973, Mar. 21
C155 AP40 110m dp ultra, blk & rose 4.75 2.25

Sound and light at Karnak.

1973, May 1   Perf. 11x11½
C156 AP41 110m multicolored 6.00 1.75

Israeli attack on Libyan civilian plane, Feb. 1973.

WMO Emblem, Weather Vane — AP42

1973, Oct. 24   Perf. 11x11½
C157 AP42 110m blue, gold & pur 2.75 1.75

Cent. of intl. meteorological cooperation.

Refugees, Map of Palestine AP43

1973, Oct. 24   Perf. 11½
C158 AP43 30m dk brn, yel & bl 1.60 .50

Plight of Palestinian refugees.

INTERPOL Emblem AP44

Postal and UPU Emblems AP45

1973, Dec. 8   Photo.   Perf. 11x11½   Wmk. 342
C159 AP44 110m black & multi 3.50 1.75

Intl. Criminal Police Organization, 50th anniv.

1974, Jan. 2   Unwmk.   Perf. 11

Post Day (UPU Emblems and): 30m, APU emblem. 55m, African Postal Union emblem. 110m, UPU emblem.

Size: 26x46½mm
C160 AP45 20m gray, red & blk .40 .20
C161 AP45 30m sal, blk & pur .60 .20

C162 AP45 55m emerald, blk & brt mag 1.25 .50
Size: 37x37½mm
Perf. 11½
C163 AP45 110m lt bl, blk & gold 1.50 1.00
    Nos. C160-C163 (4) 3.75 1.90

Solar Bark of Khufu (Cheops) — AP46

Wmk. 342
1974, Mar. 21   Photo.   Perf. 11½
C164 AP46 110m blue, gold & brn 3.00 2.10

Solar Bark Museum.

Hotel Meridien AP47

1974, Oct. 6   Perf. 11½x11
C165 AP47 110m multicolored 2.00 1.10

Opening of Hotel Meridien, Cairo.

Suez Canal Type of 1975
1975, June 5   Perf. 11½
C166 A448 30m bl, yel grn & ind 1.50 .45
C167 A448 110m indigo & blue 2.50 1.25

Irrigation Commission Emblem — AP48

1975, July 20
C168 AP48 110m orange & dk grn 2.00 1.00

9th Intl. Congress on Irrigation and Drainage, Moscow, and 25th anniv. of the Intl. Commission on Irrigation and Drainage.

Refugees and UNWRA Emblem — AP49

Woman and IWY Emblem — AP50

Perf. 11x11½
1975, Oct. 24   Photo.   Wmk. 342
C169 AP49 30m multicolored 1.25 .40
Unwmk.
C170 AP50 110m olive, org & blk 3.00 1.75

UN Day. 30m publicizes UN help for refugees; 110m is for Intl. Women's Year 1975.

Step Pyramid, Sakhara, and Entrance Gate AP51

Designs: 45m, 60m, Plane over Giza Pyramids. 140m, Plane over boats on Nile.

Perf. 11½x11
1978-82   Photo.   Wmk. 342
C171   AP51 45m yel & brown .55 .20
C171A AP51 60m olive 1.25 .75
C172   AP51 115m blue & brown .85 .50
C173   AP51 140m blue & purple 1.90 .85
C173A AP51 185m bl, sep & gray brn 4.50 1.75
    Nos. C171-C173A (5) 9.05 4.05

Issued: 60m, 1/15/82; 185m, 1982; others, 1/1/78.

Flyer and UN ICAO Emblem — AP52

Perf. 11x11½
1978, Dec. 30   Photo.   Wmk. 342
C174 AP52 140m blue, blk & brn 1.90 .95

75th anniversary of 1st powered flight.

Seeing Eye Medallion AP53

Perf. 11½x11
1981, Oct. 1   Photo.   Wmk. 342
C175 AP53 230m multicolored 2.25 1.00

Hilton Ramses Hotel Opening — AP54

Perf. 11x11½
1982, Mar. 15   Photo.   Wmk. 342
C176 AP54 18½p multi 1.75 .75

Temple of Horus, Edfu AP55

Designs: 15p, like 6p. 18½p, 25p, Statue of Akhnaton, Thebes, hieroglyphics, vert. 23p, 30p, Giza pyramids.

1985   Photo.   Perf. 11½x11, 11x11½
C177 AP55 6p lt blue & dk bl grn .75 .30
C178 AP55 15p grnsh bl & brn 1.25 .45
C179 AP55 18½p grn, sep & dp yel 1.60 .90

C180 AP55 23p grnsh bl, sep &
yel bis 2.00 1.10
C181 AP55 25p lt bl, sep & yel
bis 1.75 .80
a. Unwmkd. ('87) 2.25 1.00
C182 AP55 30p grnsh bl, sep &
org yel 1.75 .70
a. Unwmkd. ('87) 2.25 1.00
Nos. C177-C182 (6) 9.10 4.25

Issued: 6p, 18½p, 23p, 3/1; 15p, 25p, 30p, 5/1.
See No. C236.

Post Day — AP56

Narmer Board, oldest known hieroglyphic inscriptions: No. C183a, Tablet obverse. No. C183b, Reverse.

1986, Jan. 2 Photo. Perf. 13½x13
C183 AP56 Pair 2.00 2.00
a.-b. 15p any single 1.00 1.00

Map, Jet, AFRAA Emblem AP57

1986, Apr. 7 Photo. Perf. 11½
C184 AP57 15p blue, yel & blk 1.00 1.00

African Airlines Assoc., 18th General Assembly, Cairo, Apr. 7-10.

World Food Day AP58

UNESCO, 40th Anniv. — AP59

Perf. 13½x13, 13x13½
1986, Oct. 24 Litho.
C185 AP58 15p multicolored .80 .80
C186 AP59 15p multicolored .80 .80
UN Day.

Tourism Year — AP60

Design: Column and Sphinx in Alexandria, St. Catherine's Monastery in Mt. Sinai, Colossi of Thebes and Temple of Theban Triad in Luxor.

Unwmk.
1987, Sept. 30 Litho. Imperf.
Size: 140x90mm
C187 AP60 30p multicolored 4.00 4.00

Palestinian Uprising — AP61

1988, Sept. 28 Litho. Perf. 12x13½
C188 AP61 25p multicolored 1.25 1.25

UN Day AP62

1988, Oct. 20 Litho. Perf. 13x13½
C189 AP62 25p multicolored 1.25 1.25

Nobel Prize Type of 1988
1988, Nov. 7
C190 A769 25p multicolored 1.25 1.25

Arab Cooperation Council — AP63

Architecture and Art — AP64

1989, May 10 Litho. Perf. 13½x13
C191 AP63 25p Flags 1.00 1.00
Size: 89x80mm
Imperf
C192 AP63 50p Flags, seal 3.25 3.25

1989-91 Photo. Perf. 11x11½
C193 AP64 20p Balcony .60 .60
C194 AP64 25p Brazier .80 .80
C195 AP64 35p shown 1.00 1.00
C196 AP64 45p Tapestry 1.40 1.40
C197 AP64 45p like #C195 1.40 1.40
C198 AP64 50p Stag (dish) 1.50 1.50
C199 AP64 55p 4 animals
(plate) 1.75 1.75
C200 AP64 60p like #C198 2.00 2.00
C201 AP64 65p like #C198 2.25 2.25
C202 AP64 70p like #C193 2.40 2.40
C203 AP64 85p like #C199 2.75 2.75
Nos. C193-C203 (11) 17.85 17.85

Issued: 35p, 60p, 10/1/89; 55p, 1/1/90; No. C197, C202, 1/25/91; 65p, 85p, 7/20/91; others, 4/1/89.

AP65

Funerary Mask of King Tutankhamen — AP66

King Tutankhamen AP66a

1993-99 Litho. Perf. 11½
C204 AP65 55p multicolored 1.75 .95
C205 AP66 80p multicolored 3.00 1.25
Photo.
Perf. 11x11¼
C206 AP66a £1 black & brown 1.25 1.25
b. Wmk. 342 1.25 1.25
Nos. C204-C206 (3) 6.00 3.45
Issued: 55p, 80p, 3/1/93; £1, 1997; No. C206b, 1999.
See No. C231.

ICAO, 50th Anniv. — AP67

1994, Sept. 16 Litho. Perf. 13
C207 AP67 80p multicolored 1.00 1.00

Intl. Year of the Family — AP68

1994, Oct. 24 Litho. Perf. 13
C208 AP68 80p multicolored 1.00 1.00

Arab League for Education, Culture, & Science Organization — AP69

1995, July 25 Litho. Perf. 13x13½
C209 AP69 55p multicolored .70 .70

UN Organizations, 50th Anniv. — AP70

Perf. 12½x13, 13x12½
1995, Oct. 24 Litho.
C210 AP70 80p UN 1.75 1.75
C211 AP70 80p FAO 1.75 1.75
C212 AP70 80p UNESCO, vert. 1.75 1.75
Nos. C210-C212 (3) 5.25 5.25

Arab Summit, Cairo — AP71

1996, June 21 Litho. Perf. 13x12½
C213 AP71 55p multicolored .60 .60

16th Intl. Conference on Irrigation and Drainage, Cairo — AP72

1996, Sept. 15 Litho. Perf. 12½x13
C214 AP72 80p multicolored 1.10 1.10

Intl. Tourism Day — AP73

1996, Sept. 27 Perf. 13
C215 AP73 80p multicolored .90 .90

Arabian Horse Day — AP74

World Post Day — AP75

1996 Perf. 13x12½
C216 AP74 55p grn, blk & gray .60 .60

1996, Oct. 9 Litho. Perf. 13x12½
C217 AP75 80p multicolored 1.10 1.10

AP76
AP77

1996, Oct. 24
C218 AP76 55p multicolored .60 .60
Cairo, Arab cultural capital of 1996.

1996, Oct. 24
C219 AP77 80p multicolored 1.00 1.00
UNICEF, 50th anniv.

World Meteorological Day — AP78

Thutmose III — AP79

1997, Mar. 23   Litho.   Perf. 13x12½
C220 AP78   £1 multicolored   1.25 1.25

1997, Mar. 25   Photo.   Perf. 11x11½
C221 AP79   75p blk, bl & gray   1.10 1.10

Heinrich von Stephan (1831-97) — AP80

1997, Apr. 15   Litho.   Perf. 13
C222 AP80   £1 multicolored   1.25 1.25

AP81

1997, Sept. 11
C223 AP81   £1 multicolored   .90 .90
98th Intl. Parliamentary Conference, Cairo.

AP82   AP83

1997, Sept. 10   Litho.   Perf. 13
C224 AP82   75p multicolored   .90 .90
1997 Egyptian Team, top medal winners of
8th Pan Arab Games, Beirut, Lebanon.

1997, Sept. 27   Perf. 13x12½
C225 AP83   £1 multicolored   1.25 1.25
Sarabas (180-211), mumified Egyptian.

World Book and Copyright Day AP84

1997, Oct. 24   Litho.   Perf. 12½x13
C226 AP84   £1 multicolored   1.25 1.25

African Ministries of Transport and Communications, 11th Conference — AP85

1997, Nov. 22   Litho.   Perf. 13x12½
C227 AP85   75p multicolored   .90 .90

Arab Scout Movement, 85th Anniv. — AP86

1997, Nov. 24   Perf. 12½x13
C228 AP86   75p multicolored   .90 .90

8th G-15 Summit Meeting — AP87

Lighthouse of Alexandria AP88

1998, May 11   Litho.   Perf. 13
C229 AP87   £1 multicolored   1.00 1.00

1998, May 20   Litho.   Perf. 13
C230 AP88   £1 multicolored   1.25 1.25

King Tut Type of 1997
1998, July 25   Litho.   Perf. 11x11¼
C231 AP66a 125p Tutankhamen   1.50 1.50
  a.   Wmk. 342 ('99)   1.50 1.50

AP90

AP91

1998, Aug. 3   Perf. 13
C232 AP90   £1 multicolored   1.10 1.10
    Arab Post Day.

1998, Oct. 9   Litho.   Perf. 13
C233 AP91   125p multicolored   1.25 1.25
    World Post Day.

AP92

AP93

1998, Oct. 22
C234 AP92   125p multicolored   1.25 1.25
    67th Interpol Meeting, Cairo.

1998, Oct. 24
C235 AP93   125p multicolored   1.25 1.25
    Universal Declaration of Human Rights,
50th anniv.

Statue of Akhnaton Type of 1985
1998   Litho.   Perf. 13
C236 AP55   25p lt bl, brn & tan   1.00 1.00

AP94

AP95

1999, Oct. 12   Litho.   Perf. 13x12¾
C237 AP94   125p multicolored   1.75 1.75
Performance of opera "Aida" at the Pyramids.

1999, Oct. 16
C238 AP95   125p multicolored   1.75 1.75
Discovery of the Rosetta Stone, bicent.

World Tourism Day — AP96

Perf. 13¼x12¾
2000, Sept. 27   Litho.
C239 AP96   125p multi   1.50 1.50

Awarding of Nobel Prize for Chemistry
to Dr. Ahmed Zewail — AP97

Illustration reduced.

1999, Dec. 10   Imperf.
C240 AP97   125p multi   1.50 1.50

UN High Commissioner for Refugees, 50th Anniv. — AP98

2000, Dec. 13
C241 AP98   125p multi   1.75 1.75

_____

AIR POST SEMI-POSTAL STAMPS

Catalogue values for unused
stamps in this section are for
Never Hinged items.

United Arab Republic

Pharaonic Mail Carriers and Papyrus Plants SPAP1

Design: 115m+55m, Jet plane, world map and stamp of Egypt, 1926 (No. C1).

Wmk. 342

1966, Jan. 2	Photo.		Perf. 11½	
CB1	SPAP1	80m + 40m multi	2.50	2.00
CB2	SPAP1	115m + 55m multi	3.00	2.25
a.	Pair, #CB1-CB2		7.50	7.00

Post Day, Jan. 2.

SPECIAL DELIVERY STAMPS

Motorcycle Postman — SD1

Perf. 13x13½

1926, Nov. 28	Photo.	Wmk. 195		
E1	SD1	20m dark green	30.00	8.50

1929, Sept.

E2	SD1	20m brown red & black	4.50	1.50

Inscribed "Postes Expres"

1943-44			Litho.	
E3	SD1	26m brn red & gray blk	4.00	6.00
E4	SD1	40m dl brn & pale gray ('44)	2.50	1.00

For overprints see Nos. E5, NE1.

> Catalogue values for unused stamps in this section, from this point to the end of the section, are for Never Hinged items.

No. E4 Overprinted in Black

Overprint 27mm Wide

1952, Jan.				
E5	SD1	40m dl brn & pale gray	2.00	2.00

See notes after No. 316.

POSTAGE DUE STAMPS

D1   D2

Wmk. Crescent and Star (119)

1884, Jan. 1		Litho.	Perf. 10½	
J1	D1	10pa red	40.00	9.00
a.	Horiz. pair, imperf. vert.		150.00	
J2	D1	20pa red	175.00	50.00
J3	D1	1pi red	125.00	40.00
J4	D1	2pi red	225.00	11.00
J5	D1	5pi red	20.00	60.00

1886, Aug. 1   Unwmk.

J6	D1	10pa red	52.50	7.00
a.	Horiz. pair, imperf. vert.		135.00	

J7	D1	20pa red	225.00	30.00
J8	D1	1pi red	26.00	5.00
a.	Pair, imperf. between		200.00	
J9	D1	2pi red	26.00	5.00
a.	Pair, imperf. between		175.00	

1888, Jan. 1			Perf. 11½	
J10	D2	2m green	10.00	15.00
a.	Horiz. pair, imperf. between		225.00	
J11	D2	5m rose red	35.00	14.00
J12	D2	1pi blue	140.00	40.00
a.	Pair, imperf. between		300.00	
J13	D2	2pi yellow	150.00	20.00
J14	D2	5pi gray	210.00	190.00
a.	Period after "PIASTRES"		275.00	250.00

Excellent counterfeits of Nos. J1-J14 are plentiful.

There are 4 types each of Nos. J1-J14, so placed that any block of 4 contains all types.

D3

Perf. 14x13½

1889	Wmk. 119		Typo.	
J15	D3	2m green	7.00	.55
a.	Half used as 1m on cover			275.00
J16	D3	4m maroon	2.50	.55
J17	D3	1pi ultra	6.25	.55
J18	D3	2pi orange	6.00	.80
a.	Half used as 1p on cover			

Nos. J15-J18 exist on both ordinary and chalky paper. Imperf. examples of Nos. J15-J17 are proofs.

Black Surcharge

D4

1898

J19	D4	3m on 2pi orange	.65	2.75
a.	Inverted surcharge		65.00	82.50
c.	Pair, one without surcharge		—	
f.	Double surcharge		225.00	

There are two types of this surcharge. In type I, the spacing between the last two Arabic characters at the right is 2mm. In type II, this spacing is 3mm, and there is an added sign on top of the second character from the right. See *Scott Classic Specialized Catalogue of Stamps & Covers* for detailed listing.

D5   D6

1921	Wmk. 120		Perf. 14x13½	
J20	D5	2m green	.25	.25
J21	D5	4m vermilion	1.10	.90
J22	D6	10m deep blue	1.25	1.00
	Nos. J20-J22 (3)		2.60	2.15

1921-22

J23	D5	2m vermilion	.25	.20
J24	D5	4m green	.25	.20
J25	D6	10m lake ('22)	.50	.40

Nos. J18, J23-J25 Overprinted

1922, Oct. 10		Wmk. 119		
J26	D3	2pi orange	5.00	5.00
a.	Overprint right side up		25.00	25.00
		Wmk. 120		
J27	D5	2m vermilion	.60	.90
J28	D5	4m green	.90	.90
J29	D6	10m lake	1.25	.90

Overprint on Nos. J26-J29 is inverted.

Arabic Numeral — D7

Perf. 13x13½

1927-56		Litho.	Wmk. 195	
	Size: 18x22½mm			
J30	D7	2m slate	.60	.40
J31	D7	2m orange ('38)	.80	.50
J32	D7	4m green	.60	.45
J33	D7	4m ol brn ('32)	6.25	4.25
J34	D7	5m brown	3.50	.80
J35	D7	6m gray grn ('41)	1.50	1.50
J36	D7	8m brn vio	1.00	.40
J37	D7	10m brick red ('29)	1.00	.30
a.	10m deep red		1.10	.35
J38	D7	12m rose lake ('41)	1.50	1.50
J38A	D7	20m dk red ('56)	2.00	2.00
	Perf. 14			
	Size: 22x28mm			
J39	D7	30m purple	4.25	2.25

See Nos. J47-J59. For overprints see Nos. J40-J46, NJ1-NJ7.

> Catalogue values for unused stamps in this section, from this point to the end of the section, are for Never Hinged items.

Postage Due Stamps and Type of 1927 Overprinted in Various Colors

1952, Jan. 16		Perf. 13x13½		
J40	D7	2m orange (Bl)	1.25	1.00
J41	D7	4m green	1.25	1.00
J42	D7	6m gray grn (RV)	1.50	1.25
J43	D7	8m brn vio (Bl)	2.00	1.75
J44	D7	10m dl rose (Bl)	3.50	2.75
a.	10m brown red (Bk)		3.00	3.00
J45	D7	12m rose lake (Bl)	1.75	1.75
	Perf. 14			
J46	D7	30m purple (C)	2.75	2.75

See notes after No. 316.

United Arab Republic

1960	Wmk. 318		Perf. 13x13½	
	Size: 18x22½mm			
J47	D7	2m orange	.50	.25
J48	D7	4m light green	1.00	.25
J49	D7	6m green	1.50	.50
J50	D7	8m brown vio	3.00	1.25
J51	D7	12m rose brown	5.00	1.65
J52	D7	20m dull rose brn	1.00	.25
	Perf. 14			
	Size: 22x28mm			
J53	D7	30m violet	5.00	1.50

1962	Wmk. 328		Perf. 13x13½	
	Size: 18x22½mm			
J54	D7	2m salmon	.50	.50
J55	D7	4m light green	.75	.75
J56	D7	10m red brown	1.50	1.50
J57	D7	12m rose brown	3.50	3.50
J58	D7	20m dull rose brn	7.50	7.50
	Perf. 14			
	Size: 22x28mm			
J59	D7	30m light violet	10.00	10.00

D8

1965	Unwmk.	Photo.	Perf. 11	
J60	D8	2m org & vio blk	.60	.50
J61	D8	8m lt bl & dk bl	1.00	.60
J62	D8	10m yel & emer	1.50	.75
J63	D8	20m lt bl & vio blk	2.00	1.25
J64	D8	40m org & emer	3.75	2.00

MILITARY STAMPS

The "British Forces" and "Army post" stamps were special issues provided at a reduced rate for the purchase and use by the British military forces in Egypt and their families for ordinary letters sent to Great Britain and Ireland by a concessionary arrangement made with the Egyptian government. From Nov. 1, 1932 to Feb. 29, 1936, in order to take advantage of the concessionary rate, it was mandatory to use Nos. M1-M11 by affixing them to the backs of envelopes. An "Egypt Postage Prepaid" handstamp was applied to the face of the envelopes. Envelopes bearing these stamps were to be posted only at British military post boxes. Envelopes bearing the 1936-39 "Army Post" stamps (Nos. M12-M15, issued by the Egyptian Postal Administration), also were sold at the concessionary rate and also were to be posted only at British military post boxes. The "Army Post" stamps were withdrawn in 1941, but the concession continued without the use of special stamps. The concession was finally canceled in 1951.

Imperf examples of Nos. M1-M4, M6, M9 (without overprint) and M10 are proofs.

M1

Unwmk.

1932, Nov. 1		Typo.	Perf. 11	
M1	M1	1pi red & deep blue	100.00	4.25

For similar design see No. M3.

M2

1932, Nov. 26		Typo.	Perf. 11½	
M2	M2	3m blk, *sage grn*	55.00	77.50

See Nos. M4, M6, M10.

M3

1933, Aug.		Typo.	Perf. 11	
M3	M3	1pi red & deep blue	32.50	1.10

Camel Type of 1932

1933, Nov. 13		Typo.	Perf. 11½	
M4	M2	3m brown lake	8.75	57.50

M4

1934, June 1		Photo.	Perf. 14½x14	
M5	M4	1pi bright carmine	50.00	1.25

See Nos. M7-M8. For overprint and surcharge see Nos. M9, M11.

Camel Type of 1932

1934, Nov. 17		Typo.	Perf. 11½	
M6	M2	3m deep blue	8.25	30.00

Type of 1934

1934, Dec. 5		Photo.	Perf. 14½x14	
M7	M4	1pi green	6.00	6.00

Type of 1934

1935, Apr. 24 — *Perf. 13½x14*
M8 M4 1pi bright carmine 2.90 3.75

Type of 1934 Overprinted in Red

1935, May 6 — *Perf. 14*
M9 M4 1pi ultramarine 325.00 240.00

Camel Type of 1932

1935, Nov. 23 Typo. — *Perf. 11½*
M10 M2 3m vermilion 2.25 42.50

No. M8 Surcharged

1935, Dec. 16 Photo. — *Perf. 13½x14*
M11 M4 3m on 1pi brt car 25.00 100.00

Fuad Type of 1927
Inscribed "Army Post"

M5

1936, Mar. 1 — **Wmk. 195**
M12 M5 3m green 2.50 2.50
M13 M5 10m carmine 5.50 .20

King Farouk — M6

1939, Dec. 16 — *Perf. 13x13½*
M14 M6 3m green 3.75 12.00
M15 M6 10m carmine rose 4.75 .20

> Catalogue values for unused stamps in this section, from this point to the end of the section, are for Never Hinged items.

United Arab Republic

Arms of UAR and Military Emblems — M7

Perf. 11x11½
1971, Apr. 15 Photo. — **Wmk. 342**
M16 M7 10m purple .30 .30

OFFICIAL STAMPS

O1

Wmk. Crescent and Star (119)
1893, Jan. 1 Typo. — *Perf. 14x13½*
O1 O1 orange brown 3.00 .20

No. O1 exists on ordinary and chalky paper.
Imperf. examples of No. O1 are proofs.

Regular Issues of 1884-93 Overprinted

1907
O2 A18 1m brown 2.40 .35
O3 A19 2m green 2.40 .20
O4 A20 3m orange 2.40 .20
O5 A22 5m car rose 6.00 .20
O6 A14 1pi ultra 4.75 .20
O7 A16 5pi gray 17.00 4.75
Nos. O2-O7 (6) 34.95 5.90

Nos. O2-O3, O5-O7 imperf. are proofs.

Overprinted

1913
O8 A22 5m carmine rose 7.50 .60
  a. Inverted overprint 90.00
  b. No period after "S" 65.00 19.00

Regular Issues Overprinted

1914-15
On Issues of 1888-1906
O9 A19 2m green 2.00 1.50
  a. Inverted overprint 42.50 42.50
  b. Double overprint 450.00
  c. No period after "S" 16.00 16.00
O10 A21 4m brown red 2.00 1.50
  a. Inverted overprint 225.00 160.00
On Issue of 1914
O11 A24 1m olive brown 1.75 1.50
  a. No period after "S" 14.00 30.00
O12 A26 3m orange 1.75 1.50
  a. No period after "S" 16.00 30.00
O13 A28 5m lake 4.75 1.50
  a. No period after "S" 17.50 26.00
  b. Two periods after "S" 17.50 26.00
Nos. O9-O13 (5) 12.25 7.50

Regular Issues Overprinted

1915, Oct.
On Issues of 1888-1906
O14 A19 2m green 3.00 5.00
  a. Inverted overprint 24.00 24.00
  b. Double overprint 30.00
O15 A21 4m brown red 7.50 9.00
On Issue of 1914
O16 A28 5m lake 10.00 1.50
  a. Pair, one without overprint 325.00
Nos. O14-O16 (3) 20.50 15.50

Regular Issues Overprinted

1922 — **Wmk. 120**
On Issue of 1921-22
O17 A24 1m olive brown 4.25 13.00
O18 A25 2m red 9.50 20.00
O19 A26 3m orange 77.50 150.00
O20 A28 5m pink 21.00 5.00
Nos. O17-O20 (4) 112.25 188.00

Regular Issues of 1921-22 Overprinted

1922
O21 A24 1m olive brn .65 2.25
O22 A25 2m red 1.00 3.25
O23 A26 3m orange 2.25 3.50

O24 A27 4m green 6.00 6.00
  a. Two periods after "H" none after "S" 1750.00 175.00
O25 A28 5m pink 3.00 .75
  a. Two periods after "H" none after "S" 75.00 75.00
O26 A29 10m deep blue 5.00 2.50
O27 A29 10m lake ('23) 7.00 2.25
  a. Two periods after "H" none after "S" 100.00 100.00
O28 A34 15m indigo 6.00 5.00
O29 A35 15m indigo 100.00 100.00
  a. Two periods after "H" none after "S" 250.00 250.00
O30 A31 50m maroon 20.00 15.00

Regular Issue of 1923 Overprinted in Black or Red

1924 — *Perf. 13½x14*
O31 A36 1m orange 1.50 1.50
O32 A36 2m gray (R) 2.00 2.00
O33 A36 3m brown 5.00 5.00
O34 A36 4m yellow green 6.00 6.00
O35 A36 5m orange brown 1.50 .75
O36 A36 10m rose 4.00 3.00
O37 A36 15m ultra 7.00 5.00
Perf. 14
O38 A36 50m myrtle green 18.00 7.00
Nos. O31-O38 (8) 45.00 30.25

O2   O3

Perf. 13x13½
1926-35 Litho. — **Wmk. 195**
Size: 18½x22mm
O39 O2 1m lt orange .75 .40
O40 O2 2m black .50 .30
O41 O2 3m olive brn 1.40 1.00
O42 O2 4m lt green 1.25 1.10
O43 O2 5m brown 1.50 .40
O44 O2 10m dull red 3.75 .40
O45 O2 10m brt vio ('34) 2.25 .45
O46 O2 15m dp blue 3.75 .90
O47 O2 15m brown vio ('34) 3.75 .80
O48 O2 20m dp blue ('35) 3.75 1.10
Perf. 13½
Size: 22½x27½mm
O49 O2 20m olive green 6.00 2.25
O50 O2 50m myrtle green 8.00 1.60
Nos. O39-O50 (12) 36.65 10.70

1938, Dec.
Size: 22½x19mm
O51 O3 1m orange .30 .30
O52 O3 2m red .30 .30
O53 O3 3m olive brown 1.25 1.25
O54 O3 4m yel green .80 .80
O55 O3 5m brown .40 .40
O56 O3 10m brt violet .50 .50
O57 O3 15m rose violet 1.25 1.25
O58 O3 20m blue 1.25 1.25
Perf. 14x13½
Size: 26½x22mm
O59 O3 50m myrtle green 3.00 2.50
Nos. O51-O59 (9) 9.05 8.55

> Catalogue values for unused stamps in this section, from this point to the end of the section, are for Never Hinged items.

Nos. O51 to O59 Overprinted in Various Colors

Overprint 19mm Wide
1952, Jan. — *Perf. 13x13½*
O60 O3 1m orange (Br) 1.75 1.75
O61 O3 2m red (Br) 1.75 1.75
O62 O3 3m olive brn (Bl) 2.00 2.00
O63 O3 4m yel green (Bl) 2.00 2.00
O64 O3 5m brown (Bl) 2.00 2.00
O65 O3 10m brt violet (Bl) 2.00 2.00
O66 O3 15m rose violet (Bl) 2.50 2.50
O67 O3 20m blue 3.00 3.00

Overprint 24½mm Wide
Perf. 14x13½
O68 O3 50m myrtle grn (RV) 6.50 6.50
Nos. O60-O68 (9) 23.50 23.50

See notes after No. 316.

United Arab Republic

O4   Arms of UAR — O5

Perf. 13x13½
1959 Litho. — **Wmk. 318**
O69 O4 10m brown violet .65 .25
O70 O4 35m chalky blue 1.75 .30

1962-63 — **Wmk. 328**
O71 O4 1m orange ('63) .30 .30
O72 O4 4m yel grn ('63) .60 .60
O73 O4 5m brown .60 .25
O74 O4 10m dk brown .75 .30
O75 O4 35m dark blue 2.25 .50
O76 O4 50m green 3.50 .60
O77 O4 100m violet ('63) 7.00 1.75
O78 O4 200m rose red ('63) 15.00 8.00
O79 O4 500m gray ('63) 22.50 15.00
Nos. O71-O79 (9) 52.50 27.30

Perf. 11½x11
1966-68 Unwmk. — **Photo.**
O80 O5 1m ultra .20 .20
O81 O5 4m brown .25 .20
O82 O5 5m olive .30 .20
O83 O5 10m brown blk 1.00 .35
O84 O5 20m magenta .60 .30
O85 O5 35m dk purple 1.00 .35
O86 O5 50m orange 1.10 .45
O87 O5 55m dk purple 1.10 .45
Wmk. 342
O88 O5 100m brt grn & brick red 2.25 1.00
O89 O5 200m blue & brick red 4.50 2.00
O90 O5 500m olive & brick red 10.00 6.25
Nos. O80-O90 (11) 22.30 11.75

1969 — **Wmk. 342**
O91 O5 10m magenta 1.10 .65

Arab Republic of Egypt

Arms of Egypt
O6   O7

Wmk. 342
1972, June 30 Photo. — *Perf. 11*
O92 O6 1m black & vio blue .30 .25
  a. 1m black & light blue ('75) .20 .20
O93 O6 10m black & car .65 .30
  a. 10m black & rose red ('76) .20 .20
O94 O6 20m black & olive .90 .40
O95 O6 50m black & orange .50 .50
O96 O6 55m black & purple 3.00 1.00

1973
O97 O6 20m lilac & sepia .90 .40
  a. 20m purple & light brown ('76) 2.50 .75
O98 O6 70m black & grn ('79) .75 .40

1982 Photo. Unwmk. — *Perf. 11*
O99 O6 30m purple & brown .30 .30
O100 O6 60m black & orange .60 .30
O101 O6 80m black & green .65 .35
Nos. O92-O101 (10) 8.55 4.25

Issued: 30m, 2/12; 60m, 2/24; 80m, 2/18.

1985-89 Photo. — *Perf. 11½*
Size: 21x25mm
O102 O7 1p vermilion .20 .20
O103 O7 2p brown .20 .20
O104 O7 3p sepia .20 .20

O105	O7	5p orange yel	.35 .30
O106	O7	8p green	.50 .35
O107	O7	10p brown olive	.20 .20
O108	O7	15p dull violet	1.00 .65
O109	O7	20p blue	.75 .75
O110	O7	25p red	.80 .80
O111	O7	30p dull violet	.60 .60
O112	O7	50p green	2.25 2.25
O113	O7	60p myrtle green	1.10 1.10
	Nos. O102-O113 (12)		8.15 7.60

Issued: 1p, 3p, 5p, 8p, 15p, 5/1/85; 20p, 50p, 4/88; 10p, 30p, 60p, 12/1/89; 2p, 25p, 1989.

1991-99   Wmk. 342   Perf. 11½x11
Size: 18x22mm

O114	O7	5p orange yellow	.20 .20
O115	O7	10p brown violet	.20 .20
O116	O7	15p brown	.20 .20
O117	O7	20p blue	.20 .20
O118	O7	20p violet	.20 .20
O119	O7	25p purple	.25 .25
O120	O7	30p dk violet	.45 .20
O121	O7	50p green	.75 .50
O122	O7	55p red	.60 .30
O123	O7	75p brown	.75 .50
O124	O7	£1 green blue	1.25 .75
O125	O7	£2 green	2.50 1.50
	Nos. O114-O125 (12)		7.55 5.05

Issued: 10p, 30p, 7/1/91; 50p, 12/1/91; 55p, 4/1/93; £1, £2, 3/22/94; No. O123, 75p, 2/1/97; No. O118, 4/11/99.

Arms Type of 1985-89
Perf. 11½x11

2001, Mar. 25   Photo.   Unwmk.
Size: 18x22mm

O127	O7	10p brown	2.00 .50

Issued: 10p, 3/25.

Arms Type of 1985-89
Perf. 11½x11

2002 ?   Photo.   Unwmk.

O131	O7	30p violet	3.00 .60

OCCUPATION STAMPS

Catalogue values for unused stamps in this section are for Never Hinged items.

For Use in Palestine

Stamps of 1939-46 Overprinted in Red, Green or Black — a

Perf. 13x13½, 13½x13
1948, May 15   Wmk. 195

N1	A77	1m yellow brn (G)	.20 .20
N2	A77	2m red org (G)	.20 .20
N3	A66	3m brown (G)	.20 .20
N4	A77	4m dp green	.20 .20
N5	A77	5m red brown (Bk)	.20 .20
N6	A66	6m lt yel grn (Bk)	.20 .20
N7	A77	10m dp violet	.20 .20
N8	A66	13m rose car (G)	.25 .25
N9	A77	15m dk violet	.25 .25
N10	A77	17m olive green	.25 .25
N11	A77	20m dk gray	.30 .30
N12	A77	22m deep blue	.40 .40
N13	A74	50pi green & sep	20.00 20.00
N14	A75	£1 dp bl & dk brn	35.00 35.00

The two lines of the overprint are more widely separated on Nos. N13 and N14.

Nos. 267-269, 237 and 238 Overprinted in Red

b

Perf. 14x13½

N15	A73	30m olive green	.60 .60
N16	A73	40m dark brown	.75 .75
N17	A73	50m Prus green	1.10 1.10
N18	A73	100m brown violet	3.00 2.50
N19	A73	200m dark violet	8.00 8.00
	Nos. N1-N19 (19)		71.30 70.80

Overprint arranged to fit size of stamps.

Nos. N1-N19 Overprinted in Black with Three Bars to Obliterate Portrait
Perf. 13x13½, 13½x13, 14x13½
1953   Wmk. 195

N20	A77	1m yellow brown	.20 .20
N21	A77	2m red orange	.20 .20
N22	A66	3m brown	.20 .20
N23	A77	4m deep green	.20 .20
N24	A77	5m red brown	.20 .20
N25	A66	6m lt yel grn	.20 .20
N26	A77	10m deep violet	.30 .30
N27	A66	13m rose carmine	.40 .40
N28	A77	15m dark violet	.40 .40
N29	A77	17m olive green	.45 .45
N30	A77	20m dark gray	.55 .55
N31	A77	22m deep blue	.70 .70
N32	A73	30m olive green	.70 .70
N33	A73	40m dark brown	1.00 1.00
N34	A73	50m Prus green	4.25 4.25
N35	A73	100m brown violet	7.25 7.25
N36	A73	200m dark violet	16.00 16.00
N37	A74	50pi green & sepia	32.50 32.50
N38	A75	£1 dp bl & dk brn	95.00 95.00
	Nos. N20-N38 (19)		160.70 160.70

Regular Issue of 1953-55 Overprinted Type "a" in Blue or Red
1954-56   Perf. 13x13½

N39	A115	1m red brown	.20 .20
N40	A115	2m dark lilac	.20 .20
N41	A115	3m brt blue (R)	.20 .20
N42	A115	4m dark green (R)	.20 .20
N43	A115	5m deep carmine	.20 .20
N44	A110	10m dark brown	.20 .20
N45	A110	15m gray (R)	.20 .20
N46	A110	17m dk grnsh bl (R)	.20 .20
N47	A110	20m purple (R) ('54)	.30 .30

Nos. 331-333 and 335-340 Overprinted in Blue or Red — c

Perf. 13½

N48	A111	30m dull green (R)	.50 .50
N49	A111	32m brt blue (R)	.60 .60
N50	A111	35m violet (R)	.70 .70
N51	A111	40m red brown	1.10 1.10
N52	A111	50m violet brown	1.25 1.25
N53	A112	100m henna brown	3.00 3.00
N54	A112	200m dk grnsh bl (R)	10.00 10.00
N55	A112	500m purple (R)	40.00 40.00
N56	A112	£1 dk grn, blk & red (R) ('56)	72.50 72.50
	Nos. N39-N56 (18)		131.55 131.55

Type of 1957 Overprinted in Red — d

1957		**Wmk. 195 Perf. 13½x13**	
N57	A127	10m blue green	2.00 2.00

Nos. 414-417 Overprinted Type "d" in Red

1957-58		**Wmk. 315 Perf. 13½**	
N58	A137	10m violet	.30 .30
		Wmk. 318	
N59	A136	1m lt bl grn ('58)	.30 .30
N60	A138	5m brown ('58)	.30 .30
N61	A137	10m violet ('58)	.30 .30
	Nos. N58-N61 (4)		1.20 1.20

United Arab Republic

Nos. 438-444 Overprinted Type "d" in Red or Green
Perf. 13½x14

1958		**Wmk. 318 Photo.**	
N62	A136	1m crimson	.30 .30
N63	A138	2m blue	.30 .30
N64	A143	3m dk red brn (G)	.30 .30
N65	A217	4m green	.30 .30
N66	A138	5m brown	.30 .30
N67	A137	10m violet	.30 .30
N68	A138	35m lt ultra	2.50 2.50
	Nos. N62-N68 (7)		4.30 4.30

Same Overprint in Red on Freedom Struggle Type of 1958

1958		**Perf. 13½x13**	
N69	A145	10m dark brown	1.10 1.10

Same Overprint in Green on Declaration of Human Rights Type

1958		**Perf. 13½x13**	
N70	A151	10m rose violet	1.10 1.10
N71	A151	35m red brown	2.00 2.00

No. 460 Overprinted Type "d" in Green

1959		**Wmk. 195 Perf. 13½**	
N72	A112	55m on 100m henna brn	1.00 1.00

World Refugee Year Type
"PALESTINE" Added in English and Arabic to Stamps of Egypt

OS1

	Perf. 13x13½ Wmk. 328		
1960			
N73	OS1	10m orange brown	.40 .40
N74	OS1	35m dk blue gray	.60 .60

Type of Regular Issue 1959-60

1960		**Perf. 13½x14**	
N75	A136	1m brown orange	.30 .30
N76	A137	4m olive gray	.30 .30
N77	A138	5m dk dull pur	.30 .30
N78	A137	10m dk olive grn	.30 .30
	Nos. N75-N78 (4)		1.20 1.20

Palestine Day Type

1961, May 15		**Perf. 13½x13**	
N79	A184	10m purple	.30 .30

WHO Day Type

1961		**Wmk. 328 Perf. 13½x13**	
N80	A182	10m blue	.30 .30

U.N.T.A.P. Type

1961, Oct. 24			
N81	A191	10m dk blue & org	.30 .30
N82	A191	35m vermilion & blk	.30 .30

Education Day Type

1961, Dec. 18		**Photo. Perf. 13½**	
N83	A194	10m red brown	.30 .30

Victory Day Type

1961, Dec. 23		**Unwmk. Perf. 11½**	
N84	A195	10m brn org & brn	.30 .30

Gaza Strip Type
Perf. 13½x13

1962, Mar. 7		**Wmk. 328**	
N85	A200	10m red brown	.30 .30

Arab Publicity Week Type

1962, Mar. 22		**Perf. 13½x13**	
N86	SP16	10m dark purple	.30 .30

Anti-Malaria Type

1962, June 20		**Photo.**	
N87	A204	10m brn & dk car rose	.30 .30
N88	A204	35m black & yellow	.50 .50

Hammarskjold Type
Perf. 11½x11

1962, Oct. 24		**Wmk. 342**	
		Portrait in Slate Blue	
N89	A214	5m bright rose	.30 .30
N90	A214	10m brown	.30 .30
N91	A214	35m blue	.50 .50
	Nos. N89-N91 (3)		1.10 1.10

Lamp Type of Regular Issue
Perf. 11x11½

1963, Feb. 20		**Unwmk.**	
N92	A217	4m dk brn, org & ultra	.30 .30

"Freedom from Hunger" Type
Perf. 11½x11, 11x11½

1963, Mar. 21		**Wmk. 342**	
N93	A220	5m lt grn & dp org	.30 .30
N94	A220	10m olive & yellow	.30 .30
N95	A220	35m dull pur, yel & blk	.50 .50
	Nos. N93-N95 (3)		1.10 1.10

Red Cross Centenary Type

Designs: 10m, Centenary emblem, bottom panel added. 35m, Globe and emblem, top and bottom panels added.

1963, May 8		**Unwmk. Perf. 11x11½**	
N96	A221	10m dk blue & crim	.30 .30
N97	A221	35m crim & dk blue	.50 .50

"Save Abu Simbel" Type, 1963

1963, Oct. 15		**Wmk. 342 Perf. 11**	
N98	A224	5m black & yellow	.30 .30
N99	A224	10m gray, blk & yellow	.30 .30
N100	A224	35m org yel & violet	.50 .50
	Nos. N98-N100 (3)		1.10 1.10

Human Rights Type

1963, Dec. 10		**Photo. Perf. 11½x11**	
N101	A228	5m dk brown & yellow	.30 .30
N102	A228	10m dp claret, gray & blk	.30 .30
N103	A228	35m lt grn, pale grn & blk	.50 .50
	Nos. N101-N103 (3)		1.10 1.10

Types of Regular Issue

1964		**Unwmk. Perf. 11**	
N104	A231	1m citron & lt vio	.30 .30
N105	A230	2m orange & slate	.30 .30
N106	A230	3m blue & ocher	.30 .30
N107	A235	4m ol gray, ol, brn & rose	.30 .30
N108	A230	5m rose & brt blue	.30 .30
a.		5m rose & dark blue	1.25 1.25
N109	A231	10m ol, rose & brn	.30 .30
N110	A230	15m lilac & yellow	.40 .40
N111	A230	20m brown blk & ol	.60 .60
N112	A231	30m dp org & ind	1.25 1.25
N113	A231	35m buff, ocher & emer	1.00 1.00
N114	A231	40m ultra & emer	1.25 1.25
N115	A231	60m grnsh bl & brn org	2.00 2.00
		Wmk. 342	
N116	A232	100m bluish blk & yel brn	3.00 3.00
	Nos. N104-N116 (13)		11.30 11.30

Arab League Council Type

1964, Jan. 13		**Photo.**	
N117	A234	10m olive & black	.30 .30

Minaret Type

1964		**Unwmk. Perf. 11**	
N118	A235	4m ol, red brn & red	.30 .30

Arab Postal Union Type

1964, Apr. 1		**Wmk. 342 Perf. 11**	
N119	A239	10m emer & ultra, *lt grn*	.30 .30

WHO Type

1964, Apr. 7			
N120	A240	10m violet blk & red	.30 .30

Minaret Type

1965, Jan. 20		**Unwmk. Perf. 11**	
N121	A255	4m green & dk brn	.30 .30

Arab League Type

1965, Mar. 22		**Wmk. 342 Perf. 11**	
N122	A258	10m green, red & blk	.30 .30
N123	A258	20m green & brown	.30 .30

World Health Day Type

1965, Apr. 7		**Wmk. 342 Perf. 11**	
N124	A259	10m brt green & crim	.30 .30

Massacre Type

1965, Apr. 9		**Photo.**	
N125	A260	10m slate blue & red	.30 .30

ITU Type

1965, May 17		**Wmk. 342 Perf. 11**	
N126	A261	5m sl grn, sl bl & yel	.30 .30
N127	A261	10m car, rose red & gray	.30 .30
N128	A261	35m vio bl, ultra & yel	.30 .30
	Nos. N126-N128 (3)		.90 .90

United Nations Type

5m, WHO Headquarters Building, Geneva. 10m, UN Refugee emblem. 35m, UNICEF emblem.

1966, Oct. 24   Wmk. 342   Perf. 11

N129	A288	5m rose & brt pur	.30	.30
N130	A288	10m yel brn & brt pur	.30	.30
N131	A288	35m brt green & brt pur	.30	.30
		Nos. N129-N131 (3)	.90	.90

Victory Day Type
Wmk. 342

1966, Dec. 23   Photo.   Perf. 11½

N132	A290	10m olive & car rose	.30	.30

Arab Publicity Week Type
Perf. 11x11½

1967, Mar. 22   Photo.   Wmk. 342

N133	A294	10m vio blue & brn	.30	.30

Labor Day Type
Perf. 11½x11

1967, May 1   Photo.   Wmk. 342

N134	A296	10m olive & sepia	.30	.30

OCCUPATION AIR POST STAMPS

> Catalogue values for unused stamps in this section are for Never Hinged items.

Nos. C39-C50 Overprinted Type "b" in Black, Carmine or Red

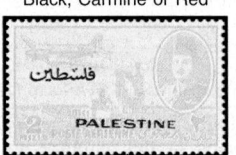

Perf. 13x13½

1948, May 15   Wmk. 195

NC1	AP3	2m red org (Bk)	.25	.25
NC2	AP3	3m dk brn (C)	.25	.25
NC3	AP3	5m red brn (Bk)	.25	.25
NC4	AP3	7m dp yel org (Bk)	.50	.50
NC5	AP3	8m green (C)	.50	.50
NC6	AP3	10m violet	.60	.60
NC7	AP3	20m brt bl	1.00	1.00
NC8	AP3	30m brn vio (Bk)	2.00	2.00
NC9	AP3	40m car rose (Bk)	1.50	1.50
NC10	AP3	50m Prus grn	2.00	2.00
NC11	AP3	100m olive grn	4.00	4.00
NC12	AP3	200m dark gray	10.00	10.00
		Nos. NC1-NC12 (12)	22.85	22.85

Nos. NC1-NC12 Overprinted in Black with Three Bars to Obliterate Portrait

1953

NC13	AP3	2m red org	.70	.70
NC14	AP3	3m dk brn	.50	.50
NC15	AP3	5m red brn	4.00	4.00
NC16	AP3	7m dp yel org	.50	.50
NC17	AP3	8m green	.60	.60
NC18	AP3	10m violet	.50	.50
NC19	AP3	20m brt bl	1.00	1.00
NC20	AP3	30m brn vio	1.25	1.25
NC21	AP3	40m car rose	4.50	4.50
NC22	AP3	50m Prus grn	4.50	4.50
NC23	AP3	100m olive grn	12.00	12.00
NC24	AP3	200m dk gray	6.00	6.00
		Nos. NC13-NC24 (12)	36.05	36.05

Nos. NC1-NC3, NC6, NC10, NC11 with Additional Overprint in Various Colors

Overprinted in Black with Three Bars to Obliterate Portrait

1953

NC25	AP3	2m red org (Bk + Bl)	.50	.50
NC26	AP3	3m dk brn (Bk + RV)	10.00	10.00
NC27	AP3	5m red brn (Bk)	2.00	2.00
NC28	AP3	10m vio (R + G)	19.00	19.00
NC29	AP3	50m Prus grn (R + RV)	5.00	5.00
NC30	AP3	100m ol grn (R + Bk)	37.50	37.50
		Nos. NC25-NC30 (6)	74.00	74.00

Nos. C65-C66 Overprinted Type "b" in Black or Red

1955   Wmk. 195   Perf. 13x13½

NC31	AP4	5m red brn	4.00	4.00
NC32	AP4	15m ol grn (R)	4.75	4.75

United Arab Republic

OAP1

Designs: 80m, Al Azhar University. 115m, Temple of Queen Nefertari, Abu Simbel. 140m, Ramses II, Abu Simbel.

Perf. 11½x11

1963, Oct. 24   Photo.   Wmk. 342

NC33	OAP1	80m blk & brt bl	2.25	2.25
NC34	OAP1	115m blk & yel	3.25	3.25
NC35	OAP1	140m bl, ultra & org red	4.00	4.00
		Nos. NC33-NC35 (3)	9.50	9.50

Cairo Tower Type, 1964

1964, Nov. 2   Unwmk.   Perf. 11x11½

NC36	AP11	50m dl vio & lt bl	1.00	1.00

World Meteorological Day Type

1965, Mar. 23   Wmk. 342   Perf. 11

NC37	AP12	80m dk bl & org	2.00	2.00

Tutankhamen Type of 1965

1965, July 1   Photo.   Perf. 11

NC38	AP13	10m brn org & brt grn	.90	.90

OCCUPATION SPECIAL DELIVERY STAMP

> Catalogue values for unused stamps in this section are for Never Hinged items.

No. E4 Overprinted Type "b" in Carmine

1948   Wmk. 195   Perf. 13x13½

NE1	SD1	40m dl brn & pale gray	6.00	6.00

OCCUPATION POSTAGE DUE STAMPS

> Catalogue values for unused stamps in this section are for Never Hinged items.

Postage Due Stamps of Egypt, 1927-41, Overprinted Type "a" in Black or Rose

1948   Wmk. 195   Perf. 13x13½

NJ1	D7	2m orange	.50	.50
NJ2	D7	4m green (R)	.50	.50
NJ3	D7	6m gray green	.50	.50
NJ4	D7	8m brown violet	.75	.75
NJ5	D7	10m brick red	.75	.75
NJ6	D7	12m rose lake	.75	.75

Overprinted Type "b" in Red
Perf. 14
Size: 22x28mm

NJ7	D7	30m purple	2.25	2.25
		Nos. NJ1-NJ7 (7)	6.00	6.00

ELOBEY, ANNOBON AND CORISCO

ˌel-ə-ˈbā, ˌan-ə-ˈbän and kə-ˈris-ˌkō

LOCATION — A group of islands near the Guinea Coast of western Africa
GOVT. — Spanish colonial possessions administered as part of the Continental Guinea District. A second district under the same governor-general included Fernando Po.
AREA — 13¾ sq. mi.
POP. — 2,950 (estimated 1910)

CAPITAL — Santa Isabel

100 Centimos = 1 Peseta

King Alfonso XIII — A1

1903   Unwmk.   Typo.   Perf. 14
Control Numbers on Back

1	A1	¼c carmine	.70	.50
2	A1	½c dk violet	.70	.50
3	A1	1c black	.70	.50
4	A1	2c red	.70	.50
5	A1	3c dk green	.70	.50
6	A1	4c dk blue grn	.70	.50
7	A1	5c violet	.70	.50
8	A1	10c rose lake	1.50	1.50
9	A1	15c orange buff	4.25	1.60
10	A1	25c dark blue	7.50	5.50
11	A1	50c red brown	9.25	9.75
12	A1	75c black brn	9.25	13.00
13	A1	1p orange red	14.50	18.50
14	A1	2p chocolate	39.00	55.00
15	A1	3p dp olive grn	60.00	67.50
16	A1	4p claret	140.00	95.00
17	A1	5p blue green	160.00	97.50
18	A1	10p dull blue	300.00	150.00
		Nos. 1-18 (18)	750.15	518.35
		Set, never hinged	1,150.	

Dated "1905"

1905
Control Numbers on Back

19	A1	1c carmine	1.25	.70
20	A1	2c dp violet	5.00	.70
21	A1	3c black	1.25	.70
22	A1	4c dull red	1.25	.70
23	A1	5c dp green	1.25	.70
24	A1	10c blue grn	4.50	.90
25	A1	15c violet	5.00	4.75
26	A1	25c rose lake	5.00	4.75
27	A1	50c orange buff	9.00	7.25
28	A1	75c dark blue	9.00	7.25
29	A1	1p red brown	18.50	16.00
30	A1	2p black brn	20.00	22.50
31	A1	3p orange red	20.00	23.00
32	A1	4p dk brown	150.00	72.50
33	A1	5p bronze grn	160.00	80.00
34	A1	10p claret	360.00	225.00
		Nos. 19-34 (16)	771.00	467.40
		Set, never hinged	1,250.	

Nos. 19-22 Surcharged in Black or Red

1906

35	A1	10c on 1c rose (Bk)	10.00	6.00
a.		Inverted surcharge	10.00	6.00
b.		Value omitted	30.00	16.00
c.		Frame omitted	16.00	7.25
d.		Double surcharge	10.00	6.00
e.		Surcharged "15 cents"	30.00	16.00
f.		Surcharged "25 cents"	52.50	22.50
g.		Surcharged "50 cents"	37.50	22.50
h.		"1906" omitted	17.50	7.25
36	A1	15c on 2c dp vio (R)	10.00	6.00
a.		Frame omitted	12.00	5.50
b.		Surcharged "25 cents"	16.00	6.00
c.		Inverted surcharge	10.00	6.00
d.		Double surcharge	10.00	6.00
37	A1	25c on 3c blk (R)	10.00	6.00
a.		Inverted surcharge	10.00	6.00
b.		Double surcharge	10.00	6.00
c.		Surcharged "15 cents"	16.00	6.00
d.		Surcharged "50 cents"	25.00	11.00
38	A1	50c on 4c red (Bk)	10.00	6.00
a.		Inverted surcharge	10.00	6.00
b.		Value omitted	35.00	17.50
c.		Frame omitted	17.50	8.00
d.		Double surcharge	10.00	6.00
e.		"1906" omitted	17.50	8.00
f.		Surcharged "10 cents"	32.50	16.00
h.		Surcharged "25 cents"	32.50	16.00
		Nos. 35-38 (4)	40.00	24.00

Eight other surcharges were prepared but not issued: 10c on 50c, 75c, 1p, 2p and 3p; 15c on 50c and 5p; 50c on 5c.

Exist with surcharges in different colors; #35 in blue, red or violet, #36 in black or violet, #37 in black or violet, #38 in blue, violet or red. Value, set of 10, $135.

King Alfonso XIII — A2

1907
Control Numbers on Back

39	A2	1c dk violet	.50	.40
40	A2	2c black	.50	.40
41	A2	3c red orange	.50	.40
42	A2	4c dk green	.50	.40
43	A2	5c blue green	.50	.40
44	A2	10c violet	5.00	5.00
45	A2	15c carmine	1.60	1.60
46	A2	25c orange	1.60	1.60
47	A2	50c blue	1.60	1.60
48	A2	75c brown	5.25	2.25
49	A2	1p black brn	8.50	4.25
50	A2	2p orange red	11.50	6.75
51	A2	3p dk brown	11.00	7.50
52	A2	4p bronze grn	11.50	7.00
53	A2	5p claret	17.00	7.50
54	A2	10p rose	42.50	22.50
		Nos. 39-54 (16)	119.55	69.55
		Set, never hinged	190.00	

Stamps of 1907 Surcharged

1908-09
Black Surcharge

55	A2	5c on 3c red org ('09)	2.25	1.25
56	A2	5c on 4c dk grn ('09)	2.25	1.25
57	A2	5c on 10c violet	4.75	5.00
58	A2	25c on 10c violet	25.00	15.00
		Nos. 55-58 (4)	34.25	22.50

1910
Red Surcharge

59	A2	5c on 1c dark violet	1.75	.90
60	A2	5c on 2c black	1.75	.90

Nos. 55-60 exist with surcharge inverted (value set, $125 unused or used); with double surcharge, one black, one red (value set, $300 unused or used); with "PARA" omitted (value set, $150.00 unused or used).

The same 5c surcharge was also applied to Nos. 45-54, but these were not issued (value set, $250).

In 1909, stamps of Spanish Guinea replaced those of Elobey, Annobon and Corisco.

CORREOS
10 cen de peseta
1909

Revenue stamps surcharged as above were unauthorized although some were postally used.

EPIRUS

i-'pī-rəs

LOCATION — Southeastern Europe comprising parts of Greece and Albania.

This territory formerly belonged to Turkey but is now divided between Greece and Albania. The northern part of the Greek section, now a part of Albania, set up a provisional government during 1912-13 and issued postage stamps but it collapsed in 1916, following Greek occupation. The name "Epirus" is taken from the Greek word meaning "Mainland."

100 Lepta = 1 Drachma

Chimarra Issue

Double-headed Eagle, Skull and Crossbones — A1

Handstamped
1914 (Feb.)   **Unwmk.**   *Imperf.*
Control Mark in Blue
Without Gum

1	A1	1 l black & blue	210.00	150.00
2	A1	5 l blue & red	210.00	150.00
3	A1	10 l red & blk	210.00	150.00
4	A1	25 l blue & red	210.00	150.00
		Nos. 1-4 (4)	840.00	600.00

All values exist without control mark. This mark is a solid blue oval, about 12x8mm, containing the colorless Greek letters "SP," the first two letters of Spiromilios, the Chimarra commander.

All four exist with value inverted and the 1, 5 and 10 l with value double.

Some experts question the official character of this issue. Reprints exist, using original handstamps. Counterfeits are plentiful.

Provisional Government Issues

Infantryman with Rifle
A2   A3

Serrate Roulette 13½
1914 (Mar.)				**Litho.**
5	A2	1 l orange	.45	.45
6	A2	5 l green	.45	.45
7	A3	10 l carmine	.45	.45
8	A3	25 l deep blue	.45	.45
9	A2	50 l brown	1.00	1.00
10	A2	1d violet	2.00	2.00
11	A2	2d blue	11.00	11.00
12	A2	5d gray green	13.50	13.50
		Nos. 5-12 (8)	29.30	29.30

15 values, 5 l to 5d, of Turkish stamps surcharged "Epirus Autonomous" and new values in Greek were on sale for a few days in Argyrokastron (Gjirokaster).

Flag of Epirus — A5

1914 (Aug.)				
15	A5	1 l brown & blue	.55	.65
16	A5	5 l green & blue	.55	.65
17	A5	10 l rose red & blue	.60	.70
18	A5	25 l dk blue & blue	.75	.75
19	A5	50 l violet & blue	.95	1.25
20	A5	1d carmine & blue	4.75	7.00

21	A5	2d orange & blue	1.40	2.00
22	A5	5d dk green & blue	9.00	9.25
		Nos. 15-22 (8)	18.55	22.25

Koritsa Issue

A7

1914				
26	A7	25 l dk blue & blue	5.00	4.75
27	A7	50 l violet & blue	9.00	11.00

Chimarra Issue

1911-23 Issues of Greece Overprinted

1914 (Aug.)				
34	A24	1 l green	25.00	25.00
35	A25	2 l carmine	22.50	22.50
36	A24	3 l vermilion	22.50	22.50
37	A26	5 l green	25.00	25.00
38	A24	10 l carmine	25.00	25.00
39	A25	20 l slate	47.50	47.50
40	A25	25 l blue	77.50	77.50
41	A26	50 l violet brn	100.00	100.00
		Nos. 34-41 (8)	345.00	345.00

The 2 l and 3 l are engraved stamps of the 1911-21 issue, the others are lithographed stamps of the 1912-23 issue.

Overprint reads: "Greek Chimarra 1914."

Stamps of this issue are with or without a black monogram (S.S., for S. Spiromilios) in manuscript. Counterfeits are plentiful.

Stamps of the following designs were not regularly issued for postal purposes in the opinion of the editors.

From 1914: 1st design, 3 varieties. 2nd design, 6 varieties. 3rd design, 7 varieties. 4th and 5th designs, 15 varieties.

From 1920: 6th design, 4 varieties.

OCCUPATION STAMPS

Issued under Greek Occupation
Greek Occupation Stamps of 1913 Overprinted Horizontally

Serrate Roulette 13½
1914-15		**Black Overprint**		**Unwmk.**
N1	O1	1 l brown	.80	.80
N2	O2	2 l red	.80	.80
b.		2 l rose	1.25	1.25
N4	O2	3 l orange	.80	.80
N5	O1	5 l green	2.00	2.00
N6	O1	10 l rose red	2.75	2.75
N7	O1	20 l violet	7.50	7.50
N8	O2	25 l pale blue	2.75	2.75
N9	O1	30 l gray green	11.50	11.50
N10	O2	40 l indigo	14.50	14.50
N11	O1	50 l dark blue	16.00	16.00
N12	O2	1d violet brown	72.50	72.50
		Nos. N1-N12 (11)	131.90	131.90

The overprint exists double on 6 denominations (1 l, 2 l both, 3 l, 5 l, 10 l and 1d); inverted on all but 25 l, 40 l; double, one inverted, 5 l. Values, $15 and up.

Red Overprint
N1a	O1	1 l brown		5.75
N2a	O2	2 l red		5.75
N4a	O2	3 l orange		5.75
N5a	O1	5 l green		5.75

Nos. N1a-N5a were not issued. Exist canceled.

Regular Issues of Greece, 1911-23, Overprinted

On Issue of 1911-21

1916				**Engr.**
N17	A24	3 l vermilion	7.50	7.50
N18	A26	30 l carmine rose	62.50	60.00
N19	A27	1d ultra	50.00	50.00
N20	A27	2d vermilion	62.50	62.50
N21	A27	3d carmine rose	75.00	75.00
N22	A27	5d ultra	400.00	400.00
a.		Double overprint	600.00	600.00
		Nos. N17-N22 (6)	657.50	655.00

Overprints on Nos. N18-N21 read up, on No. N22 reads down. Overprint on N17 exists reading down but most read up.

On Issue of 1912-23

1916				**Litho.**
N23	A24	1 l green	.90	.90
N24	A25	2 l carmine	.90	.90
N25	A24	3 l vermilion	1.40	1.40
N26	A26	5 l green	.90	.90
N27	A24	10 l carmine	1.25	1.25

N28	A25	20 l slate	1.50	1.50
N29	A25	25 l blue	2.25	2.25
N30	A26	30 l rose	7.50	7.50
N31	A25	40 l indigo	7.25	7.25
N32	A26	50 l violet brown	9.50	9.50
		Nos. N23-N32 (10)	33.35	33.35

Overprints on Nos. N28-N29, N31-N32 read up. Nos. N23-N27 N30 exist reading down but most read up.

In each sheet there are two varieties in the overprint: the "I" in "Epirus" omitted and an inverted "L" in place of the first letter of the word.

Counterfeits exist of Nos. N1-N32.

Postage stamps issued in 1940-41, during Greek occupation, are listed under Greece.

EQUATORIAL GUINEA

ē-kwə-'tō-ē-əl 'gi-nē

LOCATION — Gulf of Guinea, West Africa
GOVT. — Republic
AREA — 10,832 sq. mi.
POP. — 465,746 (1999 est.)
CAPITAL — Malabo

The Spanish provinces Fernando Po and Rio Muni united and became independent as the Republic of Equatorial Guinea, Oct. 12, 1968.

100 Centimos = 1 Peseta

100 centimos = 1 ekuele, bipkwele is plural (1973)

100 centimes = 1 CFA franc (1985)

Catalogue values for all unused stamps in this country are for Never Hinged items.

Clasped Hands and Laurel — A1   Pres. Francisco Macias Nguema — A2

1968, Oct. 12		**Unwmk.** Photo.		**Perf. 13**
1	A1	1p dp bl, gold & sep	.30	.30
2	A1	1.50p dk grn, gold & brn	.30	.30
3	A1	6p cop red, gold & brn	.30	.30
		Nos. 1-3 (3)	.90	.90

Attainment of independence, Oct. 12, 1968.

1970, Jan. 27				**Perf. 13x12½**
4	A2	50c dl org, brn & crim	.20	.20
5	A2	1p pink, grn & lil	.20	.20
6	A2	1.50p pale ol, brn & bl grn	.25	.20
7	A2	2p buff, grn & ol	.25	.20
8	A2	2.50p pale grn, dk grn & dk bl	.30	.20
9	A2	10p bis, Prus bl & vio brn	1.00	.20
10	A2	25p gray, blk & brn	2.10	.20
		Nos. 4-10 (7)	4.30	1.40

Pres. Macias Nguema and Cock — A3

1971, Apr.		**Photo.**		**Perf. 13**
11	A3	3p lt bl & multi	.25	.20
12	A3	5p buff & multi	.30	.20
13	A3	10p pale lilac & multi	.70	.20
14	A3	25p pale grn & multi	1.25	.20
		Nos. 11-14 (4)	2.50	.80

2nd anniv. of independence, Oct. 12, 1970.

Torch, Bow and Arrows — A4

1972   **Photo.**   **Perf. 11½**
15 A4 50p ocher & multi   1.50 .50
"3rd Triumphal Year."

Apollo 15, set of seven, 1p, 3p, 5p, 8p, 10p, airmail 15p, 25p, plus two airmail semi-postal gold foil perf. 200p+25p, imperf. 250p+50p, and two souv. sheets, perf. 25p+200p, imperf. 50p+250p, issued Jan. 28. Nos. 7201-7211.

1972 Winter Olympics, Sapporo, set of seven, 1p, 2p, 3p, 5p, 8p, airmail 15p, 50p, plus two airmail semi-postal gold foil perf., imperf., 200p+25p, 250p+50p, and two souv. sheets, perf. 200p+25p, imperf. 250p+50p, issued Feb. 3, 1972. Nos. 7212-7222.

Christmas, paintings, set of seven, 1p, 3p, 5p, 8p, 10p, airmail 15p, 25p, plus two airmail semi-postal gold foil perf. 200p+25p, imperf. 250p+50p, and two souv. sheets, perf. 25p+200p, imperf. 50p+250p (Virgin and Child by da Vinci, Murillo, Raphael, Mabuse, van der Weyden, Durer), issued Feb. 20. Nos. 7223-7233.

Easter, set of seven, 1p, 3p, 5p, 8p, 10p, airmail 15p, 25p, plus two airmail semi-postal gold foil perf., imperf., 200p+25p, 250p+50p (designs by Velazquez and El Greco), two souv. sheets, perf. (25p, 200p), and imperf. 250p+50p, issued Apr. 28. Nos. 7234-7244.

1972 Summer Olympics, Munich, set of seven, 1p, 2p, 3p, 5p, 8p, airmail 15p, 50p, plus two airmail semi-postal souv. sheets, perf. 200p+25p, imperf. 250p+50p, and presentation folder with two gold foil, perf. 200p+25p, imperf. 250p+50p, issued May 5, 1972. Nos. 7245-7255.

Gold Medal Winners, Sapporo, set of seven, 1p, 2p, 3p, 5p, 8p, airmail 15p, 50p, plus 12 airmail semi-postal gold foil perf. 200p+25p (6), imperf. 250p+50p (6), imperf. souv. sheet 250p+50p, and perf. souv. sheet of two (25p, 200p), issued May 25. Nos. 7256-7276.

Black Gold Medal Winners, Munich, set of seven, 1p, 2p, 3p, 5p, 8p, airmail 15p, 50p, plus 18 gold foil airmail semi-postal perf. 200p+25p (9), imperf. 250p+50p (9), and two souv. sheets, perf. 200p+25p, imperf. 250p+50p, issued June 26. Nos. 7277-72103.

Olympic Games, Regatta in Kiel and Oberschleissheim, set of seven, 1p, 2p, 3p, 5p, 8p, airmail 15p, 50p, plus four airmail semi-postal gold foil, perf. 200p+25p (2), imperf. 250p+50p (2), and two souv. sheets, perf. 200p+25p, imperf. 250p+50p, issued July 25. Nos. 72104-72116.

1972 Summer Olympics, Munich, set of seven, 1p, 2p, 3p, 5p, 8p, airmail 15p, 50p, plus two airmail semi-postal souv. sheets, perf. 200p+25p, imperf. 250p+50p, issued Aug. 10, 1972; and 20 gold foil, perf. 200p+25p (10), imperf. 250p+50p (10), issued Aug. 17. Nos. 72117-72145.

Olympic Equestrian Events, set of seven, 1p, 2p, 3p, 5p, 8p, airmail 15p, 50p, plus two airmail semi-postal souv. sheets, perf. 200p+25p, imperf. 250p+50p, two gold foil, perf. 200p+25p, imperf. 250p+50p, four gold foil souv. sheets of two, 200p+25p (2 perf., 2 imperf.), and 16 souv. sheets, perf. 200p+25p (8), imperf. 250p+50p (8), issued Aug. 24. Nos. 72146-72176.

Japanese Railroad Cent. (locomotives), set of seven, 1p, 3p, 5p, 8p, 10p, airmail 15p, 25p, plus 2 airmail semi-postal souv. sheets, perf. 200p+25p, imperf. 250p+50p, 11 gold foil souv. sheets of 1, perf. 200p+25p (9), imperf. 200p+25p (2), and 2 souv. sheets of 2, perf., imperf., 200p+25p, issued Sept. 21. Nos. 72177-72198.

Gold Medal Winners, Munich, set of seven, 1p, 2p, 3p, 5p, 8p, airmail 15p, 50p, plus two airmail semi-postal souv. sheets, perf. 200p+25p, imperf. 250p+50p, and four gold foil souv. sheets, perf. 200p+25p (2), imperf. 250p+50p (2), issued Oct. 30. Nos. 72199-72211.

Christmas and 500th Birth Anniv. of Lucas Cranach, Madonnas and Christmas seals, set of seven, 1p, 3p, 5p, 8p, 10p, airmail 15p, 25p (Giotto, Schongauer, Fouquet, de Morales, Fini, David, Sassetta), plus two airmail semi-postal souv. sheets, perf. 200p+25p, imperf. 250p+50p, 12 gold foil souv. sheets, perf. 200p+25p (6), imperf. 250p+50p (6), two souv. sheets of two, perf., imperf., 200p+25p, and ovptd. 200p+25p stamp, issued Nov. 22. Nos. 72212-72234.

American and Russian Astronaut Memorial, set of seven, 1p, 3p, 5p, 8p, 10p, airmail 15p, 25p, plus two airmail semi-postal souv. sheets, perf. 200p+25p, imperf. 250p+50p, and four gold foil ovptd. "Apollo 16 and 17" perf. 200p+25p (2), imperf. 250p+50p (2), issued Dec. 14. Nos. 72235-72247.

United Natl. Workers' Party Emblem — A5

1973   **Litho.**   **Perf. 13½x13**
16 A5 1p multi   .25 .25
17 A5 1.50p multi   .25 .25
18 A5 2p multi   .25 .25
19 A5 4p multi   .25 .25
20 A5 5p multi   .25 .25
    Nos. 16-20 (5)   1.25 1.25

Natl. Independence, 4th Anniv. — A6

Pres. Macias Nguema and: 1.50p, Agriculture. 2p, 4p, Education. 3p, 5p, Natl. defense.

1973   **Perf. 13½**
21 A6 1.50p multi   .25 .25
22 A6 2p multi   .25 .25
23 A6 3p multi   .25 .25
24 A6 4p multi   .25 .25
25 A6 5p multi   .25 .25
    Nos. 21-25 (5)   1.25 1.25

1973
Transatlantic Yacht Race, set of seven, 1p, 2p, 3p, 5p, 8p, airmail 15p, 50p, and two airmail semi-postal souv. sheets, perf. 200p+25p, imperf. 250p+50p, issued Jan. 22. Nos. 7301-7309.

Renoir paintings, set of seven, 1p, 2p, 3p, 5p, 8p, airmail 15p, 50p, plus two airmail semi-postal gold foil, perf. 200p+25p, imperf. 250p+50p, and two souv. sheets, perf. 200p+25p, imperf. 250p+50p, issued Feb. 22. Nos. 7310-7320.

Conquest of Venus (spacecraft), set of seven, 1p, 3p, 5p, 8p, 10p, airmail 5p, 25p, and two airmail semi-postal souv. sheets, perf. 200p+25p, imperf. 250p+50p, issued Mar. 22. Nos. 7321-7329.

Apollo 11-17 Flights, gold foil airmail semi-postal souv. sheets, perf. 200p+25p (7), 250p+50p (7), and four souv. sheets of two, perf. 200p+25p (2), imperf. 250p+50p (2), issued Mar. 22. Nos. 7330-7347.

Easter, paintings, set of seven, 1p, 3p, 5p, 8p, 10p, airmail 15p, 25p (Verrocchio, Perugino, Tintoretto, Witz, Pontormo), plus two airmail semi-postal souv. sheets, perf. 200p+25p, imperf. 250p+50p, and four gold foil issue of 1972 souv. sheets ovptd., perf. 200p+25p (2), imperf. 250p+50p (2), issued Apr. 25. Nos. 7348-7360.

Copernicus, 500th birth anniv. (US and USSR space explorations), four gold foil airmail semi-postal souv. sheets, perf. 200p+25p (2), imperf. 250p+50p (2), issued May 15. Nos. 7361-7364.

Tour de France bicycle race, set of seven, 1p, 2p, 3p, 5p, 8p, airmail 15p, 50p, and two airmail semi-postal souv. sheets, perf. 200p+25p, imperf. 250p+50p, issued May 22. Nos. 7365-7373.

Paintings, set of seven, 1p, 2p, 3p, 5p, 8p, airmail 15p, 50p, and two airmail semi-postal souv. sheets, perf. 200p+25p, imperf. 250p+50p, issued June 29. Nos. 7374-7382.

1974 World Cup Soccer Championships, Munich, set of nine, 5c, 10c, 15c, 20c, 25c, 55c, 60c, airmail 5p, 70p, and two airmail souv. sheets, perf. 130p, imperf. 200p, issued Aug. 30. Nos. 7383-7393.

Rubens paintings, set of seven, 1p, 2p, 3p, 5p, 8p, airmail 15p, 50p, and two airmail semi-postal souv. sheets, perf. (25p, 200p), imperf. (50p, 250p), issued Sept. 23. Nos. 7394-73102.

1974 World Cup Soccer Championships, Munich, four gold foil airmail souv. sheets, perf. 130e (2), imperf. 200e (2), and two souv. sheets of two, perf. 130e, imperf. 200e, issued Oct. 24. Nos. 73103-73108.

Christmas, paintings, set of seven, 1p, 3p, 5p, 8p, 10p, airmail 15p, 25p, and two airmail semi-postal souv. sheets, perf. 200p+25p, imperf. 250p+50p (Nativity, by van der Weyden, Bosco, de Carvajal, Mabuse, Lucas Jordan, P. Goecke, Maino, Fabriano, Lochner), issued Oct. 30. Nos. 73109-73117.

Apollo Program and J.F. Kennedy, two gold foil airmail semi-postals, perf. 200p+25p, imperf. 250p+50p, and two souv. sheets, perf. 200p+25p, imperf. 250p+50p, issued Nov. 10. Nos. 73118-73121.

World Cup Soccer (famous players), set of nine, 30c, 35c, 40c, 45c, 50c, 65c, 70c, airmail 8p, 60p, and two airmail souv. sheets, perf. 130p, imperf. 200p, issued Nov. 20. Nos. 73122-73132.

Princess Anne's Wedding, six gold foil airmail souv. sheets, perf., imperf., two sheets of one, each 250e, one sheet of two 250e, issued Dec. 17. Nos. 73133-73141.

Pablo Picasso Memorial (Blue Period paintings), set of seven, 30c, 35c, 40c, 45c, 50c, airmail 8e, 60e, and two airmail souv. sheets, perf. 130e, imperf. 200e, issued Dec. 20. Nos. 73142-73150.

1974
Copernicus, 500th birth anniv., set of seven, 5c, 10c, 15c, 20c, 4e, airmail 10e, 70e, two airmail souv. sheets, perf. 130e, imperf. 200e, issued Feb. 8, 1974; eight gold foil airmail souv. sheets, perf. 130e (3), 250e, imperf.

200e (3), 300e, and four souv. sheets of two, perf. 250e (2), imperf. 250e (2), issued Apr. 10. Nos. 7401-7421.

World Cup Soccer Championships (final games), set of nine, 75c, 80c, 85c, 90c, 95c, 1e, 1.25e, airmail 10e, 50e, and two airmail souv. sheets, perf. 130e, imperf. 200e, issued Feb. 28. Nos. 7422-7432.

Easter, paintings, set of seven, 1p, 3p, 5p, 8p, 10p, airmail 15p, 25p (Fra Angelico, Castagno, Allori, Multscher, della Francesca, Pleydenwurff, Correggio), and two airmail semi-postal souv. sheets, perf. 200p+25p, imperf. 250p+50p, issued Mar. 27. Nos. 7433-7441.

Holy Year 1975 (famous churches), set of seven, 5c, 10c, 15c, 20c, 3.50e, airmail 10e, 70e, and two airmail souv. sheets, perf. 130e, imperf. 200e, issued Apr. 11. Nos. 7442-7450.

World Cup Soccer (contemporary players), set of nine, 1.50, 1.75, 2, 2.25, 2.50, 3, 3.50e, airmail 10, 60e, and 2 airmail souv. sheets of 2, perf. (2x65e), imperf. (2x100e), issued Apr. 30. Nos. 7451-7461.

UPU Cent. (transportation from messenger to rocket), set of seven, 60c, 70c, 80c, 1e, 1.50e, airmail 30e, 50e, and two airmail souv. sheets, perf. 225e, imperf. (150e, 150e), issued May 30; three airmail deluxe souv. sheets, 130e, and 2x130e, issued June 8. Nos. 7462-7472A.

Picasso Memorial (Pink Period paintings), set of seven, 55c, 60c, 65c, 70c, 75c, airmail 10e, 50e, and two airmail souv. sheets, perf. 130e, imperf. 200e, issued June 28. Nos. 7473-7481.

World Cup Soccer Championships, gold foil airmail souv. sheets, four sheets of one, 130e (2), 250e (2), two sheets of two (2x130e; 2x250e), issued July 8. Nos. 7482-7487.

Aleksander Solzhenitsyn, two gold foil airmail souv. sheets, perf. 250e, imperf. 300e, issued July 25. Nos. 7488-7489.

Opening of American West, set of seven, 30c, 35c, 40c, 45c, 50c, airmail 8p, 60p, and two souv. sheets, perf. 130p, imperf. 200p, issued July 30. Nos. 7490-7498.

Flowers, set of 14, 5c, 10c, 15c, 20c, 25c, 1p, 3p, 5p, 8p, 10p, airmail 5p, 15p, 25p, 70p, and 4 airmail souv. sheets, perf. 130e, 25p+200p, imperf. 200p, 50p+250p, issued Aug. 20. Nos. 7499-74116.

Christmas, set of seven, 60c, 70c, 80c, 1e, 1.50e, airmail 30e, 50e, and two souv. sheets, perf. 225e, imperf. 300e, issued Sept. 16. Nos. 74117-74125.

Barcelona Soccer Team, 75th anniv., set of seven, 1e, 3e, 5e, 8e, 10e, airmail 15e, 60e, miniature sheet of seven plus label, two airmail souv. sheets, perf. 200e, imperf. 300e, and two gold foil airmail souv. sheets, perf., imperf., 200e each, issued Sept. 25. Nos. 74126-74137.

UPU Cent. and ESPANA 75, set of seven, 1.25e, 1.50e, 1.75e, 2e, 2.25e, airmail 35e, 50e, and 2 airmail souv. sheets, perf. 225e, imperf. 300e, issued Oct. 9; 6 gold foil sheets, perf. 250e, 250e, 2x250e, imperf. 300e, 300e, 2x300e, issued Oct. 14. Nos. 74138-74152.

Nature Protection
Australian Animals, set of seven, 80c, 85c, 90c, 95c, 1e, airmail 15e, 40e, and two airmail souv. sheets, perf. 130e, imperf. 200e, issued Oct. 25. Nos. 74153-74161.

African Animals, set of seven, 55c, 60c, 65c, 70c, 75c, airmail 10e, 70e, and two airmail souv. sheets, perf. 130e, imperf. 200e, issued Nov. 6. Nos. 74162-74170.

Australian and South American Birds, set of 14, 1.25p, 1.50p, 1.75p, 2p, 2.25p, 2.50p, 2.75p, 3p, 3.50p, 4p, airmail 20p, 25p, 30p, 35p, and four souv. sheets, perf. 130p (2), imperf. 200p (2), issued Nov. 26. Nos. 74171-74188.

Endangered Species, set of 15, 10c, 15c, 20c, 25c, 30c, 35c, 40c, 45c, 50c, 55c, 60c, 1e, 2e, airmail 10e, 70e, se-tenant in sheet of 15, issued Dec. 17. Nos. 74189-74203.

Monkeys, various species, set of 16, 5c, 10c, 15c, 20c, 25c, 30c, 35c, 40c, 45c, 50c, 55c, 60c, 1e, 2e, airmail 10e, 70e, se-tenant in sheet of 16, issued Dec. 27. Nos. 74204-74219.

Cats, various species, set of 16, 5c, 10c, 15c, 20c, 25c, 30c, 35c, 40c, 45c, 50c, 55c, 60c, 1e, 2e, airmail 10e, 70e, se-tenant in sheet of 16, issued Dec. 27. Nos. 74220-74235.

Fish, various species, set of 16, 5c, 10c, 15c, 20c, 25c, 30c, 35c, 40c, 45c, 50c, 55c, 60c, 1e, 2e, airmail 10e, 70e, se-tenant in sheet of 16, issued Dec. 27. Nos. 74236-74251.

Butterflies, various species, set of 16, 5c, 10c, 15c, 20c, 25c, 30c, 35c, 40c, 45c, 50c, 55c, 60c, 1e, 2e, airmail 10e, 70e, se-tenant in sheet of 16, issued Dec. 27. Nos. 74252-74267.

1975
Picasso Memorial (paintings from last period), set of seven, 5c, 10c, 15c, 20c, 25c, airmail 5e, 70e, and two souv. sheets, perf. 130e, imperf. 200e, issued Jan. 27. Nos. 7501-7509.
ARPHILA 75 Phil. Exhib., Paris, 8 gold foil airmail souv. sheets: perf. 3 sheets of 1 250e, 1 sheet of 2 250e, imperf. 3 sheets of 1 300e, 1 sheet of 2 300e issued Jan. 27. Nos. 7510-7517.

Easter and Holy Year 1975, set of seven, 60c, 70c, 80c, 1e, 1.50e, airmail 30e, 50e, and two airmail souv. sheets, perf. 225e, imperf. 300e, issued Feb. 15. Nos. 7518-7526.

1976 Winter Olympics, Innsbruck, set of 11, 5c, 10c, 15c, 20c, 25c, 30c, 35c, 40c, 45c, 25e, 70e, two airmail souv. sheets, perf. 130e, imperf. 200e, and two gold foil airmail souv. sheets, 1 sheet of 2 250e, 1 sheet of 2 250e, issued Mar. 10. Nos. 7527-7541.

Don Quixote, set of seven, 30c, 35c, 40c, 45c, 50c, airmail 25e, 60e, and two airmail souv. sheets, perf. 130e, imperf. 200e, issued Apr. 4. Nos. 7542-7550.
American Bicent. (1st issue), set of nine, 5c, 20c, 40c, 75c, 2e, 5e, 8e, airmail 25e, 30e, and two airmail souv. sheets, perf. 130e, imperf. 200e, issued Apr. 30. Nos. 7551-7561.
American Bicent. (2nd issue), set of nine, 10c, 30c, 50c, 1e, 3e, 6e, 10e, airmail 12e, 40e, and two airmail souv. sheets, perf. 130e, imperf. 200e, issued Apr. 30. Nos. 7562-7572.

American Bicent. (Presidents), set of 18, 5c, 10c, 20c, 30c, 40c, 50c, 75c, 1e, 2e, 3e, 5e, 6e, 8e, 10e, airmail 12e, 25e, 30e, 40e, four airmail souv. sheets, perf. 225e (2), imperf. 300e (2), and six embossed gold foil airmail souv. sheets, perf. 200e, 200e, 2x200e, imperf. 300e, 300e, 2x300e, issued July 4. Nos. 7573-75100.
Bull Fight, set of seven, 80c, 85c, 90c, 95c, 8e, airmail 35e, 40e, and two airmail souv. sheets, perf. 130e, imperf. 200e, issued May 26. Nos. 75101-75109.
Apollo-Soyuz Space Project, set of 11, 1e, 2e, 3e, 5e, 5.50e, 7e, 7.50e, 9e, 15e, airmail 20e, 30e, and two airmail souv. sheets, perf. 225e, imperf. 300e, issued June 20, 1975; airmail souv. sheet, perf. 250e, issued July 17. Nos. 75110-75123.

Famous Painters, Nudes, set of 16, 5c, 10c, 15c, 20c, 25c, 30c, 35c, 40c, 45c, 50c, 55c, 60c, 1e, 2e, airmail 10e, 70e (Egyptian Greek, Roman, Indian art, Goes, Dürer, Liss, Beniort, Renoir, Gauguin, Stenlen, Picasso, Modigliani, Matisse, Padua), se-tenant in sheet of

16, and 20 airmail embossed gold foil souv. sheetlets, perf. 200p+25p (10), imperf. 250p+50p (10), issued Aug. 10. Nos. 75124-75159.

Conquerors of the Sea, set of 14, 30c, 35c, 40c, 45c, 50c, 55c, 60c, 65c, 70c, 75c, airmail 8p, 10p, 50p, 60p, and four airmail souv. sheets, perf. 130p (2), imperf. 200p (2), issued Sept. 5. Nos. 75160-75177.

Christmas and Holy Year, 1975, set of seven, 60c, 70c, 80c, 1e, 1.50e, airmail 30e, 50e (Jordan, Barocci, Vereycke, Rubens, Mengs, Del Castillo, Cavedone), two airmail souv. sheets, perf. 225e, imperf. 300e, plus four embossed gold foil souv. sheets, perf. 200e (2), imperf. 300e (2), and two gold foil miniature sheets of two, perf. 200e+200e, imperf. 300e+300e, issued Oct. Nos. 75178-75192.

President Macias, IWY, set of eight, 1.50e, 3e, 3.50e, 5e, 7e, 10e, airmail 100e, 300e, and two imperf. airmail souv. sheets (world events), 100e (US 2c Yorktown), 300e, issued Dec. 25. Nos. 75193-75202.

1976
Cavalry Uniforms, set of seven, 5c, 10c, 15c, 20c, 25c, airmail 5p, 70p, and two airmail souv. sheets, perf. 130p, imperf. 200p, issued Feb. 2. Nos. 7601-7609.
1976 Winter Olympics, Innsbruck, set of 11, 50c, 55c, 60c, 65c, 70c, 75c, 80c, 85c, 90c, airmail 35e, 60e, and two airmail souv. sheets, perf. 130e, imperf. 200e, issued Feb. Nos. 7610-7622.
1976 Summer Olympics, Montreal, Ancient to Modern Games, set of seven, 50c, 60c, 70c, 80c, 90c, airmail 35e, 60e, and two airmail souv. sheets, perf. 225e, imperf. 300e, issued Feb. Nos. 7623-7631.
1976 Summer Olympics, Montreal, set of seven, 50c, 60c, 70c, 80c, 90c, airmail 30e, 60e, plus two airmail souv. sheets, perf. 225e, imperf. 300e, four embossed gold foil airmail souv. sheets, per. 250e (2), imperf. 300e (2), and two imperf. miniature sheets of two, perf. 2x250e, imperf. 2x300e, issued Mar. 5. Nos. 7632-7646.

El Greco, paintings, set of seven, 1e, 3e, 5e, 8e, 10e, airmail 15e, 25e, and two airmail semi-postal souv. sheets, perf. 200e+25e, imperf. 250e+50e, issued Apr. 5. Nos. 7647-7655.

1976 Summer Olympics, modern games, set of 11, 50c, 55c, 60c, 65c, 70c, 75c, 80c, 85c, 90c, airmail 35e, 60e, plus two airmail souv. sheets, perf. 225e, imperf. 300e, four embossed gold foil airmail souv. sheets, perf. 250e (2), imperf. 300e (2), and two miniature sheets of two, perf. 2x250e, imperf. 2x300e, issued May 7. Nos. 7656-7674.

UN 30th Anniv., airmail souv. sheet, 250e issued June. No. 7675.
Contemporary Automobiles, set of seven, 1p, 3p, 5p, 8p, 10p, airmail 15p, 25p, and two airmail semi-postal souv. sheets, perf. 200p+24p, imperf. 250p+50p, issued June 10. Nos. 7675-7684.

Nature Protection
European Animals, set of seven, 5c, 10c, 15c, 20c, 25c, airmail 5p, 70p, and two airmail souv. sheets, perf. 130p, imperf. 200p, issued July 1. Nos. 7685-7693.

Asian Animals, set of seven, 30c, 35c, 40c, 45c, 8p, airmail 50c, 60p, and two airmail souv. sheets, perf. 130p, imperf. 200p, issued Sept. 20. Nos. 7694-74102.
Asian Birds, set of seven, 55c, 60c, 65c, 70c, 75c, airmail 10p, 50p, and two airmail souv. sheets, perf. 130p, imperf. 200p, issued Sept. 20. Nos. 76103-76111.
European Birds, set of seven, 5c, 10c, 15c, 20c, 25c, airmail 5p, 70p, and

two airmail souv. sheets, perf. 130p, imperf. 200p, issued Sept. 20. Nos. 76112-76120.
North American Birds, set of seven, 80c, 85c, 90c, 95c, 1p, airmail 15p, 40p, and two airmail souv. sheets, perf. 130p, imperf. 200p, issued Sept. 20. Nos. 76121-76129.

Motorcycle Aces, set of 16, two each 1e, 2e, 3e, 4e, 5e, 10e, 30e, 40e, in se-tenant blocks of eight diff. values, issued July 22. Nos. 76130-76145.

1976 Summer Olympics, Montreal, set of five, 10e, 25e se-tenant strip of 3, airmail 200e, and imperf. airmail souv. sheet, 300e, issued Aug. 7. Nos. 76146-76151.
South American Flowers, set of seven, 30c, 35c, 40c, 45c, 50c, airmail 8p, 60p, and two airmail souv. sheets, perf. 130p, imperf. 200p, issued Aug. 16. Nos. 76152-76160.
Oceania, set of seven, 80c, 85c, 90c, 95c, 1p, airmail 15p, 40p, and two airmail souv. sheets, perf. 130p, imperf. 200p, issued 1976. Nos. 76161-76169.

1977
Butterflies, set of seven, 80c, 85c, 90c, 95c, 8e, airmail 35e, 40e, and two airmail souv. sheets, perf. 130e, imperf. 200e, issued Jan. Nos. 7701-7709.
Madrid Real, 75th Anniv., set of nine, 2e, 4e, 5e, 8e, 10e, 15e, airmail 20e, 35e, 150e, issued Jan. Nos. 7710-7718.

Ancient Carriages, set of 16, 5c, 10c, 15c, 20c, 25c, 30c, 35c, 40c, 45c, 50c, 55c, 60c, 1e, 2e, airmail 10e, 70e, issued Feb. Nos. 7719-7734.
Chinese Art, set of seven, 60c, 70c, 80c, 1e, 1.50e, airmail 30e, 50e, and two airmail souv. sheets, perf. 130e, imperf. 200e, issued Feb. Nos. 7735-7743.

African Masks, set of seven, 5c, 10c, 15c, 20c, 25c, airmail 5e, 70e, and two airmail souv. sheets, perf. 130e, imperf. 200e, issued Mar. Nos. 7744-7752.
North American Animals, set of seven, 1.25e, 1.50e, 1.75e, 2e, 2.25e, airmail 20e, 50e, and two airmail souv. sheets, perf. 130e, imperf. 200e, issued 1977. Nos. 7753-7761.

World Cup Soccer Championships, Argentina '78 (famous players), set of eight, 2e, 4e, 5e, 8e, 10e, 15e, airmail 20e, 35e, and two airmail souv. sheets, perf. 150e, imperf. 250e, issued July 25. Nos. 7762-7771.

World Cup Soccer (famous teams), se-tenant set of eight, 2e, 4e, 5e, 8e, 10e, 15e, airmail 20e, 35e, and two gold foil embossed souv. sheets, 500e (AMPHILEX '77, Cutty Sark, Concorde), airmail 500e (World Cup), issued Aug. 25.Nos. 7772-7781.
Napoleon, Life and Battle Scenes, se-tenant sheet of 16, 5c, 10c, 15c, 20c, 25c, 30c, 35c, 40c, 45c, 50c, 55c, 60c, 1e, 2e, airmail 10e, 70e, issued Aug. 20. Nos. 7782-7797.
Napoleon, Military Uniforms, se-tenant sheet of 16, 5c, 10c, 15c, 20c, 25c, 30c, 35c, 40c, 45c, 50c, 55c, 60c, 1e, 2e, airmail 10e, 70e, issued Aug. 20. Nos. 7798-77113.
South American Animals, set of seven, 2.50e, 2.75e, 3e, 3.50e, 4e, airmail 25e, 35e, and two airmail souv. sheets, perf. 130e, imperf. 200e, issued Aug. Nos. 77114-77122.

USSR Space Program, 20th Anniv., set of eight, 2e, 4e, 5e, 8e, 10e, 15e, airmail 20e, 35e, and two airmail souv. sheets, imperf. 150e, perf. 250e, issued Dec. 15. Nos. 77123-77132.

1978
Ancient Sailing Ships, set of 12, 5c, 10c, 15c, 20c, 25c, airmail 5e, 70e, also 5e, 10e, 20e, 25e, 70e, plus four airmail souv. sheets, perf. 150e, 225e, imperf. 250e, 300e, and two embossed gold foil airmail souv. sheets, perf., imperf., 500e, issued Jan. 6. Nos. 7801-7818.

1980 Winter Olympics, Lake Placid, set of five, 5e, 10e, 20e, 25e, airmail 70e, two airmail souv. sheets, perf. 150e, imperf. 250e, and two embossed gold foil airmail souv. sheets, perf., imperf., 500e, issued Jan. 17. Nos. 7819-7827.
1980 Summer Olympics, Moscow, set of eight, 2e, 3e, 5e, 8e, 10e, 15e, airmail 30e, 50e, two airmail souv. sheets, perf. 150e, imperf. 250e, and two embossed gold foil airmail souv. sheets, perf., imperf., 500e, issued Jan. 17. Nos. 7828-7839.
1980 Summer Olympic Water Games, Tallinn, set of five, 5e, 10e, 20e, 25e, airmail 70e, two airmail souv. sheets, perf. 150e, imperf. 250e, and two embossed gold foil airmail souv. sheets, perf., imperf., 500e issued Jan. 17. Nos. 7840-7848.

Eliz. II Coronation, 25th Anniv., set of eight, 2e, 5e, 8e, 10e, 12e, 15e, airmail 30e, 50e, and two airmail souv. sheets, perf. 150e, imperf. 250e, issued Apr. 25. Nos. 7849-7858.
English Knights of 1200-1350 A.D., set of seven, 5e, 10e, 15e, 20e, 25e, airmail 15e, 70e, and two airmail souv. sheets, perf. 130e, imperf. 250e, issued Apr. 25. Nos. 7859-7867.

Old Locomotives, set of seven, 1e, 2e, 3e, 5e, 10e, airmail 25e, 70e, and two airmail souv. sheets, perf. 150e, imperf. 250e, issued Aug. Nos. 7868-7876.
Prehistoric Animals, set of seven, 30e, 35e, 40e, 45e, 50e, airmail 25e, 60e, and airmail souv. sheet, 130e, issued Aug. Nos. 7877-7884.
Francisco Goya, "Maja Vestida," airmail souv. sheet, 150e, issued Aug. No. 7885.
Peter Paul Rubens — UNICEF, airmail souv. sheet, 250e, issued Aug. No. 7886.
Europa — CEPT — Europhila '78, airmail souv. sheet, 250e, issued Aug. No. 7887.
30th Intl. Stamp Fair, Riccione, airmail souv. sheet, 150e, issued Aug. Nos. 7888.
Eliz. II Coronation, 25th anniv., airmail souv. sheet of three, 150e, issued CEPT, airmail souv. sheet, 250e, issued Aug. Nos. 7890.
World Cup Soccer Championships, Argentina '78 and Spain '82, airmail souv. sheet, 150e, issued Aug. Nos. 7891.
Christmas, Titian painting, "The Virgin," airmail souv. sheet, 150e, issued Aug. Nos. 7892.

Natl. Independence, 5th Anniv. (in 1973) — A7

1979			**Perf. 13x13½**	
26	A7	1e Ekuele coin	1.10	.25

Natl. Independence, 5th Anniv. (in 1973) — A8

1979				
27	A8	1e Port Bata	.20	.20
28	A8	1.50e State Palace	.25	.25
29	A8	2b Central Bank, Bata	.30	.30

30 A8 2.50b Nguema Biyogo
Bridge .35 .35
31 A8 3b Port, palace, bank,
bridge .60 .60
Nos. 27-31 (5) 1.70 1.70

Pres.
Nguema — A9

Independence
Martyrs — A10

1979 **Perf. 13½x13**
32 A9 1.50e multi .50 .35
United Natl. Workers's Party (PUNT), 3rd
Congress.

1979
33 A10 1e Enrique Nvo .20 .20
34 A10 1.50e Salvador Ndongo
Ekang .30 .30
35 A10 2b Acacio Mane .40 .40
Nos. 33-35 (3) .90 .90

Agricultural
Experiment
Year
A11

1979 **Perf. 13x13½**
36 A11 1e multi .65 .25
37 A11 1.50e multi, diff. .95 .35

Independence
Martyrs — A12

Natl. Coat of
Arms — A13

1981, Mar. **Photo.** **Perf. 13½x12½**
38 A12 5b Obiang Esono
Nguema .55 .20
39 A12 15b Fermando Nvara
Engonga .55 .20
40 A12 25b Ela Edjodjomo
Mangue .55 .20
41 A12 35b Obiang Nguema
Moasogo, presi-
dent .75 .20
42 A12 50b Hipolito Micha
Eworo 1.10 .20
43 A13 100b multi 2.25 .35
Nos. 38-43 (6) 5.75 1.35
Dated 1980.

Christmas
1980
A14

1981, Mar. 30 **Perf. 13½**
44 A14 8b Cathedral, infant .25 .20
45 A14 25b Bells, youth .30 .20
Dated 1980.

Souvenir Sheet

Pres. Obiang Nguema
Mbasogo — A15

1981, Aug. 30 **Litho.** **Imperf.**
46 A15 400b multi 7.75 2.25

State Visit of King Juan Carlos of
Spain — A16

Perf. 13x13½, 13½x13
1981, Nov. 30
47 A16 50b Government reception .95 .20
48 A16 100b Arrival at airport 1.75 .35
49 A16 150b King, Pres.
Mbasogo, vert. 2.75 .60
Nos. 47-49 (3) 5.45 1.15

State Visit of Pope John Paul II — A17

1982, Feb. 18
50 A17 100b Papal and natl.
arms 1.90 .70
51 A17 200b Pres. Mbasogo
greeting Pope 3.50 1.40
52 A17 300b Pope, vert. 5.25 2.10
Nos. 50-52 (3) 10.65 4.20

Christmas
1981
A18

1982, Feb. 25 **Photo.**
53 A18 100b Carolers, vert. 1.25 .35
54 A18 150b Magi, African youth 1.90 .60
Dated 1981.

1982 World Cup Soccer
Championships, Spain — A19

1982, June 13 **Perf. 13½**
55 A19 40b Emblem .55 .25
56 A19 60b Naranjito character
trademark .80 .35
57 A19 100b World Cup trophy 1.40 .45

58 A19 200b Players, palm tree,
emblem 2.75 1.10
Nos. 55-58 (4) 5.50 2.30

Fauna
A20

1983, Feb. 4 **Litho.**
59 A20 40b Gorilla .65 .20
60 A20 60b Hippopotamus 1.10 .25
61 A20 80b Atherurus africanus 1.50 .35
62 A20 120b Felis pardus 2.25 .50
Nos. 59-62 (4) 5.50 1.30
Dated 1982.

Christmas
1982
A21

1983, Feb. 25 **Photo.**
63 A21 100b Stars .95 .35
64 A21 200b King offering frank-
incense 2.25 .75
Dated 1982.

World Communications Year — A22

1983, July 18 **Litho.**
65 A22 150b Postal runner 1.00 .45
66 A22 200b Microwave station,
drimmer 2.40 1.00

Banana
Trees
A23

1983, Oct. 8
67 A23 300b shown 3.25 1.00
68 A23 400b Forest, vert. 4.50 1.40

Christmas
1983
A24

1984
69 A24 80b Folk dancer, musical
instruments .90 .30
70 A24 100b Holy Family 1.10 .50
Dated 1983.

Constitution of State Powers — A25

Scales of justice, fundamental lawbook and
various maps.

1984, Feb. 15
71 A25 50b Annobon and Bioko .60 .25
72 A25 100b Mainland regions 1.10 .50

Turtle Hunting, Rio
Muni — A26

World Food
Day — A27

1984, May 1
73 A26 125b Hunting Whales,
horiz. 1.25 .50
74 A26 150b shown 1.50 .60

1984, Sept.
75 A27 60b Papaya 1.00 .40
76 A27 80b Malanga 1.25 .50

Abstract Wood-Carved Figurines and
Art — A28

Designs: 25b, Black Gazelle and Anxiety.
30b, Black Gazelle, diff., and Woman. 60b,
Man and woman, vert. 75b, Poster, vert. 100b,
Mother and Child, vert. 150b, Man and
Woman, diff., and Bust of a Woman.

1984, Nov. 15
77 A28 25b multi .25 .20
78 A28 30b multi .35 .20
79 A28 60b multi .65 .25
80 A28 75b multi .85 .30
81 A28 100b multi 1.10 .40
82 A28 150b multi 1.60 .60
Nos. 77-82 (6) 4.80 1.95

Christmas
A29

1984, Dec. 24
83 A29 60b Mother and child,
vert. .70 .25
84 A29 100b Musical instruments 1.00 .40

Immaculate Conception Missions,
Cent. — A30

50fr, Emblem, vert. 60fr, Map, nun and
youths, vert. 80fr, First Guinean nuns. 125fr,
Missionaries landing at Bata Beach, 1885.

1985, Apr. **Perf. 14**
85 A30 50fr multi .45 .20
86 A30 60fr multi .50 .20
87 A30 80fr multi .60 .20
88 A30 125fr multi 1.10 .40
Nos. 85-88 (4) 2.65 1.00

Jose Mavule Ndjong, First Postmaster A31

1985, July   *Perf. 13½*
89 A31 50fr Postal emblem, vert. .85 .20
90 A31 80fr shown   1.50 .35

Equatorial Guinea Postal Service.

Christmas A32

1985, Dec.
91 A32 40fr Nativity   .55 .20
92 A32 70fr Folk band, dancers, mother and child   .90 .35

Nature Conservation — A33

1985
93 A33 15fr Crab, snail   .75 .20
94 A33 35fr Butterflies, bees, birds   1.40 .25
95 A33 45fr Flowering plants   2.10 .35
96 A33 65fr Spraying and harvesting cacao   3.25 .50
   Nos. 93-96 (4)   7.50 1.30

Folklore — A34

1986, Apr. 15
97 A34 10fr Ndowe dance, Mekuyo, horiz.   .25 .20
98 A34 50fr Fang dance, Mokom   .50 .20
99 A34 65fr Cacha Bubi, Bisila   .65 .25
100 A34 80fr Fang dance, Ndong-Mba   .80 .35
   Nos. 97-100 (4)   2.20 1.00

A35

1986, June 25
   1986 World Cup Soccer Championships, Mexico: Various soccer plays.
101 A35 50fr multi, horiz.   .25 .20
102 A35 75fr multi   .75 .25
103 A35 150fr multi   1.10 .40
104 A35 200fr multi   1.40 .55
   Nos. 101-104 (4)   3.50 1.40

Christmas — A36

Conf. of the Union of Central African States — A37

1986, Dec. 12
105 A36 100fr Musical instruments, horiz.   .85 .35
106 A36 150fr Holy Family, lamb   1.40 .50

1986, Dec. 29
107 A37 80fr Flags, map   .80 .35
108 A37 100fr Emblem, map, horiz.   1.00 .40

Campaign Against Hunger A38

1987, June 5
109 A38 60fr Chicken   .65 .25
110 A38 80fr Fish   .95 .35
111 A38 100fr Wheat   1.10 .40
   Nos. 109-111 (3)   2.70 1.00

Intl. Peace Year A39

1987, July 15   **Litho.**   *Perf. 13½*
112 A39 100fr shown   .75 .40
113 A39 200fr Hands holding dove   1.60 .80

Stamp Day 1987 A40

1987, Oct. 5   **Litho.**   *Perf. 13½*
114 A40 150fr shown   1.25 .50
115 A40 300fr Posting envelope   2.75 .85

Christmas 1987 — A41

Mother and child (wood carvings).

1987, Dec. 22   **Litho.**   *Perf. 13½*
116 A41 80fr multi   .95 .35
117 A41 100fr multi, diff.   1.40 .50

Climbing Palm Tree — A42

Democratic Party — A43

1988, May 4   **Litho.**   *Perf. 13½*
118 A42 50fr shown   .50 .20
119 A42 75fr Woman carrying fish   .60 .30
120 A42 150fr Chopping down trees   1.25 .60
   Nos. 118-120 (3)   2.35 1.10

1988, Nov. 16
121 A43 40fr Crest   .35 .20
122 A43 75fr Torch, motto, horiz.   .60 .30
123 A43 100fr Torch, flag, weaving, horiz.   .85 .40
   Nos. 121-123 (3)   1.80 .90

Cultural Revolution Day — A44

Geometric shapes.

1988, June 4
124 A44 35fr shown   .25 .20
125 A44 50fr Squares, sphere   .35 .20
126 A44 100fr Bird   .75 .50
   Nos. 124-126 (3)   1.35 .90

Christmas — A45

1988, Dec. 22
127 A45 50fr shown   .40 .20
128 A45 100fr Mother and child   .95 .40

Natl. Independence, 20th Anniv. — A46

Designs: 10fr, Lumber on truck. 35fr, Folk dancers. 45fr, Officials on dais.

1989, Apr. 14   **Litho.**   *Perf. 14*
129 A46 10fr multicolored   .25 .20
130 A46 35fr multicolored   .30 .20
131 A46 45fr multicolored   .35 .20
   Nos. 129-131 (3)   .90 .60

Youths Bathing, Ilachi Falls — A47

25fr, Waterfall in the jungle. 60fr, Boy drinking from fruit, boys swimming at Luba Beach.

1989, July 7   *Perf. 13½*
132 A47 15fr shown   .20 .20
133 A47 25fr multicolored   .25 .20
134 A47 60fr multicolored   .45 .25
   Nos. 132-134 (3)   .90 .65

1st Congress of the Democratic Party of Equatorial Guinea A48

1989, Oct. 23   **Litho.**   *Perf. 13½*
135 A48 25fr shown   .30 .20
136 A48 35fr Torch, vert.   .50 .20
137 A48 40fr Pres. Nguema, vert.   .60 .20
   Nos. 135-137 (3)   1.40 .60

Christmas — A49

1989, Dec. 18   **Litho.**   *Perf. 13½*
138 A49 150fr shown   1.60 .75
139 A49 300fr Nativity, horiz.   2.00 1.00

Boy Scouts A50

1990, Mar. 23   **Litho.**   *Perf. 13*
140 A50 100fr Lord Baden-Powell   1.75 .50
141 A50 250fr Salute   4.00 1.10
142 A50 350fr Bugler   5.25 1.50
   Nos. 140-142 (3)   11.00 3.10

World Cup Soccer Championships, Italy — A51

1990, June 8   **Litho.**   *Perf. 13*
143 A51 100fr Soccer player, map   .75 .35
144 A51 250fr Goalkeeper   1.50 .65
145 A51 350fr Trophy   2.25 1.00
   Nos. 143-145 (3)   4.50 2.00

Musical Instruments of the Ndowe People — A52

Instruments of the: 250fr, Fang. 350fr, Bubi.

1990, June 19
146	A52	100fr multicolored		.60	.20
147	A52	250fr multicolored		1.25	.55
148	A52	350fr multicolored		1.60	.85
		Nos. 146-148 (3)		3.45	1.60

Discovery of America, 500th Anniv. (in 1992) — A53

1990, Oct. 10
149	A53	170fr Arrival in New World		1.00	.35
150	A53	300fr Columbus' fleet		1.75	.55

Christmas — A54

1990, Dec. 23 Litho. Perf. 13½
151	A54	170fr shown		1.00	.45
152	A54	300fr Bubi tribesman		1.75	.75

1992 Summer Olympics, Barcelona — A55

1991, Apr. 22 Litho. Perf. 13½x14
153	A55	150fr Tennis		2.10	.75
154	A55	250fr Cycling		3.25	1.10

Souvenir Sheet
155	A55	500fr Equestrian		14.50	6.00

La Maja Desnuda by Goya A56

Designs: 250fr, Eve by Durer, vert. 350fr, The Three Graces by Rubens, vert.

1991, May 6 Litho. Perf. 14
156	A56	100fr shown		1.75	.50
157	A56	250fr multicolored		3.75	1.10
158	A56	350fr multicolored		5.00	1.50
		Nos. 156-158 (3)		10.50	3.10

Madrillus Sphinx — A57

1991, July 1 Litho. Perf. 13½x14
159	A57	25fr shown		2.50	1.10
160	A57	25fr Face		2.50	1.10
161	A57	25fr Seated		2.50	1.10
162	A57	25fr Walking, horiz.		2.50	1.10
		Nos. 159-162 (4)		10.00	4.40

World Wildlife Fund.

Discovery of America, 500th Anniv. A58

Captains, ships: 150fr, Vicente Yanez Pinzon, Nina. 260fr, Martin Alonso Pinzon, Pinta. 350fr, Christopher Columbus, Santa Maria.

1991 Litho. Perf. 13½x14
163	A58	150fr multicolored		1.10	.40
164	A58	250fr multicolored		2.00	.75
165	A58	350fr multicolored		2.75	1.25
		Nos. 163-165 (3)		5.85	2.40

Locomotives — A59

150fr, Electric, Japan, 1932. 250fr, Steam, US, 1873. 500fr, Steam, Germany, 1841.

1991, Sept. 10
166	A59	150fr multicolored		1.25	.50
167	A59	250fr multicolored		2.00	.75

Souvenir Sheet
168	A59	500fr multicolored		12.50	6.00

1992 Summer Olympics, Barcelona — A60

1992, Feb. 12 Litho. Perf. 13½x14
169	A60	200fr Basketball		1.75	.75
170	A60	300fr Swimming		2.50	1.10

Souvenir Sheet
171	A60	400fr Baseball		22.50	12.50

Souvenir Sheet

Discovery of America, 500th Anniv. — A61

Columbus: a, 300fr, Departing from Palos, Spain. b, 500fr, Landing in New World.

1992, Apr. 8
172	A61	Sheet of 2, #a.-b.		22.50	12.50

Motion Pictures, Cent. A61a

Scenes from movies: 100fr, Humphrey Bogart, Ingrid Bergman, Dooley Wilson in "Casablanca," 1942. 250fr, "Viridiana," 1961. 350fr, Laurel and Hardy in "Sons of the Desert," 1933.

1992, Sept. Litho. Perf. 14
172C	A61a	100fr multicolored		.90	.20
172D	A61a	250fr multicolored		1.75	.45
172E	A61a	350fr multicolored		2.75	.60
		Nos. 172C-172E (3)		5.40	1.25

A62

A62a

Mushrooms: 75fr, Termitomyces globulus. 125fr, Termitomyces le testui. 150fr, Termitomyces robustus.

1992, Nov. Litho. Perf. 14x13½
173	A62	75fr multicolored		.75	.20
174	A62	125fr multicolored		1.10	.35
175	A62	150fr multicolored		1.50	.45
		Nos. 173-175 (3)		3.35	1.00

1992 Litho. Perf. 14x13½

Wildlife Protection: 150fr, Halcyon malimbicus. 250fr, Corythaeola cristata. 500fr, Mariposa nymphalidae, horiz.

175A	A62a	150fr multicolored		1.75	.50
175B	A62a	350fr multicolored		3.25	1.00

Souvenir Sheet
Perf. 13½x14
175C	A62a	500fr multicolored		14.50	6.50

Virgin and Child with Virtuous Saints, by Claudio Coello (c. 1635-1693) — A63

Paintings, by Jacob Jordaens (1593-1678): 300fr, Apollo Conquering Marsias. 400fr, Meleager and Atalanta.

1993, Mar. Litho. Perf. 13½x14
176	A63	200fr multicolored		2.50	.75
177	A63	300fr multicolored		3.50	1.25

Souvenir Sheet
178	A63	400fr multicolored		17.00	8.00

1992 Olympic Gold Medalists A64

Designs: 100fr, Quincy Watts, 400-meter dash, US. 250fr, Martin Lopez Zubero, swimming, Spain. 350fr, Petra Kronberger, women's slalom, Austria. 400fr, Flying Dutchman class yachting, Spain.

1993 Litho. Perf. 13½x14
179	A64	100fr multicolored		.90	.35
180	A64	250fr multicolored		1.90	.75
181	A64	350fr multicolored		2.50	1.00
182	A64	400fr multicolored		3.00	1.25
		Nos. 179-182 (4)		8.30	3.35

Scene from Romeo and Juliet, by Tchaikovsky — A65

Design: 200fr, Scene from Faust, by Charles-Francois Gounod (1818-93).

1993, June Litho. Perf. 13½x14
183	A65	100fr multicolored		.85	.40
184	A65	200fr multicolored		1.50	.75

First Ford Gasoline Engine, Cent. A66

1993 Perf. 13½x14, 14x13½
185	A66	200fr First Ford vehicle		3.50	1.00
186	A66	300fr Ford Model T		5.50	1.50
187	A66	400fr Henry Ford, vert.		7.75	2.10
		Nos. 185-187 (3)		16.75	4.60

25th Anniv. of Independence — A67

Designs: 150fr, Pres. Obiang Nguema Mbasogo, vert. 250fr, Cargo ship, map, communications . 300fr, Hydroelectric plant, Riaba. 350fr, Bridge.

Perf. 14x13½, 13½x14
1993, Oct. 12 Litho.
188	A67	150fr multicolored		1.25	.50
189	A67	250fr multicolored		2.00	.75
190	A67	300fr multicolored		2.50	1.00
191	A67	350fr multicolored		2.75	1.10
		Nos. 188-191 (4)		8.50	3.35

1994 World Cup Soccer Championships, US — A68

Designs: 200fr, German team, 1990 champions. 300fr, Rose Bowl Stadium, Pasadena, Calif. 500fr, Player kicking ball, vert.

1994 Litho. Perf. 13½x14, 14x13½
192	A68	200fr multicolored		1.25	.45
193	A68	300fr multicolored		1.75	.65
194	A68	500fr multicolored		3.25	1.10
		Nos. 192-194 (3)		6.25	2.20

First Manned Moon Landing, 25th Anniv. A69

Designs: 500fr, Lunar module, Eagle. 700fr, "Buzz" Aldrin, Michael Collins, Neil Armstrong. 900fr, Footprint on moon, astronaut.

1994 Perf. 13½x14
195	A69	500fr multicolored		2.75	.70
196	A69	700fr multicolored		4.25	1.00
197	A69	900fr multicolored		6.50	1.75
		Nos. 195-197 (3)		13.50	3.45

Dinosaurs A70

Designs: 300fr, Chasmosaurus. 500fr, Tyrannosaurus rex. 700fr, Triceratops. 800fr, Styracosaurus, deinonychus.

1994

198	A70	300fr multicolored	1.50	.65
199	A70	500fr multicolored	2.75	1.10
200	A70	700fr multicolored	3.75	1.60
		Nos. 198-200 (3)	8.00	3.35

Souvenir Sheet

201	A70	800fr multicolored	16.00	16.00

Famous Men
A71

Designs: 300fr, Jean Renoir (1894-1979), French film director. 500fr, Ferdinand de Lesseps (1805-94), French diplomat, promoter of Suez Canal. 600fr, Antoine de Saint Exupery (1900-44), French aviator, writer. 700fr, Walter Gropius (1883-1969), architect.

1994   Litho.   Perf. 13½x14

202	A71	300fr multicolored	2.00	.75
203	A71	500fr multicolored	3.25	1.25
204	A71	600fr multicolored	3.75	1.50
205	A71	700fr multicolored	4.50	1.75
		Nos. 202-205 (4)	13.50	5.25

Establishment of The Bauhaus, 75th anniv. (#205).

Minerals
A72

1994   Litho.   Perf. 13½x14

206	A72	300fr Aurichalcite	2.00	1.00
207	A72	400fr Pyromorphite	2.50	1.40
208	A72	600fr Fluorite	3.25	1.90
209	A72	700fr Halite	4.25	2.25
		Nos. 206-209 (4)	12.00	6.55

Domestic Animals
A73

Designs: a, Cat. b, Dog. c, Pig.

1995   Litho.   Perf. 13½x14

210		Strip of 3, #a.-c.	8.50	8.50
a.-c.	A73	500fr Any single	1.50	1.50

Butterflies & Orchids
A74

a, Hypolimnas salmacis. b, Myrina silenus. c, Palla ussheri. d, Pseudacraea boisduvali.

1995

211		Strip of 4, #a.-d.	8.50	8.50
a.-d.	A74	400fr Any single	1.50	1.50

Anniversaries — A75

Designs: a, 350fr, End of World War II, 50th Anniv. b, 450fr, UN, 50th anniv. c, 600fr, Sir Rowland Hill, birth bicent.

1995   Litho.   Perf. 13½x14

212		Strip of 3, #a.-c.	8.50	8.50
a.	A75	350fr multi	1.25	1.25
b.	A75	450fr multi	1.50	1.50
c.	A75	600fr multi	2.25	2.25

Trains
A76

Designs: No. 213a, English steam engine. b, German diesel engine. c, Japanese Shinkansen train.
800fr, Swiss electric locomotive.

1995

213		Strip of 3, #a.-c.	12.50	12.50
a.-c.	A76	500fr Any single	2.00	2.00

Souvenir Sheet

214	A76	800fr multicolored	9.00	9.00

Formula 1 Driving Champions
A77

Designs: a, Juan Manuel Fangio. b, Ayrton Senna. c, Jim Clark. d, Jochen Rindt.

1995   Litho.   Perf. 14

215		Strip of 4, #a.-d.	10.00	10.00
a.-d.	A77	400fr Any single	1.50	1.50

Motion Pictures, Cent.
A78

Designs: a, Marilyn Monroe. b, Elvis Presley. c, James Dean. d, Vittorio de Sica.

1996   Litho.   Perf. 14

216		Strip of 4, #a.-d.	9.00	9.00
a.-d.	A78	350fr Any single	1.50	1.50

Famous People
A79

Designs: a, Alfred Nobel (1833-96), inventor, philanthropist. b, Anton Bruckner (1824-96), composer. c, Abraham and Three Angels, by Giovanni B. Tiepolo (1696-1770).
800fr, Family of Charles IV, by Francisco de Goya, (1746-1828).

1996

217		Strip of 3, #a.-c.	12.50	12.50
a.-c.	A79	500fr Any single	2.00	2.00

Souvenir Sheet

218	A79	800fr multicolored	7.75	7.75

Chess
A80

Designs: a, World Chess Festival for youth and children, Minorca, Spain. b, Women's World Chess Championship, Jaén, Spain. c, Men's World Chess Championship, Karpov versus Kamsky, Elista, Kalmyk. d, Chess Olympiad, Yerevan, Armenia.

1996   Litho.   Perf. 14

219		Strip of 4, #a.-d.	10.00	10.00
a.-d.	A80	400fr Any single	1.50	1.50

1996 Summer Olympic Games, Atlanta
A81

Designs: a, Olympic Stadium, Athens, 1896. b, Cycling. c, Tennis. d, Equestrian show jumping.

1996   Litho.   Perf. 14

220		Strip of 4, #a.-d.	10.00	10.00
a.-d.	A81	400fr Any single	1.50	1.50

Ships
A82

Designs: a, Paddle steamer with sails, 19th cent. b, Bark "Galatea," 1896. c, Modern ferry.

1996

221		Strip of 3, #a.-c.	11.00	11.00
a.-c.	A82	500fr Any single	2.00	2.00

Franz Schubert (1797-1828), Composer — A83

Miguel de Cervantes (1547-1616), Novelist — A84

Designs: a, shown. b, Chinese Lunar New Year, 1997, (Year of the Ox). c, Johannes Brahms (1833-97), composer.
Illustration A84 reduced.

1997, Apr. 23   Litho.   Perf. 14

222		Strip of 3, #a.-c.	9.00	9.00
a.-c.	A83	500fr Any single	2.00	2.00

Souvenir Sheet

223	A84	800fr multicolored	5.50	5.50

Mushrooms — A85

a, Sparassis laminosa. b, Amanita pantherina. c, Morchella esculenta. d, Aleuria aurantia.

1997

224		Strip of 4, #a.-d.	11.00	11.00
a.-d.	A85	400fr Any single	1.75	1.75

1998 World Cup Soccer Championships, France — A86

Designs: a, Players with ball on field. b, Stadium. c, Kicking ball.

1997   Litho.   Perf. 14

225		Strip of 3, #a.-c.	6.00	6.00
a.-c.	A86	300fr Any single	1.10	1.10

Fauna
A88

a, Snake. b, Snail. c, Turtle. d, Monitor lizard.

1998   Litho.   Perf. 14

230		Strip of 4, #a.-d.	10.00	10.00
a.-d.	A88	400fr Any single	1.50	1.50

A89   A90

Military Uniforms: a, Alsace Regiment, French Infantry, 18th cent. b, English Marine, 18th cent. c, Georgian Hussars Regiment, Russian Calvary, 18th cent. d, Prussian Artillery, 19th cent.

1998

231		Strip of 4, #a.-d.	10.00	10.00
a.-d.	A89	400fr Any single	1.50	1.50

1999   Litho.   Perf. 14

Easter (Museum paintings): a, Crucifixion of Christ, by Velázquez. b, Adoration of the Magi, by Rubens. c, Holy Family, by Michelangelo.

232		Strip of 3, #a.-c.	10.00	10.00
a.-c.	A90	500fr Any single	2.00	2.00

Orchids — A91

Designs: a, Angraecum eburneum. b, Paphiopedilum insigne. c, Ansellia africana. d, Cattleya leopoldii.

1999

233		Strip of 4, #a.-d.	10.00	10.00
a.-d.	A91	400fr Any single	1.50	1.50

Birth and Death Anniversaries
A92

No. 234: a, 750fr, Portrait of Frederic Chopin (1810-49), by Eugene Delacroix. b, 100fr, Christ Crowned With Thorns, by Anthony Van Dyck (1599-1641). c, 250fr, Portrait of Johann Wolfgang von Goethe (1749-1832), by Joseph Carl Stieler. d, 500fr, Jacques-Etienne Montgolfiere (1745-1799) and balloon.

	1999	Litho.	Perf. 14x13¾		
234		Horiz. strip of 4, #a-d		10.00	10.00
a.	A92	750fr multi		3.00	3.00
b.	A92	100fr multi		.35	.35
c.	A92	250fr multi		1.10	1.10
d.	A92	500fr multi		2.00	2.00

Parrots — A93

No. 235: a, Aratinga guarouba. b, Ara ambigua. c, Anodorhynchus hyacinthinus. 800fr, Alisterus amboinensis.

	1999				
235		Vert. strip of 3, #a-c		9.00	9.00
a.-c.	A93	500fr any single		2.00	2.00
		Souvenir Sheet			
236	A93	800fr multi		6.00	6.00

Locomotives — A94

No. 237: a, Swiss. b, German. c, Japanese.

	2000	Litho.	Perf. 13¾x14		
237		Horiz. strip of 3		7.00	7.00
a.-c.	A94	500fr Any single		2.25	2.25
		Souvenir Sheet			
238	A94	800fr AVE Train		3.50	3.50

Butterflies A95

a, Fabriciana niobe. b, Palaeochrysophanus hippothoe. c, Inachis io. d, Apatura iris.

	2000				
239		Horiz. strip of 4		7.50	7.50
a.-d.	A95	400fr Any single		1.75	1.75

UPU, 125th Anniv. (in 1999) A96

	2000	Litho.	Perf. 13¾		
240	A96	400fr multi		1.75	1.75

Mushrooms A97

No. 241: a, Gyroporus cyanescens. b, Terfezia arenaria. c, Battarrea stevenii. d, Amanita muscaria.

	2001	Litho.	Perf. 13¾		
241		Horiz. strip of 4		6.00	6.00
a.-d.	A97	400fr Any single		1.50	1.50

Fire Trucks A98

No. 242: a, Truck, 1915. b, Tanker, 1943. c, Ladder truck, 1966. d, Merryweather pumper, 1888.

	2001				
242		Horiz. strip of 4		4.50	4.50
a.-d.	A98	400fr Any single		1.10	1.10

Soldiers — A99

No. 243: a, Infantry officer, 1700. b, Harquebusier, 1534. c, Musketeer, 17th cent. d, Fusilier, 1815.

	2001	Litho.	Perf. 14x13¾		
243		Horiz. strip of 4		6.00	6.00
a.-d.	A99	400fr Any single		1.50	1.50

Prehistoric Animals A100

No. 244: a, Carnotaurus sastrei. b, Iberomesornis romerali. c, Troodon. 800fr, Diplodocus carnegiei.

	2001		Perf. 13¾x14		
244		Horiz. strip of 3		4.25	4.25
a.-c.	A100	500fr Any single		1.40	1.40
		Souvenir Sheet			
245	A100	800fr multi		2.25	2.25

Millennium A101

Designs: No. 246, 200fr, Intl. Conference Center. No. 247, 200fr, Offshore petroleum exploration. No. 248, 200fr, Women's Plaza, Malabo.
400fr, Statue at Intl. Conference Center, vert.

	2001	Litho.	Perf. 13¾x14		
246-248	A101	Set of 3		3.50	3.50
		Souvenir Sheet			
			Perf. 14x13¾		
249	A101	400fr multi		1.10	1.10

Flora — A102

No. 250: a, Alstonia congensis. b, Harongana madagascariensis. c, Caloncoba glauca. d, Cassia occidentalis.

	2002		Perf. 14x13¾		
250		Horiz. strip of 4		5.25	5.25
a.-d.	A102	400fr Any single		1.25	1.25

Automobiles — A103

No. 251: a, 1924 Rochet Schneider 20,000. b, 1930 Bugatti T49. c, 1931 Ford Model A. d, 1925 Alfa Romeo RLSS.

	2002		Perf. 13¾x14		
251		Vert. strip of 4		5.25	5.25
a.-d.	A103	400fr Any single		1.25	1.25

Butterflies A104

No. 252: a, Papilio menestheus canui. b, Papilio policenes. c, Papilio tynderaeus. d, Papilio zalmoxis.

	2002				
252		Strip of 4		5.25	5.25
a.-d.	A104	400fr Any single		1.25	1.25

Famous Men A105

No. 253: a, Victor Hugo (1802-85), writer. b, Santiago Ramón y Cajal (1852-1934), histologist. c, Emile Zola (1840-1902), writer.

	2002				
253		Horiz. strip of 3		3.75	3.75
a.-c.	A105	400fr Any single		1.25	1.25

2002 World Cup Soccer Championships, Japan and Korea — A106

No. 254: a, Player with yellow shirt with knee on ground. b, Stadium. c, Player with yellow shirt on ground.

	2002				
254		Horiz. strip of 3		4.75	4.75
a.-c.	A106	500fr Any single		1.50	1.50

Souvenir Sheet

2002 Chess Olympiad, Bled, Slovenia — A107

	2002				
255	A107	800fr multi		2.60	2.60

Anniversaries and Events — A108

No. 256: a, Painting by Henri de Toulouse-Lautrec (1864-1901). b, Year of Dialogue Among Civilizations. c, Giuseppe Verdi (1813-1901), composer.

	2004 ?	Litho.	Perf. 14x13¾		
256		Vert. strip of 3		4.50	4.50
a.-c.	A108	400fr Any single		1.50	1.50

Dated 2001. Stamps did not appear in philatelic market until 2004.

Anniversaries and Events — A109

No. 257: a, Tour de France bicycle race, cent. b, Painting by Vincent van Gogh (1853-90). c, Wright Brothers and Wright Flyer.

	2004 ?		Perf. 13¾x14		
257		Horiz. strip of 3		8.50	8.50
a.	A109	400fr multi		2.25	2.25
b.	A109	500fr multi		2.75	2.75
c.	A109	600fr multi		3.50	3.50

Dated 2003. Stamps did not appear in philatelic market until 2004.

Minerals A110

	2004 ?				
258		Vert. strip of 4		8.50	8.50
a.	A110	400fr Realgar		1.75	1.75
b.	A110	450fr Gypsum		2.00	2.00
c.	A110	550fr Red quartz		2.25	2.25
d.	A110	600fr Chrysoberyl		2.50	2.50

Dated 2003. Stamps did not appear in philatelic market until 2004.

Lighthouses A111

Designs: a, Marina Lighthouse, Luba, Equatorial Guinea. b, La Plata Lighthouse, Spain. c, Prodecao Lighthouse, Luba. d, Torre de Hércules, Spain.

	2004 ?		Perf. 14x13¾		
259		Horiz. strip of 4		11.00	11.00
a.	A111	400fr multi		2.25	2.25
b.	A111	450fr multi		2.50	2.50
c.	A111	550fr multi		2.75	2.75
d.	A111	600fr multi		3.50	3.50

Dated 2003. Stamps did not appear in philatelic market until 2004.

Space Shuttle
Columbia
Accident — A112

No. 260: a, Rocket lift-off. b, Rocket on launch pad. c, Flight crew patch.
1000fr, View of earth from outer space.

2004 ?
260	Vert. strip of 3		6.75	6.75
a.	A112 500fr multi		1.90	1.90
b.	A112 600fr multi		2.25	2.25
c.	A112 700fr multi		2.60	2.60

Souvenir Sheet
261	A112 1000fr multi	3.75 3.75

Dated 2003. Stamps did not appear in philatelic market until 2004.

Motorcycles — A113

No. 262: a, 1944-47 Soriano Tigre. b, 1970 Derbi 50 Grand Prix. c, 1938 DKW 250 with sidecar.
1000fr, Harley-Davidson VRSCA V-Rod.

2004 ?   **Perf. 13¾x14**
262	Horiz. strip of 3	7.00	7.00
a.	A113 450fr multi	1.90	1.90
b.	A113 500fr multi	2.25	2.25
c.	A113 550fr multi	2.75	2.75

Souvenir Sheet
263	A113 1000fr multi	5.50 5.50

Dated 2003. Stamps did not appear in philatelic market until 2004.

Souvenir Sheet

Wedding of Spanish Prince Felipe and
Letizia Ortiz Rocasolano — A114

2004   Litho.   Perf. 13¾x14
264	A114 1400fr multi	5.75 5.75

2004
Summer
Olympics,
Athens
A115

2004
265	Horiz. strip of 4	8.25	8.25
a.	A115 400fr Basketball	1.60	1.60
b.	A115 450fr Track	1.90	1.90
c.	A115 550fr Tennis	2.25	2.25
d.	A115 600fr Cycling	2.50	2.50

2004
Anniversaries
A116

No. 266: a, FIFA (Fédération Internationale de Football Association), cent. b, Pablo Neruda (1904-73), poet. c, Anton Dvorak (1841-1904), composer.

2005 ?   Litho.   Perf. 14x13¾
266	Vert. strip of 3	5.50	5.50
a.	A116 450fr multi	1.60	1.60
b.	A116 500fr multi	1.75	1.75
c.	A116 550fr multi	2.00	2.00

Dated 2004. Stamps did not appear in philatelic marketplace until 2005.

Airplanes
A117

No. 267: a, Concorde. b, Airbus A340-600. c, Boeing 747-400. d, Eurofighter C-16 Typhoon.

2005 ?   Perf. 13¾x14
267	Vert. strip of 4	7.00	7.00
a.	A117 400fr multi	1.40	1.40
b.	A117 450fr multi	1.60	1.60
c.	A117 500fr multi	1.75	1.75
d.	A117 600fr multi	2.25	2.25

Dated 2004. Stamps did not appear in philatelic marketplace until 2005.

Churches — A118

No. 268: a, Cathedral, Pisa, Italy. b, Notre-Dame-la-Grande Church, Poitiers, France. c, Speyer Cathedral, Germany. d, Cathedral, Santiago de Compostela, Spain.

2005   Perf. 14x13¾
268	Horiz. strip of 4	7.25	7.25
a.	A118 400fr multi	1.40	1.40
b.	A118 450fr multi	1.60	1.60
c.	A118 550fr multi	2.00	2.00
d.	A118 600fr multi	2.25	2.25

Paintings by
Salvador Dali
(1904-89) — A119

Various unnamed paintings.

2005   Perf. 14x13¾
269	Vert. strip of 3	7.00	7.00
a.	A119 500fr multi	1.75	1.75
b.	A119 600fr multi	2.25	2.25
c.	A119 700fr multi	2.50	2.50

Souvenir Sheet
270	A119 1000fr multi	3.75 3.75

Art and Architecture — A120

No. 271: a, Statue of African Woman, Malabo. b, Building, Bioko Sur. c, Eyi Muan Ndong, troubadour.

2005   Litho.   Perf. 13¾x14
271	Horiz. strip of 3	5.75	5.75
a.	A120 450fr multi	1.60	1.60
b.	A120 550fr multi	2.00	2.00
c.	A120 600fr multi	2.10	2.10

Trains
A121

No. 272: a, Tren Basculante. b, Tren Talgo Pendular. c, Tren Electrotrén. d, Tren T. A. F.

2005
272	Strip of 4	7.25	7.25
a.	A121 400fr multi	1.50	1.50
b.	A121 450fr multi	1.60	1.60
c.	A121 550fr multi	2.00	2.00
d.	A121 600fr multi	2.10	2.10

Publication of
Don Quixote,
400th
Anniv. — A122

No. 273: a, Emblem. b, Don Quixote and Sancho Panza riding. c, Quixote catching falling Panza. d, Quixote on horse, windmill.

2005   Perf. 14x13¾
273	Horiz. strip of 4	7.25	7.25
a.	A122 400fr multi	1.50	1.50
b.	A122 450fr multi	1.60	1.60
c.	A122 550fr multi	2.00	2.00
d.	A122 600fr multi	2.10	2.10

Famous
People
A123

No. 274: a, Christopher Columbus (1451-1506), explorer. b, Federico García Lorca (1898-1936), poet. c, Wolfgang Amadeus Mozart (1756-91), composer.

2006   Perf. 13¾x14
274	Horiz. strip of 3	6.25	6.25
a.	A123 450fr multi	1.75	1.75
b.	A123 550fr multi	2.10	2.10
c.	A123 600fr multi	2.40	2.40

Pope
Benedict
XVI
A124

No. 275: a, Coat of Arms. b, St. Peter's Basilica.
1000fr, Pope Benedict XVI.

2006
275	Vert. pair	4.00	4.00
a.	A124 450fr multi	1.75	1.75
b.	A124 550fr multi	2.10	2.10

Souvenir Sheet
276	A124 1000fr multi	4.00 4.00

Tourism
A125

No. 277: a, Road from Boloko to Luba. b, Malabo Intl. Airport Terminal. c, Sculpture, Avenida de Juan Pablo II. d, National Parliament.

2006   Litho.   Perf. 13¾x14
277	Strip of 4	8.00	8.00
a.	A125 400fr multi	1.60	1.60
b.	A125 450fr multi	1.75	1.75
c.	A125 550fr multi	2.25	2.25
d.	A125 600fr multi	2.40	2.40

Spain, 2006
World Basketball
Champions
A126

No. 278: a, Emblem of Spanish Basketball Federation. b, Basketball and hoop. c, Players.

2006   Perf. 14x13¾
278	Vert. strip of 3	6.50	6.50
a.	A126 450fr multi	1.75	1.75
b.	A126 550fr multi	2.25	2.25
c.	A126 600fr multi	2.40	2.40

Christmas
A127

No. 279 — Baby and: a, People and drummer. b, People. c, People and airplane.

2006   Perf. 13¾x14
279	Horiz. strip of 3	6.50	6.50
a.	A127 450fr multi	1.75	1.75
b.	A127 550fr multi	2.25	2.25
c.	A127 600fr multi	2.40	2.40

European Economic Community, 50th
Anniv. — A128

No. 280: a, Orchard, Spain. b, Mountain, France. c, Farm fields, Italy. d, Village, Germany.

2007   Litho.   Perf. 13¾x14
280	Horiz. strip of 4	9.25	9.25
a.	A128 400fr multi	1.75	1.75
b.	A128 500fr multi	2.25	2.25
c.	A128 550fr multi	2.50	2.50
d.	A128 600fr multi	2.75	2.75

Locomotives in Madrid Train
Museum — A129

No. 281: a, Steam locomotive 242F-2009. b, Diesel locomotive 1615. c, Electric locomotive 6101. d, Talgo II train.
1000fr, Steam locomotive, diff.

2007
281	Strip of 4	10.50	10.50
a.	A129 450fr multi	2.00	2.00
b.	A129 550fr multi	2.50	2.50

c.	A129 600fr multi	2.75	2.75	
d.	A129 650fr multi	3.00	3.00	

Souvenir Sheet

282	A129 1000fr multi	4.50	4.50

SPECIAL DELIVERY STAMPS

Archer with Crossbow — SD1

1971, Oct. 12   Photo.   Perf. 12½x13

E1	SD1	4p blue & multi	.75	.20
E2	SD1	8p rose & multi	1.25	.20

3rd anniversary of independence.

ERITREA

ˌer-ə-ˈtrē-ə

LOCATION — In northeast Africa, bordering on the Red Sea, Sudan, Ethiopia and Djibouti.
GOVT. — Independent state
AREA — 45,300 (?) sq. mi.
POP. — 3,984,723 (1999 est.)
CAPITAL — Asmara

Formerly an Italian colony, Eritrea was incorporated as a State of Italian East Africa in 1936.

Under British occupation (1941-52) until it became part of Ethiopia as its northernmost region. Eritrea became independent May 24, 1993.

100 Centesimi = 1 Lira
100 cents = 1 birr (1991)
100 cents = 1 nakfa (1997)

Catalogue values for unused stamps in this country are for Never Hinged items, beginning with Scott 200 in the regular postage section.

All used values to about 1916 are for postally used stamps. From 1916-1934, used values in italics are for postally used stamps. CTO's, for stamps valued postally used, sell for about the same as unused, hinged stamps.

Watermark

Wmk. 140 — Crown

Stamps of Italy Overprinted

a   b

1892   Wmk. 140   Perf. 14
Overprinted Type "a" in Black

1	A6	1c bronze grn	8.00	8.00
a.	Inverted overprint	525.00	475.00
b.	Double overprint	1,450.	
	Never hinged	1,850.	

c.	Vert. pair, one without overprint	2,750.	
	Never hinged	3,400.	
2	A7	2c orange brn	4.00	4.00
a.	Inverted overprint	475.00	450.00
b.	Double overprint	1,450.	
	Never hinged	1,850.	
3	A33	5c green	110.00	12.00
a.	Inverted overprint	5,500.	3,250.
	Never hinged	6,750.	

Overprinted Type "b" in Black

4	A17	10c claret	140.00	12.00
5	A17	20c orange	275.00	8.00
6	A17	25c blue	1,000.	40.00
7	A25	40c brown	9.75	24.00
8	A26	45c slate green	9.75	28.00
9	A27	60c violet	9.75	55.00
10	A28	1 l brown & yel	32.50	55.00
11	A38	5 l blue & rose	525.00	400.00
	Nos. 1-11 (11)	2,123.	646.00
	Set, never hinged	5,350.	

1895-99
Overprinted type "a" in Black

12	A39	1c brown ('99)	14.50	9.75
13	A40	2c org brn ('99)	2.40	1.60
14	A41	5c green	2.40	1.60
a.	Inverted overprint	400.00	3,250.

Overprinted type "b" in Black

15	A34	10c claret ('98)	2.40	1.60
16	A35	20c orange	3.25	2.00
17	A36	25c blue	3.25	4.00
18	A37	45c olive grn	22.50	22.50
	Nos. 12-18 (7)	50.70	43.05
	Set, never hinged	125.00	

1903-28
Overprinted type "a" in Black

19	A42	1c brown	.80	1.25
a.	Inverted overprint	127.50	127.50
	Never hinged		
20	A43	2c orange brn	.80	.60
21	A44	5c blue green	40.00	.60
22	A45	10c claret	47.50	.60
23	A45	20c orange	3.25	1.25
24	A45	25c blue	350.00	16.00
a.	Double overprint	650.00	
25	A45	40c brown	400.00	24.00
26	A45	45c olive grn	4.00	8.00
27	A45	50c violet	110.00	27.50
28	A46	75c dk red & rose ('28)	65.00	5.75
29	A46	1 l brown & grn	4.00	.80
30	A46	1.25 l bl & ultra ('28)	32.50	3.25
31	A46	2 l dk grn & org ('25)	52.50	72.50
32	A46	2.50 l dk grn & org ('28)	140.00	52.50
33	A46	5 l blue & rose	27.50	40.00
	Nos. 19-33 (15)	1,277.	254.60
	Set, never hinged	3,250.	

Surcharged in Black

Colonia Eritrea
C. 15

1905

34	A45	15c on 20c orange	35.00	9.25
	Never hinged	92.50	

1908-28
Overprinted type "a" in Black

35	A48	5c green	1.00	.95
36	A48	10c claret ('09)	1.00	.95
37	A48	15c slate ('20)	16.00	9.50
38	A49	20c green ('25)	16.00	11.00
39	A49	20c lilac brn ('28)	4.75	3.25
40	A49	25c blue ('09)	4.50	2.25
41	A49	30c gray ('25)	16.00	16.00
42	A49	40c brown ('16)	36.00	32.50
43	A49	50c violet ('16)	12.00	2.00
44	A49	60c brn car ('18)	20.00	2.00
a.	Printed on both sides		1,200.
45	A49	60c brn org ('28)	80.00	160.00
46	A51	10 l gray grn & red ('16)	325.00	600.00
	Nos. 35-46 (12)	532.25	860.90
	Set, never hinged	1,300.	

See No. 53.

Government Building at Massaua — A2

1910-29   Unwmk.   Engr.   Perf. 13½

47	A1	15c slate	240.00	22.00
a.	Perf. 11 ('29)	32.50	47.50
	Never hinged	77.50	
48	A2	25c dark blue	4.75	14.00
a.	Perf. 12	600.00	600.00

For surcharges see Nos. 51-52.

A3

Farmer Plowing — A4

1914-28

49	A3	5c green	.80	2.40
a.	Perf. 11 ('28)	160.00	60.00
	Never hinged	400.00	
50	A4	10c carmine	4.00	4.25
a.	Perf. 11 ('28)	12.00	40.00
	Never hinged	30.00	
b.	Perf. 13½x14	60.00	60.00

No. 47 Surcharged in Red or Black

1916

51	A1	5c on 15c slate (R)	6.50	14.50
52	A1	20c on 15c slate	2.40	4.00
a.	"CEN" for "CENT"	32.50	32.50
b.	"CENT" omitted	175.00	175.00
c.	"ENT"	47.50	47.50
	Set, never hinged	22.00	

Italy No. 113 Overprinted in Black — f

1921   Wmk. 140   Perf. 14

53	A50	20c brown orange	4.00	12.00
	Never hinged	10.00	

Victory Issue

Italian Victory Stamps of 1921 Overprinted type "f" 13mm long

1922

54	A64	5c olive green	2.00	7.25
55	A64	10c red	2.00	7.50
56	A64	15c slate green	2.00	11.00
57	A64	25c ultra	2.00	11.00
	Nos. 54-57 (4)	8.00	36.75
	Set, never hinged	20.00	

Somalia Nos. 10-16 Overprinted In Black and Bars over Original Values

g

1922   Wmk. 140

58	A1	2c on 1b brn	4.75	16.00
59	A1	5c on 2b bl grn	4.75	11.00
60	A2	10c on 1a claret	4.75	2.40
61	A2	15c on 2a brn org	4.75	2.40
62	A2	25c on 2½a blue	4.75	2.40
63	A2	50c on 5a yellow	16.00	11.00
64	A2	1 l on 10a lilac	16.00	20.00
a.	"ERITREA" double	1,000.	1,000.
	Nos. 58-64 (7)	55.75	65.20
	Set, never hinged	132.50	

See Nos. 81-87.

Propagation of the Faith Issue

Italy Nos. 143-146 Overprinted

1923

65	A68	20c ol grn & brn org	8.00	40.00
66	A68	30c claret & brn org	8.00	40.00
67	A68	50c vio & brn org	4.75	47.50
68	A68	1 l bl & brn org	4.75	60.00
	Nos. 65-68 (4)	25.50	187.50
	Set, never hinged	62.50	

Fascisti Issue

Italy Nos. 159-164 Overprinted in Red or Black — j

1923   Unwmk.   Perf. 14

69	A69	10c dk green (R)	8.00	14.50
70	A69	30c dk violet (R)	8.00	14.50
71	A69	50c brown carmine	8.00	16.00

Wmk. 140

72	A70	1 l blue	8.00	40.00
73	A70	2 l brown	8.00	47.50
74	A71	5 l black & blue (R)	8.00	65.00
	Nos. 69-74 (6)	48.00	197.50
	Set, never hinged	115.00	

Manzoni Issue

Italy Nos. 165-170 Overprinted in Red

1924   Perf. 14

75	A72	10c brn red & blk	13.00	40.00
76	A72	15c blue grn & blk	13.00	40.00
77	A72	30c black & slate	13.00	40.00
78	A72	50c org brn & blk	13.00	40.00
79	A72	1 l blue & blk	80.00	275.00
80	A72	5 l violet & blk	525.00	2,200.
	Nos. 75-79 (5)	132.00	435.00

On Nos. 79 and 80 the overprint is placed vertically at the left side.

Somalia Nos. 10-16 Overprinted type "g" in Blue or Red

1924

Bars over Original Values

81	A1	2c on 1b brn	13.00	27.50
82	A1	5c on 2b bl grn (R)	13.00	17.50

Bottom Center

A1

83	A2	10c on 1a rose red	8.00	16.00
84	A2	15c on 2a brn org	8.00	16.00
a.		Pair, one without "ERI-TREA"	1,600.	
		Never hinged	2,000.	
85	A2	25c on 2½a bl (R)	8.00	11.00
a.		Double surcharge	800.00	
86	A2	50c on 5a yellow	8.00	20.00
87	A2	1 l on 10a lil (R)	8.00	27.50
		Nos. 81-87 (7)	66.00	135.50
		Set, never hinged	160.00	

Stamps of Italy, 1901-08 Overprinted type "j" in Black

1924

88	A42	1c brown	8.00	9.75
a.		Inverted overprint	275.00	
89	A43	2c orange brown	4.75	8.00
90	A48	5c green	8.00	9.00
		Nos. 88-90 (3)	20.75	26.75
		Set, never hinged	50.00	

Victor Emmanuel Issue

Italy Nos. 175-177 Overprinted — k

1925-26   Unwmk.   Perf. 11

91	A78	60c brown car	1.60	6.50
a.		Perf. 13½	10.00	24.00
92	A78	1 l dark blue	1.60	9.75
a.		Perf. 13½	21,000.	5,600.
		Never hinged	26,000.	

Perf. 13½

93	A78	1.25 l dk blue ('26)	3.25	20.00
a.		Perf. 11	6.50	28.00
		Nos. 91-93 (3)	6.45	36.25
		Set, never hinged	17.50	

Saint Francis of Assisi Issue

Italian Stamps of 1926 Overprinted

1926   Wmk. 140   Perf. 14

94	A79	20c gray green	2.40	11.00
95	A80	40c dark violet	2.40	11.00
96	A81	60c red violet	2.40	20.00

Overprinted in Red

Unwmk.   Perf. 11

97	A82	1.25 l dark blue	2.40	28.00

Perf. 14

98	A83	5 l + 2.50 l ol grn	6.50	55.00
		Nos. 94-98 (5)	16.10	125.00
		Set, never hinged	36.00	

Italian Stamps of 1926 Overprinted type "f" in Black

1926   Wmk. 140   Perf. 14

99	A46	75c dk red & rose	55.00	16.00
a.		Double overprint	325.00	
100	A46	1.25 l blue & ultra	32.50	16.00
101	A46	2.50 l dk grn & org	110.00	45.00
		Nos. 99-101 (3)	197.50	77.00
		Set, never hinged	475.00	

Volta Issue

Type of Italy, 1927, Overprinted — o

1927

102	A84	20c purple	6.50	32.50
103	A84	50c deep orange	8.00	20.00
a.		Double overprint	175.00	
104	A84	1.25 l brt blue	12.50	52.50
		Nos. 102-104 (3)	27.00	105.00
		Set, never hinged	65.00	

Italian Stamps of 1925-28 Overprinted type "a" in Black

1928-29

105	A86	7½c lt brown ('29)	16.00	65.00
106	A86	50c brt violet	55.00	55.00
		Set, never hinged	180.00	

Italian Stamps of 1927-28 Overprinted type "f"

1928-29

107	A86	50c brt violet	47.50	47.50
		Never hinged	120.00	

Unwmk.   Perf. 11

107A	A85	1.75 l deep brown	72.50	32.50
		Never hinged	180.00	

Italy No. 192 Overprinted type "o"

1928   Wmk. 140   Perf. 14

108	A85	50c brown & slate	16.00	8.00
		Never hinged	40.00	

Monte Cassino Issue

Types of 1929 Issue of Italy Overprinted in Red or Blue

1929   Perf. 14

109	A96	20c dk green (R)	4.75	17.50
110	A96	25c red orange (Bl)	4.75	17.50
111	A98	50c + 10c crim (Bl)	4.75	20.00
112	A98	75c + 15c ol brn (R)	4.75	20.00
113	A96	1.25 l + 25c dl vio (R)	11.00	40.00
114	A98	5 l + 1 l saph (R)	11.00	60.00

Overprinted in Red

Unwmk.

115	A100	10 l + 2 l gray brn	11.00	55.00
		Nos. 109-115 (7)	52.00	230.00
		Set, never hinged	125.00	

Royal Wedding Issue

Type of Italian Stamps of 1930 Overprinted

1930   Wmk. 140

116	A101	20c yellow green	1.60	4.75
117	A101	50c + 10c dp org	1.25	8.00
118	A101	1.25 l + 25c rose red	1.25	16.00
		Nos. 116-118 (3)	4.10	28.75
		Set, never hinged	10.00	

Lancer — A5

Scene in Massaua A6

2c, 35c, Lancer. 5c, 10c, Postman. 15c, Lineman. 25c, Askari (infantryman). 2 l, Railroad viaduct. 5 l, Asmara Deghe Selam. 10 l, Camels.

1930   Wmk. 140   Litho.   Perf. 14

119	A5	2c brt bl & blk	2.40	12.00
120	A5	5c dk vio & blk	4.00	2.40
121	A5	10c yel brn & blk	4.00	1.25
122	A5	15c dk grn & blk	4.00	1.60
123	A5	25c gray grn & blk	4.00	1.25
124	A5	35c red brn & blk	10.00	22.50
125	A6	1 l dk bl & blk	4.00	1.25
126	A6	2 l choc & blk	10.00	24.00
127	A6	5 l ol grn & blk	13.00	36.00
128	A6	10 l dl bl & blk	20.00	65.00
		Nos. 119-128 (10)	75.40	167.25
		Set, never hinged	160.00	

Ferrucci Issue
Types of Italian Stamps of 1930 Overprinted type "f" in Red or Blue

1930

129	A102	20c violet (R)	4.75	4.75
130	A103	25c dk green (R)	4.75	4.75
131	A103	50c black (R)	4.75	9.75
132	A103	1.25 l dp brown (R)	4.75	17.50
133	A104	5 l + 2 l dp car (Bl)	9.75	32.50
		Nos. 129-133 (5)	28.75	69.25
		Set, never hinged	60.00	

Virgil Issue
Types of Italian Stamps of 1930 Overprinted in Red or Blue

1930   Photo.

134	A106	15c violet black	1.25	8.00
135	A106	20c orange brown	1.25	3.25
136	A106	25c dark green	1.25	3.25
137	A106	30c lt brown	1.25	3.25
138	A106	50c dull violet	1.25	3.25
139	A106	75c rose red	1.25	6.50
140	A106	1.25 l gray blue	1.25	8.00

Unwmk.   Engr.

141	A106	5 l + 1.50 l dk vio	3.75	40.00
142	A106	10 l + 2.50 l ol brn	3.75	60.00
		Nos. 134-142 (9)	16.25	135.50
		Set, never hinged	36.00	

Saint Anthony of Padua Issue
Types of Italian Stamps of 1931 Overprinted type "f" in Blue, Red or Black

1931   Photo.   Wmk. 140

143	A116	20c brown (Bl)	1.60	17.50
144	A116	25c green (R)	1.60	6.50
145	A118	30c gray brn (Bl)	1.60	6.50
146	A118	50c dl violet (Bl)	1.60	6.50
147	A120	1.25 l slate bl (R)	1.60	17.50

Unwmk.   Engr.

148	A121	75c black (R)	1.60	32.50
149	A122	5 l + 2.50 l dk brn (Bk)	6.50	67.50
		Nos. 143-149 (7)	16.10	154.50
		Set, never hinged	40.00	

Victor Emmanuel III — A13

1931   Photo.   Wmk. 140

150	A13	7½c olive brown	1.25	4.00
151	A13	20c slate bl & car	1.25	.20
152	A13	30c ol grn & brn vio	1.25	.20
153	A13	40c bl & yel grn	1.60	.20
154	A13	50c bis brn & ol	.80	.20
155	A13	75c carmine rose	3.25	.20
156	A13	1.25 l violet & indigo	4.00	4.00
157	A13	2.50 l dull green	4.00	9.75
		Nos. 150-157 (8)	17.40	18.75
		Set, never hinged	42.50	

Camel A14

Temple Ruins — A18

Designs: 2c, 10c, Camel. 5c, 15c, Shark fishery. 25c, Baobab tree. 35c, Pastoral scene. 2 l, African elephant. 5 l, Eritrean man. 10 l, Eritrean woman.

1934   Photo.   Wmk. 140

158	A14	2c deep blue	1.60	4.75
159	A14	5c black	3.25	.40
160	A14	10c brown	3.25	.35
161	A14	15c orange brn	4.00	1.60
162	A14	25c gray green	3.25	.35
163	A14	35c purple	6.50	9.75
164	A18	1 l dk blue gray	.80	.35
165	A18	2 l olive black	17.50	3.25
166	A18	5 l carmine rose	9.75	6.50
167	A18	10 l red orange	13.00	22.50
		Nos. 158-167 (10)	62.90	49.80
		Set, never hinged	145.00	

Abruzzi Issue

Types of 1934 Issue Overprinted in Black or Red

1934

168	A14	10c dull blue (R)	13.00	20.00
169	A14	15c blue	9.75	20.00
170	A14	35c green (R)	5.75	20.00
171	A18	1 l copper red	5.75	20.00
172	A14	2 l rose red	17.50	20.00
173	A18	5 l purple (R)	9.75	32.50
174	A18	10 l olive grn (R)	9.75	40.00
		Nos. 168-174 (7)	71.25	172.50
		Set, never hinged	165.00	

Grant's Gazelle A22

1934   Photo.

175	A22	5c ol grn & brn	4.00	20.00
176	A22	10c yel brn & blk	4.00	20.00
177	A22	20c scar & indigo	4.00	16.00
178	A22	50c dk vio & brn	4.00	16.00
179	A22	60c org brn & ind	4.00	24.00
180	A22	1.25 l blk & grn	4.00	40.00
		Nos. 175-180 (6)	24.00	136.00
		Set, never hinged	57.50	

Second Colonial Arts Exhibition, Naples. See Nos. C1-C6.

Between 1981 and 1986 unofficial labels appeared showing such non-Eritrean subjects as the British royal weddings, Queen Mother, Queen's birthday, and the Duke & Duchess of York. These labels are not listed.

In 1978, two sets of stamps were issued for use within liberated areas of Eritrea and to publicize the liberation effort. A May 26 set of 5c, 10c, 80c and 1b commemorated the 8th anniv. of the Eritrean People's Liberation Front (EPLF). An August 1 set of 80c, 1b, 1.50b featured the Future of Eritrea theme. A September 1, 1991 set of 5c, 15c and 20c was issued with a Freedom Fighter design in orange and black almost identical to design A24. Although the 80c from the 1st 1978 issue was available at the Asmara post office in late 1992 and early 1993, there is no evidence that any of these stamps were available at the time of independence. Thus these stamps are more properly considered locals and provisionals.

Freedom Fighter with EPLF Flags
A23   A24

1991, Jan. 16   Typo.   Perf. 11 rough
192 A23 5c lt bl, blk & org   —
193 A23 15c pale green, blk & org   —
194 A23 20c pale yel, blk & org   —
195 A23 3b silver, blk & org   25.00 25.00
196 A23 5b gold, blk & org   25.00 25.00

See footnotes following #199.

1993, Feb. 1   Litho.   Perf. 10
197 A24 5c lt bl, blk & org   4.50 4.50
198 A24 15c pale grn, blk & org 4.50 4.50
199 A24 20c pale yel, blk & org 4.50 4.50

Nos. 192-199 commemorate 30 years of the war for national liberation.
Nos. 192-199 were issued for local use, and became valid for international mail on Sept. 13, 1993.

> Catalogue values for unused stamps in this section, from this point to the end of the section, are for Never Hinged items.

Referendum for Independence
A25

Designs: 15c, Placing ballot in box. 60c, Group of arrows pointing right, one pointing left. 75c, Signs indicating "yes" & "no." 1b, Candle burning. 2b, Peace dove, horn over country map.

Perf. 14x15
1993, Apr. 22   Litho.   Wmk. 373
200 A25 15c multicolored   1.00 1.00
201 A25 60c multicolored   2.00 2.00
202 A25 75c multicolored   3.00 3.00
203 A25 1b multicolored   5.00 5.00
204 A25 2b multicolored   7.00 7.00
    Nos. 200-204 (5)   18.00 18.00

Natl. Flag — A26

1993   Litho.   Perf. 11 rough
Blue Border
205 A26 5c multicolored   3.00 .50
206 A26 20c multicolored
207 A26 35c multicolored   5.00 2.00
208 A26 50c multicolored   7.00 2.50
209 A26 70c multicolored   4.00 3.50
210 A26 80c multicolored   4.00 4.00

The border of the 40c, No. 215, is similar to that of this issue but it was issued with next set. And the type face of the "0.40" matches that set.

1994   Litho.   Perf. 11 rough
Color of Border
211 A26 5c brown   1.50 1.50
212 A26 15c red   1.50 1.50
213 A26 20c gold   15.00
214 A26 25c lt blue   1.50 1.50
215 A26 40c blue   15.00 15.00
216 A26 60c yellow   2.00 2.00
217 A26 70c purple   2.25 2.25
218 A26 3b light green 6.00 6.00
219 A26 5b silver   6.00 6.00

Flag & Map — A27

1994, Sept. 2   Litho.   Perf. 13½x14
Color of Border
220 A27 5c deep yellow   .45 .40
221 A27 10c yellow green .50 .45
222 A27 20c salmon   .70 .65
223 A27 25c red   1.25 1.25
224 A27 40c lilac rose   1.40 1.25
225 A27 60c blue green   1.50 1.25
226 A27 70c dark green   1.60 1.50
227 A27 1b yellow   1.60 1.50
228 A27 2b orange   1.75 1.50
229 A27 3b blue violet 1.90 1.75
230 A27 5b red lilac   2.25 2.00
231 A27 10b pale violet 3.75 3.50
    Nos. 220-231 (12)   18.65 17.00

World Tourism Organization, 20th Anniv. — A29

Perf. 14x13½, 13½x14
1995, Jan. 2   Litho.
232 A29 10c Fishing from boat 1.25 1.25
233 A29 35c Monument, vert.   1.25 1.25
234 A29 85c Winding road   2.50 2.50
235 A29 2b Stone dwelling, vert. 4.25 4.25
    Nos. 232-235 (4)   9.25 9.25

Fish — A30

Designs: 30c, Horned butterflyfish. 55c, Gonochaetodon larvatus. 70c, Shrimp lobster. 1b, Bluestripe snapper.

1995, Apr. 1   Perf. 14x13½
236 A30 30c multicolored   .60 .60
237 A30 55c multicolored   .85 .85
238 A30 70c multicolored 1.25 1.25
239 A30 1b multicolored 1.50 1.50
    Nos. 236-239 (4)   4.20 4.20

Independence Day — A31

Designs: 25c, Breaking chains, mountain, buildings, animals. 40c, Raising natl. flag, vert.

70c, Three men, holding natl. flag, sword, vert. 3b, Natl. flag, fireworks, vert.

Perf. 14x13½, 13½x14
1995, May 23   Litho.
240 A31 25c multicolored   .40 .40
241 A31 40c multicolored   .45 .45
242 A31 70c multicolored   .70 .70
243 A31 3b multicolored 1.40 1.40
    Nos. 240-243 (4)   2.95 2.95

Future Development Plan — A32

1995, Aug. 28   Litho.   Perf. 13
244 A32 60c Building bridge .40 .40
245 A32 80c Trees   .55 .55
246 A32 90c Rural village   .65 .65
247 A32 1b Camels   .70 .70
    Nos. 244-247 (4)   2.30 2.30

A33

A34

1995, Oct. 23   Perf. 13½x14
248 A33 40c shown   .25 .25
249 A33 60c Tree, emblem   .35 .35
250 A33 70c Dove, "50," emblem .45 .45
251 A33 2b like No. 248   2.00 2.00
    Nos. 248-251 (4)   3.05 3.05

UN, 50th anniv.

1995, Oct. 2   Perf. 13½x14, 14x13½
COMESA, Committee for Economic Growth and Development in Southern Africa: 40c, Map of African member countries. 50c, Tree with country names on branches. 60c, Emblem, 3b, Emblem surrounded by country flags, horiz.

252 A34 40c multicolored   .25 .25
253 A34 50c multicolored   .45 .45
254 A34 60c multicolored   .45 .45
255 A34 3b multicolored 1.75 1.75
    Nos. 252-255 (4)   2.90 2.90

FAO, 50th Anniv. — A35

5c, Food bowl with world map on it, spoon. 25c, Men with tractor. 80c, Mother bird feeding chicks. 3b, Vegetables in horn of plenty.

1995, Dec. 18   Litho.   Perf. 13x14
256 A35 5c multicolored   .40 .40
257 A35 25c multicolored   .40 .40
258 A35 80c multicolored   .80 .80
259 A35 3b multicolored 2.50 2.50
    Nos. 256-259 (4)   4.10 4.10

Endangered Fauna — A36

No. 260: a, Green monkey. b, Aardwolf. c, Dugong. d, Maned rat.
Beisa oryx: No. 261: a, With young. b, One facing left. c, Two with heads together. d, One facing right.
White-eyed gull: No. 262: a, Preening. b, In flight. c, Two standing. d, One facing right.

1996, July 15   Litho.   Perf. 14
260-262 A36 3b Set of 3 strips 24.00 24.00

Nos. 260-262 were each issued in sheets of 12 stamps, containing three strips of four stamps, #a.-d. No. 261 for World Wildlife Fund.

Martyrs Day — A37

1996, June 17   Litho.   Perf. 13½x14
263 A37 40c People, flag   .40 .40
264 A37 60c At grave   .40 .40
265 A37 70c Mother, child   .80 .80
266 A37 80c Planting crops 1.00 1.00
    Nos. 263-266 (4)   2.60 2.60

1996 Summer Olympic Games, Atlanta A38

No. 267, Cycling. No. 268, Basketball, vert. No. 269, Volleyball, vert. No. 270, Soccer.
No. 271, vert: a, Volleyball. b, Laurel wreath. c, Basketball. d, Torch. e, Cycling, yellow shirt. f, Torch, diff. g, Cycling, green shirt. h, Gold medal. i, Soccer.
Each 10b: #272, Soccer, vert. #273, Cycling, vert.

1996, Nov. 20   Litho.   Perf. 14
267-270 A38 3b Set of 4   7.50 7.50
271 A38 2b Sheet of 9, #a.-i. 11.00 11.00
Souvenir Sheets
272-273 A38 Set of 2   11.00 11.00

UNICEF, 50th Anniv. A39

UNICEF emblem and: 40c, Mother with child. 55c, Nurse helping child. 60c, Weighing baby. 95c, Boy with one leg walking with crutch.

1996   Litho.   Perf. 14x13½
274 A39 40c multicolored   .25 .25
275 A39 55c multicolored   .25 .25
276 A39 60c multicolored   .40 .40
277 A39 95c multicolored   .40 .40
    Nos. 274-277 (4)   1.30 1.30

Revival of Eritrea Railway A40

Designs: 40c, Repairing track. 55c, Steam train arriving at station. 60c, Train shuttle transporting people. 95c, Train tunnel.

1996

278	A40	40c multicolored	.45	.45
279	A40	55c multicolored	.45	.45
280	A40	60c multicolored	.45	.45
281	A40	95c multicolored	.90	.90
		Nos. 278-281 (4)	2.25	2.25

National Service
A41

40c, Service members, speaker's platform, flags, vert. 55c, People looking over mountainside, vert. 60c, People digging ditches. 95c, Man standing on mountain top, overlooking valley, lake.

1996   Perf. 13½x14, 14x13½

282	A41	40c multicolored	.45	.45
283	A41	55c multicolored	.45	.45
284	A41	60c multicolored	.85	.85
285	A41	95c multicolored	1.25	1.25
		Nos. 282-285 (4)	3.00	3.00

Butterflies and Moths
A42

1b, Pieris napi. 2b, Heliconius melpomerie. 4b, Ornithoptera goliath. 8b, Heliconius astraea.

No. 290, vert, each 3b: a, Psaphis eusehemoides. b, Papilio brookiana. c, Parnassius charitonius. d, Morpho cypris. e, Darius plexippus. f, Precis octavia. g, Teinopalpus imperialis. h, Samia gloreri. i, Automeris nyctimene.

No. 291, each 3b: a, Papilio polymnestar. b, Ornithoptera paradiseo. c, Graphium marcellus. d, Panaxia quadripunctaria. e, Cardui japonica. f, Papilio childrence. g, Philosamea cynthis. h, Actias luna. i, Heticopis acit.

Each 10b: No. 292, Papilio glaucus. No. 293, Parnassius phoebus.

1997, June 16   Litho.   Perf. 14

| 286-289 | A42 | Set of 4 | 8.50 | 8.50 |

Sheets of 9

| 290-291 | A42 | 3b Set of 2 Sheets, #a.- | 24.00 | 24.00 |

Souvenir Sheets

| 292-293 | A42 | 10b Set of 2 Sheets | 9.00 | 9.00 |

Environmental Protection — A43

1997   Litho.   Perf. 14x13½

294	A43	60c Irrigation	.60	.60
295	A43	90c Reforestation	.60	.60
296	A43	95c Preventing erosion	1.25	1.25
		Nos. 294-296 (3)	2.45	2.45

Marine Life
A44

No. 297, each 3n: a, Sergeant major, white tipped reef shark. b, Hawksbill turtle, devil ray (e). c, Surgeonfish. d, Red sea houndfish, humpback whale (a, g). e, Devil ray (b, f, h). f, Devil ray (e, c), two-banded clownfish. g, Long-nosed butterflyfish. h, Red sea houndfish (g), yellow sweetlips (i). i, White moray eel.

No. 298, each 3n: a, Masked butterflyfish. b, Suckerfish (a), whale shark (a). c, Sunrise dottyback, bluefin trevally. d, Moon wrasse (a), purple moon angel (a), two-banded anemonefish. e, Lionfish (b, f). f, White tipped shark, sand diver fish. g, Golden jacks (d), lunar tailed grouper. h, Batfish (e, i). i, Black triggerfish.

Each 10n: No. 299, Powder-blue surgeonfish. No. 300, Twin-spot wrasse.

1997, Dec. 29   Litho.   Perf. 14

Sheets of 9

| 297-298 | A44 | Set of 2 Sheets, #a.-i. | 20.00 | 20.00 |

Souvenir Sheets

| 299-300 | A44 | Set of 2 Sheets | 12.50 | 12.50 |

A45

A46

Natl. Constitution: 10c, Speaker, crowd seated beneath tree. 40c, Dove, scales of justice. 85c, Hands holding constitution.

1997   Litho.   Perf. 13½x14

| 301-303 | A45 | Set of 3 | 1.25 | 1.25 |

1998, Mar. 16   Litho.   Perf. 14

Birds — No. 304, each 3n: a, African darter (b, d, e). b, White-headed vulture (e). c, Egyptian vulture (f). d, Yellow-billed hornbill (g). e, Helmeted guineafowl (d, f). f, Secretary bird (d, e, i). g, Martial eagle (h). h, Bateleur eagle (i). i, Red-billed queleas.

No. 305, each 3n: a, Black-headed weaver. b, Abyssinian roller (c, f). c, Abyssinian ground hornbill (b, e, f). d, Lichtenstein's sandgrouse. e, Erckel's francolin (d, g, h). f, Arabian bustard (e, i). g, Chestnut-backed finch-lark. h, Desert lark. i, Bifasciated lark.

Each 10n: #306, Peregrine falcon. #307, Hoopoe.

Sheets of 9

| 304-305 | A46 | Set of 2 Sheets, #a.-i. | 22.00 | 22.00 |

Souvenir Sheets

| 306-307 | A46 | Set of 2 Sheets | 8.00 | 8.00 |

Dwellings — A47

Traditional Hair Styles — A48

1998, July 1   Litho.   Perf. 13½x14

308	A47	50c Highlanders	.50	.50
309	A47	60c Lowlanders	.50	.50
310	A47	85c Danakils (Afars)	.75	.75
		Nos. 308-310 (3)	1.75	1.75

1998   Litho.   Perf. 13½x14

311	A48	10c Cunama	.30	.30
312	A48	50c Tignnys	.35	.35
313	A48	85c Bllen	.65	.65
314	A48	95c Tigre	.75	.75
		Nos. 311-314 (4)	2.05	2.05

Dated 1997.

A49

A50

Traditional Musical Instruments: 15c, Chirawata. 60c, Imbilta, malaket, shambeko. 75c, Kobero. 85c, K'rar.

1998, Dec. 28   Litho.   Perf. 13½x14

315	A49	15c multicolored	.35	.35
316	A49	60c multicolored	.45	.45
317	A49	75c multicolored	.65	.65
318	A49	85c multicolored	.75	.75
		Nos. 315-318 (4)	2.20	2.20

1999   Litho.   Perf. 13¼x14

319	A50	60c green & multi	.45	.45
320	A50	1n red & multi	.70	.70
321	A50	3n blue & multi	2.25	2.25
		Nos. 319-321 (3)	3.40	3.40

Independence, 8th Anniv.

1997 Introduction of Nakfa Currency — A51

Bank notes: 10c, 1 Nakfa. 60c, 5 Nakfa. 80c, 10 Nakfa. 1n, 20 Nakfa. 2n, 50 Nakfa. 3n, 100 Nakfa.

1999, Nov. 8   Litho.   Perf. 13¼

322	A51	10c multicolored	.45	.45
323	A51	60c multicolored	.45	.45
324	A51	80c multicolored	.45	.45
325	A51	1n multicolored	.70	.70
326	A51	2n multicolored	1.40	1.40
327	A51	3n multicolored	2.00	2.00
		Nos. 322-327 (6)	5.45	5.45

Natl. Union of Eritrean Women, 20th Anniv.
A52

Designs: 5c, Woman and child, vert. 10c, Three women. 25c, Women and flag. 1n, Woman with binoculars.

1999   Perf. 13¼x14, 14x13¼

328	A52	5c multicolored	.25	.25
329	A52	10c multicolored	.25	.25
330	A52	25c multicolored	.25	.25
331	A52	1n multicolored	.40	.40
		Nos. 328-331 (4)	1.15	1.15

A53

Marine Life
A54

No. 332, each 3n: a, Coachwhip ray. b, Sulfur damselfish. c, "Gray moray." d, Sabre squirrelfish. e, Rusty parrotfish. f, "Striped eel catfish."

No. 333, each 3n: a, Spangled emperor. b, Devil scorpionfish. c, Crown squirrelfish. d, Vanikoro sweeper. e, Sergeant major. f, Giant manta.

No. 334, each 3n: a, Chilomycterus spilostylus. b, Dascyllus marginatus. c, Balistapus undulatus. d, Pomacanthus semicirculatus. e, Rhinecanthus assasi. f, Millepora.

No. 335, each 3n: a, Epinephalus fasciata. b, Pygoplites diacanthus. c, Cephalopholis miniata. d, Centropyge eibli. e, Ostracion cubicus. f, Heniochus acuminatus.

Each 10n: No. 336, Centropyge flavissimus. No. 337, Larabicus quadrilineatus. No. 338, Anthias squamipinnis. 15n, Pomacanthus maculosus.

2000, Apr. 17   Litho.   Perf. 14

Sheets of 6, #a.-f.

| 332-333 | A53 | Set of 2 | 13.50 | 13.50 |
| 334-335 | A54 | Set of 2 | 13.50 | 13.50 |

Souvenir Sheets

| 336-338 | A54 | Set of 3 | 12.00 | 12.00 |
| 339 | A54 | 15n multi | 4.50 | 4.50 |

Illustrations on Nos. 332c and 332f were switched.

A55

Flag and: 5c, Man with sword. 10c, Ship Denden Assab. 25c, Independence Day festivities. 60c, Soldiers and barracks. 1n, Finger, heart and map. 2n, People under tree. 3n, Ballot box. 5n, Eritrean seal, military plane, tank, ship. 7n, Seal. 10n, Ten-nakfa note.

Perf. 13¾x13¼

2000, Mar. 17   Litho.

| 340-349 | A55 | Set of 10 | 11.00 | 11.00 |

See Nos. 363A, 363E.

Worldwide Fund for Nature (WWF) — A56

Proteles cristatus: a, Laying down. b, Pair in den. c, Walking. d, Close-up. Illustration reduced.

2001, Oct. 1   Litho.   Perf. 14

| 350 | A56 | 3n Block or strip of 4, #a-d | 4.50 | 4.50 |

Wild Animals — A57

No. 351, 3n: a, Salt's dik-dik. b, Klipspringer. c, Greater kudu. d, Soemmering's gazelle. e, Dorcas gazelle. f, Somali wild ass.

No. 352, 3n: a, Aardvark. b, Black-backed jackal. c, Striped hyena. d, Spotted hyena. e, East African leopard. f, African elephant.

2001, Oct. 29
Sheets of 6, #a-f
351-352 A57 Set of 2   10.00 10.00

Struggle for Independence, 10th Anniv. — A58

Designs: 20c, Women, flag, jewelry. 60c, Doves, stylized flag, vert. 1n, Bees, honeycomb, flag, vert. 3n, Men with sticks, vert.

Perf. 13x13¼, 13¼x13
2001, May 23   Litho.
353-356 A58 Set of 4   2.25 2.25

Liberation of Nakfa, 25th Anniv. A59

Designs: 50c, Denden. 1n, Town of Nakfa, 1977 (77x27mm). 3n, First Organizational Congress of the Eritrean People's Liberation Front (77x27mm).

2002, Mar. 23 Litho. Perf. 14x13¼
357-359 A59 Set of 3   1.50 1.50

Martyr's Day — A60

Designs: 1n, People and map. 2n, Hand, map of Badma area, and flag. 3n, Map and ship. 5n, Dove, map and dead man (49x29mm, triangular).

Perf. 14x13¼, 13½ (5n)
2002, June 20
360-363 A60 Set of 4   4.00 4.00

Type of 2000 Redrawn

Flag and: 30c, People under tree. 75c, Ship Denden Assab.

2002, Oct. 21 Litho. Perf. 13¼x14¼
363A A55 30c multi   —
363E A55 75c multi   —

Four additional stamps were issued in this set. The editors would like to examine any examples.

Dr. Fred C. Hollows (1929-93), Ophthalmologist A61

Designs: 50c, Portrait. 1n, Hollows wearing ophthalmological equipment. 2n, Hollows with man.

2003, Feb. 10   Perf. 13¼x14
364-366 A61 Set of 3   1.25 1.25

Eritrea — People's Republic of China Diplomatic Relations, 10th Anniv. A62

2003, May 24   Perf. 12
367 A62 4.50n multi   1.50 1.50

Eritrean postal authorities have declared "illegal" the following items:

Sheetlet of nine 5n stamps depicting Trains;

Sheetlets of nine 3n stamps depicting Marilyn Monroe (two different), Dogs, The Beatles "Yellow Submarine," September 11 firefighters, Brigitte Bardot, Grace Kelly, Sophia Loren, Golf etiquette, Sexy actresses, Sexy models, Boris Vallejo nudes, Dorian Cleavenger, Michael Möbius, Olivia, Ricky Carralero, Concorde;

Sheetlets of six stamps with various denominations depicting Lighthouses (with Rotary emblem) (two different), Hopper paintings (two different), Vettriano paintings (two different), Marilyn Monroe (two different), Elvgren pin-ups (two different), Teddy bears (two different);

Sheetlets of six 3n stamps depicting Van Gogh paintings, Paintings of nudes;

Sheetlets of five 3n stamps depicting Corot paintings, Pisarro paintings, Renoir paintings, Elvis Presley, Marilyn Monroe;

Sheetlets of four stamps with various denominations depicting Pandas (with Scouting emblem), Crocodiles (with Scouting emblem), Buffalos (with Rotary emblem), Elephants (with Rotary emblem), Monkeys (with Scouting emblem), Lizards (with Scouting emblem), Snakes (with Scouting Emblem), Turtles (with Rotary emblem), Wild cats (with Scouting emblem), Birds of prey (with Rotary emblem), Fowl (with Rotary emblem), Parrots (with Scouting emblem), Penguins (with Rotary emblem), Fish (with Rotary emblem), Marine life (with Scouting emblem), Mushrooms (with Rotary emblem), Butterflies (with Scouting emblem), Bees (with Scouting emblem), Spiders (with Scouting emblem);

Sheetlets of four 3n stamps depicting Dinosaurs (with Scouting emblem), Dinosaurs (with Rotary emblem) Elephants (with Scouting emblem), Elephants (with Rotary emblem), Horses (with Scouting emblem), Horses (with Rotary emblem), Birds (with Scouting emblem), Birds (with Rotary emblem), Penguins (with Scouting emblem), Penguins (with Rotary emblem), Orchids (with Scouting emblem), Orchids (with Rotary emblem), Butterflies (with Scouting emblem), Butterflies (with Rotary emblem), Cars (with Scouting emblem), Cars (with Rotary emblem), Motorcycles (with Scouting emblem), Motorcycles (with Rotary emblem), Trains (with Scouting emblem), Trains (with Rotary emblem);

Sheetlets of three 5n stamps depicting Dinosaurs (with Rotary emblem) (two different), Pandas;

Strips of three 5n stamps depicting Steam trains (four different);

Souvenir sheet with one 8n stamp depicting Steam Trains (with Rotary emblem) (two different), Dinosaurs (with Rotary emblem), Pandas (with Scouting emblem), Elephants (with Scouting emblem), Tigers (with Scouting emblem), Birds of prey (with Scouting emblem);

Souvenir sheets with one 5n stamp depicting Marilyn Monroe (six different), Lighthouses (with Rotary emblem) (four different), Teddy bears (four different), Hopper paintings (two different), Vettriano paintings (two different).

Eritrean Railway — A63

Independence Celebrations A63a

Massawa A63b

2003   Litho.   Perf. 14x13¼
Denomination Color

368	A63	5c	Prussian blue	.20	.20
369	A63	10c	greenish blk	.20	.20
370	A63	15c	lilac	.20	.20
371	A63	35c	violet	.20	.20
372	A63	50c	orange	.20	.20
373	A63	90c	olive green	.25	.25
374	A63	1n	red	.25	.25
375	A63	2n	blue violet	.55	.55
376	A63	10n	red	2.75	2.75
376A	A63a	50n	white	12.00	12.00
376B	A63b	75n	white	18.00	18.00
376C	A63b	100n	white	24.00	24.00
	Nos. 368-376C (12)			58.80	58.80

Issued: 50n, 75n, 100n, 8/29.

Liberation of Massawa, 14th Anniv. A64

Designs: 40c, Tanks as fountains. 50c, Boat with soldiers.

No. 379: a, 3n, Crashed airplane, people, soldiers in shallow water. b, 3n, Tank, soldier, flag, boat. c, 4n, People, buildings at shore.

2004
377-378 A64 Set of 2   .40 .40

Miniature Sheet

379 A64 Sheet of 3, #a-c   3.00 3.00

Man and Camels — A65

Man and Cattle A66

Highland Woman, Child and Camel — A67

2004, July 12　　Litho.　　Perf. 12
Frame Color

380	A65	20c violet blue	.20	.20
381	A65	25c red violet	.20	.20
382	A65	40c brown	.20	.20
383	A66	50c red	.20	.20
384	A66	55c green	.20	.20
385	A66	60c light blue	.20	.20
386	A67	80c olive green	.30	.30
387	A67	1n orange	.30	.30
388	A67	4.50n blue	.95	.95
		Nos. 380-388 (9)	2.75	2.75

China - Africa Cooperation Forum, Beijing — A71

2006, Nov. 3　　Litho.　　Perf. 12

| 392 | A71 | 7n multi | .95 | .95 |

SEMI-POSTAL STAMPS

Many issues of Italy and Italian Colonies include one or more semipostal denominations. To avoid splitting sets, these issues are generally listed as regular postage, airmail, etc., unless all values carry a surtax.

Italy Nos. B1-B3 Overprinted type "f"

1915-16　　Wmk. 140　　Perf. 14

B1	SP1	10c + 5c rose	4.00	16.00
a.		"EPITREA"	28.00	40.00
b.		Inverted overprint	500.00	500.00
B2	SP2	15c + 5c slate	16.00	32.50
B3	SP2	20c + 5c orange	4.75	32.50
a.		"EPITREA"	32.50	52.50
b.		Inverted overprint	525.00	525.00
c.		Pair, one without ovpt.	—	2,800.
		Nos. B1-B3 (3)	24.75	76.50
		Set, never hinged	60.00	

No. B2 Surcharged

1916

B4	SP2	20c on 15c+5c slate	16.00	32.50
		Never hinged	40.00	
a.		"EPITREA"	57.50	95.00
b.		Pair, one without overprint	1,300.	
		Never hinged	1,600.	

Counterfeits exist of the minor varieties of Nos. B1, B3-B4.

Holy Year Issue
Italy Nos. B20-B25 Overprinted in Black or Red

1925　　　　　　　　　Perf. 12

B5	SP4	20c + 10c dk grn & brn	3.25	20.00
B6	SP4	30c + 15c dk brn & brn	3.25	22.50
a.		Double overprint		
B7	SP4	50c + 25c vio & brn	3.25	20.00
B8	SP4	60c + 30c dp rose & brn	3.25	25.00
a.		Inverted overprint		
B9	SP8	1 l + 50c dp bl & vio (R)	3.25	32.50
B10	SP8	5 l + 2.50 l org brn & vio (R)	3.25	47.50
		Nos. B5-B10 (6)	19.50	167.50
		Set, never hinged	47.50	

The existence of Nos. B6a, B8a has been questioned.

Colonial Institute Issue

"Peace" Substituting Spade for Sword — SP1

1926　　Typo.　　Perf. 14

B11	SP1	5c + 5c brown	1.00	8.00
B12	SP1	10c + 5c olive grn	1.00	8.00
B13	SP1	20c + 5c blue grn	1.00	8.00
B14	SP1	40c + 5c brown red	1.00	8.00
B15	SP1	60c + 5c orange	1.00	8.00
B16	SP1	1 l + 5c blue	1.00	17.50
		Nos. B11-B16 (6)	6.00	57.50
		Set, never hinged	13.50	

The surtax of 5c on each stamp was for the Italian Colonial Institute.

Types of Italian Semi-Postal Stamps of 1926 Overprinted type "k"

1927　　Unwmk.　　Perf. 11½

B17	SP10	40c + 20c dk brn & blk	2.40	32.50
B18	SP10	60c + 30c brn red & ol brn	2.40	32.50
B19	SP10	1.25 l + 60c dp bl & blk	2.40	52.50
B20	SP10	5 l + 2.50 l dk grn & blk	4.00	72.50
		Nos. B17-B20 (4)	11.20	190.00
		Set, never hinged	28.00	

The surtax on these stamps was for the charitable work of the Voluntary Militia for Italian National Defense.

Fascism and Victory SP2

Agriculture SP3

1928　　Wmk. 140　　Typo.　　Perf. 14

B21	SP2	20c + 5c blue grn	2.40	12.00
B22	SP2	30c + 5c red	2.40	12.00
B23	SP2	50c + 10c purple	2.40	20.00
B24	SP2	1.25 l + 20c dk blue	3.25	24.00
		Nos. B21-B24 (4)	10.45	68.00
		Set, never hinged	25.00	

The surtax was for the Society Africana d'Italia, whose 46th anniv. was commemorated by the issue.

Types of Italian Semi-Postal Stamps of 1928 Overprinted type "f"

1929　　Unwmk.　　Perf. 11

B25	SP10	30c + 10c red & blk	4.00	20.00
B26	SP10	50c + 20c vio & blk	4.00	24.00
B27	SP10	1.25 l + 50c brn & bl	4.75	40.00
B28	SP10	5 l + 2 l olive grn & blk	4.75	72.50
		Nos. B25-B28 (4)	17.50	156.50
		Set, never hinged	45.00	

Surtax for the charitable work of the Voluntary Militia for Italian Natl. Defense.

Types of Italian Semi-Postal Stamps of 1929 Overprinted type "f" in Black or Red

1930　　　　　　　　　Perf. 14

B29	SP10	30c + 10c dk grn & bl grn (Bk)	21.00	32.50
B30	SP10	50c + 10c grn & vio	21.00	45.00
B31	SP10	1.25 l + 30c ol brn & red brn	21.00	55.00

B32	SP10	5 l + 1.50 l ind & grn	65.00	160.00
		Nos. B29-B32 (4)	128.00	292.50
		Set, never hinged	300.00	

Surtax for the charitable work of the Voluntary Militia for Italian Natl. Defense.

1930　　Photo.　　Wmk. 140

B33	SP3	50c + 20c ol brn	4.00	20.00
B34	SP3	1.25 l + 20c dp bl	4.00	20.00
B35	SP3	1.75 l + 20c green	4.00	22.50
B36	SP3	2.55 l + 50c purple	6.50	36.00
B37	SP3	5 l + 1 l dp car	6.50	52.50
		Nos. B33-37 (5)	25.00	151.00
		Set, never hinged	57.50	

Italian Colonial Agricultural Institute, 25th anniv. The surtax aided that institution.

AIR POST STAMPS

Desert Scene AP1

Design: 80c, 1 l, 2 l, Plane and globe.

Wmk. Crowns (140)
1934　　Photo.　　Perf. 14

C1	AP1	25c sl bl & org red	4.00	20.00
C2	AP1	50c grn & indigo	4.00	16.00
C3	AP1	75c brn & org red	4.00	16.00
C4	AP1	80c org brn & ol grn	4.00	20.00
C5	AP1	1 l scar & ol grn	4.00	24.00
C6	AP1	2 l dk bl & brn	4.00	40.00
		Nos. C1-C6 (6)	24.00	136.00
		Set, never hinged	57.50	

Second Colonial Arts Exhibition, Naples.

Plowing AP3

Plane and Cacti AP6

25c, 1.50 l, Plowing. 50c, 2 l, Plane over mountain pass. 60c, 5 l, Plane and trees. 75c, 10 l, Plane and cacti. 1 l, 3 l, Bridge.

1936　　　　　　　　　Photo.

C7	AP3	25c deep green	3.25	4.00
C8	AP3	50c dark brown	2.40	.35
C9	AP3	60c brown orange	4.00	12.00
C10	AP6	75c orange brown	3.25	1.60
C11	AP3	1 l deep blue	1.60	.35
C12	AP3	1.50 l purple	4.00	.80
C13	AP3	2 l gray blue	4.00	3.25
C14	AP3	3 l copper red	19.00	22.50
C15	AP3	5 l green	14.50	6.50
C16	AP6	10 l rose red	32.50	22.50
		Nos. C7-C16 (10)	88.50	73.85
		Set, never hinged	200.00	

AIR POST SEMI-POSTAL STAMPS

King Victor Emmanuel III — SPAP1

1934　　Wmk. 140　　Photo.　　Perf. 14

CB1	SPAP1	25c + 10c	6.50	14.50
CB2	SPAP1	50c + 10c	6.50	14.50
CB3	SPAP1	75c + 15c	6.50	14.50
CB4	SPAP1	80c + 15c	6.50	14.50

CB5	SPAP1	1 l + 20c	6.50	14.50
CB6	SPAP1	2 l + 20c	6.50	14.50
CB7	SPAP1	3 l + 25c	22.50	72.50
CB8	SPAP1	5 l + 25c	22.50	72.50
CB9	SPAP1	10 l + 30c	22.50	72.50
CB10	SPAP1	25 l + 2 l	22.50	72.50
		Nos. CB1-CB10 (10)	129.00	377.00
		Set, never hinged	300.00	

65th birthday of King Victor Emmanuel III and the nonstop flight from Rome to Mogadiscio. Used values are for stamps canceled to order.

AIR POST SEMI-POSTAL OFFICIAL STAMP

Type of Air Post Semi-Postal Stamps, 1934, Overprinted Crown and "SERVIZIO DI STATO" in Black

1934　　Wmk. 140　　Perf. 14

| CBO1 | SPAP1 | 25 l + 2 l cop red | 2,800. | |
| | | Never hinged | 4,200. | |

SPECIAL DELIVERY STAMPS

Special Delivery Stamps of Italy, Overprinted type "a"

1907　　Wmk. 140　　Perf. 14

E1	SD1	25c rose red	20.00	20.00
		Never hinged	50.00	
a.		Double overprint	—	—

1909

| E2 | SD2 | 30c blue & rose | 110.00 | 175.00 |
| | | Never hinged | 275.00 | |

1920

| E3 | SD1 | 50c dull red | 2.40 | 22.00 |
| | | Never hinged | 6.00 | |

"Italia" SD1

1924　　Engr.　　Unwmk.

E4	SD1	60c dk red & brn	5.50	22.50
a.		Perf. 13½	14.00	35.00
E5	SD1	2 l dk blue & red	14.00	26.00
		Set, never hinged	47.50	

For surcharges see Nos. E6-E8.

Nos. E4 and E5 Surcharged in Dark Blue or Red:

v

w

1926

E6	SD1	70c on 60c (Bl)	5.50	14.00
E7	SD1	2.50 l on 2 l (R)	14.00	25.00
		Set, never hinged	47.50	

Type of 1924 Surcharged in Blue or Black:

1927-35 **Perf. 11**
E8 SD1 1.25 l on 60c dk
    red &
    brn (Bl) 11.00 3.25
  Never hinged 28.00
  a. Perf. 14 (Bl) ('37) 100.00 20.00
    Never hinged 200.00
  b. Perf. 11 (Bk) ('35) 8,750. 725.00
    Never hinged 11,000.
  c. Perf. 14 (Bk) ('35) 275.00 47.50
    Never hinged 550.00

AUTHORIZED DELIVERY STAMP

Authorized Delivery Stamp of Italy, No. EY2, Overprinted Type "f" in Black

1939-41 **Wmk. 140** **Perf. 14**
EY1 AD2 10c dk brown ('41) .65
  a. 10c reddish brown 17.50 40.00
    Never hinged 45.00

On No. EY1a, which was used in Italian East Africa, the overprint hits the figures "10." On No. EY1, which was sold in Rome, the overprint falls above the 10's.

POSTAGE DUE STAMPS

Postage Due Stamps of Italy Overprinted type "a" at Top

1903 **Wmk. 140** **Perf. 14**
J1 D3 5c buff & mag 22.50 40.00
  a. Double overprint 500.00
J2 D3 10c buff & mag 17.50 40.00
J3 D3 20c buff & mag 17.50 27.50
J4 D3 30c buff & mag 25.00 32.50
J5 D3 40c buff & mag 65.00 65.00
J6 D3 50c buff & mag 87.50 65.00
J7 D3 60c buff & mag 25.00 65.00
J8 D3 1 l blue & mag 17.50 36.00
J9 D3 2 l blue & mag 175.00 160.00
J10 D3 5 l blue & mag 300.00 275.00
J11 D3 10 l blue & mag 2,800. 550.00
    Never hinged 4,200.
  Set #J1-J10, never
  hinged 1,100.

Same with Overprint at Bottom

1920-22
J1b D3 5c buff & magenta 4.75 13.00
  c. Numeral and ovpt. invtd. 525.00 525.00
J2a D3 10c buff & magenta 8.00 13.00
J3a D3 20c buff & magenta 875.00 350.00
J4a D3 30c buff & magenta 60.00 36.00
J5a D3 40c buff & magenta 52.50 40.00
J6a D3 50c buff & magenta 28.00 36.00
J7a D3 60c buff & magenta 28.00 36.00
J8a D3 1 l blue & magenta 47.50 36.00
J9a D3 2 l blue & magenta 1,600. 750.00
J10a D3 5 l blue & magenta 400.00 260.00
J11a D3 10 l blue & magenta 57.50 67.50
  Set, never hinged 4,750.

1903 **Wmk. 140**
J12 D4 50 l yellow 725.00 260.00
J13 D4 100 l blue 475.00 140.00
  Set, never hinged 1,800.

1927
J14 D3 60c buff & brown 120.00 145.00
  Never hinged 180.00

Postage Due Stamps of Italy, 1934, Overprinted type "j" in Black

1934
J15 D6 5c brown .80 12.00
J16 D6 10c blue .80 2.40
J17 D6 20c rose red 2.40 4.00
  a. Inverted overprint
J18 D6 25c green 2.40 4.75
J19 D6 30c red orange 2.40 12.00
J20 D6 40c black brown 2.40 12.00
J21 D6 50c violet 2.40 1.60
J22 D6 60c black 5.00 20.00
J23 D7 1 l red orange 2.40 2.40
J24 D7 2 l green 14.50 45.00
J25 D7 5 l violet 25.00 52.50
J26 D7 10 l blue 30.00 55.00
J27 D7 20 l carmine rose 40.00 65.00
  Nos. J15-J27 (13) 130.50 288.65
  Set, never hinged 325.00

The existence of No. J17a has been questioned.

PARCEL POST STAMPS

These stamps were used by affixing them to the way bill so that one half remained on it following the parcel, the other half staying on the receipt given the sender. Most used halves are right halves. Complete stamps were obtainable canceled, probably to order. Both unused and used values are for complete stamps.

Parcel Post Stamps of Italy, 1914-17, Overprinted type "j" in Black on Each Half

1916 **Wmk. 140** **Perf. 13½**
Q1 PP2 5c brown 120.00 175.00
Q2 PP2 10c deep blue 2,500. 3,200.
  Never hinged 3,800.
Q3 PP2 25c red 275.00 275.00
Q4 PP2 50c orange 65.00 175.00
Q5 PP2 1 l violet 120.00 175.00
Q6 PP2 2 l green 87.50 175.00
Q7 PP2 3 l bister 800.00 475.00
Q8 PP2 4 l slate 800.00 475.00
  Set #Q1, Q3-Q8, never hinged 3,400.

Halves Used, Each
Q1, Q7-Q8 2.50
Q2 75.00
Q3 3.25
Q4 1.00
Q5-Q6 4.00

Overprinted type "f" on Each Half

1917-24
Q9 PP2 5c brown 3.25 8.00
Q10 PP2 10c deep blue 3.25 8.00
Q11 PP2 20c black 3.25 8.00
Q12 PP2 25c red 3.25 8.00
Q13 PP2 50c orange 6.50 12.00
Q14 PP2 1 l violet 6.50 12.00
Q15 PP2 2 l green 6.50 12.00
Q16 PP2 3 l bister 6.50 12.00
Q17 PP2 4 l slate 6.50 20.00
Q18 PP2 10 l rose lil ('24) 95.00 160.00
Q19 PP2 12 l red brn ('24) 210.00 300.00
Q20 PP2 15 l olive grn ('24) 210.00 300.00
Q21 PP2 20 l brn vio ('24) 275.00 400.00
  Nos. Q9-Q21 (13) 835.50 1,260.
  Set, never hinged 1,200.

Halves Used, Each
Q9-Q16 .20
Q17 .75
Q18 5.00
Q19 7.50
Q20 7.50
Q21 10.00

Parcel Post Stamps of Italy, 1927-39, Overprinted type "f" on Each Half

1927-37
Q21A PP3 10c dp bl ('37) 8,000. 725.00
  Never hinged 9,000.
Q22 PP3 25c red ('37) 475.00 47.50
Q23 PP3 30c ultra ('29) 4.00 16.00
Q24 PP3 50c orange ('36) 650.00 32.50
Q25 PP3 60c red ('29) 4.00 16.00
Q26 PP3 1 l brn vio ('36) 275.00 32.50
  a. 1 l lilac 325.00 32.50
Q27 PP3 2 l green ('36) 275.00 32.50
Q28 PP3 3 l bister ('36) 9.50 28.00
Q29 PP3 4 l gray ('36) 9.50 28.00
Q30 PP3 10 l rose lil ('36) 525.00 600.00
Q31 PP3 20 l lil brn ('36) 525.00 600.00
  Nos. Q22-Q31 (10) 2,752.
  Set, never hinged 4,000.
  Nos. Q21A-Q31 (11) 2,158.

Halves Used, Each
Q21A 26.00
Q22-Q25, Q27-Q28 .40
Q26, Q26a, Q29 .40
Q30 10.00
Q31 15.00

ESTONIA

e-'stō-nē-ə

LOCATION — Northern Europe, bordering on the Baltic Sea and the Gulf of Finland
GOVT. — Independent republic
AREA — 17,462 sq. mi.
POP. — 1,408,523 (1999 est.)
CAPITAL — Tallinn

Formerly a part of the Russia empire, Estonia declared its independence in 1918. In 1940 it was incorporated in the Union of Soviet Socialist Republics. Estonia declared the restoration of its independence from the USSR on Aug. 20, 1991. Estonian independence was

recognized by the Soviet Union on Sept. 6, 1991.

100 Kopecks = 1 Ruble (1918, 1991)
100 Penni = 1 Mark (1919)
100 Sents = 1 Kroon (1928, 1992)

Catalogue values for unused stamps in this country are for Never Hinged items, beginning with Scott 200 in the regular postage section, Scott B60 in the semipostal section, and Scott F1 in the registration section.

Watermark

Wmk. 207 — Arms of Finland in the Sheet

Illustration reduced. Watermark covers a large part of sheet.

A1 A2

1918-19 **Unwmk.** **Litho.** **Imperf.**
1 A1 5k pale red .85 .85
2 A1 15k bright blue .85 .85
3 A2 35p brown ('19) 1.00 .90
  a. Printed on both sides 100.00
  b. 35p olive 35.00 30.00
4 A2 70p olive grn ('19) 1.50 1.25
  Nos. 1-4 (4) 4.20 3.85

Nos. 1-4 exist privately perforated.

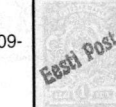

Russian Stamps of 1909-17 Handstamped in Violet or Black

1919, May 7 **Perf. 14, 14½x15, 13½**
8 A14 1k orange 1,750. 1,750.
9 A14 2k green 25.00 25.00
10 A14 3k red 30.00 26.00
11 A14 5k claret 25.00 22.50
12 A15 10k dk bl (Bk) 45.00 42.50
13 A15 10k dk bl 150.00 150.00
14 A14 10k on 7k lt bl 400.00 400.00
15 A11 15k red brn & bl 35.00 35.00
16 A11 25k grn & vio 40.00 37.50
17 A11 35k red brn & grn 1,500. 1,500.
18 A8 50k vio & grn 87.50 87.50
19 A9 1r pale brn, brn & org 150.00 150.00
20 A13 10r scar, yel & gray 3,250. 3,250.

Imperf.
21 A14 1k orange 22.50 22.50
22 A14 2k green 325.00 325.00
23 A14 3k red 42.50 42.50
24 A9 1r pale brn, brn & red org 210.00 210.00
25 A12 3½r maroon & grn 400.00 400.00
26 A13 5r dk bl, grn & pale bl 500.00 500.00

Provisionally issued at Tallinn. This overprint has been extensively counterfeited. Values are for genuine examples competently expertized. No. 20 is always creased.

Gulls — A3

1919, May 13 **Imperf.**
27 A3 5p yellow 2.25 3.25

A4 A5 A6

A7 Viking Ship — A8

1919-20 **Perf. 11½**
28 A4 10p green .25 .25

Imperf
29 A4 5p orange .20 .20
30 A4 10p green .20 .20
31 A5 15p rose .20 .20
32 A6 35p blue .25 .20
33 A7 70p dl vio ('20) .25 .20
34 A1 1m bl & blk brn 1.25 .55
  a. Gray granite paper ('20) .65 .40
35 A8 5m yel & blk 3.00 .95
  a. Gray granite paper ('20) 1.00 .50
36 A8 15m yel grn & olv ('20) 3.25 .65
37 A8 25m ultra & blk brn ('20) 4.75 2.50
  Nos. 28-37 (10) 13.60 5.90
  Set, never hinged 16.50

The 5m exists with inverted center. Not a postal item.
See #76-77. For surcharges see #55, 57.

Skyline of Tallinn — A9

1920-24 **Imperf.**
Pelure Paper
39 A9 25p green .25 .25
40 A9 25p yellow ('24) .25 .30
41 A9 35p rose .25 .25
42 A9 50p green ('21) .25 .25
43 A9 1m vermilion .65 .25
44 A9 2m blue .55 .25
45 A9 2m ultramarine .45 .25
46 A9 2.50m blue .65 .25
  Nos. 39-46 (8) 3.30 2.05
  Set, never hinged 9.00

Nos. 39-46 with sewing machine perforation are unofficial.
For surcharge see No. 56.

Stamps of 1919-20 Surcharged

1920 **Imperf.**
55 A5 1m on 15p rose .50 .50
56 A9 1m on 35p rose .60 .50
57 A7 2m on 70p dl vio .85 .60
  Nos. 55-57 (3) 1.95 1.60
  Set, never hinged 4.00

Weaver Blacksmith
A10 A11

1922-23   Typo.   Imperf.

58	A10	½m orange ('23)	2.00	3.00
59	A10	1m brown ('23)	2.75	2.25
60	A10	2m yellow green	2.00	2.00
61	A10	2½m claret	5.00	3.00
62	A11	5m rose	5.00	3.00
63	A11	9m red ('23)	8.00	6.00
64	A11	10m deep blue	6.00	5.00
		Nos. 58-64 (7)	30.75	24.25
		Set, never hinged	60.00	

1922-25   Perf. 14

65	A10	½m orange ('23)	.65	.20
66	A10	1m brown ('23)	.80	.20
67	A10	2m yellow green	1.40	.20
68	A10	2½m claret	1.40	.20
69	A10	3m blue green ('24)	1.50	.20
70	A11	5m rose	5.00	.20
71	A11	9m red ('23)	3.00	1.00
72	A11	10m deep blue	4.00	.20
73	A11	12m red ('25)	4.00	.90
74	A11	15m plum ('25)	4.00	.25
75	A11	20m ultra ('25)	15.00	.20
		Nos. 65-75 (11)	40.75	3.75
		Set, never hinged	75.00	

See No. 89. For surcharges see Nos. 84-88.

Viking Ship Type of 1920

1922, June 8   Perf. 14x13½

76	A8	15m yel grn & vio	5.00	.60
77	A8	25m ultra & blk brn	9.00	2.00
		Set, never hinged	22.50	

Map of
Estonia — A13

1923-24

Paper with Lilac Network

78	A13	100m ol grn & bl	20.00	2.75

Paper with Buff Network

79	A13	300m brn & bl ('24)	50.00	12.50
		Set, never hinged	110.00	

For surcharges see Nos. 106-107.

National
Theater,
Tallinn — A14

1924, Dec. 9   Perf. 14x13½

Paper with Blue Network

81	A14	30m violet & blk	10.00	2.75

Paper with Rose Network

82	A14	70m car rose & blk	15.00	5.00
		Set, never hinged	25.00	

For surcharge see No. 105.

Vanemuine
Theater,
Tartu — A15

1927, Oct. 25

Paper with Lilac Network

83	A15	40m dp bl & ol brn	10.00	2.75
		Never hinged	15.00	

Stamps of 1922-25
Surcharged in New
Currency in Red or
Black

1928   Perf. 14

84	A10	2s yellow green	1.50	.20
85	A11	5s rose red (B)	1.50	.20
86	A11	10s deep blue	2.00	.20
a.		Imperf., pair	750.00	—
87	A11	15s plum (B)	6.50	.20
88	A11	20s ultra	4.50	.30
		Nos. 84-88 (5)	16.00	1.15
		Set, never hinged	26.00	

10th anniversary of independence.

3rd Philatelic Exhibition Issue
Blacksmith Type of 1922-23

1928, July 6

89	A11	10m gray	5.00	7.50
		Never hinged	9.00	

Sold only at Tallinn Philatelic Exhibition.
Exists imperf.

Arms — A16

Paper with Network in Parenthesis

1928-40   Perf. 14, 14½x14

90	A16	1s dk gray (bl)	.30	.20
a.		Thick gray-toned laid paper ('40)	7.50	4.50
91	A16	2s yel grn (org)	.40	.20
92	A16	4s grn (brn) ('29)	.50	.20
93	A16	5s red (grn)	3.00	.20
a.		5 feet on lowest lion	35.00	25.00
94	A16	8s vio (buff) ('29)	1.60	.20
95	A16	10s lt bl (lilac)	2.00	.20
96	A16	12s crimson (grn)	1.50	.20
97	A16	15s yel (blue)	1.75	.20
98	A16	15s car (gray) ('35)	6.00	.45
99	A16	20s slate bl (red)	2.75	.20
100	A16	25s red vio (grn) ('29)	6.00	.20
101	A16	25s bl (brn) ('35)	6.00	.40
102	A16	40s red org (bl) ('29)	7.00	.30
103	A16	60s gray (brn) ('29)	10.00	.50
104	A16	80s brn (bl) ('29)	10.00	1.00
		Nos. 90-104 (15)	58.80	4.65
		Set, never hinged	85.00	

Types of 1924 Issues Surcharged:

1930, Sept. 1   Perf. 14x13½

Paper with Green Network

105	A14	1k on 70m car & blk	7.00	3.00

Paper with Rose Network

106	A13	2k on 300m brn & bl	14.50	7.50

Paper with Blue Network

107	A13	3k on 300m brn & bl	35.00	18.00
		Nos. 105-107 (3)	56.50	28.50
		Set, never hinged	125.00	

University
Observatory
A17

University of
Tartu
A18

Paper with Network as in Parenthesis

1932, June 1   Perf. 14

108	A17	5s red (yellow)	5.50	.60
109	A18	10s light bl (lilac)	1.50	.60
110	A17	12s car (blue)	8.00	2.75
111	A18	20s dk bl (green)	6.00	1.10
		Nos. 108-111 (4)	21.00	5.05
		Set, never hinged	55.00	

University of Tartu tercentenary.

Narva Falls — A19

Ancient Bard
Playing
Harp — A20

1933, Apr. 1   Photo.   Perf. 14x13½

112	A19	1k gray black	7.00	.65
		Never hinged	15.00	

See No. 149.

Paper with Network as in Parenthesis

1933, May 29   Typo.   Perf. 14

113	A20	2s green (orange)	1.50	.20
114	A20	5s red (green)	2.00	.20
115	A20	10s blue (lilac)	2.50	.20
		Nos. 113-115 (3)	6.00	.60
		Set, never hinged	12.50	

Tenth National Song Festival.
Nos. 113-115 exist imperf. Value $100.

Woman
Harvester
A21

Pres.
Konstantin
Päts
A22

1935, Mar. 1   Engr.   Perf. 13½

116	A21	3k black brown	.50	1.00
		Never hinged	.65	

1936-40   Typo.   Perf. 14

117	A22	1s chocolate	.40	.25
118	A22	2s yellow green	.40	.25
119	A22	3s dp org ('40)	10.00	7.50
120	A22	4s rose vio	.75	.25
121	A22	5s lt blue grn	.75	.30
122	A22	6s rose lake	.90	.25
123	A22	6s dp green ('40)	25.00	25.00
124	A22	10s greenish blue	.80	.25
125	A22	15s crim rose ('37)	1.25	.25
126	A22	15s dp bl ('40)	4.00	2.25
127	A22	18s dp car ('39)	25.00	9.00
128	A22	20s brt vio	1.25	.35
129	A22	25s dk bl ('38)	6.00	.35
130	A22	30s bister ('38)	4.25	.35
131	A22	30s ultra ('39)	20.00	5.00
132	A22	50s org brn	7.00	.85
133	A22	60s brt pink	12.50	4.50
		Nos. 117-133 (17)	120.25	56.95
		Set, never hinged	175.00	

St. Brigitta
Convent
Entrance
A23

Ruins of
Convent, Pirita
River
A24

Front View of
Convent — A25

Seal of
Convent — A26

Paper with Network as in Parenthesis

1936, June 10   Perf. 13½

134	A23	5s green (buff)	.35	.20
135	A24	10s blue (lil)	.55	.20
136	A25	15s red (org)	.85	1.25
137	A26	25s ultra (brn)	1.25	1.75
		Nos. 134-137 (4)	3.00	3.40
		Set, never hinged	6.00	

St. Brigitta Convent, 500th anniversary.

Harbor at
Tallinn — A27

1938, Apr. 11   Engr.   Perf. 14

138	A27	2k blue	.75	1.25
		Never hinged	.90	

Friedrich R.
Faehlmann
A28

Friedrich R.
Kreutzwald
A29

1938, June 15   Typo.   Perf. 13½

139	A28	5s dark green	.70	.50
140	A29	10s deep brown	.70	.50
141	A29	15s dark carmine	1.00	.90
142	A28	25s ultra	1.60	1.40
a.		Sheet of 4, #139-142	10.00	12.00
		Nos. 139-142 (4)	4.00	3.30
		Set, never hinged	9.00	

Society of Estonian Scholars centenary.

Hospital at
Pärnu — A30

Beach
Hotel — A31

1939, June 20   Typo.   Perf. 14x13½

144	A30	5s dark green	.70	.35
145	A31	10s deep red violet	.50	.40
146	A30	18s dark carmine	1.50	1.50
147	A31	30s deep blue	1.75	1.75
a.		Sheet of 4, #144-147	15.00	25.00
		Nos. 144-147 (4)	4.45	4.00
		Set, never hinged	10.00	

Cent. of health resort and baths at Pärnu.

Narva Falls Type of 1933

1940, Apr. 15   Engr.

149	A19	1k slate green	.70	1.25
		Never hinged	.85	

The sky consists of heavy horizontal lines
and the background consists of horizontal and
vertical lines.

Carrier Pigeon
and Plane — A32

1940, July 30   Typo.

150	A32	3s red orange	.20	.20
151	A32	10s purple	.20	.20
152	A32	15s rose brown	.20	.20
153	A32	30s dark blue	1.00	.75
		Nos. 150-153 (4)	1.60	1.35
		Set, never hinged		

Centenary of the first postage stamp.
The 15s exists imperf. Value $5.

> **Catalogue values for unused
> stamps in this section, from this
> point to the end of the section, are
> for Never Hinged items.**

Natl.
Arms — A40   A41

1991, Oct. 1   Litho.   Perf. 13x12½
200	A40	5k salmon & red	.20	.20
201	A40	10k lt grn & dk bl grn	.20	.20
202	A40	15k lt bl & dk bl	.20	.20
203	A40	30k vio & gray	.20	.20
204	A40	50k org & brn	.25	.25
205	A40	70k pink & purple	.25	.25
206	A40	90k pur & rose lilac	.30	.30

Size: 20½x27mm
Engr.
Perf. 12½ Horiz.
207	A40	1r dark brown	.35	.35
208	A40	2r lt bl & dk bl	.70	.70
	Nos. 200-208 (9)	2.65	2.65

See Nos. 211-213, 215, 216, 230, 299-301, 314-314A, 317, 333-334, 339-340. For surcharge, see No. 217.

Perf. 13½x14, 14x13½
1991, Nov. 1   Litho.
|209|A41|1.50r Flag, vert.|.90|.90|
|210|A41|2.50r shown|1.25|1.25|

National Arms — A42

1992, Mar. 16   Litho.   Perf. 13x12½
211	A42	E (1r) lemon	.20	.20
212	A42	I (20r) blue green	.75	.75
213	A42	A (40r) blue	1.90	1.90
	Nos. 211-213 (3)	2.85	2.85

No. 211 was valid for postage within Estonia. No. 212 was valid for postage within Europe. No. 213 was valid for overseas mail. See Nos. 214, 219, 220, 224-229.

No. 202 Surcharged and Arms Types of 1991-1992

And

Natl. Arms — A42a

Perf. 14, 13x12½ (#214, 217, 219-220)
1992-96
214	A42	E (10s) orange	.20	.20
215	A40	10s blue & gray	.20	.20
216	A40	50s gray & brt bl	.20	.20
217	A40	60s on 15k #202	.20	.20
218	A40	60s lilac & olive	.20	.20
219	A42	I (1k) emerald	.60	.60
220	A42	A (2k) violet blue	1.25	1.25
221	A42a	5k bis & red vio	1.00	1.00
221a.		5k yel orange & red violet	2.00	2.00
222	A42a	10k blue & olive	2.00	2.00
223	A42a	20k pale lilac & slate grn	3.75	3.75
	Nos. 214-223 (10)	9.60	9.60

Coil Stamps
Engr.
Size: 20½x27mm
Perf. 12½ Horiz.
224	A42	X (10s) brown	.20	.20
225	A42	X (10s) olive	.20	.20
226	A42	X (10s) black	.20	.20
227	A42	Z (30s) red lilac	.20	.20
228	A42	Z (30s) red	.20	.20
229	A42	Z (30s) dark blue	.20	.20

Litho.
|230|A40|60s lilac brown|.20|.20|
| |Nos. 224-230 (7)|1.40|1.40|

Issued: #214, 219-220, 6/22; #224, 8/29; #225, 9/25; #226, 10/31; #227, 11/16; #228, 12/1; #229, 12/22; #230, 1/8/93; #217, 3/5/93; 10s, 50s, 3/23 1993; 10k, 5/25/93; 5k, 7/7/93; #218, 8/5/93; 20k, 9/8/93; #221a, 9/19/96.
See note after No. 213. Nos. 224-229 were valid for postage within Estonia. See No. F1.

A44

A45

Birds of the Baltic shores.

1992, Oct. 3   Litho. & Engr.   Perf. 13
Booklet Stamps
231	A44	1k Pandion haliaetus	.20	.20
232	A44	1k Limosa limosa	.20	.20
233	A44	1k Mergus merganser	.20	.20
234	A44	1k Tadorna tadorna	.20	.20
a.		Booklet pane of 4, #231-234	1.25	

See Latvia Nos. 332-335a, Lithuania Nos. 427-430a and Sweden Nos. 1975-1978a.

1992, Dec. 15   Litho.   Perf. 14
|235|A45|30s gray & multi|.20|.20|
|236|A45|2k light brown & multi|.40|.40|

Christmas.
Exist on ordinary and fluorescent paper. Values are for former.

Friendship A46

1993, Feb. 8   Litho.   Perf. 14
|237|A46|1k multicolored|.20|.20|
|a.| |Booklet pane of 6|1.25| |

See Finland No. 906.

A47   A48

1993, Feb. 16   Perf. 13½x13½
238	A47	60s black & multi	.20	.20
239	A47	1k violet & multi	.25	.25
240	A47	2k blue & multi	.35	.35
	Nos. 238-240 (3)	.80	.80

First Republic, 75th anniv.

1993, June 9   Litho.   Perf. 13½x14
241	A48	60s Wrestling	.20	.20
242	A48	1k +25s Viking ship, map	.25	.25
243	A48	2k Shot put with rock	.40	.40
	Nos. 241-243 (3)	.85	.85

First Baltic sea games.

Tallinn Castle — A49

Designs: 1k, Toolse Castle. #245, Paide Castle, vert. #245A, Purtse Castle. 2.70k, Narva Fortress. 2.90k, Haapsalu Cathedral. 3k, Monks' Tower, Kiiu. 3.20k, Rakvere Castle. 4k, Kuressaare Castle. 4.80k, Viljandi Castle.

1993-97   Litho.   Perf. 14
244	A49	1k gray & black	.20	.20
245	A49	2k tan & brown	.35	.35
246	A49	2.50k lt vio & dk vio	.45	.45
247	A49	2.50k gray	.45	.45
248	A49	2.70k lt blue & dk blue	.45	.45
249	A49	2.90k lt grn & dk grn	.50	.50
250	A49	3k rose & brown	.50	.50
251	A49	3.20k lt grn & dk grn	.75	.75
252	A49	3.20k lt gray vio & gray vio	.75	.75
253	A49	4.80k dull org & brn	.80	.80
	Nos. 244-253 (10)	5.20	5.20

Issued: 1k, 2/22/94; 2k, 10/12/93; 2.70k, 12/10/93; 2.90k, 12/23/93; 3k, 3/31/94; 3.20, 12/28/94; 4k, 9/20/94; #246, 1/25/96; 247, 7/25/96; 4.80k, 1/21/97.

First Estonian Postage Stamp, 75th Anniv. — A50

1993, Nov. 13   Litho.   Perf. 14
|259|A50|1k multicolored|.20|.20|

Souvenir Sheet
Imperf
|260|A50|4k multicolored|2.75|2.75|
|a.| |Ovptd. in sheet margin|15.00|15.00|

No. 260 sold for 5k. Overprint on No. 260a reads "FILATEELIANAITUS / MARE BALTICUM '93 / 24.-28. NOVEMBER 1993".

Christmas A51

80s, Haapsalu Cathedral. 2k, Tallinn Church.

1993, Nov.   Litho.   Perf. 14
|261|A51|80s red|.20|.20|
|262|A51|2k blue, vert.|.35|.35|

See Nos. 279-280.

Lydia Koidula — A52

1993, Dec. 14   Litho.   Perf. 14
|263|A52|1k multicolored|.25|.25|

A53   A54

1994, Jan. 26
|264|A53|1k +25s Ski jumping|.25|.25|
|265|A53|2k Speed skating|.35|.35|

1994 Winter Olympics, Lillehammer.

1994, May 31   Litho.   Perf. 13½x14
Festival badges: 1k+25s, Tartu, 1869. 2k, Tallinn, 1923. 3k, Tallinn, 1969. 15k, Anniversary badge.
266	A54	1k +25s olive & multi	.20	.20
267	A54	2k blue & brown	.35	.35
268	A54	3k brown, buff & bister	.50	.50
	Nos. 266-268 (3)	1.05	1.05

Souvenir Sheet
|269|A54|15k multicolored|2.50|2.50|

All Estonian Song Festival, 125th anniv.

Flying Squirrel — A55

A56

1994, June 27   Litho.   Perf. 13½x14
270	A55	1k shown	.40	.40
271	A55	2k On leafy branch	.50	.50
272	A55	3k In fir tree	.85	.85
273	A55	4k With young	1.10	1.10
	Nos. 270-273 (4)	2.85	2.85

World Wildlife Fund.

1994, July 19
Europa (Estonian Inventions): 1k, Rotating horizontal millstones, by Aleksander Mikiver. 2.70k, First mini-camera, by Walter Zapp.
|274|A56|1k multicolored|.25|.25|
|275|A56|2.70k multicolored|.45|.45|

A57   A58

Folk Costumes.

1994, Aug. 23   Litho.   Perf. 14
|276|A57|1k Jamaja|.25|.25|
|277|A57|1k Mustjala|.25|.25|

See Nos. 286-287, 303-304, 325-326, 347-348, 369-370.

1994, Sept. 27   Litho.   Perf. 13½
|278|A58|1.70k multicolored|.30|.30|

Estonian Art Museum, 75th anniv.

Christmas Type of 1993
Designs: 1.20k, Ruhnu Church, vert. 2.50k, Urvaste Church.

1994, Nov. 15   Litho.   Perf. 14
|279|A51|1.20k brown|.25|.25|
|280|A51|2.50k green|.50|.50|

For surcharge see No. B63.

A59   A60

1994, Oct. 18
|281|A59|1.70k multicolored|.35|.35|

Intl. Year of the Family.

1994, Dec. 9

Gustavus II Adolphus (1594-1632), King of Sweden.

282   A60 2.50k lilac   .60   .60

A61

A62

1995, Jan. 26   Litho.   Perf. 14
283   A61 1.70k Branta leucopsis   .30   .30
284   A61 3.20k Anser anser   .55   .55

Matsalu Nature Reserve.

1995, Feb. 28   Litho.   Perf. 14

Farm Laborer's Family at Table, by Efraim Allsalu.

285   A62 2.70k multicolored   .50   .50

FAO, 50th anniv.

Folk Costumes Type of 1994

1995, Mar. 30   Litho.   Perf. 14
286   A57 1.70k Muhu couple   .50   .50
287   A57 1.70k Three Muhu girls   .50   .50

A63

A64

Via Baltica Highway Project: #288, 289a, Beach Hotel, Parnu. #289b, Castle, Bauska, Latvia. #289c, Kaunas, Lithuania.

1995, Apr. 20   Litho.   Perf. 14
288   A63 1.70k multicolored   .35   .35
Souvenir Sheet
289   A63 3.20k Sheet of 3, #a.-c.   1.75 1.75

See Latvia Nos. 394-395, Lithuania Nos. 508-509.

1995, Apr. 20   Litho.   Perf. 14
290   A64 2.70k multicolored   .45   .45

Europa. Liberation of Nazi Concentration Camps, 50th anniv.

UN, 50th Anniv. — A65

1995, June 1   Litho.   Perf. 14
291   A65 4k multicolored   .70   .70

Pakri Lighthouse A66

1995, July 5   Litho.   Perf. 14
292   A66 1.70k multicolored   .30   .30
See Nos. 309, 318, 338, 356, 388-389, 408.

Vanemuine Theater, 125th Anniv. — A67

1995, Aug. 14   Litho.   Perf. 14
293   A67 1.70k multicolored   .30   .30

Louis Pasteur (1822-95) A68

1995, Sept. 20   Litho.   Perf. 14
294   A68 2.70k multicolored   .45   .45

Finno-Ugric Peoples A69

Aleksander Kunileid (1845-75), Composer A70

Ethnographic object, languages: a, 2.50k, Drawing on shaman's drum, Saami. b, 3.50k, Duck-shaped brooch, Mordva, Mari. c, 4.50k, Duck-feet necklace pendant, Udmurdi, Komi. d, 2.50k, Khanty band ornament, Ungari, Mansi, Handi. e, 3.50k, Bronze amulet, Neenetsi, Eenetsi, Nganassaani, Solkupi, Kamassi. f, 4.50k, Karelian writing on birchbark, Eesti, Vadia, Soome, Liivi, Isuri, Karjala, Vespa.

1995, Oct. 17   Litho.   Perf. 14
Miniature Sheet
295   A69 Sheet of 6, #a.-f.   3.25 3.25

1995, Nov. 1   Engr.   Perf. 12½ Horiz.
296   A70 2k dark blue black   .35   .35

Christmas — A71

Churches: 2k, St. Martin's, Türi. 3.50k, Charles' Church of the Toompea Congregation, Tallinn.

1995, Nov. 15   Litho.   Perf. 14
297   A71 2k yellow orange   .35   .35
298   A71 3.50k dull carmine   .60   .60

See Nos. 315-316, 331.

Natl. Arms Type of 1991
1995, Oct. 26   Litho.   Perf. 14
299   A40 20s blue green & black   .20   .20
300   A40 30s gray & magenta   .20   .20
301   A40 80s lilac & blue black   .25   .25
a.   Perf. 13   .25   .25
     Nos. 299-301 (3)   .65   .65

No. 301a issued in 1996.

Submarine Lembit — A72

1996, Feb. 29   Litho.   Perf. 14
302   A72 2.50k multicolored   .45   .45
See No. 308, 328.

Folk Costume Type of 1994
1996, Mar. 26   Litho.   Perf. 14
303   A57 2.50k Emmaste   .60   .60
304   A57 2.50k Reigi   .60   .60

A73

A74

Designs: a, 2.50k, First gold medal, 1896. b, 3.50k, Alfred Neuland, weight lifter, first to win gold medal for Estonia, 1920. c, 4k, Cyclist.

1996, Apr. 25   Litho.   Perf. 14
305   A73 Sheet of 3, #a.-c.   1.90 1.90
Modern Olympic Games, Cent. & 1996 Summer Olympics, Atlanta.

1996, May 10
Europa: Marie Under (1883-1980), poet.
306   A74 2.50k multicolored   .45   .45

Radio, Cent. — A75

1996, June 27   Litho.   Perf. 14
307   A75 3.50k Guglielmo Marconi   .60   .60

Ship Type of 1996
Design: Icebreaker, Suur Toll.

1996, Aug. 30   Litho.   Perf. 14
308   A72 2.50k multicolored   .50   .50

Lighthouse Type of 1995
1996, Sept. 25   Litho.   Perf. 14
309   A66 2.50k Vaindloo   .55   .55

Estonian Narrow Gauge Railway, Cent. — A76

Designs: 3.20k, Class Gk steam locomotive. 3.50k, DeM 1 diesel motor wagon. 4.50k, Class Sk steam locomotive.

1996, Oct. 17   Litho.   Perf. 14
310   A76 3.20k multicolored   .55   .55
311   A76 3.50k multicolored   .60   .60
312   A76 4.50k multicolored   .75   .75
     Nos. 310-312 (3)   1.90 1.90
See No. 397.

Christmas A77

1996, Nov. 27   Litho.   Perf. 14
313   A77 2.50k multicolored   .45   .45

Natl. Arms Type of 1991
1996-97   Perf. 14
314   A40 3.30k lilac and claret   .55   .55
Perf. 13x13¼
314A A40 3.30k blue & lt claret   .60   .60
Issued: #314, 12/2; #314A, 12/10/97.

Church Type of 1995
Christmas: 3.30k, Harju-Madise Church. 4.50k, Holy Spirit Church, Tallinn.

1996, Dec. 12
315   A71 3.30k blue   .55   .55
316   A71 4.50k pink   .75   .75

Natl. Arms Type of 1991
1996, Oct. 24   Litho.   Perf. 13½
317   A40 2.50k grn & dark grn   .45   .45

Lighthouse Type of 1995
1997, Feb. 11   Litho.   Perf. 14
318   A66 3.30k Ruhnu   .65   .65

Tallinn Zoo — A78

a, Haliaeetus pelagicus. b, Mustela lutreola. c, Aegypius monachus. d, Panthera pardus orientalis. e, Diceros bicornis. f, Capra cylindricornis.

1997, Mar. 26   Litho.   Perf. 14
319   A78 3.30k Sheet of 6, #a.-f.   3.50 3.50

Heinrich von Stephan (1831-97), Founder of UPU — A79

1997, Apr. 8   Litho.   Perf. 14
320   A79 7k black & bister   1.25 1.25

A80

1997, May 5   Litho.   Perf. 14
321   A80 4.80k Goldspinners Fairy Tale   .85   .85
Europa.

A81

1997, May 10
No. 323: a, like #322. b, Linijkugis, 17th cent. c, Kurenas, 16th cent.
322   A81 3.30k multicolored   .60   .60
Perf. 14x14½
323   A81 4.50k Sheet of 3, #a.-c.   3.00 3.00
Maasilinn ship, 16th cent.
See Latvia Nos. 443-444, Lithuania Nos. 571-572.

Folk Costume Type of 1994

1997, June 10   Litho.   Perf. 14
325 A57 3.30k Ruhnu   .60   .60
326 A57 3.30k Vormsi   .60   .60

One Kroon
Coin — A82

1997, June 12   Litho.   Perf. 14
327 A82 50k bl grn, blk & gray   8.50 8.50
See Nos. 345, 363, 391.

Ship Type of 1996
Design: Four-masted barkentine, Tormilind.

1997, July 2
328 A72 5.50k multicolored   .95   .95

Stone Bridge,
Tartu — A83

1997, Sept. 16   Litho.   Perf. 14
329 A83 3.30k multicolored   .60   .60

Wastne
Testament,
Estonian Bible
Translation,
1686 — A84

1997, Oct. 14   Litho.   Perf. 14
330 A84 3.50k multicolored   .60   .60

Church Type of 1995
Christmas: St. Anne's, Halliste.

1997, Nov. 27   Litho.   Perf. 14
331 A71 3.30k brown   .55   .55

Christmas
A85

1997, Dec. 3
332 A85 2.90k Elves   .50   .50

Natl. Arms Type of 1991
1998, Jan. 19   Litho.   Perf. 13x13½
333 A40 3.10k lt violet & rose   .55   .55
334 A40 3.60k lt blue & ultra   .60   .60
a.   3.60k gray & vio bl   .60   .60
Issued: #334a, 8/4/98.

1998 Winter
Olympic Games,
Nagano — A86

1998, Jan. 28   Litho.   Perf. 14
335 A86 3.60k multicolored   .60   .60

Republic of Estonia, 80th
Anniv. — A87

Illustration reduced.

1998, Feb. 6   Litho.   Imperf.
336 A87 7k Proclamation, arms   1.25 1.25

Eduard Viiralt
(1898-1954), Print
Artist — A88

Various sections of print, "Hell," showing faces: a, 3.60k, shown. b, 3.60k, Explosion coming from center figure. c, 5.50k, Cat on top of one figure's head. d, 5.50k, Faces within faces.

1998, Feb. 18   Perf. 14
337 A88 Sheet of 4, #a.-d.   3.00 3.00

Lighthouse Type of 1995
1998, Mar. 12   Litho.   Perf. 14
338 A66 3.60k Kunda   .60   .60

Natl. Arms Type of 1991
1998, Mar. 16   Perf. 13
339 A40 10s grn bl & brn blk   .20   .20
340 A40 4.50k pale orange &
               brick red   .75   .75
Issued: 10s, 3/25/97; 4.50k, 3/16/98.

A88a   A89

1998, Apr. 16   Litho.   Perf. 14
341 A88a 7k multicolored   1.25 1.25
1998 World Cup Soccer Championship, France.

1998, May 5   Litho.   Perf. 14
342 A89 5.20k St. John's Day   .85   .85
Europa.

Use of Lübeck
Charter in
Tallinn, 750th
Anniv. — A90

1998, June 1
343 A90 4.80k multicolored   .80   .80

Beautiful
Homes
Year — A91

1998, June 16   Litho.   Perf. 14
344 A91 3.60k multicolored   .60   .60

One Kroon Coin Type of 1997
1998, June 18
345 A82 25k green, gray & black 4.75 4.75

A92   A93

1998, Aug. 4   Litho.   Perf. 14
346 A92 5.50k multicolored   .95   .95
470 Class World Yachting Championships.

Folk Costume Type of 1994
1998, Aug. 21   Litho.   Perf. 14
347 A57 3.60k Kihnu couple   .70   .70
348 A57 3.60k Kihnu family   .70   .70

1998, Sept. 3
349 A93 3.60k yel, blue & blk   .60   .60
Juhan Jaik (1899-1948), author.

Tallinn Zoo — A94

Design: Panthera tigris altaica.

1998, Sept. 17
350 A94 3.60k multicolored   .65   .65
See No. 357.

Estonian Post,
80th
Anniv. — A95

1998, Oct. 22   Litho.   Perf. 14
351 A95 3.60k multicolored   .60   .60

Military Aid from
Finland, 90th
Anniv. — A96

1998, Nov. 5   Litho.   Perf. 14
352 A96 4.50k Freedom Cross   .75   .75

Christmas
A97

1998, Nov. 26   Litho.   Perf. 14
353 A97 3.10k Santa, child, vert.   .55   .55
354 A97   5k shown   .85   .85

Friedrich Robert
Faehlmann,
Founder of Learned
Estonian Society,
Birth Bicent. — A98

1998, Dec. 2
355 A98 3.60k multicolored   .60   .60

Lighthouse Type of 1995
1999, Jan. 20   Litho.   Perf. 14
356 A66 3.60k Vilsandi   .70   .70

Tallinn Zoo Type of 1998
1999, Feb. 18   Litho.   Perf. 14
357 A94 3.60k Uncia uncia   .60   .60

Council of Europe,
50th Anniv. — A99

1999, Mar. 24   Litho.   Perf. 14
358 A99 5.50k multicolored   .95   .95

Estonian Pres.
Lennart Meri,
70th Birthday
A100

1999, Mar. 29
359 A100 3.60k multicolored   .60   .60

Tolkuse
Bog — A101

1999, Apr. 27   Litho.   Perf. 14
360 A101 5.50k multicolored   .95   .95
Europa.

Bank of
Estonia, 80th
Anniv. — A102

1999, May 3   Litho.   Perf. 14
361 A102 5k multicolored   .85   .85

Olustvere
Manor — A103

1999, June 1
362 A103 3.60k multicolored   .60   .60
See Nos. 395, 414, 433, 456, 490, 520, 551, 562.

One Kroon Coin Type of 1997
1999, June 18   Litho.   Perf. 14
363 A82 100k bl, bister & blk   17.00 17.00

Estonian Natl.
Anthem — A104

1999, June 30   Litho.   Perf. 14
364 A104 3.60k multicolored   .60   .60
No. 364 is printed se-tenant with label.

Tower on Suur
Munamägi,
Highest Point in
Baltic Countries
A105

1999, July 17
365 A105 5.20k multicolored   .90   .90

A106

A107

Families holding hands and: 3.60k, Estonian flag.
No. 367: a, like #366. b, Latvian flag. c, Lithuanian flag.

1999, Aug. 23   Litho.   Perf. 14
366 A106 3.60k multicolored   .60   .60
Souvenir Sheet
367 A106 5.50k Sheet of 3, #a.-c. 2.75 2.75

Baltic Chain, 10th Anniv.
See Latvia #493-494, Lithuania #639-640.

1999, Sept. 23   Litho.   Perf. 14x13¾
368 A107 7k multicolored   1.25   1.25
UPU, 125th Anniv.

Folk Costumes Type of 1994
1999, Oct. 12   Litho.   Perf. 13¾x14
369 A57 3.60k Setu couple   .60   .60
370 A57 5k Setu man, boy   .85   .85

Three Lions — A108

Perf. 13x13¼, 13¾x14 (#371, 373, 374, 378-382)
1999-2002   Litho.
371 A108 10s brn & dk brn   .20   .20
372 A108 30s lt bl & dk bl   .20   .20
  a.   Perf. 13¾x14   .20   .20
373 A108 30s blue & slate blue, dated 2003   .20   .20
374 A108 50s olive & dk grn   .20   .20
375 A108 1k brown & fawn   .20   .20
376 A108 2k gray   .35   .35
377 A108 3.60k sky bl & dk bl   .60   .60
  a.   Bright blue green ('00)   .60   .60

378 A108 4.40k grn & bl grn   .75   .65
379 A108 4.40k bl grn & brt bl grn, wide 2001 date   .75   .25
380 A108 4.40k Prus bl & lt bl, narrow 2001 date   .75   .25
381 A108 4.40k green & lt grn, dated 2002   .75   .25
382 A108 4.40k grn & apple grn, dated 2002   .75   .25
382A A108 4.40k ol grn & apple grn, dated 2003   .75   .30
382B A108 5k grn & lt grn   .85   .85
382C A108 6k bis & yel   1.00   1.00
382D A108 6.50k bis & org   1.10   1.10
382E A108 8k lake & pink   1.40   1.40
    Nos. 371-382E (17)   10.80 8.25

Issued: 30s, 2k, 11/4; 3.60k (378), 10/22; #377a, 3/31/00; No. 378, 8/21/00; 6k, 10/12/00; 6.50k, 10/5/00; 8k, 10/19/00; No. 372a: 4/17/01; 1k, 5k, 8/28/01; 10s, 2/2/02. 50s, 1/7/03; No. 373, 3/11/03; No. 379, 4/17/01; No. 380, 9/24/01; No. 381, 2/2/02; No. 382, 11/14/02; No. 382A, 3/11/03.
No. 378 exists dated 2001 and 2002. No. 382B exists dated 2002.
The background color of No. 379 is bolder than that on No. 380.

Christmas
A109

1999, Nov. 25   Litho.   Perf. 14x13¾
383 A109 3.10k multicolored   .55   .55

A110

A111

1999, Nov. 25   Perf. 13¾x14
384 A110 7k multicolored   1.25   1.25
1st public Christmas tree in Tallinn, 1441.

Christmas
Lottery
A110a

1999, Dec. 1   Litho.   Perf. 14x13¾
384A A110a 3.10k + 1.90k multi   .65   .65

1999, Dec. 14   Litho.   Perf. 13¾x14
385 A111 5.50k Millennium   .95   .95

2000
Census — A112

2000, Jan. 5
386 A112 3.60k multicolored   .60   .60

Tartu Peace
Treaty, 80th
Anniv. — A113

2000, Feb. 2   Litho.   Perf. 14x13¾
387 A113 3.60k multi   .60   .60

Lighthouse Type of 1995
2000, Feb. 25
388 A66 3.60k Ristna   .60   .60
389 A66 3.60k Kopu   .60   .60
  a.   Pair, #388-389   1.25   1.25

Congress, 10th
Anniv. — A114

2000, Mar. 9   Perf. 13¾x14
390 A114 3.60k multi   .60   .60

One Kroon Coin Type of 1997
2000, Mar. 14   Perf. 14x13¾
391 A82 10k red, sil & blk   1.75   1.75

Cornflower
(Natl.
Flower) — A115

2000, Apr. 7
392 A115 4.80k multi   .80   .80

Natl. Book
Year — A116

2000, Apr. 22   Perf. 13¾x14
393 A116 3.60k multi   .60   .60
First book printed in Estonian language, 475th anniv.

Europa, 2000
Common Design Type
2000, May 9
394 CD17 4.80k multi   .75   .75

Manor Type of 1999
2000, May 23   Litho.   Perf. 14x13¾
395 A103 3.60k Palmse Hall   .60   .60

Tallinn
Zoo — A117

2000, June 13   Litho.   Perf. 14x13¾
396 A117 3.60k Naemorhedus caudatus   .70   .70

Railway Type of 1996
4.50k, Viljandi-Tallinn Railway, cent.

2000, June 30
397 A76 4.50k multi   .80   .80

9th Intl. Finno-
Ugric Congress
A118

2000, Aug. 1
398 A118 5k multi   .85   .85

2000 Summer
Olympics,
Sydney — A119

2000, Sept. 5   Litho.   Perf. 13¾x14
399 A119 8k multi   1.40   1.40

Folk Costume Type of 1994
Designs: 4.40k, Hargla. 8k, Polva.

2000, Sept. 12
400-401 A57 Set of 2   2.10   2.10

August Mälk
(1900-87),
Writer — A120

2000, Sept. 20   Perf. 14x13¾
402 A120 4.40k multi   .75   .75

Lake Peipus
Fish — A121

No. 403: a, Osmerus eperlanus spirinchus. b, Stizostedion lucioperka.

2000, Oct. 25
403   Horiz. pair + central label   2.50   2.50
  a.-b. A121 6.50k Any single   1.10   1.10
    See Russia No. 6607.

Souvenir Sheet

Estonian Bookplates, Cent. — A122

Various bookplates. Denominiations in: a, LR. b, UR.
Illustration reduced.

2000, Nov. 11   Perf. 13¾x14
404 A122 6k Sheet of 2, #a-b   2.10   2.10

Christmas
A123

3.60k, Horn and bow. 6k, Ornament.

2000, Nov. 29   Perf. 14x13¾
405-406 A123 Set of 2   1.60   1.60

Erki Nool,
Olympic
Decathlon
Champion
A124

2001, Jan. 10   Litho.   Perf. 14x13¾
407 A124 4.40k multi   1.00   1.00

Lighthouse Type of 1995

2001, Jan. 24
408 A66 4.40k Mohni   .75 .75

Valentine's Day — A125

2001, Feb. 6   Litho.   *Perf. 13¾x14*
409 A125 4.40k multi   .75 .75

Stenbock House, Seat of Government A126

2001, Feb. 20   *Perf. 14x13¾*
410 A126 6.50k multi   1.10 1.10

Souvenir Sheet

Paintings of Johann Köler (1826-99) — A127

No. 411: a, Girl on the Spring, 1858-62. b, Eve of the Pomegranate, 1879-80.

2001, Feb. 27
411 A127 4.40k Sheet of 2, #a-b   1.50 1.50

European Year of Languages A128

2001, Mar. 6
412 A128 4.40k multi   .75 .75

Vanellus Vanellus A129

2001, Apr. 4   *Perf. 12¾x13*
413 A129 4.40k multi   .75 .75

Manor Type of 1999

2001, Apr. 17   *Perf. 14x13¾*
414 A103 4.40k Laupa Hall   .75 .75

Europa — A130

2001, May 9   *Perf. 13¾x14*
415 A130 6.50k multi   1.10 1.10

Kalev Sports Association, Cent. — A131

2001, May 24
416 A131 6.50k multi   1.10 1.10

Pärnu, 750th Anniv. — A132

2001, June 5   Litho.   *Perf. 14x13¾*
417 A132 4.40k multi   .75 .75

Illustrations from Pokuland, by Edgar Valter — A133

Characters and — No. 418: a, Lake. b, Owl. c, Crane. d, Bird in nest.
No. 419: a, Fence. b, Flowers. c, Dog. d, Moon.

2001, June 19
418   Booklet pane of 4   2.25
   a.-d. A133 3.60k Any single   .60 .60
419   Booklet pane of 4   3.00
   a.-d. A133 4.40k Any single   .75 .75
   Booklet, #418-419   6.00

Entire booklet sold for 35k, 3k of which went to the Pokuland Project of the Estonian Nature Fund.

Restoration of Independence, 10th Anniv. — A134

2001, Aug. 7   *Perf. 13¾x14*
420 A134 4.40k multi   .75 .75

Establishment of St. Mary's Land, 800th Anniv. — A135

2001, Aug. 15   *Perf. 14x13¾*
421 A135 6.50k multi   1.10 1.10

Resumption of Issuing Stamps, 10th Anniv. — A136

2001, Sept. 4   *Perf. 13¾x14*
422 A136 4.40k #200   .75 .75

Baltic Coast Landscapes A137

Designs: 4.40k, No. 424a, Lahemaa. No. 424b, Vidzeme. No. 424c, Palanga.

2001, Sept. 15   *Perf. 14x13¾*
423 A137 4.40k multi   .75 .75

Souvenir Sheet
Perf. 13¼x13½
424   Sheet of 3   3.00 3.00
   a.-c. A137 6k Any single   1.00 1.00

No. 424 contains three 35x29mm stamps. See Lithuania Nos.
See Latvia Nos. 534-535, Lithuania Nos. 698-699.

Tallinn Zoo — A138

2001, Oct. 4   *Perf. 14x13¾*
425 A138 4.40k Alligator sinensis   .85 .85

Estonia 26/9 Racing Car — A139

2001, Oct. 23
426 A139 6k multi   1.10 1.10

Folk Costume Type of 1994

Designs: 4.40k, Paistu woman. 7.50k, Tarvastu man.

2001, Nov. 7   Litho.   *Perf. 13¾x14*
427-428 A57   Set of 2   2.25 2.25

A140

Christmas A141

Perf. 13¾x14, 14x13¾
2001, Nov. 22
429 A140 3.60k multi   .60 .60
430 A141 6.50k multi   1.10 1.10

Radio Broadcasting in Estonia, 75th Anniv. — A142

2001, Dec. 4   *Perf. 14x13¾*
431 A142 4.40k multi   1.25 1.25

2002 Winter Olympics, Salt Lake City — A143

2002, Jan. 10   Litho.   *Perf. 14x13¾*
432 A143 8k multi   1.40 1.40

Manor Type of 1999

2002, Jan. 22
433 A103 4.40k Sangaste Hall   .75 .75

Lighthouse Type of 1995

2002, Feb. 20
434 A66 4.40k Laidunina   .85 .85

Bird Type of 2001

Design: Passer domesticus and Passer montanus.

2002, Mar. 7   *Perf. 12¾x13*
435 A129 4.40k multi   .75 .75

Spring Flowers — A144

2002, Mar. 20   *Perf. 14x13¾*
436 A144 4.40k multi   .85 .85

Estonian Puppet Theater, 50th Anniv. — A145

2002, Mar. 27   *Perf. 13¾x14*
437 A145 4.40k multi + label   .75 .75

PTO-4 Training Airplane — A146

2002, Apr. 10   *Perf. 14x13¾*
438 A146 6k multi   1.00 1.00

Andrus Veerpalu, Gold Medalist at 2002 Winter Olympics A147

2002, Apr. 12
439 A147 4.40k multi   .75 .75

Tartu University Anniversaries — A148

No. 440: a, Main building, 1806-09, founding act of 1632. b, University Library, 1982, text from Biblia Latina.

2002, Apr. 24
440 A148 4.40k Horiz. pair, #a-b,
      + central label   1.50 1.50

Europa
A149

2002, May 9   *Perf. 12¾x13*
441 A149 6.50k multi   1.10 1.10

Re-adoption of Constitution, 10th Anniv. — A150

2002, May 23   *Perf. 13¾x14*
442 A150 4.40k multi   .75 .75

Adoption of Lübeck Charter by Town of Rakvere, 700th Anniv. — A151

2002, June 5
443 A151 4.40k multi   .75 .75

Souvenir Sheet

Re-introduction of the Kroon, 10th Anniv. — A152

No. 444 — Portraits from bank notes: a, Lydia Koidula, poet. b, Carl Rober Jakobson, journalist.

2002, June 10   *Perf. 14x13¾*
444 A152 4.40k Sheet of 2, #a-b 1.50 1.50

Souvenir Sheet

Adamson-Eric (1902-68), Painter — A153

2002, Aug. 8 Litho.   *Perf. 14x13¾*
445 A153 4.40k Sheet of 4, #a-d 3.00 3.00

Sus Scrofa
A154

2002, Aug. 21   *Perf. 12¾x13*
446 A154 4.40k multi   .75 .75

Limestone, Estonia's National Stone A155

2002, Sept. 18
447 A155 4.40k multi   .75 .75

Folk Costume Type of 1994

Designs: 4.40k, Kolga-Jaani women. 5.50k, Suure-Jaani boy and girl.

2002, Oct. 1   *Perf. 13¾x14*
448-449 A57 Set of 2   1.75 1.75

A156

Christmas — A157

Perf. 14x13¾, 13¾x14
2002, Nov. 20   Litho.
450 A156 3.60k Reindeer   .60 .60
451 A157 6.50k Christmas tree 1.10 1.10

Lighthouse Type of 1995
2003, Jan. 15   *Perf. 14x13¾*
452 A66 4.40k Keri   .75 .75

Anton Hansen Tammsaare (1878-1940), Novelist — A158

2003, Jan. 30 Litho.   *Perf. 14x13¾*
453 A158 4.40k multi   .75 .40

Pica Pica
A159

2003, Feb. 13   *Perf. 12¾x13*
454 A159 4.40k multi   .75 .40
      See Nos. 485, 509, 540, 566.

Spring Flowers — A160

No. 455: a, Tulips. b, Helleborus purpurascens. c, Narcissus poeticus. d, Crocus vernus.

2003, Mar. 20   *Perf. 13¾x14*
455 A160 4.40k Sheet of 4, #a-d 3.00 1.50
  e. Booklet pane, like #455, without
        date in margin   3.00   —
      Complete booklet, #455e   3.00

Manor Type of 1999
2003, Apr. 9   *Perf. 14x13¾*
456 A103 4.40k Alatskivi Hall   .75 .40

Pres. Arnold Rüütel, 75th Birthday — A161

2003, Apr. 24
457 A161 4.40k multi + label   .75 .40

Europa — A162

2003, May 8   *Perf. 13¾x14*
458 A162 6.50k multi   1.10 .55

Tartu University Botanical Gardens, Bicent. — A163

2003, June 11 Litho. *Perf. 14x13¾*
459 A163 4.40k multi   .75 .40

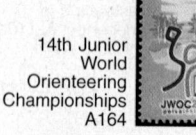

14th Junior World Orienteering Championships A164

2003, June 27
460 A164 7.50k multi   1.25 .65

Circumnavigation of Adam Johann von Krusenstern (1770-1846) — A165

2003, Aug. 6   *Perf. 12½*
461 A165 8k multi   1.40 .70

Phoca Hispida A166

2003, Aug. 27   *Perf. 12¾x13*
462 A166 4.40k multi   .75 .40

Adm. Fabian Gottlieb von Bellingshausen (1778-1852) — A167

2003, Sept. 10
463 A167 8k multi   1.40 .70

Ancient Trade Routes — A168

Map and: No. 464, 6.50k, Silver coin of Prince Volodymyr Sviatoslavovych, Slavic warship with sail. No. 465, 6.50k, Arrival of Scandinavian Seamen, coin of Danish King Svend Estridsen.

2003, Sept. 10   *Perf. 11½*
464-465 A168 Set of 2   2.25 1.10

See Ukraine No. 524.

Three Lions Type of 1999-2002
2003-04 Litho.   *Perf. 13¾x14*
467 A108 20s blk & gray   .20 .20
472 A108 4.40k ol grn & apple
                   grn   .75 .40
473 A108 5k dk grn & apple
                   grn, dated 2004 .80 .80
474 A108 5.50k dk grn & yel grn .85 .85

Issued: 20s, 4.40k, 8/22; 5k, 1/20/04; 5.50k, 3/25/04.

Folk Costume Type of 1994

Designs: 4.40k, Aksi woman and girl. 6.50k, Otepää man, woman and girl.

2003, Oct. 9 Litho.   *Perf. 13¾x14*
476-477 A57 Set of 2   1.90 .95

A169

Christmas A170

2003, Nov. 26   *Perf. 14x13¾*
478 A169 3.60k multi   .60 .30
479 A170 6k multi   1.00 .50

Souvenir Sheet

Friedrich Reinhold Kreutzwald (1803-82), Writer — A171

No. 480: a, 4.40k, Illustration by Kristjan Raud of "Voyage to the End of the World," from "Kalevipoeg," by Kreutzwald. b, 6.50k, Portrait of Kreutzwald.

2003, Dec. 4   *Perf. 13x12¾*
480   A171   Sheet of 2, #a-b   1.90   1.90

Lighthouse Type of 1995
2004, Jan. 7   Litho.   *Perf. 14x13¾*
481   A66   4.40k Sorgu   .75   .75

Canis Lupus A172

2004, Feb. 3   *Perf. 12¾x13*
482   A172   4.40k multi   .75   .75

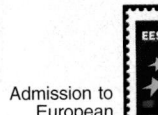

Voyage Around Cape Horn of the Hioma, 150th Anniv. — A173

2004, Feb. 18   *Perf. 13¾x14*
483   A173   8k multi   1.25   1.25

Spring Flowers Type of 2003
No. 484: a, Viola riviniana. b, Anemone nemorosa. c, Hepatica nobilis. d, Trollius europaeus.

2004, Mar. 17
484   A160   4.40k Sheet of 4, #a-d   2.75   2.75
   e.   Booklet pane, like #484 without
     date in margin   2.75   —
     Complete booklet, #484e   2.75

Bird Type of 2003
2004, Apr. 6   *Perf. 12¾x13*
485   A159   4.40k Ciconia ciconia   .70   .70

Admission to European Union A174

2004, May 1   *Perf. 13¼x13*
486   A174   6.50k multi   1.00   1.00

Europa — A175

Illustration reduced.

2004, May 4   *Perf. 13*
487   A175   6.50k multi   *1.00 1.00*

Tallinn Town Hall, 600th Anniv. A176

2004, May 13   Litho.   *Perf. 12¾x13*
488   A176   4.40k multi   .70   .70

Consecration of Estonian Flag, 120th Anniv. — A177

2004, June 4   *Perf. 13¾x14*
489   A177   4.40k multi   .70   .70

Manor Type of 1999
2004, June 15   *Perf. 14x13¾*
490   A103   4.40k Vasalemma Hall   .70   .70

Admission to NATO — A178

2004, June 28   *Perf. 13¾x14*
491   A178   6k multi   .95   .95

2004 Summer Olympics, Athens — A179

2004, July 15   Litho.   *Perf. 13¾x14*
492   A179   8k multi   1.25   1.25

Dragon Class Yachting European Championships — A180

2004, Aug. 17   *Perf. 14x13¾*
493   A180   6k multi   .95   .95

Taraxacum Officinale — A181

2004, Sept. 14   *Serpentine Die Cut 12½*
Self-Adhesive
494   A181   30s multi   .20   .20
   See Nos. 547, 560, 572.

County Arms — A182

2004, Sept. 28   **Self-Adhesive**
495   A182   4.40k Harjumaa   .70   .70
496   A182   4.40k Hiiumaa   .70   .70
   See Nos. 506-507, 518-519, 532-533, 536, 552, 561, 573.

Folk Costumes Type of 1994
Designs: 4.40k, Viru-Jaagupi boy and girl. 7.50k, Jõhvi woman and girl.

2004, Oct. 5   Litho.   *Perf. 13¾x14*
497-498   A57   Set of 2   1.90   1.90

A183

Christmas A184

2004, Nov. 23   *Perf. 13¾x14*
499   A183   4.40k multi   .80   .80
     Perf. 14x13¾
500   A184   6.50k multi   1.10   1.10

Lighthouse Type of 1995
Norrby Lighthouse with: 4.40k, White top, vert. 6.50k, Red top, vert.

2005, Jan. 11   Litho.   *Perf. 14*
501-502   A66   Set of 2   1.90   1.90

Castor Fiber A185

2005, Jan. 25   *Perf. 12¾x13*
503   A185   4.40k multi   .75   .75

Rotary International, Cent. — A186

2005, Feb. 11   *Perf. 13¾x14*
504   A186   8k multi   1.40   1.40

Flag Over Pikk Hermann Tower, Tallinn — A187

Serpentine Die Cut 12½
2005, Feb. 22
Self-Adhesive
505   A187   5k multi   .85   .85
   See Nos. 530, 559.

County Arms Type of 2004
2005   Litho.
Self-Adhesive
506   A182   4.40k Ida-Virumaa   .75   .75
507   A182   4.40k Järvamaa   .75   .75
   Issued: No. 506, 3/8; No. 507, 3/15.

Souvenir Sheet

Spring — A188

No. 508: a, Two swans, denomination at UL. b, One swan, denomination at UL. c, One swan, denomination at LL. d, Two swans, denomination at LR.

2005, Mar. 22   Litho.   *Perf. 14x13¾*
508   A188   4.40k Sheet of 4, #a-d   3.00   3.00

Bird Type of 2003
2005, Apr. 5   *Perf. 12¾x13*
509   A159   4.40k Accipiter gentilis   .75   .75

Mother's Day — A189

2005, Apr. 20   *Perf. 14x13¾*
510   A189   4.40k multi   .75   .75

Europa — A190

Designs: 6k, Vegetable wrap. 6.50k, Tomato, carrots, egg yolk, parsley, fish, onion, beet.

2005, May 3
511-512   A190   Set of 2   2.10   2.10

Eduard Tubin (1905-82), Composer A191

2005, May 18
513   A191   6k multi   .95   .95

Intl. Children's Day — A192

No. 514: a, Birds. b, Butterflies. Illustration reduced.

2005, June 1   *Perf. 13¼x13¾*
514   A192   4.40k Horiz. pair, #a-b,
     + central label   1.40   1.40

Orchids — A193

Designs: 4.40k, Epipactis palustris. 8k, Epipogium aphyllum.

2005, June 16   Litho.   *Perf. 13¾x14*
515-516   A193   Set of 2   2.25   2.25

Restoration of St.
John's Cathedral,
Tartu — A194

2005, June 29
517 A194 4.40k multi   .70 .70
Tartu, 975th anniv.

County Arms Type of 2004
Serpentine Die Cut 12½
2005   *Litho.*
Self-Adhesive
518 A182 4.40k Jõgevamaa   .70 .70
519 A182 4.40k Läänemaa   .70 .70
Issued: No. 518, 7/5; No. 519, 7/8.

Manor Type of 1999
2005, July 12   *Perf. 14x13¾*
520 A103 4.40k Kiltsi Hall   .70 .70

St. Catherine's
Church,
Karja — A195

2005, Sept. 20
521 A195 4.40k multi   .70 .70

Souvenir Sheet

Sculptures by Amandus Adamson
(1855-1929) — A196

No. 522: a, Igavesti Voidutsev Armastus,
1889. b, Lüüriline Muusika, 1891. c, Memento
Mori, 1907. d, Koit ja Hämarik, 1895.

2005, Oct. 12   *Perf. 13½*
522 A196 650s Sheet of 4, #a-d   4.00 4.00

Dogs — A197

No. 523: a, Kazakh hound (Kasaahi hurt). b,
Estonian hound (Eesti hagijas).

2005, Oct. 19   *Perf. 14x13¾*
523 A197 6.50k Horiz. pair, #a-b   2.00 2.00
See Kazakhstan No. 495.

Folk Costumes Type of 1994
Designs: 4.40k, Ambla man, woman and
girl. 8k, Türi women.

2005, Oct. 28   *Perf. 13¾x14*
524-525 A57   Set of 2   2.25 2.25

New Year's   Adoration of the
Goat — A198   Magi — A199

2005, Nov. 22
526 A198 4.40k multi   .70 .70
527 A199   8k sil & red lil   1.25 1.25
Christmas and New Year's Day.

Due to the postponed conversion to
the euro, originally scheduled for Jan. 1,
2007, Estonian stamps of 2006 until
conversion will show denominations in
kroons and the as-yet-uncirculating
euros.

Europa
Stamps, 50th
Anniv. — A200

CEPT emblem and: 6k, Superimposed letters. 6.50k, Map of Europe.

2006, Jan. 4   Litho.   *Perf. 14x13¾*
528 A200   6k multi   .95 .95
Souvenir Sheet
529 A200 6.50k multi   1.00 1.00

**Flag Over Pikk Hermann Tower
Type of 2005 With Euro
Denominations Added**
2006, Jan. 11   *Die Cut Perf. 12½*
Self-Adhesive
530 A187 11k multi   1.75 1.75

2006 Winter
Olympics,
Turin,
Italy — A201

2006, Jan. 18   *Perf. 14x13¾*
531 A201   8k multi   1.25 1.25

**County Arms Type of 2004 With
Euro Denominations Added**
2006   *Die Cut Perf. 12½*
Self-Adhesive
532 A182 4.40k Lääne-Virumaa   .70 .70
533 A182 4.40k Polvamaa   .70 .70
Issued: No. 532, 1/25; No. 533, 2/8.

Alces
Alces
A202

2006, Feb. 1   *Perf. 12¾x13*
534 A202 4.40k multi   .70 .70

Opening of KUMU
Art
Museum — A203

2006, Feb. 17   Litho.   *Perf. 13¾x14*
535 A203 4.40k multi   .70 .70

**County Arms Type of 2004 With
Euro Denominations Added**
2006, Mar. 8   *Die Cut Perf. 12½*
Self-Adhesive
536 A182 4.40k Pärnumaa   .70 .70

Souvenir Sheet

National Opera, Cent. — A204

No. 537: a, Characters from Vikerlased, first
opera staged in 1928. b, Ballerina.

2006, Mar. 27   *Perf. 13¾x14*
537 A204 6.50k Sheet of 2, #a-b,
            + central label   2.00 2.00

A205

Gold Medalists at 2006 Winter
Olympics — A206

No. 539: a, Andrus Veerpalu. b, Kristina
Smigun.
Illustrations reduced.

2006, Mar. 30   *Perf. 14x13¾*
538 A205 4.40k multi   .70 .70
Souvenir Sheet
539 A206   8k Sheet of 2, #a-b 2.50 2.50

**Bird Type of 2003 With Euro
Denominations Added**
2006, Apr. 5   *Perf. 12¾x13*
540 A159 4.40k multi   .70 .70

Lighthouses
A207

Designs: 4.40k, Tallinn Bay lower lighthouse. 6.50k, Tallinn Bay upper lighthouse.

2006, Apr. 12   *Perf. 13¾x14*
541-542 A207   Set of 2   1.75 1.75
See No. 564.

Estonian Shooting
Sport Federation,
75th
Anniv. — A208

2006, Apr. 26
543 A208 4.40k car & sil   .75 .75

Europa — A209

2006, May 3
544 A209 6.50k multi   1.10 1.10

Confectionery
Industry in
Estonia,
Bicent.
A210

2006, May 18   *Perf. 14x13¾*
545 A210 4.40k multi   .75 .75

Posthorns — A211

2006, May 22   *Die Cut Perf. 10*
Self-Adhesive
546 A211 4.40k gray brn + label   .75 .75
Labels could be personalized.
See No. 563.

**Flower Type of 2004 with Euro
Denominations Added**
2006, May 24   *Die Cut Perf. 12½*
Self-Adhesive
547 A181 30s Hepatica nobilis   .20 .20

Souvenir Sheet

Tori Stud Farm, 150th Anniv. — A212

No. 548: a, Three horses, denomination at
UL. b, Pony and three horses, denomination at
UR.

2006, June 7   *Perf. 14x13¾*
548 A212 4.40k Sheet of 2, #a-b 1.50 1.50

Victory
Day — A213

2006, June 23
549 A213 4.40k multi   .75 .75

20th Intl. Organ
Music Festival,
Tallinn — A214

2006, July 28   Litho.   *Perf. 14x13¾*
550 A214 4.40k multi   .75 .75

**Manor Type of 1999 With Added
Euro Denomination**
2006, Aug. 16
551 A103 4.40k Taagepera Hall   .75 .75

County Arms Type of 2004 With Added Euro Denomination

2006, Sept. 6   *Die Cut Perf. 12½*
Self-Adhesive
552 A182 4.40k Raplamaa   .75   .75

St. Lawrence's
Church,
Noo — A215

2006, Sept. 20   *Perf. 13¾x14*
553 A215 4.40k multi   .75   .75

Betti Alver (1906-89), Writer — A216

2006, Oct. 11   *Perf. 13*
554 A216 4.40k multi   .75   .75

Antarctic Wildlife — A217

No. 555 — Estonian and Chilean flags and:
a, Aptenodytes forsteri. b, Balaenoptera
acutorostrata.
Illustration reduced.

2006, Oct. 25   *Perf. 13½*
555 A217 8k Pair, #a-b   2.60   2.60
See Chile No. 1468.

A218

Christmas — A219

2006, Nov. 22   **Litho.**   *Perf. 13¾x14*
556 A218 4.40k multi   .75   .75
557 A219 6k multi   1.10   1.10

Estonia's conversion to euro currency
was postponed until certain mandated
economic requirements are met. Until
the conversion, stamps will continue to
show denominations in kroons and the
as-yet-uncirculating euros.

Lotte From
Gadgetville
A220

2007, Jan. 4   *Perf. 14x13¾*
558 A220 4.40k multi   .75   .75

Flag Over Pikk Hermann Tower Type of 2005 With Euro Denomination Added

2007, Jan. 11   *Die Cut Perf. 12½*
Self-Adhesive
559 A187 5k tan & multi   .85   .85

Flower Type of 2004 With Euro Denomination Added

2007, Jan. 17   *Die Cut Perf. 12½*
Self-Adhesive
560 A181 30s Leucanthemum
vulgare   .20   .20

County Arms Type of 2004 With Euro Denomination Added

2007, Jan. 25   *Die Cut Perf. 12½*
Self-Adhesive
561 A182 4.40k Saaremaa   .75   .75

Manor Type of 1999 With Euro Denomination Added

2007, Feb. 14   *Perf. 14x13¾*
562 A103 5.50k Sagadi Hall   .95   .95

Posthorns Type of 2006

2007, Feb. 22   *Die Cut Perf. 10*
Self-Adhesive
563 A211 5.50k bl grn + label   .95   .95
Labels could be personalized.

Lighthouse Type of 2006

2007, Mar. 8   *Perf. 14x13¾*
564 A207 6k Juminda, horiz.   1.00   1.00

Meles
Meles
A221

2007, Mar. 22   *Perf. 12¾x13*
565 A221 4.40k multi   .75   .75

Bird Type of 2003 With Euro Denomination Added

2007, Apr. 5   *Perf. 12¾x13*
566 A159 4.40k Cygnus bewickii   .75   .75

Miniature Sheet

Summer Flowers — A222

No. 567: a, Paeonia officinalis. b, Lilium
lancifolium. c, Rosa ecae Golden Chersonese.
d, Iris latifolia.

2007, Apr. 19   *Perf. 13¾x14*
567 A222 4.40k Sheet of 4, #a-d   3.25   3.25

Europa — A223

2007, May 3   *Perf. 12½*
568 A223 20.50k multi   3.75   3.75
Scouting, cent.

Intl. Children's
Day — A224

2007, June 1   **Litho.**   *Perf. 13½*
569 A224 10k multi   1.75   1.75

Souvenir Sheet

1941-51 Deportation of
Estonians — A225

2007, June 14   *Perf. 13*
570 A225 8k multi   1.40   1.40

Pirita Convent, 600th Anniv. — A226

2007, June 15   **Litho.**   *Perf. 12½*
571 A226 5.50k multi   .95   .95

Flower Type of 2004 With Euro Denominations Added

2007, July 2   *Die Cut Perf. 12½*
Self-Adhesive
572 A181 1.10k Centaurea
phrygia   .20   .20

County Arms Type of 2004 With Euro Denominations Added

2007, July 2
Self-Adhesive
573 A182 5.50k Tartumaa   .95   .95

Flag Over Pikk Hermann Tower Type of 2005 With Euro Denominations Added

2007, Aug. 1
Self-Adhesive
574 A187 10k multi   1.75   1.75

Hellenurme
Mill — A227

2007, Aug. 9   *Perf. 14x13¾*
575 A227 5.50k multi   1.00   1.00

Hirvepark Demonstration, 20th
Anniv. — A228

2007, Aug. 23   *Perf. 14x14¼*
576 A228 5.50k multi   1.00   1.00

Souvenir Sheet

Matthias Johann Eisen (1857-1934),
Folklorist — A229

2007, Sept. 14   *Imperf.*
577 A229 10k multi   1.90   1.90
No. 577 has simulated perforations.

Ragnar Nurkse (1907-59),
Economist — A230

2007, Oct. 5   *Perf. 13*
578 A230 10k multi   1.90   1.90

St. John's Church,
Kanepi — A231

2007, Oct. 11   *Perf. 13¾x14*
579 A231 5.50k multi   1.00   1.00

Arms of
Viljandi — A232

2007, Oct. 25   **Litho.**   *Perf. 13¾x14*
580 A232 5.50k multi   1.00   1.00

A233

Christmas
A234

Die Cut Perf. 11¼ Syncopated
2007, Nov. 22
Self-Adhesive
581	A233	5.50k multi	1.00	1.00
582	A234	8k multi	1.50	1.50

SEMI-POSTAL STAMPS

Assisting Wounded Soldier — SP1

Offering Aid to Wounded Hero — SP2

1920, June　Unwmk.　Litho.　Imperf.
B1	SP1	35p + 10p red & ol grn	.25	.35
B2	SP2	70p + 15p dp bl & brn	.25	.35

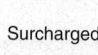

Surcharged

1920
B3	SP1	1m on No. B1	.30	.25
B4	SP2	2m on No. B2	.30	.25

Nurse and Wounded Soldier — SP3

1921, Aug. 1　　　　　Imperf.
B5	SP3	2½ (3½)m org, brn & car	.90	1.00
B6	SP3	5 (7)m ultra, brn & car	.90	1.00

1922, Apr. 26　　　Perf. 13½x14
B7	SP3	2½ (3½)m org, brn & car	.90	1.00
a.		Vert. pair, imperf. horiz.	30.00	30.00
B8	SP3	5 (7)m ultra, brn & car	.90	1.00
a.		Vert. pair, imperf. horiz.	30.00	30.00

Nos. B5-B8
Overprinted

1923, Oct. 8　　　　　Imperf.
B9	SP3	2½ (3½)m	25.00	25.00
B10	SP3	5 (7)m	30.00	30.00

Perf. 13½x14
B11	SP3	2½ (3½)m	40.00	40.00
a.		Vert. pair, imperf. horiz.	100.00	160.00
B12	SP3	5 (7)m	40.00	40.00
a.		Vert. pair, imperf. horiz.	100.00	160.00
		Nos. B9-B12 (4)	135.00	135.00

Excellent forgeries are plentiful.

Nos. B7 and B8
Surcharged

1926, June 15
B13	SP3	5 (6)m on #B7	3.50	3.50
a.		Vert. pair, imperf. horiz.	20.00	20.00
B14	SP3	10 (12)m on #B8	4.00	4.00
a.		Vert. pair, imperf. horiz.	20.00	20.00

Nos. B5-B14 had the franking value of the lower figure. They were sold for the higher figure, the excess going to the Red Cross Society.

Kuressaare Castle SP4

Tartu Cathedral SP5

Tallinn Castle SP6

Narva Fortress SP7

View of Tallinn — SP8

Laid Paper
Perf. 14½x14
1927, Nov. 19　　Typo.　　Wmk. 207
B15	SP4	5m + 5m bl grn & ol, grysh	.90	1.00
B16	SP5	10m + 10m dp bl & brn, cream	.90	1.00
B17	SP6	12m + 12m rose red & ol grn, bluish	.90	2.00

Perf. 14x13½
B18	SP7	20m + 20m bl & choc, gray	1.75	2.00
B19	SP8	40m + 40m org brn & slate, buff	1.75	3.00
		Nos. B15-B19 (5)	6.20	9.00

The money derived from the surtax was donated to the Committee for the commemoration of War for Liberation.

Red Cross Issue

Symbolical of Succor to Injured — SP9

Symbolical of "Light of Hope" — SP10

1931, Aug. 1　　Unwmk.　　Perf. 13½
B20	SP9	2s + 3s grn & car	6.00	5.00
B21	SP10	5s + 3s red & car	6.00	5.00
B22	SP10	10s + 3s lt bl & car	6.00	5.00
B23	SP9	20s + 3s dk bl & car	7.50	7.50
		Nos. B20-B23 (4)	25.50	22.50
		Set, never hinged	35.00	

Nurse and Child SP11

Taagepera Sanatorium SP12

Lorraine Cross and Flower — SP13

Paper with Network as in Parenthesis
1933, Oct. 1　　　　Perf. 14, 14½
B24	SP11	5s + 3s ver (grn)	5.00	5.00
B25	SP12	10s + 3s lt bl & red (vio)	5.00	5.00
B26	SP13	12s + 3s rose & red (grn)	5.00	5.00
B27	SP12	20s + 3s dk bl & red (org)	7.50	7.50
		Nos. B24-B27 (4)	22.50	22.50
		Set, never hinged	40.00	

The surtax was for a fund to combat tuberculosis.

Coats of Arms

Narva — SP14

Pärnu — SP15

Tartu — SP16

Tallinn — SP17

Paper with Network as in Parenthesis
1936, Feb. 1　　　　　Perf. 13½
B28	SP14	10s + 10s grn & ultra (gray)	3.50	5.00
B29	SP15	15s + 15s car & bl (gray)	3.50	5.00
B30	SP16	25s + 25s gray bl & red (brn)	4.50	7.00
B31	SP17	50s + 50s blk & dl org (ol)	10.00	18.00
		Nos. B28-B31 (4)	21.50	35.00
		Set, never hinged	35.00	

Paide SP18

Rakvere SP19

Valga SP20

Viljandi SP21

Paper with Network as in Parenthesis
1937, Jan. 2　　　　Perf. 13½x14
B32	SP18	10s + 10s grn (gray)	3.00	5.00
B33	SP19	15s + 15s red brn (gray)	3.00	5.00
B34	SP20	25s + 25s dk bl (lil)	5.00	6.00
B35	SP21	50s + 50s dk vio (gray)	9.00	10.00
		Nos. B32-B35 (4)	20.00	26.00
		Set, never hinged	40.00	

Baltiski — SP22

Võru — SP23

Haapsalu SP24

Kuressaare SP25

Designs are the armorial bearings of various cities

1938, Jan. 21
Paper with Gray Network
B36	SP22	10s + 10s dk brn	3.00	3.25
B37	SP23	15s + 15s car & grn	3.50	3.50
B38	SP24	25s + 25s dk bl & car	5.00	5.00
B39	SP25	50s + 50s blk & org yel	7.00	8.75
a.		Sheet of 4, #B36-B39	35.00	30.00
		Nos. B36-B39 (4)	18.50	20.50
		Set, never hinged	40.00	

Annual charity ball, Tallinn, Jan. 2, 1938.

Viljandimaa SP27

Pärnumaa SP28

Tartumaa SP29

Harjumaa SP30

Designs are the armorial bearings of various districts

1939, Jan. 10　　　　　Perf. 13½
Paper with Gray Network
B41	SP27	10s + 10s dk bl grn	3.50	4.50
B42	SP28	15s + 15s carmine	4.00	5.00
B43	SP29	25s + 25s dk blue	5.50	7.25
B44	SP30	50s + 50s brn lake	8.50	15.00
a.		Sheet of 4, #B41-B44	30.00	40.00
		Nos. B41-B44 (4)	21.50	31.75
		Set, never hinged	40.00	

Võrumaa SP32

Järvamaa SP33

Läänemaa SP34

Saaremaa SP35

Designs are the armorial bearings of various districts

1940, Jan. 2   Typo.   Perf. 13½
Paper with Gray Network

B46	SP32	10s + 10s dp grn & ultra	2.50 3.00
B47	SP33	15s + 15s dk car & ultra	2.50 3.00
B48	SP34	25s + 25s dk bl & scar	3.00 5.00
B49	SP35	50s + 50s ocher & ultra	4.00 8.00
		Nos. B46-B49 (4)	12.00 19.00
		Set, never hinged	25.00

Catalogue values for unused stamps in this section, from this point to the end of the section, are for Never Hinged items.

1992 Summer Olympics, Barcelona — SP40

1992, June 22   Litho.   Perf. 14

B60	SP40	1r +50k red	.25 .25
B61	SP40	3r +1.50r green	1.00 1.00
B62	SP40	5r +2.50r blue & blk	.50 .50
		Nos. B60-B62 (3)	1.75 1.75

While face values are shown in kopecks and rubles, the stamps were sold in the new currency at the rate of 1 ruble = 10 sents.

No. 280 Surcharged

1994, Nov. 18   Litho.   Perf. 14

B63	A51	2.50k +20k green	5.00 4.00

Surtax for benefit of survivors of sinking of ferry "Estonia."

Haliaeetus Albicilla — SP41

1995, Aug. 29   Litho.   Perf. 14

B64	SP41	2k +25k black & blue	.45 .45

Surtax for Keep the Estonian Sea Clean Assoc.

UNICEF, 60th Anniv. SP42

2006, June 1   Litho.   Perf. 13½

B65	SP42	4.40k +1k multi	.90 .90

AIR POST STAMPS

Airplane AP1

Unwmk.
1920, Mar. 13   Typo.   Imperf.

C1	AP1	5m yel, blk & lt grn	3.00 5.00

No. C1 Overprinted "1923" in Red
1923, Oct. 1

C2	AP1	5m multicolored	7.00 15.00

No. C1 Surcharged in Red
1923, Oct. 1

C3	AP1	15m on 5m multi	10.00 17.50

Pairs of No. C1 Surcharged in Black or Red

1923, Oct.

C4	AP1	10m on 5m+5m (B)	7.50 10.00
C5	AP1	20m on 5m+5m	20.00 22.50
C6	AP1	45m on 5m+5m	80.00 100.00

Rough Perf. 11½

C7	AP1	10m on 5m+5m (B)	425.00 450.00
C8	AP1	20m on 5m+5m	175.00 225.00
		Nos. C4-C8 (5)	707.50 807.50

The pairs comprising Nos. C7 and C8 are imperforate between. Forged surcharges and perforations abound. Authentication is required.

Monoplane in Flight — AP2

Designs: Various views of planes in flight.

1924, Feb. 12   Imperf.

C9	AP2	5m yellow & blk	2.00 4.00
C10	AP2	10m blue & blk	2.00 4.00
C11	AP2	15m red & blk	2.00 4.00
C12	AP2	20m green & blk	2.00 3.00
C13	AP2	45m violet & blk	2.00 6.00
		Nos. C9-C13 (5)	10.00 21.00

The paper is covered with a faint network in pale shades of the frame colors. There are four varieties of the frames and five of the pictures.

1925, July 15   Perf. 13½

C14	AP2	5m yellow & blk	1.50 2.00
C15	AP2	10m blue & blk	1.50 2.00
C16	AP2	15m red & blk	1.50 3.00
C17	AP2	20m green & blk	1.50 2.50
C18	AP2	45m violet & blk	1.50 3.00
		Nos. C14-C18 (5)	7.50 12.50

Counterfeits of Nos. C1-C18 are plentiful.

REGISTRATION STAMP

Catalogue values for unused stamps in this section are for Never Hinged items.

Arms Type of 1992
1992, Mar. 16   Litho.   Perf. 13x12½

F1	A42	R (10r) pink & red	.50 .50

OCCUPATION STAMPS

Issued under German Occupation
For Use in Tartu (Dorpat)

Russian Stamps of 1909-12 Surcharged

1918   Unwmk.   Perf. 14x14½

N1	A15	20pf on 10k dk bl	35.00 50.00
N2	A8	40pf on 20k bl & car	35.00 50.00
		Set, never hinged	77.50

Forged overprints exist.

Estonian Arms and Swastika — OS1

Perf. 11½
1941, Aug.   Typo.   Unwmk.

N3	OS1	15k brown	10.00 10.00
N4	OS1	20k green	10.00 10.00
N5	OS1	30k dark blue	10.00 10.00
		Nos. N3-N5 (3)	30.00 30.00
		Set, never hinged	50.00

Exist imperf. Value, set, $100.
Nos. N3-N5 were issued on both ordinary paper with colorless gum and thick chalky paper with yellow gum. Same values.

OCCUPATION SEMI-POSTAL STAMPS

Castle Tower, Tallinn — OSP1

Designs: 20k+20k, Stone Bridge, Tartu, horiz. 30k+30k, Narva Castle, horiz. 50k+50k, Tallinn view, horiz. 60k+60k, Tartu University. 100k+100k, Narva Castle, close view.

Paper with Gray Network
Perf. 11½
1941, Sept. 29   Photo.   Unwmk.

NB1	OSP1	15k + 15k dk brn	.60 1.00
NB2	OSP1	20k + 20k red lil	.60 1.00
NB3	OSP1	30k + 30k dk bl	.60 1.00
NB4	OSP1	50k + 50k bluish grn	.70 2.50
NB5	OSP1	60k + 60k car	1.00 2.50
NB6	OSP1	100k + 100k gray	1.50 3.00
		Nos. NB1-NB6 (6)	5.00 11.00
		Set, never hinged	12.00

Nos. NB1-NB6 exist imperf. Value, set unused $20, used $40.
A miniature sheet containing one each of Nos. NB1-NB6, imperf., exists in various colors. Value, mint $40, used $60. It was not postally valid. Reproductions are common.

ETHIOPIA
ˌē-thē-ˈō-pē-ə

(Abyssinia)

LOCATION — Northeastern Africa
GOVT. — Republic (1988)
AREA — 426,260 sq. mi.
POP. — 59,680,383 (1999 est.)
CAPITAL — Addis Ababa

During the Italian occupation (1936-1941) Nos. N1-N7 were used, also stamps of Italian East Africa, Eritrea and Somalia.

During the British administration (1941-42) stamps of Great Britain and Kenya were used when available.

16 Guerche = 1 Menelik Dollar or 1 Maria Theresa Dollar
100 Centimes = 1 Franc (1905)
40 Paras = 1 Piaster (1908)
16 Mehalek = 1 Thaler or Talari (1928)
100 Centimes = 1 Thaler (1936)
100 Cents = 1 Ethiopian Dollar (1946)
100 Cents = 1 Birr (1978)

Catalogue values for unused stamps in this country are for Never Hinged items, beginning with Scott 247 in the regular postage section, Scott B6 in the semipostal section, Scott C18 in the airpost section, Scott E1 in the special delivery section, and Scott J57 in the postage due section.

Watermarks

Wmk. 140 — Crown

Wmk. 282 — Ethiopian Star and Amharic Characters, Multiple

Excellent forgeries of Nos. 1-86 exist.

Very Fine examples of Nos. 1-86 and J1-J42 will have perforations touching the design on one or more sides due to the narrow spacing of the stamps on the plates and imperfect perforating methods. Stamps with margins clear on all sides are scarce and command high premiums.

On March 9, 1894 Menelik II awarded Alfred Ilg a concession to develop a railway, including postal service. Ilg's stamps, Nos. 1-79, were valid locally and to Djibouti. Mail to other countries had to bear stamps of Obock, Somali Coast, etc.
Ethiopia joined the UPU Nov. 1, 1908.

Menelik II A1

Lion of Judah A2

Amharic numeral "8"

Perf. 14x13½
1895, Jan.   Unwmk.   Typo.

1	A1	¼g green	3.00 2.00
2	A1	½g red	3.00 2.00
3	A1	1g blue	3.00 2.00

4	A1	2g dark brown	3.00	2.00
5	A2	4g lilac brown	3.00	2.00
6	A2	8g violet	3.00	2.00
7	A2	16g black	3.00	2.00
		Nos. 1-7 (7)	21.00	14.00

For 4g, 8g and 16g stamps of type A1, see Nos. J3a, J4a and J7a.
Earliest reported use is Jan. 29, 1895.
Forged cancellations are plentiful.
For overprints see #8-86, J8-J28, J36-J42.
For surcharges see #94-100, J29-J35.

**Nos. 1-7 Handstamped
in Violet or Blue**

Overprint 9¼x2½mm, Serifs on "E"

1901, July 18

8	A1	¼g green	24.00	24.00
9	A1	½g red	24.00	24.00
10	A1	1g blue	24.00	24.00
11	A1	2g dark brown	24.00	24.00
12	A2	4g lilac brown	27.50	27.50
13	A2	8g violet	42.50	42.50
14	A2	16g black	52.50	52.50
		Nos. 8-14 (7)	218.50	218.50

Violet overprints were issued July 18, 1901, for postal use, while the blue overprints were issued in Jan. 1902 for philatelic purposes. The blue overprints were not used in the mails. Values for unused stamps are for examples with blue overprints. Unused stamps with violet overprints are worth much more.
Overprints 8¼mm wide are unofficial reproductions.

**Nos. 1-7 Handstamped
in Violet, Blue or Black**

Overprint 11x3mm, Low Colons

1902, Apr. 1

15	A1	¼g green	6.00	6.00
16	A1	½g red	9.00	7.00
17	A1	1g blue	10.00	10.00
18	A1	2g dark brown	14.00	14.00
19	A2	4g lilac brown	27.50	27.50
20	A2	8g violet	40.00	40.00
21	A2	16g black	65.00	65.00
		Nos. 15-21 (7)	171.50	169.50

The handstamp reads "Bosta" (Post).
Overprints 10¾mm and 11mm wide with raised colons are unofficial reproductions.

**Nos. 1-7 Handstamped
in Black**

Overprint 16x3¾mm

1903, Apr. 15

22	A1	¼g green	7.00	7.00
23	A1	½g red	11.00	11.00
24	A1	1g blue	14.00	14.00
25	A1	2g dark brown	17.50	17.50
26	A2	4g lilac brown	25.00	25.00
27	A2	8g violet	35.00	35.00
28	A2	16g black	52.50	52.00
		Nos. 22-28 (7)	162.00	161.50

The handstamp reads "Malekt." (Also "Melekt," message).
Original stamps have blurred colons. Unofficial reproductions have clean colons.
Nos. 22-28 have black overprints only. All other colors are fakes.

**Nos. 1-7 Handstamped
in Violet or Blue**

Overprint 18¼mm Wide

1904, Dec.

36	A1	¼g green	15.00	15.00
37	A1	½g red	20.00	
38	A1	1g blue	25.00	
39	A1	2g dark brown	27.50	
40	A2	4g lilac brown	35.00	
41	A2	8g violet	57.50	
42	A2	16g black	75.00	
		Nos. 36-42 (7)	255.00	

The handstamp reads "Malekathe" (message). This set was never issued.

**Preceding Issues Surcharged with
New Values in French Currency in
Blue, Violet, Rose or Black:**

a　　　　　　　b

Overprint 3mm High

1905, Jan. 1

On Nos. 1-7

43	A1 (a)	5c on ¼g	10.00	10.00
44	A1 (a)	10c on ½g	10.00	10.00
45	A1 (a)	20c on 1g	10.00	10.00
46	A1 (a)	40c on 2g	11.00	11.00
47	A2 (a)	80c on 4g	18.50	18.50
48	A2 (b)	1.60fr on 8g	22.50	22.50
49	A2 (b)	3.20fr on 16g	32.50	32.50
		Nos. 43-49 (7)	114.50	114.50

Nos. 48-49 exist with period or comma.

On No. 8, "Ethiopie" in Blue

| 50 | A1 (a) | 5c on ¼g | 100.00 | 100.00 |

On No. 15, "Bosta" in Black

| 51 | A1 (a) | 5c on ¼g | 40.00 | 40.00 |

On No. 22, "Malekt" in Black

| 52 | A1 (a) | 5c on ¼g | 75.00 | 75.00 |

Unofficial reproductions exist of Nos. 50, 51, 52. The 5c on #36, 10c, 20c, 40c, 80c, and 1.60fr surcharges exist as unofficial reproductions only.

---

c　　　　　　　d

1905

On No. 2

| 54 | A1 (c) | 5c on half of ½g | 7.50 | 7.50 |

On No. 21, "Bosta" in Black

| 55 | A2 (d) | 5c on 16g blk | 200.00 | 100.00 |

On #55, "Bosta" is in black.

On No. 28, "Malekt" in Black

56	A2 (d)	5c on 16g blk	250.00	250.00
		Nos. 54-56 (3)	457.50	357.50

Nos. 55-56 issued Mar. 30.
The overprints and surcharges on Nos. 8 to 56 inclusive were handstamped, the work being very roughly done.
As is usual with handstamped overprints and surcharges there are many inverted and double, but most of them are fakes or unofficial reproductions.

**Surcharged with New Values in
Various Colors**

and in Violet:

Overprint 14¾x3½mm

1906, Jan. 1

57	A1	5c on ¼g green	10.00	10.00
58	A1	10c on ½g red	12.00	12.00
59	A1	20c on 1g blue	12.00	12.00
60	A1	40c on 2g dk brn	12.00	12.00
61	A2	80c on 4g lilac brn	18.00	18.00
62	A2	1.60fr on 8g violet	27.50	27.50
63	A2	3.20fr on 16g black	27.50	27.50
		Nos. 57-63 (7)	136.50	136.50

Two types of the 4-character overprint ("Menelik"): 14¾x3½mm and 16x4mm.

Surcharged with New Values

and in Violet Brown:

Overprint 16x4¼mm

1906, July 1

64	A1	5c on ¼g grn	8.50	8.50
a.		Surcharged "20"	75.00	75.00
65	A1	10c on ½g red	10.00	10.00
66	A1	20c on 1g blue	16.00	16.00
67	A1	40c on 2g dk brn	16.00	16.00
68	A2	80c on 4g lil brn	22.50	22.50
69	A2	1.60fr on 8g vio	22.50	22.50
70	A2	3.20fr on 16g blk	55.00	55.00
		Nos. 64-70 (7)	150.50	150.50

The control overprint reads "Menelik."

Surcharged in Violet:

e　　　　　　　f

1907, June 21

71	A1 (e)	¼ on ¼g grn	8.00	8.00
72	A1 (e)	½ on ½g red	8.00	8.00
73	A1 (f)	1 on 1g blue	9.50	9.50
74	A1 (f)	2 on 2g dk brn	11.00	11.00
a.		Surcharged "40"	65.00	
75	A2 (f)	4 on 4g lil brn	12.00	12.00
a.		Surcharged "80"	57.50	
76	A2 (f)	8 on 8g vio	27.50	27.50
77	A2 (f)	16 on 16g blk	35.00	35.00
		Nos. 71-77 (7)	111.00	111.00

Nos. 71-72 are also found with stars farther away from figures.
The control overprint reads "Dagmawi" ("Second"), meaning Emperor Menelik II.

**Nos. 2, 23 Surcharged
in Bluish Green**

1908, Aug. 14

78	A1	1pi on ½g red (#2)	10.00	10.00
79	A1	1pi on ½g red (#23)	850.00	

Official reproductions exist. Value, set $25.
Forgeries exist.
The surcharges on Nos. 57-78 are handstamped and are found double, inverted, etc.

Surcharged in Black

1908, Nov. 1

80	A1	¼p on ¼g grn	1.25	1.25
81	A1	½p on ½g red	1.25	1.25
82	A1	1p on 1g blue	1.75	1.75
83	A1	2p on 2g dk brn	3.00	3.00
84	A2	4p on 4g lil brn	4.25	4.25
85	A2	8p on 8g vio	10.00	10.00
86	A2	16p on 16g blk	15.00	15.00
		Nos. 80-86 (7)	36.50	36.50

Surcharges on Nos. 80-85 are found double, inverted, etc. Forgeries exist.
These are the 1st stamps valid for international mail.

King Solomon's
Throne — A3　　　Menelik in
Native
Costume — A4

Menelik in Royal
Dress — A5

1909, Jan. 29　　　　**Perf. 11½**

87	A3	¼g blue green	.80	.60
88	A3	½g rose	.90	.60
89	A3	1g green & org	4.50	1.75
90	A4	2g blue	3.50	2.25
91	A4	4g green & car	5.00	4.00
92	A5	8g ver & dp grn	11.00	7.50
93	A5	16g ver & car	16.50	12.00
		Nos. 87-93 (7)	42.20	28.70

For overprints see Nos. 101-115, J43-J49, J55-J56. For surcharges see Nos. 116-119.

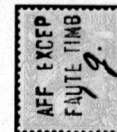

**Nos. 1-7 Handstamped
and Surcharged in ms.**

1911, Oct. 1　　　　**Perf. 14x13½**

94	A1	¼g on ¼g grn	50.00	
95	A1	½g on ½g red	50.00	
96	A1	1g on 1g blue	50.00	
97	A1	2g on 2g dk brn	50.00	
98	A2	4g on 4g lil brn	50.00	
99	A2	8g on 8g violet	50.00	
100	A2	16g on 16g black	50.00	
		Nos. 94-100 (7)	350.00	

Nos. 94-100 are provisionals used at Dire-Dawa for 5 days. The overprint is abbreviated from "Affranchissement Exceptionnel Faute Timbres" (Special Franking Lacking Stamps). The overprints and surcharges were applied to stamps on cover and then canceled.
Nos. 94-100 without surcharges are forgeries.

Stamps of 1909 Handstamped in Violet or Black:

Nos. 101-102   Nos. 104-107

1917, Mar. 30   **Perf. 11½**

101	A3	¼g blue grn (V)	4.25	4.25
102	A3	½g rose (V)	4.25	4.25
104	A4	2g blue (Bk)	5.25	5.25
105	A4	4g grn & car (Bk)	11.00	11.00
106	A5	8g ver & dp grn (Bk)	16.00	16.00
107	A5	16g ver & car (Bk)	32.50	32.50
		Nos. 101-107 (6)	73.25	73.25

Coronation of Empress Zauditu and appointment of Prince Tafari as Regent and Heir to the throne.

Exist with overprint inverted and double.

Stamps of 1909 Overprinted in Blue, Black or Red:

Nos. 108-111   Nos. 112-115

1917, Oct. 1

108	A3	¼g blue grn (Bl)	1.25	1.25
109	A3	½g rose (Bl)	1.25	1.25
110	A3	1g grn & org (Bl)	2.25	2.25
111	A4	2g blue (R)	82.50	87.25
112	A4	2g blue (Bk)	1.25	1.25
113	A4	4g grn & car (Bl)	1.25	1.25
a.		Black overprint	11.00	11.00
114	A5	8g ver & dp grn (Bl)	1.25	1.25
115	A5	16g ver & car (Bl)	2.25	2.25
		Nos. 108-115 (8)	93.25	98.00

Coronation of Empress Zauditu.

Nos. 108-115 all exist with double overprint, inverted overprint, double overprint, one inverted, and various combinations.

Nos. 114-115 with Additional Surcharge

k   l

m   n

1917, May 28

116	A5 (k)	¼g on 8g	3.00	2.50
117	A5 (l)	½g on 8g	3.00	2.50
118	A5 (m)	1g on 16g	9.00	6.50
119	A5 (n)	2g on 16g	10.00	7.00
		Nos. 116-119 (4)	25.00	18.50

Nos. 116-119 all exist with the numerals double and inverted and No. 116 with the Amharic surcharge missing.

Sommering's Gazelle — A6   Prince Tafari — A9

Cathedral of St. George A12

Empress Waizeri Zauditu — A18

¼g, Giraffes. ½g, Leopard. 2g, Prince Tafari, diff. 4g, Prince Tafari, diff. 8g, White rhinoceros. 12g, Somali ostriches. 1t, African elephant. 2t, Water buffalo. 3t, Lions. 5t, 10t, Empress Zauditu.

1919, July 16   **Typo.**   **Perf. 11½**

120	A6	⅛g violet & brn	.20	.20
121	A6	¼g bl grn & drab	.20	.20
122	A6	½g scar & ol grn	.20	.20
123	A9	1g rose lil & gray grn	.20	.20
124	A9	2g dp ultra & fawn	.20	.20
125	A9	4g turq bl & org	.20	2.50
126	A12	6g lt blue & org	.25	.20
127	A12	8g ol grn & blk brn	.35	.20
128	A12	12g red vio & gray	.50	.30
129	A12	1t rose & gray blk	.90	.40
130	A12	2t black & brown	2.50	
131	A12	3t grn & dp org	2.50	1.90
132	A18	4t brn & lil rose	3.00	2.50
133	A18	5t carmine & gray	4.00	4.00
134	A18	10t gray grn & bis	8.00	5.25
		Nos. 120-134 (15)	23.20	
		Nos. 120-129,131-134 (14)		18.25

No. 130 was not issued.

For overprints see Nos. J50-J54. For surcharges see Nos. 135-154.

Reprints have brownish gum that is cracked diagonally. Originals have smooth, white gum. Reprints exist imperf. and some values with inverted centers. Value for set, unused or canceled, $5.

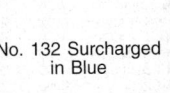

No. 132 Surcharged in Blue

1919, Oct.

135	A18	4g on 4t brn & lil rose	3.00	3.00

Nos. 135-154

The Amharic surcharge indicates the new value and, therefore, varies on Nos. 135-154. There are numerous defective letters and figures, several types of the "2" of "½," the errors "guerhce," "gnerche," etc.

Many varieties of surcharge, such as double, inverted, lines transposed or omitted, and inverted "2" in "½," exist.

There are many irregularly produced settings in imitation of Nos. 136-154 which differ slightly from the originals. These may be essays or proofs.

Stamps of 1919 Surcharged

1921-22

136	A6	½g on ⅛g vio & brn ('22)	1.00	1.00
137	A6	1g on ¼g grn & db	2.50	1.00
138	A9	2g on 1g lil brn & gray grn ('22)	1.00	1.50
139	A18	2g on 4t brn & lil rose ('22)	35.00	15.00
140	A6	2½g on ½g scar & ol grn	1.00	1.50
141	A9	4g on 2g ultra & fawn ('22)	1.00	1.25
		Nos. 136-141 (6)	41.50	21.25

No. 139 has been forged.

Stamps and Type of 1919 Surcharged

1925-28

142	A12	½g on 1t rose & gray blk ('26)	1.00	1.00
a.		Without colon ('28)	12.50	12.50
143	A18	½g on 5t car & gray ('26)	2.00	1.00
144	A12	1g on 6g bl & org	1.00	1.00
145	A12	1g on 12g lil & gray	400.00	400.00
146	A12	1g on 3t grn & org ('26)	22.50	16.00
147	A18	1g on 10t gray grn & bis ('26)	1.00	1.00
		Nos. 142-147 (6)	427.50	420.00

On #142 the surcharge is at the left side of the stamp, reading upward. On #142a it is at the right, reading downward. The two surcharges are from different, though similar, settings. On #146 the surcharge is at the right, reading upward. See note following #154.

Type of 1919 Surcharged

1926

147A	A12	1g on 12g lil & gray	400.00	

Forgeries exist.

Nos. 126-128 Surcharged

1926

148	A12	½g on 8g	3.00	1.25
149	A12	1g on 6g	80.00	50.00
150	A12	1g on 12g	350.00	
		Nos. 148-150 (3)	433.00	51.25

The Amharic line has 7 (½g) or 6 characters (1g).

Nos. 126-128, 131 Surcharged

1927

151	A12	½g on 8g	1.50	1.50
152	A12	1g on 6g	60.00	40.00
153	A12	1g on 12g	5.00	1.50
154	A12	1g on 3t	400.00	
		Nos. 151-154 (4)	466.50	43.00

The Amharic line has 7 (½g) or 4 characters (1g). No. 152 has the lines closer together than do the others.

Forgeries of No. 154 exist.

Prince Tafari — A22   Empress Zauditu — A23

1928, Sept. 5   **Typo.**   **Perf. 13½x14**

155	A22	⅛m org & lt bl	.50	.45
156	A23	¼m ind & red org	.30	.45
157	A22	½m gray grn & blk	.50	.45
158	A23	1m dk car & blk	.30	.45
159	A22	2m dk bl & blk	.30	.45
160	A23	4m yel & olive	.30	.45
161	A22	8m vio & olive	.80	.45
162	A23	1t org brn & vio	.95	.65
163	A22	2t grn & bister	1.40	1.10
164	A23	3t choc & grn	2.25	1.25
		Nos. 155-164 (10)	7.60	6.15

For overprints and surcharges see Nos. 165-209, 217-230, C1-C10.

Preceding Issue Overprinted in Black, Violet or Red

1928, Sept. 1

165	A22	⅛m (Bk)	1.25	1.25
166	A23	¼m (V)	1.25	1.25
167	A22	½m (V)	1.25	1.25
168	A23	1m (V)	1.25	1.25
169	A22	2m (R)	1.25	1.25
170	A23	4m (Bk)	1.25	1.25
171	A22	8m (R)	1.25	1.25
172	A23	1t (Bk)	1.25	1.25
173	A22	2t (R)	1.90	1.90
174	A23	3t (R)	2.75	2.75
		Nos. 165-174 (10)	14.65	14.65

Opening of General Post Office, Addis Ababa.

Exist with overprint inverted, double, double, one inverted, etc.

Nos. 155, 157, 159, 161, 163 Handstamped in Violet, Red or Black

1928, Oct. 7

175	A22	⅛m (V)	1.40	1.40
176	A22	½m (R)	1.40	1.40
177	A22	2m (R)	1.40	1.40

178	A22	8m (Bk)	1.40	1.40
179	A22	2t (V)	1.40	1.40
		Nos. 175-179 (5)	7.00	7.00

Crowning of Prince Tafari as king (Negus) on Oct. 7, 1928.
Nos. 175-177 exist with overprint vertical, inverted, double, etc.
Forgeries exist.

Nos. 155-164
Overprinted in Red
or Green

1930, Apr. 3

180	A22	⅛m org & lt bl (R)	.25	.35
181	A23	¼m ind & red org (G)	.35	.35
182	A22	½m gray grn & blk (R)	.25	.35
183	A22	1m dk car & blk (R)	.35	.35
184	A22	2m dk bl & blk (R)	.35	.35
185	A23	4m yel & ol (R)	.50	.50
186	A22	8m vio & ol (R)	1.00	1.00
187	A23	1t org brn & vio (R)	2.25	2.25
188	A23	2t grn & bis (R)	3.00	3.00
189	A23	3t choc & grn (R)	4.00	4.00
		Nos. 180-189 (10)	12.30	12.50

Proclamation of King Tafari as King of Kings of Abyssinia under the name "Haile Selassie."
A similar overprint, set in four vertical lines, was printed on all denominations of the 1928 issue. It was not considered satisfactory and was rejected. The trial impressions were not placed on sale to the public, but some copies reached private hands and have been passed through the post.

Nos. 155-164
Overprinted in Red
or Olive Brown

1930, Apr. 3

190	A22	⅛m orange & lt bl	.35	.35
191	A23	¼m ind & red org (OB)	.35	.35
192	A22	½m gray grn & blk	.75	.75
193	A23	1m dk car & blk (OB)	.35	.35
194	A22	2m dk blue & blk	.35	.35
195	A23	4m yellow & ol	.60	.60
196	A22	8m violet & ol	1.00	1.00
197	A23	1t org brn & vio	2.25	2.25
198	A22	2t green & bister	3.00	3.00
199	A23	3t chocolate & grn	3.75	3.75
		Nos. 190-199 (10)	12.75	12.75

Proclamation of King Tafari as Emperor Haile Selassie.
All stamps of this series exist with "H" of "HAILE" omitted and with many other varieties.

Nos. 155-164
Handstamped in
Violet or Red

1930, Nov. 2

200	A22	⅛m (V)	.50	.50
201	A23	¼m (V)	.50	.50
202	A22	½m (R)	.50	.50
203	A23	1m (V)	.50	.50
204	A22	2m (R)	.50	.50
205	A23	4m (V)	.50	.50
206	A22	8m (V or R)	1.00	1.00
207	A23	1t (V)	1.50	1.50
208	A22	2t (V or R)	2.50	2.50
209	A23	3t (V or R)	3.50	3.50
		Nos. 200-209 (10)	11.50	11.50

Coronation of Emperor Haile Selassie, Nov. 2, 1930.

Haile Selassie
Coronation
Monument, Symbols
of Empire — A24

1930		**Engr.**		**Perf. 12½**
210	A24	1g orange	.40	.40
211	A24	2g ultra	.40	.40
212	A24	4g violet	.40	.40
213	A24	8g dull green	.70	.65
214	A24	1t brown	1.00	1.00
215	A24	3t green	1.50	1.50
216	A24	5t red brown	1.50	1.50
		Nos. 210-216 (7)	5.90	5.85

Coronation of Emperor Haile Selassie.
Issued: 4g, 11/2; others, 11/23.
Reprints of Nos. 210 to 216 exist. Colors are more yellow and the ink is thicker and slightly glossy. Ink on the originals is dull and granular. Value 35c each.

Nos. 158-160, 164 Surcharged in
Green, Red or Blue

		Type I	**Type II**	
1931			**Perf. 13½x14**	
217	A23	⅛m on 1m	.45	.45
218	A22	⅛m on 2m (R)	.45	.45
219	A23	⅛m on 4m	.45	.45
220	A23	¼m on 1m (Bl)	.45	.45
221	A22	¼m on 2m (R)	1.50	1.50
222	A23	¼m on 4m	1.50	1.50
225	A23	½m on 1m (Bl)	1.50	1.50
226	A22	½m on 2m (R)	1.50	1.50
227	A23	½m on 4m, type II	1.50	1.50
a.		½m on 4m, type I	10.00	10.00
228	A23	½m on 3t (R)	11.00	11.00
230	A22	½m on 2m (R)	1.75	1.75
		Nos. 217-230 (11)	22.05	22.05

The ½m on ⅛m orange & light blue and ½m on ¼m indigo & red orange were clandestinely printed and never sold at the post office.
No. 230 with double surcharge in red and blue is a color trial.
Many varieties exist.
Issued: 1m, Apr.; others, 4/20.

Prince
Makonnen
A25

Empress Menen
A27

View of
Hawash
River and
Railroad
Bridge
A26

Designs: 2g, 8g, Haile Selassie (profile). 4g, 1t, Statue of Menelik II. 3t, Empress Menen (full face). 5t, Haile Selassie (full face).

	Perf. 12½, 12x12½, 12½x12			
1931, June 27				**Engr.**
232	A25	⅛g red	.40	.20
233	A26	¼g olive green	.40	.20
234	A25	½g dark violet	.40	.20
235	A27	1g red orange	.50	.25
236	A27	2g ultra	.50	.25
237	A25	4g violet	.90	.40
238	A27	8g blue green	2.00	2.00
239	A21	1t chocolate	24.00	10.00
240	A27	3t yellow green	7.00	3.00
241	A27	5t red brown	12.00	5.50
		Nos. 232-241 (10)	48.10	22.00

For overprints see Nos. B1-B5. For surcharges see Nos. 242-246.
Reprints of Nos. 232-236, 238-240 are on thinner and whiter paper than the originals. On originals the ink is dull and granular. On reprints, heavy, caked and shiny. Value 20c each.

Nos. 232-236 Surcharged in Blue or
Carmine similar to cut

1936, Jan. 29		**Perf. 12x12½, 12½x12**		
242	A25	1c on ⅛g red	2.00	1.00
243	A26	2c on ¼g ol grn (C)	2.00	1.00
244	A25	3c on ½g dk vio	2.00	1.10
245	A27	5c on 1g red org	2.50	1.50
246	A27	10c on 2g ultra (C)	3.25	1.90
		Nos. 242-246 (5)	11.75	6.50

Catalogue values for unused stamps in this section, from this point to the end of the section, are for Never Hinged items.

Haile Selassie I
A32 A33

1942, Mar. 23		**Litho.**	**Perf. 14x13½**	
247	A32	4c lt bl grn, ind & blk	.50	.25
248	A32	10c rose, indigo & blk	1.50	.45
249	A32	20c dp ultra, ind & blk	3.00	.80
		Nos. 247-249 (3)	5.00	1.50

1942-43				**Unwmk.**
250	A33	4c lt bl grn & indigo	.75	.20
251	A33	8c yel org & indigo	.85	.20
252	A33	10c rose & indigo	1.00	.20
253	A33	12c dull vio & indigo	1.00	.25
254	A33	20c dp ultra & indigo	1.50	.40
255	A33	25c dull grn & indigo	2.00	.60
256	A33	50c dull brn & indigo	4.00	1.00
257	A33	60c lilac & indigo	6.00	1.25
		Nos. 250-257 (8)	17.10	4.10

Issued: 25c, 50c, 60c, 4/1/43; others, 6/22/42.
For surcharges see #258-262, 284, C18-C20.

Nos. 250-254
Surcharged in Black
or Brown

1943, Nov. 3

258	A33	5c on 4c	50.00	50.00
259	A33	10c on 8c	50.00	50.00
260	A33	15c on 10c	50.00	50.00

261	A33	20c on 12c (Br)	50.00	50.00
262	A33	30c on 20c (Br)	50.00	50.00
		Nos. 258-262 (5)	250.00	250.00

Restoration of the Obelisk in Myazzia Place, Addis Ababa, and the 14th anniv. of the coronation of Emperor Haile Selassie.
On No. 262, "3" is surcharged on "2" of "20" to make "30."
A small number of sets exist with a somewhat different handstamped surcharge.

Palace of
Menelik II
A34

Menelik
II — A35

Statue — A36

50c, Mausoleum. 65c, Menelik II (with scepter).

1944, Dec. 31		**Litho.**	**Perf. 10½**	
263	A34	5c green	1.25	.65
264	A35	10c red lilac	1.75	.85
265	A36	20c deep blue	3.00	1.75
266	A34	50c dull purple	3.50	1.75
267	A35	65c bister brown	6.50	2.75
		Nos. 263-267 (5)	16.00	7.75

Cent. of the birth of Menelik II, 8/18/44.
Printed on gum-impregnated paper.

Unissued Semi-Postal Stamps
Overprinted in Carmine:

Nurse &
Baby — A39

Various Designs
Inscribed "Croix Rouge"

1945, Aug. 7		**Photo.**	**Perf. 11½**	
268	A39	5c brt green	.95	.45
269	A39	10c brt red	.95	.45
270	A39	25c blue	.95	.45
271	A39	50c dk yellow brn	5.00	2.00
272	A39	1t brt violet	7.75	2.75
		Nos. 268-272 (5)	15.60	6.10

Nos. 268-272 without overprint were ordered printed in Switzerland before Ethiopia fell to the invading Italians, so were not delivered to Addis Ababa. After that country's liberation, the set was overprinted "V" and issued for ordinary postage. These stamps exist without overprint, but were not so issued. Value $1.25.
Some values exist inverted or double.
Forged overprints exist.
For surcharges see #B11-B15, B36-B40.

Lion of
Judah — A44

Menelik II — A45

Mail Transport, Old and New A46

Designs: 50c, Old Post Office, Addis Ababa. 70c, Menelik II and Haile Selassie.

1947, Apr. 18   Engr.   Perf. 13
273 A44 10c yellow org   2.50   .50
274 A45 20c deep blue   3.75   .75
275 A46 30c orange brn   5.75   1.25
276 A46 50c dk slate grn   13.00   5.00
277 A46 70c red violet   25.00   5.00
      Nos. 273-277 (5)   50.00 10.00

50th anniv. of Ethiopia's postal system.

Haile Selassie and Franklin D. Roosevelt — A49

Design: 65c, Roosevelt and US Flags.

Engraved and Photogravure
1947, May 23   Unwmk.   Perf. 12½
278 A49 12c car lake & bl grn   .80   1.00
279 A49 25c dk blue & rose   .80   1.00
280 A49 65c blk, red & dp bl   1.60   2.00
      Nos. 278-280,C21-C22 (5)   15.20 15.00

King Sahle Selassie Reclining A50

King Sahle Selassie — A52

Design: 30c, View of Ankober.

1947, May 1   Engr.   Perf. 13
281 A50 20c deep blue   1.75   .75
282 A50 30c dark purple   2.75   1.00
283 A52 $1 deep green   6.50   3.00
      Nos. 281-283 (3)   11.00   4.75

150th anniversary of Selassie dynasty.

No. 255 Surcharged in Orange

1947, July 14   Perf. 14x13½
284 A33 12c on 25c   60.00 60.00

Amba Alagaie A53

Designs: 2c, Trinity Church. 4c, Debra Sina. 5c, Mecan, near Achanguie. 8c, Lake Tana. 12c, 15c, Parliament Building, Addis Ababa. 20c, Aiba, near Mai Cheo. 30c, Bahr Bridge over Blue Nile. 60c, 70c, Canoe on Lake Tana. $1, Omo Falls. $3, Mt. Alamata. $5, Ras Dashan Mountains.

Perf. 13x13½
1947-53   Engr.   Wmk. 282
285   A53   1c rose violet   .20   .20
286   A53   2c blue violet   .20   .20
  a.   Unwatermarked ('51)   37.50 15.00
287   A53   4c green   .25   .20
288   A53   5c dark green   .25   .20
289   A53   8c deep orange   .45   .20
290   A53 12c red   .55   .20
290A A53 15c dk ol brn ('53)   .50   .20
291   A53 20c blue   .80   .30
292   A53 30c orange brown   1.40   .40
292A A53 60c red ('51)   1.60   .70
293   A53 70c rose lilac   2.25   .50
294   A53 $1 dk carmine rose   3.75   .50
295   A53 $3 bright rose   10.00   2.00
296   A53 $5 olive   16.00   4.00
      Nos. 285-296 (14)   38.20   9.80

Issue dates: 15c, May 25, 1953; 60c, Feb. 10, 1951; others, Aug. 23, 1947.
Shades exist.
For overprints see Nos. 355-356. For surcharges see Nos. B6-B10, B16-B20.

Empress Waizero Menen and Emperor Haile Selassie A54

1949, May 5   Wmk. 282   Perf. 13
297 A54 20c blue   1.50   .70
298 A54 30c yellow org   1.50   .90
299 A54 50c purple   3.00   1.60
300 A54 80c green   3.50   2.00
301 A54 $1 red   6.25   3.00
      Nos. 297-301 (5)   15.75   8.20

Central ornaments differ on each denomination.
8th anniv. of Ethiopia's liberation from Italian occupation.

Dejach Balcha Hospital A55

Abuna Petros — A56

Designs: 20c, Haile Selassie raising flag. 30c, Lion of Judah statue. 50c, Empress Waizero Menen, Haile Selassie and building.

Perf. 13x13½, 13½x13
1950, Nov. 2   Engr.   Wmk. 282
302 A55   5c purple   .95   .30
303 A56 10c deep plum   2.50   .60
304 A56 20c deep carmine   3.50   .75
305 A56 30c green   5.75   1.50
306 A55 50c deep blue   10.00   3.00
      Nos. 302-306 (5)   22.70   6.15

20th anniv. of the coronation of Emperor Haile Selassie and Empress Menen.

Abbaye Bridge — A57

1951, Jan. 1   Unwmk.   Perf. 14
308 A57   5c dk green & dk brn   4.25   .50
309 A57 10c dp orange & blk   5.75   .50
310 A57 15c dp blue & org brn   8.25   .50
311 A57 30c olive & lil rose   15.00   .80

312 A57 60c brown & dp bl   20.00   2.00
313 A57 80c purple & green   30.00   3.00
      Nos. 308-313 (6)   83.25   7.30

Opening of the Abbaye Bridge over the Blue Nile.

Tomb of Prince Makonnen A58

1951, Mar. 2
Center in Black
314 A58   5c dark green   3.00   .60
315 A58 10c deep ultra   3.00   .35
316 A58 15c blue   5.00   .35
317 A58 30c claret   10.00   1.35
318 A58 80c rose carmine   15.00   2.00
319 A58 $1 orange brown   20.00   2.00
      Nos. 314-319 (6)   56.00   6.65

55th anniversary of the Battle of Adwa.

Emperor Haile Selassie — A59

1952, July 23   Perf. 13½
320 A59   5c dark green   .60   .20
321 A59 10c red orange   .85   .25
322 A59 15c black   1.25   .35
323 A59 25c ultra   1.60   .35
324 A59 30c violet   2.00   .60
325 A59 50c rose red   3.00   .85
326 A59 65c chocolate   6.00   1.50
      Nos. 320-326 (7)   15.30   4.10

60th birthday of Haile Selassie.

Open Road to Sea A60

Designs: 25c, 50c, Road and broken chain. 65c, Map. 80c, Allegory: Reunion. $1, Haile Selassie raising flag. $2, Ethiopian flag and seascape. $3, Haile Selassie addressing League of Nations.

Wmk. 282
1952, Sept. 11   Engr.   Perf. 13
327 A60 15c brown carmine   .85   .20
328 A60 25c red brown   1.10   .40
329 A60 30c yellow brown   2.00   .60
330 A60 50c purple   2.25   .75
331 A60 65c gray   3.50   .90
332 A60 80c blue green   4.00   .60
333 A60 $1 rose carmine   8.00   1.25
334 A60 $2 deep blue   14.00   2.00
335 A60 $3 magenta   30.00   3.50
      Nos. 327-335 (9)   65.70 10.20

Issued to celebrate Ethiopia's federation with Eritrea, effected Sept. 11, 1952.

Haile Selassie and New Ethiopian Port A61

15c, 30c, Haile Selassie on deck of ship.

1953, Oct. 4
337 A61 10c red & dk brn   2.75   1.00
338 A61 15c blue & dk grn   3.00   1.00
339 A61 25c orange & dk brn   5.25   2.00
340 A61 30c red brn & dk grn 9.50   3.00
341 A61 50c purple & dk brn 17.00   4.00
      Nos. 337-341 (5)   37.50 11.00

Federation of Ethiopia and Eritrea, 1st anniv.

Princess Tsahai at a Sickbed A62

Perf. 13x13½
1955, July 8   Engr.   Wmk. 282
Cross Typo. in Red
342 A62 15c choc & ultra   1.00   .50
343 A62 20c green & orange   1.50   .60
344 A62 30c ultra & green   2.50   .75
      Nos. 342-344 (3)   5.00   1.85

Ethiopian Red Cross, 20th anniv.
For surcharges see Nos. B33-B35.

Promulgating the Constitution — A63

Bishops' Consecration by Archbishop — A64

25c, Kagnew Battalion. 35c, Reunion with the Motherland. 50c, "Progress." 65c, Empress Waizero Menen & Emperor Haile Selassie.

Perf. 12½
1955, Nov. 3   Unwmk.   Engr.
345 A63   5c green & choc   .50   .25
346 A64 20c carmine & brn   1.10   .40
347 A64 25c magenta & gray   1.50   .60
348 A63 35c brown & red org   2.00   .75
349 A64 50c dk brn & ultra   3.00   1.10
350 A64 65c violet & car   4.25   1.75
      Nos. 345-350 (6)   12.35   4.85

Silver jubilee of the coronation of Emperor Haile Selassie and Empress Waizero Menen.

Emperor Haile Selassie and Fair Emblem — A65

1955, Nov. 5   Wmk. 282
351 A65   5c green & ol grn   .60   .20
352 A65 10c car & dp ultra   .90   .25
353 A65 15c vio blk & grn   1.25   .35
354 A65 50c mag & red brn   1.75   .90
      Nos. 351-354 (4)   4.50   1.70

Silver Jubilee Fair, Addis Ababa.

Nos. 291 and 292A Overprinted

1960, Apr. 7   Perf. 13x13½
355 A53 20c blue   1.50   1.00
356 A53 60c red   2.50   2.00

WRY, July 1, 1959-June 30, 1960.
The 60c without serifs is a trial printing.

Map of Africa, "Liberty" and Haile Selassie — A66

Emperor Haile Selassie — A67

Perf. 13½

1960, June 14   Engr.   Unwmk.
357	A66	20c orange & green	.60 .60
358	A66	80c orange & violet	1.50 .60
359	A66	$1 orange & maroon	1.75 .80
		Nos. 357-359 (3)	3.85 2.00

2nd Conf. of Independent African States at Tunis. Issued in sheets of 10.

1960, Nov. 2   Wmk. 282   Perf. 14
360	A67	10c brown & blue	.40 .20
361	A67	25c violet & emerald	.85 .30
362	A67	50c dk bl & org yel	1.50 1.00
363	A67	65c slate grn & sal pink	2.00 1.00
364	A67	$1 indigo & rose vio	3.25 1.50
		Nos. 360-364 (5)	8.00 4.00

30th anniv. of the coronation of Emperor Haile Selassie.

Africa Hall, UN Economic Commission for Africa — A68

1961, Apr. 15   Wmk. 282   Perf. 14
365	A68	80c ultra	1.00 .50

Africa Freedom Day, Apr. 15. Sheets of 10.

Map of Ethiopia, Olive Branch A69

1961, May 5   Perf. 13x13½
366	A69	20c green	.25 .20
367	A69	30c violet blue	.35 .20
368	A69	$1 brown	1.40 .60
		Nos. 366-368 (3)	1.40 .60

20th anniv. of Ethiopia's liberation from Italian occupation.

African Wild Ass A70

1961, June 16   Wmk. 282   Perf. 14
369	A70	5c shown	.60 .20
370	A70	15c Eland	.60 .20
371	A70	25c Elephant	.75 .40
372	A70	35c Giraffe	1.75 .50
373	A70	50c Beisa	1.75 .50
374	A70	$1 Lion	3.50 1.50
		Nos. 369-374 (6)	8.95 3.30

Issued in sheets of 10. Used values are for CTO's.

Emperor Haile Selassie and Empress Waizero Menen — A71

1961, July 27   Unwmk.   Perf. 11
375	A71	10c green	.50 .25
376	A71	50c violet blue	.90 .45
377	A71	$1 carmine rose	1.60 .90
		Nos. 375-377 (3)	3.00 1.60

Golden wedding anniv. of the Emperor and Empress.

Warlike Horsemanship (Guks) — A72

15c, Hockey. 20c, Bicycling. 30c, Soccer. 50c, 1960 Olympic marathon winner, Abebe Bikila.

Photogravure and Engraved
1962, Jan. 14   Perf. 12x11½
378	A72	10c yel grn & car	.20 .20
379	A72	15c pink & dk brn	.20 .20
380	A72	20c red & black	.25 .20
381	A72	30c ultra & dl pur	.45 .20
382	A72	50c yellow & green	.90 .20
		Nos. 378-382 (5)	2.00 1.00

Third Africa Football (soccer) Cup, Addis Ababa, Jan. 14-22.

Malaria Eradication Emblem, World Map and Mosquito — A73

Wmk. 282
1962, Apr. 7   Engr.   Perf. 13½
383	A73	15c black	.20 .20
384	A73	30c purple	.40 .25
385	A73	60c red brown	1.00 .55
		Nos. 383-385 (3)	1.60 1.00

WHO drive to eradicate malaria.

Abyssinian Ground Hornbill A74

Birds: 15c, Abyssinian roller. 30c, Bateleur, vert. 50c, Double-toothed barbet, vert. $1, Didric cuckoo.

Perf. 11½
1962, May 5   Unwmk.   Photo.
Granite Paper
386	A74	5c multicolored	.90 .20
387	A74	15c emer, brn & ultra	1.50 .45
388	A74	30c lt brn, blk & red	1.75 1.00
389	A74	50c multicolored	3.25 1.25
390	A74	$1 multicolored	7.25 2.00
		Nos. 386-390 (5)	14.65 4.90

See Nos. C77-C81, C97-C101, C107-C111.

Assab Hospital A75

15c, School at Assab. 20c, Church at Massawa. 50c, Mosque at Massawa. 60c, Assab port.

Wmk. 282
1962, Sept. 11   Engr.   Perf. 13½
391	A75	3c purple	.20 .20
392	A75	15c dark blue	.20 .20
393	A75	20c green	.25 .20
394	A75	50c brown	.50 .20
395	A75	60c carmine rose	.75 .35
		Nos. 391-395 (5)	1.90 1.20

Federation of Ethiopia and Eritrea, 10th anniv.

King Bazen, Madonna and Stars over Bethlehem — A76

15c, Ezana, obelisks & temple. 20c, Kaleb & sailing fleet. 50c, Lalibela, rock-church and frescoes, vert. 60c, King Yekuno Amlak & Abuna Tekle Haimanot preaching in Ankober. 75c, King Zara Yacob & Maskal celebration. $1, King Lebna Dengel & battle against Mohammed Gragn.

Perf. 14½
1962, Nov. 2   Unwmk.   Photo.
396	A76	10c multicolored	.20 .20
397	A76	15c multicolored	.25 .20
398	A76	20c multicolored	.30 .20
399	A76	50c multicolored	.50 .20
400	A76	60c multicolored	.60 .30
401	A76	75c multicolored	.90 .50
402	A76	$1 multicolored	1.25 .75
		Nos. 396-402 (7)	4.00 2.35

32nd anniv. of the coronation of Emperor Haile Selassie and to commemorate ancient kings and saints.

Map of Ethiopian Telephone Network — A77

Wheat Emblem — A78

Designs: 50c, Radio mast and waves. 60c, Telegraph pole and rising sun.

Perf. 13½x14
1963, Jan. 1   Engr.   Wmk. 282
403	A77	10c dark red	.40 .20
404	A77	50c ultra	1.00 .40
405	A77	60c brown	1.25 .50
		Nos. 403-405 (3)	2.65 1.10

10th anniv. of the Imperial Board of Telecommunications.

1963, Mar. 21   Unwmk.   Perf. 13½
406	A78	5c deep rose	.20 .20
407	A78	10c rose carmine	.20 .20
408	A78	15c violet blue	.20 .20
409	A78	30c emerald	.30 .20
		Nos. 406-409 (4)	.90 .80

FAO "Freedom from Hunger" campaign.

Abuna Salama — A79

Queen of Sheba — A80

Spiritual Leaders: 15c, Abuna Aregawi. 30c, Abuna Tekle Haimanot. 40c. Yared. 60c, Zara Yacob.

1964, Jan. 3   Unwmk.   Perf. 13½
410	A79	10c blue	.45 .20
411	A79	15c dark green	.75 .20
412	A79	30c brown red	1.10 .45
413	A79	40c dark blue	2.00 .75
414	A79	60c brown	2.75 1.40
		Nos. 410-414 (5)	7.05 3.00

1964, Mar. 2   Photo.   Perf. 11½

Ethiopian Empresses: 15c, Helen. 50c, Seble Wongel. 60c, Mentiwab. 80c, Taitu, consort of Menelik II.

Granite Paper
415	A80	10c multicolored	.50 .30
416	A80	15c multicolored	.80 .50
417	A80	50c multicolored	1.40 .90
418	A80	60c multicolored	3.00 1.50
419	A80	80c multicolored	4.00 2.00
		Nos. 415-419 (5)	9.70 5.20

Priest Teaching Alphabet to Children — A81

Eleanor Roosevelt (1884-1962) — A82

10c, Classroom. 15c, Woman learning to read. 40c, Students in chemistry laboratory. 60c, Graduation procession.

1964, June 1   Unwmk.   Perf. 11½
Granite Paper
420	A81	5c multicolored	.20 .20
421	A81	10c emerald	.20 .20
422	A81	15c rose vio, vert.	.20 .20
423	A81	40c vio blue, vert.	.60 .20
424	A81	60c dark pur, vert.	1.00 .50
		Nos. 420-424 (5)	2.20 1.35

Issued to publicize education.

1964, Oct. 11   Photo.
Granite Paper
Portrait in Slate Blue
425	A82	10c yellow bister	.20 .20
426	A82	60c orange brown	.80 .50
427	A82	80c green & gold	1.00 .70
		Nos. 425-427 (3)	2.00 1.40

King Serse Dengel and View of Gondar, 1563 A83

Ethiopian Leaders: 10c, King Fasiladas and Gondar in 1632. 20c, King Yassu the Great and Gondar in 1682. 25c, Emperor Theodore II and map of Ethiopia. 60c, Emperor John IV and Battle of Gura, 1876. 80c, Emperor Menelik II and Battle of Adwa, 1896.

1964, Dec. 12   Photo.   Perf. 14½x14
428	A83	5c multicolored	.20 .20
429	A83	10c multicolored	.20 .20
430	A83	20c multicolored	.30 .20
431	A83	25c multicolored	.50 .20
432	A83	60c multicolored	.95 .50
433	A83	80c multicolored	1.10 .70
		Nos. 428-433 (6)	3.25 2.00

Ethiopian Rose — A84

Flowers: 10c, Kosso tree. 25c, St.-John's-wort. 35c, Parrot's-beak. 60c, Maskal daisy.

1965, Mar. 30   *Perf. 12x13½*
434 A84	5c multicolored	.20	.20
435 A84	10c multicolored	.20	.20
436 A84	25c multicolored	.45	.20
437 A84	35c multicolored	.85	.25
438 A84	60c green, yel & org	1.10	.40
	Nos. 434-438 (5)	2.80	1.25

ITU Emblem, Old and New Communication Symbols — A85

Perf. 13½x14½
1965, May 17   Litho.   Unwmk.
439 A85	5c blue, indigo & yel	.20	.20
440 A85	10c blue, indigo & org	.25	.20
441 A85	60c blue, indigo & lil rose	.90	.50
	Nos. 439-441 (3)	1.35	.90

Cent. of the ITU.

Laboratory A86

Designs: 5c, Textile spinning mill. 10c, Sugar factory. 20c, Mountain road. 25c, Autobus. 30c, Diesel locomotive and bridge. 35c, Railroad station, Addis Ababa.

1965, July 19   Photo.   *Perf. 11½*
Granite Paper
Portrait in Black
442 A86	3c sepia	.20	.20
443 A86	5c dull pur & buff	.20	.20
444 A86	10c black & gray	.20	.20
445 A86	20c green & pale yel	.25	.20
446 A86	25c dk brown & yel	.35	.20
447 A86	30c maroon & gray	.55	.25
448 A86	65c dk blue & gray	.65	.35
	Nos. 442-448 (7)	2.40	1.60

For overprints see Nos. 609-612.

ICY Emblem A87

1965, Oct. 24   Unwmk.   *Perf. 11½*
Granite Paper
449 A87	10c blue & red brn	.25	.20
450 A87	50c dp blue & red brn	.75	.40
451 A87	80c vio blue & red brn	1.00	.60
	Nos. 449-451 (3)	2.00	1.20

International Cooperation Year, 1965.

National Bank Emblem A88

Designs: 10c, Commercial Bank emblem. 60c, Natl. and Commercial Bank buildings.

1965, Nov. 2   Photo.   *Perf. 13*
452 A88	10c dp car, blk & indigo	.35	.20
453 A88	30c ultra, blk & indigo	.65	.30
454 A88	60c black, yel & indigo	1.00	.50
	Nos. 452-454 (3)	2.00	1.00

Natl. and Commercial Banks of Ethiopia.

"Light and Peace" Press Building A89

1966, Apr. 5   Engr.   *Perf. 13*
455 A89	5c pink & black	.20	.20
456 A89	15c lt yel grn & blk	.35	.20
457 A89	30c orange yel & blk	.60	.30
	Nos. 455-457 (3)	1.15	.70

Opening of the "Light and Peace" Printing Press building.

Kabaro Drum — A90

Musical Instruments: 10c, Bagana harp. 35c, Messenko guitar. 50c, Krar lyre. 60c, Wachent flutes.

1966, Sept. 9   Photo.   *Perf. 13½*
458 A90	5c brt green & blk	.20	.20
459 A90	10c dull blue & blk	.20	.20
460 A90	35c orange & blk	.60	.25
461 A90	50c yellow & blk	.90	.35
462 A90	60c rose car & blk	1.10	.60
	Nos. 458-462 (5)	3.00	1.60

Emperor Haile Selassie — A91

1966, Nov. 1   Unwmk.   *Perf. 12*
463 A91	10c black, gold & grn	.25	.20
464 A91	15c black, gold & dp car	.40	.20
465 A91	40c black & gold	1.25	.60
	Nos. 463-465 (3)	1.90	1.00

50 years of leadership of Emperor Haile Selassie.

UNESCO Emblem and Map of Africa A92

Wmk. 282
1966, Nov. 30   Litho.   *Perf. 13½*
| 466 A92 | 15c blue car & blk | .35 | .20 |
| 467 A92 | 60c olive, brn & dk bl | .90 | .45 |

20th anniv. of UNESCO.

WHO Headquarters, Geneva — A93

1966, Nov. 30
| 468 A93 | 5c olive, ultra & brn | .80 | .20 |
| 469 A93 | 40c brown, pur & emer | 2.50 | .35 |

Opening of WHO Headquarters, Geneva.

Expo '67 Ethiopian Pavilion and Columns of Axum (Replica) — A94

Perf. 12x13½
1967, May 2   Photo.   Unwmk.
470 A94	30c brt blue & multi	.50	.50
471 A94	45c multicolored	.65	.30
472 A94	80c gray & multi	1.25	.45
	Nos. 470-472 (3)	2.40	1.00

EXPO '67, Intl. Exhibition, Montreal, Apr. 28-Oct. 27, 1967.

Diesel Train and Map — A95

1967, June 7   Photo.   *Perf. 12*
473 A95	15c multicolored	.60	.30
474 A95	30c multicolored	1.40	.75
475 A95	50c multicolored	2.00	.95
	Nos. 473-475 (3)	4.00	2.00

Djibouti-Addis Ababa railroad, 50th anniv.

Papilionidae Aethiops — A96

Various Butterflies.

Perf. 13½x13
1967, June 30   Photo.   Unwmk.
476 A96	5c buff & multi	.35	.20
477 A96	10c lilac & multi	1.00	.30
478 A96	20c multicolored	1.50	.50
479 A96	35c blue & multi	2.75	1.00
480 A96	40c multicolored	4.25	1.40
	Nos. 476-480 (5)	9.85	3.40

Emperor Haile Selassie and Lion of Judah A97

1967, July 21   *Perf. 11½*
Granite Paper
481 A97	10c dk brn, emer & gold	.25	.20
482 A97	15c dk brn, yel & gold	.40	.20
483 A97	$1 dk brn, red & gold	1.75	.75
	Nos. 481-483 (3)	2.40	1.15

Souvenir Sheet
| 484 A97 | $1 dk brn, pur & gold | 12.00 | 12.00 |

75th birthday of Emperor Haile Selassie.

Microscope and Ethiopian Flag — A98

1967, Nov. 6   Litho.   *Perf. 13*
Flag in Grn, Yel, Red & Blk
485 A98	5c blue	.20	.20
486 A98	30c ocher	.50	.25
487 A98	$1 violet	1.75	.80
	Nos. 485-487 (3)	2.45	1.25

2nd Intl. Conf. on the Global Impact of Applied Microbiology, Addis Ababa, 11/6-12.

Wall Painting from Debre Berhan Selassie Church, Gondar, 17th Century — A99

ITY Emblem and: 25c, Votive throne from Atsbe Dera, 4th Cent. B.C., vert. 35c, Prehistoric cave painting, Harar Province. 50c, Prehistoric stone tools, Melke Kontoure, vert.

1967, Nov. 20   Photo.   *Perf. 14½*
488 A99	15c multicolored	2.00	1.00
489 A99	25c yel grn, buff & blk	2.25	1.00
490 A99	35c green, brn & blk	2.00	1.25
491 A99	50c yellow & blk	3.50	2.00
	Nos. 488-491 (4)	9.75	5.25

International Tourist Year, 1967.

A100   A101

Crosses of Lalibela: 5c, Processional Bronze Cross, Biet-Maryam Church. 10c, Processional copper cross. 15c, Copper cross, Biet-Maryam church. 20c, Lalibela-style cross. 50c, Chiseled copper cross, Madhani Alem church.

1967, Dec. 7   Photo.   *Perf. 14½*
Crosses in Silver
492 A100	5c yellow & blk	.20	.20
493 A100	10c red orange & blk	.20	.20
494 A100	15c violet & blk	.30	.20
495 A100	20c brt rose & blk	.45	.20
496 A100	50c orange yel & blk	1.40	.50
	Nos. 492-496 (5)	2.55	1.30

Perf. 14x13½
1968, Apr. 18   Litho.   Unwmk.

Designs: 10c, Emperor Theodore (1818?-1868). 20c, Emperor Theodore and lions, horiz. 50c, Imperial crown.

497 A101	10c lt vio, ocher & brn	.30	.20
498 A101	20c lilac, brn & dk vio	.50	.20
499 A101	50c dk brn, org & rose cl	1.00	.40
	Nos. 497-499 (3)	1.80	.80

Human Rights Flame A102

1968, May 31   Unwmk.   *Perf. 14½*
| 500 A102 | 15c pink, red & blk | .30 | .30 |
| 501 A102 | $1 lt bl, brt bl & blk | 1.50 | 1.50 |

International Human Rights Year, 1968.

Shah Riza Pahlavi, Emperor and Flags A103

1968, June 3   Litho.   *Perf. 13½*
502 A103	5c multicolored	.20	.20
503 A103	15c multicolored	.25	.25
504 A103	30c multicolored	.85	.85
	Nos. 502-504 (3)	1.30	1.30

Visit of Shah Mohammed Riza Pahlavi of Iran.

Emperor Haile Selassie Appealing to
League of Nations, 1935 — A104

35c, African Unity Building and map of
Africa. $1, World map, symbolizing intl.
relations.

1968, July 22   Photo.   Perf. 14x13½
505 A104 15c bl, red, blk & gold   .25   .20
506 A104 35c blk, emer, red &
gold   .50   .50
507 A104 $1 dk bl, lil, blk & gold 1.50 2.00
Nos. 505-507 (3)   2.25 2.70

Ethiopia's struggle for peace. Issued with
tabs on bottom row.

WHO
Emblem
A105

Perf. 14x13½
1968, Aug. 30   Litho.   Unwmk.
508 A105 15c brt green & blk   .25 .25
509 A105 60c red lilac & blk   .90 .90

20th anniv. of the WHO.

Abebe
Bikila,
Marathon
Runner
A106

1968, Oct. 12   Perf. 11½
510 A106 10c shown   .20   .20
511 A106 15c Soccer   .25   .25
512 A106 20c Boxing   .30   .30
513 A106 40c Basketball   .60   .60
514 A106 50c Bicycling   .90   .90
Nos. 510-514 (5)   2.25 2.25

19th Olympic Games, Mexico City, 10/12-27.

Arrussi
Woman — A107

Regional Costumes: 15c, Man from Gemu
Gefa. 20c, Gojam man. 30c, Kefa man. 35c,
Harar woman. 50c, Ilubabor grass coat. 60c,
Woman from Eritrea.

Perf. 13½x13
1968, Dec. 10   Photo.   Unwmk.
515 A107 5c silver & multi   .25   .20
516 A107 15c silver & multi   .25   .20
517 A107 20c silver & multi   .25   .20
518 A107 30c silver & multi   .35   .30
519 A107 35c silver & multi   .40   .35
520 A107 50c silver & multi   .80   .60
521 A107 60c silver & multi   1.10   .85
Nos. 515-521 (7)   3.40 2.70

See Nos. 575-581.

Message
Stick and
Amharic
Postal
Emblem
A108

1969, Mar. 10   Litho.   Perf. 14
522 A108 10c emerald, blk & brn   .50   .50
523 A108 15c yellow, blk & brn   .50   .50
524 A108 35c multicolored   .75   .75
Nos. 522-524 (3)   1.75 1.75

Ethiopian postal service, 75th anniv.

ILO
Emblem
A109

1969, Apr. 11   Litho.   Perf. 14½
525 A109 15c orange & blk   .30   .30
526 A109 60c emerald & blk   1.25 1.25

50th anniv. of the ILO.

Dove, Red
Cross,
Crescent,
Lion and
Sun
Emblems
A110

1969, May 8   Wmk. 282   Perf. 13
527 A110 5c lt ultra, blk & red   .20   .20
528 A110 15c lt ultra, grn & red   .30   .30
529 A110 30c lt ultra, vio bl & red   .60   .60
Nos. 527-529 (3)   1.10 1.10

League of Red Cross Societies, 50th anniv.

Endybis Silver Coin,
3rd Century — A111

Ancient Ethiopian Coins: 10c, Gold of
Ezana, 4th cent. 15c, Gold of Kaleb, 6th cent.
30c, Bronze of Armah, 7th cent. 40c, Bronze
of Wazena, 7th cent. 50c, Silver of Gersem,
8th cent.

1969, June 19   Photo.   Perf. 14½
530 A111 5c ultra, blk & sil   .20   .20
531 A111 10c brt red, blk & gold   .25   .25
532 A111 15c brown, blk & gold   .35   .35
533 A111 30c dp car, blk & brnz   .65   .65
534 A111 40c dk green, blk &
brnz   .80   .80
535 A111 50c dp violet, blk & sil   1.25 1.25
Nos. 530-535 (6)   3.50 3.50

Zebras
and
Tourist
Year
Emblem
A112

Designs: 10c, Camping. 15c, Fishing. 20c,
Water skiing. 25c, Mountaineering, vert.

Perf. 13x13½, 13½x13
1969, Aug. 29   Litho.   Unwmk.
536 A112 5c multicolored   .20   .20
537 A112 10c multicolored   .20   .20
538 A112 15c multicolored   .25   .30

539 A112 20c multicolored   .40   .50
540 A112 25c multicolored   .50   .80
Nos. 536-540 (5)   1.55 2.00

International Year of African Tourism.

Stylized
Bird and
UN
Emblem
A113

UN 25th anniv.: 30c, Stylized flowers, UN
and peace emblems, vert. 60c, Stylized bird,
UN emblem and plane.

1969, Oct. 24   Unwmk.   Perf. 11½
541 A113 10c lt blue & multi   .20   .20
542 A113 30c lt blue & multi   .45   .45
543 A113 60c lt blue & multi   1.00 1.00
Nos. 541-543 (3)   1.65 1.65

Ancient
Cross
and Holy
Family
A114

Designs: Various ancient crosses.

Perf. 14½x13½
1969, Dec. 10   Photo.
544 A114 5c black, yel & dk bl   .20   .20
545 A114 10c black & yellow   .20   .30
546 A114 25c black, yel & grn   .50   .75
547 A114 60c black & ocher   1.25 1.50
Nos. 544-547 (4)   2.15 2.75

Ancient Figurines — A115

Ancient Ethiopian Pottery: 20c, Vases, Yeha
period, 4th-3rd centuries B.C. 25c, Vases and
jugs, Axum, 4th-6th centuries A.D. 35c, Bird-
shaped jug and jugs, Matara, 4th-6th centuries
A.D. 60c, Decorated pottery, Adulis, 6th-7th
centuries A.D.

1970, Feb. 6   Photo.   Perf. 14½
548 A115 10c black & multi   .50   .50
549 A115 20c black & multi   .50   .50
550 A115 25c black & multi   .50   .50
551 A115 35c black & multi   1.00 1.00
552 A115 60c black & multi   2.00 2.00
Nos. 548-552 (5)   4.50 4.50

Medhane Alem Church — A116

Rock Churches of Lalibela, 12th-13th Centuries: 10c, Bieta Emmanuel. 15c, The four
Rock Churches of Lalibela. 20c, Bieta Mariam.
50c, Bieta Giorgis.

1970, Apr. 15   Unwmk.   Perf. 13
553 A116 5c brown & multi   .20   .20
554 A116 10c brown & multi   .20   .20
555 A116 15c brown & multi   .30   .30
556 A116 20c brown & multi   .50   .50
557 A116 50c brown & multi   1.15 1.15
Nos. 553-557 (5)   2.35 2.35

Sailfish
Tang
A117

Tropical Fish: 10c, Undulate triggerfish. 15c,
Orange butterflyfish. 25c, Butterflyfish. 50c,
Imperial Angelfish.

1970, June 19   Photo.   Perf. 12½
558 A117 5c multicolored   .20   .20
559 A117 10c multicolored   .20   .20
560 A117 15c multicolored   .30   .30
561 A117 25c multicolored   .70   .70
562 A117 50c multicolored   1.40 1.40
Nos. 558-562 (5)   2.80 2.80

Education Year
Emblem — A118

1970, Aug. 14   Unwmk.   Perf. 13½
563 A118 10c multicolored   .20   .20
564 A118 20c gold, ultra & emer   .35   .35
565 A118 50c gold, emer & org   .85   .85
Nos. 563-565 (3)   1.40 1.40

Issued for International Education Year.

Map of Africa — A119

30c, Flag of Organization of African Unity.
40c, OAU Headquarters, Addis Ababa.

1970, Sept. 21   Photo.   Perf. 13½
566 A119 20c multicolored   .25   .25
567 A119 30c multicolored   .40   .40
568 A119 40c green & multi   .75   .75
Nos. 566-568 (3)   1.40 1.40

Africa Unity Day and Organization of African
Unity.

Emperor Haile
Selassie — A120

1970, Oct. 30   Unwmk.   Perf. 14½
569 A120 15c Prus bl & multi   .20   .20
570 A120 50c multicolored   .65   .65
571 A120 60c multicolored   1.50 1.25
Nos. 569-571 (3)   2.35 2.10

Coronation, 40th anniv.

Buildings — A121

1970, Dec. 30   Litho.   Perf. 13½

572	A121	10c ver & multi	.20	.20
573	A121	50c brown & multi	1.00	1.00
574	A121	80c multicolored	1.25	1.25
		Nos. 572-574 (3)	2.45	2.45

Opening of new Posts, Telecommunications and General Post Office buildings.

Costume Type of 1968

Regional Costumes: 5c, Warrior from Begemdir and Semien. 10c, Woman from Bale. 15c, Warrior from Welega. 20c, Woman from Shoa. 25c, Man from Sidamo. 40c, Woman from Tigre. 50c, Man from Welo.

1971, Feb. 17   Photo.   Perf. 11½
Granite Paper

575	A107	5c gold & multi	.20	.20
576	A107	10c gold & multi	.20	.20
577	A107	15c gold & multi	.25	.25
578	A107	20c gold & multi	.30	.30
579	A107	25c gold & multi	.40	.40
580	A107	40c gold & multi	.55	.55
581	A107	50c gold & multi	1.10	1.10
		Nos. 575-581 (7)	3.00	3.00

Plane's Tail with Emblem — A122

Designs: 10c, Ethiopian scenes. 20c, Nose of Boeing 707. 60c, Pilots in cockpit, and engine. 80c, Globe with routes shown.

1971, Apr. 8   Perf. 14½x14

582	A122	5c multicolored	.35	.35
583	A122	10c multicolored	.35	.35
584	A122	20c multicolored	.45	.45
585	A122	60c multicolored	1.40	1.40
586	A122	80c multicolored	2.10	2.10
		Nos. 582-586 (5)	4.65	4.65

Ethiopian Airlines, 25th anniversary. Issued with tabs on bottom row.

Fountain of Life, 15th Century Gospel Book — A123

Ethiopian Paintings: 10c, King David, 15th cent. manuscript. 25c, St. George, 17th cent. painting on canvas. 50c, King Lalibela, 18th cent. painting on wood. 60c, Yared singing before King Kaleb. Mural in Axum Cathedral.

1971, June 15   Photo.   Perf. 11½
Granite Paper

587	A123	5c tan & multi	.20	.20
588	A123	10c pale sal & multi	.20	.20
589	A123	25c lemon & multi	.30	.30
590	A123	50c yellow & multi	.80	.80
591	A123	60c gray & multi	1.25	1.25
		Nos. 587-591 (5)	2.75	2.75

Black and White Heads, Globes — A124

Designs: 60c, Black and white hand holding globe. 80c, Four races, globes.

1971, Aug. 31   Unwmk.

592	A124	10c org, red brn & blk	.30	.30
593	A124	60c green, bl & blk	1.10	1.10
594	A124	80c bl, org, yel & blk	1.90	1.90
		Nos. 592-594 (3)	3.30	3.30

Intl. Year Against Racial Discrimination.

Emperor Menelik II and Reading of Treaty of Ucciali A125

Contemporary Paintings: 30c, Menelik II on horseback gathering the tribes. 50c, Ethiopians and Italians in Battle of Adwa. 60c, Menelik II and Taitu at head of their armies.

1971, Oct. 20   Litho.   Perf. 13½

595	A125	10c multicolored	.30	.30
596	A125	30c multicolored	.75	.75
597	A125	50c multicolored	1.10	1.10
598	A125	80c multicolored	2.00	2.00
		Nos. 595-598 (4)	4.15	4.15

75th anniversary of victory of Adwa over the Italians, March 1, 1896.

Two telephones, 1897, Menelik II and Prince Makonnen — A126

Designs: 10c, Haile Selassie Broadcasting and Map of Ethiopia. 30c, Ethiopians around television set. 40c, Telephone microwave circuits. 60c, Map of Africa on globe and telephone dial.

1971, Nov. 2

599	A126	5c brown & multi	.35	.35
600	A126	10c yellow & multi	.35	.35
601	A126	30c vio bl & multi	.45	.45
602	A126	40c black & multi	1.00	1.00
603	A126	60c vio bl & multi	2.00	2.00
		Nos. 599-603 (5)	4.15	4.15

Telecommunications in Ethiopia, 75th anniv.

UNICEF Emblem, Mother and Child — A127

UNICEF Emblem and: 10c, Children drinking milk. 15c, Man holding sick child. 30c, Kindergarten class. 50c, Father and son.

1971, Dec. 15   Unwmk.

604	A127	5c yellow & multi	.30	.30
605	A127	10c pale brn & multi	.30	.30
606	A127	15c rose & multi	.30	.30
607	A127	30c violet & multi	.70	.70
608	A127	50c green & multi	1.25	1.25
		Nos. 604-608 (5)	2.85	2.85

25th anniv. of UNICEF.

Nos. 445-448 Overprinted

1972, Jan. 28   Photo.   Perf. 11
Portrait in Black

609	A86	20c grn & pale yel	.45	.45
610	A86	25c dk brn & yel	.70	.70
611	A86	30c maroon & gray	2.25	2.25
612	A86	35c dk blue & gray	2.25	2.25
		Nos. 609-612 (4)	5.65	5.65

1st meeting of UN Security Council in Africa.

River Boat on Lake Haik — A128

1972, Feb. 7   Litho.   Perf. 11½
Granite Paper

613	A128	10c shown	.30	.30
614	A128	20c Boats on Lake Abaya	.55	.55
615	A128	30c on Lake Tana	1.00	1.00
616	A128	60c on Baro River	1.75	1.75
		Nos. 613-616 (4)	3.60	3.60

Proclamation of Cyrus the Great — A129

1972, Mar. 28   Photo.   Perf. 14x14½

617	A129	10c red & multi	.30	.30
618	A129	60c emerald & multi	1.50	1.50
619	A129	80c gray & multi	2.10	2.10
		Nos. 617-619 (3)	3.90	3.90

2500th anniversary of the founding of the Persian empire by Cyrus the Great.

Houses, Sidamo Province A130

Ethiopian Architecture: 10c, Tigre Province. 20c, Eritrea Province. 40c, Addis Ababa. 80c, Shoa Province.

1972, Apr. 11   Litho.   Perf. 13½

620	A130	5c black & multi	.30	.30
621	A130	10c black, gray & brn	.30	.30
622	A130	20c black & multi	.50	.50
623	A130	40c black, bl grn & brn	.85	.85
624	A130	80c black, brn & red brn	2.00	2.00
		Nos. 620-624 (5)	3.95	3.95

Hands Holding Map of Ethiopia — A131

10c, Hands shielding Ethiopians. 25c, Map of Africa, hands reaching for African Unity emblem. 50c, Brown & white hands clasped, UN emblem. 60c, Hands protecting dove. Each denomination shows different portrait of the Emperor.

Perf. 14½x14
1972, July 21   Litho.   Unwmk.

625	A131	5c scarlet & multi	.30	.30
626	A131	10c ultra & multi	.30	.30
627	A131	25c vio bl & multi	.50	.50
628	A131	50c lt blue & multi	1.00	1.00
629	A131	60c brown & multi	1.25	1.25
		Nos. 625-629 (5)	3.35	3.35

80th birthday of Emperor Haile Selassie.

Running, Flags of Mexico, Japan, Italy — A132

1972, Aug. 25   Perf. 13½x13

630	A132	10c shown	.30	.30
631	A132	30c Soccer	.65	.65
632	A132	50c Bicycling	1.25	1.25
633	A132	60c Boxing	1.75	1.75
		Nos. 630-633 (4)	3.95	3.95

20th Olympic Games, Munich, Germany, Aug. 26-Sept. 11.

Open Bible, Cross and Orbit A133

Designs: 50c, First and 1972 headquarters of the British and Foreign Bible Society, vert. 80c, First Amharic Bible.

1972, Sept. 25   Photo.   Perf. 13½

634	A133	20c deep red & multi	.50	.50
635	A133	50c deep red & multi	1.00	1.00
636	A133	80c deep red & multi	1.90	1.90
		Nos. 634-636 (3)	3.40	3.40

United Bible Societies World Assembly, Addis Ababa, Sept. 1972.

Security Council Meeting A134

Designs: 60c, Building where Security Council met. 80c, Map of Africa with flags of participating members.

1972, Nov. 1   Litho.   Perf. 13½

637	A134	10c lt bl & vio bl	.25	.25
638	A134	60c multicolored	1.00	1.00
639	A134	80c multicolored	1.75	1.75
		Nos. 637-639 (3)	3.00	3.00

First United Nations Security Council meeting, Addis Ababa, Jan. 28-Feb. 4, 1972.

Fish in Polluted Sea A135

Designs: 30c, Fisherman, beacon, family. 80c, Polluted seashore.

1973, Feb. 23   Photo.   Perf. 13½

640	A135	20c gold & multi	.50	.50
641	A135	30c gold & multi	.75	.75
642	A135	80c gold & multi	2.25	2.25
		Nos. 640-642 (3)	3.50	3.50

World message from the sea, Ethiopian anti-pollution campaign.

INTERPOL and Ethiopian Police Emblems — A136

50c, INTERPOL emblem & General Secretariat, Paris. 60c, INTERPOL emblem.

1973, Mar. 20   Photo.   Perf. 13½

643	A136	40c dull orange & blk	.95	.95
644	A136	50c blue, blk & yel	1.25	1.25
645	A136	60c dk carmine & blk	1.50	1.50
		Nos. 643-645 (3)	3.70	3.70

50th anniversary of International Criminal Police Organization (INTERPOL).

Virgin of Emperor Zara Yaqob A137

Ethiopian Art: 15c, Crucifixion, Zara Yaqob period. 30c, Virgin and Child, from Entoto Mariam Church. 40c, Christ, contemporary mosaic. 80c, The Evangelists, contemporary bas-relief.

1973, May 15   Photo.   Perf. 11½
Granite Paper

646	A137	5c brown & multi	.30	.30
647	A137	15c dp blue & multi	.45	.45
648	A137	30c gray grn & multi	.80	.80
649	A137	40c multicolored	.95	.95
650	A137	80c slate & multi	2.50	2.50
		Nos. 646-650 (5)	5.00	5.00

Free African States in 1963 and 1973 A138

Designs (Map of Africa and): 10c, Flags of OAU members. 20c, Symbols of progress. 40c, Dove and people. 80c, Emblems of various UN agencies.

1973 May 25   Perf. 14½x14

651	A138	5c red & multi	.25	.25
652	A138	10c ol gray & multi	.30	.30
653	A138	20c green & multi	.45	.45
654	A138	40c sepia & multi	.90	.90
655	A138	80c lt blue & multi	1.90	1.90
		Nos. 651-655 (5)	3.80	3.80

OAU, 10th anniv.

Scouts Saluting Ethiopian and Scout Flags — A139

Designs: 15c, Road and road sign. 30c, Girl Scout reading to old man. 40c, Scout and disabled people. 60c, Ethiopian Boy Scout.

1973, July 10   Photo.   Perf. 11½
Granite Paper

656	A139	5c blue & multi	.30	.30
657	A139	15c lt green & multi	.45	.45
658	A139	30c yellow & multi	.85	.85
659	A139	40c crimson & multi	1.00	1.00
660	A139	60c violet & multi	2.10	2.10
		Nos. 656-660 (5)	4.70	4.70

24th Boy Scout World Conference, Nairobi, Kenya, July 16-21.

WMO Emblem A140

50c, WMO emblem, anemometer. 60c, Weather satellite over earth, WMO emblem.

1973, Sept. 4   Photo.   Perf. 13½

661	A140	40c black, bl & dl bl	.90	.90
662	A140	50c dull blue & blk	1.00	1.00
663	A140	60c dull blue & multi	1.60	1.60
		Nos. 661-663 (3)	3.50	3.50

Cent. of intl. meteorological cooperation.
Printed with tabs at top of sheet inscribed in Amharic and tabs at bottom with "ETHIOPIA."

Prince Makonnen, Duke of Harar — A141

Human Rights Flame — A142

5c, Old wall of Harar. 20c, Operating room. 40c, Boy Scouts learning 1st aid & hospital. 80c, Prince Makonnen & hospital.

1973, Nov. 1   Unwmk.   Perf. 14½

664	A141	5c gray & multi	.30	.30
665	A141	10c red brn & multi	.30	.30
666	A141	20c green & multi	.50	.50
667	A141	40c brown red & multi	1.25	1.25
668	A141	80c ultra & multi	2.25	2.25
		Nos. 664-668 (5)	4.60	4.60

Opening of Prince Makonnen Memorial Hospital.

Perf. 11½
1973, Nov. 16   Photo.   Unwmk.
Granite Paper

669	A142	40c yel, gold & dk grn	.70	.70
670	A142	50c lt grn, gold & dk grn	1.00	1.00
671	A142	60c org, gold & dk grn	1.25	1.25
		Nos. 669-671 (3)	2.95	2.95

25th anniversary of the Universal Declaration of Human Rights.

Emperor Haile Selassie — A143

1973, Nov. 5   Photo.   Perf. 11½

672	A143	5c yellow & multi	.30	.25
673	A143	10c brt blue & multi	.30	.25
674	A143	15c green & multi	.40	.35
675	A143	20c dull yel & multi	.50	.35
676	A143	25c multicolored	.60	.35
677	A143	30c multicolored	.70	.35
678	A143	35c multicolored	.75	.35
679	A143	40c ultra & multi	.85	.35
680	A143	45c multicolored	1.00	.45
681	A143	50c orange & multi	1.10	.45
682	A143	55c magenta & multi	1.50	.75
683	A143	60c multicolored	1.60	1.00
684	A143	70c red org & multi	1.90	1.10
685	A143	90c brt vio & multi	2.40	1.25
686	A143	$1 multicolored	3.00	1.75
687	A143	$2 orange & multi	5.75	3.00
688	A143	$3 multicolored	9.00	4.50
689	A143	$5 multicolored	15.00	7.50
		Nos. 672-689 (18)	46.65	24.35

Wicker Furniture A144

Designs: Various wicker baskets, wall hangings, dinnerware.

1974, Jan. 31   Photo.   Perf. 11½
Granite Paper

690	A144	5c violet bl & multi	.25	.25
691	A144	10c violet bl & multi	.30	.30
692	A144	30c violet bl & multi	.55	.55
693	A144	40c violet bl & multi	1.00	1.00
694	A144	60c violet bl & multi	1.10	1.10
		Nos. 690-694 (5)	3.20	3.20

Cow, Calf, Syringe — A145

Designs: 15c, Inoculation of cattle. 20c, Bullock and syringe. 50c, Laboratory technician, cow's head, syringe. 60c, Map of Ethiopia, cattle, syringe.

1974, Feb. 20   Litho.   Perf. 13½x13

695	A145	5c sepia & multi	.20	.20
696	A145	15c ultra & multi	.40	.40
697	A145	20c ultra & multi	.50	.50
698	A145	50c orange & multi	1.25	1.25
699	A145	60c gold & multi	1.75	1.75
		Nos. 695-699 (5)	4.10	4.10

Campaign against cattle plague.

Umbrella Makers A146

Designs: 30c, Weaving. 50c, Child care. 60c, Foundation headquarters.

1974, Apr. 17   Photo.   Perf. 14½

700	A146	10c lt lilac & multi	.30	.30
701	A146	30c multicolored	.45	.45
702	A146	50c multicolored	.85	.85
703	A146	60c blue & multi	1.00	1.00
		Nos. 700-703 (4)	2.60	2.60

20th anniv. of Haile Selassie Foundation.

Ceremonial Robe — A147

Designs: Ceremonial robes.

1974, June 26   Litho.   Perf. 13

704	A147	15c multicolored	.40	.40
705	A147	25c ocher & multi	.60	.60
706	A147	35c green & multi	1.10	1.10
707	A147	40c lt brown & multi	1.25	1.25
708	A147	60c gray & multi	2.50	2.50
		Nos. 704-708 (5)	5.85	5.85

World Population Statistics — A148

Designs: 50c, "Larger families-lower living standard." 60c, Rising population graph.

1974, Aug. 19   Photo.   Perf. 14½

709	A148	40c yellow & multi	1.10	1.10
710	A148	50c violet & multi	1.40	1.40
711	A148	60c green & multi	1.75	1.75
		Nos. 709-711 (3)	4.25	4.25

World Population Year 1974.

UPU Emblem, Letter Carrier's Staff — A149

Celebration Around "Damara" Pillar — A150

UPU Emblem and: 50c, Letters and flags. 60c, Globe. 70c, Headquarters, Bern.

1974, Oct. 9   Photo.   Perf. 11½
Granite Paper

712	A149	15c yellow & multi	.40	.30
713	A149	50c multicolored	1.10	.85
714	A149	60c ultra & multi	1.40	1.10
715	A149	70c multicolored	1.60	1.25
		Nos. 712-715 (4)	4.50	3.50

Centenary of Universal Postal Union.

1974, Dec. 17   Photo.   Perf. 14x14½

5c, Site of Gishen Mariam Monastery. 20c, Cross and festivities. 80c, Torch (Chibos) Parade.

716	A150	5c yellow & multi	.40	.40
717	A150	10c yellow & multi	.45	.45
718	A150	20c yellow & multi	.55	.55
719	A150	80c yellow & multi	2.25	2.25
		Nos. 716-719 (4)	3.65	3.65

Meskel Festival, Sept. 26-27, commemorating the finding in the 4th century of the True Cross, of which a fragment is kept at Gishen Mariam Monastery in Welo Province.

Precis Clelia — A151

Adoration of the Kings — A152

Butterflies: 25c, Charaxes achaemenes. 45c, Papilio dardanus. 50c, Charaxes druceanus. 60c, Papilio demodocus.

1975, Feb. 18   Photo.   Perf. 12x12½

720	A151	10c silver & multi	.60	.35
721	A151	25c gold & multi	1.25	.75
722	A151	45c purple & multi	2.50	1.60
723	A151	50c green & multi	3.00	2.25
724	A151	60c brt blue & multi	4.25	2.75
		Nos. 720-724 (5)	11.60	7.70

1975, Apr. 23   Photo.   Perf. 11½

10c, Baptism of Jesus. 15c, Jesus teaching in the Temple. 30c, Jesus giving sight to the blind. 40c, Crucifixion. 80c, Resurrection.

Granite Paper

725	A152	5c brown & multi	.35	.35
726	A152	10c black & multi	.40	.40
727	A152	15c dk brown & multi	.45	.45
728	A152	30c dk brown & multi	.70	.70
729	A152	40c black & multi	1.50	1.50
730	A152	80c slate & multi	2.60	2.60
		Nos. 725-730 (6)	6.00	6.00

Murals from Ethiopian churches.

Wild Animals A153

1975, May 27   Photo.   Perf. 11½
Granite Paper

731	A153	5c Warthog	.90	.90
732	A153	10c Aardvark	.90	.90
733	A153	20c Semien wolf	1.25	1.25
734	A153	40c Gelada baboon	2.50	2.50
735	A153	80c Civet	5.00	5.00
		Nos. 731-735 (5)	10.55	10.55

"Peace," Dove, Globe, IWY Emblem — A154

50c, Symbols of development. 90c, Equality between men and women.

1975, June 30   Litho.   Perf. 14x14½
736 A154 40c blue & black   .70   .70
737 A154 50c salmon & multi   .90   .90
738 A154 90c multicolored   1.75   1.75
    Nos. 736-738 (3)   3.35   3.35

International Women's Year 1975.

Postal Museum A155

Various interior views of Postal Museum.

1975, Aug. 19   Photo.   Perf. 13x12½
739 A155 10c ocher & multi   .35   .30
740 A155 30c pink & multi   .65   .50
741 A155 60c multicolored   1.50   1.10
742 A155 70c lt green & multi   1.75   1.25
    Nos. 739-742 (4)   4.25   3.15

Ethiopian Natl. Postal Museum, opening.

Map of Ethiopia and Sun — A156

1975, Sept. 11   Photo.   Perf. 11½
Granite Paper
743 A156 5c lilac & multi   .20   .20
744 A156 10c ultra & multi   .20   .20
745 A156 25c brown & multi   .35   .35
746 A156 50c yellow & multi   .90   .90
747 A156 90c brt green & multi   1.75   1.75
    Nos. 743-747 (5)   3.40   3.40

1st anniv. of Ethiopian revolution.

UN Emblem A157

1975, Oct. 24   Photo.   Perf. 11½
748 A157 40c lilac & multi   .90   .90
749 A157 50c multicolored   1.00   1.00
750 A157 90c blue & multi   2.00   2.00
    Nos. 748-750 (3)   3.90   3.90

United Nations, 30th anniversary.

Regional Hair Styles — A158   Delphinium Wellbyi — A159

1975, Dec. 15   Photo.   Perf. 11½
751 A158 5c Ilubabor   .30   .30
752 A158 15c Arusi   .40   .40
753 A158 20c Eritrea   .60   .60
754 A158 30c Bale   .85   .85
755 A158 35c Kefa   1.10   1.10

756 A158 50c Begemir   1.50   1.50
757 A158 60c Shoa   2.00   2.00
    Nos. 751-757 (7)   6.75   6.75
    See Nos. 832-838.

1976, Jan. 15   Photo.   Perf. 11½

Flowers: 10c, Plectocephalus varians. 20c, Brachystelma asmarensis, horiz. 40c, Ceropegia inflata. 80c, Erythrina brucei.

758 A159 5c multicolored   .35   .35
759 A159 10c multicolored   .40   .40
760 A159 20c multicolored   .60   .60
761 A159 40c multicolored   1.50   1.50
762 A159 80c multicolored   2.50   2.50
    Nos. 758-762 (5)   5.35   5.35

Goalkeeper, Map of Africa, Games' Emblem A160

Designs: Various scenes from soccer, map of Africa and ball.

1976, Feb. 27   Photo.   Perf. 14½
763 A160 5c orange & multi   .20   .20
764 A160 10c yellow & multi   .35   .35
765 A160 25c lilac & multi   .70   .70
766 A160 50c green & multi   1.40   1.40
767 A160 90c brt grn & multi   2.40   2.40
    Nos. 763-767 (5)   5.05   5.05

10th African Cup of Nations, Addis Ababa and Dire Dawa, Feb. 29-Mar. 14.

Telephones, 1876 and 1976 — A161   Ethiopian Jewelry — A162

Designs: 60c, Alexander Graham Bell. 90c, Transmission tower.

1976, Mar. 10   Litho.   Perf. 12x13½
768 A161 30c lt ocher & multi   .85   .75
769 A161 60c emerald & multi   1.60   1.25
770 A161 90c ver, blk & buff   2.50   2.00
    Nos. 768-770 (3)   4.95   4.00

Centenary of first telephone call by Alexander Graham Bell, Mar. 10, 1876.

1976, May 14   Photo.   Perf. 11½

Designs: Women wearing various kinds of Ethiopian jewelry.

Granite Paper
771 A162 5c blue & multi   .25   .20
772 A162 10c plum & multi   .35   .25
773 A162 20c gray & multi   .75   .50
774 A162 40c green & multi   1.25   .90
775 A162 80c orange & multi   2.50   1.75
    Nos. 771-775 (5)   5.10   3.60

Boxing — A163   Hands Holding Map of Ethiopia — A164

Designs (Montreal Olympic Emblem and): 80c, Runner and maple leaf. 90c, Bicycling.

1976, July 15   Litho.   Perf. 12½x12
776 A163 10c multicolored   .50   .40
777 A163 80c brt red, blk & grn 2.25   1.75
778 A163 90c brt red & multi   2.75   2.00
    Nos. 776-778 (3)   5.50   4.15

21st Olympic Games, Montreal, Canada, July 17-Aug. 1.

1976, Aug. 5   Photo.   Perf. 14½
779 A164 5c rose & multi   .25   .20
780 A164 10c olive & multi   .30   .25
781 A164 25c orange & multi   .40   .30
782 A164 50c multicolored   .95   .70
783 A164 90c dk blue & multi   1.75   1.40
    Nos. 779-783 (5)   3.65   2.85

Development through cooperation.

Revolution Emblem: Eye and Map A165

1976, Sept. 9   Photo.   Perf. 13½
784 A165 5c multicolored   .20   .20
785 A165 10c multicolored   .30   .25
786 A165 25c multicolored   .40   .30
787 A165 50c yellow & multi   .95   .70
788 A165 90c green & multi   1.60   1.25
    Nos. 784-788 (5)   3.45   2.70

2nd anniversary of the revolution.

Sunburst Around Crest — A166   Plane Over Man with Donkey — A167

1976, Sept. 13   Photo.   Perf. 11½
789 A166 5c green, gold &
           blk   .20   .20
790 A166 10c org, gold & blk   .25   .20
791 A166 15c grnsh bl, gold &
           blk   .40   .20
792 A166 20c lilac, gold & blk   .50   .25
793 A166 25c brt grn, gold &
           blk   .60   .25
794 A166 30c car, gold & blk   .75   .25
795 A166 35c yel, gold & blk   .90   .25
796 A166 40c ol, gold & blk   1.00   .40
797 A166 45c brt grn, gold &
           blk   1.10   .50
798 A166 50c car rose, gold &
           blk   1.25   .70
799 A166 55c ultra, gold & blk   1.50   .90
800 A166 60c fawn, gold & blk   1.75   .90
801 A166 70c rose, gold & blk   2.00   .90
802 A166 90c blue, gold & blk   2.25   .90
803 A166 $1 dull grn, gold &
           blk   2.75   1.00
804 A166 $2 gray, gold & blk   6.00   2.00
805 A166 $3 brn vio, gold &
           blk   8.00   3.25
806 A166 $5 slate bl, gold &
           blk   15.00 5.00
    Nos. 789-806 (18)   46.20 18.05

Denomination Expressed as "BIRR"
1983, June 16
806A A166 1b dull grn, gold &
           blk   3.75   2.25
806B A166 2b gray, gold & blk   7.50   4.50
806C A166 3b brn vio, gold &
           blk   9.00   6.25

1976, Oct. 28   Litho.   Perf. 12x12½

10c, Globe showing routes. 25c, Crew and passengers forming star. 50c, Propeller and jet engine. 90c, Airplanes surrounding map of Ethiopia.

807 A167 5c dull bl & multi   .40   .30
808 A167 10c lilac & multi   .50   .35
809 A167 25c multicolored   .70   .50
810 A167 50c orange & multi   1.40   1.25
811 A167 90c olive & multi   2.75   2.25
    Nos. 807-811 (5)   5.75   4.65

Ethiopian Airlines, 30th anniversary.

Tortoises A168   Hand Holding Makeshift Hammer A169

Reptiles: 20c, Chameleon. 30c, Python. 40c, Monitor lizard. 80c, Nile crocodiles.

1976, Dec. 15   Photo.   Perf. 14½
812 A168 10c multicolored   .50   .40
813 A168 20c multicolored   .75   .50
814 A168 30c multicolored   1.00   .80
815 A168 40c multicolored   1.50   1.10
816 A168 80c multicolored   3.00   2.25
    Nos. 812-816 (5)   6.75   5.05

1977, Jan. 20   Litho.   Perf. 12½

Designs: 5c, Hands holding bowl and plane dropping food. 45c, Infant with empty bowl, and bank note. 60c, Map of affected area, footprints and tire tracks. 80c, Film strip, camera and Ethiopian sitting between eggshells.

817 A169 5c multicolored   .30   .25
818 A169 10c multicolored   .45   .40
819 A169 45c multicolored   1.00   .85
820 A169 60c multicolored   1.25   1.00
821 A169 80c multicolored   1.75   1.60
    Nos. 817-821 (5)   4.75   4.10

Ethiopian Relief and Rehabilitation Commission for drought and disaster areas.

Elephant and Ruins, Axum, 7th Century A170

Designs: 10c, Ibex and temple, 5th century, B.C., Yeha. 25c, Megalithic dolmen and pottery, Sourre Kabanawa. 50c, Awash Valley, stone axe, Acheulean period. 80c, Omo Valley, hominid jawbone.

1977, Mar. 15   Photo.   Perf. 13½
822 A170 5c gold & multi   .50   .35
823 A170 10c gold & multi   .60   .45
824 A170 25c gold & multi   .75   .65
825 A170 50c gold & multi   1.25   1.00
826 A170 80c gold & multi   2.25   1.50
    Nos. 822-826 (5)   5.35   4.05

Archaeological sites and finds in Ethiopia.

Map of Africa with Trans-East Highway — A171

1977, Mar. 30   Perf. 14
827 A171 10c gold & multi   .40   .35
828 A171 20c gold & multi   .50   .40
829 A171 40c gold & multi   .90   .80
830 A171 40c gold & multi   1.25   1.00
831 A171 60c gold & multi   1.75   1.25
    Nos. 827-831 (5)   4.80   3.80

Addis Ababa to Nairobi Highway and projected highways to Cairo, Egypt, and Gaborone, Botswana.

Hairstyle Type of 1975
1977, Apr. 28   Photo.   Perf. 11½
832 A158 5c Welega   .20   .20
833 A158 10c Gojam   .30   .25
834 A158 15c Tigre   .40   .35
835 A158 20c Harar   .70   .65
836 A158 25c Gemu Gefa   .85   .70
837 A158 40c Sidamo   1.40   1.25
838 A158 50c Welo   1.75   1.50
    Nos. 832-838 (7)   5.60   4.90

Addis Ababa
A172

Towns of Ethiopia: 10c, Asmara. 25c, Harar. 50c, Jima. 90c, Dese.

1977, June 20   Photo.   Perf. 14½

839	A172	5c silver & multi	.30	.25
840	A172	10c silver & multi	.40	.35
841	A172	25c silver & multi	.60	.55
842	A172	50c silver & multi	1.25	1.00
843	A172	90c silver & multi	2.25	1.50
		Nos. 839-843 (5)	4.80	3.65

Terebratula
Abyssinica — A173

Fractured Imperial
Crown — A174

Fossil Shells: 10c, Terebratula subalata. 25c, Cuculloea lefeburiaua. 50c, Ostrea plicatissima. 90c, Trigonia cousobrina.

1977, Aug. 15   Photo.   Perf. 14x13½

844	A173	5c multicolored	.75	.25
845	A173	10c multicolored	.95	.40
846	A173	25c multicolored	1.25	.65
847	A173	50c multicolored	2.00	1.25
848	A173	90c multicolored	3.00	2.00
		Nos. 844-848 (5)	7.95	4.55

1977, Sept. 9   Litho.   Perf. 15

Designs: 10c, Symbol of the Revolution (spade, axe, torch). 25c, Warriors, hammer and sickle, map of Ethiopia. 60c, Soldier, farmer and map. 80c, Map and emblem of revolutionary government.

849	A174	5c multicolored	.25	.20
850	A174	10c multicolored	.40	.35
851	A174	25c multicolored	.50	.45
852	A174	60c multicolored	1.25	1.00
853	A174	80c multicolored	1.50	1.25
		Nos. 849-853 (5)	3.90	3.25

Third anniversary of the revolution.

Cicindela
Petitii — A175

Lenin, Globe,
Map of Ethiopia
and
Emblem — A176

Insects: 10c, Heliocopris dillonii. 25c, Poekilocerus vignaudii. 50c, Pepsis heros. 90c, Pepsis dedjaz.

1977, Sept. 30   Photo.   Perf. 14x13½

854	A175	5c multicolored	.55	.50
855	A175	10c multicolored	.75	.75
856	A175	25c multicolored	1.50	1.50
857	A175	50c multicolored	3.50	3.50
858	A175	90c multicolored	5.50	5.50
		Nos. 854-858 (5)	11.80	11.75

1977, Nov. 15   Litho.   Perf. 12

859	A176	5c orange & multi	.40	.25
860	A176	10c multi & multi	.45	.35
861	A176	25c salmon & multi	.50	.40
862	A176	50c lt blue & multi	1.00	.85
863	A176	90c yellow & multi	1.75	1.25
		Nos. 859-863 (5)	4.10	3.10

60th anniv. of Russian October Revolution.

Chondrostoma Dilloni — A177

Salt-water Fish: 10c, Ostracion cubicus. 25c, Serranus summana. 50c, Serranus luti. 90c, Tetraodon maculatus.

1978, Jan. 20   Litho.   Perf. 15½

864	A177	5c multicolored	.65	.65
865	A177	10c multicolored	.75	.75
866	A177	25c multicolored	1.25	1.25
867	A177	50c multicolored	2.25	2.25
868	A177	90c multicolored	4.00	4.00
		Nos. 864-868 (5)	8.90	8.90

Domestic
Animals — A178

1978, Mar. 27   Litho.   Perf. 13½x14

869	A178	5c Cattle	.25	.20
870	A178	10c Mules	.40	.35
871	A178	25c Goats	.75	.55
872	A178	50c Dromedaries	1.50	1.25
873	A178	90c Horses	2.75	2.25
		Nos. 869-873 (5)	5.65	4.50

Weapons and
Shield, Map of
Ethiopia — A179

Bronze Ibex, 5th
Century
B.C. — A180

"Call of the Motherland." (Map of Ethiopia and): 10c, Civilian fighters. 25c, Map of Africa. 60c, Soldiers. 80c, Red Cross nurse and wounded man.

1978, May   Litho.   Perf. 15½

874	A179	5c multicolored	.30	.25
875	A179	10c multicolored	.40	.35
876	A179	25c multicolored	.70	.60
877	A179	60c multicolored	1.25	1.00
878	A179	80c multicolored	2.25	1.50
		Nos. 874-878 (5)	4.90	3.70

1978, June 21   Litho.   Perf. 15½

Ancient Bronzes: 10c, Lion, Yeha, 5th cent. B.C., horiz. 25c, Lamp with ibex attacked by dog, Matara, 1st cent. B.C. 50c, Goat, Axum, 3rd cent. A.D., horiz. 90c, Ax, chisel and sickle, Yeha, 5th-4th centuries B.C.

879	A180	5c multicolored	.25	.20
880	A180	10c multicolored	.35	.30
881	A180	25c multicolored	.60	.50
882	A180	50c multicolored	1.50	1.25
883	A180	90c multicolored	2.50	1.75
		Nos. 879-883 (5)	5.20	4.00

See Nos. 1024-1027.

Globe and
Argentina
'78 Emblem
— A181

20c, Soccer player kicking ball. 30c, Two players embracing, net and ball. 55c, World map and ball. 70c, Soccer field, vert.

Perf. 14x13½, 13½x14

1978, July 19   Litho.

884	A181	5c multicolored	.45	.40
885	A181	20c multicolored	.70	.50
886	A181	30c multicolored	1.00	.65
887	A181	55c multicolored	1.75	1.25
888	A181	70c multicolored	2.25	1.75
		Nos. 884-888 (5)	6.15	4.55

11th World Cup Soccer Championship, Argentina, June 1-25.

Map of Africa,
Oppressed
African — A182

Namibia Day: 10c, Policeman pointing gun. 25c, Sniper with gun. 60c, African caught in net. 80c, Head of free man.

1978, Aug. 25   Perf. 12½x13½

889	A182	5c multicolored	.30	.25
890	A182	10c multicolored	.50	.45
891	A182	25c multicolored	.60	.50
892	A182	60c multicolored	1.50	1.00
893	A182	80c multicolored	2.25	1.50
		Nos. 889-893 (5)	5.15	3.70

Soldiers,
Guerrilla
and Jets
A183

Design: 1b, People looking toward sun, crushing snake, flags.

1978, Sept. 8   Photo.   Perf. 14

894	A183	80c multicolored	1.75	1.25
895	A183	1b multicolored	2.50	1.75

4th anniversary of revolution.

Hand and
Globe with
Tools — A184

Designs: 15c, Symbols of energy, communications, education, medicine, agriculture and industry. 25c, Cogwheels and world map. 60c, Globe and hands passing wrench. 70c, Flying geese and turtle over globe.

1978, Nov. 14   Litho.   Perf. 12x12½

896	A184	10c multicolored	.30	.25
897	A184	15c multicolored	.35	.30
898	A184	25c multicolored	.55	.50
899	A184	60c multicolored	1.40	1.00
900	A184	70c multicolored	1.75	1.25
		Nos. 896-900 (5)	4.35	3.30

Technical Cooperation Among Developing Countries Conference, Buenos Aires, Argentina, Sept. 1978.

Human Rights
Emblem — A185

1978, Dec. 7   Photo.   Perf. 12½x13½

901	A185	5c multicolored	.30	.25
902	A185	15c multicolored	.30	.25
903	A185	25c multicolored	.45	.40
904	A185	35c multicolored	.75	.70
905	A185	1b multicolored	2.25	1.75
		Nos. 901-905 (5)	4.05	3.35

Declaration of Human Rights, 30th anniv.

Broken Chain, Anti-
Apartheid
Emblem — A186

Stele from
Osole — A187

1978, Dec. 28   Litho.   Perf. 12½x12

906	A186	5c multicolored	.30	.25
907	A186	20c multicolored	.45	.40
908	A186	30c multicolored	.75	.65
909	A186	55c multicolored	1.25	1.00
910	A186	70c multicolored	1.50	1.25
		Nos. 906-910 (5)	4.25	3.55

Anti-Apartheid Year.

1979, Jan. 25   Perf. 14

Ancient Carved Stones, Soddo Region: 10c, Anthropomorphous stele, Gorashino. 25c, Leaning stone, Wado. 60c, Round stones, Ambeut. 80c, Bas-relief, Tiya.

911	A187	5c multicolored	.30	.25
912	A187	10c multicolored	.40	.30
913	A187	25c multicolored	.65	.50
914	A187	60c multicolored	1.75	1.25
915	A187	80c multicolored	2.25	1.75
		Nos. 911-915 (5)	5.35	4.05

Cotton
Plantation
A188

Shemma Industry: 10c, Women spinning cotton yarn. 20c, Man reeling cotton. 65c, Weaver. 80c, Shemma (Natl. dress).

1979, Mar. 15   Litho.   Perf. 15½

916	A188	5c multicolored	.40	.25
917	A188	10c multicolored	.45	.35
918	A188	20c multicolored	.60	.40
919	A188	65c multicolored	1.75	1.25
920	A188	80c multicolored	2.25	1.50
		Nos. 916-920 (5)	5.45	3.75

Ethiopian
Trees — A189

1979, Apr. 26   Photo.   Perf. 13½x14

921	A189	5c Grar	.35	.25
922	A189	10c Weira	.45	.30
923	A189	25c Tidh	.65	.40
924	A189	50c Shola	1.25	1.00
925	A189	90c Zigba	2.00	1.50
		Nos. 921-925 (5)	4.70	3.45

Agricultural
Development
A190

Revolutionary Development Campaign: 15c, Industry. 25c, Transportation and communication. 60c, Education and health. 70c, Commerce.

1979, July 3   Litho.   Perf. 12x12½
926 A190 10c multicolored ..... .30 .25
927 A190 15c multicolored ..... .45 .30
928 A190 25c multicolored ..... .60 .50
929 A190 60c multicolored 1.25 1.00
930 A190 70c multicolored 1.75 1.50
    Nos. 926-930 (5) 4.35 3.55

IYC Emblem — A191

Intl. Year of the Child: 15c, Adults leading children. 25c, Adult helping child. 60c, IYC emblem surrounded by children. 70c, Adult and children embracing.

1979, Aug. 16   Litho.   Perf. 12x12½
931 A191 10c multicolored ..... .40 .35
932 A191 15c multicolored ..... .50 .40
933 A191 25c multicolored ..... .75 .65
934 A191 60c multicolored 1.75 1.40
935 A191 70c multicolored 2.00 1.75
    Nos. 931-935 (5) 5.40 4.55

Guerrilla Fighters — A192

15c, Soldiers. 25c, Map of Africa within cogwheel, star. 60c, Students with book, torch. 70c, Family, hammer & sickle emblem.

1979, Sept. 11   Photo.   Perf. 14
936 A192 10c multicolored ..... .40 .35
937 A192 15c multicolored ..... .50 .45
938 A192 25c multicolored ..... .75 .65
939 A192 60c multicolored 1.75 1.25
940 A192 70c multicolored 2.25 1.75
    Nos. 936-940 (5) 5.65 4.45

Fifth anniversary of revolution.

Telephone Receiver A193   Incense Container A194

Telecom Emblem and: 5c, Symbolic waves. 35c, Satellite beaming to earth. 45c, Dish antenna. 65c, Television cameraman.

1979, Sept.   Photo.   Perf. 11½
941 A193 5c multicolored ..... .35 .30
942 A193 30c multicolored ..... .75 .60
943 A193 35c multicolored ..... .95 .75
944 A193 45c multicolored 1.50 1.00
945 A193 65c multicolored 2.25 1.50
    Nos. 941-945 (5) 5.80 4.15

3rd World Telecommunications Exhibition, Geneva, Sept. 20-26.

1979, Nov. 15   Litho.   Perf. 15
946 A194 5c shown ..... .45 .30
947 A194 10c Vase ..... .85 .45
948 A194 25c Earthenware cover ..... 1.00 .75
949 A194 60c Milk container 1.75 1.25
950 A194 80c Storage container 2.50 1.75
    Nos. 946-950 (5) 6.55 4.50

Wooden Grain Bowl — A195   Lappet-faced Vulture — A196

1980, Jan.   Litho.   Perf. 13½x13
951 A195 5c shown ..... .50 .35
952 A195 30c Chair, stool ..... .90 .50
953 A195 35c Mortar, pestle ..... 1.00 .75
954 A195 45c Buckets 1.75 1.25
955 A195 65c Storage jars 2.75 2.00
    Nos. 951-955 (5) 6.90 4.85

1980, Feb. 12   Perf. 13½x14
Birds of Prey: 15c, Long-crested hawk eagle. 25c, Secretary bird. 60c, Abyssinian long-eared owl. 70c, Lanner falcon.
956 A196 10c multicolored 1.25 1.25
957 A196 15c multicolored 1.50 1.50
958 A196 25c multicolored 2.25 2.25
959 A196 60c multicolored 4.00 4.00
960 A196 70c multicolored 6.00 6.00
    Nos. 956-960 (5) 15.00 15.00

Fight Against Cigarette Smoking — A197

1980, Apr. 7   Photo.   Perf. 13x13½
961 A197 20c multicolored 1.25 1.00
962 A197 60c Cigarette 1.75 1.25
963 A197 1b Respiratory system 3.00 2.50
    Nos. 961-963 (3) 6.00 4.75

"110" and Lenin House Museum A198

Lenin, 110th "Birthday" (Paintings): 15c, In hiding. 20c, As a young man. 40c, Returning to Russia. 1b, Speaking on the Goelro Plan.

1980, Apr. 22   Litho.   Perf. 12x12½
964 A198 5c multicolored ..... .35 .30
965 A198 15c multicolored ..... .40 .35
966 A198 20c multicolored ..... .50 .45
967 A198 40c multicolored ..... .95 .80
968 A198 1b multicolored 2.25 2.00
    Nos. 964-968 (5) 4.45 3.90

Grévy's Zebras A199

1980, June 10   Litho.   Perf. 12½x12
969 A199 10c shown ..... .75 .75
970 A199 15c Gazelles 1.00 1.00
971 A199 25c Wild hunting dogs 1.50 1.50
972 A199 60c Swayne's hartebeests 2.75 2.75
973 A199 70c Cheetahs 3.50 3.50
    Nos. 969-973 (5) 9.50 9.50

Runner, Moscow '80 Emblem — A200

1980, July 19   Photo.   Perf. 11½x12
974 A200 30c shown 1.00 1.00
975 A200 70c Gymnast 2.25 2.25
976 A200 80c Boxing 3.00 3.00
    Nos. 974-976 (3) 6.25 6.25

22nd Summer Olympic Games, Moscow, July 19-Aug. 3.

Removing Blindfold — A201   Bamboo Folk Craft — A202

1980, Sept. 11   Photo.   Perf. 14x13½
977 A201 30c shown ..... .75 .50
978 A201 40c Revolutionary ..... 1.00 .65
979 A201 50c Woman breaking chain 1.50 1.00
980 A201 70c Russian & Ethiopian flags 2.25 1.25
    Nos. 977-980 (4) 5.50 3.40

6th anniversary of revolution.

1980, Oct. 23   Litho.   Perf. 14
981 A202 5c Bamboo food basket ..... .30 .25
982 A202 15c Lamp shade ..... .40 .35
983 A202 25c Stool ..... .75 .60
984 A202 35c Fruit basket 1.25 1.00
985 A202 1b Lamp shade 2.75 1.75
    Nos. 981-985 (5) 5.45 3.95

Mekotkocha (Used in Weeding) A203

Traditional Harvesting Tools: 15c, Layda (grain separator). 40c, Mensh (fork). 45c, Mededekia (soil turner). 70c, Mofer & Kenber (plow and yoke).

1980, Dec. 18   Litho.   Perf. 12½x12
986 A203 10c multicolored ..... .30 .25
987 A203 15c multicolored ..... .35 .30
988 A203 40c multicolored ..... .90 .75
989 A203 45c multicolored 1.25 1.00
990 A203 70c multicolored 2.50 1.75
    Nos. 986-990 (5) 5.30 4.05

Baro River Bridge Opening A204

1981, Feb. 28   Photo.   Perf. 13½x13
991 A204 15c Canoes and ferry ..... .50 .40
992 A204 65c Bridge construction 1.75 1.25
993 A204 1b shown 3.00 2.25
    Nos. 991-993 (3) 5.25 3.90

Semien National Park — A205

World Heritage Year: 5c, Wawel Castle, Poland. 15c, Quito Cathedral, Ecuador. 20c, Old Slave Quarters, Goree Island, Senegal. 30c, Mesa Verde Indian Village, US. 1b, L'Anse aux Meadows excavation, Canada.

Perf. 11x11½, 11½x11
1981, Mar. 10   Photo.
994 A205 5c multicolored ..... .40 .30
995 A205 15c multicolored ..... .55 .45
996 A205 20c multicolored ..... .70 .55
997 A205 30c multicolored ..... 1.00 .75
998 A205 80c multicolored 2.25 1.50
999 A205 1b multicolored 3.00 2.25
    Nos. 994-999 (6) 7.90 5.80

1981, June 16   Photo.
10c, Biet Medhanialem Church, Ethiopia. 15c, Nahanni Natl. Park, Canada. 20c, Yellowstone River Lower Falls, U.S. 30c, Aachen Cathedral, Germany. 80c, Kicker Rock, San Cristobal Island, Ecuador. 1b, The Lizak corridor, Holy Cross Chapel, Cracow, Poland.
1000 A205 10c multi ..... .45 .30
1001 A205 15c multi ..... .55 .45
1002 A205 20c multi ..... .75 .60
1003 A205 30c multi ..... .95 .80
1004 A205 80c multi 3.25 2.25
1005 A205 1b multi, vert. 4.50 2.75
    Nos. 1000-1005 (6) 10.45 7.15

Ancient Drinking Vessel A206

1981, May 5   Litho.   Perf. 12½x12
1006 A206 20c shown ..... .40 .30
1007 A206 25c Spice container ..... .50 .40
1008 A206 35c Jug ..... 1.00 .75
1009 A206 40c Cooking pot holder 1.50 1.10
1010 A206 60c Animal figurine 2.25 1.60
    Nos. 1006-1010 (5) 5.65 4.15

Intl. Year of the Disabled — A207

7th Anniv. of Revolution A208

1981, July 16   Photo.   Perf. 11½x12
1011 A207 5c Prostheses ..... .30 .20
1012 A207 15c Boys writing ..... .35 .25
1013 A207 20c Activities ..... .65 .50
1014 A207 40c Knitting 1.25 1.00
1015 A207 1b Weaving 3.00 2.25
    Nos. 1011-1015 (5) 5.55 4.20

1981, Sept. 10   Perf. 14
1016 A208 20c Children's Center ..... .65 .35
1017 A208 60c Heroes' Center 1.25 1.00
1018 A208 1b Serto Ader (state newspaper) 2.25 1.75
    Nos. 1016-1018 (3) 4.15 3.10

World Food Day — A209

1981, Oct. 15   Litho.   Perf. 13½x12½
1019 A209 5c Wheat airlift ..... .20 .20
1020 A209 15c Plowing ..... .30 .25
1021 A209 20c Malnutrition ..... .40 .30
1022 A209 40c Agriculture education ..... .85 .70
1023 A209 1b Cattle, corn 2.25 1.75
    Nos. 1019-1023 (5) 4.00 3.20

Ancient Bronze Type of 1978
1981, Dec. 15   Litho.   Perf. 14x13½
1024 A180 15c Pitcher ..... .35 .35
1025 A180 45c Tsenatsil (musical instrument) 1.00 1.00
1026 A180 50c Pitcher, diff. 1.25 1.25
1027 A180 70c Pot 1.50 1.50
    Nos. 1024-1027 (4) 4.10 4.10

Horn
Artifacts — A210

1982, Feb. 18 Photo. Perf. 12x12½
1028 A210 10c Tobacco containers   .25   .20
1029 A210 15c Cup   .35   .30
1030 A210 40c Container, diff.   .90   .70
1031 A210 45c Goblet   1.25   .95
1032 A210 70c Spoons   1.75 1.25
Nos. 1028-1032 (5)   4.50 3.40

Coffee
Cultivation
A211

1982, May, 6 Photo. Perf. 13½
1033 A211 5c Plants   .20   .20
1034 A211 15c Bushes   .35   .30
1035 A211 25c Mature bushes   .60   .50
1036 A211 35c Picking beans   1.00   .75
1037 A211 1b Drinking coffee   2.25 1.75
Nos. 1033-1037 (5)   4.40 3.50

1982 World
Cup — A212

Various soccer plays.

Perf. 13½x12½
1982, June 10   Litho.
1038 A212 5c multicolored   .25   .20
1039 A212 15c multicolored   .40   .30
1040 A212 20c multicolored   .55   .50
1041 A212 40c multicolored   1.25 1.10
1042 A212 1b multicolored   2.50 2.25
Nos. 1038-1042 (5)   4.95 4.35

TB Bacillus
Centenary
A213

1982, July 12 Litho. Perf. 13½x12½
1043 A213 15c Cow   .50   .40
1044 A213 20c Magnifying glass   .60   .50
1045 A213 30c Koch, microscope   .80   .70
1046 A213 35c Koch   1.00   .85
1047 A213 80c Man coughing   2.00 1.75
Nos. 1043-1047 (5)   4.90 4.20

8th Anniv. of
Revolution — A214

Designs: Symbols of justice.

1982, Sept. 10   Perf. 12½x13½
1048 A214 80c multicolored   2.00 1.50
1049 A214 1b multicolored   2.25 1.75

World
Standards
Day — A215

1982, Oct. 14 Litho. Perf. 13½x12½
1050 A215 5c Hand, foot,
square   .20   .20
1051 A215 15c Scales   .40   .30
1052 A215 20c Rulers   .50   .40
1053 A215 40c Weights   1.00   .80
1054 A215 1b Emblem   2.50 1.75
Nos. 1050-1054 (5)   4.60 3.45

10th Anniv.
of UN
Conference
on Human
Environment
A216

1982, Dec. 13   Litho.   Perf. 12
1055 A216 5c Wildlife conservation   .20   .20
1056 A216 15c Environmental
health and set-
tlement   .40   .35
1057 A216 20c Forest protection .60   .45
1058 A216 40c Natl. literacy
campaign   1.00   .90
1059 A216 1b Soil and water
conservation   2.50 2.00
Nos. 1055-1059 (5)   4.70 3.90

Cave of
Sof Omar
A217

Various views.

1983, Feb. 10 Photo. Perf. 13½
1060 A217 5c multicolored   .20   .20
1061 A217 10c multicolored   .30   .25
1062 A217 15c multicolored   .40   .35
1063 A217 70c multicolored   1.50 1.10
1064 A217 80c multicolored   1.75 1.50
Nos. 1060-1064 (5)   4.15 3.40

A218   A219

1983, Apr. 29 Photo. Perf. 14
1065 A218 80c multicolored   2.00 1.50
1066 A218 1b multicolored   2.25 2.00
25th Anniv. of Economic Commission for
Africa.

Perf. 12½x11½
1983, June 3   Photo.
1067 A219 85c Emblem   1.60 1.25
1068 A219 1b Lighthouse, ship   3.25 2.25
25th Anniv. of Intl. Maritime Org.

WCY
A220

1983, July 22   Litho.
1069 A220 25c UPU emblem   .70   .60
1070 A220 55c Dish antenna,
emblems   1.40 1.25
1071 A220 1b Bridge, tunnel   3.25 2.50
Nos. 1069-1071 (3)   5.35 4.35

9th Anniv. of
Revolution
A221

1983, Sept. 10 Litho. Perf. 14½
1072 A221 25c Dove   .50   .40
1073 A221 55c Star   1.40 1.00
1074 A221 1b Emblems   2.00 1.60
Nos. 1072-1074 (3)   3.90 3.00

Musical
Instruments — A222

Charaxes
Galawadiwosi
A223

1983, Oct. 17 Litho. Perf. 12½x13½
1075 A222 5c Hura   .25   .20
1076 A222 15c Dinke   .45   .40
1077 A222 20c Meleket   .75   .65
1078 A222 40c Embilta   1.25 1.00
1079 A222 1b Tom   2.25 2.00
Nos. 1075-1079 (5)   4.95 4.25

1983, Dec. 13 Photo. Perf. 14
1080 A223 10c shown   1.25 1.00
1081 A223 15c Epiphora
elianae   1.75 1.50
1082 A223 55c Batuana rouge-
oti   4.75 3.00
1083 A223 1b Achaea
saboeareginae   9.00 7.50
Nos. 1080-1083 (4)   16.75 13.00

Intl. Anti-Apartheid Year
(1983) — A224

Perf. 13½x12½
1984, Feb. 10   Litho.
1084 A224 5c multicolored   .35   .30
1085 A224 15c multicolored   .55   .50
1086 A224 20c multicolored   .75   .65
1087 A224 40c multicolored   1.25 1.00
1088 A224 1b multicolored   2.50 2.00
Nos. 1084-1088 (5)   5.40 4.45

Local
Flowers — A225

Traditional
Houses — A226

1984, Apr. 13 Litho. Perf. 13½
1089 A225 5c Protea gaguedi   .30   .25
1090 A225 25c Sedum epiden-
drum   1.25   .90
1091 A225 50c Echinops amplex-
icaulis   2.25 1.75
1092 A225 1b Canarina eminii   4.25 3.25
Nos. 1089-1092 (4)   8.05 6.15

1984, Aug. 3   Photo.
1093 A226 15c Konso   .55   .40
1094 A226 65c Dorze   1.75 1.40
1095 A226 1b Harer   3.00 2.50
Nos. 1093-1095 (3)   5.30 4.30

10th Anniv. of
the Revolution
A227

1984, Sept. 10 Photo. Perf. 11½
1096 A227 5c Sept. 12, 1974   .25   .20
1097 A227 10c Mar. 4, 1975   .35   .25
1098 A227 15c Apr. 20, 1976   .45   .35

1099 A227 20c Feb. 11, 1977   .60   .50
1100 A227 25c Mar. 1978   .75   .60
1101 A227 40c July 8, 1980   1.10   .80
1102 A227 45c Dec. 17, 1980   1.40 1.00
1103 A227 50c Sept. 15, 1980   1.75 1.25
1104 A227 70c Sept. 18, 1981   2.00 1.50
1105 A227 1b June 6, 1983   2.75 2.00
Nos. 1096-1105 (10)   11.40 8.35

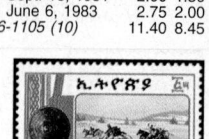

Traditional
Sports
A228

1984, Dec. 7 Photo. Perf. 14
1106 A228 5c Gugs   .25   .20
1107 A228 25c Tigil   .55   .50
1108 A228 50c Genna   1.25 1.00
1109 A228 1b Gebeta   2.25 1.75
Nos. 1106-1109 (4)   4.30 3.45

Birds — A229

1985, Jan. 4 Photo. Perf. 14½
1110 A229 5c Francolinus
harwoodi   .50   .40
1111 A229 15c Rallus rougetti   1.00   .75
1112 A229 80c Merops pusillus   3.50 3.00
1113 A229 85c Malimbus rub-
riceps   4.00 3.50
Nos. 1110-1113 (4)   9.00 7.65

Indigenous
Fauna
A230

1985, Feb. 4 Litho. Perf. 12½x12
1114 A230 20c Hippopotamus
amphibius   .90   .75
1115 A230 25c Litocranius walleri 1.25 1.00
1116 A230 40c Sylvicapra grim-
mia   2.00 1.50
1117 A230 1b Rhynchotragus
guentheri   4.50 3.25
Nos. 1114-1117 (4)   8.65 6.50

Freshwater Fish — A231

1985, Apr. 3   Perf. 13½
1118 A231 10c Barbus degeni   .45   .40
1119 A231 20c Labeo cylindricus .75   .60
1120 A231 55c Protopterus an-
nectens   1.75 1.50
1121 A231 1b Alestes dentex   3.75 3.25
Nos. 1118-1121 (4)   6.70 5.75

Medicinal
Plants
A232

1985, May 23   Perf. 11½x12½
1122 A232 10c Securidaca
longepeduncu-
lata   .40   .30
1123 A232 20c Plumbago zey-
lanicum   .65   .45
1124 A232 55c Brucea an-
tidysenteric   1.50 1.25
1125 A232 1b Dorstenia
barminiana   3.50 2.75
Nos. 1122-1125 (4)   6.05 4.75

Ethiopian Red
Cross Soc., 50th
Anniv. — A233

1985, Aug. 6   Litho.   Perf. 13½x13
1126 A233 35c multicolored ... .90 .75
1127 A233 55c multicolored ... 1.50 1.25
1128 A233 1b multicolored ... 3.00 2.50
Nos. 1126-1128 (3) ... 5.40 4.50

Ethiopian
Revolution,
11th Anniv.
A234

10c, Kombolcha Mills, Welo Region. 80c,
Muger Cement Factory, Mokoda, Shoa. 1b,
Relocating famine and drought victims.

1985, Sept. 10   Litho.   Perf. 13½
1129 A234 10c multicolored ... .30 .25
1130 A234 80c multicolored ... 2.25 2.00
1131 A234 1b multicolored ... 3.00 2.50
Nos. 1129-1131 (3) ... 5.55 4.75

UN 40th
Anniv. — A235

1985, Nov. 22   Litho.   Perf. 13½x14
1132 A235 25c multicolored ... .90 .75
1133 A235 55c multicolored ... 1.75 1.50
1134 A235 1b multicolored ... 3.25 2.50
Nos. 1132-1134 (3) ... 5.90 4.75

Anti-Polio
Campaign
A236

1986, Jan. 10   Litho.   Perf. 11½x12½
1135 A236 5c Boy, prosthesis ... .25 .20
1136 A236 10c Boy on crutches ... .35 .30
1137 A236 20c Nurse, boy ... .65 .50
1138 A236 55c Man, sewing machine ... 1.75 1.25
1139 A236 1b Nurse, mother, child ... 3.00 2.50
Nos. 1135-1139 (5) ... 6.00 4.75

Indigenous
Trees
A237

1986, Feb. 10   Perf. 13½x14½
1140 A237 10c Millettia ferruginea ... .40 .35
1141 A237 30c Syzygium guineense ... 1.00 .75
1142 A237 50c Cordia africana ... 1.50 1.25
1143 A237 1b Hagenia abyssinica ... 3.25 2.75
Nos. 1140-1143 (4) ... 6.15 5.10

Spices — A238

1986, Mar. 10   Perf. 13½
1144 A238 10c Zingiber officinale rosc ... .50 .40
1145 A238 15c Ocimum bacilicum ... .75 .50
1146 A238 55c Sinapsis alba ... 1.75 1.50
1147 A238 1b Cuminum cyminum ... 3.50 3.00
Nos. 1144-1147 (4) ... 6.50 5.40

Current
Coins,
Obverse
and
Reverse
A239

1986, May 9   Litho.   Perf. 13½x14
1148 A239 5c 1-cent ... .25 .20
1149 A239 10c 25-cent ... .40 .35
1150 A239 35c 5-cent ... 1.25 1.00
1151 A239 50c 50-cent ... 1.50 1.25
1152 A239 1b 10-cent ... 3.00 2.50
Nos. 1148-1152 (5) ... 6.40 5.30

Discovery of 3.5
Million Year-old
Hominid
Skeleton,
"Lucy" — A240

1986, July 4   Perf. 13½
1153 A240 2b multicolored ... 7.00 7.00

Ethiopian Revolution, 12th
Anniv. — A241

Designs: 20c, Military service. 30c,
Tiglachin monument. 55c, Delachin Exhibition
emblem. 85c, Food processing plant, Merti.

1986, Sept. 10   Litho.   Perf. 14
1154 A241 20c multicolored ... .50 .40
1155 A241 30c multicolored ... .75 .60
1156 A241 55c multicolored ... 1.50 1.00
1157 A241 85c multicolored ... 2.00 1.75
Nos. 1154-1157 (4) ... 4.75 3.75

Ethiopian Airlines,
40th
Anniv. — A242

Intl. Peace
Year — A243

1986, Oct. 14   Perf. 13½
1158 A242 10c DC-7 ... .40 .30
1159 A242 20c DC-3 ... .60 .50
1160 A242 30c Personnel, jet tail ... 1.00 .75
1161 A242 40c Engine ... 1.25 1.00
1162 A242 1b DC-7, map ... 2.75 2.25
Nos. 1158-1162 (5) ... 6.00 4.80

1986, Nov. 13   Perf. 13½
1163 A243 10c multicolored ... .40 .30
1164 A243 80c multicolored ... 2.25 2.00
1165 A243 1b multicolored ... 3.00 2.50
Nos. 1163-1165 (3) ... 5.65 4.80

UN Child Survival Campaign — A244

1986, Dec. 11   Perf. 12½
1166 A244 10c Breast feeding ... .35 .30
1167 A244 35c Immunization ... 1.00 .75
1168 A244 50c Hygiene ... 1.25 1.00
1169 A244 1b Growth monitoring ... 2.50 2.00
Nos. 1166-1169 (4) ... 5.10 4.05

Umbrellas
A245

1987, Feb. 10   Perf. 13½
1170 A245 35c Axum ... 1.00 .85
1171 A245 55c Negele-Borena ... 1.50 1.25
1172 A245 1b Jimma ... 3.00 2.50
Nos. 1170-1172 (3) ... 5.50 4.60

Artwork by
Afewerk
Tekle
(b. 1932)
A246

Designs: 50c, Defender of His Country —
Afar, stained glass window. 2b, Defender of
His Country — Adwa, painting.

1987, Mar. 19   Litho.   Perf. 13½
1173 A246 50c multicolored ... 1.50 1.00
1174 A246 2b multicolored ... 5.25 4.50

Stained Glass Windows by Afewerk
Tekle — A247

1987, June 16   Photo.   Perf. 11½x12
Granite Paper
1175 A247 50c multicolored ... 6.00 4.00

Size: 26x38mm
1176 A247 80c multicolored ... 8.00 5.50
1177 A247 1b multicolored ... 12.00 8.00
Nos. 1175-1177 (3) ... 26.00 17.50
Struggle of the African People.
Sold out in Addis Ababa on date of issue.

Simien Fox
A248

1987, June 29   Litho.   Perf. 13½
1178 A248 5c multicolored ... .25 .25
1179 A248 10c multicolored ... .40 .25
1180 A248 15c multicolored ... .60 .40
1181 A248 20c multicolored ... .75 .50
1182 A248 25c multicolored ... 1.00 .75
1183 A248 45c multicolored ... 1.50 1.00
1184 A248 55c multicolored ... 1.75 1.50
Nos. 1178-1184 (7) ... 6.25 4.60

For overprints see Nos. 1234-1237. For similar design see A294a.

Ethiopian
Revolution,
13th Anniv.
A249

1987, Sept. 10   Perf. 12½
1185 A249 5c Constitution, freedom of press ... .35 .30
1186 A249 10c Popular elections ... .45 .40
1187 A249 80c Referendum ... 1.75 1.50
1188 A249 1b Bahir Dar Airport, map ... 2.50 2.00
Nos. 1185-1188 (4) ... 5.05 4.20

Addis
Ababa,
Cent.
A251

"100" and views: 5c, Emperor Menelik II,
Empress Taitu and city. 10c, Traditional buildings. 80c, Central Addis Ababa. 1b, Aerial
view of city.

1987, Sept. 7   Perf. 13½
1193 A251 5c multicolored ... .50 .30
1194 A251 10c multicolored ... .65 .40
1195 A251 80c multicolored ... 2.00 1.50
1196 A251 1b multicolored ... 2.50 2.00
Nos. 1193-1196 (4) ... 5.65 4.20

Wooden
Spoons
A252

1987, Nov. 30
1197 A252 85c Hurso, Harerge ... 1.75 1.75
1198 A252 1b Borena, Sidamo ... 2.25 2.25

Intl. Year
of Shelter
for the
Homeless
A253

1988, Jan.   Litho.   Perf. 13
1199 A253 10c Village revitalization program ... .50 .40
1200 A253 35c Resettlement program ... 1.00 .90
1201 A253 50c Urban improvement ... 1.25 1.00

1202 A253 1b Cooperative and
government
housing   2.00 1.50
Nos. 1199-1202 (4)   4.75 3.80

October Revolution, Russia, 70th
Anniv. (in 1987) — A254

Painting: 1b, Lenin receiving Workers'
Council delegates in the Smolny Institute.

1988, Feb. 17   **Perf. 12½x12**
1203 A254 1b multicolored   2.50 1.75

Traditional
Hunting Methods
and Prey — A255

1988, Mar. 30   **Litho.**   **Perf. 13½**
1204 A255 85c Bow and arrow   2.50 2.25
1205 A255 1b Double-pronged
spear   3.75 3.50

A256

1988, May 6
1206 A256 85c multicolored   1.75 1.50
1207 A256 1b multicolored   2.25 1.75

Intl. Red Cross and Red Crescent Organizations, 125th annivs.

1988, June 7   **Photo.**   **Perf. 11½x12**
1208 A257 2b multicolored   3.50 2.25

Organizaton of African Unity, 25th anniv.

A257

Ethiopian
Revolution,
14th Anniv.
A258

Design: Various details of *The Victory of
Ethiopia*, six-panel mural by Afewerk Tekle (b.
1932) in the museum of the Heroes Center,
Debre Zeit.

1988, June 28   **Litho.**   **Perf. 13½x13**
1209 A258 10c Jet over farm,
vert.   .35 .30
1210 A258 20c Farm workers on
road, vert.   .45 .35
1211 A258 35c Allegory of unity,
vert.   .75 .50
1212 A258 55c Jet over industry 1.25 1.00

1213 A258 80c Steel works   1.75 1.25
1214 A258 1b Weaving   2.25 2.00
Nos. 1209-1214 (6)   6.80 5.40
Nos. 1209-1211 vert.

Women,
Bracelets
and Maps
A259

1988, July 27   **Litho.**   **Perf. 13x13½**
1215 A259 15c Sidamo   .40 .30
1216 A259 85c Arsi   1.75 1.25
1217 A259 1b Harerge   2.50 2.00
Nos. 1215-1217 (3)   4.65 3.55

Immunize
Every Child
A260

1988, June 14   **Litho.**   **Perf. 13x13½**
1218 A260 10c Measles   .35 .25
1219 A260 35c Tetanus   .75 .60
1220 A260 50c Whooping cough   1.25 1.00
1221 A260 1b Diphtheria   2.25 1.75
Nos. 1218-1221 (4)   4.60 3.60

Intl. Fund for Agricultural Development
(IFAD), 10th Anniv. — A261

1988, Aug. 16   **Perf. 13½**
1222 A261 15c Monetary aid   .30 .25
1223 A261 85c Farming activities 1.50 1.10
1224 A261 1b Harvest   2.25 1.25
Nos. 1222-1224 (3)   4.05 2.60

People's Democratic Republic of
Ethiopia, 1st Anniv. — A262

5c, 1st Session of the natl. Shengo (congress). 10c, Mengistu Haile-Mariam, 1st president of the republic. 80c, Natl. crest, flag &
crowd. 1b, State assembly building.

1988, Sept. 9   **Perf. 14**
1225 A262 5c multicolored   .20 .20
1226 A262 10c multicolored   .30 .25
1227 A262 80c multicolored   1.75 1.50
1228 A262 1b multicolored   2.25 2.00
Nos. 1225-1228 (4)   4.50 3.95

Bank
Notes
A263

1988, Nov. 10   **Photo.**   **Perf. 13**
1229 A263 5c 1-Birr   .20 .20
1230 A263 10c 5-Birr   .35 .30
1231 A263 20c 10-Birr   .75 .50
1232 A263 75c 50-Birr   1.75 1.50
1233 A263 85c 100-Birr   2.25 2.00
Nos. 1229-1233 (5)   5.30 4.50

Nos. 1181-1184 Overprinted "WORLD
AIDS DAY" in Two Languages

1988, Dec. 1   **Litho.**   **Perf. 13½**
1234 A248 20c multicolored   4.75 4.50
1235 A248 25c multicolored   6.25 5.50
1236 A248 45c multicolored   12.50 10.50
1237 A248 55c multicolored   13.00 11.00
Nos. 1234-1237 (4)   36.50 31.50

Intl. Day for the Fight Against AIDS.

WHO, 40th
Anniv.
A264

1988, Dec. 30   **Litho.**   **Perf. 14**
1238 A264 50c multicolored   1.00 .80
1239 A264 65c multicolored   1.40 1.00
1240 A264 85c multicolored   1.75 1.50
Nos. 1238-1240 (3)   4.15 3.30

Traditional
Musical
Instruments
A265

1989, Feb. 9   **Perf. 13x13½**
1241 A265 30c Gere   .75 .45
1242 A265 40c Fanfa   1.00 .65
1243 A265 50c Chancha   1.25 .90
1244 A265 85c Negareet   1.75 1.25
Nos. 1241-1244 (4)   4.75 3.25

Ethiopian
Shipping
Lines,
25th
Anniv.
A266

1989, Mar. 27   **Litho.**   **Perf. 14**
1245 A266 15c Abyot   .40 .30
1246 A266 30c Wolwol   .75 .60
1247 A266 55c Queen of Sheba   1.40 1.25
1248 A266 1b Abbay Wonz   2.75 2.25
Nos. 1245-1248 (4)   5.30 4.40

Birds — A267

1989, May 18   **Litho.**   **Perf. 13½x13**
1249 A267 10c Yellow-fronted
parrot   .40 .30
1250 A267 35c White-winged cliff
chat   1.25 1.00
1251 A267 50c Yellow-throated
seed eater   1.75 1.25
1252 A267 1b Black-headed forest oriole   2.75 2.25
Nos. 1249-1252 (4)   6.15 4.80

Production of Early
Manuscripts — A268

1989, June 16   **Litho.**   **Perf. 13½**
1253 A268 5c Preparing vellum .20 .20
1254 A268 10c Ink horns, pens .30 .25
1255 A268 20c Scribe   .50 .40
1256 A268 75c Book binding   1.50 1.25

1257 A268 85c Illuminated manuscript   2.00 1.75
Nos. 1253-1257 (5)   4.50 3.85

Indigenous
Wildlife — A269

1989, July 18
1258 A269 30c Greater kudu   1.00 .75
1259 A269 40c Lesser kudu   1.25 1.00
1260 A269 50c Roan antelope   1.50 1.25
1261 A269 85c Nile lechwe   2.50 1.50
Nos. 1258-1261 (4)   6.25 5.00

People's
Democratic
Republic of
Ethiopia,
2nd Anniv.
A270

Designs: 15c, Melka Wakana Hydroelectric
Power Station. 75c, Adea Berga Dairy Farm.
1b, Pawe Hospital.

1989, Sept. 8
1262 A270 15c multicolored   .35 .25
1263 A270 75c multicolored   1.50 1.25
1264 A270 1b multicolored   2.50 2.00
Nos. 1262-1264 (3)   4.35 3.50

African
Development
Bank, 25th
Anniv. — A271

1989, Nov. 10   **Litho.**   **Perf. 13½x13**
1265 A271 20c multicolored   .35 .30
1266 A271 80c multicolored   1.50 1.25
1267 A271 1b multicolored   2.75 2.00
Nos. 1265-1267 (3)   4.60 3.55

Pan-African
Postal Union,
10th
Anniv. — A272

1990, Jan. 18   **Litho.**   **Perf. 13½**
1268 A272 50c multicolored   1.00 .75
1269 A272 70c multicolored   1.50 1.25
1270 A272 80c multicolored   2.00 1.75
Nos. 1268-1270 (3)   4.50 3.75

UNESCO World
Literacy
Year — A273

15c, Illiterate man holding newspaper
upside down. 85c, Adults learning alphabet in
school. 1b, Literate man holding newspaper
upright.

1990, Mar. 13
1271 A273 15c multicolored .50 .40
1272 A273 85c multicolored 1.75 1.50
1273 A273 1b multicolored 2.50 2.25
Nos. 1271-1273 (3) 4.75 4.15

Abebe Bikila, Marathon Runner A274

1990, Apr. 17
1274 A274 5c Race .20 .20
1275 A274 10c Flag bearer, Olympic team .30 .25
1276 A274 20c Race, Rome Olympics .60 .50
1277 A274 75c Race, Tokyo Olympics 1.75 1.50
1278 A274 85c Bikila, trophies, vert. 2.25 2.00
Nos. 1274-1278 (5) 5.10 4.45

Flag — A275

1990, Apr. 30 Litho. Perf. 13½x13
1279 A275 5c multicolored .20 .20
1280 A275 10c multicolored .20 .20
1281 A275 15c multicolored .30 .20
1282 A275 20c multicolored .40 .30
1283 A275 25c multicolored .45 .35
1284 A275 30c multicolored .55 .40
1285 A275 35c multicolored .65 .45
1286 A275 40c multicolored .80 .50
1287 A275 45c multicolored .90 .65
1288 A275 50c multicolored 1.00 .65
1289 A275 55c multicolored 1.10 .70
1290 A275 60c multicolored 1.20 .80
1291 A275 70c multicolored 1.25 .90
1292 A275 75c multicolored 1.40 1.00
1293 A275 85c multicolored 1.50 1.10
1294 A275 90c multicolored 1.60 1.25
1295 A275 1b multicolored 1.75 1.25
1296 A275 2b multicolored 3.75 2.75
1297 A275 3b multicolored 5.50 4.00
Nos. 1279-1297 (19) 24.50 17.65
Dated 1989.

Sowing of Teff A276

1990, May 18 Litho. Perf. 13½
1298 A276 5c shown .20 .20
1299 A276 10c Harvesting .25 .20
1300 A276 20c Threshing .50 .40
1301 A276 75c Storage, preparation 1.75 1.50
1302 A276 85c Consumption 2.25 2.00
Nos. 1298-1302 (5) 4.95 4.30

Walia Ibex — A277

1990, June 18 Perf. 14x13½
1303 A277 5c multi .75 .50
1304 A277 15c multi 1.75 1.00
1305 A277 20c multi 2.50 1.50
1306 A277 1b multi, horiz. 10.00 5.75
Nos. 1303-1306 (4) 15.00 8.75

World AIDS Day A278

1991, Jan. 31 Litho. Perf. 14
1307 A278 15c Stages of disease .40 .30
1308 A278 85c Education 1.75 1.50
1309 A278 1b Causes, preventatives 2.25 2.00
Nos. 1307-1309 (3) 4.40 3.80

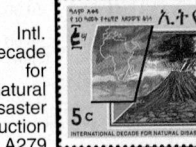

Intl. Decade for Natural Disaster Reduction A279

Map of disaster-prone African areas and: 5c, Volcano. 10c, Earthquake. 15c, Drought. 30c, Flood. 50c, Red Cross health education. 1b, Red Cross assisting fire victims.

1991, Apr. 9 Litho. Perf. 14
1310 A279 5c multicolored .20 .20
1311 A279 10c multicolored .25 .20
1312 A279 15c multicolored .30 .25
1313 A279 30c multicolored .60 .50
1314 A279 50c multicolored 1.25 1.00
1315 A279 1b multicolored 2.25 2.00
Nos. 1310-1315 (6) 4.85 4.15

The Cannon of Tewodros A280

Designs: 15c, Villagers receiving cannon. 85c, Warriors leaving with cannon. 1b, Hauling cannon up mountainside.

1991, June 18 Litho. Perf. 13½
1316 A280 15c multicolored .50 .40
1317 A280 85c multicolored 1.75 1.50
1318 A280 1b multicolored 2.25 2.00
Nos. 1316-1318 (3) 4.50 3.90

Fish A281

1991, Sept. 6 Litho. Perf. 13½
1319 A281 5c Lacepede .50 .30
1320 A281 15c Black-finned butterflyfish .60 .40
1321 A281 80c Regal angelfish 2.25 1.75
1322 A281 1b Bleeker 3.00 2.50
Nos. 1319-1322 (4) 6.35 4.95

A282   A283

Traditional Ceremonial Robes: Various robes.

1992, Jan. 1 Litho. Perf. 13½x14
1323 A282 5c yellow & multi .35 .20
1324 A282 15c orange & multi .40 .25
1325 A282 80c yel green & multi 1.75 1.50
1326 A282 1b blue & multi 2.00 1.75
Nos. 1323-1326 (4) 4.50 3.70

1992, Mar. 5 Litho. Perf. 13½x14
Flowers: 5c, Cissus quadrangularis. 15c, Delphinium dasycaulon. 80c, Epilobium hirsutum. 1b, Kniphofia foliosa.
1327 A283 5c multicolored .40 .30
1328 A283 15c multicolored .50 .40
1329 A283 80c multicolored 2.25 1.75
1330 A283 1b multicolored 2.75 2.00
Nos. 1327-1330 (4) 5.90 4.45

Traditional Homes A284

1992, May 14 Litho. Perf. 12½x12
1331 A284 15c Afar .40 .30
1332 A284 35c Anuak .80 .60
1333 A284 50c Gimira 1.00 .90
1334 A284 1b Oromo 2.25 1.75
Nos. 1331-1334 (4) 4.45 3.55

A285

Pottery.

1992, May Litho. Perf. 13x13½
1335 A285 15c Cover .40 .30
1336 A285 85c Jug 1.50 1.25
1337 A285 1b Tall jar 2.25 1.75
Nos. 1335-1337 (3) 4.15 3.30

A286

1992, Sept. 29 Perf. 14x13½
1338 A286 20c multicolored .40 .30
1339 A286 80c multicolored 1.50 1.25
1340 A286 1b multicolored 2.00 1.75
Nos. 1338-1340 (3) 3.90 3.30

Pan-African Rinderpest campaign.

A287

Musical instruments.

1993, Feb. 16 Litho. Perf. 14x13½
1341 A287 15c Catchel .40 .30
1342 A287 35c Huldudwa .75 .55
1343 A287 50c Dita 1.00 .75
1344 A287 1b Atamo 2.50 2.00
Nos. 1341-1344 (4) 4.65 3.60

Birds — A288

1993, Apr. 22 Litho. Perf. 14x13½
1345 A288 15c Banded barbet .45 .45
1346 A288 35c Ruppell's chat .80 .75
1347 A288 50c Abyssinian catbird 1.25 1.00
1348 A288 1b White-billed starling 3.00 2.25
Nos. 1345-1348 (4) 5.50 4.45

Animals A289

1993, May 14 Perf. 13½x14
1349 A289 15c Honey badger .30 .25
1350 A289 35c Spotted necked otter .50 .40
1351 A289 50c Rock hyrax .80 .60
1352 A289 1b White-tailed mongoose 1.50 1.25
Nos. 1349-1352 (4) 3.10 2.50

Herbs — A290

1993, June 10 Perf. 14x13½
1353 A290 5c Caraway seed .65 .50
1354 A290 15c Garlic .75 .50
1355 A290 80c Turmeric 1.50 1.00
1356 A290 1b Capsicum peppers 2.50 2.25
Nos. 1353-1356 (4) 5.40 4.35

Butterflies A291

1993, July 9 Litho. Perf. 14x13½
1357 A291 20c Papilio echeriodes .75 .60
1358 A291 30c Papilio rex .90 .75
1359 A291 50c Graphium policenes 1.25 1.00
1360 A291 1b Graphium leonidas 2.50 1.75
Nos. 1357-1360 (4) 5.40 4.10

Insects — A292

1993, Aug. 10
1361 A292 15c C. Variabilis .40 .30
1362 A292 35c Lycus trabeatus .60 .50
1363 A292 50c Malachius bifasciatus .80 .70
1364 A292 1b Homoeogryllus xanthographus 1.60 1.25
Nos. 1361-1364 (4) 3.40 2.75

Trees A293

1993, Oct. 12　Litho.　Perf. 13½x14
1365	A293	15c Euphorbia am-		
		pliphylla	.25	.20
1366	A293	35c Erythrina brucei	.35	.30
1367	A293	50c Draceana		
		steudneri	.65	.50
1368	A293	1b Allophylus abys-		
		sinicus	1.25	1.00
		Nos. 1365-1368 (4)	2.50	2.00

Lakes
A294

1993, Dec. 14
1369	A294	15c Wonchi	.25	.20
1370	A294	35c Zuquala	.35	.30
1371	A294	50c Ashengi	.60	.50
1372	A294	1b Tana	1.10	.90
		Nos. 1369-1372 (4)	2.30	1.90

Simien Fox
A294a

Rough Perf. 13½
1994, Jan. 18　　　　　　　Litho.
Color of Border
1372A	A294a	5c violet	
1372B	A294a	10c brown	
1372C	A294a	15c lemon	
1372D	A294a	20c salmon	
1372E	A294a	40c pale rose	
1372F	A294a	55c dull green	
1372G	A294a	60c dark blue	
1372H	A294a	80c bright blue	
1372I	A294a	85c gray green	
1372J	A294a	1b bright green	
		Nos. 1372A-1372J (10)	27.50

Nos. 1372A-1372J have rough perforations and a poor quality printing impression. Dated "1991."

See Nos. 1393A-1393T. For overprints see Nos. 1393U-1393X, 1396A-1396D.

A295

A296

Transitional government: 15c, First anniversary of EPRDF's control of Addis Ababa. 35c, Transition Conference. 50c, National, regional elections. 1b, Coat of arms of Transitional Government.

1994, Mar. 31　Litho.　Perf. 14
1373	A295	15c multicolored	.35	.25
1374	A295	35c multicolored	.40	.30
1375	A295	50c multicolored	.45	.35
1376	A295	1b multicolored	.90	.55
		Nos. 1373-1376 (4)	2.10	1.45

1994, May 17　　　　　　　Perf. 13½
1377	A296	15c blue & multi	.35	.25
1378	A296	85c green & multi	.55	.40
1379	A296	1b violet & multi	.75	.50
		Nos. 1377-1379 (3)	1.65	1.15

Intl. Year of the Family.

Ethiopian Postal Service, Cent. A297

Designs: 60c, Early, modern postal workers, Scott Type A1. 75c, Early letter carriers. 80c, Older building, methods of transportation. 85c, People, mail buses. 1b, Modern methods of transportation, modern high-rise building.

1994, July 4　Litho.　Perf. 13½
1380	A297	60c multicolored	.50	.35
1381	A297	75c multicolored	.60	.40
1382	A297	80c multicolored	.75	.45
1383	A297	85c multicolored	.80	.50
1384	A297	1b multicolored	.95	.70
a.		Souvenir sheet, #1380-1384 +		
		label	4.00	3.25
		Nos. 1380-1384 (5)	3.60	2.40

Enset Plant — A298

Hair Ornaments
A299

1994, Aug. 3
1385	A298	10c shown	.25	.20
1386	A298	15c Young plants, hut	.30	.25
1387	A298	25c Root, women		
		processing		
		leaves	.35	.30
1388	A298	50c Mature plants	.50	.35
1389	A298	1b Uses as food	.75	.55
		Nos. 1385-1389 (5)	2.15	1.65

1994, Sept. 2
1390	A299	5c Gamo gofa	.35	.25
1391	A299	15c Sidamo	.40	.30
1392	A299	80c Gamo gofa, diff.	.60	.40
1393	A299	1b Wello	.75	.55
		Nos. 1390-1393 (4)	2.10	1.50

Simien Fox Type of 1994
1994, Oct. 18　Litho.　Perf. 14
Size: 39x25mm
Color of Border
1393A	A294a	5c dull lilac	
1393B	A294a	10c brown	
1393C	A294a	15c lemon	
1393D	A294a	20c salmon	
1393E	A294a	25c lemon	
1393F	A294a	30c yellow	
		brown	
1393G	A294a	35c orange	
1393H	A294a	40c pale rose	
1393I	A294a	45c pale red	
		org	
1393J	A294a	50c rose lilac	
1393K	A294a	55c pale	
		green	
1393L	A294a	60c dark blue	
1393M	A294a	65c pale lilac	
1393N	A294a	70c bright	
		green	
1393O	A294a	75c pale bl	
		grn	
1393P	A294a	80c bright blue	
1393Q	A294a	85c dark	
		greenish	
		blue	
1393R	A294a	90c pale	
		brown	
1393S	A294a	1b greenish	
		blue	
1393T	A294a	2b yellow	
		brown	
		Nos. 1393A-1393T (20)	500.00　40.00

Nos. 1393A-1393T have sharp impressions, Questa imprint, clean perforations. Dated "1993."

Nos. 1393L, 1393P-1393Q, 1393S
Ovptd. in Blue

1994, Oct. 20　Litho.　Perf. 14
1393U	A294a	60c on		
		#1393L	20.00	3.00
1393V	A294a	80c on		
		#1393P	25.00	4.00
1393W	A294a	85c on		
		#1393Q	50.00	7.50
1393X	A294a	1b on		
		#1393S	55.00	8.00
		Nos. 1393U-1393X (4)	150.00	22.50

UNFPA, 50th anniv.

ICAO, 50th Anniv. A300

1994, Dec. 7　Litho.　Perf. 13½
1394	A300	20c mag, lt bl & yel	.40	.35
1395	A300	80c yel & lt bl	.60	.45
1396	A300	1b dk bl, lt bl & yel	.80	.70
		Nos. 1394-1396 (3)	1.80	1.50

Nos. 1393M-1393O, 1393R Ovptd.

1994, Dec. 20　Litho.　Perf. 14
1396A	A294a	65c on		
		#1393M	20.00	3.00
1396B	A294a	70c on		
		#1393N	25.00	4.00
1396C	A294a	75c on		
		#1393O	50.00	7.50
1396D	A294a	90c on		
		#1393R	55.00	8.00
		Nos. 1396A-1396D (4)	150.00	22.50

African Development Bank, 30th anniv.

Baskets for Serving Food A301

1995, June 7　Litho.　Perf. 13½
1397	A301	30c Erbo	.30	.25
1398	A301	70c Sedieka	.70	.55
1399	A301	1b Tirar	1.00	.80
		Nos. 1397-1399 (3)	2.00	1.60

Traditional Hair Styles — A302

1995, July 5　Litho.　Perf. 13½
1400	A302	25c Kuncho	.25	.20
1401	A302	75c Gamme	.75	.55
1402	A302	1b Sadulla	1.00	.80
		Nos. 1400-1402 (3)	2.00	1.55

FAO, 50th Anniv. A303

1995, Aug. 29　Litho.　Perf. 13½
1403	A303	20c green & multi	.20	.20
1404	A303	80c blue & multi	.55	.45
1405	A303	1b brown & multi	.80	.65
		Nos. 1403-1405 (3)	1.55	1.30

Cultivating Tools
A304

1995, Sept. 7
1406	A304	15c Dangora	.25	.20
1407	A304	35c Gheso	.35	.30
1408	A304	50c Akafa	.55	.45
1409	A304	1b Ankasse	.80	.65
		Nos. 1406-1409 (4)	1.95	1.60

UN, 50th Anniv. — A305

1995, Oct. 18　Litho.　Perf. 13½
Color of UN Emblem
1410	A305	20c black	.50	.40
1411	A305	80c bister	.60	.50
1412	A305	1b blue	.85	.75
		Nos. 1410-1412 (3)	1.95	1.65

Intergovernmental Authority on Drought and Development (IGADD), 10th Anniv. — A306

Flags of member nations and: 15c, Seedling being planted in arid region. 35c, People carrying supplies through desert. 50c, Person picking fruit. 1b, Map of member nations.

1995, Dec. 27　Litho.　Perf. 13½
1413	A306	15c multicolored	.35	.25
1414	A306	35c multicolored	.45	.35
1415	A306	50c multicolored	.55	.45
1416	A306	1b multicolored	.85	.75
		Nos. 1413-1416 (4)	2.20	1.80

Victory at Battle of Adwa, Cent. — A307

Designs: 40c, Battle sites. 50c, Map of Africa focused at Ethiopia. 60c, Troops, ship. 70c, Warriors, soldiers in two battle scenes. 80c, Italians surrendering, Ethiopian troops, cannons. 1b, Emperor Menelik II, constitution, Empress Taitu.

1996, Mar. 2　Litho.　Perf. 13½x14½
1417	A307	40c multicolored	.25	.20
1418	A307	50c multicolored	.30	.25
1419	A307	60c multicolored	.45	.35
1420	A307	70c multicolored	.55	.40
1421	A307	80c multicolored	.75	.60

1422	A307	1b multicolored	1.00 .80
a.		Souvenir sheet, #1417-1422	4.50 4.50
		Nos. 1417-1422 (6)	3.30 2.60

UN Volunteers, 25th Anniv. A308

Designs: 20c, People, temporary housing huts. 30c, Planting seedlings. 50c, Instructing students. 1b, Caring for infant.

1996, June 6   Litho.   Perf. 13½

1423	A308	20c multicolored	.25 .20
1424	A309	30c multicolored	.35 .30
1425	A309	50c multicolored	.50 .40
1426	A309	1b multicolored	.95 .80
		Nos. 1423-1426 (4)	2.05 1.65

1996 Summer Olympic Games, Atlanta A310

1996, Aug. 1   Litho.   Perf. 12½x12
Overprint in Black

1427	A310	15c Boxing	.35 .25
1428	A310	20c Swimming	.40 .30
1429	A310	40c Cycling	.45 .35
1430	A310	85c Athletics	.60 .50
1431	A310	1b Soccer	.75 .65
		Nos. 1427-1431 (5)	2.55 2.05

Nos. 1427-1431 were originally prepared for the 1984 Summer Olympic Games in Los Angeles, but were not released due to the Soviet-led boycott.

A311

A312

UNICEF, 50th Anniv.: 10c, Emblems. 15c, Mother, child receiving vaccination. 25c, Woman carrying water, boy drinking from faucet. 50c, Children studying. 1b, Mother breastfeeding infant.

1996, Sept. 10   Litho.   Perf. 13½

1432	A311	10c multicolored	.25 .20
1433	A311	15c multicolored	.30 .25
1434	A311	25c multicolored	.35 .30
1435	A311	50c multicolored	.60 .45
1436	A311	1b multicolored	.95 .75
		Nos. 1432-1436 (5)	2.45 1.95

1996, Dec. 26   Litho.   Perf. 13½

Creation of Federal Democratic Republic of Ethiopia: 10c, People discussing new Constitution, approved Dec. 8, 1994. 20c, Ballot boxes, hand placing ballot in box. 30c, Marking ballot, placing into box, tower building, items from country's environment. 40c, Building, ballot, assembly hall. 1b, Natl. flag, transition of power.

1437	A312	10c multicolored	.20 .20
1438	A312	20c multicolored	.20 .20
1439	A312	30c multicolored	.30 .25
1440	A312	40c multicolored	.35 .30
1441	A312	1b multicolored	.75 .60
		Nos. 1437-1441 (5)	1.80 1.55

Traditional Baskets — A313

1997, Feb. 20   Litho.   Perf. 13½

1442	A313	5c Jimma	.50 .35
1443	A313	15c Wello	.50 .35
1444	A313	80c Welega	.85 .40
1445	A313	1b Shewa	1.00 .60
		Nos. 1442-1445 (4)	2.85 1.70

Traditional Baskets A314

1997, May 22   Litho.   Perf. 13½

1446	A314	35c Arssi	.30 .25
1447	A314	65c Gojam	.55 .45
1448	A314	1b Harer	.85 .75
		Nos. 1446-1448 (3)	1.70 1.45

See Nos. 1464-1466.

UN Decade Against Drug Abuse & Illicit Trafficking A315

1997, Sept. 9   Litho.   Perf. 14

1449	A315	20c green & multi	.50 .35
1450	A315	80c brown & multi	.70 .55
1451	A315	1b blue & multi	1.00 .80
		Nos. 1449-1451 (3)	2.20 1.70

Historic Buildings, Addis Ababa A316

45c, Bitweded Haile Giorgis' house. 55c, Alfred Ilg's house, vert. 3b, Menelik's Elfgin.

Perf. 14½x14, 14x14½
1997, Dec. 23   Litho.

1452	A316	45c multicolored	.35 .30
1453	A316	55c multicolored	.45 .40
1454	A316	3b multicolored	1.60 1.25
		Nos. 1452-1454 (3)	2.40 1.95

Addis Ababa's Oldest Historical Buildings A317

Designs: 60c, Ras Biru W/Gabriel's house. 75c, Sheh Hojele Alhassen's house. 80c, Fitawrari H/Giorgis Dinegde's house. 85c, Etege Taitu Hotel. 1b, Dejazmach Wube Atnafseged's house.

1997, Dec. 30   Litho.   Perf. 14½x14

1455	A317	60c multicolored	.35 .30
1456	A317	75c multicolored	.40 .35
1457	A317	80c multicolored	.45 .40
1458	A317	85c multicolored	.50 .45
1459	A317	1b multicolored	.75 .60
		Nos. 1455-1459 (5)	2.45 2.10

Pan African Postal Union, 18th Anniv. A318

Union's emblem and wildlife: 45c, Deculla bushback. 55c, Soemmering's gazelle. 1b, Defassa waterbuck. 2b, Black buffalo.

1998, Mar. 25   Litho.   Perf. 14½x14

1460	A318	45c multicolored	.50 .35
1461	A318	55c multicolored	.55 .45
1462	A318	1b multicolored	.90 .65
1463	A318	2b multicolored	1.75 1.25
		Nos. 1460-1463 (4)	3.70 2.70

Traditional Basket Type of 1997

1998, May 21   Litho.   Perf. 13½

1464	A314	45c Gonder	.25 .20
1465	A314	55c Harere	.35 .30
1466	A314	3b Tigray	1.50 1.25
		Nos. 1464-1466 (3)	2.10 1.75

Golden-Backed Woodpecker A319

1998, Jan. 12   Photo.   Perf. 11½
Granite Paper
Panel Color

1467	A319	5c green blue	.45 .30
1468	A319	10c yellow	.45 .30
1469	A319	15c blue	.45 .30
1470	A319	20c light brown	.45 .30
1471	A319	25c violet	.45 .30
1472	A319	30c light blue	.45 .30
1473	A319	35c salmon rose	.45 .30
1474	A319	40c lilac	.45 .30
1475	A319	45c green	.45 .30
1476	A319	50c salmon	.50 .35
1477	A319	55c blue	.50 .35
1478	A319	60c brick red	.55 .40
1479	A319	65c light gray	.60 .45
1480	A319	70c bright yellow	.65 .50
1481	A319	75c pale violet	.75 .65
1482	A319	80c apple green	.80 .70
1483	A319	85c gray	.85 .75
1484	A319	90c orange	.95 .80
1485	A319	1b yellow green	1.25 .95
1486	A319	2b pale rose	1.50 1.25
1487	A319	3b lilac rose	2.50 2.00
1488	A319	5b bister	3.50 3.00
1489	A319	10b orange yellow	7.00 6.00
		Nos. 1467-1489 (23)	25.95 20.85

Agreement for Return of Axum Obelisk from Italy — A320

45c, Map of Italy, pieces of obelisk. 55c, Obelisk in Rome. 3b, Map of E. Africa, obelisk, ruins of Axum.

1998, Sept. 3   Litho.   Perf. 13½

1490	A320	45c multicolored	.40 .25
1491	A320	55c multicolored	.50 .45
1492	A320	3b multicolored	1.60 1.25
		Nos. 1490-1492 (3)	2.50 1.95

Ethiopia-Djibouti Railway, Cent. — A321

Designs: 45c, Men carrying rails during construction. 55c, Early steam train, CFE 404. 1b, Terminal building. 2b, Modern train, BB 1212.

1998, Nov. 24   Litho.   Perf. 11½
Granite Paper

1493	A321	45c multicolored	.40 .35
1494	A321	55c multicolored	.50 .45
1495	A321	1b multicolored	.85 .75
1496	A321	2b multicolored	1.75 1.25
		Nos. 1493-1496 (4)	3.50 2.80

Universal Declaration of Human Rights, 50th Anniv. A322

1998, Dec. 23   Litho.   Perf. 13x13½

1497	A322	45c red & multi	.35 .25
1498	A322	55c yellow & multi	.35 .30
1499	A322	1b green & multi	.60 .50
1500	A322	2b blue & multi	.90 .75
		Nos. 1497-1500 (4)	2.20 1.80

Mother Teresa (1910-97) — A323

Various portraits.

1999, Mar. 9   Litho.   Perf. 13½x13

1501	A323	45c brown & multi	.55 .35
1502	A323	55c green & multi	.60 .45
1503	A323	1b yel org & multi	.75 .60
1504	A323	2b blue & multi	1.75 1.25
		Nos. 1501-1504 (4)	3.65 2.65

Intl. Year of the Ocean A324

1999, May 6   Litho.   Perf. 13½x13¼

1505	A324	45c black & multi	.35 .25
1506	A324	55c red & multi	.45 .30
1507	A324	1b blue & multi	.60 .50
1508	A324	2b green & multi	1.25 1.00
		Nos. 1505-1508 (4)	2.65 2.05

World Environment Day — A325

1999, June 17   Litho.   Perf. 13½

1509	A325	45c pink & multi	.45 .30
1510	A325	55c vio & multi	.55 .40
1511	A325	1b yel org & multi	.90 .70
1512	A325	2b grn & multi	1.50 1.00
		Nos. 1509-1512 (4)	3.40 2.40

National Parks — A326

45c, Abijata, Shalla Lakes. 70c, Nechisar. 85c, Bale Mountains. 2b, Awash.

Perf. 13¾x13¼, 13¼x13¾

1999, Sept. 8			Litho.	
1513	A326	45c multi, vert.	.60	.50
1514	A326	70c multi, vert.	.80	.70
1515	A326	85c multi, vert.	1.00	.90
1516	A326	2b multi	2.50	1.50

See Nos. 1521-1524.

Nos. 1513-1516 (4)   4.90   3.60

UPU, 125th
Anniv. — A327

1999, Oct. 28			Perf. 13¼x13	
1517	A327	20c multicolored	.30	.25
1518	A327	80c multicolored	.40	.35
1519	A327	1b multicolored	.70	.60
1520	A327	2b multicolored	1.00	.80
		Nos. 1517-1520 (4)	2.40	2.00

National Parks Type of 1999

Designs: 50c, Omo, vert. 70c, Mago, vert. 80c, Yangudi-Rassa, vert. 2b, Gambella.

1999, Nov. 30		Litho.	Perf. 13¼	
1521-1524	A326	Set of 4	3.25	2.50

Intl. Year of
Older Persons
A328

45c, Woman attending to sick man. 70c, Older people gardening. 85c, Four men, bench. 2b, Older man, two young people.

1999, Dec. 30			Perf. 13¾x13¼	
1525-1528	A328	Set of 4	3.25	2.50

Alexander
Pushkin,
Writer, Birth
Bicent. (in
1999) — A329

Various portraits: 45c, 70c, 85c, 2b.

2000, Mar. 9		Litho.	Perf. 13¾x13¼	
1529-1532	A329	Set of 4	3.25	2.50

Worldwide Fund for Nature
(WWF) — A330

Grevy's zebra: a, Grazing. b, Running. c, Resting. d, Head.

2001, Jan. 31	Litho.	Perf. 13¼x13¾	
1533	Strip of 4	7.50	5.00
a.	A330 45c multi	.60	.45
b.	A330 55c multi	.75	.55
c.	A330 1b multi	1.40	1.00
d.	A330 3b multi	4.25	3.00

Operation
Sunset — A331

Designs: 45c, Lecturer, students. 55c, Soldiers, flag ceremony. 1b, People, house. 2b, Agriculture, construction.

2000, June 27			Perf. 13¾	
1534-1537	A331	Set of 4	3.25	2.50

Flags
A332

Designs: 25c, Harar Region. 30c, Oromia Region. 50c, Amhara Region. 60c, Tigre Region. 70c, Benishangi Region. 80c, Somalia Region. 90c, Peoples of the South Region. 95c, Gambella Region. 1b, Afar Region. 2b, Ethiopia.

2000, Oct. 26			Perf. 13¼x13¾	
1538-1547	A332	Set of 10	4.75	4.00

Afro Ayigeba,
Cross of St.
Lalibela
A333

2000, Apr. 27			Perf. 13¾x13¼	
1548	A333	4b multi	2.75	2.25

Menelik's
Bushbuck
A334

Perf. 13¾x13¼

2000, June 19			Litho.	
		Frame Color		
1548A	A334	5c dk Prus blue		
1549	A334	10c lilac		
1549A	A334	15c blue		
1549B	A334	20c yellow bister		
1549C	A334	25c purple		
1549D	A334	30c lt Prus blue		
1549E	A334	35c brt red		
1549F	A334	40c lilac		
1549G	A334	45c emerald		
1549H	A334	50c red		
1549I	A334	55c blue		
1549J	A334	60c yellow orange		
1549K	A334	65c deep blue		
1549L	A334	70c dull blue		
1549M	A334	75c orange yellow		
1549N	A334	80c carmine		
1549O	A334	85c light blue		
1550	A334	90c ocher		
1551	A334	1b green		
1552	A334	2b red violet		
1553	A334	3b purple		
1554	A334	5b dark carmine		
1555	A334	10b light carmine		
	Nos. 1548A-1555 (23)		—	40.00

Haile Gebreselassie, Runner — A335

Design: #1557, 50c, Gebreselassie running. #1557A, 60c, Gebreselassie running, diff. #1557B, 90c, Gebreselassie running, diff. #1558, 2b, Gebreselassie with arms raised.

2000, Nov. 9		Litho.	Perf. 13½	
1557-1558	A335	Set of 4	2.75	2.00

World Meteorological Organization,
50th Anniv. — A336

Color of inscriptions: 40c, Gray. 75c, Green. 85c, Brown. 2b, Blue.

2000, Oct. 10		Litho.	Perf. 13½	
1559-1562	A336	Set of 4	3.25	2.50

Addis Ababa University, 50th
Anniv. — A337

2000, Nov. 30			Perf. 13½x14¼	
1563	A337	4b multi	3.25	2.50

UN High Commissioner for Refugees,
50th Anniv. — A338

Frame color: 40c, Brown. 75c, Green. 85c, Blue. 2b, Gold.

2000 Dec. 14			Perf. 13½x14	
1564-1567	A338	Set of 4	3.25	2.50

Freshwater Fish — A340

Designs: 45c, Catfish. 55c, Tilapia. 3b, Nile perch.

2001, July 26		Litho.	Perf. 14¼	
1572-1574	A340	Set of 3	3.50	2.75

Traditional Means of
Transportation — A341

Designs: 40c, Man on horseback, horse-drawn cart. 60c, Camel caravan. 1b, Man on horseback, horse carrying load. 2b, Man on donkey, donkeys carrying goods.

2001, Aug. 30			Perf. 13¼x13½	
1575-1578	A341	Set of 4	3.50	2.75

Year of Dialogue
Among
Civilizations
A342

Color of country name: 25c, Light blue. 75c, White. 1b, Light yellow. 2b, Pink.

2001, Oct. 9			Perf. 14	
1579-1582	A342	Set of 4	3.00	2.75

Birds — A343

Designs: 50c, White-tailed swallow. 60c, Spot-breasted plover. 90c, Abyssinian long-claw. 2b, Prince Ruspoli's turaco.

2001, Nov. 29			Perf. 14¼	
1583-1586	A343	Set of 4	3.75	3.00

Traditional
Beehives
A344

Various beehives: 40c, 70c, 90c, 2b.

2002, Jan. 24		Litho.	Perf. 14	
1587-1590	A344	Set of 4	3.50	2.75

Traditional Grain Storage — A345

Designs: 30c, Gota. 70c, Bekollo Gotera. 1b, Gotera. 2b, Gotera, diff.

2002, Mar. 28			**Perf. 13½x14**		
1591-1594	A345	Set of 4		2.50	2.00

Lions Club Intl. — A346

Lions Club Intl. emblem and: 45c, Quality emblem. 55c, Woman at pump. 1b, Eye doctor treating patient. 2b, Man in wheelchair.

2002, Apr. 26	**Litho.**		**Perf. 13x13¼**		
1595-1598	A346	Set of 4		2.75	2.25

Trees A347

Designs: 50c, Acacia abyssinica. 60c, Boswellia papyrifera, vert. 90c, Aningeria adolfi-freiderici, vert. 2b, Prunus africana, vert.

	Perf. 13½x13¼, 13¼x13½				
2002, June 27					
1599-1602	A347	Set of 4		2.50	2.00

Traditional Beehives A348

Various beehives with panel colors of: 45c, Pink. 55c, Yellow. 1b, Light blue. 2b, Light green.

2002, Sept. 19	**Litho.**		**Perf. 13¼x13**		
1603-1606	A348	Set of 4		2.25	1.75

Granite — A349

Designs: 45c, Sidamo. 55c, Harrar. 1b, Tigray. 2b, Wollega.

2002, Oct. 24			**Perf. 13x13¼**		
1607-1610	A349	Set of 4		4.00	3.50

Konso Waka A350

Various wooden sculptures with background colors of: 40c, Green. 60c, Blue. 1b, Yellow. 2b, Red.

2002, Nov. 28			**Perf. 14**		
1611-1614	A350	Set of 4		3.00	2.25

Menelik's Bushbuck — A351

2002, Dec. 12			**Perf. 13½x13¾**		
	Frame Color				
1615	A351	5c brt grn blue		.20	.20
1616	A351	10c lilac		.20	.20
1617	A351	15c bright blue		.20	.20
1618	A351	20c brn orange		.25	.20
1619	A351	25c purple		.25	.20
1620	A351	30c bright blue		.25	.20
1621	A351	35c carmine		.25	.20
1622	A351	40c purple		.25	.20
1623	A351	45c emerald		.25	.20
1624	A351	50c red		.25	.20
1625	A351	55c blue		.25	.20
1626	A351	60c bright yel		.35	.25
1627	A351	65c red		.35	.25
1628	A351	70c light blue		.35	.25
1629	A351	75c bright yel		.40	.35
1630	A351	80c carmine		.40	.35
1631	A351	85c bright blue		.50	.40
1632	A351	90c orange brn		.50	.40
1633	A351	95c green		.50	.40
1634	A351	1b red violet		.60	.50
1635	A351	2b purple		.85	.75
1636	A351	3b blue		1.00	.90
1637	A351	5b dull red		2.00	1.50
1638	A351	10b light green		4.00	3.00
1639	A351	20b rose pink		8.00	6.00
	Nos. 1615-1639 (25)			22.40	17.50

Oil Crops A352

Designs: 40c, Abyssinian mustard. 60c, Linseed. 3b, Niger seed.

2002, Dec. 31	**Litho.**		**Perf. 13¼x13**		
1640-1642	A352	Set of 3		2.00	2.00

Pan-African Postal Union, 23rd Anniv. — A353

Background color: 20c, Green. 80c, Blue green. 1b, Orange brown. 2b, Purple.

2003, Feb. 18			**Perf. 13x13¼**		
1643-1646	A353	Set of 4		2.00	2.00

Opals — A354

Designs: 45c, Milk opal. 60c, Brown precious opal. 95c, Fire opal. 2b, Yellow precious opal.

2003, May 8			**Perf. 14**		
1647-1650	A354	Set of 4		2.50	2.50

Emperor Tewodros's Amulet — A355

Various views with frame color of: 40c, Green. 60c, Yellow orange. 3b, Red.

2003, Sept. 4	**Litho.**		**Perf. 13x13¼**		
1651-1653	A355	Set of 3		2.00	2.00

Flowers — A356

Designs: 45c, Kniphofia isoetfolia. 55c, Kniphofia insignis. 1b, Crinum bambusetum. 2b, Crinum abyssinicum, horiz.

2003, Nov. 27	**Litho.**		**Perf. 13x13¼**		
1654-1657	A356	Set of 4		2.50	2.50

Konso Terracing System A357

Designs: 40c, Village, crops. 60c, Man and woman, ears of grains. 1b, Terraces, tool. 2b, Farmers working on terraces, crops.

2003, Dec. 30			**Perf. 13¼x13¾**		
1658-1661	A357	Set of 4		2.00	2.00

Amaranths A358

Designs: 20c, Seeds. 80c, White amaranth. 1b, Red amaranth. 2b, Amaranth bread.

2004, Mar. 11	**Litho.**		**Perf. 13¼x14**		
1662-1665	A358	Set of 4		2.25	2.25

Marble A359

Designs: 25c, Sabian multicolored marble. 75c, Eshet blue marble. 1b, Sabian rose green marble. 2b, Sabian purple marble.

2004, July 27			**Perf. 14**		
1666-1669	A359	Set of 4		1.50	1.50

FIFA (Fédération Internationale de Football Association), Cent. — A360

Soccer field, "100" and: 5c, FIFA emblem. 95c, Old soccer ball. 1b, Cleats. 2b, Modern soccer ball.

2004, Sept. 7	**Litho.**		**Perf. 14**		
1670-1673	A360	Set of 4		1.25	1.25

2004 Summer Olympics, Athens A361

Designs: 20c, Track. 35c, Hammer throw. 45c, Boxing. 3b, Cycling.

2004, Dec. 7					
1674-1677	A361	Set of 4		1.25	1.25

Gesho — A362

Designs: 40c, Chopped plant. 60c, Plants, horiz. 1b, Cut logs. 2b, Branch with berries.

2004, Dec. 28					
1678-1681	A362	Set of 4		1.25	1.25

Black Rhinoceros A363

2005, June 20	**Litho.**		**Perf. 14**		
	Background Color				
1682	A363	5c bright blue		.20	.20
1683	A363	10c lilac		.20	.20
1684	A363	15c dark blue		.20	.20
1685	A363	20c bister		.40	.40
1686	A363	25c dark purple		.40	.40
1687	A363	30c blue		.40	.40
1688	A363	35c red		.40	.40
1689	A363	40c purple		.40	.40
1690	A363	45c green		.40	.40
1691	A363	4b bright red		1.75	1.75
	Nos. 1682-1691 (10)			4.75	4.75

Sabean Inscriptions — A364

Various inscriptions with background colors of: 15c, Green. 40c, Red, vert. 45c, Orange, vert. 3b, Blue, vert.

	Perf. 13¾x14, 14x13¾				
2005, Aug. 20			**Litho.**		
1692-1695	A364	Set of 4		1.25	1.25

Surma Hairstyles
A365

Various hairstyles with background colors of: 15c, Red. 40c, Green. 45c, Blue. 3b, Lilac.

2005, Dec. 20   *Perf. 14x13¾*
1696-1699 A365   Set of 4   1.50 1.50

Flowers
A366

Designs: 45c, Chlorophytum neghellense. 55c, Aloe bertemariae, vert. 3b, Aloe schelpei, vert.

Perf. 13¾x14, 14x13¾
2006, June 6   Litho.
1700-1702 A366   Set of 3   .95 .95

Ethiopian Airlines, 60th Anniv.
A367

Designs: 15c, Douglas C-47A Dakota III. 40c, Douglas DC-6B Super Cloudmaster. 45c, Boeing 720-060B. 1b, Boeing 767-300ER. 2b, Boeing 787 Dreamliner.

2006, Sept. 28   *Perf. 13x13¼*
1703-1707 A367   Set of 5   .95 .95

Intl. Year of Deserts and Desertification — A368

Emblem and: 15c, United Nations emblem. 40c, Map of Ethiopia showing desertification vulnerability. 45c, Map of Africa showing climate types. 3b, Map of world showing climate types.

2006, Oct. 31   *Perf. 14x13½*
1708-1711 A368   Set of 4   .95 .95

SEMI-POSTAL STAMPS

Types of 1931, Overprinted in Red at Upper Left

Perf. 12x12½, 12½x12
1936, Feb. 24   Unwmk.
B1 A27 1g light green .45 .45
B2 A27 2g rose .45 .45
B3 A25 4g blue .45 .45

B4 A27 8g brown .65 .65
B5 A25 1t purple .65 .65
   Nos. B1-B5 (5) 2.65 2.65
Nos. B1-B5 were sold at twice face value, the surtax going to the Red Cross.

> **Catalogue values for unused stamps in this section, from this point to the end of the section, are for Never Hinged items.**

Nos. 289, 290, 292-294 Surcharged in Blue

Perf. 13x13½
1949, June 13   Wmk. 282
B6 A53 8c + 8c deep org 2.00 2.00
B7 A53 12c + 5c red 2.00 2.00
B8 A53 30c + 15c org brn 3.00 3.00
B9 A53 70c + 70c rose lilac 18.00 18.00
B10 A53 $1 + 80c dk car rose 24.00 24.00
   Nos. B6-B10 (5) 49.00 49.00
No. B10 exists with "80+" error.
See Nos. B16-B20.

Type A39 Surcharged in Red or Carmine

Perf. 11½
1950, May 8   Unwmk.   Photo.
Various Designs
Inscribed "Croix Rouge"
B11 A39 5c + 10c brt grn .85 1.25
B12 A39 10c + 10c brt red 1.25 1.50
B13 A39 25c + 10c brt bl 2.00 2.75
B14 A39 50c + 10c dk yel brn 5.75 4.50
B15 A39 1t + 10c brt vio 9.00 10.00
   Nos. B11-B15 (5) 18.85 20.00
The surtax was for the Red Cross.
The surcharge includes two dots which invalidate the original surtax. The original surcharge with uneven cross was red, a 1951 printing with even cross was carmine. Forgeries exist.

Nos. B6-B10 Overprinted in Black

Perf. 13x13½
1951, Nov. 17   Wmk. 282
B16 A53 8c + 8c dp org .70 .70
B17 A53 12c + 5c red .70 .70
B18 A53 30c + 15c org brn 1.10 1.10
B19 A53 70c + 70c rose lilac 9.50 9.50
B20 A53 $1 + 80c dk car rose 14.00 14.00
   Nos. B16-B20 (5) 26.00 26.00

Tree, Staff and Snake — SP1

Wmk. 282
1951, Nov. 25   Engr.   *Perf. 13*
Lower Panel in Red
B21 SP1 5c + 2c dp bl grn .35 .20
B22 SP1 10c + 3c orange .50 .25
B23 SP1 15c + 3c dp bl .65 .40
B24 SP1 30c + 5c red 1.50 1.00
B25 SP1 50c + 7c red brn 3.25 2.00
B26 SP1 $1 + 10c purple 5.75 3.00
   Nos. B21-B26 (6) 12.00 6.85
The surtax was for anti-tuberculosis work.

1958, Dec. 1
Lower Panel in Red
B27 SP1 20c + 3c dl pur .40 .30
B28 SP1 25c + 4c emerald .50 .35
B29 SP1 35c + 5c rose vio .75 .40
B30 SP1 60c + 7c vio bl 1.50 .80
B31 SP1 65c + 7c violet 2.00 1.75
B32 SP1 80c + 9c car rose 5.00 3.00
   Nos. B27-B32 (6) 11.15 6.60
   Nos. B21-B32 (12) 23.15 13.45
The surtax was for anti-tuberculosis work.
Nos. B21-B32 were the only stamps on sale from Dec. 1-25, 1958.

Type of Regular Issue, 1955, Overprinted and Surcharged

Engr.; Cross Typo. in Red
1959, May 30   Wmk. 282
B33 A62 15c + 2c olive bister & rose red .60 .60
B34 A62 20c + 3c vio & emer .75 .75
B35 A62 30c + 5c rose car & grnsh bl 1.25 1.25
   Nos. B33-B35 (3) 2.60 2.60
Cent. of the Intl. Red Cross idea. Surtax for the Red Cross.
The overprint includes the cross, "RED CROSS CENTENARY" and date in two languages. The surcharge includes the date in Amharic and the new surtax. The surcharge was applied locally.

Design A39 Surcharged

Perf. 11½
1960, May 7   Photo.   Unwmk.
B36 A39 5c + 1c brt green .50 .50
B37 A39 10c + 2c brt red .75 .60
B38 A39 25c + 3c brt blue 1.10 .75
B39 A39 50c + 4c dk yel brn 1.75 1.50
B40 A39 1t + 5c brt vio 3.00 2.75
   Nos. B36-B40 (5) 7.10 6.10
25th anniversary of Ethiopian Red Cross. Forgeries exist.

Crippled Boy on Crutches — SP2

Wmk. 282
1963, July 23   Engr.   *Perf. 13½*
B41 SP2 10c + 2c ultra .25 .25
B42 SP2 15c + 3c red .35 .30
B43 SP2 50c + 5c brt green 1.10 1.00
B44 SP2 60c + 5c brt lilac 1.75 1.25
   Nos. B41-B44 (4) 3.45 2.80
The surtax was to aid the disabled.

AIR POST STAMPS

Regular Issue of 1928 Handstamped in Violet, Red, Black or Green

Perf. 13½x14
1929, Aug. 17   Unwmk.
C1 A22 ⅛m orange & lt bl .90 1.00
C2 A23 ¼m ind & red org .90 1.00
C3 A22 ½m gray grn & blk .90 1.00
C4 A23 1m dk car & blk .90 1.00
C5 A22 2m dk blue & blk 1.00 1.25
C6 A23 4m yellow & olive 1.00 1.25
C7 A22 8m violet & olive 1.00 1.25
C8 A23 1t org brn & vio 1.25 1.25
C9 A22 2t green & bister 1.60 2.00
C10 A23 3t choc & grn 1.75 2.00
   Nos. C1-C10 (10) 11.20 13.00
The overprint signifies "17 August 1929-Airplane of the Ethiopian Government." The stamps commemorate the arrival at Addis Ababa of the 1st airplane of the Ethiopian Government.
There are 3 types of the overprint: (I) 19½mm high; "colon" at right of bottom word. (II) 20mm high; same "colon." (III) 19½mm high; no "colon." Many errors exist.

Symbols of Empire, Airplane and Map — AP1

1931, June 17   Engr.   *Perf. 12½*
C11 AP1 1g orange red .20 .25
C12 AP1 2g ultra .20 .30
C13 AP1 4g violet .20 .40
C14 AP1 8g blue green .50 .80
C15 AP1 1t olive brown 1.25 1.00
C16 AP1 2t carmine 2.25 3.75
C17 AP1 3t yellow green 3.25 5.00
   Nos. C11-C17 (7) 7.85 11.50
Nos. C11 to C17 exist imperforate.
Reprints of C11 to C17 exist. Paper is thinner and gum whiter than the originals and the ink is heavy and shiny. Originals have ink that is dull and granular. Reprints usually sell at about one-tenth of above values.

> **Catalogue values for unused stamps in this section, from this point to the end of the section, are for Never Hinged items.**

Nos. 250, 255 and 257 Surcharged in Black

a   b

Perf. 14x13½

1947, Mar. 20　　　　　　　**Unwmk.**

C18	A33 (a) 12c on 4c	50.00	50.00
C19	A33 (b) 50c on 25c	45.00	45.00
a.	"26-12-46"	225.00	
C20	A33 (b) $2 on 60c	75.00	75.00
a.	"26-12-46"	300.00	
	Set, hinged	110.00	

Nos. C18-C20 (3)　170.00 170.00

Resumption of airmail service, 12/29/46.

Franklin D. Roosevelt AP2

Design: $2, Haile Selassie.

Engraved and Photogravure

1947, May 23　　　　**Perf. 12½**

C21	AP2 $1 dk purple & sepia	5.00	4.00
C22	AP2 $2 carmine & dp blue	7.00	7.00

Farmer Plowing AP3

Designs: 10c, 25c, Zoquala, extinct volcano. 30c, 35c, Tesissat Falls, Abai River. 65c, 70c, Amba Alaguie. $1, Sacala, source of Nile. $3, Gorgora and Dembia, Lake Tana. $5, Magdala, former capital. $10, Ras Dashan, mountain peak.

Perf. 13x13½

1947-55　　**Wmk. 282**　　**Engr.**

C23	AP3 8c purple brown	.20	.20
C24	AP3 10c bright green	.20	.20
C25	AP3 25c dull pur ('52)	.35	.20
C26	AP3 30c orange yellow	.50	.20
C27	AP3 35c blue ('55)	.50	.25
C28	AP3 65c purple ('51)	.60	.40
C29	AP3 70c red	.90	.40
C30	AP3 $1 deep blue	1.00	.50
C31	AP3 $3 rose lilac	4.00	2.50
C32	AP3 $5 red brown	7.50	3.50
C33	AP3 $10 rose violet	15.00	9.00

Nos. C23-C33 (11)　30.75 17.35

For overprints see Nos. C64-C70.

UPU Monument, Bern — AP4

1950, Apr. 3　　**Unwmk.**　　**Perf. 12½**

C34	AP4 5c green & red	.20	.20
C35	AP4 15c dk sl grn & car	.25	.25
C36	AP4 25c org yel & grn	.30	.25
C37	AP4 50c carmine & ultra	.75	.60

Nos. C34-C37 (4)　1.50 1.30

75th anniv. of the UPU.

Convair Plane over Mountains AP5

Engraved and Lithographed

1955, Dec. 30　**Unwmk.**　**Perf. 12½**
Center Multicolored

C38	AP5 10c gray green	.40	.20
C39	AP5 15c carmine	.50	.25
C40	AP5 20c violet	.75	.40

Nos. C38-C40 (3)　1.65 .85

10th anniversary of Ethiopian Airlines.

Promulgating the Constitution — AP6

Perf. 14x13½

1956, July 16　**Engr.**　**Wmk. 282**

C41	AP6 10c redsh brn & ultra	.25	.30
C42	AP6 15c dk car rose & ol grn	.40	.45
C43	AP6 20c blue & org red	.60	.45
C44	AP6 25c purple & green	.75	.70
C45	AP6 30c dk grn & red brn	1.00	1.10

Nos. C41-C45 (5)　3.00 3.00

25th anniversary of the constitution.

Aksum AP7

Ancient Capitals: 10c, Lalibela. 15c, Gondar. 20c, Mekele. 25c, Ankober.

1957, Feb. 7　　　　　**Perf. 14**
Centers in Green

C46	AP7 5c red brown	.50	.25
C47	AP7 10c rose carmine	.50	.25
C48	AP7 15c red orange	.60	.30
C49	AP7 20c ultramarine	.85	.45
C50	AP7 25c claret	1.25	.65

Nos. C46-C50 (5)　3.70 1.90

Amharic "A" — AP8

Designs: Various Amharic characters and views of Addis Ababa. The characters, arranged by values, spell Addis Ababa.

1957, Feb. 14　　　　　**Engr.**
Amharic Letters in Scarlet

C51	AP8 5c ultra, sal pink	.20	.20
C52	AP8 10c ol grn, pink	.25	.20
C53	AP8 15c dl pur, yel	.40	.20
C54	AP8 20c grn, buff	.50	.25
C55	AP8 25c plum, pale bl	.75	.30
C56	AP8 30c red, pale grn	.90	.35

Nos. C51-C56 (6)　3.00 1.50

70th anniversary of Addis Ababa.

Map, Rock Church at Lalibela and Obelisk AP9

1958, Apr. 15　**Wmk. 282**　**Perf. 13½**

C57	AP9 10c green	.20	.20
C58	AP9 20c rose red	.30	.20
C59	AP9 30c bright blue	.50	.25

Nos. C57-C59 (3)　1.00 .60

Conf. of Independent African States, Accra, Apr. 15-22.

Map of Africa and UN Emblem AP10

1958, Dec. 29　　　　**Perf. 13**

C60	AP10 5c emerald	.20	.20
C61	AP10 20c carmine rose	.25	.20
C62	AP10 25c ultramarine	.30	.25
C63	AP10 50c pale purple	.60	.35

Nos. C60-C63 (4)　1.35 1.00

1st session of the UN Economic Conf. for Africa, opened in Addis Ababa Dec. 29.

Nos. C23-C29 Overprinted

Perf. 13x13½

1959, Aug. 16　**Engr.**　**Wmk. 282**

C64	AP3 8c purple brown	.30	.25
C65	AP3 10c brt green	.40	.30
C66	AP3 25c dull purple	.60	.35
C67	AP3 30c orange yellow	.65	.50
C68	AP3 35c blue	.85	.55
C69	AP3 65c purple	1.25	.85
C70	AP3 70c red	1.60	1.10

Nos. C64-C70 (7)　5.65 3.90

30th anniv. of Ethiopian airmail service.

Ethiopian Soldier and Map of Congo — AP11

Globe with Map of Africa — AP12

Perf. 11½

1962, July 23　**Unwmk.**　**Photo.**
Granite Paper

C71	AP11 15c org, bl, brn & grn	.20	.20
C72	AP11 50c pur, bl, brn & grn	.40	.30
C73	AP11 60c red, bl, brn & grn	.70	.35

Nos. C71-C73 (3)　1.30 .85

2nd anniv. of the Ethiopian contingent of the UN forces in the Congo and in honor of the 70th birthday of Emperor Haile Selassie.

1963, May 22
Granite Paper

C74	AP12 10c magenta & blk	.20	.20
C75	AP12 40c emerald & blk	.40	.25
C76	AP12 60c blue & blk	.70	.35

Nos. C74-C76 (3)　1.30 .80

Conf. of African heads of state for African Unity, Addis Ababa.

Bird Type of Regular Issue

Birds: 10c, Black-headed forest oriole. 15c, Broad-tailed paradise whydah, vert. 20c, Lammergeier, vert. 50c, White-checked touraco. 80c, Purple indigo bird.

1963, Sept. 12　　　　**Perf. 11½**
Granite Paper

C77	A74 10c multicolored	.25	.20
C78	A74 15c multicolored	.30	.20
C79	A74 20c blue, blk & ocher	.60	.25
C80	A74 50c lemon & multi	.95	.45
C81	A74 80c ultra, blk & brn	1.90	.75

Nos. C77-C81 (5)　4.00 1.85

Swimming AP13

Sport: 10c, Basketball, vert. 15c, Javelin. 80c, Soccer game in stadium.

Perf. 14x13½

1964, Sept. 15　**Litho.**　**Unwmk.**

C82	AP13 5c multicolored	.20	.20
C83	AP13 10c multicolored	.20	.20
C84	AP13 15c multicolored	.35	.30
C85	AP13 80c multicolored	1.25	.60

Nos. C82-C85 (4)　2.00 1.30

18th Olympic Games, Tokyo, Oct. 10-25.

Queen Elizabeth II and Emperor Haile Selassie — AP14

1965, Feb. 1　**Photo.**　**Perf. 11½**
Granite Paper

C86	AP14 5c multicolored	.20	.20
C87	AP14 35c multicolored	.50	.30
C88	AP14 60c multicolored	.85	.50

Nos. C86-C88 (3)　1.55 1.00

Visit of Queen Elizabeth II, Feb. 1-8.

Koka Dam and Power Plant — AP15

Designs: 15c, Sugar cane field. 50c, Blue Nile bridge. 60c, Gondar castles. 80c, Coffee tree. $1, Cattle at water hole. $3, Camels at well. $5, Ethiopian Air Lines jet plane.

1965, July 19　**Unwmk.**　**Perf. 11½**
Granite Paper
Portrait in Black

C89	AP15 15c vio brn & buff	.20	.20
C90	AP15 40c vio bl & lt bl	.45	.30
C91	AP15 50c grn & lt bl	.60	.35
C92	AP15 60c claret & yel	.75	.45
C93	AP15 80c grn, yel & red	.90	.50
C94	AP15 $1 brn & lt bl	1.10	.60
C95	AP15 $3 claret & pink	3.50	1.60
C96	AP15 $5 ultra & lt bl	7.50	3.00

Nos. C89-C96 (8)　15.00 7.00

Bird Type of Regular Issue

Birds: 10c, White-collared kingfisher. 15c, Blue-breasted bee-eater. 25c, African paradise flycatcher. 40c, Village weaver. 60c, White-collared pigeon.

1966, Feb. 15　**Photo.**　**Perf. 11½**
Granite Paper

C97	A74 10c dull yel & multi	.25	.20
C98	A74 15c lt blue & multi	.35	.20
C99	A74 25c gray & multi	.70	.35
C100	A74 40c pink & multi	1.40	.50
C101	A74 60c multicolored	1.60	.75

Nos. C97-C101 (5)　4.30 2.00

Black Rhinoceros — AP16

Animals: 10c, Leopard. 20c, Black-and-white colobus (monkey). 30c, Mountain nyala. 60c, Nubian ibex.

1966, June 20   **Litho.**   *Perf. 13*

C102	AP16	5c dp grn, blk & gray	.20 .20
C103	AP16	10c grn, blk & ocher	.25 .20
C104	AP16	20c cit, blk & grn	.50 .20
C105	AP16	30c yel grn, blk & ocher	.75 .20
C106	AP16	60c yel grn, blk & dk brn	1.50 .30
		Nos. C102-C106 (5)	3.20 1.10

Bird Type of Regular Issue

Birds: 10c, Blue-winged goose, vert. 15c, Yellow-billed duck. 20c, Wattled ibis. 25c, Striped swallow. 40c, Black-winged lovebird, vert.

1967, Sept. 29   **Photo.**
Granite Paper   *Perf. 11½*

C107	A74	10c lt ultra & multi	.20 .20
C108	A74	15c green & multi	.35 .20
C109	A74	20c yellow & multi	.40 .20
C110	A74	25c salmon & multi	.65 .20
C111	A74	40c pink & multi	1.40 .50
		Nos. C107-C111 (5)	3.00 1.30

SPECIAL DELIVERY STAMPS

> Catalogue values for unused stamps in this section are for Never Hinged items.

Motorcycle Messenger — SD1

Addis Ababa Post Office SD2

Unwmk.

1947, Apr. 24   **Engr.**   *Perf. 13*

E1	SD1	30c orange brown	3.00 .75
E2	SD2	50c blue	5.00 2.00

1954-62   **Wmk. 282**

E3	SD1	30c org brown ('62)	3.00 2.00
E4	SD2	50c blue	2.00 .75

POSTAGE DUE STAMPS

> Very Fine examples of Nos. J1-J42 will have perforations touching the design on one or more sides.

Nos. 1-4 and unissued values Overprinted

1895   **Unwmk.**   *Perf. 14x13½*

Black Overprint

J1	A1	¼g green	1.25
J2	A1	½g red	1.25
J3	A1	4g lilac brown	.90
a.		Without overprint	.90
J4	A1	8g violet	.90
a.		Without overprint	.90

Red Overprint

J5	A1	1g blue	1.25
J6	A1	2g dark brown	1.25
J7	A1	16g black	.90
a.		Without overprint	
		Nos. J1-J7 (7)	7.70

Nos. J1-J7 were not issued.

Nos. 1-7 Handstamped in Various Colors:

a   b

1905, Apr.

J8	A1 (a)	¼g green	42.50 42.50
J9	A1 (a)	½g red	42.50 42.50
J10	A1 (a)	1g blue	42.50 42.50
J11	A1 (a)	2g dk brown	42.50 42.50
J12	A2 (a)	4g lilac brown	42.50 42.50
J13	A2 (a)	8g violet	42.50 42.50
J14	A2 (a)	16g black	42.50 42.50
		Nos. J7-J14 (8)	298.40 297.50

1905, June 1

J15	A1 (b)	¼g green	42.50 42.50
J16	A1 (b)	½g red	42.50 42.50
J17	A1 (b)	1g blue	42.50 42.50
J18	A1 (b)	2g dark brown	42.50 42.50
J19	A2 (b)	4g lilac brown	42.50 42.50
J20	A2 (b)	8g violet	42.50 42.50
J21	A2 (b)	16g black	42.50 42.50
		Nos. J15-J21 (7)	297.50 297.50

Excellent forgeries of Nos. J8-J42 exist.

Nos. 1-7 Handstamped in Blue or Violet

1905, Dec.

J22	A1	¼g green	10.00 10.00
J23	A1	½g red	10.00 10.00
J24	A1	1g blue	10.00 10.00
J25	A1	2g dark brown	10.00 10.00
J26	A2	4g lilac brown	10.00 10.00
J27	A2	8g violet	15.00 15.00
J28	A2	16g black	21.00 21.00
		Nos. J22-J28 (7)	86.00 86.00

Nos. J22-J27 exist with inverted overprint, also No. J22 with double overprint. Forgeries exist.

With Additional Surcharge of Value Handstamped as on Nos. 71-77

1907, July 1

J29	A1 (e)	¼ on ¼g grn	14.00 14.00
J30	A1 (e)	½ on ½g red	14.00 14.00
J31	A1 (f)	1 on 1g blue	14.00 14.00
J32	A1 (f)	2 on 2g dk brown	14.00 14.00
J33	A2 (f)	4 on 4g lilac brn	14.00 14.00
J34	A2 (f)	8 on 8g violet	14.00 14.00
J35	A2 (f)	16 on 16g blk	22.50 22.50
		Nos. J29-J35 (7)	106.50 106.50

Many errors exist, most of them are unofficial reproductions.

Nos. 1-7 Handstamped in Black

1908, Dec. 1

J36	A1	¼g green	1.00 .90
J37	A1	½g red	1.00 .90
J38	A1	1g blue	1.00 .90
J39	A1	2g dark brown	1.25 1.10
J40	A2	4g lilac brown	1.75 1.75
J41	A2	8g violet	4.00 4.50
J42	A2	16g black	12.50 12.00
		Nos. J36-J42 (7)	22.50 24.05

Nos. J36 to J42 exist with inverted overprint and Nos. J36, J37, J38 and J40 with double overprint.

Forgeries of Nos. J36-J56 exist.

Same Handstamp on Nos. 87-93

1912, Dec. 1   *Perf. 11½*

J43	A3	¼g blue green	1.25 .85
J44	A3	½g rose	1.25 1.10

1913, July 1

J45	A3	1g green & org	4.25 3.00
J46	A4	2g blue	5.00 4.25
J47	A4	4g green & car	7.50 5.00

J48	A5	8g ver & dp grn	10.00 8.00
J49	A5	16g ver & car	25.00 19.00
		Nos. J43-J49 (7)	54.25 41.20

Nos. J43-J49, all exist with inverted, double and double, one inverted overprint.

Same Handstamp on Nos. 120-124 in Blue Black

1925-27   *Perf. 11½*

J50	A6	⅛g violet & brn	18.00 18.00
J51	A6	¼g bl grn & db	18.00 18.00
J52	A6	½g scar & ol grn	20.00 20.00
J53	A9	1g rose lil & gray grn	20.00 20.00
J54	A9	2g dp ultra & fawn	20.00 20.00
		Nos. J50-J54 (5)	96.00 96.00

Same Handstamp on Nos. 110, 112

1930 (?)

J55	A3	1g green & orange	30.00 30.00
J56	A4	2g blue	30.00 30.00

The status of Nos. J55-J56 is questioned.

> Catalogue values for unused stamps in this section, from this point to the end of the section, are for Never Hinged items.

D2

Perf. 11½

1951, Apr. 2   **Unwmk.**   **Litho.**

J57	D2	1c emerald	.35 .20
J58	D2	5c rose red	.55 .20
J59	D2	10c violet	.75 .30
J60	D2	20c ocher	1.10 .65
J61	D2	50c bright ultra	2.00 1.50
J62	D2	$1 rose lilac	4.25 2.00
		Nos. J57-J62 (6)	9.00 4.85

OCCUPATION STAMPS

Issued under Italian Occupation
100 Centesimi = 1 Lira

OS1

Emperor Victor Emmanuel III — OS2

1936   **Wmk. 140**   *Perf. 14*

N1	OS1	10c orange brown	8.25 5.50
N2	OS1	20c purple	7.75 1.75
N3	OS2	25c dark green	3.75 .35
N4	OS2	30c dark brown	3.75 .85
N5	OS2	50c rose carmine	1.00 .20
N6	OS1	75c deep orange	15.00 4.00
N7	OS1	1.25 l deep blue	16.00 6.25
		Nos. N1-N7 (7)	55.50 18.90
		Set, never hinged	135.00

Issued: #N3-N5, May 22; others Dec. 5. For later issues see Italian East Africa.

FALKLAND ISLANDS

ˈfȯl-klənd ˈī-lənds

LOCATION — A group of islands about 300 miles east of the Straits of Magellan at the southern limit of South America
GOVT. — British Crown Colony
AREA — 4,700 sq. mi.
POP. — 2,607 (1996)
CAPITAL — Stanley

Dependencies of the Falklands are South Georgia and South Sandwich. In March 1962, three other dependencies — South Shetland Islands, South Orkneys and Graham Land—became the new separate colony of British Antarctic Territory. In 1985 South Georgia and the South Sandwich Islands became a separate colony.

12 Pence = 1 Shilling
20 Shillings = 1 Pound
100 Pence = 1 Pound (1971)

Catalogue values for unused stamps in this country are for **Never Hinged items, beginning with Scott 97** in the regular postage section, Scott B1 in the semi-postal section, Scott J1 in the postage due section, Scott 1L1 in Falkland Island Dependencies regular issues, Scott 1LB1 in Falkland Island Dependencies semi-postals, and Scott 2L1, 3L1, 4L1, 5L1 in the Issues for Separate Islands.

Values for unused stamps are for examples with original gum as defined in the catalogue introduction.
Nos. 1-4, and some printings of Nos. 5-6, exist with straight edges on one or two sides, being the imperforate margins of the sheets. This occurs in 24 out of 60 stamps. Catalogue values are for stamps with perforations on all sides.

Queen Victoria — A1

1878-79		**Unwmk.**	**Engr.**	*Perf. 14*	
1	A1	1p claret		850.00	*500.00*
2	A1	4p dark gray ('79)		1,400.00	200.00
3	A1	6p green		100.00	85.00
4	A1	1sh bister brown		80.00	80.00

1883-95			**Wmk. 2**	
5	A1	1p brt claret ('94)	130.00	95.00
a.		1p claret	425.00	175.00
b.		Horiz. pair, imperf. vert.	65.00	
c.		1p red brown ('91)	240.00	90.00
d.		Diag. half of #5c used as ½p on cover		3,500.
6	A1	4p olive gray ('95)	14.00	27.50
a.		4p gray black	500.00	100.00
b.		4p olive gray black ('89)	180.00	65.00
c.		4p brownish black ('94)	900.00	400.00

No. 6c has watermark reversed.
For surcharge see No. 19E.

1886			**Wmk. 2 Sideways**	
7	A1	1p claret	95.00	65.00
a.		1p brownish claret	125.00	60.00
b.		Diagonal half of #7a used as 1p on cover		3,250.
8	A1	4p olive gray	525.00	60.00
a.		4p pale gray black	825.00	90.00

For surcharge see No. 19.

1891-1902			**Wmk. 2**	
9	A1	½p green ('92)	19.00	18.00
a.		½p blue green	27.50	32.50
10	A1	½p yel green ('99)	2.25	3.50
11	A1	1p orange brown	100.00	80.00
a.		Diagonal half used as ½p on cover		2,750.
11B	A1	1p pale red	9.00	5.00
11A	A1	1p org red ('02)	16.00	4.75
a.		1p Venetian red ('95)	32.50	20.00

13	A1	2p magenta ('96)	7.00	14.00
14	A1	2½p deep blue ('94)	275.00	160.00
15	A1	2½p ultra ('94)	37.50	14.00
a.		2½p pale ultra ('98)	40.00	20.00
b.		2½p dull blue	190.00	30.00
c.		2½p deep ultra ('01)	45.00	40.00
d.		2½p pale chalky ultra	190.00	60.00
16	A1	6p yellow ('96)	42.50	55.00
a.		6p orange ('92)	100.00	75.00
17	A1	9p ver ('96)	50.00	65.00
a.		9p salmon	57.50	70.00
18	A1	1sh gray brn ('95)	67.50	65.00
a.		1sh bister brown ('96)	65.00	55.00
		Nos. 9-18 (11)	625.75	484.25

Nos. 7 and 5a Surcharged in Black

1891			**Wmk. 2 Sideways**	
19	A1	½p on half of 1p, #7	725.	360.
d.		Unsevered pair	3,500.	1,350.

			Wmk. 2	
19E	A1	½p on half of 1p, #5a	825.	325.
f.		Unsevered pair	4,500.	1,800.

Genuine used bisects should be canceled with a segmented circular cork cancel. Any other cancel must be linked by date to known mail ship departures. This surcharge exists on "souvenir" bisects, including copies of No. 11, and can be found inverted, double and sideways.

A3   A4

1898			**Wmk. 1**	
20	A3	2sh6p dark blue	300.00	300.00
21	A4	5sh brown red	240.00	275.00

King Edward VII
A5   A6

1904-07			**Wmk. 3**		*Perf. 14*
22	A5	½p yellow green		5.25	1.80
23	A5	1p red, wmk. sideways ('07)		1.20	*2.50*
a.		Wmk. upright ('04)		15.00	*1.80*
24	A5	2p dull vio ('05)		20.00	32.50
25	A5	2½p ultramarine		35.00	10.00
a.		2½p deep blue		300.00	200.00
26	A5	6p orange ('05)		50.00	*57.50*
27	A5	1sh bis brn ('05)		50.00	40.00
28	A6	3sh gray green		175.00	160.00
29	A6	5sh dull red ('05)		240.00	180.00
		Nos. 22-29 (8)		576.45	484.30

King George V
A7   A8

1912-14				
30	A7	½p yellow green	3.00	3.25
31	A7	1p red	5.50	2.75
32	A7	2p brown violet	9.50	19.00
33	A7	2½p deep ultra	9.50	*19.00*
34	A7	6p orange	17.50	22.50
35	A7	1sh bister brown	40.00	*37.50*
36	A8	3sh dark green	100.00	95.00
37	A8	5sh brown red	95.00	120.00
38	A8	5sh plum ('14)	250.00	250.00

39	A8	10sh red, *green*	200.00	*300.00*
40	A8	£1 black, *red*	525.00	*600.00*
		Nos. 30-40 (11)	1,255.	*1,469.*

For overprints see Nos. MR1-MR3.

1921-29			**Wmk. 4**	
41	A7	½p yellow green	3.50	*4.50*
42	A7	1p red ('24)	6.00	1.50
43	A7	2p brown vio ('23)	9.50	8.50
44	A7	2½p dark blue	9.00	20.00
a.		2½p Prussian blue ('29)	375.00	550.00
45	A7	2½p yel vio ('23)	6.00	42.50
46	A7	6p orange ('25)	9.50	45.00
47	A7	1sh bister brown ('23)	20.00	57.50
48	A8	3sh dk green ('23)	100.00	190.00
		Nos. 41-48 (8)	163.50	369.50

No. 43 Surcharged

1928				
52	A7	2½p on 2p brn vio	1,200.	1,200.
a.		Double surcharge	45,000.	

Beware of forged surcharges.

King George V — A9

1929-31			*Perf. 14*	
54	A9	½p green	1.40	*3.25*
55	A9	1p scarlet	4.00	.90
56	A9	2p gray	3.25	3.00
57	A9	2½p blue	3.25	2.50
58	A9	4p deep orange	20.00	15.00
59	A9	6p brown violet	20.00	15.00

60	A9	1sh black, *green*	25.00	*37.50*
a.		1sh black, *emerald*	26.00	*30.00*
61	A9	2sh6p red, *blue*	60.00	60.00
62	A9	5sh green, *yel*	100.00	*120.00*
63	A9	10sh red, *green*	190.00	*225.00*

			Wmk. 3	
64	A9	£1 black, *red*	350.00	425.00
		Nos. 54-64 (11)	776.90	907.15

Issue dates: 4p, 1931, others, Sept. 2.

Romney Marsh Ram — A10

Iceberg A11

Whaling Ship — A12

Port Louis A13

Map of the Islands
A14

South Georgia
A15

Blue Whale
A16

Government House
A17

Battle Memorial — A18

King Penguin — A19

Coat of Arms — A20

King George V — A21

1933, Jan. 2   Wmk. 4   Perf. 12

65	A10	½p green & blk	2.25	6.50
66	A11	1p dl red & blk	4.00	2.50
67	A12	1½p lt bl & blk	19.00	20.00
68	A13	2p ol brn & blk	12.50	25.00
69	A14	3p dl vio & blk	20.00	22.50
70	A15	4p orange & blk	20.00	20.00
71	A16	6p gray & black	57.50	75.00
72	A17	1sh ol grn & blk	50.00	85.00
73	A18	2sh6p dp vio & blk	200.00	200.00
74	A19	5sh yellow & blk	700.00	1,000.
a.		5sh yellow orange & black	2,000.	2,500.
75	A20	10sh lt brn & blk	725.00	1,100.
76	A21	£1 rose & black	2,000.	2,500.
		Nos. 65-76 (12)	3,810.	5,056.

Cent. of the permanent occupation of the islands as a British colony.

Common Design Types pictured following the introduction.

Silver Jubilee Issue
Common Design Type

1935, May 7   Perf. 11x12

77	CD301	1p carmine & blue	2.00	.50
78	CD301	2½p ultra & brown	4.25	2.10

79	CD301	4p indigo & grn	8.75	5.50
80	CD301	1sh brn vio & ind	20.00	4.75
		Nos. 77-80 (4)	35.00	12.85
		Set, never hinged	52.50	

Coronation Issue
Common Design Type

1937, May 12   Perf. 11x11½

81	CD302	½p deep green	.20	.20
82	CD302	1p dark carmine	.35	.50
83	CD302	2½p deep ultra	.60	.80
		Nos. 81-83 (3)	1.15	1.50
		Set, never hinged	3.50	

Whale Jawbones (Centennial Monument) — A22

#85, 86A, Black-necked swan. #85B, 86, Battle memorial. 2½p, 3p, Flock of sheep. 4p, Upland goose. 6p, R.R.S. "Discovery II." 9p, R.R.S. "William Scoresby." 1sh, Mt. Sugar Top. 1sh3p, Turkey vultures. 2sh6p, Gentoo penguins. 5sh, Sea lions. 10sh, Deception Island. £1, Arms of Colony.

1938-46   Perf. 12

84	A22	½p green & blk	.20	.20
85	A22	1p red & black	2.50	2.75
a.		1p rose carmine & black	16.00	1.75
85B	A22	1p dk vio & blk	.20	.20
86	A22	2p dk vio & blk	1.75	1.90
86A	A22	2p rose car & black	.25	.30
87	A22	2½p ultra & blk	1.50	1.40
87A	A22	3p dp bl & blk	.75	.80
88	A22	4p rose vio & blk	1.75	1.90
89	A22	6p brown & blk	5.00	4.75
90	A22	9p sl bl & blk	1.75	1.60
91	A22	1sh dull blue	7.75	3.25
92	A22	1sh3p car & blk	1.75	3.25
93	A22	2sh6p gray black	37.50	22.50
94	A22	5sh org brown & ultra	55.00	47.50
a.		5sh yel brown & indigo	625.00	300.00
95	A22	10sh org & blk	60.00	47.50
96	A22	£1 dk vio & blk	125.00	92.50
		Nos. 84-96 (16)	302.65	232.30
		Set, never hinged	550.00	

Issued: #85B, 86A, 3p, 7/14/41; 1sh3p, 12/10/46; No. 94a, 1942; others, 1/3/38.
See Nos. 101-102. For overprints see Nos. 2L1-2L8, 3L1-3L8, 4L1-4L8, 5L1-5L8.

> Catalogue values for unused stamps in this section, from this point to the end of the section, are for Never Hinged items.

Peace Issue
Common Design Type
Perf. 13½x14

1946, Oct. 7   Engr.   Wmk. 4

97	CD303	1p purple	.35	.25
98	CD303	3p deep blue	.55	.25

Silver Wedding Issue
Common Design Types

1948, Nov. 1   Photo.   Perf. 14x14½

99	CD304	2½p bright ultra	1.25	.70

Engr.; Name Typo.
Perf. 11½x11

100	CD305	£1 purple	110.00	82.50

Types of 1938-46
2½p, Upland goose. 6p, R.R.S. "Discovery II."

Perf. 12

1949, June 15   Engr.   Wmk. 4

101	A22	2½p dp blue & black	5.50	7.25
102	A22	6p gray black	4.75	3.50

UPU Issue
Common Design Types
Engr.; Name Typo. on 3p, 1sh3p

1949, Oct. 10   Perf. 13½, 11x11½

103	CD306	1p violet	.60	.60
104	CD307	3p indigo	1.50	1.50
105	CD308	1sh3p green	5.00	4.50
106	CD309	2sh blue	11.00	9.50
		Nos. 103-106 (4)	18.10	16.10

Sheep
A35

Arms of the Colony — A36

Designs: 1p, R.M.S. Fitzroy. 2p Upland goose. 2½p, Map. 4p, Auster plane. 6p, M.S.S. John Biscoe. 9p, "Two Sisters" peaks. 1sh, Gentoo penguins. 1sh 3p, Kelp goose and gander. 2sh 6p, Sheep shearing. 5sh, Battle memorial. 10sh, Sea lion and clapmatch. £1, Hulk of "Great Britain."

Perf. 13½x13, 13x13½

1952, Jan. 2   Engr.   Wmk. 4

107	A35	½p green	1.00	1.40
108	A35	1p red	2.10	.70
109	A35	2p violet	4.75	4.50
110	A35	2½p ultra & blk	1.25	.95
111	A36	3p deep ultra	1.40	1.75
112	A35	4p claret	10.00	2.75
113	A35	6p yellow brn	16.00	1.75
114	A35	9p orange yel	12.50	3.50
115	A36	1sh black	29.00	1.50
116	A35	1sh3p red orange	18.00	9.25
117	A36	2sh6p olive	22.50	20.00
118	A36	5sh red violet	14.00	15.00
119	A35	10sh gray	30.00	25.00
120	A35	£1 black	37.50	32.50
		Nos. 107-120 (14)	200.00	120.55

Coronation Issue
Common Design Type

1953, June 4   Perf. 13½x13

121	CD312	1p car & black	.95	1.25

Types of 1952 with Portrait of Queen Elizabeth II

1955-57   Perf. 13½x13, 13x13½

122	A35	½p green ('57)	.75	1.50
123	A35	1p red ('57)	1.25	1.25
124	A35	2p violet ('56)	3.50	6.25
125	A35	6p light brown	8.75	.70
126	A35	9p ocher ('57)	13.00	21.00
127	A36	1sh black	7.75	1.40
		Nos. 122-127 (6)	35.00	32.10

Marsh Starling
A37

Birds: ½p, Falkland Islands Thrush. 1p, Dominican gull. 2p, Gentoo penguins. 2½p, Upland geese. 4p, Steamer ducks. 5½p, Rock-hopper penguin. 6p, black-browed albatross. 9p, Silver grebe. 1sh, Pied oystercatchers. 1sh3p, Yellow-billed teal. 2sh, Kelp geese. 5sh, King shag. 10sh, Guadelupe caracara. £1, Black-necked swan.

Perf. 13½x13

1960, Feb. 10   Engr.   Wmk. 314
Center in Black

128	A37	½p green	3.75	.50
a.		Wmk. sideways ('66)	.45	.30
129	A37	1p rose red	1.40	.80
130	A37	2p blue	3.75	1.00
131	A37	2½p bister brn	1.25	.30
132	A37	3p olive	.70	.30
133	A37	4p rose car	1.00	1.00
134	A37	5½p violet	1.75	2.25
135	A37	6p sepia	2.00	.30
136	A37	9p orange	1.75	1.25
137	A37	1sh dull purple	.65	.30
138	A37	1sh3p ultra	9.50	13.00
139	A37	2sh brown car	27.50	2.50
140	A37	5sh grnsh blue	27.50	11.00
141	A37	10sh rose lilac	47.50	13.00
142	A37	£1 yellow org	50.00	32.50
		Nos. 128-142 (15)	180.00	80.00

Morse Key — A38

1962, Oct. 5   Photo.   Perf. 11½x11

143	A38	6p dp org & dk red	1.00	.60
144	A38	1sh brt ol grn & dp green	1.10	1.00
145	A38	2sh brt ultra & violet	1.90	1.90
		Nos. 143-145 (3)	4.00	3.50

Falkland Islands radio station, 50th anniv.

Freedom from Hunger Issue
Common Design Type

1963, June 4   Perf. 14x14½

146	CD314	1sh ultramarine	13.50	5.00

Red Cross Centenary Issue
Common Design Type
Wmk. 314

1963, Sept.2   Litho.   Perf. 13

147	CD315	1p black & red	3.00	1.00
148	CD315	1sh ultra & red	20.00	6.00

Shakespeare Issue
Common Design Type

1964, Apr. 23   Photo.   Perf. 14x14½

149	CD316	6p black	1.75	.50

H.M.S. Glasgow
A39

6p, H.M.S. Kent. 1sh, H.M.S. Invincible. 2sh, Falkland Islands Battle Memorial, vert.

1964, Dec. 8   Engr.   Perf. 13

150	A39	2½p ver & black	9.75	3.75
151	A39	6p blue & black	.45	.30
a.		"Glasgow" vignette	17,000.	
152	A39	1sh carmine & blk	.45	1.10
				Perf. 13x14
153	A39	2sh dk blue & blk	.35	.85
		Nos. 150-153 (4)	11.00	6.00

Battle of the Falkland Islands between the British and German navies, 50th anniv.

ITU Issue
Common Design Type
Perf. 11x11½

1965, May 26   Litho.   Wmk. 314

154	CD317	1p blue & dl dk bl	.65	.40
155	CD317	2sh lilac & dl yel	9.50	3.25

Intl. Cooperation Year Issue
Common Design Type

1965, Oct. 25   Perf. 14½

156	CD318	1p blue grn & claret	1.00	.25
157	CD318	1sh lt violet & grn	7.50	1.75

Churchill Memorial Issue
Common Design Type

1966, Jan. 24   Photo.   Perf. 14
Design in Black, Gold and Carmine Rose

158	CD319	½p bright blue	.40	.20
159	CD319	1p green	1.60	.30
160	CD319	1sh brown	4.00	1.75
161	CD319	2sh violet	8.50	4.25
		Nos. 158-161 (4)	14.50	6.50

Human Rights Flame and Globe
A40

Perf. 14x14½

1968, July 4		**Photo.**	**Wmk. 314**	
162	A40	2p brt rose & multi	.20	.20
163	A40	6p brt green & multi	.40	.40
164	A40	1sh orange & multi	.65	.65
165	A40	2sh ultra & multi	1.25	1.25
		Nos. 162-165 (4)	2.50	2.50

International Human Rights Year.

Dusty Miller — A41

Falkland Islands flora: 1½p, Pig vine, horiz. 2p, Pale maiden. 3p, Dog orchard. 3½p, Sea cabbage, horiz. 4½p, Vanilla daisy. 5½p, Arrowleaf marigold, horiz. 6p, Diddle-dee, horiz. 1sh, Scurvy grass, horiz. 1sh6p, Prickly burr. 2sh, Fachine. 3sh, Lavender. 5sh, Felton's flower, horiz. £1, Yellow orchid.

1968, Oct. 9		**Photo.**	**Perf. 14**	
166	A41	½p multicolored	.20	.20
167	A41	1½p multicolored	.45	.20
168	A41	2p multicolored	.60	.20
169	A41	3p multicolored	6.00	.40
170	A41	3½p multicolored	.35	.55
171	A41	4½p multicolored	1.75	.75
172	A41	5½p multicolored	1.75	1.00
173	A41	6p multicolored	.85	1.25
174	A41	1sh multicolored	.85	2.40
175	A41	1sh6p multicolored	4.75	11.00
176	A41	2sh multicolored	6.00	5.50
177	A41	3sh multicolored	8.50	8.75
178	A41	5sh multicolored	30.00	15.00
179	A41	£1 multicolored	13.25	8.75
		Nos. 166-179 (14)	75.30	55.20

See #210-222. For surcharges see #197-209.

Beaver DHC 2 Seaplane A42

Designs: 6p, Norseman seaplane. 1sh, Auster plane. 2sh, Falkland Islands arms.

1969, Apr. 8		**Litho.**	**Perf. 14**	
180	A42	2p multicolored	.20	.20
181	A42	6p multicolored	.35	.35
182	A42	1sh multicolored	.70	.70
183	A42	2sh multicolored	1.75	1.25
		Nos. 180-183 (4)	3.00	2.50

21st anniv. of Government Air Service.

Bishop Stirling A43

2p, Holy Trinity Church, 1869. 6p, Christ Church Cathedral, 1969. 2sh, Bishop's miter.

1969, Oct. 30			**Perf. 14**	
184	A43	2p emerald & black	.60	.60
185	A43	6p red orange & black	.60	.60
186	A43	1sh lilac & black	.60	.60
187	A43	2sh yellow & multi	.70	.70
		Nos. 184-187 (4)	2.50	2.50

Consecration of Waite Hocking Stirling (1829-1923), as first Bishop of the Bishopric of the Falkland Islands, cent.

Gun Emplacement — A44

2p, Volunteer on horseback, vert. 1sh, Volunteer in dress uniform, vert. 2sh, Defense Force badge.

Perf. 13½x13, 13x13½

1970, Apr. 30		**Litho.**	**Wmk. 314**	
188	A44	2p ultra & multi	.65	.30
189	A44	6p multicolored	1.25	.75
190	A44	1sh buff & multi	2.50	1.25
191	A44	2sh yellow & multi	5.25	2.50
		Nos. 188-191 (4)	9.65	4.80

Falkland Islands Defense Force, 50th anniv.

The Great Britain, 1843 A45

The Great Britain in: 4p, 1845. 9p, 1876. 1sh, 1886. 2sh, 1970.

1970, Oct. 30		**Litho.**	**Perf. 14½**	
192	A45	2p lemon & multi	.35	.20
193	A45	4p lilac & multi	.70	.50
194	A45	9p bister & multi	1.40	1.10
195	A45	1sh org brn & multi	2.25	1.75
196	A45	2sh multicolored	4.75	3.75
		Nos. 192-196 (5)	9.45	7.30

Nos. 166-178 Surcharged with New Value (Decimal Currency) and Bar

1971, Feb. 15		**Photo.**	**Perf. 14**	
197	A41	½p on ½p multi	1.00	1.00
198	A41	1p on 1½p multi	.20	.20
199	A41	1½p on 2p multi	.35	.35
200	A41	2p on 3p multi	.40	.40
201	A41	2½p on 3½p multi	.60	.60
202	A41	3p on 4½p multi	.65	.65
203	A41	4p on 5½p multi	.90	.90
204	A41	5p on 6p multi	1.25	1.25
205	A41	6p on 1sh multi	1.90	1.60
206	A41	7½p on 1sh6p multi	2.25	2.10
207	A41	10p on 2sh multi	3.50	3.00
208	A41	15p on 3sh multi	6.50	5.25
209	A41	25p on 5sh multi	13.50	11.00
		Nos. 197-209 (13)	33.00	28.30

Flower Type of 1968
"p" instead of "d"

Designs as before. 1p, 2½p, 4p, 5p, 6p, 25p, horizontal.

Wmk. 314, Sideways on Vert. Stamps

1972, June 1			**Perf. 14**	
210	A41	½p Dusty miller	1.25	1.00
	a.	Wmk. upright ('74)	12.50	22.50
	b.	Wmk. 373 (75)	3.25	3.50
211	A41	1p Pig vine	.40	.30
212	A41	1½p Pale maiden	.55	.40
213	A41	2p Dog orchid	3.50	3.00
	a.	Wmk. upright ('74)	27.50	3.50
214	A41	2½p Sea cabbage	.95	.70
215	A41	3p Vanilla daisy	.95	.85
216	A41	4p Arrowleaf marigold	1.25	.85
217	A41	5p Diddle-dee	1.50	1.00
218	A41	6p Scurvy grass	17.00	12.50
	a.	Wmk. sideways ('74)	1.90	2.25
219	A41	7½p Prickly burr	3.50	3.00
220	A41	10p Fachine	7.25	6.50
221	A41	15p Lavender	6.25	5.50
222	A41	25p Felton's flower	11.50	11.50
		Nos. 210-222 (13)	55.85	47.10

No. 213 has watermark sideways.

Silver Wedding Issue, 1972
Common Design Type

Design: Queen Elizabeth II, Prince Philip, Romney Marsh sheep and giant sea lions.

1972, Nov 20		**Photo.**	**Perf. 14x14½**	
223	CD324	1p sl grn & multi	.30	.30
224	CD324	10p ultra & multi	1.00	1.00

Princess Anne's Wedding Issue
Common Design Type

1973, Nov. 14		**Litho.**	**Perf. 14**	
225	CD325	5p lilac & multi	.20	.20
226	CD325	15p citron & multi	.70	.70

Fur Seals A46

Tourist Publicity: 4p, Trout fishing. 5p, Rockhopper penguins. 15p, Military starling.

1974, Mar. 6		**Litho.**	**Wmk. 314**	
227	A46	2p lt ultra & multi	2.50	.95
228	A46	4p brt blue & multi	3.50	1.40
229	A46	5p yellow & multi	11.50	1.40
230	A46	15p lt ultra & multi	13.50	3.00
		Nos. 227-230 (4)	31.00	6.75

Early 19th Cent. Mail Coach, UPU Emblem — A47

UPU Cent.: 5p, Packet, 1841. 8p, First British mail planes, 1911. 16p, Catapult mail, 1920's.

1974, July 31			**Perf. 14**	
231	A47	2p multicolored	.25	.25
232	A47	5p multicolored	.40	.40
233	A47	8p multicolored	.45	.45
234	A47	16p multicolored	.65	.65
		Nos. 231-234 (4)	1.75	1.75

Churchill, Parliament and Big Ben A48

Design: 20p, Churchill and warships.

1974, Nov. 30			**Perf. 13x13½**	
235	A48	16p multicolored	1.50	1.50
236	A48	20p multicolored	2.00	2.00
	a.	Souvenir sheet of 2, #235-236	8.50	8.50

Sir Winston Churchill (1874-1965).

HMS Exeter A49

Battleships: 6p, HMNZS Achilles. 8p, Admiral Graf Spee. 16p, HMS Ajax.

1974, Dec. 13			**Perf. 14**	
237	A49	2p multicolored	2.25	.85
238	A49	6p multicolored	3.75	2.00
239	A49	8p multicolored	4.75	3.00
240	A49	16p multicolored	12.00	8.00
		Nos. 237-240 (4)	22.75	13.85

35th anniv. of the Battle of the River Plate between British ships and the German battleship Graf Spee.

Seal and Flag Badge — A50

7½p, Coat of arms, 1925. 10p, Arms, 1948. 16p, Arms (Falkland Islands Dependencies), 1952.

1975, Oct. 28		**Litho.**	**Wmk. 373**	
241	A50	2p multicolored	1.00	1.00
242	A50	7½p multicolored	1.90	1.90
243	A50	10p multicolored	2.10	2.10
244	A50	16p multicolored	3.00	3.00
		Nos. 241-244 (4)	8.00	8.00

Falkland Islands heraldic arms, 50th anniv.

½p-Coin and Trout A51

New Coinage: 5½p, 1p-coin and gentoo penguins, 8p, 2p-coin and upland geese. 10p, 5p-coin and black-browed albatross. 16p, 10p-coin and sea lions.

1975, Dec. 31		**Litho.**	**Wmk. 373**	
245	A51	2p copper & multi	.20	.20
246	A51	5½p copper & multi	.65	.65
247	A51	8p copper & multi	1.25	1.25
248	A51	10p silver & multi	1.90	1.90
249	A51	16p silver & multi	5.50	5.50
		Nos. 245-249 (5)	9.50	9.50

Gathering Sheep — A52

Sheep Farming: 7½p, Shearing. 10p, Dipping sheep. 20p, Motor Vessel Monsunen collecting wool.

1976, Apr. 28		**Litho.**	**Perf. 13½**	
250	A52	2p multicolored	.50	.25
251	A52	7½p multicolored	1.00	.50
252	A52	10p multicolored	1.50	.75
253	A52	20p multicolored	3.50	1.90
		Nos. 250-253 (4)	6.50	3.40

Prince Philip, 1957 Visit A53

11p, Queen, ampulla and spoon. 33p, Queen awaiting anointment, and Knights of the Garter.

1977, Feb. 7			**Perf. 13½x14**	
254	A53	6p multicolored	.35	.35
	a.	Booklet pane of 4, wmk. 314	9.00	
	b.	Single stamp from #254a	2.25	
255	A53	11p multicolored	.60	.60
	a.	Booklet pane of 4	3.50	
256	A53	33p multicolored	1.50	1.50
	a.	Booklet pane of 4	8.00	
		Nos. 254-256 (3)	2.45	2.45

25th anniv. of the reign of Elizabeth II.

Map of West and East Falkland with Communications Centers — A54

Telecommunications: 11p, Ship to shore communications at Fox Bay. 40p, Globe with Telex tape and telephone.

1977, Oct. 24		**Litho.**	**Perf. 14½x14**	
257	A54	3p yel brown & multi	.40	.25
258	A54	11p lt ultra & multi	1.00	.60
259	A54	40p rose & multi	4.25	3.00
		Nos. 257-259 (3)	5.65	3.85

A.E.S., 1957-1974 — A55

Designs: Mail ships.

1978, Jan. 25　Wmk. 373　Perf. 14

260	A55	1p shown	.25	.25
261	A55	2p Darwin, 1957-75	.25	.25
262	A55	3p Merak-N 1951-53	.25	.25
263	A55	4p Fitzroy, 1936-57	.25	.25
264	A55	5p Lafonia 1936-41	.30	.40
265	A55	6p Fleurus, 1924-33	.35	.50
266	A55	7p S.S. Falkland, 1914-34	.50	.70
267	A55	8p Oravia, 1900-12	.55	.75
268	A55	9p Memphis, 1890-97	.60	.85
269	A55	10p Black Hawk, 1873-80	.75	1.00
270	A55	20p Foam, 1963-72	.95	1.40
271	A55	25p Fairy, 1857-61	1.25	1.75
272	A55	50p Amelia, 1852-54	2.00	2.75
273	A55	£1 Nautilus, 1846-48	4.25	6.00
274	A55	£3 Hebe, 1842-46	12.00	14.00
		Nos. 260-274 (15)	24.50	31.10

The 1p, 3p, 5p, 6p and 10p were also issued in booklet panes of 4.
Nos. 260-274 also issued inscribed 1982.
For overprints see Nos. 352-353.

Elizabeth II Coronation Anniversary Issue
Souvenir Sheet
Common Design Type

1978, June 2　Unwmk.　Perf. 15

275	Sheet of 6	4.00	4.00
a.	CD326 25p Red Dragon of Wales	.60	.60
b.	CD327 25p Elizabeth II	.60	.60
c.	CD328 25p Hornless ram	.60	.60

No. 275 contains 2 se-tenant strips of Nos. 275a-275c, separated by horizontal gutter with commemorative and descriptive inscriptions.

Short Sunderland Mark III — A56

Design: 33p, Pane in flight and route Southampton to Stanley.

1978, Apr. 28　Wmk. 373　Perf. 14

276	A56	11p multicolored	2.40	1.90
277	A56	33p multicolored	5.00	3.25

First direct flight Southampton, England to Stanley, Falkland Islands, 26th anniv.

First Fox Bay PO and No. 1 — A57　Macrocystis Pyrifera — A58

Designs: 11p, Second Stanley Post Office and #2. 15p, New Island Post Office and #3. 22p, 1st Stanley Post Office and #4.

1978, Aug. 8　Litho.　Perf. 13½x13

278	A57	3p multicolored	.20	.20
279	A57	11p multicolored	.40	.40
280	A57	15p multicolored	.55	.55
281	A57	22p multicolored	.85	.85
		Nos. 278-281 (4)	2.00	2.00

Falkland Islands postage stamps, cent.

1979, Feb. 19　Litho.　Perf. 14

Kelp: 7p, Durvillea. 11p, Lessoniae. horiz. 15p, Callophyllis, horiz. 25p, Iridea.

282	A58	3p multicolored	.20	.20
283	A58	7p multicolored	.40	.40
284	A58	11p multicolored	.60	.60
285	A58	15p multicolored	.75	.75
286	A58	25p multicolored	1.25	1.25
		Nos. 282-286 (5)	3.20	3.20

Britten-Norman Islander over Map — A59

Opening of Stanley Airport: 11p, Fokker F27 over map. 15p, Fokker F28 over Stanley. 25p, Cessna 172 Skyhawk, Islander and Fokkers F27, F28 over runway.

1979, May 1　Litho.　Perf. 13½

287	A59	3p multicolored	.20	.20
288	A59	11p multicolored	.75	.75
289	A59	15p multicolored	1.00	1.00
290	A59	25p multicolored	1.75	1.75
		Nos. 287-290 (4)	3.70	3.70

Rowland Hill and No. 121 A60

Sir Rowland Hill (1795-1879), originator of penny postage, and: 11p, Falkland Islands No. 1, vert. 25p, Penny Black. 33p, Falkland Islands No. 37, vert.

1979, Aug. 27　Perf. 14

291	A60	3p multicolored	.20	.20
292	A60	11p multicolored	.45	.45
293	A60	25p multicolored	.90	.90
		Nos. 291-293 (3)	1.55	1.55

Souvenir Sheet

294	A60	33p multicolored	1.40	1.40

Mail Delivery by Air, UPU Emblem A61

UPU Membership Cent. (Modes of Mail Delivery): 11p, Horseback. 25p, Schooner Gwendolin.

1979, Nov. 26

295	A61	3p multicolored	.20	.20
296	A61	11p multicolored	.45	.45
297	A61	25p multicolored	.95	.95
		Nos. 295-297 (3)	1.60	1.60

Commerson's Dolphin — A62

1980, Feb. 25　Wmk. 373　Perf. 14

298	A62	3p Peale's porpoise, vert.	.20	.20
299	A62	6p shown	.30	.30
300	A62	7p Hour-glass dolphin	.35	.35
301	A62	11p Spectacled porpose, vert.	.55	.55
302	A62	15p Dusky dolphin	.90	.90
303	A62	25p Killer whale	1.60	1.60
		Nos. 298-303 (6)	3.90	3.90

Miniature Sheet

Falkland Islands Cancel, 1878 A63

Designs: b, New Islds., 1915. c, Falklands Islds., 1901. d, Port Stanley, 1935. e, Port Stanley airmail, 1952. f, Fox Bay, 1934.

1980, May 6　Litho.　Perf. 14

304		Sheet of 6	2.25	2.25
a.-f.		A63 11p any single	.35	.35

London 1980 Intl. Stamp Exhib., May 6-14.

Queen Mother Elizabeth Birthday
Common Design Type

1980, Aug. 4　Litho.　Perf. 14

305	CD330	11p multicolored	.50	.50

Striated Caracara A64

1980, Aug. 11　Wmk. 373　Perf. 13½

306	A64	3p shown	.35	.20
307	A64	11p Red-backed buzzard	.70	.60
308	A64	15p Crested caracara	.85	.70
309	A64	25p Cassin's falcon	1.60	1.40
		Nos. 306-309 (4)	3.50	2.90

Port Egmont, Early Settlement — A65

1980, Dec. 22　Litho.　Perf. 14

310	A65	3p Stanley	.20	.20
311	A65	11p shown	.45	.45
312	A65	25p Port Louis	.95	.50
313	A65	33p Mission House, Keppel Island	1.10	.95
		Nos. 310-313 (4)	2.70	2.10

Polwarth Sheep A66

1981, Jan. 19　Litho.　Perf. 14

314	A66	3p shown	.20	.20
315	A66	11p Frisian cow and calf	.40	.40
316	A66	25p Horse	.85	.85
317	A66	33p Welsh collies	1.10	1.10
		Nos. 314-317 (4)	2.55	2.55

Map of Falkland Islands, Bowles and Carver, 1779 A67

1981, May 22　Litho.　Perf. 14

318	A67	3p shown	.20	.20
319	A67	10p Hawkin's Mainland, 1773	.30	.25
320	A67	13p New Isles, 1747	.40	.35
321	A67	15p French & British Islands	.50	.40
322	A67	25p Falklands, 1771	.75	.60
323	A67	26p Falklands, 1764	.85	.65
		Nos. 318-323 (6)	3.00	2.45

Royal Wedding Issue
Common Design Type

1981, July 22　Litho.　Perf. 13½x13

324	CD331	10p Bouquet	.25	.25
325	CD331	13p Charles	.35	.35
326	CD331	52p Couple	1.10	1.10
		Nos. 324-326 (3)	1.70	1.70

Duke of Edinburgh's Awards, 25th Anniv. — A68

1981, Sept. 28　Litho.　Perf. 14

327	A68	10p Spinning	.30	.30
328	A68	13p Camping	.35	.35
329	A68	15p Kayaking	.45	.45
330	A68	26p Duke of Edinburgh	.80	.80
		Nos. 327-330 (4)	1.90	1.90

The Holy Virgin, by Guido Reni (1575-1642) A69

Christmas: 3p, Adoration of the Holy Child, 16th cent. Dutch. 13p, Holy Family in an Italian Landscape, 17th cent. Italian.

1981, Nov. 2　Litho.　Perf. 14

331	A69	3p multicolored	.20	.20
332	A69	13p multicolored	.45	.45
333	A69	26p multicolored	.80	.80
		Nos. 331-333 (3)	1.45	1.45

Rock Cod — A70

1981, Dec. 7

Designs: Shelf fish. 5p, 15p, 25p horiz.

334	A70	5p Falkland herring	.20	.20
335	A70	13p shown	.40	.40
336	A70	15p Patagonian hake	.50	.50
337	A70	25p Southern blue whiting	.80	.80
338	A70	26p Gray-tailed skate	.80	.80
		Nos. 334-338 (5)	2.70	2.70

Shipwrecks — A71

1982, Feb. 15　Wmk. 373　Perf. 14½

339	A71	5p Lady Elizabeth, 1913	.20	.20
340	A71	13p Capricorn, 1882	.45	.45
341	A71	15p Jhelum, 1870	.55	.55
342	A71	25p Snowsquall, 1864	.75	.75
343	A71	26p St. Mary, 1890	.75	.75
		Nos. 339-343 (5)	2.70	2.70

Sesquicentennial of Charles Darwin's Visit — A72

1982, Apr. 19   Litho.   Perf. 14
344 A72 5p Darwin .... .20 .20
345 A72 17p Microscope ...... .65 .65
346 A72 25p Warrah 1.00 1.00
347 A72 34p Beagle 1.25 1.25
  Nos. 344-347 (4) 3.10 3.10

Princess Diana Issue
Common Design Type

1982, July 5   Wmk. 373   Perf. 13
348 CD333 5p Arms .... .40 .20
349 CD333 17p Diana .... 1.40 .50
350 CD333 37p Wedding 2.75 1.00
351 CD333 50p Portrait 3.75 1.40
  Nos. 348-351 (4) 8.30 3.10

Nos. 264, 271 Overprinted: "1st
PARTICIPATION / COMMONWEALTH
GAMES 1982"

1982, Oct. 7   Litho.   Perf. 14
352 A55 5p multicolored ... .20 .20
353 A55 25p multicolored ... .65 .65

12th Commonwealth Games, Brisbane,
Australia, Sept. 30-Oct. 9.

Tussock Bird — A73

1982, Dec. 6   Perf. 15x14½
354 A73 5p shown .... .20 .20
355 A73 10p Black-chinned siskin .25 .25
356 A73 13p Grass wren ..... .45 .45
357 A73 17p Black-throated finch .60 .60
358 A73 25p Falkland-correndera
       pipit 1.00 1.00
359 A73 34p Dark-faced ground-
       tyrant 1.10 1.10
  Nos. 354-359 (6) 3.60 3.60

British Occupation
Sesquicentennial — A74

1p, Raising the Standard, Port Louis, 1833.
2p, Chelsea pensioners & barracks, 1849. 5p,
Wool trade, 1874. 10p, Ship repairing trade,
1850-90. 15p, Government House, early 20th
cent. 20p, Battle of the Falkland Islands, 1914.
25p, Whalebone Arch centenary, 1933. 40p,
Contribution to World War II effort, 1939-45.
50p, Visit of Duke of Edinburgh, 1957. £1,
Royal Marines, 1933, 1983, vert. £2, Queen
Elizabeth II.

1983, Jan. 1   Litho.   Perf. 14
360 A74 1p multi, vert. .... .25 .30
361 A74 2p multi .... .25 .25
362 A74 5p multi, vert. .... .25 .30
363 A74 10p multi .... .25 .30
364 A74 15p multi .... .30 .40
365 A74 20p multi, vert. .... .45 .60
366 A74 25p multi .... .60 .70
367 A74 40p multi, vert. .... .90 1.10
368 A74 50p multi 1.10 1.40
369 A74 £1 multi 1.75 3.00
370 A74 £2 multi, vert. 4.00 6.50
  Nos. 360-370 (11) 10.10 14.90

For surcharges see Nos. 402-403.

A75

1983, Mar. 14
371 A75 5p No. 69 .... .25 .25
372 A75 17p No. 65 .... .50 .50
373 A75 34p No. 75, vert. ... .75 1.00
374 A75 50p No. 91, vert. ... .90 1.00
  Nos. 371-374 (4) 2.40 2.75

Commonwealth Day.

First
Anniv. of
Liberation
A76

1983, June 14   Wmk. 373   Perf. 14
375 A76 5p Army .... .20 .20
376 A76 13p Merchant Navy ... .30 .30
377 A76 17p Royal Air Force .. .45 .45
378 A76 50p Royal Navy 1.25 1.25
  a.   Souvenir sheet of 4, #375-378 3.25 3.25
  Nos. 375-378 (4) 2.20 2.20

Local
Fruit
A77

1983, Oct. 10   Litho.   Perf. 14
379 A77 5p Diddle dee ...... .20 .20
380 A77 17p Tea berries ..... .40 .40
381 A77 25p Mountain berries . .60 .60
382 A77 34p Native strawberries .80 .80
  Nos. 379-382 (4) 2.00 2.00

Britten-Norman Islander — A78

1983, Nov. 14   Litho.   Perf. 14
383 A78 5p shown .... .25 .20
384 A78 13p DHC-2 Beaver .... .40 .25
385 A78 17p Noorduyn Norse-
       man .... .50 .30
386 A78 50p Auster .... 1.25 .85
  Nos. 383-386 (4) 2.40 1.60

Green
Spider
A79

Insects and Spiders.

1984, Jan. 1   Litho.   Perf. 14
387 A79 1p shown .... .20 .20
388 A79 1p Ichneumon-Fly ... .20 .20
389 A79 3p Brocade Moth .... .20 .20
390 A79 4p Black Beetle .... .20 .20
391 A79 5p Fritillary ..... .20 .20
392 A79 6p Green Spider,
       diff. .... .30 .30
393 A79 7p Ichneumon-Fly,
       diff. .... .30 .30
394 A79 8p Ochre Shoulder .. .30 .30
395 A79 9p Clocker Weevil .. .30 .45
396 A79 10p Hover Fly ...... .30 .45
397 A79 20p Weevil .... .60 1.00
398 A79 25p Metallic Beetle . .80 1.25
399 A79 50p Camel Cricket ... 1.50 2.50
400 A79 £1 Beauchene Spi-
       der 3.25 5.50
401 A79 £3 Southern Painted
       Lady 9.75 15.00
  Nos. 387-401 (15) 18.40 28.05

No. 388 exists inscribed "1986." Value $4.

Nos. 364, 366 Surcharged

1984, Jan. 3   Litho.   Perf. 14
402 A74 17p on 15p multi ... .45 .45
403 A74 22p on 25p multi ... .55 .55

Lloyd's List Issue
Common Design Type

1984, May 7   Wmk. 373   Perf. 14½
404 CD335 6p Wavertree .... .25 .25
405 CD335 17p Port Stanley,
       1910 .... .65 .65
406 CD335 22p Oravia .... .80 .80
407 CD335 52p Cunard Count-
       ess 2.00 2.00
  Nos. 404-407 (4) 3.70 3.70

Great
Grebe — A80

1984, Aug. 6   Perf. 14½x14
408 A80 17p shown 1.10 1.10
409 A80 22p Silver grebe 1.40 1.40
410 A80 52p Rolland's grebe . 4.00 4.00
  Nos. 408-410 (3) 6.50 6.50

See Nos. 450-453.

1984
UPU
Congress
A81

1984, June 22   Litho.   Perf. 14
411 A81 22p Emblem, jet, ship .60 .60

Wildlife
Conservation
A82

1984, Nov. 5   Litho.   Perf. 14½
412 A82 6p Birds .... .60 .40
413 A82 17p Plants .... 1.25 .90
414 A82 22p Mammals 1.40 1.00
415 A82 52p Marine Life 3.00 2.25
  a.   Souvenir sheet of 4, #412-415 8.50 6.00
  Nos. 412-415 (4) 6.25 4.55

Camber
Railway,
1915-1927
A83

1985, Feb. 18   Litho.   Perf. 14
416 A83 7p multicolored ... .35 .30
417 A83 22p multicolored ... .85 .75
418 A83 27p multicolored ... .90 1.00

Size: 77x26mm
419 A83 54p multicolored ... 1.90 1.90
  Nos. 416-419 (4) 4.00 3.95

Queen Mother 85th Birthday
Common Design Type

Designs: 7p, Commonwealth Visitor's
Reception. 22p, With Prince Charles, Mark
Phillips, Princess Anne. 27p, 80th birthday celebration. 54p, Holding Prince Henry. £1, In
coach with Princess Diana.

Perf. 14½x14
1985, June 7   Litho.   Wmk. 384
420 CD336 7p multicolored .. .20 .20
421 CD336 22p multicolored .. .85 .85
422 CD336 27p multicolored .. 1.10 1.10
423 CD336 54p multicolored .. 2.10 2.10
  Nos. 420-423 (4) 4.25 4.25

Souvenir Sheet
424 CD336 £1 multicolored .. 4.50 4.50

Mount
Pleasant
Airport
Opening
A84

1985, May 12   Litho.   Perf. 14½
425 A84 7p Pioneer camp,
       docked ship .... .40 .40
426 A84 22p Construction site . 1.25 1.25

427 A84 27p Runway layout ... 1.60 1.60
428 A84 54p Aircraft landing . 3.00 3.00
  Nos. 425-428 (4) 6.25 6.25

Captain J.
McBride,
HMS Jason,
1765 — A85

18th-19th century naval explorers: 22p,
Commodore J. Byron, HMS Dolphin and
Tamar, 1765. 27p, Vice-Adm. R. Fitzroy, HMS
Beagle, 1831. 54p, Adm. Sir B.J. Sulivan,
HMS Philomel, 1842.

1985, Sept. 23
429 A85 7p multicolored ... .50 .50
430 A85 22p multicolored ... 1.40 1.40
431 A85 27p multicolored ... 1.50 1.50
432 A85 54p multicolored ... 3.25 3.25
  Nos. 429-432 (4) 6.65 6.65

Philibert
Commerson
(1727-1773),
Commerson's
Dolphin — A86

Naturalists, endangered species: 22p, Rene
Primevere Lesson (1794-1849), kelp. 27p,
Joseph Paul Gaimard (1796-1858), diving petrel. 54p, Charles Darwin (1803-1882), Calceo-
laria darwinii.

1985, Nov. 4   Perf. 14½
433 A86 7p multicolored ... .50 .35
434 A86 22p multicolored ... 1.50 1.10
435 A86 27p multicolored ... 1.75 1.25
436 A86 54p multicolored ... 3.50 2.50
  Nos. 433-436 (4) 7.25 5.20

Seashells
A87

1986, Feb. 10   Wmk. 384   Perf. 14½
437 A87 7p Painted keyhole lim-
       pet .... .40 .40
438 A87 22p Magellanic volute . 1.50 1.50
439 A87 27p Falkland scallop . 2.00 2.00
440 A87 54p Rough thorn drupe . 4.00 4.00
  Nos. 437-440 (4) 7.90 7.90

Queen Elizabeth II 60th Birthday
Common Design Type

Designs: 10p, With Princess Margaret at St.
Paul's, Waldenbury, 1932. 24p, Christmas
broadcast from Sandringham, 1958. 29p,
Order of the Thistle, St. Giles Cathedral, Edinburgh, 1962. 45p, Royal reception on the Britannia, US visit, 1976. 58p, Visiting Crown
Agents' offices, 1983.

1986, Apr. 21   Litho.   Perf. 14x14½
441 CD337 10p scar, blk & sil . .30 .30
442 CD337 24p ultra, blk & sil . .65 .65
443 CD337 29p green & multi . .85 .85
444 CD337 45p violet & multi . 1.40 1.40
445 CD337 58p rose vio & multi . 1.75 1.75
  Nos. 441-445 (5) 4.95 4.95

AMERIPEX '86 — A88

SS Great Britain's arrival in the Falkland
Isls., Cent.: 10p, Maiden voyage, crossing the
Atlantic, 1845. 24p, Wreck in Sparrow Cove,
1937. 29p, Refloating wreck, 1970. 58p,
Restored vessel, Bristol, 1986.

1986, May 22

446	A88	10p multicolored	.25	.25
447	A88	24p multicolored	.75	.75
448	A88	29p multicolored	1.00	1.00
449	A88	58p multicolored	2.00	2.00
a.		Souvenir sheet of 4, #446-449	4.00	4.00
		Nos. 446-449 (4)	4.00	4.00

Bird Type of 1984

Rockhopper Penguins.

1986, Aug. 25 Wmk. 373 Perf. 14½

450	A80	10p Adult	.65	.50
451	A80	24p Adults swimming	1.50	1.25
452	A80	29p Adults, diff.	2.00	1.75
453	A80	58p Adult and young	4.00	3.50
		Nos. 450-453 (4)	8.15	7.00

Wedding of Prince Andrew and Sarah Ferguson — A90

Various photographs: 17p, Presenting Queen's Polo Cup, Windsor, 1986. 22p, Open carriage, wedding. 29p, Andrew wearing military fatigues.

1986, Nov. 10 Wmk. 384 Perf. 14½

454	A90	17p multicolored	.80	.80
455	A90	22p multicolored	1.00	1.00
456	A90	29p multicolored	1.40	1.40
		Nos. 454-456 (3)	3.20	3.20

Royal Engineers, 200th Anniv. A91

1987, Feb. 9 Litho. Perf. 14½

457	A91	10p Surveying Sapper Hill	.55	.55
458	A91	24p Explosives disposal	1.90	1.90
459	A91	29p Boxer Bridge, Pt. Stanley	2.25	2.25
460	A91	58p Postal services, Stanley Airport	5.00	5.00
		Nos. 457-460 (4)	9.70	9.70

Seals A92

1987, Apr. 27

461	A92	10p Southern sea lion	.80	.80
462	A92	24p Falkland fur seal	2.25	2.25
463	A92	29p Southern elephant seal	2.40	2.40
464	A92	58p Leopard seal	4.25	4.25
		Nos. 461-464 (4)	9.70	9.70

Hospitals A93

Designs: 10p, Victorian Cottage Home, c. 1912. 24p, King Edward VII Memorial Hospital, c. 1914. 29p, Churchill Wing, 1953. 58p, Prince Andrew Wing, 1987.

1987, Dec. 8 Perf. 14

465	A93	10p multicolored	.50	.50
466	A93	24p multicolored	1.10	1.10
467	A93	29p multicolored	1.40	1.40
468	A93	58p multicolored	2.50	2.50
		Nos. 465-468 (4)	5.50	5.50

Fungi — A94

1987, Sept. 14 Litho. Perf. 14½

469	A94	10p Suillus luteus	1.50	1.50
470	A94	24p Mycena	2.75	2.75
471	A94	29p Camarophyllus adonis	3.75	3.75
472	A94	58p Gerronema schusteri	8.00	8.00
		Nos. 469-472 (4)	16.00	16.00

1940 Morris Truck, Fitzroy A95

Classic automobiles: 24p, 1929 Citroen Kegresse, San Carlos. 29p, 1933 Ford 1-Ton Truck, Port Stanley. 58p, 1935 Ford Model T Saloon, Darwin.

1988, Apr. 11 Litho. Perf. 14

473	A95	10p multicolored	.45	.45
474	A95	24p multicolored	1.10	1.10
475	A95	29p multicolored	1.40	1.40
476	A95	58p multicolored	2.50	2.50
		Nos. 473-476 (4)	5.45	5.45

Geese A96

1988, July 25

477	A96	10p Kelp	1.50	.35
478	A96	24p Upland	3.00	.85
479	A96	29p Ruddy-headed	3.75	1.00
480	A96	58p Ashy-headed	7.75	2.25
		Nos. 477-480 (4)	16.00	4.45

Lloyds of London, 300th Anniv.
Common Design Type

Designs: 10p, Lloyd's Nelson Collection silver service. 24p, Hydroponic Gardens, horiz. 29p, Supply ship A.E.S., horiz. 58p, Wreck of the Charles Cooper near the Falklands, 1866.

1988, Nov. 14 Litho. Wmk. 373

481	CD341	10p multicolored	.50	.50
482	CD341	24p multicolored	1.00	1.00
483	CD341	29p multicolored	1.25	1.25
484	CD341	58p multicolored	2.50	2.50
		Nos. 481-484 (4)	5.25	5.25

Ships of Cape Horn A97

1989, Feb. 28 Perf. 373

485	A97	1p Padua	.45	.25
486	A97	2p Priwall, vert.	.45	.25
a.		Wmk. 384	.60	.45
487	A97	3p Passat	.45	.25
a.		Wmk. 384	.60	.45
488	A97	4p Archibald Russell, vert.	.45	.25
489	A97	5p Pamir, vert.	.45	.25
490	A97	6p Mozart	.45	.25
a.		Wmk. 384	.60	.45
491	A97	7p Pommern	.45	.25
492	A97	8p Preussen	.60	.45
493	A97	9p Fennia	.65	.50
a.		Wmk. 384	1.00	.75
494	A97	10p Cassard	.75	.60
495	A97	20p Lawhill	1.60	1.25
496	A97	25p Garthpool	1.90	1.40
497	A97	50p Grace Harwar	3.75	2.75
498	A97	£1 Criccieth Castle	8.50	5.50
a.		Wmk. 384	7.75	6.00

499	A97	£3 Cutty Sark, vert.	29.00	18.00
500	A97	£5 Flying Cloud	40.00	22.50
		Nos. 485-500 (16)	89.90	54.70

Nos. 486a, 487a, 490a, 493a, 498a are dated "1991."

Whales — A98

1989, May 15 Wmk. 384 Perf. 14

501	A98	10p Southern right	.90	.90
502	A98	24p Minke	2.10	2.10
503	A98	29p Humpback	2.75	2.75
504	A98	58p Blue	5.75	5.75
		Nos. 501-504 (4)	11.50	11.50

Sports Assoc. Activities A99

Children's drawings.

1989, Sept. 16

505	A99	5p Gymkhana	.20	.20
506	A99	10p Steer Riding	.25	.25
507	A99	17p Sheep shearing	.55	.55
508	A99	24p Dog trial	.70	.70
509	A99	29p Horse racing	.95	.95
510	A99	45p Sack race	1.50	1.50
		Nos. 505-510 (6)	4.15	4.15

Battles — A100

Commanders, ships and ship crests: 10p, Vice-Adm. Sturdee, HMS *Invincible*. 24p, Vice-Adm. Von Spee, SMS *Scharnhorst*. 29p, Commodore Harwood, HMS *Ajax*. 58p, Capt. Langsdorff, *Admiral Graff Spee*.

1989, Dec. 8 Perf. 14x13½

511	A100	10p multicolored	.55	.55
512	A100	24p multicolored	1.60	1.60
513	A100	29p multicolored	2.10	2.10
514	A100	58p multicolored	3.75	3.75
		Nos. 511-514 (4)	8.00	8.00

Battle of the Falklands, 75th anniv. (10p, 24p); Battle of the River Plate, 50th anniv. (29p, 58p).

Emblems and Presentation Spitfires, 1940 — A101

1990, May 3 Wmk. 373 Perf. 14

515	A101	12p No. 92 Squadron	.60	.60
516	A101	26p No. 611 Squadron	1.40	1.40
517	A101	31p No. 92 Squadron, diff.	1.75	1.75
518	A101	62p Spitfires scramble	3.25	3.25
		Nos. 515-518 (4)	7.00	7.00

Souvenir Sheet

519	A101	£1 Battle of Britain	7.50	7.50

Stamp World London '90.
For souvenir sheet similar to #519, see #530.

A102

A103

1990, Apr. 1 Wmk. 384 Perf. 14½

520	A102	12p Kidney Is.	.50	.50
521	A102	26p Beauchene Is.	1.25	1.25
522	A102	31p Bird Is.	1.50	1.50
523	A102	62p Elephant Jason Is.	3.00	3.00
		Nos. 520-523 (4)	6.25	6.25

Nature reserves and bird sanctuaries.

Queen Mother, 90th Birthday
Common Design Types

1990, Aug. 4 Wmk. 384 Perf. 14x15

524	CD343	26p Queen Mother in Dover	1.00	1.00

Perf. 14½

525	CD344	£1 Steering the "Queen Elizabeth," 1946	4.25	4.25

Wmk. 384

1990, Oct. 3 Litho. Perf. 14

526	A103	12p Black browed albatross	.75	.75
527	A103	26p Adult bird	1.75	1.75
528	A103	31p Adult, chick	2.25	2.25
529	A103	62p Bird in flight	4.50	4.50
		Nos. 526-529 (4)	9.25	9.25

Battle of Britain Type of 1990 inscribed "SECOND VISIT OF / HRH THE DUKE OF EDINBURGH" Souvenir Sheet

1991, Mar. 7

530	A101	£1 multicolored	10.50	10.50

Orchids — A104

King Penguin — A105

1991, Mar. 18 Wmk. 373

531	A104	12p Gavilea australis	.70	.70
532	A104	26p Codonorchis lessonii	1.60	1.60
533	A104	31p Chlorea gaudichaudii	2.00	2.00
534	A104	62p Gavilea littoralis	4.00	4.00
		Nos. 531-534 (4)	8.30	8.30

1991, Aug. 26 Wmk. 384

535	A105	2p Two adults crossing bills	1.00	1.00
536	A105	6p Two adults, one brooding	2.00	1.50

537	A105	12p Adult with two young	3.00	1.75
538	A105	20p Adult swimming	4.00	2.00
539	A105	31p Adult feeding young	2.00	2.00
540	A105	62p Two adults, diff.	3.00	3.00
		Nos. 535-540 (6)	15.00	11.25

World Wildlife Fund.

Falkland Islands Bisects, Cent. A106

1991, Sept. 10   Wmk. 384   Perf. 14½

541	A106	12p #9, #15	.65	.65
542	A106	26p On cover	1.50	1.50
543	A106	31p Unsevered pair	1.60	1.60
544	A106	62p S.S. Isis	3.25	3.25
		Nos. 541-544 (4)	7.00	7.00

Discovery of America, 500th Anniv. (in 1992) — A107

Sailing ships: 14p, STV Eye of the Wind. 29p, STV Soren Larsen. 34p, Nina, Santa Maria, Pinta. 68p, Columbus and Santa Maria.

1991, Dec. 12   Wmk. 373   Perf. 14

545	A107	14p multicolored	.85	.85
546	A107	29p multicolored	1.75	1.75
547	A107	34p multicolored	2.25	2.25
548	A107	68p multicolored	4.25	4.25
		Nos. 545-548 (4)	9.10	9.10

World Columbian Stamp Expo '92, Chicago and Genoa '92 Intl. Philatelic Exhibitions.

Queen Elizabeth II's Accession to the Throne, 40th Anniv.
Common Design Type

1992, Feb. 6

549	CD349	7p multicolored	.40	.40
550	CD349	14p multicolored	.65	.65
551	CD349	29p multicolored	1.25	1.25
552	CD349	34p multicolored	1.50	1.50
553	CD349	68p multicolored	3.00	3.00
		Nos. 549-553 (5)	6.80	6.80

Christ Church Cathedral, Cent. — A108

1992, Feb. 21   Wmk. 384   Perf. 14½

554	A108	14p Laying foundation stone	.70	.70
555	A108	29p Interior, 1920	1.60	1.60
556	A108	34p Bishop's chair	2.10	2.10
557	A108	68p Without tower c. 1900, horiz.	4.00	4.00
		Nos. 554-557 (4)	8.40	8.40

First Sighting of Falkland Islands by Capt. John Davis, 400th Anniv. A109

Designs: 22p, Capt. John Davis using backstaff. 29p, Capt. Davis working on chart. 34p, Queen Elizabeth I, Queen Elizabeth II. 68p, The Desire sights Falkland Islands.

1992, Aug. 14   Wmk. 373

558	A109	22p multicolored	1.25	1.25
559	A109	29p multicolored	1.50	1.50
560	A109	34p multicolored	1.75	1.75
561	A109	68p multicolored	3.50	3.50
		Nos. 558-561 (4)	8.00	8.00

Falkland Islands Defense Force and West Yorkshire Regiment — A110

7p, Private, Falkland Islands Volunteers, 1892. 14p, Officer, Falkland Islands Defense Corps, 1914. 22p, Officer, Falkland Islands Defense Force, 1920. 29p, Private, Falkland Islands Defense Force, 1939-45. 34p, Officer, West Yorkshire Regiment, 1942. 68p, Private, West Yorkshire Regiment, 1942.

1992, Oct. 1   Perf. 14

562	A110	7p multicolored	.35	.35
563	A110	14p multicolored	.70	.70
564	A110	22p multicolored	1.10	1.10
565	A110	29p multicolored	1.50	1.50
566	A110	34p multicolored	1.60	1.60
567	A110	68p multicolored	3.25	3.25
		Nos. 562-567 (6)	8.50	8.50

Gulls and Terns A111

Perf. 14x14½

1993, Jan. 2   Litho.   Wmk. 384

568	A111	15p South American tern	.85	.85
569	A111	31p Pink breasted gull	1.75	1.75
570	A111	36p Dolphin gull	2.00	2.00
571	A111	72p Dominican gull	4.00	4.00
		Nos. 568-571 (4)	8.60	8.60

Souvenir Sheet

Visit of Liner QE II to Falkland Islands — A112

Wmk. 373

1993, Jan. 22   Litho.   Perf. 14

572	A112	£2 multicolored	10.00	10.00

Royal Air Force, 75th Anniv.
Common Designs Type

Designs: No. 573, Lockheed Tristar. No. 574, Lockheed Hercules. No. 575, Boeing Vertol Chinook. No. 576, Avro Vulcan.
No. 577a, Hawker Siddeley Andover. b, Westland Wessex. c, Panavia Tornado F3. d, McDonnell Douglas Phantom.

Wmk. 373

1993, Apr. 3   Litho.   Perf. 14

573	CD350	15p multicolored	1.25	1.25
574	CD350	15p multicolored	1.25	1.25
575	CD350	15p multicolored	1.25	1.25
576	CD350	15p multicolored	1.25	1.25
		Nos. 573-576 (4)	5.00	5.00

Souvenir Sheet of 4

577	CD350	36p #a.-d.	6.25	6.25

Fisheries A113

Designs: 15p, Short-finned squid. 31p, Stern haul of whiptailed hake. 36p, Fishery Patrol Vessel Falkalnds Protector. 72p, Aerial surveillance by Britten-Norman Islander.

Wmk. 384

1993, July 1   Litho.   Perf. 14

578	A113	15p multicolored	.85	.85
579	A113	31p multicolored	1.60	1.60
580	A113	36p multicolored	2.10	2.10
581	A113	72p multicolored	3.75	3.75
		Nos. 578-581 (4)	8.30	8.30

Launch of SS Great Britain, 150th Anniv. — A114

Perf. 14x13½

1993, July 19   Litho.   Wmk. 384

582	A114	8p In drydock, Bristol	.40	.40
583	A114	£1 At sea	5.00	5.00

Cruise Ships and Penguins A115

Wmk. 373

1993, Oct. 1   Litho.   Perf. 14

584	A115	16p Explorer	1.00	1.00
585	A115	34p Rockhopper penguins	2.25	2.25
586	A115	39p World Discoverer	2.50	2.50
587	A115	78p Columbus Caravelle	5.25	5.25
		Nos. 584-587 (4)	11.00	11.00

Pets — A116

Perf. 14x14½

1993, Dec. 1   Litho.   Wmk. 384

588	A116	8p Pony	.50	.35
589	A116	16p Lamb	.90	.65
590	A116	34p Puppy, kitten	2.10	1.50

Perf. 14½x14

591	A116	39p Kitten, vert.	2.50	1.75
592	A116	78p Collie, vert.	5.00	3.50
		Nos. 588-592 (5)	11.00	7.75

Ovptd. with Hong Kong '94 Emblem

1994, Feb. 18

593	A116	8p on #588	.65	.65
594	A116	16p on #589	1.10	1.10
595	A116	34p on #590	2.25	2.25
596	A116	39p on #591	2.50	2.50
597	A116	78p on #592	5.00	5.00
		Nos. 593-597 (5)	11.50	11.50

Inshore Marine Life A117

Wmk. 384

1994, Apr. 4   Litho.   Perf. 14

598	A117	1p Goose barnacles, vert.	.30	.30
599	A117	2p Painted shrimp	.30	.30
600	A117	8p Common limpet	.30	.30
601	A117	9p Mullet	.35	.35
602	A117	10p Sea anemones	.40	.40
603	A117	20p Rock eel	.85	.85
604	A117	25p Spider crab	1.10	1.10
605	A117	50p Lobster krill, vert.	2.50	2.50
606	A117	80p Falkland skate	3.75	3.75
607	A117	£1 Centollon crab	5.00	5.00
a.		Souv. sheet of 1, wmk. 373	8.00	8.00
608	A117	£3 Rock cod	13.00	13.00
609	A117	£5 Octopus, vert.	22.50	22.50
		Nos. 598-609 (12)	50.35	50.35

No. 607a for return of Hong Kong to China. Issued 7/1/97.
See No. 671.

Founding of Stanley, 150th Anniv. A118

9p, Blacksmith's shop, dockyard, Sir James Clark Ross, explorer. 17p, James Leith Mody, 1st colonial chaplain, home at 21 Fitzroy Road. 30p, Stanley cottage, Dr. Henry J. Hamblin, 1st colonial surgeon. 35p, Pioneer row, Sergeant Major Henry Felton. 40p, Government House, Governor R. C. Moody R.E. 65p, View of Stanley, Edward Stanley, 14th Earl of Derby, Secretary of State for Colonies.

Wmk. 373

1994, July 1   Litho.   Perf. 14

610	A118	9p multicolored	.50	.50
611	A118	17p multicolored	.95	.95
612	A118	30p multicolored	1.75	1.75
613	A118	35p multicolored	1.90	1.90
614	A118	40p multicolored	2.40	2.40
615	A118	65p multicolored	3.50	3.50
		Nos. 610-615 (6)	11.00	11.00

Methods of Transportation — A119

17p, Tristar over Gypsy Cove. 35p, Cruise ship, Sea Lion Island. 40p, FIGAS Islander, Pebble Island Beach. 65p, Land Rover, Volunteer Beach.

Wmk. 384

1994, Oct. 24   Litho.   Perf. 14

616	A119	17p multicolored	.95	.95
617	A119	35p multicolored	2.00	1.10
618	A119	40p multicolored	2.40	1.25
619	A119	65p multicolored	3.25	2.00
		Nos. 616-619 (4)	8.60	4.90

South American Missionary Society, 150th Anniv. — A120

Designs: 5p, Mission House, Keppel Island. 17p, Thomas Bridges, compiler of Yahgan dictionary. 40p, Fuegian Indians. 65p, Schooner Allen Gardiner, Capt. Allen Gardiner.

1994, Dec. 1

620	A120	5p multicolored	.25	.25
621	A120	17p multicolored	.75	.75
622	A120	40p multicolored	1.75	1.75
623	A120	65p multicolored	2.75	2.75
		Nos. 620-623 (4)	5.50	5.50

Flowering
Shrubs — A121

Designs: 9p, Lupinus arboreus. 17p, Box-
wood. 30p, Fuchsia magellanica. 35p,
Berberis ilicifolia. 40p, Gorse. 65p, Veronica.

1995, Jan. 3   Perf. 14½x14
Litho.   Wmk. 384

624	A121	9p multicolored	.35	.35
625	A121	17p multicolored	.70	.70
626	A121	30p multicolored	1.60	1.60
627	A121	35p multicolored	2.10	2.10
628	A121	40p multicolored	2.25	2.25
629	A121	65p multicolored	4.00	4.00
		Nos. 624-629 (6)	11.00	11.00

Shore
Birds
A122

Designs: 17p, Magellanic oystercatcher.
35p, Rufous chested dotterel. 40p, Black oystercatcher. 65p, Two banded plover.

1995, Mar. 1   Perf. 13½
Litho.   Wmk. 373

630	A122	17p multicolored	1.00	1.00
631	A122	35p multicolored	2.40	2.40
632	A122	40p multicolored	2.75	2.75
633	A122	65p multicolored	4.25	4.25
		Nos. 630-633 (4)	10.40	10.40

End of World War II, 50th Anniv.
Common Design Types

17p, Falkland Islands Victory Parade contingent. 35p, Governor Sir Alan Wolsey Cardinall
on Bren gun carrier. 40p, HMAS Esperance
Bay, 1942. 65p, HMS Exeter, 1939.
£1, Reverse of War Medal 1939-45.

1995, May 8   Wmk. 373
**   Perf. 14**

634	CD351	17p multicolored	1.10	1.10
635	CD351	35p multicolored	2.25	2.25
636	CD351	40p multicolored	2.75	2.75
637	CD351	65p multicolored	4.25	4.25
		Nos. 634-637 (4)	10.35	10.35

Souvenir Sheet

638	CD352	£1 multicolored	5.00	5.00

Transporting Peat — A123

1995, Aug. 1   Perf. 14
Litho.   Wmk. 384

639	A123	17p Ox, cart	.70	.70
640	A123	35p Horse, cart	2.10	2.10
641	A123	40p Tractor, sledge	2.10	2.10
642	A123	65p Truck, peat bank	3.50	3.50
		Nos. 639-642 (4)	8.40	8.40

Miniature Sheet of 6

Wildlife — A124

Designs: a, Kelp geese. b, Albatross. c, Cormorants. d, Magellanic penguins. e, Fur seals.
f, Rockhopper penguins.

1995, Sept. 11

643	A124	35p #a.-f.	12.50	12.50

No. 643 is a continuous design.

Wild
Animals
A125

1995, Nov. 6   Wmk. 373

644	A125	9p Rabbit	.60	.60
645	A125	17p Hare	1.00	1.00
646	A125	35p Guanaco	2.40	2.40
647	A125	40p Fox	2.75	2.75
648	A125	65p Otter	4.25	4.25
		Nos. 644-648 (5)	11.00	11.00

Visit by
Princess
Anne
A126

Princess Anne and: 9p, Government House.
19p, San Carlos Cemetery. 30p, Christ
Church Cathedral. 73p, Goose Green.

1996, Jan. 30   Perf. 14½

649	A126	9p multicolored	.50	.50
650	A126	19p multicolored	1.50	1.50
651	A126	30p multicolored	2.50	2.50
652	A126	73p multicolored	5.50	5.50
		Nos. 649-652 (4)	10.00	10.00

Queen Elizabeth II, 70th Birthday
Common Design Type

Various portraits of Queen, scenes from Falkland Islands: 17p, Steeple Jason. 40p, Ship,
KV Tamar. 45p, New Island with shipwreck on
beach. 65p, Community School.
£1, Queen in formal dress at Sandringham
Ball.

1996, Apr. 21   Perf. 13½

653	CD354	17p multicolored	.65	.65
654	CD354	40p multicolored	1.75	1.75
655	CD354	45p multicolored	2.10	2.10
656	CD354	65p multicolored	3.00	3.00
		Nos. 653-656 (4)	7.50	7.50

Souvenir Sheet

657	CD354	£1 multicolored	4.25	4.25

CAPEX
'96
A127

Mail delivery: 9p, Horseback, 1890. 40p,
Norseman floatplane. 45p, Inter-island ship.
76p, Beaver floatplane.
£1, LMS Jubilee Class 4-6-0 locomotive.

1996, June 8   Wmk. 384   Perf. 14

658	A127	9p multicolored	.50	.50
659	A127	40p multicolored	1.75	1.75
660	A127	45p multicolored	2.00	2.00
661	A127	76p multicolored	3.75	3.75
		Nos. 658-661 (4)	8.00	8.00

Souvenir Sheet

662	A127	£1 multicolored	4.00	4.00

No. 662 contains one 48x32mm stamp.

Beaked Whales — A128

Designs: 9p, Southern bottlenose whale.
30p, Cuvier's beaked whale. 35p,

Straptoothed beaked whale. 75p, Gray's
beaked whale.

**   Wmk. 373**
1996, Sept. 2   Litho.   Perf. 14

663	A128	9p multicolored	.50	.50
664	A128	30p multicolored	1.75	1.75
665	A128	35p multicolored	1.75	1.75
666	A128	75p multicolored	4.25	4.25
		Nos. 663-666 (4)	8.25	8.25

Magellanic Penguins — A129

Designs: 17p, Two adults. 35p, Young in
nest. 40p, Chick, adult. 65p, Swimming.

**   Wmk. 373**
1997, Jan. 2   Litho.   Perf. 14

667	A129	17p multicolored	1.00	1.00
668	A129	35p multicolored	2.50	2.50
669	A129	40p multicolored	2.75	2.75
670	A129	65p multicolored	4.50	4.50
		Nos. 667-670 (4)	10.75	10.75

Fish Type of 1994
Souvenir Sheet
**   Wmk. 373**
1997, Feb. 3   Litho.   Perf. 14

671	A117	£1 Smelt	5.00	5.00

Hong Kong '97.

Ferns — A130

Perf. 14½x14
1997, Mar. 3   Litho.   Wmk. 373

672	A130	17p Coral	1.00	1.00
673	A130	35p Adder's tongue	2.25	2.25
674	A130	40p Fuegian tall	2.50	2.50
675	A130	65p Small fern	4.25	4.25
		Nos. 672-675 (4)	10.00	10.00

Lighthouses — A131

**   Wmk. 373**
1997, July 1   Litho.   Perf. 14

676	A131	9p Bull Point	1.25	1.25
677	A131	30p Cape Pem-		
		broke	2.50	2.50
678	A131	£1 Cape Meredith	9.25	9.25
		Nos. 676-678 (3)	13.00	13.00

Queen Elizabeth II and Prince Philip,
50th Wedding Anniv. — A132

#679, Queen holding flowers. #680, Prince
with horse. #681, Queen riding in open carriage. #682, Prince in uniform. #683, Queen in
red coat & hat, Prince. #684, Princes William
and Harry on horseback.
£1.50, Queen, Prince riding in open
carriage.

1997   Wmk. 384   Perf. 14½x14

679		9p multicolored	.75	.75
680		9p multicolored	.75	.75
a.	A132	Pair, #679-680	1.75	1.75
681		17p multicolored	1.50	1.50
682		17p multicolored	1.50	1.50
a.	A132	Pair, #681-682	3.50	3.50
683		40p multicolored	3.25	3.25
684		40p multicolored	3.25	3.25
a.	A132	Pair, #683-684	7.25	7.25
		Nos. 679-684 (6)	11.00	11.00

Souvenir Sheet

685	A132	£1.50 multicolored	10.00	10.00

Endangered Species — A133

Designs: 17p, Phalcoboenus australis. 19p,
Otaria flavescens. 40p, Calandrinia feltonii.
73p, Aplochiton zebra.

**   Wmk. 373**
1997, Oct. 16   Litho.   Perf. 14½

686	A133	17p multicolored	1.50	1.50
687	A133	19p multicolored	2.00	2.00
688	A133	40p multicolored	4.00	4.00
689	A133	73p multicolored	7.50	7.50
		Nos. 686-689 (4)	15.00	15.00

Fire Service in
Falkland Islands,
Cent. — A134

Equipment, manufacturer: 9p, Greenwich
Gem, Merryweather & Son. 17p, Hatfield
trailer pump, Merryweather & Son. 40p,
Godiva trailer pump, Coventry Climax. 65p,
Water tender type B, Carmichael Bedford.

**   Wmk. 384**
1998, Feb. 26   Litho.   Perf. 14½

690	A134	9p multicolored	1.00	1.00
691	A134	17p multicolored	2.25	2.25
692	A134	40p multicolored	6.00	6.00
693	A134	65p multicolored	9.75	9.75
		Nos. 690-693 (4)	19.00	19.00

Diana, Princess of Wales (1961-97)
Common Design Type

Portraits: a, Looking left. b, In red dress. c,
Hand on cheek. d, Investigating land mines.

Perf. 14½x14
1998, Mar. 31   Wmk. 373

694	CD355	30p Sheet of 4, #a-d	6.00	6.00

No. 694 sold for £1.20 + 20p, with surtax
from international sales being donated to the
Princess Diana Memorial Fund and surtax
from national sales being donated to designated local charity.

Birds
A135

1p, Tawny-throated dotterel. 2p, Hudsonian
godwit. 5p, Eared dove. #698, Great grebe.
#699, Roseate spoonbill. 10p, Southern lap-
wing. 16p, Buff-necked ibis. 17p, Astral parakeet. 30p, Ashy-headed goose. 35p, American
kestrel. 65p, Red-legged shag. 88p, Red shoveler. £1, Red-fronted coot. £3, Chilean flamingo. £5, Fork-tailed flycatcher.

**   Wmk. 373**
1998, July 14   Litho.   Perf. 14

695	A135	1p multicolored	.30	.30
696	A135	2p multicolored	.30	.30
697	A135	5p multicolored	.30	.30
698	A135	9p multicolored	.45	.45
699	A135	9p multicolored	.45	.45
700	A135	10p multicolored	.50	.50
701	A135	16p multicolored	.70	.70

702	A135	17p multicolored	.80	.80
a.		Booklet pane, 2 #699, 8 #702 + 2 labels	7.25	
		Complete booklet, #702a	7.25	
703	A135	30p multicolored	1.40	1.40
704	A135	35p multicolored	1.60	1.60
		Complete booklet, 6 #704	9.75	
705	A135	65p multicolored	3.00	3.00
706	A135	88p multicolored	4.00	4.00
707	A135	£1 multicolored	4.50	4.50
708	A135	£3 multicolored	15.00	15.00
709	A135	£5 multicolored	24.00	22.50
		Nos. 695-709 (15)	57.30	55.80

Boats — A136

Boat, country flag, year: 17p, Penelope, Germany, 1926. 35p, Ilen, Italy, 1926. 40p, Weddell, Chile, 1940. 65p, Lively, Scotland, 1940.

Wmk. 373

1998, Sept. 30   Litho.   Perf. 14

710	A136	17p multicolored	1.25	1.25
711	A136	35p multicolored	2.50	2.50
712	A136	40p multicolored	2.75	2.75

Size: 29x18mm

713	A136	65p multicolored	4.50	4.50
		Nos. 710-713 (4)	11.00	11.00

FIGAS (First Medivac Air Ambulance Service), 50th Anniv. — A137

17p, Man carrying patient, airplane. £1, Airplane, map of Islands, float plane.

Wmk. 373

1998, Dec. 1   Litho.   Perf. 14

714	A137	17p multicolored	1.75	1.75
715	A137	£1 multicolored	12.00	12.00

Military Uniforms — A138

Uniform, background location: 17p, Marine Private, 1776, The Block House at Port Egmont, Saunders Island. 30p, Marine Officer, 1833, Port Louis, East Falkland. 35p, Royal Marine Corporal, 1914, HMS Kent. 65p, Royal Marine Bugler, 1976, Government House.

Wmk. 373

1998, Dec. 8   Litho.   Perf. 14½

716	A138	17p multicolored	2.00	2.00
717	A138	30p multicolored	4.00	4.00
718	A138	35p multicolored	4.25	4.25
719	A138	65p multicolored	8.75	8.75
		Nos. 716-719 (4)	19.00	19.00

St. Mary's Church, Cent. A139

Wmk. 373

1999, Feb. 12   Litho.   Perf. 14

720	A139	17p Inside view	1.25	1.25
721	A139	40p Outside view	4.00	4.00
722	A139	75p Laying cornerstone, 1899	7.75	7.75
		Nos. 720-722 (3)	13.00	13.00

Australia '99, World Stamp Expo A140

25p, HMS Beagle. 35p, HMAS Australia. 40p, SS Canberra. #726, SS Great Britain. #727, All-England Eleven visit Australia, 1861-62.

1999, Mar. 5   Wmk. 384

723	A140	25p multicolored	2.50	2.50
724	A140	35p multicolored	3.50	3.50
725	A140	40p multicolored	4.00	4.00
726	A140	50p multicolored	4.75	4.75
727	A140	50p multicolored	4.75	4.75
a.		Pair, #726-727	9.50	9.50
		Nos. 723-727 (5)	19.50	19.50

1999 Visit of HRH Prince of Wales — A141

Perf. 14x13½

1999, Mar. 13   Litho.   Wmk. 384

728	A141	£2 multicolored	14.50	14.50

Wedding of Prince Edward and Sophie Rhys-Jones
Common Design Type

Perf. 13¾x14

1999, June 15   Litho.   Wmk. 384

729	CD356	80p Separate portraits	5.25	5.25
730	CD356	£1.20 Couple	8.25	8.25

PhilexFrance '99, World Philatelic Exhibition — A142

Designs: 35p, French cruiser, Jeanne d'Arc, Port Stanley, 1931. 40p, CAMS 37/11 Flying Boat's first flight.
£1, CAMS 37 Flying Boat over Port Stanley, 1931.

1999, June 21   Wmk. 373   Perf. 14

731	A142	35p multicolored	3.75	3.75
732	A142	40p multicolored	4.25	4.25

Souvenir Sheet

733	A142	£1 multicolored	12.00	12.00

No. 733 contains one 48x31mm stamp.

Queen Mother's Century
Common Design Type

Queen Mother: 9p, With King George VI at Port of London. 20p, With Queen Elizabeth at Women's Institute, Sandringham. 30p, With Princes Charles, William and Harry at Clarence House, 95th birthday. 67p, As Colonel-in-Chief of the Queen's Royal Hussars.
£1.40, With Ernest Shackleton, Robert F. Scott and Edward A. Wilson.

Wmk. 384

1999, Aug. 18   Litho.   Perf. 13½

734	CD358	9p multicolored	1.00	1.00
735	CD358	20p multicolored	2.10	2.10
736	CD358	30p multicolored	3.25	3.25
737	CD358	67p multicolored	7.50	7.50
		Nos. 734-737 (4)	13.85	13.85

Souvenir Sheet

738	CD358	£1.40 multicolored	15.00	15.00

For overprint see #767.

Waterfowl A143

Perf. 14¼x14½

1999, Sept. 9   Litho.   Wmk. 384

739	A143	9p Chiloe wigeon	.85	.85
740	A143	17p Crested duck	1.90	1.90
741	A143	30p Brown pintail	3.50	3.50
742	A143	35p Silver teal	4.00	4.00
743	A143	40p Yellow billed teal	5.25	5.25
744	A143	65p Flightless steamer duck	7.50	7.50
		Nos. 739-744 (6)	23.00	23.00

California Gold Rush A144

Designs: 9p, Vicar of Bray, 1999. 35p, Gold panning, 1849. 40p, Gold rocking cradle, 1849. 80p, Vicar of Bray, 1849.
£1, Vicar of Bray in San Francisco Harbor, 1849.

Wmk. 373

1999, Nov. 3   Litho.   Perf. 14

745	A144	9p multicolored	1.00	1.00
746	A144	35p multicolored	3.75	3.75
747	A144	40p multicolored	4.25	4.25
748	A144	80p multicolored	9.00	9.00
		Nos. 745-748 (4)	18.00	18.00

Souvenir Sheet
Perf. 13¾

749	A144	£1 multicolored	12.00	12.00

No. 749 contains one 48x31mm stamp.

Millennium A145

Designs: No. 750, Kelp gull. No. 751, Upland goose. No. 752, Christchurch Cathedral. No. 753, Night heron. No. 754, King penguin. No. 755, Christmas at home.

1999, Dec. 6   Perf. 14x14½

750	A145	9p multicolored	1.00	1.00
751	A145	9p multicolored	1.00	1.00
752	A145	9p multicolored	1.00	1.00
753	A145	30p multicolored	4.25	4.25
754	A145	30p multicolored	4.25	4.25
755	A145	30p multicolored	4.25	4.25
		Nos. 750-755 (6)	15.75	15.75

Visit of Princess Alexandra A146

Designs: 9p, Princess in blue dress, trees. £1, Princess in patterned dress, trees.

Perf. 13¼x13¾

2000, Feb. 1   Litho.   Wmk. 373

756	A146	9p multi	1.00	1.00
757	A146	£1 multi	10.00	10.00

Sir Ernest Shackleton (1874-1922), Polar Explorer — A147

17p, Ship Endurance, discovery of the Caird Coast. 45p, Endurance trapped in pack ice. 75p, Shackleton, Chilean tugboat Yelcho.

2000, Feb. 10   Wmk. 373   Perf. 14

758	A147	17p multi	2.00	2.00
759	A147	45p multi	7.00	7.00
760	A147	75p multi	12.00	12.00
		Nos. 758-760 (3)	21.00	21.00

See British Antarctic Territory Nos. 285-287, South Georgia and South Sandwich Islands Nos. 254-256.

British Monarchs — A148

a, Elizabeth I. b, James II. c, George I. d, William IV. e, Edward VIII. f, Elizabeth II.

2000, Feb. 29   Wmk. 373   Perf. 14

761	A148	40p Sheet of 6, #a.-f.	15.00	15.00

The Stamp Show 2000, London.

Prince William, 18th Birthday
Common Design Type

William: 10p, As toddler with fireman's helmet, vert. 20p, In checked suit and in navy suit, vert. 37p, With blue shirt. 43p, In gray suit and in navy suit holding flowers. 50p, As child with dog.

Perf. 13¾x14¼, 14¼x13¾

2000, June 21   Litho.   Wmk. 373
Stamps with White Border

762	CD359	10p multi	.65	.65
763	CD359	20p multi	1.60	1.60
764	CD359	37p multi	3.00	3.00
765	CD359	43p multi	3.25	3.25
		Nos. 762-765 (4)	8.50	8.50

Souvenir Sheet
Stamps Without White Border
Perf. 14¼

766		Sheet of 5	12.00	12.00
a.	CD359	10p multi	.60	.60
b.	CD359	20p multi	1.25	1.25
c.	CD359	37p multi	2.25	2.25
d.	CD359	43p multi	2.50	2.50
e.	CD359	50p multi	3.00	3.00

No. 738 Ovptd. in Gold

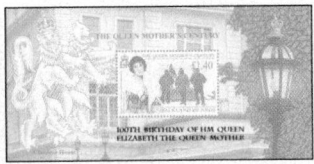

Wmk. 384

2000, Aug. 4   Perf. 13½

767	CD358	£1.40 multi	14.00	14.00

Gold overprint in sheet margin reads "100TH BIRTHDAY OF HM QUEEN / ELIZABETH THE QUEEN MOTHER."

Bridges A149

Bridges over: 20p, Malo River. 37p, Bodie Creek. 43p, Fitzroy River.

2000, Oct. 16   Perf. 14¼x14½

768-770	A149	Set of 3	15.00	15.00

Christmas — A150

Designs: 10p, Shepherd, sheep. 20p, Shepherds, sheep, angel. 33p, Holy family, shepherds, Magus, donkey, sheep. 43p, Angel, two Magi. 78p, Camel.

2000, Nov. 1   **Wmk. 373**
771-775 A150   Set of 5   14.00   14.00
775a   Souvenir sheet, #771-775   17.00   17.00

Sunrises and Sunsets A151

Various photos: 10p, 20p, 37p, 43p.

2001, Jan. 10   **Perf. 14½x14¼**
776-779 A151   Set of 4   12.00   12.00

Souvenir Sheet

New Year 2001 (Year of the Snake) — A152

Birds: a, Striated caracara. b, Mountain hawk eagle.

Perf. 14½x14¼
2001, Feb. 1   **Litho.**   **Wmk. 373**
780 A152   37p Sheet of 2, #a-b   8.00   8.00

Hong Kong 2001 Stamp Exhibition.

Age of Victoria — A153

Designs: 3p, Falkland Islands #1. 10p, S.S. Great Britain, horiz. 20p, Stanley Harbor, 1888, horiz. 43p, Cape Pembroke Lighthouse, telephones, 1897. 93p, Royal Marines, 1900. £1.50, Queen Victoria, by Franz Xavier Winterhalter, 1859.
£1, Funeral procession for Queen Victoria.

2001, May 24   **Perf. 14**
781-786 A153   Set of 6   22.50   22.50
Souvenir Sheet
787 A153   £1 multi   9.00   9.00

Royal Navy Connections to Falkland Islands — A154

Designs: 10p, Welfare, ship that made first recorded landing, 1690. 17p, HMS Invincible, ship in Battle of the Falklands, 1914. 20p,

HMS Exeter, ship in Battle of the River Plate, 1939. 37p, SN.R6 Hovercraft, 1967. 43p, Antarctic patrol ship HMS Protector and Wasp helicopter, 1955. 68p, Desire, ship that made first sighting, 1592.

2001, July 24
788-793 A154   Set of 6   18.00   18.00

Carcass Island and its Flora and Fauna — A155

No. 794, 37p: a, Yellow violet. b, Tussac bird.
No. 795, 43p: a, Carcass Island settlement. b, Black-crowned night heron.

Wmk. 373
2001, Sept. 28   **Litho.**   **Perf. 13¾**
Pairs, #a-b
794-795 A155   Set of 2   11.00   11.00

Gentoo Penguins — A156

Designs: 10p, Birds flapping wings. 33p, Feeding young. 37p, Bird with beak open. 43p, Four birds walking.

2001, Oct. 26   **Perf. 14½x14¼**
796-799 A156   Set of 4   9.00   9.00

Falkland Islands Company, 150th Anniv. A157

Designs: 10p, Company coat of arms, and gathering of cattle. 20p, Company flag, and ship Amelia. 43p, Manager F. E. Cobb, and company buildings. £1, Sheep farmer William Wickham Bertrand, sheep dip.

Wmk. 373
2002, Jan. 10   **Perf. 14**
800-803 A157   Set of 4   12.00   12.00

Reign Of Queen Elizabeth II, 50th Anniv. Issue
Common Design Type

Designs: Nos. 804, 808a, 20p, Princess Elizabeth reading, 1945. Nos. 805, 808b, 37p, In 1977. Nos. 806, 808c, 43p, Holding Prince Charles, 1949. Nos. 807, 808d, 50p, At Garter ceremony, 1994. No. 808e, 50p, 1955 portrait by Annigoni (38x50mm).

Perf. 14¼x14½, 13¾ (#808e)
2002, Feb. 6   **Litho.**   **Wmk. 373**
With Gold Frames
804-807 CD360   Set of 4   7.00   7.00
Souvenir Sheet
Without Gold Frames
808 CD360   Sheet of 5, #a-e   9.50   9.50

Falkland Islands War, 20th Anniv. — A158

No. 809, 22p: a, HMS Hermes, 1982. b, Fishery patrol vessel, 2002.
No. 810, 40p: a, Troops landing, 1982. b, Mine clearing, 2002.

No. 811, 45p: a, RAF Harrier on HMS Hermes, 1982. b, RAF Tristar, 2002.
Illustration reduced.

Wmk. 373
2002, June 14   **Litho.**   **Perf. 14**
Horiz. pairs, #a-b
809-811 A158   Set of 3   12.00   12.00

Queen Mother Elizabeth (1900-2002)
Common Design Type

Designs: 22p, Wearing hat and scarf (black and white photograph). 25p, Wearing blue hat with polka dots. Nos. 814, 816a, 95p, Wearing feathered hat (black and white photograph). Nos. 815, 816b, £1.20, Wearing blue hat.

Wmk. 373
2002, Aug. 5   **Litho.**   **Perf. 14¼**
With Purple Frames
812-815 CD361   Set of 4   11.50   11.50
Souvenir Sheet
Without Purple Frames
Perf. 14½x14¼
816 CD361   Sheet of 2, #a-b   11.50   11.50

Worldwide Fund for Nature (WWF) — A159

Penguins: 36p, Rockhopper. 40p, Magellanic. 45p, Gentoo. 70p, Macaroni.

Wmk. 373
2002, Aug. 30   **Litho.**   **Perf. 14¼**
817-820 A159   Set of 4   9.50   9.50
a.   Horiz. strip of 4, #817-820   9.50   9.50

West Point Island and its Flora and Fauna — A160

No. 821, 40p: a, Felton's flower. b, Black-browed albatross.
No. 822, 45p: a, Rockhopper penguin. b, Island settlement.
Illustration reduced.

Perf. 14¼x14½
2002, Oct. 31   **Litho.**   **Wmk. 373**
Horiz. Pairs, #a-b
821-822 A160   Set of 2   10.00   10.00

Visit of Prince Andrew — A161

No. 823: a, 22p, In uniform. b, £1.52, In suit and tie.

2002, Nov. 11   **Perf. 13¼x13½**
823 A161   Horiz. pair, #a-b   9.50   9.50

Shepherds' Houses — A162

Designs: 10p, Gun Hill shanty, Little Chartres. 22p, Paragon House, Lafonia. 45p, Dos Lomas, Lafonia. £1, Old House, Shallow Bay Farm.

Wmk. 373
2003, Mar. 31   **Litho.**   **Perf. 14**
824-827 A162   Set of 4   9.00   9.00

Head of Queen Elizabeth II
Common Design Type
Wmk. 373
2003, June 2   **Litho.**   **Perf. 13¾**
828 CD362   £2 multi   8.00   8.00

Prince William, 21st Birthday
Common Design Type

Color photographs: a, In suit at right. b, With Prince Harry at left.

Wmk. 373
2003, June 21   **Litho.**   **Perf. 14¼**
829   Horiz. pair   10.00   10.00
a.-b.   CD364 95p Either single   4.50   4.50

Birds — A163

Designs: 1p, Chiloe widgeon. 2p, Dolphin gull, vert. 5p, Falkland flightless steamer duck. 10p, Black-throated finch, vert. 22p, White-tufted grebe. 25p, Rufous-chested dotterel, vert. 45p, Upland goose. 50p, Dark-faced ground-tyrant, vert. 95p, Black-crowned night heron. £1, Red-backed hawk, vert. £3, Black-necked swan. £5, Short-eared owl, vert.

Perf. 13x13¼, 13¼x13
2003, July 21   **Litho.**   **Wmk. 373**
830 A163   1p multi   .20   .20
831 A163   2p multi   .20   .20
832 A163   5p multi   .20   .20
833 A163   10p multi   .35   .35
834 A163   22p multi   .80   .80
835 A163   25p multi   .90   .90
836 A163   45p multi   1.60   1.60
837 A163   50p multi   1.90   1.90
838 A163   95p multi   3.50   3.50
839 A163   £1 multi   3.75   3.75
840 A163   £3 multi   11.00   11.00
841 A163   £5 multi   19.00   19.00
   Nos. 830-841,C1 (13)   44.65   44.65

Bird Life International A164

Black-browed albatross: No. 842, Adult on nest, facing right. No. 843, Chick. 40p, Heads of two adults, vert. £1, Adult on nest, facing left, vert.
16p, In flight.

Perf. 14¼x13¾, 13¾x14¼
2003, Sept. 26
842 A164   22p multi   1.10   1.10
  a.   Perf. 14¼x14½   1.10   1.10
843 A164   22p multi   1.10   1.10
  a.   Perf. 14¼x14½   1.10   1.10
844 A164   40p multi   2.00   2.00
  a.   Perf. 14½x14¼   1.90   1.90
845 A164   £1 multi   5.25   5.25
  a.   Perf. 14½x14¼   4.75   4.75
   Nos. 842-845 (4)   9.45   9.45
Souvenir Sheet
846   Sheet, #842a-846a   9.00   9.00
  a.   A164 16p multi, perf. 14¼x14½   .50   .50

New Island and its Flora and Fauna A165

No. 847, 40p: a, Striated caracara. b, Lady's slipper.
No. 848, 45p: a, Stone Cottage. b, King penguin.

Wmk. 373
2003, Oct. 24 **Litho.** *Perf. 13¾*
Pairs, #a-b
847-848 A165 Set of 2 8.50 8.50

Christmas — A166

Various depictions of Pale maiden flower: 16p, 30p, 40p, 95p.

2003, Nov. 3 *Perf. 14x14¼*
849-852 A166 Set of 4 8.75 8.75

Sheep Farming A167

Designs: 19p, Traditional hand shearing. 22p, Driving the sheep. 45p, Big House, Hill Cove. 70p, The early years. £1, Wool collection, SS Fitzroy.

Unwmk.
2004, Apr. 30 **Litho.** *Perf. 14*
853-857 A167 Set of 5 9.25 9.25

Wildlife Conservation in Falkland Islands, 25th Anniv. — A168

Designs: 20p, Man planting tussac grass. 24p, People cleaning beach. 50p, Satellite tracking of rockhopper penguins. £1, Weighing of albatross chick.

2004, June 17 **Litho.** *Perf. 14*
858-861 A168 Set of 4 8.00 8.00

Sir Rowland Hill (1795-1879) and Falkland Islands Postage Stamps — A169

Hill and: 24p, #20. 50p, #74. 75p, #94. £1, #151a.

2004, Aug. 31 **Litho.** *Perf. 13¼*
862-865 A169 Set of 4 9.00 9.00

Sea Lion Island and its Flora and Fauna — A170

No. 866, 42p: a, King cormorant. b, Dog orchid.
No. 867, 50p: a, Magellanic penguin. b, Sea Lion Lodge.
Illustration reduced.

2004, Sept. 15 *Perf. 13¾*
Pairs, #a-b
866-867 A170 Set of 2 7.50 7.50

Owls — A171

Designs: 18p, Head of short-eared owl. 45p, Short-eared owl. 50p, Barn owl in flight. £1.50, Barn owl. £2, Barn owl in flight, horiz.

2004, Oct. 25
868-871 A171 Set of 4 10.50 10.50
Souvenir Sheet
872 A171 £2 multi 7.50 7.50

Battle of the Falkland Islands, 90th Anniv. A172

No. 873: a, HMS Kent, HMS Inflexible, half of HMS Carnarvon, half of HMS Cornwall. b, British Navy flag, HMS Glasgow, half of HMS Carnarvon, half of HMS Cornwall, half of HMS Invincible. c, Medals, half of HMS Invincible.
No. 874: a, Medals, half of SMS Scharnhorst. b, German imperial war ensign, SMS Dresden, half of SMS Scharnhorst, half of SMS Leipzig. c, SMS Nürnberg, SMS Gneisenau, half of SMS Leipzig.

2004, Dec. 8 **Litho.** *Perf. 14*
873 Horiz. strip of 3 3.50 3.50
a.-c. A172 24p Any single 1.00 1.00
874 Horiz. strip of 3 7.50 7.50
a.-c. A172 50p Any single 2.00 2.00

Camber Railway, 90th Anniv. — A173

Designs: 3p, Old track bed. 24p, Kerr Stuart Wren Class locomotive at Camber Depot, horiz. 50p, Kerr Stuart Wren Class locomotive Falkland Islands Express, horiz. £2, Camber sailing wagon.

2005, Feb. 28 *Perf. 13¾*
875-878 A173 Set of 4 11.00 11.00

Wedding of Prince Charles and Camilla Parker Bowles A174

Designs: 24p, Couple. 50p, Couple in formal wear, vert. £2, Couple, Windsor Castle.

2005, Apr. 29 *Perf. 14*
879-880 A174 Set of 2 3.00 3.00
Souvenir Sheet
881 A174 £2 multi 7.75 7.75

End of World War II, 60th Anniv. — A175

No. 882, 24p: a, Walrus reconnaissance seaplane. b, Presentation Spitfire X4616.
No. 883, 80p: a, HMS Exeter at Port Stanley. b, Governor, King Edward Memorial Hospital staff, Rear Admiral Harwood and Capt. Bell.
No. 884, £1: a, Fitzroy. b, HMS William Scoresby.
Illustration reduced.

Perf. 13¼x13½
2005, June 29 **Litho.**
Horiz. Pairs, #a-b
882-884 A175 Set of 3 14.50 14.50

Maritime Heritage A176

Designs: 24p, Snow Squall escaping CSS Tuscaloosa, 1863. No. 886, 55p, Jhelum, 1870. No. 887, 55p, Charles Cooper, 1866. £1.20, SS Imo colliding with the Mont Blanc, Halifax Harbor, 1917.

2005, Aug. 29 **Litho.** *Perf. 14*
885-888 A176 Set of 4 10.50 10.50

Pebble Island and its Flora and Fauna — A177

No. 889, 45p: a, Gentoo penguin. b, Falkland lavender.
No. 890, 55p: a, Pebble Island Lodge. b, Black-necked swan.
Illustration reduced.

2005, Sept. 12 *Perf. 13¾*
Pairs, #a-b
889-890 A177 Set of 2 8.25 8.25

Souvenir Sheet

The Fall of Nelson, Battle of Trafalgar, 21 October 1805, by Denis Dighton — A178

2005, Oct. 21
891 A178 £2 multi 8.50 8.50
Battle of Trafalgar, bicent.

Hans Christian Andersen (1805-75), Author — A179

Stories: 18p, The Little Mermaid. 30p, The Snowman. 45p, The Ugly Duckling. £1, Thumbelina.

2005, Oct. 28 *Perf. 14*
892-895 A179 Set of 4 8.25 8.25
Stanley Infant and Junior School, 50th anniv.

Black-crowned Night Heron — A180

Designs: 24p, Head. 55p, Bird on one leg. 80p, Juvenile standing. £1, Head of juvenile.

2006, Feb. 10 **Litho.** *Perf. 13¾*
896-899 A180 Set of 4 9.00 9.00

Queen Elizabeth II, 80th Birthday — A181

Queen wearing: 24p, Yellow hat. 55p, Green hat. 80p, Blue hat. £1, Red hat. £2, Tiara and white hat, horiz.

2006, Apr. 21 *Perf. 14*
900-903 A181 Set of 4 9.75 9.75
Souvenir Sheet
904 A181 £2 multi 7.50 7.50

SS Great Britain — A182

View of: 24p, Bow. 55p, Stern. £1.50, Deck and masts.

2006, May 19 *Perf. 13¾x13¼*
905-907 A182 Set of 3 8.75 8.75

Birds A183

Designs: No. 908, 25p, Gentoo penguin chicks. No. 909, 25p, King cormorants. No. 910, 60p, King penguin. No. 911, 60p, Wandering albatross.

2006, Aug. 30 **Litho.** *Perf. 14¼x14*
908-911 A183 Set of 4 6.50 6.50

Bleaker Island and its Flora and Fauna — A184

No. 912, 50p: a, Woolly Falkland ragwort. b, Macaroni penguin.
No. 913, 60p: a, The Outlook and sheep. b, Long-tailed meadowlark.
Illustration reduced.

2006, Sept. 18 *Perf. 13¼x13*
Pairs, #a-b
912-913 A184 Set of 2 8.25 8.25

Victoria Cross, 150th Anniv. — A185

Designs: Nos. 914, 916a, 60p, Lt. Col. H. Jones. Nos. 915, 916b, 60p, Sgt. Ian McKay. No. 916c, £1, Victoria Cross.

2006, Nov. 11   *Perf. 13¼*
Stamps With White Frames
914-915 A185   Set of 2   4.75 4.75
Souvenir Sheet
Stamps Without White Frames
916 A185   Sheet of 3, #a-c   8.75 8.75

Bird Type of 2003

Designs: 20p, Black-browed albatross, vert. 25p, Rufous-chested dotterel, vert. £5, Short-eared owl, vert.

2006, Nov. 15   Litho.   Unwmk.
917 A163 20p multi   .80 .80
918 A163 25p multi   1.00 1.00
919 A163 £5 multi   20.00 20.00
   Nos. 917-919 (3)   21.80 21.80

Nos. 918-919 differ from Nos. 835 and 841 by having less color around the Queen's head. Nos. 917-919 are dated "2006."

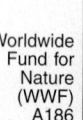

Worldwide Fund for Nature (WWF) A186

Striated caracara: 25p, Heads of two birds. 50p, Bird in flight. 60p, Bird standing. 85p, Bird eating shellfish.

2006, Dec. 20   Litho.   *Perf. 13¾*
920-923 A186   Set of 4   8.50 8.50
923a   Miniature sheet, 4 each #920-923   34.00 34.00

Fisheries, 20th Anniv. A187

Designs: 3p, Fishermen at sea. 11p, Fishing boat at night. 25p, Fishermen leaving boat. 30p, Japanese jigger. 60p, Fishery protection boat Dorada. £1.05, Trawler transferring fish to a freezer container ship.

2007, Feb. 24   *Perf. 14¼*
924-929 A187   Set of 6   9.25 9.25

HMS Plymouth A188

HMS Plymouth: 25p, Joining Falkland Islands Task Force. 40p, Supporting SBS. 60p, Under attack by Argentine fighters. £1.05, Docked at Port Stanley.

2007, Mar. 27
930-933 A188   Set of 4   9.25 9.25

Souvenir Sheet

Falkland Islands War, 25th Anniv. — A189

No. 934: a, Avro Vulcan prototype VX770. b, Avro Vulcan XM597. c, Avro Vulcan XM607. d, Vulcan in the Sky Project.

2007, May 25   Litho.   *Perf. 13¼*
934 A189 60p Sheet of 4, #a-d   9.50 9.50

Miniature Sheets

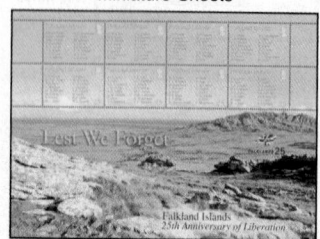

British and Falkland Islander Casualties of the Falkland Islands War — A190

No. 935, 25p — Casualties beginning with: a, Doreen Bonner. b, G. W. J. Batt. c, J. R. Carlyle. d, S. J. Dixon. e, I. R. Farrell. f, G. C. Grace. g, R. R. Heath. h, A. S. James.
No. 936, 60p: a, D. Lee. b, P. B. McKay. c, G. T. Nelson. d, J. B. Pashley. e, M. Sambles. f, D. A. Strickland. g, R. G. Thomas. h, P. A. West.

2007, June 14   Litho.   *Perf. 14¼*
Sheets of 8, #a-h
935-936 A190   Set of 2   27.00 27.00

Scouting, Cent. — A191

Designs: 10p, Scouts on ladder of RRS Discovery. 20p, Dignitaries on ship's deck. 25p, Dignitaries, diff. £2, RRS Discovery.

2007, July 23   Litho.   *Perf. 13½x13¼*
937-940 A191   Set of 4   10.50 10.50

Voyage of RRS Discovery from Falkland Islands for presentation to British Scout Association, 70th anniv.

Princess Diana (1961-97) — A192

2007, Aug. 31   *Perf. 14*
941 A192 60p multi   2.50 2.50
Printed in sheets of 8 stamps + 21 labels.

Saunders Island and its Flora and Fauna — A193

No. 942, 50p: a, Rockhopper penguin. b, Dusty miller.
No. 943, 55p: a, Crested caracara. b, Earliest British settlement at Port Egmont. Illustration reduced.

2007, Sept. 28   Litho.   *Perf. 13¾*
Pairs, #a-b
942-943 A193   Set of 2   8.75 8.75

SEMI-POSTAL STAMPS

> Catalogue values for unused stamps in this section are for Never Hinged items.

Rebuilding after Conflict with Argentina — SP1

Wmk. 373
1982, Sept. 13   Litho.   *Perf. 11*
B1 SP1 £1 + £1 Battle sites   3.00 3.00

Liberation of Falkland Islands, 10th Anniv. — SP2

Designs: 14p+6p, San Carlos Cemetery. 29p+11p, 1982 War Memorial, Port Stanley. 34p+16p, South Atlantic Medal. 68p+32p, Government House, Port Stanley.

Wmk. 373
1992, June 14   Litho.   *Perf. 14*
B2 SP2 14p + 6p multicolored   .75 .75
B3 SP2 29p + 11p multicolored   1.50 1.50
B4 SP2 34p + 16p multicolored   2.00 2.00
B5 SP2 68p + 32p multicolored   3.75 3.75
a.   Souvenir sheet of 4, #B2-B5   9.50 9.50
   Nos. B2-B5 (4)   8.00 8.00

Surtax for Soldiers', Sailors' and Airmen's Families Association.

AIR POST STAMPS

Bird Type of 2003
Design: Rockhopper penguins, vert.

Serpentine Die Cut 6x6½ Syncopated
2003, Sept. 19   Litho.
Booklet Stamp
Self-Adhesive
C1 A163 (40p) multi   1.25 1.25
a.   Booklet pane of 8   10.00

POSTAGE DUE STAMPS

> Catalogue values for unused stamps in this section are for never hinged items.

Penguin — D1

1991, Jan. 7   Litho.   Wmk. 373
J1 D1 1p lilac rose & lake   .20 .50
J2 D1 2p buff & brown org   .20 .50
J3 D1 3p yel & orange yel   .20 .50
J4 D1 4p lt bl grn & dk bl grn   .25 .50
J5 D1 5p sky blue & Prus bl   .25 .50
J6 D1 10p lt blue & dk blue   .35 .70
J7 D1 20p lt violet & dk vio   .90 1.50
J8 D1 50p brt yel grn & dk yel green   2.00 3.25
   Nos. J1-J8 (8)   4.35 7.95

Penguins D2

Various penguins.

2005, Dec. 2   Litho.   *Perf. 13¾*
J9 D2 1p multi   .20 .20
J10 D2 3p multi   .20 .20
J11 D2 5p multi   .20 .20
J12 D2 10p multi   .50 .50
J13 D2 20p multi   .90 .90
J14 D2 50p multi   2.00 2.00
J15 D2 £1 multi   4.00 4.00
J16 D2 £2 multi   8.00 8.00
J17 D2 £3 multi   12.00 12.00
J18 D2 £5 multi   20.00 20.00
   Nos. J9-J18 (10)   48.00 48.00

WAR TAX STAMPS

Regular Issue of 1912-14 Overprinted

1918, Oct. 7   Wmk. 3   *Perf. 14*
MR1 A7 ½p yellow green   .55 7.25
MR2 A7 1p red   .55 4.00
a.   Double overprint   2,500.
MR3 A7 1sh bister brown   6.50 52.50
a.   Pair, one without overprint   8,000.
   Nos. MR1-MR3 (3)   7.60 63.75

No. MR3a probably is caused by a foldover and is not constant.

FALKLAND ISLANDS DEPENDENCIES

> Catalogue values for unused stamps in this section are for Never Hinged items.

Map of Falkland Islands — A1

Engr., Center Litho. in Black
1946, Feb. 1   Wmk. 4   *Perf. 12*
1L1 A1 ½p yellow green   .95 1.50
1L2 A1 1p blue violet   .95 1.90
1L3 A1 2p deep carmine   .95 1.90
1L4 A1 3p ultramarine   1.90 1.90
1L5 A1 4p deep plum   1.90 3.00
1L6 A1 6p orange yellow   1.90 3.00

1L7	A1	9p brown	3.00	3.50
1L8	A1	1sh rose violet	5.75	7.50
		Nos. 1L1-1L8 (8)	18.40	24.70

Nos. 1-8 were reissued in 1948, printed on more opaque paper with the lines of the map finer and clearer. Value for set, unused or used $120.
See No. 1L13.

Common Design Types
pictured following the introduction.

Peace Issue
Common Design Type
1946, Oct. 4   Perf. 13½x14

1L9	CD303	1p purple	.60	.20
1L10	CD303	3p deep blue	1.10	.20

Silver Wedding Issue
Common Design Types
1948, Dec. 6   Photo.   Perf. 14x14½

1L11	CD304	2½p brt ultra	1.25	1.25

Perf. 11½x11
Engr.

1L12	CD305	1sh blue violet	5.75	5.75

Type of 1946
1949, Mar. 6   Perf. 12
Center Litho. in Black

1L13	A1	2½p deep blue	12.50	12.00

UPU Issue
Common Design Types
Engr.; Name Typo. on 2p, 3p
1949, Oct. 10   Perf. 13½, 11x11½

1L14	CD306	1p violet	1.60	1.90
1L15	CD307	2p deep carmine	4.25	1.90
1L16	CD308	3p indigo	6.50	4.25
1L17	CD309	6p red orange	11.00	8.50
		Nos. 1L14-1L17 (4)	23.35	16.55

Coronation Issue
Common Design Type
1953, June 4   Perf. 13½x13

1L18	CD312	1p purple & black	1.50	1.50

John Biscoe — A2

Trepassey — A3

Ships: 1½p, Wyatt Earp. 2p, Eagle. 2½p, Penola. 3p, Discovery II. 4p, William Scoresby. 6p, Discovery. 9p, Endurance. 1sh, Deutschland. 2sh, Pourquoi-pas? 2sh6p, Français. 5sh, Scotia. 10sh, Antarctic. £1, Belgica.

1954, Feb. 1   Engr.   Perf. 12½
Center in Black

1L19	A2	½p blue green	.20	2.00
1L20	A3	1p sepia	1.75	1.50
1L21	A3	1½p olive	2.00	1.75
1L22	A3	2p rose red	1.25	.20
1L23	A3	2½p yellow	1.25	.20
1L24	A3	3p ultra	1.25	.20
1L25	A3	4p red violet	3.00	.45
1L26	A2	6p rose violet	3.50	.45
1L27	A2	9p black	3.50	1.25
1L28	A3	1sh org brown	3.50	1.00
1L29	A3	2sh lilac rose	18.00	10.00
1L30	A2	2sh6p blue gray	19.00	6.25
1L31	A2	5sh violet	40.00	6.75
1L32	A3	10sh brt blue	55.00	18.00
1L33	A2	£1 black	87.50	50.00
		Nos. 1L19-1L33 (15)	240.70	100.00

Nos. 20, 23-24, 26 Overprinted in Black

1956, Jan 30   Center in Black

1L34	A3	1p sepia	.20	.20
1L35	A3	2½p yellow	.50	.50
1L36	A3	3p ultramarine	.60	.60
1L37	A3	6p rose violet	.70	.70
		Nos. 1L34-1L37 (4)	2.00	2.00

Trans-Antarctic Expedition, 1955-1958.

A4

Wmk. 373
1980, May 5   Litho.   Perf. 13½

1L38	A4	1p Map of Dependencies	.20	.25
1L39	A4	2p Shag Rocks	.20	.25
1L40	A4	3p Bird and Willis Islds.	.20	.25
1L41	A4	4p Gulbrandsen Lake	.20	.25
1L42	A4	5p King Edward Point	.20	.25
1L43	A4	6p Shackleton's Memorial Cross	.20	.25
1L44	A4	7p Shackleton's grave	.20	.25
1L45	A4	8p Grytviken Church	.20	.25
1L46	A4	9p Coaling Hulk "Louise"	.25	.30
1L47	A4	10p Clerke Rocks	.25	.30
1L48	A4	20p Candlemas Island	.45	.55
1L49	A4	25p Twitcher Rock, Cook Island	.60	.70
1L50	A4	50p "John Biscoe"	1.10	1.25
1L51	A4	£1 "Bransfield"	2.25	2.75
1L52	A4	£3 "Endurance"	7.50	9.00
		Nos. 1L38-1L52 (15)	14.00	16.85

Nos. 38-50 exist dated 1984; issued May 3, 1984. Value, set $10.

1985, Nov. 18   Wmk. 384

1L48a	A4	20p	.75	1.10
1L49a	A4	25p	1.00	1.25
1L50a	A4	50p	2.75	3.50
1L51a	A4	£1	4.00	5.00
1L52a	A4	£3	12.50	16.00
		Nos. 1L48a-1L52a (5)	21.00	26.85

Magellanic Clubmoss — A5

1981, Feb. 5   Litho.   Perf. 14

1L53	A5	3p shown	.25	.25
1L54	A5	6p Alpine cat's-tail	.25	.25
1L55	A5	7p Greater burnet	.25	.25
1L56	A5	11p Antarctic bedstraw	.35	.35
1L57	A5	15p Brown rush	.50	.50
a.		Brown missing		
1L58	A5	25p Antarctic hair grass	.75	.75
		Nos. 1L53-1L58 (6)	2.35	2.35

Royal Wedding Issue
Common Design Type
1981, July 22   Litho.   Perf. 14

1L59	CD331	10p Bouquet	.25	.25
1L60	CD331	13p Charles	.35	.35
1L61	CD331	52p Couple	.85	.85
		Nos. 1L59-1L61 (3)	1.45	1.45

Reindeer in Spring — A6

1982, Jan. 29   Litho.   Perf. 14

1L62	A6	5p shown	.20	.20
1L63	A6	13p Autumn	.45	.45
1L64	A6	25p Winter	.80	.80
1L65	A6	26p Late winter	.85	.85
		Nos. 1L62-1L65 (4)	2.30	2.30

Gamasellus Racovitzai — A7

1982, Mar. 16   Litho.   Perf. 14

1L66	A7	5p shown	.20	.20
1L67	A7	10p Alaskozetes antarcticus	.25	.25
1L68	A7	13p Cryptopygus antarcticus	.30	.30
1L69	A7	15p Notiomaso australis	.40	.40
1L70	A7	25p Hydromedion sparsutum	.60	.60
1L71	A7	26p Parochlus steinenii	.65	.65
		Nos. 1L66-1L71 (6)	2.40	2.40

Princess Diana Issue
Common Design Type
1982, July 1   Litho.   Perf. 14x14½

1L72	CD333	5p Arms	.45	.20
1L73	CD333	17p Diana	1.40	.60
a.		Perf. 14	9.00	9.00
1L74	CD333	37p Wedding	3.25	1.40
1L75	CD333	50p Portrait	4.25	1.75
		Nos. 1L72-1L75 (4)	9.35	3.95

Crustacea — A8

Perf. 14½x14
1984, Mar. 23   Wmk. 373

1L76	A8	5p Euphausia superba	.20	.20
1L77	A8	17p Glyptonotus antarcticus	.65	.65
1L78	A8	25p Epimeria monodon	1.00	1.00
1L79	A8	34p Serolis pagenstecheri	1.40	1.40
		Nos. 1L76-1L79 (4)	3.25	3.25

Manned Flight Bicentenary — A9

1983, Dec. 23   Litho.   Perf. 14

1L80	A9	5p Westland Whirlwind	.20	.20
1L81	A9	13p Westland Wasp	.45	.45
1L82	A9	17p Saunders-Roe Walrus	.65	.65
1L83	A9	50p Auster	2.00	2.00
		Nos. 1L80-1L83 (4)	3.30	3.30

South Sandwich Islds. Volcanoes — A10

1984, Nov. 8   Wmk. 373   Perf. 14½

1L84	A10	6p Zavodovski Isld.	.60	.60
1L85	A10	17p Mt. Michael, Saunders Isld.	1.40	1.40
1L86	A10	22p Bellingshausen Isld.	2.00	2.00
1L87	A10	52p Bristol Isld.	4.75	4.75
		Nos. 1L84-1L87 (4)	8.75	8.75

Albatrosses — A11

1985, May 5   Wmk. 384   Perf. 14½

1L88	A11	7p Diomedea chrysostoma	.80	.80
1L89	A11	22p Diomedea melanophris	2.50	2.50
1L90	A11	27p Diomedea exulans	2.75	2.75
1L91	A11	54p Phoebetria palpebrata	5.75	5.75
		Nos. 1L88-1L91 (4)	11.80	11.80

Queen Mother 85th Birthday
Common Design Type

Designs: 7p, 14th birthday celebration. 22p, With Princess Anne, Lady Sarah Armstrong-Jones, Prince Edward. 27p, Queen Mother. 54p, Holding Prince Henry. £1, On the Britannia.

1985, June 23   Perf. 14½x14

1L92	CD336	7p multicolored	.25	.25
1L93	CD336	22p multicolored	.75	.75
1L94	CD336	27p multicolored	1.00	1.00
1L95	CD336	54p multicolored	2.00	2.00
		Nos. 1L92-1L95 (4)	4.00	4.00

Souvenir Sheet

1L96	CD336	£1 multicolored	3.75	3.75

Falkland Islands Naturalists Type of 1985

Naturalists, endangered species: 7p, Dumont d'Urville (1790-1842), kelp. 22p, Johann Reinhold Forster (1729-1798), king penguin. 27p, Johann Georg Adam Forster (1754-1794), tussock grass. 54p, Sir Joseph Banks (1743-1820), dove prion.

1985, Nov. 4   Perf. 13½x14

1L97	A86	7p multicolored	.65	.65
1L98	A86	22p multicolored	1.60	1.60
1L99	A86	27p multicolored	2.40	2.40
1L100	A86	54p multicolored	4.75	4.75
		Nos. 1L97-1L100 (4)	9.40	9.40

SEMI-POSTAL STAMP

Rebuilding Type of Falkland Islands
Wmk. 373
1982, Sept. 13   Litho.   Perf. 11

1LB1	SP1	£1 Map of So. Georgia	3.00	3.00

ISSUES FOR THE SEPARATE ISLANDS

Graham Land

Nos. 84, 85B, 86A, 87A, 88-91 Overprinted in Red

1944, Feb. 12   Wmk. 4   Perf. 12

2L1	A22	½p green & black	.55	.50
2L2	A22	1p dk vio & black	.60	.60
2L3	A22	2p rose car & blk	.90	.85
2L4	A22	3p deep bl & blk	1.25	1.10
2L5	A22	4p rose vio & blk	1.50	1.50
2L6	A22	6p brown & black	4.00	3.50
2L7	A22	9p slate bl & blk	3.00	3.00
2L8	A22	1sh dull blue	3.00	2.75
		Nos. 2L1-2L8 (8)	14.80	13.80

South Georgia

1944, Apr. 3   Wmk. 4   Perf. 12

3L1	A22	½p green & black	.60	.50
3L2	A22	1p dark vio & blk	.65	.60
3L3	A22	2p rose car & blk	1.00	.85
3L4	A22	3p deep bl & blk	1.40	1.10
3L5	A22	4p rose vio & blk	1.60	1.50
3L6	A22	6p brown & black	4.25	4.00
3L7	A22	9p slate bl & blk	3.25	3.00
3L8	A22	1sh dull blue	3.25	3.00
		Nos. 3L1-3L8 (8)	16.00	14.55

South Orkneys

1944, Feb. 21   Wmk. 4   Perf. 12

4L1	A22	½p green & black	.55	.50
4L2	A22	1p dark vio & blk	.60	.60
4L3	A22	2p rose car & blk	.90	.85
4L4	A22	3p deep bl & blk	1.25	1.10
4L5	A22	4p rose vio & blk	1.50	1.50
4L6	A22	6p brown & black	4.00	3.50
4L7	A22	9p slate bl & blk	3.00	3.00
4L8	A22	1sh dull blue	3.00	2.75
		Nos. 4L1-4L8 (8)	14.80	13.80

South Shetlands

1944   Wmk. 4   Perf. 12

5L1	A22	½p green & black	.50	.50
5L2	A22	1p dark vio & blk	.60	.60
5L3	A22	2p rose car & blk	.90	.85
5L4	A22	3p deep bl & blk	1.25	1.10
5L5	A22	4p rose vio & blk	1.50	1.50
5L6	A22	6p brown & black	4.00	3.50
5L7	A22	9p slate bl & blk	3.00	3.00
5L8	A22	1sh dull blue	3.00	2.75
		Nos. 5L1-5L8 (8)	14.75	13.80

FAR EASTERN REPUBLIC

'fär 'ē-stərn ri-'pə-blik

LOCATION — In Siberia east of Lake Baikal
GOVT. — Republic
AREA — 900,745 sq. mi.
POP. — 1,560,000 (approx. 1920)
CAPITAL — Chita

A short-lived independent government was established here in 1920.

100 Kopecks = 1 Ruble

Watermark

Wmk. 171 — Diamonds

Vladivostok Issue
Russian Stamps Surcharged or Overprinted:

a

b

c

On Stamps of 1909-17
Perf. 14, 14½x15, 13½

1920   Unwmk.

2	A14(a)	2k green	10.00	*10.00*
3	A14(a)	3k red	10.00	*10.00*
4	A11(b)	3k on 35k red brn & grn	30.00	*50.00*
5	A15(a)	4k carmine	10.00	*12.00*
6	A11(b)	4k on 70k brn & org	10.00	*8.00*
8	A11(b)	7k on 15k red brn & bl	2.00	2.00
a.		Inverted surcharge	60.00	
b.		Pair, one ovptd. "DBP" only	100.00	
9	A15(a)	10k dark blue	50.00	*55.00*
a.		Overprint on back	80.00	
10	A12(c)	10k on 3½r mar & lt grn	25.00	*25.00*
11	A11(a)	14k blue & rose	35.00	*35.00*
12	A11(a)	15k red brn & bl	25.00	*25.00*
13	A8(a)	20k blue & car	75.00	*100.00*
14	A11(b)	20k on 14k bl & rose	10.00	*8.00*
a.		Surcharge on back	30.00	
15	A11(a)	25k green & vio	25.00	*15.00*
16	A11(a)	35k red brn & grn	35.00	*35.00*
17	A8(a)	50k brn vio & grn	10.00	*12.00*
18	A9(a)	1r pale brn, dk brn & org	750.00	*750.00*

On Stamps of 1917
Imperf

21	A14(a)	1k orange	10.00	*10.00*
22	A14(a)	2k gray grn	10.00	*5.00*
23	A14(a)	3k red	10.00	*10.00*
25	A11(b)	7k on 15k red brn & dp bl	2.00	*5.00*
a.		Pair, one without surcharge	100.00	
b.		Pair, one ovptd. "DBP" only	100.00	
26	A12(c)	10k on 3½r mar & lt grn	15.00	*15.00*
27	A9(a)	1r pale brn, brn & red org	20.00	*20.00*

On Stamps of Siberia 1919
Perf. 14, 14½x15

30	A14(a)	35k on 2k green	5.00	*8.00*
a.		"DBP" on back	25.00	*50.00*

Imperf

31	A14(a)	35k on 2k green	25.00	25.00
32	A14(a)	70k on 1k orange	10.00	*10.00*

Counterfeit surcharges and overprints abound, including digital forgeries.

Postal Savings Stamps Surcharged for Postal Use

A1

Perf. 14½x15
Wmk. 171

35	A1(b)	1k on 5k green, *buff*	20.00	15.00
36	A1(b)	2k on 10k brown, *buff*	35.00	35.00

The letters on these stamps resembling "DBP," are the Russian initials of "Dalne Vostochnaya Respublika" (Far Eastern Republic).

Chita Issue

A2

A2a

1921   Unwmk.   Typo.   Imperf.

38	A2	2k gray green	1.50	1.50
39	A2a	4k rose	3.00	3.00
40	A2	5k claret	3.00	3.00
41	A2a	10k blue	2.50	2.50
		Nos. 38-41 (4)	10.00	10.00

For overprints see Nos. 62-65.

Blagoveshchensk Issue

A3

1921   Litho.   Imperf.

42	A3	2r red	2.75	2.00
43	A3	3r dark green	2.75	2.00
44	A3	5r dark blue	2.75	2.00
a.		Tête bêche pair	30.00	50.00
45	A3	15r dark brown	2.75	2.00
46	A3	30r dark violet	3.00	2.00
a.		Tête bêche pair	35.00	60.00
		Nos. 42-46 (5)	13.75	10.00

Remainders of Nos. 42-46 were canceled in colored crayon or by typographed bars. These sell for half of foregoing values.

Chita Issue

A4

A5

1922   Litho.   Imperf.

49	A4	1k orange	.55	.85
50	A4	3k dull red	.30	.45
51	A5	4k dp rose & buff	.30	.45
52	A4	5k orange brown	.65	.45
53	A4	7k light blue	.65	1.25
a.		Perf. 11½	1.00	2.00
b.		Rouletted 9	2.00	2.00
c.		Perf. 11½x rouletted	4.00	3.00
54	A5	10k dk blue & red	.40	.65
55	A4	15k dull rose	.55	.85
56	A5	20k blue & red	.55	.85
57	A5	30k green & red org	.65	1.10
58	A5	50k black & red org	1.25	1.75
		Nos. 49-58 (10)	5.85	8.65

The 4k exists with "4" omitted. Value $100.

Vladivostok Issue

Stamps of 1921
Overprinted in Red

1922   Imperf.

62	A2	2k gray green	35.00	25.00
a.		Inverted overprint	250.00	
63	A2a	4k rose	35.00	25.00
a.		Inverted overprint	250.00	
b.		Double overprint	250.00	
64	A2	5k claret	35.00	35.00
a.		Inverted overprint	100.00	
b.		Double overprint	350.00	
65	A2a	10k blue	35.00	35.00
a.		Inverted overprint	100.00	
		Nos. 62-65 (4)	140.00	120.00

Russian revolution of Nov. 1917, 5th anniv. Once in the setting the figures "22" of 1922 have the bottom stroke curved instead of straight. Value, each $75.

Vladivostok Issue

Russian Stamps of 1922-23 Surcharged in Black or Red

1923   Imperf.

66	A50	1k on 100r red	.40	1.00
a.		Inverted surcharge	60.00	
67	A50	2k on 70r violet	.40	.75
68	A49	5k on 10r blue (R)	.40	.75
69	A50	10k on 50r brown	.90	1.25
a.		Inverted surcharge	60.00	

Perf. 14½x15

70	A50	1k on 100r red	.90	1.25
		Nos. 66-70 (5)	3.00	5.00

OCCUPATION STAMPS

Issued under Occupation of General Semenov
Chita Issue
Russian Stamps of 1909-12 Surcharged:

р. 1 р.   2р.50к.
a   b

c
Р. 5 Р.

1920   Unwmk.   Perf. 14, 14x15½

N1	A15 (a)	1r on 4k car	50.00	*100.00*
N2	A8 (b)	2r50k on 20k bl & car	20.00	*40.00*
N3	A14 (c)	5r on 5k claret	20.00	*50.00*
a.		Double surcharge	65.00	
N4	A11 (a)	10r on 70k brn & org	20.00	*40.00*
		Nos. N1-N4 (4)	110.00	*230.00*

FAROE ISLANDS

ˈfar-ˌü ˈī-lənds

(The Faroes)

LOCATION — North Atlantic Ocean
GOVT. — Self-governing part of King-
  dom of Denmark
AREA — 540 sq. mi.
POP. — 41,059 (1999 est.)
CAPITAL — Thorshavn

100 Ore = 1 Krone

> Catalogue values for unused
> stamps in this country are for
> Never Hinged items, beginning
> with Scott 7.

Denmark No. 97
Handstamp Surcharged

1919, Jan.   Typo.   Perf. 14x14½
1   A16 2o on 5o green   1,400. 400.00

Counterfeits of surcharge exist.
Denmark No. 88a, the bisect, was used with
Denmark No. 97 in Faroe Islands Jan. 3-23,
1919.

Denmark Nos. 220, 224, 238A, 224C
Surcharged in Blue or Black

Nos. 2, 5-6   No. 3

No. 4

1940-41   Engr.   Perf. 13
2   A32 20o on 1o ('41)   45.00 110.00
3   A32 20o on 5o ('41)   45.00   35.00
4   A30 20o on 15o (Bk)   60.00   22.50
5   A32 50o on 5o (Bk)   300.00   90.00
6   A32 60o on 6o (Bk)   125.00 175.00
    Nos. 2-6 (5)   575.00 432.50
    Set, never hinged   900.00

Issued during British administration.

> Catalogue values for unused
> stamps in this section, from this
> point to the end of the section, are
> for Never Hinged items.

Map of Islands,
1673 — A1

Map of North
Atlantic, 1573 — A2

West Coast,
Sandoy — A3

Vidoy and
Svinoy, by
Eyvindur
Mohr — A4

Designs: 200o, like 70o. 250o, 300o, View
of Streymoy and Vagar. 450o, Houses, Nes,
by Ruth Smith. 500o, View of Hvitanes and
Skalafjordur, by S. Joensen-Mikines.

Unwmk.

1975, Jan. 30   Engr.   Perf. 13
7   A1   5o sepia   .20   .20
8   A2   10o emer & dark blue .20   .20
9   A1   50o graysh green   .20   .20
10   A2   60o brown & dark blue 1.00 1.00
11   A3   70o vio bl & slate grn 1.00 1.00
12   A2   80o ocher & dark blue .40   .50
13   A1   90o red brown   1.00 1.00
14   A2   120o brt bl & dark bl .40   .45
15   A3   200o vio bl & slate grn .40 .50
16   A3   250o multicolored   .35   .45
17   A3   300o multicolored   5.00 2.25

Photo.
Perf. 12½x13
18   A4   350o multicolored   .65   .80
19   A4   450o multicolored   .75   .80
20   A4   500o multicolored   .85   .95
    Nos. 7-20 (14)   12.40 10.30

Faroe
Boat — A5

Faroe
Flag — A6

Faroe Mailman — A7

Perf. 12½x13, 12 (A6)
1976, Apr. 1   Engr.; Litho. (A6)
21   A5   125o copper red   2.00 1.25
22   A6   160o multicolored   .40   .30
23   A7   800o olive   1.60 1.10
    Nos. 21-23 (3)   4.00 2.65

Faroe Islands independent postal service,
Apr. 1, 1976.

Motor
Fishing
Boat — A8

Faroese Fishing Vessels and Map of
Islands: 125o, Inland fishing cutter. 160o,
Modern seine fishing vessel. 600o, Deep-sea
fishing trawler.

1977, Apr. 28   Photo.   Perf. 14½x14
24   A8   100o green & black   6.00 5.50
25   A8   125o carmine & black 1.75 1.75
26   A8   160o blue & black   .55   .55
27   A8   600o brown & black   .85   .85
    Nos. 24-27 (4)   9.15 8.65

Common
Snipe
A9

Photogravure & Engraved
1977, Sept. 29   Perf. 14½x14
28   A9   70o shown   .25   .20
29   A9   180o Oystercatcher   .50   .40
30   A9   250o Whimbrel   .90   .65
    Nos. 28-30 (3)   1.65 1.25

North Coast,
Puffins — A10

Mykines
Village — A11

Mykines Island: 140o, Tilled fields and
coast. 150o, Aerial view. 180o, Map.

Perf. 13x13½, 13½x13
1978, Jan. 26   Photo.
Size: 21x28mm, 28x21mm
31   A10 100o multicolored   .25   .25
32   A11 130o multicolored   .35   .35
33   A11 140o multicolored   .55   .55
34   A10 150o multicolored   .40   .40
Size: 37x26mm
Perf. 14½x14
35   A11 180o multicolored   .40   .40
    Nos. 31-35 (5)   1.95 1.95

Sea Birds — A12

Old
Library — A13

Lithographed and Engraved
1978, Apr. 13   Perf. 12x12½
36   A12 140o Gannets   .90   .90
37   A12 180o Puffins   1.25 1.25
38   A12 400o Guillemots   .90   .90
    Nos. 36-38 (3)   3.05 3.05

1978, Dec. 7   Perf. 13
39   A13 140o shown   .60   .55
40   A13 180o New library   .60   .65

Completion of New Library Building.

Girl Guide, Tent
and Fire — A14

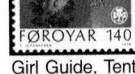

Ram — A15

1978, Dec. 7   Photo.   Perf. 13½
41   A14 140o multicolored   .70   .70

Faroese Girl Guides, 50th anniversary.

Lithographed and Engraved
1979, Mar. 19   Perf. 12
42   A15 25k multicolored   6.25 5.75

Denmark No.
88a — A16

Europa: 180o, Faroe Islands No. 1.

1979, May 7   Perf. 12½
43   A16 140o yellow & blue   .40   .40
44   A16 180o rose, grn & blk .40   .40

Girl Wearing
Festive
Costume — A17

Children's Drawings and IYC Emblem:
150o, Fisherman. 200o, Two friends.

1979, Oct. 1   Perf. 12
45   A17 110o multicolored   .30   .30
46   A17 150o multicolored   .45   .45
47   A17 200o multicolored   .55   .55
    Nos. 45-47 (3)   1.30 1.30

International Year of the Child.

Sea Plantain — A18

1980, Mar. 17 Photo. Perf. 12x11½
48   A18 90o shown   .30   .30
49   A18 110o Glacier buttercup .30 .30
50   A18 150o Purple saxifrage .45   .45
51   A18 200o Starry saxifrage .60   .60
52   A18 400o Lady's mantle   1.00 1.00
    Nos. 48-52 (5)   2.65 2.65

Jakob Jakobsen
(1864-1918),
Linguist — A19

Coat of Arms,
Virgin and Child,
Gothic Pew
Gable — A20

Europa: 200o, Vensel Ulrich Hammer-
shaimb (1819-1909), theologian, linguist and
folklorist.

1980, Oct. 6   Engr.   Perf. 11½
53   A19 150o dull green   .30   .30
54   A19 200o dull red brown   .50   .50

Photo. & Engr.
1980, Oct. 6   Perf. 13½

Kirkjubour Pew Gables, 15th Century: 140o,
Norwegian coat of arms, John the Baptist.
150o, Christ's head, St. Peter. 200o, Hand in
halo, Apostle Paul.

55   A20 110o multicolored   .25   .25
56   A20 140o multicolored   .45   .45
57   A20 150o multicolored   .45   .45
58   A20 200o multicolored   .60   .60
    Nos. 55-58 (4)   1.75 1.75

See Nos. 102-105.

A21

Sketches of Old Torshavn by Ingalzur Reyni

1981, Mar. 2   **Engr.**
59 A21 110o dark green   .25 .25
60 A21 140o black   .45 .45
61 A21 150o dark brown   .45 .45
62 A21 200o dark blue   .55 .55
    Nos. 59-62 (4)   1.70 1.70

The Ring Dance A22

Europa: 200o, The garter dance.

1981, June 1   Engr.   Perf. 13x14
63 A22 150o pale rose & grn   .30 .30
64 A22 200o pale yel grn & dk brn .45 .45

Rune Stones, 800-1000 AD — A23

Historic Writings: 1k, Folksong, 1846. 3k, Sheep Letter excerpt, 1298. 6k, Seal and text, 1533. 10k, Titlepage from Faeroae et Faeroa, by Lucas Jacobson Debes, library.

Photo. & Engr.

1981, Oct. 19   Perf. 11½
65 A23 10o multicolored   .20 .20
66 A23 1k multicolored   .30 .30
67 A23 3k multicolored   .75 .70
68 A23 6k multicolored   1.50 1.25
69 A23 10k multicolored   2.50 2.50
    Nos. 65-69 (5)   5.25 4.95

Nos. 70-80 not assigned.

Europa 1982 — A24

1982, Mar. 15   Engr.   Perf. 13½
81 A24 1.50k Viking North Atlantic routes .35 .35
82 A24 2k Viking house foundation .50 .50

View of Gjogv, by Ingalvur av Reyni A25

1982, June 7   Litho.   Perf. 12½x13
83 A25 180o shown   .35 .35
84 A25 220o Hvalvik   1.40 1.10
85 A25 250o Kvivik   .50 .50
    Nos. 83-85 (3)   2.25 1.95

Ballad of Harra Paetur and Elinborg — A26

Scenes from the medieval ballad of chivalry.

1982, Sept. 27   Litho.
86 A26 220o multicolored   .55 .55
87 A26 250o multicolored   .65 .65
88 A26 350o multicolored   .90 .90
89 A26 450o multicolored   1.40 1.40
    Nos. 86-89 (4)   3.50 3.50

Cargo Ships A27

1983, Feb. 21   Litho.   Perf. 14x14½
90 A27 220o Arcturus, 1856   .75 .75
91 A27 250o Laura, 1882   .80 .80
92 A27 700o Thyra, 1866   2.25 2.25
    Nos. 90-92 (3)   3.80 3.80

Chessmen, by Pol i Buo (1791-1857) — A28

1983, May 2   Engr.   Perf. 13 Vert.
Booklet Stamps
93   250o King   3.00 3.00
94   250o Queen   3.00 3.00
 a. Bklt. pane of 6, 3 each #93-94 17.50
 b. A28 Pair, #93-94   6.00 6.00

Europa 1983 — A29

Nobel Prizewinners in Medicine: 250o, Niels R. Finsen (1860-1903), ultraviolet radiation pioneer. 400o, Alexander Fleming (1881-1955), discoverer of penicillin.

1983, June 6   Engr.   Perf. 12x11½
95 A29 250o dark blue   .55 .55
96 A29 400o red brown   .95 .95

A30

1983, Sept. 19   Litho.   Perf. 12½x13
97   A30 250o Tusk   .90 .90
98   A30 280o Haddock   1.25 1.25
99   A30 500o Halibut   1.50 1.50
100 A30 900o Catfish   2.75 2.75
     Nos. 97-100 (4)   6.40 6.40

Souvenir Sheet

Traditional Costumes — A31

Various national costumes.

1983, Nov. 4   Litho.   Perf. 12
101 A31 Sheet of 3   9.25 9.25
 a.-c. 250o multicolored 2.10 2.10

Nordic House Cultural Center opening. Margin shows Scandinavian flags.

Pew Gables Type of 1980

Designs: 250o, John, shield with three crowns. 300o, St. Jacob, shield with crossed keys. 350o, Thomas, shield with crossbeam. 400o, Judas Taddeus, Toulouse cross halo.

Photo. & Engr.

1984, Jan. 30   Perf. 14x13½
102 A20 250o lil, pur & dk brn   .75 .75
103 A20 300o red brn, dk buff & dk brn .90 .90
104 A20 350o blk, lt gray & dk brn 1.10 1.10
105 A20 400o ol grn, pale yel & dk brn 1.25 1.25
     Nos. 102-105 (4)   4.00 4.00

Europa (1959-84) A33

1984, Apr. 2   Engr.   Perf. 13½
106 A33 250o red   .60 .60
107 A33 500o dark blue   1.40 1.40

Sverri Patursson (1871-1960), Writer — A34

Poets: 2.50k, Joannes Patursson (1866-1946). 3k, J. H. O. Djurhuus (1881-1948). 4.50k, H.A. Djurhuus (1883-1951).

1984, May 28   Engr.   Perf. 13½
108 A34   2k olive green   .60 .60
109 A34 2.50k red   .75 .75
110 A34   3k dark blue   .90 .90
111 A34 4.50k violet   1.50 1.50
     Nos. 108-111 (4)   3.75 3.75

Faroese Smack (Fishing Boat) — A35

Perf. 12½x13, 13x12½
1984, Sept. 10   Engr.
112 A35 280o shown   .95 .95
113 A35 300o Fishermen, vert. 1.10 1.10
114 A35 12k Helmsman, vert. 4.00 4.00
     Nos. 112-114 (3)   6.05 6.05

Fairytale Illustrations by Elinborg Lutzen — A36

1984, Oct. 29   Litho.   Perf. 13 Vert.
Booklet Stamps
115 A36 140o Beauty of the Veils 5.00 5.00
116 A36 280o Veils, diff.   5.00 5.00
117 A36 280o Girl Shy Prince 5.00 5.00
118 A36 280o The Glass Sword 5.00 5.00
119 A36 280o Little Elin   5.00 5.00
120 A36 280o The Boy and the Ox 5.00 5.00
 a. Booklet pane of 6, #115-120 32.50

View of Torshavn and the Forts, by Edward Dayes A37

Dayes' Landscapes, 1789: 280o, Skaeling. 550o, View Towards the North Seen from the Hills Near Torshavn in Stremoy, Faroes. 800o, The Moving Stones in Eysturoy, Faroes.

Litho. & Engr.

1985, Feb. 4   Perf. 13
121 A37 250o multicolored   .75 .75
122 A37 280o multicolored   .85 .75
123 A37 550o multicolored   2.00 1.90
124 A37 800o multicolored   2.75 2.75
     Nos. 121-124 (4)   6.35 6.15

Europa 1985 — A38

Children taking music lessons.

1985, Apr. 1   Litho.   Perf. 13½x14½
125 A38 280o multicolored   .85 .85
126 A38 550o multicolored   1.90 1.90

Paintings, Faroese Museum of Art A39

Designs: 550o, Winter's Day in Nolsoy, 1959, by Steffan Danielsen (1922-76). 450o, Self-Portrait, 1952, by Ruth Smith (1913-58), vert. 280o, The Garden, Hoyvik, 1973, by Thomas Arge (1942-78).

Litho. & Engr.

1985, June 3   Perf. 12½
127 A39 280o multicolored   1.25 1.25
128 A39 450o multicolored   1.75 1.75
129 A39 550o multicolored   2.50 2.10
     Nos. 127-129 (3)   5.50 5.10

Lighthouses — A40

1985, Sept. 23   Litho.   Perf. 13½x14
130 A40 270o Nolsoy, 1893   1.00 .90
131 A40 320o Thorshavn, 1909 1.40 1.25
132 A40 350o Mykines, 1909 1.50 1.40
133 A40 470o Map of locations 2.10 1.90
     Nos. 130-133 (4)   6.00 5.45

Passenger Aviation in the Faroes, 22nd Anniv. A41

Perf. 13½ Horiz.
1985, Oct. 28   Photo.
Booklet Stamps
134 A41 300o Douglas DC-3   2.75 2.75
135 A41 300o Fokker Friendship 2.75 2.75
136 A41 300o Boeing 737   2.75 2.75
137 A41 300o Interisland LM-IKB 2.75 2.75
138 A41 300o Helicopter Snipan 2.75 2.75
 a. Booklet pane of 5, #134-138 14.50 14.50

Skrimsla, Ancient Folk Ballad — A42

1986, Feb. 3   Litho.   Perf. 12½x13
139 A42 300o Peasant in woods 1.00 1.00
140 A42 420o Meets Giant   1.40 1.40
141 A42 550o Giant loses game 1.75 1.75

142 A42 650o Giant grants Peasant's wish 2.00 1.75
Nos. 139-142 (4) 6.15 5.90

Europa 1986 — A43

Amnesty Intl., 25th Anniv. — A44

1986, Apr. 7   Litho.   Perf. 13½
143 A43   3k shown   1.00 1.00
144 A43   5.50k Sea pollution   1.75 1.75

1986, June 2   Perf. 14x13½
Winning design competition artwork.
145 A44   3k Olivur vid Neyst   1.00 .75
146 A44   4.70k Eli Smith   1.75 1.25
147 A44   5.50k Ranna Kunoy   2.25 1.75
Nos. 145-147 (3) 5.00 3.75

Nos. 145-146 horiz.

Souvenir Sheet

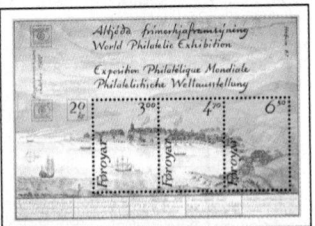

HAFNIA '87, Copenhagen — A45

Design: East Bay of Torshavn, watercolor, 1782, by Christian Rosenmeyer (1728-1802).

1986, Aug. 29   Litho.   Perf. 13x13½
148 A45   Sheet of 3   9.00 9.00
a.   3k multicolored   3.00 3.00
b.   4.70k multicolored   3.00 3.00
c.   6.50k multicolored   3.00 3.00

Sold for 20k.

Old Stone Bridges A46

2.70k, Glyvrar on Eysturoy. 3k, Leypanagjogv on Vagar, vert. 13k, Skaelinger on Streymoy.

Perf. 13½x14½, 14½x13½
1986, Oct. 13   Engr.
149 A46   2.70k dp brown vio   1.90 1.60
150 A46   3k bluish blk   1.60 1.40
151 A46   13k gray green   3.50 3.00
Nos. 149-151 (3) 7.00 6.00

Farmhouses — A47

Traditional architecture: 300o, Depil on Borooy, 1814. 420o, Depil, diff. 470o, Frammi vio Gjonna on Streymoy, c. 1814. 650o, Frammi, diff.

1987, Feb. 9   Engr.   Perf. 13x14½
152 A47   300o pale blue & blue   1.00 .90
153 A47   420o buff & brown   1.60 1.40
154 A47   470o pale grn & dp grn   2.00 1.60
155 A47   650o pale gray & black   2.50 2.25
Nos. 152-155 (4) 7.10 6.15

Europa 1987 — A48

Nordic House.

1987, Apr. 6   Perf. 13x14
156 A48   300o Exterior   .85 .85
157 A48   550o Interior   1.90 1.60

Fishing Trawlers A49

1987, June 1   Litho.   Perf. 14x13½
158 A49   3k Joannes Patursson   .90 .80
159 A49   5.50k Magnus Heinason   1.90 1.75
160 A49   8k Sjurdarberg   4.00 3.75
Nos. 158-160 (3) 6.80 6.30

Hestur (Horse) Island A50

1987, Sept. 7   Litho. & Engr.   Perf. 13
161 A50   270o Map   .90 .85
162 A50   300o Seaport   .70 .60
163 A50   420o Bird cliff   1.60 1.40
164 A50   470o Pasture, sheep   1.90 1.75
165 A50   550o Seashore   1.90 1.75
Nos. 161-165 (5) 7.00 6.35

Nos. 161, 163 and 165 vert.

Collages by Zacharias Heinesen A51

1987, Oct. 16   Litho.   Perf. 13½x14
166 A51   4.70k Eystaravag   1.75 1.60
167 A51   6.50k Vestarvag   2.25 2.00

Souvenir Sheet
Perf. 13½x13
168 A52   3k multicolored   3.50 3.50

West Bay of Torshavn, Watercolor by Rosenmeyer — A52

HAFNIA '87. Sold for 4k.

Flowers — A53   Europa — A54

1988, Feb. 8   Litho.   Perf. 11½
Granite Paper
169 A53   2.70k Bellis perennis   1.40 1.40
170 A53   3k Dactylorchis maculata   .75 .75
171 A53   4.70k Potentilla erecta   2.10 2.10
172 A53   9k Pinguicula vulgaris   3.00 3.00
Nos. 169-172 (4) 7.25 7.25

1988, Apr. 11   Photo.   Perf. 11½
Communication and transport.
173 A54   3k Satellite dish, satellite   1.10 1.10
174 A54   5.50k Fork lift, crane, ship   1.90 1.90

A55   A56

Writers: 270o, Jorgen-Frantz Jacobsen (1900-38). 300o, Christian Matras (b. 1900). 470o, William Heinesen (b. 1900). 650o, Hedin Bru (1901-87).

1988, June 6   Engr.   Perf. 13½
175 A55   270o myrtle green   1.40 1.40
176 A55   300o rose lake   1.25 1.25
177 A55   470o dark blue   1.90 1.90
178 A55   650o brown black   2.10 2.10
Nos. 175-178 (4) 6.65 6.65

1988, Sept. 5   Photo.   Perf. 12
Text, illustrations and cameo portraits of organizers: 3k, Announcement and Djoni Geil, Enok Baerentsen and H.H. Jacobsen. 3.20k, Meeting, Rasmus Effersoe, C.L. Johannesen and Samal Krakusteini. 12k, Oystercatcher and lyrics of *Now the Hour Has Come,* by poet Sverri Patursson (1871-1960), Just A. Husum, Joannes Patursson and Jens Olsen.

Granite Paper
179 A56   3k multicolored   1.25 1.25
180 A56   3.20k multicolored   1.25 1.25
181 A56   12k multicolored   4.50 4.50
Nos. 179-181 (3) 7.00 7.00

1888 Christmas meeting to preserve cultural traditions and the natl. language, cent.

Kirkjubour Cathedral Ruins A57

270o, Exterior. 300o, Arch. 470o, Crucifixion, bas-relief. 550o, Interior.

1988, Oct. 17   Engr.   Perf. 13
182 A57   270o dark green   1.60 1.60
183 A57   300o dark bl, vert.   1.25 1.25
184 A57   470o dark brn, vert.   1.75 1.75
185 A57   550o dark violet   1.90 1.90
Nos. 182-185 (4) 6.50 6.50

Havnar Church, Torshavn, 200th Anniv. A58

Designs: 350o, Church exterior. 500o, Crypt, vert. 15k, Bell, vert.

1989, Feb. 6   Engr.   Perf. 13
186 A58   350o dark green   1.25 1.25
187 A58   500o dark brown   2.25 2.25
188 A58   15k deep blue   4.50 4.50
Nos. 186-188 (3) 8.00 8.00

Folk Costumes — A59

Photo. & Engr.
1989, Apr. 10   Perf. 13½
189 A59   350o Man   1.25 1.25
190 A59   600o Woman   2.50 2.50

Europa 1989 — A60

Wooden children's toys.

1989, Apr. 10   Photo.   Perf. 12x11½
Granite Paper
191 A60   3.50k Boat   1.25 1.25
192 A60   6k Horse   2.00 2.00

Island Games, July 5-13 — A61

1989, June 5   Photo.   Perf. 12½
Granite Paper
193 A61   2000o Rowing   .75 .75
194 A61   3500o Handball   1.50 1.50
195 A61   6000o Soccer   2.25 2.25
196 A61   7000o Swimming   2.50 2.50
Nos. 193-196 (4) 7.00 7.00

A62   A63

Bird cliffs of Suduroy.

1989, Oct. 2   Engr.   Perf. 14x13½
197 A62   320o Tvoran   1.10 1.10
198 A62   350o Skuvanes   1.40 1.40
199 A62   500o Beinisvord   1.90 1.90
200 A62   600o Asmundarstakkur   2.10 2.10
Nos. 197-200 (4) 6.50 6.50

1990, Feb. 5   Litho.   Perf. 14x13½
Modern fish factory (filleting station).
201 A63   3.50k Unloading fish   1.00 1.00
202 A63   3.70k Cleaning and sorting   1.75 1.75
203 A63   5k Filleting   2.00 2.00
204 A63   7k Packaged frozen fish   2.25 2.25
Nos. 201-204 (4) 7.00 7.00

Europa 1990 — A64

Post offices.

1990, Apr. 9   Litho.   Perf. 13½x14
205 A64   3.50k Gjogv   1.10 1.10
206 A64   6k Klaksvik   2.00 2.00

Souvenir Sheet

Recognition of the Merkid, Flag of the Faroes, by the British, 50th Anniv. — A65

Designs: a, Flag. b, Fishing trawler *Nyggjaberg*, disappeared, 1942. c, Sloop *Saana*, sunk by the Germans, 1942.

1990, Apr. 9   Photo.   Perf. 12
Granite Paper
207 A65 Sheet of 3   4.50 4.50
a.-c.   3.50k any single   1.50 1.50

Whales
A66

1990, June 6   Photo.   Perf. 11½
Granite Paper
208 A66 320o Mesoplodon
                bidens   1.50 1.25
209 A66 350o Balaena mys-
                ticetus   2.00 1.75
210 A66 600o Eubalaena
                glacialis   3.25 2.00
211 A66 700o Hyperoodon
                ampullatus   5.25 2.50
          Nos. 208-211 (4)   12.00 7.50

Nolsoy Island by Steffan Danielsen A67

1990, Oct. 8   Photo.   Perf. 11½
Granite Paper
212 A67   50o shown   .25   .25
213 A67 350o Coastline   1.40 1.40
214 A67 500o Town   1.75 1.75
215 A67 1000o Coastline, cliffs 3.75 3.75
          Nos. 212-215 (4)   7.15 7.15

Flora and
Fauna — A68   Europa — A69

1991, Feb. 4   Litho.   Perf. 13
216 A68 3.70k Plantago lanceo-
                 lata   1.40 1.40
217 A68   4k   Rumex longifolius 1.40 1.40
218 A68 4.50k Amara aulica   1.75 1.75
219 A68 6.50k Lumbricus ter-
                 restris   3.00 3.00
          Nos. 216-219 (4)   7.55 7.55

1991, Apr. 4   Litho.   Perf. 13
Designs: 3.70k, Weather satellite. 6.50k, Celestial navigation.
220 A69 3.70k multicolored   1.00 1.00
221 A69 6.50k multicolored   2.00 2.00

Town of Torshavn, 125th Anniv. — A70

1991, Apr. 4   Perf. 14x13½
222 A70 3.70k Town Hall   1.25 1.25
223 A70 3.70k View of town   1.50 1.50

Birds — A71

1991, June 3   Litho.   Perf. 13½
224 A71 3.70k Rissa tridactyla 1.50 1.50
225 A71 3.70k Sterna paradisaea 1.50 1.50
a.   Bklt. pane, 3 each #224-225   9.00

Village of
Saksun
A72

1991, June 3
226 A72 370o shown   1.50 1.50
227 A72 650o Cliffs of Vestman-
                na   2.50 2.50

Samal Joensen-Mikines (1906-1979),
Painter — A73

1991, Oct. 7   Litho.   Perf. 13½
228 A73 340o Funeral Proces-
                sion   1.25 1.25
229 A73 370o The Farewell   1.40 1.40
230 A73 550o Handanagarthur   2.00 2.00
231 A73 1300o Winter morning   4.50 4.50
          Nos. 228-231 (4)   9.15 9.15

Mail Boats
A74

1992, Feb. 10   Litho.   Perf. 13½x14
232 A74 200o Ruth   .75   .75
233 A74 370o Ritan   1.25 1.25
234 A74 550o Sigmundur   1.90 1.90
235 A74 800o Masin   2.75 2.75
          Nos. 232-235 (4)   6.65 6.65

Europa
A75

Designs: 3.70k, Map of North Atlantic, Viking ship. 6.50k, Map of Central Atlantic region, one of Columbus' ships.

1992, Apr. 6   Litho.   Perf. 13½x14
236 A75 3.70k multicolored   .90   .90
237 A75 6.50k multicolored   2.10 2.10

Souvenir Sheet
238 A75 Sheet of 2, #236-237   9.00 4.75

First landing in the Americas by Leif Erikson (#236). Discovery of America by Christopher Columbus, 500th anniv. (#237).

Seals
A76

1992, June 9   Litho.   Perf. 14x13½
239 A76 3.70k Halichoerus
                 grypus   1.50 1.50
240 A76 3.70k Phoca vitulina   1.50 1.50
a.   Bklt. pane, 3 #239, 3 #240   19.00

Minerals — A77

1992, June 9   Photo.   Perf. 12
Granite Paper
241 A77 370o Stilbite   1.75 1.75
242 A77 650o Mesolite   2.25 2.25

Traditional
Houses
A78

1992, Oct. 5   Litho.   Perf. 13½
243 A78 3.40k Hja Glyvra Hanusi 1.25 1.25
244 A78 3.70k I Nordragotu   1.90 1.90
245 A78 6.50k Blasastova   2.25 2.25
246 A78   8k   Jakupsstova   2.50 2.50
          Nos. 243-246 (4)   7.90 7.90

Nordic House Entertainers — A79

1993, Feb. 8   Litho.   Perf. 13½
247 A79 400o Dancers   1.50 1.50
248 A79 400o Pianist   1.50 1.50
249 A79 400o Trio   1.50 1.50
a.   Souv. sheet, #247-249, perf 12½   4.50 4.50
          Nos. 247-249 (3)   4.50 4.50

Village of
Gjogv
A80

1993, Apr. 5
250 A80 4k View toward sea   1.75 1.75
251 A80 4k Ravine, village   1.75 1.75
a.   Booklet pane, 3 each #250-251   10.50

Europa — A81   Horses — A82

Sculptures by Hans Pauli Olsen: 4k, Movement. 7k, Reflection.

1993, Apr. 5
252 A81 4k multicolored   1.00 1.00
253 A81 7k multicolored   2.00 2.00

Perf. 13½x13, 13x13½
1993, June 7   Engr.
254 A82 400o shown   1.50 1.50
255 A82 20k Mare, foal, horiz. 7.50 7.50

Butterflies
A83

1993, Oct. 4   Litho.   Perf. 14½
256 A83 350o Apamea zeta   1.50 1.50
257 A83 400o Hepialus humuli   1.75 1.75
258 A83 700o Vanessa atalanta   2.40 2.40
259 A83 900o Perizoma albulata 3.25 3.25
          Nos. 256-259 (4)   8.90 8.90

Fish — A84

1994, Feb. 7   Litho.   Perf. 14½
260 A84 10o Gasterosteus
               aculeatus   .50   .50
261 A84   4k Neocyttus helgae   1.75 1.75
262 A84   7k Salmo trutta fario 2.25 2.25
263 A84 10k Hoplostethus atlan-
               ticus   3.50 3.50
          Nos. 260-263 (4)   8.00 8.00

Voyages of
St.
Brendan
(484-577)
A85

Europa: 4k, St. Brendan on island with sheep, Irish monks in boat. 7k, St. Brendan, monks sailing past volcano.

1994, Apr. 18   Litho.   Perf. 14½x14
264 A85 4k multicolored   1.10 1.10
265 A85 7k multicolored   2.25 1.90
a.   Miniature sheet of 2, #264-265   4.00 4.00

Nos. 264-265 have designers name below the design. Stamps in No. 265a do not.
See Iceland Nos. 780-781; Ireland Nos. 923-924.

Sheepdogs — A86

School of
Navigation
A87

Design: No. 267, Dog watching over sheep.

1994, June 6   Litho.   Perf. 13½
266 A86 4k multicolored   1.50 1.50
Size: 39x25mm
267 A86 4k multicolored   1.50 1.50
a.   Booklet pane, 3 each #266-267   9.00
          Complete booklet,
          #267a   10.00

1994, June 6
Designs: 3.50k, Man using sextant, schooner. 7k, Ship, man at computer.
268 A87 3.50k multicolored   1.25 1.25
269 A87 7k   multicolored   2.75 2.75

Brusajokil's Lay — A88

Scenes, verses of the ballad: 1k, Ship at sea. 4k, Asbjorn entering Brasajokil's cave. 6k, Ormar with cat, trolls. 7k, Ormar pulling Brusajokil's beard.

1994, Sept. 19   Litho.   *Perf. 14*
270	A88 1k multicolored	.30	.30
271	A88 4k multicolored	1.75	1.75
272	A88 6k multicolored	2.25	2.25
273	A88 7k multicolored	2.75	2.75
	Nos. 270-273 (4)	7.05	7.05

Twelve Days of Christmas A89

#274, Goats, men, deer, hides. #275, Ducks, cattle, sheep, horses, banners, barrels.

1994, Oct. 31   Litho.   *Perf. 14x13*
274	A89 4k multicolored	1.50	1.50
275	A89 4k multicolored	1.50	1.50
a.	Bklt. pane, 3 each #274-275	9.00	
	Complete booklet, #275a	9.00	

Leafhoppers — A90

Designs: 50o, Ulopa reticulata. 4k, Streptanus sordidus. 5k, Anoscopus flavostriatus. 13k, Macrosteles alpinus.

1995, Feb. 6   Litho.   *Perf. 14*
276	A90 50o multicolored	.25	.25
277	A90 4k multicolored	1.60	1.60
278	A90 5k multicolored	1.60	1.60
279	A90 13k multicolored	5.00	5.00
	Nos. 276-279 (4)	8.45	8.45

Tourism A91

1995, Apr. 10   Litho.   *Perf. 13½x14*
280	A91 4k Village of Famjin	1.50	1.50
281	A91 4k Vatnsdalur valley	1.50	1.50

Peace & Freedom A92

Europa: 4k, Island couple, "Vidar, vali og baldur." 7k, Couple looking toward sun, "Liv og livtrasir."

1995, Apr. 10   *Perf. 13x14*
282	A92 4k multicolored	*1.25*	*1.25*
283	A92 7k multicolored	*2.25*	*2.25*

Nordic Art — A93

Designs: 2k, Museum of Art, Torshavn. 4k, Woman, by Frimod Joensen, vert. 5.50k, Self-portrait, by Joensen, vert.

Perf. 13½x14, 14x13½

1995, June 12   Litho.
284	A93 2k multicolored	.75	.75
285	A93 4k multicolored	1.50	1.50
286	A93 5.50k multicolored	2.00	2.00
	Nos. 284-286 (3)	4.25	4.25

Corvus Corax A94

1995, June 12   *Perf. 13½x14*
287	A94 4k Black raven	1.60	1.60
288	A94 4k White-speckled raven	1.60	1.60
a.	Booklet pane, 5 each #287-288	16.00	
	Complete booklet, #288a	16.00	

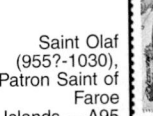

Saint Olaf (955?-1030), Patron Saint of Faroe Islands — A95

Litho. & Engr.

1995, Sept. 12   *Perf. 13½x13*
289	A95 4k multicolored	1.60	1.60

See Aland Islands No. 119.

Early Folk Life — A95a

4k, Dairy maids carrying buckets. 6k, Peasants fleecing sheep. 15k, Schooners, saltfish being brought ashore, vert.

1995, Sept. 12   Engr.   *Perf. 12½*
290	A95a 4k dark green	1.50	1.50
291	A95a 6k dark brn, vert.	2.25	2.25
292	A95a 15k dark blue	5.50	5.50
	Nos. 290-292 (3)	9.25	9.25

Church of Mary Catholic Church — A96

Designs: No. 293, Stained glass window. No. 294, Exterior view of church.

1995, Nov. 9   Litho.   *Perf. 13½*
293	A96 4k multicolored	1.60	1.60
294	A96 4k multicolored	1.60	1.60
a.	Booklet pane, 5 ea #293-294	16.00	
	Complete booklet, #294a	16.00	

Rocky Coastline — A97   Seaweed — A98

1996, Jan. 1   Litho.   *Perf. 14*
295	A97 4.50k multicolored	1.75	1.75

1996, Feb. 12   *Perf. 15*

4k, Ptilota plumosa. 5.50k, Fucus spiralis. 6k, Ascophyllum nodosum. 9k, Laminaria hyperborea.
296	A98 4k multicolored	1.40	1.40
297	A98 5.50k multicolored	2.00	2.00
298	A98 6k multicolored	2.00	2.00
299	A98 9k multicolored	3.25	3.25
	Nos. 296-299 (4)	8.65	8.65

Birds — A99

A100

1996, Apr. 15   Litho.   *Perf. 14x15*
300	A99 4.50k Laxia curvirostra	1.60	1.60
301	A99 4.50k Bombycilla garrulus	1.60	1.60
a.	Booklet pane, 5 each #300-301	17.00	
	Complete booklet, #301a	17.00	

See Nos. 313-314.

1996, Apr. 15   *Perf. 15x14½, 14½x15*

Europa (Wives of Faroese Seamen): 4.50k, Woman standing beside sea coast. 7.50k, Portrait of a woman, vert.
302	A100 4.50k multicolored	*1.50*	*1.50*
303	A100 7.50k multicolored	*2.50*	*2.50*

A101

Nordatlantex '96 (Children's drawings): a, Boy playing with hoop, stick, by Bugvi. b, Two girls on steet, road sign, by Gudrid. c, Girl on bicycle, car on street, by Herborg.

1996, June 7   Litho.   *Perf. 14½*
Souvenir Sheet of 3
304	A101 4.50k #a.-c.	5.00	5.00

A102

Litho. & Engr.

1996, June 7   *Perf. 13*

Sea bed off the Faroes.
305	A102 10k violet & multi	3.50	3.50
306	A102 16k green & multi	5.50	5.50

See Nos. 319-320, 343, 377-378.

James Kamban (b. 1913), Sculptor, Graphic Artist A103

Works of art: 4.50k, Flock of Sheep. 6.50k, Fisherman on the Way Home. 7.50k, View from Tórshavn's Old Quarter.

1996, Sept. 16   Litho.   *Perf. 14*
307	A103 4.50k multicolored	1.60	1.60
308	A103 6.50k multicolored	2.40	2.40
309	A103 7.50k multicolored	2.75	2.75
	Nos. 307-309 (3)	6.75	6.75

A104

Christianschurch, Klaksvík — A105

1996, Nov. 4   Litho.   *Perf. 14x15*
310	A104 4.50k Exterior	1.60	1.60
311	A105 4.50k Interior, altar fresco	1.60	1.60
a.	Booklet pane, 6 #310, 4 #311	16.00	
	Complete booklet, #311a	16.00	

Christmas.

Souvenir Sheet

Reign of Queen Margaret II, 25th Anniv. — A106

Illustration reduced.

1997, Jan. 14   Litho.   *Perf. 14½*
312	A106 4.50k multicolored	2.25	2.25

Bird Type of 1996

1997, Feb. 27   Litho.   *Perf. 14x15*
313	A99 4.50k Pyrrhula pyrrhula	1.60	1.60
314	A99 4.50k Carduelis flammea	1.60	1.60
a.	Booklet pane, 5 each #313-314	16.00	—
	Complete booklet, #314a	16.00	

Mushrooms — A107

Designs: 4.50k, Hygrocybe helobia. 6k, Hygrocybe chlorophana. 6.50k, Hygrocybe virginea. 7.50k, Hygrocybe psittacina.

1997, Feb. 17   *Perf. 14½*
315	A107 4.50k multicolored	1.50	1.50
316	A107 6k multicolored	2.10	2.10
317	A107 6.50k multicolored	2.40	2.40
318	A107 7.50k multicolored	2.75	2.75
	Nos. 315-318 (4)	8.75	8.75

Map Type of 1996
Litho. & Engr.
1997, May 20 *Perf. 13*
319 A102 11k red & multi 3.75 3.75
320 A102 18k claret & multi 6.00 6.00

Europa — A108   Kalmar Union, 600th Anniv. — A109

Legends illustrated by William Heinesen: 4.50k, The Temptations of Saint Anthony. 7.50k, The Merman sitting at bottom of sea eating fish bait.

1997, May 20 Litho. *Perf. 14½*
321 A108 4.50k multicolored 1.40 1.25
322 A108 7.50k multicolored 2.40 2.25

1997, May 20 Engr. *Perf. 12½*
323 A109 4.50k deep blue violet 1.75 1.75

A110

A111

Barbara, Film Shot in Faroe Islands (Scenes from film): 4.50k, Danish theologian Poul Aggerso arriving at Faroe Islands. 6.50k, Barbara and Poul. 7.50k, Barbara with men on boat. 9k, Barbara in row boat, sailing ship.

1997, Sept. 15 Litho. *Perf. 14*
324 A110 4.50k multicolored 1.50 1.50
325 A110 6.50k multicolored 2.25 2.25
326 A110 7.50k multicolored 2.50 2.50
327 A110 9k multicolored 3.00 3.00
  Nos. 324-327 (4) 9.25 9.25

1997, Sept. 15
Hvalvik church.
328 A111 4.50k Interior 1.60 1.60
329 A111 4.50k Exterior 1.60 1.60
a. Booklet pane, 5 each #328-329 16.00 —
  Complete booklet, #329a 16.00

Birds — A112   A113

1998, Feb. 23 Litho. *Perf. 14x14½*
330 A112 4.50k Sturnus vulgaris 1.60 1.60
331 A112 4.50k Turdus merula 1.60 1.60
a. Bklt. pane, 5 each #330-331 16.00
  Complete booklet, #331a 16.00

1998, Feb. 23 *Perf. 14*
Scenes from the Sigurd poem "Brynhild's Ballad": 4.50k, King Buole, daughter Brynhild. 6.50k, Sigurd riding through wall of fire on

horseback. 7.50k, Sigurd, Brynhild together. 10k, Guthrun alone leading horse.
332 A113 4.50k multicolored 1.50 1.50
333 A113 6.50k multicolored 2.25 2.25
334 A113 7.50k multicolored 2.50 2.50
335 A113 10k multicolored 3.50 3.50
  Nos. 332-335 (4) 9.75 9.75

Europa — A114   A115

1998, May 18 Litho. *Perf. 14*
336 A114 4.50k Parade 1.40 1.25
337 A114 7.50k Processional 2.40 1.75
Olavsoka, Natl. Festival of Faroe Islands.

1998, May 18 *Perf. 14½*
338 A115 7.50k multicolored 2.50 2.50
UN Declaration of Human Rights, 50th anniv.

Intl. Year of the Ocean A116

Toothed whales: 4k, Lagenorhynchus acutus. 4.50k, Orcinus orca. 7k, Tursiops truncatus. 9k, Delphinapterus leucas.

1998, May 18 *Perf. 14½x14*
339 A116 4k multicolored 1.40 1.40
340 A116 4.50k multicolored 1.50 1.50
341 A116 7k multicolored 2.40 2.40
342 A116 9k multicolored 3.00 3.00
  Nos. 339-342 (4) 8.30 8.30

Map Type of 1996
Litho. & Engr.
1998, Sept. 14 *Perf. 13*
343 A102 14k multicolored 4.50 4.50

Frederickschurch A117

1998, Sept. 14 Litho. *Perf. 14*
344 A117 4.50k Exterior, coast-line 1.60 1.60
345 A117 4.50k Interior 1.60 1.60
a. Bklt. pane, 5 each #344-345 16.00
  Complete booklet, #345a 16.00

A118   A119

Paintings by Hans Hansen (1920-70): 4.50k, Fell-field, 1966. 5.50k, Village Interior, 1965. 6.50k, Portrait of Farmer Ólavur í Útistovu from Mikladalur, 1968. 8k, Self-portrait, 1968.

Perf. 13½x14, 14x13½
1998, Sept. 14
346 A118 4.50k multi 1.50 1.50
347 A118 5.50k multi 1.90 1.90
348 A118 6.50k multi, vert. 2.25 2.25
349 A118 8k multi, vert. 2.75 2.75
  Nos. 346-349 (4) 8.40 8.40

1999, Feb. 22 Litho. *Perf. 13½*
Birds.
350 A119 4.50k Passer domesticus 1.60 1.60
351 A119 4.50k Troglodytes troglodytes 1.60 1.60
a. Bklt. pane, 5 each #350-351 16.00
  Complete booklet, #351a 16.00

Ships Named "Smyril" A120

1999, Feb. 22 *Perf. 14½x14*
352 A120 4.50k 1895 1.50 1.50
353 A120 5k 1932 1.75 1.75
354 A120 8k 1967 2.75 2.75
355 A120 13k 1975 4.50 4.50
  Nos. 352-355 (4) 10.50 10.50

Northern Islands A121

1999, May 25 Litho. *Perf. 13½*
356 A121 50o Kalsoy .20 .20
357 A121 100o Vithoy .35 .35
358 A121 400o Svinoy 1.40 1.40
359 A121 450o Fugloy 1.50 1.50
360 A121 600o Kunoy 2.10 2.10
361 A121 800o Borthoy 3.00 3.00
  Nos. 356-361 (6) 8.55 8.55
See Nos. 383-386.

Waterfalls — A122

Europa: 6k, Svartifossur. 8k, Foldarafossur.

1999, May 25 *Perf. 14x14½*
362 A122 6k multicolored 2.00 2.00
363 A122 8k multicolored 2.75 2.75

Abstract Paintings of Ingálvur av Reyni — A123

1999, Sept. 27 Litho. *Perf. 12½*
364 A123 4.50k Bygd 1.50 1.50
365 A123 6k Húsavik 2.00 2.00
366 A123 8k Reytt regn 2.75 2.75
367 A123 20k Genta 6.75 6.75
  Nos. 364-367 (4) 13.00 13.00

Bible Stories — A124

1999, Sept. 27 *Perf. 14½x14*
368 A124 450o John 1:1-5 1.50 1.50
a. Booklet pane of 6 9.00
  Complete booklet, #368a 9.00
369 A124 600o Luke 1:26-28 2.00 2.00
a. Booklet pane of 6 12.00
  Complete booklet, #369a 12.00
See Nos. 387-388.

A125   A126

Christianity in the Faroes, 1000th Anniv.: 4.50k, Man on rocks in ocean. 5.50k, Monk with cross, man with sword. 8k, People, flags. 16k, Cross in sky.

Perf. 13½x13¼
2000, Feb. 21 Litho.
370 A125 4.50k multi 1.50 1.50
371 A125 5.50k multi 1.90 1.90
372 A125 8k multi 2.75 2.75
373 A125 16k multi 5.50 5.50
  Nos. 370-373 (4) 11.65 11.65

2000, Feb. 21
School and: No. 374, Sanna av Skarthi, Anna Suffia Rasmussen, wives of founders. No. 375, Rasmus Rasmussen (1871-1962), Símun av Skarthi (1872-1942), school founders.
374 A126 4.50k multi 1.50 1.50
375 A126 4.50k multi 1.50 1.50
a. Bklt. pane, 4 ea #374-375 12.00
  Complete booklet, #375a 12.00
Faroese Folk High School, cent.

Europa, 2000
Common Design Type
2000, May 9 Litho. *Perf. 13¼x13*
376 CD17 8k multi 3.00 3.00

Map Type of 1996
Litho. & Engr.
2000, May 22 *Perf. 13¼x13*
377 A102 15k multi 5.00 5.00
378 A102 22k multi 7.50 7.50

Stampin' The Future Children's Stamp Design Contest Winners A127

Art by: 4k, Katrin Mortensen. 4.50k, Sigga Andreassen. 6k, Steingrímur Joensen. 8k, Dion Dam Frandsen.

2000, May 22 Litho. *Perf. 13x13¼*
379 A127 4k multi 1.40 1.40
380 A127 4.50k multi 1.50 1.50
381 A127 6k multi 2.00 2.00
382 A127 8k multi 2.75 2.75
  Nos. 379-382 (4) 7.65 7.65

Island Type of 1999
2000, Sept. 18 Litho. *Perf. 13½*
383 A121 200o Skúvoy .70 .70
384 A121 650o Hestoy 2.25 2.25
385 A121 750o Koltur 2.50 2.50
386 A121 1000o Nólsoy 3.50 3.50
  Nos. 383-386 (4) 8.95 8.95

Bible Story Type of 1999
2000, Sept. 18 Litho. *Perf. 13x13¼*
387 A124 4.50k Micah 5:1 1.50 1.50
a. Booklet pane of 6 9.00
  Booklet, #387a 9.00
388 A124 6k John 1:14 2.00 2.00
a. Booklet pane of 6 12.00
  Booklet, #388a 12.00

Pew Gables Type of 1980
Kirkjubour pew gables: 430o, St. Andrew with cross. 650o, St. Bartholomew. 800o, Unknown apostle. 18k, Unknown apostle, diff.

Photo. & Engr.
2001, Feb. 12 *Perf. 12¾x12½*
389 A20 450o multi 1.50 1.50
390 A20 650o multi 2.25 2.25
391 A20 800o multi 2.75 2.75
392 A20 18k multi 6.00 6.00
  Nos. 389-392 (4) 12.50 12.50

Faroese Red Cross, 75th Anniv. A128

Designs: 4.50k, Old person. 6k, Relief worker.

2001, Feb. 12   Litho.   Perf. 14½x14
393	A128	4.50k multi	1.50	1.50
a.	Booklet pane of 6		9.00	
	Booklet, #393a		9.00	
394	A128	6k multi	2.00	2.00
a.	Booklet pane of 6		12.00	
	Booklet, #394a		12.00	

Souvenir Sheet

Faroe Islands Postal Service, 25th Anniv. — A129

No. 395: a, Boat for interisland mail transport, 19th cent. b, Tórshavn post office, 1906. c, Simon Pauli Poulsen (Morkabóndin), mail carrier.

Photo. & Engr.
2001, Apr. 1   Perf. 13x13¼
395 A129 4.50k Sheet of 3, #a-c   4.50 4.50

Nordic Myths and Legends About Light and Darkness — A130

No. 396: a, The Death of Hogni. b, The Tree of the Year. c, The Harp. d, Gram and Grane. e, The Ballad of Nornagest. f, Gudrun's Evil Magic.

Litho. with Foil Application
2001, Apr. 1   Perf. 13½x13¼
396 A130 6k Sheet of 6, #a-f   12.00 12.00

Hafnia 2001 Philatelic Exhibition, Copenhagen.

Paintings by Zacharias Heinesen A131

Designs: 4k, The Artist's Mother, 1992. 4.50k, Úti á Reyni, 1974. 10k, Ur Vágunum, 2000. 15k, Sunrise, 1975.

2001, June 11   Litho.   Perf. 13¼x13
397	A131	4k multi	1.40	1.40
398	A131	4.50k multi	1.50	1.50
399	A131	10k multi	3.50	3.50
400	A131	15k multi	5.00	5.00
	Nos. 397-400 (4)		11.40	11.40

Europa A132

Hydroelectric power stations: 6k, Fossáverkith. 8k, Eithisverkith.

2001, June 11   Perf. 13x13½
401 A132 6k multi   2.00 2.00
402 A132 8k multi   2.75 2.75

Whales — A133

Designs: 4.50k, Physeter macrocephalus. 6.50k, Balaenoptera physalus. 9k, Balaenoptera musculus. 20k, Balaenoptera borealis.

Perf. 13¾x13¼
2001, Sept. 17   Litho.
403	A133	4.50k multi	1.50	1.50
404	A133	6.50k multi	2.25	2.25
405	A133	9k multi	3.00	3.00
406	A133	20k multi	6.75	6.75
	Nos. 403-406 (4)		13.50	13.50

Bible Stories Type of 1999
2001, Sept. 17   Perf. 13
407	A124	5k Luke 2:34-35	1.75	1.75
a.	Booklet pane of 6		8.50	
	Booklet, #407a		8.50	
408	A124	6.50k Matthew 2:18	2.25	2.25
a.	Booklet pane of 6		11.50	
	Booklet, #408a		11.50	

Mollusks — A134

Designs: 5k, Sepiola atlantica. 7k, Modiolus modiolus. 7.50k, Polycera faeroensis. 18k, Buccinum undatum.

2002, Feb. 11   Litho.   Perf. 13
409	A134	5k multi	1.75	1.75
410	A134	7k multi	2.40	2.40
411	A134	7.50k multi	2.50	2.50
412	A134	18k multi	6.00	6.00
	Nos. 409-412 (4)		12.65	12.65

Portions of the designs were applied by a thermographic process producing a shiny, raised effect.

Souvenir Sheet

Viking Voyages — A135

No. 413: a, Navigation tool. b, Viking sailor on boat. c, Viking boat.

Litho. & Engr.
2002, Feb. 11   Perf. 13
413 A135 6.50k Sheet of 3, #a-c   6.75 6.75

Europa A136

Designs: 6.50k, Clowns. 8k, Various circus performers.

2002, Apr. 8   Litho.   Perf. 13¼x13½
414 A136 6.50k multi   2.25 2.25
415 A136 8k multi   2.75 2.75

Art by Tróndur Paturssson A137

Designs: 5k, Bládypi. 6.50k, Kosmiska Rúmith.

2002, Apr. 8
416	A137	5k multi	1.75	1.75
417	A137	6.50k multi	2.25	2.25
a.	Booklet pane of 8, 4 each #416-417		16.00	—
	Booklet, #417a		16.00	

Eggs and Chicks — A138

Designs: 5k, Numenius phaeopus. 7.50k, Gallinago gallinago. 12k, Haematopus ostralegus. 20k, Pluvialis apricaria.

2002, June 17   Perf. 14x14½
418	A138	5k multi	1.75	1.75
419	A138	7.50k multi	2.50	2.50
420	A138	12k multi	4.00	4.00
421	A138	20k multi	6.75	6.75
	Nos. 418-421 (4)		15.00	15.00

Souvenir Sheet

Faroese Representative Council, 150th Anniv. — A139

Designs: 5k, Royal book and seal. 6.50k, Royal book, Protocol of 1852.

2002, June 17   Perf. 14
422 A139 Sheet of 2, #a-b   4.00 4.00

Falco Columbarius Subaesalon — A140

Litho. & Embossed
2002, Sept. 23   Perf. 13¼
423 A140 30k multi   10.00 10.00

Gota Church — A141

2002, Sept. 23   Litho.   Perf. 12½
424	A141	5k Exterior	1.75	1.75
425	A141	6.50k Interior	2.25	2.25
a.	Booklet pane, 5 each #424-425		20.00	—
	Booklet, #425a		20.00	

Souvenir Sheet

Intl. Council for the Exploration of the Sea, Cent. — A142

No. 426: a, Micromesistius poutassou and island. b, Exploration ship Magnus Heinason and fish.

Litho. & Engr.
2002, Sept. 23   Perf. 13
426 A142 8k Sheet of 2, #a-b   5.50 5.50

See Denmark Nos. 1237-1238, Greenland Nos. 401-402.

Opening of Vagár-Streymoy Tunnel, Nov. 2002 — A143

Designs: No. 427, Wheeled tunneling machine at right. No. 428, Workers in red uniforms at left.

2003, Feb. 24   Litho.   Perf. 13¼x13
427	A143	5k multi	1.50	1.50
428	A143	5k multi	1.50	1.50
a.	Booklet pane, 5 each #427-428		15.00	—
	Complete booklet, #428a		15.00	

Voluspá, Ancient Norse Poem — A144

No. 429: a, Seeress Heid holding staff. b, Heid sees animal and man in vision. c, Nude man and woman. d, Scribe and horseman. e, Battle between group with swords and man with hammer. f, Horseman and warriors. g, Men, large sword. h, Longboat. i, Attack on man holding spear, fire. j, Two figures with staffs, winged serpent.

2003, Feb. 24   Perf. 14
429	A144	Sheet of 10	21.00	21.00
a.-j.	6.50k Any single		2.10	2.10

Europa — A145

Poster art for Nordic House: 6.50k, Fish Tree, by Astrid Andreasen, 1991. 8k, Ceramics by Guthrith Poulsen, 1997.

2003, Apr. 14　　　**Perf. 13½x13¼**
430　A145　6.50k multi　　　1.90　1.90
431　A145　8k multi　　　　2.25　2.25

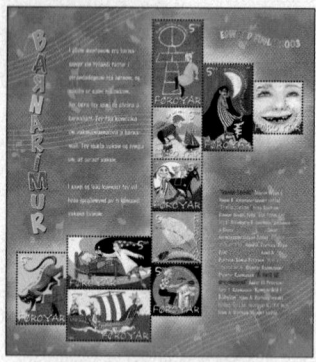

Children's Songs — A146

No. 432: a, Woman playing hopscotch (26x44mm). b, Boy on rocks, moon (26x44mm). c, Girl with missing teeth (26x26mm). d, Boy with toy sailboat (26x26mm). e, Cat, horse and girl (26x26mm). f, Butterfly and fly (26x26mm). g, Girl in bed, boy with stars (44x26mm). h, Cat on stairs, mouse (26x36mm). i, Man playing drums (26x26mm). j, King and queen in longboat (44x26mm).

Perf. 13¼, 13¼x13¼x13¼x14 (#432g, 432j), 13¼x14 (#432h)
2003, Apr. 14
432　A146　Sheet of 10　15.00　15.00
　a.-j.　5k Any single　　　1.50　1.50

Small Towns A147

2003, June 10　Litho.　Perf. 13x13¼
433　A147　5k Bour　　　　1.60　1.60
434　A147　5k Gásadalur　　1.60　1.60

Communities With Post Offices 100 Years Old — A148

No. 435: a, Fuglafjorthur. b, Strendur. c, Sandur. d, Eithi. e, Vestmanna. f, Vágur. g, Mithvágur. h, Hvalba.

2003, June 10　　　**Perf. 13¼x13**
435　A148　Sheet of 8　　13.00　13.00
　a.-h.　5k Any single　　　1.60　1.60

Theologians — A149

Designs: 5k, Jesper Rasmussen Brochmand (1585-1652). 6.50k, Thomas Kingo (1634-1703).

2003, Sept. 22　　　**Perf. 13x13¼**
436　A149　5k multi　　　　1.50　1.50
437　A149　6.50k multi　　　2.00　2.00
　a.　Booklet pane, 5 each #436-437　17.50
　　Complete booklet, #437a　　17.50

Souvenir Sheet

Dancing in the Inn's Smoking Room, by Emil Krause — A150

Litho. & Engr.
2003, Sept. 22　　　**Perf. 12¼**
438　A150　25k multi　　　　9.00　9.00
100th Faroese stamp engraved by Czeslaw Slania.

Islands Type of 1999
2004, Jan. 26　　Litho.　　Perf. 13½
439　A121　550o Stóra Dímun　1.90　1.90
440　A121　700o Lítla Dímun　2.40　2.40

Suthuroy Island — A151

No. 441: a, Sigmundargjogv, Sandvik. b, Fiskieithi, Hvalba. c, A Hamri, Frothba. d, Tjaldavíkshólmur, Oravík. e, Fossurin Stóri, Fámjin. f, Hovsfjorthur, Hov. g, I Eystrum, Porkeri. h, A Okrum. i, I Horg, Sumba. j, I Akrabergi.

2004, Jan. 26　　　**Perf. 13x13¼**
441　A151　5k Sheet of 10, #a-j　17.00　17.00

1854 Cruise of Yacht "Maria" — A152

No. 442: a, Gáshólmur and Tindhólmur. b, Framvith "Diamantunum." c, Hús av tí betra slagnum. d, Mylingur sunnanífrá. e, Mylingur northanífrá. f, Kalsoyggin northanífrá. g, Raetha teir infoddu. h, Sunnari endi av Kunoynni.

2004, Mar. 26　　Litho.　　Perf. 13
442　A152　6.50k Sheet of 8, #a.-h.　18.00　18.00

Souvenir Sheet

Norse Gods — A153

No. 443: a, Thor, in boat, fighting Midgard serpent. b, Ran in fishing net.

2004, Mar. 26
443　A153　6.50k Sheet of 2, #a.-b.　4.50　4.50

Souvenir Sheet

Wedding of Crown Prince Frederik and Mary Donaldson — A154

Litho. & Photo.
2004, May 14　　　**Perf. 13¼**
444　A154　Sheet of 2 + central label　4.00　4.00
　a.　5k Couple facing right　1.60　1.60
　b.　6.50k Couple facing left　2.10　2.10

Soccer Organization Centenaries A155

Soccer players and emblems of: 5k, Klaksvík and Tórshavn teams. 6.50k, FIFA (Fédération Internationale de Football Association).

2004, May 24　Litho.　　Perf. 13¼x13
445　A155　5k multi　　　　1.75　1.75
446　A155　6.50k multi　　　2.25　2.25
　a.　Booklet pane, 4 each #445-446　16.00　—
　　Complete booklet, #446a　16.00

Europa A156

Designs: 6.50k, Tourists in gorge, Hestur. 8k, Tourists at shore, Stóra Dímun.

2004, May 24　　　**Perf. 13x13¼**
447　A156　6.50k multi　　　2.10　2.10
448　A156　8k multi　　　　2.60　2.60

Churches A157

2004, Sept. 20　Litho.　Perf. 13¼x13
449　A157　5.50k Vágur　　1.90　1.90
450　A157　7.50k Tvoroyri　2.50　2.50
　a.　Booklet pane, 4 each #449-450　18.00
　　Complete booklet, #450a　18.00

Poems by Janus Djurhuus (1881-1948) — A158

No. 451: a, Atlantis. b, Grímur Kamban. c, Gandkvaethi Tróndar. d, Til Foroya I-III. e, Mín sorg. f, Loki. g, I búri og Slatur. h, Heimferth Nólsoyar Páls. i, Móses á Sinai fjalli. j, Cello.

2004, Sept. 20　　　**Perf. 13**
451　A158　Sheet of 10　26.00　26.00
　a.-j.　7.50k Any single　2.60　2.60

Souvenir Sheet

Life of the Vikings — A159

No. 452: a, Men tending sheep. b, Men with farm implements. c, Women weaving and woman milking cow.

Litho. & Engr.
2005, Feb. 7　　　**Perf. 13**
452　A159　Sheet of 3　8.00　8.00
　a.-c.　7.50k Any single　2.60　2.60

Miniature Sheet

Vágar Island — A160

No. 453: a, Víkar. b, Gásadalur. c, Bour. d, Slaettanes. e, Kvígandalsá. f, Sorvágur. g, Sandavágur. h, Vatnsoyrar. i, Fjallavatn. j, Mithvágur.

2005, Feb. 7　　Litho.　Perf. 13x13¼
453　A160　Sheet of 10　19.00　19.00
　a.-j.　5.50k Any single　1.90　1.90

Lepus Timidus — A161

2005, Apr. 18 — Perf. 13¼x13½

454 A161 5.50k shown 1.90 1.90
455 A161 5.50k Brown fur 1.90 1.90
a. Booklet pane, 4 each #454-455 15.50
Complete booklet, #455a 15.50

Europa — A162

Various traditional foods with: 7.50k, Brown panel. 10k, Green panel. Illustration reduced.

2005, Apr. 18 — Perf. 13¼x13

456 A162 7.50k multi 2.60 2.60
457 A162 10k multi 3.50 3.50

Worldwide Fund for Nature (WWF) A163

Petrels: 8.50k, Oceanodroma leucorhoa. 9k, Hydrobates pelagicus. 12k, Oceanodroma leucorhoa on ground. 20k, Hydrobates pelagicus on ground.

2005, June 6 — Perf. 13

458 A163 8.50k multi 2.75 2.75
459 A163 9k multi 3.25 3.25
460 A163 12k multi 4.25 4.25
461 A163 20k multi 6.75 6.75
Nos. 458-461 (4) 17.00 17.00

Miniature Sheet

Landscapes by Jógvan Waagstein (1879-1949) — A164

No. 462: a, Path and wall at LL, denomination in red, year date in black in grass. b, Path and wall at LL, denomination in white, year date in black on wall. c, Stone hut at left, denomination in red, year date in black. d, Path at right, denomination in red, year date in black. e, Two large rocks at right, denomination in red, year date in black. f, Rocks at LL, denomination in red, year date in white. g, Path at center, denomination in white, year date in black on path. h, Buildings at LL, denomination in red, year date in black in path. i, Churches, denomination in white, year date in black in water.

2005, Sept. 19 Litho. — Perf. 14x14¼

462 A164 Sheet of 9 22.00 22.00
a.-i. 7.50k Any single 2.40 2.40

End of British Occupation In World War II, 60th Anniv. A165

Soldiers with: 5.50k, Arms. 9k, Children.

2005, Sept. 19 — Perf. 14

463 A165 5.50k blue & blk 2.00 2.00
464 A165 9k yel & blk 3.25 3.25

Christmas — A166

Ballads: 5.50k, Jólavísan. 7.50k, Rudisar Vísa.

2005, Nov. 7 — Perf. 13½x13¼

465 A166 5.50k multi 1.75 1.75
466 A166 7.50k multi 2.40 2.40
466a Booklet pane, 5 each #465-466 16.00 —
Complete booklet, #466a 16.00

Villages A167

2006, Feb. 13 Litho. — Perf. 13¾

467 A167 7k Sythrugota 2.25 2.25
468 A167 12k Fuglafjorthur 4.25 4.25
469 A167 20k Leirvík 6.75 6.75
Nos. 467-469 (3) 13.25 13.25

Miniature Sheet

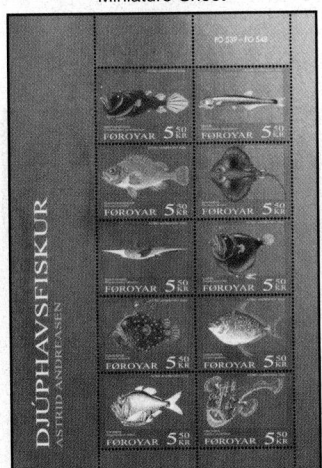

Fish — A168

No. 470: a, Himantolophus groenlandicus. b, Gonostoma elongatum. c, Sebastes mentella. d, Neoraja caerulea. e, Rhinochimaera atlantica. f, Linophryne lucifer. g, Ceratias holboelli. h, Lampris guttatus. i, Argyropelecus olfersi. j, Lophius piscatorius.

2006, Feb. 13 — Perf. 14

470 A168 Sheet of 10 19.00 19.00
a.-j. 5.50k Any single 1.90 1.90

Souvenir Sheet

Norse Folklore — A169

No. 471: a, Norns surrounding sleeping child. b, Sea ghost.

2006, Mar. 29 — Perf. 13

471 A169 7.50k Sheet of 2, #a-b 5.00 5.00

Miniature Sheet

Ballad of the Long Serpent, by Jens Christian Djurhuus — A170

No. 472: a, Building of ship. b, Launch of ship. c, King on throne. d, King's fleet at sea (brown ship at LL, blue ship at LR). e, King and sailors on shore. f, King pointing. g, Ship with red sail at R. h, Battle scene (injured men falling into water). i, Battle scene (men with shields jumping from ship to ship). j, Dead men on ship's deck.

2006, Mar. 29 — Perf. 13¼x13

472 A170 Sheet of 10 18.00 18.00
a.-j. 5.50k Any single 1.75 1.75

Opening of Northoy Tunnel — A171

Tunnel and: No. 473, Fish. No. 474, Canoe.

2006, June 12 — Perf. 13¼

473 A171 5.50k multi 1.90 1.90
474 A171 5.50k multi 1.90 1.90
a. Booklet pane, 4 each #473-474 15.50
Complete booklet, #474a 15.50

Europa A172

2006, June 12 — Perf. 13¾

475 A172 7.50k shown 2.60 2.60
476 A172 10k Hands, diff. 3.50 3.50

Miniature Sheet

Sandoy Island — A173

No. 477: a, Sunnan fyri Skopun. b, Dalur. c, Soltuvík. d, Skálavík. e, Skopun. f, Sandur. g, Skarvanes. h, Húsavík.

2006, Sept. 18 Litho. — Perf. 13x13¼

477 A173 Sheet of 8 20.00 20.00
a.-h. 7.50k Any single 2.50 2.50

Sandur Church A174

Designs: 5.50k, Building exterior, steeple cross. 7.50k, Interior.

2006, Sept. 18 — Perf. 14

478 A174 5.50k multi 1.90 1.90
479 A174 7.50k multi 2.60 2.60
a. Booklet pane, 4 each #478-479 18.00 —
Complete booklet, #479a 18.00

Wave Energy A175

2007, Feb. 12 Litho. — Perf. 12½x13

480 A175 7.50k multi 2.60 2.60

Art From 1838 La Recherche Expedition A176

Art by Barthélemy Lauvergne: 5.50k, La Recherche off Nólsoy. 7.50k, Skaelingsfjall.

2007, Feb. 12

481 A176 5.50k multi 1.90 1.90
482 A176 7.50k multi 2.60 2.60
a. Booklet pane, 4 each #481-482 18.00 —
Complete booklet, #482a 18.00

Miniature Sheet

Legend of the Seal Woman — A177

No. 483: a, Man, head of white seal. b, Woman and seals in ring. c, Man, nude woman, seals. d, Man and nude woman seated on chest. e, Ship and two seals. f, Children, seal woman nursing child. g, Seal woman and man. h, Sleeping man and seal woman with hands open. i, Man and dead seals. j, Seal woman.

2007, Feb. 12 — Perf. 14

483 A177 Sheet of 10 19.00 19.00
a.-j. 5.50k Any single 1.90 1.90

Miniature Sheet

The Old Man and His Sons, Novel by Hethin Brú — A178

No. 484: a, Ketil cutting whale's throat. b, Men carrying injured Klávus on log. c, Kálvur and fiancee, Klávusardóttir with pot and kettle.

d, Ketil and Kálvur in fishing boat. e, Ketil's wife arguing with daughter-in-law. f, Ketil catching flying northern fulmars. g, Kálvur and stone fence. h, Ketil, Kálvur and cow.

2007, Apr. 10   Litho.   Perf. 13x12½

484	A178	Sheet of 8	22.00	22.00
a.-h.		7.50k Any single	2.75	2.75

Europa — A179

Design: 5.50k, Scout holding bird. 10k, Tent.

2007, Apr. 10

485	A179	5.50k multi	2.00	2.00
486	A179	10k multi	3.75	3.75

Scouting, cent.

Souvenir Sheet

Bible Translators — A180

No. 487: a, Jákup Dahl (1878-1944). b, Kristian O. Videro (1906-91). c, Victor Danielsen (1894-1961).

2007, June 11   Litho.   Perf. 13x12½

487	A180	Sheet of 3	6.00	6.00
a.-c.		5.50k Any single	2.00	2.00

Domesticated Birds — A181

Designs: 9k, Chickens and rooster. 20k, Ducks. 25k, Geese.

2007, June 11   Perf. 12½x13

488	A181	9k multi	3.25	3.25
489	A181	20k multi	7.25	7.25
490	A181	25k multi	9.25	9.25
		Nos. 488-490 (3)	19.75	19.75

Hoyvík — A182

Illustration reduced.

2007, Oct. 1   Perf. 13½

491	A182	7.50k multi	2.75	2.75

Wooden Religious Statues of Kirkjubour Cathedral — A183

2007, Oct. 1   Perf. 13x12½

492	A183	5.50k Jesus	2.10	2.10
493	A183	7.50k Mary	2.75	2.75
a.		Booklet pane, 4 each #492-493	19.50	
		Complete booklet, #493a	19.50	

Miniature Sheet

Stone Fence and Wildlife — A184

No. 494: a, Bird, worm. b, Two red beetles, fern. c, Mouse, purple flowers. d, Mosquito, pink flowers. e, Large black and white bird, dandelions. f, Bird with black wings, buttercups. g, Earwigs, grass. h, Bird and eggs.

2007, Oct. 1   Perf. 13½x14¼

494	A184	Sheet of 8	17.00	17.00
a.-h.		5.50k Any single	2.10	2.10

FERNANDO PO

fər-'nan-ˌdō 'pō

LOCATION — An island in the Gulf of Guinea off west Africa.
GOVT. — Former province of Spain
AREA — 800 sq. mi.
POP. — 62,612 (1960)
CAPITAL — Santa Isabel

Together with the islands of Elobey, Annobon and Corisco, Fernando Po came under the administration of Spanish Guinea. Postage stamps of Spanish Guinea were used until 1960.
The provinces of Fernando Po and Rio Muni united Oct. 12, 1968, to form the Republic of Equatorial Guinea.

100 Centimos = 1 Escudo = 2.50 Pesetas
100 Centimos = 1 Peseta
1000 Milesimas = 100 Centavos = 1 Peso (1882)

> Catalogue values for unused stamps in this country are for Never Hinged items, beginning with Scott 181 in the regular postage section and Scott B1 in the semi-postal section.

Isabella II — A1   Alfonso XII — A2

1868   Unwmk.   Typo.   Perf. 14

1	A1	20c brown	475.00	135.00
a.		20c red brown	500.00	135.00

No. 1 is valued in the grade of fine, as illustrated. Examples with very fine centering are uncommon and sell for more.
Forgeries exist.

1879

Centimos de Peseta

2	A2	5c green	60.00	15.00
3	A2	10c rose	30.00	15.00
4	A2	50c blue	105.00	15.00
		Nos. 2-4 (3)	195.00	45.00

1882-89

Centavos de Peso

5	A2	1c green	11.00	5.00
6	A2	2c rose	16.50	8.00
7	A2	5c gray blue	55.00	11.00
8	A2	10c dk brown ('89)	75.00	6.00
		Nos. 5-8 (4)	157.50	30.00

Nos. 5-7 Handstamp Surcharged Type "a" in Blue, Black or Violet

a

1884-95

9	A2	50c on 1c green ('95)	95.00	19.00
11	A2	50c on 2c rose	29.00	6.00
12	A2	50c on 5c blue ('87)	105.00	25.00
		Nos. 9-12 (3)	229.00	50.00

Values above are for examples surcharged in black. Stamps surcharged in violet or blue are worth about 25% more.
Inverted and double surcharges exist. No. 12 exists overprinted in carmine. Value $90.

King Alfonso XIII — A4

1894-97   Perf. 14

13	A4	⅛c slate ('96)	20.00	2.75
14	A4	2c rose ('96)	14.50	2.25
15	A4	5c blue grn ('97)	15.00	2.25
16	A4	6c dk violet ('96)	12.00	2.75
17	A4	10c blk vio ('94)	350.00	90.00
18	A4	10c lake ('95)	45.00	8.25
19	A4	10c org brn ('96)	9.50	2.25
20	A4	12½c dk brown ('96)	10.50	2.75
21	A4	20c slate bl ('96)	10.50	2.75
22	A4	25c claret ('96)	21.00	2.75
		Nos. 13-22 (10)	508.00	118.75

Stamps of 1894-97 Handstamped in Blue, Black or Red

b   c

Type "b" Surcharge

1896-98

23	A4	5c on 2c rose (Bl)	37.50	5.75
24	A4	5c on 10c brn vio (Bl)	110.00	16.00
25	A4	5c on 12½c brn (Bl)	25.00	4.75
a.		Black surcharge	25.00	4.75
		Nos. 23-25 (3)	172.50	26.50

Type "c" Surcharge

26	A4	5c on ⅛c slate (Bk)	22.00	6.25
27	A4	5c on 2c rose (Bl)	22.00	6.25
a.		Black surcharge	22.00	6.25
28	A4	5c on 5c green (R)	110.00	20.00
29	A4	5c on 6c dk vio (R)	17.50	12.50
a.		Violet surcharge	18.50	14.00
30	A4	5c on 10c org brn (Bk)	125.00	25.00
31	A4	5c on 12½c brn (R)	50.00	10.00
32	A4	5c on 20c sl bl (R)	27.50	9.50
33	A4	5c on 25c claret (Bk)	27.50	10.00
a.		Blue surcharge	27.50	12.00
		Nos. 26-33 (8)	401.50	99.50

Exist surcharged in other colors.

Type "a" Surch. in Blue or Black

1898-99

34	A4	50c on 2c rose	70.00	8.50
35	A4	50c on 10c brn vio	160.00	25.00
36	A4	50c on 10c lake	170.00	25.00
37	A4	50c on 10c org brn	160.00	25.00
38	A4	50c on 12½c brn (Bk)	140.00	16.50

The "a" surch. also exists on ⅛c, 5c & 25c. Values, $300, $200 and $190, respectively.

Arms

A5   A6

Revenue Stamps Handstamped in Blue

1897-98   Imperf.

39	A5	5c on 10c rose	31.00	14.00
40	A6	10c rose	26.00	12.00

A7

A8

A9

Arms — A9a

Revenue Stamps Handstamped in Black or Red

1899   Imperf.

41	A7	15c on 10c green	40.00	21.00
a.		Blue surcharge, vertical	35.00	19.00
42	A8	10c on 25c green	110.00	60.00
43	A9	15c on 25c green	175.00	110.00
43A	A9a	15c on 25c green (R)	1,600.	1,000.
b.		Black surcharge	1,600.	1,000.

Surcharge on No. 41 is either horizontal, inverted or vertical.
On No. 42 "CORREOS" is ovptd. in red.

King Alfonso XIII — A10

Double-lined shaded letters at sides.

1899   Perf. 14

44	A10	1m orange brn	1.90	.40
45	A10	2m orange brn	1.90	.40
46	A10	3m orange brn	1.90	.40
47	A10	4m orange brn	1.90	.40
48	A10	5m orange brn	1.90	.40
49	A10	1c black vio	1.90	.40
50	A10	2c dk blue grn	1.90	.40
51	A10	3c dk brown	1.90	.40
52	A10	4c orange	11.50	1.00
53	A10	5c carmine rose	1.90	.40
54	A10	6c dark blue	1.90	.40

55	A10	8c gray brn	7.00	.40
56	A10	10c vermilion	4.50	.40
57	A10	15c slate grn	4.50	.40
58	A10	20c maroon	12.00	1.00
59	A10	40c violet	82.50	17.50
60	A10	60c black	82.50	17.50
61	A10	80c red brown	82.50	17.50
62	A10	1p yellow grn	300.00	85.00
63	A10	2p slate blue	300.00	87.50
		Nos. 44-63 (20)	906.00	232.20

Nos. 44-63 exist imperf. Value for set, $1,275.
See Nos. 66-85. For surcharges see Nos. 64-65, 88-88B.

1900

Surcharged type "a"

64	A10	50c on 20c maroon	15.00	2.25
a.		Blue surcharge	30.00	4.50

Surcharged type "b"

64B	A10	5c on 20c maroon	200.00	10.00

Surcharged type "c"

65	A10	5c on 20c maroon	8.50	2.25
		Nos. 64-65 (3)	223.50	14.50

Dated "1900"

Solid letters at sides.

1900

66	A10	1m black	2.75	.50
67	A10	2m black	2.75	.50
68	A10	3m black	2.75	.50
69	A10	4m black	2.75	.50
70	A10	5m black	2.75	.50
71	A10	1c green	2.75	.50
72	A10	2c violet	2.75	.50
73	A10	3c rose	2.75	.50
74	A10	4c black brn	2.75	.50
75	A10	5c blue	2.75	.50
76	A10	6c orange	2.75	.50
77	A10	8c bronze grn	2.75	.50
78	A10	10c claret	2.75	.50
79	A10	15c dk violet	2.75	.50
80	A10	20c olive brn	2.75	.50
81	A10	40c brown	7.00	2.25
82	A10	60c green	15.00	2.50
83	A10	80c dark blue	16.00	3.75
84	A10	1p red brown	90.00	30.00
85	A10	2p orange	160.00	62.50
		Nos. 66-85 (20)	329.25	108.50
		Set, never hinged	475.00	

Nos. 66-85 exist imperf. Value, set $1,600.

A11

A12

Revenue Stamps Overprinted or Surcharged with Handstamp in Red or Black

1900 Imperf.

86	A11	10c blue (R)	35.00	16.00
87	A12	5c on 10c blue	90.00	37.50
		Set, never hinged	165.00	

Nos. 52 and 80 Surcharged type "a" in Violet or Black

1900

88	A10	50c on 4c orange (V)	14.00	4.00
a.		Green surcharge	22.50	12.00
88B	A10	50c on 20c ol brn	14.00	3.50
		Set, never hinged	37.50	

A13

A14

1901 Perf. 14

89	A13	1c black	2.50	.90
90	A13	2c orange brn	2.50	.90
91	A13	3c dk violet	2.50	.90
92	A13	4c lt violet	2.50	.90
93	A13	5c orange red	1.60	.90
94	A13	10c violet brn	1.60	.90
95	A13	25c dp blue	1.60	.90
96	A13	50c claret	2.50	.90
97	A13	75c dk brown	1.75	.90
98	A13	1p blue grn	57.50	6.00
99	A13	2p red brown	35.00	9.00
100	A13	3p olive grn	35.00	12.00
101	A13	4p dull red	36.00	12.00
102	A13	5p dk green	42.50	12.00
103	A13	10p buff	95.00	35.00
		Nos. 89-103 (15)	320.05	94.10
		Set, never hinged	575.00	

Dated "1902"

1902

Control Numbers on Back

104	A13	5c dk green	2.25	.40
105	A13	10c slate	2.40	.45
106	A13	25c claret	5.50	.85
107	A13	50c violet brn	13.00	2.75
108	A13	75c lt violet	13.00	2.75
109	A13	1p car rose	16.00	3.50
110	A13	2p olive grn	34.00	8.00
111	A13	5p orange red	50.00	17.50
		Nos. 104-111 (8)	136.15	36.20
		Set, never hinged	200.00	

Exist imperf. Value for set, $850.

1903 Perf. 14

Control Numbers on Back

112	A14	¼c dk violet	.40	.25
113	A14	½c black	.40	.25
114	A14	1c scarlet	.40	.25
115	A14	2c dk green	.40	.30
116	A14	3c blue grn	.40	.30
117	A14	4c violet	.40	.30
118	A14	5c rose lake	.45	.30
119	A14	10c orange buff	.55	.45
120	A14	15c blue green	2.25	1.00
121	A14	25c red brown	2.50	1.25
122	A14	50c black brn	4.25	2.00
123	A14	75c carmine	15.00	3.50
124	A14	1p dk brown	22.50	6.00
125	A14	2p dk olive grn	30.00	7.50
126	A14	3p claret	30.00	7.50
127	A14	4p dark brown	37.50	12.50
128	A14	5p dp dull blue	55.00	16.00
129	A14	10p dull red	120.00	27.50
		Nos. 112-129 (18)	322.40	87.15
		Set, never hinged	450.00	

Dated "1905"

1905

Control Numbers on Back

136	A14	1c dp violet	.40	.30
137	A14	2c black	.40	.30
138	A14	3c vermilion	.40	.30
139	A14	4c dp green	.40	.30
140	A14	5c blue grn	.45	.35
141	A14	10c violet	1.60	.75
142	A14	15c car lake	1.60	.75
143	A14	25c orange buff	12.50	2.25
144	A14	50c green	8.00	2.75
145	A14	75c red brown	11.00	7.50
146	A14	1p dp gray brn	12.50	7.50
147	A14	2p carmine	20.00	12.50
148	A14	3p deep brown	32.50	14.00
149	A14	4p bronze grn	40.00	18.00
150	A14	5p claret	62.50	25.00
151	A14	10p deep blue	90.00	35.00
		Nos. 136-151 (16)	294.25	127.55
		Set, never hinged	525.00	

King Alfonso XIII — A15

1907

Control Numbers on Back

152	A15	1c blue black	.20	.20
153	A15	2c car rose	.20	.20
154	A15	3c dp violet	.20	.20
155	A15	4c black	.20	.20
156	A15	5c orange buff	.25	.20
157	A15	10c maroon	1.50	.75
158	A15	15c bronze grn	.45	.30
159	A15	25c dk brown	24.00	10.00
160	A15	50c blue green	.25	.25
161	A15	75c vermilion	.35	.25
162	A15	1p dull blue	2.25	.55
163	A15	2p brown	8.50	3.25
164	A15	3p lake	8.50	3.25
165	A15	4p violet	8.50	3.25
166	A15	5p black brn	8.50	3.25
167	A15	10p orange brn	8.50	3.25
		Nos. 152-167 (16)	72.35	29.35
		Set, never hinged	125.00	

No. 157 Handstamp Surcharged in Black or Blue

1908

168	A15	5c on 10c mar (Bk)	2.75	2.00
169	A15	5c on 10c mar (Bl)	10.00	5.50
		Set, never hinged	16.00	

The surcharge on Nos. 168-169 exist inverted, double, etc. The surcharge also exists on other stamps. A 25c on 10c also exists.

Seville-Barcelona Issue of Spain, 1929, Overprinted in Blue or Red

1929 Perf. 11

170	A52	5c rose lake	.20	.20
171	A53	10c green (R)	.20	.20
a.		Perf. 14	.65	.65
172	A50	15c Prus bl (R)	.25	.20
173	A51	20c purple (R)	.25	.20
174	A50	25c brt rose	.25	.20
175	A52	30c black brn	.25	.20
176	A53	40c dk blue (R)	.70	.70
177	A51	50c dp orange	1.50	1.50
178	A52	1p blue blk (R)	5.75	5.75
179	A53	4p deep rose	27.50	27.50
180	A53	10p brown	35.00	35.00
		Nos. 170-180 (11)	71.85	71.65
		Set, never hinged	135.00	

Catalogue values for unused stamps in this section, from this point to the end of the section, are for Never Hinged items.

Virgin Mary — A16

1960 Unwmk. Photo. Perf. 13x12½

181	A16	25c dull gray vio	.25	.20
182	A16	50c brown olive	.25	.20
183	A16	75c violet brn	.25	.20
184	A16	1p orange ver	.25	.25
185	A16	1.50p lt blue grn	.25	.25
186	A16	2p red lilac	.25	.25
187	A16	3p dark blue	3.00	.80
188	A16	5p lt red brn	.25	.25
189	A16	10p lt olive brn	.45	.30
		Nos. 181-189 (9)	5.20	2.70

Tricorn and Windmill from "The Three-Cornered Hat" by Falla — A17

Manuel de Falla A18

1960 Perf. 13x12½, 12½x13

190	A17	35c slate green	.50	.50
191	A18	80c Prus green	.60	.60

Issued to honor Manuel de Falla (1876-1946), Spanish composer.

See Nos. B1-B2.

Map of Fernando Po — A19

General Franco A20

Designs: 70c, Santa Isabel Cathedral.

Perf. 13x12½, 12½x13

1961, Oct. 1 Photo. Unwmk.

192	A19	25c gray violet	.25	.25
193	A20	50c olive brown	.25	.25
194	A19	70c brt green	.30	.30
195	A20	1p red orange	.35	.35
		Nos. 192-195 (4)	1.15	1.15

25th anniv. of the nomination of Gen. Francisco Franco as Chief of State.

Ocean Liner A21

Design: 50c, S.S. San Francisco.

1962, July 10 Perf. 12½x13

196	A21	25c dull violet	.25	.25
197	A21	50c gray olive	.25	.25
198	A21	1p orange brn	.25	.25
		Nos. 196-198 (3)	.75	.75

Mailman — A22

Mail Transport Symbols A23

Perf. 13x12½, 12½x13

1962, Nov. 23 Unwmk.

199	A22	15c dark green	.25	.25
200	A23	35c lilac rose	.25	.25
201	A22	1p brown	.25	.25
		Nos. 199-201 (3)	.75	.75

Issued for Stamp Day.

Fetish — A24

1963, Jan. 29 Perf. 13x12½

202	A24	50c olive gray	.25	.25
203	A24	1p deep magenta	.25	.25

Issued to help victims of the Seville flood.

Nuns
A25

Design: 50c, Nun and child, vert.

Perf. 12½x13, 13x12½

1963, July 6   Photo.   Unwmk.
204 A25   25c bright lilac   .25 .25
205 A25   50c dull green   .25 .25
206 A25   1p red orange   .25 .25
    Nos. 204-206 (3)   .75 .75

Issued for child welfare.

Child and
Arms
A26

1963, July 12   Perf. 12½x13
207 A26   50c brown olive   .25 .25
208 A26   1p carmine rose   .25 .25

Issued for Barcelona flood relief.

Governor
Chacon
A27

Orange
Blossoms
A28

Men in Dugout
Canoe
A29

1964, Mar. 6   Perf. 12½x13, 13x12½
209 A27   25c violet black   .25 .25
210 A28   50c dark olive   .25 .25
211 A27   1p brown red   .25 .25
    Nos. 209-211 (3)   .75 .75

Issued for Stamp Day 1963.

1964, June 1   Photo.   Perf. 13x12½

Design: 50c, Pineapple.

212 A29   25c purple   .25 .25
213 A28   50c dull olive   .25 .25
214 A29   1p deep claret   .25 .25
    Nos. 212-214 (3)   .75 .75

Issued for child welfare.

Ring-necked
Francolin — A30

Designs: 15c, 70c, 3p, Ring-necked francolin. 25c, 1p, 5p, Two mallards. 50c, 1.50p, 10p,
Head of great blue touraco.

1964, July 1
215 A30   15c chestnut   .25 .25
216 A30   25c dull violet   .25 .25
217 A30   50c dk olive grn   .25 .25
218 A30   70c green   .25 .25
219 A30   1p brown orange   .30 .25
220 A30   1.50p grnsh blue   .35 .25
221 A30   3p violet blue   .65 .25
222 A30   5p dull purple   1.50 .30
223 A30   10p bright green   2.25 .85
    Nos. 215-223 (9)   6.05 2.90

The Three
Kings
A31

Designs: 50c, 1.50p, Caspar, vert.

Perf. 13x12½, 12½x13

1964, Nov. 23   Unwmk.
224 A31   50c green   .25 .25
225 A31   1p orange ver   .25 .25
226 A31   1.50p deep green   .30 .25
227 A31   3p ultra   1.50 .90
    Nos. 224-227 (4)   2.30 1.65

Issued for Stamp Day, 1964.

Boy — A32   Woman Fruit
            Picker — A33

1.50p, Girl learning to write, and church.

1964, Mar. 1   Photo.   Perf. 13x12½
228 A32   50c indigo   .25 .25
229 A33   1p dark red   .25 .25
230 A33   1.50p grnsh blue   .30 .25
    Nos. 228-230 (3)   .80 .75

Issued to commemorate 25 years of peace.

Plectrocnemia
Cruciata — A34

Design: 1p, Metopodontus savagei, horiz.

Perf. 13x12½, 12½x13

1965, June 1   Photo.   Unwmk.
231 A34   50c slate green   .30 .25
232 A34   1p rose red   .30 .25
233 A34   1.50p Prus blue   .35 .30
    Nos. 231-233 (3)   .95 .80

Issued for child welfare.

Pole Vault
A35

Arms of Fernando
Po — A36

Perf. 12½x13, 13x12½

1965, Nov. 23   Photo.   Unwmk.
234 A35   50c yellow green   .25 .25
235 A36   1p brt org brn   .25 .25
236 A35   1.50p brt blue   .30 .25
    Nos. 234-236 (3)   .80 .75

Issued for Stamp Day, 1965.

Children
Reading
A37

1.50p, St. Elizabeth of Hungary, vert.

Perf. 12½x13, 13x12½

1966, June 1   Photo.   Unwmk.
237 A37   50c dark green   .25 .25
238 A37   1p brown red   .25 .25
239 A37   1.50p dark blue   .25 .25
    Nos. 237-239 (3)   .75 .75

Issued for child welfare.

White-nosed
Monkey — A38

Stamp Day: 40c, 4p, Head of moustached
monkey, vert.

1966, Nov. 23   Photo.   Perf. 13
240 A38   10c dk blue & yel   .30 .25
241 A38   40c lt brn, bl & blk   .30 .25
242 A38   1.50p ol bis, brn org &
           blk   .35 .30
243 A38   4p sl grn, brn org &
           blk   .45 .35
    Nos. 240-243 (4)   1.40 1.15

Flowers — A39

Designs: 40c, 4p, Six flowers.

1967, June 1   Photo.   Perf. 13
244 A39   10c brt car & pale grn   .25 .25
245 A39   40c red brn & org   .25 .25
246 A39   1.50p red lil & lt red brn   .30 .25
247 A39   4p dk blue & lt grn   .35 .30
    Nos. 244-247 (4)   1.15 1.05

Issued for child welfare.

Linsang — A40

Stamp Day: 1.50p, Needle-clawed galago,
vert. 3.50p, Fraser's scaly-tailed flying squirrel.

1967, Nov. 23   Photo.   Perf. 13
248 A40   1p black & bister   .30 .25
249 A40   1.50p brown & olive   .30 .25
250 A40   3.50p rose lake & dl grn   .40 .30
    Nos. 248-250 (3)   1.00 .80

Stamp of
1868, No.
1, and
Arms of
San Carlos
A41

Fernando Po No. 1 and: 1.50p, Arms of
Santa Isabel. 2.50p, Arms of Fernando Po.

1968, Feb. 4   Photo.   Perf. 13
251 A41   1p brt plum & brn org   .25 .25
252 A41   1.50p dp blue & brn org   .30 .25
253 A41   2.50p brn & brn org   .40 .30
    Nos. 251-253 (3)   .95 .80

Centenary of the first postage stamp.

Signs of the
Zodiac — A42

1968, Apr. 25   Photo.   Perf. 13
254 A42   1p Libra   .25 .25
255 A42   1.50p Leo   .30 .25
256 A42   2.50p Aquarius   .40 .30
    Nos. 254-256 (3)   .95 .80

Issued for child welfare.

SEMI-POSTAL STAMPS

Catalogue values for unused
stamps in this section are for
Never Hinged items.

Types of Regular Issue, 1960

Designs: 10c+5c, Manuel de Falla. 15c+5c,
Dancers from "Love, the Magician."

Perf. 12½x13, 13x12½

1960   Photo.   Unwmk.
B1   A18   10c + 5c maroon   .25 .25
B2   A17   15c + 5c dk brn & bister   .25 .25

The surtax was for child welfare.

Whale
SP1

Design: Nos. B4, B6, Harpooning whale.

1961   Perf. 12½x13
B3   SP1   10c + 5c rose brown   .30 .25
B4   SP1   20c + 5c dk slate grn   .30 .25
B5   SP1   30c + 10c olive brn   .30 .25
B6   SP1   50c + 20c dark brn   .30 .25
    Nos. B3-B6 (4)   1.20 1.00

Issued for Stamp Day, 1960.

Hand Blessing
Woman — SP2

Design: 25c+10c, Boy making sign of the
cross, and crucifix.

1961, June 21   Perf. 13x12½
B7   SP2   10c + 5c rose brn   .30 .25
B8   SP2   25c + 10c gray vio   .30 .25
B9   SP2   80c + 20c dk brn   .35 .30
    Nos. B7-B9 (3)   .95 .80

The surtax was for child welfare.

Ethiopian
Tortoise
SP3

Stamp Day: 25c+10c, 1p+10c, Native carriers, palms and shore.

1961, Nov. 23   Perf. 12½x13
B10   SP3   10c + 5c rose red   .30 .25
B11   SP3   25c + 10c dk pur   .30 .25
B12   SP3   30c + 10c vio brn   .30 .25
B13   SP3   1p + 10c red org   .35 .30
    Nos. B10-B13 (4)   1.25 1.05

FIJI

ˈfē-ˌjē

LOCATION — Group of 332 islands (106 inhabited) in the South Pacific Ocean east of Vanuatu
GOVT. — Independent nation in British Commonwealth
AREA — 7,078 sq. mi.
POP. — 812,918 (1999 est.)
CAPITAL — Suva

A British colony since 1874, Fiji became fully independent in 1970.

12 Pence = 1 Shilling
20 Shillings = 1 Pound
100 Cents = 1 Dollar (1872-74, 1969)

Syncopated Perforations
Type A (1st stamp #873): On shorter sides, the seventh hole from the larger side is an oval hole equal in width to three holes.

Catalogue values for unused stamps in this country are for Never Hinged items, beginning with Scott 137 in the regular postage section and Scott B1 in the semi-postal section.

Values for unused stamps are for examples with original gum as defined in the catalogue introduction except for Nos. 1-10 which are valued without gum. Additionally, Nos. 1-10 are valued with roulettes showing on two or more sides, but expect small faults which do not detract from the appearance of the stamps. Very few examples of Nos. 1-10 will be found free of faults and these will command substantial premiums.

Watermark

Wmk. 17 — FIJI POSTAGE Across Center Row of Sheet

A1

1870   Unwmk.   Typeset   *Roulletted*
Quadrille Paper

1	A1	1p black, *pink*	3,750.	4,000.
2	A1	3p black, *pink*	4,000.	4,000.
3	A1	6p black, *pink*	2,350.	2,750.
5	A1	1sh black, *pink*	1,750.	2,250.

1871   **Laid Batonne Paper**

6	A1	1p black, *pink*	1,000.	2,000.
7	A1	3p black, *pink*	1,750.	3,250.
8	A1	6p black, *pink*	1,300.	2,000.
9	A1	9p black, *pink*	2,200.	3,500.
10	A1	1sh black, *pink*	1,500.	1,600.

This service was established by the *Fiji Times*, a weekly newspaper, for the delivery of the newspaper. Since there was no postal service to the other islands, delivery of letters to agents of the newspaper on the islands was offered to the public.

Nos. 1-5 were printed in the same sheet, one horizontal row of 6 of each (6p, 1sh, 1p, 3p). Nos. 6-10 were printed from the same plate with three 9p replacing three 3p.

Most used examples have pen cancels.

Up to three sets of imitations exist. One on pink laid paper, pin-perforated, measuring 22½x16mm. Originals measure 22½x18½mm. A later printing was made on pink wove paper. Forgeries also exist plus fake cancellations.

Crown and "CR" (Cakobau Rex)
A2   A3

A4

1871   Typo.   Wmk. 17   *Perf. 12½*
Wove Paper

15	A2	1p blue	62.50	140.00
16	A3	3p green	125.00	400.00
17	A4	6p rose	150.00	325.00
		Nos. 15-17 (3)	337.50	865.00

Sheets of 50 (10x5).
For overprints and surcharges see #18-39.

Stamps of 1871 Surcharged in Black

1872, Jan. 13

18	A2	2c on 1p blue	37.50	57.50
19	A3	6c on 3p green	75.00	75.00
20	A4	12c on 6p rose	100.00	85.00
		Nos. 18-20 (3)	212.50	217.50

Nos. 18-20 with Additional Overprint in Black:

b   c

1874, Oct. 10

21	A2(b)	2c on 1p blue	1,150.	325.00
22	A2(c)	2c on 1p blue	1,000.	300.00
a.		Invtd. "A" instead of "V"	2,600.	1,500.
b.		Period after "R" is a Maltese Cross	2,600.	1,500.
23	A3(b)	6c on 3p green	2,100.	1,000.
24	A3(c)	6c on 3p green	1,650.	775.00
a.		Inverted "A"	4,250.	1,850.
b.		Period after "R" is a Maltese Cross	4,250.	1,850.
25	A4(b)	12c on 6p rose	900.00	250.00
a.		"V.R." inverted	5,750.	
26	A4(c)	12c on 6p rose	725.00	275.00
a.		Inverted "A"	2,250.	1,350.
b.		Period after "R" is a Maltese Cross	2,250.	1,350.
c.		"V.R." inverted	—	5,000.

Types "b" and "c" were in the same sheet.

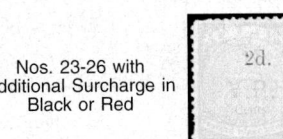

Nos. 23-26 with Additional Surcharge in Black or Red

1875

27	A3(b)	2c on 6c on 3p	1,950.	750.00
a.		Period btwn. "2" and "d"	3,500.	1,400.
b.		"V.R." double	4,000.	3,750.
28	A3(b)	2p on 6c on 3p (R)	750.00	325.00
a.		Period btwn. "2" and "d"	1,750.	750.00
29	A3(c)	2p on 6c on 3p	1,650.	525.00
a.		Inverted "A"	3,750.	1,400.
b.		Period after "R" is a Maltese Cross	3,750.	1,400.
c.		No period after "2d"	3,750.	1,400.

30	A3(c)	2p on 6c on 3p (R)	600.00	225.00
a.		Inverted "A"	1,750.	750.00
b.		Period after "R" is a Maltese Cross	1,750.	750.00
c.		No period after "2d"	1,850.	750.00
31	A4(b)	2p on 12c on 6p	2,250.	950.00
a.		Period btwn. "2" and "d"		
b.		No period after "2d"		
c.		"2d, VR" double		4,250.
32	A4(c)	2p on 12c on 6p	2,100.	900.00
a.		Inverted "A"	2,750.	1,250.
b.		No period after "2d"		
c.		"2d, VR" double		4,250.

Types of 1871 Overprinted or Surcharged in Black:

e   f

1876, Jan. 31   Unwmk.
Wove Paper

33	A2(e)	1p ultramarine	57.50	57.50
a.		Inverted surcharge	1,000.	
b.		Dbl. impression of stamp	1,000.	
c.		Horiz. pair, imperf vert.	1,000.	
34	A3(e+f)	2p on 3p dk grn	52.50	60.00
a.		Dbl. surch. "Two Pence"		
35	A4(e)	6p rose	70.00	65.00
b.		Surcharge inverted		
c.		Dbl. impression of stamp	2,850.	
		Nos. 33-35 (3)	180.00	182.50

1877   Laid Paper

36	A2(e)	1p ultramarine	20.00	32.50
a.		Horiz. pair, imperf. vert.	1,100.	
37	A3(e+f)	2p on 3p dk grn	65.00	75.00
38	A3(e+f)	4p on 3p lilac	95.00	30.00
a.		Horiz. pair, imperf. vert.	1,000.	
39	A4(e)	6p rose	55.00	32.50
a.		Horiz. pair, imperf. vert.	800.00	
		Nos. 36-39 (4)	235.00	*170.00*

Many of the preceding stamps are known imperforate. They are printer's waste and were never issued.

A12   A13

Queen Victoria
A14   A15

Perf. 10-13½ & Compound

1878-90   Wove Paper   Typo.

40	A12	1p ultra ('79)	10.00	7.50
a.		1p blue	60.00	3.75
41	A12	2p green	15.00	1.10
b.		2p ultramarine (error)	28,500.	
42	A12	4p brt vio ('90)	8.50	7.00
a.		4p mauve	11.50	8.50
43	A13	6p brt rose ('80)	7.50	4.25
a.		Printed on both sides	1,150.	975.00
44	A14	1sh yel brn ('99)	40.00	10.00
a.		1sh deep brown ('81)	95.00	22.50

Litho.

45	A15	5sh blk & red brn ('82)	62.50	37.50
		Nos. 40-45 (6)	143.50	67.35

Official facsimiles of the 5sh were officially made in 1900, differing in shades and detail of design from No. 45. They exist imperf., perf. 10 and 12; are all canceled "SUVA" and usually dated "15 Dec., 00."
No. 41b was not put on sale. All copies were supposed to be destroyed.
For surcharges see Nos. 46-52.

Surcharged type "f" in Black

1878-90   Typo.

46	A12	2p on 3p green	6.50	22.50
47	A12	4p on 1p vio ('90)	47.50	30.00
48	A12	4p on 2p lilac ('83)	85.00	12.50
		Nos. 46-48 (3)	139.00	65.00

Nos. 40-43 Surcharged in Black:

g   h

j   k

1891-92   *Perf. 10*

49	A12(g)	½p on 1p ('92)	50.00	75.00
50	A12(h)	2½p on 2p	50.00	57.50
a.		Wider space (2mm) between "2" and "½"	150.00	160.00
51	A12(j)	5p on 4p ('92)	57.50	75.00
52	A13(k)	5p on 6p ('92)	62.50	80.00
a.		"FIVE" and "PENCE" 3mm apart	75.00	80.00
		Nos. 49-52 (4)	220.00	287.50

A18

Fijian Canoe — A19

A20

1891-96   *Perf. 10-12 & Compound*

53	A18	½p grnsh blk ('92)	1.40	3.00
a.		½p gray	3.50	6.00
54	A19	1p black ('93)	5.00	5.50
55	A19	1p lilac rose ('96)	5.00	1.00
56	A19	2p green ('93)	6.50	1.10
a.		Perf. 10x12 ('94)	700.00	425.00
57	A20	2½ red brown	5.75	5.75
58	A19	5p ultra ('93)	15.00	8.50
		Nos. 53-58 (6)	38.65	24.85

Edward VII   George V
A22   A23

1903, Feb. 1   Wmk. 2   *Perf. 14*

59	A22	½p pale green & gray green	2.60	2.25
60	A22	1p black & violet, red	15.00	.65
61	A22	2p orange & violet	4.50	1.40
62	A22	2½p ultramarine & violet, blue	16.00	4.00
63	A22	3p red violet & violet	1.75	4.50
64	A22	4p black & violet	1.75	2.75
65	A22	5p green & violet	1.75	3.00
66	A22	6p carmine rose & violet	1.75	3.00
67	A22	1sh carmine rose & green	12.50	70.00
68	A22	5sh black & green	62.50	150.00
69	A22	£1 ultramarine & gray	400.00	550.00
		Revenue cancel		70.00
		Nos. 59-68 (10)	120.10	241.55

Numerals of 2p, 4p, 6p and 5sh of type A22 are in color on plain tablet.

1904-12   Wmk. 3
Ordinary Paper
70	A22	½p pale green & green ('04)	15.00	3.50
70A	A22	½p green ('08)	12.50	3.50
71	A22	1p black & violet, red ('04)	30.00	.20
72	A22	1p carmine ('06)	11.00	.20
73	A22	2½p ultramarine ('10)	7.50	8.50

Chalky Paper
74	A22	6p violet ('10)	15.00	30.00
75	A22	1sh carmine rose & green ('09)	30.00	45.00
76	A22	1sh black, green ('11)	5.00	11.00
77	A22	5sh scarlet & green, yellow ('11)	65.00	75.00
78	A22	£1 black & violet, red ('12)	375.00	325.00
		Nos. 70-77 (9)	191.00	176.90

Die I
For description of Dies I and II see "Dies of British Colonial Stamps" in Table of Contents.

1912-23
Ordinary Paper
79	A23	¼p brown ('16)	1.50	.45
80	A23	½p green	1.40	.55
81	A23	1p scarlet	2.25	.75
a.		1p carmine ('16)	2.25	.25
82	A23	2p gray ('14)	2.00	.20
83	A23	2½p ultramarine ('14)	3.50	4.00
84	A23	3p violet, yellow	2.25	4.00
a.		Die II ('21)	2.75	25.00
85	A23	4p red & black, yellow ('14)	3.75	15.00
a.		Die II ('23)	3.75	27.50

Chalky Paper
86	A23	5p ol green & dl violet ('14)	5.50	12.50
87	A23	6p red violet & dl violet ('14)	2.40	6.00
88	A23	1sh black, green	1.10	14.00
a.		1sh blk, blue green, olive back	4.50	11.00
b.		1sh black, emerald ('21)	6.25	45.00
c.		Die II ('22)	3.25	27.50
89	A23	2sh 6p red & black, blue	37.50	35.00
90	A23	5sh scarlet & green, yellow	37.50	45.00
91	A23	£1 black & violet, red	300.00	325.00
a.		Die II ('21)	300.00	325.00
		Revenue cancel		52.50

Surface-colored Paper
92	A23	1sh black, green	1.25	12.50
		Nos. 79-90,92 (13)	101.90	149.95

Numerals of ¼p, 1½p, 2p, 4p, 6p, 2sh, 2sh6p and 5sh of type A23 are in color on plain tablet.

For overprints see Nos. MR1-MR2.

Die II
1922-27   Wmk. 4
Ordinary Paper
93	A23	¼p dark brown	3.00	27.50
94	A23	½p green	.85	2.40
95	A23	1p rose red	2.75	1.25
96	A23	1p violet ('27)	1.40	.20
97	A23	1½p rose red ('27)	4.50	2.00
98	A23	2p gray	1.40	.20
99	A23	3p ultramarine ('23)	3.00	1.20
100	A23	4p red & black, yellow	5.75	7.50
101	A23	5p ol green & dl violet	1.75	2.25
102	A23	6p red violet & dull violet	2.40	1.50

Chalky Paper
103	A23	1sh black, emerald	5.50	6.75
104	A23	2sh ultra & violet, blue ('27)	30.00	67.50
105	A23	2sh6p red & black, blue	12.50	35.00
106	A23	5sh scarlet & green, yellow	37.50	75.00
		Nos. 93-106 (14)	112.30	230.25

Common Design Types pictured following the introduction.

Silver Jubilee Issue
Common Design Type
1935, May 6   Perf. 13½x14
110	CD301	1½p carmine & blue	1.10	7.50
111	CD301	2p gray blk & ultra	1.75	.50
112	CD301	3p blue & brown	3.00	4.00

113	CD301	1sh brt vio & indigo	6.00	7.50
		Nos. 110-113 (4)	11.85	19.50
		Set, never hinged	22.50	

Coronation Issue
Common Design Type
1937, May 12   Perf. 11x11½
114	CD302	1p dark violet	.45	.25
115	CD302	2p gray black	.45	.85
116	CD302	3p indigo	.45	.85
		Nos. 114-116 (3)	1.35	1.95
		Set, never hinged	2.00	

Outrigger Canoe — A24

Fijian Village — A25

Outrigger Canoe A26

Map of Fiji Islands A27

Canoe and Arms of Fiji — A28

Sugar Cane — A29   Spear Fishing at Night — A30

Arms of Fiji — A31

Suva Harbor — A32

River Scene — A33

Fijian House — A34

Papaya Tree — A35

Bugler — A36

Designs: No. 121, Government buildings. 8p, 1sh5p, 1sh6p, Arms of Fiji.

Perf. 13½, 12½ (1p)
1938-55   Engr.   Wmk. 4
117	A24	½p green	.25	1.00
c.		Perf. 14 ('41)	16.00	4.50
d.		Perf. 12 ('48)	.80	4.00
118	A25	1p blue & brn	.40	.25
119	A26	1½p rose car (empty canoe)	.40	.25
120	A27	2p grn & org brn (no "180 degree")	30.00	2.00
121	A27	2p mag & grn	.45	.80
a.		Perf. 12 ('46)	.45	.90

Perf. 12½, 13x12 (6p), 14 (8p)
122	A28	3p dp ultra	.80	.40
123	A29	5p rose red & bl	32.50	13.00
124	A29	5p rose red & yel grn	.25	.40
125	A27	6p blk (no "180 degree")	50.00	16.00
126	A31	8p rose car	.80	3.00
a.		Perf. 13 ('50)	.55	3.50
127	A30	1sh black & yel	.60	.90

Perf. 14
128	A31	1sh5p car & black	.20	.20
128A	A31	1sh6p ultra	2.75	3.50
b.		Perf. 13 ('55)	1.10	20.00

Perf. 12½
129	A32	2sh vio & org	2.00	.55
130	A33	2sh6p brn & grn	2.25	2.00
131	A34	5sh dk vio & brn org	2.25	2.25
131A	A35	10sh emer & brn org	27.50	52.50
131B	A36	£1 car & ultra	37.50	65.00
		Nos. 117-131B (18)	202.50	164.25

Issued: 1sh5p, 6/13/40; 5p, 10/1/40; #121, 5/19/42; 8p, 11/15/48; 10sh, 1, 3/13/50; 1sh6p, 8/1/50; others, 4/5/38.

Types of 1938-40 Redrawn
Perf. 13½ (1½p, 2p, 6p), 14 (2½p)
1940-49   Wmk. 4
132	A26	1½p rose car (man in canoe)	1.00	1.00
a.		Perf. 12 ('49)	.80	1.60
b.		Perf. 14 ('42)	14.50	25.00
133	A27	2p grn & org brn ("180 degree")	12.50	21.00
134	A27	2½p grn & org brn	.50	1.25
a.		Perf. 12 ('48)	.80	.60
b.		Perf. 13½ ('42)	.55	1.00
135	A27	6p blk ("180 degree")	2.50	3.00
a.		Perf. 12 ('47)	1.40	2.00
		Nos. 132-135 (4)	16.50	26.25

No. 132, type A26, has a man sitting in the canoe.

Nos. 133-135, type A27, have 180 degree added to the lower right hand corner of the design.

Issued: 2½p, 1/6/42; others 10/1/40.

No. 133 Surcharged in Black

1941, Feb. 10   Perf. 13½
136	A27	2½p on 2p grn & org brn	1.50	.40
		Never hinged	2.50	

> Catalogue values for unused stamps in this section, from this point to the end of the section, are for Never Hinged items.

Peace Issue
Common Design Type
1946, Aug. 17   Perf. 13½
137	CD303	2½p bright green	.20	.60
138	CD303	3p deep blue	.20	.20

Silver Wedding Issue
Common Design Types
1948, Dec. 17   Photo.   Perf. 14x14½
139	CD304	2½p dark green	.70	1.00

Engr.; Name Typo.
Perf. 11½x11
140	CD305	5sh blue violet	22.50	16.00

UPU Issue
Common Design Types
Engr.; Name Typo. on 3p, 8p
Perf. 13½, 11x11½
1949, Oct. 10   Wmk. 4
141	CD306	2p red violet	.65	.50
142	CD307	3p indigo	4.00	2.50
143	CD308	8p dp carmine	.65	2.50
144	CD309	1sh6p blue	.70	1.10
		Nos. 141-144 (4)	6.00	6.60

Coronation Issue
Common Design Type
1953, June 2   Perf. 13½x13
145	CD312	2½p dk green & blk	1.00	.60

Type of 1938-40 with Portrait of Queen Elizabeth II Inscribed: "Royal Visit 1953"
1953, Dec. 16   Perf. 13
146	A31	8p carmine lake	.65	.35

Visit of Queen Elizabeth II and the Duke of Edinburgh, 1953.

Types of 1938-50 with Portrait of Queen Elizabeth II, and:

A39

Loading Copra A40

Designs: 1sh6p, Sugar cane train. 2sh, Bananas for export. 5sh, Gold industry.

Perf. 11½, 11½x11, 12, 12½, 13
1954-56   Engr.
147	A24	½p green	.20	1.25
148	A39	1p grnsh blue	2.00	.20
149	A39	1½p brown	1.10	.65
150	A27	2p mag & green	1.40	.20
151	A39	2½p blue vio	2.75	.20
152	A40	3p purple & brn	3.00	.20
153	A27	6p black	3.00	.85
154	A31	8p carmine lake	4.25	1.25
155	A30	1sh black & yel	2.75	.20
156	A40	1sh6p grn & dp ultra	21.00	1.00
157	A40	2sh brt car & black	6.25	.50
158	A33	2sh6p brn & bl grn	1.40	.20
159	A40	5sh dp ultra & yel	17.00	1.25
160	A35	10sh emer & brn org	8.00	20.00
161	A36	£1 car & ultra	42.50	19.00
		Nos. 147-162 (15)	116.60	47.15

Issued: 2p, 1sh, 2sh6p, 2/1/54; ½p, 6p, 8p, 10sh, £1, 7/1/54; 1p, 6/1/56; 1½p, 2½p, 3p, 1sh6p, 2sh, 5sh, 10/1/56.

Types of 1954-56 and:

Nautilus Shells — A41

Hibiscus — A42

Kandavu Parrot A43

½p, 2p, 2½p, Queen Elizabeth II (A39). 1p, Queen, turtles in bottom panels. 6p, Fijian beating drum (lali). 10p, Yaqona ceremony. 1sh, South Pacific map. 2sh6p, Nadi Airport. 10sh, Cutting sugar cane. £1, Arms of Fiji.

Perf. 11½ (A39, A41); 11½x11 (A40); 14½x14 (A42); 14x14½ (A43)
Engr. (A39, A40, A41); others Photo.
1959-63   **Wmk. 4**

163	A39	½p green ('61)	.25	2.75
164	A41	1p dk blue ('62)	4.00	2.75
165	A41	1½p dk brown ('62)	3.25	2.00
166	A39	2p crim rose ('61)	.90	.20
167	A39	2½p brown org ('62)	2.75	4.25
168	A40	6p blk & car rose ('61)	2.25	.20
169	A42	8p gray, red, yel & grn ('61)	.90	.40
170	A40	10p car & brn ('63)	1.10	.80
171	A40	1sh dk bl & bl ('61)	2.75	.75
172	A40	2sh6p pur & blk ('61)	4.50	1.40
173	A43	4sh dk grn, red, bl & emer	3.25	2.40
174	A40	10sh sep & emer ('61)	8.00	8.00
175	A40	£1 org & blk ('61)	24.00	10.00
		Nos. 163-175 (13)	57.90	35.90

Issued: 4sh, 7/13; 8p, 8/1; ½p, 2p, 6p, 1sh, 2sh6p, 10sh, £1, 11/14; 1p, 1½p, 2½p, 12/3; 10p, 4/1.

For type overprinted see No. 205.

Types of 1954-63 and:

Elizabeth II — A44

1sh6p, 180th meridian and Intl. Date Line. 2sh, White orchids. 5sh, Orange dove.

Perf. 11½ (A41); 12½ (A44); 11½x11 (A40); 14x14½ (A43)
Engr. (A40, A41); others Photo.
1962-67   **Wmk. 314**

176	A41	1p dark blue ('64)	.75	4.25
177	A39	2p crim rose ('65)	.95	.20
178	A44	3p rose cl & multi	.20	.20
179	A40	6p blk & car rose ('64)	1.10	.20
180	A42	9p ultra, red, yel & grn ('63)	1.10	1.00
181	A40	10p car & brn ('64)	1.10	.85
182	A40	1sh dk bl & bl ('66)	1.90	.75
183	A43	1sh6p dk bl & multi	2.25	1.60
184	A42	2sh gold, yel grn & grn	11.00	5.75
185	A40	2sh6p pur & blk ('65)	2.25	1.25
186	A43	4sh grn & multi, wmk. sideways ('67)	4.75	3.25
a.		As #186, wmk. upright ('64)	3.50	6.50
b.		4sh dark green & multi ('66)	4.00	5.25
187	A43	5sh dk gray, yel & red	8.00	1.00
188	A40	10sh sep & emer ('64)	5.50	5.75
189	A40	£1 org & blk ('64)	21.00	15.00
		Nos. 176-189 (14)	61.85	41.05

Issued: 3p, 1sh6p, 2sh, 5sh, 12/3; 9p, #186a, 4/1; 1p, 10p, 10sh, 1/14; 6p, £1, 6/9; 2p, 2sh6p, 8/3; #186b, 3/1; #186, 2/16.

Nos. 178 and 171 Overprinted:
"ROYAL VISIT 1963"

1963, Feb. 1

196	A44	3p multicolored	.50	.35
197	A40	1sh dark blue & blue	.50	.35

Visit of Elizabeth II & Prince Philip, Feb. 3.

Freedom from Hunger Issue
Common Design Type

1963, June 4   **Photo.**   *Perf. 14x14½*

198	CD314	2sh ultramarine	8.25	4.50

Running A45

9p, Throwing the discus, vert. 1sh, Field hockey, vert. 2sh6p, Women's high jump.

Perf. 14½x14, 14x14½
1963, Aug. 6   **Wmk. 314**

199	A45	3p yel, blk & brn	.75	.20
200	A45	9p violet, blk & brn	.75	1.50
201	A45	1sh green, blk & brn	.75	.25
202	A45	2sh6p blue, blk & brn	1.75	1.75
		Nos. 199-202 (4)	4.00	3.70

1st So. Pacific Games, Suva, 8/29-9/7.

Red Cross Centenary Issue
Common Design Type

1963, Sept. 2   **Litho.**   *Perf. 13*

203	CD315	2p black & red	1.50	.30
204	CD315	2sh ultra & red	4.50	4.50

Type of 1959-63 Overprinted

1963, Dec. 2   **Engr.**   *Perf. 11½x11*

205	A40	1sh dark blue & blue	1.00	.35

Opening of the Commonwealth Pacific (telephone) Cable service, COMPAC.

Fiji Scout Badge — A46   Scouts of India, Fiji and Europe Tying Knot — A47

1964, Aug. 3   **Photo.**   *Perf. 12½*

206	A46	3p multicolored	.65	.50
207	A47	1sh ocher & purple	1.00	.75

50th anniv. of the founding of the Fiji Boy Scouts.

Amphibian "Aotearoa," 1939 — A48

Map of Fiji and Tonga Islands and Plane A49

Design: 6p, Heron plane.

1964, Oct. 24   *Perf. 12½, 14½*

208	A48	3p brt red & black	.65	.35
209	A48	6p ultra & red	1.10	1.10
210	A49	1sh grnsh blue & black	1.10	1.10
		Nos. 208-210 (3)	2.85	2.55

Fiji-Tonga airmail service, 25th anniv.

ITU Issue
Common Design Type
Perf. 11x11½

1965, May 17   **Litho.**   **Wmk. 314**

211	CD317	3p blue & rose red	.50	.30
212	CD317	2sh yel & bister	3.50	3.50

Intl. Cooperation Year Issue
Common Design Type

1965, Oct. 25   *Perf. 14½*

213	CD318	2p blue grn & claret	.40	.40
214	CD318	2sh6p lt vio & grn	2.60	2.10

Churchill Memorial Issue
Common Design Type

1966, Jan. 24   **Photo.**   *Perf. 14*
Design in Black, Gold and Carmine Rose

215	CD319	3p brt blue	1.25	.35
216	CD319	9p green	1.75	1.75
217	CD319	1sh brown	1.75	.35
218	CD319	2sh6p violet	2.00	2.00
		Nos. 215-218 (4)	6.75	4.45

World Cup Soccer Issue
Common Design Type

1966, July 1   **Litho.**   *Perf. 14*

219	CD321	2p multicolored	.60	.30
220	CD321	2sh multicolored	1.75	.90

H.M.S. Pandora and Split Island, Rotuma A50

Designs: 10p, Rotuma chiefs, Pandora, and Rotuma's position in Pacific. 1sh6p, Rotuma islanders welcoming Pandora.

1966, Aug. 29   **Photo.**   *Perf. 14x13*

221	A50	3p multicolored	.60	.25
222	A50	9p multicolored	.75	.40
223	A50	1sh6p multicolored	1.00	1.00
		Nos. 221-223 (3)	2.35	1.65

175th anniv. of the discovery of Rotuma, a group of eight islands forming part of the colony of Fiji.

WHO Headquarters Issue
Common Design Type

1966, Sept. 20   **Litho.**   *Perf. 14*

224	CD322	6p multicolored	2.10	.50
225	CD322	1sh6p multicolored	4.50	4.00

Woman Runner A51

Designs: 9p, Shot put, vert. 1sh, Diver.

1966, Dec. 8   **Photo.**   *Perf. 14x14½*

226	A51	3p ol, black & lt brn	.40	.40
227	A51	9p brt blue, blk & brn	.65	.65
228	A51	1sh blue green & multi	.65	.65
		Nos. 226-228 (3)	1.70	1.70

2nd South Pacific Games, Noumea, New Caledonia, Dec. 8-18.

Military Band A52

Intl. Tourist Year: 9p, Reef diving. 1sh, Beqa fire walkers. 2sh, Liner Oriana and Mt. Rama volcano.

1967, Oct. 20   *Perf. 14x13*

229	A52	3p multi & gold	.90	.20
230	A52	9p multi & silver	.35	.35
231	A52	1sh multi & gold	.35	.35
232	A52	2sh multi & silver	.90	.60
		Nos. 229-232 (4)	2.50	1.40

Admiral Bligh, H.M.S. Providence and Old Map of "Feejee" A53

Designs: 1sh, Bligh's longboat being chased by double canoe and map of Fiji Islands. 2sh6p, Bligh's tomb, St. Mary's Cemetery, Lambeth, London.

Perf. 15x14, 12½x13 (1sh)
1967, Dec. 7   **Photo.**   **Wmk. 314**
Size: 35x21mm

233	A53	4p emer, blk & yel	.30	.30

Size: 54x20mm

234	A53	1sh brt bl, brn org & blk	.45	.45

Size: 35x21mm

235	A53	2sh6p sepia & multi	1.25	1.25
		Nos. 233-235 (3)	2.00	2.00

150th anniv. of the death of Adm. William Bligh (1754-1817), captain of the Bounty and principal discoverer of the Fiji Islands.

Simmonds "Spartan" Seaplane — A54

Designs: 6p, Fiji Airways Hawker-Siddeley H748 and emblems of various airlines. 1sh, Fokker "Southern Cross," Capt. Charles Kingsford-Smith, his crew and Southern Cross constellation. 2sh, Lockheed Altair "Lady Southern Cross."

Perf. 14x14½
1968, June 5   **Wmk. 314**

236	A54	2p green & black	.30	.30
237	A54	6p brt blue, car & blk	.30	.30
238	A54	1sh dp violet & green	.50	.50
239	A54	2sh orange brn & dk blue	.90	.90
		Nos. 236-239 (4)	2.00	2.00

40th anniv. of the first Trans-Pacific Flight through Fiji under Capt. Charles Kingsford-Smith.

Fijian Bures — A55

Eastern Reef Heron — A56

1p, Passion fruit flowers. 2p, Nautilus pompilius shell. 4p, Hawk moth. 6p, Reef butterlyfish. 9p, Bamboo raft (bilibili). 10p, Tiger moth. 1sh, Black marlin. 1sh6p, Orangebreasted honey eaters. 2sh, Ringed sea snake, horiz. 2sh6p, Outrigger canoes (takia), horiz. 3sh, Golden cowrie shell. 4sh, Emperor gold mine and gold ore. 5sh, Bamboo orchids, horiz. 10sh, Tabua (ceremonial whale's tooth). £1, Coat of Arms and Queen Elizabeth II, horiz.

Perf. 13½ (A55), 14 (A56)
1968, July 15   **Photo.**   **Wmk. 314**

240	A55	½p multicolored	.20	.20
241	A55	1p multicolored	.20	.20
242	A55	2p multicolored	.20	.20
243	A56	3p multicolored	.30	.20
244	A56	4p multicolored	.65	.20
245	A55	6p multicolored	.25	.30
246	A55	9p multicolored	.20	.45
247	A55	10p multicolored	1.00	.60
248	A56	1sh multicolored	1.25	.65
249	A56	1sh6p multicolored	2.75	.75
250	A55	2sh multicolored	1.50	1.50
251	A56	2sh6p multicolored	1.50	1.50
252	A55	3sh multicolored	3.00	2.00
253	A56	4sh multicolored	5.25	1.75
254	A56	5sh multicolored	2.60	2.25
255	A56	10sh multicolored	4.00	3.50
256	A56	£1 red & multi	5.00	4.00
		Nos. 240-256 (17)	29.85	20.25

See Nos. 260-276.

WHO Emblem, Map of Fiji and
Nurses — A57

WHO Emblem and: 9p, Medical team loading patient on stretcher on dinghy and medical ship "Vuniwai." 3sh, People playing on beach.

1968, Dec. 9   Litho.   Perf. 14

257	A57	3p blue green & multi	.20	.20
258	A57	9p brt blue & multi	.30	.30
259	A57	3sh dk blue & multi	.90	.90
		Nos. 257-259 (3)	1.40	1.40

WHO, 20th anniv.

Types of 1968
Values in Cents and Dollars

Designs: 1c, Passion fruit flowers. 2c, Nautilus pompilius shell. 3c, Reef heron. 4c, Hawk moth. 5c, Reef butterflyfish. 6c, Fijian bures. 8c, Bamboo raft. 9c, Tiger moth. 10c, Black marlin. 15c, Orange-breasted honey-eater. 20c, Ringed sea snake, horiz. 25c, Outrigger canoes (takia), horiz. 30c, Golden cowrie shell. 40c, Emperor gold mine and gold ore. 50c, Bamboo orchids, horiz. $1, Tabua (ceremonial whale's tooth). $2, Coat of Arms and Queen Elizabeth II, horiz.

Perf. 13½ (A55), 14 (A56)

1969, Jan. 13   Photo.   Wmk. 314

260	A55	1c multicolored	.20	.20
261	A55	2c multicolored	.20	.20
262	A56	3c multicolored	.50	.35
263	A55	4c multicolored	1.25	.35
264	A55	5c multicolored	.20	.20
265	A55	6c multicolored	.20	.20
266	A55	8c multicolored	.20	.20
267	A55	9c multicolored	1.25	1.60
268	A56	10c multicolored	.20	.20
269	A56	15c multicolored	7.25	3.50
270	A56	20c multicolored	.90	.65
271	A55	25c multicolored	.90	.25
272	A55	30c multicolored	5.25	1.40
273	A56	40c multicolored	6.00	3.25
274	A56	50c multicolored	3.50	.25
275	A55	$1 multicolored	5.00	2.00
276	A56	$2 red & multi	6.00	5.00
		Nos. 260-276 (17)	39.00	19.80

For overprints & surcharges see #286-288, B5-B6.

Fiji Soldiers and Map of Solomon Islands A58

Designs: 10c, Flags of Fiji Military Force, soldiers in full and battle dress. 25c, Cpl. Sefanaia Sukanaivalu and Victoria Cross.

1969, June 23   Wmk. 314   Perf. 14

277	A58	3c emerald & multi	.80	.80
278	A58	10c red & multi	.95	.95
279	A58	25c black & multi	1.25	1.25
		Nos. 277-279 (3)	3.00	3.00

25th anniv. of the Fiji Military Forces campaign in the Solomon Islands and of the posthumous award of the Victoria Cross to Cpl. Sefanaia Sukanaivalu.

Yachting — A59

Designs: 4c, Javelin. 20c, Winners and South Pacific Games medal.

1969, Aug. 18   Photo.   Perf. 14½x14

280	A59	4c red, brown & blk	.45	.45
281	A59	8c blue & black	.60	.60
282	A59	20c olive grn, blk & ocher	1.25	1.25
		Nos. 280-282 (3)	2.30	2.30

3rd South Pacific Games, Port Moresby, Papua New Guinea, Aug. 13-23.

Students in Laboratory — A60

2c, Map of South Pacific and mortarboard. 8c, Site of University at Royal New Zealand Air Force Seaplane Station, Laucala Bay, RNZAF badge and Sunderland flying boat.

1969, Nov. 10   Perf. 14x14½

283	A60	2c multicolored	.30	.30
284	A60	8c red & multi	.50	.50
285	A60	25c dk green & multi	1.40	1.40
		Nos. 283-285 (3)	2.20	2.20

Inauguration of the University of the South Pacific, Laucala Bay, Suva.

Nos. 261, 268 and 271 Overprinted:
"ROYAL VISIT / 1970"

1970, Mar. 4   Perf. 13½, 14

286	A55	2c multicolored	.30	.30
287	A56	10c multicolored	.40	.40
288	A55	25c multicolored	1.75	1.75
		Nos. 286-288 (3)	2.45	2.45

Visit of Queen Elizabeth II, Prince Philip and Princess Anne, Mar. 4-5.

Nuns Sitting under Chaulmoogra Tree, and Chaulmoogra Fruit — A61

Designs: 10c, Paintings by Semisi Maya (former patient). No. 290, Cascade, vert. No. 291, Sea urchins, vert. 30c, Aerial view of Makogai Hospital.

Perf. 14x14½, 14½x14

1970, May 25   Photo.   Wmk. 314

289	A61	2c brt pink & multi	.50	.50
290	A61	10c gray green & blk	.75	.75
291	A61	10c blue, car & blk	.75	.75
a.		Pair, #290-291	1.50	1.50
292	A61	30c orange & multi	2.00	2.00
		Nos. 289-292 (4)	4.00	4.00

Closing of the Leprosy Hospital on Makogai Island in 1969.

Abel Tasman and Ship's Log, 1643 — A62

3c, Capt. James Cook & "Endeavour." 8c, Capt. William Bligh & longboat, 1789. 25c, Man of Fiji & Fijian ocean-going canoe.

1970, Aug. 18   Litho.   Perf. 13x12½

293	A62	2c blue green & multi	1.00	1.00
294	A62	3c gray green & multi	1.25	1.25
295	A62	8c multicolored	1.50	1.50
296	A62	25c dull lilac & multi	2.25	2.25
		Nos. 293-296 (4)	6.00	6.00

Discoverers and explorers of Fiji Islands.

King Cakobau and Cession Stone at Lavuka A63

Designs: 3c, Chinese, Fijian, Indian and European children. 10c, Prime Minister Ratu Sir Kamisese Mara and flag of Fiji. 25c, Fijian male dancer and Indian female dancer.

1970, Oct. 10   Wmk. 314   Perf. 14

297	A63	2c multicolored	.25	.25
298	A63	3c multicolored	.35	.35
299	A63	10c multicolored	.55	.55
300	A63	25c multicolored	1.60	1.60
		Nos. 297-300 (4)	2.75	2.75

Fijian independence.

Fiji Nos. 1 and 3 — A64

15c, Fiji #15, 44, 59, 81, 127, 166. 20c, Fiji Times Office, Levuka, & G. P. O., Suva.

1970, Nov. 2   Photo.   Perf. 14½x14
Size: 35x21mm

301	A64	4c multicolored	.40	.40

Size: 60x21½mm

302	A64	15c multicolored	1.10	1.10

Size: 35x21mm

303	A64	20c multicolored	1.50	1.50
		Nos. 301-303 (3)	3.00	3.00

Centenary of first postage stamps of Fiji.

Gray-backed White Eyes — A65

Yellow-breasted Musk Parrots — A66

Designs: 1c, Cirrhopetalum umbellatum. 2c, Cardinal honey eaters. 3c, Calanthe furcata. 4c, Bulbophyllum. 6c, Phaius tancarviliae. 8c, Blue-crested broadbills. 10c, Acanthephippiumvitiense. 15c, Dendrobium tokai. 20c, Slaty flycatchers. 25c, Kandavu honey eaters. 30c, Dendrobium gordonii. 50c, White-throated pigeon. $1, Collared lories (kula). $2, Dendrobium platygastrium. (Orchids shown on 1c, 3c, 4c, 6c, 10c, 15c, 30c, $2.)

Wmk. 314 Upright

1971-72   Litho.   Perf. 13½x14

305	A65	1c blk & multi ('72)	.20	.20
306	A65	2c carmine & multi	.20	.20
307	A65	3c multi ('72)	.85	.20
308	A65	4c blk & multi ('72)	.75	1.50
309	A65	5c brown & multi	2.75	.25
310	A65	6c lt bl & multi ('72)	.45	.30
311	A65	8c black & multi	.50	.35
312	A65	10c multi ('72)	.55	.40
313	A65	15c multi ('72)	2.50	.55
314	A65	20c gray & multi	1.50	.60

Perf. 14

315	A66	25c sepia & multi	1.50	.95
316	A66	30c grn & multi ('72)	3.00	1.10
317	A66	40c blue & multi	3.50	1.50
318	A66	50c gray & multi	4.00	1.90
319	A66	$1 red & multi	6.25	3.75
320	A66	$2 multi ('72)	12.50	7.25
		Nos. 305-320 (16)	41.00	21.00

Issued: 5c, 20c, 40c, 50c, 8/6; 2c, 8c, 25c, $1, 11/22; 1c, 10c, 30c, $2, 1/4; 3c, 4c, 6c, 15c, 6/23.

1972-74   Wmk. 314 Sideways

306c	A65	2c ('73)	.70	11.00
307a	A65	3c ('73)	2.00	.60
308a	A65	4c ('73)	6.50	.90
309a	A65	6c ('73)	6.50	4.25
310a	A65	6c ('73)	8.75	1.60
311a	A65	8c ('73)	4.25	1.00
313a	A65	15c ('73)	3.75	2.75
314a	A65	20c	14.00	2.50
315a	A66	25c ('73)	2.00	1.10
317a	A66	40c ('74)	3.25	8.75
318a	A66	50c ('74)	3.25	4.25
319a	A66	$1	3.25	6.50
320a	A66	$2	4.25	7.00
		Nos. 306c-320a (13)	62.45	52.20

Issued: 20c, $1, $2, 11/17; 3c, 5c, 3/8; 4c, 6c, 8c, 15c, 25c, 4/11; 2c, 12/12; 40c, 50c, 3/15.

1975-77   Wmk. 373

305b	A65	1c	1.00	4.75
306d	A65	2c	1.00	4.75
307b	A65	3c	.50	4.75
308b	A65	4c ('76)	4.50	.20
309b	A65	5c	1.60	4.75
310b	A65	6c ('76)	3.75	.20
311b	A65	8c ('76)	.45	.20
312b	A65	10c	.50	2.25
313b	A65	15c ('76)	3.25	.50
314b	A65	20c ('77)	4.75	.65
316b	A66	25c ('76)	6.75	1.10
317b	A66	40c ('76)	3.75	.70
318b	A66	50c ('76)	3.75	.80
319b	A66	$1 ('76)	3.75	1.75
320b	A66	$2 ('76)	1.90	1.75
		Nos. 305b-320b (15)	41.20	29.10

Issued: 1c, 2c, 3c, 5c, 10c, 4/9; 20c, 7/15; others, 9/3.

Women's Basketball — A67

Community Education — A68

1971, Sept. 6   Wmk. 314   Perf. 14

321	A67	8c multicolored	.50	.50
322	A67	10c Running	.75	.75
323	A67	25c Weight lifting	1.50	1.50
		Nos. 321-323 (3)	2.75	2.75

4th South Pacific Games, Papeete, French Polynesia, Sept. 8-19.

1972, Feb. 7

Designs: 4c, Public health. 50c, Economic growth (farm scenes).

324	A68	2c bright rose & multi	.20	.20
325	A68	4c gray & multi	.30	.30
326	A68	50c bright blue & multi	2.00	2.00
		Nos. 324-326 (3)	2.50	2.50

South Pacific Commission, 25th anniv.

Arts Festival Emblem — A69

Rugby — A70

1972, Apr. 10

327	A69	10c blue, org & black	.50	.50

South Pacific Festival of Arts, May 6-20.

Silver Wedding Issue, 1972
Common Design Type

Queen Elizabeth II, Prince Philip, flowers, shells.

1972, Nov. 20   Photo.   Perf. 14x14½

328	CD324	10c slate grn & multi	.40	.40
329	CD324	25c red lilac & multi	.60	.60

1973, Mar. 9   Litho.   Perf. 14

330	A70	2c shown	.40	.40
331	A70	8c Tackle	.80	.80
332	A70	25c Kicking ball	1.25	1.25
		Nos. 330-332 (3)	2.45	2.45

60th anniversary of Fiji Rugby Union.

Forestry Development — A71

Development projects: 8c, Irrigation of rice field. 10c, Low income housing. 25c, Highway construction.

1973, July 23 — Perf. 14

333	A71	5c multicolored	.30	.30
334	A71	8c multicolored	.40	.40
335	A71	10c multicolored	.45	.45
336	A71	25c multicolored	1.25	1.25
		Nos. 333-336 (4)	2.40	2.40

Holy Family — A72

Runners — A73

Festivals: 10c, Diwali (Candles; Indian New Year). 20c, Id-Ul-Fitar (Friendly greeting and mosque; Moslem, Ramadan). 25c, Chinese New Year (dragon dance).

1973, Oct. 26 — Perf. 14x14½

337	A72	3c blue & multi	.45	.45
338	A72	10c purple & multi	.45	.45
339	A72	20c emerald & multi	.75	.75
340	A72	25c red & multi	.75	.75
		Nos. 337-340 (4)	2.40	2.40

Festivals celebrated by various groups in Fiji.

1974, Jan. 7

341	A73	3c shown	.60	.35
342	A73	8c Boxing	.60	.35
343	A73	50c Lawn bowling	2.25	2.25
		Nos. 341-343 (3)	3.45	2.95

10th British Commonwealth Games, Christchurch, N.Z., Jan. 24-Feb. 2.

Centenary of Cricket in Fiji — A74

Designs: 3c, Bowler. 25c, Batsman and wicketkeeper. 40c, Fielder, horiz.

Perf. 14x14½, 14½x14

1974, Feb. 21 — Litho.

344	A74	3c multicolored	1.00	1.00
345	A74	25c multicolored	1.40	1.40
346	A74	40c multicolored	1.60	1.60
		Nos. 344-346 (3)	4.00	4.00

Mailman and UPU Emblem A75

UPU Emblem and: 8c, Loading mail on ship. 30c, Post office and truck. 50c, Jet.

1974, May 22 — Wmk. 314 — Perf. 14

347	A75	3c orange & multi	.40	.40
348	A75	8c multicolored	.45	.45
349	A75	30c lt blue & multi	.75	.75
350	A75	50c multicolored	1.40	1.40
		Nos. 347-350 (4)	3.00	3.00

Centenary of the Universal Postal Union.

Cub Scouts A76

Designs: 10c, Boy Scouts reading map. 40c, Scouts and Fiji flag, vert.

1974, Aug. 30

351	A76	3c multicolored	.25	.25
352	A76	10c multicolored	.75	.75
353	A76	40c multicolored	2.00	2.00
		Nos. 351-353 (3)	3.00	3.00

First National Boy Scout Jamboree, Lautoka, Viti Levu Island.

Cakobau Club and Flag — A77

King Cakobau, Queen Victoria A78

Design: 50c, Signing ceremony at Levuka.

1974, Oct. 9 — Litho. — Perf. 13½x13

354	A77	3c multicolored	.20	.20
355	A78	8c multicolored	.40	.40
356	A78	50c multicolored	1.10	1.10
		Nos. 354-356 (3)	1.70	1.70

Deed of Cession, cent. and 4th anniv. of independence.

Diwali, Hindu Festival of Lights — A79

Designs: 15c, Id-Ul-Fitar (women exchanging greetings under moon). 25c, Chinese New Year (girl twirling streamer, and fireworks). 30c, Christmas (man and woman singing hymns, and star).

1975, Oct. 31 — Wmk. 373 — Perf. 14

357	A79	3c black & multi	.20	.20
358	A79	15c black & multi	.45	.45
359	A79	25c black & multi	.90	.90
360	A79	30c black & multi	1.10	1.10
a.		Souvenir sheet of 4, #357-360	7.00	7.00
		Nos. 357-360 (4)	2.65	2.65

Festivals celebrated by various groups in Fiji.

Steam Locomotive No. 21 — A80

Sugar mill trains: 15c, Diesel locomotive No. 8. 20c, Diesel locomotive No. 1. 30c, Free passenger train.

1976, Jan. 26 — Litho. — Perf. 14½

361	A80	4c yellow & multi	.45	.45
362	A80	15c salmon & multi	1.10	1.10
363	A80	20c multicolored	1.50	1.50
364	A80	30c blue & multi	2.25	2.25
		Nos. 361-364 (4)	5.30	5.30

Fiji Blind Society and Rotary Emblems A81

Rotary Intl. of Fiji, 40th Anniv.: 25c, Ambulance and Rotary emblems.

Perf. 13x13½

1976, Mar. 26 — Wmk. 373

365	A81	10c lt green, brn, ultra	.40	.40
366	A81	25c multicolored	1.00	1.00

De Havilland Drover — A82

Planes: 15c, BAC One-Eleven. 25c, Hawker-Siddeley 748. 30c, Britten Norman Trislander.

1976, Sept. 1 — Litho. — Perf. 14

367	A82	4c multicolored	.20	.20
368	A82	15c multicolored	.80	.80
369	A82	25c multicolored	2.00	2.00
370	A82	30c multicolored	2.25	2.25
		Nos. 367-370 (4)	5.25	5.25

Fiji air service, 25th anniversary.

Queen's Visit, 1970 — A83

Designs: 25c, King Edward's Chair. 30c, Queen wearing cloth-of-gold supertunica.

1977, Feb. 7 — Litho. — Perf. 14x13½

371	A83	10c silver & multi	.25	.25
372	A83	25c silver & multi	.75	.75
373	A83	30c silver & multi	.90	.90
		Nos. 371-373 (3)	1.90	1.90

25th anniv. of reign of Elizabeth II.

World Map, Sinusoidal Projection — A84

Design: 30c, Map showing Fiji Islands.

Wmk. 373

1977, Apr. 12 — Litho. — Perf. 14½

374	A84	4c multicolored	.20	.20
375	A84	30c multicolored	1.10	1.10

First Joint Council of Ministers Conference of the European Economic Community (EEC) and of African, Caribbean and Pacific States (ACP).

Hibiscus A85

1977, Aug. 27 — Wmk. 373 — Perf. 14

376	A85	4c red	.20	.20
377	A85	15c orange	.40	.35
378	A85	30c pink	.90	.70
379	A85	35c yellow	1.10	.90
		Nos. 376-379 (4)	2.60	2.15

Fiji Hibiscus Festival, 21st anniversary.

Drua, Double Canoe A86

Canoes: 15c, Tabilai. 25c, Takia, dugout outrigger canoe. 40c, Camakau.

1977, Nov. 7 — Litho. — Perf. 14½

380	A86	4c multicolored	.20	.20
381	A86	15c multicolored	.40	.30
382	A86	25c multicolored	.70	.60
383	A86	40c multicolored	.90	.90
		Nos. 380-383 (4)	2.20	2.00

Elizabeth II Coronation Anniversary Issue
Common Design Types
Souvenir Sheet
Unwmk.

1978, Apr. 21 — Litho. — Perf. 15

384		Sheet of 6	3.25	3.25
a.		CD326 25c White hart of Richard II	.60	.60
b.		CD327 25c Elizabeth II	.60	.60
c.		CD328 25c Banded iguana	.60	.60

No. 384 contains 2 se-tenant strips of Nos. 348a-348c, separated by horizontal gutter.

Southern Cross on Naselai Beach — A87

4c, Fiji Defence Force surrounding Southern Cross. 25c, Wright Flyer. 30c, Bristol F2B.

1978, June 26 — Wmk. 373 — Perf. 14½

385	A87	4c multicolored	.20	.20
386	A87	15c multicolored	.40	.30
387	A87	25c multicolored	.75	.60
388	A87	30c multicolored	1.10	.75
		Nos. 385-388 (4)	2.45	1.85

50th anniv. of Kingsford-Smith's Trans-Pacific flight, May 31-June 10, 1928 (4c, 15c); 75th anniv. of Wright brothers' first powered flight, Dec. 17, 1903 (25c); 60th anniv. of Royal Air Force, Apr. 1, 1918 (30c).

Necklace of Sperm Whale Teeth A88

Fiji artifacts: 4c, Wooden oil dish in shape of man, vert. 25c, Twin water bottles. 30c, Carved throwing club (Ula), vert.

1978, Aug. 14 — Litho. — Perf. 14

389	A88	4c multicolored	.30	.30
390	A88	15c multicolored	.35	.35
391	A88	25c multicolored	.60	.60
392	A88	30c multicolored	.75	.75
		Nos. 389-392 (4)	2.00	2.00

Christmas Wreath and Candles A89

Festivals: 15c, Diwali (oil lamps). 25c, Id-Ul-Fitr (fruit, coffeepot and cups). 40c, Chinese New Year (paper dragon).

1978, Oct. 30 — Perf. 14

393	A89	4c multicolored	.25	.25
394	A89	15c multicolored	.35	.35
395	A89	25c multicolored	.55	.55
396	A89	40c multicolored	.85	.85
		Nos. 393-396 (4)	2.00	2.00

Banded Iguana A90

Endangered species and Wildlife Fund emblem: 15c, Tree frog. 25c, Long-legged warbler. 30c, Pink-billed parrot finch.

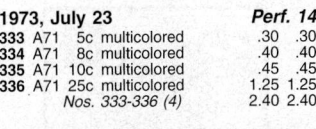

1979, Mar. 19 Litho. Wmk. 373

397	A90	4c multicolored	2.00	2.00
398	A90	15c multicolored	5.00	5.00
399	A90	25c multicolored	8.00	8.00
400	A90	30c multicolored	10.00	10.00
		Nos. 397-400 (4)	25.00	25.00

Indian Women Making Music A91

15c, Indian men sitting around kava bowl. 30c, Indian sugar cane, houses. 40c, Sailing ship Leonidas, map of South Pacific.

1979, May 11 Wmk. 373 Perf. 14

401	A91	4c multicolored	.20	.20
402	A91	15c multicolored	.25	.25
403	A91	30c multicolored	.45	.45
404	A91	40c multicolored	.65	.65
		Nos. 401-404 (4)	1.55	1.55

Arrival of Indians as indentured laborers, cent.

Soccer A92

Games Emblem and: 15c, Rugby. 30c, Tennis. 40c, Weight lifting.

1979, July 2 Litho. Perf. 14

405	A92	4c multicolored	.30	.30
406	A92	15c multicolored	.45	.45
407	A92	30c multicolored	.90	.90
408	A92	40c multicolored	1.25	1.25
		Nos. 405-408 (4)	2.90	2.90

6th South Pacific Games.

Old Town Hall, Suva A93

2c, Dudley Church, Suva. 3c, Telecommunications building, Suva. 4c, 5c, Lautoka Mosque. 6c, GPO, Suva. 8c, 12c, Levuka Public School. 10c, Visitors' Bureau, Suva. 15c, Colonial War Memorial Hospital Suva. 18c, Labasa Sugar Mill. 20c, Rewa Bridge, Nausori. 30c Sacred Heart Cathedral, Suva. 35c Grand Pacific Hotel, Suva. 45c, Shiva Temple, Suva. 50c Serua Island Village. $1, Solo Lighthouse. $2, Baker memorial Hall, Nausori. $5, Government House.

1979-91 Wmk. 373 Perf. 14

409	A93	1c multi	.20	.20
410	A93	2c multi	.20	.20
411	A93	3c multi	.20	.20
411B	A93	4c multi	.20	.20
412	A93	5c multi	.20	.20
413	A93	6c multi	.20	.20
414	A93	10c multi	.20	.20
415	A93	12c multi	.20	.20
416	A93	15c multi	.20	.20
417	A93	18c multi	.25	.25
418	A93	20c multi	.30	.30
419	A93	30c multi, vert.	.35	.35
420	A93	35c multi	.40	.40
421	A93	45c multi	.45	.45
422	A93	50c multi	.60	.60

Perf. 14x13½, 13½x14
Size: 45x29mm, 29x45mm (#423)

423	A93	$1 multi, vert.	1.10	1.10
424	A93	$2 multi	2.25	2.25
425	A93	$5 multi	5.50	5.50
		Nos. 409-425 (18)	13.00	13.00

All denominations except 4c issued without inscribed dates. 4c inscribed 1991. Reissues include: 1c inscribed 1994; 2c inscribed 1983, 1986, 1991, 1993 and 1994; 3c inscribed 1993; 4c inscribed 1993 and 1994; 10c inscribed 1991; 12c inscribed 1993 and 1994; 15c inscribed 1991; 20c inscribed 1993 and 1994; 50c inscribed 1994.

Issued: 5c, 6c, 12c, 18c, 35c-$2, 12/22/80; #411B, 11/1991; others, 11/11/79.

1986-91 Wmk. 384

409a	A93	1c	.75	.75
410a	A93	2c	.75	.75
411a	A93	3c	.75	.75
411c	A93	4c	.75	.75
413A	A93	8c	1.00	1.00
414a	A93	10c	.75	.75
416a	A93	15c	.75	.75
418a	A93	20c	1.25	1.25
420a	A93	35c	1.50	1.75
422a	A93	50c	2.25	2.50
423a	A93	$1	3.75	4.75
		Nos. 409a-423a (11)	14.25	15.75

1c inscribed 1991, reissued inscribed 1992; 2c inscribed 1986, reissued inscribed 1988 and 1991; 3c inscribed 1988, reissued inscribed 1991 and 1992; 4c inscribed 1988, reissued inscribed 1991 and 1992; 8c inscribed 1986; 10c inscribed 1990, reissued inscribed 1991; 15c inscribed 1991, reissued inscribed 1992; 20c inscribed 1988, reissued inscribed 1990 and 1992; 35c, 50c and $1 each inscribed 1991, each reissued inscribed 1992.

Issued: 2c, 4/86; 8c, 12/1/86; 3c, 4c, 20c, 6/1/88; 10c, 3/1/90; 1c, 15c, 35c, 50c, $1, 3/11/90.

Southern Cross, 1873, London 1980 Emblem A94

1980, Apr. 28 Wmk. 373 Perf. 13½

426	A94	6c shown	.25	.25
427	A94	20c Levuka, 1910	.30	.30
428	A94	45c Matua, 1936	.70	.70
429	A94	50c Oronsay, 1951	.75	.75
		Nos. 426-429 (4)	2.00	2.00

London 80 Intl. Stamp Exhib., May 6-14.

Sovi Bay A95

1980, Aug. 18 Perf. 13½x14

430	A95	6c shown	.20	.20
431	A95	20c Yanuca Island, evening scene	.25	.25
432	A95	45c Dravuni Beach	.55	.55
433	A95	50c Wakaya Island	.65	.65
		Nos. 430-433 (4)	1.65	1.65

Opening of Parliament, 1979 — A96

1980, Oct. 6 Litho. Perf. 13

434	A96	6c shown	.20	.20
435	A96	20c Coat of arms, vert.	.25	.25
436	A96	45c Fiji flag	.50	.50
437	A96	50c Elizabeth II, vert.	.60	.60
		Nos. 434-437 (4)	1.55	1.55

Independence, 10th anniversary.

Coastal Scene, by Semisi Maya A97

Intl. Year of the Disabled: Paintings and portrait of disabled artist Semisi Maya.

1981, Apr. 21 Wmk. 373 Perf. 14

438	A97	6c shown	.20	.20
439	A97	35c Underwater Scene	.45	.45
440	A97	50c Maya Painting, vert.	.60	.60
441	A97	60c Peacock, vert.	.75	.75
		Nos. 438-441 (4)	2.00	2.00

Royal Wedding Issue
Common Design Type

1981, July 22 Wmk. 373 Perf. 14

442	CD331	6c Bouquet	.20	.20
443	CD331	45c Charles	.50	.50
444	CD331	$1 Couple	1.10	1.10
		Nos. 442-444 (3)	1.80	1.80

Operator Assistance Center — A98

1981, Aug. 7 Litho. Perf. 14

445	A98	6c shown	.25	.20
446	A98	35c Microwave station, map	.60	.55
447	A98	50c Satellite earth station	1.00	.75
448	A98	60c Cableship Retriever	1.10	.90
		Nos. 445-448 (4)	2.95	2.40

World Food Day — A99

1981, Sept. 21 Litho. Perf. 14½x14

449	A99	20c multicolored	.50	.50

Ratu Sir Lala Sukuna, First Legislative Council Speaker — A100

1981, Oct. 19 Litho. Perf. 14

450	A100	6c shown	.20	.20
451	A100	35c Mace, flag	.55	.55
452	A100	50c Suva Civic Center	.75	.75
		Nos. 450-452 (3)	1.50	1.50

Souvenir Sheet

453	A100	60c Emblem, participants' flags	.90	.90

27th Commonwealth Parliamentary Assoc. Conf., Suva.

World War II Aircraft A101

1981, Dec. 7 Litho. Perf. 14

454	A101	6c Bell P-39 Aircobra	1.10	.20
455	A101	18c Consolidated PBY-5 Catalina	2.40	.30
456	A101	35c Curtiss P-40 Warhawk	4.00	.65
457	A101	60c Short Singapore	4.50	1.00
		Nos. 454-457 (4)	12.00	2.15

Scouting Year A102

1982, Feb. 22 Litho. Perf. 14½

458	A102	6c Building	.25	.25
459	A102	20c Sailing, vert.	.50	.50
460	A102	45c Campfire	1.10	1.10
461	A102	60c Baden-Powell, vert.	1.25	1.25
		Nos. 458-461 (4)	3.10	3.10

Disciplined Forces — A103

1982, May 10 Wmk. 373 Perf. 14

462	A103	12c UN checkpoint	.50	.20
463	A103	30c Construction project	1.25	.50
464	A103	40c Police, car	2.00	.65
465	A103	70c Navy ship	2.25	1.25
		Nos. 462-465 (4)	6.00	2.60

1982 World Cup A104

1982, June 15 Litho. Perf. 14

466	A104	6c Fiji Soccer Assoc. emblem	.20	.20
467	A104	18c Flag, ball	.35	.35
468	A104	50c Stadium	.90	.90
469	A104	90c Emblem	1.75	1.75
		Nos. 466-469 (4)	3.20	3.20

Princess Diana Issue
Common Design Type

1982, July 1 Perf. 14½x14

470	CD333	20c Arms	.60	.60
471	CD333	35c Diana	1.00	1.00
472	CD333	45c Wedding	1.50	1.50
473	CD333	$1 Portrait	3.25	3.25
		Nos. 470-473 (4)	6.35	6.35

October Royal Visit — A105

1982, Nov. 1 Litho. Perf. 14

474	A105	6c Duke of Edinburgh	.20	.20
475	A105	45c Elizabeth II	.80	.80

Souvenir Sheet

476		Sheet of 3	3.75	3.75
c.		A105 $1 Britannia	1.60	1.60

No. 476 contains Nos. 474-475 and 476c.

Christmas A106

1982, Nov. 22 Perf. 14x14½

477	A106	6c Holy Family	.20	.20
478	A106	20c Adoration of the Kings	.40	.40
479	A106	35c Carolers	.75	.75
		Nos. 477-479 (3)	1.35	1.35

Souvenir Sheet

480	A106	$1 Faith, from The Three Virtues, by Raphael	2.00	2.00

Red-throated Lory — A107

Parrots.

1983, Feb. 14   Litho.   Perf. 14
481 A107 20c shown   1.50 1.50
482 A107 40c Blue-crowned lo-
          ry   2.25 2.25
483 A107 55c Sulphur-breast-
          ed musk parrot   3.50 3.50
484 A107 70c Red-breasted
          musk parrot   4.25 4.25
    Nos. 481-484 (4)   11.50 11.50

8c FIJI   A108

1983, Mar. 14
485 A108 8c Traditional house   .20   .20
486 A108 25c Barefoot
          firewalkers   .35   .35
487 A108 50c Sugar cane crop   .70   .70
488 A108 80c Kava Yagona cere-
          mony   1.10 1.10
    Nos. 485-488 (4)   2.35 2.35

Commonwealth Day.

Manned Flight Bicentenary — A109

1983, July 18   Wmk. 373   Perf. 14
489 A109 8c Montgolfiere, 1783   .45   .20
490 A109 20c Wright Flyer   .55   .35
491 A109 25c DC-3   .65   .40
492 A109 40c DeHavilland Comet   1.00   .70
493 A109 50c Boeing 747   1.25   .85
494 A109 58c Columbia space
          shuttle   1.60 1.00
    Nos. 489-494 (6)   5.50 3.50

Cordia   Earth Satellite
Subcordata   Station, Fijian
A110   Playing Lali
                  A111

Flowers.

1983, Sept. 26   Litho.   Perf. 14
495 A110 8c shown   .20   .20
496 A110 25c Gmelina vitiensis   .35   .35
497 A110 40c Carruthersia
          scandens   .60   .60
498 A110 $1 Amylotheca insu-
          larum   1.50 1.50
    Nos. 495-498 (4)   2.65 2.65

See Nos. 505-508.

Perf. 14x13½
1983, Nov. 7   Wmk. 373
499 A111 50c multicolored   .85   .85

Dacryopinax
Spathularia
A112

Various fungi.

1984, Jan. 9   Perf. 14x13½, 13½x14
500 A112 8c shown   .65   .20
501 A112 15c Podoscypha in-
          voluta   1.10   .45
502 A112 40c Lentinus squar-
          rosulus   2.25 1.10
503 A112 50c Scleroderma
          flavidum   3.50 1.50
504 A112 $1 Phillipsia dom-
          ingensis   6.50 2.75
    Nos. 500-504 (5)   14.00 6.00

Flower Type of 1983

1984   Litho.   Perf. 14x14½
505 A110 15c Pseuderanthemum
          laxiflorum   .25   .25
506 A110 20c Storkiella vitiensis .30   .30
507 A110 50c Paphia vitiensis   .80   .80
508 A110 70c Elaeocarpus storkii 1.10 1.10
    Nos. 505-508 (4)   2.45 2.45

Lloyd's List Issue
Common Design Type
Perf. 14½x14
1984, May 7   Wmk. 373
509 CD335 8c Tui Lau on reef   .40   .40
510 CD335 40c Tofua   1.50 1.50
511 CD335 55c Canberra   2.00 2.00
512 CD335 60c Suva Wharf   2.25 2.25
    Nos. 509-512 (4)   6.15 6.15

Souvenir Sheet

1984 UPU Congress — A113

1984, June 14   Litho.   Perf. 14½
513 A113 25c Map   2.25 2.25

Ausipex
'84 — A114

1984, Sept. 17   Wmk. 373   Perf. 14
514 A114 8c Yalavou cattle   .20   .20
515 A114 25c Wailoa Power Sta-
          tion, vert.   .55   .55
516 A114 40c Boeing 737   .95   .95
517 A114 $1 Cargo ship Fua
          Kavenga   2.50 2.50
    Nos. 514-517 (4)   4.20 4.20

Christmas
A115

1984, Nov. 5   Litho.   Perf. 14
518 A115 8c Church on hill   .20   .20
519 A115 20c Sailing   .35   .35
520 A115 25c Santa, children,
          tree   .40   .40
521 A115 40c Going to church   .65   .65
522 A115 $1 Family, tree, vert. 1.75 1.75
    Nos. 518-522 (5)   3.35 3.35

Butterflies
A116

1985, Feb. 4   Perf. 14
523 A116 8c Monarch   1.00   .25
524 A116 25c Common eggfly   2.50   .80
525 A116 40c Long-tailed blue,
          vert.   4.00 1.40

526 A116 $1 Meadow argus,
          vert.   10.50 3.50
    Nos. 523-526 (4)   18.00 5.95

EXPO '85,
Tsukuba,
Japan — A117

1985, Mar. 18   Litho.   Perf. 14
527 A117 20c Outrigger canoe,
          Toberua Isl.   .55   .50
528 A117 25c Wainivula Falls   .60   .55
529 A117 50c Mana Island   1.60 1.40
530 A117 $1 Sawa-I-Lau Caves   2.75 2.50
    Nos. 527-530 (4)   5.50 4.95

Queen Mother 85th Birthday Issue
Common Design Type
Perf. 14½x14
1985, June 7   Wmk. 384
531 CD336 8c Holding Prince
          Andrew   .20   .20
532 CD336 25c With Prince
          Charles   .60   .60
533 CD336 40c On Oaks Day,
          Epsom Races   .95   .95
534 CD336 50c Holding Prince
          Henry   1.25 1.25
    Nos. 531-534 (4)   3.00 3.00

Souvenir Sheet
535 CD336 $1 In Royal Wed-
          ding Cavalcade,
          1981   4.00 4.00

Shallow
Water
Fish
A118

1985, Sept. 23   Perf. 14½
536 A118 40c Horned squirrel
          fish   1.50 1.10
537 A118 50c Yellow-banded
          goatfish   2.25 1.40
538 A118 55c Fairy cod   2.25 1.50
539 A118 $1 Peacock rock cod   4.00 2.75
    Nos. 536-539 (4)   10.00 6.75

Sea Birds — A119

1985, Nov. 4   Perf. 14
540 A119 15c Collared petrel   1.25   .45
541 A119 20c Lesser frigate
          bird   2.25   .70
542 A119 50c Brown booby   6.00 1.75
543 A119 $1 Crested tern   11.50 4.25
    Nos. 540-543 (4)   21.00 7.15

**Queen Elizabeth II 60th Birthday
Issue**
Common Design Type

20c, With the Duke of York at the Royal
Tournament, 1936. 25c, On Buckingham Palace balcony, wedding of Princess Margaret
and Anthony Armstrong-Jones, 1960. 40c,
Inspecting the Guard of Honor, Suva, 1982.
50c, State visit to Luxembourg, 1976. $1, Visit-
ing Crown Agents' offices, 1983.

Perf. 14x14½
1986, Apr. 21   Wmk. 384
544 CD337 20c scar, blk & sil   .40   .40
545 CD337 25c ultra & multi   .45   .45
546 CD337 40c green & multi   .75   .75
547 CD337 50c violet & multi   .95   .95
548 CD337 $1 rose vio & multi   1.90 1.90
    Nos. 544-548 (5)   4.45 4.45

Intl. Peace   Halley's
Year — A120   Comet — A121

1986, June 23 Wmk. 373 Perf. 14½
549 A120 8c shown   .20   .20
550 A120 40c Dove   1.10 1.10

1986, July 7   Perf. 13½
551 A121 25c Newton's reflector
          telescope   .90   .60
552 A121 40c Comet over
          Lomaiviti   1.10   .95
553 A121 $1 Comet nucleus,
          Giotto probe   6.00 2.50
    Nos. 551-553 (3)   8.00 4.05

Reptiles and Amphibians — A122

1986, Aug. 1   Perf. 14½
554 A122 8c Ground frog   .40   .20
555 A122 20c Burrowing snake   .65   .70
556 A122 25c Spotted gecko   .70   .90
557 A122 40c Crested iguana   1.10 1.25
558 A122 50c Blotched skink   3.00 1.60
559 A122 $1 Speckled skink   6.00 3.50
    Nos. 554-559 (6)   11.85 8.15

Ancient War   Cone
Clubs — A123   Shells — A124

1986, Nov. 10 Wmk. 384 Perf. 14
560 A123 25c Gatawaka   .90   .80
561 A123 40c Siriti   1.25 1.00
562 A123 50c Bulibuli   1.60 1.40
563 A123 $1 Culacula   3.25 2.75
    Nos. 560-563 (4)   7.00 5.95

1987, Feb. 26 Litho. Perf. 14x14½
564 A124 15c Weasel   .60   .35
565 A124 20c Pertusus   .65   .45
566 A124 25c Admiral   1.10   .60
567 A124 40c Leaden   1.40   .95
568 A124 50c Imperial   2.75 1.25
569 A124 $1 Geography   5.50 2.50
    Nos. 564-569 (6)   12.00 6.10

Souvenir Sheet

Tagimoucia Flower — A125

1987, Apr. 23 Wmk. 373 Perf. 14½
570 A125 $1 multicolored   5.50 3.75

No. 570 Overprinted with CAPEX '87 Emblem

1987, June 13
571 A125 $1 multicolored　　35.00 35.00

Intl. Year of Shelter for the Homeless
A126

1987, July 20　　　　　　**Perf. 14**
572 A126 55c Hut　　　　　　　.70 .70
573 A126 70c Government housing　　　　　　　.95 .95

Beetles — A127

1987, Sept. 7　　　　　　**Wmk. 384**
574 A127 20c Bulbogaster ctenostomoides　　　1.00 .45
575 A127 25c Paracupta flaviventris　　　1.75 .65
576 A127 40c Cerambyrhynchus schoenherri　　2.25 1.00
577 A127 50c Rhinoscapha lagopyga　　3.75 1.25
578 A127 $1 Xixuthrus heros　　8.25 2.50
　　Nos. 574-578 (5)　　17.00 5.85

Christmas — A128

1987, Nov. 19
579 A128 8c Holy Family, vert.　　.25 .20
580 A128 40c Shepherds see star　　1.00 .65
581 A128 50c Three Kings follow star　　2.75 .75
582 A128 $1 Adoration of the Magi　　5.75 1.50
　　Nos. 579-582 (4)　　9.75 3.10

World Expo '88, Apr. 30-Oct. 30, Brisbane, Australia A129

1988, Apr. 27　　**Litho.**　　**Perf. 14**
583 A129 30c Windsurfing　　1.75 1.75

Intl. Council of Women, Cent. A130

1988, June 14
584 A130 45c Fiji Nouna　　1.25 1.25

Pottery A131

Wmk. 384, 373 (69c)
1988, Aug. 29　**Litho.**　**Perf. 13½**
585 A131 9c Lapita (bowl)　　.20 .20
586 A131 23c Kuro (cooking pot)　　.35 .35
587 A131 58c Saqa (ritual drinking vessel)　　.75 .75
588 A131 63c Saqa, diff.　　.80 .80
589 A131 69c Ramarama (oil lamp)　　.90 .90
590 A131 75c Kuro, diff., vert.　　1.00 1.00
　　Nos. 585-590 (6)　　4.00 4.00

Fiji Tree Frog — A132

Indigenous Flowering Plants — A133

1988, Oct. 3　　**Wmk. 384**　　**Perf. 14**
591 A132 18c multi　　5.00 5.00
592 A132 23c multi, diff.　　5.75 5.75
593 A132 30c multi, diff.　　7.25 7.25
594 A132 45c multi, diff.　　12.00 12.00
　　Nos. 591-594 (4)　　30.00 30.00

World Wildlife Fund.

1988, Nov. 21　　　　**Wmk. 373**
595 A133 9c Dendrobium mohlianum　　.20 .20
596 A133 30c Dendrobium cattilare　　.70 .65
597 A133 45c Degeneria vitiensis　1.10 .90
598 A133 $1 Degeneria roseiflora　　2.75 2.10
　　Nos. 595-598 (4)　　4.75 3.85

Intl. Red Cross and Red Crescent Orgs., 125th Anniv. — A134

1989, Feb. 6　　　　**Wmk. 384**
599 A134 58c Battle of Soferino, 1859　　1.75 1.10
600 A134 63c Jean-Henri Dunant, vert.　　2.00 1.10
601 A134 69c Medicine　　2.25 1.25
602 A134 $1 Anniv. emblem, vert.　　5.00 1.90
　　Nos. 599-602 (4)　　11.00 5.35

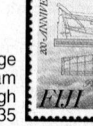

Epic Voyage of William Bligh A135

Designs: 45c, Plans (line drawing) of the Bounty's launch. 58c, Diary and inscription on artifacts "The cup I eat my miserable allowance out of." 80c, Silhouette, lightning, quote "O Almighty God, relieve us. . ." $1, Map of Bligh's Islands, launch and compass rose.

1989, Apr. 28　　　　**Perf. 14½**
603 A135 45c multicolored　　2.10 .70
604 A135 58c multicolored　　2.50 .95
605 A135 80c multicolored　　4.50 1.25
606 A135 $1 multicolored　　6.00 1.50
　　Nos. 603-606 (4)　　15.10 4.40

Coral A136

1989, Aug. 21　　**Wmk. 373**　　**Perf. 14**
607 A136 46c Platygyra daedalea　　2.50 2.50
608 A136 60c Caulastrea furcata　　3.25 3.25
609 A136 75c Acropora echinata　　4.00 4.00
610 A136 90c Acropora humilis　5.25 5.25
　　Nos. 607-610 (4)　　15.00 15.00

Nos. 609-610 vert.

1990 World Cup Soccer Championships, Italy — A137

Various Fijian soccer players.

1989, Sept. 25　**Wmk. 384**　**Perf. 14½**
611 A137 35c shown　　1.60 1.60
612 A137 63c multi, diff.　　2.50 2.50
613 A137 70c multi, diff.　　3.00 3.00
614 A137 85c multi, diff.　　3.50 3.50
　　Nos. 611-614 (4)　　10.60 10.60

Christmas A138

1989, Nov. 1　　　　**Wmk. 373**
615 A138 9c Church service　　.35 .35
616 A138 45c Delonix regia tree　　1.10 1.10
617 A138 $1 Holy family　　2.10 2.10
618 A138 $1.40 Tree, Fijian children　　3.00 3.00
　　Nos. 615-618 (4)　　6.55 6.55

Fish A139

1990, Apr. 23　**Litho.**　**Wmk. 384**
619 A139 50c Mangrove jack　　3.00 3.00
620 A139 70c Orange-spotted therapon perch　4.50 4.50
621 A139 85c Spotted scat　　5.00 5.00
622 A139 $1 Flagtail　　6.00 6.00
　　Nos. 619-622 (4)　　18.50 18.50

Souvenir Sheet

Stamp World London '90 — A140

1990, May 1
623 A140　Sheet of 2　13.50 6.00
a.　$1 No. 243　　4.25 1.75
b.　$2 No. 249　　8.50 4.25

Soil Conservation — A141

50c, Vertiver grass contours. 70c, Mulching. 90c, Contour cultivation. $1, Proper land use.

1990, July 23　**Litho.**　**Wmk. 373**
625 A141 50c multi　　1.10 1.10
626 A141 70c multi　　1.60 1.60
627 A141 90c multi　　2.10 2.10
628 A141 $1 multi, vert.　　2.25 2.25
　　Nos. 625-628 (4)　　7.05 7.05

Trees — A142

1990, Oct. 2
629 A142 25c Dacrydium nidulum　　.90 .90
630 A142 35c Decussocarpus vitiensis　　1.10 1.10
631 A142 $1 Agathis vitiensis　　3.50 3.50
632 A142 $1.55 Santalum yasi　5.00 5.00
　　Nos. 629-632 (4)　　10.50 10.50

Christmas — A143

Christmas carols: 10c, Hark! The Herald Angels Sing. 35c, Silent Night. 65c, Joy to the World! $1, The Race that Long in Darkness Pined.

1990, Nov. 26　**Wmk. 373**　**Perf. 14**
633 A143 10c multicolored　　.40 .40
634 A143 35c multicolored　　1.10 1.10
635 A143 65c multicolored　　2.00 2.00
636 A143 $1 multicolored　　3.00 3.00
　　Nos. 633-636 (4)　　6.50 6.50

Scenic Views — A144

1991, Feb. 25　　　　**Wmk. 384**
637 A144 35c Sigatoka sand dunes　　1.50 1.50
638 A144 50c Monu, Monuriki Islands　　2.75 2.75
639 A144 65c Ravilevu Nature Reserve　　3.25 3.25
640 A144 $1 Colo-I-Suva Forest Park　　5.50 5.50
　　Nos. 637-640 (4)　　13.00 13.00

Discovery of Rotuma Island, Bicent. A145

1991, Aug. 8　　**Wmk. 373**　　**Perf. 14**
641 A145 54c HMS Pandora　　2.75 2.75
642 A145 70c Map of Rotuma Island　　3.50 3.50
643 A145 75c Natives　　3.75 3.75
644 A145 $1 Mt. Solroroa, Uea Island　　5.00 5.00
　　Nos. 641-644 (4)　　15.00 15.00

Crabs
A146

Designs: 38c, Scylla serrata. 54c, Metopograpsus messor. 96c, Parasesarma erythrodactyla. $1.65, Cardisoma carnifex.

1991, Sept. 26   Perf. 14½x14
645	A146	38c multicolored	1.10	1.10
646	A146	54c multicolored	1.75	1.75
647	A146	96c multicolored	2.75	2.75
648	A146	$1.65 multicolored	5.50	5.50
		Nos. 645-648 (4)	11.10	11.10

Christmas
A147

Designs: 11c, Mary, Joseph travelling to Bethlehem. 75c, Manger scene. 96c, Jesus being blessed at temple in Jerusalem. $1, Baby Jesus.

1991, Oct. 31   Wmk. 384   Perf. 14
649	A147	11c multicolored	.45	.45
650	A147	75c multicolroed	2.10	2.10
651	A147	96c multicolored	2.50	2.50
652	A147	$1 multicolored	2.50	2.50
		Nos. 649-652 (4)	7.55	7.55

Air Pacific, 40th Anniv. A148

Airplanes: 54c, Dragon Rapide, Harold Gatty, founder. 75c, Douglas DC3. 96c, ATR 42. $1.40, Boeing 767.

1991, Nov. 18   Perf. 14½
653	A148	54c multicolored	3.00	3.00
654	A148	75c multicolored	3.25	3.25
655	A148	96c multicolored	4.25	4.25
656	A148	$1.40 multicolored	6.50	6.50
		Nos. 653-656 (4)	17.00	17.00

Expo '92, Seville A149

Designs: 27c, Traditional dance and costumes. 75c, Faces of people. 96c, Train and gold bars. $1.40, Cruise ship in port.

1992, Mar. 23   Litho.   Wmk. 373
Perf. 14½x14
657	A149	27c multicolored	1.50	1.50
658	A149	75c multicolored	4.00	4.00
659	A149	96c multicolored	5.75	5.75
660	A149	$1.40 multicolored	7.75	7.75
		Nos. 657-660 (4)	19.00	19.00

Inter-Islands Shipping — A150

1992, June 22   Perf. 14
661	A150	38c Tabusoro	2.00	2.00
662	A150	54c Degei II	2.75	2.75
663	A150	$1.40 Dausoko	6.25	6.25
664	A150	$1.65 Nivanga	7.00	7.00
		Nos. 661-664 (4)	18.00	18.00

1992 Summer Olympics, Barcelona — A151

1992, July 30   Perf. 13½
665	A151	20c Running	.65	.65
666	A151	86c Yachting	2.75	2.75
667	A151	$1.34 Swimming	4.00	4.00
668	A151	$1.50 Judo	5.00	5.00
		Nos. 665-668 (4)	12.40	12.40

Levuka A152

30c, European War Memorial. 42c, Map. 59c, Beach Street. 77c, Sacred Heart Church, vert. $2, Deed of Cession Site, vert.

1992, Sept. 21   Perf. 14½
669	A152	30c multicolored	.45	.45
670	A152	42c multicolored	.60	.60
671	A152	59c multicolored	.90	.90
672	A152	77c multicolored	1.10	1.10
673	A152	$2 multicolored	3.25	3.25
		Nos. 669-673 (5)	6.30	6.30

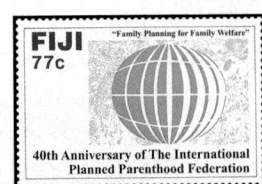

Intl. Planned Parenthood Federation, 40th Anniv. — A153

1992, Nov. 2   Perf. 15x14½
674	A153	77c Globe	1.50	1.50
675	A153	$2 Family	3.75	3.75

Christmas — A154

Bible interpretations: 12c, "God so loved the world..." 77c, "We love because God first loved us." 83c, "It is more blessed to give..." $2, "Every good gift..."

1992, Nov. 17
676	A154	12c multicolored	.35	.35
677	A154	77c multicolored	1.90	1.90
678	A154	83c multicolored	2.25	2.25
679	A154	$2 multicolored	5.50	5.50
		Nos. 676-679 (4)	10.00	10.00

Peace Corps in Fiji, 25th Anniv. A155

Designs: 59c, Voluntary service. 77c, Fiji/US friendship. $1, Education. $2, Income generating business through volunteer help.

1993, Feb. 22   Wmk. 373   Litho.   Perf. 14½
680	A155	59c multicolored	1.25	1.25
681	A155	77c multicolored	1.60	1.60
682	A155	$1 multicolored	2.00	2.00
683	A155	$2 multicolored	4.25	4.25
		Nos. 680-683 (4)	9.10	9.10

Hong Kong Rugby Sevens — A156

Designs: 77c, Players performing traditional Cibi Dance. $1.06, Two players, map of Fiji, Hong Kong, and Australia. $2, Stadium, players in scrum.

Perf. 14x15
1993, Mar. 26   Litho.   Wmk. 384
684	A156	77c multicolored	1.75	1.75
685	A156	$1.06 multicolored	2.50	2.50
686	A156	$2 multicolored	4.50	4.50
		Nos. 684-686 (3)	8.75	8.75

Royal Air Force, 75th Anniv.
Common Design Type

Designs: 59c, Gloster Gauntlet. 77c, Armstrong Whitworth Whitley. 83c, Bristol F2b. $2, Hawker Tempest.
No. 691: a, Vickers Vildebeest. b, Handley Page Hampden. c, Vickers Vimy. d, British Aerospace Hawk.

1993, Apr. 1   Perf. 14
687	CD350	59c multicolored	1.25	1.25
688	CD350	77c multicolored	1.60	1.60
689	CD350	83c multicolored	1.60	1.60
690	CD350	$2 multicolored	4.50	4.50
		Nos. 687-690 (4)	8.95	8.95

Souvenir Sheet of 4
691	CD350	$1 #a.-d.	10.00	10.00
a.		Overprinted in sheet margin	9.00	9.00

Overprint on No. 691a is exhibition emblem for Hong Kong '94.

Nudibranchs A157

Wmk. 373
1993, July 27   Litho.   Perf. 14
692	A157	12c Chromodoris fidelis	.50	.50
693	A157	42c Halgerda carlsoni	1.25	1.25
694	A157	53c Chromodoris lochi	1.75	1.75
695	A157	83c Glaucus atlanticus	2.75	2.75
696	A157	$1 Phyllidia bourguini	3.25	3.25
697	A157	$2 Hexabranchus sanguineus	6.50	6.50
		Nos. 692-697 (6)	16.00	16.00

Tropical Fruit — A158

Wmk. 373
1993, Oct. 25   Litho.   Perf. 13½
698	A158	30c Mango	1.25	1.25
699	A158	42c Guava	2.25	2.25
700	A158	$1 Lemon	4.50	4.50
701	A158	$2 Soursop	9.00	9.00
		Nos. 698-701 (4)	17.00	17.00

Hong Kong '94 — A159

Butterflies: a, Caper white. b, Blue branded king crow. c, Vagrant. d, Glasswing.

Perf. 14½x13
1994, Feb. 18   Litho.   Wmk. 373
702	A159	$1 Sheet of 4, #a.-d.	11.00	11.00

Easter A160

59c, The Last Supper. 77c, The Crucifixion. $1, The Resurrection. $2, Jesus showing his wounds to his disciples.

Perf. 14x15, 15x14
1994, Mar. 31   Litho.   Wmk. 373
703	A160	59c multi	1.25	1.25
704	A160	77c multi, vert.	1.75	1.75
705	A160	$1 multi	2.00	2.00
706	A160	$2 multi, vert.	4.25	4.25
		Nos. 703-706 (4)	9.25	9.25

Edible Seaweeds A161

42c, Codium bulbopilum. 83c, Coulerpa racemosa. $1, Hypnea pannosa. $2, Gracilaria.

Wmk. 384
1994, June 6   Litho.   Perf. 14
707	A161	42c multicolored	1.25	.95
708	A161	83c multicolored	2.25	1.90
709	A161	$1 multicolored	2.75	2.40
710	A161	$2 multicolored	5.75	4.75
		Nos. 707-710 (4)	12.00	10.00

White-Collared Kingfisher — A162

Designs: a, On branch. b, In flight.

Wmk. 373
1994, Aug.   Litho.   Perf. 13½
711	A162	$1.50 Sheet of 2, #a.-b.	12.50	12.50
c.		Overprinted in sheet margin	12.00	12.00

Overprint on No. 711c consists of exhibition emblem and "JAKARTA '95."
Issued: #711, 8/16; #711c, 8/19.

Souvenir Sheet

Singpex '94 — A163

Neoveitchia storckii: a, Complete tree. b. Fruits, inflorescence.

1994, Aug. 31   Wmk. 384   Perf. 14
712 A163 $1.50 Sheet of 2,
               #a.-b.   11.00 11.00

First Catholic Missionaries in Fiji, 150th Anniv. — A164

Wmk. 373
1994, Dec. 16   Litho.   Perf. 14
713 A164 23c Father Ioane
              Batita   .60   .60
714 A164 31c Local catechist   .70   .70
715 A164 44c Sacred Heart
              Cathedral   .95   .95
716 A164 63c Lomary Church   1.25 1.25
717 A164 81c Pope Gregory
              XVI   1.75 1.75
718 A164 $2 Pope John Paul
              II   4.00 4.00
    Nos. 713-718 (6)   9.25 9.25

Souvenir Sheet

Ecotourism in Fiji — A165

Designs: a, Waterfalls, banded iguana. b, Mountain trekking, Fiji tree frog. c, Bilibili River trip, kingfisher. d, Historic sites, flying fox.

Wmk. 373
1995, Mar. 27   Litho.   Perf. 14
719 A165 81c Sheet of 4, #a.-d.   9.00 9.00

End of World War II, 50th Anniv.
Common Design Types

Designs: 13c, Fijian regiment guarding crashed Japanese Zero Fighter. 63c, Kameli Airstrip, Solomon Islands, built by Fijian regiment. 87c, Corp. Sukanaivalu VC, Victoria Cross. $1.12, HMS Fiji. $2, Reverse side of War Medal 1939-45.

Wmk. 373
1995, May 8   Litho.   Perf. 13½
720 CD351 13c multicolored   .50   .50
721 CD351 63c multicolored   2.75 2.75
722 CD351 87c multicolored   3.75 3.75
723 CD351 $1.12 multicolored   5.00 5.00
    Nos. 720-723 (4)   12.00 12.00

Souvenir Sheet
Perf. 14
724 CD352 $2 multicolored   5.00 5.00

Birds — A166

1995   Litho.   Wmk. 373   Perf. 13
725 A166 1c Red-headed
             parrotfinch   .20   .20
726 A166 2c Golden whis-
             tler   .20   .20

---

727 A166 3c Ogea flycatch-
             er   .20   .20
728 A166 4c Peale's pigeon   .20   .20
729 A166 6c Blue-crested
             broadbill   .20   .20
730 A166 13c Island thrush   .20   .20
731 A166 23c Many-colored
             fruit dove   .40   .40
732 A166 31c Mangrove her-
             on   .55   .55
733 A166 44c Purple
             swamphen   1.00 1.00
734 A166 63c Fiji goshawk   1.25 1.25
735 A166 81c Kadavu fantail   1.60 1.60
736 A166 87c Collared lory   1.75 1.75
737 A166 $1 Scarlet robin   2.00 2.00
738 A166 $2 Peregrine fal-
             con   4.00 4.00
739 A166 $3 Barn owl   5.75 5.75
739A A166 $5 Yellow-breast-
             ed musk par-
             rot   10.50 10.50
    Nos. 725-739A (16)   30.00 30.00

Issued: 13c, 23c, 31c, 44c, 63c, 81c, $2, $3, 7/25; 1c, 2c, 3c, 4c, 6c, 87c, $1, $5, 11/7. See No. 1011.

Souvenir Sheet

Singapore '95 — A167

Orchids: a, Arundina graminifolia. b, Phaius tankervilliae.

Wmk. 373
1995, Sept. 1   Litho.   Perf. 14
740 A167 $1 Sheet of 2, #a.-b.   9.00 9.00

Independence, 25th Anniv. — A168

Designs: 81c, Pres. Kamisese Mara, Parliament Building. 87c, Fijian youth. $1.06, Playing rugby. $2, Air Pacific Boeing 747.

Wmk. 373
1995, Oct. 4   Litho.   Perf. 14
741 A168 81c multicolored   1.60 1.60
742 A168 87c multicolored   1.90 1.90
743 A168 $1.06 multicolored   2.25 2.25
744 A168 $2 multicolored   4.25 4.25
    Nos. 741-744 (4)   10.00 10.00

Christmas — A169

Paintings: 10c, Praying Madonna with the Crown of Stars, from Correggio Workshop. 63c, Madonna and Child with Crowns on porcelain. 87c, The Holy Virgin with the Holy Child and St. John, after Titian. $2, The Holy Family and St. John, from Rubens Workshop.

Wmk. 373
1995, Nov. 22   Litho.   Perf. 13
745 A169 10c multicolored   .25   .25
746 A169 63c multicolored   1.25 1.25
747 A169 87c multicolored   1.75 1.75
748 A169 $2 multicolored   4.00 4.00
    Nos. 745-748 (4)   7.25 7.25

Arrival of Banabans in Fiji, 50th Anniv. A170

Perf. 14x14½, 14½x14
1996, Jan. 24   Litho.   Wmk. 373
749 A170 81c Trolling lure   2.25 2.25
750 A170 87c Canoes   2.50 2.50
751 A170 $1.12 Warrior, vert.   2.75 2.75
752 A170 $2 Frigate bird,
             vert.   5.25 5.25
    Nos. 749-752 (4)   12.75 12.75

A172

Radio, Cent.: 44c, L2B portable tape recorder. 63c, Fiji Broadcasting Center. 81c, Communications satellite in orbit. $3, Marconi.

Wmk. 373
1996, Mar. 11   Litho.   Perf. 14½
753 A171 44c multicolored   .90   .90
754 A171 63c multicolored   1.25 1.25
755 A171 81c multicolored   1.60 1.60
756 A171 $3 multicolored   6.25 6.25
    Nos. 753-756 (4)   10.00 10.00

Wmk. 384
1996, Apr. 25   Litho.   Perf. 13½

Ancient Chinese artifacts: 63c, Bronze monster mask and ring, c. 450 BC. 81c, Archer, 210 BC. $1, Plate, Hsuan Te Period, 1426-35. $2, Central Asian horseman, dated 706. 30c, Yan Deng Mountain.

757 A172 63c multicolored   1.25 1.25
758 A172 81c multicolored   1.50 1.50
759 A172 $1 multicolored   2.00 2.00
760 A172 $2 multicolored   4.25 4.25
    Nos. 757-760 (4)   9.00 9.00

Souvenir Sheet
Perf. 13½x13
761 A172 30c multicolored   2.50 2.50

No. 761 contains one 48x76mm stamp. CHINA '96, 9th Asian Intl. Philatelic Exhibition.

A173

A174

Wmk. 373
1996, June 18   Litho.   Perf. 14
762 A173 31c Hurdling   .65   .65
763 A173 63c Judo   1.50 1.50
764 A173 87c Sailboarding   2.10 2.10
765 A173 $1.12 Swimming   2.50 2.50
    Nos. 762-765 (4)   6.75 6.75

Souvenir Sheet
766 A173 $2 Athlete, 1896   4.00 4.00

Modern Olympic Games, cent.

1996, July 1

31c, Computerized telephone exchange, horiz. 44c, Mail being unloaded, horiz. 81c, Manual switchboard operator. $1, Mail delivery.

No. 771: a, #117. b, #527.

767 A174 31c multicolored   .60   .60
768 A174 44c multicolored   .80   .80
769 A174 81c multicolored   1.40 1.40
770 A174 $1 multicolored   1.90 1.90
    Nos. 767-770 (4)   4.70 4.70

Souvenir Sheet of 2
771 A174 $1.50 #a.-b.   5.00 5.00

Creation of independent Postal, Telecommunications Companies.

UNICEF, 50th Anniv. A175

Designs: 81c, "Our children, our future." 87c, Village scene. $1, "Living in harmony the world over." $2, "Their future."

Wmk. 384
1996, Aug. 13   Litho.   Perf. 14
772 A175 81c multicolored   2.00 2.00
773 A175 87c multicolored   2.00 2.00
774 A175 $1 multicolored   2.25 2.25
775 A175 $2 multicolored   4.50 4.50
    Nos. 772-775 (4)   10.75 10.75

Nadi Intl. Airport, 50th Anniv. A176

Designs: 31c, First airplane in Fiji, 1921. 44c, Nadi Airport commences Commercial Operations, 1946. 63c, First jet in Fiji, 1959. 87c, Airport entrance. $1, Control tower, 1996. $2, Global positioning system, first commercial use, 1994.

Wmk. 373
1996, Oct. 1   Litho.   Perf. 14
776 A176 31c multicolored   .75   .75
777 A176 44c multicolored   1.00 1.00
778 A176 63c multicolored   1.50 1.50
779 A176 87c multicolored   2.00 2.00
780 A176 $1 multicolored   2.25 2.25
781 A176 $2 multicolored   4.50 4.50
    Nos. 776-781 (6)   12.00 12.00

Christmas — A177

Scene from the Christmas story and native story or scene: 13c, Angel Gabriel & Mary, beating of Lali. 81c, Shepherds with sheep, Fijian canoe. $1, Wise men on camels, multiracial Fiji. $3, Mary, Christ Child in stable, blowing of conch shell.

1996, Nov. 20   Wmk. 373
782 A177 13c multicolored   .30   .30
783 A177 81c multicolored   2.00 2.00
784 A177 $1 multicolored   2.40 2.40
785 A177 $3 multicolored   7.25 7.25
    Nos. 782-785 (4)   11.95 11.95

Hong Kong '97
A178

Cattle: a, Brahman. b, Freisian (Holstein). c, Hereford. d, Fiji draught bullock.

1997, Feb. 12
786 A178 $1 Sheet of 4, #a.-d. 9.00 9.00

Souvenir Sheet

Black-Faced Shrikebill — A179

Illustration reduced.

1997, Feb. 21 *Perf. 14x15*
787 A179 $2 multicolored 4.50 4.50

Singpex '97.

Orchids — A180

Designs: 81c, Dendrobium biflorum. 87c, Dendrobium dactylodes. $1.06, Spathoglottis pacifica. $2, Dendrobium macropus.

Wmk. 384
1997, Apr. 22 Litho. *Perf. 14*
788 A180 81c multicolored 1.75 1.75
789 A180 87c multicolored 1.75 1.75

Wmk. 373
790 A180 $1.06 multicolored 2.25 2.25
791 A180 $2 multicolored 4.00 4.00
Nos. 788-791 (4) 9.75 9.75

Souvenir Sheet

Hawksbill Turtle
A181

Designs: a, 63c, Female laying eggs. b, 81c, Baby turtles emerging from nest. c, $1.06 Young turtles in water. d, $2, One adult in water, coral.

1997, May 26 Wmk. 373
792 A181 Sheet of 4, #a.-d. 11.00 11.00

Coral
A182

Designs: 63c, Branching hard coral 87c, Massive hard coral. $1, Soft coral, sinularia. $3, Soft coral, dendronephthya.

Wmk. 373
1997, July 16 Litho. *Perf. 14*
793 A182 63c multicolored 1.40 1.40
794 A182 87c multicolored 1.90 1.90
795 A182 $1 multicolored 2.25 2.25
796 A182 $3 multicolored 6.75 6.75
Nos. 793-796 (4) 12.30 12.30

Fijian Monkey-faced Bat — A183

63c, With nose pointed downward. 81c, Hanging below flower. $2, Between leaves on tree branch.

Perf. 13½
1997, Oct. 15 Litho. Unwmk.
797 A183 44c multicolored 1.25 1.00
798 A183 63c multicolored 1.75 1.50
799 A183 81c multicolored 2.25 1.75
800 A183 $2 multicolored 4.75 4.25
a. Sheet, 2 each #797-800 21.00 21.00
Nos. 797-800 (4) 10.00 8.50

World Wildlife Fund.

Christmas
A184

Designs: 13c, Angel, shepherd. 31c, Birth of Jesus. 87c, Magi. $3, Madonna and Child.

Perf. 14x14½
1997, Nov. 18 Wmk. 373
801 A184 13c multicolored .20 .20
802 A184 31c multicolored .60 .60
803 A184 87c multicolored 1.60 1.60
804 A184 $3 multicolored 5.50 5.50
Nos. 801-804 (4) 7.90 7.90

A185

A186

1997 Rugby World Cup Sevens Champions: a, 50c, Waisale Serevi, captain, highest point scorer. b, 50c, Taniela Qauqau. c, 50c, Jope Tuikabe. d, 50c, Leveni Duvuduvukula. e, 50c, Inoke Maraiwai. f, 50c, Aminiasi Naituyaga. g, 50c, Lemeki Koroi. h, 50c, Marika Vunibaka, highest try scorer. i, 50c, Luke Erenavula. j, 50c, Manasa Bari. k, $1, Entire team.

Wmk. 373
1997, Oct. 30 Litho. *Perf. 14*
805 A185 Sheet of 11, #a.-k. 13.00 13.00

No. 805k is 53x39mm.

Wmk. 373
1998, Jan. 20 Litho. *Perf. 14*

Chief's Traditional Costumes: 81c, War dress. 87c, Formal dress. $1.12, Presentation dress. $2, Highland war dress.

806 A186 81c multicolored 1.25 1.25
807 A186 87c multicolored 1.25 1.25
808 A186 $1.12 multicolored 1.75 1.75
809 A186 $2 multicolored 3.00 3.00
Nos. 806-809 (4) 7.25 7.25

Asian and Pacific Decade of Disabled Persons, 1993-2000
A187

63c, Mastering modern technology. 87c, Assisting the will to overcome. $1, Using natural born skills. $2, Competing to win.

Wmk. 373
1998, Mar. 18 Litho. *Perf. 13*
810 A187 63c multicolored 1.00 1.00
811 A187 87c multicolored 1.40 1.40
812 A187 $1 multicolored 1.50 1.50
813 A187 $2 multicolored 3.00 3.00
Nos. 810-813 (4) 6.90 6.90

Royal Air Force, 80th Anniv.

Common Design Type of 1993 Re-Inscribed

Designs: 44c, R34 Airship. 63c, Handley Page Heyford. 87c, Supermarine Swift FR.5. $2, Westland Whirlwind.

No. 818: a, Sopwith Dolphin. b, Avro 504K. c, Vickers Warwick V. d, Shorts Belfast.

1998, Apr. 1 *Perf. 13½x14*
814 CD350 44c multicolored 1.00 1.00
815 CD350 63c multicolored 1.25 1.25
816 CD350 87c multicolored 1.75 1.75
817 CD350 $2 multicolored 4.00 4.00
Nos. 814-817 (4) 8.00 8.00

Souvenir Sheet of 4
818 CD350 $1 #a.-d. 7.50 7.50

Diana, Princess of Wales (1961-97)

Common Design Type

Design: No. 819, Wearing plaid jacket.
No. 820: a, Wearing blue jacket. b, In high-collared blouse. c, Holding flowers.

1998, Mar. 31 Litho. *Perf. 14x14½*
819 CD355 81c multicolored .75 .75
820 CD355 81c Sheet of 4, #819, a.-c. 5.25 5.25

No. 820 sold for $3.24 + 50c, with surtax from international sales being donated to the Princess Diana Memorial Fund and surtax from national sales being donated to designated local charity.

Sperm Whale
A188

Wmk. 373
1998, June 22 Litho. *Perf. 14*
821 A188 63c shown 1.40 1.40
822 A188 81c Adult, calf 1.90 1.90
823 A188 87c Breaching 1.90 1.90
824 A188 $2 Sperm whale tooth 4.50 4.50
a. Souvenir sheet 6.75 6.75
Nos. 821-824 (4) 9.70 9.70

16th Commonwealth Games, Kuala Lumpur, Malaysia — A189

Wmk. 384
1998, Sept. 11 Litho. *Perf. 14*
825 A189 44c Athletics .70 .70
826 A189 63c Lawn bowls 1.00 1.00
827 A189 81c Javelin 1.40 1.40
828 A189 $1.12 Weight lifting 1.90 1.90
Nos. 825-828 (4) 5.00 5.00

Souvenir Sheet
829 A189 $2 Waisale Serevi, rugby sevens 4.00 4.00

Maritime Heritage
A190

Designs: 13c, Takia, hollowed-out log with outrigger. 44c, Camakau, sailing canoe. 87c, Drua, twin-hulled sailing canoe. $3, MV Pioneer motor yacht.

$1.50, Camakau, map of Fiji.

Wmk. 384
1998, Oct. 26 Litho. *Perf. 13½*
830 A190 13c multicolored .30 .30
831 A190 44c multicolored .85 .85
832 A190 87c multicolored 1.60 1.60
833 A190 $3 multicolored 5.25 5.25
Nos. 830-833 (4) 8.00 8.00

Souvenir Sheet
834 A190 $1.50 multicolored 4.75 4.75

Australia '99, World Stamp Expo (#834).
See Nos. 843-847.

Christmas
A191

Children's drawings: 13c, "Jesus in a Manger." 50c, "A Time for Family and Friends." $1, "What Christmas Means to Me," vert. $2, "The Joy of Christmas," vert.

1998, Nov. 23 Wmk. 373
835 A191 13c multicolored .25 .25
836 A191 50c multicolored .80 .80
837 A191 $1 multicolored 1.60 1.60
838 A191 $2 multicolored 3.25 3.25
Nos. 835-838 (4) 5.90 5.90

Traditional Dances — A192

Designs: 13c, Vakamalolo (women's sitting dance). 81c, Mekeiwau (club dance). 87c, Seasea (women's fan dance). $3, Meke ni yaqona (Kava serving dance).

Wmk. 373
1999, Jan. 20 Litho. *Perf. 14½*
839 A192 13c multicolored .25 .25
840 A192 81c multicolored 1.60 1.60
841 A192 87c multicolored 1.90 1.90
842 A192 $3 multicolored 5.75 5.75
Nos. 839-842 (4) 9.50 9.50

Maritime Heritage Type of 1998

Designs: 63c, SS Toufua, 1920-30's. 81c, MF Adi Beti, 1920-30's. $1, SS Niagara, 1920-30's. $2, MV Royal Viking Sun, 1990's.

$1.50, SS. Makatea, 1920's.

1999, Mar. 19 Wmk. 384 *Perf. 13½*
843 A190 63c multicolored 1.10 1.10
844 A190 81c multicolored 1.90 1.90
845 A190 $1 multicolored 2.25 2.25
846 A190 $2 multicolored 4.50 4.50
Nos. 843-846 (4) 9.75 9.75

Souvenir Sheet
847 A190 $1.50 multicolored 4.50 4.50

Australia '99, World Stamp Exhibition (#847).

Souvenir Sheet

Ducks — A193

a, Wandering whistling. b, Pacific black.

1999, Apr. 27   **Wmk. 373**
848 A193 $2 Sheet of 2, #a.-b.   8.00 8.00
    IBRA '99, Intl. Philatelic Exhibition, Nuremberg.

Orchids — A194

Designs: 44c, Calanthe ventilabrum. 63c, Dendrobium prasinum. 81c, Dendrobium macrophyllum. $3, Dendrobium tokai.

1999, June 28
849 A194 44c multicolored   .75 .75
850 A194 63c multicolored   1.00 1.00
851 A194 81c multicolored   1.25 1.25
852 A194 $3 multicolored   5.00 5.00
    Nos. 849-852 (4)   8.00 8.00

1st Manned Moon Landing, 30th Anniv.
Common Design Type

13c, Astronaut waves goodbye. 87c, Stage 3 fires towards moon. $1, Aldrin walks on lunar surface. $2, Command module fires towards earth.
$2, Looking at earth from moon.

Perf. 14x13¾
1999, July 20   **Wmk. 384**
853 CD357 13c multicolored   .25 .25
854 CD357 87c multicolored   1.50 1.50
855 CD357 $1 multicolored   1.75 1.75
856 CD357 $2 multicolored   3.50 3.50
    Nos. 853-856 (4)   7.00 7.00

Souvenir Sheet
Perf. 14
857 CD357 $2 multicolored   4.00 4.00
    No. 857 contains one circular stamp 40mm in diameter.

Queen Mother's Century
Common Design Type

Queen Mother: 13c, Visiting Hull to see bomb damage. 63c, With Prince Charles. 81c, As Colonel-in-Chief of Light Infantry. $3, With Prince Charles at Clarence House.
$2, With crowd on Armistice Day.

Wmk. 384
1999, Aug. 18   **Litho.**   **Perf. 13½**
858 CD358 13c multicolored   .50 .50
859 CD358 63c multicolored   1.25 1.25
860 CD358 81c multicolored   1.75 1.75
861 CD358 $3 multicolored   5.50 5.50
    Nos. 858-861 (4)   9.00 9.00

Souvenir Sheet
862 CD358 $2 multicolored   6.00 6.00

UPU,
125th
Anniv.
A195

Sugar Mills rolling stock: 50c, Diesel locomotive. 87c, Steam locomotive. $1, Diesel locomotive, diff. $2, Free passenger train.

Wmk. 373
1999, Oct. 26   **Litho.**   **Perf. 13¾**
863 A195 50c multicolored   .60 .60
864 A195 87c multicolored   1.25 1.25
865 A195 $1 multicolored   1.40 1.40
866 A195 $2 multicolored   2.75 2.75
    Nos. 863-866 (4)   6.00 6.00

Christmas — A196

Designs: 13c, Giving gifts. 31c, Angels and star. 63c, Bible, Magi, Holy family. 87c, Joseph, mary, donkey, vert. $1, Mary, Jesus, animals, vert. $2, Children, Santa, vert.

Perf. 13¼x13
1999, Nov. 29   **Litho.**   **Wmk. 373**
867 A196 13c multicolored   .20 .20
868 A196 31c multicolored   .45 .45
869 A196 63c multicolored   .90 .90
870 A196 87c multicolored   1.25 1.25
871 A196 $1 multicolored   1.40 1.40
872 A196 $2 multicolored   2.75 2.75
    Nos. 867-872 (6)   6.95 6.95

Millennium
A197

Designs: No. 873, Outstretched hands, islands (arch at top). No. 874, Map, flag (arch at right). No. 875, Globe, warrior beating lali, temple (arch at bottom). No. 876, Globe, drua, red line (arch at left).
    No. 877: a, Fiji petrel (arch at top). b, Crested iguana, islands (arch at top). c, Red prawns (arch at bottom). d, Tagimaucia (arch at bottom).

Perf. 13¼ Syncopated Type A
Litho. with Foil Application
2000, Jan. 1   **Unwmk.**
873 A197 $5 gold & multi   8.00 8.00
874 A197 $5 gold & multi   8.00 8.00
875 A197 $5 gold & multi   8.00 8.00
876 A197 $5 gold & multi   8.00 8.00
    Nos. 873-876 (4)   32.00 32.00

Souvenir Sheet
877 A197 $10 Sheet of 4, #a-d   65.00 65.00

Beetles — A198

Designs: 15c, Paracupta sulcata. 87c, Agrilus sp. $1.06, Cyphogastra abdominalis. $2, Paracupta sp.

Perf. 13¾x14
2000, Mar. 14   **Litho.**   **Wmk. 373**
878 A198 15c multi   .25 .25
879 A198 87c multi   1.50 1.50
880 A198 $1.06 multi   1.75 1.75
881 A198 $2 multi   3.00 3.00
    Nos. 878-881 (4)   6.50 6.50

Sesame Street — A199

No. 882: a, Big Bird. b, Oscar the Grouch. c, Cookie Monster. d, Grover. e, Elmo. f, Ernie. g, Zoe. h, The Count. i, Bert.
    No. 883, Big Bird, Elmo and Ernie, horiz. No. 884, Cookie Monster, Bert and Ernie, horiz.
    Illustration reduced.

Perf. 14½x14¾
2000, Apr. 20   **Litho.**   **Wmk. 373**
882 A199 50c Sheet of 9, #a-i   7.00 7.00

Souvenir Sheets
Perf. 14¾x14½
883 A199 $2 multi   3.50 3.50
884 A199 $2 multi   3.50 3.50
    The Stamp Show 2000, London (#882).

Pres. Ratu Sir
Kamisese Mara,
80th
Birthday — A200

President with: 15c, Lumberjack, timber truck. 81c, Women. $1, Workers in cane field. $3, Ships.

2000, May 13   **Perf. 14x13¾**
885 A200 15c multi   .25 .25
886 A200 81c multi   1.25 1.25
887 A200 $1 multi   1.50 1.50
888 A200 $3 multi   5.50 5.50
    Nos. 885-888 (4)   8.50 8.50

Prince William, 18th Birthday
Common Design Type

William: Nos. 889, 893a, As child, wearing fireman's helmet, vert. Nos. 890, 893b, Wearing navy suit, vert. Nos. 891, 893c, Wearing scarf. Nos. 892, 893d, Wearing suit and wearing blue shirt. No. 893e, As child, wearing camouflage and beret.

Perf. 13¾x14¼, 14¼x13¾
2000, June 21   **Wmk. 373**
Stamps With White Border
889 CD359 $1 multi   1.50 1.50
890 CD359 $1 multi   1.50 1.50
891 CD359 $1 multi   1.50 1.50
892 CD359 $1 multi   1.50 1.50
    Nos. 889-892 (4)   6.00 6.00

Souvenir Sheet
Stamps Without White Border
Perf. 14¼
893 CD359 $1 Sheet of 5, #a-e   9.00 9.00

2000 Summer Olympics,
Sydney — A201

Wmk. 373
2000, Aug. 8   **Litho.**   **Perf. 13¾**
894 A201 44c Swimming, vert.   .50 .50
895 A201 87c Judo, vert.   1.25 1.25
896 A201 $1 Running   1.50 1.50
897 A201 $2 Windsurfing   2.75 2.75
    Nos. 894-897 (4)   6.00 6.00

Souvenir Sheet

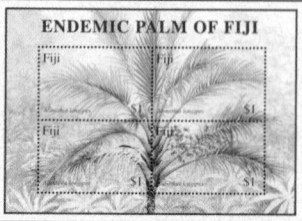

Alsmithia Longipes — A202

No. 898: a, Red frond at R. b, Red frond at L. c, Yellow frond. d, Fruit.
Illustration reduced.

Wmk. 373
2000, Sept. 12   **Litho.**   **Perf. 13½**
898 A202 $1 Sheet of 4, #a-d   7.00 7.00

Lapita Pottery Shards and Discovery
Sites — A203

44c, Yanuca Island. 63c, Mago Island. $1, Ugaga Island. $2, Sigatoka sand dunes.

2000, Oct. 24   **Perf. 13¾**
899-902 A203 Set of 4   7.00 7.00

Christmas
A204

Designs: 15c, Jungle. 81c, Cliffside trail. 87c, Coastal village. $3, Outrigger canoe.

2000, Nov. 21
903-906 A204 Set of 4   8.00 8.00

Souvenir Sheet

Taveuni Rain Forest — A205

Designs: a, Orange dove. b, Xixuthrus heyrovskyi.

Perf. 13¾x13½
2001, Feb. 1   Litho.   Unwmk.
907 A205 $2 Sheet of 2, #a-b   6.25 6.25

Moths
A206

Designs: 17c, Macroglossum hirundo vitiensis. 48c, Hippotion celerio. 69c, Gnathothlibus erotus eras. 89c, Theretra pinastrina intersecta. $1.17, Deilephila placida torenia. $2, Psilogramma jordana.

2001, Mar. 20   Perf. 13¼x13
908-913 A206   Set of 6   8.00 8.00

Souvenir Sheet

Gallus Gallus — A207

Designs: a, Hen. b, Rooster.

2001, May 22   Perf. 13¾x14
914 A207 $2 Sheet of 2, #a-b   6.50 6.50

Society for
Prevention of
Cruelty — A208

Designs: 34c, Girl, cat. 96c, Boy, dogs. $1.23, Girl, cat, diff. $2, Boy, dog.

Perf. 14x13¾
2001, June 26   Litho.   Unwmk.
915-918 A208   Set of 4   6.25 6.25

Pigeons — A209

Designs: 69c, White-throated. 89c, Pacific, vert. $1.23, Peal's, vert. $2, Rock.

2001, July 20   Perf. 14x14¾, 14¾x14
919-922 A209   Set of 4   7.25 7.25

Westpac Pacific Bank, 100th Anniv. in
Fiji — A210

Bank office in: 48c, 1901. 96c, 1916. $1, 1934. $2, 2001.

2001, Aug. 10   Perf. 13¼x13¾
923-926 A210   Set of 4   6.00 6.00

Fish
A211

Designs: 50c, Yellowfin tuna. 96c, Wahoo. $1.17, Dolphin fish. $2, Pacific blue marlin.

2001, Aug. 23
927-930 A211   Set of 4   6.50 6.50

Christmas
A212

Designs: 17c, Angel appears to Mary. 34c Nativity. 48c, Adoration of the shepherds. 69c, Adoration of the Magi. 89c, Flight to Egypt. $2, Fijian Chirst child.

2001, Oct. 29   Litho.   Perf. 13¾x13¼
931-936 A212   Set of 6   7.00 7.00

Colonial Financial Services Group,
125th Anniv. in Fiji — A213

Designs: 17c, Bank office. 48c, Women using automatic teller machine. $1, Suva Private Hospital. $3, Hoisting of British flag.

2001, Nov. 16   Litho.   Perf. 13¼
937-940 A213   Set of 4   7.00 7.00

Air Pacific, 50th
Anniv. — A214

No. 941: a, De Havilland Drover. b, Hawker Siddley HS-748. c, Douglas DC-10-30. d, Boeing 747-200.

2001, Nov. 30   Litho.   Perf. 13
941   Horiz. strip of 4   7.25 7.25
  a. A214 89c multi   1.25 1.00
  b. A214 96c multi   1.40 1.10
  c. A214 $1 multi   1.50 1.25
  d. A214 $2 multi   3.00 1.50

Spices — A215

Designs: 69c, Pepper. 89c, Nutmeg. $1, Vanilla. $2, Cinnamon.

2002, Mar. 12   Litho.   Perf. 13¼
942-945 A215   Set of 4   6.25 6.25

Souvenir Sheet

Balaka Palm — A216

Palm and: a, Bird, butterfly, beetle. b, Lizard, butterfly

2002, Apr. 29
946 A216 $2 Sheet of 2, #a-b   5.25 5.25

Freshwater Fish — A217

Designs: 48c, Redigobius sp. 96c, Spotted flagtail. $1.23, Silverstripe mudskipper. $2, Snakehead gudgeon.

2002, May 13
947-950 A217   Set of 4   7.00 7.00

Fruit — A218

Designs: 25c, Breadfruit. 34c, Wi. $1, Jakfruit. $3, Avocado.

2002, July 25   Litho.   Perf. 13¾x13¼
951-954 A218   Set of 4   6.25 6.25

Murex
Shells — A219

Designs: 69c, Saul's murex. 96c, Caltrop murex. $1, Purple Pacific drupe. $2, Ramose murex.

2002, Aug. 20   Perf. 13¾
955-958 A219   Set of 4   5.75 5.75

Fiji
Goshawk — A220

Designs: 48c, Goshawk and eggs. 89c, Chicks in nest. $1, Juvenile on branch. $3, Adult.

2002, Sept. 10
959-962 A220   Set of 4   6.75 6.75

2002 Operation Open Heart Visit to
Fiji — A221

Designs: 34c, Doctors performing operation, vert. 69c, Doctor listening to patient's heart with stethoscope. $1.17, Technician administering echocardiogram. $2, Administration of anesthesia to patient, vert.

2002, Oct. 30   Perf. 13¼
963-966 A221   Set of 4   5.50 5.50

Fiji Natural Artesian Water — A222

Designs: 25c, Bottle of water, flowers, vert. 48c, Bottling plant. $1, Delivery truck. $3, Children with bottled water, vert.

2002, Nov. 5
967-970 A222   Set of 4   7.00 7.00

Christmas — A223

Designs: 17c, Christian church. 89c, Mosque. $1, Hindu temple. $3, Christian church, diff.

2002, Nov. 20
971-974 A223   Set of 4   6.50 6.50

Post Fiji, Ltd. Improvements — A224

Designs: 48c, General Post Office. 96c, Post Fiji Mail Center. $1, Post Fiji Logistics Center. $2, Smart Mail.

2003, Mar. 19   Litho.   Perf. 13¼
975-978 A224   Set of 4   6.50 6.50

Souvenir Sheet

Intl. Year of Fresh Water — A225

No. 979: a, Top of waterfall, flowers. b, Base of waterfall, butterfly.

2003, Apr. 22
979 A225 $2 Sheet of 2, #a-b   6.00 6.00

2003 South Pacific Games, Suva — A226

Designs: 10c, Track athlete with arms raised. 14c, Baseball. 20c, Netball. No. 983, $5, Shot put.
No. 984, $5, Flags of participating nations, venues, volleyball players.

2003   **Perf. 13¼**
980-983 A226   Set of 4   6.50 6.50
              Size: 120x85mm
                    Imperf
984 A226 $5 multi   8.00 8.00
Issued: Nos. 980-983, 5/26; No. 984, 6/28.

Fish
A227

Siganus uspi: 58c, Fish, crab and coral. 83c, Two fish and coral. $1.15, Two fish, coral, and other fish species. $3, Fish and coral.

2003, Aug. 12   **Perf. 13¼**
985-988 A227   Set of 4   8.00 8.00

Bird Life International
A228

Designs: 41c, Long-legged warbler. 60c, Silktail. $1.07, Red-throated lorikeet. $3, Pink-billed parrot finch.

2003, Sept. 16
989-992 A228   Set of 4   12.00 12.00

Geckos
A229

Designs: 83c, Pacific slender-toed gecko. $1.07, Indopacific tree gecko. $1.15, Mann's gecko. $2, Voracious gecko.

2003, Oct. 21   Litho.   Perf. 13¼
993-996 A229   Set of 4   10.50 10.50

Christmas — A230

Children's art: 18c, Children, Christmas tree. 41c, Children, flag of Fiji. 58c, Children, Santa Claus, reindeer pulling sleighs, vert. 83c, Santa Claus on chimney, gifts, children, Christmas tree, vert. $1.07, Children with candles, Christmas tree, vert. $1.15, Santa Claus, children, bell, rainbow, vert.
$1.41, Handshake.

2003, Nov. 26   Litho.   Perf. 13¼
997-1002 A230   Set of 6   7.50 7.50
              Souvenir Sheet
1003 A230 $1.41 multi   3.50 3.50

Tagimoucia — A231

2003, Dec. 1   Litho.   Perf. 14½x14
1004 A231 50c multi + label   1.75 1.75
Sold in sheets of 10 stamps + 10 labels that could be personalized for $15 per sheet.

Xixuthrus Heyrovskyi, Longest Beetle in the World — A232

Illustration reduced.

2003, Feb. 27   **Imperf.**
1005 A232 $5 multi   8.50 8.50

Miniature Sheet

Worldwide Fund for Nature (WWF) — A233

No. 1006: a, 58c, Skipjack tuna. b, 83c, Albacore tuna. c, $1.07, Yellowfin tuna. d, $3, Bigeye tuna.

2004, Apr. 7   **Perf. 13¼**
1006 A233   Sheet of 4, #a-d   8.50 8.50
  e.   Like #1006, with artist's name
           at LL of each stamp   8.50 8.50

Land Snails
A234

Designs: 18c, Malleated placostyle. 41c, Kandavu placostyle. $1.15, Fragile orpiella. $3, Thin Fijian placostyle.

2004, May 28
1007-1010 A234   Set of 4   8.50 8.50

Bird Type of 1995
Perf. 13¼x13
2004, June 26   **Unwmk.**
1011 A166 18c Island thrush   .20 .20

Coral Reef Shrimp — A235

Designs: 58c, Boxer shrimp. 83c, Bumblebee shrimp. $1.07, Mantis shrimp. $3, Anemone shrimp.

2004, June 30   **Perf. 13¼**
1012-1015 A235   Set of 4   9.00 9.00

Birds
A236

Designs: 41c, Wandering tattler. 58c, Whimbrel. $1.15, Pacific golden plover. $3, Bristle-thighed curlew.

2004, July 28
1016-1019 A236   Set of 4   11.50 11.50

2004 Summer Olympics, Athens A237

Designs: 41c, Swimming. 58c, Judo, vert. $1.40, Weight lifting, vert. $2, Makelesi Buliki-obo, runner.

2004, Aug. 12
1020-1023 A237   Set of 4   8.75 8.75

Musket Cove to Port Vila Yacht Race, 25th Anniv. — A238

Various yachts: 83c, $1.07, $1.15, $2. $1.07 and $2 are vert.

2004, Sept. 18   **Perf. 14¼**
1024-1027 A238   Set of 4   10.00 10.00
1027a   Souvenir sheet of 1   4.00 4.00
See Vanuatu Nos. 858-861.

Souvenir Sheet

Coconut Crab — A239

2004, Oct. 20   Litho.   Perf. 14
1028 A239 $5 multi   10.00 10.00

Papilio Schmeltzii — A240

Designs: 58c, Newly-emerged adult, vert. 83c, Larva. $1.41, Adult. $3, Pupa, vert.

Perf. 14x14½, 14½x14
2004, Nov. 10
1029-1032 A240   Set of 4   11.00 11.00

Christmas A241

Designs: 18c, Annunciation. 58c, Infant in manger. $1.07, Madonna and child. $3, Adoration of the Shepherds.

2004, Dec. 1   Litho.   Perf. 13¼
1033-1036 A241   Set of 4   15.00 15.00

Birds — A242

No. 1037: a, Little heron. b, Great white egret. c, White-faced heron. d, Pacific reef heron.

2005, Jan. 26
1037   Horiz. strip of 4   11.00 11.00
  a.-d. A242 $1 Any single   2.75 2.75

Flowers For Perfume — A243

Designs: 58c, Cananga odorata. $1.15, Euodia hortensis. $1.41, Pandanus tecorius. $2, Santalum yasi.

2005, Feb. 20   *Perf. 14x14½*
1038-1041 A243   Set of 4   10.00 10.00

Peregrine Falcons — A244

Designs: 41c, Head of falcon. 83c, Adult at nest. $1.07, Chicks. $3, Adult on rock.

2005, Mar. 14 Litho.   *Perf. 14½x14*
1042-1045 A244   Set of 4   12.00 12.00

Triggerfish — A245

Designs: 58c, Whitebanded triggerfish. 83c, Yellow-spotted triggerfish. $1.15, Orange-lined triggerfish. $2, Clown triggerfish.

2005, Apr. 27
1046-1049 A245   Set of 4   9.00 9.00

European Philatelic Cooperation, 50th Anniv. (in 2006) — A246

Color of arches: 58c, Red. 83c, Blue green. $1.41, Purple. $4, Yellow bister.

2005, June 1   *Perf. 13¾*
1050-1053 A246   Set of 4   13.00 13.00
1053a   Souvenir sheet, #1050-1053   13.00 13.00

Europa stamps, 50th anniv. (in 2006).

Miniature Sheet

End of World War II, 60th Anniv. — A247

No. 1054: a, HMNZS Achilles. b, Japanese Yokosuka E14Y "Glen" over Suva Harbor. c, Fijian South Pacific Scouts in Solomon Islands. d, USS Chicago. e, Patrol vessel HMS Viti. f, British Prime Minister Winston Churchill. g, HMS Hood. h, Dambusters Raid. i, German King Tiger tank in Ardennes. j, Gen. Dwight D. Eisenhower.

2005, June 27 Litho.   *Perf. 13¾*
1054 A247 83c Sheet of 10, #a-j   16.00 16.00

Game Fish A248

Designs: 41c, Great barracuda. 58c, Narrow-barred Spanish mackerel. $1.07, Giant trevally. $3, Indo-Pacific sailfish.

2005, July 27 Litho.   *Perf. 14½x14*
1055-1058 A248   Set of 4   10.00 10.00

Pope John Paul II (1920-2005) A249

2005, Aug. 18   *Perf. 14*
1059 A249 $1 multi   2.75 2.75

Dragonflies — A250

Designs: 83c, Yellow-striped flutterer. $1.07, Agrionoptera insignis. $1.15, Green skimmer. $2, Common percher.

2005, Aug. 30 Litho.   *Perf. 13¼*
1060-1063 A250   Set of 4   9.75 9.75

Albert Einstein (1879-1955), Physicist — A251

Einstein: 83c, As a child. $1.07, In 1905. $1.15, And blackboard. $2, And galaxies.

2005, Sept. 27 Litho.   *Perf. 14¼x14*
1064-1067 A251   Set of 4   6.00 6.00

Intl. Year of Physics.

Root Crops — A252

Designs: 41c, Manihot utilissima. 83c, Ipomoea satatas. $1.41, Colocasia esculenta. $2, Dioscorea sativa.

2005, Oct. 13   *Perf. 13¼*
1068-1071 A252   Set of 4   5.50 5.50

Tall Ships A253

Designs: 83c, Eliza of Province. $1.15, Elbe. $1.41, HMS Rosario. $2, L'Astrolabe.

2005, Nov. 21 Litho.   *Perf. 14x14¼*
1072-1075 A253   Set of 4   6.25 6.25

Barn Owls — A254

Owl: 18c, And eggs. $1.15, Juvenile. $1.41, With prey. $2, Perched.

2006, Jan. 10 Litho.   *Perf. 14¼x14*
1076-1079 A254   Set of 4   5.50 5.50

Platymantis Vitianus — A255

Various depictions: 50c, 83c, $1.15, $2.

2006, Feb. 8 Litho.   *Perf. 14x14¼*
1080-1083 A255   Set of 4   5.25 5.25

Skinks A256

Designs: 18c, Pygmy snake-eyed skink. 58c, Brown-tailed copper striped skink. $1.15, Pacific black skink. $3, Pacific blue-tailed skink.

2006, Mar. 22
1084-1087 A256   Set of 4   5.50 5.50

Queen Elizabeth II, 80th Birthday A257

Designs: 50c, As child. 65c, Wearing tiara. 90c, Wearing blue hat. $3, Wearing blue hat, diff.
No. 1092: a, Like 65c. b, Like 90c.

2006, Apr. 21 Litho.   *Perf. 14*
With White Frames
1088-1091 A257   Set of 4   6.00 6.00
Souvenir Sheet
Without White Frames
1092 A257 $2 Sheet of 2, #a-b   4.75 4.75

Nos. 725 and 729 Surcharged

Methods and Perfs. As Before
2006   Wmk. 373
1093 A166 2c on 1c #725   .20 .20
1094 A166 3c on 1c #725   .20 .20
1095 A166 4c on 1c #725   .20 .20
1096 A166 18c on 6c #729   .20 .20
   Nos. 1093-1096 (4)   .80 .80

Issued: No. 1093, 4/3; No. 1094, 3/13; No. 1095, 6/27; No. 1096, 6/8.

Miniature Sheet

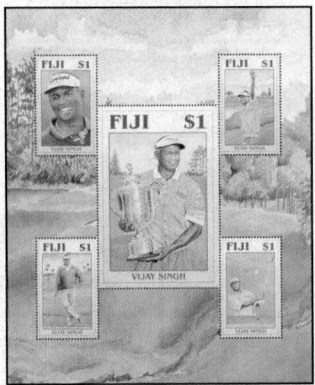
Vijay Singh, Golfer — A258

No. 1097 — Singh: a, Head. b, With arm raised. c, Leaning on golf club. d, Hitting ball from sand trap. e, Holding trophy (60x87mm).

Perf. 14x14¼
2006, May 26 Litho.   Unwmk.
1097 A258 $1 Sheet of 5, #a-e   5.75 5.75

2006 World Cup Soccer Championships, Germany — A259

Various players: 65c, 90c, $1.20, $2.

2006, June 9   *Perf. 14¼x14*
1098-1101 A259   Set of 4   5.50 5.50

Souvenir Sheet

Purple Swamphen — A260

No. 1102: a, Swamphen and flowers. b, Swamphen on nest.

2006, July 20   *Perf. 14½x14*
1102 A260 $2 Sheet of 2, #a-b   4.75 4.75

Extinct Species A261

Designs: 50c, Brachylophus vitiensis. $1.10, Natunaornis gigoura, vert. $1.20, Vitirallus watlingi, vert. $1.50, Platymantis megabotoniviti.

Perf. 14x14¼, 14¼x14
2006, Aug. 15   Litho.
1103-1106 A261 Set of 4   5.00 5.00

Phasmids — A262

Designs: 10c, Hermarchus apollonius. $1.10, Cotylosoma dipneusticum. $1.20, Chitoniscus feejeeanus. $2, Graeffea crouanii.

2006, Sept. 7   **Perf. 14½x14**
1107-1110 A262 Set of 4   5.25 5.25

Honey Production A263

Designs: 18c, Bees and honeycomb. 40c, Apiarist examining honeycomb, horiz. $1, Woman and beehives, horiz. $3, Man and bottle of honey.

2006, Oct. 16 Perf. 14x14½, 14½x14
1111-1114 A263 Set of 4   5.50 5.50

Christmas A264

Flowering plants: 18c, Decaspermum vitiense. 65c, Quisqualis indica. 90c, Mussaenda raiateensis. $3, Delonix regia.

2006, Dec. 5   **Perf. 14x14½**
1115-1118 A264 Set of 4   5.75 5.75

Anemonefish — A265

Designs: 18c, Spine-cheek anemonefish. 60c, Pink anemonefish. 90c, Orange-fin anemonefish. $3, Dusky anemonefish.

Perf. 14½x14, 14x14½
2006, Nov. 7   Litho.
1119-1122 A265 Set of 4   5.75 5.75

Souvenir Sheet

Thalassina Anomala — A266

2007, Jan. 24   **Perf. 13½**
1123 A266 $4 multi   4.75 4.75

Traditional Architecture — A267

Designs: 20c, Coastal dwelling. 65c, Inland dwelling. $1.10, Temple, Bau. $3, Lauan-style house.

2007, Mar. 20 Litho. **Perf. 13¼**
1124-1127 A267 Set of 4   6.00 6.00

Freshwater Gobies — A268

Designs: 20c, Sicyopterus lagocephalus. $1.10, Stiphodon rutilaureus. $1.20, Sicyopus zosterophorum. $2, Stiphodon sp.

2007, Apr. 5 Litho. **Perf. 13¼**
1128-1131 A268 Set of 4   5.50 5.50

Birds Introduced to Fiji — A269

Designs: 50c, Red-vented bulbul. 65c, Spotted dove, horiz. $1.50, Australian magpie, horiz. $2, Java sparrow.

2007, May 22
1132-1135 A269 Set of 4   5.75 5.75

Scouting, Cent. A270

Designs: 50c, Scout in kayak, hand holding compass. 90c, Three Scouts wearing helmets, hands tying knot. No. 1138, $1.50, Scout in harness climbing, Scout saluting. $2, Scout writing observation notes, hands tying neckerchief.
No. 1140, $1.50, vert.: a, Scout emblem. b, Lord Robert Baden-Powell.

2007, July 9   **Perf. 13¾**
1136-1139 A270 Set of 4   6.25 6.25

Souvenir Sheet
1140 A270 $1.50 Sheet of 2, #a-b   3.75 3.75

Snails A271

Designs: 40c, Clithon diadema. 90c, Neritina variegata. $1.20, Fijidoma maculata. $2, Neritina squamaepicta.

2007, Aug. 18   **Perf. 14x14¼**
1141-1144 A271 Set of 4   5.50 5.50

Orchids — A272

Designs: 20c, Liparis layardii. 65c, Dendrobium catillare, horiz. $1.10, Dendrobium mohlianum, horiz. $3, Glomera montana.

Perf. 14¼x14, 14x14¼
2007, Aug. 21
1145-1148 A272 Set of 4   6.25 6.25

Nos. 725 and 729 Surcharged

l — Large "XX"   m — Small "XX"

n — Small "2," Small "XX"   o — Large "2," Small "XX"

Methods, Types and Watermarks As Before
2006-07
1149 A166(l) 1c on 6c #729 2.00 2.00
1150 A166(m) 1c on 6c #729 6.00 6.00
1151 A166(n) 2c on 1c #725 2.00 2.00
1152 A166(o) 2c on 1c #725 4.00 4.00
1153 A166(l) 2c on 6c #729 2.00 2.00
1154 A166(m) 3c on 1c #725 2.00 2.00
1155 A166(m) 4c on 1c #725 2.00 2.00
1156 A166(l) 4c on 6c #729 2.00 2.00
1157 A166(l) 18c on 6c #729 3.00 3.00
1158 A166(m) 18c on 6c #729 8.00 8.00
1159 A166(l) 20c on 6c #729 3.00 3.00
1160 A166(l) 20c on 6c #729 8.00 8.00
Nos. 1149-1160 (12)   44.00 44.00

Issued: No. 1149, 5/30/07; No. 1150, 9/19/07; No. 1151, 4/3; No. 1152, 11/13; No. 1153, 2/19/07; No. 1154, 3/13; No. 1155, 6/27; No. 1156, 6/6/07; No. 1157, 6/8; No. 1158, 9/8; No. 1159, 1/19/07; No. 1160, 3/8/07.

Fish A273

Designs: 50c, Coronation trout. 90c, Roving coral trout. $1.50, Squaretail coral trout. $2, Chinese footballer.

2007, Oct. 15 Litho. **Perf. 13¼**
1161-1164 A273 Set of 4   6.50 6.50

SEMI-POSTAL STAMPS

Catalogue values for unused stamps in this section are for Never Hinged items.

Children at Play — SP1

Rugby Player — SP2

Perf. 13x13½
1951, Sept. 17 Engr. Wmk. 4
B1 SP1 1p + 1p brown .25 .25
B2 SP2 2p + 1p deep green .30 .30

Bamboo River Raft — SP3

Design: 2½p+ ½p, Cross of Lorraine.

1954, Apr. 1   **Perf. 11x11½**
B3 SP3 1½p + ½p green & brn .25 .25
B4 SP3 2½p + ½p black & org .30 .30

Nos. 269 and 272 Surcharged

1972, Dec. 4 Photo. Perf. 14, 13½
B5 A56 15c + 5c multi .50 .50
B6 A55 30c + 10c multi 1.10 1.10

Indian Boy, Map of Fiji SP4

Map of Fiji and: 15c+2c, European girl. 30c+3c, Chinese girl. 40c+4c, Fijian boy.

Wmk. 373
1979, Sept. 17 Litho. **Perf. 14½**
B7 SP4 4c + 1c multicolored .20 .20
B8 SP4 15c + 2c multicolored .25 .25
B9 SP4 30c + 3c multicolored .50 .50
B10 SP4 40c + 4c multicolored .70 .70
Nos. B7-B10 (4)   1.65 1.65

The surtax was for IYC fund.

POSTAGE DUE STAMPS

D1

D2

D3

1917 Unwmk. Typeset Perf. 11
Laid Papers; Without Gum

J1	D1	½p black	850.00	425.00
J2	D2	½p black	550.00	300.00
J3	D3	1p black	375.00	92.50
J4	D3	2p black	325.00	75.00
J5	D3	3p black	400.00	92.50
J6	D3	4p black	850.00	425.00
a.	Strip of 8, 3 #J3, 1 ea. #J1 and #J6, and 3 #J5		16,000.	
	Nos. J1-J6 (6)		3,350.	1,410.

There were two printings of this issue. In the first printing, the 2d was printed in sheets of 84 (7x12), and the other four values were printed together in sheets of 96 (8x12), with each row consisting of three 1p, one ½p, one 4p and three 3p values. Setenant multiples exist. Sheets were not perforated on the margins, so that marginal stamps were not perforated on the outer edge. Examples from the first printing are 25mm wide (including margins).

In the second printing, the ½p, 1p and 2p were printed in separate sheets of 84 (7x12). The clichés were set a little closer, and so that examples of this printing are 23mm wide.

D4

D5

Perf. 14
1918, June 1 Typo. Wmk. 3

J7	D4	½p black	4.25	20.00
J8	D4	1p black	4.25	15.00
J9	D4	2p black	5.50	22.50
J10	D4	3p black	7.00	27.50
J11	D4	4p black	8.25	40.00
	Nos. J7-J11 (5)		29.25	125.00

1940 Wmk. 4 Perf. 12½

J12	D5	1p bright green	4.75	62.50
J13	D5	2p bright green	8.50	62.50
J14	D5	3p bright green	11.00	77.50
J15	D5	4p bright green	12.00	82.50
J16	D5	5p bright green	15.00	82.50
J17	D5	6p bright green	8.00	87.50
J18	D5	1sh dk carmine	20.00	140.00
J19	D5	1sh6p dk carmine	20.00	200.00
	Nos. J12-J19 (8)		99.25	795.00
	Set, never hinged		140.00	

WAR TAX STAMPS

Regular Issue of 1912-16 Overprinted

Die I

1916 Wmk. 3 Perf. 14

MR1	A23	½p green	.85	3.00
a.	Inverted overprint		700.00	
b.	Double overprint			
MR2	A23	1p scarlet	2.00	.75
a.	1p carmine		30.00	26.00
b.	Pair, one without ovpt.		9,000.	
c.	Inverted overprint		800.00	

Most examples of #MR2b are within horiz. strips of 12.

FINLAND

'fin-lənd

(Suomi)

LOCATION — Northern Europe bordering on the Gulfs of Bothnia and Finland
GOVT. — Republic
AREA — 130,119 sq. mi.
POP. — 5,147,349 (1997)
CAPITAL — Helsinki

Finland was a Grand Duchy of the Russian Empire from 1809 until December 1917, when it declared its independence.

100 Kopecks = 1 Ruble
100 Pennia = 1 Markka (1866)
100 Cents = 1 Euro (2002)

> Catalogue values for unused stamps in this country are for Never Hinged items, beginning with Scott 220 in the regular postage section, Scott B39 in the semipostal section, Scott C2 in the airpost section, Scott M1 in the military stamp section, and Scott Q6 in the parcel post section.

Unused stamps are valued with original gum as defined in the catalogue introduction except for Nos. 1-3B which are valued without gum. Used values for Nos. 1-3B are for pen-canceled examples. Very fine examples of the serpentine rouletted issues, Nos. 4-13c, will have roulettes cutting the design slightly on one or more sides and will have all "teeth" complete and intact. Stamps with roulettes clear of the design on all four sides are extremely scarce and sell for substantial premiums.

Watermarks

Wmk. 121 — Multiple Swastika

Wmk. 208 — Post Horn

Wmk. 168 — Wavy Lines and Letters

Wmk. 273 — Roses

Wmk. 363 — Tree Stump

Syncopated Perforations

Type A (1st stamp #1065): On one longer side, groups of five holes are separated by an oval hole equal in width to eight holes.

Type B (1st stamp, #1142): On the top groups of 3 holes at left and right and a middle group of 4 holes separated by rectangular perforations equal in width to 4 holes.

Issues under Russian Empire

Coat of Arms — A1

1856 Unwmk. Typo. Imperf.
Small Pearls in Post Horns
Wove Paper

1	A1	5k blue	6,750.	1,500.
	Cut to shape			150.00
	Pen and town cancellation			1,900.
	Cut to shape			200.00
	Town cancellation			3,250.
	Cut to shape			250.00
a.	Tête bêche pair	80,000.	65,000.	
	Pen and town cancellation			90,000.
2	A1	10k rose	8,750.	400.00
	Cut to shape			65.00
	Pen and town cancellation			575.00
	Cut to shape			90.00
	Town cancellation			925.00
	Cut to shape			100.00
a.	Tête bêche pair	80,000.	60,000.	
	Pen and town cancellation			65,000.

1858
Wide Vertically Laid Paper

2C	A1	10k rose	—	1,400.
	Cut to shape			225.00
	Pen and town cancellation			1,800.
	Cut to shape			275.00
	Town cancellation			2,500.
	Cut to shape			350.00
d.	Tête bêche pair			—

The wide vertically laid paper has 13-14 distinct lines per 2cm. The 10k rose also exists on a narrow laid paper with lines sometimes indistinct. Value, about 45 per cent of that for a wide laid paper example.

A 5k blue with small pearls exists on narrow vertically laid paper. It is rare.

Stamps on diagonally laid paper are envelope cut squares.

Large Pearls in Post Horns
Wove Paper

3	A1	5k blue	8,500.	1,400.
	Cut to shape			125.
	Pen and town cancellation			1,550.
	Cut to shape			175.
	Town cancellation			2,500.
	Cut to shape			225.
a.	Tête bêche pair		60,000.	
	Pen and town cancellation			65,000.

1859 Wide Vertically Laid Paper

3B	A1	5k blue	—	18,000.
	Cut to shape			2,250.
	Pen and town cancellation			25,000.
	Cut to shape			3,500.

Reprints of Nos. 2 and 3, made in 1862, are on brownish paper, on vertically laid paper, and in tête bêche pairs on normal and vertically laid paper. Reprints of 1871, 1881 and 1893 are on yellowish or white paper. Value for least costly of each, $85.

In 1956, Nos. 2 and 3 were reprinted for the Centenary with post horn watermark and gum. Value, $85 each.

Coat of Arms — A2

1860 Serpentine Roulette 7½, 8

Four types of indentation are noted:

I — Depth 1-1¼mm

II — Depth 1½-1¾mm

III — Depth 2-2¼mm

IV — Shovel-shaped teeth. Depth 1¼-1½mm

Wove Paper

4	A2	5k blue, *bluish*, I	725.00	200.00
a.		Roulette II	875.00	275.00
b.		Perf. vert.		
5	A2	10k rose, *pale rose*, I	625.00	65.00
a.		Roulette II	1,300.	190.00

A3   A4

1866-74   *Serpentine Roulette*

6	A3	5p pur brn, *lil*, I ('73)	450.00	200.00
a.		Roulette II		4,500.
b.		5p red brn, *lil*, III ('71)	400.00	200.00
7	A3	8p blk, *grn*, III ('67)	325.00	200.00
a.		Ribbed paper ('72)	1,300.	1,000.
b.		Roulette II ('74)	400.00	300.00
c.		As "b," ribbed paper ('74)	400.00	275.00
d.		Roulette I ('73)	575.00	375.00
e.		As "d," ribbed paper ('74)	1,100.	475.00
f.		Serpentine roulette 10½ ('67)		15,000.
8	A3	10p blk, *yel*, III ('70)	750.00	400.00
a.		10p blk, *buff*, II	850.00	450.00
b.		10p blk, *buff*, I ('73)	800.00	425.00
9	A3	20p bl, *bl*, III	650.00	67.50
a.		Roulette II	650.00	97.50
b.		Roulette I ('73)	750.00	150.00
c.		Roulette IV ('74)		1,300.
d.		Perf. horiz.		
e.		Printed on both sides (40p blue on back)		—
10	A3	40p rose, *lil rose*, III	575.00	77.50
a.		Ribbed paper, III ('73)	750.00	250.00
b.		Roulette II	575.00	92.50
c.		As "b," ribbed paper ('73)	750.00	200.00
d.		Roulette I	800.00	200.00
e.		As "d," ribbed paper	750.00	150.00
f.		Roulette IV	—	2,500.
g.		As "f," ribbed paper		
h.		Serpentine roulette 10½		

11	A4	1m yel brn, III ('67)	2,500.	900.00
a.		Roulette II	3,100.	1,900.

Nos. 7f and 10h are private roulettes and are also known in compound serpentine roulette 10½ and 7½.

Nos. 4-11 were reprinted in 1893 on thick wove paper. Colors differ from originals. Roulette type IV. Value for Nos. 4-5, each $40, Nos. 6-10, each $50. Value for No. 11, $55.

Thin or Thick Laid Paper

12	A3	5p red brn, *lil*, III	300.00	160.00
a.		Roulette II	325.00	325.00
b.		Roulette I	300.00	325.00
d.		5p blk, *buff*, roul. III (error)		22,500.
e.		Tête bêche pair		
13	A3	10p black, *buff*, III	750.00	300.00
a.		10p black, *yel*, II	900.00	300.00
b.		10p black, *yel*, I	1,300.	800.00
c.		10p red brown, *lil*, III (error)	8,500.	7,750.

Forgeries of No. 13c exist.

A5

1875   Perf. 14x13½

16	A5	32p lake	2,400.	500.00

1875-81   Perf. 11

17	A5	2p gray	55.00	65.00
18	A5	5p orange	140.00	15.00
a.		5p yellow	140.00	15.00
19	A5	8p blue green	275.00	65.00
a.		8p yellow green	275.00	77.50
20	A5	10p brown ('81)	625.00	67.50
21	A5	20p ultra	160.00	3.75
a.		20p blue	175.00	6.00
b.		20p Prussian blue	350.00	40.00
c.		Tête bêche pair		3,500.
22	A5	25p carmine ('79)	300.00	16.00
a.		25p rose	425.00	65.00
23	A5	32p carmine	410.00	57.50
a.		32p rose	500.00	160.00
24	A5	1m violet ('77)	875.00	175.00
		Nos. 17-24 (8)	2,840.	464.75

A souvenir card issued in 1974 for NORDIA 1975 reproduced a block of four of the unissued "1 MARKKAA" design.

Nos. 19, 23 were reprinted in 1893, perf. 12½. Value $17.50 each.

1881-83   Perf. 12½

25	A5	2p gray	15.00	17.00
a.		Imperf., pair	575.00	
26	A5	5p orange	57.50	7.00
a.		Tête bêche pair	7,500.	4,500.
b.		Imperf. vert., pair		—
c.		Imperf. horiz., pair		—
27	A5	10p brown	100.00	20.00
28	A5	20p ultra	60.00	2.00
a.		20p blue	60.00	2.00
b.		Tête bêche pair	3,000.	2,400.
c.		Imperf., pair		—
29	A5	25p rose	50.00	10.00
a.		25p carmine	67.50	20.00
b.		Tête bêche pair		
30	A5	1m violet ('82)	400.00	50.00
		Nos. 25-30 (6)	682.50	106.00

Nos. 27-29 were reprinted in 1893 in deeper shades, perf. 12½. Value $35 each.

Most examples of No. 28c are from printer's waste.

1881   Perf. 11x12½

26d	A5	5p orange	500.00	100.00
27a	A5	10p brown	1,000.	275.00
28d	A5	20p ultra	650.00	50.00
28e	A5	20p blue	650.00	50.00
29c	A5	25p rose	750.00	200.00
29d	A5	25p carmine	650.00	125.00
30a	A5	1m violet		1,600.

1881   Perf. 12½x11

26e	A5	5p orange	500.00	100.00
27b	A5	10p brown	—	350.00
28f	A5	20p ultra	650.00	50.00
28g	A5	20p blue	650.00	50.00
29e	A5	25p rose	—	300.00
29f	A5	25p carmine	650.00	125.00

1885   Perf. 12½

31	A5	5p emerald	19.00	.65
a.		5p yellow green	21.00	1.25
b.		Tête bêche pair		10,000.
32	A5	10p carmine	29.00	3.00
a.		10p rose	29.00	3.00
33	A5	20p orange	32.50	.50
a.		20p yellow	37.50	1.75
b.		Tête bêche pair		3,500.
34	A5	25p ultra	62.50	3.50
a.		25p blue	57.50	3.00
35	A5	1m gray & rose	30.00	20.00
36	A5	5m green & rose	500.00	375.00
37	A5	10m brown & rose	625.00	625.00

A6

1889-92   Perf. 12½

38	A6	2p slate ('90)	.65	1.00
39	A6	5p green ('90)	32.50	.40
40	A6	10p carmine ('90)	62.50	.55
a.		10p rose ('90)	77.50	.60
b.		Imperf.	100.00	100.00
41	A6	20p orange ('92)	72.50	.35
a.		20p yellow ('90)	77.50	1.25
42	A6	25p ultra ('91)	72.50	1.00
a.		25p blue	77.50	1.25
43	A6	1m slate & rose ('92)	4.75	3.75
a.		1m brnsh gray & rose ('90)	27.50	4.00
44	A6	5m green & rose ('90)	27.50	72.50
45	A6	10m brown & rose ('90)	40.00	95.00
		Nos. 38-45 (8)	312.90	174.55

The 2p slate, perf. 14x13, is believed to be an essay.
See Nos. 60-63.

See Russia for types similar to A7-A18.
Finnish stamps have "dot in circle" devices or are inscribed "Markka," "Markkaa," "Pen." or "Pennia."

Imperial Arms of Russia
A7   A8   A9

A10   A11

Laid Paper

1891-92   Wmk. 168   Perf. 14½x15

46	A7	1k orange yel	5.25	11.00
47	A7	2k green	6.25	9.50
48	A7	3k carmine	12.50	17.50
49	A8	4k rose	15.00	15.00
50	A8	7k dark blue	6.25	2.50
51	A8	10k dark blue	15.00	16.00
52	A9	14k blue & rose	21.00	27.50
53	A9	20k blue & car	19.00	18.00
54	A9	35k violet & grn	26.00	57.50
55	A8	50k violet & grn	35.00	40.00

Perf. 13½

56	A10	1r brown & org	90.00	90.00
57	A11	3½r black & gray	325.00	475.00
a.		3½r black & yellow (error)	14,000.	17,000.
58	A11	7r black & yellow	225.00	300.00
		Nos. 46-58 (13)	801.25	1,079.

Forgeries of Nos. 57, 57a, 58 exist.

Type of 1889-90   Wove Paper

1895-96   Unwmk.   Perf. 14x13

60	A6	5p green	.60	.40
61	A6	10p rose	.70	.50
62	A6	20p orange	.60	.25
a.		Imperf.	150.00	
63	A6	25p ultra	1.00	.70
a.		25p blue	1.75	.75
b.		Imperf.	100.00	
		Nos. 60-63 (4)	2.90	1.85

A12   A13

A14   A15

1901   Litho.   Perf. 14½x15
Chalky Paper

64	A12	2p yellow	5.25	5.25
65	A12	5p green	10.00	1.00
66	A13	10p carmine	27.50	1.25
67	A12	20p dark blue	62.50	.85
68	A14	1m violet & grn	325.00	9.25

Perf. 13½

69	A15	10m black & gray	300.00	300.00
		Nos. 64-69 (6)	730.25	317.60

Imperf sheets of 10p and 20p, stolen during production, were privately perforated 11½ to defraud the P.O. Uncanceled imperfs. of Nos. 65-68 are believed to be proofs.
See Nos. 70-75, 82.

Types of 1901 Redrawn

No. 64   No. 70

2p. On No. 64, the "2" below "II" is shifted slightly leftward. On No. 70, the "2" is centered below "II."

No. 65   No. 71

5p. On No. 65, the frame lines are very close. On No. 71, a clear white space separates them.

Nos. 66, 67   Nos. 72, 73

10p, 20p. On Nos. 66-67, the horizontal central background lines are faint and broken. On Nos. 72-73, they are clear and solid, though still thin.

20p. On No. 67, "H" close to "2" with period midway. On No. 73 they are slightly separated with period close to "H."

No. 68   Nos. 74, 74a

1m. On No. 68, the "1" following "MARKKA" lacks serif at base. On Nos. 74-74a, this "1" has serif.

No. 69   No. 75

10m. On No. 69, the serifs of "M" and "A" in top and bottom panels do not touch. On No. 75, the serifs join.

Perf. 14¼x14¾ (#70-73), 14¼x14 (#74)

1901-14   Typo.
Ordinary Paper

70	A12	2p orange ('03)	.60	1.10
71	A12	5p green	1.75	.50
a.		Perf 14¼x14 ('06)	1.75	.50

72	A13	10p carmine	10.00	.50
a.		Perf 14¼x14 ('07)	55.00	.50
b.		Background inverted	16.00	2.50
c.		Background inverted, perf 14¼x14	62.50	2.50
73	A12	20p dark blue	5.25	.50
a.		Perf 14¼x14 ('06)	70.00	.65
74	A14	1m lil & grn, perf. 14¼x14 ('14)	1.40	.65
a.		1m violet & blue green, perf. 14¼x14¾ ('02)	10.00	1.00
		Nos. 70-74 (5)	19.00	3.25

Perf. 13½

75	A15	10m blk & drab ('03)	150.00	52.50

Imperf.

70a	A12	2p	290.00	410.00
71b	A12	5p	77.50	160.00
72a	A13	10p	90.00	160.00
73a	A13	20p	160.00	160.00
74b	A14	1m	150.00	160.00
		Nos. 70a-74b (5)	767.50	1,050.

A16	A17	A18

1911-16   Perf. 14¼x14

77	A16	2p orange	.30	.25
78	A16	5p green	.35	.25
a.		Imperf.	410.00	
b.		Perf. 14¼x14¾	425.00	75.00
79	A17	10p rose	.30	.25
a.		Imperf.	77.50	160.00
80	A16	20p deep blue	.30	.25
a.		Imperf.	150.00	1.10
81	A18	40p violet & blue	.30	.25
a.		Perf. 14¼x14¾	4,000.	4,000.
		Nos. 77-81 (5)	1.55	1.25

There are three minor types of No. 79.

Perf. 14½

82	A15	10m blk & grnsh gray ('16)	125.00	175.00
a.		Horiz. pair, imperf. vert.	3,750.	

Republic
Helsinki Issue

Arms of the Republic
A19   A20

Two types of the 40p.
Type I — Thin figures of value.
Type II — Thick figures of value.

1917-29   Unwmk.   Perf. 14

83	A19	5p green	.25	.20
84	A19	5p gray ('19)	.25	.20
85	A19	10p rose	.30	.20
a.		Imperf., pair	240.00	375.00
86	A19	10p green ('19)	2.00	.50
a.		Perf. 14½x15		2,600.
87	A19	10p lt blue ('21)	.30	.20
88	A19	20p buff	.30	.20
89	A19	20p rose ('20)	.60	.20
90	A19	20p brown ('24)	.60	.20
a.		Perf 14¼x14¾	.60	32.50
91	A19	25p blue	.25	.20
92	A19	25p lt brown ('19)	.25	.20
93	A19	30p green ('23)	.30	.20
94	A19	40p violet (I)	.25	.20
a.		Perf 14¼x14¾	350.00	19.00
95	A19	40p bl grn (II) ('29)	.35	1.25
a.		Type I ('24)	12.00	5.00
b.		Perf 14¼x14¾	1.10	16.00
96	A19	50p orange brn	.25	.20
97	A19	50p dp blue ('19)	3.50	.20
a.		Perf 14¼x14¾		1,400.
98	A19	50p green ('21)	4.50	.30
a.		Perf 14¼x14¾	.30	2.50
99	A19	60p red vio ('21)	.35	.20
a.		Imperf., pair	75.00	100.00
100	A19	75p yellow ('21)	.25	.45
101	A19	1m dull rose & blk	13.00	.20
102	A19	1m red org ('25)	7.00	22.50
103	A19	1½m bl grn & red vio ('29)	.25	1.25
a.		Perf 14¼x14¾	.25	1.10
104	A19	2m grn & blk ('21)	2.75	.70
105	A19	2m dk blue & ind ('22)	2.00	.30
a.		Perf 14¼x14¾	.60	2.25
106	A19	3m bl & blk ('21)	70.00	.20
107	A19	5m red vio & blk	17.00	.20

108	A19	10m brn & gray blk, perf. 14	.90	1.25
a.		10m light brown & black, perf. 14¼x14¾ ('29)	3.75	450.00
110	A19	25m dull red & yel ('21)	.90	.20
		Nos. 83-108,110 (27)	128.65	59.70

Examples of a 2½p gray of this type exist. They are proofs from the original die which were distributed through the UPU. No plate was made for this denomination.
See Nos. 127-140, 143-152. For surcharge and overprints see Nos. 119-126, 153-154.

Vasa Issue

1918   Litho.   Perf. 11½

111	A20	5p green	.35	.90
112	A20	10p red	.35	.90
113	A20	30p slate	.80	2.25
114	A20	40p brown vio	.30	.90
115	A20	50p orange brn	.40	2.25
116	A20	70p gray brown	2.40	17.50
117	A20	1m red & gray	.45	1.40
118	A20	5m red violet & gray	40.00	80.00
		Nos. 111-118 (8)	45.05	106.10

Nos. 111-118 exist imperforate but were not regularly issued in that condition.
Sheet margin examples, perf. on 3 sides, imperf. on margin side, were sold by post office.

Stamps and Type of 1917-29 Surcharged

1919   Perf. 14

119	A19	10p on 5p green	.35	.60
120	A19	20p on 10p rose	.35	.60
121	A19	50p on 25p blue	.90	.35
122	A19	75p on 20p orange	.35	.60
		Nos. 119-122 (4)	1.95	2.15

Stamps and Type of 1917-29 Surcharged:

Nos. 123-125   No. 126

1921

123	A19	30p on 10p grn	.65	.90
124	A19	60p on 40p red violet	3.75	1.10
125	A19	90p on 20p rose	.40	.30
126	A19	1½m on 50p blue	1.40	.40
a.		Thin "2" in "½"	11.00	6.75
b.		Imperf., pair	250.00	375.00
		Nos. 123-126 (4)	6.20	2.70

Arms Type of 1917-29
Perf. 14, 14½x15

1925-29   Wmk. 121

127	A19	10p ultra ('27)	.50	2.00
128	A19	20p brown	.50	1.40
129	A19	25p brn org ('29)	.80	75.00
130	A19	30p yel green	.25	.20
a.		Perf. 14¼x14¾	.25	
131	A19	40p blue grn (I)	2.75	.40
a.		Perf. 14¼x14¾ ('26)	4.00	.60
b.		Type II ('28)	125.00	55.00
c.		As "b", perf. 14¼x14¾ ('28)	4.00	.60
132	A19	50p gray grn ('27)	1.00	.50
a.		Perf. 14¼x14¾ ('26)	.35	.50
133	A19	60p red violet	.25	.25
134	A19	1m dp orange	4.75	.20
a.		Perf. 14¼x14¾	100.00	.60
135	A19	1½m blue grn & red vio, perf. 14¼x14¾ ('26)	5.00	.45
a.		Perf. 14 ('26)	50.00	.45
136	A19	2m dk bl & ind	1.00	.45
a.		Perf. 14¼x14¾	.60	.45
137	A19	3m chlky blue & blk	1.00	.45
138	A19	5m red vio & blk	1.10	.45
139	A19	10m lt brn & blk ('27)	4.00	18.00
140	A19	25m dp org & yel ('27)	20.00	275.00
		Nos. 127-140 (14)	42.90	374.75

A21

Wmk. 208

1927, Dec. 6   Typo.   Perf. 14

141	A21	1½m deep violet	.20	.35
142	A21	2m deep blue	.25	1.75

10th anniv. of Finnish independence.

Arms Type of 1917-29

1927-29   Wmk. 208   Perf. 14½x15

143	A19	20p lt brown ('29)	1.60	15.00
144	A19	40p bl grn (II) ('28)	.20	.20
145	A19	50p gray grn ('28)	.20	.20
146	A19	1m dp orange	.20	1.00
a.		Imperf., pair	125.00	200.00
b.		Perf. 14	1.00	1.00
147	A19	1½m bl grn & red vio ('28)	2.50	.65
a.		Perf. 14	900.00	19.00
148	A19	2m dk bl & ind ('28)	.40	.35
149	A19	3m chlky bl & blk ('28)	.40	.35
a.		Perf. 14	1.75	4.50
150	A19	5m red vio & blk ('28)	.60	.60
151	A19	10m lt brown & blk	1.40	37.50
152	A19	25m brown org & yel	1.60	175.00
		Nos. 143-152 (10)	9.10	230.85

Nos. 146-147 Overprinted

1928, Nov. 10   Litho.   Wmk. 208

153	A19	1m deep orange	7.75	19.00
154	A19	1½m bl grn & red vio	7.75	19.00

Nos. 153 and 154 were sold exclusively at the Helsinki Philatelic Exhibition, Nov. 10-18, 1928, and were valid only during that period.

S. S. "Bore" Leaving Turku — A23

Turku Cathedral — A24

Turku Castle — A25

Wmk. 208

1929, May 22   Typo.   Perf. 14

155	A23	1m olive green	1.50	4.00
156	A24	1½m chocolate	2.40	4.00
157	A25	2m dark gray	.85	4.50
		Nos. 155-157 (3)	4.75	12.50

Founding of the city of Turku (Abo), 700th anniv.

A26

1930-46   Unwmk.   Perf. 14

158	A26	5p chocolate	.20	.20
159	A26	10p dull violet	.20	.20
160	A26	20p yel grn	.30	.35
161	A26	25p yel brn	.20	.20

162	A26	40p bl grn	1.90	.35
163	A26	50p yellow	.50	.35
164	A26	50p blue grn ('32)	.20	.20
b.		Imperf., pair	140.00	140.00
165	A26	60p dark gray	.35	.45
165A	A26	75p dp org ('42)	.20	.20
166	A26	1m red org	.45	.20
166B	A26	1m yel grn ('42)	.20	.20
167	A26	1.20m crimson	.35	.60
168	A26	1.25m yel ('32)	.20	.20
169	A26	1½m red vio	2.10	.20
170	A26	1½m car ('32)	.20	.20
170A	A26	1½m sl ('40)	.20	.20
170B	A26	1.75m org yel ('40)	.60	.20
171	A26	2m indigo	.30	.20
172	A26	2m dp vio ('32)	6.25	.20
173	A26	2m car ('36)	.20	.20
		Complete booklet, panes of 4 #161, 164, 166, 168, 173	5.50	
173B	A26	2m yel org ('42)	.30	.20
173C	A26	2m blue grn ('45)	.20	.20
174	A26	2½m brt bl ('32)	3.00	.35
174A	A26	2½m car ('42)	.20	.20
174B	A26	2.75m rose vio ('40)	.20	.20
175	A26	3m olive blk	26.00	.20
175B	A26	3m car ('45)	.20	.20
175C	A26	3m yel ('45)	.35	.60
176	A26	3½m brt bl ('36)	8.50	.35
176A	A26	3½m olive ('42)	.35	.20
176B	A26	4m olive ('45)	.35	.20
176C	A26	4½m saph ('42)	.20	.20
176D	A26	5m saph ('45)	.35	.20
176E	A26	5m pur ('45)	.35	.20
j.		Imperf., pair	150.00	150.00
176F	A26	5m yel ('46)	.70	.20
k.		Imperf., pair	150.00	190.00
176G	A26	6m car ('45)	.35	.20
m.		Imperf., pair	190.00	225.00
176H	A26	8m pur ('46)	.20	.20
176I	A26	10m saph ('45)	1.00	.20
		Nos. 158-176I (38)	57.75	9.40

See #257-262, 270-274, 291-296, 302-304. For surcharges & overprints see #195-196, 212, 221-222, 243, 250, 275, M2-M3.

Stamps of types A26-A29 overprinted "ITA KARJALA" are listed under Karelia, Nos. N1-N15.

Castle in Savonlinna A27

Lake Saima — A28

Woodchopper A29

1930   Engr.

177	A27	5m blue	.20	.20
178	A28	10m gray lilac	60.00	4.75
179	A29	25m black brown	.95	.20
		Nos. 177-179 (3)	61.15	5.15

See #205, 305. For overprint see #C1.

Elias Lönnrot — A30

Seal of Finnish Literary Society — A31

1931, Jan. 1 — Typo.
180 A30 1m olive brown 2.75 6.00
181 A31 1½m dull blue 14.00 6.00
Centenary of Finnish Literary Society.

A32

1931, Feb. 28
182 A32 1½m red 2.75 10.00
183 A32 2m blue 2.75 11.00
1st use of postage stamps in Finland, 75th anniv.

Nos. 162-163 Surcharged

1931, Dec.
195 A26 50p on 40p blue grn 1.40 .60
196 A26 1.25m on 50p yellow 4.25 1.75

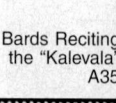
Svinhufvud A33
Alexis Kivi A34

1931, Dec. 15
197 A33 2m gray blue & blk 1.50 3.50
Pres. Pehr Eyvind Svinhufvud, 70th birthday.

Lake Saima Type of 1930
1932-43 — Re-engraved
205 A28 10m red violet ('43) .35 .20
a. 10m dark violet 21.00 .75
On Nos. 205 and 205a the lines of the islands, the clouds and the foliage are much deeper and stronger than on No. 178.

1934, Oct. 10 — Typo.
206 A34 2m red violet 2.25 2.25
Never hinged 5.00
Alexis Kivi, Finnish poet (1834-1872).

Bards Reciting the "Kalevala" A35

Goddess Louhi, As Eagle Seizing Magic Mill — A36

Kullervo — A37

1935, Feb. 28 — Engr.
207 A35 1¼m brown lake 1.25 1.25
208 A36 2m black 3.50 1.50
209 A37 2½m blue 3.00 2.25
Nos. 207-209 (3) 7.75 5.00
Set, never hinged 17.00
Cent. of the publication of the "Kalevala" (Finnish National Epic).

No. 170 Surcharged in Black

1937, Feb.
212 A26 2m on 1½m car 4.75 .90
Never hinged 10.00

Gustaf Mannerheim — A38

Swede-Finn Co-operation in Colonization A39

1937, June 4 — Photo. — Perf. 14
213 A38 2m ultra .60 1.25
Never hinged 1.50
70th birthday of Field Marshal Baron Carl Gustaf Mannerheim, June 4th, 1937.

1938, June 1
214 A39 3½m dark brown 1.25 3.25
Never hinged 2.75
Tercentenary of the colonization of Delaware by Swedes and Finns.

Early Post Office — A40
Designs: 1¼m, Mail delivery in 1700. 2m, Modern mail plane. 3½m, Helsinki post office.

1938, Sept. 6 — Photo. — Perf. 14
215 A40 50p green .35 .75
216 A40 1¼m dk blue 1.25 3.50
217 A40 2m scarlet 1.25 1.25
218 A40 3½m slate black 3.75 7.00
Nos. 215-218 (4) 6.60 12.50
Set, never hinged 10.00
300th anniv. of the Finnish Postal System. Margin strips of each denomination (3 of #215, 2 each of #216, 217, 218) were pasted on to advertising sheets and stapled into a booklet. Value, $110.

Post Office, Helsinki — A44

1939-42 — Photo.
219 A44 4m brown black .20 .20
— Engr.
219A A44 7m black brn ('42) .35 .20
219B A44 9m rose lake ('42) .35 .20
Nos. 219-219B (3) .90 .60
Set, never hinged 2.75
See No. 248.

Catalogue values for unused stamps in this section, from this point to the end of the section, are for Never Hinged items.

University of Helsinki — A45

1940, May 1 — Photo.
220 A45 2m dp blue & blue .60 1.00
300th anniv. of the founding of the University of Helsinki.

Nos. 168 and 173 Surcharged in Black

1940, June 16 — Typo.
221 A26 1.75m on 1.25m yel 1.90 1.90
222 A26 2.75m on 2m carmine 6.00 .70

President Kallio Reviewing Military Band — A46

1941, May 24 — Engr.
223 A46 2.75m black .60 .90
Pres. Kyösti Kallio (1873-1940).

Castle at Viborg — A47

1941, Aug. 30 — Typo.
224 A47 1.75m yellow orange .60 .85
225 A47 2.75m rose violet .60 .85
226 A47 3.50m blue .90 1.75

Field Marshal Mannerheim A48

Pres. Risto Ryti A49

1941, Dec. 31 — Engr. — Wmk. 273
227 A48 50p dull green 1.10 1.50
228 A48 1.75m deep brown 1.10 1.50
229 A48 2m dark red 1.10 1.50
230 A48 2.75m dull vio brn 1.10 1.50
231 A48 3.50m deep blue 1.10 1.50
232 A48 5m slate blue 1.10 1.50
Nos. 227-232 (6) 6.60 9.00
233 A49 50p dull green 1.10 1.50
234 A49 1.75m deep brown 1.10 1.50
235 A49 2m dark red 1.10 1.50
236 A49 2.75m dull vio brn 1.10 1.50
237 A49 3.50m deep blue 1.10 1.50
238 A49 5m slate blue 1.10 1.50
Nos. 233-238 (6) 6.60 9.00
Types A48-A49 overprinted "ITA KARJALA" are listed under Karelia, Nos. N16-N27.

Häme Bridge, Tampere A50

South Harbor, Helsinki — A51

1942 — Unwmk.
239 A50 50m dull brown vio 3.00 .20
240 A51 100m indigo 4.00 .20
See No. 350.

Altar and Open Bible — A52
17th Century Printer — A53

1942, Oct. 10
241 A52 2.75m dk brown .50 1.10
242 A53 3.50m violet blue .90 1.75
300th anniv. of the printing of the 1st Bible in Finnish.

No. 174B Surcharged in Black

1943, Feb. 1
243 A26 3.50m on 2.75m rose vio .35 .35

Minna Canth (1844-96), Author and Playwright — A54

1944, Mar. 20
244 A54 3.50m dk olive grn .60 1.00

Pres. P. E. Svinhufvud A55
K. J. Stahlberg A56

1944, Aug. 1
245 A55 3.50m black .40 1.00
Death of President Svinhufvud (1861-1944).

1945, May 16 — Engr. — Perf. 14
246 A56 3.50m brown vio .35 .60
80th birthday of Dr. K. J. Stahlberg.

Castle in Savonlinna A57

Jean Sibelius — A58

1945, Sept. 4
247 A57 15m lilac rose 1.75 .20
248 A44 20m sepia 1.75 .20

For a 35m of type A57, see No. 280.

1945, Dec. 8
249 A58 5m dk slate green .40 .40

Jean Sibelius (1865-1957), composer.

No. 176E Surcharged with New Value and Bars in Black

1946, Mar. 16
250 A26 8(m) on 5m purple .45 .20

Victorious Athletes — A59 | Lighthouse at Uto — A60

1946, June 1   Engr.   Perf. 13½
251 A59 8m brown violet .35 .60

3rd Sports Festival, Helsinki, June 27-30, 1946.

1946, Sept. 19
252 A60 8m deep violet .45 .60

250th anniv. of the Finnish Department of Pilots and Lighthouses.

Post Bus — A61

1946-47   Unwmk.   Perf. 14
253 A61 16m gray black .75 .75
253A A61 30m gray black ('47) 2.25 .20

Issue dates: 16m, Oct. 16, 30m, Feb. 10.

Old Town Hall, Porvoo — A62

Cathedral, Porvoo — A63

1946, Dec. 3
254 A62 5m gray black .35 .60
255 A63 8m deep claret .45 .60

600th anniv. of the founding of the city of Porvoo (Borga).

Waterfront, Tammisaari A64

1946, Dec. 14
256 A64 8m grnsh black .35 .60

400th anniv. of the founding of the town of Tammisaari (Ekenas).

Lion Type of 1930

1947   Typo.   Perf. 14
257 A26 2½m dark green .35 .20
258 A26 3m slate gray .35 .20
259 A26 6m deep orange 1.75 .50
260 A26 7m carmine .80 .20

261 A26 10m purple 3.25 .20
262 A26 12m deep blue 2.50 .20
Nos. 257-262 (6) 9.00 1.50

Issued: 3m, 6/9; 7m, 12m, 2/10; others, 1/20.

Pres. Juho K. Paasikivi — A65 | Postal Savings Emblem — A66

1947, Mar. 15   Engr.
263 A65 10m gray black .35 .50

1947, Apr. 1
264 A66 10m brown violet .35 .50

60th anniv. of the foundation of the Finnish Postal Savings Bank.

Ilmarinen, the Plowman A67 | Girl and Boy Athletes A68

1947, June 2
265 A67 10m gray black .35 .50

2nd year of peace following WW II.

1947, June 2
266 A68 10m bright blue .35 .50

Finnish Athletic Festival, Helsinki, June 29-July 3, 1947.

Wheat and Savings Bank Assoc. Emblem — A69 | Sower — A70

1947, Aug. 21
267 A69 10m red brown .35 .75

Finnish Savings Bank Assoc., 125th anniv.

1947, Nov. 1
268 A70 10m gray black .35 .60

150th anniv. of Finnish Agricultural Societies.

Koli Mountain and Lake Pielisjärvi A71

Statue of Michael Agricola — A72

1947, Nov. 1
269 A71 10m indigo .35 .60

60th anniv. of the Finnish Touring Assoc.

Lion Type of 1930

1948   Typo.   Perf. 14
270 A26 3m dark green 3.00 .20
271 A26 6m yellow green 1.25 .65
272 A26 9m carmine 1.10 .20
273 A26 15m dark blue 4.50 .20
274 A26 24m brown lake 1.40 .20
Nos. 270-274 (5) 11.25 1.45

Issued: 3m, 2/9; 24m, 4/26; others, 9/13.

No. 261 Surcharged with New Value and Bars in Black

1948, Feb. 9
275 A26 12(m) on 10m purple 1.10 .20

1948, Oct. 2   Engr.   Perf. 14

12m, Agricola translating New Testament.

276 A72 7m rose violet 1.00 1.75
277 A72 12m gray blue 1.00 1.75

400th anniv. of publication of the Finnish translation of the New Testament, by Michael Agricola.

Sveaborg Fortress A73

Post Rider — A74

1948, Oct. 15
278 A73 12m deep green 1.40 2.25

200th anniv. of the construction of Sveaborg Fortress on the Gulf of Finland.

1948, Oct. 27
279 A74 12m green 9.00 20.00

Helsinki Philatelic Exhibition. Sold only at exhibition for 62m, of which 50m was entrance fee.

Castle Type of 1945

1949
280 A57 35m violet 8.00 .20

Sawmill and Cellulose Plant — A75

Pine Tree and Globe — A76

Woman with Torch — A77

1949, June 15
281 A75 9m brown 2.75 3.25
282 A76 15m dull green 2.75 3.25

Issued to publicize the Third World Forestry Congress, Helsinki, July 10-20, 1949.

1949, July 16   Engr.   Perf. 14
283 A77 5m dull green 5.00 9.00
284 A77 15m red (Worker) 5.00 9.00

50th anniv. of the Finnish labor movement.

Harbor of Lappeenranta (Willmanstrand) — A78

Raahe (Brahestad) — A79

1949
285 A78 5m dk blue grn .75 .70
286 A79 9m brown carmine .95 .95
287 A78 15m brt blue (Kristiinan-kaupunki) 1.75 2.50
Nos. 285-287 (3) 3.45 4.15

300th anniv. of the founding of Willmanstrand, Brahestad and Kristinestad (Kristiinan-kaupunki).

Issued: 5m, 8/6; 9m, 8/13; 15m, 7/30.

Technical High School Badge — A80 | Hannes Gebhard — A81

1949, Sept. 13
288 A80 15m ultra .95 1.00

Founding of the technical school, cent.

1949, Oct. 2
289 A81 15m dull green .95 1.00

Establishment of Finnish cooperatives, 50th anniv.

Finnish Lake Country — A82

1949, Oct. 8
290 A82 15m blue 1.25 1.10

75th anniv. of the UPU.

Lion Type of 1930

1950, Jan. 9   Typo.   Perf. 14
291 A26 8m brt green 3.00 3.00
292 A26 9m red orange 2.10 .50
293 A26 10m violet brown 7.25 .20
294 A26 12m scarlet 1.40 .20
295 A26 15m plum 17.00 .20
296 A26 20m deep blue 8.50 .20
Nos. 291-296 (6) 39.25 4.30

Forsell's Map of Old Helsinki — A83

J. A. Ehrenstrom and C. L. Engel — A84

City Hall — A85

1950, June 11   **Engr.**
297 A83   5m emerald   .50   *.70*
298 A84   9m brown   .75   *1.00*
299 A85   15m deep blue   .60   *.75*
    Nos. 297-299 (3)   1.85 2.45

400th anniv. of the founding of Helsinki.

J. K. Paasikivi — A86   View of Kajaani — A87

1950, Nov. 27
300 A86   20m deep ultra   .60 .35

80th birthday of Pres. J. K. Paasikivi.

1951, July 7   **Unwmk.**   *Perf. 14*
301 A87   20m red brown   .60 .50

Tercentenary of Kajaani.

Lion and Chopper Types of 1930
1952, Jan. 18   **Typo.**
302 A26   10m emerald   4.00   .20
303 A26   15m red   4.25   .20
304 A26   25m blue   4.25   .20
             Engr.
305 A29   40m black brown   4.25   .20
    Nos. 302-305 (4)   16.75   .80

Arms of Pietarsaari A88   Rooftops of Vaasa A89

1952, June 19   **Unwmk.**   *Perf. 14*
306 A88   25m blue   .90 .90

300th anniv. of the founding of Pietarsaari (Jacobstad).

1952, Aug. 3
307 A89   25m brown   .90 .90

Centenary of the burning of Vaasa.

Chess Symbols — A90   Torch Bearers — A91

1952, Aug. 10
308 A90   25m gray   2.00 *2.25*

10th Chess Olympics, Helsinki, 8/10-31/52.

1953, Jan. 27
309 A91   25m blue   1.10 1.00

Temperance movement in Finland, cent.

Air View of Hamina (Fredrikshamn) A92

Ivar Wilskman — A93

1953, June 20
310 A92   25m dk gray green   .90 .80

Tercentenary of Hamina.

1954, Feb. 26
311 A93   25m blue   .80 .80

Centenary of the birth of Prof. Ivar Wilskman, "father of gymnastics in Finland."

Arms of Finland A94   "In the Outer Archipelago" A95

1954-59   *Perf. 11½*
312   A94   1m red brown ('55)   .50   .20
313   A94   2m green ('55)   .50   .20
314   A94   3m deep orange   .50   .20
314A   A94   4m gray ('58)   .45   .20
315   A94   5m violet blue   .85   .20
316   A94   10m blue green   1.25   .20
   a.   Bklt. pane of 5 (vert. strip)   22.50 22.50
       Complete booklet, #316a   25.00
317   A94   15m rose red   3.75   .20
318   A94   15m yellow org ('57)   20.00   .20
319   A94   20m rose lilac   12.00   .20
320   A94   20m rose red ('56)   2.75   .20
321   A94   25m deep blue   4.00   .20
322   A94   25m rose lilac ('59)   13.00   .20
323   A94   30m lt ultra ('56)   2.75   .20
    Nos. 312-323 (13)   50.80 2.60

See Nos. 398, 400-405A, 457-459, 461A-462, 464-464B.

1954, July 21   *Perf. 14*
324 A95   25m black   .75 .60

Cent. of the birth of Albert Edelfelt, painter.

J. J. Nervander A96

1955, Feb. 23
325 A96   25m blue   .90 .70

150th anniv. of the birth of J. J. Nervander, astronomer and poet.

Composite of Finnish Public Buildings A97   Bishop Henrik with Foot on Lalli, his Murderer A98

1955, Mar. 30   **Engr.**   *Perf. 14*
326 A97   25m gray   12.50 *15.00*

Sold for 125m, which included the price of admission to the Natl. Postage Stamp Exhibition, Helsinki, Mar. 30-Apr. 3, 1955.

1955, May 19

25m, Arrival of Bishop Henrik and monks.
327 A98   15m rose brown   1.00 .75
328 A98   25m green   1.00 .75

Adoption of Christianity in Finland, 800th anniv.

Conference Hall, Helsinki — A99

1955, Aug. 25
329 A99   25m bluish green   1.25 *1.40*

44th conf. of the Interparliamentarian Union, Helsinki, Aug. 25-31, 1955.

Sailing Vessel and Merchant A100

1955, Sept. 2
330 A100   25m sepia   1.50 1.50

350th anniv. of founding of Oulu.

Town Hall, Lahti — A101   Radio Sender, Map of Finland — A102

1955, Nov. 1   *Perf. 14x13½*
331 A101   25m violet blue   1.25 1.25

50th anniversary of founding of Lahti.

1955, Dec. 10   *Perf. 14*

Designs: 15m, Otto Nyberg. 25m, Telegraph wires and pines under snow.

Inscribed: Lennatin 1855-1955 Telegrafen
332 A102   10m green   1.50 1.50
333 A102   15m dull violet   1.50 1.50
334 A102   25m lt ultra   1.50 1.50
    Nos. 332-334 (3)   4.50 4.50

Cent. of the telegraph in Finland.

A103

A104

1956, Jan. 26   **Unwmk.**   *Perf. 14*
335 A103   25m Lighthouse, Porkkala Peninsula   .80 .60

Return of the Porkkala Region to Finland by Russia, Jan. 1956.

1956-57   *Perf. 11½*

30m, 50m, Church at Lammi. 40m, House of Parliament. 60m, Fortress of Olavinlinna (Olofsborg).

336   A104   30m gray olive   1.25   .20
337   A104   40m dull purple   3.00   .20
338   A104   50m gray ol ('57)   7.50   .20
338A   A104   60m pale pur ('57)   13.00   .20
    Nos. 336-338A (4)   24.75   .80

Issued: 30m, 3/4; 40m, 3/11; 50m, 3/3; 60m, 4/7. See Nos. 406-408A.

Johan V. Snellman A105   Gymnast and Athletes A106

1956, May 12   **Engr.**   *Perf. 14*
339 A105   25m dk violet brn   .80 .65

Johan V. Snellman (1806-81), statesman.

1956, June 28
340 A106   30m violet blue   1.00 .70

Finnish Gymnastic and Sports Games, Helsinki, June 28-July 1, 1956.

A107

Wmk. 208
1956, July 7   **Typo.**   *Rouletted*
341 A107   30m deep ultra   4.00 *6.00*
   a.   Tête bêche pair   8.50 *12.50*
   b.   Pane of 10   42.50 *65.00*

Issued to publicize the FINLANDIA Philatelic Exhibition, Helsinki, July 7-15, 1956.

Printed in sheets containing four 2x5 panes, with white margins around each group. The stamps in each double row are printed tete-beche, making the position of the watermark differ in the vertical row of each pane of ten.

Sold for 155m, price including entrance ticket to exhibition.

Town Hall at Vasa — A108

Unwmk.
1956, Oct. 2   **Engr.**   *Perf. 14*
342 A108   30m bright blue   .85 .60

350th anniversary of Vasa.

Northern Countries Issue

Whooper Swans — A108a

1956, Oct. 30   *Perf. 12½*
343 A108a   20m rose red   2.75 1.25
344 A108a   30m ultra   10.00 1.10

See footnote after Denmark No. 362.

University Clinic, Helsinki A109

Scout Sign, Emblem and Globe — A110

1956, Dec. 17   *Perf. 11½*
345 A109 30m dull green   2.25 .75

Public health service in Finland, bicent.

1957, Feb. 22   *Perf. 14*
346 A110 30m ultra   2.00 .90

50th anniversary of Boy Scouts.

Arms Holding Hammers and Laurel — A111

"Lex" from Seal of Parliament — A112

Design: 20m, Factories and cogwheel.

1957   Engr.   *Perf. 13½*
347 A111 20m dark blue   .90 .55
348 A111 30m carmine   .90 .70

50th anniv.: Central Fed. of Finnish Employers (20m, issued 9/27); Finnish Trade Union Movement (30m, issued 4/15).

1957, May 23   *Perf. 14*
349 A112 30m olive gray   1.00 .60

50th anniv. of the Finnish parliament.

Harbor Type of 1942

1957   Unwmk.   *Perf. 14*
350 A51 100m grnsh blue   15.00 .20

Ida Aalberg — A114

Arms of Finland A115

1957, Dec. 4   *Perf. 14*
351 A114 30m vio gray & mar   .80 .65

Birth cent. of Ida Aalberg, Finnish actress.

1957, Dec. 6   *Perf. 11½*
352 A115 30m blue   .85 .65

40th anniv. of Finland's independence.

Jean Sibelius — A116

Ski Jump — A117

1957, Dec. 8   *Perf. 14*
353 A116 30m black   1.25 .55

Jean Sibelius (1865-1957), composer.

1958, Feb. 1   Engr.   *Perf. 11½*

Design: 30m, Skier, vert.

354 A117 20m slate green   .75 .95
355 A117 30m blue   .85 .55

Nordic championships of the Intl. Ski Federation, Lahti.

"March of the Bjorneborgienses," by Edelfelt — A118

1958, Mar. 8
356 A118 30m violet gray   1.25 .65

400th anniv. of the founding of Pori (Bjorneborg).

South Harbor, Helsinki A119

1958, June 2   Unwmk.   *Perf. 11½*
357 A119 100m bluish green   20.00 .20
See No. 410.

Seal of Jyväskylä Lyceum A120

1958, Oct. 1   *Perf. 11½*
358 A120 30m rose carmine   1.60 .85

Cent. of the founding of the 1st Finnish secondary school.

Chrismon and Globe — A121

Diet at Porvoo, 1809 — A122

1959, Jan. 19
359 A121 30m dull violet   .85 .60

Finnish Missionary Society, cent.

1959, Mar. 22   *Perf. 11½*
360 A122 30m dk blue gray   .85 .60

150th anniv. of the inauguration of the Diet at Porvoo.

Saw Cutting Log — A123

Pyhakoski Power Station — A124

1959, May 13   Engr.
361 A123 10m shown   .60 .60
362 A123 30m Forest   .85 .85

No. 361 for the cent. of the establishment of the 1st steam saw-mill in Finland; No. 362, the cent. of the Dept. of Forestry.

1959, May 24
363 A124 75m gray   4.50 .20
See No. 409.

Oil Lamp — A125

Woman Gymnast A126

1959, Dec. 19
364 A125 30m blue   .85 .50

Cent. of the liberation of the country trade.

1959, Nov. 14   Unwmk.
365 A126 30m rose lilac   .95 .60

Finnish women's gymnastics and the cent. of the birth of Elin Oihonna Kallio, pioneer of Finnish women's physical education.

Arms of Six New Towns — A127

1960, Jan. 2   *Perf. 14*
366 A127 30m light violet   .85 .50

Issued to commemorate the founding of new towns in Finland: Hyvinkaa, Kouvola, Riihimaki, Rovaniemi, Salo and Seinajoki.

Type of 1860 Issue A128

1960, Mar. 25   Typo.   *Rouletted 4½*
367 A128 30m blue & gray   7.50 8.75

Cent. of Finland's serpentine roulette stamps, and in connection with HELSINKI 1960, 40th anniv. exhib. of the Federation of Philatelic Societies of Finland, Mar. 25-31. Sold only at the exhibition for 150m including entrance ticket.

Mother and Child, Waiting Crowd and Uprooted Oak Emblem A129

1960, Apr. 7   Engr.   *Perf. 11½*
368 A129 30m rose claret   .75 .65
369 A129 40m dark blue   .75 .65

World Refugee Year, 7/1/59-6/30/60.

Johan Gadolin A130

Hj. Nortamo A131

1960, June 4   *Perf. 11½*
370 A130 30m dark brown   .80 .80

Bicent. of the birth of Gadolin, chemist.

1960, June 13   Unwmk.
371 A131 30m gray green   .80 .50

Cent. of the birth of Hj. Nortamo (Hjalmar Nordberg), writer.

Symbolic Tree and Cuckoo A132

1960, June 18
372 A132 30m vermilion   .85 .50

Karelian Natl. Festival, Helsinki, June 18-19.

Geodetic Instrument A133

Urho Kekkonen — A134

Design: 30m, Aurora borealis and globe.

1960, July 26   Unwmk.   *Perf. 13½*
373 A133 10m blue & pale brn   .50 .40
374 A133 30m ver & rose car   .85 .50

12th General Assembly of the Intl. Union of Geodesy and Geophysics, Helsinki.

1960, Sept. 3   Engr.   *Perf. 11½*
375 A134 30m violet blue   .90 .50

Issued to honor President Urho Kekkonen on his 60th birthday.

Common Design Types pictured following the introduction.

Europa Issue, 1960
Common Design Type

1960, Sept. 19   *Perf. 13½*
Size: 30½x21mm.

376 CD3 30m dk bl & Prus bl   .60 .60
377 CD3 40m dk brn & plum   .60 .60

A 30m gray similar to No. 376 was printed with simulated perforations in a non-valid souvenir sheet privately released in London for STAMPEX 1961.

Uno Cygnaeus
A135

"Pommern" and Arms
of Mariehamn
A136

1960, Oct. 13   **Perf. 11½**
378 A135 30m dull violet   1.00 .50
150th anniv. of the birth of Pastor Uno Cygnaeus, founder of elementary schools.

1961, Feb. 21   **Perf. 11½**
379 A136 30m grnsh blue   3.25 1.40
Centenary of the founding of Mariehamn.

Lake and
Rowboat
A137

Turku
Castle — A138

1961   **Engr.**   **Unwmk.**
380 A137 5m green   .40 .20
381 A138 125m slate green   19.00 .40
See Nos. 399, 411.

Postal Savings Bank
Emblem — A139

Symbol of Standardization — A140

1961, May 24
382 A139 30m Prus green   .85 .50
75th anniv. of Finland's Postal Savings Bank.

1961, June 5   **Litho.**   **Perf. 14x13½**
383 A140 30m dk sl grn & org   .85 .50
Meeting of the Intl. Organization for Standardization (ISO), Helsinki, June 5.

Juhani Aho
A141

Various
Buildings
A142

Perf. 11½
1961, Sept. 11   **Unwmk.**   **Engr.**
384 A141 30m red brown   .85 .50
Juhani Aho (1861-1921), writer.

1961, Oct. 16   **Perf. 11½**
385 A142 30m slate   .85 .50
150 years of the Central Board of Buildings.

Arvid Jarnefelt
A143

1961, Nov. 16
386 A143 30m deep claret   .85 .50
Cent. of the birth of Arvid Jarnefelt, writer.

Bank of
Finland — A144

First Finnish
Locomotive — A145

1961, Dec. 12   **Engr.**   **Perf. 11½**
387 A144 30m brown violet   .85 .50
150th anniversary of Bank of Finland.

1962, Jan. 31   **Unwmk.**   **Perf. 11½**
30m, Steam locomotive & timber car. 40m, Diesel locomotive & passenger train.
388 A145 10m gray green   1.50 .65
389 A145 30m violet blue   2.25 .65
390 A145 40m dull red brown   5.25 .90
Nos. 388-390 (3)   9.00 2.20
Centenary of the Finnish State Railways.

Mora
Stone — A146

1962, Feb. 15
391 A146 30m gray brown   .85 .50
Issued to commemorate 600 years of political rights of the Finnish people.

Senate Place,
Helsinki
A147

1962, Apr. 8   **Unwmk.**   **Perf. 11½**
392 A147 30m violet brown   .85 .50
Sesquicentennial of the proclamation of Helsinki as capital of Finland.

Customs
Emblem
A148

Staff of
Mercury — A149

1962, Apr. 11
393 A148 30m red   .85 .50
Finnish Board of Customs, sesquicentennial.

1962, May 21   **Engr.**
394 A149 30m bluish green   .85 .50
Cent. of the 1st commercial bank in Finland.

Santeri
Alkio — A150

Finnish Labor
Emblem and
Conveyor
Belt — A151

1962, June 17   **Unwmk.**   **Perf. 11½**
395 A150 30m brown carmine   .85 .50
Cent. of the birth of Santeri Alkio, writer and pioneer of the young people's societies in Finland.

1962, Oct. 19
396 A151 30m chocolate   .85 .50
National production progress.

Survey Plane and
Compass — A152

1962, Nov. 14
397 A152 30m yellow green   1.00 .60
Finnish Land Survey Board, 150th anniv.

Types of 1954-61 and

House of
Parliament —
A152a

Church at
Lammi —
A152b

Fortress of
Olavinlinna —
A152c

Log Floating
A153

Parainen
Bridge — A154

Farm on Lake
Shore — A155

Aerial View of
Punkaharju —
A155a

Ristikallio in
Kuusamo
A156

1963-67   **Engr.**   **Perf. 11½**
398 A94 5p violet blue   .40 .20
 a. Booklet pane of 2 (vert. pair)   22.50 20.00
 b. Bklt. pane of 2 (horiz. pair)   12.00 10.00
399 A137 5p green   .30 .20
400 A94 10p blue green   .45 .20
 a. Booklet pane of 2 (vert. pair)   22.50 20.00
401 A94 15p yellow org   1.10 .20
402 A94 20p rose red   .70 .20
 a. Booklet pane of 2 (vert. pair)   24.00
   Complete booklet, #398a, 400a, 402a   75.00
 b. Bklt. pane, 2 #400, 1 #402 + label; horiz. strip   45.00 35.00
   Complete booklet, #398b, 402b   97.50
 c. Bklt. pane, 2 #398, 2 #400, 1 #402; horiz. strip   3.50 3.50
   Complete booklet, #402c   4.50
403 A94 25p rose lilac   1.10 .20
404 A94 30p lt ultra   6.00 .20
404A A94 30p blue gray ('65)   .70 .20
405 A94 35p blue   1.10 .20
405A A94 40p ultra ('67)   1.50 .20
406 A152a 40p dull purple   3.50 .20
407 A152b 50p gray olive   5.00 .20
408 A152c 60p pale purple   8.50 .20
408A A152c 65p pale pur ('67)   1.10 .20
409 A124 75p gray   1.75 .20
410 A119 1m bluish grn   .50 .20
411 A138 1.25m slate grn   1.60 .20
412 A153 1.50m dk grnsh gray   1.60 .20
413 A154 1.75m blue   1.50 .20
414 A155 2m green ('64)   14.00 .20
414A A155a 2.50m ultra & yel grn ('67)   7.00 .20
415 A156 5m dk slate grn ('64)   17.00 .30
Nos. 398-415 (22)   76.40 4.50

Pennia denominations expressed: "0.05," "0.10," etc.
Four stamps of type A94 (5p, 10p, 20p, 25p) come in two types: I. Four vertical lines in "O" of SUOMI. II. Three lines in "O."
For similar designs see #457-470A.

Mother and
Child — A157

1963, Mar. 21   **Unwmk.**   **Perf. 11½**
416 A157 40p red brown   .70 .45
FAO "Freedom from Hunger" campaign.

"Christ
Today" — A158

Design: 10p, Crown of thorns and medieval cross of consecration.

1963, July 30   **Engr.**   **Perf. 11½**
417 A158 10p maroon   .50 .45
418 A158 30p dark green   .75 .60
4th assembly of the Lutheran World Federation, Helsinki, July 30-Aug. 8.

Europa Issue, 1963
Common Design Type
1963, Sept. 16
Size: 30x20mm
419 CD6 40p red lilac   1.60 .50

Assembly
Building,
Helsinki
A159

1963, Sept. 18
420 A159 30p violet blue .80 .40
Representative Assembly of Finland, cent.

Convair Metropolitan
A160
M. A. Castrén
A161

Design: 40p, Caravelle jetliner.

1963, Nov. 1
421 A160 35p slate green 1.00 .45
422 A160 40p brt ultra 1.00 .45
40th anniversary of Finnish air traffic.

1963, Dec. 2 Unwmk.
423 A161 35p violet blue .90 .40
Matthias Alexander Castrén (1813-52), ethnologist and philologist.

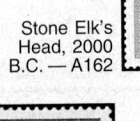
Stone Elk's
Head, 2000
B.C. — A162

Emil Nestor
Setälä — A163

1964, Feb. 5 Litho. Perf. 11½
424 A162 35p ocher & slate grn .90 .40
Cent. of the Finnish Artists' Association. The soapstone sculpture was found at Huittinen.

1964, Feb. 27 Engr.
425 A163 35p dk red brown .90 .40
Emil Nestor Setälä (1864-1946), philologist, minister of education and foreign affairs and chancellor of Abo University.

Staff of
Aesculapius
A164

1964, June 13 Unwmk. Perf. 11½
426 A164 40p slate green 1.25 .50
18th General Assembly of the World Medical Association, Helsinki, June 13-19, 1964.

Ice
Hockey — A165

1965, Jan. 4 Engr.
427 A165 35p dark blue .85 .40
World Ice Hockey Championships, Finland, March 3-14, 1965.

Design from
Centenary
Medal — A166

1965, Feb. 6 Unwmk. Perf. 11½
428 A166 35p olive gray .85 .40
Centenary of communal self-government in Finland.

K. J. Stahlberg
and "Lex" by
W. Runeberg
A167

1965, Mar. 22 Engr.
429 A167 35p brown .85 .40
Kaarlo Juho Stahlberg (1865-1952), 1st Pres. of Finland.

International
Cooperation
Year Emblem
A168

1965, Apr. 2 Litho. Perf. 14
430 A168 40p bis, dull red, blk & grn .85 .40
UN International Cooperation Year.

"Fratricide" by Gallen-Kallela
A169

Sibelius, Piano
and
Score — A170

35p, Girl's Head by Akseli Gallen-Kallela.

1965, Apr. 26 Perf. 13½x14
431 A169 25p multicolored 1.25 .45
432 A169 35p multicolored 1.25 .45
Centenary of the birth of the painter Aksell Gallen-Kallela.

1965, May 15 Engr. Perf. 11½
Design: 35p, Musical score and bird.
433 A170 35p violet .85 .45
434 A170 35p dull green .85 .45
Jean Sibelius (1865-1957), composer.

Antenna for Satellite
Telecommunication — A171

"Winter Day" by
Pekka
Halonen — A172

1965, May 17
435 A171 35p blue .80 .40
Cent. of the ITU.

Perf. 14x13½
1965, Sept. 23 Litho. Unwmk.
436 A172 35p gold & multi .90 .45
Centenary of the birth of the painter Pekka Halonen.

Europa Issue, 1965
Common Design Type
Engraved and Lithographed
1965, Sept. 27 Perf. 13½x14
437 CD8 40p bister, red brn, dk bl & grn 1.10 .40

"Growth" — A173

Old Post
Office — A174

1966, May 11 Litho. Perf. 14
438 A173 35p vio blue & blue .80 .40
Centenary of the promulgation of the Elementary School Decree.

1966, June 11 Litho. Perf. 14
439 A174 35p ocher, yel, dk bl & blk 7.00 8.00
Cent. of the 1st postage stamps in Finnish currency, and in connection with the NORDIA Stamp Exhibition, Helsinki, June 11-15. The stamp was sold only to buyers of a 1.25m exhibition entrance ticket.

UNESCO
Emblem and
World
Map — A175

Finnish Police
Emblem — A176

Lithographed and Engraved
1966, Oct. 9 Perf. 14
440 A175 40p grn, yel, blk & brn org .80 .40
20th anniv. of UNESCO.

1966, Oct. 15
441 A176 35p dp ultra, blk & sil .80 .40
Issued to honor the Finnish police.

Insurance Sesquicentennial
Medal — A177

1966, Oct. 28 Engr. & Photo.
442 A177 35p maroon, olive & blk .80 .40
150th anniv. of the Finnish insurance system.

UNICEF
Emblem
A178

1966, Nov. 14
443 A178 15p lt ultra, pur & grn .40 .30
Activities of UNICEF.

"FINEFTA,"
Finnish Flag
and
Circle — A179

1967, Feb. 15 Engr. Perf. 14
444 A179 40p ultra 1.00 .30
European Free Trade Association, EFTA. See note after Denmark No. 431.

Windmill and
Arms of
Uusikaupunki
A180
Mannerheim
Monument by
Aimo Tukiainen
A181

Lithographed and Engraved
1967, Apr. 19 Perf. 14
445 A180 40p multicolored .80 .40
350th anniv. of Uusikaupunki (Nystad).

1967, June 4 Perf. 14
446 A181 40p violet & multi .80 .40
Cent. of the birth of Field Marshal Carl Gustav Emil Mannerheim.

Double Mortise
Corner — A182

Watermark of
Thomasböle Paper
Mill — A183

1967, June 16 Litho. & Photo.
447 A182 40p multicolored .70 .35
Issued to honor Finnish settlers in Sweden.

1967, Sept. 6 Perf. 14
448 A183 40p olive & black .70 .35
300th anniv. of the Finnish paper industry.

Martin Luther, by Lucas Cranach A184

Photogravure and Engraved
1967, Nov. 4   *Perf. 14*
449 A184 40p bister & brown   .70 .35
450th anniversary of the Reformation.

"Wood and Water" Globe and Flag — A185

Designs (Globe, Flag and): 25p, Flying swan. 40p, Ear of wheat.

1967, Dec. 5   *Perf. 11½*
450 A185 20p green & blue   .85 .35
451 A185 25p ultra & blue   .85 .35
452 A185 40p magenta & bl   .85 .35
     Nos. 450-452 (3)   2.55 1.05
50th anniv. of Finland's independence.

Zachris Topelius and Blue Bird — A186

1968, Jan. 14   *Litho.*   *Perf. 14*
453 A186 25p blue & multi   .70 .35
Topelius (1818-98), writer and educator.

Skiers and Ski Lift — A187

1968, Feb. 19   *Photo.*   *Perf. 14*
454 A187 25p multicolored   .70 .35
Winter Tourism in Finland.

Paper Making, by Hannes Autere — A188

1968, Mar. 12   *Litho.*   *Wmk. 363*
455 A188 45p dk red, brn & org   .70 .35
Finnish paper industry and 150th anniv. of the oldest Finnish paper mill, Tervakoski, whose own watermark was used for this stamp.

World Health Organization Emblem A189

Lithographed and Photogravure
1968, Apr. 6   *Unwmk.*   *Perf. 14*
456 A189 40p red org, dk blue & gold   .70 .35
To honor World Health Organization.

Lion Type of 1954-58 and

Market Place and Mermaid Fountain, Helsinki A190

Keuru Wooden Church, 1758 — A191

Häme Bridge, Tampere A192

Finnish Arms from Grave of King Gustav Vasa, 1581 — A194

25p, Post bus. 30p, Aquarium-Planetarium, Tampere. No. 463, P.O., Tampere. #465, National Museum, Helsinki, vert. #467A, like 70p. 1.30m, Helsinki railroad station.

Engr. (type A94, except #459A);
Litho. (#459A, 465 & type A190);
Engr. & Litho. (others)
Perf. 11½; 12½ (type A190); 14
(#465, 470A); 13½ (#470)
1968-78
457 A94 1p lt red brn   .40 .20
458 A94 2p gray green   .40 .20
459 A94 4p gray   .40 .20
459A A94 5p violet blue   .40 .20
460 A192 25p multi ('71)   .40 .20
461 A191 30p multi ('71)   1.25 .20
461A A94 35p dull org ('74)   .40 .20
  b. Bklt. pane of 4, #459A,
      461A, 400, 464A + label 2.50 2.50
      Complete booklet, #461b 3.00
462 A94 40p orange ('73)   .80 .20
  a. Bklt. pane of 3, #462, 2
      #404A + 2 labels   5.50 5.50
      Complete booklet, #462a 7.00
463 A192 40p multi ('73)   1.00 .20
464 A94 50p lt ultra ('70) 2.25 .20
  c. Bklt. pane of 5, #401, 403,
      464, 2 #459A + 5 labels 11.00 10.50
      Complete booklet, #464c 12.00
464A A94 50p rose lake
          ('74)   .80 .20
  d. Bklt. pane of 4, #400, 464A,
      2 #402 + label   1.75 1.75
      Complete booklet, #464Ad 2.00
464B A94 60p blue ('73)   .70 .20
465 A191 60p multi ('73)   .75 .20
466 A190 70p multi ('73)   .90 .20
467 A191 80p multi ('70)   5.00 .20
467A A190 80p multi ('76)   .45 .20
468 A192 90p multicolored   2.00 .20
469 A191 1.30m multi ('71)   1.00 .20
470 A194 10m multi ('74)   5.00 .50
470A A194 20m multi ('78)   10.00 .85
     Nos. 457-470A (20)   34.30 4.95
     Issued: 5p, 6/72.

Infantry Monument, Vaasa — A195

Camping Ground A196

Designs: 25p, War Memorial (cross), Hietaniemi Cemetery. 40p, Soldier, 1968.

1968, June 4   *Photo.*   *Perf. 14*
471 A195 20p lt violet & multi   .80 .35
472 A195 25p lt blue & multi   .80 .35
473 A195 40p orange & multi   .80 .35
     Nos. 471-473 (3)   2.40 1.05
To honor Finnish national defense.

1968, June 10   *Litho.*
474 A196 25p multicolored   .70 .35
Issued to publicize Finland for summer vacations.

Paper, Pulp and Pine — A197

Mustola Lock, Saima Canal — A198

Lithographed and Embossed
1968, July 2   *Unwmk.*   *Perf. 14*
475 A197 40p multicolored   .70 .35
Finnish wood industry.

1968, Aug. 5   *Litho.*   *Perf. 14*
476 A198 40p multicolored   .70 .35
Opening of the Saima Canal.

Oskar Merikanto and Pipe Organ — A199

1968, Aug. 5   *Unwmk.*
477 A199 40p vio, silver & lt brn .70 .35
Centenary of the birth of Oskar Merikanto, composer.

Ships in Harbor and Emblem of Central Chamber of Commerce A200

Welder — A201

1968, Sept. 13   *Litho.*   *Perf. 14*
478 A200 40p lt bl, brt bl & blk   .70 .35
Publicizing economic development and for the 50th anniv. of the Central Chamber of Commerce of Finland.

1968, Oct. 11   *Litho.*   *Perf. 14*
479 A201 40p blue & multi   .70 .35
Finnish metal industry.

Lyre, Students' Emblem — A202

Five Ancient Ships — A203

Lithographed and Engraved
1968, Nov. 24   *Perf. 14*
480 A202 40p ultra, vio bl & gold .70 .35
Issued to publicize the work of the student unions in Finnish social life.

Nordic Cooperation Issue
1969, Feb. 28   *Engr.*   *Perf. 11½*
481 A203 40p lt ultra   2.00 .40
See footnote after Denmark No. 455.

Town Hall and Arms of Kemi — A203a

1969, Mar. 5   *Photo.*   *Perf. 14*
482 A203a 40p multicolored   .70 .35
Centenary of the town of Kemi.

Europa Issue, 1969
Common Design Type
1969, Apr. 28   *Photo.*   *Perf. 14*
Size: 30x20mm
483 CD12 40p dl rose, vio bl & dk bl   3.75 1.00

ILO Emblem A204

Armas Järnefelt — A205

Lithographed and Engraved
1969, June 2   *Perf. 11½*
484 A204 40p dp rose & vio blue .70 .35
50th anniv. of the ILO.

1969, Aug. 14   *Photo.*   *Perf. 14*
485 A205 40p multicolored   .70 .35
Järnefelt (1869-1958), composer and conductor. Portrait on stamp by Vilho Sjöström.

Emblems and Flag — A206

Johannes Linnankoski — A207

1969, Sept. 19   Photo.   Perf. 14
486 A206 40p lt bl, blk, grn & lil   .70 .35

Publicizinge the importance of National and International Fairs in Finnish economy.

1969, Oct. 18   Litho.
487 A207 40p dk brn red & multi   .70 .35

Linnankoski (1869-1913), writer.

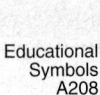

Educational Symbols A208

Lithographed and Engraved
1969, Nov. 24   Perf. 11½
488 A208 40p gray, vio & grn   .70 .35

Centenary of the Central School Board.

DC-8-62 CF Plane and Helsinki Airport — A209

1969, Dec. 22   Photo.   Perf. 14
489 A209 25p sky blue & multi   1.00 .40

Golden Eagle — A210

1970, Feb. 10   Litho.   Perf. 14
490 A210 30p multicolored   3.00 .75

Year of Nature Conservation, 1970.

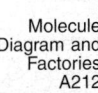

Swatches in Shape of Factories A211

1970, Mar. 9   Litho.   Perf. 14
491 A211 50p multicolored   .75 .35

Finnish textile industry.

Molecule Diagram and Factories A212

UNESCO Emblem and Lenin — A213

Atom Diagram and Laurel — A214

UN Emblem and Globe — A215

1970, Mar. 26   Photo.   Perf. 14
492 A212 50p multicolored   .75 .35

Finnish chemical industry.

1970   Litho. and Engr.
493 A213 30p gold & multi   .75 .30
494 A214 30p red & multi   .75 .30

Photogravure and Gold Embossed
495 A215 50p bl, vio bl & gold   .75 .30
         Nos. 493-495 (3)   2.25 .90

25th anniv. of the UN. No. 493 also publicizes the UNESCO-sponsored Lenin Symposium, Tampere, Apr. 6-10. No. 494 also publicizes the Nuclear Data Conf. of the Atomic Energy Commission, Otaniemi (Helsinki), June 15-19.
Issued: #493, 4/6; #494, 6/15; #495, 10/24.

Handicapped Volleyball Player — A216

Meeting of Auroraseura Society — A217

1970, June 27   Litho.   Perf. 14
496 A216 50p orange, red & blk   .80 .35

Issued to publicize the position of handicapped civilians and war veterans in society and their potential contributions to it.

1970, Aug. 15   Photo.   Perf. 14
497 A217 50p multicolored   .70 .35

200th anniv. of the Auroraseura Soc., dedicated to the study of Finnish history, geography, economy and language. The design of the stamp is after a painting by Eero Jarnefelt.

Uusikaarlepyy Arms, Church and 17th Cent. Building A218

Design: No. 499, Arms of Kokkola, harbor, Sports Palace and 17th century building.

1970   Perf. 14
498 A218 50p multicolored   .75 .35
499 A218 50p multicolored   .75 .35

Towns of Uusikaarlepyy and Kokkola, 350th anniv.
Issued: #498, Aug. 21; #499, Sept. 17.

Urho Kekkonen, Medal by Aimo Tukiainen — A219

1970, Sept. 3   Litho. & Engr.
500 A219 50p ultra, sil & blk   .80 .35

70th birthday of Pres. Urho Kekkonen.

Globe, Maps of US, Finland, USSR A220

Pres. Paasikivi by Essi Renavall A221

Lithographed and Gold Embossed
1970, Nov. 2
501 A220 50p blk, bl, pink & gold   .75 .35

Strategic Arms Limitation Talks (SALT) between the US & USSR, Helsinki, 11/2-12/18.

1970, Nov. 27   Photo.   Perf. 14
502 A221 50p gold, brt bl & slate   .85 .35

Centenary of the birth of Juho Kusti Paasikivi (1870-1956), President of Finland.

Cogwheels A222

1971, Jan. 28   Litho.   Perf. 14
503 A222 50p multicolored   .75 .35

Finnish industry.

Europa Issue, 1971
Common Design Type
1971, May 3   Litho.   Perf. 14
Size: 30x20mm
504 CD14 50p dp rose, yel & blk   3.75 .55

Tornio Church — A223

Front Page, January 15, 1771 — A224

1971, May 12   Litho.   Perf. 14
505 A223 50p multicolored   .90 .35

350th anniversary of the town of Tornio.

1971, June 1   Litho.   Perf. 14
506 A224 50p multicolored   .70 .35

Bicentenary of the Finnish press.

Athletes in Helsinki Stadium A225

50p, Running & javelin in Helsinki Stadium.

1971, July 5   Litho.   Perf. 14
507 A225 30p multicolored   1.00 .45
508 A225 50p multicolored   2.00 .45

European Athletic Championships.

Sailboats A226

1971, July 14
509 A226 50p multicolored   1.10 .35

International Lightning Class Championships, Helsinki, July 14-Aug. 1.

Silver Tea Pot, Guild's Emblem, Tools — A227

1971, Aug. 6
510 A227 50p lilac & multi   .75 .35

600th anniv. of Finnish goldsmiths' art.

"Plastic Buttons and Houses" A228

Photogravure and Embossed
1971, Oct. 20   Perf. 14
511 A228 50p multicolored   .80 .35

Finnish plastics industry.

Europa Issue 1972
Common Design Type
1972, May 2   Litho.   Perf. 14
Size: 20x30mm
512 CD15 30p dk red & multi   2.50 .50
513 CD15 50p lt brn & multi   3.50 .50

Finnish National Theater A229

1972, May 22.   Litho.   Perf. 14
514 A229 50p lt violet & multi   .75 .35

Centenary of the Finnish National Theater, founded by Kaarlo and Emilie Bergbom.

Globe, US and USSR Flags — A230

1972, June 2
515 A230 50p multicolored   1.40 .35

Strategic Arms Limitation Talks (SALT), final meeting, Helsinki, Mar. 28-May 26; treaty signed, Moscow, May 26.

Map and Arms of Aland — A231

Training Ship
Suomen
Joutsen — A232

1972, June 9
516 A231 50p multicolored   4.00 .75
1st Provincial Meeting of Aland, 50th anniv.

1972, June 19
517 A232 50p orange & multi   1.25 .40
Tall Ships' Race 1972, Helsinki, Aug. 20.

Costume from
Perni, 12th
Cent. — A233

Circle
Surrounding
Map of
Europe — A234

1972, Nov. 19   Litho.   Perf. 13
518 A233 50p shown   2.50 .65
519 A233 50p Couple, Tenho-
     la, 18th cent.   2.50 .65
520 A233 50p Girl, Nastola,
     19th cent.   2.50 .65
521 A233 50p Man, Voyni,
     19th cent.   2.50 .65
522 A233 50p Lapps, Inari,
     19th cent.   2.50 .65
  a.   Strip of 5, #518-522   12.50 14.50
       Complete booklet, 2 each
       #518-522   30.00
Regional costumes.
See Nos. 533-537.

1972, Dec. 11   Perf. 14x13½
523 A234 50p multicolored   2.50 .50
Preparatory Conference on European
Security and Cooperation.

Book, Finnish
and Soviet
Colors — A235

Litho.; Gold Embossed
1973, Apr. 6   Perf. 14
524 A235 60p gold & multi   .65 .35
Soviet-Finnish Treaty of Friendship, 25th
anniv.

Kyösti Kallio
(1873-1940), Pres.
of Finland — A236

1973, Apr. 10   Litho.   Perf. 13
525 A236 60p multicolored   .65 .35

Europa Issue 1973
Common Design Type
1973, Apr. 30   Photo.   Perf. 14
Size: 31x21mm
526 CD16 60p bl, brt bl & emer   1.40 .40

Nordic
House,
Reykjavik
A236a

Nordic Cooperation Issue

1973, June 26   Engr.   Perf. 12½
527 A236a 60p multicolored   .90 .30
528 A236a 70p multicolored   .90 .30
A century of postal cooperation among Denmark, Finland, Iceland, Norway and Sweden,
and in connection with the Nordic Postal Conference, Reykjavik.

Map of Europe,
"EUROPA" as a
Maze — A237

Litho. & Embossed
1973, July 3   Perf. 13
529 A237 70p multicolored   .85 .35
Conference for European Security and
Cooperation, Helsinki, July 1973.

Paddling
A238

Radiosonde, WMO
Emblem — A239

1973, July 18   Litho.   Perf. 14
530 A238 60p multicolored   .65 .35
Canoeing World Championships, Tampere,
July 26-29.

1973, Aug. 6   Litho.   Perf. 14
531 A239 60p multicolored   .65 .35
Cent. of intl. meteorological cooperation.

Eliel
Saarinen
and
Design for
Parliament,
Helsinki
A240

1973, Aug. 20   Perf. 12½x13
532 A240 60p multicolored   .65 .35
Eliel Saarinen (1873-1950), architect.

Costume Type of 1972
1973, Oct. 10   Litho.   Perf. 13
533 A233 60p Woman, Kauko-
     la   5.25 .65
534 A233 60p Woman, Jaaski   5.25 .65
535 A233 60p Married couple,
     Koivisto   5.25 .65
536 A233 60p Mother and son,
     Sakyla   5.25 .65
537 A233 60p Girl, Hainavesi   5.25 .65
  a.   Strip of 5, #533-537   27.50 14.00
Regional costumes.

DC10-30
Jet — A241

1973, Nov. 1   Litho.   Perf. 14
538 A241 60p multicolored   .80 .40
50th anniv. of regular air service, Finnair.

Santa Claus in
Reindeer
Sleigh — A242

1973, Nov. 15   Litho.   Perf. 14
539 A242 30p multicolored   .80 .30
Christmas 1973.

"The Barber of
Seville"
A243

1973, Nov. 21
540 A243 60p multicolored   .75 .35
Centenary of opera in Finland.

Production of
Porcelain
Jug — A244

Nurmi, by Waino
Aaltonen — A245

1973, Nov. 23
541 A244 60p blue & multi   .75 .35
Finnish porcelain.

1973, Dec. 11
542 A245 60p multicolored   .80 .40
Paavo Nurmi (1897-1973), runner, Olympic
winner, 1920-1924-1928.

Arms, Map
and Harbor of
Hanko — A246

1974, Jan. 10   Litho.   Perf. 14
543 A246 60p blue & multi   .75 .35
Centenary of the town of Hanko.

Ice Hockey
A247

1974, Mar. 5   Litho.   Perf. 14
544 A247 60p multicolored   .75 .35
European and World Ice Hockey Championships, held in Finland.

Seagulls (7
Baltic
States)
A248

1974, Mar. 18   Perf. 12½
545 A248 60p multicolored   .75 .35
Protection of marine environment of the Baltic Sea.

Goddess of
Freedom, by
Waino
Aaltonen — A249

Ilmari Kianto and
Old Pine — A250

1974, Apr. 29   Litho.   Perf. 13x12½
546 A249 70p multicolored   4.00 .35
Europa.

1974, May 7   Perf. 13
547 A250 60p multicolored   .70 .35
Ilmari Kianto (1874-1970), writer.

Society
Emblem,
Symbol
A251

Lithographed and Embossed
1974, June 12   Perf. 13½x14
548 A251 60p gold & multi   .70 .35
Centenary of Adult Education.

Grid
A252

UPU Emblem
A253

1974, June 14   Litho.   Perf. 14x13½
549 A252 60p multicolored   .70 .35
Rationalization Year in Finland, dedicated to
economic and business improvements.

1974, Oct. 10   Litho.   Perf. 13½x14
550 A253 60p multicolored   .70 .35
551 A253 70p multicolored   .70 .35
Centenary of Universal Postal Union.

Elves
Distributing
Gifts — A254

1974, Nov. 16   Litho.   Perf. 14x13½
552 A254 35p multicolored   1.25 .40
Christmas 1974.

Concrete Bridge and Granite Bridge, Aunessilta — A255

Litho. & Engr.
1974, Dec. 17   *Perf. 14*
553 A255 60p multicolored   .70 .35
Royal Finnish Directorate of Roads and Waterways, 175th anniversary.

Coat of Arms, 1581 — A256   Chimneyless Log Sauna — A256a

Carved Wooden Distaffs A258   Kirvu Weather Vane A258a

Cheese Frames A257

1.50m, Wood-carved high drinking bowl, 1542.

1975-90   Engr.   *Perf. 11½; 14 (2m)*
555   A256   10p red lilac ('78)   .25 .20
  a.   Bklt. pane of 4 (#555, 2 #556, #559) + label   2.25 2.25
    Complete booklet, #555a   2.50
  b.   Bklt. pane of 5 (2 #555, #557, #563, #564)   2.50 2.25
    Complete booklet, #555b   3.00
  c.   As "a," no label   2.50 2.50
    Complete booklet, #555c   3.00
  d.   Perf. 13x12½   .35 .20
556   A256   20p olive ('77)   .25 .20
  a.   20p yellow bister ('87)   .25 .20
  b.   As "a," perf. 13x12½   .25 .20
557   A256   30p carmine ('77)   .25 .20
557A A256   30p car, litho.   .25 .20
558   A256   40p orange   .25 .20
  a.   Perf. 13x12½, litho. & engr.   1.25 .20
559   A256   50p green ('76)   .25 .20
  a.   Perf. 13x12½   .25 .20
560   A256   60p blue   .30 .20
  a.   Perf. 13x12½   .35 .20
561   A256   70p sepia   .40 .20
562   A256   80p dl red & bl grn ('76)   .50 .20
  a.   Perf. 13x12½   1.20 1.20
563   A256   90p vio bl ('77)   .50 .20
564   A256   1.10m yellow ('79)   .60 .20
565   A256   1.20m dk blue ('79)   .60 .20
566   A258   1.50m multi ('76)   .75 .20

Litho.
567   A256a   2m multi ('77)   .90 .20

Lithographed and Engraved
568   A257   2.50m multi ('76)   1.25 .20
  a.   Perf. 14   2.25 .20
569   A258   4.50m multi ('76)   2.25 .20
  a.   Perf. 14   3.25 .20
570   A258a   5m multi ('77)   2.50 .20
    Nos. 555-570 (17)   12.05 3.40

No. 562a was only issued within the booklet pane No. 715a.
Issued: #557A, 6/3/80; #560a, 7/25/88; #555d, 7/25/89; #562a, 3/1/90; #558a, 8/18/94; #568a, 12/28/88; #569a, 9/26/88; No. 556b, 4/3/98.
See Nos. 629, 631-633, 711-715, 861.

Finland No. 16 — A259

Lithographed and Typographed
1975, Apr. 26   *Perf. 13*
571 A259 70p multicolored   3.75 4.00
Nordia 75 Philatelic Exhibition, Helsinki, Apr. 26-May 1. Sold only at exhibition for 3m including entrance ticket.

1975, Apr. 28   Litho.   *Perf. 13x12½*
Europa: 90p, Washerwoman, by Tyko Sallinen (1879-1955).
572 A260 70p gray & multi   2.25 .35
573 A260 90p tan & multi   2.25 .35

Girl Combing Hair, by Magnus Enckell — A260

Balance of Justice, Sword of Legality — A261

Rescue Boat and Sinking Ship — A262

1975, May 7   *Perf. 14*
574 A261 70p vio blue & multi   .60 .30
Sesquicentennial of State Economy Comptroller's Office.

1975, June 2   Litho.   *Perf. 14*
575 A262 70p multicolored   .75 .35
12th Intl. Salvage Conf., Finland, stressing importance of coordinating sea, air and communications resources in salvage operations.

Safe and Unsafe Levels of Drugs — A263

1975, July 21   Litho.   *Perf. 14*
576 A263 70p multicolored   .60 .30
Importance of pharmacological studies and for the 6th Intl. Pharmacology Cong., Helsinki.

Olavinlinna Castle A264

1975, July 29   *Perf. 13*
577 A264 70p multicolored   .65 .30
500th anniversary of Olavinlinna Castle.

Swallows over Finlandia Hall — A265

"Men and Women Working for Peace" — A266

1975, July 30
578 A265 90p multicolored   .90 .30
European Security and Cooperation Conference, Helsinki, July 30-Aug. 1. (The swallows of the design represent freedom, mobility and continuity.) See No. 709.

1975, Oct. 24   Litho.   *Perf. 13x12½*
579 A266 70p multicolored   .65 .30
International Women's Year 1975.

"Continuity and Growth" — A267

Boys as Three Kings and Herod — A268

1975, Oct. 29   *Perf. 13*
580 A267 70p brown & multi   .65 .30
Industrial Art and for the centenary of the Finnish Society of Industrial Art.

1975, Nov. 8   *Perf. 14*
581 A268 40p blue & multi   1.00 .25
Christmas 1975.

Top Border of State Debenture A269

Lithographed and Engraved
1976, Jan. 9   *Perf. 11½*
582 A269 80p multicolored   .65 .30
Centenary of State Treasury.

Glider over Lake Region A270

1976, Jan. 13   Litho.   *Perf. 14*
583 A270 80p multicolored   .90 .30
15th World Glider Championships, Rayskala, June 13-27.

Prof. Heikki Klemetti (1876-1953), Musician & Writer — A271

1976, Feb. 14   Litho.   *Perf. 13*
584 A271 80p green & multi   .65 .30

Map with Areas of Different Dialects — A272

Aino Ackté, by Albert Edelfelt — A273

1976, Mar. 10   Litho.   *Perf. 13*
585 A272 80p multicolored   .65 .30
Finnish Language Society, centenary.

1976, Apr. 23
586 A273 70p yellow & multi   .80 .30
Aino Ackté (1876-1944), opera singer.

Europa Issue 1976

Knife from Voyri, Sheath and Belt — A274

1976, May 3   Litho.   *Perf. 13*
587 A274 80p violet bl & multi   3.75 .55

Radio and Television A275

1976, Sept. 9   Litho.   *Perf. 13*
588 A275 80p multicolored   .65 .30
Radio broadcasting in Finland, 50th anniv.

Christmas Morning Ride to Church A276

1976, Oct. 23   Litho.   *Perf. 14*
589 A276 50p multicolored   .85 .25
Christmas 1976.

Turku
Chapter
Seal
(Virgin and
Child)
A277

1976, Nov. 1   Litho.   Perf. 12½
590 A277 80p buff, brn & red   .65 .30
Cathedral Chapter of Turku, 700th anniv.

Alvar Aalto,
Finlandia
Hall,
Helsinki
A278

1976, Nov. 4
591 A278 80p multicolored   .65 .30
Hugo Alvar Henrik Aalto (1898-1976),
architect.

Ice
Dancers — A280

Five Water
Lilies — A281

1977, Jan. 25   Litho.   Perf. 13
592 A280 90p multicolored   .65 .30
European Figure Skating Championships,
Finland, Jan. 25-29.

Photogravure and Engraved
1977, Feb. 2   Perf. 12½
593 A281 90p brt green & multi   .80 .30
594 A281 1m ultra & multi   .80 .30
Nordic countries cooperation for protection
of the environment and 25th Session of Nordic
Council, Helsinki, Feb. 19.

Icebreaker
Rescuing
Merchantman
A282

1977, Mar. 2   Litho.   Perf. 13
595 A282 90p multicolored   .70 .30
Winter navigation between Finland and
Sweden, centenary.

Nuclear
Reactor
A283

1977, Mar. 3   Perf. 12½x13
596 A283 90p multicolored   .60 .30
Opening of nuclear power station on Häs-
tholmen Island.

Europa Issue 1977

Autumn Landscape, Northern
Finland — A284

1977, May 2   Litho.   Perf. 12½x13
597 A284 90p multicolored   3.25 .35

Tree, Birds and
Nest — A285

Orthodox
Church, Valamo
Cloister — A286

1977, May 4   Perf. 13x12½
598 A285 90p multicolored   .65 .30
75th anniversary of cooperative banks.

1977, May 31   Litho.   Perf. 14
599 A286 90p multicolored   .60 .30
Consecration festival of new Orthodox
Church at Valamo Cloister, Heinävesi; 800th
anniversary of introduction of orthodoxy in
Karelia and of founding of Valamo Cloister.

Paavo
Ruotsalainen
(1777-1852), Lay
Leader of Pietists
in Finland — A287

1977, July 8   Litho.   Perf. 13
600 A287 90p multicolored   .60 .30

People Fleeing
Fire and
Water — A288

1977, Sept. 14   Litho.   Perf. 14
601 A288 90p multicolored   .55 .30
Civil defense for security.

Volleyball — A289

1977, Sept. 15
602 A289 90p multicolored   .65 .30
European Women's Volleyball Championships, Finland, Sept. 29-Oct. 2.

Children
Bringing Water
for
Sauna — A290

1977, Oct. 25
603 A290 50p multicolored   .75 .25
Christmas 1977.

Finnish
Flag — A291

Wall Telephone,
1880, New
Telephone — A292

1977, Dec. 5   Litho.   Perf. 14
Size: 31x21mm
604 A291 80p multicolored   .65 .25
Size: 37x25mm
Perf. 13
605 A291 1m multicolored   .95 .25
Finland's declaration of independence, 60th
anniv.

1977, Dec. 9   Perf. 14
606 A292 1m multicolored   .60 .30
Centenary of first telephone in Finland.

Harbor, Sunila
Factory, Kotka
Arms — A293

1978, Jan. 2   Litho.   Perf. 14
607 A293 1m multicolored   .65 .30
Centenary of founding of Kotka.

Paimio Sanitarium
by Alvar
Aalto — A294

Europa: 1.20m, Hvittrask studio house,
1902, horiz.

1978, May 2   Litho.   Perf. 13
608 A294   1m multicolored   6.00 .70
609 A294 1.20m multicolored   6.00 3.75

Rural Bus
Service
A295

1978, June 8   Litho.   Perf. 14
610 A295 1m multicolored   .65 .30

Eino Leino
and
Eagle — A296

1978, July 6   Litho.   Perf. 13
611 A296 1m multicolored   .65 .30
Eino Leino (1878-1926), poet.

Function
Theory and
Rhythmical
Lines — A297

1978, Aug. 15   Litho.   Perf. 14
612 A297 1m multicolored   .65 .30
ICM 78, International Congress of Mathematicians, Helsinki, Aug. 15-23.

Child Feeding
Birds — A298

1978, Oct. 23   Litho.   Perf. 14
613 A298 50p multicolored   .75 .25
Christmas 1978.

A299

A300

1979, Jan. 2   Litho.   Perf. 13
614 A299 1.10m multicolored   2.00 .30
International Year of the Child.

1979, Feb. 7   Litho.   Perf. 14
615 A300 1.10m Runner   .80 .30
8th Orienteering World Championships, Finland, Sept. 1-4.

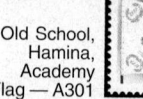

Old School,
Hamina,
Academy
Flag — A301

1979, Mar. 20   Litho.   Perf. 14
616 A301 1.10m multicolored   .60 .30
200th anniv. of Finnish Military Academy.

A302   A303

Design: Turku Cathedral and Castle, Prink-
kala house, Brahe statue.

1979, Mar. 31
617 A302 1.10m multicolored   .60 .30

1979, May 2   Litho.   Perf. 14
618 A303 1.10m Streetcar, Helsinki   .65 .30
Non-polluting urban transportation.

View of Tampere, 1779 — A304

View of Tampere, 1979 — A305

1979, May 2
619 A304 90p multicolored .60 .30

1979, Oct. 1 **Perf. 13**
620 A305 1.10m multicolored .65 .30
Bicentenary of founding of Tampere.

Optical Telegraph, 1796, Map of Islands A306

Europa: 1.10m, Letter of Queen Christina to Per Brahe, 1638, establishing postal service.

1979, May 2 **Perf. 13**
621 A306 1.10m multi 2.00 .35
622 A306 1.30m multi, vert 4.50 .85

Shops and Merchants' Signs — A307

1979, Sept. 26 **Perf. 14**
623 A307 1.10m multicolored .60 .30
Business and industry regulation centenary.

Old and New Cars, Street Crossing A308

1979, Oct. 1
624 A308 1.10m multicolored .65 .30
Road safety.

Elves Feeding Horse — A309

1979, Oct. 24
625 A309 60p multicolored .90 .25
Christmas 1979.

Korppi House, Lapinjarvi A310

Farm houses, First Row: Syrjala House, Tammela, 2 stamps in continuous design; Murtovaara House, Valtimo; Antila House, Lapua. Second row: Lofts, Pohjanmaa; Court-yard gate, Kanajarvi House, Kalvola; Main door, Havuselka House, Kauhajoki; Maki-

Rasinpera House and dinner bell tower; Gable and eaves, Rasula Kuortane granary.

1979, Oct. 27 **Litho.** **Perf. 13**
626 Booklet pane of 10 6.00 6.00
a.-j. A310 1.10m single stamp .60 .35
Complete booklet, #626 6.00
See design A349a.

Type of 1975 and

Kauhaneva Swamp A315

Hame Castle, Hameenlinna A316

Windmill, Harrstrom A318

Multiharju Forest, Seitseminen Natl. Park — A319

Shuttle, Raanu Designs A322

Kaspaikka Towel Design — A323

Bridal Rug, Teisko, 1815 — A324

Iron-forged Door, Hollola Church — A325

Iron Fish Spear c. 1100 — A326

Design: 1.80m, Eastern Gulf natl. park.

Litho. & Engr., Litho., Engr.
1979-98 **Perf. 14, 11½ (A256, A318)**
627 A315 70p multicolored .35 .20
628 A316 90p brown red .30 .20
629 A256 1m red brown .90 .40
a. Perf. 13x12½ ('98) .90 .20
630 A318 1m bl & red brn .30 .20
631 A256 1.30m dk green .65 .20
631A A256 1.30m dk green, litho. .65 .25
b. Booklet pane, #555-556, 557A, 560, 631A 2.00 2.00
Complete booklet, #631Ab 2.25
632 A256 1.40m purple .65 .20
633 A256 1.50m grnsh blue .70 .20
634 A319 1.60m multicolored .75 .20
635 A315 1.80m multicolored 1.40 .20
636 A322 3m multicolored 1.40 .20
637 A323 6m multicolored 2.75 .20
638 A324 7m multicolored 3.25 .75

639 A325 8m multicolored 3.75 .25
640 A326 9m blk & dk bl 4.25 .30
Nos. 627-640 (15) 22.05 3.95

Coil Stamps
Perf. 11½ Vert.
641 A316 90p brown red .45 .25
Perf. 12½ Horiz.
642 A318 1m blue & red brn .55 .25
Issued: 3m, 10/27/79; 6m, 4/9/80; #629, 1/2/81; 70p, 1/12/81; 90p, 9/1/82; 1.60m, 2/8/82; 7m, 2/15/82; #631, 1/3/83; #630, 642, 1/12/83; 1.80m, 8m, 2/10/83; 1.40m, 9m, 1/2/84; 1.50m, 1/2/85; #631A, 11/1/85.

Maria Jotuni (1880-1943), Writer — A327

1980, Apr. 9 **Litho.**
643 A327 1.10m multicolored .60 .25

Frans Eemil Sillanpaa (1888-1964), Writer — A328

Europa: 1.30m, Artturi Ilmari Virtanen (1895-1973), chemist, vert.

1980, Apr. 28 **Perf. 13**
644 A328 1.10m multicolored 1.25 .40
645 A328 1.30m multicolored 1.50 .70

Pres. Urho Kekkonen, 80th Birthday — A329

1980, Sept. 3 **Litho.** **Perf. 13**
646 A329 1.10m multicolored .65 .25

Nordic Cooperation Issue

Back-piece Harness, 19th century A330

1980, Sept. 9 **Perf. 14**
647 A330 1.10m shown .60 .30
648 A330 1.30m Collar harness, vert. .60 .40

Biathlon A331

1980, Oct. 17 **Litho.** **Perf. 14**
649 A331 1.10m multicolored .60 .25
World Biathlon Championship, Lahti, Feb. 10-15, 1981.

Pull the Roller, Weighing out the Salt — A332

Christmas 1980 (Traditional Games): 1.10m, Putting out the shoemaker's eye.

1980, Oct. 27
650 A332 60p multicolored .90 .25
651 A332 1.10m multicolored .90 .25

Boxing Match — A333

Glass Blowing A334

1981, Feb. 28 **Litho.** **Perf. 14**
652 A333 1.10m multicolored .60 .25
European Boxing Championships, Tampere, May 2-10.

1981, Mar. 12
653 A334 1.10m multicolored .60 .25
Glass industry, 300th anniversary.

Mail Boat Furst Menschikoff, 1836 — A335

Litho. & Engr.
1981, May 6 **Perf. 13**
654 A335 1.10m brown & tan 3.50 3.25
Nordia '81 Stamp Exhibition, Helsinki, May 6-10. Sold only at exhibition for 3m including entrance ticket.

Europa Issue 1981

Rowing to Church A336

1981, May 18 **Litho.** **Perf. 13**
655 A336 1.10m shown .75 .30
656 A336 1.50m Midsummer's Eve dance 1.50 .50

Traffic Conference Emblem — A337

Boy and Girl Riding Pegasus A338

1981, May 26 **Litho.** **Perf. 14**
657 A337 1.10m multicolored .50 .25
European Conference of Ministers of Trans-port, May 25-28.

1981, June 11
658 A338 1m multicolored .50 .25
Youth associations centenary.

Intl. Year of the
Disabled — A339

1981, Sept. 2   Litho.   Perf. 13
659 A339 1.10m multicolored   .60 .25

Christmas
1981 — A340

1981, Oct. 27   Litho.   Perf. 14
660 A340 70p Children, Christ-
                mas tree   .90 .20
661 A340 1.10m Decorating tree,
                vert.   .90 .30

"Om Konsten
att Ratt
Behaga" First
Issue
(Periodicals
Bicentenary)
A341

1982, Jan. 15
662 A341 1.20m multicolored   .60 .25

Kuopio   Score, String
Bicentenary   Instrument Neck
A343   A344

1982, Mar. 4   Litho.   Perf. 14
664 A343 1.20m multicolored   .60 .25

1982, Mar. 11   Perf. 13
665 A344 1.20m multicolored   .70 .25

Centenaries of Sibelius Academy of Music
and Helsinki Orchestra.

Electric Power
Plant
Centenary
A345

1982, Mar. 15   Perf. 14
666 A345 1.20m multicolored   .60 .25

Gardening
A346

1982, Apr. 16   Litho.   Perf. 14
667 A346 1.10m multicolored   .55 .25

Europa — A347

1.20m, Publication of Abckiria (1st Finnish
book), 1543 (Sculpture of Mikael Agricola,
translator, by Oskari Jauhiainen, 1951).
1.50m, Turku Academy, 1st Finnish university
(Turku Academy Inaugural Procession, 1640,
after Albert Edelfelt).

1982, Apr. 29   Litho.   Perf. 13x12½
668 A347 1.20m multicolored   1.50 .45
           Size: 47x31mm
           Perf. 12½
669 A347 1.50m multicolored   1.60 .45

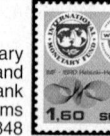

Intl. Monetary
Fund and
World Bank
Emblems
A348

1982, May 12   Perf. 14
670 A348 1.60m multicolored   .75 .30

IMF Interim Committee and IMF-WB Joint
Development Committee Meeting, Helsinki,
May 12-14.

75th Anniv. of
Unicameral
Parliament
A349

1982, May 25
671 A349 2.40m Future, by Waino
                Aaltonen, Parlia-
                ment   1.10 .45

Manor
Houses
A349a

1st Row: a, Kuitia, Parainen, 1490. b,
Louhisaari, Askainen, 1655. c, Frugard,
Joroinen, 1780. d, Jokioinen, 1798. e, Moisio,
Elimaki, 1820.
2nd Row: f, Sjundby, Siuntio, 1560. g,
Fagervik, Inkoo, 1773. h, Mustio, Karjaa,
1792. i, Fiskars, Pohja, 1818. j, Kotkaniemi,
Vihti, 1836.

1982, June 14   Litho.   Perf. 13x13½
672   Booklet pane of 10   8.50 8.50
a.-j. A349a 1.20m single stamp   .85   .45
       Complete booklet, #672   9.50 9.50

See design A310.

Christmas
1982 — A350

1982, Oct. 25
673 A350 90p Feeding forest ani-
                mals   .80 .25
674 A350 1.20m Children eating
                porridge   .80 .25

Nordic
Cooperation
A351

1983, Mar. 24   Litho.   Perf. 14
675 A351 1.20m Panning for gold   .55 .25
676 A351 1.30m Kitkajoki River
                rapids   .65 .25

World
Communications
Year — A352

1983, Apr. 9   Litho.   Perf. 13
677 A352 1.30m Postal services   .65 .25
678 A352 1.70m Sound waves, opti-
                cal cables   .80 .40

Europa
1983
A353

1983, May 2   Litho.   Perf. 12½x13
679 A353 1.30m Flash smelting
                method   5.00 .45
680 A353 1.70m Temppeliaukio
                Church   6.00 .90

Pres. Lauri   Running
Kristian   A355
Relander
(1883-1942)
A354

1983, May 31   Litho.   Perf. 14
681 A354 1.30m multicolored   .65 .30

1983, June 6
682 A355 1.20m Javelin, horiz.   .65 .40
683 A355 1.30m shown   .70 .30

First World Athletic Championships, Helsinki, Aug. 7-14.

Toivo Kuula (1883-
1918),
Composer — A356

1983, July 7   Perf. 14
684 A356 1.30m multicolored   .65 .30

Christmas
1983 — A357

Childrens drawings: 1m, Santa, reindeer,
sled and gifts by Eija Myllyviita. 1.30m, Two
candles by Camilla Lindberg.

Engr., Litho.
1983, Nov. 4   Perf. 12, 14
685 A357 1m dark blue   .80 .30
686 A357 1.30m multi, vert.   .80 .30

A358

A360

1983, Nov. 25   Litho.   Perf. 14
687 A358 1.30m brt blue & blk   .65 .30

President Mauno Henrik Koivisto, 60th
birthday.

1984, Mar. 1   Engr.   Perf. 12
689 A360 1.10m Letters (2nd class
                rate)   .50 .20
           Photo. & Engr.
690 A360 1.40m Automated sorting
                (1st class rate),
                vert.   .65 .20

Inauguration of Nordic postal rates.

Museum   Work and
Pieces — A361   Skill — A362

Designs: No. 691, Pottery, 3200 B.C.; Silver
chalice, 1416; Crossbow, 16th cent. No. 692,
Kaplan hydraulic turbine.

1984, Apr. 30   Litho.   Perf. 13½
691 A361 1.40m multicolored   .65 .30
692 A362 1.40m multicolored   .65 .30

Europa
(1959-84)
A363

1984, May 7   Perf. 12½x13
693 A363 1.40m multicolored   4.00 .25
694 A363 2m multicolored   4.00 .80

Dentistry — A364

1984, Aug. 27   Litho.   Perf. 14
695 A364 1.40m Dentist, teeth   .70 .30

Astronomy
A365

1984, Sept. 12
696 A365 1.10m Observatory, plan-
                ets, sun   .50 .25

Aleksis Kivi
(1934-72),
Writer — A366

1984, Oct. 10   Litho.   Perf. 14
697 A366 1.40m Song of my Heart   .65 .30

Christmas
1984 — A367

Litho. & Engr.

1984, Nov. 30 *Perf. 12*
698 A367 1.10m Father Christmas,
brownie   .90 .30

Common Law of
1734 — A368

1984, Dec. 6 *Perf. 14*
699 A368 2m Statute Book   .95 .40

25th Anniv. of
EFTA — A369

1985, Feb. 2 *Litho.*
700 A369 1.20m multicolored   .60 .25

100th Anniv. of
Society of
Swedish
Literature in
Finland
A370

1985, Feb. 5 *Litho.*
701 A370 1.50m Johan Ludvig
Runeberg   .70 .30

A371   A372

1985, Feb. 18 *Litho.* *Perf. 11½x12*
702 A371 1.50m Icon   .70 .30

Order of St. Sergei and St. Herman, 100th
anniv.

Litho. & Engr.

1985, Feb. 28 *Perf. 13x12½*
703 A372 1.50m Pedri Semeikka   .70 .30
704 A372 2.10m Larin Paraske   1.00 .45

150th anniv. of Kalevala.

A373

A374

Litho. & Engr.

1985, May 15 *Perf. 13*
705 A373 1.50m Mermaid and
sea lions   5.00 6.25

NORDIA 1985 philatelic exhibition, May 15-
19. Sold for 10m, which included admission
ticket.

Photo. & Engr.

1985, May 18 *Perf. 11½*
Finnish Banknote Cent.: banknotes of 1886,
1909, 1922, 1945 and 1955.
706   Booklet pane of 8   6.50 8.00
a.-h. A374 1.50m any single   .75 .35
       Complete booklet, #706   7.00

A375

A376

Europa: 1.50m, Children playing the
recorder. 2.10m, Excerpt "Ramus Virens
Olivarum" from the "Piae Cantiones," 1582.

1985, June 17 *Litho.* *Perf. 13*
707 A375 1.50m multicolored   5.50 .25
708 A375 2.10m multicolored   6.50 .85

Security Conference Type of 1975

1985, June 19 *Litho.*
709 A265 2.10m multicolored   1.00 .45

European Security and Cooperation Conference, 10th Anniv.

1985, Sept. 5 *Litho.* *Perf. 14*
710 A376 1.50m Provincial arms,
Count's seal   .85 .30

Provincial Administration Established by
Count Per Brahe, 350th Anniv.

Arms Type of 1975 and

Kerimaki
Church
A376a

Urho Kekkonen
Natl.
Park — A376b

Tulip Damask Table
Cloth, 18th Cent.
A377

Postal Service
A377a

Brown
Bear — A377b

Perf. 11½, 13x12½ (2m)
1985-90 **Engr., Litho. (2m)**
711 A256 1.60m vermilion   .75 .20
712 A256 1.70m black   .80 .20
a.   Bkt. pane, #558, 560, 2
      each #555, 556a, 712 + 2
      labels   6.00 6.00
      Complete booklet, #712a 8.50
713 A256 1.80m olive green .85 .20
a.   Bkt. pane, 2 ea #555d,
      560a, 713b   2.50 2.50
      Complete booklet, #713a 2.75
b.   Perf. 13x12½   .80 .30
714 A256 1.90m brt orange   .90 .25
715 A256 2m blue grn,
          bklt. stamp   1.10 .75
a.   Bkt. pane, #562a, 2 ea
      #715, 555d   5.00 5.50
      Complete booklet, #715a 5.50

          Litho. *Perf. 14*
716 A376a 2.20m multi   1.00 .25
717 A376b 2.40m multi   1.10 .25
718 A377 12m multi   5.75 .75

Litho. & Engr.
Perf. 13x12½
719 A377b 50m blk, grn & lt
          red brn   24.00 5.50
      Nos. 711-719 (9)   36.25 8.35

No. 712a contains two labels inscribed to
publicize FINLANDIA '88.
Issued: 12m, 9/13/85; 1.60m, 1/2/86; 1.70m,
1/2/87; #712a, 8/10/87; 1.80m, 1/4/88; 2.20m,
2.40m, 1/20/88; #713b, 7/25/88; 1.90m,
1/2/89; 2m, 1/19/90; 50m, 8/30/89.

Booklet Stamps

#720, Telephone, mailbox. #721, Postal
truck, transport plane. #722, Transport plane,
fork lift. #723, Postman delivering letter. #724,
Woman accepting letter.

Perf. 12½ on 3 Sides
1988, Feb. 1 **Litho.**
720 A377a 1.80m multicolored .85 .35
721 A377a 1.80m multicolored .85 .35
722 A377a 1.80m multicolored .85 .35
723 A377a 1.80m multicolored .85 .35
724 A377a 1.80m multicolored .85 .35
a.   Bkt. pane, 2 each #720-724 9.50 8.50
      Complete booklet, #724a 9.50
      Nos. 720-724 (5)   4.25 1.75

Nos. 721-722 and 723-724 printed se-tenant in continuous designs. No. 724c sold for
14m to households on mainland Finland. Each
household entitled to buy 2 booklets at discount price from Feb. 1 to May 31, with
coupon.

Miniature Sheet

Postal Map,
1698
A378

Designs: a, Postman on foot. c, Sailing vessel, diff. d, Postrider, vert.

Litho. & Engr.

1985, Oct. 16 *Perf. 14*
728   Sheet of 4   10.00 10.00
a.-d. A378 1.50m any single 2.50 2.50

FINLANDIA '88, 350th anniv. of Finnish
Postal Service, founded in 1638 by Gov.-Gen.
Per Brahe. Sheet sold for 8m.

Intl. Youth   Christmas
Year — A379   1985 — A380

1985, Nov. 1 *Litho.* *Perf. 13*
729 A379 1.50m multicolored .70 .30

1985, Nov. 29 *Perf. 14*
730 A380 1.20m Bird, tulips   .90 .30
731 A380 1.20m Cross of St.
          Thomas, hy-
          acinths   .90 .30

Natl.
Geological
Society,
Cent. — A390

1986, Feb. 8 *Litho.* *Perf. 14*
732 A390 1.30m Orbicular granite .70 .30
733 A390 1.60m Rapaviki   .85 .55
734 A390 2.10m Veined gneiss 1.10 .55
      Nos. 732-734 (3)   2.65 1.40

Europa
1986
A391

1986, Apr. 10 *Perf. 12½x13*
735 A391 1.60m Saimaa ringed
          seal   5.00 .25
736 A391 2.20m Environmental
          conservation   5.50 .80

Conference
Palace,
Baghdad,
1982 — A392

Natl. Construction Year. b, Lahti Theater,
1983. c, Kuusamo Municipal Offices, 1978. d,
Hamina Court Building, 1983. e, Finnish

Embassy, New Delhi, 1986. f, Western Sakyla Daycare Center, 1980.

1986, Apr. 19   *Perf. 14*
737   Booklet pane of 6   5.00 4.50
a.-f. A392 1.60m, any single   .80 .50
         Complete booklet, #737   5.00

Nordic
Cooperation
Issue
1986 — A393

Sister towns.

1986, May 27   Litho.   Perf. 14
738 A393 1.60m Joensuu   .75 .40
739 A393 2.20m Jyvaskyla   1.00 .50

Souvenir Sheet

FINLANDIA '88 — A394

Postal ships: a, Iron paddle steamer Aura, Stockholm-St. Petersburg, 1858. b, Screw vessel Alexander, Helsinki-Tallinn-Lubeck, 1859. c, Steamship Nicolai, Helsinki-Tallinn-St. Petersburg, 1858. d, 1st Ice steamship Express II, Helsinki-Stockholm, 1877-98, vert.

Litho. & Engr.
1986, Aug. 29   *Perf. 13*
740   Sheet of 4   10.00 11.00
a.-b. 1.60m, any single   2.50 2.75
c.-d. 2.20m, any single   2.50 2.75

Sold for 10k.

Pierre-Louis Moreau de Maupertuis
(1698-1759) — A395

1986, Sept. 5   Litho.   Perf. 12½x13
741 A395 1.60m multicolored   .80 .30

Lapland Expedition, 250th anniv., proved Earth's poles are flattened.
See France No. 2016.

Urho Kaleva   Intl. Peace
Kekkonen   Year — A397
(1900-86),
Pres. — A396

1986, Sept. 30   Engr.   Perf. 14
742 A396 5m black   2.50 2.25

1986, Oct. 13   Litho.   Perf. 13
743 A397 1.60m multicolored   .75 .30

A398

Christmas
A399

Photo. & Engr.
1986, Oct. 31   *Perf. 12*
744   1.30m Denomination at
         L   .80 .35
745   1.30m Denomination at
         R   .80 .35
a.   A398 Pair, #744-745   1.60 .85
746 A399 1.60m Elves   1.10 .45
         Nos. 744-746 (3)   2.70 1.15

No. 745a has a continuous design.

Postal Savings
Bank,
Cent. — A400

1987, Jan. 2   Litho.   Perf. 14
747 A400 1.70m multicolored   .80 .40

Natl. Tourism,
Cent. — A401

1987, Feb. 4   Litho.   Perf. 14
748 A401 1.70m Winter   .80 .40
749 A401 2.30m Summer   1.10 .55

A402

A403

1987, Feb. 4   *Perf. 14*
750 A402 1.40m multicolored   .65 .30
     Metric system in Finland, cent.

1987, Feb. 17   Litho.   Perf. 14
751 A403 2.10m multicolored   1.00 .50
     Leevi Madetoja (1887-1947), composer.

European   1987 World
Wrestling   Bowling
Championships   Championships
A404   A405

1987, Feb. 17
752 A404 1.70m multicolored   .80 .40

1987, Apr. 13
753 A405 1.70m multicolored   .80 .40

Mental
Health — A406

1987, Apr. 13
754 A406 1.70m multicolored   .80 .40

Souvenir Sheet

FINLANDIA '88 — A407

Locomotives and mail cars: a, Steam locomotive, 6-wheeled tender. b, 4-window mail car. c, 7-window mail car.

Litho. & Engr.
1987, May 8   *Perf. 12½x13*
755   A407 Sheet of 4   13.00 13.00
a.-c. 1.70m any single   3.25 3.25
d.   2.30m multicolored   3.25 3.25

Sold for 10m.

Europa
1987
A408

Modern architecture: 1.70m, Tampere Main Library, 1986, designed by Raili and Reima Pietila. 2.30m, Stoa Monument, Helsinki, c. 1981, by sculptor Hannu Siren.

1987, May 15   Litho.   Perf. 13
756 A408 1.70m multicolored   5.25 .25
757 A408 2.30m multicolored   5.25 .90

Natl. Art Museum,
Ateneum,
Cent. — A409

Paintings: a, Strawberry Girl, by Nils Schillmark (1745-1804). b, Still-life on a Lady's Work Table, by Ferdinand von Wright (1822-1906). c, Old Woman with Basket, by Albert Edelfelt (1854-1906). d, Boy and Crow, by Akseli Gallen-Kallela (1865-1931). e, Late Winter, by Tyko Sallinen (1879-1955).

1987, May 15
758   Booklet pane of 5   8.00
a.-e. A409 1.70m any single   1.50 .50
         Complete booklet, #758   8.00

A410   A411

1987, Aug. 12   *Perf. 14*
759 A410 1.70m multicolored   .80 .25
     European Physics Soc. 7th gen. conf., Helsinki, Aug. 10-14.

1987, Oct. 12
760 A411 1.70m ultra, sil & pale
          lt gray   .80 .25

Size: 30x41mm
761 A411 10m dark ultra, lt
           blue & sil   5.00 1.75
     Natl. independence, 70th anniv.

Ylppo, Child
and
Lastenlinna
Children's
Hospital
A412

1987, Oct. 27
762 A412 1.70m multicolored   .80 .25
     Arvo Ylppo (b. 1887), pediatrics pioneer.

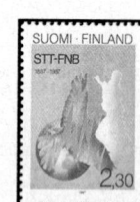

Christmas   Finnish News
A413   Agency (STT),
                   Cent.
                   A414

1987, Oct. 30
763 A413 1.40m Santa Claus,
          youths, horiz.   .75 .20
764 A413 1.70m shown   .85 .20

1987, Nov. 1
765 A414 2.30m multicolored   1.10 .70

Lauri "Tahko" Pihkala (1888-1981),
Promulgator of Sports and Physical
Education
A415

1988, Jan. 5   Litho.   Perf. 14
766 A415 1.80m blk, chalky blue &
          brt blue   .85 .25

A416

1988, Mar. 14   *Litho.*
767 A416 1.40m multicolored   .65 .20
     Meteorological Institute, 150th anniv.

Settlement of New Sweden in
America, 350th Anniv. — A417

Design: 17th Century European settlers negotiating with 3 American Indians, map of New Sweden, the Swedish ships Kalmar Nyckel and Fogel Grip, based on an 18th cent. illustration from a Swedish book about the American Colonies.

Litho. & Engr.
1988, Mar. 29   *Perf. 13*
768 A417 3m multicolored   1.50 .70
     See US No. C117 and Sweden No. 1672.

FINLANDIA '88, June 1-12, Helsinki
Fair Center — A418

Agathon Faberge (1876-1951), famed philatelist, & rarities from his collection.

Booklet Stamp
1988, May 2   **Litho.**   **Perf. 13**
769 A418 5m Pane of 1+2 la-
    bels   14.00 16.00
  Complete booklet, #769   14.00

350th Anniv. of the Finnish Postal Service.
No. 769 sold for 30m to include the price of
adult admission to the exhibition.

Achievements of
Finnish Athletes
at the 1988
Winter
Olympics,
Calgary — A419

Design: Matti Nykanen, gold medalist in all 3
ski jumping events at the '88 Games.

1988, Apr. 6   **Perf. 14**
770 A419 1.80m multicolored   .85   .25

Europa
1988
A420

Communication and transport.

1988, May 23   **Litho.**   **Perf. 13**
771 A420 1.80m shown   5.00   .25
772 A420 2.40m Horse-drawn
    tram, 1890   5.00   .90

Souvenir Sheet

FINLANDIA '88 — A421

1st airmail flights: a, Finnish air force
Breguet 14 biplane transporting mail from Helsinki to Tallinn, Feb. 12, 1920. b, AERO
Junkers F-13 making 1st airmail night flight
from Helsinki to Copenhagen, May 15, 1930.
c, AERO Douglas DC-3, 1st intl. route, Hel-
sinki-Norrkoping-Copenhagen-Amsterdam,
1947. d, Douglas DC 10-30, 1975-88, inauguration of Helsinki-Beijing route, June 2, 1988.

Litho. & Engr.
1988, June 2   **Perf. 13½**
773   Sheet of 4   13.00 13.00
 a.-c.   A421 1.80m any single   3.25 3.25
 d.   A421 2.40m multicolored   3.25 3.25

Sold for 11m.

Turku Fire
Brigade, 150th
Anniv. — A422

Design: 1902 Horse-drawn, steam-driven
fire pump, preserved at the brigade.

1988, Aug. 15   **Litho.**   **Perf. 14**
774 A422 2.20m multicolored   1.10   .60

A423   A424

Missale Aboense, the 1st printed book in
Finland, 500th anniv.

1988, Aug. 17
775 A423 1.80m multicolored   .85   .25

Booklet Stamps
1988, Sept. 6   **Litho.**   **Perf. 13**
Finnish Postal Service, 350th Anniv.: #776,
Postal tariff issued by Queen Christina of Sweden, Sept. 6, 1638. #777, Postal cart, c. 1880.
#778, Leyland Sherpa 185 mail van, 1976.
#779, Malmi P.O. interior. #780, Skier using
mobile telephone, c. 1970. #781, Telecommunications satellite in orbit.

776 A424 1.80m multicolored   1.00   .50
777 A424 1.80m multicolored   1.00   .50
778 A424 1.80m multicolored   1.00   .50
779 A424 1.80m multicolored   1.00   .50
780 A424 1.80m multicolored   1.00   .50
781 A424 1.80m multicolored   1.00   .50
 a.   Booklet pane of 6, #776-781   6.25 6.25
   Complete booklet, #781a   6.50

Children's
Playgroups
(Preschool)
A425

1988, Oct. 10   **Perf. 14**
782 A425 1.80m multicolored   .85   .25

Christmas
A426

1988, Nov. 4   **Litho.**
783 A426 1.40m multicolored   .85   .20
784 A426 1.80m multicolored   .85   .20

Hameenlinna
Township,
350th
Anniv. — A427

Design: Market square, coat of arms and
17th century plan of the town.

1989, Jan. 19   **Litho.**
785 A427 1.90m multicolored   .90   .25

1989 Nordic Ski
Championships,
Lahti, Feb. 17-
26 — A428

1989, Jan. 25
786 A428 1.90m multicolored   .90   .25

Salvation Army   Photography,
in Finland,   150th
Cent. — A429   Anniv. — A430

1989, Feb. 6   **Litho.**
787 A429 1.90m multicolored   .90   .25

1989, Feb. 6
788 A430 1.50m Photographer,
    box camera,
    c.1900   .70   .30

31st Intl.
Physiology
Congress,
Basel, July 9-
14 — A431

Design: Congress emblem, silhouettes of
Robert Tigerstedt and Ragnar Granit, eye,
flowmeter measuring flow of blood through
heart, color-sensitive retinal cells and
microelectrode.

1989, Mar. 2
789 A431 1.90m multicolored   .90   .25

Sports — A432

1989, Mar. 10   **Booklet Stamps**
790 A432 1.90m Skiing   .90   .30
791 A432 1.90m Jogging   .90   .30
792 A432 1.90m Cycling   .90   .30
793 A432 1.90m Canoeing   .90   .30
 a.   Booklet pane of 4, #790-793   3.75 3.50
   Complete booklet, #793a   4.00

Souvenir Sheet

Finnish Kennel Club, Cent. — A433

Dogs: a, Lapponian herder. b, Finnish spitz.
c, Karelian bear dog. d, Finnish hound.

1989, Mar. 17   **Litho.**   **Perf. 14**
794   A433   Sheet of 4   5.00 5.00
 a.-d.   1.90m any single   1.25   .70

Europa — A434   A435

1989, Mar. 31   **Perf. 13**
795 A434 1.90m Hopscotch   2.50   .25
796 A434 2.50m Sledding   2.50   .65

1989, Apr. 20   **Perf. 14**
Nordic Cooperation Year: Folk Costumes.
797 A435 1.90m Sakyla (man)   .90   .25
798 A435 2.50m Veteli (woman)   1.25   .60

Finnish
Pharmacies,
300th
Anniv. — A436

Foxglove, distilling apparatus, mortar, flask.

1989, June 2   **Litho.**
799 A436 1.90m multicolored   .90   .25

A437

A438

1989, June 2
800 A437 1.90m multicolored   .90   .25
Savonlinna Municipal Charter, 350th anniv.

1989, June 12
801 A438 1.90m *Panthera uncia*   .90   .25
802 A438 2.50m *Capra falconeri*   1.25   .80
Helsinki Zoo, cent.

Vocational
Training, 150th
Anniv. — A439

Interparliamentary Union,
Cent. — A440

Council of
Europe, 40th
Anniv. — A441

1989, Sept. 4   **Litho.**   **Perf. 14**
803 A439 1.50m multicolored   .70   .30
804 A440 1.90m multicolored   .90   .25
805 A441 2.50m multicolored   1.25   .55
   Nos. 803-805 (3)   2.85 1.10

Admission of Finland to the Council of
Europe (2.50m).

A442

A443

1989, Oct. 9 — Litho.
806 A442 1.90m multicolored .90 .25

Hannes Kolehmainen (1889-1966) winning the 5000-meter race at the Stockholm Olympics, 1912.

1989, Oct. 20
807 A443 1.90m multicolored .90 .25

Continuing Education in Finland, cent.

A444   A445

Christmas: 1.90m, Sodankyla Church, Siberian jays in snow.

1989, Nov. 3
808 A444 1.50m shown .90 .20
809 A444 1.90m multicolored .90 .20

1990, Jan. 19 Litho. Perf. 13x13½
810 A445 1.90m multicolored 1.00 1.00
811 A445 2.50m multicolored 1.25 1.10

Incorporation of the State Posts and Telecommunications Services.
Emblem of the corporation was produced by holography. Soaking may affect the design.

Musical Soc. of Turku and Finnish Orchestras, 200th Annivs. A446

1990, Jan. 26 Perf. 14
812 A446 1.90m multicolored .90 .25

Disabled Veteran's Assoc., 50th Anniv. — A447

1990, Mar. 13 Litho.
813 A447 2m multicolored .95 .25

End of the Winter (Russo-Finnish) War, 50th Anniv. — A448

1990, Mar. 13
814 A448 2m blue .95 .25

University of Helsinki, 350th Anniv. — A449

University crest and: 2m, Queen Christina on horseback. 3.20m, Degree ceremony procession in front of the main university building.

1990, Mar. 26 Litho. Perf. 13
815 A449 2m multicolored .95 .25
816 A449 3.20m multicolored 1.50 .75

Europa 1990 A450

Post Offices: 2m, Lapp man, P.O. at Nuvvus, Mt. Nuvvus Ailigas. 2.70m, Turku main P.O.

1990, Mar. 26 Perf. 12½x13
817 A450 2m multicolored 6.00 .25
818 A450 2.70m multicolored 6.00 .65

Rural Postal Service and Address Reform, Cent. — A451

1990, Apr. 19 Litho. Perf. 13
819 A451 2m multicolored .95 .25

"Ali Baba and the Forty Thieves" A452   "Story of the Great Musician" A453

"Story of the Giants, the Witches and the Daughter of the Sun" A454   "The Golden Bird, the Golden Horse and the Princess" A455

"Lamb Brother" A456   "The Snow Queen" A457

Fairy tale illustrations by Rudolf Koivu.

Booklet Stamps
Perf. 14 on 3 sides

1990, Aug. 29 Litho.
820 A452 2m multicolored 1.25 .30
821 A453 2m multicolored 1.25 .30
822 A454 2m multicolored 1.25 .30
823 A455 2m multicolored 1.25 .30
824 A456 2m multicolored 1.25 .30
825 A457 2m multicolored 1.25 .30
a. Booklet pane of 6, #820-825 8.00 9.00
Complete booklet, #825a 9.00

Souvenir Sheet

Horse Care — A458

a, Feeding. b, Riding. c, Watering. d, Currying.

1990, Oct. 10 Litho. Perf. 14
826 A458 Sheet of 4 4.00 3.00
a.-d. 2m any single .95 .45

Christmas A459

1990, Nov. 2
827 A459 1.70m Santa's elves 1.10 .20
828 A459 2m Santa, reindeer 1.25 .20

Provincial Flowers

A460   A460a

A460b   A460c

A460d   A460e

A460f   A460g

A460h   A460i

A460j   A460k

1990-99 Perf. 13x12½
829 A460 2m Wood anemone .95 .20
830 A460 2.10m Rowan 1.00 .20
831 A460 2.70m Heather 1.25 .35
832 A460 2.90m Sea buckthorn 1.40 .35
833 A460 3.50m Oak 1.75 .45
834 A460a 2 Globeflower 1.40 .30
835 A460b 1 Hepatica 1.60 .20
Nos. 829-835 (7) 9.35 2.05

Self-Adhesive
Die Cut

836 A460c 2 Iris 1.40 .20
a. Booklet pane of 20 28.00 15.00
837 A460 2.10m like #830 1.00 .20
838 A460d 1 Rosebay willowherb 1.60 .20
839 A460e 1 Labrador tea 1.60 .20
a. Booklet pane of 10 16.00 12.50
840 A460f 1 Karelian rose 1.60 .20
841 A460g 1 Daisy 1.60 .20
842 A460h 1 Water lily 1.60 .20
843 A460i 1 Bird cherry 1.60 .20

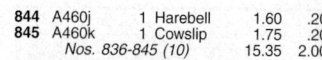

844 A460j 1 Harebell 1.60 .20
845 A460k 1 Cowslip 1.75 .20
Nos. 836-845 (10) 15.35 2.00

Issued: 2m, 2.70m, 1/19/90; #830, 2.90m, 3.50m, 2/5/90; 2.10m, 1991; #834-835, 3/2/92; #838, 10/9/92; #836, 3/1/93; #839, 6/14/93; #840, 5/5/94; #841, 3/15/95; #842, 6/3/96; #843, 3/18/97; #844, 3/12/98; #845, 4/28/99.
#834 sold for 1.60m, #836 sold for 1.90m, #835, 838 for 2.10m, #839-840 for 2.30m, #841-844 sold for 2.80m, #845 sold for 3m at time of release.
#837-838, 840-843 issued in sheets of 10. Nos. 836a and 839a were issued as complete booklets. The peelable backing serves as a booklet cover.
The numbers on the stamps represent the class of mail for which each was intended at time of release.

A461

1991, Mar. 1 Perf. 14
846 A461 2.10m multicolored 1.00 .25
World Hockey Championships, Turku.

A462

1991, Mar. 1
847 A462 2.10m Cooking class 1.00 .25
Home economics teacher education, cent.

Sauna Type of 1977 and:

Birds — A463

Perf. 13x12½, 14 (#861)
1991-99 Litho.
Booklet Stamps (#848-859)
848 A463 10p Great tit .50 .20
849 A463 10p Wagtail .25 .20
850 A463 10p Aegolius funereus .40 .60
850A A463 20p Phoenicurus phoenicurus 1.75 .70
851 A463 60p Chaffinches 1.75 .40
852 A463 60p Robin 1.75 .60
856 A463 2.10m Bullfinch 1.25 .20
a. Bklt. pane, #851, 2 each #848, 856 4.00 4.00
Complete booklet, #856a 4.25
857 A463 2.10m Waxwing 1.25 .25
a. Bklt. pane, #852, 2 each #849, 857 4.00 4.00
Complete booklet, #857a 4.25
859 A463 2.30m Dendrocopos leucotos 1.40 .40
a. Booklet pane of #850A, 2 each #850, #859 + 1 label 5.00 5.00
Complete booklet, #859a 5.25

Sheet Stamp
861 A256a 4.80m multicolored 2.50 .75
Nos. 848-861 (10) 12.80 4.30

Issued: #848, 851, 856, 3/20/91; #849, 852, 857, 4/22/92; #850, 850A, 859, 6/4/93. 861, 7/1/99.
"SUOMI" is in upper left on #849, 852, 857.

Fishing A464   Tourism A465

Designs: a, Fly fisherman, trout. b, Perch, bobber. c, Crayfish, trap. d, Trawling for herring. e, Stocking powan.

1991, Mar. 20   *Perf. 14*
863   Booklet pane of 5   5.25 5.50
a.-e.   A464 2.10m any single   1.00 .35
   Complete booklet, #863   5.50

1991, June 4   Litho.   *Perf. 14*
864 A465 2.10m Seurasaari Island   1.00 .25
865 A465 2.90m Steamship, Lake Saimaa   1.40 .70

Europa
A466

European map and: 2.10m, Human figures. 2.90m, Satellites, dish antennae.

1991, June 7   Litho.   *Perf. 12½x13*
866 A466 2.10m multicolored   5.50 .25
867 A466 2.90m multicolored   5.50 .70

Alfred W. Finch (1854-1930)
A467

Designs: 2.10m, Iris, ceramic vase. 2.90m, Painting, The English Coast at Dover.

1991, Sept. 7   Litho.   *Perf. 13*
868 A467 2.10m multicolored   1.50 .25
869 A467 2.90m multicolored   1.50 .60

See Belgium No. 1410.

Finnish Candy Industry, Cent. — A468

1991, Sept. 17   Photo.   *Perf. 11½*
870 A468 2.10m multicolored   1.00 .25

Souvenir Sheets

Children's Stamp Designs — A469

a, Sun. b, Rainbow. c, Cows grazing.

1991, Sept. 17   Litho.   *Perf. 13½*
871 A469 Sheet of 3   3.00 2.25
a.-c.   2.10m any single   1.00 .55

Skiing — A470

1991, Oct. 4   *Perf. 14*
Color of skisuit: a, red. b, green. c, yellow. d, blue.
872 A470 Sheet of 4   4.00 3.25
a.-d.   2.10m any single   1.00 .55

Town Status for Iisalmi, Cent. — A471

1991, Oct. 18   Litho.   *Perf. 14*
873 A471 2.10m multicolored   1.00 .60

Christmas A472

1.80m, Santa, animals carrying candles. 2.10m, Reindeer pulling Santa's sleigh.

1991, Nov. 1   Litho.   *Perf. 14*
874 A472 1.80m multi   1.10 .25
875 A472 2.10m multi, vert.   1.10 .25

Chemists' Club, Finnish Chemists' Society, Cent. — A473

1991, Nov. 1
876 A473 2.10m multi   1.00 .25
877 A473 2.10m multi, diff.   1.00 .25
a.   Pair, #876-877 + label   2.50 2.50

Second and third vertical branches merge while second and third branches below almost touch in the upper left part of camphor molecular structure on No. 877. Nos. 876-877 are designed to produce a three dimensional effect when viewed together.

1992 Olympic Games A474

Designs: No. 878, Skier, Albertville. No. 879, Swimmer, Barcelona.

1992, Feb. 4   Litho.   *Perf. 14*
878 A474 2.10m multicolored   1.10 .25
879 A474 2.90m multicolored   1.50 .55

Expo '92, Seville — A475

1992, Mar. 20   Litho.   *Perf. 14*
880 A475 3.40m multicolored   1.60 .80

Conference on Security and Cooperation in Europe, Helsinki A476

1992, Mar. 20   *Perf. 14½x15*
881 A476 16m multicolored   7.75 2.75

Town of Rauma, 550th Anniv. — A477

1992, Mar. 27   *Perf. 14*
882 A477 2.10m multicolored   1.00 .25

Healthy Brains — A478

1992, Mar. 27
883 A478 3.50m multicolored   1.75 .95

Discovery of America, 500th Anniv. A479

1992, May 8   Litho.   *Perf. 12½x13*
884 A479 2.10m Santa Maria, map   2.25 .30
885 A479 2.10m Map, Columbus   2.25 .30
a.   Pair, #884-885   5.00 4.00

Europa.

Finnish Technology A480

Hologram of trees and: 2.10m, Drawing of blowing machine. 2.90m, Schematic of electronic circuits. 3.40m, Triangles and grid.

1992, May 8   *Perf. 13x12½*
886 A480 2.10m multicolored   1.10 .35
887 A480 2.90m multicolored   1.50 .60
888 A480 3.40m multicolored   1.75 1.00
  Nos. 886-888 (3)   4.35 1.95

First Finnish patent granted, sesqui. (#886), Finnish chairmanship of Eureka (#887), Government Technology Research Center, 50th anniv. (#888).
Nos. 886-888 have holographic images. Soaking in water may affect the hologram.

Natl. Board of Agriculture, Cent. — A481

1992, June 4   Litho.   *Perf. 14*
889 A481 2.10m Currant harvesting   1.00 .25

Finnish Women A482

#890, Aurora Karamzin (1808-1902), founder of Deaconesses' Institution of Helsinki. #891, Baroness Sophie Mannerheim (1863-1928), reformer of nursing education. #892, Laimi Leidenius (1877-1938), physician and educator. #893, Miina Sillanpaa (1866-1952), Minister for social affairs. #894, Edith Sodergran (1892-1923), poet. #895, Kreeta Haapasalo (1813-1893), folk singer.

Litho. & Engr.
1992, June 8   *Perf. 14*
Booklet Stamps
890 A482 2.10m multicolored   1.00 .45
891 A482 2.10m multicolored   1.00 .45
892 A482 2.10m multicolored   1.00 .45
893 A482 2.10m multicolored   1.00 .45
894 A482 2.10m multicolored   1.00 .45
895 A482 2.10m multicolored   1.00 .45
a.   Booklet pane of 6, #890-895   6.00 5.50
   Complete booklet, #895a   6.00 5.50

Child's Painting A483

Independence, 75th Anniv. — A484

1992, Oct. 5   Litho.   *Perf. 13*
896 A483 2.10m multicolored   1.00 .25
Souvenir Sheet
Perf. 13½
897 A484 2.10m multicolored   1.00 .80

Nordia '93 — A485

A486

Illustrations depicting "Moomin" characters, by Tove Jansson: No. 898, Winter scene, ice covered bridges. No. 899, Winter scene in forest. No. 900, Boats in water. No. 901, Characters on beach.

Perf. 13 on 3 Sides
1992, Oct. 9   Litho.
Booklet Stamps
898 A485 2.10m multicolored   1.75 .45
899 A485 2.10m multicolored   1.75 .45
900 A485 2.10m multicolored   1.75 .45
901 A485 2.10m multicolored   1.75 .45
a.   Booklet pane of 4, #898-901   7.50 7.50
   Complete booklet, #901a   7.75

1992, Oct. 20   *Perf. 13*
902 A486 2.10m multicolored   1.00 .25

Printing in Finland, 350th anniv.

Christmas A487

Designs: 1.80m, Church of St. Lawrence, Vantaa. 2.10m, Stained glass window of nativity scene, Karkkila Church, vert.

1992, Oct. 30   Litho.   *Perf. 14*
903 A487 1.80m multicolored   1.10 .20
904 A487 2.10m multicolored   1.10 .20

Central Chamber of Commerce, 75th Anniv. — A488

1993, Feb. 8   Litho.   *Perf. 14*
905 A488 1.60m multicolored   .75 .30

Friendship
A489

1993, Feb. 8   Litho.   Perf. 14
906 A489 1 multicolored   1.60   .30
a.   Booklet pane of 5 + label   8.00   8.00
      Complete booklet, 2 #906a   16.00

No. 906 sold for 2m at time of release. See note following No. 845.
See Estonia No. 237.

Alopex Lagopus — A490

a, Adult with winter white coat. b, Face, full view, winter white coat. c, Mother, kits, summer coat. d, Two on rock, summer coat.

1993, Mar. 19   Litho.   Perf. 12½x13
907 A490 2.30m Block of 4, #a-d   5.50 5.50

World Wildlife Fund.

Sculptures
A491

Europa: 2m, Rumba, by Martti Aiha. 2.90m, Complete Works, by Kari Caven.

1993, Apr. 26   Perf. 13
908 A491   2m multicolored   1.90   .25
909 A491 2.90m multicolored   1.40   .60

Organized
Philately in
Finland,
Cent. — A492

1993, May 6   Perf. 13x12½
910 A492 2.30m Rosa pimpinel-
             lifolia   1.10   .45

Vyborg
Castle, 700th
Anniv.
A493

1993, May 6   Perf. 13½
911 A493 2.30m multicolored   1.10   .25

Tourism
A494

1993, May 7   Perf. 13x12½
912 A494 2.30m Naantali   1.10   .45
913 A494 2.90m Imatra   1.40   .45

550th anniv. of Naantali (#912).

A495   A496

Independent Finland Defense Forces, 75th Anniv.: 2.30m, Finnish landscape in form of soldier's silhouette. 3.40m, UN checkpoint of Finnish battalion, Middle East.

1993, June 4   Litho.   Perf. 14
914 A495 2.30m multicolored   1.10   .25
915 A495 3.40m multicolored   1.60   .95

1993, June 14   Litho.   Perf. 12½x13
Art by Martta Wendelin (1893-1986): #916, Boy on skis, 1936. #917, Mother, daughter knitting, 1931. #918, Children building snowman, 1931. #919, Mother, children at fence, 1935. #920, Girl with lamb, 1936.

Booklet Stamps
916 A496 2.30m multicolored   1.25   .50
917 A496 2.30m multicolored   1.25   .50
918 A496 2.30m multicolored   1.25   .50
919 A496 2.30m multicolored   1.25   .50
920 A496 2.30m multicolored   1.25   .50
a.   Booklet pane of 5, #916-920   6.25   6.25
      Complete booklet, #920a   6.50

Water Birds — A497

#921, Flock of gavia arctica. #922, Pair of gavia arctica. #923, Mergus merganser. #924, Anas platyrhynchos. #925, Mergus serrator.

Perf. 12½x13 on 3 or 4 Sides
1993, Sept. 20   Litho.
Booklet Stamps
921 A497 2.30m multicolored   1.25   .35
922 A497 2.30m multicolored   1.25   .35
Size: 26x40mm
923 A497 2.30m multicolored   1.25   .35
924 A497 2.30m multicolored   1.25   .35
925 A497 2.30m multicolored   1.25   .35
a.   Booklet pane of 5, #921-925   6.25   6.25
      Complete booklet, #925a   6.50

Physical Education in
Finnish Schools,
150th Anniv. — A498

1993, Oct. 8   Perf. 14
926 A498 2.30m multicolored   1.10   .25

Souvenir Sheet

New Opera
House,
Helsinki
A499

Operas and ballet: a, 2.30m, Ostrobothnians, by Leevi Madetoja. b, 2.30m, The Faun (four dancers), by Claude Debussy. c, 2.90m, Giselle, by Adolphe Adam. d, 3.40m, The Magic Flute, by Wolfgang Amadeus Mozart.

1993, Oct. 8   Perf. 13
927 A499   Sheet of 4, #a.-d.   5.25 5.25

Christmas   Pres. Mauno
A500   Koivisto, 70th
                   Birthday
                   A501

1993, Nov. 5   Litho.   Perf. 14
928 A500 1.80m Christmas
             tree, elves   .85   .25
a.   Booklet pane of 10   12.00   12.00
      Complete booklet, #928a   12.00
929 A500 2.30m Three angels   1.10   .25

1993, Nov. 25
930 A501 2.30m multicolored   1.10   .25

Friendship — A502

Moomin characters: No. 931, Two standing. No. 932, Seven running.

1994, Jan. 27   Litho.   Perf. 12½x13
Booklet Stamps
931 A502 1 multicolored   1.60   .25
932 A502 1 multicolored   1.60   .25
a.   Bklt. pane, 4 each #931-932 13.50 12.00
      Complete booklet, #932a   13.50

Nos. 931-932 each sold for 2.30m at time of release. See note following No. 845.

Souvenir Sheet

Intl. Olympic Committee,
Cent. — A503

Winter Olympics medalists from Finland: a, Marja-Liisa Kirvesniemi, Marjo Matikainen, cross-country skiing. b, Clas Thunberg, speed skating. c, Veikko Kankkonen, ski jumping. d, Veikko Hakulinen, cross-country skiing.

1994, Jan. 27   Perf. 13
933 A503 4.20m Sheet of 4, #a-d   8.00 8.00

See No. 939.

A504

Waino Aaltonen
(1894-1966),
Sculptor — A505

1994, Mar. 8
934 A504 2m "Peace"   .95   .25
935 A505 2m "Muse"   .95   .25
a.   Pair, #934-935   2.00   1.50

Postal Service
Civil Servants'
Federation,
Cent. — A506

1994, Mar. 11
936 A506 2.30m multicolored   1.10   .25

Finnish
Technology
A507

Europa: 2.30m, Paper roll, nitrogen fixation, safety lock, ice breaker MS Fennica. 4.20m, Radiosonde, fishing lure, mobile phone, wind power plant.

1994, Mar. 18
937 A507 2.30m multicolored   1.40   .25
938 A507 4.20m multicolored   1.90   1.10

Olympic Athlete Type of 1994
Souvenir Sheet

Finnish athletes: a, Riitta Salin, Pirjo Haggman, runners. b, Lasse Viren, runner. c, Tiina Lillak, javelin thrower. d, Pentti Nikula, pole vaulter.

1994, May 5   Litho.   Perf. 13
939 A503 4.20m Sheet of 4, #a-d   8.00 8.00

European Track & Field Championships, Finlandia '95.

Finlandia '95, Helsinki — A508

1994, May 10   Perf. 13½x13
940 A508 16m Coccinella
             septempunctata   7.75 7.75

See Nos. 962, 1009.

Miniature Sheet

Wildflowers — A509

Designs: a, Hypericum perforatum (b). b, Lychnis viscaria. c, Campanula rotundifolia. d, Campanula glomerata. e, Geranium sanguineum (d). f, Fragaria vesca. g, Veronica chamaedrys (f, h). h, Saxifraga granulata (c, i). i, Viola tricolor (j). j, Potentilla anserina.

1994, June 1   Perf. 12
941 A509 1 Sheet of 10, #a.-j.   17.50 12.50

No. 941 sold for 23m at time of release. See note following No. 845.

Finland-Sweden
Track and Field
Meet — A510

#942, Seppo Raty, Finland, javelin. #943, Patrick Sjoberg, Sweden, high jump.

1994, Aug. 26 Litho. Perf. 12½
Booklet Stamps
942 A510 2.40m multicolored 1.10 .25
943 A510 2.40m multicolored 1.10 .25
  a. Booklet pane, 2 each #942-943 4.75 3.50
    Complete booklet, #943a 4.75

See Sweden Nos. 2091-2092.

Population Registers, 450th Anniv. — A511

1994, Sept. 1
944 A511 2.40m multicolored 1.10 .25

Intl. Year of the Family — A512

1994, Sept. 1
945 A512 3.40m multicolored 1.60 .70

Souvenir Sheet

Letter Writing Day — A513

Dog Hill Kids in the Post Office: a, At Post Office window. b, Standing in doorway, mail cart. c, Blowing horn, pig. d, Putting letters in mailbox.

1994, Oct. 7 Litho. Perf. 14
946 A513 2.80m Sheet of 4, #a-d 5.50 5.50

Christmas A514

2.10m, Reindeer, bullfinches on antlers. 2.80m, Elves among snow-covered trees.

1994, Nov. 4
947 A514 2.10m multi 1.00 .25
  a. Booklet pane of 10 10.00 11.00
    Complete booklet, #947a 10.00
948 A514 2.80m multi, vert. 1.40 .45

Greetings — A515

"Dog Hill Kids," sending/receiving greetings: No. 949, Delivering mail to Moon, spaceman. No. 950, Cat writing letter, clown. No. 951, Receiving mail from postman, baby. No. 952, Writing in bed, friend. No. 953, Winter scene at mailbox, characters at beach. No. 954, On bus, girl friend. No. 955, Standing at microphone with guitar, fan. No. 956, Baby in play pen, teddy bear.

Perf. 13 on 3 Sides
1995, Jan. 30 Litho.
Booklet Stamps
949 A515 2.80m multicolored 1.50 .60
950 A515 2.80m multicolored 1.50 .60
951 A515 2.80m multicolored 1.50 .60
952 A515 2.80m multicolored 1.50 .60
953 A515 2.80m multicolored 1.50 .60
954 A515 2.80m multicolored 1.50 .60
955 A515 2.80m multicolored 1.50 .60
956 A515 2.80m multicolored 1.50 .60
  a. Booklet pane, #949-956 12.00
    Complete booklet, 956a 12.00

Nos. 949-952 are printed tete beche with Nos. 953-956. Soaking in water may affect the holographic images on Nos. 949-956.

Souvenir Sheet

Team Sports — A516

a, Paivi Ikola, pesapallo. b, Jari Kurri, ice hockey. c, Jari Litmanen, soccer. d, Lea Hakala, basketball.

1995, Jan. 30 Perf. 13
957 A516 3.40m Sheet of 4, #a-d 6.50 6.50
See No. 961.

Membership in European Union — A517

1995, Jan. 30 Perf. 14
958 A517 3.50m multicolored 1.75 .85

Peace & Liberty — A518

Europa: 2.90m, Stylized parachutists.

1995, Mar. 1 Litho. Perf. 14
959 A518 2.90m multicolored 1.40 .45

Endangered Species — A519

Designs: a, Felis lynx. b, Lake, forest. c, Rocks, lake. d, Pusa hispida.

1995, Mar. 1 Perf. 13
960 A519 2.90m Block of 4, #a-d 5.50 5.50

Nos. 960a-960b, 960c-960d are continuous designs. See Russia No. 6249.

Athlete Type of 1995
Souvenir Sheet

Motor sports drivers in cars, on motorcycles: a, Timo Makinen. b, Juha Kankkunen. c, Tommi Ahvala. d, Heikki Mikkola.

1995, May 10 Litho. Perf. 13
961 A516 3.50m Sheet of 4, #a.-d. 6.75 6.75

Insect Type of 1994
1995, May 11
962 A508 19m Geotrupes stercorarius 9.25 9.25

Tourism — A520

Designs: 2.80m, Linnanmaki amusement park, Helsinki. 2.90m, Town of Mantyharju.

1995, May 12
963 A520 2.80m multicolored 1.25 .55
964 A520 2.90m multicolored 1.25 .65

Town of Loviisa, 250th Anniv. — A521

1995, June 30 Litho. Perf. 14
965 A521 3.20m multicolored 1.50 1.10

Intl. Union of Forestry Research Organizations, 20th World Congress, Tampere — A522

Designs: No. 966, Betula pendula. No. 967, Pinus sylvestris. No. 968, Picea abies. No. 969, Research, tree grown from needle.

Perf. 14 on 2 or 3 Sides
1995, Aug. 8 Litho.
Booklet Stamps
966 A522 2.80m multicolored 1.25 .50
967 A522 2.80m multicolored 1.25 .50
968 A522 2.80m multicolored 1.25 .50
969 A522 2.80m multicolored 1.25 .50
  a. Booklet pane of 4, #966-969 5.00 4.25
    Complete booklet, #969a 5.00 4.25

Wilhelm Roentgen (1845-1923), Discovery of the X-Ray, Cent. — A523

1995, Aug. 8 Perf. 14
970 A523 4.30m multicolored 2.10 1.25

Cats — A525

1995, Oct. 9 Litho. Perf. 13½
972 A525 2.80m Somali 1.40 .60
973 A525 2.80m Siamese 1.40 .60
974 A525 2.80m Norwegian forest 1.40 .60
975 A525 2.80m Persian 1.40 .60
Size: 59x35mm
976 A525 2.80m European domestic female 1.40 .60
977 A525 2.80m Three kittens, frog 1.40 .60
  a. Booklet pane of 6, #972-977 8.50
    Complete booklet, #977a 8.50

UN, 50th Anniv. — A526

1995, Oct. 20 Perf. 14
978 A526 3.40m multicolored 1.60 1.00

A527

Christmas A528

1995, Nov. 3 Litho. Perf. 14
979 A527 2m Santa on skates .95 .20
980 A528 2.80m Poinsettias 1.40 .70

Letter Stamps A529

UNICEF, 50th Anniv. A530

1996, Feb 2 Litho. Perf. 13½x14
Booklet Stamps
981 A529 1m "M" .50 .35
982 A529 1m "O" .50 .35
983 A529 1m "I" .50 .35
984 A529 1m "H" .50 .35
985 A529 1m "E" .50 .35
986 A529 1m "J" .50 .35
987 A529 1m "A" .50 .35
988 A529 1m "N" .50 .35
989 A529 1m "T" .50 .35
990 A529 1m "P" .50 .35
991 A529 1m "U" .50 .35
992 A529 1m "S" .50 .35
  a. Booklet pane of 12, #981-992 6.00
    Complete booklet, No. 992a 6.00

1996, Feb. 2 Perf. 14
993 A530 2.80m multicolored 1.40 .50

Women's Gymnastics in Finland, Cent. — A531

1996, Feb. 26 Litho. Perf. 13
994 A531 2.80m multicolored 1.40 .55

Woman Suffrage, 90th Anniv. A532

Litho. & Engr.
1996, Mar. 8 Perf. 13
995 A532 3.20m multicolored 1.25 .75
Europa.

Cinema,
Cent. — A533

Finnish films: No. 996, "Juha," 1937. No.
997, "Laveata Tieta," 1931. No. 998,
"Tuntematon Sotilas," 1935. No. 999, Oldest
known photo of a motion picture show, 1896.
No. 1000, "Jäniksen Vuosi," 1977. No. 1001,
"Valkoinen Peura," 1952. No. 1002, "Kaikki
Rakastavat," 1935. No. 1003, "Varjoja Parati-
isissa," 1986.

1996, Apr. 1   Litho.   Perf. 14x13½
Booklet Stamps

996	A533	2.80m multicolored	1.40	.55
997	A533	2.80m multicolored	1.40	.55
998	A533	2.80m multicolored	1.40	.55
999	A533	2.80m multicolored	1.40	.55
1000	A533	2.80m multicolored	1.40	.55
1001	A533	2.80m multicolored	1.40	.55
1002	A533	2.80m multicolored	1.40	.55
1003	A533	2.80m multicolored	1.40	.55
a.		Bklt. pane of 8, #996-1003	11.50	
		Complete booklet, #1003a	11.50	

Radio,
Cent. — A534

1996, Apr. 25   Perf. 14

1004	A534	4.30m multicolored	2.10	1.10

1996 Summer
Olympic Games,
Atlanta — A535

1996, June 3   Litho.   Perf. 12 Vert.
Booklet Stamps

1005	A535	3.40m Kayaking	1.60	1.00
1006	A535	3.40m Sailing	1.60	1.00
1007	A535	3.40m Rowing	1.60	1.00
1008	A535	3.40m Swimming	1.60	1.00
a.		Booklet pane of 4, #1005-1008	6.50	
		Complete booklet, #1008a	6.50	

Insect Type of 1994

1996, July 1   Litho.   Perf. 13

1009	A508	19m Dytiscus marginalis	8.25	9.00

Shore
Birds — A536

#1010, Gallinago gallinago. #1011,
Haematopus ostralegus. #1012, Scolopax rus-
ticola. #1013, Vanellus vanellus. #1014,
Numenius arquata.

Perf. 13½ on 3 Sides
1996, Sept. 6   Litho. & Engr.

1010	A536	2.80m multicolored	1.40	.55
1011	A536	2.80m multicolored	1.40	.55
1012	A536	2.80m multicolored	1.40	.55
1013	A536	2.80m multicolored	1.40	.55

Size: 30x52mm

1014	A536	2.80m multicolored	1.40	.55
a.		Sheet of 5, #1010-1014	7.00	6.00

Finnish Comic
Strips — A537

#1015, "Professor Itikainen" examining plant
with magnifying glass, by Ilmari Vainio. #1016,
"Pekka Puupää (Peter Blockhead)" taking letter from mailbox, by Ola Fogelberg. #1017,
"Joonas" holding drawing pencil, by Veikko
Savolainen. #1018, "Mämmilä" wearing helmet, by Tarmo Koivisto. #1019, "Rymy-Eetu"
smoking pipe, by Erkki Tanttu. #1020, "Kieku"
writing letter, by Asmo Alho. # 1021, "Pikku
Risunen" with animal, by Riitta Uusitalo. #
1022, "Kiti" holding up pencil, by Kati Kovács.

1996, Oct. 9   Litho.   Perf. 13½
Booklet Stamps

1015	A537	2.80m black & red	1.40	.55
1016	A537	2.80m black & red	1.40	.55
1017	A537	2.80m red & black	1.40	.55
1018	A537	2.80m black & red	1.40	.55
1019	A537	2.80m black & red	1.40	.55
1020	A537	2.80m red & black	1.40	.55
1021	A537	2.80m red & black	1.40	.55
1022	A537	2.80m red & black	1.40	.55
a.		Bklt. pane of 8, #1015-1022	11.50	
		Complete booklet, #1022a	11.50	

Christmas
A538

2m, Snowman, Santa, gnome playing mus-
cical instruments. 2.80m, Rabbit, reindeer
watching northern lights. 3.20m, Santa reading letters.

1996, Nov. 1   Litho.   Perf. 14

1023	A538	2m multi	1.00	.20
1024	A538	2.80m multi	1.40	.55
1025	A538	3.20m multi, vert.	1.50	.65
		Nos. 1023-1025 (3)	3.90	1.40

Greetings
Stamps — A539

End of 19th cent.: #1026, Two angels.
#1027, Flowers in basket. #1028, Hand reach-
ing through garland, bluebird. #1029, Boy, girl
dancing. #1030, Boy, envelope, shamrocks.
#1031, Clasping hands through heart-shaped
garlands. #1032, Roses. #1033, Angel.

Perf. 13x12½ on 3 Sides
1997, Jan. 30   Litho.
Booklet Stamps

1026	A539	1 multicolored	1.60	.50
1027	A539	1 multicolored	1.60	.50
1028	A539	1 multicolored	1.60	.50
1029	A539	1 multicolored	1.60	.50
1030	A539	1 multicolored	1.60	.50
1031	A539	1 multicolored	1.60	.50
1032	A539	1 multicolored	1.60	.50
1033	A539	1 multicolored	1.60	.50
a.		Bklt. pane of 8, #1026-1033	13.50	
		Complete booklet, #1033a	13.50	

Nos. 1026-1033 sold for 2.80m on day of
issue.
Number on stamp represents class of mail.

Mail Order
Sales in
Finland,
Cent. — A540

1997, Jan. 30   Perf. 13½x14

1034	A540	2.80m multicolored	1.40	.25

1997 Ice Hockey
World
Championships,
Helsinki — A541

1997, Jan. 30

1035	A541	2.80m multicolored	1.40	.25

On each stamp from the right vertical row of
the sheet, No. 1035 exists without the thin,
curved black line at the center right edge of
the stamp.

Lepus Timidus
A542

1997, Mar. 4   Litho.   Perf. 14

1036	A542	2.80m multicolored	1.40	.25

Saami Folktale, "Girl Who Turned into
a Golden Merganser" — A543

Europa: 3.20m, Duck, girl, prince. 3.40m,
Girl falling into crevice.

1997, Mar. 4   Perf. 13

1037	A543	3.20m multicolored	1.50	.50
1038	A543	3.40m multicolored	1.60	.60

Paavo Nurmi
(1897-1973),
Winner of 9
Olympic Gold
Medals — A544

1997, Mar. 18   Perf. 14

1039	A544	3.40m multicolored	1.60	.90

Southwest
Archipelago
Natl.
Park — A545

Litho. & Engr.
1997, Apr. 25   Perf. 14

1040	A545	4.30m multicolored	2.10	1.10

Tango — A546

A547

1997, May 19   Litho.

1041	A546	1 multicolored	1.60	.25
		Complete booklet of 5	8.25	

No. 1041 sold for 2.80m on day of release.
Number on stamp represents class of mail.

1997, May 19   Perf. 13½

Sailing Ships: #1042, Astrid. #1043, Jacob-
stads Wapen. #1044, Tradewind. #1045, Mer-
ikokko. #1046, Suomen Joutsen. #1047,
Sigyn.

Booklet Stamps

1042	A547	2.80m multicolored	1.40	.55
1043	A547	2.80m multicolored	1.40	.55
1044	A547	2.80m multicolored	1.40	.55
1045	A547	2.80m multicolored	1.40	.55

Size: 48x25½mm

1046	A547	2.80m multicolored	1.40	.55
1047	A547	2.80m multicolored	1.40	.55
a.		Booklet pane of 6, #1042-1047	8.50	
		Complete booklet, #1047a	8.50	

Pres. Martti
Ahtisaari, 60th
Birthday
A548

1997, June 23   Litho.   Perf. 14

1048	A548	2.80m multicolored	1.40	.25

Independence,
80th
Anniv. — A549

Four seasons: No. 1049, Spring, lily-of-the-
valley (natl. flower). No. 1050, Summer, white
clouds. No. 1051, Fall, colorful leaves. No.
1052, Winter, snow crystals.

Perf. 13x12½ on 2 or 3 Sides
1997, June 23
Booklet Stamps

1049	A549	2.80m multicolored	1.40	.55
1050	A549	2.80m multicolored	1.40	.55
1051	A549	2.80m multicolored	1.40	.55
1052	A549	2.80m multicolored	1.40	.55
a.		Booklet pane, #1049-1052	5.75	
		Complete booklet, #1052a	5.75	

Souvenir Sheet

A550

Grus Grus (Cranes): a, With young. b, With
frog. c, Performing mating dance. d, In flight.

1997, Aug. 19   Litho.   Perf. 14

1053	A550	2.80m Sheet of 4, #a.-d.	5.50	5.50

A551

1997, Oct. 9   Litho.   Perf. 14¼, 14½

Finnish Writers Assoc. (Covers from books):
No. 1054, "Seven Brothers," by Aleksis Kivi.
No. 1055, "Sinuhe the Egyptian," by Mika
Waltari. No. 1056, "Täällä Pohjantähden alla
I," by Väinö Linna. No. 1057, "Hyvästi Iijoki,"
by Kalle Päätalo. No. 1058, "Haukka, minum
rakkaani," by Kaari Utrio. No. 1059, "Juhan-
nustanssit," by Hannu Salama. No. 1060,
"Manillaköysi," by Veijo Meri. No. 1061, "Uppo-
Nalle ja Kumma," by Elina Karjalainen.

Booklet Stamps

1054	A551	2.80m multicolored	1.40	.55
1055	A551	2.80m multicolored	1.40	.55
1056	A551	2.80m multicolored	1.40	.55
1057	A551	2.80m multicolored	1.40	.55
1058	A551	2.80m multicolored	1.40	.55

1059	A551	2.80m multicolored	1.40	.55
1060	A551	2.80m multicolored	1.40	.55
1061	A551	2.80m multicolored	1.40	.55
a.		Booklet pane, #1054-1061	11.50	
		Complete booklet, #1061a	11.50	

No. 1056 exists perf 14½x14¼. The other values also should exist thus. The editors would like to examine such stamps.

Christmas
A552

1997, Oct. 31

1062	A552	2m Village	.95	.20
1063	A552	2.80m Candelabra, vert.	1.40	.55
1064	A552	3.20m Church, vert.	1.50	.65
	Nos. 1062-1064 (3)		3.85	1.40

Wildlife
A553

2nd, Stizostedion lucioperca. 1st, Turdus merula.

Die Cut 10 Horiz., Syncopated Type A

1998, Jan. 15   *Litho.*

Self-Adhesive
Coil Stamps

1065	A553	2 multicolored	1.50	.25
1066	A553	1 multicolored	1.60	.25

Nos. 1065-1066 were valued at 2.40m and 2.80m, respectively, on date of issue. Number on stamp represents class of mail.
See Nos. 1099-1100.

A554   A555

Moomin Cartoon Characters, by Tove Jansson: No. 1067, Boy Moomin drawing with pad and pencil. No. 1068, Girl Moomin in sunshine. No. 1069, Organ grinder. No. 1070, Boy Moomin giving flower to girl Moomin.

1998, Jan. 15   *Perf. 13 (on 3 Sides)*

Booklet Stamps

1067	A554	1 multicolored	1.60	.50
1068	A554	1 multicolored	1.60	.50
1069	A554	1 multicolored	1.60	.50
1070	A554	1 multicolored	1.60	.50
a.		Booklet pane, #1067-1070	6.50	
		Complete booklet, #1070a	6.50	

Nos. 1067-1070 each sold for 2.80m on day of issue. Number on stamp represents class of mail.
See No. 1127.

1998, Feb. 3   *Perf. 14*

1071	A555	2.80m multicolored	1.40	.25

Finnish Federation of Nurses, cent.

A556   A557

Valentine's Day Surprise Stamps. (Designs beneath scratch-off heart): a, Musical notes, two dogs. b, Elephant, mouse and flowers. c, Puppy, sealed envelope. d, Kittens, kittens hugging. e, Dog with nose in air, bouquet of flowers. f, Flowers, two rodents.

1998, Feb. 3   *Perf. 12*

1072		1 Sheet of 6	10.00	6.25
a.-f.		A556 Any single, unscratched	1.60	.50

Nos. 1072a-1072f were each valued at 2.80m on day of issue. Number on stamp represents class of mail. Unused values are for singles with attached selvage. Inscriptions are shown in selvage above or below each stamp. Each stamp bears a heart-shaped, golden scratch-off overlay. Values are for unscratched examples. Scratched stamps, with hearts partially or fully removed, sell for about 20 percent less.

1998, Mar. 27   *Litho.*   *Perf. 14*

1073	A557	2.80m Tussilago farfara	1.40	.25

National
Festivals
A558

Europa: 3.20m, Boy and girl, balloons, "Vappu" (May Day). 3.40m, Boy and girl in a dream floating over water, Midsummer Festival.

1998, Mar. 27   *Perf. 14x14½*

1074	A558	3.20m multicolored	1.50	.50
1075	A558	3.40m multicolored	1.60	.60

Finnish Marine
Research
Institute, 80th
Anniv. — A559

Designs: 2.80m, Research vessel, "Aranda." 3.20m, "Vega," chart showing route of Nils Adolf Erik Nordenskjold's expedition.

Litho. & Engr.

1998, May 7   *Perf. 14x13*

1076	A559	2.80m multicolored	1.40	.55
1077	A559	3.20m multicolored	1.50	.65

First Performance of National Anthem,
150th Anniv. — A560

1998, May 7   *Perf. 13*

1078	A560	5m multicolored	2.40	.30

Puppies
A561

#1079, Bernese Mountain dog. #1080, Puli. #1081, Boxer. #1082, Bichon Frisé. #1083, Finnish lapphound. #1084, Wire-haired dachshund. #1085, Scottish cairn terrier. #1086, Labrador retriever.

Perf. 13½x13 on 2 or 3 Sides

1998, June 4   *Litho.*

Booklet Stamps

1079	A561	1 multicolored	1.60	.50
1080	A561	1 multicolored	1.60	.50
1081	A561	1 multicolored	1.60	.50
1082	A561	1 multicolored	1.60	.50
1083	A561	1 multicolored	1.60	.50
1084	A561	1 multicolored	1.60	.50
1085	A561	1 multicolored	1.60	.50
1086	A561	1 multicolored	1.60	.50
a.		Booklet pane, #1079-1086	13.50	
		Complete booklet, #1086a	13.50	

Nos. 1079-1086 each sold for 2.80m on day of issue. Number on stamp represents class of mail.

Owls — A562   Cycling — A563

Designs: a, Bubo bubo. b, Wing of bubo bubo. c, Bubo bubo, aegolius funereus. d, Strix nebulosa. e, Nyctea scandiaca.

1998, Sept. 4   *Litho.*   *Perf. 13½*

1087		Sheet of 5 + label	7.25	7.25
a.-e.		A562 3m any single	1.40	.55

#1087b is 52x27mm; #1087c-1087d, 26x44mm; #1087e, 30x44mm.
See No. 1113.

1998, Sept. 4   *Perf. 14*

1088	A563	3m multicolored	1.25	.25

Finnish Design — A564

#1089, Savoy vases, by Alvar Aalto. #1090, Karuselli chair, by Yrjö Kukkapuro. #1091, Tasaraita knitwear, designed by Annika Rimala for Marimekko. #1092, Kilta tableware set, by Kaj Franck. #1093, Cast iron pot, by Timo Sarpaneva. #1094, Carelia cutlery set, by Bertel Gardberg.
Illustration reduced.

Perf. 13½ on 3 Sides

1998, Oct. 9   *Litho.*

Booklet Stamps

1089	A564	3m multicolored	1.40	.55
1090	A564	3m multicolored	1.40	.55
1091	A564	3m multicolored	1.40	.55
1092	A564	3m multicolored	1.40	.55
1093	A564	3m multicolored	1.40	.55
1094	A564	3m multicolored	1.40	.55
a.		Booklet pane, #1089-1094	8.50	
		Complete booklet, #1094a	8.50	

Nos. 1090-1091, 1093-1094 are 29x34mm.

Christmas
A565

Designs: 2m, Christmas tree, children, vert. 3m, Children, dog riding sled. 3.20m, Winter scene of cottage in center of island.

1998, Oct. 30   *Perf. 14*

1095	A565	2m multicolored	.95	.20
1096	A565	3m multicolored	1.40	.55
1097	A565	3.20m multicolored	1.50	.65
	Nos. 1095-1097 (3)		3.85	1.40

Souvenir Sheet

Mika Häkkinen, Formula 1 Driving
Champion — A566

Illustration reduced.

1999, Jan. 15   *Perf. 13½*

1098	A566	3m multicolored	1.40	1.40

Native Wildlife Type of 1998

2nd, Salmo salar. 1st, Luscinia svecica.

1999, Jan. 27   *Litho.*   *Die Cut*

Coil Stamps
Self-Adhesive

1099	A553	2 multi	1.50	.25

Die Cut

1100	A553	1 multi, vert.	1.60	.25

Nos. 1099-1100 were valued at 2.40m and 3m, respectively, on day of issue. Number on stamp represents class of mail.

Friendship
A567

Animals' tails: No. 1101, Zebra, lion. No. 1102, Dog, cat.

Serpentine Die Cut Perf. 13xDie Cut

1999, Jan. 27

Booklet Stamps
Self-Adhesive

1101	A567	3m multicolored	1.40	.55
1102	A567	3m multicolored	1.40	.55
a.		Bklt. pane, 3 each #1101-1102	8.50	

No. 1102a is a complete booklet.

Finnish Labor
Movement,
Cent. — A568

1999, Jan. 27   *Perf. 13½*

1103	A568	4.50m multicolored	2.10	1.10

Finland's Roads — A569

#1104, Snow-covered landscape, Arctic Ocean Road. #1105, Freeway interchanges, Jyväsjtkä Lakeshore Road. #1106, Raippaluoto Bridge. #1107, Wooded drive, Kitee.

1999, Feb. 15   *Litho.*   *Perf. 14 Horiz.*

Booklet Stamps

1104	A569	3m multicolored	1.40	.55
a.		Perf. 12¾ horiz.	6.00	.55
1105	A569	3m multicolored	1.40	.55
a.		Perf. 12¾ horiz.	6.00	.55
1106	A569	3m multicolored	1.40	.55
a.		Perf. 12¾ horiz.	6.00	.55
1107	A569	3m multicolored	1.40	.55
a.		Booklet pane, #1104-1107	5.75	
		Complete booklet, #1107a	6.75	
b.		Perf. 12¾ horiz.	6.00	.55
c.		Booklet pane, #1104a, 1105a, 1106a, 1107b	24.00	
		Complete booklet, #1107c	25.00	

A570   A571

Women's Kalevala-style brooches: a, Horse clasp. b, Bird clasp. c, Virusmäki clasp.

1999, Feb. 15   *Perf. 13½x14*
1108   Sheet of 3   4.25   3.25
   a.-c.   A570 3m any single   1.40   .55

1st Publication of Legend of the Kalevala, 150th Anniv.

1999, Mar. 15   *Perf. 13x13½*
1109   A571 3m Crocus vernus   1.40   .55

Martha Organization, Cent. — A572

1999, Mar. 15   *Perf. 13½x13*
1110   A572 3m multicolored   1.40   .55

Europa A573

1999, Mar. 15   *Perf. 13½x14*
1111   A573 2.70m Esplanade Park   *1.25*   *.50*
1112   A573 3.20m Ruissalo Park   *1.50*   *.60*

Bird Type of 1998

Designs: a, Luscinia luscinia. b, Cuculus canorus. c, Botaurus stellaris. d, Caprimulgus europaeus. e, Crex crex.

1999, May 18   *Perf. 13½*
1113   Sheet of 5 + label   7.00   7.00
   a.-e.   A562 3m any single   1.40   .55

No. 1113b is 25x43mm. No. 1113c is 45x30mm. No. 1113d-1113e are 26x37mm.

Finland's Presidency of European Union — A574

1999, July 1 Litho.   *Perf. 13¾x13½*
1114   A574 3.50m multicolored   1.60   .65

Finnish Entertainers A575

a, Harmony Sisters, Vera (1914-97), Maire (1916-95) & Raija (1918-97) Valtonen. b, Olavi Virta (1915-72), singer. c, Georg Malmstén (1902-81), composer, conductor. d, Topi Kärki (1915-22), composer, and Reino (Repe) Helismaa (1913-65), lyricist. e, Tapio Rautavaara (1915-79), singer. f, Esa Parkarinen (1911-89), musician, actor.

Perf. 13¼ on 3 Sides
1999, Sept. 6   **Litho.**
1115   Booklet pane of 6   9.75
   a.-f.   A575 3.50m any single   1.60   .65
   Complete booklet, #1115   9.75

Nos. 1115a, 1115d are each 60x34mm.

Finnish Commercial Product Design — A576

a, Fiskars cutting tools. b, Zoel/Versoul guitars. c, Ergo II/Silenta hearing protectors. d, Ponsse Cobra HS 10 tree harvester. e, Suunto compass. f, Exel Avanti QLS ski pole.
Illustration reduced.

Perf. 13¼ on 3 sides
1999, Oct 8   **Litho.**
1116   Booklet pane of 6   9.75
   a.-f.   A576 3.50m any single   1.60   .65
   Complete booklet, #1116   9.75

Size of b, c, e, f: 30x35mm.

"The Nativity," by Giorgio di Chirico (1888-1978) A577

Rabbits, Birds — A578

1999, Nov. 5   *Perf. 14*
1117   A578 2.50m Santa Claus, vert.   1.25   .20
1118   A577   3m multicolored   1.40   .55
1119   A578 3.50m multicolored   1.60   .65
   Nos. 1117-1119 (3)   4.25   1.40

Christmas. See Italy Nos. 2314-2315.

Sveaborg Fortress — A579

2000, Jan. 12 Litho.   *Perf. 13¾x13½*
1120   A579 7.20m multi   3.50   .65

Helsinki, 450th Anniv. A580

Designs: No. 1121, Baltic herring market (designer's name at UL).
No. 1122: a, Museum of Contemporary Art (blue building), vert. b, Cathedral, Senate Square (green building). c, Finlandia Hall (orange building). d, Glass Palace Film and Media Center (red building), vert.
No. 1123: a, Quest for the Lost Crown, Sveaborg Fortress (children and arch), vert. b, Like No. 1121, no designer's name. c, Forces of Light City Festival. d, Cellist at outdoor concert, Kaivopuisto Park.

2000, Jan. 12   *Perf. 14*
1121   A580 3.50m multi   1.60   .65
   Perf. 14½x14¾ (vert. stamps), 14¾x14½
1122   Booklet pane of 4   6.50
   a.-d.   A580 3.50m Any single   1.60   .65
1123   Booklet pane of 4   6.50
   a.-d.   A580 3.50m Any single   1.60   .65
   Complete booklet, #1122-1123   13.00

Valentine's Day — A581

Designs: a, Earth as backpack. b, Painters on ladder. c, Birds in balloon. d, Alien with magnet. e, Boy with heart-shaped balloon. f, Polar bear and igloo.

Perf. 13x12¾ on 3 sides
2000, Jan. 12
1124   Bklt. pane of 6 + 4 labels   8.75
   a.-f.   A581 3.50m Any single   1.60   .65
   Complete booklet, #1124   8.75

Souvenir Sheet of 2

Tommi Mäkinen, 1999 Rally World Champion — A582

a, Mäkinen behind wheel. b, Race car.
Illustration reduced.

2000, Mar. 3   *Perf. 13x13¼*
1125   A582 3.50m #a.-b.   3.25   3.25

Easter — A583

2000, Mar. 15   *Perf. 13¾x13¼*
1126   A583 3.50m Caltha palustris   1.60   .65

Moomin Type of 1998

a, Rat with broom looking at Moomins. b, Moomin with uniform, figures sprouting from ground. c, Moomin with hat in forest. d, Moomin with hat, children, in front of stove.

Perf. 13x12¾ on 3 sides
2000, Mar. 15
1127   Booklet pane of 4   6.75
   a.-d.   A554 1 Any single   1.60   .65
   Complete booklet, #1127   6.75
   e. As #1127, perf. 13¼ on 3 sides   6.75
   f.-i. As #a-d, perf. 13¼ on 3 sides   1.60   .65
   Booklet, #1127e   6.75

Nos. 1127a-1127d sold for 3.50m on day of issue. Number on stamp represents class of mail.
Issued: No. 1127e, 7/10/00.

Jubilee Year — A584

Turku Cathedral: a, Nave. b, Woman, votive candles. c, Christ on the Mount of Transfiguration, alterpiece. d, Infant baptism.

2000, Mar. 15 Litho.   *Perf. 14 Vert.*
1128   Booklet pane of 4   6.50
   a.-d.   A584 3.50m Any single   1.60   .65
   Complete booklet, #1128   6.50

Europa, 2000
Common Design Type
2000, May 9   *Perf. 13¼x13*
1129   CD17 3.50m multi   1.60   .65

Provincial Flowers

Spring Anemone A585

Blue Cornflower A586

Pulsatilla Patens — A587

Die Cut Perf. 13x12½
2000-2001   **Litho.**
Self-Adhesive
1130   A585 1 multi   1.60   .20
1131   A586 1 multi   1.60   .20
1132   A587 1 multi   1.60   .20
   a.   Pane, 5 each #1131-1132   17.00

Number on stamp represents class of mail. No. 1130 sold for 3.50m at time of release and was issued in sheets of 10. Nos. 1131-1132 each sold for 3.60m on day of issue.
Issued: No. 1130, 5/9. Nos. 1131-1132, 5/16/01.

Souvenir Sheet

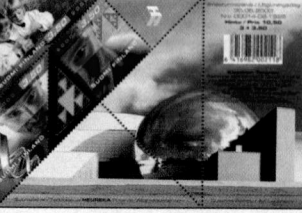

Science — A595

Designs: a, Children, molecuar model (triangular stamp). b, Man's face, DNA strand (rhomboid stamp). c, Man's face, Sierpinski triangles (square stamp).
Illustration reduced.

2000, May 30   *Perf. 14¼*
1140   A595 3.50m Sheet of 3, #a.-c.   5.00   5.00

No. 1140 has holographic image. Soaking in water may affect the hologram.

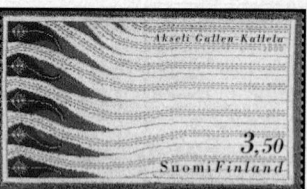

Finnish Design — A596

No. 1141: a, Rug, by Akseli Gallen-Kallela (1865-1931). b, Pearl Bird, by Birger Kaipiainen (1915-88). c, Pot, by Kyllikki Salmenhaara (1915-81). d, Leaf, by Tapio Wirkkala (1915-85). e, Detail from damask, by Dora Jung (1906-80). f, Glass vase, by Valter Jung (1879-1946).
Illustration reduced.

Perf. 13¼ on 3 sides
2000, Sept. 5   **Litho.**
1141   Booklet pane of 6   9.75
   a.-f.   A596 3.50m Any single   1.60   .65
   Booklet, #1141   9.75

Size of b, c, e, f: 30x35mm.

Coregonus Lavaretus A597

Lagopus Lagopus A598

Die Cut 10 Horiz. Sync. Type B
2000, Sept. 5
Self-Adhesive
Coil Stamps
1142 A597 2 multi   1.50   .25
Die Cut 10 Horiz. Sync. Type A
1143 A598 1 multi   1.60   .25
Nos. 1142-1143 sold for 3m and 3.50m respectively on day of sale.

> On modern stamps bearing the "denominations" "1" or "2," the number represents the class of mail.

Christmas
A599

2.50m, Costumed Tiernapojat carol singers. 3.50m, Bullfinch on door ornament, vert.

Serpentine Die Cut 14¼
2000, Nov. 3   **Photo.**
Self-Adhesive
1144-1145 A599 Set of 2   2.75   .85

Christmas Type of 2000
Design: No. 1146, Like #1145.

Serpentine Die Cut 13¾
2000, Nov. 3   **Litho.**
Self-Adhesive
1146 A599 3.50m multi + label   3.50 3.50
No. 1146 issued in sheets of 20 that sold for 120m, together with a separate sheet of stickers that could be affixed on the label. The labels attached to the stamps are separated by a row of interrupted serpentine die cutting. Labels could be personalized with photographs taken at some sale sites.

European
Year of
Languages
A600

2001, Jan. 17   Litho.   Perf. 13¼
1147 A600 1 multi   1.60   .65
No. 1147 sold for 3.50m on day of sale.

World Ski Championships,
Lahti — A601

No. 1148: a, Ski jumper Janne Ahonen (yellow helmet). b, Skier Mika Myllylä. Illustration reduced.

2001, Jan. 17
1148 A601 3.50m Horiz. pair,
           #a-b   3.25 3.25

Valentine's
Day — A602

No. 1149: a, Oval wreath. b, Basket of flowers, letter. c, Heart-shaped wreath. d, Bouquet of flowers, letter. e, Flowers, tea set. f, Flowers, heart-shaped pastry.

Serpentine Die Cut 11½x11¾ on 3 Sides
2001, Jan. 17   **Photo.**
Self-Adhesive
1149   Booklet pane of 6   10.00
a.-f.   A602 1 Any single   1.60   .65
        Booklet, #1149   10.00
Nos. 1149a-1149f each sold for 3.50m on day of issue.

Souvenir Sheet

Donald Duck Comics in Finland, 50th
Anniv. — A603

No. 1150: a, Mickey Mouse, Donald Duck, Santa Claus, Goofy. b, First comics, silhouette of boy. c, Tin soldier with Finnish flag, Chip and Dale (25x30mm). d, Finnish epic hero Väinämöinen, silhouette of Donald Duck. e, Helsinki Cathedral, Donald Duck.

Perf. 7¾ on 3 or 4 Sides
2001, Mar. 13   **Litho.**
1150 A603 1 Sheet of 5, #a-e   8.50 5.25
Nos. 1150a-1150e sold for 3.50m each on day of issue.

Santa Claus and
Sleigh — A604

2001-04   Serpentine Die Cut 14½x14
Self-Adhesive
1151 A604 1 multi   1.60   .65
a.   Serpentine die cut 13¾x13¼
        ('04)   1.75 1.75
No. 1151 sold for 3.60m on day of issue. No. 1151a sold for 65c on day of issue. No. 1151, 4/2/01. No. 1151a, 12/04.

Europa
A605

2001, Apr. 2   **Perf. 13x13½**
1152 A605 5.40m multi   2.50 1.25

Easter — A606

No. 1153: a, Chick. b, Decorated egg. Illustration reduced.

2001, Apr. 2   **Perf. 13¼**
1153 A606 3.60m Horiz. pair,
           #a-b   3.25 3.25

Souvenir Sheet

Verla Mill, UNESCO World Heritage
Site — A607

Denominations in: a, UL. b, UR. c, LL. d, LR.

2001, Apr. 2
1154 A607 3.60m Sheet of 4,
                    #a-d   7.00 7.00

Orienteering
World
Championships,
Tampere — A608

2001, May 16
1155 A608 3.60m multi   1.60   .65
Values are for stamps with surrounding selvage.

Souvenir Sheet

Woodpeckers — A609

No. 1156: a, Dendrocopos minor (32x36mm). b, Picoides tridactylus (29x36mm). c, Dendrocopos leucotos (32x42mm). d, Dendrocopos major (29x42mm). e, Picus canus (32x41mm). f, Dryocopus martius (29x41mm).

Perf. 14½x14¼ on 2, 3 or 4 Sides
2001, May 16
1156 A609 3.60m Sheet of 6,
                    #a-f   9.00 9.00

Marine
Life — A610

No. 1157: a, Lampetra fluviatilis. b, Aspius aspius. c, Coregonus albula.
Type C Syncopation (1st stamp, #1157): On the top, groups of 3 holes at left and right and a central group of four holes, separated by 2 oval holes equal in width to 4 holes.

Perf. 10 Horiz. Sync. Type C
2001, Sept. 6   **Photo.**
Self-Adhesive
Coil Stamps
1157   Horiz. strip of 3   4.75
a.-c.   A610 2 Any single   1.50   .50
Nos. 1157a-1157c were sold in boxes of 100 stamps that sold at a discount price of 270m on day of sale. The franking value on the day of sale for each stamp was 3m.

Birds
A611

No. 1158: a, Parus caeruleus. b, Motacilla alba. c, Oriolus oriolus.

Perf. 10 Horiz. Sync. Type B
2001, Sept. 6   **Photo.**
Self-Adhesive
Coil Stamps
1158   Horiz. strip of 3   5.00 3.50
a.-c.   A611 1 Any single   1.60   .65
Nos. 1158a-1158c were sold in boxes of 100 stamps that sold at a discount price of 330m on day of sale. The franking value on the day of sale for each stamp was 3.60m.

History of Gulf
of Finland
A612

No. 1159: a, Utö Lighthouse. b, Wreck of the St. Mikael. c, Diver exploring St. Mikael. d, Opossum shrimp, isopod. e, Ship's cabin and nautical chart (32x55mm).

Perf. 13¼x13¾ on 2 or 3 Sides
2001, Sept. 6   **Litho.**
1159   Booklet pane of 5   9.00   —
a.-e.   A612 1 Any single   1.75   .70
        Booklet, #1159   9.00
Nos. 1159a-1159e each sold for 3.60m on day of sale.

Christmas
A613

Designs: 2.50m, Elf reading Santa's book, candle. 3.60m, Elf delivering package on sled, horiz.

Serpentine Die Cut 14¼
2001, Oct. 26   **Photo.**
Self-Adhesive
1160 A613 2.50m multi   1.25   .50
1161 A613 3.60m multi   1.75   .70
Slightly larger examples of Nos. 1160-1161 serpentine die cut 14 are known on first day and other covers produced by the postal service. They were not sold unused to the public.

100 Cents = 1 Euro (€)

Flowers — A614

National Symbols
A615

Heraldic Lion — A616

Type A614 — No. 1162, Myosotis scorpioides: a, Forty-one flowers. b, Four flowers, five buds. c, One flower, four buds. d, Entire plant. e, Five flowers.
No. 1163, Convallaria majallis: a, Leaf, stem with five flowers. b, Two leaves, stem with eight flowers. c, Two flowers. d, Two leaves, stem with five flowers. e, Entire plants.
Type A615: 50c, Swan, vert. 60c, Birch. 1, Flag and bird. 90c, Kymintehtaalta, by Victor Westerholm. €1.30, Granite cliff. €2.50, Spruce. €3.50, Pine.

Die Cut Perf. 15
2002, Jan. 1　　　　　　　**Photo.**
Self-Adhesive

1162		Vert. strip of 5	.75 .75
a.-e.		A614 5c Any single	.20 .20
f.		As #1162, die cut perf 14	.75
g.-k.		A614 5c Any single, die cut perf 14	.20 .20
1163		Vert. strip of 5	1.50 1.50
a.-e.		A614 10c Any single	.30 .20

Die Cut Perf. 14

1164	A615	50c multi	1.40 .95
1165	A615	60c multi	1.75 1.25

Die Cut Perf. 13¾

1166	A615	1 multi	1.75 1.25
a.		Booklet pane of 8	14.50
		Booklet, #1166a	14.50

Die Cut Perf. 14¾x15

1167	A615	90c multi	2.50 1.75

Die Cut Perf. 12 Syncopated

1168	A616	€1 blue & multi	3.00 2.10

Die Cut Perf. 14¾x15

1169	A615	€1.30 multi	3.75 2.75
a.		Die cut perf 14 ('04)	3.75 2.75

Die Cut Perf. 14

1170	A615	€2.50 multi	7.25 5.25
1171	A615	€3.50 multi	10.00 7.00

Die Cut Perf. 12 Syncopated

1172	A616	€5 red & multi	14.50 10.50
		Nos. 1162-1172 (11)	48.15 35.05

No. 1166 sold for 60c on day of issue.
Die cut perf 14 examples of No. 1167 exist on first day and other covers produced by the postal service. They were not sold unused to the public.
No. 1169a issued 7/04. No. 1169a has a duller blue panel and a duller black denomination than that found on No. 1169, and a die cut perf. 14 version of No. 1169 that was available only on first day covers with 1/1/02 cancels, and which was not made available to the public unused. Nos. 1169 and 1169a were produced by different printers.
Nos. 1162f-1162k were printed and put on first day and other covers in 2002 but were not sold to the public until 2006.

Easter — A617

Die Cut Perf. 14
2002, Mar. 6　　　　　　**Photo.**
Self-Adhesive

1173	A617	60c multi	1.75 1.75

Souvenir Sheet

Elias Lönnrot (1802-84), Botanist, Linguist — A618

No. 1174: a, Plantain. b, Opening lines of "Kalevala" (denomination at UL). c, Closing lines of "Kalevala" (denomination at UR). d, Portrait.

Perf. 13¼ on 3 or 4 Sides
2002, Mar. 6　　　　　　**Litho.**

1174	A618	60c Sheet of 4, #a-d	7.00 7.00

Souvenir Sheet

Old Rauma, UNESCO World Heritage Site — A619

Denominations at: a, UL. b, UR. c, LL. d, LR.

2002, Mar. 6　　　　　　**Perf. 13½**

1175	A619	60c Sheet of 4, #a-d	7.00 7.00

Europa — A620

2002, Apr. 15　　　　　　**Perf. 13**

1176	A620	60c multi	1.75 1.75

Gulf of Finland Type of 2001

No. 1177: a, Birds, fish. b, Sailboat, plankton. c, Flounder on sea bed. d, Shrimp, herring. e, Tvärminne Zoological Station, ship, isopod, oceanographic equipment, mussels (32x55mm).

Perf. 13¼x13¾ on 2 or 3 Sides
2002, Apr. 15

1177		Booklet pane of 5	8.75 —
a.-e.	A612	1 Any single	1.75 1.10
		Booklet, #1177	8.75

Nos. 1177a-1177e each sold for 60c on day of issue.

Sibelius Monument, Helsinki, by Eila Hiltunen A621

2002, May 3　　　　　　**Perf. 13**

1178	A621	60c multi	1.75 1.75

National Symbols Type of 2002 Without Finland Post Emblem

Designs: 60c, Juniperus communis. 1, Reindeer in Lapland.

Die Cut Perf. 14
2002, Oct. 9　　　　　　**Photo.**
Self-Adhesive

1179	A615	60c multi	1.75 1.25
1180	A615	1 multi	1.75 1.25

No. 1180 sold for 60c on day of issue.

Christmas
A622

Designs: 45c, Horse-drawn sleigh. 60c, Angel with trumpet, vert.

Serpentine Die Cut 14¼
2002, Nov. 1
Self-Adhesive

1181-1182	A622	Set of 2	3.00 3.00

Fish — A623

No. 1183: a, Abramis brama. b, Salmo trutta lacustris. c, Esox lucius.

Syncopated Die Cut Perf. 10 Horiz.
2003, Jan. 15
Self-Adhesive
Coil Stamps

1183		Horiz. strip of 3	4.75 3.00
a.-c.		A623 2 Any single	1.50 1.00

Nos. 1183a-1183c were sold in boxes of 100 that sold at a discount price of €47 on day of issue. The franking value on the day of issue for each stamp was 50c.

Birds — A624

No. 1184: a, Cuculus canorus. b, Alauda arvensis. c, Perisoreus infaustus.

Syncopated Die Cut Perf. 10 Horiz.
2003, Jan. 15
Self-Adhesive
Coil Stamps

1184		Horiz. strip of 3	5.25 3.75
a.-c.		A624 1 Any single	1.75 1.25

Nos. 1184a-1184c were sold in boxes of 100 that sold at a discount price of €57 on day of issue. The franking value on the day of issue for each stamp was 60c.

Viivi and Wagner, by Jussi Tuomola — A625

No. 1185: a, Viivi and Wagner running. b, Viivi and Wagner dancing. c, Viivi writing love letter. d, Wagner and Viivi in bed. e, Viivi and Wagner kissing. f, Wagner reading love letter.

Serpentine Die Cut 11½x11¾ on 3 Sides
2003, Jan. 15
Self-Adhesive

1185		Booklet pane of 6	11.00
a.-f.		A625 1 Any single	1.75 1.25
		Booklet, #1185	11.00

Nos. 1185a-1185f each sold for 60c on day of issue.

Ice Hockey World Championships — A626

2003, Mar. 3　**Litho.**　**Perf. 13¼x13¾**

1186	A626	65c multi	1.90 1.90

St. Bridget (1303-73) A627　　Viola Wittrockiana A628

2003, Mar. 3　　　　　　**Perf. 13**

1187	A627	65c multi	1.90 1.90

Die Cut Perf. 13¾x14
2003, Mar. 3　　　　　　**Photo.**
Self-Adhesive

1188	A628	65c multi	1.90 1.90

Fighting Wood Grouses, by Ferdinand von Wright — A629

2003, Mar. 3　**Die Cut Perf. 13¾**
Self-Adhesive

1189	A629	90c multi	2.50 2.50

Airplanes A630

No. 1190: a, Super Caravelle. b, Airbus 320. c, Junkers Ju 52/3m. d, Douglas DC-3.

Perf. 14x14½ on 3 Sides
2003, Mar. 3

1190		Booklet pane of 4 + 4 etiquettes	7.75
a.-d.	A630	65c Any single	1.90 1.90
		Complete booklet, #1190	7.75

Finnair, 80th anniv.; Powered flight, cent.

Europa A631

No. 1191 — Posters by Lasse Hietala: a, Woman with newspaper. b, Hearts.

2003, May 7　**Litho.**　**Perf. 13¾x13¼**

1191	A631	65c Pair, #a-b	3.75 3.75

Souvenir Sheet

Flora and Fauna Seen in
Summer — A632

No. 1192: a, Moth, flowers (35x29mm). b,
Dragonfly, grasshopper (44x35mm). c, Grasshopper, caterpillar, thistle (35x25mm). d, Frog,
flowers, butterfly, insects (44x36mm). e, Magpie, snail, flowers (35x46mm). f, Hedgehog,
bee, ant, spider, flowers (44x29mm).

Perf. 14½ on 2 or 3 Sides
2003, May 7
1192 A632 65c Sheet of 6, #a-
       f   11.50 11.50

Moomins
A633

No. 1193: a, Moomin ancestors. b, Moomins
around stove. c, Moomin standing on hands in
water. d, Moomin and fox. e, Moomin looking
at film negative. f, Moomin with hat, flowers.

Serpentine Die Cut 11½x11¾ on 3
Sides
2003, May 7   **Photo.**
Self-Adhesive
1193   Booklet pane of 6   11.50
a.-f.   A633 1 Any single   1.90 1.90
         Complete booklet, #1193   11.50

Nos. 1193a-1193f each sold for 65c on day
of issue.

Cupid
A634

Serpentine Die Cut 11½ Syncopated
2003, May 14   **Litho.**
Self-Adhesive
1194 A634 1 multi   1.90 1.90

No. 1194 could be personalized. It sold for
65c on day of issue.

Lingonberries — A635

Serpentine Die Cut 14
2003, Sept. 10   **Photo.**
Self-Adhesive
1195 A635 65c multi   1.90 1.90

Philanthropists
A636

No. 1196: a, Juho (1852-1913) and Maria
(1858-1923) Lallukka. b, Emil Aaltonen (1869-
1949), vert. c, Heikki Huhtamäki (1900-70),
vert. d, Antti (1883-1962) and Jenny Wihuri. e,
Alfred Kordelin (1868-1917), vert. f, Amos
Anderson (1878-1961), vert.

Perf. 13¼x13¾, 13¾x13¼ on 3 Sides
2003, Sept. 10   **Litho.**
1196   Booklet pane of 6   11.50   —
a.-f.   A636 65c Any single   1.90 1.90
         Complete booklet, #1196   11.50

Lighthouses — A637

No. 1197: a, Bengtskär. b, Russarö. c,
Rönnskär. d, Harmaja Grahara. e, Söderskär.

2003, Sept. 10   **Perf. 13¼x13¾**
1197 A637 Sheet of 5   9.50 9.50
a.-e.   1 Any single   1.90 1.90

Nos. 1197a-1197e sold for 65c on day of
issue. Size of No. 1197a, 28x45mm; Nos.
1197b-1197e, 21x36mm.

Christmas
A638

Designs: 45c, Elf mailing letter. 65c, Elf with
ginger biscuit on baking pan, vert.

Serpentine Die Cut 14x14¼, 14¼x14
2003, Oct. 31   **Photo.**
Self-Adhesive
1198-1199 A638 Set of 2   3.25 3.25

Slightly larger versions of No. 1198 with a
serpentine die cutting of 13¼x13¾ and of No.
1199 with a serpentine die cutting of 13¾x13¼
exist only on first day and other covers produced by the postal service. They were not
sold unused to the public.

Apples
A639

Serpentine Die Cut 11½ Syncopated
2003, Oct. 31   **Litho.**
Self-Adhesive
1200 A639 1 multi   1.90 1.90

No. 1200 could be personalized. It sold for
65c on day of issue.

Pres. Tarja Halonen,
60th
Birthday — A640

2003, Dec. 1   Litho.   Perf. 13
1201 A640 65c multi
                                     1.90 1.90

Linnaea
Borealis — A641

Die Cut Perf. 14
2004, Jan. 14   **Photo.**
Self-Adhesive
1202 A641 30c multi   .85   .85

Souvenir Sheet

Johan Ludvig Runeberg (1804-77),
Poet — A642

No. 1203: a, Title page of *Tales of Ensign
Stahl.* b, Sven Dufva with gun. c, Illustration for
"Our Country." d, Sculpture of Runeberg.

Perf. 13½x13¼ on 3 or 4 Sides
2004, Jan. 14   **Litho.**
1203 A642 65c Sheet of 4, #a-d   7.50 7.50

Jean Sibelius
(1865-1957),
Composer
A643

No. 1204: a, Satu, and Sibelius, paintings by
Akseli Gallen-Kallela. b, Hands of Sibelius on
piano keyboard. c, Swans, musical score by
Sibelius.
No. 1205: a, Sibelius' house, Ainola. b,
Sibelius and wife, Aino. c, Score of "Voces
Intimae."

Die Cut Perf. 10 Horiz., Syncopated
at Top
2004, Jan. 14   **Photo.**
Coil Stamps
Self-Adhesive
1204   Horiz. strip of 3   5.00
a.-c.   A643 2 Any single   1.60 1.60
1205   Horiz. strip of 3   5.75
a.-c.   A643 1 Any single   1.90 1.90

Nos. 1204a-1204c each sold for 55c on day
of issue and have two short syncopations;
Nos. 1205a-1205c each sold for 65c on day of
issue, and have one large syncopation.

Love — A644

Text and: a, Rose. b, Man kissing. c,
Woman's eye. d, Man and woman embracing.
e, Elderly woman. f, Hand pulling petal from
daisy.

Serpentine Die Cut 11½x11¾ on 3
Sides
2004, Jan. 14
Self-Adhesive
1206   Booklet pane of 6   11.50
a.-f.   A644 1 Any single   1.90 1.90

Nos. 1206a-1206f each sold for 65c on day
of issue.

Ursus Arctos — A645

2004, Mar. 1   Die Cut Perf. 14
Self-Adhesive
1207 A645 2 multi   1.60 1.60

No. 1207 sold for 55c on day of issue.

Rose — A646

2004, Mar. 1   Booklet Stamp
Self-Adhesive
1208 A646 1 multi   1.90 1.90
a.   Booklet pane of 10   19.00

No. 1208 sold for 65c on day of issue. Booklet pane was sold folded.

Easter
Flowers — A647

Die Cut Perf. 14
2004, Mar. 1   **Litho.**
Self-Adhesive
1209 A647 65c multi   1.90 1.90

Heraldic Lion Type of 2002
Die Cut Perf. 12 Syncopated
2004, Mar. 1
Self-Adhesive
1210 A616 €3 multi   8.75 8.75

Swallows
A648

Orchid
A649

Serpentine Die Cut 11½ Syncopated
2004, Mar. 26
Self-Adhesive
1211 A648 1 multi   1.90 1.90
1212 A649 1 multi   1.90 1.90

Nos. 1211-1212 each sold for 65c on day of
issue, and they could be personalized.

Souvenir Sheet

Norse Gods — A650

No. 1213: a, Head of Luonnotar (33x30mm). b, Luonnotar with arms extended (22x42mm).

Perf. 14¼x14½ (#1213a), 14½x14 (#1213b)

2004, Mar. 26
1213 A650 65c Sheet of 2, #a-b   3.75 3.75

Forest Animals — A651

No. 1214: a, Red squirrel (40x40mm). b, Raven (40x31mm). c, Variable hare (40x34mm). d, Stoat (40x37mm). e, Lizard (40x34mm). f, Red fox (40x40mm).

Perf. 13¼x14 on 2 or 3 Sides
2004, Apr. 28
1214 A651 65c Sheet of 6, #a-
f   11.50 11.50

Fragaria
Vesca — A652

Die Cut Perf. 14
2004, Apr. 28   Photo.
Self-Adhesive
1215 A652 65c multi   1.90 1.90

Luxembourg Gardens, by Albert Edelfelt (1854-1905) A653

2004, Apr. 28   Self-Adhesive
1216 A653 1 multi   1.90 1.90
No. 1216 sold for 65c on day of issue.

Europa — A654

No. 1217: a, People around campfire. b, Family in rowboat.

2004, Apr. 28   Litho.   *Perf. 13*
1217 A654 65c Horiz. pair, #a-b   *3.75 3.75*

Snufkin and Moomintroll A655

Litho. & Embossed
2004, Sept. 8   *Perf. 13*
Flocked Paper
1218 A655 1 multi   1.90 1.90
No. 1218 sold for 65c on day of issue.

Shipwreck Treasures A656

No. 1219: a, Tankard. b, Fabric seal. c, Gold watch. d, Powder keg. e, Figurehead (23x40mm).

Perf. 14¼x13 on 3 or 4 Sides
2004, Sept. 8
1219   Booklet pane of 5   9.50   —
a.-e. A656 1 Any single   1.90 1.90
        Complete booklet, #1219   9.50
Stamps sold for 65c each on day of issue.

Souvenir Sheet

Sammallahdenmäki, UNESCO World Heritage Site — A657

No. 1220: a, Stone wall and trees. b, Lichen-covered rocks.

2004, Sept. 8 Litho. *Perf. 14¾x14¼*
1220 A657 65c Sheet of 2, #a-b   3.75 3.75

Rights of the Child — A658

No. 1221: a, Two girls. b, Boy painting. Illustration reduced.

2004, Oct. 29   *Perf. 13*
1221 A658 65c Horiz. pair, #a-b   4.00 4.00

Christmas A659

Designs: 45c, Boy writing Santa Claus. 65c, Christmas tree branch, candle, ornaments, vert.

Serpentine Die Cut 13¼x13¾, 13¾x13¼
2004, Oct. 29   Photo.
Self-Adhesive
1222-1223 A659   Set of 2   3.25 3.25

Rotary International, Cent. — A660

2005, Jan. 14   Litho.   *Perf. 13*
1224 A660 65c blue & gold   1.90 1.90

Lahti, Cent. — A661

No. 1225: a, Sibelius Concert Hall. b, Illuminated radio towers.

2005, Jan. 14
1225 A661 65c Pair, #a-b   3.75 3.75

Oulo, 400th Anniv. — A662

No. 1226: a, Child with pail and shovel. b, Woman riding bicycle. Illustration reduced.

2005, Jan. 14
1226 A662 65c Horiz. pair, #a-b 3.75 3.75

Publishing of First Finnish Almanac, 300th Anniv. — A663

Die Cut Perf. 14
2005, Jan. 14   Photo.
Self-Adhesive
1227 A663 65c multi   1.90 1.90

Children's Toys — A664

No. 1228: a, Stuffed lion and tiger. b, Stuffed elephant and dog. c, Airplane, train and car. d, Stuffed bear and rabbit.

Serpentine Die Cut 9¼x8½ on 3 Sides
2005, Jan. 14
Self-Adhesive
1228   Booklet pane of 4   7.75
a.-d. A664 1 Any single   1.90 1.90
Stamps sold for 65c each on day of issue.

End of Winter War, 65th Anniv. — A665

2005, Mar. 2   Litho.   *Perf. 13*
1229 A665 65c multi   1.90 1.90

Easter — A666

2005, Mar. 2 *Serpentine Die Cut 14*
Self-Adhesive
1230 A666 65c multi   1.90 1.90

Apple Blossom — A667

Die Cut Perf. 14
2005, Mar. 2   Photo.
Self-Adhesive
Booklet Stamp
1231 A667 1 multi   1.90 1.90
a.   Booklet pane of 10   19.00
No. 1231 sold for 65c on day of issue.

Door Decoration, by Eliel Saarinen A668

Copper Stove Door — A669

Chair Back — A670

Stained Glass Window, by Olga Gummerus-Ehrström — A671

Dining Room A672

Exterior of Hvitträsk
A673

Die Cut Perf. 10 Horiz., Syncopated at Top
2005, Mar. 2   Litho.
Self-Adhesive
Coil Stamps

1232	Horiz. strip of 3	5.00	
a.	A668 2 multi	1.60	1.60
b.	A669 2 multi	1.60	1.60
c.	A670 2 multi	1.60	1.60
1233	Horiz. strip of 3	5.75	
a.	A671 1 multi	1.90	1.90
b.	A672 1 multi	1.90	1.90
c.	A673 1 multi	1.90	1.90

Hvitträsk, home and studio of architects Eliel Saarinen, Armas Lindgren and Herman Gesellius. Nos. 1232a-1232c each sold for 55c on day of issue and have two short syncopations. Nos. 1233a-1233c each sold for 65c on day of issue and have one large syncopation.

Miniature Schnauzer
A674

Serpentine Die Cut 11½ Syncopated
2005, Apr. 6
1234   A674 1 multi   1.90   1.90

Sold for 65c on day of issue. Sheets could be personalized.

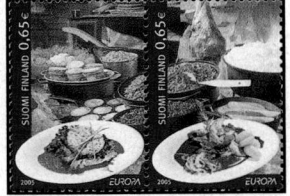

Europa — A675

No. 1235 — Plates with: a, Whitefish and beetroot tartare on lettuce. b, Sauteed reindeer and grouse breast.

2005, May 11   **Perf. 13**
1235   A675 65c Pair, #a-b   3.75   3.75

Souvenir Sheet

Golf — A676

No. 1236: a, Man driving ball (44x31mm). b, Boy holding flag, vert. (30x44mm). c, Boy putting, vert. (33x44mm). d, Putter and golf ball (44x32mm).

Perf. 13¼ on 3 or 4 Sides
2005, May 11
1236   A676 65c Sheet of 4, #a-d   7.50   7.50

World Track Championships, Helsinki — A677

Serpentine Die Cut 12½
2005, May 11
Self-Adhesive
1237   A677 65c multi   1.90   1.90

Buses in Finland, Cent. A678

Die Cut Perf. 14
2005, May 11   **Photo.**
Self-Adhesive
1238   A678 65c brown & black   1.90   1.90

Horses — A679

No. 1239: a, Icelandic horse with saddle. b, White Welsh Mountain pony. c, New Forest pony with blanket. d, Shetland Pony.

Serpentine Die Cut 9¼x8½ on 3 Sides
2005, May 11
Self-Adhesive

1239	Booklet pane of 4	7.50	
a.-d.	A679 1 Any single	1.90	1.90

Stamps sold for 65c each on day of issue.

Cloudberries — A680

Die Cut Perf. 14
2005, Sept. 7   **Photo.**
Self-Adhesive
1240   A680 1 multi   1.90   1.90

Sold for 65c on day of issue.

Fruits I, by Kari Huhtamo
A681

Die Cut Perf. 11½ Syncopated
2005, Sept. 7   Litho.
Self-Adhesive
1241   A681 90c multi   2.50   2.50

Sheets could be personalized.

Souvenir Sheet

Petäjävesi Church, UNESCO World Heritage Site — A682

No. 1242: a, Bell tower (26x47mm). b, Church (34x39mm). c, Angel (26x39mm). d, Chandelier (27x39mm).

2005, Sept. 7   Litho.   **Perf. 13**
1242   A682 65c Sheet of 4, #a-d   7.50   7.50

Icebreakers — A683

No. 1243: a, Urho, 1975. b, Otso, 1986. c, Fennica, 1993. d, Botnica, 1998.

2005, Sept. 7   **Perf. 13¼ Horiz.**

1243	Booklet pane of 4	7.50	—
a.-d.	A683 1 Any single	1.90	1.90

Each stamp sold for 65c on day of issue.

Souvenir Sheet

Imperial Winter Egg, by Carl Fabergé — A684

No. 684: a, Flowers in egg. b, Frost detail of egg.

Litho. & Embossed with Foil Application
2005, Oct. 28   **Perf. 13**
1244   A684 €3.50 Sheet of 2, #a-b   20.00   20.00

A limited quantity of 2,500 numbered sheets, which sold for €30, exist. Value, $100.

Christmas — A685

Designs: 50c, Santa Claus reading letters. 1, Santa Claus and wife dancing, horiz.

Serpentine Die Cut 13¾x13¼, 13¼x13¾
2005, Oct. 28   **Photo.**
Self-Adhesive
1245-1246   A685   Set of 2   3.75   3.75

No. 1246 sold for 65c on day of issue.

Postal Employees Union, Cent. — A686

2006, Jan. 11   Litho.   **Perf. 13**
1247   A686 65c multi   1.90   1.90

Heart — A687

2006, Jan. 11   **Die Cut**
Self-Adhesive
1248   A687 65c bright pink   1.90   1.90

Renaming of Helsinki University Library as National Library of Finland
A688

2006, Jan. 11   **Die Cut Perf. 14x13¾**
Self-Adhesive
1249   A688 1 multi   1.90   1.90

Sold for 65c on day of issue.

Forest in Winter — A689

2006, Jan. 11   **Photo.**
Self-Adhesive
1250   A689 1 multi   1.90   1.90

Sold for 65c on day of issue.

Taxis, Cent. — A690

No. 1251: a, Women passengers in taxi, 1906. b, Driver standing in front of 1929 Chevrolet taxi. c, Driver leaning on 1957 Pobeda taxi. d, Driver on phone at taxi stand next to Mercedes-Benz taxi.

Serpentine Die Cut 11¼ Vert.
2006, Jan. 11   Litho.
Self-Adhesive

1251	Booklet pane of 4	7.50	
a.-d.	A690 65c Any single	1.90	1.90

Souvenir Sheet

Johan Vilhelm Snellman (1806-81), Philosopher — A691

No. 1252: a, Caricature of Snellman, masthead of his newspaper "Saima." b, Snellman's portrait on 1940 five thousand mark note. c, Snellman and European railway map. d, Ilmarinen, first Finnish locomotive, and European railway map.

2006, Jan. 11   **Perf. 13¼x13¾**
1252 A691 65c Sheet of 4, #a-d   7.50 7.50

Parliament, Cent. — A692

Serpentine Die Cut 14
2006, Feb. 3   **Litho.**
Self-Adhesive
1253 A692 1 multi   1.90 1.90
Sold for 65c on day of sale.

Flag — A693

2006, Mar. 1
Self-Adhesive
1254 A693 1 multi   1.90 1.90
Sold for 65c on day of sale.

Lilacs — A694

Die Cut Perf. 13¾x14
2006, Mar. 1   **Photo.**
Self-Adhesive
1255 A694 1 multi   1.90 1.90
Sold for 65c on day of sale.

Easter — A695

2006, Mar. 1   **Litho.**   *Die Cut*
Self-Adhesive
1256 A695 65c multi   1.90 1.90

Fortune Teller, by Helene Schjerfbeck — A696

Die Cut Perf. 13¾x14
2006, Mar. 1   **Photo.**
Self-Adhesive
1257 A696 95c multi   2.75 2.75

Bil-Bol Poster A697

Errotaja 2 Poster A698

Concert Finnois Poster A699

Madonna A700   **Self-Portrait A701**

Home of Artist Akseli Gallen-Kallela, Tarvaspää — A702

Die Cut Perf. 10 Horiz., Syncopated at Top
2006, Mar. 1
Coil Stamps
Self-Adhesive
1258   Horiz. strip of 3   5.00
   a.   A697 2 multi   1.60 1.60
   b.   A698 2 multi   1.60 1.60
   c.   A699 2 multi   1.60 1.60

Die Cut Perf. 10, Syncopated at Right
1259   Vert. strip of 3   5.75
   a.   A700 1 multi   1.90 1.90
   b.   A701 1 multi   1.90 1.90
   c.   A702 1 multi   1.90 1.90

Akseli Gallen-Kallela (1865-1931), artist. Nos. 1258a-1258c each sold for 55c and Nos. 1259a-1259c each sold for 65c on day of issue.

Souvenir Sheet

Norse Mythology — A703

No. 1260 — Fairy tale book cover illustrations by Rudolf Koivu: a, Fairy. b, Fairy dancing with Santa Claus, vert.

Perf. 13½x13¼, 13¼x13½ (#1260b)
2006, Mar. 29   **Litho.**
1260 A703 65c Sheet of 2, #a-b   3.75 3.75

Europa A704

2006, May 4   **Perf. 13**
1261 A704 65c multi   1.90 1.90

Vaasa, 400th Anniv. — A705

2006, May 4
1262 A705 1 multi   1.90 1.90
Sold for 65c on day of issue.

A706

Serpentine Die Cut 10 Syncopated
2006, May 4
Booklet Stamp
Self-Adhesive
1263 A706 1 multi   1.90 1.90
   a.   Booklet pane of 8   15.00

No. 1263 sold for 65c on day of issue. Design portion of stamp could be personalized.

Summer Activities A707

No. 1264: a, Woman fishing. b, Children making flower garlands. c, Man making sauna whisk. d, Woman weeding flower garden.

Serpentine Die Cut 11¼ Vert.
2006, May 4
Self-Adhesive
1264   Booklet pane of 4   7.50
   a.-d.   A707 1 Any single   1.90 1.90

Nos. 1264a-1264d each sold for 65c on day of issue.

Cats — A708

No. 1265: a, Striped house cat. b, British shorthair (gray cat). c, Ragdoll cat (brown and white). d, Chocolate Persian cat.

2006, May 4
Self-Adhesive
1265   Booklet pane of 4   7.50
   a.-d.   A708 1 Any single   1.90 1.90

Nos. 1265a-1265d each sold for 65c on day of issue.

Suomenlinna (Sveaborg) Fortress, Helsinki — A709

No. 1266: a, Ship without oars. b, Ship with oars facing fortress. c, Ship with oars, windmill.

Litho. & Engr.
2006, May 4   **Perf. 13x12¾**
1266   A709   Booklet pane of 3   5.75 —
   a.-c.   1 Any single   1.90 1.90
     Complete booklet, #1266   5.75

Nos. 1266a-1266c each sold for 65c on day of issue. See Sweden No. 2530.

Blueberries and Blueberry Pie — A710

Die Cut Perf. 14
2006, Aug. 24   **Photo.**
Self-Adhesive
1267 A710 1 multi   2.00 2.00
Sold for 70c on day of issue.

Miniature Sheet

Family Life — A711

No. 1268: a, Family watching television. b, Woman writing letter to husband.

2006, Aug. 24   *Die Cut*
Self-Adhesive
1268 A711 1 Sheet of 2, #a-b   4.00 4.00
   Nos. 1268a-1268b each sold for 70c on day of issue.

Newspaper Journalism — A712

Die Cut Perf. 14
2006, Sept. 22   Litho.
Self-Adhesive
1269 A712 70c multi   2.00 2.00

Points, Textile Art by Ritva Puotila — A713

Serpentine Die Cut 11½ Syncopated
2006, Sept. 22
Self-Adhesive
1270 A713 1 multi   2.00 2.00
   Sold for 70c on day of issue.

Dryas Octopetala A714

Serpentine Die Cut 14
2006, Sept. 22   Photo.
Self-Adhesive
1271 A714 1 multi   2.00 2.00
   Sold for 70c on day of issue.

Art of Snow and Ice — A715

No. 1272: a, Horse. b, Kemi Snow Castle. c, Wall of ice tiles. d, Snowball lantern.

Serpentine Die Cut 11¾ Vert.
2006, Sept. 22
Self-Adhesive
1272   Booklet pane of 4   8.00
  a.-d.   A715 1 Any single   2.00 2.00
   Nos. 1272a-1272d each sold for 70c on day of issue. Denominations are printed in thermographic ink that changes color when warmed.

Miniature Sheet

Finnish Postage Stamps, 150th Anniv. — A716

No. 1273: a, 70c, Heraldic lion and fleurons in white. b, 95c, Part of vignette of type A1. c, €1.40, Heraldic lion in gold, fleurons in red.

Litho. & Embossed With Foil Application
2006, Oct. 27   *Perf. 13½x13*
1273 A716   Sheet of 3, #a-c   8.75 8.75

A717

Christmas — A718

Serpentine Die Cut 13¼x13¾
2006, Oct. 27   Photo.
Self-Adhesive
1274 A717 50c multi   1.40 1.40
Serpentine Die Cut 13¾x13¼
1275 A718   1 multi   2.00 2.00
   No. 1275 sold for 70c on day of issue.

Television Broadcasting in Finland, 50th Anniv. — A719

Die Cut Perf. 14
2007, Jan. 24   Litho.
Self-Adhesive
1276 A719 70c multi   1.90 1.90

Faces — A720

2007, Jan. 24
Self-Adhesive
1277 A720 70c multi   1.90 1.90

Winter Landscape, Haminalahti, by Ferdinand von Wright A721

2007, Jan. 24   Photo.
Self-Adhesive Booklet Stamp
1278 A721 1 multi   1.90 1.90
  a.   Booklet pane of 10   19.00
   Sold for 70c on day of issue.

Sun Setting Over Flower Field — A722

2007, Jan. 24   Litho.
Self-Adhesive
1279 A722 €1.40 multi   3.75 3.75

Souvenir Sheet

Intl. Polar Year — A723

No. 1280: a, Snowflake. b, Aurora borealis.

Perf. 13 Syncopated (#1280a), 13 (#1280b)
Litho. With Hologram Affixed
2007, Jan. 24
1280 A723 70c Sheet of 2, #a-b   3.75 3.75
       + label

Truck Transport — A724

No. 1281: a, Log truck. b, Milk truck. c, Dump truck. d, Tractor trailer.

Serpentine Die Cut 12¼ Horiz.
2007, Jan. 24   Litho.
Self-Adhesive
1281   Booklet pane of 4   7.75
  a.-d.   A724 70c Any single   1.90 1.90

Central Organization of Finnish Trade Unions — A725

2007, Mar. 7   *Perf. 13*
1282 A725 70c multi   1.90 1.90

Soccer Association of Finland, Cent. — A726

2007, Mar. 7   *Die Cut*
Self-Adhesive
1283 A726 70c multi   1.90 1.90

Easter — A727

2007, Mar. 7   *Die Cut Perf. 14*
Self-Adhesive
1284 A727 1 multi   1.90 1.90
   Sold for 70c on day of issue. Portions of design were applied by a thermographic process producing a shiny, raised effect.

Lilium Enchantment A728

2007, Mar. 7   Litho.
Booklet Stamp
Self-Adhesive
1285 A728 1 multi   1.90 1.90
  a.   Booklet pane of 10   19.00
   No. 1285 sold for 70c on day of issue.

Souvenir Sheet

Bishop Michael Agricola (1509-57) — A729

No. 1286: a, Text and open book. b, Agricola preaching.

2007, Mar. 7   *Perf. 13½*
1286 A729 70c Sheet of 2, #a-b   3.75 3.75

Tampere Cathedral, Cent. A730

2007, May 9   *Perf. 13¼*
1287 A730 70c multi   1.90 1.90

Europa — A731

No. 1288: a, Scouts on sailboat. b, Scouts around campfire.
Illustration reduced.

2007, May 9   *Perf. 12½x13*
1288 A731   Horiz. pair   3.80 3.80
  a.-b.   70c Either single   1.90 1.90
   Scouting, cent.

Helsinki Public Transportation — A732

No. 1289: a, Commuter train in station. b, Tram on street. c, Subway train on bridge. d, People in Kamppi Bus Station.

Serpentine Die Cut 12¼ Horiz.
2007, May 9
Self-Adhesive
1289   Booklet pane of 4   7.75
  a.-d.   A732 1 Any single   1.90 1.90
   Nos. 1289a-1289d each sold for 70c on day of issue.

Moomins A733

No. 1290: a, Little My in water. b, Moomintroll running across rocks. c, Moominpappa at typewriter. d, Snork Maiden picking flowers. e, Moominmamma making pancakes. f, Snufkin amid flowers.

Serpentine Die Cut 11¾ Vert.
2007, May 9   **Photo.**
Self-Adhesive

1290	Booklet pane of 6	11.50	
a.-f.	A733 1 Any single	1.90	1.90

Nos. 1290a-1290f each sold for 70c on day of issue.

Souvenir Sheet

2007 Eurovision Song Contest, Helsinki — A734

No. 1291: a, Eurovision Song Contest emblem. b, Finnish singers Laila Kinnunen, Marion Rung, Kirka Babitzin and Katri Helena. c, 2006 Finnish contest-winning band, Lordi. d, Lead singer of Lordi.

Litho. With Foil Application
2007, May 9   ***Die Cut***
Self-Adhesive

1291	A734 70c Sheet of 4, #a-d	7.75	7.75

A735

Serpentine Die Cut 11½ Syncopated
2007, Aug. 24   **Litho.**
Self-Adhesive

1292	A735 1 multi	1.90	1.90

No. 1292 sold for 70c on day of issue. Design portion of stamp could be personalized.

Home Furnishings — A736

No. 1293 — Picture frame and: a, Empire-style chair, "Porvoo Garland" wallpaper, 19th

cent. (country name at LR). b, Paimio chair, "2+3" wallpaper, 20th cent. (country name at LL).

Die Cut Perf. 14
2007, Aug. 24   **Litho.**
Self-Adhesive

1293	Pair	3.80	
a.-b.	A736 1 Either single	1.90	1.90

Nos. 1293a-1293b each sold for 70c on day of issue.

Raspberries and Raspberry Cake — A737

Die Cut Perf. 14
2007, Aug. 24   **Photo.**
Self-Adhesive
Booklet Stamp

1294	A737 1 multi	1.90	1.90

No. 1294 sold for 70c on day of issue.

Finnish Olympic Committee, Cent. — A738

2007, Aug. 24   **Litho.**
Self-Adhesive
Booklet Stamp

1295	A738 1 multi	1.90	1.90

No. 1295 sold for 70c on day of issue.

Butterflies — A739

No. 1296: a, Apatura iris. b, Scolitantides orion. c, Colias palaeno.

Die Cut Perf. 10 Vert., Syncopated at Right
2007, Aug. 24
Self-Adhesive
Coil Stamps

1296	Vert. strip of 3	5.75	
a.-c.	A739 1 Any single	1.90	1.90

Nos. 1296a-1296c had a franking value of 70c on day of issue. A roll of 100 stamps sold for €68.

Miniature Sheet

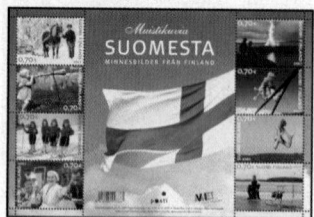

Independence, 90th Anniv. — A740

No. 1297 — Photographs of people at work and play: a, Man and horse hauling wood. b, Girl blowing horn. c, Four boys with skis. d, People at coffee break. e, People near bonfire. f, Boy ski jumping. g, Boy diving. h, Ice fisherman. Nos. 1297a-1297d are black and white photos.

2007, Nov. 2   **Perf. 13¼**

1297	A740 Sheet of 8	16.50	16.50
a.-h.	70c Any single	2.00	2.00

Souvenir Sheet

Woodwork — A741

No. 1298: a, Zitan armchair with dragon design, China (denomination at left). b, Modern Finnish bowls (denomination at right).

2007, Nov. 2   **Perf. 13¼x14¼**

1298	A741	Sheet of 2	4.25	4.25
a.-b.		70c Either single	2.00	2.00

See Hong Kong Nos. 1298-1299.

A742

Christmas — A743

Serpentine Die Cut 13¼x13¾
2007, Nov. 2   **Photo.**
Self-Adhesive

1299	A742 55c multi	1.60	1.60

Serpentine Die Cut 13¾x13¼

1300	A743 1 multi	2.00	2.00

No. 1300 sold for 70c on day of issue.

SEMI-POSTAL STAMPS

Arms — SP1

1922, May 15   **Unwmk.**   **Typo.**   **Perf. 14**

B1	SP1 1m + 50p gray & red	.80	8.50
	Never hinged	1.75	
a.	Perf. 13x13½	8.00	
	Never hinged	12.00	

Red Cross Standard SP2

Symbolic SP3

Ship of Mercy — SP4

1930, Feb. 6

B2	SP2 1m + 10p red org & red	1.75	9.00
B3	SP3 1½m + 15p grysh grn & red	1.50	9.00

B4	SP4 2m + 20p dk bl & red	3.75	42.50
	Nos. B2-B4 (3)	7.00	60.50
	Set, never hinged	10.00	

The surtax on this and subsequent similar issues was for the benefit of the Red Cross Society of Finland.

Church in Hattula — SP5

SP8

Designs: 1½m+15p, Castle of Hameenlinna. 2m+20p, Fortress of Viipuri.

1931, Jan. 1   **Engr.**
Cross in Red

B5	SP5 1m + 10p gray grn	1.60	11.00
B6	SP5 1½m + 15p lil brn	9.00	14.00
B7	SP5 2m + 20p dull bl	1.60	30.00
	Nos. B5-B7 (3)	12.20	55.00
	Set, never hinged	30.00	

1931, Oct. 15   **Typo.**   **Rouletted 4, 5**

B8	SP8 1m + 4m black	15.00	30.00
	Never hinged	22.50	

The surtax was to assist the Postal Museum of Finland in purchasing the Richard Granberg collection of entire envelopes.

Helsinki University Library — SP9

Nikolai Church at Helsinki — SP10

2½m+25p, Parliament Building, Helsinki.

1932, Jan. 1   **Perf. 14**

B9	SP9 1¼m + 10p ol bis & red	1.60	11.00
B10	SP10 2m + 20p dp vio & red	.75	7.00
B11	SP9 2½m + 25p lt blue & red	1.25	27.50
	Nos. B9-B11 (3)	3.60	45.50
	Set, never hinged	7.00	

Bishop Magnus Tawast SP12

Michael Agricola SP13

Design: 2½m+25p, Isacus Rothovius.

1933, Jan. 20   **Engr.**

B12	SP12 1¼m + 10p blk brn & red	2.75	9.50
B13	SP13 2m + 20p brn vio & red	.75	3.50
B14	SP13 2½m + 25p indigo & red	.80	6.00
	Nos. B12-B14 (3)	4.30	19.00
	Set, never hinged	8.50	

Evert
Horn — SP15

Designs: 2m+20p, Torsten Stalhandske.
2½m+25p, Jakob (Lazy Jake) de la Gardie.

1934, Jan.
Cross in Red

B15	SP15	1¼m + 10p brown	.80	3.00
B16	SP15	2m + 20p gray lil	1.40	5.00
B17	SP15	2½m + 25p gray	.80	3.50
	Nos. B15-B17 (3)		3.00	11.50
	Set, never hinged		4.75	

Mathias	Robert Henrik
Calonius	Rehbinder
SP18	SP21

Designs: 2m+20p, Henrik C. Porthan.
2½m+25p, Anders Chydenius.

1935, Jan. 1
Cross in Red

B18	SP18	1¼m + 15p brown	.80	2.75
B19	SP18	2m + 20p gray lil	1.75	5.00
B20	SP18	2½m + 25p gray bl	.65	3.00
	Nos. B18-B20 (3)		3.20	10.75
	Set, never hinged		4.75	

1936, Jan. 1

2m+20p, Count Gustaf Mauritz Armfelt.
2½m+25p, Count Arvid Bernard Horn.
Cross in Red

B21	SP21	1¼m + 15p dk brn	.65	2.75
B22	SP21	2m + 20p vio brn	2.75	6.50
B23	SP21	2½m + 25p blue	.65	3.00
	Nos. B21-B23 (3)		4.05	12.25
	Set, never hinged		8.00	

Type
"Uusimaa"
SP24

Type
"Turunmaa" — SP25

Design: 3½m+35p, Type "Hameenmaa."

1937, Jan. 1
Cross in Red

B24	SP24	1¼m + 15p brown	.65	2.50
B25	SP25	2m + 20p brn lake	12.00	7.00
B26	SP25	2½m + 25p indigo	.65	3.00
	Nos. B24-B26 (3)		13.30	12.50
	Set, never hinged		37.50	

Aukuste	Skiing
Makipeska	SP31
SP27	

Designs: 1¼m+15p, Robert Isidor Örn.
2m+20p, Edward Bergenheim. 3½m+35p,
Johan Mauritz Nordenstam.

1938, Jan. 5   Engr.
Cross in Red

B27	SP27	50p + 5p dk grn	.50	1.25
B28	SP27	1¼m + 15p dk brn	.90	2.50
B29	SP27	2m + 20p rose lake	6.75	6.75
B30	SP27	3½m + 35p dk blue	.60	2.75
	Nos. B27-B30 (4)		8.75	13.25
	Set, never hinged		17.50	

1938, Jan. 18

Designs: #B32, Skijumper. #B33, Skier.

B31	SP31	1.25m + 75p sl grn	3.00	11.00
B32	SP31	2m + 1m dk car	3.00	11.00
B33	SP31	3.50m + 1.50m dk blue	3.00	11.00
	Nos. B31-B33 (3)		9.00	33.00
	Set, never hinged		17.50	

Ski championships held at Lahti.

Soldier — SP34

Battlefield at
Solferino
SP35

1938, May 16

B34	SP34	2m + ½m blue	1.25	4.00
	Never hinged		3.25	

Victory of the White Army over the Red
Guards. The surtax was for the benefit of the
members of the Union of the Finnish Front.

1939, Jan. 2
Cross in Scarlet

B35	SP35	50p + 5p dk grn	.65	1.40
B36	SP35	1¼m + 15p dk brn	.75	2.25
B37	SP35	2m + 20p lake	11.00	11.00
B38	SP35	3½m + 35p dk bl	.65	2.50
	Nos. B35-B38 (4)		13.05	17.15
	Set, never hinged		30.00	

Intl. Red Cross Soc., 75th anniv.

> Catalogue values for unused
> stamps in this section, from this
> point to the end of the section, are
> for Never Hinged items.

Soldiers with	Arms of
Crossbows	Finland
SP36	SP40

1¼m+15p, Cavalryman. 2m+20p, Soldier of
Charles XII of Sweden. 3½m+35p, Officer and
soldier of War with Russia, 1808-1809.

1940, Jan. 3
Cross in Red

B39	SP36	50p + 5p dk grn	1.10	1.60
B40	SP36	1¼m + 15p dk brn	2.25	2.40
B41	SP36	2m + 20p lake	4.00	2.75
B42	SP36	3½m + 35p dp ultra	3.00	3.75
	Nos. B39-B42 (4)		10.35	10.50

The surtax aided the Finnish Red Cross.

1940, Feb. 15   Litho.

B43	SP40	2m + 2m indigo	.50	1.25

The surtax was given to a fund for the preservation of neutrality.

Mason	Soldier's
SP41	Emblem
	SP45

1.75m+15p, Farmer plowing. 2.75m+25p,
Mother and child. 3.50m+35p, Finnish flag.

1941, Jan. 2   Engr.
Cross in Red

B44	SP41	50p + 5p green	.55	.70
B45	SP41	1.75m + 15p brown	1.40	2.00
B46	SP41	2.75m + 25p brn car	7.00	8.00
B47	SP41	3.50m + 35p dp ultra	1.60	2.75
	Nos. B44-B47 (4)		10.55	13.45

See Nos. B65-B68.

1941, May 24   Unwmk.

B48	SP45	2.75m + 25p brt ultra	.80	.80

The surtax was for the aid of the soldiers
who fought in the Russo-Finnish War.

Aland	Lapland
Arms — SP46	Arms — SP51

Coats of Arms: 1.75m+15p, Nyland.
2.75m+25p, Finland's first arms. 3.50m+35p,
Karelia. 4.75m+45p, Satakunta.

1942, Jan. 2   Perf. 14
Cross in Red

B49	SP46	50p + 5p green	1.25	1.25
B50	SP46	1.75m + 15p brown	1.40	2.25
B51	SP46	2.75m + 25p dark red	1.40	2.25
B52	SP46	3.50m + 35p deep ultra	1.40	2.25
B53	SP46	4.75m + 45p dk sl grn	1.10	2.75
	Nos. B49-B53 (5)		6.55	10.75

The surtax aided the Finnish Red Cross.

1943, Jan. 6   Inscribed "1943"

Coats of Arms: 2m+20p, Hame.
3.50m+35p, Eastern Bothnia. 4.50m+45p,
Savo.
Cross in Red

B54	SP51	50p + 5p green	.40	1.00
B55	SP51	2m + 20p brown	1.00	2.00
B56	SP51	3.50m + 35p dark red	1.00	2.00
B57	SP51	4.50m + 45p brt ultra	2.25	5.50
	Nos. B54-B57 (4)		4.65	10.50

The surtax aided the Finnish Red Cross.

Soldier's
Helmet and
Sword — SP55

Mother and
Children — SP56

1943, Feb. 1   Perf. 13

B58	SP55	2m + 50p dk brown	.50	.85
B59	SP56	3.50m + 1m brown red	.50	.85

The surtax was for national welfare.

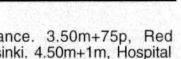

Red Cross
Train — SP57

2m+50p, Ambulance. 3.50m+75p, Red
Cross Hospital, Helsinki. 4.50m+1m, Hospital
plane.

1944, Jan. 2   Perf. 14
Cross in Red

B60	SP57	50p + 25p green	.30	.30
B61	SP57	2m + 50p sepia	.50	.80
B62	SP57	3.50m + 75p ver	.50	.80
B63	SP57	4.50m + 1m brt ultra	1.10	2.75
	Nos. B60-B63 (4)		2.40	4.65

The surtax aided the Finnish Red Cross.

Symbols of	Wrestling
Peace	SP62
SP61	

1944, Dec. 1

B64	SP61	3.50m + 1.50m dk red brn	.40	.85

The surtax was for national welfare.

Type of 1941 Inscribed "1945"
1945, May 2   Photo. & Engr.
Cross in Red

B65	SP41	1m + 25p green	.20	.50
B66	SP41	2m + 50p brown	.20	.65
B67	SP41	3.50m + 75p brn car	.20	.65
B68	SP41	4.50m + 1m dp ultra	.60	1.25
	Nos. B65-B68 (4)		1.20	3.05

The surtax was for the Finnish Red Cross.

1945, Apr. 16   Engr.   Perf. 13½

2m+1m, Gymnast. 3.50m+1.75m, Runner.
4.50m+2.25m, Skier. 7m+3.50m, Javelin
thrower.

B69	SP62	1m + 50p bluish grn	.20	.80
B70	SP62	2m + 1m dp red	.20	.80
B71	SP62	3.50m + 1.75m dull vio	.20	.80
B72	SP62	4.50m + 2.25m ultra	.50	1.00
B73	SP62	7m + 3.50m dull brn	.80	2.00
	Nos. B69-B73 (5)		1.90	5.40

Fishing	Nurse and
SP67	Children
	SP71

Designs: 3m+75p, Churning. 5m+1.25m,
Reaping. 10m+2.50m, Logging.

Engraved; Cross Typo. in Red
1946, Jan. 7

B74	SP67	1m + 25p dull grn	.40	.60
B75	SP67	5m + 75p lilac brn	.30	.40
B76	SP67	5m + 1.25m rose red	.40	.60
a.		Red cross omitted	650.00	
B77	SP67	10m + 2.50m ultra	.50	1.10
	Nos. B74-B77 (4)		1.60	2.70

The surtax was for the Finnish Red Cross.

1946, Sept. 2   Engr.

Design: 8m+2m, Doctor examining infant.

B78	SP71	5m + 1m green	.40	.60
B79	SP71	8m + 2m brown vio	.40	.60

The surtax was for the prevention of
tuberculosis.

Nos. B78 and B79 Surcharged with New Values in Black

1947, Apr. 1

B80	SP71	6m + 1m on 5m + 1m	.40	.70
B81	SP71	10m + 2m on 8m + 2m	.40	.70

The surtax was for the prevention of tuberculosis.

Medical Examination of Infants — SP74

Designs: 10m+2.50m, Infant held by the feet. 12m+3m, Mme. Alli Paasikivi and a child. 20m+5m, Infant standing.

1947, Sept. 15   Engr.

B82	SP73	2.50m + 1m green	.50	1.00
B83	SP74	6m + 1.50m dk red	.60	1.50
B84	SP74	10m + 2.50m red brn	.70	1.50
B85	SP73	12m + 3m dp blue	1.10	2.10
B86	SP74	20m + 5m dk red vio	1.50	3.25
		Nos. B82-B86 (5)	4.40	9.35

The surtax was for the prevention of tuberculosis.
For surcharges see Nos. B91-B93.

Zachris Topelius — SP78

7m+2m, Fredrik Pacius. 12m+3m, Johan L. Runeberg. 20m+5m, Fredrik Cygnaeus.

Engraved; Cross Typo. in Red
1948, May 10   Unwmk.   Perf. 14

B87	SP78	3m + 1m green	.50	.80
B88	SP78	7m + 2m rose red	.60	.85
B89	SP78	12m + 3m brt blue	.65	.95
B90	SP78	20m + 5m dk vio	.75	1.25
		Nos. B87-B90 (4)	2.50	3.85

The surtax was for the Finnish Red Cross.

Nos. B83, B84 and B86 Surcharged with New Values and Bars in Black

1948, Sept. 13   Engr.   Perf. 13½

B91	SP74	7m + 2m on #B83	1.40	3.00
B92	SP74	15m + 3m on #B84	1.40	3.00
B93	SP74	24m + 6m on #B86	2.00	3.75
		Nos. B91-B93 (3)	4.80	9.75

The surtax was for the prevention of tuberculosis.

Tying Birch Boughs SP79   Wood Anemone SP83

9m+3m, Bathers in Sauna house. 15m+5m, Rural bath house. 30m+10m, Cold plunge in lake.

Engraved; Cross Typo. in Red
1949, May 5   Perf. 13½x14

B94	SP79	5m + 2m dull grn	.45	.75
B95	SP79	9m + 3m dk car	.70	1.10
B96	SP79	15m + 5m dp blue	.70	1.10
B97	SP79	30m + 10m dk vio brn	1.90	3.25
		Nos. B94-B97 (4)	3.75	6.20

The surtax was for the Finnish Red Cross.

1949, June 2   Engr.
Inscribed: "1949"

B98	SP83	5m + 2m shown	.60	.85
B99	SP83	9m + 3m Wild rose	.65	1.00
B100	SP83	15m + 5m Coltsfoot	.75	1.50
		Nos. B98-B100 (3)	2.00	3.35

The surtax was for the prevention of tuberculosis.

Similar to Type of 1949

Designs: 5m+2m, Water lily. 9m+3m, Pasqueflower. 15m+5m, Bell flower cluster.

1950, Apr. 1
Inscribed: "1950"

B101	SP83	5m + 2m emer	2.25	2.25
B102	SP83	9m + 3m rose car	2.10	2.10
B103	SP83	15m + 5m blue	2.10	2.10
		Nos. B101-B103 (3)	6.45	6.45

The surtax was for the prevention of tuberculosis.

Hospital Entrance, Helsinki SP84   Blood Donor's Medal SP86

Design: 12m+3m, Giving blood.

Engraved; Cross Typo. in Red
1951, Mar. 17   Unwmk.   Perf. 14

B104	SP84	7m + 2m chocolate	1.10	1.50
B105	SP84	12m + 3m bl vio	1.10	1.50
B106	SP84	20m + 5m blue	2.00	3.00
		Nos. B104-B106 (3)	4.20	6.00

The surtax was for the Finnish Red Cross.

Capercaillie — SP87

Designs: 12m+3m, European cranes. 20m+5m, Caspian terns.

1951, Oct. 26   Engr.

B107	SP87	7m + 2m dk grn	1.90	2.50
B108	SP87	12m + 3m rose brn	1.90	2.50
B109	SP87	20m + 5m blue	1.90	2.50
		Nos. B107-B109 (3)	5.70	7.50

The surtax was for the prevention of tuberculosis.

Diver — SP88

Soccer Players SP89

#B112, Stadum, Helsinki. #B113, Runners.

1951-52

B110	SP88	12m + 2m rose car	1.10	1.60
B111	SP89	15m + 2m grn ('52)	1.10	1.60
B112	SP88	20m + 3m deep blue	1.10	1.60
B113	SP89	25m + 4m brn ('52)	1.10	1.60
		Nos. B110-B113 (4)	4.40	6.40

XV Olympic Games, Helsinki, 1952. The surtax was to help finance the games.
Issued: B110, B112, 11/16; B111, B113, 2/15/52.
Margin blocks of four of each denomination were cut from regular or perf-through-margin sheets and pasted by the selvage, overlapping, in a printed folder to create a kind of souvenir booklet. Value $60.

Field Marshal Mannerheim SP90   Great Titmouse SP91

Engraved; Cross Typo. in Red
1952, Mar. 4

B114	SP90	10m + 2m gray	1.50	2.10
B115	SP90	15m + 3m rose vio	1.50	2.10
B116	SP90	25m + 5m blue	1.50	2.10
		Nos. B114-B116 (3)	4.50	6.30

The surtax was for the Red Cross.

1952, Dec. 4   Engr.

Designs: 15m+3m, Spotted flycatchers and nest. 25m+5m, Swift.

B117	SP91	10m + 2m green	2.00	2.50
B118	SP91	15m + 3m plum	2.00	2.50
B119	SP91	25m + 5m deep blue	2.00	2.50
		Nos. B117-B119 (3)	6.00	7.50

The surtax was for the prevention of tuberculosis.

European Red Squirrel SP92

#B121, Brown bear. #B122, European elk.

Unwmk.
1953, Nov. 16   Engr.   Perf. 14

B120	SP92	10m + 2m red brown	2.25	2.50
B121	SP92	15m + 3m violet	2.25	2.50
B122	SP92	25m + 5m dark grn	2.25	2.50
		Nos. B120-B122 (3)	6.75	7.50

Surtax for the prevention of tuberculosis.

Children Receiving Parcel from Welfare Worker — SP93

Designs: 15m+3m, Aged woman knitting. 25m+5m, Blind basket-maker and dog.

Engraved; Cross Typo. in Red
1954, Mar. 8   Perf. 11½

B123	SP93	10m + 2m dk ol grn	1.25	1.40
B124	SP93	15m + 3m dk blue	1.40	1.75
B125	SP93	25m + 5m dk brown	1.40	1.75
		Nos. B123-B125 (3)	4.05	4.90

The surtax was for the Finnish Red Cross.

Bumblebees, Dandelions — SP94

European Perch — SP95

15m+3m, Butterfly. 25m+5m, Dragonfly.

Engraved; Cross Typo. in Red
1954, Dec. 7   Perf. 14

B126	SP94	10m + 2m brown	2.00	1.40
B127	SP94	15m + 3m carmine	2.00	1.60
B128	SP94	25m + 5m blue	2.00	1.60
		Nos. B126-B128 (3)	6.00	4.60

The surtax was for the prevention of tuberculosis.

Engraved; Cross Typo. in Red
1955, Sept. 26   Perf. 14

Designs: 15m+3m, Northern pike. 25m+5m, Atlantic salmon.

B129	SP95	10m + 2m dl grn	2.00	1.40
B130	SP95	15m + 3m vio brn	2.00	1.60
B131	SP95	25m + 5m dk bl	2.00	1.60
		Nos. B129-B131 (3)	6.00	4.60

Surtax for the Anti-Tuberculosis Society.

Gen. von Dobeln in Battle of Juthas, 1808 SP96   Waxwing SP97

Illustrations by Albert Edelfelter from J. L. Runeberg's "Tales of Ensign Stal": 15m+3m, Col. J. Z. Duncker holding flag. 25m+5m, Son of fallen Soldier.

Engraved; Cross Typo. in Red
1955, Nov. 24

B132	SP96	10m + 2m dp ultra	1.25	1.25
B133	SP96	15m + 3m dk red brn	1.50	1.50
B134	SP96	25m + 5m green	1.50	1.50
		Nos. B132-B134 (3)	4.25	4.25

The surtax was for the Red Cross.

Engraved; Cross Typo. in Red
1956, Sept. 25   Perf. 11½

Birds: 20m+3m, Eagle owl. 30m+5m, Mute swan.

B135	SP97	10m + 2m dl red brn	1.90	1.25
B136	SP97	20m + 3m bl grn	2.10	1.75
B137	SP97	30m + 5m blue	2.10	1.90
		Nos. B135-B137 (3)	6.10	4.90

Surtax for the Anti-Tuberculosis Society.

Pekka Aulin SP98   Wolverine (Glutton) SP99

Portraits: 10m+2m, Leonard von Pfaler. 20m+3m, Gustaf Johansson. 30m+5m, Viktor Magnus von Born.

Engraved; Cross Typo. in Red
1956, Nov. 26   Unwmk.

B138	SP98	5m + 1m grysh grn	.80	.75
B139	SP98	12m + 2m brown	1.40	1.40
B140	SP98	20m + 3m magenta	2.00	2.00
B141	SP98	30m + 5m lt ultra	2.00	2.00
		Nos. B138-B141 (4)	6.20	6.15

The surtax was for the Red Cross.

Engraved; Cross Typo. in Red
1957, Sept. 5   *Perf. 11½*

20m+3m, Lynx. 30m+5m, Reindeer.

B142	SP99	10m + 2m dull purple	1.75	1.40
B143	SP99	20m + 3m sepia	1.90	1.75
B144	SP99	30m + 5m dark blue	2.00	1.75
		Nos. B142-B144 (3)	5.65	4.90

The surtax was for the Anti-Tuberculosis Society. See Nos. B160-B165.

Red Cross Flag
SP100

Raspberry
SP101

1957, Nov. 25   Engr.
Cross in Red   *Perf. 14*

B145	SP100	10m + 2m ol grn	1.75	1.50
B146	SP100	20m + 3m maroon	1.75	1.50
B147	SP100	30m + 5m dull blue	1.75	1.50
		Nos. B145-B147 (3)	5.25	4.50

80th anniv. of the Finnish Red Cross.

Type of 1952

Flowers: 10m+2m, Lily of the Valley. 20m+3m, Red clover. 30m+5m, Hepatica.

Engraved; Cross Typo. in Red
1958, May 5   Unwmk.   *Perf. 14*

B148	SP91	10m + 2m green	1.75	1.25
B149	SP91	20m + 3m lilac rose	2.25	1.60
B150	SP91	30m + 5m ultra	2.25	1.60
		Nos. B148-B150 (3)	6.25	4.45

Surtax for the Anti-Tuberculosis Society.

Engraved; Cross Typo. in Red
1958, Nov. 20   *Perf. 11½*

20m+3m, Cowberry. 30m+5m, Blueberry.

B151	SP101	10m + 2m orange	1.25	1.00
B152	SP101	20m + 3m red	1.75	1.40
B153	SP101	30m + 5m dk blue	1.75	1.40
		Nos. B151-B153 (3)	4.75	3.80

The surtax was for the Red Cross.

Daisy — SP102

Reindeer
SP103

20m+5m, Primrose. 30m+5m, Cornflower.

Engraved; Cross Typo. in Red
1959, Sept. 7   Unwmk.

B154	SP102	10m + 2m green	2.50	1.75
B155	SP102	20m + 3m lt brown	3.50	2.25
B156	SP102	30m + 5m blue	3.50	2.25
		Nos. B154-B156 (3)	9.50	6.25

Surtax for the Anti-Tuberculosis Society.

Engraved; Cross Typo. in Red
1960, Nov. 24   *Perf. 11½*

#B158, Lapp & lasso. #B159, Mountains.

B157	SP103	10m + 2m dk gray	1.40	1.40
B158	SP103	20m + 3m gray vio	2.00	1.75
B159	SP103	30m + 5m rose vio	2.00	1.75
		Nos. B157-B159 (3)	5.40	4.90

The surtax was for the Red Cross.

Animal Type of 1957

Designs: 10m+2m, Muskrat. 20m+3m, Otter. 30m+5m, Seal.

Engr.; Cross at right, Typo. in Red
1961, Sept. 4

B160	SP99	10m + 2m brn car	1.75	1.50
B161	SP99	20m + 3m slate bl	2.25	2.00
B162	SP99	30m + 5m bl grn	2.25	2.00
		Nos. B160-B162 (3)	6.25	5.50

Surtax for the Anti-Tuberculosis Society.

Animal Type of 1957.

Designs: 10m+2m, Hare. 20m+3m, Pine marten. 30m+5m, Ermine.

Engraved; Cross Typo. in Red
1962, Oct. 1

B163	SP99	10m + 2m gray	2.00	1.25
B164	SP99	20m + 3m dl red brn	2.50	1.75
B165	SP99	30m + 5m vio bl	2.50	1.75
		Nos. B163-B165 (3)	7.00	4.75

The surtax was for the Anti-Tuberculosis Society.

Cross and Outstretched Hands
SP104

Engraved; Cross Typo. in Red
1963, May 8   Unwmk.   *Perf. 11½*

B166	SP104	10p + 2p red brn	.90	.90
B167	SP104	20p + 3p violet	1.10	1.10
B168	SP104	30p + 5p green	1.10	1.10
		Nos. B166-B168 (3)	3.10	3.10

The surtax was for the Red Cross.

Attending the Wounded
SP105

Red Cross Activities: 25p+4p, Hospital ship. 35p+5p, Prisoner-of-war health examination. 40p+7p, Gift parcel distribution.

Engraved; Cross Typo. in Red
1964, May 26   *Perf. 11½*

B169	SP105	15p + 3p vio bl	.75	.75
B170	SP105	25p + 4p green	1.00	.85
B171	SP105	35p + 5p vio brn	1.00	.85
B172	SP105	40p + 7p dk ol grn	1.00	.85
		Nos. B169-B172 (4)	3.75	3.30

The surtax was for the Red Cross.

Finnish Spitz — SP106

Artificial Respiration — SP107

Designs: 25p+4p, Karelian bear dog. 35p+5p, Finnish hunting dog.

Engraved; Cross Typo. in Red
1965, May 10   *Perf. 11½*

B173	SP106	15p + 3p org brn	2.00	1.40
B174	SP106	25p + 4p black	2.25	1.75
B175	SP106	35p + 5p gray brn	2.25	1.75
		Nos. B173-B175 (3)	6.50	4.90

Surtax for Anti-Tuberculosis Society.

1966, May 7   Litho.   *Perf. 14*

First Aid: 25p+4p, Skin diver rescuing occupants of submerged car. 35p+5p, Helicopter rescue in winter.

B176	SP107	15p + 3p multi	1.00	.90
B177	SP107	25p + 4p multi	1.00	.90
B178	SP107	35p + 5p multi	1.00	.90
		Nos. B176-B178 (3)	3.00	2.70

The surtax was for the Red Cross.

Birch — SP108

Horse-drawn Ambulance
SP109

Trees: 25p+4p, Pine. 40p+7p, Spruce.

1967, May 12   Litho.   *Perf. 14*

B179	SP108	20p + 3p multi	.75	.75
B180	SP108	25p + 4p multi	.75	.75
B181	SP108	40p + 7p multi	.75	.75
		Nos. B179-B181 (3)	2.25	2.25

Surtax for Anti-Tuberculosis Society. See Nos. B185-B187.

1967, Nov. 24   Litho.   *Perf. 14*

25p+4p, Ambulance, 1967. 40p+7p, Red Cross.

Cross in Red

B182	SP109	20p + 3p dl yel, grn & blk	.75	.75
B183	SP109	25p + 4p vio & blk	.75	.75
B184	SP109	40p + 7p dk grn, blk & dk ol	.75	.75
		Nos. B182-B184 (3)	2.25	2.25

The surtax was for the Red Cross.

Tree Type of 1967

Trees: 20p+3p, Juniper. 25p+4p, Aspen. 40p+7p, Chokecherry.

1969, May 12   Litho.   *Perf. 14*

B185	SP108	20p + 3p multi	.75	.75
B186	SP108	25p + 4p multi	.75	.75
B187	SP108	40p + 7p multi	.75	.75
		Nos. B185-B187 (3)	2.25	2.25

Surtax for Anti-Tuberculosis Society.

"On the Lapp's Magic Rock"
SP110

Designs: 30p+6p, Juhani blowing horn on Impivaara Rock, vert. 50p+10p, The Pale Maiden. The designs are from illustrations by Askeli Gallen-Kallelas for "The Seven Brothers" by Aleksis Kivi.

1970, May 8   Litho.   *Perf. 14*

B188	SP110	25p + 5p multi	.70	.60
B189	SP110	30p + 6p multi	.70	.60
B190	SP110	50p + 10p multi	.70	.60
		Nos. B188-B190 (3)	2.10	1.80

The surtax was for the Red Cross.

Cutting and Loading Timber
SP111

Designs: 30p+6p, Floating logs downstream. 50p+10p, Sorting logs at sawmill.

1971, Apr. 25   Litho.   *Perf. 14*

B191	SP111	25p + 5p multi	.70	.60
B192	SP111	30p + 6p multi	.70	.60
B193	SP111	50p + 10p multi	.70	.60
		Nos. B191-B193 (3)	2.10	1.80

Surtax for Anti-Tuberculosis Society.

Blood Donor and Nurse
SP112

30p+6p, Blood research (microscope, slides), vert. 50p+10p, Blood transfusion.

1972, Oct. 23

B194	SP112	25p + 5p multi	.65	.65
B195	SP112	30p + 6p multi	.65	.65
B196	SP112	50p + 10p multi	.65	.65
		Nos. B194-B196 (3)	1.95	1.95

Surtax was for the Red Cross.

Girl with Lamb, by Hugo Simberg — SP113

Paintings: 40p+10p, Summer Evening, by Vilho Sjöström. 60p+15p, Woman at Mountain Foun ain, by Juho Rissanen.

1973, Sept. 12   Litho.   *Perf. 13x12½*

B197	SP113	30p + 5p multi	.90	.90
B198	SP113	40p + 10p multi	1.40	1.40
B199	SP113	60p + 15p multi	1.40	1.40
		Nos. B197-B199 (3)	3.70	3.70

Surtax for the Finnish Anti-Tuberculosis Assoc. Birth centenaries of featured artists.

Morel
SP114

Mushrooms: 50p+10p, Chanterelle. 60p+15p, Boletus edulis.

1974, Sept. 24   Litho.   *Perf. 12½x13*

B200	SP114	35p + 5p multi	1.75	1.25
B201	SP114	50p + 10p multi	1.75	1.25
B202	SP114	60p + 15p multi	1.75	1.25
		Nos. B200-B202 (3)	5.25	3.75

Finnish Red Cross.

Echo, by Ellen Thesleff (1869-1954)
SP115

Paintings: 60p+15p, Hilda Wiik, by Maria Wiik (1853-1928). 70p+20p, At Home (old woman in chair), by Helene Schjerfbeck (1862-1946).

1975, Sept. 30   Litho.   *Perf. 13x12½*

B203	SP115	40p + 10p multi	.80	.75
B204	SP115	60p + 15p multi	1.10	1.00
B205	SP115	70p + 20p multi	1.10	1.00
		Nos. B203-B205 (3)	3.00	2.75

Finnish Red Cross. In honor of International Women's Year paintings by women artists were chosen.

Disabled Veterans' Emblem
SP116

Lithographed and Photogravure
1976, Jan. 15   *Perf. 14*

B206	SP116	70p + 30p multi	1.00	.95

The surtax was for hospitals for disabled war veterans.

Wedding
Procession
SP117

Designs: 70p+15p, Wedding dance, vert.
80p+20p, Bride, groom, matron and pastor at
wedding dinner.

1976, Sept. 15   Litho.   Perf. 13
B207 SP117 50p + 10p multi   .55   .55
B208 SP117 70p + 15p multi   .70   .70
B209 SP117 80p + 20p multi   .75   .75
    Nos. B207-B209 (3)   2.00 2.00

Surtax for Anti-Tuberculosis Society.

Disaster Relief
SP118

Designs: 80p+15p, Community work.
90p+20p, Blood transfusion service.

1977, Jan. 19   Litho.   Perf. 14
B210 SP118 50p + 10p multi   .50   .50
B211 SP118 80p + 15p multi   .70   .70
B212 SP118 90p + 20p multi   .70   .70
    Nos. B210-B212 (3)   1.90 1.90

Finnish Red Cross centenary.

Long-distance
Skiing
SP119

Design: 1m+50p, Ski jump.

1977, Oct. 5   Litho.   Perf. 13
B213 SP119 80p + 40p multi   2.50 2.50
B214 SP119 1m + 50p multi   1.50 1.50

Surtax was for World Ski Championships,
Lahti, Feb. 17-26, 1978.

Saffron
Milkcap
SP120

Edible Mushrooms: 80p+15p, Parasol, vert.
1m+20p, Gypsy.

1978, Sept. 13   Litho.   Perf. 13
B215 SP120 50p + 10p multi   1.00   .80
B216 SP120 80p + 15p multi   1.25 1.25
B217 SP120 1m + 20p multi   1.25 1.25
    Nos. B215-B217 (3)   3.50 3.30

Surtax was for Red Cross. See Nos. B221-
B223.

Pehr Kalm,
1716-1779
SP121

Finnish Scientists: 90p+15p, Title page of
Pehr Adrian Gadd's (1727-97) book, vert.
1.10m+20p, Petter Forsskal (1732-63).

Perf. 12½x13, 13x12½
1979, Sept. 26   Litho.
B218 SP121 60p + 10p multi   .40   .40
B219 SP121 90p + 15p multi   .65   .65
B220 SP121 1.10m + 20p multi .65   .65
    Nos. B218-B220 (3)   1.70 1.70

Surtax for Finnish Anti-Tuberculosis Assoc.

Mushroom Type of 1978
Edible Mushrooms: 60p+10p, Woolly milkcap. 90p+15p, Orange-cap boletus, vert.
1.10m+20p, Russula paludosa.

1980, Apr. 19   Litho.   Perf. 13
B221 SP120 60p + 10p multi   .70   .50
B222 SP120 90p + 15p multi   .90   .70
B223 SP120 1m + 20p multi   .90   .70
    Nos. B221-B223 (3)   2.50 1.90

Surtax was for Red Cross.

Fuchsia — SP122

1981, Aug. 24   Litho.   Perf. 13
B224 SP122 70p + 10p shown   .55   .55
B225 SP122 1m + 15p African
                violet   .75   .75
B226 SP122 1.10m + 20p Gera-
                nium   .95   .95
    Nos. B224-B226 (3)   2.25 2.25

Surtax for Finnish Anti-Tuberculosis Assoc.

Garden
Dormouse
SP123

1982, Aug. 16   Litho.   Perf. 13
B227 SP123 90p + 10p shown   .75   .65
B228 SP123 1.10m + 15p Flying
                squirrels   1.10   .75
B229 SP123 1.20m + 20p Euro-
                pean minks 1.25   .95
    Nos. B227-B229 (3)   3.10 2.35

Surtax was for Red Cross. No. B228 vert.

Forest and
Wetland
Plants
SP124

1m+20p, Chickweed wintergreen.
1.20m+25p, Marsh violet. 1.30m+30p, Marsh
marigold.

1983, July 7   Litho.   Perf. 13
B230 SP124 1m + 20p multi   .70   .50
B231 SP124 1.20m + 25p multi .90   .70
B232 SP124 1.30m + 30p multi .90   .70
    Nos. B230-B232 (3)   2.50 1.90

Surtax for Finnish Anti-Tuberculosis Assoc.

Globe
Puzzle — SP125

2m+40p, Symbolic world communication.

1984, May 28   Litho.   Perf. 13
B233 SP125 1.40m + 35p multi .85   .85
B234 SP125 2m + 40p multi   1.25 1.25

Surtax for Red Cross.

Butterflies
SP126

1986, May 22   Litho.   Perf. 13
#B235, Anthocharis cardamines. #B236,
Nymphalis antiopa. #B237, Parnassius apollo.
B235 SP126 1.60m + 40p multi 1.10   .80
B236 SP126 2.10m + 45p multi 1.60 1.25
B237 SP126 5m + 50p multi   3.25 3.25
    Nos. B235-B237 (3)   5.95 5.30

Surtax for Red Cross.

Festivals
SP127

1988, Mar. 14   Litho.   Perf. 13
B238 SP127 1.40m +40p Christ-
                mas   .85   .85
B239 SP127 1.80m +45p Easter 1.25 1.25
B240 SP127 2.40m +50p Mid-
                summer   1.50 1.50
    Nos. B238-B240 (3)   3.60 3.60

Surtax for the Red Cross.

Heodes
virgaureae on
Goldrod Plant
SP128

Butterflies and plants: No. B242,
Agrodiaetus amandus on meadow vetchling.
No. B243, Inachis io on tufted vetch.

1990, Apr. 6   Photo.   Perf. 12x11½
B241 SP128 1.50m +40p multi 1.00 1.00
B242 SP128 2m +50p multi   1.25 1.25
B243 SP128 2.70m +60p multi 1.50 1.50
    Nos. B241-B243 (3)   3.75 3.75

Surtax for the natl. Red Cross Soc.

Paintings by Helene
Schjerfbeck — SP129

Designs: #B244a, The Little Convalescent,
#B244b, Green Still-Life.

1991, Mar. 8   Litho.   Perf. 13
B244 SP129 Pair   3.00 3.00
a.-b.   2.10m +50p any single 1.50 1.50

Surtax for philately.

Butterflies
SP130

#B245, Xestia brunneopicta. #B246,
Acerbia alpina. #B247, Baptria tibiale.

Litho. & Embossed
1992, Apr. 22   Perf. 13
B245 SP130 1.60m +40p multi 1.00 1.00
B246 SP130 2.10m +50p multi 1.25 1.25
B247 SP130 5m +60p multi   2.75 2.75
    Nos. B245-B247 (3)   5.00 5.00

Surtax for Finnish Red Cross. Embossed
"Arla 100" in braille for Arla Institute, training
center for the blind, cent.

Autumn
Landscape of
Lake
Pielisjarvi, by
Eero Jarnefelt
SP131

a, Tree-covered hill. b, Lake shoreline.

1993, Mar. 19   Litho.   Perf. 13
B248 SP131 2.30m + 70p Pair,
    #a.-b.   3.00 3.00

Surtax for philately.

Finnhorses
SP132

1994, Mar. 11   Litho.   Perf. 13
B249 SP132 2m +40p Draft
                horses   1.25 1.25
B250 SP132 2.30m +50p Trotter 1.25 1.25
B251 SP132 4.20m +60p War
                horses, vert. 2.25 2.25
    Nos. B249-B251 (3)   4.75 4.75

Surtax for Finnish Red Cross.

Paintings, by Albert Edelfelt (1854-
1905) — SP133

#B252, Playing Boys on the Shore. #B253,
Queen Blanche.

1995, Mar. 1   Litho.   Perf. 13½
B252 2.40m +60p multi   1.50 1.50
    Size: 22x31mm
B253 2.40m +60p multi   1.50 1.50
    a. SP133 Pair, #B252-B253   3.00 3.00

Surtax for philately.

Chickens
SP134

1996, Mar. 18   Litho.   Perf. 13
B254 SP134 2.80m +60p Chicks 1.60 1.60
B255 SP134 3.20m +70p Hens   1.90 1.90
B256 SP134 3.40m +70p Roost-
                er, vert.   2.00 2.00
    Nos. B254-B256 (3)   5.50 5.50

Surtax for Finnish Red Cross.

The Aino Myth, by
Akseli Gallen-
Kallela (1865-
1931)
SP135

Designs: No. B257, Väinämöinen proposing
marriage to Aino in forest. No. B258, Aino
jumping into water to escape Väinämöinen.
No. B259, Aino at shore for bath.

1997, Sept. 5   Litho.   Perf. 13½x13
Booklet Stamps
B257	SP135	2.80m +60p multi	1.60	1.60
B258	SP135	2.80m +60p multi	1.60	1.60
B259	SP135	2.80m +60p multi	1.60	1.60
a.		Booklet pane, #B257-B259	5.00	5.00
		Complete booklet, #B259a	5.00	

No. B258 is 33x46mm.

Pigs — SP136

2.80m+60p, Sow, piglets. 3.20m+70p,
Three piglets. 3.40m+70p, Pig's head.

1998, Mar. 12   Litho.   Perf. 13
B260	SP136	2.80m +60p multi	1.60	1.60
B261	SP136	3.20m +70p multi	1.90	1.90
B262	SP136	3.40m +70p multi	2.00	2.00
		Nos. B260-B262 (3)	5.50	5.50

Surtax for Finnish Red Cross.

Paintings by
Hugo Simberg
(1873-1917)
SP137

a, Garden of Death. b, Wounded Angel.

Perf. 13¼x13¾
1999, Sept. 24   Litho.
B263		Booklet pane of 2	4.00	4.00
a.-b.		SP137 3.50m +50p any single	1.90	
		Complete booklet, #B263	4.00	

Surtax for philately.

Cow and
Calf — SP138

Perf. 13¾x13¼
2000, Mar. 15   Litho.
B264	SP138	3.50m +70p Bull, vert.	2.00	2.00

Perf. 13¼x13¾
B265	SP138	4.80m +80p shown	2.75	2.75

Surtax for Finnish Red Cross.

AIR POST STAMPS

No. 178
Overprinted in
Red

1930, Sept. 24   Unwmk.   Perf. 14
C1	A28	10m gray lilac	140.00	250.00
		Never hinged	225.00	
a.		1830 for 1930	2,500.	3,750.

Overprinted expressly for use on mail carried in "Graf Zeppelin" on return flight from Finland to Germany on Sept. 24, 1930, after which trip the stamps ceased to be valid for postage. Forgeries are almost always on No. 205, rather than No. 178.

Catalogue values for unused stamps in this section, from this point to the end of the section, are for Never Hinged items.

Douglas DC-
2 — AP1

1944   Engr.
C2	AP1	3.50m dark brown	.50	.90

Air Transport Service anniv., 1923-43.

Douglas DC-6 Over
Winter
Landscape — AP2

1950, Feb. 13
C3	AP2	300m blue	20.00	6.25

Available also for ordinary postage.

Redrawn
1958, Jan. 20   Perf. 11½
C4	AP2	300(m) blue	35.00	1.00

On No. C4 "mk" is omitted.
See Nos. C9-C9a.

Convair 440
over
Lakes — AP3

1958, Oct. 31   Unwmk.   Perf. 11½
C5	AP3	34m blue	1.25	.95

No. C5 Surcharged with New Value
and Bars

1959, Apr. 5
C6	AP3	45m on 34m blue	2.25	2.25

1959, Nov. 2
C7	AP3	45m blue	2.00	.50

1963, Feb. 15
C8	AP3	45p blue	1.60	.55

On No. C7 the denomination is "45." On No.
C8 it is "0.45."

DC-6 Type, Comma After "3"
Type I — 16 lines in "O"
Type II — 13 lines in "O"

1963, Oct. 10
C9	AP2	3m blue, Type II ('73)	2.00	.25
a.		Type I	30.00	1.00

Convair Type of 1958
1970, July 15
C10	AP3	57p ultra	2.00	1.25

MILITARY STAMPS

Catalogue values for unused stamps in this section are for Never Hinged items.

M1

Unwmk.
1941, Nov. 1   Typo.   Imperf.
M1	M1	(4m) blk, dk org	.35	.55

#M1 has simulated roulette printed in black.

Type of 1930-46
Overprinted in Black

1943, Oct. 16   Perf. 14
M2	A26	2m deep orange	.35	.75
M3	A26	3½m greenish blue	.35	.75

Post Horn and
Sword — M2

1943   Size: 29½x19½mm
M4	M2	(2m) green	.20	.35
M5	M2	(3m) rose violet	.20	.35

1944   Size: 20x16mm
M6	M2	(2m) green	.20	.20
M7	M2	(3m) rose violet	.20	.20

Post Horns
and Arms of
Finland — M3

1963, Sept. 26   Litho.   Perf. 14
M8	M3	violet blue	160.00	160.00

Used during maneuvers Sept. 30-Oct. 5,
1963. Valid from Sept. 26.

No. M8 Overprinted "1983"
1983, Apr. 20
M9	M3	violet blue	250.00	100.00

Used during maneuvers Apr. 24-30.

PARCEL POST STAMPS

PP1

Wmk. Rose & Triangles Multiple
Rouletted 6 on 2 or 3 Sides
1949-50   Typo.
Q1	PP1	1m brt grn & blk	1.25	4.50
Q2	PP1	5m red & blk	10.50	14.00
Q3	PP1	20m org & blk	20.00	22.50
Q4	PP1	50m bl & blk ('50)	7.25	11.00
Q5	PP1	100m brn & blk ('50)	8.25	11.00
		Nos. Q1-Q5 (5)	47.25	63.00
		Set, never hinged	75.00	

Catalogue values for unused stamps in this section, from this point to the end of the section, are for Never Hinged items.

Mail
Bus — PP2

1952-58   Unwmk.   Engr.   Perf. 14
Q6	PP2	5m car rose	5.00	5.00
Q7	PP2	20m orange	12.50	8.50
Q8	PP2	50m blue ('54)	30.00	12.50
Q9	PP2	100m brn ('58)	37.50	18.00
		Nos. Q6-Q9 (4)	85.00	44.00

Mail
Bus — PP3

1963   Perf. 12
Q10	PP3	5p red & blk	4.00	4.00
Q11	PP3	20p org & blk	3.50	1.90
Q12	PP3	50p blue & blk	6.50	2.50
Q13	PP3	1m brn & blk	1.90	1.90
		Nos. Q10-Q13 (4)	15.90	10.30

Nos. Q1-Q13 were issued only in booklets: panes of 6 for Nos. Q1-Q5, 10 for Nos. Q6-Q9 and 5 for Nos. Q10-Q13.
Used values are for regular postal or mail-bus cancels. Pen strokes, cutting or other cancels sell for half as much.

1981 SISU
Bus — PP4

Photo. & Engr.
1981, Dec. 7   Perf. 12 Horiz.
Q14	PP4	50p dk bl & blk	.60	3.00
Q15	PP4	1m dk brn & blk	.90	3.00
Q16	PP4	5m grn & blk	3.50	6.25
Q17	PP4	10m red & blk	7.25	12.50
		Nos. Q14-Q17 (4)	12.25	24.75

Parcel post stamps invalid after Jan. 9, 1985.

ALAND ISLANDS

LOCATION — A group of 6,554 islands at the mouth of the Gulf of Bothnia, between Finland and Sweden.
GOVT. — Province of Finland
AREA — 590 sq. mi.
POP. — 23,761
CAPITAL — Mariehamn

The province of Aland was awarded to Finland in 1921 by the League of Nations. The Swedish language is spoken and the province has a considerable amount of self-determination.

Catalogue values for unused stamps in this country are for Never Hinged items.

Gaff-rigged
Sloop — A1

Aland Flag — A2

Midsummer
Pole — A3

Landscapes — A4

Map of
Scandinavia — A5

Seal of St. Olaf and Aland Province, 1326 — A6

Artifacts — A7

Sea Birds — A8

Gothic Tower, Jomala Church, 12th Cent. — A9

Mariehamn Town Hall, Designed by Architect Lars Sonck — A9a

Designs: 1.50m, Statue of Frans Petter von Knorring, vicar from 1834 to 1875, and St. Michael's Church, Finstrom, 12th cent. 1.60m, Burial site, clay hands. 1.70m, Somateria mollissima. 2.20m, Bronze Staff of Finby, apostolic decoration. 2.30m, Aythya fuligula. 5m, Outer Aland Archipelago. 8m, Farm and windmill. 12m, Melantha fusca. 20m, Ancient court site, contemporary monument.

		1984-90	Engr.	Unwmk.	Perf. 12	
1	A1	10p magenta			.20	.20
2	A1	20p brown olive			.20	.20
3	A1	50p bright green			.20	.20
4	A1	1.10m deep blue			.50	.35
5	A1	1.20m black			.55	.45
6	A1	1.30m dark green			.60	.45

Litho.
Perf. 14, 13x14 (#8)

7	A2	1.40m multi	.75	.45
8	A9	1.40m multi	1.50	1.50
9	A3	1.50m multi, I	1.50	.45
9A	A3	1.50m multi, II	.85	.45
10	A9	1.50m multi	1.50	1.25

Perf. 13, 14 (#13)

11	A7	1.60m multi, vert.	1.50	.50
12	A9	1.70m multi	4.00	4.00
13	A9a	1.90m multi	1.00	.70
14	A4	2m multi	1.50	.60
15	A7	2.20m multi, vert.	1.00	.75
16	A8	2.30m multi	3.00	3.00

17	A5	3m multi	2.00	2.00
18	A4	5m multi, horiz.	2.50	1.75
19	A4	8m multi, horiz.	4.00	3.00

Litho. & Engr.

20	A6	10m multi	4.75	4.75

Litho.

21	A8	12m multi	6.00	6.00
22	A7	20m multi	9.75	9.75
		Nos. 1-22 (23)	49.35	42.75

On No. 9A (type II) "Aland" is 10½mm long, figure support is 2mm wide, pole supports are thinner, diagonal black highlighting lines in pole greenery and horizontal black line on support under the man removed.
Issued: #2-4, 7, 17, 20, 3/1/84; #1, 5, 6, 9, 1/2/85; #14, 18-19, 9/16/85; #11, 15, 22, 4/4/86; #12, 16, 21, 1/2/87; #8, 8/26/88; #13, 1/2/89; #10, 9/4/89; #9A, 5/21/90.
See Nos. 39-42, 87-92.

A10

A11

Bark Pommern and car ferries, Mariehamn West Harbor

		1984, Mar. 1	Litho.	Perf. 14	
23	A10	2m multicolored		3.00	3.00

		1986, Jan. 2	Litho.	Perf. 14	
24	A11	1.60m multicolored		1.90	1.90

1986 Nordic Orienteering Championships, Aug. 30-31.

Onningeby Artists' Colony, Cent. — A12

Design: Pallette, pen and ink drawing of Onningeby landscape, 1891, by Victor Westerholm (1860-1919), founder.

		1986, Sept. 1	Litho.	
25	A12	3.70m multicolored	1.75	1.75

Mariehamn Volunteer Fire Brigade, Cent. — A13

		1987, Apr. 27	Litho.	Perf. 14	
26	A13	7m multicolored		6.00	6.00

Farjsund Bridge, 50th Anniv., Rebuilt in 1980 — A14

		1987, Apr. 27	Engr.	Perf. 13x13½	
27	A14	1m greenish black		.50	.50

Municipal Meeting, Finstrom, 1917 — A15

		1987, Aug. 20	Litho.	Perf. 14	
28	A15	1.70m multicolored		1.25	1.25

Movement for reunification with Sweden, 70th anniv.

Loading of Mail Barrels on Sailboat, Post Office, Eckero — A16

		1988, Jan. 4	Litho.	Perf. 14	
29	A16	1.80m multicolored		2.25	2.00

Postal Service, 350th anniv. From Feb. 1 to May 31, Alanders were entitled to buy 20 stamps for 28m with a discount coupon.

New Aland Farm School, Horse-Drawn Plow — A17

		1988, Mar. 29	Litho.	Perf. 14	
30	A17	2.20m multicolored		1.75	2.25

Haga Farm School, cent.; Aland Farm School, 75th anniv.; 50th anniv. of experimental farming on Aland.

Sailing Ships — A18

		1988, June 4	Litho.	Perf. 13	
31	A18	1.80m Albanus, 1904, vert.		2.00	1.25
32	A18	2.40m Ingrid, c. 1900		3.00	2.50
33	A18	11m Pamir, c. 1900		9.50	8.00
		Nos. 31-33 (3)		14.50	11.75

Type of 1988 and

Orchids — A19

Fish
A20

Handicrafts
A21

Fresco, St. Anna's Church of Kumlinge
A22

Mammals
A23

Geological Formations
A24   A25

Designs: 10p, Boulder field, Geta. #35, *Dactylorhiza sambucina.* #36, *Clupea harengus membras.* #37, *Erinaceus europauus.* #38, Drumlin, Finstrom. 1.70m, St. Andrew Church, Lumparland. #40, Vardo Church. #41, Hammarland Church. #42, Sottunga Church. #43, *Esox lucius.* #45, Diabase dike, Sottunga, Basskar. 2.10m, *Sciurus vulgaris.* 2.50m, *Cephalanthera longifolia.* #48, *Platichthys flesus.* #49, Pillow lava, Kumlinge, western Varpskar. #50, *Capreolus capreolus.* #51, Rouche Moutonne, Roda Kon, Lumparn. 6m, Folded gneiss, Sottunga, Gloskar. 13m, Tapestry, 1793. 14m, *Cypripedium calceolus.*

Perf. 13, 14 (#39-42, 44, 53), 15x14½ (10p, #38, 45, 49, 51-52)

		1989-94		Litho.	
34	A25	10p multicolored		.20	.20
35	A19	1.50m multicolored		2.75	2.25
36	A20	1.50m multicolored		1.25	.95
37	A23	1.60m multicolored		1.25	.60
38	A25	1.60m multicolored		.90	.60
39	A9	1.70m multicolored		1.25	1.10
40	A9	1.80m multicolored		1.25	.95
41	A9	1.80m multicolored		1.25	1.00
42	A9	1.80m multicolored		1.00	1.00
43	A20	2m multicolored		1.25	.85
44	A22	2m multicolored		1.00	.85
45	A24	2m multicolored		.85	.70
46	A23	2.10m multicolored		1.50	.45
47	A19	2.50m multicolored		3.25	2.50
48	A20	2.70m multicolored		1.50	1.40
49	A24	2.70m multicolored		1.25	.95
50	A23	2.90m multicolored		1.50	1.50
51	A25	2.90m multicolored		1.25	1.10
52	A24	6m multicolored		2.50	2.50
53	A21	13m multicolored		6.50	5.75
54	A19	14m multicolored		9.50	9.00
		Nos. 34-54 (21)		42.95	36.00

Issued: 2.50m, 14m, #35, 4/10/89; 2.70m, #36, 43, 3/1/90; 13m, 4/19/90; 1.70m, #44, 9/10/90; 1.60m, 2.10m, #50, 3/3/91; #40, 10/9/91; #41 10/5/92; #45, 49, 52, 9/3/93; #42, 10/8/93; 10p, #38, 51, 2/1/94.
See Nos. 96, 102, 105.

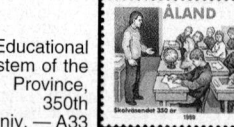

Educational System of the Province, 350th Anniv.— A33

		1989, May 31	Litho.	Perf. 14	
57	A33	1.90m multicolored		1.50	1.25

Souvenir Sheet

1991 Aland Island Games — A34

a, Volleyball. b, Shooting. c, Soccer. d, Running.

1991, Apr. 5   Litho.   Perf. 13x12½
58 A34 2.10m Sheet of 4, #a.-d.   5.00 5.00

Autonomy of Aland, 70th Anniv. — A35

1991, June 4   Perf. 13
59 A35 16m multicolored   8.75 8.00

Kayaking A36

1991, June 4   Perf. 14
60 A36 2.10m shown   1.25 .75
61 A36 2.90m Cycling   1.75 1.25

Rev. Frans Peter Von Knorring (1792-1875), Educator — A37

Cape Horn Congress, Mariehamn, June 8-11 — A38

1992, Mar. 2   Litho.   Perf. 13
62 A37 2 multicolored   1.25 1.25
Litho. & Engr.
Perf. 13½x14
63 A38 1 multicolored   1.75 1.75
No. 62 sold for 1.60m, No. 63 for 2.10m.

On stamps bearing the "denominations" "1" or "2," the number represents the class of mail.

Lighthouses A39

1992, May 8   Litho.   Perf. 13
Booklet Stamps
64 A39 2.10m Ranno   5.25 4.00
65 A39 2.10m Salskar   5.25 4.00
66 A39 2.10m Lagskar   5.25 4.00
67 A39 2.10m Market   5.25 4.00
  a.   Booklet pane of 4, #64-67   22.50 22.50

First Aland Provincial Parliament, 70th Anniv. — A40

1992, June 8   Litho.   Perf. 13
68 A40 3.40m multicolored   1.75 1.75

Joel Pettersson (1892-1937), Painter — A41

1992, June 8
69 A41 2.90m Landscape from Lemland   1.50 1.50
70 A41 16m Self-Portrait   8.50 8.25

Arms of Aland — A42

1993, Mar. 1   Litho.   Perf. 14
71 A42 1.60m gray, sepia & blue   1.00 1.00
Autonomy Act, Jan. 1.

Souvenir Sheet

Autonomous Postal Administration — A43

Designs: a, Inscriptions from old letter canceled in Kastelholm, vert. b, Mariehamn post office. c, Ferry, mail truck. d, New post office emblem, vert.

Perf. 12½x13, 14 (#b.-c.)
1993, Mar. 1   Litho., Engr. (#b.-c.)
72 A43 1.90m Sheet of 4, #a.-d.   3.75 3.75

Fiddler, Jan Karlsgarden Museum — A44

Folk Dresses — A45

2.30m, Boat Shed, Jan Karlsgarden Museum.

Perf. 13x12½, 12½x13
1993, May 7   Litho.
73 A44 2m multicolored   1.10 1.00
74 A44 2.30m multi, horiz.   1.40 1.25

1993, June 1   Perf. 12½
Clothing from: 1.90m, Saltvik. 3.50m, Brando, Eckero, Mariehamn. 17m, Finstrom.
75 A45 1.90m multicolored   1.25 1.00
76 A45 3.50m multicolored   1.75 1.50
77 A45 17m multicolored   9.00 8.50
    Nos. 75-77 (3)   12.00 11.00

Butterflies A46

A47

Perf. 14 on 3 Sides
1994, Mar. 1   Litho.
Booklet Stamps
78 A46 2.30m Melitaea cinxia   1.25 1.10
79 A46 2.30m Quercusia quercus   1.25 1.10
80 A46 2.30m Parnassius mnemosyne   1.25 1.10
81 A46 2.30m Hesperia comma   1.25 1.10
    a.   Booklet pane, 2 each #78-81   10.00 11.00
    Nos. 78-81 (4)   5.00 4.40

1994, May 5   Litho.   Perf. 13
Europa, Inventions and Discoveries: 2.30m, Diagram showing transmission of von Willebrand's Disease, discovered by E. A. von Willebrand. 2.90m, Purification of heparin, by Erik Jorpes.
82 A47 2.30m multicolored   2.75 2.50
83 A47 2.90m multicolored   1.90 1.60

Types of 1989-93 and:

Ice Age Survivors — A48   Fossils — A49

Sea Birds — A50

Bronze Age — A51

Stone Age — A52

Ships — A53

Lichens — A54

Primula Veris — A55

30p, Saduria entomon, mysis relicta. 40p, Trilobita asaphus. 1.80m, Sterna paradisaea. #87, Church of Mariehamn. #88, Church of Eckerö. #89, St. Bridget's Church, Lemland. #90, Church of St. John the Baptist, Sund. #91, St. George Church, Geta. #92, Church of Brando. #93, Bronze sword, bronze dagger. #94, Ship tumulus grave. #95, Larus canus. 2.30m, Pitcher of Kallskar. #97, Pottery. #98, Myoxocephalus quadricornis. 2.60m, Larus marinus. #100, Stone tools. #101, SS Thornbury. 3.40m, Erratic boulders. 3.50m, SS Osmo. 4.30m, Phoca hispida. 7m, Potholes. 9m, Gastropoda euomophalus. 18m, Settlement. 2, Hypogmnia physodes. 1, Xanthoria parietina.

Perf. 13 (A48, A50, A52), 15x14½, 14½x15, 14½ (40p, #88-89), 14 (#87, 90),

				Engr.
1994-2000				
84	A48	30p multi	.20	.20
85	A49	40p multi	.20	.20
86	A50	1.80m multi	.85	.85
87	A9	1.90m multi	.85	.85
88	A9	1.90m multi	.85	.85
89	A9	1.90m multi	.85	.85
90	A9	2m multi	.95	.70
91	A9	2m multi	.95	.95
92	A9	2m multi	.95	.95
93	A51	2m multi	.95	.95
94	A51	2.20m multi, vert.	1.10	1.10
95	A50	2.20m multi, vert.	1.10	1.10
96	A24	2.30m multi	1.10	1.00
97	A52	2.40m multi, vert.	1.25	1.10
98	A48	2.40m multi	1.25	1.10
99	A50	2.60m multi	1.25	1.10
100	A52	2.80m multi, vert.	1.50	.85
101	A53	2.80m multi	1.50	1.25
102	A24	3.40m multi, horiz.	1.75	1.50
103	A53	3.50m multi	1.75	1.50
104	A48	4.30m multi	2.25	1.90
105	A24	7m multi, horiz.	4.00	3.00
106	A49	9m multi	5.00	4.00
107	A52	18m multi	8.75	8.25

Perf. 13
107A A54 2 multi   1.10 .95
107B A54 1 multi   1.50 1.25

Self-Adhesive
Serpentine Die Cut Perf. 10
108 A55 2.40m multi   1.25 1.25
    Nos. 84-108 (27)   45.00 39.55

No. 108 was issued in sheets of 10.
Nos. 107A-107B sold for 2m and 2.40m, respectively, on day of issue.
Issued: #97, 100, 18m, 8/16/94; #90, 10/7/94; 2.30m, 3.40m, 7m, 1/2/95; #91, 9/15/95; 40p, #92, 9m, 10/9/96; 30p, #98, 4.30m, 2/3/97; #101, 103, 9/8/97; #87, 10/9/97; #88, 10/9/98; #93-94, 2/1/99; #108, 4/28/99; #107A-107B, 9/25/99; #89, 10/8/99; 1.80m, #95, 2.60m, 1/3/00.

Cargo Vessels — A58

Perf. 14 on 3 Sides
1995, Mar. 1   Litho.
Booklet Stamps
109 A58 2.30m Skuta   1.10 1.00
110 A58 2.30m Sump   1.10 1.00
111 A58 2.30m Storbat   1.10 1.00
112 A58 2.30m Jakt   1.10 1.00
    a.   Booklet pane, 2 each #109-112   9.00 10.00
    Complete booklet, #112b   9.50
    Nos. 109-112 (4)   4.40 4.00

Entry into European Union — A59

1995, Mar. 1   Litho.   Perf. 13x14
113 A59 2.90m multicolored   1.50 1.75

Europa — A60   Tourism — A61

1995, May 5   Litho.   Perf. 13x14
114 A60 2.80m shown   1.40 1.25
115 A60 2.90m Dove, island in sea   1.40 1.25

1995, May 12
116 A61 2 Golf   1.25 1.00
117 A61 1 Fishing   1.50 1.00
    Nos. 116-117 sold for value 2m and 2.30m, respectively.

Optimist Dinghy World Championships — A62

1995, June 2   Litho.   Perf. 13½x14
118 A62 3.40m multicolored   1.75 1.50

St. Olaf (995?-1030), Patron Saint of Aland — A63

Litho. & Engr.
1995, Sept. 15   Perf. 13½x13
119 A63 4.30m multicolored   2.25 2.00
    See Faroe Islands No. 289

A64   A65

Greeting Stamps (stylized designs): No. 120, Fish with natl. flag, "Hälsningar fran Aland." No. 121, Yellow bird with flower, "Grattis."

1996, Feb. 14   Litho.   Perf. 13x14
120 A64 1 multicolored   1.25 .90
121 A64 1 multicolored   1.25 .90
    Nos. 120-121 had a face value of 2.30m on day of issue.

1996, Mar. 1   Perf. 14 on 3 Sides
    Eagle owl (bubo bubo): No. 122, Landing on tree branch over lake. No. 123, Perched on branch over lake. No. 124, Male, darker feathers. No. 125, Female, lighter feathers.

Booklet Stamps
122 A65 2.40m multicolored   1.40 1.10
123 A65 2.40m multicolored   1.40 1.10
124 A65 2.40m multicolored   1.40 1.10
125 A65 2.40m multicolored   1.40 1.10
  a. Booklet pane, 2 ea #122-125   11.50 11.50
      Complete booklet, No. 125a   12.50
      Nos. 122-125 (4)   5.60 4.40
    World Wildlife Fund.

Famous Women A66

    Europa: 2.80m, Sally Salminen (1906-76), writer. 2.90m, Fanny Sundström (1883-1944), politician.

1996, May 6   Litho.   Perf. 14x13
126 A66 2.80m multicolored   1.40 1.25
127 A66 2.90m multicolored   1.40 1.25

A67

A68

1996, June 7   Litho.   Perf. 13½x14
128 A67 2.40m multicolored   1.25 1.10
    Aland '96 Song and Music Festival.

1996, June 7   Perf. 13
    "Haircut," by Karl Emanuel Jansson (1846-74).
129 A68 18m multicolored   9.00 8.00

Spring Flowers — A69

    Designs: No. 130, Tussilago farfara. No. 131, Hepatica nobilis. No. 132, Anemone nemorosa. No. 133, Anemone ranunculoides.

1997, Feb. 3   Perf. 14
Booklet Stamps
130 A69 2.40m multicolored   1.10 1.10
131 A69 2.40m multicolored   1.10 1.10
132 A69 2.40m multicolored   1.10 1.10
133 A69 2.40m multicolored   1.10 1.10
  a. Booklet pane, 2 each #130-133 9.00 10.00
      Complete booklet, #133a   9.50

A70   A71

1997, May 3   Litho.   Perf. 14x13½
134 A70 3.40m multicolored   1.60 1.60
    1st Floorball World Championships, Aland.

1997, May 9   Perf. 13x14
    Devil's Dance with Clergyman's Wife.
135 A71 2.90m multicolored   1.40 1.10
    Europa.

Kalmar Union, 600th Anniv. — A72

    Design: Kastelholm Castle, arms of Lord High Chancellor Bo Jonsson Grip.

1997, May 30   Litho.   Perf. 14x13
136 A72 2.40m multicolored   1.25 1.10

Souvenir Sheet

Autonomy, 75th Anniv. — A73

    Illustration reduced.

1997, June 9   Perf. 13
137 A73 20m multicolored   10.00 10.00
    No. 137 contains a holographic image. Soaking in water may affect the hologram.

Horticulture A74

1998, Feb. 2   Litho.   Perf. 14½x15
138 A74 2m Apples   .95 .95
139 A74 2.40m Cucumbers   1.10 1.10

Youth Activities A75

    #140, Riding moped. #141, Computer. #142, Listening to music. #143, Aerobics.

1998, Mar. 28   Perf. 14 on 3 Sides
Booklet Stamps
140 A75 2.40m multicolored   1.10 1.10
141 A75 2.40m multicolored   1.10 1.10
142 A75 2.40m multicolored   1.10 1.10
143 A75 2.40m multicolored   1.10 1.10
  a. Booklet pane, 2 each #140-143 9.00 10.00
      Complete booklet, #143a   9.50

Midsummer Celebration in Aland — A76

1998, Apr. 27   Litho.   Perf. 14
144 A76 4.20m multicolored   2.00 1.75
    Europa.

Passenger Ferry — A77

1998, May 8   Perf. 14½
145 A77 2.40m multicolored   1.10 1.10

Intl. Year of the Ocean — A78

1998, May 8
146 A78 6.30m multicolored   3.00 3.00

ATP Senior Tour of Champions Tennis Tournament, Mariehamn A79

Serpentine Die Cut
1998, June 25   Litho.
Self-Adhesive
147 A79 2.40m multicolored   1.25 1.25
    Issued in sheets of 10.

Scouting — A80

1998, Aug. 1   Perf. 14
148 A80 2.80m multicolored   1.40 1.40

Foyers — A81

    Homesteads: 1.60m, Seffers. 2m, Labbas. 2.90m, Abras.

1998, Sept. 11   Litho.   Perf. 14½
149 A81 1.60m multicolored   .75 .75
150 A81 2m multicolored   .95 .95
151 A81 2.90m multicolored   1.40 1.40
    Nos. 149-151 (3)   3.10 3.10

18th Century Furniture Ornamentation A82

Perf. 14 on 3 Sides
1999, Feb. 1   Litho.
Booklet Stamps
152 A82 2.40m Wardrobe   1.10 1.10
153 A82 2.40m Distaff   1.10 1.10
154 A82 2.40m Chest   1.10 1.10
155 A82 2.40m Spinning wheel   1.10 1.10
  a. Booklet pane, 2 each #152-155 9.00 10.00
      Complete booklet, #155a   9.50

Passage of Cape Horn by Grain Ships Pamir & Passat, 50th Anniv. A83

1999, Mar. 19   Litho.   Perf. 14½
156 A83 3.40m multicolored   1.60 1.60

    Beginning with No. 157, denominations are indicated on many stamps in both Markkas and Euros. The value shown is in Markkas.

Nature Reserve, Kökar — A84

1999, Apr. 28 **Litho.** **Perf. 13**
157 A84 2.90m multicolored 1.40 1.25

Europa.

Match Sailboat Racing — A85

1999, Aug. 5 **Litho.** **Perf. 14½x15**
158 A85 2.70m multicolored 1.25 1.25

UPU, 125th Anniv. A86

1999, Sept. 25
159 A86 2.90m multicolored 1.40 1.40

Finnish Cross-Country Championships, Mariehamn — A87

1999, Oct. 9 **Litho.** **Perf. 14¾x14½**
160 A87 3.50m multicolored 1.75 1.75

Souvenir Sheet

Peace Symbol, Aland Flag — A88

Background colors: a, Yellow. b, Red. c, Blue. d, White.

Litho. & Embossed
2000, Jan. 3 **Perf. 13**
161 A88 3.40m Sheet of 4, #a.-d. 6.50 6.50

Elk — A89

Elk in: No. 162, Spring. No. 163, Summer. No. 164, Autumn. No. 165, Winter.

Perf. 11¾on 3 sides
2000, Mar. 1 **Litho.**
Booklet Stamps
162 A89 2.60m multicolored 1.25 1.25
163 A89 2.60m multicolored 1.25 1.25
164 A89 2.60m multicolored 1.25 1.25
165 A89 2.60m multicolored 1.25 1.25
  a. Block of 4, #162-165 5.00 5.00
  b. Booklet pane, 2 #165a 10.00 11.00
    Complete booklet, #165b 10.50

Europa, 2000
Common Design Type
2000, May 9 **Perf. 13**
166 CD17 3m multicolored 1.75 1.25

A90 A91

2000, June 9 **Die Cut Perf. 13x13¼**
Self-Adhesive
Coil Stamp
167 A90 2.60m multicolored 1.25 1.25
Gymnastics Festival, Mariehamn.

2000, July 21 Litho. Perf. 13½x13¼
168 A91 3.40m multicolored 1.60 1.60
Cutty Sark Tall Ships race to Mariehamn.

Vikings From Aland — A92

2000, July 28
169 A92 4.50m multicolored 2.10 2.10
Recreation of Viking market, Saltvik.

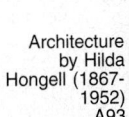

Architecture by Hilda Hongell (1867-1952) A93

2000, Aug. 25 **Perf. 13¼x13¾**
170 A93 3.80m shown 1.75 1.75
171 A93 10m House, diff. 4.75 4.75

Christianity, 2000th Anniv. — A94

2000, Oct. 9 **Perf. 13**
172 A94 3m multicolored 1.40 1.25

Church Type of 1984-90 and:

Swamp Plants — A95

Swamp plants: 1.90m, Equisetum fluviatile. 2.80m, Lycopodium annotinum. 3.50m, Polypodium vulgare. Churches: No. 179, Föglö Church, Föglö. 2m, Kökar Church, Kökar.

Perf. 13x13¼, 13 (#178)
2000-01 **Litho.**
177 A95 1.90m multicolored .90 .85
178 A9 2m multicolored .95 .90
179 A9 2m multi .95 .90

180 A95 2.80m multicolored 1.40 1.40
182 A95 3.50m multicolored 1.75 1.75
  Nos. 177-182 (5) 5.95 5.80

These stamps are part of an ongoing definitive set. Numbers have been reserved for additional stamps.
Issued: 2m, 10/9; 1.90m, 2.80m, 3.50m, 1/2/01; No. 179, 10/9/01.

Worldwide Fund for Nature (WWF) — A100

Polysticta stelleri: a, Pair in flight. b, Pair on rock. c, Pair in water. d, Male in water.

Perf. 13¼ on 3 sides
2001, Jan. 2 **Litho.**
Booklet Stamps
185 A100 Block of 4 5.00 5.00
  a.-d. 2.70m any single 1.25 1.10
  e. Booklet pane, 2 #185 10.00 11.00
    Booklet, #185e 11.00

Valentine's Day — A101

2001, Feb. 14 **Perf. 14½x14¾**
186 A101 3.20m multicolored 1.50 1.50

Europa A102

2001, May 9 **Litho.** **Perf. 14½x14¾**
187 A102 3.20m multi 1.60 1.25

Windmills A103

Windmill types: 3m, Archipelago. 7m, Timbered, horiz. 20m, Nest, horiz.

Perf. 13¾x14¼, 14¼x13¾
2001, June 8
188-190 A103 Set of 3 14.50 14.50

Puppies — A104

Designs: 2, Golden retriever. 1, Wire-haired dachshund.

2001, Sept. 3 **Perf. 13¼**
191-192 A104 Set of 2 2.75 2.75

Nos. 191-192 sold for 2.30m and 2.70m respectively on day of issue.

100 Cents = 1 Euro (€)
Church Type of 1998 with Euro Denominations and

Fauna — A105

Post Terminal — A106

Mushrooms A107

Designs: 5c, Coronella austriaca. 10c, Chanterelle mushroom. 35c, Saltviks Church. 50c, King Bolete mushroom. 70c, Triturus cristatus. €2.50, Parasol mushroom.

Perf. 12½, 13 (#193, 196), 13¼ (#198), 14¾x14 (#195)
2002-03 **Litho.**
193 A105 5c multi .20 .20
194 A107 10c multi .30 .30
195 A9 35c multi 1.00 1.00
196 A9 40c multi 1.10 1.10
197 A107 50c multi 1.40 1.40
198 A105 70c multi 2.00 2.00
199 A106 €1 multi 3.00 2.75
200 A107 €2.50 multi 7.25 7.25
  Nos. 193-200 (8) 16.25 16.00

Issue dates: 5c, 70c, 1/2/02; €1, 2/28/02; 35c, 10/9/02; 10c, 50c, €2.50, 1/2/03. No. 196, 10/9/03.
This is an expanding set. Numbers may change.

Introduction of the Euro — A108

2002, Jan. 2 **Litho.** **Perf. 12½**
201 A108 60c multi 1.75 1.50

St. Canute's Day — A109

2002, Jan. 2
202 A109 €2 multi 5.75 5.75

Cuisine — A110

Flowers and: a, Gravlax, boiled potatoes. b, Fried herring, beets, mashed potatoes. c, Black bread, cheese, butter. d, Pancake with prune sauce and whipped cream, coffee. Illustration reduced.

Perf. 13½x13¼ on 3 Sides

2002, Feb. 28   **Litho.**
203	A110	Block of 4	7.00 6.00
a.-d.		1 Any single	1.75 1.40
e.		Booklet pane 2 #203	14.00 11.00
		Booklet, #203e	15.00

Nos. 203a-203d each sold for 55c on day of issue.

Europa — A111

2002, May 3   **Perf. 13¼**
204	A111 40c multi	1.25 1.00

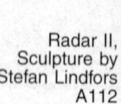

Radar II, Sculpture by Stefan Lindfors A112

2002, May 3   **Perf. 13**
205	A112 €3 multi	8.75 8.50

"My Aland," by Lill Lindfors A113

2002, Aug. 12   **Litho.**   **Perf. 13¼**
206	A113 90c multi	2.50 2.50

Iron Age Artifacts — A114

Designs: No. 207, 2, Buckle found in Persby. No. 208, 1, Ornamental pin found in Syllöda.

2002, Sept. 2   **Perf. 13x13¼**
207-208	A114 Set of 2	3.00 2.50

Nos. 207-208 sold for 45c and 55c respectively on day of issue.

Janne Holmén, Marathon Gold Medalist in European Track and Field Championships A115

2002, Nov. 1   **Perf. 12½**
209	A115 1 multi	1.60 1.50

Sold for 55c on day of issue.

House Cats — A116

2003, Mar. 14   **Litho.**   **Perf. 13¼**
210	A116 2 Tovis	1.25 1.00
211	A116 1 Randi, horiz.	1.75 1.50

Nos. 210-211 sold for 45c and 55c respectively on day of issue.

Landscape in Summer, by Elin Danielson-Gambogi (1861-1919) — A117

No. 212: a, Woman at fence. b, Tree without leaves. c, Sun. d, Boat. Illustration reduced.

2003, Mar. 28   **Perf. 14 Vert.**
Booklet Stamps
212	A117	Horiz. strip of 4	6.25 6.25
a.-d.		1 Any single	1.50 1.25
e.		Booklet pane, 2 #212	12.50 12.50
		Complete booklet, #212e	13.00

Nos. 212a-212d each sold for 55c on day of issue.

Europa — A118

2003, May 9   **Perf. 13¼**
213	A118 45c multi	1.25 1.00

Museum Ship "Pommern," Cent. A119

2003, June 6   **Die Cut Perf. 9¼x9½**
Booklet Stamp
Self-Adhesive
214	A119 55c multi	1.60 1.60
a.	Booklet pane of 4	6.50 6.50
	Complete booklet, 2 #214a	13.00

Mark and Stephen Levengood on Beach — A120

2003, June 18   **Perf. 12½**
215	A120 55c multi	1.60 1.60

Aland Folk Music Association, 50th Anniv. — A121

2003, Aug. 1   **Perf. 14¼**
216	A121 €1.10 buff & black	3.25 3.25

St. Lucia's Day Celebrations A122

2003, Oct. 9   **Litho.**   **Perf. 12½**
217	A122 60c multi	1.75 1.75

Mammals — A123

Designs: 20c, Mustela erminea. 60c, Vulpes vulpes. €3, Martes martes.

2004, Feb. 2   **Litho.**   **Perf. 14½x14¼**
218	A123 20c multi	.75 .50
219	A123 60c multi	1.75 1.50
220	A123 €3 multi	8.75 8.50
	Nos. 218-220 (3)	11.25 10.50

Souvenir Sheet

Norse Gods Fenja and Menja — A124

2004, Mar. 26   **Perf. 14¼x14¾**
221	A124 55c multi	1.60 1.60

Aland Flag, 50th Anniv. — A125

Serpentine Die Cut 12½
2004, Apr. 23
Booklet Stamp
Self-Adhesive
222	A125 1 multi	1.50 1.50
a.	Booklet pane of 4	6.00 5.75
	Complete booklet, 2 #222a	12.50

No. 222a was reprinted in 2007 with a hole for a pegboard hook.

Finnish Pres. Mauno Koivisto and Guests on Boat — A126

2004, Apr. 23   **Perf. 12½**
223	A126 90c multi	2.50 2.50

Europa — A127

2004, May 10   **Perf. 13¾x14¼**
224	A127 75c multi	2.00 1.75

Destruction of Bomarsund Fortress, 150th Anniv. — A128

No. 225: a, Fortress, six ships in harbor. b, Fortress, three ships in harbor. c, Three soldiers in foreground. d, Six soldiers in foreground.

2004, June 9   **Perf. 13**
225	Booklet pane of 4	8.50 8.25
a.-d.	A128 75c Any single	2.10 2.10
	Complete booklet, 2 #225	17.00

2004 Summer Olympics, Athens A183

2004, Aug. 13   **Litho.**   **Perf. 14¼**
226	A183 80c multi	2.25 2.25

Landscapes A184

Designs: 2, Storklynkan, Brändö. 1, Prästgardsnäset Nature Reserve, Finström.

2004, Aug. 13   **Perf. 12½**
227-228	A184 Set of 2	3.25 3.00

Nos. 227-228 sold for 50c and 60c respectively on day of issue.

Christmas A185

2004, Oct. 8   **Perf. 14½x14¾**
229	A185 45c multi	1.75 1.40

Birds — A186

Designs: 15c, Phalacrocorax carbo sinensis. 65c, Cygnus cygnus. €4, Ardea cinerea, vert.

2005, Jan. 14   **Litho.**   **Perf. 13¼**
230	A186 15c multi	.45 .45
231	A186 65c multi	1.90 1.90
232	A186 €4 multi	11.50 11.50
	Nos. 230-232 (3)	13.85 13.85

Automobiles — A187

No. 233: a, 1928 Oakland Sport Cabriolet. b, 1939 Ford V8. c, 1957 Buick Super 4D HT. d, 1964 Volkswagen 1200.

2005, Mar. 4   *Perf. 13¼ Horiz.*
Booklet Stamps
233		Vert. strip of 4	7.00	7.00
a.-d.	A187	1 Any single	1.75	1.75
e.		Booklet pane, 2 #233	14.00	—
		Complete booklet, #233e	14.00	

Stamps sold for 60c each on day of issue.

Europa A188

2005, Apr. 29   *Perf. 13¼*
234 A188 90c multi   2.50 2.10

Walpurgis Night Bonfire A189

Serpentine Die Cut 12½
2005, Apr. 29
Self-Adhesive
Booklet Stamp
235	A189	2 multi	1.40	1.40
a.		Booklet pane of 4	5.75	
		Complete booklet, 2 #235a	11.50	

Stamp sold for 50c on day of issue.

Tennis Player Bjorn Borg — A190

2005, May 26   *Perf. 12½*
236 A190 55c multi   1.60 1.60

Mr. Black and Mr. Smith at Bomarsund, by Fritz von Dardel A191

2005, Aug. 12   *Litho.*   *Perf. 13¾*
237 A191 €1.30 multi   3.75 3.75

Schooner Linden — A192

2005, Aug. 26   *Perf. 13¼*
238 A192 60c multi   1.75 1.75

Landscapes Type of 2004
Designs: 70c, Pine tree on Sandö Island. 80c, Cliffs, Gröndal.

2005, Aug. 26   *Perf. 12½*
239-240 A184   Set of 2   4.25 4.25

Christmas — A193

Litho. with Hologram Applied
2005, Oct. 10   *Perf. 13*
241 A193 45c multi   1.25 1.25

Stars in hologram differ on each stamp.

Beetles A194

Designs: 40c, Potosia cuprea. 65c, Coccinella septempunctata. €2, Oryctes nasicornis.

Litho. & Embossed
2006, Jan. 2   *Perf. 13½*
242	A194	40c multi	1.10	1.10
243	A194	65c multi	1.90	1.90
244	A194	€2 multi	5.75	5.75
		Nos. 242-244 (3)	8.75	8.75

Woman Suffrage in Finland, Cent. — A195

2006, Mar. 8   *Litho.*   *Perf. 12½*
245 A195 85c multi   2.50 2.50

Demilitarization of Aland, 150th Anniv. — A196

2006, Mar. 29   *Perf. 13¾*
246 A196 €1.50 multi   4.25 4.25

Souvenir Sheet

Lettesgubbe, Mythological Being — A197

2006, Mar. 29   *Perf. 12½x13*
247 A197 85c multi   2.50 2.50

Europa — A198

2006, May 4
248 A198 €1.30 multi   3.75 3.75

A199

Serpentine Die Cut 10 Syncopated
2006, May 26
| 249 | A199 | 1 multi | 2.00 | 2.00 |
| a. | | Booklet pane of 8 | 16.00 | |

No. 249 sold for 65c on day of issue. Design portion of stamp could be personalized at €10.40 per booklet with a minimum purchase of three booklets.

Tattoos — A200

No. 250: a, Tribal tattoo on man's biceps. b, Sailor's tattoo on man's forearm. c, Flower tattoo, on woman's torso.

2006, Sept. 7   *Perf. 14 Vert.*
Booklet Stamps
250		Horiz. strip of 3	5.75	5.75
a.-c.	A200	65c Any single	1.90	1.90
d.		Booklet pane, 3 #250	17.50	
		Complete booklet, #250d	17.50	

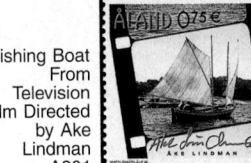
Fishing Boat From Television Film Directed by Ake Lindman A201

2006, Aug. 4   *Litho.*   *Perf. 12½*
251 A201 75c multi   2.25 2.25

Landscapes Type of 2004
Designs: 55c, Foggy grove, windmill and houses, Söderby, Lemland. €1.20, Rocks, Norra Essvik, Sottunga.

2006, Aug. 4
252-253 A184   Set of 2   5.00 5.00

Christmas A202

Litho. With Holograms Affixed
2006, Oct. 9   *Perf. 13*
254 A202 (50c) multi   1.40 1.40

Flowers A203

Designs: 80c, Tripolium vulgare. 90c, Lythrum salicaria. €5, Angelica archangelica.

2007, Feb. 1   *Litho.*   *Perf. 12½x13*
255	A203	80c multi	2.10	2.10
256	A203	90c multi	2.40	2.40
257	A203	€5 multi	13.00	13.00
		Nos. 255-257 (3)	17.50	17.50

Mail Planes A204

Designs: 2, Junkers F13. 1, Saab 340.

2007, Mar. 1   *Perf. 12½*
258-259 A204   Set of 2   3.25 3.25

No. 258 sold for 55c, and No. 259 sold for 70c on day of issue.

Landscapes Type of 2004
2007, Mar. 13
260 A194 2 Skaftö, Kumlinge   1.50 1.50

Sold for 55c on day of issue.

Untitled Painting by Tove Jansson A205

2007, Apr. 18   *Perf. 13¼x13¾*
261 A205 85c multi   2.40 2.40

Europa — A206

2007, May 9   *Perf. 12½x13¼*
262 A206 70c multi   1.90 1.90

Scouting, cent.

Contemporary Crafts — A207

Designs: No. 263, Bridal crown, by Titti Sundblom. No. 264, Floral textile design, by Maria Korpi-Gordon and Adam Gordon. No. 265, Cups, bowl and plate, by Judy Kuyitunen.

2007, May 18   *Perf. 13 Horiz.*
Booklet Stamps
263	A207	1 multi	1.90	1.90
264	A207	1 multi	1.90	1.90
265	A207	1 multi	1.90	1.90
a.		Booklet pane, 3 each #263-265	17.50	—
		Complete booklet, #265a	17.50	

Nos. 263-265 each sold for 70c on day of issue.

A208

Serpentine Die Cut 10 Syncopated
2007, June 7
Booklet Stamp
Self-Adhesive

266 A208 1 multi   1.90 1.90
   a. Booklet pane of 8   15.50

No. 266 sold for 70c on day of issue. Design portion of stamp could be personalized at €10.40 per booklet with a minimum purchase of three booklets.

Emigration to America
A209

2007, Aug. 9 Litho.   Perf. 13¼x12½
267 A209 75c multi   2.10 2.10

Kjusan, Hammarland
A210

2007, Oct. 1   Perf. 12½
268 A210 1 multi   2.00 2.00

No. 268 sold for 70c on day of issue.

Christmas — A211

2007, Oct. 9   Perf. 14
269 A211 (50c) multi   1.50 1.50

FIUME

'fyü-ₔmã

LOCATION — A city and surrounding territory on the Adriatic Sea
GOVT. — Formerly a part of Italy
AREA — 8 sq. mi.
POP. — 44,956 (estimated 1924)

Fiume was under Hapsburg rule after 1466 and was transferred to Hungarian control after 1870. Of mixed Italian and Croatian population and strategically important - it was Hungary's only international seaport - Fiume was disputed between Italy and the newly-created Kingdom of the Serbs, Croats and Slovenes (later Yugoslavia), following World War I. A force of Allied troops occupied the city in Nov. 1918, while its future status was negotiated at the Paris Peace Conference.

In Sept., 1919, the Italian nationalist poet Gabriele d'Annunzio organized his legionnaires and seized Fiume,

together with the islands of Arbe, Carnaro and Veglia, in the name of Italy. D'Annunzio established an autonomous administration, which soon came into conflict with the Italian government. There followed several years of instability, with three Italian interventions after 1920. In Jan. 1924, the Treaty of Rome between Italy anf Yugoslavia established formal Italian sovereignty over Fiume, and Fiume stamps were replaced by those of Italy after March 31, 1924.

100 Filler = 1 Korona
100 Centesimi = 1 Corona (1919)
100 Centesimi = 1 Lira

See note on FIUME-KUPA Zone, Italian Occupation, after Yugoslavia No. NJ22.

The overprints on Nos. 1-23a have been extensively forged. Even the inexpensive values are difficult to find with genuine overprints. Forgeries of many later issues also exist, most created for the packet trade in the 1920s. Values are for genuine stamps. Collectors should be aware that stamps sold "as is" are likely to be forgeries, and unexpertized collections should be assumed to consist of mostly forged stamps. Education plus working with knowledgeable dealers is mandatory in this collecting area. More valuable stamps should be expertized.

Hungarian Stamps of 1916-18 Overprinted

1918, Dec. 2   Wmk. 137   Perf. 15
On Stamps of 1916
White Numerals

1a A8 10f rose   87.50 40.00
2 A8 15f violet   37.50 26.00

Value for Nos. 1 is for handstamped overprint. Value for No. 2 is for typographed overprint.

On Stamps of 1916-18
Colored Numerals

3	A9	2f brown orange	3.00	1.50
4	A9	3f red violet	3.00	1.50
5	A9	5f green	3.00	1.50
6	A9	6f grnsh blue	3.00	1.50
7a	A9	10f rose red	*60.00*	*22.50*
8	A9	15f violet	3.00	1.50
9	A9	20f gray brown	3.00	1.50
10	A9	25f deep blue	11.00	1.75
11	A9	35f brown	6.00	3.00
12a	A9	40f olive green	87.50	37.50

White Numerals

13	A10	50f red vio & lil	3.75	2.25
14	A10	75f brt bl & pale bl	8.75	3.00
15	A10	80f grn & pale grn	8.75	2.25
16	A10	1k red brn & claret	30.00	7.50
17	A10	2k ol brn & bis	3.75	2.25
18	A10	3k dk vio & ind	37.50	18.00
19	A10	5k dk brn & lt brn	80.00	30.00
20a	A10	10k vio brn & vio	250.00	130.00

Inverted or double overprints exist on most of Nos. 4-15.

On Stamps of 1918

21	A11	10f scarlet	3.00	3.00
22	A11	20f dark brown	2.25	1.50
23a	A12	40f olive green	24.00	10.50

The overprint on Nos. 3-23a was applied by 2 printing plates and 6 handstamps. Values are for the less costly. Values of Nos. 7a, 12a, 20a and 23a are for handstamps. See the *Scott Specialized Catalogue of Stamps and Covers* for detailed listings.

Postage Due Stamps of Hungary, 1915-20 Ovptd. & Surcharged in Black

1919, Jan.
24 D1 45f on 6f green & red   10.50 11.00
25 D1 45f on 20f green & red   26.50 11.00
  Set, never hinged   85.00

Hungarian Savings Bank Stamp Surcharged in Black — A2

1919, Jan. 29
26 A2 15f on 10f dk violet   16.00 15.00
  Never hinged   40.00

"Italy" — A3   Italian Flag on Clock-Tower in Fiume — A4

"Revolution" A5   Sailor Raising Italian Flag at Fiume (1918) A6

Nos. 30-43 exist on three types of paper: (A) grayish, porous paper, printed in sheets of 70 stamps (Jan, Feb. printings); (B) translucent or semi-translucent good quality white paper, printed in sheets of 70 stamps (March printing); and (C) good quality medium white paper, plain and opaque, sometimes grayish or yellowish, printed in sheets of 100 (April printing). Values are for the least expensive variety. See the *Scott Specialized Catalogue of Stamps and Covers* for detailed listings.

1919   Unwmk.   Litho.   Perf. 11½

27	A3	2c dull blue (C)	1.50	1.50
28	A3	3c gray brown (C)	1.50	1.50
29	A3	5c yellow green (C)	1.50	1.50
30a	A4	10c rose (A)	22.50	9.00
31	A4	15c violet (C)	1.50	1.50
32a	A4	20c green (A)	3.00	3.00
33	A5	25c dark blue (C)	2.25	1.50
34	A5	30c deep violet (C)	2.25	1.50
35	A5	40c brown (C)	2.25	1.50
36	A5	45c orange (C)	2.25	2.25
37	A6	50c yellow green (C)	2.25	1.50
38	A6	60c claret (C)	2.25	1.50
39	A6	1cor brown orange (C)	3.75	2.25
40	A6	2cor brt blue (C)	3.75	2.25
41	A6	3cor orange red (C)	4.50	2.25
42	A6	5cor deep brown (C)	22.50	22.50
43a	A6	10cor olive green (A)	24.00	52.50

   Nos. 27-43a (17)   103.50 109.50

The earlier printings of Jan. and Feb. are on thin grayish paper, the Mar. printing is on semi-transparent white paper, all in sheets of 70. An Apr. printing is on white paper of medium thickness in sheets of 100. Part-perf. examples of most of this series are known.
For surcharges see Nos. 58, 60, 64, 66-69.

A7   A8

A9

A10

1919, July 28   Perf. 11½

46	A7	5c yellow green	1.50	.75
47	A8	10c rose	1.50	.75
48	A9	30c violet	6.00	2.25
49	A10	40c yellow brown	1.50	*1.50*
50	A10	45c orange	6.00	5.25
51	A9	50c yellow green	6.00	5.25
52	A9	60c claret	6.00	5.25
a.		Perf. 13x12½	160.00	—
		Never hinged	240.00	
b.		Perf. 10½	325.00	
		Never hinged	500.00	
53	A9	10cor olive green	6.00	*15.00*
a.		Perf. 13x12½	52.50	*87.50*
		Never hinged	77.50	
b.		Perf. 10½	325.00	325.00
		Never hinged	500.00	

   Nos. 46-53 (8)   34.50 36.00
  Set, never hinged   85.00

Five other denominations (25c, 1cor, 2cor, 3cor and 5cor) were not officially issued. Some copies of the 25c are known canceled. For surcharges see Nos. 59, 61-63, 65, 70.

Stamps of 1919 Handstamp Surcharged

1919-20

58	A4	5c on 20c green ('20)	1.50	1.50
59	A10	5c on 25c blue	1.50	1.50
60	A5	10c on 45c orange	1.50	1.50
61	A9	15c on 30c vio ('20)	1.50	1.50
62	A10	15c on 45c orange	1.50	1.50
63	A9	15c on 60c cl ('20)	1.50	1.50
64	A6	25c on 50c yel grn ('20)	14.00	*25.00*
65	A9	25c on 50c yel grn ('20)	1.00	1.50
66	A6	55c on 1cor brn org	35.00	25.00
67	A6	55c on 2cor brt bl	4.50	*7.50*
68	A6	55c on 3cor org red	4.50	7.00
69	A6	55c on 5cor dp brn	4.50	7.00
70	A9	55c on 10cor ol grn	25.00	27.50

   Nos. 58-70 (13)   98.00 109.50
  Set, never hinged   225.00

Semi-Postal Stamps of 1919 Surcharged:

a

b

1919-20

73	SP6(a)	5c on 5c green	1.50	1.50
74	SP6(a)	10c on 10c rose	1.50	1.50
75	SP6(a)	15c on 15c gray	1.50	1.50
76	SP6(a)	20c on 20c org	1.50	1.50
77	SP9(a)	25c on 25c bl ('20)	1.50	1.50
78	SP7(b)	45c on 45c ol grn	1.50	1.50
79	SP7(b)	60c on 60c rose	1.50	1.50
80	SP7(b)	80c on 80c violet	1.75	1.75
81	SP7(b)	1cor on 1cor sl	1.75	1.75
82	SP8(a)	2cor on 2cor red brn	2.50	2.50
83	SP8(a)	3cor on 3cor blk	5.00	5.00
84	SP8(a)	5cor on 5cor yel	7.50	7.50
85	SP8(a)	10cor on 10cor dk vio ('20)	2.50	2.50
		Nos. 73-85 (13)	31.50	31.50
		Set, never hinged	75.00	

Double or inverted surcharges, or imperf. varieties, exist on most of Nos. 73-85.

There were three settings of the surcharges on Nos. 73-85 except No. 77 which is known only with one setting.

Gabriele d'Annunzio — A11

Severing the Gordian Knot — A12

1920, Sept. 12   Typo.   Perf. 11½
Pale Buff Background

86	A11	5c green	1.50	1.50
87	A11	10c carmine	1.50	1.50
88	A11	15c dark gray	1.50	1.50
89	A11	20c orange	1.50	1.50
90	A11	25c dark blue	2.00	2.00
91	A11	30c red brown	2.00	2.00
92	A11	45c olive gray	3.00	3.00
93	A11	50c lilac	3.00	3.00
94	A11	55c bister	3.00	3.00
95	A11	1 l black	15.00	22.50
96	A11	1 l red violet	15.00	22.50
97	A11	3 l dark green	15.00	22.50
98	A11	5 l brown	75.00	42.50
99	A11	10 l gray violet	17.50	27.50
		Nos. 86-99 (14)	156.50	156.50
		Set, never hinged	350.00	

Counterfeits of Nos. 86 to 99 are plentiful. For overprints see Nos. 134-148.

1920, Sept. 12

Designs: 10c, Ancient emblem of Fiume. 20c, Head of "Fiume." 25c, Hands holding daggers.

100	A12	5c green	57.50	32.50
101	A12	10c deep rose	30.00	25.00
102	A12	20c brown orange	57.50	25.00
103	A12	25c indigo	30.00	55.00
a.		25c blue	125.00	125.00
		Nos. 100-103 (4)	175.00	137.50
		Set, never hinged	425.00	

Anniv. of the occupation of Fiume by d'Annunzio. They were available for franking the correspondence of the legionnaires on the day of issue only, Sept. 12, 1920.

Counterfeits of Nos. 100-103 are plentiful. For overprints and surcharges see Nos. 104-133, E4-E9.

Nos. 100-103 Overprinted or Surcharged in Black or Red and New Values

1920, Nov. 20

104	A12	1c on 5c green	1.50	1.00
105	A12	2c on 25c indi- go (R)	1.25	1.00
a.		2c on 25c blue (R)	80.00	80.00
106	A12	5c green	20.00	1.75
107	A12	10c rose	20.00	1.75
108	A12	15c on 10c rose	1.75	1.75
109	A12	15c on 20c brn org	1.50	1.75
110	A12	15c on 25c ind (R)	1.75	1.75
a.		15c on 25c blue (R)	175.00	175.00
111	A12	20c brown or- ange	1.75	1.75
112	A12	25c indigo (R)	1.75	1.75
a.		25c blue (R)	7.50	7.50
113	A12	25c indigo (Bk)	175.00	175.00
a.		25c blue (Bk)	225.00	225.00
114	A12	25c on 10c rose	2.00	3.75
115	A12	50c on 20c brn org	5.00	2.00
116	A12	55c on 5c green	21.00	3.75
117	A12	1 l on 10c rose	40.00	22.50
118	A12	1 l on 25c ind (R)	100.00	100.00
a.		1 l on 25c blue (R)	600.00	600.00
119	A12	2 l on 5c green	40.00	30.00
120	A12	5 l on 10c rose	200.00	200.00
121	A12	10 l on 20c brn org	700.00	550.00
		Nos. 104-121 (18)	1,334.	1,101.
		Set, never hinged	3,000.	

The Fiume Legionnaires of d'Annunzio occupied the islands of Arbe and Veglia in the Gulf of Carnaro Nov. 13, 1920-Jan. 5, 1921.

Varieties of overprint or surcharge exist for most of Nos. 104-121.

#113, 117-121, 125, 131 have a backprint.

Nos. 106-107, 111, 113, 115-116 Overprinted or Surcharged at top

1920, Nov. 18

122	A12	5c green	15.00	15.00
123	A12	10c rose	30.00	35.00
124	A12	20c brown org	60.00	40.00
125	A12	25c deep blue	35.00	40.00
126	A12	50c on 20c brn org	65.00	40.00
127	A12	55c on 5c green	65.00	40.00
		Nos. 122-127 (6)	270.00	210.00
		Set, never hinged	625.00	

The overprint on Nos. 122-125 comes in two widths: 11mm and 14mm. Values are for the 11mm width.

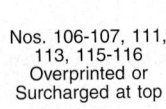

Nos. 106-107, 111, 113, 115-116 Overprinted or Surcharged at top

1920, Nov. 18

128	A12	5c green	15.00	15.00
129	A12	10c rose	30.00	35.00
130	A12	20c brown orange	60.00	40.00
131	A12	25c deep blue	35.00	40.00
132	A12	50c on 20c brn org	65.00	40.00
133	A12	55c on 5c green	65.00	40.00
		Nos. 128-133 (6)	270.00	210.00
		Set, never hinged	625.00	

The overprint on Nos. 128-131 comes in two widths: 17mm and 19mm. Values are for the 17mm width.

Nos. 122-133 exist with double and inverted overprints.

Counterfeits of these overprints exist.

Nos. 86-99 Overprinted

1921, Feb. 2
Pale Buff Background

134	A11	5c green	1.50	1.50
135	A11	10c carmine	1.50	1.50
136	A11	15c dark gray	1.50	1.50
137	A11	20c orange	2.00	2.00
138	A11	25c dark blue	2.00	2.00
139	A11	30c red brown	2.00	2.00
140	A11	45c olive gray	1.75	1.75
141	A11	50c lilac	2.75	2.00
142	A11	55c bister	2.50	2.00
143	A11	1 l black	140.00	140.00
144	A11	2 l red violet	40.00	40.00
145	A11	3 l dark green	40.00	40.00
146	A11	5 l brown	40.00	40.00
147	A11	10 l gray violet	40.00	40.00

With Additional Surcharge

148	A11	1 l on 30c red brn	1.50	1.50
		Nos. 134-148 (15)	319.00	317.75
		Set, never hinged	750.00	

Most of Nos. 134-143, 148 and E10-E11 exist with inverted or double overprint. See Nos. E10-E11.

First Constituent Assembly

Nos. B4-B15 Overprinted

1921, Apr. 24

149	SP6	5c blue green	4.00	3.00
150	SP6	10c rose	4.00	3.00
151	SP6	15c gray	4.00	3.00
152	SP6	20c orange	4.00	3.00
153	SP7	45c olive green	9.75	7.50
154	SP7	60c car rose	9.75	7.50
155	SP7	80c brt violet	15.00	12.00

With Additional Overprint "L"

156	SP7	1 l on 1cor dk sl	20.00	20.00
157	SP8	2 l on 2cor red brn	80.00	2.50
158	SP8	3 l on 3cor blk brn	80.00	85.00
159	SP8	5 l on 5cor yel brn	80.00	3.75
160	SP8	10 l on 10cor dk vio	110.00	110.00
		Nos. 149-160 (12)	420.50	260.25
		Set, never hinged	1,000.	

The overprint exists inverted on several denominations.

Second Constituent Assembly
"Constitution" Issue of 1921 With Additional Overprint "1922"

1922

161	SP6	5c blue green	3.25	2.75
162	SP6	10c rose	1.50	1.50
163	SP6	15c gray	17.50	8.00
164	SP6	20c orange	1.75	1.75
165	SP7	45c olive grn	11.50	9.50
166	SP7	60c car rose	1.50	2.75
167	SP7	80c brt violet	1.75	2.75
168	SP7	1 l on 1cor dk slate	1.75	2.25
169	SP8	2 l on 2cor red brn	17.50	12.00
170	SP8	3 l on 3cor blk brn	1.75	2.75
171	SP8	5 l on 5cor yel brn	1.75	2.75
		Nos. 161-171 (11)	61.25	48.75
		Set, never hinged	140.00	

Nos. 161-171 have the overprint in heavier type than Nos. 149-160 and "IV" in Roman instead of sans-serif numerals.

The overprint exists inverted or double on almost all values.

Venetian Ship — A16

Roman Arch — A17

St. Vitus — A18

Rostral Column — A19

1923, Mar. 23   Perf. 11½
Pale Buff Background

172	A16	5c blue green	1.50	1.50
173	A16	10c violet	1.50	1.50
174	A16	15c brown	1.50	1.50
175	A17	20c orange red	1.50	1.50
176	A17	25c dark gray	1.50	1.50
177	A17	30c dark green	1.50	1.50
178	A18	50c dull blue	1.50	1.50
179	A18	60c rose	2.50	2.00
180	A18	1 l dark blue	2.50	2.50
181	A19	2 l violet brown	55.00	11.00
182	A19	3 l olive bister	45.00	37.50
183	A19	5 l yellow brown	45.00	45.00
		Nos. 172-183 (12)	160.50	108.50
		Set, never hinged	325.00	

Nos. 172-183 Overprinted

1924, Feb. 22
Pale Buff Background

184	A16	5c blue green	1.50	3.75
185	A16	10c violet	1.50	3.75
186	A16	15c brown	1.50	3.75
187	A17	20c orange red	1.50	3.75
188	A17	25c dk gray	1.50	3.75
189	A17	30c dk green	1.50	3.75
190	A18	50c dull blue	1.50	3.75
191	A18	60c red	1.50	3.75
192	A18	1 l dark blue	1.50	3.75
193	A19	2 l violet brown	3.00	13.00
194	A19	3 l olive	6.00	16.50
195	A19	5 l yellow brown	6.00	16.50
		Nos. 184-195 (12)	28.50	79.75
		Set, never hinged	60.00	

The overprint exists inverted on almost all values.

Nos. 172-183 Overprinted

1924, Mar. 1
Pale Buff Background

196	A16	5c blue green	1.50	2.25
197	A16	10c violet	1.50	2.25
198	A16	15c brown	1.50	2.25
199	A17	20c orange red	1.50	2.25
200	A17	25c dark gray	1.50	2.25
201	A17	30c dark green	1.50	2.25
202	A18	50c dull blue	1.50	2.25
203	A18	60c red	1.50	2.25
204	A18	1 l dark blue	1.50	2.25
205	A19	2 l violet brown	2.25	5.00
206	A19	3 l olive	2.75	5.00
207	A19	5 l yellow brown	2.75	5.00
		Nos. 196-207 (12)	21.25	35.25
		Set, never hinged	36.00	

Postage stamps of Fiume were superseded by stamps of Italy.

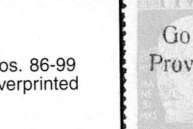

Nos. 100-103 Overprinted or Surcharged at top

SEMI-POSTAL STAMPS

Semi-Postal Stamps of
Hungary, 1916-17
Overprinted

1918, Dec. 2   Wmk. 137   *Perf. 15*

B1	SP3	10f + 2f rose	4.00	3.00
a.		Inverted overprint	65.00	40.00
B2	SP4	15f + 2f dl vio	4.00	3.00
a.		Inverted overprint	125.00	40.00
B3	SP5	40f + 2f brn car	8.00	3.00
a.		Inverted overprint	67.50	37.50
		Nos. B1-B3 (3)	16.00	9.00
		Set, never hinged	42.50	

Examples of Nos. B1-B3 with overprint
handstamped sell for higher prices.

Statue of Romulus
and Remus Being
Suckled by
Wolf — SP6

Venetian
Galley — SP7

Church of St.
Mark's,
Venice — SP8

Perf. 11½

1919, May 18		**Unwmk.**		**Typo.**
B4	SP6	5c +5 l bl grn	17.50	9.50
B5	SP6	10c +5 l rose	17.50	9.50
B6	SP6	15c +5 l dk gray	17.50	9.50
B7	SP6	20c +5 l orange	17.50	9.50
B8	SP7	45c +5 l ol grn	17.50	9.50
B9	SP7	60c +5 l car rose	17.50	9.50
B10	SP7	80c +5 l lilac	17.50	9.50
B11	SP7	1cor +5 l dk slate	17.50	9.50
B12	SP8	2cor +5 l red brn	17.50	9.50
B13	SP8	3cor +5 l blk brn	17.50	9.50
B14	SP8	5cor +5 l yel brn	17.50	9.50
B15	SP8	10cor +5 l dk vio	17.50	9.50
		Nos. B4-B15 (12)	210.00	114.00
		Set, never hinged	400.00	

200th day of peace. The surtax aided Fiume
students in Italy. "Posta di Fiume" is printed on
the back of Nos. B4-B16.
    The surtax is shown on the stamps as "LIRE
5" but actually was 5cor.
    For surcharges and overprints see Nos. 73-
85, 149-171, J15-J26.

Dr. Antonio
Grossich — SP9

1919, Sept. 20

B16	SP9	25c + 2 l blue	3.00	3.00
		Never hinged	7.25	

Surtax for the Dr. Grossich Foundation.

SPECIAL DELIVERY STAMPS

Special Delivery Stamp of Hungary,
1916, Overprinted like Nos. 1-23

1918, Dec. 2   Wmk. 137   *Perf. 15*

E1	SD1	2f gray green & red	4.00	3.25
		Never hinged	8.75	

Handstamped overprints sell for more.

SD3

Perf. 11½

1920, Sept. 12		**Unwmk.**		**Typo.**
E2	SD3	30c slate blue	25.00	25.00
E3	SD3	50c rose	25.00	25.00
		Set, never hinged	120.00	

For overprints see Nos. E10-E11.

Nos. 102 and 100
Surcharged

1920, Nov.

E4	A12	30c on 20c brn org	150.00	100.00
E5	A12	50c on 5c green	200.00	80.00

Nos. E4-E5 have a backprint.

Same Surcharge as on Nos. 124, 122

E6	A12	30c on 20c brn org	200.00	100.00
E7	A12	50c on 5c green	160.00	100.00

Overprint on Nos. E6-E7 is 11mm wide.

Same Surcharge as on Nos. 130, 128

E8	A12	30c on 20c brn org	200.00	100.00
E9	A12	50c on 5c green	160.00	100.00
		Nos. E4-E9 (6)	1,070.	580.00
		Set, never hinged	2,100.	

Overprint on Nos. E8-E9 is 17mm wide.

Nos. E2 and E3 Overprinted

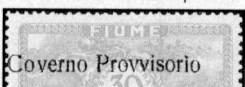

1921, Feb. 2

E10	SD3	30c slate blue	10.00	12.00
E11	SD3	50c rose	15.00	12.00
		Set, never hinged	60.00	

Fiume in
16th
Century
SD4

1923, Mar. 23   *Perf. 11, 11½*

E12	SD4	60c rose & buff	20.00	13.50
E13	SD4	2 l dk bl & buff	20.00	15.00
		Set, never hinged	85.00	

Nos. E12-E13 Overprinted

1924, Feb. 22

E14	SD4	60c car & buff	2.25	7.00
E15	SD4	2 l dk bl & buff	2.25	7.00
		Set, never hinged	9.00	

Nos. E12-E13 Overprinted

1924, Mar. 1

E16	SD4	60c car & buff	2.75	6.00
E17	SD4	2 l dk bl & buff	2.75	6.00
		Set, never hinged	10.00	

POSTAGE DUE STAMPS

Postage Due
Stamps of Hungary,
1915-1916,
Overprinted

1918, Dec.   Wmk. 137   *Perf. 15*

J1	D1	6f green & black	175.00	85.00
J2	D1	12f green & black	190.00	60.00
J3	D1	50f green & black	60.00	27.50
		Set, never hinged	900.00	
J4	D1	1f green & red	29.00	17.50
J5	D1	2f green & red	2.00	1.00
J6	D1	5f green & red	15.00	5.00
J7	D1	6f green & red	2.00	1.75
J8	D1	10f green & red	17.50	5.00
J9	D1	12f green & red	2.25	2.00
J10	D1	15f green & red	27.50	15.00
J11	D1	20f green & red	2.50	2.25
J12	D1	30f green & red	27.50	20.00
		Nos. J4-J12 (9)	125.25	69.50
		Set, never hinged	275.00	

The overprint on Nos. J1-J12 was applied
both by press and handstamp. Values are for
the less costly. Inverted and double overprints
exist. Excellent forgeries exist.

Eagle — D2

Perf. 11½

1919, July 28		**Unwmk.**		**Typo.**
J13	D2	2c brown	1.75	1.50
J14	D2	5c brown	1.75	1.50
		Set, never hinged	8.00	

Semi-Postal Stamps of 1919 with
Overprint "Valore Globale" Surcharged:

1921, Mar. 21

J15	SP6	2c on 15c gray	3.00	2.00
J16	SP6	4c on 10c rose	2.25	1.50
J17	SP9	5c on 25c blue	2.25	1.50
J18	SP6	6c on 20c orange	2.25	1.50
J19	SP6	10c on 20c orange	3.50	2.50

Surcharged:

J20	SP7	20c on 45c olive grn	2.00	2.25
J21	SP7	30c on 1cor dk slate	4.00	2.25
J22	SP7	40c on 80c violet	2.25	2.00
J23	SP7	50c on 60c carmine	2.50	2.00
J24	SP7	60c on 45c olive grn	2.00	2.25
J25	SP7	80c on 45c olive grn	2.00	2.25

Surcharged like Nos. J15-J19

J26	SP8	1 l on 2cor red brown	5.00	5.00
		Nos. J15-J26 (12)	33.00	27.00
		Set, never hinged	60.00	

See note below No. 85 regarding settings of
"Valore Globale" overprint.

NEWSPAPER STAMPS

Newspaper Stamp of Hungary, 1914,
Overprinted like Nos. 1-23

1918, Dec. 2   Wmk. 137   *Imperf.*

P1	N5	(2f) orange	3.75	2.25
		Never hinged	8.50	

Handstamped overprints sell for more.

Eagle
N1

1919   Unwmk.   *Perf. 11½*

P2	N1	2c deep buff	7.00	11.00

Re-engraved

P3	N1	2c deep buff	7.00	11.00
		Set, never hinged	35.00	

In the re-engraved stamp the top of the "2" is
rounder and broader, the feet of the eagle
show clearly and the diamond at bottom has
six lines instead of five.

Steamer — N2

1920, Sept. 12

P4	N2	1c gray green	2.75	1.75
		Never hinged	6.00	

No. P4 exists imperf.

FRANCE

'fran̩t̩s

LOCATION — Western Europe
GOVT. — Republic
AREA — 210,033 sq. mi.
POP. — 58,978,172 (1999 est.)
CAPITAL — Paris

100 Centimes = 1 Franc
100 Cents = 1 Euro (2002)

Catalogue values for unused stamps in this country are for Never Hinged items, beginning with Scott 299 in the regular postage section, Scott B42 in the semipostal section, Scott C18 in the airpost section, Scott CB1 in the airpost semi-postal section, Scott J69 in the postage due section, Scott M10 in the military stamps section, Scott 1O1 in the section for official stamps for the Council of Europe, Scott 2O1 for the section for UNESCO, Scott S1 for franchise stamps, Scott N27 for occupation stamps, and Scott 2N1 for AMG stamps.

Ceres — A1

FORTY CENTIMES

4
Type I

4
Type II

1849-50 Typo.		Unwmk.	Imperf.
1	A1 10c bis, yelsh ('50)	2,000.	275.00
a.	10c dark bister, yelsh	2,300.	350.00
b.	10c greenish bister	2,750.	425.00
e.	Tête bêche pair	132,500.	18,500.
2	A1 15c green, grnsh ('50)	23,000.	900.00
a.	15c yellow green, grnsh	22,500.	900.00
c.	Tête bêche pair	—	
3	A1 20c blk, yelsh	400.00	40.00
a.	20c black	475.00	50.00
b.	20c black, buff	1,400.	225.00
c.	Tête bêche pair	10,000.	6,600.
4	A1 20c dark blue	2,850.	
a.	20c blue, bluish	2,200.	
b.	20c blue, yelsh	3,500.	
c.	Tête bêche pair	70,000.	
6	A1 25c lt bl, bluish	6,750.	32.50
a.	25c blue, bluish ('50)	6,750.	32.50
b.	25c blue, yelsh	6,400.	45.00
c.	Tête bêche pair	185,000.	13,500.
7	A1 40c org, (I) ('50)	3,750.	450.00
a.	40c org ver, yelsh (I)	4,250.	500.00
b.	40c orange, yelsh (II)	25,000.	6,750.
c.	Pair, types I and II	40,000.	13,250.
g.	Vertical half used as 20c on cover		215,000.

8	A1 1fr ver, yelsh	100,000.	15,500.
a.	1fr dull org red	100,000.	19,500.
b.	Tête bêche pair	95,000.	172,500.
c.	1fr pale ver ("Vervelle")	26,500.	
9	A1 1fr light carmine	11,000.	750.00
a.	Tête bêche pair	235,000.	23,500.
b.	1fr brown carmine	13,250.	1,100.
c.	1fr dk car, yelsh	13,250.	775.00

No. 4, which lacks gum, was not issued due to a rate change to 25c after the stamps were prepared. An essay with a red "25" surcharge on No. 4 was rejected.

An ungummed sheet of No. 8c was found in 1895 among the effects of Anatole A. Hulot, the printer. It was sold to Ernest Vervelle, a Parisian dealer, by whose name the stamps are known.

See Nos. 329-329e, 612-613, 624.

Nos. 1, 4a, 6a, 7 and 13 are of similar designs and colors to French Colonies Nos. 9, 11, 12, 14, and 8. There are numerous shades of each. Identification by those who are not experts can be difficult, though cancellations can be used as a guide for used stamps. Because of the date of issue the Colonies stamps are similar in shades and papers to the perforated French stamps,

Nos. 23a, 54, 57-59, and are not as clearly printed. Except for No. 13, unused, the French Colonies stamps sell for much less than the values shown here for properly identified French versions.

Expertization of these stamps is recommended.

1862			**Re-issue**
1g	A1	10c bister	550.
2d	A1	15c yellow green	700.
3d	A1	20c black, yellowish	450.
4d	A1	20c blue	450.
6d	A1	25c blue	500.
7d	A1	40c orange (I)	700.
7e	A1	40c orange (II)	11,500.
h.		Pair, types I and II	16,500.
9d	A1	1fr pale lake	750.

The re-issues are fine impressions in lighter colors and on whiter paper than the originals. An official imitation of the essay, 25c on 20c blue, also in a lighter shade and on whiter paper, was made at the same time as the re-issues.

President Louis Napoleon — A2

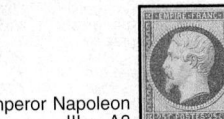

Emperor Napoleon III — A3

1852				
10	A2 10c pale bister, yelsh	34,500.	575.00
a.	10c dark bister, yelsh	37,000.	650.00
11	A2 25c blue, bluish	2,900.	40.00
b.	25c dark blue, blush	3,500.	70.00

1862			**Re-issue**
10b	A2	10c bister	700.00
11a	A2	25c blue	450.00

The re-issues are in lighter colors and on whiter paper than the originals.

1853-60			**Imperf.**

Die I. The curl above the forehead directly below "R" of "EMPIRE" is made up of two lines very close together, often appearing to form a single thick line. There is no shading across the neck.

Die II. The curl is made of two distinct, more widely separated lines. There are lines of shading across the upper neck.

12	A3 1c ol grn, pale bl ('60)	190.00	77.50
a.	1c bronze grn, pale bluish	200.00	95.00
13	A3 5c grn, grnsh (I) ('54)	700.00	85.00
14	A3 10c bis, yelsh (I)	425.00	9.00
a.	10c yellow, yelsh	1,500.	37.50
b.	10c bister brn, yelsh (I)	550.00	25.00
c.	10c bis, yelsh (II) ('60)	550.00	22.50
15	A3 20c bl, bluish (I) ('54)	175.00	1.50
a.	20c dark bl, bluish	250.00	2.00
b.	20c milky blue	275.00	12.50
c.	20c blue, lilac (I)	4,500.	82.50
d.	20c bl, bluish (II) ('60)	325.00	4.75
e.	Half used as 10c on cover		18,500.
16	A3 20c bl, grnsh (II)	5,000.	190.00
a.	20c blue, greenish (I)	4,250.	125.00
17	A3 25c bl, bluish (I)	2,300.	250.00
18	A3 40c bl, yelsh	2,250.	12.50
a.	40c org ver, yellowish	2,750.	20.00
b.	Half used as 20c on cover		135,000.
19	A3 80c lake, yelsh (I) ('54)	3,400.	82.50
a.	Tête bêche pair	325,000.	17,500.
b.	Half used as 40c on cover		40,000.
20	A3 80c rose, pnksh (I) ('60)	1,900.	47.50
a.	Tete bêche pair	57,500.	12,000.
21	A3 1fr lake, yelsh (I)	7,000.	2,600.
a.	Tête bêche pair	310,000.	130,000.

Most values of the 1853-60 issue are known privately rouletted, pin-perf., perf. 7 and percé en scie.

1862			**Re-issue**
17c	A3	25c blue (I)	425.
19c	A3	80c lake (I)	1,500.
21c	A3	1fr lake (I)	1,800.
d.		Tête bêche pair	30,000.

The re-issues are in lighter colors and on whiter paper than the originals.

1862-71			**Perf. 14x13½**
22	A3 1c ol grn, pale bl (II)	160.00	40.00
a.	1c bronze grn, pale bl (II)	160.00	40.00
23	A3 5c yel grn, grnsh (I)	375.00	20.00
a.	5c deep green, grnsh (I)	250.00	16.00
24	A3 5c grn, pale bl ('71)	1,950.	100.00
25	A3 10c bis, yelsh	1,450.	4.25
a.	10c yel brn, yelsh (II)	2,000.	10.50
26	A3 20c bl, bluish (II)	225.00	1.25
a.	Tête bêche pair (II)	4,000.	1,000.
27	A3 40c org, yelsh (I)	1,300.	7.50

28	A3 80c rose, pnksh (I)	1,200.	37.50
a.	80c brt rose, pinkish (I)	1,500.	57.50
c.	Tête bêche pair (I)	20,500.	8,250.

No. 26a imperf is from a trial printing.

A4   A5

Napoleon III — A6

1863-70			**Perf. 14x13½**
29	A4 1c brnz grn, pale bl ('70)	35.00	14.50
a.	1c olive green, pale blue	29.00	14.00
30	A4 2c red brn, yelsh	82.50	25.00
b.	Half used as 1c on cover		42,500.
31	A4 4c gray	200.00	52.50
a.	Tete beche pair	20,000.	13,250.
d.	Half used as 2c on cover		60,000.
32	A5 10c bis, yelsh ('67)	325.00	6.00
c.	Half used as 5c on cover with other stamps		3,750.
33	A5 20c bl, bluish ('67)	225.00	1.60
c.	Half used as 10c on cover		52,500.
34	A5 30c brn, yelsh ('67)	750.00	17.00
a.	30c dk brn, yellowish	1,225.	37.50
35	A5 40c pale org, yellowish	750.00	10.00
a.	40c org, yelsh ('68)	750.00	10.00
c.	Half used as 20c on cover		42,500.
36	A5 80c rose, pnksh ('68)	1,000.	21.00
a.	80c carmine, yellowish	1,400.	40.00
d.	Half used as 40c on cover		50,000.
e.	Quarter used as 20c on cover		57,500.
37	A6 5fr gray lil, lav ('69)	5,500.	825.00
a.	"5" and "F" omitted		112,500.
c.	5fr bluish gray, lavender	6,000.	1,000.
d.	As #37, "5" and "F" in light blue	7,500.	1,100.

No. 33 exists in two types, differing in the size of the dots at either side of POSTES.

On No. 37, the "5" and "F" vary in height from 3¾mm to 4½mm. These figures normally appear in gray but exist in blue or black.

All known copies of No. 37a are more or less damaged.

No. 29 was reprinted in 1887 by authority of Granet, Minister of Posts. The reprints show a yellowish shade under the ultraviolet lamp. Value $850.

For surcharge see No. 49.

Original Issue Imperfs

31c	A4	4c gray	400.	175.
32b	A5	10c bister, yellowish	450.	175.
33b	A5	20c blue, bluish	375.	160.
36c	A5	80c rose, pinkish		
37b	A6	5fr gray lilac, lavender	8,500.	8,500.

Imperfs, "Rothschild" Re-issue
Paper Colors are the Same

29b	A4	1c olive green	1,200.
30a	A4	2c pale red brown	190.
31b	A4	4c pale gray	140.
32a	A5	10c pale bister	140.
33a	A5	20c pale blue	250.
34c	A5	30c pale brown	150.
35b	A5	40c pale orange	225.
36b	A5	80c pale rose	425.

The re-issues constitute the "Rothschild Issue." These stamps were authorized exclusively for the banker to use on his correspondence. Used copies exist.

Ceres
A7   A8

A9   A10

A11

Bordeaux Issue

On the lithographed stamps, except for type I of the 20c, the shading on the cheek and neck is in lines or dashes, not in dots. On the typographed stamps the shading is in dots. The 2c, 10c and 20c (types II and III) occur in two or more types. The most easily distinguishable are:

2c — Type A. To the left of and within the top of the left "2" are lines of shading composed of dots.

2c — Type B. These lines of dots are replaced by solid lines.

10c — Type A. The inner frame lines are of the same thickness as all other frame lines.

10c — Type B. The inner frame lines are much thicker than the others.

Three Types of the 20c.
A9 — The inscriptions in the upper and lower labels are small and there is quite a space between the upper label and the circle containing the head. There is also very little shading under the eye and in the neck.

A10 — The inscriptions in the labels are similar to those of the first type, the shading under the eye and in the neck is heavier and the upper label and circle almost touch.

A11 — The inscriptions in the labels are much larger than the those of the two preceding types, and are similar to those of the other values of the same type in the set.

1870-71   Litho.   *Imperf.*

38	A7	1c ol grn, pale bl	160.00	115.00
a.		1c bronze grn, pale blue	200.00	150.00
39	A7	2c red brn, yelsh (B)	275.00	250.00
a.		2c brick red, yelsh (B)	825.00	625.00
b.		2c chestnut, yelsh (B)	1,500.	850.00
c.		2c chocolate, yelsh (A)	825.00	725.00
40	A7	4c gray	275.00	225.00
41	A8	5c yel green, greenish	275.00	175.00
a.		5c grn, greenish	350.00	175.00
b.		5c emerald, greenish	3,600.	1,250.
42	A8	10c bis, yelsh (A)	1,000.	60.00
a.		10c bister, yellowish (B)	1,000.	90.00
43	A9	20c bl, bluish	22,000.	575.00
a.		20c dark blue, bluish	24,500.	825.00
44	A10	20c bl, bluish	950.00	45.00
a.		20c dark blue, bluish	1,250.	100.00
b.		20c ultra, bluish	22,000.	3,300.
45	A11	20c bl, bluish ('71)	950.00	18.00
a.		20c ultra, bluish	2,750.	1,250.
46	A8	30c brn, yelsh	375.00	225.00
a.		30c blk brn, yelsh	2,000.	825.00
47	A8	40c org, yelsh	475.00	115.00
a.		40c yel orange, yelsh	1,450.	250.00
b.		40c red orange, yelsh	725.00	190.00
c.		40c scarlet, yelsh	3,200.	775.00
48	A8	80c rose, pinkish	525.00	250.00
a.		80c dull rose, pinkish	1,000.	275.00

All values of the 1870 issue are known privately rouletted, pin-perf. and perf. 14. See Nos. 50-53.

A12

Dark Blue Surcharge

1871   Typo.   *Perf. 14x13½*

49	A12	10c on 10c bister	1,500.	
a.		Pale blue surcharge	1,400.	

#49 was never placed in use. Counterfeits exist.

A13   A14

Two types of the 40c as in the 1849-50 issue.

1870-73   Typo.   *Perf. 14x13½*

50	A7	1c ol grn, pale bl	45.00	13.00
a.		1c bronze grn, pale bl ('72)	52.50	15.00
51	A7	2c red brn, yelsh ('70)	90.00	15.00
52	A7	4c gray ('70)	275.00	45.00
53	A7	5c yel grn, pale bl ('72)	175.00	8.25
a.		5c green	175.00	8.25
54	A13	10c bis, yelsh	600.00	65.00
a.		Tête beche pair	6,250.	2,600.
b.		Half used as 5c on cover		5,000.
55	A13	10c bis, rose ('73)	300.00	10.50
a.		Tête beche pair	4,250.	2,000.
56	A13	15c bis, yelsh ('71)	350.00	5.00
a.		Tête beche pair	42,500.	13,500.

57	A13	20c dl bl, bluish	250.00	7.50
a.		20c bright blue, bluish	400.00	9.00
b.		Tête beche pair	4,250.	1,650.
c.		Half used as 10c on cover		62,500.
d.		Quarter used as 5c on cover		57,500.
58	A13	25c bl, bluish ('71)	125.00	1.25
a.		25c dk bl, bluish	150.00	1.25
b.		Tête beche pair	7,500.	3,500.
59	A13	40c org, yelsh (I)	525.00	7.00
a.		40c orange yel, yelsh (I)	650.00	10.00
b.		40c orange, yelsh (II)	3,500.	150.00
c.		40c orange yel, yelsh (II)	3,500.	150.00
d.		Pair, types I and II	7,250.	575.00
f.		Half used as 20c on circular		25,000.
g.		Half used as 20c on cover		50,000.

No. 58 exists in three main plate varieties, differing in one or another of the flower-like corner ornaments.

Margins on this issue are extremely small. Nos. 54, 57 and 58 were reprinted imperf. in 1887. See note after No. 37.

Imperf.

50b	A7	1c	300.00
51a	A7	2c	400.00
52a	A7	4c	500.00
53b	A7	5c yel grn, pale bl	325.00
55b	A13	10c	400.00
56b	A13	15c	425.00

1872-75   *Perf. 14x13½*
Larger Numerals

60	A14	10c bis, rose ('75)	375.00	12.00
a.		Cliché of 15c in plate of 10c	4,250.	4,750.
b.		Pair, #60, 60a	7,500.	9,500.
61	A14	15c bister ('73)	375.00	4.00
62	A14	30c brn, yelsh	650.00	6.50
63	A14	80c rose, pnksh	725.00	13.50
		Nos. 60-63 (4)	2,125.	36.00

Imperf.

62a	A14	30c	575.00
63a	A14	80c	825.00

Peace and Commerce ("Type Sage") — A15

Type I. The "N" of "INV" is under the "B" of "REPUBLIQUE."
Type II. The "N" of "INV" is under the "U" of "REPUBLIQUE."

1876-78   *Perf. 14x13½*
Type I

64	A15	1c grn, grnsh	140.00	70.00
65	A15	2c grn, grnsh	1,450.	250.00
66	A15	4c grn, grnsh	160.00	55.00
67	A15	5c grn, grnsh	700.00	45.00
68	A15	10c grn, grnsh	825.00	22.50
69	A15	15c gray lil, grysh	825.00	18.00
70	A15	20c red brn, straw	600.00	18.00
71	A15	20c bl, bluish	32,500.	
72	A15	25c ultra, bluish	7,750.	57.50
73	A15	30c brn, yelsh	425.00	8.25
74	A15	40c red, straw ('78)	600.00	35.00
75	A15	75c car, rose	950.00	13.50
76	A15	1fr brnz grn, straw	925.00	11.00

No. 71 was never put into use.
The reprints of No. 71 are type II. They are imperforate or with forged perforation.

For overprints and surcharges see Offices in China Nos. 1-17, J7-J10, J20-J22, Offices in Egypt, Alexandria 1-15, Port Said 1-17, Offices in Turkish Empire 1-7, Cavalle 1-8, Dedeagh 1-8, Port Lagos 1-5, Vathy 1-9, Offices in Zanzibar 1-33, 50-54, Offices in Morocco 1-8, and Madagascar 14-27.

Imperf.

64a	A15	1c	175.00
65a	A15	2c	1,100.
66a	A15	4c	190.00
67a	A15	5c	575.00
68a	A15	10c	650.00
69a	A15	15c	650.00
70a	A15	20c	425.00
73a	A15	30c	300.00
74a	A15	40c	275.00
75a	A15	75c	600.00
76a	A15	1fr	450.00

Beware of French Colonies #24-29.

1876-77   *Perf. 14x13½*
Type II

77	A15	2c grn, grnsh	115.00	19.00
78	A15	5c grn, grnsh	25.00	.60
a.		Imperf.	175.00	
79	A15	10c grn, grnsh	1,100.	240.00
80	A15	15c gray lil, grysh	675.00	1.90
81	A15	25c ultra, bluish	425.00	1.00
a.		25c blue, bluish	475.00	1.50
b.		Pair, types I & II	65,000.	17,500.
c.		Imperf.	325.00	
82	A15	30c yel brn, yelsh	82.50	1.40
a.		30c brown, yellowish	90.00	1.40
b.		Imperf.	525.00	
83	A15	75c car, rose ('77)	1,775.	110.00
84	A15	1fr brnz grn, straw ('77)	150.00	7.50
a.		Imperf.	925.00	

Beware of French Colonies #31, 35.

1877-80

86	A15	1c blk, lil bl	3.75	1.75
a.		1c black, gray blue	3.75	1.75
b.		Imperf.	75.00	
87	A15	1c blk, Prus bl ('80)	11,000.	4,350.

Values for No. 87 are for copies with the perfs touching the design on at least one side.

88	A15	2c brn, straw	4.50	1.90
a.		2c brown, yellow	4.50	1.90
b.		Imperf.	200.00	
89	A15	3c yel, straw ('78)	200.00	42.50
a.		Imperf.	150.00	
90	A15	4c claret, lav	5.00	1.90
a.		4c vio brown, lavender	8.25	4.00
b.		Imperf.	60.00	
91	A15	10c blk, lavender	35.00	1.00
a.		10c black, rose lilac	37.50	1.00
b.		10c black, lilac	37.50	1.00
c.		Imperf.	70.00	
92	A15	15c blue ('78)	22.50	.60
a.		Imperf.	95.00	
b.		15c blue, bluish	450.00	15.00
93	A15	25c blk, red ('78)	1,075.	25.00
a.		Imperf.	675.00	
94	A15	35c blk, yel ('78)	525.00	35.00
a.		35c blk, yel org	525.00	35.00
b.		Imperf.	250.00	
95	A15	40c red, straw ('80)	90.00	2.10
a.		Imperf.	250.00	
96	A15	5fr vio, lav	450.00	70.00
a.		5fr red lilac, lavender	650.00	90.00
b.		Imperf.	750.00	

Beware of French Colonies #38-40, 42, 44.

1879-90

97	A15	3c gray, grysh ('80)	4.00	1.75
a.		Imperf.	65.00	
98	A15	20c red, yel grn	37.50	4.25
a.		20c red, deep green ('84)	70.00	5.75
b.		Imperf.	100.00	
99	A15	25c yel, straw	325.00	5.00
a.		Imperf.	250.00	
100	A15	25c blk, pale rose ('86)	70.00	1.00
a.		Imperf.	150.00	
101	A15	50c rose, rose ('90)	200.00	2.75
a.		50c carmine, rose	225.00	3.25
102	A15	75c dp vio, org ('90)	200.00	32.50
a.		75c deep violet, yellow	275.00	45.00
		Nos. 97-102 (6)	836.50	47.25

Beware of French Colonies #43.

1892
Quadrille Paper

103	A15	15c blue	12.50	.35
a.		Imperf.	175.00	

1898-1900
Ordinary Paper

104	A15	5c yellow green	16.00	1.25
a.		Imperf.	82.50	

Type I

105	A15	5c yellow green	14.00	1.25
a.		Imperf.	550.00	
106	A15	10c blk, lavender	21.00	2.50
a.		Imperf.	250.00	
107	A15	50c car, rose	200.00	30.00
108	A15	2fr brn, azure ('00)	110.00	40.00
b.		Imperf.	2,225.	
		Nos. 104-108 (5)	361.00	75.00

See No. 226.
Reprints of A15, type II, were made in 1887 and left imperf. See note after No. 37. Value for set of 27, $3,300.

Liberty, Equality, Fraternity A16

"The Rights of Man" A17

Liberty and Peace A18

1900-29   Perf. 14x13½

109	A16	1c gray	.55	.40
110	A16	2c violet brn	.70	.25
111	A16	3c orange	.45	.45
a.		3c red	19.00	7.50
112	A16	4c yellow brn	3.25	1.60
113	A16	5c green	2.00	.35
b.		Booklet pane of 10	350.00	
114	A16	7½c lilac ('26)	.60	.40
115	A16	10c lilac ('29)	4.00	.60
116	A17	10c carmine	25.00	1.50
a.		Numerals printed separately	24.00	10.00
117	A17	15c orange	8.00	.60
118	A17	20c brown vio	55.00	9.00
119	A17	25c blue	125.00	1.75
a.		Numerals printed separately	115.00	9.00
120	A17	30c violet	70.00	5.75
121	A18	40c red & pale bl	15.00	.85
122	A18	45c green & bl ('06)	29.00	2.10
123	A18	50c bis brn & gray	100.00	1.65
124	A18	60c vio & ultra ('20)	1.00	1.25
125	A18	1fr claret & ol grn	26.50	.85
126	A18	2fr gray vio & yel	600.00	75.00
127	A18	2fr org & pale bl ('20)	42.50	.60
128	A18	3fr vio & bl ('25)	26.50	7.50
129	A18	3fr brt vio & rose ('27)	55.00	2.75
130	A18	5fr dk bl & buff ('26)	125.00	16.50
131	A18	10fr grn & red ('26)	125.00	16.50
132	A18	20fr mag & grn ('26)	200.00	37.50
		Nos. 109-132 (24)	1,597.	174.20

In the 10c and 25c values, the first printings show the numerals to have been impressed by a second operation, whereas, in later printings, the numerals were inserted in the plates. Two operations were used for all 20c and 30c, and one operation for the 15c.

No. 114 was issued precanceled only. Values for precanceled stamps in first column are for those which have not been through the post and have original gum. Values in the second column are for postally used, gumless stamps.

See Off. in China #34, 40-44, Off. in Crete 1-5, 10-15, Off. in Egypt, Alexandria 16-20, 26-30, 77, 84-86, Port Said 18-22, 28-32, 83, 90-92, Off. in Turkish Empire 21-26, 31-33, Cavalle 9, Dedeagh 9.

For overprints & surcharge see #197, 246, C1-C2, M1, P7. Off. in China 57, 62-65, 71, 73, 75, 83-85, J14, J27, Off. in Crete 17-20, Off. in Egypt, Alexandria 31-32, 34-35, 40-48, 57-64, 66, 71-73, Port Said 33, 35-40, 43, 46-57, 59, 65-71, 73, 78-80, Off. in Turkish Empire 35-38, 47-49, Cavalle 13-15, Dedeagh 16-18, Off. in Zanzibar 39, 45-49, 55, Off. in Morocco 11-15, 20-22, 26-29, 35-41, 49-54, 72-76, 84-85, 87-89, B6.

Imperf.

109a	A16	1c	62.50	
110a	A16	2c	75.00	60.00
111b	A16	3c	62.50	
112a	A16	4c	175.00	125.00
113a	A16	5c	82.50	
116b	A17	10c #116 or 116a	275.00	140.00
117a	A17	15c	200.00	175.00
119b	A17	25c #119 or 119a	350.00	
121a	A18	40c	225.00	160.00
122a	A18	45c	300.00	
123a	A18	50c	425.00	375.00
124a	A18	60c	575.00	
125a	A18	1fr	275.00	325.00
126a	A18	2fr	1,450.	
127a	A18	2fr	525.00	
128a	A18	3fr	800.00	500.00
129a	A18	3fr	475.00	
130a	A18	5fr	1,050.	

Nos. 112a and 126a are valued without gum.

Flat Plate & Rotary Press

The following stamps were printed by both flat plate and rotary press: Nos. 109-113, 144-146, 163, 166, 168, 170, 177-178, 185, 192 and P7.

A19

Sower A20

1902

133	A19	10c rose red	26.50	.90
134	A19	15c pale red	11.00	.60
135	A19	20c brown violet	82.50	14.00
136	A19	25c blue	100.00	2.25
137	A19	30c lilac	250.00	14.50
		Nos. 133-137 (5)	470.00	32.25

Imperf

133a	A19	10c rose red	450.00	275.00
134a	A19	15c pale red	450.00	325.00
135a	A19	20c brown violet	800.00	475.00
136a	A19	25c blue	950.00	625.00
137a	A19	30c lilac	1,100.	

See Off. in China #35-39, Off. in Crete 6-10, Off. in Egypt, Alexandria 21-25, 81-82, Port Said 23-27, 87-88, Off. in Turkish Empire 26-30, Cavalle 10-11, Dedeagh 10-11.

For overprints and surcharges see #M2, Off. in China 45, 58-61, 66-70, 76-82, J15-J16, J28-J30, Off. in Crete 16, Off. in Egypt, Alexandria 33, 36-39, 49-50, 52-56, 65, 67-70, B1-B4, Port Said 34, 41-42, 44-45, 57, 60-64, 77, 74-77, B1-B4, Off. in Turkish Empire 34, 39, Cavalle 12, Dedeagh 15, Off. in Zanzibar 40-44, 56-59, Off. in Morocco 16-19, 30-34, 42-48, 77-83, 86, B1-B5, B7, B9.

1903-38

138	A20	10c rose	8.00	.40
139	A20	15c slate grn	13.00	.25
b.		Booklet pane of 10	450.00	
140	A20	20c violet brn	67.50	1.90
141	A20	25c dull blue	75.00	1.40
142	A20	30c violet	175.00	5.25
143	A20	45c lt violet ('26)	6.00	1.90
144	A20	50c dull blue ('21)	27.50	1.40
145	A20	50c gray grn ('26)	6.25	1.25
146	A20	50c vermilion ('26)	1.25	.25
a.		Booklet pane of 10	40.00	
147	A20	50c grnsh bl ('38)	1.00	.35
148	A20	60c lt vio ('24)	6.25	2.10
149	A20	65c rose ('24)	3.00	1.75
150	A20	65c gray grn ('27)	6.50	2.10
151	A20	75c rose lil ('26)	5.25	.60
152	A20	80c ver ('25)	26.50	9.50
153	A20	85c ver ('24)	13.50	3.25
154	A20	1fr dull blue ('26)	6.00	.75
		Nos. 138-154 (17)	447.50	34.40
		Set, never hinged	940.00	

See Nos. 941, 942A. For surcharges and overprints see Nos. 229-230, 232-233, 255, 256, B25, B29, B32, B36, B40, M3-M4, M6, Offices in Turkish Empire 46, 54.

Imperf.

138a	A20	10c	175.00	
139a	A20	15c	140.00	55.00
140a	A20	20c	300.00	160.00
141a	A20	25c	350.00	
142a	A20	30c	625.00	
144a	A20	50c	140.00	
145a	A20	50c	125.00	
146b	A20	50c	70.00	
147a	A20	50c	67.50	
149a	A20	65c	300.00	
151a	A20	75c	450.00	
154a	A20	1fr	1,000.	

No. 146b is valued without gum.

Ground A21

No Ground A22

1906, Apr. 13
With Ground Under Feet of Figure

155	A21	10c red	2.50	1.75
a.		Imperf., pair, without gum	275.00	225.00
		As "a," with gum	450.00	

1906-37

TEN AND THIRTY-FIVE CENTIMES
Type I — Numerals and letters of the inscriptions thin.
Type II — Numerals and letters thicker.

No Ground Under the Feet

156	A22	1c olive bis ('33)	.20	.30
157	A22	2c dk green ('33)	.20	.30
158	A22	3c ver ('33)	.20	.30
159	A22	5c green ('07)	1.50	.25
a.		Imperf., pair	40.00	30.00
b.		Booklet pane of 10	100.00	
160	A22	5c orange ('21)	1.25	.30
a.		Booklet pane of 10	72.50	
161	A22	5c cerise ('34)	.20	.25
162	A22	10c red (II) ('07)	1.50	.25
a.		Imperf., pair	37.50	115.00
b.		10c red (I) ('06)	8.25	1.00
c.		Booklet pane of 10 (I)	125.00	
d.		Booklet pane of 10 (II)	75.00	
e.		Booklet pane of 6 (II)	240.00	
163	A22	10c grn (II) ('21)	1.00	.55
a.		10c green (I) ('27)	32.50	37.50
b.		Booklet pane of 10 (II, "Phena")	150.00	
c.		Booklet pane of 10 (I, "Mineraline")	3,200.	
164	A22	10c ultra ('32)	1.40	.25
165	A22	15c red brn ('26)	.25	.20
a.		Booklet pane of 10	27.50	
166	A22	20c brown	3.00	.65
a.		Imperf., pair	82.50	100.00
167	A22	20c red vio ('26)	.25	.25
a.		Booklet pane of 10	7.50	
168	A22	25c blue	2.40	.25
a.		Imperf., pair	37.50	
b.		Booklet pane of 10	45.00	60.00
169	A22	25c lt brown ('27)	.20	.20
170	A22	30c orange	13.50	1.40
a.		Imperf., pair	200.00	175.00
171	A22	30c red ('21)	6.50	2.25
172	A22	30c cerise ('25)	1.25	.80
a.		Booklet pane of 10	13.50	
173	A22	30c lt blue ('25)	3.75	.60
a.		Booklet pane of 10	35.00	
174	A22	30c cop red ('37)	.25	.30
a.		Booklet pane of 10	9.00	
175	A22	35c vio (II) ('26)	8.25	.90
a.		Imperf., pair	150.00	115.00
b.		35c violet (I) ('06)	150.00	7.50
c.		As "b," Imperf., pair, without gum	575.00	
176	A22	35c green ('37)	.50	.55
177	A22	40c olive ('25)	1.40	.55
b.		Booklet pane of 10	30.00	
178	A22	40c ver ('26)	2.50	.80
a.		Booklet pane of 10	25.00	
179	A22	40c violet ('27)	2.00	.90
180	A22	40c lt ultra ('28)	1.25	.50
181	A22	1.05fr ver ('25)	9.50	5.25
182	A22	1.10fr cerise ('27)	11.50	2.50
183	A22	1.40fr cerise ('26)	20.00	22.50
184	A22	2fr Prus grn ('31)	14.00	1.75
		Nos. 156-184 (29)	109.70	45.85
		Set, never hinged	225.00	

The 10c and 35c, type I, were slightly retouched by adding thin white outlines to the sack of grain, the underside of the right arm and the back of the skirt. It is difficult to distinguish the retouches except on clearly-printed copies. The white outlines were made stronger on the stamps of type II.

Stamps of types A16, A18, A20 and A22 were printed in 1916-20 on paper of poor quality, usually grayish and containing bits of fiber. This is called G. C. (Grande Consommation) paper.

#160, 162b, 163, 175b, 176 exist imperf.

See #241-241b. For surcharges & overprint see #227-228, 234, 238, 240, 400, B1, B24, B28, B31, B35, B37, B39, B41, M5, P8, Off. in Turkish Empire 40-45, 52, 55.

Louis Pasteur — A23

1923-26

185	A23	10c green	.55	.30
a.		Booklet pane of 10	15.00	
186	A23	15c green ('24)	1.40	.30
187	A23	20c green ('26)	2.75	.90
188	A23	30c red	.90	1.50
189	A23	30c green ('26)	.55	.50
190	A23	45c red ('24)	1.90	2.10
191	A23	50c blue	4.50	.50
192	A23	75c blue ('24)	3.75	1.00
a.		Imperf., pair	250.00	
193	A23	90c red ('26)	11.00	3.50
194	A23	1fr blue ('25)	21.00	.50
195	A23	1.25fr blue ('26)	25.00	8.00
196	A23	1.50fr blue ('26)	5.25	.50
		Nos. 185-196 (12)	78.55	19.60
		Set, never hinged	150.00	

Nos. 185, 188 and 191 were issued to commemorate the cent. of the birth of Pasteur.
For surcharges and overprint see Nos. 231, 235, 257, B26, B30, B33, C4.

No. 125 Overprinted in Blue

1923, June 15

197	A18	1fr claret & ol grn	400.00	440.00
		Never hinged	825.00	

Allegory of Olympic Games at Paris A24

The Trophy A25

Milo of Crotona — A26

Victorious Athlete — A27

1924, Apr. 1   *Perf. 14x13½, 13½x14*
198	A24	10c gray grn & yel grn	2.25	1.25
199	A25	25c rose & dk rose	3.00	.80
200	A26	30c brn red & blk	9.50	11.00
201	A27	50c ultra & dk bl	26.00	5.75
		Nos. 198-201 (4)	40.75	18.80
		Set, never hinged	125.00	

8th Olympic Games, Paris. Exist imperf.

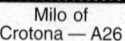

Pierre de Ronsard (1524-85), Poet — A28

1924, Oct. 6   *Perf. 14x13½*
219	A28	75c blue, *bluish*	1.90	1.40
		Never hinged	2.75	

"Light and Liberty" Allegory A29

Majolica Vase — A30

Potter Decorating Vase — A31

Terrace of Château A32

1924-25   *Perf. 14x13½, 13½x14*
220	A29	10c dk grn & yel ('25)	.55	.75
221	A30	15c ind & grn ('25)	.55	.85
a.		Imperf.	375.00	
		Never hinged	600.00	
222	A31	25c vio brn & garnet	.80	.50
223	A32	25c gray bl & vio ('25)	1.60	.65
a.		Imperf.	425.00	150.00
		Never hinged	700.00	
224	A31	75c indigo & ultra	3.50	2.25
225	A29	75c dk bl & lt bl ('25)	18.00	6.50
a.		Imperf.	375.00	
		Never hinged	600.00	
		Nos. 220-225 (6)	25.00	11.50
		Set, never hinged	52.50	

Intl. Exhibition of Decorative Modern Arts at Paris, 1925.

Philatelic Exhibition Issue
Souvenir Sheet

A32a

1925, May 2   *Perf. 14x13½*
226	A32a	Sheet of 4, A15 II	1,000.	850.00
		Never hinged	2,850.	
a.		Imperf. sheet	5,000.	1,750.
		Never hinged	7,750.	
b.		5fr carmine, perf.	110.00	140.00
c.		5fr carmine, imperf.	900.00	
		Never hinged	1,325.	

These were on sale only at the Intl. Phil. Exhib., Paris, May, 1925. Size: 140x220mm.

Nos. 148-149, 152-153, 173, 175, 181, 183, 192, 195 Surcharged

1926-27
227	A22	25c on 30c lt bl	.20	.50
228	A22	25c on 35c violet	.20	.50
a.		Double surcharge	525.00	350.00
229	A20	50c on 60c lt vio ('27)	1.40	1.10
230	A20	50c on 65c rose ('27)	.75	.55
a.		Inverted surcharge	1,225.	1,400.
231	A23	50c on 75c blue	3.25	1.50
232	A20	50c on 80c ver ('27)	1.25	1.10
233	A20	50c on 85c ver ('27)	2.25	1.00
234	A22	50c on 1.05fr ver	1.25	.75
235	A23	50c on 1.25fr blue	2.75	2.25
236	A20	55c on 60c lt vio	125.00	52.50
238	A22	90c on 1.05fr ver ('27)	2.25	2.75
240	A22	1.10fr on 1.40fr cer	1.00	1.10
		Nos. 227-240 (12)	141.55	65.60
		Set, never hinged	275.00	

Issue dates: Nos. 229-230, 232-234, 1927. No. 236 is known only precanceled. See second note after No. 132.

Nos. 229, 230, 234, 238 and 240 have three bars instead of two. The 55c surcharge has thinner, larger numerals and a rounded "c." Width, including bars, is 17mm, instead of 13mm.

The 55c was used only precanceled at the Department stores of Louvre in Paris, August 1926.

Strasbourg Exhibition Issue
Souvenir Sheet

A32b

1927, June 4
241	A32b	Sheet of 2	1,000.	1,000.
		Never hinged	2,150.	
a.		5fr light ultra (A22)	180.00	225.00
		Never hinged	300.00	225.00
b.		10fr carmine rose (A22)	190.00	225.00
		Never hinged	300.00	225.00

Sold at the Strasbourg Philatelic Exhibition as souvenirs. Size: 111x140mm.

Marcelin Berthelot (1827-1907), Chemist and Statesman — A33

1927, Sept. 7
242	A33	90c dull rose	1.90	.60
		Never hinged	3.00	

For surcharge see No. C3.

Lafayette, Washington, S. S. Paris and Airplane "Spirit of St. Louis" — A34

1927, Sept. 15
243	A34	90c dull red	1.25	1.75
a.		Value omitted	2,000.	1,725.
244	A34	1.50fr deep blue	4.00	2.50
a.		Value omitted	1,450.	
		Set, never hinged	10.00	

Visit of American Legionnaires to France, September, 1927. Exist imperf.

Joan of Arc — A35

1929, Mar.
245	A35	50c dull blue	1.90	.20
		Never hinged	2.75	
a.		Booklet pane of 10	125.00	
b.		Imperf.	140.00	

500th anniv. of the relief of Orleans by the French forces led by Joan of Arc.

No. 127 Overprinted in Blue

1929, May 18
246	A18	2fr org & pale bl	500.00	550.00
		Never hinged	1,325.	

Sold exclusively at the Intl. Phil. Exhib., Le Havre, May, 1929, for 7fr, which included a 5fr admission ticket.

Excellent counterfeits of No. 246 exist.

Reims Cathedral — A37

Die I, II, III   Die IV

Die I   Die II   Die III

Die I — The window of the 1st turret on the left is made of 2 lines. The horizontal line of the frame surrounding 3F is not continuous.

Die II — Same as Die I but the line under 3F is continuous.

Die III — Same as Die II but there is a deeply cut line separating 3 and F.

Die IV — Same as Die III but the window of the first turret on the left is made of three lines.

Mont-Saint-Michel — A38

Die I   Die II

Die I — The line at the top of the spire is broken.

Die II — The line is unbroken.

Port of La Rochelle — A39

 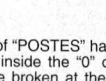

Dies I & II   Die III

Die I — The top of the "E" of "POSTES" has a serif. The oval of shading inside the "0" of "10 fr" and the outer oval are broken at their bases.

Die II — The same top has no serif. Interior and exterior of "0" broken as in Die I.

Die III — Top of "E" has no serif. Interior and exterior of "0" complete.

Pont du Gard, Nimes A40

Dies I & II

Die III

Die I — Shading of the first complete arch in the left middle tier is made of horizontal lines. Size 36x20¾mm. Perf. 13½.
Die II — Same, size 35½x21mm. Perf. 11.
Die III — Shading of same arch is made of three diagonal lines. Thin paper. Perf. 13.

1929-33   Engr.   Perf. 11, 13, 13½

247	A37	3fr dk gray ('30) (I)	62.50	2.40
		Never hinged	115.00	
247A	A37	3fr dk gray ('30) (II)	125.00	3.50
		Never hinged	200.00	
247B	A37	3fr dk gray ('30) (III)	375.00	24.00
		Never hinged	600.00	
248	A37	3fr bluish sl ('31) (IV)	60.00	2.40
		Never hinged	115.00	
249	A38	5fr brn ('30) (I)	24.00	4.25
		Never hinged	40.00	
250	A38	5fr brn ('31) (II)	21.00	.75
		Never hinged	32.50	
251	A39	10fr lt ultra (I)	95.00	15.00
		Never hinged	160.00	
251A	A39	10fr ultra (II)	140.00	26.00
		Never hinged	225.00	
252	A39	10fr dk ultra ('31) (III)	70.00	6.50
		Never hinged	140.00	
253	A40	20fr red brown (I)	275.00	40.00
		Never hinged	500.00	
254	A40	20fr brt red brn ('30) (II)	1,000.	350.00
		Never hinged	1,650.	
254A	A40	20fr org brn ('31) (III)	250.00	35.00
		Never hinged	450.00	
		Nos. 247-254A (12)	2,497.	509.80

View of Algiers A41

1929, Jan. 1   Typo.

255	A41	50c blue & rose red	2.40	.50
		Never hinged	5.00	

Cent. of the 1st French settlement in Algeria.

Nos. 146 and 196 Overprinted

1930, Apr. 23   Perf. 14x13½

256	A20	50c vermilion	3.00	3.25
257	A23	1.50fr blue	20.00	14.50
		Set, never hinged	47.50	

Intl. Labor Bureau, 48th Congress, Paris.

Colonial Exposition Issue

Fachi Woman — A42

French Colonials A43

1930-31   Typo.   Perf. 14x13½

258	A42	15c gray black	1.10	.30
259	A42	40c dark brown	2.40	.30
260	A42	50c dark red	.65	.20
a.		Booklet pane of 10	12.50	
261	A42	1.50fr deep blue	9.00	.65

Perf. 13½
Photo.

262	A43	1.50fr dp blue ('31)	45.00	2.75
		Nos. 258-262 (5)	58.15	4.20
		Set, never hinged	90.00	

No. 260 has two types: type 1 shows four short downward hairlines near top of head, type 2 has no lines. Booklet stamps are type 2.

Arc de Triomphe A44

1931   Engr.   Perf. 13

263	A44	2fr red brown	32.50	1.00
		Never hinged	65.00	

Peace with Olive Branch — A45

1932-39   Typo.   Perf. 14x13½

264	A45	30c dp green	1.00	.55
265	A45	40c brt violet	.30	.30
266	A45	45c yellow brown	1.75	1.00
267	A45	50c rose red	.20	.25
a.		Imperf., pair	140.00	
b.		Booklet pane of 10	5.50	
268	A45	55c dull vio ('37)	.60	.25
269	A45	60c ocher ('37)	.30	.25
270	A45	65c violet brown	.50	.50
271	A45	65c brt ultra ('37)	.25	.20
a.		Booklet pane of 10	7.00	
272	A45	75c olive green	.20	.30
273	A45	80c orange ('38)	.20	.20
274	A45	90c dk red	32.50	2.00
275	A45	90c brt green ('38)	.20	.20
276	A45	90c ultra ('38)	.90	.20
a.		Booklet pane of 10	8.50	
277	A45	1fr orange	3.25	.25
278	A45	1fr rose pink ('38)	3.25	.25
279	A45	1.25fr brown ol	75.00	4.75
280	A45	1.25fr rose car ('39)	1.90	2.25
281	A45	1.40fr brt red vio ('39)	5.75	5.25
282	A45	1.50fr deep blue	.30	.30
283	A45	1.75fr magenta	4.00	.50
		Nos. 264-283 (20)	132.35	20.00
		Set, never hinged	275.00	

The 50c is found in 4 types, differing in the lines below belt and size of "c."
For surcharges and overprints see Nos. 298, 333, 401-403, 405-409, M7-M9, S1.

Le Puy-en-Velay — A46

1933   Engr.   Perf. 13

290	A46	90c rose	3.00	1.10
		Never hinged	5.75	

Aristide Briand A47

Paul Doumer A48

Victor Hugo — A49

1933, Dec. 11   Typo.   Perf. 14x13½

291	A47	30c blue green	17.00	8.00
292	A48	75c red violet	27.50	1.90
293	A49	1.25fr claret	6.00	2.25
		Nos. 291-293 (3)	50.50	12.15
		Set, never hinged	110.00	

Dove and Olive Branch A50

Joseph Marie Jacquard A51

1934, Feb. 20

294	A50	1.50fr ultra	50.00	15.00
		Never hinged	95.00	

1934, Mar. 14   Engr.   Perf. 14x13

295	A51	40c blue	3.00	1.10
		Never hinged	4.50	

Jacquard (1752-1834), inventor of an improved loom for figured weaving.

Jacques Cartier A52

1934, July 18   Perf. 13

296	A52	75c rose lilac	27.50	2.25
297	A52	1.50fr blue	50.00	4.25
		Set, never hinged	225.00	

Cartier's discovery of Canada, 400th anniv.

No. 279 Surcharged

1934, Nov.   Perf. 14x13½

298	A45	50c on 1.25fr brn ol	3.75	.65
		Never hinged	7.00	

> **Catalogue values for unused stamps in this section, from this point to the end of the section, are for Never Hinged items.**

Breton River Scene A53

1935, Feb.   Engr.   Perf. 13

299	A53	2fr blue green	70.00	1.00

S. S. Normandie A54

1935, Apr.
300	A54	1.50fr dark blue	29.00	2.00
a.		1.50fr blue ('36)	140.00	19.00
b.		1.50fr blue green ('36)	19,000.	12,500.
		Hinged	24,500.	
c.		1.50fr turquoise ('36)	275.00	40.00
		Hinged	400.00	

Maiden voyage of the transatlantic steamship, the "Normandie."

Benjamin Delessert A55

1935, May 20
301	A55	75c blue green	42.50	1.75

Opening of the International Savings Bank Congress, May 20, 1935.

View of St. Trophime at Arles A56

Victor Hugo (1802-85) A57

1935, May 3
302	A56	3.50fr dark brown	70.00	4.25

1935, May 30   *Perf. 14x13*
303	A57	1.25fr magenta	8.25	2.00

Cardinal Richelieu — A58   Jacques Callot — A59

1935, June 12   *Perf. 13*
304	A58	1.50fr deep rose	55.00	1.75

Tercentenary of the founding of the French Academy by Cardinal Richelieu.

1935, Nov.   *Perf. 14x13*
305	A59	75c red	19.00	.75

300th anniv. of the death of Jacques Callot, engraver.

André Marie Ampère (1775-1836), Scientist, by Louis Boilly — A60

1936, Feb. 27   *Perf. 13*
306	A60	75c brown	37.50	2.00

Windmill at Fontvielle, Immortalized by Daudet — A61

1936, Apr. 27
307	A61	2fr ultra	5.75	.40

70th anniv. of the publication, in 1866, of Alphonse Daudet's "Lettres de mon Moulin".

Pilâtre de Rozier and his Balloon A62

1936, June 4
308	A62	75c Prus blue	37.50	2.75

150th anniversary of the death of Jean Francois Pilâtre de Rozier, balloonist.

Rouget de Lisle — A63

"La Marseillaise" — A64

1936, June 27
309	A63	20c Prus green	5.75	2.00
310	A64	40c dark brown	11.50	3.25

Cent. of the death of Claude Joseph Rouget de Lisle, composer of "La Marseillaise."

Canadian War Memorial at Vimy Ridge A65

1936, July 26
311	A65	75c henna brown	24.50	2.00
312	A65	1.50fr dull blue	32.50	9.50

Unveiling of the Canadian War Memorial at Vimy Ridge, July 26, 1936.

A66

Jean Léon Jaurès A67

1936, July 30
313	A66	40c red brown	5.75	1.40
314	A67	1.50fr ultra	29.00	3.75

Assassination of Jean Léon Jaurès (1859-1914), socialist and politician.

Herald — A68

Allegory of Exposition A69

1936, Sept. 15   **Typo.**   *Perf. 14x13½*
315	A68	20c brt violet	1.00	.50
316	A68	30c Prus green	4.00	1.75
317	A68	40c ultra	2.50	.50
318	A68	50c red orange	2.25	.25
319	A69	90c carmine	25.00	7.50
320	A69	1.50fr ultra	67.50	4.00
	Nos. 315-320 (6)		102.25	14.50

Publicity for the 1937 Paris Exposition.

"Peace" A70

1936, Oct. 1   **Engr.**   *Perf. 13*
321	A70	1.50fr blue	27.50	4.00

Skiing A71

1937, Jan. 18
322	A71	1.50fr dark blue	14.00	1.75

Intl. Ski Meet at Chamonix-Mont Blanc.

Pierre Corneille, Portrait by Charles Le Brun — A72

1937, Feb. 15
323	A72	75c brown carmine	3.75	1.40

300th anniv. of the publication of "Le Cid."

Paris Exposition Issue

Exposition Allegory A73

1937, Mar. 15
324	A73	1.50fr turq blue	4.00	1.25

Jean Mermoz (1901-36), Aviator A74

Memorial to Mermoz — A75

1937, Apr. 22
325	A74	30c dk slate green	1.00	.55
326	A75	3fr dark violet	13.50	3.75
a.		3fr violet	15.00	4.50

Electric Train A76

Streamlined Locomotive A77

1937, May 31
327	A76	30c dk green	1.90	1.75
328	A77	1.50fr dk ultra	15.00	8.25

13th International Railroad Congress.

Intl. Philatelic Exhibition Issue
Souvenir Sheet

Ceres Type A1 of 1849-50 — A77a

1937, June 18   **Typo.**   *Perf. 14x13½*
329	A77a	Sheet of 4	700.00	300.00
		Hinged in margins	200.00	
a.		5c ultra & dark brown	90.00	47.50
b.		15c red & rose red	90.00	47.50
c.		30c ultra & rose red	90.00	47.50
d.		50c red & dark brown	90.00	47.50
e.		Sheet of 4, imperf.	3,000.	
		Hinged in margins	2,350.	

Issued in sheets measuring 150x220mm. The sheets were sold only at the exhibition in Paris, a ticket of admission being required for each sheet purchased.

René Descartes, by Frans Hals — A78

1937, June   **Engr.**   *Perf. 13*
Inscribed "Discours sur la Méthode"
330	A78	90c copper red	3.25	1.40

Inscribed "Discours de la Méthode"
331	A78	90c copper red	11.00	1.75

3rd centenary of the publication of "Discours de la Méthode" by René Descartes.

France Congratulating USA — A79

1937, Sept. 17
332 A79 1.75fr ultra   4.50 2.00
150th anniv. of the US Constitution.

No. 277 Surcharged in Red

1937, Oct.   *Perf. 14x13½*
333 A45 80c on 1fr orange   1.90 .85
 a. Inverted surcharge   1,225.

Mountain Road at Iseran A80

1937, Oct. 4 Engr. *Perf. 13*
334 A80 90c dark green   3.75 .30
Issued in commemoration of the opening of the mountain road at Iseran, Savoy.

Ceres — A81

1938-40 Typo. *Perf. 14x13½*
335 A81 1.75fr dk ultra   1.40 .55
336 A81 2fr car rose ('39)   .30 .30
337 A81 2.25fr ultra ('39)   15.00 1.10
338 A81 2.50fr green ('39)   3.00 .50
339 A81 2.50fr vio blue ('40)   1.25 .75
340 A81 3fr rose lilac ('39)   1.25 .50
 Nos. 335-340 (6)   22.20 3.70
For surcharges see Nos. 397-399.

Léon Gambetta (1838-82), Lawyer and Statesman — A82

1938, Apr. 2 Engr. *Perf. 13*
341 A82 55c dark violet   .55 .40

Arc de Triomphe of Orange A82a

Miners A83
Keep and Gate of Vincennes A86

Palace of the Popes, Avignon A84

Medieval Walls of Carcassonne — A85

Port of St. Malo — A87

1938
342 A82a 2fr brown black   3.75 2.50
343 A83 2.15fr violet brn   9.50 1.00
344 A84 3fr car brown   26.50 5.00
345 A85 5fr deep ultra   1.50 .40
346 A86 10fr brown, *blue*   3.25 1.90
347 A87 20fr dk blue green   80.00 19.00
 Nos. 342-347 (6)   124.50 29.80
For surcharges see Nos. 410-414.

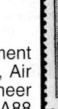

Clément Ader, Air Pioneer A88

1938, June 16
348 A88 50fr ultra (thin paper)   150.00 65.00
 Hinged   95.00
 a. 50fr dark ultra (thick paper)   175.00 77.50
 Hinged   100.00

Soccer Players A89

1938, June 1
349 A89 1.75fr dark ultra   29.00 13.50
World Cup Soccer Championship.

Costume of Champagne Region — A90
Jean de La Fontaine — A91

1938, June 13
350 A90 1.75fr dark ultra   7.50 4.50
Tercentenary of the birth of Dom Pierre Pérignon, discoverer of the champagne process.

1938, July 8
351 A91 55c dk blue green   1.00 .80
Jean de La Fontaine (1621-1695) the fabulist.

Seal of Friendship and Peace, Victoria Tower and Arc de Triomphe A92

1938, July 19
352 A92 1.75fr ultra   1.25 .80
Visit of King George VI and Queen Elizabeth of Great Britain to France.

Mercury A93
Self-portrait A95

1938-42 Typo. *Perf. 14x13½*
353 A93 1c dark brown ('39)   .20 .20
354 A93 2c slate grn ('39)   .20 .20
355 A93 5c rose   .20 .20
356 A93 10c ultra   .20 .20
357 A93 15c red orange   .20 .20
358 A93 15c orange brn ('39)   1.00 .50
359 A93 20c red violet   .20 .20
360 A93 25c blue green   .20 .20
361 A93 30c rose red ('39)   .20 .20
362 A93 40c dk violet ('39)   .20 .20
363 A93 45c lt green ('39)   .80 .50
364 A93 50c deep blue ('39)   4.00 .40
365 A93 50c dk green ('41)   .55 .35
366 A93 50c grnsh blue ('42)   .20 .20
367 A93 60c red orange ('39)   .25 .25
368 A93 70c magenta ('39)   .25 .25
369 A93 75c dk org brn ('39)   7.50 2.50
 Nos. 353-369 (17)   16.35 6.70
No. 366 exists imperforate. See Nos. 455-458. For overprints and surcharge see #404, 499-502.

1939, Mar. 15 Engr. *Perf. 13*
370 A95 2.25fr Prussian blue   8.25 3.50
Paul Cézanne (1839-1906), painter.

Georges Clemenceau and Battleship Clemenceau — A96

1939, Apr. 18
371 A96 90c ultra   1.00 .75
Laying of the keel of the warship "Clemenceau," Jan. 17, 1939.

Statue of Liberty, French Pavilion, Trylon and Perisphere A97

1939-40
372 A97 2.25fr ultra   17.00 6.50
373 A97 2.50fr ultra ('40)   22.50 9.50
New York World's Fair.

Joseph Nicéphore Niepce and Louis Jacques Mandé Daguerre A98

1939, Apr. 24
374 A98 2.25fr dark blue   16.00 7.00
Centenary of photography.

Iris — A99

Pumping Station at Marly A100

1939-44 Typo. *Perf. 14x13½*
375 A99 80c red brown ('40)   .25 .20
376 A99 80c yellow grn ('44)   .20 .20
377 A99 1fr green   1.00 .20
378 A99 1fr crimson ('40)   .40 .35
 a. Booklet pane of 10   7.50
379 A99 1fr grnsh blue ('44)   .20 .20
380 A99 1.20fr violet ('44)   .20 .20
381 A99 1.30fr ultra ('40)   .25 .25
382 A99 1.50fr red org ('41)   .20 .20
383 A99 1.50fr henna brn ('44)   .20 .20
384 A99 2fr violet brn ('44)   .20 .20
385 A99 2.40fr car rose ('44)   .20 .20
386 A99 3fr orange ('44)   .20 .20
387 A99 4fr ultra ('44)   .20 .20
 Nos. 375-387 (13)   3.70 2.80

1939 Engr. *Perf. 13*
388 A100 2.25fr brt ultra   25.00 5.00
France's participation in the International Water Exposition at Liège.

St. Gregory of Tours — A101

1939, June 10
389 A101 90c red   .90 .55
14th centenary of the birth of St. Gregory of Tours, historian and bishop.

"The Oath of the Tennis Court" by Jacques David A102

1939, June 20
390 A102 90c deep slate green   3.50 1.90
150th anniversary of French Revolution.

Cathedral of
Strasbourg — A103

1939, June 23
391 A103 70c brown carmine   1.50 1.00
   500th anniv. of the completion of Strasbourg
Cathedral.

Porte
Chaussée,
Verdun
A104

1939, June 23
392 A104 90c black brown   1.00 .80
   23rd anniv. of the Battle of Verdun.

View of
Pau
A105

1939, Aug. 25
393 A105 90c brt rose, *gray bl*   1.25 .90

Maid of
Languedoc
A106

Bridge at
Lyons
A107

1939
394 A106 70c black, *blue*   .50 .40
395 A107 90c dull brown vio   1.00 .90

Imperforates
Nearly all French stamps issued from
1940 onward exist imperforate. Officially 20 sheets, ranging from 25 to 100
subjects, were left imperforate.

Georges Guynemer
(1894-1917), World
War I Ace — A108

1940, Nov. 7
396 A108 50fr ultra   16.00 9.00

Stamps of 1938-39 Surcharged in
Carmine

1940-41   **Perf. 14x13½**
397 A81 1fr on 1.75fr dk ultra   .25 .25
398 A81 1fr on 2.25fr ultra ('41) .25 .25
399 A81 1fr on 2.50fr grn ('41) 1.40 1.40
   Nos. 397-399 (3)   1.90 1.90

Stamps of 1932-39
Surcharged in Carmine,
Red (#408) or Black
(#407)

1940-41   **Perf. 13, 14x13½**
400 A22   30c on 35c grn   .25 .25
401 A45   50c on 55c dl vio   .25 .25
  a. Inverted surcharge   1,000.
402 A45   50c on 65c brt ul-
          tra   .20 .20
403 A45   50c on 75c ol grn   .25 .25
404 A93   50c on 75c dk org
          brn   .25 .25
405 A45   50c on 80c org   .25 .25
406 A45   50c on 90c ultra   .20 .20
  a. Inverted surcharge   525.00
  b. "05" instead of "50"   8,250.
407 A45   1fr on 1.25fr rose
          car (Bk)   .25 .25
408 A45   1fr on 1.40fr brt
          red vio (R)   .40 .40
  a. Double surcharge   1,300.
409 A45   1fr on 1.50fr dk bl 1.40 1.40
410 A83   1fr on 2.15fr vio
          brn   .40 .40
411 A85 2.50fr on 5fr dp ultra .40 .40
  a. Double surcharge   325.00 140.00
412 A86   5fr on 10fr brn, *bl* 1.90 1.90
413 A87 10fr on 20fr dk bl
          grn   1.60 1.60
414 A88 20fr on 50fr dk ul-
          tra (#348a)   70.00 37.50
  a. 20fr on 50fr ultra, thin paper
       (#348)   75.00 50.00
   Nos. 400-414 (15)   78.00 45.50
   Issued: #410, 1940; others, 1941.

Marshal Pétain
A109

Frédéric
Mistral
A110

1941   **Perf. 13**
415 A109 40c red brown   .40 .40
416 A109 80c turq blue   .55 .55
417 A109 1fr red   .25 .25
418 A109 2.50fr deep ultra   1.50 1.10
   Nos. 415-418 (4)   2.70 2.30

1941, Feb. 20   **Perf. 14x13**
419 A110 1fr brown lake   .25 .25
   Issued in honor of Frédéric Mistral, poet and
Nobel prize winner for literature in 1904.

Beaune
Hospital
A111

View of
Angers
A112

Ramparts of St. Louis,
Aiguesmortes — A113

1941
420 A111   5fr brown black   .40 .25
421 A112 10fr dark violet   .90 .55
422 A113 20fr brown black   1.40 1.00
   Nos. 420-422 (3)   2.70 1.80

Inscribed "Postes Francaises"

1942
Imprint: "FELTESSE" at right
423 A111 15fr brown lake   .65 .55

A114

A115

Marshal Pétain — A116

A117

A118

1941-42   **Typo.**   **Perf. 14x13½**
427 A114 20c lilac ('42)   .20 .20
428 A114 30c rose red   .20 .20
429 A114 40c ultra   .20 .20
431 A115 50c dp green   .20 .20
432 A115 60c violet ('42)   .20 .20
433 A115 70c saph ('42)   .20 .20
434 A115 70c orange ('42)   .20 .20
435 A115 80c brown   .25 .25
436 A115 80c emerald ('42)   .20 .20
437 A115 1fr rose red   .20 .20
438 A115 1.20fr red brn ('42) .20 .20
439 A115 1.50fr rose   .20 .20
440 A115 1.50fr dl red brn ('42) .20 .20
  a. Booklet pane of 10   2.75
441 A116   2fr blue grn ('42) .20 .20
443 A116 2.40fr rose red ('42) .25 .25
444 A116 2.50fr ultra   .85 .85
445 A116   3fr orange   .20 .20
446 A115   4fr ultra ('42)   .25 .25
447 A115 4.50fr dk green ('42) 1.00 .65
   Nos. 427-447 (19)   5.40 5.05

Nos. 431 to 438 measure 16½x20½mm.
   No. 440 was forged by the French Underground ("Defense de la France") and used to
frank clandestine journals, etc., from Feb. to
June, 1944. The forgeries were ungummed,
both perf. 11½ and imperf., with a back handstamp covering six stamps and including the
words: "Atelier des Faux."
   For surcharge see No. B134.

1942   **Engr.**   **Perf. 14x13**
448 A115   4fr brt ultra   .25 .25
449 A115 4.50fr dark green   .25 .25
450 A117   5fr Prus green   .25 .25

               Perf. 13
451 A118 50fr black   4.50 4.00
   Nos. 448-451 (4)   5.25 4.75

Nos. 448 and 449 measure 18x21½mm.

Jules
Massenet
A119

Stendhal (Marie
Henri Beyle)
A120

1942, June 22   **Perf. 14x13**
452 A119 4fr Prus green   .25 .25
   Jules Massenet (1842-1912), composer.

1942, Sept. 14   **Perf. 13**
453 A120 4fr blk brn & org red .55 .55
   Stendhal (1783-1842), writer.

André
Blondel — A121

Town-Hall Belfry,
Arras — A122

1942, Sept. 14
454 A121 4fr dull blue   .55 .55
   André Eugène Blondel (1863-1938),
physicist.

Mercury Type of 1938-42
Inscribed "Postes Françaises"
1942   **Perf. 14x13½**
455 A93 10c rose red   .20 .20
456 A93 30c rose red   .20 .20
457 A93 40c dark violet   .25 .25
458 A93 50c turq blue   .20 .20
   Nos. 455-458 (4)   .85 .85

1942, Dec. 8   **Engr.**   **Perf. 13**
459 A122 10fr green   .25 .25

Coats of Arms

Lyon — A123

1943   **Typo.**   **Perf. 14x13½**
460 A123 5fr shown   .40 .40
461 A123 10fr Brittany   .65 .55
462 A123 15fr Provence   1.90 1.40
463 A123 20fr Ile de France   1.60 1.60
   Nos. 460-463 (4)   4.55 3.95

Antoine Lavoisier
(1743-94), French
Scientist — A127

1943, July 5 **Engr.**   **Perf. 14x13**
464 A127 4fr ultra   .25 .25

Lake Lerie
and Meije
Dauphiné
Alps
A128

1943, July 5   **Perf. 13**
465 A128 20fr dull gray grn   .90 .90

Nicolas Rolin, Guigone de Salins and Hospital of Beaune
A129

1943, July 21
466 A129 4fr blue .25 .25
500th anniv. of the founding of the Hospital of Beaune.

Arms of Flanders — A130

1944, Mar. 27 Typo. Perf. 14x13½
467 A130 5fr shown .25 .25
468 A130 10fr Languedoc .25 .25
469 A130 15fr Orleans .85 .85
470 A130 20fr Normandy 1.25 1.00
Nos. 467-470 (4) 2.60 2.35

Edouard Branly — A134

Early Postal Car
A135

1944, Feb. 21 Engr. Perf. 14x13
471 A134 4fr ultra .25 .25
Cent. of the birth of Edouard Branly, electrical inventor.

1944, June 10 Perf. 13
472 A135 1.50fr dark blue green .85 .65
Cent. of France's traveling postal service.

Chateau de Chenonceaux — A136

Claude Chappe — A137

1944, June 10
473 A136 15fr lilac brown .65 .55
a. 15fr black brown 9.00 1.90
b. 15fr black 55.00 55.00

See No. 496.

1944, Aug. 14 Perf. 14x13
474 A137 4fr dark ultra .20 .20
150th anniv. of the invention of an optical telegraph by Claude Chappe (1763-1805).

Arc de Triomphe — OS2

Unwmk.
1944, Oct. 9 Litho. Perf. 11
475 OS2 5c brt red violet .35 .35
476 OS2 10c lt gray .35 .35
476A OS2 25c brown .35 .35
476B OS2 50c olive bis .50 .50
476C OS2 1fr pck green .90 .90
476D OS2 1.50fr rose pink 1.90 .90
476E OS2 2.50fr purple .90 .90
476F OS2 4fr ultra 1.90 1.90
476G OS2 5fr black 1.90 1.90
476H OS2 10fr yellow org 37.50 35.00
Nos. 475-476H (10) 46.55 43.05

Nos 475-476H were printed by the U.S. Bureau of Engraving and Printing and were intended to be used by an Allied Military government expected to administer the liberated areas of France. Instead, the Allies recognized the authority of Gen. de Gaulle's Provisional Government's over these territories, and these stamps were transferred to the Free French in July, 1944. They were put on sale in liberated areas as the Allied armies advanced, and on Oct. 9, they were officially issued in Paris. See Nos. 523A-523J.

Gallic Cock
A138

Marianne
A139

1944 Litho. Perf. 12
477 A138 10c yellow grn .20 .20
478 A138 30c dk rose vio .40 .40
479 A138 40c blue .20 .20
480 A138 50c dark red .20 .20
481 A139 60c olive brown .20 .20
482 A139 70c rose lilac .20 .20
483 A139 80c yellow grn 1.10 1.10
484 A139 1fr violet .25 .25
485 A139 1.20fr dp carmine .25 .25
486 A139 1.50fr deep blue .20 .20
487 A139 2fr indigo .20 .20
488 A139 2.40fr red orange 1.50 1.50
489 A139 3fr dp blue grn .25 .25
490 A139 4fr grnsh blue .25 .25
491 A139 4.50fr black .20 .20
492 A139 5fr violet blue 4.50 4.50
493 A138 10fr violet 5.00 5.00
494 A138 15fr olive brown 5.00 5.00
495 A138 20fr dk slate grn 4.50 4.50
Nos. 477-495 (19) 24.60 24.60

Nos. 477-495 were issued first in Corsica after the Allied landing, and released in Paris Nov. 15, 1944.

Chateau Type Inscribed "RF"
1944, Oct. 30 Engr. Perf. 13
496 A136 25fr black .85 .65

Thomas Robert Bugeaud — A141

1944, Nov. 20
497 A141 4fr myrtle green .25 .25
Battle of Isly, Aug. 14th, 1844.

Church of St. Denis
A142

1944, Nov. 20
498 A142 2.40fr brown carmine .40 .40
800th anniv. of the Church of St. Denis.

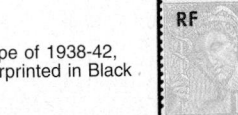

Type of 1938-42, Overprinted in Black

Inscribed "Postes Francaises"
1944 Perf. 14x13½
499 A93 10c ultra .20 .20
500 A93 30c rose red .20 .20
501 A93 40c dark violet .20 .20
502 A93 50c grnsh blue .20 .20
Nos. 499-502 (4) .80 .80

The overprint "RF" in various forms, with or without Lorraine Cross, was also applied to stamps of the French State at Lyon and fourteen other cities.

French Forces of the Interior and Symbol of Liberation — A143

1945, Jan.
503 A143 4fr dark ultra .40 .40
Issued to commemorate the Liberation.

Stamps of the above design, and of one incorporating "FRANCE" in the top panel, were printed by photo. in England during WW II upon order of the Free French Government. They were not issued. There are 3 values in each design; 25c green, 1fr red, 2.50fr blue. Value: set, above design, $100; set inscribed "FRANCE," $500.

Marianne — A144

Perf. 11½x12½
1944-45 Engr. Unwmk.
504 A144 10c ultra .20 .20
505 A144 30c bister .20 .20
506 A144 40c indigo .20 .20
507 A144 50c red orange .20 .20
508 A144 60c chalky blue .20 .20
509 A144 70c sepia .20 .20
510 A144 80c deep green .20 .20
511 A144 1fr lilac .20 .20
512 A144 1.20fr dk ol grn .20 .20
513 A144 1.50fr rose ('44) .20 .20
514 A144 2fr dk brown .20 .20
515 A144 2.40fr red .20 .20
516 A144 3fr brt ol grn .20 .20
517 A144 4fr brt ultra .25 .25
518 A144 4.50fr slate gray .25 .25
519 A144 5fr brt orange .25 .25
520 A144 10fr yellow grn .30 .30
521 A144 15fr lake .40 .40
522 A144 20fr brown org 1.75 1.50
523 A144 50fr deep purple 3.50 2.50
Nos. 504-523 (20) 9.30 8.05

The 2.40fr exists imperf. in a miniature sheet of 4 which was not issued. Value: never hinged $375; unused $275.

Arc de Triomphe Type of 1944
1945, Feb. 12 Litho. Perf. 11
Denominations in Black
523A OS2 30c orange .30 .30
523B OS2 40c pale gray .30 .30
523C OS2 50c olive bis .30 .30
523D OS2 60c violet .30 .30
523E OS2 80c emerald .30 .30
523F OS2 1.20fr brown .30 .30
523G OS2 1.50fr vermilion .30 .30
523H OS2 2fr yellow .30 .30
523I OS2 2.40fr dark rose .30 .30
523J OS2 3fr brt red violet .30 .30
Nos. 523A-523J (10) 3.00 3.00

Coat of Arms
A145

Ceres
A146

Marianne — A147

1945-47 Typo. Perf. 14x13½
524 A145 10c brown black .20 .20
525 A145 30c dk blue green .20 .20
526 A145 40c lilac rose .30 .30
527 A145 50c violet blue .20 .20
528 A146 60c brt ultra .20 .20
530 A146 80c brt green .20 .20
531 A146 90c dull grn ('46) .65 .55
532 A146 1fr rose red .20 .20
533 A146 1.20fr brown black .20 .20
534 A146 1.50fr rose lilac .20 .20
535 A147 1.50fr rose pink .20 .20
536 A147 2fr myrtle green .20 .20
536A A146 2fr lt bl grn ('46) .85 .65
537 A147 2.40fr scarlet .40 .40
538 A146 2.50fr brown ('46) 1.00 .85
539 A147 3fr sepia .20 .20
540 A147 3fr deep rose ('46) .20 .20
541 A147 4fr ultra .20 .20
541A A147 4fr violet ('46) .20 .20
541B A147 4.50fr ultra ('47) .20 .20
542 A147 5fr lt green .25 .20
542A A147 5fr rose pink ('47) .20 .20
543 A147 6fr brt ultra .35 .25
544 A147 6fr crim rose ('46) 1.60 1.10
545 A147 10fr red orange .65 .55
546 A147 10fr indigo ('46) 1.60 .85
547 A147 15fr brt red vio 3.25 1.90
Nos. 524-547 (27) 14.10 10.80

No. 531 is known only precanceled. See second note after No. 132.
Due to a reduction of the domestic postage rate, No. 542A was sold for 4.50fr.
See Nos. 576-580, 594-602, 614, 615, 650-654. For surcharges see Nos. 589, 610, 706, Reunion 270-276, 278, 285, 290-291, 293, 295.

1945-46 Engr. Perf. 14x13
548 A147 4fr dark blue .25 .25
549 A147 10fr dp blue ('46) 1.25 .55
550 A147 15fr brt red vio ('46) 9.00 2.00
551 A147 20fr blue grn ('46) 1.25 .55
552 A147 25fr red ('46) 9.00 1.50
Nos. 548-552 (5) 20.75 4.85

Marianne — A148

1945 Engr. Perf. 13
553 A148 20fr dark green 1.25 1.10
554 A148 25fr violet 1.65 1.25
555 A148 50fr red brown 2.00 2.00
556 A148 100fr brt rose car 12.50 6.25
Nos. 553-556 (4) 17.40 10.60

CFA
French stamps inscribed or surcharged "CFA" and new value are listed under Réunion at the end of the French listings.

Arms of Metz
A149

Arms of
Strasbourg
A150

1945, Mar. 3   **Perf. 14x13**
557 A149 2.40fr dull blue   .25 .25
558 A150 4fr black brown   .25 .25
    Liberation of Metz and Strasbourg.

Costumes of Alsace and Lorraine and
Cathedrals of Strasbourg and Metz
A151

1945, May 16   **Perf. 13**
559 A151 4fr henna brown   .25 .25
    Liberation of Alsace and Lorraine.

World Map Showing French
Possessions — A152

1945, Sept. 17
560 A152 2fr Prussian blue   .25 .25

No. B193 Surcharged with New Value
in Black

1946   **Perf. 14x13½**
561 SP147 3fr on 2fr+1fr red org   .25 .25

Arms of
Corsica — A153

1946 Unwmk. Typo. Perf. 14x13½
562 A153 10c shown   .20 .20
563 A153 30c Alsace   .20 .20
564 A153 50c Lorraine   .20 .20
565 A153 60c County of Nice   .20 .20
    Nos. 562-565 (4)   .80 .80

For surcharges see Reunion Nos. 268-269.

Reaching for
"Peace" — A157

Holding the
Dove of
Peace — A158

1946, July 29   **Engr.**   **Perf. 13**
566 A157 3fr Prussian green   .25 .25
567 A158 10fr dark blue   .25 .25
    Peace Conference of Paris, 1946.

Vézelay
A159

Luxembourg Palace — A160

Rocamadour
A161

Pointe du
Raz,
Finistère
A162

1946   **Unwmk.**   **Perf. 13**
568 A159 5fr rose violet   .25 .25
569 A160 10fr dark blue   .25 .25
570 A161 15fr dk violet brn   4.25 .25
571 A162 20fr slate gray   1.25 .25
    Nos. 568-571 (4)   6.00 1.30

See Nos. 591-592. For surcharges see
Reunion Nos. 277, 279.

Globe and
Wreath — A163

1946, Nov.
572 A163 10fr dark blue   .25 .25
    Gen. conf. of UNESCO, Paris, 1946.

Cannes
A164

Stanislas
Square,
Nancy
A165

1946-48   **Engr.**   **Perf. 13**
573 A164 6fr rose red   1.50 .65
574 A165 25fr black brown   4.25 .40
575 A165 25fr dark blue ('48)   11.50 1.25
    Nos. 573-575 (3)   17.25 2.30

For surcharges see Reunion Nos. 280-281.

Ceres & Marianne Types of 1945
1947 Unwmk. Typo. Perf. 14x13½
576 A146 1.30fr dull blue   .20 .20
577 A147 3fr green   1.90 .40
578 A147 3.50fr brown red   .85 .55
579 A147 5fr blue   .25 .25
580 A147 6fr carmine   .25 .20
    Nos. 576-580 (5)   3.45 1.60

Colonnade
of the
Louvre
A166

La Conciergerie, Paris Prison — A167

La Cité,
Oldest
Section of
Paris
A168

Place de la
Concorde
A169

1947, May 7   **Engr.**   **Perf. 13**
581 A166 3.50fr chocolate   .40 .40
582 A167 4.50fr dk slate gray   .60 .40
583 A168 6fr red   1.10 1.00
584 A169 10fr bright ultra   1.10 1.00
    Nos. 581-584 (4)   3.20 2.80

    12th UPU Cong., Paris, May 7-July 7.

Auguste
Pavie — A170

Francois
Fénelon — A171

1947, May 30
585 A170 4.50fr sepia   .40 .40
    Cent. of the birth of Auguste Pavie, French
pioneer in Laos.

1947, July 12
586 A171 4.50fr chocolate   .40 .40
    Issued to honor Francois de Salignac de la
Mothe-Fénelon, prelate and writer.

Fleur-de-Lis and
Double Carrick
Bend — A172

1947, Aug. 2   **Unwmk.**
587 A172 5fr brown   .40 .40
    6th World Boy Scout Jamboree held at
Moisson, Aug. 9th-18th, 1947.

Captured Patriot
A173

View of Conques
A174

1947, Nov. 10   **Engr.**   **Perf. 13**
588 A173 5fr sepia   .40 .35

No. 576 Surcharged in Carmine

1947, Nov.   **Typo.**   **Perf. 14x13½**
589 A146 1fr on 1.30fr dull blue   .20 .20

1947, Dec. 18   **Engr.**   **Perf. 13**
590 A174 15fr henna brown   4.50 1.00
    For surcharge see Reunion No. 282.

Types of 1946-47
1948   **Re-engraved**
591 A160 12fr rose carmine   3.25 .65
592 A160 15fr bright red   .85 .85
593 A174 18fr dark blue   4.50 .40
    Nos. 591-593 (3)   8.60 1.90
"FRANCE" substituted for inscriptions "RF"
and "REPUBLIQUE FRANCAISE."

Marianne Type of 1945
1948-49   **Typo.**   **Perf. 14x13½**
594 A147 2.50fr brown   2.75 1.25
595 A147 3fr lilac rose   .25 .25
596 A147 4fr lt blue grn   .25 .25
597 A147 4fr brown org   3.00 .90
598 A147 5fr lt blue grn   .85 .25
599 A147 8fr blue   .40 .25
600 A147 10fr brt violet   .25 .20
601 A147 12fr ultra ('49)   3.00 .40
602 A147 15fr crim rose ('49)   1.00 .20
   a. Booklet pane of 10   150.00
    Nos. 594-602 (9)   11.75 3.95
No. 594 known only precanceled. See second note after No. 132.

François René de
Chateaubriand — A175

1948, July 3   **Engr.**   **Perf. 13**
603 A175 18fr dark blue   .40 .40
    Vicomte de Chateaubriand (1768-1848).

Philippe François M. de Hautecloque
(Gen. Jacques Leclerc) — A176

1948, July 3
604 A176 6fr gray black   .40 .40
    See Nos. 692-692A.

Chaillot
Palace
A177

A178

1948, Sept. 21
605 A177 12fr carmine rose   .55 .55
606 A178 18fr indigo   .55 .55
    Meeting of the UN General Assembly, Paris,
1948.

Genissiat
Dam
A179

Paul Langevin — A180

1948, Sept. 21
607 A179 12fr carmine rose .85 .85

1948, Nov. 17 **Perf. 14x13**
608 A180 5fr shown .40 .25
609 A180 8fr Jean Perrin .40 .25

Placing of the ashes of physicists Langevin (1872-1946) and Perrin (1870-1942) in the Pantheon.

No. 580 Surcharged with New Value and Bars in Black
1949, Jan. **Perf. 14x13½**
610 A147 5fr on 6fr carmine .25 .25

Arctic Scene — A181

1949, May 2 **Perf. 13**
611 A181 15fr indigo .40 .40
French polar explorations.

Types of 1849 and 1945
1949, May 9 **Engr.** **Imperf.**
612 A1 15fr red 3.25 3.25
613 A1 25fr deep blue 3.25 3.25

Perf. 14x13
614 A147 15fr red 3.25 3.25
615 A147 25fr deep blue 3.25 3.25
a. Strip of 4, #612-615 + label 16.50 16.50
Nos. 612-615 (4) 13.00 13.00

Cent. of the 1st French postage stamps.

Arms of Burgundy — A182

Arms: 50c, Guyenne (Aquitania). 1fr, Savoy. 2fr, Auvergne. 4fr, Anjou.

1949, May 11 Typo. **Perf. 14x13½**
616 A182 10c blue, red & yel .20 .20
617 A182 50c blue, red & yel .20 .20
618 A182 1fr brown & red .55 .40
619 A182 2fr green, yel & red .55 .25
620 A182 4fr blue, red & yel .40 .40
Nos. 616-620 (5) 1.90 1.45

See Nos. 659-663, 694-699, 733-739, 782-785. For surcharges see Reunion Nos. 283-284, 288-289, 297, 301, 305, 311.

Collegiate Church of St. Barnard and Dauphiné Arms A183

1949, May 14 **Engr.** **Perf. 13**
621 A183 12fr red brown .40 .40

600th anniv. of France's acquisition of the Dauphiné region.

US and French Flags, Plane and Steamship A184

1949, May 14
622 A184 25fr blue & carmine .65 .65
Franco-American friendship.

Cloister of St. Wandrille Abbey A185

1949, May 18
623 A185 25fr deep ultra .40 .25

See No. 649. For surcharge see Reunion No. 287.

Type of 1849 Inscribed "1849-1949" in Lower Margin
1949, June 1
624 A1 10fr brown orange 55.00 45.00
a. Sheet of 10 700.00 500.00

Cent. of the 1st French postage stamp. No. 624 has wide margins, 40x52mm from perforation to perforation. Sold for 110fr, which included cost of admission to the Centenary Intl. Exhib., Paris, June 1949.

Claude Chappe — A186 | Jean Racine — A187

15fr, François Arago & André M. Ampère. 25fr, Emile Baudot. 50fr, Gen. Gustave A. Ferrié.

Inscribed: "C.I.T.T. PARIS 1949"

1949, June 13 Unwmk. **Perf. 13**
625 A186 10fr vermilion .90 .85
626 A186 15fr sepia 1.00 .90
627 A186 25fr deep claret 2.50 2.25
628 A186 50fr deep blue 4.50 4.00
Nos. 625-628 (4) 8.90 8.00

International Telegraph and Telephone Conference, Paris, May-July 1949.

1949
629 A187 12fr sepia .40 .40

Death of Jean Racine, dramatist, 250th anniv.

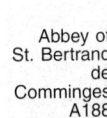

Abbey of St. Bertrand de Comminges A188

Meuse Valley, Ardennes A189

Mt. Gerbier de Jonc, Vivarais A190

1949 **Engr.**
630 A188 20fr dark red .25 .20
631 A189 40fr Prus green 15.00 .30
632 A190 50fr sepia 2.50 .20
Nos. 630-632 (3) 17.75 .70

For surcharge see Reunion No. 286.

A191

1949, Oct. 18
633 A191 15fr deep carmine .25 .25

50th anniv. of the Assembly of Presidents of Chambers of Commerce of the French Union.

UPU Allegory A192

1949, Nov. 7
634 A192 5fr dark green .25 .25
635 A192 15fr deep carmine .40 .25
636 A192 25fr deep blue 1.25 .90
Nos. 634-636 (3) 1.90 1.40

UPU, 75th anniversary.

Raymond Poincaré — A193

1950, May 27 **Unwmk.** **Perf. 13**
637 A193 15fr indigo .35 .25

Charles Péguy and Cathedral at Chartres A194

François Rabelais — A195

1950, June
638 A194 12fr dk brown .40 .25
639 A195 12fr red brown .85 .75

Chateau of Chateaudun — A196

1950, Nov. 25
640 A196 8fr choc & bis brn .70 .45

Madame Récamier A197 | Marie de Sévigné A198

1950
641 A197 12fr dark green .65 .40
642 A198 15fr ultra .65 .40

Palace of Fontainbleau — A199

1951, Jan. 20
643 A199 12fr dark brown .90 .75

Jules Ferry — A200 | Jean-Baptiste de la Salle — A202

Hands Holding Shuttle A201

1951, Mar. 17
644 A200 15fr bright red .55 .55

1951, Apr. 9
645 A201 25fr deep ultra 1.00 .65
Intl. Textile Exposition, Lille, April-May, 1951.

1951, Apr. 28
646 A202 15fr chocolate .65 .55

300th anniv. of the birth of Jean-Baptiste de la Salle, educator and saint.

Map and Anchor A203

1951, May 12
647 A203 15fr deep ultra .60 .40

50th anniv. of the creation of the French colonial troops.

Vincent d'Indy A204

1951, May 15
648 A204 25fr deep green 2.00 2.00
Vincent d'Indy, composer, birth cent.

Abbey Type of 1949

1951
649 A185 30fr bright blue   6.00 4.50

Marianne Type of 1945-47

1951	**Typo.**		**Perf. 14x13½**
650	A147	5fr dull violet	.50 .20
651	A147	6fr green	6.50 .60
652	A147	12fr red orange	.85 .25
653	A147	15fr ultra	.35 .20
a.		Booklet pane of 10	30.00
654	A147	18fr cerise	16.00 1.40
		Nos. 650-654 (5)	24.20 2.65

Professors Nocard, Bouley and
Chauveau; Gate at Lyons School
A205

1951, June 8   Engr.   Perf. 13
655 A205 12fr red violet   .60 .55
Issued to honor Veterinary Medicine.

Gen. Picqué, Cols. Roussin and
Villemin; Val de Grace Dome
A206

1951, June 17   Unwmk.
656 A206 15fr red brown   .75 .55
Issued to honor Military Medicine.

St. Nicholas, by
Jean Didier — A207

1951, June 23
657 A207 15fr ind, dp claret &
           org   1.40 1.00

Chateau
Bontemps,
Arbois
A208

1951, June 23
658 A208 30fr indigo   1.00 .25
For surcharge see Reunion No. 296.

Arms Type of 1949

Arms of: 10c, Artois. 50c, Limousin. 1fr,
Béarn. 2fr, Touraine. 3fr, Franche-Comté.

1951, June	**Typo.**		**Perf. 14x13½**
659	A182	10c red, vio bl & yel	.20 .20
660	A182	50c green, red & blk	.20 .20
661	A182	1fr blue, red & yel	.25 .25
662	A182	2fr vio bl, red & yel	.90 .40
663	A182	3fr red, vio bl & yel	.85 .40
		Nos. 659-663 (5)	2.40 1.45

Seal of
Paris — A209

Maurice Noguès
and
Globe — A210

Unwmk.
1951, July 7   Engr.   Perf. 13
664 A209 15fr dp bl, dk brn & red   .65 .40
2,000th anniv. of the founding of Paris.

1951, Oct. 13
665 A210 12fr indigo & blue   .90 .85
Maurice Nogues, aviation pioneer.

Charles
Baudelaire
A211

Poets: 12fr, Paul Verlaine. 15fr, Arthur
Rimbaud.

1951, Oct. 27
666 A211 8fr purple   .85 .75
667 A211 12fr gray   .85 .75
668 A211 15fr dp green   .85 .75
       Nos. 666-668 (3)   2.55 2.25

Georges
Clemenceau, Birth
Cent. — A212

1951, Nov. 11
669 A212 15fr black brown   .55 .45

Chateau du
Clos,
Vougeot
A213

1951, Nov. 17
670 A213 30fr blk brn & brn   6.25 2.50

Chaillot
Palace and
Eiffel Tower
A214

1951, Nov. 6
671 A214 18fr red   1.10 .60
672 A214 30fr deep ultra   2.00 1.10
Opening of the Geneva Assembly of the
United Nations, Paris, Nov. 6, 1951.

Observatory, Pic du Midi — A215

Abbaye aux
Hommes,
Caen — A216

1951, Dec. 22
673 A215 40fr violet   5.50 .20
674 A216 50fr black brown   5.00 .20
For surcharge see Reunion No. 294.

Marshal
Jean de
Lattre de
Tassigny,
1890-1952
A217

1952, May 8   Unwmk.   Perf. 13
675 A217 15fr violet brown   1.00 .45
See No. 717.

Gate of France,
Vaucouleurs — A218

1952, May 11
676 A218 12fr brown black   1.50 .90

Flags and
Monument
at Narvik,
Norway
A219

1952, May 28
677 A219 30fr violet blue   3.25 2.00
Battle of Narvik, May 27, 1940.

Chateau
de
Chambord
A220

1952, May 30
678 A220 20fr dark purple   .45 .20
For surcharge see Reunion No. 292.

Assembly
Hall,
Strasbourg
A221

1952, May 31
679 A221 30fr dark green   8.00 5.75
Issued to honor the Council of Europe.

Monument, Bir-Hacheim
Cemetery — A222

1952, June 14
680 A222 30fr rose lake   3.75 2.00
10th anniv. of the defense of Bir-Hacheim.

Abbey of the Holy
Cross,
Poitiers — A223

1952, June 21
681 A223 15fr bright red   .55 .55
14th cent. of the foundation of the Abbey of
the Holy Cross at Poitiers.

Leonardo da Vinci, Amboise Chateau
and La Signoria, Florence
A224

1952, July 9
682 A224 30fr deep ultra   8.25 7.00
Leonardo da Vinci, 500th birth anniv.

Garabit
Viaduct
A225

1952, July 5
683 A225 15fr dark blue   .65 .55

Sword and
Military Medals,
1852-1952
A226

Dr. René
Laennec
A227

1952, July 5
684 A226 15fr choc, grn & yel   .60 .50
Cent. of the creation of the Military Medal.

1952, Nov. 7
685 A227 12fr dark green   .50 .50

Versailles
Gate,
Painted by
Utrillo
A228

1952, Dec. 20
686 A228 18fr violet brown   2.90 1.90
Publicity for the restoration of Versailles Palace. See No. 728.

Mannequin — A229

1953, Apr. 24   Unwmk.   Perf. 13
687 A229 30fr blue blk & rose vio   .90   .35
Dressmaking industry of France.

Gargantua of
François
Rabelais
A230

Célimène from
The Misanthrope
A231

Figaro, from the
Barber of
Seville — A232

Hernani of Victor
Hugo — A233

1953
688 A230 6fr dp plum & car   .25   .20
689 A231 8fr indigo & ultra   .25   .20
690 A232 12fr vio brn & dk grn   .25   .20
691 A233 18fr vio brn & blk brn   .60   .30
      Nos. 688-691 (4)   1.35   .90
For surcharge see Reunion No. 298.

Type of 1948
Inscribed "Général Leclerc Maréchal
de France"

1953-54
692 A176 8fr red brown   1.00   .90
692A A176 12fr dk grn & gray
      grn ('54)   3.00   1.90
Issued to honor the memory of General Jacques Leclerc.

Map and
Cyclists,
1903-1953
A234

1953, July 26
693 A234 12fr red brn, ultra &
      blk   2.25   1.25
50th anniv. of the Bicycle Tour de France.

Arms Type of 1949
50c, Picardy. 70c, Gascony. 80c, Berri. 1fr,
Poitou. 2fr, Champagne. 3fr, Dauphiné.

1953   Typo.   Perf. 14x13½
694 A182 50c blue, yel & red   .25   .20
695 A182 70c red, blue & yel   .25   .20
696 A182 80c blue, red & yel   .25   .20
697 A182 1fr black, red & yel   .25   .20
698 A182 2fr brown, bl & yel   .50   .25
699 A182 3fr red, blue & yel   .65   .25
      Nos. 694-699 (6)   2.15   1.30

Swimming
A235

1953, Nov. 28   Engr.   Perf. 13
700 A235 20fr shown   2.50   .25
701 A235 25fr Track   13.00   .55
702 A235 30fr Fencing   2.50   .40
703 A235 40fr Canoe racing   11.50   .55
704 A235 50fr Rowing   8.25   .25
705 A235 75fr Equestrian   35.00   12.50
      Nos. 700-705 (6)   72.75   14.50
For surcharges see Reunion Nos. 299-300.

No. 654 Surcharged with New Value
and Bars in Black

1954   Perf. 14x13½
706 A147 15fr on 18fr cerise   .55   .20

Farm
Woman
A236

Gallic Cock
A237

1954   Typo.
707 A236 4fr blue   .25   .20
708 A236 8fr brown red   5.50   1.25
709 A237 12fr cerise   3.75   .85
710 A237 24fr blue green   20.00   5.00
      Nos. 707-710 (4)   29.50   7.30
Nos. 707-710 are known only precanceled.
See second note after No. 132.
See #833-834, 840-844, 910-913, 939, 952-955. For surcharges see Reunion #324, 326-327.

Tapestry and
Gobelin
Workshop
A238

Entrance to
Exhibition Park
A239

Designs: 30fr, Book manufacture. 40fr, Porcelain and glassware. 50fr, Jewelry and metalsmith's work. 75fr, Flowers and perfumes.

1954, May 6   Engr.   Perf. 13
711 A238 25fr red brn car & blk
      brn   14.00   .55
712 A238 30fr dk grn & lil gray   2.50   .20
713 A238 40fr dk brn, vio brn &
      org brn   4.00   .20
714 A238 50fr brt ultra, dl grn &
      org brn   2.50   .20
715 A238 75fr dp car & magenta   14.00   1.10
      Nos. 711-715 (5)   37.00   2.25
For surcharges see Reunion Nos. 303-304.

1954, May 22
716 A239 15fr blue & dk car   .35   .30
Founding of the Fair of Paris, 50th anniv.

De Lattre Type of 1952
1954, June 5
717 A217 12fr vio bl & indigo   4.50   3.75

Allied
Landings
A240

1954, June 5
718 A240 15fr scarlet & ultra   1.75   1.00
The 10th anniversary of the liberation.

View of
Lourdes
A241

Street Corner,
Quimper — A242

Views: 8fr, Seine valley, Les Andelys. 10fr,
Beach at Royan. 18fr, Cheverny Chateau.
20fr, Beach, Gulf of Ajaccio.

1954
719 A241 6fr ultra, ind & dk grn   .40   .30
720 A241 8fr brt blue & dk grn   .30   .20
721 A241 10fr aqua & org brn   .30   .20
722 A242 12fr rose vio & dk vio   .50   .20
723 A241 18fr bl, dk grn & ind   3.25   .90
724 A241 20fr blk brn, bl grn &
      red brn   2.75   .20
      Nos. 719-724 (6)   7.50   2.00
See No. 873. For surcharges see Reunion
Nos. 302, 306-310.

Abbey Ruins,
Jumièges
A243

St. Philibert
Abbey, Tournus
A244

1954, June 13
725 A243 12fr vio bl, ind & dk
      grn   1.60   1.00
13th centenary of Abbey of Jumièges.

1954, June 18
726 A244 30fr indigo & blue   6.00   4.50
1st conf. of the Intl. Center of Romance
Studies.

View of
Stenay
A245

1954, June 26
727 A245 15fr dk brn & org brn   .85   .60
Acquisition of Stenay by France, 300th anniv.

Versailles Type of 1952
1954, July 10
728 A228 18fr dp bl, ind & vio
      brn   9.00   6.25

Villandry
Chateau
A246

1954, July 17
729 A246 18fr dk bl & dk bl grn   5.00   3.25

Napoleon
Awarding
Legion of
Honor
Decoration
A247

1954, Aug. 14
730 A247 12fr scarlet   1.60   1.25
150th anniv. of the 1st Legion of Honor
awards at Camp de Boulogne.

Cadets
Marching
Through
Gateway
A248

1954, Aug. 1
731 A248 15fr vio gray, dk bl &
      car   1.25   1.25
150th anniversary of the founding of the Military School of Saint-Cyr.

Allegory
A249

Duke de Saint-
Simon
A250

1954, Oct. 4
732 A249 30fr indigo & choc   6.00   4.00

Issued to publicize the fact that the metric system was first introduced in France.

Arms Type of 1949

Arms: 50c, Maine. 70c, Navarre. 80c, Nivernais. 1fr, Bourbonnais. 2fr, Angoumois. 3fr, Aunis. 5fr, Saintonge.

1954		Typo.	Perf. 14x13½	
733	A182	50c multicolored	.20	.20
734	A182	70c green, red & yel	.25	.20
735	A182	80c blue, red & yel	.25	.20
736	A182	1fr red, blue & yel	.20	.20
737	A182	2fr black, red & yel	.20	.20
738	A182	3fr brown, red & yel	.20	.20
739	A182	5fr blue & yellow	.20	.20
		Nos. 733-739 (7)	1.50	1.40

1955, Feb. 5		Engr.	Perf. 13	
740	A250	12fr dk brn & vio brn	.70	.60

Louis de Rouvroy, Duke de Saint-Simon (1675-1755).

Allegory
and Rotary
Emblem
A251

Marianne — A252

1955, Feb. 23
741 A251 30fr vio bl, bl & org   1.90   1.00

50th anniv. of Rotary International.

1955-59		Typo.	Perf. 14x13½	
751	A252	6fr fawn	2.75	1.75
752	A252	12fr green	3.25	1.25
a.		Bklt. pane of 10 + 2 labels	45.00	
753	A252	15fr carmine	.20	.20
a.		Booklet pane of 10	10.00	
754	A252	18fr green ('58)	.25	.20
755	A252	20fr ultra ('57)	.45	.20
756	A252	25fr rose red ('59)	1.40	.20
a.		Booklet pane of 8	15.00	
b.		Booklet pane of 10	16.00	
		Nos. 751-756 (6)	8.30	3.80

No. 751 was issued in coils of 1,000.
No. 752 was issued in panes of 10 stamps and two labels with marginal instructions for folding to form a booklet.
Nos. 754-755 are found in two types, distinguished by the numerals. On the 18fr there is no serif at left of base of the "1" on the 1st type. The 2nd type has a shorter "1" with no serifs at base. On the 20fr the 2nd type has a well formed "2" and the horiz. lines of the "F" of the denomination are longer and of equal length.
No. 756 also in two types, distinguished by border width. On the 1st type, the border is thicker than the width of the letters. On the 2nd type, the border is thinner than the width of the letters.
For surcharges see Reunion Nos. 330-331.

Philippe
Lebon,
Inventor of
Illuminating
Gas
A253

Inventors: 10fr, Barthélemy Thimonnier, sewing machine. 12fr, Nicolas Appert, canned

---

foods. 18fr, Dr. E. H. St. Claire Deville, aluminum. 25fr, Pierre Martin, steel making. 30fr, Bernigaud de Chardonnet, rayon.

1955, Mar. 5			Engr.	
757	A253	5fr dk vio bl & bl	.75	.75
758	A253	10fr dk brn & org brn	.90	.90
759	A253	12fr dk green	1.25	1.25
760	A253	18fr dk vio bl & ind	2.90	1.90
761	A253	25fr dk brnsh pur & vio	3.25	2.00
762	A253	30fr rose car & scar	3.25	2.00
		Nos. 757-762 (6)	12.30	8.80

St. Stephen
Bridge,
Limoges
A254

1955, Mar. 26		Unwmk.	Perf. 13	
763	A254	12fr yel brn & dk vio brn	1.60	1.25

Gloved Model in
Place de la
Concorde — A255

1955, Mar. 26
764 A255 25fr blk brn, vio bl & blk   1.00   .20

French glove manufacturing.

Jean Pierre
Claris de
Florian
A256

1955, Apr. 2
765 A256 12fr blue green   .85   .60

200th anniv. of the birth of Jean Pierre Claris de Florian, fabulist.

Eiffel Tower
and
Television
Antennas
A257

1955, Apr. 16
766 A257 15fr indigo & ultra   1.00   .90

French advancement in television.

Wire Fence
and Guard
Tower
A258

1955, Apr. 23
767 A258 12fr dk gray bl & brn blk   1.00   .90

10th anniv. of the liberation of concentration camps.

Electric
Train
A259

1955, May 11
768 A259 12fr blk brn & slate bl   2.75   1.25

Issued to publicize the electrification of the Valenciennes-Thionville railroad line.

Jacquemart of
Moulins — A260

1955, May 28
769 A260 12fr black brown   1.50   1.25

Jules Verne
and
Nautilus
A261

1955, June 3
770 A261 30fr indigo   8.00   5.00

50th anniv. of the death of Jules Verne.

Auguste
and Louis
Lumière
and Motion
Picture
Projector
A262

1955, June 12
771 A262 30fr rose brown   6.25   4.50

Invention of motion pictures, 60th anniv.

Jacques
Coeur and
His
Mansion at
Bourges
A263

1955, June 18
772 A263 12fr violet   2.25   1.60

5th centenary of the death of Jacques Coeur (1395?-1456), French merchant.

Corvette "La Capricieuse" — A264

1955, July 9
773 A264 30fr aqua & dk blue   6.00   4.50

Centenary of the voyage of La Capricieuse to Canada.

Bordeaux
A265

Designs: 8fr, Marseille. 10fr, Nice. 12fr, Valentre bridge, Cahors. 18fr, Uzerche. 25fr, Fortifications, Brouage.

1955, Oct. 15
774	A265	6fr carmine lake	.20	.20
775	A265	8fr indigo	.45	.20
776	A265	10fr dp ultra	.20	.20
777	A265	12fr violet & brn	.20	.20
778	A265	18fr bluish grn & ind	.85	.20
779	A265	25fr org brn & red brn	1.25	.20
		Nos. 774-779 (6)	3.15	1.20

See Nos. 838-839. For surcharges see Reunion Nos. 312-317, 323.

Mount
Pelée,
Martinique
A266

1955, Nov. 1
780 A266 20fr dk & lt purple   3.50   .20

Gérard de
Nerval — A267

1955, Nov. 11
781 A267 12fr lake & sepia   .55   .35

Centenary of the death of Gérard de Nerval (Labrunie), author.

Arms Type of 1949

Arms of: 50c, County of Foix. 70c, Marche. 80c, Roussillon. 1fr, Comtat Venaissin.

		Perf. 14x13½		
1955, Nov. 19		Typo.	Unwmk.	
782	A182	50c multicolored	.20	.20
783	A182	70c red, blue & yel	.20	.20
784	A182	80c brown, yel & red	.20	.20
785	A182	1fr blue, red & yel	.20	.20
		Nos. 782-785 (4)	.80	.80

Concentration
Camp Victim
and Monument
A268

Belfry at Douai
A269

1956, Jan. 14		Engr.	Perf. 13	
786	A268	15fr brn blk & red brn	.65	.50

Natl. memorial for Nazi deportation victims erected at the Natzwiller Struthof concentration camp in Alsace.

1956, Feb. 11
787 A269 15fr ultra & indigo   .55   .55

Col. Emil
Driant
A270

1956, Feb. 21
788 A270 15fr dark blue   .40   .35

40th anniv. of the death of Col. Emil Driant during the battle of Verdun.

Trench Fighting — A271

1956, Mar. 3
789 A271 30fr indigo & dk olive   2.00 1.50
40th anniversary of Battle of Verdun.

Jean Henri Fabre, Entomology A272

Scientists: 15fr, Charles Tellier, Refrigeration. 18fr, Camille Flammarion, Popular Astronomy. 30fr, Paul Sabatier, Catalytic Chemistry.

1956, Apr. 7
790 A272 12fr vio brn & org brn   1.00   .65
791 A272 15fr vio bl & int blk   1.00   .65
792 A272 18fr brt ultra   1.90 1.60
793 A272 30fr Prus grn & dk grn   4.75 2.90
　　Nos. 790-793 (4)   8.65 5.80

Grand Trianon, Versailles A273

1956, Apr. 14
794 A273 12fr vio brn & gray grn 1.50 1.00

Symbols of Latin American and French Culture A274

1956, Apr. 21
795 A274 30fr brown & red brn   2.50   1.60
Issued in recognition of the friendship between France and Latin America.

"The Smile of Reims" and Botticelli's "Spring" A275

1956, May 5
796 A275 12fr black & green   .75 .55
Issued to emphasize the cultural and artistic kinship of Reims and Florence.

Leprosarium and Maltese Cross — A276

1956, May 12
797 A276 12fr sepia, red brn & red .40 .35
Issued in honor of the Knights of Malta.

St. Yves de Treguier A277

1956, May 19
798 A277 15fr bluish gray & blk   .35   .25
St. Yves, patron saint of lawyers.

Marshal Franchet d'Esperey A278

Miners Monument A279

1956, May 26
799 A278 30fr deep claret   2.75   1.90
Centenary of the birth of Marshal Louis Franchet d'Esperey.

1956, June 2
800 A279 12fr violet brown   .45 .40
Town Montceau-les-Mines, 100th anniv.

Basketball A280

"Rebuilding Europe" A281

Sports: 40fr, Pelota (Jai alai). 50fr, Rugby. 75fr, Mountain climbing.

1956, July 7
801 A280 30fr gray vio & blk   1.50   .20
802 A280 40fr brown & vio brn   6.00   .30
803 A280 50fr rose vio & vio   2.00   .20
804 A280 75fr indigo, grn & bl   12.00 2.00
　　Nos. 801-804 (4)   21.50 2.70

For surcharges see Reunion Nos. 318-321.

Europa Issue
Perf. 13½x14
1956, Sept. 15   Typo.   Unwmk.
805 A281 15fr rose & rose lake   1.00   .25

Perf. 13
Engr.
806 A281 30fr lt blue & vio bl   6.00   .85

Issued to symbolize the cooperation among the six countries comprising the Coal and Steel Community.
No. 805 measures 21x35½mm, No. 806 measures 22x35½mm.

Dam at Donzère-Mondragon — A282

Cable Railway to Pic du Midi — A283

Rhine Port of Strasbourg A284

1956, Oct. 6   Engr.   Perf. 13
807 A282 12fr gray vio & vio brn   1.60 1.10
808 A283 18fr indigo   3.25 2.25
809 A284 30fr indigo & dk blue   14.00 6.25
　　Nos. 807-809 (3)   18.85 9.60
French technical achievements.

Antoine-Augustin Parmentier — A285

1956, Oct. 27
810 A285 12fr brown red & brown   .75 .65
Parmentier, nutrition chemist, who popularized the potato in France.

Petrarch — A286

Portraits: 12fr, J. B. Lully. 15fr, J. J. Rousseau. 18fr, Benjamin Franklin. 20fr, Frederic Chopin. 30fr, Vincent van Gogh.

1956, Nov. 10
811 A286   8fr green   .85   .65
812 A286 12fr claret   .85   .65
813 A286 15fr dark red   1.25   .65
814 A286 18fr ultra   2.75 2.25
815 A286 20fr brt violet   3.75 1.75
816 A286 30fr brt grnsh blue   5.75 3.00
　　Nos. 811-816 (6)   15.20 8.95

Famous men who lived in France.

Pierre de Coubertin and Olympic Stadium A287

1956, Nov. 24
817 A287 30fr dk blue gray & pur 2.00 1.25
Issued in honor of Baron Pierre de Coubertin, founder of the modern Olympic Games.

Homing Pigeon A288

1957, Jan. 12
818 A288 15fr dp ultra, ind & red
　　　　　　　 brn   .45 .25

Victor Schoelcher — A289

1957, Feb. 16   Engr.
819 A289 18fr lilac rose   .65   .65
Issued in honor of Victor Schoelcher, who freed the slaves in the French Colonies.

Sèvres Porcelain A290

1957, Mar. 23   Unwmk.   Perf. 13
820 A290 30fr ultra & vio blue   .85   .40
Bicentenary of the porcelain works at Sèvres (in 1956).

Gaston Planté and Storage Battery A291

Designs: 12fr, Antoine Béclère and X-ray apparatus. 18fr, Octave Terrillon, autoclave, microscope and surgical instruments. 30fr, Etienne Oemichen and early helicopter.

1957, Apr. 13
821 A291   8fr gray blk & dp cl   .50   .50
822 A291 12fr dk bl, blk & emer   .55   .55
823 A291 18fr rose red & mag   1.40 1.40
824 A291 30fr green & slate grn   2.50 2.50
　　Nos. 821-824 (4)   4.95 4.95

Uzès Chateau A292

1957, Apr. 27
825 A292 12fr slate bl & bis brn   .40 .40

Jean Moulin A293

Le Quesnoy A294

Portraits: 10fr, Honoré d'Estienne d'Orves. 12fr, Robert Keller. 18fr, Pierre Brossolette. 20fr, Jean-Baptiste Lebas.

1957, May 18
826 A293   8fr violet brown   1.00   .45
827 A293 10fr black & vio bl   1.00   .45
828 A293 12fr brown & sl grn   1.00   .80
829 A293 18fr purple & blk   1.60 1.25
830 A293 20fr Prus bl & dk bl   1.50   .90
　　Nos. 826-830 (5)   6.10 3.85

Issued in honor of the heroes of the French Underground of World War II.
See #879-882, 915-919, 959-963, 990-993.

1957, June 1
831 A294   8fr dk slate green   .25   .20
See No. 837. For surcharge see Reunion No. 322.

Symbols of Justice
A295

1957, June 1
832 A295 12fr sepia & ultra　　.25　.20
French Cour des Comptes, 150th anniv.

Farm Woman Type of 1954
1957-59　　　　　　**Perf. 14x13½**
833　A236　6fr orange　　　　.20　.20
833A A236 10fr brt green ('59)　.75　.20
834　A236 12fr red lilac　　　.25　.20
　　　Nos. 833-834 (3)　　1.20　.60
Nos. 833-834 issued without precancellation.

Symbols of Public Works
A296

1957, June 20　Engr.　Perf. 13
835 A296 30fr sl grn, brn & ocher 1.90 1.10

Brest
A297

1957, July 6
836 A297 12fr gray grn & brn ol　1.00 1.00

Scenic Types of 1955, 1957
Designs: 15fr, Le Quesnoy. 35fr, Bordeaux. 70fr, Valentre bridge, Cahors.

1957, July 19　　Unwmk.
837 A294 15fr dk bl grn & sep　.40　.20
838 A265 35fr dk grn & sl grn　3.25 1.10
839 A265 70fr black & dull grn　22.50 2.00
　　Nos. 837-839 (3)　　26.15 3.30

Gallic Cock Type of 1954
1957　Typo.　　Perf. 14x13½
840 A237　5fr olive bister　　.40　.20
841 A237 10fr bright blue　　1.75　.35
842 A237 12fr plum　　　　2.25　.75
843 A237 30fr bright red　　10.00 3.00
844 A237 45fr green　　　21.00 12.50
　　Nos. 840-844 (5)　　35.40 16.80
Nos. 840-844 are known only precanceled. See second note after No. 132.

Leo Lagrange and Stadium
A298

1957, Aug. 31　Engr.　Perf. 13
845 A298 18fr lilac gray & blk　.55　.55
Intl. University Games, Paris, 8/31-9/8.

"United Europe" — A299　　Auguste Comte — A300

1957, Sept. 16
846 A299 20fr red brown & green　.40　.30
847 A299 35fr dk brown & blue　1.00　.65
A united Europe for peace and prosperity.

1957, Sept. 14
848 A300 35fr brown red & sepia　.45　.35
Centenary of the death of Auguste Comte, mathematician and philosopher.

Roman Amphitheater, Lyon — A301

1957, Oct. 5　　　　Perf. 13
849 A301 20fr brn org & brn vio　.45　.35
2,000th anniv. of the founding of Lyon.

Sens River, Guadeloupe
A302

Beynac-Cazenac, Dordogne
A303

Nicolaus Copernicus
A304

Designs: 10fr, Elysee Palace. 25fr, Chateau de Valencay, Indre. 35fr, Rouen Cathedral. 50fr, Roman Ruins, Saint-Remy. 65fr, Evian-les-Bains.

1957, Oct. 19
850 A302　8fr green & lt brn　.20　.20
851 A302 10fr dk ol bis & vio brn　.20　.20
852 A303 18fr indigo & dk brn　.20　.20
853 A302 25fr bl gray & vio brn　.60　.20
854 A303 35fr car rose & lake　.20　.20
855 A302 50fr ol grn & ol bister　.50　.20
856 A302 65fr dk blue & indigo　.65　.35
　　Nos. 850-856 (7)　　2.55 1.55
See #907-909. For overprint and surcharges see #1O1, Reunion 325, 328-329, 332-334.

1957, Nov. 9　Engr.　Perf. 13
Portraits: 10fr, Michelangelo. 12fr, Miguel de Cervantes. 15fr, Rembrandt. 18fr, Isaac Newton. 25fr, Mozart. 35fr, Johann Wolfgang von Goethe.
857 A304　8fr dark brown　　.90　.65
858 A304 10fr dark green　　.90　.65
859 A304 12fr dark purple　　.90　.80
860 A304 15fr brown & org brn　1.10　.90
861 A304 18fr deep blue　　1.60 1.00
862 A304 25fr lilac & claret　1.60 1.00
863 A304 35fr blue　　　　1.90 1.10
　　Nos. 857-863 (7)　　8.90 6.10

Louis Jacques Thénard
A305

1957, Nov. 30　　　　Unwmk.
864 A305 15fr ol bis & grnsh blk　.40　.30
Centenary of the death of L. J. Thenard, chemist, and the founding of the Charitable Society of the Friends of Science.

Dr. Philippe Pinel
A306

Joseph Louis Lagrange
A307

French Physicians: 12fr, Fernand Widal. 15fr, Charles Nicolle. 35fr, René Leriche.

1958, Jan. 25
865 A306　8fr brown olive　　.90　.60
866 A306 12fr brt vio blue　　.90　.60
867 A306 15fr deep blue　　1.40　.80
868 A306 35fr black　　　1.75 1.10
　　Nos. 865-868 (4)　　4.95 3.10

1958, Feb. 15　　　　Perf. 13
French Scientists: 12fr, Urbain Jean Joseph Leverrier. 15fr, Jean Bernard Leon Foucault. 35fr, Claude Louis Berthollet.
869 A307　8fr blue grn & vio bl　.90　.55
870 A307 12fr sepia & gray　　1.00　.70
871 A307 15fr slate grn & grn　1.90　.95
872 A307 35fr maroon & cop red　2.40 1.25
　　Nos. 869-872 (4)　　6.20 3.45

Lourdes Type of 1954
1958
873 A241 20fr grnsh bl & ol　.30　.20

Le Havre
A308

Maubeuge — A309

Designs: 18fr, Saint-Die. 25fr, Sete.

1958, Mar. 29　Engr.　Perf. 13
874 A308 12fr ol grn & car rose　.65　.40
875 A309 15fr brt purple & brn　.65　.40
876 A309 18fr ultra & indigo　1.00　.80
877 A308 25fr dk bl, bl grn & brn　1.25　.80
　　Nos. 874-877 (4)　　3.55 2.40
Reconstruction of war-damaged cities.

French Pavilion, Brussels
A310

1958, Apr. 12
878 A310 35fr brn, dk grn & bl　.30　.25
Issued for the Universal and International Exposition at Brussels.

Heroes Type of 1957
8fr, Jean Cavaillès. 12fr, Fred Scamaroni. 15fr, Simone Michel-Levy. 20fr, Jacques Bingen.

1958, Apr. 19
879 A293　8fr violet & black　.65　.65
880 A293 12fr ultra & green　.65　.65
881 A293 15fr brown & gray　1.60　.90
882 A293 20fr olive & ultra　1.25 1.00
　　Nos. 879-882 (4)　　4.15 3.20
Issued in honor of the heroes of the French Underground in World War II.

Bowling
A311

Sports: 15fr, Naval joust. 18fr, Archery, vert. 25fr, Breton wrestling, vert.

1958, Apr. 26
883 A311 12fr rose & brown　　.85　.75
884 A311 15fr bl, ol gray & grn　1.10　.85
885 A311 18fr green & brown　2.00 1.10
886 A311 25fr brown & indigo　2.90 1.75
　　Nos. 883-886 (4)　　6.85 4.45

Senlis Cathedral — A312

1958, May 17
887 A312 15fr ultra & indigo　.40　.40

Bayeux Tapestry Horsemen
A313

1958, June 21
888 A313 15fr blue & carmine　.35　.25

Common Design Types pictured following the introduction.

Europa Issue, 1958
Common Design Type
1958, Sept. 13　Engr.　Perf. 13
Size: 22x36mm
889 CD1 20fr rose red　　.40　.20
890 CD1 35fr ultra　　　1.25　.30

Foix Chateau
A314

1958, Oct. 11
891 A314 15fr ultra, grn & ol brn　.40　.30

City Halls, Paris and Rome
A315

1958, Oct. 11
892 A315 35fr gray, grnsh bl & rose red　.40　.30
Issued to publicize the cultural ties between Rome and Paris and the need for European unity.

UNESCO Building, Paris
A316

Design: 35fr, Different view of building.

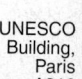

1958, Nov. 1 — Perf. 13
893 A316 20fr grnsh blue & ol bis .20 .20
894 A316 35fr dk sl grn & red org .20 .20
UNESCO Headquarters in Paris opening, Nov. 3.

Soldier's Grave in Wheat Field A317

Arms of Marseille A318

1958, Nov. 11
895 A317 15fr dk green & ultra .30 .25
40th anniv. of the World War I armistice.

1958-59 — Typo. Perf. 14x13½
Cities: 70c, Lyon. 80c, Toulouse. 1fr, Bordeaux. 2fr, Nice. 3fr, Nantes. 5fr, Lille. 15fr, Algiers.
896 A318 50c dk blue & ultra .20 .20
897 A318 70c multicolored .20 .20
898 A318 80c red, blue & yel .20 .20
899 A318 1fr dk bl, yel & red .20 .20
900 A318 2fr dk bl, red & grn .20 .20
901 A318 3fr multicolored .20 .20
902 A318 5fr dk brown & red .20 .20
903 A318 15fr multi ('59) .20 .20
　Nos. 896-903 (8) 1.60 1.60

See Nos. 938, 940, 973, 1040-1042, 1091-1095, 1142-1144. For surcharges see Reunion Nos. 336, 345-346, 350-351, 353.

Arc de Triomphe and Flowers — A319

1959, Jan. 17 — Engr. Perf. 13
904 A319 15fr brn, bl, grn, cl & red .45 .30
Paris Flower Festival.

Symbols of Learning and Medal A320

1959, Jan. 24 — Perf. 13
905 A320 20fr lake, blk & vio .25 .20
Sesquicentennial of the Palm Leaf Medal of the French Academy.

Charles de Foucauld A321

1959, Jan. 31
906 A321 50fr dp brn, bl & mar .50 .35
Issued to honor Father Charles de Foucauld, explorer and missionary of the Sahara.

Type of 1957
Designs: 30fr, Elysee Palace. 85fr, Evian-les Bains. 100fr, Sens River, Guadeloupe.

1959, Feb. 10
907 A302 30fr dk slate green 2.25 .25
908 A302 85fr deep claret 3.25 .30
909 A302 100fr deep violet 27.50 .45
　Nos. 907-909 (3) 33.00 1.00

Gallic Cock Type of 1954
1959 — Typo. Perf. 14x13½
910 A237 8fr violet .55 .25
911 A237 20fr yellow grn 1.75 .65
912 A237 40fr henna brn 4.00 2.25
913 A237 55fr emerald 17.00 10.00
　Nos. 910-913 (4) 23.30 13.15
Nos. 910-913 were issued with precancellation. See second note after No. 132. See Nos. 952-955.

Miners' Tools and School A322

1959, Apr. 11 — Engr. Perf. 13
914 A322 20fr red, blk & blue .25 .20
175th anniv. of the National Mining School.

Heroes Type of 1957
Portraits: No. 915, The five martyrs of the Buffon school. No. 916, Yvonne Le Roux. No. 917, Médéric-Védy. No. 918, Louis Martin-Bret. 30fr, Gaston Moutardier.

1959, Apr. 25 — Engr. Perf. 13
915 A293 15fr black & vio .40 .20
916 A293 15fr mag & rose vio .40 .40
917 A293 20fr green & grnsh bl .40 .40
918 A293 20fr org brn & brn .50 .50
919 A293 30fr magenta & vio .65 .50
　Nos. 915-919 (5) 2.35 2.00

Dam at Foum el Gherza A323

Marcoule Atomic Center — A324

Designs: 30fr, Oil field at Hassi Messaoud, Sahara. 50fr, C. N. I. T. Building (Centre National des Industries et des Techniques).

1959, May 23
920 A323 15fr olive & grnsh bl .35 .20
921 A324 20fr brt car & red brn .50 .50
922 A324 30fr dk blue, brn & grn .50 .50
923 A323 50fr ol grn & sl blue .75 .55
　Nos. 920-923 (4) 2.10 1.75
French technical achievements.

Marceline Desbordes-Valmore — A325

1959, June 20
924 A325 30fr blue, brn & grn .25 .20
Centenary of the death of Marceline Desbordes-Valmore, poet.

Pilots Goujon and Rozanoff A326

1959, June 13
925 A326 20fr lt blue & org brn .50 .40
Issued in honor of Charles Goujon and Col. Constantin Rozanoff, test pilots.

Tancarville Bridge A327

1959, Aug. 1 — Engr. Perf. 13
926 A327 30fr dk blue, brn & ol .50 .20

Marianne and Ship of State A328

Jean Jaures A329

1959, July — Typo. Perf. 14x13½
927 A328 25fr black & red .30 .20
See No. 942. For surcharge see No. B336.

1959, Sept. 12 — Engr. Perf. 13
928 A329 50fr chocolate .40 .25
Jean Jaures, socialist leader, birth cent.

Europa Issue, 1959
Common Design Type
1959, Sept. 19
Size: 22x36mm
929 CD2 25fr bright green .75 .35
930 CD2 50fr bright violet 1.10 .55

Blood Donors A330

1959, Oct. 17 — Engr.
931 A330 20fr magenta & gray .25 .20

French-Spanish Handshake — A331

1959, Oct. 24 — Perf. 13
932 A331 50fr blue, rose car & org .55 .35
300th anniv. of the signing of the Treaty of the Pyrenees.

Polio Victim Holding Crutches A332

Henri Bergson A333

1959, Oct. 31
933 A332 20fr dark blue .25 .20
Vaccination against poliomyelitis.

1959, Nov. 7
934 A333 50fr lt red brown .40 .25
Henri Bergson, philosopher, birth cent.

Avesnes-sur-Helpe — A334

Design: 30fr, Perpignan.

1959, Nov. 14
935 A334 20fr sepia & blue .40 .20
936 A334 30fr brn, dp claret & bl .40 .20

New NATO Headquarters, Paris — A335

1959, Dec. 12
937 A335 50fr green, brn & ultra .60 .40
10th anniv. of the NATO.

Types of 1958-59 and

Farm Woman A336

Sower A337

Designs: 5c, Arms of Lille. 15c, Arms of Algiers. 25c, Marianne and Ship of State.

Perf. 14x13½
1960-61 — Unwmk. — Typo.
938 A318 5c dk brown & red 7.25 .20
939 A336 10c brt green .25 .20
940 A318 15c red, ultra, yel & grn .60 .20
941 A337 20c grnsh bl & car rose .20 .20
942 A328 25c ver & ultra 2.25 .20
　b. Booklet pane of 8 27.50
　c. Booklet pane of 10 32.50
942A A337 30c gray & ultra ('61) 2.00 .30
　Nos. 938-942A (6) 12.55 1.30

See Nos. 707-708, 833-834 for the Farm Woman type (A336), but with no decimals in denominations.
For surcharges see Reunion Nos. 337-338, 341. For overprint see Algeria No. 286.

Laon Cathedral A338

Kerrata Gorge — A339

Designs: 30c, Fougères Chateau. 50c, Mosque, Tlemcen. 65c, Sioule Valley. 85c, Chaumont Viaduct. 1fr, Cilaos Church, Reunion.

1960, Jan. 16 — Engr. Perf. 13
943 A338 15c blue & indigo .40 .20
944 A338 30c blue, sepia & grn 3.75 .20
945 A338 45c brt vio & ol gray .85 .20
946 A339 50c sl grn & lt cl 2.50 .20
947 A338 65c sl grn, bl & blk brn 1.25 .20
948 A339 85c blue, sep & grn 3.00 .20
949 A339 1fr vio bl, bl & grn 3.00 .20
　Nos. 943-949 (7) 14.75 1.40

For surcharges see Reunion Nos. 335, 340, 342. For overprint see Algeria No. 288-289.

Pierre de Nolhac
A340

1960, Feb. 13
950 A340 20c black & gray　　.50　.35
　Centenary of the birth of Pierre de Nolhac, curator of Versailles and historian.

Museum of Art and Industry, Saint-Etienne — A341

1960, Feb. 20
951 A341 30c brn, car & slate　　.60　.30

Gallic Cock Type of 1954

1960　　　**Typo.**　　**Perf. 14x13½**
952 A237 8c violet　　　　.95　.30
953 A237 20c yellow grn　　3.25　.30
954 A237 40c henna brn　　9.00　2.00
955 A237 55c emerald　　29.00 16.00
　　Nos. 952-955 (4)　　42.20 18.50

　Nos. 952-955 were issued only precanceled. See second note after No. 132. See Nos. 910-913.

View of Cannes
A342

1960, Mar. 5　　**Engr.**　　**Perf. 13**
956 A342 50c red brn & lt grn　.70　.50
　Meeting of European municipal administrators, Cannes, Mar., 1960.

Woman of Savoy and Alps
A343

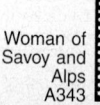

Woman of Nice and Shore
A344

1960　　**Unwmk.**　　**Perf. 13**
957 A343 30c slate green　　.65　.50
958 A344 50c brn, yel & rose　.65　.40
　Cent. of the annexation of Nice and Savoy.

Heroes Type of 1957

　Portraits: No. 959, Edmund Debeaumarché. No. 960, Pierre Massé. No. 961, Maurice Ripoche. No. 962, Leonce Vieljeux. 50c, Abbé René Bonpain.

1960, Mar. 26
959 A293 20c bister & blk　　2.50　1.50
960 A293 20c pink & rose cl　　1.90　1.50
961 A293 30c vio & brt vio　　1.90　1.50
962 A293 30c sl bl & brt bl　　3.50　2.50
963 A293 30c sl grn & red brn　3.50　3.25
　　Nos. 959-963 (5)　　13.30 10.25

　Issued in honor of the heroes of the French Underground of World War II.

"Education" and Children
A345

1960, May 21　　**Engr.**　　**Perf. 13**
964 A345 20c rose lilac, pur & blk　.25　.20
　1st secondary school in Strasbourg, 150th anniv.

Blois Chateau
A346

View of La Bourboule
A347

1960, May
965 A346 30c dk bl, sep & grn　.85　.65
966 A347 50c ol brown, car & grn　.65　.50

Lorraine Cross
A348

Marianne
A349

1960, June 18
967 A348 20c red brn, dk brn & yel grn　.65　.25
　20th anniv. of the French Resistance Movement in World War II.

1960, June 18　　**Typo.**　　**Perf. 14x13½**
968 A349 25c lake & gray　　.20　.20
　a.　Booklet pane of 8　　4.50
　b.　Booklet pane of 10　　3.50
　For surcharge see Reunion No. 339. For overprint see Algeria No. 287.

Jean Bouin and Stadium
A350

1960, July 9　　**Engr.**　　**Perf. 13**
969 A350 20c blue, mag & ol gray　.35　.25
　17th Olympic Games, Rome, 8/25-9/11.

Europa Issue, 1960
Common Design Type
1960, Sept. 17　　　**Perf. 13**
Size: 36x22mm
970 CD3 25c green & bluish grn　.20　.20
971 CD3 50c maroon & red lilac　.30　.20

Lisieux Basilica
A351

1960, Sept. 24　　　**Perf. 13**
972 A351 15c blue, gray & blk　.25　.20

Arms Type of 1958-59
　Design: Arms of Oran.

1960, Oct. 15　**Typo.**　**Perf. 14x13½**
973 A318 5c red, bl, yel & emer　.20　.20

Madame de Stael by François Gerard — A352

1960, Oct. 22　　**Engr.**　　**Perf. 13**
974 A352 30c dull claret & brn　.35　.25
　Madame de Stael (1766-1817), writer.

Gen. J. B. E. Estienne
A353

1960, Nov. 5
975 A353 15c lt lilac & black　　.25　.20
　Centenary of the birth of Gen. Jean Baptiste Eugene Estienne.

Marc Sangnier and Youth Hostel at Bierville
A354

1960, Nov. 5
976 A354 20c blue, blk & lilac　.25　.20
　Issued to honor Marc Sangnier, founder of the French League for Youth Hostels.

Badge of Order of Liberation — A355

1960, Nov. 14　　**Engr.**　　**Perf. 13**
977 A355 20c black & brt green　.40　.25
　Order of Liberation, 20th anniversary.

Lapwings
A356

　Birds: 30c, Puffin. 45c, European teal. 50c, European bee-eaters.

1960, Nov. 12
978 A356 20c multicolored　　.30　.20
979 A356 30c multicolored　　.30　.25
980 A356 45c multicolored　　.95　.50
981 A356 50c multicolored　　.85　.25
　　Nos. 978-981 (4)　　2.40 1.20
　Issued to publicize wildlife protection.

André Honnorat
A357

1960, Nov. 19
982 A357 30c blue, blk & green　.30　.25
　Honnorat, statesman, fighter against tuberculosis and founder of the University City of Paris, an intl. students' community.

St. Barbara and Medieval View of School
A358

1960, Dec. 3　　　　**Engr.**
983 A358 30c red, bl & ol brn　.35　.25
　St. Barbara School, Paris, 500th anniv.

"Mediterranean" by Aristide Maillol — A359

1961, Feb. 18　　**Unwmk.**　　**Perf. 13**
984 A359 20c carmine & indigo　.25　.20
　Aristide Maillol, sculptor, birth cent.

Marianne by Cocteau — A360

1961, Feb. 23
985 A360 20c blue & carmine　　.25　.20
　A second type has an extra inverted V-shaped mark (a blue flag top) at right of hair tip. Value unused $3.25, used 60 cents.
　For surcharge see Reunion No. 357.

Paris Airport, Orly
A361

1961, Feb. 25
986 A361 50c blk, dk bl, & bluish grn　.45　.35
　Inauguration of new facilities at Orly airport.

George Méliès and Motion Picture Screen
A362

1961, Mar. 11
987 A362 50c pur, indigo & ol bis　.60　.40
　Cent. of the birth of George Méliès, motion picture pioneer.

Jean Baptiste Henri
Lacordaire — A363

1961, Mar. 25 *Perf. 13*
988 A363 30c lt brown & black   .30 .30
Cent. of the death of the Dominican monk
Lacordaire, orator and liberal Catholic leader.

A364

1961, Mar. 25
989 A364 30c grn, red brn & red   .30 .25
Introduction of tobacco use into France,
fourth centenary. By error stamp portrays Jan
Nicquet instead of Jean Nicot.

Heroes Type of 1957
Portraits: No. 990, Jacques Renouvin. No.
991, Lionel Dubray. No. 992, Paul Gateaud.
No. 993, Mère Elisabeth.

1961, Apr. 22
990 A293 20c blue & lilac   1.00 .50
991 A293 20c gray grn & blue   1.00 .50
992 A293 30c brown org & blk   1.60 .90
993 A293 30c violet & blk   1.25 1.00
   Nos. 990-993 (4)   4.85 2.90

Bagnoles-de-l'Orne — A365

1961, May 6
994 A365 20c olive, ocher, bl & grn   .20 .20

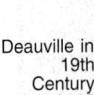

Dove, Olive Branch
and Federation
Emblem — A366

1961, May 6
995 A366 50c brt bl, grn & mar   .30 .20
World Federation of Ex-Service Men.

Deauville in
19th
Century
A367

1961, May 13 *Engr.*
996 A367 50c rose claret   1.90 1.20
Centenary of Deauville.

La Champmeslé
A368

Mont-Dore,
Snowflake and
Cable Car
A369

French actors: #998, Talma. #999, Rachel.
#1000, Gérard Philipe. #1001, Raimu.

1961, June 10   Unwmk.   Perf. 13
Dark Carmine Frame
997 A368 20c choc & yel grn   1.00 .40
998 A368 30c brown & crimson   1.00 .40
999 A368 30c yel grn & sl grn   1.00 .40
1000 A368 50c olive & choc   1.40 .60
1001 A368 50c bl grn & red brn   1.40 .60
   Nos. 997-1001 (5)   5.80 2.40

Issued to honor great French actors and in
connection with the Fifth World Congress of
the International Federation of Actors.

1961, July 1
1002 A369 20c orange & rose lilac   .20 .20

Pierre Fauchard
A370

St. Theobald's
Church, Thann
A371

1961, July 1
1003 A370 50c dk green & blk   .55 .30
Bicentenary of the death of Pierre Fauchard,
1st surgeon dentist.

1961, July 1
1004 A371 20c sl grn, vio & brn   .65 .35
800th anniversary of Thann.

Europa Issue, 1961
Common Design Type
1961, Sept. 16 *Perf. 13*
Size: 35x22mm
1005 CD4 25c vermilion   .20 .20
1006 CD4 50c ultramarine   .25 .25

Beach and
sailboats,
Arcachon
A372

15c, Saint-Paul, Maritime Alps. 45c, Sully-
sur-Loire Chateau. 50c, View of Cognac. 65c,
Rance Valley and Dinan. 85c, City hall and
Rodin's Burghers, Calais. 1fr, Roman gates of
Lodi, Medea, Algeria.

1961, Oct. 9   Engr.   Perf. 13
1007 A372 15c blue & purple   .20 .20
1008 A372 30c ultra, sl grn & lt brn   .25 .20
1009 A372 45c vio bl, red brn & grn   .25 .20
1010 A372 50c grn, Prus bl & sl   1.25 .20
1011 A372 65c red brn, sl grn & bl   .50 .20
1012 A372 85c sl grn, sl & red brn   .60 .25
1013 A372 1fr dk bl, sl & bis   5.00 .25
   Nos. 1007-1013 (7)   8.05 1.50

For surcharges see Reunion Nos. 347-348.
For overprint see Algeria No. 290.

Blue Nudes, by Matisse — A373

Paintings: 50c, "The Messenger," by
Braque. 85c, "The Cardplayers," by Cézanne.
1fr, "The 14th July," by Roger de La Fresnaye.

1961, Nov. 10 *Perf. 13x12*
1014 A373 50c dk brn, bl, blk & gray   2.90 1.60
1015 A373 65c grn, vio, & ultra   5.00 2.50
1016 A373 85c blk, brn, red & ol   2.50 1.25
1017 A373 1fr multicolored   4.00 2.50
   Nos. 1014-1017 (4)   14.40 7.85

Liner
France
A374

1962, Jan. 11   Engr.   Perf. 13
1018 A374 30c dk blue, blk & car   .60 .45
New French liner France.

Skier Going
Downhill — A375

Maurice
Bourdet — A376

1962, Jan. 27 *Perf. 13*
1019 A375 30c shown   .20 .20
1020 A375 50c Slalom   .40 .30
Issued to publicize the World Ski Championships, Chamonix, Feb. 1962.

1962, Feb. 17
1021 A376 30c slate   .30 .20
60th anniv. of the birth of Maurice Bourdet,
radio commentator and resistance hero.

Pierre-Fidele Bretonneau — A377

1962, Feb. 17
1022 A377 50c brt lilac & blue   .35 .25
Centenary of the death of Pierre-Fidele
Bretonneau, physician.

Chateau and
Bridge, Laval,
Mayenne
A378

Gallic Cock
A379

1962, Feb. 24
1023 A378 20c bis brn & slate grn   .25 .20

1962-65 *Perf. 13*
1024 A379 25c ultra, car & brn   .25 .20
 a. Bklt. pane of 4 (horiz. strip)   2.50
1024B A379 30c gray grn, red & brn ('65)   .85 .20
 c. Booklet pane of 5   5.00
 d. Booklet pane of 10   10.00

No. 1024 was also issued on experimental
luminescent paper in 1963. Value $750.

Ramparts
of Vannes
A380

Dunkirk — A381

Paris
Beach, Le
Touquet
A381a

1962   Engr.   Perf. 13
1025 A380 30c dark blue   .80 .50
1026 A381 95c grn, bis & red lil   1.60 .90
1027 A381a 1fr, red brn & bl   .45 .20
   Nos. 1025-1027 (3)   2.85 1.60
No. 1026 for the 300th anniv. of Dunkirk.

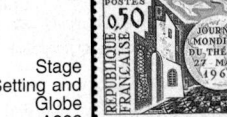

Stage
Setting and
Globe
A382

1962, Mar. 24 *Unwmk.*
1028 A382 50c sl grn, ocher & mag   .55 .30
International Day of the Theater, Mar. 27.

Memorial to
Fighting
France,
Mont
Valerien
A383

Resistance Heroes'
Monument,
Vercors — A384

Design: 50c, Ile de Sein monument.

1962, Apr. 7
1029	A383	20c olive & slate grn	.80	.50
1030	A384	30c bluish black	.80	.50
1031	A384	50c blue & indigo	1.00	.80
		Nos. 1029-1031 (3)	2.60	1.80

Issued to publicize memorials for the French Underground in World War II.

Malaria Eradication Emblem and Swamp — A385

Nurses with Child and Hospital — A386

1962, Apr. 14   Engr.
1032	A385	50c dk blue & dk red	.35	.30

WHO drive to eradicate malaria.

1962, May 5   Unwmk.   Perf. 13
1033	A386	30c bl grn, gray & red brn	.35	.30

National Hospital Week, May 5-12.

Glider A387

20c, Planes showing development of aviation.

1962, May 12
1034	A387	15c orange red & brn	.30	.20
1035	A387	20c lil rose & rose cl	.35	.25

Issued to publicize sports aviation.

School Emblem — A388

1962, May 19   Engr.
1036	A388	50c mar, ocher & dk vio	.50	.30

Watchmaker's School at Besançon, cent.

Louis XIV and Workers Showing Modern Gobelin A389

1962, May 26   Unwmk.   Perf. 13
1037	A389	50c ol, sl grn & car	.50	.30

Gobelin tapestry works, Paris, 300th anniv.

Blaise Pascal A390

1962, May 26
1038	A390	50c slate grn & dp org	.50	.30

Blaise Pascal (1623-1662), mathematician, scientist and philosopher.

Palace of Justice, Rennes A391

1962, June 12
1039	A391	30c blk, grysh bl & grn	1.40	.60

Arms Type of 1958-59

5c, Amiens. 10c, Troyes. 15c, Nevers.

1962-63   Typo.   Perf. 14x13½
1040	A318	5c ver, ultra & yel	.20	.20
1041	A318	10c red, ultra & yel ('63)	.20	.20
1042	A318	15c ver, ultra & yel	.20	.20
		Nos. 1040-1042 (3)	.60	.60

Phosphor Tagging

In 1970 France began to experiment with luminescence. Phosphor bands have been added to Nos. 1041, 1143, 1231, 1231C, 1292A-1294B, 1494-1498, 1560-1579B, etc.

Rose — A392

Design: 30c, Old-fashioned rose.

1962, Sept. 8   Engr.   Perf. 13
1043	A392	20c ol, grn & brt car	.65	.40
1044	A392	30c dk sl grn, ol & car	.65	.40

Europa Issue, 1962
Common Design Type
1962, Sept. 15
Size: 36x22mm
1045	CD5	25c violet	.20	.20
1046	CD5	50c henna brown	.35	.20

Space Communications Center, Pleumeur-Bodou, France — A394

Telstar, Earth and Television Set — A395

1962, Sept. 29   Engr.   Perf. 13
1047	A394	25c gray, yel & grn	.25	.20
1048	A395	50c dk bl, grn & ultra	.40	.30

1st television connection of the US and Europe through Telstar satellite, July 11-12.
For surcharges see Reunion Nos. 343-344.

"Bonjour Monsieur Courbet" by Gustave Courbet — A396

Paintings: 65c, "Madame Manet on Blue Sofa," by Edouard Manet. 1fr, "Guards officer on horseback," by Theodore Géricault, vert.

1962, Nov. 9   Perf. 13x12, 12x13
1049	A396	50c multicolored	3.25	2.50
1050	A396	65c multicolored	2.50	1.60
1051	A396	1fr multicolored	5.75	3.25
		Nos. 1049-1051 (3)	11.50	7.35

Bathyscaph "Archimede" — A397

1963, Jan. 26   Unwmk.   Perf. 13
1052	A397	30c dk blue & blk	.25	.20

French deep-sea explorations.

Flowers and Nantes Chateau A398

1963, Feb. 11
1053	A398	30c vio bl, car & sl grn	.25	.20

Nantes flower festival.

St. Peter, Window at St. Foy de Conches A399

50c, Jacob Wrestling with the Angel, by Delacroix.

1963, Mar. 2   Perf. 12x13
1054	A399	50c multicolored	3.00	1.50
1055	A399	1fr multicolored	4.00	2.50

See Nos. 1076-1077.

Hungry Woman and Wheat Emblem A400

1963, Mar. 21   Engr.   Perf. 13
1056	A400	50c slate grn & brn	.30	.20

FAO "Freedom from Hunger" campaign.

Cemetery and Memorial, Glières — A401

Design: 50c, Memorial, Ile de la Cité, Paris.

1963, Mar. 23   Unwmk.   Perf. 13
1057	A401	30c dk brown & olive	.55	.55
1058	A401	50c indigo	.55	.55

Heroes of the resistance against the Nazis.

Beethoven, Birthplace at Bonn and Rhine A402

#1060, Emile Verhaeren, memorial at Roisin & residence. #1061, Giuseppe Mazzini, Marcus Aurelius statue & Via Appia, Rome. #1062, Emile Mayrisch, Colpach Chateau & blast furnace, Esch. #1063, Hugo de Groot, Palace of Peace, The Hague & St. Agatha Church, Delft.

1963, Apr. 27   Unwmk.   Perf. 13
1059	A402	20c ocher, sl & brt grn	.35	.25
1060	A402	20c purple, blk & mar	.35	.25
1061	A402	20c maroon, sl & ol	.35	.25
1062	A402	20c mar, dk brn & ocher	.35	.25
1063	A402	30c dk brn, vio & ocher	.35	.25
		Nos. 1059-1063 (5)	1.75	1.25

Issued to honor famous men of the European Common Market countries.

Hotel des Postes and Stagecoach, 1863 — A403

1963, May 4
1064	A403	50c grayish black	.35	.25

1st Intl. Postal Conference, Paris, 1863.

Lycée Louis-le-Grand, Belvédère, Panthéon and St. Etienne du Mont Church — A404

1963, May 18
1065	A404	30c slate green	.30	.25

400th anniversary of the Jesuit Clermont secondary school, named after Louis XIV.

St. Peter's Church and Ramparts, Caen A405

1963, June 1   Unwmk.   Perf. 13
1066	A405	30c gray blue & brn	.25	.25

Radio Telescope, Nançay — A406

1963, June 8   Engr.
1067	A406	50c dk bl & dk brn	.45	.35

Amboise Chateau A407

Saint-Flour — A408

Designs: 50c, Côte d'Azur Varoise. 85c, Vittel. 95c, Moissac.

1963, June 15
1068 A407 30c slate, grn & bis .25 .20
1069 A407 50c dk grn, dk bl & hn brn .40 .20
1070 A408 60c ultra, dk grn & hn brn .45 .20
1071 A407 85c dk grn, yel grn & brn 1.40 .30
1072 A408 95c dk brown & black .85 .25
Nos. 1068-1072 (5) 3.35 1.15

For surcharge see Reunion No. 355.

Water Skiing Slalom A409

1963, Aug. 31 Unwmk. Perf. 13
1073 A409 30c sl grn, blk & car .30 .20
World Water Skiing Championships, Vichy.

Europa Issue, 1963
Common Design Type
1963, Sept. 14
Size: 36x22mm
1074 CD6 25c red brown .25 .25
1075 CD6 50c green .35 .25

Art Type of 1963
Designs: 85c, "The Married Couple of the Eiffel Tower," by Marc Chagall. 95c, "The Fur Merchants," window, Chartres Cathedral.
1963, Nov. 9 Engr. Perf. 12x13
1076 A399 85c multicolored 1.75 1.25
1077 A399 95c multicolored .65 .65

Philatec Issue
Common Design Type
1963, Dec. 14 Unwmk. Perf. 13
1078 CD118 25c dk gray, sl grn & dk car .20 .20
For surcharge see Reunion No. 349.

Radio and Television Center, Paris A411

1963, Dec. 15 Engr.
1079 A411 20c org brn, slate & ol .20 .20

Fire Brigade Insignia, Symbols of Fire, Water and Civilian Defense A412

1964, Feb. 8 Engr. Perf. 13
1082 A412 30c blue, org & red .50 .25
Issued to honor the fire brigades and civilian defense corps.

Handicapped Laboratory Technician — A413

1964, Feb. 22 Unwmk. Perf. 13
1083 A413 30c grn, red brn & brn .25 .20
Rehabilitation of the handicapped.

John II the Good (1319-64) by Girard d'Orleans A414

1964, Apr. 25 Perf. 12x13
1084 A414 1fr multicolored 1.60 1.10

Stamp of 1900 A415 / Mechanized Mail Handling A416

Designs: No. 1086, Stamp of 1900, Type A17. No. 1088, Telecommunications.

1964, May 9 Perf. 13
1085 A415 25c bister & dk car .30 .30
1086 A415 25c bister & blue .30 .30
1087 A416 30c blk, bl & org brn .30 .30
1088 A416 30c blk, car rose & bluish grn .30 .30
a. Strip of 4, #1085-1088 + label 1.25 1.25
Printed in sheets of 20 stamps, containing five No. 1088a. The label shows the Philatec emblem in green.

Type of Semi-Postal Issue
with "25e ANNIVERSAIRE" added
1964, May 9
1089 SP208 25c multicolored .25 .20
25th anniversary, night airmail service.

Madonna and Child from Rose Window of Notre Dame A417

1964, May 23 Perf. 12x13
1090 A417 60c multicolored .55 .55
Notre Dame Cathedral, Paris, 800th anniv.

Arms Type of 1958-59
Arms: 1c, Niort. 2c, Guéret. 12c, Agen. 18c, Saint-Denis, Réunion. 30c, Paris.

1964-65 Typo. Perf. 14x13½
1091 A318 1c vio blue & yel .20 .20
1092 A318 2c emer, vio bl & yel .20 .20
1093 A318 12c black, red & yel .20 .20
1094 A318 18c multicolored .40 .25
1095 A318 30c vio bl & red ('65) .50 .20
a. Booklet pane of 10 15.00
Nos. 1091-1095 (5) 1.50 1.05

Gallic Coin — A418

Perf. 13½x14
1964-66 Typo. Unwmk.
1096 A418 10c emer & bister .75 .20
1097 A418 15c org & bister ('66) .30 .20
1098 A418 25c lilac & brn .45 .20
1099 A418 50c brt blue & brn .85 .75
Nos. 1096-1099 (4) 2.35 1.35

Nos. 1096-1099 are known only precanceled. See second note after No. 132. See Nos. 1240-1242, 1315-1318, 1421-1424.

Postrider, Rocket and Radar Equipment — A419

1964, June 5 Engr. Perf. 13
1100 A419 1fr brn, dk red & dk bl 25.00 20.00

Sold for 4fr, including 3fr admission to PHILATEC. Issued in sheets of 8 stamps and 8 labels (2x8 subjects with labels in horizontal rows 1, 4, 5, 8; stamps in rows 2, 3, 6, 7). Commemorative inscriptions on side margins. Value $200.

Caesar's Tower, Provins — A420

Chapel of Notre Dame du Haut, Ronchamp A421

1964-65
1101 A421 40c sl grn, dk brn & brn ('65) .25 .20
1102 A420 70c slate, grn & car .35 .20
1103 A421 1.25fr brt bl, sl grn & ol .75 .30
Nos. 1101-1103 (3) 1.35 .70

The 40c was issued in vertical coils in 1971. Every 10th coil stamp has a red control number printed twice on the back.
For surcharges see Reunion Nos. 352, 361.

Mandel — A422

Judo — A423

1964, July 4 Unwmk. Perf. 13
1104 A422 30c violet brown .25 .20
Georges Mandel (1885-1944), Cabinet minister, executed by the Nazis.

1964, July 4
1105 A423 50c dk blue & vio brn .25 .20
18th Olympic Games, Tokyo, 10/10-25/64.

Champlevé Enamel from Limoges, 12th Century A424

Design: No. 1107, The Lady (Claude Le Viste?) with the Unicorn, 15th cent. tapestry.

1964 Perf. 12x13
1106 A424 1fr multicolored 1.25 .80
1107 A424 1fr multicolored .65 .45

No. 1106 shows part of an enamel sepulchral plate portraying Geoffrey IV, Count of Anjou and Le Maine (1113-1151), who was called Geoffrey Plantagenet.
Issue dates: #1106, July 4. #1107, Oct. 31.

Paris Taxis Carrying Soldiers to Front, 1914 A425

1964, Sept. 5 Unwmk. Perf. 13
1108 A425 30c black, blue & red .25 .20
50th anniversary of Battle of the Marne.

Europa Issue, 1964
Common Design Type
1964, Sept. 12 Engr.
Size: 22x36mm
1109 CD7 25c dk car, dp ocher & grn .20 .20
1110 CD7 50c vio, yel grn & dk car .25 .20

Cooperation Issue
Common Design Type
1964, Nov. 6 Unwmk. Perf. 13
1111 CD119 25c red brn, dk brn & dk bl .25 .20

Joux Chateau — A427

1965, Feb. 6 Engr.
1112 A427 1.30fr redsh brn, brn red & dk brn 1.50 .35

"The English Girl from the Star" by Toulouse-Lautrec — A428

St. Paul on the Damascus Road, Window, Cathedral of Sens — A429

Leaving for the Hunt — A430

Apocalypse Tapestry, 14th Century A431

"The Red Violin" by Raoul Dufy — A432

Designs: No. 1115, "August" miniature of Book of Hours of Jean de France, Duc de Berry ("Les Très Riches Heures du Duc de Berry"), painted by Flemish brothers, Pol, Hermant and Jannequin Limbourg, 1411-16. No. 1116, Scene from oldest existing set of French tapestries, showing the Winepress of the Wrath of God (Revelations 14: 19-20).

1965		Perf. 12x13, 13x12	
1113	A428 1fr multicolored	.50	.40
1114	A429 1fr multicolored	.50	.40
1115	A430 1fr multicolored	.30	.30
1116	A431 1fr multicolored	.30	.30
1117	A432 1fr blk, pink & car	.30	.30
	Nos. 1113-1117 (5)	1.90	1.70

No. 1114 issued to commemorate the 800th anniversary of the Cathedral of Sens.
Issued: #1113, 3/12; #1114, 6/5; #1115, 9/25; #1116, 10/30; #1117, 11/6.

Returning Deportees, 1945 — A433

1965, Apr. 1   Unwmk.   Perf. 13
1118 A433 40c Prussian green   .50 .30
20th anniv. of the return of people deported during World War II.

House of Youth and Culture, Troyes A434

1965, Apr. 10   Engr.
1119 A434 25c ind, brn & dk grn   .25 .20
20th anniv. of the establishment of recreational cultural centers for young people.

Woman Carrying Flowers A435

Flags of France, US, USSR and Great Britain Crushing Swastika A436

1965, Apr. 24   Unwmk.   Perf. 13
1120 A435 60c dk grn, dp org & ver   .35 .20
Tourist Campaign of Welcome & Amiability.

1965, May 8
1121 A436 40c black, car & ultra   .40 .20
20th anniv. of victory in World War II.

Telegraph Key, Syncom Satellite and Pleumeur-Bodou Station — A437

1965, May 17
1122 A437 60c dk blue, brn & blk   .50 .30
Centenary of the ITU.

Croix de Guerre — A438

1965, May 22   Engr.
1123 A438 40c red, brn & brt grn   .55 .35
50th anniv. of the Croix de Guerre medal.

Cathedral of Bourges — A439

Moustiers-Sainte-Marie — A440

Views: 30c, Road and tunnel, Mont Blanc. 60c, Aix-les-Bains, sailboat. 75c, Tarn Gorge, Lozère mountains. 95c, Vendée River, man poling boat, and windmill. 1fr, Prehistoric stone monuments, Carnac.

1965			
1124	A439 30c bl, vio bl & brn vio	.25	.20
1125	A439 40c gray bl & redsh brn	.40	.20
1126	A440 50c grn, bl gray & bis	.40	.20
1127	A439 60c blue & red brn	.85	.25
1128	A439 75c brown, bl & grn	1.25	.90
1129	A440 95c brown, grn & bl	5.75	.90
1130	A440 1fr gray, grn & brn	1.40	.25
	Nos. 1124-1130 (7)	10.30	2.90

No. 1124 for the opening of the Mont Blanc Tunnel. No. 1125 (Bourges Cathedral) was issued in connection with the French Philatelic Societies Federation Congress, held at Bourges.
Issued: 40c, June 5; 50c, June 19; 30c, 60c, July 17; others, July 10.
For surcharges see Reunion #354, 362, 365.

Europa Issue, 1965
Common Design Type
1965, Sept. 25   Perf. 13
Size: 36x22mm
1131 CD8 30c red   .25 .30
1132 CD8 60c gray   .50 .50

Planting Seedling A441

Etienne Régnault, "Le Taureau" and Coast of Reunion A442

1965, Oct. 2
1133 A441 25c slate grn, yel grn & red brn   .20 .20
National reforestation campaign.

1965, Oct. 2
1134 A442 30c indigo & dk car   .20 .20
Tercentenary of settlement of Reunion.

Atomic Reactor and Diagram, Symbols of Industry, Agriculture and Medicine — A443

1965, Oct. 9
1135 A443 60c brt blue & blk   .50 .30
Atomic Energy Commission, 20th anniv.

Air Academy and Emblem A444

1965, Nov. 6   Perf. 13
1136 A444 25c dk blue & green   .35 .30
Air Academy, Salon-de-Provence, 50th anniv.

French Satellite A-1 Issue
Common Design Type
Design: 60c, A-1 satellite.

1965, Nov. 30   Engr.   Perf. 13
1137 CD121 30c Prus bl, brt bl & blk   .25 .20
1138 CD121 60c blk, Prus bl & brt bl   .40 .25
a.   Strip of 2, #1137-1138 + label   .65 .65
Launching of France's 1st satellite, 11/26/65.
For surcharges see Reunion Nos. 358-359.

Arms of Auch — A446

Cities: 20c, Saint-Lô. 25c, Mont-de-Marsan.

Typographed, Photogravure (20c)
1966   Perf. 14x13; 14 (20c)
1142 A446 5c blue & red   .20 .20
1143 A446 20c vio bl, sil, gold & red   .20 .20
1144 A446 25c red brown & ultra   .60 .60
| | Nos. 1142-1144 (3)   1.00 .60

The 5c and 20c were issued in sheets and in vertical coils. In the coils, every 10th stamp has a red control number on the back.
For surcharges see Reunion Nos. 360-360A.

French Satellite D-1 Issue
Common Design Type
1966, Feb. 18   Engr.   Perf. 13
1148 CD122 60c blue blk, grn & cl   .25 .20

Horses from Bronze Vessel of Vix — A448

"The Newborn" by Georges de La Tour — A449

The Baptism of Judas (4th Century Bishop of Jerusalem) — A450

"The Moon and the Bull" Tapestry by Jean Lurçat A451

"Crispin and Scapin" by Honoré Daumier — A452

1966 **Perf. 13x12, 12x13**
1149 A448 1fr multicolored .40 .35
1150 A449 1fr multicolored .40 .35
1151 A450 1fr multicolored .40 .35
1152 A451 1fr multicolored .40 .30
1153 A452 1fr multicolored .40 .30
Nos. 1149-1153 (5) 2.00 1.65

The design of No. 1149 is a detail from a 6th century B.C. vessel, found in 1953 in a grave near Vix, Cote d'Or.
The design of No. 1151 is from a stained glass window in the 13th century Sainte-Chapelle, Paris.
No. 1150 exists in an imperf, ungummed souv. sheet with 2 progressive die proofs, issued for benefit of the Postal Museum, and not postally valid. Value $2.
Issued: #1149, 3/26; #1150, 6/25; #1151, 10/22; #1152, 11/19; #1153, 12/10.

Chessboard, Knight, Emblems for King and Queen — A453

St. Michael Slaying the Dragon — A455

Rhone Bridge, Pont-Saint-Esprit — A454

1966, Apr. 2 **Engr.** **Perf. 13**
1154 A453 60c sepia, gray & dk vio bl .60 .45
Issued to publicize the Chess Festival.

1966, Apr. 23 **Unwmk.** **Perf. 13**
1155 A454 25c black & dull blue .20 .20

1966, Apr. 30 **Litho. & Engr.**
1156 A455 25c multicolored .20 .20
Millenium of Mont-Saint-Michel.

Stanislas Leszczynski, Lunéville Chateau — A456

1966, May 6 **Engr.**
1157 A456 25c slate, grn & brn .20 .20
200th anniv. of the reunion of Lorraine and Bar (Barrois) with France.

St. Andrew's and Sèvre River, Niort — A457

1966, May 28 **Engr.** **Perf. 13**
1158 A457 40c brt bl, indigo & grn .30 .20

Bernard Le Bovier de Fontenelle and 1666 Meeting Room A458

1966, June 4
1159 A458 60c dk car rose & brn .30 .25
300th anniversary, Académie des Sciences.

William the Conqueror, Castle and Norman Ships — A459

1966, June 4
1160 A459 60c brown red & dp bl .40 .30
900th anniversary of Battle of Hastings.

Tracks, Globe and Eiffel Tower A460

1966, June 11
1161 A460 60c dk brn, car & dull bl .85 .45
19th International Railroad Congress.

Oléron Bridge A461

1966, June 20
1162 A461 25c Prus bl, brn & bl .20 .20
Issued to commemorate the opening of Oléron Bridge, connecting Oléron Island in the Bay of Biscay with the French mainland.

Europa Issue, 1966
Common Design Type
1966, Sept. 24 **Engr.** **Perf. 13**
Size: 22x36mm
1163 CD9 30c Prussian blue .25 .25
1164 CD9 60c red .35 .25

Vercingetorix at Gergovie, 52 B.C. — A462

Bishop Remi Baptizing King Clovis, 496 A.D. — A463

Design: 60c, Charlemagne attending school (page holding book for crowned king).

1966, Nov. 5 **Perf. 13**
1165 A462 40c choc, grn & gray bl .35 .30
1166 A463 40c dk red brn & blk .35 .30
1167 A463 60c pur, rose car & brn .35 .30
Nos. 1165-1167 (3) 1.05 .90

Map of Pneumatic Post and Tube A464

1966, Nov. 11
1168 A464 1.60fr maroon & indigo .75 .40
Centenary of Paris pneumatic post system.

Val Chateau — A465

1966, Nov. 19 **Engr.** **Perf. 13**
1169 A465 2.30fr dk bl, sl grn & brn 2.00 .30

Rance Power Station A466

1966, Dec. 3
1170 A466 60c dk bl, sl grn & brn .45 .45
Tidal power station in the estuary of the Rance River on the English Channel.

European Broadcasting Union Emblem — A467

1967, Mar. 4 **Engr.** **Perf. 13**
1171 A467 40c dk blue & rose brn .25 .20
3rd Intl. Congress of the European Broadcasting Union, Paris, Mar. 8-22.

Father Juniet's Gig by Henri Rousseau — A468

Francois I by Jean Clouet A469

The Bather by Jean-Dominique Ingres — A470

St. Eloi, the Goldsmith, at Work — A471

1967 **Engr.** **Perf. 13x12, 12x13**
1172 A468 1fr multicolored .40 .40
1173 A469 1fr multicolored .40 .40
1174 A470 1fr multicolored .40 .35
1175 A471 1fr multicolored .40 .35
Nos. 1172-1175 (4) 1.60 1.50

The design of No. 1175 is from a 16th century stained glass window in the Church of Sainte Madeleine, Troyes.
Issued: #1172, 4/15; #1173, 7/1; #1174, 9/9; #1175, 10/7.

Snow Crystal and Olympic Rings — A472

1967, Apr. 22 **Photo.** **Perf. 13**
1176 A472 60c brt & lt blue & red .40 .25
Issued to publicize the 10th Winter Olympic Games, Grenoble, Feb. 6-18, 1968.

French Pavilion, EXPO '67 — A473

1967, Apr. 22   Engr.
1177 A473 60c dull bl & bl grn   .35   .30
    Intl. Exhibition EXPO '67, Montreal, Apr. 28-
Oct. 27, 1967.
    For surcharge see Reunion No. 363.

Europa Issue, 1967
Common Design Type
1967, Apr. 29
Size: 22x36mm
1178 CD10 30c blue & gray   .25   .25
1179 CD10 60c brown & lt blue   .55   .45

Great Bridge, Bordeaux A474

1967, May 8
1180 A474 25c olive, blk & brn   .25   .20

Nungesser, Coli and "L'Oiseau Blanc" A475

1967, May 8
1181 A475 40c slate, dk & lt brn   .50   .35
    40th anniv. of the attempted transatlantic
flight of Charles Nungesser and François Coil,
French aviators.

Goüin House, Tours — A476

1967, May 13   Engr.   Perf. 13
1182 A476 40c vio bl, red brn & red .55 .25
    Congress of the Federation of French Phila-
telic Societies in Tours.

Ramon and Alfort Veterinary School A477

1967, May 27
1183 A477 25c brn, dp bl & yel grn .25 .20
    200th anniv. of the Alfort Veterinary School
and to honor Professor Gaston Ramon (1886-
1963).

Robert Esnault-Pelterie, Diamant Rocket and A-1 Satellite — A478

1967, May 27
1184 A478 60c slate & vio blue   .50   .30
    Issued to honor Robert Esnault-Pelterie
(1881-1957), aviation and space expert.

City Hall, Saint-Quentin A479

Saint-Germain-en-Laye — A480

    Views: 60c, Clock Tower, Vire. 75c, Beach,
La Baule, Brittany. 95c, Harbor, Boulogne-sur-
Mer. 1fr, Rodez Cathedral. 1.50fr, Morlaix; old
houses, grotesque carving, viaduct.

1967
1185 A479   50c bl, sl bl & brn   .40   .20
1186 A479   60c dp bl, sl bl & dk
               red brn   .60   .50
1187 A480   70c rose car, red
               brn & bl   .40   .20
1188 A480   75c multicolored   1.60 1.25
1189 A480   95c sky bl, lil & sl
               grn   1.25 1.10
1190 A479   1fr indigo & bl gray   .65   .20
1191 A479   1.50fr brt bl, brt grn &
               red brn   1.25   .30
    Nos. 1185-1191 (7)   6.15 3.75

    Issued: 1fr, 1.50fr, June 10; 70c, June 17;
50c, 60c, 95c, July 8; 75c, July 24.

Orchids — A481

1967, July 29   Engr.   Perf. 13
1192 A481 40c dp car, brt pink &
             pur   .90   .50
    Orleans flower festival.

Scales of Justice, City and Harbor A482

1967, Sept. 4
1193 A483 60c dk plum, dl bl &
             ocher   .50   .30
    9th Intl. Accountancy Cong., Paris, 9/6-12.

Cross of Lorraine, Soldiers and Sailors — A483

1967, Oct. 7   Engr.   Perf. 13
1194 A482 25c brn, dp ultra & bl   .20   .20
    25th anniv. of the Battle of Bir Hacheim.

Marie Curie, Bowl Glowing with Radium A484

1967, Oct. 23   Engr.   Perf. 13
1195 A484 60c dk blue & ultra   .40   .30
    Marie Curie (1867-1934), scientist who dis-
covered radium and polonium, Nobel prize
winner for physics and chemistry.

Lions Emblem A485

Marianne (by Cheffer) — A486

1967, Oct. 28
1196 A485 40c dk car & vio bl   1.00 .50
    50th anniversary of Lions International.
For surcharge see Reunion No. 364.

1967, Nov. 4   Engr.
1197 A486 25c dark blue   .40   .20
1198 A486 30c bright lilac   .45   .20
  a.   Booklet pane of 5   6.00
  b.   Booklet pane of 10   12.00

    Coils (vertical) of Nos. 1197 and 1231 show
a red number on the back of every 10th stamp.
See Nos. 1230-1231C. For surcharges see
Reunion Nos. 367-368, 389.

King Philip II (Philip Augustus) at Battle of Bouvines A487

    Designs: No. 1200, Election of Hugh Capet
as King, horiz. 60c, King Louis IX (St. Louis)
holding audience for the poor.

1967, Nov. 13   Engr.   Perf. 13
1199 A487 40c gray & black   .40   .30
1200 A487 40c steel bl & ultra   .40   .30
1201 A487 60c grn & dk red brn   .50   .30
    Nos. 1199-1201 (3)   1.30   .90

Commemorative Medal — A488

1968, Jan. 6   Engr.   Perf. 13
1202 A488 40c dk slate grn & bis   .25   .20
    50th anniversary of postal checking service.

Various Road Signs — A489

1968, Feb. 24
1203 A489 25c lil, red & dk bl grn   .25   .20
    Issued to publicize road safety.

Prehistoric Paintings, Lascaux Cave — A490

Arearea (Merriment) by Paul Gauguin — A491

The Dance by Emile Antoine Bourdelle A492

Portrait of the Model by Auguste Renoir A493

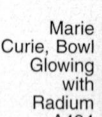

1968 Engr. Perf. 13x12, 12x13
1204 A490 1fr multicolored .55 .40
1205 A491 1fr multicolored .65 .40
1206 A492 1fr car & gray olive .65 .40
1207 A493 1fr multicolored .65 .40
Nos. 1204-1207 (4) 2.50 1.60
Issue dates: #1204, Apr. 13; #1205, Sept. 21; #1206, Oct. 26; #1207, Nov. 9.

Audio-visual Institute, Royan — A494

1968, Apr. 13 Perf. 13
1208 A494 40c slate grn, brn & Prus bl .25 .20
5th Conference for World Cooperation with the theme of teaching living languages by audio-visual means.

Europa Issue, 1968
Common Design Type
1968, Apr. 27 Size: 36x22mm
1209 CD11 30c brt red lil & ocher .30 .20
1210 CD11 60c brown & lake .60 .30

Alain René Le Sage — A495

1968, May 4
1211 A495 40c blue & rose vio .25 .20
Alain René Le Sage (1668-1747), novelist and playwright.

Chateau de Langeais A496

1968, May 4
1212 A496 60c slate bl, grn & red brn .50 .40

Pierre Larousse A497

1968, May 11 Engr. Perf. 13
1213 A497 40c rose vio & brown .25 .20
Pierre Larousse (1817-75), grammarian, lexicographer and encyclopedist.

Gnarled Trunk and Fir Tree — A498

1968, May 18 Engr. Perf. 13
1214 A498 25c grnsh bl, brn & grn .25 .20
Twinning of Rambouillet Forest in France and the Black Forest in Germany.

Map of Papal Enclave, Valréas, and John XXII Receiving Homage A499

1968, May 25
1215 A499 60c brn, bis brn & pur .55 .40
Papal enclave at Valréas, 650th anniv.

Louis XIV, Arms of France and Flanders A500

1968, June 29
1216 A500 40c rose car, gray & lemon .25 .20
300th anniv. of the Treaty of Aachen which reunited Flanders with France.

Martrou Bridge, Rochefort A501

1968, July 20
1217 A501 25c sky bl, blk & dk red brn .25 .20

Letord Lorraine Bimotor Plane over Map of France A502

1968, Aug. 17 Engr. Perf. 13
1218 A502 25c brt blue, indigo & red .50 .30
1st regularly scheduled air mail route in France from Paris to St. Nazaire, 50th anniv.

Tower de Constance, Aigues-Mortes A503

1968, Aug. 31
1219 A503 25c red brn, sky bl & olive bister .25 .20
Bicentenary of the release of Huguenot prisoners from the Tower de Constance, Aigues-Mortes.

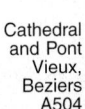
Cathedral and Pont Vieux, Beziers A504

1968, Sept. 7 Engr. Perf. 13
1220 A504 40c ind, bis & grn .85 .50

"Victory" over White Tower of Salonika — A505

1968, Sept. 28
1221 A505 40c red lilac & plum .25 .20
50th anniv. of the armistice on the eastern front in World War I, Sept. 29, 1918.

Louis XV, Arms of France and Corsica A506

1968, Oct. 5 Perf. 13
1222 A506 25c ultra, grn & blk .25 .20
Return of Corsica to France, 200th anniv.

Relay Race A507

1968, Oct. 12
1223 A507 40c ultra, brt grn & ol brn .50 .30
19th Olympic Games, Mexico City, 10/12-27.

Polar Camp with Helicopter, Plane and Snocat Tractor — A508

1968, Oct. 19
1224 A508 40c Prus bl, lt grnsh bl & brn red .35 .20
20 years of French Polar expeditions. For surcharge see Reunion No. 366.

Leon Bailby, Paris Opera Staircase and Hospital Beds — A509 "Victory" over Arc de Triomphe and Eternal Flame — A510

1968, Oct. 26
1225 A509 40c ocher & maroon .25 .20
50th anniv. of the "Little White Beds" children's hospital fund.

1968, Nov. 9 Engr. Perf. 13
1226 A510 25c dk car rose & dp blue .25 .20
50th anniv. of the armistice which ended World War I.

Death of Bertrand Du Guesclin at Chateauneuf-de-Randon, 1380 — A511

#1228, King Philip IV (the Fair) and first States-General assembly, 1302, horiz. 60c. Joan of Arc leaving Vaucouleurs, 1429.

1968, Nov. 16
1227 A511 40c green, ultra & brn .40 .30
1228 A511 40c cop red, grn & gray .40 .30
1229 A511 60c vio bl, sl bl & bis .40 .30
Nos. 1227-1229 (3) 1.20 .90
See No. 1260.

Marianne Type of 1967
1969-70 Engr. Perf. 13
1230 A486 30c green .35 .20
a. Booklet pane of 10 8.50
1231 A486 40c deep carmine .45 .20
a. Booklet pane of 5 (horiz. strip) 7.50
b. Booklet pane of 10 8.50
d. With label ('70) .50 .25

Typo. Perf. 14x13
1231C A486 30c blue green .20 .20
Nos. 1230-1231C (3) 1.00 .60
No. 1231d was issued in sheets of 50 with alternating labels showing coat of arms of Perigueux, arranged checkerwise, to commemorate the inauguration of the Perigueux stamp printing plant.
The 40c coil is noted after No. 1198.

Church of Brou, Bourg-en-Bresse — A512

Views: 80c, Vouglans Dam, Jura. 85c, Chateau de Chantilly. 1.15fr, Sailboats in La Trinité-sur-Mer harbor.

1969 Engr. Perf. 13
1232 A512 45c olive, bl & red brn .25 .20
1233 A512 80c ol bis, brn red & dk brn .45 .20
1234 A512 85c sl grn, dl bl & gray .90 .45
1235 A512 1.15fr brt bl, gray grn & brn .90 .40
Nos. 1232-1235 (4) 2.50 1.25

"February" Bas-relief from Amiens Cathedral A513

Philip the Good, by Roger van der Weyden A514

Sts. Savin and Cyprian before Ladicius, Mural, St. Savin, Vienne — A515

The Circus, by Georges Seurat A515a

1969   **Perf. 12x13**
1236 A513 1fr dk green & brn .60 .45
1237 A514 1fr multicolored .60 .45
1238 A515 1fr multicolored .60 .45
1239 A515a 1fr multicolored .60 .45
   Nos. 1236-1239 (4) 2.40 1.80

Issue dates: No. 1236, Feb. 22; No. 1237, May 3; No. 1238, June 28; No. 1239, Nov. 8.

Gallic Coin Type of 1964-66
1969   **Typo.**   **Perf. 13½x14**
1240 A418 22c brt green & vio .80 .20
1241 A418 35c red & ultra 1.65 .40
1242 A418 70c ultra & red brn 6.00 2.00
   Nos. 1240-1242 (3) 8.45 2.60

Nos. 1240-1242 are known only precanceled. See note after No. 132.

Hautefort Chateau A516

1969, Apr. 5   **Engr.**   **Perf. 13**
1243 A516 70c blue, slate & bister .40 .30

Irises A517

1969, Apr. 12   **Photo.**
1244 A517 45c multicolored .40 .30
3rd Intl. Flower Show, Paris, 4/23-10/5.

Europa Issue, 1969
Common Design Type
1969, Apr. 26   **Engr.**   **Perf. 13**
    Size: 36x22mm
1245 CD12 40c carmine rose .20 .20
1246 CD12 70c Prussian blue .30 .25

Albert Thomas and Thomas Memorial, Geneva A518

1969, May 10   **Engr.**   **Perf. 13**
1247 A518 70c brn, ol bis & ind .40 .30
ILO, 50th anniv., and honoring Thomas (1878-1932), director of the ILO (1920-32).

Garigliano Battle Scene, 1944 — A519

1969, May 10
1248 A519 45c black & violet .50 .50
25th anniv. of the Battle of the Garigliano against the Germans.

Chateau du Marché, Chalons-sur-Marne A520

1969, May 24
1249 A520 45c bis, dull bl & grn .50 .40
Federation of French Philatelic Societies, 42nd congress.

Parachutists over Normandy Beach A521

1969, May 31
1250 A521 45c dk blue & vio bl 1.25 .55
Landing of Special Air Service and Free French commandos in Normandy, June 6, 1944, 25th anniv.

Monument of the French Resistance, Mt. Mouchet — A522

1969, June 7
1251 A522 45c dk grn, slate & ind .90 .65
25th anniv. of the battle of Mt. Mouchet between French resistance fighters and the Germans, June 2 and 10, 1944.

French Troops Landing in Provence — A523

1969, Aug. 23   **Engr.**   **Perf. 13**
1252 A523 45c slate & blk brn 1.00 .65
25th anniv. of the landing of French and American forces in Provence, Aug. 15, 1944.

Russian and French Aviators — A524

1969, Oct. 18   **Engr.**   **Perf. 13**
1253 A524 45c slate, dp bl & car 1.00 .80
Issued to honor the French aviators of the Normandy-Neman Squadron who fought on the Russian Front, 1942-45.

Kayak on Isère River A525

1969, Aug. 2   **Engr.**   **Perf. 13**
1254 A525 70c org brn, ol & dk bl .45 .30
Intl. Canoe and Kayak Championships, Bourg-Saint-Maurice, Savoy, July 31-Aug. 6.

Napoleon as Young Officer and his Birthplace, Ajaccio — A526

1969, Aug. 16
1255 A526 70c brt grnsh bl, ol & rose vio .45 .30
Napoleon Bonaparte (1769-1821). For surcharge see Reunion No. 370.

Drops of Water and Diamond A527

Mediterranean Mouflon A528

1969, Sept. 27
1256 A527 70c blk, dp bl & brt grn .50 .30
European Water Charter.

1969, Oct. 11
1257 A528 45c ol, blk & org brn 3.25 1.25
Issued to publicize wildlife protection.

Central School of Arts and Crafts A529

1969, Oct. 18
1258 A529 70c dk grn, yel grn & org .40 .30
Inauguration of the Central School of Arts and Crafts at Chatenay-Malabry.

Nuclear Submarine "Le Redoutable" — A530

1969, Oct. 25
1259 A530 70c dp bl, grn & sl grn .40 .30

Type of 1968 and

Henri IV and Edict of Nantes — A531

Designs: No. 1260, Pierre Terrail de Bayard wounded at Battle of Brescia (after a painting in Versailles). No. 1262, Louis XI, Charles the Bold and map of France.

1969, Nov. 8   **Engr.**   **Perf. 13**
1260 A511 80c brn, bister & blk .50 .30
1261 A531 80c blk & vio bl .50 .30
1262 A531 80c ol, dp grn & dk red brn .50 .30
   Nos. 1260-1262 (3) 1.50 .90

"Firecrest" and Alain Gerbault — A532

1970, Jan. 10   **Engr.**   **Perf. 13**
1263 A532 70c ind, brt bl & gray .75 .50
Completion of Alain Gerbault's trip around the world aboard the "Firecrest," 1923-29, 40th anniv.

Gendarmery Emblem, Mountain Climber, Helicopter, Motorcyclists and Motorboat — A533

1970, Jan. 31
1264 A533 45c sl grn, dk bl & brn 1.25 .50
National Gendarmery, founded 1791.

Field Ball
Player — A534

1970, Feb. 21   Engr.   Perf. 13
1265 A534 80c slate green   .50 .50
7th Intl. Field Ball Games, Feb. 26-Mar. 8.

Alphonse Juin and Church of the
Invalides — A535

1970, Feb. 28
1266 A535 45c gray bl & dk brn   .35 .20
Issued to honor Marshal Alphonse Pierre
Juin (1888-1967), military leader.

Aerotrain
A536

1970, Mar. 7
1267 A536 80c purple & gray   .65 .50
Introduction of the aerotrain, which reaches
a speed of 320 miles per hour.

Pierre Joseph Pelletier, Joseph
Bienaimé Caventou, Quinine Formula
and Cell — A537

1970, Mar. 21   Engr.   Perf. 13
1268 A537 50c slate grn, sky bl &
    dp car   .35 .30
Discovery of quinine, 150th anniversary.

Pink Flamingos   Diamant B Rocket
A538   and Radar
                      A539

1970, Mar. 21
1269 A538 45c olive, gray & pink   .35 .25
European Nature Conservation Year, 1970.

1970, Mar. 28
1270 A539 45c bright green   .65 .40
Space center in Guyana and the launching
of the Diamant B rocket, Mar. 10, 1970.

Europa Issue, 1970
Common Design Type

1970, May 2   Engr.   Perf. 13
Size: 36x22mm
1271 CD13 40c deep carmine   .25 .20
1272 CD13 80c sky blue   .50 .20

Annunication, by Primitive Painter of
Savoy, 1480 — A540

The Triumph of Flora, by Jean
Baptiste Carpeaux — A541

Diana Returning from the Hunt, by
François Boucher — A542

Dancer
with
Bouquet,
by Edgar
Degas
A543

1970   Perf. 12x13, 13x12
1273 A540 1fr multicolored   .85 .45
1274 A541 1fr red brown   .85 .45
1275 A542 1fr multicolored   .85 .45
1276 A543 1fr multicolored   .85 .45
    Nos. 1273-1276 (4)   3.40 1.80
Issue dates: #1273, May 9; #1274, July 4;
#1275, Oct. 10; #1276, Nov. 14.

Arms of
Lens,
Miner's
Lamp and
Pit Head
A544

1970, May 16   Engr.   Perf. 13
1277 A544 40c scarlet   .25 .20
43rd Natl. Congress of the Federation of
French Philatelic Societies, Lens, May 14-21.

Diamond
Rock,
Martinique
A545

Haute Provence
Observatory and
Spiral
Nebula — A546

Designs: 95c, Chancelade Abbey, Dordogne. 1fr, Gosier Islet, Guadeloupe.

1970, June 20   Engr.   Perf. 13
1278 A545 50c sl grn, brt bl &
    plum   .45 .20
1279 A545 95c lt ol, car & brn   1.25 1.00
1280 A545 1fr sl grn, brt bl &
    dk car rose   .55 .20
1281 A546 1.30fr dk bl, vio bl &
    dk grn   1.90 1.00
    Nos. 1278-1281 (4)   4.15 2.40

Hand Reaching   Handicapped
for Freedom   Javelin Thrower
A547   A548

1970, June 27
1282 A547 45c vio bl, bl & bister   .40 .25
Liberation of concentration camps, 25th
anniv.

1970, June 27
1283 A548 45c rose car, ultra &
    emer   .40 .25
Issued to publicize the International Games
of the Handicapped, St. Etienne, June 1970.

Pole Vault — A549

1970, Sept. 11   Engr.   Perf. 13
1284 A549 45c car, bl & indigo   .45 .25
First European Junior Athletic Championships, Colombes, Sept. 11-13.

Royal Salt Works, Arc-et-
Senans — A550

1970, Sept. 26
1285 A550 80c bl, brn & dk grn   1.50 .65
Restoration of the 18th cent. Royal Salt
Works buildings, by Claude Nicolas Ledoux
(1736-1806) at Arc-et-Senans, for use as a
center for studies of all aspects of future
human life.

Armand Jean du Plessis, Duc de
Richelieu — A551

Designs: No. 1287, Battle of Fontenoy,
1745. No. 1288, Louis XIV and Versailles.

1970, Oct. 17   Engr.   Perf. 13
1286 A551 45c blk, sl & car rose   .65 .35
1287 A551 45c org, brn & indigo   .65 .35
1288 A551 45c sl grn, lem & org
    brn   .65 .35
    Nos. 1286-1288 (3)   1.95 1.05

UN Headquarters in New York and
Geneva — A552

1970, Oct. 24   Engr.   Perf. 13
1289 A552 80c ol, dp ultra & dk pur .55 .40
25th anniversary of the United Nations.

View of Bordeaux and France No.
43 — A553

1970, Nov. 7
1290 A553 80c vio bl & gray bl   .55 .35
Centerary of the Bordeaux issue.

Col. Denfert-Rochereau and Lion of
Belfort, by Frederic A.
Bartholdi — A554

1970, Nov. 14
1291 A554 45c dk bl, ol & red brn   .40 .25
Centenary of the siege of Belfort during
Franco-Prussian War.

Marianne (by
Bequet) — A555

1971-74   Typo.   Perf. 14x13
1292 A555 45c sky blue   .30 .20
1292A A555 60c green ('74)   .90 .20
For surcharges see Reunion #371, 397-398.

Engr.   Perf. 13
1293 A555 50c rose carmine   .30 .20
    a. Bklt. pane of 5 (horiz. strip)   5.00
    b. Booklet pane of 10   10.00
1294 A555 60c green ('74)   5.00 .35
    a. Booklet pane of 10   65.00
1294B A555 80c car rose ('74)   .50 .20
    c. Booklet pane of 5   9.00
    d. Booklet pane of 10   12.00
    Nos. 1293-1294B (3)   5.80 .75
Nos. 1294 and 1294B issued also in vertical
coils with control number on back of every
10th stamp.

No. 1293 issued only in booklets and in vertical coils with red control number on back of every 10th stamp.
See Nos. 1494-1498.

St. Matthew, Sculpture from Strasbourg Cathedral A556

Winnower, by François Millet A557

The Dreamer, by Georges Rouault A558

1971   Engr.   Perf. 12x13
1295 A556 1fr dark red brown   .85   .50
1296 A557 1fr multicolored   .85   .40
1297 A558 1fr multicolored   .85   .40
    Nos. 1295-1297 (3)   2.55   1.30

Issued: #1295, 1/23; #1296, 4/3; #1297, 6/5.

Figure Skating Pair A560

1971, Feb. 20   Engr.   Perf. 13
1299 A560 80c vio bl, sl & aqua   .55   .30
  World Figure Skating Championships, Lyons, Feb. 23-28.

Underwater Exploration — A561

1971, Mar. 6
1300 A561 80c blue blk & bl grn   .55   .30
  International Exhibition of Ocean Exploration, Bordeaux, Mar. 9-14.

Cape Horn Clipper "Antoinette" and Solidor Castle, Saint-Malo — A562

1971, Apr. 10   Engr.   Perf. 13
1301 A562 80c blue, pur & slate   1.25   .90
  For surcharge see Reunion No. 372.

Pyrenean Chamois — A563

1971, Apr. 24   Engr.   Perf. 13
1302 A563 65c bl, dk brn & brn ol   .65   .30
  National Park of Western Pyrenees.

Europa Issue, 1971
Common Design Type and

Santa Maria della Salute, Venice A564

1971, May 8   Engr.   Perf. 13
1303 A564 50c blue gray & ol bis   .30   .25
    Size: 36x22mm
1304 CD14 80c rose lilac   .45   .40

Cardinal, Nobleman and Lawyer — A565

Storming of the Bastille — A566

Design: No. 1306, Battle of Valmy.

1971
1305 A565 45c bl, rose red & pur   .55   .40
1306 A565 45c bl, ol bis & brn red   .65   .40
1307 A566 65c dk brn, gray bl & mag   1.00   .40
    Nos. 1305-1307 (3)   2.20   1.20
  No. 1305 commemorates the opening of the Estates General, May 5, 1789; No. 1306, Battle of Valmy (Sept. 20, 1792) between French and Prussian armies; 65c, Storming of the Bastille, Paris, July 14, 1789.
  Issued: #1305, 5/8; #1306, 9/18; 65c, 7/10.

Grenoble A568

1971, May 29   Engr.   Perf. 13
1308 A568 50c ocher, lil & rose red   .35   .20
  44th Natl. Cong. of the Federation of French Philatelic Societies, Grenoble, May 30-31.

"Rural Family Aid" Shedding Light on Village — A569

1971, June 5
1309 A569 40c vio, bl & grn   .25   .20
  Aid for rural families.
  For surcharge see Reunion No. 373.

Chateau and Fort de Sedan A570

Pont d'Arc, Ardèche Gorge — A571

  Views: 60c, Sainte Chapelle, Riom. 65c, Fountain and tower, Dole. 90c, Tower and street, Riquewihr.

1971   Engr.   Perf. 13
1310 A571 60c black, grn & bl   .25   .20
1311 A571 65c lil, ocher & blk   .35   .20
1312 A571 90c grn, vio brn & red brn   .50   .20
1313 A570 1.10fr sl grn, Prus bl & brn   .60   .30
1314 A571 1.40fr sl grn, bl & dk brn   .75   .40
    Nos. 1310-1314 (5)   2.45   1.10
  Issued: 60c, 6/19; 65c, 90c, 7/3; 1.10fr, 1.40fr, 6/12.
  For surcharges see Reunion Nos. 374, 381.

Gallic Coin Type of 1964-66
1971, July 1   Typo.   Perf. 13½x14
1315 A418 26c lilac & brn   .50   .20
1316 A418 30c lt brown & brn   .90   .20
1317 A418 45c dull green & brn   1.75   .30
1318 A418 90c red & brown   2.25   .50
    Nos. 1315-1318 (4)   5.40   1.20
  Nos. 1315-1318 are known only precanceled. See second paragraph after No. 132.

Bourbon Palace A572

1971, Aug. 28   Engr.   Perf. 13
1319 A572 90c violet blue   .75   .25
  59th Conf. of the Interparliamentary Union.

Embroidery and Tool Making A573

1971, Oct. 16
1320 A573 90c brn red, brt lil & cl   .50   .30
  40th anniv. of the first assembly of presidents of artisans' guilds.
  For surcharge see Reunion No. 375.

Reunion Chameleon A574

1971, Nov. 6   Photo.   Perf. 13
1321 A574 60c brn, yel, grn & blk   1.10   .65
  Nature protection.

De Gaulle Issue
Common Design Type and

De Gaulle in Brazzaville, 1944 — A576

  Designs: No. 1324, De Gaulle entering Paris, 1944. No. 1325, Pres. de Gaulle, 1970.

1971, Nov. 9   Engr.
1322 CD134 50c black   1.10   .65
1323 A576 50c ultra   1.10   .65
1324 A576 50c rose red   1.10   .65
1325 CD134 50c black   1.10   .65
  a. Strip of 4, #1322-1325 + label   4.50   4.00
  1st anniv. of the death of Charles de Gaulle.
  See Reunion Nos. 377, 380.

Antoine Portal and first Session of Academy — A577

1971, Nov. 13
1326 A577 45c dk purple & mag   .35   .30
  Sesquicentennial of the founding of the National Academy of Medicine; Baron Antoine Portal was first president.

L'Etude, by Jean Honoré Fragonard A578

Women in Garden, by Claude Monet A579

St. Peter Presenting Pierre de Bourbon, by Maitre de Moulins A580

Boats, by André Derain — A581

1972   Engr.   Perf. 12x13, 13x12
1327 A578 1fr black & multi   .90   .75
1328 A579 1fr slate grn & multi   1.75   .75
1329 A580 2fr dk brown & multi   2.50   1.25
1330 A581 2fr yellow & multi   3.50   1.50
        Nos. 1327-1330 (4)   8.65   4.25
   Issue dates: #1327, Jan. 22; #1328, June 17; #1329, Oct. 14; #1330, Dec. 16.

Map of South Indian Ocean, Penguin and Ships — A582

1972, Jan. 29   Perf. 13
1331 A582 90c black, bl & ocher   .65   .40
   Bicentenary of discovery of the Crozet and Kerguelen Islands.

Slalom and Olympic Emblems A583

1972, Feb. 7
1332 A583 90c dk olive & dp car   .55   .35
   11th Winter Olympic Games, Sapporo, Japan, Feb. 3-13.

Hearts, UN Emblem, Caduceus and Pacemaker A584

1972, Apr. 8   Engr.   Perf. 13
1333 A584 45c dk car, org & gray   .35   .25
   "Your heart is your health," world health month.

Red Deer, Sologne Plateau — A585

Charlieu Abbey A585a

Bazoches-du-Morvand Chateau — A586

Saint-Just Cathedral, Narbonne A587

1972   Perf. 13
1334 A585   1fr ocher & red brn   .65   .20
1335 A585a 1.20fr sl & dull brn   .65   .20
1336 A586   2fr sl grn, blk & red brn 1.00   .20
1337 A587   3.50fr bl, gray ol & car rose 1.90 .55
         Nos. 1334-1337 (4)   4.20   1.15
   Issued: 1fr, 9/10; 1.20fr, 4/29; 2fr, 9/9; 3.50fr, 4/8.
   For surcharge see Reunion No. 388.

Eagle Owl — A588

   Nature protection: 60c, Salmon, horiz.

1972
1338 A588 60c grn, ind & brt bl   2.25   .60
1339 A588 65c sl, ol brn & sep   1.40   .30
   Issue dates: 60c, May 27; 65c, Apr. 15.

Europa Issue 1972
Common Design Type and

Aix-la-Chapelle Cathedral — A589

1972, Apr. 22   Engr.   Perf. 13
1340 A589 50c yel, vio brn & dk ol   .25 .25
Photo.
Size: 22x36mm
1341 CD15 90c red org & multi   .50   .45

Bouquet Made of Hearts and Blood Donors' Emblem A590

Newfoundlander "Côte d'Emeraude" A591

1972, May 5   Engr.
1342 A590 40c red   .30   .20
   20th anniv. of the Blood Donors Association of Post and Telecommunications Employees. For surcharge see Reunion No. 383.

1972, May 6
1343 A591 90c org, vio bl & sl grn 1.00 .80

Cathedral, Saint-Brieuc A592

1972, May 20
1344 A592 50c lilac rose   .30   .20
   45th Congress of the Federation of French Philatelic Societies, Saint-Brieuc, May 21-22.

Hand Holding Symbol of Postal Code A593

1972, June 3   Typo.   Perf. 14x13
1345 A593 30c green, blk & car   .20   .20
1346 A593 50c car, blk & yel   .30   .20
   Introduction of postal code system. For surcharges see Reunion Nos. 384-385.

Old and New Communications A594

1972, July 1   Engr.   Perf. 13
1347 A594 45c slate & vio blue   .40   .20
   21st Intl. Congress of P.T.T. (Post, Telegraph & Telephone) Employees, Paris, 7/1-7.

Hurdler and Olympic Rings A595

1972, July 8
1348 A595 1fr deep olive   .50   .20
   20th Olympic Games, Munich, 8/26-9/11.

Hikers and Mt. Aigoual — A596   Bicyclist — A597

1972, July 15   Photo.   Perf. 13
1349 A596 40c brt rose & multi   1.50   .60
   Intl. Year of Tourism and 25th anniv. of the Natl. Hikers Association.

1972, July 22   Engr.
1350 A597 1fr gray, brn & lil   1.90   .60
   World Bicycling Championships, Marseille, July 29-Aug. 2.

"Incroyables and Merveilleuses," 1794 — A598

   French History: 60c, Bonaparte at the Arcole Bridge. 65c, Egyptian expedition (soldiers and scientists finding antiquities; pyramids in background).

1972   Engr.   Perf. 13
1351 A598 45c ol, dk grn & car rose   .40   .30
1352 A598 60c red, blk & ind   .85   .40
1353 A598 65c ocher, ultra & choc   .85   .40
         Nos. 1351-1353 (3)   2.10   1.10
   . Issued: 45c, Oct. 7; 60c, 65c, Nov. 11.

Champollion, Rosetta Stone with Key Inscription — A599

1972, Oct. 14
1354 A599 90c vio bl, brn red & blk   .60   .30
   Sesquicentennial of the deciphering of hieroglyphs by Jean-François Champollion.

St. Teresa, Portal of Notre Dame of Alençon
A600

1973, Jan. 6   **Engr.**   *Perf. 13*
1355 A600 1fr Prus blue & indigo   .60   .45

   Centenary of the birth of St. Teresa of Lisieux, the Little Flower (Thérèse Martin, 1873-1897), Carmelite nun.

Anthurium (Martinique) — A601

1973, Jan. 20   **Photo.**
1356 A601 50c gray & multi   .40   .20

Colors of France and Germany Interlaced — A602

1973, Jan. 22
1357 A602 50c multicolored   .40   .20

   10th anniv. of the Franco-German Cooperation Treaty. See Germany No. 1101.

Polish Immigrants — A603

1973, Feb. 3   **Engr.**   *Perf. 13*
1358 A603 40c slate grn & dp car & brn   .25   .25

   50th anniversary of Polish immigration into France, 1921-1923.

Last Supper, St. Austremoine Church, Issoire — A604

Kneeling Woman, by Charles Le Brun
A605

Angel, Wood, Moutier-D'Ahun — A606

Lady Playing Archlute, by Antoine Watteau
A607

1973   **Engr.**   *Perf. 12x13*
1359 A604 2fr brown & multi   1.75   1.25
1360 A605 2fr dk red & yel   1.75   1.40
1361 A606 2fr ol brn & vio brn   1.75   1.25
1362 A607 2fr black & multi   1.75   1.25
    Nos. 1359-1362 (4)   7.00   5.15

   Issue dates: #1359, Feb. 10; #1360, Apr. 28; #1361, May 26; #1362, Sept. 22.

Tuileries Palace, Telephone Relays
A608

Oil Tanker, Francis I Lock
A609

Airbus A300-B
A610

1973
1363 A608 45c ultra, sl grn & bis   .30   .20
1364 A609 90c plum, blk & bl   .55   .20
1365 A610 3fr dk brn, bl & blk   1.90   .80
    Nos. 1363-1365 (3)   2.75   1.20

   French technical achievements.
   Issued: 45c, 5/15; 90c, 10/27; 3fr, 4/7.

Europa Issue 1973
Common Design Type and

City Hall, Brussels, CEPT Emblem — A611

1973, Apr. 14   **Engr.**   *Perf. 13*
1366 A611 50c brt pink & choc   .45   .25
     Photo.
     Size: 36x22mm
1367 CD16 90c slate grn & multi   *1.60*   .75

Masonic Lodge Emblem
A612

1973, May 12   **Engr.**   *Perf. 13*
1368 A612 90c magenta & vio bl   .55   .30

   Bicentenary of the Free Masons of France.

Guadeloupe Raccoon
A613

White Storks
A614

1973
1369 A613 40c lilac, sepia & olive   .35   .20
1370 A614 60c blk, aqua & org red   .50   .25

   Nature protection.
   Issue dates: 40c, June 23; 60c, May 12.

Tourist Issue

Doubs Waterfall
A615

Clos-Lucé, Amboise
A617

Palace of Dukes of Burgundy, Dijon
A616

   Design: 90c, Gien Chateau.

1973   **Engr.**   *Perf. 13*
1371 A615 60c multicolored   .30   .20
1372 A616 65c red & purple   .30   .20
1373 A616 90c Prus bl, ind & brn   .35   .20
1374 A617 1fr ocher, bl & sl grn   .35   .20
    Nos. 1371-1374 (4)   1.30   .80

   Issued: 60c, 9/8; 65c, 5/19; 90c, 8/18; 1fr, 6/23.
   For surcharge see Reunion No. 387.

Academy Emblem — A618

1973, May 26
1375 A618 1fr lil, slate grn & red   .50   .30
   Academy of Overseas Sciences, 50th anniv.

Racing Car and Clocks
A619

1973, June 2
1376 A619 60c dk brown & blue   .65   .50
   24-hour automobile race at Le Mans, 50th anniv.

Five-master France II — A620

1973, June 9
1377 A620 90c ultra, Prus bl & ind   1.25   .65
   For surcharge see Reunion No. 386.

Tower and Square, Toulouse — A621

1973, June 9
1378 A621 50c purple & red brn   .35   .20
   46th Congress of the Federation of French Philatelic Societies, Toulouse, June 9-12.

Dr. Armauer G. Hansen — A622

Ducretet and his Transmission Diagram — A623

1973, Sept. 29   **Engr.**   *Perf. 13*
1379 A622 45c grn, dk ol & ocher   .30   .20
   Centenary of the discovery of the Hansen bacillus, the cause of leprosy.

1973, Oct. 6
1380 A623 1fr yel grn & magenta   .55   .40
   75th anniversary of the first transmission of radio signals from the Eiffel Tower to the Pantheon by Eugene Ducretet (1844-1915).

Molière as Sganarelle — A624

1973, Oct. 20
1381 A624 1fr dk red & olive brn   .55   .35
   Moliere (Jean-Baptiste Poquelin; 1622-1673), playwright and actor.

Pierre Bourgoin and Philippe Kieffer A625

1973, Oct. 27
1382 A625 1fr red, rose cl & vio bl   .50 .30
Pierre Bourgoin (1907-70), and Philippe Kieffer (1899-1963), heroes of the Free French forces in World War II.

Napoleon, Jean Portalis and Palace of Justice, Paris — A626

Exhibition Halls — A627

The Coronation of Napoleon, by Jean Louis David — A628

1973   **Engr.**   **Perf. 13**
1383 A626 45c blue, choc & gray   .55 .30
1384 A627 60c ol, sl grn & brn   .55 .50
1385 A628 1fr sl grn, ol & claret   .65 .55
Nos. 1383-1385 (3)   1.75 1.35
History of France. 45c, for the preparation of the Code Napoleon; 60c, Napoleon's encouragement of industry; 1fr, his coronation. Issued: 45c, 11/3; 60c, 11/24; 1fr, 11/12.

Eternal Flame, Arc de Triomphe A629

Weather Vane A630

1973, Nov. 10
1386 A629 40c pur, vio bl & red   .40 .30
50th anniv. of the Eternal Flame at the Arc de Triomphe, Paris.

1973, Dec. 1
1387 A630 65c ultra, blk & grn   .40 .30
50th anniv. of the Dept. of Agriculture.

Human Rights Flame and Man — A631

Postal Museum — A632

1973, Dec. 8   **Engr.**   **Perf. 13**
1388 A631 45c car, org & blk   .30 .25
25th anniversary of the Universal Declaration of Human Rights.

1973, Dec. 19
1389 A632 50c maroon & bister   .30 .25
Opening of new post and philately museum, Paris.

ARPHILA 75 Emblem A633

1974, Jan. 19   **Engr.**   **Perf. 13**
1390 A633 50c brn, bl & brt lil   .25 .20
ARPHILA 75 Philatelic Exhibition, Paris, June 1975. For surcharge see Reunion No. 390.

Concorde over Charles de Gaulle Airport A634

Turbotrain T.G.V. 001 A635

Phenix Nuclear Power Station A636

1974   **Engr.**   **Perf. 13**
1391 A634 60c pur & ol gray   .40 .30
1392 A635 60c multicolored   1.10 .55
1393 A636 65c multicolored   .40 .30
Nos. 1391-1393 (3)   1.90 1.15
French technical achievements. Issued: #1391, 3/18; #1392, 8/31; 65c, 9/21.

Cardinal Richelieu, by Philippe de Champaigne — A637

Painting by Joan Miró A638

Canal du Loing, by Alfred Sisley — A639

"In Honor of Nicolas Fouquet," Tapestry by Georges Mathieu A640

Engr., Photo. (#1395, 1397)
1974   **Perf. 12x13, 13x12**
1394 A637 2fr multicolored   1.25 1.00
1395 A638 2fr multicolored   1.25 1.25
1396 A639 2fr multicolored   1.75 1.25
1397 A640 2fr multicolored   1.75 1.25
Nos. 1394-1397 (4)   6.00 4.75
Nos. 1394-1397 are printed in sheets of 25 with alternating labels publicizing "ARPHILA 75," Paris, June 6-16, 1975. Issue dates: #1394, Mar. 23; #1395, Sept. 14; #1396, Nov. 9; #1397, Nov. 16. For surcharges see Reunion Nos. 391-394.

French Alps and Gentian A641

1974, Mar. 30   **Engr.**   **Perf. 13**
1398 A641 65c vio blue & gray   .40 .25
Centenary of the French Alpine Club.

Europa Issue 1974

"Age of Bronze," by Auguste Rodin — A642

"Air," by Aristide Maillol A643

1974, Apr. 20   **Perf. 13**
1399 A642 50c brt rose lil & blk   .30 .25
1400 A643 90c olive & brown   .90 .50

Sea Rescue — A644

1974, Apr. 27
1401 A644 90c multicolored   .50 .40
Reorganized sea rescue organization. For surcharge see Reunion No. 395.

Council Building, View of Strasbourg and Emblem — A645

1974, May 4   **Engr.**   **Perf. 13**
1402 A645 45c indigo, bister & bl   .30 .25
25th anniversary of the Council of Europe.

Tourist Issue

View of Salers A646

Basilica of St. Nicolas de Porte — A647

Seashell over Corsica — A648

Design: 1.10fr, View of Lot Valley.

1974   **Engr.**   **Perf. 13**
1403 A646 65c yel grn & choc   .25 .20
1404 A646 1.10fr choc & sl grn   .45 .30
1405 A647 2fr gray & lilac   .80 .30
1406 A648 3fr multicolored   1.00 .40
Nos. 1403-1406 (4)   2.50 1.20
Issued: 65c, 6/22; 1.10fr, 9/7; 2fr, 10/12; 3fr, 5/11.

Bison A649

Giant Armadillo of Guyana A650

1974
1407 A649 40c bis, choc & bl   .35 .20
1408 A650 65c slate, olive & grn   .35 .20
Nature protection. Issued: #1407, May 25; #1408, Oct. 19.

Americans Landing in Normandy and Arms of Normandy — A651

General Marie-Pierre Koenig — A652

Order of the French Resistance — A653

1974

1409	A651	45c grn, rose & ind	.80	.50
1410	A652	1fr multicolored	.50	.35
1411	A653	1fr multicolored	.65	.50
		Nos. 1409-1411 (3)	1.95	1.35

30th anniversary of the liberation of France from the Nazis. Design of No. 1410 includes diagram of battle of Bir-Hakeim and Free French and Bir-Hakeim memorials.
Issued: 45c, 6/8; #1410, 5/25; #1411, 11/23.
See No. B478.

Pfister House, 16th Century, Colmar — A654

1974, June 1

1412	A654	50c multicolored	.25	.20

47th Congress of the Federation of French Philatelic Societies, Colmar, May 30-June 4.

Chess A655

1974, June 8

1413	A655	1fr dk brown & multi	.60	.35

21st Chess Olympiad, Nice, June 6-30.

Facade with Statue of Louis XIV, and 1675 Medal — A656

1974, June 15

1414	A656	40c indigo, bl & brn	.30	.20

300th anniversary of the founding of the Hotel des Invalides (Home for poor and sick officers and soldiers).

Peacocks Holding Letter, and Globe — A657

1974, Oct. 5   Engr.   Perf. 13

1415	A657	1.20fr ultra, dp grn & dk car	.50	.30

Centenary of Universal Postal Union. For surcharge see Reunion No. 396.

Copernicus and Heliocentric System — A658

1974, Oct. 12

1416	A658	1.20fr multicolored	.45	.30

500th anniversary of the birth of Nicolaus Copernicus (1473-1543), Polish astronomer.

Tourist Issue

Palace of Justice, Rouen A659

Saint-Pol-de-Leon A660

Chateau de Rochechouart — A661

1975   Engr.   Perf. 13

1417	A659	85c multicolored	.35	.30
1418	A660	1.20fr bl, bis & choc	.40	.30
1419	A661	1.40fr brn, ind & grn	.50	.30
		Nos. 1417-1419 (3)	1.25	.90

Issued: 85c, 1/25; 1.20fr, 1/18; 1.40fr, 1/11.

Snowy Egret — A662

Gallic Coin — A663

1975, Feb. 15   Engr.   Perf. 13

1420	A662	70c brt blue & bister	.40	.30

Nature protection.

1975, Feb. 16   Typo.   Perf. 13½x14

1421	A663	42c orange & mag	1.25	.50
1422	A663	48c lt bl & red brn	1.50	.80
1423	A663	70c brt pink & red	2.50	1.25
1424	A663	1.35fr lt green & brn	2.75	1.50
		Nos. 1421-1424 (4)	8.00	4.05

Nos. 1421-1424 are known only precanceled. See second note after No. 132. See Nos. 1460-1463, 1487-1490.

The Eye — A664

Ionic Capital — A665

Graphic Art — A666

Ceres — A667

1975   Engr.   Perf. 13

1425	A664	1fr red, pur & org	.45	.30
1426	A665	2fr grn, sl grn & mag	.80	.55
1427	A666	3fr dk car & ol grn	1.25	.90
1428	A667	4fr red, sl grn & bis	1.60	1.25
		Nos. 1425-1428 (4)	4.10	3.00

Souvenir Sheet

1429		Sheet of 4	7.50	7.50
a.		A664 2fr dp car & slate blue	1.00	1.00
b.		A665 3fr brt bl, sl bl & dp car	1.40	1.40
c.		A666 4fr slate blue, brt bl & plum	2.00	2.00
d.		A667 6fr brt bl, sl bl & plum	2.50	2.50

ARPHILA 75, Intl. Philatelic Exhibition, Paris, 6/6-16. Issued: 1fr, 3/1; 2fr, 3/22; 3fr, 4/19; 4fr, 5/17; #1429, 4/2.

Pres. Georges Pompidou A668

Paul as Harlequin, by Picasso A669

1975, Apr. 3   Engr.   Perf. 13

1430	A668	80c black & gray	.30	.20

Georges Pompidou (1911-74), President of France, 1969-74.

1975, Apr. 26   Photo.   Perf. 13

Europa; 1.20fr, Woman on Balcony, by Kees van Dongen.

1431	A669	80c multi	.45	.35
1432	A669	1.20fr multi, horiz.	.90	.70

Machines, Globe, Emblem A670

1975, May 3   Engr.

1433	A670	1.20fr blue, blk & red	.65	.30

World Machine Tool Exhib., Paris, 6/7-26.

Senate Assembly Hall A671

1975, May 24   Engr.   Perf. 13

1434	A671	1.20fr olive & dk car	.65	.40

Centenary of the Senate of the Republic.

Meter Convention Document, Atom Diagram and Waves — A672

1975, May 31

1435	A672	1fr multicolored	.55	.30

Cent. of Intl. Meter Convention, Paris, 1875.

Metro Regional Train A673

"Gazelle" Helicopter A674

1975

1436	A673	1fr indigo & brt bl	.90	.30
1437	A674	1.30fr vio bl & grn	.65	.40

French technical achievements. Issue dates: 1fr, June 21; 1.30fr, May 31.

Youth and Flasks, Symbols of Study and Growth — A675

1975, June 21
1438 A675 70c red pur & blk .30 .20
Student Health Foundation.

People's Theater, Bussang, and Maurice Pottecher A676

1975, Aug. 9 **Engr.** **Perf. 13**
1439 A676 85c multicolored .30 .20
80th anniversary of the People's Theater at Bussang, founded by Maurice Pottecher.

Regions of France

Central France A677

Aquitaine A678

Limousin A679

Picardy A680

Burgundy A681

Loire A682

Guyana A683

Auvergne A684

Poitou-Charentes A685

Southern Pyrenees A686

Pas-de-Calais — A687

1975-76 **Engr.** **Perf. 13**
1440 A677 25c blue & yel grn .25 .20
1441 A678 60c multicolored .25 .20
1442 A679 70c multicolored .50 .35
1443 A680 85c bl, grn & org .70 .35
1444 A681 1fr red, yel & mar .70 .35
1445 A682 1.15fr bl, bis & grn .70 .35
1446 A683 1.25fr multicolored .65 .50
1447 A684 1.30fr dk bl & red .85 .50
1448 A685 1.90fr sl, ol & Prus bl 1.00 .50
1449 A686 2.20fr multicolored 1.10 1.00
1450 A687 2.80fr car, bl & blk 1.40 1.00
Nos. 1440-1450 (11) 8.10 5.30

Issued: 85c, 11/15; 1fr, 10/25; 1.15fr, 9/6; 1.30fr, 10/4/75; 1.90fr, 12/6; 2.80fr, 12/13; 25c, 1/31/76; 2.20fr, 1/10/76; 60c, 5/22/76; 70c, 5/29/76; 1.25fr, 10/16/76.

A690   A691

French Flag, F.-H. Manhes, Jean Verneau, Pierre Kaan

1975, Sept. 27
1453 A690 1fr multicolored .50 .30
Liberation of concentration camps, 30th anniversary. F.-H. Manhes (1889-1959), Jean Verneau (1890-1944) and Pierre Kaan (1903-1945) were French resistance leaders, imprisoned in concentration camps.

1975, Oct. 11
Monument, by Joseph Riviere.
1454 A691 70c multicolored .40 .30
Land Mine Demolition Service, 30th anniversary. Monument was erected in Alsace to honor land mine victims.

Symbols of Suburban Living A692

1975, Oct. 18
1455 A692 1.70fr brown, bl & grn .75 .50
Creation of new towns.

Women and Rainbow — A693

1975, Nov. 8 **Photo.**
1456 A693 1.20fr silver & multi .45 .40
International Women's Year 1975.

Saint-Nazaire Bridge — A694

1975, Nov. 8 **Engr.**
1457 A694 1.40fr bl, ind & grn .60 .30

French and Russian Flags — A695

Frigate Melpomene A696

1975, Nov. 22
1458 A695 1.20fr bl, red & ocher .50 .30
Franco-Soviet diplomatic relations, 50th anniv.

1975, Dec. 6
1459 A696 90c multicolored 1.25 .65

Gallic Coin Type of 1975
1976, Jan. 1 **Typo.** **Perf. 13½x14**
1460 A663 50c lt green & brn 1.10 .70
1461 A663 60c lilac & brn 1.75 1.00
1462 A663 90c orange & brn 2.25 1.25
1463 A663 1.60fr violet & brn 4.00 2.00
Nos. 1460-1463 (4) 9.10 4.95

Nos. 1460-1463 are known only precanceled. See second note after No. 132.

Lintel, St. Genis des Fontaines Church A697

Venus of Brassempouy (Paleolithic) — A698

"The Joy of Life," by Robert Delaunay A699

Ramses II, from Abu Simbel Temple, Egypt — A700

Still Life, by Maurice de Vlaminck — A701

1976 **Engr.** **Perf. 13**
1464 A697 2fr blue & slate bl 1.25 .75
1465 A698 2fr dk brn & yel 1.25 .60

Photo. **Perf. 12½x13**
1466 A699 2fr multicolored 1.25 .80

Engr. **Perf. 13x12½**
1467 A700 2fr multicolored .95 .75

Perf. 13
1468 A701 2fr multicolored .95 .60
Nos. 1464-1468 (5) 5.65 3.50

Issued: #1464, 1/24; #1465, 3/6; #1466, 7/24; #1467, 9/4; #1468, 12/18.

Tourist Issue

Chateau Fort de Bonaguil A702

Lodève Cathedral — A703

Biarritz
A704

Thiers — A705

Ussel — A706

Chateau de
Malmaison
A707

1976   **Engr.**   **Perf. 13**
1469 A702   1fr multicolored   .35   .20
1470 A703   1.10fr violet blue   .50   .30
1471 A704   1.40fr multicolored   .65   .30
1472 A705   1.70fr multicolored   .65   .25
1473 A706   2fr multicolored   .90   .25
1474 A707   3fr multicolored   1.10   .25
    Nos. 1469-1474 (6)   4.15   1.60

Issue dates: 1fr, 2fr, July 10; 1.10fr, Nov. 13; 1.40fr, Sept. 25; 1.70fr, Oct. 9; 3fr, Apr. 10.

Destroyers,
Association
Emblem
A708

1976, Apr. 24
1475 A708 1fr vio bl, mag & lem   .50   .30
Naval Reserve Officers Assoc., 50th anniv.

Gate,
Rouen — A709

Young
Person — A710

1976, Apr. 24   •
1476 A709 80c olive gray & sal   .35   .20
49th Congress of the Federation of French Philatelic Societies, Rouen, Apr. 23-May 2.

1976, Apr. 27
1477 A710 60c bl grn, ind & car   .35   .25
JUVAROUEN 76, International Youth Philatelic Exhibition, Rouen, Apr. 25-May 2.

Europa Issue 1976

Ceramic
Pitcher,
Strasbourg,
18th
Century
A711

1.20fr, Sevres porcelain plate & CEPT emblem.

1976, May 8   **Photo.**   **Perf. 13**
1478 A711   80c multicolored   .30   .30
1479 A711   1.20fr multicolored   .65   .55

Count de Vergennes and Benjamin
Franklin — A712

1976, May 15   **Engr.**   **Perf. 13**
1480 A712 1.20fr multicolored   .50   .30
American Bicentennial.

— A713   A714

Battle of Verdun Memorial.

1976, June 12   **Engr.**
1481 A713 1fr multicolored   .45   .20
Battle of Verdun, 60th anniversary.

1976, June 12   **Photo.**
1482 A714 1.20fr Communication   .50   .40

Troncais
Forest — A715

Cross of
Lorraine — A716

1976, June 19   **Engr.**
1483 A715 70c green & multi   .35   .20
Protection of the environment.

1976, June 19
1484 A716 1fr multicolored   .60   .25
Association of Free French, 30th anniv.

Symphonie Communications
Satellite — A717

1976, June 26   **Photo.**
1485 A717 1.40fr multicolored   .65   .50
French technical achievements.

Gallic Coin Type of 1975
1976, July 1   **Typo.**   **Perf. 13½x14**
1487 A663   52c ver & dk brn   .65   .40
1488 A663   62c vio & dk brn   1.25   .75
1489 A663   95c tan & dk brn   1.65   1.00
1490 A663   1.70fr dk bl & dk brn   3.00   1.50
    Nos. 1487-1490 (4)   6.55   3.65

Nos. 1487-1490 are known only precanceled. See second note after No. 132.

Paris Summer
Festival — A719

1976, July 10   **Engr.**
1491 A719 1fr multicolored   .65   .30
Summer festival in Tuileries Gardens, Paris.

Emblem
and
Soldiers
A720

1976, July 8
1492 A720 1fr blk, dp bl & mag   .50   .25
Officers Reserve Corps, centenary.

Sailing
A721

1976, July 17
1493 A721 1.20fr blue, blk & vio   .65   .35
21st Olympic Games, Montreal, Canada, July 17-Aug. 1.

Marianne Type of 1971-74
1976   **Typo.**   **Perf. 14x13**
1494 A555 80c green   .50   .20

    Engr.   **Perf. 13**
1495 A555   80c green   1.25   .50
   a.   Booklet pane of 10   15.00
1496 A555   1fr carmine rose   .55   .20
   a.   Booklet pane of 5   4.00
   b.   Booklet pane of 10   8.00
    Nos. 1495-1496 (2)   1.80   .70

No. 1495 issued in booklets only. "POSTES" 6mm long on Nos. 1292A and 1494; 4mm on others.
#1494, 1496 were issued untagged in 1977.

Coil Stamps
1976, Aug. 1   **Engr.**   **Perf. 13 Horiz.**
1497 A555   80c green   .65   .55
1498 A555   1fr carmine rose   .65   .55

Red control number on back of every 10th stamp.

Woman's Head, by Jean
Carzou — A722

1976, Sept. 18   **Engr.**   **Perf. 13x12½**
1499 A722 2fr multicolored   .90   .65

Old and
New
Telephones
A723

1976, Sept. 25   **Engr.**   **Perf. 13**
1500 A723 1fr multicolored   .50   .25
Centenary of first telephone call by Alexander Graham Bell, Mar. 10, 1876.

Festival Emblem
and Trophy,
Pyrenees, Hercules
and Pyrène — A724

Police
Emblem — A725

1976, Oct. 2
1501 A724 1.40fr multicolored   .65   .45
10th Intl. Tourist Film Festival, Tarbes, 10/4-10.

1976, Oct. 9   **Engr.**   **Perf. 13**
1502 A725 1.10fr ultra, red & ol   .50   .30
National Police, help and protection.

Atomic
Particle
Accelerator,
Diagram
A726

1976, Oct. 22   **Photo.**
1503 A726 1.40fr multicolored   .85   .55
European Center for Nuclear Research (CERN).

"Exhibitions" — A727

1976, Nov. 20   **Engr.**   **Perf. 13**
1504 A727 1.50fr multicolored   .75   .50
Trade Fairs and Exhibitions.

Abstract
Design
A728

1976, Nov. 27   **Photo.**
1505 A728 1.10fr multicolored   .50   .40
Customs Service.

Atlantic Museum, Port Louis — A729

1976, Dec. 4   **Engr.**
1506 A729 1.45fr grnsh bl & olive   .65   .50

Regions of France

Réunion
A730

Martinique
A731

Dunkirk
Harbor
A739

1977, Feb. 12
1516 A739 50c multicolored   .25 .20
Expansion of Dunkirk harbor facilities.

Hand Holding
Torch and
Sword — A744

Pisces — A745

Battle of
Cambray
A749

1977, May 14
1538 A749 80c multicolored   .40 .30
Capture of Cambray and the incorporation
of Cambresis District into France, 300th anniv.

Franche-Comté
A732

Brittany
A733

Bridge at Mantes, by Corot — A740

1977, Mar. 5   Engr.   Perf. 13
1521 A744 80c ultra & multi   .50 .30
"France remembers its dead."

1977-78   Engr.   Perf. 13
Zodiac Signs: 58c, Cancer. 61c, Sagittarius.
68c, Taurus. 73c, Aries. 78c, Libra. 1.05fr,
Scorpio. 1.15fr, Capricorn. 1.25fr, Leo. 1.85fr,
Aquarius. 2fr, Virgo. 2.10fr, Gemini.

1522 A745   54c violet blue   .65 .30
1523 A745   58c emerald   1.00 .40
1524 A745   61c brt blue   .55 .30
1525 A745   68c deep brown   .85 .35
1526 A745   73c rose carmine   1.50 .80
1527 A745   78c vermilion   .65 .35
1528 A745   1.05fr brt lilac   1.50 .75
1529 A745   1.15fr orange   2.25 1.40
1530 A745   1.25fr lt olive grn   1.25 .60
1531 A745   1.85fr slate grn   2.75 1.25
1532 A745   2fr blue green   3.00 1.75
1533 A745   2.10fr lilac rose   1.65 1.00
      Nos. 1522-1533 (12)   17.60 9.25
Issued: 54c, 68c, 1.05fr, 1.85fr, 4/1/77;
others, 1978.
Nos. 1522-1533 are known only precanceled. See second note after No. 132.

Carmes Church,
School, Map of
France
A750

Modern
Constructions
A751

1977, May 14
1539 A750 1.10fr multicolored   .50 .30
Catholic Institutes in France.

1977, May 21
1540 A751 1.10fr multicolored   .55 .30
European Federation of the Construction
Industry.

Languedoc-Roussillon — A734

Virgin and
Child, by
Rubens
A741

Village in
Provence
A746

Europa: 1.40fr, Brittany port.

1977, Apr. 23
1534 A746   1fr multicolored   .45 .25
1535 A746 1.40fr multicolored   1.00 .35

Annecy
Castle
A752

1977, May 28
1541 A752 1fr multicolored   .60 .30
Congress of the Federation of French Philatelic Societies, Annecy, May 28-30.

Rhône-Alps
A735

Tridimensional Design, by Victor
Vasarely — A742

Flowers
and
Gardening
A747

1977, Apr. 23   Engr.   Perf. 13
1536 A747 1.70fr multicolored   .80 .50
National Horticulture Society, centenary.

Tourist Issue

Abbey, Pont-à-Mousson — A753

Champagne-
Ardennes
A736

Alsace
A737

Photo. (1.45fr, 1.50fr, 2.50fr); Engr.
1977   Perf. 13
1507 A730 1.45fr grn & lil rose   .65 .40
1508 A731 1.50fr multicolored   .65 .60
1509 A732 2.10fr multicolored   .90 .65
1510 A733 2.40fr multicolored   1.10 .35
1511 A734 2.50fr multicolored   1.10 .35
1512 A735 2.75fr Prus blue   1.50 .90
1513 A736 3.20fr multicolored   1.60 1.00
1514 A737 3.90fr multicolored   2.25 1.50
      Nos. 1507-1514 (8)   9.75 6.25
Issued: 1.45fr, 2/5; 1.50fr, 1/29; 2.10fr, 1/8;
2.40fr, 2/19; 2.50fr, 1/15; 2.75fr, 1/22; 3.20fr,
4/16; 3.90fr, 2/26.

Head and
Eagle, by
Pierre-Yves
Tremois
A743

1977   Engr.   Perf. 13x12½
1517 A740 2fr multicolored   1.10 .85
      Perf. 12x13
1518 A741 2fr multicolored   1.25 .85
      Perf. 12½x13
1519 A742 3fr ultra & sl grn   1.50 .85
      Photo.
1520 A743 3fr dark red & blk   1.90 1.40
      Nos. 1517-1520 (4)   5.75 3.95
Issue dates: No. 1517, Feb. 12; No. 1518,
Nov. 5; No. 1519, Apr. 7; No. 1520, Sept. 17.

Symbolic
Flower
A748

1977, May 7
1537 A748 1.40fr multicolored   .65 .45
Intl. Flower Show, Nantes, May 12-23.

Abbey Tower,
Saint-Amand-
les-Eaux
A754

Collegiate
Church of Dorat
A755

Fontenay
Abbey
A756

Pompidou Cultural Center — A738

1977, Feb. 5   Engr.   Perf. 13
1515 A738 1fr multicolored   .35 .20
Inauguration of the Georges Pompidou
National Center for Art and Culture, Paris.

Bayeux
Cathedral — A757

Chateau de
Vitré
A758

1977   Engr.   Perf. 13
1542 A753 1.25fr multicolored   .60 .35
1543 A754 1.40fr multicolored   .65 .35
1544 A755 1.45fr multicolored   .75 .45
1545 A756 1.50fr multicolored   .75 .25
1546 A757 1.90fr black & yel   1.00 .35
1547 A758 2.40fr black & yel   1.10 .35
    Nos. 1542-1547 (6)   4.85 2.10

Issued: 1.25fr, 10/1; 1.40fr, 9/17; 1.45fr,
7/16; 1.50fr, 6/4; 1.90fr, 7/9; 2.40fr, 9/24.

Polytechnic
School and
"X" — A759

1977, June 4   Engr.   Perf. 13
1548 A759 1.70fr multicolored   .75 .30

Relocation at Palaiseau of Polytechnic
School, founded 1794.

Soccer and Cup — A760

1977, June 11
1549 A760 80c multicolored   .90 .50

Soccer Cup of France, 60th anniversary.

De Gaulle   Stylized Map of
Memorial — A761   France — A762

Photo. & Embossed
1977, June 18
1550 A761 1fr gold & multi   1.00 .50

5th anniversary of dedication of De Gaulle
memorial at Colombey-les-Deux-Eglises.

1977, June 18   Engr.   Perf. 13
1551 A762 1.10fr ultra & red   .55 .30

French Junior Chamber of Commerce.

Battle of Nancy
A763

Arms of
Burgundy
A764

1977, June 25
1552 A763 1.10fr blue & slate   1.10 .40

Battle of Nancy between the Dukes of Burgundy and Lorraine, 500th anniversary.

1977, July 2
1553 A764 1.25fr ol brn & slate
          grn   .55 .25

Annexation of Burgundy by the French
Crown, 500th anniversary.

Association
Emblem
A765

1977, July 8
1554 A765 1.40fr ultra, olive & red .55 .25

French-speaking Parliamentary Association.

Red Cicada — A766

1977, Sept. 10   Photo.   Perf. 13
1555 A766 80c multicolored   .55 .30

Nature protection.

French
Handicrafts
A767

1977, Oct. 1   Engr.   Perf. 13
1556 A767 1.40fr multicolored   .65 .45

French craftsmen.

Industry and
Agriculture — A768

1977, Oct. 22
1557 A768 80c brown & olive   .30 .25

Economic & Social Council, 30th anniv.

Table
Tennis
A769

1977, Dec. 17   Engr.   Perf. 13
1558 A769 1.10fr multicolored   3.25 1.00

French Table Tennis Federation, 50th anniv.,
and French team, gold medal winner,
Birmingham.

Abstract, by Roger Excoffon — A770

1977, Dec. 17   Perf. 13x12½
1559 A770 3fr multicolored   2.00 1.00

Sabine, after
David — A771

1977-78   Engr.   Perf. 13
1560 A771   1c slate   .20 .20
1561 A771   2c brt violet   .20 .20
1562 A771   5c slate green   .20 .20
1563 A771   10c red brown   .20 .20
1564 A771   15c Prus blue   .20 .20
1565 A771   20c brt green   .20 .20
1566 A771   30c orange   .20 .20
1567 A771   50c red lilac   .20 .20
1568 A771   80c green   1.10 .20
  a.   Booklet pane of 10   11.00
1569 A771   80c olive   .30 .20
1570 A771   1fr red   1.25 .20
  a.   Booklet pane of 5   8.50
  b.   Booklet pane of 10   15.00
1571 A771   1fr green   .55 .20
  a.   Booklet pane of 10   5.50
1572 A771 1.20fr red   .55 .20
  a.   Booklet pane of 5   4.25
  b.   Booklet pane of 10   7.75
1573 A771 1.40fr brt blue   2.00 .20
1574 A771 1.70fr grnsh blue   .70 .20
1575 A771   2fr emerald   .70 .20
1576 A771 2.10fr lilac rose   .75 .20
1577 A771   3fr dark brown   1.00 .30
    Nos. 1560-1577 (18)   10.50 3.70

Issued: #1560-1567, 1573, 1575, 1577,
4/3/78; #1568, 1570, 12/19/77; #1569, 1571,
1572, 1574, 1576, 6/5/78.

Coil Stamps
1978   Perf. 13 Horiz.
1578 A771   80c bright green 1.40 1.00
1579 A771   1fr bright green 1.10 1.00
1579A A771   1fr bright red   1.40 1.00
1579B A771 1.20fr bright red 1.10 1.00
    Nos. 1578-1579B (4)   5.00 4.00

See Nos. 1658-1677.
For similar design inscribed "REPUBLIQUE
FRANCAISE" see type A900.

Percheron,
by Jacques
Birr
A772

Osprey — A773

1978   Photo.   Perf. 13
1580 A772 1.70fr multicolored   1.00 .80
          Engr.
1581 A773 1.80fr multicolored   .90 .50
Nature protection.
Issue dates: 1.70fr, Jan. 7; 1.80fr, Oct. 14.

Tournament, 1662, Etching — A774

Institut de France and Pont des Arts,
Paris, by Bernard Buffet — A776

Horses, by Yves Brayer — A777

1978   Engr.   Perf. 12x13
1582 A774 2fr black   3.00 1.25
          Perf. 13x12
1584 A776 3fr multicolored   2.75 1.40
1585 A777 3fr multicolored   2.00 1.20
    Nos. 1582-1585 (3)   7.75 3.85

Issued: 2fr, 1/14; #1584, 2/4; #1585, 12/9.

Communications
School and
Tower — A778

1978, Jan. 19   Engr.   Perf. 13
1586 A778 80c Prussian blue   .30 .25

Natl. Telecommunications School, cent.

Swedish and French Flags, Map of Saint Barthelemy
A779

1978, Jan. 19
1587 A779 1.10fr multicolored .45 .25
Centenary of the reunion with France of Saint Barthelemy Island, West Indies.

Regions of France

Ile de France — A780

Tanker, Refinery, Flower, Upper Normandy A781

Lower Normandy A782

1978 Photo. Perf. 13
1588 A780 1fr red, blue & blk .50 .20
Engr.
1589 A781 1.40fr multicolored .75 .35
Photo.
1590 A782 1.70fr multicolored 1.10 .50
Nos. 1588-1590 (3) 2.35 1.05
Issued: 1fr, 3/4; 1.40fr, 1/21; 1.70fr, 3/31.

Stylized Map of France A788   Young Stamp Collector A789

1978, Feb. 11 Engr. Perf. 13
1596 A788 1.10fr violet & green .45 .25
Program of administrative changes, 15th anniv.

1978, Feb. 25
1597 A789 80c multicolored .30 .25
JUVEXNIORT, Youth Philatelic Exhibition, Niort, Feb. 25-March 5.

Tourist Issue

Verdon Gorge — A790   Saint-Saturnin Church — A792

Pont Neuf, Paris A791

Our Lady of Bec-Hellouin Abbey — A793

Chateau D'Esquelbecq — A794

Aubazine Abbey A795

Fontevraud Abbey A796

1978 Engr. Perf. 13
1598 A790 50c multicolored .20 .20
1599 A791 80c multicolored .35 .25
1600 A792 1fr black .35 .25
1601 A793 1.10fr multicolored .50 .25
1602 A794 1.10fr multicolored .50 .25
1603 A795 1.25fr carmine & brn .85 .30
1604 A796 1.70fr multicolored .90 .40
Nos. 1598-1604 (7) 3.65 1.85
Issued: 1.25fr, 2/18; 50c, 3/6; #1601, 3/26; 80c, 5/27; 1fr, 6/10; 1.70fr, 6/3; #1602, 6/17.

Fish and Corals — A797

1978, Apr. 15 Photo. Perf. 13
1605 A797 1.25fr multicolored 1.00 .85
Port Cros National Park, 15th anniversary.

Flowers, Butterflies and Houses — A798

1978, Apr. 22 Engr. Perf. 13
1606 A798 1.70fr multicolored 2.75 .35
Beautification of France campaign, 50th anniv.

Hands Shielding Source of Heat and Light A799

1978, Apr. 22
1607 A799 1fr multicolored .60 .25
Energy conservation.

World War I Memorial near Lens — A800   Fountain of the Innocents, Paris — A801

1978, May 6
1608 A800 2fr lemon & magenta 1.00 .30
Colline Notre Dame de Lorette memorial of World War I.

1978, May 6
Europa: 1.40fr, Flower Park Fountain, Paris.
1609 A801 1fr multicolored .40 .25
1610 A801 1.40fr multicolored .90 .50

Maurois Palace, Troyes — A802

1978, May 13
1611 A802 1fr multicolored .55 .30
51st Congress of the Federation of French Philatelic Societies, Troyes, May 13-15.

Roland Garros Tennis Court and Player — A803

1978, May 27
1612 A803 1fr multicolored 2.50 .40
Roland Garros Tennis Court, 50th anniv.

Hand and Plant — A804   Printing Office Emblem — A805

1978, Sept. 9 Engr. Perf. 13
1613 A804 1.30fr brown, red & grn .60 .25
Encouragement of handicrafts.

1978, Sept. 23
1614 A805 1fr multicolored .50 .20
National Printing Office, established 1538.

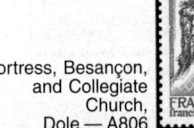

Fortress, Besançon, and Collegiate Church, Dole — A806

Valenciennes and Maubeuge — A807

1978
1615 A806 1.20fr multicolored .55 .20
1616 A807 1.20fr multicolored .55 .20
Reunion of Franche-Comté and Valenciennes and Maubeuge with France, 300th anniversary.
Issued: #1615, Sept. 23; #1616, Sept. 30.

Sower Type of 1906-1937 and Academy Emblem — A808   Gymnasts, Strasbourg Cathedral, Storks — A809

1978, Oct. 7
1617 A808 1fr multicolored .45 .30
Academy of Philately, 50th anniversary.

1978, Oct. 21
1618 A809 1fr multicolored .70 .30
19th World Gymnastics Championships, Strasbourg, Oct. 23-26.

Various Sports A810   Polish Veterans' Monument A811

1978, Oct. 21
1619 A810 1fr multicolored 1.10 .40
Sports for all.

1978, Nov. 11
1620 A811 1.70fr multicolored .80 .50
Polish veterans of World War II.

Railroad Car and Monument, Compiègne Forest, Rethondes A812

1978, Nov. 11 Engr. Perf. 13
1621 A812 1.20fr indigo .75 .30
60th anniversary of World War I armistice.

Handicapped People — A813

1978, Nov. 18
1622 A813 1fr multicolored   .45   .25
Rehabilitation of the handicapped.

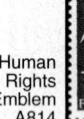

Human
Rights
Emblem
A814

1978, Dec. 9   Engr.   Perf. 13
1623 A814 1.70fr dk brown & blue   .80   .40
30th anniversary of Universal Declaration of
Human Rights.

Child and
IYC
Emblem
A815

1979, Jan. 6   Engr.   Perf. 13
1624 A815 1.70fr multicolored   4.00 2.50
International Year of the Child.

"Music," 15th Century
Miniature — A816

1979, Jan. 13   Perf. 13x12½
1625 A816 2fr multicolored   1.50   .90

Diana
Taking a
Bath,
d'Ecouen
Castle
A817

Church at Auvers-on-Oise, by Vincent
Van Gogh — A818

Head of
Marianne,
by
Salvador
Dali
A819

Fire
Dancer
from The
Magic
Flute, by
Chaplain
Midy
A820

1979   Photo.   Perf. 12½x13
1626 A817 2fr multicolored   1.40 1.00
1627 A818 2fr multicolored   5.50 1.25
1628 A819 3fr multicolored   1.50 1.00
1629 A820 3fr multicolored   1.50 1.00
  Nos. 1626-1629 (4)   9.90 4.25
Issue dates: #1626, Sept. 22; #1627, Oct.
27; #1628, Nov. 19; #1629, Nov. 26.

Orange
Agaric — A821

Mushrooms: 83c, Death trumpet. 1.30fr,
Olive wood pleurotus. 2.25fr, Cauliflower
claveria.

1979, Jan. 15   Engr.   Perf. 13
1630 A821   64c orange   .50   .25
1631 A821   83c brown   .50   .30
1632 A821   1.30fr yellow bister 1.00   .50
1633 A821   2.25fr brown purple   1.50 1.00
  Nos. 1630-1633 (4)   3.50 2.05
Nos. 1630-1633 are known only precanceled. See second note after No. 132.

Victor
Segalen
A822

1979, Jan. 20
1634 A822 1.50fr multicolored   .70   .30
Physician, explorer and writer (1878-1919).

Hibiscus and
Palms — A823

1979, Feb. 3
1635 A823 35c multicolored   .20   .20
International Flower Festival, Martinique.

Buddha,
Stupas,
Temple of
Borobudur
A824

1979, Feb. 24
1636 A824 1.80fr ol & slate grn   .85   .40
Save the Temple of Borobudur, Java,
campaign.

Boy, by Francisque
Poulbot (1879-1946)
A825

1979, Mar. 24   Photo.
1637 A825 1.30fr multicolored   .60   .25

Tourist Issue

Chateau de
Maisons,
Laffitte
A826

Bernay and St.
Pierre sur Dives
Abbeys — A827

View of
Auray — A827a

Steenvorde
Windmill — A828

Wall
Painting,
Niaux Cave
A829

Royal
Palace,
Perpignan
A830

1979   Engr.   Perf. 13
1638 A826   45c multicolored   .30   .20
1639 A827   1fr multicolored   .45   .25
1640 A827a   1fr multicolored   .45   .25
1641 A828   1.20fr multicolored   .55   .25
1642 A829   1.50fr multicolored   .70   .40
1643 A830   1.70fr multicolored   .75   .60
  Nos. 1638-1643 (6)   3.20 1.95
Issued: 45c, 10/6; #1639, 6/16; #1640, 6/30;
1.20fr, 6/12; 1.50fr, 7/9; 1.70fr, 4/21.

Honey Bee
A831

1979, Mar. 31   Engr.   Perf. 13
1644 A831 1fr multicolored   .85   .30
Nature protection.

St. Germain
des Prés
Abbey
A832

1979, Apr. 21
1645 A832 1.40fr multicolored   .65   .35

Simoun Mail Monoplanes, 1935, and
Map of Mail Routes — A833

Europa: 1.70fr, Floating spheres used on
Seine during siege of Paris, 1870.

1979, Apr. 28
1646 A833 1.20fr multicolored   .75   .35
1647 A833 1.70fr multicolored   1.00   .50

Ship and
View of
Nantes
A834

1979, May 5   Engr.   Perf. 13
1648 A834 1.20fr multicolored   .55   .30
52nd National Congress of French Philatelic
Societies, Nantes, May 5-7.

Royal Palace,
1789 — A835

1979, May 19
1649 A835 1fr car rose & pur   .45   .25

European
Elections
A836

1979, May 19   Photo.   Perf. 13
1650 A836 1.20fr multicolored   .55   .25
European Parliament, 1st direct elections,
June 10.

Joan of Arc
Monument
A837

1979, May 24   **Engr.**
1651 A837 1.70fr brt lilac rose   .75   .40
Joan of Arc, the Maid of Orleans (1412-1431).

Felix Guyon
and
Catheters
A840

1979, June 23
1652 A840 1.80fr sepia & blue   .60   .20
Felix Guyon (1831-1920), urologist.

Lantern Tower,
La Rochelle
A841

Telecom '79
A842

Towers: 88c, Chartres Cathedral. 1.40fr, Bourges Cathedral. 2.35fr, Amiens Cathedral.

1979, Aug. 13   **Engr.**   **Perf. 13**
1653 A841 68c vio brn & blk   .30   .30
1654 A841 88c ultra & blk   .40   .30
1655 A841 1.40fr gray grn & blk   .65   .50
1656 A841 2.35fr dull brn & blk   1.10   .60
   Nos. 1653-1656 (4)   2.45   1.70

Nos. 1653-1656 are known only precanceled. See second note after No. 132. See Nos. 1684-1687, 1719-1722, 1814-1817.

1979, Sept. 22
1657 A842 1.10fr multicolored   .40   .20
3rd World Telecommunications Exhibition.

Sabine Type of 1977-78
1979-81   **Engr.**   **Perf. 13**
1658 A771 40c brown ('81)   .20   .20
1659 A771 60c red brn ('81)   .25   .20
1660 A771 70c violet blue   .30   .25
1661 A771 90c brt lilac ('81)   .40   .30
1662 A771 1fr gray olive   .45   .20
1663 A771 1.10fr green   .70   .25
1664 A771 1.20fr green ('80)   .55   .20
1665 A771 1.30fr rose red   .70   .20
1666 A771 1.40fr rose red ('80)   .65   .20
1667 A771 1.60fr purple   1.00   .30
1668 A771 1.80fr ocher   .85   .60
1669 A771 3.50fr lt ol grn ('81)   1.60   .60
1670 A771 4fr brt car ('81)   1.80   .40
1671 A771 5fr brt grnsh bl ('81)   2.25   .30
   Nos. 1658-1671 (14)   11.70   4.20

Coil Stamps
1979-80   **Perf. 13 Horiz.**
1674 A771 1.10fr green   1.75   .60
1675 A771 1.20fr green ('80)   .65   .50
1676 A771 1.30fr rose red   1.75   .60
1677 A771 1.40fr rose red ('80)   .90   .40
   Nos. 1674-1677 (4)   5.05   2.10

Lorraine
Region — A845

1979, Nov. 10
1678 A845 2.30fr multicolored   1.00   .30

Gears
A847

1979, Nov. 17   **Perf. 13**
1680 A847 1.80fr multicolored   .85   .40
Central Technical School of Paris, 150th anniv.

Judo Throw
A848

1979, Nov. 24   **Engr.**
1681 A848 1.60fr multicolored   .75   .40
World Judo Championships, Paris, Dec.

Violins — A849

1979, Dec. 10
1682 A849 1.30fr multicolored   .60   .35

Eurovision
A850

1980, Jan. 12   **Engr.**   **Perf. 13x13½**
1683 A850 1.80fr multicolored   1.00   .70

Tower Type of 1979
Designs: 76c, Chateau d'Angers. 99c, Chateau de Kerjean. 1.60fr, Chateau de Pierrefonds. 2.65fr, Chateau de Tarascon.

1980, Jan. 21   **Engr.**
1684 A841 76c grnsh bl & blk   .35   .30
1685 A841 99c slate grn & blk   .45   .30
1686 A841 1.60fr red & blk   .75   .55
1687 A841 2.65fr brn org & blk   1.25   .65
   Nos. 1684-1687 (4)   2.80   1.80

Nos. 1684-1687 are known only precanceled. See second note after No. 132.

Self-portrait, by Albrecht Dürer,
Philexfrance '82 Emblem — A851

Woman
Holding
Fan, by
Ossip
Zadkine
A852

Abstract, by Raoul Ubak — A853

Hommage to J.S. Bach, by Jean
Picart Le Doux — A854

Peasant,
by Louis
Le Nain
A855

Woman
with Blue
Eyes, by
Modigliani
A856

Abstract,
by Hans
Hartung
A857

Engraved, Photogravure (#1691, 1694)
1980   **Perf. 12½x13, 13x12½**
1688 A851 2fr multicolored   1.00   .90
1689 A852 3fr multicolored   1.50   1.00
1690 A853 3fr multicolored   1.50   1.00
1691 A854 3fr multicolored   1.50   1.00
1692 A855 3fr multicolored   1.50   1.00
1693 A856 4fr multicolored   3.00   1.25
1694 A857 4fr ultra & black   2.00   1.25
   Nos. 1688-1694 (7)   12.00   7.40

Issued: #1688, 6/7; #1689, 1/19; #1690, 2/2; #1691, 9/20; #1693, 10/26; #1692, 11/10; #1694, 12/20.

Giants of the
North
Festival — A858

French
Cuisine — A859

1980, Feb. 16   **Perf. 13**
1695 A858 1.60fr multicolored   .75   .35

1980, Feb. 23
1696 A859 90c red & lt brown   .80   .40

Woman
Embroidering
A860

Fight Against
Cigarette
Smoking
A861

Photogravure and Engraved
1980, Mar. 29   **Perf. 13**
1697 A860 1.10fr multicolored   .50   .30

1980, Apr. 5   **Photo.**   **Perf. 13**
1698 A861 1.30fr multicolored   .60   .20

Aristide
Briand — A862

Europa : 1.80fr, St. Benedict.

1980, Apr. 26   **Engr.**   **Perf. 13**
1699 A862 1.30fr multicolored   .60   .30
1700 A862 1.80fr red & red brown   .85   .50

Aristide Briand (1862-1932), prime minister, 1909-1911, 1921-1922; St. Benedict, patron saint of Europe.

Liancourt, College, Map of
Northwestern France — A863

1980, May 19   **Engr.**   **Perf. 13**
1701 A863 2fr dk green & pur   .90   .35

National College of Arts and Handicrafts (founded by Larochefoucauld Liancourt) bicentenary.

Cranes, Town Hall
Tower,
Dunkirk — A864

1980, May 24
1702 A864 1.30fr multicolored .60 .20

53rd Natl. Congress of French Federation of
Philatelic Societies, Dunkirk, May 24-26.

Tourist Issue

Chateau de
Maintenon
A866

Cordes
A865

Montauban
A867

St. Peter's
Abbey,
Solesmes
A868

Puy Cathedral
A869

1980		**Engr.**	**Perf. 13**	
1703	A865	1.50fr multicolored	.70	.30
1704	A866	2fr multicolored	.90	.30
1705	A867	2.30fr multicolored	1.00	.30
1706	A868	2.50fr multicolored	1.10	.30
1707	A869	3.20fr multicolored	1.50	.55
	Nos. 1703-1707 (5)		5.20	1.75

Issued: #1703, 4/5; #1704, 6/7; #1705, 5/7;
#1706, 9/20; #1707, 5/12.

Graellsia
Isabellae
A870

1980, May 31 **Photo.**
1708 A870 1.10fr multicolored .75 .35

Association
Emblem — A871

1980, June 10 **Photo.**
1709 A871 1.30fr red & blue .60 .25

Intl. Public Relations Assoc., 25th anniv.

Marianne,
French
Architecture
A872

1980, June 21 **Engr.**
1710 A872 1.50fr bluish & gray blk .70 .30

Heritage Year.

Earth
Sciences
A873

1980, July 5
1711 A873 1.60fr dk brown & red .75 .50

International Geological Congress.

Rochambeau's
Landing — A874

1980, July 15
1712 A874 2.50fr multicolored 1.10 .50

Rochambeau's landing at Newport, R.I.
(American Revolution), bicentenary.

Message of Peace, by Yaacov
Agam — A875

1980, Oct. 4 **Photo.** **Perf. 11½x13**
1713 A875 4fr multicolored 3.50 1.00

French Golf
Federation
A876

1980, Oct. 18 **Engr.**
1714 A876 1.40fr multicolored .65 .30

Comedie
Francaise,
300th
Anniversary
A877

1980, Oct. 18
1715 A877 2fr multicolored .90 .45

Charles de Gaulle — A878

1980, Nov. 10 **Photo.** **Perf. 13**
1716 A878 1.40fr multicolored 1.00 .50

40th anniversary of De Gaulle's appeal of
June 18, and 10th anniversary of his death.

Guardsman — A879

1980, Nov. 24 **Engr.** **Perf. 13**
1717 A879 1.70fr multicolored .80 .45

Rambouillet
Chateau
A880

1980, Dec. 6 **Engr.** **Perf. 13**
1718 A880 2.20fr multicolored 1.00 .35

Tower Type of 1979

Designs: 88c, Imperial Chapel, Ajaccio.
1.14fr, Astronomical Clock, Besancon. 1.84fr,
Coucy Castle ruins. 3.05fr, Font-de-Gaume
cave drawing, Les Eyzies de Tayac.

1981, Jan. 11		**Engr.**	**Perf. 13**	
1719	A841	88c dp mag & blk	.40	.20
1720	A841	1.14fr ultra & blk	.55	.30
1721	A841	1.84fr dk green & blk	.85	.50
1722	A841	3.05fr brn red & blk	1.40	.80
	Nos. 1719-1722 (4)		3.20	1.80

Nos. 1719-1722 are known only precanceled. See second note after No. 132.

Microelectronics — A881

1981			**Photo.**	
1723	A881	1.20fr shown	.75	.30
1724	A881	1.20fr Biology	.55	.30
1725	A881	1.40fr Energy	.65	.30
1726	A881	1.80fr Marine explora-tion	.85	.50
1727	A881	2fr Telemetry	.90	.65
	Nos. 1723-1727 (5)		3.70	2.05

Issue dates: #1723, Feb. 5; others, Mar. 28.

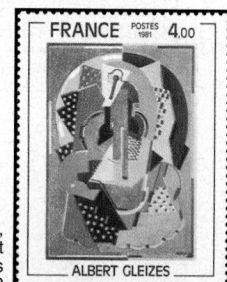

Abstract,
by Albert
Gleizes
A882

1981, Feb. 28 **Perf. 12½x13**
1728 A882 4fr multicolored 2.00 .90

The Footpath by Camille
Pissaro — A883

1981, Apr. 18 **Engr.** **Perf. 13x12½**
1729 A883 2fr multicolored 1.25 .90

Child Watering
Smiling Map of
France — A884

1981, Mar. 14 **Engr.** **Perf. 13**
1730 A884 1.40fr multicolored .65 .25

Sully Chateau, Rosny-sur-
Seine — A885

1981, Mar. 21
1731 A885 2.50fr multicolored 1.10 .40

Tourist Issue

Roman Temple,
Nimes — A886

Church of St.
Jean,
Lyon — A887

St. Anne d'Auray
Basilica — A888

Vaucelles
Abbey
A889

Notre Dame
of Louviers
A890

1981, Apr. 11 **Engr.** **Perf. 13**
1732 A886 1.70fr multicolored .85 .30

1981

1733 A887 1.40fr dk red & dk brn .65 .30
1734 A888 2.20fr blue & black 1.00 .50

Issue dates: 1.40fr, May 30; 2.20fr, July 4.

1981

1735 A889 2fr red & black .90 .40
1736 A890 2.20fr red brn & dk brn 1.00 .50
Nos. 1732-1736 (5) 4.40 2.00

Issue dates: 2fr, Sept. 19; 2.20fr, Sept. 26.

Europa Issue 1981

Folkdances A891

1981, May 4 *Perf. 13*
1737 A891 1.40fr Bouree *.65 .25*
1738 A891 2fr Sardane *1.25 .40*

Bookbinding A892

Cadets A893

1981, Apr. 4 *Perf. 13*
1739 A892 1.50fr olive & car rose .70 .40

1981, May 16
1740 A893 2.50fr multicolored 1.10 .30

Military College at St. Maixent centenary.

Man Drawing Geometric Diagram — A894

1981, May 23 **Photo.**
1741 A894 2fr shown 1.40 .90
1742 A894 2fr Faces 1.40 .90
a. Pair, #1741-1742 + label 3.50 3.00

PHILEXFRANCE '82 Stamp Exhibition, Paris, June 11-21, 1982.

Theophraste Renaudot and Emile de Girardin — A895

Public Gardens, Vichy — A896

1981, May 30 **Engr.**
1743 A895 2.20fr black & red 1.00 .40

350th anniversary of La Gazette (founded by Renaudot), and death centenary of founder of Le Journal (de Girardin).

1981, June 6
1744 A896 1.40fr multicolored .65 .30

54th National Congress of French Federation of Philatelic Societies, Vichy.

Higher National College for Commercial Studies Centenary A897

1981, June 20 *Perf. 13*
1745 A897 1.40fr multicolored .65 .30

Sea Shore Conservation — A898

1981, June 20
1746 A898 1.60fr multicolored .75 .55

World Fencing Championship, Clermont-Ferrand, July 2-13 — A899

1981, June 27
1747 A899 1.80fr multicolored .85 .45

Sabine, after David — A900

1981, Sept. 1 **Engr.**
1755 A900 1.40fr green .85 .20
1756 A900 1.60fr red 1.00 .25
1757 A900 2.30fr blue 1.40 .85
Nos. 1755-1757 (3) 3.25 1.30

Coil Stamps

1981 **Engr.** *Perf. 13 Horiz.*
1758 A900 1.40fr green .75 .50
1759 A900 1.60fr red .75 .40

Highway Safety ("Drink or Drive") A901

1981, Sept. 5 *Perf. 13*
1768 A901 1.60fr multicolored .75 .35

45th Intl. PEN Club Congress A902

Jules Ferry, Statesman A903

1981, Sept. 19 *Perf. 13*
1769 A902 2fr multicolored .90 .35

1981, Sept. 26 *Perf. 12½x13*
1770 A903 1.60fr multicolored .75 .35

Free compulsory public school centenary.

Natl. Savings Bank Centenary A904

1981, Sept. 21 **Photo.** *Perf. 13*
1771 A904 1.40fr multicolored .65 .20
1772 A904 1.60fr multicolored .75 .20

The Divers, by Edouard Pignon — A905

1981, Oct. 3 *Perf. 13x12½*
1773 A905 4fr multicolored 1.90 .90

Alleluia, by Alfred Manessier A906

1981, Dec. 19 **Photo.** *Perf. 12x13*
1774 A906 4fr multicolored 1.90 .90

Tourist Issue

Saint-Emilion — A907

Crest — A908

1981 **Engr.** *Perf. 13x12½*
1775 A907 2.60fr dk red & lt ol grn 1.20 .35

Perf. 13

1776 A908 2.90fr dk green 1.40 .25

Issued: #1775, Oct. 10; #1776, Nov. 28.

150th Anniv. of Naval Academy A909

1981, Oct. 17 *Perf. 13*
1777 A909 1.40fr multicolored .65 .35

A910

A911

St. Hubert Kneeling before the Stag, 15th cent. sculpture.

1981, Oct. 24
1778 A910 1.60fr multicolored .75 .35

Museum of hunting and nature.

1981, Nov. 2

V. Schoelcher, J. Jaures, J. Moulin, the Pantheon.

1779 A911 1.60fr blue & dull pur .75 .30

Intl. Year of the Disabled A912

1981, Nov. 7
1780 A912 1.60fr multicolored .75 .25

Men Leading Cattle, 2nd Cent. Roman Mosaic — A913

1981, Nov. 14 *Perf. 13x12*
1781 A913 2fr multicolored 1.10 .90

Virgil's birth bimillennium.

Martyrs of Chateaubriant A914

1981, Dec. 12 **Engr.** *Perf. 13*
1782 A914 1.40fr multicolored .65 .25

Liberty, after Delacroix — A915

1982 **Engr.** *Perf. 13*
1783 A915 5c dk green .20 .20
1784 A915 10c dull red .20 .20
1785 A915 15c brt rose lilac .35 .35
1786 A915 20c brt green .20 .20
1787 A915 30c orange .20 .20
1788 A915 40c brown .20 .20
a. Bklt. pane of 5, 4 No. 1784, No. 1788 ('87) 1.00
1789 A915 50c lilac .25 .20
1790 A915 60c lt red brn .30 .20
1791 A915 70c ultra .30 .20
1792 A915 80c lt olive grn .35 .20
1793 A915 90c brt lilac .40 .20
1794 A915 1fr olive green .45 .20
1795 A915 1.40fr green .65 .20
1796 A915 1.60fr green .75 .20
1797 A915 1.60fr red .75 .20
1798 A915 1.80fr red .85 .20

1799	A915	2fr brt yel grn	.90	.20
1800	A915	2.30fr blue	2.00	1.25
1801	A915	2.60fr blue	2.00	1.00
1802	A915	3fr chocolate	1.40	.30
1803	A915	4fr brt carmine	1.90	.30
1804	A915	5fr gray blue	2.25	.20
	Nos. 1783-1804 (22)		16.85	6.60

Coil Stamps
Perf. 13 Horiz.

1805	A915	1.40fr green	1.25	.90
1806	A915	1.60fr red	1.25	.90
1807	A915	1.60fr green	.85	.90
1807A	A915	1.80fr red	.90	.50
	Nos. 1805-1807A (4)		4.25	2.80

Issued: 5c-50c, 1fr-1.40fr, 2fr, 2.30fr, 5fr, #1797, 1/2; 1.80fr, 2.60fr, #1796, 6/1; 60c-90c, 3fr, 4fr, 11/3.

See Nos. 1878-1897A, 2077-2080. For surcharge see No. 2115.

Tourist Issue

St. Pierre and Miquelon
A916

Corsica A917

Renaissance Fountain, Aix-en Provence — A918

Collonges-la-Rouge — A919

Castle of Henry IV, Pau A920

Lille — A921

Chateau Ripaille, Haute-Savoie — A921a

1982		**Engr.**		***Perf. 12½***
1808	A916	1.60fr dk blue & blk	.75	.20
1809	A917	1.90fr blue & red	.90	.25
		Perf. 13		
1810	A918	2fr multicolored	.90	.40
1811	A919	3fr multicolored	1.40	.30
1812	A920	3fr ultra & dk bl	1.40	.40

Issued: 1.60fr, 1.90fr, Jan. 9; 2fr, June 21, No. 1811, July 5, No. 1812, May 15.

1982			***Perf. 13x12½***	
1813	A921	1.80fr dull red & ol	.85	.25
1813A	A921a	2.90fr multicolored	1.40	.80
	Nos. 1808-1813A (7)		7.60	2.65

Issue dates: 1.80fr, Oct. 16; 2.90fr, Sept. 4.

Tower Type of 1979

97c, Tanlay Castle, Yonne. 1.25fr, Salses Fort, Pyrenees-Orientales. 2.03fr, Montlhery Tower, Essonne. 3.36fr, Chateau d'If Bouches-du-Rhone.

1982, Jan. 11		**Engr.**		***Perf. 13***
1814	A841	97c olive grn & blk	.45	.20
1815	A841	1.25fr red & blk	.55	.25
1816	A841	2.03fr sepia & blk	.95	.50
1817	A841	3.36fr ultra & blk	1.50	.80
	Nos. 1814-1817 (4)		3.45	1.75

Nos. 1814-1817 are known only precanceled. See second note after No. 132.

800th Birth Anniv. of St. Francis of Assisi A922

1982, Feb. 6		**Photo. & Engr.**		
1818	A922	2fr black & blue	.90	.50

Posts and Mankind — A923

Posts and Technology — A924

Illustration reduced.

1982, Feb. 13		**Photo.**		
1819	A923	2fr multicolored	3.50	2.00
1820	A924	2fr multicolored	3.50	2.00
a.	Pair, #1819-1820 + label		9.00	6.50

PHILEXFRANCE '82 Stamp Exhibition, Paris, June 11-21.

Souvenir Sheet

Marianne, by Jean Cocteau — A925

1982, June 11				
1821	A925	Sheet of 2	14.00	14.00
a.	4fr red & blue		6.00	6.00
b.	6fr blue & red		6.00	6.00

Sold only with 20fr show admission ticket.

Scouting Year A926

1982, Feb. 20		**Engr.**		
1822	A926	2.30fr yel grn & blk	1.00	.30

31st Natl. Census — A927

1982, Feb. 27		**Photo.**		
1823	A927	1.60fr multicolored	.75	.20

Bale-Mulhouse Airport Opening — A928

1982, Mar. 15		**Engr.**		***Perf. 13***
1824	A928	1.90fr multicolored	.90	.50

Fight Against Racism A929

1982, Mar. 20				
1825	A929	2.30fr brn & red org	1.00	.50

Blacksmith — A930

1982, Apr. 17				
1826	A930	1.40fr multicolored	.65	.40

Europa 1982 A931

1982, Apr. 24				
1827	A931	1.60fr Treaty of Rome, 1957	.75	.30
1828	A931	2.30fr Treaty of Verdun, 843	1.30	.40

1982 World Cup A932

1982, Apr. 28				
1829	A932	1.80fr multicolored	1.60	.35

Young Greek Soldier, Hellenic Sculpture, Agude A933

1982, May 15			***Perf. 12½x13***	
1830	A933	4fr multicolored	1.90	1.00

Embarkation for Ostia, by Claude Gellee — A934

The Lacemaker, by Vermeer A935

Turkish Chamber, by Balthus — A936

1982		**Photo.**	***Perf. 13x12½, 12½x13***	
1831	A934	4fr multicolored	1.90	1.00
1832	A935	4fr multicolored	1.90	1.00
1833	A936	4fr multicolored	1.90	1.00
	Nos. 1831-1833 (3)		5.70	3.00

Issued: #1831, 6/19; #1832, 9/4; #1833, 11/6.

35th Intl. Film Festival, Cannes — A937

Natl. Space Studies Center, 20th Anniv. — A938

1982, May 15		**Photo.**		***Perf. 13***
1834	A937	2.30fr multicolored	1.00	.80

1982, May 15				**Engr.**
1835	A938	2.60fr multicolored	1.20	1.00

A939

 — Jules Vallès — A940

1982, June 4   **Photo.**
1836 A939 2.60fr multicolored   1.20 .50
Industrialized Countries' Summit Meeting, Versailles, June 4-6.

1982, June 4   **Engr.**   *Perf. 13*
1837 A940 1.60fr ol grn & dk grn   .75 .20
Jules Valles (1832-1885), writer.

Frederic and Irene Curie, Radiation Diagrams
A941

1982, June 26
1838 A941 1.80fr multicolored   .85 .35

Electric Street Lighting Centenary
A942

1982, July 10
1839 A942 1.80fr dk blue & vio   .85 .25

The Family, by Marc Boyan
A943

Photogravure and Engraved
1982, Sept. 18   *Perf. 12½x13*
1840 A943 4fr multicolored   2.00 1.00

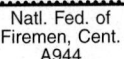

Natl. Fed. of Firemen, Cent.
A944

Marionettes
A945

1982, Sept. 18   **Engr.**   *Perf. 13*
1841 A944 3.30fr red & sepia   1.75 .40

1982, Sept. 25
1842 A945 1.80fr multicolored   .85 .35

Rugby
A946

1982, Oct. 9
1843 A946 1.60fr multicolored   2.00 .35

Higher Education
A947

1982, Oct. 16
1844 A947 1.80fr red & black   .85 .35

TB Bacillus Centenary
A948

1982, Nov. 13
1845 A948 2.60fr red & black   1.20 .40

St. Teresa of Avila (1515-82)
A949

Leon Blum (1872-1950), Politician
A950

1982, Nov. 20
1846 A949 2.10fr multicolored   .95 .45

1982, Dec. 18   **Engr.**   *Perf. 13*
1847 A950 1.80fr dk brn & brn   .85 .25

Cavelier de la Salle (1643-1687), Explorer — A951

1982, Dec. 18   *Perf. 13x12½*
1848 A951 3.25fr multicolored   1.50 .50

Spring — A952

1983, Jan. 17   **Engr.**   *Perf. 13*
1849 A952 1.05fr shown   .50 .40
1850 A952 1.35fr Summer   .60 .50
1851 A952 2.19fr Autumn   1.00 .75
1852 A952 3.63fr Winter   1.60 1.25
    Nos. 1849-1852 (4)   3.70 2.90
Nos. 1849-1852 known only precanceled. See second note after No. 132.

Provence-Alpes-Cote d'Azur — A953

Brantome (Perigord)
A954

Concarneau — A955

Noirlac Abbey
A956

Jarnac
A957

Charleville-Mezieres — A958

Illustration A958 reduced.

1983   **Photo.**   *Perf. 13*
1853 A953   1fr multicolored   .45 .25
    Engr.
    Perf. 13x12½
1854 A954 1.80fr multicolored   .85 .20
    Perf. 13
1855 A955   3fr multicolored   1.40 .60
    Perf. 13x12½
1856 A956 3.60fr multicolored   1.60 .35
    Issued: 1fr, 1/8; 1.80fr, 2/5; 3fr, 6/11; 3.60fr, 7/2.

1983   *Perf. 13x12½*
1857 A957   2fr multicolored   .90 .35
1858 A958 3.10fr multicolored   1.40 .85
    Nos. 1853-1858 (6)   6.60 2.60
    Issued: 2fr, Oct. 8; 3.10fr, Sept. 17.

Martin Luther (1483-1546) — A959

1983, Feb. 12   **Engr.**   *Perf. 13*
1859 A959 3.30fr dk brn & tan   1.50 .55

Alliance Francaise Centenary
A960

1983, Feb. 19
1860 A960 1.80fr multicolored   .85 .35

Danielle Casanova (d. 1942), Resistance Leader
A961

1983, Mar. 8
1861 A961 3fr blk & red brn   1.40 .35

World Communications Year — A962

1983, Mar. 12   **Photo.**
1862 A962 2.60fr multicolored   1.20 .75

Manned Flight Bicentenary — A963

1983, Mar. 19   **Photo.**   *Perf. 13*
1863   2fr Hot air balloon   .90 .65
1864   3fr Hydrogen balloon   1.40 .80
   a.   A963 Pair, #1863-1864 + label 2.50 2.50

Female Nude, by Raphael
A964

Aurora-Set, by Dewasne — A965

1983   **Engr.**   *Perf. 13*
1865 A964 4fr multicolored   1.90 1.00
      Photo.
1866 A965 4fr multicolored   1.90 1.00
   Issue dates: #1866, Mar. 19; #1865, Apr. 9.

Illustration from Perrault's Folk Tales, by Gustave Dore
A966

1983, June 18   **Engr.**   *Perf. 13*
1867 A966 4fr red & black   1.90 1.00

Homage to
Jean Effel
A967

1983, Oct. 15
1868 A967 4fr multicolored   1.90 1.00

Le Lapin Agile, by Utrillo — A968

1983, Dec. 3   *Perf. 13x12½*
1869 A968 4fr multicolored   1.90 1.00

Thistle — A969   Europa
               1983 — A970

1983, Apr. 23   **Engr.**   *Perf. 12½x12*
1870 A969 1fr shown   .45 .30
1871 A969 2fr Martagon lily   .90 .30
1872 A969 3fr Aster   1.40 .60
1873 A969 4fr Aconite   1.90 .60
     Nos. 1870-1873 (4)   4.65 1.80

1983, Apr. 29   *Perf. 13*
1874 A970 1.80fr Symbolic shut-
          ter   2.00 .50
1875 A970 2.60fr Lens-to-screen
          diagram   2.10 .75

Centenary of Paris
Convention for the
Protection of
Industrial
Property — A971

1983, May 14   **Photo.**   *Perf. 13*
1876 A971 2fr multicolored   .90 .30

French
Philatelic
Societies
Congress,
Marseille
A972

1983, May 21   **Engr.**   *Perf. 13*
1877 A972 1.80fr multicolored   .85 .35

Liberty Type of 1982
1983-87   **Engr.**   *Perf. 13*
1878 A915 1.70fr green   .75 .20
1879 A915 1.80fr green   .80 .20
1880 A915 1.90fr green   .85 .20
1881 A915 2fr red   .90 .20
1882 A915 2fr green   .90 .20
1883 A915 2.10fr red   .95 .20

1884 A915 2.20fr red   1.00 .20
   a.   Booklet pane of 10   10.00
   b.   Bklt. pane of #1788, 4 #1884   5.00
   c.   With label ('87)   1.00 .20
1885 A915 2.80fr blue   1.25 .90
1886 A915 3fr blue   1.40 .90
1887 A915 3.20fr blue   1.50 .90
1888 A915 3.40fr blue   1.60 .75
1889 A915 3.60fr blue   1.60 .65
1890 A915 10fr purple   4.50 .20
1891 A915 (1.90fr) green   .90 .20
1892 A915 (2fr) green   .90 .20
    Nos. 1878-1892 (15)   19.80 5.70

Coil Stamps
     Engr.   *Perf. 13 Horiz.*
1893 A915 1.70fr green   1.00 .80
1894 A915 1.80fr green   1.00 .50
1895 A915 1.90fr green   1.25 .30
1896 A915 2fr red   1.00 .30
1897 A915 2.10fr red   1.10 .60
1897A A915 2.20fr red   1.00 .50
    Nos. 1893-1897A (6)   6.35 3.00

#1891 is inscribed "A," #1892 "B."
No. 1884c was issued in sheets of 50 plus
50 alternating labels picturing the PHILEX-
FRANCE '89 emblem to publicize the international philatelic exhibition.
Issued: 2.80fr, 10fr, #1881, 6/1; 1.70fr,
2.10fr, 3fr, 7/1/84; 1.80fr, 2.20fr, 3.20fr, 8/1/85;
3.40fr, #1891, 8/1/86; 1.90fr, 9/13/86; #1882,
10/15/87; 3.60fr, #1892, 8/1/87.
For surcharge see No. 2115.

50th Anniv.
of Air
France
A973

1983, June 18
1898 A973 3.45fr multicolored   1.60 .85

Treaties of Versailles and Paris
Bicentenary — A974

1983, Sept. 2   *Perf. 13x12½*
1899 A974 2.80fr multicolored   1.25 .60

Jewelry
Making
A975

1983, Sept. 10   **Photo.**   *Perf. 13*
1900 A975 2.20fr multicolored   1.00 .35

30th Anniv. of Customs Cooperation
Council — A976

1983, Sept. 22   **Engr.**   *Perf. 13x12½*
1901 A976 2.30fr multicolored   1.00 .45

Michaux's
Bicycle
A977

1983, Oct. 1   **Engr.**   *Perf. 13*
1902 A977 1.60fr multicolored   .75 .40

Natl. Weather
Forecasting — A978

1983, Oct. 22   **Engr.**   *Perf. 12½x13*
1903 A978 1.50fr multicolored   .70 .20

Berthie Albrecht (1893-1943) — A979

1983, Nov. 5
1904 A979 1.60fr dk brown & olive .75 .35
1905 A979 1.60fr Rene Levy
          (1906-1943)   .75 .35
    Resistance heroines.

A980   A981

1983, Dec. 16
1906 A980 2fr dk gray & red   .90 .25
Pierre Mendes France (1907-1982), Premier.

1984, Mar. 22   *Perf. 13*
1907 A981 3.60fr Union leader
          Waldeck-
          Rousseau   1.60 .35
    Trade Union centenary.

Homage to
the
Cinema,
by Cesar
A982

1984, Feb. 4   **Engr.**   *Perf. 12½x13*
1908 A982 4fr multicolored   2.00 1.00

Four Corners of the Sky, by Jean
Messagier — A983

1984, Mar. 31   **Photo.**   *Perf. 13x12½*
1909 A983 4fr multicolored   2.00 1.00

Dining Room Corner, at Cannet, by
Pierre Bonnard — A984

Photogravure and Engraved
1984, Apr. 14   *Perf. 12½x12*
1910 A984 4fr multicolored   2.00 1.00

Pythia, by
Andre
Masson
A985

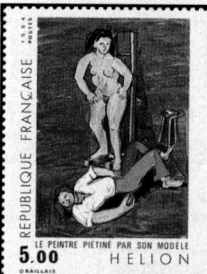

Painter at
the Feet of
His Model,
by Helion
A986

1984   **Photo.**   *Perf. 12x13*
1911 A985 5fr multicolored   2.25 1.00
1912 A986 5fr multicolored   2.25 1.00
Issue dates: #1911, Oct. 13; #1912, Dec. 1.

Guadeloupe — A987

1984, Feb. 25   *Perf. 13*
1913 A987 2.30fr Map, West Indi-
          an dancers   1.00 .35

Vauban
Citadel,
Belle Ile-
en-Mer
A988

Cordouan
Lighthouse — A989

La Grande
Chartreuse
Monastery,
900th
Anniv.
A990

Palais Ideal, Hauterives-Drome — A991

Montsegur Chateau A992

1984 Engr. Perf. 13
1914 A988 2.50fr multicolored 1.10 .35
1915 A989 3.50fr multicolored 1.60 .40
Issued: #1914, 5/26; #1915, 6/23.

1984
1916 A990 1.70fr multicolored .80 .40
1917 A991 2.10fr multicolored .95 .30
1917A A992 3.70fr multicolored 1.75 .40
Nos. 1914-1917A (5) 6.20 1.85
Issued: 1.70fr, 7/7; 2.10fr, 6/30; 3.70fr, 9/15.

Flora Tristan (1803-44), Feminist A992a

1984, Mar. 8
1918 A992a 2.80fr multicolored 1.25 .50

Playing Card Suits — A993

1984, Apr. 11 Engr.
1919 A993 1.14fr Hearts .55 .50
1920 A993 1.47fr Spades .70 .60
1921 A993 2.38fr Diamonds 1.10 .85
1922 A993 3.95fr Clubs 1.80 1.40
Nos. 1919-1922 (4) 4.15 3.35

Nos. 1919-1922 known only precanceled.
See second note after No. 132.

450th Anniv. of Cartier's Landing in Quebec A994

1984, Apr. 20 Photo. & Engr.
1923 A994 2fr multicolored .90 .25
See Canada No. 1011.

Philex '84, Dunkirk A995

1984, Apr. 21 Perf. 13x12½
1924 A995 1.60fr multicolored .75 .35

Europa (1959-84) A996

1984, Apr. 28 Engr. Perf. 13
1925 A996 2fr red brown 1.10 .35
1926 A996 2.80fr blue 1.75 .60

2nd European Parliament Election A997

1984, Mar. 24 Photo. Perf. 13
1927 A997 2fr multicolored .90 .25

Foreign Legion A998

1984, Apr. 30 Engr. Perf. 13x12½
1928 A998 3.10fr multicolored 1.40 .50

40th Anniv. of Liberation A999

Photogravure and Engraved
1984, May 8 Perf. 12½x13
1929 A999 2fr Resistance .90 .50
1930 A999 3fr Landing 1.40 .60
a. Pair, #1929-1930 + label 2.50 2.50

Olympic Events — A1000

Illustration reduced.

1984, June 1 Perf. 13
1931 A1000 4fr multicolored 1.90 .80
Intl. Olympic Committee, 90th anniv. and 1984 Summer Olympics.

Engraving — A1001

1984, June 8 Engr.
1932 A1001 2fr multicolored .90 .25

Bordeaux A1002

1984, June 9 Perf. 13x12½
1933 A1002 2fr red .90 .25
French Philatelic Societies Congress, Bordeaux.

Natl. Telecommunications College, 40th Anniv. — A1003

1984, June 16 Photo. Perf. 13
1934 A1003 3fr Satellite, phone, keyboard 1.40 .35

25th Intl. Geography Congress, Paris — A1004

Illustration reduced.

1984, Aug. 25 Engr. Perf. 13x12½
1935 A1004 3fr Alps 1.40 .50

Telecom I Satellite A1005

1984, Sept. 1 Photo. Perf. 13
1936 A1005 3.20fr multicolored 1.50 .50

High-speed Train Mail Transport A1006

1984, Sept. 8
1937 A1006 2.10fr Electric train, Paris-Lyon 1.00 .25

Local Birds A1007

Marx Dormoy (1888-1941) A1008

Photogravure and Engraved
1984, Sept. 22 Perf. 12½x12
1938 A1007 1fr Gypaetus barbatus .45 .25
1939 A1007 2fr Circaetus gallicus .90 .25
1940 A1007 3fr Accipiter nisus 1.40 .75
1941 A1007 5fr Peregrine falcon 2.25 .55
Nos. 1938-1941 (4) 5.00 1.80

1984, Sept. 22 Perf. 12½x13
1942 A1008 2.40fr multicolored 1.10 .35

A1009

— A1010

1984, Oct. 6 Engr. Perf. 12½x13
1943 A1009 3fr Automobile plans 1.40 .35
100th anniv. of the automobile.

1984, Nov. 3
1944 A1010 2.10fr multicolored .95 .25
Pres. Vincent Auriol (1884-1966).

9th 5-Year Plan A1011

1984, Dec. 8 Photo. Perf. 13
1945 A1011 2.10fr dk blue & scar .95 .25

French Language Promotion — A1012

1985, Jan. 15 Engr. Perf. 12½x13
1946 A1012 3fr multicolored 1.40 .35

Tourism Issue

View of Vienne A1013

Cathedral at Montpelier A1014

St. Michel de Cuxa (Codalet) Abbey — A1015

Talmont Church, Saintonge Romane A1016

Solutre A1017

1985 Perf. 13x12½
1947 A1013 1.70fr ol blk & dk grn .75 .25
1948 A1014 2.10fr sepia & org .95 .25
1949 A1015 2.20fr multicolored 1.00 .35
1950 A1016 3fr multicolored 1.40 .55
1951 A1017 3.90fr multicolored 1.75 .40
Nos. 1947-1951 (5) 5.85 1.80

Issue dates: 1.70fr, Jan. 19; 2.10fr, Mar. 30; 2.20fr, July 6; 3fr, June 15; 3.90fr, Sept. 28.

French TV, 50th Anniv. A1018

1985, Jan. 26 Photo. Perf. 13
1952 A1018 2.50fr multicolored 1.10 .50

Months of the Year — A1019

1985, Feb. 11 Engr.
1953 A1019 1.22fr January .65 .35
1954 A1019 1.57fr February .75 .50
1955 A1019 2.55fr March 1.25 1.00
1956 A1019 4.23fr April 2.25 1.50

1986, Feb. 10 Engr. *Perf. 13*
1957 A1019 1.28fr May .65 .35
1958 A1019 1.65fr June .75 .50
1959 A1019 2.67fr July 1.25 1.10
1960 A1019 4.44fr August 2.25 1.60

1987, Feb. 16 Engr.
1961 A1019 1.31fr September .70 .35
1962 A1019 1.69fr October .90 .50
1963 A1019 2.74fr November 1.40 1.10
1964 A1019 4.56fr December 2.50 1.90
Nos. 1953-1964 (12) 15.30 10.75

Nos. 1953-1964 are known only precanceled. See second note after No. 132.

St. Valentine, by Raymond Peynet A1020

1985, Feb. 14 Photo. *Perf. 13x12½*
1965 A1020 2.10fr multicolored .95 .25

Pauline Kergomard (1838-1925) A1021

1985, Mar. 8 Engr. *Perf. 13x12½*
1966 A1021 1.70fr int bl & cop red .75 .25

Stained Glass Window, Strasbourg Cathedral A1022

Still-life with Candle, Nicolas de Stael — A1023

1985 **Engraved** *Perf. 12x13*
1967 A1022 5fr multicolored 4.00 1.25
Photo.
Perf. 13x12
1968 A1023 5fr multicolored 3.00 1.00
Issue dates: #1967, Apr. 13; #1968, June 1.

Untitled Abstract by Jean Dubuffet — A1024

Octopus Overlaid on Manuscript, by Pierre Alechinsky — A1025

Photogravure; Engraved (#1970)
1985 *Perf. 13x12½*
1969 A1024 5fr multicolored 2.50 1.25
1970 A1025 5fr multicolored 2.50 1.00
Issued: #1969, Sept. 14; #1970, Oct. 12.

The Dog, Abstract by Alberto Giacometti (1901-1966) — A1026

1985, Dec. 7 Engr. *Perf. 13x12½*
1971 A1026 5fr grnsh blk & lt lem 2.50 1.00

Housing in Givors A1027

Contemporary architecture by Jean Renaude.

1985, Apr. 20 Engr. *Perf. 13*
1972 A1027 2.40fr blk, yel org & ol grn 1.10 .50

Landevennec Abbey, 1500th Anniv. — A1028

1985, Apr. 20 *Perf. 13x12½*
1973 A1028 1.70fr green & brn vio .60 .20

A1029 A1030

Europa: 2.10fr, Adam de la Halle (1240-1285), composer. 3fr, Darius Milhaud (1892-1974), composer.

1985, Apr. 27 *Perf. 12½x13*
1974 A1029 2.10fr dr bl, blk, & brt bl 1.00 .40
1975 A1029 3fr dk bl, brt bl & blk 1.75 .65

1985, May 8 *Perf. 13x12½*
1976 A1030 2fr Return of peace .80 .55
1977 A1030 3fr Return of liberty 1.40 .55
a. Pair, #1976-1977 + label 2.25 2.25
Liberation of France from German occupation forces, 40th anniv.

Natl. Philatelic Congress, Tours — A1031

1985, May 25 *Perf. 12½x13*
1978 A1031 2.10fr Tours Cathedral .95 .35

Rabies Vaccine Cent. A1032

1985, June 1 *Perf. 13x12½*
1979 A1032 1.50fr Pasteur inoculating patient .70 .25

Mystere Falcon-900 A1033

1985, June 1 *Perf. 13*
1980 A1033 10fr blue 4.50 2.00

Lake Geneva Life-Saving Society Cent. A1034

1985, June 15
1981 A1034 2.50fr blk, red & brt ultra 1.10 .50

UN, 40th Anniv. — A1035

Huguenot Cross — A1036

1985, June 26 *Perf. 13x12½*
1982 A1035 3fr multicolored 1.40 .35

1985, Aug. 31 Engr. *Perf. 12½x13*
1983 A1036 2.50fr dp vio, dk red brn & dk red 1.10 .35

King Louis XIV revoked the Edict of Nantes on Oct. 18, 1685, dispossessing French Protestants of religious and civil liberty.

A1037 A1038

Trees, leaves and fruit of the beech, elm, oak and spruce varieties.

1985, Sept. 21 Engr. *Perf. 12½*
1984 A1037 1fr shown .45 .25
1985 A1037 2fr Ulmus montana .90 .25
1986 A1037 3fr Quercus pedunculata 1.40 .60
1987 A1037 5fr Picea abies 2.25 .35
Nos. 1984-1987 (4) 5.00 1.45

1985, Nov. 2 Engr. *Perf. 12½x13*
La France Mourning the Dead, Eternal Flame.
1988 A1038 1.80fr brn, org & lake .85 .25
Memorial Day.

A1039 A1040

1985, Nov. 9 Engr.
1989 A1039 3.20fr black & blue 1.50 .50
Charles Dullin, 1885-1949, impresario, theater.

1985, Nov. 16 Engr. *Perf. 13x12½*
1990 A1040 2.20fr red & black 1.00 .20
National information system.

Thai Ambassadors at the Court of King Louis XIV, Painting A1041

1986, Jan. 25 Engr. *Perf. 13*
1991 A1041 3.20fr rose lake & blk 1.50 .75
Normalization of diplomatic relations with Thailand, 300th anniv.

Leisure, by Fernand Leger A1042

1986, Feb. 1 **Photo.** *Perf. 13*
1992 A1042 2.20fr multicolored 1.00 .20
1936 Popular Front, 50th anniv.

Venice Carnival, Paris — A1043

1986, Feb. 12   *Perf. 12½x13*
1993 A1043 2.20fr multicolored   1.00 .20

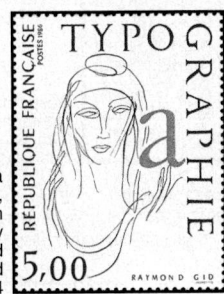

La Marianne, Typograph by Raymond Gid A1044

Photogravure & Engraved
1986, Mar. 3   *Perf. 12½x13½*
1994 A1044 5fr black & dk red   2.25 1.00

Tourism Issue

Filitosa, South Corsica A1045

Loches Chateau A1046

Norman Manor, St. Germain de Livet A1047

Notre-Dame-en-Vaux Monastery, Marne — A1048

Market Square, Bastide de Monpazier, Dordogne — A1049

Illustration A1049 reduced.

1986   **Engr.**   *Perf. 13*
1995 A1045 1.80fr multicolored   .85 .25
1996 A1046 2fr int blue & blk   .90 .50
1997 A1047 2.20fr grnsh bl, brn & grn   1.00 .35
1998 A1048 2.50fr henna brn & sepia   1.10 .40

     Perf. 13x12½
1999 A1049 3.90fr blk & yel org   1.75 .90
   Nos. 1995-1999 (5)   5.60 2.40

Issued: 2.20fr, 3/3; 2fr, 6/14; 2.50fr, 6/9; 1.80fr, 3.90fr, 7/5.

Louise Michel (1830-1905), Anarchist — A1050

1986, Mar. 10   **Engr.**
2000 A1050 1.80fr dk red & gray blk   .80 .20

City of Science and Industry, La Villette — A1051

1986, Mar. 17
2001 A1051 3.90fr multicolored   1.75 .50

Center for Modern Asia-Africa Studies A1052

1986, Apr. 12   **Photo.**   *Perf. 13*
2002 A1052 3.20fr Map   1.50 .30

Skibet, Abstract by Maurice Esteve — A1053

Virginia, Abstract by Alberto Magnelli — A1054

Abstract, by Pierre Soulages — A1055

The Dancer, by Jean Arp A1056

Isabelle d'Este, by Leonardo da Vinci A1057

Perf. 12½x13, 13x12½ (#2005, 2006)
1986   **Photo., Engr. (#2005, 2007)**
2003 A1053 5fr multicolored   2.25 1.00
2004 A1054 5fr multicolored   2.25 1.00
2005 A1055 5fr brt vio, blk & brn gray   2.25 1.00
2006 A1056 5fr multicolored   2.25 1.00
2007 A1057 5fr blk, red brn & grnsh yel   2.25 1.00
   Nos. 2003-2007 (5)   11.25 5.00

Issued: #2003, Apr. 14; #2004, June 25; #2005, Dec. 22; #2006, 2007, Nov. 10.

Victor Basch (1863-1944), IPY Emblem — A1058

1986, Apr. 28   **Engr.**   *Perf. 13*
2008 A1058 2.50fr black & yel grn   1.10 .30
   International Peace Year.

Europa 1986 A1059

1986, Apr. 28   *Perf. 13x12½*
2009 A1059 2.20fr Civet cat   1.00 .35
2010 A1059 3.20fr Bat   1.50 .65

St. Jean-Marie Vianney, Curé of Ars A1060

1986, May 3   **Engr.**   *Perf. 13x12½*
2011 A1060 1.80fr sepia, brn org & brn   .80 .25

Philatelic Societies Federation Congress, Nancy — A1061

1986, May 17   *Perf. 13*
2012 A1061 2.20fr Exposition Center   1.00 .25

Mens World Volleyball Championship A1062

Statue of Liberty, Cent. A1063

1986, May 24   **Engr.**   *Perf. 13*
2013 A1062 2.20fr dk vio, brn vio & scar   1.00 .35

1986, July 4   *Perf. 13*
2014 A1063 2.20fr scar & dk blue   1.00 .25
   See US No. 2224.

1st Ascent of Mt. Blanc, 1786 A1064

1986, Aug. 8   **Engr.**   *Perf. 13x12½*
2015 A1064 2fr J. Balmat, M.G. Paccard   .90 .50

Pierre-Louis Moreau de Maupertuis (1698-1759), La Condamine and Sextant — A1065

1986, Sept. 5
2016 A1065 3fr multicolored   1.40 .55
   Lapland Expedition, 250th anniv., proved Earth's poles are flattened.
   See Finland No. 741.

Marcassite A1066

1986, Sept. 13   *Perf. 12½*
2017 A1066 2fr shown   .90 .25
2018 A1066 3fr Quartz   1.40 .25
2019 A1066 4fr Calcite   1.75 .70
2020 A1066 5fr Fluorite   2.25 .70
   Nos. 2017-2020 (4)   6.30 1.90

Souvenir Sheet

Natl. Film Industry, 50th Anniv. A1067

Personalities and film scenes: a, Louis Feuillade, The Vampires. b, Max Linder. c, Sacha Guitry, Romance of the Trickster. d, Jean Renoir, The Grand Illusion. e, Marcel Pagnol, The Baker's Woman. f, Jean Epstein, The Three-Sided Mirror. g, Rene Clair, Women of the Night. h, Jean Gremillon, Talk of Love. i, Jacques Becker, Helmet of Gold. j, Francois Truffaut, The Young Savage.

1986, Sept. 20 Photo.   *Perf. 13x12½*
2021   Sheet of 10   10.00 10.00
   a.-j. A1067 2.20fr any single   1.00 1.00

Scene from Le Grand Meaulnes, by Henry Alain-Fournier (b. 1886), Novelist A1068

Professional Education, Cent. A1069

1986, Oct. 4   Engr.   Perf. 12½x13
2022 A1068 2.20fr black & dk red   1.00 .25

1986, Oct. 4
2023 A1069 1.90fr brt vio & dp lil rose   .85 .25

World Energy Conf., Cannes A1070

Mulhouse Technical Museum A1071

1986, Oct. 5   Photo.   Perf. 13
2024 A1070 3.40fr multicolored   1.50 .50

1986, Dec. 1   Engr.
2025 A1071 2.20fr int blue, dk red & blk   1.00 .45

Museum at Orsay, Opening — A1072

1986, Dec. 10   Photo.
2026 A1072 3.70fr bluish blk & pck bl   1.75 .60

Fulgence Bienvenue (1852-1934), and the Metro — A1073

1987, Jan. 17   Engr.   Perf. 13
2027 A1073 2.50fr vio brn, brn & dk grn   1.10 .35

A1074

A1075

1987, Jan. 24
2028 A1074 1.90fr grn & grnsh blk   .85 .20
Raoul Follereau (1903-1977), care for lepers.

1987, Mar. 7   Engr.   Perf. 12½x13
2029 A1075 1.90fr black & red   .85 .20
Cutlery industry, Thiers.

Tourist Issue

Redon, Ille et Vilaine A1076

Azay-le-Rideau Chateau — A1077

Meuse District — A1078

De Gaulle's Home, Etretat A1079

Les Baux-de-Provence — A1080

Illustration A1078 reduced.

1987   Engr.   Perf. 13
2030 A1076 2.20fr dp rose lil, blk & brn ol   1.10 .25
2031 A1077 2.50fr Prus blue & olive grn   1.25 .25
Perf. 12½
2032 A1078 3.70fr multicolored   1.75 .25
Photo.   Perf. 13
2033 A1079 2.20fr multicolored   1.00 .25
Engr.
2034 A1080   3fr dk ol bis & dp vio   1.40 .90
Nos. 2030-2034 (5)   6.50 1.90

Issued: #2030, 3/7; #2033, 6/12; 2.50fr, 5/9; 3fr, 6/27; 3.70fr, 5/30.

Charles Edouard Jenneret (Le Corbusier) (1887-1965), Architect — A1081

1987, Apr. 11   Photo.   Perf. 13x12½
2035 A1081 3.70fr Abstract   1.75 .50

Europa 1987 A1082

Modern architecture: 2.20fr, Metal factory at Boulogne-Billancourt, by architect Claude Vasconi. 3.40fr, Rue Mallet-Stevens housing, by Robert Mallet-Stevens.

1987, Apr. 25   Engr.   Perf. 13x12½
2036 A1082 2.20fr dk blue & grn   1.25 .50
2037 A1082 3.40fr brn & dk grn   1.75 .65

Abstract Painting, by Bram van Velde — A1083

Woman under Parasol, by Eugene Boudin (1824-1898) — A1084

Precambrien, by Camille Bryen — A1085

World, Bronze Sculpture by Antoine Pevsner — A1086

Perf. 12½x13, 13x12½ (Nos. 2039, 2041)
Photo., Engr. (Nos. 2039, 2041)
1987
2038 A1083 5fr multicolored   2.25 1.00
2039 A1084 5fr multicolored   2.25 1.00
2040 A1085 5fr multicolored   2.25 1.00
2041 A1086 5fr bister & blk   2.25 1.00
Nos. 2038-2041 (4)   9.00 4.00

Issue dates: #2038, Apr. 25; #2039, May 23; #2040, Sept. 12; #2041, Nov. 14.

Gaspard de Montagnes, from a Manuscript Illustration — A1087

1987, May 9   Engr.   Perf. 13
2042 A1087 1.90fr dp grn & sepia   .85 .20
Henri Pourrat (1887-1959), novelist.

Natl. Philatelic Societies Congress, Lens A1088

1987, June 6   Perf. 13x13½
2043 A1088 2.20fr choc & red   1.00 .30

Involvement of U.S. Forces in WW I, 70th Anniv. A1089

Design: Stars and Stripes, troops, Gen. John J. Pershing (1860-1948), American army commander.

1987, June 13   Perf. 13
2044 A1089 3.40fr olive grn, saph & ver   1.50 .70

A1090

A1091

1987, June 17   Photo.
2045 A1090 2fr multicolored   .90 .60
6th Intl. Cable Car Transport Congress, Grenoble.

1987, June 20   Litho.
2046 A1091 1.90fr pale chalky blue & blk   .90 .55
Accession of Hugh Capet (c.938-996), 1st king of France, millenary.

A1092 — A1093

1987, June 20 Engr. Perf. 12½x13
2047 A1092 2.20fr multicolored 1.00 .30
La Fleche Natl. Military School.

1987, June 27 Photo. Perf. 13
2048 A1093 1.90fr multicolored .90 .55
World Assembly of Expatriate Algerians, Nice.

World Wrestling
Championships — A1094

1987, Aug. 21 Engr.
2049 A1094 3fr brt pur, vio gray
& brt olive grn 1.40 .60

Mushrooms — A1095 / William the Conqueror (c. 1027-1087) A1096

1987, Sept. 5 Perf. 12½
2050 A1095 2fr Gyroporus cyanescens .90 .25
2051 A1095 3fr Gomphus
clavatus 1.40 .35
2052 A1095 4fr Morchella conica 1.75 .60
2053 A1095 5fr Russula
virescens 2.25 .60
Nos. 2050-2053 (4) 6.30 1.80

1987, Sept. 5 Perf. 13
2054 A1096 2fr Bayeux Tapestry
detail .90 .35

Montbenoit Le Saugeais A1097

Design: Abbey of Medieval Knights, cloisters, winter scene.

1987, Sept. 19
2055 A1097 2.50fr saph, blk &
scar 1.10 .55

Pasteur Institute, Cent. — A1098

1987, Oct. 3
2056 A1098 2.20fr dp blue & dk
red 1.00 .20

Blaise Cendrars (1887-1961), Poet and Novelist — A1099 / Treaty of Andelot, 1400th Anniv. — A1100

Pen and ink portrait by Modigliani.

1987, Nov. 6 Perf. 12½
2057 A1099 2fr brt grn, buff & blk .90 .35

1987, Nov. 28 Perf. 12½x13
2058 A1100 3.70fr multicolored 1.75 .55

Gen. Leclerc (1902-1947), Marshal of France — A1101

1987, Nov. 28 Perf. 13x12½
2059 A1101 2.20fr multicolored 1.00 .25

Liberty Type of 1982
1987-90 Perf. 13
2077 A915 3.70fr brt lilac rose 1.75 .35
2078 A915 (2.10fr) green ('90) .95 .20
2079 A915 (2.30fr) red ('90) 1.00 .20
Nos. 2077-2079 (3) 3.70 .75
Coil Stamp
Engr.
Perf. 13 Horiz.
2080 A915 2fr emerald green .90 .30
Issued: 2fr, 8/1; 3.70fr, 11/16; #2078-2079, 1/2.
Nos. 2078-2079 are inscribed "C."

Franco-German Cooperation Treaty, 25th Anniv. — A1102

1988, Jan. 15 Perf. 13
2086 A1102 2.20fr Adenauer, De
Gaulle 1.00 .35
See Fed. Rep. of Germany No. 1546.

Marcel Dassault (1892-1986), Aircraft Designer — A1103

1988, Jan. 23 Photo.
2087 A1103 3.60fr brt ultra, gray
blk & dk red 1.60 .70

Communications A1104 / Great Synagogue, Rue Victoire, Paris A1105

Angouleme Festival prize-winning cartoons.

1988, Jan. 29 Photo. Perf. 13½x13
Booklet Stamps
2088 A1104 2.20fr Pellos 1.00 .50
2089 A1104 2.20fr Reiser 1.00 .50
2090 A1104 2.20fr Marijac 1.00 .50
2091 A1104 2.20fr Fred 1.00 .50
2092 A1104 2.20fr Moebius 1.00 .50
2093 A1104 2.20fr Gillon 1.00 .50
2094 A1104 2.20fr Bretecher 1.00 .50
2095 A1104 2.20fr Forest 1.00 .50
2096 A1104 2.20fr Mezieres 1.00 .50
2097 A1104 2.20fr Tardi 1.00 .50
2098 A1104 2.20fr Lob 1.00 .50
2099 A1104 2.20fr Bilal 1.00 .50
a. Bklt. pane of 12, #2088-2099 12.00

1988, Feb. 7 Litho. Perf. 13
2100 A1105 2fr black & gold .90 .25

The Four Elements — A1106

1988, Feb. 1 Engr. Perf. 13
2101 A1106 1.36fr Air .65 .40
2102 A1106 1.75fr Water .80 .40
2103 A1106 2.83fr Fire 1.25 1.00
2104 A1106 4.75fr Earth 2.25 1.75
Nos. 2101-2104 (4) 4.95 3.55
Nos. 2101-2104 known only precanceled. See second note after No. 132.

PHILEXFRANCE '89 — A1107

1988, Mar. 4
2105 A1107 2.20fr #1885, emblem 1.00 .20

Postal Training College, Cent. A1108

1988, Mar. 29
2106 A1108 3.60fr multicolored 1.60 .40

Philex-Jeunes '88, Youth Stamp Show — A1109

1988, Apr. 8 Perf. 13x12½
2107 A1109 2fr multicolored .90 .25

Blood Donation — A1110

1988, Apr. 9 Photo. Perf. 13½x13
2108 A1110 2.50fr multicolored 1.10 .40

Europa 1988 A1111

Communication and transportation.

1988, Apr. 30 Engr. Perf. 13
2109 A1111 2.20fr Cables, satellites 1.75 .35
2110 A1111 3.60fr Rail cars 2.50 .60

Jean Monnet (1888-1979), Economist — A1112

1988, May 10 Perf. 12½x13
2111 A1112 2.20fr black & brn ol 1.00 .25

Philatelic Congress, Valence A1113

1988, May 21 Perf. 13x12½
2112 A1113 2.20fr multicolored 1.00 .35

Intl. Medical Assistance A1114

1988, May 28 Photo. Perf. 13
2113 A1114 3.60fr multicolored 1.60 .50

Aid to the Handicapped — A1115

1988, May 28
2114 A1115 3.70fr multicolored 1.75 .50

No. 1884 Surcharged in European Currency Units

1988, Apr. 16 Engr.
2115 A915 2.20fr red 1.00 .25

Tourist Issue

Hermes Dicephalus (Roman Empire), Frejus — A1116

Ship Museum, Douarnenez — A1117

Chateau Sedieres, Correze — A1118

Cirque de Gavarnie A1119

View of Perouges, Ain A1120

1988, June 12   Engr.   Perf. 13x12½
2116 A1116 3.70fr multicolored   1.75 .80

1988   Perf. 13, 12½x13 (#2118)
2117 A1117   2fr multicolored   .90 .25
2118 A1118   2.20fr multicolored   1.00 .35
2119 A1119   3fr multicolored   1.40 .40

Issued: 2.20fr, 7/2; 2fr, 7/4; 3fr, 7/23.

1988, Sept. 10   Perf. 13x12½
2120 A1120 2.20fr multicolored   1.00 .25
    Nos. 2116-2120 (5)   6.05 2.05

RÉPUBLIQUE FRANÇAISE

1788 ASSEMBLÉE DES 3 ORDRES, VIZILLE

French Revolution, Bicent. — A1121

Designs: 3fr, Assembly of the Three Estates, Vizille. 4fr, Day of the Tiles (Barricades), Grenoble.

1988, June 18   Engr.
2121 A1121 3fr multicolored   1.40 1.00
2122 A1121 4fr multicolored   1.90 1.00
  a.   Pair, #2121-2122 + label   3.50 3.00

PHILEXFRANCE '89.

Buffon's Natural History — A1122

Alpine Troops, Cent. — A1123

1988, June 18   Perf. 12½
2123 A1122 2fr Otters   .90 .20
2124 A1122 3fr Stag   1.40 .30
2125 A1122 4fr Fox   1.90 .70
2126 A1122 5fr Badger   2.25 .60
    Nos. 2123-2126 (4)   6.45 1.80

1988, June 25   Perf. 13
2127 A1123 2.50fr multicolored   1.10 .65

Roland Garros (1888-1918), 1st Pilot to Fly Across the Mediterranean, Sept. 23, 1913 — A1124

1988, July 2   Engr.   Perf. 13x12½
2128 A1124 2fr brt grn bl & olive   .90 .25

Nov. 11, 1918 Armistice Ending World War I, 70th Anniv. A1125

1988, Sept. 10   Engr.   Perf. 13
2129 A1125 2.20fr brt blue, gray & blk   1.00 .25

Homage to Leon Degand, Sculpture by Robert Jacobsen A1126

1988, Sept. 22   Perf. 12½x13
2130 A1126 5fr blk & dp claret   2.25 1.00
French-Danish cultural exchange program, 10th anniv. See Denmark No. 860.

Strasbourg, 2000th Anniv. — A1127

1988, Sept. 24   Perf. 13
2131 A1127 2.20fr Municipal arms 1.00 .25

St. Mihiel Sepulcher, by Ligier Richier (c. 1500-1567), Sculptor — A1128

Composition, 1954, by Serge Poliakoff (1906-1969) — A1129

La Pieta de Villeneuve-les-Avignon, by Enguerrand Quarton (1444-1466) — A1130

Anthropometry of the Blue Period, by Yves Klein — A1131

1988-89   Engr.   Perf. 13x12½
2132 A1128 5fr black brown   2.25 1.00
                Photo.
2133 A1129 5fr multicolored   2.25 1.00
2134 A1130 5fr multicolored   2.25 1.00
2135 A1131 5fr multi ('89)   2.25 1.00
    Nos. 2132-2135 (4)   9.00 4.00

Issue dates: #2132, Oct. 15; #2133, Oct. 22; #2134, Dec. 10; #2135, Jan. 21.

Thermal Springs A1132

1988, Nov. 21   Engr.   Perf. 13x12½
2136 A1132 2.20fr multicolored   1.00 .25

Metamecanique, by Jean Tinguely — A1133

1988, Nov. 25   Photo.
2137 A1133 5fr multicolored   3.00 1.00
    See Switzerland No. 828.

UN Declaration of Human Rights, 40th Anniv. A1134

1988, Dec. 12   Litho.   Perf. 13
2138 A1134 2.20fr dk bl & grnsh bl 1.00 .25

French Revolution, Bicent. — A1135

1989, Jan. 1   Photo.   Perf. 13x12½
2139 A1135 2.20fr red & vio blue 1.00 .20

Valentin Hauy (1745-1822), Founder of the School for the Blind, Paris, 1791 — A1136

Photo. & Embossed
1989, Jan. 28
2140 A1136 2.20fr multicolored   1.00 .40

Estienne School, Cent. — A1137

1989, Feb. 4   Engr.   Perf. 12½
2141 A1137 2.20fr gray, black & red   1.00 .25

European Parliament Elections A1138

1989, Mar. 4   Litho.   Perf. 13
2142 A1138 2.20fr multicolored   1.00 .20

A1139

1989   Engr.   Perf. 12½x13
2143 A1139 2.20fr Liberty   1.00 .25
2144 A1139 2.20fr Equality   1.00 .25
2145 A1139 2.20fr Fraternity   1.00 .25
  a.   Strip of 3, #2143-2145 + label 3.00 2.50

Bicent. of the French revolution and the Declaration of Rights of Man and the Citizen. No. 2145a contains inscribed label picturing PHILEXFRANCE '89 emblem.
Issue dates: #2143, Mar. 18; #2144, Apr. 22; #2145, May 27; #2145a, July 14.

French-Soviet Joint Space
Flight — A1140

1989, Mar. 4   Litho.   Perf. 13
2146 A1140 3.60fr multicolored   1.60 .60

Historic Sights,
Paris — A1141

Designs: No. 2147, Arche de la Defense.
No. 2148, Eiffel Tower. No. 2149, Grand Louvre. No. 2150, Notre Dame Cathedral. No.
2151, Bastille Monument and Opera de la
Bastille. #2151a has a continuous design.

1989, Apr. 21   Engr.   Perf. 13x12½
2147 A1141 2.20fr multicolored   1.00 .85
2148 A1141 2.20fr multicolored   1.00 .85
2149 A1141 2.20fr multicolored   1.00 .85
2150 A1141 2.20fr multicolored   1.00 .85
2151 A1141 2.20fr multicolored   1.00 .85
   a.   Strip of 5, #2147-2151   5.00 5.00

Europa
1989
A1142

Children's games.

1989, Apr. 29   Perf. 13
2152 A1142 2.20fr Hopscotch   1.00 .30
2153 A1142 3.60fr Catch (ball)   2.50 .70

ITU Plenipotentiaries Conference,
Nice — A1143

1989, May 23   Litho.
2154 A1143 3.70fr dk bl, dl org &
       red   1.75 .40

Tourist Issue

Fontainebleau Forest — A1144

Vaux le Vicomte — A1145

La Brenne — A1146

Illustrations A1145-A1146 reduced.

1989, May 20   Engr.   Perf. 13
2155 A1144 2.20fr multicolored   1.00 .30

Perf. 13x12½
2156 A1145 3.70fr ol bis & blk   1.75 .75
2157 A1146 4fr violet blue   1.90 .75
   Nos. 2155-2157 (3)   4.65 1.80
Issued: 2.20fr, 5/20; 3.70fr, 7/14; 4fr, 8/25.

World Cycling Championships,
Chambery — A1147

1989, June 3   Litho.   Perf. 13
2158 A1147 2.20fr multi   1.00 .25

Jehan de Malestroit,
Dept. of
Morbihan — A1148

1989, June 10   Engr.   Perf. 12½x13
2159 A1148 3.70fr multicolored   1.75 .55

Preliminary Sketch (Detail) for *Oath of
the Tennis Court*, by David — A1149

*Regatta
with Wind
Astern*, by
Charles
Lapicque
A1150

1989, June 19   Photo.   Perf. 13x12½
2160 A1149 5fr multicolored   2.25 1.00
Perf. 12½
2161 A1150 5fr multicolored   2.25 1.00
No. 2160 for French revolution bicent.
Issued: #2160, 6/19; #2161, 9/23.

Souvenir Sheet

Revolution Bicentennial — A1151

Revolutionaries: a, Madame Roland (1754-
1793). b, Camille Desmoulins (1760-1794). c,
Condorcet (1743-1794). d, Kellermann (1735-
1820).

1989, June 26   Engr.   Perf. 13
2162 A1151   Sheet of 4   4.00 3.50
   a.-d.   2.20fr any single   1.00 .75

15th Summit of the Arch Meeting of
Leaders from Industrial Nations, July
14-16
A1152

1989, July 14   Photo.
2163 A1152 2.20fr multicolored   1.00 .35

Declaration of the Rights of Man and
the Citizen, Versailles, Aug. 26,
1789 — A1153

Details of an anonymous 18th-19th cent.
painting in Carnavalet Museum: No. 2168a,
Preamble, Article I. No. 2168b, Articles VII-XI.
No. 2168c, Articles II-VI. No. 2168d, Articles
XII-XVII.

Litho. & Engr.
1989, Aug. 26   Perf. 13x11½
2164 A1153 2.50fr Preamble,
       Article I   1.00 .90
2165 A1153 2.50fr Art. II-VI   1.00 .90
2166 A1153 2.50fr Art. VII-XI   1.00 .90
2167 A1153 2.50fr Art. XII-XVII   1.00 .90
   a.   Strip, #2164-2167 + label   4.00 3.50
Souvenir Sheet
Perf. 13x12½
2168   Sheet of 4   20.00 20.00
   a.-d.   A1153 5fr any single   5.00 5.00
No. 2168 contains 4 52x41mm stamps. Sold
for 50fr, including admission fee to PHILEX-
FRANCE '89.
Value of No. 2168 is for examples on plain
paper. Examples on fluorescent paper seem
to have been distributed in North America, and
may not have been distributed widely or made
available in Europe. Value $250.

Musical
Instruments — A1154

1989   Litho.   Perf. 12x12½
2169 A1154 1.39fr Harp   .65 .40
2170 A1154 1.79fr Piano   .80 .40
2171 A1154 2.90fr Trumpet   1.25 .90
2172 A1154 4.84fr Violin   2.25 1.75
   Nos. 2169-2172 (4)   4.95 3.45
Nos. 2169-2172 are known only precanceled. See second note after No. 132.
See #2233-2239, 2273-2283, 2368-2371.

TGV
Atlantic
A1155

1989, Sept. 23   Photo.   Perf. 13
2173 A1155 2.50fr dk bl, sil & red 1.10 .50

Clermont-Ferrand
Tramway,
Cent. — A1156

1989, Oct. 28   Engr.
2174 A1156 3.70fr blk & dk ol bis 1.75 .40

Villers-Cotterets Ordinance, 450th
Anniv. — A1157

1989, Oct. 28   Engr.
2175 A1157 2.20fr blk, dp cl &
       red   1.00 .25

Baron Augustin-Louis Cauchy (1789-
1857), Mathematician — A1158

1989, Nov. 10   Perf. 13x12½
2176 A1158 3.60fr red, blk & bl
       grn   1.60 .50

Marshal Jean de Lattre de Tassigny
(1889-1952) — A1159

1989, Nov. 18   Perf. 13
2177 A1159 2.20fr bl, blk & red   1.00 .35

Harki
Soldiers of
France
A1160

1989, Dec. 9   **Photo.**
2178 A1160 2.20fr multicolored   1.00 .35

Marianne — A1161

1990-92		**Engr.**		**Perf. 13**
2179	A1161	10c brn blk	.20	.20
a.		Bklt. pane, #2180, 4 #2179	1.00	
2180	A1161	20c lt green	.20	.20
2181	A1161	50c brt violet	.20	.20
2182	A1161	1fr orange	.45	.20
2183	A1161	2fr apple grn	.90	.20
2184	A1161	2.10fr dark grn	.95	.20
2185	A1161	2.20fr dark grn	1.00	.20
2186	A1161	2.20fr emerald	1.00	.20
2187	A1161	2.30fr red	1.00	.20
a.		Bklt. pane, #2180, 4 #2187	5.00	
2188	A1161	2.50fr red	1.10	.20
2189	A1161	3.20fr blue	1.50	.75
2190	A1161	3.40fr blue	1.60	.40
2191	A1161	3.80fr lilac rose	1.75	.30
2192	A1161	4fr lilac rose	1.90	.20
2193	A1161	4.20fr lilac rose	1.90	.20
2194	A1161	5fr greenish blue	2.25	.20
2195	A1161	10fr violet	4.50	.25
2196	A1161	(2.20fr) dk grn	1.00	.20
2197	A1161	(2.50fr) red	1.10	.20
		Nos. 2179-2197 (19)	24.50	4.70

Coil Stamps
Perf. 13 Horiz.

2198	A1161	2.10fr dk grn	1.00	.20
2199	A1161	2.20fr dk grn	1.00	.60
2200	A1161	2.30fr red	1.00	.20
2201	A1161	2.50fr red	1.10	.20
		Nos. 2198-2201 (4)	4.10	1.20

Die Cut
Self-Adhesive

2202	A1161	2.30fr red	1.00	.20
a.		Booklet pane of 10	10.00	
2203	A1161	2.50fr red	1.10	.20
a.		Booklet pane of 10	11.00	
b.		Booklet pane of 5	5.50	
2204	A1161	(2.50fr) red	1.10	.20
a.		Booklet pane of 10	11.00	
		Nos. 2202-2204 (3)	3.20	.60

Issued: #2187, 1/2; #2198, 1/1; 10c, 20c,
50c, 3.20fr, 3.80fr, 3/26; #2202, 1/29; #2182-
2183, 2194-2195, 5/21; #2196-2197, 8/19/91;
2.20fr, 2.50fr, 3.40fr, 4fr, 9/30/91; #2179a,
2187a, 2199, 2201, 1991; 4.20fr, 9/24/92;
#2203-2204, 1992; 2.10fr, 1993.
Peelable paper backing serves as booklet
cover for Nos. 2202, 2203. No. 2203b has separate backing with no printing.
Nos. 2196-2197, 2204 inscribed "D."
See Nos. 2333-2348.

Lace Work
A1162

1990, Feb. 3   **Engr.**   **Perf. 13x12½**
2205 A1162 2.50fr red   1.10 .40

1992 Winter
Olympics,
Albertville — A1163

1990, Feb. 9   **Photo.**   **Perf. 13**
2206 A1163 2.50fr multicolored   1.10 .20

Charles de
Gaulle (1890-
1970)
A1164

Max Hymans
(1900-1961),
Planes and ACC
Emblem
A1165

1990, Feb. 24   **Engr.**   **Perf. 12½x13**
2207 A1164 2.30fr brt vio, vio bl & blk   1.00 .25

1990, Mar. 3   **Perf. 13**
2208 A1165 2.30fr brt vio, brt bl & dk ol grn   1.00 .25

Profile of a
Woman,
by Odilon
Redon
A1166

Head of Christ,
Wissembourg — A1167

Cambodian Dancer by Auguste
Rodin — A1168

Jaune et
Gris by
Roger
Bissiere
A1169

1990   **Litho.**   **Perf. 13½x14**
2209 A1166 5fr multicolored   2.25 1.00

Perf. 12½x13
Engr.
2210 A1167 5fr multicolored   2.25 1.00
2211 A1168 5fr multicolored   2.25 1.00

Photo.
2212 A1169 5fr multicolored   2.25 1.00
   Nos. 2209-2212 (4)   9.00 4.00

   Issue dates: No. 2209, Mar. 3; No. 2210,
June 16; No. 2211, June 9; No. 2212, Dec. 8.

Jean Guehenno
(1890-1978)
A1170

Litho. & Engr.

1990, Mar. 24   **Perf. 13**
2213 A1170 3.20fr buff & red brn   1.50 .40

Tourism Series

Flaran
Abbey,
Gers
A1171

Cluny
A1172

Pont Canal
de Briare
A1173

Cap
Canaille,
Cassis
A1174

1990, Apr. 21   **Engr.**   **Perf. 13**
2214 A1171 3.80fr sepia & blk   1.75 .50

1990
2215 A1172 2.30fr multicolored   1.00 .25
2216 A1173 2.30fr multicolored   1.00 .25
2217 A1174 3.80fr multicolored   1.75 .50
   Nos. 2215-2217 (3)   3.75 1.00

Issued: #2215, 6/23; #2216, 7/7; 3.80fr, 7/14.

Europa
1990
A1175

Post offices.

1990, Apr. 28   **Engr.**   **Perf. 13**
2218 A1175 2.30fr Macon   *1.50* *.50*
2219 A1175 3.20fr Cerizay   *2.25* *.80*

Arab World
Institute — A1176

1990, May 5   **Perf. 12½x13**
2220 A1176 3.80fr brt bl, dk red & dp bl   1.75 .45

Labor Day,
Cent.
A1177

1990, May 1   **Photo.**   **Perf. 13**
2221 A1177 2.30fr multicolored   1.00 .25

Villefranche-sur-Saone — A1178

1990, June 2   **Engr.**   **Perf. 13x12½**
2222 A1178 2.30fr multicolored   1.00 .25
   National philatelic congress.

A1179   A1181

1990, June 6   **Perf. 13x12½**
2223 A1179 2.30fr La Poste   1.00 .25
   Whitbread trans-global yacht race.

1990, June 17   **Perf. 12½x13**
2225 A1181 2.30fr multicolored   1.00 .25
   De Gaulle's Call for French Resistance, 50th
anniv.

Franco-Brazilian House, Rio de
Janeiro — A1182

1990, July 14   **Perf. 13**
2226 A1182 3.20fr multicolored   1.50 .75
   See Brazil No. 2255.

A1183

A1184

Designs: Fish.

1990, Oct. 6   Engr.   Perf. 12½
2227	A1183	2fr Rutilus rutilus	.90	.20
2228	A1183	3fr Perca fluviatilis	1.40	.25
2229	A1183	4fr Salmo salar	1.90	.50
2230	A1183	5fr Esox lucius	2.25	.50
		Nos. 2227-2230 (4)	6.45	1.45

1990, Sept. 29   Photo.   Perf. 12½x13
| 2231 | A1184 | 2.30fr multicolored | 1.00 | .50 |

Natl. Institute of Geography, 50th anniv.

Souvenir Sheet

French Revolution,
Bicentennial — A1185

Designs: a, Gaspard Monge. b, Abbe Gregoire. c, Creation of the Tricolor. d, Creation of the French departments.

1990, Oct. 15   Engr.   Perf. 13
| 2232 | A1185 | Sheet of 4 | 4.50 | 4.50 |
| a.-d. | | 2.50fr any single | 1.10 | 1.10 |

Musical Instrument Type of 1989

1990, Sept. 1   Litho.   Perf. 13
2233	A1154	1.46fr Accordion	.65	.40
2234	A1154	1.89fr Breton bag-pipe	.85	.60
2235	A1154	3.06fr Tambourin	1.75	1.50
2236	A1154	5.10fr Hurdy-gurdy	3.00	2.40
		Nos. 2233-2236 (4)	6.25	4.90

1990, Nov.   Litho.   Perf. 13
2237	A1154	1.93fr like #2169	1.10	.75
2238	A1154	2.39fr like #2170	1.25	.90
2239	A1154	2.74fr like #2172	2.00	1.25
		Nos. 2237-2239 (3)	4.35	2.90

Nos. 2233-2239 are known only precanceled. See second note after No. 132.

Maurice Genevoix
(1890-1980),
Novelist — A1186

1990, Nov. 12   Engr.   Perf. 13
| 2240 | A1186 | 2.30fr lt green & blk | 1.00 | .20 |

Organization for Economic
Cooperation and Development, 30th
Anniv. — A1187

1990, Dec. 15   Litho.
| 2241 | A1187 | 3.20fr dk & lt blue | 1.50 | .75 |

"The Swing" by Auguste Renoir (1841-1919) — A1188

1991, Feb. 23   Engr.   Perf. 12½x13
| 2242 | A1188 | 5fr multicolored | 2.25 | 1.00 |

Youth
Philatelic
Exhibition,
Cholet
A1189

1991, Mar. 30   Litho.   Perf. 13
| 2243 | A1189 | 2.50fr multicolored | 1.10 | .40 |

Art Series

Le Noeud Noir by Georges Seurat
(1859-1891) — A1190

Apres Nous La Maternite, by Max
Ernst (1891-1976) — A1191

Volte
Faccia by
Francois
Rouan
A1192

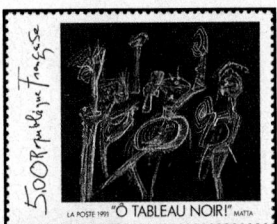

O Tableau Noir by Roberto Matta (b.
1911) — A1193

1991   Engr.   Perf. 12½x13
| 2244 | A1190 | 5fr pale yellow & blk | 2.25 | 1.00 |

Photo.   Perf. 13
| 2245 | A1191 | 2.50fr multicolored | 1.10 | .80 |

Engr.   Perf. 12½x13
| 2246 | A1192 | 5fr black | 2.25 | 1.00 |

Photo.   Perf. 13x12½
| 2247 | A1193 | 5fr multicolored | 2.25 | 1.00 |
| | | *Nos. 2244-2247 (4)* | 7.85 | 3.80 |

Issued: #2244, 4/13; #2245, 10/10; #2246, 11/9; #2247, 11/30.

Wolfgang Amadeus Mozart (1756-1791), Composer — A1194

1991, Apr. 9   Photo.   Perf. 13
| 2248 | A1194 | 2.50fr bl, blk & red | 1.10 | .60 |

National Printing
Office, 350th
Anniv. — A1195

1991, Apr. 13
| 2249 | A1195 | 4fr multicolored | 1.90 | .60 |

Tourism Series

Chevire Bridge,
Nantes — A1196

Carennac
Castle
A1197

Pipe
Organ,
Wasquehal
A1198

Valley of
Munster
A1199

1991   Engr.   Perf. 13
| 2250 | A1196 | 2.50fr multicolored | 1.10 | .25 |

Perf. 12x13
| 2251 | A1197 | 2.50fr multicolored | 1.10 | .30 |

Perf. 12
| 2252 | A1198 | 4fr black & buff | 1.90 | .55 |

Perf. 13x12½
| 2253 | A1199 | 4fr violet | 1.90 | .55 |
| | | *Nos. 2250-2253 (4)* | 6.00 | 1.65 |

Issue dates: No. 2250, Apr. 27; Nos. 2251, 2253, July 6; No. 2252, June 22.

Europa
A1200

Concours
Lepine, 90th
Anniv.
A1201

1991, Apr. 27   Perf. 12½x13
| 2254 | A1200 | 2.50fr Ariane launch site, French Guiana | 1.10 | .20 |
| 2255 | A1200 | 3.50fr Television satellite | 1.60 | .55 |

Compare with No. 2483.

1991, Apr. 27   Perf. 13
| 2256 | A1201 | 4fr multicolored | 1.90 | .80 |

French Assoc. of Small Manufacturers and Inventors.

Philatelic
Society
Congress,
Perpignan
A1202

1991, May 18
| 2257 | A1202 | 2.50fr multicolored | 1.10 | .25 |

French Open Tennis
Championships,
Cent. — A1203

1991, May 24   Engr.   Perf. 13
| 2258 | A1203 | 3.50fr multicolored | 1.60 | .50 |

Souvenir Sheet

French Revolution, Bicent. — A1204

Designs: a, Theophile Malo Corret, La Tour
d'Auvergne (1743-1800). b, Liberty Tree. c,

National police, bicent. d, Louis Antoine-Leon de St. Just (1767-1794).

1991, June 1   Engr.   Perf. 13
2259 A1204 Sheet of 4   4.50 3.00
a.-d. 2.50fr any single   1.10 .75

A1205

A1206

1991, June 13   Photo.   Perf. 13
2260 A1205 2.50fr multicolored   1.10 .45

Gaston III de Foix (Febus) (1331-1391), general.

1991, Sept. 14   Engr.   Perf. 12½

Designs: Wildlife.
2261 A1206 2fr Ursus arctos   .90 .30
2262 A1206 3fr Testudo hermanni   1.40 .30
2263 A1206 4fr Castor fiber   1.90 .75
2264 A1206 5fr Alcedo atthis   2.25 .75
     Nos. 2261-2264 (4)   6.45 2.10

10th World Forestry Congress A1207

1991, Sept. 22   Engr.   Perf. 13x12½
2265 A1207 2.50fr multicolored   1.10 .25

School of Public Works, Cent. A1208

1991, Oct. 5   Litho. & Engr.   Perf. 13
2266 A1208 2.50fr multicolored   1.10 .35

Marcel Cerdan (1916-1949), Middleweight Boxing Champion — A1209

1991, Oct. 19   Photo.   Perf. 13
2267 A1209 2.50fr black & red   1.10 .35

Amnesty International, 30th Anniv. — A1210

1991, Oct. 19
2268 A1210 3.40fr multicolored   1.60 .60

A1211

A1212

1991, Nov. 14   Engr.   Perf. 13
2269 A1211 2.50fr Olympic flame   1.10 .25

1992 Winter Olympics, Albertville.

1991, Dec. 7   Perf. 13
2270 A1212 2.50fr dk & lt blue   1.10 .30

Fifth Handicapped Olympics.

Voluntary Attachment of Mayotte to France, Sesquicentennial — A1213

1991, Dec. 21   Engr.
2271 A1213 2.50fr multicolored   1.10 .25

French Pavilion, Expo '92, Seville A1214

Litho. & Engr.
1992, Jan. 18   Perf. 13
2272 A1214 2.50fr multicolored   1.10 .25

Musical Instruments Type of 1989
1992, Jan. 31   Litho.   Perf. 13
2273 A1154 1.60fr Guitar   45.00 25.00
2274 A1154 1.98fr like
            #2233   4.00   3.00
2275 A1154 2.08fr Saxo-
            phone   2.00   1.50
2276 A1154 2.46fr like
            #2234   2.00   1.50
2277 A1154 2.98fr Banjo   2.00   1.50
2278 A1154 3.08fr like
            #2235   6.00   4.00
2279 A1154 3.14fr like
            #2236   2.75   2.00
2280 A1154 3.19fr like
            #2169   7.00   4.00
2281 A1154 5.28fr Xylo-
            phone   5.50   3.50
2282 A1154 5.30fr like
            #2170   3.50   2.00
2283 A1154 5.32fr like
            #2172   3.50   2.50
     Nos. 2273-2283 (11)   83.25 50.50

Perf. 12
2273a A1154 1.60fr Guitar   7.50   4.50
2274a A1154 1.98fr like #2233   150.00 140.00
2275a A1154 2.08fr Saxophone   40.00 30.00
2276a A1154 2.46fr like #2234   12.00   7.50
2278a A1154 3.08fr like #2235   12.00   7.50
2279a A1154 3.14fr like #2236   60.00 50.00
2280a A1154 3.19fr like #2169   8.00   5.00
2281a A1154 5.28fr Xylophone   30.00 20.00
2282a A1154 5.30fr like #2170   75.00 60.00
2283a A1154 5.32fr like #2172   25.00 20.00
     Nos. 2273a-2283a (10)   419.50 344.50

Nos. 2273-2283 are known only precanceled. See 2nd note after No. 132. See Nos. 2303-2306.

1992 Summer Olympics, Barcelona A1215

1992, Apr. 3   Photo.   Perf. 13
2284 A1215 2.50fr multicolored   1.10 .25

See Greece No. 1730.

Marguerite d'Angouleme (1492-1549) A1216

1992, Apr. 11   Litho.   Perf. 13
2285 A1216 3.40fr multicolored   1.60 .90

Founding of Ajaccio, 500th Anniv. A1217

Virgin and Child Beneath a Garland by Botticelli.

1992, Apr. 30   Photo.   Perf. 13
2286 A1217 4fr multicolored   1.90 .60

A1218

A1219

Discovery of America, 500th Anniv.: 2.50fr, Map, navigation instruments. 3.40fr, Sailing ship, map.

1992, May 9   Engr.   Perf. 13x12½
2287 A1218 2.50fr multicolored   1.25 .30
2288 A1218 3.40fr multicolored   2.00 .65

Europa.

1992, May 30   Litho.   Perf. 13
2289 A1219 3.40fr multicolored   1.60 .80

Intl. Bread and Cereal Congress.

Tourism Series

Ourcq Canal A1220

Mt. Aiguille A1221

Biron Castle A1223

Lorient A1222

1992, May 30   Engr.   Perf. 13
2290 A1220 4fr black, blue & grn   1.90 .50

1992, June 27   Engr.   Perf. 13
2291 A1221 3.40fr multicolored   1.60 .75

First ascension of Mt. Aiguille, 500th anniv.

1992, July 4   Engr.   Perf. 13
2292 A1222 4fr multicolored   1.90 .25

1992, July 4   Perf. 12½x13
2293 A1223 2.50fr multicolored   1.10 .50

Natl. Philatelic Societies Congress, Niort A1224

1992, June 6   Photo.   Perf. 13
2294 A1224 2.50fr multicolored   1.10 .25

Natl. Art Festival.

1992 Olympic Games, Albertville and Barcelona A1225

1992, June 19   Perf. 12½x13½
2295 A1225 2.50fr multicolored   1.10 .35

Tautavel Man A1226

1992, June 20   Photo.   Perf. 13
2296 A1226 3.40fr multicolored   1.60 .60

Portrait of Jacques Callot (1592-1635), by Claude Deruet — A1227

1992, June 27   Engr.   Perf. 12x13
2297 A1227 5fr buff & brown   2.25 .75

Flowers — A1228

2fr, Pancratium maritimum. 3fr, Drosera rotundifolia. 4fr, Orchis palustris. 5fr, Nuphar luteum.

1992, Sept. 12　Engr.　Perf. 12½

2298	A1228	2fr multicolored	.90	.30
2299	A1228	3fr multicolored	1.40	.30
2300	A1228	4fr multicolored	1.90	.70
2301	A1228	5fr multicolored	2.25	.70
		Nos. 2298-2301 (4)	6.45	2.00

First French Republic, Bicent. A1229

1992, Sept. 26　Perf. 13

2302	A1229	2.50fr multicolored	1.10	.20

Musical Instruments Type of 1989

1992, Oct.		Litho.	Perf. 13	
2303	A1154	1.73fr like #2273	.80	.20
2304	A1154	2.25fr like #2275	1.00	.50
2305	A1154	3.51fr like #2277	1.60	1.00
2306	A1154	5.40fr like #2281	2.50	1.75
		Nos. 2303-2306 (4)	5.90	3.45

Nos. 2303-2306 are known only precancelled. See second note after No. 132.

Proclamation of First French Republic, Bicent. — A1230

Paintings or drawings by contemporary artists: No. 2307, Tree of Freedom, by Pierre Alechinsky. No. 2308, Portrait of a Young Man, by Martial Raysse. No. 2309, Marianne with Body and Head of Rooster, by Gerard Garouste. No. 2310, "Republique Francaise," by Jean-Charles Blais.

1992, Sept. 26　Engr.　Perf. 13

2307	A1230	2.50fr red	1.10	.20
2308	A1230	2.50fr red	1.10	.20
2309	A1230	2.50fr red	1.10	.20
2310	A1230	2.50fr red	1.10	.20
		Nos. 2307-2310 (4)	4.40	.80

Single European Market A1231

1992, Nov. 6　Photo.　Perf. 12½x13½

2311	A1231	2.50fr multicolored	1.10	.35

First Mail Flight from Nancy to Luneville, 80th Anniv. A1232

1992, Nov. 12　Perf. 13

2312	A1232	2.50fr multicolored	1.10	.45

Marcel Paul (1900-1982), Minister of Industrial Production — A1233

1992, Nov. 13　Engr.

2313	A1233	4.20fr claret & blue	1.90	.55

Contemporary Art — A1234

#2314, Le Rendezvous d'Ephese, by Paul Delvaux, Belgium. #2315, Abstract painting, by Alberto Burri, Italy. #2316, Abstract painting, by Antoni Tapies, Spain. #2317, Portrait of John Edwards, by Francis Bacon, Great Britain.

1992　Photo.　Perf. 13x12½

2314	A1234	5fr multicolored	2.25	1.00
2315	A1234	5fr multicolored	2.25	1.00
2316	A1234	5fr multicolored	2.25	1.00
2317	A1234	5fr multicolored	2.25	1.00
		Nos. 2314-2317 (4)	9.00	4.00

Issued: #2314, 11/20; #2315-2317, 11/21. See Nos. 2379-2390.

Gypsy Culture — A1235

1992, Dec. 5　Photo.　Perf. 13

2318	A1235	2.50fr multicolored	1.10	.30

Yacht "La Poste," Entrant in Whitbread Trans-Global Race — A1236

1993, Feb. 6　Engr.　Perf. 12

2319	A1236	2.50fr multicolored	1.10	.40

See No. 2375.

Water Birds — A1237

1993, Feb. 6　Perf. 12½x12

2320	A1237	2fr Harle piette	.90	.30
2321	A1237	3fr Fuligule nyroca	1.40	.30
2322	A1237	4fr Tadorne de belon	1.90	.75
2323	A1237	5fr Harle huppe	2.25	.70
		Nos. 2320-2323 (4)	6.45	2.05

Memorial to Indochina War, Frejus A1238

Litho. & Engr.

1993, Feb. 16　Perf. 13x13½

2324	A1238	4fr multicolored	1.90	.60

Stamp Day — A1239

1993, Mar. 6　Photo.　Perf. 13

2325	A1239	2.50fr red & multi	1.75	1.00
2326	A1239	2.50fr +60c red & multi	1.40	.80
a.		Bklt. pane of 4 #2325, 3 #2326 + label	13.00	

Mediterranean Youth Games, Agde — A1240

1993, Mar. 13　Photo.　Perf. 13

2327	A1240	2.50fr multicolored	1.10	.20

Human Rights, Intl. Mixed Masonic Order, Cent. — A1241

1993, Apr. 3　Engr.　Perf. 13

2328	A1241	3.40fr blue & black	1.60	.50

Contemporary Art — A1242

Europa: 2.50fr, Painting, Rouge Rythme Bleu, by Olivier Debre. 3.40fr, Sculpture, Le Griffu, by Germaine Richier, vert.

Perf. 13x12½, 12½x13

1993, Apr. 17			Litho.	
2329	A1242	2.50fr multicolored	1.10	.35
2330	A1242	3.40fr multicolored	1.60	.80

Marianne Type of 1990

1993-96		Engr.	Perf. 13	
2333	A1161	2fr blue	1.75	.20
2334	A1161	2.40fr emerald	1.40	.20
2335	A1161	2.70fr emerald	1.60	.25
2336	A1161	3.50fr apple green	1.75	.30
2337	A1161	3.80fr blue	1.90	.50
2338	A1161	4.40fr blue	2.25	.40
2339	A1161	4.50fr mag	2.25	.40
2340	A1161	(2.50fr) red	1.25	.20
		Nos. 2333-2340 (8)	14.15	2.45

Perf. 13 Horiz.

Coil Stamps

2341	A1161	2.40fr emerald	1.40	.60
2342	A1161	2.70fr emerald	3.00	.20
2343	A1161	(2.80fr) red	1.75	.20

Self-Adhesive

Die Cut

2344	A1161	70c brown	13.00	12.00

Serpentine Die Cut Vert.

2345	A1161	70c brown	13.00	10.00
2346	A1161	1fr orange	7.00	2.50
a.		Booklet pane, 3 #2348, 1 #2346	9.00	

		Complete bklt., 2 #2346a	20.00	

Die Cut

2347	A1161	(2.50fr) red	1.50	.20
a.		Booklet pane of 10 (see footnote)	16.00	
b.		Bklt. pane of 4 + label	6.00	
c.		Booklet pane, #2344, 3 #2348 + label	30.00	
d.		Booklet pane of 10 (see footnote)	15.00	

Serpentine Die Cut Vert.

2348	A1161	(2.80fr) red	1.25	.20
a.		Bklt. pane of 4 + label	5.00	
b.		Booklet pane of 10 (see footnote)	13.00	
c.		Booklet pane, #2345, 3 #2347 + label	18.00	
d.		Booklet pane of 10 (see footnote)	13.00	
e.		Booklet pane of 10 (see footnote)	13.00	
f.		Booklet pane of 10 (see footnote)	—	

Nos. 2340, 2347 pay postage for the first class letter rate and sold for 2.50fr when first released. They have no denomination or letter inscription. Nos. 2343 and 2348 had a face value of 2.80fr when released.

No. 2347a has all stamps adjoining and has selvage covering backing paper (booklet cover), No. 2347d is comprised of two strips of 5 stamps each with yellow backing paper showing.

No. 2348b has the same format as No. 2347a. No. 2348d has a format similar to No. 2347d except there is a narrow selvage strip between the left six stamps and the right four stamps. No. 2348e is like No. 2348f but lacks the selvage strip. No. 2348f has a format similar to No. 2347a except it has a wide selvage strip between the left four stamps and the right six stamps.

Backing paper of Nos. 2347b and 2347c may have cuts along fold and were sold in a booklet for 20fr.

Issued: #2340, 2347, 4/19/93; 70c, July; 2fr, 7/31/94; #2341-2343, 4/1/94; #2345, 2348, 2/14/94; 1fr, 2.70fr, 3.80fr, 4.50fr, 3/18/96.

Tourism Series

Chinon — A1243

Illustration reduced.

Village of Minerve — A1244

Chaise-Dieu Abbey — A1245

Montbeliard — A1246

1993, Apr. 24　Engr.　Perf. 13x12½

2355	A1243	4.20fr dk grn, ol grn & brn	2.00	.80

1993, July 17　Perf. 13

2356	A1244	4.20fr red brown & yel grn	2.00	.50

1993

2357	A1245	2.80fr multicolored	1.25	.35
2358	A1246	4.40fr multicolored	2.00	.60
		Nos. 2355-2358 (4)	7.25	2.25

Issued: #2357, Sept. 4; #2358, Sept. 11.

Ninth European Conference on
Protection of Human Rights — A1247

1993, May 8　Engr.　Perf. 12½x13
2359　A1247　2.50fr multicolored　1.10　.30

Django Reinhardt (1910-1953),
Musician — A1248

1993, May 14　Litho.　Perf. 13
2360　A1248　4.20fr multicolored　1.90　.60

Louise Weiss (1893-
1983),
Suffragist — A1249

1993, May 15　Engr.　Perf. 13x12½
2361　A1249　2.50fr blk, buff & red　1.10　.35

Philatelic
Society
Congress,
Lille
A1250

1993, May 29　Engr.　Perf. 13x12½
2362　A1250　2.50fr bl, dk bl & lil　1.10　.45

Natural
History
Museum,
Bicent.
A1251

Litho. & Engr.
1993, June 5　　　　　Perf. 13
2363　A1251　2.50fr multicolored　1.10　.30

Martyrs and Heroes of the
Resistance — A1252

1993, June 18　Photo.　Perf. 13
2364　　2.50fr red, black & gray　1.10　.60
2365　　4.20fr red, black & gray　1.90　1.00
　　a.　A1252 Pair, #2364-2365　3.00　2.50

A1254　　　　　A1255

1993, July 10　Engr.　Perf. 13x12½
2366　A1254　2.50fr multicolored　1.10　.30
Claude Chappe's Semaphore Telegraph,
bicent.

1993, July 10　Engr.　Perf. 12½x13
2367　A1255　3.40fr bl, grn & red　1.60　.75
Train to Lake Artouste, Laruns, highest train
ride in Europe.

Musical Instruments Type of 1989
1993, July 1　Litho.　Perf. 13
2368　A1154　1.82fr like #2171　　.85　.40
2369　A1154　2.34fr like #2235　1.10　.75
2370　A1154　3.86fr like #2236　1.75　1.00
2371　A1154　5.93fr like #2281　2.75　2.00
　　　Nos. 2368-2371 (4)　6.45　4.15
Nos. 2368-2371 are known only precanceled. See note after No. 132.

Liberation of
Corsica, 50th
Anniv. — A1256

1993, Sept. 9　Engr.　Perf. 13
2372　A1256　2.80fr lake, bl & blk　1.25　.30

Saint Thomas, by Georges de la Tour
(1593-1652) — A1257

1993, Sept. 9　Photo.　Perf. 12½x13
2373　A1257　5fr multicolored　2.25　1.00

Service as Military
Hospital of Val de
Grace Monastery,
Bicent. — A1258

1993, Sept. 25　Engr.　　Perf. 13
2374　A1258　3.70fr multicolored　1.75　.35

Whitbread Trans-Global Race Type
1993, Sept. 27　Engr.　　Perf. 12
2375　A1236　2.80fr multicolored　1.25　.40

The Muses, by Maurice Denis (1870-
1943) — A1259

1993, Oct. 2　Photo.　Perf. 12½x13
2376　A1259　5fr multicolored　2.25　1.00

The Clowns, by
Albert Gleizes
(1881-1953)
A1260

1993, Oct. 2　Photo.　Perf. 13½x12½
2377　A1260　2.80fr multicolored　1.25　.30
Natl. Circus Center, Chalons-sur-Marne.

Clock Tower
Bellringer Statues of
Lambesc — A1261

1993, Oct. 9　Engr.　Perf. 13x12½
2378　A1261　4.40fr multicolored　2.00　.70

European Contemporary Art Type
Designs: No. 2379, Abstract, by Takis. No.
2380, Abstract, by Maria Helena Vieira da
Silva. No. 2381, Abstract Squares, by Sean
Scully. No. 2382, Abstract, by Georg Baselitz,
Germany.

1993-94　　Photo.　Perf. 13x12½
2379　A1234　5fr blk & ver　2.25　1.00
2380　A1234　5fr multicolored　2.25　1.00
2381　A1234　6.70fr multicolored　3.00　1.00
**　　　　　Perf. 13**
2382　A1234　6.70fr multicolored　3.00　1.00
　　　Nos. 2379-2382 (4)　10.50　4.00
Issued: #2379, 10/9/93; #2380, 12/11/93;
#2381, 1/29/94; #2382, 11/19/94.

Greetings
A1266

Greeting, artist: #2383, Happy Birthday,
Claire Wendling. #2384, Happy Birthday, Ber-
nard Olivie. #2385, Happy Anniversary,
Stephane Colman. #2386, Happy Anniversary,
Guillaune Sorel. #2387, With Love, Jean-
Michel Thiriet. #2388, Please Write, Etienne
Davodeau. #2389, Congratulations, Johan de
Moor. #2390, Good luck, "Mezzo." #2391,
Best Wishes, Nicolas de Crecy. #2392, Best
Wishes, Florence Magnin. #2393, Merry
Christmas, Thierry Robin. #2394, Merry
Christmas, Patrick Prugne.

1993, Oct. 21　Photo.　Perf. 13½x13
Booklet Stamps
2383　A1266　2.80fr multicolored　1.25　.30
2384　A1266　2.80fr multicolored　1.25　.30
2385　A1266　2.80fr multicolored　1.25　.30

2386　A1266　2.80fr multicolored　1.25　.30
2387　A1266　2.80fr multicolored　1.25　.30
2388　A1266　2.80fr multicolored　1.25　.30
2389　A1266　2.80fr multicolored　1.25　.30
2390　A1266　2.80fr multicolored　1.25　.30
2391　A1266　2.80fr multicolored　1.25　.30
2392　A1266　2.80fr multicolored　1.25　.30
2393　A1266　2.80fr multicolored　1.25　.30
2394　A1266　2.80fr multicolored　1.25　.30
　　a.　Bklt. pane, #2383-2394　12.50
**　　　　　Perf. 12½**
2383a　A1266　2.80fr　1.25　.30
2384a　A1266　2.80fr　1.25　.30
2385a　A1266　2.80fr　1.25　.30
2386a　A1266　2.80fr　1.25　.30
2387a　A1266　2.80fr　1.25　.30
2388a　A1266　2.80fr　1.25　.30
2389a　A1266　2.80fr　1.25　.30
2390a　A1266　2.80fr　1.25　.30
2391a　A1266　2.80fr　1.25　.30
2392a　A1266　2.80fr　1.25　.30
2393a　A1266　2.80fr　1.25　.30
2394b　A1266　2.80fr　1.25　.30
　　c.　Booklet pane of 12,
　　　　#2383a-2393a, 2394b　14.00

Souvenir Sheet

European
Stamp
Exhibition,
Salon du
Timbre
A1267

a, Rhododendrons. b, Flowers in park,
Paris.

1993, Nov. 10　　　　Perf. 13
2395　A1267　2.40fr #a.-b.+ 2
　　　　labels　16.00　16.00
　　　Sold for 15fr.

Louvre
Museum,
Bicent.
A1268

1993, Nov. 20
2396　A1268　2.80fr Louvre, 1793　1.25　1.00
2397　A1268　4.40fr Louvre, 1993　2.00　1.25
　　a.　Pair, #2396-2397　3.50　2.50

Glassware,
1901 — A1269

Cast Iron,
c. 1900 — A1270

Furniture,
c. 1902 — A1271

Stoneware,
c. 1898 — A1272

Decorative arts by: No. 2398, Emile Galle
(1846-1904). No. 2399, Hector Guimard
(1867-1942). No. 2400, Louis Majorelle (1859-
1926). No. 2401, Pierre-Adrien Dalpayrat
(1844-1910).

Perf. 13½x12½
1994, Jan. 22 **Photo.**
2398 A1269 2.80fr multicolored 1.25 .35
2399 A1270 2.80fr multicolored 1.25 .35
2400 A1271 4.40fr multicolored 2.00 .65
2401 A1272 4.40fr multicolored 2.00 .65
Nos. 2398-2401 (4) 6.50 2.00

Stained
Glass
Window,
St. Julian's
Cathedral,
Le Mans
A1273

1994, Feb. 12 **Engr.** **Perf. 12½x13**
2402 A1273 6.70fr multicolored 3.00 1.00

City of
Bastia — A1274

1994, Feb. 19 **Perf. 13x12½**
2403 A1274 4.40fr blue & brown 2.00 .30

Tourism Series

Argentat
A1275

1994, June 18 **Engr.** **Perf. 12x12½**
2404 A1275 4.40fr red brown &
rose carmine 2.00 .60

European Parliamentary
Elections — A1276

1994, Feb. 26 **Litho.** **Perf. 13**
2405 A1276 2.80fr multicolored 1.25 .25

Laurent Mourguet (1769-1844),
Creator of Puppet, Guignol — A1277

1994, Mar. 4 **Photo.** **Perf. 13**
2406 A1277 2.80fr multicolored 1.25 .35

French
Polytechnic
Institute,
Bicent.
A1277a

1994, Mar. 11
2407 A1277a 2.80fr multicolored 1.25 .35

Stamp Day
A1278

1994, Mar. 12 **Engr.** **Perf. 13**
2408 A1278 2.80fr blue & red 5.00 2.25
2409 A1278 2.80fr +60c blue &
red 1.40 1.25
a. Booklet pane of 4 #2408, 3
#2409 + 1 label 25.00
No. 2408 issued only in booklets.

Swedish Ballet
Costume — A1279

Banquet for Gustavus III at the
Trianon, 1784, by Lafrensen — A1280

French-Swedish cultural relations: No. 2411,
Tuxedo costume for Swedish ballet. No. 2412,
Viking ships. No. 2413, Viking ship. No. 2415,
Swedish, French flags.

1994, Mar. 18 **Engr.** **Perf. 13**
2410 A1279 2.80fr multicolored 3.50 1.25
2411 A1279 2.80fr multicolored 3.50 1.25
2412 A1279 2.80fr multicolored 3.50 1.25
2413 A1279 2.80fr multicolored 3.50 1.25
2414 A1280 3.70fr multicolored 4.00 2.00
2415 A1280 3.70fr multicolored 4.00 2.00
a. Booklet pane of #2410-2415 25.00

See Sweden Nos. 2065-2070.

Pres. Georges
Pompidou (1911-
1974)
A1281

1994, Apr. 9 **Engr.** **Perf. 13**
2416 A1281 2.80fr olive brown 1.25 .30

Resistance
of the
Maquis,
50th Anniv.
A1282

1994, Apr. 9
2417 A1282 2.80fr multicolored 1.25 .30

Philexjeunes '94, Grenoble — A1283

1994, Apr. 22 **Photo.**
2418 A1283 2.80fr multicolored 1.25 .30

Europa
A1284

Discoveries: 2.80fr, AIDS virus, by scientists
of Pasteur Institute. 3.70fr, Formula for wave
properties of matter, developed by Louis de
Brogile.

1994, Apr. 30 **Photo. & Engr.**
2419 A1284 2.80fr multicolored 1.25 .30
a. With label 1.25 .75
2420 A1284 3.70fr multicolored 1.75 .85
No. 2419a issued Dec. 1, 1994.

Opening of Channel Tunnel — A1285

Designs: Nos. 2421, 2423, British lion,
French rooster, meeting over Channel. Nos.
2422, 2424, Joined hands above speeding
train.

1994, May 3 **Photo.** **Perf. 13**
2421 A1285 2.80fr dk blue & multi 1.25 .30
2422 A1285 2.80fr dk blue & multi 1.25 .30
a. Pair, #2421-2422 2.75 1.50
2423 A1285 4.30fr lt blue & multi 2.00 .90
2424 A1285 4.30fr multicolored 2.00 .90
a. Pair, #2423-2424 4.50 2.25
Nos. 2421-2424 (4) 6.50 2.40

See Great Britain Nos. 1558-1561.

Asian Development Bank, Board of
Governors Meeting, Nice — A1286

1994, May 3 **Photo.** **Perf. 13**
2425 A1286 2.80fr multicolored 1.25 .30

Federation
of French
Philatelic
Societies,
67th
Congress,
Martigues
A1287

1994, May 20 **Engr.** **Perf. 12x12½**
2426 A1287 2.80fr multicolored 1.25 .30

Court of
Cassation
A1288

Litho. & Engr.
1994, June 3 **Perf. 13**
2427 A1288 2.80fr multicolored 1.25 .30

D-Day,
50th Anniv.
A1289

No. 2429, Tank, crowd waving Allied flags.

1994, June 4 **Engr.**
2428 A1289 4.30fr multicolored 2.00 .50
2429 A1289 4.30fr multicolored 2.00 .50
Liberation of Paris, 50th anniv. (#2429).

Mount St. Victoire, by Paul Cezanne
(1839-1906) — A1290

1994, June 18 **Photo.** **Perf. 13**
2430 A1290 2.80fr multicolored 1.25 .30

Intl.
Olympic
Committee,
Cent.
A1291

1994, June 23 **Litho.** **Perf. 13**
2431 A1291 2.80fr multicolored 1.25 .25

Saulx River
Bridge,
Rupt aux
Nonains
A1292

1994, July 2 **Engr.**
2432 A1292 2.80fr blackish blue 1.25 .25

Organ, Poitiers
Cathedral — A1293

1994, July 2   *Perf. 13x12½*
2433 A1293 4.40fr multicolored   2.00 .55

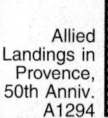

Allied
Landings in
Provence,
50th Anniv.
A1294

1994, Aug. 13   Engr.   *Perf. 13*
2434 A1294 2.80fr multicolored   1.25 .30

Moses and the Daughters of Jethro,
by Nicolas Poussin (1594-
1665) — A1295

Illustration reduced.

1994, Sept. 10
2435 A1295 4.40fr yel brn & blk   1.90 .90

Natl. Conservatory of Arts and Crafts,
Bicent. — A1296

1994, Sept. 24   *Perf. 13x12½*
2436 A1296 2.80fr Foucault's
       pendulum   1.25 .30

The Great Cascade,
St. Cloud
Park — A1297

1994, Sept. 24   *Perf. 12½x13*
2437 A1297 3.70fr multicolored   1.75 .50

Leaves — A1298

1994   Litho.   *Perf. 13*
2438 A1298 1.91fr Oak   .85 .40
2439 A1298 2.46fr Sycamore   1.10 .70
2440 A1298 4.24fr Chestnut   2.00 1.00
2441 A1298 6.51fr Holly   3.00 2.00
    Nos. 2438-2441 (4)   6.95 4.10

Nos. 2438-2441 are known only precanceled. See second note after No. 132.
See Nos. 2517-2520.

Ecole Normale
Superieure
(Teachers' School),
Bicent. — A1299

1994, Oct. 8   Engr.   *Perf. 13*
2442 A1299 2.80fr red & dk bl   1.25 .45

Georges
Simenon
(1903-89),
Writer
A1300

Litho. & Engr.
1994, Oct. 15   *Perf. 13*
2443 A1300 2.80fr multicolored   1.25 .25
See Belgium No. 1567, Switzerland No. 948.

Souvenir Sheet

European Stamp Exhibition — A1301

a, Flowers in park, Paris. b, Dalhias, vert.

1994, Oct. 15   Photo.   *Perf. 13*
2444 A1301 2.80fr Sheet of 2,
      #a.-b.   15.00 15.00
No. 2444 sold for 16fr.

Natl. Drug Addiction
Prevention
Day — A1302

1994, Oct. 15
2445 A1302 2.80fr multicolored   1.25 .25

Grand
Lodge of
France,
Cent.
A1303

1994, Nov. 5   Engr.
2446 A1303 2.80fr multicolored   1.25 .25

Alain Colas
(1943-78),
Sailor
A1304

1994, Nov. 19
2447 A1304 3.70fr green & black   1.75 .60

French
Natl. Press
Federation,
50th Anniv.
A1305

1994, Dec. 9   Photo.   *Perf. 13*
2448 A1305 2.80fr multicolored   1.25 .30

Champs Elysees — A1306

Illustration reduced.

1994, Dec. 31
2449 A1306 4.40fr multicolored   2.00 .75
No. 2449 printed with se-tenant label.

Souvenir Sheet

Motion Pictures, Cent. — A1307

Faces on screen and: a, Projector at right. b,
Projector facing away from screen. c, Projector
facing screen. d, Reels of film.

1995, Jan. 14   Photo.   *Perf. 13*
2450 A1307   Sheet of 4   5.50 5.50
   a.-d.   2.80fr any single   1.25 1.25

Normandy Bridge — A1308

Illustration reduced.

1995, Jan. 20   Engr.   *Perf. 13*
2451 A1308 4.40fr multicolored   2.00 .75

A1309   A1310

1995, Jan. 21   *Perf. 13x12*
2452 A1309 2.80fr multicolored   1.25 .30
European Notaries Public.

1995, Feb. 18   Photo.   *Perf. 13*
2453 A1310 3.70fr multicolored   1.75 1.00
Louis Pasteur (1822-95).

Art Series

St.
Taurin's
Reliquary,
Evreaux
A1311

Study for the Dream of Happiness, by
Pierre Prud'hon (1758-1823) — A1312

Abstract, by Zao Wou-ki — A1313

Abstract, by Per Kirkeby,
Denmark — A1314

1995   Photo. & Engr.   *Perf. 12x13*
2454 A1311 6.70fr multicolored   3.00 1.10
         Engr.
        Perf. 13x12
2455 A1312 6.70fr slate & blue   3.00 1.10
         Litho.
        Perf. 14
2456 A1313 6.70fr multicolored   3.00 1.10
         Photo.
        Perf. 13
2457 A1314 6.70fr multicolored   3.00 1.10
    Nos. 2454-2457 (4)   12.00 4.40
  Issued: #2454, 2/25/95; #2455, 5/12/95;
#2456, 6/10/95; #2457, 9/23/95.

Tourism Series

Stenay Malt
Works
A1315

Remiremont, Vosges — A1316

Nyons Bridge, Drome A1317

Barbizon, Home of Landscape Artists A1318

1995, Feb. 25   Engr.   Perf. 13x12½
2458 A1315 2.80fr ol & dk grn   1.25   .30
2459 A1316 2.80fr brn, grn & bl   1.25   .30
Perf. 12½x13
2460 A1317 4.40fr multicolored   2.00   .75
Photo.
Perf. 13½
2461 A1318 4.40fr multicolored   2.00   .75
  Nos. 2458-2461 (4)   6.50 2.10
Issued: #2458, 2/25/95; #2459, 5/13/95; #2460, 5/20/95; #2461, 9/30/95.

A1319

John J. Audubon (1785-1851) A1320

Designs: No. 2462, Snowy egret. No. 2463, Band-tailed pigeon. 4.30fr, Common tern. 4.40fr, Brown-colored rough-legged buzzard.

1995, Feb. 25 Photo. Perf. 12½x12
2462 A1319 2.80fr multicolored   1.25 .40
2463 A1320 2.80fr multicolored   1.25 .40
2464 A1319 4.30fr multicolored   2.00 .75
2465 A1320 4.40fr multicolored   2.00 .75
  a. Souvenir sheet of 4, #2462-
      2465, perf. 13   7.00 7.00
  Nos. 2462-2465 (4)   6.50 2.30

Stamp Day A1321

1995, Mar. 4   Engr.   Perf. 13
2466 A1321 2.80fr multicolored   6.00 3.00
2467 A1321 2.80fr +60c multi   1.60 1.40
  a. Booklet pane, 4 #2466, 3
      #2467+label   29.00
      Complete booklet, #2467   30.00
  No. 2466 issued only in booklets.

Work Councils, 50th Anniv. — A1322

1995, Mar. 7   Engr.   Perf. 13
2468 A1322 2.80fr dk bl, brn &
             sky bl   1.25 .30

Advanced Institute of Electricity, Cent. A1323

1995, Mar. 11   Photo.
2469 A1323 3.70fr multicolored 1.75 .40

Institute of Oriental Languages, Bicent. A1324

1995, Mar. 25   Photo.   Perf. 13
2470 A1324 2.80fr multicolored 1.25 .30

Jean Giono (1895-1970), Writer — A1325

1995, Mar. 25   Engr.
2471 A1325 3.70fr multicolored 1.75 1.00

Iron and Steel Industry in Lorraine — A1326

1995, Apr. 1   Perf. 13x12
2472 A1326 2.80fr multicolored 1.25 .30

End of World War II, 50th Anniv. A1327

Europa: 2.80fr, Barbed wire, laurel wreath. 3.70fr, Broken sword, emblem of European Union.

1995, Apr. 29   Photo.   Perf. 13
2473 A1327 2.80fr multicolored 1.25 .30
2474 A1327 3.70fr multicolored 1.75 .75

Forestry Profession, Ardennes — A1328

1995, May 2   Engr.   Perf. 12½x13
2475 A1328 4.40fr multicolored 2.00 .80

End of World War II, 50th Anniv. A1329

1995, May 8   Photo.   Perf. 13
2476 A1329 2.80fr multicolored 1.25 .35

Natl. Assembly — A1330

1995, May 13 Photo. Perf. 13x12½
2477 A1330 2.80fr multicolored 1.25 .60

French's People's Relief Assoc., 50th Anniv. A1331

1995, May 20   Engr.   Perf. 12½x13
2478 A1331 2.80fr multicolored 1.25 .30

Scenes of France — A1332

#2479, Forest, Vosges. #2480, Massif, Brittany. #2481, Wetlands, cattle, Camargue. #2482, Volcanoes, Auvergne.

1995, May 27   Perf. 13
2479 A1332 2.40fr green 1.10 .25
2480 A1332 2.40fr green 1.10 .25
2481 A1332 2.80fr red   1.25 .30
2482 A1332 2.80fr red   1.25 .30
  Nos. 2479-2482 (4)   4.70 1.10

Ariane Rocket on Launch Pad, French Guiana — A1333

1995, June 1   Engr.   Perf. 12½x13
2483 A1333 2.80fr bl, grn & red 1.25 .30
  Compare with No. 2254.

A1334   A1335

1995, June 2   Engr.   Perf. 13
2484 A1334 2.80fr multicolored 1.25 .30
68th Congress of French Federation of Philatelic Organizations, Orleans.

1995, June 3
2485 A1335 4.40fr Town of Correze   2.00 .75

A1336   A1337

Fables of Jean de la Fontaine (1621-95): No. 2486, The Grasshopper and The Ant. No. 2487, The Frog Who Could Make Himself Larger than an Ox. No. 2488, The Wolf and the Lamb. No. 2489, The Crow and the Fox. No. 2490, The Cat, the Weasel, and the Small Rabbit. No. 2491, The Tortoise and the Hare.

1995, June 24   Photo.   Perf. 13
2486 A1336 2.80fr multicolored 1.40 .75
2487 A1336 2.80fr multicolored 1.40 .75
2488 A1336 2.80fr multicolored 1.40 .75
2489 A1336 2.80fr multicolored 1.40 .75
2490 A1336 2.80fr multicolored 1.40 .75
2491 A1336 2.80fr multicolored 1.40 .75
  a. Strip, #2486-2491 + 2 labels 9.00 8.00

1995, July 9   Photo.   Perf. 13
2492 A1337 2.80fr multicolored 1.25 .30
  Velodrome d'Hiver raid.

André Maginot (1877-1932), Creator of Maginot Line — A1338

1995, Sept. 9   Engr.   Perf. 13
2493 A1338 2.80fr multicolored 1.25 .30

Women's Grand Masonic Lodge of France, 50th Anniv. — A1339

1995, Sept. 16   Perf. 13x12½
2494 A1339 2.80fr multicolored 1.25 .30

Hospital Pharmacies, 500th Anniv. — A1340

1995, Sept. 23   Perf. 12½x13
2495 A1340 2.80fr multicolored 1.25 .30

Natl. School of Administration, 50th Anniv. — A1341

1995, Oct. 5   Photo.   Perf. 13
2496 A1341 2.80fr multicolored 1.25 .30

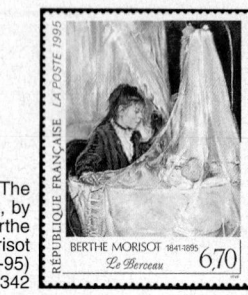

The Cradle, by Berthe Morisot (1841-95) A1342

1995, Oct. 7   Litho.   Perf. 13½x14
2497 A1342 6.70fr multicolored   3.00 1.00

The French Institute, Bicent. — A1343

1995, Oct. 14   Engr.   Perf. 12½x13
2498 A1343 2.80fr blk, grn & red   1.25   .30

Automobile Club of France, Cent. A1344

1995, Nov. 4   Engr.   Perf. 13x12½
2499 A1344 4.40fr blk, bl & red   2.00   .60

UN, 50th Anniv. A1345

1995, Nov. 16   Photo.   Perf. 13
2500 A1345 4.30fr multicolored   2.00 1.00

Francis Jammes (1868-1938), Poet — A1346

1995, Dec. 2   Engr.   Perf. 13
2501 A1346 3.70fr black & blue   1.75 1.00

A1347

A1348

1995, Dec. 9   Litho. & Engr.
2502 A1347 2.80fr Evry Cathedral   1.25   .30

1995, Dec. 12   Photo.   Perf. 13
2503 A1348 2.80fr multicolored   1.25   .30

1998 World Cup Soccer Championships, France.

Art Series

Abstract, by Lucien Wercollier — A1349

Design: No. 2505, The Netherlands (Horizon), abstract photograph, by Jan Dibbets.

1996   Perf. 13x12½
2504 A1349 6.70fr multicolored   3.00 1.00
2505 A1349 6.70fr multicolored   3.00 1.00
    Issued: #2504, 1/20; #2505, 2/10.

Arawak Civilization, Saint Martin — A1350

Design: 2.80fr, Dog figurine, 550 B.C.

1996, Feb. 10   Engr.   Perf. 13
2506 A1350 2.80fr multicolored   1.25   .40

The Augustus Bridge over the Nera River, by Camille Corot (1796-1875) — A1351

1996, Mar. 2   Litho.   Perf. 13
2507 A1351 6.70fr multicolored   3.00 1.00

St. Patrick A1352

1996, Mar. 16   Photo.   Perf. 13
2508 A1352 2.80fr multicolored   1.25   .50

The Sower, 1903 — A1353

1996, Mar. 16   Litho. & Engr.
2509 A1353 2.80fr multicolored   6.00 5.00
2510 A1353 2.80fr +60c multi   1.75 1.25
    a. Booklet pane, 4 #2509, 3
            #2510 + label   30.00
        Complete booklet, #2510a   32.50
    Stamp Day.

Jacques Rueff (1896-1978), Economist — A1354

1996, Mar. 23   Engr.   Perf. 13x12½
2511 A1354 2.80fr multicolored   1.25   .50

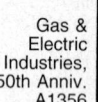

René Descartes (1596-1650) A1355

1996, Mar. 30   Engr.   Perf. 12½x13
2512 A1355 4.40fr red   2.00 1.00

Gas & Electric Industries, 50th Anniv. A1356

1996, Apr. 6   Photo.   Perf. 13
2513 A1356 3fr multicolored   1.40   .35

Natl. Parks A1357

1996, Apr. 20
2514 A1357 3fr Cévennes   1.40   .60
2515 A1357 4.40fr Vanoise   2.00 1.00
2516 A1357 4.40fr Mercantour   2.00 1.25
    Nos. 2514-2516 (3)   5.40 2.85
    See Nos. 2569-2572.

Leaf Type of 1994
1996, Mar.   Litho.   Perf. 13
2517 A1298 1.87fr Ash   .85   .30
2518 A1298 2.18fr Beech   1.00   .65
2519 A1298 4.66fr Walnut   2.10 1.25
2520 A1298 7.11fr Elm   3.25 2.00
    Nos. 2517-2520 (4)   7.20 4.20

Nos. 2517-2520 are known only precanceled. Values for precanceled stamps in first column are for those which have not been through the post and have original gum. Values in second column are for postally used, gumless stamps.

Madame Marie de Sévigné (1626-96), Writer — A1358

1996, Apr. 27   Photo.   Perf. 13
2521 A1358 3fr multicolored   1.40   .65
    Europa.

Natl. Institute of Agronomy Research, 50th Anniv. A1359

1996, May 4   Photo.   Perf. 13
2522 A1359 3.80fr multicolored   1.75 1.00

Joan of Arc's House, Domremy-La-Pucelle — A1360

1996, May 11
2523 A1360 4.50fr multicolored   2.10   .70

RAMOGE Agreement Between France, Italy, Monaco, 20th Anniv. A1361

1996, May 14   Photo. & Engr.
2524 A1361 3fr multicolored   1.40   .35
    See Monaco No. 1998, Italy No. 2077.

69th Congress of Federation of Philatelic Assoc., Clermont-Ferrand — A1362

1996, May 24   Engr.   Perf. 13
2525 A1362 3fr brn, red & grn   1.40   .35

Tourism Series

Bitche, Moselle A1363

Iles Sanguinaires, Ajaccio, Southern Corsica — A1364

Thoronet
Abbey, Var
A1365

Chambéry
Cathedral,
Savoie
A1366

1996　　**Engr.**　　**Perf. 12½x13**
2526 A1363　3fr multicolored　　1.40　.35
2527 A1364　3fr multicolored　　1.40　.35
　　　　　　Perf. 13x12½
2528 A1365　3.80fr brn & claret　1.75　.70
　　　　　　Photo.
　　　　　　Perf. 13
2529 A1366　4.50fr multicolored　2.10　.75
　Issued: #2526, 5/25/96; #2527, 6/1/96;
3.80fr, 7/6/96; 4.50fr, 6/8/96.

1998 World Cup
Soccer
Championships,
France — A1367

Various stylized soccer plays, name of host
city in France.

1996, June 1　　**Photo.**　　**Perf. 13**
2530 A1367　3fr Lens　　　　1.40　.35
2531 A1367　3fr Toulouse　　1.40　.35
2532 A1367　3fr Saint-Etienne　1.40　.35
2533 A1367　3fr Montpellier　1.40　.35
　　Nos. 2530-2533 (4)　　　5.60 1.40

　See Nos. 2584-2587, 2623-2624, sheet of
10, #2624a.

Art Series

Gallo-Roman Bronze Statue of Horse,
Neuvy-en-Sullias, Loiret — A1368

Imprints of Cello Fragments, by
Arman — A1369

1996　　**Engr.**　　**Perf. 13**
2534 A1368　6.70fr multicolored　3.00 1.00
　　　　　　Photo.
2535 A1369　6.70fr multicolored　3.00 1.00
　Issued: #2534, 6/8/96; #2535, 9/21/96.

A1371

A1372

1996, June 15　　**Photo.**　　**Perf. 13**
2537 A1371　3fr multicolored　　1.40　.50
　Modern Olympic Games, cent.

1996, June 15　**Engr.**　**Perf. 12½x13**
2538 A1372　4.40fr deep purple　2.00 1.00
　Jacques Marette (1922-84), Member of
Parliament.

A1373

A1374

1996, June 29　　**Photo.**　　**Perf. 13**
2539 A1373　3fr multicolored　　1.40　.35
　Train between Ajaccio and Vizzavona, cent.

1996, Sept. 6　**Engr.**　**Perf. 13x12½**
2540 A1374　3fr dark blue & yel　1.40　.30
　Notre Dame de Fourvière Basilica, Lyon,
cent.

Baptism of
Clovis,
1500th
Anniv.
A1375

1996, Sept. 14　　　　　**Perf. 13**
2541 A1375　3fr multicolored　　1.40　.30

Henri IV High
School,
Bicent. — A1376

1996, Oct. 12　**Engr.**　**Perf. 12½x13**
2542 A1376　4.50fr brown & blue　2.10　.80

UNICEF,
50th Anniv.
A1377

1996, Oct. 19　　**Photo.**　　**Perf. 13**
2543 A1377　4.50fr multicolored　2.10　.80

Economic and
Social Council, 50th
Anniv. — A1378

1996, Oct. 26　　**Engr.**　　**Perf. 13**
2544 A1378　3fr red, black & blue　1.40　.30

UNESCO,
50th Anniv.
A1379

1996, Nov. 2　　**Litho.**　　**Perf. 13**
2545 A1379　3.80fr multicolored　1.75　.75

A1380

A1381

1996, Nov. 7　　**Photo.**　　**Perf. 13**
2546 A1380　3fr multicolored　　1.40　.30
　Autumn Stamp Show, 50th anniv.

1996, Nov. 16
2547 A1381　3fr multicolored　　1.40　.30
　Creation of French Overseas Departments,
50th anniv.

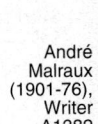
André
Malraux
(1901-76),
Writer
A1382

1996, Nov. 23　　**Engr.**　　**Perf. 13**
2548 A1382　3fr deep green black　1.40　.30

French
School in
Athens,
150th
Anniv.
A1383

1996, Nov. 23　　　　　　**Photo.**
2549 A1383　3fr multicolored　　1.40　.30

Cannes
Film
Festival,
50th Anniv.
A1384

1996, Nov. 30
2550 A1384　3fr multicolored　　1.40　.30

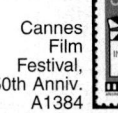
New
National
Library of
France
A1385

1996, Dec. 14
2551 A1385　3fr multicolored　　1.40　.30

A1386

A1387

1997, Jan. 4
2552 A1386　3fr multicolored　　1.40　.30
　Francois Mitterrand (1916-96).

1997, Jan. 24　　**Photo.**　　**Perf. 13**
2553 A1387　3fr multicolored　　1.40　.30
　Participatory innovation.

Georges Pompidou Natl. Center of Art
and Culture, 20th Anniv.
A1388

1997, Jan. 31　**Engr.**　**Perf. 12½x13**
2554 A1388　3fr multicolored　　1.40　.30

Happy
Holiday
A1389

1997, Feb. 8　　**Photo.**　　**Perf. 13**
2555 A1389　3fr shown　　　　1.40　.30
2556 A1389　3fr Happy birthday　1.40　.30

Natl. School of Bridges and Highways,
250th Anniv.
A1390

Photo. & Engr.
1997, Feb. 14　　　　**Perf. 12½x13**
2557 A1390　3fr multicolored　　1.40　.30

Saint-Laurent-du-Maroni, French
Guiana — A1391

Photo. & Engr.
1997, Feb. 22　　　　**Perf. 12½x13**
2558 A1391　3fr multicolored　　1.40　.30

Art Series

Church
Fresco,
Tavant
A1392

Painting by Bernard Moninot — A1393

The Thumb, Polished Bronze, by César A1394

Grapes and Pomegranates, by Jean Baptiste Chardin — A1395

1997   Engr.   Perf. 13
2559 A1392 6.70fr multicolored   3.00 1.00
      Photo.
2560 A1393 6.70fr multicolored   3.00 1.00
2561 A1394 6.70fr multicolored   3.00 1.00
2562 A1395 6.70fr multicolored   3.00 1.00
      Nos. 2559-2562 (4)   12.00 4.00
   Issued: #2559, 3/1; #2560, 3/29; #2561, 9/13; #2562, 9/27.

Tourism Series

Millau — A1396

Guimiliau Church Close — A1398

Fresco, Saint Eutrope des Salles-Lavauguyon — A1397

Sablé-Sur-Sarthe — A1399

1997   Engr.   Perf. 12½x13
2563 A1396 3fr grn & dk bl
                 grn   1.40 .30
      Perf. 13
2564 A1397 4.50fr multicolored   2.10 .75
2565 A1398 3fr multicolored   1.40 .30

Perf. 12½x13
2566 A1399 3fr multicolored   1.40 .20
      Nos. 2563-2566 (4)   6.30 1.55
   Issued: #2563, 3/15; #2564, 6/14; #2565, 7/12; #2566, 9/20.

Vignette of Type A17 — A1400

1997, Mar. 15   Litho. & Engr.   Perf. 13½x13
2567 A1400 3fr multicolored   6.00 5.00
2568 A1400 3fr +60c multi   2.50 2.00
  a. Booklet pane, 4 #2567, 3
      #2568 + label   32.50
      Complete booklet, #2568a   35.00
   Stamp Day.
   No. 2567 issued only in booklets.

National Parks Type of 1996
1997, Apr. 12   Photo.   Perf. 13
2569 A1357 3fr Parc des
                 Ecrins   1.40 .40
2570 A1357 3fr Guadeloupe
                 Park   1.40 .40
2571 A1357 4.50fr Parc des Pyr-
                 énées   2.10 .90
2572 A1357 4.50fr Port-Cros
                 Park   2.10 .90
      Nos. 2569-2572 (4)   7.00 2.60

Puss-in-Boots A1401

1997, Apr. 26   Engr.   Perf. 13
2573 A1401 3fr blue   1.40 .30
   Europa.

Philexjeunes '97, Nantes — A1402

1997, May 2   Litho.   Perf. 13
2574 A1402 3fr multicolored   1.40 .30

Cartoon Journey of a Letter A1403

   "Envelope": No. 2575, Writing letter. No. 2576, Climbing ladder to go into letter box. No. 2577, On wheels. No. 2578, Following postman carrying another "Envelope." No. 2579, Held by girl. No. 2580, At feet of girl reading long letter.

1997, May 8   Photo.   Perf. 13
2575 A1403 3fr multicolored   2.50 1.00
2576 A1403 3fr multicolored   2.50 1.00
2577 A1403 3fr multicolored   2.50 1.00
2578 A1403 3fr multicolored   2.50 1.00
2579 A1403 3fr multicolored   2.50 1.00
2580 A1403 3fr multicolored   2.50 1.00
  a. Strip of 6, #2575-2580
      + label   18.00 12.00

Self-Adhesive
Serpentine Die Cut 11
2580B A1403 3fr like #2575   2.00 1.25
2580C A1403 3fr like #2576   2.00 1.25
2580D A1403 3fr like #2577   2.00 1.25
2580E A1403 3fr like #2578   2.00 1.25
2580F A1403 3fr like #2579   2.00 1.25
2580G A1403 3fr like #2580   2.00 1.25
  h. Booklet pane, 2 each
      #2580B-2580G   27.50 27.50
   By its nature No. 2580h is a complete booklet. The peelable paper backing serves as a booklet cover.
   See Nos. 2648-2659.

Honoring French Soldiers in North Africa (1952-62) A1404

1997, May 10   Litho.   Perf. 13
2581 A1404 3fr multicolored   1.40 .30

French Federation of Philatelic Associations, 70th Congress, Versailles — A1405

   Illustration reduced.

1997, May 17   Photo.   Perf. 13
2582 A1405 3fr multicolored   1.40 .30
   Printed with se-tenant label.

Château de Plessis-Bourré, Maine and Loire Rivers — A1406

1997, May 24   Litho. & Engr.
2583 A1406 4.40fr multicolored   2.00 1.00

1998 World Cup Soccer Championships Type
   Stylized action scenes, name of host city in France.

1997, May 31   Photo.   Perf. 13½
2584 A1367 3fr Lyon   1.40 .35
2585 A1367 3fr Marseilles   1.40 .35
2586 A1367 3fr Nantes   1.40 .35
2587 A1367 3fr Paris   1.40 .35
      Nos. 2584-2587 (4)   5.60 1.40

Saint Martin of Tours (316-97) Apostle of the Gauls A1408

1997, July 5   Engr.   Perf. 13
2588 A1408 4.50fr multicolored   2.00 .65

Marianne — A1409

1997, July 14   Engr.   Perf. 13
2589 A1409 10c brown   .20 .20
2590 A1409 20c brt blue
                 grn   .20 .20
2591 A1409 50c purple   .25 .20
2592 A1409 1fr bright org   .45 .20
2593 A1409 2fr bright blue   .90 .30
2594 A1409 2.70fr bright grn   1.25 .30
2595 A1409 (3fr) red   1.40 .20
2596 A1409 3.50fr apple grn   1.60 .25
2597 A1409 3.80fr blue   1.75 .25
2598 A1409 4.20fr dark org   1.90 .30
2599 A1409 4.40fr blue   2.00 .30
2600 A1409 4.50fr bright pink 2.10 .30
2601 A1409 5fr brt grn
                 blue   5.25 .30

2602 A1409 6.70fr dark
                 green   3.00 .30
  a. Souvenir sheet, #2594-
      2600, 2602   14.00 14.00
2603 A1409 10fr violet   4.50 .35
  a. Souvenir sheet, #2589-
      2593, 2601, 2603   12.00 12.00
      Nos. 2589-2603 (15)   26.75 3.90
Self-Adhesive
Booklet Stamps
Die Cut x Serpentine Die Cut 7
2603B A1409 1fr brt org   2.25 .50
  c. Booklet pane, #2603B, 3
      #2604   7.75
      Booklet, 2 #2603Bc   16.00
2604 A1409 (3fr) red   1.40 .25
  a. Booklet pane of 10   14.00
Coil Stamps
Perf. 13 Horiz.
2604B A1409 2.70fr bright grn 1.25 .50
2605 A1409 (3fr) red   1.40 .40
   Nos. 2595, 2604-2605 were valued at 3fr on day of issue.
   Issued: Nos. 2602a, 2603a, 11/12/01. No. 2603B, 9/1/97.
   See Nos. 2835-2835C.

1997 World Rowing Championships, Savoie — A1410

1997, Aug. 30   Engr.   Perf. 13x12½
2606 A1410 3fr blue & magenta   1.40 .30

Basque Corsairs A1411

1997, Sept. 13   Perf. 13
2607 A1411 3fr multicolored   1.40 .30

Saint-Maurice Basilica, Epinal — A1412

1997, Sept. 20   Perf. 13x12½
2608 A1412 3fr multicolored   1.40 .30

Fresh Fish Merchants, Port of Boulogne A1413

1997, Sept. 26   Perf. 13
2609 A1413 3fr multicolored   1.40 .30

Japan Year — A1414

1997, Oct. 4   Engr.   Perf. 13
2610 A1414 4.90fr multicolored   2.25 1.25

1997 World Judo Championships — A1415

1997, Oct. 9   **Photo.**   *Perf. 13*
2611 A1415 3fr multicolored   1.40   .35

Sceaux Estate, Hauts-de-Seine — A1416

1997, Oct. 11
2612 A1416 3fr multicolored   1.40   .30

Saar-Lorraine-Luxembourg Summit — A1417

1997, Oct. 16   **Photo.**   *Perf. 13*
2613 A1417 3fr multicolored   1.40   .30
   See Germany #1982, Luxembourg #972.

College of France A1418

1997, Oct. 18   **Engr.**
2614 A1418 4.40fr multicolored   2.00   .90

Quality — A1419

1997, Oct. 18   **Photo.**
2615 A1419 4.50fr multicolored   2.10   .60

A1420

Season's Greetings A1421

1997   **Photo.**   *Perf. 13*
2616 A1420 3fr Cat & mouse   1.40   .30
   Photo. & Embossed
2617 A1421 3fr Mailman   1.40   .30
   Issued: No. 2616, 11/8; No. 2617, 11/22.

Protection of Abused Children — A1422

1997, Nov. 20   **Photo.**
2618 A1422 3fr multicolored   1.40   .30

Marshal Jacques Leclerc (Philippe de Haute Cloque) (1902-47) A1423

1997, Nov. 28   **Photo.**   *Perf. 13*
2619 A1423 3fr multicolored   1.40   .30

Philexfrance '99, World Stamp Exposition — A1424

1997, Dec. 6   **Engr.**
2620 A1424 3fr red & blue   1.40   .30

Abbey of Moutier D'Ahun, Creuse A1425

1997, Dec. 13
2621 A1425 4.40fr multicolored   2.00   1.00

Michel Debré (1912-96), Politician A1426

1998, Jan. 15   **Photo.**
2622 A1426 3fr multicolored   1.40   .30

1998 World Cup Soccer Championships Type

Stylized action scenes, name of host city in France.

1998, Jan. 24   *Perf. 13½*
2623 A1367 3fr Saint-Denis   1.40   .30
2624 A1367 3fr Bordeaux   1.40   .30
   a.   Sheet of 10, #2530-2533,
      #2584-2587, #2623-2624
      + label   14.00   14.00

National Assembly, Bicent. — A1427

1998, Jan. 24   *Perf. 13*
2625 A1427 3fr multicolored   1.40   .30

Valentine's Day A1428

1998, Jan. 31
2626 A1428 3fr multicolored   1.40   .30

Office of Mediator of the Republic, 25th Anniv. A1429

1998, Feb. 5
2627 A1429 3fr multicolored   1.40   .30

A1430

1998, Feb. 28   **Photo.**   *Perf. 12½*
2628 A1430 3fr multicolored   1.40   .30
   Self-Adhesive
   Serpentine Die Cut
2629 A1430 3fr like #2628   1.40   .30
   a.   Booklet pane of 10   14.00   14.00
   b.   Sheet of 1 + 7 labels   14.00   14.00
   1998 World Cup Soccer Championships, France.
   The peelable paper backing of No. 2629a serves as a booklet cover.
   See No. 2665.

A1431

1998, Feb. 21   **Engr.**   *Perf. 13½x13*
2630 A1431 3fr Detail of design
      A16   6.50   4.50
2631 A1431 3fr +60c like #2630   2.50   2.50
   a.   Booklet pane, 4 #2630, 3
      #2631 + label   34.00
      Complete booklet, #2631a   35.00

   Stamp Day. No. 2630 issued only in booklets.

A1432

1998, Feb. 28   **Engr.**   *Perf. 13*
2632 A1432 4.50fr blue   2.10   .75
   Father Franz Stock (1904-48), prison chaplain.

Happy Birthday A1433

1998, Mar. 13   **Photo.**   *Perf. 13x13½*
2633 A1433 3fr multicolored   1.40   .30

Union of Mulhouse with France, Bicent. A1434

1998, Mar. 14
2634 A1434 3fr multicolored   1.40   .30

Citeaux Abbey, 900th Anniv. A1435

1998, Mar. 14   **Engr.**   *Perf. 13*
2635 A1435 3fr multicolored   1.40   .30

Sous-Préfecture Hotel, Saint-Pierre, Réunion — A1436

1998, Apr. 4   **Engr.**   *Perf. 13*
2636 A1436 3fr multicolored   1.40   .30
   Réunion's architectural heritage.

"The Return," by René Magritte — A1437

1998, Apr. 18   **Photo.**
2637 A1437 3fr multicolored   1.40   .50
   See Belgium No. 1691.

Edict of Nantes, 400th Anniv. A1438

1998, Apr. 18   **Litho.**
2638 A1438 4.50fr Henry IV   2.10   .75

Art Series

Detail from "Entry of the Crusaders into Constantinople," by Delacroix (1798-1863) — A1439

Le Printemps, by Pablo Picasso
(1881-1973) — A1440

Neuf Moules Malic, by Marcel
Duchamp (1887-1968) — A1441

Vision After the Sermon, by Paul
Gauguin (1848-1903) — A1442

1998   Engr.   Perf. 12x13
2639 A1439 6.70fr multicolored   3.00 1.00
Litho.
Perf. 13
2640 A1440 6.70fr multicolored   3.00 1.00
Photo.
2641 A1441 6.70fr multicolored   3.00 1.00
2642 A1442 6.70fr multicolored   3.00 1.00

Issued: #2639, 4/25; #2640, 5/15; #2641,
10/17; #2642, 12/5.

Abolition of
Slavery,
150th
Anniv.
A1443

1998, Apr. 25   Litho.   Perf. 13
2643 A1443 3fr multicolored   1.40   .30

Tourism Series

Le Gois Causeway, Island of
Noirmoutier, Vendée — A1444

Bay of Somme,
Picardy — A1445

Château de
Crussol,
Ardèche
A1446

Collegiate Church
of
Mantes — A1447

1998, May 2   Photo.
2644 A1444   3fr multicolored   1.40   .30
2645 A1445   3fr multicolored   1.40   .30
Engr.
2646 A1446   3fr multicolored   1.40   .30
2647 A1447   4.40fr multicolored   2.00 1.00
Nos. 2644-2647 (4)   6.20 1.90

Issued: #2644, 5/2; #2645, 6/27; #2646, 7/4;
#2647, 9/19.

Journey of a Letter Type

Historic "letters:" No. 2648, Dove carrying
letter, Noah's Ark. No. 2649, Egyptian writing
letter on papyrus. No. 2650, Soldier running to
Athens with letter to victory at Marathon. No.
2651, Knight carrying letter on horseback. No.
2652, Writing letters with quill and ink. No.
2653, Astronaut carrrying letter in space from
earth to the moon.

1998, May 9   Photo.   Perf. 13x13½
2648 A1403 3fr multicolored   2.50 1.00
2649 A1403 3fr multicolored   2.50 1.00
2650 A1403 3fr multicolored   2.50 1.00
2651 A1403 3fr multicolored   2.50 1.00
2652 A1403 3fr multicolored   2.50 1.00
2653 A1403 3fr multicolored   2.50 1.00
 a.   Strip of #2648-2653 + label   16.00 10.00
Booklet Stamps
Self-Adhesive
Serpentine Die Cut 11
2654 A1403 3fr like #2648   2.25 1.25
2655 A1403 3fr like #2649   2.25 1.25
2656 A1403 3fr like #2650   2.25 1.25
2657 A1403 3fr like #2651   2.25 1.25
2658 A1403 3fr like #2652   2.25 1.25
2659 A1403 3fr like #2653   2.25 1.25
 a.   Bkt. pane, 2 ea #2654-
         2659   27.50 27.50

By its nature No. 2659a is a complete booklet. The peelable paper backing serves as a
booklet cover.

League of Human
Rights,
Cent. — A1448

1998, May 9   Perf. 13
2660 A1448 4.40fr multicolored   2.00 1.00

Henri Collet (1885-1951),
Composer — A1449

1998, May 15   Engr.   Perf. 12x13
2661 A1449 4.50fr black, gray &
                 buff   2.10   .90

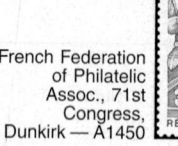

French Federation
of Philatelic
Assoc., 71st
Congress,
Dunkirk — A1450

Photo. & Engr.
1998, May 29   Perf. 13
2662 A1450 3fr multicolored   1.40   .30

Mont-Saint-Michel — A1451

1998, June 6   Photo.   Perf. 13
2663 A1451 3fr multicolored   1.40   .30

Natl. Music
Festival — A1452

1998, June 13
2664 A1452 3fr multicolored   1.40   .50

Europa.

**1998 World Cup Soccer
Championships Type with Added
Inscription, "Champion du Monde"**
1998, July 12   Photo.   Perf. 12½
2665 A1430 3fr multicolored   1.40   .30

Stéphane
Mallarmé
(1842-98),
Poet
A1453

Photo. & Engr.
1998, Sept. 5   Perf. 13
2666 A1453 4.40fr multicolored   2.00   .90

Flowers — A1453a

1998, Sept. 9   Litho.   Perf. 13
2666A   A1453a 1.87fr Liseron   .85   .30
2666B   A1453a 2.18fr Coqueli-
                     cot   1.00   .55
2666C   A1453a 4.66fr Violette   2.10 1.25
2666D   A1453a 7.11fr Bouton
                     d'or   3.25 2.00
 Nos. 2666A-2666D (4)   7.20 4.10

Nos. 2666A-2666D are known only precanceled. See second note after #132.

A1454   A1455

1998, Sept. 12   Photo.
2667 A1454 3fr multicolored   1.40   .30

Aéro Club of France, cent.

1998, Oct. 23   Photo.   Perf. 13

"The Little Prince," by Antoine de Saint-
Exupéry (1900-44): a, Standing in uniform with
sword, horiz. b, Seated on wall. c, "The Little
Prince on Asteroid B-612." d, Pouring water
from sprinkling can. e, Walking along cliff, fox,
horiz.

2668   Strip of 5 + 2 labels   7.00 6.00
 a.-e. A1455 3fr any single   1.40   .60
 f.   Souv. sheet, #2668a-2668e   9.00 9.00

Philexfrance '99. No. 2668f was released
9/12 and sold for 25fr.

Hall of
Heavenly
Peace,
Imperial
Palace,
Beijing,
China
A1456

1998, Sept. 12   Photo.   Perf. 13x13½
2669 A1456   3fr shown   1.40   .40
2670 A1456   4.90fr The Louvre,
                     France   2.25 1.00

See China People's Republic #2895-2896.

Garnier Palace,
Home of the Paris
Opera — A1457

1998, Sept. 19   Photo.   Perf. 13
2671 A1457 4.50fr multicolored   2.10   .75

Horses
A1458

1998, Sept. 27
2672 A1458 2.70fr Camargue   1.25   .30
2673 A1458 3fr Pottok   1.40   .50
2674 A1458 3fr French trotter   1.40   .50
2675 A1458 4.50fr Ardennais   2.10   .80
 Nos. 2672-2675 (4)   6.15 2.10

Paris Auto
Show,
Cent.
A1459

1998, Oct. 1   Perf. 12
2676 A1459 3fr multicolored   1.40   .30

5th Republic, 40th Anniv. A1460

1998, Oct. 3   Photo.   Perf. 13
2677 A1460 3fr blue, gray & red   1.40   .30

Saint-Dié, Capital of Vosges Mountain Region — A1461

1998, Oct. 3   Engr.   Perf. 13
2678 A1461 3fr Tower of Liberty   1.40   .30

End of World War I, 80th Anniv. A1462

1998, Oct. 17   Photo.   Perf. 13x13½
2679 A1462 3fr multicolored   1.40   .40

Intl. Union for the Conservation of Nature and Natural Resources, 50th Anniv. — A1463

1998, Nov. 3   Litho.
2680 A1463 3fr multicolored   1.40   .40

New Year A1464   Christmas A1465

1998, Nov. 7   Photo.   Perf. 13
Background Colors
2681 A1464 3fr deep blue   1.40   .75
2682 A1465 3fr green   1.40   .75
2683 A1464 3fr yellow   1.40   .75
2684 A1465 3fr red   1.40   .75
2685 A1464 3fr green   1.40   .75
  a.   Strip of 5, #2681-2685   7.00   6.00

Issued in sheets of 10 stamps. Location of "Bonne Annee" and "Meilleurs Voeux" varies.

Doctors Without Borders A1466

1998, Nov. 21   Perf. 13x13½
2686 A1466 3fr multicolored   1.40   .30

European Parliament, Strasbourg A1467

1998, Dec. 5   Photo.   Perf. 13
2687 A1467 3fr multicolored   1.40   .30

Universal Declaration of Human Rights, 50th Anniv. A1468

#2688, Faces of people of various races, globe. #2689, René Cassin (1887-1976), principal author of Declaration, Eleanor Roosevelt (1884-1962), Chaillot Palace, Paris.

1998, Dec. 10   Litho.   Perf. 13
2688 A1468 3fr multicolored   1.40   .30
2689 A1468 3fr multicolored   1.40   .30

Discovery of Radium, Cent., ZOE Reactor, 50th Anniv. A1469

1998, Dec. 15   Photo.   Perf. 13
2690 A1469 3fr multicolored   1.40   .40

Introduction of the Euro — A1470

1999   Engr.   Perf. 13
2691 A1470 3fr red & blue   1.40   .25
Booklet Stamps
Self-Adhesive
Die Cut x Serpentine Die Cut 7
2691A A1470 3fr red & blue   1.40   .25
  b.   Booklet pane of 10   14.00

Issued: No. 2691, 1/1/99. No. 2691A, 2/15/99. Values are shown in both Francs and Euros on Nos. 2691-2691A. No. 2691Ab is a complete booklet.
Euro currency did not circulate until 2002.

French Postage Stamps, 150th Anniv. A1471

1999, Jan. 1   Photo.   Perf. 13
Booklet Stamps
2692 A1471 3fr black & red   6.50   4.50
2693 A1471 3fr red & black   1.25   .75
  a.   Booklet pane, #2692, 4 #2693 + label   11.50
        Complete booklet, #2693a   12.00

No. 2692 has black denomination; No. 2693 has red denomination.
Stamp Day.

Public Assistance Hospital, Paris, 150th Anniv. A1472

1999, Jan. 9
2694 A1472 3fr multicolored   1.40   .30

Diplomatic Relations with Israel, 50th Anniv. — A1473

1999, Jan. 24
2695 A1473 4.40fr multicolored   2.00   .75

Festival Stamps A1474

1999, Feb. 6   Photo.   Perf. 13
2696 A1474 3fr Stars, "Je t'aime"   1.40   .30
2697 A1474 3fr Rose   1.40   .30
Booklet Stamps
Self-Adhesive
Die Cut Perf. 10
2698 A1474 3fr like #2696   1.40   .30
2699 A1474 3fr like #2697   1.40   .30
  a.   Bklt. pane, 5 ea #2698-2699   14.00

No. 2699a is a complete booklet.

Art Series

St. Luke the Evangelist, Sculpture by Jean Goujon (1510-66) A1475

Painting, "Waterlillies in Moonlight," by Claude Monet (1840-1926) — A1476

Stained Glass, Cathedral of Auch, by Arnauld de Moles, 16th Cent. A1477

Charles I, King of England, by Sir Anthony Van Dyck A1478

1999   Engr.   Perf. 13
2700 A1475 6.70fr multicolored   3.00 1.00
Litho.
2701 A1476 6.70fr multicolored   3.00 1.00
Engr.
2702 A1477 6.70fr multicolored   3.00 1.00
Photo.
Perf. 13¼x13
2703 A1478 6.70fr multicolored   3.00 1.00
    Nos. 2700-2703 (4)   12.00 4.00

Issued: #2700, 2/13; #2701, 5/29; #2702, 6/19; #2703, 11/11.

National Census — A1479

1999, Feb. 20   Photo.   Perf. 13½
2704 A1479 3fr multicolored   1.40   .30

Cultural Heritage of Lebanon A1480

Mosaic illustrating transformation of Zeus into bull, Natl. Museum of Beirut.

1999, Feb. 27   Perf. 12½
2705 A1480 4.40fr multicolored   2.00   .90

Asterix, by Albert Uderzo and Rene Goscinny A1481

1999, Mar. 6   Photo.   Perf. 13¼
2706 A1481 3fr multicolored   1.75   .50
  a.   Perf. 13¼x12¾   1.75   .90
Booklet Stamp
Perf. 13¼x12¾
2707 A1481 3fr +60c like #2706   3.50 2.00
  b.   Booklet pane, 4 #2706a, 3 #2707 + label   15.00
        Complete booklet, #2707b   16.00
Souvenir Sheet
2707A A1481 3fr +60c like #2706   3.00 2.50

Stamp Day. Stamp design in #2707A continues into the margins.

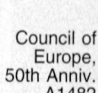

Council of Europe, 50th Anniv. A1482

1999, Mar. 19
2708 A1482 3fr multicolored   1.40   .30

A1483

Announcements — A1483a

1999, Mar. 20   **Perf. 13**
2709 A1483 3fr Marriage (Oui)   1.40   .30
2710 A1483 3fr It's a boy (C'est un garcon)   1.40   .30
2711 A1483 3fr It's a girl(C'est une fille)   1.40   .30
2712 A1483a 3fr Thank you   1.40   .30
   Nos. 2709-2712 (4)   5.60   1.20

See Nos. 2721-2722.

Souvenir Sheet

PhilexFrance '99 — A1484

Works of art: a, Venus de Milo. b, Mona Lisa, by Da Vinci. c, Liberty Guiding the People, by Delacroix.

Litho. & Engr.
1999, Mar. 26   **Perf. 13¼**
2713 A1484   Sheet of 3   50.00   50.00
  a.-b.   5fr each   10.00   10.00
  c.   10fr multicolored   20.00   20.00

No. 2713 sold for 50fr, with 30fr serving as a donation to the Assoc. for the Development of Philately.

Elections to the European Parliament A1485

1999, Mar. 27   **Photo.**   **Perf. 13**
2714 A1485 3fr multicolored   1.40   .30

Richard I, the Lion-Hearted (1157-1199), King of England — A1486

1999, Apr. 10   **Engr.**   **Perf. 13x12½**
2715 A1486 3fr multicolored   1.40   .35

Tourism Series

Dieppe A1487

Haut-Koenigsbourg Castle, Bas-Rhin — A1488

Birthpalce of Champollion, Figeac — A1489

Chateau, Arnac-Pompadour — A1490

Illustration reduced (A1488).

1999   **Engr.**   **Perf. 13½**
2716 A1487 3fr multicolored   1.40   .30
   Litho. & Engr.
    Perf. 13
2717 A1488 3fr multicolored   1.40   .50
2718 A1489 3fr multicolored   1.40   .30
   Engr.
2719 A1490 3fr multicolored   1.40   .30
   Nos. 2716-2719 (4)   5.60   1.40
   Issued: #2716, 4/17; #2717, 5/15; #2718, 6/26; #2719, 7/10.

The Camargue Nature Preserve A1491

1999, Apr. 24   **Photo.**   **Perf. 13x13½**
2720 A1491 3fr multicolored   1.40   .50
   Europa.

Announcements Type of 1999 and

A1492

1999, May 13   **Photo.**   **Perf. 13**
2721 A1483 3fr Nice Holiday (bonnes vacances)   1.40   .30
2722 A1483 3fr Happy Birthday (joyeux anniversaire)   1.40   .30
2723 A1492 3fr Long Live Vacations (Vive les vacances)   1.40   .30
   Nos. 2721-2723 (3)   4.20   .90

Saint Pierre, Martinique A1493

1999, May 15
2724 A1493 3fr multicolored   1.10   .25

Detail of "Noctuelles" Dish, by Émile Gallé, School of Nancy Museum A1494

1999, May 22
2725 A1494 3fr multicolored   1.40   .30

Souvenir Sheet

World Old Roses Competition, Lyon — A1495

a, 4.50fr, Mme. Caroline Testout. b, 3fr, Mme. Alfred Carrière. c, 4.50fr, La France.

1999, May 28   **Perf. 13½x13**
2726 A1495   Sheet of 3, #a.-c.   8.00   8.00

Court of Saint-Emilion, 800th Anniv. — A1496

1999, May 29   **Engr.**   **Perf. 13¼x13**
2727 A1496 3.80fr multicolored   1.75   .90

Hotel de la Monnaie, French Mint Headquarters — A1497

1999, June 5   **Engr.**   **Perf. 13**
2728 A1497 4.50fr brn org & bl   2.10   .75

A1498   A1499

1999, June 12   **Photo.**   **Perf. 13¼**
2729 A1498 3fr multicolored   1.40   .40
   Countess of Segur (1799-1874), children's storyteller.

1999, June 19   **Perf. 13**
2730 A1499 3fr Welcome   1.40   .30

René Caillié (1799-1838), Explorer of Africa — A1500

1999, June 26   **Engr.**   **Perf. 13¼**
2731 A1500 4.50fr multicolored   2.10   .75

1st French Postage Stamps, 150th Anniv. A1501

1999, July 2   **Photo.**   **Perf. 11¾x13**
2732 A1501 6.70fr multicolored   3.00   1.75

PhilexFrance '99, World Philatelic Exhibition. No. 2732 was printed with a se-tenant label and contains a holographic image. Soaking in water may affect the hologram.

Celebrating the Year 2000 A1502

1999, July 5   **Photo.**   **Perf. 13**
2733 A1502 3fr multicolored   1.40   .30

Year 2000 Stamp Design Contest Winner — A1503

1999, July 6
2734 A1503 3fr multicolored   1.40   .30

Total Solar Eclipse, Aug. 11, 1999 A1504

1999, July 8   **Perf. 12x12¼**
2735 A1504 3fr multicolored   1.40   .40

Gathering of Tall Ships, Rouen, July 9-18 A1505

Sailing ships: a, Simón Bolivar. b, Iskra. c, Statsraad Lehmkuhl. d, Asgard II. e, Belle Poule. f, Belem. g, Amerigo Vespucci. h, Sagres. i, Europa. j, Cuauhtemoc.

1999, July 10   **Photo.**   **Perf. 13**
2736   1fr Sheet of 10   6.00   6.00
  a.-j.   A1505 any single   .50   .50

1999 Rugby
World Cup,
Cardiff,
Wales
A1506

1999, Sept. 11   Photo.   Perf. 13¼
2737 A1506 3fr multicolored   1.40   .40
  a. Miniature sheet of 10   11.00

Value is for copy with surrounding selvage.
One stamp in No. 2737a has a missing "F"
in the printer's mark.

Frédéric Ozanam
(1813-53),
Historian — A1507

1999, Sept. 11   Engr.   Perf. 13
2738 A1507 4.50fr multicolored   2.10   .75

Emmaus
Movement,
50th Anniv.
A1508

1999, Sept. 26   Photo.   Perf. 13
2739 A1508 3fr multicolored   1.40   .40

Cats and
Dogs — A1509

1999, Oct. 2   Photo.   Perf. 13¼
2740 A1509 2.70fr Chartreux cat   1.25   .30
2741 A1509 3fr European cat   1.40   .30
2742 A1509 3fr Pyrenean
        Mountain
        dog   1.40   .30
2743 A1509 4.50fr Brittany span-
        iel   2.10   .75
    Nos. 2740-2743 (4)   6.15 1.65

Frédéric
Chopin
(1810-49),
Composer
A1510

1999, Oct. 17   Engr.   Perf. 13¼
2744 A1510 3.80fr multicolored   1.75   .75
    See Poland No. 3484.

A1511

Best
Wishes for
Year 2000
A1512

1999, Nov. 20   Photo.   Perf. 13x13¼
2745 A1511 3fr multi   1.40   .30
2746 A1512 3fr multi   1.40   .30
    No. 2746 was printed with se-tenant label.

Paris
Metro,
Cent.
A1513

1999, Dec. 4   Photo.   Perf. 13
2747 A1513 3fr multi   1.40   .30

Council of State,
Bicent. — A1514

1999, Dec. 11
2748 A1514 3fr multi   1.40   .30

Reconstruction of
Lighthouses — A1515

2000, Jan. 1   Photo.   Perf. 13x12¾
2749 A1515 3fr multi   1.40   .30

Reconstruction of San Juan de Salvamento
Lighthouse, Argentina and replication of its
design at La Rochelle, France.

Hearts
A1516

2000, Jan. 8   Photo.   Perf. 13
2750 A1516 3fr Snakes   1.40   .30
2751 A1516 3fr Face   1.40   .30
  a. Souvenir sheet, 3 #2750, 2
    #2751   9.00 9.00

Self-Adhesive Booklet Stamps
Serpentine Die-Cut
2752 A1516 3fr Like #2750   1.40   .30
2753 A1516 3fr Like #2751   1.40   .30
  a. Bklt. pane, 5 ea #2752-2753   14.00

Values for Nos. 2750-2751 are for copies
with surrounding selvage. No. 2753a is a complete booklet.

Bank of France,   Prefectorial
Bicent. — A1517   Corps,
              Bicent. — A1518

2000, Jan. 15   Litho.   Perf. 13
2754 A1517 3fr multi   1.40   .30

2000, Feb. 17   Photo.   Perf. 13x12¼
2755 A1518 3fr multi   1.40   .30

Art Series

Venus and the Graces Offering Gifts to
a Young Girl, by Sandro Botticelli
(1445-1510) — A1519

The Waltz,
by Camille
Claudel
A1520

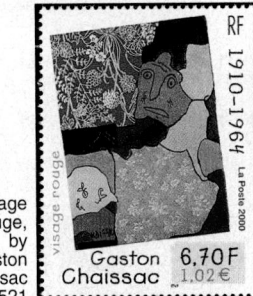

Visage
Rouge,
by
Gaston
Chaissac
A1521

Carolingian Mosaic, Germigny-des-
Prés — A1522

2000   Photo.   Perf. 13¼x13
2756 A1519 6.70fr multi   3.00 1.00
2757 A1520 6.70fr multi   3.00 1.00
2758 A1521 6.70fr multi   3.00 1.00
2759 A1522 6.70fr multi   3.00 1.00
    Issued: #2756, 2/25; #2757, 4/8; #2758,
9/23; 10/21.

Tourism Series

Carcassonne — A1523

Saint-Guilhem-Le-Désert — A1524

Gérardmer
A1525

Abbey Church of
Ottmarsheim — A1526

Illustration A1523 reduced.

2000   Photo.   Perf. 13
2760 A1523 3fr multi   1.40   .30
        Engr.
        Perf. 13¼
2761 A1524 3fr multi   1.40   .30
2762 A1525 3fr multi   1.40   .30
      Perf. 12¼x13
2763 A1526 3fr multi   1.40   .30
    Nos. 2760-2763 (4)   5.60 1.20
    Issued: #2760, 3/3; #2761, 4/8; #2762, 4/17;
#2763, 6/17.

Tintin — A1527

2000, Mar. 11   Photo.   Perf. 13¼
2764 A1527 3fr multi   1.40   .50
  a. Perf. 13½x13   2.00   .75
     Perf. 13½x13
2765 A1527 3fr + 60c multi   4.00 2.00
  a. Booklet pane, 4 #2764a, 3
    #2765 + label   20.00
    Complete booklet, #2765a   21.00
  b. Souvenir sheet of 1   3.00 2.50
     Stamp Day.

Bretagne Parliament Building
Restoration — A1528

2000, Mar. 25   Photo.   Perf. 13¼
2766 A1528 3fr multi   1.40   .30

Madagascar Periwinkles — A1529

2000, Mar. 25   Litho.   Perf. 13x13¼
2767 A1529 4.50fr multi   2.10   .60

Felicitations A1530

2000, Apr. 7   Photo.   Perf. 13x13¼
2768 A1530 3fr multi   1.40   .30

The 20th Century — A1531

No. 2769: a, France as World Cup soccer champions, 1998, vert. b, Marcel Cerdan wins middleweight boxing title, 1948. c, Charles Lindbergh flies solo across Atlantic, 1927. d, Jean-Claude Killy wins three Winter Olympics gold medals, 1968, vert. e, Carl Lewis wins four Olympic gold medals, 1984, vert.
Illustration reduced.

Perf. 13¼x13 (vert. stamps), 13x13¼
2000, Apr. 15
2769 A1531 Sheet, 2 ea #a-e 14.00 14.00
  a.-e.   3fr any single   1.40   .75

Top part of No. 2769 contains Nos. 2769a-2769e and is separated from bottom part of sheet by a row of rouletting.
See No. 2787, 2804, 2837, 2881, 2915.

Automobiles — A1532

No. 2770: a, Bugatti 35. b, Citroen Traction. c, Renault 4CV. d, Simca Chambord. e, Hispano-Suiza K6. f, Volkswagen Beetle. g, 1962 Cadillac. h, Peugeot 203. i, Citroen DS19. j, Ferrari 250 GTO.
Illustration reduced.

2000, May 5   Perf. 13¼x13
2770 A1532 Sheet of 10, #a.-j. 7.50 7.50
  a.-e.   1fr any single   .45   .35
  f.-j.   2fr any single   .90   .60

Europa, 2000
Common Design Type

2000, May 9   Photo.   Perf. 13¼
2771 CD17 3fr multi   1.40   .40

Henry-Louis Duhamel du Monceau (1700-82), Agronomist — A1533

2000, May 13   Engr.   Perf. 13
2772 A1533 4.50fr multi   2.10   .65

French Federation of Philatelic Associations, 73rd Congress, Nevers — A1534

2000, May 19   Engr.   Perf. 13¼
2773 A1534 3fr multi   1.40   .30

A1535   A1536

2000, June 1   Photo.   Perf. 13¼x13
2774 A1535 3fr Happy Vacation 1.40   .30

2000, June 3   Engr.   Perf. 13x12¼
2775 A1536 3fr multi   1.40   .30

First Ascent of Annapurna, 50th anniv.

Nature A1537

2.70fr, Agrias sardanapalus butterfly. #2777, Giraffe. #2778, Allosaurus. 4.50fr, Tulipa lutea.

2000, June 17   Photo.   Perf. 13¼
2776 A1537 2.70fr multi   1.25   .50
2777 A1537 3fr multi, vert.   1.40   .50
2778 A1537 3fr multi   1.40   .50
2779 A1537 4.50fr multi, vert   2.10   .90
  a.   Souvenir sheet, #2776-2779 7.00 7.00
       Nos. 2776-2779 (4)   6.15 2.40

Antoine de Saint-Exupéry (1900-44), Aviator, Writer — A1538

2000, June 24   Photo.   Perf. 13¼x13
2780 A1538 3fr multi   1.40   .30

Yellow Train of Cerdagne, Cent. A1539

2000, July 14   Perf. 13x13¼
2781 A1539 3fr multi   1.40   .30

Folklore A1540

2000, Aug. 12   Photo.   Perf. 13
2782 A1540 4.50fr multi   2.10   .65

2000 Summer Olympics, Sydney A1541

Designs: No. 2783, Cycling, fencing, relay racer. No. 2784, Relay racer, judo, diving.

2000, Sept. 9
2783 A1541 3fr multi   1.40   .50
2784 A1541 3fr multi   1.40   .50
  a.   Pair, #2783-2784   3.00 2.00
  b.   Sheet, 5 #2784a + label 15.00 15.00

Olymphilex 2000, Sydney (#2784b).

Brother Alfred Stanke (1904-75) A1542

2000, Sept. 23   Engr.
2785 A1542 4.40fr multi   2.00   .90

S.O.S. Amitié, 40th Anniv. A1543

2000, Sept. 30   Litho.   Perf. 13
2786 A1543 3fr multi   1.40   .30

20th Century Type

No. 2787: a, Man on the Moon, 1969, vert. b, Paid vacations, 1936. c, Invention of washing machine, 1901, vert. d, Woman suffrage, 1944, vert. e, Universal Declaration of Human Rights, 1948.

Perf. 13¼x13 (vert. stamps), 13x13¼
2000, Sept. 30   Photo.
2787 A1531 Sheet, 2 each
         #a-e   14.00 14.00
  a.-e.   3fr Any single   1.40   .50

The top and bottom parts of No. 2787 contains Nos. 2787a-2787e and are separated by a row of rouletting.

2001, Start of New Millennium A1544

2000, Oct. 14   Litho.   Perf. 13
2788 A1544 3fr multi   1.40   .30

The Lovers' Kiosk, by Peynet A1545

2000, Nov. 4   Engr.   Perf. 13¼x13
2789 A1545 3fr multi   1.40   .50

Endangered Birds — A1546

2000, Nov. 4   Photo.   Perf. 13¼
2790 A1546 3fr Kiwi   1.40   .40
2791 A1546 5.20fr Falcon   2.50 1.50
  See New Zealand Nos. 1688, 1694.

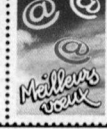

Start of the 3rd Millennium — A1547

Illustration reduced.

2000, Nov. 9   Photo.   Perf. 13x13¼
2792 A1547 3fr multi + label 1.40   .30

Issued in sheets of 10 stamps + 10 labels, which could be personalized for an extra fee.

Holiday Greetings A1548

2000, Nov. 11   Perf. 12¼x13
2793 A1548 3fr Meilleurs voeux 1.40   .30
              Perf. 13¼
2794 A1548 3fr Bonne année   1.40   .30

Union of Metallurgical & Mining Industries, Cent. — A1549

Engr. with Foil Application
2000, Dec. 9   Perf. 13x13¼
2795 A1549 4.50fr multi   2.10   .90

World Handball
Championships — A1550

2001, Jan. 20   Photo.   *Perf. 13¼*
2796 A1550 3fr multi   1.40   .30

Heart
A1551

2001, Jan. 27
2797 A1551 3fr multi   1.40   .30
  a.   Souvenir sheet of 5   10.00 10.00

Value of No. 2797 is for copy with surrounding selvage.

Art Series

The Peasant Dance, by Pieter
Breughel, the Elder — A1552

Hotel des Chevaliers de Saint-Jean-
de-Jérusalem — A1553

Yvette Guilbert Singing "Linger,
Longer, Loo," by Henri de Toulouse-
Lautrec (1864-1901) — A1554

Honfleur at Low Tide, by Johan
Barthold Jongkind — A1555

Engr., Photo (#2800), Litho (#2801)
2001   *Perf. 13x13¼, 13¼x13 (#2800)*
2798 A1552 6.70fr multi   3.00   1.00
2799 A1553 6.70fr multi   3.00   1.00
2800 A1554 6.70fr multi   3.00   1.00
2801 A1555 6.70fr multi   3.00   1.00
  Nos. 2798-2801 (4)   12.00   4.00

Issued: No. 2798, 2/3; No. 2799, 4/21; No. 2800, 9/8; No. 2801, 10/27.

Gaston Lagaffe,
by André
Franquin
A1556

2001, Feb. 24   Photo.   *Perf. 13¼*
2802 A1556   3fr multi   1.40   .50
  a.   Perf. 13¼x13   1.40   .65

          Perf. 13¼x13
2803 A1556   3fr +60c multi   5.00   3.50
  a.   Souvenir sheet of 1   3.50   2.50
  b.   Booklet pane, 5 #2802a, 3
        #2803   22.00
       Booklet, #2803b   22.50

          Stamp Day.

20th Century Type of 2000
No. 2804 — Communications: a, Television.
b, Compact disc. c, Advertisements, vert. d,
Radio, vert. e, Portable telephone, vert.

Perf. 13¼x13 (vert. stamps), 13x13¼
2001, Mar. 17   Photo.
2804 A1531 Sheet, 2 each
        #a-e   14.00 14.00
  a.-e. 3fr Any single   1.40   .75

Top part of No. 2804 contains Nos. 2804a-
2804e and is separated from bottom part by a
row of rouletting.

Announcements — A1557

Designs: No. 2805, It's a girl. No. 2806, It's
a boy. No. 2807, Thank you. 4.50fr, Yes
(marriage).

2001   *Perf. 13*
          Frame Color
2805 A1557   3fr brt pink   1.40   .30
  a.   Litho., stamp + label   6.50   6.50
2806 A1557   3fr brt blue   1.40   .30
  a.   Litho., stamp + label   6.50   6.50
2807 A1557   3fr brt yel grn   1.40   .30
  a.   Litho., stamp + label   6.50   6.50
2808 A1557   4.50fr orange   2.10   .75
  Nos. 2805-2808 (4)   6.30   1.65

Issued: Nos. 2805-2808, 3/23; Nos. 2805a-
2807a, 11/8.
Nos. 2805a-2807a were issued in sheets of
10 stamps and 10 labels that sold for 60fr on
day of issue. The labels could be personalized. Frames on Nos. 2805 and 2806 look
splotchy, while those on Nos. 2805a and
2806a have a distinct dot structure. The frame
on No. 2807 has tightly spaced small dots,
while on No. 2807a, the dots are more widely
spaced.

Wildlife — A1558

2001, Apr. 21   Photo.   *Perf. 13¼*
2809 A1558 2.70fr Squirrel   1.25   .40
2810 A1558 3fr Roe deer   1.40   .40
2811 A1558 3fr Hedgehog,
                    horiz.   1.40   .40
2812 A1558 4.50fr Ermine   2.10   .75
  a.   Souvenir sheet, #2809-2812 7.00   6.50

          Tourism Issue

Nogent-le-Rotrou
A1559

Besançon
A1560

Calais
A1561

Château
de
Grignan
A1562

Engr., Litho & Engr. (#2813)
2001   *Perf. 13¼x13 (#2813), 13*
2813 A1559 3fr multi   1.40   .40
2814 A1560 3fr multi   1.40   .30
2815 A1561 3fr multi   1.40   .30
2816 A1562 3fr multi   1.40   .30
  Nos. 2813-2816 (4)   5.60   1.30

Issued: No. 2813, 4/28; No. 2814, 5/5; No.
2815, 6/16; No. 2816, 7/7.

Europa — A1563

2001, May 8   Photo.   *Perf. 13*
2817 A1563 3fr multi   1.40   .35

Gardens of Versailles — A1564

Illustration reduced.

2001, May 12
2818 A1564 4.40fr multi   2.00   1.00

Singers — A1565

Designs: No. 2819, Claude François (1939-
78). No. 2820, Léo Ferré (1916-93). No. 2821,
Serge Gainsbourg (1928-91). No. 2822,
Dalida (1933-87). No. 2823, Michel Berger
(1947-92). No. 2824, Barbara (1930-97).

2001, May 19   Photo.   *Perf. 13*
2819 A1565 3fr multi   1.40   .75
2820 A1565 3fr multi   1.40   .75
2821 A1565 3fr multi   1.40   .75
2822 A1565 3fr multi   1.40   .75
2823 A1565 3fr multi   1.40   .75
2824 A1565 3fr multi   1.40   .75
  a.   Souvenir sheet, #2819-
        2824   11.00 11.00
  Nos. 2819-2824 (6)   8.40   4.50

No. 2824a sold for 28fr with the Red Cross
receiving 10fr of that.

Old
Lyon — A1566

2001, May 19   Engr.   *Perf. 13¼*
2825 A1566 3fr multi   1.40   .30

French
Federation of
Philatelic
Associations 74th
Congress,
Tours — A1567

2001, June 1
2826 A1567 3fr multi   1.40   .30

Jean Vilar
(1912-71),
Actor
A1568

          Litho. & Engr.
2001, June 7   *Perf. 13*
2827 A1568 3fr multi   1.40   .40

Vacation
A1569

2001, June 10   Litho.   *Perf. 13*
2828 A1569 3fr multi   1.40   .30
          Booklet Stamp
          Self-Adhesive
2829 A1569 3fr multi   1.40   .30
  a.   Booklet of 10   14.00

1 Euro Coin
A1570

2001, June 23   Photo.   *Perf. 12½*
2830 A1570 3fr multi   1.40   .30

Value is for copy with surrounding selvage.

Albert Caquot (1881-1976),
Engineer — A1571

2001, June 30   Engr.   Perf. 13¼
2831 A1571 4.50fr multi   2.00 .75

Law Guaranteeing Freedom of
Association, Cent. — A1572

2001, July 1   Photo.   Perf. 13
2832 A1572 3fr multi   1.40 .30

Trains — A1573

No. 2833: a, Eurostar. b, American 220. c,
Crocodile. d, Crampton. e, Garratt 59. f,
Pacific Chapelon. g, Mallard. h, Capitole. i,
Autorail Panoramique. j, 230 Class P8.

2001, July 6   Photo.   Perf. 13¼
2833 A1573   Sheet of 10   7.50 7.50
a.-j.   1.50fr Any single   .75 .65

Geneva Convention on Refugees, UN
High Commisioner for Refugees, 50th
Anniv. — A1574

2001, July 28   Perf. 13
2834 A1574 4.50fr multi   2.00 .75

**Marianne Type of 1997 Inscribed
"RF" at Lower Left**
2001   Engr.   Perf. 13
2835 A1409 (3fr) red   1.40 .25
d.   Sheet of 15 + 15 labels   60.00
Serpentine Die Cut 6¾ Vert.
**Self-Adhesive
Booklet Stamp**
2835A A1409 (3fr) red   1.40 .25
b.   Booklet of 10   15.00

2001, Aug. 1   Engr.   Perf. 13 Horiz.
Coil Stamp
Water-Activated Gum
2835C A1409 (3fr) red   1.40 .25
Issued: Nos. 2835, 2835C, 8/1; No. 2835A,
9/24.
No. 2835d sold for €10.03. Labels could be
personalized for an additional price.
"La Poste" and engraver are at right.

Pierre de Fermat (1601-65),
Mathematician — A1575

2001, Aug. 19   Engr.   Perf. 13¼x13
2836 A1575 4.50fr multi   2.00 .75

20th Century Type of 2000
No. 2837 — Science: a, First man in space.
b, DNA. c, Chip cards. d, Laser. e, Penicillin.

Perf. 13¼x13 (vert. stamps), 13
2001, Sept. 22   Photo.
2837 A1531   Sheet, 2 each
#a-e   14.00 14.00
a.-e.   3fr Any single   1.40 .70
Top part of No. 2837 contains Nos. 2837a-
2837e and is separated from bottom part of
sheet by a row of rouletting.

Astrolabe
Sculpture,
Val-de-Reuil
A1576

2001, Sept. 29   Perf. 13
2838 A1576 3fr multi   1.40 .30

Halloween
A1577

2001, Oct. 20
2839 A1577 3fr multi   1.40 .30
a.   Souvenir sheet of 5 + 4 labels 8.00 8.00

Jean Pierre-Bloch
(1905-99), Human
Rights
Advocate — A1578

2001, Nov. 8   Engr.   Perf. 13
2840 A1578 4.50fr multi   2.00 .75

Albert
Decaris
(1901-88),
Artist
A1579

2001, Nov. 9   Engr.   Perf. 13¼x13
2841 A1579 3fr multi   1.40 .40

Jacques Chaban-
Delmas (1915-2000),
Politician — A1580

2001, Nov. 10   Engr.   Perf. 13x13¼
2842 A1580 3fr multi   1.40 .40

Holiday
Greetings
A1581

Designs: Nos. 2843, 2845 Bonne Année
(Happy New Year). Nos. 2844, 2846 Meilleurs
Voeux (Best wishes).

2001, Nov. 9   Litho.   Perf. 13
2843 A1581 3fr multi   1.40 .30
2844 A1581 3fr multi   1.40 .30

Serpentine Die Cut 11
**Self-Adhesive
Booklet Stamps**
2845 A1581 3fr multi   1.40 .30
2846 A1581 3fr multi   1.40 .30
a.   Booklet, 5 each # 2845-2846 14.00

Fountains
A1582

Designs: 3fr, Nejjarine Fountain, Fez,
Morocco. 3.80fr, Wallace Fountain, Paris.

2001, Dec. 14   Photo.   Perf. 13¼
2847 A1582   3fr multi   1.40 .40
2848 A1582   3.80fr multi   1.75 1.00
See Morocco Nos. 914-915.

100 Cents = 1 Euro (€)

Marianne
(With Euro
Denominations)
A1583

Orchids
A1584

2002, Jan. 1   Engr.   Perf. 13
2849 A1583   1c yellow   .20 .20
2850 A1583   2c brown   .20 .20
2851 A1583   5c brt bl grn .20 .20
2852 A1583   10c purple   .25 .20
2853 A1583   20c brt org   .60 .30
2854 A1583   41c brt green 1.20 .20
2855 A1583   50c dk blue   1.50 .25
2856 A1583   53c apple grn 1.60 .40
2857 A1583   58c blue   1.75 .50
2858 A1583   64c dark org 1.90 .50
2859 A1583   67c brt blue 2.00 .50
a.   deep blue   2.00 .50
2860 A1583   69c brt pink 2.10 .60
2861 A1583   €1 Prus blue 3.00 .80
2862 A1583   €1.02 dk green 3.00 .90
a.   Souvenir sheet, #2835,
2854, 2856-2858, 2859a,
2860, 2862   15.00 15.00
2863 A1583   €2 violet   6.00 1.50
a.   Souvenir sheet, #2849-
2853, 2855, 2861, 2863 12.00 12.00
Nos. 2849-2863 (15)   25.50 7.25
Coil Stamp
Perf. 13 Horiz.
2864 A1583   41c brt green 1.25 .30

2002, Jan. 2   Litho.   Perf. 13
Designs: 29c, Orchis insularis. 33c, Ophrys
fuciflora.
2865 A1584 29c multi   .80 .30
2866 A1584 33c multi   1.00 .40
Nos. 2865-2866 are known only precanceled. See second note after #132.

Heart of Voh, Photograph by Yann
Arthurs-Bertrand — A1585

2002, Jan. 18   Photo.   Perf. 13¼
2867 A1585 46c multi   1.40 .40
a.   Souvenir sheet of 5   7.00 7.00
Value of No. 2867 is for copy with surrounding selvage.

2002 Winter
Olympics, Salt Lake
City — A1586

2002, Jan. 26   Perf. 13
2868 A1586 46c multi   1.40 .30

Art Series

Sphere
Concorde,
by Jesús
Rafael Soto
A1587

The Kiss,
by Gustav
Klimt
A1588

The
Dancers,
by
Fernando
Botero
A1589

Self-Portrait, by Elisabeth Vigée-
Lebrun — A1590

2002　　**Photo.**　　**Perf. 13¼x13**
2869 A1587 75c multi　　　2.25　1.00
2870 A1588 €1.02 multi　　3.00　1.00
2871 A1589 €1.02 multi　　3.00　1.00

Engr.
2872 A1590 €1.02 multi　　3.00　1.00
　　Nos. 2869-2872 (4)　　11.25　4.00

　Issued: No. 2869, 11/11. No. 2870, 2/8; No.
2871, 4/27. No. 2872, 10/12.

Alain Bosquet (1919-
98), Poet — A1591

2002, Feb. 16　**Engr.**　**Perf. 13**
2873 A1591 58c multi　　　1.75　1.00

It's A Girl
A1592

It's A Boy
A1593

Yes
A1594

2002, Feb. 23　　　**Photo.**
2874 A1592 46c multi　　　1.40　.30
2875 A1593 46c multi　　　1.40　.30
2876 A1594 69c multi　　　2.00　.30
　　Nos. 2874-2876 (3)　　4.80　.90

Europa — A1595

2002, Mar. 2　　**Perf. 13¼**
2877 A1595 46c multi　　　1.40　.30

Boule and Bill, by
Jean
Roba — A1596

　Designs: 46c, Boule, Bill, bird. 46c+9c,
Boule, Bill, ball.

2002, Mar. 16　　**Perf. 13¼**
2878 A1596 46c multi　　　1.40　.50
a.　　Perf. 13¼x13　　　2.00　.60
　　　Perf. 13¼x13
2879 A1596 46c +9c multi　4.00　3.00
a.　Souvenir sheet of 1　3.00　2.50
b.　Booklet pane, 5 #2878a, 3
　　　#2879　　　　　　22.00
　　Booklet, #2879b　　22.50

Stamp Day. Stamp on No. 2879a has continuous design.

Nimes Amphitheater — A1597

Litho. & Engr.
2002, Mar. 22　　**Perf. 13**
2880 A1597 46c multi　　　1.40　.30

20th Century Type of 2000
　No. 2881 — Transportation: a, Concorde
supersonic airplane. b, TGV train. c, Ocean
liner France, vert. d, Mobylette motor scooter,
vert. e, Citroen 2 CV automobile, vert.

Perf. 13, 13¼x13 (vert. stamps)
2002, Mar. 23　　　　**Photo.**
2881 A1531　Sheet, 2 each
　　　#a-e　　　　　　14.00　14.00
a.-e.　46c Any single　　1.40　.75

　Top part of No. 2881 contains Nos. 2881a-
2881e and is separated from bottom part of
sheet by a row of rouletting.

Encounter
of Matthew
Flinders and
Nicolas
Boudin,
Bicent.
A1598

　Map of Australia, portrait and ship of: 46c,
Flinders. 79c, Boudin.

2002, Apr. 4　　**Perf. 13¼**
2882 A1598 46c multi　　　1.40　.40
2883 A1598 79c multi　　　2.25　1.25

　See Australia Nos. 2053-2054.

Tourism Series

La Charité-sur-Loire — A1599

Collioure
A1600

Locronan
A1601

Neufchateau — A1602

Engraved (#2884, 2886), Photo.
(#2885)
2002　　　　　　**Perf. 13¼**
2884 A1599 46c multi　　　1.40　.30
2885 A1600 46c multi　　　1.40　.30
2886 A1601 46c multi　　　1.40　.30
2887 A1602 46c multi　　　1.40　.30
　　Nos. 2884-2887 (4)　　5.60　1.20

　Issue dates: No. 2884, 4/6; No. 2885, 6/22;
No. 2886, 7/13; No. 2887, 10/12/02.
　Numbers have been reserved for additional
stamps in this set.

Birthday
Greetings
A1603

Anniversaire

Invitation
A1604

2002, Apr. 6　　**Photo.**　**Perf. 13**
2888 A1603 46c multi　　　1.40　.30
a.　Litho., stamp + label　6.00　6.00
2889 A1604 46c multi　　　1.40　.30
a.　Litho., stamp + label　6.00　6.00

　Issued: Nos. 2888a, 2889a, 11/7. Nos.
2888a and 2889a were issued in sheets of 10
stamps and 10 labels that sold for €6.19 on
day of issue. The labels could be
personalized.
　No. 2888a has a duller blue in "Anniversaire" than No. 2888, but is otherwise quite
similar in appearance. The gold ink on No.
2889a has a more coppery look than that on
No. 2889.

100th Paris-Roubaix
Bicycle
Race — A1605

2002, Mar. 13
2890 A1605 46c multi　　　1.40　.30

2002 World Cup Soccer
Championships, Japan and
Korea — A1606

　No. 2891: a, Flags, soccer ball and field
(32mm diameter). b, Soccer player, year of
French championship.
　Illustration reduced.

2002, Apr. 27　　　**Perf. 12¾**
2891 A1606　Horiz. pair　2.75　2.50
a.-b.　46c Any single　　1.40　.30
c.　Sheet, 5 #2891　　15.00　15.00

　Issued: No. 2891c, 5/18.
　See Argentina No. 2184, Brazil No. 2840,
Germany No. 2163, Italy No. 2526 and Uru-
guay No. 1946.

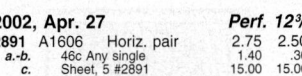

Marine Life
A1607

　Designs: 41c, Sea turtle (tortue luth), vert.
No. 2893, Killer whale (orque). No. 2894,
Dolphin (grand dauphin). 69c, Seal (phoque
veau marin).

2002, May 4　　**Perf. 13¼**
2892 A1607 41c multi　　　1.25　.30
2893 A1607 46c multi　　　1.25　.30
2894 A1607 46c multi　　　1.25　.30
2895 A1607 69c multi　　　2.00　.75
a.　Souvenir sheet, #2892-2895　6.50　6.50
　　Nos. 2892-2895 (4)　　5.75　1.65

　Worldwide Fund for Nature (#2895a).

French Federation of Philatelic
Associations 75th Congress,
Marseilles — A1608

　Illustration reduced.

2002, May 17　**Engr.**　**Perf. 13**
2896 A1608 46c multi　　　1.40　.30

Legion of
Honor, Bicent.
A1609

Rocamadour
A1610

2002, May 18　　　**Photo.**
2897 A1609 46c multi　　　1.40　.30

2002, May 25　　**Perf. 13¼**
2898 A1610 46c multi　　　1.40　.30

Louis Delgrés (1766-1802),
Soldier — A1611

2002, May 25
2899 A1611 46c multi　　　1.40　.30

Vacation
A1612

2002, June 8　**Litho.**　**Perf. 13**
2900 A1612 46c multi　　　1.40　.30

Self-Adhesive
Serpentine Die Cut 11
2901 A1612 46c multi　　　1.40　.30
a.　Booklet pane of 10　14.00

World Disabled Athletics
Championships — A1613

2002, June 15 Photo. Perf. 13¼
2902 A1613 46c multi   1.40 .30

Saint-Ser
Chapel — A1614

2002, June 22 Engr. Perf. 13x13¼
2903 A1614 46c multi   1.40 .30

Metz
Cathedral
Stained
Glass
A1615

2002, July 6 Engr. Perf. 13¼x13
2904 A1615 46c multi   1.40 .40

Jazz
Musicians — A1616

Designs: No. 2905, Louis Armstrong (1901-71). No. 2906, Ella Fitzgerald (1918-96). No. 2907, Duke Ellington (1899-1974). No. 2908, Stéphane Grappelli (1908-97). No. 2909, Michel Petrucciani (1962-99), horiz. No. 2910, Sidney Bechet (1897-1959), horiz.

2002, July 13 Photo. Perf. 13
2905 A1616 46c multi   1.40 .75
2906 A1616 46c multi   1.40 .75
2907 A1616 46c multi   1.40 .75
2908 A1616 46c multi   1.40 .75
2909 A1616 46c multi   1.40 .75
2910 A1616 46c multi   1.40 .75
a.   Souvenir sheet, #2905-2910   12.00 12.00
      Nos. 2905-2910 (6)   8.40 4.50

No. 2910a sold for €4.36, with the Red Cross receiving €1.60 of that.

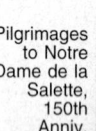

Pilgrimages
to Notre
Dame de la
Salette,
150th
Anniv.
A1617

2002, Aug. 15 Engr. Perf. 13¼x13
2911 A1617 46c multi   1.40 .30

Choreography — A1618

Illustration reduced.
2002, Sept. 13 Photo. Perf. 13x13¼
2912 A1618 53c multi   1.50 .60

Motorcycles — A1619

No. 2913: a, Honda 750 four. b, Terrot 500 RGST. c, Majestic. d, Norton Commando 750. e, Voxan 1000 Café Racer. f, BMW R90S. g, Harley Davidson Hydra Glide. h, Triumph Bonneville 650. i, Ducati 916. j, Yamaha 500 XT.

2002, Sept. 14 Perf. 13¼x13
2913 A1619 Sheet of 10   12.00 12.00
a.-e. 16c any single   .75 .60
f.-j. 30c any single   .90 .75

Georges Perec
(1936-82),
Writer — A1620

2002, Sept. 21 Engr. Perf. 13¼
2914 A1620 46c multi   1.40 .30

20th Century Type of 2000
No. 2915 — Photographs of everyday life: a, Family on motor scooter, 1955, vert. b, Man, horse and wagon, 1947. c, Woman ironing, 1950. d, Boy at fountain, 1950, vert. e, Girl in classroom, 1965, vert.

Perf. 13¼x13 (vert. stamps), 13
2002, Sept. 28 Photo.
2915 A1531 Sheet, 2 each
      #a-e   14.00 14.00
a.-e. 46c Any single   1.40 .75

Top part of No. 2915 contains Nos. 2915a-2915e and is separated from bottom part of sheet by a row of rouletting.

Emile Zola (1840-1902),
Novelist — A1621

2002, Oct. 5 Perf. 13
2916 A1621 46c multi   1.40 .30

Souvenir Sheet

European Capitals — A1622

Attractions in Rome: a, Trevi Fountain. b, Coliseum, horiz. c, Trinità de Monti Church and Spanish Steps. d, St. Peter's Basilica, horiz.

2002, Nov. 7 Perf. 13¼x13, 13x13¼
2917 A1622 Sheet of 4   6.00 6.00
a.-d. 46c Any single   1.40 .75
      See No. 2985.

Globe and
Microcircuits
A1623

2002, Nov. 8 Photo. Perf. 13
2918 A1623 46c multi   1.40 .30
a.   Litho., stamp + label   6.00 6.00

Issued: No. 2918a, 11/7. No. 2918a was issued in sheets of 10 stamps and 10 labels that sold for €6.19 on day of issue. The labels could be personalized.
No. 2918a has a hairline at top, above "RF" that No. 2888 does not have, but is otherwise quite similar in appearance.

Holiday
Greetings
A1624

2002, Nov. 8 Photo. Perf. 13
2919 A1624 46c multi   1.40 .30
a.   Litho., stamp + label   6.00 6.00

Booklet Stamp
Self-Adhesive
Serpentine Die Cut 11
2920 A1624 46c multi   1.40 .30
a.   Booklet pane of 10   14.00

Issued: No. 2919a, 11/7. No. 2919a was issued in sheets of 10 stamps and 10 labels that sold for €6.19 on day of issue. The labels could be personalized.
No. 2919a has a finer dot structure, which is most noticeable in the chimney smoke, than No. 2888.

Marianne Type of 1997 Inscribed "RF" at Lower Left
2002, Nov. 9 Engr. Perf. 13
2921 A1409 (41c) bright green 1.20 .25
Coil Stamp
Perf. 13 Horiz.
2922 A1409 (41c) bright green 1.20 .25

Alexandre
Dumas
(Father)
(1802-70),
Writer
A1625

2002, Nov. 30 Photo. Perf. 13
2924 A1625 46c multi   1.40 .30

Léopold Sédar Senghor (1906-2001),
President of Senegal, Poet — A1626

2002, Dec. 20
2925 A1626 46c multi   1.40 .30

Hearts
A1627

2003, Jan. 11 Perf. 13¼
2926 A1627 46c Four hearts   1.40 .30
a.   Souvenir sheet of 5   7.00 7.00
2927 A1627 69c Roses   2.00 .60

Values for Nos. 2926-2927 are for copies with surrounding selvage.

Thank You
A1628

Birth
A1629

2003, Jan. 11 Perf. 13
2928 A1628 46c multi   1.40 .30
2929 A1629 46c brt org & brt bl 1.40 .30

Franco-German Cooperation Treaty,
40th Anniv. — A1630

2003, Jan. 16 Perf. 13¼
2930 A1630 46c multi   1.40 .40

Delegation for Land-use Planning and
Regional Action, 40th Anniv.
A1631

2003, Feb. 8 Photo. Perf. 13
2931 A1631 46c multi   1.40 .30

Geneviève de Gaulle Anthonioz (1920-2002), World War II Resistance Fighter — A1632

2003, Feb. 11
2932 A1632 46c blk & ol brn   1.40 .30

Paris Chamber of Commerce and Industry, Bicent. — A1633

2003, Feb. 22   **Perf. 13¼**
2933 A1633 46c multi   1.40   .30

Lucky Luke, by Morris (Maurice De Bevere) — A1634

Lucky Luke and Jolly Jumper: 46c, Skipping rope on ball on high wire. 46c+9c, Following dog, Rantanplan.

2003, Mar. 15   Photo.   Perf. 13¼
2934 A1634 46c multi   1.40   .65
  a.   Perf. 13¼x13   1.40   .65

          Perf. 13¼x13
2935 A1634 46c +9c multi   3.50   2.00
  a.   Souvenir sheet of 1   3.00   2.50
  b.   Booklet pane, 5 #2934a, 3
         #2935   17.50   —
       Complete booklet, #2935b 18.00

Stamp Day.

Birds A1635

Designs: 41c, Colibri à tete bleue (Cyanophaia bicolor). No. 2937, Toucan ariel (Ramphastos vitellinus). No. 2938, Colibri grenat (Eulampis jugularis), vert. 69c, Terpsiphone de Bourbon (Terpsiphone bourbonnensis).

2003, Mar. 22   Photo.   Perf. 13¼
2936 A1635 41c multi   1.20   .30
2937 A1635 46c multi   1.40   .30
2938 A1635 46c multi   1.40   .30
2939 A1635 69c multi   2.00   .75
  a.   Souvenir sheet, #2936-2939 7.00 7.00
       Nos. 2936-2939 (4)   6.00   1.65

Nantes A1636

2003, Apr. 4   Engr.
2940 A1636 46c multi   1.40   .30

Pierre Bérégovoy (1925-93), Prime Minister — A1637

2003, Apr. 30   Engr.   Perf. 13x13¼
2941 A1637 46c multi   1.40   .30

Milan Stefanik (1880-1919), Czechoslovakian General — A1638

2003, May 3   Perf. 13¼
2942 A1638 50c multi   1.50   .40

See Slovakia No. 428.

Europa — A1639

2003, May 8   Photo.
2943 A1639 50c multi   1.50   .40

Charter of Fundamental Rights of the European Union — A1640

2003, May 8
2944 A1640 50c multi   1.50   .30

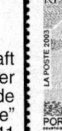

Aircraft Carrier "Charles de Gaulle" A1641

2003, May 8   Engr.
2945 A1641 50c multi   1.50   .30

Aspects of Life in the French Regions A1642

No. 2946: a, Beach cabins. b, Fishing net. c, Vineyards of Champagne. d, Camembert cheese, vert. e, Foie gras, vert. f, Petanque. g, Puppet show (Guignol), vert. h, Crepe, vert. i, Cassoulet. j, Limoges porcelain.

2003, May 24   Photo.   Perf. 13
2946   Sheet of 10   15.00 15.00
  a.-j.   A1642 50c Any single 1.40   1.25

No. 2946 has three vertical rows of rouletting, separating sheet into quarters.
Nos. 2946a-2946j were also issued in large booklets containing panes of 1 of each stamp. The booklet sold for €19.
See No. 2978.

"The Dying Slave" and "The Rebel Slave," by Michelangelo — A1643

The Red Buoy, by Paul Signac A1644

Untitled Abstract by Vassily Kandinsky A1645

Marilyn, by Andy Warhol A1646

2003   Engr.   Perf. 13¼x13
2947 A1643   75c multi   2.25   1.00
          Photo.
2948 A1644   75c multi   2.25   1.00
          Litho.
2949 A1645   €1.11 multi   3.25   1.25
2950 A1646   €1.11 multi   3.25   1.40
       Nos. 2947-2950 (4)   11.00   4.65

Issued: No. 2947, 5/24. Nos. 2948, 2949, 7/5. No. 2950, 11/8.
A sheet containing 3 No. 2949 and 12 imperforate color progressive proofs was bound in a book that sold for €60.

Happy Birthday A1647

2003, May 31   Photo.   Perf. 13¼
2951 A1647 50c multi   1.40   .35
  a.   Souvenir sheet of 5   7.00   7.00
  b.   Litho., stamp + label   1.75   1.75

Issued: No. 2951b, 2004. No. 2951b was issued in sheets of 10 stamps + 10 labels that sold for €6.67 on day of issue. The labels could be personalized. The background on

No. 2951 looks splotchy while that of No. 2951b has a dot structure.

Marianne With Euro Denominations Type of 2002

2003, June 1   Engr.   Perf. 13
2952 A1583 58c apple grn   1.60   .40
2953 A1583 70c yellow grn   2.00   .50
2954 A1583 75c bright blue   2.25   .50
2955 A1583 90c dark blue   2.60   1.00
2956 A1583 €1.11 red lilac   3.25   1.00
2957 A1583 €1.90 violet
                   brown   5.50   1.25
  a.   Souvenir sheet, #2835,
         2921, 2952-2957   19.00 19.00
       Nos. 2952-2957 (6)   17.20   4.65

No. 2957a issued 2/28/04.

Orchids Type of 2002

Designs: 30c, Platanthera chlorantha. 35c, Dactylorhiza savogiensis.

2003, June 1   Litho.   Perf. 13
2958 A1584 30c multi   .85   .30
2959 A1584 35c multi   1.00   .40

Nos. 2958-2959 are known only precanceled. See second note after #132.

French Federation of Philatelic Associations 76th Congress, Mulhouse A1648

2003, June 6   Engr.   Perf. 13¼
2960 A1648 50c multi   1.50   .40

Vacation — A1649

          Perf. 12¾x13¼
2003, June 14   Litho.
2961 A1649 50c multi   1.50   .30

**Self-Adhesive
Booklet Stamp
Serpentine Die Cut 11**
2962 A1649 50c multi   1.50   .30
  a.   Booklet pane of 10   15.00

Tourism Issue

Notre Dame de l'Epine Basilica — A1650

Tulle A1651

Arras — A1652

Pontarlier
A1653

Perf. 13x13¼, 13 (#2965)

2003, June 21   **Engr.**

2963	A1650	50c multi	1.50	.30
2964	A1651	50c multi	1.50	.30
2965	A1652	50c multi	1.50	.40
2966	A1653	50c multi	1.50	.40
	Nos. 2963-2966 (4)		6.00	1.40

Issued: Nos. 2963, 2964, 6/21. No. 2965, 9/20. No. 2966, 10/11.
No. 2965, illustration reduced.

French Freemasonry, 275th
Anniv. — A1654

2003, June 28   Engr.   Perf. 13¼x13

2967	A1654	50c multi	1.40	.30

Tour de France Bicycle Race, Cent. A1655

No. 2968: a, Maurice Garin, winner of 1903 race. b, Cyclist with arms raised.

2003, June 28   Photo.   Perf. 13

2968	A1655	Vert. pair	3.00	2.00
a.-b.		50c Either single	1.50	.30

Values are for stamps with surrounding selvage.

Saint-Père Church, Yonne — A1656

2003, July 12   Engr.   Perf. 13¼

2969	A1656	50c multi	1.50	.30

World Track and Field Championships, Paris — A1657

Illustration reduced.

2003, July 19   Photo.   Perf. 13

2970	A1657	50c multi	1.50	.30

Characters From French Literature — A1658

Designs: No. 2971, Eugène-François Vidocq (1775-1857), convict and police official. No. 2972, Esmerelda, from *Notre-Dame de Paris*, by Victor Hugo. No. 2973, Claudine, from *Claudine* novels, by Colette. No. 2974, Nana, from *Rougon-Macquart*, by Emile Zola. No. 2975, La Comte de Monte-Cristo, from *La Comte de Monte-Cristo*, by Alexandre Dumas (pere). No. 2976, Gavroche, from *Les Miserables*, by Hugo.

2003, Aug. 30   Photo.   Perf. 13

2971	A1658	50c multi	1.50	.75
2972	A1658	50c multi	1.50	.75
2973	A1658	50c multi	1.50	.75
2974	A1658	50c multi	1.50	.75
2975	A1658	50c multi	1.50	.75
2976	A1658	50c multi	1.50	.75
a.	Souvenir sheet, #2971-2976		14.00	14.00
	Nos. 2971-2976 (6)		9.00	4.50

No. 2976a sold for €4.60, with the Red Cross receiving €1.60 of that.

Ahmad Shah Massoud (1953-2001), Afghan Northern Alliance Leader — A1659

2003, Sept. 9

2977	A1659	50c multi	1.50	.30

Aspects of Life in French Regions Type of 2003

No. 2978: a, Chateau de Chenonceau. b, House, Alsace. c, Roof, Bourgogne. d, Genoese Tower, Corsica, vert. e, Arc de Triomphe, vert. f, Farm house, Provence. g, Pointe du Raz, vert. h, Mont Blanc, vert. i, Basque house. j, Pont du Gard.

2003, Sept. 20   Photo.   Perf. 13

2978		Sheet of 10	15.00	15.00
a.-j.		A1642 50c Any single	1.50	1.25

No. 2978 has three vertical rows of rouletting, separating sheet into quarters.
Nos. 2978a-2978j were also issued in large booklets containing panes of 1 of each stamp. The booklet sold for €19.

Gardens and Parks — A1660

No. 2979: a, Buttes-Chaumont Park. b, Jardin du Luxembourg.

2003, Sept. 27   Perf. 13¼x13

2979		Sheet of 2	11.00	11.00
a.-b.		A1660 €1.90 Either single	5.50	5.50

Salon du Timbre 2004. No. 2979 has four vertical rows of rouletting, separating sheet into fifths, with the two stamps in the central fifth.

Motor Vehicles — A1661

No. 2980: a, 1954 Isobloc 648 DP 102 bus (Autocar). b, 1950 SFV 302 Tractor. c, 1938 Delahaye fire truck with mechanical aerial ladder. d, Renault Kangaroo Express postal van. e, 1932 Renault TN6 Paris city bus. f, 1910 Berliet 22hp Type M delivery truck. g, 1957 Berliet T100 heavy-duty truck. h, Citroen police van. i, Citroen DS ambulance. j, 1964 Hotchkiss fire truck.

2003, Oct. 24   Photo.   Perf. 13¼

2980	A1661	Sheet of 10	9.00	9.00
a.-e.		20c Any single	.55	.45
f.-j.		30c Any single	.85	.65

Philexjeunes 2003 Philatelic Exhibition, Dunkerque.

A1662

Holiday Greetings A1663

2003, Nov. 6   Photo.   Perf. 13

2981	A1662	50c multi	1.50	.35
a.		Litho., stamp + label	6.00	6.00

Litho.

2982	A1663	50c multi	1.50	.35
a.		Sheet of 10 + 10 labels	60.00	60.00

**Booklet Stamp
Self-Adhesive
*Serpentine Die Cut 11¼***

2983	A1663	50c multi	1.50	.35
a.		Booklet pane of 10	15.00	

Nos. 2981a, 2982a, 2004. Nos. 2981a and 2982 were issued in sheets of 10 stamps + 10 labels that sold for €6.67 each on day of issue. The labels could be personalized. The background on No. 2981a looks splotchy while that of No. 2982a has a dot structure.

A souvenir sheet containing No. 2982 was sold for €6 by mail order only. It was not available through standing order subscriptions and was not offered in the philatelic bureau's sales catalog. 50,000 copies of this sheet were printed. Value $250.

Sower Type of 1903, Cent. — A1664

**2003, Nov. 6   Engr.
Booklet Stamp**

2984	A1664	50c red	3.50	3.00
a.		Booklet pane, 5 each #2984, 2835A	25.00	

European Capitals Type of 2002

No. 2985 — Attractions in Luxembourg: a, Citadelle Saint-Esprit. b, Notre Dame Cathedral, horiz. c, Adolphe Bridge, horiz. d, Grand Duke's Palace.

Perf. 13¼x13, 13x13¼

2003, Nov. 7   Photo.

2985	A1622	Sheet of 4	7.50	7.50
a.-d.		50c Any single	1.50	1.00

Indian and French Artisan's Work A1665

Designs: 50c, Illumination depicting rooster, France, 15th cent. 90c, Jewelry design, India, 19th cent.

2003, Nov. 29   Engr.   Perf. 13¼x13

2986	A1665	50c multi	1.50	.40
2987	A1665	90c multi	2.60	1.50

See India No. 2040.

Launch of the Queen Mary 2 — A1666

2003, Dec. 12   Photo.   Perf. 13¼

2988	A1666	50c multi	1.40	.30

Greetings A1667

Holes punched through dots in "i's."

2004, Jan. 9   Photo.   Perf. 13

2989	A1667	50c shown	1.50	.30
2990	A1667	50c Un grand merci	1.50	.30

**No Holes Punched Through Dots of "i's"
Stamp + Label**

2991	A1667	50c Like No. 2989	6.00	6.00
2992	A1667	50c Like No. 2990	6.00	6.00

Nos. 2991-2992 were issued in sheets of 10 stamps + 10 labels that sold for €6.67 on day of issue. The labels could be personalized.

It's a Boy A1668

It's a Girl A1669

2004   Litho.   *Perf. 13*
Stamp + Label
2993 A1668 50c multi   6.00 6.00
2994 A1669 50c multi   6.00 6.00

Booklet Stamps
Self-Adhesive
Serpentine Die Cut 11
2995 A1668 50c multi   1.50 .35
a.   Booklet pane of 10   15.00
2996 A1669 50c multi   1.50 .35
a.   Booklet pane of 10   15.00

Nos. 2993-2994 were issued in sheets of 10 stamps + 10 labels that sold for €6.67 on day of issue. The labels could be personalized. Nos. 2995-2996 issued 1/9/04.

Hearts
A1670

Designs: 50c, Chanel No. 5 perfume bottle. 75c, Woman, Eiffel Tower.

2004, Jan. 9   Photo.   *Perf. 13*
2997 A1670 50c multi   1.50 .35
a.   Souvenir sheet of 5   7.50 7.50
b.   Litho., stamp + label, perf.
      13¼   6.00 6.00
2998 A1670 75c multi   2.25 .75
a.   Litho., stamp + label, perf.
      13¼   6.00 6.00

Nos. 2997b and 2998a were each printed in sheets of 10 stamps + 10 labels that could be personalized and sold for €6.69 and €10 respectively. On No. 2997b, there are large brown dots arranged in circles in the shading on the green rectangles, while on No. 2997 the brown dots are small and arranged in rows. On No. 2998a, the dots in the sky are larger and father apart than the tiny dots found on No. 2998.
Values are for stamps with surrounding selvage.

Tourism Issue

Lille, 2004 European Cultural Capital A1671

2004, Jan. 10   Photo.   *Perf. 13*
2999 A1671 50c multi   1.50 .35

Art Series

Statue of Liberty, Sculpted by Frederic Auguste Bartholdi (1834-1904) — A1672

2004, Feb. 21   Engr.   *Perf. 13¼x13*
3000 A1672 90c multi   2.60 1.50

Queen Eleanor of Aquitaine (c. 1122-1204) A1673

2004, Feb. 28   *Perf. 13x13¼*
3001 A1673 50c multi   1.50 .35

Stamp Day — A1674

Characters of Walt Disney: 45c, Donald Duck. 50c, Mickey Mouse. 75c, Minnie Mouse.

2004, Mar. 6   Photo.   *Perf. 13¼*
3002 A1674 50c multi   1.50 .35
a.   Perf. 13¼x13 (from booklet
      pane)   1.50 .35

Booklet Stamps
Perf. 13¼x13
3003 A1674 45c multi   1.30 .30
3004 A1674 75c multi   2.25 .60
a.   Booklet pane, 2 #3003, 4
      each #3002a, 3004   17.50 —
      Complete booklet, #3004a 18.00

Civil Code, Bicent. A1675

2004, Mar. 12   Engr.   *Perf. 13¼x13*
3005 A1675 50c multi   1.50 .35

George Sand (1804-76), Writer A1676

2004, Mar. 20   Engr.   *Perf. 13¼x13*
3006 A1676 50c multi   1.50 .35

Aspects of Life in French Regions
Type of 2003

No. 3007: a, Cutlery. b, Produce of Provence, vert. c, Beaujolais grapes, vert. d, Bread. e, Woman wearing coif, vert. f, Oysters, vert. g, Quiche Lorraine. h, Bullfighting. i, Clafoutis. j, Bagpipers.

2004, Mar. 26   Photo.   *Perf. 13*
3007 Sheet of 10   15.00 15.00
a.-j. A1642 50c Any single   1.50 1.00

No. 3007 has three vertical rows of rouletting, separating sheet into quarters.

Clermont-Ferrand — A1677

2004, Mar. 26   Engr.   *Perf. 13¼*
3008 A1677 50c multi   1.50 .35

Entente Cordiale, Cent. — A1678

Designs: 50c, Coccinelle, by Sonia Delaunay. 75c, Lace 1 (trial proof) 1968, by Sir Terry Frost.

2004, Apr. 6   Photo.   *Perf. 13¼*
3009 A1678 50c multi   1.50 .35
3010 A1678 75c multi   2.25 .75
See Great Britain Nos. 2200-2201.

Road Safety — A1679

2004, Apr. 7
3011 A1679 50c multi   1.50 .35
See United Nations Offices in Geneva No. 424.

Art Series

La Méridienne d'Après Millet, by Vincent van Gogh — A1680

2004, July 2   Photo.   *Perf. 13x13¼*
3012 A1680 75c multi   2.25 .95

Art Series

Un Combat de Coqs, by Jean-Léon Gérôme — A1681

Galatée aux Sphères, by Salvador Dali A1682

2004   Photo.   *Perf. 13x13¼*
3013 A1681 €1.11 multi   3.25 1.40
3014 A1682 €1.11 multi   3.25 1.40
Issued: No. 3013, 4/17; No. 3014, 6/19.

Tourism Issue

Bordeaux — A1683

Vaux-sur-Mer — A1684

Notre Dame de l'Assomption Cathedral, Luçon — A1685

Illustration reduced.

2004   Litho. & Engr.   *Perf. 13*
3015 A1683 50c multi   1.50 .35
Engr.
Perf. 13¼
3016 A1684 50c multi   1.50 .35
3017 A1685 50c multi   1.50 .35
Issued: No. 3015, 4/26; No. 3016, 7/17; No. 3017, 10/2.

Farm Animals A1686

2004, Apr. 26   Photo.   *Perf. 13¼*
3018 A1686 45c Rabbit   1.25 .30
3019 A1686 50c Cow, vert.   1.50 .35
3020 A1686 50c Chicken   1.50 .35
3021 A1686 75c Burro, vert. 2.25 .60
a.   Souvenir sheet, #3018-3021 7.00 6.50

Expansion of the European Union A1687

2004, May 1   Photo.   *Perf. 13¼*
3022 A1687 50c multi   1.50 .40

Battle of Dien Bien Phu, 50th Anniv. — A1688

2004, May 7   *Perf. 13¼x13*
3023 A1688 50c multi   1.50 .40

Europa
A1689

2004   Photo.   Perf. 13x13¼
3024 A1689 50c multi   1.50   .35
Litho.
Booklet Stamp
Self-Adhesive
Serpentine Die Cut 11

3025 A1689 50c multi   1.50   .35
  a.   Booklet pane of 10   15.00
  Issued: No. 3024, 5/9; No. 3025, 6/4.

Blake and
Mortimer,
Comic
Book
Characters
by Edgar
P. Jacobs
A1690

Blake and Mortimer and: 50c, Brick wall,
vert. €1, Blue background.

2004, May 15   Photo.   Perf. 13¼
3026 A1690 50c multi   1.50   .35
3027 A1690 €1 multi   3.00 1.25
  See Belgium No. 2020.

FIFA (Fédération
Internationale de
Football
Association),
Cent. — A1691

2004, May 20   Perf. 13¼x13
3028 A1691 50c multi   1.50   .35

Gardens and Parks Type of 2003
No. 3029: a, Jardin des Tuileries. b, Parc
Floral de Paris.

2004, June 4   Perf. 13¼x13
3029   Sheet of 2   11.50 11.50
  a.-b.   Either single   5.75   5.75
  c.   Souvenir sheet, #2979a-
          2979b, 3029a-3029b   25.00 25.00
  Salon du Timbre 2004. No. 3029 has four
vertical rows of rouletting, separating sheet
into fifths, with the two stamps in the central
fifth.

D-Day Invasion of
France, 60th
Anniv. — A1692

2004, June 5   Perf. 13
3030 A1692 50c multi   1.50   .35

Organ Donation
A1693

2004, June 22   Perf. 13¼
3031 A1693 50c multi   1.50   .35

Pierre
Dugua de
Mons,
Leader of
First
French
Settlement
in Acadia,
and Ship
A1694

Litho. & Engr.
2004, June 26   Perf. 13
3032 A1694 90c multi   2.75 1.50
  See Canada No. 2044.

Napoleon I and the
Imperial
Guard — A1695

Designs: No. 3033, Light cavalry (Chasseur
à cheval). No. 3034, Artilleryman and cannon
(Artilleur à pied), horiz. No. 3035, Dragoon.
No. 3036, Mameluke. No. 3037, Napoleon I.
No. 3038, Grenadier (Grenadier à pied).

2004, June 26   Photo.
3033 A1695 50c multi   1.50   .75
3034 A1695 50c multi   1.50   .75
3035 A1695 50c multi   1.50   .75
3036 A1695 50c multi   1.50   .75
3037 A1695 50c multi   1.50   .75
3038 A1695 50c multi   1.50   .75
  a.   Souvenir sheet, #3033-
          3038   12.50 12.50
          Nos. 3033-3038 (6)   9.00   4.50
  No. 3038a sold for €4.60, with the Red
Cross receiving €1.60 of that.

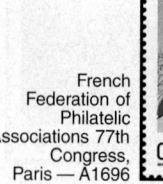

French
Federation of
Philatelic
Associations 77th
Congress,
Paris — A1696

Litho. & Engr.
2004, June 27   Perf. 13¼x13
3039 A1696 50c multi   1.50   .35

2004 Summer Olympics,
Athens — A1697

2004, June 28   Photo.   Perf. 13¼
3040   50c Modern athletes   1.50   .60
3041   50c Ancient athletes   1.50   .60
  a.   A1697 Pair, #3040-3041   3.25 2.25
  Printed in sheets containing five of each
stamp.
  A souvenir sheet containing No. 3041 was
issued Aug. 2 and sold for €2.51.

Happy
Birthday
A1698

2004, June 30   Photo.   Perf. 13¼
3042 A1698 50c multi   1.50   .35
  a.   Souvenir sheet of 5   7.50   7.50
  b.   Litho. stamp + label   6.00   6.00
  No. 3042b printed in sheets of 10 stamps +
10 labels that could be personalized that sold
for €8. No. 3042b has a dark green inscription
at left with a distinct dot pattern. No. 3042 has
a lighter green inscription.

**Marianne Type of 1997 Inscribed
"RF" at Lower Left and Type of
2002 With Euro Denominations**

2004   Litho.   Perf. 13
3043   Sheet of 15 + 15 la-
          bels   50.00 50.00
  a. A1583 1c orange yellow   .20   .20
  b. A1583 2c brown   .20   .20
  c. A1583 5c brt bl green   .20   .20
  d. A1583 10c purple   .30   .30
  e. A1583 20c orange   .60   .60
  f. A1583 58c apple green   1.75   1.75
  g. A1583 70c olive   2.10   2.10
  h. A1583 75c sky blue   2.25   2.25
  i. A1583 90c dark blue   2.75   2.75
  j. A1583 €1 Prussian blue   3.00   3.00
  k. A1583 €1.11 red lilac   3.25   3.25
  l. A1583 €1.90 violet brown   5.75   5.75
  m. A1583 €2 violet   6.00   6.00
  n. A1409 (45c) green   1.40   1.40
  o. A1409 (50c) red   1.50   1.50
  No. 3043 sold for €10.03. Stamps have a
glossy varnish.

Marianne and Emblem of World Fund
to Combat AIDS, Tuberculosis and
Smoking — A1699

2004, July 1   Engr.   Perf. 13
3044 A1699 (50c) red   1.50   .35

Extreme Sports — A1700

No. 3045: a, Skateboarding. b, Parachuting.
c, Sailboarding. d, Surfing. e, Luge. f, BMX
bicycling. g, Paragliding. h, Jetskiing. i,
Snowboarding. j, Rollerblading.

2004, July 3   Photo.   Perf. 13¼x13
3045 A1700   Sheet of 10   7.50   7.50
  a.-e.   20c Any single   .60   .50
  f.-j.   30c Any single   .90   1.25

Orchid Type of 2002
Design: 39c, Orchis insularis.

2004, Sept. 1   Litho.   Perf. 13
3046 A1584 39c multi   1.20   .75
  No. 3046 known only precanceled. See second note after No. 132.

**Aspects of Life in the French
Regions Type of 2003**

No. 3047: a, House, Normandy. b,
Chambord Chateau. c, Gorges, Tarn, vert. d,
Notre Dame Cathedral, Paris, vert. e, Windmill, vert. f, Cave dwellings. g, Creek, Cassis,
vert. h, Cap-Ferret Lighthouse, vert. i, Castle
ruins. j, Alpine chalet.

2004, Sept. 18   Photo.   Perf. 13
3047   Sheet of 10   15.00 15.00
  a.-j. A1642 Any single   1.50   1.25
  No. 3047 has three vertical rows of rouletting separating sheet into quarters.
  Each stamp exists in booklet pane of 1 from
booklet that sold for €19.

Halloween
A1701

2004, Oct. 9   Litho.   Perf. 13
3048 A1701 50c multi   1.50   .35

Félix Eboué (1884-
1944), Colonial
Governor — A1702

2004, Oct. 16   Photo.
3049 A1702 50c multi   1.50   .40

Ouistreham
Lighthouse
A1703

2004, Oct. 30 *Perf. 13¼*
3050 A1703 50c multi 1.50 .40

Marianne — A1704

Serpentine Die Cut 6¾ Vert.
2004, Nov. 10 **Engr.**
Booklet Stamp
Self-Adhesive
3051 A1704 50c multi 2.50 2.00
a. Booklet pane, 5 each
#2835A, 3051 20.00

European Capitals Type of 2002

No. 3052 — Attractions in Athens: a, Greek Academy. b, Parthenon. c, Odeon of Herodes Atticus. d, Church of the Holy Apostles, vert.

Perf. 13x13¼, 13¼x13
2004, Nov. 11 **Photo.**
3052 A1622 Sheet of 4 7.50 7.50
a.-d. 50c Any single 1.50 .90

A1705

A1706

A1707

A1708

A1709

Holiday
Greetings
A1710

2004, Nov. 12 **Photo.** *Perf. 13*
3053 A1705 50c multi 1.50 .40

Litho.
3054 A1706 50c multi + label 6.00 6.00
3055 A1707 50c multi + label 6.00 6.00
3056 A1708 50c multi + label 6.00 6.00
3057 A1709 50c multi + label 6.00 6.00
3058 A1710 50c multi + label 6.00 6.00
a. Vert. strip of 5, #3054-3059
+ 5 labels 30.00 30.00
Miniature sheet, 2 #3058a
+ 10 labels 60.00 60.00

Booklet Stamps
Self-Adhesive
Serpentine Die Cut 11¼x11
3059 A1706 50c multi 1.50 .40
3060 A1707 50c multi 1.50 .40
3061 A1708 50c multi 1.50 .40
3062 A1709 50c multi 1.50 .40
3063 A1710 50c multi 1.50 .40
a. Booklet pane, 2 each
#3059-3063 15.00
Nos. 3053-3063 (11) 39.00 32.40

Miniature sheet containing Nos. 3054-3058 sold for €6.69. Labels could be personalized. No. 3055 exists in a souvenir sheet of 1 stamp without label that sold for €3.

Henri Wallon (1812-
1904), Historian
and
Politician — A1711

2004, Nov. 13 **Photo.** *Perf. 13*
3064 A1711 50c multi 1.50 .40

Opening of Millau Viaduct — A1712

Illustration reduced.

2004, Dec. 14 **Photo.** *Perf. 13*
3065 A1712 50c multi 1.50 .40

Marianne — A1713

Inscribed "ITVF" at Bottom

2005 **Engr.** *Perf. 13*
3066 A1713 1c yellow .20 .20
a. Inscribed "Phil@poste" at
bottom .20 .20
3067 A1713 5c brown
black .20 .20
a. Inscribed "Phil@poste" at
bottom .20 .20
3068 A1713 10c violet .25 .20
3069 A1713 (45c) green 1.25 .25
a. Inscribed "Phil@poste" at
bottom 1.25 .25
3070 A1713 (50c) red 1.50 .25
a. Sheet of 15 + 15 labels 60.00 60.00
b. Inscribed "Phil@poste" at
bottom 1.40 .25
3071 A1713 55c dark blue 1.60 .50
3072 A1713 58c olive green 1.75 .40
3073 A1713 64c dark green 1.90 .40
3074 A1713 70c dark green 2.10 .50
3075 A1713 75c light blue 2.25 .40
3076 A1713 82c fawn 2.40 .45
3077 A1713 90c dark blue 2.75 .90
3078 A1713 €1 orange 3.00 1.00
a. Inscribed "Phil@poste" at
bottom 2.60 .55
3079 A1713 €1.11 red violet 3.25 .80
3080 A1713 €1.22 red violet 3.50 .75
3081 A1713 €1.90 chocolate 5.75 1.20
3082 A1713 €1.98 chocolate 6.00 2.00
Nos. 3066-3082 (17) 39.65 10.40

Booklet Stamp
Self-Adhesive
Serpentine Die Cut 6¾ Vert.
3083 A1713 (50c) red 1.50 .20
a. Booklet pane of 10 (see
footnote) 15.00
b. Booklet pane of 10 (see
footnote) 15.00
c. Booklet pane of 20 30.00
d. As #3083, with
"Phil@poste" inscription 1.50 .20
e. Booklet pane, 10 #3083d 15.00
f. Booklet pane of 12 #3083d 17.00

Coil Stamps
Perf. 13 Horiz.
3086 A1713 (45c) green 1.25 .30
3087 A1713 (50c) red 1.50 .25
3087A A1713 55c dark blue 1.60 .60

Issued: Nos. 1c, 10c, (45c), (50c), 58c, 70c, 75c, 90c, €1, €1.11, €1.90, 1/8. 5c, No. 3071, 64c, 82c, €1.22, €1.98, 3/1. No. 3087A, 7/15. Nos. 3083d, 3083e, 10/1/06. Face values shown for Nos. 3069, 3070, 3083, 3086 and 3087 are those the stamps sold for on the day of issue. No. 3070a sold for €10.03 and the labels could be personalized for an additional fee. No. 3083a has a narrow strip of selvage separating the four stamps at left, from the six stamps, at right, and is on a white backing paper. No. 3083b is comprised of two horizontal strips of five stamps on a yellow backing paper. No. 3083d sold for 54c on day of issue.
Nos. 3066a, 3067a, 3069a, 3070b issued 2006. No. 3083f, Jan. 2007. On day of issue, No. 3069a sold for 49c; No. 3070b for 54c.
A sheet of 10 litho. stamps similar to No. 3067 + 10 labels exists, but was not sold.

Rabbi Shlomo Yitshaqi (Rashi) (1040-
1105) — A1714

2005, Jan. 16 **Engr.** *Perf. 13¼*
3088 A1714 50c multi 1.50 .40

Hearts
A1715

Designs: 53c, Polka dots. 82c, Bird and flowers.

2005, Jan. 29 **Photo.** *Perf. 13¼*
3089 A1715 53c multi 1.50 .40
a. Souvenir sheet of 5 7.50 7.50
b. Litho, stamp + label 5.00 5.00
3090 A1715 82c multi 2.50 1.00
a. Litho, stamp + label 6.00 6.00

Values are for stamps with surrounding selvage.
Sheets of 10 of No. 3089b sold for €6.86, and sheets of 10 of No. 3090a sold for €8.78. Labels could be personalized for an additional fee.
See Nos. 3134, 3136.

New Year 2005
(Year of the
Rooster)
A1716

Photo. & Embossed
2005, Jan. 29 *Perf. 13½x13*
3091 A1716 (50c) multi 1.50 .40
Printed in sheets of 10.

Rotary
International,
Cent. — A1717

2005, Feb. 19 **Photo.** *Perf. 13¼*
3092 A1717 53c multi 1.50 .40

Titeuf — A1718

Nadia — A1719

Manu — A1720

2005, Feb. 28 **Photo.** *Perf. 13¼*
3093 A1718 (50c) red & multi 1.50 .40
a. Perf. 13¼x13 (booklet
stamp) 1.50 .40

Booklet Stamps
3094 A1719 (45c) green & multi 1.40 .35
3095 A1720 (90c) blue & multi 2.75 .70
a. Booklet pane, 2 #3094, 4
each #3093a, 3095 20.00 —
Complete booklet, #3095a 21.00

Characters from Titeuf, comic strip by Zep. Stamp Day.

Greetings Type of 2004 Inscribed
"Lettre 20g"

Designs: Nos. 3096, 3097A, "Ceci est une invitation." Nos. 3097, 3097B, "Un grand merci."
No. 3097C, "Ceci est une invitation." No. 3097D, "Un grand merci."

2005-06 **Photo.** *Perf. 13*
Holes Punched Through Dots of
"i's"
3096 A1667 (53c) brt lil rose &
yel 1.50 .40
3097 A1667 (53c) brt yel grn &
red lil 1.50 .40

Litho.
No Holes Punched Through Dots of
"i's"
Stamp + Label
3097A A1667 (53c) brt lil rose &
yel 4.50 4.50
3097B A1667 (53c) brt yel grn &
red lil 4.50 4.50

Self-Adhesive
No Holes Punched Through Dots of "i's"
Stamp + Label

3097C A1667 (53c) brt lil rose & yel ... 2.40 2.40
3097D A1667 (53c) brt yel grn & rrd lil ... 2.40 2.40

Nos. 3097A-3097B were issued in sheets of 10 stamps + 10 labels that sold for €8 on day of issue. The labels could be personalized.
Nos. 3097C-3097D were each issued in sheets of 10 stamps + 10 labels that sold for €8.61. Labels could be personalized.
Issued: Nos. 2096-3097B, 3/1/05. Nos. 3097C-3097D, 2006.

Art Series

The Guitarist, by Jean-Baptiste Greuze (1725-1805) — A1721

White Bear, Sculpture by François Pompon — A1722

Sicile, by Nicolas de Stael — A1723

2005 **Photo.** **Perf. 13x13¼**
3098 A1721 82c multi ... 2.40 1.00
3099 A1722 90c multi ... 2.75 1.50
3100 A1723 €1.22 multi ... 3.50 1.60
Issued: €1.22, 3/5. 90c, 7/2. 82c, 9/24.

Orchids — A1725

Designs: No. 3102, Cypripedium calceolus. No. 3103, Paphiopedilum Mabel Sanders. 55c, Oncidium papilio. 82c, Paphinia cristata, horiz.

2005, Mar. 11 **Photo.** **Perf. 13¼**
3102 A1725 53c multi ... 1.60 .40
3103 A1725 53c multi ... 1.60 .40
3104 A1725 55c multi ... 1.60 .45
3105 A1725 82c multi ... 2.40 1.00
a. Souvenir sheet, #3102-3105 ... 7.50 7.50
Nos. 3102-3105 (4) ... 7.20 2.25

Aspects of Life in French Regions Type of 2003

No. 3106: a, Nautical jousting. b, Clocks of Franche-Comte, vert. c, Cantal cheese and bread, vert. d, Dancers and accordion player.

e, Bouillabaisse. f, P'tit Quinquin statue, vert. g, Rillettes (chopped pork). h, Sauerkraut and sausage, beer stein. i, Pelota, vert. j, Sugar cane, vert.

2005, Mar. 19 **Photo.** **Perf. 13**
3106 Sheet of 10 ... 16.00 16.00
a.-j. A1642 53c Any single ... 1.50 1.25
No. 3106 has three vertical rows of rouletting, separating sheet into quarters.
Each stamp exists in a booklet pane of 1 from a booklet that sold for €19.

Tourism Issue

Aix-en-Provence — A1726

Gulf of Morbihan — A1727

Villefranche-sur-Mer — A1728

La Roque-Gageac — A1729

Illustration A1727 is reduced.

2005 **Engr.** **Perf. 13¼, 13 (#3108)**
3107 A1726 53c multi ... 1.60 .40
Photo.
3108 A1727 53c multi ... 1.60 .40
3109 A1728 53c multi ... 1.60 .40
Engr.
3110 A1729 53c multi ... 1.60 .40
Issued: No. 3107, 4/1; No. 3108, 5/5; No. 3109, 6/4; No. 3110, 7/23.

Happy Birthday A1730

2005, Apr. 2 **Photo.** **Perf. 13**
3111 A1730 (53c) multi ... 1.60 .40
a. Souvenir sheet of 5 ... 8.00 8.00
b. Litho., stamp + label ... 6.00 6.00
Sheets of 10 and 10 labels of No. 3111b sold for €6.86. Labels could be personalized for an additional fee.

Albert Einstein (1879-1955), Physicist — A1731

2005, Apr. 16 **Perf. 13¼**
3112 A1731 53c multi ... 1.60 .40

Alexis de Tocqueville (1805-59), Writer — A1732

2005, Apr. 23 **Engr.** **Perf. 13x13¼**
3113 A1732 90c multi ... 2.75 1.00

Liberation of Concentration Camp Internees, 60th Anniv. — A1733

2005, Apr. 24 **Photo.** **Perf. 13¼**
3114 A1733 53c multi ... 1.60 .40

Battle of Austerlitz, Bicent. A1734

Litho. & Engr.
2005, May 4 **Perf. 13¼**
3115 A1734 55c multi ... 1.60 .45
See Czech Republic No. 3273.

French Federation of Philatelic Associations, 78th Congress, Nancy — A1735

Illustration reduced.

2005, May 5 **Engr.** **Perf. 13**
3116 A1735 53c multi + label ... 1.60 .40
A souvenir sheet of one stamp without label exists.

Europa — A1736

2005, May 8 **Photo.** **Perf. 13¼**
3117 A1736 53c multi ... 1.60 .50

Gardens and Parks Type of 2003
Souvenir Sheet

No. 3118 — Sculptures in Jardin de la Fontaine, Nimes: a, Denomination in green. b, Denomination in white.

2005, May 15 **Perf. 13¼x13**
3118 Sheet of 2 ... 12.00 12.00
a.-b. A1660 €1.98 Either single ... 6.00 6.00
Salon du Timbre 2005. No. 3118 has four vertical rows of rouletting, separating sheet into fifths, with the two stamps in the central fifth.

Vacation A1737

Serpentine Die Cut 11
2005, May 23 **Litho.**
Booklet Stamp
Self-Adhesive

3119 A1737 (53c) multi ... 1.60 .40
a. Booklet pane of 10 ... 16.00

Stories by Jules Verne (1828-1905) A1738

Designs: No. 3120, Five Weeks in a Balloon (Cinq Semaines en Ballon). No. 3121, From the Earth to the Moon (De la Terre à la Lune). No. 3122, Journey to the Center of the Earth (Voyage au Centre de la Terre), horiz. No. 3123, Michael Strogoff, horiz. No. 3124, Around the World in Eighty Days (Le Tour du Monde en Quatre-vingts Jours). No. 3125, 20,000 Leagues Under the Sea (Vingt Mille Lieues Sous les Mers).

2005, May 28 **Photo.** **Perf. 13**
3120 A1738 53c multi ... 1.60 .75
3121 A1738 53c multi ... 1.60 .75
3122 A1738 53c multi ... 1.60 .75
3123 A1738 53c multi ... 1.60 .75
3124 A1738 53c multi ... 1.60 .75
3125 A1738 53c multi ... 1.60 .75
a. Souvenir sheet, #3120-3125 ... 12.00 12.00
Nos. 3120-3125 (6) ... 9.60 4.50
No. 3125a sold for €4.80 with the Red Cross receiving €1.62 of that.

Miniature Sheet

Gordon Bennett Cup, Cent. — A1739

No. 3126 — Inscriptions: a, La Coupe Gordon Bennett (Car No. 1 facing right). b, La Coupe Gordon Bennett (Car No. 1 facing left). c, La Formule 1, vert. d, Le Rallye-Raid, vert. e, Les Rallyes. f, La Course d'endurance.

2005, June 2 **Photo.** **Perf.**
3126 A1739 Sheet of 10,
#a-b, 2 each
#c-f ... 16.00 16.00
a.-f. 53c Any single ... 1.60 .85
A souvenir sheet containing No. 3126a sold for €3.

Environmental Charter — A1740

Illustration reduced.

2005, June 5   **Litho.**   *Perf. 13*
3127 A1740 53c multi, *lt green*   1.60 .40

Enactment of Handicapped Persons Rights Law — A1741

2005, June 18   **Photo.**   *Perf. 13¼*
3128 A1741 53c multi   1.60 .35

It's a Boy A1742

It's a Girl A1743

2005   **Litho.**   *Perf. 13x13¼*
3129 A1742 (53c) multi + label   4.00 4.00
3130 A1743 (53c) multi + label   4.00 4.00

Booklet Stamps
Self-Adhesive
Serpentine Die Cut 11¼x11
3131 A1742 (53c) multi   1.60 .35
  a.   Booklet pane of 10   16.00
  b.   Sheet of 10 + 10 labels   23.00
3132 A1743 (53c) multi   1.60 .35
  a.   Booklet pane of 10   16.00
  b.   Sheet of 10 + 10 labels   23.00

Sheets of 10 stamps and 10 labels of Nos. 3129 and 3130 each sold for €6.86. Nos. 3131b and 3132b each sold for €8.61. Labels could be personalized for an additional fee.

Hearts Types of 2004-05
Serpentine Die Cut
2005, July 15   **Photo.**
Self-Adhesive
3133 A1670 50c Like #2997   4.00 3.00
3134 A1715 53c Like #3089   5.00 4.00
3135 A1670 75c Like #2998   5.00 4.00
3136 A1715 82c Like #3090   6.00 5.00
  Nos. 3133-3136 (4)   20.00 16.00

Haras du Pin Natl. Stud Farm A1744

2005, July 16   *Perf. 13*
3137 A1744 53c multi   1.60 .40

European Capitals Type of 2002

No. 3138 — Attractions in Berlin: a, Brandenburg Gate. b, Kaiser Wilhelm Memorial Church, vert. c, Philharmonic Hall. d, Reichstag.

Perf. 13x13¼, 13¼x13
2005, Aug. 27   **Photo.**
3138 A1622   Sheet of 4   6.50 6.50
  a.-d.   53c Any single   1.60 1.00

Aspects of Life in the French Regions Type of 2003

No. 3139: a, Lake Annecy. b, Etretat Cliffs, vert. c, Pigeon house, vert. d, Wash house (lavoir). e, Banks of the Seine. f, Carnac megaliths. g, House, Sologne. h, Pilat Sand Dune. i, Stiff Lighthouse, vert. j, Stone hut (borie), vert.

2005, Sept. 17   *Perf. 13*
3139   Sheet of 10   16.00 16.00
  a.-j.   A1642 53c Any single   1.60 1.25

No. 3139 has three vertical rows of rouletting, separating sheet into quarters.
Nos. 3139a-3139j were also issued in large booklets containing panes of 1 of each stamp. The booklet sold for €19.

Art Series

Les Halles Centrales, Designed by Victor Baltard (1805-74) — A1745

2005, Sept. 17   **Engr.**   *Perf. 13x13¼*
3140 A1745 €1.22 multi   3.50 1.25

Breast Cancer Awareness A1746

2005, Oct. 1   **Photo.**   *Perf. 13¼*
3141 A1746 53c multi   1.60 .35

A1747

A1748

A1749

A1750

A1751

A1752

A1753

A1754

A1755

Cat, Comics by Philippe Geluck A1756

Serpentine Die Cut 11¼x11
2005, Oct. 1   **Litho.**
Booklet Stamps
Self-Adhesive
3142 A1747 (53c) multi   1.60 .35
3143 A1748 (53c) multi   1.60 .35
3144 A1749 (53c) multi   1.60 .35
3145 A1750 (53c) multi   1.60 .35
3146 A1751 (53c) multi   1.60 .35
3147 A1752 (53c) multi   1.60 .35
3148 A1753 (53c) multi   1.60 .35
3149 A1754 (53c) multi   1.60 .35
3150 A1755 (53c) multi   1.60 .35
3151 A1756 (53c) multi   1.60 .35
  a.   Booklet pane of 10, #3142-3151   16.00

Raymond Aron (1905-83), Philosopher A1757

2005, Oct. 7   **Engr.**   *Perf. 13¼x13*
3152 A1757 53c multi   1.60 .35

Souvenir Sheet

The Annunciation, by Raphael — A1758

No. 3153: a, Drawing of Angel, painting of Virgin Mary. b, Painting of Angel, drawing of Virgin Mary.

Litho. & Engr.
2005, Nov. 10   *Perf. 13x13¼*
3153 A1758   Sheet of 2   4.00 4.00
  a.   53c multi   1.60 1.60
  b.   55c multi   1.60 1.60

See Vatican City Nos. 1312-1314.

Marianne — A1759

Serpentine Die Cut 6¾ Vert.
2005, Nov. 11   **Engr.**
Booklet Stamp
Self-Adhesive
3154 A1759 53c red   3.00 2.50
  a.   Booklet pane, 5 each #3083, 3154   22.50

Video Game Characters — A1760

No. 3155: a, Link. b, Pac-Man. c, Prince of Persia. d, Spyro. e, Donkey Kong. f, Mario. g, Adibou. h, Rayman. i, Lara Croft. j, The Sims.

2005, Nov. 11   **Photo.**   *Perf. 13¼x13*
3155 A1760   Sheet of 10   9.00 9.00
  a.-e.   20c Any single   .60 .50
  f.-j.   33c Any single   1.00 .75

Avicenna (980-1037), Scientist — A1761

2005, Nov. 12   **Engr.**   *Perf. 13x13¼*
3156 A1761 53c multi   1.60 .35

Holiday Greetings A1762

Designs: Nos. 3157, 3162, Bear, three penguins and sled. Nos. 3158, 3163, Two penguins, reindeer and sled. Nos. 3159, 3164, Two penguins, bear and sled. Nos. 3160, 3165, Three penguins. Nos. 3161, 3166, Two penguins, reindeer and snowman.

2005, Nov. 12   **Litho.**   *Perf. 13*
3157 A1762 (53c) multi + label   6.00 4.00
3158 A1762 (53c) multi + label   6.00 4.00
3159 A1762 (53c) multi + label   6.00 4.00
3160 A1762 (53c) multi + label   6.00 4.00
3161 A1762 (53c) multi + label   6.00 4.00
  a.   Vert. strip of 5, #3157-3161, + 5 labels   30.00 30.00
     Miniature sheet, 2 #3161a   60.00 60.00

Booklet Stamps
Self-Adhesive
Serpentine Die Cut 11¼x11
3162 A1762 (53c) multi   1.60 .35
3163 A1762 (53c) multi   1.60 .35
3164 A1762 (53c) multi   1.60 .35
3165 A1762 (53c) multi   1.60 .35
3166 A1762 (53c) multi   1.60 .35
  a.   Booklet pane, 2 each #3162-3166   16.00
  Nos. 3157-3166 (10)   38.00 21.75

Miniature sheet containing Nos. 3157-3161 sold for €6.86. Labels could be personalized.

No. 3161 exists in a souvenir sheet of one stamp without label, that sold for €3. Value $35.

Jacob Kaplan (1895-1994), Grand Rabbi of France — A1763

2005, Nov. 14   **Engr.**   **Perf. 13**
3167   A1763   53c multi   1.60   .35

Orchid Type of 2002

Design: Orchis insularis.

2005   **Litho.**   **Perf. 13**
3168   A1584   42c multi   1.25   .75

No. 3168 is known only precanceled. See second note after #132.

Law Separating Church and State, Cent. — A1764

2005, Dec. 3   **Photo.**   **Perf. 13¼x13**
3169   A1764   53c multi   1.60   .35

Hearts A1765

Designs: (53c), Hearts, octagons and diamonds. (82c), Heart and stripes.

2006, Jan. 7   **Photo.**   **Perf. 13¼**
3170   A1765   (53c) multi   1.60   .40
  a.   Souvenir sheet of 5   8.00   8.00
  b.   Litho., stamp + label   4.00   4.00
3171   A1765   (82c) multi   2.40   .70
  a.   Litho., stamp + label   4.00   4.00

Self-Adhesive
Serpentine Die Cut

3172   A1765   (53c) Like #3170   3.00   1.50
  a.   Sheet of 10 + 10 labels   23.00
3173   A1765   (82c) Like #3171   4.00   3.00
  a.   Sheet of 10 + 10 labels   30.00

Values are for stamps with surrounding selvage. Sheets of 10 of No. 3170b sold for €6.86, and sheets of No. 3172a. No. 3172a sold for €8.61; No. 3173a for €11.54. Labels could be personalized for an additional fee.

New Year 2006 (Year of the Dog) — A1766

2006, Jan. 21   **Photo.**   **Perf. 13¼x13**
3174   A1766   (53c) multi   1.60   .40

A souvenir sheet containing No. 3174 sold for €3.

Impressionist Paintings — A1767

Designs: Nos. 3175a, 3176, Portraits from the Country, by Gustave Caillebotte. Nos. 3175b, 3183, Dancers, by Edgar Degas. Nos. 3175c, 3181, Marguerite Gachet in the Garden, by Vincent van Gogh. Nos. 3175d, 3179, Two Young Girls at the Piano, by Auguste Renoir. Nos. 3175e, 3177, The Butterfly Hunt, by Berthe Morisot. Nos. 3175f, 3184, Luncheon on the Grass, by Edouard Manet. Nos. 3175g, 3182, Evening Air, by Henri-Edmond Cross. Nos. 3175h, 3180, The Shepherdess (Young Peasant Girl with a Stick), by Camille Pissarro. Nos. 3175i, 3178, Mother and Child, by Mary Cassatt. Nos. 3175j, 3185, Women of Tahiti on the Beach, by Paul Gauguin.

2006   **Litho.**   **Perf. 13¼**
3175   Sheet of 10 +10 labels   35.00   35.00
  a.-j.   A1767 (53c) Any single + label   3.50   3.50

Booklet Stamps
Self-Adhesive
Serpentine Die Cut 11¼x11

3176   A1767   (53c) multi   1.60   .40
3177   A1767   (53c) multi   1.60   .40
3178   A1767   (53c) multi   1.60   .40
3179   A1767   (53c) multi   1.60   .40
3180   A1767   (53c) multi   1.60   .40
3181   A1767   (53c) multi   1.60   .40
3182   A1767   (53c) multi   1.60   .40
3183   A1767   (53c) multi   1.60   .40
3184   A1767   (53c) multi   1.60   .40
3185   A1767   (53c) multi   1.60   .40
  a.   Booklet pane of 10, #3176-3185   16.00
  b.   Sheet of 10, #3176-3185, + 10 labels   23.00

Issued: No. 3175, 6/1; Nos. 3176-3185, 1/21. No. 3175 sold for €6.86. No. 3185b sold for €8.61. Labels could be personalized.

2006 Winter Olympics, Turin — A1768

2006, Feb. 4   **Photo.**   **Perf. 13**
3186   A1768   53c multi   1.60   .35

Spirou — A1769

Fantasio, Spip and Spirou — A1770

Fantasio A1771

2006, Feb. 25   **Perf. 13¼**
3187   A1769   (53c) multi   1.60   .40
  a.   Perf. 13¼x13 (booklet stamp)   1.60   .40

Booklet Stamps
Perf. 13¼x13

3188   A1770   (48c) multi   1.40   .35
3189   A1771   (90c) multi   2.75   .65
  a.   Booklet pane, 4 each #3187a, 3188, 2 #3189   17.50   —
    Complete booklet, #3189a   18.00

Characters from Spirou, by Robert Velter. Stamp Day.

Courrières Coal Mine Disaster, Cent. — A1772

2006, Feb. 25   **Perf. 13¼**
3190   A1772   53c multi   1.60   .40

Douaumont Ossuary — A1773

2006, Mar. 4   **Engr.**
3191   A1773   53c multi   1.60   .40

Aspects of Life in the French Regions Type of 2003

No. 3192: a, Yellow plums (mirabelle). b, Salt marsh (marais salants). c, Butter (beurre). d, Roquefort cheese, vert. e, Olive oil, vert. f, Carnival, vert. g, Grape harvests (vendanges), vert. h, Waiter at café, vert. i, Transhumance of livestock. j, Marshland gardens (hortillonages).

2006, Mar. 25   **Photo.**   **Perf. 13**
3192   Sheet of 10   16.00   16.00
  a.-j.   A1642 53c Any single   1.60   1.25

No. 3192 has three vertical rows of rouletting, separating sheet into quarters. Nos. 3192a-3192j were also issued in large booklets containing panes of 1 of each stamp. The booklet sold for €19.

Tourism Issue

Yvoire A1774

Dijon A1775

Antibes Juan-les-Pins — A1776

Thionville A1777

2006   **Photo.**   **Perf. 13**
3193   A1774   53c multi   1.60   .40

Engr.
Perf. 13¼
3194   A1775   53c multi   1.60   .40

Litho. & Engr.
Perf. 13x13¼
3195   A1776   53c multi   1.60   .40

Engraved
3196   A1777   54c multi   1.60   .40
   Nos. 3193-3196 (4)   6.40   1.60

Issued: No. 3193, 3/25; No. 3194, 4/7. No. 3195, 7/15. No. 3196, 9/16.

Art Series

Prehistoric Drawings in Rouffignac Cave — A1778

Bathers, by Paul Cézanne — A1779

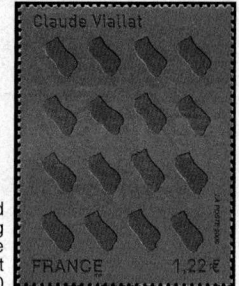

Untitled Painting by Claude Viallat A1780

Beggars Receiving Alms at the Door of a House, by Rembrandt A1781

Engr., Photo (#3198, 3199)

2006			Perf. 13x13¼	
3197	A1778	55c multi	1.60	.75
3198	A1779	82c multi	2.40	.75

			Perf. 13¼x13	
3199	A1780	€1.22 brt pink & bl grn	3.50	1.00
3200	A1781	€1.30 multi	3.75	1.00
		Nos. 3197-3200 (4)	11.25	3.50

Issued: 82c, 4/8; 55c, 5/27; No. 3199, 6/3. No. 3200, 11/10.

Gardens and Parks Type of 2003
Souvenir Sheet

No. 3201: a, Vallée-aux-Loups Park. b, Albert Kahn Gardens.

2006, Apr. 22	Photo.		Perf. 13¼x13	
3201		Sheet of 2	12.50	12.50
a.-b.	A1660	€1.98 Either single	6.00	6.00
c.		Souvenir sheet, #3118a, 3118b, 3201a, 3201b	25.00	25.00

Salon du Timbre 2006. No. 3201 has four vertical rows of rouletting, separating sheet into fifths, with the two stamps in the central fifth.

No. 3201c issued 6/16.

Young Animals
A1782

Designs: No. 3202, Puppy. No. 3203, Kitten. 55c, Foal, horiz. 82c, Lamb, horiz..

2006, Apr. 22			Perf. 13¼	
3202	A1782	53c multi	1.60	.40
3203	A1782	53c multi	1.60	.40
3204	A1782	55c multi	1.60	.40
3205	A1782	82c multi	2.40	.65
a.		Souvenir sheet, #3202-3205	7.50	7.50
		Nos. 3202-3205 (4)	7.20	1.85

Europa
A1783

2006, Apr. 30				
3206	A1783	53c multi	1.60	.40

Pierre Bayle (1647-1706), Philiosopher
A1784

2006, May 2	Engr.		Perf. 13x13¼	
3207	A1784	53c blk & brn	1.60	.40

Remembrance of Slavery Day, 5th Anniv. — A1785

2006, May 10	Photo.		Perf. 13¼	
3208	A1785	53c multi	1.60	.40

Vacation
A1786

Serpentine Die Cut 11¼x11

2006, May 27			Litho.	

Booklet Stamp
Self-Adhesive

3209	A1786	(53c) multi	1.60	.40
a.		Booklet pane of 10	16.00	

Miniature Sheet

2006 World Cup Soccer Championships, Germany — A1787

No. 3210: a, Replacement players (39x25mm). b, Fans (39x25mm). c, Player with ball near chest (32mm diameter). d, Player kicking ball (32mm diameter). e, Goalie throwing ball (32mm diameter). f, Player making scissor kick (32mm diameter). g, Two players (32mm diameter). h, Referee (25x39mm). i, Coach (39x25mm). j, Cameramen (39x25mm).

2006, May 27	Photo.		Perf. 12¾	
3210	A1787	Sheet of 10	16.00	16.00
a.-j.		53c Any single	1.60	1.25

Marianne Type of 2005

2006		Litho.	Perf. 13	
3211		Sheet of 15, #a-k, 2 each #l-m, + 15 labels	35.00	35.00
a.	A1713	1c yellow orange	.20	.20
b.	A1713	5c dark brown	.20	.20
c.	A1713	10c violet	.30	.30
d.	A1713	55c blue	1.75	1.75
e.	A1713	64c olive green	2.00	2.00
f.	A1713	75c light blue	2.25	2.25
g.	A1713	82c fawn	2.50	2.50
h.	A1713	90c dark blue	2.75	2.75
i.	A1713	€1 dull orange	3.00	3.00
j.	A1713	€1.22 red violet	3.75	3.75
k.	A1713	€1.98 brown	6.00	6.00
l.	A1713	(48c) green	1.50	1.50
m.	A1713	(53c) red	1.60	1.60

Etched on Foil
Die Cut Perf. 13
Self-Adhesive

3212	A1713	€5 silver	17.50	17.50

No. 3211 has stamps with a glossy varnish. It sold for €12.04 and labels could be personalized. Nos. 3211a-3211m and 3212 have "Phil@poste" inscription at bottom. No. 3212 was sold in a protective package.

Serpentine Die Cut 11¼
Litho.
Self-Adhesive

3211N		Sheet of 15, #3211No-3211Ny, 2 each #3211Nz, 3211Naa, + 15 labels	40.00	
o.	A1713	1c yellow orange	.20	.20
p.	A1713	5c dark brown	.20	.20
q.	A1713	10c violet	.40	.40
r.	A1713	55c blue	2.25	2.25
s.	A1713	64c olive green	2.60	2.60
t.	A1713	75c light blue	3.00	3.00
u.	A1713	82c fawn	3.25	3.25
v.	A1713	90c dark blue	3.75	3.75
w.	A1713	€1 dull orange	4.00	4.00
x.	A1713	€1.22 red violet	5.00	5.00
y.	A1713	€1.98 brown	7.00	7.00
z.	A1713	(48c) green	1.90	1.90
aa.	A1713	(53c) red	2.10	2.10

No. 3211N has stamps with a glossy varnish and "Phil@poste" inscription at bottom. It sold for €15.05 and labels could be personalized.

Costumes From Operas by Wolfgang Amadeus Mozart — A1788

Designs: No. 3213, The Magic Flute. No. 3214, Don Giovanni. No. 3215, The Marriage of Figaro. No. 3216, The Clemency of Titus. No. 3217, The Abduction from the Seraglio (L'enlèvement au Sérail). No. 3218, Cosi Fan Tutte.

2006, June 17	Photo.		Perf. 13	
3213	A1788	53c multi	1.60	.75
3214	A1788	53c multi	1.60	.75
3215	A1788	53c multi	1.60	.75
3216	A1788	53c multi	1.60	.75
3217	A1788	53c multi	1.60	.75
3218	A1788	53c multi	1.60	.75
a.		Souvenir sheet, #3213-3218	12.00	12.00
		Nos. 3213-3218 (6)	9.60	4.50

Nos. 3213-3218 were each printed in souvenir sheets containing one stamp that sold as a set for €15, and in booklet panes containing one stamp in a large book that sold for €19. Value: set of 6 sheets $35; set of 6 panes in book $45. No. 3218a sold for €4.80, with the Red Cross receiving €1.62 of that.

UNESCO World Heritage Sites
A1789

Designs: 53c, Provins. 90c, Mont Saint-Michel.

2006, June 17	Photo.		Perf. 13¼	
3219	A1789	53c multi	1.60	.40
3220	A1789	90c multi	2.60	.70

See United Nations Offices in Geneva Nos. 459-461.

Garnier Opera House, Paris — A1790

2006, June 18	Engr.		Perf. 13x13¼	
3221	A1790	53c multi + label	1.60	.40

French Federation of Philatelic Associations 79th Congress, Paris.

Happy Birthday
A1791

2006, June 19	Photo.		Perf. 13	
3222	A1791	(53c) multi	1.60	.40
a.		Souvenir sheet of 5	8.00	8.00
b.		Litho. stamp + label	4.00	4.00

Serpentine Die Cut 11
Self-Adhesive

3222C	A1791	(53c) multi + label	2.40	2.40

Sheets of 10 of No. 3222b sold for €6.86. No. 3222C was printed in sheets of 10 stamps + 10 labels that sold for €8.61. Labels could be personalized for an additional fee.

European Capitals Type of 2002
Souvenir Sheet

No. 3223 — Attractions in Nicosia, Cyprus: a, Chrysaliniotissa Church. b, Archaeological

---

Museum. c, Famagusta Gate. d, Archbishop's residence (Archeveché).

2006, June 20	Photo.		Perf. 13x13¼	
3223	A1622	Sheet of 4	7.00	7.00
a.-d.		53c Any single	1.60	1.00

Tango Dancing
A1792

2006, June 21	Photo.		Perf. 12¼	
3224	A1792	53c Dancers	1.60	.40
3225	A1792	90c Musician	2.60	.70

See Argentina Nos. 2395-2396.

La Poste's Business Foundation, 10th Anniv. — A1793

2006, June 22	Litho.		Perf. 13	
3226	A1793	(53c) multi, tan	1.60	.40

French Open Golf Championship, Cent. — A1794

Photo. & Embossed

2006, June 24			Perf. 13	
3227	A1794	53c multi	1.60	.40

A souvenir sheet containing No. 3227 sold for €3.

Rotary International Type of 2005
Serpentine Die Cut 11

2006, July 1			Photo.	

Self-Adhesive

3227A	A1717	53c multi	1.60	.40

French Soccer Team's Second-Place Showing in 2006 World Cup — A1795

2006, July 5	Photo.		Perf. 13¼	
		Size: 35x26mm		
3228	A1795	53c multi	1.60	.40

Litho.
Size: 35x22mm
Perf. 13

3229	A1795	53c multi + label	4.00	4.00

Serpentine Die Cut 11¼x11
Self-Adhesive

3229A	A1795	53c multi + label	2.40	2.40

No. 3229 was printed in sheets of 10 stamps and 10 labels that sold for €6.94. No. 3229A was printed in sheets of 10 stamps + 10 labels that sold for €8.61. Labels could be personalized.

Quai Branly Museum — A1796

Illustration reduced.

2006, July 8   Photo.   Perf. 13x13¼
3230   A1796   53c multi   1.60   .40

Reinstatement of Capt. Alfred Dreyfus, Cent. — A1797

2006, July 12   Engr.
3231   A1797   53c multi   1.60   .40

Claude-Joseph Rouget de Lisle (1760-1836), Composer of "La Marseillaise" — A1798

2006, July 13   Photo.   Perf. 13¼
3232   A1798   53c multi   1.60   .40

Pablo Casals (1876-1973), Cellist — A1799

2006, July 29
3233   A1799   53c multi   1.60   .40

Aspects of Life in French Regions Type of 2003

No. 3234: a, Catalan Towers. b, La Croisette, Cannes. c, Brocéliande Forest. d, Volcanic craters, Auvergne, vert. e, Les Invalides, Paris, vert. f, Chateau de Chaumont, Chaumont-sur-Loire. g, Ardèche Gorges, vert. h, Flour mill, Valmy, vert. i, Grotto of Messabielle, Lourdes. j, Calanches de Piana, Corsica.

2006, Sept. 2   Photo.   Perf. 13
3234   Sheet of 10   16.00 16.00
     a.-j.   A1642 54c Any single   1.60   1.25

No. 3234 has three vertical rows of rouletting, separating sheet into quarters.
Nos. 3234a-3234j were also issued in large booklets containing panes of 1 of each stamp. The booklet sold for €19.

A1800

A1801

A1802

A1803

A1804

A1805

A1806

A1807

A1808

Cubitus, Comics by Michel Rodrigue and Pierre Aucaigne A1809

Serpentine Die Cut 11¼x11
2006, Sept. 20   Litho.
Self-Adhesive
Booklet Stamps
3235   A1800   (54c) multi   1.60   .40
3236   A1801   (54c) multi   1.60   .40
3237   A1802   (54c) multi   1.60   .40
3238   A1803   (54c) multi   1.60   .40
3239   A1804   (54c) multi   1.60   .40
3240   A1805   (54c) multi   1.60   .40
3241   A1806   (54c) multi   1.60   .40
3242   A1807   (54c) multi   1.60   .40
3243   A1808   (54c) multi   1.60   .40
3244   A1809   (54c) multi   1.60   .40
     a.   Booklet pane of 10, #3235-3244   16.00

Sculptures by Constantin Brancusi (1876-1957) — A1810

Designs: 54c, Sleeping Muse. 85c, Sleep.

2006, Sept. 25   Photo.   Perf. 13¼
3245   A1810   54c multi   1.60   .40
3246   A1810   85c multi   2.50   .75

See Romania Nos. 4878-4879.

Marianne Type of 2005
2006, Oct. 1   Engr.   Perf. 13
Inscribed "Phil@poste" at Bottom
3247   A1713   10c gray   .30   .20
3248   A1713   60c dark blue   1.75   .40
3249   A1713   70c yel green   2.00   .40
3250   A1713   85c purple   2.50   .50
3251   A1713   86c fawn   2.50   .50
3252   A1713   €1.15 blue   3.25   .75
3253   A1713   €1.30 red violet   3.75   .75
3254   A1713   €2.11 chocolate   6.00   1.40
     Nos. 3247-3254 (8)   22.05   4.90

Coil Stamp
Perf. 13 Horiz.
3255   A1713   60c dark blue   1.75   .50

Serpentine Die Cut 11¼
2006   Engr.
Self-Adhesive
3255A   A1713   (54c) red + label   2.40   2.40
3255C   A1713   60c dark blue + label   2.50   2.50
3255D   A1713   86c fawn + label   3.00   3.00
     Nos. 3255A-3255D (3)   7.90   7.90

A number has been reserved for an additional stamp. Nos. 3255A, 3255C and 3255D were printed in sheets of 15 stamps + 15 labels that could be personalized. Sheets of No. 3255A sold for €13.29; No. 3255C, €14.04; No. 3255D, €17.31.

Aviation Without Borders — A1811

2006, Oct. 7   Photo.   Perf. 13
3256   A1811   54c multi   1.60   .40

Henri Moissan (1852-1907), 1906 Nobel Chemistry Laureate — A1812

2006, Oct. 14   Engr.   Perf. 13¼x13
3257   A1812   54c multi   1.60   .40

"Shared Memories," Intl. Conference on Veterans, Paris — A1813

2006, Oct. 26   Photo.   Perf. 13¼
3258   A1813   54c multi   1.60   .40

Marianne — A1814

Serpentine Die Cut 6¾ Vert.
2006, Nov. 8   Engr.
Self-Adhesive
Booklet Stamp
3259   A1814   54c red   3.00   2.50
     a.   Booklet pane, 5 each #3083d, 3259   22.50

Flying Machines — A1815

No. 3260: a, Gustave Ponton d'Amécourt's helicopter. b, Alberto Santos-Dumont's monoplane, "Demoiselle," horiz. c, Jean Marie Le Bris's bird-shaped glider, horiz. d, Clément Ader's "Avion III," horiz. e, Henri Fabré's seaplane, horiz. f, Jean-Pierre Blanchard's balloon.

Litho. & Engr.
2006, Nov. 9   Perf. 13
3260   A1815   Sheet of 6   10.00 10.00
     a.-f.   54c Any single   1.60   1.25

Inauguration of Aulnay-sous-Bois to Bondy Tram-Train Line — A1816

2006, Nov. 18   Photo.   Perf. 13x13¼
3261   A1816   54c multi   1.60   .50

Holiday Greetings A1817

Designs: No. 3262, Reindeer, sleigh, four penguins. No. 3263, Reindeer with fishing pole, three penguins. No. 3264, Reindeer, Christmas tree, two penguins. No. 3265, Reindeer skating, three penguins. No. 3266, Reindeer with gift boxes, three penguins.

2006, Nov. 25   Litho.   Perf. 13¼
3261A   A1817   (54c) multi + label   1.90   1.90
3261B   A1817   (54c) multi + label   1.90   1.90
3261C   A1817   (54c) multi + label   1.90   1.90
3261D   A1817   (54c) multi + label   1.90   1.90
3261E   A1817   (54c) multi + label   1.90   1.90
     f.   Vert. strip of 5, #3261A-3261E, + 5 labels   9.50   9.50
        Miniature sheet, 2 #3261Ef   19.00 19.00

Self-Adhesive
Booklet Stamps
Serpentine Die Cut 11¼x11
3262   A1817   (54c) multi   1.60   .50
3263   A1817   (54c) multi   1.60   .50
3264   A1817   (54c) multi   1.60   .50
3265   A1817   (54c) multi   1.60   .50
3266   A1817   (54c) multi   1.60   .50
     a.   Booklet pane, 2 each #3262-3266   16.00
     Nos. 3262-3266 (5)   8.00   2.50

Miniature sheet containing Nos. 3261A-3261E sold for €6.94. Labels could be personalized.
A souvenir sheet containing a perf. 13 example of No. 3266 sold for €3. A sheet containing 5 No. 3261A + 5 labels exists, but was not sold.

Grand Masonic Lodge of France A1818

2006, Dec. 1   Photo.   Perf. 13x13¼
3267   A1818   54c multi   1.50   .50

Alain Poher (1909-96), Politician, and Senate Building A1819

2006, Dec. 2   Engr.   Perf. 13¼
3268 A1819 54c multi   1.50 .50

Opening of New Paris Tramway A1820

2006, Dec. 16   Photo.   Perf. 13¼
3269 A1820 54c multi   1.40 .45

Orchids Type of 2002

Designs: 31c, Platanthera chlorantha. 36c, Dactylorhiza savogiensis. 43c, Orchis insularis.

2007, Jan. 2   Litho.   Perf. 13
3270 A1584 31c multi   .80   .20
3271 A1584 36c multi   .95   .20
3272 A1584 43c multi   1.10 .20
  Nos. 3270-3272 (3)   2.85 .60

Nos. 3270-3272 are known only precanceled. See second note after #132.

Hearts A1821

"Givenchy" in: (54c), Black and white. (86c), Red.

2007, Jan. 6   Photo.   Perf. 13¼
Inscribed "Lettre 20 g"
3273 A1821 (54c) red & black 1.40 .45
  a. Souvenir sheet of 5   7.00 7.00
Inscribed "Lettre 50 g"
3274 A1821 (86c) black & red 2.25 .75
Values are for stamps with surrounding selvage.

Serpentine Die Cut
Self-Adhesive
3275 A1821 (54c) Like #3273   1.40 .45
Inscribed "Lettre 50 g"
3276 A1821 (86c) Like #3274   2.25 .75

New Year 2007 (Year of the Pig) — A1822

2007, Jan. 27 Photo. Perf. 13¼x13
3277 A1822 (54c) multi   1.40 .45
  a. Litho., stamp + label   1.90 1.90
Serpentine Die Cut 11
Self-Adhesive
3277B A1822 (54c) multi + label 2.40 2.40

No. 3277 has a somewhat blurrier image than No. 3277a. Sheets of 5 #3277a + 5 labels sold for €3.51. Labels could be personalized. No. 3277 exists in a souvenir sheet of 1 that sold for €3.
No. 3277B was printed in sheets of 10 + 10 labels that sold for €8.86. Labels could be personalized.

Egyptian Hippopotamus Figurine — A1823

Head of Aphrodite A1824

Winged Victory of Samothrace A1825

Fresco, Pompeii A1826

King Amenemhet III of Egypt A1827

Statue of Juno A1828

Egyptian Harpist A1829

Etruscan Sarcophagus of Husband and Wife — A1830

Egyptian Statue of Seated Scribe A1831

Head of Pericles A1832

Serpentine Die Cut 11¼x11
2007, Jan. 27   Litho.
Booklet Stamps
Self-Adhesive
3279 A1823 (54c) multi   1.40 .45
3280 A1824 (54c) multi   1.40 .45
3281 A1825 (54c) multi   1.40 .45
3282 A1826 (54c) multi   1.40 .45
3283 A1827 (54c) multi   1.40 .45
3284 A1828 (54c) multi   1.40 .45
3285 A1829 (54c) multi   1.40 .45
3286 A1830 (54c) multi   1.40 .45
3287 A1831 (54c) multi   1.40 .45
3288 A1832 (54c) multi   1.40 .45
  a. Booklet pane of 10, #3279-3288 14.00

Tourism Issue

Valenciennes A1833

2007   Engr.   Perf. 13¼
3289 A1833 54c red & blue   1.50 .50
  Issued: No. 3289, 2/3.

Tourism Issue

Limoges A1834

2007   Engr.   Perf. 13¼
3290 A1834 54c multi   1.50 .50
  Issued: No. 3290, 3/23.

Tourism Issue

Arcachon A1835

2007, May 19   Photo.   Perf. 13¼
3291 A1835 54c multi   1.50 .50

Tourism Issue

Castres A1836

2007, July 20   Engr.   Perf. 13¼
3292 A1836 54c multi   1.50 .50

Tourism Issue

Firminy — A1837

2007, Sept. 15   Engr.   Perf. 13¼
3293 A1837 54c multi   1.60 .55

Rights of France A1838

2007, Feb. 5   Photo.   Perf. 13¼
3294 A1838 54c multi   1.50 .50

Art Issue

Book Illumination from Sélestat Library — A1839

Galerie des Glaces, Versailles Palace — A1840

La Barrière Fleurie, by Paul Sérusier A1841

Gallic Boar Ensign — A1842

Perf. 12¼x13, 13¼x13 (#3297),
13x13¼ (#3296, 3298)
Engraved, Photo. (#3296, 3297)
2007
3295 A1839 60c multi   1.60 .80
3296 A1840 85c multi   2.50 1.25
3297 A1841 86c multi   2.50 1.25
3298 A1842 €1.30 multi   3.50 1.75

Issued: No. 3295, 2/10. No. 3297, 10/13. No. 3298, 6/2. No. 3296, 11/10.

Aspects of Life in the French Regions Type of 2003

No. 3299: a, Baux-de-Provence. b, Banks of the Loire. c, Grande-Chartreuse Massif. d, Saint-Tropez. e, Doubs Waterfall, vert. f, Fontainebleau Forest, vert. g, Chantilly Castle. h, Saint-Malo. i, Ballon d'Alsace, vert. j, Midi Canal, vert.

2007, Feb. 24   Photo.   Perf. 13
3299   Sheet of 10   15.00 15.00
  a.-j. A1642 54c Any single   1.50 .50

No. 3299 has three vertical rows of rouletting, separating sheet into quarters.
Nos. 3299a-3299j were also issued in large booklets containing panes of 1 of each stamp. The booklet sold for €19.

Aspects of Life in French Regions
Type of 2003 Inscribed "Lettre Prioritaire 20g"

2007, Feb. Photo. *Perf. 13*

3300 A1642 (54c) Arc de Triomphe, vert. 1.90 1.90

No. 3300 was printed in sheets of 10 stamps + 10 different labels that sold for €6.85.

Marianne Type of 2005

2007 Litho. *Perf. 13*
Stamps Inscribed "Phil@poste"
Without Varnish

3302	Sheet of 15, #a-k, 2 each #l-m, + 15 labels	40.00	40.00
a.	A1713 1c yellow orange	.20	.20
b.	A1713 5c brown	.25	.25
c.	A1713 10c gray	.35	.35
d.	A1713 60c blue	2.25	2.25
e.	A1713 70c lt yellow green	2.60	2.60
f.	A1713 85c purple	3.00	3.00
g.	A1713 86c pink	3.25	3.25
h.	A1713 €1 orange	3.75	3.75
i.	A1713 €1.15 light blue	4.25	4.25
j.	A1713 €1.30 red violet	4.75	4.75
k.	A1713 €2.11 maroon	7.75	7.75
l.	A1713 (49c) blue green	1.75	1.75
m.	A1713 (54c) red	2.00	2.00

No. 3302 sold for €14.40 and has personalizable labels.

Harry Potter — A1843

Designs: (49c), Hermione Granger. (85c), Ron Weasley.

2007, Mar. 12 Photo. *Perf. 13¼*

3303	A1843 (54c) red & multi	1.50	.50
a.	Souvenir sheet of 1	1.50	1.50
b.	Perf. 13¼x13 (booklet stamp)	1.50	.50

Booklet Stamps
Perf. 13¼x13

3304	A1843 (49c) blue & multi	1.40	.45
3305	A1843 (85c) grn & multi	2.25	.75
a.	Booklet pane of 10, 4 #3303b, 3 each #3304-3305	17.00	
	Complete booklet, #3305a	17.00	

Stamp Day. Sheets of five serpentine die cut 11 self-adhesive stamps of each denomination and five labels that could not be personalized exist. Each sheet sold for €6.50.

Albert Londres (1884-1932), Journalist — A1844

2007, Mar. 16 Engr. *Perf. 13x13¼*

3306 A1844 54c multi 1.50 .50

Six different souvenir sheets containing one No. 3306 exist. The set sold for €15.

Audit Office, Bicent. A1845

2007, Mar. 17 *Perf. 13¼x13*

3307 A1845 54c multi 1.50 .50

Treaty of Rome, 50th Anniv. A1846

2007, Mar. 23 Photo. *Perf. 13¼*

3308 A1846 54c multi 1.50 .50

Sébastaen Le Prestre de Vauban (1633-1707), Military Engineer — A1847

2007, Mar. 30 Engr.

3309 A1847 54c multi 1.50 .50

2007 Rugby World Cup A1848

2007, Apr. 14 Photo. *Perf. 13¼*

3310	A1848 54c multi	1.50	.50
a.	Perf. 13¼x13¼ + label	2.25	2.25

No. 3310a was printed in sheets of 5 stamps and 5 labels that could be personalized that sold for €4.20.

Endangered Animals in Overseas Departments A1849

Designs: No. 3312, Antillean iguana. No. 3313, Raccoon, horiz. 60c, Jaguar, horiz. 86c, Barau's petrel, vert.

2007, Apr. 28 Photo. *Perf. 13¼*

3312	A1849 54c multi	1.50	.50
3313	A1849 54c multi	1.50	.50
3314	A1849 60c multi	1.75	.60
3315	A1849 86c multi	2.40	.80
a.	Souvenir sheet, #3312-3315	7.25	7.25
	Nos. 3312-3315 (4)	7.15	2.40

Gardens and Parks Type of 2003
Souvenir Sheet

No. 3316 — Parc de la Tete d'Or, Lyon: a, Red flowers. b, White flowers.

2007, Apr. 28 *Perf. 13¼x13*

3316	Sheet of 2	11.50	11.50
a.-b.	A1660 €2.11 Either single	5.75	3.00

Salon du Timbre. No. 3316 has four vertical rows of rouletting, separating sheet into fifths, with the two stamps in the central fifth.

Vacations A1850

Designs: No. 3317, Wooden fence and red hollyhocks. No. 3318, Angelfish. No. 3319, Blue flowers. No. 3320, Blueberries. No. 3321, Canoes. No. 3322, Dyed wool hanging on rods. No. 3323, Glacier. No. 3324, Palm tree. No. 3325, Beach umbrellas and woman. No. 3326, Boxes of color pigments.

Serpentine Die Cut 11¼x11
2007, Apr. 28 Litho.
Booklet Stamps
Self-Adhesive

3317	A1850 (54c) multi	1.50	.50
3318	A1850 (54c) multi	1.50	.50
3319	A1850 (54c) multi	1.50	.50
3320	A1850 (54c) multi	1.50	.50
3321	A1850 (54c) multi	1.50	.50
3322	A1850 (54c) multi	1.50	.50
3323	A1850 (54c) multi	1.50	.50
3324	A1850 (54c) multi	1.50	.50
3325	A1850 (54c) multi	1.50	.50
3326	A1850 (54c) multi	1.50	.50
a.	Booklet pane of 10, #3317-3326	15.00	

Europa A1851

2007, May 1 Photo. *Perf. 13¼*

3327 A1851 60c multi 1.75 .60

Scouting, cent.

Intl. Sailing Federation, Cent. — A1852

Illustration reduced.

2007, May 4 *Perf. 13*

3328 A1852 85c multi 2.40 .80

A souvenir sheet containing No. 3328 sold for €3.

Tintin and Snowy — A1853

Characters from Tintin comic strips and books, by Hergé: No. 3330, Professor Calculus (Tournesol). No. 3331, Captain Haddock. No. 3332, Thomson and Thompson (Dupondt). No. 3333, Bianca Castafiore. No. 3334, Chang (Tchang).

2007, May 12

3329	A1853 54c multi	1.50	.50
3330	A1853 54c multi	1.50	.50
3331	A1853 54c multi	1.50	.50
3332	A1853 54c multi	1.50	.50
3333	A1853 54c multi	1.50	.50
3334	A1853 54c multi	1.50	.50
a.	Souvenir sheet, #3329-3334	13.50	13.50

No. 3334a sold for €5, with the Red Cross receiving €1.76 of that.

Religious Art — A1854

Designs: 54c, Nativity, 15th cent. miniature, from Armenia. 85c, The Smile of Reims.

2007, May 22 *Perf. 13¼*

3335	A1854 54c multi	1.50	.50
3336	A1854 85c multi	2.40	.80

See Armenia Nos. 749-750.

Inauguration of Eastern France TGV Train Service — A1855

2007, June 9 *Perf. 13*

3337 A1855 54c multi 1.50 .50

French Federation of Philatelic Associations 80th Congress, Poitiers — A1856

Illustration reduced.

2007, June 15 Engr. *Perf. 13x13¼*

3338 A1856 54c multi + label 1.50 .50

Miniature Sheet

2007 Rugby World Cup, France — A1857

No. 3339 — Inscriptions: a, Touche (Throw-in, 30x39mm elliptical). b, Melée (scrum). c, Attaque (player running with ball). d, Essai (try). e, Transformation (kick, 30x39mm elliptical). f, Passe (pass). g, Raffut (stiff-arm). h, Haka (dance). i, Plaquage (tackle). j, Supporteurs (fans).

2007, June 23 *Perf. 13x13¼*

3339	A1857	Sheet of 10	15.00	15.00
a.-j.		54c Any single	1.50	.50

European Capitals Type of 2002
Souvenir Sheet

No. 3340 — Attractions in Brussels: a, Maison du Roi (Royal Palace). b, Hotel de Ville (City Hall), vert. c, Mannekin Pis, vert. d, Atomium.

Perf. 13x13¼, 13¼x13 (vert. stamps)
2007, June 30

3340	A1622	Sheet of 4	6.00	6.00
a.-d.		54c Any single	1.50	.50

Association of French Mayors, Cent. — A1858

2007, July 5 Photo. *Perf. 13¼*

3341 A1858 54c multi 1.50 .50

Pierre Pfimlin (1907-2000), Mayor of Strasbourg
A1859

2007, July 7 Photo. *Perf. 13¼*
3342 A1859 60c multi 1.75 .60

2007 Rugby World Cup, France
A1860

Litho. With Three-Dimensional Plastic Affixed
2007, Sept. 5 *Serpentine Die Cut 11*
Self-Adhesive
3343 A1860 €3 multi 8.25 4.25

Happy Birthday
A1861

2007, Sept. 8 Photo. *Perf. 13x13¼*
3344 A1861 (54c) multi 1.60 .55
a. Litho., with attached label 2.40 2.40

No. 3344 was printed in a sheet of 5; No. 3344a was printed in a sheet of 5 + 5 labels that sold for €4.20.

Gift Boxes — A1862

Boxes and: Nos. 3345a, 3346, Butterflies. Nos. 3345b, 3348, Flowers. Nos. 3345c, 3347, Hearts. Nos. 3345d, 3350, Musical notes. Nos. 3345e, 3349, Bubbles.

2007, Sept. 8 Litho. *Perf. 13¼*
3345 Sheet of 5 + 5 labels 12.00 12.00
a.-e. A1862 (54c) Any single + label 2.40 2.40

Self-Adhesive
Booklet Stamps
Serpentine Die Cut 11

3346 A1862 (54c) multi 1.60 .55
3347 A1862 (54c) multi 1.60 .55
3348 A1862 (54c) multi 1.60 .55
3349 A1862 (54c) multi 1.60 .55
3350 A1862 (54c) multi 1.60 .55
a. Booklet pane of 5 #3346-3350 8.00

No. 3345 sold for €4.20.

Sully Prudhomme (1839-1907), Poet — A1863

2007, Sept. 15 Engr. *Perf. 13¼*
3351 A1863 €1.30 multi 3.75 1.25

A1864

A1865

A1866

A1867

Cows
A1868

Serpentine Die Cut 11
2007, Sept. 20 Litho.
Self-Adhesive
Booklet Stamps

3352 A1864 (54c) multi 1.60 .55
3353 A1865 (54c) multi 1.60 .55
3354 A1866 (54c) multi 1.60 .55
3355 A1867 (54c) multi 1.60 .55
3356 A1868 (54c) multi 1.60 .55
a. Booklet pane, 2 each #3352-3356 16.00
Nos. 3352-3356 (5) 8.00 2.75

Aspects of Life in French Regions Type of 2003

No. 3357: a, Sèvres porcelain. b, Grasse perfume. c, Christmas market. d, Marseille soap. e, Giants, vert. f, Basque beret, vert. g, Aubusson tapestries. h, Lyonnaise tavern. i, Slipper, vert. j, Canteloupe, vert.

2007, Sept. 29 Photo. *Perf. 13*
3357 Sheet of 10 16.00 16.00
a.-j. A1642 54c Any single 1.60 .55

No. 3357 has three vertical rows of rouletting separating sheet into quarters.

Nos. 3357a-3357j were also issued in large booklets containing panes of 1 of each stamp. The booklet sold for €19.

Space Age, 50th Anniv. — A1869

2007, Oct. 4 *Perf. 13x12½*
3358 A1869 85c multi 2.40 .80

Medical Research Foundation, 60th Anniv. — A1870

2007, Oct. 20 *Perf. 13¼*
3359 A1870 54c multi 1.60 .55

Guy Moquet (1924-41), World War II Resistance Fighter — A1871

2007, Oct. 22 Engr.
3360 A1871 54c multi 1.60 .55

Dole
A1872

2007, Nov. 2
3361 A1872 54c multi 1.60 .55

Personalized Stamp With Country Name on Short Side — A1873

Personalized Stamp With Country Name on Long Side
A1874

Serpentine Die Cut 11¼ Syncopated
2007, Nov. Litho.
Self-Adhesive
Inscribed: "Lettre Prioritaire 20 g"

3362 A1873 (54c) multi 3.00 3.00
3363 A1874 (54c) multi 3.00 3.00

Inscribed: "Monde 20 g"

3364 A1873 (85c) multi 4.00 4.00
3365 A1874 (85c) multi 4.00 4.00

Inscribed: "Lettre Prioritaire 50 g"

3366 A1873 (86c) multi 4.00 4.00
3367 A1874 (86c) multi 4.00 4.00
Nos. 3362-3367 (6) 22.00 22.00

Nos. 3362-3367 were each printed in sheets of ten, having vignettes that could be personalized or chosen from a library of stock designs, two of which are shown on the illustrated stamps. Sheets of Nos. 3362 and 3363 each sold for €10.03, and sheets of Nos. 3364-3367 each sold for €13.38.

Jean-Baptiste Charcot (1867-1936), Polar Explorer
A1875

Ship Pourquoi-Pas? — A1876

2007, Nov. 8 Engr. *Perf. 13x12¾*
3368 A1875 54c multi 1.60 .55
3369 A1876 60c multi 1.75 .60
a. Horiz. pair, #3368-3369 3.50 1.25

See Greenland No. 505.

Marianne — A1877

Serpentine Die Cut 6¾ Vert.
2007, Nov. 8 Engr.
Self-Adhesive
Booklet Stamp

3370 A1877 54c red 1.60 .55
a. Booklet pane, 6 each #3083d, 3370 19.50

Miniature Sheet

Lighthouses — A1878

No. 3371: a, Cap Fréhel Lighthouse. b, Espiguette Lighthouse. c, D'ar-Men Lighthouse. d, Grand-Léjon Lighthouse. e, Porquerolles Lighthouse, horiz. f, Chassiron Lighthouse, horiz.

Litho. & Engr.
2007, Nov. 9 *Perf. 13*
3371 A1878 Sheet of 6 9.75 9.75
a.-f. 54c Any single 1.60 .55

2007 Women's World Handball Championships, France — A1879

2007, Nov. 10 Photo. *Perf. 13¼*
3372 A1879 54c multi 1.60 .55

Subject Index of French Commemorative Issues

FRANCE

SEMI-POSTAL STAMPS

No. 162 Surcharged in Red and:

No. B1

SP2

1914 Unwmk. Typo. *Perf. 14x13½*

B1	A22	10c + 5c red	5.00	4.25
		Never hinged	7.00	
B2	SP2	10c + 5c red	32.50	3.25
		Never hinged	70.00	
a.		Booklet pane of 10	600.00	
		Never hinged	800.00	

Issue dates: #B1, Aug. 11; #B2, Sept. 10.
For overprint see Offices in Morocco #B8.

Widow at Grave SP3

War Orphans SP4

Woman Plowing — SP5

"Trench of Bayonets" SP6

Lion of Belfort SP7

"La Marseillaise" — SP8

1917-19

B3	SP3	2c + 3c vio brn	4.50	5.00
		Never hinged	10.00	
B4	SP4	5c + 5c grn ('19)	19.00	9.00
		Never hinged	45.00	
B5	SP5	15c + 10c gray grn	30.00	27.50
		Never hinged	70.00	
B6	SP5	25c + 15c dp bl	77.50	57.50
		Never hinged	175.00	
B7	SP6	35c + 25c sl & vio	135.00	125.00
		Never hinged	350.00	
B8	SP7	50c + 50c pale brn & dk brn	225.00	180.00
		Never hinged	650.00	
B9	SP8	1fr + 1fr cl & mar	425.00	400.00
		Never hinged	1,100.	
B10	SP8	5fr + 5fr dp bl & blk	1,550.	1,450.
		Never hinged	3,500.	
		Nos. B3-B10 (8)	2,466.	2,254.

See #B20-B23. For surcharges see #B12-B19.

Hospital Ship and Field Hospital SP9

1918, Aug.

B11	SP9	15c + 5c sl & red	125.00	60.00
		Never hinged	250.00	

Semi-Postal Stamps of 1917-19 Surcharged

1922, Sept. 1

B12	SP3	2c + 1c violet brn	.50	.80
		Never hinged	1.00	
B13	SP4	5c + 2½c green	.80	1.25
		Never hinged	1.50	
B14	SP5	15c + 5c gray grn	1.25	1.60
		Never hinged	2.60	
B15	SP5	25c + 5c deep bl	2.30	2.50
		Never hinged	4.75	
B16	SP6	35c + 5c sl & vio	13.00	15.00
		Never hinged	30.00	
B17	SP7	50c + 10c pale brn & dk brn	19.00	24.00
		Never hinged	39.00	
a.		Pair, one without surcharge		
B18	SP8	1fr + 25c cl & mar	32.50	37.50
		Never hinged	60.00	
B19	SP8	5fr + 1fr bl & blk	150.00	155.00
		Never hinged	275.00	
		Nos. B12-B19 (8)	219.35	237.65
		Set, never hinged	415.00	

Style and arrangement of surcharge differs for each denomination.

Types of 1917-19

1926-27

B20	SP3	2c + 1c violet brn	1.50	1.40
		Never hinged	3.25	
B21	SP7	50c + 10c ol brn & dk brn	20.00	12.50
		Never hinged	50.00	
B22	SP8	1fr + 25c dp rose & red brn	55.00	42.50
		Never hinged	130.00	
B23	SP8	5fr + 1fr sl bl & blk	105.00	100.00
		Never hinged	240.00	
		Nos. B20-B23 (4)	181.50	156.40

Sinking Fund Issues

Types of Regular Issues of 1903-07 Surcharged in Red or Blue

1927, Sept. 26

B24	A22	40c + 10c lt blue (R)	5.75	5.75
		Never hinged	10.50	
B25	A20	50c + 25c green (Bl)	8.25	9.00
		Never hinged	14.00	

Surcharge on #B25 differs from illustration.

Type of Regular Issue of 1923 Surcharged in Black

B26	A23	1.50fr + 50c orange	14.50	14.00
		Never hinged	37.50	
		Nos. B24-B26 (3)	28.50	28.75

See Nos. B28-B33, B35-B37, B39-B41.

Industry and Agriculture SP10

1928, May **Engr.** *Perf. 13½*

B27	SP10	1.50fr + 8.50fr dull blue	130.00	150.00
		Never hinged	200.00	
a.		Blue green	510.00	550.00
		Never hinged	725.00	

Types of 1903-23 Issues Surcharged like Nos. B24-B26

1928, Oct. 1 *Perf. 14x13½*

B28	A22	40c + 10c gray lilac (R)	13.00	14.00
		Never hinged	32.50	
B29	A20	50c + 25c orange brn (Bl)	32.50	29.00
		Never hinged	60.00	
B30	A23	1.50fr + 50c rose lilac (Bk)	52.50	42.50
		Never hinged	100.00	
		Nos. B28-B30 (3)	98.00	85.50

Types of 1903-23 Issues Surcharged like Nos. B24-B26

1929, Oct. 1

B31	A22	40c + 10c green	18.00	19.00
		Never hinged	37.50	
B32	A20	50c + 25c lil rose	30.00	30.00
		Never hinged	60.00	
B33	A23	1.50fr + 50c chestnut	60.00	65.00
		Never hinged	130.00	
		Nos. B31-B33 (3)	108.00	114.00

"The Smile of Reims" SP11

1930, Mar. 15 **Engr.** *Perf. 13*

B34	SP11	1.50fr + 3.50fr red vio	75.00	82.50
		Never hinged	130.00	
a.		Booklet pane of 4	300.00	
		Never hinged	525.00	
b.		Booklet pane of 8	600.00	
		Never hinged	1,050.	

Booklets containing No. B34 have two panes of 4 (#B34a) connected by a gutter, the complete piece constituting #B34b, which is stapled into the booklet through the gutter.

Types of 1903-07 Issues Surcharged like Nos. B24-B25

1930 Oct. 1 *Perf. 14x13½*

B35	A22	40c + 10c cerise	20.00	21.00
		Never hinged	70.00	
B36	A20	50c + 25c gray brown	37.50	42.50
		Never hinged	120.00	
B37	A22	1.50fr + 50c violet	65.00	70.00
		Never hinged	190.00	
		Nos. B35-B37 (3)	122.50	133.50

Allegory, French Provinces SP12

1931, Mar. 1 *Perf. 13*

B38	SP12	1.50fr + 3.50fr grn	125.00	140.00
		Never hinged	300.00	

Types of 1903-07 Issues Surcharged like Nos. B24-B25

1931, Oct. 1 *Perf. 14x13½*

B39	A22	40c + 10c ol grn	40.00	45.00
		Never hinged	90.00	
B40	A20	50c + 25c gray vio	100.00	110.00
		Never hinged	190.00	
B41	A22	1.50fr + 50c deep red	100.00	110.00
		Never hinged	175.00	
		Nos. B39-B41 (3)	240.00	265.00

> Catalogue values for unused stamps in this section, from this point to the end of the section, are for Never Hinged items.

"France" Giving Aid to an Intellectual SP13

Symbolic of Music SP14

1935, Dec. 9 **Engr.** *Perf. 13*

B42	SP13	50c + 10c ultra	4.00	2.50
B43	SP14	50c + 2fr dull red	125.00	45.00

The surtax was for the aid of distressed and exiled intellectuals.
For surcharge see No. B47.

Statue of Liberty SP15

Children of the Unemployed SP16

1936-37

B44	SP15	50c + 25c dk blue ('37)	7.50	5.00
B45	SP15	75c + 50c violet	20.00	10.00

Surtax for the aid of political refugees.
For surcharge see No. B47.

1936, May

B46	SP16	50c + 10c copper red	7.50	5.00

The surtax was for the aid of children of the unemployed.

No. B43 Surcharged in Black

1936, Nov.

B47	SP14	20c on 50c + 2fr dull red	4.00	3.00

Jacques Callot SP17

Anatole France (Jacques Anatole Thibault) — SP18

Hector Berlioz SP19

Victor Hugo SP20

Auguste Rodin SP21

Louis Pasteur SP22

1936-37   **Engr.**
B48 SP17 20c + 10c brown
              car   4.50   2.50
B49 SP18 30c + 10c emer
              ('37)   5.00   2.75
B50 SP19 40c + 10c emer   4.50   2.75
B51 SP20 50c + 10c copper
              red   6.50   3.75
B52 SP21 90c + 10c rose
              red ('37)   13.00   6.50
B53 SP22 1.50fr + 50c deep
              ultra   37.50   20.00
     Nos. B48-B53 (6)   71.00   38.25

The surtax was used for relief of unemployed intellectuals.

1938
B54 SP18 30c +10c brn car   3.00   1.75
B55 SP17 35c +10c dull grn   3.50   2.40
B56 SP19 55c +10c dull vio   10.00   4.00
B57 SP20 65c +10c ultra   11.50   4.00
B58 SP21 1fr +10c car lake   8.50   4.50
B59 SP22 1.75fr + 25c dp blue   35.00   17.00
     Nos. B54-B59 (6)   71.50   33.65

Tug of War
SP23

Foot Race
SP24

Hiking — SP25

1937, June 16
B60 SP23 20c + 10c brown   3.00   2.25
B61 SP24 40c + 10c red brown   3.00   2.25
B62 SP25 50c + 10c black brn   3.00   2.25
     Nos. B60-B62 (3)   9.00   6.75

The surtax was for the Recreation Fund of the employees of the Post, Telephone and Telegraph.

Pierre Loti
(Louis
Marie Julien
Viaud)
SP26

1937, Aug.
B63 SP26 50c + 20c rose car   7.50   5.00
The surtax was for the Pierre Loti Monument Fund.

"France"
and Infant
SP27

1937-39
B64 SP27 65c + 25c brown vio   5.25   2.75
B65 SP27 90c + 30c pck bl ('39) 3.50   2.75
The surtax was used for public health work.

Winged Victory   Jean Baptiste
of Samothrace   Charcot
SP28   SP29

1937, Aug.
B66 SP28 30c blue green   175.00   40.00
B67 SP28 55c red   175.00   40.00
     Set, hinged   130.00

On sale at the Louvre for 2.50fr. The surtax of 1.65fr was for the benefit of the Louvre Museum.

1938-39
B68 SP29 65c + 35c dk bl grn   3.25   3.25
B69 SP29 90c + 35c brt red
              vio ('39)   37.50   19.00
Surtax for the benefit of French seamen.

Palace of
Versailles
SP30

1938, May 9
B70 SP30 1.75fr + 75c dp bl   37.50   19.00
Natl. Exposition of Painting and Sculpture at Versailles.
The surtax was for the benefit of the Versailles Concert Society.

French Soldier   Monument
SP31   SP32

1938, May 16
B71 SP31 55c + 70c brown vio   8.50   5.25
B72 SP31 65c + 1.10fr pck bl   8.50   5.25
The surtax was for a fund to erect a monument to the glory of the French Infantrymen.

1938, May 25
B73 SP32 55c + 45c vermilion   22.50   12.50
The surtax was for a fund to erect a monument in honor of the Army Medical Corps.

Reims Cathedral   "France"
SP33   Welcoming Her
                          Sons
                          SP34

1938, July 10
B74 SP33 65c + 35c ultra   17.50   10.50
Completion of the reconstruction of Reims Cathedral, July 10, 1938.

1938, Aug. 8
B75 SP34 65c + 60c rose car   8.50   5.75
The surtax was for the benefit of French volunteers repatriated from Spain.

Curie Issue
Common Design Type
1938, Sept. 1
B76 CD80 1.75fr + 50c dp ultra 21.00   12.50

Victory
Parade
Passing Arc
de
Triomphe
SP36

1938, Oct. 8
B77 SP36 65c + 35c brown car   5.75   4.50
20th anniversary of the Armistice.

Student and
Nurse — SP37

1938, Dec. 1
B78 SP37 65c + 60c pck blue   15.00   8.25
The surtax was for Student Relief.

Blind Man
and Radio
SP38

1938, Dec.
B79 SP38 90c + 25c brown vio   15.00   9.00
The surtax was used to help provide radios for the blind.

Civilian Facing   Red Cross
Firing   Nurse — SP40
Squad — SP39

1939, Feb. 1
B80 SP39 90c + 35c black brn   17.00   10.50
The surtax was used to erect a monument to civilian victims of World War I.

1939, Mar. 24
B81 SP40 90c + 35c dk sl grn,
             turq bl & red   13.00   8.25
75th anniv. of the Intl. Red Cross Soc.

Army
Engineer
SP41

1939, Apr. 3
B82 SP41 70c + 50c vermilion   12.50   8.25
Army Engineering Corps. The surtax was used to erect a monument to those members who died in World War I.

Ministry of
Post,
Telegraph
and
Telephone
SP42

1939, Apr. 8
B83 SP42 90c + 35c turq blue   37.50   20.00
The surtax was used to aid orphans of employees of the postal system. Opening of the new building for the Ministry of Post, Telegraph and Telephones.

Mother and   Eiffel
Child — SP43   Tower — SP44

1939, Apr. 24
B84 SP43 90c + 35c red   3.75   2.50
The surtax was used to aid children of the unemployed.

1939, May 5
B85 SP44 50c + 50c red violet   15.00   9.00
50th anniv. of the Eiffel Tower. The surtax was used for celebration festivities.

Puvis de
Chavannes — SP45

Claude
Debussy
SP46

Honoré de
Balzac
SP47

Claude
Bernard
SP48

1939-40
B86   SP45 40c + 10c ver   1.75   1.00
B87   SP46 70c + 10c brn
             vio   8.25   2.50
B87A SP46 80c + 10c brn
             vio ('40)   9.00   7.50
B88   SP47 90c + 10c brt
             red vio   7.25   2.50
B88A SP47 1fr + 10c brt
             red vio
             ('40)   9.00   7.50
B89   SP48 2.25fr + 25c brt
             ultra   28.00   11.50
B89A SP48 2.50fr + 25c brt
             ultra ('40)   9.00   7.50
     Nos. B86-B89A (7)   72.25   40.00

The surtax was used to aid unemployed intellectuals.

Mothers and Children
SP49   SP50

1939, June 15
B90 SP49 70c + 80c bl, grn & vio   5.25 4.50
B91 SP50 90c + 60c dk brn, dl vio & brn   8.50 5.25

The surtax was used to aid France's repopulation campaign.

"The Letter" by Jean Honoré Fragonard SP51

Statue of Widow and Children SP52

1939, July 6
B92 SP51 40c + 60c brn, sep & pur   4.25 2.75

The surtax was used for the Postal Museum.

1939, July 20
B93 SP52 70c + 30c brown vio 25.00 12.00

Surtax for the benefit of French seamen.

French Soldier SP53

Colonial Trooper SP54

1940, Feb. 15
B94 SP53 40c + 60c sepia   3.75 2.75
B95 SP54 1fr + 50c turq blue   3.75 2.75

The surtax was used to assist the families of mobilized men.

World Map Showing French Possessions — SP55

1940, Apr. 15
B96 SP55 1fr + 25c scarlet   2.75 2.75

Marshal Joseph J. C. Joffre SP56

Marshal Ferdinand Foch — SP57

Gen. Joseph S. Gallieni SP58

Woman Plowing SP59

1940, May 1
B97 SP56 80c + 45c choc   8.25 6.00
B98 SP57 1fr + 50c dk vio   7.50 6.00
B99 SP58 1.50fr + 50c brn red   7.50 4.00
B100 SP59 2.50fr + 50c indigo & dl bl   15.00 11.50
Nos. B97-B100 (4)   38.25 27.50

The surtax was used for war charities.

Doctor, Nurse, Soldier and Family SP60

Nurse and Wounded Soldier SP61

1940, May 12
B101 SP60 80c + 1fr dk grn & red   8.25 6.00
B102 SP61 1fr + 2fr sep & red   11.50 6.50

The surtax was used for the Red Cross.

Nurse with Injured Children — SP62

1940, Nov. 12
B103 SP62 1fr + 2fr sepia   1.25 .80

The surtax was used for victims of the war.

Wheat Harvest SP63

Sowing SP64

Picking Grapes SP65

Grazing Cattle SP66

1940, Dec. 2
B104 SP63 80c + 2fr brn blk   3.25 2.10
B105 SP64 1fr + 2fr chestnut   3.25 2.10
B106 SP65 1.50fr + 2fr brt vio   3.25 2.10
B107 SP66 2.50fr + 2fr dp grn   4.00 2.25
Nos. B104-B107 (4)   13.75 8.55

The surtax was for national relief.

Prisoners of War
SP67   SP68

1941, Jan. 1
B108 SP67 80c + 5fr dark grn   1.60 1.50
B109 SP68 1fr + 5fr rose brn   1.75 1.60

The surtax was for prisoners of war.

Science Fighting Cancer SP69

1941, Feb. 20
B110 SP69 2.50fr + 50c slate blk & brn   1.60 1.40

Surtax used for the control of cancer.

Type of 1941 Surcharged "+10c" in Blue

1941, Mar. 4
B111 A109 1fr + 10c crimson   .25 .20

Men Hauling Coal SP70

"France" Aiding Needy Man SP71

1941
B112 SP70 1fr + 2fr sepia   2.75 1.40
B113 SP71 2.50fr + 7.50fr dk bl   9.00 3.00

The surtax was for Marshal Pétain's National Relief Fund.

Liner Pasteur SP72

Red Surcharge
1941, July 17
B114 SP72 1fr + 1fr on 70c dk bl grn   .40 .40

World Map, Mercator Projection SP73

1941
B115 SP73 1fr + 1fr multi   .80 .50

Fisherman — SP74

1941, Oct. 23
B116 SP74 1fr + 9fr dk blue grn 1.00 .90

Surtax for benefit of French seamen.

Arms of Various Cities

Nancy SP75   Lille SP76

Rouen SP77   Bordeaux SP78

Toulouse SP79   Clermont-Ferrand SP80

Marseille SP81   Lyon SP82

Rennes SP83   Reims SP84

Montpellier SP85   Paris SP86

1941   **Perf. 14x13**

B117	SP75	20c + 30c brn blk	2.75 2.75
B118	SP76	40c + 60c org brn	2.75 2.75
B119	SP77	50c + 70c grnsh blue	2.75 2.75
B120	SP78	70c + 80c rose vio	2.75 2.75
B121	SP79	80c + 1fr dp rose	2.75 2.75
B122	SP80	1fr + 1fr black	2.75 2.75
B123	SP81	1.50fr + 2fr dk bl	2.75 2.75
B124	SP82	2fr + 2fr dk vio	2.75 2.75
B125	SP83	2.50fr + 3fr brt grn	2.75 2.75
B126	SP84	3fr + 5fr org brn	2.75 2.75
B127	SP85	5fr + 6fr brt ultra	2.75 2.75
B128	SP86	10fr + 10fr dk red	2.75 2.75
	Nos. B117-B128 (12)		33.00 33.00

Count de
La Pérouse
SP87

1942, Mar. 23   **Perf. 13**

B129 SP87 2.50fr + 7.50fr ultra   1.50 1.50

Jean Francois de Galaup de La Pérouse, (1741-88), French navigator and explorer. The surtax was for National Relief.

Planes over
Fields
SP88

1942, Apr. 4

B130 SP88 1.50fr + 3.50fr lt vio   2.40 2.40

The surtax was for the benefit of French airmen and their familes.

Alexis
Chabrier
SP89

1942, May 18

B131 SP89 2fr + 3fr sepia   1.25 1.25

Emmanuel Chabrier (1841-1894), composer, birth centenary. The surtax was for works of charity among musicians.

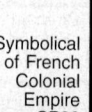

Symbolical
of French
Colonial
Empire
SP90

1942, May 18

B132 SP90 1.50fr + 8.50fr black   1.10 1.10

The surtax was for National Relief.

Jean de
Vienne
SP91

1942, June 16

B133 SP91 1.50fr + 8.50fr sepia   1.10 1.10

600th anniv. of the birth of Jean de Vienne, 1st admiral of France. The surtax was for the benefit of French seamen.

Type of Regular Issue,
1941 Surcharged in
Carmine

1942, Sept. 10   **Perf. 14x13½**

B134 A116 1.50fr + 50c brt ultra   .20 .20

The surtax was for national relief ("Secours National").

Arms of Various Cities

Chambéry   La Rochelle
SP92   SP93

Poitiers   Orléans
SP94   SP95

Grenoble   Angers
SP96   SP97

Dijon   Limoges
SP98   SP99

Le Havre   Nantes
SP100   SP101

Nice   St. Etienne
SP102   SP103

Perf. 14x13

1942, Oct.   **Unwmk.**   **Engr.**

B135	SP92	50c + 60c blk	3.50	3.50
B136	SP93	60c + 70c grnsh blue	3.50	3.50
B137	SP94	80c + 1fr rose	3.50	3.50
B138	SP95	1fr + 1.30fr dk green	3.50	3.50
B139	SP96	1.20fr + 1.50fr rose vio	3.50	3.50
B140	SP97	1.50fr + 1.80fr slate bl	3.50	3.50
B141	SP98	2fr + 2.30fr deep rose	3.50	3.50
B142	SP99	2.40fr + 2.80fr slate grn	3.50	3.50
B143	SP100	3fr + 3.50fr dp violet	3.50	3.50
B144	SP101	4fr + 5fr lt ultra	3.50	3.50
B145	SP102	4.50fr + 6fr red	3.50	3.50
B146	SP103	5fr + 7fr brt red vio	3.50	3.50
	Nos. B135-B146 (12)		42.00	42.00

The surtax was for national relief.

Tricolor
Legion
SP104

1942, Oct. 12   **Perf. 13**

B147	SP104	1.20 + 8.80fr dk blue	10.00 10.00
a.		Vert. pair, #B147, B148 + albino impression	22.50 25.00
B148	SP104	1.20 + 8.80fr crim	10.00 10.00

These stamps were printed in sheets of 20 stamps and 5 albino impressions arranged: 2 horizontal rows of 5 dark blue stamps, 1 row of 5 albino impressions, and 2 rows of 5 crimson stamps.

Marshal Henri Philippe Pétain
SP105   SP106

1943, Feb. 8

B149	SP105	1fr + 10fr rose red	2.75 2.75
B150	SP105	1fr + 10fr blue	2.75 2.75
B151	SP106	2fr + 12fr rose red	2.75 2.75
B152	SP106	2fr + 12fr blue	2.75 2.75
a.		Strip, #B149-B152 + label	12.50 12.50

The surtax was for national relief. Printed in sheets of 20, the 10 blue stamps at left, the 10 rose red at right, separated by a vert. row of 5 white labels bearing a tri-colored battle-ax.

Marshal   "Work" — SP108
Pétain — SP107

"Family"   "State"
SP109   SP110

Marshal
Pétain — SP111

1943, June 7

B153	SP107	1.20fr + 1.40fr dull vio	15.00 15.00
B154	SP108	1.50fr + 2.50fr red	15.00 15.00
B155	SP109	2.40fr + 7fr brown	15.00 15.00
B156	SP110	4fr + 10fr dk violet	15.00 15.00
B157	SP111	5fr + 15fr red brown	15.00 15.00
a.		Strip of 5, #B153-B157	110.00 110.00

Pétain's 87th birthday.

The surtax was for national relief.

Civilians Under   Civilians Doing
Air   Farm
Attack — SP112   Work — SP113

Prisoner's
Family
Doing Farm
Work
SP114

1943, Aug. 23

B158 SP112 1.50fr + 3.50fr black   .50 .50

Surtax was for bomb victims at Billancourt, Dunkirk, Lorient, Saint-Nazaire.

1943, Sept. 27

B159	SP113	1.50fr + 8.50fr sepia	.90 .90
B160	SP114	2.40fr + 7.60fr dk grn	1.00 1.00

The surtax was for families of war prisoners.

Michel de   Picardy Costume
Montaigne   SP121
SP115

1.20fr+1.50fr, Francois Clouet. 1.50fr+3fr, Ambrose Paré. 2.40fr+4fr, Chevalier Pierre de Bayard. 4fr+6fr, Duke of Sully. 5fr+10fr, Henri IV.

1943, Oct. 2

B161	SP115	60c + 80c Prus green	2.00 2.00
B162	SP115	1.20fr + 1.50fr black	2.00 2.00
B163	SP115	1.50fr + 3fr deep ultra	2.00 2.00
B164	SP115	2.40fr + 4fr red	2.00 2.00
B165	SP115	4fr + 6fr dull brn red	2.00 2.00
B166	SP115	5fr + 10fr dull green	2.00 2.00
	Nos. B161-B166 (6)		12.00 12.00

The surtax was for national relief. Issued to honor famous 16th century Frenchmen.

1943, Dec. 27

Designs: 18th Century Costumes: 1.20fr+2fr, Brittany. 1.50fr+4fr, Ile de France. 2.40fr+5fr, Burgundy. 4fr+6fr, Auvergne. 5fr+7fr, Provence.

B167	SP121	60c + 1.30fr sepia	2.00 2.00
B168	SP121	1.20fr + 2fr lt vio	2.00 2.00
B169	SP121	1.50fr + 4fr turq blue	2.00 2.00
B170	SP121	2.40fr + 5fr rose car	2.00 2.00
B171	SP121	4fr + 6fr chlky blue	3.00 3.00
B172	SP121	5fr + 7fr red	3.00 3.00
	Nos. B167-B172 (6)		14.00 14.00

The surtax was for national relief.

Admiral Tourville
SP127

Charles
Gounod
SP128

1944, Feb. 21
B173 SP127 4fr + 6fr dull red brn .75 .75
   300th anniv. of the birth of Admiral Anne-Hilarion de Cotentin Tourville (1642-1701).

1944, Mar. 27   Perf. 14x13
B174 SP128 1.50fr + 3.50fr sepia 1.00 .80
   50th anniv. of the death of Charles Gounod, composer (1818-1893).

Marshal
Pétain
SP129

Farming
SP130

Industry
SP131

1944, Apr. 24   Perf. 13
B175 SP129 1.50fr + 3.50fr sepia 3.50 3.50
B176 SP130 2fr + 3fr dp ultra .60 .60
B177 SP131 4fr + 6fr rose red .60 .60
   Nos. B175-B177 (3)   4.70 4.70
   Marshal Henri Pétain's 88th birthday.

Modern
Streamliner, 19th
Cent. Train
SP132

Molière (Jean-Baptiste
Poquelin)
SP133

1944, Aug. 14
B178 SP132 4fr + 6fr black   2.10 1.90
   Centenary of the Paris-Rouen, Paris-Orléans railroad.

1944, July 31
   Designs: 80c+2.20fr, Jules Hardouin Mansart. 1.20fr+2.80fr, Blaise Pascal. 1.50fr+3.50fr, Louis II of Bourbon. 2fr+4fr, Jean-Baptiste Colbert. 4fr+6fr, Louis XIV.
B179 SP133 50c + 1.50fr rose
                    car   1.50 1.50
B180 SP133 80c + 2.20fr dk
                    green   1.50 1.50
B181 SP133 1.20fr + 2.80fr black 1.50 1.50

B182 SP133 1.50fr + 3.50fr brt
                    ultra   1.50 1.50
B183 SP133 2fr + 4fr dull brn
                    red   1.50 1.50
B184 SP133 4fr + 6fr red   1.50 1.50
   Nos. B179-B184 (6)   9.00 9.00
   Noted 17th century Frenchmen.

Angoulême
SP139

Chartres
SP140

Amiens
SP141

Beauvais
SP142

Albi — SP143

1944, Nov. 20
B185 SP139 50c + 1.50fr black .60 .60
B186 SP140 80c + 2.20fr rose
                    vio   .60 .60
B187 SP141 1.20fr + 2.80fr brn
                    car   .60 .60
B188 SP142 1.50fr + 3.50fr dp
                    blue   .60 .60
B189 SP143 4fr + 6fr orange
                    red   .60 .60
   Nos. B185-B189 (5)   3.00 3.00
   French Cathedrals.

Coat of Arms of
Renouard de
Villayer
SP144

Sarah Bernhardt
SP145

1944, Dec. 9   Engr.
B190 SP144 1.50fr + 3.50fr dp brn .25 .25
   Stamp Day.

1945, May 16   Unwmk.   Perf. 13
B191 SP145 4fr + 1fr dk violet brn .30 .30
   100th anniv. of the birth of Sarah Bernhardt, actress.

War
Victims
SP146

1945, May 16
B192 SP146 4fr + 6fr dk violet brn .20 .20
   The surtax was for war victims of the P.T.T.

Tuberculosis
Patient — SP147

1945, May 16 Typo. Perf. 14x13½
B193 SP147 2fr + 1fr red orange .20 .20
   Surtax for the aid of tuberculosis victims.
   For surcharge see No. 561.

Boy and Girl
SP148

Burning of
Oradour Church
SP149

1945, July 9   Engr.   Perf. 13
B194 SP148 4fr + 2fr Prus green .20 .20
   The surtax was used for child welfare.

1945, Oct. 13
B195 SP149 4fr + 2fr sepia   .20 .20
   Destruction of Oradour, June, 1944.

Louis XI
and Post
Rider
SP150

1945, Oct. 13
B196 SP150 2fr + 3fr deep ultra .40 .40
   Stamp Day.
   For overprint see French West Africa #B2.

Ruins of
Dunkirk
SP151

Ruins of
Rouen
SP152

Ruins of
Caen
SP153

Ruins of
Saint-Malo
SP154

1945, Nov. 5
B197 SP151 1.50fr + 1.50fr red
                    brown   .40 .40
B198 SP152 2fr + 2fr violet   .50 .50
B199 SP153 2.40fr + 2.60fr blue   .50 .50
B200 SP154 4fr + 4fr black   .60 .60
   Nos. B197-B200 (4)   2.00 2.00
   The surtax was to aid the suffering residents of Dunkirk, Rouen, Caen and Saint Malo.

Alfred Fournier
SP155

Henri Becquerel
SP156

1946, Feb. 4   Engr.   Perf. 13
B201 SP155 2fr + 3fr red brown   .30 .30
B202 SP156 2fr + 3fr violet   .30 .30
   Issued to raise funds for the fight against venereal disease (#B201) and for the struggle against cancer (#B202).
   No. B202 for the 50th anniv. of the discovery of radioactivity by Henri Becquerel.
   See No. B221.

Church of the
Invalides,
Paris — SP157

1946, Mar. 11
B203 SP157 4fr + 6fr red brown   .40 .40
   The surtax was to aid disabled war veterans.

French
Warships
SP158

1946, Apr. 8
B204 SP158 2fr + 3fr gray black .65 .65
   The surtax was for naval charities.

"The Letter" by
Jean Siméon
Chardin
SP159

Fouquet de la
Varane
SP160

1946, May 25
B205 SP159 2fr + 3fr brown red   .50 .50
   The surtax was used for the Postal Museum.

1946, June 29
B206 SP160 3fr + 2fr sepia   .50 .50
   Stamp Day.

François
Villon — SP161

Designs: 3fr+1fr, Jean Fouquet. 4fr+3fr, Philippe de Commynes. 5fr+4fr, Joan of Arc. 6fr+5fr, Jean de Gerson. 10fr+6fr, Charles VII.

1946, Oct. 28

B207	SP161	2fr + 1fr dk Prus grn	1.50	1.50
B208	SP161	3fr + 1fr dk blue vio	1.50	1.50
B209	SP161	4fr + 3fr henna brn	1.50	1.50
B210	SP161	5fr + 4fr ultra	1.50	1.50
B211	SP161	6fr + 5fr sepia	1.50	1.50
B212	SP161	10fr + 6fr red	1.50	1.50
		Nos. B207-B212 (6)	9.00	9.00

Church of St. Sernin, Toulouse SP167

Notre Dame du Port, Clermont-Ferrand SP168

Cathedral of St. Front, Perigueux SP169

Cathedral of St. Julien, Le Mans SP170

Cathedral of Notre Dame, Paris SP171

François Michel le Tellier de Louvois SP172

1947 Engr.

B213	SP167	1fr + 1fr car rose	1.10	1.10
B214	SP168	3fr + 2fr dk bl vio	3.00	3.00
B215	SP169	4fr + 3fr henna brn	1.10	1.10
B216	SP170	6fr + 4fr dp bl	1.10	1.10
B217	SP171	10fr + 6fr dk gray grn	3.00	3.00
		Nos. B213-B217 (5)	9.30	9.30

1947, Mar. 15

B218	SP172	4.50fr + 5.50fr car rose	1.50	1.50

Stamp Day, Mar. 15, 1947.

Submarine Pens, Shipyard and Monument SP173

1947, Aug. 2

B219	SP173	6fr + 4fr bluish black	.60	.60

British commando raid on the Nazi U-boat base at St. Nazaire, 1942.

Liberty Highway Marker — SP174

Louis Braille — SP175

1947, Sept. 5

B220	SP174	6fr + 4fr dk green	1.00	1.00

The surtax was to help defray maintenance costs of the Liberty Highway.

Fournier Type of 1946

1947, Oct. 20

B221	SP155	2fr + 3fr indigo	.40	.40

1948, Jan. 19

B222	SP175	6fr + 4fr purple	.40	.40

Etienne Arago SP176

Alphonse de Lamartine SP177

1948, Mar. 6

B223	SP176	6fr + 4fr black brn	.50	.50

Stamp Day, March 6-7, 1948.

1948, Apr. 5 Engr. Perf. 13

Designs: 3fr+2fr, Alexandre A. Ledru-Rollin. 4fr+3fr, Louis Blanc. 5fr+4fr, Albert (Alexandre Martin). 6fr+5fr, Pierre J. Proudhon. 10fr+6fr, Louis Auguste Blanqui. 15fr+7fr, Armand Barbés. 20fr+8fr, Dennis A. Affre.

B224	SP177	1fr + 1fr dk grn	1.25	1.25
B225	SP177	3fr + 2fr henna brn	1.25	1.25
B226	SP177	4fr + 3fr vio brn	1.25	1.25
B227	SP177	5fr + 4fr lt bl grn	3.25	3.25
B228	SP177	6fr + 5fr indigo	2.50	2.50
B229	SP177	10fr + 6fr car rose	2.50	2.50
B230	SP177	15fr + 7fr sl blk	3.25	3.25
B231	SP177	20fr + 8fr purple	3.25	3.25
		Nos. B224-B231 (8)	18.50	18.50

Centenary of the Revolution of 1848.

Dr. Léon Charles Albert Calmette SP178

1948, June 18

B232	SP178	6fr + 4fr dk grnsh bl	.50	.50

1st Intl. Congress on the Calmette-Guerin bacillus vaccine.

Farmer — SP179

Designs: 5fr+3fr, Fisherman. 8fr+4fr, Miner. 10fr+6fr, Metal worker.

1949, Feb. 14

B233	SP179	3fr + 1fr claret	.90	.75
B234	SP179	5fr + 3fr dk blue	.90	.75
B235	SP179	8fr + 4fr indigo	.90	.75
B236	SP179	10fr + 6fr dk red	1.00	.75
		Nos. B233-B236 (4)	3.70	3.00

Étienne François de Choiseul and Post Cart SP180

Baron de la Brède et de Montesquieu SP181

1949, Mar. 26

B237	SP180	15fr + 5fr dk green	1.20	1.20

Stamp Day, Mar. 26-27, 1949.

1949, Nov. 14

Designs: 8fr+2fr, Voltaire. 10fr+3fr, Antoine Watteau. 12fr+4fr, Georges de Buffon. 15fr+5fr, Joseph F. Dupleix. 25fr+10fr, A. R. J. Turgot.

B238	SP181	5fr + 1fr dk grn	3.50	3.50
B239	SP181	8fr + 2fr indigo	3.50	3.50
B240	SP181	10fr + 3fr brn red	3.50	3.50
B241	SP181	12fr + 4fr purple	3.50	3.50
B242	SP181	15fr + 5fr rose car	5.00	5.00
B243	SP181	25fr + 10fr ultra	6.00	6.00
		Nos. B238-B243 (6)	25.00	25.00

"Spring" SP182

Designs: 8fr+2fr, Summer. 12fr+3fr, Autumn. 15fr+4fr, Winter.

1949, Dec. 19

B244	SP182	5fr + 1fr green	1.90	1.75
B245	SP182	8fr + 2fr yel org	2.50	2.00
B246	SP182	12fr + 3fr purple	2.50	2.00
B247	SP182	15fr + 4fr dp blue	4.00	3.75
		Nos. B244-B247 (4)	10.90	9.50

Postman — SP183

1950, Mar. 11

B248	SP183	12fr + 3fr dp bl	3.75	3.00

Stamp Day, Mar. 11-12, 1950.

André de Chénier SP184

Alexandre Brongniart, Bust by Houdon SP185

8fr+3fr, J. L. David. 10fr+4fr, Lazare Carnot. 12fr+5fr, G. J. Danton. 15fr+6fr, Maximilian Robespierre. 20fr+10fr, Louis Hoche.

1950, July 10 Engr. Perf. 13
Frames in Indigo

B249	SP184	5fr + 2fr brn vio	10.00	10.00
B250	SP184	8fr + 3fr blk brn	10.00	10.00
B251	SP184	10fr + 4fr lake	11.00	11.00
B252	SP184	12fr + 5fr red brn	13.00	13.00
B253	SP184	15fr + 6fr dk grn	14.00	14.00
B254	SP184	20fr + 10fr dk vio bl	14.00	14.00
		Nos. B249-B254 (6)	72.00	72.00

1950, Dec. 22

15fr+3fr, "L'Amour" by Etienne M. Falconet.

B255	SP185	8fr + 2fr ind & car	2.50	2.50
B256	SP185	15fr + 3fr red brn & car	2.50	2.50

The surtax was for the Red Cross.

Mail Car Interior SP186

Alfred de Musset SP187

1951, Mar. 10 Unwmk. Perf. 13

B257	SP186	12fr + 3fr lilac gray	3.75	3.75

Stamp Day, Mar. 10-11, 1951.

1951, June 2

8fr+2fr, Eugène Delacroix. 10fr+3fr, J.-L. Gay-Lussac. 12fr+4fr, Robert Surcouf. 15fr+5fr, C. M. Talleyrand. 30fr+10fr, Napoleon I.

Frames in Dark Brown

B258	SP187	5fr + 1fr dk grn	7.50	5.75
B259	SP187	8fr + 2fr vio brn	7.50	5.75
B260	SP187	10fr + 3fr grnsh black	8.00	5.75
B261	SP187	12fr + 4fr dk vio brn	8.00	5.75
B262	SP187	15fr + 5fr brn car	9.00	5.75
B263	SP187	30fr + 10fr indigo	14.00	11.00
		Nos. B258-B263 (6)	54.00	39.75

Child at Prayer by Le Maître de Moulins SP188

18th Century Child by Quentin de la Tour SP189

1951, Dec. 15
Cross in Red

B264	SP188	12fr + 3fr dk brown	3.25	3.25
B265	SP189	15fr + 5fr dp ultra	3.75	3.75

The surtax was for the Red Cross.

Stagecoach
of 1844
SP190

1952, Mar. 8 *Perf. 13*
B266 SP190 12fr + 3fr dp green 5.00 5.00
Stamp Day, Mar. 8, 1952.

Gustave
Flaubert — SP191

Portraits: 12fr+3fr, Edouard Manet. 15fr+4fr, Camille Saint-Saens. 18fr+5fr, Henri Poincaré. 20fr+6fr, Georges-Eugene Haussmann. 30fr+7fr, Adolphe Thiers.

1952, Oct. 18
Frames in Dark Brown
B267 SP191 8fr + 2fr indigo 7.00 7.00
B268 SP191 12fr + 3fr vio blue 7.00 7.00
B269 SP191 15fr + 4fr dk grn 7.00 7.00
B270 SP191 18fr + 5fr dk brn 9.00 9.00
B271 SP191 20fr + 6fr car 9.00 9.00
B272 SP191 30fr + 7fr purple 9.00 9.00
Nos. B267-B272 (6) 48.00 48.00

Cupid from
Diana
Fountain
Versailles
SP192

15fr+5fr, Similar detail, cupid facing left.

1952, Dec. 13
Cross in Red
B273 SP192 12fr + 3fr dk grn 5.00 5.00
B274 SP192 15fr + 5fr indigo 5.00 5.00
  a. Booklet pane of 10 225.00
    Complete booklet 375.00
The surtax was for the Red Cross.

Count
d'Argenson
SP193

St. Bernard
SP194

1953, Mar. 14
B275 SP193 12fr + 3fr dp blue 2.75 2.75
Day of the Stamp. Surtax for the Red Cross.

1953, July 9
12fr+3fr, Olivier de Serres. 15fr+4fr, Jean Philippe Rameau. 18fr+5fr, Gaspard Monge. 20fr+6fr, Jules Michelet. 30fr+7fr, Marshal Hubert Lyautey.
B276 SP194 8fr + 2fr ultra 6.25 6.25
B277 SP194 12fr + 3fr dk grn 6.25 6.25
B278 SP194 15fr + 4fr brn car 10.00 10.00
B279 SP194 18fr + 5fr dk blue 11.00 11.00
B280 SP194 20fr + 6fr dk pur 11.00 11.00
B281 SP194 30fr + 7fr brown 11.50 11.50
Nos. B276-B281 (6) 56.00 56.00
The surtax was for the Red Cross.

Madame Vigée-
Lebrun and her
Daughter
SP195

Count Antoine
de La Vallette
SP196

Design: 15fr+5fr, "The Return from Baptism," by Louis Le Nain.

1953, Dec. 12
Cross in Red
B282 SP195 12fr + 3fr red brn 7.50 7.00
  a. Bkt. pane, 4 each, gutter
    btwn. 85.00
B283 SP195 15fr + 5fr indigo 10.00 9.50
The surtax was for the Red Cross.

1954, Mar. 20 *Engr.* *Perf. 13*
B284 SP196 12fr + 3fr dp grn & choc 4.50 3.25
Stamp Day, Mar. 20, 1954.

Louis IX
SP197

"The Sick Child,"
by Eugene
Carrière
SP198

Portraits: 15fr+5fr, Jacques Benigne Bossuet. 18fr+6fr, Sadi Carnot. 20fr+7fr, Antoine Bourdelle. 25fr+8fr, Dr. Emile Roux. 30fr+10fr, Paul Valéry.

1954, July 10
B285 SP197 12fr + 4fr dp bl 21.00 21.00
B286 SP197 15fr + 5fr pur 21.00 21.00
B287 SP197 18fr + 6fr dk brn 21.00 21.00
B288 SP197 20fr + 7fr crim 29.00 29.00
B289 SP197 25fr + 8fr ind 29.00 29.00
B290 SP197 30fr + 10fr dp claret 29.00 29.00
Nos. B285-B290 (6) 150.00 150.00
See Nos. B303-B308, B312-B317.

1954, Dec. 18
Design: 15fr+5fr, "Young Girl with Doves," by Jean Baptiste Greuze.
Cross in Red
B291 SP198 12fr + 3fr vio gray & indigo 11.00 11.00
  a. Bkt. pane, 4 each, gutter
    btwn. 110.00
B292 SP198 15fr + 5fr dk brn & org brn 11.00 11.00
No. B291a for 90th anniv. of the Red Cross. The surtax was for the Red Cross.

Balloon
Post, 1870
SP199

1955, Mar. 19 *Unwmk.* *Perf. 13*
B293 SP199 12fr + 3fr multi 5.00 4.00
Stamp Day, Mar. 19-20, 1955.

King Philip
II — SP200

Child with Cage
by
Pigalle — SP201

Portraits: 15fr+6fr, Francois de Malherbé. 18fr+7fr, Sebastien de Vauban. 25fr+8fr, Charles G. de Vergennes. 30fr+9fr, Pierre S. de Laplace. 50fr+15fr, Pierre Auguste Renoir.

1955, June 11
B294 SP200 12fr + 5fr brt pur 16.00 16.00
B295 SP200 15fr + 6fr dp bl 16.00 16.00
B296 SP200 18fr + 7fr dp green 16.00 16.00
B297 SP200 25fr + 8fr gray 25.00 25.00
B298 SP200 30fr + 9fr rose brn 26.00 26.00
B299 SP200 50fr + 15fr blue grn 30.00 30.00
Nos. B294-B299 (6) 129.00 129.00
See Nos. B321-B326.

1955, Dec. 17
Design: 15fr+5fr, Child with Goose, by Boethus of Chalcedon.
Cross in Red
B300 SP201 12fr + 3fr claret 7.50 7.50
B301 SP201 15fr + 5fr dk bl 5.25 5.25
  a. Booklet pane of 10 150.00
    Complete booklet 300.00
The surtax was for the Red Cross.

Francois of
Taxis
SP202

1956, Mar. 17 *Engr.* *Perf. 13*
B302 SP202 12fr + 3fr ultra, grn & dk brn 2.75 2.75
Stamp Day, Mar. 17-18, 1956.

Portrait Type of 1954
Portraits: No. 303, Guillaume Budé. No. B304, Jean Goujon. No. B305, Samuel de Champlain. No. B306, Jean Simeon Chardin. No. B307, Maurice Barrès. No. B308, Maurice Ravel.

1956, June 9 *Perf. 13*
B303 SP197 12fr + 3fr saph 5.25 5.25
B304 SP197 12fr + 3fr lil gray 5.25 5.25
B305 SP197 12fr + 3fr brt red 5.25 5.25
B306 SP197 15fr + 5fr green 7.75 7.75
B307 SP197 15fr + 5fr vio brn 7.75 7.75
B308 SP197 15fr + 5fr dp vio 7.75 7.75
Nos. B303-B308 (6) 39.00 39.00

Peasant Boy by Le
Nain — SP203

Design: 15fr+5fr, Gilles by Watteau.

1956, Dec. 8 *Unwmk.*
Cross in Red
B309 SP203 12fr + 3fr ol gray 3.00 3.00
  a. Bkt. pane, 4 ea, gutter
    btwn. 40.00
B310 SP203 15fr + 5fr rose lake 3.00 3.00
The surtax was for the Red Cross.

Genoese
Felucca,
1750
SP204

1957, Mar. 16 *Perf. 13*
B311 SP204 12fr +3fr bluish gray & brn blk 1.90 1.60
Day of the Stamp, Mar. 16, 1957, and honoring the Maritime Postal Service.

Portrait Type of 1954
Portraits: No. B312, Jean de Joinville. No. B313, Bernard Palissy. No. B314, Quentin de la Tour. No. B315, Hugues Félicité Robert de Lamennais. No. B316, George Sand. No. B317, Jules Guesde.
B312 SP197 12fr + 3fr ol gray & ol grn 2.75 2.75
B313 SP197 12fr + 3fr grnsh blk & grnsh bl 2.75 2.75
B314 SP197 15fr + 5fr cl & brt red 3.25 3.25
B315 SP197 15fr + 5fr ultra & ind 3.25 3.25
B316 SP197 18fr + 7fr grnsh blk & dk grn 4.50 4.50
B317 SP197 18fr + 7fr dk vio brn & red brn 4.50 4.50
Nos. B312-B317 (6) 21.00 21.00

Blind Man and
Beggar, Engraving
by Jacques
Callot — SP205

Design: 20fr+8fr, Women beggars.

1957, Dec. 7 *Engr.* *Perf. 13*
B318 SP205 15fr + 7fr ultra & red 4.50 4.50
  a. Bkt. pane, 4 ea, gutter
    btwn. 45.00 45.00
B319 SP205 20fr + 8fr dk vio brn & red 4.50 4.50
The surtax was for the Red Cross.

Motorized
Mail
Distribution
SP206

1958, Mar. 15
B320 SP206 15fr + 5fr multi 1.90 1.50
Stamp Day, Mar. 15.

Portrait Type of 1955
Portraits: No. B321, Joachim du Bellay. No. B322, Jean Bart. No. B323, Denis Diderot. No. B324, Gustave Courbet. 20fr+8fr, J. B. Carpeaux. 35fr+15fr, Toulouse-Lautrec.

1958, June 7 *Engr.* *Perf. 13*
B321 SP200 12fr + 4fr yel grn 1.75 1.75
B322 SP200 12fr + 4fr dk blue 1.75 1.75
B323 SP200 15fr + 5fr dull cl 2.00 2.00
B324 SP200 15fr + 5fr ultra 2.25 2.25
B325 SP200 20fr + 8fr brt red 2.25 2.25
B326 SP200 35fr + 15fr green 2.25 2.25
Nos. B321-B326 (6) 12.25 12.25

St. Vincent de
Paul — SP207

Portrait: 20fr+8fr, J. H. Dunant.

1958, Dec. 6   Unwmk.
Cross in Carmine

B327 SP207 15fr + 7fr grayish
                              grn   1.25   1.25
  a.   Bklt. pane, 4 each, gutter
       btwn.   20.00
B328 SP207 20fr + 8fr violet   1.25   1.25
The surtax was for the Red Cross.

Plane
Landing at
Night
SP208

1959, Mar. 21

B329 SP208 20fr + 5fr sl grn, blk
                              & rose   .50   .50
Issued for Stamp Day, Mar. 21, and to publicize night air mail service.
The surtax was for the Red Cross.
See No. 1089.

Geoffroi de Villehardouin and
Ships — SP209

Designs: No. B331, André Le Nôtre and formal garden. No. B332, Jean Le Rond d'Alembert, books and wheel. No. B333, David d'Angers, statue and building. No. B334, M. F. X. Bichat and torch. No. B335, Frédéric Auguste Bartholdi, Statue of Liberty and Lion of Belfort.

1959, June 13   Engr.   Perf. 13

B330 SP209 15fr + 5fr vio blue   1.25   1.25
B331 SP209 15fr + 5fr dk sl grn 1.25   1.25
B332 SP209 20fr + 10fr olive bis 1.25   1.25
B333 SP209 20fr + 10fr dk gray   1.25   1.25
B334 SP209 30fr + 10fr dk car
                              rose   1.75   1.75
B335 SP209 30fr + 10fr org brn   1.75   1.75
    Nos. B330-B335 (6)   8.50   8.50
The surtax was for the Red Cross.

No. 927 Surcharged

FREJUS
+5ᶠ

1959, Dec.   Typo.   Perf. 14x13½

B336 A328 25fr + 5fr black & red   .30   .30
Surtax for the flood victims at Frejus.

Charles Michel de
l'Épée — SP210

Design: 25fr+10fr, Valentin Hauy.

1959, Dec. 5   Engr.   Perf. 13
Cross in Carmine

B337 SP210 20fr + 10fr blk & cl   2.00   2.00
  a.   Bklt. pane, 4 each, gutter
       btwn.   30.00
B338 SP210 25fr + 10fr dk blue
                              & blk   2.50   2.50
The surtax was for the Red Cross.

Ship Laying
Underwater
Cable
SP211

1960, Mar. 12

B339 SP211 20c + 5c grnsh bl
                              & dk bl   1.50   1.50
Issued for the Day of the Stamp. The surtax went to the Red Cross.

Refugee Girl Amid
Ruins — SP212

1960, Apr. 7

B340 SP212 25c + 10c grn, brn &
                              ind   .30   .25
World Refugee Year, July 1, 1959-June 30, 1960. The surtax was for aid to refugees.

Michel de
L'Hospital
SP213

#B342, Henri de la Tour D'Auvergne, Viscount of Turenne. #B343, Nicolas Boileau (Despreaux). #B344, Jean-Martin Charcot, M.D. #B345, Georges Bizet. 50c+15c, Edgar Degás.

1960, June 11   Engr.   Perf. 13

B341 SP213 10c + 5c pur &
                              rose car   2.50   2.50
B342 SP213 20c + 10c ol &
                              vio brn   3.25   3.25
B343 SP213 20c + 10c Prus
                              grn & dp yel
                              grn   3.25   3.25
B344 SP213 30c + 10c rose
                              car & rose
                              red   5.00   5.00
B345 SP213 30c + 10c dk bl &
                              vio bl   5.00   5.00
B346 SP213 50c + 15c sl bl &
                              gray   5.50   5.50
    Nos. B341-B346 (6)   24.50 24.50
The surtax was for the Red Cross.
See Nos. B350-B355.

Staff of the
Brotherhood of
St.
Martin — SP214

Letter Carrier,
Paris
1760 — SP215

25c+10c, St. Martin, 16th cent. wood sculpture.

1960, Dec. 3   Unwmk.   Perf. 13

B347 SP214 20c + 10c rose cl
                              & red   3.25   3.25
  a.   Bklt. pane, 4 each, gutter
       btwn.   32.50
B348 SP214 25c + 10c lt ultra
                              & red   3.25   3.25
The surtax was for the Red Cross.

1961, Mar. 18   Perf. 13

B349 SP215 20c + 5c sl grn, brn
                              & red   .75   .75
Stamp Day. Surtax for Red Cross.

Famous Men Type of 1960

Designs: 15c+5c, Bertrand Du Guesclin. B351, Pierre Puget. #B352, Charles Coulomb. 30c+10c, Antoine Drouot. 45c+10c, Honoré Daumier. 50c+15c, Guillaume Apollinaire.

1961, May 20   Engr.

B350 SP213 15c + 5c red brn
                              & blk   2.50   2.50
B351 SP213 20c + 10c dk grn
                              & lt bl   2.50   2.50
B352 SP213 20c + 10c ver &
                              rose car   2.50   2.50
B353 SP213 30c + 10c blk &
                              brn org   3.50   3.50
B354 SP213 45c + 10c choc &
                              dk grn   3.50   3.50
B355 SP213 50c + 15c dk car
                              rose & vio   4.00   4.00
    Nos. B350-B355 (6)   18.50 18.50

"Love" by
Rouault
SP216

Medieval Royal
Messenger
SP217

Designs from "Miserere" by Georges Rouault: 25c+10c, "The Blind Consoles the Seeing."

1961, Dec. 2   Perf. 13

B356 SP216 20c + 10c brn,
                              blk & red   2.50   2.50
  a.   Bklt. pane, 4 each, gutter
       btwn.   30.00
B357 SP216 25c + 10c brn,
                              blk & red   2.50   2.50
The surtax was for the Red Cross.

1962, Mar. 17

B358 SP217 20c + 5c rose red, bl
                              & sepia   .80   .80
Stamp Day. Surtax for Red Cross.

Denis Papin,
Scientist
SP218

Rosalie
Fragonard by
Fragonard
SP219

Portraits: No. B360, Edme Bouchardon, sculptor. No. B361, Joseph Lakanal, educator. 30c+10c, Gustave Charpentier, composer. 45c+15c, Edouard Estaunië, writer. 50c+20c, Hyacinthe Vincent, physician and bacteriologist.

1962, June 2   Engr.

B359 SP218 15c + 5c bluish
                              grn & dk
                              gray   2.25   2.25
B360 SP218 20c + 10c cl brn   2.25   2.25
B361 SP218 20c + 10c gray &
                              sl   2.50   2.50
B362 SP218 30c + 10c brt bl
                              & ind   3.00   3.00
B363 SP218 45c + 15c org brn
                              & choc   3.00   3.00
B364 SP218 50c + 20c grnsh
                              bl & blk   3.50   3.50
    Nos. B359-B364 (6)   16.50 16.50
The surtax was for the Red Cross.

1962, Dec. 8

Design: 25c+10c, Child dressed as Pierrot.

Cross in Red

B365 SP219 20c + 10c redsh
                              brown   1.75   1.75
  a.   Bklt. pane, 4 ea, gutter
       btwn.   32.00
B366 SP219 25c + 10c dull grn   2.25   2.25
The surtax was for the Red Cross.
For surcharges see Reunion Nos. B16-B17.

Jacques
Amyot,
Classical
Scholar
SP220

30c+10c, Pierre de Marivaux, playwright. 50c+20c, Jacques Daviel, surgeon.

1963, Feb. 23   Unwmk.   Perf. 13

B367 SP220 20c + 10c mar, gray
                              & pur   1.25   1.25
B368 SP220 30c + 10c Prus grn
                              & mar   1.25   1.25
B369 SP220 50c + 20c ultra,
                              ocher & ol   1.50   1.50
    Nos. B367-B369 (3)   4.00   4.00
The surtax was for the Red Cross.

Roman
Chariot
SP221

1963, Mar. 16   Engr.

B370 SP221 20c + 5c brn org &
                              vio brn   .25   .25
Stamp Day. Surtax for Red Cross.

Étienne
Méhul,
Composer
SP222

Designs: 30c+10c, Nicolas-Louis Vauquelin, chemist. 50c+20c, Alfred de Vigny, poet.

1963, May 25   Unwmk.   Perf. 13

B371 SP222 20c + 10c dp bl,
                              dk brn & dp
                              org   1.25   1.25
B372 SP222 30c + 10c mag,
                              gray ol & blk 1.25   1.25
B373 SP222 50c + 20c sl, blk &
                              brn   1.50   1.50
    Nos. B371-B373 (3)   4.00   4.00
The surtax was for the Red Cross.

"Child with Grapes"
by David d'Angers
and Centenary
Emblem — SP223

25c+10c, "The Fifer," by Edouard Manet.

1963, Dec. 9   Unwmk.   Perf. 13

B374 SP223 20c + 10c black &
                              red   .75   .75
  a.   Bklt. pane, 4 each, gutter
       btwn.   9.00   9.00
B375 SP223 25c + 10c sl grn &
                              red   .75   .75
Cent. of the Intl. and French Red Cross. Surtax for the Red Cross.
For surcharges see Reunion Nos. B18-B19.

Post Rider,
18th
Century
SP224

1964, Mar. 14   Engr.

B376 SP224 20c + 5c Prus green   .30   .30
Issued for Stamp Day.

Resistance Memorial by Watkin, Luxembourg Gardens — SP225

De Gaulle's 1940 Poster "A Tous les Francais" SP226

Street Fighting in Paris and Strasbourg. SP227

Designs: 20c+5c, "Deportation," concentration camp with watchtower and barbed wire. No. B381, Allied troops landing in Normandy and Provence.

1964	Engr.	Perf. 13	
B377	SP225 20c + 5c slate blk	.50	.50
	Perf. 12x13		
B378	SP226 25c + 5c dk red, bl, red & blk	.65	.65
	Perf. 13		
B379	SP227 30c + 5c blk, bl & org brn	.75	.75
B380	SP227 30c + 5c org brn, cl & blk	.75	.75
B381	SP225 50c + 5c dk grn	.90	.90
	Nos. B377-B381 (5)	3.55	3.55

20th anniv. of liberation from the Nazis. Issue dates: #B377, B381, Mar. 21; #B378, June 18; #B379, June 6; #B380, Aug. 22.

President René Coty SP229

Jean Nicolas Corvisart SP230

Portraits: No. B383, John Calvin. No. B384, Pope Sylvester II (Gerbert).

1964	Unwmk.	Perf. 13	
B382	SP229 30c + 10c dp cl & blk	.25	.25
B383	SP229 30c + 10c dk grn, blk & brn	.25	.25
B384	SP229 30c + 10c slate & cl	.25	.25
	Nos. B382-B384 (3)	.75	.75

The surtax was for the Red Cross. Issued: #B382, 4/25; #B383, 5/25; #B384, 6/1.

1964, Dec. 12   Engr.

Portrait: 25c+10c, Dominique Larrey.

Cross in Carmine

B385	SP230 20c + 10c black	.35	.35
a.	Bklt. pane, 4 ea, gutter btwn.	3.50	
B386	SP230 25c + 10c black	.35	.35

Jean Nicolas Corvisart (1755-1821), physician of Napoleon I, and Dominique Larrey (1766-1842), Chief Surgeon of the Imperial Armies. The surtax was for the Red Cross. For surcharges see Reunion Nos. B20-B21.

Paul Dukas, Composer — SP231

#B387, Duke François de La Rochefoucauld, writer. #B388, Nicolas Poussin, painter. #B389, Duke Charles of Orléans, poet.

1965, Feb.	Engr.	Perf. 13	
B387	SP231 30c + 10c org brn & dk bl	.40	.40
B388	SP231 30c + 10c car & dk red brn	.40	.40
B389	SP231 40c + 10c dk red brn, dk red & Prus bl	.50	.50
B390	SP231 40c + 10c dk brn & sl bl	.50	.50
	Nos. B387-B390 (4)	1.80	1.80

The surtax was for the Red Cross. Issued: #B387, B390 2/13; #B388-B389 2/20.

Packet "La Guienne" SP232

1965, Mar. 29   Unwmk.   Perf. 13

B391	SP232 25c + 10c multi	.75	.50

Issued for Stamp Day, 1965. "La Guienne" was used for transatlantic mail service. Surtax was for the Red Cross.

Infant with Spoon by Auguste Renoir — SP233

Design: 30c+10c, Coco Writing (Renoir's daughter Claude).

1965, Dec. 11   Engr.   Perf. 13

Cross in Carmine

B392	SP233 25c + 10c slate	.30	.30
a.	Bklt. pane, 4 ea, gutter btwn.	2.75	
B393	SP233 30c + 10c dull red brn	.30	.30

The surtax was for the Red Cross. For surcharges see Reunion Nos. B22-B23.

Francois Mansart and Carnavalet Palace, Paris SP234

#B395, St. Pierre Fourier and Basilica of St. Pierre Fourier, Mirecourt. #B396, Marcel Proust and St. Hilaire Bridge, Illiers. #B397, Gabriel Fauré, monument and score of "Penelope." #B398, Elie Metchnikoff, microscope and Pasteur Institute. #B399, Hippolyte Taine and birthplace.

1966	Engr.	Perf. 13	
B394	SP234 30c + 10c dk red brn & grn	.35	.35
B395	SP234 30c + 10c blk & gray grn	.35	.35
B396	SP234 30c + 10c ind, sep & grn	.35	.35
B397	SP234 30c + 10c bis brn & ind	.35	.35
B398	SP234 30c + 10c blk & dl brn	.35	.35
B399	SP234 30c + 10c grn & ol brn	.35	.35
	Nos. B394-B399 (6)	2.10	2.10

The surtax was for the Red Cross. Issued: #B394-B396, 2/12; others, 6/25.

Engraver Cutting Die and Tools SP235

1966, Mar. 19   Engr.   Perf. 13

B400	SP235 25c + 10c slate, dk brn & dp org	.30	.30

Stamp Day. Surtax for Red Cross.

Angel of Victory, Verdun Fortress, Marching Troops — SP236

First Aid on Battlefield, 1859 — SP237

1966, May 28   Perf. 13

B401	SP236 30c + 5c Prus bl, ultra & dk bl	.20	.20

Victory of Verdun, 50th anniversary.

1966, Dec. 10   Engr.   Perf. 13

#B403, Nurse giving first aid to child, 1966.

Cross in Carmine

B402	SP237 25c + 10c green	.35	.35
a.	Bklt. pane, 4 ea, gutter btwn.	3.50	
B403	SP237 30c + 10c slate	.40	.40

The surtax was for the Red Cross. For surcharges see Reunion Nos. B24-B25.

Emile Zola — SP238

Letter Carrier, 1865 — SP239

No. B405, Beaumarchais (pen name of Pierre Augustin Caron). No. B406, St. François de Sales (1567-1622). No. B407, Albert Camus (1913-1960).

1967	Engr.	Perf. 13	
B404	SP238 30c + 10c sl bl & bl	.35	.35
B405	SP238 30c + 10c rose brn & lil	.35	.35
B406	SP238 30c + 10c dl vio & pur	.35	.35
B407	SP238 30c + 10c brn & dl cl	.35	.35
	Nos. B404-B407 (4)	1.40	1.40

The surtax was for the Red Cross. Issued: #B404-B405, 2/4; others, 6/24.

1967, Apr. 8

B408	SP239 25c + 10c indigo, grn & red	.30	.25

Issued for Stamp Day.

Ivory Flute Player — SP240

Ski Jump and Long Distance Skiing — SP241

30c+10c, Violin player, ivory carving.

1967, Dec. 16   Engr.   Perf. 13

Cross in Carmine

B409	SP240 25c + 10c dl vio & lt brn	.40	.40
a.	Bklt. pane, 4 ea, gutter btwn.	3.50	
B410	SP240 30c + 10c grn & lt brn	.40	.40

The surtax was for the Red Cross. For surcharges see Reunion Nos. B26-B27.

1968, Jan. 27

Designs: 40c+10c, Ice hockey. 60c+20c, Olympic flame and snowflakes. 75c+25c, Woman figure skater. 95c+35c, Slalom.

B411	SP241 30c + 10c ver, gray & brn	.35	.35
B412	SP241 40c + 10c lil, lem & brt mag	.35	.35
B413	SP241 60c + 20c dk grn, org & brt vio	.50	.50
B414	SP241 75c + 25c brt pink, yel grn & blk	.60	.60
B415	SP241 95c + 35c bl, brt pink & red brn	.60	.60
	Nos. B411-B415 (5)	2.40	2.40

Issued for the 10th Winter Olympic Games, Grenoble, Feb. 6-18.

Rural Mailman, 1830 — SP242

1968, Mar. 16   Engr.   Perf. 13

B416	SP242 25c + 10c multi	.25	.25

Issued for Stamp Day.

François Couperin, Composer, and Instruments SP243

Portraits: No. B418, Gen. Louis Desaix de Veygoux (1768-1800) and scene showing his death at the Battle of Marengo, Italy. No. B419, Saint-Pol-Roux (pen name of Paul-Pierre Roux, 1861-1940), Christ on the Cross and ruins of Camaret-sur-Mer. No. B420, Paul Claudel (poet and diplomat, 1868-1955) and Joan of Arc at the stake.

1968	Engr.	Perf. 13	
B417	SP243 30c + 10c pur & rose lil	.25	.25
B418	SP243 30c + 10c dk grn & brn	.25	.25
B419	SP243 30c + 10c cop red & ol bis	.25	.25
B420	SP243 30c + 10c dk brn & lil	.25	.25
	Nos. B417-B420 (4)	1.00	1.00

Issue dates: Nos. B417-B418, Mar. 23; Nos. B419-B420, July 6.

Spring, by Nicolas Mignard — SP244

Paintings by Nicolas Mignard; 30c+10c, Fall. No. B423, Summer. No. B424, Winter.

1968-69   Engr.   Perf. 13

Cross in Carmine

B421	SP244 25c + 10c pur & sl bl	.30	.30
a.	Bklt. pane, 4 ea #B421-B422 with gutter btwn.)	3.00	
B422	SP244 30c + 10c brn & rose car	.30	.30
B423	SP244 40c + 15c dk brn & brn ('69)	.50	.50
a.	Bklt. pane, 4 ea #B423, B424 with gutter btwn.)	3.50	

B424 SP244 40c + 15c pur &
  Prus bl ('69) .50 .50
 Nos. B421-B424 (4) 1.60 1.60

The surtax was for the Red Cross.
For surcharges see Reunion Nos. B28-B31.

Mailmen's Omnibus, 1881
SP245

1969, Mar. 15 Engr. *Perf. 13*
B425 SP245 30c + 10c brn, grn &
  blk .25 .25

Issued for Stamp Day.
For surcharge see Reunion No. B32.

Gen. Francois Marceau — SP246

Portraits: No. B427, Charles Augustin Sainte-Beuve (1804-1869), writer. No. B428, Albert Roussel (1869-1937), musician. No. B429, Marshal Jean Lannes (1769-1809). No. B430, Georges Cuvier (1769-1832), naturalist. No. B431, André Gide, (1869-1951), writer.

1969
B426 SP246 50c + 10c brn red .50 .50
B427 SP246 50c + 10c slate bl .50 .50
B428 SP246 50c + 10c dp vio bl .50 .50
B429 SP246 50c + 10c choc .50 .50
B430 SP246 50c + 10c dp plum .50 .50
B431 SP246 50c + 10c blue grn .50 .50
 Nos. B426-B431 (6) 3.00 3.00

The surtax was for the Red Cross.
Issued: Nos. B426-B428, Mar. 24; No. B429, May 10; Nos. B430-B431, May 17.

Gen. Jacques Leclerc, La Madeleine and Battle — SP247

1969, Aug. 23 Engr. *Perf. 13*
B432 SP247 45c + 10c slate & ol 1.00 1.00

Liberation of Paris, 8/25/44, 25th anniv.

Same Inscribed "Liberation de Strasbourg"

1969, Nov. 22 Engr. *Perf. 13*
B433 SP247 70c + 10c brn,
  choc & olive 3.50 3.50

25th anniv. of the liberation of Strasbourg.

Philibert Delorme, Architect, and Chateau d'Anet
SP248

Designs: No. B435, Louis Le Vau (1612-1670), architect, and Vaux-le-Vicomte Chateau, Paris. No. B436, Prosper Merimée (1803-1870), writer, and Carmen. No. B437, Alexandre Dumas (1802-1870), writer, and Three Musketeers. No. B438, Edouard Branly (1844-1940), physicist, electric circuit and convent of the Carmes, Paris. No. B439, Maurice de Broglie (1875-1960), physicist, and X-ray spectrograph.

1970 Engr. *Perf. 13*
B434 SP248 40c + 10c slate grn .50 .50
B435 SP248 40c + 10c dk car .50 .50
B436 SP248 40c + 10c Prus blue .50 .50
B437 SP248 40c + 10c violet bl .50 .50

B438 SP248 40c + 10c dp brown .50 .50
B439 SP248 40c + 10c dk gray .50 .50
 Nos. B434-B439 (6) 3.00 3.00

The surtax was for the Red Cross.
Issued: #B434-B436, 2/14; others, 4/11.

City Mailman, 1830 — SP249 "Life and Death" — SP250

1970, Mar. 14
B440 SP249 40c + 10c blk, ultra &
  dk car rose .40 .40

Issued for Stamp Day.
For surcharge see Reunion No. B33.

1970, Apr. 4
B441 SP250 40c + 10c brt bl, ol &
  car rose .25 .25

Issued to publicize the fight against cancer in connection with Health Day, Apr. 7.

Marshal de Lattre de Tassigny — SP251

1970, May 8 Engr. *Perf. 13*
B442 SP251 40c + 10c slate & vio
  bl .50 .50

25th anniv. of the entry into Berlin of French troops under Marshal Jean de Lattre de Tassigny, May 8, 1945.

Lord and Lady, Dissay Chapel Fresco — SP252

#B444, Angel holding whips, from fresco in Dissay Castle Chapel, Vienne, c. 1500.

1970, Dec. 12 Engr. *Perf. 13*
  Cross in Carmine
B443 SP252 40c + 15c green .55 .55
 a. Bklt. pane, 4 ea, gutter btwn. 12.50
B444 SP252 40c + 15c cop red .55 .55

The surtax was for the Red Cross.
For surcharges see Reunion Nos. B34-B35.

Daniel-Francois Auber and "Fra Diavolo" Music — SP253

#B446, Gen. Charles Diego Brosset (1898-1944), Basilica of Fourvière. #B447, Victor Grignard (1871-1935), chemist, Nobel Prize medal. #B448, Henri Farman (1874-1958), plane. #B449, Gen. Charles Georges Delestraint (1879-1945), scroll. #B450, Jean Eugène Robert-Houdin (1805-71), magician's act.

1971 Engr. *Perf. 13*
B445 SP253 50c + 10c brn vio
  & brn .75 .75
B446 SP253 50c + 10c dk sl
  grn & ol gray .75 .75
B447 SP253 50c + 10c brn red
  & olive .75 .75
B448 SP253 50c + 10c vio bl &
  vio .75 .75
B449 SP253 50c + 10c pur & cl .85 .85
B450 SP253 50c + 10c sl grn &
  bl grn .85 .85
 Nos. B445-B450 (6) 4.70 4.70

The surtax was for the Red Cross.
Issued: #B445-B446, 3/6; #B447, 5/8; #B448, 5/29; #B449-B450, 10/16.

Army Post Office, 1914-1918
SP254

1971, Mar. 27 Engr. *Perf. 13*
B451 SP254 50c + 10c ol, brn &
  bl .45 .45

Stamp Day, 1971.
For surcharge see Reunion No. B36.

Girl with Dog, by Greuze
SP255 Aristide Bergès (1833-1904)
SP256

Design: 50c+10c, "The Dead Bird," by Jean-Baptiste Greuze (1725-1805).

1971, Dec. 11
  Cross in Carmine
B452 SP255 30c + 10c violet bl .70 .70
 a. Bklt. pane, 4 each, gutter btwn. 6.00
B453 SP255 50c + 10c dp car .70 .70

The surtax was for the Red Cross.
For surcharges see Reunion Nos. B37-B38.

1972 Engr. *Perf. 13*
#B455, Paul de Chomedey (1612-76), founder of Montreal, and arms of Neuville-sur-Vanne. #B456, Edouard Belin (1876-1963), inventor. #B457, Louis Blériot (1872-1936), aviation pioneer. #B458, Adm. François Joseph, Count de Grasse (1722-88), hero of the American Revolution. #B459, Théophile Gautier (1811-72), writer.

B454 SP256 50c + 10c blk & grn .75 .75
B455 SP256 50c + 10c blk & bl .75 .75
B456 SP256 50c + 10c blk & lil
  rose .75 .75
B457 SP256 50c + 10c red & blk .75 .75
B458 SP256 50c + 10c org & blk 1.00 1.00
B459 SP256 50c + 10c blk & brn 1.00 1.00
 Nos. B454-B459 (6) 5.00 5.00

The surtax was for the Red Cross.
Issued: #B454-B455, Feb. 19; #B456, June 24; #B457, July 1; #B458-B459, Sept. 9.

Rural Mailman, 1894
SP257 Nicolas Desgenettes
SP258

1972, Mar. 18 Engr. *Perf. 13*
B460 SP257 50c + 10c bl, yel &
  ol gray 1.00 .75

Stamp Day 1972.
For surcharge see Reunion No. B39.

1972, Dec. 16 Engr. *Perf. 13*
Designs: 30c+10c, René Nicolas Dufriche, Baron Desgenettes, M.D. (1762-1837). 50c+10c, François Joseph Broussais, M.D. (1772-1838).

B461 SP258 30c + 10c sl grn &
  red .65 .50
 a. Bklt. pane, 4 ea, gutter btwn. 7.00
B462 SP258 50c + 10c red .65 .50

The surtax was for the Red Cross.
For surcharges see Reunion Nos. B40-B41.

Tony Garnier (1869-1948), architect — SP259

#B463, Gaspard de Coligny (1519-1572), admiral and Huguenot leader. #B464, Ernest Renan (1823-1892), philologist and historian. #B465, Alberto Santos Dumont (1873-1932), Brazilian aviator. #B466, Gabrielle-Sidonie Colette (1873-1954), writer. #B467, René Duguay-Trouin (1673-1736), naval commander. #B468, Louis Pasteur (1822-1895), chemist, bacteriologist. #B469, Tony Garnier (1869-1948), architect.

1973 Engr. *Perf. 13*
B463 SP259 50c + 10c multi .85 .85
B464 SP259 50c + 10c multi .85 .85
B465 SP259 50c + 10c multi .85 .85
B466 SP259 50c + 10c multi .85 .85
B467 SP259 50c + 10c multi .85 .85
B468 SP259 50c + 10c multi .85 .85
B469 SP259 50c + 10c multi .85 .85
 Nos. B463-B469 (7) 5.95 5.95

Issued: #B463, 2/17; #B464, 4/28; #B465, 5/26; #B466, 6/2; #B467, 6/9; #B468, 10/6; #B469, 11/17.

Mail Coach, 1835
SP260

1973, Mar. 24 Engr. *Perf. 13*
B470 SP260 50c + 10c grnsh blue .35 .35

Stamp Day, 1973.
For surcharge see Reunion No. B42.

Mary Magdalene
SP261 St. Louis-Marie de Montfort
SP262

50c+10c, Mourning woman. Designs are from 15th cent. Tomb of Tonnerre.

1973, Dec. 1
B471 SP261 30c + 10c sl grn &
  red .55 .55
 a. Bklt. pane, 4 each, gutter
  btwn. 6.00
B472 SP261 50c + 10c dk gray &
  red .55 .55

Surtax was for the Red Cross.
For surcharges see Reunion Nos. B43-B44.

1974, Feb. 23 Engr. *Perf. 13*
Portraits: No. B474, Francis Poulenc (1899-1963), composer. No. B475, Jules Barbey

d'Aurevilly (1808-1889), writer. No. B476, Jean Giraudoux (1882-1944), writer.

B473 SP262 50c + 10c multi 1.10 1.10
B474 SP262 50c + 10c multi .70 .70
B475 SP262 80c + 15c multi .80 .80
B476 SP262 80c + 15c multi .80 .80
Nos. B473-B476 (4) 3.40 3.40

Issue dates: No. B473, Mar. 9; No. B474, July 20; Nos. B475-B476, Nov. 16.

Automatically Sorted Letters — SP263

1974, Mar. 9 **Engr.** **Perf. 13**
B477 SP263 50c + 10c multi .30 .25

Stamp Day 1974. Automatic letter sorting center, Orleans-la-Source, opened 1/30/73. For surcharge see Reunion No. B45.

Order of Liberation and 5 Honored Cities — SP264

1974, June 15 **Engr.** **Perf. 13**
B478 SP264 1fr + 10c multi .75 .40

30th anniv. of liberation from the Nazis.

"Summer" SP265   "Winter" SP266

Designs: B481, "Spring" (girl on swing). B482, "Fall" (umbrella and rabbits).

1974, Nov. 30 **Engr.** **Perf. 13**
B479 SP265 60c + 15c multi .60 .60
a. Bklt. pane, 4 ea, gutter btwn. 12.00
B480 SP266 80c + 15c multi .60 .60

For surcharges see Reunion Nos. B46-B47.

1975, Nov. 29
B481 SP265 60c + 15c multi .50 .50
a. Bklt. pane, 4 ea, gutter btwn. 4.75
B482 SP266 80c + 20c multi .50 .50

Surtax was for the Red Cross.

Dr. Albert Schweitzer SP267   Edmond Michelet SP268

André Siegfried and Map SP269

#B483, Albert Schweitzer (1875-1965), medical missionary. #B484, Edmond Michelet (1899-1970), Resistance hero, statesman. #B485, Robert Schuman (1886-1963), promoter of United Europe. #B486, Eugene Thomas (1903-69), minister of PTT. #B487, André Siegfried (1875-1959), political science professor, writer.

1975 **Engr.** **Perf. 13**
B483 SP267 80c + 20c multi .50 .50
B484 SP268 80c + 20c bl & ind .50 .50
B485 SP268 80c + 20c blk & ind .50 .50
B486 SP268 80c + 20c blk & sl .50 .50
B487 SP269 80c + 20c blk & bl .50 .50
Nos. B483-B487 (5) 2.50 2.50

Issued: #B483, 1/11; #B484, 2/22; #B485, 5/10; #B486, 6/28; #B487, 11/15.

Second Republic Mailman's Badge — SP270

1975, Mar. 8 **Photo.**
B488 SP270 80c + 20c multi .50 .40

Stamp Day.

"Sage" Type of 1876 SP271   Marshal A. J. de Moncey SP272

1976, Mar. 13 **Engr.** **Perf. 13**
B489 SP271 80c + 20c blk & lil .45 .45

Stamp Day 1976.

1976 **Engr.** **Perf. 13**
#B491, Max Jacob (1876-1944), Dadaist writer, by Picasso. #B492, Jean Mounet-Sully (1841-1916), actor. #B493, Gen. Pierre Daumesnil (1776-1832). #B494, Eugène Fromentin (1820-1876), painter.
B490 SP272 80c + 20c multi .50 .50
B491 SP272 80c + 20c red brn & ol .50 .50
B492 SP272 80c + 20c multi .50 .50
B493 SP272 1fr + 20c multi .50 .50
B494 SP272 1fr + 20c multi .50 .50
Nos. B490-B494 (5) 2.50 2.50

Issued: #B490, 5/22; #B491, 7/22; #B492, 8/28; #B493, 9/4; #B494, 9/25.

Anna de Noailles SP273   St. Barbara SP274

1976, Nov. 6 **Engr.** **Perf. 13**
B495 SP273 1fr + 20c multi .60 .60

Anna de Noailles (1876-1933), writer & poet.

1976, Nov. 20

Design: 1fr+25c, Cimmerian Sibyl. Sculptures from Brou Cathedral.

Cross in Carmine

B496 SP274 80c + 20c violet .60 .60
a. Bklt. pane, 4 ea, gutter btwn. 6.00
B497 SP274 1fr + 25c dk brown .80 .80

Surtax was for the Red Cross.

Marckolsheim Relay Station Sign — SP275

1977, Mar. 26 **Engr.** **Perf. 13**
B498 SP275 1fr + 20c multi .40 .40

Stamp Day.

Edouard Herriot, Statesman and Writer SP276   Christmas Figurine, Provence SP277

Designs: No. B500, Abbé Breuil (1877-1961), archaeologist. No. B501, Guillaume de Machault (1305-1377), poet and composer. No. B502, Charles Cross (1842-1888).

1977 **Engr.** **Perf. 13**
B499 SP276 1fr + 20c multi .60 .60
B500 SP276 1fr + 20c multi .60 .60
B501 SP276 1fr + 20c multi .60 .60
B502 SP276 1fr + 20c multi .60 .60
Nos. B499-B502 (4) 2.40 2.40

Issued: #B499, Oct. 8; #B500, Oct. 15; #B501, Nov. 12; #B502, Dec. 3.

1977, Nov. 26

1fr+25c, Christmas figurine (woman), Provence.

B503 SP277 80c + 20c red & ind .45 .45
a. Bklt. pane, 4 ea, gutter btwn. 4.50
B504 SP277 1fr + 25c red & sl grn .55 .55

Surtax was for the Red Cross.

Marie Noel, Writer — SP278   Mail Collection, 1900 — SP279

#B506, Georges Bernanos (1888-1948), writer. #B507, Leo Tolstoi (1828-1910), Russian writer. #B508, Charles Marie Leconte de Lisle (1818-1894), poet. #B509, Voltaire (1694-1778) and Jean Jacques Rousseau (1712-1778). #B510, Claude Bernard (1813-1878), physiologist.

1978 **Engr.** **Perf. 13**
B505 SP278 1fr + 20c multi .55 .55
B506 SP278 1fr + 20c multi .55 .55
B507 SP278 1fr + 20c multi .55 .55
B508 SP278 1fr + 20c multi .55 .55
B509 SP278 1fr + 20c multi .55 .55
B510 SP278 1fr + 20c multi .55 .55
Nos. B505-B510 (6) 3.30 3.30

Issued: #B505, 2/11; #B506, 2/18; #B507, 4/15; #B508, 3/26; #B509, 7/1; #B510, 9/16.

1978, Apr. 8 **Engr.** **Perf. 13**
B511 SP279 1fr + 20c multi .50 .40

Stamp Day 1978.

SP280   SP281

1fr+25c, The Hare & the Tortoise. 1.20fr+30c, The City Mouse & the Country Mouse.

1978, Dec. 2 **Engr.** **Perf. 13**
B512 SP280 1fr + 25c multi .75 .65
a. Bklt. pane, 4 ea, gutter btwn. 6.00
B513 SP280 1.20fr + 30c multi .75 .65

Surtax was for the Red Cross.

1979 **Engr.** **Perf. 13**
#B514, Ladislas Marshal de Berchény (1689-1778). #B515, Leon Jouhaux (1879-1954), labor leader. #B516, Peter Abelard (1079-1142), theologian and writer. #B517, Georges Courteline (1860-1929), humorist. #B518, Simone Weil (1909-1943), social philosopher. #B519, André Malraux (1901-1976), novelist.

B514 SP281 1.20fr + 30c multi .60 .60
B515 SP281 1.20fr + 30c multi .60 .60
B516 SP281 1.20fr + 30c multi .60 .60
B517 SP281 1.20fr + 30c multi .60 .60
B518 SP281 1.30fr + 30c multi .60 .60
B519 SP281 1.30fr + 30c multi .60 .60
Nos. B514-B519 (6) 3.60 3.60

Issued: #B514, 1/13; #B515, 5/12; #B516, 6/9; #B517, 6/25; #B518, 11/12; #B519, 11/26.

General Post Office, from 1908 Post Card SP282

1979, Mar. 10 **Engr.** **Perf. 13**
B520 SP282 1.20fr + 30c multi .60 .40

Stamp Day 1979.

Woman, Stained-Glass Window — SP283

Stained-glass windows, Church of St. Joan of Arc, Rouen: 1.30fr+30c, Simon the Magician.

1979, Dec. 1
B521 SP283 1.10fr + 30c multi .50 .40
a. Bklt. pane, 4 each, gutter btwn., perf. 12½x13 6.00
B522 SP283 1.30fr + 30c multi .60 .45

Surtax was for the Red Cross.

Eugene Viollet le Duc (1814-1879), Architect — SP284

Jean-Marie de Le Mennais (1780-1860), Priest and Educator — SP285

#B524, Jean Monnet (1888-1979), economist and diplomat. #B525, Viollet le Duc (1814-1879), architect and writer. #B526, Frederic Mistral (1830-1914), poet. #B527, Saint-John Perse (Alexis Leger, 1887-1975), poet and diplomat. #B528, Pierre Paul de Riquet (1604-1680), canal builder.

1980	Engr.		Perf. 13	
B523	SP284	1.30fr + 30c multi	.70	.70
B524	SP285	1.30fr + 30c multi	.70	.70
B525	SP285	1.40fr + 30c blue	.70	.70
B526	SP285	1.40fr + 30c black	.70	.70
B527	SP285	1.40fr + 30c multi	.70	.70
B528	SP284	1.40fr + 30c multi	.70	.70
	Nos. B523-B528 (6)		4.20	4.20

Issued: #B523, Feb. 16; #B524-B526, Sept. 6; #B527-B528, Oct. 11.

The Letter to Melie, by Avati, Stamp Day, 1980 — SP286

1980, Mar. 8			Photo.	
B529	SP286	1.30fr + 30c multi	.60	.45

Filling the Granaries, Choir Stall Detail, Amiens Cathedral — SP287

#B531, Grapes from the Promised Land.

1980, Dec. 6			Engr.	Perf. 13
B530	SP287	1.20fr + 30c red & dk red brn	.70	.70
B531	SP287	1.40fr + 30c red & dk red brn	.80	.80
a.	Bklt. pane, 4 each, gutter btwn., perf. 12½x13		5.00	

Sister Anne-Marie Javouhey (1779-1851), Founded Congregation of St. Joseph of Cluny — SP288

#B532, Louis Armand (1905-71), railway engineer. #B533, Louis Jouvet (1887-1951), theater director. #B534, Marc Boegner (1881-1970), peace worker. #B536, Jacques Offenbach (1819-80), composer. #B537, Pierre Teilhard de Chardin (1881-1955), philosopher. Nos. B532-B533, B537 vert.

1981	Engr.		Perf. 13	
B532	SP288	1.20 + 30c multi	.65	.65
B533	SP288	1.20 + 30c multi	.65	.65
B534	SP288	1.40 + 30c multi	.65	.65
B535	SP288	1.40 + 30c multi	.65	.65
B536	SP288	1.40 + 30c multi	.65	.65
B537	SP288	1.40 + 30c multi	.65	.65
	Nos. B532-B537 (6)		3.90	3.90

Issued: #B532, 5/23; #B533, 6/13; #B534, 11/14; #B535, 2/7; #B536, 2/14; #B537, 5/23.

The Love Letter, by Goya — SP289

1981, Mar. 7			Perf. 13x12½	
B538	SP289	1.40 + 30c multi	1.00	.90

Stamp Day 1981.

Scourges of the Passion SP290

Guillaume Postel (1510-1581), Theologian — SP291

Stained-glass Windows, Church of the Sacred Heart, Audincourt: 1.60fr+30c, "Peace."

1981, Dec. 5			Photo.	Perf. 13
B539	SP290	1.40 + 30c multi	.75	.65
B540	SP290	1.60 + 30c multi	.70	.45
a.	Bklt. pane, 4 ea, gutter btwn.		6.00	

1982	Engr.		Perf. 13	
	#B542, Henri Mondor (1885-1962), physi-			

#B542, Henri Mondor (1885-1962), physician. #B543, Andre Chantemesse (1851-1919), Scientist. #B544, Louis Pergaud (1882-1915), writer. #B545, Robert Debre (1882-1978), writer. #B546, Gustave Eiffel (1832-1923), engineer.

B541	SP291	1.40 + 30c multi	.65	.45
B542	SP291	1.40 + 30c dk brn & dk bl	.65	.40
B543	SP291	1.60 + 30c multi	.70	.70
B544	SP291	1.60 + 40c multi	.70	.70
B545	SP291	1.60 + 40c dk blue	.90	.70
B546	SP291	1.80 + 40c sepia	.90	.70
	Nos. B541-B546 (6)		4.50	3.65

Woman Reading, by Picasso — SP292

1982, Mar. 27			Perf. 13x12½	
B547	SP292	1.60 + 40c multi	1.00	.75

Stamp Day.

SP293

SP294

Jules Verne books: 1.60fr+30c, Five Weeks in a Balloon. 1.80fr+40c, 20,000 Leagues under the Sea.

1982, Nov. 20			Perf. 13	
B548	SP293	1.60 + 30c multi	.75	.65
B549	SP293	1.80 + 40c multi	.75	.65
a.	Bklt. pane, 4 each, gutter btwn., perf. 12½x13		8.00	

Surtax was for Red Cross.

1983	Engr.		Perf. 12½x13	

#B550, Andre Messager (1853-1929). #B551, J.A. Gabriel (1698-1782), architect. #B552, Hector Berlioz (1803-69), composer. #B553, Max Fouchet (1913-80). #B554, Rene Cassin (1887-1976). #B555, Stendhal (Marie Henri Beyle, 1783-1842).

B550	SP294	1.60 + 30c multi	.65	.65
B551	SP294	1.60 + 30c multi	.65	.65
B552	SP294	1.80 + 40c dp lil & blk	.75	.75
B553	SP294	1.80 + 40c multi	.75	.75
B554	SP294	2fr + 40c multi	.80	.80
B555	SP294	2fr + 40c multi	.80	.80
	Nos. B550-B555 (6)		4.40	4.40

Issued: #B550, 1/15; #B551, 4/16; #B552, 1/22; #B553, 4/30; #B554, 6/25; #B555, 11/12.

Man Dictating a Letter, by Rembrandt — SP295

	Photo. & Engr.			
1983, Feb. 26			Perf. 13X12½	
B556	SP295	1.80 + 40c multi	1.20	.75

Stamp Day.

Virgin with Child, Baillon, 14th Cent. — SP296

Design: No. B558, Virgin with Child, Genainville, 16th Cent.

1983, Nov. 26			Engr.	Perf. 13
B557	SP296	1.60 + 40c shown	.65	.45
B558	SP296	2fr + 40c multi	.85	.55
a.	Bklt. pane, 4 each, gutter btwn., perf. 12½x13		6.50	

Emile Littre (1801-1881), Physician — SP297

#B560, Jean Zay (1904-44). #B561, Pierre Corneille (1606-1684). #B562, Gaston Bachelard (1884-1962), writer. #B563, Jean Paulhan (1884-1968). #B564, Evariste Galois (1811-1832).

1984	Engr.		Perf. 13	
B559	SP297	1.60fr + 40c plum & blk	.85	.85
B560	SP297	1.60fr + 40c dk grn & blk	.85	.85
B561	SP297	1.70fr + 40c dp vio & blk	.85	.85
B562	SP297	2fr + 40c gray & blk	.85	.85
B563	SP297	2.10fr + 40c dk brn & blk	.90	.80
B564	SP297	2.10fr + 40c ultra & blk	.90	.80
	Nos. B559-B564 (6)		5.20	5.00

SP298

SP299

Diderot Holding a Letter, by L.M. Van Loo.

1984, Mar. 17			Engr.	Perf. 12½x13
B565	SP298	2fr + 40c multi	1.25	.90

1984, Nov. 24			Photo.	Perf. 12½x13

The Rose Basket, by Caly.

B566	SP299	2.10fr + 50c pnksh (basket) & multi	1.10	.90
a.	Salmon (basket) & multi, perf. 13½x13		1.10	.90
b.	As "a," bklt. pane of 10 + 2 labels		11.00	

Surtax was for the Red Cross.

Jules Romains (1885-1972) — SP300

Authors: No. B568, Jean-Paul Sartre (1905-1980). No. B569, Romain Rolland (1866-1944). No. B570, Roland Dorgeles (1885-1973). No. B571, Victor Hugo (1802-1885). No. B572, Francois Mauriac (1885-1970).

1985, Feb. 23			Engr.	Perf. 13
B567	SP300	1.70fr + 40c	3.25	3.25
B568	SP300	1.70fr + 40c	3.25	3.25
B569	SP300	1.70fr + 40c	3.25	3.25
B570	SP300	2.10fr + 50c	3.75	3.75
B571	SP300	2.10fr + 50c	3.75	3.75
B572	SP300	2.10fr + 50c	3.75	3.75
a.	Bklt. pane, 1 each + 2 labels, perf. 15x14½		32.50	
	Nos. B567-B572 (6)		21.00	21.00

SP301 　　　　SP302

Stamp Day: Canceling apparatus invented by Eugene Daguin (1849-1888).

1985, Mar. 16			Engr.	Perf. 12½x13
B573	SP301	2.10fr + 50c brn blk & bluish gray	1.00	.85

1985, Nov. 23			Photo.	

Issenheim Altarpiece retable.

B574	SP302	2.20fr + 50c multi	1.00	.85
a.	As "b," bklt. pane of 10		10.00	
b.	Perf. 13½x13		1.00	.85

Surtax for the Red Cross.

SP303 　　　　SP304

Famous men: No. B575, Francois Arago (1786-1853), physician, politician. No. B576, Henri Moissan (1852-1907), chemist. No. B577, Henri Fabre (1882-1984), engineer. No. B578, Marc Seguin (1786-1875), engineer. No. B579, Paul Heroult (1863-1914), chemist.

1986, Feb. 22 Engr. Perf. 13
B575 SP303 1.80fr + 40c multi .95 .95
B576 SP303 1.80fr + 40c multi .95 .95
B577 SP303 1.80fr + 40c multi .95 .95
B578 SP303 2.20fr + 50c multi 1.10 1.10
B579 SP303 2.20fr + 50c multi 1.10 1.10
  a. Bklt. pane of 5, #B575-B579,
     + 3 labels 8.00
  Nos. B575-B579 (5) 5.05 5.05

1986, Mar. 1 Engr. Perf. 13x12½
B580 SP304 2.20fr + 50c brn blk 6.00 6.00
Pierre Cot (1895-1977).

Mail
Britzska
SP305

1986, Apr. 5 Perf. 13
B581 SP305 2.20fr + 60c pale
     tan & dk vio
     brn 1.10 1.00

Booklet Stamp
B582 SP305 2.20fr + 60c buff &
     blk 1.20 1.00
  a. Bklt. pane of 6 + 2 labels 7.50
Stamp Day. See Nos. B590-B591, B599-
B600, B608-B609.

Stained Glass
Window (detail),
by Vieira da Silva,
St. Jacques of
Reims Church,
Marne — SP306

1986, Nov. 24 Photo. Perf. 12½x13
B583 SP306 2.20fr + 60c multi 1.20 .95
  a. As "b," bklt. pane of 10 12.00
  b. Perf. 13½x13 1.20 .95
Surtaxed to benefit the natl. Red Cross.

Physicians
and
Biologists
SP307

#B584, Charles Richet (1850-1935). #B585,
Eugene Jamot (1879-1937). #B586, Bernard
Halpern (1904-1978). #B587, Alexandre Yer-
sin (1863-1943). #B588, Jean Rostand (1894-
1977). #B589, Jacques Monod (1910-1976).

1987, Feb. 21 Engr. Perf. 13
B584 SP307 1.90fr + 50c deep
     ultra .95 .95
B585 SP307 1.90fr + 50c dull lil .95 .95
B586 SP307 1.90fr + 50c grnish
     gray .95 .95
B587 SP307 2.20fr + 50c grnish
     gray 1.10 1.10
B588 SP307 2.20fr + 50c deep
     ultra 1.10 1.10
B589 SP307 2.20fr + 50c dull lil 1.10 1.10
  a. Bklt. pane of 6, #B584-B589 6.50
  Nos. B584-B589 (6) 6.15 6.15

Stamp Day Type of 1986
Stamp Day 1987: Berline carriage.

1987, Mar. 14 Engr.
B590 SP305 2.20fr + 60c buff &
     sepia 1.10 .95

Booklet Stamp
B591 SP305 2.20fr + 60c pale &
     dk bl 1.25 .95
  a. Bklt. pane of 6 + 2 labels 8.00

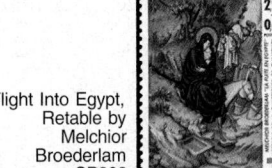
Flight Into Egypt,
Retable by
Melchior
Broederlam
SP308

1987, Nov. 21 Photo. Perf. 12½x13
B592 SP308 2.20fr +60c multi 1.10 .95
  a. As "b," bklt. pane of 10 + 2
     labels 11.00
  b. Perf. 13½x13 1.10 .95
Surtaxed to benefit the Red Cross.

Explorers
SP309

Profiles & maps: #B593, Marquis Abraham
Duquesne (1610-1688), naval commander.
#B594, Pierre Andre de Suffren (1729-1788).
#B595, Jean-Francois de La Perouse (1741-
1788). #B596, Mahe de La Bourdonnais
(1699-1753). #B597, Louis-Antoine de Bougainville (1729-1811). #B598, Jules Dumont
d'Urville (1790-1842).

1988, Feb. 20 Engr. Perf. 13
B593 SP309 2fr + 50c multi .90 .80
B594 SP309 2fr + 50c multi .90 .80
B595 SP309 2fr + 50c multi .90 .80
B596 SP309 2.20fr + 50c multi 1.00 .85
B597 SP309 2.20fr + 50c multi 1.00 .85
B598 SP309 2.20fr + 50c multi 1.00 .85
  a. Bklt. pane of 6, #B593-B598 6.00

Stamp Day Type of 1986
Stamp Day 1988: Postal coach.

1988, Mar. 29 Engr.
B599 SP305 2.20fr +60c dk lilac 1.10 1.00

Booklet Stamp
B600 SP305 2.20fr +60c sepia 1.10 1.00
  a. Bklt. pane of 6 + 2 labels 6.50

Intl. Red Cross,
125th
Anniv. — SP310

1988, Nov. 19 Engr. Perf. 12½x13
B601 SP310 2.20fr +60c multi 1.10 1.00
  a. As "b," bklt. pane of 10+2
     labels 11.00
  b. Perf. 13½x13 1.10 1.00

Revolution
Leaders
and
Heroes
SP311

#B602, Emmanuel Joseph Sieyes (1748-
1836). #B603, Honore Gabriel Riqueti, Comte
de Mirabeau (1749-91). #B604, Louis Marie
de Noailles (1756-1804). #B605, Lafayette.
#B606, Antoine Pierre Joseph Marie Barnave
(1761-93). #B607, Jean Baptiste Drouet
(1763-1824).

1989, Feb. 25 Engr. Perf. 13
B602 SP311 2.20fr +50c multi 1.10 .90
B603 SP311 2.20fr +50c multi 1.10 .90
B604 SP311 2.20fr +50c multi 1.10 .90
B605 SP311 2.20fr +50c multi 1.10 .90
B606 SP311 2.20fr +50c multi 1.10 .90
B607 SP311 2.20fr +50c multi 1.10 .90
  a. Bklt. pane, 1 each + 2 labels 6.00
French Revolution, bicent.

Stamp Day Type of 1986
Design: Paris-Lyon stagecoach.

1989, Apr. 15 Engr. Perf. 13
B608 SP305 2.20fr +60c pale bl
     & dk bl 1.10 .95

Booklet Stamp
B609 SP305 2.20fr +60c pale lil
     & pur 1.00 .95
  a. Bklt. pane of 6 + 2 labels 8.00
Stamp Day 1989.

Bird From a Silk
Tapestry, Lyon,
18th
Cent. — SP312

1989, Nov. 18 Photo. Perf. 12½x13
B610 SP312 2.20fr +60c multi 1.10 .90
  a. As "b," bklt. pane of 10 12.00
  b. Perf. 13½x13 1.10 .90
Surtax for the natl. Red Cross.

1992
Winter
Olympics,
Albertville
SP313

1990, Feb. 9 Engr. Perf. 13
B611 SP313 2.30fr +20c red, bl
     & blk 1.10 .85
See Nos. B621-B627, B636-B637, B639.

Stamp Day
SP314

1990, Mar. 17 Photo.
B612 SP314 2.30fr +60c ultra, bl
     & brt yel 1.20 1.00

Booklet Stamp
B613 SP314 2.30fr +60c ultra,
     grn, yel &
     brt grn 1.20 1.00
  a. Bklt. pane of 6 + 2 labels 8.00

SP315 SP316
Quimper or Brittany Ware Faience plate.

1990, May 5 Photo. Perf. 12½x13
B614 SP315 2.30fr +60c multi 1.10 1.00
  a. As "b," bklt. pane of 10+2 la-
     bels 12.00
  b. Perf. 13½x13 1.20 1.00
Surcharge benefited the Red Cross.

1990, June 16 Photo. Perf. 13
#B615, Aristide Bruant. #B616, Maurice
Chevalier. #B617, Tino Rossi. #B618, Edith
Piaf. #B619, Jacques Brel. #B620, Georges
Brassens.

B615 SP316 2.30fr +50c multi 1.00 1.00
B616 SP316 2.30fr +50c multi 1.00 1.00
B617 SP316 2.30fr +50c multi 1.00 1.00
B618 SP316 2.30fr +50c multi 1.00 1.00
B619 SP316 2.30fr +50c multi 1.00 1.00
B620 SP316 2.30fr +50c multi 1.00 1.00
  a. Bklt. pane, 1 each +2 labels 6.00

Albertville Olympic Type
Designs: No. B621, Ski jumping. No. B622,
Speed skiing. No. B623, Slalom skiing. No.
B624, Cross-country skiing. No. B625, Ice
hockey. No. B626, Luge. No. B627, Curling.

1990-91 Engr. Perf. 13
B621 SP313 2.30fr +20c multi 1.00 .95
B622 SP313 2.30fr +20c multi 1.00 .95
B623 SP313 2.30fr +20c multi 1.00 .95
B624 SP313 2.30fr +20c multi 1.00 .95
B625 SP313 2.30fr +20c multi 1.00 .95

B626 SP313 2.50fr +20c multi 1.10 1.10
B627 SP313 2.50fr +20c multi 1.10 1.10
  Nos. B621-B627 (7) 7.20 6.95
Issued: #B621, 12/22/90; #B622, 12/29/90;
#B623, 1/19/91; #B624, 2/2/91; #B625, 2/9/91;
#B626, 3/2/91; #B627, 4/20/91.
No. B624 inscribed "La Poste 1992."

Paul Eluard (1895-1952) — SP317

Poets: No. B629, Andre Breton (1896-
1966). No. B630, Louis Aragon (1897-1982).
No. B631, Francis Ponge (1899-1988). No.
B632, Jacques Prevert (1900-1977). No.
B633, Rene Char (1907-1988).

1991, Feb. 23 Engr. Perf. 12½x13
B628 SP317 2.50fr +50c multi 1.10 1.10
B629 SP317 2.50fr +50c multi 1.10 1.10
B630 SP317 2.50fr +50c multi 1.10 1.10
B631 SP317 2.50fr +50c multi 1.10 1.10
B632 SP317 2.50fr +50c multi 1.10 1.10
B633 SP317 2.50fr +50c multi 1.10 1.10
  a. Bklt. pane, 1 each +2 labels,
     perf. 13 7.50

Stamp Day
SP318

1991, Mar. 16 Photo. Perf. 13
B634 SP318 2.50fr +60c blue
     machine 1.25 1.25
B635 SP318 2.50fr +60c purple
     machine 1.25 1.25
  a. Bklt. pane of 6 + 2 labels 8.50

Winter Olympics Type of 1990
#B636, Acrobatic skiing. #B637, Alpine
skiing.

1991 Engr. Perf. 13
B636 SP313 2.50fr +20c multi 1.10 .95
B637 SP313 2.50fr +20c multi 1.10 .95
Issued: #B636, Aug. 3; #B637, Aug. 17.
Nos. B636-B637 inscribed "La Poste 1992."

The Harbor of
Toulon by
Francois
Nardi
SP319

1991, Dec. 2 Photo. Perf. 13x12½
B638 SP319 2.50fr +60c multi 1.20 1.10
  a. Perf. 13x13½ 1.20 1.10
  b. As "a," bklt. pane of 10 + 2
     labels 12.00
Surtax for the Red Cross.

Winter Olympics Type of 1990
Miniature Sheet
a, like #B611. b, like #B621. c, like #B622. d,
like #B623. e, like #B624. f, like #B625.

1992, Feb. 8 Engr. Perf. 13
B639 Sheet of 10 + label 18.00 18.00
  a.-f. SP313 2.50fr +20c multi 1.75 1.75
No. B639 contains one each #B626-B627,
B636-B637, B639a-B639f. Central label is
litho.

Stamp Day
SP320

1992, Mar. 7 Litho. Perf. 13
B640 SP320 2.50fr +60c gray
     people 1.10 1.10

Booklet Stamp
Photo.
B641 SP320 2.50fr +60c red people   1.25 1.10
  a. Bklt. pane of 6 + 2 labels   8.00

SP321

SP322

Composers: No. B642, Cesar Franck (1822-1890). No. B643, Erik Satie (1866-1925). No. B644, Florent Schmitt (1870-1958). No. B645, Arthur Honegger (1892-1955). No. B646, Georges Auric (1899-1983). No. B647, Germaine Tailleferre (1892-1983).

1992, Apr. 11   Photo.   Perf. 13
B642 SP321 2.50fr +50c multi   1.10 1.10
B643 SP321 2.50fr +50c multi   1.10 1.10
B644 SP321 2.50fr +50c multi   1.10 1.10
B645 SP321 2.50fr +50c multi   1.10 1.10
B646 SP321 2.50fr +50c multi   1.10 1.10
B647 SP321 2.50fr +50c multi   1.10 1.10
  a. Bklt. pane of 6, #B642-B647   8.00

1992, Nov. 28   Photo.   Perf. 13½x13
B648 SP322 2.50fr +60c multi   1.20 1.10
  a. Bklt. pane of 10 + 2 labels   12.00

Mutual Aid, Strasbourg. Surtax for the Red Cross.

Writers
SP323

#B649, Guy de Maupassant (1850-93). #B650, Alain (Emile Chartier) (1868-1951). #B651, Jean Cocteau (1889-1963). #B652, Marcel Pagnol (1895-1974). #B653, Andre Chamson (1900-83). #B654, Marguerite Yourcenar (1903-87).

1993, Apr. 24   Engr.   Perf. 13
B649 SP323 2.50fr +50c multi   1.10 1.10
B650 SP323 2.50fr +50c multi   1.10 1.10
B651 SP323 2.50fr +50c multi   1.10 1.10
B652 SP323 2.50fr +50c multi   1.10 1.10
B653 SP323 2.50fr +50c multi   1.10 1.10
B654 SP323 2.50fr +50c multi   1.10 1.10
  a. Bklt. pane of 6, #B649-B654 + 2 labels   8.00

When Nos. B650-B654 are normally centered, inscriptions at base of the lower panel are not parallel to the perforations at bottom. On all six stamps the lower panel is not centered between the side perforations.

SP324

SP325

St. Nicolas, Image of Metz.

1993, Nov. 27   Engr.   Perf. 12½x13
B655 SP324 2.80fr +60c multi   1.25 1.10
  a. Perf. 13½x13   1.25 1.10
  b. As "a," Bklt. pane of 10 +2 labels   15.00

Surtax for Red Cross.

1994, Sept. 17   Photo.   Perf. 13

Stage and Screen Personalities: No. B656, Yvonne Printemps (1894-1977). No. B657, Fernandel (1903-71). No. B658, Josephine Baker (1906-75). No. B659, Bourvil (1917-70).

No. B660, Yves Montand (1921-91). No. B661, Coluche (1944-86).
B656 SP325 2.80fr +60c multi   1.25 1.25
B657 SP325 2.80fr +60c multi   1.25 1.25
B658 SP325 2.80fr +60c multi   1.25 1.25
B659 SP325 2.80fr +60c multi   1.25 1.25
B660 SP325 2.80fr +60c multi   1.25 1.25
B661 SP325 2.80fr +60c multi   1.25 1.25
  a. Bklt. pane, #B656-B661 + 2 labels   8.00

SP326

SP327

Designs: #B662, St. Vaast, Arras Tapestry. #B663, Brussels tapestry from Reydams workshop, Horse Museum, Saumur.

1994-95   Photo.   Perf. 12½x13
B662 SP326 2.80fr +60c multi   1.50 1.40
  a. Perf. 13½x13   1.50 1.40
  b. Bklt. pane, 10 #B662a + 2 labels   15.00
    Complete booklet, #B662b   16.00
B663 SP326 2.80fr +60c multi   1.50 1.50
  a. Perf. 13½x13   1.50 1.50
  b. Bklt. pane, 10 #B663a + 2 labels   15.00
    Complete booklet, #B663b   15.00

Surtax for Red Cross.
Issued: #B662, 11/26/94; #B663, 5/13/95.

1995, Nov. 25   Engr.   Perf. 13
Provencal Nativity Figures: No. B664, The Shepherd. No. B665, The Miller. No. B666, The Simpleton and the Tambour Player. No. B667, The Fishmonger. No. B668, The Scissor Grinder. No. B669, The Elders.
B664 SP327 2.80fr +60c multi   1.40 1.40
B665 SP327 2.80fr +60c multi   1.40 1.40
B666 SP327 2.80fr +60c multi   1.40 1.40
B667 SP327 2.80fr +60c multi   1.40 1.40
B668 SP327 2.80fr +60c multi   1.40 1.40
B669 SP327 2.80fr +60c multi   1.40 1.40
  a. Booklet pane, Nos. B664-B669 + 2 labels   10.00
    Complete booklet, No. B669a   11.00

SP328

Famous Fictional Detectives and Criminals: #B670, Rocambole. #B671, Arsène Lupin. #B672, Joseph Rouletabille. #B673, Fantômas. #B674, Commissioner Maigret. #B675, Nestor Burma.

1996, Oct. 5   Photo.   Perf. 13
B670 SP328 3fr +60c multi   1.40 1.40
B671 SP328 3fr +60c multi   1.40 1.40
B672 SP328 3fr +60c multi   1.40 1.40
B673 SP328 3fr +60c multi   1.40 1.40
B674 SP328 3fr +60c multi   1.40 1.40
B675 SP328 3fr +60c multi   1.40 1.40
  a. Booklet pane, #B670-B675 + 2 labels   9.00
    Complete booklet, #B675a   11.00

Christmas
SP329

1996, Nov. 16   Photo.   Perf. 12¾x13
B676 SP329 3fr +60c multi   1.45 1.45
  a. Perf. 13¼x13   1.50 1.50
  b. Booklet pane, 10 #B676a + 2 labels   15.00
    Complete booklet, #B676b   15.00

Surtax for Red Cross.

Adventure Heroes
SP330

1997, Oct. 25   Photo.   Perf. 13
B677 SP330 3fr +60c Sir Lancelot   1.40 1.40
B678 SP330 3fr +60c Pardaillan   1.40 1.40
B679 SP330 3fr +60c D'Artagnan   1.40 1.40
B680 SP330 3fr +60c Cyrano de Bergerac   1.40 1.40
B681 SP330 3fr +60c Captain Fracasse   1.40 1.40
B682 SP330 3fr +60c Le Bossu   1.40 1.40
  a. Booklet pane, #B677-B682 + 2 labels   9.00
    Complete booklet, #682a   9.00

Christmas, New Year — SP331

1997, Nov. 6   Photo.   Perf. 12¾x13
B683 SP331 3fr +60c multi   1.40 1.25
  a. Perf. 13¼x13   1.40 1.25
  b. Booklet pane, 10 #B683a + 2 labels   14.00   —
    Complete booklet, #B683b   15.00

Surtax for the Red Cross.

SP332

Actors of the French Cinema: #B684, Romy Schneider (1938-82). #B685, Simone Signoret (1921-85). #B686, Jean Gabin (1904-76). #B687, Louis de Funés (1914-83). #B688, Bernard Blier (1916-89). #B689, Lino Ventura (1919-87).

1998, Oct. 3   Photo.   Perf. 13
B684 SP332 3fr +60c multi   1.40 1.40
B685 SP332 3fr +60c multi   1.40 1.40
B686 SP332 3fr +60c multi   1.40 1.40
B687 SP332 3fr +60c multi   1.40 1.40
B688 SP332 3fr +60c multi   1.40 1.40
B689 SP332 3fr +60c multi   1.40 1.40
  a. Booklet pane, #B684-B689 + label   9.50
    Complete booklet, #B689a   10.00

Christmas
SP333

1998, Nov. 5   Photo.   Perf. 12½x13
B690 SP333 3fr +60c multi   1.40 1.40
  a. Perf. 13½x13   1.40 1.40
  b. Booklet pane, 10 #B690a + 2 labels   14.00
    Complete booklet, #B690b   15.00

Surtax for Red Cross.

Famous Photographers — SP334

Photographs by: #B691, Robert Doisneau (1912-94). #B692, Brassai (Gyula Halasz) (1899-1984). #B693, Jacques Lartigue (1894-

1986). #B694, Henri Cartier-Bresson (b. 1908). #B695, Eugene Atget (1857-1927). #B696, Felix Nadar (1820-1910).

1999, July 10   Photo.   Perf. 13
B691 SP334 3fr +60c multi   1.40 1.40
B692 SP334 3fr +60c multi   1.40 1.40
B693 SP334 3fr +60c multi   1.40 1.40
B694 SP334 3fr +60c multi   1.40 1.40
B695 SP334 3fr +60c multi   1.40 1.40
B696 SP334 3fr +60c multi   1.40 1.40
  a. Booklet pane, #B691-B696   8.50
    Complete booklet, #B696a   9.00

New Year 2000 — SP335

1999, Nov. 10   Photo.   Perf. 12¾x13
B697 SP335 3fr +60c multi   1.40 1.40
  a. Perf. 13½x13   1.40 1.40
  b. Booklet pane, 10 #B697a + 2 labels   14.00
    Complete booklet, #B697b   14.00

Surtax for Red Cross.

Adventurers
SP336

#B698, Eric Tabarly (1931-98), sailor. #B699, Alexandra David-Néel (1868-1969), opera singer, Asian traveler. #B700, Haroun Tazieff (1914-98), vulcanologist. #B701, Paul-Emile Victor (1907-55), ethnologist, polar explorer. #B702, Jacques-Yves Cousteau (1910-97), oceanographer. #B703, Norbert Casteret (1897-1987), speleologist.

2000, Sept. 16   Photo.   Perf. 13¼x13
B698 SP336 3fr +60c multi   1.40 1.40
B699 SP336 3fr +60c multi   1.40 1.40
B700 SP336 3fr +60c multi   1.40 1.40
B701 SP336 3fr +60c multi   1.40 1.40
B702 SP336 3fr +60c multi   1.40 1.40
B703 SP336 3fr +60c multi   1.40 1.40
  a. Booklet pane, #B698-B703   8.50
    Booklet, #B703a   8.50

Toy Airplane — SP337

2000, Nov. 9   Photo.   Perf. 13¼x13
B704 SP337 3fr +60c multi   1.40 1.40
  a. Booklet pane of 10 + 2 labels   14.00
    Booklet, #B704a   15.00

Surtax for Red Cross.

Santa Claus and Tree Ornaments
SP338

2001, Nov. 8   Photo.   Perf. 12¾x13
B705 SP338 3fr +60c multi   1.40 1.40
  a. Perf 13½x13   1.40 1.40
  b. Booklet pane of 10   14.00
    Booklet, #B705a   14.00

Surtax for Red Cross.

Infant Jesus Asleep, by Giovanni Battista Salvi — SP339

2002, Nov. 7 Photo. *Perf. 12¾x13*
B706 SP339 46c +9c multi 1.40 1.40
a. Perf. 13½x13 1.40 1.40
b. As "a," booklet pane of 10 14.00 —
  Booklet, #B706b 14.00

Surtax for Red Cross.

Virgin with Grapes, by Pierre Mignard — SP340

2003, Nov. 6 Photo. *Perf. 13¼x13*
Booklet Stamp
B707 SP340 50c +(16c) multi 1.50 1.50
a. Booklet pane of 10 15.00
  Complete booklet, #B707a 15.00

Surtax for Red Cross.

Virgin With Child, Attributed to Cretan School — SP341

2004, Nov. 10 Photo. *Perf. 13¼x13*
Booklet Stamp
B708 SP341 50c +(16c) multi 1.75 1.75
a. Booklet pane of 10 + 2 labels 17.50 —
  Complete booklet, #B708a 17.50

Surtax for Red Cross.

Dec. 26, 2004 Tsunami Victim Relief SP342

2005, Jan. 13 Engr. *Perf. 13*
B709 SP342 (50c) +20c red 1.90 1.90

Virgin and Child, by Hans Memling SP343

2005, Nov. 10 Photo. *Perf. 13½x13*
Booklet Stamp
B710 SP343 53c +(17c) multi 1.75 1.75
a. Booklet pane of 10 + 2 labels 17.50 —
  Complete booklet, #B710a 17.50

Surtax for Red Cross.

SP344

Children's Art — SP345

2006, Nov. 25 Photo. *Perf. 13½x13*
Booklet Stamps
B711 SP344 (54c) +(17c) multi 1.90 1.90
B712 SP345 (54c) +(17c) multi 1.90 1.90
a. Booklet pane, 5 each
  #B711-B712, + 2 labels 19.00 —
  Complete booklet, #B712a 19.00

Surtax for Red Cross.

Red Cross
SP346   SP347
Serpentine Die Cut 11

2007, Nov. 24 Photo.
Self-Adhesive
Booklet Stamps
B713 SP346 (54c) +(17c) multi 2.10 2.10
B714 SP347 (54c) +(17c) multi 2.10 2.10
a. Booklet pane, 5 each
  #B713-B714 21.00

Surtax for Red Cross.

AIR POST STAMPS

Nos. 127, 130 Overprinted in Dark Blue or Black

Perf. 14x13½
1927, June 25 Unwmk.
C1 A18 2fr org & bl (DB) 200.00 225.00
  Never hinged 400.00
C2 A18 5fr dk bl & buff 200.00 225.00
  Never hinged 400.00

On sale only at the Intl. Aviation Exhib. at Marseilles, June, 1927. One set could be purchased by each holder of an admission ticket. Excellent counterfeits exist.

Nos. 242, 196 Surcharged

1928, Aug. 23
C3 A33 10fr on 90c 1,800. 1,800.
  Never hinged 2,500.
a. Inverted surcharge 16,500. 16,500.
  Never hinged 25,000.
b. Space between "10" and bars 6½mm 3,100. 3,100.
  Never hinged 5,100.

C4 A23 10fr on 1.50fr 8,250. 8,250.
  Never hinged 12,500.
a. Space between "10" and bars 6½mm 10,750. 10,750.
  Never hinged 16,500.

Nos. C3-C4 received their surcharge in New York by order of the French consul general. They were for use in paying the 10fr fee for letters leaving the liner Ile de France on a catapulted hydroplane when the ship was one day off the coast of France on its eastward voyage.

The normal space between "10" and bars is 4½mm, but on 10 stamps in each pane of 50 the space is 6½mm. Counterfeits exist.

View of Marseille, Church of Notre Dame at Left — AP1

1930-31 Engr. *Perf. 13*
C5 AP1 1.50fr dp carmine 21.00 4.00
  Never hinged 40.00
C6 AP1 1.50fr dk bl ('31) 19.00 2.25
  Never hinged 35.00
a. 1.50fr ultramarine 50.00 21.00
  Never hinged 90.00
b. As "a," with perf. initials "E.I.P.A.30" 450.00 350.00
  Never hinged 700.00

No. C6a was sold at the Intl. Air Post Exhib., Paris, Nov. 6-20, 1930, at face value plus 5fr, the price of admission.

Forgeries abound of No. C6b. Certificates from recognized authorities are recommended.

Blériot's Monoplane AP2

1934, Sept. 1 *Perf. 13*
C7 AP2 2.25fr violet 24.00 6.00
  Never hinged 32.50

1st flight across the English Channel, by Louis Blériot.

Plane over Paris AP3

1936
C8 AP3 85c dp green 2.25 2.25
  Never hinged 5.00
C9 AP3 1.50fr blue 10.50 5.50
  Never hinged 18.00
C10 AP3 2.25fr violet 18.00 7.00
  Never hinged 35.00
C11 AP3 2.50fr rose 32.50 8.25
  Never hinged 45.00
C12 AP3 3fr ultra 26.00 2.50
  Never hinged 37.50
C13 AP3 3.50fr orange brn 62.50 24.00
  Never hinged 105.00
C14 AP3 50fr emerald 825.00 325.00
  Never hinged 1,450.
a. 50fr deep green 1,000. 525.00
  Never hinged 1,650.
  Nos. C8-C14 (7) 976.75 374.50

Monoplane over Paris — AP4

Paper with Red Network Overprint

1936, July 10 *Perf. 12½*
C15 AP4 50fr ultra 575.00 310.00
  Never hinged 1,150.

Airplane and Galleon — AP5

Airplane and Globe AP6

1936, Aug. 17 *Perf. 13*
C16 AP5 1.50fr dk ultra 17.50 5.25
  Never hinged 35.00
C17 AP6 10fr Prus green 290.00 130.00
  Never hinged 700.00

100th air mail flight across the South Atlantic.

> **Catalogue values for unused stamps in this section, from this point to the end of the section, are for Never Hinged items.**

Centaur and Plane — AP7   Iris — AP8

Zeus Carrying Hebe AP9

Chariot of the Sun AP10

1946-47 Engr. Unwmk.
C18 AP7 40fr dk green .65 .20
C19 AP8 50fr rose pink .65 .20
C20 AP9 100fr dk blue ('47) 7.00 4.00
C21 AP10 200fr red 6.00 1.50
  Nos. C18-C21 (4) 14.30 5.90

Issued: 50fr, 200fr, 5/27; 40fr, 7/1; 100fr, Jan.

For surcharges see Reunion Nos. C35-C38.

Ile de la Cité, Paris, and Gull — AP11

1947, May 7
C22 AP11 500fr dk Prus grn 50.00 45.00
  UPU 12th Cong., Paris, May 7-July 7.

View of Lille
AP12

Air View of Paris — AP13

200fr, Bordeaux. 300fr, Lyon. 500fr, Marseille.

1949-50   **Unwmk.**   **Perf. 13**
C23 AP12 100fr sepia   1.40   .40
C24 AP12 200fr dk bl grn   12.50   .75
C25 AP12 300fr purple   15.00   10.00
C26 AP12 500fr brt red   57.50   5.75
C27 AP13 1000fr sep & blk, bl ('50)   150.00   27.50
Nos. C23-C27 (5)   236.40   44.40

For surcharges see Reunion Nos. C39-C41.

Alexander III Bridge and Petit Palais, Paris — AP14

1949, June 13
C28 AP14 100fr brown car   7.50   5.75
International Telegraph and Telephone Conference, Paris, May-July 1949.

Jet Plane, Mystère IV — AP15

Planes: 200fr, Noratlas. 500fr, Miles Magister. 1000fr, Provence.

1954, Jan. 16
C29 AP15 100fr red brn & bl   3.00   .20
C30 AP15 200fr blk brn & vio bl   11.00   .25
C31 AP15 500fr car & org   200.00   12.50
C32 AP15 1000fr vio brn, bl grn & ind   110.00   16.00
Nos. C29-C32 (4)   324.00   28.95

See No. C37. For surcharges see Reunion Nos. C42-C45, C48.

Maryse Bastié and Plane AP16

1955, June 4   **Unwmk.**   **Perf. 13**
C33 AP16 50fr dp plum & rose pink   6.50   4.00
Issued to honor Maryse Bastié, 1898-1952.

Caravelle
AP17

Designs: 300fr, Morane Saulnier 760 "Paris." 1000fr, Alouette helicopter.

1957-59   **Engr.**   **Perf. 13**
C34 AP17 300fr sl grn, grnsh bl & sep ('59)   5.00   3.00
C35 AP17 500fr dp ultra & blk   30.00   3.75
C36 AP17 1000fr lil, ol blk & blk ('58)   52.50   19.00
Nos. C34-C36 (3)   87.50   25.75
See Nos. C38-C41. For surcharges see Reunion Nos. C46-C47, C49-C51.

Types of 1954-59

Planes: 2fr, Noratlas. 3fr, MS760, Paris. 5fr, Caravelle. 10fr, Alouette helicopter.

1960, Jan. 11
C37 AP15 2fr vio bl & ultra   1.60   .20
a.   2fr ultramarine   3.25   .40
C38 AP17 3fr sl grn, grnsh bl & sep   1.60   .20
C39 AP17 5fr dp ultra & blk   3.25   .75
C40 AP17 10fr lil, ol blk & blk   13.00   2.00
Nos. C37-C40 (4)   19.45   3.15

Type of 1957-59

Design: 2fr, Jet plane, Mystère 20.

1965, June 12   **Engr.**   **Perf. 13**
C41 AP17 2fr slate bl & indigo   .85   .20

Concorde Issue
Common Design Type

1969, Mar. 2   **Engr.**   **Perf. 13**
C42 CD129 1fr indigo & brt bl   1.00   .35

Jean Mermoz, Antoine de Saint-Exupéry and Concorde — AP19

1970, Sept. 19   **Engr.**   **Perf. 13**
C43 AP19 20fr blue & indigo   9.00   .60
Jean Mermoz (1901-36) and writer Antoine de Saint-Exupéry (1900-44), aviators and air mail pioneers.

Balloon, Gare d'Austerlitz, Paris — AP20

1971, Jan. 16   **Engr.**   **Perf. 13**
C44 AP20 95c bl, vio bl, org & sl grn   .90   .55
Centenary of the balloon post from besieged Paris, 1870-71.

Didier Daurat, Raymond Vanier and Plane Landing at Night — AP21

1971, Apr. 17   **Engr.**   **Perf. 13**
C45 AP21 5fr Prus bl, blk & lt grn   2.00   .20
Didier Daurat (1891-1969) and Raymond Vanier (1895-1965), aviation pioneers.
For surcharge see Reunion No. C52.

Hélène Boucher, Maryse Hilsz and Caudron-Renault and Moth-Morane Planes — AP22

Design: 15fr, Henri Guillaumet, Paul Codos, Latécoère 521, Guillaumet's crashed plane in Andes, skyscrapers.

1972-73   **Engr.**   **Perf. 13**
C46 AP22 10fr plum, red & sl   4.50   .40
C47 AP22 15fr dp car, gray & brn ('73)   6.50   .65
Hélène Boucher (1908-34), Maryse Hilsz (1901-46), Henri Guillaumet (1902-40) and Paul Codos (1896-1960), aviation pioneers. Issue dates: 10fr, June 10; 15fr, Feb. 24.

Concorde AP23

1976, Jan. 10   **Engr.**   **Perf. 13**
C48 AP23 1.70fr brt bl, red & blk   1.00   .50
First flight of supersonic jet Concorde from Paris to Rio de Janeiro, Jan. 21.

Planes over the Atlantic, New York-Paris — AP24

1977, June 4   **Engr.**   **Perf. 13**
C49 AP24 1.90fr multicolored   .90   .50
1st transatlantic flight by Lindbergh from NY to Paris, 50th anniv., and 1st attempted westbound flight by French aviators Charles Nungesser and Francois Coli.

Plane over Flight Route AP25

1978, Oct. 14   **Engr.**   **Perf. 13**
C50 AP25 1.50fr multicolored   .90   .35
75th anniversary of first airmail route from Villacoublay to Pauillac, Gironde.

Rocket, Concorde, Exhibition Hall — AP26

1979, June 9   **Engr.**   **Perf. 13**
C51 AP26 1.70fr ultra, org & brn   1.25   .80
33rd International Aerospace and Space Show, Le Bourget, June 11-15.

First Nonstop Transatlantic Flight, Paris-New York — AP27

1980, Aug. 30   **Engr.**   **Perf. 13**
C52 AP27 2.50fr vio brn & ultra   1.00   .40

34th Intl. Space and Aeronautics Exhibition, June 5-14 AP28

1981, June 6   **Engr.**   **Perf. 13**
C53 AP28 2fr multicolored   2.00   .50

Dieudonné Costes and Joseph Le Brix and their Breguet Bi-plane — AP29

1981, Sept. 12   **Engr.**
C54 AP29 10fr dk brown & red   4.50   .40
1st So. Atlantic crossing, Oct. 14-15, 1927.

Seaplane Late-300 — AP30

1982, Dec. 4   **Engr.**
C55 AP30 1.60fr multicolored   .80   .60

Farman F-60 Goliath — AP31

Planes: 20fr, CAMS-53 seaplane. 30fr, Wibault 283 Monoplane. 50fr, Dewoitine 338.

1984-87   **Engr.**
C56 AP31 15fr dark blue   5.00   .60
C57 AP31 20fr dp org ('85)   7.50   .60
C58 AP31 30fr brt vio ('86)   10.00   1.50
C59 AP31 50fr green ('87)   15.00   4.50
Nos. C55-C59 (5)   38.30   7.80
Issued: 15fr, 3/3; 20fr, 3/2; 30fr, 10/11; 50fr, 4/11.

Breguet XIV — AP32

1997, Nov. 15   **Photo.**   **Perf. 13x13¼**
C60 AP32 20fr shown   10.00   4.00
a.   Perf. 13x12½   9.00   1.75
C61 AP32 30fr Potez 25   15.00   4.00
a.   Perf. 13x12½   14.00   2.50
Issued: No. C60 11/15/97; No. C60a, 7/13/98; 30fr, 7/13/98.

Nos. C60 and C61 were issued in panes of 40 (5x8), Nos. C60a and C61a in panes of 10 (2x5).

Airbus A300-B4 — AP33

1999, Apr. 10   Photo.   Perf. 13x13¼
C62   AP33   15fr multicolored   12.00   4.00
a.   Perf. 13x12½   7.00   1.25

No. C62 was issued in panes of 40 (5x8), No. C62a in panes of 10 (2x5).

Couzinet 70 — AP34

2000, Feb. 12   Perf. 13¼x13¼
C63   AP34   50fr multi   22.50   9.00
a.   Perf. 13x12½   22.50   6.00

No. C63 was issued in panes of 40 (5x8), No. C63a in panes of 10 (2x5).

First Flight of Airbus A300, 30th Anniv. — AP35

2002, Oct. 26   Photo.   Perf. 13x13¼
C64   AP35   €3 multi   9.00   1.75

No. C64 was issued both in panes of 40 and 10, same perforation.

Jacqueline Auriol (1917-2000), Pilot, and Jet — AP36

Litho. & Engr.
2003, June 21   Perf. 13
C65   AP36   €4 multi   12.00   2.50
a.   Miniature sheet of 10   120.00   —

Marie Marvingt (1875-1963), Pilot — AP37

Litho. & Engr.
2004, June 29   Perf. 13¼x13
C66   AP37   €5 multi   15.00   3.00
a.   Sheet of 10   150.00   —

Adrienne Bolland (1895-1975), Pilot — AP38

Litho. & Engr.
2005, Oct. 22   Perf. 13
C67   AP38   €2 multi   6.00   1.50
a.   Miniature sheet of 10   60.00   —

Airbus A380 — AP39

2006, June 23   Photo.   Perf. 13x13¼
C68   AP39   €3 multi   9.00   1.75
a.   Miniature sheet of 10   90.00   —

Helicopters, Cent. — AP40

2007, Feb. 19   Photo.   Perf. 13x12½
C69   AP40   €3 multi   8.00   1.60
a.   Perf. 13x13¼   8.00   1.60

No. C69 was issued in panes of 40; No. C69a in panes of 10.

AIR POST SEMI-POSTAL STAMPS

> **Catalogue values for unused stamps in this section are for Never Hinged items.**

Antoine de Saint-Exupéry — SPAP1

Col. Jean Dagnaux SPAP2

1948   Unwmk.   Engr.   Perf. 13
CB1   SPAP1   50fr + 30fr vio brn   2.75   1.60
CB2   SPAP2   100fr + 70fr dk blue   3.75   2.25

Modern Plane and Ader's "Eole" SPAP3

1948, Feb.
CB3   SPAP3   40fr + 10fr dk blue   1.60   1.50

50th anniv. of the flight of Clément Ader's plane, the Eole, in 1897.

POSTAGE DUE STAMPS

D1   D2

1859-70   Unwmk.   Litho.   Imperf.
J1   D1   10c black   26,000.   240.00
J2   D1   15c black ('70)   130.00   250.00

In the lithographed stamps the central bar of the "E" of "CENTIMES" is very short, and the accent on "a" slants at an angle of 30 degree, for the 10c and 17 degree for the 15c, while on the typographed the central bar of the "E" is almost as wide as the top and bottom bars and the accent on the "a" slants at an angle of 47 degree.

No. J2 is known rouletted unofficially.

1859-78   Typo.
J3   D1   10c black   30.00   17.50
J4   D1   15c black ('63)   35.00   15.00
J5   D1   20c black ('71)   4,100.
J6   D1   25c black ('71)   150.00   50.00
J7   D1   30c black ('78)   225.00   125.00
J8   D1   40c blue ('71)   325.00   425.00
a.   40c ultramarine   6,500.   5,700.
b.   40c Prussian blue   2,600.
J9   D1   60c yellow ('71)   475.00   1,050.
J10   D1   60c blue ('78)   60.00   110.00
a.   60c dark blue   600.00   725.00
J10B   D1   60c black   2,700.

The 20c & 60c black were not put into use.
Nos. J3, J4, J6, J8 and J9 are known rouletted unofficially and Nos. J4, J6, J7 and J10 pin-perf. unofficially.

1882-92   Perf. 14x13½
J11   D2   1c black   2.50   2.50
J12   D2   2c black   30.00   26.00
J13   D2   3c black   30.00   25.00
J14   D2   4c black   60.00   40.00
J15   D2   5c black   130.00   32.50
J16   D2   10c black   110.00   2.50
J17   D2   15c black   77.50   10.50
J18   D2   20c black   350.00   140.00
J19   D2   30c black   210.00   2.50
J20   D2   40c black   140.00   60.00
J21   D2   50c blk ('92)   600.00   175.00
J22   D2   60c blk ('84)   600.00   57.50
J23   D2   1fr black   750.00   350.00
J24   D2   2fr blk ('84)   1,400.   825.00
J25   D2   5fr blk ('84)   3,000.   1,600.

Excellent counterfeits exist of Nos. J23-J25.
See Nos. J26-J45A. For overprints and surcharges see Offices in China Nos. J1-J6, J33-J40, Offices in Egypt, Alexandria J1-J5, Port Said J1-J8, Offices in Zanzibar 60-62, J1-J5, Offices in Morocco 9-10, 24-25, J1-J5, J10-J12, J17-J22, J35-J41.

1884
J26   D2   1fr brown   400.00   90.00
J27   D2   2fr brown   190.00   130.00
J28   D2   5fr brown   450.00   325.00

1893-1941
J29   D2   5c blue ('94)   .25   .30
J30   D2   10c brown   .25   .30
J31   D2   15c lt grn ('94)   28.00   1.40
J32   D2   20c ol grn ('06)   6.50   .65
J33   D2   25c rose ('23)   6.50   3.75
J34   D2   30c red ('94)   .25   .20
J35   D2   30c org red ('94)   475.00   85.00
J36   D2   40c rose ('25)   11.50   4.50
J37   D2   45c grn ('24)   9.00   5.25
J38   D2   50c brn vio ('95)   .50   .30
a.   50c lilac   .50   .30
J39   D2   60c bl grn ('25)   1.00   .55
J40   D2   1fr rose, straw ('96)   475.00   375.00
J41   D2   1fr red brn, straw ('20)   9.50   .30
J42   D2   1fr red brn ('35)   1.25   .40
J43   D2   2fr red org ('10)   225.00   65.00
J44   D2   2fr brt vio ('26)   .65   .75
J45   D2   3fr magenta ('26)   .65   .75
J45A   D2   5fr red org ('41)   1.40   2.25

D3   D4

1908-25
J46   D3   1c olive grn   1.00   1.25
J47   D3   10c violet   1.10   .30
a.   Imperf., pair   175.00

J48   D3   20c bister ('19)   40.00   1.25
J49   D3   30c bister ('09)   14.00   .40
J50   D3   50c red ('09)   275.00   60.00
J51   D3   60c red ('25)   2.75   3.75
Nos. J46-J51 (6)   333.85   66.95

"Recouvrements" stamps were used to recover charges due on undelivered or refused mail which was returned to the sender.
For surcharges see Offices in Morocco Nos. J6-J9, J13-J16, J23-J26, J42-J45.

Nos. J49-J50 Surcharged

1917
J52   D3   20c on 30c bister   20.00   4.00
J53   D3   40c on 50c red   10.50   4.00
a.   Double surcharge   475.00

In Jan. 1917 several values of the current issue of postage stamps were handstamped "T" in a triangle and used as postage due stamps.

Recouvrements Stamps of 1908-25 Surcharged

1926
J54   D3   50c on 10c lilac   3.50   3.25
J55   D3   60c on 1c ol grn   7.00   5.00
J56   D3   1fr on 60c red   18.00   10.00
J57   D3   2fr on 60c red   18.00   10.50
Nos. J54-J57 (4)   46.50   28.75

1927-31
J58   D4   1c olive grn ('28)   1.00   1.00
J59   D4   10c rose ('31)   1.90   1.40
J60   D4   30c bister   4.50   .50
J61   D4   60c red   4.50   .50
J62   D4   1fr violet   14.00   3.25
J63   D4   1fr Prus grn ('31)   17.00   .55
J64   D4   2fr blue   80.00   42.50
J65   D4   2fr olive brn ('31)   150.00   26.00
Nos. J58-J65 (8)   272.90   75.70

Nos. J62 to J65 have the numerals of value double-lined.

Nos. J64, J62 Surcharged in Red or Black

1929
J66   D4   1.20fr on 2fr blue   42.50   11.00
J67   D4   5fr on 1fr vio (Bk)   65.00   15.00
Set, never hinged   250.00

No. J61 Surcharged

1931
J68   D4   1fr on 60c red   30.00   2.75
Never hinged   60.00

> **Catalogue values for unused stamps in this section, from this point to the end of the section, are for Never Hinged items.**

Sheaves of Wheat
D5   D6

Perf. 14x13½

1943-46		Unwmk.		Typo.
J69	D5	10c sepia	.20	.20
J70	D5	30c brt red vio	.20	.20
J71	D5	50c blue grn	.20	.20
J72	D5	1fr brt ultra	.20	.20
J73	D5	1.50fr rose red	.45	.40
J74	D5	2fr turq blue	.45	.40
J75	D5	3fr brn org	.45	.40
J76	D5	4fr dp vio ('45)	5.50	3.00
J77	D5	5fr brt pink	.60	.40
J78	D5	10fr red org ('45)	3.50	.40
J79	D5	20fr ol bis ('46)	10.00	2.75
		Nos. J69-J79 (11)	21.75	8.55

Type of 1943
Inscribed "Timbre Taxe"

1946-53				
J80	D5	10c sepia ('47)	1.25	1.25
J81	D5	30c brt red vio ('47)	1.25	1.25
J82	D5	50c blue grn ('47)	25.00	9.50
J83	D5	1fr brt ultra ('47)	.25	.25
J85	D5	2fr turq blue	.25	.25
J86	D5	3fr brown org	.25	.25
J87	D5	4fr deep violet	.25	.25
J88	D5	5fr brt pink ('47)	.25	.25
J89	D5	10fr red org ('47)	.25	.25
J90	D5	20fr olive bis ('47)	2.00	.45
J91	D5	50fr dk green ('50)	25.00	1.40
J92	D5	100fr dp green ('53)	77.50	6.75
		Nos. J80-J92 (12)	133.50	22.10

For surcharges see Reunion Nos. J36-J44.

1960		Typo.	Perf. 14x13½	
J93	D6	5c bright pink	3.25	.40
J94	D6	10c red orange	5.00	.30
J95	D6	20c olive bister	4.00	.30
J96	D6	50c dark green	12.50	1.25
J97	D6	1fr deep green	50.00	2.00
		Nos. J93-J97 (5)	74.75	4.25

For surcharges see Reunion Nos. J46-J48.
For overprints see Algeria Nos. J49-J53.

D7

D8

Flowers: 5c, Centaury. 10c, Gentian. 15c, Corn poppy. 20c, Violets. 30c, Forget-me-not. 40c, Columbine. 50c, Clover. 1fr, Soldanel.

1964-71		Typo.	Perf. 14x13½	
J98	D7	5c car rose, red & grn ('65)	.20	.20
J99	D7	10c car rose, brt bl & grn ('65)	.20	.20
J100	D7	15c brn, grn & red	.20	.20
J101	D7	20c dk grn, grn & vio ('71)	.20	.20
J102	D7	30c brn, ultra & grn	.20	.20
J103	D7	40c dk grn, scar & yel ('71)	.25	.20
J104	D7	50c vio bl, car & grn ('65)	.25	.20
J105	D7	1fr vio bl, lil & grn ('65)	.40	.20
		Nos. J98-J105 (8)	1.90	1.60

For surcharges see Reunion Nos. J49-J55.

1982-83		Engr.	Perf. 13	
J106	D8	10c Ampedus Cinnabarinus	.20	.20
J107	D8	20c Dorcadion fuliginator	.20	.20
J108	D8	30c Leptura cordigera	.20	.20
J109	D8	40c Paederus littoralis	.20	.20
J110	D8	50c Pyrochroa coccinea	.20	.20
J111	D8	1fr Scarites laevigatus	.30	.20
J112	D8	2fr Trichius gallicus	.55	.20
J113	D8	3fr Adalia alpina	.90	.20
J114	D8	4fr Apoderus coryli	.20	.20
J115	D8	5fr Trichodes alvearius	1.50	.20
		Nos. J106-J115 (10)	5.45	2.00

Issued: 30c, 40c, 3fr, 5fr, 1/3/83; others, 1/4/82.

MILITARY STAMPS

Regular Issue
Overprinted in Black or Red

F. M.

1901-39		Unwmk.	Perf. 14x13½	
M1	A17	15c orange ('01)	65.00	6.00
a.		Inverted overprint	300.00	150.00
b.		Imperf., pair	425.00	
M2	A19	15c pale red ('03)	65.00	6.00
M3	A20	15c slate grn ('04)	52.50	6.00
a.		No period after "M"	110.00	57.50
b.		Imperf., pair	290.00	
M4	A20	10c rose ('06)	30.00	8.25
a.		No period after "M"	82.50	45.00
b.		Imperf., pair	350.00	
M5	A22	10c red ('07)	1.75	1.00
a.		Inverted overprint	105.00	65.00
b.		Imperf., pair	190.00	
M6	A20	50c vermilion ('29)	4.75	1.00
a.		No period after "M"	32.50	18.00
b.		Period in front of F	32.50	18.00
M7	A45	50c rose red ('34)	2.75	.55
a.		No period after "M"	29.00	16.00
b.		Inverted overprint	150.00	110.00
M8	A45	65c brt ultra (R) ('38)	.30	.30
a.		No period after "M"	29.00	16.00
M9	A45	90c ultra (R) ('39)	.40	.35
		Nos. M1-M9 (9)	222.45	29.45

"F. M." are initials of Franchise Militaire (Military Frank). See No. S1.

Catalogue values for unused stamps in this section, from this point to the end of the section, are for Never Hinged items.

M1

Flag — M2

1946-47			Typo.	
M10	M1	dark green	1.75	.65
M11	M1	rose red ('47)	.30	.20

Nos. M10-M11 were valid also in the French colonies.

1964, July 20			Perf. 13x14	
M12	M2	multicolored	.30	.35

OFFICIAL STAMPS

FOR THE COUNCIL OF EUROPE

For use only on mail posted in the post office in the Council of Europe Building, Strasbourg.

Catalogue values for unused stamps in this section are for Never Hinged items.

For French stamp inscribed "Conseil de l'Europe" see No. 679.

France No. 854 Overprinted: "CONSEIL DE L'EUROPE"
Unwmk.

1958, Jan. 14		Engr.	Perf. 13	
1O1	A303	35fr car rose & lake	1.25	2.25

Council of Europe
Flag — O1

1958-59				
		Flag in Ultramarine		
1O2	O1	8fr red org & brn vio	.25	.25
1O3	O1	20fr yel & lt brn	.35	.35
1O4	O1	25fr lil rose & sl grn ('59)	1.10	1.10
1O5	O1	35fr red	.55	.55
1O6	O1	50fr lilac rose ('59)	2.25	2.25
		Nos. 1O2-1O6 (5)	4.50	4.50

1963, Jan. 3				
		Flag in Ultramarine		
1O7	O1	20c yel & lt brn	1.25	1.25
1O8	O1	25c lil rose & sl grn	2.00	2.00
1O9	O1	50c lilac rose	2.50	2.50
		Nos. 1O7-1O9 (3)	5.75	5.75

Centime value stamps shown the denomination as "0,20," etc.

1965-71				
		Flag in Ultramarine & Yellow		
1O10	O1	25c ver, yel & sl grn	1.10	1.10
1O11	O1	30c ver & yel	1.10	1.10
1O12	O1	40c ver, yel & gray	1.75	1.75
1O13	O1	50c red, yel & grn	2.25	2.25
1O14	O1	60c ver, yel & vio	1.50	1.50
1O15	O1	70c ver, yel & dk brn	5.50	5.50
		Nos. 1O10-1O15 (6)	13.20	13.20

Issue dates: 25c, 30c, 60c, Jan. 16, 1965; 50c, Feb. 20, 1971; others, Mar. 24, 1969.

Type of 1958 Inscribed "FRANCE"

1975-76		Engr.	Perf. 13	
		Flag in Ultramarine & Yellow		
1O16	O1	60c org, yel & emer	.85	.85
1O17	O1	80c yel & mag	1.25	1.25
1O18	O1	1fr car, yel & gray ol ('76)	5.50	5.50
1O19	O1	1.20fr org, yel & bl	4.50	4.50
		Nos. 1O16-1O19 (4)	12.10	12.10

Issue dates: 1fr, Oct. 16; others, Nov. 22.

New Council Headquarters,
Strasbourg — O2

1977, Jan. 22		Engr.	Perf. 13	
1O20	O2	80c car & multi	1.00	.50
1O21	O2	1fr brown & multi	1.00	.50
1O22	O2	1.40fr gray & multi	2.00	1.00
		Nos. 1O20-1O22 (3)	4.00	2.00

Human Rights Emblem in Upper Left Corner

1978, Oct. 14				
1O23	O2	1.20fr red lilac & multi	.45	.40
1O24	O2	1.70fr blue & multi	.75	.55

30th anniversary of the Universal Declaration of Human Rights.

Council Headquarters Type of 1977

1980, Nov. 24		Engr.	Perf. 13	
1O25	O2	1.40fr olive	.50	.50
1O26	O2	2fr blue gray	.90	.90

New Council Headquarters,
Strasbourg — O3

1981-84			Engr.	
1O27	O3	1.40fr multicolored	.50	.50
1O28	O3	1.60fr multicolored	.50	.40
1O29	O3	1.70fr emerald	.75	.75
1O30	O3	1.80fr multicolored	.70	.70
1O31	O3	2fr multicolored	.90	.90
1O32	O3	2.10fr red	1.00	1.00
1O33	O3	2.30fr multicolored	1.00	1.00
1O34	O3	2.60fr multicolored	1.00	1.00
1O35	O3	2.80fr multicolored	1.00	1.00
1O36	O3	3fr brt blue	1.25	1.25
		Nos. 1O27-1O36 (10)	8.60	8.50

Issued: 1.40, 1.60, 2.30fr, 11/21; 1.80, 2.60fr, 11/13/82; 2, 2.80fr, 11/21/83; 1.70, 2.10, 3fr, 11/5/84.

Youth's Leg, Sneaker, Shattered Eggshell O4

1985, Aug. 31		Engr.	Perf. 13	
1O37	O4	1.80fr brt green	.90	.90
1O38	O4	2.20fr vermilion	.90	.90
1O39	O4	3.20fr brt blue	1.40	1.40
		Nos. 1O37-1O39 (3)	3.20	3.20

New Council Headquarters,
Strasbourg — O5

1986-87		Engr.	Perf. 13	
1O40	O5	1.90fr green	.90	.90
1O41	O5	2fr brt yel grn	1.10	1.10
1O42	O5	2.20fr red	.90	.90
1O43	O5	3.40fr blue	1.75	1.75
1O44	O5	3.60fr brt blue	2.25	2.25
		Nos. 1O40-1O44 (5)	6.90	6.90

Issued: 1.90, 2.20, 3.40fr, 12/13; 2, 3.60fr, 10/10/87.

Council of Europe, 40th Anniv. O6

1989, Feb. 4		Litho. & Engr.		
1O45	O6	2.20fr multicolored	1.40	1.40
1O46	O6	3.60fr multicolored	2.25	2.25

Denominations also inscribed in European Currency Units (ECUs).

Map of Europe O7

1990-91		Litho.	Perf. 13	
1O47	O7	2.30fr multicolored	1.00	1.00
1O48	O7	2.50fr multicolored	1.00	1.00
1O49	O7	3.20fr multicolored	1.60	1.60
1O50	O7	3.40fr multicolored	1.60	1.60
		Nos. 1O47-1O50 (4)	5.20	5.20

Issued: 2.30fr, 3.20fr, 5/26/90; 2.50fr, 3.40fr, 11/23/91.

36 Heads, by Hundertwasser O8

1994, Jan. 15		Litho.	Perf. 13	
1O51	O8	2.80fr multicolored	1.40	1.40
1O52	O8	3.70fr multicolored	1.75	1.75

Palace of Human Rights, Strasbourg O9

1996, June 1		Litho.	Perf. 13	
1O53	O9	3fr multicolored	.90	.90
1O54	O9	3.80fr multicolored	1.60	1.60

Charioteer of Delphi — O10

1999, Sept. 18		Photo.	Perf. 13	
1O55	O10	3fr shown	1.40	1.40
1O56	O10	3.80fr Nike	1.75	1.75

Girl, Penguin and Boy — O11

2001, Dec. 1   Litho.   Perf. 13
1057 O11 3fr red & multi   .90 .90
1058 O11 3.80fr grn & multi   1.40 1.40

Hiker on Stars — O12

2003, Oct. 18   Litho.   Perf. 13
1059 O12 50c Hiker facing left   1.25 1.25
1060 O12 75c Hiker facing right 1.75 1.75

O13

O14

2005, Sept. 18   Litho.   Perf. 13
1061 O13 55c multi   1.40 1.40
1062 O14 75c multi   1.90 1.90

Map of Europe O15

Sculpture by Mariano González Beltrán O16

2007, June 23   Litho.   Perf. 13
1063 O15 60c multi   1.75 1.75
1064 O16 85c multi   2.40 2.40

FOR THE UNITED NATIONS EDUCATIONAL, SCIENTIFIC AND CULTURAL ORGANIZATION

For use only on mail posted in the post office in the UNESCO Building, Paris.

Catalogue values for unused stamps in this section are for Never Hinged items.

For French stamps inscribed "UNESCO" see Nos. 572, 893-894, 2545.

Khmer Buddha and Hermes by Praxiteles O1

1961-65   Unwmk.   Engr.   Perf. 13
201 O1 20c dk gray, ol bis & bl   .25 .55
202 O1 25c blk, lake & grn   .40 .90
203 O1 30c choc & bis brn ('65)   .60 .60
204 O1 50c blk, red & vio bl   1.50 1.75
205 O1 60c grnsh bl, red brn & rose lil ('65)   1.40 1.40
      Nos. 201-205 (5)   4.15 5.20

Book and Globe — O2

1966, Dec. 17
206 O2 25c gray   .50 .50
207 O2 30c dark red   .65 .65
208 O2 60c green   1.10 1.10
      Nos. 206-208 (3)   2.25 2.25
20th anniversary of UNESCO.

Human Rights Flame — O3

1969-71   Engr.   Perf. 13
209   O3 30c sl grn, red & dp brn   .60 .60
2010 O3 40c dk car rose, red & dp brn   .95 .95
2011 O3 50c ultra, car & brn ('71)   2.00 2.00
2012 O3 70c pur, red & sl   3.00 3.00
      Nos. 209-2012 (4)   6.55 6.55
Universal Declaration of Human Rights.

Type of 1969 Inscribed "FRANCE"

1975, Nov. 15   Engr.   Perf. 13
2013 O3 60c grn, red & dk brn   1.10 1.10
2014 O3 80c ocher, red & red brn   1.65 1.65
2015 O3 1.20fr ind, red & brn   4.25 4.25
      Nos. 2013-2015 (3)   7.00 7.00

O4

1976-78   Engr.   Perf. 13
2016 O4 80c multi   .85 .85
2017 O4 1fr multi   .85 .85
2018 O4 1.20fr multi   .50 .50
2019 O4 1.40fr multi   2.25 1.25
2020 O4 1.70fr multi   .75 .75
      Nos. 2016-2020 (5)   5.20 4.20
Issued: 1.20, 1.70fr, 10/14/78; others, 10/23/76.

Slave Quarters, Senegal O5

Designs: 1.40fr, Mohenjo-Daro excavations, Pakistan. 2fr, Sans-Souci Palace, Haiti.

1980, Nov. 17   Engr.   Perf. 13
2021 O5 1.20fr multi   .45 .45
2022 O5 1.40fr multi   .50 .50
2023 O5 2fr multi   .65 .65
      Nos. 2021-2023 (3)   1.60 1.60

Hue, Vietnam — O7

Designs: 1.40fr, Building, Fez, Morocco. 1.60fr, Seated deity, Sukhotai, Thailand. 2.30fr, Fort St. Elmo, Malta, horiz. 2.60fr, St. Michael Church ruins, Brazil.

1981-82
2024 O7 1.40fr multi   .60 .60
2025 O7 1.60fr multi   .60 .60
2026 O7 1.80fr shown   .70 .70
2027 O7 2.30fr multi   .80 .80
2028 O7 2.60fr multi   .90 .90
      Nos. 2024-2028 (5)   3.60 3.60
Issued: 1.80fr, 2.60fr, 10/23/82; others, 12/12/81.

Mosque, Chinguetti, Mauritania O8

Roman Theater and female standing sculpture, Carthage, Tunisia — O8a

Architecture: 1.70fr, Church, Lalibela, Ethiopia. 2.10fr, San'a, Yemen. 2.20fr, Old Town Square and wrought iron latticework, Havana. 2.80fr, Enclosure wall interior, Istanbul. 3fr, Church, Kotor, Yugoslavia. 3.20fr, Temple of Anuradhapura and bas-relief of two women, Sri Lanka.

1983-85   Engr.
2029 O8   1.70fr multi   .70 .70
2030 O8a 1.80fr multi   .80 .80
2031 O8   2fr multi   .75 .75
2032 O8   2.10fr multi   .80 .80
2033 O8a 2.20fr multi   .90 .90
2034 O8   2.80fr multi   1.00 1.00
2035 O8   3fr multi   1.10 1.10
2036 O8a 3.20fr multi   1.50 1.50
      Nos. 2029-2036 (8)   7.55 7.55
Issued: 2fr, 2.80fr, 10/10; 1.70fr, 2.10fr, 3fr, 10/22/84; 1.80fr, 2.20fr, 3.20fr, 10/26/85.

Tikal Temple, Guatemala — O9

1986, Dec. 6   Engr.   Perf. 13
2037 O9 1.90fr shown   1.00 1.00
2038 O9 3.40fr Bagerhat Mosque, Bangladesh   1.75 1.75

The Parthenon, Athens O10

1987, Dec. 5   Engr.   Perf. 13x12½
2039 O10 2fr shown   .90 .90
2040 O10 3.60fr Temple of Philae, Egypt   1.60 1.60

Shibam, Yemen People's Democratic Republic O11

Perf. 13x12½, 12½x13
1990, Apr. 7   Engr.
2041 O11 2.30fr San Francisco de Lima, Peru, vert.   1.10 1.10
2042 O11 3.20fr shown   1.50 1.50

Bagdaon Temple, Nepal — O12

3.40fr, Citadel of Harat, Afghanistan, horiz.

1991, Nov. 23
2043 O12 2.50fr choc & dk red   1.25 1.25
2044 O12 3.40fr grn, brn & ol   1.50 1.50

Tassili N'Ajjer Natl. Park, Algeria O13

Design: 2.80fr, Angkor Wat Archaeological Park, Cambodia, vert.

1993, Oct. 23   Litho.   Perf. 13
2045 O13 2.80fr multicolored   1.25 1.25
2046 O13 3.70fr multicolored   2.00 2.00

UNESCO, 50th Anniv. O14

Designs: 3fr, Uluru Natl. Park, Australia. 3.80fr, Los Glaciares Natl. Park, Argentina.

1996, June 1   Litho.   Perf. 13
2047 O14 3fr multicolored   1.50 1.50
2048 O14 3.80fr multicolored   2.00 2.00

Detail of Dionysus Fresco, Pompeii — O15

Moai Statues, Easter Island O16

1998, Oct. 24   Litho.   Perf. 13
2049 O15 3fr multicolored   1.50 1.50
2050 O16 3.80fr multicolored   1.90 1.90

Sphinx and
Pyramids,
Egypt
O17

Komodo
Dragon,
Komodo
Natl. Park,
Indonesia
O18

2001, Dec. 1   Litho.   Perf. 13

2O51	O17	3fr multi	1.60 1.60
2O52	O18	3.80fr multi	2.00 2.00

Reindeer,
Lapland
O19

Church of the
Resurrection, St.
Petersburg,
Russia — O20

2003, Dec. 6   Litho.   Perf. 13

2O53	O19	50c multi	1.40 1.40
2O54	O20	75c multi	2.00 2.00

Bison in Bialowieza
Forest,
Poland — O21

Petra,
Jordan
O22

2005, Nov. 26   Litho.   Perf. 13

2O55	O21	55c multi	1.50 1.50
2O56	O22	90c multi	2.25 2.25

Siberian
Tiger — O23

Luang
Prabang,
Laos
O24

2006, Dec. 7   Litho.   Perf. 13

2O57	O23	60c multi	1.60 .40
2O58	O24	85c multi	2.25 .60

FOR THE UNITED NATIONS EDUCATIONAL, SCIENTIFIC AND CULTURAL ORGANIZATION

Ksar d'Ait-Ben-Haddou,
Morocco — O25

Koala,
Australia — O26

2007, Dec. 13   Litho.   Perf. 13

2O59	O25	60c multi	1.75 1.75
2O60	O26	85c multi	2.50 2.50

NEWSPAPER STAMPS

Coat of Arms — N1

1868   Unwmk.   Typo.   Imperf.

P1	N1 2c lilac	300.00	65.00
P2	N1 2c (+ 2c) blue	600.00	275.00

Perf. 12½

P3	N1 2c lilac	52.50	25.00
P4	N1 2c (+ 4c) rose	250.00	100.00
P5	N1 2c (+ 2c) blue	75.00	35.00
P6	N1 5c lilac	1,250.	550.00

Nos. P2, P4, and P5 were sold for face plus an added fiscal charge indicated in parenthesis. Nos. P1, P3 and P6 were used simply as fiscals.

The 2c rose and 5c lilac imperforate and the 5c rose and 5c blue, both imperforate and perforated, were never put into use.

Nos. P1-P6 were reprinted for the 1913 Ghent Exhibition and the 1937 Paris Exhibition (PEXIP).

No. 109 Surcharged in
Red

1919   Perf. 14x13½

P7	A16 ½c on 1c gray	.30 .30
a.	Inverted surcharge	1,200. 1,150.

No. 156 Surcharged

1933

P8	A22 ½c on 1c olive bister	.30 .30

FRANCHISE STAMP

No. 276 Overprinted "F"

1939   Unwmk.   Perf. 14x13½

S1	A45 90c ultramarine	1.90 *2.50*
	Never hinged	2.75
a.	Period following "F"	20.00 20.00
	Never hinged	20.00

No. S1 was for the use of Spanish refugees in France. "F" stands for "Franchise."

OCCUPATION STAMPS

Issued under German Occupation (Alsace and Lorraine)

OS1

1870   Typo.   Unwmk.   Perf. 13½x14
Network with Points Up

N1	OS1	1c bronze grn	100.00 *110.00*
a.		1c olive green	100.00 *110.00*
N2	OS1	2c dark brown	190.00 190.00
a.		2c red brown	190.00 190.00
N3	OS1	4c gray	200.00 115.00
N4	OS1	5c yel grn	200.00 15.00
N5	OS1	10c yel bister brn	155.00 6.50
a.		10c yel brown	170.00 7.00
b.		Network lemon yellow	200.00 10.00
N6	OS1	20c ultra	190.00 17.50
N7	OS1	25c brown	210.00 110.00
		25c blk brown	160.00 80.00

There are three varieties of the 4c and two of the 10c, differing in the position of the figures of value, and several other setting varieties.

Network with Points Down

N8	OS1	1c olive grn	525.00 *725.00*
N9	OS1	2c red brn	265.00 *625.00*
N10	OS1	4c gray	265.00 *625.00*
N11	OS1	5c yel grn	6,500. 650.00
N12	OS1	10c bister	265.00 21.50
a.		Network lemon yellow	325.00 *57.50*
N13	OS1	20c ultra	340.00 100.00
N14	OS1	25c brown	725.00 325.00

Official imitations have the network with points downward. The "P" of "Postes" is 2½mm from the border in the imitations and 3mm in the originals.

The word "Postes" measures 12¾ to 13mm on the imitations, and from 11 to 12½mm on the originals.

The imitations are perf. 13½x14½; originals, perf. 13½x14¼.

The stamps for Alsace and Lorraine were replaced by stamps of the German Empire on Jan. 1, 1872.

German Stamps of 1905-16
Surcharged:

1916   Wmk. 125   Perf. 14, 14½

N15	A16	3c on 3pf brown	1.25 1.25
N16	A16	5c on 5pf green	1.25 1.25
N17	A22	8c on 7½pf org	2.00 2.00
N18	A16	10c on 10pf car	2.00 2.00
N19	A22	15c on 15pf yel brn	1.25 1.25
N20	A16	25c on 20pf blue	1.25 1.25
a.		25c on 20pf ultramarine	2.00 2.00
N21	A16	40c on 30pf org & blk, *buff*	2.90 2.75
N22	A16	50c on 40pf lake & blk	2.90 2.75
N23	A16	75c on 60pf mag	12.50 12.50
N24	A16	1fr on 80pf lake & blk, *rose*	12.50 12.50

N25	A17	1fr25c on 1m car	47.50 47.50
a.		Double surcharge	
N26	A21	2fr50c on 2m gray bl	47.50 47.50
a.		Double surcharge	
		Nos. N15-N26 (12)	134.80 134.50

These stamps were also used in parts of Belgium occupied by the German forces.

Catalogue values for unused stamps in this section, from this point to the end of the section, are for Never Hinged items.

Alsace
Issued under German Occupation

Stamps of Germany
1933-36 Overprinted in
Black

1940   Wmk. 237   Perf. 14

N27	A64	3pf olive bister	.80	.55
N28	A64	4pf dull blue	.80	.55
N29	A64	5pf brt green	.80	.55
N30	A64	6pf dark green	.80	.55
N31	A64	8pf vermilion	.80	.55
N32	A64	10pf chocolate	.80	.55
N33	A64	12pf dp carmine	1.00	.55
N34	A64	15pf maroon	1.00	.55
N35	A64	20pf brt blue	1.65	.75
N36	A64	25pf ultra	1.65	.75
N37	A64	30pf olive grn	1.65	.75
N38	A64	40pf red violet	2.90	.75
N39	A64	50pf dk grn & blk	7.00	3.25
N40	A64	60pf claret & blk	7.00	3.25
N41	A64	80pf dk blue & blk	17.50	7.00
N42	A64	100pf orange & blk	17.50	7.00
		Nos. N27-N42 (16)	63.65	28.15

Lorraine
Issued under German Occupation

Stamps of Germany
1933-36 Overprinted in
Black

1940   Wmk. 237   Perf. 14

N43	A64	3pf olive bister	1.00	.75
N44	A64	4pf dull blue	1.00	.75
N45	A64	5pf brt green	1.00	4.00
N46	A64	6pf dark green	1.00	.75
N47	A64	8pf vermilion	1.00	.75
N48	A64	10pf chocolate	1.50	.85
N49	A64	12pf deep carmine	1.50	.85
N50	A64	15pf maroon	1.50	.75
a.		Inverted surcharge	—	
N51	A64	20pf brt blue	1.65	1.00
N52	A64	25pf ultra	1.40	1.00
N53	A64	30pf olive grn	2.10	1.00
N54	A64	40pf red violet	2.50	1.25
N55	A64	50pf dk grn & blk	6.00	3.00
N56	A64	60pf claret & blk	6.00	3.00
N57	A64	80pf dk blue & blk	18.00	7.50
N58	A64	100pf orange & blk	18.00	7.50
		Nos. N43-N58 (16)	65.15	34.70

Besetztes Gebiet Nordfrankreich

These three words, in a rectangular frame covering two stamps, were handstamped in black on Nos. 267, 367 and 369 and used in the Dunkerque region in July-August, 1940. The German political officer of Dunkerque authorized the overprint. The prevalence of forgeries and later favor overprints makes expertization mandatory.

ALLIED MILITARY GOVERNMENT

Stamps formerly listed in this section as Nos. 2N1-2N20 are now listed with regular stamps of France as Nos. 475-476H and 523A-523J.

FRENCH OFFICES ABROAD

Prior to 1923 several of the world powers maintained their own post offices in China for the purpose of sending and receiving overseas mail. French offices were maintained in Canton, Hoi Hao (Hoihow), Kwangchowan (Kouangtchéou-wan), Mongtseu (Mong-tseu), Packhoi (Paknoi), Tong King (Tchongking), Yunnan Fou (Yunnanfu).

100 Centimes = 1 Franc
100 Cents = 1 Piaster
100 Cents = 1 Dollar

OFFICES IN CHINA

Peace and Commerce Stamps of France Overprinted in Red or Black

1894-1900		**Unwmk.**		**Perf. 14x13½**	
1	A1	5c grn, *grnsh* (R)		2.90	2.50
2	A1	5c yel grn, I (R)		2.90	2.50
		('00)		2.90	2.50
a.		Type II		45.00	29.00
3	A1	10c blk, *lav*, I (R)		8.25	2.50
a.		Type II		25.00	16.50
4	A1	15c bl (R)		11.50	4.00
5	A1	20c red, *grn*		7.00	4.50
6	A1	25c blk, *rose* (R)		8.25	2.50
a.		Double overprint		200.00	
b.		Pair, one without overprint		500.00	
7	A1	30c brn, *bis*		8.25	5.25
8	A1	40c red, *straw*		9.00	6.50
9	A1	50c car, *rose*, I		25.00	15.00
a.		Red overprint		57.50	
b.		Type II (Bk)		15.00	8.25
10	A1	75c dp vio, *org* (R)		75.00	52.50
11	A1	1fr brnz grn, *straw*		15.00	6.50
a.		Double overprint		375.00	400.00
12	A1	2fr brn, *az* ('00)		30.00	29.00
12A	A1	5fr red lil, *lav*		70.00	55.00
b.		Red overprint		475.00	
		Nos. 1-12A (13)		273.05	188.25

For surcharges and overprints see Nos. 13-17, J7-J10, J20-J23.

No. 11 Surcharged in Black **25**

13	A1	25c on 1fr brnz grn, *straw*		125.00	75.00

No. 6 Surcharged in Red

1901					
14	A1	2c on 25c blk, *rose*		1,000.	325.00
15	A1	4c on 25c blk, *rose*		1,250.	450.00
16	A1	6c on 25c blk, *rose*		1,000.	375.00
17	A1	16c on 25c blk, *rose*		300.00	190.00
a.		Black surcharge			6,750.
		Nos. 14-17 (4)		3,550.	1,340.

Stamps of Indo-China Surcharged in Black

1902-04					
18a	A3	1c blk, *lil bl* ('04)		2.50	2.50
19	A3	2c brn, *buff*		3.75	3.75
20a	A3	4c claret, *lav* ('04)		3.75	2.90
21a	A3	5c yellow grn ('04)		4.50	2.90
22	A3	10c red		5.75	5.00
23	A3	15c gray		6.50	5.75
24a	A3	20c red, *grn* ('04)		8.25	7.50
25a	A3	25c blk, *rose* ('04)		11.00	11.00
26	A3	30c blue ('04)		9.00	7.50
27a	A3	30c brn, *bis* ('04)		8.25	7.50
28a	A3	40c red, *straw* ('04)		24.00	18.00
29	A3	50c car, *rose*		62.50	62.50
30	A3	50c brn, *azure* ('04)		9.00	8.25
31a	A3	75c vio, *org* ('04)			6.00
32a	A3	1fr brnz grn, *straw* ('04)		40.00	40.00
33a	A3	5fr red lil, *lavender* ('04)		82.50	80.00
		Nos. 18a-33a (16)		287.25	297.55

The Chinese characters surcharged on Nos. 18-33 are the Chinese equivalents of the French values and therefore differ on each denomination. Two printings exist, differing slightly in the size of "CHINE." Values above are for the less expensive variety. See the *Scott Classic Specialized Catalouge of Stamps* and Covers for detailed listings. Many varieties of surcharge exist.

Liberty, Equality and Fraternity A3

"Rights of Man" A4

A5

1902-03				**Typo.**	
34	A3	5c green		5.00	3.25
35	A4	10c rose red ('03)		2.50	1.90
36	A4	15c pale red		2.50	1.90
37	A4	20c brn vio ('03)		7.50	6.50
38	A4	25c blue ('03)		5.75	3.00
39	A4	30c lilac ('03)		8.25	7.00
40	A5	40c red & pale bl		16.50	14.50
41	A5	50c bis brn & lav		22.50	16.00
42	A5	1fr claret & ol grn		29.00	16.50
43	A5	2fr gray vio & yel		57.50	45.00
44	A5	5fr dk bl & buff		82.50	70.00
		Nos. 34-44 (11)		239.50	185.55

For surcharges and overprints see Nos. 45, 57-85, J14-J16, J27-J30.

Surcharged in Black **5**

1903					
45	A4	5c on 15c pale red		16.50	16.50
a.		Inverted surcharge		125.00	75.00

Stamps of Indo-China, 1904-06, Surcharged as Nos. 18-33 in Black

1904-05					
46	A4	1c olive grn		2.00	2.00
47	A4	2c vio brn, *buff*		2.00	2.00
47A	A4	4c cl, *bluish*		900.00	750.00
48	A4	5c deep grn		2.00	2.00
49	A4	10c carmine		2.90	2.90
50	A4	15c org brn, *bl*		2.90	2.90
51	A4	20c red, *grn*		11.00	11.00
52	A4	25c deep blue		10.00	5.75
53	A4	40c blk, *bluish*		8.25	5.75
54	A4	1fr pale grn		325.00	275.00
55	A4	2fr brn, *org*		37.50	32.50
56	A4	10fr org brn, *grn*		145.00	135.00
		Nos. 46-56 (12)		1,448.	1,226.

Many varieties of the surcharge exist.

Stamps of 1902-03 Surcharged in Black

1907					
57	A3	2c on 5c green		2.50	1.65
58	A4	4c on 10c rose red		1.80	1.50
a.		Pair, one without surcharge		—	
59	A4	6c on 15c pale red		2.75	2.25
60	A4	8c on 20c brn vio		5.00	5.00
a.		"8" inverted		65.00	67.50
61	A4	10c on 25c blue		1.65	1.25
62	A5	20c on 50c bis brn & lav		5.25	3.25
a.		Double surcharge		425.00	425.00
b.		Triple surcharge		425.00	425.00
63	A5	40c on 1fr claret & ol grn		21.00	13.50
64	A5	2pi on 5fr dk bl & buff		21.00	13.50
a.		Double surcharge		2,100.	1,650.
		Nos. 57-64 (8)		60.95	41.90

Stamps of 1902-03 Surcharged in Black

1911-22					
65	A3	2c on 5c green		1.80	1.40
66	A4	4c on 10c rose red		1.90	1.50
67	A4	6c on 15c org		4.50	1.80
68	A4	8c on 20c brn vio		2.00	1.80
69	A4	10c on 25c bl ('21)		3.75	1.90
70	A4	20c on 50c bl ('22)		50.00	55.00
71	A5	40c on 1fr cl & ol grn		6.50	4.25

No. 44 Surcharged

73	A5	$2 on 5fr bl & buff ('22)		165.00	190.00
		Nos. 65-73 (8)		235.45	257.65

Types of 1902-03 Surcharged like Nos. 65-71

1922					
75	A3	1c on 5c org		5.00	5.25
76	A4	2c on 10c org		5.75	6.25
77	A4	3c on 15c org		8.25	9.00
78	A4	4c on 20c red brn		10.00	12.00
79	A4	5c on 25c dk vio		5.00	4.50
80	A4	6c on 30c red		11.00	9.00
82	A4	10c on 50c blue		13.00	9.00
83	A5	20c on 1fr claret & ol grn		32.50	40.00
84	A5	40c on 2fr org & pale bl		42.50	50.00
85	A5	$1 on 5fr dk bl & buff		135.00	145.00
		Nos. 75-85 (10)		268.00	290.00

POSTAGE DUE STAMPS

Postage Due Stamps of France Handstamped in Red or Black

1901-07		**Unwmk.**		**Perf. 14x13½**	
J1	D2	5c lt bl (R)		6.50	3.75
J2	D2	10c choc (R)		10.00	5.25
J3	D2	15c lt grn (R)		10.00	6.50
J4	D2	20c on grn (R) ('07)		11.50	10.00
J5	D2	30c carmine		16.00	11.00
J6	D2	50c lilac		16.00	11.00
		Nos. J1-J6 (6)		70.00	47.50

Stamps of 1894-1900 Handstamped in Carmine **A PERCEVOIR**

1903					
J7	A1	5c yel grn		—	2,250.
a.		Purple handstamp		—	
b.		5c green, *greenish*		—	
J8	A1	10c blk, *lavender*		—	
a.		Purple handstamp		—	
J9	A1	15c blue		—	1,250.
a.		Purple handstamp		—	
J10	A1	30c brn, *bister*		—	350.
a.		Purple handstamp		—	

Same Handstamp on Stamps of 1902-03 in Carmine

1903					
J14	A3	5c green		—	2,000.
a.		Purple handstamp		—	
J15	A4	10c rose red		—	425.
a.		Purple handstamp		—	
J16	A4	15c pale red		—	325.
a.		Purple handstamp		—	

Stamps of 1894-1900 Handstamped in Carmine

1903					
J20	A1	5c yellow green		—	1,100.
a.		Purple handstamp			
b.		5c green, *greenish*			

J21	A1	10c blk, *lavender*		—	—
a.		Purple handstamp			
J22	A1	15c blue		—	350.
a.		Purple handstamp			
J23	A1	30c brn, *bister*		—	325.
a.		Purple handstamp			

Same Handstamp on Stamps of 1902-03 in Carmine or Purple

1903					
J27	A3	5c green (C)		—	1,750.
a.		Purple handstamp			
J28	A4	10c rose red (C)		—	225.00
a.		Purple handstamp			
J29	A4	15c pale red (C)		—	225.00
a.		Purple handstamp			
J30	A4	30c lilac (P)		—	

The handstamps on Nos. J7-J30 are found inverted, double, etc.

The cancellations on these stamps should have dates between Sept. 1, and Nov. 30, 1903, to be genuine.

Postage Due Stamps of France, 1893-1910 Surcharged like Nos. 65-71

1911					
J33	D2	2c on 5c blue		2.50	2.10
a.		Double surcharge		125.00	
J34	D2	4c on 10c choc		2.50	2.10
a.		Double surcharge		125.00	
J35	D2	8c on 20c ol grn		2.90	2.50
J36	D2	20c on 50c lilac		2.90	2.50
		Nos. J33-J36 (4)		10.80	9.20

1922					
J37	D2	1c on 5c blue		82.50	95.00
J38	D2	2c on 10c brn		145.00	165.00
J39	D2	4c on 10c ol grn		145.00	165.00
J40	D2	10c on 50c brn vio		125.00	185.00
		Nos. J37-J40 (4)		497.50	610.00

CANTON

Stamps of Indo-China, 1892-1900, Overprinted in Red

1901		**Unwmk.**		**Perf. 14x13½**	
1	A3	1c blk, *lil bl*		1.75	1.75
1A	A3	2c brn, *buff*		2.25	2.25
2	A3	4c claret, *lav*		3.75	3.75
2A	A3	5c grn, *grnsh*		575.00	575.00
3	A3	5c yel grn		2.60	2.60
4	A3	10c blk, *lavender*		6.50	6.50
5	A3	15c blue, quadrille paper		5.25	5.25
6	A3	15c gray		6.25	6.25
a.		Double overprint		19.00	
7	A3	20c red, *grn*		20.00	20.00
8	A3	25c blk, *rose*		11.50	11.50
9	A3	30c brn, *bister*		28.00	28.00
10	A3	40c red, *straw*		28.00	28.00
11	A3	50c car, *rose*		32.50	32.50
12	A3	75c dp vio, *org*		32.50	32.50
13	A3	1fr brnz grn, *straw*		40.00	40.00
14	A3	5fr red lil, *lav*		225.00	225.00
		Nos. 1-14 (16)		1,020.	1,020.

The Chinese characters in the overprint on Nos. 1-14 read "Canton." On Nos. 15-64, they restate the denomination of the basic stamp.

Surcharged in Black

1903-04					
15	A3	1c blk, *lil bl*		3.75	3.25
16	A3	2c brn, *buff*		3.75	3.25
17	A3	4c claret, *lav*		3.75	3.25
18	A3	5c yellow green		3.90	3.40
19	A3	10c rose red		3.90	3.40
20	A3	15c gray		3.90	3.40
21	A3	20c red, *grn*		17.50	15.00
22	A3	25c blue		6.00	6.00
23	A3	25c blk, *rose* ('04)		9.50	6.50
24	A3	30c brn, *bister*		24.00	16.00
25	A3	40c red, *straw*		60.00	47.50
26	A3	50c car, *rose*		310.00	280.00
27	A3	50c brn, *az* ('04)		67.50	60.00
28	A3	75c dp vio, *org*		60.00	55.00
a.		"INDO-CHINE" inverted		47,500.	
29	A3	1fr brnz grn, *straw*		60.00	55.00
30	A3	5fr red lil, *lav*		60.00	55.00
		Nos. 15-30 (16)		697.45	615.95

Many varieties of the surcharge exist on #15-30.

Stamps of Indo-China, 1892-1906, Surcharged in Red or Black

A second printing of the 1906 surcharges of Canton, Hoi Hao, Kwangchowan, Mongtseu, Packhoi, Tong King and Yunnan Fou was made in 1908. The inks are grayish instead of full black and vermilion instead of carmine. Values are for the cheaper variety which usually is the second printing.

The 4c and 50c of the 1892 issue of Indo-China are known with this surcharge and similarly surcharged for other cities in China. The surcharges on these two stamps are always inverted. It is stated that they were irregularly produced and never issued.

1906
31	A4	1c ol grn (R)	2.00	2.00
32	A4	2c vio brn, *buff*	2.00	2.00
33	A4	4c cl, *bluish* (R)	2.00	2.00
34	A4	5c dp grn (R)	1.75	1.75
35	A4	10c carmine	2.60	2.60
36	A4	15c org brn, *bl*	20.00	20.00
37	A4	20c red, *grn*	11.00	11.00
38	A4	25c deep blue	4.75	4.75
39	A4	30c pale brn	16.00	16.00
40	A4	35c blk, *yel*	12.00	12.00
41	A4	40c blk, *bluish* (R)	20.00	20.00
42	A4	50c bister brn	13.00	13.00
43	A3	75c dp vio, *org* (R)	60.00	60.00
44	A4	1fr pale grn	24.00	24.00
45	A4	2fr brn, *org* (R)	35.00	35.00
46	A3	5fr red lil, *lav*	80.00	80.00
47	A4	10fr org brn, *grn*	72.50	72.50
		Nos. 31-47 (17)	378.60	378.60

Surcharge exists inverted on 1c, 25c & 1fr.

Stamps of Indo-China, 1907, Surcharged "CANTON", and Chinese Characters, in Red or Blue

1908
48	A5	1c ol brn & blk	.95	.95
49	A5	2c brn & blk	1.00	1.00
50	A5	4c bl & blk	2.00	1.20
51	A5	5c grn & blk	2.00	1.60
52	A5	10c red & blk (Bl)	2.40	2.00
53	A5	15c vio & blk	3.25	2.75
54	A6	20c vio & blk	4.50	3.50
55	A6	25c bl & blk	4.50	3.50
56	A6	30c brn & blk	7.25	6.75
57	A6	35c ol grn & blk	7.50	6.75
58	A6	40c brn & blk	9.50	6.75
59	A6	50c car & blk (Bl)	9.50	6.75
60	A7	75c ver & blk (Bl)	9.50	8.75
61	A8	1fr car & blk (Bl)	16.00	16.00
62	A9	2fr grn & blk	40.00	35.50
63	A10	5fr bl & blk	55.00	47.50
64	A11	10fr pur & blk	80.00	80.00
		Nos. 48-64 (17)	254.85	227.25

Nos. 48-64 Surcharged with New Values in Cents or Piasters in Black, Red or Blue

1919
65	A5	⅖c on 1c	1.00	.95
66	A5	⅘c on 2c	1.00	.95
67	A5	1⅗c on 4c (R)	1.00	.95
68	A5	2c on 5c	1.40	1.40
69	A5	4c on 10c (Bl)	1.60	1.60
a.		Chinese "2" instead of "4"	30.00	30.00
70	A6	6c on 15c	2.00	1.60
71	A6	8c on 20c	3.50	1.60
72	A6	10c on 25c	4.50	1.60
73	A6	12c on 30c	1.75	1.75
a.		Double surcharge	120.00	120.00
74	A6	14c on 35c	1.75	1.60
a.		Closed "4"	8.75	8.75
75	A6	16c on 40c	1.75	1.60
76	A6	20c on 50c (Bl)	2.10	1.60
77	A7	30c on 75c (Bl)	1.60	1.60
78	A8	40c on 1fr (Bl)	11.00	6.50
79	A9	80c on 2fr (R)	17.00	8.50
80	A10	2pi on 5fr (R)	29.00	29.00
81	A11	4pi on 10fr (R)	29.00	29.00
		Nos. 65-81 (17)	111.45	91.80

HOI HAO

Stamps of Indo-China Overprinted in Red

1901   Unwmk.   Perf. 14x13½
1	A3	1c blk, *lil bl*	3.25	3.25
2	A3	2c brn, *buff*	4.00	4.00
3	A3	4c claret, *lav*	4.00	4.00
4	A3	5c yel grn	4.00	4.00
5	A3	10c blk, *lavender*	12.00	9.50

6	A3	15c blue	1,700.	725.00
7	A3	15c gray	6.40	4.00
8	A3	20c red, *grn*	27.50	22.50
9	A3	25c blk, *rose*	16.00	12.00
10	A3	30c brn, *bister*	60.00	60.00
11	A3	40c red, *straw*	60.00	60.00
12	A3	50c car, *rose*	60.00	60.00
13	A3	75c dp vio, *org*	225.00	195.00
14	A3	1fr brnz grn, *straw*	725.00	675.00
15	A3	5fr red lil, *lav*	725.00	650.00
		Nos. 1-15 (15)	3,632.	2,488.

The Chinese characters in the overprint on Nos. 1-15 read "Hoi Hao." On Nos. 16-66, they restate the denomination of the basic stamp.

Surcharged in Black

1903-04
16	A3	1c blk, *lil bl*	1.75	1.75
17	A3	2c brn, *buff*	1.80	1.80
18	A3	4c claret, *lav*	2.90	2.90
19	A3	5c yel grn	3.00	3.00
20	A3	10c red	3.40	3.40
21	A3	15c gray	3.75	3.75
22	A3	20c red, *grn*	7.25	7.25
23	A3	25c blue	5.00	5.00
24	A3	25c blk, *rose* ('04)	7.25	7.25
25	A3	30c brn, *bister*	5.50	5.50
26	A3	40c red, *straw*	32.50	32.50
27	A3	50c car, *rose*	28.00	28.00
28	A3	50c brn, *az* ('04)	130.00	130.00
29	A3	75c dp vio, *org*	42.50	42.50
a.		"INDO-CHINE" inverted		42,500.
30	A3	1fr brnz grn, *straw*	62.50	62.50
31	A3	5fr red lil, *lav*	200.00	200.00
		Nos. 16-31 (16)	537.10	537.10

Many varieties of the surcharge exist on #1-31.

Stamps of Indo-China, 1892-1906, Surcharged in Red or Black

1906
32	A4	1c ol grn (R)	8.00	8.00
33	A4	2c vio brn, *buff*	8.00	8.00
34	A4	4c cl, *bluish* (R)	8.00	8.00
35	A4	5c dp grn (R)	8.00	8.00
36	A4	10c carmine	8.00	8.00
37	A4	15c org brn, *bl*	30.00	30.00
38	A4	20c red, *grn*	12.00	12.00
39	A4	25c deep blue	9.50	9.50
40	A4	30c pale brn	12.00	12.00
41	A4	35c blk, *yel* (R)	20.00	20.00
42	A4	40c blk, *bluish* (R)	20.00	20.00
43	A4	50c gray brn	20.00	20.00
44	A3	75c dp vio, *org* (R)	60.00	60.00
45	A4	1fr pale grn	60.00	60.00
46	A4	2fr brn, *org* (R)	60.00	60.00
47	A3	5fr red lil, *lav*	120.00	120.00
48	A4	10fr org brn, *grn*	140.00	140.00
		Nos. 32-48 (17)	603.50	603.50

Stamps of Indo-China, 1907, Surcharged "HOI HAO" and Chinese Characters, in Red or Blue

1908
49	A5	1c ol brn & blk	1.35	1.35
50	A5	2c brn & blk	1.40	1.40
51	A5	4c bl & blk	1.60	1.60
52	A5	5c grn & blk	2.40	2.40
53	A5	10c red & blk (Bl)	2.40	2.40
54	A5	15c vio & blk	6.50	6.50
55	A6	20c vio & blk	6.50	6.50
56	A6	25c bl & blk	6.50	6.50
57	A6	30c brn & blk	6.50	6.50
58	A6	35c ol grn & blk	6.50	6.50
59	A6	40c brn & blk	7.25	7.25
60	A6	50c car & blk (Bl)	9.25	9.25
61	A7	75c ver & blk (Bl)	8.75	8.75
62	A8	1fr car & blk (Bl)	26.00	26.00
63	A9	2fr grn & blk	40.00	40.00
64	A10	5fr bl & blk	67.50	67.50
66	A11	10fr pur & blk	100.00	100.00
		Nos. 49-66 (17)	300.40	300.40

Nos. 49-66 Surcharged with New Values in Cents or Piasters in Black, Red or Blue

1919
67	A5	⅖c on 1c	1.20	1.20
68	A5	⅘c on 2c	1.20	1.20
69	A5	1⅗c on 4c (R)	1.60	1.60
70	A5	2c on 5c	2.00	2.00
71	A5	4c on 10c (Bl)	2.40	2.40
a.		Chinese "2" instead of "4"	8.75	8.75

72	A5	6c on 15c	2.00	2.00
73	A6	8c on 20c	4.00	4.00
a.		"S" of "CENTS" omitted	110.00	110.00
74	A6	10c on 25c	5.50	5.50
75	A6	12c on 30c	4.00	4.00
76	A6	14c on 35c	3.25	3.25
a.		Closed "4"	40.00	40.00
77	A6	16c on 40c	4.00	4.00
79	A6	20c on 50c (Bl)	3.25	3.25
80	A7	30c on 75c (Bl)	9.50	9.50
81	A8	40c on 1fr (R)	20.00	20.00
82	A9	80c on 2fr (R)	55.00	55.00
83	A10	2pi on 5fr (R)	80.00	80.00
a.		Triple surch. of new value	675.00	675.00
84	A11	4pi on 10fr (R)	200.00	200.00
		Nos. 67-84 (17)	398.90	398.90

KWANGCHOWAN

A Chinese Territory leased to France, 1898 to 1945.

Stamps of Indo-China, 1892-1906, Surcharged in Red or Black

1906   Unwmk.   Perf. 14x13½
1	A4	1c ol grn (R)	8.00	8.00
2	A4	2c vio brn, *buff*	8.00	8.00
3	A4	4c cl, *bluish* (R)	8.00	8.00
4	A4	5c dp grn (R)	8.00	8.00
5	A4	10c carmine	8.00	8.00
6	A4	15c org brn, *bl*	30.00	30.00
7	A4	20c red, *grn*	12.00	12.00
8	A4	25c deep blue	9.50	9.50
9	A4	30c pale brn	12.00	12.00
10	A4	35c blk, *yel* (R)	20.00	20.00
11	A4	40c blk, *bluish* (R)	20.00	20.00
12	A4	50c bister brn	20.00	20.00
13	A3	75c dp vio, *org* (R)	60.00	60.00
14	A4	1fr pale grn	40.00	40.00
15	A4	2fr brn, *org* (R)	52.50	52.50
16	A3	5fr red lil, *lav*	190.00	190.00
17	A4	10fr org brn, *grn*	240.00	240.00
		Nos. 1-17 (17)	746.00	746.00

Various varieties of the surcharge exist on Nos. 2-10.

Stamps of Indo-China, 1907, Surcharged "KOUANG-TCHEOU" and Value in Chinese in Red or Blue

1908
18	A5	1c ol brn & blk	1.35	1.35
19	A5	2c brn & blk	1.35	1.35
20	A5	4c bl & blk	1.35	1.35
21	A5	5c grn & blk	1.40	1.40
22	A5	10c red & blk (Bl)	1.40	1.40
23	A5	15c vio & blk	3.00	3.00
24	A6	20c vio & blk	5.50	5.50
25	A6	25c bl & blk	6.00	6.00
26	A6	30c brn & blk	8.75	8.75
27	A6	35c ol grn & blk	12.00	12.00
28	A6	40c brn & blk	12.00	12.00
29	A6	50c car & blk (Bl)	13.50	13.50
30	A7	75c ver & blk (Bl)	13.50	13.50
31	A8	1fr car & blk (Bl)	20.00	20.00
32	A9	2fr grn & blk	30.00	30.00
34	A10	5fr bl & blk	65.00	65.00
35	A11	10fr pur & blk	92.50	92.50
a.		Double surcharge	800.00	
b.		Triple surcharge	800.00	
		Nos. 18-35 (17)	288.60	288.60

The Chinese characters overprinted on Nos. 1 to 35 repeat the denomination of the basic stamp.

Nos. 18-35 Surcharged with New Values in Cents or Piasters in Black, Red or Blue

1919
36	A5	⅖c on 1c	.95	.80
37	A5	⅘c on 2c	.95	.80
38	A5	1⅗c on 4c (R)	.95	.80
39	A5	2c on 5c	1.40	.80
a.		"2 CENTS" inverted	80.00	
40	A5	4c on 10c (Bl)	3.00	2.50
41	A5	6c on 15c	1.60	1.60
42	A6	8c on 20c	4.00	4.00
43	A6	10c on 25c	12.00	12.00
44	A6	12c on 30c	2.75	2.75
45	A6	14c on 35c	2.75	2.75
a.		Closed "4"	40.00	32.50
46	A6	16c on 40c	2.00	2.00
48	A6	20c on 50c (Bl)	2.00	2.00
49	A7	30c on 75c (Bl)	9.50	9.50
50	A8	40c on 1fr (Bl)	9.50	9.50
a.		"40 CENTS" inverted	9.50	9.50
51	A9	80c on 2fr (R)	16.00	16.00
52	A10	2pi on 5fr (R)	160.00	150.00
53	A11	4pi on 10fr (R)	30.00	30.00
		Nos. 36-53 (17)	259.35	247.80

Stamps of Indo-China, 1922-23, Overprinted in Black, Red or Blue

1923
54	A12	⅒c blk & sal (Bl)	.30	.30
55	A12	⅕c dp bl & blk (R)	.30	.30
a.		Black overprint	120.00	
56	A12	⅖c ol brn & blk (R)	.30	.30
57	A12	⅘c brt rose & blk	.45	.45
58	A12	1c yel brn & blk (R)	.45	.45
59	A12	2c gray grn & blk (R)	.80	.80
60	A12	3c vio & blk (R)	.80	.80
61	A12	4c org & blk	.95	.95
62	A12	5c car & blk	.95	.95
63	A12	6c dl red & blk	.95	.95
64	A13	7c ol grn & blk	1.35	1.35
65	A13	8c black (R)	2.00	2.00
66	A13	9c yel & blk	2.00	2.00
67	A13	10c bl & blk	1.75	1.75
68	A13	11c vio & blk	1.90	1.90
69	A13	12c brn & blk	1.90	1.90
70	A13	15c org & blk	2.25	2.25
71	A13	20c bl & blk, *straw* (R)	2.25	2.25
72	A13	40c ver & blk, *bluish* (Bl)	2.75	2.75
73	A13	1pi bl grn & blk, *grnsh*	6.50	6.50
74	A13	2pi lt brn & blk, *pnksh* (Bl)	14.00	14.00
		Nos. 54-74 (21)	44.90	44.90

Indo-China Stamps of 1927 Overprinted in Black or Red

1927
75	A14	⅒c lt ol grn (R)	.30	.30
76	A14	⅕c yellow	.30	.30
77	A14	⅖c lt blue (R)	.45	.45
78	A14	⅘c dp brown	.45	.45
79	A14	1c orange	.65	.65
80	A14	2c blue grn (R)	.95	.95
81	A14	3c indigo (R)	.95	.95
82	A14	4c lilac rose	.95	.95
83	A14	5c deep violet	.95	.95
84	A15	6c deep red	.95	.95
85	A15	7c lt brown	.95	.95
86	A15	8c gray grn (R)	1.10	1.10
87	A15	9c red violet	1.25	1.25
88	A15	10c lt bl (R)	1.25	1.25
89	A15	11c orange	1.25	1.25
90	A15	12c myr grn (R)	1.25	1.25
91	A16	15c dl rose & ol brn	2.40	2.40
92	A16	20c vio & sl (R)	2.10	2.10
93	A17	25c org brn & lil rose	2.10	2.10
94	A17	30c dp bl & ol gray (R)	1.35	1.35
95	A18	40c ver & lt bl	1.35	1.35
96	A18	50c lt grn & sl (R)	2.10	2.10
97	A19	1pi dk bl, blk & yel (R)	3.50	3.50
98	A19	2pi red, dp bl & org (R)	4.25	4.25
a.		Double surcharge	130.00	
		Nos. 75-98 (24)	33.10	33.10

Stamps of Indo-China, 1931-41, Overprinted in Black or Red

1937-41   Perf. 13, 13½
99	A20	⅒c Prus blue	.25	.25
100	A20	⅕c lake	.25	.25
101	A20	⅖c orange red	.40	.40
102	A20	⅕c red brown	.30	.30
103	A20	⅘c dk violet	.30	.30
104	A20	1c black brown	.30	.30
105	A20	2c dk green	.30	.30
a.		Inverted overprint	120.00	
106	A21	3c dk green	.75	.75
107	A21	3c yel brn ('41)	.30	.30
108	A21	4c dk blue (R)	.95	.95
109	A21	4c dk green ('41)	.30	.30
110	A21	4c yel org ('41)	2.10	2.10
111	A21	5c dp violet	.85	.85
112	A21	5c dp green ('41)	.45	.45
113	A21	6c orange red	.65	.65
114	A21	7c black ('41)	.65	.65
115	A21	8c rose lake ('41)	.65	.65
116	A21	9c blk, yel ('41)	.75	.75
d.		Black overprint	8.75	8.75
117	A22	10c dk blue (R)	1.00	1.00
118	A22	10c ultra, *pink* (R) ('41)	.75	.75
119	A22	15c dk bl (R)	.75	.75
120	A22	18c bl (R) ('41)	.45	.45

121	A22	20c rose	.75	.75
122	A22	21c olive grn	.75	.75
123	A22	22c green ('41)	.55	.55
124	A22	25c dp violet	2.75	2.75
125	A22	25c dk bl (R) ('41)	.75	.75
126	A22	30c orange brn	.75	.75
127	A23	50c dk brown	.95	.95
128	A23	60c dl violet	.95	.95
129	A23	70c lt bl (R) ('41)	.75	.75
130	A23	1pi yel green	1.90	1.90
131	A23	2pi red	2.10	2.10
		Nos. 99-131 (33)	26.50	26.50

For types A20-A23 without "RF," see Nos. 137-153.

Common Design Types pictured following the introduction.

Colonial Arts Exhibition Issue
Common Design Type
Souvenir Sheet

		1937	**Engr.**	**Imperf.**
132	CD79	30c green & sepia	8.75	10.00

New York World's Fair Issue
Common Design Type

		1939	**Unwmk.**	**Perf. 12½x12**
133	CD82	13c carmine lake	1.00	1.00
134	CD82	23c ultramarine	1.00	1.00

Petain Issue
Indo-China Nos. 209-209A
Overprinted "KOUANG TCHEOU" in
Blue or Red

		1941	**Engr.**	**Perf. 12½x12**
135	A27a	10c car lake (B)		.65
136	A27a	25c blue (R)		.65

Nos. 135-136 were issued by the Vichy government in France, but were not placed on sale in Kwangchowan.
For surcharges, see Nos. B9-B10.

Indo-China Types of 1937-41 without "RF" Overprinted "KOUANG TCHEOU" in Blue or Red

1942-44

137	A20	⅖c orange red		.25
138	A20	½c red brown		.25
139	A20	1c black brown		.30
140	A20	2c dark green		.65
141	A21	3c yellow brown		.65
142	A21	4c yellow orange		.30
143	A21	5c deep green		.45
144	A21	9c black, yellow		.30
145	A22	10c ultramarine, pink (R)		.55
146	A22	18c blue (R)		160.00
147	A22	22c green		.55
148	A22	30c orange brown		.65
149	A23	50c dark brown		.55
150	A23	60c dull violet		.55
151	A23	70c light blue (R)		.75
152	A23	1pi yellow green		1.20
153	A23	2pi red		1.25
		Nos. 137-153 (17)		169.20

Nos. 137-153 were issued by the Vichy government in France, but were not placed on sale in Kwangchowan.

SEMI-POSTAL STAMPS

French Revolution Issue
Common Design Type

		1939	**Unwmk.**	**Photo.**	**Perf. 13**
		Name and Value typo. in Black			
B1	CD83	6c + 2c green		8.75	8.75
B2	CD83	7c + 3c brown		8.75	8.75
B3	CD83	9c + 4c red org		8.75	8.75
B4	CD83	13c + 10c rose pink		8.75	8.75
B5	CD83	23c + 20c blue		8.75	8.75
		Nos. B1-B5 (5)		43.75	43.75

Indo-China Nos. B19A and B19C
Overprinted "KOUANG-TCHEOU" in
Blue or Red, and Common Design
Type

		1941	**Photo.**	**Perf. 13½**
B6	SP1	10c + 10c red (B)		.65
B7	CD86	15c + 30c mar & car		.85
B8	SP2	25c + 10c blue (R)		.65
		Nos. B6-B8 (3)		2.15

Nos. B6-B8 were issued by the Vichy government in France, but were not placed on sale in Kwangchowan.

Indo-China Nos. B21A-B21B
Overprinted "KOUANG-TCHEOU" in
Blue or Red

		1944	**Engr.**	**Perf. 12½x12**
B9	A27a	5c + 15c on 25c deep blue (R)		.75
B10	A27a	+ 25c on 10c car lake		.75

Colonial Development Fund.
Nos. B9-B10 were issued by the Vichy government in France, but were not placed on sale in Kwangchowan.

AIR POST SEMI-POSTAL STAMPS

Indo-China Nos. CB2-CB4 Overprinted
"KOUANG-TCHEOU" in Blue or Red
Methods and Perfs as Before

		1942, June 22	
CB1	SPAP1	15c + 35c green	.85
CB2	SPAP2	20c + 60c brown	.85
CB3	SPAP3	30c + 90c car red	.85
		Nos. CB1-CB3 (3)	2.55

Native children's welfare fund.
Nos. CB1-CB3 were issued by the Vichy government in France, but were not placed on sale in Kwangchowan.

Colonial Education Fund
Indo-China No. CB5 Overprinted
"KOUANG-TCHEOU" in Blue or Red
Perf. 12½x13½

		1942, June 22	**Engr.**
CB4	CD86a	12c + 18c blue & red	.85

No. CB4 was issued by the Vichy government in France, but was not placed on sale in Kwangchowan.

MONGTSEU (MENGTSZ)

Stamps of Indo-China
Surcharged in Black

		1903-04	**Unwmk.**	**Perf. 14x13½**
1	A3	1c blk, lil bl	7.25	7.25
2	A3	2c brn, buff	6.50	6.50
3	A3	4c claret, lav	8.00	8.00
4	A3	5c yel grn	5.50	5.50
5	A3	10c red	8.00	8.00
6	A3	15c gray	9.50	9.50
7	A3	20c red, grn	11.00	11.00
7C	A3	25c blk, rose	650.00	650.00
8	A3	25c blue	11.00	11.00
9	A3	30c brn, bister	9.00	9.00
10	A3	40c red, straw	67.50	67.50
11	A3	50c car, rose	400.00	400.00
12	A3	50c brn, az ('04)	110.00	110.00
13	A3	75c dp vio, org	87.50	87.50
a.		"INDO-CHINE" inverted	60,000.	
14	A3	1fr brnz grn, straw	95.00	95.00
15	A3	5fr red lil, lav	100.00	100.00
		Nos. 1-15 (16)	1,585.	1,585.

Many Surcharge varieties exist on #1-15.

Stamps of Indo-China,
1892-1906, Surcharged
in Red or Black

1906

16	A4	1c ol grn (R)	4.75	4.75
17	A4	2c vio brn, buff	4.75	4.75
18	A4	4c cl, bluish (R)	4.75	4.75
19	A4	5c dp grn (R)	5.50	5.50
20	A4	10c carmine	4.75	4.75
21	A4	15c org brn, bl	30.00	30.00
22	A4	20c red, grn	12.00	12.00
23	A4	25c deep blue	9.50	9.50
24	A4	30c pale brn	12.00	12.00
25	A4	35c blk, yel (R)	11.00	11.00
26	A4	40c blk, bluish (R)	16.00	16.00
27	A4	50c bister brn	20.00	20.00
28	A3	75c dp vio, org (R)	60.00	60.00
a.		"INDO-CHINE" inverted	60,000.	
29	A4	1fr pale grn	40.00	40.00
30	A4	2fr brn, org (R)	52.50	52.50
31	A3	5fr red lil, lav	120.00	120.00

32	A4	10fr org brn, grn	140.00	140.00
a.		Chinese characters inverted	1,600.	1,850.
		Nos. 16-32 (17)	547.50	547.50

Inverted varieties of the surcharge exist on Nos. 19, 22 and 32.

Stamps of Indo-China, 1907, Surcharged "MONGTSEU" and Value in Chinese in Red or Blue

1908

33	A5	1c ol brn & blk	.95	.95
34	A5	2c brn & blk	1.00	1.00
35	A5	4c bl & blk	1.00	1.00
36	A5	5c grn & blk	1.00	1.00
37	A5	10c red & blk (Bl)	2.40	2.40
38	A5	15c vio & blk	2.40	2.40
39	A6	20c vio & blk	4.75	4.75
40	A6	25c bl & blk	14.00	14.00
41	A6	30c brn & blk	5.50	5.50
42	A6	35c ol grn & blk	6.50	6.50
43	A6	40c brn & blk	4.25	4.25
44	A6	50c car & blk (Bl)	5.50	5.50
46	A7	75c ver & blk (Bl)	12.50	12.50
47	A8	1fr car & blk (Bl)	12.00	12.00
48	A9	2fr grn & blk	17.50	17.50
49	A10	5fr bl & blk	92.50	92.50
50	A11	10fr pur & blk	110.00	110.00
		Nos. 33-50 (17)	293.75	293.75

The Chinese characters overprinted on Nos. 1 to 50 repeat the denomination of the basic stamp.

Nos. 33-50 Surcharged with New Values in Cents or Piasters in Black, Red or Blue

1919

51	A5	⅖c on 1c	1.35	1.35
52	A5	1¹⁄₅c on 2c	1.45	1.45
53	A5	1⅗c on 4c	1.60	1.60
54	A5	2c on 5c	1.35	1.35
55	A5	4c on 10c (Bl)	2.40	2.40
56	A5	6c on 15c	2.60	2.60
57	A6	8c on 20c	5.50	5.50
58	A6	10c on 25c	4.50	4.50
59	A6	12c on 30c	4.50	4.50
60	A6	14c on 35c	2.75	2.75
a.		Closed "4"	16.00	16.00
61	A6	16c on 40c	3.75	3.75
63	A6	20c on 50c (Bl)	4.25	4.25
64	A7	30c on 75c (Bl)	8.00	8.00
65	A8	40c on 1fr (Bl)	8.00	8.00
66	A9	80c on 2fr (R)	8.00	8.00
a.		Triple surch., one inverted	475.00	475.00
67	A10	2pi on 5fr (R)	160.00	160.00
a.		Triple surch., one inverted	475.00	475.00
b.		Double surcharge	800.00	800.00
68	A11	4pi on 10fr (R)	27.50	27.50
		Nos. 51-68 (17)	247.50	247.50

PAKHOI

Stamps of Indo-China
Surcharged in Black

		1903-04	**Unwmk.**	**Perf. 14x13½**
1	A3	1c blk, lil bl	6.00	6.00
2	A3	2c brn, buff	5.25	5.25
3	A3	4c claret, lav	5.25	5.25
4	A3	5c yel grn	4.00	4.00
5	A3	10c red	4.50	4.50
6	A3	15c gray	4.50	4.50
7	A3	20c red, grn	9.50	9.50
8	A3	25c blue	7.50	7.50
9	A3	25c blk, rose ('04)	6.00	6.00
10	A3	30c brn, bister	7.25	7.25
11	A3	40c red, straw	50.00	50.00
12	A3	50c car, rose	310.00	310.00
13	A3	50c brn, az ('04)	45.00	45.00
14	A3	75c dp vio, org	60.00	60.00
a.		"INDO-CHINE" inverted	45,000.	
15	A3	1fr brnz grn, straw	60.00	60.00
16	A3	5fr red lil, lav	120.00	120.00
		Nos. 1-16 (16)	704.75	704.75

Many varieties of the surcharge exist.

Stamps of Indo-China
1892-1906, Surcharged
in Red or Black

1906

17	A4	1c ol grn (R)	8.00	8.00
18	A4	2c vio brn, buff	8.00	8.00
19	A4	4c cl, bluish (R)	8.00	8.00
20	A4	5c dp grn (R)	8.00	8.00
21	A4	10c carmine	8.00	8.00
22	A4	15c org brn, bl	30.00	30.00
23	A4	20c red, grn	12.00	12.00
24	A4	25c deep blue	9.50	9.50
25	A4	30c pale brn	12.00	12.00
26	A4	35c blk, yel (R)	20.00	20.00
27	A4	40c blk, bluish (R)	20.00	20.00
28	A4	50c bister brn	20.00	20.00
29	A3	75c dp vio, org (R)	60.00	60.00
30	A4	1fr pale grn	40.00	40.00
31	A4	2fr brn, org (R)	52.50	52.50
32	A3	5fr red lil, lav	120.00	120.00
33	A4	10fr org brn, grn	140.00	140.00
		Nos. 17-33 (17)	576.00	576.00

Various surcharge varieties exist on #17-24.

Stamps of Indo-China, 1907, Surcharged "PAKHOI" and Value in Chinese in Red or Blue

1908

34	A5	1c ol brn & blk	.80	.80
35	A5	2c brn & blk	.80	.80
36	A5	4c bl & blk	.80	.80
37	A5	5c grn & blk	1.25	1.25
38	A5	10c red & blk (Bl)	1.25	1.25
39	A5	15c vio & blk	1.75	1.75
40	A5	20c vio & blk	1.75	1.75
41	A6	25c bl & blk	2.40	2.40
42	A6	30c brn & blk	3.00	3.00
43	A6	35c ol grn & blk	3.00	3.00
44	A6	40c brn & blk	3.00	3.00
46	A6	50c car & blk (Bl)	3.00	3.00
47	A7	75c ver & blk (Bl)	5.40	5.40
48	A8	1fr car & blk (Bl)	6.75	6.75
49	A9	2fr grn & blk	15.00	15.00
50	A10	5fr bl & blk	75.00	75.00
51	A11	10fr pur & blk	130.00	130.00
		Nos. 34-51 (17)	254.95	254.95

The Chinese characters overprinted on Nos. 1 to 51 repeat the denomination of the basic stamps.

Nos. 34-51 Surcharged with New Values in Cents or Piasters in Black, Red or Blue

1919

52	A5	⅖c on 1c	.80	.80
a.		"PAK-HOI" and Chinese double	150.00	
53	A5	⅖c on 2c	.80	.80
54	A5	1⅗c on 4c (R)	.80	.80
55	A5	2c on 5c	2.00	2.00
56	A5	4c on 10c (Bl)	3.00	3.00
57	A6	6c on 15c	1.35	1.35
58	A6	8c on 20c	3.00	3.00
59	A6	10c on 25c	3.75	3.75
60	A6	12c on 30c	1.35	1.35
a.		"12 CENTS" double	550.00	
61	A6	14c on 35c	.95	.95
a.		Closed "4"	12.00	12.00
62	A6	16c on 40c	2.40	2.40
64	A6	20c on 50c (Bl)	1.80	1.80
65	A7	30c on 75c (Bl)	8.00	8.00
66	A8	40c on 1fr (Bl)	10.00	10.00
67	A9	80c on 2fr (R)	9.25	9.25
68	A10	2pi on 5fr (R)	14.00	14.00
69	A11	4pi on 10fr (R)	32.50	32.50
		Nos. 52-69 (17)	95.75	95.75

TCHONGKING (CHUNGKING)

Stamps of Indo-China
Surcharged in Black

		1903-04	**Unwmk.**	**Perf. 14x13½**
1	A3	1c blk, lil bl	4.00	4.00
2	A3	2c brn, buff	4.00	4.00
3	A3	4c claret, lav	4.75	4.75
4	A3	5c yel grn	4.75	4.75
5	A3	10c red	4.75	4.75
6	A3	15c gray	4.75	4.75
7	A3	20c red, grn	7.25	7.25
8	A3	25c blue	47.50	47.50
9	A3	25c blk, rose ('04)	8.75	8.75
10	A3	30c brn, bister	12.50	12.50
11	A3	40c red, straw	52.50	52.50
12	A3	50c car, rose	200.00	200.00
13	A3	50c brn, az ('04)	110.00	110.00
14	A3	75c vio, org	40.00	40.00
15	A3	1fr brnz grn, straw	52.50	52.50
16	A3	5fr red lil, lav	92.50	92.50
		Nos. 1-16 (16)	650.50	650.50

Many surcharge varieties exist on #1-14. Stamps of Indo-China and French China, issued in 1902 with similar overprint, but without Chinese characters, were not officially authorized.

Stamps of Indo-China, 1892-1906, Surcharged in Red or Black

1906

17	A4	1c ol grn (R)	8.00	8.00
18	A4	2c vio brn, buff	8.00	8.00
19	A4	4c cl, bluish (R)	8.00	8.00
20	A4	5c dp grn (R)	8.00	8.00
21	A4	10c carmine	8.00	8.00
22	A4	15c org brn, bl	30.00	30.00
23	A4	20c red, grn	12.00	12.00
24	A4	25c deep blue	9.50	9.50
25	A4	30c pale brn	12.00	12.00
26	A4	35c blk, yellow (R)	20.00	20.00
27	A4	40c blk, bluish (R)	20.00	20.00
28	A4	50c bis brn	20.00	20.00
29	A3	75c dp vio, org (R)	60.00	60.00
30	A4	1fr pale grn	40.00	40.00
31	A4	2fr brn, org (R)	52.50	52.50
32	A3	5fr red lil, lav	120.00	120.00
33	A4	10fr org brn, grn	140.00	140.00
		Nos. 17-33 (17)	576.00	576.00

Variety "T" omitted in surcharge occurs once in each sheet of Nos. 17-33. Other surcharge varieties exist, such as inverted surcharge on 1c and 2c.

Stamps of Indo-China, 1907, Surcharged "TCHONGKING" and Value in Chinese in Red or Blue

1908

34	A5	1c ol brn & blk	.55	.55
35	A5	2c brn & blk	.80	.80
36	A5	4c bl & blk	1.00	1.00
37	A5	5c grn & blk	1.60	1.60
38	A5	10c red & blk (Bl)	1.60	1.60
39	A5	15c vio & blk	2.40	2.40
40	A6	20c vio & blk	2.40	2.40
41	A6	25c bl & blk	4.50	4.50
42	A6	30c brn & blk	2.75	2.75
43	A6	35c ol grn & blk	6.50	6.50
44	A6	40c brn & blk	12.00	12.00
45	A6	50c car & blk (Bl)	9.50	9.50
46	A7	75c ver & blk (Bl)	8.00	8.00
47	A8	1fr car & blk (Bl)	12.00	12.00
48	A9	2fr grn & blk	80.00	80.00
49	A10	5fr bl & blk	35.00	35.00
50	A11	10fr pur & blk	200.00	200.00
		Nos. 34-50 (17)	380.60	380.60

The Chinese characters overprinted on Nos. 1 to 50 repeat the denomination of the basic stamp.

Nos. 34-50 Surcharged with New Values in Cents or Piasters in Black, Red or Blue

1919

51	A5	⅖c on 1c	1.00	.95
52	A5	⅘c on 2c	1.00	.95
53	A5	1⅗c on 4c (R)	1.00	.95
54	A5	2c on 5c	1.35	1.35
55	A5	4c on 10c (Bl)	1.00	.95
56	A5	6c on 15c	1.25	1.20
57	A6	8c on 20c	2.50	.95
58	A6	10c on 25c	7.25	6.50
59	A6	12c on 30c	2.40	1.20
60	A6	14c on 35c	1.60	1.60
a.		Closed "4"	27.50	27.50
61	A6	16c on 40c	1.80	1.80
		"16 CENTS" double	110.00	110.00
62	A6	20c on 50c (Bl)	9.50	8.00
63	A7	30c on 75c (Bl)	8.00	5.75
64	A8	40c on 1fr (Bl)	8.00	6.00
65	A9	80c on 2fr (R)	8.00	5.50
66	A10	2pi on 5fr (R)	8.00	8.00
67	A11	4pi on 10fr (R)	16.00	16.00
		Nos. 51-67 (17)	79.65	67.65

YUNNAN FOU

(Formerly Yunnan Sen, later known as Kunming)

Stamps of Indo-China Surcharged in Black

1903-04		**Unwmk.**	**Perf. 14x13½**	
1	A3	1c blk, lil bl	6.00	6.00
2	A3	2c brn, buff	6.00	6.00
3	A3	4c claret, lav	6.75	6.75
4	A3	5c yel green	6.00	6.00
5	A3	10c red	6.75	6.75
6	A3	15c gray	6.75	6.75
7	A3	20c red, grn	10.00	10.00
8	A3	25c blue	6.00	6.00
9	A3	30c brn, bister	10.00	10.00
10	A3	40c red, straw	70.00	50.00

11	A3	50c car, rose	330.00	320.00
12	A3	50c brn, az ('04)	160.00	160.00
13	A3	75c dp vio, org	55.00	52.50
a.		"INDO-CHINE" inverted	45,000.	
14	A3	1fr brnz grn, straw	55.00	52.50
15	A3	5fr red lil, lav	110.00	110.00
		Nos. 1-15 (15)	844.25	809.25

The Chinese characters overprinted on Nos. 1 to 15 repeat the denomination of the basic stamp.

Many varieties of the surcharge exist.

Stamps of Indo-China, 1892-1906, Surcharged in Red or Black

1906		**Unwmk.**	**Perf. 14x13½**	
17	A4	1c ol grn (R)	4.75	4.75
18	A4	2c vio brn, buff	4.75	4.75
19	A4	4c cl, bluish (R)	4.75	4.75
20	A4	5c dp grn (R)	4.75	4.75
21	A4	10c carmine	4.75	4.75
22	A4	15c org brn, bl	30.00	30.00
23	A4	20c red, grn	12.00	12.00
24	A4	25c deep blue	9.50	9.50
25	A4	30c pale brn	12.00	12.00
26	A4	35c blk, yel (R)	16.00	16.00
27	A4	40c blk, bluish (R)	16.00	16.00
28	A4	50c bister brn	16.00	16.00
29	A3	75c dp vio, org (R)	60.00	60.00
30	A4	1fr pale grn	40.00	40.00
31	A4	2fr brn, org (R)	52.50	52.50
32	A3	5fr red lil, lav	120.00	120.00
33	A4	10fr org brn, grn	140.00	140.00
		Nos. 17-33 (17)	547.75	547.75

Various varieties of the surcharge exist on Nos. 18, 20, 21 and 27.

Stamps of Indo-China, 1907, Surcharged "YUNNANFOU," and Value in Chinese in Red or Blue

1908

34	A5	1c ol brn & blk	.95	.95
35	A5	2c brn & blk	1.20	1.20
36	A5	4c bl & blk	1.40	1.40
37	A5	5c grn & blk	2.40	2.40
38	A5	10c red & blk (Bl)	2.40	2.40
39	A5	15c vio & blk	5.50	5.50
40	A6	20c vio & blk	5.25	5.25
41	A6	25c bl & blk	8.00	8.00
42	A6	30c brn & blk	6.50	6.50
43	A6	35c ol grn & blk	6.50	6.50
44	A6	40c brn & blk	7.25	7.25
45	A6	50c car & blk (Bl)	8.00	8.00
46	A7	75c ver & blk (Bl)	8.75	8.75
47	A8	1fr car & blk (Bl)	13.50	13.50
48	A9	2fr grn & blk	22.50	22.50
a.		"YUNANNFOU"	2,200.	2,200.
49	A10	5fr bl & blk	52.50	52.50
a.		"YUNANNFOU"	2,200.	2,200.
50	A11	10fr pur & blk	100.00	100.00
a.		"YUNANNFOU"	2,200.	2,200.
		Nos. 34-50 (17)	252.60	252.60

The Chinese characters overprinted on Nos. 17-50 repeat the denomination of the basic stamp.

Nos. 34-50 Surcharged with New Values in Cents or Piasters in Black, Red or Blue

1919

51	A5	⅖c on 1c	.95	.95
a.		New value double	120.00	
52	A5	⅘c on 2c	1.20	1.20
53	A5	1⅗c on 4c (R)	1.20	1.20
54	A5	2c on 5c	1.75	1.75
a.		Triple surcharge	180.00	
55	A5	4c on 10c (Bl)	1.25	1.25
56	A5	6c on 15c	2.40	2.40
57	A6	8c on 20c	1.60	1.60
58	A6	10c on 25c	3.25	3.25
59	A6	12c on 30c	8.00	8.00
60	A6	14c on 35c	12.50	12.50
a.		Closed "4"	120.00	120.00
61	A6	16c on 40c	8.00	8.00
62	A6	20c on 50c (Bl)	1.60	1.60
63	A7	30c on 75c (Bl)	8.00	8.00
64	A8	40c on 1fr (Bl)	32.50	32.50
65	A9	80c on 2fr (R)	12.00	12.00
a.		Triple surch., one inverted	225.00	
66	A10	2pi on 5fr (R)	60.00	60.00
67	A11	4pi on 10fr (R)	32.50	32.50
		Nos. 51-67 (17)	188.70	188.70

OFFICES IN CRETE

Austria, France, Italy and Great Britain maintained their own post offices in Crete during the period when that country was an autonomous state.

100 Centimes = 1 Franc

Liberty, Equality and Fraternity A1

"Rights of Man" A2

Liberty and Peace (Symbolized by Olive Branch) A3

Perf. 14x13½

1902-03		**Unwmk.**	**Typo.**	
1	A1	1c gray	2.00	2.00
2	A1	2c violet brown	2.00	2.00
3	A1	3c red orange	2.00	2.00
4	A1	4c yellow brown	2.00	2.00
5	A1	5c green	2.00	2.00
6	A2	10c rose red	2.40	2.40
7	A2	15c pale red ('03)	3.25	2.40
8	A2	20c brown vio ('03)	4.00	3.25
9	A2	25c blue ('03)	5.50	3.25
10	A2	30c lilac ('03)	5.50	3.25
11	A3	40c red & pale bl	11.00	9.50
12	A3	50c bis brn & lav	16.00	11.00
13	A3	1fr claret & ol grn	20.00	18.00
14	A3	2fr gray vio & yel	32.50	27.50
15	A3	5fr dk blue & buff	52.50	47.50
		Nos. 1-15 (15)	162.65	137.65

A4

A5

Black Surcharge

1903

16	A4	1pi on 25c blue	47.50	40.00
17	A5	2pi on 50c bis brn & lav	67.50	52.50
18	A5	4pi on 1fr claret & ol grn	105.00	92.50
19	A5	8pi on 2fr gray vio & yel	120.00	120.00
20	A5	20pi on 5fr dk bl & buff	200.00	195.00
		Nos. 16-20 (5)	540.00	500.00

OFFICES IN EGYPT

French post offices formerly maintained in Alexandria and Port Said.

100 Centimes = 1 Franc

ALEXANDRIA

Stamps of France Overprinted in Red, Blue or Black

1899-1900		**Unwmk.**	**Perf. 14x13½**	
1	A15	1c blk, lil bl (R)	2.00	2.00
a.		Double overprint	140.00	
b.		Triple overprint	160.00	
2	A15	2c brn, buff (Bl)	2.75	2.40
3	A15	3c gray, grysh (Bl)	2.75	2.40
4	A15	4c cl, lav (Bl)	3.25	2.75
5	A15	5c yel grn, (I) (R)	5.50	3.25
a.		Type II	140.00	92.50
6	A15	10c blk, lav, (I) (R)	8.00	6.50
a.		Type II	55.00	32.50
7	A15	15c blue (R)	8.00	3.50
8	A15	20c red, grn	13.00	7.25
a.		Double overprint		
9	A15	25c blk, rose (R)	6.50	3.50
a.		Inverted overprint	87.50	
b.		Double ovpt., one invtd.	140.00	

10	A15	30c brn, bis	14.00	10.00
11	A15	40c red, straw	12.00	12.00
12	A15	50c car, rose (II)	30.00	16.00
a.		Type I	140.00	24.00
13	A15	1fr brnz grn, straw	29.00	21.00
14	A15	2fr brn, az ('00)	75.00	75.00
15	A15	5fr red lil, lav	110.00	100.00
		Nos. 1-15 (15)	321.75	267.55

A2 A3

A4

1902-03

16	A2	1c gray	.65	.40
17	A2	2c violet brn	.65	.55
18	A2	3c red orange	.65	.55
19	A2	4c yellow brn	.90	.80
20	A2	5c green	4.00	3.75
21	A3	10c rose red	1.25	.75
22	A3	15c orange	1.50	1.00
a.		15c pale red ('03)	3.90	1.20
23	A3	20c brn vio ('03)	2.40	1.40
24	A3	25c blue ('03)	1.40	.65
25	A3	30c violet ('03)	6.50	4.00
26	A4	40c red & pale bl	4.25	2.00
27	A4	50c bis brn & lav	8.75	2.50
28	A4	1fr cl & ol grn	8.00	3.50
29	A4	2fr gray vio & yel	20.00	10.00
30	A4	5fr dk bl & buff	24.00	15.00
		Nos. 16-30 (15)	84.90	46.85

The 2c, 5c, 10c, 20c and 25c exist imperf. Value, each $45.

See #77-86. For surcharges see #31-73, B1-B4.

Stamps of 1902-03 Surcharged Locally in Black

1921

31	A2	2m on 5c green	6.50	4.00
32	A2	3m on 3c red org	12.00	9.50
a.		Larger numeral	120.00	100.00
33	A2	4m on 10c rose	5.50	4.75
34	A3	5c on 1c dk gray	12.00	9.50
35	A2	5m on 4c yel brn	16.00	11.00
36	A3	6m on 15c orange	5.50	4.75
a.		Larger numeral	100.00	100.00
37	A3	8m on 20c brn vio	6.50	4.75
a.		Larger numeral	72.50	52.50
38	A3	10m on 25c blue	4.00	4.00
a.		Inverted surcharge	40.00	40.00
b.		Double surcharge	40.00	40.00
39	A3	12m on 30c vio	14.00	14.00
40	A2	15m on 2c vio brn	12.00	12.00

Nos. 26-30 Surcharged

41	A4	15m on 40c	20.00	16.00
42	A4	15m on 50c	9.50	8.75
43	A4	30m on 1fr	140.00	140.00
44	A4	60m on 2fr	225.00	225.00
a.		Larger numeral	800.00	800.00
45	A4	150m on 5fr	300.00	300.00

Port Said Nos. 20 and 19 Surcharged like Nos. 32 and 40

45A	A2	3m on 3c red org	125.00	125.00
46	A2	15m on 2c vio brn	125.00	125.00
		Nos. 31-46 (17)	1,038.	1,018.

Alexandria No. 28 Surcharged with Two New Values

1921

46A	A4	30m on 15m on 1fr	1,100.	1,200.

The surcharge "15 Mill." was made in error and is canceled by a bar.

The surcharges were lithographed on Nos. 31, 33, 38, 39 and 42 and typographed on the other stamps of the 1921 issue. Nos. 34, 36 and 37 were surcharged by both methods.

Alexandria Stamps of 1902-03 Surcharged in Paris

1921-23

47	A2	1m on 1c gray	2.75	2.10
48	A2	2m on 5c green	2.10	1.75
49	A3	4m on 10c rose	2.75	2.40
50	A3	4m on 10c green ('23)	2.00	2.00
51	A3	5m on 3c red org ('23)	6.00	4.25
52	A3	6m on 15c orange	1.80	1.50
53	A3	8m on 20c brn vio	2.00	.95
54	A3	8m on 25c blue	1.20	1.10
55	A3	10m on 30c vio	3.25	2.75
56	A3	15m on 50c bl ('23)	2.75	2.75

Nos. 27-30 and Type of 1902 Surcharged

57	A4	15m on 50c	4.50	2.75
58	A4	30m on 1fr	3.50	2.25
59	A4	60m on 2fr	2,000.	2,200.
60	A4	60m on 2fr org & pale bl ('23)	10.00	10.00
61	A4	150m on 5fr	12.00	8.00
		Nos. 47-58,60-61 (14)	56.60	44.55

Stamps and Types of 1902-03 Surcharged with New Values and Bars in Black

1925

62	A2	1m on 1c gray	1.00	1.00
63	A2	2m on 5c orange	1.00	1.00
64	A2	2m on 5c green	1.30	1.30
65	A3	4m on 10c green	.95	.80
66	A3	5m on 3c red org	1.25	1.00
67	A3	6m on 15c orange	1.10	.95
68	A3	8m on 20c brn vio	1.40	1.20
69	A3	10m on 25c blue	.85	.75
70	A3	15m on 50c blue	1.90	1.20
71	A4	30m on 1fr cl & ol grn	3.00	2.40
72	A4	60m on 2fr org & pale bl	3.50	3.25
73	A4	150m on 5fr dk bl & buff	5.00	4.00
		Nos. 62-73 (12)	22.25	18.85

Types of 1902-03 Issue

1927-28

77	A2	3m orange ('28)	2.00	1.60
81	A3	15m slate blue	2.00	1.60
82	A3	20m rose lil ('28)	5.50	4.00
84	A4	50m org & blue	9.50	8.00
85	A4	100m sl bl & buff	12.00	10.00
86	A4	250m gray grn & red	21.00	14.00
		Nos. 77-86 (6)	52.00	39.20

SEMI-POSTAL STAMPS

Regular Issue of 1902-03 Surcharged in Carmine

1915   Unwmk.   Perf. 14x13½

B1	A3	10c + 5c rose	1.10 1.10

Sinking Fund Issue

Type of 1902-03 Issue Surcharged in Blue or Black

1927-30

B2	A3	15m + 5m deep org	4.75	4.75
B3	A3	15m + 5m red vio ('28)	8.00	8.00
a.		15m + 5m violet ('30)	12.00	12.00

Type of 1902-03 Issue Surcharged as in 1927-28

1929

B4	A3	15m + 5m fawn	9.50	9.50

POSTAGE DUE STAMPS

Postage Due Stamps of France, 1893-1920, Surcharged in Paris in Black

1922   Unwmk.   Perf. 14x13½

J1	D2	2m on 5c blue	2.00	2.00
J2	D2	4m on 10c brown	2.00	2.00
J3	D2	10m on 30c rose red	2.40	2.40
J4	D2	15m on 50c brn vio	2.75	2.75
J5	D2	30m on 1fr red brn, straw	4.00	4.00
		Nos. J1-J5 (5)	13.15	13.15

D3

1928   Typo.

J6	D3	1m slate	1.60	1.60
J7	D3	2m light blue	1.00	1.00
J8	D3	4m lilac rose	1.60	1.60
J9	D3	5m gray green	1.75	1.75
J10	D3	10m light red	2.10	2.10
J11	D3	20m violet brn	1.90	1.90
J12	D3	30m green	4.50	4.50
J13	D3	40m lt violet	4.75	4.75
		Nos. J6-J13 (8)	19.20	19.20

#J6-J13 were also available for use in Port Said.

PORT SAID

Stamps of France Overprinted in Red, Blue or Black

1899-1900   Unwmk.   Perf. 14x13½

1	A15	1c blk, lil bl (R)	1.60	1.10
2	A15	2c brn, buff (bl)	1.60	1.25
3	A15	3c gray, grysh (Bl)	1.60	1.60
4	A15	4c claret, lav (Bl)	1.60	1.60
5	A15	5c yel grn (I) (R)	8.00	4.00
a.		Type II (R)	45.00	14.00
6	A15	10c blk, lav (I) (R)	12.00	12.00
a.		Type II (R)	60.00	47.50
7	A15	15c blue (R)	12.00	8.00
8	A15	20c red, grn	13.50	10.00
9	A15	25c blk, rose (R)	12.00	4.00
a.		Double overprint	240.00	
b.		Inverted overprint	240.00	
10	A15	30c brn, bister	13.50	12.00
a.		Inverted overprint	240.00	
11	A15	40c red, straw	12.00	12.00
12	A15	50c car, rose (R)	18.00	12.00
a.		Type I	280.00	100.00
b.		Double overprint (II)	340.00	
13	A15	1fr brnz grn, straw	27.50	16.00
14	A15	2fr brn, az ('00)	67.50	60.00
15	A15	5fr red lil, lav	110.00	87.50
		Nos. 1-15 (15)	312.40	243.05

PORT SAID
VINGT
CINQ

Regular Issue Surcharged in Red

1899

16	A15	25c on 10c blk, lav	120.00	27.50
a.		Inverted surcharge		225.00

With Additional Surcharge "25" in Red

17	A15	25c on 10c blk, lav	440.00	160.00
a.		"25" inverted	1,400.	1,200.
b.		"25" in black		2,400.
c.		As "b," "VINGT CINQ" inverted		3,000.
d.		As "b," "25" vertical		3,000.
e.		As "c" and "d"		3,000.

A2   A3

A4

1902-03   Typo.

18a	A2	1c gray	.65	.65
19	A2	2c violet brn	.65	.65
20	A2	3c red orange	.75	.65
21	A2	4c yellow brown	1.00	.80
22	A2	5c blue green	1.10	.80
a.		5c yellow green	4.00	2.75
23	A3	10c rose red	1.50	1.10
24	A3	15c pale red ('03)	2.75	1.80
a.		15c orange	4.00	2.40
25	A3	20c brn vio ('03)	2.75	2.00
26	A3	25c blue ('03)	2.25	1.40
27	A3	30c violet ('03)	5.50	4.50
28	A4	40c red & pale bl	5.25	3.50
29	A4	50c bis brn & lav	8.00	6.50
30	A4	1fr claret & ol grn	10.00	8.25
31	A4	2fr gray vio & yel	13.50	13.50
32	A4	5fr dk bl & buff	32.50	27.50
		Nos. 18a-32 (15)	88.15	73.60

See #83-92. For surcharges see #33-80, B1-B4.

Stamps of 1902-03 Surcharged Locally

1921

33	A2	2m on 5c green	8.00	8.00
a.		Inverted surcharge	40.00	40.00
34	A3	4m on 10c rose	7.25	7.25
a.		Inverted surcharge	40.00	40.00
35	A2	5m on 1c	9.50	9.50
a.		Inverted surcharge	65.00	65.00
c.		Surcharged "2 Milliemes"	47.50	47.50
36	A2	5m on 2c	15.00	15.00
a.		Surcharged "2 Milliemes"	60.00	60.00
b.		As "a," inverted	140.00	140.00
37	A2	5m on 3c	12.50	12.50
a.		Inverted surcharge	47.50	47.50
b.		On Alexandria #18	340.00	340.00
38	A2	5m on 4c	8.75	8.75
a.		Inverted surcharge	65.00	65.00
39	A2	10m on 2c	15.00	15.00
40	A2	10m on 4c	27.50	27.50
a.		Inverted surcharge	80.00	80.00
41	A3	10m on 25c	7.25	7.25
a.		Inverted surcharge	60.00	60.00
42	A3	12m on 30c	32.50	32.50
43	A2	15m on 4c	8.00	8.00
a.		Inverted surcharge	67.50	67.50
44	A3	15m on 15c pale red	47.50	47.50
a.		Inverted surcharge	120.00	120.00
45	A3	15m on 20c	47.50	47.50
a.		Inverted surcharge	120.00	120.00
46	A4	30m on 50c	260.00	260.00
47	A4	60m on 50c	300.00	300.00
48	A4	150m on 50c	340.00	340.00

Nos. 46, 47 and 48 have a bar between the numerals and "Milliemes," which is in capital letters.

Same Surcharge on Stamps of French Offices in Turkey, 1902-03

49	A2	2m on 2c vio brn	140.00	140.00
50	A2	5m on 1c gray	120.00	120.00
a.		"5" inverted	6,750.	
		Nos. 33-50 (18)	1,406.	1,406.

Nos. 28-32 Surcharged

51	A4	15m on 40c	52.50	52.50
52	A4	15m on 50c	72.50	72.50
b.		Bar below 15	45.00	45.00
53	A4	30m on 1fr	250.00	250.00
54	A4	60m on 2fr	67.50	67.50
55	A4	150m on 5fr	225.00	225.00
		Nos. 51-55 (5)	667.50	667.50

Overprinted "MILLtEMES"

51a	A4	15m on 40c	350.00	350.00
52a	A4	15m on 50c	400.00	400.00
53a	A4	30m on 1fr	1,200.	1,200.

54a	A4	60m on 2fr	340.00	340.00
55a	A4	150m on 5fr	925.00	925.00
		Nos. 51a-55a (5)	3,215.	3,215.

Stamps of 1902-03 Surcharged in Paris

1921-23

56	A2	1m on 1c gray	1.10	1.10
57	A2	2m on 5c green	1.10	1.10
58	A3	4m on 10c rose	2.10	2.10
59	A2	5m on 3c red org	7.50	7.50
60	A3	6m on 15c orange	3.25	3.25
a.		6m on 15c pale red	12.00	12.00
61	A3	8m on 20c brn vio	4.00	4.00
62	A3	10m on 25c blue	2.40	2.40
63	A3	10m on 30c violet	6.50	6.50
64	A3	15m on 50c blue	5.50	5.50

Nos. 29-32 and Type of 1902 Surcharged

65	A4	15m on 50c	5.00	5.00
66	A4	30m on 1fr	8.00	8.00
67	A4	60m on 2fr	120.00	120.00
68	A4	60m on 2fr org & pale blue	11.00	11.00
69	A4	150m on 5fr	16.00	16.00
		Nos. 56-69 (14)	193.45	193.45

Stamps and Types of 1902-03 Surcharged with New Values and Bars

1925

70	A2	1m on 1c gray	.75	.75
71	A2	2m on 5c green	1.00	1.00
72	A3	4m on 10c rose red	.85	.85
73	A2	5m on 3c red org	1.00	1.00
74	A3	6m on 15c orange	1.00	1.00
75	A3	8m on 20c brn vio	.95	.95
76	A3	10m on 25c blue	1.40	1.40
77	A3	15m on 50c blue	1.60	1.60
78	A4	30m on 1fr cl & ol grn	2.50	2.50
79	A4	60m on 2fr org & pale blue	2.25	2.25
80	A4	150m on 5fr dk bl & buff	3.00	3.00
		Nos. 70-80 (11)	16.30	16.30

Types of 1902-03 Issue

1927-28

83	A2	3m orange ('28)	1.50	1.50
87	A3	15m slate bl	1.80	1.80
88	A3	20m rose lil ('28)	2.25	2.25
90	A4	50m org & blue	4.00	4.00
91	A4	100m slate bl & buff	4.75	4.75
92	A4	250m gray grn & red	8.00	8.00
		Nos. 83-92 (6)	22.30	22.30

SEMI-POSTAL STAMPS

Regular Issue of 1902-03 Surcharged in Carmine

1915   Unwmk.   Perf. 14x13½

B1	A3	10c + 5c rose	1.20 1.20

Sinking Fund Issue

Type of 1902-03 Issue Surcharged like Alexandria Nos. B2-B3 in Blue or Black

1927-30

B2	A3	15m + 5m dp org (Bl)	4.75	4.75
B3	A3	15m + 5m red vio ('28)	8.00	8.00
a.		15m + 5m violet	12.00	12.00
B4	A3	15m + 5m fawn ('29)	9.50	9.50
		Nos. B2-B4 (3)	22.25	22.25

POSTAGE DUE STAMPS

Postage Due Stamps of France, 1893-1906, Surcharged Locally in Black

15
Millièmes

1921　　Unwmk.　　Perf. 14x13½

J1	D2	12m on 10c brown	52.50	55.00
J2	D2	15m on 5c blue	80.00	87.50
J3	D2	30m on 20c ol grn	80.00	87.50
a.		Inverted surcharge	1,000.	1,000.
J4	D2	30m on 50c red vio	3,000.	3,400.

Same Surcharged in
Red or Blue

1921

J5	D2	2m on 5c bl (R)	47.50	52.50
a.		Blue surcharge	275.00	275.00
J6	D2	4m on 10c brn (Bl)	47.50	52.50
a.		Surcharged "15 Milliemes"	650.00	650.00
J7	D2	10m on 30c red (Bl)	47.50	52.50
a.		Inverted surcharge	140.00	140.00
J8	D2	15m on 50c brn vio (Bl)	60.00	65.00
a.		Inverted surcharge	140.00	140.00
		Nos. J5-J8 (4)	8.20	8.20

Nos. J5-J8 exist with second "M" in "Milliemes" inverted, also with final "S" omitted.
Value, each $150-175.

Alexandria Nos. J6-J13 were also available for use in Port Said.

OFFICES IN TURKEY

Various powers maintained post offices in the Turkish Empire before World War I by authority of treaties which ended with the signing of the Treaty of Lausanne in 1923. The foreign post offices were closed Oct. 27, 1923.

100 Centimes = 1 Franc
25 Centimes = 40 Paras = 1 Piaster

2ovpt

Stamps of France Surcharged in Black or Red

1885-1901　　Unwmk.　　Perf. 14x13½

1	A1	1pi on 25c yel, straw	460.00	12.00
a.		Inverted surcharge	2,250.	2,100.
2	A1	1pi on 25c blk, rose (R) ('86)	3.50	.95
a.		Inverted surcharge	350.00	300.00
3	A1	2pi on 50c car, rose (II) ('90)	16.00	2.40
a.		Type I ('01)	325.00	45.00
4	A1	3pi on 75c car, rose	24.00	12.00
5	A1	4pi on 1fr brnz grn, straw	24.00	12.00
6	A1	8pi on 2fr brn, az ('00)	32.50	20.00
7	A1	20pi on 5fr red lil, lav ('90)	95.00	52.50
		Nos. 1-7 (7)	655.00	111.85

A2

A3

A4

A5

A6

1902-07　　Typo.　　Perf. 14x13½

21	A2	1c gray	.65	.65
22	A2	2c vio brn	.65	.65
23	A2	3c red org	.65	.65
24	A2	4c yel brn	2.40	1.00
a.		Imperf., pair	80.00	
25	A2	5c grn ('06)	.95	.65
26	A2	10c rose red	.95	.65
27	A3	15c pale red ('03)	2.40	1.20
28	A3	20c brn vio ('03)	3.00	1.90
29	A3	25c blue ('07)	40.00	47.50
a.		Imperf., pair	360.00	
30	A3	30c lilac ('03)	4.75	2.40
31	A4	40c red & pale bl	4.75	2.60
32	A4	50c bis brn & lav ('07)	175.00	200.00
a.		Imperf., pair	800.00	
33	A4	1fr claret & ol grn ('07)	375.00	400.00
a.		Imperf., pair	950.00	

Black Surcharge

34	A5	1pi on 25c bl ('03)	.95	.65
a.		Second "I" omitted	27.50	20.00
b.		Double surcharge	65.00	52.50
35	A6	2pi on 50c bis brn & lavender	3.50	1.20
36	A6	4pi on 1fr cl & ol grn	4.00	1.60
a.		Imperf., pair	650.00	
37	A6	8pi on 2fr gray vio & yel	17.50	12.00
38	A6	20pi on 5fr dk bl & buff	8.00	4.00
		Nos. 21-38 (18)	645.10	679.30

Nos. 29, 32-33 were used during the early part of 1907 in the French Offices at Harar and Diredawa, Ethiopia. Djibouti and Port Said stamps were also used.

1 Piastre

No. 27 Surcharged in Green

Beyrouth

1905

39	A3	1pi on 15c pale red	1,900.	300.
a.		"Piastte"	5,750.	1,300.

Stamps of France 1900-21 Surcharged:

On A22 　　　 On A20

On A18

1921-22

40	A22	30pa on 5c grn	.80	.80
41	A22	30pa on 5c org	.80	.80
42	A22	1pi20pa on 10c red	.80	.80
43	A22	1pi20pa on 10c grn	1.00	.80
44	A22	3pi30pa on 25c bl	1.35	.80
45	A22	4pi20pa on 30c org	1.40	.95
a.		"4" omitted	875.00	
46	A20	7pi20pa on 50c bl	1.40	.95
47	A18	15pi on 1fr car & ol grn	2.10	1.60
48	A18	30pi on 2fr org & pale bl	10.00	8.00
49	A18	75pi on 5fr dk bl & buff	9.50	6.00
		Nos. 40-49 (10)	29.15	21.50

Stamps of France, 1903-07, Handstamped

3 PIASTRES
30 PARAS

1923

52	A22	1pi20pa on 10c red	52.50	50.00
54	A20	3pi30pa on 15c gray grn	20.00	20.00

55	A22	7pi20pa on 35c vio	24.00	24.00
a.		1pi20pa on 35c violet	1,200.	1,200.
		Nos. 52-55 (3)	96.50	94.00

CAVALLE (CAVALLA)

Stamps of France Overprinted or Surcharged in Red, Blue or Black

1893-1900　　Unwmk.　　Perf. 14x13½

1	A15	5c grn, grnsh (R)	20.00	16.00
2	A15	5c yel grn (I) ('00) (R)	21.00	20.00
3	A15	10c blk, lav (II)	40.00	21.00
a.		10c black, lavender (I)	150.00	120.00
4	A15	15c blue (R)	40.00	21.00
5	A15	1pi on 25c blk, rose	26.00	18.00
6	A15	2pi on 50c car, rose	80.00	60.00
7	A15	4pi on 1fr brnz grn, straw (R)	100.00	90.00
8	A15	8pi on 2fr brn, az ('00) (Bk)	110.00	110.00
		Nos. 1-8 (8)	437.00	356.00

A3

A4

A5

A6

1902-03

9	A3	5c green	2.00	1.60
10	A4	10c rose red ('03)	2.00	1.60
11	A4	15c orange	2.40	1.60
a.		15c pale red ('03)	9.50	9.50

Surcharged in Black

12	A5	1pi on 25c bl	3.50	2.40
13	A6	2pi on 50c bis brn & lav	10.00	6.50
14	A6	4pi on 1fr cl & ol grn	12.50	8.75
15	A6	8pi on 2fr gray vio & yel	16.00	13.50
		Nos. 9-15 (7)	48.40	35.95

DEDEAGH (DEDEAGATCH)

Stamps of France Overprinted or Surcharged in Red, Blue or Black

1893-1900　　Unwmk.　　Perf. 14x13½

1	A15	5c grn, grnsh (II) (R)	13.50	12.00
2	A15	5c yel grn (I) ('00) (R)	12.00	11.00
3	A15	10c blk, lav (II)	22.50	16.00
a.		Type I	35.00	27.50
4	A15	15c blue (R)	27.50	24.00
5	A15	1pi on 25c blk, rose	32.50	27.50
6	A15	2pi on 50c car, rose	52.50	40.00
7	A15	4pi on 1fr brnz grn, straw (R)	67.50	55.00

8	A15	8pi on 2fr brn, az ('00) (Bk)	100.00	80.00
		Nos. 1-8 (8)	328.00	265.50

A3 　　　 A4

A5

A6

1902-03

9	A3	5c green	2.40	2.00
10	A4	10c rose red ('03)	2.40	2.00
11	A4	15c orange	5.25	4.00

Black Surcharge

15	A5	1pi on 25c bl ('03)	2.75	2.40
16	A6	2pi on 50c bis brn & lav	9.50	8.00
a.		Double surcharge	240.00	
17	A6	4pi on 1fr cl & ol grn	16.00	13.50
18	A6	8pi on 2fr gray vio & yel	25.00	24.00
		Nos. 9-18 (7)	63.30	55.90

PORT LAGOS

Stamps of France Overprinted or Surcharged in Red or Blue

1893　　Unwmk.　　Perf. 14x13½

1	A15	5c grn, grnsh (R)	24.00	24.00
2	A15	10c blk, lav	47.50	40.00
3	A15	15c blue (R)	72.50	55.00
4	A15	1pi on 25c blk, rose	60.00	47.50
5	A15	2pi on 50c car, rose	160.00	80.00
6	A15	4pi on 1fr brnz grn, straw (R)	100.00	80.00
		Nos. 1-6 (6)	464.00	326.50

VATHY (SAMOS)

Stamps of France Overprinted or Surcharged in Red, Blue or Black

1894-1900　　Unwmk.　　Perf. 14x13½

1	A15	5c grn, grnsh (R)	7.25	6.50
2	A15	5c yel grn (I) ('00) (R)	7.25	6.50
a.		Type II	70.00	70.00
3	A15	10c blk, lav (R)	14.00	12.00
a.		Type II	45.00	35.00
4	A15	15c blue (R)	12.50	12.50
5	A15	1pi on 25c blk, rose	16.00	8.00
6	A15	2pi on 50c car, rose	25.00	20.00
7	A15	4pi on 1fr brnz grn, straw (R)	30.00	27.50
8	A15	8pi on 2fr brn, az ('00) (Bk)	65.00	65.00

9	A15	20pi on 5fr lil, *lav* ('00) (Bk)	87.50	87.50
		Nos. 1-9 (9)	264.50	245.50

OFFICES IN ZANZIBAR

Until 1906 France maintained post offices in the Sultanate of Zanzibar, but in that year Great Britain assumed direct control over this protectorate and the French withdrew their postal system.

16 Annas = 1 Rupee

A1

A2

Stamps of France Surcharged in Red, Blue or Black

1894-96   Unwmk.   Perf. 14x13½

1	A1	½a on 5c grn, *grnsh*	9.50	7.25
2	A1	1a on 10c blk, *lav* (Bl)	14.00	12.00
3	A1	1½a on 15c bl ('96)	21.00	20.00
a.		"ANNAS"	100.00	87.50
4	A1	2a on 20c red, *grn* ('96) (Bk)	18.00	14.00
a.		"ANNA"	2,200.	2,200.
5	A1	2½a on 25c blk, *rose* (Bl)	12.00	8.75
a.		Double surcharge	240.00	240.00
6	A1	3a on 30c brn, *bis* ('96) (Bk)	20.00	17.50
7	A1	4a on 40c red, *straw* ('96) (Bk)	27.50	24.00
8	A1	5a on 50c car, *rose* (Bl)	35.00	32.50
9	A1	7½a on 75c vio, *org* ('96)	475.00	390.00
10	A1	10a on 1fr brnz grn, *straw*	65.00	52.50
11	A1	50a on 5fr red lil, *lav* ('96) (Bk)	300.00	250.00
		Nos. 1-11 (11)	997.00	828.50

1894

12	A2	½a & 5c on 1c blk, *lil bl* (R)	190.00	*210.00*
13	A2	1a & 10c on 3c gray, *grysh* (R)	175.00	*190.00*
14	A2	2½a & 25c on 4c cl, *lav* (Bk)	225.00	*260.00*
15	A2	5a & 50c on 20c red, *grn* (Bk)	240.00	*265.00*
16	A2	10a & 1fr on 40c red, *straw* (Bk)	460.00	*500.00*
		Nos. 12-16 (5)	1,290.	1,425.

There are two distinct types of the figures 5c, four of the 25c and three of each of the others of this series.

Stamps of France Surcharged in Red, Blue or Black

1896-1900

17a	A15	½a on 5c grn, *grnsh* (C)	10.00	8.00
18	A15	½a on 5c yel grn (I) (R)	7.25	6.50
a.		Type II	8.75	7.25
19	A15	1a on 10c blk, *lav* (II) (Bl)	8.75	7.25
a.		Type I	21.00	18.00
20	A15	1½a on 15c bl (R)	10.00	8.75
a.		Carmine surcharge	10.00	8.75
21	A15	2a on 20c red, *grn*	8.75	8.75
a.		"ZANZIBAR" double	200.00	200.00
b.		"ZANZIBAR" triple	200.00	200.00
22	A15	2½a on 25c blk, *rose* (Bl)	10.00	8.75
a.		Inverted surcharge	260.00	200.00
23	A15	3a on 30c brn, *bis*	10.00	8.75

24	A15	4a on 40c red, *straw*	12.50	9.50
25	A15	5a on 50c rose, *rose* (II) (Bl)	45.00	32.50
a.		Type I	120.00	100.00
26	A15	10a on 1fr brnz grn, *straw* (R)	27.50	24.00
27	A15	20a on 2fr brn, *az*	35.00	27.50
a.		"ZANZIBAS"	640.00	725.00
b.		"ZANZIBAR" triple		1,600.
28	A15	50a on 5fr lil, *lav*	65.00	60.00
a.		"ZANZIBAS"	8,750.	
		Nos. 17a-28 (12)	249.75	210.25

For surcharges see Nos. 50-54.

A4   A5

1897

29	A4	2½a & 25c on ½a on 5c grn, *grnsh*	1,100.	150.
30	A4	2½a & 25c on 1a on 10c *lav*	3,600.	800.
31	A4	2½a & 25c on 1½a on 15c blue	3,600.	675.
32	A5	5a & 50c on 3a on 30c brn, *bis*	3,600.	600.
33	A5	5a & 50c on 4a on 40c red, *straw*	3,600.	800.

A6   A7

Printed on the Margins of Sheets of French Stamps

Perf. 14x13½ on one or more sides

1897

34	A6	2½a & 25c on grn, *grnsh*	1,050.
35	A6	2½a & 25c blk, *lav*	3,250.
36	A6	2½a & 25c blue	2,600.
37	A7	5a & 50c brn, *bis*	2,750.
38	A7	5a & 50c red, *straw*	3,250.

There are 5 varieties of figures in the above surcharges.

A8   A9

A10

Surcharged in Red or Black

1902-03   Perf. 14x13½

39	A8	½a on 5c grn (I)	6.50	5.50
40	A9	1a on 10c rose red ('03)	7.25	7.25
41	A9	1½a on 15c pale red ('03)	14.00	13.50
42	A9	2a on 20c brn vio ('03)	17.50	14.00
43	A9	2½a on 25c bl ('03)	17.50	14.00
44	A9	3a on 30c lil ('03)	12.50	12.50
a.		5a on 30c (error)	325.00	*360.00*
45	A10	4a on 40c red & pale bl	27.50	24.00
46	A10	5a on 50c bis brn & *lav*	24.00	20.00
47	A10	10a on 1fr cl & ol grn	32.50	27.50
48	A10	20a on 2fr gray vio & yel	80.00	72.50

49	A10	50a on 5fr dk bl & buff	100.00	87.50
		Nos. 39-49 (11)	339.25	298.25

For see Reunion Nos. 55-59.

Nos. 23-24 Surcharged in Black:

25 ▬ 2½   50 ▬ 5
a   b

1 fr ▬ 10
c

1904

50	A15	25c & 2½a on 4a on 40c		1,000.
51	A15	50c & 5a on 3a on 30c		1,200.
52	A15	50c & 5a on 4a on 40c	6,500.	1,200.
53	A15	1fr & 10a on 3a on 30c		1,900.
54	A15	1fr & 10a on 4a on 40c		1,900.

Nos. 39-40, 44 Surcharged in Red or Black:

2   25ᶜ
25   2½
d   e

50ᶜ   1 fr

cinq   dix
f   g

55	A8	25c & 2a on ½a on 5c (R)	3,000.	130.00
56	A9	25c & 2½a on 1a on 10c	6,500.	150.00
a.		Inverted surcharge		1,500.
57	A9	25c & 2½a on 3a on 30c		2,250.
a.		Inverted surcharge		3,900.
b.		Double surch., both invtd.		2,600.
58	A9	50c & 5a on 3a on 30c		1,200.
59	A9	1fr & 10a on 3a on 30c		1,900.

No. J1-J3 With Various Surcharges Overprinted:

"Timbre" in Red

60	D1	½a on 5c blue	425.00

Overprinted "Affranchi" in Black

61	D1	1a on 10c brown	425.00

With Red Bars Across "CHIFFRE" and "TAXE"

62	D1	1½a on 15c green	1,000.

The illustrations are not exact reproductions of the new surcharges but are merely intended to show their relative positions and general styles.

POSTAGE DUE STAMPS

Postage Due Stamps of France Surcharged in Red, Blue or Black Like Nos. 17-28

1897   Unwmk.   Perf. 14x13½

J1	D2	½a on 5c blue (R)	20.00	12.00
J2	D2	1a on 10c brn	20.00	12.00
a.		Inverted surcharge	160.00	*180.00*
J3	D2	1½a on 15c grn (R)	32.50	12.00
J4	D2	3a on 30c car (Bk)	27.50	20.00
J5	D2	5a on 50c lil (Bl)	32.50	24.00
a.		2½a on 50c lilac (Bl)	1,400.	1,250.
		Nos. J1-J5 (5)	132.50	80.00

For overprints see Nos. 60-62.

REUNION

LOCATION — An island in the Indian Ocean about 400 miles east of Madagascar
GOVT. — Department of France
AREA — 970 sq. mi.
POP. — 490,000 (est. 1974)

CAPITAL — St. Denis

The colony of Réunion became an integral part of the Republic, acquiring the same status as the departments in metropolitan France, under a law effective Jan. 1, 1947.

On Jan. 1, 1975, stamps of France replaced those inscribed or overprinted "CFA."

100 Centimes = 1 Franc

> Catalogue values for unused stamps in this country are for Never Hinged items, beginning with Scott 224 in the regular postage section, Scott B15 in the semipostal section, Scott C18 in the airpost section, and Scott J26 in the postage due section.

For French stamps inscribed "Reunion" see Nos. 949, 1507.

A1   A2

1852   Unwmk.   Typo.   Imperf.

1	A1	15c black, *blue*	32,000.	17,500.
2	A2	30c black, *blue*	30,000.	17,500.

Four varieties of each value.
The reprints are printed on a more bluish paper than the originals. They have a frame of a thick and a thin line, instead of one thick and two thin lines. Value, $45 each.

Stamps of French Colonies Surcharged or Overprinted in Black:

5c. R
a   b

1885

3	A1(a)	5c on 40c org, *yelsh*	325.00	300.00
a.		Inverted surcharge	1,050.	1,050.
4	A1(a)	25c on 40c org, *yelsh*	42.50	35.00
a.		Inverted surcharge	500.00	500.00
b.		Double surcharge	500.00	500.00
5	A5(a)	5c on 30c brn, *yelsh*	42.50	35.00
a.		"5" inverted	2,100.	2,100.
b.		Double surcharge	500.00	500.00
6	A4(a)	5c on 40c org, *yelsh* (I)	35.00	29.00
a.		5c on 40c org, *yelsh* (II)	1,850.	1,850.
b.		Inverted surcharge (I)	500.00	500.00
c.		Double surcharge (I)	500.00	500.00
7	A8(a)	5c on 30c brn, *yelsh*	11.00	10.50
8	A8(a)	5c on 40c ver, *straw*	92.50	77.50
a.		Inverted surcharge	500.00	500.00
b.		Double surcharge	500.00	500.00
9	A8(a)	10c on 40c ver, *straw*	13.00	11.00
a.		Inverted surcharge	500.00	500.00
b.		Double surcharge	525.00	525.00
10	A8(a)	20c on 30c brn, *yelsh*	57.50	50.00

Overprint Type "b" With or Without Accent on "E"

1891

11	A4	40c org, *yelsh* (I)	425.00	400.00
a.		40c orange, *yelsh* (II)	5,000.	5,000.
b.		Double overprint	350.00	350.00
12	A7	80c car, *pnksh*	57.50	45.00
13	A8	30c brn, *yelsh*	32.50	32.50
14	A8	40c ver, *straw*	25.00	25.00
15	A8	75c car, *rose*	325.00	325.00
16	A8	1fr brnz grn, *straw*	35.00	32.50

Perf. 14x13½

17	A9	1c blk, *lil bl*	3.50	2.75
a.		Inverted overprint	25.00	25.00
b.		Double overprint	42.50	42.50
18	A9	2c brn, *buff*	4.25	3.50
a.		Inverted overprint	25.00	25.00
19	A9	4c claret, *lav*	7.50	5.75
a.		Inverted overprint	65.00	60.00
20	A9	5c grn, *grnsh*	7.50	5.75
a.		Inverted overprint	40.00	40.00
b.		Double overprint	40.00	40.00

21	A9	10c blk, *lav*	27.00	5.75
a.		Inverted overprint	50.00	50.00
b.		Double overprint	55.00	47.50
22	A9	15c blue	42.50	5.75
a.		Inverted overprint	85.00	77.50
23	A9	20c red, *grn*	30.00	22.50
a.		Inverted overprint	95.00	90.00
b.		Double overprint	90.00	85.00
24	A9	25c blk, *rose*	30.00	5.50
a.		Inverted overprint	95.00	90.00
25	A9	35c dp vio, *yel*	25.00	18.00
b.		Inverted overprint	125.00	125.00
26	A9	40c red, *straw*	60.00	47.50
a.		Inverted overprint	150.00	150.00
27	A9	75c car, *rose*	600.00	500.00
a.		Inverted overprint	950.00	950.00
28	A9	1fr brnz grn, *straw*	475.00	400.00
a.		Inverted overprint	1,250.	1,250.
b.		Double overprint	1,000.	1,000.

The varieties "RUNION," "RUENION," "REUNIONR," "ERUNION," "EUNION," "REUNIN," "REUNIOU" and "REUNOIN" are found on most stamps of this group. See *Scott Classic Specialized Catalogue of Stamps and Covers* for detailed listings. There are also many broken letters.

For surcharges see Nos. 29-33, 53-55.

No. 23 with Additional Surcharge in Black:

c

d

e

f

1891

29	A9(c)	02c on 20c red, *grn*	9.25	9.25
a.		Inverted surcharge	40.00	40.00
30	A9(c)	15c on 20c red, *grn*	11.50	11.50
a.		Inverted surcharge	40.00	40.00
31	A9(d)	2c on 20c red, *grn*	3.50	3.50
32	A9(e)	2c on 20c red, *grn*	2.50	2.50
33	A9(f)	2c on 20c red, *grn*	5.50	5.50
		Nos. 29-33 (5)	32.25	32.25

Navigation and Commerce — A14

1892-1905   Typo.   Perf. 14x13½
Name of Colony in Blue or Carmine

34	A14	1c blk, *lil bl*	1.40	.95
35	A14	2c brn, *buff*	1.40	.95
36	A14	4c claret, *lav*	2.00	1.60
37	A14	5c grn, *grnsh*	5.00	1.60
38	A14	5c yel grn ('00)	1.10	1.00
39	A14	10c blk, *lav*	8.00	2.00
40	A14	10c red ('00)	2.50	2.00
41	A14	15c bl, quadrille paper	24.00	2.40
42	A14	15c gray ('00)	5.75	2.00
43	A14	20c red, *grn*	14.50	6.50
44	A14	25c blk, *rose*	16.00	2.50
a.		"Reunion" double	300.00	300.00
45	A14	25c blue ('00)	18.00	18.00
46	A14	30c brn, *bis*	17.00	8.50
47	A14	40c red, *straw*	22.50	16.00
48	A14	50c car, *rose*	62.50	30.00
a.		"Reunion" in red and blue	350.00	350.00
49	A14	50c brn, *az* ("Reunion" in car) ('00)	42.50	37.50
50	A14	50c brn, *az* ("Reunion" in bl) ('05)	42.50	37.50
51	A14	75c dp vio, *org*	55.00	32.50
a.		"Reunion" double	325.00	325.00
52	A14	1fr brnz grn, *straw*	42.50	27.50
a.		"Reunion" double	300.00	300.00
		Nos. 34-52 (19)	384.15	231.00

Perf. 13½x14 stamps are counterfeits.
For surcharges and overprint see Nos. 56-59, 99-106, Q1.

French Colonies No. 52 Surcharged in Black:

g   h

j

1893

53	A9(g)	2c on 20c red, *grn*	2.10	2.10
54	A9(h)	2c on 20c red, *grn*	3.50	3.50
55	A9(j)	2c on 20c red, *grn*	16.00	16.00
		Nos. 53-55 (3)	21.60	21.60

Reunion Nos. 47-48, 51-52 Surcharged in Black

1901

56	A14	5c on 40c red, *straw*	4.25	4.25
a.		Inverted surcharge	29.00	29.00
b.		No bar	140.00	140.00
c.		Thin "5"	—	—
d.		"5" inverted	450.00	450.00
57	A14	5c on 50c car, *rose*	5.00	5.00
a.		Inverted surcharge	29.00	29.00
b.		No bar	140.00	140.00
c.		Thin "5"	—	—
58	A14	5c on 75c vio, *org*	14.50	14.50
a.		Inverted surcharge	35.00	35.00
b.		No bar	140.00	140.00
c.		Thin "5" and small "1"	27.50	27.50
d.		As "c," inverted	—	—
59	A14	15c on 1fr brnz grn, *straw*	12.50	12.50
a.		Inverted surcharge	35.00	35.00
b.		No bar	140.00	140.00
c.		Thin "5" and small "1"	27.50	27.50
d.		As "c," inverted	—	—
		Nos. 56-59 (4)	36.25	36.25

Map of Réunion A19

Coat of Arms and View of St. Denis A20

View of St. Pierre — A21

1907-30   Typo.

60	A19	1c vio & car rose	.25	.25
61	A19	2c brn & ultra	.25	.25
62	A19	4c ol grn & red	.25	.25
63	A19	5c grn & red	.85	.25
64	A19	5c org & vio ('22)	.25	.25
65	A19	10c car & grn	2.00	.25
66	A19	10c grn ('22)	.25	.25
67	A19	10c brn red & org red, *bluish* ('26)	.50	.50
68	A19	15c blk & ultra	.30	.30
69	A19	15c gray grn & bl grn ('26)	.30	.30
70	A19	15c bl & lt red ('28)	.30	.30
71	A20	20c gray grn & bl grn	.30	.30
72	A20	25c dp bl & vio brn	4.75	2.50
73	A20	25c lt brn & bl ('22)	.30	.30
74	A20	30c yel brn & grn	1.00	.55
75	A20	30c rose & pale rose ('22)	1.10	1.00
76	A20	30c gray & car rose ('26)	.40	.40
77	A20	30c dp grn & yel ('28)	.90	.90
78	A20	35c ol grn & bl	1.25	.75
79	A20	40c gray grn & brn ('25)	.50	.50

80	A20	45c vio & car rose	1.40	.75
81	A20	45c red brn & ver ('26)	.65	.65
82	A20	45c vio & red org ('28)	2.00	2.00
83	A20	50c red brn & ultra	3.25	1.10
84	A20	50c bl & ultra ('22)	1.00	1.00
85	A20	50c yel & vio ('26)	.80	.80
86	A20	60c dk bl & yel brn ('26)	.80	.80
87	A20	65c vio & lt bl ('28)	1.25	1.25
88	A20	75c red & car rose	.65	.55
89	A20	75c ol brn & red vio ('28)	1.75	1.75
90	A20	90c brn red & brt red ('30)	5.75	5.50
91	A21	1fr ol grn & bl	1.10	1.10
92	A21	1fr blue ('26)	.65	.65
93	A21	1fr yel brn & lav ('28)	1.10	.60
94	A21	1.10fr org brn & rose lil ('28)	1.00	.75
95	A21	1.50fr dk bl & ultra ('30)	9.75	9.75
96	A21	2fr red & grn	3.75	2.40
97	A21	3fr red vio ('30)	9.50	6.50
98	A21	5fr car & vio brn	6.75	4.50
		Nos. 60-98 (39)	68.90	52.75

For surcharges see #107-121, 178-180, B1-B3.

Stamps of 1892-1900 Surcharged in Black or Carmine

1912

99	A14	5c on 2c brn, *buff*	1.10	1.10
100	A14	5c on 15c gray (C)	1.00	1.00
a.		Inverted surcharge	125.00	125.00
101	A14	5c on 20c red, *grn*	1.50	1.50
102	A14	5c on 25c blk, *rose* (C)	1.00	1.00
103	A14	5c on 30c brn, *bis* (C)		
104	A14	10c on 40c red, *straw*	.80	.80
105	A14	10c on 50c brn, *az*	.95	.95
106	A14	10c on 75c dp vio, *org*	4.00	4.00
		Nos. 99-106 (8)	7.25 / 17.60	7.25 / 17.60

Two spacings between the surcharged numerals are found on Nos. 99 to 106. For detailed listings, see the *Scott Classic Specialized Catalogue of Stamps and Covers.*

No. 62 Surcharged

1917

107	A19	1c on 4c ol grn & red	1.25	1.25
a.		Inverted surcharge	40.00	40.00
b.		Double surcharge	60.00	60.00

Stamps and Types of 1907-30 Surcharged in Black or Red

1922-33

108	A20	40c on 20c grn & yel	.50	.50
109	A20	50c on 45c red brn & ver ('33)	.85	.75
109A	A20	50c on 45c vio & red org ('33)	210.00	200.00
b.		Double surcharge	1,000.	
110	A20	50c on 65c vio & lt bl ('33)	.85	.75
111	A20	60c on 75c red & rose	.65	.65
112	A19	50c on 15c blk & ultra (R) ('25)	1.50	1.50
113	A19	85c on 15c blk & ultra ('25)	1.50	1.50
114	A20	50c on 75c red & cer ('25)	1.60	1.60
115	A20	90c on 75c brn red & rose red ('27)	1.60	1.60
		Nos. 108-109,110-115 (8)	9.05	8.85

Stamps and Type of 1907-30 Surcharged with New Value and Bars in Black or Red

1924-27

116	A21	25c on 5fr car & brn	.80	.80
a.		Double surcharge	72.50	
117	A21	1.25fr on 1fr bl (R) ('26)	.75	.50
a.		Double surcharge	85.00	
118	A21	1.50fr on 1fr ind & ultra, *bluish* ('27)	1.00	.90
a.		Double surcharge	100.00	
119	A21	3fr on 5fr dl red & lt bl ('27)	2.50	2.10
120	A21	10fr on 5fr bl grn & brn red ('27)	14.00	11.50
121	A21	20fr on 5fr blk brn & rose ('27)	17.50	13.00
		Nos. 116-121 (6)	36.55	28.80

Common Design Types pictured following the introduction.

Colonial Exposition Issue
Common Design Types

1931   Engr.   Perf. 12½
Name of Country Typo. in Black

122	CD70	40c dp green	4.00	4.00
123	CD71	50c violet	4.00	4.00
124	CD72	90c red orange	4.00	4.00
125	CD73	1.50fr dull blue	4.00	4.00
		Nos. 122-125 (4)	16.00	16.00

Cascade of Salazie — A22

Waterfowl Lake and Anchain Peak — A23

Léon Dierx Museum, St. Denis — A24

Perf. 12, 12½ and Compound
1933-40   Engr.

126	A22	1c violet	.20	.20
127	A22	2c dark brown	.20	.20
128	A22	3c rose vio ('40)	.20	.20
129	A22	4c olive green	.20	.20
130	A22	5c red orange	.20	.20
131	A22	10c ultramarine	.20	.20
132	A22	15c black	.20	.20
133	A22	20c indigo	.25	.25
134	A22	25c red brown	.25	.25
135	A22	30c dark green	.25	.25
136	A23	35c green ('38)	.40	.40
137	A23	40c ultramarine	.40	.40
138	A23	40c brn blk ('40)	.30	.30
139	A23	45c red violet	.60	.60
140	A23	45c green ('40)	.30	.30
141	A23	50c red	.25	.25
142	A23	55c brn org ('38)	.95	.65
143	A23	60c dull bl ('40)	.30	.30
144	A23	65c olive green	.75	.60
145	A23	70c ol grn ('40)	.45	.45
146	A23	75c dark brown	3.50	2.75
147	A23	80c black ('38)	.60	.55
148	A23	90c carmine	1.75	1.50
149	A23	90c dl rose vio ('39)	.65	.65
150	A23	1fr green	1.40	.40
151	A23	1fr dk car ('38)	1.75	.40
152	A23	1fr black ('40)	.50	.50
153	A24	1.25fr orange brown	.50	.40
154	A24	1.25fr brt car rose ('39)	.65	.65
155	A22	1.40fr pck bl ('40)	.65	.65
156	A24	1.50fr ultramarine	.25	.25
157	A24	1.60fr dk car rose ('40)	1.00	1.00
158	A24	1.75fr olive green	.60	.35
159	A22	1.75fr dk bl ('38)	1.25	.45
160	A24	2fr vermilion	.40	.40
161	A22	2.25fr brt ultra ('39)	1.25	1.25
162	A22	2.50fr chnt ('40)	.95	.95
163	A24	3fr purple	.40	.40
164	A24	5fr magenta	.40	.40

165 A24	10fr dark blue	.75	.65
166 A24	20fr red brown	1.10	1.10
	Nos. 126-166 (41)	27.15	22.05

For overprints and surcharges see Nos. 177A, 181-220, 223, C1.

60c, 1fr without "RF," see Nos. 237A-237B.

Paris International Exposition Issue
Common Design Types

1937		Perf. 13	
167 CD74	20c dp vio	1.75	1.75
168 CD75	30c dk grn	1.75	1.75
169 CD76	40c car rose	1.75	1.75
170 CD77	50c dk brn & blk	1.90	1.90
171 CD78	90c red	1.90	1.90
172 CD79	1.50fr ultra	1.90	1.90
	Nos. 167-172 (6)	10.95	10.95

Colonial Arts Exhibition Issue
Souvenir Sheet
Common Design Type

1937		Imperf.	
173 CD74	3fr ultra	7.00	8.50

New York World's Fair Issue
Common Design Type

1939	Engr.	Perf. 12½x12	
174 CD82	1.25fr car lake	1.00	1.00
175 CD82	2.25fr ultra	1.00	1.00

For overprints see Nos. 221-222.

St. Denis
Roadstead
and
Marshal
Pétain
A25

1941	Unwmk.	Perf. 11½x12	
176 A25	1fr brown		.60
177 A25	2.50fr blue		.60

Nos. 176-177 were issued by the Vichy government in France, but were not placed on sale in Réunion.

For surcharges, see Nos. B13-B14.

No. 144
Surcharged
in Carmine

1943			
177A	1fr on 65c olive grn	.80	.35

De Pronis Landing on
Reunion — A25a

1943		Perf. 12½x12	
177B A25a	60c blk brn & red		.35
177C A25a	80c green & blue		.30
177D A25a	1.50fr dk brn red		.25
177E A25a	4fr ultra & red		.25
177F A25a	5fr red brn & black		.35
177G A25a	10fr violet & green		.35
	Nos. 177B-177G,C13A-C13F (12)		3.65

300th Ann. of French settlement on Réunion.
Nos. 177B-177G were issued by the Vichy government in France, but were not placed on sale in Réunion.

Stamps of 1907 Overprinted in Blue Violet

q

1943	Unwmk.	Perf. 14x13½	
178 A19(q)	4c ol gray & pale red	3.50	3.50
179 A20(q)	75c red & lil rose	.95	.95
180 A21(q)	5fr car & vio brn	47.50	47.50

Stamps of 1933-40 Overprinted in Carmine, Black or Blue Violet

181 A22(r)	1c rose vio (C)	.65	.65
182 A22(r)	2c blk brn (C)	.65	.65
183 A22(r)	3c rose vio (C)	.65	.65
184 A22(r)	4c ol yel (C)	.65	.65
185 A22(r)	5c red org	.65	.65
186 A22(r)	10c ultra (C)	.65	.65
187 A22(r)	15c blk (C)	.65	.65
188 A22(r)	20c ind (C)	.65	.65
189 A22(r)	25c red brn (BIV)	.85	.85
190 A22(r)	30c dk grn (C)	.95	.95
191 A23(q)	35c green	.55	.55
192 A23(q)	40c dl ultra (C)	.55	.55
193 A23(q)	40c brn blk (C)	.55	.55
194 A23(q)	45c red vio	.55	.55
195 A23(q)	45c green	.55	.55
196 A23(q)	50c org red	.55	.55
197 A23(q)	55c brn org	.55	.55
198 A23(q)	60c dl bl (C)	2.25	2.25
199 A23(q)	65c ol grn	.55	.55
200 A23(q)	70c ol grn (C)	1.50	1.50
201 A23(q)	75c dk brn (C)	3.50	3.50
202 A23(q)	80c blk (C)	.65	.65
203 A23(q)	90c dl rose vio	.65	.65
204 A23(q)	1fr green	.65	.65
205 A23(q)	1fr dk car	.65	.65
206 A23(q)	1fr blk (C)	1.90	1.90
207 A24(q)	1.25fr org brn (BIV)	.65	.65
208 A24(q)	1.25fr brt car rose	2.00	2.00
209 A22(r)	1.40fr pck bl (C)	1.40	1.40
210 A24(q)	1.50fr ultra (C)	.65	.65
211 A22(r)	1.60fr dk car rose	1.50	1.50
212 A24(q)	1.75fr ol grn (C)	1.75	1.75
213 A22(r)	1.75fr dk bl (C)	3.00	3.00
214 A24(q)	2fr vermilion	.65	.65
215 A22(r)	2.25fr brt ultra (C)	3.00	3.00
216 A22(r)	2.50fr chnt (BIV)	4.75	4.75
217 A24(q)	3fr pur (C)	.65	.65
218 A24(q)	5fr brn lake (BIV)	1.40	1.40
219 A24(q)	10fr dk bl (C)	5.50	5.50
220 A24(q)	20fr red brn (BIV)	8.00	8.00

New York World's Fair Issue
Overprinted in Black or Carmine

221 CD82(q)	1.25fr car lake	2.50	2.50
222 CD82(q)	2.25fr ultra (C)	2.50	2.50
	Nos. 178-222 (45)	115.00	115.00

No. 177A Overprinted Type "q"

1943	Unwmk.	Perf. 12½	
223 A23	1fr on 65c ol grn	.65	.65

Catalogue values for unused stamps in this section, from this point to the end of the section, are for Never Hinged items.

Produce of
Réunion
A26

1943	Photo.	Perf. 14½x14	
224 A26	5c dull brown	.20	.20
225 A26	10c dk blue	.20	.20
226 A26	15c emerald	.20	.20
227 A26	30c dp orange	.20	.20
228 A26	40c dk slate grn	.20	.20
229 A26	80c rose violet	.35	.35
230 A26	1fr red brown	.20	.20
231 A26	1.50fr crimson	.35	.35
232 A26	2fr black	.35	.35
233 A26	2.50fr ultra	.50	.50
234 A26	4fr dk violet	.65	.65
235 A26	5fr bister	.65	.65

236 A26	10fr dark brown	.95	.95
237 A26	20fr dark green	1.25	1.25
	Nos. 224-237 (14)	6.25	6.25

For surcharges see Nos. 240-247.

Type of 1933-40 without "RF"

1944	Engr.	Perf. 12½	
237A A23	60c dull blue		.75
237B A23	1fr black & blue		.75

Nos. 237A-237B were issued by the Vichy government in France, but were not placed on sale in Réunion.

Eboue Issue
Common Design Type

1945	Engr.	Perf. 13	
238 CD91	2fr black	.50	.50
239 CD91	25fr Prussian green	.75	.50

Nos. 224, 226 and 233 Surcharged with New Values and Bars in Carmine or Black

1945		Perf. 14½x14	
240 A26	50c on 5c dl brn (C)	.20	.20
241 A26	60c on 5c dl brn (C)	.20	.20
242 A26	70c on 5c dl brn (C)	.20	.20
243 A26	1.20fr on 5c dl brn (C)	.35	.35
244 A26	2.40fr on 25c emer	.35	.35
245 A26	3fr on 25c emer	.65	.65
246 A26	4.50fr on 25c emer	.65	.65
247 A26	15fr on 2.50fr ultra (C)	.80	.80
	Nos. 240-247 (8)	3.40	3.40

Cliff — A27

Cutting Sugar
Cane — A28

Cascade
A29

Banana Tree
A30

Mountain
Scene
A31

Ship Approaching Réunion — A32

1947	Unwmk.	Photo.	Perf. 13½	
249 A27	10c org & grnsh blk		.20	.20
250 A27	30c org & brt bl		.20	.20
251 A27	40c org & brn		.20	.20
252 A28	50c bl grn & brn		.20	.20
253 A28	60c dk bl & brn		.20	.20
254 A28	80c brn & ol brn		.35	.35
255 A29	1fr dl bl & vio brn		.35	.35
256 A29	1.20fr bl grn & gray		.50	.50
257 A29	1.50fr org & vio brn		.50	.50
258 A30	2fr gray bl & bl grn		.50	.50
259 A30	3fr vio brn & bl grn		.50	.50
260 A30	3.60fr red & rose red		.55	.55
261 A30	4fr gray bl & buff		.50	.50
262 A31	5fr rose lil & brn		.70	.50
263 A31	6fr bl & brn		.80	.55
264 A31	10fr org & ultra		1.90	1.10
265 A32	15fr gray bl & vio brn		2.75	2.00
266 A32	20fr bl & org		3.75	3.00
267 A32	25fr rose lil & brn		4.50	3.25
	Nos. 249-267 (19)		19.15	15.15

Stamps of France, 1945-49, Surcharged type "a" or "b" in Black or Carmine

On A147

Others

1949	Unwmk.	Perf. 14x13½, 13	
268 A153	10c on 30c	.20	.20
269 A153	30c on 50c	.45	.20
270 A146	50c on 1fr	1.10	.70
271 A146	60c on 2fr	6.00	1.10
272 A147	1fr on 3fr	1.50	.55
273 A147	2fr on 4fr	5.75	1.25
274 A147	2.50fr on 5fr	15.50	8.00
275 A147	3fr on 6fr	1.75	1.10
276 A147	4fr on 10fr	1.60	1.25
277 A162	5fr on 20fr (C)	7.75	1.10
278 A147	6fr on 12fr	22.50	1.75
279 A160	7fr on 12fr	7.00	2.25
280 A165	8fr on 25fr (C)	30.00	2.50
281 A165	10fr on 25fr (C)	2.10	1.10
282 A174	11fr on 18fr (C)	13.00	1.60
	Nos. 268-282 (15)	116.20	24.65

The letters "C. F. A." are the initials of "Colonies Francaises d'Afrique," referring to the currency which is expressed in French Africa francs.

The surcharge on Nos. 277, 279, 282 includes two bars.

1950		Perf. 14x13½	
283 A182	10c on 50c bl, red & yel	.55	.55
284 A182	1fr on 2fr grn, yel & red (#619)	8.00	2.25
285 A147	2fr on 5fr lt grn	14.00	2.75
	Nos. 283-285 (3)	22.55	5.55

Surcharged Type "a" and Bars

1950-51		Perf. 13	
286 A188	5fr on 20fr dk red	8.00	1.10
287 A185	8fr on 25fr dp ultra ('51)	8.00	1.10

Stamps of France, 1951-52, Surcharged in Black or Red

1951-52		Perf. 14x13½, 13	
288 A182	50c on 1fr bl, red & yel	.55	.55
289 A182	1fr on 2fr vio bl, red & yel (#662)	.55	.55
290 A147	2fr on 5fr dl vio	3.25	1.50
291 A147	3fr on 6fr grn	6.50	1.25
292 A220	5fr on 20fr dk pur (R; '52)	2.25	1.25
293 A147	6fr on 12fr red org ('52)	7.00	1.60
294 A215	8fr on 40fr vio (R) ('52)	5.00	.55
295 A147	9fr on 18fr cerise	16.00	3.25
296 A208	15fr on 30fr ind (R)	8.50	1.75
	Nos. 288-296 (9)	49.60	12.25

The surcharge on Nos. 292, 294 and 296 include two bars.

France No. 697 Surcharged Type "a" in Black

1953		Perf. 14x13½	
297 A182	50c on 1fr blk, red & yel	.35	.20

France No. 688 Surcharged type "c" in Black

	Perf. 13		
298 A230	3fr on 6fr dp plum & car	.90	.55

France Nos. 703 and 705 Surcharged Type "a" in Red or Blue

1954			
299 A235	8fr on 40fr (R)	29.00	7.00
300 A235	20fr on 75fr	62.50	27.50

France Nos. 698, 721, 713, and 715 Surcharged Type "a" in Black

Perf. 14x13½, 13

301	A182	1fr on 2fr	3.50	1.60
302	A241	4fr on 10fr	3.25	1.10
303	A238	8fr on 40fr	7.75	.55
304	A238	20fr on 75fr	10.00	1.25

The surcharge on Nos. 303 and 304 includes two bars.

France Nos. 737, 719 and 722-724 Surcharged in Black or Red

305	A182(b)	1fr on 2fr	.35	.35
306	A241(a)	2fr on 6fr (R)	.55	.55
307	A242(a)	6fr on 12fr	7.25	1.25
308	A241(b)	9fr on 18fr	8.25	3.75
309	A241(a)	10fr on 20fr	6.00	1.10
		Nos. 299-309 (11)	138.40	45.80

The surcharge on Nos. 306-308 includes two bars; on No. 309 three bars.

France No. 720 Surcharged Type "c" in Red, Bars at Lower Left

1955　　　　**Perf. 13**

310	A241	3fr on 8fr brt bl & dk grn	1.10	.90

France Nos. 785, 774-779 Surcharged Type "a" in Black or Red

Perf. 14x13½, 13

1955-56　　　　**Typo., Engr.**

311	A182	50c on 1fr	.20	.20
312	A265	2fr on 6fr ('56)	.95	.55
313	A265	3fr on 8fr	.80	.35
314	A265	4fr on 10fr	.95	.35
315	A265	5fr on 12fr (R)	.95	.35
316	A265	6fr on 18fr (R)	.80	.35
317	A265	10fr on 25fr	1.10	.35
		Nos. 311-317 (7)	5.75	2.50

The surcharge on Nos. 312-317 includes two bars.

France Nos. 801-804 Surcharged Type "a" or "b" in Black or Red

1956　　　　**Engr.**　　　　**Perf. 13**

318	A280(a)	8fr on 30fr (R)	4.00	.90
319	A280(b)	9fr on 40fr	5.50	2.40
320	A280(a)	15fr on 50fr	7.00	1.25
321	A280(a)	20fr on 75fr (R)	6.50	1.75
		Nos. 318-321 (4)	23.00	6.30

The surcharge on Nos. 318, 319 and 321 includes two bars.

France Nos. 837 and 839 Surcharged Type "a" in Red

1957　　　　**Perf. 13**

322	A294	7fr on 15fr	.90	.50
323	A265	17fr on 70fr	5.00	1.60

The surcharge on Nos. 322-323 includes two bars.

No. 322 has three types of "7" in the sheet of 50. There are 34 of the "normal" 7; 10 of a slightly thinner 7, and 6 of a slightly thicker 7.

France Nos. 755-756, 833-834, 851-855, 908, 949 Surcharged in Black or Red Type "a", "b" or

d

Typographed, Engraved

1957-60　　　　**Perf. 14x13½, 13**

324	A236(b)	2fr on 6fr	.20	.20
325	A302(b)	3fr on 10fr ('58)	.35	.35
326	A236(b)	4fr on 12fr	2.75	.55
327	A236(b)	5fr on 10fr	1.60	.80
328	A303(b)	6fr on 18fr	.90	.35
329	A302(a)	9fr on 25fr (R)		
		('58)	.90	.45
330	A252(a)	10fr on 20fr (R)	1.25	.30
331	A302(b)	12fr on 25fr	5.00	.35
332	A303(b)	17fr on 35fr	2.25	1.25
333	A302(a)	20fr on 50fr	1.25	.55
334	A302(a)	25fr on 85fr	3.00	1.10
335	A339(d)	50fr on 1fr ('60)	21.70	6.70
		Nos. 324-335 (12)	21.70	6.70

The surcharge includes two bars on Nos. 324, 326-327, 329-331, 333 and 335.

France Nos. 973, 939 and 968 Surcharged

e

f

1961-63　　　　**Typo.**　　　　**Perf. 14x13½**

336	A318(e)	2fr on 5c multi	.30	.20
337	A336(b)	5fr on 10c brt grn	1.25	.35
338	A336(b)	5fr on 10c brt grn		
		('63)	1.40	.55
339	A349(f)	12fr on 25c lake & gray	.30	.20
		Nos. 336-339 (4)	3.25	1.30

The surcharge on No. 337 includes three bars. No. 338 has "b" surcharge and two bars.

France Nos. 943, 941 and 946 Surcharged "CFA" and New Value in Two Lines in Black or Red

Engraved, Typographed

1961　　　　**Unwmk.**　　　　**Perf. 13, 14x13½**

340	A338	7fr on 15c	.80	.55
341	A337	10fr on 20c	.25	.20
342	A339	20fr on 50c (R)	13.00	3.25
		Nos. 340-342 (3)	14.05	4.00

Surcharge on No. 342 includes 3 bars.

France Nos. 1047-1048 Surcharged with New Value, "CFA" and Two Bars

1963, Jan. 2　　　　**Engr.**　　　　**Perf. 13**

343	A394	12fr on 25c	.70	.70
344	A395	25fr on 50c	.70	.70

1st television connection of the US and Europe through the Telstar satellite, July 11-12, 1962.

France Nos. 1040-1041, 1007 and 1009 Surcharged Similarly to Type "e"

Typographed, Engraved

1963　　　　**Perf. 14x13½, 13**

345	A318	2fr on 5c	.25	.20
346	A318	5fr on 10c	.25	.20
347	A372	7fr on 15c	.35	.35
348	A372	20fr on 45c	1.25	.55
		Nos. 345-348 (4)	2.10	1.30

Two-line surcharge on No. 345; No. 347 has currency expressed in capital "F" and two heavy bars through old value; two thin bars on No. 348.

France No. 1078 Surcharged Type "e" in Two Lines in Dark Blue

1964, Feb. 8　　　　**Engr.**　　　　**Perf. 13**

349	CD118	12fr on 25c	.90	.80

"PHILATEC," Intl. Philatelic and Postal Techniques Exhib., Paris, June 5-21, 1964.

France Nos. 1092, 1094 and 1102 Surcharged with New Value and "CFA"

Typographed, Engraved

1964　　　　**Perf. 14x13½, 13**

350	A318	1fr on 2c	.20	.20
351	A318	6fr on 18c	.30	.20
352	A420	35fr on 70c	1.10	.70
		Nos. 350-352 (3)	1.60	1.10

Surcharge on No. 352 includes two bars.

France Nos. 1095, 1126, 1070 Surcharged with New Value and "CFA"

1965

353	A318	15fr on 30c	.35	.20
354	A440	25fr on 50c	.80	.70
355	A408	30fr on 60c	1.10	.80
		Nos. 353-355 (3)	2.25	1.70

Two bars obliterate old denomination on Nos. 354-355.

Etienne Regnault, "Le Taureau" and Coast of Reunion — A33

1965, Oct. 3　　　　**Engr.**　　　　**Perf. 13**

356	A33	15fr bluish blk & dk car	.70	.45

Tercentenary of settlement of Reunion.

France No. 985 Surcharged with New Value, Two Bars and "CFA"

1966, Feb. 13　　　　**Engr.**　　　　**Perf. 13**

357	A360	10fr on 20c bl & car	1.10	.55

French Satellite A-1 Issue

France Nos. 1137-1138 Surcharged with New Value, Two Bars and "CFA" and Red

1966, Mar. 27　　　　**Engr.**　　　　**Perf. 13**

358	CD121	15fr on 30c	.90	.80
359	CD121	30fr on 60c	1.00	.90
a.		Strip of 2 + label	2.25	2.25

France Nos. 1142, 1143, 1101 and 1127 Surcharged with New Value, "CFA" and Two Bars

1967-69　　　　**Typo.**　　　　**Perf. 14x13**

360	A446	2fr on 5c bl & red	.20	.20

Photo.　　　　**Perf. 13**

360A	A446	10fr on 20c multi ('69)	.20	.20

Engr.

361	A421	20fr on 40c multi	.90	.70
362	A439	30fr on 60c bl & red brn	1.90	1.25

EXPO '67 Issue

France No. 1177 Surcharged with New Value, "CFA" and Two Bars

1967, June 12　　　　**Engr.**　　　　**Perf. 13**

363	A473	30fr on 60c dl bl & bl grn	1.90	1.25

EXPO '67, Montreal, Apr. 28-Oct. 27.

Lions Issue

France No. 1196 Surcharged in Violet Blue with New Value, "CFA" and Two Bars

1967, Oct. 29　　　　**Engr.**　　　　**Perf. 13**

364	A485	20fr on 40c	2.25	1.00

50th anniversary of Lions International.

France No. 1130 Surcharged in Violet Blue with New Value, "CFA" and Two Bars

1968, Feb. 26　　　　**Engr.**　　　　**Perf. 13**

365	A440	50fr on 1fr	2.00	1.25

France No. 1224 Surcharged with New Value, "CFA" and Two Bars

1968, Oct. 21　　　　**Engr.**　　　　**Perf. 13**

366	A508	20fr on 40c multi	1.10	.70

20 years of French Polar expeditions.

France Nos. 1230-1231 Surcharged with New Value, "CFA" and Two Bars

1969, Apr. 13　　　　**Engr.**　　　　**Perf. 13**

367	A486	15fr on 30c green	.45	.35
368	A486	20fr on 40c dp car	.55	.20

France No. 1255 Surcharged with New Value, "CFA" and Two Bars

1969, Aug. 18　　　　**Engr.**　　　　**Perf. 13**

370	A526	35fr on 70c multi	1.10	1.00

Napoleon Bonaparte (1769-1821).

France No. 1293 Surcharged with New Value and "CFA"

1971, Jan. 16　　　　**Engr.**　　　　**Perf. 13**

371	A555	25fr on 50c rose car	.55	.20

France No. 1301 Surcharged with New Value and "CFA"

1971, Apr. 13　　　　**Engr.**　　　　**Perf. 13**

372	A562	40fr on 80c multi	1.40	1.10

France No. 1309 Surcharged with New Value, "CFA" and 2 Bars

1971, June 5　　　　**Engr.**　　　　**Perf. 13**

373	A569	15fr on 40c multi	.70	.55

Aid for rural families.

France No. 1312 Surcharged with New Value and "CFA"

1971, Aug. 30　　　　**Engr.**　　　　**Perf. 13**

374	A571	45fr on 90c multi	.90	.70

France No. 1320 Surcharged with New Value and "CFA"

1971, Oct. 18　　　　**Engr.**　　　　**Perf. 13**

375	A573	45fr on 90c multi	1.10	.80

40th anniversary of the first assembly of presidents of artisans' guilds.

Réunion Chameleon A34

1971, Nov. 8　　　　**Photo.**　　　　**Perf. 13**

376	A34	25fr multi	1.25	.70

Nature protection.

Common Design Type and

De Gaulle in Brazzaville, 1944 — A35

Designs: No. 377, Gen. de Gaulle, 1940. No. 379, de Gaulle entering Paris, 1944. No. 380, Pres. de Gaulle, 1970.

1971, Nov. 9　　　　**Engr.**

377	CD134	25fr black	1.10	1.10
378	A35	25fr ultra	1.10	1.10
379	A35	25fr rose red	1.10	1.10
380	CD134	25fr black	1.10	1.10
a.		Strip of 4 + label	6.50	6.50

Charles de Gaulle (1890-1970), president of France. Nos. 377-380 printed se-tenant in sheets of 20 containing 5 strips of 4 plus labels with Cross of Lorraine and inscription.

France No. 1313 Surcharged with New Value and "CFA"

1972, Jan. 17　　　　**Engr.**　　　　**Perf. 13**

381	A570	50fr on 1.10fr multi	1.10	.90

Map of South Indian Ocean, Penguin and Ships — A36

1972, Jan. 31　　　　**Engr.**　　　　**Perf. 13**

382	A36	45fr blk, bl & ocher	1.75	1.75

Bicentenary of the discovery of the Crozet and Kerguelen Islands.

France No. 1342 Surcharged with New New Value, "CFA" and 2 Bars in Red

1972, May. 8　　　　**Engr.**　　　　**Perf. 13**

383	A590	15fr on 40c red	.70	.70

20th anniv. of Blood Donors' Assoc. of Post and Telecommunications Employees.

France Nos. 1345-1346 Surcharged with New Value, "CFA" and 2 Bars
1972, June 5 Typo. Perf. 14x13
384 A593 15fr on 30c multi .35 .35
385 A593 25fr on 50c multi .55 .45
Introduction of postal code system.

France No. 1377 Surcharged with New Value, "CFA" and 2 Bars in Ultramarine
1973, June 12 Engr. Perf. 13
386 A620 45fr on 90c multi 1.50 1.00

France Nos. 1374, 1336 Surcharged with New Value and "CFA" in Ultramarine or Red
1973 Engr. Perf. 13
387 A617 50fr on 1fr multi (U) .90 .70
388 A586 100fr on 2fr multi (R) 1.40 .80
On No. 388, two bars cover "2.00".
Issue dates: 50fr, June 24; 100fr, Oct. 13.

France No. 1231C Surcharged with New Value, "CFA" and 2 Bars
1973, Nov. Typo. Perf. 14x13
389 A486 15fr on 30c bl grn 3.75 .55

France No. 1390 Surcharged with New Value, "CFA" and 2 Bars in Red
1974, Jan. 20 Engr. Perf. 13
390 A633 25fr on 50c multi .55 .55
ARPHILA 75 Phil. Exhib., Paris, June 1975.

France Nos. 1394-1397 Surcharged "100 FCFA" in Black, Ultramarine or Brown
Engr. (#391, 393), Photo. (#392, 394)
1974 Perf. 12x13, 13x12
391 A637 100fr on 2fr (Bk) 1.90 1.10
392 A638 100fr on 2fr (U) 2.40 1.90
393 A639 100fr on 2fr (Br) 2.40 1.90
394 A640 100fr on 2fr (U) 2.40 1.90
Nos. 391-394 (4) 9.10 6.80
Nos. 391-394 printed in sheets of 25 with alternating labels publicizing "ARPHILA 75," Paris June 6-16, 1975.
Two bars obliterate original denomination on Nos. 391-393.

France No. 1401 Surcharged "45 FCFA" and 2 Bars in Red
1974, Apr. 29 Engr. Perf. 13
395 A644 45fr on 90c multi 1.40 1.10
Reorganized sea rescue organization.

France No. 1415 Surcharged with New Value, 2 Bars and "FCFA" in Ultramarine
1974, Oct. 6 Engr. Perf. 13
396 A657 60fr on 1.20fr multi 1.25 1.00
Centenary of Universal Postal Union.

France Nos. 1292A and 1294B Surcharged with New Value and "FCFA" in Ultramarine
1974, Oct. 19 Typo. Perf. 14x13
397 A555 30fr on 60c grn 1.25 1.25
Engr.
Perf. 13
398 A555 40fr on 80c car rose 1.50 1.25

SEMI-POSTAL STAMPS

No. 65 Surcharged in Black or Red

1915 Unwmk. Perf. 14x13½
B1 A19 10c + 5c (Bk) 110.00 80.00
a. Inverted surcharge 275.00 210.00
B2 A19 10c + 5c (R) 1.10 1.10
a. Inverted surcharge 57.50 57.50

No. 65 Surcharged in Red

1916
B3 A19 10c + 5c 1.25 1.25

Curie Issue
Common Design Type
1938 Perf. 13
B4 CD80 1.75fr + 50c brt ultra 11.00 11.00

French Revolution Issue
Common Design Type
1939 Photo. Unwmk.
Name and Value Typo. in Black
B5 CD83 45c + 25c grn 10.00 10.00
B6 CD83 70c + 30c brn 10.00 10.00
B7 CD83 90c + 35c red org 10.00 10.00
B8 CD83 1.25fr + 1fr rose pink 10.00 10.00
B9 CD83 2.25fr + 2fr blue 10.00 10.00
Nos. B5-B9 (5) 50.00 50.00

Common Design Type and

Artillery Colonel — SP1

Colonial Infantry SP2

1941 Unwmk. Perf. 13½
B10 SP1 1fr + 1fr red 1.00
B11 CD86 1.50fr + 3fr claret 1.00
B12 SP2 2.50fr + 1fr blue 1.00
Nos. B10-B12 (3) 3.00
Nos. B10-B12 were issued by the Vichy government in France, but were not placed on sale in Reunion.

Nos. 176-177 Surcharged in Black or Red

1944 Engr. Perf. 12½x12
B13 50c + 1.50fr on 2.50fr deep blue (R) .55
B14 + 2.50fr on 1fr yel brn .55
Colonial Development Fund.
Nos. B13-B14 were issued by the Vichy government in France, but were not placed on sale in Réunion.

Catalogue values for unused stamps in this section, from this point to the end of the section, are for Never Hinged items.

Red Cross Issue
Common Design Type
1944 Perf. 14½x14
B15 CD90 5fr + 20fr black .85 .85
The surtax was for the French Red Cross and national relief.

France Nos. B365-B366 Surcharged with New Value, "CFA" and Two Bars
1962, Dec. 10 Engr. Perf. 13
B16 SP219 10 + 5fr on 20 + 10c 1.90 1.90
B17 SP219 12 + 5fr on 25 + 10c 2.00 2.00
The surtax was for the Red Cross.

France Nos. B374-B375 Surcharged with New Value, "CFA" and Two Bars in Red
1963, Dec. 9
B18 SP223 10 + 5fr on 20 + 10c 2.40 2.40
B19 SP223 12 + 5fr on 25 + 10c 2.40 2.40
Centenary of the Intl. Red Cross. The surtax was for the Red Cross.

France Nos. B385-B386 Surcharged with New Value, "CFA" and Two Bars in Dark Blue
1964, Dec. 13 Unwmk. Perf. 13
B20 SP230 10 + 5fr on 20 + 10c 1.25 1.25
B21 SP230 12 + 5fr on 25 + 10c 1.40 1.40
Jean Nicolas Corvisart (1755-1821) and Dominique Larrey (1766-1842), physicians. The surtax was for the Red Cross.

France Nos. B392-B393 Surcharged with New Value, "CFA" and Two Bars
1965, Dec. 12 Engr. Perf. 13
B22 SP233 12 + 5fr on 25 + 10c 1.25 1.25
B23 SP233 15 + 5fr on 30 + 10c 1.40 1.40
The surtax was for the Red Cross.

France Nos. B402-B403 Surcharged with New Value, "CFA" and Two Bars
1966, Dec. 11 Engr. Perf. 13
B24 SP237 12 + 5fr on 25 + 10c 1.10 1.10
B25 SP237 15 + 5fr on 30 + 10c 1.10 1.10
The surtax was for the Red Cross.

France Nos. B409-B410 Surcharged with New Value, "CFA" and Two Bars
1967, Dec. 17 Engr. Perf. 13
B26 SP240 12 + 5fr on 25 + 10c 2.10 2.10
B27 SP240 15 + 5fr on 30 + 10c 2.75 2.75
Surtax for the Red Cross.

France Nos. B421-B424 Surcharged with New Value, "CFA" and Two Bars
1968-69 Engr. Perf. 13
B28 SP244 12 + 5fr on 25 + 10c 1.25 1.10
B29 SP244 15 + 5fr on 30 + 10c 1.40 1.10
B30 SP244 20 + 7fr on 40 + 15c 1.10 1.10
B31 SP244 20 + 7fr on 40 + 15c ('69) 1.10 1.10
Nos. B28-B31 (4) 4.85 4.40
The surtax was for the Red Cross.

France No. B425 Surcharged with New Value, "CFA" and Two Bars
1969, Mar. 17 Engr. Perf. 13
B32 SP245 15fr + 5fr on 30c + 10c 1.10 1.10
Stamp Day.

France No. B440 Surcharged with New Value, "CFA" and Two Bars
1970, Mar. 16 Engr. Perf. 13
B33 SP249 20fr + 5fr on 40c + 10c .90 .80
Stamp day.

France Nos. B443-B444 Surcharged with New Value "CFA" and Two Bars
1970, Dec. 14 Engr. Perf. 13
B34 SP252 20 + 7fr on 40 + 15c 2.00 1.60
B35 SP252 20 + 7fr on 40 + 15c 2.00 1.90
The surtax was for the Red Cross.

France No. B451 Surcharged with New Value, "CFA" and Two Bars
1971, Mar. 29 Engr. Perf. 13
B36 SP254 25fr + 5fr on 50c + 10c .90 .70
Stamp Day.

France Nos. B452-B453 Surcharged with New Value, "CFA" and Two Bars
1971, Dec. 13
B37 SP255 15fr + 5fr on 30c + 10c 1.10 1.10
B38 SP255 25fr + 5fr on 50c + 10c 1.10 1.10
The surtax was for the Red Cross.

France No. B460 Surcharged with New Value and "CFA"
1972, Mar. 20 Engr. Perf. 13
B39 SP257 25fr + 5fr on 50c + 10c .90 .90
Stamp Day.

France Nos. B461-B462 Surcharged with New Value, "CFA" and Two Bars in Red or Green
1972, Dec. 16 Engr. Perf. 13
B40 SP258 15 + 5fr on 30 + 10c .90 .90
B41 SP258 25 + 5fr on 50 + 10c (G) 1.00 1.00
Surtax was for the Red Cross.

France No. B470 Surcharged with New Value, "CFA" and Two Bars in Red
1973, Mar. 26 Engr. Perf. 13
B42 SP260 25fr +5fr on 50c +10c 1.10 1.10
Stamp Day.

France Nos. B471-B472 Surcharged with New Value, "CFA" and Two Bars in Red
1973, Dec. 3 Engr. Perf. 13
B43 SP261 15 +5fr on 30c +10c 1.10 1.10
B44 SP261 25 +5fr on 50c +10c 1.10 1.10
Surtax was for the Red Cross.

France No. B477 Surcharged "25 + 5 FCFA"
1974, Mar. 11 Engr. Perf. 13
B45 SP263 25fr + 5fr on 50c + 10c .80 .80
Stamp Day.

France Nos. B479-B480 Surcharged with New Value, "FCFA" and Two Bars in Green or Red
1974, Nov. 30 Engr. Perf. 13
B46 SP265 30 + 7fr on 60 + 15c (G) 1.10 1.10
B47 SP266 40 + 7fr on 80 + 15c (R) 1.10 1.10
Surtax was for the Red Cross.

AIR POST STAMPS

No. 141 Overprinted in Blue

1937, Jan. 23 Unwmk. Perf. 12½
C1 A23 50c red 225.00 200.00
a. Vert. pair, one without overprint 1,300. 1,300.
b. Inverted overprint 3,500.
Flight of the "Roland Garros" from Reunion to France by aviators Laurent, Lenier and Touge in Jan.-Feb., 1937.

Airplane and Landscape — AP2

1938, Mar. 1 Engr. Perf. 12½
C2 AP2 3.65fr slate blue & car .75 .60
C3 AP2 6.65fr brown & org red .75 .60
C4 AP2 9.65fr car & ultra .75 .60
C5 AP2 12.65fr brown & green 1.50 1.25
Nos. C2-C5 (4) 3.75 3.05
For overprints see Nos. C14-C17.

Plane and
Bridge over
East River
AP3

Plane and
Landscape
AP4

1942, Oct. 19   **Perf. 12x12½**

C6	AP3	50c olive & pur	.25
C7	AP3	1fr dk bl & scar	.25
C8	AP3	2fr brn & blk	.40
C9	AP3	3fr rose lil & grn	.80
C10	AP3	5fr red org & red brn	.80

Frame Engr., Center Photo.

C11	AP4	10fr dk grn, red org & vio	.80
C12	AP4	20fr dk bl, brn vio & red	.80
C13	AP4	50fr brn car, Prus grn & bl	1.00
		Nos. C6-C13 (8)	5.10

Nos. C6-C13 were issued by the Vichy government in France, but were not placed on sale in Réunion.

De Poivre
AP4a

1943   **Perf. 12½x12**

C13A	AP4a	1fr sepia & red	.20
C13B	AP4a	2fr green & blue	.20
C13C	AP4a	3fr dk brown red	.20
C13D	AP4a	5fr ultramarine & red	.35
C13E	AP4a	10fr red brown & black	.35
C13F	AP4a	20fr violet & green	.50
		Nos. C13A-C13F (6)	1.80

300th Ann. of French settlement on Réunion. Nos. C13A-C13F were issued by the Vichy government in France, but were not placed on sale in Réunion.

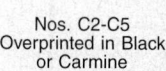

Nos. C2-C5
Overprinted in Black
or Carmine

1943   **Unwmk.**   **Perf. 12½**

C14	AP2	3.65fr sl bl & car	4.00	4.00
C15	AP2	6.65fr brn & org red	4.00	4.00
C16	AP2	9.65fr car & ultra (C)	4.00	4.00
C17	AP2	12.65fr brn & grn	4.00	4.00
		Nos. C14-C17 (4)	16.00	16.00

Catalogue values for unused stamps in this section, from this point to the end of the section, are for Never Hinged items.

Common Design Type

1944   **Photo.**   **Perf. 14½x14**

C18	CD87	1fr dk org	.25	.25
C19	CD87	1.50fr brt red	.25	.25
C20	CD87	5fr brn red	.35	.35
C21	CD87	10fr black	.60	.60
C22	CD87	25fr ultra	.75	.75
C23	CD87	50fr dk grn	.75	.75
C24	CD87	100fr plum	1.00	1.00
		Nos. C18-C24 (7)	3.95	3.95

Victory Issue
Common Design Type

1946, May 8   **Engr.**   **Perf. 12½**

C25	CD92	8fr olive gray	.75	.75

European victory of the Allied Nations in WWII.

Chad to Rhine Issue
Common Design Types

1946, June 6

C26	CD93	5fr orange	.85	.85
C27	CD94	10fr sepia	.85	.85
C28	CD95	15fr grnsh blk	.85	.85
C29	CD96	20fr lilac rose	1.10	1.10
C30	CD97	25fr greenish blue	1.10	1.10
C31	CD98	50fr green	1.25	1.25
		Nos. C26-C31 (6)	6.00	6.00

Shadow of Plane — AP5

Plane over
Réunion — AP6

Air View of Réunion and Shadow of
Plane — AP7

Perf. 13x12½

1947, Mar. 24   **Photo.**   **Unwmk.**

C32	AP5	50fr ol grn & bl gray	6.50	6.50
C33	AP6	100fr dk brn & org	10.00	10.00
C34	AP7	200fr dk bl & org	12.50	12.50
		Nos. C32-C34 (3)	29.00	29.00

France, Nos. C18-C21 Surcharged
and Bars, in Carmine or Black

c

1949   **Unwmk.**   **Perf. 13**

C35	AP7	20fr on 40fr (C)	2.75	1.10
C36	AP8	25fr on 50fr	3.50	1.10
C37	AP9	50fr on 100fr (C)	7.75	3.25
C38	AP10	100fr on 200fr	42.50	16.00
		Nos. C35-C38 (4)	56.50	21.45

France Nos. C24, C26 and C27
Surcharged Type "c" and Bars in Black

1949-51

C39	AP12	100fr on 200fr		
		('51)	110.00	22.50
C40	AP12	200fr on 500fr	45.00	16.50
C41	AP13	500fr on 1000fr		
		('51)	250.00	175.00
		Nos. C39-C41 (3)	405.00	214.00

France Nos. C29-C32 Surcharged
"CFA," New Value and Bars in Blue or
Red

1954, Feb. 10

C42	AP15(c)	50fr on 100fr	2.10	1.10
C43	AP15	100fr on 200fr (R)	4.25	.75
C44	AP15(c)	200fr on 500fr	32.50	11.00
C45	AP15	500fr on 1000fr	26.00	10.00
		Nos. C42-C45 (4)	64.85	22.85

France Nos. C35-C36 Surcharged
"CFA," New Values and Bars in Red or
Black

1957-58   **Engr.**   **Perf. 13**

C46	AP17	200fr on 500fr (R)	20.00	5.75
C47	AP17	500fr on 1000fr		
		('58)	20.00	11.00

France Nos. C37, C39-C40
Surcharged "CFA," New Value and
Bars in Red or Black

1961-64

C48	AP15	100fr on 2fr	5.00	1.10
C49	AP17	200fr on 5fr	5.00	2.50
C50	AP17	500fr on 10fr (B;'64)	12.00	5.00
		Nos. C48-C50 (3)	22.00	8.60

France No. C41 Surcharged "CFA,"
New Value and Two Bars in Red

1967, Jan. 27

C51	AP17	100fr on 2fr sl bl & ind	1.60	.55

France No. C45 Surcharged in Red
with "CFA," New Value and Two Bars
in Red

1972, May 14   **Engr.**   **Perf. 13**

C52	AP21	200fr on 5fr multi	4.00	1.40

AIR POST SEMI-POSTAL STAMPS

French Revolution Issue
Common Design Type

1939   **Unwmk.**   **Perf. 13**
Name and Value Typo. in Orange

CB1	CD83	3.65fr + 4fr brn blk	18.00	18.00

Felix Guyon Hospital, St.
Denis — SPAP1

Perf. 13½x12½

1942, June 22   **Engr.**

CB2	SPAP1	1.50fr + 3.50fr lt green	.60
CB3	SPAP1	2fr + 6fr yellow brown	.60

Native children's welfare fund.
Nos. CB2-CB3 were issued by the Vichy government in France, but were not placed on sale in Réunion.

Colonial Education Fund
Common Design Type

1942, June 22

CB4	CD86a	1.20fr + 1.80fr blue & red	.60

No. CB4 was issued by the Vichy government in France, but was not placed on sale in Réunion.

POSTAGE DUE STAMPS

D1   D2

1889-92   **Unwmk. Type-set**   **Imperf.**
Without Gum

J1	D1	5c black	19.00	9.25
J2	D1	10c black	24.00	9.25
J3	D1	15c black ('92)	46.50	29.00
J4	D1	20c black	32.50	18.00
J5	D1	30c black	30.00	18.00
		Nos. J1-J5 (5)	152.00	83.50

Ten varieties of each value.
Nos. J1-J2, J4-J5 issued on yellowish paper in 1889; Nos. J1-J3, J5 on bluish white paper in 1892.
Nos. J1-J5 exist with double impression. Values $125-$190.

1907   **Typo.**   **Perf. 14x13½**

J6	D2	5c carmine, yel	.60	.60
J7	D2	10c blue, bl	.60	.60
J8	D2	15c black, bluish	.95	.95
J9	D2	20c carmine	.95	.95
J10	D2	30c green, grnsh	1.50	1.50
J11	D2	50c red, green	1.75	1.75
J12	D2	60c carmine, bl	1.75	1.75
J13	D2	1fr violet	2.00	2.00
		Nos. J6-J13 (8)	10.10	10.10

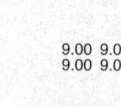

Type of 1907 Issue
Surcharged

1927

J14	D2	2fr on 1fr org red	9.00	9.00
J15	D2	3fr on 1fr org brn	9.00	9.00

Arms of
Réunion
D3

Numeral
D4

1933   **Engr.**   **Perf. 13x13½**

J16	D3	5c deep violet	.20	.20
J17	D3	10c dark green	.20	.20
J18	D3	15c orange brown	.20	.20
J19	D3	20c light red	.25	.25
J20	D3	30c olive green	.25	.25
J21	D3	50c ultramarine	.60	.60
J22	D3	60c black brown	.60	.60
J23	D3	1fr light violet	.60	.60
J24	D3	2fr deep blue	.60	.60
J25	D3	3fr carmine	.80	.80
		Nos. J16-J25 (10)	4.30	4.30

Catalogue values for unused stamps in this section, from this point to the end of the section, are for Never Hinged items.

1947   **Unwmk.**   **Photo.**   **Perf. 13**

J26	D4	10c dark violet	.20	.20
J27	D4	30c brown	.20	.20
J28	D4	50c blue green	.20	.20
J29	D4	1fr orange	.30	.30
J30	D4	2fr red violet	.30	.30
J31	D4	3fr red brown	.45	.45
J32	D4	4fr blue	.80	.80
J33	D4	5fr henna brown	.95	.95
J34	D4	10fr slate green	.95	.95
J35	D4	20fr violet blue	.95	.60
		Nos. J26-J35 (10)	5.30	4.95

France, Nos. J83-J92
Surcharged in Black

1949-53

J36	D5	10c on 1fr brt ultra	.20	.20
J37	D5	50c on 2fr turq bl	.35	.35
J38	D5	1fr on 3fr brn org	.45	.35
J39	D5	2fr on 4fr dp vio	.45	.35
J40	D5	3fr on 5fr brt pink	5.00	2.00
J41	D5	5fr on 10fr red org	.80	.55
J42	D5	10fr on 20fr ol bis	1.60	1.50
J43	D5	20fr on 50fr dk grn ('50)	10.00	4.00
J44	D5	50fr on 50fr dp grn ('53)	24.00	10.00
		Nos. J36-J44 (9)	42.85	19.30

Same Surcharge on France Nos. J93,
J95-J96

1962-63   **Typo.**   **Perf. 14x13½**

J46	D6	1fr on 5c brt pink ('63)	2.25	.90
J47	D6	10fr on 20c ol bis ('63)	4.50	2.50
J48	D6	20fr on 50c dk grn	16.50	10.00
		Nos. J46-J48 (3)	23.25	13.40

France Nos. J98-J102, J104-J105
Surcharged with New Value and "CFA"

1964-71   **Unwmk.**   **Perf. 14x13½**

J49	D7	1fr on 5c	.20	.20
J50	D7	5fr on 10c	.25	.20
J51	D7	7fr on 15c	.40	.35
J52	D7	10fr on 20c ('71)	1.10	.45
J53	D7	15fr on 30c	.50	.35

J54	D7	20fr on 50c	.60 .45
J55	D7	50fr on 1fr	1.10 1.00
		Nos. J49-J55 (7)	4.15 3.00

PARCEL POST STAMP

No. 40 Overprinted

1906		**Unwmk.**	**Perf. 14x13½**
Q1	A14	10c red	14.50 14.50

FRENCH COLONIES

ˈfrench ˈkä-lə-nēz

From 1859 to 1906 and from 1943 to 1945 special stamps were issued for use in all French Colonies which did not have stamps of their own.

100 Centimes = 1 Franc

> Catalogue values for unused stamps in this country are for Never Hinged items, beginning with Scott B1 in the semi-postal section and Scott J23 in the postage due section.

Perforations: Nos. 1-45 are known variously perforated privately.

Gum: Many of Nos. 1-45 were issued without gum. Some were gummed locally.

Reprints: Nos. 1-7, 9-12, 24, 26-42, 44 and 45 were reprinted officially in 1887. These reprints are ungummed and the colors of both design and paper are deeper or brighter than the originals. Value for Nos. 1-6, $20 each.

Eagle and Crown — A1

			Typo.	Imperf.
1859-65		**Unwmk.**		
1	A1	1c ol grn, *pale bl* ('62)	16.50	*19.00*
2	A1	5c yel grn, *grnsh* ('62)	19.00	12.00
3	A1	10c bister, *yel*	25.00	6.50
a.		Pair, one sideways	800.00	400.00
4	A1	20c bl, *bluish* ('65)	29.00	11.00
5	A1	40c org, *yelsh*	22.00	11.00
6	A1	80c car rose, *pnksh* ('65)	90.00	50.00
		Nos. 1-6 (6)	201.50	109.50

For surcharges see Reunion Nos. 3-4.

Napoleon III
A2   A3

Ceres   Napoleon III
A4   A5

				Imperf.
1871-72				
7	A2	1c ol grn, *pale bl* ('72)		57.50 50.00
8	A3	5c yel grn, *grnsh* ('72)		825.00 350.00

9	A4	10c bis, *yelsh*	300.00	110.00
a.		Tête bêche pair	35,000.	16,500.
10	A4	15c bis, *yelsh*	275.00	11.00
		('72)		
11	A4	20c blue, *bluish*	425.00	100.00
a.		Tête bêche pair	—	12,000.
12	A4	25c bl, *bluish*	140.00	11.00
		('72)		
13	A5	30c brn, *yelsh*	125.00	40.00
14	A4	40c org, *yelsh* (I)	210.00	11.00
a.		Type II	2,750.	500.00
b.		Pair, types I & II	5,750.	1,400.
15	A5	80c rose, *pnksh*	850.00	92.50
		Nos. 7-15 (9)	3,207.	775.50

For 40c types I-II see illustrations over France #1.

For surcharges see Reunion Nos. 5-6.

See note after France No. 9 for additional information on Nos. 8-9, 11-12, 14.

Ceres
A6   A7

				Imperf.
1872-77				
16	A6	1c ol grn, *pale bl* ('73)		11.00 *12.00*
17	A6	2c red brn, *yelsh* ('76)		400.00 650.00
18	A6	4c gray ('76)		*8,900.* 475.00
19	A6	5c grn, *pale bl*		12.00 8.00
20	A7	10c bis, *rose* ('76)		190.00 11.00
21	A7	15c bister ('77)		425.00 82.50
22	A7	30c brn, *yelsh*		90.00 17.50
23	A7	80c rose, *pnksh* ('73)		500.00 125.00

No. 17 was used only in Cochin China, 1876-77. Excellent forgeries of Nos. 17 and 18 exist.

With reference to the stamps of France and French Colonies in the same designs and colors see the note after France No. 9.

Peace and   Commerce
Commerce   A9
A8

			Type I	Imperf.
1877-78				
24	A8	1c grn, *grnsh*	22.00	32.50
25	A8	4c grn, *grnsh*	14.50	14.50
26	A8	30c brn, *yelsh* ('78)	32.50	42.50
27	A8	40c ver, *straw*	21.00	18.00
28	A8	75c rose, *rose* ('78)	62.50	72.50
29	A8	1fr brnz grn, *straw*	37.50	16.00
		Nos. 24-29 (6)	190.00	196.00
			Type II	
30	A8	2c grn, *grnsh*	11.00	8.50
31	A8	5c grn, *grnsh*	14.50	4.25
32	A8	10c grn, *grnsh*	72.50	10.50
33	A8	15c gray, *grnsh*	225.00	62.50
34	A8	20c red brn, *straw*	45.00	7.25
35	A8	25c ultra *bluish*	32.50	7.50
a.		25c blue, *bluish* ('78)	*3,750.*	140.00
36	A8	35c vio blk, *org* ('78)	40.00	22.50
		Nos. 30-36 (7)	440.50	123.00
		Nos. 24-36 (13)	630.50	319.00
1878-80				
			Type II	
38	A8	1c blk, *lil bl*	14.00	14.00
39	A8	2c brn, *buff*	14.00	*19.00*
40	A8	4c claret, *lav*	21.00	21.00
41	A8	10c blk, *lav* ('79)	90.00	19.00
42	A8	15c blue	22.50	11.00
43	A8	20c red, *grn* ('79)	62.50	11.00
44	A8	25c blk, *red* ('79)	500.00	225.00
45	A8	25c yel, *straw* ('80)	600.00	25.00
		Nos. 38-45 (8)	1,324.	345.00

No. 44 was used only in Mayotte, Nossi-Be and New Caledonia. Forgeries exist.

The 3c yellow, 3c gray, 15c yellow, 20c blue, 25c rose and 5fr lilac were printed together with the reprints, and were never issued.

				Perf. 14x13½
1881-86				
46	A9	1c blk, *lil bl*		4.25 3.50
47	A9	2c brn, *buff*		4.25 3.75
48	A9	4c claret, *lav*		4.25 4.25
49	A9	5c grn, *grnsh*		5.00 2.25
50	A9	10c blk, *lavender*		8.50 3.75
51	A9	15c blue		12.50 2.25

52	A9	20c red, *yel grn*	42.50	15.00
53	A9	25c yel, *straw*	11.00	4.25
54	A9	25c blk, *rose* ('86)	14.50	2.25
55	A9	30c brn, *bis*	32.50	18.00
56	A9	35c vio blk, *yel org*	32.50	25.00
a.		35c violet blk, *yellow*	82.50	42.50
57	A9	40c ver, *straw*	35.00	24.00
58	A9	75c car, *rose*	100.00	50.00
59	A9	1fr brnz grn, *straw*	62.50	37.50
		Nos. 46-59 (14)	369.25	195.75

Nos. 46-59 exist imperforate. They are proofs and were not used for postage, except the 10c.

For stamps of type A9 surcharged with numerals see: Cochin China, Diego Suarez, Gabon, Malagasy (Madagascar), Nossi-Be, New Caledonia, Reunion, Senegal, Tahiti.

SEMI-POSTAL STAMPS

> Catalogue values for unused stamps in this section are for Never Hinged items.

Resistance
Fighters — SP1

1943		**Unwmk. Litho.**	*Rouletted*
B1	SP1	1.50fr + 98.50fr ind & gray	40.00 40.00
		Without label	17.50 10.50

The surtax was for the benefit of patriots and the French Committee of Liberation.

No. B1 was printed in sheets of 10 (5x2) with adjoining labels showing the Lorraine cross.

Colonies
Offering Aid
to France
SP2

1943			**Perf. 12**
B2	SP2	9fr + 41fr red violet	2.90 2.50

Surtax for the benefit of French patriots.

Patriots
and Map of
France
SP3

1943			
B3	SP3	50c + 4.50fr yel grn	1.10 *1.40*
B4	SP3	1.50fr + 8.50fr cerise	1.10 *1.40*
B5	SP3	3fr + 12fr grnsh bl	1.10 *1.40*
B6	SP3	5fr + 15fr olive gray	1.10 *1.40*
		Nos. B3-B6 (4)	4.40 5.60

Surtax for the aid of combatants and patriots.

Refugee
Family
SP4

1943			
B7	SP4	10fr + 40fr dull blue	4.25 *5.00*

The surtax was for refugee relief work.

Woman and Child
with Wing — SP5

1944			
B8	SP5	10fr + 40fr grnsh blk	5.75 *5.00*

Surtax for the benefit of aviation.

Nos. B1-B8 were prepared for use in the French Colonies, but after the landing of Free French troops in Corsica they were used there and later also in Southern France. They became valid throughout France in Nov. 1944.

POSTAGE DUE STAMPS

D1

			Typo.	Imperf.
1884-85		**Unwmk.**		
J1	D1	1c black		2.75 2.75
J2	D1	2c black		2.75 2.75
J3	D1	3c black		2.75 2.75
J4	D1	4c black		3.25 2.75
J5	D1	5c black		4.25 2.10
J6	D1	10c black		6.50 4.25
J7	D1	15c black		10.50 8.25
J8	D1	20c black		10.50 8.75
J9	D1	30c black		12.00 6.50
J10	D1	40c black		16.00 6.50
J11	D1	60c black		25.00 13.50
J12	D1	1fr brown		25.00 16.00
a.		1fr black		250.00

   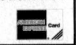

J13	D1	2fr brown	22.00	16.00
a.		2fr black	250.00	
J14	D1	5fr brown	75.00	50.00
a.		5fr black	325.00	

Nos. J12a, J13a and J14a were not regularly issued.

1894-1906

J15	D1	5c pale blue	.80	.80
J16	D1	10c gray brown	.80	.80
J17	D1	15c pale green	.90	.90
J18	D1	20c olive grn ('06)	.90	.90
J19	D1	30c carmine	1.75	1.10
J20	D1	50c lilac	1.75	1.10
J21	D1	60c brown, buff	3.00	1.75
a.		60c dark violet, buff	4.00	2.10
J22	D1	1fr red, buff	4.25	3.25
a.		1fr rose, buff	18.00	15.00
		Nos. J15-J22 (8)	14.15	10.60

For overprints see New Caledonia Nos. J1-J8.

> Catalogue values for unused stamps in this section, from this point to the end of the section, are for Never Hinged items.

D2

1945   Litho.   Perf. 12

J23	D2	10c slate blue	.20	.20
J24	D2	15c yel green	.20	.20
J25	D2	25c deep orange	.20	.20
J26	D2	50c greenish blk	.55	.45
J27	D2	60c copper brn	.55	.45
J28	D2	1fr deep red lil	.55	.35
J29	D2	2fr red	.55	.45
J30	D2	4fr slate gray	2.25	2.00
J31	D2	5fr brt ultra	2.25	2.00
J32	D2	10fr purple	13.50	10.50
J33	D2	20fr dull brown	2.75	2.10
J34	D2	50fr deep green	5.00	4.25
		Nos. J23-J34 (12)	28.55	23.15

FRENCH CONGO

'french 'kär͟,gō

LOCATION — Central Africa
GOVT. — French possession

French Congo was originally a separate colony, but was joined in 1888 to Gabon and placed under one commissioner-general with a lieutenant-governor presiding in Gabon and another in French Congo. In 1894 the military holdings in Ubangi were attached to French Congo, and in 1900 the Chad military protectorate was added. Postal service was not established in Ubangi or Chad, however, at that time. In 1906 Gabon and Middle Congo were separated and French Congo ceased to exist as such. Chad and Ubangi remained attached to Middle Congo as the joint dependency of "Ubangi-Chari-Chad," and Middle Congo stamps were used there.

Issues of the Republic of the Congo are listed under Congo People's Republic (ex-French).

100 Centimes = 1 Franc

Watermarks

Wmk. 122 — Thistle Branch

Wmk. 123 — Rose Branch

Wmk. 124 — Olive Branch

Stamps of French Colonies Surcharged Horizontally in Red or Black

1891   Unwmk.   Perf. 14x13½

1	A9	5c on 1c blk, lil bl (R)	5,100.	3,500.
2	A9	5c on 1c blk, lil bl	140.00	72.50
a.		Double surcharge	475.00	325.00
3	A9	5c on 15c blue	225.00	110.00
a.		Double surcharge	525.00	250.00
5	A9	5c on 25c blk, rose	80.00	32.50
a.		Inverted surcharge		

First "O" of "Congo" is a Capital, "Francais" with Capital "F"

1891-92

6	A9	5c on 20c red, grn	900.00	350.00
7	A9	5c on 25c blk, rose	140.00	65.00
a.		Surcharge vertical	190.00	60.00
8	A9	10c on 25c blk, rose	175.00	50.00
a.		Inverted surcharge	325.00	110.00
b.		Surcharge vertical	150.00	72.50
c.		First "o" of "Congo" small		
d.		Double surcharge	300.00	140.00
9	A9	10c on 40c red, straw	1,900.	300.00
10	A9	15c on 25c blk, rose	160.00	35.00
a.		Surcharge vertical	190.00	57.50
b.		Inverted surcharge		
c.		Double surcharge	275.00	140.00

First "O" of Congo small Surcharge Vert., Down or Up No period

11	A9	5c on 25c blk, rose	200.00	85.00
12	A9	10c on 25c blk, rose	—	
13	A9	15c on 25c blk, rose	275.00	110.00

Postage Due Stamps of French Colonies Surcharged in Red or Black Reading Down or Up

1892   Imperf.

14	D1	5c on 5c blk (R)	125.00	100.00
15	D1	5c on 20c blk (R)	125.00	95.00
16	D1	5c on 30c blk (R)	160.00	125.00
17	D1	10c on 1fr brown	125.00	95.00
a.		Double surcharge	3,250.	3,300.
b.		Surcharge horiz.		1,800.
		Nos. 14-17 (4)	535.00	415.00

Excellent counterfeits of Nos. 1-17 exist.

Navigation and Commerce — A3

1892-1900   Typo.   Perf. 14x13½
Colony Name in Blue or Carmine

18	A3	1c blk, lil bl	1.25	1.10
19	A3	2c brn, buff	2.25	1.75
a.		Name double	125.00	125.00
20	A3	4c claret, lav	2.25	2.10
a.		Name in blk and in blue	125.00	125.00
21	A3	5c grn, grnsh	4.25	4.25
22	A3	10c blk, lavender	16.50	14.00
a.		Name double	625.00	450.00
23	A3	10c red ('00)	2.10	1.40
24	A3	15c blue, quadrille paper	42.50	14.00
25	A3	15c gray ('00)	7.50	5.00
26	A3	20c red, grn	17.50	13.00
27	A3	25c blk, rose	19.50	13.00
28	A3	25c blue ('00)	8.50	8.00
29	A3	30c brn, bis	22.50	15.00
30	A3	40c red, straw	42.50	24.00
31	A3	50c car, rose	37.50	23.00
32	A3	50c brn, az ('00)	10.00	8.50
a.		Name double	600.00	600.00
33	A3	75c dp vio, org	30.00	23.00
34	A3	1fr brnz grn, straw	42.50	22.50
		Nos. 18-34 (17)	309.10	193.60

Perf. 13½x14 stamps are counterfeits.
For surcharges see Nos. 50-51.

Leopard — A4

	Bakalois Woman — A5		Coconut Grove — A6	

1900   Wmk. 122   Perf. 11

35	A4	1c brn vio & gray lilac	.55	.55
a.		Background inverted	62.50	62.50
36	A4	2c brn & org	.55	.55
a.		2c dark red & red	140.00	190.00
b.		Imperf., pair	50.00	50.00
37	A4	4c scar & gray bl	1.10	.85
a.		4c dark red & red	550.00	
b.		Background inverted	60.00	60.00
38	A4	5c grn & gray grn	2.00	.85
a.		Imperf., pair	110.00	110.00
39	A4	10c dk red & red	5.50	2.25
a.		Imperf., pair	110.00	110.00
40	A4	15c dl vio & ol grn	2.00	1.00
a.		Imperf. pair	75.00	75.00

Wmk. 123

41	A5	20c yel grn & org	1.75	1.50
42	A5	25c bl & pale bl	2.40	1.50
43	A5	30c car rose & org	3.50	1.60
44	A5	40c org brn & brt grn	4.25	2.00
a.		Imperf., pair	75.00	75.00
b.		Center inverted	125.00	125.00
45	A5	50c gray vio & lil	5.50	5.00
46	A5	75c red vio & org	11.00	6.50
a.		Imperf., pair	75.00	75.00

Wmk. 124

47	A6	1fr gray lil & ol	17.50	12.00
a.		Center inverted	225.00	225.00
b.		Imperf., pair	100.00	100.00
48	A6	2fr car & brn	30.00	20.00
a.		Imperf., pair	200.00	200.00
49	A6	5fr brn org & gray	65.00	57.50
a.		5fr ocher & gray	650.00	700.00
b.		Center inverted	325.00	325.00
c.		Wmk. 123	325.00	225.00
d.		Imperf., pair	350.00	350.00
		Nos. 35-49 (15)	152.60	113.65

For surcharges see Nos. 52-53.

Nos. 26 and 29 Surcharged in Black

Valeur
15

1900   Unwmk.   Perf. 14x13½

50	A3	5c on 20c red, grn	20,000.	5,000.
a.		Double surcharge		13,750.
51	A3	15c on 30c brn, bis	13,750.	2,000.
a.		Double surcharge		5,000.

Nos. 43 and 48 Surcharged in Black:

5°c

a

b

0,10

1903   Wmk. 123   Perf. 11

52	A5	5c on 30c	225.00	110.00
a.		Inverted surcharge	2,150.	

Wmk. 124

53	A6	10c on 2fr	275.00	110.00
a.		Inverted surcharge	2,200.	
b.		Double surcharge	2,400.	

Counterfeits of the preceding surcharges are known.

FRENCH EQUATORIAL AFRICA

'french ̦ē-kwə-'tōr-ē-əl 'a-fri-kə

LOCATION — North of Belgian Congo and south of Libya
GOVT. — French Colony
AREA — 959,256 square miles
POP. — 4,491,785
CAPITAL — Brazzaville

In 1910 Gabon and Middle Congo, with its military dependencies, were politically united as French Equatorial Africa. The component colonies were granted administrative autonomy. In 1915 Ubangi-Chari-Chad was made an autonomous civilian colony and in 1920 Chad was made a civil colony. In 1934 the four colonies were administratively united as one colony, but this federation was not completed until 1936. Each colony had its own postal administration until 1936. The postal issues of the former colonial subdivisions are listed under the names of those colonies.

In 1958, French Equatorial Africa was divided into four republics: Chad, Congo, Gabon and Central African Republic (formerly Ubangi-Chari).

Stamps other than Nos. 189-192 are inscribed with "Afrique Equatoriale Francaise" or "AEF" and the name of one of the component colonies are listed under those colonies.

100 Centimes = 1 Franc

Catalogue values for unused stamps in this country are for Never Hinged items, beginning with Scott 142 in the regular postage section, Scott B8A in the semi-postal section, Scott C17 in the airpost section, and Scott J12 in the postage due section.

Stamps of Gabon, 1932, Overprinted "Afrique Equatoriale Francaise" and Bars Similar to "a" and "b" in Black

Perf. 13x13½, 13½x13

1936   Unwmk.

1	A16	1c brown violet	.20	.20
2	A16	2c black, *rose*	.35	.35
3	A16	4c green	.85	.85
4	A16	5c grnsh blue	.95	.95
5	A16	10c red, *yel*	.85	.85
6	A17	40c brown violet	2.50	2.00
7	A17	50c red brown	1.90	1.50
8	A17	1fr yel grn, *bl*	22.50	10.00
9	A18	1.50fr dull blue	6.25	2.25
10	A18	2fr brown red	13.00	9.00
		Nos. 1-10 (10)	49.35	27.95

Stamps of Middle Congo, 1933 Overprinted in Black:

a

b

c

1936

11	A4 (b)	1c lt brown	.20	.20
12	A4 (b)	2c dull blue	.20	.20
13	A4 (b)	4c olive green	1.10	1.10
14	A4 (b)	5c red violet	.65	.65
15	A4 (b)	10c slate	1.10	.70
16	A4 (b)	15c dk violet	1.50	1.00
17	A4 (b)	20c red, *pink*	1.50	1.00
18	A4 (b)	25c orange	2.40	1.00
19	A5 (a)	40c orange brn	3.25	1.75
20	A5 (a)	50c black violet	3.25	2.25
21	A5 (c)	75c black, *pink*	4.00	3.25
22	A5 (a)	90c carmine	4.00	2.50
23	A5 (c)	1.50fr dark blue	2.50	1.50
24	A6 (a)	5fr slate blue	42.50	22.50
25	A6 (a)	10fr black	25.00	16.00
26	A6 (a)	20fr dark brown	22.50	20.00
		Nos. 11-26 (16)	115.65	76.30

Common Design Types pictured following the introduction.

Paris International Exposition Issue
Common Design Types

1937, Apr. 15			Engr.		Perf. 13
27	CD74	20c dark violet		1.75	1.75
28	CD75	30c dark green		1.75	1.75
29	CD76	40c carmine rose		1.75	1.75
30	CD77	50c dk brn & bl		1.75	1.75
31	CD78	90c red		2.00	2.00
32	CD79	1.50fr ultra		2.00	2.00
		Nos. 27-32 (6)		11.00	11.00

Logging on Loéme River — A1

People of Chad — A2

Pierre Savorgnan de Brazza A3

Emile Gentil — A4

Paul Crampel A5

Governor Victor Liotard A6

Two types of 25c:
Type I — Wide numerals (4mm).
Type II — Narrow numerals (3½mm).

1937-40		Photo.	Perf. 13½x13	
33	A1	1c brown & yel	.20	.20
34	A1	2c violet & grn	.20	.20
35	A1	3c blue & yel ('40)	.20	.20
36	A1	4c magenta & bl	.20	.20
37	A1	5c dk & lt green	.40	.20
38	A2	10c magenta & blue	.25	.20
39	A2	15c blue & buff	.25	.20
40	A2	20c brown & yellow	.40	.55
41	A2	25c cop red & bl (I)	.65	.20
	a.	Type II	2.25	1.60
42	A3	30c gray grn & grn	.65	.45
43	A3	30c chlky bl, ind & buff ('40)	.30	.30
44	A2	35c dp grn & yel ('38)	.80	.55
45	A3	40c green	.30	.30
46	A3	45c dk bl & lt grn	3.75	3.00
47	A3	45c dp grn & yel grn ('40)	.45	.45
48	A3	50c brown & yellow	.30	.20
49	A3	55c pur & bl ('38)	.65	.55
50	A3	60c mar & gray bl ('40)	.50	.50
51	A4	65c dk bl & lt green	.65	.30
52	A4	70c dp vio & buff ('40)	.55	.55
53	A4	75c ol blk & dl yel	4.50	3.75
54	A4	80c brn & yel ('38)	.45	.45
55	A4	90c copper red & buff	.45	.30
56	A4	1fr dk vio & lt grn	1.75	.85
57	A3	1fr cer & dl org ('38)	2.50	.95
58	A4	1fr bl grn & sl grn ('40)	.45	.45
59	A5	1.25fr cop red & buff	1.00	.65
60	A5	1.40fr dk brn & pale grn	.90	.90
61	A5	1.50fr dk & lt blue	1.25	.50
62	A5	1.60fr dp vio & buff ('40)	.80	.80
63	A5	1.75fr brn & yel	1.50	.65
64	A5	1.75fr bl & lt bl ('38)	.55	.45
65	A5	2fr dk & lt green	.85	.55
66	A6	2.15fr brn, vio & yel ('38)	.65	.50
67	A6	2.25fr bl & lt bl ('39)	1.25	1.25
68	A6	2.50fr rose lake & buff ('40)	.90	.90
69	A6	3fr dk blue & buff	.60	.25
70	A6	5fr dk & lt green	1.25	.75
71	A6	10fr dk violet & bl	2.75	2.00
72	A6	20fr ol blk & dl yel	3.00	2.50
		Nos. 33-72 (40)	39.00	28.65

For overprints and surcharges see Nos. 80-127, 129-141, B2-B3, B10-B13, B22-B23.

Colonial Arts Exhibition Issue
Souvenir Sheet
Common Design Type

1937			Imperf.
73	CD79	3fr red brown	11.00 *12.00*
		Never hinged	15.00

Count Louis Edouard Bouet-Willaumez and His Ship "La Malouine" — A7

1938, Dec. 5			Perf. 13½	
74	A7	65c gray brown	.90	.90
75	A7	1fr deep rose	1.10	1.10
76	A7	1.75fr blue	1.25	1.25
77	A7	2fr dull violet	1.50	1.50
		Nos. 74-77 (4)	4.75	4.75
		Set, never hinged	8.50	

Centenary of Gabon.

New York World's Fair Issue
Common Design Type

1939, May 10			Engr.	Perf. 12½x12	
78	CD82	1.25fr carmine lake		1.25	1.25
79	CD82	2.25fr ultra		1.25	1.25
		Set, never hinged		5.00	

Libreville View and Marshal Petain A7a

1941		Engr.	Perf. 12½x12	
79A	A7a	1fr bluish green	.90	
79B	A7a	2.50fr blue	.90	
		Set, never hinged	3.50	

Nos. 79A-79B were issued by the Vichy government in France, but were not placed on sale in French Equatorial Africa.
For surcharges, see Nos. B36-B37.

Stamps of 1936-40, Overprinted in Carmine or Black:

Nos. 80-82, 84-88, 93

Nos. 83, 89-92, 94-125

1940-41			Perf. 13½x13	
80	A1	1c brn & yel (C)	1.25	1.25
81	A1	2c vio & grn (C)	1.25	1.25
82	A1	3c blue & yel (C)	1.25	1.25
83	A4	4c ol grn (No. 13)	10.00	8.50
84	A1	5c dk grn & lt grn (C)	1.25	1.25
85	A2	10c magenta & bl	1.75	1.75
86	A2	15c blue & buff (C)	1.50	1.50
87	A2	20c brn & yel (C)	1.50	1.50
88	A2	25c cop red & bl	7.00	7.00
89	A3	30c gray grn & grn (C)	14.50	9.25
90	A3	30c gray grn & grn ('41)	2.25	2.25
91	A3	30c chlky bl, ind & buff (C) ('41)	7.25	6.00
92	A3	30c chlky bl, ind & buff ('41)	9.50	8.50
93	A3	35c dp grn & yel (C)	1.60	1.60
94	A3	40c cop red & bl	1.10	1.10
95	A3	45c dp grn & yel grn (C)	.85	.85
96	A3	45c dp grn & yel grn ('41)	1.10	1.10
97	A3	50c brn & yel (C)	5.75	4.75
98	A3	50c brn & yel ('41)	4.75	4.75
99	A3	55c pur & bl (C)	.85	.80
100	A3	55c pur & bl ('41)	1.10	1.10
101	A3	60c mar & gray bl	.80	.80
102	A4	65c dk bl & lt green	.80	.80
103	A4	70c dp vio & buff	.80	.80
104	A4	75c ol blk & dl yel	45.00	45.00
105	A4	80c brown & yellow	.80	.80
106	A4	90c cop red & buff	1.00	1.00
107	A4	1fr bl grn & sl grn	7.25	7.25
108	A4	1fr bl grn & sl grn (C) ('41)	4.50	4.00
109	A3	1fr cer & dl org	2.00	2.00
110	A5	1.40fr dk brn & pale grn	.80	.80
111	A5	1.50fr dk bl & lt bl	.80	.80
112	A5	1.60fr dp vio & buff	.80	.80
113	A5	1.75fr brn & yel	1.40	1.40
114	A6	2.15fr brn, vio & yel	1.25	1.25
115	A6	2.25fr bl & lt bl (C)	.85	.85
116	A6	2.25fr bl & lt bl (C) ('41)	2.50	2.50
117	A6	2.50fr rose lake & buff	.85	.85
118	A6	3fr dk bl & buff (C)	1.25	1.25
119	A6	3fr dk bl & buff ('41)	2.75	2.75
120	A6	5fr dk grn & lt grn (C)	3.00	3.00
121	A6	5fr dk grn & lt grn ('41)	90.00	50.00
122	A6	10fr dk vio & bl (C)	2.00	2.00
123	A6	10fr dk vio & bl ('41)	72.50	50.00
124	A6	20fr ol blk & dl yel (C)	1.75	1.75
125	A6	20fr ol blk & dl yel ('41)	11.50	10.00
		Nos. 80-125 (46)	334.30	259.55

For overprints and surcharges see Nos. 129-132, B12-B13, B22-B23.
For types of Nos. 38//61 without "RF," see Nos. 155A-155B.

Double Overprint

94a	A3	40c	21.00
96a	A3	45c	25.00
98a	A3	50c	25.00
100a	A4	55c	25.00
102a	A4	65c	21.00
103a	A4	70c	25.00
105a	A4	80c	25.00
106a	A4	90c	21.00
b.		one inverted	85.00
109a	A4	1fr One inverted	85.00
110a	A5	1.40fr	25.00
111a	A5	1.50fr	25.00
114a	A6	2.15fr	18.00
115a	A6	2.25fr	25.00
116a	A6	2.25fr	25.00
117a	A6	2.50fr	25.00
119a	A6	3fr	25.00
123a	A6	10fr	25.00
124a	A6	20fr	25.00
		Nos. 96a-124a (17)	470.00

Nos. 48, 51 Surcharged in Black or Carmine

1940

126	A3	75c on 50c	.55	.55
a.		Double surcharge	25.00	
127	A4	1fr on 65c (C)	.55	.55
a.		Double surcharge	18.00	
		Set, never hinged	4.50	

Middle Congo No. 67 Overprinted in Carmine like No. 80

Perf. 13½

128	A4	4c olive green	45.00	37.50

Stamps of 1940 With Additional Overprint in Black

1940   **Perf. 13½x13**
129 A4 80c brown & yel   12.50 10.00
 a. Overprint without "2"   110.00
130 A4 1fr bl grn & sl grn   12.50 10.00
131 A3 1fr cer & dull org   12.50 10.00
132 A5 1.50fr dk bl & lt bl   12.50 10.00
      Nos. 129-132 (4)   50.00 40.00
      Set, never hinged   80.00

Arrival of General de Gaulle in Brazzaville, capital of Free France, Oct. 24, 1940.
These stamps were sold affixed to post cards and at a slight increase over face value to cover the cost of the cards.
For surcharges see #B12-B13, B22-B23.

Stamps of 1937-40 Overprinted in Black

1941
133 A1 1c brown & yel   1.25 1.25
134 A1 2c violet & grn   1.25 1.25
135 A1 3c blue & yel   1.25 1.25
136 A1 5c dk & lt green   1.25 1.25
137 A2 10c magenta & bl   1.25 1.25
138 A2 15c blue & buff   1.25 1.25
139 A2 20c brown & yel   1.40 1.40
140 A2 25c copper red & bl   4.25 4.25
141 A2 35c dp grn & yel   4.50 4.50
 a. Double overprint   100.00
      Nos. 133-141 (9)   17.65 17.65
      Set, never hinged   30.00

There are 2 settings of the overprint on Nos. 133-141 & C10. The 1st has 1mm between lines of the overprint, the 2nd has 2mm.

> **Catalogue values for unused stamps in this section, from this point to the end of the section, are for Never Hinged items.**

Phoenix — A8

1941   **Photo.**   **Perf. 14x14½**
142 A8 5c brown   .20   .20
143 A8 10c dark blue   .20   .20
144 A8 25c emerald   .20   .20
145 A8 30c deep orange   .20   .20
146 A8 40c dk slate grn   .35   .20
147 A8 80c red brown   .35   .20
148 A8 1fr deep red lilac   .35   .20
149 A8 1.50fr brt red   .45   .25
150 A8 2fr gray   .45   .25
151 A8 2.50fr brt ultra   .50   .50
152 A8 4fr dull violet   .50   .50
153 A8 5fr yellow bister   .50   .50
154 A8 10fr deep brown   .80   .80
155 A8 20fr deep green   .95   .95
      Nos. 142-155 (14)   6.00 5.15

For surcharges see #158-165, B14-B21, B24-B35.

Types of 1937-40 without "RF"
1944   **Perf. 13½**
155A A2 10c magenta & blue   .75
155B A2 15c blue & buff   1.10
155C A3 60c maroon & gray
            blue   1.25
155D A5 1.50fr dk & lt blue   1.60
      Nos. 155A-155D (4)   4.70

Nos. 155A-155D were issued by the Vichy government in France, but were not sold in French Equatorial Africa.

Eboue Issue
Common Design Type
1945   **Unwmk.**   **Engr.**   **Perf. 13**
156 CD91 2fr black   .35   .35
157 CD91 25fr Prussian green   1.25 1.25
      Nos. 156 and 157 exist imperforate.

Nos. 142, 144 and 151 Surcharged with New Values and Bars in Red, Carmine or Black

1946   **Perf. 14x14½**
158 A8 50c on 5c (R)   .50   .50
159 A8 60c on 5c (R)   .50   .50
160 A8 70c on 5c (R)   .50   .50
161 A8 1.20fr on 5c (C)   .50   .50
162 A8 2.40fr on 25c   .80   .80
163 A8 3fr on 25c   .85   .85
164 A8 4.50fr on 25c   .85   .85
165 A8 15fr on 2.50fr (C)   .95   .95
      Nos. 158-165 (8)   5.45 5.45

Black Rhinoceros and Rock Python A9

Jungle Scene — A10

Mountainous Shore Line — A11

Gabon Forest — A12

Niger Boatman — A13

Young Bacongo Woman — A14

1946   **Unwmk.**   **Engr.**   **Perf. 12½**
166 A9   10c deep blue   .20   .20
167 A9   30c violet blk   .20   .20
168 A9   40c dp orange   .20   .20
169 A10 50c violet bl   .40   .40
170 A10 60c dk carmine   .40   .40
171 A10 80c dk ol grn   .40   .40
172 A11 1fr dp orange   .70   .30
173 A11 1.20fr dp claret   .70   .55
174 A11 1.50fr dk green   1.00   .75
175 A12 2fr dk vio brn   .25   .25
176 A12 3fr rose carmine   .60   .35
177 A12 3.60fr red brown   2.75 1.90
178 A12 4fr deep vio   .50   .20
179 A13 5fr dk brown   .75   .20
180 A13 6fr deep blue   .75   .25
181 A13 10fr black   1.60   .35
182 A14 15fr brown   1.60   .35
183 A14 20fr dp claret   1.60   .35
184 A14 25fr dark brown   2.00   .35
      Nos. 166-184 (19)   16.60 7.90

Imperforates
Most French Equatorial Africa stamps from 1951 onward exist imperforate in issued and trial colors, and also in small presentation sheets in issued colors.

Pierre Savorgnan de Brazza — A15

1951, Nov. 5   **Perf. 13**
185 A15 10fr indigo & dk grn   .80   .20

Cent. of the birth of Pierre Savorgnan de Brazza, explorer.

Military Medal Issue
Common Design Type
Engraved and Typographed
1952, Dec. 1   **Perf. 13**
186 CD101 15fr multicolored   4.25 4.25

Lt. Gov. Adolphe L. Cureau A16

1954, Sept. 20   **Engr.**
187 A16 15fr ol grn & red brn 1.00   .40

Savannah Monitor A17

1955, May 2   **Unwmk.**
188 A17 8fr dk grn & claret   2.00 1.50

International Exhibition for Wildlife Protection, Paris, May 1955.

FIDES Issue

Boali Waterfall and Power Plant, Ubangi-Chari — A18

10fr, Cotton, Chad. 15fr, Brazzaville Hospital, Middle Congo. 20fr, Libreville Harbor, Gabon.

1956, Apr. 25   **Perf. 13x12½**
189 A18 5fr dk brn & claret   .35   .20
190 A18 10fr blk & bluish grn   .35   .20
191 A18 15fr ind & gray vio   .50   .30
192 A18 20fr dk red & red org   .55   .45
      Nos. 189-192 (4)   1.75 1.15

See note after Common Design Type CD103.

Coffee Issue

Coffee A19

1956, Oct.   **Engr.**   **Perf. 13**
193 A19 10fr brn vio & vio bl   .60   .20

Leprosarium at Mayumba and Maltese Cross — A20

1957, Mar. 11
194 A20 15fr grn, bl grn & red 1.10   .55

Issued in honor of the Knights of Malta.

Giant Eland A21

1957, Nov. 4
195 A21 1fr shown   .50   .25
196 A21 2fr Lions   .50   .25
197 A21 3fr Elephant, vert.   .50   .25
198 A21 4fr Greater kudu, vert. .50   .25
      Nos. 195-198 (4)   2.00 1.00

WHO Building, Brazzaville A22

1958, May 19   **Engr.**   **Perf. 13**
199 A22 20fr dk green & org brn .80   .55

10th anniv. of WHO.

Flower Issue
Common Design Type
1958, July 7   **Photo.**   **Perf. 12x12½**
200 CD104 10fr Euadania   .75   .35
201 CD104 25fr Spathodea   1.25   .55

Human Rights Issue
Common Design Type
1958, Dec. 10   **Engr.**   **Perf. 13**
202 CD105 20fr Prus grn & dk bl 1.40 .80

SEMI-POSTAL STAMPS

Common Design Type
1938, Oct. 24   **Engr.**
B1 CD80 1.75fr + 50c brt ultra 18.00 18.00
      Never hinged   27.50

Nos. 51, 64 Surcharged in Black or Red

1938, Nov. 7   **Perf. 13x13½**
B2 A4 65c + 35c dk bl & lt
            grn (R)   1.60 1.60
B3 A4 1.75fr + 50c bl & lt bl   1.60 1.60
      Set, never hinged   6.00

The surtax was for welfare.

French Revolution Issue
Common Design Type
Name and Value Typo. in Black
1939, July 5   **Photo.**
B4 CD83 45c + 25c green   12.00 12.00
B5 CD83 70c + 30c brown   12.00 12.00
B6 CD83 90c + 35c red org   12.00 12.00
B7 CD83 1.25fr + 1fr rose pink 12.00 12.00
B8 CD83 2.25fr + 2fr blue   12.00 12.00
      Nos. B4-B8 (5)   60.00 60.00
      Set, never hinged   60.00

Surtax used for the defense of the colonies.

> **Catalogue values for unused stamps in this section, from this point to the end of the section, are for Never Hinged items.**

Common Design Type and

Native
Artilleryman
SP1

Gabon
Infantryman
SP2

1941		Photo.	Perf. 13½	
B8A	SP1	1fr + 1fr red	2.25	
B8B	CD86	1.50fr + 3fr maroon	2.25	
B8C	SP2	2.50fr + 1fr blue	2.25	
		Nos. 8A-8C (3)	6.75	

Nos. B8A-B8C were issued by the Vichy government in France, but were not placed on sale in French Equatorial Africa.

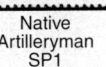

Brazza and
Stanley
Pool
SP3

1941		Photo.	Perf. 14½x14	
B9	SP3	1fr + 2fr dk brn & red	.85	.85

The surtax was for a monument to Pierre Savorgnan de Brazza.

Nos. 67, 71 Surcharged in Red

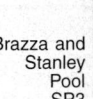

1943, June 28			Perf. 13½x13	
B10	A6	2.25fr + 50fr	10.50	10.50
B11	A6	10fr + 100fr	32.50	32.50

Nos. 129 and 132 with additional
Surcharge in Carmine

1944				
B12	A4	80c + 10fr	20.00	20.00
B13	A5	1.50fr + 15fr	20.00	20.00

Same surcharge printed Vertically
on Nos. 142-146, 148, 150-151
Perf. 14x14½

B14	A8	5c + 10fr brown	6.50	6.50
B15	A8	10c + 10fr dk bl	6.50	6.50
B16	A8	25c + 10fr emer	6.50	6.50
B17	A8	30c + 10fr dp org	6.50	6.50
B18	A8	40c + 10fr dk sl grn	6.50	6.50
B19	A8	1fr + 10fr dp red lil	6.50	6.50
B20	A8	2fr + 20fr gray	6.50	6.50
B21	A8	2.50fr + 25fr brt ultra	6.50	6.50
		Nos. B12-B21 (10)	92.00	92.00

Nos. 129 and 132 with additional
Surcharge in Carmine

1944			Perf. 13½x13	
B22	A4	80c + 10fr	20.00	20.00
B23	A5	1.50fr + 15fr	20.00	20.00

Same Surcharge printed Vertically
on Nos. 142-146, 148, 150-155
Perf. 14x14½

B24	A8	5c + 10fr brn	5.50	5.50
B25	A8	10c + 10fr dk bl	5.50	5.50
B26	A8	25c + 10fr emer	6.00	6.00
B27	A8	30c + 10fr dp org	6.00	6.00
B28	A8	40c + 10fr dk sl grn	6.00	6.00
B29	A8	1fr + 10fr dp red lil	6.00	6.00
B30	A8	2fr + 20fr gray	6.00	6.00
B31	A8	2.50fr + 25fr brt ultra	6.00	6.00
B32	A8	4fr + 40fr dl vio	6.00	6.00
B33	A8	5fr + 50fr yel bis	6.00	6.00
B34	A8	10fr + 100fr dp brn	7.00	7.00
B35	A8	20fr + 200fr dp grn	7.00	7.00
		Nos. B22-B35 (14)	113.00	113.00

Nos. B12 to B35 were issued to raise funds for the Committee to Aid the Fighting Men and Patriots of France.

Nos. 79A-79B
Surcharged in Black or Red

1944	Engr.	Perf. 12½x12	
B36	50c + 1.50fr on 2.50fr deep blue (R)	.80	
B37	+ 2.50fr on 1fr green	.80	

Colonial Development Fund.
Nos. B36-B37 were issued by the Vichy government in France, but were not placed on sale in French Equatorial Africa.

Red Cross Issue
Common Design Type

1944		Photo.	Perf. 14½x14	
B38	CD90	5fr + 20fr royal blue	.80	.80

The surtax was for the French Red Cross and national relief.

Tropical Medicine Issue
Common Design Type

1950, May 15		Engr.	Perf. 13	
B39	CD100	10fr + 2fr dk bl grn & vio brn	4.75	4.75

The surtax was for charitable work.

AIR POST STAMPS

Hydroplane over Pointe-Noire — AP1

Trimotor over Stanley Pool — AP2

1937		Unwmk.	Photo.	Perf. 13½	
C1	AP1	1.50fr ol blk & yel		.20	.20
C2	AP1	2fr mag & blue		.35	.35
C3	AP1	2.50fr grn & buff		.35	.35
C4	AP1	3.75fr brn & lt grn		.55	.55
C5	AP2	4.50fr cop red & bl		.55	.55
C6	AP2	6.50fr bl & lt grn		1.10	1.10
C7	AP2	8.50fr red brn & yel		1.25	1.25
C8	AP2	10.75fr vio & lt grn		1.25	1.25
		Nos. C1-C8 (8)		5.60	5.60

For overprints and surcharges see #C9-C16, CB2.
For types AP1, AP2 without "RF," see Nos. C23A-C23L.

Nos. C1, C3-C7 Overprinted in Black
like Nos. 133-141

1940-41				
C9	AP1	1.50fr ('41)	175.00	175.00
C10	AP1	2.50fr	1.40	1.40
C11	AP1	3.75fr ('41)	175.00	175.00

C12	AP2	4.50fr	1.75	1.75
C13	AP2	6.50fr	2.50	2.50
C14	AP2	8.50fr	1.40	1.40

No. C8
Surcharged
in Carmine

C15	AP2	50fr on 10.75fr	7.50	7.50

No. C3
Surcharged
in Black

C16	AP1	10fr on 2.50fr ('41)	65.00	65.00
		Nos. C9-C16 (8)	429.55	429.55

Counterfeits of Nos. C9 and C11 exist.
See note following No. 141.

Catalogue values for unused stamps in this section, from this point to the end of the section, are for Never Hinged items.

Common Design Type

1941		Photo.	Perf. 14½x14	
C17	CD87	1fr dark orange	.50	.35
C18	CD87	1.50fr brt red	.55	.35
C19	CD87	5fr brown red	.90	.55
C20	CD87	10fr black	1.00	.70
C21	CD87	25fr ultra	.90	.85
C22	CD87	50fr dark green	.90	.70
C23	CD87	100fr plum	1.10	.90
		Nos. C17-C23 (7)	5.85	4.40

Types of 1937 without "RF" and

Sikorsky
5.43
Seaplane
and Canoe
— AP2a

Perf. 13½, 13 (#C23M)

1943, Oct. 18-1944			Unwmk.	
C23A	AP1	1.50fr ol blk & yel	.20	
C23B	AP1	2fr mag & blue	.20	
C23C	AP1	2.50fr grn & buff	.20	
C23D	AP1	3.75fr brn & lt grn	.35	
C23E	AP2	4.50fr cop red & bl	.35	
C23F	AP2	5fr green	.55	
C23G	AP2	6.50fr bl & lt grn	.50	
C23H	AP2	8.50fr red brn & yel	.45	
C23I	AP2	10fr gray & brn ('44)	.50	
C23J	AP2	10.75fr vio & lt grn	.50	
C23K	AP2	20fr yel & brn red ('44)	.50	
C23L	AP2	50fr gray grn & blk ('44)	.85	
C23M	AP2a	100fr red brown ('44)	.55	
		Nos. C23A-C23M (13)	5.70	

Issue dates: Nos. C23I, C23K-L, 4/3/44; C23M, 6/26/44.
Nos. C23A-C23M were issued by the Vichy government in France, but were not sold in French Equatorial Africa.

Victory Issue
Common Design Type
Perf. 12½

1946, May 8		Unwmk.	Engr.	
C24	CD92	8fr lilac rose	.70	.55

Chad to Rhine Issue
Common Design Types

1946, June 6				
C25	CD93	5fr dk violet	.90	.90
C26	CD94	10fr slate green	.90	.90
C27	CD95	15fr deep blue	1.50	1.50
C28	CD96	20fr red orange	1.50	1.50
C29	CD97	25fr sepia	1.50	1.50
C30	CD98	50fr brown carmine	1.75	1.75
		Nos. C25-C30 (6)	8.05	8.05

Palms and Village — AP3

Village and Waterfront — AP4

Bearers in Jungle — AP5

1946		Engr.	Perf. 13	
C31	AP3	50fr red brn	2.00	.60
C32	AP4	100fr grnsh blk	3.25	.90
C33	AP5	200fr deep blue	7.00	1.50
		Nos. C31-C33 (3)	12.25	3.00

UPU Issue
Common Design Type

1949, July 4				
C34	CD99	25fr green	9.00	9.00

Brazza Holding Map — AP6

1951, Nov. 5				
C35	AP6	15fr brn, indigo & red	1.10	.55

Cent. of the birth of Pierre Savorgnan de Brazza, explorer.

Archbishop Augouard and St. Anne
Cathedral, Brazzaville — AP7

1952, Dec. 1				
C36	AP7	15fr ol grn, dk brn & vio brn	3.75	1.75

Cent. of the birth of Archbishop Philippe-Prosper Augouard.

Anhingas — AP8

1953, Feb. 16				
C37	AP8	500fr grnsh blk, blk & slate	30.00	5.50

Liberation Issue
Common Design Type

1954, June 6				
C38	CD102	15fr vio & vio brn	5.75	5.75

Log Rafts — AP9

Designs: 100fr, Fishing boats and nets, Lake Chad. 200fr, Age of mechanization.

1955, Jan. 24   *Engr.*
C39 AP9 50fr ind, brn & dk grn   1.25   .55
C40 AP9 100fr aqua, dk grn &
     blk brn   4.50   .95
C41 AP9 200fr red & deep plum   7.00 1.75
     Nos. C39-C41 (3)   12.75 3.25

Gov. Gen. Félix Eboué, View of Brazzaville and the Pantheon — AP10

1955, Apr. 30   Unwmk.   *Perf. 13*
C42 AP10 15fr sep, brn & slate
     bl   3.50 1.60

Gen. Louis Faidherbé and African Sharpshooter AP11

1957, July 20
C43 AP11 15fr sepia & org ver   2.10 1.40
Centenary of French African Troops.

AIR POST SEMI-POSTAL STAMPS

French Revolution Issue
Common Design Type
1939   Unwmk.   Photo.   *Perf. 13*
Name and Value Typo. in Orange
CB1 CD83 4.50fr + 4fr brn blk   27.50 27.50

SPAP1

SPAP2

SPAP3

Unwmk.
1942, June 22   Engr.   *Perf. 13*
CB2 SPAP1 1.50fr + 3.50fr green   1.10
CB3 SPAP2   2fr + 6fr brown   1.10
CB4 SPAP3   3fr + 9fr carmine   1.10
     Nos. CB2-CB4 (3)   3.30

Native children's welfare fund.
Nos. CB2-CB4 were issued by the Vichy government in France, but were not placed on sale in French Equatorial Africa.

Colonial Education Fund
Common Design Type
1942, June 22
CB5 CD86a 1.20fr + 1.80fr bl &
     red   1.10

No. CB5 was issued by the Vichy government in France, but was not placed on sale in French Equatorial Africa.

#C8 Surcharged in Red like #B10-B11
1943, June 28   *Perf. 13½*
CB6 AP2 10.75fr + 200fr   140.00 140.00

Counterfeits exist.

POSTAGE DUE STAMPS

Numeral of Value on Equatorial Butterfly — D1

1937   Unwmk.   Photo.   *Perf. 13*
J1 D1 5c redsh pur & lt bl   .20   .20
J2 D1 10ccop red & buff   .20   .20
J3 D1 20cdk grn & grn   .25   .20
J4 D1 25cred brn & buff   .25   .20
J5 D1 30ccop red & lt bl   .35   .35
J6 D1 45cmag & yel grn   .50   .50
J7 D1 50cdk ol grn & buff   .50   .50
J8 D1 60credsh pur & yel   .65   .65
J9 D1 1fr brown & yel   .80   .80
J10 D1 2fr dk bl & buff   1.40 1.00
J11 D1 3fr red brn & lt grn   1.50 1.10
     Nos. J1-J11 (11)   6.60 5.70
Set, never hinged   10.00 10.00

Catalogue values for unused stamps in this section, from this point to the end of the section, are for Never Hinged items.

D2

1947   *Engr.*
J12 D2 10c red   .20   .20
J13 D2 30c dp org   .20   .20
J14 D2 50c greenish bl   .20   .20
J15 D2 1fr carmine   .25   .25
J16 D2 2fr emerald   .25   .25
J17 D2 3fr dp red lil   .25   .25
J18 D2 4fr dp ultra   .90   .90
J19 D2 5fr red brown   .90   .90
J20 D2 10fr peacock blue   1.25 1.25
J21 D2 20fr sepia   1.40 1.40
     Nos. J12-J21 (10)   5.80 5.80

FRENCH GUIANA
ˈfrench gē-ˈä-nə

LOCATION — On the northeast coast of South America bordering on the Atlantic Ocean.
GOVT. — French colony
AREA — 34,740 sq. mi.

POP. — 28,537 (1946)
CAPITAL — Cayenne

French Guiana became an overseas department of France in 1946.

100 Centimes = 1 Franc

Catalogue values for unused stamps in this country are for Never Hinged items, beginning with Scott 171 in the regular postage section, Scott B12 in the semipostal section, Scott C9 in the airpost section, and Scott J22 in the postage due section.

See France No. 1446 for French stamp inscribed "Guyane."

Stamps of French Colonies Surcharged in Black

Déc. 1886. GUY. FRANÇ. **0f 05**

1886, Dec.   Unwmk.   *Imperf.*
1 A8 5c on 2c grn, *grnsh*   575.00 500.00
  b.   No "f" after "0"   725.00 675.00

     Perf. 14x13½
2 A9 5c on 2c brn, *buff*   450.00 450.00
  b.   No "f" after "0"   400.00 350.00

Two types of No. 1: Surcharge 12mm high, and surcharge 10½mm high.

Avril 1887.
—
GUY FRANÇ **0f 20**

Avril 1887. — GUY. FRANÇ. 0f 25

"Av" of Date Line Inverted-Reversed
1887, Apr.   *Imperf.*
4 A8 20c on 35c blk, *org*   50.00 40.00
     Date Line Reads "Avril 1887"
5 A8 5c on 2c grn, *grnsh*   110.00 95.00
6 A8 30c on 35c blk, *org*   250.00 210.00
7 A7 25c on 30c brn, *yelsh*   35.00 29.00

Variety "small f omitted" occurs on #5-7.

French Colonies Nos. 22 & 26 Surcharged

DÉC. 1887. GUY. FRANÇ. 5c

8 A7 5c on 30c brn,
     yelsh   115.00 110.00
  a.   Double surcharge   575.00   575.00
  b.   Inverted surcharge   850.00 850.00
  c.   Pair, one without
       surcharge   1,150.
9 A8 5c on 30c brn,
     yelsh   1,100.   1,100.

French Colonies Nos. 22 and 28 Surcharged:

Février 1888 GUY. FRANÇ 5   Février 1888 GUY. FRANÇ 10

1888
10 A7 5c on 30c brn, *yelsh*   110.00 90.00
  b.   Double surcharge   575.00 575.00
  c.   Inverted surcharge   425.00 400.00
11 A8 10c on 75c car, *rose*   250.00 250.00

Stamps of French Colonies Overprinted in Black

GUYANE.

1892, Feb. 20   *Imperf.*
12 A8   2c grn, *grnsh*   650.00 725.00
13 A7 30c brn, *yelsh*   115.00 115.00
  a.   Inverted overprint   450.00 425.00
14 A8 35c blk, *orange*   2,100.   2,100.
15 A8 40c red, *straw*   110.00 110.00
16 A8 75c car, *rose*   115.00 110.00
  a.   Inverted overprint   350.00 350.00
17 A8   1fr brnz grn,
     straw   130.00 125.00
  a.   Inverted overprint   600.00 525.00
  b.   Double overprint   600.00 525.00

1892   *Perf. 14x13½*
18 A9   1c blk, *lil bl*   35.00 27.50
19 A9   2c brn, *buff*   32.50 30.00
20 A9   4c claret, *lav*   30.00 30.00
21 A9   5c grn, *grnsh*   32.50 27.50
  a.   Inverted overprint   92.50
  b.   Double overprint   92.50
22 A9 10c blk, *lavender*   55.00 35.00
  a.   Inverted overprint   125.00 125.00
23 A9 15c blue   45.00 32.50
24 A9 20c red, *grn*   40.00 32.50
25 A9 25c blk, *rose*   65.00 30.00
26 A9 30c brn, *bis*   32.50 29.00
27 A9 35c blk, *orange*   175.00 175.00
28 A9 40c red, *straw*   100.00 100.00
  a.   Inverted overprint   175.00 175.00
29 A9 75c car, *rose*   110.00 77.50
30 A9   1fr brnz grn, *straw*   180.00 160.00
     Nos. 18-30 (13)   932.50 786.50

French Colonies No. 51 Surcharged

GUYANE. DÉC. 92. 0.05

1892, Dec.
31 A9 5c on 15c blue   42.50 29.00
    On cover   900.00

Navigation and Commerce — A12

1892-1904   Typo.   *Perf. 14x13½*
Name of Colony in Blue or Carmine
32 A12   1c blk, *lil bl*   1.50 1.50
33 A12   2c brn, *buff*   1.00 .90
34 A12   4c claret, *lav*   1.50 1.10
  a.   "GUYANE" double   175.00
35 A12   5c grn, *grnsh*   8.50 7.50
36 A12   5c yel grn ('04)   1.50 .90
37 A12 10c blk, *lavender*   9.75 5.75
38 A12 10c red ('00)   3.25 1.00
39 A12 15c blue, quadrille
     paper   27.50 2.50
40 A12 15c gray, *lt gray*
     ('00)   100.00 67.50
41 A12 20c red, *grn*   18.00 11.00
42 A12 25c blk, *rose*   16.00 3.25
43 A12 25c blue ('00)   13.00 13.00
44 A12 30c brn, *bis*   17.00 11.00
45 A12 40c red, *straw*   17.00 12.00
46 A12 50c car, *rose*   25.00 13.00
47 A12 50c brn, *az* ('00)   20.00 16.00
48 A12 75c dp vio, *org*   30.00 16.00
49 A12   1fr brn grn, *straw*   12.50 10.50
50 A12   2fr vio, *rose* ('02)   140.00 7.50
     Nos. 32-50 (19)   463.00 201.20

Perf. 13½x14 stamps are counterfeits.
For surcharges see Nos. 87-93.

Great Anteater — A13   Washing Gold — A14

Palm Grove at Cayenne A15

1905-28
51 A13   1c black   .30   .30
52 A13   2c blue   .30   .30
53 A13   4c red brn   .30   .30
54 A13   5c green   .90   .65
55 A13   5c org ('22)   .25   .25
56 A13 10c rose   1.00   .65
57 A13 10c grn ('22)   .50   .50
58 A13 10c red, *bluish* ('25)   .35   .35
59 A13 15c violet   1.10   .90

60	A14	20c red brn	.45	.35
61	A14	25c blue	2.00	1.25
62	A14	25c vio ('22)	.55	.50
63	A14	30c black	1.40	.60
64	A14	30c rose ('22)	.40	.40
65	A14	30c red org ('25)	.25	.25
66	A14	30c dk grn, grnsh ('28)	1.00	1.00
67	A14	35c blk, yel ('06)	.35	.30
68	A14	40c rose	.65	.60
69	A14	40c black ('22)	.25	.25
70	A14	45c olive ('07)	.70	.60
71	A14	50c violet	3.00	2.25
72	A14	50c blue ('22)	.45	.40
73	A14	50c gray ('25)	.65	.40
74	A14	60c lil, rose ('25)	.55	.50
75	A14	65c myr grn ('26)	.75	.60
76	A14	75c green	1.25	.80
77	A14	85c magenta ('26)	.60	.60
78	A15	1fr rose	.75	.75
79	A15	1fr bl, bluish ('25)	.80	.70
80	A15	1fr bl, yel grn ('28)	2.25	2.25
81	A15	1.10fr lt red ('28)	1.25	1.25
82	A15	2fr blue	1.00	1.00
83	A15	2fr org red, yel ('26)	2.25	1.50
84	A15	5fr black	5.50	4.00
85	A15	10fr grn, yel ('24)	11.00	10.00
a.		Printed on both sides	42.50	42.50
86	A15	20fr brn lake ('24)	14.00	13.00
		Nos. 51-86 (36)	59.05	50.15

For surcharges see Nos. 94-108, B1-B2.

Issue of 1892 Surcharged in Black or Carmine

1912

87	A12	5c on 2c brn, buff	.75	.75
88	A12	5c on 4c cl, lav (C)	.75	.75
89	A12	5c on 20c red, grn	1.00	1.00
90	A12	5c on 25c blk, grn (C)	3.00	3.00
91	A12	5c on 30c brn, bis	.95	.95
92	A12	10c on 40c red, straw	.75	.75
93	A12	10c on 50c car, rose	3.00	3.00
a.		Double surcharge	400.00	
		Nos. 87-93 (7)	10.20	10.20

Two spacings between the surcharged numerals are found on Nos. 87 to 93. For detailed listings, see the *Scott Classic Specialized Catalogue of Stamps and Covers.*

No. 59 Surcharged in Various Colors

1922

94	A13	1c on 15c vio (Bk)	.45	.45
95	A13	2c on 15c vio (Bl)	.45	.45
a.		Inverted surcharge	65.00	
96	A13	4c on 15c vio (G)	.45	.45
a.		Double surcharge	57.50	
97	A13	5c on 15c vio (R)	.45	.45
		Nos. 94-97 (4)	1.80	1.80

Type of 1905-28 Surcharged in Blue

1923

98	A15	10fr on 1fr grn, yel	16.00	16.00
99	A15	20fr on 5fr lilac, rose	16.00	16.00

Stamps and Types of 1905-28 Surcharged with New Value and Bars in Black or Red

1924-27

100	A13	25c on 15c vio ('25)	.50	.50
101	A15	25c on 2fr bl ('24)	.60	.60
a.		Double surcharge	100.00	
b.		Triple surcharge	110.00	
102	A14	65c on 45c ol (R) ('25)	1.10	1.10
103	A14	85c on 45c ol (R) ('25)	1.10	1.10
104	A14	90c on 75c red ('27)	.95	.95
105	A15	1.05fr on 2fr lt yel brn ('27)	.95	.95

106	A15	1.25fr on 1fr ultra (R) ('26)	1.10	1.10
107	A15	1.50fr on 1fr lt bl ('27)	1.10	1.10
108	A15	3fr on 5fr vio ('27)	1.25	1.25
a.		No period after "F"	8.50	8.50
		Nos. 100-108 (9)	8.65	8.65

Carib Archer — A16

Shooting Rapids, Maroni River — A17

Government Building, Cayenne — A18

1929-40   **Perf. 13½x14**

109	A16	1c gray lil & grnsh bl	.20	.20
110	A16	2c dk red & bl grn	.20	.20
111	A16	3c gray lil & grnsh bl ('40)	.20	.20
112	A16	4c ol brn & red vio	.20	.20
113	A16	5c Prus bl & red org	.20	.20
114	A16	10c mag & brn	.25	.25
115	A16	15c yel brn & red org	.25	.25
116	A16	20c dk bl & ol grn	.25	.25
117	A16	25c dk red & dk brn	.40	.40

        Perf. 14x13½

118	A17	30c dl & lt grn	.50	.50
119	A17	30c grn & brn ('40)	.30	.30
120	A17	35c Prus grn & ol grn ('38)	.75	.75
121	A17	40c org brn & ol gray	.25	.25
122	A17	45c grn & dk brn	.75	.75
123	A17	45c ol grn & lt grn ('40)	.55	.55
124	A17	50c dk bl & ol gray	.30	.30
125	A17	55c vio bl & car ('38)	1.25	1.25
126	A17	60c sal & grn ('40)	.50	.50
127	A17	65c sal & grn	.75	.75
128	A17	70c ind & sl bl ('40)	.90	.90
129	A17	75c ind & sl bl	.90	.90
130	A17	80c blk & vio bl ('38)	.70	.70
131	A17	90c dk red & ver	.75	.75
132	A17	90c red vio & brn ('39)	.80	.80
133	A17	1fr lt vio & brn	.50	.50
134	A17	1fr car & lt red ('38)	1.75	1.75
135	A17	1fr blk & vio bl ('40)	.55	.55
136	A18	1.05fr ver & olivine	4.75	4.50
137	A18	1.10fr ol brn & red vio	5.25	4.00
138	A18	1.25fr blk brn & bl grn ('33)	.65	.65
139	A18	1.25fr rose & lt red ('39)	.70	.70
140	A18	1.40fr ol brn & red vio ('40)	.90	.90
141	A18	1.50fr dk bl & lt bl	.35	.35
142	A18	1.60fr ol brn & bl grn ('40)	.90	.90
143	A18	1.75fr brn red & blk brn ('33)	1.90	1.75
144	A18	1.75fr vio bl ('38)	1.40	.75
145	A18	2fr dk grn & rose red	.50	.50
146	A18	2.25fr vio bl ('39)	.90	.90
147	A18	2.50fr cop red & brn ('40)	1.00	1.00
148	A18	3fr brn red & red vio	.70	.70
149	A18	5fr dl vio & yel grn	1.00	1.00
150	A18	10fr ol gray & dp ultra	1.25	1.25
151	A18	20fr indigo & ver	1.75	1.75
		Nos. 109-151 (43)	38.80	36.50

For types A16-A18 without "RF," see Nos. 170C-170E.

Common Design Types

pictured following the introduction.

Colonial Exposition Issue
Common Design Types

1931   **Engr.**   **Perf. 12½**
Name of Country in Black

152	CD70	40c dp green	4.50	4.50
153	CD71	50c violet	4.50	4.50
154	CD72	90c red orange	4.50	4.50
155	CD73	1.50fr dull blue	4.50	4.50
		Nos. 152-155 (4)	18.00	18.00

Recapture of Cayenne by d'Estrées, 1676 — A19

Products of French Guiana A20

1935, Oct. 21   **Perf. 13**

156	A19	40c gray brn	3.50	3.50
157	A19	50c dull red	7.25	5.75
158	A19	1.50fr ultra	3.50	3.50
159	A20	1.75fr lilac rose	9.50	8.50
160	A20	5fr brown	7.25	7.25
161	A20	10fr blue green	7.25	7.25
		Nos. 156-161 (6)	38.25	35.75

Tercentenary of the founding of French possessions in the West Indies.

Paris International Exposition Issue
Common Design Types

1937, Apr. 15

162	CD74	20c deep violet	1.15	1.15
163	CD75	30c dark green	1.15	1.15
164	CD76	40c carmine rose	1.15	1.15
165	CD77	50c dark brown	1.25	1.25
166	CD78	90c red	1.25	1.25
167	CD79	1.50fr ultra	1.40	1.40
		Nos. 162-167 (6)	7.35	7.35

Colonial Arts Exhibition Issue
Souvenir Sheet
Common Design Type

1937   **Imperf.**

168	CD75	3fr violet	8.00	10.00

New York World's Fair Issue
Common Design Type

1939, May 10   **Engr.**   **Perf. 12½x12**

169	CD82	1.25fr car lake	.95	.95
170	CD82	2.25fr ultra	.95	.95

View of Cayenne and Marshal Petain A21a

1941   **Engr.**   **Perf. 12½x12**

170A	A21a	1fr deep lilac	.60	—
170B	A21a	2.50fr blue	.60	—

For surcharges, see Nos. B11A-B11B.

Types of 1929-40 without "RF"

1944   *Methods and Perfs as Before*

170C	A16	15c yel brn & red org	.90	
170D	A17	1fr black & vio blue	.90	
170E	A18	1.50fr dk blue & lt blue	1.00	
		Nos. 170C-170E (3)	2.80	

Nos. 170C-170E were issued by the Vichy government in France, but were not issued in French Guiana.

> Catalogue values for unused stamps in this section, from this point to the end of the section, are for Never Hinged items.

Eboue Issue
Common Design Type

1945   **Engr.**   **Perf. 13**

171	CD91	2fr black	.50	.50
172	CD91	25fr Prussian green	.95	.95

This issue exists imperforate.

Arms of Cayenne A22

1945   **Litho.**   **Perf. 12**

173	A22	10c dp gray violet	.20	.20
174	A22	30c brown org	.20	.20
175	A22	40c lt blue	.20	.20
176	A22	50c violet brn	.35	.35
177	A22	60c orange yel	.35	.35
178	A22	70c pale brown	.35	.35
179	A22	80c lt green	.35	.35
180	A22	1fr blue	.35	.35
181	A22	1.20fr brt violet	.35	.35
182	A22	1.50fr dp orange	.50	.50
183	A22	2fr black	.60	.60
184	A22	2.40fr red	.60	.60
185	A22	3fr pink	.65	.65
186	A22	4fr dp ultra	.80	.80
187	A22	4.50fr dp yel grn	.80	.80
188	A22	5fr orange brn	.80	.80
189	A22	10fr dk violet	.80	.80
190	A22	15fr rose carmine	.80	.80
191	A22	20fr olive green	.90	.90
		Nos. 173-191 (19)	9.95	9.95

Hammock A23   Guiana Girl A26

Maroni River Bank A24

Inini Scene A25

Toucans A27

Parrots A28

         Perf. 13.
1947, June 2   **Unwmk.**   **Engr.**

192	A23	10c dk blue grn	.20	.20
193	A23	30c brt red	.20	.20
194	A24	50c dk vio brn	.20	.20
195	A24	60c grnsh blk	.20	.20
196	A24	1fr red brn	.35	.35
197	A24	1.50fr black brn	.35	.35
198	A25	2fr dp yel grn	.55	.50
199	A25	2.50fr dp ultra	.55	.50
200	A25	3fr red brn	.50	.50
201	A26	4fr black brn	1.40	.80
202	A26	5fr deep blue	1.00	.85
203	A26	6fr red brown	1.00	.85
204	A27	10fr deep ultra	4.50	3.50
205	A27	15fr black brn	4.50	4.00
206	A27	20fr red brn	6.50	4.00
207	A28	25fr brt bl grn	7.75	6.00
208	A28	40fr black brn	6.50	5.75
		Nos. 192-208 (17)	36.25	28.75

SEMI-POSTAL STAMPS

Regular Issue of
1905-28 Surcharged
in Red

	1915	Unwmk.	Perf. 13½x14		
B1	A13	10c + 5c rose		12.00	12.00
a.		Inverted surcharge		190.00	190.00
b.		Double surcharge		190.00	190.00

Regular Issue of
1905-28 Surcharged
in Rose

B2	A13	10c + 5c rose		.95	.95

Curie Issue
Common Design Type

	1938		Perf. 13		
B3	CD80	1.75fr + 50c brt ultra	10.00	10.00

French Revolution Issue
Common Design Type

	1939		Photo.		
	Name and Value in Black				
B4	CD83	45c + 25c green		9.25	9.25
B5	CD83	70c + 30c brown		9.25	9.25
B6	CD83	90c + 35c red org		9.25	9.25
B7	CD83	1.25fr + 1fr rose pink		9.25	9.25
B8	CD83	2.25fr + 2fr blue		9.25	9.25
	Nos. B4-B8 (5)			46.25	46.25

Common Design Type and

Colonial
Infantryman — SP1

Colonial
Policeman
SP2

	1941	Photo.		Perf. 13½	
B9	SP1	1fr + 1fr red			.95
B10	CD86	1.50fr + 3fr maroon			1.00
B11	SP2	2.50fr + 1fr blue			.95
	Nos. B9-B11 (3)				2.90

Nos. B9-B11 were issued by the Vichy government in France, but were not placed on sale in French Guiana.

Nos. 170A-170B
Surcharged in Black or Red

	1944	Engr.	Perf. 12½x12		
B11A		50c + 1.50fr on 2.50fr			
		deep blue (R)			.60
B11B		+ 2.50fr on 1fr dp lilac			.60

Colonial Development Fund.
Nos. B11A-B11B were issued by the Vichy government in France, but were not placed on sale in French Guiana.

Catalogue values for unused
stamps in this section, from this
point to the end of the section, are
for Never Hinged items.

Red Cross Issue
Common Design Type

	1944		Perf. 14½x14		
B12	CD90	5fr + 20fr dk copper			
		brn		.90	.90

The surtax was for the French Red Cross
and national relief.

AIR POST STAMPS

Cayenne
AP1

	Perf. 13½				
	1933, Nov. 20	Unwmk.		Photo.	
C1	AP1	50c orange brn		.20	.20
C2	AP1	1fr yellow grn		.35	.35
C3	AP1	1.50fr dk blue		.50	.50
C4	AP1	2fr orange		.50	.50
C5	AP1	3fr black		.65	.65
C6	AP1	5fr violet		.65	.65
C7	AP1	10fr olive grn		.65	.65
C8	AP1	20fr scarlet		.80	.80
	Nos. C1-C8 (8)			4.30	4.30

For No. C1 without "RF," see No. C8A.

Catalogue values for unused
stamps in this section, from this
point to the end of the section, are
for Never Hinged items.

Type of 1933 without "RF" and

AP1a

AP1b

	Perf. 13½, 13 (#C8C)				
	1941-44		Photo, Engr. (#C8C)		
C8A	AP1	50c orange brn			.65
C8B	AP1a	50f bl grn & red			
		brown ('42)			.90
C8C	AP1b	100f dk blue ('44)			.85
	Nos. C8A-C8C (3)				2.40

Nos. C8A-C8C were issued by the Vichy government in France, but were not placed on sale in French Guiana.

Common Design Type

	1945	Photo.		Perf. 14½x14	
C9	CD87	50fr dark green		1.00	1.00
C10	CD87	100fr plum		1.75	1.75

Victory Issue
Common Design Type

	1946, May 8	Engr.		Perf. 12½	
C11	CD92	8fr black		1.00	1.00

Chad to Rhine Issue
Common Design Types

	1946, June 6				
C12	CD93	5fr dk slate bl		1.15	1.15
C13	CD94	10fr lilac rose		1.15	1.15
C14	CD95	15fr dk vio brn		1.15	1.15
C15	CD96	20fr dk slate grn		1.40	1.40
C16	CD97	25fr vio brown		1.50	1.50
C17	CD98	50fr bright lilac		1.75	1.75
	Nos. C12-C17 (6)			8.10	8.10

Eagles — AP2

Tapir — AP3

Toucans — AP4

	1947, June 2	Engr.		Perf. 13	
C18	AP2	50fr deep green		13.50	13.50
C19	AP3	100fr red brown		10.00	10.00
C20	AP4	200fr dk gray bl		19.50	19.50
	Nos. C18-C20 (3)			43.00	43.00

AIR POST SEMI-POSTAL STAMPS

French Revolution Issue
Common Design Type
Unwmk.

	1939, July 5	Photo.	Perf. 13		
	Name & Value Typo. in Orange				
CB1	CD83	5fr + 4fr brn blk	16.00	16.00	

Nurse with Mother & Child — SPAP1

Unwmk.

	1942, June 22	Engr.		Perf. 13	
CB2	SPAP1	1.50fr + 50c green			.80
CB3	SPAP1	2fr + 6fr brn &			
		red			.80

Native children's welfare fund.
Nos. CB2-CB3 were issued by the Vichy government in France, but were not placed on sale in French Guiana.

Colonial Education Fund
Common Design Type

	1942, June 22				
CB4	CD86a	1.20fr + 1.80fr blue			
		& red			.70

No. CB4 was issued by the Vichy government in France, but was not placed on sale in French Guiana.

POSTAGE DUE STAMPS

Postage Due Stamps of
France, 1893-1926,
Overprinted

	1925-27	Unwmk.		Perf. 14x13½	
J1	D2	5c light blue		.45	.45
J2	D2	10c brown		.55	.55
J3	D2	20c olive green		.75	.75
J4	D2	50c violet brown		.95	.95
J5	D2	3fr magenta ('27)		7.75	7.75

Surcharged in Black

J6	D2	15c on 20c ol grn		.50	.50
a.		Blue surcharge		32.50	
J7	D2	25c on 5c lt bl		.80	.80
J8	D2	30c on 20c ol grn		1.00	1.00
J9	D2	45c on 10c brn		.95	.95
J10	D2	60c on 5c lt bl		.95	.95
J11	D2	1fr on 20c ol grn		1.40	1.40
J12	D2	2fr on 50c vio brn		1.50	1.50
	Nos. J1-J12 (12)			17.55	17.55

Royal
Palms — D3

Guiana
Girl — D4

	1929, Oct. 14	Typo.		Perf. 13½x14	
J13	D3	5c indigo & Prus bl		.30	.30
J14	D3	10c bis brn & Prus grn		.30	.30
J15	D3	20c grn & rose red		.30	.30
J16	D3	30c ol brn & rose red		.30	.30
J17	D3	50c vio & ol brn		.65	.65
J18	D3	60c brn red & ol brn		.95	.95
J19	D4	1fr dp bl & org brn		1.25	1.25
J20	D4	2fr brn red & bluish grn		1.40	1.40
J21	D4	3fr violet & blk		3.25	3.25
	Nos. J13-J21 (9)			8.70	8.70

Catalogue values for unused
stamps in this section, from this
point to the end of the section, are
for Never Hinged items.

D5

	1947, June 2	Engr.		Perf. 14x13	
J22	D5	10c dk car rose		.20	.20
J23	D5	30c dull green		.20	.20
J24	D5	50c black		.20	.20
J25	D5	1fr brt ultra		.35	.35
J26	D5	2fr dk brown red		.35	.35
J27	D5	3fr deep violet		.50	.50
J28	D5	4fr red		.70	.70
J29	D5	5fr brown violet		.85	.85
J30	D5	10fr blue green		1.40	1.40
J31	D5	20fr lilac rose		1.90	1.90
	Nos. J22-J31 (10)			6.65	6.65

FRENCH GUINEA

'french 'gi-nē

LOCATION — On the coast of West Africa, between Portuguese Guinea and Sierra Leone.
GOVT. — French colony
AREA — 89,436 sq. mi.
POP. — 2,058,442 (est. 1941)
CAPITAL — Conakry

French Guinea stamps were replaced by those of French West Africa around 1944-45. French Guinea became the Republic of Guinea Oct. 2, 1958. See "Guinea" for issues of the republic.

100 Centimes = 1 Franc

See French West Africa No. 66 for additional stamp inscribed "Guinee" and "Afrique Occidentale Francaise."

Navigation and Commerce A1

Fulah Shepherd A2

Perf. 14x13½
1892-1900   Typo.   Unwmk.
Name of Colony in Blue or Carmine

1	A1	1c black, *lilac bl*	1.10	1.10
2	A1	2c brown, *buff*	1.60	1.60
3	A1	4c claret, *lav*	2.00	2.00
4	A1	5c green, *grnsh*	6.50	3.50
5	A1	10c blk, *lavender*	5.75	3.50
6	A1	10c red ('00)	32.50	29.00
7	A1	15c blue, quadrille paper	11.00	5.50
8	A1	15c gray, *lt gray* ('00)	80.00	75.00
9	A1	20c red, *grn*	16.00	10.00
10	A1	25c black, *rose*	10.00	6.00
11	A1	25c blue ('00)	19.00	17.50
12	A1	30c brown, *bis*	30.00	25.00
13	A1	40c red, *straw*	30.00	25.00
a.		"GUINEE FRANCAISE" double	350.00	350.00
14	A1	50c car, *rose*	32.50	26.00
15	A1	50c brown, *az* ('00)	29.00	25.00
16	A1	75c dp vio, *org*	45.00	37.50
17	A1	1fr brnz grn, *straw*	37.50	30.00
		Nos. 1-17 (17)	389.45	323.20

Perf. 13½x14 stamps are counterfeits.
For surcharges see Nos. 48-54.

1904

18	A2	1c black, *yel grn*	.90	.55
19	A2	2c vio brn, *buff*	.75	.75
20	A2	4c carmine, *bl*	1.10	.95
21	A2	5c green, *grnsh*	1.25	.95
22	A2	10c carmine	2.75	1.50
23	A2	15c violet, *rose*	7.50	3.50
24	A2	20c carmine, *grn*	10.00	9.50
25	A2	25c blue	12.50	7.50
26	A2	30c brown	17.50	16.00
27	A2	40c red, *straw*	24.00	18.00
28	A2	50c brown, *az*	24.00	18.00
29	A2	75c green, *org*	27.50	21.00
30	A2	1fr brnz grn, *straw*	37.50	32.50
31	A2	2fr red, *org*	72.50	72.50
32	A2	5fr green, *yel grn*	87.50	87.50
		Nos. 18-32 (15)	327.25	290.70

For surcharges see Nos. 55-62.

Gen. Louis Faidherbé A3

Oil Palm — A4

Dr. Noel Eugène Ballay A5

1906-07
Name of Colony in Red or Blue

33	A3	1c gray	.60	.60
34	A3	2c brown	.85	.75
35	A3	4c brown, *bl*	1.10	1.10
36	A3	5c green	2.50	1.60
37	A3	10c carmine (B)	20.00	2.00
38	A4	20c black, *blue*	5.00	3.00
39	A4	25c blue, *pnksh*	5.00	5.00
40	A4	30c brown, *pnksh*	6.25	3.00
41	A4	35c black, *yellow*	3.75	2.00
42	A4	45c choc, *grnsh gray*	5.00	3.25
43	A4	50c dp violet	10.00	8.00
44	A4	75c blue, *org*	6.25	3.00
45	A5	1fr black, *az*	16.00	16.00
46	A5	2fr blue, *pink*	32.50	32.50
47	A5	5fr car, *straw* (B)	50.00	45.00
		Nos. 33-47 (15)	164.80	126.80

Regular Issues Surcharged in Black or Carmine

1912

On Issue of 1892-1900

48	A1	5c on 2c brown, *buff*	.80	.80
49	A1	5c on 4c cl, *lav* (C)	.80	.80
50	A1	5c on 15c blue (C)	.80	.80
51	A1	5c on 20c red, *grn*	3.00	3.00
52	A1	5c on 30c brn, *bis* (C)	3.50	3.50
53	A1	10c on 40c red, *straw*	1.75	1.75
54	A1	10c on 75c dp vio, *org*	6.25	6.25
a.		Double surcharge, inverted	210.00	

On Issue of 1904

55	A2	5c on 2c vio brn, *buff*	.80	.80
a.		Pair, one without surcharge	450.00	
56	A2	5c on 4c car, *blue*	.80	.80
57	A2	5c on 15c violet, *rose*	.80	.80
58	A2	5c on 20c car, *grn*	.80	.80
59	A2	5c on 25c blue (C)	1.10	1.10
60	A2	5c on 30c brown (C)	1.50	1.50
61	A2	10c on 40c red, *straw*	1.25	1.25
62	A2	10c on 50c brn, *az* (C)	3.50	3.50
		Nos. 48-62 (15)	27.45	27.45

Two spacings between the surcharged numerals are found on Nos. 48 to 62. For detailed listings, see the *Scott Classic Specialized Catalogue of Stamps and Covers.*

Ford at Kitim — A6

1913-33   Perf. 13½x14

63	A6	1c violet & bl	.20	.20
64	A6	2c brn & vio brn	.20	.20
65	A6	4c gray & black	.20	.20
66	A6	5c yel grn & bl grn	.80	.25
67	A6	5c brn vio & grn ('22)	.20	.20
68	A6	10c red org & rose	.75	.25
69	A6	10c yel grn & bl grn ('22)	.25	.25
70	A6	10c vio & ver ('25)	.45	.25
71	A6	15c vio brn & rose ('16)	.30	.25
72	A6	15c gray grn & yel grn ('25)	.25	.25
73	A6	15c red brn & rose lil ('27)	.25	.25

74	A6	20c brown & violet	.30	.25
75	A6	20c grn & bl grn ('26)	.65	.50
76	A6	20c brn red & brn ('27)	.65	.30
77	A6	25c ultra & blue	2.00	1.00
78	A6	25c black & vio ('22)	.50	.50
79	A6	30c vio brn & grn	1.10	.75
80	A6	30c red org & rose ('22)	.80	.75
81	A6	30c rose red & grn ('25)	.25	.25
82	A6	30c dl grn & bl grn ('28)	1.25	.90
83	A6	35c blue & rose	.40	.20
84	A6	40c green & gray	.80	.65
85	A6	45c brown & red	.85	.75
86	A6	50c ultra & black	5.75	3.25
87	A6	50c ultra & bl ('22)	.85	.50
88	A6	50c yel brn & ol ('25)	.45	.35
89	A6	60c vio, *pnksh* ('25)	.45	.35
90	A6	65c yel brn & sl bl ('26)	1.40	1.00
91	A6	75c red & ultra	1.25	1.00
92	A6	75c indigo & dl bl ('25)	.90	.80
93	A6	75c mag & yel grn ('27)	1.40	1.00
94	A6	85c ol grn & red brn ('26)	1.00	1.00
95	A6	90c brn red & rose ('30)	5.25	4.25
96	A6	1fr violet & black	1.25	1.00
97	A6	1.10fr vio & ol brn ('28)	5.50	4.25
98	A6	1.25fr vio & yel brn ('33)	1.90	1.00
99	A6	1.50fr dk bl & lt bl ('30)	5.00	1.90
100	A6	1.75fr ol brn & vio ('33)	1.50	1.25
101	A6	2fr orange & vio brn	3.00	1.25
102	A6	3fr red violet ('30)	7.50	1.00
103	A6	5fr black & vio	11.00	11.00
104	A6	5fr dl bl & blk ('22)	3.00	2.25
		Nos. 63-104 (42)	71.75	51.65

Nos. 66 and 68 exist on both ordinary and chalky paper, No. 71 on chalky paper only.
For surcharges see Nos. 105-115, B1.
Nos. 66, 68 and 77 pasted on colored cardboard and overprinted "VALEUR D'ECHANGE" were used as emergency currency in 1920.

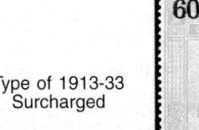

Type of 1913-33 Surcharged

1922

105	A6	60c on 75c violet, *pnksh*	.50	.50

Stamps and Type of 1913-33 Surcharged with New Value and Bars

1924-27

106	A6	25c on 2fr org & brn (R)	.35	.35
107	A6	25c on 5fr dull bl & blk	.35	.35
108	A6	65c on 75c rose & ultra ('25)	1.00	1.00
109	A6	85c on 75c rose & ultra ('25)	1.25	1.25
110	A6	90c on 75c brn red & cer ('27)	1.75	1.75
111	A6	1.25fr on 1fr dk bl & ultra ('26)	.85	.85
112	A6	1.50fr on 1fr dp bl & lt bl ('27)	1.40	1.40
113	A6	3fr on 5fr mag & sl ('27)	3.25	3.25
114	A6	10fr on 5fr bl & bl grn, *bluish* ('27)	6.50	6.50
115	A6	20fr on 5fr rose lil & brn ol, *pnksh* ('27)	14.50	14.50
		Nos. 106-115 (10)	31.20	31.20

Common Design Types pictured following the introduction.

Colonial Exposition Issue
Common Design Types
1931   Engr.   Perf. 12½
Name of Country in Black

116	CD70	40c deep green	3.75	3.75
117	CD71	50c violet	3.75	3.75
118	CD72	90c red orange	3.75	3.75
119	CD73	1.50fr dull blue	3.75	3.75
		Nos. 116-119 (4)	15.00	15.00
		Set, never hinged	19.00	

Paris International Exposition Issue
Common Design Types
1937   Perf. 13

120	CD74	20c deep violet	1.25	1.25
121	CD75	30c dark green	1.25	1.25
122	CD76	40c carmine rose	1.40	1.40

123	CD77	50c dark brown	1.40	1.40
124	CD78	90c red	1.50	1.50
125	CD79	1.50fr ultra	1.50	1.50
		Nos. 120-125 (6)	8.30	8.30
		Set, never hinged	12.00	

Colonial Arts Exhibition Issue
Souvenir Sheet
Common Design Type
1937   Imperf.

126	CD76	3fr Prussian green	5.75	7.00
		Never hinged	8.50	

Guinea Village A7

Hausa Basket Workers A8

Forest Waterfall A9

Guinea Women — A10

1938-40   Perf. 13

128	A7	2c vermilion	.20	.20
129	A7	3c ultra	.20	.20
130	A7	4c green	.20	.20
131	A7	5c rose car	.20	.20
132	A7	10c peacock blue	.20	.20
133	A7	15c violet brown	.20	.20
134	A8	20c dk carmine	.20	.20
135	A8	25c pck blue	.20	.20
136	A8	30c ultra	.20	.20
137	A8	35c green	.45	.40
138	A8	40c blk brn ('40)	.20	.20
139	A8	45c dk green ('40)	.20	.20
140	A8	50c red brown	.40	.40
141	A9	55c dk ultra	.85	.75
142	A9	60c dk ultra ('40)	.65	.65
143	A9	65c green	.90	.65
144	A9	70c green ('40)	1.25	1.00
145	A9	80c rose violet	.50	.45
146	A9	90c rose vio ('39)	1.00	.95
147	A9	1fr orange red	2.50	1.40
148	A9	1fr brn blk ('40)	.40	.40
149	A9	1.25fr org red ('39)	1.10	1.00
150	A9	1.40fr brown ('40)	1.10	1.00
151	A9	1.50fr violet	2.25	1.40
152	A10	1.60fr org red ('40)	1.25	1.00
153	A10	1.75fr ultra	.60	.55
154	A10	2fr magenta	.85	.50
155	A10	2.25fr brt ultra ('39)	1.75	1.25
156	A10	2.50fr brn blk ('40)	1.25	1.00
157	A10	3fr peacock blue	.70	.30
158	A10	5fr rose violet	.70	.55
159	A10	10fr slate green	1.00	.80
160	A10	20fr chocolate	2.50	1.40
		Nos. 128-160 (33)	26.15	20.00
		Set, never hinged	67.50	

For surcharges see Nos. B8-B11.
For types A7-A10 without "RF," see Nos. 168-174.

Caillié Issue
Common Design Type
1939   Engr.   Perf. 12½x12

161	CD81	90c org brn & org	.75	.75
162	CD81	2fr brt violet	.85	.85
163	CD81	2.25fr ultra & dk bl	.85	.85
		Nos. 161-163 (3)	2.45	2.45

René Caillié, French explorer, death cent.

New York World's Fair Issue
Common Design Type
1939

164	CD82	1.25fr carmine lake	.95	.95
165	CD82	2.25fr ultra	.95	.95

Ford at Kitim and Marshal Petain — A11

1941   *Perf. 12x12½*
166 A11 1fr green .60 1.25
167 A11 2.50fr deep blue .60 1.25
For surcharges, see Nos. B15-B16.

Types of 1933-40 without "RF"

1943-44   *Perf. 13*
168 A7 10c peacock blue .35
169 A8 20c dk carmine .55
170 A8 30c ultramarine .55
171 A8 40c black brown .80
172 A9 60c dk ultramarine 1.00
173 A9 1.50fr violet 1.00
174 A10 2fr magenta 1.10
    Nos. 168-174 (7) 5.35

Nos. 168-174 were issued by the Vichy government in France, but were not placed on sale in French Guinea.

SEMI-POSTAL STAMPS

Regular Issue of 1913 Surcharged in Red

1915   *Unwmk.*   *Perf. 13½x14*
B1 A6 10c + 5c org & rose 1.10 1.00
Exists on both ordinary and chalky paper.

Curie Issue
Common Design Type
1938   *Engr.*   *Perf. 13*
B2 CD80 1.75fr + 50c brt ultra 7.50 7.50

French Revolution Issue
Common Design Type
1939   *Photo.*
Name and Value Typo. in Black
B3 CD83 45c + 25c green 7.50 7.50
B4 CD83 70c + 30c brown 7.50 7.50
B5 CD83 90c + 35c red org 7.50 7.50
B6 CD83 1.25fr + 1fr rose pink 7.50 7.50
B7 CD83 2.25fr + 2fr blue 7.50 7.50
    Nos. B3-B7 (5) 37.50 37.50
Set, never hinged 50.00

Stamps of 1938, Surcharged in Black

1941   *Unwmk.*   *Perf. 13*
B8 A8 50c + 1fr red brn 1.75 1.75
B9 A9 80c + 2fr rose vio 4.75 4.75
B10 A9 1.50fr + 2fr brn 4.75 4.75
B11 A10 2fr + 3fr magenta 4.75 4.75
    Nos. B8-B11 (4) 16.00 16.00

Common Design Type and

Senegalese Soldier SP1   Colonial Infantryman SP2

1941   *Unwmk.*   *Perf. 13*
B12 SP1 1fr + 1fr red 1.00
B13 CD86 1.50fr + 3fr maroon 1.00
B14 SP2 2.50fr + 1fr blue 1.00
    Nos. B12-B14 (3) 3.00

Nos. B12-B14 were issued by the Vichy government in France, but were not placed on sale in the French Guinea.

Nos. 166-167
Surcharged in Black or Red

1944   *Engr.*   *Perf. 12½x12*
B15 50c + 1.50fr on 2.50fr deep
    blue (R) .60
B16 + 2.50fr on 1fr green .60
Colonial Development Fund.
Nos. B15-B16 were issued by the Vichy government in France, but were not placed on sale in French Guinea.

AIR POST STAMPS

Common Design Type
1940   *Unwmk. Engr.*   *Perf. 12½x12*
C1 CD85 1.90fr ultra .45 .45
C2 CD85 2.90fr dark red .50 .50
C3 CD85 4.50fr dk gray grn .65 .65
C4 CD85 4.90fr yellow bis .65 .65
C5 CD85 6.90fr dp orange 1.00 1.00
    Nos. C1-C5 (5) 3.25 3.25

Common Design Types
1942   *Engr.*
C6 CD88 50c car & blue .20
C7 CD88 1fr brown & blk .20
C8 CD88 2fr dk grn & red brn .20
C9 CD88 3fr dk bl & scar .35
C10 CD88 5fr vio & brn red .55

Frame Engraved, Center Typographed
C11 CD89 10fr multicolored .55
C12 CD89 20fr multicolored .65
C13 CD89 50fr multicolored .85 2.50
    Nos. C6-C13 (8) 3.55

There is doubt whether Nos. C6-C12 were officially placed in use.

AIR POST SEMI-POSTAL STAMPS

Dahomey types SPAP1-SPAP3
inscribed "Guinée Frcaise" or "Guinée"
Perf. 13½x12½, 13 (#CB3)
Photo, Engr. (#CB3)
1942, June 22
CB1 SPAP1 1.50fr + 3.50fr
     green .60 3.75
CB2 SPAP2 2fr + 6fr brown .60 3.75
CB3 SPAP3 3fr + 9fr car red .60 3.75
    Nos. CB1-CB3 (3) 1.80 11.25
Native children's welfare fund.

Colonial Education Fund
Common Design Type
Perf. 12½x13½
1942, June 22   *Engr.*
CB4 CD86a 1.20fr + 1.80fr blue
     & red .65 3.50

POSTAGE DUE STAMPS

Fulah Woman D1   Heads and Coast D2

1905   *Unwmk. Typo.*   *Perf. 14x13½*
J1 D1 5c blue 1.40 1.40
J2 D1 10c brown 1.40 1.40
J3 D1 15c green 4.25 2.75
J4 D1 30c rose 4.25 2.75
J5 D1 50c black 7.25 7.25
J6 D1 60c dull orange 10.00 8.00
J7 D1 1fr violet 32.50 29.00
    Nos. J1-J7 (7) 61.05 52.55

"Guinèe" in Red or Blue
1906-08
J8 D2 5c grn, *grnsh* ('08) 16.00 10.50
J9 D2 10c violet brn ('08) 4.25 4.25
J10 D2 15c dk blue ('08) 4.25 4.25
J11 D2 20c blk, *yellow* 4.25 3.25
J12 D2 30c red, *straw* ('08) 22.50 20.00
J13 D2 50c violet ('08) 18.00 18.00
J14 D2 60c blk, *buff* ('08) 18.00 16.00
J15 D2 1fr blk, *pnksh* ('08) 11.00 9.00
    Nos. J8-J15 (8) 98.25 85.25

D3   D4

1914
J16 D3 5c green .20 .20
J17 D3 10c rose .20 .20
J18 D3 15c gray .35 .35
J19 D3 20c brown .50 .50
J20 D3 30c blue .50 .50
J21 D3 50c black .90 .70
J22 D3 60c orange 1.40 1.40
J23 D3 1fr violet 1.40 1.40
    Nos. J16-J23 (8) 5.45 5.25

Type of 1914 Issue
Surcharged

1927
J24 D3 2fr on 1fr lil rose 5.75 5.75
J25 D3 3fr on 1fr org brn 5.75 5.75

1938   *Engr.*
J26 D4 5c dk violet .20 .20
J27 D4 10c carmine .20 .20
J28 D4 15c green .20 .20
J29 D4 20c red brown .20 .20
J30 D4 30c rose violet .20 .20
J31 D4 50c chocolate .50 .50
J32 D4 60c peacock blue .80 .80
J33 D4 1fr vermilion .80 .80
J34 D4 2fr ultra .80 .80
J35 D4 3fr black 1.25 1.25
    Nos. J26-J35 (10) 5.15 5.15
For No. J27 without "RF," see No. J36.

Type of 1938 without "RF"
1944
J36 D4 10c carmine .35
No. J36 was issued by the Vichy government in France, but was not placed on sale in French Guinea.

FRENCH INDIA

ˈfrench ˈin-dē-ə

LOCATION — East coast of India bordering on Bay of Bengal.
GOVT. — French Territory
AREA — 196 sq. mi.
POP. — 323,295 (1941)
CAPITAL — Pondichéry

French India was an administrative unit comprising the five settlements of Chandernagor, Karikal, Mahé, Pondichéry and Yanaon. These united with India in 1949 and 1954.

100 Centimes = 1 Franc
24 Caches = 1 Fanon (1923)
8 Fanons = 1 Rupie

> Catalogue values for unused stamps in this country are for **Never Hinged** items, beginning with Scott 210 in the regular postage section, Scott B14 in the semi-postal section, and Scott C7 in the airpost section.

Navigation and Commerce — A1

A2

Perf. 14x13½
1892-1907   *Typo.*   *Unwmk.*
Colony Name in Blue or Carmine
1 A1 1c blk, *lil bl* .95 .70
2 A1 2c brn, *buff* 1.40 1.10
3 A1 4c claret, *lav* 1.75 1.60
4 A1 5c grn, *grnsh* 4.00 2.75
5 A1 10c blk, *lavender* 9.50 2.50
6 A1 10c red ('00) 3.25 1.75
7 A1 15c bl, quadrille paper 10.50 4.25
8 A1 15c gray, *lt gray* ('00) 25.00 22.50
9 A1 20c red, *grn* 5.25 4.00
10 A1 25c blk, *rose* 3.50 1.75
11 A1 25c blue ('00) 13.50 11.00
12 A1 30c brn, *bis* 47.50 40.00
13 A1 35c blk, *yel* ('06) 13.50 7.00
14 A1 40c red, *straw* 5.25 5.00
15 A1 45c blk, *gray grn* ('07) 4.00 3.50
16 A1 50c car, *rose* 5.25 5.00
17 A1 50c brn, *az* ('00) 12.00 12.00
18 A1 75c dp vio, *org* 7.00 7.00
19 A1 1fr brnz grn, *straw* 9.50 9.50
    Nos. 1-19 (19) 182.60 142.90

Perf. 13½x14 stamps are counterfeits.

Nos. 10 and 16
Surcharged in Carmine or Black

1903
20 A1 5c on 25c blk, *rose* 260.00 165.00
21 A1 10c on 25c blk, *rose* 275.00 180.00
22 A1 15c on 25c blk, *rose* 90.00 90.00
23 A1 40c on 50c car, *rose*
     (Bk) 425.00 325.00
    Nos. 20-23 (4) 1,050. 760.00

Counterfeits of Nos. 20-23 abound.

1903
Revenue Stamp Surcharged in Black
24 A2 5c gray blue 22.50 22.50
The bottom of the revenue stamps were cut off.

Brahma — A5

Kali Temple
near
Pondichéry
A6

1914-22   *Perf. 13½x14, 14x13½*

25	A5	1c gray & blk	.25	.20
26	A5	2c brn vio & blk	.25	.20
27	A5	2c grn & brn vio ('22)	.25	.20
28	A5	3c brown & blk	.30	.25
29	A5	4c orange & blk	.30	.25
30	A5	5c bl grn & blk	.45	.45
31	A5	5c vio brn & blk ('22)	.25	.25
32	A5	10c dp rose & blk	.95	.95
33	A5	10c grn & blk ('22)	.60	.60
34	A5	15c vio & blk	.75	.75
35	A5	20c org red & blk	1.25	1.25
36	A5	25c blue & blk	1.25	1.25
37	A5	25c ultra & fawn ('22)	.80	.80
38	A5	30c ultra & blk	2.40	2.40
39	A5	30c rose & blk ('22)	.90	.90
40	A6	35c choc & blk	1.40	1.40
41	A6	40c org red & blk	1.40	1.40
42	A6	45c bl grn & blk	1.40	1.40
43	A6	50c dp rose & blk	1.25	1.25
44	A6	50c ultra & bl ('22)	1.50	1.50
45	A6	75c blue & blk	2.75	2.75
46	A6	1fr yellow & blk	2.75	2.75
47	A6	2fr violet & blk	4.25	4.25
48	A6	5fr ultra & blk	1.90	1.90
49	A6	5fr rose & blk ('22)	3.50	3.50
		Nos. 25-49 (25)	33.05	32.80

For surcharges see Nos. 50-79, 113-116, 156A, B1-B5.

No. 34 Surcharged in
Various Colors

1922

50	A5	1c on 15c (Bk)	.60	.60
51	A5	2c on 15c (Bl)	.60	.60
53	A5	5c on 15c (R)	.60	.60
		Nos. 50-53 (3)	1.80	1.80

Stamps and Types of 1914-22
Surcharged with New Values in
Caches, Fanons and Rupies in Black,
Red or Blue:

1923-28

54	A5	1ca on 1c gray & blk (R)	.20	.20
55	A5	2ca on 5c vio brn & blk	.30	.30
a.		Horizontal pair, imperf. between	—	
56	A5	3ca on 3c brn & blk	.40	.40
57	A5	4ca on 4c org & blk	.60	.60
58	A5	6ca on 10c grn & blk	.65	.65
59	A6	6ca on 45c bl grn & blk (R)	.65	.65
60	A5	10ca on 20c dp red & bl grn ('28)	2.00	2.00
61	A5	12ca on 15c vio & blk	.65	.65
62	A5	15ca on 20c org & blk	1.00	1.00
63	A6	16ca on 35c lt bl & yel brn ('28)	2.00	2.00
64	A5	18ca on 30c rose & blk	1.75	1.75
65	A6	20ca on 45c grn & dl red ('28)	1.50	1.10
66	A5	1fa on 25c dp grn & rose red ('28)	2.75	2.75
67	A6	1fa3ca on 35c choc & blk (Bl)	.80	.80
68	A6	1fa6ca on 40c org & blk (R)	1.00	.90
69	A6	1fa12ca on 50c ultra & bl (Bl)	1.25	.90
70	A6	1fa12ca on 75c bl & blk (Bl)	1.00	.90
a.		Double surcharge	95.00	
71	A6	1fa16ca on 75c brn red & grn ('28)	2.50	2.25
72	A5	2fa9ca on 25c ultra & fawn (Bl)	1.00	.80
73	A6	2fa12ca on 1fr vio & dk brn ('28)	2.25	2.25
74	A6	3fa3ca on 1fr yel & blk ('28)	1.10	1.00
a.		Double surcharge	125.00	
75	A6	6fa6ca on 2fr vio & blk (Bl)	3.50	3.50
76	A6	1r on 1fr grn & dp bl (R) ('26)	7.00	5.00
77	A6	2r on 5fr rose & blk (R)	5.50	5.00
a.		Double surcharge	100.00	
78	A6	3r on 2fr gray & bl vio (R) ('26)	15.00	12.50
79	A6	5r on 5fr rose & blk, grnsh ('26)	19.00	19.00
		Nos. 54-79 (26)	75.35	69.35

Nos. 60, 63, 66 and 73 have the original value obliterated by bars.

A7

A8

1929

80	A7	1ca dk gray & blk	.20	.20
81	A7	2ca vio brn & blk	.20	.20
82	A7	3ca brn & blk	.20	.20
83	A7	4ca org & blk	.25	.25
84	A7	6ca gray grn & grn	.25	.25
85	A7	10ca brn, red & grn	.25	.25
86	A8	12ca grn & lt grn	.60	.60
87	A7	16ca brt bl & blk	.75	.75
88	A7	18ca brn red & ver	.75	.75
89	A7	20ca dk bl & grn, bluish	.60	.60
90	A8	1fa gray grn & rose red	.60	.55
91	A8	1fa6ca red org & blk	.60	.55
92	A8	1fa12ca dp bl & ultra	.60	.55

93	A8	1fa16ca rose red & grn	.75	.75
94	A8	2fa12ca brt vio & brn	1.00	.80
95	A8	6fa6ca dl vio & blk	1.00	.80
96	A8	1r gray grn & dp bl	.95	.80
97	A8	2r rose & blk	1.40	.95
98	A8	3r lt gray & gray lil	2.50	1.60
99	A8	5r rose & blk, grnsh	2.50	1.75
		Nos. 80-99 (20)	15.95	13.15

For overprints and surcharges see Nos. 117-134, 157-176, 184-209G.

Common Design Types
pictured following the introduction.

Colonial Exposition Issue
Common Design Types

1931			*Perf. 12½*	
100	CD70	10ca deep green	3.00	3.00
101	CD71	12ca violet	3.00	3.00
102	CD72	18ca red orange	3.00	3.00
103	CD73	1fa12ca dull blue	3.00	3.00
		Nos. 100-103 (4)	12.00	12.00

Paris International Exposition Issue
Common Design Types

1937			*Perf. 13*	
104	CD74	8ca dp violet	1.10	1.10
105	CD75	12ca dk green	1.10	1.10
106	CD76	16ca car rose	1.25	1.25
107	CD77	20ca dk brown	1.25	1.25
108	CD78	1fa12ca red	1.25	1.25
109	CD79	2fa12ca ultra	1.25	1.25
		Nos. 104-109 (6)	7.20	7.20

For overprints see Nos. 135-139, 177-181.

Colonial Arts Exhibition Issue
Souvenir Sheet
Common Design Type

1937			*Imperf.*	
110	CD79	5fa red violet	6.50	8.75

For overprint see No. 140.

New York World's Fair Issue
Common Design Type

1939		Engr.	*Perf. 12½x12*	
111	CD82	1fa12ca car lake	.95	.95
112	CD82	2fa12ca ultra	1.25	1.25

For overprints see Nos. 141-142, 182-183.

Temple
near
Pondichéry
and
Marshal
Petain
A9

1941		Engr.	*Perf. 12½x12*	
112A	A9	1fa16ca car & red	.50	
112B	A9	4fa4ca blue	.50	

Nos. 112A-112B were issued by the Vichy government in France, but were not placed on sale in French India.
For surcharges, see Nos. B13B-B13C.

Nos. 62, 64, 67, 72 Overprinted in
Carmine or Blue (#116):

a

**FRANCE
LIBRE**

b

1941		Unwmk.	*Perf. 13½x14*	
113	A5 (a)	15ca on 20c	62.50	62.50
114	A5 (a)	18ca on 30c	2.50	2.50
115	A6 (a)	1fa3ca on 35c	80.00	80.00
a.		Horiz. overprint	80.00	80.00
116	A5 (b)	2fa9ca on 25c	1,100.	800.00
a.		Overprint "a" (Bl)	975.00	800.00
b.		Overprint "b" (C)	1,500.	1,500.

Nos. 81-99 Overprinted Type "a" in
Carmine or Blue

1941				
117	A7	2ca (C)	9.50	9.50
118	A7	3ca (C)	2.75	2.75
119	A7	4ca (C)	6.50	6.50
120	A7	6ca (C)	2.00	2.00
121	A7	10ca (Bl)	3.00	3.00
122	A8	12ca (C)	2.25	2.25
123	A7	16ca (C)	2.40	2.40
123A	A7	18ca (Bl)	500.00	500.00
124	A7	20ca (C)	2.00	2.00
125	A8	1fa (Bl)	1.90	1.90
126	A8	1fa6ca (C)	2.75	2.75
127	A8	1fa12ca (C)	4.50	4.50
128	A8	1fa16ca (C)	2.25	2.25
129	A8	2fa12ca (C)	2.50	2.50
130	A8	6fa6ca (C)	2.50	2.50
131	A8	1r (C)	2.50	2.50
132	A8	2r (C)	2.50	2.50
133	A8	3r (C)	3.25	3.25
134	A8	5r (C)	7.50	7.50
		Nos. 117-123,124-134 (18)	62.55	62.55

Same Overprints on Paris Exposition
Issue of 1937

1941			*Perf. 13*	
135	CD74 (b)	8ca (C)	6.25	6.25
135A	CD74 (b)	8ca (Bl)	175.00	175.00
135B	CD74 (a)	8ca (C)	125.00	125.00
135C	CD74 (a)	8ca (Bl)	160.00	160.00
136	CD75 (a)	12ca (C)	3.50	3.50
137	CD76 (a)	16ca (Bl)	3.50	3.50
138	CD78 (a)	1fa12ca (C)	3.50	3.50
139	CD79 (a)	2fa12ca (C)	3.50	3.50
		Nos. 135-139 (8)	480.25	480.25

Inverted overprints exist.

Souvenir Sheet
No. 110 Overprinted "FRANCE LIBRE"
Diagonally in Blue Violet

Two types of overprint:
I — Overprint 37mm. With serifs.
II — Overprint 24mm, as type "a" shown above No. 113. No serifs.

1941		Unwmk.	*Imperf.*	
140	CD79	5fa red vio (I)	575.00	450.00
a.		Type II	600.00	600.00

Overprinted on New York World's Fair
Issue, 1939
Perf. 12½x12

141	CD82 (a)	1fa12ca (Bl)	2.40	2.40
142	CD82 (a)	2fa12ca (C)	2.75	2.75

Lotus
Flowers — A10

1942	Unwmk. Photo.		*Perf. 14x14½*	
143	A10	2ca brown	.25	.25
144	A10	3ca dk blue	.25	.25
145	A10	4ca emerald	.25	.25
146	A10	6ca dk orange	.25	.25
147	A10	12ca grnsh blk	.25	.25
148	A10	16ca rose violet	.25	.25
149	A10	20ca dk red brn	.50	.50
150	A10	1fa brt red	.55	.50
151	A10	1fa18ca slate blk	.70	.65
152	A10	6fa6ca brt ultra	1.25	1.25
153	A10	1r dull violet	.95	.95
154	A10	2r bister	1.25	1.10
155	A10	3r chocolate	1.25	1.25
156	A10	5r dk green	1.75	1.75
		Nos. 143-156 (14)	9.70	9.45

Stamps of 1923-39 Overprinted in
Blue or Carmine

c

d

1942-43   **Perf. 13½x14, 14x13½**
Overprinted on No. 64
156A A5 (c) 18ca on 30c (B) 210.00 175.00

Overprinted on #81-82, 84, 86-99
157	A7 (c)	2ca (C)	1.25	1.25
a.		Black overprint	150.00	125.00
158	A7 (c)	3ca (C)	1.25	1.25
159	A7 (c)	6ca (C)	1.10	1.10
160	A8 (d)	12ca (Bl)	2.75	2.75
161	A7 (c)	16ca (C)	1.10	1.10
162	A7 (c)	18ca (Bl)	1.25	1.25
163	A7 (c)	20ca (Bl)		
		('43)	5.00	4.00
164	A7 (c)	20ca (Bl)	1.10	1.10
165	A8 (d)	1fa (C)	1.10	1.10
166	A8 (d)	1fa6ca (C)	2.00	2.00
167	A8 (d)	1fa12ca (C)	1.25	1.25
168	A8 (d)	1fa16ca (Bl)	1.50	1.50
169	A8 (d)	2fa12ca (Bl)	62.50	62.50
170	A8 (d)	2fa12ca (C)	2.25	2.25
171	A8 (d)	6fa6ca (C)	2.75	2.75
172	A8 (d)	1r (C)	5.00	5.00
173	A8 (d)	2r (C)	4.75	4.75
174	A8 (d)	3r (C)	4.75	4.75
175	A8 (d)	3r (Bl)		
		('43)	125.00	125.00
176	A8 (d)	5r (C)	4.75	4.75
		Nos. 156A-176 (21)	442.40	406.40

**Same Overprints on Paris International
Exposition Issue of 1937
Perf. 13**
177	CD74 (c)	8ca (Bl)	5.00	4.50
178	CD75 (d)	12ca (Bl)	4.25	4.25
179	CD76 (d)	16ca (Bl)	975.00	975.00
180	CD78 (d)	1fa12ca (Bl)	2.00	2.00
181	CD79 (d)	2fa12ca (C)	2.40	2.40

**Same Overprint on New York World's
Fair Issue, 1939
Perf. 12½x12**
182	CD82 (d)	1fa12ca (Bl)	3.00	3.00
183	CD82 (d)	2fa12ca (C)	4.00	4.00

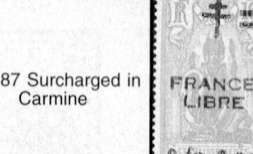

No. 87 Surcharged in
Carmine

1942-43   **Perf. 13½x14**
184	A7	1ca on 16ca	57.50	35.00
185	A7	4ca on 16ca ('43)	57.50	35.00
186	A7	10ca on 16ca	32.50	14.00
187	A7	15ca on 16ca	30.00	14.00
188	A7	1fa3ca on 16ca ('43)	55.00	29.00
189	A7	2fa9ca on 16ca ('43)	45.00	39.00
190	A7	3fa3ca on 16ca ('43)	32.50	17.00
		Nos. 184-190 (7)	310.00	183.00

Nos. 95-99 Surcharged in Carmine

1943   **Perf. 14x13½**
191	A8	1ca on 6fa6ca	6.75	6.75
192	A8	4ca on 6fa6ca	9.00	9.00
193	A8	10ca on 6fa6ca	2.50	2.50
194	A8	15ca on 6fa6ca	5.50	5.50
195	A8	1fa3ca on 6fa6ca	7.25	7.25
196	A8	2fa9ca on 6fa6ca	9.00	9.00
197	A8	3fa3ca on 6fa6ca	9.00	9.00
198	A8	1ca on 1r	3.50	3.50
199	A8	2ca on 1r	.95	.95
200	A8	4ca on 1r	.95	.95
201	A8	6ca on 2r	.95	.95
202	A8	10ca on 2r	1.25	1.25
203	A8	12ca on 2r	.95	.95
204	A8	16ca on 3r	.95	.95
205	A8	16ca on 3r	.85	.85
206	A8	1fa3ca on 3r	.95	.95
207	A8	1fa6ca on 5r	1.25	1.25
208	A8	1fa12ca on 5r	2.40	2.40
209	A8	1fa16ca on 5r	2.40	2.40
		Nos. 191-209 (19)	66.35	66.35

In 1943, 200 each of 27 stamps were overprinted in red or dark blue, "FRANCE TOUJOURS" and a Lorraine Cross within a circle measuring 17½mm in diameter. Overprinted were Nos. 81-99, 104-109, 111-112.

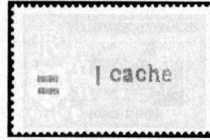

No. 95 Surcharged in Carmine with
New Value and Bars

1943   **Unwmk.**   **Perf. 14x13½**
209A	A8	1ca on 6fa6ca	21.00	15.00
209B	A8	4ca on 6fa6ca	21.00	15.00
209C	A8	10ca on 6fa6ca	11.00	6.50
209D	A8	15ca on 6fa6ca	11.00	6.50
209E	A8	1fa3ca on 6fa6ca	15.00	14.00
209F	A8	2fa9ca on 6fa6ca	15.00	14.00
209G	A8	3fa3ca on 6fa6ca	20.00	17.50
		Nos. 209A-209G (7)	114.00	88.50

> Catalogue values for unused stamps in this section, from this point to the end of the section, are for Never Hinged items.

Eboue Issue
Common Design Type
1945   **Engr.**   **Perf. 13**
210	CD91	3fa8ca black	.50	.50
211	CD91	5r1fa16ca Prus grn	.95	.95

Nos. 210 and 211 exist imperforate.

Apsaras — A11   Brahman
                                 Ascetic — A12

Designs: 6ca, 8ca, 10ca, Dvarabalagar. 12ca, 15ca, 1fa, Vishnu. 1fa6ca, 2fa, 2fa2ca, Dvarabalagar (foot raised). 2fa12ca, 3fa, 5fa, Temple Guardian. 7fa12ca, 1r2fa, 1r4fa12ca, Tigoupalagar.

1948   **Photo.**   **Perf. 13x13½**
212	A11	1ca dk ol grn	.20	.20
213	A11	2ca orange brn	.20	.20
214	A11	4ca vio, *cr*	.20	.20
215	A11	6ca yellow org	.85	.50
216	A11	8ca gray blk	.85	.85
217	A11	10ca dl yel grn, pale grn	.85	.85
218	A11	12ca violet brn	.55	.55
219	A11	15ca Prus grn	.55	.50
220	A11	1fa vio, pale rose	.85	.65
221	A11	1fa6ca brown red	.85	.65
222	A11	2fa dk green	.85	.65
223	A11	2fa2ca blue, *cr*	1.25	.85
224	A11	2fa12ca brown	1.25	.95
225	A11	3fa dp orange	1.75	.95
226	A11	5fa red vio, rose	1.60	.85
227	A11	7fa12ca dk brown	1.75	.85
228	A11	1r2fa brown blk	4.00	4.00
229	A11	1r4fa12ca olive grn	4.50	4.00
		Nos. 212-229 (18)	22.90	18.10

1952
230	A12	18ca rose red	1.25	1.25
231	A12	1fa15ca vio blue	1.75	1.75
232	A12	4fa olive grn	2.25	2.25
		Nos. 230-232 (3)	5.25	5.25

Military Medal Issue
Common Design Type
1952   **Engr. and Typo.**   **Perf. 13**
233 CD101 1fa multi 3.50 3.50

SEMI-POSTAL STAMPS

Regular Issue of
1914 Surcharged in
Red

1915   **Unwmk.**   **Perf. 14x13½**
B1 A5 10c + 5c rose & blk 1.25 1.25
a. Inverted surcharge 140.00 140.00

There were two printings of this surcharge; in the first it was placed at the bottom of the stamp, in the second it was near the top.

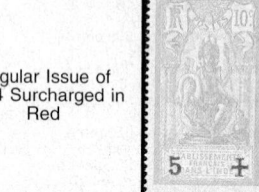

Regular Issue of
1914 Surcharged in
Red

1916
B2 A5 10c + 5c rose & blk 13.00 13.00
a. Inverted surcharge 140.00 140.00
b. Double surcharge 140.00 140.00

Surcharged

B3 A5 10c + 5c rose & blk 2.50 2.50

Surcharged

B4 A5 10c + 5c rose & blk 1.10 1.10

Surcharged

B5 A5 10c + 5c rose & blk 1.50 1.50

Curie Issue
Common Design Type
1938   **Engr.**   **Perf. 13**
B6 CD80 2fa12ca + 20ca brt ul-
        tra 7.25 7.25

French Revolution Issue
Common Design Type
1939   **Photo.**
Name and Value Typo. in Black
B7	CD83	18ca + 10ca grn	6.50	6.50
B8	CD83	1fa6ca + 12ca brn	6.50	6.50
B9	CD83	1fa12ca + 16ca red org	6.50	6.50

B10	CD83	1fa16ca + 1fa16ca rose pink	6.50	6.50
B11	CD83	2fa12ca + 3fa blue	6.50	6.50
		Nos. B7-B11 (5)	32.50	32.50

Common Design Type and

Non-Commissioned
Officer, Native
Guard — SP1

Sepoy
SP2

1941   **Photo.**   **Perf. 13½**
B12	SP1	1fa16ca + 1fa16ca red		.95
B13	CD86	2fa12ca + 5fa mar		.80
B13A	SP2	4fa4ca + 1fa16ca bl		.80
		Nos. B12-B13A (3)		2.55

Nos. B12-B13A were issued by the Vichy government in France, but were not placed on sale in French India.

Nos. 112A-112B
Surcharged in Black or Red

1944   **Engr.**   **Perf. 12½x12**
B13B	20ca + 2fa12ca on 4fa4ca deep blue (R)		.70
B13C	+ 4fa4ca on 1fa16ca car & red		.70

Colonial Development Fund.
Nos. B13B-B13C were issued by the Vichy government in France, but were not placed on sale in French India.

> Catalogue values for unused stamps in this section, from this point to the end of the section, are for Never Hinged items.

Red Cross Issue
Common Design Type
1944   **Photo.**   **Perf. 14½x14**
B14 CD90 3fa + 1r4fa dk ol brn .90 .90

The surtax was for the French Red Cross and national relief.

Tropical Medicine Issue
Common Design Type
1950   **Engr.**   **Perf. 13**
B15 CD100 1fa + 10ca ind & dp bl 2.50 2.50

The surtax was for charitable work.

AIR POST STAMPS

Common Design Type
1942   **Unwmk. Photo.**   **Perf. 14½x14**
C1	CD87	4fa dark orange	.75	.75
C2	CD87	1r bright red	.75	.75
C3	CD87	2r brown red	1.10	1.10
C4	CD87	5r black	1.10	1.10
C5	CD87	8r ultra	1.75	1.75
C6	CD87	10r dark green	1.75	1.75
		Nos. C1-C6 (6)	7.20	7.20

> Catalogue values for unused stamps in this section, from this point to the end of the section, are for Never Hinged items.

Victory Issue
Common Design Type

1946   **Engr.**   *Perf. 12½*
C7 CD92 4fa dk blue green   .75   .75

Chad to Rhine Issue
Common Design Types

1946, June 6
C8	CD93	2fa12ca olive bis	.75	.75
C9	CD94	5fa dark blue	.75	.75
C10	CD95	7fa12ca dk purple	1.10	1.10
C11	CD96	1r2fa green	1.10	1.10
C12	CD97	1r4fa12ca dk car	1.40	1.40
C13	CD98	3r1fa violet brn	2.40	2.40
		Nos. C8-C13 (6)	7.50	7.50

A 3r ultramarine and red, picturing the Temple of Chindambaram, was sold at Paris June 7 to July 8, 1948, but not placed on sale in the colony. Value $5.75.

Bas-relief Figure of Goddess — AP1

Wing and Temple — AP2

Bird over Palms — AP3

Perf. 12x13, 13x12
1949   **Photo.**   **Unwmk.**
C14	AP1	1r yellow & plum	4.00	2.75
C15	AP2	2r green & dk grn	4.00	3.50
C16	AP3	5r lt bl & vio brn	17.00	13.50
		Nos. C14-C16 (3)	25.00	19.75

UPU Issue
Common Design Type

1949   **Engr.**   *Perf. 13*
C17 CD99 6fa lilac rose   6.50   6.50

Universal Postal Union, 75th anniv.

Liberation Issue
Common Design Type

1954, June 6
C18 CD102 1fa sepia & vio brn   5.75   5.75

AIR POST SEMI-POSTAL STAMPS

Girl's School SPAP1

Perf. 12½x13½
1942, June 22   **Unwmk.**   **Photo.**
CB1	SPAP1	2fa12ca + 5fa20ca green	.75
CB2	SPAP1	3fa8ca + 1r2fa yel brn	.75

Native children's welfare fund.
Nos. CB1-CB2 were issued by the Vichy government in France, but were not placed on sale in French India.

Colonial Education Fund
Common Design Type

1942, June 22
CB3 CD86a 2fa + 3fa blue & red   .75

No. CB3 was issued by the Vichy government in France, but was not placed on sale in French India.

POSTAGE DUE STAMPS

Postage Due Stamps of France
Surcharged like Nos. 54-75 in Black,
Blue or Red
1923   **Unwmk.**   *Perf. 14x13½*
J1	D2	6ca on 10c brn	.80	.80
J2	D2	12ca on 25c rose (Bk)	.85	.85
J3	D2	15ca on 20c ol grn (R)	1.10	1.10
J4	D2	1fa6ca on 30c red	1.10	1.10
J5	D2	1fa12a on 50c brn vio	1.90	1.90
J6	D2	1fa15ca on 5c bl (Bk)	2.00	2.00
J7	D2	3fa3ca on 1fr red brn, straw	2.10	2.10
		Nos. J1-J7 (7)	9.85	9.85

Types of Postage Due Stamps of French Colonies, 1884-85, Surcharged with New Values as in 1923 in Red or Black Bars over Original Values
1928
J8	D1	4ca on 20c gray lil	1.10	1.10
J9	D1	1fa on 30c orange	2.10	2.10
J10	D1	1fa16ca on 5c bl blk (R)	2.10	2.10
J11	D1	3fa on 1fr lt grn	2.50	2.50
		Nos. J8-J11 (4)	7.80	7.80

D3

1929   **Typo.**
J12	D3	4ca deep red	.35	.35
J13	D3	6ca blue	.50	.50
J14	D3	12ca green	.50	.50
J15	D3	1fa brown	.95	.95
J16	D3	1fa12ca lilac gray	.95	.95
J17	D3	1fa16ca buff	1.25	1.25
J18	D3	3fa lilac	1.60	1.60
		Nos. J12-J18 (7)	6.10	6.10

D4

1948   **Unwmk.**   **Photo.**   *Perf. 13x13½*
J19	D4	1ca dk violet	.20	.20
J20	D4	2ca dk brown	.35	.35
J21	D4	6ca blue green	.35	.35
J22	D4	12ca dp orange	.50	.50
J23	D4	1fa dk car rose	.55	.55
J24	D4	1fa12ca brown	.55	.55
J25	D4	2fa dk slate bl	.95	.95
J26	D4	2fa12ca henna brn	1.25	1.25
J27	D4	5fa dk olive grn	1.75	1.75
J28	D4	1r dk blue vio	2.25	2.25
		Nos. J19-J28 (10)	8.70	8.70

FRENCH MOROCCO

'french mə-'rä-ₐkō

LOCATION — Northwest coast of Africa
GOVT. — French Protectorate
AREA — 153,870 sq. mi.
POP. — 8,340,000 (estimated 1954)
CAPITAL — Rabat

French Morocco was a French Protectorate from 1912 until 1956 when it, along with the Spanish and Tangier zones of Morocco, became the independent country, Morocco.

Stamps inscribed "Tanger" were for use in the international zone of Tangier in northern Morocco.

100 Centimos = 1 Peseta
100 Centimes = 1 franc (1917)

> Catalogue values for unused stamps in this country are for Never Hinged items, beginning with Scott 177 in the regular postage section, Scott B26 in the semipostal section, Scott C27 in the airpost section, Scott CB23A in the airpost semi-postal section, and Scott J46 in the postage due section.

French Offices in Morocco

A1

A2

Stamps of France Surcharged in Red or Black
1891-1900   **Unwmk.**   *Perf. 14x13½*
1	A1	5c on 5c grn, grnsh (R)	8.50	3.50
a.		Imperf., pair	110.00	
2	A1	5c on 5c yel grn (II) (R) ('99)	24.00	21.00
a.		Type I	24.00	17.50
3	A1	10c on 10c blk, lav (II) (R)	24.00	2.10
a.		Type I	29.00	16.00
b.		10c on 25c black, rose	775.00	
4	A1	20c on 20c red, grn	27.50	20.00
5	A1	25c on 25c blk, rose (R)	21.00	2.50
a.		Double surcharge	160.00	
b.		Imperf., pair	125.00	
6	A1	50c on 50c car, rose (II)	70.00	29.00
a.		Type I	300.00	210.00
7	A1	1p on 1fr brnz grn, straw	82.50	52.50
8	A1	2p on 2fr brn, az (Bk) ('00)	190.00	175.00
		Nos. 1-8 (8)	447.50	305.60

No. 3b was never sent to Morocco.

France Nos. J15-J16 Overprinted in Carmine
1893
9	A2	5c black	1,900.	800.00
10	A2	10c black	1,650.	575.00

Counterfeits exist.

A3

18srch

A5

Surcharged in Red or Black
1902-10
11	A3	1c on 1c gray (R) ('08)	1.40	.80
a.		Surcharge omitted		
12	A3	2c on 2c vio brn ('08)	1.40	.95
13	A3	3c on 3c red org ('08)	1.50	.95
14	A3	4c on 4c yel brn ('08)	7.75	5.25
15	A3	5c on 5c grn (R)	6.00	2.50
a.		Double surcharge		175.00
16	A4	10c on 10c rose red ('03)	4.50	1.50
a.		Surcharge omitted		
17	A4	20c on 20c brn vio ('03)	21.00	14.00
18	A4	25c on 25c bl ('03)	21.00	1.75
19	A4	35c on 35c vio ('10)	29.00	16.00
20	A5	50c on 50c bis brn & lav ('03)	40.00	9.25
21	A5	1p on 1fr cl & ol grn ('03)	82.50	55.00
22	A5	2p on 2fr gray vio & yel ('03)	110.00	67.50
		Nos. 11-22 (12)	326.05	175.45

Nos. 11-14 exist spelled CFNTIMOS or GENTIMOS.
The 25c on 25c with surcharge omitted is listed as No. 81a.
For overprints and surcharges see Nos. 26-37, 72-79, B1, B3.

Postage Due Stamps
Nos. J1-J2
Handstamped

1903
24	D2	5c on 5c light blue	1,100.	925.00
25	D2	10c on 10c choc	2,100.	1,600.

Nos. 24 and 25 were used only on Oct. 10, 1903. Used copies were not canceled, the overprint serving as a cancellation.
Counterfeits exist.

Types of 1902-10 Issue Surcharged in Red or Blue

1911-17
26	A3	1c on 1c gray (R)	.55	.50
27	A3	2c on 2c vio brn	.55	.50
28	A3	3c on 3c orange	.55	.50
29	A3	5c on 5c green (R)	.80	.35
30	A4	10c on 10c rose	.65	.35
a.		Imperf., pair	200.00	
31	A4	15c on 15c org ('17)	2.25	1.60
32	A4	20c on 20c brn vio	3.50	2.50
33	A4	25c on 25c blue (R)	1.75	1.25
34	A4	35c on 35c violet (R)	6.75	2.75
35	A5	40c on 40c red & pale bl ('17)	6.00	4.00
36	A5	50c on 50c bis brn & lav (R)	17.50	9.25
37	A5	1p on 1fr cl & ol grn	13.00	5.00
		Nos. 26-37 (12)	53.85	28.55

For surcharges see Nos. B1, B3.

Stamps of this design were issued by the Cherifien posts in 1912-13. The Administration Cherifinne des Postes, Telegraphes et Telephones was formed in 1911 under French guidance. See Morocco in Vol. 4 for listings.

French Protectorate

A6

A7

A8

Issue of 1911-17 Overprinted "Protectorat Francais"

1914-21
38	A6	1c on 1c gray	.45	.30
39	A6	2c on 2c vio brn	.45	.30
40	A6	3c on 3c orange	.80	.35
41	A6	5c on 5c green	.55	.35
a.		New value omitted	210.00	210.00
42	A7	10c on 10c rose	.45	.20
a.		New value omitted	450.00	450.00
43	A7	15c on 15c org ('17)	.65	.55
a.		New value omitted	82.50	82.50
44	A7	20c on 20c brn vio	3.50	2.10
a.		"Protectorat Francais" double	210.00	210.00
45	A7	25c on 25c blue	1.60	.35
a.		New value omitted	250.00	250.00
46	A7	25c on 25c violet ('21)	1.00	.20
a.		"Protectorat Francais" omitted	60.00	60.00
b.		"Protectorat Francais" dbl.	125.00	125.00
c.		"Protectorat Francais" dbl. (R + Bk)	125.00	125.00
47	A7	30c on 30c vio ('21)	12.00	6.75
48	A7	35c on 35c violet	4.00	1.25
49	A8	40c on 40c red & pale bl	12.00	6.50
a.		New value omitted	240.00	240.00
50	A8	45c on 45c grn & bl ('21)	32.50	29.00
51	A8	50c on 50c bis brn & lav	1.10	.35
a.		"Protectorat Francais" invtd.	110.00	110.00
b.		"Protectorat Francais" dbl.	175.00	175.00
52	A8	1p on 1fr cl & ol grn	2.40	.50
a.		"Protectorat Francais" invtd.	240.00	240.00
b.		New value double	140.00	140.00
c.		New value dbl., one invtd.	140.00	140.00
53	A8	2p on 2fr gray vio & yel	4.00	1.10
a.		"Protectorat Francais" omitted	125.00	125.00
b.		New value double	85.00	85.00
c.		New value dbl., one invtd.	125.00	125.00
54	A8	5p on 5fr dk bl & buff	10.50	3.25
		Nos. 38-54 (17)	87.95	53.40

For surcharges see Nos. B2, B4-B5.

Tower of Hassan, Rabat — A9

Mosque of the Andalusians, Fez — A10

City Gate Chella A11

Koutoubiah, Marrakesh A12

Bab Mansour, Meknes A13

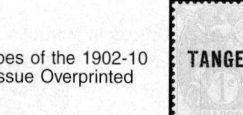

Roman Ruins, Volubilis A14

1917 Engr. Perf. 13½x14, 14x13½
55	A9	1c grnsh gray	.35	.35
56	A9	2c brown lilac	.50	.35
57	A9	3c orange brn	.50	.35
a.		Imperf., pair	65.00	65.00
58	A10	5c yellow grn	.50	.20
59	A10	10c rose red	.65	.20
60	A10	15c dark gray	.65	.20
a.		Imperf., pair	47.50	47.50
61	A11	20c red brown	2.50	1.75
62	A11	25c dull blue	2.90	.70
63	A11	30c gray violet	3.25	2.10
64	A12	35c orange	3.25	2.10
65	A12	40c ultra	1.25	.70
66	A12	45c gray green	21.00	8.50
67	A13	50c dk brown	4.00	2.10
a.		Imperf., pair	47.50	47.50
68	A13	1fr slate	8.50	2.75
a.		Imperf., pair	47.50	47.50
69	A14	2fr black brown	125.00	70.00
70	A14	5fr dk gray grn	32.50	29.00
71	A14	10fr black	32.50	29.00
		Nos. 55-71 (17)	239.80	150.35

See note following #115. See #93-105. For surcharges see #120-121.

Types of the 1902-10 Issue Overprinted

TANGER

1918-24 Perf. 14x13½
72	A3	1c gray	.30	.30
73	A3	2c violet brn	.35	.35
74	A3	3c red orange	.55	.55
75	A3	5c green	.55	.35
76	A3	5c orange ('23)	1.25	1.25
77	A4	10c rose	1.25	.95
78	A4	10c green ('24)	1.10	.95
79	A4	15c orange	1.10	.70
80	A4	20c violet brn	1.90	1.40
81	A4	25c blue	1.60	1.40
a.		"TANGER" omitted	325.00	300.00
82	A4	30c red org ('24)	1.90	1.90
83	A4	35c violet	2.25	1.75
84	A5	40c red & pale bl	2.50	1.60
85	A5	50c bis brn & lav	17.50	10.50
86	A4	50c blue	12.00	8.25
87	A5	1fr claret & ol grn	9.50	4.50
88	A5	2fr org & pale bl ('24)	57.50	55.00
89	A5	5fr dk bl & buff ('24)	47.50	47.50
		Nos. 72-89 (18)	160.60	139.20

Types of 1917 and

Tower of Hassan, Rabat — A15

Bab Mansour, Meknes A16

Roman Ruins, Volubilis A17

1923-27 Photo. Perf. 13½
90	A15	1c olive green	.20	.20
91	A15	2c brown vio	.20	.20
92	A15	3c yellow brn	.20	.20
93	A10	5c orange	.20	.20
94	A10	10c yellow grn	.20	.20
95	A10	15c dk gray	.20	.20
96	A11	20c red brown	.20	.20
97	A11	20c red vio ('27)	.45	.45
98	A11	25c ultra	.20	.20
99	A11	30c deep red	.20	.20
100	A11	30c turq bl ('27)	.85	.50
101	A12	35c violet	.80	.50
102	A12	40c orange red	.20	.20
103	A12	45c deep green	.20	.20
104	A16	50c dull turq	.20	.20
105	A12	50c olive grn ('27)	.65	.20
106	A16	60c lilac	.70	.20
107	A16	75c red vio ('27)	.70	.35
108	A16	1fr deep brown	.50	.35
109	A16	1.05fr red brn ('27)	1.40	.60
110	A16	1.40fr dull rose ('27)	.65	.50
111	A16	1.50fr turq bl ('27)	1.10	.25
112	A17	2fr olive brn	1.25	.75
113	A17	3fr dp red ('27)	1.50	.75
114	A17	5fr dk gray grn	3.00	1.75
115	A17	10fr black	8.50	3.75
		Nos. 90-115 (26)	24.60	13.30

Nos. 90-110, 112-115 exist imperf. The stamps of 1917 were line engraved. Those of 1923-27 were printed by photogravure and have in the margin at lower right the imprint "Helio Vaugirard."
See #B36. For surcharges see #122-123.

No. 102 Surcharged in Black

1930
120	A12	15c on 40c orange red	1.25	1.25

Nos. 100, 106 and 110 Surcharged in Blue Similarly to No. 176

1931
121	A11	25c on 30c turq blue	2.00	1.60
a.		Inverted surcharge	85.00	85.00
122	A16	50c on 60c lilac	.80	.25
a.		Inverted surcharge	95.00	95.00
123	A16	1fr on 1.40fr rose	2.50	1.25
a.		Inverted surcharge	95.00	95.00
		Nos. 121-123 (3)	5.30	3.10

Old Treasure House and Tribunal, Tangier A18

Roadstead at Agadir A19

Post Office at Casablanca A20

Moulay Idriss of the Zehroun A21

Kasbah of the Oudayas, Rabat A22

Court of the Medersa el Attarine at Fez A23

Saadiens' Tombs at Marrakesh A25

Kasbah of Si Madani el Glaoui at Ouarzazat A24

1933-34 Engr. Perf. 13
124	A18	1c olive blk	.20	.20
125	A18	2c red violet	.20	.20
126	A19	3c dark brown	.20	.20
127	A19	5c brown red	.20	.20
128	A20	10c blue green	.20	.20
129	A20	15c black	.20	.20
130	A20	20c red brown	.20	.20
131	A21	25c dark blue	.20	.20
132	A21	30c emerald	.35	.20
133	A21	40c black brn	.35	.20
134	A22	45c brown vio	.55	.50
135	A22	50c dk blue grn	.55	.20
a.		Booklet pane of 10	12.00	
b.		Booklet pane of 20	25.00	
136	A22	65c brown red	.20	.20
a.		Booklet pane of 10	12.00	
b.		Booklet pane of 20	25.00	
137	A23	75c red violet	.55	.20
138	A23	90c orange red	.35	.20
139	A23	1fr deep brown	.80	.35
140	A23	1.25fr black ('34)	1.10	.80
141	A24	1.50fr ultra	.35	.20
142	A24	1.75fr myr grn ('34)	.55	.20
143	A24	2fr yellow brn	3.25	.55
144	A24	3fr car rose	42.50	5.00
145	A25	5fr red brown	8.50	1.50
146	A25	10fr black	6.75	5.25
147	A25	20fr bluish gray	6.50	5.25
		Nos. 124-147 (24)	74.80	22.40

Booklets containing Nos. 135 and 136 each have two panes of 10 (#135a, 136a) connected by a gutter, the complete piece constituting No. 135b or 136b, which is stapled into the booklet through the gutter.

For surcharges see #148, 176, B13-B20.

No. 135 Surcharged in Red

1939
148	A22	40c on 50c dk bl grn	.55	.20

Mosque of Salé — A26

Sefrou — A27

Cedars — A28

Goatherd
A29

Ramparts
of
Salé — A30

Scimitar-horned
Oryxes — A31

Fez — A33

Valley of
Draa
A32

1939-42
149	A26	1c rose violet	.20	.20
150	A27	2c emerald	.20	.20
151	A27	3c ultra	.20	.20
152	A26	5c dk bl grn	.20	.20
153	A27	10c brt red vio	.20	.20
154	A28	15c dk green	.20	.20
155	A28	20c black grn	.20	.20
156	A29	30c deep blue	.20	.20
157	A29	40c chocolate	.20	.20
158	A29	45c Prus green	.55	.20
159	A30	50c rose red	1.50	.70
159A	A30	50c Prus grn ('40)	.20	.20
160	A30	60c turq blue	1.50	.55
160A	A30	60c choc ('40)	.20	.20
161	A31	70c dk violet	.20	.20
162	A32	75c grnsh blk	.35	.20
163	A32	80c pck bl ('40)	.20	.20
163A	A32	80c dk grn ('42)	.20	.20
164	A30	90c ultra	.20	.20
165	A28	1fr chocolate	.20	.20
165A	A32	1.20fr rose vio ('42)	.50	.20
166	A32	1.25fr henna brn	1.00	.50
167	A32	1.40fr rose violet	.35	.20
168	A30	1.50fr cop red ('40)	.20	.20
168A	A30	1.50fr rose ('42)	.20	.20
169	A33	2fr Prus green	.20	.20
170	A33	2.25fr dark blue	.50	.20
170A	A26	2.40fr red ('42)	.20	.20
171	A26	2.50fr scarlet	1.00	.50
171A	A26	2.50fr dp blue ('40)	.90	.50
172	A33	3fr black brown	.35	.20
172A	A26	4fr dp ultra ('42)	.20	.20
172B	A32	4.50fr grnsh blk ('42)	.55	.20
173	A31	5fr dark blue	.55	.35
174	A31	10fr red	.90	.55
174A	A31	15fr Prus grn ('42)	4.25	3.00
175	A31	20fr dk vio brn	1.60	1.40
		Nos. 149-175 (37)	20.55	13.65
		Set, never hinged	30.00	

See Nos. 197-219. For surcharges see Nos. 244, 261-262, B21-B24, B26, B28, B32.

No. 136 Surcharged in Black

1940
176	A22	35c on 65c brown red	1.40	.60
a.		Pair, one without surcharge	2.50	2.50

The surcharge was applied on alternate rows in the sheet, making No. 176a. This was done to make a pair equal 1fr, the new rate.

One Aim
Alone-Victory
A34

Tower of
Hassan,
Rabat
A35

1943   Litho.   Perf. 12
177	A34	1.50fr deep blue	.25	.20

1943
178	A35	10c rose lilac	.20	.20
179	A35	30c blue	.20	.20
180	A35	40c lake	.20	.20
181	A35	50c blue green	.20	.20
182	A35	60c dk vio brn	.20	.20
183	A35	70c rose violet	.20	.20
184	A35	80c gray green	.20	.20
185	A35	1fr car lake	.20	.20
186	A35	1.20fr violet	.20	.20
187	A35	1.50fr red	.20	.20
188	A35	2fr lt bl grn	.20	.20
189	A35	2.40fr car rose	.20	.20
190	A35	3fr olive brn	.20	.20
191	A35	4fr dk ultra	.20	.20
192	A35	4.50fr slate blk	.20	.20
193	A35	5fr dull blue	.35	.20
194	A35	10fr orange brn	.35	.20
195	A35	15fr slate grn	1.00	.50
196	A35	20fr deep plum	1.75	.65
		Nos. 178-196 (19)	6.45	4.55

Types of 1939-42
Perf. 13½x14, 14x13½
1945-47   Typo.   Unwmk.
197	A27	10c red violet	.20	.20
199	A29	40c chocolate	.20	.20
200	A30	50c Prus grn	.20	.20
203	A28	1fr choc ('46)	.20	.20
204	A32	1.20fr vio brn ('46)	.20	.20
205	A32	1.30fr blue ('47)	.35	.20
206	A30	1.50fr deep red	.20	.20
207	A33	2fr Prus grn	.20	.20
209	A33	3fr black brn	.20	.20
210	A29	3.50fr dk red ('47)	.50	.40
212	A31	4.50fr magenta ('47)	.20	.20
214	A31	5fr indigo	.55	.35
215	A32	6fr chlky bl ('46)	.30	.20
216	A31	10fr red	1.10	.55
217	A31	15fr Prus grn	1.25	.50
218	A31	20fr dk vio brn	1.40	1.00
219	A31	25fr black brn	1.90	1.75
		Nos. 197-219 (17)	9.15	6.75

For surcharges see #261-263, B26, B28, B32.

The
Terraces — A37

Mountain
District — A39

Fortress
A38

Marrakesh
A40

Gardens of
Fez — A41

Ouarzazat
District — A42

1947-48   Engr.   Unwmk.   Perf. 13
221	A37	10c black brn	.20	.20
222	A37	30c brt red	.20	.20
223	A37	50c brt grnsh bl	.20	.20
224	A37	60c brt red vio	.20	.20
225	A38	1fr black	.20	.20
226	A38	1.50fr blue	.20	.20
227	A39	2fr brt green	.40	.20
228	A39	3fr brown red	.30	.20
229	A40	4fr dk bl vio	.20	.20
230	A41	5fr dk green	.65	.40
231	A40	6fr crimson	.20	.20
232	A41	10fr dp blue ('47)	.55	.20
233	A42	15fr dk grn ('47)	1.00	.75
234	A42	20fr henna brn ('47)	.95	.40
235	A42	25fr purple ('47)	1.40	.40
		Nos. 221-235 (15)	6.85	4.15

1948-49
236	A37	30c purple	.20	.20
237	A38	2fr vio brn ('49)	.20	.20
238	A40	4fr green	.30	.20
239	A41	8fr org ('49)	.80	.50
240	A41	10fr blue	.55	.20
241	A42	10fr car rose	.35	.20
242	A38	12fr red	.55	.35
243	A42	18fr deep blue	1.10	.80
		Nos. 236-243 (8)	4.05	2.80

For surcharges see Nos. 263, 293-294.

No. 175 Surcharged with New Value and Wavy Lines in Carmine
1948
244	A31	8fr on 20fr dk vio brn	.70	.50

Fortified
Oasis
A43

Walled
City — A44

1949
245	A43	5fr blue green	.50	.20
246	A44	15fr red	.90	.20
247	A44	25fr ultra	.90	.35
		Nos. 245-247 (3)	2.30	.75

See No. 300.

Detail, Gate
of Oudayas,
Rabat — A45

Nejjarine
Fountain,
Fez — A46

Garden,
Meknes — A47

1949   Perf. 14x13
248	A45	10c black	.20	.20
249	A45	50c rose brn	.20	.20
250	A45	1fr blue vio	.20	.20
251	A46	2fr dk car rose	.20	.20
252	A46	3fr dark blue	.30	.20
253	A46	5fr brt green	.65	.20
254	A47	8fr dk bl grn	.85	.40
255	A47	10fr brt red	.85	.40
		Nos. 248-255 (8)	3.45	2.00

Postal Administration Building,
Meknes — A48

1949, Oct.   Perf. 13
256	A48	5fr dark green	1.50	1.40
257	A48	15fr deep carmine	1.60	1.50
258	A48	25fr deep blue	2.00	1.75
		Nos. 256-258 (3)	5.10	4.65

75th anniv. of the UPU.

Todra Valley
A49

1950
259	A49	35fr red brown	.95	.30
260	A49	50fr indigo	.95	.30

See No. 270.

Nos. 204 and 205 Surcharged in Black or Blue

1950   Perf. 14x13½, 13½x14
261	A32	1fr on 1.20fr vio brn (Bk)	.35	.20
262	A27	1fr on 1.30fr blue (Bl)	.35	.20

The surcharge is transposed and spaced to fit the design on No. 262.

No. 231 Surcharged with New Value and Wavy Lines in Black
1951   Perf. 13
263	A40	5fr on 6fr crimson	.25	.20

Statue of Gen.
Jacques
Leclerc — A50

1951, Apr. 28   Engr.
264	A50	10fr blue green	1.50	1.50
265	A50	15fr deep carmine	1.75	1.75
266	A50	25fr indigo	1.75	1.75
		Nos. 264-266 (3)	5.00	5.00

Unveiling of a monument to Gen. Leclerc at Casablanca, Apr. 28, 1951. See No. C39.

Loustau
Hospital,
Oujda
A51

Designs: 15fr, New Hospital, Meknes. 25fr, New Hospital, Rabat.

1951
267	A51	10fr indigo & pur	1.25	1.25
268	A51	15fr Prus grn & red brn	1.25	1.25
269	A51	25fr dk brn & ind	1.50	1.50
		Nos. 267-269 (3)	4.00	4.00

Todra Valley Type of 1950
1951
270	A49	30fr ultramarine	1.00	.25

Pigeons at
Fountain
A52

Karaouine
Mosque, Fez
A53

Patio,
Oudayas
A54

Oudayas
Point, Rabat
A55

Patio of Old
House — A56

MAROC
Type I (No. 275)

MAROC
Type II (No. 276)

Perf. 14x13, 13

1951-53		Engr.	Unwmk.	
271	A52	5fr magenta ('52)	.25	.20
272	A53	6fr bl grn ('52)	.45	.20
273	A52	8fr brown ('52)	.45	.20
273A	A53	10fr rose red ('53)	.45	.20
274	A53	12fr dp ultra ('52)	.75	.40
275	A54	15fr red brn (I)	3.50	.20
276	A54	15fr red brn (II)	1.25	.20
277	A55	15fr pur ('52)	1.25	.20
278	A55	15fr red ('52)	2.00	.75
279	A56	20fr dp grnsh bl ('52)	2.00	.50
		Nos. 271-279 (10)	12.35	3.05

See Nos. 297-299.

8th-10th Cent.
Capital
A57

Casablanca
Monument
A58

Capitals: 20fr, 12th Cent. 25fr, 13th-14th
Cent. 50fr, 17th Cent.

1952, Apr. 5			Perf. 13	
280	A57	15fr deep blue	2.75	1.90
281	A57	20fr red	2.75	1.90
282	A57	25fr purple	2.75	1.90
283	A57	50fr deep green	2.75	2.10
		Nos. 280-283 (4)	11.00	7.80

1952 Sept. 22			Engr. & Typo.	
284	A58	15fr multicolored	2.25	1.75

Creation of the French Military Medal, cent.

Daggers of
South Morocco
A59

Post Rider and
Public Letter-
writer
A60

Designs: 20fr and 25fr, Antique brooches.

1953, Mar. 27			Engr.	
285	A59	15fr dk car rose	2.50	2.25
286	A59	20fr violet brn	2.50	2.25
287	A59	25fr dark blue	2.50	2.25
		Nos. 285-287 (3)	7.50	6.75

See No. C46.

1953, May 16				
288	A60	15fr violet brown	1.40	1.40

Stamp Day, May 16, 1953.

Bine el
Ouidane
Dam — A61

1953, Nov. 3			Perf. 13	
290	A61	15fr indigo	1.50	1.10

See No. 295.

Mogador
Fortress — A62

Design: 30fr, Moorish knights.

1953, Dec. 4				
291	A62	15fr green	1.75	1.25
292	A62	30fr red brown	1.75	1.25

Issued to aid Army Welfare Work.

**Nos. 226 and 243 Surcharged with
New Value and Wavy Lines in Black**

1954				
293	A38	1fr on 1.50fr blue	.20	.20
294	A42	15fr on 18fr dp bl	1.00	.50

Dam Type of 1953

1954, Mar. 8				
295	A61	15fr red brn & indigo	.80	.80

Station of
Rural
Automobile
Post — A63

1954, Apr. 10				
296	A63	15fr dk blue grn	.80	.65

Stamp Day, April 10, 1954.

Types of 1951-53

1954		Engr.	Perf. 14x13	
297	A52	15fr dk blue green	.50	.20

Typo.

298	A52	5fr magenta	.50	.20
299	A55	15fr rose violet	.80	.25
		Nos. 297-299 (3)	1.80	.65

Walled City Type of 1949

1954		Engr.	Perf. 13	
300	A44	25fr purple	1.00	.35

Marshal
Lyautey at
Rabat
A64

Lyautey, Builder of
Cities — A65

Designs: 15fr, Marshal Lyautey at Khenifra.
50fr, Hubert Lyautey, Marshal of France.

1954, Nov. 17				
301	A64	5fr indigo	1.75	1.75
302	A64	15fr dark green	1.75	1.75
303	A65	30fr rose brown	2.50	2.50
304	A65	50fr dk red brn	2.50	2.50
		Nos. 301-304 (4)	8.50	8.50

Marshal Hubert Lyautey, birth cent.

Franco-Moslem Education — A66

Moslem Student at
Blackboard — A67

Designs: 30fr, Moslem school at Camp
Boulhaut. 50fr, Moulay Idriss College at Fez.

1955, Apr. 16		Unwmk.	Perf. 13	
305	A66	5fr indigo	1.25	1.25
306	A67	15fr rose lake	1.40	1.40
307	A66	30fr chocolate	1.40	1.40
308	A67	50fr dk blue grn	1.75	1.75
		Nos. 305-308 (4)	5.80	5.80

Franco-Moslem solidarity.

Map and
Rotary
Emblem
A68

1955, June 11				
309	A68	15fr bl & org brn	1.00	.80

Rotary Intl., 59th anniv.

Post Office,
Mazagan
A69

1955, May 24				
310	A69	15fr red	1.00	.50

Stamp Day.

Bab el
Chorfa, Fez
A70

Mahakma
(Courthouse),
Casablanca
A71

Fortress,
Safi — A72

Designs: 50c, 1fr, 2fr, 3fr, Mrissa Gate,
Salé. 10fr, 12fr, 15fr, Minaret at Rabat. 30fr,
Menara Garden Marrakesh. 40fr, Tafraout Vil-
lage. 50fr, Portuguese cistern, Mazagan. 75fr,
Garden of Oudaya, Rabat.

1955		Perf. 13½x13, 13x13½, 13		
311	A70	50c brn vio	.20	.20
312	A70	1fr blue	.20	.20
313	A70	2fr red lilac	.20	.20
314	A70	3fr bluish blk	.20	.20
315	A70	5fr vermilion	.80	.20
316	A70	6fr green	.35	.20
317	A70	8fr orange brn	.70	.35
318	A70	10fr violet brn	.95	.20
319	A70	12fr greenish bl	.50	.35
320	A70	15fr magenta	.80	.20
321	A71	18fr dk green	1.00	.60
322	A71	20fr brown lake	.60	.20
323	A72	25fr brt ultra	1.60	.20
324	A72	30fr green	1.40	.35
325	A72	40fr orange red	1.40	.20
326	A72	50fr black brn	4.00	.35
327	A71	75fr greenish bl	1.40	.70
		Nos. 311-327 (17)	16.30	4.90

Succeeding issues, released under the
Kingdom, are listed under Morocco in Vol. 4.

SEMI-POSTAL STAMPS

French Protectorate

No. 30 Surcharged in Red   5c

1914		Unwmk.	Perf. 14x13½	
B1	A4	10c + 5c on 10c	18,500.	22,000.

Known only with inverted red surcharge.

Same Surcharge on No. 42 with
"Protectorat Francais"

B2	A7	10c + 5c on 10c		
		rose	4.25	4.25
a.		Double surcharge	125.00	125.00
b.		Inverted surcharge	140.00	140.00
c.		"c" omitted	67.50	67.50

On Nos. B1 and B2 the cross is set up from
pieces of metal (quads), the horizontal bar
being made from two long pieces, the vertical
bar from two short pieces. Each cross in the
setting of twenty-five differs from the others.

No. 30 Handstamp   5c
Surcharged in Red

B3	A4	10c + 5c on 10c		
		rose	1,250.	975.

No. B3 was issued at Oujda. The surcharge
ink is water-soluble.

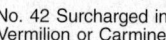

No. 42 Surcharged in
Vermilion or Carmine

B4	A7	10c + 5c on 10c		
		(V)	16.00	16.00
a.		Double surcharge	160.00	160.00
b.		Inverted surcharge	160.00	160.00
c.		Double surch., one invtd.	140.00	140.00
B5	A7	10c +5c on 10c (C)	350.00	400.00

On #B4-B5 the horizontal bar of the cross is
single and not as thick as on #B1-B2.
No. B5 was sold largely at Casablanca.

SP1

SP2

Carmine Surcharge
1915
B6 SP1 5c + 5c green   2.25 1.75
  a. Inverted surcharge   225.00 225.00
B7 SP2 10c + 5c rose   3.00 3.00

No. B6 was not issued without the Red Cross surcharge. No. B7 was also used in Tangier.

SP3   SP4

France No. B2 Overprinted in Black
B8 SP3 10c + 5c red   5.25 5.25

Carmine Surcharge
1917
B9 SP4 10c + 5c on 10c rose   2.10 2.10

On No. B9 the horizontal bar of the cross is made from a single, thick piece of metal.

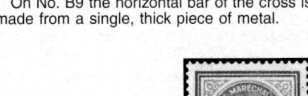
Marshal Hubert Lyautey — SP5

1935, May 15 Photo. Perf. 13x13½
B10 SP5 50c + 50c red   8.25 8.25
B11 SP5 1fr + 1fr dk grn   8.25 8.25
B12 SP5 5fr + 5fr blk brn   32.50 32.50
  Nos. B10-B12 (3)   49.00 49.00
  Set, never hinged   110.00

Stamps of 1933-34 Surcharged in Blue or Red

1938   Perf. 13
B13 A18 2c + 2c red vio   4.00 4.00
B14 A19 3c + 3c dk brn   4.00 4.00
B15 A20 20c + 20c red brn   4.00 4.00
B16 A21 40c + 40c blk brn (R) 4.00 4.00
B17 A22 65c + 65c brn red   4.00 4.00
B18 A23 1.25fr + 1.25fr blk (R) 4.00 4.00
B19 A24 2fr + 2fr yel brn   4.00 4.00
B20 A25 5fr + 5fr red brn   4.00 4.00
  Nos. B13-B20 (8)   32.00 32.00
  Set, never hinged   45.00

Stamps of 1939 Surcharged in Black

1942
B21 A29 45c + 2fr Prus grn   3.50 3.50
B22 A30 90c + 4fr ultra   3.50 3.50
B23 A32 1.25fr + 6fr henna brn 3.50 3.50
B24 A26 2.50fr + 8fr scarlet 3.50 3.50
  Nos. B21-B24 (4)   14.00 14.00
  Set, never hinged   22.50

The arrangement of the surcharge differs slightly on each denomination.

Catalogue values for unused stamps in this section, from this point to the end of the section, are for Never Hinged items.

No. 207 Surcharged in Black

1945   Unwmk.   Perf. 13½x14
B26 A33 2fr + 1fr Prus green   .40 .35
  For surcharge see No. B28.

Mausoleum of Marshal Lyautey — SP7 / Statue of Marshal Lyautey — SP8

1945   Litho.   Perf. 11½
B27 SP7 2fr + 3fr dark blue   .50 .20
  The surtax was for French works of solidarity.

No. B26 Surcharged in Red

1946   Perf. 13½x14
B28 A33 3fr (+ 1fr) on 2fr + 1fr .20 .20

Perf. 13½x14, 13
1946, Dec. 16   Engr.
B29 SP8 2fr + 10fr black   1.25 1.25
B30 SP8 3fr + 15fr cop red   1.25 1.25
B31 SP8 10fr + 20fr brt bl   2.00 2.00
  Nos. B29-B31 (3)   4.50 4.50
The surtax was for works of solidarity.

No. 212 Surcharged in Rose Violet

1947, Mar. 15   Perf. 13½x14
B32 A31 4.50fr + 5.50fr magenta 2.50 1.50
  Stamp Day, 1947.

Map and Symbols of Prosperity from Phosphates SP9

1947   Perf. 13
B33 SP9 4.50fr + 5.50fr green   1.00 .70
25th anniv. of the exploitations of the Cherifien Office of Phosphates.

Power — SP10 / Health — SP11

1948, Feb. 9
B34 SP10 6fr + 9fr red brn   2.00 2.00
B35 SP11 10fr + 20fr dp ultra 2.00 2.00
The surtax was for combined works of Franco-Moroccan solidarity.

Type of Regular Issue of 1923, Inscribed: "Journee du Timbre 1948"
1948, Mar. 6
B36 A16 6fr + 4fr red brown   1.10 .70
  Stamp Day, Mar. 6, 1948.

Battleship off Moroccan Coast SP12

1948, Aug.
B37 SP12 6fr + 9fr purple   2.00 1.10
  The surtax was for naval charities.

Wheat Field near Meknes SP13

Designs: 2fr+5fr, Olive grove, Taroudant. 3fr+7fr, Net and coastal view. 5fr+10fr, Aguedal Gardens, Marrakesh.

1949, Apr. 12   Engr.   Unwmk.
Inscribed: "SOLIDARITÉ 1948"
B38 SP13 1fr + 2fr orange   1.25 1.25
B39 SP13 2fr + 5fr car   1.25 1.25
B40 SP13 3fr + 7fr pck bl   1.25 1.25
B41 SP13 5fr + 10fr dk brn vio 1.25 1.25
  a. Sheet of 4, #B38-B41   14.00 14.00
  Nos. B38-B41,CB31-CB34 (8)   10.60 10.60

Gazelle Hunter, from 1899 Local Stamp SP14

1949, May 1
B42 SP14 10fr + 5fr choc & car rose 1.10 1.10
Stamp Day and 50th anniversary of Mazagan-Marrakesh local postage stamp.

Moroccan Soldiers, Flag SP15 / Rug Weaving SP16

1949
B43 SP15 10fr + 10fr bright red 1.00 1.00
The surtax was for Army Welfare Work.

1950, Apr. 11
Designs: 2fr+5fr, Pottery making, 3fr+7fr, Bookbinding. 5fr+10fr, Copper work.
Inscribed: "SOLIDARITE 1949"
B44 SP16 1fr + 2fr dp car   1.60 1.60
B45 SP16 2fr + 5fr dk brnsh bl 1.75 1.75
B46 SP16 3fr + 7fr dk pur   1.75 1.75
B47 SP16 5fr + 10fr red brn   1.75 1.75
  a. Sheet of 4, #B44-B47   14.00 14.00
  Nos. B44-B47,CB36-CB39 (8)   12.45 12.45

Ruins of Sala Colonia at Chella SP17

1950, Sept. 25   Engr.   Perf. 13
B48 SP17 10fr + 10fr dp magenta 1.50 1.50
B49 SP17 15fr + 15fr indigo   1.50 1.50
The surtax was for Army Welfare Work.

AIR POST STAMPS
French Protectorate

Biplane over Casablanca AP1

1922-27   Photo. Unwmk.   Perf. 13½
C1 AP1 5c dp orange ('27)   .35 .35
C2 AP1 25c dp ultra   .85 .50
C3 AP1 50c grnsh blue   .35 .35
C4 AP1 75c dp blue   62.50 9.25
C5 AP1 75c dp green   .50 .20
C6 AP1 80c vio brn ('27)   1.40 .35
C7 AP1 1fr vermilion   .80 .35
C8 AP1 1.40fr brn lake ('27)   2.00 .95
C9 AP1 1.90fr dp blue ('27)   2.00 1.40
C10 AP1 2fr black vio   1.90 .80
  a. 2fr deep violet   1.90 1.10
C11 AP1 3fr gray blk   2.00 1.35
  Nos. C1-C11 (11)   74.65 15.85

The 25c, 50c, 75c deep green and 1fr each were printed in two of three types, differing in frameline thickness, or hyphen in "Helio-Vaugirard" imprint.

Imperf., Pairs
C1a AP1 5c   42.50
C2a AP1 25c   55.00
C3a AP1 50c   42.50
C4a AP1 75c   475.00
C5a AP1 75c   60.00
C6a AP1 80c   47.50
C7a AP1 1fr   55.00
C10b AP1 2fr   175.00

Nos. C8-C9 Surcharged in Blue or Black

1931, Apr. 10
C12 AP1 1fr on 1.40fr   1.40 1.40
  a. (B)   —
  a. Inverted surcharge   240.00 240.00
C13 AP1 1.50fr on 1.90fr   1.40 1.40
  (Bk)

Rabat and Tower of Hassan AP2

Casablanca
AP3

1933, Jan.   **Engr.**
C14	AP2	50c dark blue	.60	.50
C15	AP2	80c orange brn	.60	.45
C16	AP2	1.50fr brown red	.60	.50
C17	AP3	2.50fr carmine rose	4.25	.85
C18	AP3	5fr violet	2.10	1.25
C19	AP3	10fr blue green	.80	.80
		Nos. C14-C19 (6)	8.95	4.35

For surcharges see Nos. CB22-CB23.

Storks and Minaret, Chella — AP4

Plane and Map of Morocco AP5

1939-40   **Perf. 13**
C20	AP4	80c Prus green	.20	.20
C21	AP4	1fr dk red	.20	.20
C22	AP5	1.90fr ultra	.30	.20
C23	AP5	2fr red vio ('40)	.30	.20
C24	AP5	3fr chocolate	.30	.20
C25	AP4	5fr violet	1.10	.60
C26	AP5	10fr turq blue	1.00	.35
		Nos. C20-C26 (7)	3.40	1.95

> Catalogue values for unused stamps in this section, from this point to the end of the section, are for Never Hinged items.

Plane over Oasis — AP6

1944   **Litho.**   **Perf. 11½**
C27	AP6	50c Prus grn	.25	.20
C28	AP6	2fr ultra	.25	.20
C29	AP6	5fr scarlet	.25	.20
C30	AP6	10fr violet	1.00	1.00
C31	AP6	50fr black	1.50	1.50
C32	AP6	100fr dp bl & red	2.75	2.75
		Nos. C27-C32 (6)	6.00	5.85

For surcharge see No. CB24.

Plane AP7

1945   **Engr.**   **Perf. 13**
C33	AP7	50fr sepia	.80	.70

Moulay Idriss — AP8

La Medina AP9

1947-48
C34	AP8	9fr dk rose car	.20	.20
C35	AP8	40fr dark blue	.65	.35
C36	AP8	50fr dp claret ('47)	.85	.20
C37	AP9	100fr dp grnsh bl	1.90	.80
C38	AP9	200fr henna brn	4.00	1.25
		Nos. C34-C38 (5)	7.60	2.80

Leclerc Type of Regular Issue

1951, Apr. 28
C39	A50	50fr purple	2.00	1.75

Unveiling of a monument to Gen. Leclerc at Casablanca, Apr. 28, 1951.

Kasbah of the Oudayas, Rabat AP11

1951, May 22
C40	AP11	300fr purple	14.50	7.75

Ben Smine Sanatorium AP12

1951, June 4
C41	AP12	50fr pur & Prus grn	3.00	2.10

Fortifications, Chella — AP13

Plane Near Marrakesh AP14

Fort, Anti-Atlas Mountains AP15   View of Fez AP16

1952, Apr. 19   **Unwmk.**   **Perf. 13**
C42	AP13	10fr blue green	.70	.35
C43	AP14	40fr red	1.10	.35
C44	AP15	100fr brown	2.25	.55
C45	AP16	200fr purple	6.00	4.25
		Nos. C42-C45 (4)	10.05	5.50

Antique Brooches — AP17

1953, Mar. 27
C46	AP17	50fr dark green	2.75	2.10

"City" of the Agdal, Meknes AP18

20fr, Yakoub el Mansour, Rabat. 40fr, Ainchock, Casablanca. 50fr, El Aliya, Fedala.

1954, Mar. 8
C47	AP18	10fr olive brown	2.10	1.90
C48	AP18	20fr purple	2.10	1.90
C49	AP18	40fr red brown	2.25	2.00
C50	AP18	50fr deep green	2.25	2.00
		Nos. C47-C50 (4)	8.70	7.80

Franco-Moroccan solidarity.

Naval Vessel and Sailboat AP19   Village in the Anti-Atlas AP20

"Ksar es Souk," Rabat and Plane AP21

1954, Oct. 18
C51	AP19	15fr dk blue green	1.75	1.25
C52	AP19	30fr violet blue	2.25	1.60

1955, July 25   **Engr.**   **Perf. 13**

200fr, Estuary of Bou Regreg, Rabat and Plane.
C53	AP20	100fr brt violet	1.75	.35
C54	AP20	200fr brt carmine	3.50	.80
C55	AP21	500fr grnsh blue	9.00	2.75
		Nos. C53-C55 (3)	14.25	3.90

AIR POST SEMI-POSTAL STAMPS

French Protectorate

Moorish Tribesmen SPAP1

Designs: 25c, Moor plowing with camel and burro. 50c, Caravan nearing Saffi. 75c, Walls, Marrakesh. 80c, Sheep grazing at Azrou. 1fr, Gate at Fez. 1.50fr, Aerial view of Tangier. 2fr, Aerial view of Casablanca. 3fr, Storks on old wall, Rabat. 5fr, Moorish fete.

Perf. 13½

1928, July 26   **Photo.**   **Unwmk.**
CB1	SPAP1	5c dp blue	4.00	4.00
CB2	SPAP1	25c brn org	4.00	4.00
CB3	SPAP1	50c red	4.00	4.00
CB4	SPAP1	75c org brn	4.00	4.00
CB5	SPAP1	80c olive grn	4.00	4.00
CB6	SPAP1	1fr orange	4.00	4.00
CB7	SPAP1	1.50fr Prus bl	4.00	4.00
CB8	SPAP1	2fr dp brown	4.00	4.00

CB9	SPAP1	3fr dp violet	4.00	4.00
CB10	SPAP1	5fr brown blk	4.00	4.00
		Nos. CB1-CB10 (10)	40.00	40.00

These stamps were sold in sets only and at double their face value. The money received for the surtax was divided among charitable and social organizations. The stamps were not sold at post offices but solely by subscription to the Moroccan Postal Administration.

Overprinted in Red or Blue (25c, 50c, 75c, 1fr)

1929, Feb. 1
CB11	SPAP1	5c dp blue	4.00	4.00
CB12	SPAP1	25c brown org	4.00	4.00
CB13	SPAP1	50c red	4.00	4.00
CB14	SPAP1	75c org brn	4.00	4.00
CB15	SPAP1	80c olive grn	4.00	4.00
CB16	SPAP1	1fr orange	4.00	4.00
CB17	SPAP1	1.50fr Prus bl	4.00	4.00
CB18	SPAP1	2fr dp brown	4.00	4.00
CB19	SPAP1	3fr dp violet	4.00	4.00
CB20	SPAP1	5fr brown blk	4.00	4.00
		Nos. CB11-CB20 (10)	40.00	40.00

These stamps were sold at double their face values and only in Tangier. The surtax benefited various charities.

Marshal Hubert Lyautey SPAP10

1935, May 15   **Perf. 13½**
CB21	SPAP10	1.50fr + 1.50fr blue	17.00	17.00

Nos. C14, C19 Surcharged in Red

1938   **Perf. 13**
CB22	AP2	50c + 50c dk bl	4.50	4.50
CB23	AP3	10fr + 10fr bl grn	4.50	4.50

> Catalogue values for unused stamps in this section, from this point to the end of the section, are for Never Hinged items.

Plane over Oasis SPAP11   Statue of Marshal Lyautey SPAP12

1944   **Litho.**   **Perf. 11½**
CB23A	SPAP11	1.50fr + 98.50fr	1.50	1.25

The surtax was for charity among the liberated French.

No. C29
Surcharged in Black

1946, June 18 — *Perf. 11*
CB24 AP6 5fr + 5fr scarlet .80 .70
6th anniv. of the appeal made by Gen. Charles de Gaulle, June 18, 1940. The surtax was for the Free French Association of Morocco.

1946, Dec. — **Engr.** — *Perf. 13*
CB25 SPAP12 10fr +30fr dk grn 1.60 1.60
The surtax was for works of solidarity.

Replenishing Stocks of
Food — SPAP13

Agriculture
SPAP14

1948, Feb. 9 — **Unwmk.**
CB26 SPAP13 9fr +26fr dp grn 2.00 1.50
CB27 SPAP14 20fr +35fr brown 2.00 1.50
The surtax was for combined works of Franco-Moroccan solidarity.

Tomb of Marshal
Hubert
Lyautey — SPAP15

1948, May 18 — *Perf. 13*
CB28 SPAP15 10fr +25fr dk grn .95 .95
Lyautey Exposition, Paris, June, 1948.

P.T.T.
Clubhouse
SPAP16

1948, June 7 — **Engr.**
CB29 SPAP16 6fr + 34fr dk grn 2.00 1.50
CB30 SPAP16 9fr + 51fr red brn 2.00 1.50
The surtax was used for the Moroccan P.T.T. employees vacation colony at Ifrane.

View of Agadir
SPAP17

Plane over
Globe
SPAP18

Designs: 6fr+9fr, Fez. 9fr+16fr, Atlas Mountains. 15fr+25fr, Valley of Draa.

1949, Apr. 12 — *Perf. 13*
Inscribed: "SOLIDARITÉ 1948"
CB31 SPAP17 5fr +5fr dk grn 1.40 1.40
CB32 SPAP17 6fr +9fr org red 1.40 1.40
CB33 SPAP17 9fr +16fr blk brn 1.40 1.40
CB34 SPAP17 15fr +25fr ind 1.40 1.40
a. Sheet of 4, #CB31-CB34 16.00 16.00
Nos. CB31-CB34 (4) 5.60 5.60

1950, Mar. 11 — **Engr. & Typo.**
CB35 SPAP18 15fr + 10fr bl grn & car .85 .85
Day of the Stamp, Mar. 11-12, 1950, and 25th anniv. of the 1st post link between Casablanca and Dakar.

Scenes and
Map:
Northwest
Corner
SPAP19

Designs (quarters of map): 6fr+9fr, NE, 9fr+16fr, SW. 15fr+25fr, SE.

1950, Apr. 11 — **Engr.**
Inscribed: "SOLIDARITE 1949"
CB36 SPAP19 5fr +5fr dp ultra 1.40 1.40
CB37 SPAP19 6fr +9fr Prus grn 1.40 1.40
CB38 SPAP19 9fr +16fr dk brn 1.40 1.40
CB39 SPAP19 15fr +25fr brn red 1.40 1.40
a. Sheet of 4, #CB36-CB39 16.00 16.00
Nos. CB36-CB39 (4) 5.60 5.60

Arch of
Triumph of
Caracalla at
Volubilis
SPAP20

1950, Sept. 25 — **Unwmk.**
CB40 SPAP20 10fr + 10fr sepia 1.25 1.25
CB41 SPAP20 15fr + 15fr bl grn 1.25 1.25
The surtax was for Army Welfare Work.

Casablanca
Post Office
and First
Air Post
Stamp
SPAP21

1952, Mar. 8 — *Perf. 13*
CB42 SPAP21 15fr + 5fr red brn & dp grn 4.00 4.00
Day of the Stamp, Mar. 8, 1952, and 30th anniv. of French Morocco's 1st air post stamp.

POSTAGE DUE STAMPS

French Offices in Morocco

Postage Due Stamps
and Types of France
Surcharged in Red or
Black

1896 — **Unwmk.** — *Perf. 14x13½*
On Stamps of 1891-93
J1 D2 5c on 5c lt bl (R) 5.75 3.50
J2 D2 10c on 10c choc (R) 8.50 3.50
J3 D2 30c on 30c car 21.00 16.00
a. Pair, one without surcharge
J4 D2 50c on 50c lilac 21.00 16.00
a. "S" of "CENTIMOS" omitted 240.00 175.00
J5 D2 1p on 1fr lil brn 275.00 250.00

1909-10 — **On Stamps of 1908-10**
J6 D3 1c on 1c ol grn (R) 1.75 1.75
J7 D3 10c on 10c violet 26.00 22.50
J8 D3 30c on 30c bister 32.50 29.00
J9 D3 50c on 50c red 45.00 45.00
Nos. J6-J9 (4) 105.25 98.25

Postage Due Stamps of
France Surcharged in
Red or Blue

1911 — **On Stamps of 1893-96**
J10 D2 5c on 5c blue (R) 2.90 2.90
J11 D2 10c on 10c choc (R) 11.00 11.00
a. Double surcharge 110.00 110.00
J12 D2 50c on 50c lil (BI) 13.00 13.00
On Stamps of 1908-10
J13 D3 1c on 1c ol grn (R) 1.75 1.75
J14 D3 10c on 10c vio (R) 5.25 5.25
J15 D3 30c on 30c bis (R) 5.75 5.75
J16 D3 50c on 50c red (BI) 11.00 11.00
Nos. J10-J16 (7) 50.65 50.65
For surcharges see Nos. JN23-J26.

French Protectorate

D4   D5

Type of 1911 Issue Overprinted
"Protectorat Francais"

1915-17
J17 D4 1c on 1c black .35 .35
a. New value double 125.00
J18 D4 5c on 5c blue 1.40 1.10
J19 D4 10c on 10c choc 1.75 1.25
J20 D4 20c on 20c ol grn 1.75 1.25
J21 D4 30c on 30c rose red 4.50 4.00
J22 D4 50c on 50c vio brn 6.50 4.20
Nos. J17-J22 (6) 16.25 12.45

Nos. J13 to J16 With Additional
Overprint "Protectorat Francais"

1915
J23 D3 1c on 1c ol grn .95 .95
J24 D3 10c on 10c violet 1.90 1.60
J25 D3 30c on 30c bister 2.10 1.90
J26 D3 50c on 50c red 2.10 2.00
Nos. J23-J26 (4) 7.05 6.45

1917-26 — **Typo.**
J27 D5 1c black .20 .20
J28 D5 5c deep blue .20 .20
J29 D5 10c brown .45 .20
J30 D5 20c olive green 2.00 1.10
J31 D5 30c rose .20 .20
J32 D5 50c lilac brown .45 .20
J33 D5 1fr red brn, straw ('26) .90 .60
J34 D5 2fr violet ('26) 1.50 .90
Nos. J27-J34 (8) 5.90 3.60
See #J49-J56, Morocco #J1-J4. For surcharges see #J46-J48.

Postage Due Stamps of
France, 1882-1906
Overprinted

1918
J35 D2 1c black .60 .60
J36 D2 5c blue 1.25 1.25
J37 D2 10c chocolate 1.25 1.25
J38 D2 15c green 3.00 3.00
J39 D2 20c olive green 4.25 4.00
J40 D2 30c rose red 8.75 8.50
J41 D2 50c violet brown 14.00 13.50
Nos. J35-J41 (7) 33.10 32.10

Postage Due Stamps of
France, 1908-19
Overprinted

1918
J42 D3 1c olive green .60 .60
J43 D3 10c violet 1.75 1.75
J44 D3 20c bister 5.50 5.50
J45 D3 50c on 50c red 13.00 13.00
Nos. J42-J45 (4) 20.85 20.85

> Catalogue values for unused stamps in this section, from this point to the end of the section, are for Never Hinged items.

Nos. J31 and J29
Surcharged

1944 — **Unwmk.** — *Perf. 14x13½*
J46 D5 50c on 30c rose 3.00 2.50
J47 D5 1fr on 10c brown 4.75 3.75
J48 D5 3fr on 10c brown 8.50 8.25
Nos. J46-J48 (3) 16.25 14.50

Type of 1917-1926

1945-52 — **Typo.**
J49 D5 1fr brn lake ('47) .65 .55
J50 D5 2fr rose lake ('47) .90 .75
J51 D5 3fr ultra .40 .40
J52 D5 4fr red orange .60 .25
J53 D5 5fr green 1.00 .45
J54 D5 10fr yellow brn 1.25 .45
J55 D5 20fr carmine ('50) 1.50 1.00
J56 D5 30fr dull brn ('52) 2.25 1.50
Nos. J49-J56 (8) 8.55 5.35

PARCEL POST STAMPS

French Protectorate

PP1

1917 — **Unwmk.** — *Perf. 13½x14*
Q1 PP1 5c green .70 .35
Q2 PP1 10c carmine .70 .35
Q3 PP1 20c lilac brown .70 .50
Q4 PP1 25c blue 1.25 .50
Q5 PP1 40c dark brown 1.90 .80
Q6 PP1 50c red orange 2.40 .60
Q7 PP1 75c pale slate 3.00 1.90
Q8 PP1 1fr ultra 4.00 .55
Q9 PP1 2fr gray 5.75 1.00
Q10 PP1 5fr violet 9.00 1.00
Q11 PP1 10fr red 13.00 1.00
Nos. Q1-Q11 (11) 42.40 8.55

FRENCH POLYNESIA

'french ˌpä-lə-'nē-zhə

(French Oceania)

LOCATION — South Pacific Ocean
GOVT. — French Overseas Territory
AREA — 1,522 sq. mi.
POP. — 242,073 (1999 est.)
CAPITAL — Papeete

In 1903 various French Establishments in the South Pacific were united to form a single colony. Most important of the island groups are the Society Islands, Marquesas Islands, the Tuamotu group and the Gambier, Austral, and Rapa Islands. Tahiti, largest of the Society group, ranks first in importance.

100 Centimes = 1 Franc

Catalogue values for unused stamps in this country are for Never Hinged items, beginning with Scott 136 in the regular postage section, Scott B11 in the semi-postal section, Scott C2 in the airpost section, Scott CB1 in the airpost semi-postal section, Scott J18 in the postage due section, and Scott O1 in the officials section.

Navigation and Commerce — A1

Perf. 14x13½

1892-1907   Typo.   Unwmk.
Name of Colony in Blue or Carmine

1	A1	1c black, *lil bl*	1.10	1.10
2	A1	2c brown, *buff*	1.90	1.50
3	A1	4c claret, *lav*	3.00	2.25
4	A1	5c green, *grnsh*	7.75	5.75
5	A1	5c yellow grn ('06)	1.90	1.25
6	A1	10c blk, *lavender*	22.50	9.00
7	A1	10c red ('00)	1.90	1.25
8	A1	15c blue, quadrille paper	19.00	7.75
9	A1	15c gray, *lt gray* ('00)	3.75	3.00
10	A1	20c red, *grn*	15.00	6.00
11	A1	25c black, *rose*	45.00	20.00
12	A1	25c blue ('00)	15.00	10.00
13	A1	30c brown, *bis*	14.00	10.00
14	A1	35c black, *yel* ('06)	6.00	6.00
15	A1	40c red, *straw*	110.00	65.00
16	A1	45c blk, *gray grn* ('07)	5.25	5.50
17	A1	50c car, *rose*	8.50	7.00
18	A1	50c brown, *az* ('00)	225.00	175.00
19	A1	75c dp vio, *org*	10.00	7.75
20	A1	1fr brnz grn, *straw*	11.50	9.00
		Nos. 1-20 (20)	528.05	354.10

Perf. 13½x14 stamps are counterfeits.
For overprint and surcharge see #55, B1.

Tahitian Girl — A2

Kanakas — A3

Fautaua Valley — A4

1913-30

21	A2	1c violet & brn	.20	.20
22	A2	2c brown & blk	.20	.20
23	A2	4c orange & bl	.20	.20
24	A2	5c grn & yel grn	.70	.40

25	A2	5c bl & blk ('22)	.25	.25
26	A2	10c rose & org	1.25	.70
27	A2	10c bl grn & yel grn ('22)	.70	.70
28	A2	10c org red & brn red, *bluish* ('26)	1.10	1.10
29	A2	15c org & blk ('15)	.50	.35
a.		Imperf., pair	125.00	
30	A2	20c black & vio	.80	.65
a.		Imperf., pair	125.00	
31	A2	20c grn & bl grn ('26)	.70	.70
32	A2	20c brn red & dk brn ('27)	1.10	1.10
33	A3	25c ultra & blue	1.10	.80
34	A3	25c vio & rose ('22)	.35	.35
35	A3	30c gray & brown	3.25	2.25
a.		Imperf., pair	225.00	
36	A3	30c rose & red org ('22)	2.00	1.75
37	A3	30c blk & red org	.50	.50
38	A3	30c slate bl & bl grn ('27)	1.25	1.25
39	A3	35c green & rose	.80	.80
40	A3	40c black & green	.80	.80
41	A3	45c orange & red	.80	.80
42	A3	50c dk brown & blk	11.50	8.75
43	A3	50c ultra & bl ('22)	.70	.70
44	A3	50c gray & bl vio ('26)	.50	.50
45	A3	60c green & blk ('26)	.75	.75
46	A3	65c ol brn & red vio ('27)	2.25	2.25
47	A3	75c vio brn & vio	1.75	1.60
48	A3	90c brn red & rose ('30)	12.50	12.00
49	A4	1fr rose & black	3.50	2.25
50	A4	1.10fr vio & dk brn ('28)	1.25	1.10
51	A4	1.40fr bis brn & vio ('29)	3.25	2.90
52	A4	1.50fr ind & bl ('30)	12.50	12.00
53	A4	2fr dk brown & grn	3.50	2.25
54	A4	5fr violet & bl	8.25	7.00
		Nos. 21-54 (34)	80.75	69.90

For surcharges see Nos. 56-71, B2-B4.

No. 7 Overprinted

1915

55	A1	10c red	3.50	3.50
a.		Inverted overprint	125.00	125.00

For surcharge see No. B1.

No. 29 Surcharged

1916

56	A2	10c on 15c org & blk	2.00	1.75

Nos. 22, 41 and 29 Surcharged

1921

57	A2	5c on 2c brn & blk	25.00	25.00
58	A3	10c on 45c org & red	25.00	25.00
59	A2	25c on 15c org & blk	5.75	5.75
		Nos. 57-59 (3)	55.75	55.75

On No. 58 the new value and date are set wide apart and without bar.

Types of 1913-30 Issue Surcharged in Black or Red

1923-27

60	A3	60c on 75c bl & brn	.40	.40
61	A4	65c on 1fr dk bl & ol (R) ('25)	1.25	1.25
62	A4	85c on 1fr dk bl & ol (R) ('25)	1.25	1.25
63	A3	90c on 75c brn red & cer ('27)	1.90	1.90
		Nos. 60-63 (4)	4.80	4.80

No. 26 Surcharged

1924

64	A2	45c on 10c rose & org	1.75	1.75
a.		Inverted surcharge	1,800.	1,800.

Stamps and Type of 1913-30 Surcharged with New Value and Bars in Black or Red

1924-27

65	A4	25c on 2fr dk brn & grn	.80	.80
66	A4	25c on 5fr vio & bl	.85	.85
67	A4	1.25fr on 1fr dk bl & ultra (R) ('26)	.85	.85
68	A4	1.50fr on 1fr dk bl & lt bl ('27)	2.10	2.10
69	A4	20fr on 5fr org & brt vio ('27)	24.00	18.00
		Nos. 65-69 (5)	28.60	22.60

Surcharged in Black or Red

1926

70	A4	3fr on 5fr gray & blue	2.10	1.75
71	A4	10fr on 5fr grn & blk (R)	4.75	4.25

Papetoai Bay, Moorea A5

1929, Mar. 25

72	A5	3fr green & dk brn	5.75	5.75
73	A5	5fr lt blue & dk brn	11.00	11.00
74	A5	10fr lt red & dk brn	32.50	32.50
75	A5	20fr lilac & dk brn	40.00	40.00
		Nos. 72-75 (4)	89.25	89.25

For overprints see Nos. 128, 130, 132, 134.

Common Design Types pictured following the introduction.

Colonial Exposition Issue
Common Design Types

1931, Apr. 13   Engr.   Perf. 12½
Name of Country Printed in Black

76	CD70	40c deep green	5.75	5.75
77	CD71	50c violet	5.75	5.75
78	CD72	90c red orange	5.75	5.75
79	CD73	1.50fr dull blue	5.75	5.75
		Nos. 76-79 (4)	23.00	23.00

Spear Fishing A12

Tahitian Girl — A13

Idols A14

1934-39   Photo.   Perf. 13½, 13½x13

80	A12	1c gray black	.20	.20
81	A12	2c claret	.20	.20
82	A12	3c lt blue ('39)	.20	.20
83	A12	4c orange	.35	.35
84	A12	5c violet	.55	.55
85	A12	10c dark brown	.20	.20
86	A12	15c green	.35	.35
87	A12	20c red	.35	.35
88	A13	25c gray blue	.55	.55
89	A13	30c yellow green	.95	.95
90	A13	30c org brn ('39)	.50	.50
91	A14	35c dp green ('38)	2.75	2.75
92	A13	40c red violet	.35	.35
93	A13	45c brown orange	6.25	6.25
94	A13	45c dk green ('39)	.95	.95
95	A13	50c violet	.35	.35
96	A13	55c blue ('38)	5.00	5.00
97	A13	60c black ('39)	.50	.50
98	A13	65c brown	2.25	2.25
99	A13	70c brt pink ('39)	.80	.80
100	A13	75c olive green	6.25	6.25
101	A13	80c violet brn ('38)	1.10	1.10
102	A13	90c rose red	.55	.55
103	A14	1fr red brown	.55	.55
104	A14	1.25fr brown violet	5.75	5.75
105	A14	1.25fr rose red ('39)	.70	.70
106	A14	1.40fr org yel ('39)	.70	.70
107	A14	1.50fr blue	.55	.55
108	A14	1.60fr dull vio ('39)	.95	.95
109	A14	1.75fr olive	5.00	5.00
110	A14	2fr red	.55	.55
111	A14	2.25fr deep blue ('39)	.70	.70
112	A14	2.50fr black ('39)	.80	.80
113	A14	3fr brown org ('39)	1.25	1.25
114	A14	5fr red violet ('39)	.75	.75
115	A14	10fr dk grn ('39)	2.25	2.25
116	A14	20fr dk brn ('39)	2.25	2.25
		Nos. 80-116 (37)	54.25	54.25

For overprints see #126-127, 129, 131, 133, 135.
For types A12-A14 without "RF," see Nos. 135A-135E.

Paris International Exposition Issue
Common Design Types

1937   Engr.   Perf. 13

117	CD74	20c deep violet	2.25	2.25
118	CD75	30c dark green	2.25	2.25
119	CD76	40c carmine rose	2.25	2.25
120	CD77	50c dk brn & bl	3.00	3.00
121	CD78	90c red	3.00	3.00
122	CD79	1.50fr ultra	3.75	3.75
		Nos. 117-122 (6)	16.50	16.50

Colonial Arts Exhibition Issue
Souvenir Sheet
Common Design Type

1937   Imperf.

123	CD78	3fr emerald	30.00	42.50
		Never hinged		42.50

New York World's Fair Issue
Common Design Type

1939, May 10   Engr.   Perf. 12½x12

124	CD82	1.25fr carmine lake	1.00	1.00
125	CD82	2.25fr ultra	1.00	1.00
		Set, never hinged	3.50	

Fautaua Valley and Marshal Petain A15

1941 Engr. Perf. 12½x12

125A	A15	1fr bluish green	.80
125B	A15	2.50fr deep blue	.95
		Set, never hinged	2.40

Nos. 125A-125B were issued by the Vichy government in France, but were not placed on sale in the French Polynesia.

For surcharges, see Nos. B12B-B12C.

Stamps of 1929-39 Overprinted in Black or Red

1941 Perf. 14x13½, 13½x13

126	A14	1fr red brown (Bk)	3.50	3.75
127	A14	2.50fr black	4.50	5.00
128	A5	3fr grn & dk brn	5.00	5.00
129	A5	3fr brn org (Bk)	5.50	5.50
130	A5	5fr lt bl & dk brn	5.00	5.00
131	A5	5fr red vio (Bk)	5.50	5.50
132	A5	10fr lt red & dk brn	16.00	16.00
133	A14	10fr dark green	50.00	
134	A14	20fr lil & dk brn	82.50	82.50
135	A14	20fr dark brown	47.50	
		Nos. 126-135 (10)	225.00	
		Set, never hinged	300.00	

Types of 1934-39 without "RF"

1942-44 Photo. Perf. 13½

135A	A12	10c dark brown	.50
135B	A13	30c orange brown	.55
135C	A14	1.50fr blue	.70
135D	A14	10fr dark green	1.10
135E	A14	20fr dark brown	1.75
		Nos. 135A-135E (5)	4.60

Nos. 135A-135E were issued by the Vichy government in France, but were not placed on sale in French Polynesia.

Catalogue values for unused stamps in this section, from this point to the end of the section, are for Never Hinged items.

Ancient Double Canoe A16

1942 Photo. Perf. 14½x14

136	A16	5c dark brown	.30	.20
137	A16	10c dk gray bl	.30	.20
138	A16	25c emerald	.30	.20
139	A16	30c red orange	.30	.20
140	A16	40c dk slate grn	.30	.20
141	A16	80c red brown	.30	.20
142	A16	1fr rose violet	.35	.25
143	A16	1.50fr brt red	.50	.35
144	A16	2fr gray black	.75	.55
145	A16	2.50fr brt ultra	1.75	1.40
146	A16	4fr dull violet	1.10	.85
147	A16	5fr bister	1.10	.85
148	A16	10fr deep brown	1.75	1.40
149	A16	20fr deep green	2.00	1.60
		Nos. 136-149 (14)	11.10	8.45

For surcharges see Nos. 152-159.

Eboue Issue
Common Design Type

1945 Engr. Perf. 13

150	CD91	2fr black	.75	.55
151	CD91	25fr Prus green	2.25	1.60

Nos. 150 and 151 exist imperforate.

Nos. 136, 138 and 145 Surcharged with New Values and Bars in Carmine or Black

1946 Perf. 14½x14

152	A16	50c on 5c (C)	.50	.40
153	A16	60c on 5c (C)	.50	.40
154	A16	70c on 5c (C)	.50	.50
155	A16	1.20fr on 5c (C)	.65	.50
156	A16	2.40fr on 25c (Bk)	1.25	1.00
157	A16	3fr on 25c (Bk)	.80	.55
158	A16	4.50fr on 25c (Bk)	1.60	1.15
159	A16	15fr on 2.50fr (C)	1.90	1.40
		Nos. 152-159 (8)	7.70	6.00

Coast of Mooréa A17

Fisherman and Catch — A18

Tahitian Girl — A20

House at Faa — A19

Island of Borabora A21

Island Women A22

1948 Unwmk. Engr. Perf. 13

160	A17	10c brown	.35	.25
161	A17	30c blue green	.35	.25
162	A17	40c deep blue	.35	.25
163	A18	50c red brown	.35	.25
164	A18	60c dk brown ol	.55	.40
165	A19	80c brt blue	.55	.40
166	A19	1fr red brown	.55	.30
167	A19	1.20fr slate	.55	.40
168	A19	1.50fr deep ultra	.55	.40
169	A20	2fr sepia	1.10	.65
170	A20	2.40fr red brown	1.10	.80
171	A20	3fr purple	10.00	2.25
172	A20	4fr blue black	1.60	.95
173	A21	5fr sepia	2.75	1.20
174	A21	6fr steel blue	2.75	1.75
175	A21	10fr dk brown ol	3.50	1.40
176	A22	15fr vermilion	4.50	2.00
177	A22	20fr slate	5.00	2.25
178	A22	25fr sepia	7.00	3.50
		Nos. 160-178 (19)	43.45	19.65

Imperforates
Most French Polynesia stamps from 1948 onward exist imperforate in issued and trial colors, and also in small presentation sheets in issued colors.

Military Medal Issue
Common Design Type

1952, Dec. 1 Engr. & Typo.

179	CD101	3fr multicolored	11.00	8.50

Girl of Borabora — A23

Girl Playing Guitar — A24

1955, Sept. 26 Engr.

180	A23	9fr dk brn, blk & red	8.50	5.50

FIDES Issue
Common Design Type

Design: 3fr, Dry dock at Papeete.

1956, Oct. 22 Engr. Perf. 13x12½

181	CD103	3fr grnsh blue	3.00	1.40

1958, Nov. 3 Unwmk. Perf. 13

Designs: 4fr, 7fr, 9fr, Man with headdress. 10fr, 20fr, Girl with shells on beach.

182	A24	10c grn & redsh brn	.55	.45
183	A24	25c slate grn, cl & car	.65	.50
184	A24	1fr brt bl, brn & red org	.85	.55
185	A24	2fr brn, vio brn & vio	.95	.55
186	A24	4fr sl grn & org yel	1.25	.90
187	A24	7fr red brn, grn & org	2.50	1.40
188	A24	9fr vio brn, grn & org	4.50	2.00
189	A24	10fr dk bl, brn & car	4.00	2.00
190	A24	20fr pur, rose red & brn	7.25	4.25
		Nos. 182-190 (9)	22.50	12.60

See Nos. 304-306.

Human Rights Issue
Common Design Type

1958, Dec. 10

191	CD105	7fr dk gray & dk bl	10.00	7.00

Flower Issue
Common Design Type

1959, Jan. 3 Photo. Perf. 12½x12

192	CD104	4fr Breadfruit	5.00	3.00

Spear Fishing — A25

Tahitian Dancers A26

1960, May 16 Engr. Perf. 13

193	A25	5fr green, brn & lil	1.25	.90
194	A26	17fr ultra, brt grn & red brn	5.25	2.25

Post Office, Papeete A27

1960, Nov. 19 Unwmk. Perf. 13

195	A27	16fr green, bl & claret	5.00	2.90

Saraca Indica — A28

1962, July 12 Photo. Perf. 13

196	A28	15fr shown	14.00	11.00
197	A28	25fr Hibiscus	18.00	12.50

Map of Australia and South Pacific — A29

1962, July 18 Perf. 13x12

198	A29	20fr multicolored	15.00	6.25

5th South Pacific Conf., Pago Pago, July 1962.

Spined Squirrelfish A30

Fish: 10fr, One-spot butterflyfish. 30fr, Radiate lionfish. 40fr, Horned boxfish.

1962, Dec. 15 Engr. Perf. 13

199	A30	5fr black, mag & bis	4.50	2.00
200	A30	10fr multicolored	6.50	3.00
201	A30	30fr multicolored	13.00	8.00
202	A30	40fr multicolored	16.00	10.00
		Nos. 199-202 (4)	40.00	25.00

Soccer — A30a

Design: 50fr, Throwing the javelin.

1963, Aug. 29 Photo. Perf. 12½

203	A30a	20fr brt ultra & brn	8.00	4.50
204	A30a	50fr brt car rose & ultra	13.00	6.75

South Pacific Games, Suva, 8/29-9/7.

Red Cross Centenary Issue
Common Design Type

1963, Sept. 2 Engr. Perf. 13

205	CD113	15fr vio brn, gray & car	11.50	9.00

Human Rights Issue
Common Design Type

1963, Dec. 10 Unwmk. Perf. 13

206	CD117	7fr green & vio bl	11.50	8.00

Philatec Issue
Common Design Type

1964, Apr. 9 Perf. 13

207	CD118	25fr grn, dk sl grn & red	13.50	10.00

Tahitian Dancer A31

1964, May 14 Engr. Perf. 13

208	A31	1fr multicolored	.35	.35
209	A31	3fr dp claret, blk & org	.80	.80

Soldiers, Truck and Battle Flag — A32

1964, July 10　Photo.　Perf. 12½
210　A32　5fr multicolored　　9.00　2.75

Issued to honor the Tahitian Volunteers of the Pacific Battalion. See No. C31.

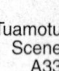

Tuamotu Scene A33

Views: 4fr, Borabora. 7fr, Papeete Harbor. 8fr, Paul Gauguin's tomb, Marquesas. 20fr, Mangareva, Gambier Islands.

1964, Dec. 1　Litho.　Perf. 12½x13
211　A33　2fr multicolored　　.95　.55
212　A33　4fr multicolored　　1.60　.55
213　A33　7fr multicolored　　3.25　1.40
214　A33　8fr multicolored　　4.25　2.00
215　A33　20fr multicolored　10.00　3.25
　　　Nos. 211-215,C32 (6)　28.80　10.50

Painting from a School Dining Room — A34

1965, Nov. 29　Engr.　Perf. 13
216　A34　20fr dk brn, sl grn &
　　　　　dk car　　　17.50　10.00

Publicizing the School Canteen Program. See #C38.

Outrigger Canoe on Lagoon A35

Ships: 11fr, Large cruising yacht, vert. 12fr, Motorboat for sport fishing. 14fr, Outrigger canoes with sails. 19fr, Schooner, vert. 22fr, Modern coaster "Oiseau des Isles II."

1966, Aug. 30　Engr.　Perf. 13
217　A35　10fr brt ultra, emer &
　　　　　mar　　　3.00　.80
218　A35　11fr mar, dk bl & sl
　　　　　grn　　　3.00　1.40
219　A35　12fr emer, dk bl & red
　　　　　lil　　　4.00　1.60
220　A35　14fr brn, bl & slate
　　　　　grn　　　6.00　1.75
221　A35　19fr scar, sl grn & dp
　　　　　　　　　7.00　1.90
222　A35　22fr multicolored　10.00　3.50
　　　Nos. 217-222 (6)　33.00　10.95

High Jump A36

Designs: 20fr, Pole vault, vert. 40fr, Women's basketball, vert. 60fr, Hurdling.

1966, Dec. 15　Engr.　Perf. 13
223　A36　10fr dk red, lem & blk　2.00　1.25
224　A36　20fr blue, emer & blk　4.50　1.60
225　A36　40fr emer, brt pink &
　　　　　blk　　　8.75　4.00
226　A36　60fr dull yel, bl & blk　14.50　7.50
　　　Nos. 223-226 (4)　29.75　14.35

2nd South Pacific Games, Nouméa, New Caledonia, Dec. 8-18.

Poi Pounder — A37　　Javelin Throwing — A38

1967, June 15　Engr.　Perf. 13
227　A37　50fr orange & blk　14.50　8.00

Society for Oceanic Studies, 50th anniv.

1967, July 11

5fr, Spring dance. 15fr, Horse race. 16fr, Fruit carriers' race. 21fr, Canoe race.

228　A38　5fr multi, horiz.　1.10　.75
229　A38　13fr multi　　3.50　1.25
230　A38　15fr multi　　3.50　1.40
231　A38　16fr multi　　3.50　2.25
232　A38　21fr multi, horiz.　7.25　4.00
　　　Nos. 228-232 (5)　18.85　9.65

Issued to publicize the July Festival.

Earring — A39

Art of the Marquesas Islands: 10fr, Carved mother-of-pearl. 15fr, Decorated canoe paddle. 23fr, Oil vessel. 25fr, Carved stilt stirrups. 30fr, Fan handles. 35fr, Tattooed man. 50fr, Tikis.

1967-68　Engr.　Perf. 13
233　A39　10fr dp cl, dl red & ul-
　　　　　tra　　　2.50　.70
234　A39　15fr black & emerald　3.25　1.50
235　A39　20fr ol gray, dk car &
　　　　　lt bl　　　4.50　1.75
236　A39　23fr dk brn, ocher &
　　　　　bl　　　5.75　3.25
237　A39　25fr dk brn, dk bl & lil　5.75　3.00
238　A39　30fr brown & red lilac　7.25　3.25
239　A39　35fr ultra & dk brn　12.00　5.00
240　A39　50fr brn, sl grn & lt bl　13.00　5.75
　　　Nos. 233-240 (8)　54.00　24.20

Issued: 20fr, 25fr, 30fr, 50fr, 12/19/67; others 2/28/68.

WHO Anniversary Issue
Common Design Type

1968, May 4　Engr.　Perf. 13
241　CD126　15fr bl grn, mar & dp
　　　　　vio　　　8.75　3.50
242　CD126　16fr org, lil & bl grn　8.75　5.75

Human Rights Year Issue
Common Design Type

1968, Aug. 10　Engr.　Perf. 13
243　CD127　15fr blue, red & brn　9.00　4.75
244　CD127　16fr brn, brt pink &
　　　　　ultra　　　9.00　5.75

Tiare Apetahi A40

Flower: 17fr, Tiare Tahiti.

1969, Mar. 27　Photo.　Perf. 12½x13
245　A40　9fr multicolored　2.00　.90
246　A40　17fr multicolored　4.00　1.60

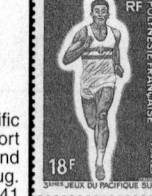

3rd South Pacific Games, Port Moresby, Papua and New Guinea, Aug. 13-23 — A41

1969, Aug. 13　Engr.　Perf. 13
247　A41　9fr Boxer, horiz.　2.90　1.10
248　A41　17fr High jump　5.75　1.75
249　A41　18fr Runner　7.25　2.90
250　A41　22fr Long jump　9.50　5.75
　　　Nos. 247-250 (4)　25.40　11.50

ILO Issue
Common Design Type

1969, Nov. 24　Engr.　Perf. 13
251　CD131　17fr org, emer & ol　8.75　4.25
252　CD131　18fr org, dk brn & vio
　　　　　bl　　　8.75　5.00

Territorial Assembly A42

Buildings: 14fr, Governor's Residence. 17fr, House of Tourism. 18fr, Maeva Hotel. 24fr, Taharaa Hotel.

1969, Dec. 22　Photo.　Perf. 12½x12
253　A42　13fr black & multi　2.75　1.10
254　A42　14fr black & multi　3.75　1.40
255　A42　17fr black & multi　6.00　2.90
256　A42　18fr black & multi　6.75　3.25
257　A42　24fr black & multi　11.50　5.75
　　　Nos. 253-257 (5)　30.75　14.40

Stone Figure with Globe — A43

Designs: 40fr, Globe, plane, map of Polynesia and men holding "PATA" sign, horiz. 60fr, Polynesian carrying globe.

1970, Apr. 7　Engr.　Perf. 13
258　A43　20fr deep plum, gray
　　　　　& bl　　　5.75　2.75
259　A43　40fr emer, rose lil &
　　　　　ultra　　　9.50　4.25
260　A43　60fr red brn, bl & dk
　　　　　brn　　　16.00　8.25
　　　Nos. 258-260 (3)　31.25　15.25

Issued to publicize the 1970 Pacific Area Travel Association Congress (PATA).

UPU Headquarters Issue
Common Design Type

1970, May 20　Engr.　Perf. 13
261　CD133　18fr maroon, pur &
　　　　　brn　　　8.00　4.00
262　CD133　20fr lilac rose, ol &
　　　　　ind　　　8.00　4.25

Night Fishing — A44

1971, May 11　Photo.　Perf. 13
263　A44　10fr multicolored　11.00　4.25
　　　Nos. 263,C71-C73 (4)　35.75　16.25

Flowers — A45

Designs: Various flowers. 12fr is horiz.

Perf. 12½x13, 13x12½

1971, Aug. 27
264　A45　8fr multicolored　1.75　.90
265　A45　12fr multicolored　3.00　1.40
266　A45　22fr multicolored　4.75　2.25
　　　Nos. 264-266 (3)　9.50　4.55

Day of a Thousand Flowers.

Water-skiing Slalom — A46

Designs: 20fr, Water-skiing, jump, vert. 40fr, Figure water-skiing.

1971, Oct. 11　Engr.　Perf. 13
267　A46　10fr grnsh bl, dk red
　　　　　& brn　　　5.00　1.75
268　A46　20fr car, emer & brn　7.25　3.25
269　A46　40fr brn, grn & lil　17.00　10.00
　　　Nos. 267-269 (3)　29.25　15.00

World water-skiing championships, Oct. 1971.

De Gaulle Issue
Common Design Type

30fr, As general, 1940. 50fr, As president, 1970.

1971, Nov. 9　Engr.　Perf. 13
270　CD134　30fr red lilac & blk　15.00　8.25
271　CD134　50fr red lilac & blk　21.00　12.50

Map of Tahiti and Jerusalem Cross A47

1971, Dec. 18　Photo.　Perf. 13x12½
272　A47　28fr lt blue & multi　12.00　6.75

2nd rally of French Boy Scouts and Guides, Taravao, French Polynesia.

"Alcoholism"　　Mother and Child
A48　　　　　　　A49

1972, Mar. 24　Photo.　Perf. 13
273　A48　20fr brown & multi　9.50　4.00

Fight against alcoholism.

1973, Sept. 26　Photo.　Perf. 12½x13
274　A49　28fr pale yellow & multi　10.00　4.00

Day nursery.

Polynesian Golfer — A50

Design: 24fr, Atimaono Golf Course.

1974, Feb. 27   Photo.   Perf. 13
275 A50 16fr multicolored   8.75 2.50
276 A50 24fr multicolored   11.00 4.00

Atimaono Golf Course.

Hand Throwing Life Preserver to Puppy — A51

1974, May 9   Photo.   Perf. 13
277 A51 21fr brt blue & multi   10.50 4.50

Society for the Protection of Animals.

Around a Fire, on the Beach A52

Polynesian Views: 2fr, Lagoons and mountains. 6fr, Pebble divers. 10fr, Lonely Mountain and flowers, vert. 15fr, Sailing ship at sunset. 20fr, Lagoon and mountain.

1974, May 22
278 A52 2fr multicolored   .75   .50
279 A52 5fr multicolored   .95   .75
280 A52 6fr multicolored   1.60   .90
281 A52 10fr multicolored   1.75 1.10
282 A52 15fr multicolored   3.50 1.50
283 A52 20fr multicolored   5.75 1.75
  Nos. 278-283 (6)   14.30 6.50

Polynesian Woman and UPU Emblem — A53

Lion, Sun and Emblem — A54

1974, Oct. 9   Engr.   Perf. 13
284 A53 65fr multicolored   10.50 6.75

Centenary of Universal Postal Union.

1975, June 17   Photo.
285 A54 26fr multicolored   12.50 4.50

15th anniv. of Lions Intl. in Tahiti.

Fish and Leaf A55

1975, July 9   Litho.   Perf. 12
286 A55 19fr dp ultra & green 10.00 3.25

Polynesian Association for the Protection of Nature.

Georges Pompidou, Pres. of France — A55a

1976, Feb. 16   Engr.   Perf. 13
287 A55a 49fr dk violet & black 10.50 6.00

See France No. 1430.

Alain Gerbault and Sailboat A56

1976, May 25   Photo.   Perf. 13
288 A56 90fr multicolored   11.50 8.00

Alain Gerbault's arrival in Bora Bora, 50th anniv.

Turtle — A57

Design: 42fr, Hand protecting bird.

1976, June 24   Litho.   Perf. 12½
289 A57 18fr multicolored   12.50 3.25
290 A57 42fr multicolored   17.00 8.00

World Ecology Day.

A. G. Bell, Telephone, Radar and Satellite — A58

1976, Sept. 15   Engr.   Perf. 13
291 A58 37fr multicolored   9.00 4.50

Centenary of first telephone call by Alexander Graham Bell, Mar. 10, 1876.

Dugout Canoes — A59

1976, Dec. 16   Litho.   Perf. 13x12½
292 A59 25fr Marquesas   4.00 3.00
293 A59 30fr Raiatea   5.00 4.00
294 A59 75fr Tahiti   10.00 6.00
295 A59 100fr Tuamotu   12.50 7.50
  Nos. 292-295 (4)   31.50 20.50

Sailing Ship — A60

Designs: Various sailing vessels.

1977, Dec. 22   Litho.   Perf. 13
296 A60 20fr multicolored   5.50 1.75
297 A60 50fr multicolored   6.25 2.00
298 A60 85fr multicolored   7.50 3.25
299 A60 120fr multicolored   13.00 5.00
  Nos. 296-299 (4)   32.25 12.00

Hibiscus — A61   Girl with Shells on Beach — A62

Designs: 10fr, Vanda orchids. 16fr, Pua (fagraea berteriana). 22fr, Gardenia.

1978-79   Photo.   Perf. 12½x13
300 A61 10fr multicolored   1.00   .45
301 A61 13fr multicolored   2.25   .90
302 A61 16fr multicolored   2.50 1.40
303 A61 22fr multicolored   1.75   .90
  Nos. 300-303 (4)   7.50 3.65

Issued: 13fr, 16fr, 8/23; 10fr, 22fr, 1/25/79.

1978, Nov. 3   Engr.   Perf. 13
Design A24 with "1958 1978" added: 28fr, Man with headdress. 36fr, Girl playing guitar.

304 A62 20fr multicolored   3.25   .60
305 A62 28fr multicolored   4.00 1.40
306 A62 36fr multicolored   6.00 2.00
  a. Souvenir sheet of 3   30.00 30.00
  Nos. 304-306 (3)   13.25 4.00

20th anniv. of stamps inscribed: Polynesie Francaise. #306a contains #304-306 in changed colors.

Ships — A63

1978, Dec. 29   Litho.   Perf. 13x12½
307 A63 15fr Tahiti   1.50   .75
308 A63 30fr Monowai   2.50 1.00
309 A63 75fr Tahitien   4.00 2.50
310 A63 100fr Mariposa   7.50 2.50
  Nos. 307-310 (4)   15.50 6.75

Porites Coral A64

Design: 37fr, Montipora coral.

1979, Feb. 15   Perf. 13x12½
311 A64 32fr multicolored   2.75   .90
312 A64 37fr multicolored   4.00 1.40

Raiatea A65

Landscapes: 1fr, Moon over Bora Bora. 2fr, Mountain peaks, Ua Pou. 3fr, Sunset over Motu Tapu. 5fr, Motu. 6fr, Palm and hut, Tuamotu.

1979, Mar. 8   Photo.   Perf. 13x13½
313 A65 1fr multicolored   .20   .20
314 A65 2fr multicolored   .20   .20
315 A65 3fr multicolored   .25   .20
316 A65 4fr multicolored   .35   .20
317 A65 5fr multicolored   .60   .30
318 A65 6fr multicolored   .75   .50
  Nos. 313-318 (6)   2.35 1.60

See Nos. 438-443 for redrawn designs.

Dance Costumes A66

1979, July 14   Litho.   Perf. 12½
319 A66 45fr Fetia   1.60   .80
320 A66 51fr Teanuanua   2.25   .90
321 A66 74fr Temaeva   3.25 1.75
  Nos. 319-321 (3)   7.10 3.45

Hill, Great
Britain
No. 53,
Tahiti
No. 28
A67

1979, Aug. 1   Engr.   Perf. 13
322 A67 100fr multicolored   4.00 2.75
Sir Rowland Hill (1795-1879), originator of
penny postage.

Hastula
Strigilata — A68

Statue Holding
Rotary
Emblem — A69

Shells: 28fr, Scabricola variegata. 35fr,
Fusinus undatus.

1979, Aug. 22   Litho.   Perf. 12½
323 A68 20fr multicolored   2.00 .80
324 A68 28fr multicolored   2.75 .90
325 A68 35fr multicolored   3.75 2.50
  Nos. 323-325 (3)   8.50 4.20

1979, Nov. 30   Litho.   Perf. 13
326 A69 47fr multicolored   2.75 1.60
Rotary International, 75th anniversary;
Papeete Rotary Club, 20th anniversary.
For overprint see No. 330.

Myripristis
Murdjan
A70

Fish: 8fr, Napoleon. 12fr, Emperor.

1980, Jan. 21   Litho.   Perf. 12½
327 A70 7fr multicolored   2.00 .45
328 A70 8fr multicolored   2.00 .60
329 A70 12fr multicolored   2.50 .75
  Nos. 327-329 (3)   6.50 1.80

No. 326 Overprinted and Surcharged
in Gold: "75eme / ANNIVERSAIRE /
1905-1980"
1980, Feb. 23   Litho.   Perf. 13
330 A69 77fr on 47fr multi   5.00 2.75
Rotary International, 75th anniversary.

CNEXO
Fish
Hatchery
A71

1980, Mar. 17   Photo.   Perf. 13x13½
331 A71 15fr shown   1.25 .75
332 A71 22fr Crayfish   1.25 .75

Papeete
Post Office
Building
Opening
A72

1980, Apr. 30   Photo.   Perf. 13x12½
333 A72 50fr multicolored   2.25 1.40

Tiki and Festival
Emblem — A73

1980, June 30   Photo.   Perf. 13½
334 A73 34fr shown   1.50 .75
335 A73 39fr Drum (pahu)   1.90 1.10
336 A73 49fr Ax (to'i)   2.50 1.50
  a.   Souv. sheet of 3, #334-336 11.50 11.50
  Nos. 334-336 (3)   5.90 3.35
South Pacific Arts Festival, Port Moresby,
Papua New Guinea.

Titmouse
Henparrot — A74

Charles de
Gaulle — A75

Perf. 13x12½, 12½x13
1980, Oct. 20   Photo.
337 A74 25fr White sea-swallow,
            horiz.   2.50 .75
338 A74 35fr shown   3.00 1.00
339 A74 45fr Minor frigate bird,
            horiz.   4.00 1.25
  Nos. 337-339 (3)   9.50 3.00

1980, Nov. 9   Engr.   Perf. 12½x13
340 A75 100fr multicolored   4.50 2.75

Naso
Vlamingi
(Karaua)
— A76

1981, Feb. 5   Litho.   Perf. 12½
341 A76 13fr shown   2.25 .50
342 A76 16fr Lutjanus vaigensis
            (toau)   2.25 .60
343 A76 24fr Plectropomus le-
            opardus (tonu)   3.00 .75
  Nos. 341-343 (3)   7.50 1.85

Indoor Fish
Breeding
Tanks,
Cnexo
Hatchery
A77

1981, May 14   Photo.   Perf. 13x13½
344 A77 23fr shown   1.25 .80
345 A77 41fr Mussels   2.00 1.10

Folk
Dancers
A78

Perf. 13x13½, 13½x13
1981, July 10   Litho.
346 A78 26fr shown   1.25 .55
347 A78 28fr Dancer   1.25 .55
348 A78 44fr Dancers, vert.   2.00 1.10
  Nos. 346-348 (3)   4.50 2.40

Sterna Bergii — A79

1981, Sept. 24   Litho.   Perf. 13
349 A79 47fr shown   1.50 .80
350 A79 53fr Ptilinopus
            purpuratus, vert.   1.50 .90
351 A79 65fr Estrilda astrild,
            vert.   2.00 1.25
  Nos. 349-351 (3)   5.00 2.95
  See Nos. 370-372.

Huahine
Island
A80

1981, Oct. 22   Litho.   Perf. 12½
352 A80 34fr shown   1.40 .60
353 A80 134fr Maupiti   3.00 1.60
354 A80 136fr Bora-Bora   3.00 1.60
  Nos. 352-354 (3)   7.40 3.80

A81

1982, Feb. 4   Photo.   Perf. 13x13½
355 A81 30fr Parrotfish   1.00 .70
356 A81 31fr Regal angel   1.40 .70
357 A81 45fr Spotted bass   1.50 1.00
  Nos. 355-357 (3)   3.90 2.40

Pearl
Industry
A82

1982, Apr. 22   Photo.   Perf. 13x13½
358 A82 7fr Pearl beds   1.25 .35
359 A82 8fr Extracting pearls   1.50 .35
360 A82 10fr Pearls   2.00 .50
  Nos. 358-360 (3)   4.75 1.20

Tahiti "No. 1A," Emblem — A83

1982, May 12   Engr.   Perf. 13
361 A83 150fr multicolored   5.00 3.50
  a.   Souvenir sheet   15.00 15.00
PHILEXFRANCE Stamp Exhibition, Paris,
June 11-21. No. 361a contains No. 361 in
changed colors.

King Holding
Carved
Scepter — A84

Designs: Coronation ceremony.

1982, July 12   Photo.   Perf. 13½x13
362 A84 12fr shown   .50 .20
363 A84 13fr King, priest   .50 .20
364 A84 17fr Procession   1.00 .50
  Nos. 362-364 (3)   2.00 .90

Championship Emblem — A85

1982, Aug. 13   Perf. 13
365 A85 90fr multicolored   2.25 1.60
4th Hobie-Cat 16 World Catamaran Sailing
Championship, Tahiti, Aug. 15-21.

First Colloquium
on New Energy
Sources — A86

1982, Sept. 29   Litho.
366 A86 46fr multicolored   2.75 .90

Motu,
Tuamotu
Islet — A87

1982, Oct. 12   Litho.   Perf. 13
367 A87 20fr shown   .75 .35
368 A87 33fr Tupai Atoll   1.00 .50
369 A87 35fr Gambier Islds.   1.50 .60
  Nos. 367-369 (3)   3.25 1.45

Bird Type of 1981
1982, Nov. 17   Litho.   Perf. 13
370 A79 37fr Sacred egret   2.25 .50
371 A79 39fr Pluvialis dominica,
            vert.   2.25 .60

372 A79 42fr Lonchura castane-
　　　　othorax　　　　4.50　.75
　　Nos. 370-372 (3)　　9.00 1.85

Fish — A88

1983, Feb. 9　Litho.　Perf. 13x13½
373 A88　8fr Acanthurus lineatus　.75　.35
374 A88 10fr Caranx me-
　　　　lampygus　　　　1.00　.35
375 A88 12fr Carcharhinus mela-
　　　　nopterus　　　　1.50　.50
　　Nos. 373-375 (3)　　3.25 1.20

The Way of the
Cross, Sculpture
by Damien
Haturau — A89

1983, Mar. 9　Litho.　Perf. 13
376 A89　7fr shown　　　1.00　.25
377 A89 21fr Virgin and Child　1.50　.50
378 A89 23fr Christ　　　1.75　.35
　　Nos. 376-378 (3)　　4.25 1.10

Traditional
Hats — A90

1983, May 24　Litho.　Perf. 13x12½
379 A90 11fr Acacia　　　.75　.35
380 A90 13fr Niau　　　　.75　.35
381 A90 25fr Ofe　　　　1.00　.50
382 A90 35fr Ofe, diff.　　1.25　.50
　　Nos. 379-382 (4)　　3.75 1.70
　　See Nos. 393-396.

Chieftain in
Traditional
Costume, Sainte-
Christine
Isld. — A91

Traditional Costumes, Marquesas Islds.

1983, July 12　Photo.　Perf. 13
383 A91 15fr shown　　　.75　.50
384 A91 17fr Man　　　　1.00　.50
385 A91 28fr Woman　　　1.25　.50
　　Nos. 383-385 (3)　　3.00 1.50
　　See Nos. 397-399, 419-421.

Polynesian Crowns — A92

Various flower garlands.

1983, Oct. 19　Litho.　Perf. 13
386 A92 41fr multicolored　1.40　.60
387 A92 44fr multicolored　1.60　.60
388 A92 45fr multicolored　2.00　.80
　　Nos. 386-388 (3)　　5.00 2.00
　　See Nos. 400-402.

Martin Luther
(1483-1546)
A93

Tiki
Carvings — A94

1983, Nov. 10　Engr.　Perf. 13
389 A93 90fr black, brn & lil gray　2.50 1.25

1984, Feb. 8　Litho.　Perf. 12½x13
Various carvings.
390 A94 14fr multicolored　.80　.25
391 A94 16fr multicolored　1.00　.50
392 A94 19fr multicolored　1.25　.40
　　Nos. 390-392 (3)　　3.05 1.15

Hat Type of 1983

1984, June 20　Litho.　Perf. 13x12½
393 A90 20fr Aeho ope　　.50　.35
394 A90 24fr Paeore　　　.60　.35
395 A90 26fr Ofe fei　　　.75　.50
396 A90 33fr Hua　　　　.80　.50
　　Nos. 393-396 (4)　　2.65 1.70

Costume Type of 1983

1984, July 11　Litho.　Perf. 13
397 A91 34fr Tahitian playing
　　　　nose flute　　　.75　.50
398 A91 35fr Priest, Oei-eitia　.90　.50
399 A91 39fr Tahitian adult and
　　　　child　　　　.90　.50
　　Nos. 397-399 (3)　　2.55 1.50

Garland Type of 1983

1984, Oct. 24　Litho.　Perf. 13x12½
400 A92 46fr Moto'i Lei　　.90　.50
401 A92 47fr Pitate Lei　　1.00　.60
402 A92 53fr Bougainvillea Lei　1.25　.80
　　Nos. 400-402 (3)　　3.15 1.90

4th Pacific Arts Festival, Noumea, New
Caledonia, Dec. 8-22 — A95

1984, Nov. 20　Litho.　Perf. 13
403 A95 150fr Statue, head-
　　　　dress　　　3.50　2.25
　　See No. C213.

Paysage D'Anaa, by Jean
Masson — A96

Paintings: 50fr, Sortie Du Culte, by Jacques
Boulaire. 75fr, La Fete, by Robert Tatin. 85fr,
Tahitiennes Sur La Plage, by Pierre Heyman.

Perf. 12½x13, 13x12½

1984, Dec. 12　　　　Litho.
404 A96 50fr multi, vert.　1.25　.60
405 A96 65fr multicolored　1.40　.75
406 A96 75fr multicolored　1.90　.90
407 A96 85fr multicolored　2.25 1.50
　　Nos. 404-407 (4)　　6.80 3.75

Tiki
Carvings — A97

Polynesian
Faces — A98

1985, Jan. 23　Litho.　Perf. 13½
408 A97 30fr multicolored　.60　.35
409 A97 36fr multicolored　.80　.45
410 A97 44fr multicolored　.90　.70
　　Nos. 408-410 (3)　　2.30 1.55

1985, Feb. 20　Photo.　Perf. 12½x13
411 A98 22fr multicolored　.45　.35
412 A98 39fr multicolored　.80　.45
413 A98 44fr multicolored　1.00　.75
　　Nos. 411-413 (3)　　2.25 1.55

Early Tahiti — A99

Perf. 13x12½, 12½x13

1985, Apr. 24　　　　Litho.
414 A99 42fr Entrance to Papee-
　　　　te　　　　1.00　.60
415 A99 45fr Girls, vert.　　1.40　.80
416 A99 48fr Papeete market　1.50　.90
　　Nos. 414-416 (3)　　3.90 2.30

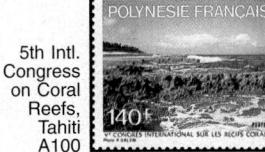

5th Intl.
Congress
on Coral
Reefs,
Tahiti
A100

1985, May 28　Litho.　Perf. 13½
417 A100 140fr Local reef for-
　　　　mation　　3.00 2.00
Printed se-tenant with label picturing congress emblem.

National
Flag
A101

1985, June 28
418 A101 9fr Flag, natl. arms　1.50 1.00

Costume Type of 1983
18th-19th Cent. Prints, Beslu Collection.

1985, July 17　　　　Perf. 13
419 A91 38fr Tahitian dancer　1.25　.50
420 A91 55fr Man and woman
　　　　from Otahiti, 1806　1.75　.75
421 A91 70fr Traditional chief　2.50　.90
　　Nos. 419-421 (3)　　5.50 2.15

Local Foods — A103

1985-86　　　　Litho.　Perf. 13
422 A103 25fr Roasted pig　1.00　.40
423 A103 35fr Pit fire　　　1.50　.60
423A A103 80fr Fish in coco-
　　　　nut milk　　2.00 1.40
423B A103 110fr Fafaru　　1.75　.90
　　Nos. 422-423B (4)　　7.00 4.15
Issued: 25fr, 35fr, 11/14; 80fr, 110fr, 5/20/86.
See Nos. 458-459, 474-475.

Catholic Churches — A104

1985, Dec. 11　Litho.　Perf. 13
424 A104 90fr St. Anne's,
　　　　Otepipi　　1.90 1.10
425 A104 100fr St. Michael's
　　　　Cathedral, Rik-
　　　　itea　　　2.00 1.10
426 A104 120fr Cathedral, exte-
　　　　rior　　　2.40 1.60
　　Nos. 424-426 (3)　　6.30 3.80
Nos. 424-426 printed se-tenant with labels
picturing local religious art.

Crabs
A105

1986, Jan. 22　　　　Perf. 13½
427 A105 18fr Fiddler　　　.50　.35
428 A105 29fr Hermit　　　.75　.35
429 A105 31fr Coconut　　1.25　.50
　　Nos. 427-429 (3)　　2.50 1.20

Faces of
Polynesia
A106

1986, Feb. 19　Perf. 12½x13, 13x12½
430 A106 43fr Boy, fish　　1.00　.50
431 A106 49fr Boy, coral　　1.25　.50
432 A106 51fr Boy, turtle, vert.　1.40　.60
　　Nos. 430-432 (3)　　3.65 1.60

Old Tahiti — A107

1986, Mar. 18   *Perf. 13x12½*
433 A107 52fr Papeete   1.10 .60
434 A107 56fr Harpoon fishing   1.25 .60
435 A107 57fr Royal Palace, Papeete   1.40 .75
    Nos. 433-435 (3)   3.75 1.95

Tiki Rock Carvings — A108

1986, Apr. 16
436 A108 58fr Atuona, Hiva Oa   1.75 .70
437 A108 59fr Ua Huka Hill, Hane Valley   1.75 .70

Landscapes Type Redrawn
1986-88   Litho.   *Perf. 13½*
438 A65 1fr multi, type 2 ('88)   2.00 .35
   a.   Type 1 ('86)   4.25 1.00
   b.   Type 3 ('91)   15.00 4.00
439 A65 2fr multicolored   .40 .20
440 A65 3fr multicolored   .45 .20
441 A65 4fr multicolored ('87)   .75 .30
442 A65 5fr multicolored   .75 .30
443 A65 6fr multicolored   .65 .30
    Nos. 438-443 (6)   5.00 1.65

Nos. 438-443 printed in sharper detail, and box containing island name is taller. Nos. 439-443 margin is inscribed "CARTOR" instead of "DELRIEU."

No. 438 has three types of inscription below design: type 1, photographer's name at left, no inscription at right; type 2, photographer's name at left 9.5mm long, printer's name (Cartor) at right; type 3, photographer's name at left 12.5mm long, Cartor at right.

Traditional Crafts A109

    Perf. 13x12½, 12½x13
1986, July 17   Litho.
444 A109 8fr Quilting, vert.   .25 .20
445 A109 10fr Baskets, hats   .25 .25
446 A109 12fr Grass skirts   .85 .30
    Nos. 444-446 (3)   1.35 .75

Building a Pirogue (Canoe) A110

1986, Oct. 21   Litho.   *Perf. 13½*
447 A110 46fr Boat-builders   1.25 .60
448 A110 50fr Close-up   1.50 .80

Medicinal Plants — A111

Polynesians A112

1986, Nov. 19   *Perf. 13*
449 A111 40fr Phymatosorus   .80 .50
450 A111 41fr Barringtonia asiatica   .90 .50
451 A111 60fr Ocimum bacilicum   1.50 .90
    Nos. 449-451 (3)   3.20 1.90
    See Nos. 495-497.

1987, Jan. 21   Litho.   *Perf. 13½*
452 A112 28fr Old man   .60 .35
453 A112 30fr Mother and child   .75 .50
454 A112 37fr Old woman   1.00 .60
    Nos. 452-454 (3)   2.35 1.45

Crustaceans — A113

1987, Feb. 18   *Perf. 12½x13*
455 A113 34fr Carpilius maculatus   1.00 .50
456 A113 35fr Parribacus antarticus   1.00 .50
457 A113 39fr Justitia longimana   1.25 .50
    Nos. 455-457 (3)   3.25 1.50

Local Foods Type of 1985
1987, Mar. 19   Litho.   *Perf. 13*
458 A103 33fr Papaya poe   2.00 .60
459 A103 65fr Chicken fafa   3.00 .90

Polynesian Petroglyphs A114

1987, May 13   *Perf. 12½*
460 A114 13fr Tipaerui, Tahiti   .35 .20
461 A114 21fr Turtle, Raiatea Is.   .60 .35

Calling Devices and Musical Instruments, Museum of Tahiti and the Isles — A115

1987, July 1   *Perf. 13½*
462 A115 20fr Wood horn   .80 .20
463 A115 26fr Triton's conch   .80 .50
464 A115 33fr Nose flutes   1.00 .60
    Nos. 462-464 (3)   2.60 1.30

Medicinal Plants — A116

1987, Sept. 16   *Perf. 12½x13*
465 A116 46fr Thespesia populnea   1.00 .60
466 A116 53fr Ophioglossum reticulatum   1.40 .60
467 A116 54fr Dicrocephala latifolia   1.40 .60
    Nos. 465-467 (3)   3.80 1.80

Ancient Weapons and Tools — A117

Designs: 25fr, Adze, war club, chisel, flute. 27fr, War clubs, tatooing comb, mallet. 32fr, Headdress, necklaces, nose flute.

1987, Oct. 14   Engr.   *Perf. 13*
468 A117 25fr lt olive grn & blk   .60 .40
469 A117 27fr Prus grn & int blue   .75 .45
470 A117 32fr brt olive bis & brn blk   .80 .55
    Nos. 468-470 (3)   2.15 1.40

Catholic Missionaries — A118

Monsignors: 95fr, Rene Ildefonse Dordillon (1808-1888), bishop of the Marquesas Isls. 105fr, Tepano Jaussen (1815-1891), first bishop of Polynesia. 115fr, Paul Laurent Maze (1885-1976), archbishop of Papeete.

1987, Dec. 9   Litho.
471 A118 95fr multicolored   2.00 1.50
472 A118 105fr multicolored   2.25 1.75
473 A118 115fr multicolored   2.50 1.90
    Nos. 471-473 (3)   6.75 5.15

Local Foods Type of 1985
1988, Jan. 12   Litho.   *Perf. 13*
474 A103 40fr Crayfish (varo)   2.00 .60
475 A103 75fr Bananas in coconut milk   3.00 1.25
    Nos. 474-475 are vert.

Authors — A119

62fr, James Norman Hall (1887-1951). 85fr, Charles Bernard Nordhoff (1887-1947).

1988, Feb. 10
476 A119 62fr multicolored   1.50 .80
477 A119 85fr multicolored   2.00 .90

Traditional Housing — A120

11fr, Taranpoo Opoa Is., Raiatea. 15fr, Tahaa Village. 17fr, Community meeting house, Tahiti.

1988, Mar. 16   Litho.   *Perf. 13x12½*
478 A120 11fr multicolored   1.00 .30
479 A120 15fr multicolored   1.00 .30
480 A120 17fr multicolored   1.50 .30
    Nos. 478-480 (3)   3.50 .90

Point Venus Lighthouse, 120th Anniv. — A121

1988, Apr. 21   Litho.   *Perf. 13*
481 A121 400fr multicolored   9.00 6.00

Tapa-cloth Paintings by Paul Engdahl A122

1988, May 20
482 A122 52fr multicolored   1.40 .80
483 A122 54fr multicolored   1.50 .90
484 A122 64fr multicolored   1.60 1.25
    Nos. 482-484 (3)   4.50 2.95

POLYSAT (Domestic Communications Network) — A123

1988, June 15   Litho.   *Perf. 12½x12*
485 A123 300fr multicolored   6.00 4.75

Tahitian Dolls — A124

Designs: 42fr, Wearing grass skirt and headdress. 45fr, Wearing print dress and straw hat, holding guitar. 48fr, Wearing print dress and straw hat, holding straw bag.

1988, June 27   *Perf. 13x12½*
486 A124 42fr multicolored   1.00 .60
487 A124 45fr multicolored   1.25 .60
488 A124 48fr multicolored   1.50 .75
    Nos. 486-488 (3)   3.75 1.95

Visiting a Marae at Nuku Hiva, Engraving by J. & E. Verreaux A125

1988, Aug. 1   Engr.   Perf. 13
489 A125 68fr black brown   2.00 1.25
Size: 143x101mm
490 A125 145fr violet brn & grn   5.25 4.00

SYDPEX '88, July 30-Aug. 7, Australia. No. 490 pictures a Russian navy officer (probably Krusenstern) visiting the Marquesas Islanders; denomination LR.

Map Linking South America and South Pacific Islands — A126

1988, Aug. 30   Engr.
491 A126 350fr multicolored   7.50 4.50

Eric de Bisschop (1890-1958), explorer who tried to prove that there was an exchange of peoples between the South Pacific islands and So. America, rather than that the island populations originated from So. America.

Seashells A127

1988, Sept. 21   Litho.   Perf. 13½
492 A127 24fr Kermia barnardi   .60 .35
493 A127 35fr Vexillum suavis   1.00 .50
494 A127 44fr Berthelinia   1.40 .75
Nos. 492-494 (3)   3.00 1.60

Medicinal Plants Type of 1986
1988, Oct. 18   Engr.   Perf. 13
495 A111 23fr Davallia solida   .75 .35
496 A111 36fr Rorippa sarmentosa   1.10 .50
497 A111 49fr Lindernia crustacea   1.40 .75
Nos. 495-497 (3)   3.25 1.60

Protestant Missionaries — A128

1988, Dec. 7   Litho.
498 A128 80fr Henry Nott (1774-1844)   1.50 .90
499 A128 90fr Papeiha (1800-40)   2.00 1.25
500 A128 100fr Samuel Raapoto (1921-76)   2.25 1.40
Nos. 498-500 (3)   5.75 3.55

Tahiti Post Office A129

1989, Jan. 12   Engr.
501 A129 30fr P.O., 1875   .75 .40
502 A129 40fr P.O., 1915   1.00 .55

Center for Arts and Crafts A130

1989, Feb. 15   Litho.   Perf. 12½
503 A130 29fr Marquesas Is. lidded bowl   .85 .40
504 A130 31fr Mother-of-pearl pendant   .95 .45

Copra Industry

Extracting Coconut Meat From Shell — A131a

Drying Coconut Meat in Sun — A131

1989, Mar. 16   Litho.   Perf. 13
505 A131a 55fr multicolored   75.00 75.00
506 A131 70fr multicolored   2.50 2.50

Tapa Art — A132

43fr, Wood statue (pole), Marquesas Islands, vert. 51fr, Hand-painted bark tapestry, Society Is. 56fr, Concentric circles, Tubuai, Austral Islands.

1989, Apr. 18   Litho.   Perf. 13½
507 A132 43fr multicolored   .90 .60
508 A132 51fr shown   1.25 .75
509 A132 56fr multicolored   1.50 .90
Nos. 507-509 (3)   3.65 2.25

Polynesian Environment A133

1989, May 17   Litho.   Perf. 13x12½
510 A133 120fr shown   3.00 1.60
511 A133 140fr Diving for seashells   3.50 1.90

Polynesian Folklore A134

Perf. 13x12½, 12½x13
1989, June 28   Litho.
512 A134 47fr Stone-lifting contest, vert.   1.25 .60
513 A134 61fr Dancer, vert.   1.50 .75
514 A134 67fr Folk singers   1.90 .80
Nos. 512-514 (3)   4.65 2.15

Bounty Castaways, from an Etching by Robert Dodd — A135

1989, July 7   Engr.   Perf. 13
515 A135 100fr dp blue & bl grn   2.50 1.60
Souvenir Sheet
Imperf
516 A135 200fr dk ol grn & dk brn   12.50 12.50

PHILEXFRANCE '89 and 200th annivs. of the mutiny on the Bounty and the French revolution.
No. 515 printed se-tenant with label picturing exhibition emblem.

Reverend-Father Patrick O'Reilly (1900-1988) A136

1989, Aug. 7   Engr.   Perf. 13x13½
517 A136 52fr yel brn & myrtle grn   1.40 .75

Miniature Sheet

Messages A137

a, Get well soon. b, Good luck. c, Happy birthday. d, Keep in touch. e, Congratulations.

1989, Sept. 27   Litho.   Perf. 12½
518 A137 42fr Sheet of 5, #a.-e.   7.50 7.50

Sea Shells A138

1989, Oct. 12   Litho.   Perf. 13½
523 A138 60fr Triphoridae   1.60 .80
524 A138 69fr Muricidae favartia   1.75 .90
525 A138 73fr Muricidae morula   2.00 1.00
Nos. 523-525 (3)   5.35 2.70

Te Faaturama, c. 1892, by Gauguin A139

1989, Nov. 19   Litho.   Perf. 12½x13
526 A139 1000fr multicolored   22.50 13.00

Legends — A140

Designs: 66fr, Maui, birth of the islands, vert. 82fr, Mt. Rotui, the pierced mountain. 88fr, Princess Hina and the eel King of Lake Vaihiria.

1989, Dec. 6   Litho.   Perf. 13
527 A140 66fr olive brn & blk   1.25 .90
528 A140 82fr buff & blk   1.75 1.10
529 A140 88fr cream & blk   1.90 1.15
Nos. 527-529 (3)   4.90 3.15

Vanilla Orchid — A141

1990, Jan. 11   Litho.
530 A141 34fr Flower   1.40 .60
531 A141 35fr Bean pods   1.75 .60

Marine Life A142

1990, Feb. 9   Litho.   Perf. 13½
532 A142 40fr Kuhlia marginata   1.40 .60
533 A142 50fr Macrobrachium   1.60 .75

Tahiti, Center of Polynesian Triangle — A143

Maohi settlers and maps of island settlements: 58fr, Hawaiian Islands. 59fr, Easter Island. 63fr, New Zealand.

1990, Mar. 14   Engr.   Perf. 13
534 A143 58fr black   1.75 .85
535 A143 59fr bluish gray   47.50 22.50
536 A143 63fr olive green   2.25 .95
537 A143 71fr Prussian blue   2.50 1.10
Nos. 534-537 (4)   54.00 25.40

See Nos. 544-545.

Papeete Village, Cent. — A144

1990, May 16   Litho.
538 A144 150fr New City Hall   3.50 2.00
539 A144 250fr Old Town Hall   5.00 3.25

A145

A146

Designs: Endangered birds.

1990, June 5   *Perf. 13½*
540 A145 13fr Porzana tabuensis .75 .20
541 A145 20fr Vini ultramarina 1.75 .35

1990, July 10   *Perf. 13*
542 A146 39fr multicolored 1.00 .60

Lions Club in Papeete, 30th anniv.

Gen. Charles de Gaulle, Birth
Cent. — A147

1990, Sept. 2   Litho.
543 A147 200fr multi 4.00 3.00

No. 536 with Different Colors and
Inscriptions

1990, Aug. 24   Engr.   *Perf. 13*
544 A143 125fr Man, map 3.00 2.00

Souvenir Sheet
Imperf
545 A143 230fr like No. 544 6.00 6.00

New Zealand 1990.

Intl. Tourism
Day — A148

1990, Sept. 27   Litho.   *Perf. 12½*
546 A148 8f red & yellow pareo 1.00 .35
547 A148 10fr yellow pareo 1.00 .35
548 A148 12fr blue pareo 1.00 .75
     Nos. 546-548 (3) 3.00 1.45

Polynesian Legends — A149

170fr, Legend of the Uru. 290fr, Pipiri-ma,
vert. 375fr, Hiro, God of Thieves, vert.

1990, Nov. 7   Litho.   *Perf. 13*
549 A149 170fr multicolored 4.00 2.50
550 A149 290fr multicolored 7.50 4.50
551 A149 375fr multicolored 11.00 5.75
     Nos. 549-551 (3) 22.50 12.75

Tiare
Flower — A150

Pineapple
A151

Designs: 28fr, Flower crown, lei. 30fr, Flowers in bloom. 37fr, Lei.

1990, Dec. 5   *Perf. 12½*
552 A150 28fr multicolored .75 .45
553 A150 30fr multicolored 1.00 .50
554 A150 37fr multicolored 1.25 .60
     Nos. 552-554 (3) 3.00 1.55

1991, Jan. 9   *Die Cut*
Self-adhesive
555 A151 42fr shown 1.10 .90
556 A151 44fr Pineapple field 1.40 1.10

#555-556 are on paper backing perf. 12½.

Marine Life
A152

1991, Feb. 7   *Perf. 12½*
557 A152 7fr Nudibranch .50 .20
558 A152 9fr Galaxaura tenera .75 .20
559 A152 11fr Adusta cumingii .75 .20
     Nos. 557-559 (3) 2.00 .60

Maohi Islands — A153

18th Century scenes of: 68fr, Woman of
Easter Island, vert. 84fr, Twin-hulled canoe,
Hawaii. 94fr, Maori village, New Zealand.

1991, Mar. 13   Engr.   *Perf. 13*
560 A153 68fr olive 47.50 32.50
561 A153 84fr black 2.50 1.75
562 A153 94fr brown 3.00 1.75
     Nos. 560-562 (3) 53.00 36.00

Basketball, Cent. — A154

1991, May 15   Litho.   *Perf. 13*
563 A154 80fr multicolored 1.75 1.25

Birds — A155

1991, June 5   *Perf. 13½*
564 A155 17fr Halcyon gambieri .60 .25
565 A155 21fr Vini kuhlii .90 .35

Still Life with Oranges in Tahiti by Paul
Gauguin — A156

1991, June 9   Litho.   *Perf. 13*
566 A156 700fr multicolored 17.50 12.00

Sculptures of the Marquesas
Islands — A157

56fr, White Tiki with Club, vert. 102fr, Warriors Carrying Tired Man, vert. 110fr, Native
Canoe.

1991, July 17   Litho.   *Perf. 13*
567 A157 56fr multicolored 1.25 .85
568 A157 102fr multicolored 2.25 1.50
569 A157 110fr multicolored 2.50 1.75
     Nos. 567-569 (3) 6.00 4.10

Wolfgang Amadeus Mozart, Death
Bicent. — A158

1991, Aug. 28   Engr.   *Perf. 13x12½*
570 A158 100fr multicolored 3.50 1.75

Stone Fishing — A159

1991, Oct. 9   Litho.   *Perf. 13*
571 A159 25fr Fishing boats,
     vert. .60 .40
572 A159 57fr Man hurling stone,
     vert. 1.25 .90
573 A159 62fr Trapped fish 1.50 1.25
     Nos. 571-573 (3) 3.35 2.55

Phila
Nippon '91
A160

Designs: 50fr, Drawings of marine life by
Jules-Louis Lejeune, vert. 70fr, Sailing ship,
La Coquille. 250fr, Contains designs from
Nos. 574-575.

Perf. 12½x13, 13x12½
1991, Nov. 16   Engr.
574 A160 50fr multicolored 1.25 .60
575 A160 70fr multicolored 1.75 1.00

Size: 100x75mm
Imperf
576 A160 250fr multicolored 6.00 6.00
     Nos. 574-576 (3) 9.00 7.60

Central Bank for Economic Cooperation, 50th Anniv. — A161

1991, Dec. 2   Litho.   *Perf. 13x12½*
577 A161 307fr multicolored 7.00 4.50

Christmas
A162

Perf. 12½x13, 13x12½
1991, Dec. 11   Litho.
578 A162 55fr Scuba divers 1.25 .75
579 A162 83fr Underwater scene 1.75 1.35
580 A162 86fr Nativity, vert. 1.75 1.35
     Nos. 578-580 (3) 4.75 3.45

Tourism — A163

1992, Feb. 12   *Perf. 13*
581 A163 1fr shown .20 .20
582 A163 2fr Horses, beach .35 .25
583 A163 3fr Girl holding fish .50 .30
584 A163 4fr Waterfalls, vert. .60 .35
585 A163 5fr Sailing .75 .40
586 A163 6fr Waterfalls, helicop-
     ter, vert. 1.00 .45
     Nos. 581-586 (6) 3.40 1.95

Views from Space — A164

1992, Mar. 18   Litho.   Perf. 13x12½
587 A164 46fr Tahiti   1.10   .90
588 A164 72fr Mataiva   1.60 1.40
589 A164 76fr Bora Bora   1.75 1.50
    Size: 130x100mm
    Imperf
590 A164 230fr Satellite imaging
                system   5.75 5.75
    Nos. 587-590 (4)   10.20 9.55
    International Space Year.

World
Health Day
A165

1992, Apr. 7   Perf. 13½
591 A165 136fr multicolored   3.00 2.25

Discovery of America, 500th
Anniv. — A166

1992, May 22   Perf. 13
592 A166 130fr multicolored   3.00 2.25
    Size: 140x100mm
    Imperf
593 A166 250fr multicolored   6.00 6.00
World Columbian Stamp Expo '92, Chicago.

Traditional Dances — A167

Dance from: 95fr, Tahiti. 105fr, Hawaii.
115fr, Tonga.

1992, June 17   Engr.   Perf. 13
594 A167 95fr brown black   2.25 1.65
595 A167 105fr olive brown   2.50 1.85
596 A167 115fr red brn & olive
                grn   2.75 2.00
    Nos. 594-596 (3)   7.50 5.50

Tattoos
A168

1992, July 8   Litho.   Perf. 12½
597 A168 61fr Hand   1.75 1.00
598 A168 64fr Man, vert.   1.75 1.00

Children's
Games
A169

1992, Aug. 5   Perf. 13½
599 A169 22fr Outrigger canoe
                models   .50   .35
600 A169 31fr String game   .75   .45
601 A169 45fr Stilt game, vert.   1.25   .70
    Nos. 599-601 (3)   2.50 1.50

Herman Melville,
150th Anniv. of
Arrival in French
Polynesia — A170

1992, Sept. 16   Perf. 12½
602 A170 78fr multicolored   4.50 1.25

6th Festival of Pacific Arts,
Rarotonga — A171

40fr, Men on raft. 65fr, Pirogues, Tahiti.

1992, Oct. 16   Engr.   Perf. 13
603 A171 40fr lake   1.00   .60
604 A171 65fr blue   1.75 1.00

First French Polynesian Postage
Stamps, Cent. — A172

1992, Nov. 18   Photo.   Perf. 13
605 A172 200fr multicolored   4.75 3.25

Paintings
A173

55fr, Two Women Talking, by Erhard Lux.
60fr, Bouquet of Flowers, by Uschi. 75fr,
Spearfisherman, by Pierre Kienlen. 85fr,
Mother Nursing Child, by Octave Morillot.

1992, Dec. 9   Perf. 12½x13
606 A173 55fr multicolored   1.50   .75
607 A173 60fr multicolored   1.75 1.40
608 A173 75fr multicolored   1.90 1.50
609 A173 85fr multicolored   2.50 1.60
    Nos. 606-609 (4)   7.65 5.25

Net Thrower
A174

Bonito Fishing
A175

1993, Feb. 10   Litho.
    Self-Adhesive   Die Cut
    Size: 26x36mm
610 A174 46fr blue & multi   1.50 1.00
    Size: 17x23mm
611 A174 46fr green & multi   1.50 1.00
    a.   Booklet pane of 10   15.00

1993, Mar. 10   Perf. 13½
612 A175 68fr Line & hook   1.60 1.25
613 A175 84fr Boat, horiz.   1.90 1.50
614 A175 86fr Drying catch   2.10 1.50
    Nos. 612-614 (3)   5.60 4.25

Allied Airfield on Bora Bora, 50th
Anniv. — A176

1993, Apr. 5   Perf. 13
615 A176 120fr multicolored   3.00 2.25

Jacques Boullaire, Artist, Birth
Cent. — A177

Various scenes depicting life on: 32fr,
Moorea. 36fr, Tuamotu. 39fr, Rururu. 51fr,
Nuku Hiva.

1993, May 6   Engr.
616 A177 32fr brown black   .75   .60
617 A177 36fr brick red   .85   .65
618 A177 39fr violet   1.00   .75
619 A177 51fr light brown   1.40 1.00
    Nos. 616-619 (4)   4.00 3.00

Sports
Festival — A178

1993, May 15   Litho.   Perf. 12½
620 A178 30fr multicolored   .75   .60

Australian Mathematics Competition,
15th Anniv. — A179

1993, July 1   Litho.   Perf. 13½
621 A179 70fr multicolored   1.60 1.10

Intl. Symposium
on Inter-Plate
Volcanism,
French University
of the Pacific,
Punaauia
A180

1993, Aug. 2   Litho.   Perf. 13
622 A180 140fr tan, blk & brn   3.50 2.50

Taipei '93 — A181

Tourism — A182

1993, Aug. 14   Litho.   Perf. 13½
623 A181 46fr multicolored   2.50   .85
    Exists without the Cartor imprint. Value,
unused $15.

1993, Sept. 27
    14fr, Boat tour. 20fr, Groom preparing for
traditional wedding. 29fr, Beachside brunch.
624 A182 14fr multi, horiz.   .60   .35
625 A182 20fr multi   .65   .35
626 A182 29fr multi, horiz.   .75   .45
    Nos. 624-626 (3)   2.00 1.15
    Exist without the Cartor imprint. Value, set
unused $20.

Arrival of First French Gendarme in
Tahiti, 150th Anniv. — A183

1993, Oct. 14   Perf. 13
627 A183 100fr multicolored   2.50 1.60
    Exists without the Cartor imprint. Value,
unused $15.

Alain Gerbault (1893-1941),
Sailor — A184

1993, Nov. 17   Engr.   Perf. 13
628 A184 150fr red, green & blue 4.00 2.75

Paintings — A185

Artists: 40fr, Vaea Sylvain. 70fr, A. Marere, vert. 80fr, J. Shelsher. 90fr, P.E. Victor, vert.

1993, Dec. 3 **Photo.** **Perf. 13**
629 A185 40fr multicolored   1.00   .70
630 A185 70fr multicolored   1.75 1.25
631 A185 80fr multicolored   1.90 1.25
632 A185 90fr multicolored   2.25 1.50
    Nos. 629-632 (4)   6.90 4.70

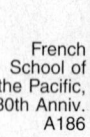

French
School of
the Pacific,
30th Anniv.
A186

1993, Dec. 7 **Litho.** **Perf. 12½**
633 A186 200fr multicolored   5.00 3.50

Whales and
Dolphins
A187

1994, Jan. 12 **Litho.** **Perf. 13½**
634 A187 25fr Whale breeching   .75   .45
635 A187 68fr Dolphins   1.75 1.10
636 A187 72fr Humpback whales,
     vert.   2.00 1.25
    Nos. 634-636 (3)   4.50 2.80

A188

1994, Feb. 18 **Litho.** **Perf. 13½**
637 A188 51fr multicolored   2.00   .95

Hong Kong '94. New Year 1994 (Year of the Dog).

A189

1994, Mar. 16
638 A189 180fr Sister Germaine
     Bruel   4.00 3.00

Arrival of Nuns from St. Joseph of Cluny, 150th anniv.

Church of Jesus Christ of Latter-day
Saints in French Polynesia, 150th
Anniv.
A190

1994, Apr. 30 **Litho.** **Perf. 13½**
639 A190 154fr Tahiti temple   3.50 2.75

Conservatory of Arts and Crafts,
Bicent. — A191

1994, May 25 **Photo.** **Perf. 13**
640 A191 316fr multicolored   7.50 5.50

Regional Associated Center of Papeete, 15th anniv.

Internal Self-Government, 10th
Anniv. — A192

1994, June 29 **Litho.** **Perf. 13**
641 A192 500fr multicolored   12.00 7.50

Tahitian Academy, 20th Anniv. — A193

1994, July 2 **Engr.** **Perf. 13**
642 A193 136fr multicolored   3.00 2.00

Scenes of Old Tahiti — A194

1994, Aug. 10 **Litho.** **Perf. 13**
643 A194 22fr Papara   .75   .40
644 A194 26fr Mataiea   .85   .45
645 A194 51fr Taravao, vert.   1.60   .95
    Nos. 643-645 (3)   3.20 1.80

    See Nos. 673-675.

Faaturuma,
by Paul
Gauguin
(1848-1903)
A195

1994, Sept. 14 **Litho.** **Perf. 13**
646 A195 1000fr multicolored   22.50 15.00

Epiphyllum
Oxypetalum
A196

1994, Oct. 15 **Litho.** **Perf. 13½**
647 A196 51fr multicolored   1.75   .95

Hawaiki Nui
Va'a '94
(Canoe
Race)
A197

Designs: a, 52fr, Yellow canoe, bow paddler. b, 76fr, Paddlers. c, 80fr, Paddlers, blue canoe. d, 94fr, Stern paddler, yellow canoe.

1994, Nov. 10 **Litho.** **Perf. 13½x13**
648 A197 Strip of 4, #a.-d.   8.00 4.75

    No. 648 is a continuous design.

Paintings of French Polynesia — A198

62fr, Young girl, by Michelle Villemin. 78fr, Ocean tide, fish, by Michele Dallet. 102fr, Native carrying bundles of fruit, by Johel Blanchard. 110fr, View of coastline, by Pierre Lacouture.

1994, Dec. 19 **Litho.** **Perf. 13**
649 A198 62fr multi, vert.   1.60   .95
650 A198 78fr multi, vert.   1.90 1.25
651 A198 102fr multi, vert.   2.10 1.60
652 A198 110fr multi   2.40 1.75
    Nos. 649-652 (4)   8.00 5.55

Don Domingo de Boenechea's Tautira
Expedition, 220th Anniv. — A199

1995, Jan. 1
653 A199 92fr multicolored   2.75 1.40

South Pacific
Tourism
Year — A200

1995, Jan. 11 **Litho.** **Perf. 13½**
654 A200 92fr multicolored   2.25 1.40

New Year
1995 (Year
of the
Boar)
A201

1995, Feb. 1 **Litho.**
655 A201 51fr multicolored   1.75   .80

Portions of the design on No. 655 were applied by a thermographic process producing a shiny, raised effect.

Exists without the Cartor imprint. Value, unused $9.

University
Teacher's Training
Institute of the
Pacific — A202

1995, Mar. 8 **Litho.** **Perf. 13½**
656 A202 59fr multicolored   1.50   .95

Nature
Protection
A203

1995, May 4 **Litho.** **Perf. 13**
657   Strip of 3 + 2 labels   4.25 4.25
  a. A203 22fr Head of turtle   .75   .35
  b. A203 29fr Turtle swimming   1.00   .50
  c. A203 91fr Black coral   2.50 1.50

Louis Pasteur (1822-95) — A204

1995, May 8
658 A204 290fr dk blue & blue   7.25 5.00

Loti's Marriage, Novel by Julien Viaud
(1850-1923) — A205

1995, May 19 **Photo.** **Perf. 13**
659 A205 66fr multicolored   1.75 1.10

A206

Birds — A207

1995, May 24   Litho.   Perf. 13½
660 A206 150fr multicolored   3.50 2.25
Tahitian Monoi beauty aid.

1995, June 7
661 A207 22fr Ptilinopus huttoni   .55   .35
662 A207 44fr Ducula galeata   1.10   .75

Tahitian
Pearls
A208

1995, June 14
663 A208 66fr shown   1.60 1.10
664 A208 84fr Eight pearls   2.10 1.40

On Nos. 663-664 portions of the design were applied by a thermographic process producing a shiny, raised effect.

Discovery of Marquesas Islands, 400th Anniv. — A209

a, Alvaro de Mendana de Neira, sailing ships. b, Pedro Fernandez de Quiros, map of islands.

1995, July 21   Litho.   Perf. 13
665 Pair + label   8.00 6.00
  a. A209 161fr multicolored   3.50 2.75
  b. A209 195fr multicolored   4.50 3.25

A210

A211

1995, Aug. 12   Litho.   Perf. 13
666 A210 83fr multicolored   2.00 1.40
10th South Pacific Games, Tahiti.

1995, Sept. 1   Perf. 13½x13
Pandanus plant: No. 667a, Entire plant. b, Flower. c, Fruit. d, Using dry leaves for weaving.
667   Strip of 4   8.50 6.00
  a.-d. A211 91fr any single   2.00 1.50
Singapore '95.

UN, 50th Anniv. — A212

1995, Oct. 24   Litho.   Perf. 13
668 A212 420fr multicolored   9.50 6.00

Paintings — A213

Designs: 57fr, The Paddler with the Yellow Dog, by Philippe Dubois, vert. 76fr, An Afternoon in Vaitape, by Maui Seaman, vert. 79fr, The Mama with the White Hat, by Simone Testeguide. 100fr, In Front of the Kellum House in Moorea, by Christian Deloffre.

1995, Dec. 6   Photo.   Perf. 13
669 A213 57fr multicolored   1.25   .90
670 A213 76fr multicolored   1.60 1.25
671 A213 79fr multicolored   1.75 1.25
672 A213 100fr multicolored   2.25 1.60
    Nos. 669-672 (4)   6.85 5.00

Scenes of Old Tahiti Type
1996, Jan. 17   Litho.   Perf. 13
673 A194 18fr Fautaua   .55   .30
674 A194 30fr District of
            Punaauia   .85   .50
675 A194 35fr Tautira   1.10   .60
    Nos. 673-675 (3)   2.50 1.40

New Year 1996
(Year of the
Rat) — A214

1996, Feb. 19   Photo.   Perf. 13
676 A214 51fr multicolored   1.75   .80
Portions of the design on No. 676 were applied by a thermographic process producing a shiny, raised effect.

Paul-Emile Victor (1907-95), Explorer, Writer — A215

1996, Mar. 7   Litho.
677 A215 500fr multicolored   12.00 8.00

Queen Pomare
IV — A216

1996, Mar. 1   Litho.   Perf. 13
678 A216 (51fr) multicolored   1.50   .80
Serpentine Die Cut 7 Vert.
Self-Adhesive
Size: 17x24mm
678A A216 (51fr) multicolored   2.00 1.15
  b.   Booklet pane of 5   10.00
        Complete booklet, 2 #678b   20.00

Sea Shells
A217

10fr, Conus pertusus. 15fr, Cypraea alisonae. 25fr, Vexillum roseotinctum.

1996, Apr. 10   Photo.   Perf. 13½x13
679 A217 10fr multicolored   .40   .20
680 A217 15fr multicolored   .45   .25
681 A217 25fr multicolored   .90   .40
    Nos. 679-681 (3)   1.75   .85

Portions of the designs on Nos. 679-681 were applied by a thermographic process producing a shiny, raised effect.

Return of the Pacific Battalion, 50th Anniv. — A218

1996, May 5   Litho.   Perf. 13
682 A218 100fr multicolored   3.00 1.60

CHINA '96,
9th Asian
Intl.
Philatelic
Exhibition
A219

Design: 200fr, Chinese School, Tahiti, 1940. Illustration reduced.

1996, May 18   Perf. 13x13½
683 A219 50fr multicolored   1.25   .80
Souvenir Sheet
Imperf
684 A219 200fr multicolored   4.50 3.40

Birds
A220

1996, June 12   Litho.   Perf. 13x13½
685 A220 66fr Sula sula   1.50 1.10
686 A220 79fr Fregata minor   2.00 1.25
687 A220 84fr Anous stolidus   2.00 1.40
    Nos. 685-687 (3)   5.50 3.75

Musical
Instruments
A221

1996, July 10   Perf. 13x13½
688 A221 5fr Pahu, ukulele,
            toere   .30   .20
689 A221 9fr Toere   .40   .20
690 A221 14fr Pu, vivo   .50   .20
    Nos. 688-690 (3)   1.20   .60

Raiateana
Oulietea
A222

1996, Aug. 7   Litho.   Perf. 13x13½
691 A222 66fr multicolored   1.75 1.10

A223

A224

1996, Sept. 9   Litho.   Perf. 13
692 A223 70fr Ruahatu, God of
            the Ocean   1.75 1.10
7th Pacific Arts Festival.

1996, Oct. 16   Engr.   Perf. 13
Stamp Day: Young Tahitian girl (Type A2), Noho Mercier, taken from photo by Henry Lemasson (1870-1956), postal administrator.
693 A224 92fr black, red & blue   2.50 1.50

First Representative Assembly, 50th
Anniv. — A225

1996, Nov. 7   Litho.   Perf. 13
694 A225 85fr multicolored   2.25   .90

Paintings of Tahitian Women — A226

Designs: 70fr, Woman lounging on Bora
Bora Beach, by Titi Bécaud. 85fr, "Woman
with Crown of Auti leaves," by Maryse Noguier,
vert. 92fr, "Dreamy Woman," by Christine de
Dinechin, vert. 96fr, Two working women, by
Andrée Lang, vert.

1996, Dec. 4   Litho.   Perf. 13
695 A226 70fr multicolored   1.75   .75
696 A226 85fr multicolored   1.90   .90
697 A226 92fr multicolored   2.25 1.00
698 A226 96fr multicolored   2.50 1.00
        Nos. 695-698 (4)   8.40 3.65

A227

A228

1997, Jan. 2   Litho.   Perf. 13
699 A227 55fr brown   1.25   .55

Society of South Sea Studies, 80th anniv.

1997, Feb. 7   Photo.   Perf. 13½x13
700 A228 13fr multicolored   .75   .20

New Year 1997 (Year of the Ox). Portions of
the design were applied by a thermographic
process producing a shiny, raised effect.

Arrival of Evangelists in Tahiti,
Bicent. — A229

Designs: a, Sailing ship, "Duff." b, Painting,
"Transfer of the Matavai District to the L.M.S.
Missionaries," by Robert Smirke.

1997, Mar. 5   Litho.   Perf. 13
701 A229 43fr Pair, #a.-b. + label 3.00   .85

Tifaifai
(Tahitian
Bedspread)
A230

Various leaf and floral patterns.

1997, Apr. 16
702 A230 1fr multicolored   .20   .20
703 A230 5fr multicolored   .20   .20
704 A230 70fr multicolored   1.60   .70
        Nos. 702-704 (3)   2.00 1.10

PACIFIC
97 — A231

Sailing ships carrying mail, passengers
between Tahiti and San Francisco: No. 705,
Tropic Bird, 1897. No. 706, Papeete/Zélee,
1892.

1997, May 29   Litho.   Perf. 13
705 A231 92fr multicolored   2.25   .90
706 A231 92fr multicolored   2.25   .90
   a.   Pair, #705-706   5.25 5.25
   b.   Souvenir sheet, #705-706   45.00 45.00

No. 706b sold for 400fr.

Island
Scenes
A232

#707, Flower. #708, Rowing canoe, sun
behind mountain. #709, Throwing spears.
#710. Aerial view of island. #711, Fish. #712,
Women walking on beach. #713, Holding oyster shell with pearls. #714, Boat with sail
down, sunset across water. #715, Snorkeling,
sting ray. #716, Bananas, pineapples. #717,
Palm tree, beach. #718, Women dancers in
costume.

1997, June 25   Litho.   Perf. 13
Booklet Stamps
707 A232 85fr multicolored   10.00 9.00
708 A232 85fr multicolored   10.00 9.00
709 A232 85fr multicolored   10.00 9.00
710 A232 85fr multicolored   10.00 9.00
711 A232 85fr multicolored   10.00 9.00
712 A232 85fr multicolored   10.00 9.00
   a.   Bklt. pane of 6, #707-712   60.00
713 A232 85fr multicolored   10.00 9.00
714 A232 85fr multicolored   10.00 9.00
715 A232 85fr multicolored   10.00 9.00
716 A232 85fr multicolored   10.00 9.00
717 A232 85fr multicolored   10.00 9.00
718 A232 85fr multicolored   10.00 9.00
   a.   Bklt. pane of 6, #713-718   60.00
        Complete booklet, 2 each
        #712a, #718a   240.00

Traditional Dance
Costumes
A233

Designs: 4fr, Warrior's costume. 9fr,
Women's costume. 11fr, Couple.

1997, July 10   Litho.   Perf. 13½x13
719 A233 4fr multicolored   .40   .20
720 A233 9fr multicolored   .50   .20
721 A233 11fr multicolored   .75   .20
        Nos. 719-721 (3)   1.65   .60

Kon-Tiki Expedition, 50th
Anniv. — A234

1997, Aug. 7   Litho.   Perf. 13
722 A234 88fr multicolored   2.25   .80

Artists in Tahiti — A235

Designs: 85fr, Painting, "The Fruit Carrier,"
by Monique "Mono" Garnier-Bissol. 96fr,
"Revival of Our Resources," mother of pearl
painting, by Camélia Maraea. 110fr, "Tahitian
Spirit," pottery, by Peter Owen, vert. 126fr,
"Monoi," surrealist painting, by Elisabeth
Stefanovitch.

1997, Oct. 15   Litho.   Perf. 13
723 A235 85fr multicolored   1.90   .80
724 A235 96fr multicolored   2.00   .90
725 A235 110fr multicolored   2.50 1.00
726 A235 126fr multicolored   3.00 1.10
        Nos. 723-726 (4)   9.40 3.80

Te Arii Vahine, by Paul Gauguin
(1848-1903) — A236

1997, Nov. 6   Litho.   Perf. 13
727 A236 600fr multicolored   15.00 5.75

Christmas
A237

1997, Dec. 3   Litho.   Perf. 13
728 A237 118fr multicolored   3.00 1.10

New Year
1998 (Year
of the
Tiger)
A238

1998, Jan. 28   Photo.   Perf. 13
729 A238 96fr multicolored   2.50   .90

Portions of the design on No. 729 were
applied by a thermographic process producing
a shiny, raised effect.

Domestic Airline
Network — A239

Designs: a, 70fr, Grumman Widgeon, 1950.
b, 85fr, DHC 6 Twin-Otter, 1968. c, 70fr,
Fairchild FH 227, 1980. d, 85fr, ATR 42-500,
1998.

1998, Apr. 16   Photo.   Perf. 13
730 A239 Strip of 4, #a.-d. + la-
           bel   6.50 2.90

Orchids
A240

5fr, Dendrobium "Royal King." 20fr, Oncidium "Ramsey." 50fr, Ascodenca "Laksi." 100fr,
Cattleya "hybride."

1998, May 14   Photo.   Perf. 13
731 A240 5fr multi   .25   .20
732 A240 20fr multi, vert.   .50   .20
733 A240 50fr multi, vert.   1.25   .45
734 A240 100fr multi   2.25   .95
        Nos. 731-734 (4)   4.25 1.80

On Nos. 731-734 portions of the design
were applied by a thermographic process producing a shiny, raised effect.

The Lovers, by Paul Gauguin (1848-
1903) — A241

1998, June 7   Photo.   Perf. 13x12½
735 A241 1000fr multicolored   22.50 9.00

Printed se-tenant with label.

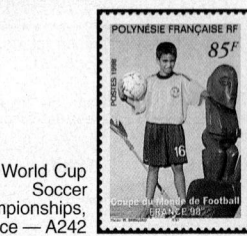

1998 World Cup
Soccer
Championships,
France — A242

1998, June 10
736 A242 85fr multicolored   2.00   .75

For overprint see No. 742.

Tahiti Festival of
Flower and Shell
Garlands — A243

Women wearing various garlands of flowers
or shells.

1998, July 16   Photo.   Perf. 13½
737 A243 55fr multicolored   1.25   .50
738 A243 65fr multicolored   1.60   .60
739 A243 70fr multicolored   1.75   .65
740 A243 80fr multicolored   2.00   .75
        Nos. 737-740 (4)   6.60 2.50

Painting, "Underwater World of Polynesia," by Stanley Haumani
A244

1998, Sept. 10   Photo.   Perf. 12½x13
741 A244 200fr multicolored   4.25 2.00

No. 736 Ovptd. in Blue & Black "France / Championne / du Munde"
1998, Oct. 28   Photo.   Perf. 13½
742 A242 85fr multicolored   2.00 .80

Autumn Philatelic Fair, Paris — A246

Watercolor paintings of Papeete Bay, by René Gillotin (1814-61): a, Beach at left, people. b, Beach at right, people.

1998, Nov. 5   Perf. 13
743 A246 250fr Pair, #a.-b. + label   12.00 5.00
 c.   Souvenir sheet, #a.-b., imperf.   12.00 5.00

Life in Tahiti and the Islands
A247

Paintings by André Deymonaz: 70fr, Return to the Market, vert. 100fr, Bonito Fish Stalls, vert. 102fr, Going Fishing. 110fr, Discussion after Church Services.

1998, Dec. 10   Photo.   Perf. 13
744 A247 70fr multicolored   1.60 .70
745 A247 100fr multicolored   2.50 1.00
746 A247 102fr multicolored   2.50 1.00
747 A247 110fr multicolored   2.75 1.10
     Nos. 744-747 (4)   9.35 3.80

St. Valentine's Day — A248

1999, Feb. 11   Litho.   Perf. 13
748 A248 96fr multicolored   2.50 .90

New Year 1999 (Year of the Rabbit)
A249

1999, Feb. 16
749 A249 118fr Rabbits, flowers   2.50 1.10

Portions of the design of No. 749 were applied by a thermographic process producing a shiny, raised effect.

Marine Life
A250

Designs: 70fr, Ptérois volitans. 85fr, Hippocampus histrix. 90fr, Antennarius pictus. 120fr, Taenianotus triacanthus.

1999, Mar. 18   Photo.   Perf. 13
750 A250 70fr multicolored   1.50 .65
751 A250 85fr multicolored   1.90 .80
752 A250 90fr multicolored   2.00 .80
753 A250 120fr multicolored   2.75 1.10
     Nos. 750-753 (4)   8.15 3.35

Portions of the designs on Nos. 750-753 were applied by a thermographic process producing a shiny, raised effect.

IBRA '99, World Philatelic Exhibition, Nuremberg
A251

Tatooed men of Marquesas Islands, 1804: 90fr, Holding staff, fan. 120fr, Wearing blue cape.

Photo. & Engr.
1999, Apr. 27   Perf. 13¼
754 A251 90fr multicolored   2.00 .90
755 A251 120fr multicolored   2.75 1.25

Mother's Day
A252

1999, May 27   Litho.   Perf. 13¼
756 A252 85fr Children, vert.   1.90 .75
757 A252 120fr shown   2.75 1.00

Island Fruits
A254

#758, Breadfruit, vert. 120fr, Coconut.
#760: a, Papaya. b, Guava (goyave). c, Mombin. d, Rambutan. e, Star apple (pomme-etoile). f, Otaheite gooseberry (seurette). g, Rose apple. h, Star fruit (carambole). i, Spanish lime (quenette). j, Sweetsop (pomme-cannelle). k, Cashew (pomme de caju). l, Passion fruit.

1999   Litho.   Perf. 13½x13, 13x13½
758 A253 85fr multicolored   1.90 .75
759 A253 120fr multicolored   2.75 1.10
Souvenir Booklet
760   Complete bklt.   30.00
 a.-l. A254 85fr Any single   2.00 1.40

Issued: #758, 120fr, 7/21; #760, 7/21.
No. 760 sold for 1200fr, and contains two booklet panes, containing Nos. 760a-760f, and Nos. 760g-760l.

No. 720, 1856 Letter, 1864 Postmark — A255

1999, July 2   Litho.   Perf. 13
761 A255 180fr multicolored   4.00 2.25
 a.   Souvenir sheet of 1   12.00 12.00

150th anniv. of French postage stamps, PhilexFrance 99.
No. 761 issued se-tenant with label. No. 761a sold for 500fr.

Frédéric Chopin (1810-49), Composer — A256

1999, July 2   Litho.   Perf. 13
762 A256 250fr multicolored   5.50 2.50

Malardé Medical Research Institute, 50th Anniv. — A257

1999, Sept. 27
763 A257 400fr multicolored   8.75 3.75

Nudes
A258

Paintings by: 85fr, J. Sorgniard. 120fr, J. Dubrusk. 180fr, C. Deloffre. 250fr, J. Gandouin.

1999, Oct. 14   Litho.   Perf. 13
764 A258 85fr multi   2.00 .75
765 A258 120fr multi   3.00 1.10
766 A258 180fr multi   4.25 1.60
767 A258 250fr multi   5.75 2.25
     Nos. 764-767 (4)   15.00 5.70

Tahiti on the Eve of the Year 2000
A259

1999, Nov. 10   Litho.   Perf. 13
768 A259 85fr multi   2.25 .75

5th Marquesas Islands Arts Festival
A260

1999, Dec. 10
769 A260 90fr multi   2.00 .80

Year 2000
A261

85fr, Hands of adult and infant. 120fr, Eye.

2000, Jan. 3   Perf. 13¼x13, 13x13¼
770 A261 85fr multi, vert.   1.90 .75
771 A261 120fr multi   2.75 1.10

New Year 2000 (Year of the Dragon)
A262

2000, Feb. 5   Litho.   Perf. 13x13¼
772 A262 180fr multi   4.00 1.50

Portions of the design were applied by a thermographic process producing a shiny, raised effect.

Postal Service Emblem and Stamps
A263

2000, Mar. 15   Litho.   Perf. 13x13¼
773 A263 90fr multi   2.00 .75

First Intl. Tattoo Festival, Raiatea — A264

Various tattoos.

2000, Apr. 28   *Perf. 13*
774 A264 85fr multi   1.90   .70
775 A264 120fr multi   2.75   .95
776 A264 130fr multi   2.90 1.00
777 A264 160fr multi   3.50 1.25
     Nos. 774-777 (4)   11.05 3.90

Beautiful Women of French
Polynesia — A265

2000, May 30
778 A265 300fr multi   6.75 3.00
 a.   Souvenir sheet of 1   12.00 11.50
     No. 778a sold for 500fr.

Traditional
Dresses — A266

Denominations: 85fr, 120fr, 160fr, 250fr.

2000, June 21 Litho. Perf. 13¼x13
779-782 A266   Set of 4   13.50 6.00

Mountains
A267

Designs: 90fr, Mts. Aorai and Orohena.
180fr, Mts. Orohena and Aorai.

2000, July 10   Perf. 13x13¼
783-784 A267   Set of 2   6.00 2.60

Traditional
Sports
A268

120fr, Fruit carrying. 250fr, Stone lifting,
vert.

Perf. 13x13¼, 13¼x13
2000, Sept. 15
785-786 A268   Set of 2   8.25 3.50

Native
Woven
Crafts
A269

No. 787, Fans. No. 788, Hat.

2000, Oct. 3   Litho.   Perf. 13x13¼
787-788 A269 85fr Set of 2   3.75 1.75

Year of
Ancient
Tahitian
Language
Reo
Ma'ohi
A270

2000, Nov. 9   Litho.   Perf. 13x13¼
789 A270 120fr multi   2.75 1.20
     Portions of the design were applied by a
thermographic process producing a shiny,
raised effect.

Advent of New Millennium — A271

2000, Dec. 28
790 A271 85fr multi   1.90   .90

Central School, Cent. — A272

Designs: No. 791, 85fr, Central School. No.
792, 85fr, Paul Gauguin High School.

2001, Jan. 16
791-792 A272   Set of 2   3.75 1.75

New Year 2001
(Year of the
Snake) — A273

2001, Jan. 24   Perf. 13¼x13
793 A273 120fr multi   2.75 1.20
     Portions of the design were applied by a
thermographic process producing a shiny,
raised effect.

Landscapes
A274

Designs: 35fr, Vaiharuru Waterfall. 50fr,
Vahiria Lake, horiz. 90fr, Hakaui Valley.

Perf. 13¼x13, 13x13¼
2001, Feb. 26   Litho.
794-796 A274   Set of 3   4.00 1.75

Year of the Polynesian Child — A275

2001, Mar. 28   Litho.   Perf. 13x13¼
797 A275 55fr multi   1.25   .55

Polynesian
Singers — A276

Designs: 85fr, Eddie Lund. 120fr, Charley
Mauu. 130fr, Bimbo. 180fr, Marie Mariteragi
and Emma Terangi, horiz.

2001, Apr. 12   Perf. 13¼x13, 13x13¼
798-801 A276   Set of 4   11.50 5.00

Volunteers
of the
Pacific
Batallion,
60th
Anniv.
A277

2001, Apr. 21   Perf. 13x13¼
802 A277 85fr multi   1.90   .90

Surfing
Waves of
Teahupoo
A278

2001, May 4
803 A278 120fr multi   2.75 1.20

Internal
Autonomy,
17th Anniv.
A279

2001, June 29 Litho.   Perf. 13
804 A279 250fr multi   5.50 2.50
 a.   Souvenir sheet of 1   11.00 11.00
     No. 804a sold for 500fr.

Pirogue
Racing — A280

Designs: 85fr, Male racers. 120fr, Female
racers.

2001, July 12   Perf. 13¼x13
805-806 A280   Set of 2   4.50 2.00
 a.   Souvenir sheet, #805-806, imperf. 5.50 5.50
     No. 806a sold for 250fr.

Hardwood
Trees
A281

Designs: 90fr, Tou. 130fr, Ati. 180fr, Miro.

2001, Oct. 23   Litho.   Perf. 13x13½
807-809 A281   Set of 3   9.00 8.00

AIDS
Prevention
A282

2001, Sept. 20   Litho.   Perf. 13x13¼
810 A282 55fr multi   2.50 1.10

Year of
Dialogue
Among
Civilizations
A283

2001, Oct. 9   Perf. 13
811 A283 500fr multi   11.50 10.00

Perfume
Flowers — A284

Designs: 35fr, Gardenia tahitensis. 50fr,
Fagraea berteriana. 85fr, Gardenia
jasminoides.

2001, Nov. 8   Perf. 13¼x13
812-814 A284   Set of 3   4.25 3.50
     Portions of the designs were applied by a
thermographic process producing a shiny,
raised effect.

Christmas
A285

2001, Dec. 6   Perf. 13x13¼
815 A285 120fr multi   2.75 2.40

New Year
2002 (Year
of the
Horse)
A286

2002, Feb. 12   Litho.   Perf. 13x13¼
816 A286 130fr multi   2.90 2.60
     Portions of the design were applied by a
thermographic process producing a shiny,
raised effect.

Happy Holidays A287

Greetings A288

2002, Feb. 28   **Background Colors**
817	A287	55fr	red	1.25 1.10
818	A288	55fr	blue	1.25 1.10
819	A287	85fr	blue	1.90 1.75
820	A288	85fr	green	1.90 1.75
	Nos. 817-820 (4)			6.30 5.70

10th World Outrigger Canoe Championships — A289

Canoe rowers and emblems: 120fr, 180fr.

2002, Mar. 9   **Photo.**   **Perf. 13¼**
821-822	A289	Set of 2	6.75 6.25

Sea Urchins A290

Designs: 35fr, Echinometra sp. 50fr, Heterocentrotus trigonarius. 90fr, Echinothrix calamaris. 120fr, Toxopneustes sp.

2002, Apr. 18   **Litho.**   **Perf. 13x13¼**
823-826	A290	Set of 4	6.50 6.25

Blood Donation — A291

2002, May 3   **Litho.**   **Perf. 13¼x13**
827	A291	130fr multi	3.25 3.25

2002 World Cup Soccer Championships, Japan and Korea — A292

2002, May 30
828	A292	85fr multi	1.90 1.75

Traditional Sports — A293

Designs: 85fr, Coconut husking. 120fr, Fruit carrying. 250fr, Javelin throwing.

2002, June 27
829-831	A293	Set of 3	10.00 9.00

House of James Norman Hall — A294

2002, July 4   **Perf. 13x13¼**
832	A294	90fr multi	2.00 1.90

Papeete Market — A295

2002, Aug. 30   **Litho.**   **Perf. 13**
833	A295	400fr multi	8.75 8.00
a.		Souvenir sheet of 1	11.00 11.00

Amphilex 2002 Stamp Exhibition, Amsterdam (#833a). No. 833a sold for 500fr.

Pacific Oceanology Center, Vairao A296

Designs: 55fr, Research pond, fish, shrimp, oyster, and flasks. 90fr, Aerial view of center, fish, shrimp and oyster.

2002, Sept. 26   **Photo.**   **Perf. 13¼**
834-835	A296	Set of 2	3.50 2.40

Taapuna Master 2002 Surfing Competition A297

2002, Oct. 21   **Litho.**   **Perf. 13x13¼**
836	A297	120fr multi	2.75 2.00

Halophilic Flowers A298

Designs: 85fr, Hibiscus tiliaceus. 130fr, Scaveola sericea. 180fr, Guettarda speciosa.

2002, Nov. 7
837-839	A298	Set of 3	8.75 6.75

Polynesians at Festivals A299

Designs: 55fr, Dancers and bus. 120fr, Musicians, vert.

2002, Dec. 5   **Perf. 13x13¼, 13¼x13**
840-841	A299	Set of 2	3.75 3.00

New Year 2003 (Year of the Ram) — A300

2003, Feb. 1   **Litho.**   **Perf. 13¼x13**
842	A300	120fr multi	2.75 2.25

Portions of the design was applied by a thermographic process producing a shiny, raised effect.

Polynesian Women — A301

2003, Mar. 8   **Litho.**   **Perf. 13¼x13**
843	A301	55fr multi	1.25 1.00

Waterfalls — A302

2003, Apr. 10   **Perf. 13**
844	A302	330fr multi	7.25 6.00

Old Papeete A303

Designs: 55fr, Automobiles and buildings, vert. 85fr, Ship in harbor. 90fr, People with bicycles in front of buildings (50x28mm). 120fr, Tree-lined street (50x28mm).

Perf. 13¼x13, 13x13¼, 13
2003, May 15
845-848	A303	Set of 4	7.75 7.00
848a		Souvenir sheet, #845-848	12.00 12.00

No. 848a sold for 550fr.

Fish — A304

2003, June 12   **Litho.**   **Perf. 13**
849	A304	460fr multi	9.00 9.00

Portions of the design were applied by a thermographic process producing a shiny, raised effect.

Outrigger Canoes A305

Designs: No. 850, 85fr, shown. No. 851, 85fr, Three sailors on canoe at sea. No. 852, 85fr, Three sailors on canoe, vert. No. 853, 85fr, Sailor sitting on outrigger, vert.

Perf. 13x13¼, 13¼x13
2003, July 11   **Litho.**
850-853	A305	Set of 4	7.50 6.50

Firewalkers A306

Orange-banded Cowrie — A307

2003, Aug. 14   **Photo.**   **Perf. 13¼**
854	A306	130fr multi	2.50 2.50

Perf. 13x13¼
855	A307	420fr multi	8.50 8.50

Are You Jealous? by Paul Gauguin (1848-1903) — A308

2003, Sept. 11   **Perf. 13x12¼**
856	A308	250fr multi	5.00 5.00

Office of Posts and Telecommunications Emblem — A308a

Type I: "Postes 2003" at right.
Type II: "Postes" only at right.

Serpentine Die Cut 6½ Vert.
2003, Oct. 1   **Engr.**
   Booklet Stamp
   Self-Adhesive
856A	A308a	(60fr) blue (type	
		II, *2006*	1.25 1.25
b.		Booklet pane of 10	12.50
c.		Type I	25.00 25.00
d.		As "c," booklet pane of 10	250.00

e. As #856A, inscribed
"Phil@poste" 1.40 1.40
f. Booklet pane of 10 #856Ae 14.00

Issued: No. 856Ac, 10/1/03. No. 856A,
2006. No. 856Ae, 2007 (?).
See No. 869.

French
Polynesian
Flag
A309

2003, Oct. 1   Litho.   Perf. 13x13¼
857 A309 (60fr) multi   1.25 1.25

Tiki — A310

2003, Oct. 1   Perf. 13¼x13
858 A310 100fr multi   2.00 2.00

Reissued in 2006 on shiny paper with much
deeper colors. Values the same.

Flowers
A311

Designs: 90fr, Orchid. 130fr, Rose de porcelain (torch ginger).

2003, Oct. 4   Litho.   Perf. 13x13¼
859-860 A311   Set of 2   4.50 4.50

Portions of the designs were applied by a
thermographic process producing a shiny,
raised effect.

Bora Bora
A312

Designs: No. 861, 60fr, Painting of Bora
Bora by A. Van Der Heyde. No. 862, 60fr,
Aerial photograph of Bora Bora.

2003, Nov. 6   Litho.   Perf. 13x13¼
861-862 A312   Set of 2   2.75 2.75

Tiki — A313

2003, Dec. 6   Perf. 13
863 A313 190fr multi   4.00 4.00

Buildings
and Palm
Trees
A314

2003, Dec. 19   Perf. 13x13¼
864 A314 90fr multi   1.90 1.90

New Year 2004
(Year of the
Monkey) — A315

2004, Jan. 22   Litho.   Perf. 13¼x13
865 A315 130fr multi   3.50 3.50

A portion of the design was applied by a
thermographic process producing a shiny,
raised effect.

Scenes
From
Everyday
Life
A316

Designs: 60fr, Women working with cloth.
90fr, Street scene, vert.

Perf. 13x13¼, 13¼x13
2004, Feb. 13   Litho.
866-867 A316   Set of 2   3.25 3.25

Polynesian
Woman — A317

2004, Mar. 8   Perf. 13¼x13
868 A317 90fr multi   2.00 1.90

Post Emblem Type of 2003
Serpentine Die Cut 6½ Vert.
2004, Apr. 22   Engr.
Booklet Stamp
Self-Adhesive
869 A308a (90fr) red   7.50 2.00
a. Booklet pane of 10   75.00

No. 869 lacks year date.

Polynesian Economic
Development — A318

2004, Apr. 23   Litho.   Perf. 13x12¾
870 A318 500fr multi   11.00 10.00

Arahurahu Marae, Paea — A319

2004, Apr. 23
871 A319 500fr multi   11.00 10.00

Vanilla — A320

2004, May 14   Perf. 13¼x13
872 A320 90fr multi   1.90 1.90

No. 872 is impregnated with a vanilla scent.

Mobile Snack Bars — A321

2004, May 28   Perf. 13x12¾
873 A321 300fr multi   6.50 6.25

Handicrafts
A322

Designs: No. 874, 60fr, Artisan braiding
fibers. No. 875, 60fr, Mother-of-pearl carving.
No. 876, 90fr, Artisan carving statue. No. 877,
90fr, Hat.

2004, June 26   Perf. 13x13¼
874-877 A322   Set of 4   7.00 6.25

Portion of the designs were applied by a
thermographic process producing a shiny,
raised effect.

Involvement in South Pacific Area of
Office of Posts and
Telecommunications — A323

Designs: 100fr, Earth, Sun on horizon.
130fr, Satellite dish, building.

2004, July 23   Photo.   Perf. 13¼
878-879 A323   Set of 2   5.00 4.75

Information
Technology and
Communications
A324

Designs: No. 880, 190fr, Computer keyboard, "@." No. 881, 190fr, Satellite, satellite
dish.

2004, Sept. 23   Litho.   Perf. 13¼x13
880-881 A324   Set of 2   8.00 8.00

Omai,
Polynesian Capt.
James Cook
Brought to
England — A325

2004, Oct. 14   Perf. 13
882 A325 250fr multi   5.25 5.25

Shell
Collectors
A326

2004, Nov. 10   Photo.   Perf. 13¼
883 A326 60fr multi   1.40 1.40

A souvenir sheet of one sold for 250fr.

Adenium
Obesum
A327

Alpinia
Purpurata
A328

Ixora
Chinensis
A329

Gardenia
Taitensis
A330

Heliconia Psittacorum — A331

Allamanda Blanchetii A332

Otacanthus Caeruleus — A333

Hibiscus Rosa-sinensis — A334

Euphorba Milii A335

Asocenda Hybrid of Vanda x Ascocentrum — A336

Mussaenda Erythrophylia — A337

Bougainvillea Glabra — A338

2004, Nov. 10   Litho.   Perf. 13x13¼

884	Booklet pane of 6	15.00	—
a.	A327 90fr multi	2.50	2.50
b.	A328 90fr multi	2.50	2.50
c.	A329 90fr multi	2.50	2.50
d.	A330 90fr multi	2.50	2.50
e.	A331 90fr multi	2.50	2.50
f.	A332 90fr multi	2.50	2.50
885	Booklet pane of 6	15.00	—
a.	A333 90fr multi	2.50	2.50
b.	A334 90fr multi	2.50	2.50
c.	A335 90fr multi	2.50	2.50
d.	A336 90fr multi	2.50	2.50
e.	A337 90fr multi	2.50	2.50
f.	A338 90fr multi	2.50	2.50
	Complete booklet, #884-885	30.00	

Complete booklet sold for 1200fr.

Christmas A339

2004, Dec. 17
886 A339 60fr multi   1.40 1.40

A portion of the design was applied by a thermographic process producing a shiny, raised effect.

Bamboo — A340

2005, Feb. 9   Perf. 13¼x13
887 A340 130fr multi   3.00 3.00

New Year 2005. A portion of the design was applied by a thermographic process producing a shiny, raised effect.

People and Hut A341

2005, Feb. 25   Perf. 13x13¼
888 A341 90fr multi   2.00 2.00

Polynesian Women — A342

Designs: 60fr, Woman wearing lei. 90fr, Woman wearing flower garland on head and robe.

2005, Mar. 8   Perf. 13¼x13
889-890 A342   Set of 2   3.50 3.50

Woman Making Tapa Cloth — A343

2005, Apr. 22   Perf. 13
891 A343 250fr multi   5.50 5.50

Tifaifai A344

2005, Mar. 23   Litho.   Perf. 13x13¼
892 A344 5fr multi   .25 .20

Angelfish A345

Designs: No. 893, 90fr, Centropyge bispinosa. No. 894, 90fr, Centropyge loricula. No. 895, 130fr, Centropyge heraldi. No. 896, 130fr, Centropyge flavissima.

2005, May 27   Litho.   Perf. 13x13¼
893-896 A345   Set of 4   9.00 9.00
896a   Souvenir sheet, #893-896   9.00 9.00

Portions of the designs were applied by a thermographic process producing a shiny, raised effect.

Historic Airplanes A346

Designs: No. 897, 60fr, TAI DC-8, first jet in Tahiti, 1961. No. 898, 60fr, Pan American Boeing 707, first foreign flight, 1963. No. 899, 100fr, Air France Boeing 707, first Air France flight to Tahiti, 1973. No. 900, 100fr, Air Tahiti Nui Airbus A340-300, first Tahitian airline, 2000.

2005, June 24
897-900 A346   Set of 4   6.50 6.50

Musical Instruments A347

Designs: No. 901, 130fr, Drum. No. 902, 130fr, Nose flutes, horiz.

2005, July 22   Perf. 13¼x13, 13x13¼
901-902 A347   Set of 2   5.50 5.50

Polynesian Landscapes — A348

2005, Aug. 26   Perf. 13
903 A348 300fr multi   6.25 6.25

Pineapples A349

Designs: 90fr, Close-up of spines. 130fr, Entire fruit.

2005, Sept. 23   Litho.   Perf. 13¼x13
904-905 A349   Set of 2   4.50 4.50

Nos. 904-905 are impregnated with pineapple scent.

Marae — A350

Marquesan Tohua — A351

2005, Oct. 21   Perf. 13
906 A350 500fr multi   10.00 10.00
907 A351 500fr multi   10.00 10.00

Autonomy, 20th Anniv. (in 2004) — A352

2005, Nov. 10   Perf. 13¼x13
908 A352 60fr multi   1.75 1.75

No. 908 was printed in France and distributed there in June 2004 but was not sold in French Polynesia until 2005, where it was available from the philatelic bureau upon request, and not through standing orders.

O'Parrey Harbor, Tahiti A353

2005, Nov. 10   Engr.   Perf. 13x12½
909 A353 100fr multi   2.00 2.00

Christmas A354

2005, Dec. 16   Litho.   Perf. 13x13¼
910 A354 90fr multi   2.00 2.00

Lotus
Flower
A355

Litho. & Silk-screened

2006, Jan. 30   **Perf. 13x13¼**
911 A355 130fr multi   2.60 2.60

A356

Hearts
A357

2006, Feb. 14   Photo.   Perf. 13
912 A356 60fr multi   1.25 1.25
913 A357 90fr multi   1.90 1.90

Values are for stamps with surrounding selvage.

Polynesian
Women — A358

Woman: 60fr, At water's edge. 90fr, With oil lamp.

2006, Mar. 8   Litho.   Perf. 13¼x13
914-915 A358 Set of 2   3.25 3.25

Maupiti — A359

2006, Apr. 26   Engr.   Perf. 13x13¼
916 A359 500fr multi   11.00 11.00

History of the
Marquesas
(Washington)
Islands — A360

Designs: 60fr, Native man and woman. 130fr, Ships.

2006, May 27   Litho.   Perf. 13¼x13
917-918 A360 Set of 2   4.00 4.00
918a   Souvenir sheet, #917-918   4.00 4.00

Diners and Musicians — A361

2006, June 6   Perf. 13
919 A361 300fr multi   6.50 6.50

Polynesian
Ground
Dove
A362

Tuamotu
Sandpiper
A363

2006, June 21   Perf. 13x13¼
920 A362 250fr multi   5.25 5.25
921 A363 250fr multi   5.25 5.25

Heiva — A364

Designs: 90fr, Canoe race. 130fr, Stone lifting. 190fr, Dancer.

2006, July 19   Perf. 13¼x13
922-924 A364 Set of 3   8.75 8.75

Frangipani
Flowers
A365

2006, Aug. 23   Litho.   Perf. 13x13½
925 A365 90fr multi   1.90 1.90

No. 925 is impregnated with frangipani scent.

A366

World
Tourism
Day
A367

Designs: 40fr, Ruins. No. 927, 90fr, Waterfall, woman and child. 130fr, Clothing at open-air market.

No. 929: a, Dancers with yellow skirts. b, Surfer. c, House and palm tree. d, Pearls. e, Fish and coral. f, Islanders in outrigger canoes.

No. 930: a, Woman in hammock. b, Stilt houses. c, Tower and boats. d, Horses and riders. e, Aerial view of island. f, Diver and sting ray.

2006, Sept. 22   Perf. 13¼x13
926-928 A366 Set of 3   5.50 5.50

Booklet Stamps
Perf. 13x13¼
929   Booklet pane of 6   12.50   —
a.-f.   A367 90fr Any single   2.00 2.00
930   Booklet pane of 6   12.50   —
a.-f.   A367 90fr Any single   2.00 2.00
          Complete booklet, #929-930 25.00

Complete booklet sold for 1200fr.

Paintings
A368

Designs: 60fr, Javelin Throwing, by Monique Garnier Bissol. 90fr, Market Life, by Albert Luzuy, horiz. 100fr, Island Quay, by Gilbert Chaussoy, horiz. 190fr, Vahine, by Olivier Louzé.

2006, Oct. 25   Perf. 13
931-934 A368 Set of 4   9.50 9.50

Engravings by Paul Gauguin (1848-1903) — A369

Engravings depicting: 60fr, Women. 130fr, Cow and man carrying items on stick.

2006, Nov. 8   Engr.   Perf. 13¼
935-936 A369 Set of 2   4.25 4.25

Children's
Art
A370

2006, Dec. 13   Litho.   Perf. 13x13¼
937 A370 90fr multi   2.00 2.00

Beach
Gear — A371

Designs: 60fr, Flip-flops. 90fr, Surfboards.

Serpentine Die Cut 11x11¼
2007   Photo.
Self-Adhesive
938 A371 60fr multicolored   1.25 1.25
a.   Blue tips of die cutting along left   1.25 1.25
      side

939 A371 90fr multicolored   2.00 2.00
a.   Light blue tips of die cutting   2.00 2.00
      along bottom

Issued: Nos. 938a, 939a, 1/24; Nos. 938-939, Feb. Nos. 938a and 939a are from the original printing, and are from sheets having adjacent stamps and die cutting that does not extend through the backing paper. Nos. 938-939, which were distributed to the philatelic trade, are from sheets with selvage around each stamp, and with rouletting that extends through the backing paper that allows the stamps to be removed from the sheet more easily.

New Year
2007 (Year
of the Pig)
A372

2007, Feb. 19   Litho.   Perf. 13x13¼
940 A372 130fr multi   3.00 3.00

Portions of the design were applied by a thermographic process producing a shiny, raised effect.

Painting of
Polynesian
Woman by
Mathius — A373

Photograph of Polynesian Woman by
John Stember — A374

2007, Mar. 8   Litho.   Perf. 13¼x13
941 A373 60fr multi   1.40 1.40
                          Perf. 13x13¼
942 A374 90fr multi   2.00 2.00

Audit
Office,
Bicent.
A375

2007, Mar. 17   Engr.   Perf. 13¼x13
943 A375 90fr multi   2.00 2.00

Shells — A376

Designs: 10fr, Lambis crocata pilsbryi. 60fr, Cypraea thomasi. 90fr, Cyrtulus serotinus. 130fr, Chicoreus laqueatus.

2007, Apr. 25   Litho.
944-947 A376 Set of 4   6.75 6.75
947a   Souvenir sheet, #944-947   6.75 6.75

Coconut
A377

2007, May 23   *Perf. 13x13¼*
948 A377 90fr multi   2.00 2.00
No. 948 is impregnated with a coconut scent.

Ships — A378

Designs: No. 949, 250fr, Gunboat Zélée.
No. 950, 250fr, Passenger and cargo liner
Sagittaire.

2007, June 22   *Perf. 13*
949-950 A378 Set of 2   11.50 11.50

Heiva
Festival — A379

Various women dancers: 65fr, 100fr, 140fr.

2007, July 4   *Perf. 13¼x13*
951-953 A379 Set of 3   7.00 7.00

Arrival of Kon-Tiki Expedition in
Polynesia, 60th Anniv. — A380

Litho. & Silk-screened
2007, Aug. 7   *Perf. 13*
954 A380 300fr multi   7.00 7.00

Arrival of Ship at Papeete
Dock — A381

2007, Aug. 29 Litho.   *Perf. 13*
955 A381 190fr multi   4.50 4.50

Old and Modern Photos of
Papeete — A382

Designs: 65fr, Rue Gauguin, 2007. 100fr,
Rue de la Petite-Pologne (now Rue Gauguin),
1907.

2007, Sept. 26
956-957 A382 Set of 2   4.00 4.00

Old Franc and Centime Notes — A383

Designs: 65fr, 1919 2-franc Chamber of
Commerce note. 140fr, 1942 2-franc note.
500fr, 1943 50-centime note.

2007, Oct. 26 Engr.   *Perf. 13*
958-960 A383 Set of 3   17.00 17.00

Flowers
A384

Designs: 100fr, Hibiscus. 140fr, Bird-of-paradise (Oiseaux de paradis).

Litho. & Silk-screened
2007, Nov. 8   *Perf. 13x13¼*
961-962 A384 Set of 2   6.00 6.00

SEMI-POSTAL STAMPS

Nos. 55 and 26
Surcharged in Red

1915 Unwmk.   *Perf. 14x13½*
B1 A1 10c + 5c red   22.50 22.50
  a. "e" instead of "c"   57.50 57.50
  b. Inverted surcharge   160.00 160.00
B2 A2 10c + 5c rose & org   7.50 7.50
  a. "e" instead of "c"   40.00 40.00
  b. "c" inverted   47.50 47.50
  c. Inverted surcharge   225.00 225.00

Surcharged in
Carmine

B3 A2 10c + 5c rose & org   3.25 3.25
  a. "e" instead of "c"   25.00 25.00
  b. Inverted surcharge   150.00 150.00

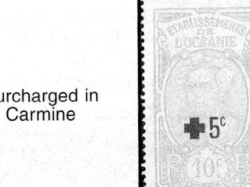

Surcharged in
Carmine

1916
B4 A2 10c + 5c rose & org   3.25 3.25

Curie Issue
Common Design Type
1938 Engr.   *Perf. 13*
B5 CD80 1.75fr + 50c brt ultra 14.00 14.00

French Revolution Issue
Common Design Type
1939   **Photo.**
Name and Value Typo. in Black
B6 CD83 45c + 25c grn   14.00 14.00
B7 CD83 70c + 30c brn   14.00 14.00
B8 CD83 90c + 35c red
           org   14.00 14.00
B9 CD83 1.25fr + 1fr rose
           pink   14.00 14.00
B10 CD83 2.25fr + 2fr blue   14.00 14.00
     Nos. B6-B10 (5)   70.00 70.00
Set, never hinged   120.00

Catalogue values for unused stamps in this section, from this point to the end of the section, are for Never Hinged items.

Common Design Type and

Marine Officer — SP1

"L'Astrolabe" — SP2

1941   Photo.   *Perf. 13½*
B11 SP1 1fr + 1fr red   2.50
B12 CD86 1.50fr + 3fr maroon   2.50
B12A SP2 2.50fr + 1fr blue   2.50
     Nos. B11-B12A (3)   7.50
  Nos. B11-B12A were issued by the Vichy
government in France, and were not placed on
sale in French Polynesia.

Nos. 125A-125B
Surcharged in Black or Red

1944   Engr.   *Perf. 12½x12*
B12B 50c + 1.50fr on 2.50fr
       deep blue (R)   1.25
B12C + 2.50fr on 1fr green   1.50
  Colonial Development Fund.
  Nos. B12B-B12C were issued by the Vichy
government in France, but were not placed on
sale in French Polynesia.

Red Cross Issue
Common Design Type
1944   Photo.   *Perf. 14½x14*
B13 CD90 5fr + 20fr peacock
            blue   1.60 1.10
The surtax was for the French Red Cross
and national relief.

Tropical Medicine Issue
Common Design Type
1950, July 17 Engr.   *Perf. 13*
B14 CD100 10fr + 2fr dk bl grn &
             dk grn   9.00 5.75
The surtax was for charitable work.

AIR POST STAMPS

Seaplane
in Flight
AP1

Perf. 13½
1934, Nov. 5 Unwmk. Photo.
C1 AP1 5fr green   .75   .75
  For overprint see No. C2.
  For Type AP1 without "RF," see Nos. C1A-
C1D.

Type of 1934 without "RF" and

Beach
Scene —
AP1a

Perf. 13½, 13 (#C1E)
1944   Photo, Engr. (#C1E)
C1A AP1 5fr green   .60
C1B AP1 10fr black   .90
C1C AP1 20fr orange   .95
C1D AP1 50fr gray blue   1.25
C1E AP1a 100fr turquoise blue   3.00
     Nos. C1A-C1E (5)   6.70
  Nos. C1A-C1E were issued by the Vichy
government in France, but were not placed on
sale in French Polynesia.

Catalogue values for unused stamps in this section, from this point to the end of the section, are for Never Hinged items.

No. C1
Overprinted
in Red

1941
C2 AP1 5fr green   3.75 3.00

Common Design Type
1942   *Perf. 14½x14*
C3 CD87 1fr dark orange   .75   .50
C4 CD87 1.50fr bright red   .75   .60
C5 CD87 5fr brown red   1.00   .80
C6 CD87 10fr black   1.50 1.10
C7 CD87 25fr ultra   2.25 1.60
C8 CD87 50fr dark green   2.25 1.60
C9 CD87 100fr plum   2.25 1.60
     Nos. C3-C9 (7)   10.75 7.80

Victory Issue
Common Design Type
1946, May 8 Engr.   *Perf. 12½*
C10 CD92 8fr dark green   2.25 1.60

Chad to Rhine Issue
Common Design Types
1946, June 6
C11 CD93 5fr red orange   1.75 1.50
C12 CD94 10fr dk olive bis   1.75 1.50
C13 CD95 15fr dk yellow grn   1.75 1.50
C14 CD96 20fr carmine   2.25 1.75
C15 CD97 25fr dk rose violet   3.00 2.50
C16 CD98 50fr black   3.50 3.00
     Nos. C11-C16 (6)   14.00 11.75

Shearwater and Moorea
Landscape — AP2

Fishermen — AP3

Shearwater over Maupiti
Shoreline — AP4

1948, Mar. 1   Unwmk.   *Perf. 13*
C17 AP2 50fr red brown   21.00   8.75
C18 AP3 100fr purple   17.50   5.75
C19 AP4 200fr blue green   37.50   15.00
   Nos. C17-C19 (3)   76.00   29.50

UPU Issue
Common Design Type
1949
C20 CD99 10fr deep blue   14.50   11.50

Gauguin's "Nafea
faaipoipo" — AP5

1953, Sept. 24
C21 AP5 14fr dk brn, dk gray
         grn & red   62.50   50.00
50th anniv. of the death of Paul Gauguin.

Liberation Issue
Common Design Type
1954, June 6
C22 CD102 3fr dk grnsh bl & bl
         grn   7.50   5.75

Bahia Peak, Borabora — AP6

1955, Sept. 26   Unwmk.   *Perf. 13*
C23 AP6 13fr indigo & blue   8.00   4.00

Mother-of-Pearl
Artist — AP7

Designs: 50fr, "Women of Tahiti," Gauguin,
horiz. 100fr, "The White Horse," Gauguin.
200fr, Night fishing at Moorea, horiz.

1958, Nov. 3   Engr.   *Perf. 13*
C24 AP7 13fr multicolored   11.50   3.75
C25 AP7 50fr multicolored   11.00   3.75
C26 AP7 100fr multicolored   17.00   5.75
C27 AP7 200fr lilac & slate   37.50   17.00
   Nos. C24-C27 (4)   77.00   30.25

Airport, Papeete — AP8

1960, Nov. 19
C28 AP8 13fr rose lil, vio, & yel
         grn   3.00   1.90

Telstar Issue
Common Design Type
1962, Dec. 5   *Perf. 13*
C29 CD111 50fr red lil, mar &
         vio bl   10.50   7.00

Tahitian
Dancer — AP10

1964, May 14   Photo.   *Perf. 13*
C30 AP10 15fr multicolored   4.00   2.00

Map of Tahiti and Free French
Emblems — AP11

1964, July 10   Unwmk.
C31 AP11 16fr multicolored   13.50   6.75
Issued to commemorate the rallying of
French Polynesia to the Free French cause.

Moorea Scene — AP12

1964, Dec. 1   Litho.   *Perf. 13*
C32 AP12 23fr multicolored   8.75   2.75

ITU Issue
Common Design Type
1965, May 17   Engr.   *Perf. 13*
C33 CD120 50fr vio, red brn &
         bl   85.00   45.00

Paul Gauguin — AP13

Design: 25fr, Gauguin Museum (stylized).
40fr, Primitive statues at Gauguin Museum.

1965   Engr.   *Perf. 13*
C34 AP13 25fr olive green   8.00   3.75
C35 AP13 40fr blue green   15.00   6.75
C36 AP13 75fr brt red brown   22.50   12.50
   Nos. C34-C36 (3)   45.50   23.00
Opening of Gauguin Museum, Papeete.
Issued: 25fr, 75fr, 6/13. 40fr, 11/7.

Skin Diver with Spear Gun — AP14

1965, Sept. 1   Engr.   *Perf. 13*
C37 AP14 50fr red brn, dl bl
         & dk grn   75.00   47.50
World Championships in Underwater Fish-
ing, Tuamotu Archipelago, Sept. 1965.

Painting from a
School Dining
Room — AP15

1965, Nov. 29
C38 AP15 80fr brn, bl, dl bl &
         red   20.00   14.50
School Canteen Program.

1965, Dec. 29   Engr.   *Perf. 13*
C39 AP16 60fr org, grn & dk
         brn   17.50   12.50
50th anniversary of the first radio link
between Tahiti and France.

Radio Tower,
Globe and
Palm — AP16

French Satellite A-1 Issue
Common Design Type
Designs: 7fr, Diamant Rocket and launching
installations. 10fr, A-1 satellite.

1966, Feb. 7
C40 CD121   7fr choc, dp grn
         & lil   5.00   4.25
C41 CD121 10fr lil, dp grn &
         dk brn   5.00   4.25
   a.   Pair, #C40-C41 + label   15.00   15.00

French Satellite D-1 Issue
Common Design Type
1966, May 10   Engr.   *Perf. 13*
C42 CD122 20fr multicolored   6.00   4.00

Papeete Harbor — AP17

1966, June 30   Photo.   *Perf. 13*
C43 AP17 50fr multicolored   14.50   9.00

"Vive Tahiti" by A. Benichou — AP18

1966, Nov. 28   Photo.   *Perf. 13*
C44 AP18 13fr multicolored   11.00   5.00

Explorer's Ship and Canoe — AP19

Designs: 60fr, Polynesian costume and
ship. 80fr, Louis Antoine de Bougainville, vert.

1968, Apr. 6   Engr.   *Perf. 13*
C45 AP19 40fr multicolored   6.75   3.25
C46 AP19 60fr multicolored   9.00   4.50
C47 AP19 80fr multicolored   11.00   6.75
   a.   Souv. sheet, #C45-C47   125.00   125.00
   Nos. C45-C47 (3)   26.75   14.50
200th anniv. of the discovery of Tahiti by
Louis Antoine de Bougainville.
Issued: 40fr, 4/6/68.

The Meal, by Paul Gauguin — AP20

1968, July 30   Photo.   *Perf. 12x12½*
C48 AP20 200fr multicolored   37.50   25.00
See #C63-C67, C78-C82, C89-C93, C98.

Shot Put — AP21

PATA 1970
Poster — AP22

1968, Oct. 12   Engr.   *Perf. 13*
C49 AP21 35fr dk car rose &
         brt grn   14.50   7.00
19th Olympic Games, Mexico City, 10/12-27.

Concorde Issue
Common Design Type
1969, Apr. 17
C50 CD129 40fr red brn & car
rose   50.00 30.00

1969, July 9 Photo. Perf. 12½x13
C51 AP22 25fr blue & multi   17.00 6.00

Issued to publicize PATA 1970 (Pacific Area Travel Association Congress), Tahiti.

Underwater Fishing — AP23

52fr, Hand holding fish made up of flags, vert.

1969, Aug. 5 Photo. Perf. 13
C52 AP23 48fr blk, grnsh bl &
red lil   32.50 10.50
C53 AP23 52fr bl, blk & red   37.50 17.50

Issued to publicize the World Underwater Fishing Championships.

Gen. Bonaparte as Commander of the Army in Italy, by Jean Sebastien Rouillard — AP24

1969, Oct. 15 Photo. Perf. 12½x12
C54 AP24 100fr car & multi   75.00 55.00

Bicentenary of the birth of Napoleon Bonaparte (1769-1821).

Eiffel Tower, Torii and EXPO Emblem — AP25

Pearl Diver Descending, and Basket — AP26

Design: 30fr, Mount Fuji, Tower of the Sun and EXPO emblem, horiz.

1970, Sept. 15 Photo. Perf. 13
C55 AP25 30fr multicolored   17.50 8.00
C56 AP25 50fr multicolored   25.00 11.00

EXPO '70 International Exposition, Osaka, Japan, Mar. 15-Sept. 13.

1970, Sept. 30 Engr. Perf. 13
Designs: 5fr, Diver collecting oysters. 18fr, Implantation into oyster, horiz. 27fr, Open oyster with pearl. 50fr, Woman with mother of pearl jewelry.
C57 AP26 2fr slate, grnsh bl
& red brn   1.25   .75
C58 AP26 5fr grnsh blue, ul-
tra & org   2.25 1.25
C59 AP26 18fr sl, mag & org   4.75 2.25
C60 AP26 27fr brt pink, brn &
dl lil   8.00 4.00
C61 AP26 50fr gray, red brn &
org   13.00 6.25
Nos. C57-C61 (5)   29.25 14.50

Pearl industry of French Polynesia.

The Thinker, by Auguste Rodin and Education Year Emblem — AP27

1970, Oct. 15 Engr. Perf. 13
C62 AP27 50fr bl, ind & fawn   16.00 8.75

International Education Year.

Painting Type of 1968
Paintings by Artists Living in Polynesia: 20fr, Woman on the Beach, by Yves de Saint-Front. 40fr, Abstract, by Frank Fay. 60fr, Woman and Shells, by Jean Guillois. 80fr, Hut under Palms, by Jean Masson. 100fr, Polynesian Girl, by Jean-Charles Boulloc.

Perf. 12x12½, 12½x12
1970, Dec. 14   Photo.
C63 AP20 20fr brn & multi   9.00   4.00
C64 AP20 40fr brn & multi   13.50   7.50
C65 AP20 60fr brn & multi   18.00 11.00
C66 AP20 80fr brn & multi   22.50 16.00
C67 AP20 100fr brn & multi   30.00 22.50
Nos. C63-C67 (5)   93.00 61.00

South Pacific Games Emblem — AP28

1971, Jan. 26 Perf. 12½
C68 AP28 20fr ultra & multi   7.00   4.50

Publicity for 4th South Pacific Games, held in Papeete, Sept. 8-19, 1971.

Memorial Flame — AP29

1971, Mar. 19 Photo. Perf. 12½
C69 AP29 5fr multicolored   7.50   4.00

In memory of Charles de Gaulle.

Soldier and Badge — AP30

1971, Apr. 21
C70 AP30 25fr multicolored   9.50   5.50

30th anniversary of departure of Tahitian volunteers to serve in World War II.

Water Sports Type
Designs: 15fr, Surfing, vert. 16fr, Skin diving, vert. 20fr, Water-skiing with kite.

1971, May 11 Photo. Perf. 13
C71 A44 15fr multicolored   6.25   2.75
C72 A44 16fr multicolored   7.50   3.25
C73 A44 20fr multicolored 11.00   6.00
Nos. C71-C73 (3)   24.75 12.00

Sailing AP31

1971, Sept. 8 Perf. 12½
C74 AP31 15fr shown   5.75   3.00
C75 AP31 18fr Golf   7.25   4.00
C76 AP31 27fr Archery 11.50   6.00
C77 AP31 53fr Tennis 18.50 11.00
a. Souv. sheet, #C74-C77 175.00 175.00
Nos. C74-C77 (4)   43.00 24.00

4th So. Pacific Games, Papeete, Sept. 8-19.

Painting Type of 1968
Paintings by Artists Living in Polynesia: 20fr, Hut and Palms, by Isabelle Wolf. 40fr, Palms on Shore, by André Dobrowolski. 60fr, Polynesian Woman, by Françoise Séli, vert. 80fr, Holy Family, by Pierre Heymann, vert. 100fr, Crowd, by Nicolai Michoutouchkine.

1971, Dec. 15 Photo. Perf. 13
C78 AP20 20fr multicolored   8.00   4.50
C79 AP20 40fr multicolored 12.50   7.50
C80 AP20 60fr multicolored 15.00 10.00
C81 AP20 80fr multicolored 21.00 12.50
C82 AP20 100fr multicolored 35.00 22.50
Nos. C78-C82 (5)   91.50 57.00

Papeete Harbor — AP32

1972, Jan. 13
C83 AP32 28fr violet & multi 13.50 6.75

Free port of Papeete, 10th anniversary.

Figure Skating and Dragon AP33

1972, Jan. 25 Engr. Perf. 13
C84 AP33 20fr ultra, lake & brt
grn   10.00 7.00

11th Winter Olympic Games, Sapporo, Japan, Feb. 3-13.

South Pacific Commission Headquarters, Noumea — AP34

1972, Feb. 5 Photo. Perf. 13
C85 AP34 21fr blue & multi   11.50 4.25

South Pacific Commission, 25th anniv.

Festival Emblem — AP35

1972, May 9 Engr. Perf. 13
C86 AP35 36fr orange, bl & grn 7.25 4.50

So. Pacific Festival of Arts, Fiji, May 6-20.

Kon Tiki and Route, Callao to Tahiti — AP36

1972, Aug. 18 Photo. Perf. 13
C87 AP36 16fr dk & lt bl, blk &
org   11.00 5.00

25th anniversary of the arrival of the raft Kon Tiki in Tahiti.

Charles de Gaulle and Memorial — AP37

1972, Dec. 9 Engr. Perf. 13
C88 AP37 100fr slate   55.00 35.00

Painting Type of 1968
Paintings by Artists Living in Polynesia: 20fr, Horses, by Georges Bovy. 40fr, Sailboats, by Ruy Juventin, vert. 60fr, Harbor, by André Brooke. 80fr, Farmers, by Daniel Adam, vert. 100fr, Dancers, by Aloysius Pilioko, vert.

1972, Dec. 14   Photo.
C89 AP20 20fr gold & multi   8.25   3.50
C90 AP20 40fr gold & multi 10.00   5.25
C91 AP20 60fr gold & multi 17.50   7.25
C92 AP20 80fr dk grn, buff
& dk brn   22.50 10.00
C93 AP20 100fr gold & multi 27.50 20.00
Nos. C89-C93 (5)   85.75 46.00

St. Teresa
and Lisieux
Basilica
AP38

1973, Jan. 23   Engr.   Perf. 13
C94 AP38 85fr multicolored   22.50 13.50
  Centenary of the birth of St. Teresa of
Lisieux (1873-1897), Carmelite nun.

Nicolaus Copernicus — AP39

1973, Mar. 7   Engr.   Perf. 13
C95 AP39 100fr brn, vio bl &
         red lil   28.50 13.50
  Copernicus (1473-1543), Polish astronomer.

Plane over Tahiti — AP40

1973, Apr. 3   Photo.   Perf. 13
C96 AP40 80fr ultra, gold & lt
         grn   20.00 13.50
  Air France's World Tour via Tahiti.

DC-10 at Papeete Airport — AP41

1973, May 18   Engr.   Perf. 13
C97 AP41 20fr bl, ultra & sl grn 18.00 5.00
  Start of DC-10 service.

Painting Type of 1968
  Design: 200fr, "Ta Matete" (seated women),
by Paul Gauguin.

1973, June 7   Photo.   Perf. 13
C98 AP20 200fr multicolored 25.00 17.00
  Paul Gauguin (1848-1903), painter.

Pierre Loti and Characters from his
Books — AP42

1973, July 4   Engr.   Perf. 13
C99 AP42 60fr multicolored   37.50 20.00
  Pierre Loti (1850-1923), French naval officer
and writer.

Woman
with
Flowers, by
Eliane de
Gennes
AP43

  Paintings by Artists Living in Polynesia: 20fr,
Sun, by Jean Francois Favre. 60fr, Seascape,
by Alain Sidet. 80fr, Crowded Bus, by Francois
Ravello. 100fr, Stylized Boats, by Jackie
Bourdin, horiz.

1973, Dec. 13   Photo.   Perf. 13
C100 AP43 20fr gold & multi   7.50   2.25
C101 AP43 40fr gold & multi   10.00   4.75
C102 AP43 60fr gold & multi   15.00   8.00
C103 AP43 80fr gold & multi   20.00 13.00
C104 AP43 100fr gold & multi   24.00 16.00
    Nos. C100-C104 (5)   76.50 44.00

Bird, Fish, Flower
and
Water — AP44

Catamaran under
Sail — AP45

1974, June 12   Photo.   Perf. 13
C105 AP44 12fr blue & multi   7.50   3.25
  Nature protection.

1974, July 22   Engr.   Perf. 13
C106 AP45 100fr multicolored 22.50 13.50
  2nd Catamaran World Championships.

Still-life, by Rosine Temarui-
Masson — AP46

  Paintings by Artists Living in Polynesia: 40fr,
Palms and House on Beach, by Marcel
Chardon. 60fr, Man, by Marie-Françoise Avril.
80fr, Polynesian Woman, by Henriette Robin.
100fr, Lagoon by Moon-light, by David Farsi,
horiz.

1974, Dec. 12   Photo.   Perf. 13
C107 AP46 20fr gold & multi 16.00   7.00
C108 AP46 40fr gold & multi 21.00   8.00
C109 AP46 60fr gold & multi 25.00 10.00

C110 AP46 80fr gold & multi 35.00 13.50
C111 AP46 100fr gold & multi 50.00 22.50
    Nos. C107-C111 (5)   147.00 61.00
    See Nos. C122-C126.

Polynesian Gods of Travel — AP47

  Designs: 75fr, Tourville hydroplane, 1929.
100fr, Passengers leaving plane.

1975, Feb. 7   Engr.   Perf. 13
C112 AP47 50fr sep, pur &
         brn   8.50   4.50
C113 AP47 75fr brn, bl & red 14.00   6.50
C114 AP47 100fr grn, sep &
         car   20.00 12.00
    Nos. C112-C114 (3)   42.50 23.00
  Fifty years of Tahitian aviation.

French Ceres
Stamp and
Woman — AP48

1975, May 29   Engr.   Perf. 13
C115 AP48 32fr ver, brn & blk 10.00   4.00
  ARPHILA 75 International Philatelic Exhibi-
tion, Paris, June 6-16.

Shot Put
and Games'
Emblem
AP50

1975, Aug. 1   Photo.   Perf. 13
C117 AP50 25fr shown   4.00   2.25
C118 AP50 30fr Volleyball   5.75   2.75
C119 AP50 40fr Women's
         swimming   7.50   3.75
    Nos. C117-C119 (3)   17.25   8.75
  5th South Pacific Games, Guam, Aug. 1-10.

Flowers, Athlete,
View of
Montreal — AP51

1975, Oct. 15   Engr.   Perf. 13
C120 AP51 44fr brt bl, ver & blk 9.00 5.00
  Pre-Olympic Year 1975.

UPU Emblem, Jet and Letters — AP52

1975, Nov. 5   Engr.   Perf. 13
C121 AP52 100fr brn, bl & ol 19.00 10.00
  World Universal Postal Union Day.

Paintings Type of 1974
  Paintings by Artists Living in Polynesia: 20fr,
Beach Scene, by R. Marcel Marius, horiz. 40fr,
Roofs with TV antennas, by M. Anglade, horiz.
60fr, Street scene with bus, by J. Day, horiz.
80fr, Tropical waters (fish), by J. Steimetz.
100fr, Women, by A. van der Heyde.

1975, Dec. 17   Litho.   Perf. 13
C122 AP46 20fr gold & multi   3.50   1.75
C123 AP46 40fr gold & multi   6.50   3.00
C124 AP46 60fr gold & multi 10.00   4.50
C125 AP46 80fr gold & multi 13.00   7.50
C126 AP46 100fr gold & multi 16.00 12.00
    Nos. C122-C126 (5)   49.00 28.75

Concorde — AP53

1976, Jan. 21   Engr.   Perf. 13
C127 AP53 100fr car, bl & ind 15.00 10.00
  First commercial flight of supersonic jet
Concorde from Paris to Rio, Jan. 21.

Adm. Rodney, Count de la Perouse,
"Barfleur" and "Triomphant" in
Battle — AP54

  31fr, Count de Grasse and Lord Graves,
"Ville de Paris" & "Le Terible" in Chesapeake
Bay Battle.

1976, Apr. 15   Engr.   Perf. 13
C128 AP54 24fr grnsh bl, lt brn &
         blk   4.00   2.00
C129 AP54 31fr mag, red & lt brn 4.50   2.75
  American Bicentennial.

King
Pomaré I — AP55

  Portraits: 21fr, King Pomaré II. 26fr, Queen
Pomaré IV. 30fr, King Pomaré V.

1976, Apr. 28   Litho.   Perf. 12½
C130 AP55 18fr olive & multi   1.50   .60
C131 AP55 21fr multicolored   1.75   .95
C132 AP55 26fr gray & multi   2.25   1.10
C133 AP55 30fr plum & multi   2.50   1.50
    Nos. C130-C133 (4)   8.00   4.15

  Pomaré Dynasty. See Nos. C141-C144.

Running and Maple Leaf — AP56

Designs: 34fr, Long jump, vert. 50fr, Olympic flame and flowers.

1976, July 19   Engr.   Perf. 13
C134 AP56 26fr ultra & multi   3.50   1.75
C135 AP56 34fr ultra & multi   5.00   2.25
C136 AP56 50fr ultra & multi   9.50   4.25
  a. Min. sheet, #C134-C136   85.00 85.00
  Nos. C134-C136 (3)   18.00   8.25
21st Olympic Games, Montreal, Canada, July 17-Aug. 1.

The Dream, by Paul Gauguin — AP57

1976, Oct. 17   Photo.   Perf. 13
C137 AP57 50fr multicolored   10.00 6.00

Murex Steeriae — AP58

Pocillopora AP59

Sea Shells: 27fr, Conus Gauguini. 35fr, Conus marchionatus.

1977, Mar. 14 Photo. Perf. 12½x13
C138 AP58 25fr vio bl & multi   4.25 1.25
C139 AP58 27fr ultra & multi   4.25 1.50
C140 AP58 35fr blue & multi   5.00 2.00
  Nos. C138-C140 (3)   13.50 4.75
See Nos. C156-C158.

Royalty Type of 1976

19fr, King Maputeoa, Mangareva. 33fr, King Camatoa V, Raiatea. 39fr, Queen Vaekehu, Marquesas. 43fr, King Teurarii III, Rurutu.

1977, Apr. 19   Litho.   Perf. 12½
C141 AP55 19fr dull red & multi 1.10 .80
C142 AP55 33fr dk blue & multi   1.60 1.00
C143 AP55 39fr ultra & multi   1.60 1.10
C144 AP55 43fr green & multi   2.25 1.60
  Nos. C141-C144 (4)   6.55 4.50
Polynesian rulers.

Perf. 13x12½, 12½x13
1977, May 23   Photo.
Design: 25fr, Acropora, horiz.
C145 AP59 25fr multicolored   1.75 .95
C146 AP59 33fr multicolored   2.25 1.40
3rd Symposium on Coral Reefs, Miami, Fla. See Nos. C162-C163.

De Gaulle Memorial — AP60

Tahitian Dancer — AP61

Photogravure and Embossed
1977, June 18   Perf. 13
C147 AP60 40fr gold & multi   5.50 3.50
5th anniversary of dedication of De Gaulle memorial at Colombey-les-Deux-Eglises.

1977, July 14   Litho.   Perf. 12½
C148 AP61 27fr multicolored   5.00 2.50

Charles A. Lindbergh and Spirit of St. Louis — AP62

1977, Aug. 18   Litho.   Perf. 12½
C149 AP62 28fr multicolored   7.50 3.00
Lindbergh's solo transatlantic flight from New York to Paris, 50th anniv.

Mahoe — AP63

Palms on Shore — AP64

1977, Sept. 15 Photo. Perf. 12½x13
C150 AP63 8fr shown   1.40 .55
C151 AP63 12fr Frangipani 1.75 .80

1977, Nov. 8   Photo. Perf. 12½x13
C152 AP64 32fr multicolored 10.00 3.00
Ecology, protection of trees.

Rubens' Son Albert AP65

1977, Nov. 28   Engr.   Perf. 13
C153 AP65 100fr grnsh blk & rose cl 12.00 6.50
Peter Paul Rubens (1577-1640), painter, 400th birth anniversary.

Capt. Cook and "Discovery" — AP66

Design: 39fr, Capt. Cook and "Resolution."

1978, Jan. 20   Engr.   Perf. 13
C154 AP66 33fr multicolored   2.50 1.60
C155 AP66 39fr multicolored   3.00 1.75
Bicentenary of Capt. James Cook's arrival in Hawaii.
For overprints see Nos. C166-C167.

Shell Type of 1977
Sea Shells: 22fr, Erosaria obvelata. 24fr, Cypraea ventriculus. 31fr, Lambis robusta.

1978, Apr. 13 Photo. Perf. 13½x13
C156 AP58 22fr brt blue & multi 2.50 1.25
C157 AP58 24fr brt blue & multi 2.50 1.50
C158 AP58 31fr brt blue & multi 4.00 2.50
  Nos. C156-C158 (3)   9.00 5.25

Tahitian Woman and Boy, by Gauguin AP67

1978, May 7   Perf. 13
C159 AP67 50fr multicolored 14.00 9.00
Paul Gauguin (1848-1903).

Antenna and ITU Emblem AP68

1978, May 17   Litho.   Perf. 13
C160 AP68 80fr gray & multi   5.00 2.75
10th World Telecommunications Day.

Soccer and Argentina '78 Emblem — AP69

1978, June 1
C161 AP69 28fr multicolored   6.00 3.00
11th World Cup Soccer Championship, Argentina, June 1-25.

Coral Type of 1977
Designs: 26fr, Fungia, horiz. 34fr, Millepora.

Perf. 13x12½, 12½x13
1978, July 13   Photo.
C162 AP59 26fr multicolored   3.00 2.00
C163 AP59 34fr multicolored   4.00 3.00

Radar Antenna, Polynesian Woman — AP70

1978, Sept. 5   Engr.   Perf. 13
C164 AP70 50fr blue & black   3.00 1.75
Papenoo earth station.

Bird and Rainbow over Island — AP71

1978, Oct. 5   Photo.
C165 AP71 23fr multicolored   6.00 1.75
Nature protection.

Nos. C154-C155 Overprinted in Black or Violet Blue: "1779-1979 / BICENTENAIRE / DE LA / MORT DE"
1979, Feb. 14   Engr.   Perf. 13
C166 AP66 33fr multi   4.00 2.50
C167 AP66 39fr multi (VBl) 5.00 3.50
Bicentenary of Capt. Cook's death. On No. C167 date is last line of overprint.

Children, Toys and IYC Emblem — AP72

1979, May 3   Engr.   Perf. 13
C168 AP72 150fr multicolored 15.00 7.00
International Year of the Child.

"Do you expect a letter?" by Paul Gauguin — AP73

1979, May 20   Photo.   Perf. 13
C169 AP73 200fr multicolored   17.50 8.00

Shell and Carved Head — AP74

1979, June 30   Engr.   Perf. 13
C170 AP74 44fr multicolored   3.50 2.00
Museum of Tahiti and the Islands.

Conference Emblem over Island AP75

1979, Oct. 6   Photo.   Perf. 13
C171 AP75 23fr multicolored   2.25 1.10
19th South Pacific Conf., Tahiti, Oct. 6-12.

Flying Boat "Bermuda" — AP76

Planes Used in Polynesia: 40fr, DC-4 over Papeete. 60fr, Britten-Norman "Islander." 80fr, Fairchild F-27A. 120fr, DC-8 over Tahiti.

1979, Dec. 19   Litho.   Perf. 13
C172 AP76 24fr multicolored   1.00 .50
C173 AP76 40fr multicolored   1.75 1.00
C174 AP76 60fr multicolored   2.75 1.50
C175 AP76 80fr multicolored   3.50 2.25
C176 AP76 120fr multicolored   6.00 3.00
    Nos. C172-C176 (5)   15.00 8.25
    See Nos. C180-C183.

Window on Tahiti, by Henri Matisse AP77

1980, Feb. 18   Photo.
C177 AP77 150fr multicolored   8.00 5.00

Marshi Metua No Tehamana, by Gauguin AP78

1980, Aug. 24   Photo.   Perf. 13
C178 AP78 500fr multicolored   16.00 11.00

Sydpex '80, Philatelic Exhibition, Sydney Town Hall — AP79

1980, Sept. 29   Photo.   Perf. 13
C179 AP79 70fr multicolored   7.00 4.50

Aviation Type of 1979

1980, Dec. 15   Litho.   Perf. 13
C180 AP76 15fr Catalina   1.25 .75
C181 AP76 26fr Twin Otter   2.50 1.00
C182 AP76 30fr CAMS 55   3.00 1.25
C183 AP76 50fr DC-6   4.50 1.75
    Nos. C180-C183 (4)   11.25 4.75

And The Gold of their Bodies, by Gauguin — AP80

1981, Mar. 15   Photo.   Perf. 13
C184 AP80 100fr multicolored   7.50 3.00

20th Anniv. of Manned Space Flight AP81

1981, June 15   Litho.   Perf. 12½
C185 AP81 300fr multicolored   7.50 5.00

First Intl. Pirogue (6-man Canoe) Championship — AP82

1981, July 25   Litho.   Perf. 13x12½
C186 AP82 200fr multicolored   5.00 4.00

Matavai Bay, by William Hodges — AP83

Paintings: 60fr, Poedea, by John Weber, vert. 80fr, Omai, by Joshua Reynolds, vert. 120fr, Point Venus, by George Tobin.

1981, Dec. 10   Photo.   Perf. 13
C187 AP83 40fr multicolored   1.10 .90
C188 AP83 60fr multicolored   1.75 1.25
C189 AP83 80fr multicolored   2.75 1.75
C190 AP83 120fr multicolored   3.50 2.40
    Nos. C187-C190 (4)   9.10 6.30
    See Nos. C194-C197, C202-C205.

TB Bacillus Centenary — AP84

1982, Mar. 24   Engr.   Perf. 13
C191 AP84 200fr multicolored   5.00 3.00

1982 World Cup — AP85

1982, May 18   Litho.   Perf. 13
C192 AP85 250fr multicolored   5.75 4.00

French Overseas Possessions' Week, Sept. 18-25 — AP86

1982, Sept. 17   Engr.
C193 AP86 110fr multicolored   2.75 1.65

Painting Type of 1981

Designs: 50fr, The Tahitian, by M. Radiguet, vert. 70fr, Souvenir of Tahiti, by C. Giraud. 100fr, Beating Cloth Lengths, by Atlas JL the Younger. 160fr, Papeete Harbor, by C.F. Gordon Cumming.

1982, Dec. 15   Photo.   Perf. 13
C194 AP83 50fr multicolored   1.75 .75
C195 AP83 70fr multicolored   2.25 1.10
C196 AP83 100fr multicolored   2.50 1.60
C197 AP83 160fr multicolored   4.50 3.25
    Nos. C194-C197 (4)   11.00 6.70

Wood Cutter, by Gauguin AP87

Photo. & Engr.
1983, May 8   Perf. 12½x13
C198 AP87 600fr multicolored   14.00 8.00

Voyage of Capt. Bligh — AP88

1983, June 9   Litho.   Perf. 13
C199 AP88 200fr Map, fruit   6.00 3.00

BRASILIANA '83 Intl. Stamp Exhibition, Rio de Janeiro, July 29-Aug. 7 — AP89

1983, July 29   Litho.   Perf. 13x12½
C200 AP89 100fr multicolored   2.50 1.75
    a.   Souvenir sheet   6.00 6.00

1983, Aug. 4   Litho.   Perf. 13x12½
C201 AP89 110fr Bangkok '83   3.00 2.00
    a.   Souvenir sheet   7.50 7.50

Painting Type of 1981

20th Cent. Paintings: 40fr, View of Moorea, by William Alister MacDonald (1861-1956). 60fr, The Fruit Carrier, by Adrian Herman Gouwe (1875-1965). 80fr, Arrival of the Destroyer Escort, by Nicolas Mordvinoff (1911-1977). 100fr, Women on a Veranda, by Charles Alfred Le Moine (1872-1918).

1983, Dec. 22   Photo.   Perf. 13
C202 AP83 40fr multi   1.00 .75
C203 AP83 60fr multi, vert.   1.50 1.00
C204 AP83 80fr multi, vert.   1.60 1.25
C205 AP83 100fr multi   2.00 1.60
    Nos. C202-C205 (4)   6.10 4.60

ESPANA '84 — AP90

Design: Maori canoers.

1984, Apr. 27   Engr.   Perf. 13
C206 AP90 80fr brn red & dk
    bl   2.25 1.50

Souvenir Sheet
C207 AP90 200fr dk bl & dk
    red   12.00 12.00

Woman with Mango, by Gauguin AP91

Photo. & Engr.
1984, May 27   Perf. 12½x13
C208 AP91 400fr multicolored   9.50 6.00

Ausipex '84 — AP92

Details from Human Sacrifice of the Maori in Tahiti, 18th cent. engraving.

1984, Sept. 5   Litho.   Perf. 13x12½
C209 AP92 120fr Worshippers   3.00 2.25
C210 AP92 120fr Preparation   3.00 2.25
  a.   Pair, #C209-C210 + label   7.50 7.50
Souvenir Sheet
C211 AP92 200fr Entire   9.50 9.50

Painting by Gaugin (1848-1903) — AP93

Design: Where have we come from? What are we? Where are we going? Illustration reduced.

1985, Mar. 17   Litho.   Perf. 13½x13
C212 AP93 550fr multi   12.00 7.50

4th Pacific Arts Festival Type
1985, July 3   Litho.   Perf. 13
C213 A95 200fr Islander, tiki, ar-
           tifacts   4.50 3.00

Intl. Youth Year — AP95

1985, Sept. 18   Litho.
C214 AP95 250fr Island youths,
           frigate bird   5.50 3.25

ITALIA '85 — AP96

Designs: Ship sailing into Papeete Harbor, 19th century print.

1985, Oct. 22   Engr.
C215 AP96 130fr multicolored   2.75 2.50
Souvenir Sheet
C216 AP96 240fr multicolored   7.50 7.50

1st Intl. Marlin Fishing Contest, Feb. 27-Mar. 5 — AP97

1986, Feb. 27   Litho.   Perf. 12½
C217 AP97 300fr multicolored   6.50 4.00

Arrival of a Boat, c.1880 — AP98

1986, June 24   Engr.   Perf. 13
C218 AP98 400fr intense blue   8.75 5.25

STOCKHOLMIA '86 — AP99

Design: Dr. Karl Solander and Anders Sparrmann, Swedish scientists who accompanied Capt. Cook, and map of Tahiti.

1986, Aug. 28   Engr.   Perf. 13
C219 AP99 150fr multicolored   3.25 2.25
Souvenir Sheet
C220 AP99 210fr multicolored   4.75 4.75

Protestant Churches — AP100

1986, Dec. 17   Litho.   Perf. 13
C221 AP100 80fr Tiva, 1955   1.75   .90
C222 AP100 200fr Avera, 1880   4.50 2.10
C223 AP100 300fr Papetoai,
            1822   6.50 3.25
       Nos. C221-C223 (3)   12.75 6.25

Broche Barracks, 120th Anniv. — AP101

1987, Apr. 21   Litho.   Perf. 12½x12
C224 AP101 350fr multicolored   7.75 5.00

CAPEX '87 — AP102

Design: George Vancouver (1757-1798), English navigator and cartographer, chart and excerpt from ship's log.

1987, June 15   Engr.   Perf. 13
C225 AP102 130fr multi   2.90 2.25
Imperf
Size: 143x100mm
C226 AP102 260fr multicolored   5.75 5.75

Soyez Mysterieuses, from a 5-Panel Sculpture by Paul Gauguin, Gauguin Museum — AP103

Illustration reduced.

1987, Nov. 15   Perf. 13
C227 AP103 600fr multicolored 14.00 9.50

AIR POST SEMI-POSTAL STAMPS

> Catalogue values for unused stamps in this section are for Never Hinged items.

French Revolution Issue
Common Design Type
Unwmk.
1939, July 5   Photo.   Perf. 13
Name and Value Typo. in Orange
CB1 CD83 5fr + 4fr brn blk   52.50 29.00

Mother & Children on Beach — SPAP1

Perf. 12½x13½
1942, June 22   Engr.
CB2 SPAP1 1.50fr + 3.50fr green 1.50
CB3 SPAP1 2fr + 6fr yellow
            brown   1.50

Native children's welfare fund. Nos. CB2-CB3 were issued by the Vichy government in France, but were not placed on sale in French Polynesia.

Colonial Education Fund
Common Design Type
1942, June 22
CB4 CD86a 1.20fr + 1.80fr blue
             & red   1.50

No. CB4 was issued by the Vichy government in France, but was not placed on sale in French Polynesia.

POSTAGE DUE STAMPS

Postage Due Stamps of French Colonies, 1894-1906, Overprinted

1926-27   Unwmk.   Perf. 14x13½
J1 D1 5c light blue   .60   .60
J2 D1 10c brown   .60   .60
J3 D1 20c olive green   .95   .95
J4 D1 30c dull red   1.00 1.00
J5 D1 40c rose   2.25 2.25
J6 D1 60c blue green   2.25 2.25
J7 D1 1fr red brown, straw   2.25 2.25
J8 D1 3fr magenta ('27)   9.50 9.50
With Additional Surcharge of New Value
J9 D1 2fr on 1fr orange red   2.75 2.75
       Nos. J1-J9 (9)   22.15 22.15

Fautaua Falls, Tahiti — D2   Tahitian Youth — D3

1929   Typo.   Perf. 13½x14
J10 D2 5c lt blue & dk brn   .50   .50
J11 D2 10c vermilion & grn   .60   .60
J12 D2 30c dk brn & dk red   1.25 1.25
J13 D2 50c yel grn & dk brn   1.00 1.00
J14 D2 60c dl vio & yel grn   2.75 2.75
J15 D3 1fr Prus bl & red vio 2.25 2.25
J16 D3 2fr brn red & dk brn   1.50 1.50
J17 D3 3fr bl vio & bl grn   1.50 1.50
       Nos. J10-J17 (8)   11.35 11.35

> Catalogue values for unused stamps in this section, from this point to the end of the section, are for Never Hinged items.

D4   Polynesian Club — D5

1948   Engr.   Perf. 14x13
J18 D4 10c brt blue grn   .30   .20
J19 D4 30c black brown   .30   .20
J20 D4 50c dk car rose   .40   .25
J21 D4 1fr ultra   .55   .45
J22 D4 2fr dk blue green   .75   .60
J23 D4 3fr red   1.50 1.25
J24 D4 4fr violet   1.60 1.40
J25 D4 5fr lilac rose   2.40 1.90
J26 D4 10fr slate   3.25 2.25
J27 D4 20fr red brown   4.50 3.75
       Nos. J18-J27 (10)   15.55 12.25

1958   Unwmk.   Perf. 14x13
J28 D5 1fr dk brn & grn   .55   .50
J29 D5 3fr bluish blk & hn brn .75   .75
J30 D5 5fr brown & ultra   .90   .90
       Nos. J28-J30 (3)   2.20 2.15

Tahitian Bowl — D6

1984-87   Litho.   Perf. 13
J31 D6 1fr Mother-of-pearl fish
           hook, vert.   .25   .25
J32 D6 3fr shown   .25   .25
J33 D6 5fr Marquesan fan   .25   .25
J34 D6 10fr Lamp stand, vert. .40   .40

J35	D6	20fr Wood headrest ('87)	.55	.55
J36	D6	50fr Wood scoop ('87)	1.25	1.25
		Nos. J31-J36 (6)	2.95	2.95

Issued: #J31-34, 3/15; #J35-J36, 8/18.

OFFICIAL STAMPS

> Catalogue values for unused stamps in this section are for Never Hinged items.

Breadfruit
O1

Polynesian Fruits: 2fr, 3fr, 5fr, like 1fr. 7fr, 8fr, 10fr, 15fr, "Vi Tahiti." 19fr, 20fr, 25fr, 35fr, Avocados. 50fr, 100fr, 200fr, Mangos.

1977, June 9   Litho.   Perf. 12½

O1	O1	1fr ultra & multi	.25	.25
O2	O1	2fr ultra & multi	.25	.25
O3	O1	3fr ultra & multi	.25	.25
O4	O1	5fr ultra & multi	.25	.25
O5	O1	7fr red & multi	.50	.50
O6	O1	8fr red & multi	.55	.55
O7	O1	10fr red & multi	.60	.60
O8	O1	15fr red & multi	1.00	1.00
O9	O1	19fr black & multi	1.25	1.25
O10	O1	20fr black & multi	1.50	1.50
O11	O1	25fr black & multi	1.75	1.75
O12	O1	35fr black & multi	2.25	2.25
O13	O1	50fr black & multi	2.50	2.50
O14	O1	100fr red & multi	4.50	4.50
O15	O1	200fr ultra & multi	8.00	8.00
		Nos. O1-O15 (15)	25.40	25.40

1982-86   Perf. 13

O1a	O1	1fr ultra & multi	.45	.45
O2a	O1	2fr ultra & multi	.45	.45
O3a	O1	3fr ultra & multi	.65	.65
O4a	O1	5fr ultra & multi	1.25	1.25
O5a	O1	7fr red & multi	1.50	1.50
O6a	O1	8fr red & multi	2.00	2.00
O7a	O1	10fr red & multi	2.00	2.00
O8a	O1	15fr red & multi ('84)	2.00	2.00
O10a	O1	20fr black & multi	2.00	2.00
O11a	O1	25fr black & multi ('84)	2.00	2.00
O12a	O1	35fr black & multi ('84)	4.75	4.75
O13a	O1	50fr black & multi ('84)	12.00	12.00
O14a	O1	100fr red & multi ('86)	24.00	24.00
O15a	O1	200fr ultra & multi ('86)	26.00	26.00
		Nos. O1a-O15a (14)	81.05	81.05

Nos. O1-O15 have dull finish (matte) gum. Nos. O1a-O15a have shiny gum.

Stamps and Postmarks — O2

1fr, French Colonies #5. 2fr, French Colonies #27, #12. 3fr, French Colonies #29, 1884 Papeete postmark. 5fr, Newspaper franked with surcharge of Tahiti #2, 1884 Papeete postmark. 9fr, #176. 10fr, #4, 1894 octagonal postmark. 20fr, #6, #8. 46fr, #48. 51fr, #147-148, Vaitepaua-Makatea Island postmark. 70fr, Visit Tahiti postmark on postal card piece. 85fr, #59 with 1921 manuscript cancel, vert. 100fr, #181. 200fr, #C21, 1st day cancel.

Perf. 13¼, 13¼x13 (#O26), 13x13¼ (#O27)

1993-99   Litho.

O16	O2	1fr multicolored	.20	.20
O17	O2	2fr multicolored	.20	.20
O18	O2	3fr multicolored	.20	.20
O19	O2	5fr multicolored	.20	.20
O20	O2	9fr multicolored	.75	.75
O21	O2	10fr multicolored	.20	.20
O22	O2	20fr multicolored	.50	.50
O23	O2	46fr multicolored	1.10	1.10
O24	O2	51fr multicolored	1.90	1.90
O25	O2	70fr multicolored	1.75	1.75
O26	O2	85fr multicolored	1.90	1.90
O27	O2	100fr multicolored	2.25	2.25
O28	O2	200fr multicolored	3.50	3.50
		Nos. O16-O28 (13)	14.65	14.65

Issued: 51fr, 4/6/94; 9fr, 85fr, 4/21/97; others, 1/13/93.

1997-98   Litho.   Perf. 13¼x13,

O16a	O2	1fr multicolored	.50	.50
O17a	O2	2fr multicolored	.50	.50
O18a	O2	3fr multicolored	.50	.50
O19a	O2	5fr multicolored	.75	.75
O20a	O2	10fr multicolored	.75	.75
O21a	O2	20fr multicolored	.75	.75
O23a	O2	70fr multicolored	1.50	1.50
O24a	O2	100fr multicolored	1.90	1.90
O25a	O2	200fr multicolored	4.50	4.50

Issued: Nos. O17a, O19a, O23a, O25a, 1997; Nos. O16a, O18a, 1998. Nos. O20a, O21a, O24a, 1999.

FRENCH SOUTHERN AND ANTARCTIC TERRITORIES

'french 'sə-<u>th</u>ərn and
ˌant-ärk-tik 'ter-ə-'tör-ēs

POP. — 130 staff

Formerly dependencies of Madagascar, these areas, comprising the Kerguelen Archipelago; St. Paul, Amsterdam and Crozet Islands and Adelie Land in Antarctica achieved territorial status on August 6, 1955.

100 Centimes = 1 Franc
100 Cents = 1 Euro (2002)

Catalogue values for all unused stamps in this country are for Never Hinged items.

Madagascar No. 289 Overprinted in Red:

Unwmk.
1955, Oct. 28   Engr.   Perf. 13
1   A25 15f dk grn & dp ultra   14.50 *29.00*

Rockhopper Penguins, Crozet Archipelago — A1

New Amsterdam A2

Design: 10fr, 15fr, Elephant seal.

1956, Apr. 25   Engr.   Perf. 13
2   A1 50c dk blue, sepia & yel   .45   .75
3   A1 1fr ultra, org & gray   .45   .75
4   A2 5fr blue & dp ultra   3.00   *3.25*
5   A2 8fr gray vio & dk brn   18.00 *21.00*
6   A2 10fr indigo   6.50   6.25
7   A2 15fr indigo & brn vio   8.00   7.50
     Nos. 2-7 (6)   36.40 39.50

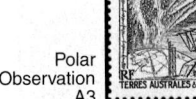

Polar Observation A3

1957, Oct. 11
8   A3 5fr black & violet   3.50   *5.00*
9   A3 10fr rose red   4.75   5.75
10   A3 15fr dark blue   5.75   *7.50*
     Nos. 8-10 (3)   14.00 18.25

International Geophysical Year, 1957-58.

Imperforates
Most stamps of this French possession exist imperforate in issued and trial colors, and also in small presentation sheets in issued colors.

Flower Issue
Common Design Type
Design: Pringlea, horiz.

1959   Photo.   Perf. 12½x12
11   CD104 10fr sal, grn & yel   10.00 8.00

Common Design Types pictured following the introduction.

Light-mantled Sooty Albatross — A4

Coat of Arms — A5

Designs: 40c, Skua, horiz. 12fr, King shag.

1959, Sept. 14   Engr.   Perf. 13
12   A4 30c blue, grn & red brn   .50   .75
13   A4 40c blk, dl red brn & bl .50   .75
14   A4 12fr lt blue & blk   13.50   8.75
     Nos. 12-14 (3)   14.50 10.25

1959, Sept. 14   Typo.   Perf. 13x14
15   A5 20fr ultra, lt bl & yel 21.00 11.50

Sheathbills — A6

4fr, Sea leopard, horiz. 25fr, Weddell seal at Kerguélen, horiz. 85fr, King penguin.

1960, Dec. 15   Engr.   Perf. 13
16   A6 2fr grnsh bl, gray & choc   1.75   2.25
17   A6 4fr bl, dk brn & dk grn   9.50   7.50
18   A6 25fr sl grn, bis brn & blk 100.00 42.50
19   A6 85fr grnsh bl, org & blk   22.50 14.50
     Nos. 16-19 (4)   133.75 66.75

Yves-Joseph de Kerguélen-Trémarec — A7

1960, Nov. 22
20   A7 25fr red org, dk bl & brn 29.00 22.50
Yves-Joseph de Kerguélen-Trémarec, discoverer of the Kerguélen Archipelago.

Charcot, Compass Rose and "Pourquoi-pas?" — A8

1961, Dec. 26   Unwmk.   Perf. 13
21   A8 25fr brn, grn & red   29.00 22.50
25th anniv. of the death of Commander Jean Charcot (1867-1936), Antarctic explorer.

Elephant Seals Fighting A9

1963, Feb. 11   Engr.   Perf. 13
22   A9 8fr dk blue, blk & claret 12.00 7.50
     See No. C4.

Penguins and Camp on Crozet Island A10

20fr, Research station & IQSY emblem.

1963, Dec. 16   Unwmk.   Perf. 13
23   A10 5fr blk, red brn & Prus bl   65.00 35.00
24   A10 20fr vio, sl & red brn   80.00 55.00
Intl. Quiet Sun Year, 1964-65. See #C6.

Great Blue Whale A11

Black-browed Albatross — A12

Aurora Australis, Map of Antarctica and Rocket — A13

10fr, Cape pigeons. 12fr, Phylica trees, Amsterdam Island. 15fr, Killer whale (orca).

1966-69   Engr.   Perf. 13
25   A11 5fr brt bl & indigo   21.00 11.50
26   A11 10fr sl, ind & ol brn   32.50 25.00
27   A11 12fr brt bl, sl grn & lemon 22.50 14.00
27A   A11 15fr ol, dk bl & ind   12.00   7.25
28   A12 20fr slate, ol & org   400.00 225.00
      Nos. 25-28 (5)   488.00 282.75

Issued: 5fr, 12/12; 20fr, 1/3/68; 10fr, 12fr, 1/6/69; 15fr, 12/21/69.

1967, Mar. 4   Engr.   Perf. 13
29   A13 20fr mag, blue & blk   29.00 22.50
Launching of the 1st space rocket from Adelie Land, Jan., 1967.

Dumont d'Urville A14

1968, Jan. 20
30   A14 30fr lt ultra, dk bl & dk brn   140.00 80.00
Jules Sébastien César Dumont D'Urville (1790-1842), French naval commander and South Seas explorer.

WHO Anniversary Issue
Common Design Type
1968, May 4   Engr.   Perf. 13
31   CD126 30fr red, yel & bl   65.00 45.00

Human Rights Year Issue
Common Design Type
1968, Aug. 10   Engr.   Perf. 13
32   CD127 30fr grnsh bl, red & brn   60.00 45.00

Polar Camp with Helicopter, Plane and Snocat Tractor — A15

1969, Mar. 17   Engr.   Perf. 13
33   A15 25fr Prus bl, lt grnsh bl & brn red   25.00 15.00
20 years of French Polar expeditions.

ILO Issue
Common Design Type
1970, Jan. 1   Engr.   Perf. 13
35   CD131 20fr org, dk bl & brn 18.50 11.00

UPU Headquarters Issue
Common Design Type
1970, May 20   Engr.   Perf. 13
36   CD133 50fr blue, plum & ol bis   45.00 29.00

Ice Fish A16

Fish: Nos. 38-43, Antarctic cods, various species. 135fr, Zanchlorhynchus spinifer.

1971   Engr.   Perf. 13

37	A16	5fr brt grn, ind & org	1.25	.85
38	A16	10fr redsh brn & dp vio	2.00	.95
39	A16	20fr dp cl, brt grn & org	4.25	2.10
40	A16	22fr pur, brn ol & mag	4.00	3.25
41	A16	25fr grn, ind & org	6.00	2.75
42	A16	30fr sep, gray & bl vio	7.50	4.25
43	A16	35fr sl grn, dk brn & ocher	6.00	3.25
44	A16	135fr Prus bl, dp org & ol grn	10.00	5.25
		Nos. 37-44 (8)	41.00	22.65

Issued: #37-39, 41-42, 1/1; #40, 43-44, 12/22.

Map of Antarctica
A17

Microzetia Mirabilis
A18

1971, Dec. 22

45	A17	75fr red	27.50	25.00

Antarctic Treaty pledging peaceful uses of and scientific cooperation in Antarctica, 10th anniv.

1972

Insects: 15fr, Christiansenia dreuxi. 22f, Phtirocoris antarcticus. 30fr, Antarctophytosus atriceps. 40fr, Paractora drenxi. 140fr, Pringleophaga Kerguelenensis.

46	A18	15fr cl, org & brn	10.00	6.00
47	A18	22fr vio bl, sl grn & yel	14.50	9.25
48	A18	25fr grn, rose lil & pur	5.75	4.75
49	A18	30fr blue & multi	18.00	10.00
50	A18	40fr dk brn, ocher & blk	8.75	4.75
51	A18	140fr bl, emer & brn	12.50	8.75
		Nos. 46-51 (6)	69.50	43.50

Issued: #48, 50-51, 1/3; #46-47, 49, 12/16.

De Gaulle Issue
Common Design Type

Designs: 50fr, Gen. de Gaulle, 1940. 100fr, Pres. de Gaulle, 1970.

1972, Feb. 1   Engr.   Perf. 13

52	CD134	50fr brt grn & blk	21.00	13.50
53	CD134	100fr brt grn & blk	26.00	20.00

Kerguelen Cabbage — A19

Designs: 61fr, Azorella selago, horiz. 87fr, Acaena ascendens, horiz.

1972-73

54	A19	45fr multicolored	10.00	5.00
55	A19	61fr multicolored	3.50	2.75
56	A19	87fr multicolored	5.75	4.00
		Nos. 54-56 (3)	19.25	11.75

Issued: 45fr, 12/18; others, 12/13/73.

Mailship Sapmer and Map of Amsterdam Island — A20

1974, Dec. 31   Engr.   Perf. 13

57	A20	75fr bl, blk & dk brn	7.25	5.25

25th anniversary of postal service.

Antarctic Tern — A21

Designs: 50c, Antarctic petrel. 90c, Sea lioness. 1fr, Weddell seal. 1.20fr, Kerguelen cormorant, vert. 1.40fr, Gentoo penguin, vert.

1976, Jan.   Engr.   Perf. 13

58	A21	40c multicolored	4.75	3.00
59	A21	50c multicolored	4.75	3.00
60	A21	90c multicolored	7.50	4.00
61	A21	1fr multicolored	12.00	9.25
62	A21	1.20fr multicolored	15.00	11.00
63	A21	1.40fr multicolored	14.00	11.50
		Nos. 58-63 (6)	58.00	41.75

James Clark Ross — A22

James Cook — A23

Design: 30c, Climbing Mount Ross.

1976, Dec. 16   Engr.   Perf. 13

64	A22	30c multicolored	4.50	3.00
65	A22	3fr multicolored	4.50	3.00

First climbing of Mount Ross, Kerguelen Island, Jan. 5, 1975.

1976, Dec. 16

66	A23	70c multicolored	13.50	10.00

Bicentenary of Capt. Cook's voyage past Kerguelen Island. See No. C46.

Commerson's Dolphins — A24

1977, Feb. 1   Engr.   Perf. 13

67	A24	1.10fr Blue whale	5.75	3.25
68	A24	1.50fr shown	5.75	4.00

Macrocystis Algae — A25

Salmon Hatchery — A26

Magga Dan — A27

Designs: 70c, Durvillea algae. 90c, Albatross. 1fr, Underwater sampling and scientists, vert. 1.40fr, Thala Dan and penguins.

1977, Dec. 20   Engr.   Perf. 13

69	A25	40c ol brn & bis	1.10	.70
70	A26	50c dk bl & pur	1.40	1.00
71	A25	70c blk, grn & brn	1.60	1.00
72	A26	90c grn, brt bl & brn	1.60	1.00
73	A26	1fr slate	1.40	1.00
74	A27	1.20fr multi	3.25	1.60
75	A27	1.40fr multi	2.00	1.60
		Nos. 69-75 (7)	12.35	7.90

See Nos. 77-79.

A28

A29

Explorer with French and Expedition Flags.

1977, Dec. 24

76	A28	1.90fr multicolored	7.75	5.00

French Polar expeditions, 1947-48.

Types of 1977

40c, Forbin, destroyer. 50c Jeanne d'Arc, helicopter carrier. 1.40fr, Kerguelen cormorant.

1979, Jan. 1   Engr.   Perf. 13

77	A27	40c black & blue	1.40	1.10
78	A27	50c black & blue	1.60	1.10
79	A26	1.40fr multicolored	1.60	1.10
		Nos. 77-79 (3)	4.60	3.30

1979, Jan. 1

80	A29	1.20fr citron & indigo	1.40	1.10

R. Rallier du Baty. See Nos. 97, 100, 111, 117, 129, 135, 188.

French Navigators Monument, Hobart — A30

1979, Jan. 1

81	A30	1fr multicolored	.90	.80

French navigators and explorers.

Petrel — A31

1979   Engr.   Perf. 13

82	A31	70c Rockhopper penguins, vert.	1.25	1.00
83	A31	1fr shown	1.50	1.25

Commandant Bourdais — A32

1979

84	A32	1.10fr Doudart de Lagree, vert.	1.25	1.00
85	A32	1.50fr shown	1.50	1.25

Adm. Antoine d'Entrecasteaux
A33

Sebastian de el Cano
A34

1979

86	A33	1.20fr multicolored	1.40	1.10

1979

Discovery of Amsterdam Island, 1522: 4fr, Victoria, horiz.

87	A34	1.40fr multicolored	1.10	.80
88	A34	4fr multicolored	2.00	1.60

Adelie Penguins — A35

Adelie Penguin — A36

Sea Leopard A37

1980, Dec. 15   Engr.   Perf. 13

89	A35	50c rose violet	1.40	1.25
90	A36	60c multicolored	1.40	.90
91	A35	1.20fr multicolored	2.00	1.10
92	A37	1.30fr multicolored	1.40	1.25
93	A37	1.80fr multicolored	1.40	1.25
		Nos. 89-93 (5)	7.60	5.75

FRENCH SOUTHERN AND ANTARCTIC TERRITORIES

20th Anniv. of Antarctic Treaty — A38

1981, June 23   Engr.   Perf. 13
94 A38 1.80fr multicolored   4.50 4.50

Alouette II — A39

1981-82   Engr.   Perf. 13
95 A39 55c brown & multi   .55 .45
96 A39 65c blue & multi   .55 .45

Explorer Type of 1979
1981
97 A29 1.40fr Jean Loranchet   .80 .55

Landing Ship Le Gros Ventre, Kerguelen — A41

1983, Jan. 3   Engr.   Perf. 13
98 A41 55c multicolored   .90 .65

Our Lady of the Winds Statue and Church, Kerguelen — A42

1983, Jan. 3
99 A42 1.40fr multicolored   .90 .90

Explorer Type of 1979
Design: Martin de Vivies, Navigator.

1983, Jan. 3
100 A29 1.60fr multicolored   .90 .75

Eaton's Ducks A44

1983, Jan. 3
101 A44 1.50fr multicolored   .90 .60
102 A44 1.80fr multicolored   .90 .75

Trawler Austral — A45

1983, Jan. 3
103 A45 2.30fr multicolored   1.40 1.10

Freighter Lady Franklin — A46

1983, Aug. 4   Engr.   Perf. 13
104 A46 5fr multicolored   4.00 3.00

Glaciology — A47

Design: Scientists examining glacier, base.

1984, Jan. 1   Engr.   Perf. 13
105 A47 15c multicolored   .35 .30
106 A47 1.70fr multicolored   .80 .55

Crab-eating Seal — A48

Penguins — A49

1984, Jan. 1
107 A48 60c multicolored   .55 .45
108 A49 70c multicolored   .45 .45
109 A49 2fr multicolored   1.25 1.00
110 A48 5.90fr multicolored   2.00 1.75
    Nos. 107-110 (4)   4.25 3.65

Explorer Type of 1979
1984, Jan. 1
111 A29 1.80fr Alfred Faure   .90 .70

Biomass — A51

1985, Jan. 1   Engr.   Perf. 13
112 A51 1.80fr multicolored   .80 .55
113 A51 5.20fr multicolored   2.00 1.75

Emperor Penguins — A52

Snowy Petrel — A53

1985, Jan. 1   Engr.   Perf. 13
114 A52 1.70fr multicolored   1.00 .80
115 A53 2.80fr multicolored   1.25 1.10

Port Martin — A54

1985, Jan. 1   Engr.   Perf. 13
116 A54 2.20fr multicolored   1.25 .80

Explorer Type of 1979
1985, Jan. 1   Engr.   Perf. 13
117 A29 2fr Andre-Frank Liotard   .90 .70

Antarctic Fulmar — A56

1986, Jan. 1   Engr.   Perf. 13
118 A56 1fr shown   .55 .45
119 A56 1.70fr Giant petrels   .80 .75
    Nos. 118-119,C91 (3)   3.35 2.95

Echinoderms — A57

1986, Jan. 1
120 A57 1.90fr shown   .90 .75

Cotula Plumosa — A58

Shipping — A59

1986, Jan. 1
121 A58 2.30fr shown   .90 .75
122 A58 6.20fr Lycopodium.
    saururus   2.50 1.90

1986, Jan. 1
123 A59 2.10fr Var research ship   .90 .85
124 A59 3fr Polarbjorn support
    ship   1.25 1.25

Marine Life — A60

1987, Jan. 1   Engr.   Perf. 13½x13
125 A60 50c dk blue & org   .50 .50

Flora — A61

1987, Jan. 1
126 A61 1.80fr Poa cookii   .70 .50
127 A61 6.50fr Lichen, Neuro-
           pogon taylori   2.00 1.90

Marret Base, Adelie Land — A62

1987, Jan. 1
128 A62 2fr yel brn, dk ultra &
           lake   .90 .70

Explorer Type of 1979
1987, Jan. 1
129 A29 2.20fr Adm. Mouchez   1.00 .75

Reindeer — A64

1987, Jan. 1
130 A64 2.50fr black   1.25 .80

Transport Ship Eure — A65

1987, Jan. 1
131 A65 3.20fr dk ultra, Prus grn
           & dk grn   1.25 1.00

Macaroni Penguins — A66

1987, Jan. 1   **Perf. 13x12½**
132 A66 4.80fr multicolored   2.50 1.90

Elephant Grass — A67

1988, Jan. 1   **Engr.**   **Perf. 13**
133 A67 1.70fr Prus grn, emer &
           olive   .75 .65

Rev.-Father Lejay,
Explorer — A68

1988, Jan. 1
134 A68 2.20fr vio, ultra & blk   .90 .80

Explorer Type of 1979
Design: Robert Gessain (1907-86).

1988, Jan. 1
135 A29 3.40fr gray, dk red & blk 1.40 1.10

Le Gros Ventre, 18th Cent. — A70

1988, Jan. 1
136 A70 3.50fr dp ultra, bl grn &
           brn   1.25 1.25

Mermaid and B.A.P. Jules Verne,
Research Vessel — A71

1988, Jan. 1
137 A71 4.90fr gray & dk blue   2.25 1.75

La Fortune, Early
19th Cent. — A72

1988, Jan. 1
138 A72 5fr blk & dull bl grn   2.25 1.75

Wilson's Petrel — A73

1988, Jan. 1
139 A73 6.80fr blk, sepia & dl bl
           grn   2.75 2.25
           See Nos. 143-144.

Mt. Ross Campaign (in 1987) — A74

1988, Jan. 1   **Perf. 13x12½**
140 A74 2.20fr Volcanic rock
           cross-sections   .75 .75
141 A74 15.10fr Kerguelen Is.   5.00 5.00
  a. Pair, #140-141 + label   6.75 6.75

Darrieus System Wind Vane Electric
Generator — A75

1988, Jan. 1   **Engr.**   **Perf. 13**
142 A75 1fr dark blue & blue   .50 .35

Fauna Type of 1988
1989, Jan. 1   **Engr.**
143 A73 1.10fr Lithodes   .40 .40
144 A73 3.60fr Blue petrel   1.40 .75

Fern
A76

1989, Jan. 1
145 A76 2.80fr Blechnum penna
           Marina   1.00 .90

Minerals
A77

1989, Jan. 1
146 A77 5.10fr Mesotype   1.75 1.75
147 A77 7.30fr Analcime   2.75 2.25

Henri and
Rene
Bossiere,
Pioneers of
the
Kerguelen
Isls. — A78

1989, Jan. 1
148 A78 2.20fr multicolored   1.10 .75

Kerguelen Is. Sheep — A79

1989, Jan. 1   **Perf. 13½x13**
149 A79 2fr multicolored   .75 .65

Scuba Diver, Adelie Coast — A80

1989, Jan. 1
150 A80 1.70fr dk olive bis, blue &
           dk grn   .75 .60

Map of Kerguelen Island, Protozoa
and Copepod — A81

1990, Jan. 1   **Engr.**   **Perf. 13**
151 A81 1.10fr blk, brt blue & red
           brn   .75 .40
       Study of protista, Kerguelan Is.

Cattle on Farm, Sea Birds — A82

1990, Jan. 1
152 A82 1.70fr Prus blue, grn & brn
           blk   .75 .60
       Rehabilitation of the environment, Amster-
dam Is.

Quoy and   Dumont d'Urville
Copendium   (1790-1842),
decollata — A83   Explorer — A84

1990, Jan. 1   **Perf. 13½x13**
153 A83 2.20fr brt blue, blk & red
           brn   .85 .75
       Jean Rene C. Quoy (1790-1869), naturalist,
navigator.

1990, Jan. 1
154 A84 3.60fr ultra & blk   1.50 1.10

Yellow-billed Albatross — A85

1990, Jan. 1   **Perf. 13x12½**
155 A85 2.80fr multicolored   1.75 .90

Aragonite A86

1990, Jan. 1
156 A86 5.10fr deep ultra & dark yel grn   2.50 1.75

Ranunculus pseudo trullifolius — A87

1990, Jan. 1   *Perf. 13*
157 A87 8.40fr dp bl, org & emer grn   3.00 2.75

Penguin Type of Airpost 1974

1991, Jan. 1
158 AP18 50c blue grn, bl & blk   .75 .20
Postal Service at Crozet Island, 30th anniv.

Moss — A88

1991, Jan. 1   *Perf. 13x12½*
159 A88 1.70fr gray, brn & blk   .80 .65

Adm. Max Douguet (1903-1989) A89

1991, Jan. 1
160 A89 2.30fr org brn, blk & bl   1.25 .90

Lighter L'Aventure — A90

1991, Jan. 1   Engr.   *Perf. 13*
161 A90 3.20fr brn, grn & bl   1.50 1.25

Sea Lions — A91

1991, Jan. 1   *Perf. 13*
162 A91 3.60fr blue & ol brn   2.25 1.40

Mordenite — A92

1991, Jan. 1
163 A92 5.20fr blk, grn bl & grn   2.75 2.00

Champsocephalus Gunnari — A93

1991, Jan. 1
164 A93 7.80fr blue & green   3.00 3.00

A94   A95

1991, Jan. 1
165 A94 9.30fr ol grn & rose red   4.00 3.50
Antarctic Treaty, 30th anniv.

1992, Jan. 1   Engr.   *Perf. 13*
Design: Colobanthus Kerguelensis.
166 A95 1fr bl grn, grn & brn   .85 .45

Globe Challenge Yacht Race — A96

1992, Jan. 1   Litho.
167 A96 2.20fr multicolored   1.25 1.00

Dissostichus Eleginoides — A97

1992, Jan. 1   Engr.
168 A97 2.30fr blue, ol grn & red brn   1.40 1.00

Paul Tchernia A98

1992, Jan. 1   Engr.   *Perf. 13*
169 A98 2.50fr brown & green   1.00 1.00

Capt. Marion Dufresne (1724-1772) — A99

1992, Jan. 1   Engr.   *Perf. 13*
170 A99 3.70fr red, blk & bl   1.50 1.50

Supply Ship Tottan, 1951 — A100

1992, Jan. 1   Engr.   *Perf. 13*
171 A100 14fr blue grn, brn & bl   5.75 5.75

WOCE Program — A101

1992, Jan. 1
172 A101 25.40fr multi   11.00 10.50

Coat of Arms — A102

1992-95   Engr.   *Perf. 13*
173 A102 10c black   .25 .20
174 A102 20c greenish blue   .25 .20
175 A102 30c red   .25 .20
176 A102 40c green   .40 .20
177 A102 50c orange   .40 .20
    Nos. 173-177 (5)   1.55 1.00
Issued: 10c, 1/1/92; 20c, 30c, 1/1/93; 40c, 1/1/94; 50c, 1/2/95.
See Nos. 295-299.

Garnet A103

1993, Jan. 1   Engr.   *Perf. 13*
183 A103 1fr multicolored   1.25 .30
See Nos. 194, 203, 212, 222, 235, 244, 259, 279, 300.

Research Ship Marion Dufresne, 20th Anniv. — A104

Lyallia Kerguelensis A105

1993, Jan. 1
184 A104 2.20fr multicolored   1.25 .60

1993, Jan. 1
185 A105 2.30fr blue & green   1.25 .60

A106

A107

1993, Jan. 1
186 A106 2.50fr Killer whale   1.50 .70
187 A107 2.50fr Skua   7.00 .70

Explorer Type of 1979 and

Weather station, Adelie Land A108

Design: 2.50fr, Andre Prudhomme (1930-1959), Meteorologist.

1993, Jan. 1   *Perf. 12½x13*
188 A29 2.50fr blue, blk & org   1.00 .65
189 A108 22fr org, blk & bl   8.50 6.00
  a.   Pair, #188-189 + label   10.00 10.00

Centriscops Obliquus — A109

1993, Jan. 1   *Perf. 13*
190 A109 3.40fr multicolored   1.50 .90

Freighter Italo Marsano — A110

1993, Jan. 1
191 A110 3.70fr multicolored   1.75 1.00

ECOPHY Program
A111

1993, Jan. 1
192 A111 14fr black, blue & brn 6.50 4.25

L'Astrolabe on Northeast Route, 1991
A112

1993, Jan. 1
193 A112 22fr multicolored 9.25 5.75

Mineral Type of 1993
1994, Jan. 1 Engr. Perf. 13
194 A103 1fr Cordierite .75 .35

Felis Catus — A113

1994, Jan. 1
195 A113 2fr green & black 3.50 1.25

A114

1994, Jan. 1 Engr. Perf. 13
196 A114 2.40fr dk brn, blk & bl 1.50 .65

A115

1994, Jan. 1
197 A115 2.80fr slate blue 1.25 .70

Robert Pommier (1919-61)
A116

1994, Jan. 1
198 A116 2.80fr multicolored 1.25 .70

A117

Designs: 2.80fr, C.A. Vincendon Dumoulin (1811-58), hydrographer. 23fr, Measuring Earth's magnetic field.

1994, Jan. 1 Perf. 12½x13
199 2.80fr black & blue 1.40 .70
200 23fr blue & black 8.75 5.75
a. A118 Pair, #199-200 + label 11.00 11.00

Rascasse — A119

1994, Jan. 1 Perf. 13
201 A119 3.70fr bl grn & red brn 1.50 .95

Kerguelen of Tremarec — A120

1994, Jan. 1
202 A120 4.30fr multicolored 1.75 1.10

Mineral Type of 1993
1995, Jan. 2 Engr. Perf. 13
203 A103 1fr Olivine 1.25 .30

Mancoglosse Antarctique — A121

1995, Jan. 2
204 A121 2.40fr ol brn, vio & bl grn 1.50 .95

Andree (1903-90) and Edgar de la Rue (1901-91)
A122

1995, Jan. 2
205 A122 2.80fr bl, red brn & mag 1.25 .85

SODAR Station — A123

1995, Jan. 2
206 A123 2.80fr vio, mag & red brn 1.25 .85

Mont D'Alsace — A124

1995, Jan. 2
207 A124 3.70fr dk bl, vio, red brn 1.75 1.10

Balaenoptera Acutorostrata — A125

1995, Jan. 2
208 A125 23fr blue, claret & ind 10.00 6.50

Sailing Ship Tamaris
A126

1995, Jan. 2
209 A126 25.80fr multicolored 11.00 7.50

L'Heroine, Crozet Islands Mission, 1837 — A127

1995, Jan. 2
210 A127 27.30fr blue 11.50 7.75

Creation of the Territories, 40th Anniv. — A128

Illustration reduced.

1995, Aug. 7 Litho. Imperf.
Size: 143x84mm
211 A128 30fr multicolored 12.50 12.50

Mineral Type of 1993
1996, Jan. 1 Engr. Perf. 13
212 A103 1fr Amazonite 1.00 .30

White-chinned Petrel — A129

1996, Jan. 1
213 A129 2.40fr blue black 1.25 .70

Expedition Ship Yves de Kerguelen — A130

1996, Jan. 1
214 A130 2.80fr multicolored 1.40 .80

Benedict Point Scientific Research Station, Amsterdam Island — A131

1996, Jan. 1
215 A131 2.80fr multicolored 1.25 .80

Paul-Emile Victor (1907-1995), Polar Explorer — A132

Designs: 2.80fr, Victor crossing Greenland with sled dogs, 1936. 23fr, Victor, penguins, Dumont d'Urville Base, Adélie Land.

1996, Jan. 1
216 A132 2.80fr multicolored 1.50 .90
217 A132 23fr multicolored 12.00 8.00
a. Pair, #216-217 + label 14.00 14.00

Admiral Jacquinot (1796-1879), Antarctic Explorer — A133

1996, Jan. 1
218 A133 3.70fr dark blue & blue 1.50 1.10

Trawler Austral — A134

1996, Jan. 1 Photo. & Engr.
219 A134 4.30fr multicolored 2.25 1.40

Lycopodium Magellanicum — A135

1996, Jan. 1 Engr.
220 A135 7.70fr multicolored 3.00 2.25

Search for Micrometeorites, Cape Prudhomme — A136

1996, Jan. 1
221 A136 15fr vio, blk & grn bl 8.00 5.00

Mineral Type of 1993
1997, Jan. 1 Engr. Perf. 13x12½
222 A103 1fr Amethyst 1.00 .40

Storm Petrel — A137

1997, Jan. 1 Perf. 13
223 A137 2.70fr blue & indigo 1.25 .90

Rene Garcia (1915-95), Windmill A138

1997, Jan. 1
224 A138 3fr multicolored 1.25 1.00

Research Ship Marion Dufresne — A139

Illustration reduced.

Photo. & Engr.
1997, Jan. 1 Perf. 13x12½
225 A139 3fr multicolored 1.75 1.00

A140 A141

1997, Jan. 1 Engr. Perf. 13
226 A140 4fr black & brown 1.75 1.25

Jean Turquet (1867-1945).

1997, Jan. 1
227 A141 5.20fr multicolored 2.25 1.60

Church of Our Lady of Birds, Crozet Island.

A142

A143

1997, Jan. 1
228 A142 8fr multicolored 4.00 2.60

Army Health Service.

1997, Jan. 1
229 A143 29.20fr Poa Kerguelensis 12.50 9.25

French Polar Expeditions, 50th Anniv. — A144

Designs: No. 230, Greenland Expedition. No. 231, Port Martin, 1950-51, Marret Base, 1952, Adélie Land. No. 232, Dumont D'Urville, 1956, Charcot Station, Magnetic Pole, 1957.

Photo. & Engr.
1997, Feb. 28 Perf. 13x12½
230 A144 1fr multicolored .75 .30
231 A144 1fr multicolored .75 .30
232 A144 1fr multicolored .75 .30
a. Strip of 3, #230-232 10.00 8.00

Yves-Joseph de Kerguelen Trémarec (1734-97) — A145

3fr, Portrait. 24fr, Cook's landing at Kerguelen Island, Dec. 1776.

1997, Mar. 3 Engr. Perf. 13
233 3fr multicolored 1.25 .90
234 24fr multicolored 9.75 7.25
a. A145 Pair, #233-234 + label 13.00 9.00

No. 234 is 37x37mm.

Mineral Type of 1993
1998, Jan. 2 Engr. Perf. 13
235 A103 1fr Rock crystal 1.00 .30

Fisheries Management — A146

Designs: No. 236, Fishing boats. No. 237, Examining fish, performing research.

1998, Jan. 2
236 A146 2.60fr multicolored 1.50 .75
237 A146 2.60fr multicolored 1.50 .75
a. Pair, #236-237 + label 3.50 3.50

Gray-headed Albatross — A147

1998, Jan. 2
238 A147 2.70fr multicolored 1.75 .75

Ecology of St. Paul Island — A148

1998, Jan. 2
239 A148 3fr bl, brn & grn 1.75 .85

A149 A150

1998, Jan. 2 Perf. 13x13½
240 A149 3fr lilac, blue & black 1.60 .85

Etienne Peau, Antarctic explorer.

1998, Jan. 2
241 A150 4fr lt org, blk & red brn 1.75 1.10

Georges Laclavere (1906-94), geographer.

Mole Shark — A151

1998, Jan. 2 Perf. 13
242 A151 27fr multicolored 11.00 7.25

"Le Cancalais" — A152

1998, Jan. 2
243 A152 29.20fr multicolored 12.00 7.75

Mineral Type of 1993
1999, Jan. 1 Engr. Perf. 13
244 A103 1fr Epidote, vert. 1.00 .30

Chinstrap Penguin — A153

1999, Jan. 1
245 A153 2.70fr brn, blk & bl 1.25 .85

Pierre Sicaud (1911-98), Antarctic Explorer, Commander of Outpost at Kerguelen Islands — A154

1999, Jan. 1
246 A154 3fr black & green 1.40 .95

Penguins of Crozet Islands — A155

Illustration reduced.

1999, Jan. 1
247 A155 3fr multicolored 1.50 .85

Jacques-André Martin (1911-49) — A156

1999, Jan. 1
248 A156 4fr multicolored 1.60 1.10

Ray — A157

1999, Jan. 1 Perf. 12½
249 A157 5.20fr mag, bl & brn 2.25 1.50

Value is for stamp with surrounding rectangular selvage.

F.S. Floreal — A158

1999, Jan. 1   **Photo.**   *Perf. 13*
250 A158 5.20fr multicolored   2.25 1.40

No. 250 was printed se-tenant with label. Value is for stamp with label attached.

"Pop Cat" Program, Kerguelen Islands — A159

1999, Jan. 1   *Engr.*
251 A159 8fr multicolored   4.25 2.75

Study of Albatrosses on Artificial Nests A160

1999, Jan. 1
252 A160 16fr olive, grn & blk   7.00 4.50

Amsterdam Base, Kerguelen Base, 50th Anniv. — A161

1999, Jan. 1
253 A161   3fr Amsterdam Base   6.00 .85
254 A161 24fr Kerguelen Base   10.50 6.50
   a.   Pair, #253-254 + label   17.00 14.00

Festuca Contracta A162

1999, Jan. 1
255 A162 24fr dk grn, ol & bl grn   10.50 6.50

Geoleta Program — A163

1999, Jan. 1   *Perf. 13x12½*
256 A163 29.20fr blk, bl & red brn   13.00 7.75

Voyage of Marion Dufresne II — A164

a, Docked, Reunion. b, Passengers in dining salon. c, Penguins, Crozet Island. d, Postal manager of Alfred Faure, Crozet Island, vert. e, Port of France, Kerguelen Island. f, Port Couvreux, Kerguelen Island. g, Offloading stores, Port of France, Kerguelen Island. h, Port Jeanne d'arc, Kerguelen Island. i, St. Paul Island. j, Ruins of lobster cannery, St. Paul Island. k, Martin de Vivies Base, Amsterdam Island. l, Offloading cargo, Amsterdam Island.

1999, May 1   **Litho.**   *Perf. 13*
257 A164 Souv. bklt., #a.-l.   65.00

Nos. 257a-257l are all non-denominated. Stamps are valid for 20 gram international letter rate. Each stamp appears on a separate booklet pane showing an enlarged design of the stamp. Booklet sold for 100fr.

Souvenir Sheet

PhilexFrance '99, World Philatelic Exhibition — A165

Antarctic postmarks on stamps: a, Malagasy Republic #280. b, Malagasy Republic #282. c, Malagasy Republic #C42. d, #21.

1999, July 2   Litho. & Engr.   Perf. 13
258 A165 5.20fr Sheet of 4, #a.-d.   11.50 7.00

Nos. 258b-258c are each 40x52mm.

Mineral Type of 1993
2000, Jan.   **Engr.**   *Perf. 12¾x13*
259 A103 1fr Mica, *vert.*   .75 .25

Puffin — A166

2000, Jan.   *Perf. 13x12¾*
260 A166 2.70fr multi   1.25 .60

André Beaugé (1913-97) A167

2000, Jan.   *Perf. 12¾x13*
261 A167 3fr multi   1.40 .70

Abby Jane Morrell — A168

Sled Dog Hobbs — A170

Oceanographic Survey — A169

2000, Jan.   *Perf. 13¼x13*
262 A168 4fr multi   1.75 .95

2000, Jan.   *Perf. 13x12½*
263 A169 4.40fr multi   1.90 1.00

2000, Jan.   *Perf. 12¾x13*
264 A170 5.20fr multi   2.25 1.25

Sleep Study — A171

Illustration reduced

2000, Jan.   Photo.   Perf. 13x12½
265 A171 8fr multi + label   3.50 1.90

Ship "La Perouse" — A172

2000, Jan.   **Engr.**   *Perf. 13x12½*
266 A172 16fr multi   7.00 3.75

Lantern Fish — A173

2000, Jan.
267 A173 24fr multi   10.50 5.50

Larose Bay — A174

2000, Jan.
268 A174 27fr multi   12.00 6.25

Explorers A175

#269, Yves Joseph de Kerguelen-Trémarec (1734-97). #270, Jules Sébastien César Dumont D'Urville (1790-1842). #271, Raymond Rallier du Baty (1881-1978). #272, Edgar Aubert de La Rüe (1901-91). #273, Paul-Emile Victor (1907-95).

2000, Jan.   *Perf. 13*
Booklet Stamps
269 A175 3fr multi   1.50 .70
270 A175 3fr multi   1.50 .70
271 A175 3fr multi   1.50 .70
272 A175 3fr multi   1.50 .70
273 A175 3fr multi   1.50 .70
   a.   Bklt. pane, #269-273 + 2 labels   8.00
     Complete booklet, #273a   9.50

Souvenir Sheet

The Third Millennium — A176

No. 274: a, Penguins, Crozet Islands. b, Seals, Kerguelen Islands. c, Crustacean, Saint-Paul and Amsterdam Islands. d, Hovering vehicle, Adelie Land.

2000, Jan.   **Photo.**   *Perf. 13*
274 A176 3fr Sheet of 4, #a.-d.   6.00 4.75

Bird Demographic Studies — A177

Designs: 5.20fr, Bird banding. 8fr, Albatross, graph. 16fr, Emperor penguins, graph.

2000, Jan.   *Perf. 13x13¼*
275 A177 5.20fr multi   2.25 1.25
Size: 50x28mm
276 A177   8fr multi   3.50 1.90
277 A177 16fr multi   7.00 3.75
   a.   Horiz. strip, #275-277   14.00 14.00

Relocation of Headquarters to Reunion — A178

2000, Aug. 6   **Litho.**   *Perf. 13*
278 A178 27fr multi   12.00 5.50

Mineral Type of 1993
2001, Jan. 1   Engr.   Perf. 13x12¾
279 A103 1fr Magnetite   1.00 .30

Diving Petrel — A179

2001, Jan. 1   *Perf. 13x13¼*
280 A179 2.70fr multi   1.25 .55

High Mountain Military Group A180

2001, Jan. 1   *Perf. 13¼x13*
281 A180 3fr multi   1.40 .65

Kerguelen Arch — A181

2001, Jan. 1   *Perf. 13*
282 A181 3fr blue gray   1.50 .65

Xavier-Charles Richert (1913-92) A182   Jean Coulomb A183

2001, Jan. 1
283 A182 3fr multi   1.40 .65

2001, Jan. 1
284 A183 4fr multi   1.75 .85

Memorial to 1874 Astronomical Observation, St. Paul Island — A184

2001, Jan. 1
285 A184 8fr brn & blk   3.50 1.75

Frigate La Fayette — A185

2001, Jan. 1   *Perf. 13x13¼*
286 A185 16fr multi   7.00 3.50

Squid — A186

2001, Jan. 1
287 A186 24fr multi   10.50 5.00

Amateur Radio Link Between Space Station Mir and Crozet Island — A187

2001, Jan. 1   *Litho.*   *Perf. 13*
288 A187 27fr multi   12.00 5.50

Bryum Laevigatum — A188

2001, Jan. 1   *Engr.*   *Perf. 13x12½*
289 A188 29.20fr multi   13.00 6.00

Souvenir Sheet

Ships — A189

No. 290: a, Carmen. b, Austral. c, Ramuntcho. d, Samper 1.

2001, Jan. 1   *Perf. 13x13½*
290 A189 5.20fr Sheet of 4, #a-d   9.00 4.50

Souvenir Sheet

Wildlife — A190

No. 291: a, Albatrosses. b, Emperor penguins, horiz. c, Sea lions, horiz. d, Whales.

2001, Jan. 1   *Litho.*   *Perf. 13*
291 A190 3fr Sheet of 4, #a-d   9.00 5.00

Antarctic Treaty, 40th Anniv. — A191

2001, June 23   *Engr.*   *Perf. 13x12¾*
292 A191 5.20fr dark & sky blue   3.25 1.00

Commission for the Conservation of Antarctic Marine Living Resources, 20th Anniv. — A192

2001, Oct. 22   *Litho.*   *Perf. 13*
293 A192 5.20fr multi   4.00 1.75

Voyage Booklet Type of 1999

Adélie Land: a, Boat in pack ice. b, Dumont d'Urville Base. c, Adélie penguin rookery. d, L'Astrolabe Glacier. e, Pointe Géologie Archipelago. f, Release of meteorological balloon. g, Equipment convoy. h, Helicopter transport of fresh supplies. i, Arrival of emperor penguins. j, Telecommunications center. k, Looking towards the Antarctic. l, Cape Prud'homme. m, Ship L'Astrolabe anchored. n, Dispatch of mail.

2001, Oct. 29   *Perf. 13*
294 A164   Souvenir booklet, 2   each #a-n   90.00

Nos. 294a-294n are all non-denominated. Stamps are valid for 20 gram international letter rate. Each stamp appears ofn a separate booklet pane showing an enlarged design of the stamp and on one pane with all of the stamps and four labels found at the center of the booklet. the booklet sold for 196.78fr.

100 Cents = 1 Euro (€)

Arms Type of 1992-95 with Euro Denominations

2002, Jan. 2   *Engr.*   *Perf. 13*
295 A102   1c black   .20 .20
296 A102   2c greenish blue   .20 .20
297 A102   5c red   .20 .20
298 A102   10c green   .30 .20
299 A102   20c orange   .60 .20
   Nos. 295-299 (5)   1.50 1.00

Mineral Type of 1993 with Euro Denomination

2002, Jan. 2   *Engr.*   *Perf. 12¾x13*
300 A103 15c Nepheline, vert.   .75 .20

Albatross A193

2002, Jan. 2   *Perf. 13¼x13*
301 A193 41c multi   1.25 .50

Ship "Marion Dufresne" — A194

2002, Jan. 2   *Perf. 13x13¼*
302 A194 46c multi   1.40 .60

1963-83 Telegraph Station, Crozet Island A195

2002, Jan. 2   *Litho.*   *Perf. 13*
303 A195 46c multi   1.50 .60

Jacques Dubois (1920-2000) A196

2002, Jan. 2   *Engr.*
304 A196 61c multi   1.90 .90

Engraved Rock, Saint Paul Island — A197

2002, Jan. 2   *Perf. 13x13¼*
305 A197 79c multi   2.40 1.25

Kerguelen Cabbage A198

2002, Jan. 2   *Perf. 12¼*
306 A198 €1.22 multi   3.50 1.75

Passage of the Ship "Gauss," Cent. — A199

2002, Jan. 2   *Perf. 13x12¼*
307 A199 €2.44 multi   7.25 3.50

Crab — A200

2002, Jan. 2   **Perf. 13x13¼**
308 A200 €3.66 multi   11.00 5.25

Pack Ice Diatoms — A201

2002, Jan. 2   **Litho.**   **Perf. 13**
309 A201 €4.12 multi   12.50 6.00

French Geographic Society Building, Paris — A202

2002, Jan. 2   **Engr.**   **Perf. 13¼x13**
310 A202 €4.45 multi + label   13.50 8.00

Cartoker Program — A203

No. 311: a, 46c, Diagram of plate tectonics. b, €3.66, Geological map of Kerguelen Island. Illustration reduced.

2002, Jan. 2   **Perf. 13x12¼**
311 A203   Horiz. pair, #a-b, +
    central label   12.50 12.50

Souvenir Sheet

Olympic Games for Antarctic Animals — A204

No. 312: a, Albatrosses flying marathon. b, Langoustines diving, vert. c, Penguins riding

bobsled course, vert. d, Killer whales performing synchronized swimming, vert.

2002, Jan. 2   **Litho.**   **Perf. 13**
312 A204 46c Sheet of 4, #a-d   5.50 5.50

Souvenir Sheet

Animals and Their Young — A205

No. 313: a, Penguins. b, Sea lions. c, Albatrosses. d, Elephant seals.

2002, Jan. 2
313 A205 79c Sheet of 4, #a-d   9.50 9.50

Introduction of the Euro A206

2002, Feb. 17
314 A206 46c blue & black   3.00 .60

Mineral Type of 1993

2003, Jan.   **Engr.**   **Perf. 13¼**
315 A103 15c Apatite, vert.   1.00 .30

Lobster Processing Plant, Saint-Paul — A207

2003, Jan.   **Perf. 13x13¼**
316 A207 41c multi   1.20 .65

Luc Marie Bayle (1914-2000), Painter — A208

2003, Jan.   **Litho.**   **Perf. 13**
317 A208 46c multi   1.40 .70

Emperor Penguins — A209

2003, Jan.
318 A209 46c multi   1.40 .70

Otice Hydroacoustic Station — A210

2003, Jan.   **Engr.**   **Perf. 13x13¼**
319 A210 61c multi   1.90 1.00

Restoration of Port Jeanne d'Arc — A211

2003, Jan.   **Perf. 13x12¼**
320 A211 79c multi   2.40 1.25

Phylica — A212

2003, Jan.   **Perf. 13x13¼**
321 A212 €1.22 multi   3.75 2.25

Ship "Bougainville" A213

2003, Jan.   **Perf. 13¼x13**
322 A213 €2.44 multi   7.25 4.25

Chub — A214

2003, Jan.   **Engr.**   **Perf. 13x13¼**
323 A214 €3.66 multi   11.00 6.50

Ile aux Pingouins — A215

2003, Jan.   **Perf. 13x12¼**
324 A215 €3.66 black   11.00 6.50

Super Darn Antenna Array — A216

Illustration reduced.

2003, Jan.   **Perf. 13**
325 A216 €4.12 multi   12.50 7.00

Souvenir Sheet

Paintings Revised to Reflect a Less Southerly Antarctica — A217

No. 326: a, Triumph of Venus with fish and lobsters. b, King Louis XV and wife with penguins, vert. c, Jules Dumont d'Urville and wife in a grassy Adélie Land. d, Chevalier Yves de Kerguelin under umbrella, seal in pool, vert.

2003, Jan.   **Litho.**
326 A217 46c Sheet of 4, #a-d   6.50 6.50

Protective Clothing — A218

Cold-weather outerwear from: a, 1898. b, 1912. c, 2002. d, 1980, e, 1996.

2003, Jan.   **Photo.**   **Perf. 13¼x13**
327   Booklet pane of 5   12.00 —
a.-e.   A218 79c Any single   2.40 1.25
    Booklet, #327   12.00

Voyage of the Ship "Français," Cent. — A219

2003, Aug. 31   Engr.   Perf. 13x13¼
328   Horiz. strip of 3   13.50 13.50
  a.   A219 79c Capt. J.-B. Charcot   2.40   1.25
  b.   A219 €1.22 Ship in ice, horiz.   3.50   2.00
  c.   A219 €2.44 Ship in harbor,
         horiz.   7.25   4.25

Stamp size: Nos. 328b-328c, 49x29mm.

Voyage Booklet Type of 1999

Recipes: a, Truite aus deux citrons (trout and waterfall). b, Veau d'Amsterdam à la savoyarde (cattle). c, Lapin "Volage" à la cannelle (rabbits, penguins). d, Rôti de légine de l'ile de l'est (fish). e, Civet de renne "Volcan du diable," (reindeer). f, Iles antarctiques flottantes. g, Langouste à la mode de Saint-Paul (lobster). h, Gigot de mouflon aux 5 épices et aux pommes (sheep). i, Cabot tropical (fish, ship). j, Tagine d'agneau aux épices de la Réunion (sheep). k, Moules au pastis (mussels). l, Glace à la menthe sauvage d'Amsterdam (mint plant).

2003, Nov. 6   Litho.   Perf. 13
329   A164   Souvenir booklet,
          #a-l   45.00

Nos. 329a-329l are all non-denominated. Stamps are valid for 20 gram international letter rate. Each stamp appears on a separate booklet pane showing an enlarged design of the stamp. The booklet sold for €17.

Mineral Type of 1993

2004, Jan. 1   Engr.   Perf. 13¼
330   A103 15c Chalcedony, vert. 1.00   .30

A220

A221

2004, Jan. 1   Engr.   Perf. 13x13¼
331   A220 45c multi   1.40   .85
Mario Marret, director of film "Terre Adélie."

2004, Jan. 1
332   A221 50c multi   1.50   .95
Col. Robert Genty (1910-2001).

Albert Faure Base, Crozet Island, 40th Anniv. — A222

Illustration reduced.

2004, Jan. 1   Litho. & Engr.
333   A222 50c multi   1.50   .95

Péron's Dolphins — A223

2004, Jan. 1   Litho.   Perf. 13
334   A223 75c multi   2.25 1.40

Twin Otter Flights A224

2004, Jan. 1   Photo.   Perf. 12¾
335   A224 90c multi   2.75 1.75
Values are for stamps with surrounding selvage.

Iceberg — A225

2004, Jan. 1   Engr.   Perf. 13x13¼
336   A225 €1.30 multi   4.00 2.40

Grave of Sailors from the Volage — A226

2004, Jan. 1   Perf. 13¼x13
337   A226 €2.50 multi   7.50 5.00

Krill — A227

2004, Jan. 1   Perf. 13x13¼
338   A227 €4 multi   12.00 8.00

Ship "Dives" — A228

2004, Jan. 1
339   A228 €4.50 multi   13.50 9.25

Souvenir Sheet

Hydrological Surveys, Adélie Land — A229

2004, Jan. 1   Litho.   Perf. 13
340   A229 €4.90 multi   15.00 10.50

Souvenir Sheet

Imaginary "TAAFland" Theme Park — A230

No. 341: a, Whale statue, pyramidal entrance structure. b, Showgirls, seals, vert. c, Boy and girl with ice cream cones, vert. d, Woman in swimsuit, penguins.

2004, Jan. 1
341   A230 50c Sheet of 4, #a-d   6.00 3.75

Souvenir Sheet

Post Offices — A231

No. 342: a, Amsterdam Island. b, Crozet Island. c, Kerguelen Island. d, Adélie Land.

2004, Jan. 1
342   A231 90c Sheet of 4, #a-d 11.00 7.25

Penguin and Liberty Cap — A232

2004, June 26   Engr.   Perf. 13¼x13
343   A232 €4.50 multi   13.50 11.50

Mineral Type of 1993

2005, Jan. 1   Engr.   Perf. 13¼
344   A103 15c Agate   .50   .50

Albert Bauer (1916-2003), Glaciologist — A233

2005, Jan. 1   Perf. 13x13¼
345   A233 45c multi   1.40 1.40

Roger Barberot (1915-2002), Administrator A234

2005, Jan. 1
346   A234 50c multi   1.50 1.50

Ship "Cap Horn" — A235

2005, Jan. 1
347   A235 50c multi   1.50 1.50

Seal Pot A236

2005, Jan. 1   Litho.   Perf. 13
348   A236 50c multi   1.50 1.50

Macgillivray's Prion — A237

2005, Jan. 1   Engr.   Perf. 13x13¼
349   A237 75c multi   2.25 2.25

Studer Valley — A238

2005, Jan. 1   Perf. 13x12½
350   A238 90c multi   2.75 2.75

Peigne
des
Néréides
A239

2005, Jan. 1   *Perf. 12¼*
351 A239 €2.50 multi   7.50 7.50

Harpovoluta Charcoti — A240

2005, Jan. 1   *Perf. 13x12½*
352 A240 €4 multi   12.00 12.00

Murray's
Ray — A241

2005, Jan. 1   Litho.   *Perf. 13*
353 A241 €4.50 multi   13.50 13.50

Elephant Seal and Oceanographic
Chart — A242

Illustration reduced.

2005, Jan. 1   Engr.
354 A242 €4.90 multi   15.00 15.00

Concordia Station — A243

Illustration reduced.

2005, Jan. 3   Litho.   *Perf. 13*
355 A243 50c multi   1.50 1.50

Return of the Ship "Français,"
Cent. — A244

Illustration reduced.

2005, Mar. 4   Engr.   *Perf. 13x13¼*
356 A244 €4.50 multi + label   13.50 13.50

Disappearance of Paul-Emile Victor,
10th Anniv. — A245

2005, Mar. 7   Litho.   *Perf. 13*
357 A245 50c multi   1.50 1.50

50th Anniversary Coat of
Arms — A246

2005, Aug. 6
358 A246 (90c) multi   2.75 2.75
   a.   Booklet pane of 1   4.00 —
   No. 358a is found in No. 359.

Voyage Booklet Type of 1999

History: a, Discovery of Amsterdam Island,
1522. b, Discovery of Crozet Island, 1772. c,
Discovery of Kerguelen Island, 1772, vert. d,
Discovery of Adélie Land, 1840. e, Astrono-
mers viewing 1874 transit of Venus on St. Paul
Island. f, Wreck of the Strathmore, 1875. g,
Port Jeanne d'Arc, 1908. h, Port-Couvreux,
1925. i, Building of Port-Martin, 1950. j,
Antarctic Treaty, 1959. k, Building of fourth
base, 1963-64.

2005, Aug. 6   Litho.   *Perf. 13*
359 A164   Souvenir booklet,
     #a-k, 358a   45.00

Nos. 359a-359k are all non-denominated.
Stamps are valid for 90c, the 20 gram international letter rate. Each stamp appears on a
separate booklet pane showing an enlarged
design of the stamp. The booklet sold for €18.

Penguins
and No.
1 — A247

2005, Nov. 2
360 A247 90c multi   2.75 2.75
French Southern & Antarctic Territories,
50th anniv.

Souvenir Sheet

Maps — A248

Maps of: a, Crozet Archipelago. b, Amsterdam and St. Paul Islands. c, Kerguelen Island.
d, Adélie Land.

Litho. & Engr.
2005, Nov. 10
361 A248 50c Sheet of 4, #a-d   6.00 6.00
French Southern & Antarctic Territories,
50th anniv.

Rutile
A249

2006, Jan. 1   Engr.   *Perf. 13x12½*
362 A249 15c multi   .50 .50

A250   A251

2006, Jan. 1   *Perf. 13x13¼*
363 A250 48c pur & red   1.40 1.40
Charles Vélain (1845-1925), geologist.

2006, Jan. 1
364 A251 53c multi   1.60 1.60
Albert Seyrolle (1887-1919), mariner.

Amsterdam Island Garden — A252

2006, Jan. 1   Litho.   *Perf. 13*
365 A252 53c multi   1.60 1.60

Ship "Osiris" — A253

2006, Jan. 1   Photo.   *Perf. 13x13¼*
366 A253 90c multi   2.75 2.75

Dumont d'Urville Base, 50th
Anniv. — A254

Illustration reduced.

2006, Jan. 1   Engr.   *Perf. 13x12½*
367 A254 90c multi   2.75 2.75

Virgin of the
Seal
Hunters — A255

2006, Jan. 1   *Perf. 12½x13*
368 A255 €2.50 multi   7.50 7.50

Lagenorhynchus Cruciger — A256

2006, Jan. 1   *Perf. 13x13¼*
369 A256 €4 multi   12.00 12.00

Keguelen Hake — A257

2006, Jan. 1
370 A257 €4.53 multi   13.50 13.50

Amsterdam Island Carbon Dioxide
Measurements, 25th Anniv. — A258

2006, Jan. 1
371 A258 €4.90 multi   15.00 15.00

Miniature Sheet

Penguins — A259

No. 372 — Penguin (background color): a,
Emperor penguin (lilac, 22x36mm). b, King
penguin (pale yellow green, 22x36mm). c,
Gentoo penguin (green, 22x27mm). d, Adélie

penguin (pink, 22x27mm). e, Macaroni penguin (orange, 22x27mm). f, Rockhopper penguin (blue, 22x27mm).

Litho. & Engr.

2006, Jan. 1			Perf. 13
372	A259	53c Sheet of 6, #a-f	9.50 9.50

Souvenir Sheet

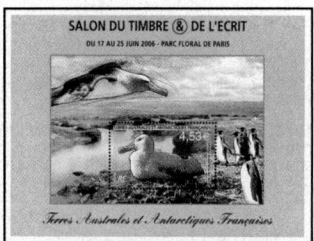

Albatross — A260

Litho. & Engr.

2006, June 1			Perf. 13
373	A260	€4.53 multi	13.50 13.50

Souvenir Sheet

Albatross — A261

Litho. & Engr.

2006, Nov. 8			Perf. 13
374	A261	90c multi	2.40 2.40

Corundum
A262

2007, Jan. 1		Engr.	Perf. 13¼
375	A262	15c multi	.40 .40

A263   A264

2007, Jan. 1			Perf. 13x13¼
376	A263	49c multi	1.40 1.40

Louis-Francois Aleno de Saint Aloüarn (1738-72), explorer who claimed Australia for France.

2007, Jan. 1			
377	A264	54c multi	1.40 1.40

Marthe Emmanuel (1901-97), assistant to explorer Jean Charcot.

Cattle, Amsterdam Island — A265

2007, Jan. 1			Perf. 13x12½
378	A265	54c multi	1.40 1.40

Ship Tonkinois — A266

2007, Jan. 1			Perf. 13x13¼
379	A266	90c multi	2.40 2.40

Ile de la Baleine — A267

2007, Jan. 1			Perf. 13x12½
380	A267	90c multi	2.40 2.40

Archaeology on Saint Paul Island — A268

2007, Jan. 1			Perf. 12½x13
381	A268	€2.50 multi	6.50 6.50

Lampris Immaculatus — A269

2007, Jan. 1			Perf. 13x12½
382	A269	€4 multi	10.50 10.50

Astonomy at Concordia — A270

Litho. & Engr.

2007, Jan. 1			Perf. 13
383	A270	€4.90 multi	13.00 13.00

French Polar Expeditions, 60th Anniv. — A271

No. 384: a, Expedition headquarters, Paris, men shaking hands over globe. b, Expedition headquarters.

2007, Jan. 1	Engr.		Perf. 13x13¼
384		Horiz. pair + central label	12.00 12.00
a.	A271	54c multi	1.40 1.40
b.	A271	€4 multi	10.50 10.50

Miniature Sheet

Albatrosses — A272

No. 385: a, Amsterdam albatross. b, Great albatross (Grand albatros). c, Black-browed albatross (Albatros à sourcils noir). d, Yellow-beaked albatross (Albatros à bec jaune). e, Sooty albatross (Albatros fuligineux).

Litho. & Engr.

2007, Jan. 1			Perf. 13
385	A272	54c Sheet of 5, #a-e	7.00 7.00

Intl. Polar Year — A273

No. 386: a, Penguins. b, Map of Antarctica, French Southern & Antarctic Territories #9.

2007, Mar. 1	Litho.		Perf. 13
386		Horiz. pair + central label	13.00 13.00
a.	A273	90c multi	2.40 2.40
b.	A273	€4 multi	10.50 10.50

Audit Office, Bicent. A274

2007 Mar. 19		Engr.	Perf. 13¼
387	A274	90c multi	2.40 2.40

Miniature Sheet

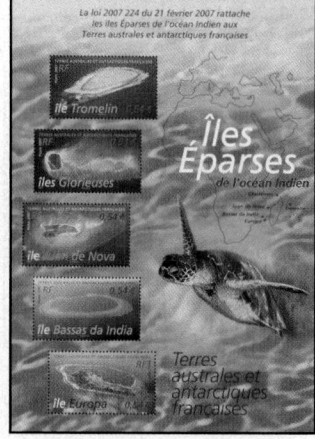

Indian Ocean Islands — A275

No. 388: a, Ile Tromelin. b, Iles Glorieuses. c, Ile Juan de Nova. d, Ile Bassas da India. e, Ile Europa.

2007, May 10		Photo.	Perf. 13x13¼
388	A275	54c Sheet of 5, #a-e	7.25 7.25

Path of Sun on June 21 Over Dumont d'Urville Base — A276

Illustration reduced.

2007, June 21			
389	A276	90c multi	2.50 2.50

AIR POST STAMPS

Emperor Penguins and Map of Antarctica — AP1

Unwmk.

1956, Apr. 25		Engr.	Perf. 13
C1	AP1	50fr lt ol grn & dk grn	42.50 29.00
C2	AP1	100fr dl bl & indigo	35.00 25.00

Wandering Albatross — AP2

1959, Sept. 14			
C3	AP2	200fr brn red, bl & blk	40.00 27.50

Adélie Penguins — AP3

1963, Feb. 11	Unwmk.		Perf. 13
C4	AP3	50fr blk, dk bl & dp cl	42.50 32.50

Telstar Issue
Common Design Type
1963, Feb. 11
C5 CD111 50fr dp bl, ol & grn 29.00 21.00

Radio Towers,
Adelie Penguins
and IQSY
Emblem — AP4

1963, Dec. 16　　　　　**Engr.**
C6 AP4 100fr bl, ver & blk　110.00 87.50
International Quiet Sun Year, 1964-65.

Discovery of Adelie Land — AP5

1965, Jan. 20　　**Engr.**　　**Perf. 13**
C7 AP5 50fr blue & indigo　125.00 87.50
125th anniversary of the discovery of Adelie Land by Dumont d'Urville.

ITU Issue
Common Design Type
1965, May 17　**Unwmk.**　**Perf. 13**
C8 CD120 30fr multi　200.00 160.00

French Satellite A-1 Issue
Common Design Type
Designs: 25fr, Diamant rocket and launching installations. 30fr, A-1 satellite.

1966, Mar. 2　　**Engr.**　　**Perf. 13**
C9 CD121 25fr dk grn, choc
　　　　　& sl　13.50 10.00
C10 CD121 30fr choc, sl & dk
　　　　　grn　13.50 10.00
　a.　Pair, #C9-C10 + label　29.00 24.00

French Satellite D-1 Issue
Common Design Type
1966, Mar. 27
C11 CD122 50fr dk pur, lil &
　　　　　org　57.50 40.00

Ionospheric
Research Pylon,
Adelie
Land — AP6

1966, Dec. 12
C12 AP6 25fr plum, bl & dk
　　　　　brn　　32.50 17.50

Port aux Français, Emperor Penguin
and Explorer — AP7

40fr, Aerial view of Saint Paul Island.

1968-69　　**Engr.**　　**Perf. 13**
C13 AP7 40fr brt bl & dk
　　　　　gray　42.50 27.50
C14 AP7 50fr lt ultra, dk grn
　　　　　& blk　175.00 110.00
Issue dates: 50fr, Jan. 21; 40fr, Jan. 5, 1969.

Kerguelen Island and Rocket — AP8

Design: 30fr, Adelie Land.

1968, Apr. 22　**Engr.**　**Perf. 13**
C15 AP8 25fr sl grn, dk brn &
　　　　　Prus bl　19.00 14.00
C16 AP8 30fr dk brn, sl grn &
　　　　　Prus bl　19.00 14.00
　a.　Pair, #C15-C16 + label　40.00 30.00
Space explorations with Dragon rockets, 1967-68.

Eiffel
Tower,
Antarctic
Research
Station,
Ship from
Paris Arms
and
Albatross
AP9

1969, Jan. 13
C17 AP9 50fr bright blue　45.00 35.00
5th Consultative Meeting of the Antarctic Treaty Powers, Paris, Nov. 18, 1968.

Concorde Issue
Common Design Type
1969, Apr. 17
C18 CD129 85fr indigo & blue　55.00 37.50
Prepared but not issued with 87fr denomination. Value $6,000.

Map of
Amsterdam
Island
AP10

Map of Kerguelen Island — AP11

Coat of
Arms
AP12

Designs: 50fr, Possession Island. 200fr, Point Geology Archipelago.

1969-71　　**Engr.**　　**Perf. 13**
C19 AP10 30fr brown　19.00 12.50
C20 AP11 50fr sl grn, bl &
　　　　　dk red　21.00 14.00
C21 AP11 100fr blue & blk　85.00 40.00
C22 AP10 200fr sl grn, brn
　　　　　& Prus bl　70.00 42.50
C23 AP12 500fr peacock
　　　　　blue　20.00 15.00
　　Nos. C19-C23 (5)　215.00 124.00
30fr for the 20th anniv. of the Amsterdam Island Meteorological Station.
Issued: 100fr, 500fr, 12/21; 30fr, 3/27/70; 50fr, 12/22/70; 200fr, 1/1/71.

Port-aux-Français, 1970 — AP13

Design: 40fr, Port-aux-Français, 1950.

1971, Mar. 9　**Engr.**　**Perf. 13**
C24 AP13 40fr bl, ocher & sl
　　　　　grn　19.00 12.00
C25 AP13 50fr bl, grn ol & sl
　　　　　grn　19.00 12.00
　a.　Pair, #C24-C25 + label　40.00 27.50
20th anniversary of Port-aux-Français on Kerguelen Island.

Marquis de Castries Taking
Possession of Crozet Island,
1772 — AP14

250fr, Fleur-de-lis flag raising on Kerguelen Is.

1972　　　**Engr.**　　**Perf. 13**
C26 AP14 100fr black　45.00 29.00
C27 AP14 250fr black & dk
　　　　　brn　100.00 45.00
Bicentenary of the discovery of the Crozet and Kerguelen Islands.
Issue dates: 100fr, Jan. 24; 250fr, Feb. 23.

M. S. Galliéni — AP15

1973, Jan. 25　**Engr.**　**Perf. 13**
C28 AP15 100fr black & blue　25.00 17.50
Exploration voyages of the Galliéni.

"Le Mascarin," 1772 — AP16

Sailing Ships: 145fr, "L'Astrolabe," 1840. 150fr, "Le Rolland," 1774. 185fr, "La Victoire," 1522.

1973, Dec. 13　**Engr.**　**Perf. 13**
C29 AP16 120fr brown olive　6.00 4.00
C30 AP16 145fr brt ultra　6.00 4.00
C31 AP16 150fr slate　7.50 5.00
C32 AP16 185fr ocher　9.50 6.00
　　Nos. C29-C32 (4)　29.00 19.00
Ships used in exploring Antarctica.
See Nos. C37-C38.

Alfred Faure Base — AP17

Design: Nos. C33-C35 show panoramic view of Alfred Faure Base.

1974, Jan. 7　　**Engr.**　　**Perf. 13**
C33 AP17 75fr Prus bl, ultra
　　　　　& brn　8.00 5.25
C34 AP17 110fr Prus bl, ultra
　　　　　& brn　11.00 8.00
C35 AP17 150fr Prus bl, ultra
　　　　　& brn　14.00 8.00
　a.　Triptych, Nos. C33-C35　37.50 30.00
Alfred Faure Antarctic Base, 10th anniv.

Penguin, Map of
Antarctica,
Letters — AP18

1974, Oct. 9　　**Engr.**　　**Perf. 13**
C36 AP18 150fr multicolored　7.00 5.50
Centenary of Universal Postal Union.

Ship Type of 1973
100fr, "Le Français." 200fr, "Pourquoi-pas?"

1974, Dec. 16　**Engr.**　**Perf. 13**
C37 AP16 100fr brt blue　5.00 3.00
C38 AP16 200fr dk car rose　8.00 4.50
Ships used in exploring Antarctica.

Rockets over Kerguelen
Islands — AP19

Design: 90fr, Northern lights over map of northern coast of Russia.

1975, Jan. 26　**Engr.**　**Perf. 13**
C39 AP19 45fr purple & multi　7.00 4.00
C40 AP19 90fr purple & multi　9.00 5.25
　a.　Pair, #C39-C40 + label　19.00 13.00
Franco-Soviet magnetosphere research.

"La Curieuse" — AP20

Ships: 2.70fr, Commandant Charcot. 4fr, Marion-Dufresne.

1976, Jan. **Engr.** *Perf. 13*
C41 AP20 1.90fr multicolored 3.25 2.00
C42 AP20 2.70fr multicolored 5.00 3.25
C43 AP20 4fr red & multi 9.00 4.25
　　Nos. C41-C43 (3) 17.25 9.50

Dumont d'Urville Base, 1956 — AP21

4fr, Dumont d'Urville Base, 1976, Adelie Land.

1976, Jan.
C44 AP21 1.20fr multicolored 9.00 4.00
C45 AP21 4fr multicolored 11.00 7.25
　a. Pair, #C44-C45 + label 24.00 16.00

Dumont d'Urville Antarctic Base, 20th anniv.

Capt. Cook's Ships Passing Kerguelen Island — AP22

1976, Dec. 31 **Engr.** *Perf. 13*
C46 AP22 3.50fr slate & blue 13.00 8.00

Bicentenary of Capt. Cook's voyage past Kerguelen Island.

Sea Lion and Cub AP23

1977-79 **Engr.** *Perf. 13*
C47 AP23 4fr dk blue grn ('79) 3.00 2.50
C48 AP23 10fr multicolored 10.00 9.00

Satellite Survey, Kerguelen — AP24

Designs: 70c, Geophysical laboratory. 1.90fr, Satellite and Kerguelen tracking station. 3fr, Satellites, Adelie Land.

1977-79 **Engr.** *Perf. 13*
C49 AP24 50c multi ('79) .90 .70
C50 AP24 70c multi ('79) .90 .70
C51 AP24 1.90fr multi ('79) 1.60 1.40

C52 AP24 2.70fr multi ('78) 2.75 2.00
C53 AP24 3fr multicolored 4.25 3.25
　　Nos. C49-C53 (5) 10.40 8.05

Elephant Seals — AP25

1979, Jan. 1
C54 AP25 10fr multicolored 5.50 4.50

Challenger — AP26

1979, Jan. 1
C55 AP26 2.70fr black & blue 2.00 1.75

Antarctic expeditions to Crozet and Kerguelen Islands, 1872-1876.

La Recherche and L'Esperance — AP27

1979
C56 AP27 1.90fr deep blue 1.25 1.10

Arrival of d'Entrecasteaux and Kermadec at Amsterdam Island, Mar. 28, 1792.

Lion Rock — AP28

1979
C57 AP28 90c multicolored .90 .70

Natural Arch, Kerguelen Island, 1840 — AP29

1979
C58 AP29 2.70fr multicolored 1.25 1.10

Phylica Nitida, Amsterdam Island — AP30

1979
C59 AP30 10fr multicolored 4.00 3.25

Charles de Gaulle, 10th Anniversary of Death AP31

1980, Nov. 9 **Engr.** *Perf. 13*
C60 AP31 5.40fr multicolored 11.00 8.00

HB-40 Castor Truck and Trailer — AP32

1980, Dec. 15
C61 AP32 2.40fr multicolored 1.25 1.00

Supply Ship Saint Marcouf — AP33

1980, Dec. 15
C62 AP33 3.50fr shown 1.60 1.10
C63 AP33 7.30fr black & Icebreaker Norsel 2.50 2.00

Glacial Landscape, Dumont d'Urville Sea — AP34

Chionis — AP35

Adele Dumont d'Urville (1798-1842) — AP36

Arcad III — AP37

25th Anniv. of Charcot Station — AP38

Antares — AP39

1981 **Engr.** *Perf. 13, 12½x13 (2fr)*
C64 AP34 1.30fr multicolored .70 .45
C65 AP35 1.50fr black .70 .50
C66 AP36 2fr black & lt brn .90 .85
C67 AP37 3.85fr multicolored 1.60 1.25
C68 AP38 5fr multicolored 1.75 1.50
C69 AP39 8.40fr multicolored 2.75 2.25
　　Nos. C64-C69 (6) 8.40 6.80

PHILEXFRANCE '82 Stamp Exhibition, Paris, June 11-21 — AP40

1982, June 11 **Engr.** *Perf. 13*
C70 AP40 8fr multicolored 5.25 5.25

French Overseas Possessions Week, Sept. 18-25 — AP41

1982, Sept. 17 **Engr.** *Perf. 13*
C71 AP41 5fr Commandant Charcot 1.75 1.75

Apostle Islands — AP42

1983, Jan. 3   **Engr.**   *Perf. 13*
C72 AP42 65c multicolored   .55   .35

Sputnik I, 25th
Anniv. of Intl.
Geophysical
Year — AP43

Orange Bay Base, Cape Horn, 1883,
Cent. — AP44

5.20fr, Scoresby Sound Base, Greenland,
50th anniv.

1983, Jan. 3
C73 AP43 1.50fr multicolored   .60   .60
C74 AP44 3.30fr multicolored   1.75   1.75
C75 AP44 5.20fr multicolored   2.00   2.00
   a.   Strip of 3, #C73-C75   4.50   4.50

AP45

1983, Jan. 3
C76 AP45 4.55fr dark blue   3.75   3.00

Abstract, by G. Mathieu — AP46

Illustration reduced.

1983, Jan. 3   **Photo.**   *Perf. 13x13½*
C77 AP46 25fr multicolored   10.00   8.00

Erebus off Antarctic Ice Cap,
1842 — AP47

Port of Joan of Arc, 1930 — AP48

1984, Jan. 1   **Engr.**   *Perf. 13*
C78 AP47 2.60fr ultra & dk blue   1.10   1.00
C79 AP48 4.70fr multicolored   1.75   1.75

Aurora Polaris — AP49

1984, Jan. 1   **Photo.**
C80 AP49 3.50fr multicolored   2.00   1.25

Manned Flight Bicentenary
(1983) — AP50

Various balloons and airships.

1984, Jan. 1   **Engr.**
C81 AP50 3.50fr multicolored   1.75   1.75
C82 AP50 7.80fr multicolored   2.75   2.75
   a.   Pair, #C81-C82 + label   5.00   5.00

Patrol Boat
Albatros — AP51

1984, July 2   **Engr.**   *Perf. 13*
C83 AP51 11.30fr multi   4.25   4.25

NORDPOSTA Exhibition — AP52

1984, Nov. 3   **Engr.**   *Perf. 13*
C84 AP52 9fr Scientific Vessel
           Gauss   4.50   3.50

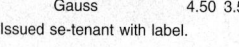

Issued se-tenant with label.

Corsican
Sheep — AP53

Amsterdam
Albatross
AP54

1985, Jan. 1   **Engr.**   *Perf. 13*
C85 AP53 70c Mouflons   .50   .35
C86 AP54 3.90fr Diomedia am-
      sterdamensis   1.50   1.25

La Novara,
Frigate
AP55

1985, Jan. 1   **Engr.**   *Perf. 13*
C87 AP55 12.80fr La Novara at
          St. Paul   5.00   4.50

Explorer and Seal, by Tremois — AP56

Design: Explorer, seal, names of territories.
Illustration reduced.

1985, Jan. 1   **Photo.**   *Perf. 13x12½*
C88 AP56 30fr + label   11.00   8.50

Sailing Ships, Ropes, Flora &
Fauna — AP57

1985, Aug. 6   **Engr.**   *Perf. 13*
C89 AP57   2fr blk, brt bl & ol
            grn   .70   .55
C90 AP57 12.80fr blk, ol grn &
         brt bl   3.75   3.75
   a.   Pair, #C89-C90 + label   5.50   5.50

French Southern & Antarctic Territories,
30th anniv. No. C90a has continuous design
with center label.

Bird Type of 1986

1986, Jan. 1   **Engr.**   *Perf. 13½x13*
C91 A56 4.60fr Sea Gulls   2.00   1.75

Antarctic Atmospheric Research, 10th
Anniv. — AP58

1986, Jan. 1
C92 AP58 14fr blk, dk red & brt
         org   5.00   4.00

Jean Charcot (1867-1936),
Explorer — AP59

1986, Jan. 1
C93 AP59 2.10fr Ship Pourquoi
          Pas   .90   .60
C94 AP59 14fr Ship in storm   4.50   4.25
   a.   Pair, #C93-C94 + label   6.00   6.00

SPOT Satellite over the
Antarctic — AP60

1986, May 26   **Engr.**   *Perf. 13*
C95 AP60 8fr dp ultra, sep & dk
         ol grn   3.25   2.50

J.B.
Charcot — AP61

1987, Jan. 1   **Engr.**   *Perf. 13x13½*
C96 AP61 14.60fr multi   5.00   4.50

Ocean Drilling Program — AP62

1987, Jan. 1   *Perf. 13½x13*
C97 AP62 16.80fr lem, dk ultra &
         bluish blk   5.50   4.50

INMARSAT — AP63

1987, Mar. 2   **Engr.**   *Perf. 13*
C98 AP63 16.80fr multi   8.00 7.50

French Polar Expeditions, 40th
Anniv. — AP64

1988, Jan. 1
C99 AP64 20fr lake, ol grn &
     plum   8.00 6.75

Views of Penguin Is. — AP65

1988, Jan. 1
C100 AP65 3.90fr dk bl & sep   1.60 1.25
C101 AP65 15.10fr dp grn, choc
     brn & dk bl   5.00 5.00

See Nos. C103, C109.

Founding of Permanent Settlements in
the Territories, 40th Anniv. — AP66

1989, Jan. 1   **Engr.**   *Perf. 13½x13*
C102 AP66 15.50fr black   5.00 4.75

Island View Type

1989, Jan. 1
C103 AP65 8.40fr Apostle Islands 2.75 2.50

La Curieuse — AP68

1989, Jan. 1   *Perf. 13x12½*
C104 AP68 2.20fr multicolored   .80 .70
C105 AP68 15.50fr multi, diff.   5.00 5.00
   a.   Pair, #C104-C105 + label   6.00 6.00

No. C105a label continues the design.

French Revolution, Bicent. — AP69

1989, July 14   **Engr.**   *Perf. 13x12½*
C106 AP69 5fr pink, dark olive
     grn & dark blue   5.00 5.00

Souvenir Sheet
Perf. 13
C107   Sheet of 4   9.75 9.75
   a.   AP69 5fr Prus green, brt ultra
     & dark red   2.40 2.40

No. C107 for PHILEXFRANCE '89.

15th Antarctic Treaty Summit
Conference — AP70

1989, Oct. 9   **Engr.**   *Perf. 13*
C108 AP70 17.70fr multicolored   6.00 5.75

Island View Type
1990, Jan. 1   **Engr.**   *Perf. 13*
C109 AP65 7.30fr Isle of Pigs,
     Crozet Isls.   3.00 2.40

L'Astrolabe, Expedition Team — AP72

1990, Jan. 1
C110 AP72 15.50fr dk red vio &
     blk   5.00 5.00

Discovery of Adelie Land by Dumont
D'Urville, 150th anniv.

L'Astrolabe, Commanded by Dumont
D'Urville, 1840 — AP73

1990, Jan. 1
C111 AP73 2.20fr L'Astrolabe,
     1988   .80 .75
C112 AP73 15.50fr shown   5.00 5.00
   a.   Pair, #C111-C112 + label   6.50 6.50

Bird, by Folon — AP74

Illustration reduced.

1990, Jan. 1   **Litho.**   *Perf. 12½x13*
C113 AP74 30fr multicolored   10.00 9.50

Albatross,
Argos
Satellite
AP75

1991, Jan. 1
C114 AP75 2.10fr red brn, bl &
     brn   1.25 .80

Climatological Research — AP76

1991, Jan. 1   **Engr.**   *Perf. 13*
C115 AP76 3.60fr Weather bal-
     loons, in-
     struments   1.40 1.40
C116 AP76 20fr Research
     ship   7.75 7.75
   a.   Pair, #C115-C116 + label   10.00 10.00

Charles de Gaulle (1890-
1970) — AP77

1991, Jan. 1
C117 AP77 18.80fr blk, red & bl   7.25 7.25

Cape
Petrel — AP78

1992, Jan. 1   **Engr.**   *Perf. 13*
C118 AP78 3.40fr multicolored   2.00 1.40

French Institute of Polar Research and
Technology — AP79

#C120, Polar bear with man offering flowers.

1991, Dec. 16   **Engr.**   *Perf. 13x12*
C119 AP79 15fr multicolored   5.75 5.75
C120 AP79 15fr multicolored   5.75 5.75
   a.   Strip, #C119-C120 + label   11.50 11.50

Christopher Columbus and Discovery
of America — AP80

1992, Jan. 1   *Perf. 13*
C121 AP80 22fr multicolored   9.75 9.75

Mapping Satellite Poseidon — AP81

1992, Jan. 1   **Engr.**   *Perf. 13*
C122 AP81 24.50fr multi   11.00 10.50

Dumont d'Urville Base, Adelie
Land — AP82

Illustration reduced.

1992, Jan. 1   **Litho.**   *Perf. 13x12½*
C123 AP82 25.70fr multi   11.50 10.50

Amateur Radio — AP83

1993, Jan. 1   **Engr.**   *Perf. 13*
C124 AP83 2fr multicolored   1.50 .55

New Animal Biology Laboratory, Adelie
Land — AP84

1993, Jan. 1
C125 AP84 25.40fr multicolored 11.00 6.75

Support Base D10 — AP85

1993, Jan. 1
C126 AP85 25.70fr ol, red & bl   11.00 7.00

Opening of Adelie Land
Airfield — AP86

1993, Jan. 1
C127 AP86 30fr multicolored   13.00 8.75

Krill — AP87

1994, Jan. 1   **Engr.**   *Perf. 13*
C128 AP87 15fr black   6.50 4.00

Fishery Management — AP88

1994, Jan. 1
C129 AP88 23fr multicolored   10.00 6.00

Satellite, Ground Station — AP89

Design: 27.30fr, Lidar Station.

1994, Jan. 1
C130 AP89 26.70fr multicolored   12.00 7.00
C131 AP89 27.30fr multicolored   12.00 7.25

Arrival of Emperor Penguins — AP90

Illustration reduced.

1994, Jan. 1   *Perf. 13x12½*
C132 AP90 28fr blue & black   12.00 7.50

Erebus Mission — AP91

1995, Jan. 2   **Engr.**   *Perf. 13*
C133 AP91 4.30fr bl, vio & slate   2.25 1.50

Moving of Winter Station,
Charcot — AP92

1995, Jan. 2   **Litho.**
C134 AP92 15fr multicolored   6.50 4.25

G. Lesquin (1803-30) — AP93

Illustration reduced.

1995, Jan. 2
C135 AP93 28fr multicolored   12.00 8.00

Map of East Island — AP94

1996, Jan. 1   **Engr.**   *Perf. 13*
C136 AP94 20fr multicolored   8.50 6.00

Expedition to Dome/C — AP95

1996, Jan. 1
C137 AP95 23fr dark blue   10.00 7.00

Blue Whale, Southern Whale
Sanctuary — AP96

1996, Jan. 1
C138 AP96 26.70fr multicolored   12.00 8.00

Port-Couvreux — AP97

1996, Jan. 1
C139 AP97 27.30fr multicolored   12.00 8.50

Jasus Paulensis
AP98

1997, Jan. 1   **Engr.**   *Perf. 12½x13*
C140 AP98 5.20fr multicolored   2.60 1.60

Racing
Yacht
Charentes
2 — AP99

1997, Jan. 1   **Litho.**   *Perf. 13*
C141 AP99 16fr multicolored   7.00 5.00

John Nunn, Shipwrecked 1825-29,
Hope Cottage — AP100

1997, Jan. 1   **Engr.**
C142 AP100 20fr multicolored   8.75 6.25

ICOTA Program — AP101

1997, Jan. 1
C143 AP101 24fr multicolored   10.50 7.50

Harpagifer Spinosus — AP102

1997, Jan. 1
C144 AP102 27fr multicolored   12.00 8.50

EPICA Program — AP103

1998, Jan. 2   **Engr.**   *Perf. 13*
C145 AP103 5.20fr dk brn & lil   2.50 1.40

First Radio Meteorological Station,
Port Aux Francais — AP104

1998, Jan. 2
C146 AP104 8fr black, blue & red 3.75 2.25

King
Penguin,
Argos
Satellite
AP105

1998, Jan. 2   *Perf. 12½x13*
C147 AP105 16fr multicolored   7.00 4.75

Ranunculas
Moseleyi
AP106

1998, Jan. 2
C148 AP106 24fr multicolored   10.50 6.50

Intl. Geophysical Year, 40th
Anniv. — AP107

Illustration reduced.

1998, Oct.   **Engr.**   *Perf. 13x12½*
C149 AP107 5.20fr dk bl, blk &
          brick red   2.50 1.40

FRENCH SUDAN

'french sü-'dan

LOCATION — In northwest Africa, north of French Guinea and Ivory Coast

GOVT. — French Colony

AREA — 590,966 sq. mi.

POP. — 3,794,270 (1941)

CAPITAL — Bamako

In 1899 French Sudan was abolished as a separate colony and was divided among Dahomey, French Guinea, Ivory Coast, Senegal and Senegambia and Niger. Issues for French Sudan were resumed in 1921.

From 1906 to 1921 a part of this territory was known as Upper Senegal and Niger. A part of Upper Volta was added in 1933. See Mali.

100 Centimes = 1 Franc

See French West Africa No. 70 for stamp inscribed "Soudan Francais" and "Afrique Occidentale Francaise."

Navigation and Commerce
A1   A2

Stamps of French Colonies, Surcharged in Black

Perf. 14x13½

1894, Apr. 12   Unwmk.
1	A1	15c on 75c car, *rose*	3,200.	1,600.
2	A1	25c on 1fr brnz grn, *straw*	3,500.	1,250.

The imperforate stamp like No. 1 was made privately in Paris from a fragment of the lithographic stone which had been used in the Colony for surcharging No. 1. Counterfeit surcharges exist.

1894-1900   Typo.   Perf. 14x13½
Name of colony in Blue or Carmine
3	A2	1c blk, *lil bl*	1.25	1.25
4	A2	2c brn, *buff*	1.75	1.75
5	A2	4c claret, *lav*	4.25	4.25
6	A2	5c grn, *grnsh*	7.25	7.25
7	A2	10c blk, *lav*	16.00	16.00
8	A2	10c red ('00)	5.50	5.50
9	A2	15c blue, quadrille paper	5.00	5.00
10	A2	15c gray, *lt gray* ('00)	5.75	5.75
11	A2	20c red, *grn*	22.00	22.00
12	A2	25c blk, *rose*	19.50	19.50
13	A2	25c blue ('00)	5.75	5.75
14	A2	30c brn, *bister*	32.50	32.50
15	A2	40c red, *straw*	26.00	26.00
16	A2	50c car, *rose*	40.00	40.00
17	A2	50c brn, *az* ('00)	9.75	9.75
18	A2	75c dp vio, *org*	37.50	37.50
19	A2	1fr brnz grn, *straw*	7.00	7.00
		Nos. 3-19 (17)	246.75	246.75

Perf. 13½x14 stamps are counterfeits.
Nos. 8, 10, 13, 17 were issued in error. They were accepted for use in the other colonies.

Camel and Rider — A3

Stamps of Upper Senegal and Niger Overprinted in Black

1921-30   Perf. 13½x14
21	A3	1c brn vio & vio	.20	.20
22	A3	2c dk gray & dl vio	.20	.20
23	A3	4c blk & blue	.20	.20
24	A3	5c ol brn & dk brn	.20	.20
25	A3	10c yel grn & bl grn	.65	.20
26	A3	10c red vio & bl ('25)	.25	.25
27	A3	15c red brn & org	.25	.20

28	A3	15c yel grn & dp grn ('25)	.25	.20
29	A3	15c org brn & vio ('27)	1.25	1.25
30	A3	20c brn vio & blk	.25	.20
31	A3	25c blk & bl grn	.75	.60
a.		Booklet pane of 4	—	
32	A3	30c red org & rose	1.10	.75
33	A3	30c bl grn & blk ('26)	.45	.45
34	A3	30c dl grn & bl grn ('28)	1.40	1.40
35	A3	35c rose & vio	.30	.25
36	A3	40c gray & rose	.90	.65
37	A3	45c bl & ol brn	.75	.60
38	A3	50c ultra & bl	1.25	.95
39	A3	50c red org & bl ('26)	.90	.80
40	A3	60c vio, *pnksh* ('26)	.80	.50
41	A3	65c bis & pale bl ('28)	1.40	1.25
42	A3	75c org & ol brn	1.00	.80
43	A3	90c brn red & pink ('30)	4.25	4.25
44	A3	1fr dk brn & dl vio	1.10	.95
45	A3	1.10fr gray lil & red vio ('28)	2.25	2.25
46	A3	1.50fr dp bl & bl ('30)	4.75	4.75
47	A3	2fr green & blue	1.60	1.40
48	A3	3fr red vio ('30)	9.50	9.50
a.		Double overprint	125.00	
49	A3	5fr violet & blk	5.00	4.25
		Nos. 21-49 (29)	43.15	39.40

Type of 1921
Surcharged

1922, Sept. 28
50	A3	60c on 75c vio, *pnksh*	.50	.50

Stamps and Type of 1921-30 Surcharged with New Values and Bars

1925-27
51	A3	25c on 45c	.50	.50
52	A3	65c on 75c	1.40	1.10
53	A3	85c on 2fr	1.40	1.40
54	A3	85c on 5fr	1.40	1.40
55	A3	90c on 75c brn red & sal pink ('27)	1.60	1.40
56	A3	1.25fr on 1fr dp bl & lt bl (R) ('26)	.95	.95
57	A3	1.50fr on 1fr dp bl & ultra ('27)	.95	.95
58	A3	3fr on 5fr dl red & brn org ('27)	4.25	3.75
59	A3	10fr on 5fr brn red & bl grn ('27)	17.00	14.00
60	A3	20fr on 5fr vio & ver ('27)	22.00	19.50
		Nos. 51-60 (10)	51.45	44.95

Sudanese Woman — A4   Entrance to the Residency at Djenné — A5

Sudanese Boatman — A6

1931-40   Typo.   Perf. 13x14
61	A4	1c dk red & blk	.20	.20
62	A4	2c dp bl & org	.20	.20
63	A4	3c dk red & blk ('40)	.20	.20
64	A4	4c gray lil & rose	.20	.20
65	A4	5c ind & grn	.20	.20
66	A4	10c ol grn & rose	.20	.20
67	A4	15c blk & brt vio	.25	.25
68	A4	20c hn brn & lt bl	.25	.25
69	A4	25c red vio & lt red	.25	.25
70	A5	30c grn & lt grn	.60	.35

71	A5	30c dk bl & red org ('40)	.25	.25
72	A5	35c ol grn & grn ('38)	.35	.35
73	A5	40c ol grn & pink	.25	.25
74	A5	45c dk bl & red org	.80	.35
75	A5	45c ol grn & grn ('40)	.35	.35
76	A5	50c red & blk	.25	.25
77	A5	55c ultra & car ('38)	.35	.35
78	A5	60c brt bl & brn ('40)	.80	.80
79	A5	65c brt vio & blk	.50	.35
80	A5	70c vio bl & car rose ('40)	.50	.50
81	A5	75c brt bl & ol brn	2.25	1.50
82	A5	80c car & brn ('38)	.35	.35
83	A5	90c dp red & red org	1.50	.75
84	A5	90c brt vio & sl blk ('39)	.60	.60
85	A5	1fr indigo & grn	6.75	1.50
86	A5	1fr rose red ('38)	4.00	1.50
87	A5	1fr car & brn ('40)	.60	.60
88	A6	1.25fr vio & dl vio ('33)	.50	.50
89	A6	1.25fr red ('39)	.60	.60
90	A6	1.40fr brt vio & blk ('40)	.65	.65
91	A6	1.50fr dk bl & ultra	.50	.35
92	A6	1.60fr brn & dp bl ('40)	.60	.60
93	A6	1.75fr dk brn & dp bl ('33)	.65	.55
94	A6	1.75fr vio bl ('38)	.65	.55
95	A6	2fr org brn & grn	.70	.40
96	A6	2.25fr vio bl & ultra ('39)	.75	.75
97	A6	2.50fr lt brn ('40)	1.25	1.25
98	A6	3fr Prus grn & brn	.65	.25
99	A6	5fr red & blk	1.75	1.00
100	A6	10fr dl bl & grn	2.00	1.60
101	A6	20fr red vio & brn	2.75	2.25
		Nos. 61-101 (41)	37.00	24.20

For surcharges see Nos. B7-B10.
For 10c and 30c, without "RF," see Nos. 120-121.

For surcharges see Nos. B7-B10.
Common Design Types pictured following the introduction.

Colonial Exposition Issue
Common Design Types

1931, Apr. 13   Engr.   Perf. 12½
Name of Country Printed in Black
102	CD70	40c deep green	3.00	3.00
103	CD71	50c violet	3.00	3.00
104	CD72	90c red orange	3.00	3.00
105	CD73	1.50fr dull blue	3.00	3.00
		Nos. 102-105 (4)	12.00	12.00

Paris International Exposition Issue
Common Design Types

1937, Apr. 15   Perf. 13
106	CD74	20c dp violet	3.00	3.00
107	CD75	30c dk green	1.25	1.25
108	CD76	40c carmine rose	1.25	1.25
109	CD77	50c dk brown	1.25	1.25
110	CD78	90c red	1.25	1.25
111	CD79	1.50fr ultra	1.25	1.25
		Nos. 106-111 (6)	9.25	9.25

Colonial Arts Exhibition Issue
Souvenir Sheet
Common Design Type

1937   Engr.   Imperf.
112	CD77	3fr magenta & blk	7.50	8.00

Caillie Issue
Common Design Type

1939, Apr. 5   Perf. 12½x12
113	CD81	90c org brn & org	.75	.75
114	CD81	2fr brt violet	.75	.75
115	CD81	2.25fr ultra & dk bl	.75	.75
		Nos. 113-115 (3)	2.25	2.25

New York World's Fair Issue
Common Design Type

1939, May 10
116	CD82	1.25fr carmine lake	.90	.90
117	CD82	2.25fr ultra	.90	.90

Entrance to the Residency at Djenné and Marshal Pétain — A7

1941   Engr.   Perf. 12x12½
118	A7	1fr green	.60	1.25
119	A7	2.50fr blue	.60	1.25

For surcharges, see Nos. B14-B15.

Types of 1931-40 without "RF"
1943-44   Typo.   Perf. 13½x14
120	A4	10c ol green & rose	.35	
121	A5	30c dk bl & red org	.50	

Nos. 120-121 were issued by the Vichy government in France, but were not placed on sale in French Sudan.

Stamps of French Sudan were superseded by those of French West Africa.

SEMI-POSTAL STAMPS

Curie Issue
Common Design Type
Unwmk.

1938, Oct. 24   Engr.   Perf. 13
B1	CD80	1.75fr + 50c brt ultra	10.00	10.00

French Revolution Issue
Common Design Type

1939, July 5   Photo.
Name and Value Typo. in Black
B2	CD83	45c + 25c green	8.50	8.50
B3	CD83	70c + 30c brown	8.50	8.50
B4	CD83	90c + 35c red orange	8.50	8.50
B5	CD83	1.25fr + 1fr rose pink	8.50	8.50
B6	CD83	2.25fr + 2fr blue	8.50	8.50
		Nos. B2-B6 (5)	42.50	42.50

Stamps of 1931-40, Surcharged in Black or Red

1941   Perf. 13x14
B7	A5	50c + 1fr red & blk (R)	1.75	1.75
B8	A5	80c + 2fr car & brn	5.50	5.50
B9	A6	1.50fr + 2fr dk bl & ultra	5.50	5.50
B10	A6	2fr + 3fr org brn & grn	5.50	5.50
		Nos. B7-B10 (4)	18.25	18.25

Common Design Type and

Native Officer — SP1   Aviation Officer — SP2

1941   Photo.   Perf. 13½
B11	SP1	1fr + 1fr red	.95	
B12	CD86	1.50fr + 3fr claret	.95	
B13	SP2	2.50fr + 1fr blue	.95	
		Nos. B11-B13 (3)	2.85	

Surtax for the defense of the colonies. Issued by the Vichy government in France, but not placed on sale in French Sudan.

Petain Type of 1941
Surcharged in Black or Red

1944	**Engr.**	**Perf. 12x12½**	
B14	50c + 1.50fr on 2.50fr deep		
	blue (R)		.60
B15	+ 2.50fr on 1fr green		.60

Colonial Development Fund.
Nos. B14-B15 were issued by the Vichy government in France, but were not placed on sale in French Sudan.

AIR POST STAMPS

Common Design Type
Perf. 12½x12

1940, Feb. 8	**Unwmk.**		**Engr.**	
C1	CD85	1.90fr ultra	.25	.25
C2	CD85	2.90fr dark red	.35	.35
C3	CD85	4.50fr dk gray green	.75	.75
C4	CD85	4.90fr yellow bister	.75	.75
C5	CD85	6.90fr deep orange	.90	.90
	Nos. C1-C5 (5)		3.00	3.00

Common Design Types

1942, Oct. 19				
C6	CD88	50c carmine & bl	.20	.55
C7	CD88	1fr brown & blk	.25	
C8	CD88	2fr dk grn & red brn	.35	
C9	CD88	3fr dk blue & scar	.55	
C10	CD88	5fr vio & brn red	.55	

Frame Engr., Center Typo.

C11	CD89	10fr ultra, ind & gray		
		blk	.80	
C12	CD89	20fr rose car, mag & lt		
		vio	.95	
C13	CD89	50fr yel grn, dl grn &		
		dl bl	1.60	2.50
	Nos. C6-C13 (8)		5.25	

There is doubt whether Nos. C7-C12 were officially placed in use.

AIR POST SEMI-POSTAL STAMPS

Types of Dahomey Air Post Semi-Postal Issue
Perf. 13½x12½, 13 (#CB3)
Photo, Engr. (#CB3)

1942, June 22				
CB1	SPAP1	1.50fr + 3.50fr		
		green	.50	3.50
CB2	SPAP2	2fr + 6fr brown	.50	3.50
CB3	SPAP2	3fr + 9fr car red	.50	3.50
	Nos. CB1-CB3 (3)		1.50	10.50

Native children's welfare fund.

Colonial Education Fund
Common Design Type
Perf. 12½x13½

1942, June 22			**Engr.**	
CB4	CD86a	1.20fr + 1.80fr blue		
		& red	.50	3.50

POSTAGE DUE STAMPS

D1   D2

Postage Due Stamps of Upper Senegal and Niger Overprinted

Perf. 14x13½

1921, Dec.		**Unwmk.**	**Typo.**	
J1	D1	5c green	.35	.35
J2	D1	10c rose	.50	.50
J3	D1	15c gray	.65	.65
J4	D1	20c brown	.85	.85
J5	D1	30c blue	.85	.85
J6	D1	50c black	1.25	1.25
J7	D1	60c orange	1.50	1.50
J8	D1	1fr violet	1.90	1.90
	Nos. J1-J8 (8)		7.85	7.85

Type of 1921 Issue Surcharged

1927, Oct. 10				
J9	D1	2fr on 1fr lilac rose	4.50	4.50
J10	D1	3fr on 1fr org brown	4.50	4.50

1931, Mar. 9				
J11	D2	5c green	.20	.20
J12	D2	10c rose	.20	.20
J13	D2	15c gray	.20	.20
J14	D2	20c dark brown	.20	.20
J15	D2	30c dark blue	.35	.35
J16	D2	50c black	.35	.35
J17	D2	60c deep orange	.50	.50
J18	D2	1fr violet	.80	.80
J19	D2	2fr lilac rose	.95	.95
J20	D2	3fr red brown	1.00	1.00
	Nos. J11-J20 (10)		4.75	4.75

FRENCH WEST AFRICA

ˈfrench ˈwest ˈa-fri-kə

LOCATION — Northwestern Africa
GOVT. — French colonial administrative unit
AREA — 1,821,768 sq. mi.
POP. — 18,777,163 (est.)
CAPITAL — Dakar

French West Africa comprised the former colonies of Senegal, French Guinea, Ivory Coast, Dahomey, French Sudan, Mauritania, Niger and Upper Volta.

In 1958, these former colonies became republics, eventually issuing their own stamps. Until the republic issues appeared, stamps of French West Africa continued in use. The Senegal and Sudanese Republics issued stamps jointly as the Federation of Mali, starting in 1959.

> **Catalogue values for all unused stamps in this country are for Never Hinged items.**

Many stamps other than Nos. 65-72 and 77 are inscribed "Afrique Occidentale Francaise" and the name of one of the former colonies. See listings in these colonies for such stamps.

Senegal No. 156 Surcharged in Red

1943		**Unwmk.**	**Perf. 12½x12**	
1	A30	1.50fr on 65c dk vio	.85	.50
2	A30	5.50fr on 65c dk vio	.90	.50
3	A30	50fr on 65c dk vio	2.75	1.25

Mauritania No. 91 Surcharged in Red

1943			**Perf. 13**	
4	A7	3.50fr on 65c dp grn	.45	.45
5	A7	4fr on 65c dp grn	.55	.55
6	A7	5fr on 65c dp grn	1.10	1.10
7	A7	10fr on 65c dp grn	1.10	1.10
	Nos. 1-7 (7)		7.70	5.45

Senegal No. 143, 148 and 188
Surcharged with New Values in Black and Orange

1944			**Perf. 12½x12**	
8	A29	1.50fr on 15c blk (O)	.50	.40
9	A29	4.50fr on 15c blk (O)	.75	.60
10	A29	5.50fr on 2c brn	1.75	1.00
11	A29	10fr on 15c blk (O)	2.50	1.40
12	CD81	20fr on 90c org brn		
		& org	1.50	1.50
13	CD81	50fr on 90c org brn		
		& org	3.25	1.75

Mauritania No. 109 Surcharged in Black

14	CD81	15fr on 90c org brn		
		& org	1.25	1.25
	Nos. 8-14 (7)		11.50	7.90

Common Design Types pictured following the introduction.

Eboue Issue
Common Design Type

1945		**Engr.**	**Perf. 13**	
15	CD91	2fr black	.50	.50
16	CD91	25fr Prussian green	1.50	1.25

Nos. 15 and 16 exist imperforate.

Colonial Soldier — A1

1945		**Litho.**	**Perf. 12½x12, 12**	
17	A1	10c indigo & buff	.20	.20
18	A1	30c olive & yel	.20	.20
19	A1	40c blue & buff	.35	.35
20	A1	50c red org & gray	.35	.35
21	A1	60c ol brn & bl	.35	.35
22	A1	70c mag & cit	.35	.35
23	A1	80c bl grn & pale lem	.35	.35
24	A1	1fr brn vio & cit	.35	.35
25	A1	1.20fr gray brn & cit	2.50	1.75
26	A1	1.50fr choc & pink	.45	.35
27	A1	2fr ocher and gray	.50	.35
28	A1	2.40fr red & gray	.70	.70
29	A1	3fr brn red & yelsh	.45	.30
30	A1	4fr ultra & pink	.45	.30
31	A1	4.50fr org brn & yelsh	.45	.30
32	A1	5fr dk pur & yelsh	.45	.30
33	A1	10fr ol grn & pink	.80	.30
34	A1	15fr orange & yel	1.40	1.00
35	A1	20fr sl grn & grnsh	1.60	1.10
	Nos. 17-35 (19)		12.25	9.65

Rifle Dance, Mauritania — A2   Shelling Coconuts, Togo — A6

Bamako Dike, French Sudan — A3

Trading Canoe, Niger River — A4

Oasis of Bilma, Niger — A5

Kouandé Weaving, Dahomey A7

Donkey Caravan, Senegal A8

Crocodile and Hippopotamus, Ivory Coast — A9

Gathering Coconuts, French Guinea — A10   Peul Woman of Dienné — A12

Bamako Fountain, French Sudan A11

Bamako Market — A13   Dahomey Laborer — A14

Woman of Mauritania A15

Fula Woman, French Guinea A16

Djenné Mosque, French Sudan A17

Monorail Train, Senegal A18

Agni Woman, Ivory Coast — A19

Azwa Women at Niger River — A20

1947	Engr.	Unwmk.	Perf. 12½	
36	A2	10c blue	.20	.20
37	A3	30c red brn	.20	.20
38	A4	40c gray grn	.25	.20
39	A5	50c red brn	.20	.20
40	A6	60c gray blk	.50	.50
41	A7	80c brown vio	.50	.50
42	A8	1fr maroon	.40	.20
43	A9	1.20fr dk blue grn	1.50	1.40
44	A10	1.50fr ultra	1.40	1.10
45	A11	2fr red orange	.50	.20
46	A12	3fr chocolate	.60	.30
47	A13	3.60fr brown red	1.40	1.40
48	A14	4fr deep blue	.40	.25
49	A15	5fr gray green	.40	.20
50	A16	6fr dark blue	.50	.25
51	A17	10fr brn red	1.00	.20
52	A18	15fr sepia	2.00	.20
53	A19	20fr chocolate	1.25	.30
54	A20	25fr grnsh blk	2.50	.50
		Nos. 36-54 (19)	15.70	8.30

Types of 1947

1948		Re-engraved		
55	A6	60c brown olive	.65	.50
56	A12	3fr chocolate	.65	.35

Nos. 40 and 46 are inscribed "TOGO" in lower margin. Inscription omitted on Nos. 55 and 56.

Imperforates

Most stamps of French West Africa from 1949 onward exist imperforate in issued and trial colors, and also in small presentation sheets in issued colors.

Military Medal Issue
Common Design Type
Engraved and Typographed

1952, Dec. 1			Perf. 13	
57	CD101	15fr multicolored	5.00	5.00

Treich Laplène and Map — A21

1952, Dec. 1		Engr.		
58	A21	40fr brown lake	1.40	.25

Marcel Treich Laplène, a leading contributor to the development of Ivory Coast.

Medical Laboratory A22

1953, Nov. 18				
59	A22	15fr brn, dk bl grn & blk brn	.85	.20

Couple Feeding Antelopes A23

1954, Sept. 20				
60	A23	25fr multicolored	1.10	.25

Gov. Noel Eugène Ballay A24

1954, Nov. 29				
61	A24	8fr indigo & brown	1.25	.55

Chimpanzee — A25

Giant Pangolin A26

1955, May 2		Unwmk.	Perf. 13	
62	A25	5fr gray & dk brn	1.10	.50
63	A26	8fr brn & bl grn	1.10	.55

International Exhibition for Wildlife Protection, Paris, May 1955.

Map, Symbols of Industry, Rotary Emblem A27

1955, July 4				
64	A27	15fr dark blue	1.25	.50

50th anniv. of the founding of Rotary Intl.

FIDES Issue

Mossi Railroad Upper Volta C103

1fr, Date grove, Mauritania. 2fr, Milo Bridge, French Guinea. 4fr, Cattle raising, Niger. 15fr, Farm machinery and landscape, Senegal. 17fr, Woman and Niger River, French Sudan. 20fr, Palm oil production, Dahomey. 30fr, Road construction, Ivory Coast.

1956		Engr.	Perf. 13x12½	
65	C103	1fr dk grn & dk bl grn	.55	.50
66	C103	2fr dk bl grn & bl	1.00	.50
67	C103	3fr dk brn & red brn	1.00	.85
68	C103	4fr dk car rose	1.25	.85
69	C103	15fr ind & ultra	1.10	.35
70	C103	17fr dk bl & ind	1.10	.55
71	C103	20fr rose lake	1.25	.50
72	C103	30fr dk pur & claret	1.25	.80
		Nos. 65-72 (8)	8.50	4.90

Coffee A28a

1956, Oct. 22			Perf. 13	
73	A28a	15fr dk blue green	.55	.20

Mobile Leprosy Clinic and Maltese Cross A29

1957, Mar. 11				
74	A29	15fr dk red brn, pur & red	1.25	.50

Issued in honor of the Knights of Malta.

Map of Africa — A30

1958, Feb.		Unwmk.	Perf. 13	
75	A30	20fr multicolored	1.00	.55

6h Intl.Cong. for African Tourism at Dakar.

"Africa" and Communications Symbols — A31

1958, Mar. 15		Engr.		
76	A31	15fr org, ultra & choc	1.10	.55

Stamp Day. See No. 86.

Abidjan Bridge A32

1958, Mar. 15				
77	A32	20fr dk sl grn & grnsh bl	1.10	.55

Bananas A33

1958, May 19			Perf. 13	
78	A33	20fr rose lil, dk grn & ol-ive	1.00	.20

Flower Issue
Common Design Type

10fr, Gloriosa. 25fr, Adenopus. 30fr, Cyrtosperma. 40fr, Cistanche. 65fr, Crinum Moorei.

1958-59		Photo.	Perf. 12x12½	
79	CD104	10fr multicolored	.50	.20
80	CD104	25fr red, yel & grn	.95	.50
81	CD104	30fr multicolored	1.10	.80
82	CD104	40fr blk brn, grn & yel	1.60	1.10
83	CD104	65fr multicolored	1.75	.95
		Nos. 79-83 (5)	5.90	3.55

Issued: 25fr, 40fr, 1/5/59; others, 7/7/58.

Moro Naba Sagha and Map — A34

1958, Nov. 1		Engr.	Perf. 13	
84	A34	20fr ol brn, car & vio	.85	.50

10th anniv. of the reestablishment of the Upper Volta territory.

Human Rights Issue
Common Design Type

1958, Dec. 10				
85	CD105	20fr maroon & dk bl	1.40	1.40

Type of 1958 Redrawn

1959, Mar. 21		Engr.	Perf. 13	
86	A31	20fr red, grnsh bl & sl grn	3.25	3.25

Name of country omitted on No. 86; "RF" replaced by "CF," inscribed "Dakar-Abidjan." Stamp Day.

SEMI-POSTAL STAMPS

Red Cross Issue
Common Design Type
Perf. 14½x14

1944, Dec.		Photo.	Unwmk.	
B1	CD90	5fr + 20fr plum	4.25	4.25

The surtax was for the French Red Cross and national relief.

Type of France, 1945, Overprinted in Black

1945, Oct. 13		Engr.	Perf. 13	
B2	SP150	2fr + 3fr orange red	.60	.60

Tropical Medicine Issue
Common Design Type

1950, May 15			Perf. 13	
B3	CD100	10fr +2fr red brn & sep	5.00	3.50

The surtax was for charitable work.

AIR POST STAMPS

Common Design Type

1945	Photo.	Unwmk.	Perf. 14½x14	
C1	CD87	5.50fr ultra	1.25	.80
C2	CD87	50fr dark green	2.25	.80
C3	CD87	100fr plum	2.25	.80
		Nos. C1-C3 (3)	5.75	2.40

Victory Issue
Common Design Type
1946, May 8 **Engr.** **Perf. 12½**
C4 CD92 8fr violet .95 .70

Chad to Rhine Issue
Common Design Types
1946, June 6
C5 CD93 5fr brown car 1.25 1.25
C6 CD94 10fr deep blue 1.25 1.25
C7 CD95 15fr brt violet 1.40 1.40
C8 CD96 20fr dk slate grn 1.50 1.50
C9 CD97 25fr olive brn 1.90 1.90
C10 CD98 50fr brown 2.40 2.40
   Nos. C5-C10 (6) 9.70 9.70

Antoine de Saint-Exupéry, Map and Natives — AP1

Plane over Dakar — AP2

Great White Egrets in Flight — AP3

Natives and Phantom Plane — AP4

1947, Mar. 24 **Engr.**
C11 AP1 8fr red brown .75 .40
C12 AP2 50fr rose violet 2.25 .70
C13 AP3 100fr ultra 9.00 3.50
C14 AP4 200fr slate gray 7.75 3.50
   Nos. C11-C14 (4) 19.75 8.10

UPU Issue
Common Design Type
1949, July 4 **Perf. 13**
C15 CD99 25fr multicolored 7.75 7.00

Vridi Canal, Abidjan — AP5

1951, Nov. 5 **Unwmk.** **Perf. 13**
C16 AP5 500fr red org, bl grn
    & dp ultra 19.00 3.50

Liberation Issue
Common Design Type
1954, June 6
C17 CD102 15fr indigo & ultra 6.00 4.25

Logging — AP6

Designs: 100fr, Radiotelephone exchange. 200fr, Baobab trees.

1954, Sept. 20
C18 AP6 50fr ol grn & org
    brn 2.75 .55
C19 AP6 100fr ind, dk brn &
    dk grn 3.75 .85
C20 AP6 200fr bl grn, grnsh
    blk & brn lake 11.00 2.10
   Nos. C18-C20 (3) 17.50 3.50

Gen. Louis Faidherbé and African Sharpshooter AP7

1957, July 20 **Unwmk.** **Perf. 13**
C21 AP7 15fr indigo & blue 1.25 1.25
  Centenary of French African troops.

Gorée Island and Woman — AP8

Designs: 20fr, Map with planes and ships. 25fr, Village and modern city. 40fr, Seat of Council of French West Africa. 50fr, Worker, ship and peanut plant. 100fr, Bay of N'Gor.

1958, Mar. 15 **Engr.**
C22 AP8 15fr blk brn, grn &
    vio .85 .65
C23 AP8 20fr blk brn, dk bl &
    red brn .85 .65
C24 AP8 25fr blk vio, bis &
    grn .85 .80
C25 AP8 40fr dk bl, brn & grn 1.10 .80
C26 AP8 50fr violet, brn &
    grn 1.75 1.10
C27 AP8 100fr brown, bl & grn 4.00 1.75
 a. Souvenir sheet of 6, #C22-
   C27 12.00 12.00
   Nos. C22-C27 (6) 9.40 5.75
  Centenary of Dakar.

Woman Playing Native Harp — AP9

1958, Dec. 1 **Unwmk.** **Perf. 13**
C28 AP9 20fr red brn, blk & gray .95 .55
  Inauguration of Nouakchott as capital of Mauritania.

POSTAGE DUE STAMPS

D1

1947 **Engr.** **Unwmk.** **Perf. 13**
J1 D1 10c red .20 .20
J2 D1 30c deep orange .20 .20
J3 D1 50c greenish blk .20 .20
J4 D1 1fr carmine .20 .20
J5 D1 2fr emerald .30 .25
J6 D1 3fr red lilac .75 .50
J7 D1 4fr deep ultra .80 .60
J8 D1 5fr red brown 1.50 1.10
J9 D1 10fr peacock blue 2.25 1.75
J10 D1 20fr sepia 4.00 3.00
   Nos. J1-J10 (10) 10.40 8.00

OFFICIAL STAMPS

Mask — O1

Designs: Various masks.

    Perf. 14x13
1958, June 2 **Typo.** **Unwmk.**
O1 O1 1fr dk brn red .55 .45
O2 O1 3fr brt green .35 .45
O3 O1 5fr crim rose .35 .20
O4 O1 10fr light ultra .50 .20
O5 O1 20fr bright red .85 .45
O6 O1 25fr purple .70 .45
O7 O1 30fr green 1.40 1.00
O8 O1 45fr gray black 1.90 1.25
O9 O1 50fr dark red 2.25 1.00
O10 O1 65fr brt ultra 2.75 1.00
O11 O1 100fr olive bister 5.75 1.40
O12 O1 200fr deep green 12.50 4.00
   Nos. O1-O12 (12) 29.85 11.85

FUJEIRA

fü-ˈjī-rə

LOCATION — Oman Peninsula, Arabia, on Persian Gulf
GOVT. — Sheikdom under British protection

  Fujeira is one of six Persian Gulf sheikdoms to join the United Arab Emirates which proclaimed independence Dec. 2, 1971. See United Arab Emirates.

  100 Naye Paise = 1 Rupee

> **Catalogue values for all unused stamps in this country are for Never Hinged items.**

Sheik Hamad bin Mohammed al Sharqi and Grebe — A1

Sheik and: 2np, 50np, Arabian oryx. 3np, 70np, Hoopoe. 4np, 1r, Wild ass. 5np, 1.50r, Herons in flight. 10np, 2r, Arabian horses. 15np, 3r, Leopard. 20np, 5r, Camels. 30np, 10r, Hawks.

   Photo. & Litho.
1964 **Unwmk.** **Perf. 14**
   Size: 36x24mm
1 A1 1np gold & multi .20 .20
2 A1 2np gold & multi .20 .20
3 A1 3np gold & multi .20 .20
4 A1 4np gold & multi .20 .20
5 A1 5np gold & multi .20 .20
6 A1 10np gold & multi .20 .20
7 A1 15np gold & multi .20 .20
8 A1 20np gold & multi .20 .20

---

9 A1 30np gold & multi .20 .20
   Size: 43x28mm
10 A1 40np gold & multi .30 .20
11 A1 50np gold & multi .30 .20
12 A1 70np gold & multi .35 .20
13 A1 1r gold & multi .50 .20
14 A1 1.50r gold & multi .75 .20
15 A1 2r gold & multi 1.00 .20
   Size: 53½x35mm
16 A1 3r gold & multi 1.50 .25
17 A1 5r gold & multi 2.00 .50
18 A1 10r gold & multi 4.75 .50
   Nos. 1-18 (18) 13.25 4.10

  Issued: 20np, 30np, 70np, 1.50r, 3r, 10r, Nov. 14; others, Sept. 22.
  Exist imperf. Value, set $16.

Sheik Hamad and Shot Put A2

1964, Dec. 6 **Perf. 14**
   Size: 43x28mm
19 A2 25np shown .20 .20
20 A2 50np Discus .20 .20
21 A2 75np Fencing .25 .25
22 A2 1r Boxing .30 .25
23 A2 1.50r Relay race .40 .35
24 A2 2r Soccer .50 .40
   Size: 53½x35mm
25 A2 3r Pole vaulting .90 .50
26 A2 5r Hurdling 2.25 .70
27 A2 7.50r Equestrian 3.50 .90
   Nos. 19-27 (9) 8.50 3.85

  18th Olympic Games, Tokyo, 10/10-25/64.
  Exist imperf. Value, set $12.

John F. Kennedy — A3

Kennedy: 10np, As sailor in the Pacific. 15np, As naval lieutenant. 20np, On speaker's rostrum. 25np, Sailing with family. 50np, With crowd of people. 1r, With Mrs. Kennedy, Lyndon B. Johnson. 2r, With Eisenhower on White House porch. 3r, With Mrs. Kennedy & Caroline. 5r, Portrait.

1965, Feb. 23 **Photo.** **Perf. 13½**
   Size: 29x44mm
Black Design with Gold Inscriptions
28 A3 5np pale gray .20 .20
29 A3 10np pale yellow .20 .20
30 A3 15np pink .20 .20
31 A3 20np pale greenish gray .20 .20
32 A3 25np pale blue .25 .20
33 A3 50np pale rose .30 .20
   Size: 33x51mm
34 A3 1r pale gray .75 .30
35 A3 2r pale green 1.25 .40
36 A3 3r pale gray 2.00 .50
37 A3 5r pale yellow 2.75 .80
   Nos. 28-37 (10) 8.10 3.20

  Pres. John F. Kennedy (1917-1963). A souvenir sheet contains 2 29x44mm stamps similar to Nos. 36-37 with pale blue (3r) and pale rose (5r) backgrounds. Value (unused): perf $7; imperf $9.
  Nos. 28-37 exist imperf. Value $10.

AIR POST STAMPS

Arabian Oryx AP1

Photo. & Litho.
1965, Aug. 16   Unwmk.   Perf. 13½
Size: 43x28mm

C1	AP1	15np Grebe	.25	.20
C2	AP1	25np shown	.25	.20
C3	AP1	35np Hoopoe	.35	.20
C4	AP1	50np Wild ass	.40	.20
C5	AP1	75np Herons in flight	.45	.20
C6	AP1	1r Arabian horses	.50	.20

Size: 53½x35mm

C7	AP1	2r Leopard	1.00	.20
C8	AP1	3r Camels	1.75	.25
C9	AP1	5r Hawks	3.75	.50
		Nos. C1-C9 (9)	8.70	2.15

Exist imperf. Value, set $10.

AIR POST OFFICIAL STAMPS

Type of Air Post Issue, 1965
Photo. & Litho.
1965, Nov. 10   Unwmk.   Perf. 13½
Size: 43x28mm

CO1	AP1	75np Arabian horses	.50	.25

Perf. 13
Size: 53½x35mm

CO2	AP1	2r Leopard	1.25	.40
CO3	AP1	3r Camels	2.00	.60
CO4	AP1	5r Hawks	3.75	1.00
		Nos. CO1-CO4 (4)	7.50	2.25

Exist imperf. Values same as perf.

OFFICIAL STAMPS

Type of Air Post Issue, 1965
Photo. & Litho.
1965, Oct. 14   Unwmk.   Perf. 13½
Size: 43x28mm

O1	AP1	25np Grebe	.20	.20
O2	AP1	40np Arabian oryx	.20	.20
O3	AP1	50np Hoopoe	.25	.20
O4	AP1	75np Wild ass	.40	.20
O5	AP1	1r Herons in flight	.75	.20
		Nos. O1-O5 (5)	1.80	1.00

Exist imperf. Values same as perf.

FUNCHAL

fün-'shäl

LOCATION — A city and administrative district in the Madeira island group in the Atlantic Ocean northwest of Africa
GOVT. — A part of the Republic of Portugal
POP. — 150,574 (1900)

Postage stamps of Funchal were superseded by those of the Azores. These, in turn, were displaced by the stamps of Portugal.

1000 Reis = 1 Milreis

King Carlos
A1   A2
Perf. 11½, 12½, 13½

1892-93		**Typo.**		**Unwmk.**
1	A1	5r yellow	3.00	1.50
a.	Diagonal half used as 2½r on entire newspaper			5.00
b.	Perf. 11½		4.00	2.75
2	A1	10r red violet	2.50	1.50
3	A1	15r chocolate	3.25	2.50
4	A1	20r lavender	3.75	2.10
a.	Perf. 13½		8.75	6.25
5a	A1	25r dark green	4.75	1.00
6	A1	50r ultra	4.75	2.10
a.	Perf. 13½		8.75	5.50
7	A1	75r carmine	7.00	5.50
8	A1	80r yel green	14.00	9.50
a.	Perf. 13½		17.50	12.00
9	A1	100r brn, yel ('93)	9.00	4.00
a.	Diagonal half used as 50r on cover			100.00

10	A1	150r car, rose ('93)	52.50	26.00
11	A1	200r dk bl, bl ('93)	60.00	37.50
12	A1	300r dk bl, sal ('93)	60.00	47.50
		Nos. 1-12 (12)	224.50	140.70

Nos. 1-12 were printed on both enamel-sur-faced and chalky papers. Values are for the most common varieties. For detailed listings, see the *Scott Classic Specialized Catalogue*.

The reprints of this issue have shiny white gum and clean-cut perforation 13½. The shades differ from those of the originals and the uncolored paper is thin.

1897-1905   Perf. 12
Name and Value in Black except Nos. 25 and 34

13	A2	2½r gray	.50	.35
14	A2	5r orange	.50	.35
15	A2	10r light green	.50	.35
16	A2	15r brown	5.00	3.00
17	A2	15r gray grn ('99)	3.25	2.25
18	A2	20r gray vio	1.40	.75
19	A2	25r sea green	2.75	.75
20	A2	25r car rose ('99)	1.40	.55
a.	Booklet pane of 6			
21	A2	50r dark blue	6.00	4.00
a.	Perf. 12½		18.00	7.25
22	A2	50r ultra ('05)	1.50	.90
23	A2	65r slate blue ('98)	1.25	.90
24	A2	75r rose	1.40	.95
25	A2	75r brn & red, yel ('05)	4.00	1.40
26	A2	80r violet	1.40	1.10
27	A2	100r dark blue, blue	1.40	1.10
a.	Diagonal half used as 50r on cover			—
28	A2	115r org brn, pink ('98)	2.25	1.40
29	A2	130r gray brown, buff ('98)	2.25	1.40
30	A2	150r lt brn, buff	2.75	1.25
31	A2	180r sl, pnksh ('98)	2.25	1.40
32	A2	200r red vio, pale lil	3.00	2.10
33	A2	300r blue, rose	3.00	2.10
34	A2	500r blk & red, bl	5.00	2.40
a.	Perf. 12½		15.00	7.75
		Nos. 13-34 (22)	52.75	30.75

STOCKBOOKS

Stockbooks are a classic and convenient storage alternative for many collectors. These German-made stockbooks feature heavyweight archival quality paper with 9 pockets on each page. The 8½" x 11⅝" pages are bound inside a handsome leatherette grain cover and include glassine interleaving between the pages for added protection. The Value Priced Stockbooks are available in two page styles, the white page stockbooks feature glassine pockets while the black page variety includes clear acetate pockets

Black Page Stockbooks
Acetate Pockets

ITEM	COLOR	PAGES	RETAIL
ST16RD	Red	16 pages	$10.95
ST16GR	Green	16 pages	$10.95
ST16BL	Blue	16 pages	$10.95
ST16BK	Black	16 pages	$10.95
ST32RD	Red	32 pages	$16.95
ST32GR	Green	32 pages	$16.95
ST32BL	Blue	32 pages	$16.95
ST32BK	Black	32 pages	$16.95
ST64RD	Red	64 pages	$29.95
ST64GR	Green	64 pages	$29.95
ST64BL	Blue	64 pages	$29.95
ST64BK	Black	64 pages	$29.95

Available from your favorite dealer or direct from:

P.O. Box 828
Sidney OH 45365-0828
www.amosadvantage.com
1-800-572-6885

Pronunciation Symbols

ə .... banana, collide, abut

ˈə, ˌə .... humdrum, abut

ə .... immediately preceding \l\, \n\, \m\, \ŋ\, as in battle, mitten, eaten, and sometimes open \ˈō-pᵊm\, lock and key \-ᵊŋ-\; immediately following \l\, \m\, \r\, as often in French table, prisme, titre

ər .... further, merger, bird

ˈər-, ˈə-r .... as in two different pronunciations of hurry \ˈhər-ē, ˈhə-rē\

a .... mat, map, mad, gag, snap, patch

ā .... day, fade, date, aorta, drape, cape

ä .... bother, cot, and, with most American speakers, father, cart

ȧ .... father as pronounced by speakers who do not rhyme it with bother; French patte

au̇ .... now, loud, out

b .... baby, rib

ch .... chin, nature \ˈnā-chər\

d .... did, adder

e .... bet, bed, peck

ˈē, ˌē .... beat, nosebleed, evenly, easy

ē .... easy, mealy

f .... fifty, cuff

g .... go, big, gift

h .... hat, ahead

hw .... whale as pronounced by those who do not have the same pronunciation for both whale and wail

i .... tip, banish, active

ī .... site, side, buy, tripe

j .... job, gem, edge, join, judge

k .... kin, cook, ache

ḵ .... German ich, Buch; one pronunciation of loch

l .... lily, pool

m .... murmur, dim, nymph

n .... no, own

ⁿ .... indicates that a preceding vowel or diphthong is pronounced with the nasal passages open, as in French un bon vin blanc \œⁿ -bōⁿ -vaⁿ -bläⁿ\

ŋ .... sing \ˈsiŋ\, singer \ˈsiŋ-ər\, finger \ˈfiŋ-gər\, ink \ˈiŋk\

ō .... bone, know, beau

ȯ .... saw, all, gnaw, caught

œ .... French bœuf, German Hölle

œ̄ .... French feu, German Höhle

ȯi .... coin, destroy

p .... pepper, lip

r .... red, car, rarity

s .... source, less

sh .... as in shy, mission, machine, special (actually, this is a single sound, not two); with a hyphen between, two sounds as in grasshopper \ˈgras-ˌhä-pər\

t .... tie, attack, late, later, latter

th .... as in thin, ether (actually, this is a single sound, not two); with a hyphen between, two sounds as in knighthood \ˈnīt-ˌhu̇d\

t͟h .... then, either, this (actually, this is a single sound, not two)

ü .... rule, youth, union \ˈyün-yən\, few \ˈfyü\

u̇ .... pull, wood, book, curable \ˈkyu̇r-ə-bəl\, fury \ˈfyu̇r-ē\

ᵫ .... German füllen, hübsch

ᵫ̄ .... French rue, German fühlen

v .... vivid, give

w .... we, away

y .... yard, young, cue \ˈkyü\, mute \ˈmyüt\, union \ˈyün-yən\

ʸ .... indicates that during the articulation of the sound represented by the preceding character the front of the tongue has substantially the position it has for the articulation of the first sound of yard, as in French digne \dēnʸ\

z .... zone, raise

zh .... as in vision, azure \ˈa-zhər\ (actually, this is a single sound, not two); with a hyphen between, two sounds as in hogshead \ˈhȯgz-ˌhed, ˈhägz-\

\ .... slant line used in pairs to mark the beginning and end of a transcription: \ˈpen\

ˈ .... mark preceding a syllable with primary (strongest) stress: \ˈpen-mən-ˌship\

ˌ .... mark preceding a syllable with secondary (medium) stress: \ˈpen-mən-ˌship\

- .... mark of syllable division

( ) .... indicate that what is symbolized between is present in some utterances but not in others: factory \ˈfak-t(ə-)rē\

÷ .... indicates that many regard as unacceptable the pronunciation variant immediately following: cupola \ˈkyü-pə-lə, ÷-ˌlō\

Illustrated Identifier

This section pictures stamps or parts of stamp designs that will help identify postage stamps that do not have English words on them.

Many of the symbols that identify stamps of countries are shown here as well as typical examples of their stamps.

See the Index and Identifier on the previous pages for stamps with inscriptions such as "sen," "posta," "Baja Porto," "Helvetia," "K.S.A.," etc.

Linn's Stamp Identifier is now available. The 144 pages include more 2,000 inscriptions and over 500 large stamp illustrations. Available from Linn's Stamp News, P.O. Box 29, Sidney, OH 45365-0029.

1. HEADS, PICTURES AND NUMERALS

GREAT BRITAIN

Great Britain stamps never show the country name, but, except for postage dues, show a picture of the reigning monarch.

Victoria

Edward VII   George V   Edward VIII

George VI

Elizabeth II

Some George VI and Elizabeth II stamps are surcharged in annas, new paisa or rupees. These are listed under Oman.

Silhouette (sometimes facing right, generally at the top of stamp)

The silhouette indicates this is a British stamp. It is not a U.S. stamp.

VICTORIA

Queen Victoria

INDIA

Other stamps of India show this portrait of Queen Victoria and the words "Service" and "Annas."

AUSTRIA

YUGOSLAVIA

(Also BOSNIA & HERZEGOVINA if imperf.)

BOSNIA & HERZEGOVINA

Denominations also appear in top corners instead of bottom corners.

HUNGARY

Another stamp has posthorn facing left

BRAZIL

AUSTRALIA

Kangaroo and Emu

GERMANY

Mecklenburg-Vorpommern

SWITZERLAND

PALAU

2. ORIENTAL INSCRIPTIONS

CHINA

Any stamp with this one character is from China (Imperial, Republic or People's Republic). This character appears in a four-character overprint on stamps of Manchukuo. These stamps are local provisionals, which are unlisted. Other overprinted Manchukuo stamps show this character, but have more than four characters in the overprints. These are listed in People's Republic of China.

Some Chinese stamps show the Sun.

Most stamps of Republic of China show this series of characters.

Stamps with the China character and this character are from People's Republic of China. 人

Calligraphic form of People's Republic of China

(一)	(二)	(三)	(四)	(五)	(六)
1	2	3	4	5	6
(七)	(八)	(九)	(十)	(一十)	(二十)
7	8	9	10	11	12

**Chinese stamps
without China character**

REPUBLIC OF CHINA

PEOPLE'S REPUBLIC OF CHINA

Mao Tse-tung

MANCHUKUO

Temple   Emperor Pu-Yi

The first 3 characters are common to
many Manchukuo stamps.

The last 3 characters are common
to other Manchukuo stamps.

Orchid Crest

Manchukuo
stamp with-
out these
elements

JAPAN

Chrysanthemum Crest   Country Name

Japanese stamps without these elements

The number of characters in the center and the
design of dragons on the sides will vary.

RYUKYU ISLANDS

Country Name

PHILIPPINES
(Japanese Occupation)

Country Name

NORTH BORNEO
(Japanese Occupation)

 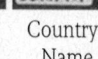

Indicates Japanese   Country
Occupation   Name

MALAYA
(Japanese Occupation)

Indicates Japanese Occupation   Country Name

BURMA
Union of Myanmar

Union of Myanmar
(Japanese Occupation)

Indicates Japanese Occupation   Country Name

Other Burma Japanese Occupation stamps without these elements

Burmese Script

KOREA

These two characters, in any order, are common to stamps from the Republic of Korea (South Korea) or of the People's Democratic Republic of Korea (North Korea).

This series of four characters can be found on the stamps of both Koreas. Most stamps of the Democratic People's Republic of Korea (North Korea) have just this inscription.

Indicates Republic of Korea (South Korea)

South Korean postage stamps issed after 1952 do not show currency expressed in Latin letters. Stamps wiith "HW," "HWAN," "WON," "WN," "W" or "W" with two lines through it, if not illustrated in listings of stamps before this date, are revenues. North Korean postage stamps do not have currency expressed in Latin letters.

Yin Yang appears on some stamps.

REPUBLIC OF KOREA

THAILAND

Country Name

King Chulalongkorn

King Prajadhipok and Chao P'ya Chakri

3. CENTRAL AND EASTERN ASIAN INSCRIPTIONS

INDIA - FEUDATORY STATES

Alwar   **Bhor**

Bundi

Similar stamps come with different designs in corners and differently drawn daggers (at center of circle).

Dhar   **Faridkot**

Hyderabad

 Similar stamps exist with straight line frame around stamp, and also with different central design which is inscribed "Postage" or "Post & Receipt."

Indore   **Jhalawar**

A similar stamp has the central figure in an oval.

Nandgaon

Nowanuggur

Poonch

Similar stamps exist
in various sizes

Rajpeepla   Soruth

BANGLADESH

Country Name

NEPAL

Similar stamps are smaller, have squares in
upper corners and have five or nine
characters in central bottom panel.

TANNU TUVA   ISRAEL

GEORGIA

This inscription is found on
other pictorial stamps.

Country Name

ARMENIA

The four characters are found somewhere
on pictorial stamps. On some stamps only
the middle two are found.

4. AFRICAN INSCRIPTIONS

ETHIOPIA

5. ARABIC INSCRIPTIONS

١ ٢ ٢ ٤ ٥
1   2   3   4   5

٧ ٧ ٨ ٩ ٠
6   7   8   9   0

AFGHANISTAN

Many early Afghanistan stamps show Tiger's head, many of these have ornaments protruding from outer ring, others show inscriptions in black.

Arabic Script

Mosque Gate & Crossed Cannons
The four characters are found somewhere on pictorial stamps. On some stamps only the middle two are found.

BAHRAIN

EGYPT

 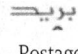

Postage

INDIA - FEUDATORY STATES

Jammu & Kashmir

Text and thickness of ovals vary. Some stamps have flower devices in corners.

India-Hyderabad

IRAN

Country Name

Royal Crown

Lion with Sword

Symbol

IRAQ

JORDAN

LEBANON

Similar types have denominations at top and slightly different design.

LIBYA

Country Name in various styles

Other Libya stamps show Eagle and Shield (head facing either direction) or Red, White and Black Shield (with or without eagle in center).

Without Country Name

SAUDI ARABIA

Tughra (Central design)

Palm Tree and Swords

SYRIA

THRACE   YEMEN

PAKISTAN

PAKISTAN - BAHAWALPUR

Country Name in top panel, star and crescent

TURKEY

Star & Crescent is a device found on many Turkish stamps, but is also found on stamps from other Arabic areas (see Pakistan-Bahawalpur)

Tughra (similar tughras can be found on stamps of Turkey in Asia, Afghanistan and Saudi Arabia)

Mohammed V

Mustafa Kemal

Plane, Star and Crescent

TURKEY IN ASIA

Other Turkey in Asia pictorials show star & crescent.
Other stamps show tughra shown under Turkey.

6. GREEK INSCRIPTIONS

GREECE

Country Name in various styles
(Some Crete stamps overprinted with the Greece country name are listed in Crete.)

Lepta

Drachma   Drachmas   Lepton

Abbreviated Country Name

Other forms of Country Name

No country name

CRETE

Country Name

These words are on other stamps

Grosion

Crete stamps with a surcharge that have the year "1922" are listed under Greece.

EPIRUS   IONIAN IS.

Country Name

---

7. CYRILLIC INSCRIPTIONS

RUSSIA

Postage Stamp

Imperial Eagle

Postage in various styles

Abbreviation   Abbreviation   Russian
for Kopeck   for Ruble

Abbreviation for Russian Soviet Federated Socialist Republic
RSFSR stamps were overprinted (see below)

Abbreviation for Union of Soviet Socialist Republics

This item is footnoted in Latvia

RUSSIA - Army of the North

 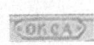

"OKCA"

RUSSIA - Wenden

RUSSIAN OFFICES IN THE TURKISH EMPIRE

    These letters appear on other stamps of the Russian offices.

The unoverprinted version of this stamp and a similar stamp were overprinted by various countries (see below).

ARMENIA

BELARUS

FAR EASTERN REPUBLIC

Country Name

SOUTH RUSSIA

Country Name

FINLAND

Circles and Dots
on stamps similar
to Imperial
Russia issues

BATUM

Forms of Country Name

TRANSCAUCASIAN FEDERATED REPUBLICS

Abbreviation for
Country Name

KAZAKHSTAN

Country Name

KYRGYZSTAN

КЫРГЫЗСТАН   Country
Name

ROMANIA

TADJIKISTAN

Country Name & Abbreviation

UKRAINE

Country Name in various forms

The trident appears
on many stamps,
usually as an overprint.

Abbreviation for
Ukrainian Soviet
Socialist Republic

WESTERN UKRAINE

Abbreviation for
Country Name

AZERBAIJAN

Country Name

Abbreviation for Azerbaijan
Soviet Socialist Republic

MONTENEGRO

ЦРНА ГОРА

Country Name in various forms

| Abbreviation for country name | No country name (A similar Montenegro stamp without country name has same vignette.) |

SERBIA

СРБИЈА

Country Name in various forms

Abbreviation for country name

No country name

SERBIA & MONTENEGRO

YUGOSLAVIA

ЈУГОСЛАВИЈА

Showing country name

No Country Name

MACEDONIA

МАКЕДОНИЈА

Country Name

МАКЕДОНСКИ

Different form of Country Name

BOSNIA & HERZEGOVINA
(Serb Administration)

РЕПУБЛИКА СРПСКА

Country Name

РЕПУБЛИКЕ СРПСКЕ

Different form of Country Name

No Country Name

BULGARIA

Country Name   Postage

Stotinka

Stotinki (plural)   Abbreviation for
                       Stotinki

Country Name in various forms and styles

No country name

  Abbreviation for
                       Lev, leva

MONGOLIA

ШУУДАН   тѳгрѳг

Country name in   Tugrik in Cyrillic
one word

МОНГОЛ
ШУУДАН   мѳнгѳ

Country name in   Mung in Cyrillic
two words

MONGOLIA
МОНГОЛ ШУУДАН
                       Mung
                       in Mongolian

MONGOLIA
МОНГОЛ ШУУДАН
                       Tugrik
                       in Mongolian

Arms

No Country Name

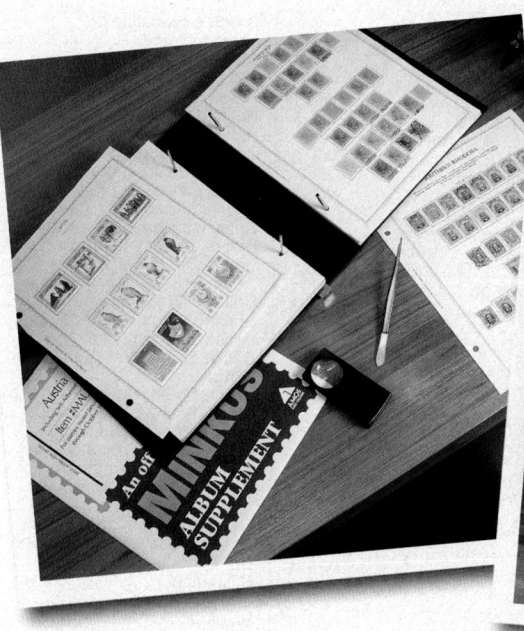

MINKUS
Album Series

The Minkus album line is now available through Amos Hobby Publishing.
The supplement schedule is listed below. Pages are punched to fit 2 or 3-ring binders.
Sold as page units only. Binders, slipcases and labels sold separately.
For more information album contents visit our web site at www.amosadvantage.com.

FEBRUARY
Global Part 1
Global Part 2
All American Regular & Commemoratives

MARCH
All American Part 3 United Nations
U.N Singles
U.N. Imprint Blocks
U.N. Postal Stationery

APRIL
All American Part 2 Postal Stationery
All American Part 4 Booklet Panes
All American Part 5 Sheetlets
All American Part 7 Postal Cards
U.S. Commemoratives
U.S. Plate Blocks
U.S. Regular Issues
U.S. Booklet Panes
U.S. Postal Stationery
U.S. Sheetlets

MAY
Albania
Austria
Bulgaria
Canada
Croatia
France
French Andorra
Germany
Gibraltar
Great Britain, Ireland
Guernsey, Jersey, Isle Of Man
Hong Kong
Ireland
Monaco
Romania
Serbia & Montenegro
Singapore
Slovenia

JUNE
Denmark
Egypt
Finland
Greece
Israel Singles
Israel Plate Blocks
Israel Tab Singles
Korea
Liechtenstein
Norway
Sweden
Switzerland

JULY
Bangladesh
India
Italy
Japan
Pakistan
People's Republic of China
Portugal/Azores/Maderia
San Marino
Spain
Sri Lanka
Thailand
Vatican City

AUGUST
Armenia
Azerbaijan
Belarus
Belgium
Czech Republic & Slovakia
Georgia
Hungary
Kazakhstan
Kyrgyzstan
Latvia, Lithuania, Estonia
Luxembourg
Moldova
Netherlands
Poland
Russia
Tajikistan
Turkmenistan
Ukraine
Uzbekistan

SEPTEMBER
Argentina
Australia
Brazil
Chile
Colombia
Dominican Republic
Haiti
Mexico
New Zealand
Venezuela

DECEMBER
All American Part 6 Plate No. Coils
U.S. Plate No. Coils

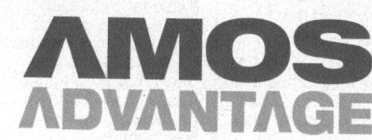

AMOS
ADVANTAGE

911 Vandemark Road
Sidney OH 45365
1-800-572-6885
www.amosadvantage.com

INDEX AND IDENTIFIER

All page numbers shown are those in this Volume 2.

Postage stamps that do not have English words on them are shown in the Identifier which begins on page 1362.

INDEX TO ADVERTISERS
2009 VOLUME 2

scott**mounts**

For stamp presentation unequaled in beauty and clarity, insist on ScottMounts. Made of 100% inert polystyrol foil, ScottMounts protect your stamps from the harmful effects of dust and moisture. Available in your choice of clear or black backs, ScottMounts are center-split across the back for easy insertion of stamps and feature crystal clear mount faces. Double layers of gum assure stay-put bonding on the album page. Discover the quality and value ScottMounts have to offer. ScottMounts are available from your favorite stamp dealer or direct from:

Discover the quality and value ScottMounts have to offer. For a complete list of ScottMount sizes call or write Scott Publishing Co.

2009
VOLUME 2
DEALER DIRECTORY
YELLOW PAGE LISTINGS

This section of your Scott Catalogue contains advertisements to help you conveniently find what you need, when you need it...!

Accessories

BROOKLYN GALLERY COIN & STAMP, INC.
8725 4th Ave.
Brooklyn, NY 11209
PH: 718-745-5701
FAX: 718-745-2775
info@brooklyngallery.com
www.brooklyngallery.com

Aerophilately

HENRY GITNER PHILATELISTS, INC.
PO Box 3077-S
Middletown, NY 10940
PH: 845-343-5151
PH: 800-947-8267
FAX: 845-343-0068
hgitner@hgitner.com
www.hgitner.com

Appraisals

PHILIP WEISS AUCTIONS
1 Neil Court
Oceanside, NY 11572
PH: 516-594-0731
FAX: 516-594-9414

Asia

MICHAEL ROGERS, INC.
415 South Orlando Ave
Winter Park, FL 32789-3683
PH: 407-644-2290
PH: 800-843-3751
FAX: 407-645-4434
Stamps@michaelrogersinc.com
www.michaelrogersinc.com

THE STAMP ACT
PO Box 1136
Belmont, CA 94002
PH: 650-703-2342
PH: 650-592-3315
FAX: 650-508-8104
thestampact@sbcglobal.net
www.thestampact.com

Auctions

DANIEL F. KELLEHER CO., INC.
20 Walnut St.
Suite 213
Wellesley, MA 02481
PH: 781-235-0990
FAX: 781-235-0945

JACQUES C. SCHIFF, JR., INC.
195 Main St.
Ridgefield Park, NJ 07660
PH: 201-641-5566
FAX: 201-641-5705

Auctions

MICHAEL ROGERS, INC.
415 South Orlando Ave
Winter Park, FL 32789-3683
PH: 407-644-2290
PH: 800-843-3751
FAX: 407-645-4434
Stamps@michaelrogersinc.com
www.michaelrogersinc.com

PHILIP WEISS AUCTIONS
1 Neil Court
Oceanside, NY 11572
PH: 516-594-0731
FAX: 516-594-9414

R. MARESCH & SON LTD.
5th Floor - 6075 Yonge St.
Toronto, ON M2M 3W2
CANADA
PH: 416-363-7777
FAX: 416-363-6511
www.maresch.com

THE STAMP CENTER DUTCH COUNTRY AUCTIONS
4115 Concord Pike
Wilmington, DE 19803
PH: 302-478-8740
FAX: 302-478-8779
auctions@thestampcenter.com
www.thestampcenter.com

Auctions - Public

ALAN BLAIR STAMPS/ AUCTIONS
5405 Lakeside Ave.
Suite 1
Richmond, VA 23228
PH/FAX: 800-689-5602
alanblair@prodigy.net

British Commonwealth

ARON R. HALBERSTAM PHILATELISTS, LTD.
PO Box 150168
Van Brunt Station
Brooklyn, NY 11215-0168
PH: 718-788-3978
FAX: 718-965-3099
arh@arhstamps.com
www.arhstamps.com

METROPOLITAN STAMP CO., INC.
PO Box 657
Park Ridge, IL 60068-0657
PH: 815-439-0142
FAX: 815-439-0143
metrostamp@aol.com
www.metropolitanstamps.com

WWW.WORLDSTAMPS.COM
242 West Saddle River Road
Suite C
Upper Saddle River, NJ 07458
PH: 201-236-8122
FAX: 201-236-8133
by mail:
Frank Geiger Philatelists
info@WorldStamps.com
www.WorldStamps.com

Auctions

British Commonwealth

Cameroons (Brit. & Ger.)

COLONIAL STAMP COMPANY
5757 Wilshire Blvd. PH #8
Los Angeles, CA 90036
PH: 323-933-9435
FAX: 323-939-9930
Toll Free in North America
PH: 877-272-6693
FAX: 877-272-6694
info@colonialstampcompany.com
www.colonialstampcompany.com

Canada

COLONIAL STAMP COMPANY
5757 Wilshire Blvd. PH #8
Los Angeles, CA 90036
PH: 323-933-9435
FAX: 323-939-9930
Toll Free in North America
PH: 877-272-6693
FAX: 877-272-6694
info@colonialstampcompany.com
www.colonialstampcompany.com

**HENRY GITNER
PHILATELISTS, INC.**
PO Box 3077-S
Middletown, NY 10940
PH: 845-343-5151
PH: 800-947-8267
FAX: 845-343-0068
hgitner@hgitner.com
www.hgitner.com

Cape of Good Hope

COLONIAL STAMP COMPANY
5757 Wilshire Blvd. PH #8
Los Angeles, CA 90036
PH: 323-933-9435
FAX: 323-939-9930
Toll Free in North America
PH: 877-272-6693
FAX: 877-272-6694
info@colonialstampcompany.com
www.colonialstampcompany.com

Caroline Islands (Ger.)

COLONIAL STAMP COMPANY
5757 Wilshire Blvd. PH #8
Los Angeles, CA 90036
PH: 323-933-9435
FAX: 323-939-9930
Toll Free in North America
PH: 877-272-6693
FAX: 877-272-6694
info@colonialstampcompany.com
www.colonialstampcompany.com

Cayman Islands

COLONIAL STAMP COMPANY
5757 Wilshire Blvd. PH #8
Los Angeles, CA 90036
PH: 323-933-9435
FAX: 323-939-9930
Toll Free in North America
PH: 877-272-6693
FAX: 877-272-6694
info@colonialstampcompany.com
www.colonialstampcompany.com

Central America

GUY SHAW
PO Box 27138
San Diego, CA 92198
PH/FAX: 858-485-8269
guyshaw@guyshaw.com
www.guyshaw.com

China

MICHAEL ROGERS, INC.
415 South Orlando Ave
Winter Park, FL 32789-3683
PH: 407-644-2290
PH: 800-843-3751
FAX: 407-645-4434
Stamps@michaelrogersinc.com
www.michaelrogersinc.com

THE STAMP ACT
PO Box 1136
Belmont, CA 94002
PH: 650-703-2342
PH: 650-592-3315
FAX: 650-508-8104
thestampact@sbcglobal.net
www.thestampact.com

China - PRC

MR. GUANLUN HONG
Jade Crown International
Stamp Company
PO Box 118
Blaine, WA 98231 USA
PH: 1-604-288-8815
PH: 1-888-482-6586
FAX: 1-604-288-8815
guanlun@hotmail.com
guanlun@shaw.ca
haitaohong@hotmail.com

China - PRC

THE STAMP ACT
PO Box 1136
Belmont, CA 94002
PH: 650-703-2342
PH: 650-592-3315
FAX: 650-508-8104
thestampact@sbcglobal.net
www.thestampact.com

Collections

**HENRY GITNER
PHILATELISTS, INC.**
PO Box 3077-S
Middletown, NY 10940
PH: 845-343-5151
PH: 800-947-8267
FAX: 845-343-0068
hgitner@hgitner.com
www.hgitner.com

Cuba

R.D.C. STAMPS
R. del Campo
Museo Historico Cubano
3131 Coral Way
Miami, FL 33145
PH: 305-815-0577
PH: 305-567-3131
FAX: 305-567-1416
rdcstamps@aol.com

Cyprus

COLONIAL STAMP COMPANY
5757 Wilshire Blvd. PH #8
Los Angeles, CA 90036
PH: 323-933-9435
FAX: 323-939-9930
Toll Free in North America
PH: 877-272-6693
FAX: 877-272-6694
info@colonialstampcompany.com
www.colonialstampcompany.com

Ducks

MICHAEL JAFFE
PO Box 61484
Vancouver, WA 98666
PH: 360-695-6161
PH: 800-782-6770
FAX: 360-695-1616
mjaffe@brookmanstamps.com
www.brookmanstamps.com

Europe

**MODLOW-ARVAI STAMPS &
COLLECTIBLES**
504 E. 118th St. Apt #2
New York, NY 10035
PH: 917-868-4850
FAX: 888-655-1655
Mastamps@aol.com
Visit our Free Auction site:
http://www.modlow-arvai.com

WWW.WORLDSTAMPS.COM
242 West Saddle River Road
Suite C
Upper Saddle River, NJ 07458
PH: 201-236-8122
FAX: 201-236-8133
by mail:
Frank Geiger Philatelists
info@WorldStamps.com
www.WorldStamps.com

Falkland Islands

**ARON R. HALBERSTAM
PHILATELISTS, LTD.**
PO Box 150168
Van Brunt Station
Brooklyn, NY 11215-0168
PH: 718-788-3978
FAX: 718-965-3099
arh@arhstamps.com
www.arhstamps.com

COLONIAL STAMP COMPANY
5757 Wilshire Blvd. PH #8
Los Angeles, CA 90036
PH: 323-933-9435
FAX: 323-939-9930
Toll Free in North America
PH: 877-272-6693
FAX: 877-272-6694
info@colonialstampcompany.com
www.colonialstampcompany.com

France & Colonies

E. JOSEPH MCCONNELL
PO Box 683
Monroe, NY 10949
PH: 845-496-5916
FAX: 845-782-0347
ejstamps@gmail.com
www.EJMcConnell.com

WULFF'S STAMPS
PO Box 661746
Sacramento, CA 95866
PH/FAX: 800-884-0656
PH/FAX: 916-489-0656
service@wulffstamps.com
www.wulffstamps.com

France & Colonies

WWW.WORLDSTAMPS.COM
242 West Saddle River Road
Suite C
Upper Saddle River, NJ 07458
PH: 201-236-8122
FAX: 201-236-8133
by mail:
Frank Geiger Philatelists
info@WorldStamps.com
www.WorldStamps.com

French S. Antarctic

E. JOSEPH MCCONNELL
PO Box 683
Monroe, NY 10949
PH: 845-496-5916
FAX: 845-782-0347
ejstamps@gmail.com
www.EJMcConnell.com

German Colonies

COLONIAL STAMP COMPANY
View our on-line price list
at our website!
5757 Wilshire Blvd. PH #8
Los Angeles, CA 90036
PH: 323-933-9435
FAX: 323-939-9930
Toll Free in North America
PH: 877-272-6693
FAX: 877-272-6694
info@colonialstampcompany.com
www.colonialstampcompany.com

Great Britain-Pricelist

COLONIAL STAMP COMPANY
5757 Wilshire Blvd. PH #8
Los Angeles, CA 90036
PH: 323-933-9435
FAX: 323-939-9930
Toll Free in North America
PH: 877-272-6693
FAX: 877-272-6694
info@colonialstampcompany.com
www.colonialstampcompany.com

Insurance

**COLLECTIBLES INSURANCE
SERVICES, LLC.**
11350 McCormick Rd., Ste. 700
Hunt Valley, MD 21031
PH: 888-837-9537
www.collectinsure.com

Japan

MICHAEL ROGERS, INC.
415 South Orlando Ave
Winter Park, FL 32789-3683
PH: 407-644-2290
PH: 800-843-3751
FAX: 407-645-4434
Stamps@michaelrogersinc.com
www.michaelrogersinc.com

Korea

MICHAEL ROGERS, INC.
415 South Orlando Ave
Winter Park, FL 32789-3683
PH: 407-644-2290
PH: 800-843-3751
FAX: 407-645-4434
Stamps@michaelrogersinc.com
www.michaelrogersinc.com

Latin America

GUY SHAW
PO Box 27138
San Diego, CA 92198
PH/FAX: 858-485-8269
guyshaw@guyshaw.com
www.guyshaw.com

Manchukuo

MICHAEL ROGERS, INC.
415 South Orlando Ave
Winter Park, FL 32789-3683
PH: 407-644-2290
PH: 800-843-3751
FAX: 407-645-4434
Stamps@michaelrogersinc.com
www.michaelrogersinc.com

Middle East-Arab

MICHAEL ROGERS, INC.
415 South Orlando Ave
Winter Park, FL 32789-3683
PH: 407-644-2290
PH: 800-843-3751
FAX: 407-645-4434
Stamps@michaelrogersinc.com
www.michaelrogersinc.com

New Issues

**DAVIDSON'S STAMP
SERVICE**
PO Box 36355
Indianapolis, IN 46236-0355
PH: 317-826-2620
davidson@in.net
www.newstampissues.com

WWW.WORLDSTAMPS.COM
242 West Saddle River Road
Suite C
Upper Saddle River, NJ 07458
PH: 201-236-8122
FAX: 201-236-8133
by mail:
Frank Geiger Philatelists
info@WorldStamps.com
www.WorldStamps.com

New Issues - Retail

BOMBAY PHILATELIC INC.
PO Box 90937
Raleigh, NC 27675
PH: 561-499-7990
FAX: 561-499-7553
sales@bombaystamps.com
www.bombaystamps.com

Proofs & Essays

**HENRY GITNER
PHILATELISTS, INC.**
PO Box 3077-S
Middletown, NY 10940
PH: 845-343-5151
PH: 800-947-8267
FAX: 845-343-0068
hgitner@hgitner.com
www.hgitner.com

Publications-Collector

**THE AMERICAN
PHILATELIST**
Dept. TZ
100 Match Factory Pl.
Bellefonte, PA 16823-1367
PH: 814-933-3803
FAX: 814-933-6128
apsinfo@stamps.org
www.stamps.org

Scandinavia

WWW.WORLDSTAMPS.COM
242 West Saddle River Road
Suite C
Upper Saddle River, NJ 07458
PH: 201-236-8122
FAX: 201-236-8133
by mail:
Frank Geiger Philatelists
info@WorldStamps.com
www.WorldStamps.com

South America

GUY SHAW
PO Box 27138
San Diego, CA 92198
PH/FAX: 858-485-8269
guyshaw@guyshaw.com
www.guyshaw.com

WWW.WORLDSTAMPS.COM
242 West Saddle River Road
Suite C
Upper Saddle River, NJ 07458
PH: 201-236-8122
FAX: 201-236-8133
by mail:
Frank Geiger Philatelists
info@WorldStamps.com
www.WorldStamps.com

STAMP STORES

Arizona

B.J.'S STAMPS
Barbara J. Johnson
6342 W. Bell Rd.
Glendale, AZ 85308
PH: 623-878-2080
FAX: 623-412-3456
info@bjstamps.com
www.bjstamps.com

California

**BROSIUS STAMP, COIN &
SUPPLIES**
2105 Main St.
Santa Monica, CA 90405
PH: 310-396-7480
FAX: 310-396-7455

STAMP STORES

California

**COLONIAL STAMP CO./
BRITISH EMPIRE
SPECIALIST**
5757 Wilshire Blvd. PH #8
(by appt.)
Los Angeles, CA 90036
PH: 323-933-9435
FAX: 323-939-9930
Toll Free in North America
PH: 877-272-6693
FAX: 877-272-6694
info@colonialstampcompany.com
www.colonialstampcompany.com

**FISCHER-WOLK
PHILATELICS**
22762 Aspan St.
Suite 211
Lake Forest, CA 92630
PH: 949-837-2932
fw@occoxmail.com

NATICK STAMPS & HOBBIES
411 E. Huntington Dr.
Suite 209
Arcadia, CA 91006
PH: 626-445-2185
natickco@att.net

Colorado

SHOWCASE STAMPS
3865 Wadsworth
Wheat Ridge, CO 80033
PH: 303-425-9252
kbeiner@colbi.net
www.showcasestamps.com

Connecticut

SILVER CITY COIN & STAMP
41 Colony St.
Meriden, CT 06451
PH: 203-235-7634
FAX: 203-237-4915

Florida

R.D.C. STAMPS
R. del Campo
Museo Historico Cubano
3131 Coral Way
Miami, FL 33145
PH: 305-815-0577
PH: 305-567-3131
FAX: 305-567-1416
rdcstamps@aol.com

Stamp Shows

Georgia

**STAMPS UNLIMITED OF
GEORGIA, INC.**
100 Peachtree St.
Suite 1460
Atlanta, GA 30303
PH: 404-688-9161
tonyroozen@yahoo.com

Illinois

**DR. ROBERT FRIEDMAN &
SONS**
2029 W. 75th St.
Woodridge, IL 60517
PH: 800-588-8100
FAX: 630-985-1588
drbobstamps@yahoo.com
www.drbobfriedmanstamps.com

SIDMORE STAMPS
145 E. Lincoln Hwy.
DeKalb, IL 60115
PH: 815-787-7000
sidmorestamps@verizon.net
Authorized APS Dealer

Indiana

KNIGHT STAMP & COIN CO.
237 Main St.
Hobart, IN 46342
PH: 219-942-4341
PH: 800-634-2646
knight@knightcoin.com
www.knightcoin.com

Massachusetts

KAPPY'S COINS & STAMPS
534 Washington St.
Norwood, MA 02062
PH: 781-762-5552
kappyscoins@aol.com

Maryland

BULLDOG STAMP COMPANY
4641 Montgomery Ave.
Bethesda, MD 20814
PH: 301-654-1138

New Jersey

AALLSTAMPS
38 N. Main St.
PO Box 249
Milltown, NJ 08850
PH: 732-247-1093
FAX: 732-247-1094
mail@aallstamps.com
www.aallstamps.com

**BERGEN STAMPS &
COLLECTIBLES**
306 Queen Anne Rd.
Teaneck, NJ 07666
PH: 201-836-8987

**TRENTON STAMP & COIN
CO.**
Thomas DeLuca
Store: Forest Glen Plaza
1804 Route 33
Hamilton Square, NJ 08690
Mail: PO Box 8574
Trenton, NJ 08650
PH: 800-446-8664
PH: 609-584-8100
FAX: 609-587-8664
TOMD4TSC@aol.com

New York

CHAMPION STAMP CO., INC.
432 W. 54th St.
New York, NY 10019
PH: 212-489-8130
FAX: 212-581-8130
championstamp@aol.com
www.championstamp.com

Ohio

HILLTOP STAMP SERVICE
Richard A. Peterson
PO Box 626
Wooster, OH 44691
PH: 330-262-8907
PH: 330-262-5378
hilltop@bright.net

THE LINK STAMP CO.
3461 E. Livingston Ave.
Columbus, OH 43227
PH/FAX: 614-237-4125
PH/FAX: 800-546-5726

Tennessee

HERRON HILL, INC.
5007 Black Rd.
Suite 140
Memphis, TN 38117
PH: 901-683-9644

Virginia

**KENNEDY'S STAMPS &
COINS, INC.**
7059 Brookfield Plaza
Springfield, VA 22150
PH: 703-569-7300
FAX: 703-569-7644
j.w.kennedy@verizon.net

LATHEROW & CO., INC.
5054 Lee Hwy.
Arlington, VA 22207
PH: 703-538-2727
PH: 800-647-4624
FAX: 703-538-5210
latherow@filatco.com

Topicals

E. JOSEPH MCCONNELL
PO Box 683
Monroe, NY 10949
PH: 845-496-5916
FAX: 845-782-0347
ejstamps@gmail.com
www.EJMcConnell.com

Topicals-Columbus

MR. COLUMBUS
PO Box 1492
Fennville, MI 49408
PH: 269-543-4755
columbus@accn.org

Topicals-Miscellaneous

**HENRY GITNER
PHILATELISTS, INC.**
PO Box 3077-S
Middletown, NY 10940
PH: 845-343-5151
PH: 800-947-8267
FAX: 845-343-0068
hgitner@hgitner.com
www.hgitner.com

United States

ACS STAMP COMPANY
10831 Chambers Way
Commerce City, CO 80022
PH: 303-841-8666
ACS@ACSStamp.com
www.acsstamp.com

BROOKMAN STAMP CO.
PO Box 90
Vancouver, WA 98666
PH: 360-695-1391
PH: 800-545-4871
FAX: 360-695-1616
larry@brookmanstamps.com
www.brookmanstamps.com

U.S.-Collections Wanted

**DR. ROBERT FRIEDMAN &
SONS**
2029 W. 75th St.
Woodridge, IL 60517
PH: 800-588-8100
FAX: 630-985-1588
drbobstamps@yahoo.com
www.drbobfriedmanstamps.com

**THE STAMP CENTER
DUTCH COUNTRY AUCTIONS**
4115 Concord Pike
Wilmington, DE 19803
PH: 302-478-8740
FAX: 302-478-8779
auctions@thestampcenter.com
www.thestampcenter.com

Want Lists

CHARLES P. SCHWARTZ
PO Box 165
Mora, MN 55051
PH: 320-679-4705
charlesp@ecenet.com

Want Lists-British Empire 1840-1935 German Cols./Offices

COLONIAL STAMP COMPANY
5757 Wilshire Blvd. PH #8
Los Angeles, CA 90036
PH: 323-933-9435
FAX: 323-939-9930
Toll Free in North America
PH: 877-272-6693
FAX: 877-272-6694
info@colonialstampcompany.com
www.colonialstampcompany.com

Wanted-Collections

BILL'S
59 Paulding Blvd.
Dallas, GA 30157
PH: 770-369-1001
cynthianix59@aol.com

Wanted-Estates

BILL'S
59 Paulding Blvd.
Dallas, GA 30157
PH: 770-369-1001
cynthianix59@aol.com

Wanted-U.S. Collections

BROOKMAN STAMP CO.
PO Box 90
Vancouver, WA 98666
PH: 360-695-1391
PH: 800-545-4871
FAX: 360-695-1616
larry@brookmanstamps.com
www.brookmanstamps.com

Wanted-Worldwide Collections

DR. ROBERT FRIEDMAN & SONS
2029 W. 75th St.
Woodridge, IL 60517
PH: 800-588-8100
FAX: 630-985-1588
drbobstamps@yahoo.com
www.drbobfriedmanstamps.com

Wanted-Worldwide Collections

THE STAMP CENTER DUTCH COUNTRY AUCTIONS
4115 Concord Pike
Wilmington, DE 19803
PH: 302-478-8740
FAX: 302-478-8779
auctions@thestampcenter.com
www.thestampcenter.com

Websites

ACS STAMP COMPANY
10831 Chambers Way
Commerce City, CO 80022
PH: 303-841-8666
ACS@ACSStamp.com
www.acsstamp.com

Wholesale

HENRY GITNER PHILATELISTS, INC.
PO Box 3077-S
Middletown, NY 10940
PH: 845-343-5151
PH: 800-947-8267
FAX: 845-343-0068
hgitner@hgitner.com
www.hgitner.com

Worldwide-Stamps

METROPOLITAN STAMP CO., INC.
PO Box 657
Park Ridge, IL 60068-0657
PH: 815-439-0142
FAX: 815-439-0143
metrostamp@aol.com
www.metropolitanstamps.com

Worldwide-Year Sets

HENRY GITNER PHILATELISTS, INC.
PO Box 3077-S
Middletown, NY 10940
PH: 845-343-5151
PH: 800-947-8267
FAX: 845-343-0068
hgitner@hgitner.com
www.hgitner.com

Worldwide-Year Sets

WWW.WORLDSTAMPS.COM
242 West Saddle River Road
Suite C
Upper Saddle River, NJ 07458
PH: 201-236-8122
FAX: 201-236-8133
by mail:
Frank Geiger Philatelists
info@WorldStamps.com
www.WorldStamps.com

Worldwide